Stanley Gibbons
STAMP CATALOGUE

PART 1

British Commonwealth 1999

Including post-independence issues of Ireland

101st edition

VOLUME 2
Countries J to Z

Stanley Gibbons Ltd
London and Ringwood

By Appointment to Her Majesty The Queen
Stanley Gibbons Ltd, London
Philatelists

Published by **Stanley Gibbons Ltd**
Editorial, Publications Sales Offices and Distribution Centre:
5 Parkside, Christchurch Road, Ringwood,
Hants BH24 3SH.

ISBN: 0-85259-447-X

Item No. 2812 (99)

Text assembled by Black Bear Press Limited, Cambridge

Made and Printed in Great Britain by William Clowes Limited, Beccles, Suffolk

Preface to the 1999 Edition

FLYING START

Stamp collecting has never stood still. One of its enduring attractions has always been its ability to evolve and add further facets to its already complex structure.

If the great collectors from the last century could return, it is an interesting speculation as to how they would react to a hobby which is now approaching the end of the next. Some would, I am sure, have heartily approved of postal history with its emphasis on research into the use of postage stamps, but I am not too sure as to their reaction to other aspects of the modern hobby. On the other hand, who is to say how we would find stamp collecting at the end of the 21st century!

As the hobby has changed the Stanley Gibbons catalogues have evolved with it. No stamp catalogue can afford to be complacent, and every trend in research, price and indeed production methods must be evaluated.

It is generally agreed that the hobby is approaching a watershed. Diverse influences, not the least of which must be the efforts of modern post office marketing departments, are influencing the ordinary collector as never before with unpredictable results.

At this critical point Stanley Gibbons has been acquired by Flying Flowers Ltd, the well-known specialist mail-order company. The new owners have announced their intention of re-asserting Stanley Gibbons' position at the very centre of philately with a commitment to maintain and improve stocks, products and, above all, the level of service provided to those most important people, our customers. Preparations have already commenced for the introduction of a new catalogue editing system with the intention that SG catalogues should lead the hobby into the new Millennium.

PRICES

There have been continued signs of consolidation in the stamp market during the last twelve months. Today's collectors are, however, becoming more selective in their interests with the result that some areas and periods have shown more movement than others.

As in previous years much of this activity has been concentrated in the period between the early 1880s and 1945. There have, however, been several changes of emphasis, with the result that a number of **British West Indies** colonies, **Leeward Islands**, **St. Lucia** and **Trinidad & Tobago** for example, have seen a spread of price rises. Changes in the classic period are less extensive, but in this edition the early stamps of **British East Africa**, **Natal**, **Uganda** and the **Samoa** Express issue of 1877 show important increases.

A number of other African territories also show considerable activity. Significant price changes can be found for **Malawi (Nyasaland)** from 1895, and there are many rises amongst the overprinted stamps of **Griqualand West**. There is also renewed interest in the issues of **Somaliland Protectorate**.

Demand for many Asian countries continues with extensive price changes in **Straits Settlements**, **Federated Malay States**, **Labuan** and **North Borneo**.

Of particular interest to postal history collectors are the revised prices provided for **India** used in the **Straits Settlements**, **Great Britain** used in either **Niger Coast** or **Niger Company Territories**, and **Mauritius** stamps used in the **Seychelles**.

The level of price changes for modern issues remains patchy. There are, however, only a few price reductions for those issues still recognised as being over-stocked, and thematic demand has initiated many increases in price for stamps appearing during the late 1980s and early 1990s.

Errors and varieties continue to be popular and there are also useful price rises for some stamp booklets, notably for **Samoa** and **Singapore**.

REVISIONS IN THIS EDITION

The listing of Commonwealth watermark varieties, started last year, has been expanded to cover issues between 1901 and 1936. This has involved considerable research as King Edward VII and King George V stamps are often found with watermark reversed, or watermark inverted and reversed in addition to watermark inverted. Watermark reversed varieties have been given "x" suffixes and those with watermark inverted and reversed "y" suffixes. Where possible prices have also been provided, but in a number of instances it is difficult to establish the true scarcity of the new listings. There are, no doubt, others to be discovered and these will be added to future editions. It is intended that similar coverage will eventually be provided for those Queen Victoria issues where the watermark position is not completely haphazard.

Adding the watermark varieties to this edition has involved not only the Colonial stamps produced by the Crown Agents, but also **New Zealand**, **Palestine** and **South Africa** where many inverted watermarks exist. The watermark positions of the **Federated Malay States** and **Kedah** are particularly complex.

Many Commonwealth printed on the gummed side errors are now listed for the first time and there have been improvements in the coverage of stamp booklets from **Jamaica** and for **Sri Lanka (Ceylon)** where the existence of the 1905 1 r. 45 booklet has now been confirmed.

Following the publication of Peter Fernbank's impressive new handbook on the King George V low value Key Plate stamps, the opportunity has been taken to revise the catalogue listings of this fascinating series. There are some number changes and additions for this volume, with the sections for **Nigeria** and **Sri Lanka (Ceylon)** being rewritten to provide improved chronological sequences. The dates for many of the listed shades have been corrected.

Further King George VI flaws have been submitted by Richard Lockyer of the King George VI Collectors' Society, and examples can be found under **Namibia** and **South Africa** in this volume.

Leeward Islands. The broken top right scroll flaw on Row 5/11, previously only recorded for Bermuda, is now listed on the 1942 printing of the 10s. having been confirmed by Harold Green.

Malawi. A number of important varieties on the **Nyasaland** high value Key Type design between 1908 and 1938 have been added with the help of David Springbett.

Malaysia. Separate listings for the two shades of the **Straits Settlements** 1883-89 2 c. rose overprinted or surcharged for various Malay States are now provided and I am grateful to Richard Hale for his advice on this project.

Much additional work has been done on the continuing saga of the different perforations for the 1986 States Agricultural Products definitives. Nigel Haworth, Len Stanway and Lim Ken Beng have all supplied information which has been incorporated into the listings.

The 1921-40 issue of **Trengganu** has been rewritten to reflect the research published by Dr W.H. Barker of the Malay Study Group. Those ordinary paper printings which were placed on sale in the state before the Japanese Occupation are now listed.

New Zealand. A number of new varieties have been added to recent issues.

Papua New Guinea. The **Papua** 1901 Lakatoi stamps and the 1906-07 surcharges have been rewritten to reflect the latest research into the various combinations of watermark format and paper thickness.

Pitcairn Islands. A further 1925 cachet is listed and illustrated.

Singapore. Further emergency printings of the 1994 Marine Life definitives are now included.

South Africa. Additional information, supplied by Martin Eichelle, has been incorporated into the **Natal** listings. Notes on the early postal history of **Zululand** have been provided by Wilson Wong.

Philatelic Foundation miniature sheets (which also occur in Namibia and the previous tribal homelands), together with the subsequent "corporate" miniature sheets, are now described in footnotes.

Tonga. Additional varieties on issues between 1893 and 1942 are now listed and illustrated based on material provided by Greg Jorgensen and Janet Klug.

As always it is impossible to individually thank all those collectors, dealers and postal professionals who have contributed to this edition. Without such assistance the task of compiling each *Part 1* would be virtually impossible.

David J. Aggersberg

Stanley Gibbons Holdings Plc Addresses

STANLEY GIBBONS LIMITED, STANLEY GIBBONS AUCTIONS

399 Strand, London WC2R 0LX
Auction Room and Specialist Stamp Departments. Open Monday–Friday 9.30 a.m. to 5 p.m.
Shop. Open Monday–Friday 8.30 a.m. to 6 p.m. and Saturday 10 a.m. to 4 p.m.
Telephone 0171 836 8444 and Fax 0171 836 7342 for all departments.

STANLEY GIBBONS PUBLICATIONS

5 Parkside, Christchurch Road, Ringwood, Hants BH24 3SH.
Telephone 01425 472363 (24 hour answer phone service), Fax 01425 470247 and E-mail info@stangib.demon.co.uk
Publications Showroom (at above address). Open Monday–Friday 9 a.m. to 3 p.m.
Publications Mail Order. FREEPHONE 0800 611622. Trade Desk. 01425 478776.
Both Monday–Friday 8.30 a.m. to 5 p.m.

URCH HARRIS & CO

(a division of Stanley Gibbons Ltd)
1 Denmark Avenue, Bristol, BS1 5HD.
UH New Issue Service
Telephone 0117 9349333 and Fax 0117 9273037
Monday–Friday 8.30 a.m. to 5 p.m.

FRASER'S

(a division of Stanley Gibbons Ltd)
399 Strand, London WC2R 0LX
Autographs, photographs, letters and documents.
Telephone 0171 836 8444 and Fax 0171 836 7342
Monday-Friday 9 a.m. to 5.30 p.m. and Saturday 10 a.m. to 4 p.m.

STANLEY GIBBONS PUBLICATIONS OVERSEAS REPRESENTATION

Stanley Gibbons Publications are represented overseas by the following sole distributors (*), distributors (**) or licensees (***).

Australia

Lighthouse Philatelic (Aust.) Pty Ltd*
PO Box 763
Strawberry Hills
New South Wales 2012
Australia

Stanley Gibbons (Australia) Pty Ltd***
Level 6, 36 Clarence Street
Sydney N.S.W. 2000
Australia

Belgium and Luxembourg**

Davo c/o Philac
Rue du Midi 48
Bruxelles 1000
Belgium

Canada*

Lighthouse Publications (Canada) Ltd
255 Duke Street
Montreal
Quebec
Canada H3C 2M2

Denmark**

Davo
c/o Lindner Falzlos
Gl Randersvej 28
8450 Hammel
Denmark

Finland**

Davo
c/o Suomen Postimerkkeily
Ludvingkatu 5
SF-00130 Helsinki
Finland

France*

Davo France (Casteilla)
10 Rue Leon Foucault
78184 St Quentin Yvelines Cesex
France

Germany and Austria*

Leuchtturm Albenverlag Gmbh u. Co.
Am Spakenberg 45
Postfach 1340
D21495 Geesthacht
Germany

Hong Kong**

Po-on Stamp Service
GPO Box 2498
Hong Kong

Israel**

Capital Stamps
PO Box 3769
Jerusalem 91036
Israel

Italy*

Secrian Srl
Via Pantelleria 2
1-20156 Milano
Italy

Japan**

Japan Philatelic Co Ltd
PO Box 2
Suginami-Minami
Tokyo
Japan

Netherlands*

Davo Publications
PO Box 411
7400 AK Deventer
Netherlands

New Zealand***

Stanley Gibbons (New Zealand) Ltd
PO Box 80
Wellington
New Zealand

Norway**

Davo Norge A/S
PO Box 738 Sentrum
N-01 05 Oslo
Norway

Singapore***

Stanley Gibbons (Singapore) Pte Ltd
Raffles City
PO Box 1689
Singapore 9117

South Africa**

Republic Coin and Stamp
Accessories (Pty) Ltd
PO Box 11199
Johannesburg
RSA 2000

Sweden*

Chr Winther Sorensen AB
Box 43
S-310 Knaered
Sweden

Switzerland**

Phila Service
Burgstrasse 160
CH 4125 Riehen
Switzerland

West Indies/Caribbean**

Hugh Dunphy
PO Box 413
Kingston 10
Jamaica
West Indies

Stanley Gibbons Stamp Catalogue
Complete List of Parts

1 British Commonwealth
(Annual in two volumes)

2 Austria & Hungary (5th edition, 1994)
Austria, Bosnia & Herzegovina, U.N. (Vienna), Hungary

3 Balkans (4th edition, 1998)
Albania, Bosnia & Herzegovina, Bulgaria, Croatia, Greece & Islands, Macedonia, Rumania, Slovenia, Yugoslavia

4 Benelux (4th edition, 1993)
Belgium & Colonies, Netherlands & Colonies, Luxembourg

5 Czechoslovakia & Poland (5th edition, 1994)
Czechoslovakia, Bohemia & Moravia, Slovakia, Poland

6 France (4th edition, 1993)
France, Colonies, Post Offices, Andorra, Monaco

7 Germany (5th edition, 1996)
Germany, States, Colonies, Post.Offices

8 Italy & Switzerland (5th edition, 1997)
Italy & Colonies, Fiume, San Marino, Vatican City, Trieste, Liechtenstein, Switzerland, U.N. (Geneva)

9 Portugal & Spain (4th edition, 1996)
Andorra, Portugal & Colonies, Spain & Colonies

10 Russia (4th edition, 1991)
Russia, Baltic States, Mongolia, Tuva

11 Scandinavia (4th edition, 1994)
Aland Island, Denmark, Faroe Islands, Finland, Greenland, Iceland, Norway, Sweden

12 Africa since Independence A-E (2nd edition, 1983)
Algeria, Angola, Benin, Bophuthatswana, Burundi, Cameroun, Cape Verde, Central African Republic, Chad, Comoro Islands, Congo, Djibouti, Equatorial Guinea, Ethiopia

13 Africa since Independence F-M (1st edition, 1981)
Gabon, Guinea, Guinea-Bissau, Ivory Coast, Liberia, Libya, Malagasy Republic, Mali, Mauritania, Morocco, Mozambique

14 Africa since Independence N-Z (1st edition, 1981)
Niger Republic, Rwanda, St. Thomas & Prince, Senegal, Somalia, Sudan, Togo, Transkei, Tunisia, Upper Volta, Venda, Zaire

15 Central America (2nd edition, 1984)
Costa Rica, Cuba, Dominican Republic, El Salvador, Guatemala, Haiti, Honduras, Mexico, Nicaragua, Panama

16 Central Asia (3rd edition, 1992)
Afghanistan, Iran, Turkey

17 China (6th edition, 1998)
China, Taiwan, Tibet, Foreign P.O.'s, Hong Kong, Macao

18 Japan & Korea (4th edition, 1997)
Japan, Ryukyus, Korean Empire, South Korea, North Korea

19 Middle East (5th edition, 1996)
Bahrain, Egypt, Iraq, Israel, Jordan, Kuwait, Lebanon, Oman, Qatar, Saudi Arabia, Syria, U.A.E., Yemen A.R., Yemen P.D.R.

20 South America (3rd edition, 1989)
Argentina, Bolivia, Brazil, Chile, Colombia, Ecuador, Paraguay, Peru, Surinam, Uruguay, Venezuela

21 South-East Asia (3rd edition, 1995)
Bhutan, Burma, Indonesia, Kampuchea, Laos, Nepal, Philippines, Thailand, Vietnam

22 United States (4th edition, 1994)
U.S. & Possessions, Canal Zone, Marshall Islands, Micronesia, Palau, U.N. (New York, Geneva, Vienna)

GREAT BRITAIN SPECIALISED CATALOGUES

Volume 1 Queen Victoria (11th edition, 1997)
Volume 2 King Edward VII to King George VI (10th edition, 1996)
Volume 3 Queen Elizabeth II Pre-decimal Issues (10th edition, 1998)
Volume 4 Queen Elizabeth II Decimal Definitive Issues (8th edition, 1996)
Volume 5 Queen Elizabeth II Decimal Special Issues (3rd edition, 1998)

THEMATIC CATALOGUES

Collect Aircraft on Stamps (1st edition, 1994)
Collect Birds on Stamps (4th edition, 1996)
Collect Butterflies and Other Insects on Stamps (out of print)
Collect Chess on Stamps (out of print)
Collect Fish on Stamps (1st edition, 1998)
Collect Fungi on Stamps (2nd edition, 1997)
Collect Mammals on Stamps (out of print)
Collect Railways on Stamps (new edition late 1998)
Collect Shells on Stamps (1st edition, 1995)
Collect Ships on Stamps (out of print)

Numbers Altered

The table below is a cross-reference for those stamps the catalogue numbers of which have altered in this edition.
For list of Numbers Added to this edition see page xxii.

Old	*New*
Jamaica	
SB6a	SB7b
Kenya, Uganda and Tanganyika	
22b	*Deleted*
33b	33c
134a	134b
Kuwait	
16a	16b
17a	17b
19a/b	19b/c
32a	*Deleted*
Malawi	
62a	62b
96c/cb	96e/eb
99a/ac	99e/ec
Malaysia—Straits Settlements	
205a	205b
211	211a
211a	211
212	212a
212a	212
225	225b
225a/ab	225/a
231b	231ba
Federated Malay States	
34a	34b
38a	38b
39a/d	39b/e
41a/b	41b/bb
42a	42b
44b	44ab
47a/bc	47c/cc
47c	47b
48a	48b
74a	74b
Kedah	
30a	30b
35a	35b
36a	36b
Negri Sembilan (Sungei Ujong)	
43b	43db
Pahang	
4a	4b
Perlis	
79w	79aw
Selangor	
38a	38b
Trengganu	
26	27
27/8	30/1
29	35
30/2	37/9
33	41
34/47	45/58
48	26
49/50	28/9
51/3	32/4
54	36
55	40
56/8	42/4
Siamese Posts in Northern Malaya	
Z220	Z221
Z308/9	Z307/8
Z338/40	Z339/41
Japanese Occupation of Malaya	
J164a/c	J164b/c
J193a/c	J1936/d
J222a	J222b
J263b	J263c
J274a	J274b
J274b	J274a
J274ca	J274cb
J274cb	J274ca
Sarawak	
74	74c
74c	74ca
Maldive Islands	
MS2608	MS2625
Malta	
47a	47b
75a	75b
221a	221b
238a/ac	238b/bc
Mauritius	
219a	219b
226a/b	226b/c
254a	254b
Montserrat	
61a/ab	61b/ba
O10b	O10c
O10c	O10b
Morocco Agencies	
3/c	3c/cc
3d/dc	3/b
Namibia	
140a	140b
New Zealand	
420a/b	420b/c
422d/e	422e/f
424b/cb	424c/db
425b/d	425c/e
430b/c	430c/d
446b/bb	446c/cb
448a	448b
449a	449b
451a	451b
468d/da	468e/ea
557a/ba	557b/ca
560a	560b
563a	563b
568b/ba	568c/ca
O76a/ab	O76b/ba
O96a/ab	O96b/ba
O100a/b	O100b/c
O102a/b	O102b/c
O105a/b	O105b/c
O111b	O111c
L62a	L62ab
Nigeria—Lagos	
47a	47b
Nigeria	
5d	5e
6d	6e
10d	10e
13	13ba
15a	15c
16a	16c
17	18
18/19	21/2
20/5	24/9
25a	15b
25b	16b
25c	18a
25d	22a
25e	25a
26	17
27/8	19/20
29	23
29a	20a
29b	24a
29c	27a
29d	28a
29e	29a
52aa/a	52a/b
57b	57ab
495/6	500/1
497/501	495/9
680/720	681/721
Pakistan—Bahawalpur	
O28a/31a	O28b/31b
Palestine	
82a	82b
SB2/3	SB3/4
Papua New Guinea—Papua	
14a/b	15/16
14c	1a
14d/e	4a/ab
15	9a
16	*Deleted*
17	11a
18/a	*Deleted*
19/a	13b/ba
20	14a
21	15a
22	16a
23/6	17/20
27/9b	24/8
30/2	21/3
38	41
38a	*Deleted*
38b	44
38c	45
38d	34a
39	35a
39a	*Deleted*
39b	35ac
40/2	38/40
42a	*Deleted*
43/4	42/3
45/a	44b/ba
46	45a
95a/c	95b/d
101a/b	101b/c
O3	O2a
Papua New Guinea	
796/7	801/2
Pitcairn Islands	
C15/16	C16/17
St. Helena	
199w	200w
St. Kitts-Nevis—Nevis	
984/93	1008/17
994/17	984/1007
St. Lucia	
82a	*Deleted*
St. Vincent	
19a	19ab
Samoa	
182a	182b
Seychelles	
88b	88c
109	107a
120	119a
Sierra Leone	
2574/606	2586/622
Singapore	
753h	753j
826a	826ba
D21/5	D23/7
South Africa—New Republic	
11a	11b
Transvaal	
119d/e	119e/f
274a	274b
South Africa	
30c/ca	30d/da
31c/ca	31d/da
34a	34b
35ba	35c
45a/ba	45b/d
46a/b	46b/c
49a	49b
54a/b	54b/c
56c/e	56d/f
57b	57c
64a	64b
114b/ba	114c/ca
130a	130b
913/31	919/37
MS932	*Deleted*
MS933/43	MS938/48
SB28/34	SB30/7
O13c/ca	O13d/da
O21a	O21b
O22a	O22b
O40	*Deleted*
Sri Lanka	
308	307a
309/10	308/a
311/12	309/a
313/14	310/a
315/16	311/a
317/18	312/a
319/20	313/ab
321/9c	314/23
340/1	341/2
342	344
343	346
343a	346c
344	348
345	350
345a	350c
346	351
346a	351b
347	352
347a	352b
348/54	353/9
355	340
356	343
357	345
358	347
358a	347b
359	349
359a	349b
360c	346b
360d	347a
360e	349a
360f	350b
360g	351a
360h	352a
360i	354a
360j	353a
Sudan	
52a	52b
76a	76b
Tanzania	
45a	45b
320b/h	320c/i
Tonga	
26a	26b
28a	28b
34a/b	34b/c
37o/oa	37p/pa
49b	49c
62a/b	62b/c
62ba	62cb
63a	63b
66b	66c
Trinidad and Tobago	
220a	220b
Tristan da Cunha	
C11	C12
C12	C11
Turks and Caicos Islands	
132a	132b
142/b	141/bb
169a	169b

Contents

General Philatelic Information

and Guidelines to the Scope of the Part 1 (British Commonwealth) Catalogue

The notes which follow seek to reflect current practice in compiling the Part 1 (British Commonwealth) Catalogue.

It scarcely needs emphasising that the *Stanley Gibbons Stamp Catalogue* has a very long history and that the vast quantity of information it contains has been carefully built up by successive generations through the work of countless individuals. Philately itself is never static and the Catalogue has evolved and developed during this long time-span. Thus, while these notes are important for today's criteria, they may be less precise the further back in the listings one travels. They are not intended to inaugurate some unwanted series of piecemeal alterations in a widely respected work, but it does seem to us useful that Catalogue users know as exactly as possible the policies currently in operation.

PRICES

The prices quoted in this Catalogue are the estimated selling prices of Stanley Gibbons Ltd at the time of publication. They are, *unless it is specifically stated otherwise*, for examples in fine condition for the issue concerned. Superb examples are worth more; those of a lower quality considerably less.

All prices are subject to change without prior notice and Stanley Gibbons Ltd may from time to time offer stamps below catalogue price. Individual low value stamps sold at 399, Strand are liable to an additional handling charge. Purchasers of new issues are asked to note that the prices charged for them contain an element for the service rendered and so may exceed the prices shown when the stamps are subsequently catalogued. Postage and handling charges are extra.

No guarantee is given to supply all stamps priced, since it is not possible to keep every catalogued item in stock. Commemorative issues may, at times, only be available in complete sets and not as individual values.

Quotation of prices. The prices in the left-hand column are for unused stamps and those in the right-hand column are for used.

A dagger (†) denotes that the item listed does not exist in that condition and a blank, or dash, that it exists, or may exist, but no market price is known.

Prices are expressed in pounds and pence sterling. One pound comprises 100 pence (£1 = 100p).

The method of notation is as follows: pence in numerals (e.g. 10 denotes ten pence); pound and pence, up to £100, in numerals (e.g. 4·25 denotes four pounds and twenty-five pence); prices above £100 expressed in whole pounds with the "£" sign shown.

Unused stamps. Great Britain and Commonwealth: the prices for unused stamps of Queen Victoria to King George V are for lightly hinged examples. Unused prices for King Edward VIII to Queen Elizabeth II issues are for unmounted mint.

Some stamps from the King George VI period are often difficult to find in unmounted mint condition. In such instances we would expect that collectors would need to pay a high proportion of the price quoted to obtain mounted mint examples. Generally speaking lightly mounted mint stamps from this reign, issued before 1945, are in considerable demand.

Mounted mint stamps from the reign of Queen Elizabeth II are frequently available at lower prices than those quoted for the stamps unmounted.

Used stamps. The used prices are normally for stamps postally used but may be for stamps cancelled-to-order where this practice exists.

A pen-cancellation on early issues can sometimes correctly denote postal use. Instances are individually noted in the Catalogue in explanation of the used price given.

Prices quoted for bisects on cover or on large piece are for those dated during the period officially authorised.

Stamps not sold unused to the public (e.g. some official stamps) are priced used only.

The use of "unified" designs, that is stamps inscribed for both postal and fiscal purposes, results in a number of stamps of very high face value. In some instances these may not have been primarily intended for postal purposes, but if they are so inscribed we include them. We only price such items used, however, where there is evidence of normal postal usage.

Cover prices. To assist collectors, cover prices are quoted for issues up to 1945 at the beginning of each country.

The system gives a general guide in the form of a factor by which the corresponding used price of the loose stamp should be multiplied when found in fine average condition on cover.

Care is needed in applying the factors and they relate to a cover which bears a single of the denomination listed; strips and blocks would need individual valuation outside the scope. If more than one denomination is present the most highly priced attracts the multiplier and the remainder are priced at the simple figure for used singles in arriving at a total.

The cover should be of non-philatelic origin, bearing the correct postal rate for the period and distance involved and cancelled with the markings normal to the offices concerned. Purely philatelic items have a cover value only slightly greater than the catalogue value for the corresponding used stamps. This applies generally to those high-value stamps used philatelically rather than in the normal course of commerce. Low-value stamps, e.g. ¼d. and ½d., are desirable when used as a single rate on cover and merit an increase in "multiplier" value.

First-day covers in the period up to 1945 are not within the scope of the system and the multiplier should not be used. As a special category of philatelic usage, with wide variations in valuation according to scarcity, they require separate treatment.

Oversized covers, difficult to accommodate on an album page, should be reckoned as worth little more than the corresponding value of the used stamps. The condition of a cover affects its value. Except for "wreck covers", serious damage or soiling reduce the value where the postal markings and stamps are ordinary ones. Conversely, visual appeal adds to the value and this can include freshness of appearance, important addresses, old-fashioned but legible hand-writing, historic town-names, etc.

The multipliers are a base on which further value would be added to take account of the cover's postal historical importance in demonstrating such things as unusual, scarce or emergency cancels, interesting routes, significant postal markings, combination usage, the development of postal rates, and so on.

For *Great Britain*, rather than multiplication factors, the cover price is shown as a third column, following the prices for unused and used stamps. It will be extended beyond King Edward VII in subsequent editions.

Minimum price. The minimum catalogue price quoted is 10p. For individual stamps prices between 10p. and 30p. are provided as a guide for catalogue users. The lowest price *charged* for individual stamps purchased from Stanley Gibbons Ltd is 30p.

Set prices. Set prices are generally for one of each value, excluding shades and varieties, but including major colour changes. Where there are alternative shades, etc., the cheapest is usually included. The number of stamps in the set is always stated for clarity. The mint prices for sets containing *se-tenant* pieces are based on the prices quoted for such combinations, and not on those for the individual stamps.

Varieties. Where plate or cylinder varieties are priced in a used condition the price quoted is for a fine used example with the cancellation well clear of the listed flaw.

Specimen stamps. The pricing of these items is explained under that heading.

Stamp booklets. Prices are for complete assembled booklets in fine condition with those issued before 1945 showing normal wear and tear. Incomplete booklets and those which have been "exploded" will, in general, be worth less than the figure quoted.

Repricing. Collectors will be aware that the market factors of supply and demand directly influence the prices quoted in this Catalogue. Whatever the scarcity of a particular stamp, if there is no one in the market who wishes to buy it it cannot be expected to achieve a high price. Conversely, the same item actively sought by numerous potential buyers may cause the price to rise.

All the prices in this Catalogue are examined during the preparation of each new edition by expert staff of Stanley Gibbons and repriced as necessary. They take many factors into account, including supply and demand, and are in close touch with the international stamp market and the auction world.

Commonwealth cover prices and advice on postal history material originally provided by Edward B. Proud.

GUARANTEE

All stamps are guaranteed genuine originals in the following terms:

If not as described, and returned by the purchaser, we undertake to refund the price paid to us in the original transaction. If any stamp is certified as genuine by the Expert Committee of the Royal Philatelic Society, London, or by B.P.A. Expertising Ltd, the purchaser shall not be entitled to make any claim against us for any error, omission or mistake in such certificate.

Consumers' statutory rights are not affected by the above guarantee.

The recognised Expert Committees in this country are those of the Royal Philatelic Society, 41 Devonshire Place, London W1N 1PE, and B.P.A. Expertising Ltd, P.O. Box 137, Leatherhead, Surrey KT22 0RG. They do not undertake valuations under any circumstances and fees are payable for their services.

THE CATALOGUE IN GENERAL

Contents. The Catalogue is confined to adhesive postage stamps, including miniature sheets. For particular categories the rules are:

(*a*) Revenue (fiscal) stamps or telegraph stamps are listed only where they have been expressly authorised for postal duty.

(*b*) Stamps issued only precancelled are included, but normally issued stamps available additionally with precancel have no separate precancel listing unless the face value is changed.

(*c*) Stamps prepared for use but not issued, hitherto accorded full listing, are nowadays footnoted with a price (where possible).

(*d*) Bisects (trisects, etc.) are only listed where such usage was officially authorised.

(*e*) Stamps issued only on first day covers or in presentation packs and not available separately are not listed but may be priced in a footnote.

(*f*) New printings are only included in this Catalogue where they show a major philatelic variety, such as a change in shade, watermark or paper. Stamps which exist with or without imprint dates are listed separately; changes in imprint dates are mentioned in footnotes.

(*g*) Official and unofficial reprints are dealt with by footnote.

(*h*) Stamps from imperforate printings of modern issues which also occur perforated are covered by footnotes, but are listed where widely available for postal use.

Exclusions. The following are excluded: (*a*) non-postal revenue or fiscal stamps; (*b*) postage stamps used fiscally; (*c*) local carriage labels and private local issues; (*d*) telegraph stamps; (*e*) bogus or phantom stamps; (*f*) railway or airline letter fee stamps, bus or road transport company labels; (*g*) cut-outs; (*h*) all types of non-postal labels and souvenirs; (*i*) documentary labels for the postal service, e.g. registration, recorded delivery, air-mail etiquettes, etc.; (*j*) privately applied embellishments to official issues and privately commissioned items generally; (*k*) stamps for training postal officers.

Full listing. "Full listing" confers our recognition and implies allotting a catalogue number and (wherever possible) a price quotation.

In judging status for inclusion in the catalogue broad considerations are applied to stamps. They must be issued by a legitimate postal authority, recognised by the government concerned, and must be adhesives valid for proper postal use in the class of service for which they are inscribed. Stamps, with the exception of such categories as postage dues and officials, must be available to the general public, at face value, in reasonable quantities without any artificial restrictions being imposed on their distribution.

We record as abbreviated Appendix entries, without catalogue numbers or prices, stamps from countries which either persist in having far more issues than can be justified by postal need or have failed to maintain control over their distribution so that they have not been available to the public in reasonable quantities at face value. Miniature sheets and imperforate stamps are not mentioned in these entries.

The publishers of this catalogue have observed, with concern, the proliferation of "artificial" stamp-issuing territories. On several occasions this has resulted in separately inscribed issues for various component parts of otherwise united states or territories.

Stanley Gibbons Ltd have decided that where such circumstances occur, they will not, in the future, list these items in the SG catalogue without first satisfying themselves that the stamps represent a genuine political, historical or postal division within the country concerned. Any such issues which do not fulfil this stipulation will be recorded in the Catalogue Appendix only.

For errors and varieties the criterion is legitimate (albeit inadvertent) sale through a postal administration in the normal course of business. Details of provenance are always important; printers' waste and deliberately manufactured material are excluded.

Certificates. In assessing unlisted items due weight is given to Certificates from recognised Expert Committees and, where appropriate, we will usually ask to see them.

New issues. New issues are listed regularly in the Catalogue Supplement published in *Gibbons Stamp Monthly*, whence they are consolidated into the next available edition of the Catalogue.

Date of issue. Where local issue dates differ from dates of release by agencies, "date of issue" is the local date. Fortuitous stray usage before the officially intended date is disregarded in listing. For ease of reference, the Catalogue displays in the top corner the date of issue of the first set listed on each page.

Catalogue numbers. Stamps of each country are catalogued chronologically by date of issue. Subsidiary classes are placed at the end of the country, as separate lists, with a distinguishing letter prefix to the catalogue number, e.g. D for postage due, O for official and E for express delivery stamps.

The catalogue number appears in the extreme left column. The boldface Type numbers in the next column are merely cross-references to illustrations. Catalogue numbers in the *Gibbons Stamp Monthly* Supplement are provisional only and may need to be altered when the lists are consolidated. For the numbering of miniature sheets and sheetlets *see* section below.

Once published in the Catalogue, numbers are changed as little as possible; really serious renumbering is reserved for the occasions when a complete country or an entire issue is being rewritten. The edition first affected includes cross-reference tables of old and new numbers.

Our catalogue numbers are universally recognised in specifying stamps and as a hallmark of status.

Illustrations. Stamps are illustrated at three-quarters linear size. Stamps not illustrated are the same size and format as the value shown, unless otherwise indicated. Stamps issued only as miniature sheets have the stamp alone illustrated but sheet size is also quoted. Overprints, surcharges, watermarks and postmarks are normally actual size. Illustrations of varieties are often enlarged to show the detail. Stamp booklet covers are illustrated half-size, unless otherwise indicated.

Designers. Designers' names are quoted where known, though space precludes naming every individual concerned in the production of a set. In particular, photographers supplying material are usually named only where they also make an active contribution in the design stage; posed photographs of reigning monarchs are, however, an exception to this rule.

CONTACTING THE CATALOGUE EDITOR

The editor is always interested in hearing from people who have new information which will improve or correct the Catalogue. As a general rule he must see and examine the actual stamps before they can be considered for listing; photographs or photocopies are insufficient evidence.

Submissions should be made in writing to the Catalogue Editor, Stanley Gibbons Publications at the Ringwood office. The cost of return postage for items submitted is appreciated, and this should include the registration fee if required.

Where information is solicited purely for the benefit of the enquirer, the editor cannot undertake to reply if the answer is already contained in these published notes or if return postage is omitted. Written communications are greatly preferred to enquiries by telephone and the editor regrets that he or his staff cannot see personal callers without a prior appointment being made. Correspondence may be subject to delay during the production period of each new edition.

The editor welcomes close contact with study circles and is interested, too, in finding reliable local correspondents who will verify and supplement official information in countries where this is deficient.

We regret we do not give opinions as to the genuineness of stamps, nor do we identify stamps or number them by our Catalogue.

TECHNICAL MATTERS

The meanings of the technical terms used in the catalogue will be found in our *Philatelic Terms Illustrated* (3rd edition), (*price* £7.50 *plus postage and packing charge*).

References below to "more specialised" listings are to be taken to indicate, as appropriate, the Stanley Gibbons *Great Britain Specialised Catalogue* in 5 volumes or the *Great Britain Concise Catalogue*.

1. Printing

Printing errors. Errors in printing are of major interest to the Catalogue. Authenticated items meriting consideration would include: background, centre or frame inverted or omitted; centre or subject transposed; error of colour; error or omission of value; double prints and impressions; printed both sides; and so on. Designs *tête-bêche*, whether intentionally or by accident, are listable. *Se-tenant* arrangements of stamps are recognised in the listings or footnotes. Gutter pairs (a pair of stamps separated by blank margin) are not included in this volume. Colours only partially omitted are not listed. Stamps with embossing omitted and (for Commonwealth countries) stamps printed on the gummed side are reserved for our more specialised listings.

Printing varieties. Listing is accorded to major changes in the printing base which lead to completely new types. In recess-printing this could be a design re-engraved; in photogravure or photolithography a screen altered in whole or in part. It can also encompass flat-bed and rotary printing if the results are readily distinguishable.

To be considered at all, varieties must be constant.

Early stamps, produced by primitive methods, were prone to numerous imperfections: the lists reflect this, recognising re-entries, retouches, broken frames, misshapen letters, and so on. Printing technology has, however, radically improved over the years, during which time photogravure and lithography have become predominant. Varieties nowadays are more in the nature of flaws and these, being too specialised for this general catalogue, are almost always outside the scope. The development of our range of specialised catalogues allows us now to list those items which have philatelic significance in their appropriate volume.

In no catalogue, however, do we list such items as: dry prints, kiss prints, doctor-blade flaws, colour shifts or registration flaws (unless they lead to the complete omission of a colour from an individual stamp), lithographic ring flaws, and so on. Neither do we recognise fortuitous happenings like paper creases or confetti flaws.

Overprints (and surcharges). Overprints of different types qualify for separate listing. These include overprints in different colours; overprints from different printing processes such as litho and typo; overprints in totally different typefaces, etc. Major errors in machine-printed overprints are important and listable. They include: overprint inverted or omitted; overprint double (treble, etc.); overprint diagonal; overprint double, one inverted; pairs with one overprint omitted, e.g. from a radical shift to an adjoining stamp; error of colour; error of type fount; letters inverted or omitted, etc. If the overprint is handstamped, few of these would qualify and a distinction is drawn. We continue, however, to list pairs of stamps where one has a handstamped overprint and the other has not.

Varieties occurring in overprints will often take the form of broken letters, slight differences in spacing, rising spaces, etc. Only the most important would be considered for footnote mention.

Sheet positions. If space permits we quote sheet positions of listed varieties and authenticated data is solicited for this purpose.

De La Rue plates. The Catalogue classifies the general plates used by De La Rue for printing British Colonial stamps as follows:

VICTORIAN KEY TYPE

Die I

1. The ball of decoration on the second point of the crown appears as a dark mass of lines.
2. Dark vertical shading separates the front hair from the bun.
3. The vertical line of colour outlining the front of the throat stops at the sixth line of shading on the neck.
4. The white space in the coil of the hair above the curl is roughly the shape of a pin's head.

Die II

1. There are very few lines of colour in the ball and it appears almost white.
2. A white vertical strand of hair appears in place of the dark shading.
3. The line stops at the eighth line of shading.
4. The white space is oblong, with a line of colour partially dividing it at the left end.

Plates numbered 1 and 2 are both Die I. Plates 3 and 4 are Die II.

GEORGIAN KEY TYPE

Die I

A. The second (thick) line below the name of the country is cut slanting, conforming roughly to the shape of the crown on each side.
B. The labels of solid colour bearing the words "POSTAGE" and "& REVENUE" are square at the inner top corners.
C. There is a projecting "bud" on the outer spiral of the ornament in each of the lower corners.

Die II

A. The second line is cut vertically on each side of the crown.
B. The labels curve inwards at the top.
C. There is no "bud" in this position.

Unless otherwise stated in the lists, all stamps with watermark Multiple Crown CA (w **8**) are Die I while those with watermark Multiple Crown Script CA (w **9**) are Die II. The Georgian Die II was introduced in April 1921 and was used for Plates 10 to 22 and 26 to 28. Plates 23 to 25 were made from Die I by mistake.

2. Paper

All stamps listed are deemed to be on "ordinary" paper of the wove type and white in colour; only departures from this are normally mentioned.

Types. Where classification so requires we distinguish such other types of paper as, for example, vertically and horizontally laid; wove and laid bâtonné; card(board); carton; cartridge; glazed; granite; native; pelure; porous; quadrillé; ribbed; rice; and silk thread.

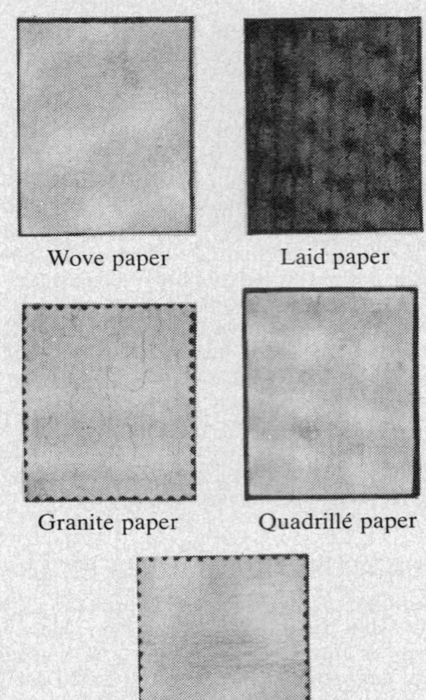

Wove paper · Laid paper · Granite paper · Quadrillé paper · Burelé band

The various makeshifts for normal paper are listed as appropriate. The varieties of double paper and joined paper are recognised. The security device of a printed burelé band on the back of a stamp, as in early Queensland, qualifies for listing.

Descriptive terms. The fact that a paper is handmade (and thus probably of uneven thickness) is mentioned where necessary. Such descriptive terms as "hard" and "soft"; "smooth" and 'rough"; "thick", "medium" and "thin" are applied where there is philatelic merit in classifying papers. We do not, for example, even in more specialised listings, classify paper thicknesses in the Wilding and Machin definitives of Great Britain. Weight standards for the paper apply to complete reels only, so that differences on individual stamps are acceptable to the printer provided the reel conforms overall.

Coloured, very white and toned papers. A coloured paper is one that is coloured right through (front and back of the stamp). In the Catalogue the colour of the paper is given in *italics*, thus:

black/*rose* = black design on rose paper.

Papers have been made specially white in recent years by, for example, a very heavy coating of chalk. We do not classify shades of whiteness of paper as distinct varieties. There does exist, however, a type of paper from early days called toned. This is off-white, often brownish or buffish, but it cannot be assigned any definite colour. A toning effect brought on by climate, incorrect storage or gum staining is disregarded here, as this was not the state of the paper when issued.

Modern developments. Two modern developments also affect the listings: printing on self-adhesive paper and the use of metallic foils. For self-adhesive stamps *see* under "Gum", below. Care should be taken not to damage the embossing on stamps impressed on metallic foils, such as Sierra Leone 1965–67, by subjecting the album pages to undue pressure. The possibility of faked "missing gold heads" is noted at the appropriate places in the listing of modern Great Britain.

"Ordinary" and "Chalk-surfaced" papers. The availability of many postage stamps for revenue purposes made necessary some safeguard against the illegitimate re-use of stamps with removable cancellations. This was at first secured by using fugitive inks and later by printing on chalk-surfaced paper, both of which made it difficult to remove any form of obliteration without also damaging the stamp design.

This catalogue lists these chalk-surfaced paper varieties from their introduction in 1905. Where no indication is given, the paper is "ordinary".

Our chalk-surfaced paper is specifically one which shows a black mark when touched with a silver wire. The paper used during the Second World War for high values, as in Bermuda, the Leeward Islands, etc., was thinly coated with some kind of surfacing which does not react to silver and is therefore regarded (and listed) as "ordinary". Stamps on chalk-surfaced paper can easily lose this coating through immersion in water.

Another paper introduced during the War as a substitute for chalk-surfaced is rather thick, very white and glossy and shows little or no watermark, nor does it show a black line when touched with silver. In the Bahamas high values this paper might be mistaken for the chalk-surfaced (which is thinner and poorer-looking) but for the silver test.

Some modern coated papers show little or no reaction to the silver test and, therefore, cannot be classed as chalk-surfaced.

Glazed paper. In 1969 the Crown Agents introduced a new general-purpose paper for use in conjunction with all current printing processes. It generally has a marked glossy surface but the degree varies according to the process used, being more marked in recess-printing stamps. As it does not respond to the silver test this presents a further test where previous printings were on chalky paper. A change of paper to the glazed variety merits separate listing.

Green and yellow papers. Issues of the First World War and immediate postwar period occur on green and yellow papers and these are given separate Catalogue listing. The original coloured papers (coloured throughout) gave way to surface-coloured papers, the stamps having "white backs"; other stamps show one colour on the front and a different one at the back. Because of the numerous variations a grouping of colours is adopted as follows:

YELLOW PAPERS

(1) The original *yellow* paper (throughout), usually bright in colour. The gum is often sparse, of harsh consistency and dull-looking. Used 1912–1920.

(2) The *white backs*. Used 1913–1914.

(3) A bright *lemon* paper. The colour must have a pronounced greenish tinge, different from the "yellow" in (1). As a rule, the gum on stamps using this lemon paper is plentiful, smooth and shiny, and the watermark shows distinctly. Care is needed with stamps printed in green on yellow paper (1) as it may appear that the paper is this lemon. Used 1914–1916.

(4) An experimental *orange-buff* paper. The colour must have a distinct brownish tinge. It is not to be confused with a muddy yellow (1) nor the misleading appearance (on the surface) of stamps printed in red on yellow paper where an engraved plate has been insufficiently wiped. Used 1918–1921.

(5) An experimental *buff* paper. This lacks the brownish tinge of (4) and the brightness of the yellow shades. The gum is shiny when compared with the matt type used on (4). Used 1919–1920.

(6) A *pale yellow* paper that has a creamy tone to the yellow. Used from 1920 onwards.

GREEN PAPERS

(7) The original "green" paper, varying considerably through shades of *blue-green* and *yellow-*

green, the front and back sometimes differing. Used 1912–1916.

(8) The *white backs*. Used 1913–1914.

(9) A paper blue-green on the surface with *pale olive* back. The back must be markedly paler than the front and this and the pronounced olive tinge to the back distinguish it from (7). Used 1916–1920.

(10) Paper with a vivid green surface, commonly called *emerald-green*; it has the olive back of (9). Used 1920.

(11) Paper with *emerald-green* both back and front. Used from 1920 onwards.

3. Perforation and Rouletting

Perforation gauge. The gauge of a perforation is the number of holes in a length of 2 cm. For correct classification the size of the holes (large or small) may need to be distinguished; in a few cases the actual number of holes on each edge of the stamp needs to be quoted.

Measurement. The Gibbons *Instanta* gauge is the standard for measuring perforations. The stamp is viewed against a dark background with the transparent gauge put on top of it. Though the gauge measures to decimal accuracy, perforations read from it are generally quoted in the Catalogue to the nearest half. For example:

Just over perf 12¾ to just under 13¼ = perf 13
Perf 13¼ exactly, rounded up = perf 13½
Just over perf 13¼ to just under 13¾ = perf 13½
Perf 13¾ exactly, rounded up = perf 14

However, where classification depends on it, actual quarter-perforations are quoted.

Notation. Where no perforation is quoted for an issue it is imperforate. Perforations are usually abbreviated (and spoken) as follows, though sometimes they may be spelled out for clarity. This notation for rectangular stamps (the majority) applies to diamond shapes if "top" is read as the edge to the top right.

P 14: perforated alike on all sides (read: "perf 14").

P 14 × 15: the first figure refers to top and bottom, the second to left and right sides (read: "perf 14 by 15"). This is a compound perforation. For an upright triangular stamp the first figure refers to the two sloping sides and second to the base. In inverted triangulars the base is first and the second figure refers to the sloping sides.

P 14–15: perforation measuring anything between 14 and 15: the holes are irregularly spaced, thus the gauge may vary along a single line or even along a single edge of the stamp (read: "perf 14 to 15").

P 14 *irregular*: perforated 14 from a worn perforator, giving badly aligned holes irregularly spaced (read: "irregular perf 14").

P comp(*ound*) 14 × 15: two gauges in use but not necessarily on opposite sides of the stamp. It could be one side in one gauge and three in the other; or two adjacent sides with the same gauge. (Read: "perf compound of 14 and 15".) For three gauges or more, abbreviated as "*P* 14, 14½, 15 *or compound*" for example.

P 14, 14½: perforated approximately 14¼ (read: "perf 14 or 14½"). It does *not* mean two stamps, one perf 14 and the other perf 14½. This obsolescent notation is gradually being replaced in the Catalogue.

Imperf: imperforate (not perforated).

Imperf × *P* 14: imperforate at top and bottom and perf 14 at sides.

Perf × imperf

P 14 × *imperf*: perf 14 at top and bottom and imperforate at sides.

Such headings as "*P* 13 × 14 (*vert*) and *P* 14 × 13 (*horiz*)" indicate which perforations apply to which stamp format—vertical or horizontal.

Some stamps are additionally perforated so that a label or tab is detachable; others have been perforated suitably for use as two halves. Listings are normally for whole stamps, unless stated otherwise.

Other terms. Perforation almost always gives circular holes; where other shapes have been used they are specified, e.g. square holes; lozenge perf. Interrupted perfs are brought about by the omission of pins at regular intervals. Perforations merely simulated by being printed as part of the design are of course ignored. With few exceptions, privately applied perforations are not listed.

In the nineteenth century perforations are often described as clean cut (clean, sharply incised holes), intermediate or rough (rough holes, imperfectly cut, often the result of blunt pins).

Perforation errors and varieties. Authenticated errors, where a stamp normally perforated is accidentally issued imperforate, are listed provided no traces of perforation (blind holes or indentations) remain. They must be provided as pairs, both stamps wholly imperforate, and are only priced in that form.

In Great Britain, numerous of these part-perforated stamps have arisen from the introduction of the Jumelle Press. This has a rotary perforator with rows of pins on one drum engaging with holes on another. Engagement is only gradual when the perforating unit is started up or stopped, giving rise to perforations "fading out", a variety mentioned above as not listed.

Stamps imperforate between stamp and sheet margin are not listed in this catalogue, but such errors on Great Britain stamps will be found in the *Great Britain Specialised Catalogue*.

Pairs described as "imperforate between" have the line of perforations between the two stamps omitted.

Imperf between (*horiz pair*): a horizontal pair of stamps with perfs all around the edges but none between the stamps.

Imperf between (*vert pair*): a vertical pair of stamps with perfs all around the edges but none between the stamps.

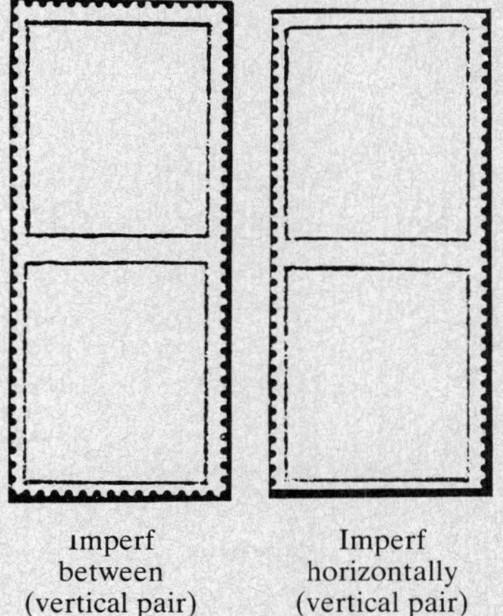
Imperf between (vertical pair)   Imperf horizontally (vertical pair)

Where several of the rows have escaped perforation the resulting varieties are listable. Thus:

Imperf vert (*horiz pair*): a horizontal pair of stamps perforated top and bottom; all three vertical directions are imperf—the two outer edges and between the stamps.

Imperf horiz (*vert pair*): a vertical pair perforated at left and right edges; all three horizontal directions are imperf—the top, bottom and between the stamps.

Straight edges. Large sheets cut up before issue to post offices can cause stamps with straight edges, i.e. imperf on one side or on two sides at right angles. They are not usually listable in this condition and are worth less than corresponding stamps properly perforated all round. This does not, however, apply to certain stamps, mainly from coils and booklets, where straight edges on various sides are the manufacturing norm affecting every stamp. The listings and notes make clear which sides are correctly imperf.

Malfunction. Varieties of double, misplaced or partial perforation caused by error or machine malfunction are not listable, neither are freaks, such as perforations placed diagonally from paper folds, nor missing holes caused by broken pins.

Centering. Well-centred stamps have designs surrounded by equal opposite margins. Where this condition affects the price the fact is stated.

Types of perforating. Where necessary for classification, perforation types are distinguished. These include:

Line perforation from one line of pins punching single rows of holes at a time.

Comb perforation from pins disposed across the sheet in comb formation, punching out holes at three sides of the stamp a row at a time.

Harrow perforation applied to a whole pane or sheet at one stroke.

Rotary perforation from toothed wheels operating across a sheet, then crosswise.

Sewing-machine perforation. The resultant condition, clean-cut or rough, is distinguished where required.

Pin-perforation is the commonly applied term for pin-roulette in which, instead of being punched out, round holes are pricked by sharp-pointed pins and no paper is removed.

Mixed perforation occurs when stamps with defective perforations are re-perforated in a different gauge.

Punctured stamps. Perforation holes can be punched into the face of the stamp. Patterns of small holes, often in the shape of initial letters, are privately applied devices against pilferage. These "perfins" are outside the scope except for Australia, Canada, Cape of Good Hope, Papua and Sudan where they were used as official stamps by the national administration. Identification devices, when officially inspired, are listed or noted; they can be shapes, or letters or words formed from holes, sometimes converting one class of stamp into another.

Rouletting. In rouletting the paper is cut, for ease of separation, but none is removed. The gauge is measured, when needed, as for perforations. Traditional French terms descriptive of the type of cut are often used and types include:

Arc roulette (*percé en arc*). Cuts are minute, spaced arcs, each roughly a semicircle.

Cross roulette (*percé en croix*). Cuts are tiny diagonal crosses.

Line roulette (*percé en ligne* or *en ligne droite*). Short straight cuts parallel to the frame of the stamp. The commonest basic roulette. Where not further described, "roulette" means this type.

Rouletted in colour or *coloured roulette* (*percé en lignes colorées* or *en lignes de couleur*). Cuts with coloured edges, arising from notched rule inked simultaneously with the printing plate.

Saw-tooth roulette (*percé en scie*). Cuts applied zigzag fashion to resemble the teeth of a saw.

Serpentine roulette (*percé en serpentin*). Cuts as sharply wavy lines.

Zigzag roulette (*percé en zigzags*). Short straight cuts at angles in alternate directions, producing sharp points on separation. U.S. usage favours "serrate(d) roulette" for this type.

Pin-roulette (originally *percé en points* and now *perforés trous d'epingle*) is commonly called pin-perforation in English.

4. Gum

All stamps listed are assumed to have gum of some kind; if they were issued without gum this is stated. Original gum (o.g.) means that which was present on the stamp as issued to the public. Deleterious climates and the presence of certain chemicals can cause gum to crack and, with early stamps, even make the paper deteriorate. Unscrupulous fakers are adept in removing it and regumming the stamp to meet the unreasoning demand often made for "full o.g." in cases where such a thing is virtually impossible.

The gum normally used on stamps has been gum arabic until the late 1960s when synthetic adhesives were introduced. Harrison and Sons Ltd for instance use *polyvinyl alcohol,* known to philatelists as PVA. This is almost invisible except for a slight yellowish tinge which was incorporated to make it possible to see that the stamps have been gummed. It has advantages in hot countries, as stamps do not curl and sheets are less likely to stick together. Gum arabic and PVA are not distinguished in the lists except that where a stamp exists with both forms this is indicated in footnotes. Our more specialised catalogues provide separate listing of gums for Great Britain.

Self-adhesive stamps are issued on backing paper, from which they are peeled before affixing to mail. Unused examples are priced as for backing paper intact, in which condition they are recommended to be kept. Used examples are best collected on cover or on piece.

5. Watermarks

Stamps are on unwatermarked paper except where the heading to the set says otherwise.

Detection. Watermarks are detected for Catalogue description by one of four methods: (1) holding stamps to the light; (2) laying stamps face down on a dark background; (3) adding a few drops of petroleum ether 40/60 to the stamp laid face down in a watermark tray; (4) by use of the Morley-Bright Detector, or other equipment, which work by revealing the thinning of the paper at the watermark (Note that petroleum ether is highly inflammable in use and can damage photogravure stamps.)

Listable types. Stamps occurring on both watermarked and unwatermarked papers are different types and both receive full listing.

Single watermarks (devices occurring once on every stamp) can be modified in size and shape as between different issues; the types are noted but not usually separately listed. Fortuitous absence of watermark from a single stamp or its gross displacement would not be listable.

To overcome registration difficulties the device may be repeated at close intervals (a *multiple watermark*), single stamps thus showing parts of several devices. Similarly, a large *sheet watermark* (or *all-over watermark*) covering numerous stamps can be used. We give informative notes and illustrations for them. The designs may be such that numbers of stamps in the sheet automatically lack watermark: this is not a listable variety. Multiple and all-over watermarks sometimes undergo modifications, but if the various types are difficult to distinguish from single stamps notes are given but not separate listings.

Papermakers' watermarks are noted where known but not listed separately, since most stamps in the sheet will lack them. Sheet watermarks which are nothing more than officially adopted papermakers' watermarks are, however, given normal listing.

Marginal watermarks, falling outside the pane of stamps, are ignored except where misplacement caused the adjoining row to be affected, in which case they are footnoted.

Watermark errors and varieties. Watermark errors are recognised as of major importance. They comprise stamps intended to be on unwatermarked paper but issued watermarked by mistake, or stamps printed on paper with the wrong watermark. Varieties showing letters omitted from the watermark are also included, but broken or deformed bits on the dandy roll are not.

Watermark positions. The diagram shows how watermark position is described in the Catalogue. Paper has a side intended for printing and watermarks are usually impressed so that they read normally when looked through from that printed side. However, since philatelists customarily detect watermarks by looking at the back of the stamp the watermark diagram also makes clear what is actually seen.

Illustrations in the Catalogue are of watermarks in normal positions (from the front of the stamps) and are actual size where possible.

Differences in watermark position are collectable as distinct varieties. This Catalogue now lists inverted, sideways inverted and reversed watermark varieties on Commonwealth stamps issued after 1900 *except* where the watermark position is completely haphazard. It is hoped to extend such listings to earlier issues in due course.

Great Britain inverted and sideways inverted watermarks can be found in the *Great Britain Specialised Catalogue* and the *Great Britain Concise Catalogue*.

Where a watermark comes indiscriminately in various positions our policy is to cover this by a general note: we do not give separate listings because the watermark position in these circumstances has no particular philatelic importance. There is a general note of this sort in modern Cyprus, for example. Issues printed since 1962 by Aspioti-Elka occur with the vertical stamps having the watermark normal or inverted, while horizontal stamps are likewise found with the watermark reading upwards or downwards.

AS DESCRIBED (Read through front of stamp)		AS SEEN DURING WATERMARK DETECTION (Stamp face down and back examined)
GvR	Normal	GvR (reversed)
GvR (inverted)	Inverted	GvR (reversed and inverted)
GvR (reversed)	Reversed	GvR
GvR (reversed and inverted)	Reversed and inverted	GvR (inverted)
GvR (sideways)	Sideways	GvR (sideways, reversed)
GvR (sideways inverted)	Sideways inverted	GvR (sideways inverted, reversed)

Standard types of watermark. Some watermarks have been used generally for various British possessions rather than exclusively for a single colony. To avoid repetition the Catalogue classifies 17 general types, as under, with references in the headings throughout the listings being given either in words or in the form "*W* w **14**" (meaning "watermark type w **14**"). In those cases where watermark illustrations appear in the listings themselves, the respective reference reads, for example, *W* **153**, thus indicating that the watermark will be found in the normal sequence of illustrations as (type) **153**.

The general types are as follows, with an example of each quoted.

W	*Description*	*Example*
w **1**	Large Star	St. Helena No. 1
w **2**	Small Star	Turks Is. No. 4
w **3**	Broad (pointed) Star	Grenada No. 24
w **4**	Crown (over) CC, small stamp	Antigua No. 13
w **5**	Crown (over) CC, large stamp	Antigua No. 31
w **6**	Crown (over) CA, small stamp	Antigua No. 21
w **7**	Crown CA (CA over Crown), large stamp	Sierra Leone No. 54
w **8**	Multiple Crown CA	Antigua No. 41
w **9**	Multiple Crown Script CA	Seychelles No. 158
w **9*a***	do. Error	Seychelles No. 158a
w **9*b***	do. Error	Seychelles No. 158b
w **10**	V over Crown	N.S.W. No. 327
w **11**	Crown over A	N.S.W. No. 347
w **12**	Multiple St. Edward's Crown Block CA	Antigua No. 149
w **13**	Multiple PTM	Johore No. 166
w **14**	Multiple Crown CA Diagonal	Antigua No. 426
w **15**	Multiple POST OFFICE	Kiribati No. 141
w **16**	Multiple Crown Script CA Diagonal	Ascension No. 376
w **17**	Multiple CARTOR	Brunei No. 357

CC in these watermarks is an abbreviation for "Crown Colonies" and CA for "Crown Agents". Watermarks w **1**, w **2** and w **3** are on stamps printed by Perkins, Bacon; w **4** onwards on stamps from De La Rue and other printers.

w **1**
Large Star

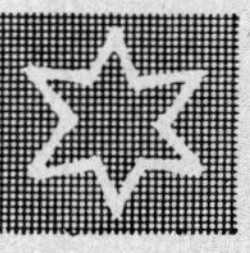

w **2**
Small Star

w **3**
Broad (pointed) Star

Watermark w **1**, *Large Star,* measures 15 to 16 mm across the star from point to point and about 27 mm from centre to centre vertically between stars in the sheet. It was made for long stamps like Ceylon 1857 and St. Helena 1856.

Watermark w **2**, *Small Star,* is of similar design but measures 12 to 13½ mm from point to point and 24 mm from centre to centre vertically. It was for use with ordinary-size stamps such as Grenada 1863–71.

When the Large Star watermark was used with the smaller stamps it only occasionally comes in the centre of the paper. It is frequently so misplaced as to show portions of two stars above and below and this eccentricity will very often help in determining the watermark.

Watermark w **3**, *Broad (pointed) Star*, resembles w **1** but the points are broader.

w **4**
Crown (over) CC

w **5**
Crown (over) CC

Two *Crown (over) CC* watermarks were used: w **4** was for stamps of ordinary size and w **5** for those of larger size.

w **6**
Crown (over) CA

w **7**
CA over Crown

Two watermarks of *Crown CA* type were used, w **6** being for stamps of ordinary size. The other, w **7**, is properly described as *CA over Crown*. It was specially made for paper on which it was intended to print long fiscal stamps: that some were used postally accounts for the appearance of w **7** in the Catalogue. The watermark occupies twice the space of the ordinary Crown CA watermark, w **6**. Stamps of normal size printed on paper with w **7** watermark show it *sideways*; it takes a horizontal pair of stamps to show the entire watermark.

w **8**
Multiple Crown CA

w **9**
Multiple Crown Script CA

Multiple watermarks began in 1904 with w **8**, *Multiple Crown CA*, changed from 1921 to w **9**, *Multiple Crown Script CA*. On stamps of ordinary size portions of two or three watermarks appear and on the large-sized stamps a greater number can be observed. The change to letters in script character with w **9** was accompanied by a Crown of distinctly different shape.

w **9a**: Error,
Crown missing

w **9b**: Error,
St. Edward's Crown

The *Multiple Crown Script CA* watermark, w **9**, is known with two errors recurring among the 1950–52 printings of several territories. In the first a crown has fallen away from the dandy-roll that impresses the watermark into the paper pulp. It gives w **9a**, *Crown missing*, but this omission has been found in both "Crown only" (*illustrated*) and "Crown CA" rows. The resulting faulty paper was used for Seychelles, Johore and the postage due stamps of nine colonies.

When the omission was noticed a second mishap occurred, which was to insert a wrong crown in the space, giving w **9b**, *St. Edward's Crown*. This produced varieties in Bahamas, St. Kitts-Nevis and Singapore and the incorrect crown likewise occurs in "Crown only" and "Crown CA" rows.

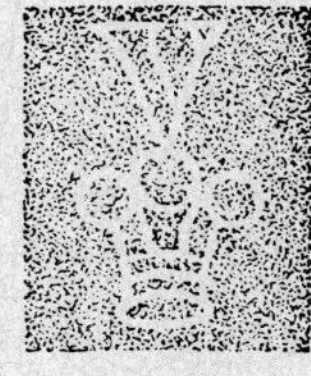

w **10**
V over Crown

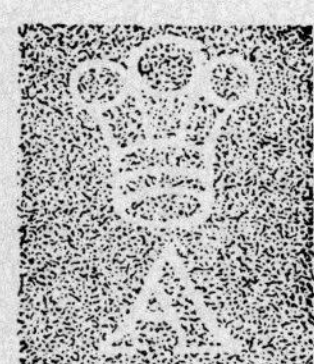

w **11**
Crown over A

Resuming the general types, two watermarks found in issues of several Australian States are: w **10**, *V over Crown*, and w **11**, *Crown over A*.

w **12**
Multiple St. Edward's
Crown Block CA

The *Multiple St. Edward's Crown Block CA* watermark, w **12**, was introduced in 1957 and besides the change in the Crown (from that used in *Multiple Crown Script CA*, w **9**) the letters reverted to block capitals. The new watermark began to appear sideways in 1966 and these stamps are generally listed as separate sets.

w **13**
Multiple PTM

The watermark w **13**, *Multiple PTM*, was introduced for new Malayan issues in November 1961.

w **14**
Multiple Crown CA
Diagonal

By 1974 the two dandy-rolls (the "upright" and the "sideways") for w **12** were wearing out; the Crown Agents therefore discontinued using the sideways-watermark one and retained the other only as a stand-by. A new dandy-roll with the pattern of w **14**, *Multiple Crown CA Diagonal*, was introduced and first saw use with some Churchill Centenary issues.

The new watermark has the design arranged in gradually spiralling rows. It is improved in design to allow smooth passage over the paper (the gaps between letters and rows had caused jolts in previous dandy-rolls) and the sharp corners and angles, where fibres used to accumulate, have been eliminated by rounding.

This watermark has no "normal" sideways position amongst the different printers using it. To avoid confusion our more specialised listings do not rely on such terms as "sideways inverted" but describe the direction in which the watermark points.

w **15**
Multiple POST OFFICE

During 1981 w **15**, *Multiple POST OFFICE*, was introduced for certain issues prepared by Philatelists Ltd, acting for various countries in the Indian Ocean, Pacific and West Indies.

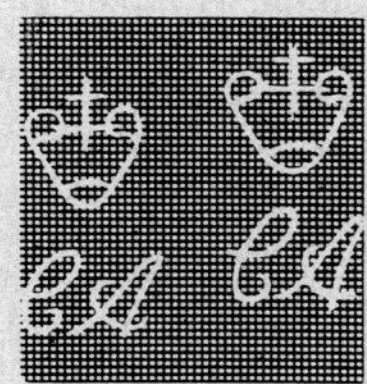

w **16**
Multiple Crown Script CA Diagonal

A new Crown Agents watermark was introduced during 1985, w **16**, *Multiple Crown Script CA Diagonal*. This was very similar to the previous w **14**, but showed "CA" in script rather than block letters. It was first used on the omnibus series of stamps commemorating the Life and Times of Queen Elizabeth the Queen Mother.

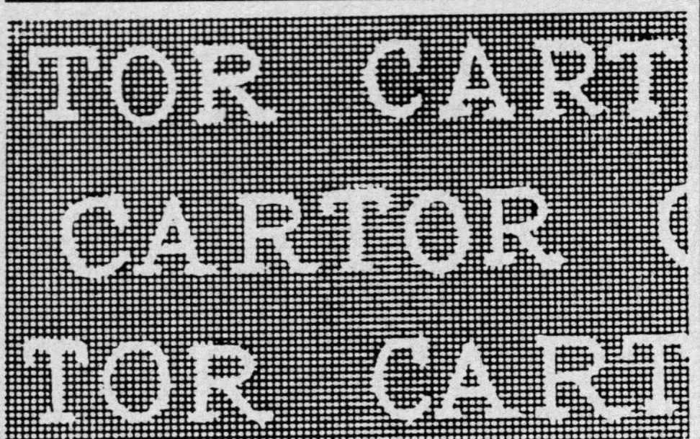

w **17**
Multiple CARTOR

Watermark w **17**, *Multiple CARTOR*, was used from 1985 for issues printed by this French firm for countries which did not normally use the Crown Agents watermark.

In recent years the use of watermarks has, to a small extent, been superseded by fluorescent security markings. These are often more visible from the reverse of the stamp (Cook Islands from 1970 onwards), but have occurred printed over the design (Hong Kong Nos. 415/30). In 1982 the Crown Agents introduced a new stock paper, without watermark, known as "C-Kurity" on which a fluorescent pattern of blue rosettes is visible on the reverse, beneath the gum. This paper was used for issues from Gambia and Norfolk Island.

6. Colours

Stamps in two or three colours have these named in order of appearance, from the centre moving outwards. Four colours or more are usually listed as multicoloured.

In compound colour names the second is the predominant one, thus:

orange-red = a red tending towards orange;

red-orange = an orange containing more red than usual.

Standard colours used. The 200 colours most used for stamp identification are given in the Stanley Gibbons Stamp Colour Key. The Catalogue has used the Stamp Colour Key as standard for describing new issues for some years. The names are also introduced as lists are rewritten, though exceptions are made for those early issues where traditional names have become universally established.

Determining colours. When comparing actual stamps with colour samples in the Stamp Colour Key, view in a good north daylight (or its best substitute: fluorescent "colour-matching" light). Sunshine is not recommended. Choose a solid portion of the stamp design; if available, marginal markings such as solid bars of colour or colour check dots are helpful. Shading lines in the design can be misleading as they appear lighter than solid colour. Postmarked portions of a stamp appear darker than normal. If more than one colour is present, mask off the extraneous ones as the eye tends to mix them.

Errors of colour. Major colour errors in stamps or overprints which qualify for listing are: wrong colours; one colour inverted in relation to the rest; albinos (colourless impressions), where these have Expert Committee certificates; colours completely omitted, but only on unused stamps (if found on used stamps the information is footnoted) and with good credentials, missing colours being frequently faked.

Colours only partially omitted are not recognised. Colour shifts, however spectacular, are not listed.

Shades. Shades in philately refer to variations in the intensity of a colour or the presence of differing amounts of other colours. They are particularly significant when they can be linked to specific printings. In general, shades need to be quite marked to fall within the scope of this Catalogue; it does not favour nowadays listing the often numerous shades of a stamp, but chooses a single applicable colour name which will indicate particular groups of outstanding shades. Furthermore, the listings refer to colours as issued: they may deteriorate into something different through the passage of time.

Modern colour printing by lithography is prone to marked differences of shade, even within a single run, and variations can occur within the same sheet. Such shades are not listed.

Aniline colours. An aniline colour meant originally one derived from coal-tar; it now refers more widely to colour of a particular brightness suffused on the surface of a stamp and showing through clearly on the back.

Colours of overprints and surcharges. All overprints and surcharges are in black unless stated otherwise in the heading or after the description of the stamp.

7. Specimen Stamps

Originally, stamps overprinted SPECIMEN were circulated to postmasters or kept in official records, but after the establishment of the Universal Postal Union supplies were sent to Berne for distribution to the postal administrations of member countries.

During the period 1884 to 1928 most of the stamps of British Crown Colonies required for this purpose were overprinted SPECIMEN in various shapes and sizes by their printers from typeset formes. Some locally produced provisionals were handstamped locally, as were sets prepared for presentation. From 1928 stamps were punched with holes forming the word SPECIMEN, each firm of printers using a different machine or machines. From 1948 the stamps supplied for U.P.U. distribution were no longer punctured.

Stamps of some other Commonwealth territories were overprinted or handstamped locally, while stamps of Great Britain and those overprinted for use in overseas postal agencies (mostly of the higher denominations) bore SPECIMEN overprints and handstamps applied by the Inland Revenue or the Post Office.

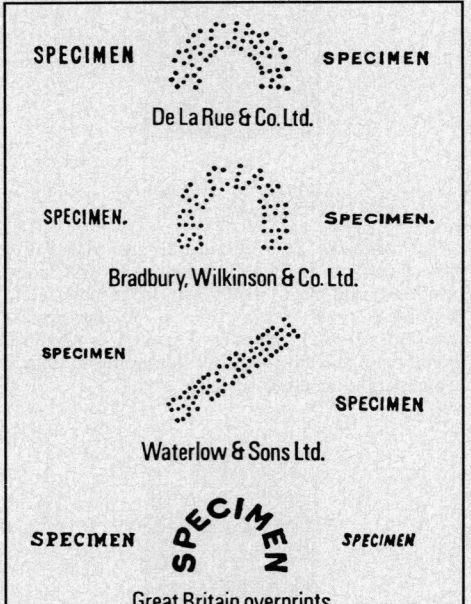

SPECIMEN SPECIMEN

De La Rue & Co. Ltd.

SPECIMEN. SPECIMEN.

Bradbury, Wilkinson & Co. Ltd.

SPECIMEN SPECIMEN

Waterlow & Sons Ltd.

SPECIMEN SPECIMEN SPECIMEN

Great Britain overprints

Some of the commoner types of overprints or punctures are illustrated here. Collectors are warned that dangerous forgeries of the punctured type exist.

The *Part* 1 (*British Commonwealth*) *Catalogue* records those Specimen overprints or perforations intended for distribution by the U.P.U. to member countries. In addition the Specimen overprints of Australia and its dependent territories, which were sold to collectors by the Post Office, are also included.

All other Specimens are outside the scope of this volume.

Specimens are not quoted in Great Britain as they are fully listed in the Stanley Gibbons *Great Britain Specialised Catalogue.*

In specifying type of specimen for individual high-value stamps, "H/S" means handstamped, "Optd" is overprinted and "Perf" is punctured. Some sets occur mixed, e.g. "Optd/Perf". If unspecified, the type is apparent from the date or it is the same as for the lower values quoted as a set.

Prices. Prices for stamps up to £1 are quoted in sets; higher values are priced singly after the colours, thus "(S. £20)". Where specimens exist in more than one type the price quoted is for the cheapest. Specimen stamps have rarely survived even as pairs; these and strips of three, four or five are worth considerably more than singles.

8. Luminescence

Machines which sort mail electronically have been introduced in recent years. In consequence some countries have issued stamps on fluorescent or phosphorescent papers, while others have marked their stamps with phosphor bands.

The various papers can only be distinguished by ultraviolet lamps emitting particular wavelengths. They are separately listed only when the stamps have some other means of distinguishing them, visible without the use of these lamps. Where this is not so, the papers are recorded in footnotes or headings.

For this Catalogue we do not consider it appropriate that collectors be compelled to have use of an ultraviolet lamp before being able to identify stamps by our listings. Some experience will also be found necessary in interpreting the results given by ultraviolet. Collectors using the lamps, nevertheless, should exercise great care in their use as exposure to their light is extremely dangerous to the eyes.

Phosphor bands are listable, since they are visible to the naked eye (by holding stamps at an angle to the light and looking along them, the bands appear dark). Stamps existing with and without phosphor bands or with differing numbers of bands are given separate listings. Varieties such as double bands, bands omitted, misplaced or printed on the back are not listed.

Detailed descriptions appear at appropriate places in the listings in explanation of luminescent papers; *see*, for example, Australia above No. 308, Canada above Nos. 472 and 611, Cook Is. above No. 249, etc.

For Great Britain, where since 1959 phosphors have played a prominent and intricate part in stamp issues, the main notes above Nos. 599, 723 and after the Decimal Machin issue (No. X841 onwards) should be studied, as well as the footnotes to individual listings where appropriate. In general the classification is as follows.

Stamps with *phosphor bands* are those where a separate cylinder applies the phosphor after the stamps are printed. Issues with "all-over" phosphor have the "band" covering the entire stamp. Parts of the stamp covered by phosphor bands, or the entire surface for "all-over" phosphor versions, appear matt. Stamps on *phosphorised paper* have the phosphor added to the paper coating before the stamps are printed. Issues on this paper have a completely shiny surface.

Further particularisation of phosphor—their methods of printing and the colours they exhibit under ultraviolet—is outside the scope. The more specialised listings should be consulted for this information.

9. Coil Stamps

Stamps issued only in coil form are given full listing. If stamps are issued in both sheets and coils the coil stamps are listed separately only where there is some feature (e.g. perforation or watermark sideways) by which singles can be distinguished. Coil strips containing different stamps *se-tenant* are also listed.

Coil join pairs are too random and too easily faked to permit of listing; similarly ignored are coil stamps which have accidentally suffered an extra row of perforations from the claw mechanism in a malfunctioning vending machine.

10. Stamp Booklets

Stamp booklets (with the exception of those from Great Britain, the Channel Islands and the Isle of Man, for which see the current editions of the *Great Britain Concise Catalogue* and *Collect Channel Islands and Isle of Man Stamps*) are now listed in this catalogue.

Single stamps from booklets are listed if they are distinguishable in some way (such as watermark or perforation) from similar sheet stamps.

Booklet panes are listed where they contain stamps of different denominations *se-tenant*, where stamp-size labels are included, or where such panes are otherwise identifiable. Booklet panes are placed in the listing under the lowest denomination present.

Particular perforations (straight edges) are covered by appropriate notes.

11. Miniature Sheets and Sheetlets

We distinguish between "miniature sheets" and "sheetlets" and this affects the catalogue numbering. An item in sheet form that is postally valid, containing a single stamp, pair, block or set of stamps, with wide, inscribed and/or decorative margins, is a *miniature sheet* if it is sold at post offices as an indivisible entity. As such the Catalogue allots a single **MS** number and describes what stamps make it up. (*See* Great Britain 1978 Historic Buildings, No. **MS**1058, as an example.) The *sheetlet* or *small sheet* differs in that the individual stamps are intended to be purchased separately for postal purposes. For sheetlets, all the component postage stamps are numbered individually and the composition explained in a footnote. (The 1978 Christmas Island Christmas sheetlet, Nos. 99/107, is an example.) Note that the definitions refer to post office sale—not how items may be subsequently offered by stamp dealers.

Production as sheetlets is a modern marketing development chosen by postal administrations to interest collectors in purchasing the item complete; if he has done so he should, as with all *se-tenant* arrangements, keep the sheetlet intact in his collection.

The Catalogue will in future no longer give full listing to designs, originally issued in normal sheets, which subsequently appear in sheetlets showing changes of colour, perforation, printing process or face value. Such stamps will be covered by footnotes.

12. Forgeries and Fakes

Forgeries. Where space permits, notes are considered if they can give a concise description that will permit unequivocal detection of a forgery. Generalised warnings, lacking detail, are not nowadays inserted, since their value to the collector is problematic.

Fakes. Unwitting fakes are numerous, particularly "new shades" which are colour changelings brought about by exposure to sunlight, soaking in water contaminated with dyes from adherent paper, contact with oil and dirt from a pocketbook, and so on. Fraudulent operators, in addition, can offer to arrange: removal of hinge marks; repairs of thins on white or coloured papers; replacement of missing margins or perforations; reperforating in true or false gauges; removal of fiscal cancellations; rejoining of severed pairs, strips and blocks; and (a major hazard) regumming. Collectors can only be urged to purchase from reputable sources and to insist upon Expert Committee certification where there is any kind of doubt.

The Catalogue can consider footnotes about fakes where these are specific enough to assist in detection.

1935 SILVER JUBILEE CROWN COLONY ISSUE

The Crown Colony Windsor Castle design by Harold Fleury is, surely, one of the most impressive produced in the 20th-century and its reproduction in the recess process by three of the leading stamp-printing firms of the era has provided a subject for philatelic research which has yet to be exhausted.

Each of the three, Bradbury, Wilkinson & Co. and Waterlow and Sons, who both produced fifteen issues, together with De La Rue & Co. who printed fourteen, used a series of vignette (centre) plates coupled with individual frame plates for each value. All were taken from dies made by Waterlow. Several worthwhile varieties exist on the frame plates, but most interest has been concentrated on the centre plates, each of which was used to print a considerable number of different stamps.

Sheets printed by Bradbury, Wilkinson were without printed plate numbers, but research has now identified eleven centre plates which were probably used in permanent pairings. A twelfth plate awaits confirmation. Stamps from some of these centre plates have revealed a number of prominent plate flaws, the most famous of which, the extra flagstaff, has been eagerly sought by collectors for many years.

Extra flagstaff (Plate "1" R. 9/1)

Short extra flagstaff (Plate "2" R. 2/1)

Lightning conductor (Plate "3" R. 2/5)

Flagstaff on right-hand turret (Plate "5" R. 7/1)

Double flagstaff (Plate "6" R. 5/2)

De La Rue sheets were initially printed with plate numbers, but in many instances these were subsequently trimmed off. Surviving examples do, however, enable a positive identification of six centre plates, 2A, 2B, (2A), (2B), 4 and 4/ to be made. The evidence of sheet markings and plate flaws clearly demonstrates that there were two different pairs of plates numbered 2A 2B. The second pair is designated (2A) (2B) by specialist collectors to avoid further confusion. The number of major plate flaws is not so great as on the Bradbury, Wilkinson sheets, but four examples are included in the catalogue.

Diagonal line by turret (Plate 2A R. 10/1 and 10/2)

Dot to left of chapel (Plate 2B R. 8/3)

Dot by flagstaff (Plate 4 R. 8/4)

Dash by turret (Plate 4/ R. 3/6)

Much less is known concerning the Waterlow centre plate system as the sheets did not show plate numbers. Ten individual plates have, so far, been identified and it is believed that these were used in pairs. The two versions of the kite and log flaw from plate "2" show that this plate exists in two states.

Damaged turret (Plate "1" R. 5/6)

Kite and vertical log (Plate "2A" R. 10/6)

Kite and horizontal log (Plate "2B" R. 10/6)

Bird by turret (Plate "7" R. 1/5)

Abbreviations

Printers

A.B.N. Co	American Bank Note Co, New York.
A. & M.	Alden & Mowbray Ltd, Oxford.
Ashton-Potter	Ashton-Potter Ltd, Toronto.
Aspioti-Elka (Aspiotis)	Aspioti-Elka, Greece.
B.A.B.N.	British American Bank Note Co, Ottawa.
B.D.T.	B.D.T. International Security Printing Ltd, Dublin, Ireland.
B.W.	Bradbury Wilkinson & Co, Ltd.
Cartor	Cartor S.A., L'Aigle, France
C.B.N.	Canadian Bank Note Co, Ottawa.
Continental B.N. Co	Continental Bank Note Co.
Courvoisier	Imprimerie Courvoisier S.A., La-Chaux-de-Fonds, Switzerland.
D.L.R.	De La Rue & Co, Ltd, London, and (from 1961) Bogota, Colombia.
Edila	Editions de l'Aubetin, S.A.
Enschedé	Joh. Enschedé en Zonen, Haarlem, Netherlands.
Format	Format International Security Printers, Ltd, London.
Harrison	Harrison & Sons, Ltd, London
Heraclio Fournier	Heraclio Fournier S.A., Vitoria, Spain.
J.W.	John Waddington Security Print Ltd., Leeds
P.B.	Perkins Bacon Ltd, London.
Questa	Questa Colour Security Printers, Ltd., London
Ueberreuter	Ueberreuter (incorporating Bruder Rosenbaum), Korneuburg, Austria.
Walsall	Walsall Security Printers, Ltd.
Waterlow	Waterlow & Sons, Ltd, London.

General Abbreviations

Alph	Alphabet
Anniv	Anniversary
Comp	Compound (perforation)
Des	Designer; designed
Diag	Diagonal; diagonally
Eng	Engraver; engraved
F.C.	Fiscal Cancellation
H/S	Handstamped
Horiz	Horizontal; horizontally
Imp, Imperf	Imperforate
Inscr	Inscribed
L	Left
Litho	Lithographed
mm	Millimetres
MS	Miniature sheet
N.Y.	New York
Opt(d)	Overprint(ed)
P or P-c	Pen-cancelled
P, Pf or Perf	Perforated
Photo	Photogravure
Pl	Plate
Pr	Pair
Ptd	Printed
Ptg	Printing
R	Right
R.	Row
Recess	Recess-printed
Roto	Rotogravure
Roul	Rouletted
S	Specimen (overprint)
Surch	Surcharge(d)
T.C.	Telegraph Cancellation
T	Type
Typo	Typographed
Un	Unused
Us	Used
Vert	Vertical; vertically
W or wmk	Watermark
Wmk s	Watermark sideways

(†)=Does not exist.

(—) (or blank price column)=Exists, or may exist, but no market price is known.

/ between colours means "on" and the colour following is that of the paper on which the stamp is printed.

Colours of Stamps

Bl (blue); blk (black); brn (brown); car, carm (carmine); choc (chocolate); clar (claret); emer (emerald); grn (green); ind (indigo); mag (magenta); mar (maroon); mult (multicoloured); mve (mauve); ol (olive); orge (orange); pk (pink); pur (purple); scar (scarlet); sep (sepia); turq (turquoise); ultram (ultramarine); verm (vermilion); vio (violet); yell (yellow).

Colour of Overprints and Surcharges

(B.) = blue, (Blk.) = black, (Br.) = brown, (C.) = carmine, (G.) = green, (Mag.) = magenta, (Mve.) = mauve, (Ol.) = olive, (O.) = orange, (P.) = purple, (Pk.) = pink, (R.)=red, (Sil.) = silver, (V.) = violet, (Vm.) or (Verm.) = vermilion, (W.) = white, (Y.) = yellow.

Arabic Numerals

As in the case of European figures, the details of the Arabic numerals vary in different stamp designs, but they should be readily recognised with the aid of this illustration.

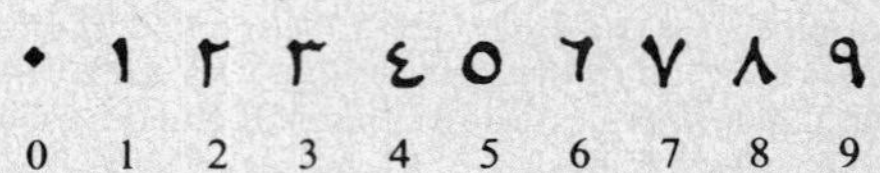

International Philatelic Glossary

English	*French*	*German*	*Spanish*	*Italian*
Agate	Agate	Achat	Agata	Agata
Air stamp	Timbre de la poste aérienne	Flugpostmarke	Sello de correo aéreo	Francobollo per posta aerea
Apple Green	Vert-pomme	Apfelgrün	Verde manzana	Verde mela
Barred	Annulé par barres	Balkenentwertung	Anulado con barras	Sbarrato
Bisected	Timbre coupé	Halbiert	Partido en dos	Frazionato
Bistre	Bistre	Bister	Bistre	Bistro
Bistre-brown	Brun-bistre	Bisterbraun	Castaño bistre	Bruno-bistro
Black	Noir	Schwarz	Negro	Nero
Blackish Brown	Brun-noir	Schwärzlichbraun	Castaño negruzco	Bruno nerastro
Blackish Green	Vert foncé	Schwärzlichgrün	Verde negruzco	Verde nerastro
Blackish Olive	Olive foncé	Schwärzlicholiv	Oliva negruzco	Oliva nerastro
Block of four	Bloc de quatre	Viererblock	Bloque de cuatro	Bloco di quattro
Blue	Bleu	Blau	Azul	Azzurro
Blue-green	Vert-bleu	Blaugrün	Verde azul	Verde azzurro
Bluish Violet	Violet bleuâtre	Bläulichviolett	Violeta azulado	Violetto azzurrastro
Booklet	Carnet	Heft	Cuadernillo	Libretto
Bright Blue	Bleu vif	Lebhaftblau	Azul vivo	Azzurro vivo
Bright Green	Vert vif	Lebhaftgrün	Verde vivo	Verde vivo
Bright Purple	Mauve vif	Lebhaftpurpur	Púrpura vivo	Porpora vivo
Bronze Green	Vert-bronze	Bronzegrün	Verde bronce	Verde bronzo
Brown	Brun	Braun	Castaño	Bruno
Brown-lake	Carmin-brun	Braunlack	Laca castaño	Lacca bruno
Brown-purple	Pourpre-brun	Braunpurpur	Púrpura castaño	Porpora bruno
Brown-red	Rouge-brun	Braunrot	Rojo castaño	Rosso bruno
Buff	Chamois	Sämisch	Anteado	Camoscio
Cancellation	Oblitération	Entwertung	Cancelación	Annullamento
Cancelled	Annulé	Gestempelt	Cancelado	Annullato
Carmine	Carmin	Karmin	Carmín	Carminio
Carmine-red	Rouge-carmin	Karminrot	Rojo carmín	Rosso carminio
Centred	Centré	Zentriert	Centrado	Centrato
Cerise	Rouge-cerise	Kirschrot	Color de ceresa	Color Ciliegia
Chalk-surfaced paper	Papier couché	Kreidepapier	Papel estucado	Carta gessata
Chalky Blue	Bleu terne	Kreideblau	Azul turbio	Azzurro smorto
Charity stamp	Timbre de bienfaisance	Wohltätigkeitsmarke	Sello de beneficenza	Francobollo di beneficenza
Chestnut	Marron	Kastanienbraun	Castaño rojo	Marrone
Chocolate	Chocolat	Schokolade	Chocolate	Cioccolato
Cinnamon	Cannelle	Zimtbraun	Canela	Cannella
Claret	Grenat	Weinrot	Rojo vinoso	Vinaccia
Cobalt	Cobalt	Kobalt	Cobalto	Cobalto
Colour	Couleur	Farbe	Color	Colore
Comb-perforation	Dentelure en peigne	Kammzähnung, Reihenzähnung	Dentado de peine	Dentellatura e pettine
Commemorative stamp	Timbre commémoratif	Gedenkmarke	Sello conmemorativo	Francobollo commemorativo
Crimson	Cramoisi	Karmesin	Carmesí	Cremisi
Deep Blue	Bleu foncé	Dunkelblau	Azul oscuro	Azzurro scuro
Deep Bluish Green	Vert-bleu foncé	Dunkelbläulichgrün	Verde azulado oscuro	Verde azzurro scuro
Design	Dessin	Markenbild	Diseño	Disegno
Die	Matrice	Urstempel, Type, Platte	Cuño	Conio, Matrice
Double	Double	Doppelt	Doble	Doppio
Drab	Olive terne	Trüboliv	Oliva turbio	Oliva smorto
Dull Green	Vert terne	Trübgrün	Verde turbio	Verde smorto
Dull Purple	Mauve terne	Trübpurpur	Púrpura turbio	Porpora smorto
Embossing	Impression en relief	Prägedruck	Impresión en relieve	Impressione a relievo
Emerald	Vert-eméraude	Smaragdgrün	Esmeralda	Smeraldo
Engraved	Gravé	Graviert	Grabado	Inciso
Error	Erreur	Fehler, Fehldruck	Error	Errore
Essay	Essai	Probedruck	Ensayo	Saggio
Express letter stamp	Timbre pour lettres par exprès	Eilmarke	Sello de urgencia	Francobollo per espresso
Fiscal stamp	Timbre fiscal	Stempelmarke	Sello fiscal	Francobollo fiscale
Flesh	Chair	Fleischfarben	Carne	Carnicino
Forgery	Faux, Falsification	Fälschung	Falsificación	Falso, Falsificazione
Frame	Cadre	Rahmen	Marco	Cornice
Granite paper	Papier avec fragments de fils de soie	Faserpapier	Papel con filamentos	Carto con fili di seta
Green	Vert	Grün	Verde	Verde
Greenish Blue	Bleu verdâtre	Grünlichblau	Azul verdoso	Azzurro verdastro

English	*French*	*German*	*Spanish*	*Italian*
Greenish Yellow	Jaune-vert	Grünlichgelb	Amarillo verdoso	Giallo verdastro
Grey	Gris	Grau	Gris	Grigio
Grey-blue	Bleu-gris	Graublau	Azul gris	Azzurro grigio
Grey-green	Vert gris	Graugrün	Verde gris	Verde grigio
Gum	Gomme	Gummi	Goma	Gomma
Gutter	Interpanneau	Zwischensteg	Espacio blanco entre dos grupos	Ponte
Imperforate	Non-dentelé	Geschnitten	Sin dentar	Non dentellato
Indigo	Indigo	Indigo	Azul indigo	Indaco
Inscription	Inscription	Inschrift	Inscripción	Dicitura
Inverted	Renversé	Kopfstehend	Invertido	Capovolto
Issue	Émission	Ausgabe	Emisión	Emissione
Laid	Vergé	Gestreift	Listado	Vergato
Lake	Lie de vin	Lackfarbe	Laca	Lacca
Lake-brown	Brun-carmin	Lackbraun	Castaño laca	Bruno lacca
Lavender	Bleu-lavande	Lavendel	Color de alhucema	Lavanda
Lemon	Jaune-citron	Zitrongelb	Limón	Limone
Light Blue	Bleu clair	Hellblau	Azul claro	Azzurro chiaro
Lilac	Lilas	Lila	Lila	Lilla
Line perforation	Dentelure en lignes	Linienzähnung	Dentado en linea	Dentellatura lineare
Lithography	Lithographie	Steindruck	Litografía	Litografia
Local	Timbre de poste locale	Lokalpostmarke	Emisión local	Emissione locale
Lozenge roulette	Percé en losanges	Rautenförmiger Durchstich	Picadura en rombos	Perforazione a losanghe
Magenta	Magenta	Magentarot	Magenta	Magenta
Margin	Marge	Rand	Borde	Margine
Maroon	Marron pourpré	Dunkelrotpurpur	Púrpura rojo oscuro	Marrone rossastro
Mauve	Mauve	Malvenfarbe	Malva	Malva
Multicoloured	Polychrome	Mehrfarbig	Multicolores	Policromo
Myrtle Green	Vert myrte	Myrtengrün	Verde mirto	Verde mirto
New Blue	Bleu ciel vif	Neublau	Azul nuevo	Azzurro nuovo
Newspaper stamp	Timbre pour journaux	Zeitungsmarke	Sello para periódicos	Francobollo per giornali
Obliteration	Oblitération	Abstempelung	Matasello	Annullamento
Obsolete	Hors (de) cours	Ausser Kurs	Fuera de curso	Fuori corso
Ochre	Ocre	Ocker	Ocre	Ocra
Official stamp	Timbre de service	Dienstmarke	Sello de servicio	Francobollo di servizio
Olive-brown	Brun-olive	Olivbraun	Castaño oliva	Bruno oliva
Olive-green	Vert-olive	Olivgrün	Verde oliva	Verde oliva
Olive-grey	Gris-olive	Olivgrau	Gris oliva	Grigio oliva
Olive-yellow	Jaune-olive	Olivgelb	Amarillo oliva	Giallo oliva
Orange	Orange	Orange	Naranja	Arancio
Orange-brown	Brun-orange	Orangebraun	Castaño naranja	Bruno arancio
Orange-red	Rouge-orange	Orangerot	Rojo naranja	Rosso arancio
Orange-yellow	Jaune-orange	Orangegelb	Amarillo naranja	Giallo arancio
Overprint	Surcharge	Aufdruck	Sobrecarga	Soprastampa
Pair	Paire	Paar	Pareja	Coppia
Pale	Pâle	Blass	Pálido	Pallido
Pane	Panneau	Gruppe	Grupo	Gruppo
Paper	Papier	Papier	Papel	Carta
Parcel post stamp	Timbre pour colis postaux	Paketmarke	Sello para paquete postal	Francobollo per pacchi postali
Pen-cancelled	Oblitéré à plume	Federzugentwertung	Cancelado a pluma	Annullato a penna
Percé en arc	Percé en arc	Bogenförmiger Durchstich	Picadura en forma de arco	Perforazione ad arco
Percé en scie	Percé en scie	Bogenförmiger Durchstich	Picado en sierra	Foratura a sega
Perforated	Dentelé	Gezähnt	Dentado	Dentellato
Perforation	Dentelure	Zähnung	Dentar	Dentellatura
Photogravure	Photogravure, Heliogravure	Rastertiefdruck	Fotograbado	Rotocalco
Pin perforation	Percé en points	In Punkten durchstochen	Horadado con alfileres	Perforato a punti
Plate	Planche	Platte	Plancha	Lastra, Tavola
Plum	Prune	Pflaumenfarbe	Color de ciruela	Prugna
Postage Due stamp	Timbre-taxe	Portomarke	Sello de tasa	Segnatasse
Postage stamp	Timbre-poste	Briefmarke, Freimarke, Postmarke	Sello de correos	Francobollo postale
Postal fiscal stamp	Timbre fiscal-postal	Stempelmarke als Postmarke verwendet	Sello fiscal-postal	Fiscale postale
Postmark	Oblitération postale	Poststempel	Matasello	Bollo
Printing	Impression, Tirage	Druck	Impresión	Stampa, Tiratura
Proof	Épreuve	Druckprobe	Prueba de impresión	Prova
Provisionals	Timbres provisoires	Provisorische Marken, Provisorien	Provisionales	Provvisori

English	*French*	*German*	*Spanish*	*Italian*
Prussian Blue	Bleu de Prusse	Preussischblau	Azul de Prusia	Azzurro di Prussia
Purple	Pourpre	Purpur	Púrpura	Porpora
Purple-brown	Brun-pourpre	Purpurbraun	Castaño púrpura	Bruno porpora
Recess-printing	Impression en taille douce	Tiefdruck	Grabado	Incisione
Red	Rouge	Rot	Rojo	Rosso
Red-brown	Brun-rouge	Rotbraun	Castaño rojizo	Bruno rosso
Reddish Lilac	Lilas rougeâtre	Rötlichlila	Lila rojizo	Lilla rossastro
Reddish Purple	Pourpre-rouge	Rötlichpurpur	Púrpura rojizo	Porpora rossastro
Reddish Violet	Violet rougeâtre	Rötlichviolett	Violeta rojizo	Violetto rossastro
Red-orange	Orange rougeâtre	Rotorange	Naranja rojizo	Arancio rosso
Registration stamp	Timbre pour lettre chargée (recommandée)	Einschreibemarke	Sello de certificado	Francobollo per lettere raccomandate
Reprint	Réimpression	Neudruck	Reimpresión	Ristampa
Reversed	Retourné	Umgekehrt	Invertido	Rovesciato
Rose	Rose	Rosa	Rosa	Rosa
Rose-red	Rouge rosé	Rosarot	Rojo rosado	Rosso rosa
Rosine	Rose vif	Lebhaftrosa	Rosa vivo	Rosa vivo
Roulette	Percage	Durchstich	Picadura	Foratura
Rouletted	Percé	Durchstochen	Picado	Forato
Royal Blue	Bleu-roi	Königblau	Azul real	Azzurro reale
Sage Green	Vert-sauge	Salbeigrün	Verde salvia	Verde salvia
Salmon	Saumon	Lachs	Salmón	Salmone
Scarlet	Écarlate	Scharlach	Escarlata	Scarlatto
Sepia	Sépia	Sepia	Sepia	Seppia
Serpentine roulette	Percé en serpentin	Schlangenliniger Durchstich	Picado a serpentina	Perforazione a serpentina
Shade	Nuance	Tönung	Tono	Gradazione de colore
Sheet	Feuille	Bogen	Hoja	Foglio
Slate	Ardoise	Schiefer	Pizarra	Ardesia
Slate-blue	Bleu-ardoise	Schieferblau	Azul pizarra	Azzurro ardesia
Slate-green	Vert-ardoise	Schiefergrün	Verde pizarra	Verde ardesia
Slate-lilac	Lilas-gris	Schieferlila	Lila pizarra	Lilla ardesia
Slate-purple	Mauve-gris	Schieferpurpur	Púrpura pizarra	Porpora ardesia
Slate-violet	Violet-gris	Schieferviolett	Violeta pizarra	Violetto ardesia
Special delivery stamp	Timbre pour exprès	Eilmarke	Sello de urgencia	Francobollo per espressi
Specimen	Spécimen	Muster	Muestra	Saggio
Steel Blue	Bleu acier	Stahlblau	Azul acero	Azzurro acciaio
Strip	Bande	Streifen	Tira	Striscia
Surcharge	Surcharge	Aufdruck	Sobrecarga	Soprastampa
Tête-bêche	Tête-bêche	Kehrdruck	Tête-bêche	Tête-bêche
Tinted paper	Papier teinté	Getöntes Papier	Papel coloreado	Carta tinta
Too-late stamp	Timbre pour lettres en retard	Verspätungsmarke	Sello para cartas retardadas	Francobollo per le lettere in ritardo
Turquoise-blue	Bleu-turquoise	Türkisblau	Azul turquesa	Azzurro turchese
Turquoise-green	Vert-turquoise	Türkisgrün	Verde turquesa	Verde turchese
Typography	Typographie	Buchdruck	Tipografia	Tipografia
Ultramarine	Outremer	Ultramarin	Ultramar	Oltremare
Unused	Neuf	Ungebraucht	Nuevo	Nuovo
Used	Oblitéré, Usé	Gebraucht	Usado	Usato
Venetian Red	Rouge-brun terne	Venezianischrot	Rojo veneciano	Rosso veneziano
Vermilion	Vermillon	Zinnober	Cinabrio	Vermiglione
Violet	Violet	Violett	Violeta	Violetto
Violet-blue	Bleu-violet	Violettblau	Azul violeta	Azzurro violetto
Watermark	Filigrane	Wasserzeichen	Filigrana	Filigrana
Watermark sideways	Filigrane couché	Wasserzeichen liegend	Filigrana acostado	Filigrana coricata
Wove paper	Papier ordinaire, Papier uni	Einfaches Papier	Papel avitelado	Carta unita
Yellow	Jaune	Gelb	Amarillo	Giallo
Yellow-brown	Brun-jaune	Gelbbraun	Castaño amarillo	Bruno giallo
Yellow-green	Vert-jaune	Gelbgrün	Verde amarillo	Verde giallo
Yellow-olive	Olive jaunâtre	Gelboliv	Oliva amarillo	Oliva giallastro
Yellow-orange	Orange jaunâtre	Gelborange	Naranja amarillo	Arancio giallastro
Zig-zag roulette	Percé en zigzag	Sägezahnartiger Durchstich	Picado en zigzag	Perforazione a zigzag

Stamps Added

Excluding new issues which have appeared in Gibbons Stamp Monthly Supplements, the following are the catalogue numbers of stamps listed in this edition for the first time. In addition watermark varieties have been added to Commonwealth Countries between 1901 and 1936 using "w", "x" or "y" suffixes.

Jamaica. 82b/c, 85c, 86b, 129a, **MS**379a

Kenya. 6a

Kenya, Uganda and Tanganyika. 33*b*, 60e, 62a/b, 134aw, 137ab

Kiribati. 36w, 200w, 232w/3w, 238w, 240w, O27a

Leeward Islands. 113ad

Malawi. 78*a*, 81c, 94d/e, 95d/e, 96d, 96ee, 98c/e, 99d, 99ee, 143c, 381w

Malaysia—Straits Settlements. Z37, 231b
Federated Malay States. 49a
Malaysia (National Issues). 191w, 345aw, 345bw, 424w, 453a, **MS**519a, 599b/ba, 600b, 604aw/b, 605b, 606aw/b, **MS**607a/b, 607*c*, 608b/ba, 609b, 639a/40a, 641a/2a
Federal Territory. K5a, K17d, K17f, K18aw, K18e, KSB10
Johore. 204f, 208cw
Kedah. 154c, 155ca
Kelantan. 143c, 145c
Malacca. 99f, 102f
Negri Sembilan (Sungei Ujong). 43*d*/da, 45*c*
(Negri Sembilan). 120f, 22aw, 123f
Pahang. 4*a*, 128c, 131aw, 131f
Penang. 100w, 102f, 103aw, 103f/fw, 106cw, 106f
Perak. 17*c*, 18*d*, 21*a*, 33*b*/7*b*, 40*b*, 200f, 203e/f
Perlis. 79c
Selangor. 35*a*, 36*a*, 38*a*, 176w, 179bw, 179cw, 182aw, 182e/f
Trengganu. 26a, 27a, 33a, 34a, 140c, 141c, 141f,
Siamese Posts in Northern Malaya. Z41, Z69, Z220, Z309/10, Z338
Japanese Occupation of Malaya. J30a, J164a, J193a, J222a, J263b,
Sabah. 188b, J16a, J34a
Sarawak. 74, 249w, 250aw, 252w, 253e/f

Malta. 158a, 221a, 221ba, 238a, 296a, 355a

Mauritius. 226a, 226ba, 226ca, 254a, 254ba, 443c, E2b

Montserrat. 60a, 61a, 61bb, 601a

Morocco Agencies. 1c, 3cd, 9d, 11d

Namibia. 109a, 117a, 125b, 126d, 140a, 159w,

Nauru. 330w

New Zealand. 354a, 812b, 835b, 875a, 930ba, 1986ba, 2064b, 2104b, 2125a, 2129a, O164a, L62a

Nigeria—Niger Coast Protectorate. Z12*a*
Nigeria. 5*d*, 6*d*, 10*d*, 12*a*, 13, 524a, 525da, **MS**680

Pakistan. 5w, 45ab, 83a, 111a, 122a, 131a, 134a, 173a, 175a, 176ac, 176bb, 179a, 180a, 204a, 464a, 465b, 466a, 471a, 473bb, 474a, 477b, 517a, 775a, O55b, O56b, O77a, O78a, O93c, O105b, O109b, O117a, O141w
Bahawalpur. O28aw

Palestine. SB2.

Papua New Guinea—New Guinea. 64pb

Pitcairn Islands. C15, Z6*a*, Z7*a*, Z13a, Z35*a*, 304aw

Rhodesia and Nyasaland. 22b

St. Kitts-Nevis. 23a, 28a

St. Lucia. 110f

St. Vincent. 16a, 19a

Seychelles. 88*b*, 147aw

Sierra Leone. 322b

Singapore. 29w, 30w, 826b, 861a

Solomon Islands. 56i, 582w

South Africa—Natal 73a
New Republic. 4b, 11a, 21a, 24a
Transvaal 119d
(Wolmaransstad) 1b
Zululand. F1a
South Africa. 3d, 4c, 5b, 6b, 45e, 75be, 80a, 91a, 101c, 104a, 114b, 130a, 267a, 904a, SB28/9, O17ab

South Georgia and South Sandwich Islands. 182w

Sri Lanka. 55ba, SB1*a*

Swaziland. 30ba

Tanzania—Zanzibar. 3m, 8p, 13n/o, 26l, 27n, 29l, 30l, 254a
Tanzania. 320*b*

Tonga. 20b, 25a, 26a, 27a, 27ba, 28a, 28ba, 29e, 30e, 31e, 34a, 34ba, 34ca, 37o, 49b, 62a, 62ca, 63a, 63ba, 66b, 80a

Trinidad and Tobago. 242e, 700w, 701w

Tristan da Cunha. 449w, 452w

Vanuatu. 416w, 417w, 517w, 518w,

Zimbabwe. 678a, D19a

Specialist Philatelic Societies

Requests for inclusion on this page should be sent to the Catalogue Editor.

British Decimal Stamps Study Circle
Secretary—Mr. S. van Kimmenade
32 Beaufort Heights, Beaufort Road,
St. George, Bristol BS5 8JX

Great Britain Philatelic Society
Membership Secretary—Mr. A. G. Lajer
The Old Post Office, Hurst,
Berks RG10 0TR

Great Britain Decimal Stamp Book Study Circle
Membership Secretary—Mr. A. J. Wilkins
3 Buttermere Close, Brierley Hill, West Midlands DY5 3SD

Channel Islands Specialists Society
Membership Secretary—Mr. T. Watkins
Holmcroft, Lewes Road, Ringmer, Lewes, East Sussex, BN8 5ES

Ascension Study Circle
Secretary—Dr. R. C. F. Baker
Greys, Tower Road, Whitstable, Kent CT5 2ER

Australian States Study Circle
Royal Sydney Philatelic Club
Honorary Secretary—Mr. B. Palmer
G.P.O. Box 1751, Sydney, N.S.W. 1043, Australia

British Society of Australian Philately
Secretary—Mr. A. J. Griffiths
c/o The British Philatelic Centre,
107 Charterhouse Street,
London EC1M 6PT

Society of Australasian Specialists/Oceania
Secretary—Mr. S. Leven
P.O. Box 24764, San Jose, CA 95154-4764, U.S.A.

Bechuanalands and Botswana Society
Membership Secretary—Mr. J. Catterall
Trevessa, Upper Castle Road, St. Mawes, Truro, Cornwall TR2 5BZ

Bermuda Collectors Society
Secretary—Mr. T. J. McMahon
P.O. Box 1949, Stuart, FL 34995, U.S.A.

British Caribbean Philatelic Study Group
Overseas Director—Mr. D. N. Druett
Pennymead Auctions, 1 Brewerton Street, Knaresborough, North Yorkshire HG5 8AZ

British West Indies Study Circle
Membership Secretary—Mr. S. A. Sharp
34 Lovelace Drive, Pyrford, Woking, Surrey GU22 8QY

Burma Philatelic Study Circle
Secretary—Mr. A. Meech
7208-91 Avenue, Edmonton, Alberta, Canada T6B 0R8

Ceylon Study Circle
Secretary—Mr. R.W.P. Frost
42 Lonsdale Road, Cannington, Bridgwater, Somerset TA5 2JS

Cyprus Study Circle
Secretary—Mr. A. R. Everett
29 Diomed Drive, Great Barton,
Bury St. Edmunds, Suffolk IP31 2TN

East Africa Study Circle
Secretary—Mr. J. G. Harvey
22 High Street, Mepal, CB6 2AW

Falklands Islands Study Group
Membership Secretary—Mr. D. W. A. Jeffery
38 Bradstock Road, Stoneleigh, Epsom, Surrey KT17 2LH

Gibraltar Study Circle
Membership Secretary—Mr. D. A. Brook
80 Farm Road, Milton, Weston-super-Mare, North Somerset, BS22 8BD

Great Britain Overprints Society
Membership Secretary—Mr. A. H. Bishop
The Coach House, Ridgemount Road, Sunningdale, Berkshire SL5 9RL

Hong Kong Stamp Society
Secretary—Dr. An-Min Chung
P.O. Box 206, Glenside, PA 19038, U.S.A.

Hong Kong Study Circle
Membership Secretary—Mr. P. V. Ball
37 Hart Court, Newcastle-under-Lyme,
Staffordshire ST5 2AL

Indian Ocean Study Circle (Western Islands)
Secretary—Mr. K. B. Fitton
50 Firlands, Weybridge, Surrey KT13 0HR

India Study Circle
Secretary—Dr. W. Fincham
10 Vallis Way, London W13 0DD

Irish Philatelic Circle
General Secretary—Mr. P. J. Wood
21 Loftus Road, London W12 7EH

King George V Silver Jubilee Study Circle
Secretary—Mr. N. Levinge
11 Broadway, Northampton NN1 4SF

King George VI Collectors Society
Secretary—Mr. F. R. Lockyer, OBE
98 Albany, Manor Road, Bournemouth, Dorset BH1 3EW

Kiribati and Tuvalu Philatelic Society
Honorary Secretary—Mr. M. J. Shaw
88 Stoneleigh Avenue, Worcester Park, Surrey KT4 8XY

Malaya Study Group
Secretary—Mr. J. Robertson
12 Lisa Court, Downsland Road, Basingstoke, Hampshire RG21 8TU

Malta Study Circle
Membership Secretary—Mr. D. Ward
40 Kingsman Road, Stanford-le-Hope, Essex SS17 0JW

New Zealand Society of Great Britain
General Secretary—Mr. K. C. Collins
13 Briton Crescent, Sanderstead,
Surrey CR2 0JN.

Orange Free State Study Circle
Secretary—Mr. J. R. Stroud
28 Oxford Street, Burnham-on-Sea, Somerset TA8 1LQ

Pacific Islands Study Circle
Honorary Secretary—Mr. J. D. Ray
24 Woodvale Avenue, London SE25 4AE

Papuan Philatelic Society
Secretary—Mr. F. J. Prophet
5 Morcom Close, Menear Road, Boscoppa,
St. Austell, Cornwall PL25 3UF

Pitcairn Islands Study Group (U.K.)
Honorary Secretary—Mr. D. Sleep
6 Palace Gardens, 100 Court Road, Eltham,
London SE9 5NS

Rhodesian Study Circle
Secretary—Mr. A. Wilson
10 Alders Road, Reigate, Surrey RH2 0ED

St. Helena, Ascension and Tristan da Cunha Philatelic Society
Secretary—Mr. J. Havill
205 N. Murray Blvd., #221, Colorado Springs, CO 80916, U.S.A.

Sarawak Specialists Society (also Brunei, North Borneo and Labuan)
Secretary—Dr. J. Higgins
31 Grimston Road, South Wootton,
Kings Lynn, Norfolk PE30 3NR

South African Collectors' Society
General Secretary—Mr. R. Ross
28 Duddon Drive, Barrow-in-Furness,
Cumbria LA14 3TW

Sudan Study Group
Secretary—Mr. N. D. Collier
34 Padleys Lane, Burton Joyce,
Nottingham NG14 5BZ

Tonga and Tin Can Mail Study Circle
Secretary/Treasurer—Mr. L. L. Benson
1832 Jean Avenue, Tallahassee
FL 32308-5227, U.S.A.

Transvaal Study Circle
Secretary—Mr. J. Woolgar
132 Dale Street, Chatham, Kent ME4 6QH

West Africa Study Circle
Secretary—Mr. J. Powell
23 Brook Street, Edlesborough, Dunstable,
Bedfordshire LU6 2JG

Select Bibliography

The literature on British Commonwealth stamps is vast, but works are often difficult to obtain once they are out of print. The selection of books below has been made on the basis of authority together with availability to the general reader, either as new or secondhand. Very specialised studies, and those covering aspects of postal history to which there are no references in the catalogue, have been excluded.

The following abbreviations are used to denote publishers:
CRL–Christie's Robson Lowe; HH–Harry Hayes; PB–Proud Bailey Co. Ltd. and Postal History Publications Co.; PC–Philip Cockrill; RPSL–Royal Philatelic Society, London; SG–Stanley Gibbons Ltd.

Where no publisher is quoted, the book is published by its author.

GENERAL. *Encyclopaedia of British Empire Postage Stamps. Vols 1–6.* Edited Robson Lowe. (CRL, 1951–1991)

Specimen Stamps of the Crown Colonies 1857–1948. Marcus Samuel. (RPSL, 1976 and 1984 Supplement)

U.P.U. Specimen Stamps. J. Bendon. (1988)

King George V Key Plates of the Imperium Postage and Revenue Design. P. Fernbank. (West Africa Study Circle, 1997)

The Printings of King George VI Colonial Stamps. W.J.W. Potter & Lt-Col R.C.M. Shelton. (1952)

King George VI Large Key Type Stamps of Bermuda, Leeward Islands, Nyasaland. R.W. Dickgiesser and E.P. Yendall. (Triad Publications, 1985)

Madame Joseph Forged Postmarks. D. Worboys (RPSL, 1994)

G.B. Used Abroad: Cancellations and Postal Markings. J. Parmenter. (The Postal History Society, 1993)

GREAT BRITAIN. For extensive bibliographies see *G.B. Specialised Catalogues. Vols 1–5.*

ASCENSION. *Ascension. The Stamps and Postal History.* J.H. Attwood. (CRL, 1981)

BARBADOS. *The Stamps of Barbados.* E.A. Bayley. (1989)

BATUM. *British Occupation of Batum.* P.T. Ashford. (1989)

BERMUDA. *The King George V High-value Stamps of Bermuda, 1917–1938.* M. Glazer. (Calaby Publishers, 1994)

BRITISH EAST AFRICA. *British East Africa. The Stamps and Postal Stationery.* J. Minns. (RPSL, 1982 and 1990 Supplement)

BRITISH GUIANA. *The Postage Stamps and Postal History of British Guiana.* W.A. Townsend and F.G. Howe. (RPSL, 1970)

BRITISH OCCUPATION OF GERMAN COLONIES. *G.R.I.* R.M. Gibbs. (CRL, 1989)

BRITISH POSTAL AGENCIES IN EASTERN ARABIA. *The Postal Agencies in Eastern Arabia and the Gulf.* N. Donaldson (HH, 1975) and Supplement (Bridger & Kay Guernsey Ltd, 1994)

BURMA. *Burma Postal History.* G. Davis and D. Martin. (CRL, 1971 and 1987 Supplement)

CAMEROONS. *The Postal Arrangements of the Anglo-French Cameroons Expeditionary Force 1914–16.* R. J. Maddocks (1996)

CANADA. *Stamps of British North America.* F. Jarrett. (Quarterman Publications Inc, 1975)

The Edward VII Issue of Canada. G.C. Marler. (National Postal Museum, Canada, 1975)

The Admiral Issue of Canada. G.C. Marler. (American Philatelic Society, 1982)

CAYMAN ISLANDS. *The Postal History of the Cayman Islands.* T.E. Giraldi and P.P. McCann. (Triad Publications, 1989)

COOK ISLANDS. *The Early Cook Islands Post Office.* A.R. Burge. (Hawthorn Press, 1978)

CYPRUS. *Cyprus 1353–1986.* W. Castle. (CRL, 3rd edition, 1987)

DOMINICA. *Dominica Postal History, Stamps and Postal Stationery to 1935.* E.V. Toeg (B.W.I. Study Circle, 1994)

FALKLAND ISLANDS. *The De La Rue Definitives of the Falkland Islands 1901–29.* J.P. Bunt. (1986 and 1996 Supplement)

FIJI. *Fiji Philatelics.* D.W.F. Alford (Pacific Islands Study Circle, 1994)

The Postal History of Fiji 1911–1952. J.G. Rodger. (Pacific Islands Study Circle, 1991)

GAMBIA. *The Stamps and Postal History of the Gambia.* Edited J.O. Andrew. (CRL, 1985)

The Postal History of The Gambia. E.B. Proud (PB, 1994)

GIBRALTAR. *Posted in Gibraltar.* W. Hine-Haycock. (CRL, 1978)

Gibraltar. The Postal History and Postage Stamps. Vol 1 (to 1885). G. Osborn. (Gibraltar Study Circle, 1995)

GOLD COAST. *The Postal History of Gold Coast.* E.B. Proud (PB, 1995)

HONG KONG. *The Philatelic History of Hong Kong. Vol 1.* (Hong Kong Study Circle, 1984)

Hong Kong Postage Stamps of the Queen Victoria Period. R.N. Gurevitch (1993)

British Post Offices in the Far East. E.B. Proud. (PB, 1991)

Cancellations of the Treaty Ports of Hong Kong. H. Schoenfeld. (1988)

INDIA. *C.E.F. The China Expeditionary Force 1900–1923.* D.S. Virk, J.C. Hume, D. Lang, G. Sattin. (Philatelic Congress of India, 1992)

A Handbook on Gwalior Postal History and Stamps. V.K. Gupta. (1980)

IRAQ. *The Postal History of Iraq.* P.C. Pearson and E. B. Proud. (PB, 1996)

KENYA. *The Postal History of Kenya.* E.B. Proud. (PB, 1992)

KIRIBATI. *Kiribati Handbook.* Edited H. Bennet. (Kiribati and Tuvalu Phil Soc., 1997)

LABUAN. *A Concise Guide to the Queen Issues of Labuan.* R. Price. (Sarawak Specialists Society, 1991)

MALAYSIA. *The Postal History of British Malaya. Vols 1–3.* E.B.Proud. (PB, 1982–84)

The Postage Stamps of Federated Malay States. W.A. Reeves. (Malaya Study Group, 1978)

Kedah and Perlis. D.R.M. Holley. (Malaya Study Group, 1995)

Kelantan. Its Stamps and Postal History. W.A. Reeves and B.E. Dexter. (Malaya Study Group, 1992)

The Postal History of the Occupation of Malaya and British Borneo 1941–1945. E.B. Proud and M.D. Rowell. (PB, 1992)

MALTA. *Malta. The Postal History and Postage Stamps.* Edited R.E. Martin. (CRL, 1980 and 1985 Supplement)

MAURITIUS. *The Postal History and Stamps of Mauritius.* P. Ibbotson. (RPSL, 1991) revisions and additions supplement (Indian Ocean Study Circle, 1995)

NEW SOUTH WALES. *The Postal History of New South Wales 1788–1901.* Edited J.S. White. (Philatelic Assoc of New South Wales, 1988)

NEW ZEALAND. *The Postage Stamps of New Zealand. Vols I–VII.* (Royal Philatelic Society of New Zealand, 1939–88)

NIGERIA. *The Postal Services of the British Nigeria Region.* J. Ince and J. Sacher. (RPSL, 1992)

The Postal History of Nigeria. E.B. Proud. (P.B, 1995)

NORTH BORNEO. *The Stamps and Postal History of North Borneo. Parts 1–3.* L.H. Shipman and P.K. Cassells. (Sarawak Specialists Society, 1976–88)

ORANGE FREE STATE. *Stamps of the Orange Free State. Parts 1–3.* G.D. Buckley & W.B. Marriott. (O.F.S. Study Circle, 1967–80)

PAPUA. *The Postal History of British New Guinea and Papua 1885–1942.* R. Lee. (CRL, 1983)

RHODESIA. *Mashonaland. A Postal History 1890–96.* A. Drysdall and D. Collis (CRL, 1990)

ST. HELENA. *St. Helena, Postal History and Stamps.* E. Hibbert. (CRL, 1979)

ST. KITTS-NEVIS. *A Study of the King George VI Stamps of St. Kitts-Nevis.* P. L. Baldwin. (Murray Payne Ltd, 2nd edition 1997)

SAMOA. *A Postal History of the Samoan Islands (Parts I and II).* Edited R. Burge. (Royal Philatelic Society of New Zealand, 1987–89)

SARAWAK. *The Stamps and Postal History of Sarawak.* W.A. Forrester-Wood. (Sarawak Specialists Society, 1959 & 1970 Supplement)

Sarawak: The Issues of 1871 and 1875. W. Batty-Smith & W. Watterson.

SIERRA LEONE. *The Postal Service of Sierra Leone.* P.O. Beale. (RPSL, 1988)

The Postal History of Sierra Leone. E.B. Proud. (P.B, 1994)

SOUTH AUSTRALIA. *The Departmental Stamps of South Australia.* A.R. Butler. (RPSL, 1978)

SOUTH WEST AFRICA. *The Overprinted Stamps of South West Africa to 1930.* N. Becker. (Philatelic Holdings (Pty) Ltd, 1990)

SUDAN. *Sudan. The Stamps and Postal Stationery of 1867 to 1970.* E.C.W. Stagg. (HH, 1977)

TANGANYIKA. *The Postal History of Tanganyika. 1915–1961.* E.B. Proud. (PB, 1989)

TASMANIA. *Stamps and Postal History of Tasmania.* W.E. Tinsley. (RPSL, 1986)

The Pictorial Stamps of Tasmania 1899–1912. K.E. Lancaster. (Royal Philatelic Society of Victoria, 1986)

TOGO. *Togo—The Postal History of the Anglo-French Occupation 1914–22.* J. Martin and F. Walton. (West Africa S.C., 1995)

TRANSVAAL. *Transvaal Philately.* Edited I.B. Mathews. (Reijger Publishers (Pty) Ltd, 1986)

Transvaal. The Provisional Issues of the First British Occupation. Dr. A.R. Drysdall (Janes Bendon, 1994)

TRINIDAD AND TOBAGO. *The Postal History of Trinidad & Tobago.* J. C. Aleong and E. B. Proud. (PB, 1997)

TURKS AND CAICOS ISLANDS. *Turks Islands and Caicos Islands to 1950.* J.J. Challis. (Roses Caribbean Philatelic Society, 1983)

UGANDA. *The Postal History of Uganda and Zanzibar.* E.B. Proud (PB, 1993)

VICTORIA. *The Stamps of Victoria.* G. Kellow. (B. & K. Philatelic Publishing, 1990)

WESTERN AUSTRALIA. *Western Australia. The Stamps and Postal History.* Ed. M. Hamilton and B. Pope. (W. Australia Study Group, 1979)

Postage Stamps and Postal History of Western Australia. Vols 1–3. M. Juhl. (1981–83)

STANLEY GIBBONS STAMP CATALOGUE

Part 1: BRITISH COMMONWEALTH

VOLUME 2: COUNTRIES J TO Z

101st EDITION—1999

Jamaica

Records show that the first local Postmaster for Jamaica on a regular basis was appointed as early as 1671, although a reasonably organised service did not evolve until 1687–8. In the early years of the 18th century overseas mail was carried by the British packets, but between 1704 and 1711 this service was run on a commercial basis by Edmund Dummer. Following the collapse of the Dummer scheme Jamaica was virtually without a Post Office until 1720 and it was not until 1755 that overseas mail was again carried by British packets.

The stamps of Great Britain were used on the island from 8 May 1858 to May 1860. Although there had been much friction between the local inhabitants and the British G.P.O. it was not until 1 August 1860 that the Jamaica authorities assumed responsibility for the postal service.

KINGSTON

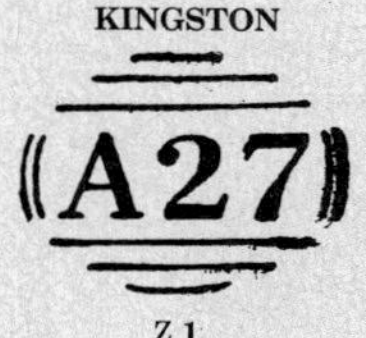

Z 1

Stamps of GREAT BRITAIN *cancelled* "A 01" *as Type* Z 1.

1858 *to* 1860.

Z1	1d. rose-red (1857), *perf* 16	£170
Z2	1d. rose-red (1857), *perf* 14	25·00
Z4	4d. rose (1857)	35·00
Z5	6d. lilac (1856)	35·00
Z6	1s. green (1856)	75·00

Z 2

Stamps of GREAT BRITAIN *cancelled* "A 01" *as Type* Z 2.

1859 *to* 1860.

Z 7	1d. rose-red (1857), *perf* 14	£160
Z 9	4d. rose (1857)	35·00
Z10	6d. lilac (1856)	35·00
Z11	1s. green (1856)	£225

Z 3

Stamps of GREAT BRITAIN *cancelled* "A 01" *as Type* Z 3.

1859 *to* 1860.

Z12	1d. rose-red (1857), *perf* 14	£200
Z14	4d. rose (1857)	£120
	a. Thick glazed paper	£400
Z15	6d. lilac (1856)	£120
Z16	1s. green (1856)	

Cancellation "A 01" was later used by the London, Foreign Branch Office.

OTHER JAMAICA POST OFFICES

British stamps were issued to several District post offices between 8 May 1858 and 1 March 1859 (i.e. before the Obliterators A 27–A 78 were issued). These can only be distinguished (off the cover) when they have the Town's date-stamp on them. They are worth about three times the price of those with an obliteration number.

Stamps of GREAT BRITAIN *cancelled* "A 27" *to* "A 78" *as Type* Z 1

1859 *to* 1860.

"A 27". ALEXANDRIA

Z17	1d. rose-red (1857), *perf* 14	£425
Z17*a*	2d. blue (1855) Large Crown, *perf* 14 (Plate 6)	£475
Z18	4d. rose (1857)	£160
Z19	6d. lilac (1856)	£375

"A 28". ANNOTTO BAY

Z20	1d. rose-red (1857), *perf* 14	£300
Z21	4d. rose (1857)	70·00
Z22	6d. lilac (1856)	£225

"A 29". BATH

Z23	1d. rose-red (1857), *perf* 14	£120
Z24	4d. rose (1857)	85·00
Z25	6d. lilac (1856)	£400

"A 30". BLACK RIVER

Z26	1d. rose-red (1857), *perf* 14	£120
Z27	4d. rose (1857)	50·00
Z28	6d. lilac (1856)	£120

"A 31". BROWN'S TOWN

Z29	1d. rose-red (1857), *perf* 14	£160
Z30	4d. rose (1857)	£160
Z31	6d. lilac (1856)	£160

"A 32". BUFF BAY

Z32	1d. rose-red (1857), *perf* 14	£120
Z33	4d. rose (1857)	£150
Z34	6d. lilac (1856)	£120

"A 33". CHAPELTON

Z35	1d. rose-red (1857), *perf* 14	£160
Z36	4d. rose (1857)	95·00
Z37	6d. lilac (1856)	£160

"A 34". CLAREMONT

Z38	1d. rose-red (1857), *perf* 14	£300
Z39	4d. rose (1857)	£150
Z40	6d. lilac (1856)	£300

"A 35". CLARENDON
(Near Four Paths)

Z41	1d. rose-red (1857), *perf* 14	£250
Z42	4d. rose (1857)	£100
Z43	6d. lilac (1856)	£160

"A 36". DRY HARBOUR

Z44	1d. rose-red (1857), *perf* 14	£375
Z45	4d. rose (1857)	£300
Z46	6d. lilac (1856)	£250

"A 37". DUNCANS

Z47	1d. rose-red (1857), *perf* 14	
Z48	4d. rose (1857)	£375
Z49	6d. lilac (1856)	£250

"A 38". EWARTON

A 38 was allocated to EWARTON but this office was closed towards the end of 1858 before the postmark arrived. A 38 was re-issued to Falmouth in 1862.

"A 39". FALMOUTH

Z53	1d. rose-red (1857), *perf* 14	75·00
Z54	4d. rose (1857)	40·00
Z55	6d. lilac (1856)	60·00
Z56	1s. green (1856)	£425

"A 40". FLINT RIVER
(Near Hopewell)

Z57	1d. rose-red (1857), *perf* 14	£150
Z58	4d. rose (1857)	£100
Z59	6d. lilac (1856)	£150
Z60	1s. green (1856)	£425

"A 41". GAYLE

Z61	1d. rose-red (1857), *perf* 14	£450
Z62	4d. rose (1857)	£120
Z63	6d. lilac (1856)	£130
Z64	1s. green (1856)	£170

"A 42". GOLDEN SPRING
(Near Stony Hill)

Z65	1d. rose-red (1857), *perf* 14	£170
Z66	4d. rose (1857)	£150
Z67	6d. lilac (1856)	£400
Z68	1s. green (1856)	£425

"A 43". GORDON TOWN

Z69	1d. rose-red (1857), *perf* 14	
Z70	4d. rose (1857)	
Z71	6d. lilac (1856)	£450

"A 44". GOSHEN
(Near Santa Cruz)

Z72	1d. rose-red (1857), *perf* 14	£120
Z73	4d. rose (1857)	£110
Z74	6d. lilac (1856)	55·00

"A 45". GRANGE HILL

Z75	1d. rose-red (1857), *perf* 14	£150
Z76	4d. rose (1857)	40·00
Z77	6d. lilac (1856)	60·00
Z77*a*	1s. green (1856)	£375

"A 46". GREEN ISLAND

Z78	1d. rose-red (1857), *perf* 14	£300
Z79	4d. rose (1857)	£150
Z80	6d. lilac (1856)	£250
Z81	1s. green (1856)	£425

"A 47". HIGHGATE

Z82	1d. rose-red (1857), *perf* 14	£170
Z83	4d. rose (1857)	£110
Z84	6d. lilac (1856)	£170

"A 48". HOPE BAY

Z85	1d. rose-red (1857), *perf* 14	£400
Z86	4d. rose (1857)	£150
Z87	6d. lilac (1856)	£400

"A 49". LILLIPUT
(Near Balaclava)

Z88	1d. rose-red (1857), *perf* 14	£150
Z89	4d. rose (1857)	£150
Z90	6d. lilac (1856)	75·00

"A 50". LITTLE RIVER

A 50 was allocated for use at LITTLE RIVER but this office was closed late in 1858, before the obliterator could be issued. Issued to Malvern in 1862.

"A 51". LUCEA

Z91	1d. rose-red (1857), *perf* 14	£225
Z92	4d. rose (1857)	50·00
Z93	6d. lilac (1856)	£150

"A 52". MANCHIONEAL

Z94	1d. rose-red (1857), *perf* 14	£300
Z95	4d. rose (1857)	£160
Z96	6d. lilac (1856)	

"A 53". MANDEVILLE

Z97	1d. rose-red (1857), *perf* 14	£160
Z98	4d. rose (1857)	50·00
Z99	6d. lilac (1856)	£140

"A 54". MAY HILL
(Near Spur Tree)

Z100	1d. rose-red (1857), *perf* 14	75·00
Z101	4d. rose (1857)	75·00
Z102	6d. lilac (1856)	50·00

"A 55". MILE GULLY

Z103	1d. rose-red (1857), *perf* 14	£250
Z104	4d. rose (1857)	£150
Z105	6d. lilac (1856)	£150

"A 56". MONEAGUE

Z106	1d. rose-red (1857), *perf* 14	£150
Z107	4d. rose (1857)	£190
Z108	6d. lilac (1856)	£400

"A 57". MONTEGO BAY

Z109	1d. rose-red (1857), *perf* 14	£160
Z110	4d. rose (1857)	40·00
Z111	6d. lilac (1856)	50·00
Z112	1s. green (1856)	£425

"A 58". MONTPELIER

Z113	1d. rose-red (1857), *perf* 14	
Z114	4d. rose (1857)	
Z115	6d. lilac (1856)	£650

"A 59". MORANT BAY

Z116	1d. rose-red (1857), *perf* 14	£300
Z117	4d. rose (1857)	50·00
Z118	6d. lilac (1856)	55·00

"A 60". OCHO RIOS

Z119	1d. rose-red (1857), *perf* 14	
Z120	4d. rose (1857)	75·00
Z121	6d. lilac (1856)	£140

"A 61". OLD HARBOUR

Z122	1d. rose-red (1857), *perf* 14	£150
Z123	4d. rose (1857)	£110
Z124	6d. lilac (1856)	£110

"A 62". PLANTAIN GARDEN RIVER
(Near Golden Grove)

Z125	1d. rose-red (1857), *perf* 14	£110
Z126	4d. rose (1857)	80·00
Z127	6d. lilac (1856)	£110

"A 63". PEAR TREE GROVE

No genuine specimen of A 63 has been found on a British stamp.

"A 64". PORT ANTONIO

Z131	1d. rose-red (1857), *perf* 14	£375
Z132	4d. rose (1857)	£225
Z133	6d. lilac (1856)	£225

"A 65". PORT MORANT

Z134	1d. rose-red (1857), *perf* 14	£225
Z135	4d. rose (1857)	85·00
Z136	6d. lilac (1856)	£225

"A 66". PORT MARIA

Z137	1d. rose-red (1857), *perf* 14	£150
Z138	4d. rose (1857)	55·00
Z139	6d. lilac (1856)	£225

"A 67". PORT ROYAL

No.	Description	Price
Z140	1d. rose-red (1857), *perf* 14	£300
Z140*a*	2d. blue (1858) (plate 9)	
Z141	4d. rose (1857)	£300
Z142	6d. lilac (1856)	£300

"A 68". PORUS

No.	Description	Price
Z143	1d. rose-red (1857), *perf* 14	£150
Z144	4d. rose (1857)	70·00
Z145	6d. lilac (1856)	£300

"A 69". RAMBLE

No.	Description	Price
Z146	1d. rose-red (1857), *perf* 14	£150
Z147	4d. rose (1857)	£150
	a. Thick glazed paper	£400
Z149	6d. lilac (1856)	£225

"A 70". RIO BUENO

No.	Description	Price
Z150	1d. rose-red (1857), *perf* 14	
Z151	4d. rose (1857)	£130
Z152	6d. lilac (1856)	85·00

"A 71". RODNEY HALL
(Now called Linstead)

No.	Description	Price
Z153	1d. rose-red (1857), *perf* 14	£120
Z154	4d. rose (1857)	80·00
Z155	6d. lilac (1856)	£110

"A 72". ST. DAVID'S
(Now called Yallahs)

No.	Description	Price
Z156	1d. rose-red (1857), *perf* 14	£150
Z157	4d. rose (1857)	£300
Z158	6d. lilac (1856)	

"A 73". ST. ANN'S BAY

No.	Description	Price
Z159	1d. rose-red (1857), *perf* 14	£150
Z160	4d. rose (1857)	75·00
Z161	6d. lilac (1856)	£150

"A 74". SALT GUT
(Near Oracabessa)

No.	Description	Price
Z162	1d. rose-red (1857), *perf* 14	£140
Z163	4d. rose (1857)	
Z164	6d. lilac (1856)	£150

"A 75". SAVANNAH-LA-MAR

No.	Description	Price
Z165	1d. rose-red (1857), *perf* 14	75·00
Z166	4d. rose (1857)	45·00
Z167	6d. lilac (1856)	£150
Z168	1s. green (1856)	£375

"A 76". SPANISH TOWN

No.	Description	Price
Z169	1d. rose-red (1857), *perf* 14	85·00
Z170	4d. rose (1857)	40·00
Z171	6d. lilac (1856)	85·00
Z172	1s. green (1856)	£250

"A 77". STEWART TOWN

No.	Description	Price
Z173	1d. rose-red (1857), *perf* 14	£400
Z174	4d. rose (1857)	£250
Z175	6d. lilac (1856)	£150

"A 78". VERE
(Now called Alley)

No.	Description	Price
Z176	1d. rose-red (1857), *perf* 14	£225
Z177	4d. rose (1857)	75·00
Z178	6d. lilac (1856)	50·00
Z179	1s. green (1856)	£425

PRICES FOR STAMPS ON COVER

Nos. 1/6	*from* × 4
Nos. 7/15	*from* × 6
Nos. 16/26	*from* × 8
Nos. 27/9	*from* × 6
No. 30	*from* × 5
Nos. 31/2	*from* × 15
Nos. 33/6	*from* × 5
Nos. 37/56	*from* × 3
No. 57	*from* × 4
Nos. 58/67	*from* × 3
Nos. 68/77	*from* × 6
Nos. 78/89	*from* × 3
Nos. 90/103	*from* × 4
Nos. 104/7	*from* × 5
Nos. 108/17	*from* × 3
Nos. 118/20	*from* × 5
Nos. 121/33*a*	*from* × 4
Nos. 134/40	*from* × 8
Nos. F1/9	*from* × 3
Nos. O1/5	*from* × 30

CROWN COLONY

PRINTERS. Until 1923, all the stamps of Jamaica were typographed by De La Rue & Co, Ltd, London, *unless otherwise stated*.

The official dates of issue are given, where known, but where definite information is not available the dates are those of earliest known use, etc.

1

2

3

4

5

6

7

A

1860 (23 Nov)–**63.** *W* **7**. *P* 14.

No.	Type	Description	Unused	Used
1	**1**	1d. pale blue	60·00	15·00
		a. Pale greenish blue	65·00	19·00
		b. Blue	50·00	12·00
		c. Deep blue	95·00	28·00
		d. Bisected (½d.) (11.61) (on cover)	†	£650
2	**2**	2d. rose	£190	45·00
		a. Deep rose	£120	45·00
3	**3**	3d. green (10.9.63)	£130	25·00
4	**4**	4d. brown-orange	£200	40·00
		a. Red-orange	£200	22·00
5	**5**	6d. dull lilac	£180	18·00
		a. Grey-purple	£275	32·00
		b. Deep purple	£800	40·00
6	**6**	1s. yellow-brown	£450	24·00
		a. Purple-brown	£500	23·00
		b. Dull brown	£180	27·00
		c. "$" for "S" in "SHILLING" (A)	£1700	£600

The diagonal bisection of the 1d. was authorized by a P.O. notice dated 20 November 1861. Specimens are only of value when on original envelope or wrapper. The authority was withdrawn as from 1 December 1872. Fakes are frequently met with. Other bisections were unauthorized.

The so-called "dollar variety" of the 1s. occurs once in each sheet of stamps in all shades and in later colours, etc, on the second stamp in the second row of the left upper pane. The prices quoted above are for the dull brown shade, the prices for the other shades being proportionate to their normal value.

All values except the 3d. are known imperf, mint only.

There are two types of watermark in the 3d. and 1s., one being short and squat and the other elongated.

8

9

10

1870–83. *Wmk Crown CC.* (*a*) *P* 14.

No.	Type	Description	Unused	Used
7	**8**	½d. claret (29.10.72)	12·00	3·50
		a. Deep claret (1883)	13·00	3·50
8	**1**	1d. blue (4.73)	55·00	75
		a. Deep blue	60·00	1·50
9	**2**	2d. rose (4.70)	55·00	70
		a. Deep rose	70·00	1·00
10	**3**	3d. green (1.70)	90·00	8·00
11	**4**	4d. brown-orange (1872)	£160	10·00
		a. Red-orange	£350	6·00
12	**5**	6d. mauve (10.3.71)	55·00	5·50
13	**6**	1s. dull-brown (*to* deep) (23.2.73)	25·00	8·50
		a. "$" for "S" in "SHILLING" (A)	£1100	£600
		(*b*) *P* 12½		
14	**9**	2s. Venetian red (27.8.75)	40·00	16·00
15	**10**	5s. lilac (27.8.75)	90·00	£130
7/15		*Set of* 9	£450	£150

The ½d., 1d., 4d., 2s. and 5s. are known imperforate.

1883–97. *Wmk Crown CA. P* 14.

No.	Type	Description	Unused	Used
16	**8**	½d. yellow-green (1885)	2·25	70
		a. Green	80	10
17	**1**	1d. blue (1884)	£300	4·50
18		1d. rose (*to* deep) (3.3.85)	50·00	75
		a. Carmine	24·00	60
19	**2**	2d. rose (*to* deep) (17.3.84)	£180	3·75
20		2d. grey (1885)	70·00	2·00
		a. Slate	50·00	50
21	**3**	3d. sage-green (1886)	4·00	85
		a. Pale olive-green	2·50	1·00
22	**4**	4d. red-orange* (9.3.83)	£350	22·00
		a. Red-brown (shades)	2·00	35
23	**5**	6d. deep yellow (4.10.90)	18·00	6·00
		a. Orange-yellow	4·00	3·50
24	**6**	1s. brown (*to* deep) (3.97)	5·00	5·00
		a. "$" for "S" in "SHILLING" (A)	£750	£450
		b. Chocolate	15·00	11·00
25	**9**	2s. Venetian red (1897)	27·00	17·00
26	**10**	5s. lilac (1897)	48·00	55·00
16/26		*Set of* 11	£550	90·00
16, 18, 20, 21, 22 and 23 Optd "Specimen"		*Set of* 6	£450	

*No. 22 is the same colour as No. 11*a*.

The 1d. carmine, 2d. slate, and 2s. are known imperf. All values to the 6d. inclusive are known perf 12. These are proofs.

NEW INFORMATION

The editor is always interested to correspond with people who have new information that will improve or correct the Catalogue.

11

TWO PENCE
HALF-PENNY

(12)

1889–91. *Value tablet in second colour. Wmk Crown CA. P* 14.

No.	Type	Description	Unused	Used
27	**11**	1d. purple and mauve (8.3.89)	2·25	10
28		2d. green (8.3.89)	19·00	3·50
		a. Deep green (brown gum)	4·50	6·00
29		2½d. dull purple and blue (25.2.91)	4·75	40
27/9		*Set of* 3	10·50	3·50
27/9 Optd "Specimen"		*Set of* 3	£100	

A very wide range of shades may be found in the 1d. The headplate was printed in many shades of purple, and the duty-plate in various shades of mauve and purple and also in carmine, etc. There are fewer shades for the other values and they are not so pronounced.

1890 (4(?) June). *No. 22a surch with T* **12** *by C. Vendyres, Kingston.*

No.	Type	Description	Unused	Used
30	**4**	2½d. on 4d. red-brown	27·00	8·50
		a. Spacing between lines of surch 1½ mm	32·00	17·00
		b. Surch double	£325	£225
		c. "PFNNY" for "PENNY"	75·00	65·00
		ca. Ditto and broken "K" for "Y"	£130	£110

This provisional was issued pending receipt of No. 29 which is listed above for convenience of reference.

Three settings exist. (1) Ten varieties arranged in a single vertical row and repeated six times in the pane. (2) Twelve varieties, in two horizontal rows of six, repeated five times, alternate rows show 1 and 1½ mm spacing between lines of surcharge. (3) Three varieties, arranged horizontally and repeated twenty times. All these settings can be reconstructed by examination of the spacing and relative position of the words of the surcharge and of the broken letters, etc, which are numerous.

A variety reading "PFNNK", with the "K" unbroken, is a forgery.

Varieties c. and ca. may be found in the double surcharge.

Surcharges misplaced either horizontally or vertically are met with, the normal position being central at the foot of the stamp with "HALF-PENNY" covering the old value.

13 Llandovery Falls, Jamaica (photo by Dr. J. Johnston)

14 Arms of Jamaica

(Recess D.L.R.)

1900–01. *Wmk Crown CC (sideways). P* 14.

No.	Type	Description	Unused	Used
31	**13**	1d. red (1.5.00)	1·25	20
32		1d. slate-black and red (25.9.01)	1·75	20
		a. Blued paper	£110	£100
		b. Imperf between (vert pair)	£6500	
31/2 Optd "Specimen"		*Set of* 2	£130	

Many shades exist of both centre and frame of the bi-coloured 1d. which was, of course, printed from two plates and the design shows minor differences from that of the 1d. red which was printed from a single plate.

(Typo D.L.R.)

1903–4. *Wmk Crown CA. P* 14.

No.	Type	Description	Unused	Used
33	**14**	½d. grey and dull green (16.11.03)	1·50	20
		a. "SER.ET" for "SERVIET"	40·00	45·00
		w. Wmk inverted	30·00	30·00
34		1d. grey and carmine (24.2.04)	1·50	10
		a. "SER.ET" for "SERVIET"	32·00	35·00
35		2½d. grey and ultramarine (16.11.03)	2·25	3·00
		a. "SER.ET" for "SERVIET"	60·00	70·00
36		5d. grey and yellow (1.3.04)	15·00	23·00
		a. "SER.ET" for "SERVIET"	£600	£700
		w. Wmk inverted	75·00	
33/6		*Set of* 4	18·00	23·00
33/6 Optd "Specimen"		*Set of* 4	75·00	

The "SER.ET" variety occurs once in each sheet of stamps on the second stamp in the fourth row of the left upper pane.

The centres of the above and later bi-coloured stamps in the Arms type vary in colour from grey to grey-black.

15 Arms type redrawn **16**

1905–11. *Wmk Mult Crown CA. P* 14. (*a*) *Arms types. Chalk-surfaced paper.*

No.	Type	Description	Unused	Used
37	**14**	½d. grey and dull green (24.11.05)	5·50	20
		a. "SER.ET" for "SERVIET"	32·00	32·00
		w. Wmk inverted		
38	**15**	½d. yell-grn (*ordinary paper*) (8.11.06)	6·50	40
		a. Dull green	3·75	20
		b. Deep green	4·50	20
39	**14**	1d. grey and carmine (20.11.05)	17·00	25
		w. Wmk inverted	—	75·00
40	**16**	1d. carmine (*ordinary paper*) (1.10.06)	1·25	10
		w. Wmk inverted	30·00	
41	**14**	2½d. grey and ultramarine (12.11.07)	2·75	1·75
42		2½d. pale ultramarine (*ordinary paper*) (21.9.10)	2·50	1·25
		a. Deep ultramarine	2·50	1·75
43		5d. grey and orange-yellow (24.4.07)	45·00	45·00
		a. "SER.ET" for "SERVIET"	£750	£900

44 14 6d. dull and bright purple (18.8.11) .. 12·00 12·00
45 5s. grey and violet (11.05) .. .. 40·00 30·00
37/45 .. .. *Set of* 9 £110 80·00
38, 40, 42, 44, 45 Optd "Specimen" *Set of* 5 £140
See note below No. 36 concerning grey centres.

(*b*) *Queen Victoria types. Ordinary paper*
46 3 3d. olive-green (15.5.05) .. .. .. 6·00 2·75
a. Sage-green (1907) .. .. .. 5·00 2·50
47 3d. purple/*yellow* (10.3.10) .. .. 4·50 3·00
a. Chalk-surfaced paper. *Pale purple/yellow* (11.7.10) .. .. .. 2·00 1·50
aw. Wmk inverted .. .. .. 40·00 40·00
48 4 4d. red-brown (6.6.08) .. .. .. 70·00 48·00
49 4d. black/*yellow* (*chalk-surfaced paper*) (21.9.10) .. .. 7·00 30·00
50 4d. red/*yellow* (3.10.11) .. .. .. 1·50 7·00
51 5 6d. dull orange (27.6.06) .. .. 15·00 24·00
a. Golden yellow (9.09) .. .. .. 22·00 40·00
52 6d. lilac (19.11.09) .. .. .. 26·00 30·00
a. Chalk-surfaced paper. *Purple* (7.10) .. 8·50 14·00
53 6 1s. brown (11.06) .. .. .. 19·00 16·00
a. Deep brown .. .. 27·00 24·00
b. "$" for "S" in "SHILLING" (A) .. £900 £900
54 1s. black/*green* (*chalk-surfaced paper*) (21.9.10) .. .. 3·75 8·50
a. "$" for "S" in "SHILLING" (A) .. £800 £1000
55 9 2s. Venetian red (11.08) .. .. 95·00 £140
56 2s. pur/*bl* (*chalk-surfaced paper*) (21.9.10) 6·00 3·50
46/56 .. .. *Set of* 11 £190 £250
47, 49, 50, 52, 54, 56 Optd "Specimen" .. *Set of* 6 £170

17

18

(T 17/18 typo D.L.R.)

1911 (3 Feb). *Wmk Mult Crown CA. P* 14.
57 17 2d. grey (Optd S. £35) .. .. .. 2·00 13·00

1912–20. *Wmk Mult Crown CA. Chalk-surfaced paper* (3*d. to* 5*s.*). *P* 14.
58 18 1d. carmine-red (5.12.12) .. .. 1·25 10
a. Scarlet (1916) .. .. .. 1·25 50
59 1½d. brown-orange (13.7.16) .. .. 1·00 60
a. Yellow-orange .. .. .. 12·00 1·00
b. Wmk sideways .. .. .. † £1300
60 2d. grey (2.8.12) .. .. .. 1·50 1·75
a. Slate-grey .. .. 1·00 3·00
61 2½d. blue (13.2.13) .. .. .. 1·00 15
a. Deep bright blue 65 75
62 3d. purple/*yellow* (6.3.12) 40 45
a. White back (2.4.13) 55 40
b. On lemon (25.9.16) (Optd S. £32) .. 3·75 1·50
w. Wmk inverted .. .. ..
63 4d. black and red/*yellow* (4.4.13) .. 50 3·00
a. White back (7.5.14) .. .. .. 70 3·50
b. On lemon (1916) (Optd S. £32) .. 23·00 19·00
c. On pale yellow (1919) .. .. 22·00 15·00
64 6d. dull and bright purple (14.11.12) .. 4·50 9·00
a. Dull purple and bright mauve (1915) 70 1·00
b. Dull purple & bright magenta (1920) 3·25 2·25
65 1s. black/*green* (2.8.12) .. .. 2·25 2·00
a. White back (4.1.15) .. .. .. 70 4·25
b. On blue-green, olive back (1920) .. 2·25 4·75
66 2s. purple and bright blue/*blue* (10.1.19) 11·00 23·00
67 5s. green and red/*yellow* (5.9.19) .. 40·00 70·00
a. On pale yellow .. .. .. 48·00 70·00
b. On orange-buff £100 £130
58/67 .. .. *Set of* 10 50·00 90·00
58/67 Optd "Specimen" .. .. *Set of* 10 £190
For the ½d. and 6d. with Script wmk see Nos. 89*a*/90.

The paper of No. 67 is a bright yellow and the gum rough and dull. No. 67*a* is on practically the normal creamy "pale yellow" paper, and the gum is smooth and shiny. The paper of No. 67*b* approaches the "coffee" colour of the true "orange-buff", and the colours of both head and frame are paler, the latter being of a carmine tone.

RED CROSS LABELS. A voluntary organization, the Jamaica War Stamp League later the Jamaica Patriotic Stamp League, was founded in November 1915 by Mr. Lewis Ashenheim, a Kingston solicitor. The aims of the League were to support the British Red Cross, collect funds for the purchase of aircraft for the Royal Flying Corps and the relief of Polish Jews.

One fund-raising method used was the sale, from 1 December 1915, of ½d. charity labels. These labels, which were available from post offices, depicted a bi-plane above a cross and were printed in red by Dennison Manufacturing Company, Framingham, U.S.A., the stamps being perforated 12 except for those along the edges of the sheet which have one side imperforate.

From 22 December 1915 supplies of the labels were overprinted "JAMAICA" in red, the colour of this overprint being changed to black from 15 January 1916. Copies sold from 11 March 1916 carried an additional "Half-Penny" surcharge, also in black.

Such labels had no postal validity when used by the general public, but, by special order of the Governor, were accepted for the payment of postage on the League's official mail. To obtain this concession the envelopes were to be inscribed "Red Cross Business" or "Jamaica Patriotic Stamp League" and the labels used endorsed with Mr. Ashenheim's signature. Such covers are rare.

WAR STAMP.
(19)

WAR
STAMP.
(20)

WAR
STAMP.
(21)

(T 19/21 optd locally)

1916 (1 Apr–Sept). *Optd with T* **19**.
68 15 ½d. yellow-green 10 35
a. No stop after "STAMP" (R. 18/2) .. 8·00 21·00
b. Opt double .. .. 95·00 £100
c. Opt inverted .. .. .. 80·00 90·00
d. Space between "W" and "A" (R. 20/1) 9·00 21·00
e. Blue-green 10 50
ea. No stop after "STAMP" (R. 3/11 or 11/1) .. .. 9·00 21·00
eb. Space between "W" and "A" (R. 20/1) 10·00 24·00
w. Wmk inverted .. .. ..
69 18 3d. purple/*yellow* (white back) .. 6·50 20·00
a. On lemon (6.16) .. .. .. 1·00 16·00
ab. No stop after "STAMP" (R. 8/6 or 9/6) 23·00 75·00
b. On pale yellow (9.16) .. .. 6·50 21·00
Minor varieties: ½d. (i) Small "P"; (ii) "WARISTAMP" (raised quad between words); (iii) Two stops after "STAMP". 3d. "WARISTAMP". There were several settings of the overprint used for each value. Where two positions are quoted for a variety these did not occur on the same sheet.

NOTE. The above and succeeding stamps with "WAR STAMP" overprint were issued for payment of a special war tax on letters and postcards or on parcels. Ordinary unoverprinted stamps could also be used for this purpose.

1916 (Sept–Dec). *Optd with T* **20**.
70 15 ½d. blue-green (*shades*) (2.10.16) .. 10 30
a. No stop after "STAMP" (R. 5/7) .. 9·00 30·00
b. Opt omitted (in pair with normal) £1100 £1000
c. "R" inserted by hand (R. 11/10) .. £500 £450
w. Wmk inverted .. .. .. 30·00
71 18 1½d. orange (1.9.16) 10 15
aa. Wmk sideways .. .. .. † £1200
a. No stop after "STAMP" (R. 4/12, 8/6, 10/10, 11/1, 18/12, 19/12) .. .. 5·00 6·50
b. "S" in "STAMP" omitted (R. 6/12) (Dec) £110 £120
c. "S" inserted by hand £250
d. "R" in "WAR" omitted (R. 1/10) .. £800 £700
e. "R" inserted by hand £450 £400
f. Inverted "d" for "P" £180 £150
w. Wmk inverted .. .. .. 15·00 15·00
72 3d. purple/*lemon* (2.10.16) 30 90
aa. Opt inverted £275
a. No stop after "STAMP" (R. 5/7) .. 22·00 55·00
b. "S" in "STAMP" omitted (R. 6/12) (Dec) £300 £275
c. "S" inserted by hand £180 £180
e. On yellow (12.16) .. .. .. 6·00 9·00
ea. "S" in "STAMP" omitted (R. 6/12) .. £450 £400
eb. "S" inserted by hand £325 £250
Nos. 70c, 71c, 71e, 72c and 72eb show the missing "R" or "S" inserted by handstamp. The 3d. is known with this "S" handstamp inverted or double.

Minor varieties, such as raised quads, small stop, double stop, spaced letters and letters of different sizes, also exist in this overprint. The setting was altered several times.

1917 (March). *Optd with T* **21**.
73 15 ½d. blue-green (*shades*) (25.3.17) .. 10 20
a. No stop after "STAMP" (R. 2/5, 8/11, 8/12) .. .. 7·50 20·00
b. Stop inserted and "P" impressed a second time (R. 7/6) £150
c. Optd on back only £140
d. Opt inverted .. .. .. 9·50 30·00
74 18 1½d. orange (3.3.17) 10 10
aa. Wmk sideways .. .. .. † £1300
a. No stop after "STAMP" (R. 2/5, 8/11, 8/12) .. .. 5·00 17·00
b. Stop inserted and "P" impressed a second time (R. 7/6) £200
c. Opt double .. .. .. 80·00 85·00
d. Opt inverted .. .. .. 80·00 75·00
e. "WAP STAMP" (R. 6/2) .. ..
w. Wmk inverted .. .. .. 15·00
75 3d. purple/*yellow* (3.3.17) 15 70
a. No stop after "STAMP" (R. 2/5, 8/11, 8/12) .. .. 13·00 27·00
b. Stop inserted and "P" impressed a second time (R. 7/6) £170
c. Opt inverted £140
d. Opt sideways (reading up) £300
da. Opt omitted (in horiz pair with No. 75d) £1800
No. 75da shows the left-hand stamp as No. 75d and the right-hand stamp without overprint.

There are numerous minor varieties in this overprint with the setting being altered several times.

WAR STAMP
(22)

1919 (4 Oct). *Optd with T* **22** *by D.L.R.*
76 15 ½d. green (R.) 10 15
77 18 3d. purple/*yellow* (R.) .. .. 2·25 3·00
a. Pale purple/buff (R.) .. .. 2·00 1·25
b. Deep purple/buff (R.) .. .. 5·50 6·00
76/7 Optd "Specimen" .. .. *Set of* 2 70·00
We list the most distinct variations in the 3d. The buff tone of the paper varies considerably in depth.

23 Jamaica Exhibition 1891

24 Arawak Woman preparing Cassava

25 War Contingent embarking

26 King's House, Spanish Town

Re-entry. Nos. 80a, 93a

The greater part of the design is re-entered, the hull showing in very solid colour and the people appear very blurred. There are also minor re-entries on stamps above (R. 7/4 and 6/4).

27 Return of War Contingent

A B

28 Landing of Columbus

29 Cathedral, Spanish Town

34

(Typo (½d., 1d.), recess (others) D.L.R.)

1919–21. *T* **23/29, 34** *and similar vert designs. Wmk Mult Crown CA* (*sideways* on* 1*d.*, 1½*d. and* 10*s.*). *Chalk-surfaced paper* (½*d.*, 1*d.*). *P* 14.
78 23 ½d. green and olive-green (12.11.20) 1·00 70
w. Wmk inverted .. .. ..
x. Wmk reversed .. .. ..
y. Wmk inverted and reversed ..
79 24 1d. carmine and orange (3.10.21) 1·75 1·75
w. Wmk Crown to left of CA ..
80 25 1½d. green (*shades*) (4.7.19) .. 40 70
a. Major re-entry (R. 8/4) .. 65·00
b. "C" of "CA" missing from wmk .. † £200
c. "A" of "CA" missing from wmk .. † —
w. Wmk Crown to left of CA .. 20·00
y. Wmk sideways inverted and reversed .. .. .. — 30·00
81 26 2d. indigo and green (18.2.21) 1·00 3·50
w. Wmk inverted .. .. 35·00
y. Wmk inverted and reversed .. 35·00
82 27 2½d. deep blue and blue (A) (18.2.21) 13·00 3·00
a. Blue-black and deep blue 1·25 1·40
b. "C" of "CA" missing from wmk ..
c. "A" of "CA" missing from wmk .. £200
w. Wmk inverted .. .. 25·00
x. Wmk reversed .. .. 30·00
y. Wmk inverted and reversed .. 30·00
83 28 3d. myrtle-green and blue (8.4.21) 1·50 2·00
w. Wmk inverted .. .. 30·00 32·00
84 29 4d. brown and deep green (21.2.21) 2·50 8·00
w. Wmk inverted .. ..
x. Wmk reversed .. ..
85 – 1s. orange-yell & red-orge (10.12.20) 3·75 5·50
a. Frame inverted £18000 £13000
b. "C" of "CA" missing from wmk .. £250
c. "A" of "CA" missing from wmk ..
w. Wmk inverted .. ..
x. Wmk reversed .. ..

86 – 2s. light blue and brown (10.12.20) 13·00 24·00
b. "C" of "CA" missing from wmk . .
c. "A" of "CA" missing from wmk . .
w. Wmk inverted . . . . . . 30·00 35·00
x. Wmk reversed . . . . . .
y. Wmk inverted and reversed . .
87 – 3s. violet-blue and orange (10.12.20) 20·00 65·00
88 – 5s. blue and yellow-orange (15.4.21) 50·00 65·00
a. Blue and pale dull orange . . 48·00 60·00
w. Wmk inverted . . . . . .
x. Wmk reversed . . . . . .
89 – 10s. myrtle-green (6.5.20) . . . . 75·00 £140
78/89 . . . . *Set of* 12 £150 £275
78/89 Optd "Specimen" . . *Set of* 12 £250

Designs: *Vert*—1s. Statue of Queen Victoria, Kingston; 2s. Admiral Rodney Memorial; 3s. Sir Charles Metcalfe Monument; 5s. Jamaican scenery.

*The normal sideways wmk on Nos. 79/80 shows Crown to right of CA, *as seen from the back of the stamp.*

The 2½d. of the above series showed the Union Jack at left, incorrectly, as indicated in illustration A. In the issue on paper with Script wmk the design was corrected (Illustration B).

No. 85 also exists with the "A" missing from an impression of the watermark on the sheet margin. An example of the "C" omitted has been reported on an example of No. 88 overprinted "Specimen".

A 6d. stamp showing the reading of the Declaration of Freedom from Slavery in 1836 was prepared and sent out in April 1921, but for political reasons was not issued and the stock was destroyed. Copies overprinted "Specimen" are known on both the Mult CA and Script CA papers, and are worth £550 each. Price without "Specimen" on Script CA £14000.

"Bow" flaw (R.18/12)

1921 (21 Oct)–**27.** *Wmk Mult Script CA. Chalk-surfaced paper (6d.). P* 14.
89*a* **18** ½d. green (Optd S. £45) (3.11.27) . . 1·00 10
ab. Bow flaw . . . . 32·00 20·00
90 6d. dull pur & brt magenta (Optd S. £35) 6·00 3·25

35 "POSTAGE & REVENUE" added

36 "Port Royal in 1853" (A. Duperly)

(Printing as before; the 6d. recess-printed)

1921–29. *As Nos. 78/89. Wmk Mult Script CA (sideways* on 1d. and* 1½*d.). Chalk-surfaced paper* (½*d.,* 1*d.). P* 14.
91 **23** ½d. green and olive-green (5.2.22) . . 50 30
a. Green and deep olive-green . . 25 30
w. Wmk inverted . . . . . . 25·00 25·00
92 **35** 1d. carmine and orange (5.12.22) . . 1·50 10
w. Wmk Crown to right of CA . . 15·00 15·00
x. Wmk reversed . . . . . . — 30·00
93 **25** 1½d. green (*shades*) (2.2.21) 30 45
a. Major re-entry (R. 8/4) . . . . 65·00
w. Wmk Crown to left of CA . . — 20·00
x. Wmk reversed . . . . . . 20·00 20·00
y. Wmk sideways inverted and reversed . . . . — 40·00
94 **26** 2d. indigo and green (4.11.21) . . 5·00 60
a. Indigo and grey-green (1925) . . 6·00 75
95 **27** 2½d. deep blue and blue (B) (4.11.21) . . 5·50 1·25
a. Dull blue and blue (B) . . . . 6·00 60
w. Wmk inverted . . . . . . 25·00 25·00
x. Wmk reversed . . . . . .
y. Wmk inverted and reversed . .
96 **28** 3d. myrtle-green and blue (6.3.22) . . 2·25 60
a. Green and pale blue 50 15
x. Wmk reversed . . . . . .
97 **29** 4d. brown and deep green (5.12.21) . . 55 30
a. Chocolate and dull green . . 55 30
w. Wmk inverted . . . . . . 25·00
x. Wmk reversed . . . . . . 35·00
98 **36** 6d. black and blue (5.12.22) . . . . 10·00 1·50
a. Grey and dull blue . . . . 10·00 95
99 – 1s. orange and red-orange (4.11.21) . . 1·40 70
a. Orange-yellow and brown-orange 1·25 40
w. Wmk inverted . . . . . .
x. Wmk reversed . . . . . .
100 – 2s. light blue and brown (5.2.22) . . 2·50 40
w. Wmk inverted . . . . . . 30·00 30·00
101 – 3s. violet-blue and orange (23.8.21) . . 8·50 8·50
102 – 5s. blue and yellow-brown (8.11.23) . . 25·00 25·00
a. Blue and pale dull orange . . 50·00 55·00
b. Blue and yellow-orange (1927) . . 23·00 23·00
c. Blue and pale bistre-brown (1929) 23·00 22·00
w. Wmk inverted . . . . . . — £100
x. Wmk reversed . . . . . .
103 **34** 10s. myrtle-green (March (?) 1922) . . 48·00 60·00
91/103 . . . . *Set of* 13 85·00 85·00
91/103 Optd "Specimen" . . . . *Set of* 13 £250

*The normal sideways wmk shows Crown to left of CA on No. 92 or Crown to right of CA on No. 93, *both as seen from the back of the stamp.*

The frame of No. 102*a* is the same colour as that of No. 88*a*.

The designs of all values of the pictorial series, with the exception of the 5s. and 10s. (which originated with the Governor, Sir Leslie Probyn), were selected by Mr. F. C. Cundall, F.S.A. The 1d. and 5s. were drawn by Miss Cundall, the 3d. by Mrs. Cundall, and the 10s. by De La Rue & Co. The 6d. is from a lithograph. The other designs are from photographs, the frames of all being the work of Miss Cundall and Miss Wood.

37

38

39

(Centres from photos by Miss V. F. Taylor. Frames des F. C. Cundall, F.S.A., and drawn by Miss Cundall. Recess B.W.)

1923 (1 Nov). *Child Welfare. Wmk Mult Script CA. P* 12.
104 **37** ½d. +½d. black and green . . . . 60 4·50
105 **38** 1d. +½d. black and scarlet . . . . 1·50 10·00
106 **39** 2½d. +½d. black and blue . . . . 7·50 18·00
104/6 . . . . *Set of* 3 8·50 29·00
104/6 Optd "Specimen" . . . . *Set of* 3 £120

Sold at a premium of ½d. for the Child Welfare League, these stamps were on sale annually from 1 November to 31 January, until 31 January 1927, when their sale ceased, the remainders being destroyed on 21 February 1927.

40

41

42

Die I

Die II

(Recess D.L.R.)

1929–32. *Wmk Mult Script CA. P* 14.
108 **40** 1d. scarlet (Die I) . . . . . . 1·25 10
a. Die II (1932) . . . . . . 2·00 10
109 **41** 1½d. chocolate . . . . 1·25 15
110 **42** 9d. maroon . . . . 3·00 1·00
108/10 . . . . *Set of* 3 5·00 1·10
108/10 Perf "Specimen" . . . . *Set of* 3 75·00

In Die I the shading below JAMAICA is formed of thickened parallel lines, and in Die II of diagonal cross-hatching.

43 Coco Palms at Don Christopher's Cove

44 Wag Water River, St. Andrew

45 Priestman's River, Portland

(Dies eng and recess Waterlow)

1932. *Wmk Mult Script CA (sideways on 2d. and* 2½*d.). P* 12½.
111 **43** 2d. black and green (late 1932) . . 6·50 2·25
a. Imperf between (vert pair) £5000
112 **44** 2½d. turquoise-blue & ultram (5.3.32) . . 1·00 1·25
a. Imperf between (vert pair) £9000 £9000
113 **45** 6d. grey-black and purple (2.32) . . 6·50 1·25
111/13 . . . . *Set of* 3 12·50 4·25
111/13 Perf "Specimen" . . . . *Set of* 3 80·00

46 Windsor Castle

(Des H. Fleury. Recess B.W.)

1935 (6 May). *Silver Jubilee. Wmk Mult Script CA. P* 11×12.
114 **46** 1d. deep blue and scarlet 20 15
d. Flagstaff on right-hand turret . . 60·00
e. Double flagstaff . . . . . . 60·00
115 1½d. ultramarine and grey-black . . 50 85
a. Extra flagstaff . . . . . . 75·00 £100
b. Short extra flagstaff . . . . 70·00
c. Lightning conductor . . . . 60·00
116 6d. green and indigo . . . . . . 4·00 8·00
a. Extra flagstaff £170 £200
b. Short extra flagstaff £170
c. Lightning conductor £140
117 1s. slate and purple . . . . . . 4·00 6·50
a. Extra flagstaff £225 £275
b. Short extra flagstaff £225
c. Lightning conductor £180
114/17 . . . . *Set of* 4 8·00 14·00
114/17 Perf "Specimen" . . . . *Set of* 4 75·00

For illustrations of plate varieties see Omnibus section following Zimbabwe.

47 King George VI and Queen Elizabeth

(Des and recess D.L.R.)

1937 (12 May). *Coronation. Wmk Mult Script CA. P* 14.
118 **47** 1d. scarlet 30 15
119 1½d. grey-black 50 30
120 2½d. bright blue 85 70
118/20 . . . . *Set of* 3 1·50 1·00
118/20 Perf "Specimen" . . . . *Set of* 3 55·00

48 King George VI

49 Coco Palms at Don Christopher's Cove

50 Bananas

51 Citrus Grove

52 Kingston Harbour

53 Sugar Industry

54 Bamboo Walk

55 King George VI

56 Tobacco Growing and Cigar Making

Repaired chimney (Centre plate 1 R. 11/1)

(Recess D.L.R. (T **48**, 5s. and 10s.), Waterlow (others))

1938 (10 Oct)–**52.** *T* **48/56** *and as Nos.* 88, 112/13, *but with inset portrait of King George VI, as in T* **49**. *Wmk Mult Script CA. P* 13½×14 (½*d.*, 1*d.*, 1½*d.*), 14 (5*s.*, 10*s.*) *or* 12½ (*others*).

No.	Type	Description	Unused	Used
121	**48**	½d. blue-green (10.10.38)	1·00	10
		a. Wmk sideways	†	£3000
121*b*		½d. orange (25.10.51)	20	30
122		1d. scarlet	80	10
122*a*		1d. blue-green (25.10.51)	30	10
123		1½d. brown	80	10
124	**49**	2d. grey and green (10.12.38) ..	50	60
		a. Perf 13×13½ (1939)	1·25	30
		b. Perf 12½×13 (1951)	75	20
125	**44**	2½d. greenish blue & ultram (10.12.38)	3·00	1·50
126	**50**	3d. ultramarine and green (10.12.38)	70	1·00
		a. "A" of "CA" missing from wmk ..	£750	
126*b*		3d. greenish blue and ultram (15.8.49)	1·75	1·40
126*c*		3d. green and scarlet (1.7.52) ..	1·50	30
127	**51**	4d. brown and green (10.12.38) ..	40	10
128	**45**	6d. grey and purple (10.12.38) ..	2·50	30
		a. Perf 13½×13 (10.10.50) ..	1·75	10
129	**52**	9d. lake (10.12.38)	40	40
		a. "A" of "CA" missing from wmk ..		
130	**53**	1s. green and purple-brown (10.12.38)	5·50	20
		a. Repaired chimney	£375	£100
131	**54**	2s. blue and chocolate (10.12.38) ..	20·00	90
132	–	5s. slate-blue & yellow-orge (10.12.38)	13·00	3·50
		a. Perf 14, line (1941)	£2750	£190
		b. Perf 13 (24.10.49)	6·50	3·00
		ba. Blue and orange (10.10.50) ..	6·50	3·00
133	**55**	10s. myrtle-green (10.12.38)	11·00	7·50
		aa. Perf 13 (10.10.50)	9·00	5·00
133*a*	**56**	£1 chocolate and violet (15.8.49) ..	27·00	26·00
121/33*a*		.. .. *Set of* 18	70·00	35·00
121/33 Perf "Specimen"		.. .. *Set of* 13	£200	

No. 130a occurred in conjunction with Frame plate 2 on printings between 1943 and 1951.

No. 132a shows the emergency use of a line perforation machine, giving an irregular gauge of 14–14.15, after the De La Rue works were damaged in December 1940. The normal comb measures 13.8×13.7.

SELF-GOVERNMENT

57 Courthouse, Falmouth

58 King Charles II and King George VI

59 Institute of Jamaica

(Recess Waterlow)

1945 (20 Aug)–**46.** *New Constitution. T* **57/9** *and similar designs. Wmk Mult Script CA. P* 12½.

No.	Type	Description	Unused	Used
134	**57**	1½d. sepia	20	30
		a. Perf 12½×13 (1946)	2·75	50
135	**58**	2d. green	6·50	90
		a. Perf 12½×13 (1945)	20	50
136	**59**	3d. ultramarine	20	50
		a. Perf 13 (1946)	90	2·25
137	–	4½d. slate	30	30
		a. Perf 13 (1946)	90	1·75
138	–	2s. red-brown	30	50
139	–	5s. indigo	1·00	1·00
140	**59**	10s. green	85	2·25
134/40		.. .. .. *Set of* 7	2·75	4·75
134/40 Perf "Specimen"		.. *Set of* 7	£140	

Designs: *Vert* (*as T* **57**)—2s. "Labour and Learning". *Horiz* (*as T* **59**)—4½d. House of Assembly; 5s. Scroll, flag and King George VI.

60 Houses of Parliament, London

(Des and recess D.L.R.)

1946 (14 Oct). *Victory. Wmk Mult Script CA. P* 13½×14.

No.	Type	Description	Unused	Used
141	**60**	1½d. purple-brown	2·00	10
		a. Perf 13½	30	45
142		3d. blue	2·00	2·00
		a. Perf 13½	30	4·00
141/2 Perf "Specimen"		.. .. *Set of* 2	50·00	

NEW INFORMATION

The editor is always interested to correspond with people who have new information that will improve or correct the Catalogue.

61 **62**
King George VI and Queen Elizabeth

(Des and photo Waterlow (T **61**). Design recess, name typo B.W. (T **62**))

1948 (1 Dec). *Royal Silver Wedding. Wmk Mult Script CA.*

No.	Type	Description	Unused	Used
143	**61**	1½d. red-brown (*p* 14×15)	30	10
144	**62**	£1 scarlet (*p* 11½×11)	24·00	45·00

63 Hermes, Globe and Forms of Transport

64 Hemispheres, Vickers Viking Airplane and Steamer

65 Hermes and Globe

66 U.P.U. Monument

(Recess Waterlow (T **63**, **66**). Design recess, name typo B.W. (T **64/5**))

1949 (10 Oct). *75th Anniv of Universal Postal Union. Wmk Mult Script CA.*

No.	Type	Description	Unused	Used
145	**63**	1½d. red-brown (*p* 13½–14)	30	15
146	**64**	2d. deep blue-green (*p* 11×11½) ..	1·00	1·75
147	**65**	3d. deep blue (*p* 11×11½)	55	1·25
148	**66**	6d. purple (*p* 13½–14)	65	2·50
145/8		.. .. *Set of* 4	2·25	5·00

67 Arms of University

68 Princess Alice

(Recess Waterlow)

1951 (16 Feb). *Inauguration of B.W.I. University College. Wmk Mult Script CA. P* 14×14½.

No.	Type	Description	Unused	Used
149	**67**	2d. black and red-brown	30	30
150	**68**	6d. grey-black and purple	35	30

69 Scout Badge and Map of Caribbean

70 Scout Badge and Map of Jamaica

(Litho B.W.)

1952 (5 Mar). *First Caribbean Scout Jamboree. Wmk Mult Script CA. P* 13½×13 (2*d.*) *or* 13×13½ (6*d.*).

No.	Type	Description	Unused	Used
151	**69**	2d. blue, apple-green and black ..	15	10
152	**70**	6d. yellow-green, carmine-red and black	15	30

71 Queen Elizabeth II

72 Coco Palms at Don Christopher's Cove

(Des and eng B.W. Recess D.L.R.)

1953 (2 June). *Coronation. Wmk Mult Script CA. P* 13½×13.

No.	Type	Description	Unused	Used
153	**71**	2d. black and deep yellow-green ..	40	10

(Recess Waterlow)

1953 (25 Nov). *Royal Visit. Wmk Mult Script CA. P* 12½×13.

No.	Type	Description	Unused	Used
154	**72**	2d. grey-black and green	30	10

73 Man-o'-War at Port Royal

(Recess D.L.R.)

1955 (10 May). *Tercentenary Issue. T* **73** *and similar horiz designs. Wmk Mult Script CA. P* 12½.

No.	Type	Description	Unused	Used
155		2d. black and olive-green	35	10
156		2½d. black and deep bright blue	15	35
157		3d. black and claret	15	30
158		6d. black and carmine-red	20	20
155/8		.. .. *Set of* 4	75	80

Designs:—2½d. Old Montego Bay; 3d. Old Kingston; 6d. Proclamation of Abolition of Slavery, 1838.

74 Coconut Palms

75 Mahoe

76 Blue Mountain Peak

77 Arms of Jamaica

78 Arms of Jamaica

(Recess B.W. (T **77/8**), D.L.R. (others))

1956 (1 May)–**58**. *T* **74/8** *and similar designs. Wmk Mult Script CA. P* 13 (½d. *to* 6*d.*), 13½ (8*d. to* 2*s.*) *or* 11½ (3*s. to* £1).

No.	Type	Description	Unused	Used
159	**74**	½d. black and deep orange-red ..	10	10
160	–	1d. black and emerald	10	10
161	–	2d. black and carmine-red (2.8.56) ..	10	10
162	–	2½d. black and deep bright blue (2.8.56)	30	40
163	**75**	3d. emerald and red-brown (17.12.56)	20	10
164	–	4d. bronze-green and blue (17.12.56)	20	10
		w. Wmk inverted	80·00	
165	–	5d. scarlet and bronze-green (17.12.56)	20	1·00
166	–	6d. black and deep rose-red (3.9.56)	1·25	10
167	**76**	8d. ultramarine & red-orge (15.11.56)	15	10
168	–	1s. yellow-green and blue (15.11.56)	50	10
169	–	1s. 6d. ultram & reddish pur (15.11.56)	50	10
170	–	2s. blue and bronze-green (15.11.56)	5·00	1·50
		a. Grey-blue & bronze-green (24.4.58)	7·00	1·50
171	**77**	3s. black and blue (2.8.56)	1·25	1·50
172		5s. black and carmine-red (15.8.56) ..	2·75	3·00
173	**78**	10s. black and blue-green (15.8.56) ..	21·00	12·00
174		£1 black and purple (15.8.56) ..	21·00	12·00
159/74		.. .. *Set of* 16	48·00	28·00

Designs: *Vert* (*as T* **74/5**)—1d. Sugar Cane; 2d. Pineapples; 2½d. Bananas; 4d. Breadfruit; 5d. Ackee; 6d. Streamertail. *Horiz* (*as T* **76**)—1s. Royal Botanic Gardens, Hope; 1s. 6d. Rafting on the Rio Grande; 2s. Fort Charles.

An earlier £1 value, in the design of No. 133*a* but showing the portrait of Queen Elizabeth II, was prepared, but not issued.

79 Federation Map

(Recess B.W.)

1958 (22 Apr). *Inauguration of British Caribbean Federation. W w* **12**. *P* 11½×11.

No.	Type	Description	Unused	Used
175	**79**	2d. deep green	55	10
176		5d. blue	95	3·00
177		6d. scarlet	95	40
175/7		.. .. *Set of* 3	2·25	3·00

81 Bristol 175 Britannia 312 flying over *City of Berlin*, 1860

83 1s. Stamps of 1860 and 1956

(Recess Waterlow)

1960 (4 Jan). *Stamp Centenary. T* **81**, **83** *and similar design. W* w **12**. *P* 13 × 13½ (1s.) *or* 13½ × 14 (*others*).

No.	Description	Unused	Used
178	2d. blue and reddish purple	45	10
179	6d. carmine and olive-green	45	20
180	1s. red-brown, yellow-green and blue	45	25
178/80	*Set of* 3	1·25	50

Design: *As T* **81**—6d. Postal mule-cart and motor-van.

INDEPENDENT

1962 INDEPENDENCE (84)

INDEPENDENCE 1962 (85)

86 Military Bugler and Map

(Des V. Whiteley. Photo D.L.R. (2, 4d., 1s. 6d., 5s.))

1962 (8 Aug)–**63**. *Independence*.

(*a*) *Nos.* 159/60, 162, 171, 173/4 *optd as T* **84** *and Nos.* 163, 165/8, 170 *optd with T* **85**

No.	Type	Description	Unused	Used
181	**74**	½d. black and deep orange-red	10	85
182	–	1d. black and emerald	10	10
183	–	2½d. black and deep bright blue	10	85
184	**75**	3d. emerald and red-brown	10	10
185	–	5d. scarlet and bronze-green	15	60
186	–	6d. black and deep rose-red	1·50	10
187	**76**	8d. ultram & red-orge (opt at upper left)	15	10
		a. Opt at lower left (17.9.63?)	15	15
188	–	1s. yellow-green and blue	15	10
189	–	2s. blue and bronze-green	80	1·25
		a. Dp blue & dp bronze-green (20.8.63)	4·50	2·25
190	**77**	3s. black and blue	90	1·50
191	**78**	10s. black and blue-green	2·50	4·25
192		£1 black and purple	2·75	5·50

(*b*) *Horiz designs as T* **86**. *W* w **12**. *P* 13

No.	Description	Unused	Used
193	2d. multicoloured	50	10
194	4d. multicoloured	50	10
195	1s. 6d. black and red	1·50	85
196	5s. multicoloured	2·25	3·00
181/96	*Set of* 16	12·00	17·00

Designs:—2, 4d. Type **86**; 1s. 6d. Gordon House and banner; 5s. Map, factories and fruit.

For these overprints on stamps watermarked w **12** see Nos. 205/13.

89 Kingston Seal, Weightlifting, Boxing, Football and Cycling

93 Farmer and Crops

(Photo Harrison)

1962 (11 Aug). *Ninth Central American and Caribbean Games, Kingston. T* **89** *and similar horiz designs. W* w **12**. *P* 14½ × 14.

No.	Description	Unused	Used
197	1d. sepia and carmine-red	15	10
198	6d. sepia and greenish blue	15	10
199	8d. sepia and bistre	15	10
200	2s. multicoloured	25	55
197/200	*Set of* 4	65	65

Designs:—6d. Kingston seal, diving, sailing, swimming and water polo; 8d. Kingston seal, pole-vaulting, javelin throwing, discus throwing, relay-racing and hurdling; 2s. Kingston coat of arms and athlete.

An imperf miniature sheet exists, but this was never available at face value or at any post office.

(Des M. Goaman. Litho D.L.R.)

1963 (4 June). *Freedom from Hunger. P* 12½.

No.	Type	Description	Unused	Used
201	**93**	1d. multicoloured	20	10
202		8d. multicoloured	60	50

COVER PRICES

Cover factors are quoted at the beginning of each country for most issues to 1945. An explanation of the system can be found on page x. The factors quoted do not, however, apply to philatelic covers.

94 Red Cross Emblem

95 Carole Joan Crawford ("Miss World 1963")

(Des V. Whiteley. Litho B.W.)

1963 (4 Sept). *Red Cross Centenary. W* w **12**. *P* 13½.

No.	Type	Description	Unused	Used
203	**94**	2d. red and black	20	10
204		1s. 6d. red and blue	50	1·00

1963–64. *As Nos.* 181/90, *but wmk* w **12**.

No.	Type	Description	Unused	Used
205	**74**	½d. black & deep orange-red (3.12.63*)	10	15
206	–	1d. black and emerald (3.4.64)	10	90
207	–	2½d. black and deep bright blue (3.4.64)	25	2·25
208	**75**	3d. emerald and red-brown (17.12.63*)	15	15
209	–	5d. scarlet and bronze-green (3.4.64)	30	2·25
210	**76**	8d. ultramarine and red-orange (3.4.64)	20	75
211	–	1s. yellow-green and blue (21.12.63*)	35	75
212	–	2s. dp blue & dp bronze-green (3.4.64)	60	5·00
213	**77**	3s. black and blue (5.2.64)	2·00	6·50
205/13		*Set of* 9	3·50	16·00

The overprint on the 8d., 1s. and 2s. is at lower left, the others are as before.

*These are the earliest known dates recorded in Jamaica.

(Des and photo D.L.R.)

1964 (14 Feb–25 May). *"Miss World 1963" Commemoration. P* 13.

No.	Type	Description	Unused	Used
214	**95**	3d. multicoloured	10	10
215		1s. multicoloured	15	10
216		1s. 6d. multicoloured	20	30
214/16		*Set of* 3	40	40
MS216*a*		153×101 mm. Nos. 214/16. Imperf (25.5.64)	80	2·00

96 *Lignum Vitae*

97 Blue Mahoe

103 Gypsum Industry

109 Arms of Jamaica

111 Multiple "J" and Pineapple

(Des V. Whiteley. Photo Harrison)

1964 (4 May)–**68**. *T* **96/7**, **103**, **109** *and similar designs. W* **111**. *P* 14½ (1*d*., 2*d*., 2½*d*., 6*d*., 8*d*.), 14×14½ (1½*d*., 3*d*., 4*d*., 10*s*.), 14½×14 (9*d*., 1*s*., 3*s*., 5*s*., £1) *or* 13½×14½ (1*s*. 6*d*., 2*s*.).

No.	Description	Unused	Used
217	1d. violet-blue, dp green & lt brn (*shades*)	10	10
218	1½d. multicoloured	15	10
219	2d. red, yellow and grey-green	15	10
	w. Wmk inverted	3·75	
220	2½d. multicoloured	80	60
221	3d. yellow, black and emerald	15	10
222	4d. ochre and violet	45	10
223	6d. multicoloured	2·25	10
	a. Blue omitted	50·00	
	b. Value omitted	£600	
	w. Wmk inverted	7·00	
224	8d mult (yellowish green background)	1·50	90
	a. Red (beak) omitted	90·00	
	b. Greyish green background (16.7.68)	5·50	3·50
225	9d. blue and yellow-bistre	1·00	10
226	1s. black and light brown	20	10
	a. Light brown omitted	£300	
	ab. Value only omitted	£400	
	b. Black omitted	£450	
	ba. "NATIONAL STADIUM" etc omitted	£500	
227	1s. 6d. black, light blue and buff	2·25	15
228	2s. red-brown, black and light blue	2·25	15
229	3s. blue and dull green	1·00	80
	aw. Wmk inverted	11·00	
	b. Perf 13½×14½	35	65
230	5s. black, ochre and blue	1·25	1·00
	w. Wmk inverted	70·00	
231	10s. multicoloured	1·25	1·00
	a. Blue ("JAMAICA", etc) omitted	£200	
232	£1 multicoloured	1·50	1·00
217/32	*Set of* 16	13·00	5·00

Designs: *Horiz*. (*As T* **96**)—1½d. Ackee; 2½d. Land shells; 3d. National flag over Jamaica; 4d. Antillean Murex (*Murex formosus*) (shell); 6d. *Papilio homerus* (butterfly); 8d. Streamertail. *As T* **103**—1s. National Stadium; 1s. 6d. Palisadoes International Airport; 2s. Bauxite mining; 3s. Blue Marlin (sport fishing); 5s. Exploration of sunken city, Port Royal; £1 Queen Elizabeth II and national flag.

No. 223b. Two left half sheets are known with the black printing shifted downwards to such an extent that the value is omitted from the top row.

Nos. 226a/ab came from a sheet on which the two bottom rows had the colour omitted with the next row showing it missing from the lower third of the stamps.

A similar sheet, but with the colour missing from the top two rows and part of the third produced Nos 226b/ba.

112 Scout Belt

113 Globe, Scout Hat and Scarf

114 Scout Badge and Alligator

(Photo Harrison)

1964 (27 Aug). *Sixth Inter-American Scout Conference, Kingston. W* **111**. *P* 14 (1*s*.) *or* 14½ × 14 (*others*).

No.	Type	Description	Unused	Used
233	**112**	3d. red, black and pink	10	10
234	**113**	8d. bright blue, olive and black	10	25
		w. Wmk inverted	18·00	
235	**114**	1s. gold, deep blue and light blue	15	25
		w. Wmk inverted	15	25
233/5		*Set of* 3	30	45

115 Gordon House, Kingston

118 Eleanor Roosevelt

(Des V. Whiteley. Photo Harrison)

1964 (16 Nov). *Tenth Commonwealth Parliamentary Conference, Kingston. T* **115** *and similar horiz designs. W* **111**. *P* 14½ × 14.

No.	Description	Unused	Used
236	3d. black and yellow-green	10	10
237	6d. black and carmine-red	10	10
238	1s. 6d. black and bright blue	25	30
236/8	*Set of* 3	40	40

Designs:—6d. Headquarters House, Kingston; 1s. 6d. House of Assembly, Spanish Town.

(Des V. Whiteley. Photo Harrison)

1964 (10 Dec). *16th Anniv of Declaration of Human Rights. W* **111**. *P* 14½ × 14.

No.	Type	Description	Unused	Used
239	**118**	1s. black, red and light green	10	10

119 Guides' Emblem on Map

120 Guide Emblems

(Photo Harrison)

1965 (17 May). *Golden Jubilee of Jamaica Girl Guides Association. W* **111** (*sideways on 3d*.). *P* 14 × 14½ (3*d*.) *or* 14 (1*s*.).

No.	Type	Description	Unused	Used
240	**119**	3d. yellow, green and light blue	10	10
241	**120**	1s. yellow, black and apple-green	20	20
		w. Wmk inverted	20	20

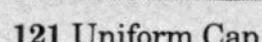

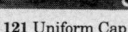

121 Uniform Cap   **122** Flag-bearer and Drummer

(Photo Harrison)

1965 (23 Aug). *Salvation Army Centenary. W* **111**. *P* 14 × 14½ (3*d*.) *or* 14½ × 14 (1*s*. 6*d*.).

242 **121** 3d. multicoloured .. 25 10
w. Wmk inverted .. 8·00
243 **122** 1s. 6d. multicoloured .. 50 35
w. Wmk inverted .. 17·00

123 Paul Bogle, William Gordon and Morant Bay Court House   **124** Abeng-blower, "Telstar", Morse Key and I.T.U. Emblem

(Photo Enschedé)

1965 (29 Dec). *Centenary of Morant Bay Rebellion. No wmk. P* 14 × 13.

244 **123** 3d. light brown, ultramarine and black 10 10
245 1s. 6d. lt brown, yellow-green & black 10 10
246 3s. light brown, rose and black 20 50
244/6 .. *Set of* 3 35 60

(Photo Harrison)

1965 (29 Dec). *I.T.U. Centenary. W* **111**. *P* 14 × 14½.

247 **124** 1s. black, grey-blue and red .. 40 15

ROYAL VISIT
MARCH 1966

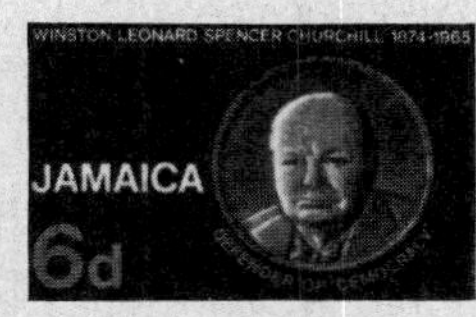

(**125**)   **126** Sir Winston Churchill

1966 (3 Mar). *Royal Visit. Nos.* 221, 223, 226/7 *optd with T* **125**.

248 3d. yellow, black and emerald .. 15 10
249 6d. multicoloured .. 1·50 10
250 1s. black and light brown .. 55 10
251 1s. 6d. black, light blue and buff .. 1·50 1·25
248/51 .. *Set of* 4 3·25 1·40

(Des Jennifer Toombs. Photo Harrison)

1966 (18 April). *Churchill Commemoration. W* **111**. *P* 14.

252 **126** 6d. black and olive-green .. 35 20
253 1s. bistre-brown and deep violet-blue .. 65 70

127 Statue of Athlete and Flags   **131** Bolivar's Statue and Flags of Jamaica and Venezuela

(Des V. Whiteley. Photo Harrison)

1966 (4 Aug). *Eighth British Empire and Commonwealth Games. T* **127** *and similar horiz designs. W* **111**. *P* 14½×14.

254 3d. multicoloured .. 10 10
255 6d. multicoloured .. 20 10
w. Wmk inverted .. 17·00
256 1s. multicoloured .. 10 10
257 3s. bright gold and deep blue .. 30 35
a. Dull gold and deep blue
w. Wmk inverted .. 17·00
254/7 .. *Set of* 4 55 45
MS258 128×103 mm. Nos. 254/7. Imperf .. 4·00 7·50

Designs:—6d. Racing cyclists; 1s. National Stadium, Kingston; 3s. Games emblem.

No. **MS**258 has been seen with the whole printing inverted except for the brown background.

(Des and photo Harrison)

1966 (5 Dec). 150*th Anniv of "Jamaica Letter". W* **111**. *P* 14×15.

259 **131** 8d. multicoloured .. 10 10
w. Wmk inverted .. 17·00

132 Jamaican Pavilion   **133** Sir Donald Sangster (Prime Minister)

(Des V. Whiteley. Photo Harrison)

1967 (28 Apr). *World Fair, Montreal. W* **111**. *P* 14½.

260 **132** 6d. multicoloured .. 10 10
261 1s. multicoloured .. 10 10
w. Wmk inverted .. 6·00

(Des and photo Enschedé)

1967 (28 Aug). *Sangster Memorial Issue. P* 13½.

262 **133** 3d. multicoloured .. 10 10
263 1s. 6d. multicoloured .. 10 10

134 Traffic Duty

135 Personnel of the Force

(Des V. Whiteley. Photo Enschedé)

1967 (28 Nov). *Centenary of the Constabulary Force. T* **134/5** *and similar horiz design. Multicoloured. W* **111**. *P* 13½ × 14.

264 3d. Type **134** .. 30 10
a. Wmk sideways .. 75 1·00
265 1s. Type **135** .. 30 10
266 1s. 6d. Badge and Constables of 1867 and 1967 (*as T* **134**) .. 40 40
264/6 .. *Set of* 3 90 50

136 Wicket-keeping   **137** Sir Alexander and Lady Bustamante

(Des V. Whiteley. Photo Harrison)

1968 (8 Feb). *M.C.C.'s West Indian Tour. T* **136** *and similar vert designs. Multicoloured. W* **111** *(sideways*). P* 14.

267 6d. Type **136** .. 50 50
a. Horiz strip of 3. Nos. 267/9 .. 1·50
w. Wmk top of J to right .. 50 50
268 6d. Batting .. 50 50
w. Wmk top of J to right .. 50 50
269 6d. Bowling .. 50 50
w. Wmk top of J to right .. 50 50
267/9 .. *Set of* 3 1·50 1·50

*The normal sideways watermark shows the top of the "J" to left, *as seen from the back of the stamp*.

Nos. 267/9 were issued in small sheets of 9 comprising three *se-tenant* strips as No. 267a.

Nos. 267/9 exist on PVA gum as well as on gum arabic.

(Des and photo Harrison)

1968 (23 May). *Labour Day. W* **111**. *P* 14.

270 **137** 3d. rose and black .. 10 10
271 1s. olive and black .. 10 10

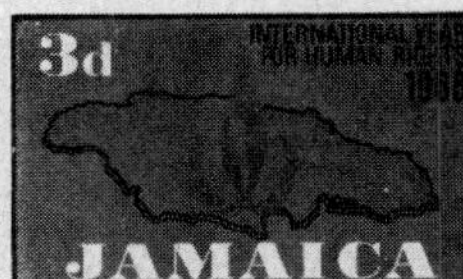

138 Human Rights Emblem over Map of Jamaica

(Photo Harrison)

1968 (3 Dec). *Human Rights Year. T* **138** *and similar multicoloured designs. W* **111**. *P* 14.

272 3d. Type **138** .. 10 10
a. Gold (flame) omitted .. 90·00
w. Wmk inverted .. 4·50
273 1s. Hands cupping Human Rights emblem (*vert*) .. 10 10
274 3s. Jamaican holding "Human Rights" .. 20 70
a. Gold (flame) omitted .. £100
272/4 .. *Set of* 3 35 80

Three designs, showing 3d. Bowls of Grain, 1s. Abacus, 3s. Hands in Prayer, were prepared but not issued (*Price for set of* 3 *mint* £100).

141 ILO Emblem   **142** Nurse, and Children being weighed and measured

(Des V. Whiteley. Litho Format)

1969 (23 May). 50*th Anniv of International Labour Organization. P* 14.

275 **141** 6d. orange-yellow and blackish brown 10 10
276 3s. bright emerald and blackish brown 20 30

(Des and photo Harrison)

1969 (30 May). 20*th Anniv of W.H.O. T* **142** *and similar designs. W* **111**. *P* 14.

277 6d. grey, brown and orange .. 10 10
278 1s. black, sepia and blue-green .. 10 10
279 3s. grey-black, brown and pale bright blue 20 30
277/9 .. *Set of* 3 30 35

Designs: *Horiz*—1s. Malaria eradication. *Vert*—3s. Trainee nurse.

(New Currency. 100 cents = 1 Jamaica dollar)

C-DAY
8th September
1969

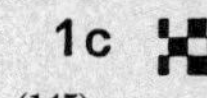

(**145**)   **146** "The Adoration of the Kings" (detail, Foppa)

1969 (8 Sept). *Decimal currency. Nos.* 217, 219, 221/3 *and* 225/32 *surch as T* **145**. *Sterling values unobliterated except* 1 c. *to* 4 c. *and* 8 c.

280 1 c. on 1d. violet-blue. dp green & lt brown 10 10
281 2 c. on 2d. red, yellow and grey-green .. 10 10
w. Wmk inverted .. 2·00
282 3 c. on 3d. yellow, black and emerald .. 10 10
283 4 c. on 4d. ochre and violet .. 90 10
a. "8t" of "8th" omitted (R. 10/1) .. 35·00
284 5 c. on 6d. multicoloured .. 1·25 10
a. Blue omitted .. 45·00
285 8 c. on 9d. blue and yellow-bistre .. 10 10
286 10 c. on 1s. black and light brown .. 10 10
287 15 c. on 1s. 6d. black, light blue and buff 30 90
288 20 c. on 2s. red-brown, black and light blue 1·50 80
a. "8th" omitted
289 30 c. on 3s. blue and dull green .. 1·50 2·75
290 50 c. on 5s. black, ochre and blue .. 1·25 3·00
291 $1 on 10s. multicoloured .. 1·50 5·00
w. Wmk inverted .. 90·00
292 $2 on £1 multicoloured .. 1·50 6·00
280/92 .. *Set of* 13 8·50 17·00

No. 281 exists with PVA gum as well as gum arabic.

Unlike the positional No. 283a the similar variety on the 20 c. on 2s. was caused by a paper fold.

(Des J. Cooter. Litho D.L.R.)

1969 (25 Oct). *Christmas. Paintings. T* **146** *and similar vert designs. Multicoloured. W* **111**. *P* 13.

293 2 c. Type **146** .. 15 30
294 5 c. "Madonna, Child and St. John" (Raphael) 20 30
295 8 c. "The Adoration of the Kings" (detail, Dosso Dossi) .. 20 30
293/5 .. *Set of* 3 50 80

MINIMUM PRICE

The minimum price quote is 10p which represents a handling charge rather than a basis for valuing common stamps. For further notes about prices see introductory pages.

149 Half Penny, 1869

151 George William Gordon

(Des G. Drummond. Litho P.B.)

1969 (27 Oct). *Centenary of First Jamaican Coins. T* **149** *and similar horiz design.* **W 111.** *P* 12½.

296 3 c. silver, black and mauve 15 25
b. Wmk sideways 40 40
297 15 c. silver, black and light emerald 10 10
Design:—15 c. One penny, 1869.

(Des G. Vasarhelyi. Litho Enschedé)

1970 (11 Mar). *National Heroes. T* **151** *and similar vert designs. Multicoloured. P* 12 × 12½.

298 1 c. Type **151** 10 10
a. Yellow (from flags) omitted £180
299 3 c. Sir Alexander Bustamante 10 10
300 5 c. Norman Manley 10 10
301 10 c. Marcus Garvey 15 10
302 15 c. Paul Bogle 20 15
298/302 . . . . *Set of* 5 40 30

156 "Christ appearing to St. Peter" (Carracci)

(159)

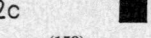

(Des G. Drummond. Photo Enschedé)

1970 (23 Mar). *Easter. T* **156** *and similar vert designs. Multicoloured.* **W 111.** *P* 12 × 12½.

303 3 c. Type **156** 10 10
w. Wmk inverted . . . . . .
304 10 c. "Christ Crucified" (Antonello da Messina) 10 10
w. Wmk inverted . . . . . .
305 20 c. Easter Lily 20 50
303/5 . . . . *Set of* 3 30 60

1970 (16 July). *No.* 219 *surch with T* **159**.

306 2 c. on 2d. red, yellow and grey-green . . 20 20

160 *Lignum Vitae*

161 Cable Ship *Dacia*

1970 (7 Sept–2 Nov). *Decimal Currency. Designs as Nos.* 217/32 *but inscr as T* **160** *in new currency.* **W 111** *(sideways on* 2, 4, 15, 20 *c. and* $1*). P* 14½ (1, 5 c.), 14 × 14½ (4 c., $1), 13½ × 14½ (15, 20 c.) *or* 14½ × 14 *(others).*

307 1 c. violet-blue, deep green & lt brown . . 50 90
308 2 c. red, yellow and grey-green (as 2d.) . . 30 10
309 3 c. yellow, black and emerald (as 3d.) . . 30 50
310 4 c. ochre and violet (as 4d.) . . . . 1·75 10
311 5 c. multicoloured (as 6d.) . . . . 2·75 30
312 8 c. blue and yellow-bistre (as 9d.) . . 1·50 10
a. Wmk sideways . . . . . . 1·50 45
313 10 c. black and light brown (as 1s.) . . 30 10
314 15 c. black, light blue and buff (as 1s. 6d.) (2.11) 1·75 2·00
315 20 c. red-brown, black & lt blue (as 2s.) (2.11) 1·25 1·75
316 30 c. blue and dull green (as 3s.) (2.11) . . 2·50 3·25
317 50 c. black, ochre and blue (as 5s.) (2.11) 1·25 3·50
318 $1 multicoloured (as 10s.) (2.11) . . 1·25 3·50
319 $2 multicoloured (as £1) (2.11) . . 1·50 3·75
307/19 . . . . . . *Set of* 13 15·00 17·00

(Des G. Drummond. Litho J.W.)

1970 (12 Oct). *Centenary of Telegraph Service. T* **161** *and similar horiz designs.* **W 111** *(sideways). P* 14½ × 14.

320 3 c. yellow, red and black 15 10
321 10 c. black and turquoise 20 10
322 50 c. multicoloured . . . . . . 50 1·00
320/2 . . . . *Set of* 3 75 1·10
Designs:—10 c. Bright's cable gear aboard *Dacia*; 50 c. Morse key and chart.

164 Bananas, Citrus, Sugar-Cane and Tobacco

165 *The Projector* (1845)

(Des G. Drummond. Litho Questa)

1970 (2 Nov). *75th Anniv of Jamaican Agricultural Society.* **W 111.** *P* 14.

323 **164** 2 c. multicoloured 20 40
w. Wmk inverted . . . . . . 7·00
324 10 c. multicoloured 40 10

(Des V. Whiteley. Litho Format)

1970 (21 Nov). *125th Anniv of Jamaican Railways. T* **165** *and similar horiz designs. Multicoloured.* **W 111** *(sideways). P* 13½.

325 3 c. Type **165** 30 10
326 15 c. Steam locomotive No. 54 (1944) . . 80 30
327 50 c. Diesel locomotive No. 102 (1967) . . 2·00 2·00
325/7 . . . . *Set of* 3 2·75 2·25

168 Church of St. Jago de la Vega

169 Henry Morgan and Ships

(Des R. Granger Barrett. Litho J.W.)

1971 (22 Feb). *Centenary of Disestablishment of the Church of England in Jamaica. T* **168** *and similar vert design. Multicoloured.* **W 111.** *P* 14½.

328 3 c. Type **168** 10 10
329 10 c. Type **168** 10 10
w. Wmk inverted . . . . . .
330 20 c. Type **168** 30 30
w. Wmk inverted . . . . . . 35·00
331 30 c. Emblem of Church of England in Jamaica 30 65
w. Wmk inverted . . . . . .
328/31 . . . . *Set of* 4 60 95

(Des J.W. Litho Questa)

1971 (10 May). *Pirates and Buccaneers. T* **169** *and similar horiz designs. Multicoloured.* **W 111** *(sideways*). P* 14.

332 3 c. Type **169** 45 10
w. Wmk top of J to right . . . . 8·50
333 15 c. Mary Read, Anne Bonny and trial pamphlet 85 15
334 30 c. Pirate schooner attacking merchantman . . . . 1·50 1·25
332/4 . . . . *Set of* 3 2·50 1·40
*The normal sideways watermark shows the top of the "J" to left, *as seen from the back of the stamp.*

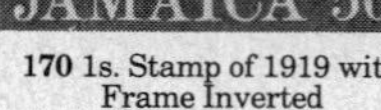

170 1s. Stamp of 1919 with Frame Inverted

171 Satellite and Dish Aerial

(Des Jennifer Toombs. Litho J.W.)

1971 (30 Oct). *Tercentenary of Post Office Establishment. T* **170** *and similar designs.* **W 111** *(sideways* except* 50 *c.). P* 13½.

335 3 c. black and lake 15 10
336 5 c. grey-black and bright green 15 10
337 8 c. black and violet 15 10
w. Wmk top of J to right . . . .
338 10 c. brown, black and indigo 15 10
339 20 c. multicoloured 40 35
340 50 c. ochre, black and slate . . . . 65 1·00
335/40 . . . . *Set of* 6 1·50 1·50
Designs: *Horiz*—3 c. Dummer packet letter, 1705; 5 c. Pre-stamp inland letter, 1793; 8 c. Harbour St. P.O., Kingston, 1820; 10 c. Modern stamp and cancellation; 20 c. British stamps used in Jamaica, 1859.
*The normal sideways watermark shows top of J to left, *as seen from the back of the stamp.*

(Des Cable & Wireless Ltd. Litho J.W.)

1972 (17 Feb). *Opening of Jamaican Earth Satellite Station.* **W 111.** *P* 14 × 13½.

341 **171** 3 c. multicoloured 15 10
w. Wmk inverted . . . . . . † —
342 15 c. multicoloured 20 15
343 50 c. multicoloured . . . . . . 65 1·25
341/3 . . . . *Set of* 3 90 1·25

172 Causeway, Kingston Harbour

173 Air Jamaica Hostess and Vickers VC-10

(Des J.W. Litho Format)

1972 (17 Apr–2 Oct). *Multicoloured designs as T* **172** (1 *to* 6 *c.*) *or* **173** (8 *c. to* $2). **W 111** *(sideways* on horiz designs). P* 14½×14 (1, 2 c.), 14×14½ (3, 4, 5, 6 c.) *or* 13½ *(others).*

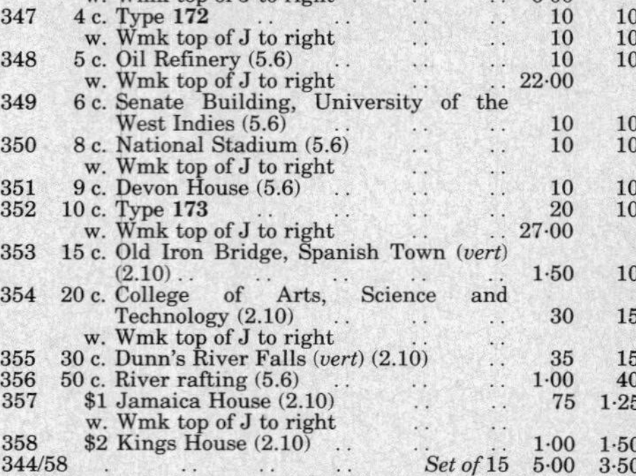

344 1 c. Pimento (*vert*) (5.6) 10 10
345 2 c. Red Ginger (*vert*) (5.6) 10 10
346 3 c. Bauxite Industry (5.6) 10 10
w. Wmk top of J to right . . . . 6·00
347 4 c. Type **172** 10 10
w. Wmk top of J to right 10 10
348 5 c. Oil Refinery (5.6) 10 10
w. Wmk top of J to right . . . . 22·00
349 6 c. Senate Building, University of the West Indies (5.6) 10 10
350 8 c. National Stadium (5.6) 10 10
w. Wmk top of J to right . . . .
351 9 c. Devon House (5.6) 10 10
352 10 c. Type **173** 20 10
w. Wmk top of J to right . . . . 27·00
353 15 c. Old Iron Bridge, Spanish Town (*vert*) (2.10) . . . . 1·50 10
354 20 c. College of Arts, Science and Technology (2.10) 30 15
w. Wmk top of J to right . . . .
355 30 c. Dunn's River Falls (*vert*) (2.10) . . 35 15
356 50 c. River rafting (5.6) . . . . . . 1·00 40
357 $1 Jamaica House (2.10) . . . . . . 75 1·25
w. Wmk top of J to right . . . .
358 $2 Kings House (2.10) . . . . . . 1·00 1·50
344/58 . . . . *Set of* 15 5·00 3·50
*The normal sideways watermark shows the top of the J to the left, *as seen from the back of the stamp.*

TENTH
ANNIVERSARY
INDEPENDENCE
1962-1972

(174)

175 Arms of Kingston

1972 (8 Aug). *Tenth Anniv of Independence. Nos.* 346, 352 *and* 356 *optd as T* **174**.

359 3 c. Bauxite Industry 10 10
w. Wmk top of J to right . . . . 12·00
360 10 c. Type **173** 15 10
w. Wmk top of J to right . . . .
361 50 c. River rafting . . . . 75 1·60
359/61 . . . . *Set of* 3 85 1·60
*The normal sideways watermark shows top of J to left, *as seen from the back of the stamp.*

(Des R. Granger Barrett. Litho J.W.)

1972 (4 Dec). *Centenary of Kingston as Capital.* **W 111** *(sideways on* 50 *c.). P* 13½ × 14 (5 *and* 30 *c.*) *or* 14 × 13½ (50 *c.*).

362 **175** 5 c. multicoloured 10 10
363 30 c. multicoloured 20 35
364 – 50 c. multicoloured . . . . . . 40 1·50
362/4 . . . . *Set of* 3 60 1·75
The 50 c. is as T **175**, but horiz.

176 Small Indian Mongoose on Map

(Des R. Granger Barrett. Litho Questa)

1973 (9 Apr). *Centenary of Introduction of the Mongoose. T* **176** *and similar horiz designs.* **W 111** *(sideways). P* 14 × 14½.

365 8 c. light apple-green, yellow-green and black 15 10
366 40 c. light cobalt, light blue and black . . 35 50
367 60 c. salmon-pink, brownish salmon & black 60 1·00
365/7 . . . . *Set of* 3 1·00 1·40
MS368 165 × 95 mm. Nos. 365/7 . . . . 1·50 3·75
Designs:—40 c. Mongoose and rat; 60 c. Mongoose and chicken.

177 *Euphorbia punicea*

(Des Sylvia Goaman. Litho Questa)

1973 (9 July). *Flora. T* **177** *and similar diamond-shaped designs. Multicoloured. W* **111**. *P* 14.

369	1 c. Type **177**	10	10
370	6 c. *Hylocereus triangularis*	15	10
371	9 c. *Columnea argentea*	15	10
372	15 c. *Portlandia grandiflora*	25	15
373	30 c. *Samyda pubescens*	50	60
374	50 c. *Cordia sebestena*	80	1·25
369/74	*Set of* 6	1·75	2·00

178 *Broughtonia sanguinea*

(Des Sylvia Goaman. Litho B.W.)

1973 (8 Oct). *Orchids. T* **178** *and similar multicoloured designs. W* **111** *(sideways) on* 5 c., $1). *P* 14×13½ (5 c., $1) *or* 13½×14 *(others).*

375	5 c. Type **178**	40	10
376	10 c. *Arpophyllum jamaicense (vert)*	50	10
	w. Wmk inverted	14·00	
377	20 c. *Oncidium pulchellum (vert)*	1·25	25
378	$1 *Brassia maculata*	2·75	2·75
375/8	*Set of* 4	4·50	2·75
MS379	161×95 mm. Nos. 375/8. Wmk sideways. P 12	4·50	5·00
	a. Printed on the gummed side (blue and brown plates only)		

No. **MS**379a has positive impressions of the blue and brown plates printed on the reverse in addition to the normal design on the front.

179 *Mary*, 1808–15

180 "Journeys"

(Des J. Cooter. Litho J.W.)

1974 (8 Apr). *Mail Packet Boats. T* **179** *and similar horiz designs. Multicoloured. W* **111** *(sideways on Nos.* 380/3, *upright on* **MS**384). *P* 13½ (5 c., 50 c.) *or* 14½ *(others).*

380	5 c. Type **179**	55	10
	a. Perf 14½	1·50	3·50
381	10 c. *Queensbury*, 1814–27	55	10
382	15 c. *Sheldrake*, 1829–34	90	40
383	50 c. *Thames I*, 1842	2·00	2·50
380/3	*Set of* 4	3·50	2·75
MS384	133×159 mm. Nos. 380/3. P 13½ *(sold at* 90 c.)	3·50	5·00

(Des R. Granger Barrett. Litho Questa)

1974 (1 Aug). *National Dance Theatre Company. T* **180** *and similar vert designs showing dance-works. Multicoloured. W* **111**. *P* 13½.

385	5 c. Type **180**	10	10
386	10 c. "Jamaican Promenade"	10	10
387	30 c. "Jamaican Promenade"	30	30
388	50 c. "Misa Criolla"	50	80
385/8	*Set of* 4	80	1·10
MS389	161 × 102 mm. Nos. 385/8 *(sold at* $1)	1·50	2·50

181 U.P.U. Emblem and Globe

(Des V. Whiteley. Litho J.W.)

1974 (9 Oct). *Centenary of Universal Postal Union. W* **111** *(sideways*). P* 14.

390	**181**	5 c. multicoloured	10	10
391		9 c. multicoloured	10	10
392		50 c. multicoloured	35	80
		w. Wmk top of J to right		
390/2		*Set of* 3	50	80

*The normal sideways watermark shows the top of the J to left, *as seen from the back of the stamp.*

182 Senate Building and Sir Hugh Wooding

183 Commonwealth Symbol

(Des R. Granger Barrett. Litho Questa)

1975 (13 Jan). *25th Anniv of University of West Indies. T* **182** *and similar horiz design. Multicoloured. W* **111** *(sideways). P* 14.

393	5 c. Type **182**	10	10
394	10 c. University Chapel and H.R.H. Princess Alice	10	10
395	30 c. Type **182**	20	25
396	50 c. As 10 c.	35	60
393/6	*Set of* 4	60	80

(Des C. Abbott. Litho Questa)

1975 (29 Apr). *Heads of Commonwealth Conference. T* **183** *and similar square designs. Multicoloured. W* **111**. *P* 13½.

397	5 c. Type **183**	10	10
398	10 c. Jamaican coat of arms	10	10
399	30 c. Dove of Peace	15	30
400	50 c. Jamaican flag	30	1·10
397/400	*Set of* 4	50	1·40

184 Jamaican Kite Swallowtail (*Eurytides marcellinus*)

185 Koo Koo or Actor Boy

(Des J. Cooter. Litho Questa)

1975 (25 Aug). *Butterflies (1st series). T* **184** *and similar vert designs showing the family Papilionidae. Multicoloured. W* **111**. *P* 14.

401	10 c. Type **184**	55	20
402	20 c. Orange Swallowtail (*Papilo thoas*)	1·10	1·10
403	25 c. False Androgeus Swallowtail (*Papilo thersites*)	1·25	1·75
404	30 c. Homerus Swallowtail (*Papilo homerus*)	1·40	2·50
401/4	*Set of* 4	4·00	5·00
MS405	134×179 mm. Nos. 401/4 *(sold at* 95 c.)	5·50	7·50

See also Nos. 429/33 and 443/47.

(Des C. Abbott. Litho J.W.)

1975 (3 Nov). *Christmas. T* **185** *and similar vert designs showing Belisario prints of "John Canoe" (Christmas) Festival (1st series). Multicoloured. W* **111**. *P* 14.

406	8 c. Type **185**	15	10
407	10 c. Red Set-girls	15	10
408	20 c. French Set-girls	35	20
409	50 c. Jaw-bone or House John Canoe	70	1·60
	w. Wmk inverted		
406/9	*Set of* 4	1·25	1·75
MS410	138×141 mm. Nos. 406/9. P 13½ *(sold at* $1)	1·75	3·25

See also Nos. 421/4.

186 Bordone Map, 1528

(Des L. Curtis. Litho Questa)

1976 (12 Mar). *16th-century Maps of Jamaica. T* **186** *and similar horiz designs. W* **111** *(sideways*). P* 13½.

411	10 c. brown, light stone and light vermilion	20	10
412	20 c. multicoloured	35	25
	w. Wmk top of J to right	17·00	
413	30 c. multicoloured	60	85
414	50 c. multicoloured	85	2·25
411/14	*Set of* 4	1·75	3·00

Designs— 20 c. Porcacchi map, 1576; 30 c. DeBry map, 1594; 50 c. Langenes map, 1598.

*The normal sideways watermark shows the top of the J to left, *as seen from the back of the stamp.*

See also Nos. 425/8.

187 Olympic Rings

(Des Sir H. McDonald: adapted V. Whiteley Studio. Litho Walsall)

1976 (14 June). *Olympic Games, Montreal. W* **111** *(sideways). P* 13½.

415	**187**	10 c. multicoloured	15	10
416		20 c. multicoloured	25	20
417		25 c. multicoloured	25	25
418		50 c. multicoloured	40	1·75
415/18		*Set of* 4	95	2·00

187*a* Map of the Caribbean

(Des PAD Studio. Litho Questa)

1976 (9 Aug). *West Indian Victory in World Cricket Cup. T* **187***a and similar design. No wmk. P* 14.

419	10 c. multicoloured	40	50
420	25 c. black and magenta	85	1·75

Design: *Vert*—25 c. Prudential Cup.

(Des C. Abbott. Litho J.W.)

1976 (8 Nov). *Christmas. Belisario Prints (2nd series). Multicoloured designs as T* **185**. *W* **111**. *P* 13½.

421	10 c. Queen of the set-girls	10	10
422	20 c. Band of the Jaw-bone John Canoe	25	10
423	50 c. Koo Koo (actor-boy)	45	1·75
	w. Wmk inverted	6·50	
421/3	*Set of* 3	70	1·75
MS424	110×140 mm. Nos. 421/3. P 14×14½ *(sold at* 90 c.)	70	2·00

(Des L. Curtis. Litho J.W.)

1977 (28 Feb). *17th Century Maps of Jamaica. Designs as T* **186**. *W* **111** *(sideways). P* 13.

425	9 c. multicoloured	30	30
426	10 c. multicoloured	30	10
427	25 c. grey-black, pale blue and bright blue	70	60
428	40 c. grey-black, light turquoise and grey-blue	80	1·25
425/8	*Set of* 4	1·90	2·00

Designs:—9 c. Hickeringill map, 1661; 10 c. Ogilby map, 1671; 25 c. Visscher map, 1680; 40 c. Thornton map, 1689.

(Des J. Cooter. Litho J.W.)

1977 (9 May). *Butterflies (2nd series). Multicoloured designs as T* **184**. *W* **111**. *P* 13½.

429	10 c. False Barred Sulphur (*Eurema elathea*)	35	10
430	20 c. Bronze Wing (*Dynamine egaea*)	75	55
431	25 c. Jamaican Harlequin (*Chlosyne pantoni*)	1·00	1·25
	w. Wmk inverted	15·00	
432	40 c. Mimic (*Hypolimnas misippus*)	1·50	2·75
	w. Wmk inverted	35·00	
429/32	*Set of* 4	3·25	4·25
MS433	139×120 mm. Nos. 429/32. P 14½ *(sold at* $1.05)	4·50	7·00

188 Map, Scout Emblem and Streamertail

189 Trumpeter

(Des Daphne Padden. Litho Questa)

1977 (5 Aug). *Sixth Caribbean Jamboree, Jamaica. Multicoloured; background colours given. W* **111** *(sideways). P* 13½.

434	**188**	10 c. new blue	25	10
435		20 c. light yellow-green	50	20
436		25 c. orange	55	25
437		50 c. light magenta	90	1·40
434/7		*Set of* 4	2·00	1·75

(Des C. Abbott, Litho Questa)

1997 (19 Dec). *50th Anniv of Jamaica Military Band. T* **189** *and similar multicoloured designs. W* **111** *(sideways on horiz designs). P* 14.

438	9 c. Type **189**	15	10
439	10 c. Clarinet players	15	10
440	20 c. Two kettle drummers *(vert)*	40	35
441	25 c. Double-bass player and trumpeter *(vert)*	55	65
438/41	*Set of* 4	1·10	1·00
MS442	120×137 mm. Nos. 438/41. Wmk sideways *(sold at* 75 c.)	2·50	4·00

(Des J. Cooter. Litho Walsall)

1978 (17 Apr). *Butterflies (3rd series). Multicoloured designs as T* **184**. *W* **111**. *P* 14.

443 10 c. Jamaican Hairstreak (*Callophrys crethona*) 40 10
444 20 c. Malachite (*Siproeta stelenes*) .. 75 20
445 25 c. Common Long-tailed Skipper (*Urbanus proteus*) 85 40
446 50 c. Troglodyte (*Anaea troglodyta*) .. 1·90 2·25
443/6 .. .. *Set of* 4 3·50 2·75
MS447 100×125 mm. Nos. 443/6 (*sold at* $1.15) 4·00 5·00
a. Error. Imperf £180

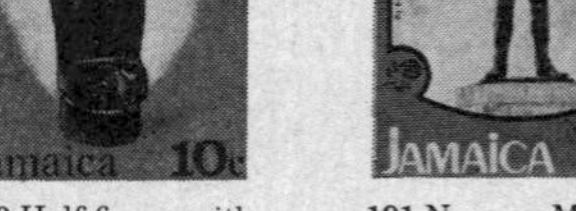

190 Half-figure with Canopy

191 Norman Manley (statue)

(Des J. Cooter. Litho J.W.)

1978 (10 July). *Arawak Artefacts (1st series). T* **190** *and similar vert designs. W* **111**. *P* 13½ × 13.

448 10 c. deep brown, yellow and black 10 10
449 20 c. deep brown, mauve and black 15 10
450 50 c. deep brown, apple-green and black .. 35 35
448/50 .. .. *Set of* 3 50 45
MS451 135 × 90 mm. Nos. 448/50. P 14 (*sold at* 90 *c.*) .. .. 60 1·25
Designs:—20 c. Standing figure; 50 c. Birdman.
See also Nos. 479/83.

(Des and litho J.W.)

1978 (25 Sept). *24th Commonwealth Parliamentary Conference. T* **191** *and similar vert designs. Multicoloured. W* **111**. *P* 13.

452 10 c. Type **191** 10 10
453 20 c. Sir Alexander Bustamante (statue) .. 20 15
454 25 c. City of Kingston Crest 20 20
455 40 c. Gordon House Chamber, House of Representatives 30 55
452/5 .. .. *Set of* 4 70 90

192 Band and Banner

193 "Negro Aroused" (sculpture by Edna Manley)

(Des V. Whiteley. Litho J.W.)

1978 (4 Dec). *Christmas. Centenary of Salvation Army. T* **192** *and similar horiz designs. Multicoloured. W* **111** (*sideways*). *P* 14.

456 10 c. Type **192** 35 10
457 20 c. Trumpeter 40 20
458 25 c. Banner 40 25
459 50 c. William Booth (founder) .. .. .. 70 2·25
456/9 .. .. *Set of* 4 1·60 2·50

(Des G. Hutchins. Litho J.W.)

1978 (11 Dec). *International Anti-Apartheid Year. W* **111**. *P* 13.

460 **193** 10 c. multicoloured 30 20

194 Tennis, Montego Bay

195 Arms and Map of Jamaica

(Des and litho Harrison ($5). Des Walsall. Litho J.W. (others))

1979 (15 Jan)–**84**. *Vert designs as T* **194**, *and T* **195**. *Multicoloured. White ordinary paper* (15, 65, 75 *c.*, $5) *or cream chalk-surfaced paper (others). W* **111** (*sideways on* $5). *P* 14½ × 14 ($5) *or* 13½ (*others*).

461 1 c. Type **194** (26.11.79) 70 55
462 2 c. Golf, Tryall, Hanover (26.11.79) .. .. 1·75 1·50
a. White ordinary paper (8.84) .. .. 2·75 2·75
463 4 c. Horse riding, Negril Beach (26.11.79) .. 40 80
a. White ordinary paper (8.84) .. .. 2·50 2·50
464 5 c. Old waterwheel, Tryall, Hanover (26.11.79) 55 20
a. White ordinary paper (27.8.82) .. .. 1·75 1·75
465 6 c. Fern Gully, Ocho Rios (26.11.79) .. 50 90
466 7 c. Dunn's River Falls, Ocho Rios (26.11.79) 40 30
467 8 c. Jamaican Tody (bird) (28.4.80) 70 65
468 10 c. Jamaican Mango (bird) (28.4.80) 70 20
a. White ordinary paper (27.8.82) 70 70
469 12 c. Yellow-billed Amazon (28.4.80) .. .. 60 1·00
470 15 c. Streamertail (bird) (28.4.80) 70 30
471 35 c. White-chinned Thrush (28.4.80) .. 70 30
472 50 c. Jamaican Woodpecker (28.4.80) 70 30
473 65 c. Rafting, Martha Brae Trelawny (28.4.80) 70 90
474 75 c. Blue Marlin Fleet, Port Antonio (28.4.80) 1·00 30
475 $1 Scuba Diving, Ocho Rios (28.4.80) .. 1·00 1·00
a. White ordinary paper (27.8.82) .. .. 2·75 2·75
476 $2 Sailing boats, Montego Bay (28.4.80) .. 75 50
a. White ordinary paper (27.8.82) .. .. 2·75 2·75
477 $5 Type **195** .. .. 1·00 1·60
461/77 .. .. *Set of* 17 11·50 10·00

TENTH ANNIVERSARY AIR JAMAICA 1st APRIL 1979

(196)

197 Grinding Stone, *circa* 400 BC.

1979 (2 Apr). *10th Anniv of Air Jamaica. No.* 352 *optd with T* **196**.

478 10 c. Type **173** 50 50

(Des D. Bowen. Litho Questa)

1979 (23 Apr). *Arawak Artefacts (2nd series). T* **197** *and similar multicoloured designs. W* **111** (*sideways on* 10, 20 *and* 25 *c.*). *P* 14.

479 5 c. Type **197** 10 10
480 10 c. Stone implements, *c.* 500 AD (*horiz*) .. 10 10
481 20 c. Cooking pot, *c.* 300 AD (*horiz*) 10 15
482 25 c. Serving boat, *c.* 300 AD (*horiz*) 15 20
483 50 c. Storage jar fragment, *c.* 300 AD 25 35
479/83 .. .. *Set of* 5 55 70

198 1962 1s. 6d. Independence Commemorative Stamp

(Des J.W. from a local design by J. Mahfood. Litho Walsall)

1979 (13 Aug). *Death Centenary of Sir Rowland Hill. T* **198** *and similar horiz designs showing stamps and Sir Rowland Hill. W* **111** (*sideways**). *P* 14.

484 10 c. black, scarlet-vermilion & brt scarlet 15 10
w. Wmk top of J to right .. .. 7·00
485 20 c. orange-yellow and yellowish brown .. 20 15
486 25 c. mauve and blue 25 20
487 50 c. multicoloured 35 70
484/7 .. .. *Set of* 4 85 1·00
MS488 146×94 mm. No. 485 (*sold at* 30 *c.*) 30 60
Designs:—20 c. 1920 1s. with frame inverted; 25 c. 1860 6d.; 50 c. 1968 3d. Human Rights Year commemorative.
*The normal sideways watermark has top of J to left, *when seen from the back of the stamp.*

199 Group of Children

(Des J.W. Litho Harrison)

1979 (1 Oct). *Christmas. International Year of the Child. T* **199** *and similar multicoloured designs. W* **111** (*sideways on* 10, 25 *and* 50 *c.*). *P* 14.

489 10 c. Type **199** 10 10
490 20 c. Doll (*vert*) 10 10
491 25 c. "The Family" (painting by child) .. 15 15
492 50 c. "House on the Hill" (painting by child) .. 25 40
489/92 .. .. *Set of* 4 50 60

200 Date Tree Hall, 1886 (original home of Institute)

(Des G. Drummond. Litho Walsall)

1980 (25 Feb). *Centenary of Institute of Jamaica. T* **200** *and similar multicoloured designs. W* **111** (*sideways on* 5, 15 *and* 50 *c.*). *P* 13½.

493 5 c. Type **200** 10 10
494 15 c. Institute building, 1980 .. .. .. 15 10
495 35 c. Microfilm reader (*vert*) 25 20
496 50 c. Hawksbill Turtle and Green Turtle .. 45 60
497 75 c. Jamaican Owl (*vert*) .. .. .. 1·50 2·50
493/7 .. .. *Set of* 5 2·25 3·00

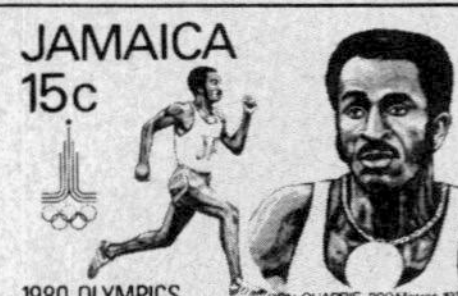

201 Don Quarrie (200 Metres, 1976)

(Des BG Studio. Litho J.W.)

1980 (21 July). *Olympic Games, Moscow. Jamaican Olympic Athletics Gold Medal Winners. T* **201** *and similar horiz designs. Multicoloured. W* **111** (*sideways**). *P* 13.

498 15 c. Type **201** 40 15
w. Wmk top of J to left .. .. .. 7·00
499 35 c. Arthur Wint (4×400 Metres Relay, 1952) 45 60
a. Horiz strip of 4. Nos. 499/502 .. .. 1·60
500 35 c. Leslie Laing (4×400 Metres Relay, 1952) 45 60
501 35 c. Herbert McKenley (4×400 Metres Relay, 1952) 45 60
502 35 c. George Rhoden (4×400 Metres Relay, 1952) 45 60
498/502 .. .. *Set of* 5 2·00 2·25
*The normal sideways watermark shows the top of J to right, *as seen from the back of the stamp.*
Nos. 499/502 were printed together, *se-tenant*, in horizontal strips of 4 throughout the sheet.

202 Parish Church

203 Blood Cup Sponge

(Des J.W. Litho Harrison)

1980 (24 Nov). *Christmas. Churches (1st series). T* **202** *and similar horiz designs. Multicoloured. W* **111** (*sideways*). *P* 14.

503 15 c. Type **202** 10 10
504 20 c. Coke Memorial Church 10 10
505 25 c. Church of the Redeemer 15 10
506 $5 Holy Trinity Cathedral .. .. .. 1·00 2·00
503/6 .. .. *Set of* 4 1·10 2·10
MS507 120 × 139 mm. Nos. 503/6. P 14½ (*sold at* $5.70) .. .. 2·00 3·00
See also Nos. 537/40 and 570/2.

(Des J. Mahfood. Litho Walsall)

1981 (27 Feb). *Marine Life (1st series). T* **203** *and similar multicoloured designs. W* **111** (*sideways on* 45 *and* 75 *c.*). *P* 14.

508 20 c. Type **203** 15 10
509 45 c. Tube Sponge (*horiz*) 25 35
510 60 c. Black Coral 35 45
511 75 c. Tyre Reef (*horiz*) 40 75
508/11 .. .. *Set of* 4 1·00 1·50
See also Nos. 541/5.

204 Brown's Hutia (or Indian Coney)

205 White Orchid

(Des D. Bowen. Litho Questa)

1981 (25 May). *Brown's Hutia (or Indian Coney). T* **204** *and similar horiz designs. Multicoloured. W* **111**. *P* 14.

512 20 c. Hutia facing right 15 20
a. Horiz strip of 4. Nos. 512/15 55
513 20 c. Type **204** 15 20
514 20 c. Hutia facing left and eating 15 20
515 20 c. Hutia family 15 20
512/15 .. .. *Set of* 4 55 70
Nos. 512/15 were printed together, *se-tenant*, in horizontal strips of 4 throughout the sheet.

(Des J.W. Litho Format)

1981 (29 July). *Royal Wedding. T* **205** *and similar vert designs. Multicoloured. W w* **14** (*sideways**). *P* 13½ ($5) *or* 15 (*others*).

516 20 c. Type **205** 10 10
aw. Wmk Crown to right of CA 25
b. Perf 15×14½ 25 25
ba. Booklet pane. Nos. 516b/19b .. .. 3·50
517 45 c. Royal Coach 15 10
aw. Wmk Crown to right of CA 40
b. Perf 15×14½ 50 50
518 60 c. Prince Charles and Lady Diana Spencer 20 20
aw. Wmk Crown to right of CA 60
b. Perf 15×14½ 60 60

519 $5 St. James' Palace 60 85
aw. Wmk Crown to right of CA .. .. 2·25
b. Perf 15×14½ .. .. .. 2·50 3·50
516/19 .. .. *Set of* 4 90 1·00
MS520 98×85 mm. No. 519. Wmk upright. P 13½ .. .. 1·00 1·75
w. Wmk inverted .. .. 2·75

*The normal sideways watermark shows Crown to left of CA, *as seen from the back of the stamp.*

Nos. 516/18 also exist perforated 13½ (*price for set of* 3 90*p. mint or used*) from additional sheetlets of 5 stamps and one label. No. 519 exists from both normal sheets and sheetlets.

Nos. 516b/19b are from $6.25 stamp booklets.

206 Blind Man at Work

207 W.F.D. Emblem on 1964 1½d. Definitive

(Des G. Vasarhelyi. Litho J.W.)

1981 (14 Sept). *International Year for Disabled Persons. T* **206** *and similar horiz designs. Multicoloured. W* **111** *(sideways). P* 13.
521 20 c. Type **206** 15 15
522 45 c. Painting with the mouth 40 40
523 60 c. Deaf student communicating with sign language 50 75
524 $1.50, Basketball players .. .. .. 1·25 1·75
521/4 .. .. *Set of* 4 2·10 2·75

(Des J. Mahfood. Litho J.W.)

1981 (16 Oct). *World Food Day. Stamps on Stamps. T* **207** *and similar designs showing W.F.D. emblems on various definitives. W* **111** *(sideways on 20 c., $2 and $4). P* 13.
525 20 c. multicoloured 35 15
526 45 c. black, rose and orange 70 40
527 $2 black, violet-blue and green .. .. 2·00 1·40
528 $4 black, green and light brown .. .. 3·25 2·50
525/8 .. .. *Set of* 4 5·50 4·00

Designs: *Vert as T* **207**—45 c. 1922 1d. (40 × 26 *mm.*)—$2 As 1938 3d. but with W.F.D. emblem replacing King's head; $4 As 1938 1s. but with W.F.D. emblem replacing King's head.

Nos. 525/8 were so designed that the face values obliterated those on the stamps depicted.

208 "Survival" (song title)

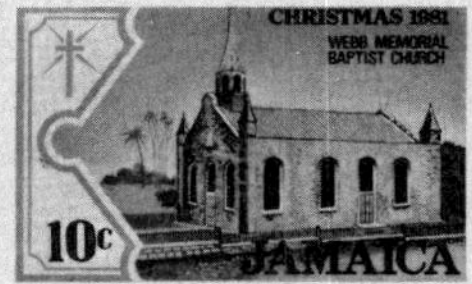

209 Webb Memorial Baptist Church

(Litho Format)

1981 (20 Oct). *Bob Marley (musician) Commemoration. T* **208** *and similar vert designs inscribed with song titles. In black and vermilion ($5.25) or multicoloured (others). W w* **14** *(sideways). P* 15.
529 1 c. Type **208** 30 40
530 2 c. "Exodus" 30 40
531 3 c. "Is this Love" 30 40
532 15 c. "Coming in from the Cold"* .. .. 1·75 30
533 20 c. "Positive Vibration"† .. .. .. 1·75 30
534 60 c. "War" .. .. 2·50 2·75
535 $3 "Could you be Loved" .. .. .. 7·50 10·00
529/35 .. .. *Set of* 7 13·00 13·00
MS536 134 × 110 mm. $5.25, Bob Marley (wmk upright) .. .. 7·00 4·75

*Part of initial "C" of song title inscription does not show on the design.

†Incorrectly inscribed "OSITIVE VIBRATION".

(Des J.W. Litho Questa)

1981 (11 Dec). *Christmas. Churches (2nd series). T* **209** *and similar horiz designs. Multicoloured. W* **111** *(sideways). P* 14.
537 10 c. Type **209** 10 10
538 45 c. Church of God in Jamaica 30 15
539 $5 Bryce United Church .. .. .. 2·25 2·50
537/9 .. .. *Set of* 3 2·40 2·50
MS540 120 × 168 mm. Nos. 537/9 (wmk upright). P 12 .. .. 3·50 3·25

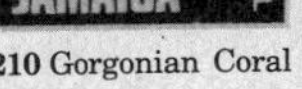

210 Gorgonian Coral

211 Cub Scout

(Des J. Mahfood; adapted PAD Studio. Litho Questa)

1982 (22 Feb). *Marine Life (2nd series). T* **210** *and similar multi-coloured designs. W* **111** *(sideways on 45, 60, 75 c. and $3). P* 14.
541 20 c. Type **210**.. .. .. 45 10
542 45 c. Hard Sponge and diver (*horiz*).. .. 65 25
543 60 c. American Manatee (*horiz*) 90 55
544 75 c. Plume Worm (*horiz*) .. .. .. 1·00 65
545 $3 Coral Banded Shrimp (*horiz*) .. .. 2·50 1·75
541/5 .. .. *Set of* 5 5·00 3·00

(Des L. Curtis. Litho J.W.)

1982 (12 July). *75th Anniv of Boy Scout Movement. T* **211** *and similar vert designs. Multicoloured. W* **111**. *P* 13½ × 13.
546 20 c. Type **211** 50 15
547 45 c. Scout camp 85 40
548 60 c. "Out of Many, One People" .. .. 1·10 90
549 $2 Lord Baden-Powell .. .. .. 1·75 2·50
546/9 .. .. *Set of* 4 3·75 3·50
MS550 80 × 130 mm. Nos. 546/9 .. .. .. 4·50 5·00

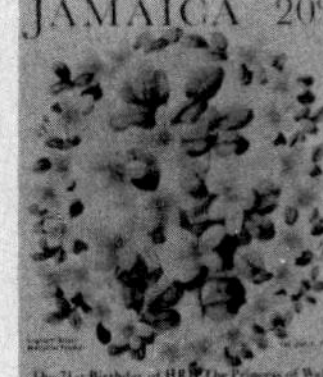

212 *Lignum vitae* (national flower)

ROYAL BABY
21.6.82

(**212***a*)

(Des R. Sauer. Litho Questa)

1982 (30 Aug). *21st Birthday of Princess of Wales. T* **212** *and similar vert designs. W* **111**. *P* 14½ × 14.
551 20 c. Type **212** 20 20
a. Booklet pane. Nos. 551/3.. .. .. 1·10
552 45 c. Carriage ride 35 35
553 60 c. Wedding 50 60
554 75 c. *Saxifraga longifolia* .. .. .. 75 1·10
a. Booklet pane. Nos. 554/6.. .. .. 2·40
555 $2 Princess of Wales .. .. .. 1·10 1·50
556 $3 *Viola gracilis major* .. .. .. 1·10 2·50
551/6 .. .. *Set of* 6 3·50 5·50
MS557 106 × 75 mm. $5 Honeymoon photograph 1·40 2·50

Nos. 554 and 556 were printed in small sheets of 6 including one *se-tenant*, stamp-size, label. The other values were printed in sheets of 40.

1982 (13 Sept). *Birth of Prince William of Wales. Nos.* 551/7 *optd with T* **212***a*.
558 20 c. Type **212** 20 20
a. Booklet pane. Nos. 558/60 80
559 45 c. Carriage ride 30 35
560 60 c. Wedding 40 60
561 75 c. *Saxifraga longifolia* .. .. .. 70 1·00
a. Booklet pane. Nos. 561/3.. .. .. 2·25
562 $2 Princess of Wales .. .. .. 75 1·50
563 $3 *Viola gracilis major* .. .. .. 1·00 2·50
558/63 .. .. *Set of* 6 3·00 5·50
MS564 106 × 75 mm. $5 Honeymoon photograph 1·75 3·00

213 Prey Captured

214 Queen Elizabeth II

(Des N. Arlott. Litho Questa)

1982 (25 Oct). *Jamaican Birds (1st series). Jamaican Lizard Cuckoo. T* **213** *and similar vert designs. Multicoloured. W* **111**. *P* 14½.
565 $1 Type **213** .. .. 95 1·00
a. Horiz strip of 5. Nos. 565/9 .. .. 4·25
566 $1 Searching for prey .. .. .. 95 1·00
567 $1 Calling prior to prey search .. .. 95 1·00
568 $1 Adult landing .. .. 95 1·00
569 $1 Adult flying in .. .. 95 1·00
565/9 .. .. *Set of* 5 4·25 4·50

Nos. 565/9 were printed in horizontal *se-tenant* strips of 5 throughout the sheet.

See also Nos. 642/5 and 707/10.

(Des and litho J.W.)

1982 (8 Dec). *Christmas. Churches (3rd series). Horiz designs as T* **209**. *Multicoloured. W* **111** *(sideways). P* 13.
570 20 c. United Pentecostal Church 40 10
571 45 c. Disciples of Christ Church 75 25
572 75 c. Open Bible Church .. .. .. 1·40 2·50
570/2 .. .. *Set of* 3 2·25 2·50

(Des D. Miller. Litho Walsall)

1983 (14 Feb). *Royal Visit. T* **214** *and similar vert design. Multi-coloured. W* **111**. *P* 14.
573 $2 Type **214** .. .. 3·00 3·50
574 $3 Coat of Arms .. .. 4·00 5·00

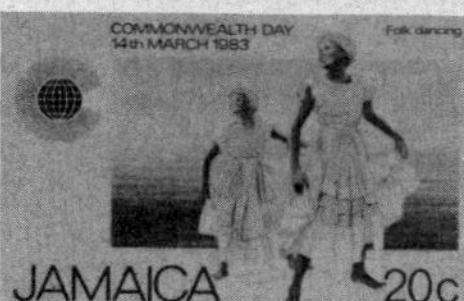

215 Folk Dancing

(Des Walsall. Litho Format)

1983 (14 Mar). *Commonwealth Day. T* **215** *and similar horiz designs. Multicoloured. W* **111** *(sideways*). P* 14.
575 20 c. Type **215** 15 15
576 45 c. Bauxite mining 35 35
577 75 c. World map showing position of Jamaica 45 45
578 $2 Coat of arms and family .. .. 80 1·40
w. Wmk top of J to right .. .. 12·00
575/8 .. .. *Set of* 4 1·60 2·10

*The normal sideways watermark has top of "J" to left, *as seen from the back of the stamp.*

216 General Cargo Ship at Wharf

217 Norman Manley and Sir Alexander Bustamante

(Des A. Theobald. Litho Format)

1983 (17 Mar). *25th Anniv of International Maritime Organiz-ation. T* **216** *and similar horiz designs. Multicoloured. P* 14.
579 15 c. Type **216** 75 30
580 20 c. *Veendam* (cruise liner) at Kingston .. 1·00 40
581 45 c. Container ship entering port .. .. 1·75 85
582 $1 Tanker passing International Seabed Headquarters Building .. .. .. 2·75 3·75
579/82 .. .. *Set of* 4 5·50 4·75

(Des D. Miller. Litho Harrison)

1983 (25 July). *21st Anniv of Independence. W* **111**. *P* 14.
583 **217** 15 c. multicoloured 15 20
584 20 c. multicoloured 15 25
585 45 c. multicoloured 30 50
583/5 .. .. *Set of* 3 55 85

218 Ship-to-Shore Radio

219 "Racing at Caymanas" (Sidney McLaren)

(Des Walsall. Litho Harrison)

1983 (18 Oct). *World Communications Year. T* **218** *and similar horiz designs. Multicoloured. W* **111** *(sideways). P* 14.
586 20 c. Type **218** 35 15
587 45 c. Postal services 65 40
588 75 c. Telephone communications .. .. 85 1·75
589 $1 T.V. via satellite .. .. 1·25 2·25
586/9 .. .. *Set of* 4 2·75 4·00

(Des D. Miller. Litho J.W.)

1983 (12 Dec). *Christmas. Paintings. T* **219** *and similar multi-coloured designs. W* **111** *(sideways on 15 c., 20 c.). P* 13 × 13½ *(15 c., 20 c.) or* 13½ × 13 *(others).*
590 15 c. Type **219** 15 10
591 20 c. "Seated Figures" (Karl Parboosingh) .. 15 10
592 75 c. "The Petitioner" (Henry Daley) (*vert*) .. 50 50
593 $2 "Banana Plantation" (John Dunkley) (*vert*) .. .. 1·25 2·25
590/3 .. .. *Set of* 4 1·90 2·75

220 Sir Alexander Bustamante

221 De Havilland D.H. 60G Gipsy Moth Seaplane

(Des D. Miller. Litho Questa)

1984 (24 Feb). *Birth Centenary of Sir Alexander Bustamante. T* **220** *and similar vert design. Multicoloured. W* **111**. *P* 14.
594 20 c. Type **220** .. .. 65 1·00
a. Horiz pair. Nos. 594/5 .. .. 1·25 2·00
595 20 c. Birthplace, Blenheim .. .. .. 65 1·00

Nos. 594/5 were printed together, *se-tenant*, in horizontal pairs throughout the sheet.

(Des A. Theobald. Litho Questa)

1984 (11 June). *Seaplanes and Flying Boats. T* **221** *and similar horiz designs. Multicoloured.* W **111** *(sideways). P* 14.

596 25 c. Type **221** 1·00 15
597 55 c. Consolidated Commodore flying boat 1·75 85
598 $1.50, Sikorsky S-38A flying boat 2·75 3·75
599 $3 Sikorsky S-40 flying boat *American Clipper* 3·50 4·75
596/9 *Set of* 4 8·00 8·50

5c

222 Cycling **223**

(Des G. Vasarhelyi. Litho J.W.)

1984 (11 July). *Olympic Games, Los Angeles. T* **222** *and similar horiz designs. Multicoloured.* W **111** *(sideways). P* 14.

600 25 c. Type **222** 45 20
601 55 c. Relay running 60 30
602 $1.50, Start of race 1·00 1·75
603 $3 Finish of race 1·40 2·75
600/3 *Set of* 4 3·00 4·50
MS604 135 × 105 mm. Nos. 600/3 (*sold at* $5.40). P 13 × 13½ 3·00 5·00

1984 (7 Aug). *Nos.* 465 *and* 469 *surch as T* **223.**

605 5 c. on 6 c. Fern Gully, Ocho Rios 15 40
606 10 c. on 12 c. Yellow-billed Amazon 85 60

224 Head of Jamaican Boa Snake

(Des I. Loe. Litho Questa)

1984 (22 Oct). *Jamaican Boa Snake. T* **224** *and similar horiz designs. Multicoloured.* W **111** *(sideways). P* 14½.

607 25 c. Type **224** 2·25 30
608 55 c. Boa snake on branch over stream 3·50 80
609 70 c. Snake with young 4·25 2·00
610 $1 Snake on log 4·75 2·75
607/10 *Set of* 4 13·00 5·25
MS611 133 × 97 mm. As Nos. 607/10 but without W.W.F. emblem (*sold at* $2.60) 5·00 2·75

225 *Enterprise* (1845) **226** "Accompong Madonna" (Namba Roy)

(Des D. Hartley-Marjoram. Litho Enschedé)

1984 (16 Nov). *Railway Locomotives* (1*st series*). *T* **225** *and similar horiz designs. Multicoloured.* W **111** *(sideways). P* 13½ × 13.

612 25 c. Type **225** 1·00 30
613 55 c. Tank locomotive (1880) 1·50 70
614 $1.50, Kitson-Meyer tank locomotive (1904) 2·25 2·75
615 $3 Super-heated locomotive (1916) 3·00 4·25
612/15 *Set of* 4 7·00 7·25

See also Nos. 634/7.

(Des G. Vasarhelyi. Litho Harrison)

1984 (6 Dec). *Christmas. Sculptures. T* **226** *and similar vert designs. Multicoloured.* W **111**. *P* 14.

616 20 c. Type **226** 25 10
617 25 c. "Head" (Alvin Marriott) 30 10
618 55 c. "Moon" (Edna Manley) 70 65
619 $1.50, "All Women are Five Women" (Mallica Reynolds (Kapo)) 1·75 3·00
616/19 *Set of* 4 2·75 3·50

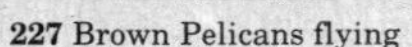

227 Brown Pelicans flying **228** The Queen Mother at Belfast University

(Des N. Arlott. Litho Walsall)

1985 (15 Apr). *Birth Bicentenary of John J. Audubon (ornithologist). Brown Pelican. T* **227** *and similar vert designs. Multicoloured.* W **111**. *P* 13½ × 13.

620 20 c. Type **227** 75 20
621 55 c. Diving for fish 1·00 40
622 $2 Young pelican taking food from adult 2·00 2·50
623 $5 "Brown Pelican" (John J. Audubon) 3·50 5·00
620/3 *Set of* 4 6·50 7·25
MS624 100 × 100 mm. Nos. 620/3 (*sold at* $7.85) 4·00 6·00

(Des A. Theobald ($5), C. Abbott (others). Litho Questa)

1985 (7 June). *Life and Times of Queen Elizabeth the Queen Mother. T* **228** *and similar vert designs. Multicoloured.* W **111**. *P* 14½ × 14.

625 25 c. With photograph album, 1963 10 10
626 55 c. With Prince Charles at Garter Ceremony, Windsor Castle, 1983 15 15
w. Wmk inverted 50
627 $1.50, Type **228** 35 50
628 $3 With Prince Henry at his christening (from photo by Lord Snowdon) 65 1·25
625/8 *Set of* 4 1·10 1·75
MS629 91 × 74 mm. $5 With the Queen, Prince Philip and Princess Anne at Ascot. Wmk sideways 1·25 1·40

229 Maps and Emblems

(Des D. Miller. Litho Harrison)

1985 (30 July). *International Youth Year and 5th Pan-American Scout Jamboree.* W **111** *(sideways). P* 14.

630 **229** 25 c. multicoloured 30 10
631 55 c. multicoloured 45 25
632 70 c. multicoloured 55 70
633 $4 multicoloured 2·25 4·00
630/3 *Set of* 4 3·25 4·50

(Des D. Hartley. Litho Harrison)

1985 (30 Sept). *Railway Locomotives* (2*nd series*). *Horiz designs as T* **225**. *Multicoloured.* W **111** *(sideways). P* 14.

634 25 c. Baldwin locomotive No. 16 85 30
635 55 c. Rogers locomotive 1·40 35
636 $1.50, Locomotive *The Projector* 1·75 1·75
637 $4 Diesel locomotive No. 102 3·00 3·75
634/7 *Set of* 4 6·25 5·50

JAMAICA 20c

230 "The Old Settlement" (Ralph Campbell) **230a** Princess Elizabeth and Princess Margaret, 1939

(Litho Format)

1985 (9 Dec). *Christmas. Jamaican Paintings. T* **230** *and similar multicoloured designs.* W **111** *(sideways on* 20, 75 *c.). P* 14.

638 20 c. Type **230** 10 10
639 55 c. "The Vendor" (Albert Huie) (*vert*) 15 15
640 75 c. "Road Menders" (Gaston Tabois) 20 35
641 $4 "Woman, must I not be about my Father's business?" (Carl Abrahams) (*vert*) 1·10 2·25
638/41 *Set of* 4 1·40 2·50

(Des N. Arlott. Litho B.D.T.)

1986 (10 Feb). *Jamaican Birds* (2*nd series*). *Vert designs as T* **213**. *Multicoloured.* W **111**. *P* 14.

642 25 c. Chestnut-bellied Cuckoo 50 10
643 55 c. Jamaican Becard 65 30
644 $1.50, White-eyed Thrush 85 1·75
645 $5 Rufous-tailed Flycatcher 1·75 4·00
642/5 *Set of* 4 3·25 5·50

(Des A. Theobald. Litho Harrison)

1986 (21 Apr). 60*th Birthday of Queen Elizabeth II. T* **230a** *and similar vert designs. Multicoloured.* W **111**. *P* 14½ × 14.

646 20 c. Type **230a** 15 10
647 25 c. With Prince Charles and Prince Andrew, 1962 15 10
648 70 c. Queen visiting War Memorial, Montego Bay, 1983 25 25
649 $3 On state visit to Luxembourg, 1976 70 90
650 $5 At Crown Agents Head Office, London, 1983 1·00 1·75
646/50 *Set of* 5 2·00 2·75

231 Bustamante Children's Hospital **231a** Prince Andrew and Miss Sarah Ferguson, Ascot, 1985

(Des D. Miller. Litho Questa)

1986 (19 May). *"Ameripex '86" International Stamp Exhibition, Chicago. T* **231** *and similar vert designs. Multicoloured.* W **111**. *P* 14½ × 14.

651 25 c. Type **231** 40 15
652 55 c. Air Jamaica Boeing 737 airliner and map of holiday resorts 80 40
653 $3 Norman Manley Law School 1·00 2·00
654 $5 Bauxite and agricultural exports 5·00 6·25
651/4 *Set of* 4 6·50 8·00
MS655 85 × 106 mm. Nos. 651/4 (*sold at* $8.90) 6·50 8·00

(Des D. Miller. Litho Walsall)

1986 (23 July). *Royal Wedding. T* **231a** *and similar square design. Multicoloured.* W **111**. *P* 14½ × 14.

656 20 c. Type **231a** 15 10
657 $5 Prince Andrew making speech, Fredericton, Canada, 1985 1·40 1·90

5c

232 Richard "Shrimpy" Clarke **(233)**

(Des G. Vasarhelyi. Litho Questa)

1986 (27 Oct). *Jamaican Boxing Champions. T* **232** *and similar vert designs. Multicoloured.* W **111**. *P* 14.

658 45 c. Type **232** 20 15
659 70 c. Michael McCallum 30 30
660 $2 Trevor Berbick 70 1·25
661 $4 Richard "Shrimpy" Clarke, Michael McCallum and Trevor Berbick 1·25 2·25
658/61 *Set of* 4 2·25 3·50

1986 (3 Nov). *Nos.* 472/3 *surch as T* **233**.

662 5 c. on 50 c. Jamaican Woodpecker 90 1·40
663 10 c. on 65 c. Rafting, Martha Brae Trelawny 90 1·40

234 *Heliconia wagneriana* **235** Crown Cone (*Conus regius*)

(Des Annette Robinson. Litho B.D.T.)

1986 (1 Dec). *Christmas. Flowers* (1*st series*). *T* **234** *and similar multicoloured designs.* W **111** *(sideways on* 25 *c.,* $5). *P* 13½.

664 20 c. Type **234** 10 10
665 25 c. *Heliconia psittacorum* (*horiz*) 10 10
666 55 c. *Heliconia rostrata* 20 30
667 $5 *Strelitzia reginae* (*horiz*) 1·60 3·50
664/7 *Set of* 4 1·75 3·50

See also Nos. 703/6 and 739/42.

(Des A. Riley. Litho Format)

1987 (23 Feb). *Sea Shells. T* **235** *and similar vert designs. Multicoloured.* W **111**. *P* 15.

668 35 c. Type **235** 45 15
669 75 c. Measled Cowrie (*Cypraea zebra*) 65 60
670 $1 Atlantic Trumpet Triton (*Charonia variegata*) 75 90
671 $5 Rooster-tail Conch (*Strombus gallus*) 1·50 3·25
668/71 *Set of* 4 3·00 4·50

COVER PRICES

Cover factors are quoted at the beginning of each country for most issues to 1945. An explanation of the system can be found on page x. The factors quoted do not, however, apply to philatelic covers.

236 Norman Manley   **237** Arms of Jamaica

(Des C. Slania (1 c. to 90 c.). Litho Enschedé)

1987 (18 May)–**97.** *Vert portraits as T* **236** *and T* **237**. *W* **111** (*sideways on* $1 *to* $50). *Cream paper* (2 *c. to* 9 *c.* (*Nos.* 673A/80A). *P* 12½×13 (1 *to* 90 *c.*) *or* 13×13½ ($1 *to* $50). A. *Without imprint.* B. *With imprint date at foot.*

			A		B	
672	**236**	1 c. scarlet and pale pink	10	10	†	
673		2 c. brt car & pale rose-pk	10	10	†	
674		3 c. yellow-ol & pale stone	10	10	†	
675		4 c. myrtle-grn & pale grn	10	10	†	
676		5 c. slate-blue and pale bluish grey	15	10	10	10
677		6 c. dull ultramarine and pale lavender-grey ..	10	10	†	
678		7 c. reddish violet and pale mauve	10	10	†	
679		8 c. deep magenta and pale rose-pink ..	10	10	†	
680		9 c. olive-sepia & pale brn	10	10	†	
681	–	10 c. dp rose-red & pale pk	30	10	10	10
		a. Chalk-surfaced paper	†		10	10
682	–	20 c. reddish orge & flesh	30	10	10	10
		a. Chalk-surfaced paper	†		10	10
683	–	30 c. brt green & pale grn	30	10	†	
		a. Chalk-surfaced paper	†		10	10
684	–	40 c. dp turquoise-green & pale turquoise-green	40	15	10	10
		a. Chalk-surfaced paper	†		10	10
685	–	50 c. grey-ol & pale ol-grey	50	15	10	10
		a. Chalk-surfaced paper	†		10	10
685*c*	–	55 c. brown-bistre & cream (*chalk-surfaced paper*)	†		10	10
686	–	60 c. brt blue & pale azure	10	10	†	
687	–	70 c. bluish vio & pale vio	10	10	†	
688	–	80 c. reddish violet and pale rose-lilac ..	10	10	†	
689	–	90 c. light reddish brown and pale grey-brown	40	40	10	10
		a. Chalk-surfaced paper	†		30	30
690	**237**	$1 olive-sepia and cream	40	30	30	30
		a. Chalk-surfaced paper	†		10	10
690*c*		$1.10, ol-sepia & cream (*chalk-surfaced paper*)	†		10	10
691		$2 bright orge & cream	30	30	†	
		a. Chalk-surfaced paper	†		10	10
692		$5 brown-ol & pale stone	40	40	†	
		a. Chalk-surfaced paper	†		20	25
693		$10 dp turquoise-blue & pale azure	35	40	†	
693*c*		$25 bluish violet and pale lavender	†		90	95
693*d*		$50 deep mauve and pale rose-lilac	†		1·75	1·90
672A/93A		.. .. *Set of* 22	3·50	2·50		
676B/93*d*B		.. .. *Set of* 13			3·25	3·50

Designs:—10 c. to 90 c. Sir Alexander Bustamante.

Dates of issue: 18.5.87, Nos. 672A/93A; 6.6.88, Nos. 676B, 682B; 12.2.91, Nos. 684B, 685B; 6.6.91, No. 690B; 9.10.91, Nos. 693*c*B, 693*d*B; 5.92, Nos. 682aB, 684*a*B, 685aB, 689aB; 11.93, Nos. 681B, 689B; 10.10.94, Nos. 681aB, 683aB, 685*c*B, 690*c*B; 30.4.97, Nos. 690aB, 691aB, 692aB.

Imprint dates: "1988", Nos. 676B, 682B; "1989", No. 682B; "1991", Nos. 684B/5B, 690B, 693*c*B/*d*B; "1992", Nos. 682aB, 684aB, 685aB, 689aB, 690B; "1993", Nos. 681B/2B, 685B, 689B/90B; "1994", Nos. 681aB, 682aB, 683aB, 684aB, 685aB, 685cB, 690cB; "1997", Nos. 690aB, 691aB, 692aB.

The background colour on printings of Type **237** from 1992 onwards is fluorescent.

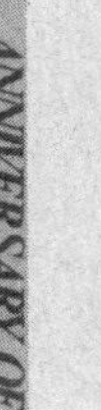

238 Jamaican Flag and Coast at Sunset   **239** Marcus Garvey

(Des D. Miller. Litho Walsall)

1987 (27 July). *25th Anniv of Independence. T* **238** *and similar multicoloured design. W* **111** (*sideways on* 70 *c.*). *P* 14.

694	55 c. Type **238**..	75	60
695	70 c. Jamaican flag and inscription (*horiz*) ..	1·00	1·75

(Des D. Miller. Litho Walsall)

1987 (17 Aug). *Birth Centenary of Marcus Garvey (founder of Universal Negro Improvement Association). T* **239** *and similar vert design, both black, emerald and lemon. W* **111**. *P* 14.

696	25 c. Type **239**..	80	1·25
	a. Horiz pair. Nos. 696/7	1·60	2·50
697	25 c. Statue of Marcus Garvey	80	1·25

Nos. 696/7 were printed together, *se-tenant*, in horizontal pairs throughout the sheet.

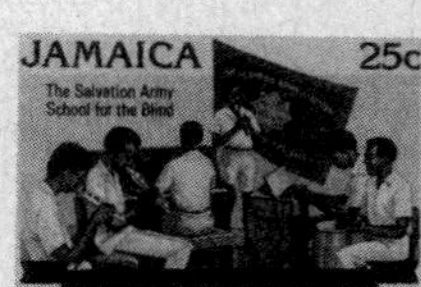

240 Salvation Army School for the Blind   **241** Hibiscus Hybrid

(Des L. Curtis. Litho Walsall)

1987 (8 Oct). *Centenary of Salvation Army in Jamaica. T* **240** *and similar horiz designs. Multicoloured. W* **111** (*sideways*). *P* 13×13½.

698	25 c. Type **240**..	90	30
699	55 c. Col. Mary Booth and Bramwell Booth Memorial Hall	1·25	30
700	$3 Welfare Service lorry, 1929	2·75	3·50
701	$5 Col. Abram Davey and S.S. *Alene*, 1887	3·50	4·75
698/701	.. .. *Set of* 4	7·50	8·00
MS702	100×80 mm. Nos. 698/701 (*sold at* $8.90)	7·50	8·50

(Des Annette Robinson. Litho Harrison)

1987 (30 Nov). *Christmas. Flowers* (2*nd series*). *T* **241** *and similar vert designs. Multicoloured. W* **111**. *P* 14½×14.

703	20 c. Type **241**..	15	10
704	25 c. *Hibiscus elatus*	15	10
705	$4 *Hibiscus cannabinus*	2·00	2·25
706	$5 *Hibiscus rosasinensis*	2·25	2·50
703/6	.. .. *Set of* 4	4·00	4·50

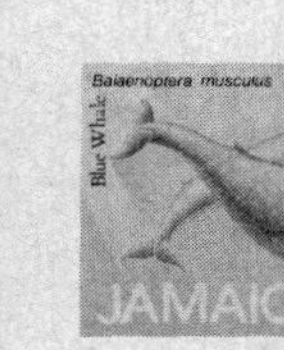

242 Chestnut-bellied Cuckoo, Black-billed Amazon and Jamaican Euphonia   **243** Blue Whales

(Des N. Arlott. Litho Walsall)

1988 (22 Jan). *Jamaican Birds* (3*rd series*). *T* **242** *and similar vert designs. Multicoloured. W* **111**. *P* 14.

707	45 c. Type **242**	1·25	1·75
	a. Horiz pair. Nos. 707/8	2·50	3·50
708	45 c. Black-billed Amazon, Jamaican White-eyed Vireo, Rufous-throated Solitaire and Yellow Elaenia	1·25	1·75
709	$5 Snowy Plover, Little Blue Heron and Great Blue Heron (white phase) ..	3·50	4·00
	a. Horiz pair. Nos. 709/10	7·00	8·00
710	$5 Black-necked Stilt, Snowy Egret, Snowy Plover and Black-crowned Night Heron	3·50	4·00
707/10	.. .. *Set of* 4	8·50	10·50

The two designs of each value were printed together, *se-tenant*, in horizontal pairs throughout the sheets, each pair forming a composite design.

(Des A. Riley. Litho Harrison)

1988 (14 Apr). *Marine Mammals. T* **243** *and similar horiz designs. Multicoloured. W* **111** (*sideways*). *P* 14.

711	20 c. Type **243**	1·50	50
712	25 c. Gervais's Whales	1·50	50
713	55 c. Killer Whales	2·50	70
714	$5 Common Dolphins	4·00	6·50
711/14	.. .. *Set of* 4	8·50	7·50

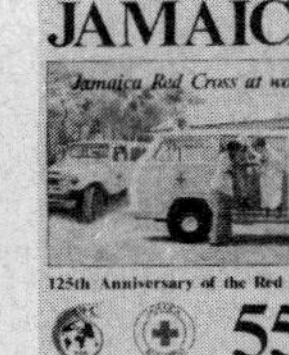

243*a* Jackie Hendriks   **244** Jamaican Red Cross Workers with Ambulance

(Des D. Hartley. Litho Walsall)

1988 (6 June). *West Indian Cricket. T* **243*a*** *and similar horiz designs, each showing portrait, cricket equipment and early belt buckle. Multicoloured. W* **111** (*sideways*). *P* 14.

715	25 c. Type **243*a***	90	30
716	55 c. George Headley	1·40	40
717	$2 Michael Holding	2·50	2·25
718	$3 R. K. Nunes	2·75	3·25
719	$4 Allan Rae	3·00	3·50
715/19	.. .. *Set of* 5	9·50	8·50

(Des S. Noon. Litho Walsall)

1988 (8 Aug). *125th Anniv of International Red Cross. T* **244** *and similar vert design. Multicoloured. W* **111**. *P* 14½ × 14.

720	55 c. Type **244**	50	30
721	$5 Henri Dunant (founder) in field hospital	2·00	3·00

245 Boxing

(Des P. Broadbent. Litho B.D.T.)

1988 (24 Aug). *Olympic Games, Seoul. T* **245** *and similar horiz designs. Multicoloured. W* **111** (*sideways*). *P* 14.

722	25 c. Type **245**	15	10
723	45 c. Cycling	55	20
724	$4 Athletics	1·25	1·75
725	$5 Hurdling	1·25	1·75
722/5	.. .. *Set of* 4	2·75	3·50
MS726	127 × 87 mm. Nos. 722/5 (*sold at* $9.90)	2·75	3·50

246 Bobsled Team Members and Logo

(Des D. Miller. Litho B.D.T.)

1988 (4 Nov). *Jamaican Olympic Bobsled Team. T* **246** *and similar horiz designs. Multicoloured. W* **111** (*sideways**). *P* 14.

727	25 c. Type **246**	30	45
	a. Horiz pair. Nos. 727/8	60	90
728	25 c. Two-man bobsled	30	45
729	$5 Bobsled team members (*different*) and logo	1·25	1·75
	a. Horiz pair. Nos. 729/30	2·50	3·50
	aw. Wmk top of J to right	3·00	
730	$5 Four-man bobsled	1·25	1·75
727/30	.. .. *Set of* 4	2·75	4·00

*The normal sideways watermark has top of "J" to left, *as seen from the back of the stamp.*

Nos. 727/8 and 729/30 were printed together, *se-tenant*, in horizontal pairs throughout the sheets.

+25c

HURRICANE GILBERT RELIEF FUND

(**247**)

1988 (11 Nov). *Hurricane Gilbert Relief Fund. Nos.* 722/5 *surch as T* **247** *by Format. A. In red. B. In black.*

		A		B	
731	25 c. + 25 c. Type **245** ..	10	15	10	15
732	45 c. + 45 c. Cycling ..	20	25	20	25
733	$4 + $4 Athletics	1·25	1·90	1·25	1·90
734	$5 + $5 Hurdling	1·50	2·25	1·50	2·25
731/4	.. .. *Set of* 4	2·75	4·00	2·75	4·00

248 Nurses and Firemen

(Des S. Noon. Litho Format)

1988 (24 Nov). *Year of the Worker. T* **248** *and similar horiz designs. Multicoloured. W* **111** (*sideways*). *P* 14.

735	25 c. Type **248**	45	20
736	55 c. Woodcarver	45	30
737	$3 Textile workers	1·00	2·50
738	$5 Workers on fish farm	1·25	3·00
735/8	.. .. *Set of* 4	2·75	5·50

(Des Annette Robinson. Litho Format)

1988 (15 Dec). *Christmas. Flowers* (3*rd series*). *Multicoloured designs as T* **241**. *W* **111** (*sideways on* 55 *c.*, $4). *P* 14.

739	25 c. *Euphorbia pulcherrima*	40	10
740	55 c. *Spathodea campanulata* (*horiz*) ..	50	15
741	$3 *Hylocereus triangularis*	1·10	1·40
742	$4 *Broughtonia sanguinea* (*horiz*) ..	1·10	1·50
739/42	.. .. *Set of* 4	2·75	2·75

249 Old York Castle School   **250** *Syntomidopsis variegata*

(Des A. Theobald. Litho B.D.T.)

1989 (19 Jan). *Bicentenary of Methodist Church in Jamaica. T* **249** *and similar horiz designs. W* **111** *(sideways). P* 13½.
743 25 c. black and bright blue 10 10
744 45 c. black and rosine 15 10
745 $5 black and yellow-green .. .. 2·00 2·50
743/5 .. .. *Set of* 3 2·00 2·50
Designs:—45 c. Revd. Thomas Coke and Parade Chapel, Kingston; $5 Father Hugh Sherlock and St. John's Church.

(Des I. Loe. Litho B.D.T.)

1989 (30 Aug). *Jamaican Moths* (1*st series*). *T* **250** *and similar vert designs. Multicoloured. W* **111**. *P* 14×13½.
746 25 c. Type **250** 50 10
747 55 c. *Himantoides perkinsae* 80 30
748 $3 *Arctia nigriplaga* .. .. .. 1·50 2·50
749 $5 *Sthenognatha toddi* .. .. .. 1·90 3·00
746/9 .. .. *Set of* 4 4·25 5·50
See also Nos. 758/61 and 790/3.

251 Arawak Fisherman with Catch

252 Girl Guide

(Des Josephine Martin. Litho Cartor)

1989 (22 Dec). 500*th Anniv of Discovery of America by Columbus* (1992) (1*st issue*). *T* **251** *and similar vert designs. Multicoloured. W* **111**. *P* 13½.
750 25 c. Type **251** 20 10
751 70 c. Arawak man smoking 45 30
752 $5 King Ferdinand and Queen Isabella inspecting caravels .. .. 2·00 2·75
753 $10 Columbus with chart .. .. 3·75 5·50
750/3 .. .. *Set of* 4 5·75 7·50
MS754 150×200 mm. Nos. 750/3. Wmk sideways. P 12½ (*sold at* $16.15) .. .. 8·00 7·50
No. **MS**754 also exists imperforate from a limited printing used in Presentation Packs.
See also Nos. 774/9 and 802/7.

(Des J. Sayer. Litho B.D.T.)

1990 (28 June). 75*th Anniv of Girl Guide Movement in Jamaica. T* **252** *and similar vert designs. Multicoloured. W* **111** (*inverted on* $5). *P* 14.
755 45 c. Type **252** 65 20
756 55 c. Guide leader 75 20
757 $5 Brownie, guide and ranger .. .. 3·50 5·50
755/7 .. .. *Set of* 3 4·50 5·50

(Des I. Loe. Litho B.D.T.)

1990 (12 Sept). *Jamaican Moths* (2*nd series*). *Vert designs as T* **250**. *Multicoloured. W* **111**. *P* 14×13½.
758 25 c. *Eunomia rubripunctata* 65 30
759 55 c. *Perigonia jamaicensis* 90 35
760 $4 *Uraga haemorrhoa* .. .. .. 2·00 3·00
761 $5 *Empyreuma pugione* .. .. .. 2·00 3·00
758/61 .. .. *Set of* 4 5·00 6·00

(253)

254 Teaching English

1990 (12 Sept). *"EXPO 90" International Garden and Greenery Exhibition, Osaka. Nos. 758/61 optd with T* **253**.
762 25 c. *Eunomia rubripunctata* 65 30
763 55 c. *Perigonia jamaicensis* 90 35
764 $4 *Uraga haemorrhoa* .. .. .. 2·00 3·00
765 $5 *Empyreuma pugione* .. .. .. 2·00 3·00
762/5 .. .. *Set of* 4 5·00 6·00

(Des G. Vasarhelyi. Litho B.D.T.)

1990 (10 Oct). *International Literacy Year. T* **254** *and similar horiz design. Multicoloured. W* **111** (*sideways*). *P* 14.
766 55 c. Type **254** 40 25
767 $5 Teaching maths .. .. .. 3·00 3·75

255 "To the Market"

(Adapted J. Mahfood and D. Miller. Litho Walsall)

1990 (7 Dec). *Christmas. Children's Paintings. T* **255** *and similar multicoloured designs. W* **111** (*sideways on horiz designs*). *P* 14×13½ ($5) *or* 13½×14 (*others*).
768 20 c. Type **255** 30 10
769 25 c. "House and Garden" 30 10
770 55 c. "Jack and Jill" 40 15
771 70 c. "Market" 50 40
772 $1.50, "Lonely" .. .. 1·25 1·75
773 $5 "Market Woman" (*vert*) .. .. 2·75 4·00
768/73 .. .. *Set of* 6 5·00 6·00

256 Map of First Voyage, 1492

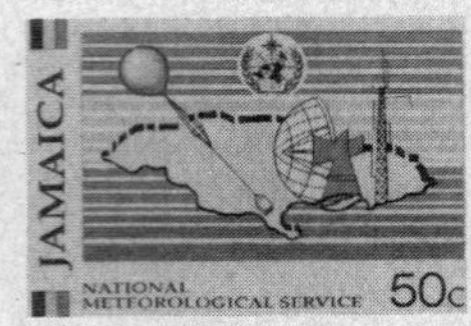

257 Weather Balloon, Dish Aerial and Map of Jamaica.

(Des Josephine Martin. Litho Questa)

1990 (19 Dec). 500*th Anniv of Discovery of America by Columbus* (1992) (2*nd issue*). *T* **256** *and similar horiz designs. Multicoloured. W* **111** (*sideways*). *P* 14.
774 25 c. Type **256** 40 15
775 45 c. Map of second voyage, 1493 .. .. 50 15
776 $5 Map of third voyage, 1498 .. .. 2·50 3·00
777 $10 Map of fourth voyage, 1502 .. .. 3·50 4·50
774/7 .. .. *Set of* 4 6·25 7·00
MS778 126×99 mm. 25, 45 c., $5, $10 Composite map of Caribbean showing routes of voyages .. 7·50 8·50
MS779 148×207 mm. Nos. 774/7. Imperf .. 6·50 8·50
Unlike the imperforate version of No. **MS**754, No. **MS**779 was freely available at face value.

(Adapted G. Vasarhelyi. Litho B.D.T.)

1991 (20 May). 11*th World Meteorological Congress, Kingston. W* **111** (*sideways*). *P* 14.
780 **257** 50 c. multicoloured 50 20
781 $10 multicoloured .. .. .. 5·00 5·50

258 Bust of Mary Seacole

259 Jamaican Iguana

(Des Jennifer Toombs. Litho B.D.T.)

1991 (24 June). *International Council of Nurses Meeting of National Representatives. T* **258** *and similar horiz designs. W* **111** (*sideways*). *P* 13½.
782 50 c. multicoloured 50 30
783 $1.10, multicoloured .. .. .. 1·25 1·75
MS784 89×60 mm. $8 agate, pale orange-brown and yellow-ochre (*sold at* $8.20) .. .. 2·00 3·00
Designs:—$1.10, Mary Seacole House; $8 Hospital at Scutari, 1854.

(Des I. Loe. Litho Cartor)

1991 (29 July). 50*th Anniv of Natural History Society of Jamaica. Jamaican Iguana. T* **259** *and similar vert designs. Multicoloured. W* **111**. *P* 13.
785 $1.10, Type **259** 55 65
a. Horiz strip of 5. Nos. 785/9 .. .. 2·50
786 $1.10, Head of iguana looking right .. 55 65
787 $1.10, Iguana climbing 55 65
788 $1.10, Iguana on rock looking left .. 55 65
789 $1.10, Close-up of iguana's head .. 55 65
785/9 .. .. *Set of* 5 2·50 2·75
Nos. 785/9 were printed together, *se-tenant*, in horizontal strips of 5 throughout the sheet.

(Des I. Loe. Litho B.D.T.)

1991 (12 Aug). *Jamaican Moths* (3*rd series*). *Multicoloured designs as T* **250**. *W* **111**. *P* 14×13½.
790 50 c. *Urania sloanus* 65 20
791 $1.10, *Phoenicoprocta jamaicensis* .. 90 60
792 $1.40, *Horama grotei* .. .. .. 1·10 85
793 $8 *Amplypterus gannascus* .. .. 3·25 5·00
790/3 .. .. *Set of* 4 5·50 6·00

(260)

261 "Doctor Bird"

1991 (23 Sept). *"Phila Nippon '91" International Stamp Exhibition, Tokyo. Nos. 790/3 optd with T* **260**.
794 50 c. *Urania sloanus* 65 20
795 $1.10, *Phoenicoprocta jamaicensis* .. 90 60
796 $1.40, *Horama grotei* .. .. .. 1·10 85
797 $8 *Amplypterus gannascus* .. .. 3·25 5·00
794/7 .. .. *Set of* 4 5·50 6·00

(Adapted J. Mahfood. Litho Enschedé)

1991 (27 Nov). *Christmas. Children's Paintings. T* **261** *and similar horiz designs. Multicoloured. W* **111** (*sideways*). *P* 14×15.
798 50 c. Type **261** 30 10
799 $1.10, "Road scene" 65 25
800 $5 "Children and house" .. .. 1·75 2·00
801 $10 "Cows grazing" .. .. .. 2·75 4·00
798/801 .. .. *Set of* 4 5·00 5·50

262 Indians threatening Ships

263 Compasses and Square Symbol

(Des Josephine Martin. Litho B.D.T.)

1991 (16 Dec). 500*th Anniv of Discovery of America by Columbus* (1992) (3*rd issue*). *T* **262** *and similar horiz designs. Multicoloured. W* **111** (*sideways*). *P* 13½.
802 50 c. Type **262** 35 10
803 $1.10, Spaniards setting dog on Indians .. 45 25
804 $1.40, Indian with gift of pineapple .. 45 25
805 $25 Columbus describes Jamaica with crumpled paper .. .. 5·00 6·00
802/5 .. .. *Set of* 4 5·50 6·00
MS806 125×102 mm. Nos. 802/5 (*sold at* $28.20) 5·50 6·00
MS807 210×150 mm. Nos. 802/5. Imperf .. 5·50 6·00

(Litho Cartor)

1992 (1 May). 250*th Anniv of First Provisional Grand Master of English Freemasonry in Jamaica. T* **263** *and similar vert designs. Multicoloured. W* **111**. *P* 13½.
808 50 c. Type **263** 45 15
809 $1.10, Symbol in stained glass window .. 60 25
810 $1.40, Compasses and square on book .. 60 25
811 $25 Eye in triangle symbol .. .. 5·00 6·00
808/11 .. .. *Set of* 4 6·00 6·00
MS812 140×80 mm. Nos. 808/11 (*sold at* $28.50) 6·00 6·50

264 Ship in Flooded Street

(Des J. Batchelor. Litho Cartor)

1992 (1 June). 300*th Anniv of Destruction of Port Royal. T* **264** *and similar horiz designs. Multicoloured. W* **111** (*sideways*). *P* 14×13½.
813 50 c. Type **264** 35 15
814 $1.10, Church tower falling 45 25
815 $1.40, Houses collapsing 45 25
816 $25 Inhabitants falling into fissure .. 3·25 4·50
813/16 .. .. *Set of* 4 4·00 4·75
MS817 116×75 mm. $5 Contemporary broadsheet of earthquake. Wmk upright. P 13×12 .. .. 1·50 2·00
No. **MS**817 has a description of the broadsheet printed on the reverse under the gum.

265 Credit Union Symbol

(Des G. Vasarhelyi. Litho Enschedé)

1992 (24 Aug). 50*th Anniv of Credit Union Movement. T* **265** *and similar horiz design. W* **111** (*sideways*). *P* 14×15.
818 50 c. dp dull bl, emer & pale turquoise-green 65 30
819 $1.40, multicoloured .. .. .. 1·10 1·50
Design:—$1.40, O'Hare Hall.

266 Jamaican Flag and Beach Scene

267 "Rainbow" (Cecil Baugh)

(Des G. Vasarhelyi. Litho Cartor)

1992 (26 Oct). *30th Anniv of Independence.* *W* **111** *(sideways). P* 13½.

820 **266** 50 c. multicoloured 10 10
821 $1.10, multicoloured 20 20
822 $25 multicoloured . . . . . . 2·75 4·50
820/2 . . . . *Set of* 3 2·75 4·50

(Des D. Bowen. Litho Cartor)

1993 (26 Apr). *Art Ceramics and Pottery. T* **267** *and similar vert designs. Multicoloured. W* **111**. *P* 13½.

823 50 c. Type **267** 10 10
824 $1.10, "Yabba Pot" (Louisa Jones) . . 20 20
825 $1.40, "Sculptured Vase" (Gene Pearson) 20 20
826 $25 "Lidded Form" (Norma Harrack) . . 3·50 4·50
823/6 . . . . *Set of* 4 3·50 4·50

268 Girls' Brigade Parade

269 Cadet, Armoured Car and Emblem

(Des G. Vasarhelyi. Litho Cartor)

1993 (9 Aug). *Centenary of Girls' Brigade. T* **268** *and similar horiz design. Multicoloured. W* **111** *(sideways). P* 14×13½.

827 50 c. Type **268** 30 20
828 $1.10, Brigade members 45 55

(Des D. Miller. Litho B.D.T.)

1993 (8 Nov). *50th Anniv of Jamaica Combined Cadet Force. T* **269** *and similar multicoloured designs. W* **111** *(sideways on $1.10, $3). P* 14.

829 50 c. Type **269** 20 15
830 $1.10, Cadet and Britten Norman Islander light aircraft *(horiz)* 30 30
831 $1.40, Cadet and patrol boats 30 30
832 $3 Cadet and emblem *(horiz)* 55 80
829/32 . . . . *Set of* 4 1·25 1·40

270 Constant Spring Golf Course

271 Norman Manley

(Des D. Miller. Litho B.D.T.)

1993 (16–21 Dec). *Golf Courses. T* **270** *and similar multicoloured designs. W* **111** *(sideways). P* 14.

833 50 c. Type **270** (21 Dec) 15 10
834 $1.10, Type **270** (21 Dec) 15 10
835 $1.40, Half Moon (21 Dec) 20 15
836 $2 As $1.40 (21 Dec) 25 25
837 $3 Jamaica Jamaica (21 Dec) 30 35
838 $10 As $3 (21 Dec) . . . . 80 1·40
833/8 . . . . *Set of* 6 1·60 2·00
MS839 66×71 mm. $25 Tryall *(vert)*. Wmk upright *(sold at $28)* . . . . 1·75 2·25

(Des R. Larson. Litho B.D.T.)

1994 (12 Jan). *Birth Centenary of Norman Manley. T* **271** *and similar vert portrait. W* **111**. *P* 14×15.

840 $25 multicoloured . . . . 2·00 2·75
a. Horiz pair. Nos. 840/1 . . . . 4·50 6·00
841 $50 multicoloured . . . . 2·50 3·25

Nos. 840/1 were printed together, *se-tenant*, in horizontal pairs throughout the sheet.

(272)

273 Flags of Great Britain and Jamaica

1994 (18 Feb). *"Hong Kong '94" International Stamp Exhibition. No.* **MS**839 *optd with T* **272**.

MS842 66×71 mm. $25 Tryall . . . . 2·75 3·25

(Des D. Miller. Litho B.D.T.)

1994 (1 Mar). *Royal Visit. T* **273** *and similar vert designs. Multicoloured. W* **111**. *P* 14×13½.

843 $1.10, Type **273** 10 10
844 $1.40, Royal Yacht *Britannia* 30 15
845 $25 Queen Elizabeth II . . . . 1·50 2·25
846 $50 Queen Elizabeth and Prince Philip . . 2·50 3·25
843/6 . . . . *Set of* 4 4·00 5·25

274 Douglas DC-9

275 Giant Swallowtail

(Des E. Nisbet. Litho Walsall)

1994 (26 Apr). *25th Anniv of Air Jamaica. T* **274** *and similar horiz designs. Multicoloured. W* **111** *(sideways). P* 14.

847 50 c. Type **274** 15 10
848 $1.10, Douglas DC-8 . . . . 15 10
849 $5 Boeing 727 . . . . 35 40
850 $50 Airbus A300 . . . . 3·00 4·50
847/50 . . . . *Set of* 4 3·25 4·50

(Des N. Shewring. Litho B.D.T.)

1994 (18 Aug). *Giant Swallowtail Butterfly Conservation. T* **275** *and similar vert designs. Multicoloured. W* **111**. *P* 13½.

851 50 c. Type **275** 25 15
852 $1.10, With wings closed 35 15
853 $10 On flower . . . . 1·25 1·75
854 $25 With wings spread . . . . 2·50 3·25
851/4 . . . . *Set of* 4 4·00 4·75
MS855 56×61 mm. $50 Pair of butterflies . . 4·50 5·50

276 "Royal Botanical Gardens" (Sidney McLaren)

(Des G. Vasarhelyi. Litho Questa)

1994 (7 Sept). *Tourism. T* **276** *and similar horiz designs. Multicoloured. W* **111** *(sideways). P* 14.

856 50 c. Type **276** 20 15
857 $1.10, Blue Mountains 30 25
858 $5 Tourist in hammock and water sports 80 1·25
856/8 . . . . *Set of* 3 1·10 1·50
MS859 105×80 mm. $25 Carolina Parakeets; $25 Silhouetted scuba diver; $25 Carolina Parakeet and foliage; $25 Tourist raft . . 5·00 6·00

277 Jamaican Red Poll Calf

(Des R. Watton. Litho Cartor)

1994 (16 Nov). *Jamaican Red Poll Cattle. T* **277** *and similar horiz designs. Multicoloured. W* **111** *(sideways). P* 13.

860 50 c. Type **277** 10 10
861 $1.10, Red Poll heifer 10 10
862 $25 Red Poll cow . . . . 1·25 2·00
863 $50 Red Poll bull . . . . 2·50 3·50
860/3 . . . . *Set of* 4 3·75 5·00

278 Refuse Collectors

279 Jamaican Band-tailed Pigeon ("Ring-tailed Pigeon")

(Des D. Miller. Litho Enschedé)

1994 (1 Dec). *Christmas. Children's Paintings. T* **278** *and similar horiz designs. Multicoloured. W* **111** *(sideways). P* 14×15.

864 50 c. Type **278** 10 10
865 90 c. Hospital ward 10 10
866 $1.10, House 10 10
867 $50 Landscape . . . . 2·75 3·75
864/7 . . . . *Set of* 4 2·75 3·75

(Des N. Arlott. Litho B.D.T.)

1995 (24 Apr). *Jamaican Wild Birds. T* **279** *and similar vert designs. Multicoloured. W w* **16**. *P* 14.

868 50 c. Type **279** 10 10
869 90 c. Yellow-billed Amazon ("Yellow-billed Parrot") 15 10
870 $1.10, Black-billed Amazon ("Black-billed Parrot") 15 10
871 $50 Jamaican Owl ("Brown Owl") . . 3·25 4·00
868/71 . . . . *Set of* 4 3·25 4·00
MS872 47×62 mm. $50 Streamertail . . 4·25 4·50

For No. **MS**872 additionally inscribed for "Singapore '95" see No. **MS**888.

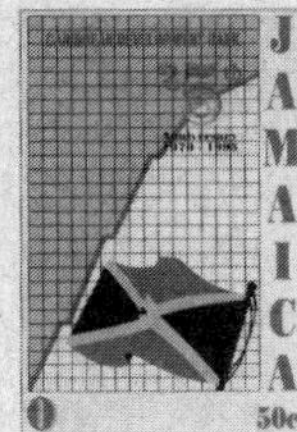

280 Graph, National Flag and Logo

281 "Song of Freedom"

(Litho Cartor)

1995 (11 May). *25th Anniv of Caribbean Development Bank. T* **280** *and similar designs. W* **111** *(sideways on horiz designs). P* 13½.

873 **280** 50 c. blue-green, black & chrome-yellow 10 10
874 $1 blue-green, black & chrome-yellow 10 10
875 – $1.10, multicoloured 10 10
876 – $50 multicoloured . . . . 2·75 3·75
873/6 . . . . *Set of* 4 2·75 3·75

Designs: *Horiz*–$1.10, Industry, agriculture and commerce; $50 Jamaican currency.

(Des D. Miller. Litho Questa)

1995 (31 July). *50th Birth Anniv of Bob Marley (reggae singer). T* **281** *and similar vert designs showing record covers. Multicoloured. W* **111**. *P* 14.

877 50 c. Type **281** 10 10
878 $1.10, "Fire" 15 15
879 $1.40, "Time will Tell" 15 15
880 $3 "Natural Mystic" 30 40
881 $10 "Live at Lyceum" . . . . 1·00 1·75
877/81 . . . . *Set of* 5 1·50 2·25
MS882 105×57 mm. $100 "Legend". Wmk sideways . . . . 6·00 7·00

282 Queen Elizabeth the Queen Mother

283 Michael Manley

(Des Jennifer Toombs. Litho B.D.T.)

1995 (4 Aug). *95th Birthday of Queen Elizabeth the Queen Mother. Sheet* 81×95 *mm. W* **111**. *P* 13½.

MS883 **282** $75 multicoloured . . . . 4·00 4·50

(Des G. Vasarhelyi. Litho B.D.T.)

1995 (23 Aug). *Recipients of the Order of the Caribbean Community. T* **283** *and similar horiz designs. Multicoloured. W* **111** *(sideways). P* 14×15.

884 50 c. Type **283** 10 10
885 $1.10, Sir Alister McIntyre 10 10
886 $1.40, Justice P. Telford Georges 10 10
887 $50 Dame Nita Barrow .. .. .. 2·75 3·75
884/7 .. .. *Set of* 4 2·75 3·75

1995 (1 Sept). *"Singapore '95" International Stamp Exhibition. No.* **MS**872 *additionally inscr with exhibition emblem on sheet margin.*

MS888 47×62 mm. $50 Streamertail .. .. 3·50 4·25

284 Dish Aerial and Landrover, Balkans

(Des A. Theobald. Litho B.D.T.)

1995 (24 Oct). *50th Anniv of United Nations. T* **284** *and similar horiz designs. Multicoloured. W* **111** *(sideways). P* 14.

889 50 c. Type **284** 10 10
890 $1.10, Antonov An-32 aircraft, Balkans 15 15
891 $3 Bedford articulated road tanker, Balkans 25 30
892 $5 Fairchild C-119 Flying Boxcar, Korea 35 45
889/92 .. .. *Set of* 4 75 85
MS893 100×70 mm. $50 U.N.T.A.G. vehicles, Namibia .. .. 1·75 2·25

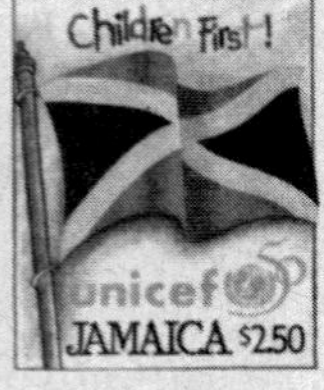

285 Landing of Indian Immigrants

286 Jamaican Flag and U.N.I.C.E.F. Emblem

(Des K. Reece. Litho Cot Printery Ltd, Barbados)

1996 (22 May). *150th Anniv of Indian Immigration to Jamaica. T* **285** *and similar horiz design. Multicoloured. W* **111** *(sideways). P* 14.

894 $2.50, Type **285** 20 10
895 $10 Indian musicians and traditional dancers 60 70

(Des K. Reece. Litho Cot Printery Ltd. Barbados)

1996 (2 Sept). *50th Anniv of U.N.I.C.E.F. W* **111**. *P* 14½×14.

896 **286** $2.50, multicoloured 15 10
897 $8 multicoloured 45 60
898 $10 multicoloured 50 70
896/8 .. .. *Set of* 3 1·00 1·25

287 Brown's Hutia

(Des W. Oliver. Litho Enschedé)

1996 (23 Sept). *Endangered Species. Brown's Hutia ("Jamaican Hutia"). T* **287** *and similar horiz designs. Multicoloured. W* **111** *(sideways). P* 13½.

899 $2.50, Type **287** 15 10
900 $10 Hutia on rock 50 55
901 $12.50, Female with young 60 70
902 $25 Head of Hutia .. .. 1·25 1·60
899/902 .. .. *Set of* 4 2·25 2·75

288 High Altar, Church of St. Thomas the Apostle

289 *Coelia triptera*

(Des W. Wright. Litho Questa)

1997 (7 Feb). *300th Anniv of the Kingston Parish Church. T* **288** *and similar multicoloured designs. P* 14.

903 $2 Type **288** 10 10
904 $8 Church of St. Thomas the Apostle .. 40 40
905 $12.50, "The Angel" (wood carving by Edna Manley) (*vert*) 60 65
903/5 .. .. *Set of* 3 1·00 1·00
MS906 106×76 mm. $60 St. Thomas the Apostle at sunset (42×56 *mm*) .. .. .. 2·10 2·25

No. 903 is inscribed "ALTER" in error.

(Litho Questa)

1997 (9 Oct). *Orchids. T* **289** *and similar multicoloured designs. W* **111** *(sideways on $2 and $5). P* 14.

907 $1 Type **289** 10 10
908 $2 *Oncidium pulchellum* (*horiz*) 10 10
909 $2.50, *Oncidium triquetrum* 10 10
910 $3 *Broughtonia negrilensis* 15 15
912 $5 *Enclyclia fragrans* (*horiz*) 25 30
907/12 .. .. *Set of* 5 60 65

STAMP BOOKLETS

1912. *Black on red covers. Stapled.*

SB1 2s. booklet containing twenty-four 1d. (No. 40) in blocks of 6 (9 Mar) .. ..
SB2 2s. booklet containing twelve ½d. and eighteen 1d. (Nos. 38, 58), each in blocks of 6 (5 Dec) .. £1300
SB3 3s. 6d. booklet containing forty-eight ½d. and eighteen 1d. (Nos. 38, 58), each in blocks of 6

1922. *Black on red cover. Stapled.*

SB4 1s. 6d. booklet containing twelve ½d. and 1d. (Nos. 78/9), each in blocks of 4 .. .. ..

1923 (Sept). *Black on red cover. Stapled.*

SB4*a* 2s. booklet containing twelve ½d. (No. 91) in blocks of 4 and eighteen 1d. (No. 92) in blocks of 6 .. .. £850

1927 (5 Jan). *Black on red cover. Stapled.*

SB5 1s. 6d. booklet containing twelve ½d. and 1d. (Nos. 91/2), each in blocks of 4 .. .. ..

1928 (5 Sept). *Black on red cover. Stapled.*

SB6 1s. 6d. booklet containing twelve ½d. and 1d. (Nos. 89*a*, 92), each in blocks of 4 .. .. ..

1929 (May). *Black on red cover. Stapled.*

SB7 2s. booklet containing twelve ½d. and eighteen 1d. (Nos. 89*a*, 108), each in blocks of 6 ..
a. With 1d. Die II (No. 108a) (1932) £750

1929 (July). *Black on red cover. Stapled.*

SB7*b* 2s. booklet containing six ½d., twelve 1d. and six 1½d. (Nos. 89*a*, 108/9) in blocks of 6 ..

1935. *Silver Jubilee. Black on red cover. Stapled.*

SB8 2s. booklet containing twenty-four 1d. (No. 114) in blocks of 6 .. .. £1200
a. In blocks of 4 .. .. £1700

1938. *Booklet containing twelve ½d. and eighteen 1d. (Nos. 121/2), each in blocks of 6. Stapled.*

SB9 2s. booklet (black on green cover) £325
SB10 2s. booklet (black on blue cover) £200
SB11 2s. booklet (black on yellow cover) £120

1946. *New Constitution. Black on blue cover. Stapled.*

SB12 2s. booklet containing sixteen 1½d. (No. 134a) in blocks of 4 .. .. £200

1951. *Black on yellow cover. Stapled.*

SB13 2s. booklet containing twelve ½d and eighteen 1d. (Nos. 121*b*, 122*a*), each in blocks of 6 .. 42·00

1956. *Black on green cover. Stitched.*

SB14 3s. booklet containing ½d., 1d., 2d. and 2½d. (Nos. 159/62) in blocks of 6 .. .. .. 11·00

1965 (15 Nov). *Black on green cover. Stitched.*

SB15 3s. booklet containing 1d., 2d. and 3d. (Nos. 217, 219, 221) in blocks of 6 .. .. 5·00

1981 (29 July). *Royal Wedding. Multicoloured cover,* 155×85 *mm, showing Prince Charles, Lady Diana Spencer and St. Paul's Cathedral. Stitched.*

SB16 $6.25, booklet containing *se-tenant* pane of 4 (No. 516ba) .. .. 3·50

1982 (30 Aug). *21st Birthday of Princess of Wales. Multicoloured cover,* 155×85 *mm, showing Princess of Wales and Highgrove House. Stitched.*

SB17 $7.50, booklet containing two different *se-tenant* panes of 3 (Nos. 551a, 554a) .. .. 3·75

1982 (13 Sept). *Birth of Prince William of Wales. No.* SB17 *optd* "ROYAL BABY 21.6.82".

SB18 $7.50, booklet containing two different *se-tenant* panes of 3 (Nos. 558a, 561a) .. .. 3·25

POSTAL FISCALS

Revenue stamps were authorised for postal use by Post Office notice of 12 October 1887.

F 1

(Typo D.L.R.)

1865–73. *P* 14. (*a*) *Wmk Pineapple* (*T* 7).

F1 **F 1** 1d. rose (1865) .. .. .. 70·00 90·00
a. Imperf (pair) £400

(*b*) *Wmk Crown CC*

F2 **F 1** 1d. rose (1871) .. .. .. 50·00 50·00

(*c*) *Wmk CA over Crown* (*Type w* **7** *sideways, covering two stamps*)

F3 **F 1** 1d. rose (1873) .. .. .. 17·00 7·00
a. Imperf .. ..

F 2

F 3

(Typo D.L.R.)

1855–74 (Issued). *Glazed paper. P* 14. (*a*) *No wmk.*

No.	Type	Description	Unused	Used
F4	F 2	1½d. blue/*blue* (1857)	45·00	45·00
		a. Imperf (1855)		
		b. Blue on white	50·00	55·00
F5		3d. purple/*blue* (1857)	42·00	50·00
		a. Imperf (1855)		
		b. Purple on lilac (1857)	42·00	50·00
		ba. Imperf (1855)		
		c. Purple on white (1857)	50·00	50·00
		(*b*) *Wmk Crown CC*		
F6	F 2	3d. purple/*lilac* (1874)	10·00	14·00

All the above stamps *imperf* are exceedingly rare postally used.

1858 (1 Jan). (Issued). *No wmk. P* 15½ × 15.

No.	Type	Description	Unused	Used
F7	F 3	1s. rose/*bluish*	70·00	75·00
F8		5s. lilac/*bluish*	£325	£375
F9		10s. green/*bluish*	£400	£450

Telegraph stamps were also used postally, but no authority was given for such use.

OFFICIAL STAMPS

OFFICIAL (O 1)   **OFFICIAL** (O 2)

1890 (1 Apr). *No.* 16*a optd with Type* O **1** *by C. Vendryes, Kingston.*

(*a*) "OFFICIAL" 17 *to* 17½ *mm long*

No.	Type	Description	Unused	Used
O1	8	½d. green	7·00	1·00
		a. "O" omitted	£450	
		b. One "I" omitted		
		c. Both "I"s omitted	£500	£500
		d. "L" omitted	£550	£550
		e. Opt inverted	65·00	70·00
		f. Opt double	65·00	70·00
		g. Opt. double, one inverted	£325	£325
		h. Opt double, one vertical	£550	
		j. Pair, overprints *tête-bêche*		
		(*b*) "OFFICIAL" 15 *to* 16 *mm long*		
O2	8	½d. green	22·00	22·00
		a. Opt double	£500	

There were four (or possibly five) settings of this overprint, all but one being of the longer type. There are numerous minor varieties, due to broken type, etc. (*e.g.* a broken "E" used for "F").

Stamps with the 17–17½ mm opt were reissued in 1894 during a temporary shortage of No. O3.

1890–1. *Optd with Type* O **2** *by D.L.R. Wmk Crown CA. P* 14.

No.	Type	Description	Unused	Used
O3	8	½d. green (1891)	5·50	40
O4	11	1d. rose (1.4.90)	4·00	65
O5		2d. grey (1.4.90)	6·50	1·00
O3/5		*Set of* 3	14·50	1·90
O3/5 Optd "Specimen"		*Set of* 3	£100	

Nos. O4/5 were not issued without overprint.

Jordan *see* Transjordan

Kenya

INDEPENDENT

(Currency. 100 cents = 1 East Africa, later Kenya Shilling)

1 Cattle Ranching

2 Wood-carving

3 National Assembly

(Des V. Whiteley. Photo Harrison)

1963 (12 Dec). *Independence. T* **1/3** *and similar designs. P* 14×15 (*small designs*) *or* 14½ (*others*).

1 5 c. brown, deep blue, green and bistre .. 10 55
2 10 c. brown 10 10
3 15 c. magenta 85 10
4 20 c. black and yellow-green 15 10
5 30 c. black and yellow 15 10
6 40 c. brown and light blue 15 30
a. Printed on the gummed side .. .. 75·00
7 50 c. crimson, black and green 15 10
8 65 c. deep turquise-green and yellow .. 55 65
9 1 s. multicoloured 20 10
10 1 s. 30, brown, black and yellow-green .. 4·25 20
11 2 s. multicoloured .. .. 1·25 40
12 5 s. brown, ultramarine and yellow-green 1·25 40
13 10 s. brown and deep blue .. .. .. 8·50 2·50
14 20 s. black and rose .. .. .. 5·50 7·50
1/14 .. .. *Set of* 14 21·00 11·50

Designs: As *T* **1/2**—15 c. Heavy industry; 20 c. Timber industry; 30 c. Jomo Kenyatta and Mt Kenya; 40 c. Fishing industry; 50 c. Kenya flag; 65 c. Pyrethrum industry. *As T* **3**—1 s. 30, Tourism (Treetops Hotel); 2 s. Coffee industry; 5 s. Tea industry; 10 s. Mombasa Port; 20 s. Royal College, Nairobi.

The 10 c. was produced in coils of 1000 in addition to normal sheets.

REPUBLIC

4 Cockerel

(Des M. Goaman. Photo J. Enschedé)

1964 (12 Dec). *Inauguration of Republic T* **4** *and similar vert designs. Multicoloured. P* 13 × 12½.

15 15 c. Type **4** 20 15
16 30 c. President Kenyatta 25 10
17 50 c. Lion 35 10
18 1 s. 30, Hartlaub's Turaco .. .. .. 3·75 50
19 2 s. 50, Nandi flame .. .. 75 3·75
15/19 .. .. *Set of* 5 4·75 4·00

5 Thomson's Gazelle

6 Sable Antelope

7 Greater Kudu

(Des Rena Fennessy. Photo Harrison)

1966 (12 Dec)–**71**. *Various designs as T* **5/7**. *Chalk-surfaced paper. P* 14 × 14½ (*5 c. to* 70 *c.*) *or* 14½ (*others*).

20 5 c. orange, black and sepia 20 20
21 10 c. black and apple-green 10 10
a. Glazed, ordinary paper (13.7.71) .. 80 3·00
22 15 c. black and orange 10 10
a. Glazed, ordinary paper (13.7.71) .. 80 1·00
23 20 c. ochre, black and blue 10 15
a. Glazed, ordinary paper (22.1.71) .. 1·00 1·50
24 30 c. Prussian blue, blue and black 20 10
25 40 c. black and yellow-brown 60 30
a. Glazed, ordinary paper (19.2.71) .. 1·25 2·00
26 50 c. black and red-orange 60 10
a. Glazed, ordinary paper (19.2.71) .. 14·00 4·75
27 65 c. black and light green .. .. .. 1·25 2·00
28 70 c. black and claret (15.9.69) .. .. 6·00 1·25
a. Glazed, ordinary paper (19.2.71) .. 19·00 12·00
29 1 s. olive-brown, black and slate-blue .. 30 10
a. Glazed, ordinary paper (22.1.71) .. 1·25 85
30 1 s. 30, indigo, light olive-green and black .. 4·00 20
31 1 s. 50, black, orange-brown and dull sage-green (15.9.69) .. .. .. 4·25 2·00
a. Glazed, ordinary paper (22.1.71) .. 3·50 6·00
32 2 s. 50, yellow, black and olive-brown .. 3·25 1·25
a. Glazed, ordinary paper (22.1.71) .. 3·50 6·50
33 5 s. yellow, black and emerald .. .. 1·00 70
a. Glazed, ordinary paper (22.1.71) .. 3·50 12·00
34 10 s. yellow-ochre, black and red-brown .. 2·50 3·00
35 20 s. yellow-ochre, yellow-orange, blk & gold 8·00 13·00
20/35 .. .. *Set of* 16 28·00 22·00
21a/33a .. .. *Set of* 10 42·00 45·00

Designs: *As T* **5/6**—15 c. Aardvark ("Ant Bear"); 20 c. Lesser Bushbaby; 30 c. Warthog; 40 c. Common Zebra; 50 c. African Buffalo; 65 c. Black Rhinoceros; 70 c. Ostrich. *As T* **7**—1 s. 30, African Elephant; 1 s. 50, Bat-eared Fox; 2 s. 50, Cheetah; 5 s. Savanna Monkey ("Vervet Monkey"); 10 s. Giant Ground Pangolin; 20 s. Lion.

On chalk-surfaced paper, all values except 30 c., 50 c. and 2 s. 50 exist with PVA gum as well as gum arabic but the 70 c. and 1 s. 50 exist with PVA gum only. The stamps on glazed, ordinary paper exist with PVA gum only.

Nos. 21 and 26 exist in coils constructed from normal sheets.

8 Perna Tellin (*Tellina perna*)

9 Ramose Murex (*Murex ramosus*)

2/-

(10)

50 c. A. Inscr "*Janthina globosa*".
B. Inscr "*Janthina janthina*".

70 c. C. Inscr "*Nautilus pompileus*".
D. Inscr "*Nautilus pompilius*".

(Des Rena Fennessy. Photo Harrison)

1971 (15 Dec)–**74**. *T* **8/9** *and similar vert designs showing sea-shells. Multicoloured.* (*a*) *Size as T* **8**. *P* 14½ × 14.

36 5 c. Type **8** 10 30
37 10 c. Episcopal Mitre (*Mitra mitra*) (yellow-green background) 15 10
a. Olive-green background (21.1.74) .. 85 10
38 15 c. Purplish Clanculus (*Clanculus puniceus*) 15 20
39 20 c. Humpback Cowrie (*Cypraea mauritania*) 15 20
40 30 c. Variable Abalone (*Haliotis varia*) .. 20 10
41 40 c. Flame Top Shell (*Trochus flammulatus*) 20 10
42 50 c. Common Purple Janthina (*Janthina janthina*) (A) 30 20
43 50 c. Common Purple Janthina (*Janthina janthina*) (B) (21.1.74) .. .. 9·50 2·25
44 60 c. Bull-mouth Helmet (*Cypraecassis rufa*) 30 85
45 70 c. Chambered, Pearly Nautilus (*Nautilus pompilius*) (C) .. .. .. 45 1·50
46 70 c. Chambered, Pearly Nautilus (*Nautilus pompilius*) (D) (21.1.74) .. .. 9·00 4·50

(*b*) *Size as T* **9**. *P* 14

47 1 s. Type **9** (yellow-buff background) .. 30 10
a. Buff background (21.1.74) 20 10
48 1 s. 50, Trumpet Triton (*Charonia tritonis*) 1·25 10
49 2 s. 50, Trapezium Horse Conch (*Fasciolaria trapezium*) .. .. 1·25 10
50 5 s. Great Green Turban (*Turbo marmoratus*) (pale olive-yellow background) .. 1·25 10
a. Pale olive-bistre background (13.6.73) 1·00 10
51 10 s. Textile or Cloth of Gold Cone (*Conus textile*) .. .. 4·25 15
52 20 s. Scorpion Conch (*Lambis scorpius*) (grey background) .. .. 6·00 75
a. Bluish slate background (12.9.73) .. 3·75 25
36/52a .. .. *Set of* 17 29·00 9·50

1975 (17 Nov). *Nos.* 48/9 *and* 52 *surch as T* **10**.

53 2 s. on 1 s. 50, Trumpet Triton (*Charonia tritonis*) .. .. 6·00 4·50
54 3 s. on 2 s. 50, Trapezium Horse Conch (*Fasciolaria trapezium*) .. .. .. 9·50 18·00
55 40 s. on 20 s. Scorpion Conch (*Lambis scorpius*) .. .. 6·00 13·00
53/5 .. .. *Set of* 3 19·00 32·00

The surcharge on No. 55 does not have a dot beneath the stroke following the face value.

For commemorative stamps, issued between 1964 and 1976, inscribed "UGANDA KENYA TANGANYIKA AND ZANZIBAR" (or "TANZANIA UGANDA KENYA") see under KENYA, UGANDA AND TANGANYIKA.

11 Microwave Tower 12 Akii Bua, Ugandan Hurdler

(Des H. Nickelsen. Litho Format)

1976 (15 Apr). *Telecommunications Development. T* **11** *and similar multicoloured designs. P* 14.

56 50 c. Type **11** 10 10
57 1 s. Cordless switchboard (*horiz*) 10 10
58 2 s. Telephones 20 30
59 3 s. Message Switching Centre (*horiz*) .. 25 45
56/9 .. .. *Set of* 4 55 75
MS60 120×120 mm. Nos. 56/9. Imperf .. 1·40 2·50

Nos. 56/7 and 59 exist imperforate from stock dispersed by the liquidator of Format International Security Printers Ltd.

(Des Beryl Moore. Litho Format)

1976 (7 July*). *Olympic Games, Montreal. T* **12** *and similar horiz designs. Multicoloured. P* 14½.

61 50 c. Type **12** 10 10
62 1 s. Filbert Bayi, Tanzanian runner 15 10
63 2 s. Steve Muchoki, Kenyan boxer 45 35
64 3 s. Olympic flame and East African flags .. 60 50
61/4 .. .. *Set of* 4 1·10 85
MS65 129 × 154 mm. Nos. 61/4. P 13 .. .. 6·00 7·50

*This is the local date of issue; the Crown Agents released the stamps two days earlier.

Nos. 61 and 63 exist imperforate from stock dispersed by the liquidator of Format Internationl Security Printers Ltd.

13 Diesel Train, Tanzania–Zambia Railway

14 Nile Perch

(Des H. Moghul. Litho Format)

1976 (4 Oct). *Railway Transport. T* **13** *and similar horiz designs. Multicoloured. P* 14½.

66 50 c. Type **13** 35 15
67 1 s. Nile Bridge, Uganda 60 15
68 2 s. Nakuru Station, Kenya .. .. .. 2·25 1·25
69 3 s. Class "A" steam locomotive, 1896 .. 2·50 1·75
66/9 .. .. *Set of* 4 5·00 3·00
MS70 154×103 mm. Nos. 66/9. P 13 .. .. 8·00 8·00

Nos. 66/70 exist imperforate from stock dispersed by the liquidator of Format International Security Printers Ltd.

(Des Adrienne Kennaway. Litho Format)

1977 (10 Jan). *Game Fish of East Africa. T* **14** *and similar vert designs. Multicoloured. P* 14*.

71 50 c. Type **14** 25 10
72 1 s. Nile Mouthbrooder ("Tilapia") 35 10
73 3 s. Sailfish .. .. 1·50 90
74 5 s. Black Marlin .. .. 2·00 1·25
71/4 .. .. *Set of* 4 3·75 2·00
MS75 153×129 mm. Nos. 71/4 .. .. .. 10·00 4·00

*On No. **MS**75 the right-hand side of the 5 s. value is perforated 13½.

15 Maasai Manyatta (village), Kenya

(Des Rena Fennessy. Litho Questa)

1977 (15 Jan). *Second World Black and African Festival of Arts and Culture, Nigeria. T* **15** *and similar horiz designs. Multicoloured. P* 13½.

76 50 c. Type **15** 15 10
77 1 s. "Heartbeat of Africa" (Ugandan dancers) 20 10
78 2 s. Makonde sculpture, Tanzania .. .. 1·00 1·50
79 3 s. "Early Man and Technology" (skinning hippopotamus) .. .. 1·50 2·25
76/9 .. .. *Set of* 4 2·50 3·50
MS80 132 × 109 mm. Nos. 76/9 .. .. .. 5·50 6·00

16 Rally-car and Villagers

(Litho Questa)

1977 (5 Apr). *25th Anniv of Safari Rally. T* **16** *and similar horiz designs. Multicoloured. P* 14.

81	50 c. Type **16**	20	10
82	1 s. President Kenyatta starting rally	30	10
83	2 s. Car fording river	80	1·00
84	5 s. Car and elephants	1·50	1·75
81/4	*Set of* 4	2·50	2·50
MS85	126 × 93 mm. Nos. 81/4	4·50	6·50

17 Canon Kivebulaya

(Des Beryl Moore. Litho Questa)

1977 (30 June). *Centenary of Ugandan Church. T* **17** *and similar horiz designs. Multicoloured. P* 14 × 13½.

86	50 c. Type **17**	10	10
87	1 s. Modern Namirembe Cathedral	10	10
88	2 s. The first Cathedral	30	55
89	5 s. Early congregation, Kigezi	50	1·00
86/9	*Set of* 4	85	1·50
MS90	126 × 94 mm. Nos. 86/9	1·40	2·50

18 Sagana Royal Lodge, Nyeri, 1952

(Des G. Vasarhelyi (50s.), J. Cooter (others). Litho Questa)

1977 (20 July). *Silver Jubilee. T* **18** *and similar multicoloured designs. P* 13½.

91	2 s. Type **18**	15	15
92	5 s. Treetops Hotel (*vert*)	20	35
93	10 s. Queen Elizabeth and President Kenyatta	30	60
94	15 s. Royal visit, 1972	45	1·00
91/4	*Set of* 4	1·00	1·90
MS95	Two sheets: (a) 140 × 60 mm, No. 94; (b) 152 × 127 mm, 50 s. Queen and Prince Philip in Treetops Hotel *Set of* 2	2·00	1·40

19 Pancake Tortoise

(Des Rena Fennessy. Litho Questa)

1977 (26 Sept). *Endangered Species. T* **19** *and similar horiz designs. Multicoloured. P* 14.

96	50 c. Type **19**	30	10
97	1 s. Nile Crocodile	40	10
98	2 s. Hunter's Hartebeest	1·60	75
99	3 s. Red Colobus	1·75	1·00
100	5 s. Dugong	2·00	1·50
96/100	*Set of* 5	5·50	3·00
MS101	127 × 101 mm. Nos. 97/100	7·00	8·50

20 Kenya–Ethiopia Border Point

(Litho Questa)

1977 (10 Nov). *Nairobi–Addis Ababa Highway. T* **20** *and similar horiz designs. Multicoloured. P* 14.

102	50 c. Type **20**	15	10
103	1 s. Archer's Post	20	10
104	2 s. Thika Flyover	75	60
105	5 s. Marsabit Game Lodge	1·75	1·50
102/5	*Set of* 4	2·50	2·00
MS106	144 × 91 mm. Nos. 102/5	3·75	5·50

21 Gypsum

22 Amethyst

(Des Rena Fennessy. Photo Harrison)

1977 (10 Dec*). *Minerals. Multicoloured designs.*

(*a*) *Vert as T* **21**. *P* 14½ × 14

107	10 c. Type **21**	1·25	20
108	20 c. Trona	1·25	20
109	30 c. Kyanite	1·40	20
110	40 c. Amazonite	1·40	10
111	50 c. Galena	1·40	10
112	70 c. Silicified wood	3·75	40
113	80 c. Fluorite	3·75	60

(*b*) *Horiz as T* **22**. *P* 14

114	1 s. Type **22**	2·00	10
	a. Gold (face value and inscr) omitted		
115	1 s. 50, Agate	2·00	30
	a. Gold (face vaue and inscr) omitted		
116	2 s. Tourmaline	2·00	20
	a. Gold (face value and inscr) omitted		
117	3 s. Aquamarine	2·25	55
118	5 s. Rhodolite Garnet	2·25	1·40
119	10 s. Sapphire	2·25	2·50
120	20 s. Ruby	6·00	3·50
121	40 s. Green Grossular Garnet	18·00	18·00
107/21	*Set of* 15	45·00	25·00

*This is the local issue date. The stamps were released in London on 9 December.

23 Joe Kadenge (Kenya) and Forwards

(Des H. Moghul. Litho Questa)

1978 (10 Apr). *World Cup Football Championship, Argentina. T* **23** *and similar horiz designs showing footballers. Multicoloured. P* 14 × 13½.

122	50 c. Type **23**	10	10
123	1 s. Mohamed Chuma (Tanzania) and Cup presentation	10	10
124	2 s. Omari Kidevu (Zanzibar) and goalmouth scene	30	70
125	3 s. Polly Ouma (Uganda) and three forwards	40	95
122/5	*Set of* 4	70	1·60
MS126	136 × 81 mm. Nos. 122/5	3·50	3·00

24 Boxing

(Des H. Moghul. Photo Heraclio Fournier)

1978 (17 July). *Commonwealth Games, Edmonton. T* **24** *and similar horiz designs. Multicoloured. P* 13 × 14.

127	50 c. Type **24**	15	10
128	1 s. Welcoming Olympic Games Team, 1968	20	10
129	3 s. Javelin throwing	60	90
130	5 s. President Kenyatta admiring boxer's trophy	75	1·40
127/30	*Set of* 4	1·50	2·25

25 "Overloading is Dangerous"

(Litho Walsall)

1978 (18 Sept). *Road Safety. T* **25** *and similar horiz designs. Multicoloured. P* 13½.

131	50 c. Type **25**	50	10
132	1 s. "Speed does not pay"	70	20
133	1 s. 50, "Ignoring Traffic Signs may cause death"	85	55
134	2 s. "Slow down at School Crossing"	1·25	1·00
135	3 s. "Never cross a continuous line"	1·40	2·25
136	5 s. "Approach Railway Level Crossing with extreme caution"	2·00	3·25
131/6	*Set of* 6	6·00	6·50

26 President Kenyatta at Mass Rally, 1963

27 Freedom Fighters, Namibia

(Des Beryl Moore. Litho J.W.)

1978 (16 Oct). *Kenyatta Day. T* **26** *and similar horiz designs. Multicoloured. P* 14.

137	50 c. "Harambee Water Project"	20	10
138	1 s. Handing over of Independence Instruments, 1963	30	10
139	2 s. Type **26**	65	45
140	3 s. "Harambee, 15 Great Years"	90	1·10
141	5 s. "Struggle for Independence, 1952"	1·10	1·75
137/41	*Set of* 5	2·75	3·00

(Des L. Curtis. Litho Questa)

1978 (11 Dec*). *International Anti-Apartheid Year. T* **27** *and similar horiz designs. P* 14 × 14½.

142	50 c. multicoloured	20	10
143	1 s. black and cobalt	25	10
144	2 s. multicoloured	60	30
145	3 s. multicoloured	80	65
146	5 s. multicoloured	90	1·00
142/6	*Set of* 5	2·50	1·90

Designs:—1 s. International seminar on apartheid, racial discrimination and colonialism in South Africa; 2 s. Steve Biko's tombstone; 3 s. Nelson Mandela; 5 s. Bishop Lamont.

*This is the local date of issue; the Crown Agents released the stamps the previous day.

28 Children Playing

(Des Beryl Moore. Litho Walsall)

1979 (5 Feb). *International Year of the Child. T* **28** *and similar horiz designs. Multicoloured. P* 13½ × 14.

147	50 c. Type **28**	20	10
148	2 s. Child fishing	60	60
149	3 s. Children singing and dancing	80	80
150	5 s. Children working with camels	1·00	1·25
147/50	*Set of* 4	2·40	2·50

29 "The Lion and the Jewel"

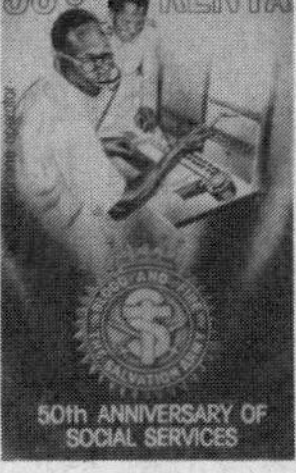

30 Blind Telephone Operator

(Des Beryl Moore. Litho Enschedé)

1979 (6 Apr). *Kenya National Theatre. T* **29** *and similar horiz designs. Multicoloured. P* 13 × 13½.

151	50 c. Type **29**	15	10
152	1 s. Scene from "Utisi"	20	10
153	2 s. "Entertainment past and present" (programmes from past productions)	40	30
154	3 s. Kenya National Theatre	60	45
155	5 s. Nairobi City Players production of "Genesis"	1·00	75
151/5	*Set of* 5	2·10	1·50

(Litho Harrison)

1979 (29 June*). *50th Anniv of Salvation Army Social Services. T* **30** *and similar multicoloured designs. P* 13½ × 13 (50 c., 1s.) *or* 13 × 13½ (*others*).

156	50 c. Type **30**	45	10
157	1 s. Care for the Aged	45	10
158	3 s. Village polytechnic (*horiz*)	1·25	1·40
159	5 s. Vocational training (*horiz*)	1·50	2·25
156/9	*Set of* 4	3·25	3·25

*This is the local date of issue; the Crown Agents released the stamps on 4 June.

MINIMUM PRICE

The minimum price quote is 10p which represents a handling charge rather than a basis for valuing common stamps. For further notes about prices see introductory pages.

31 "Father of the Nation" (Kenyatta's funeral procession)

32 British East Africa Company 1890 1 a. Stamp

(Des H. Moghul. Litho Questa)

1979 (21 Aug*). *1st Death Anniv of President Kenyatta. T* **31** *and similar vert designs. Multicoloured. P* 13½ × 14.

160 50 c. Type **31** 10 10
161 1 s. "First President of Kenya" (Kenyatta receiving independence) 15 10
162 3 s. "Kenyatta the politician" (speaking at rally) 35 50
163 5 s. "A true son of Kenya" (Kenyatta as a boy carpenter) 60 95
160/3 .. .. *Set of* 4 1·00 1·50

*This is the local date of issue; the Crown Agents did not release the stamps until 29 August.

(Des J.W. Litho Harrison)

1979 (27 Nov). *Death Centenary of Sir Rowland Hill. T* **32** *and similar vert designs showing stamps. P* 14 × 14½.

164 50 c. multicoloured 15 10
165 1 s. multicoloured 15 10
166 2 s. black, magenta and yellow-ochre 30 40
167 5 s. multicoloured .. .. 60 1·00
164/7 .. .. *Set of* 4 1·10 1·40

Designs:—1 s. Kenya, Uganda and Tanganyika 1935 1 s.; 2 s. Penny Black; 5 s. 1964 Inauguration of Republic 2 s. 50, commemorative.

33 Roads, Globe and Conference Emblem

(Des H. Moghul. Litho Questa)

1980 (10 Jan). *I.R.F. (International Road Federation) African Highway Conference, Nairobi. T* **33** *and similar horiz designs. Multicoloured. P* 14 × 13½.

168 50 c. Type **33** 15 10
169 1 s. New weighbridge, Athi River 20 10
170 3 s. New Nyali Bridge, Mombasa 55 85
171 5 s. Highway to Jomo Kenyatta International Airport .. .. 60 2·00
168/71 .. .. *Set of* 4 1·40 2·75

34 Mobile Unit in action, Masailand

35 Statue of Sir Rowland Hill

(Des Beryl Moore. Litho Questa)

1980 (20 Mar). *Flying Doctor Service. T* **34** *and similar multicoloured designs. P* 14½.

172 50 c. Type **34** 15 10
173 1 s. Donkey transport to Turkana airstrip (*vert*) 20 10
174 3 s. Surgical team in action at outstation (*vert*) 65 1·00
175 5 s. Emergency airlift from North Eastern Province .. .. 90 1·60
172/5 .. .. *Set of* 4 1·60 2·50
MS176 146 × 133 mm. Nos. 172/5 .. .. .. 1·60 2·50

(Des J.W. Litho Questa)

1980 (6 May). *"London 1980" International Stamp Exhibition. P* 14.

177 **35** 25 s. multicoloured .. .. .. 1·00 2·50
MS178 114×101 mm. No. 177 .. .. .. 1·00 2·75

36 Pope John Paul II

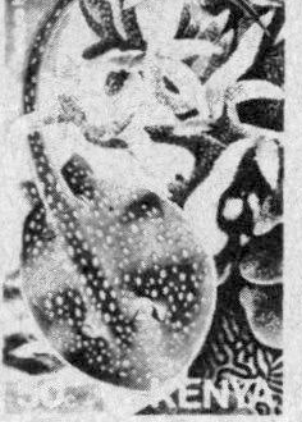

37 Blue-spotted Stingray

(Des Sister Frances Randal. Litho Italian Govt Ptg Works, Rome)

1980 (8 May). *Papal Visit. T* **36** *and similar multicoloured designs. P* 13.

179 50 c. Type **36** 40 10
180 1 s. Pope John Paul II, cathedral and coat of arms (*vert*) 50 10
181 5 s. Pope John Paul II, Papal and Kenyan flags on dove symbol (*vert*) .. .. 1·10 70
182 10 s. President Moi, Pope John Paul II and map of Africa .. .. 1·60 1·40
179/82 .. .. *Set of* 4 3·25 2·00

(Des Adrienne Kennaway. Litho Harrison)

1980 (27 June). *Marine Life. T* **37** *and similar vert designs. Multicoloured. P* 14.

183 50 c. Type **37** 30 10
184 2 s. Allard's Anemonefish .. .. .. 1·00 80
185 3 s. Four-coloured Nudibranch (*Chromodoris quadricolor*) .. .. .. 1·25 1·75
186 5 s. *Eretmochelys imbricata* .. .. .. 1·75 2·75
183/6 .. .. *Set of* 4 3·75 4·75

38 National Archives

(Des A. Odhuno; adapted L. Curtis. Litho Questa)

1980 (9 Oct). *Historic Buildings. T* **38** *and similar horiz designs. Multicoloured. P* 14.

187 50 c. Type **38** 10 10
188 1 s. Provincial Commissioner's Office, Nairobi 15 10
189 1 s. 50, Nairobi House 20 20
190 2 s. Norfolk Hotel 25 50
191 3 s. McMillan Library 35 75
192 5 s. Kipande House .. .. 55 1·25
187/92 .. .. *Set of* 6 1·40 2·50

39 "Disabled Enjoys Affection"

(Des H. Moghul. Litho Enschedé)

1981 (10 Feb). *International Year for Disabled Persons. T* **39** *and similar horiz designs. Multicoloured. P* 14 × 13.

193 50 c. Type **39** 15 10
194 1 s. President Moi presenting Kenyan flag to Disabled Olympic Games team captain 20 10
195 3 s. Blind people climbing Mount Kenya, 1975 .. .. 65 65
196 5 s. Disabled artist at work .. .. .. 95 1·00
193/6 .. .. *Set of* 4 1·75 1·60

40 Longonot Complex

(Des H. Moghul. Litho Harrison)

1981 (15 Apr). *Satellite Communications. T* **40** *and similar horiz designs. Multicoloured. P* 14 × 14½.

197 50 c. Type **40** 15 10
198 2 s. "Intelsat V" 50 35
199 3 s. "Longonot I" 60 55
200 5 s. "Longonot II" 85 85
197/200 .. .. *Set of* 4 1·90 1·60

41 Kenyatta Conference Centre

42 St. Paul's Cathedral

(Des L. Curtis. Litho Questa (**MS**206) or J.W. (others))

1981 (17 June*). *O.A.U. (Organisation of African Unity) Summit Conference, Nairobi. T* **41** *and similar horiz designs in black, bistre-yellow and new blue* (1s.) *or multicoloured (others). P* 13½.

201 50 c. Type **41** 15 10
202 1 s. "Panaftel" earth stations 20 10
203 3 s. Parliament Building 50 40
204 5 s. Jomo Kenyatta International Airport .. 90 65
205 10 s. O.A.U. flag .. .. 1·00 1·00
201/5 .. .. *Set of* 5 2·50 2·00
MS206 110 × 110 mm. No. 205. P 14½ × 14 .. 1·10 1·50

*This is the local date of issue; the Crown Agents did not release the stamps until 24 June.

(Des A. Theobald. Litho Questa)

1981 (29 July). *Royal Wedding. T* **42** *and similar vert designs. Multicoloured. P* 14.

207 50 c. Prince Charles and President Daniel Arap Moi 10 10
208 3 s. Type **42** 15 20
209 5 s. Royal Yacht *Britannia* 25 30
210 10 s. Prince Charles on safari in Kenya .. 40 55
207/10 .. .. *Set of* 4 70 1·00
MS211 85×102 mm. 25 s. Prince Charles and Lady Diana Spencer 75 80

Nos. 207/10 also exist perforated 12 (*price for set of* 4 £1.25 *mint or used*) from additional sheetlets of five stamps and one label.

Insufficient supplies of No. **MS**211 were received by 29 July for a full distribution, but subsequently the miniature sheet was freely available.

43 Giraffe

44 "Technical Development"

(Des Rena Fennessy. Litho Questa)

1981 (31 Aug). *Rare Animals. T* **43** *and similar vert designs. Multicoloured. P* 14½.

212 50 c. Type **43** 15 10
213 2 s. Bongo 35 25
214 5 s. Roan Antelope .. .. 70 1·00
215 10 s. Agile Mangabey .. .. 1·25 2·50
212/15 .. .. *Set of* 4 2·25 3·50

(Des H. Moghul, adapted L. Curtis. Litho Questa)

1981 (16 Oct). *World Food Day. T* **44** *and similar vert designs. Multicoloured. P* 14.

216 50 c. Type **44** 10 10
217 1 s. "Mwea rice projects" 15 10
218 2 s. "Irrigation schemes" 30 50
219 5 s. "Breeding livestock" .. .. 60 1·40
216/19 .. .. *Set of* 4 1·00 1·90

45 Kamba

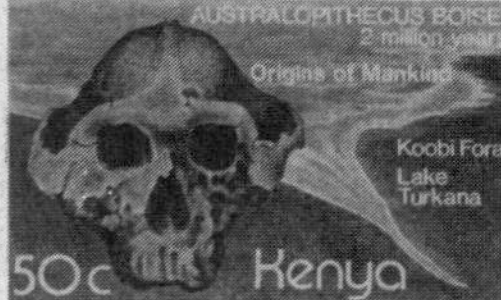

46 *Australopithecus boisei*

(Des Adrienne Kennaway. Litho Harrison)

1981 (18 Dec). *Ceremonial Costumes (1st series). T* **45** *and similar vert designs. Multicoloured. P* 14½ × 13½.

220 50 c. Type **45** 40 10
221 1 s. Turkana 45 10
222 2 s. Giriama .. .. 1·25 75
223 3 s. Masai .. .. 1·60 1·60
224 5 s. Luo .. .. 1·75 2·25
220/4 .. .. *Set of* 5 5·00 4·25

See also Nos. 329/33, 413/17 and 515/19.

(Des Adrienne Kennaway. Litho Format)

1982 (19 Jan). *"Origins of Mankind". Skulls. T* **46** *and similar horiz designs. Multicoloured. P* 13½ × 14.

225	50 c. Type **46**	95	20
226	2 s. *Homo erectus*	2·25	1·50
227	3 s. *Homo habilis*	2·75	3·50
228	5 s. *Proconsul africanus*	3·25	4·50
225/8	*Set of* 4	8·25	8·75

47 Tree-planting

(Des L. Curtis. Litho Harrison)

1982 (9 June). *75th Anniv of Boy Scout Movement (Nos. 229, 231, 233 and 235) and 60th Anniv of Girl Guide Movement (Nos. 230, 232, 234 and 236). T* **47** *and similar horiz designs. Multicoloured. P* 14½.

229	70 c. Type **47**	50	65
	a. Horiz pair. Nos. 229/30	1·00	1·25
230	70 c. Paying homage	50	65
231	3 s. 50, "Be Prepared"	1·25	1·75
	a. Horiz pair. Nos. 231/2	2·50	3·50
232	3 s. 50, "International Friendship"	1·25	1·75
233	5 s. Helping disabled	1·75	2·50
	a. Horiz pair. Nos. 233/4	3·50	5·00
234	5 s. Community service	1·75	2·50
235	6 s. 50, Paxtu Cottage (Lord Baden-Powell's home)	2·00	2·75
	a. Horiz pair. Nos. 235/6	4·00	5·50
236	6 s. 50, Lady Baden-Powell	2·00	2·75
229/36	*Set of* 8	10·00	13·00
MS237	112 × 112 mm. Nos. 229, 231, 233 and 235	3·75	3·00

The two designs of each value were printed together, *se-tenant*, in horizontal pairs throughout the sheet.

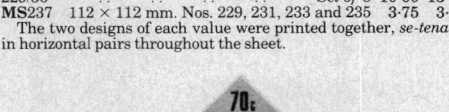

48 Footballer displaying Shooting Skill

(Des local artist. Litho Harrison)

1982 (5 July). *World Cup Football Championships, Spain. T* **48** *and similar triangular designs showing footballers silhouetted against world map. Multicoloured. P* 12½.

238	70 c. Type **48**	1·25	65
239	3 s. 50, Heading	2·50	2·50
240	5 s. Goalkeeping	3·50	4·00
241	10 s. Dribbling	5·00	7·00
238/41	*Set of* 4	11·00	12·50
MS242	101×76 mm. 20 s. Tackling. P 13×14	4·75	4·00

49 Cattle Judging

50 Micro-wave Radio System

(51)

(Des H. Moghul. Litho Harrison)

1982 (28 Sept). *80th Anniv of Agricultural Society of Kenya. T* **49** *and similar vert designs. Multicoloured. P* 14½.

243	70 c. Type **49**	70	10
244	2 s. 50, Farm machinery	1·75	1·75
245	3 s. 50, Musical ride	2·00	2·75
246	6 s. 50, Agricultural Society emblem	2·50	4·25
243/6	*Set of* 4	6·25	8·00

(Des H. Moghul. Photo Courvoisier)

1982 (21 Oct). *I.T.U. Plenipotentiary Conference, Nairobi. T* **50** *and similar vert designs. Multicoloured. P* 11½.

247	70 c. Type **50**	60	10
248	3 s. 50, Sea-to-shore service link	2·00	2·25
249	5 s. Rural telecommunications system	2·50	3·50
250	6 s. 50, I.T.U. emblem	3·00	4·25
247/50	*Set of* 4	7·25	9·00

1982 (22 Nov). *No. 113 surch with T* **51**, *in white on a black panel.*

251	70 c. on 80 c. Fluorite	1·00	1·00

52 Container Cranes

(Des R. Vigurs. Litho Questa)

1983 (20 Jan). *5th Anniv of Kenya Ports Authority. T* **52** *and similar horiz designs. P* 14.

252	70 c. Type **52**	85	10
253	2 s. Port by night	1·75	1·90
254	3 s. 50, Container cranes (*different*)	2·50	3·50
255	5 s. Map of Mombasa Port	3·25	4·50
252/5	*Set of* 4	7·50	9·00
MS256	125 × 85 mm. Nos. 252/5	7·50	9·00

53 Shada Zambarau

54 Waridi Kikuba

(Des Rena Fennessy. Photo Harrison)

1983 (15 Feb)–**85**. *Flowers. Multicoloured.*

(*a*) *Vert designs as T* **53**. *P* 14½×14

257	10 c. Type **53**	40	40
258	20 c. Kilua Kingulima	55	40
259	30 c. Mwalika Mwiya	55	40
260	40 c. Ziyungi Buluu	55	40
261	50 c. Kilua Habashia	55	30
262	70 c. Chanuo Kato	60	20
262*a*	80 c. As 40 c. (7.8.85)	4·00	1·50
262*b*	1 s. Waridi Kikuba (5.8.85*)	4·00	1·50

(*b*) *Vert designs as T* **54**. *P* 14

263	1 s. Type **54**	65	20
264	1 s. 50, Mshomoro Mtambazi	1·75	60
265	2 s. Papatuo Boti	1·75	60
266	2 s. 50, Tumba Mboni	2·25	60
266*a*	3 s. Mkuku Mrembo (12.8.85)	5·50	5·00
267	3 s. 50, Mtongo Mbeja	2·00	1·50
	a. Gold (inscr and face value) omitted		
267*b*	4 s. Mnukia Muuma (7.8.85)	4·75	6·00
268	5 s. Nyungu Chepuo	2·00	1·50
268*a*	7 s. Mlua Miba (7.8.85)	6·50	7·50
269	10 s. Muafunili	2·00	2·50
270	20 s. Mbake Nyanza	2·50	3·75
271	40 s. Njuga Pagwa	4·25	8·00
257/71	*Set of* 20	40·00	38·00

*Earliest known postmark date.

55 Coffee Plucking

56 Examining Parcels

(Des C. Fernandes. Litho Harrison)

1983 (14 Mar). *Commonwealth Day. T* **55** *and similar multicoloured designs. P* 14×14½ (70 c., 2 s.) *or* 14½×14 (*others*).

272	70 c. Type **55**	10	10
273	2 s. President Daniel Arap Moi	15	20
274	5 s. Satellite view of Earth (*horiz*)	45	45
275	10 s. Masai dance (*horiz*)	90	1·00
272/5	*Set of* 4	1·40	1·50

(Des H. Moghul. Litho Harrison)

1983 (11 May). *30th Anniv of Customs Co-operation Council. T* **56** *and similar vert designs. Multicoloured. P* 14.

276	70 c. Type **56**	25	10
277	2 s. 50, Customs Headquarters, Mombasa	65	30
278	3 s. 50, Customs Council Headquarters, Brussels	75	40
279	10 s. Customs patrol boat	2·40	2·50
276/9	*Set of* 4	3·50	3·00

57 Communications via Satellite

58 Ships in Kilindini Harbour

(Litho Harrison)

1983 (4 July). *World Communications Year. T* **57** *and similar multicoloured designs. P* 14×14½ (70 c., 2 s. 50) *or* 14½×14 (*others*).

280	70 c. Type **57**	60	10
281	2 s. 50, "Telephone and Postal Services"	1·50	1·75
282	3 s. 50, Communications by sea and air (*horiz*)	2·00	2·75
283	5 s. Road and rail communications (*horiz*)	2·50	3·75
280/3	*Set of* 4	6·00	7·50

(Litho Harrison)

1983 (22 Sept). *25th Anniv of Intergovernmental Maritime Organization. T* **58** *and similar horiz designs. Multicoloured. P* 14.

284	70 c. Type **58**	95	10
285	2 s. 50, Life-saving devices	2·00	1·75
286	3 s. 50, Mombasa container terminal	2·50	2·75
287	10 s. Marine park	3·50	6·00
284/7	*Set of* 4	8·00	9·50

59 President Moi signing Visitors' Book

(Litho Harrison)

1983 (31 Oct). *29th Commonwealth Parliamentary Conference. T* **59** *and similar multicoloured designs. P* 14.

288	70 c. Type **59**	25	10
289	2 s. 50, Parliament building, Nairobi (*vert*)	90	1·00
290	5 s. State opening of Parliament (*vert*)	1·60	2·50
288/90	*Set of* 3	2·50	3·25
MS291	122 × 141 mm. Nos. 288/90	2·50	4·00

60 Kenyan and British Flags

(Des A. Theobald. Litho Harrison)

1983 (10 Nov). *Royal Visit. T* **60** *and similar horiz designs. Multicoloured. P* 14.

292	70 c. Type **60**	50	10
293	3 s. 50, Sagana State Lodge	2·00	1·50
294	5 s. Treetops Hotel	2·25	2·25
295	10 s. Queen Elizabeth II and President Moi	3·50	6·00
292/5	*Set of* 4	7·50	8·75
MS296	126×100 mm. 25 s. Designs as Nos. 292/5, but without face values. Imperf	4·00	5·50

61 President Moi

62 White-backed Night Heron

(Des and litho Harrison)

1983 (9 Dec). *20th Anniv of Independence. T* **61** *and similar horiz designs. Multicoloured. P* 14½.

297	70 c. Type **61**	10	10
298	2 s. President Moi planting tree	20	20
299	3 s. 50, Kenyan flag and emblem	35	35
300	5 s. School milk scheme	50	50
301	10 s. People of Kenya	1·00	1·10
297/301	*Set of* 5	1·90	2·00
MS302	126×93 mm. 25 s. Designs as Nos. 297 and 299/301, but without face values. Imperf	1·75	2·75

(Des Agnes Odero. Litho Harrison)

1984 (6 Feb). *Rare Birds of Kenya. T* **62** *and similar vert designs. Multicoloured. P* 14½ × 13½.

303	70 c. Type **62**	1·50	30
304	2 s. 50, Quail Plover	2·50	2·50
305	3 s. 50, Taita Olive Thrush	3·25	3·50
306	5 s. Mufumbiri Shrike ("Yellow Gonolek")	3·50	3·75
307	10 s. White-winged Apalis	4·75	6·00
303/7	*Set of* 5	14·00	14·50

NEW INFORMATION

The editor is always interested to correspond with people who have new information that will improve or correct the Catalogue.

63 Radar Tower

64 Running

(Des C. Fernandes. Litho Harrison)

1984 (2 Apr). *40th Anniv of International Civil Aviation Organization. T* **63** *and similar multicoloured designs. P* 14.
308 70 c. Type **63** .. 15 10
309 2 s. 50, Kenya School of Aviation (*horiz*) 45 35
310 3 s. 50, Boeing 707 taking off from Moi airport (*horiz*) .. 65 55
311 5 s. Air traffic control centre .. 95 75
308/11 .. *Set of* 4 2·00 1·50

(Des and litho Harrison)

1984 (21 May). *Olympic Games, Los Angeles. T* **64** *and similar horiz designs. P* 14½.
312 70 c. black, bright yellow-green and bronze-green .. 30 10
313 2 s. 50, black, bright magenta and reddish violet .. 60 60
314 5 s. black, pale turquoise-blue and steel blue 1·50 2·25
315 10 s. black, bistre-yellow and brown .. 3·50 5·00
312/15 .. *Set of* 4 5·25 7·00
MS316 130×121 mm. 25 s. Designs as Nos. 312/15 but without face values. Imperf .. 3·25 3·25
Designs:—2 s. 50, Hurdling; 5 s. Boxing; 10 s. Hockey.

65 Conference and Kenya Library Association Logos

66 Doves and Cross

(Des and litho Harrison)

1984 (28 June). *50th Conference of the International Federation of Library Associations. T* **65** *and similar horiz designs. Multicoloured. P* 14½.
317 70 c. Type **65** .. 10 10
318 3 s. 50, Mobile library .. 50 60
319 5 s. Adult library .. 65 1·00
320 10 s. Children's library .. 1·00 2·25
317/20 .. *Set of* 4 2·00 3·50

(Des K. Bisley. Litho Harrison)

1984 (23 Aug). *4th World Conference on Religion and Peace. T* **66** *and similar vert designs, each showing a different central symbol. Multicoloured. P* 14½.
321 70 c. Type **66** .. 30 10
322 2 s. 50, Arabic inscription .. 1·25 1·50
323 3 s. 50, Peace emblem .. 1·60 1·75
324 6 s. 50, Star and Crescent .. 2·00 2·50
321/4 .. *Set of* 4 4·75 5·25

67 Export Year Logo

68 Knight and Nyayo National Stadium

(Litho Harrison)

1984 (1 Oct). *Kenya Export Year. T* **67** *and similar multicoloured designs. P* 14½.
325 70 c. Type **67** .. 30 10
326 3 s. 50, Forklift truck with air cargo (*horiz*) 1·75 2·00
327 5 s. Loading ship's cargo .. 2·50 2·75
328 10 s. Kenyan products (*horiz*) .. 3·75 5·25
325/8 .. *Set of* 4 7·50 9·00

(Litho Harrison)

1984 (5 Nov). *Ceremonial Costumes (2nd series). Vert designs as T* **45**. *Multicoloured. P* 14½ × 13½.
329 70 c. Luhya .. 70 15
330 2 s. Kikuyu .. 1·75 1·75
331 3 s. 50, Pokomo .. 2·25 2·25
332 5 s. Nandi .. 2·50 2·50
333 10 s. Rendile .. 3·50 5·00
329/33 .. *Set of* 5 9·50 10·50

(Litho Harrison)

1984 (21 Dec). *60th Anniv of International Chess Federation. T* **68** *and similar horiz designs showing Staunton chess pieces. Multicoloured. P* 14½.
334 70 c. Type **68** .. 1·50 30
335 2 s. 50, Rook and Fort Jesus .. 2·50 1·75
336 3 s. 50, Bishop and National Monument .. 3·00 2·50
337 5 s. Queen and Parliament Building .. 3·25 3·50
338 10 s. King and Nyayo Fountain .. 5·00 7·00
334/8 .. *Set of* 5 13·50 13·50

69 Cooking with Wood-burning Stove and Charcoal Fire

(Des H. Moghul. Litho J.W.)

1985 (22 Jan). *Energy Conservation. T* **69** *and similar horiz designs. Multicoloured. P* 13½.
339 70 c. Type **69** .. 20 10
340 2 s. Solar energy panel on roof .. 65 65
341 3 s. 50, Production of gas from cow dung .. 85 1·00
342 10 s. Ploughing with oxen .. 2·50 4·00
339/42 .. *Set of* 4 3·75 5·00
MS343 110×85 mm. 20 s. Designs as Nos. 339/42, but without face values .. 2·50 2·50

70 Crippled Girl Guide making Table-mat

(Litho J.W.)

1985 (27 Mar). *75th Anniv of Girl Guide Movement. T* **70** *and similar horiz designs. Multicoloured. P* 13½.
344 1 s. Type **70** .. 75 15
345 3 s. Girl Guides doing community service .. 1·75 1·50
346 5 s. Lady Olave Baden-Powell (founder) .. 2·50 2·75
347 7 s. Girl Guides gardening .. 4·00 5·50
344/7 .. *Set of* 4 8·00 9·00

71 Stylised Figures and Globe

72 Man with Malaria

(Des and litho Harrison)

1985 (8 May). *World Red Cross Day. T* **71** *and similar horiz designs. P* 14½.
348 1 s. black and rosine .. 80 15
349 4 s. multicoloured .. 2·75 2·75
350 5 s. multicoloured .. 3·00 3·25
351 7 s. multicoloured .. 4·00 5·50
348/51 .. *Set of* 4 9·50 10·50
Designs:—4 s. First aid team; 5 s. Hearts containing crosses ("Blood Donation"); 7 s. Cornucopia ("Famine Relief").

(Des H. Moghul. Litho Harrison)

1985 (25 June). *7th International Congress of Protozoology, Nairobi. T* **72** *and similar vert designs. Multicoloured. P* 14½.
352 1 s. Type **72** .. 80 15
353 3 s. Child with Leishmaniasis .. 2·50 2·50
354 5 s. Cow with Trypanosomiasis .. 3·00 3·25
355 7 s. Dog with Babesiosis .. 4·25 6·00
352/5 .. *Set of* 4 9·50 10·50

73 Repairing Water Pipes

74 The Last Supper

(Des J. Tobula and Harrison. Litho Harrison)

1985 (15 July). *United Nations Women's Decade Conference. T* **73** *and similar vert designs. Multicoloured. P* 14½.
356 1 s. Type **73** .. 20 10
357 3 s. Traditional food preparation .. 60 85
358 5 s. Basket-weaving .. 1·00 1·50
359 7 s. Dressmaking .. 1·40 2·25
356/9 .. *Set of* 4 2·75 4·25

(Des Eucharistic Congress Secretariat. Litho J.W.)

1985 (17 Aug*). *43rd International Eucharistic Congress, Nairobi. T* **74** *and similar horiz designs. Multicoloured. P* 13½.
360 1 s. Type **74** .. 50 10
361 3 s. Village family ("The Eucharist and the Christian Family") .. 2·00 1·75
362 5 s. Congress altar, Uhuru Park .. 2·25 2·50
363 7 s. St. Peter Claver's Church, Nairobi .. 2·75 4·00
360/3 .. *Set of* 4 6·75 7·50
MS364 117×80 mm. 25 s. Pope John Paul II .. 4·50 4·50
* This is the local date of issue. The Crown Agents released the stamps on 15 August and this date also appears on first day covers serviced by Kenya Posts and Telecommunications Corporation.

75 Black Rhinoceros

(Des Rena Fennessy. Litho Harrison)

1985 (10 Dec). *Endangered Animals. T* **75** *and similar horiz designs. Multicoloured. P* 14½.
365 1 s. Type **75** .. 1·50 40
366 3 s. Cheetah .. 2·75 2·50
367 5 s. De Brazza's Monkey .. 3·00 3·50
368 10 s. Grevy's Zebra .. 5·00 7·00
365/8 .. *Set of* 4 11·00 12·00
MS369 129×122 mm. 25 s. Endangered species (122×114 *mm*). Imperf .. 6·00 4·50

76 *Borassus aethiopum*

77 Dove and U.N. Logo (from poster)

(Des Rena Fennessy. Litho Questa)

1986 (24 Jan). *Indigenous Trees. T* **76** *and similar horiz designs. Multicoloured. P* 14½.
370 1 s. Type **76** .. 65 15
371 3 s. *Acacia xanthophloea* .. 2·25 2·25
372 5 s. *Ficus natalensis* .. 3·25 3·50
373 7 s. *Spathodea nilotica* .. 4·25 5·50
370/3 .. *Set of* 4 9·25 10·00
MS374 117×96 mm. 25 s. Landscape with trees (109×90 *mm*). Imperf .. 3·25 4·00

(Des Advertising Link. Litho Questa)

1986 (30 Apr*). *International Peace Year. T* **77** *and similar multicoloured designs. P* 14½.
375 1 s. Type **77** .. 30 10
376 3 s. U.N. General Assembly (*horiz*) .. 85 65
377 7 s. Nuclear explosion .. 2·00 2·25
378 10 s. Quotation from Wall of Isaiah, U.N. Building, New York (*horiz*) .. 2·25 2·50
375/8 .. *Set of* 4 4·75 5·00
*This is the local date of issue. The Crown Agents released the stamps on 17 April and this date also appears on first day covers serviced by Kenya Posts and Telecommunications Corporation.

78 Dribbling the Ball

79 Rural Post Office and Telephone

(Des C. Fernandes. Litho Harrison)

1986 (8 May). *World Cup Football Championship, Mexico. T* **78** *and similar multicoloured designs. P* 14½.
379 1 s. Type **78** .. 80 15
380 3 s. Scoring from a penalty .. 2·00 1·10
381 5 s. Tackling .. 2·75 1·75
382 7 s. Cup winners .. 3·50 2·75
383 10 s. Heading the ball .. 4·50 4·00
379/83 .. *Set of* 5 12·00 8·75
MS384 110×86 mm. 30 s. Harambee Stars football team (102×78 *mm*). Imperf .. 3·50 3·75

(Des H. Moghul. Litho Cartor)

1986 (11 June). *"Expo '86" World Fair, Vancouver. T* **79** *and similar horiz designs. Multicoloured. P* 13½×13.
385 1 s. Type **79** .. 50 15
386 3 s. Container depot, Embakasi .. 2·25 1·50
387 5 s. Piper PA-30B Twin Commanche airplane landing at game park airstrip 3·00 2·00
388 7 s. Container ship .. 3·75 3·75
389 10 s. Transporting produce to market .. 4·00 4·50
385/9 .. *Set of* 5 12·00 10·50

On 15 July 1986 Kenya was scheduled to release a set of five stamps, 1, 3, 4, 7 and 10 s., for the Commonwealth Games at Edinburgh. A political decision was taken at the last moment not to issue the stamps, but this instruction did not reach some of the sub-post offices until the morning of 15 July. About two hundred stamps, mainly the 1 s. value, were sold by these sub-post offices before the instruction arrived. Examples of the 1 s. exist used on commercial mail from Kenyatta College sub-post office from 17 July 1986 onwards.

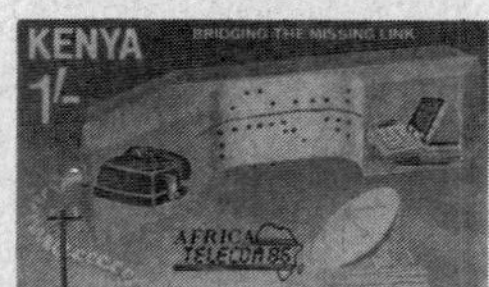

80 Telephone, Computer and Dish Aerial

(Des H. Moghul. Litho Harrison)

1986 (16 Sept). *African Telecommunications. T* **80** *and similar horiz designs. Multicoloured. P* 14½.

390	1 s. Type **80**	35	10
391	3 s. Telephones of 1876, 1936 and 1986	1·00	85
392	5 s. Dish aerial, satellite, telephones and map of Africa	1·25	1·25
393	7 s. Kenyan manufacture of telecommunications equipment	1·75	2·25
390/3	*Set of* 4	4·00	4·00

81 Mashua 82 The Nativity

(Des Mukund Arts. Litho Mardon Printers Ltd, Zimbabwe)

1986 (30 Oct). *Dhows of Kenya. T* **81** *and similar horiz designs. Multicoloured. P* 14½.

394	1 s. Type **81**	65	20
395	3 s. Mtepe	1·75	1·50
396	5 s. Dau La Mwao	2·25	2·25
397	10 s. Jahazi	3·75	4·25
394/7	*Set of* 4	7·50	7·50
MS398	118×80 mm. 25 s. Lamu dhow and map of Indian Ocean	4·00	4·50

(Des Mukund Arts. Photo Courvoisier)

1986 (5 Dec). *Christmas. T* **82** *and similar multicoloured designs. Granite paper. P* 11½.

399	1 s. Type **82**	30	10
400	3 s. Shepherd and sheep	1·00	45
401	5 s. Angel and slogan "LOVE PEACE UNITY" (*horiz*)	1·60	1·10
402	7 s. The Magi riding camels (*horiz*)	1·90	2·25
399/402	*Set of* 4	4·25	3·50

83 Immunization 84 Akamba Woodcarvers

(Des Judith D'Inca. Litho Harrison)

1987 (6 Jan). *40th Anniv of United Nations Children's Fund. T* **83** *and similar vert designs. Multicoloured. P* 14.

403	1 s. Type **83**	40	10
404	3 s. Food and nutrition	85	50
405	4 s. Oral rehydration therapy	1·50	80
406	5 s. Family planning	1·50	1·00
407	10 s. Female literacy	2·25	2·25
403/7	*Set of* 5	6·00	4·25

(Des C. Fernandes. Litho Questa)

1987 (25 Mar). *Tourism. T* **84** *and similar horiz designs. Multicoloured. P* 14½.

408	1 s. Type **84**	30	10
409	3 s. Tourists on beach	1·75	1·75
410	5 s. Tourist and guide at view point	2·50	2·75
411	7 s. Pride of lions	3·50	4·75
408/11	*Set of* 4	7·25	8·25
MS412	118×81 mm. 30 s. Geysers	7·00	7·50

(Des Mukund Arts. Litho Harrison)

1987 (20 May). *Ceremonial Costumes (3rd series). Vert designs as T* **45**. *Multicoloured. P* 14½×13½.

413	1 s. Embu	35	10
414	3 s. Kisii	1·00	60
415	5 s. Samburu	1·40	1·10
416	7 s. Taita	2·00	1·75
417	10 s. Boran	2·50	2·75
413/17	*Set of* 5	6·50	5·75

85 Telecommunications by Satellite 86 Volleyball

(Des Mukund Arts. Litho Harrison)

1987 (1 July). *10th Anniv of Kenya Posts and Telecommunications Corporation. T* **85** *and similar triangular designs. Multicoloured. P* 13½.

418	1 s. Type **85**	25	20
419	3 s. Rural post office, Kajiado	70	70
420	4 s. Awarding trophy, Welfare Sports	90	95
421	5 s. Village and telephone box	1·00	1·10
422	7 s. Speedpost labels and outline map of Kenya	1·40	1·75
418/22	*Set of* 5	3·75	4·25
MS423	110×80 mm. 25 s. Corporation flag	1·75	1·90

Nos. 418/22 were each printed as horizontal *tête-bêche* pairs within the sheet.

(Des C. Fernandes. Litho D.L.R.)

1987 (5 Aug). *4th All-Africa Games, Nairobi. T* **86** *and similar multicoloured designs. P* 14½×14.

424	1 s. Type **86**	20	10
425	3 s. Cycling	25	30
426	4 s. Boxing	35	45
427	5 s. Swimming	40	50
428	7 s. Steeplechasing	50	90
424/8	*Set of* 5	1·50	2·00
MS429	117×80 mm. 30 s. Kasarani Sports Complex (*horiz*). P 14×14½	2·10	2·25

87 *Aloe volkensii*

(Des Advertising Link. Litho Cartor)

1987 (10 Nov). *Medicinal Herbs. T* **87** *and similar vert designs. Multicoloured. P* 13½×14.

430	1 s. Type **87**	35	10
431	3 s. *Cassia didymobotrya*	90	80
432	5 s. *Erythrina abyssinica*	1·50	1·25
433	7 s. *Adenium obesum*	2·00	2·00
434	10 s. Herbalist's clinic	2·25	2·25
430/4	*Set of* 5	6·25	5·75

88 *Epamera sidus* 89 *Papilio rex*

(Des Rena Fennessy. Photo Harrison)

1988 (15 Feb)–**90**. *Butterflies. Multicoloured.*

(*a*) *Vert designs as T* **88**. *P* 15×14

434*a*	10 c. *Cyrestis camillus* (1.9.89)	60	1·00
435	20 c. Type **88**	30	60
436	40 c. *Cynthia cardui*	40	60
437	50 c. *Colotis evippe*	40	60
438	70 c. *Precis westermanni*	40	60
439	80 c. *Colias electo*	40	60
440	1 s. *Eronia leda*	40	30
440*a*	1 s. 50, *Papilio dardanus* (18.5.90)	1·25	30

(*b*) *Vert designs as T* **89**. *P* 14½

441	2 s. Type **89**	70	40
442	2 s. 50, *Colotis phisadia*	75	80
443	3 s. *Papilio desmondi*	80	80
444	3 s. 50, *Papilio demodocus*	80	60
445	4 s. *Papilio phorcas*	85	60
446	5 s. *Charaxes druceanus*	90	70
447	7 s. *Cymothoe teita*	1·00	1·25
448	10 s. *Charaxes zoolina*	1·25	1·25
449	20 s. *Papilio dardanus*	1·60	3·00
450	40 s. *Charaxes cithaeron*	3·00	5·00
434*a*/50	*Set of* 18	14·00	17·00

Examples of the 1 s. value were used in error at Kisumu from 2 February 1988.

90 Samburu Lodge and Crocodiles

(Des Advertising Link. Litho Questa)

1988 (31 May). *Kenyan Game Lodges. T* **90** *and similar horiz designs. Multicoloured. P* 14½.

451	1 s. Type **90**	30	10
452	3 s. Naro Moru River Lodge and rock climbing	75	60
453	4 s. Mara Serena Lodge and zebra with foal	85	70
454	5 s. Voi Safari Lodge and buffalo	95	90
455	7 s. Kilimanjaro Buffalo Lodge and giraffes	1·25	1·50
456	10 s. Meru Mulika Lodge and rhinoceroses	1·75	2·00
451/6	*Set of* 6	5·25	5·25

91 Athletes and Stadium, Commonwealth Games, Brisbane, 1982

(Des D. Ashby. Litho Harrison)

1988 (10 June). *"Expo '88" World Fair, Brisbane, and Bicentenary of Australian Settlement. T* **91** *and similar horiz designs. Multicoloured. P* 14½.

457	1 s. Type **91**	20	10
458	3 s. Flying Doctor Service De Havilland D.H.A.3 Drover 3 and Piper PA-30B Twin Commanche aircraft	1·00	80
459	4 s. H.M.S. *Sirius* (frigate), 1788	1·10	1·10
460	5 s. Ostrich and emu	1·40	1·40
461	7 s. Queen Elizabeth II, President Arap Moi of Kenya and Prime Minister Hawke of Australia	1·60	2·00
457/61	*Set of* 5	4·75	4·75
MS462	117×80 mm. 30 s. Entrance to Kenya Pavilion	1·90	2·00

92 W.H.O. Logo and Slogan 93 Handball

(Des Mukund Arts. Litho National Printing & Packaging, Zimbabwe)

1988 (1 July). *40th Anniv of World Health Organization. T* **92** *and similar horiz designs. P* 14½.

463	1 s. greenish blue, gold and ultramarine	25	10
464	3 s. multicoloured	85	70
465	5 s. multicoloured	1·25	1·25
466	7 s. multicoloured	1·75	2·25
463/6	*Set of* 4	3·75	3·75

Designs:—3 s. Mother with young son and nutritious food; 5 s. Giving oral vaccine to baby; 7 s. Village women drawing clean water from pump.

(Des H. Moghul. Litho D.L.R.)

1988 (1 Aug). *Olympic Games, Seoul. T* **93** *and similar vert designs. Multicoloured. P* 14½×14.

467	1 s. Type **93**	15	10
468	3 s. Judo	30	35
469	5 s. Weightlifting	40	50
470	7 s. Javelin	55	80
471	10 s. Relay racing	65	1·00
467/71	*Set of* 5	1·90	2·40
MS472	110×78 mm. 30 s. Tennis	1·90	2·00

94 Calabashes 95 Pres. Arap Moi taking Oath, 1978

(Des Mukund Arts. Litho D.L.R.)

1988 (20 Sept). *Kenyan Material Culture* (1st issue). *T* **94** *and similar multicoloured designs. P* 14½×14 (*vert*) *or* 14×14½ (*horiz*).

473	1 s. Type **94**	20	10
474	3 s. Milk gourds	60	55

475 5 s. Cooking pots (*horiz*) 70 65
476 7 s. Winnowing trays (*horiz*) .. .. 95 1·10
477 10 s. Reed baskets (*horiz*) .. .. .. 1·40 1·60
473/7 .. .. *Set of* 5 3·50 3·50
MS478 118×80 mm. 25 s. Gourds, calabash and horn (*horiz*) .. .. 1·50 1·60
See also Nos. 646/50.

(Des Mukund Arts. Litho Harrison)

1988 (13 Oct). *10th Anniv of "Nyayo" Era. T* **95** *and similar horiz designs. Multicoloured. P* 13½×14½.
479 1 s. Type **95** 25 10
480 3 s. Building soil conservation barrier .. 85 70
481 3 s. 50, Passengers boarding bus .. .. 1·00 70
482 4 s. Metalwork shop .. .. .. 1·00 90
483 5 s. Moi University, Eldoret .. .. 1·25 1·00
484 7 s. Aerial view of hospital .. .. 2·25 2·00
485 10 s. Pres. Arap Moi and Mrs. Thatcher at Kapsabet Telephone Exchange .. 3·75 3·00
479/85 .. .. *Set of* 7 9·25 7·50

96 Kenya Flag

(Des Mukund Arts. Photo Courvoisier)

1988 (9 Dec). *25th Anniv of Independence. T* **96** *and similar horiz designs. Multicoloured. Granite paper. P* 11½.
486 1 s. Type **96** 15 10
487 3 s. Coffee picking 50 50
488 5 s. Proposed Kenya Posts and Telecommunications Headquarters building .. 95 95
489 7 s. Kenya Airways Airbus Industrie A310-300 *Harambee Star* .. .. 2·00 2·00
490 10 s. New diesel locomotive No. 9401 .. 3·25 3·50
486/90 .. .. *Set of* 5 6·25 6·25

97 Gedi Ruins, Malindi

(Des Mukund Arts. Litho National Printing & Packaging, Zimbabwe)

1989 (15 Mar). *Historic Monuments. T* **97** *and similar multicoloured designs. P* 14½.
491 1 s. 20, Type **97** 25 10
492 3 s. 40, Vasco Da Gama Pillar, Malindi (*vert*) 55 55
493 4 s. 40, Ishiakani Monument, Kiunga .. 65 65
494 5 s. 50, Fort Jesus, Mombasa 80 90
495 7 s. 70, She Burnan Omwe, Lamu (*vert*) .. 1·25 1·50
491/5 .. .. *Set of* 5 3·25 3·25

98 125th Anniversary and Kenya Red Cross Logos

99 Female Giraffe and Calf

(Des H. Moghul. Litho Cartor)

1989 (8 May). *125th Anniv of International Red Cross. T* **98** *and similar horiz designs. Mulicoloured. P* 14×13½.
496 1 s. 20, Type **98** 30 10
497 3 s. 40, Red Cross workers with car crash victim 70 75
498 4 s. 40, Disaster relief team distributing blankets .. .. 85 1·00
499 5 s. 50, Henri Dunant (founder) .. .. 1·00 1·40
500 7 s. 70, Blood donor .. .. .. 1·50 2·25
496/500 .. .. *Set of* 5 4·00 5·00

(Des Doreen McGuinness. Litho Walsall)

1989 (12 July). *Reticulated Giraffe. T* **99** *and similar vert designs. Multicoloured. P* 14½.
501 1 s. 20, Type **99** .. .. 1·50 30
502 3 s. 40, Giraffe drinking .. .. .. 2·75 2·50
503 4 s. 40, Two giraffes .. .. .. 3·25 3·00
504 5 s. 50, Giraffe feeding .. .. .. 3·75 3·75
501/4 .. .. *Set of* 4 10·00 8·50
MS505 80×110 mm. 30 s. Designs as Nos. 501/4, but without face values .. .. .. 5·00 5·00
Designs from No. **MS**505 are without the Worldwide Fund for Nature logo.

NEW INFORMATION

The editor is always interested to correspond with people who have new information that will improve or correct the Catalogue.

100 *Lentinus sajor-caju*

101 Independence Monuments

(Des Dvora Bochman. Litho Questa)

1989 (6 Sept). *Mushrooms. T* **100** *and similar vert designs. Multicoloured. P* 14½.
506 1 s. 20, Type **100** .. .. 1·00 30
507 3 s. 40, *Agaricus bisporus* .. .. .. 1·75 1·50
508 4 s. 40, *Agaricus bisporus (different)* .. 2·00 2·00
509 5 s. 50, *Termitomyces schimperi* .. .. 2·50 3·00
510 7 s. 70, *Lentinus edodes* .. .. .. 3·25 4·25
506/10 .. .. *Set of* 5 9·50 10·00

(Des Conference and Exhibitions Secretariat, Nairobi. Litho Cartor)

1989 (9 Nov). *Birth Centenary of Jawaharlal Nehru (Indian statesman). T* **101** *and similar vert designs. Multicoloured. P* 13½×14.
511 1 s. 20, Type **101** 80 30
512 3 s. 40, Nehru with graduates and open book .. .. 1·50 1·50
513 5 s. 50, Jawaharlal Nehru .. .. 2·25 3·00
514 7 s. 70, Industrial complex and cogwheels 3·25 4·00
511/14 .. .. *Set of* 4 7·00 8·00

(Des Mukund Arts. Litho Harrison)

1989 (20 Dec). *Ceremonial Costumes (4th series). Vert designs as T* **45**. *Multicoloured. P* 14½×13½.
515 1 s. 20, Kipsigis 55 20
516 3 s. 40, Rabai .. .. 1·25 1·25
517 5 s. 50, Duruma .. .. 1·75 2·00
518 7 s. 70, Kuria .. .. 2·25 2·75
519 10 s. Bajuni .. .. 2·50 3·25
515/19 .. .. *Set of* 5 7·50 8·50

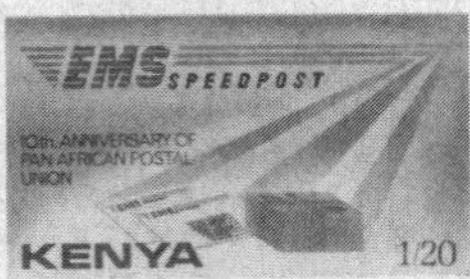

102 EMS Speedpost Letters and Parcel

(Des Conference and Exhibitions Secretariat, Nairobi. Litho Cartor)

1990 (23 Mar). *10th Anniv of Pan African Postal Union. T* **101** *and similar multicoloured designs. P* 14×13½ (*horiz*) *or* 13½×14 (*vert*).
520 1 s. 20, Type **102** 15 10
521 3 s. 40, Mail runner 35 35
522 5 s. 50, Mandera Post Office 55 70
523 7 s. 70, EMS Speedpost Letters and globe (*vert*) .. .. 80 1·40
524 10 s. P.A.P.U. logo (*vert*) .. .. 90 1·60
520/4 .. .. *Set of* 5 2·50 3·50

103 "Stamp King" with Tweezers and Magnifying Glass

104 Moi Golden Cup

(Des D. Miller. Photo Courvoisier)

1990 (3 May). *"Stamp World London 90" International Stamp Exhibition. T* **103** *and similar horiz designs. Granite paper. P* 11½.
525 1 s. 50, multicoloured 35 10
526 4 s. 50, multicoloured .. .. .. 1·00 1·00
527 6 s. 50, black, bright carmine and azure .. 1·10 1·10
528 9 s. multicoloured .. .. .. 1·50 2·25
525/8 .. .. *Set of* 4 3·50 4·00
MS529 113×77 mm. Nos. 525/8 .. .. 3·75 4·50
Designs:—4 s. 50, Penny Black and Kenya Stamp Bureau postmark; 6 s. 50, Early British cancellations; 9 s. Ronald Ngala Street Post Office, Nairobi.

(Litho Harrison)

1990 (21 May). *World Cup Football Championship, Italy. Trophies. T* **104** *and similar vert designs. Multicoloured. P* 14½.
530 1 s. 50, Type **104** 45 10
531 4 s. 50, East and Central Africa Challenge Cup .. .. 1·40 1·40
532 6 s. 50, East and Central Africa Club Championship Cup .. .. .. 2·00 2·50
533 9 s. World Cup .. .. 2·50 3·25
530/3 .. .. *Set of* 4 5·75 6·50

105 K.A.N.U. Flag

(Des Mukund Arts. Litho Harrison)

1990 (11 June). *50th Anniv of Kenya African National Union. T* **105** *and similar horiz designs. Multicoloured. P* 14½.
534 1 s. 50, Type **105** 15 10
535 2 s. 50, Nyayo Monument 15 15
536 4 s. 50, Party Headquarters 35 35
537 5 s. Jomo Kenyatta (founder) 40 40
538 6 s. 50, President Arap Moi 50 70
539 9 s. President Moi addressing rally .. 70 1·10
540 10 s. Queue of voters .. .. .. 80 1·25
534/40 .. .. *Set of* 7 2·75 3·50

106 Desktop Computer

(Litho Questa)

1990 (12 July). *125th Anniv of International Telecommunications Union. T* **106** *and similar horiz designs. Multicoloured. P* 14½.
541 1 s. 50, Type **106** 15 10
542 4 s. 50, Telephone switchboard assembly, Gilgil 35 50
543 6 s. 50, "125 YEARS" 45 80
544 9 s. Urban and rural telecommunications 70 1·75
541/4 .. .. *Set of* 4 1·50 2·75

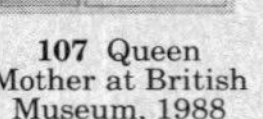

107 Queen Mother at British Museum, 1988

108 Queen Elizabeth at Hospital Garden Party, 1947

(Des D. Miller. Litho Questa)

1990 (4 Aug). *90th Birthday of Queen Elizabeth the Queen Mother. P* 14×15 (10 *s.*) *or* 14½ (40 *s.*).
545 **107** 10 s. multicoloured .. .. .. 1·25 1·50
546 **108** 40 s. black and brown-olive .. .. 3·00 4·50

109 Kenya 1988 2 s. Definitive

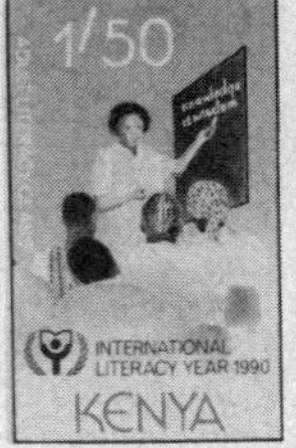

110 Adult Literacy Class

(Des D. Miller. Litho D.L.R.)

1990 (5 Sept). *Centenary of Postage Stamps in Kenya. T* **109** *and similar vert designs. Multicoloured. P* 14×14½.
547 1 s. 50, Type **109** 55 10
548 4 s. 50, East Africa and Uganda 1903 1 a. 1·00 85
549 6 s. 50, British East Africa Co 1890 ½ a. optd on G.B. 1d. .. .. .. 1·60 1·60
550 9 s. Kenya and Uganda 1922 20 c. .. 2·00 2·50
551 20 s. Kenya, Uganda, Tanzania 1971 2 s. 50, Railway commemorative .. .. 3·25 4·50
547/51 .. .. *Set of* 5 7·50 8·50

(Des H. Moghul. Litho Cartor)

1990 (30 Nov). *International Literacy Year. T* **110** *and similar vert designs. Multicoloured. P* 13½×14.
552 1 s. 50, Type **110** 30 10
553 4 s. 50, Teaching by radio 75 75
554 6 s. 50, Technical training .. .. 1·00 1·25
555 9 s. International Literacy Year logo .. 1·75 2·50
552/5 .. .. *Set of* 4 3·50 4·25

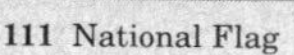

111 National Flag

112 Symbolic Man and Pointing Finger

(Des H. Moghul. Litho Cartor)

1991 (29 Nov). *Olympic Games, Barcelona* (1992) (*1st issue*). *T* **111** *and similar horiz designs. Multicoloured. P* 14×13½.

556 2 s. Type **111** 20 10
557 6 s. Basketball .. .. 1·50 1·00
558 7 s. Hockey .. .. 1·75 1·40
559 8 s. 50, Table tennis .. .. .. 1·75 2·25
560 11 s. Boxing .. .. 1·90 2·50
556/60 .. .. *Set of* 5 6·25 6·50

See also Nos. 580/4.

(Des H. Mogul. Litho Cartor)

1992 (31 Jan). *AIDS Day. T* **112** *and similar vert designs. Multicoloured. P* 13½×14.

561 2 s. Type **112** 40 15
562 6 s. Victim and drugs .. .. .. 1·00 80
563 8 s. 50, Male and female symbols .. 1·50 1·75
564 11 s. Symbolic figure and hypodermic syringe .. .. .. 2·25 3·00
561/4 .. .. *Set of* 4 4·75 5·25

113 Queen and Prince Philip with Pres. Moi

114 Leopard

(Des D. Miller. Litho Cartor)

1992 (6 Feb). *40th Anniv of Queen Elizabeth II's Accession. T* **113** *and similar horiz designs. Multicoloured. P* 14×13½.

565 3 s. Type **113** 35 10
566 8 s. Marabou Storks in tree 80 70
567 11 s. Treetops Hotel 90 90
568 14 s. Three portraits of Queen Elizabeth .. 1·10 1·25
569 40 s. Queen Elizabeth II .. .. .. 2·50 4·00
565/9 .. .. *Set of* 5 5·00 6·25

(Des Dvora Bochman. Litho National Printing & Packaging, Zimbabwe)

1992 (8 May). *Kenya Wildlife. T* **114** *and similar vert designs. Multicoloured. P* 14×14½.

570 3 s. Type **114** 65 30
571 8 s. Lion .. .. 1·25 1·25
572 10 s. Elephant .. .. 2·00 2·00
573 11 s. Buffalo .. .. 1·50 2·00
574 14 s. Black Rhinoceros .. .. .. 2·50 3·00
570/4 .. .. *Set of* 5 7·00 7·75

115 International Harvester Safari Truck, 1926

116 Kenyan Athlete winning Race

(Des Dvora Bochman. Litho National Printing & Packaging, Zimbabwe)

1992 (24 June). *Vintage Cars. T* **115** *and similar horiz designs. Multicoloured. P* 14½×14.

575 3 s. Type **115** 50 20
576 8 s. Fiat "509", 1924 .. .. .. 1·25 95
577 10 s. Hupmobile, 1923 .. .. .. 1·60 1·60
578 11 s. Chevrolet "Box Body", 1928 .. .. 1·60 1·60
579 14 s. Bentley/Parkward, 1934 .. .. 1·75 2·25
575/9 .. .. *Set of* 5 6·00 6·00

(Des Dvora Bochman. Litho National Printing & Packaging, Zimbabwe)

1992 (24 July). *Olympic Games, Barcelona* (*2nd series*). *T* **116** *and similar vert designs. Multicoloured. P* 14×14½.

580 3 s. Type **116** 45 10
581 8 s. Men's judo 90 90
582 10 s. Kenyan women's volleyball players .. 1·50 1·50
583 11 s. Kenyan men's 4×100 metres relay runners .. .. 1·50 1·50
584 14 s. Men's 10,000 metres .. .. .. 1·75 2·25
580/4 .. .. *Set of* 5 5·50 5·50

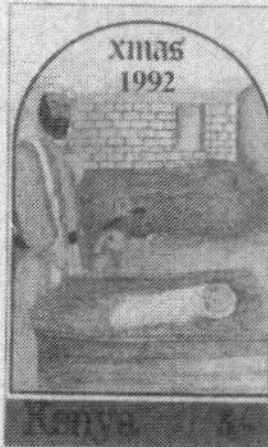

117 Holy Child, Joseph and Animals

118 Asembo Bay Lighthouse, Lake Victoria

(Litho Cartor)

1992 (14 Dec). *Christmas. T* **117** *and similar vert designs. Multicoloured. P* 13½×14.

585 3 s. Type **117** 20 10
586 8 s. Mary with Holy Child 55 50
587 11 s. Christmas tree 70 80
588 14 s. Adoration of the Magi .. .. .. 1·00 1·50
585/8 .. .. *Set of* 4 2·25 2·50

(Des H. Moghul. Litho Questa)

1993 (25 Jan). *Lighthouses. T* **118** *and similar vert designs. Multicoloured. P* 14½.

589 3 s. Type **118** 60 30
590 8 s. Old Ras Serani lighthouse, Mombasa 1·25 1·00
591 11 s. New Ras Serani lighthouse, Mombasa 1·50 1·40
592 14 s. Gingira, Lake Victoria .. .. .. 2·00 2·25
589/92 .. .. *Set of* 4 4·75 4·50

119 Superb Starling

120 Yellow-billed Hornbill

(Des Dvora Bochman. Photo Courvoisier)

1993 (22 Feb)–**94**. *Birds. Multicoloured. Granite paper.*

(*a*) *Vert designs as T* **119**. *P* 15×14

593 50 c. Type **119** 10 10
594 1 s. Red and Yellow Barbet 10 10
594*a* 1 s. 50, Lady Ross's Turaco (14.2.94) .. 10 10
595 3 s. Black-throated Honeyguide ("Greater Honeyguide") 10 10
595*a* 5 s. African Fish Eagle (14.2.94) 10 10
596 7 s. Malachite Kingfisher 15 20
597 8 s. Speckled Pigeon 15 20
598 10 s. Cinnamon-chested Bee Eater 20 25
599 11 s. Scarlet-chested Sunbird 20 25
600 14 s. Bagalafecht Weaver ("Reichenow's Weaver") 25 30

(*b*) *Vert designs as T* **120**. *P* 14½

601 50 s. Type **120** .. .. 1·00 1·10
602 80 s. Lesser Flamingo .. .. .. 1·60 1·75
603 100 s. Hadada Ibis .. .. 2·00 2·10
593/603 .. .. *Set of* 13 5·75 6·25

No. 595*a* was only issued in coils.

121 Nurse bandaging Boy's Legs

122 Maendeleo House, Nairobi

(Des Conference and Exhibitions Secretariat, Nairobi. Litho National Printing & Packaging, Zimbabwe)

1993 (1 July). *17th World Congress of Rehabilitation International. T* **121** *and similar designs. P* 14½.

611 3 s. multicoloured 40 10
612 8 s. multicoloured 55 55
613 10 s. multicoloured 60 70
614 11 s. multicoloured 60 70
615 14 s. black, new blue and yellow-orange .. 80 1·25
611/15 .. .. *Set of* 5 2·75 3·00

Designs: *Horiz*—8 s. Singing group on crutches; 10 s. Vocational training; 11 s. Wheelchair race. *Vert*—14 s. Congress emblem.

(Des Conference and Exhibitions Secretariat, Nairobi. Litho Cartor)

1994 (17 Mar). *40th Anniv of Maendeleo Ya Wanawake Organization. T* **122** *and similar multicoloured designs. P* 14×13½ (*horiz*) *or* 13½×14 (*vert*).

616 3 s. 50, Type **122** 25 10
617 9 s. Planting saplings 40 40
618 11 s. Rural family planning clinic (*vert*) .. 45 50
619 12 s. 50, Women carrying water 65 85
620 15 s. 50, Improved wood-burning cooking stove (*vert*) .. .. 80 1·25
616/20 .. .. *Set of* 5 2·25 2·75

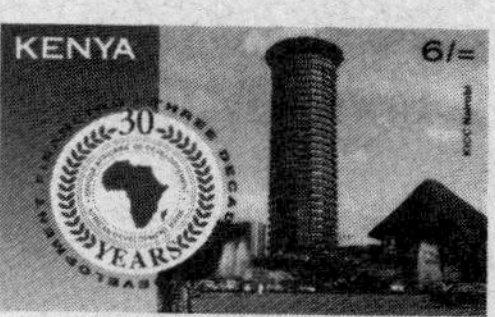

123 *Ansellia africana*

124 Emblem and K.I.C.C. Building, Nairobi

(Des Dvora Bochman. Litho Cartor)

1994 (27 June). *Orchids. T* **123** *and similar vert designs. Multicoloured. P* 13½×14.

621 3 s. 50, Type **123** 40 15
622 9 s. *Aerangis luteoalba* var *rhodosticta* .. 65 60
623 12 s. 50, *Polystachya bella* 75 85
624 15 s. 50, *Brachycorythis kalbreyeri* .. 95 1·25
625 20 s. *Eulophia guineensis* .. .. .. 1·10 1·60
621/5 .. .. *Set of* 5 3·50 4·00

(Des and litho Questa)

1994 (21 Nov). *30th Anniv of African Development Bank. T* **124** *and similar horiz design. Multicoloured. P* 14½.

626 6 s. Type **124** 40 15
627 25 s. Isinya-Kajiado project .. .. 1·40 2·00

125 Kenyan Family

126 Paul Harris (founder of Rotary)

(Des Micro General Service Ltd. Litho Questa)

1994 (22 Dec). *International Year of the Family. T* **125** *and similar multicoloured designs. P* 14½.

628 6 s. Type **125** 30 10
629 14 s. 50, Nurse with mother and baby .. 1·25 1·00
630 20 s. School children and teacher (*horiz*) .. 1·60 1·60
631 25 s. Emblem (*horiz*) .. .. .. 1·75 1·90
628/31 .. .. *Set of* 4 4·50 4·25

(Des Omak Design. Litho Cartor)

1994 (29 Dec). *50th Anniv of Rotary Club of Mombasa. T* **126** *and similar vert designs. Multicoloured. P* 13½×14.

632 6 s. Type **126** 25 10
633 14 s. 50, Anniversary logo 70 70
634 17 s. 50, Administering polio vaccine .. 80 1·00
635 20 s. Women at stand pipe .. .. .. 90 1·25
636 25 s. Rotary emblem .. .. .. 95 1·50
632/6 .. .. *Set of* 5 3·25 4·00

127 Donkey

128 Male Golfer in Bunker

(Des H. Moghul. Litho Walsall)

1995 (13 Jan). *Kenya Society for Prevention of Cruelty to Animals. T* **127** *and similar vert designs. Multicoloured. P* 14½.

637 6 s. Type **127** 20 10
638 14 s. 50, Cow 45 45
639 17 s. 50, Sheep 55 65
640 20 s. Dog .. .. 85 1·10
641 25 s. Cat .. .. 1·00 1·40
637/41 .. .. *Set of* 5 2·75 3·25

(Des Conference and Exhibitions Secretariat. Litho Questa)

1995 (28 Feb). *Golf. T* **128** *and similar vert designs. Multicoloured. P* 14½.

642 6 s. Type **128** 30 15
643 17 s. 50, Female golfer on fairway .. 90 90
644 20 s. Male golfer teeing-off .. .. 1·00 1·40
645 25 s. Head of golf club .. .. .. 1·10 1·60
642/5 .. .. *Set of* 4 3·00 3·50

129 Perfume Containers

130 Tsetse Fly

(Des Lari & Loiruk Graphic Studio. Litho Cartor)

1995 (24 Mar). *Kenyan Material Culture (2nd issue). T* **129** *and similar horiz designs. Multicoloured. P* 14×13½.

646 6 s. Type **129** 30 10
647 14 s. 50, Basketry 75 75
648 17 s. 50, Preserving pots 85 90
649 20 s. Gourds .. .. 1·10 1·40
650 25 s. Wooden containers .. .. .. 1·25 1·60
646/50 .. .. *Set of* 5 3·75 4·25

(Des Design Box Associates. Litho Enschedé)

1995 (29 Sept). *25th Anniv of I.C.I.P.E. Insect Pests. T* **130** *and similar vert designs. Multicoloured. P* 13½.

651 14 s. Type **130** 50 30
652 26 s. Tick 80 80
653 32 s. Wild Silkmoth 95 95
654 33 s. Maize Borer .. .. 1·00 1·25
655 40 s. Locust .. .. 1·60 2·00
651/5 .. .. *Set of* 5 4·25 4·75

131 Maize

132 Kenyan and United Nations Flags over Headquarters, Nairobi

(Des Dvora Bochman. Litho Cartor)

1995 (16 Oct). *50th Anniv of Food and Agriculture Organization. T* **131** *and similar vert designs. Multicoloured. P* 13½×14.

656 14 s. Type **131** 50 30
657 28 s. Cattle 80 80
658 32 s. Chickens 95 95
659 33 s. Fisherman with catch .. .. .. 1·00 1·25
660 40 s. Fruit .. .. 1·60 2·00
656/60 .. .. *Set of* 5 4·25 4·75

(Des O. Karenga. Litho Enschedé)

1995 (24 Oct). *50th Anniv of United Nations. T* **132** *and similar horiz designs. P* 13½.

661 23 s. multicoloured 70 70
662 26 s. multicoloured 80 90
663 32 s. multicoloured .. .. 95 1·10
664 40 s. brt greenish blue, dp carmine & black 1·40 1·75
661/4 .. .. *Set of* 4 3·50 4·00

Designs:—26 s. Multi-racial group with emblem; 32 s. United Nations helmet; 40 s. 50th anniversary emblem.

133 Swimming

1996 (5 Jan). *Olympic Games, Atlanta (1st issue). Events and Gold Medal Winners. T* **133** *and similar multicoloured designs. Litho. P* 14.

665 14 s. Type **133** 60 65
a. Sheetlet. Nos. 665/7 and 686/8 .. 3·75
666 20 s. Archery 60 65
667 20 s. Weightlifting 60 65
668 20 s. Pole vault (*vert*) 60 65
a. Sheetlet. Nos. 668/76 .. .. 4·75
669 20 s. Equestrian (*vert*) 60 65
670 20 s. Diving (*vert*) 60 65
671 20 s. Sprinting (*vert*) 60 65
672 20 s. Athlete carrying Olympic Torch (*vert*) 60 65
673 20 s. Hurdling (*vert*) 60 65
674 20 s. Kayak (*vert*) 60 65
675 20 s. Boxing (*vert*) 60 65
676 20 s. Gymnastics (*vert*) 60 65
677 25 s. Greg Louganis (U.S.A.) (diving, 1984 and 1988) (*vert*) 60 65
a. Sheetlet. Nos. 677/85 .. .. .. 4·75
678 25 s. Cassius Clay (U.S.A.) (boxing, 1960) (*vert*) 60 65
679 25 s. Nadia Comaneci (Rumania) (gymnastics, 1980) (*vert*) 60 65
680 25 s. Daley Thompson (Great Britain) (decathlon, 1980 and 1984) (*vert*) .. 60 65
681 25 s. Kipchoge Keino (Kenya) (running, 1968) (*vert*) 60 65
682 25 s. Kornelia Enders (Germany) (swimming, 1976) (*vert*) 60 65
683 25 s. Jackie Joyner-Kersee (U.S.A.) (long jump, 1988) (*vert*) 60 65
684 25 s. Michael Jordan (U.S.A.) (basketball, 1984) (*vert*) 60 65
685 25 s. Shun Fujimoto (Japan) (gymnastics, 1972) (*vert*) 60 65
686 32 s. Javelin 65 70
687 40 s. Fencing 80 85
688 50 s. Discus .. .. 1·00 1·10
665/88 .. .. *Set of* 24 13·50 14·50

MS689 Two sheets, each 79×109 mm. (a) 100 s. Athlete with medal (*vert*). (b) 100 s. Athlete carrying Olympic Torch (*different*) (*vert*) *Set of* 2 *sheets* 5·25 6·50

Nos. 665/7 with 686/8, 668/76 and 677/85 were printed together, *se-tenant*, in sheetlets of 6 (Nos. 665/7, 686/8) or 9 (Nos. 668/76 and 677/85) with the backgrounds forming composite designs.

See also Nos. 702/6.

134 Lions

135 Water Buck

(Litho Cartor)

1996 (31 Jan). *Tourism. Multicoloured. (a) Designs as T* **134**. *P* 14×13½.

690 6 s. Type **134** 20 10
691 14 s. Mt Kenya 35 30
692 20 s. Sailboards 55 50
693 25 s. Hippopotami .. .. 90 1·00
694 40 s. Couple in traditional dress .. .. 1·00 1·50
690/4 .. .. *Set of* 5 2·75 3·00

MS695 100×80 mm. 50 s. Female Giraffe and calf (*vert*). P 13×13½ .. .. .. 1·25 1·40

(b) Horiz designs as T **135**. *P* 13×13½

696 20 s. Type **135** 70 90
a. Booklet pane. Nos. 696/701 .. .. 3·75
697 20 s. Pair of Rhinoceroses 70 90
698 20 s. Cheetah 70 90
699 20 s. Group of Oryx 70 90
700 20 s. Pair of Giraffes 70 90
701 20 s. Monkey and Bongo 70 90
696/701 .. .. *Set of* 6 3·75 4·75

Nos. 696/701 were only available from 480 s. stamp booklets. Booklet pane No. 696a exists in two versions which differ in the order of the stamps.

136 Women's 10,000 Metres

137 Red Cross Emblem

(Des Design Box Associates. Litho Cartor)

1996 (18 July). *Olympic Games, Atlanta (2nd issue). T* **136** *and similar vert designs. Multicoloured. P* 13½×14.

702 6 s. Type **136** 20 10
703 14 s. Steeple-chasing 35 30
704 20 s. Victorious athletes with flag 60 70
705 25 s. Boxing 70 80
706 40 s. Men's 1500 metres .. .. .. 1·25 1·75
702/6 .. .. *Set of* 5 2·75 3·25

(Des Dvora Bochman. Litho National Printing & Packaging, Zimbabwe)

1996 (30 Aug). *Kenya Red Cross Society. T* **137** *and similar vert designs. P* 14½.

707 6 s. scarlet-vermilion and black 20 10
708 14 s. multicoloured 35 30
709 20 s. multicoloured 60 70
710 25 s. multicoloured 70 80
711 40 s. multicoloured .. .. 1·25 1·75
707/11 .. .. *Set of* 5 2·75 3·25

Designs:—14 s. Giving blood; 20 s. Immunization; 25 s; Refugee child with food; 40 s. Cleaning the environment.

138 Impala

139 Kenya Lions Club Logo

(Des H. Moghul. Litho Harrisons)

1996 (10 Sept). *East African Wildlife Society. T* **138** *and similar vert designs. Multicoloured. P* 14½.

712 6 s. Type **138** 20 10
713 20 s. Colobus Monkey 60 50
714 25 s. African Elephant 90 80
715 40 s. Black Rhinoceros .. .. 1·50 2·00
712/15 .. .. *Set of* 4 2·75 3·00

(Des Dvora Bochman. Litho Enschedé)

1996 (31 Oct). *Work of Lions Club International in Kenya. T* **139** *and similar vert designs. Multicoloured. P* 13½.

716 6 s. Type **139** 15 10
717 14 s. Eye operation 35 35
718 20 s. Two disabled children in wheelchair 55 65
719 25 s. Modern ambulance 60 75
716/19 .. .. *Set of* 4 1·50 1·60

140 C.O.M.E.S.A. Logo

141 *Haplochromis cinctus*

(Des O. Katenga. Litho Cartor)

1997 (15 Jan). *Inauguration of Common Market for Eastern and Southern Africa. T* **140** *and similar vert design. Multicoloured. P* 13½×14.

720 6 s. Type **140** 15 15
721 20 s. Kenyan flag and logo 60 75

(Des C. Newman. Litho Cartor)

1997 (31 Jan). *Endangered Species. Lake Victoria Cichlid Fishes. T* **141** *and similar horiz designs. Multicoloured. P* 14×13½.

722 25 s. Type **141** 60 70
723 25 s. *Haplochromis* "Orange Rock Hunter" 60 70
724 25 s. *Haplochromis chilotes* 60 70
725 25 s. *Haplochromis nigricans* 60 70
722/5 .. .. *Set of* 4 2·25 2·50

142 Class "94" Diesel Locomotive, 1981

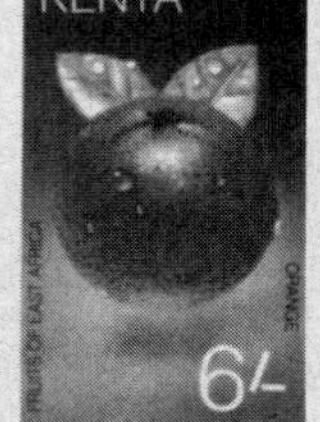

143 Orange

(Des Design Box. Litho Cartor)

1997 (20 Feb). *Kenya Railway Locomotives. T* **142** *and similar horiz designs. Multicoloured. P* 14×13½.

726 6 s. Type **142** 15 15
727 14 s. Class "87" diesel, 1964 .. .. .. 30 30
728 20 s. Class "59" steam, 1955 .. .. .. 50 45
729 25 s. Class "57" steam, 1939 .. .. .. 50 60
730 30 s. Class "23" steam, 1923 .. .. .. 55 65
731 40 s. Class "10" steam, 1914 .. .. .. 80 1·00
726/31 .. .. *Set of* 6 2·50 2·75

(Des H. Moghul. Litho Walsall)

1997 (28 Feb). *Fruits of East Africa. T* **143** *and similar vert designs. Multicoloured. P* 14½.

732 6 s. Type **143** 15 15
733 14 s. Pineapple 30 35
734 20 s. Mango 45 50
735 25 s. Pawpaw 50 65
732/5 .. .. *Set of* 4 1·25 1·50

144 Crocodile

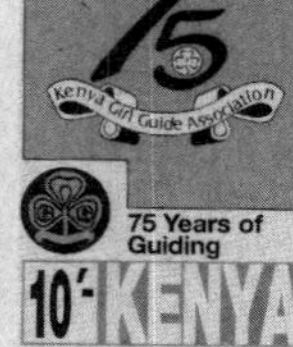

145 Girl Guides Anniversary Logo

(Des Design Box. Litho Enschedé)

1997 (9 Oct). *Local Tourist Attractions.* T **144** *and similar horiz designs. Multicoloured.* P 13½.

736	10 s. Type **144**	35	25
737	27 s. Lake Bogoria hot springs	75	65
738	30 s. Warthogs	85	75
739	33 s. Windsurfing	90	85
740	42 s. Traditional huts	1·10	1·25
736/40	*Set of* 5	3·50	3·25

(Litho Questa)

1997 (21 Nov). *75th Anniv of Kenyan Girl Guides.* T **145** *and similar vert designs. Multicoloured.* P 14½.

741	10 s. Type **145**	30	35
	a. Horiz pair. Nos. 741/2	60	70
742	10 s. Lord Baden Powell	30	35
743	27 s. Girl Guides hiking	70	75
	a. Horiz pair. Nos. 743/4	1·40	1·50
744	27 s. Rangers in camp	70	75
745	33 s. Girl Guides planting seedlings	80	90
	a. Horiz pair. Nos. 745/6	1·60	1·75
746	33 s. Boy Scouts giving first aid	80	90
747	42 s. Boy Scouts in camp	90	1·00
	a. Horiz pair. Nos. 747/8	1·75	2·00
748	42 s. Brownies entertaining the elderly	90	1·00
741/8	*Set of* 8	4·75	5·50

Nos. 741/2, 743/4, 745/6 and 747/8 were each printed together, *se-tenant*, in horizontal pairs throughout the sheets

STAMP BOOKLETS

1964. *Black on blue cover. Stitched.*

SB1	5 s. booklet containing 10 c., 15 c., 20 c., 30 c. and 50 c. (Nos. 2/5, 7) in blocks of 4	13·00

1966 (12 Dec). *Black on bluish grey (No. SB2) or buff (No. SB3) covers. Stitched.*

SB2	3 s. booklet containing four 5 c., 10 c. and eight 30 c. (Nos. 20/1, 24), each in blocks of 4	10·00
SB3	5 s. booklet containing four 5 c., 10 c., 50 c. and eight 30 c. (Nos. 20/1, 24, 26), each in blocks of 4	13·00

1971 (13 Dec). *Black on buff (No. SB4) or dull rose (No. SB5) covers. Stitched.*

SB4	5 s. booklet containing four 10 c., 15 c., 40 c. and eight 30 c. (Nos. 37, 38, 40/1), each in blocks of 4	7·50
SB5	10 s. booklet containing four 10 c., 20 c., 30 c., 50 c. and eight 70 c. (Nos. 37, 39/40, 42, 45), each in blocks of 4	13·00

1977 (10 Dec). *Black on yellow (No. SB6) or bright rose (No. SB7) covers . Stitched.*

SB6	5 s. booklet containing ten 50 c. (No. 111) in two blocks of 4 and one pair	9·00
SB7	10 s. booklet containing four 10 c., 20 c., 40 c., 80 c. and eight 50 c. (Nos. 107/8, 110/11, 113), each in blocks of 4	13·00

1983 (14 Feb). *Black on pale blue (No. SB8) or pale green (No. SB9) covers . Stitched.*

SB8	10 s. booklet containing four 10 c., 20 c., 30 c., 50 c. and eight 70 c. (Nos. 257/9, 261/2), each in blocks of 4	6·50
SB9	20 s. booklet containing eight 10 c., 20 c., 30 c., 50 c. and sixteen 70 c. (Nos. 257/9, 261/2), each in blocks of 4	11·00

1988 (15 Feb). *Black on greenish yellow (No. SB10) or yellow-orange (No. SB11) covers . Stitched.*

SB10	20 c. booklet containing eight 20 c., 50 c., 80 c., 1 s. (Nos. 435, 437, 439/40), each in blocks of 4	3·75
SB11	40 s. booklet containing sixteen 20 c., 50 c., 80 c., 1 s. (Nos. 435, 437, 439/40), each in blocks of 4	7·00

B 1
(Illustration reduced. Actual size 155×80 mm)

1996 (31 Jan). *Tourism. Multicoloured cover as Type* B **1**.

SB12	480 s. booklet containing four *se-tenant* panes of six (No. 696a)	14·00

POSTAGE DUE STAMPS

The Postage Due stamps of Kenya, Uganda and Tanganyika were used in Kenya until 2 January 1967.

D 3

(Litho D.L.R.)

1967 (3 Jan)–**70.** *Chalk-surfaced paper.* P 14×13½.

D13	D **3**	5 c. scarlet	15	2·50
		a. Perf 14. Ordinary paper. *Dull scarlet* (16.12.69)	40	4·00
D14		10 c. green	20	2·50
		a. Perf 14. Ordinary paper (16.12.69)	55	4·00
D15		20 c. blue	70	2·75
		a. Perf 14. Ordinary paper. *Deep blue* (16.12.69)	55	4·50
D16		30 c. brown	80	3·25
		a. Perf 14. Ordinary paper. *Light red-brown* (16.12.69)	80	8·50
D17		40 c. bright purple	65	5·00
		a. Perf 14. Ordinary paper. *Pale bright purple* (16.12.69)	65	9·00
D18		1 s. bright orange	1·75	7·00
		a. Perf 14. Ordinary paper. *Dull bright orange* (18.2.70)	1·25	11·00
D13/18		*Set of* 6	3·75	21·00
D13a/18a		*Set of* 6	3·75	38·00

1971 (13 July)–**73.** P 14 × 15. (*a*) *Chalk-surfaced paper* (13.7.71).

D19	D **3**	10 c. green	8·00	11·00
D20		20 c. deep dull blue	9·00	12·00
D21		30 c. red-brown	9·50	13·00
D22		1 s. dull bright orange	16·00	35·00
D19/22		*Set of* 4	38·00	65·00

(*b*) *Glazed, ordinary paper* (20.2.73)

D23	D **3**	5 c. bright scarlet	1·50	4·50
D24		10 c. dull yellow-green	1·50	4·50
D25		20 c. deep blue	1·25	4·75
D27		40 c. bright purple	1·00	7·00
D28		1 s. bright orange	1·50	11·00
D23/8		*Set of* 5	6·00	29·00

1973 (12 Dec). *Glazed, ordinary paper.* P 15.

D29	D **3**	5 c. red	30	3·75
D30		10 c. emerald	30	3·75
D31		20 c. deep blue	30	4·00
D32		30 c. red-brown	30	5·50
D33		40 c. bright purple	3·75	9·00
D34		1 s. bright orange	95	11·00
D29/34		*Set of* 6	5·50	32·00

1979 (27 Mar). *Chalk-surfaced paper.* P 14.

D35	D **3**	10 c. bright emerald	90	4·50
D36		20 c. deep dull blue	1·75	5·50
D37		30 c. dull red-brown	1·00	5·00
D38		40 c. bright reddish purple	2·00	8·50
D39		80 c. dull red	85	4·50
D40		1 s. bright reddish orange	85	4·50
D35/40		*Set of* 6	6·50	29·00

1983 (Dec). W w **14.** P 14.

D41	D **3**	10 c. yellowish green	30	50
D42		20 c. deep blue	30	50
D43		40 c. bright purple	6·00	8·00
D41/3		*Set of* 3	6·00	8·00

(Litho Harrison)

1985 (7 Aug)–**87.** *Ordinary paper.* P 14½ × 14.

D44	D **3**	30 c. red-brown (9.1.87)	15	30
D45		40 c. bright magenta (9.1.87)	15	30
D46		80 c. dull vermilion (9.1.87)	20	40
D47		1 s. bright orange (1986)	80	1·10
D48		2 s. violet	1·40	2·00
D44/8		*Set of* 5	2·40	3·50

No. D47 was issued by the Crown Agents with Nos. D44/6, but was available in Kenya by November 1986.

(Litho Enschedé)

1993 (6 Dec). *Ordinary paper.* P 14½×14.

D49	D **3**	50 c. yellowish green	10	10
D50		1 s. yellow-orange	10	10
D51		2 s. dull violet	10	10
D52		3 s. steel-blue	10	10
D53		5 s. brown-red	10	10
D49/53		*Set of* 5	30	30

Nos. D49/53 are from re-drawn plates which differ from Harrison printings of Type D 3 in that "KENYA" is 9½ mm long on the Enschedé instead of 8½ mm and "POSTAGE DUE" 11 mm long instead of 11½ mm. There are other differences in the inner frame at bottom right.

OFFICIAL STAMPS

Intended for use on official correspondence of the Kenya Government only but there is no evidence that they were so used.

OFFICIAL

(O 4)

(15 c. 30 c. opt typo; others in photogravure)

1964 (1 Oct). *Nos. 1/5 and 7 optd with Type* O 4.

O21	5 c. brown, deep blue, green and bistre	10
O22	10 c. brown	10
O23	15 c. magenta	1·25
O24	20 c. black and yellow-green	20
O25	30 c. black and yellow	30
O26	50 c. crimson, black and green	2·75
O21/26	*Set of* 6	4·00

Kenya, Uganda and Tanganyika (Tanzania)

BRITISH EAST AFRICA

The area which became British East Africa had been part of the domain of the Zanzibari Sultans since 1794. In 1887 the administration of the province was granted to the British East Africa Association, incorporated as the Imperial British East Africa Company the following year.

Company post offices were established at Lamu and Mombasa in May 1890, British mails having been previously sent via the Indian post office on Zanzibar, opened in 1875.

A German postal agency opened at Lamu on 22 November 1888 and continued to operate until 31 March 1891, using German stamps. These can be identified by the "LAMU/OSTAFRIKA" cancellations and are listed under German East Africa in our *Part* 7 (*Germany*) catalogue.

PRICES FOR STAMPS ON COVER

Nos. 1/3	*from* × 8
Nos. 4/19	*from* × 25
Nos. 20/6	*from* × 3
Nos. 27/8	*from* × 7
Nos. 29/30	*from* × 15
Nos. 31/2	*from* × 4
Nos. 33/47	*from* × 10
No. 48	*from* × 15
Nos. 49/64	*from* × 12
Nos. 65/79	*from* × 15
Nos. 80/91	*from* × 8
Nos. 92/6	*from* × 12
Nos. 97/9	—

(Currency. 16 annas = 1 rupee)

BRITISH EAST AFRICA COMPANY ADMINISTRATION

BRITISH EAST AFRICA COMPANY HALF ANNA (1)

BRITISH EAST AFRICA COMPANY 1 ANNA (2)

(Surch D.L.R.)

1890 (23 May). *Stamps of Great Britain* (*Queen Victoria*) *surch as T* **1** *or T* **2** (*1 a. and 4 a.*).

1 ½ a. on 1d. deep purple (No. 173) £275 £200
2 1 a. on 2d. grey-green and carmine (No. 200) £425 £275
3 4 a. on 5d. dull purple and blue (No. 207*a*) £425 £275

A copy of the ½ a. with the short crossbar of "F" in "HALF" omitted exists in the Royal Collection but is the only known example.

Stamps of INDIA were used in British East Africa between late July and September 1890 being postmarked "MOMBASA" or "LAMU".

3

4

5 ANNAS. (5)

(Litho B.W.)

1890 (14 Oct)–**95.** *P* 14.

4 **3** ½ a. dull brown .. .. 2·25 3·50
a. Imperf (pair) £850 £475
b. Deep brown (21.10.93) .. .. 70 3·00
ba. Imperf (pair) £750 £375
bb. Imperf between (horiz pair) .. £1500 £650
bc. Imperf between (vert pair) £800 £500
c. Pale brown (16.1.95) .. .. 1·00 4·00
5 1 a. blue-green .. .. 3·00 4·25
aa. "ANL" (broken "D") (R. 6/3) .. £375 £400
a. Imperf (pair) £950 £500
ab. "ANL" (broken "D") (R. 6/3) .. £7500
b. Deep blue-green (16.1.95) 75
ba. Imperf (pair) £1000 £600
6 2 a. vermilion .. .. 2·75 3·50
a. Imperf (pair) £1400 £600
7 2½ a. black/*yellow-buff* (9.91) .. .. 70·00 19·00
a. Black/pale buff (9.92) .. .. 65·00 9·00
b. Black/bright yellow (21.10.93) .. 4·00 5·00
bb. Imperf (pair) £900 £400
bc. Imperf between (horiz pair) .. £1100 £400
bd. Imperf between (vert pair) £1100 £500
8 3 a. black/*dull red* (30.3.91) .. .. 7·50 11·00
a. Black/bright red (21.10.93) .. .. 1·40 4·25
ab. Imperf (pair) £850 £400
ac. Imperf between (horiz pair) .. £700 £375
ad. Imperf between (vert pair) £500 £375
9 4 a. yellow-brown .. .. .. 2·50 4·75
a. Imperf (pair) £1500 £650
10 4 a. grey (*imperf*) £1200 £1400
11 **3** 4½ a. dull violet (30.3.91) .. .. 30·00 13·00
a. Brown-purple (21.10.93) .. .. 2·50 13·00
ab. Imperf (pair) £1300 £400
ac. Imperf between (horiz pair) .. £1200 £1100
ad. Imperf between (vert pair) £850 £450
12 8 a. blue .. .. 5·50 8·00
a. Imperf (pair) £2000 £650
13 8 a. grey £250 £225
14 1 r. carmine .. .. 6·00 9·00
a. Imperf (pair) £2500 £700
15 1 r. grey £225 £225
16 **4** 2 r. brick-red .. .. 12·00 23·00
17 3 r. slate-purple .. .. .. 8·00 27·00
18 4 r. ultramarine .. .. .. 12·00 27·00
19 5 r. grey-green .. .. 30·00 60·00
4/19 .. .. *Set of* 15 £500 £500

For the 5 a. and 7½ a. see Nos. 29/30.

The dates quoted for these stamps are of the earliest recorded use of the various consignments based on known shipping movements. It is possible that the initial supply may have been placed on sale before 14 October 1890 as an example has been reported postmarked on 13 October, but this is unconfirmed.

The paper of Nos. 7, 7*a*, 7*b*, 8 and 8*a* is coloured on the surface only.

Printings of 1890/92 are on thin paper having the outer margins of the sheets imperf and bearing sheet watermark "PURE LINEN WOVE BANK" and "W. C. S. & Co." in a monogram, the trademark of the makers, Messrs. William Collins, Sons & Co.

1893/94 printings are on thicker coarser paper with outer margins perforated through the selvedge and without watermark. Single specimens cannot always be distinguished by lack of watermark alone. Exceptions are the 1893 printings of the 2½ a. and 3 a. which were on Wiggins Teape paper showing a sheet watermark of "1011" in figures 1 centimetre high.

Nos. 7 (coloured through) and 16/19 on thick unwatermarked paper are from a special printing made for presentation purposes.

The printings of the 4 a., 8 a. and 1 r. values in grey were intended for fiscal purposes, but in the event, were made available for postal use.

Forgeries of the 4 a., 8 a., 1 r. grey and 2 to 5 r. exist. The latter are common and can be distinguished by the scroll above "LIGHT" where there are five vertical lines of shading in the forgeries and seven in the genuine stamps. Forged cancellations exist on the commoner stamps. Beware of "imperf" stamps made by trimming margins of stamps from marginal rows.

1891. *Mombasa Provisionals.* (*a*) *New value handstamped in dull violet, with original face value obliterated and initials added in black manuscript*

20 **3** "½ Anna" on 2 a. verm ("A.D.") (January) £3500 £750
a. "½ Anna" double .. .. .. † £3750
b. Original face value not obliterated † £1100
21 "1 Anna" on 4 a. brn ("A.B.") (February) £6000 £1500

(*b*) *Manuscript value and initials in black*

22 **3** "½ Anna" on 2 a. verm ("A.D.") (original face value not obliterated) (January) † £1700
a. Error. "½ Annas" ("A.D.") .. ..
23 "½ Anna" on 2 a. vermilion ("A.B.") (February) £3250 £750
a. Error. "½ Annas" ("A.B.") .. .. — £950
24 "½ Anna" on 3 a. black/*dull red* ("A.B.") (May) £4500 £1400
25 "1 Anna" on 3 a. black/*dull red* ("V.H.M.") (June) £4500 £900
26 "1 Anna" on 4 a. brown ("A.B.") (March) £3250 £1300

A.D. = Andrew Dick, Chief Accountant.
A.B. = Archibald Brown, Cashier of the Company.
V.H.M. = Victor H. Mackenzie, Bank Manager.

(Surch B.W.)

1894 (1 Nov). *Surch as T* **5**.

27 **3** 5 a. on 8 a. blue .. .. 55·00 75·00
28 7½ a. on 1 r. carmine .. .. .. 55·00 75·00
27/28 Handstamped "Specimen" .. *Set of* 2 90·00

Forgeries exist.

1895 (16 Jan). *No wmk. P* 14.

29 **3** 5 a. black/*grey-blue* .. .. .. 1·25 9·50
30 7½ a. black .. .. 1·25 11·00
29/30 Handstamped "Specimen" .. *Set of* 2 75·00

The date quoted is that of earliest known use of stamps from this consignment.

These two stamps have "LD" after "COMPANY" in the inscription.

The paper of No. 29 is coloured on the surface only.

1895 (Feb). *No. 8 surch with manuscript value and initials* ("T.E.C.R."). *Original face value obliterated in manuscript.*

31 **3** "½ anna" on 3 a. black/*dull red* (19.2) £350 45·00
32 "1 anna" on 3 a. black/*dull red* (22.2) £3500 £1600

T.E.C.R. = T. E. C. Remington, Postmaster at Mombasa.

Similar manuscript surcharges on the black/*bright red* shade (No. 8*a*) are believed to be forgeries.

The Company experienced considerable financial problems during 1894 with the result that the British Government agreed to assume the administration of the territory, as a protectorate, on 1 July 1895.

IMPERIAL ADMINISTRATION

BRITISH EAST AFRICA (6)

2½ (7)

(Handstamped at Mombasa)

1895 (9 July). *Handstamped with T* **6**.

33 **3** ½ a. deep brown .. .. 60·00 22·00
a. Pale brown .. .. 85·00 32·00
b. Dull brown .. .. † £1500
c. Double £400 £400
d. Inverted £2250
34 1 a. blue-green .. .. 75·00 70·00
a. Double £400 £400
b. "ANL" (broken "D") (R. 6/3) .. £1600
35 **3** 2 a. vermilion .. .. £150 95·00
a. Double £450 £450
36 2½ a. black/*bright yellow* .. .. .. £140 48·00
a. Double £450 £400
37 3 a. black/*dull red* .. .. .. 70·00 40·00
38 4 a. yellow-brown .. .. .. 40·00 35·00
a. Double £425 £425
39 4½ a. dull violet .. .. £170 85·00
a. Double £550 £500
b. Brown-purple £950 £800
ba. Double £1800 £1600
40 5 a. black/*grey-blue* £170 £100
a. Double £800 £750
b. Inverted .. .. † £2250
41 7½ a. black .. .. 90·00 75·00
a. Double £500 £500
42 8 a. blue .. .. 85·00 70·00
a. Double £550 £550
b. Inverted £2500
43 1 r. carmine .. .. 50·00 42·00
a. Double £500 £500
44 **4** 2 r. brick-red £350 £190
45 3 r. slate-purple £170 £110
a. Double £800 £800
b. Inverted .. ..
46 4 r. ultramarine £140 £130
a. Double £800 £800
47 5 r. grey-green £350 £250
a. Double £1200 £1200
33/47 .. .. *Set of* 15 £1900 £1200

Forgeries exist.

1895 (29 Sept). *No. 39 surch with T* **7** *by* The Zanzibar Gazette.

48 **3** 2½ a. on 4½ a. dull violet (R.) .. .. £120 60·00
a. Opt (T **6**) double £800 £750

British East Africa (8)

British East Africa (9)

SETTING OF TYPE 8. This consisted of 120 impressions in 10 horizontal rows of 12 stamps. This matched the size of the pane for all the Indian issues to 1 r. with the exception of the 6 a. The sheets of this value contained four panes, each 8 × 10, which meant that the outer vertical margins also received the overprint.

The setting of Type **9** is not known.

Although only the one setting was used for the low values it is known that some of the overprint errors occurred, or were corrected, during the course of the various printings.

(Overprinted at the offices of *The Zanzibar Gazette*)

1895 (27 Oct)–**96.** *Stamps of India* (*Queen Victoria*) *optd with T* **8** *or* **9** (*2 r. to 5 r.*). *W* **13** (*Elephant Head*) (*6 a.*) *or W* **34** (*Large Star*) (*others*) *of India.*

49 ½ a. blue-green (No. 85) (8.11.95) .. .. 4·50 4·75
a. "Britlsh" for "British" £3000 £2500
b. "Br1tish" for "British" (R. 10/12) .. £350
c. "Afr1ca" for "Africa" (R. 1/11) .. £350
d. Opt double, one albino £225
50 1 a. plum (No. 89) (8.11.95) .. .. 3·75 4·50
a. "Britlsh" for "British" £3500 £2250
b. "Br1tish" for "British" (R. 10/12) .. £325
c. "Afr1ca" for "Africa" (R. 1/11) .. £325
51 1 a. 6 p. sepia (No. 90) (23.11.95) .. .. 3·75 4·00
a. "Br1tish" for "British" (R. 10/12) .. £400
b. "Afr1ca" for "Africa" (R. 1/11) .. £400
52 2 a. blue (No. 92) (8.11.95) .. .. 4·50 2·50
a. "Britlsh" for "British" £2750 £3000
b. "Br1tish" for "British" (R. 10/12) .. £325 £225
c. "Afr1ca" for "Africa" (R. 1/11) .. £325 £225
53 2 a. 6 p. yellow-green (No. 103) .. .. 5·50 2·50
a. "Biitish" for "British" £4250
b. "Bpitish" for "British" £4250
c. "Britlsh" for "British" .. .. .. † £2250
d. "Eas" for "East" (R. 2/12) £900 £1200
e. "Br1tish" for "British" (R. 10/12) .. £400 £275
f. "Afr1ca" for "Africa" (R. 1/11) £400 £275
54 3 a. brown-orange (No. 94) (18.12.95) .. 7·50 9·00
a. "Br1tish" for "British" (R. 10/12) .. £425 £425
b. "Afr1ca" for "Africa" (R. 1/11) .. £425
55 4 a. olive-green (No. 95) (18.12.95) .. 28·00 24·00
a. Slate-green .. .. 26·00 24·00
b. "Br1tish" for "British" (R. 10/12) .. £500 £450
c. "Afr1ca" for "Africa" (R. 1/11) .. £500 £450
56 6 a. pale brown (No. 81) (18.12.95) .. 27·00 40·00
a. "Br1tish" for "British" (R. 10/8) .. £750
b. "Afr1ca" for "Africa" (R. 1/7) £750
c. Opt double, one albino £750
57 8 a. dull mauve (No. 98) (18.12.95) .. 55·00 60·00
a. "Br1tish" for "British" (R. 10/12) .. £850
b. "Afr1ca" for "Africa" (R. 1/11) .. £850
c. Magenta (1896) .. .. .. 28·00 48·00
ca. "Br1tish" for "British" (R. 10/12) .. £650 £600
cb. "Afr1ca" for "Africa" (R. 1/11) .. £650 £600
cc. Inverted "a" for "t" of "East" (R. 2/12) † £5500
58 12 a. purple/*red* (No. 100) (18.12.95) .. 20·00 26·00
a. "Br1tish" for "British" (R. 10/12) .. £600 £600
b. "Afr1ca" for "Africa" (R. 1/11) .. £600
59 1 r. slate (No. 101) (18.12.95) .. .. 65·00 65·00
a. "Br1tish" for "British" (R. 10/12) .. £1000
b. "Afr1ca" for "Africa" (R. 1/11) .. £1000
60 1 r. green & aniline carm (No. 106) (1896) 42·00 75·00
a. Inverted "a" for "t" of "East" (R. 2/12) £5500
b. "Br1tish" for "British" (R. 10/12) .. £750
c. "Afr1ca" for "Africa" (R. 1/11) .. £750
d. Opt double, one sideways £400 £700
e. Opt double, one albino £500
61 2 r. carm & yellow-brn (No. 107) (18.12.95) 60·00 95·00
a. "B" handstamped £2250
62 3 r. brown and green (No. 108) (18.12.95) 70·00 £110
a. "B" handstamped .. .. .. — £2250
b. Opt double, one albino £750
63 5 r. ultramarine & vio (No. 109) (18.12.95) 90·00 £130
a. Opt double £1800
b. "B" handstamped £1800 £1800
49/63 .. .. *Set of* 15 £400 £550

The relative horizontal positions of the three lines of the overprint vary considerably but the distance vertically between the lines of the overprint is constant.

In both the "Br1tish" and "Afr1ca" errors the figure one is in a smaller type size.

There are other varieties, such as inverted "s" in "British", wide and narrow "B", and inverted "V" for "A" in "Africa" (R.1/1 and R.6/7).

During the overprinting of the 2 r. and 5 r. the "B" of "British" sometimes failed to print so that only traces of the letter appeared. It was replaced by a handstamped "B" which is often out of alignment with the rest of the overprint. The handstamp is known double. The variety may also exist on the 3 r.

The 2, 3 and 5 r., normally overprinted in larger type than the lower values, are also known with a smaller overprint, for use as specimen stamps for the U.P.U. These were not issued for postal purposes (*Price £375 un per set*). The lower values were reprinted at the same time using similar type to the original overprint.

Forgeries exist.

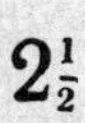
(10)

11

1895 (20 Dec). *No. 51 surch locally with* T **10** *in bright red.*
64 2½ on 1½ a. sepia 65·00 35·00
 a. Inverted "1" in fraction (R. 5/7, 10/7) £800 £600
 b. "Br1tish" for "British" (R. 10/12) £950
 c. "Afr1ca" for "Africa" (R. 1/11) £950

The setting of Type **10** was in 5 horizontal rows of 12 stamps, repeated twice for each pane.

No. 51 also exists surcharged with T **12**, **13** and **14** in brown-red. These stamps were sent to the Postal Union authorities at Berne, but were never issued to the public (*Price unused*: T **12** £85, T **13** £190, T **14** £140).

(Recess D.L.R.)

1896 (26 May)–**1901**. *Wmk Crown CA. P* 14.
65 **11** ½ a. yellow-green 1·25 70
66 1 a. carmine-rose 3·00 40
 a. Bright rose-red 3·00 40
 b. Rosine (1901) 21·00 3·75
67 2 a. chocolate 2·25 4·25
68 2½ a. deep blue 5·50 1·40
 a. Violet-blue 8·50 2·00
 b. Inverted "S" in "ANNAS" (R. 1/1) 80·00 45·00
69 3 a. grey 2·50 5·50
70 4 a. deep green 6·00 3·50
71 4½ a. orange-yellow 4·50 13·00
72 5 a. yellow-bistre 7·50 4·00
73 7½ a. mauve 5·00 22·00
74 8 a. grey-olive 2·50 5·50
75 1 r. pale dull blue 35·00 23·00
 a. Ultramarine 48·00 45·00
76 2 r. orange 50·00 25·00
77 3 r. deep violet 55·00 28·00
78 4 r. carmine-lake 55·00 55·00
79 5 r. sepia 50·00 40·00
 a. Thin "U" in "RUPEES" (R.3/2) £1100 £1100
65/79 *Set of* 15 £250 £190
65/79 Optd "Specimen" *Set of* 15 £275

(Overprinted at the offices of *The Zanzibar Gazette*)

1897 (2 Jan). *Nos.* 156/7, 159 *and* 165/7 *of Zanzibar optd with* T **8**. *Wmk Single Rosette.*
80 ½ a. yellow-green and red 48·00 45·00
81 1 a. indigo and red 85·00 85·00
82 2 a. red-brown and red 29·00 21·00
83 4½ a. orange and red 45·00 26·00
 a. No right serif to left-hand "4" £400
 b. No fraction bar at right £400
84 5 a. bistre and red 45·00 30·00
 a. "Bri" for "British" £1100 £1100
85 7½ a. mauve and red 45·00 35·00
 a. "Bri" for "British" £1200
80/5 *Set of* 6 £250 £200

Nos. 84a and 85a appear to have occurred when the type was obscured during part of the overprinting.

The above six stamps exist with an overprint similar to T **8** but normally showing a stop after "Africa". These overprints (in red on the 1 a.) were made officially to supply the U.P.U. (*Price £300 un per set*). However, the stop does not always show. Pieces are known showing overprints with and without stop *se-tenant* (including the red overprint on the 1 a.).

Stamps of Zanzibar, wmk. "Multiple Rosettes" and overprinted with T **8** are forgeries.

2½ 2½ 2½
(12) (13) (14)

SETTING OF TYPES 12/14. The setting of 60 (6×10) contained 26 examples of Type **12**, 10 of Type **13** and 24 of Type **14**.

1897 (2 Jan). *Nos.* 157 *and* 162 *of Zanzibar optd with* T **8** *and further surch locally, in red.*
86 **12** 2½ on 1 a. indigo and red 80·00 50·00
 b. Opt Type **8** double £4250
87 **13** 2½ on 1 a. indigo and red £170 90·00
88 **14** 2½ on 1 a. indigo and red 90·00 55·00
 a. Opt Type **8** double £4750
89 **12** 2½ on 3 a. grey and red 75·00 48·00
90 **13** 2½ on 3 a. grey and red £160 90·00
91 **14** 2½ on 3 a. grey and red 85·00 50·00
86/91 *Set of* 6 £600 £350

Both the notes after No. 85 also apply here.

A special printing for U.P.U. requirements was made with the 2½ surcharge on the 1 a. and 3 a. stamps overprinted as T **8** but *with stop* after "Africa". It also included a "2" over "1" error in T **14**.

15

(Recess D.L.R.)

1897 (Nov)–**1903**. *Wmk Crown CC. P* 14.
92 **15** 1 r. grey-blue 45·00 28·00
 a. Dull blue (1901) 42·00 24·00
 b. Bright ultramarine (1903) £170 £130
93 2 r. orange 65·00 65·00
94 3 r. deep violet 70·00 85·00
95 4 r. carmine £180 £225
96 5 r. deep sepia £140 £190
97 10 r. yellow-bistre (S. £60) £225 £250
98 20 r. pale green (S. £125) £550 £1200
99 50 r. mauve (S. £250) £1600 £3500
92/96 Optd "Specimen" *Set of* 5 £180

On 1 April 1901 the postal administrations of British East Africa and Uganda were merged. Subsequent issues were inscribed "EAST AFRICA AND UGANDA PROTECTORATES".

EAST AFRICA AND UGANDA PROTECTORATES

For earlier issues see BRITISH EAST AFRICA and UGANDA.

For the issues of the Mandated Territory of Tanganyika and the war-time issues that preceded them, see TANGANYIKA.

PRICES FOR STAMPS ON COVER TO 1945	
Nos. 1/43	*from* × 3
Nos. 44/75	*from* × 2
Nos. 76/95	*from* × 3
Nos. 96/105	—
Nos. 110/23	*from* × 2
Nos. 124/7	*from* × 3
Nos. 128/30	*from* × 5
Nos. 131/54	*from* × 3
Nos. D1/12	*from* × 8

PRINTERS. All the stamps issued between 1903 and 1927 were typographed by De La Rue & Co. Ltd, London.

USED HIGH VALUES. Beware of cleaned fiscally cancelled copies with faked postmarks.

1

2

1903 (24 July)–**04**. *P* 14. (*a*) *Wmk Crown CA.*
1 **1** ½ a. green (16.2.04) 3·00 7·50
2 1 a. grey and red 1·75 30
3 2 a. dull and bright purple (24.7.03) 7·50 2·50
 w. Wmk inverted 90·00 90·00
4 2½ a. blue 12·00 48·00
5 3 a. brown-purple and green 17·00 48·00
6 4 a. grey-green and black 11·00 17·00
7 5 a. grey and orange-brown 18·00 48·00
8 8 a. grey and pale blue 21·00 35·00

(*b*) *Wmk Crown CC. Ordinary paper*
9 **2** 1 r. green 14·00 50·00
 a. Chalk-surfaced paper 32·00 70·00
10 2 r. dull and bright purple 55·00 55·00
11 3 r. grey-green and black 80·00 £150
12 4 r. grey and emerald-green 75·00 £130
13 5 r. grey and red 85·00 £150
14 10 r. grey and ultramarine £140 £225
 a. Chalk-surfaced paper £170 £250
 w. Wmk inverted £275
15 20 r. grey and stone (Optd S. £120) £425 £800
16 50 r. grey and red-brown (Optd S. £250) £1100 £1800
 w. Wmk inverted £1600
1/13 *Set of* 13 £350 £650
1/14 Optd "Specimen" *Set of* 14 £275

1904–07. *Wmk Mult Crown CA. Ordinary paper* (½ *a. to* 8 *a.*) *or chalk-surfaced paper* (1 *r. to* 50 *r.*).
17 **1** ½ a. grey-green 6·50 2·00
 a. Chalk-surfaced paper 4·00 2·50
18 1 a. grey and red 3·75 50
 a. Chalk-surfaced paper 4·75 75
19 2 a. dull and bright purple 3·25 1·75
 a. Chalk-surfaced paper 2·50 1·50
20 2½ a. blue 10·00 28·00
21 2½ a. ultramarine and blue 7·50 17·00
22 3 a. brown-purple and green 3·75 30·00
 a. Chalk-surfaced paper 3·75 25·00
23 4 a. grey-green and black 7·50 16·00
 a. Chalk-surfaced paper 7·50 18·00
24 5 a. grey and orange-brown 8·00 15·00
 a. Chalk-surfaced paper 6·50 25·00
25 8 a. grey and pale blue 7·00 8·50
 a. Chalk-surfaced paper 7·00 16·00
26 **2** 1 r. green (1907) 27·00 60·00
27 2 r. dull and bright purple (1906) 35·00 55·00
28 **2** 3 r. grey-green and black (1907) 50·00 90·00
29 4 r. grey and emerald-green (1907) 55·00 £120
30 5 r. grey and red (1907) 60·00 90·00
31 10 r. grey and ultramarine (1907) £120 £150
32 20 r. grey and stone (1907) £475 £800
33 50 r. grey and red-brown (1907) £1200 £1900
17/30 *Set of* 13 £225 £450

(New Currency. 100 cents = 1 rupee)

1907–08. *Wmk Mult Crown CA. Chalk-surfaced paper* (10, 12, 25, 50, 75 *c.*). *P* 14.
34 **1** 1 c. brown 1·00 15
35 3 c. grey-green 6·00 40
 a. Blue-green 7·00 2·25
36 6 c. red 2·75 10
37 10 c. lilac and pale olive 9·00 8·50
38 12 c. dull and bright purple 7·50 2·75
39 15 c. bright blue 10·00 8·50
40 25 c. grey-green and black 4·75 6·50
41 50 c. grey-green and orange-brown 10·00 12·00
42 75 c. grey and pale blue (1908) 4·50 32·00
34/42 *Set of* 9 50·00 65·00
34/42 Optd "Specimen" *Set of* 9 £160

Original

Redrawn

1910. T **1** *redrawn. Printed from a single plate. Wmk Mult Crown CA. P* 14.
43 6 c. red 7·00 20

In the redrawn type a fine white line has been cut around the value tablets and above the name tablet separating the latter from the leaves above, EAST AFRICA AND UGANDA is in shorter and thicker letters and PROTECTORATES in taller letters than in No. 36.

3

4

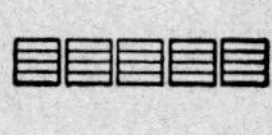
4
cents
(5)

1912–21. *Wmk Mult Crown CA. Chalk-surfaced paper* (25 *c. to* 500 *r.*). *P* 14.
44 **3** 1 c. black 30 1·40
45 3 c. green 2·00 40
 a. Deep blue-green (1917) 4·50 85
46 6 c. red 70 40
 a. Scarlet (1917) 13·00 1·75
47 10 c. yellow-orange 2·00 40
 a. Orange (1921) 9·00 2·00
48 12 c. slate-grey 2·75 50
49 15 c. bright blue 2·75 60
50 25 c. black and red/*yellow* 45 90
 a. White back (5.14) (Optd S. £27) 50 3·50
 b. On lemon (1916) (Optd S. £27) 11·00 11·00
 c. On orange-buff (1921) 45·00 17·00
 d. On pale yellow (1921) 8·00 4·25
51 50 c. black and lilac 1·50 90
52 75 c. black/*green* 1·50 16·00
 a. White back (5.14) (Optd S. £27) 90 15·00
 b. On blue-green, ol back (Optd S. £27) 6·00 6·50
 c. On emerald, olive back (1919) 42·00 £130
 d. On emerald back (1921) 11·00 38·00
53 **4** 1 r. black/*green* 1·75 3·75
 a. On emerald back (1919) 5·00 40·00
54 2 r. red and black/*blue* 20·00 30·00
 w. Wmk inverted £120
55 3 r. violet and green 20·00 60·00
56 4 r. red and green/*yellow* 45·00 £100
 a. On pale yellow 90·00 £140
57 5 r. blue and dull purple 45·00 £110
58 10 r. red and green/*green* 80·00 £130
59 20 r. black and purple/*red* £275 £300
60 20 r. purple and blue/*blue* (1918) £250 £275
61 50 r. carmine and green (Optd S. £140) £500 £600
 a. Ordinary paper. *Dull rose-red and dull greyish green* £650 £700
62 100 r. purple and black/*red* (Optd S. £250) £3250 £2250
63 500 r. green and red/*green* (Optd S. £550) £14000
44/58 *Set of* 15 £200 £400
44/60 Optd "Specimen" *Set of* 17 £475

For values in this series overprinted "G.E.A." (German East Africa) see Tanganyika Nos. 45/62.

1919 (7 Apr). *No.* 46a *surch with* T **5** *by the Swift Press, Nairobi.*
64 **3** 4 c. on 6 c. scarlet (*shades*) 75 15
 a. Bars omitted 38·00 60·00
 b. Surch double £110 £160
 c. Surch inverted £200 £275
 d. Pair, one without surch £950 £1000
64 H/S "Specimen" 55·00

1921–22. *Wmk Mult Script CA. Chalk-surfaced paper* (50 *c. to* 50 *r.*). *P* 14.
65 **3** 1 c. black 40 1·25
66 3 c. green 3·75 6·00
 a. Blue-green 13·00 10·00
67 6 c. carmine-red 3·25 7·00
68 10 c. orange (12.21) 8·00 60
69 12 c. slate-grey 3·25 70·00
70 15 c. bright blue 4·25 12·00
71 50 c. black and dull purple 12·00 80·00
72 **4** 2 r. red and black/*blue* 50·00 £130
73 3 r. violet and green 90·00 £150

74	4	5 r. blue and dull purple	£100	£180
75		50 r. carmine and green (Optd S. £250)	£1900	£3500
65/74		.. .. *Set of* 10	£250	£550
65/74 Optd "Specimen"		.. .. *Set of* 10	£250	

For values in this series overprinted "G.E.A." see Tanganyika Nos. 63/73.

KENYA AND UGANDA

(New Currency. 100 cents = 1 East Africa shilling)

On 23 July 1920 Kenya became a Crown Colony with the exception of the coastal strip, previously part of the Sultan of Zanzibar's territories, which remained a protectorate.

The northern province of Jubaland was ceded to Italy on 29 June 1925 and later incorporated into Italian Somaliland.

6

7

1922 (1 Nov)–**27**. *Wmk Script CA. P* 14.

(a) Wmk upright. Ordinary paper

76	6	1 c. pale brown	80	2·00
		a. Deep brown (1923)	1·50	2·75
		ax. Wmk reversed		
77		5 c. dull violet	3·25	50
		a. Bright violet	4·50	1·50
78		5 c. green (1927)	2·00	10
79		10 c. green	1·50	10
80		10 c. black (5.27)	3·00	10
81		12 c. jet-black	6·50	30·00
		a. Grey-black	2·50	25·00
82		15 c. rose-carmine	1·25	10
83		20 c. dull orange-yellow	3·25	10
		a. Bright orange	3·75	10
84		30 c. ultramarine	2·00	40
85		50 c. grey	2·50	10
86		75 c. olive	3·00	8·00

(b) Wmk sideways. Chalk-surfaced paper

87	7	1 s. green	3·00	2·25
88		2 s. dull purple	8·00	8·00
89		2 s. 50 c. brown (1.10.25)	18·00	65·00
90		3 s. brownish grey	17·00	6·00
		a. Jet-black	32·00	26·00
91		4 s. grey (1.10.25)	20·00	75·00
92		5 s. carmine-red	22·00	18·00
93		7 s. 50 c. orange-yellow (1.10.25) .	60·00	£140
94		10 s. bright blue	48·00	48·00
95		£1 black and orange	£140	£200
96		£2 green and purple (1.10.25) (S. £110)	£600	
97		£3 purple and yellow (1.10.25) (S. £120)	£750	
98		£4 black & magenta (1.10.25) (S. £160)	£1200	
99		£5 black and blue (S. £200)	£1500	
100		£10 black and green (S. £250) ..	£7500	
101		£20 red and green (1.10.25) (S. £375)	£13000	
102		£25 black and red (S. £400)	£16000	
103		£50 black and brown (S. £450) ..	£23000	
104		£75 purple and grey (1.10.25) (S. £550)	£48000	
105		£100 red and black (1.10.25) (S. £600)	£50000	
76/95		.. .. *Set of* 20	£325	£550
76/95 Optd "Specimen"		.. .. *Set of* 20	£425	

Specimen copies of Nos. 96/105 are all overprinted.

KENYA, UGANDA AND TANGANYIKA

The postal administrations of Kenya, Tanganyika and Uganda were amalgamated on 1 January 1933. On the independence of the three territories the combined administration became the East African Posts and Telecommunications Corporation.

8 South African Crowned Cranes

9 Dhow on Lake Victoria

10 Lion

11 Kilimanjaro

12 Jinja Railway Bridge by Ripon Falls

13 Mt. Kenya

14 Lake Naivasha

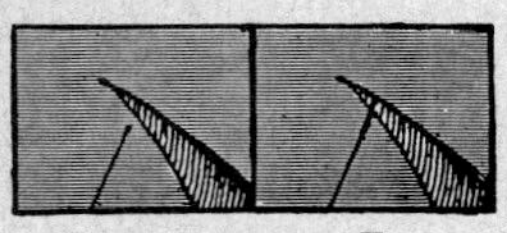

I II

(Des 1 c., 20 c., 10 s., R. C. Luck, 10 c., £1, A. Ross, 15 c., 2 s., G. Gill Holmes, 30 c., 5 s., R. N. Ambasana, 65 c., L. R. Cutts. T **10** typo, remainder recess D.L.R.).

1935 (1 May)–**37**. *Wmk Mult Script CA. Chalk-surfaced paper* (*10 c., £1*). *P* 12×13 (**10**), 14 (**9** *and* **14**) *and* 13 (*remainder*).

110	8	1 c. black and red-brown	20	1·50
111	9	5 c. black and green (I)	1·25	40
		a. Rope joined to sail (II) (1937) ..	25·00	4·00
		b. Perf 13×12 (I) (1936)	£2000	£400
		ba. Rope joined to sail (II) (1937) ..	£550	£150
112	10	10 c. black and yellow	2·25	40
113	11	15 c. black and scarlet	75	10
114	8	20 c. black and orange	1·25	10
115	12	30 c. black and blue	1·25	1·25
116	9	50 c. bright purple and black (I) ..	90	10
117	13	65 c. black and brown	2·25	2·00
118	14	1 s. black and green	75	50
		a. Perf 13×12 (1936)	£1000	£110
119	11	2 s. lake and purple	4·25	3·50
120	14	3 s. blue and black	6·00	13·00
		a. Perf 13×12 (1936)	£1600	
121	12	5 s. black and carmine	17·00	26·00
122	8	10 s. purple and blue	48·00	70·00
123	10	£1 black and red	£110	£130
110/23		.. .. *Set of* 14	£170	£225
110/23 Perf "Specimen"		.. .. *Set of* 14	£250	

Line through "0" of 1910 (R.4/2)

1935 (6 May). *Silver Jubilee. As Nos.* 114/17 *of Jamaica, but ptd by D.L.R. P* 13½×14.

124	20 c. light blue and olive-green	50	10
	f. Diagonal line by turret	55·00	
	g. Dot to left of chapel	75·00	
	h. Dot by flagstaff	75·00	
	i. Dash by turret	75·00	
125	30 c. brown and deep blue	2·25	2·75
	f. Diagonal line by turret	90·00	
	g. Dot to left of chapel	£140	
	h. Dot by flagstaff	£140	
	i. Dash by turret	£140	
126	65 c. green and indigo	1·75	2·75
	f. Diagonal line by turret	90·00	
	g. Dot to left of chapel	£140	
127	1 s. slate and purple	2·00	2·00
	f. Diagonal line by turret	95·00	
	g. Dot to left of chapel	£150	
	h. Dot by flagstaff	£150	
	l. Line through "0" of 1910	90·00	
124/7	.. .. *Set of* 4	6·00	7·00
124/7 Perf "Specimen"	.. .. *Set of* 4	£100	

For illustrations of the other plate varieties see Omnibus section following Zimbabwe.

1937 (12 May). *Coronation. As Nos.* 118/20 *of Jamaica.*

128	5 c. green	20	10
129	20 c. orange	40	30
130	30 c. bright blue	60	95
128/30	.. .. *Set of* 3	1·10	1·25
128/30 Perf "Specimen"	.. .. *Set of* 3	65·00	

15 Dhow on Lake Victoria

Damaged left-hand value tablet (Frame Pl 2–2, with Centre Pl 4B only, R. 9/6)

Retouched value tablet (Frame Pl 2–2, with Centre Pls 4B, 5, 6 or 7, R. 9/6)

Break in bird's breast (Frame Pl 2–2, with Centre Pls 4A or 4B, R. 2/5)

Retouch on 10 c. and 1 s. (Pl 7B, R. 5/10 and 6/7. Ptgs from June 1949 onwards)

With dot

Dot removed

In the 50 c. printing of 14 June 1950, using Frame-plate 3, the dot was removed by retouching on all but five stamps (R. 5/2, 6/1, 7/2, 7/4, and 9/1). In addition, other stamps show traces of the dot where the retouching was not completely effective.

PERFORATIONS. In this issue, to aid identification, the perforations are indicated to the nearest quarter.

(T **10** typo, others recess D.L.R.)

1938 (11 Apr)–**54**. *As T* **8** *to* **14** (*but with portrait of King George VI in place of King George V, as in T* **15**). *Wmk Mult Script CA. Chalk-surfaced paper* (£1).

131	8	1 c. black & red-brown (*p* 13¼) (2.5.38)	1·25	65
		a. Perf 13¼×13¾. *Black & chocolate-brown* (1942)	30	40
		ab. Damaged value tablet	80·00	
		ac. Retouched value tablet	45·00	60·00
		ad. Break in bird's breast	75·00	
		ae. Black & dp chocolate-brn (10.6.46)	1·75	1·50
		af. Ditto. Retouched tablet	50·00	65·00
		ag. Black and red-brown (26.9.51) ..	1·50	1·50
132	15	5 c. black and green (II) (*p* 13×11¾) ..	2·00	30
133		5 c. reddish brown & orange (*p* 13×11¾) (1.6.49)	40	2·50
		a. Perf 13×12½ (14.6.50)	1·25	3·00
134	14	10 c. red-brn & orge (*p* 13×11¾) (2.5.38)	1·75	10
		aw. Wmk inverted		
		b. Perf 14 (22.4.41)	£100	6·50
135		10 c. black and green (*p* 13×11¾) (1.6.49)	30	70
		a. Mountain retouch	70·00	38·00
		b. Perf 13×12½ (14.6.50)	1·25	10
136		10 c. brown and grey (*p* 13×12½) (1.4.52)	75	50
137	11	15 c. black and rose-red (*p* 13¼) (2.5.38)	8·50	50
		a. Perf 13¾×13¼ (2.43)	3·00	3·25
		ab. "A" of "CA" missing from wmk ..		
138		15 c. black & green (*p* 13¾×13¼) (1.4.52)	1·25	2·50
139	8	20 c. black and orange (*p* 13¼) (2.5.38)	35·00	20
		a. Perf 14 (19.5.41)	55·00	1·75
		b. Perf 13¼×13¾ (25.2.42)	6·00	10
		ba. Deep black and deep orange (8.51)	10·00	95
		bw. Wmk inverted	†	—
140	15	25 c. blk & carm-red (*p* 13×12½) (1.4.52)	1·25	1·75
141	12	30 c. black and dull vio-bl (*p* 13¼) (2.5.38)	50·00	40
		a. Perf 14 (3.7.41)	£140	11·00
		b. Perf 13¼×13¾ (10.5.42)	2·75	10
142		30 c. dull purple and brown (*p* 13¼×13¾) (1.4.52)	1·00	30
143	8	40 c. black & blue (*p* 13¼×13¾) (1.4.52)	1·75	2·75
144	15	50 c. purple & blk (II) (*p* 13×11¾) (2.5.38)	11·00	80
		a. Rope not joined to sail (I) (R. 2/5)	£225	£200
		b. Dull claret and black (29.7.47) ..	22·00	3·75
		c. Brown-purple and black (4.48) ..	22·00	3·75
		d. Reddish purple and black (28.4.49)	18·00	2·00
		e. Ditto. Perf 13×12½ (10.49) ..	7·00	45
		ea. Dot removed (14.6.50)	10·00	40
		eb. Ditto. In pair with normal ..	£225	95·00
145	14	1 s. black & yellowish brn (*p* 13×11¾) (2.5.38)	8·50	20
		a. Black and brown (9.42)	7·50	30
		ab. Mountain retouch (7.49)	£400	£100
		aw. Wmk inverted	†	£1600
		b. Perf 13×12½ (10.49)	8·00	60
		ba. Deep black and brown (clearer impression) (14.6.50)	9·50	1·00
146	11	2 s. lake-brn & brn-pur (*p* 13¼) (2.5.38)	£110	1·75
		a. Perf 14 (1941)	70·00	11·00
		b. Perf 13¾×13¼ (24.2.44)	13·00	30
147	14	3 s. dull ultramarine & blk (*p* 13×11¾) (2.5.38)	35·00	3·25
		a. Deep violet-blue and black (29.7.47)	45·00	6·50
		b. Ditto. Perf 13×12½ (14.6.50) ..	20·00	1·75
148	12	5 s. black and carmine (*p* 13¼) (2.5.38)	£130	12·00
		a. Perf 14 (1941)	26·00	1·75
		b. Perf 13¼×13¾ (24.2.44)	21·00	80
149	8	10 s. purple and blue (*p* 13¼) (2.5.38)	£120	19·00
		a. Perf 14. *Reddish purple & bl* (1941)	30·00	17·00
		b. Perf 13¼×13¾ (24.2.44)	30·00	3·00
150	10	£1 black and red (*p* 11¾×13) (12.10.38)	£300	£120
		a. Perf 14 (1941)	16·00	15·00
		ab. Ordinary paper (24.2.44)	16·00	15·00
		b. Perf 12½ (21.1.54)	10·00	27·00
131/50ab (*cheapest*)		.. .. *Set of* 20	£110	29·00
131/50 Perf "Specimen"		.. .. *Set of* 13	£400	

The first printing of the 50 c. utilised the King George V centre plate on which each impression had been individually corrected to show the rope joined to sail. R.2/5 was missed, however, and this continued to show Type I until replaced by a further printing from a new plate in September 1938.

Stamps perf 14, together with Nos. 131a, 137a, 139b, 141b, 146b, 148b and 149b, are the result of air raid damage to the De La Rue works which destroyed the normal perforators. Dates quoted for these stamps represent earliest known postmarks.

10c
KENYA
TANGANYIKA
UGANDA

(16)

A screw head in the surcharging forme appears as a crescent moon (R. 20/4)

1941 (1 July)–**42**. *Pictorial Stamps of South Africa variously surch as T* **16** *by Government Printer, Pretoria. Inscr alternately in English and Afrikaans.*

		Un. pair	Used pair	Used single
151	5 c. on 1d. grey & carmine (No. 56)	60	1·75	15
152	10 c. on 3d. ultramarine (No. 59)	1·00	4·50	30
153	20 c. on 6d. green & verm (No. 61*a*)	75	2·25	20
154	70 c. on 1s. brown and chalky blue (No. 62) (20.4.42)	8·50	4·50	40
	a. Crescent moon flaw	60·00		
151/4	*Set of* 4	9·75	11·50	95
151/4	Handstamped "Specimen" *Set of* 4	£180		

1946 (11 Nov). *Victory. As Nos.* 141/2 *of Jamaica.*

		Unused	Used
155	20 c. red-orange	20	10
156	30 c. blue	20	40
155/6	Perf "Specimen" *Set of* 2	50·00	

Examples of Nos. 155/6 were prereleased at Lindi on 15 October 1946.

1948 (1 Dec). *Royal Silver Wedding. As Nos.* 143/4 *of Jamaica.*

157	20 c. orange	15	10
158	£1 scarlet	35·00	48·00

1949 (10 Oct). *75th Anniv of Universal Postal Union. As Nos.* 145/8 *of Jamaica.*

159	20 c. red-orange	20	10
160	30 c. deep blue	1·25	75
161	50 c. grey	60	10
162	1 s. red-brown	75	40
159/62	*Set of* 4	2·50	1·25

17 Lake Naivasha

(Recess D.L.R.)

1952 (1 Feb). *Visit of Princess Elizabeth and Duke of Edinburgh. Wmk Mult Script CA. P* 13 × 12½.

163	**17**	10 c. black and green	10	1·00
164		1 s. black and brown	20	1·75

1953 (2 June). *Coronation. As No.* 153 *of Jamaica.*
165 20 c. black and red-orange . . 15 10

1954 (28 Apr). *Royal Visit. As No.* 171 *but inscr* "ROYAL VISIT 1954" *below portrait.*
166 30 c. black and deep ultramarine . . 20 15

18 Owen Falls Dam

19 Giraffe

20 Royal Lodge, Sagana

21 Queen Elizabeth II

(Des G. Gill Holmes (10, 50 c.), H. Grieme (15 c., 1 s. 30, 5 s.), R. McLellan Sim (10 s.), De La Rue (65 c., 2 s., £1), O.C. Meronti (others). Recess D.L.R.)

1954 (1 June)–**59**. *Designs as T* **18/21**. *Wmk Mult Script CA. P* 13 (£1); *others*, 12½×13 (*vert*) *or* 13×12½ (*horiz*).

167	5 c. black and deep brown	15	30
	a. Vignette inverted	†	£14000
168	10 c. carmine-red	75	10
169	15 c. black and light blue (28.3.58)	55	80
	a. Redrawn. Stop below "c" of "15 c" (29.4.59)	55	70
170	20 c. black and orange	70	10
	a. Imperf (pair)	£750	£850
171	30 c. black and deep ultramarine	80	10
	a. Vignette inverted	†	£10000
172	40 c. bistre-brown (28.3.58)	3·00	75
	w. Wmk inverted		
173	50 c. reddish purple	1·25	10
	a. Claret (23.1.57)	2·00	10
174	65 c. bluish green & brown-purple (1.12.55)	2·75	1·00
175	1 s. black and claret	80	10
176	1 s. 30, deep lilac and orange (1.12.55)	8·00	10
177	2 s. black and green	3·50	60
	a. Black and bronze-green (19.4.56)	4·75	90
178	5 s. black and orange	10·00	1·00
179	10 s. black and deep ultramarine	17·00	1·75
180	£1 brown-red and black	16·00	11·00
	a. Venetian red and black (19.4.56)	38·00	15·00
167/80	*Set of* 14	55·00	15·00

Designs: *Vert as T* **18/19**—5, 30 c. Type **18**; 10, 50 c. Type **19**; 20, 40 c., 1 s. Lion. *Horiz as T* **20**—15 c., 1 s. 30, 5 s. African Elephants; 65 c., 2 s. Kilimanjaro.

Only one example of No. 167a and two of No. 171a have been found, all being used.

25 Map of E. Africa showing Lakes

(Recess Waterlow)

1958 (30 July). *Centenary of Discovery of Lakes Tanganyika and Victoria by Burton and Speke. W* w **12**. *P* 12½.

181	**25**	40 c. blue and deep green	30	20
182		1 s. 30 c. green and violet	30	90

26 Sisal

27 Cotton

28 Mt Kenya and Giant Plants

29 Queen Elizabeth II

(Des M. Goaman. Photo (5 c. to 65 c.), recess (others) D.L.R.)

1960 (1 Oct). *Designs as T* **26/9**. *W* w **12**. *P* 15 × 14 (5 *c. to* 65 *c.*), 13 (20 *s.*) *or* 14 (*others*).

183	5 c. Prussian blue	10	15
184	10 c. yellow-green	10	10
185	15 c. dull purple	30	10
186	20 c. magenta	20	10
187	25 c. bronze-green	3·25	1·00
188	30 c. vermilion	15	10
189	40 c. greenish blue	15	10
190	50 c. slate-violet	15	10
191	65 c. yellow-olive	30	75
192	1 s. deep reddish violet and reddish purple	80	10
193	1 s. 30, chocolate and brown-red	1·75	15
194	2 s. deep grey-blue and greenish blue	1·75	30
195	2 s. 50, olive-green and deep bluish green	3·50	2·75
196	5 s. rose-red and purple	3·75	60
197	10 s. blackish green and olive-green	7·50	6·00
	a. Imperf (pair)	£600	
198	20 s. violet-blue and lake	16·00	15·00
183/198	*Set of* 16	35·00	24·00

Designs: *Vert as T* **26/7**—15 c. Coffee; 20 c. Blue Wildebeest; 25 c. Ostrich; 30 c. Thomson's Gazelle; 40 c. Manta; 50 c. Common Zebra; 65 c. Cheetah. *Horiz as T* **28**—1 s. 30, Murchison Falls and Hippopotamus; 2 s. Mt Kilimanjaro and Giraffe; 2 s. 50, Candelabra Tree and Black Rhinoceros; 5 s. Crater Lake and Mountains of the Moon; 10 s. Ngorongoro Crater and African Buffalo.

The 10 c. and 50 c. exist in coils with the designs slightly shorter in height, a wider horizontal gutter every eleven stamps and, in the case of the 10 c. only, printed with a coarser 200 screen instead of the normal 250. (*Price for* 10 *c.* 10*p. unused.*) Plate 2 of 30 c. shows coarser 200 screen. (*Price* 25*p. unused.*)

30 Land Tillage

(Des V. Whiteley. Photo Harrison)

1963 (21 Mar). *Freedom from Hunger. T* **30** *and similar horiz design. P* 14½.

199	**30**	15 c. blue and yellow-olive	10	10
200	–	30 c. red-brown and yellow	20	10
201	**30**	50 c. blue and orange-brown	30	10
202	–	1 s. 30, red-brown and light blue	55	1·75
199/202		*Set of* 4	1·00	1·75

Design:—30 c., 1 s. 30, African with Corncob.

31 Scholars and Open Book

(Photo Harrison)

1963 (28 June). *Founding of East African University. P* 14½.

203	**31**	30 c. lake, violet, black and greenish blue	10	10
204		1 s. 30, lake, blue, red & lt yellow-brown	20	20

32 Red Cross Emblem

(Des V. Whiteley. Photo Harrison)

1963 (2 Sept). *Centenary of Red Cross. P* 14½.

205	**32**	30 c. red and blue	1·00	10
206		50 c. red and yellow-brown	1·25	35

PRINTERS. All the following stamps were printed in photogravure by Harrison, *unless otherwise stated.*

33 Chrysanthemum Emblems **34**

35 East African "Flags"

(Des V. Whiteley)

1964 (21 Oct). *Olympic Games. Tokyo. P* 14½.

207	**33**	30 c. yellow and reddish violet	10	10
208	**34**	50 c. deep reddish violet and yellow	15	10
209	**35**	1 s. 30, orange-yellow, dp green & lt blue	25	10
210		2 s. 50, magenta, deep violet-blue & lt bl	35	1·10
207/10		*Set of* 4	75	1·25

KENYA, UGANDA AND TANZANIA

The following stamps were issued by the East African Postal Administration for use in Uganda, Kenya and Tanzania, excluding Zanzibar.

36 Rally Badge

37 Cars *en route*

1965 (15 Apr*). *13th East African Safari Rally. P* 14.

211	**36**	30 c. black, yellow and turquoise	10	10
212		50 c. black, yellow and brown	10	10
		a. Imperf (pair)	£600	
213	**37**	1 s. 30, dp bluish green, yell-ochre & blue	25	10
214		2 s. 50, dp bluish green, brn-red & lt blue	40	1·25
211/14		*Set of* 4	75	1·40

*This is the local release date. The Crown Agents in London issued the stamps the previous day.

38 I.T.U. Emblem and Symbols

1965 (17 May). *I.T.U. Centenary. P* 14½.

215	**38**	30 c. gold, chocolate and magenta	20	10
216		50 c. gold, chocolate and grey	20	10
217		1 s. 30, gold, chocolate and blue	45	10
218		2 s. 50, gold, chocolate & turquoise-grn	90	2·00
215/18		*Set of* 4	1·60	2·00

39 I.C.Y. Emblem

1965 (4 Aug). *International Co-operation Year. P* 14½ × 14.
219 **39** 30 c. deep bluish green and gold 10 10
220 50 c. black and gold 15 10
221 1 s. 30, ultramarine and gold 30 10
222 2 s. 50, carmine-red and gold . . . . 75 2·25
219/22 . . . . *Set of* 4 1·25 2·25

40 Game Park Lodge, Tanzania

(Des Rena Fennessy)

1966 (4 Apr). *Tourism. T* **40** *and similar horiz designs. Multi-coloured. P* 14½.
223 30 c. Type **40** 15 10
224 50 c. Murchison Falls, Uganda 50 10
a. Blue omitted £225
225 1 s. 30, Lesser Flamingoes, Lake Nakuru, Kenya . . . . 2·25 30
226 2 s. 50, Deep Sea Fishing, Tanzania . . . . 2·00 3·00
223/6 . . . . *Set of* 4 4·50 3·00

41 Games Emblem

(Des Harrison)

1966 (2 Aug). *Eighth British Empire and Commonwealth Games Jamaica. P* 14½.
227 **41** 30 c. black, gold, turq-green & grey . . 10 10
228 50 c. black, gold, cobalt and cerise . . 15 10
229 1 s. 30, blk, gold, rosine & dp bluish grn 20 10
230 2 s. 50, black, gold, lake and ultramarine 35 90
227/30 . . . . *Set of* 4 70 1·00

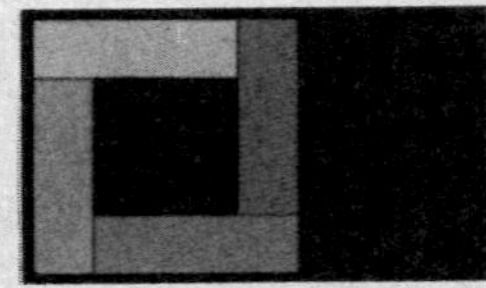

42 U.N.E.S.C.O. Emblem

(Des Harrison)

1966 (3 Oct). *20th Anniv of U.N.E.S.C.O. P* 14½ × 14.
231 **42** 30 c. black, emerald and red 25 10
232 50 c. black, emerald and light brown . . 35 10
233 1 s. 30, black, emerald and grey . . 85 15
234 2 s. 50, black, emerald and yellow . . 1·50 2·00
231/4 . . . . *Set of* 4 2·75 2·00

43 De Havilland D.H.89 Dragon Rapide

(Des R. Granger Barrett)

1967 (23 Jan). *21st Anniv of East African Airways. T* **43** *and similar horiz designs. P* 14½.
235 30 c. slate-violet, greenish blue & myrtle-grn 30 10
236 50 c. multicoloured 40 10
a. Red omitted £250
237 1 s. 30, multicoloured 85 30
238 2 s. 50, multicoloured . . . . . . 1·25 2·50
235/8 . . . . *Set of* 4 2·50 2·75
Designs:—50 c. Vickers Super VC-10; 1 s. 30, Hawker Siddeley Comet 4B; 2 s. 50, Fokker F.27 Friendship.

44 Pillar Tomb

45 Rock Painting

(Des Rena Fennessy)

1967 (2 May). *Archaeological Relics. T* **44/5** *and similar designs. P* 14½.
239 30 c. ochre, black and deep reddish purple . . 15 10
240 50 c. orange-red, black and greyish brown . . 65 10
241 1 s. 30, black, greenish, yellow and deep yellow-green 85 10
242 2 s. 50, black, ochre and brown-red . . . . 1·40 2·50
239/42 . . . . *Set of* 4 2·75 2·50
Designs:—1 s. 30, Clay head; 2 s. 50, Proconsul skull.

48 Unified Symbols of Kenya, Tanzania, and Uganda

(Des Rena Fennessy)

1967 (1 Dec). *Foundation of East African Community. P* 14½ × 14.
243 **48** 5 s. gold, black and grey . . . . 40 1·00

49 Mountaineering

(Des Rena Fennessy)

1968 (4 Mar). *Mountains of East Africa. T* **49** *and similar horiz designs. Multicoloured. P* 14.
244 30 c. Type **49** 15 10
245 50 c. Mount Kenya 30 10
246 1 s. 30, Mount Kilimanjaro 60 10
247 2 s. 50, Ruwenzori Mountains . . . . 90 2·00
244/7 . . . . *Set of* 4 1·75 2·00

50 Family and Rural Hospital

(Des Rena Fennessy. Litho D.L.R.)

1968 (13 May). *20th Anniv of World Health Organization. T* **50** *and similar horiz designs. P* 13½.
248 30 c. deep yellow-green, lilac and chocolate . . 10 10
249 50 c. slate-lilac, lilac and black 15 10
250 1 s. 30, yellow-brown, lilac and chocolate . . 20 15
251 2 s. 50, grey, black and reddish lilac . . . . 30 1·60
248/51 . . . . *Set of* 4 60 1·75
Designs:—50 c. Family and nurse; 1 s. 30, Family and microscope; 2 s. 50, Family and hypodermic syringe.

51 Olympic Stadium, Mexico City

(Des V. Whiteley)

1968 (14 Oct). *Olympic Games, Mexico. T* **51** *and similar designs. P* 14.
252 30 c. light green and black 10 10
253 50 c. black and blue-green 15 10
254 1 s. 30, carmine-red, black and grey 25 10
255 2 s. 50, blackish brown and yellow-brown . . 35 1·00
252/5 . . . . *Set of* 4 70 1·10
Designs: *Horiz*—50 c. High-diving boards; 1 s. 30, Running tracks. *Vert*—2 s. 50, Boxing ring.

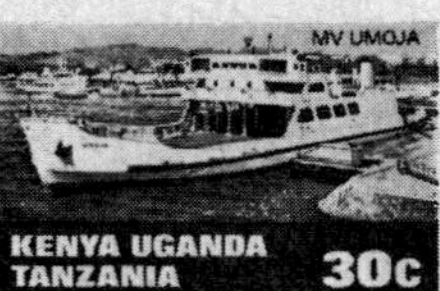

52 M.V. *Umoja*

(Des A. Grosart)

1969 (20 Jan). *Water Transport. T* **52** *and similar horiz designs. P* 14.
256 30 c. deep blue, light blue and slate-grey . . 40 10
a. Slate-grey omitted . . . . . . 42·00
257 50 c. multicoloured 45 10
258 1 s. 30, bronze-grn, greenish blue & blue . . 85 20
259 2 s. 50, red-orange, dp blue & pale blue . . 1·40 2·75
256/9 . . . . *Set of* 4 2·75 2·75
Designs:—50 c. S.S. *Harambee*; 1 s. 30, M.V. *Victoria*; 2 s. 50, *St. Michael*.

53 I.L.O. Emblem and Agriculture

54 Pope Paul VI and Ruwenzori Mountains

(Des Rena Fennessy)

1969 (14 Apr). *50th Anniv of International Labour Organization. T* **53** *and similar horiz designs. P* 14.
260 30 c. black, green and greenish yellow . . 10 10
261 50 c. black, plum, cerise and rose 10 10
262 1 s. 30, black, orange-brown & yellow-orange 10 10
263 2 s. 50, black, ultramarine & turquoise-blue 20 70
260/3 . . . . *Set of* 4 35 80
Designs:—50 c. I.L.O. emblem and building work; 1 s. 30, I.L.O. emblem and factory workers; 2 s. 50, I.L.O. emblem and shipping.

(Des Harrison)

1969 (31 July). *Visit of Pope Paul VI to Uganda. P* 14.
264 **54** 30 c. black, gold and royal blue 20 10
265 70 c. black, gold and claret 30 10
266 1 s. 50, black, gold and deep blue . . 45 20
267 2 s. 50, black, gold and violet 60 90
264/7 . . . . *Set of* 4 1·40 1·10

55 Euphorbia Tree shaped as Africa and Emblem

56 Marimba

(Des Rena Fennessy. Litho B.W.)

1969 (8 Dec). *Fifth Anniv of African Development Bank. P* 13½.
268 **55** 30 c. dp bluish green, gold & blue-green 15 10
269 70 c. dp bluish green, gold & reddish pur 15 10
270 1 s. 50, dp bluish grn, gold & lt turq-bl 30 10
271 2 s. 50, dp bluish grn, gold & orge-brn 35 80
268/71 . . . . *Set of* 4 75 90

(Des Rena Fennessy. Litho B.W.)

1970 (16 Feb). *Musical Instruments. T* **56** *and similar horiz designs. P* 11 × 12.
272 30 c. buff, yellow-brown and bistre-brown . . 15 10
273 70 c. olive-green, yellow-brown and yellow . . 25 10
274 1 s. 50, chocolate and yellow 50 10
275 2 s. 50, salmon, yellow and chocolate . . 75 1·75
272/5 . . . . *Set of* 4 1·50 1·75
Designs:—70 c. Amadinda; 1 s. 50, Nzomari; 2 s. 50, Adeudeu.

57 Satellite Earth Station

58 Athlete

(Des V. Whiteley. Litho J.W.)

1970 (18 May). *Inauguration of East African Satellite Earth Station. T* **57** *and similar horiz designs. P* 14½ × 14.
276 30 c. multicoloured 10 10
277 70 c. multicoloured 15 10
278 1 s. 50, black, slate-violet and pale orange . . 25 10
279 2 s. 50, multicoloured . . . . . . 55 2·00
276/9 . . . . *Set of* 4 90 2·00
Designs:—70 c. Transmitter in daytime; 1 s. 50, Transmitter at night; 2 s. 50, Earth and satellite.

(Des Rena Fennessy. Litho Walsall)

1970 (13 July). *Ninth Commonwealth Games. P* 14 × 14½.
280 **58** 30 c. orange-brown and black 10 10
281 70 c. olive-green and black 10 10
282 1 s. 50, slate-lilac and black 15 10
283 2 s. 50, turquoise-blue and black . . 20 90
280/3 . . . . *Set of* 4 40 1·00

59 "25" and U.N. Emblem

(Des Rena Fennessy)

1970 (19 Oct). *25th Anniv of United Nations. P 14½.*
284 **59** 30 c. multicoloured 10 10
285 70 c. multicoloured 10 10
286 1 s. 50, multicoloured 20 10
287 2 s. 50, multicoloured .. .. 45 1·75
284/7 .. .. *Set of 4* 70 1·75

60 Balance and Weight Equivalents

(Des and litho J.W.)

1971 (4 Jan). *Conversion to Metric System. T* **60** *and similar horiz designs. Multicoloured. P 14½ × 14.*
288 30 c. Type **60** 10 10
289 70 c. Fahrenheit and Centigrade Thermometers 10 10
290 1 s. 50, Petrol Pump and Liquid Capacities .. 15 10
291 2 s. 50, Surveyors and Land Measures .. 35 1·75
288/91 .. .. *Set of 4* 60 1·75

61 Class "11" Locomotive

(Des Rena Fennessy)

1971 (5 Apr). *Railway Transport. T* **61** *and similar horiz designs. Multicoloured. P 14.*
292 30 c. Type **61** 35 10
293 70 c. Class "90" locomotive 55 10
294 1 s. 50, Class "59" locomotive .. .. .. 1·25 50
295 2 s. 50, Class "30" locomotive .. .. .. 2·25 3·00
292/5 .. .. *Set of 4* 4·00 3·25
MS296 120 × 88 mm. Nos. 292/5 .. .. .. 6·50 10·00

62 Syringe and Cow

(Des Rena Fennessy. Litho)

1971 (5 July). *O.A.U. Rinderpest Campaign. T* **62** *and similar horiz design. P 14.*
297 **62** 30 c. black, pale yell-brn & pale yell-grn 10 10
298 – 70 c. black, pale slate-blue & pale yell-brn 10 10
299 **62** 1 s. 50, black, plum & pale yellow-brn 15 10
300 – 2 s. 50, black, brown-red & pale yell-brn 25 60
297/300 .. .. *Set of 4* 45 70
Design:—70 c., 2 s. 50, As T **62**, but with bull facing right.

63 Livingstone meets Stanley

(Des and litho J.W.)

1971 (28 Oct). *Centenary of Livingstone and Stanley meeting at Ujiji. P 13½ × 14.*
301 **63** 5 s. multicoloured 30 75

PRICES OF SETS

Set prices are given for many issues, generally those containing three stamps or more. Definitive sets include one of each value or major colour change, but do not cover different perforations, die types or minor shades. Where a choice is possible the set prices are based on the cheapest versions of the stamps included in the listings.

64 President Nyerere and Supporters

(Des G. Drummond. Litho J.W.)

1971 (9 Dec). *Tenth Anniv of Tanzanian Independence. T* **64** *and similar horiz designs. Multicoloured. P 13½.*
302 30 c. Type **64** 10 10
303 70 c. Ujamaa village 15 10
304 1 s. 50, Dar es Salaam University 30 25
305 2 s. 50, Kilimanjaro International Airport 1·00 3·00
302/5 .. .. *Set of 4* 1·40 3·00

65 Flags and Trade Fair Emblem

(Des Trade Fair Publicity Agents. Litho Questa)

1972 (23 Feb). *All-Africa Trade Fair. P 13½ × 14.*
306 **65** 30 c. multicoloured 10 10
307 70 c. multicoloured 10 10
308 1 s. 50, multicoloured 10 10
309 2 s. 50, multicoloured 25 65
306/9 .. .. *Set of 4* 40 75

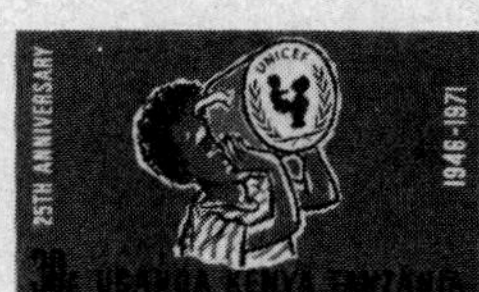

66 Child with Cup

(Des Rena Fennessy. Litho Questa)

1972 (24 Apr). *25th Anniv of UNICEF. T* **66** *and similar horiz designs. Multicoloured. P 14 × 14½.*
310 30 c. Type **66** 10 10
311 70 c. Children with ball 10 10
312 1 s. 50, Child at blackboard 10 10
313 2 s. 50, Child and tractor 25 80
310/13 .. .. *Set of 4* 35 90

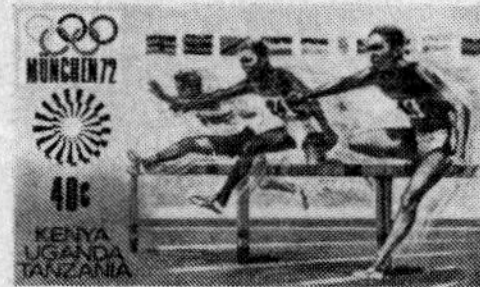

67 Hurdling

(Des G. Vasarhelyi. Litho J.W.)

1972 (28 Aug). *Olympic Games, Munich. T* **67** *and similar horiz designs. Multicoloured. P 14.*
314 40 c. Type **67** 10 10
315 70 c. Running 10 10
316 1 s. 50, Boxing 20 15
317 2 s. 50, Hockey .. .. 30 1·50
314/17 .. .. *Set of 4* 60 1·60
MS318 131 × 98 mm. Nos. 314/17 .. .. .. 4·50 7·00

68 Kobs

(Des G. Drummond. Litho D.L.R.)

1972 (9 Oct). *Tenth Anniv of Ugandan Independence. T* **68** *and similar horiz designs. Multicoloured. P 14.*
319 40 c. Type **68** 30 10
320 70 c. Conference Centre 30 10
321 1 s. 50, Makerere University 65 30
322 2 s. 50, Coat of Arms .. .. 1·00 3·00
319/22 .. .. *Set of 4* 2·00 3·00
MS323 132 × 120 mm. Nos. 319/22. P 13 × 14 .. 3·00 3·50

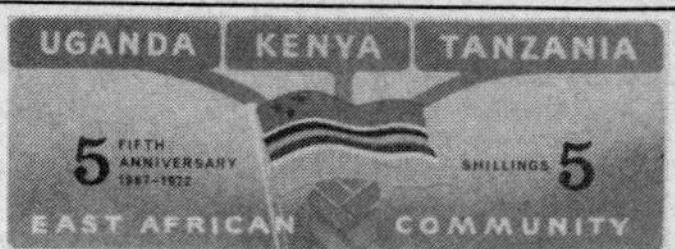

69 Community Flag

(Des Rena Fennessy. Litho)

1972 (1 Dec). *Fifth Anniv of East African Community. P 14½ × 14.*
324 **69** 5 s. multicoloured .. .. 75 1·40

70 Run-of-the-wind Anemometer

71 "Learning by Serving"

(Des P. Powell. Litho)

1973 (1 Mar*). *I.M.O./W.M.O. Centenary. T* **70** *and similar multi-coloured designs. P 14½.*
325 40 c. Type **70** 10 10
326 70 c. Weather balloon (*vert*) 15 10
327 1 s. 50, Meteorological rocket 25 15
328 2 s. 50, Satellite receiving aerial .. .. 55 2·25
325/8 .. .. *Set of 4* 90 2·25
No. 325 exists with country name at foot instead of at top, and also with country name omitted (or with imprint or plate numbers in lieu). These are because of faulty registration of the perforation comb.
*This is the local release date. The Crown Agents in London did not place the stamps on sale until 5 March.

(Des Rena Fennessy. Litho)

1973 (16 July). *24th World Scout Conference, Nairobi. T* **71** *and similar vert designs. P 14.*
329 40 c. multicoloured 15 10
330 70 c. Venetian red, reddish violet and black .. 20 10
331 1 s. 50, cobalt, reddish violet and black .. 45 30
332 2 s. 50, multicoloured .. .. 1·00 2·25
329/32 .. .. *Set of 4* 1·60 2·50
Designs:—70 c. Baden-Powell's grave, Nyeri; 1 s. 50, World Scout emblem; 2 s. 50, Lord Baden-Powell.

72 Kenyatta Conference Centre

(Des Marketing Communications Ltd, Nairobi; adapted J. Cooter. Litho D.L.R.)

1973 (29 Sept*). *I.M.F./World Bank Conference. T* **72** *and similar designs. P 13½ × 14 (1 s. 50) or 14 × 13½ (others).*
333 40 c. sage-green, light greenish grey & black 10 10
334 70 c. orange-brown, greenish grey and black 10 10
335 1 s. 50, multicoloured 25 35
336 2 s. 50, orange, greenish grey and black .. 35 1·75
333/6 .. .. *Set of 4* 65 2·00
MS337 166 × 141 mm. Nos. 333/6. Imperf .. 1·40 3·00
Designs:—Nos. 334/6 show different arrangements of Bank emblems and the Conference Centre, the 1 s. 50 being vertical.
*This is the local release date. The Crown Agents in London issued the stamps on 24 September.

73 Police Dog-handler

74 Tea Factory

(Des C. Abbott. Litho Questa)

1973 (24 Oct)–**74**. *50th Anniv of Interpol. T* **73** *and similar vert designs. P 14.*
338 40 c. yellow, blue and black 55 15
339 70 c. turquoise-green, orange-yellow & black 90 15
340 1 s. 50, light violet, yellow and black .. 1·50 90
341 2 s. 50, light yellow-green, red-orange and black (I) .. .. 3·75 6·00
342 2 s. 50, light yellow-green, red-orange, and black (II) (25.2.74) .. .. .. 3·75 6·00
338/42 .. .. *Set of 5* 9·50 12·00
Designs:—70 c. East African Policeman; 1 s. 50, Interpol emblem; 2 s. 50, Interpol H.Q.
Nos. 341/2. Type I inscribed "St. Clans"; Type II corrected to "St. Cloud".

(Des G. Drummond. Litho Enschedé)

1973 (12 Dec). *10th Anniv of Kenya's Independence. T* **74** *and similar horiz designs. Multicoloured. P* 13 × 13½.

343	40 c. Type **74**	10	10
344	70 c. Kenyatta Hospital	15	10
345	1 s. 50, Nairobi Airport	50	20
346	2 s. 50, Kindaruma hydro-electric scheme	65	1·75
343/6	*Set of* 4	1·25	1·75

75 Party H.Q.

(Des PAD Studio. Litho D.L.R.)

1974 (12 Jan). *Tenth Anniv of Zanzibar's Revolution. T* **75** *and similar horiz designs. Multicoloured. P* 13½.

347	40 c. Type **75**	10	10
348	70 c. Housing scheme	15	10
349	1 s. 50, Colour T.V.	50	30
350	2 s. 50, Amaan Stadium	90	2·50
347/50	*Set of* 4	1·50	2·75

76 "Symbol of Union"

(Des Jennifer Toombs. Litho Questa)

1974 (26 Apr). *Tenth Anniv of Tanganyika–Zanzibar Union. T* **76** *and similar horiz designs. Multicoloured. P* 14½.

351	40 c. Type **76**	10	10
352	70 c. Handclasp and map	20	10
353	1 s. 50, "Communications"	55	30
354	2 s. 50, Flags of Tanu, Tanzania and Afro-Shirazi Party	1·10	2·50
351/4	*Set of* 4	1·75	2·75

77 East African Family ("Stability of the Home")

(Des locally; adapted PAD Studio. Litho)

1974 (15 July). *17th Social Welfare Conference, Nairobi. T* **77** *and similar horiz designs. P* 14½.

355	40 c. greenish yellow, lake-brown and black	10	10
356	70 c. multicoloured	15	10
357	1 s. 50, olive-green, yellow-green and black	30	30
358	2 s. 50, light rose, reddish violet and black	1·25	2·00
355/8	*Set of* 4	1·60	2·25

Designs:—70 c. Dawn and drummer (U.N. Second Development Plan); 1 s. 50, Agricultural scene (Rural Development Plan); 2 s. 50, Transport and telephone ("Communications").

78 New Postal H.Q., Kampala

(Des Rena Fennessy. Litho)

1974 (9 Oct). *Centenary of Universal Postal Union. T* **78** *and similar horiz designs. Multicoloured. P* 14½.

359	40 c. Type **78**	10	10
360	70 c. Mail-train and post-van	20	10
361	1 s. 50, U.P.U. Building, Berne	15	20
362	2 s. 50, Loading mail into Vickers Super VC-10	55	1·50
359/62	*Set of* 4	85	1·60

79 Family-planning Clinic

(Des C. Abbott. Litho)

1974 (16 Dec). *World Population Year. T* **79** *and similar horiz designs. P* 14.

363	40 c. multicoloured	10	10
364	70 c. deep reddish violet and scarlet	10	10
365	1 s. 50, multicoloured	15	20
366	2 s. 50, apple-green, blue-green & bluish blk	30	1·90
363/6	*Set of* 4	55	2·00

Designs:—70 c. "Tug of war"; 1 s. 50, Population "scales"; 2 s. 50, W.P.Y. emblem.

80 Seronera Wild-Life Lodge, Tanzania

(Des R. Granger Barrett. Litho)

1975 (26 Feb*). *East Africa Game Lodges. T* **80** *and similar horiz designs. Multicoloured. P* 14.

367	40 c. Type **80**	15	10
368	70 c. Mweya Safari Lodge, Uganda	20	10
369	1 s. 50, "Ark"—Aberdare Forest Lodge, Kenya	35	30
370	2 s. 50, Paraa Safari Lodge, Uganda	80	2·25
367/70	*Set of* 4	1·40	2·50

*This is the local release date. The Crown Agents in London issued the stamps on 24 February.

81 Kitana (wooden comb), Bajun of Kenya

82 International Airport, Entebbe

(Des Mrs. Gombe of the E.A.P.T.; adapted C. Abbott. Litho Questa)

1975 (5 May). *African Arts. T* **81** *and similar vert designs. Multicoloured. P* 13½.

371	50 c. Type **81**	10	10
372	1 s. Earring, Chaga of Tanzania	15	10
373	2 s. Okoco (armlet), Acholi of Uganda	45	70
374	3 s. Kitete (Kamba gourd), Kenya	85	1·40
371/4	*Set of* 4	1·40	2·10

(Des PAD Studio. Litho State Ptg Wks, Warsaw)

1975 (28 July). *O.A.U. Summit Conference, Kampala. T* **82** *and similar multicoloured designs. P* 11.

375	50 c. Type **82**	30	10
376	1 s. Map of Africa and flag (*vert*)	30	10
377	2 s. Nile Hotel, Kampala	40	85
378	3 s. Martyrs' Shrine, Namugongo (*vert*)	50	1·60
375/8	*Set of* 4	1·40	2·40

83 Ahmed ("Presidential" Elephant)

84 Maasai Manyatta (village), Kenya

(Des locally. Litho State Ptg Wks, Warsaw)

1975 (11 Sept). *Rare Animals. T* **83** *and similar vert designs. Multicoloured. P* 11.

379	50 c. Type **83**	50	10
380	1 s. Albino buffalo	50	10
381	2 s. Ahmed in grounds of National Museum	1·60	1·50
382	3 s. Abbott's Duiker	1·60	3·00
379/82	*Set of* 4	3·75	4·25

(Des Rena Fennessy. Litho Questa)

1975 (3 Nov). *Second World Black and African Festival of Arts and Culture, Nigeria (1977). T* **84** *and similar horiz designs. Multicoloured. P* 13½ × 14.

383	50 c. Type **84**	15	10
384	1 s. "Heartbeat of Africa" (Ugandan dancers)	20	10
385	2 s. Makonde sculpture, Tanzania	65	85
386	3 s. "Early Man and Technology" (skinning hippopotamus)	95	1·40
383/6	*Set of* 4	1·75	2·25

For similar stamps see Nos. 76/80 of Kenya and the corresponding issues of Tanzania and Uganda.

85 Fokker F.27 Friendship at Nairobi Airport

(Des local artist. Litho State Security Ptg Wks, Warsaw)

1976 (2 Jan). *30th Anniv of East African Airways. T* **85** *and similar triangular designs. Multicoloured. P* 11½.

387	50 c. Type **85**	1·00	30
	a. Black (aircraft) and blue omitted	†	£1200
388	1 s. Douglas DC-9 at Kilimanjaro Airport	1·10	30
389	2 s. Vickers Super VC-10 at Entebbe Airport	3·50	3·00
390	3 s. East African Airways crest	3·75	3·75
387/90	*Set of* 4	8·50	6·50

Two black plates were used for each of Nos. 387/9: one for the frame and the other for the centre. No. 387a, three used copies of which are known, has the printing from the blue and centre black plates omitted.

Further commemorative issues were released during 1976–78, using common designs, but inscribed for one republic only. These are listed under KENYA, TANZANIA, or UGANDA.

Co-operation between the postal services of the three member countries virtually ceased after 30 June 1977, the postal services of Kenya, Tanzania and Uganda then operating independently.

STAMP BOOKLETS

1912. *Black on pink cover. Stapled.*

SB1	1 s. 80, booklet containing twelve 3 c. and twenty-four 6 c. (Nos. 45/6), each in blocks of 6	
SB2	1 s. 98, booklet containing six 3 c. and thirty 6 c. (Nos. 45/6), each in blocks of 6	

1938. *Black on pink cover. Stapled.*

SB3	3 s. 40, booklet containing twelve 15 c. and eight 20 c. (Nos. 137, 139), each in blocks of 4	£180

1949. *Black on yellow cover. Stapled.*

SB4	1 s. booklet containing four 5 c. and eight 10 c. (Nos. 133, 135), each in blocks of 4	£110

1952–53? *Black on yellow cover. Stapled.*

SB5	1 s. booklet containing four 5 c. and eight 10 c. (Nos. 133a, 135b), each in blocks of 4	
	a. Stitched	45·00
	ab. Contents as No. SB5, but 10 c. changed to No. 136 (1953?)	35·00

1954 (3 Sept). *Blue on yellow cover. Stitched.*

SB6	1 s. booklet containing four 5 c. and eight 10 c. (Nos. 167/8), each in blocks of 4	3·00

1956 (16 Jan). *Black on yellow cover. Stitched.*

SB7	5 s. booklet containing four 5 c., 20 c., 30 c., 50 c. and eight 10 c. (Nos. 167/8, 170/1, 173), each in blocks of 4	16·00

1958 (16 Dec)–**59.** *Black on rose-red cover. Stitched.*

SB8	5 s. booklet containing 10 c., 15 c., 20 c., 30 c. and 50 c. (Nos. 168/9, 170/1, 173), in blocks of 4	20·00
	a. Contents as No. SB8, but 15 c. changed to No. 169a (20.4.59)	20·00

1961 (1 Feb). *Black on rose-red cover. Stitched.*

SB9	5 s. booklet containing 10 c., 15 c., 20 c., 30 c. and 50 c. (Nos. 184/6, 188, 190) in blocks of 4	8·00

OFFICIAL STAMPS

For use on official correspondence of the Tanganyika Government.

OFFICIAL

(O 1)

1959 (1 July). *Nos.* 167/71, 173 *and* 175/80 *optd as Type* O **1**.

O 1	5 c. black and deep brown	10	30
O 2	10 c. carmine-red	15	30
O 3	15 c. black and light blue (No. 169a)	30	40
O 4	20 c. black and orange	20	10
	a. Opt double	—	£850
O 5	30 c. black and deep ultramarine	15	20
O 6	50 c. reddish purple	20	10
O 7	1 s. black and claret	20	20
O 8	1 s. 30, orange and deep lilac	1·90	85
O 9	2 s. black and bronze-green	1·25	85
O10	5 s. black and orange	3·00	2·25
O11	10 s. black and deep ultramarine	2·00	2·50
O12	£1 brown-red and black	6·50	11·00
O1/12	*Set of* 12	14·00	17·00

The 30 c., 50 c. and 1 s. exist with overprint double, but with the two impressions almost coincident.

OFFICIAL (O 2)

OFFICIAL (O 3)

1960 (18 Oct). *Nos.* 183/6, 188, 190, 192 *and* 196 *optd with Type* O **2** *(cents values) or* O **3**.

O13	5 c. Prussian blue	10	55
O14	10 c. yellow-green	10	40
O15	15 c. dull purple	10	55
O16	20 c. magenta	10	10
O17	30 c. vermilion	10	10
O18	50 c. slate-violet	30	30
O19	1 s. deep reddish violet and reddish purple	30	10
O20	5 s. rose-red and purple	7·50	65
O13/20	*Set of* 8	7·50	2·50

POSTAGE DUE STAMPS

D 1

D 2

(Typo Waterlow)

1928 (Sept)–**33**. *Wmk Mult Script CA. P* 15×14.
D1 D 1 5 c. violet .. .. 2·25 25
D2 10 c. vermilion .. .. 1·75 15
D3 20 c. yellow-green .. .. 1·75 2·50
D4 30 c. brown (1931) .. .. 13·00 13·00
D5 40 c. dull blue .. .. 5·50 12·00
D6 1 s. grey-green (1933) .. .. .. 42·00 85·00
D1/6 .. .. *Set of* 6 60·00 £100
D1/6 Optd/Perf "Specimen" .. .. *Set of* 6 £140

(Typo D.L.R.)

1935 (1 May)–**60**. *Wmk Mult Script CA. P* 14.
D 7 D 2 5 c. violet .. .. 2·50 1·25
D 8 10 c. scarlet 30 30
D 9 20 c. green 40 30
D10 30 c. brown 60 50
a. Bistre-brown (19.7.60) .. .. .. 2·75 6·00
D11 40 c. ultramarine .. .. 1·50 3·00
D12 1 s. grey .. .. 17·00 19·00
D7/12 .. .. *Set of* 6 20·00 22·00
D7/12 Perf "Specimen" .. .. *Set of* 6 £100

Kiribati

(*formerly* Gilbert Islands)

(Currency. 100 cents = 1 Australian dollar)

GILBERT ISLANDS

On 1 January 1976, the Gilbert Islands and Tuvalu (Ellice Islands) became separate Crown Colonies.

1 Charts of Gilbert Islands and Tuvalu (formerly Ellice) Islands

THE GILBERT ISLANDS

(2)

(Des J. Cooter. Litho Questa)

1976 (2 Jan). *Separation of the Islands. T* 1 *and similar horiz design. Multicoloured. W* w 14 (*sideways*). *P* 14.
1 4 c. Type **1** 40 75
2 35 c. Maps of Tarawa and Funafuti .. .. 70 1·50

1976 (2 Jan). *Nos.* 173/86 *of Gilbert & Ellice Is optd as T* **2**.

(*a*) *W* w 12 (*sideways* on Nos.* 5/7 *and* 9/10)
3 1 c. Cutting toddy (R.) 25 30
4 2 c. Lagoon fishing (R.) .. .. 60 1·50
5 2 c. Lagoon fishing (*wmk sideways*) (R.) .. 50 30
6 3 c. Cleaning pandanus leaves (R.) .. 17·00 23·00
w. Wmk Crown to the right of CA .. 55·00
7 4 c. Casting nets (R.) 30 80
8 20 c. Beating a pandanus leaf (R.) .. .. † £110
9 20 c. Beating a pandanus leaf (*wmk sideways*) (R.) .. .. 6·50 3·25
10 25 c. Loading copra .. .. 35·00 50·00
a. Opt double (Blk. + R.) £350
10*b* 50 c. Local handicrafts £900 £950

(*b*) *W* w 14 (*sideways* on* 3, 5, 20, 25 *and* 35 *c. inverted on others*)
11 1 c. Cutting toddy (R.) 20 80
12 3 c. Cleaning pandanus leaves (R.) 40 70
13 5 c. Gilbertese canoe (R.) 50 70
14 6 c. De-husking coconuts 50 70
15 8 c. Weaving pandanus fronds (R.) 50 70
16 10 c. Weaving a basket 50 70
17 15 c. Tiger Shark .. .. 2·00 1·25
18 20 c. Beating a pandanus leaf (R.) .. .. 1·50 1·25
w. Wmk Crown to right of CA .. .. 70·00
19 25 c. Loading copra .. .. 2·00 1·25
20 35 c. Fishing at night (Gold) .. .. .. 2·00 1·75
21 50 c. Local handicrafts .. .. 2·00 2·75
22 $1 Weaving coconut screens (R.) .. .. 4·00 9·00
a. Opt double £375
3, 4, 7 *and* 12/22 .. .. .. *Set of* 14 15·00 20·00

*The normal sideways watermark shows Crown to left of CA, *as seen from the back of the stamp.*

3 *Teraaka* (training ship)

(Des J. Cooter. Litho Questa)

1979 (1 July). *Horiz designs as T* **3**. *Multicoloured. W* w 14 (*sideways**). *P* 14.
23 1 c. Type **3** 40 60
24 3 c. *Tautunu* (inter-island freighter) 60 70
25 4 c. Moorish Idol (fish) 30 50
26 5 c. Hibiscus 30 30
27 6 c. Eastern Reef Heron 75 65
28 7 c. Catholic Cathedral, Tarawa 30 30
29 8 c. Frangipani 30 30
30 10 c. Maneaba, Bikenibeu 30 30
31 12 c. Betio Harbour 45 45
32 15 c. Evening scene 55 45
33 20 c. Marakei Atoll 35 35
34 35 c. G.I.P.C. Chapel, Tangintebu 35 40
35 40 c. Flamboyant Tree 40 45
36 50 c. *Hypolimnas bolina* (butterfly) .. .. 2·25 1·75
w. Wmk Crown to right of CA .. .. 27·00
37 $1 *Tabakea* (Tarawa Lagoon ferry) .. .. 2·00 2·50
38 $2 National flag .. .. 2·00 2·75
23/38 .. .. *Set of* 16 9·50 11·00

*The normal sideways watermark shows Crown to left of CA, *as seen from the back of the stamp.*

For similar designs inscribed "KIRIBATI" see Nos. 86/99*b* and 121/35.

4 Church

5 Porcupine Fish Helmet

(Des P. Powell. Litho Questa)

1976 (15 Sept). *Christmas. Children's Drawings. T* 4 *and similar multicoloured designs. W* w 14 (*sideways on* 5 *and* 35 *c.*). *P* 14.
39 5 c. Type **4** 25 15
40 15 c. Feasting (*vert*) 35 15
41 20 c. Maneaba (*vert*) 40 30
42 35 c. Dancing 55 45
39/42 .. .. *Set of* 4 1·40 95

(Des J. Cooter. Litho J.W.)

1976 (6 Dec). *Artefacts. T* **5** *and similar vert designs. Multicoloured. W* w 14. *P* 13.
43 5 c. Type **5** 20 15
44 15 c. Shark's Teeth Dagger 30 35
45 20 c. Fighting Gauntlet 30 40
46 35 c. Coconut Body Armour 45 55
43/6 .. .. *Set of* 4 1·10 1·25
MS47 140 × 130 mm. Nos. 43/6. P 14 .. .. 7·00 14·00

6 Queen in Coronation Robes

7 Commodore Byron and H.M.S. *Dolphin*

(Des J. Cooter. Litho Questa)

1977 (7 Feb). *Silver Jubilee. T* **6** *and similar vert designs. Multicoloured. W* w 14. *P* 14.
48 8 c. Prince Charles' visit, 1970 .. .. .. 10 10
49 20 c. Prince Philip's visit, 1959 .. .. .. 15 15
50 40 c. Type **6** 20 35
48/50 .. .. *Set of* 3 40 55

(Des J. Cooter. Litho Questa)

1977 (1 June). *Explorers. T* **7** *and similar horiz designs. Multicoloured. W* w 14 (*sideways*). *P* 14.
51 5 c. Type **7** .. .. 65 1·50
52 15 c. Capt. Fanning and *Betsey* .. .. .. 80 2·75
53 20 c. Admiral Bellingshausen and *Vostok* .. 80 2·75
54 35 c. Capt. Wilkes and U.S.S. *Vincennes* .. 1·10 4·00
51/4 .. .. *Set of* 4 3·00 10·00

8 H.M.S. *Resolution* and H.M.S. *Discovery*

9 Emblem and Island Scene

(Des J. Cooter. Litho Questa)

1977 (12 Sept). *Christmas and Bicentenary of Capt. Cook's Discovery of Christmas Is. T* **8** *and similar multicoloured designs. W* w 14 (*sideways on* 15 *and* 40 *c.*). *P* 14.
55 8 c. Type **8** 40 10
56 15 c. Logbook entry (*horiz*) 40 15
57 20 c. Capt. Cook 50 20
58 40 c. Landing party (*horiz*) 55 60
55/8 .. .. *Set of* 4 1·60 95
MS59 140 × 140 mm. Nos. 55/8. Wmk sideways 6·00 11·00

(Des J. Cooter. Litho J.W.)

1977 (5 Dec). *50th Anniv of Scouting in the Gilbert Is. T* **9** *and similar multicoloured designs. W* w 14 (*sideways on* 15 *and* 20 *c.*). *P* 13.
60 8 c. Type **9** 20 10
61 15 c. Patrol meeting (*horiz*) 25 20
62 20 c. Mat making (*horiz*) 30 20
63 40 c. Canoeing 40 55
60/3 .. .. *Set of* 4 1·00 95

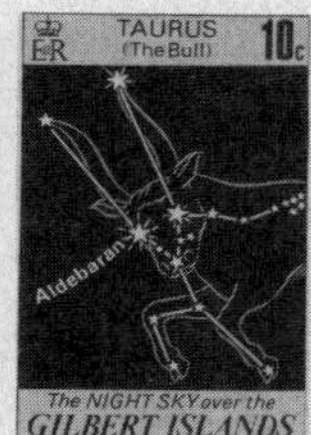

10 Taurus (The Bull)

GILBERT ISLANDS
Unicorn of Scotland
45c

11 Unicorn of Scotland

(Des J. Cooter. Litho Questa)

1978 (20 Feb). *Night Sky over the Gilbert Is.* (1*st series*). *T* **10** *and similar vert designs. W* w 14. *P* 14.
64 10 c. black and light new blue 30 15
65 20 c. black and light rose-red 35 30
66 25 c. black and sage-green 35 35
67 45 c. black and orange 55 60
64/7 .. .. *Set of* 4 1·40 1·25

Designs:—20 c. Canis Major (the Great Dog); 25 c. Scorpio (the Scorpion); 45 c. Orion (the Giant Warrior).

See also Nos. 465/8.

(Des C. Abbott. Litho Questa)

1978 (21 Apr). *25th Anniv of Coronation. T* **11** *and similar vert designs. P* 15.
68 45 c. green, bluish violet and silver 25 40
a. Sheetlet. Nos. 68/70 × 2 .. .. .. 1·25
69 45 c. multicoloured 25 40
70 45 c. green, bluish violet and silver 25 40
68/70 .. .. *Set of* 3 65 1·10

Designs:—No. 68, Type **11**; No. 69, Queen Elizabeth II; No. 70, Great Frigate Bird.

Nos. 68/70 were printed together in small sheets of 6, containing two *se-tenant* strips of 3, with horizontal gutter margin between.

12 Birds in Flight to Tarawa

(Des local artists; adapted G. Hutchins. Litho Enschedé)

1978 (5 June). *25th Anniv of Return of King George V School to Tarawa. T* **12** *and similar horiz designs. Multicoloured. W* w 14 (*sideways*). *P* 14 × 13.
71 10 c. Type **12** 10 10
72 20 c. Tarawa, Abemama and school badge .. 20 20
73 25 c. Rejoicing islanders 20 20
74 45 c. King George V School on Tarawa and Abemama 35 35
71/4 .. .. *Set of* 4 75 75

13 "Te Kaue ni Maie"

14 H.M.S. *Endeavour*

(Des W. Walsh. Litho J.W.)

1978 (25 Sept). *Christmas. Kaue (traditional head decorations). T* **13** *and similar horiz designs. Multicoloured. W* w 14 (*sideways**). *P* 14.
75 10 c. Type **13** 10 10
76 20 c. "Te Itera" 15 15
77 25 c. "Te Bau" 20 20
78 45 c. "Te Tai" 25 30
75/8 .. .. *Set of* 4 60 65
MS79 149×99 mm. Nos. 75/8. P 13×13½ .. 1·25 4·50
w. Wmk Crown to right of CA £130

*The normal sideways watermark shows Crown to left of CA *as seen from the back of the stamp.*

(Des and litho (45 c. also embossed) Walsall)

1979 (22 Feb*). *Bicentenary of Captain Cook's Voyages,* 1768–79. *T* **14** *and similar vert designs. P* 11.

80 10 c. multicoloured 25 15
81 20 c. multicoloured 30 30
82 25 c. black, light green and pale lilac 30 45
83 45 c. multicoloured 40 80
80/3 .. .. *Set of* 4 1·10 1·50

Designs:—20 c. Green Turtle; 25 c. Quadrant; 45 c. Flaxman/Wedgwood medallion of Captain Cook.

*This was the local issue date; the stamps were released in London on 15 January.

The Gilbert Islands achieved independence on 12 July 1979 and were renamed Kiribati.

KIRIBATI

INDEPENDENT

15 Kiribati Flag

(Des G. Drummond. Litho Questa)

1979 (12 July). *Independence. T* **15** *and similar horiz design. Multicoloured. W w* **14** *(sideways). P* 14.

84 10 c. Type **15** 10 25
85 45 c. Houses of Parliament and Maneaba ni Maungatabu (House of Assembly) .. 20 65

16 *Teraaka* (training ship)

17 Gilbert and Ellice Islands 1911 ½d. Stamp

(Des J. Cooter. Litho Questa)

1979 (12 July)–**80**. *Multicoloured designs as Nos.* 23/32 *and* 34/8, *some with values changed, inscribed* "KIRIBATI" *as T* **16**. *W w* **14** *(sideways*). P* 14.

86 1 c. Type **16** 10 60
w. Wmk Crown to right of CA .. .. 85·00
87 3 c. *Tautunu* (inter-island freighter) .. 30 40
w. Wmk Crown to right of CA .. .. 7·00
88 5 c. Hibiscus 10 20
w. Wmk Crown to right of CA .. .. 7·00
89 7 c. Catholic Cathedral, Tarawa 10 20
90 10 c. Maneaba, Bikenibeu 10 20
w. Wmk Crown to right of CA .. .. 7·00
91 12 c. Betio Harbour 15 20
92 15 c. Eastern Reef Heron (as No. 27) 35 25
w. Wmk Crown to right of CA £130
93 20 c. Flamboyant Tree (as No. 35) 20 25
94 25 c. Moorish Idol (fish) (as No. 25) 30 30
95 30 c. Frangipani (as No. 29) 25 30
96 35 c. G.I.P.C. Chapel, Tangintebu 25 30
97 50 c. *Hypolimnas bolina* (butterfly) 75 55
98 $1 *Tabakea* (Tarawa Lagoon ferry) .. 70 75
w. Wmk Crown to right of CA .. .. 11·00
99 $2 Evening scene (as No. 32) .. .. 70 1·00
aw. Wmk Crown to right of CA .. .. 9·00
99*b* $5 National flag (as No. 38) (27.8.80) .. 2·00 5·00
86/99*b* .. .. *Set of* 15 5·50 9·00

*The normal sideways watermark shows Crown to left of CA, *as seen from the back of the stamp.*

See also Nos. 121/35.

(Des J.W. Litho Questa)

1979 (27 Sept). *Death Centenary of Sir Rowland Hill. T* **17** *and similar vert designs showing stamps. Multicoloured. W w* **14**. *P* 14.

100 10 c. Type **17** 10 10
101 20 c. Gilbert and Ellice Islands 1956 2s. 6d. definitive 15 20
102 25 c. Great Britain 1902 2s. 6d. 15 20
103 45 c. Gilbert and Ellice Islands 1924 10s. .. 25 35
100/3 .. .. *Set of* 4 60 75
MS104 113×110 mm. Nos. 100/3 .. .. 90 1·00

18 Boy with Giant Clam Shell

(Des D. Bowen. Litho Enschedé)

1979 (28 Nov). *International Year of the Child. T* **18** *and similar multicoloured designs. W w* **14** *(sideways* on* 20 *c.). P* 13×13½ (20 *c.) or* 13½×13 *(others).*

105 10 c. Type **18** 10 10
w. Wmk inverted .. ..
106 20 c. Child climbing coconut tree (*horiz*) .. 10 10
w. Wmk Crown to left of CA .. ..
107 45 c. Girl reading 15 20
108 $1 Child in costume 30 50
w. Wmk inverted .. ..
105/8 .. .. *Set of* 4 55 75

*The normal sideways watermark shows Crown to right of CA, *as seen from the back of the stamp.*

19 Downrange Station, Christmas Island

(Des J. Cooter. Litho Format)

1980 (20 Feb). *Satellite Tracking. T* **19** *and similar multicoloured designs. P* 14½.

109 25 c. Type **19** 10 10
110 45 c. Map of South Pacific showing trajectory of Experimental Communications Satellite 15 15
111 $1 Rocket launch, Tanegashima, Japan (*vert*) 30 35
109/11 .. .. *Set of* 3 50 55

20 T.S. *Teraaka*

(Litho Format)

1980 (30 Apr). *"London 1980" International Stamp Exhibition. T* **20** *and similar horiz designs. Multicoloured. P* 14½.

112 12 c. Type **20** 15 10
113 25 c. Loading Air Tungaru Britten Norman Islander, Bonriki Airport 15 10
114 30 c. Radio operator 15 10
115 $1 Bairiki Post Office 20 35
112/15 .. .. *Set of* 4 60 50
MS116 139×116 mm. Nos. 112/15. P 14×14½. 75 85

Nos. 112/15 were each printed in sheets of 12 containing *se-tenant* stamp-size labels in positions 4 and 6.

21 *Achaea janata*

(Des J. Cooter. Litho Questa)

1980 (27 Aug). *Moths. T* **21** *and similar horiz designs. Multicoloured. P* 14.

117 12 c. Type **21** 10 10
118 25 c. *Ethmia nigroapicella* 15 15
119 30 c. *Utetheisa pulchelloides* 15 15
120 50 c. *Anua coronata* 25 25
117/20 .. .. *Set of* 4 60 60

1980 (27 Aug)–**81**. *As Nos.* 86/99*b* *but no wmk.*

121 1 c. Type **16** (4.81) 10 60
122 3 c. M.V. *Tautunu* (inter-island freighter) (6.1.81) 15 30
123 5 c. Hibiscus 15 15
124 7 c. Catholic Cathedral, Tarawa 15 15
125 10 c. Maneaba, Bikenibeu (19.11.80) 15 15
126 12 c. Betio Harbour (11.12.80) 20 30
127 15 c. Eastern Reef Heron (11.12.80) 70 40
128 20 c. Flamboyant Tree (6.1.81) 30 50
129 25 c. Moorish Idol (fish) (19.11.80) 30 30
130 30 c. Frangipani (4.81) .. .. 30 1·00
131 35 c. G.I.P.C. Chapel, Tangintebu (4.81) .. 30 1·00
132 50 c. *Hypolimnas bolina* (butterfly) (4.81) .. 85 1·75
133 $1 *Tabakea* (Tarawa Lagoon ferry) (11.12.80) .. .. 70 2·00
134 $2 Evening scene (11.12.80) .. .. .. 80 2·50
135 $5 National flag (11.12.80) .. .. .. 1·75 4·50
121/35 .. .. *Set of* 15 6·00 13·50

22 Captain Cook Hotel, Christmas Island

(Des J. Cooter. Litho Format)

1980 (19 Nov). *Development. T* **22** *and similar horiz designs. Multicoloured. P* 13½ × 14.

136 10 c. Type **22** 10 10
137 20 c. Sports Stadium 10 10
138 25 c. International Airport, Bonriki 15 10
139 35 c. National Library and Archives 15 10
140 $1 Otintai Hotel 20 40
136/40 .. .. *Set of* 5 50 65

23 *Acalypha godseffiana*

(Des J. Cooter. Litho Format)

1981 (18 Feb). *Flowers. T* **23** *and similar vert designs. Multicoloured. W w* **15**. *P* 14 × 13½.

141 12 c. Type **23** 10 10
142 30 c. *Hibiscus schizopetalus* 15 15
143 35 c. *Calotropis gigantea* 15 15
144 50 c. *Euphorbia pulcherrima* 20 20
141/4 .. .. *Set of* 4 55 55

25 Maps of Abaiang and Marakei, and String Figures

(Des J. Cooter. Litho Format)

1981 (6 May). *Island Maps (1st series). T* **25** *and similar horiz designs. Multicoloured. W w* **15** *(sideways). P* 13½ × 14.

145 12 c. Type **25** 15 10
146 30 c. Maps of Little Makin and Butaritari, and village house 20 10
147 35 c. Map of Maiana, and coral road 25 15
148 $1 Map of Christmas Island, and Captain Cook's H.M.S. *Resolution* 70 75
145/8 .. .. *Set of* 4 1·10 1·00

See also Nos. 201/4, 215/18, 237/40, 256/60 and 270/3.

26 *Katherine*

27 Prince Charles and Lady Diana Spencer

(Des D. Shults. Litho Questa)

1981 (29 July–26 Nov). *Royal Wedding. Horiz designs as T* **26**, *showing Royal Yachts, and T* **27**. *Multicoloured.* (*a*) *W w* **15**. *P* 14.

149 12 c. Type **26** 10 15
aw. Wmk inverted .. .. 7·00
b. Sheetlet. No. 149×6 and No. 150 .. 70
bw. Wmk inverted .. .. 70·00
150 12 c. Type **27** 20 30
aw. Wmk inverted .. .. 50·00
151 50 c. *Osborne* 25 40
a. Sheetlet. No. 151×6 and No. 152 .. 1·75
152 50 c. Type **27** 50 75
153 $2 *Britannia* 35 80
a. Sheetlet. No. 153×6 and No. 154 .. 3·25
154 $2 Type **27** .. .. 1·50 2·50
149/54 .. .. *Set of* 6 2·50 4·50
MS155 120×109 mm. $1.20, Type **27**. Wmk sideways. P 12 (26 Nov) .. .. .. 75 1·00

(*b*) *Booklet stamps. No wmk. P* 12 (26 Nov)

156 12 c. Type **26** 15 15
a. Booklet pane. No. 156×4 with margins all round 60
157 50 c. Type **27** 75 80
a. Booklet pane. No. 157×2 with margins all round .. .. 1·50

Nos. 149/54 were printed in sheetlets of seven stamps of the same face value, each containing six of the "Royal Yacht" design and one as Type **27**.

Nos. 156/7 come from $1.96 stamp booklets.

28 Tuna Bait Breeding Centre, Bonriki Fish Farm

(Des G. Drummond. Litho Questa)

1981 (19 Nov). *Tuna Fishing Industry. T* **28** *and similar horiz designs. Multicoloured. W* w **15**. *P* 14.

158	12 c. Type **28**	15	10
159	30 c. Tuna fishing	25	20
160	35 c. Cold storage, Betio	25	25
161	50 c. Government Tuna Fishing Vessel *Nei Manganibuka*	50	50
158/61	*Set of* 4	1·00	95
MS162	134×99 mm. Nos. 158/61. Wmk sideways*	1·25	1·40
	w. Wmk POST OFFICE reading upwards	30·00	

*The normal sideways watermark shows "POST OFFICE" reading downwards.

29 Pomarine Skua

(Des G. Drummond. Litho Questa)

1982 (18 Feb)–**85**. *Birds. Multicoloured designs as T* **29**. *P* 14.

163	1 c. Type **29**	15	15
164	2 c. Mallard	15	15
165	4 c. Collared Petrel	20	20
166	5 c. Blue-faced Booby	20	20
167	7 c. Friendly Quail Dove	20	20
168	8 c. Common Shoveler	20	20
169	12 c. Polynesian Reed Warbler	20	20
170	15 c. American Golden Plover	25	25
171	20 c. Eastern Reef Heron	30	30
171*a*	25 c. Common Noddy (31.1.83)	3·00	1·50
172	30 c. Brown Booby	30	30
173	35 c. Audubon's Shearwater	30	35
174	40 c. White-throated Storm Petrel (*vert*)	35	40
175	50 c. Bristle-thighed Curlew (*vert*)	40	45
175*a*	55 c. White Tern (*inscr* "Fairy Tern") (*vert*) (19.11.85)	11·00	14·00
176	$1 Kuhl's Lory (*vert*)	70	70
177	$2 Long-tailed Koel (*vert*)	90	1·10
178	$5 Great Frigate Bird (*vert*)	1·75	2·25
163/78	*Set of* 18	18·00	21·00

30 Riley Turbo Skyliner

31 Mary of Teck, Princess of Wales, 1893

(Des G. Drummond. Litho Format)

1982 (18 Feb). *Inauguration of Air Tungaru Airline. T* **30** *and similar horiz designs. Multicoloured. W* w **15** (*sideways**). *P* 14.

179	12 c. Type **30**	15	10
	w. Wmk POST OFFICE reading upwards	28·00	
180	30 c. Britten Norman "short nose" Trislander	20	20
181	35 c. Casa C-212 Aviocar	20	25
182	50 c. Boeing 727-200	30	35
179/82	*Set of* 4	75	75

*The normal sideways watermark shows "POST OFFICE" reading downwards.

No. 179 is inscr "De Havilland DH114 Heron" in error.

(Des D. Shults and J. Cooter. Litho Format)

1982 (19 May). *21st Birthday of Princess of Wales. T* **31** *and similar vert designs. Multicoloured. W* w **15**. *P* 13½ × 14.

183	12 c. Type **31**	10	10
184	50 c. Coat of arms of Mary of Teck	20	20
	w. Wmk inverted	10·00	
185	$1 Diana, Princess of Wales	30	35
183/5	*Set of* 3	50	55

The 12 c. design is incorrectly dated; Mary of Teck became Princess of Wales in 1901.

1982 (14 July). *Birth of Prince William of Wales. Nos. 183/5 optd with T* **19** *of St. Kitts.*

186	12 c. Type **31**	10	10
187	50 c. Coat of arms of Mary of Teck	25	25
	a. Opt inverted	14·00	
	w. Wmk inverted	17·00	
188	$1 Diana, Princess of Wales	40	45
186/8	*Set of* 3	65	70

32 First Aid Practice

(Des J. Cooter. Litho Format)

1982 (12 Aug). *75th Anniv of Boy Scout Movement. T* **32** *and similar horiz designs. Multicoloured. W* w **15** (*sideways*). *P* 13½ × 14.

189	12 c. Type **32**	20	15
190	25 c. Boat repairs	20	30
191	30 c. On parade	25	35
192	50 c. Gilbert Islands 1977 8 c. Scouting stamp and "75"	25	60
189/92	*Set of* 4	80	1·25

33 Queen and Duke of Edinburgh with Local Dancer

(Des PAD Studio. Litho Walsall)

1982 (23 Oct). *Royal Visit. T* **33** *and similar horiz designs. Multicoloured. W* w **15** (*sideways**). *P* 14.

193	12 c. Type **33**	15	15
194	25 c. Queen, Duke of Edinburgh and outrigger canoe	20	20
	w. Wmk POST OFFICE reading upwards	40·00	
195	35 c. New Philatelic Bureau building	30	30
	w. Wmk POST OFFICE reading upwards	65·00	
193/5	*Set of* 3	60	60
MS196	88×76 mm. 50 c. Queen Elizabeth II	60	60

*The normal sideways watermark shows "POST OFFICE" reading downwards.

On No. **MS**196 the captions on the map for the islands of Teraina and Tabuaeren have been transposed.

34 "Obaia, The Feathered" (Kiribati legend)

(Des J.W. Litho Format)

1983 (14 Mar). *Commonwealth Day. T* **34** *and similar horiz designs. Multicoloured. W* w **15** (*sideways**). *P* 14.

197	12 c. Type **34**	10	10
	w. Wmk POST OFFICE reading upwards	18·00	
198	30 c. Robert Louis Stevenson Hotel, Abemama	15	20
199	50 c. Container ship off Betio	15	25
	w. Wmk POST OFFICE reading upwards	7·00	
200	$1 Map of Kiribati	20	50
	w. Wmk POST OFFICE reading upwards		
197/200	*Set of* 4	50	90

*The normal sideways watermark shows "POST OFFICE" reading downwards.

(Des J. Cooter. Litho Format)

1983 (19 May). *Island Maps* (*2nd series*). *Multicoloured designs as T* **25**. *W* w **15** (*sideways** *on* 12 *and* 25 *c.*). *P* 13½×14 (*horiz*) *or* 14×13½ (*vert*).

201	12 c. Beru, Nikunau and canoe	20	15
	w. Wmk POST OFFICE reading upwards	16·00	
202	25 c. Abemama, Aranuka, Kuria and fish	20	20
	w. Wmk POST OFFICE reading upwards	13·00	
203	25 c. Nonouti and reef fishing (*vert*)	25	35
	w. Wmk inverted	18·00	
204	50 c. Tarawa and House of Assembly (*vert*)	30	50
	w. Wmk inverted	20·00	
201/4	*Set of* 4	85	1·00

*The normal sideways watermark shows "POST OFFICE" reading downwards.

35 Collecting Coconuts

(Des G. Drummond. Litho Questa)

1983 (8 Aug). *Copra Industry. T* **35** *and similar horiz designs. Multicoloured. W* w **15**. *P* 14.

205	12 c. Type **35**	25	20
206	25 c. Selecting coconuts for copra	45	35
207	30 c. Removing husks	45	40
208	35 c. Drying copra	45	45
209	50 c. Loading copra at Betio	50	55
205/9	*Set of* 5	1·90	1·75

36 War Memorials

(Des J. Cooter. Litho Format)

1983 (17 Nov). *40th Anniv of Battle of Tarawa. T* **36** *and similar horiz designs. Multicoloured. W* w **15** (*sideways**). *P* 14.

210	12 c. Type **36**	15	15
211	30 c. Maps of Tarawa and Pacific Ocean	25	30
	w. Wmk POST OFFICE reading upwards	4·00	
212	35 c. Gun emplacement	25	35
	w. Wmk POST OFFICE reading upwards	18·00	
213	50 c. Modern and war-time landscapes	35	55
	w. Wmk POST OFFICE reading upwards	18·00	
214	$1 Aircraft carrier U.S.S. *Tarawa*	55	75
210/14	*Set of* 5	1·40	1·90

*The normal sideways watermark shows "POST OFFICE" reading downwards.

(Des J. Cooter. Litho Format)

1984 (14 Feb). *Island Maps* (*3rd series*). *Multicoloured designs as T* **25**. *W* w **15** (*sideways*). *P* 13½ × 14.

215	12 c. Teraina and Captain Fanning's ship *Betsey*, 1798	25	15
216	30 c. Nikumaroro and Hawksbill Turtle	30	35
217	35 c. Kanton and local postmark	35	40
218	50 c. Banaba and Flying Fish	40	55
215/18	*Set of* 4	1·10	1·25

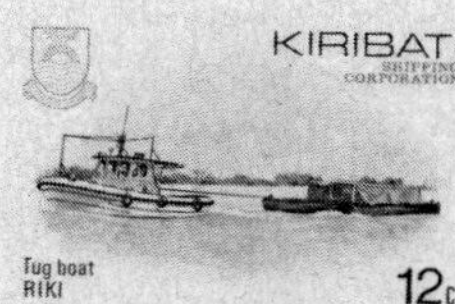

37 Tug *Riki*

(Des J. Cooter. Litho J.W.)

1984 (9 May). *Kiribati Shipping Corporation. T* **37** *and similar horiz designs. Multicoloured. W* w **15** (*sideways**). *P* 14.

219	12 c. Type **37**	40	15
	w. Wmk POST OFFICE reading downwards		
220	35 c. Ferry *Nei Nimanoa*	65	35
	w. Wmk POST OFFICE reading downwards		
221	50 c. Ferry *Nei Tebaa*	95	60
	w. Wmk POST OFFICE reading downwards		
222	$1 Cargo ship *Nei Momi*	1·50	1·10
219/22	*Set of* 4	3·25	2·00
MS223	115×98 mm. Nos. 219/22. P 13×13½	3·25	5·00
	w. Wmk POST OFFICE reading downwards		

*The normal sideways watermark shows "POST OFFICE" reading upwards.

38 Water and Sewage Schemes

(Des J. Cooter. Litho Format)

1984 (21 Aug). *"Ausipex" International Stamp Exhibition, Melbourne. T* **38** *and similar horiz designs. Multicoloured. W* w **15** (*sideways*). *P* 13½ × 14.

224	12 c. Type **38**	20	15
225	30 c. *Nouamake* (game fishing boat)	25	30
226	35 c. Overseas training schemes	25	40
227	50 c. International communications link	35	55
224/7	*Set of* 4	95	1·25

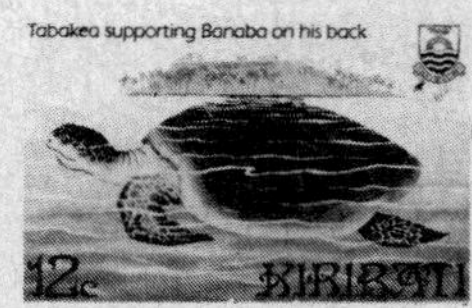

39 "Tabakea supporting Banaba"

(Des Jennifer Toombs. Litho Format)

1984 (21 Nov). *Kiribati Legends* (*1st series*). *T* **39** *and similar horiz designs. Multicoloured. W* w **15** (*sideways*). *P* 14.

228	12 c. Type **39**	15	20
229	30 c. "Nakaa, Judge of the Dead"	20	35
230	35 c. "Naareau and Dragonfly"	20	45
231	50 c. "Whistling Ghosts"	30	55
228/31	*Set of* 4	75	1·40

See also Nos. 245/8.

40 Sail-finned Tang

(Des G. Drummond. Litho Questa)

1985 (19 Feb). *Reef Fishes. T* **40** *and similar horiz designs. Multicoloured. W* w **15**. *P* 14.

232	12 c. Type **40**	60	25
	w. Wmk inverted	6·50	
233	25 c. Picasso Triggerfish	1·00	65
	w. Wmk inverted	6·50	
234	35 c. Clown Surgeonfish	1·25	85
235	80 c. Red Squirrelfish	2·00	2·50
232/5	*Set of* 4	4·25	3·75
MS236	140×107 mm. Nos. 232/5. Wmk sideways	6·00	4·75

(Des J. Cooter. Litho J.W.)

1985 (9 May). *Island Maps* (*4th series*). *Horiz designs as T* **25**. *Multicoloured. W* w **15** (*sideways**). *P* 13½.

237	12 c. Tabuaeran and Great Frigate Bird	75	15
	w. Wmk POST OFFICE reading downwards		
238	35 c. Rawaki and germinating coconuts	1·40	40
	w. Wmk POST OFFICE reading downwards	16·00	
239	50 c. Arorae and Xanthid Crab	1·60	65
	w. Wmk POST OFFICE reading downwards		
240	$1 Tamana and fish hook	2·25	1·25
	w. Wmk POST OFFICE reading downwards	8·00	
237/40	*Set of* 4	5·50	2·25

*The normal sideways watermark shows "POST OFFICE" reading upwards.

41 Youths playing Football on Beach

(Des R. Stokes. Litho Cambec Press, Melbourne)

1985 (5 Aug). *International Youth Year. T* **41** *and similar multicoloured designs. P* 13½.

241	15 c. Type **41**	60	45
242	35 c. Logos of I.Y.Y. and Kiribati Youth Year	1·00	1·10
243	40 c. Girl preparing food (*vert*)	1·10	1·40
244	55 c. Map illustrating Kiribati's youth exchange links	1·40	2·00
241/4	*Set of* 4	3·75	4·50

(Des Jennifer Toombs. Litho Questa)

1985 (19 Nov). *Kiribati Legends* (*2nd series*). *Horiz designs as T* **39**. *Multicoloured. P* 14.

245	15 c. "Nang Kineia and the Tickling Ghosts"	50	30
246	35 c. "Auriaria and Tituabine"	85	85
247	40 c. "The first coming of Babai at Arorae"	1·00	1·25
248	55 c. "Riiki and the Milky Way"	1·25	1·75
245/8	*Set of* 4	3·25	3·75

42 Map showing Telecommunications Satellite Link

(Litho Walsall)

1985 (9 Dec). *Transport and Telecommunications Decade* (*1st issue*). *T* **42** *and similar horiz design. Multicoloured. P* 14.

249	15 c. Type **42**	1·25	75
250	40 c. M.V. *Moanaraoi* (Tarawa-Suva service)	2·50	2·75

See also Nos. 268/9, 293/4 and 314/15.

(Des A. Theobald. Litho Questa)

1986 (21 Apr). *60th Birthday of Queen Elizabeth II. Vert designs as T* **230a** *of Jamaica. Multicoloured. P* 14½×14.

251	15 c. Princess Elizabeth in Girl Guide uniform, Windsor Castle, 1938	15	15
252	35 c. At Trooping the Colour, 1980	25	35
253	40 c. With Duke of Edinburgh in Kiribati, 1982	30	45
254	55 c. At banquet, Austrian Embassy, London, 1966	40	70
255	$1 At Crown Agents Head Office, London, 1983	70	1·40
251/5	*Set of* 5	1·60	2·75

(Des J. Cooter. Litho Questa)

1986 (17 June). *Island Maps* (*5th series*). *Horiz designs as T* **25**. *Multicoloured. P* 13½×14.

256	15 c. Manra and Coconut Crab	1·50	65
257	30 c. Birnie and McKean Islands and cowrie shells	2·25	1·60
258	35 c. Orona and Red-footed Booby	2·75	1·90
259	40 c. Malden Island and whaling ship, 1844	2·75	2·50
260	55 c. Vostok, Flint and Caroline Islands and Bellingshausen's *Vostok*, 1820	2·75	3·25
256/60	*Set of* 5	11·00	9·00

43 *Lepidodactylus lugubris*

44 Maps of Australia and Kiribati

(Des G. Drummond. Litho Questa)

1986 (26 Aug). *Geckos. T* **43** *and similar horiz designs. Multicoloured. P* 14.

261	15 c. Type **43**	80	55
262	35 c. *Gehyra mutilata*	1·40	1·25
263	40 c. *Hemidactylus frenatus*	1·60	1·50
264	55 c. *Gehyra oceanica*	1·75	2·00
261/4	*Set of* 4	5·00	4·75

(Des D. Miller. Litho Format)

1986 (29 Dec). *America's Cup Yachting Championship. T* **44** *and similar vert designs. Multicoloured. P* 13½×14.

265	15 c. Type **44**	20	65
	a. Horiz strip of 3. Nos. 265/7	1·75	
266	55 c. America's Cup and map of course	50	1·25
267	$1.50, *Australia II* (1983 winner)	1·25	1·50
265/7	*Set of* 3	1·75	3·00

Nos. 265/7 were printed together, *se-tenant*, in horizontal strips of 3 throughout the sheet with the $1.50 at left and the 15 c. at centre of each strip.

45 Freighter *Moamoa*

40TH WEDDING ANNIVERSARY

(**45a**)

(Des and litho Questa)

1987 (31 Mar). *Transport and Telecommunications Decade* (*2nd issue*). *T* **45** *and similar horiz design. Multicoloured. P* 13½×14.

268	30 c. Type **45**	2·00	1·75
269	55 c. Telephone switchboard and automatic exchange	3·00	3·25

(Des J. Cooter. Litho Format)

1987 (22 Sept). *Island Maps* (*6th series*). *Multicoloured designs as T* **25**, *but vert. P* 14×13½.

270	15 c. Starbuck and White-tailed Tropic Bird	55	40
271	30 c. Enderbury and White Tern	65	45
272	55 c. Tabiteuea and Pandanus Tree	65	75
273	$1 Onotoa and okai (house)	70	1·50
270/3	*Set of* 4	2·25	2·75

Nos. 271/3 exist imperforate from stock dispersed by the liquidator of Format International Security Printers Ltd.

(Des G. Drummond. Litho Format)

1987 (27 Oct). *Skinks. Horiz designs as T* **43**. *Multicoloured. P* 15.

274	15 c. *Emoia nigra*	15	20
275	35 c. *Cryptoblepharus sp.*	20	35
276	40 c. *Emoia cyanura*	25	45
277	$1 *Lipinia noctua*	40	1·00
274/7	*Set of* 4	90	1·75
MS278	130×114 mm. Nos. 274/7	1·40	3·25

Nos. 274/8 exist imperforate from stock dispersed by the liquidator of Format International Security Printers Ltd.

1987 (30 Nov). *Royal Ruby Wedding. Nos.* 251/5 *optd with T* **45a** *in silver.*

279	15 c. Princess Elizabeth in Girl Guide uniform, Windsor Castle, 1938	15	15
280	35 c. At Trooping the Colour, 1980	25	35
281	40 c. With Duke of Edinburgh in Kiribati, 1982	30	45
282	55 c. At banquet, Austrian Embassy, London, 1966	40	70
283	$1 At Crown Agents Head Office, London, 1983	70	1·40
279/83	*Set of* 5	1·60	2·75

46 Henri Dunant (founder)

47 Causeway built by Australia

(Des A. Theobald. Litho Questa)

1988 (9 May). *125th Anniv of International Red Cross. T* **46** *and similar vert designs. Multicoloured. P* 14½×14.

284	15 c. Type **46**	60	45
285	35 c. Red Cross workers in Independence parade, 1979	95	1·00
286	40 c. Red Cross workers with patient	1·00	1·10
287	55 c. Gilbert & Ellice Islands 1970 British Red Cross Centenary 10 c. stamp	1·40	1·60
284/7	*Set of* 4	3·50	3·75

(Des CPE Australia Ltd ($2), D. Miller (others). Litho CPE Australia Ltd, Melbourne ($2), Format (others))

1988 (30 July). *Bicentenary of Australian Settlement and "Sydpex '88" National Stamp Exhibition, Sydney. T* **47** *and similar horiz designs. Multicoloured. P* 14½.

288	15 c. Type **47**	25	20
289	35 c. Capt. Cook and Pacific map	60	60
290	$1 Obverse of Australian $10 Bicentenary banknote	1·25	1·75
	a. Horiz pair. Nos. 290/1	2·50	3·50
291	$1 Reverse of $10 Bicentenary banknote	1·25	1·75
288/91	*Set of* 4	3·00	3·75
MS292	95 × 76 mm. $2 *Logistic Ace* (container ship) (37 × 26 *mm*). P 13½ × 14	2·75	3·75

Nos. 290/1 were printed together, *se-tenant*, in horizontal pairs throughout the sheet.

No. **MS**292 also commemorates the 150th anniversary of the first screw-driven steamship.

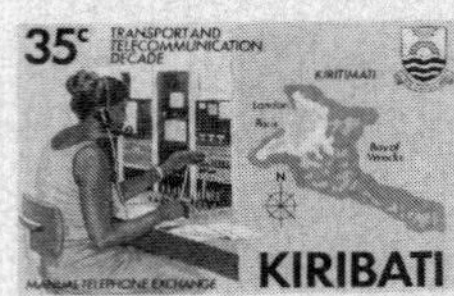

48 Manual Telephone Exchange and Map of Kiritimati

(Des A. Theobald. Litho Questa)

1988 (28 Dec). *Transport and Telecommunications Decade* (*3rd issue*). *T* **48** *and similar horiz design. Multicoloured. W* w **14** (*sideways*). *P* 14.

293	35 c. Type **48**	75	75
294	45 c. Betio–Bairiki Causeway	1·00	1·00

49 *Hound* (brigantine), 1835

50 Eastern Reef Heron

(Des E. Nisbet. Litho Questa)

1989 (26 May). *Nautical History* (*1st series*). *T* **49** *and similar horiz designs. Multicoloured. W* w **16** (*sideways*). *P* 14½.

295	15 c. Type **49**	90	55
296	30 c. *Phantom* (brig), 1854	1·50	1·10
297	40 c. H.M.S. *Alacrity* (schooner), 1873	1·60	1·60
298	$1 *Charles W. Morgan* (whaling ship), 1851	3·00	3·75
295/8	*Set of* 4	6·25	6·25

See also Nos. 343/7 and 523/6.

(Des D. Johnstone. Litho Questa)

1989 (28 June). *Birds with Young. T* **50** *and similar vert designs. Multicoloured. W* w **16**. *P* 14½.

299	15 c. Type **50**	80	90
	a. Vert pair. Nos. 299/300	1·60	1·75
300	15 c. Eastern Reef Heron chicks in nest	80	90
301	$1 White-tailed Tropic Bird	2·00	2·75
	a. Vert pair. Nos. 301/2	4·00	5·50
302	$1 Young White-tailed Tropic Bird	2·00	2·75
299/302	*Set of* 4	5·00	6·50

Nos. 299/300 and 301/2 were each printed together, *se-tenant*, in vertical pairs throughout the sheets, each pair forming a composite design.

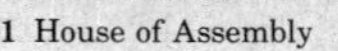

51 House of Assembly

51a "Apollo 10" on Launch Gantry

(Des D. Miller. Litho Cartor)

1989 (12 July). *10th Anniv of Independence. T* **51** *and similar vert design. Multicoloured. W* w **16** *(inverted). P* 13½×14.
303 15 c. Type **51** 25 25
304 $1 Constitution .. .. 1·25 1·75

(Des A. Theobald ($2.50), D. Miller (others). Litho Questa)

1989 (20 July). *20th Anniv of First Manned Landing on Moon. T* **51***a and similar multicoloured designs.* W w **16** *(sideways on* 50, 60 *c.) P* 14×13½ *(*20, 75 *c.) or* 14 *(others).*
305 20 c. Type **51***a* 30 30
306 50 c. Crew of "Apollo 10" (30×30 *mm*) .. 70 90
307 60 c. "Apollo 10" emblem (30×30 *mm*) .. 80 1·00
308 75 c. "Apollo 10" splashdown, Hawaii .. 95 1·25
305/8 .. .. *Set of* 4 2·50 3·00
MS309 82×100 mm. $2.50, "Apollo 11" command module in lunar orbit. P 14×13½ .. .. 5·00 6·00

51*b* Gilbert and Ellice Islands, 1949 75th Anniv of U.P.U. 3d. Stamp

51*c* Examining Fragment of Statue

(Des D. Miller. Litho Walsall)

1989 (7 Aug*). *"Philexfrance 89" International Stamp Exhibition, Paris, and "World Stamp Expo '89", Washington (1st issue). Sheet* 104×86 *mm.* W w **16**. *P* 14×13½.
MS310 **51***b* $2 multicoloured .. .. .. 3·25 4·00
*This is the local date of issue. The agents, Caphco Ltd, placed stocks on sale in London and Paris from 7 July.

(Des D. Miller, adapted Walsall. Litho Walsall)

1989 (25 Sept). *"Philexfrance 89" International Stamp Exhibition, Paris, and "World Stamp Expo '89", Washington (2nd issue). T* **51***c and similar vert designs, showing Statue of Liberty. Multicoloured.* W w **14**. *P* 14×13½.
311 35 c. Type **51***c* .. .. 1·10 1·40
a. Sheetlet. Nos. 311/13 .. .. .. 3·00
312 35 c. Workman drilling Statue .. .. 1·10 1·40
313 35 c. Surveyor with drawing .. .. 1·10 1·40
311/13 .. .. *Set of* 3 3·00 3·75
Nos. 311/13 were printed, *se-tenant*, in sheetlets of 3.

52 Telecommunications Centre

(53)

(Des L. Curtis. Litho Questa)

1989 (16 Oct). *Transport and Telecommunications Decade (4th issue). T* **52** *and similar horiz design. Multicoloured.* W w **16** *(sideways). P* 14.
314 30 c. Type **52** .. .. 1·25 1·00
315 75 c. *Mataburo* (inter-island freighter) .. 2·75 3·50

1989 (21 Oct). *"Melbourne Stampshow '89". Nos.* 301/2 *optd with T* **53**.
316 $1 White-tailed Tropic Bird .. .. 2·50 3·00
a. Vert pair. Nos. 316/17 .. .. 5·00 6·00
317 $1 Young White-tailed Tropic Bird .. .. 2·50 3·00

54 Virgin and Child (detail, "The Adoration of the Holy Child" (Denys Calvert))

55 Gilbert and Ellice Islands 1912 1d. and G.B. Twopence Blue Stamps

(Des D. Miller. Litho Questa)

1989 (1 Dec). *Christmas. T* **54** *and similar vert designs showing paintings. Multicoloured.* W w **16**. *P* 14.
318 10 c. Type **53** 55 20
319 15 c. "The Adoration of the Holy Child" (Denys Calvert) 75 30
320 55 c. "The Holy Family and St. Elizabeth" (Rubens) .. .. 2·25 1·25
321 $1 "Madonna with Child and Maria Magdalena" (School of Correggio) .. 3·50 5·00
318/21 .. .. *Set of* 4 6·25 6·00

(Des D. Miller. Litho Questa)

1990 (1 May). *150th Anniv of the Penny Black and "Stamp World London 90" International Stamp Exhibition. T* **55** *and similar horiz designs. Multicoloured.* W w **16** *(sideways). P* 14.
322 15 c. Type **55** 80 40
323 50 c. Gilbert and Ellice Islands 1911 ½d. and G.B. Penny Black .. .. .. 2·00 2·00
324 60 c. Kiribati 1982 1 c. bird and G.B. 1870 ½d. .. .. 2·00 2·00
325 $1 Gilbert Islands 1976 1 c. ship and G.B. 1841 1d. red-brown .. .. .. 2·50 3·00
322/5 .. .. *Set of* 4 6·50 6·50

56 Blue-barred Orange Parrotfish

(Des G. Drummond. Litho Questa)

1990 (12 July). *Fishes. T* **56** *and similar horiz designs. Multicoloured.* W w **14** *(sideways). "1990" imprint date. P* 14.
326 1 c. Type **56** 20 40
327 5 c. Honeycomb Grouper 30 40
328 10 c. Blue-finned Trevally 40 50
329 15 c. Hump-backed Snapper 45 30
330 20 c. Variegated Emperor 50 50
331 25 c. Rainbow Runner 55 55
332 30 c. Black-saddled Coral Grouper 65 65
333 35 c. Great Barracuda 75 75
334 40 c. Convict Tang 80 80
335 50 c. Violet Squirrelfish 90 90
336 60 c. Stocky Hawkfish .. .. 1·40 1·40
337 75 c. Pennant Coralfish .. .. 1·60 1·60
338 $1 Common Blue-striped Snapper ("Yellow and Blue Sea Perch") .. 1·90 1·90
339 $2 Sailfish .. .. 3·25 4·00
340 $5 White-tipped Reef Shark .. .. .. 6·50 8·50
326/40 .. .. *Set of* 15 18·00 21·00
For 23 c. value watermarked w **16** (sideways) see No. 356.

(Des D. Miller. Litho Questa)

1990 (4 Aug). *90th Birthday of Queen Elizabeth the Queen Mother. Vert designs as T* **107** *(*75 *c.) or* **108** *(*$2*) of Kenya.* W w **16**. *P* 14×15 *(*75 *c.) or* 14½ *(*$2*).*
341 75 c. multicoloured .. .. 1·25 1·50
342 $2 brownish black and myrtle-green .. 2·75 3·50
Designs:—75 c. Queen Elizabeth the Queen Mother; $2 King George VI and Queen Elizabeth with air raid victim, London, 1940.

(Des E. Nisbet. Litho Questa)

1990 (5 Nov). *Nautical History (2nd series). Horiz designs as T* **49**. *Multicoloured.* W w **16** *(sideways). P* 14½.
343 15 c. *Herald* (whaling ship), 1851 .. .. 75 45
344 50 c. *Belle* (barque), 1849 .. .. .. 1·50 1·50
345 60 c. *Supply* (schooner), 1851 .. .. 1·75 2·00
346 75 c. *Triton* (whaling ship), 1848 .. .. 1·75 2·00
343/6 .. .. *Set of* 4 5·25 5·50
MS347 95×75 mm. $2 *Charlotte* (convict transport), 1789 .. .. 6·50 7·00

57 Manta

58 Queen Elizabeth II

(Des G. Drummond. Litho Questa)

1991 (17 Jan). *Endangered Fishes. T* **57** *and similar horiz designs. Multicoloured.* W w **14** *(sideways). P* 14.
348 15 c. Type **57** .. .. 1·10 55
349 20 c. Manta Ray (*different*) .. .. .. 1·25 90
350 30 c. Whale Shark .. .. 1·75 2·00
351 35 c. Whale Shark (*different*) .. .. .. 2·00 2·25
348/51 .. .. *Set of* 4 5·50 5·25

1991 (30 Apr). *Horiz design as Nos.* 326/40, *but* W w **16** *(sideways). "1991" imprint date. P* 14.
356 23 c. Bennett's Pufferfish 60 60

(Des D. Miller. Litho Questa)

1991 (17 June). *65th Birthday of Queen Elizabeth II and 70th Birthday of Prince Philip. T* **58** *and similar vert design. Multicoloured.* W w **16** *(sideways). P* 14½×14.
366 65 c. Type **58** .. .. 1·00 1·25
a. Horiz pair. Nos. 366/7 separated by label .. .. 2·00 2·50
367 70 c. Prince Philip in R.A.F. uniform .. 1·00 1·25
Nos. 366/7 were printed together, *se-tenant*, in sheetlets of 10 (2×5) with designs alternating and the vertical rows separated by inscribed labels.

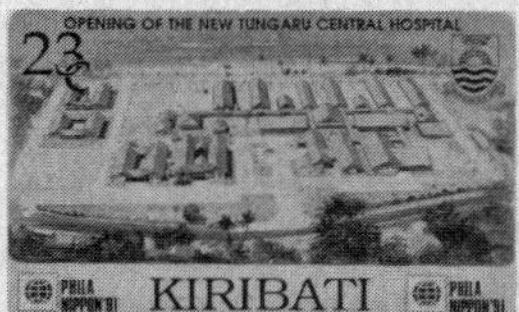

59 Aerial View of Hospital

(Des G. Vasarhelyi. Litho Questa)

1991 (16 Nov). *"Phila Nippon '91" International Stamp Exhibition, Tokyo, and Opening of Tungaru Central Hospital. T* **59** *and similar horiz designs. Multicoloured.* W w **16** *(sideways). P* 13½×14.
368 23 c. Type **59** 40 30
369 50 c. Traditional dancers 75 85
370 60 c. Hospital entrance .. .. 85 1·10
371 75 c. Foundation stone and plaques .. .. 1·25 1·60
368/71 .. .. *Set of* 4 3·00 3·50
MS372 125×83 mm. $5 Casualty on trolley and ambulance .. .. 6·00 7·00

60 Mother and Child

EXPO'92
(61)

(Des G. Vasarhelyi. Litho Questa)

1991 (2 Dec). *Christmas. T* **60** *and similar horiz designs. Multicoloured.* W w **14** *(sideways). P* 14.
373 23 c. Type **60** 50 30
374 50 c. The Holy Family in Pacific setting .. 90 90
375 60 c. The Holy Family in traditional setting 1·00 1·25
376 75 c. Adoration of the Shepherds .. .. 1·25 1·75
373/6 .. .. *Set of* 4 3·25 3·75

(Des D. Miller. Litho Questa)

1992 (6 Feb). *40th Anniv of Queen Elizabeth II's Accession. Horiz designs as T* **113** *of Kenya.* W w **14** *(sideways). P* 14.
377 23 c. Kiribati village 30 30
378 30 c. Lagoon at sunset 40 45
379 50 c. Tarawa waterfront 60 70
380 60 c. Three portraits of Queen Elizabeth .. 70 90
381 75 c. Queen Elizabeth II .. .. 90 1·10
377/81 .. .. *Set of* 5 2·50 3·00

1992 (6 June). *"EXPO '92" Worlds Fair, Seville. Nos.* 356, 336/7 *and* 339 *optd with T* **61**.
382 23 c. Bennett's Pufferfish 55 40
383 60 c. Stocky Hawkfish .. .. 1·25 1·50
384 75 c. Pennant Coralfish .. .. 1·40 1·60
385 $2 Sailfish .. .. 3·00 4·00
382/5 .. .. *Set of* 4 5·50 6·75

62 Marine Training Centre Sign

(Des A. Theobald. Litho Questa)

1992 (28 Aug). *25th Anniv of Marine Training Centre. T* **62** *and similar horiz designs. Multicoloured.* W w **16** *(sideways). P* 14.
386 23 c. Type **62** 45 40
387 50 c. Cadets on parade .. .. 80 1·00
388 60 c. Fire school .. .. 80 1·00
389 75 c. Lifeboat training .. .. 1·10 1·40
386/9 .. .. *Set of* 4 2·75 3·50

COVER PRICES

Cover factors are quoted at the beginning of each country for most issues to 1945. An explanation of the system can be found on page x. The factors quoted do not, however, apply to philatelic covers.

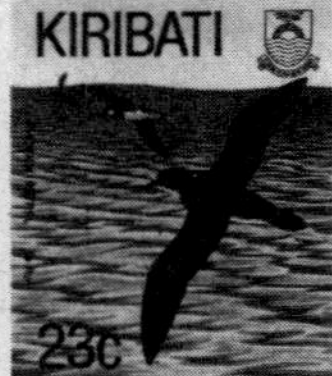

63 Healthy Children **64** Phoenix Petrel

(Des O. Ball. Litho Questa)

1992 (1 Dec). *United Nations World Health and Food/Agriculture Organizations. T* **63** *and similar horiz designs. Multicoloured.* W w **14** (*sideways*). *P* 14.

390 23 c. Type **63** 45 40
391 50 c. Fishing at night .. .. 90 1·00
392 60 c. Fruit .. .. 1·00 1·25
393 75 c. *Papuan Chief* (container ship) .. 1·50 2·00
390/3 .. .. *Set of* 4 3·50 4·25

(Des N. Arlott. Litho Questa)

1993 (28 May). *Birds. T* **64** *and similar vert designs. Multicoloured.* W w **14**. *P* 14½×14.

394 23 c. Type **64** 40 50
a. Horiz pair. Nos. 394/5 .. .. 80 1·00
395 23 c. Cook's Petrel 40 50
396 60 c. Pintail .. .. 90 1·10
a. Horiz pair. Nos. 396/7 .. .. 1·75 2·10
397 60 c. European Wigeon .. .. .. 90 1·10
398 75 c. Spectacled Tern .. .. .. 1·00 1·25
a. Horiz pair. Nos. 398/9 .. .. 2·00 2·50
399 75 c. Black-naped Tern .. .. .. 1·00 1·25
400 $1 Australian Stilt .. .. .. 1·25 1·40
a. Horiz pair. Nos. 400/1 .. .. 2·50 2·75
401 $1 Wandering Tattler .. .. .. 1·25 1·40
394/401 .. .. *Set of* 8 6·25 7·50

Nos. 394/5, 396/7, 398/9 and 400/1 were each printed together, *se-tenant*, in horizontal pairs throughout the sheets.

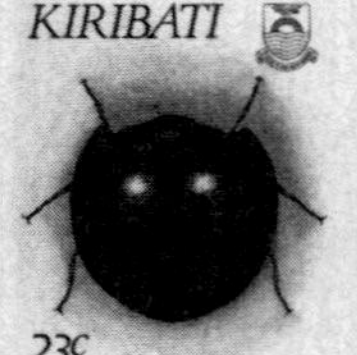

65 *Chilocorus nigritus* **66** U.S. Air Reconnaissance Consolidated B-24 Liberator

(Des I. Loe. Litho Questa)

1993 (23 Aug). *Insects. T* **65** *and similar vert designs. Multicoloured.* W w **14**. *P* 14½×14.

402 23 c. Type **65** 65 35
403 60 c. *Rodolia pumila* (ladybird) .. .. 1·25 1·50
404 75 c. *Rodolia cardinalis* (ladybird) .. 1·60 1·90
405 $1 *Cryptolaemus montrouzieri* .. .. 1·90 2·25
402/5 .. .. *Set of* 4 4·75 5·50

(Des J. Batchelor. Litho Questa)

1993 (1 Nov). *50th Anniv of Battle of Tarawa. T* **66** *and similar horiz designs. Multicoloured.* W w **14** (*sideways*). *P* 14.

406 23 c. Type **66** 60 65
a. Sheetlet. Nos. 406/15 .. .. 5·50
407 23 c. U.S.S. *Nautilus* (submarine) .. 60 65
408 23 c. U.S.S. *Indianapolis* (cruiser) .. 60 65
409 23 c. U.S.S. *Pursuit* (destroyer) .. 60 65
410 23 c. Vought Sikorsky OS2U Kingfisher spotter seaplane 60 65
411 23 c. U.S.S. *Ringgold* and U.S.S. *Dashiell* (destroyers) 60 65
412 23 c. Sherman tank on seabed 60 65
413 23 c. Grumman F6F Hellcat fighter aircraft in lagoon 60 65
414 23 c. Naval wreck on seabed 60 65
415 23 c. First U.S. aircraft to land on Betio .. 60 65
416 75 c. Landing craft leaving transports .. 1·00 1·10
a. Sheetlet. Nos. 416/25 .. .. 9·00
417 75 c. Marines landing on Betio .. .. 1·00 1·10
418 75 c. Landing craft approaching beach .. 1·00 1·10
419 75 c. Marines pinned down in surf .. 1·00 1·10
420 75 c. U.S.S. *Maryland* (battleship) .. 1·00 1·10
421 75 c. Aerial view of Betio Island .. .. 1·00 1·10
422 75 c. U.S. Navy memorial .. .. .. 1·00 1·10
423 75 c. Memorial to expatriates .. .. 1·00 1·10
424 75 c. Japanese memorial .. .. .. 1·00 1·10
425 75 c. Plan of Betio Island .. .. .. 1·00 1·10
406/25 .. .. .. *Set of* 20 14·50 16·00

Nos. 406/15 and 416/25 were each printed together, *se-tenant*, in sheetlets of 10 with the stamps arranged in two horizontal strips of 5 separated by a gutter showing Dauntless dive bomber over Betio (23 c.) and abandoned military relics (75 c.).

NEW INFORMATION

The editor is always interested to correspond with people who have new information that will improve or correct the Catalogue.

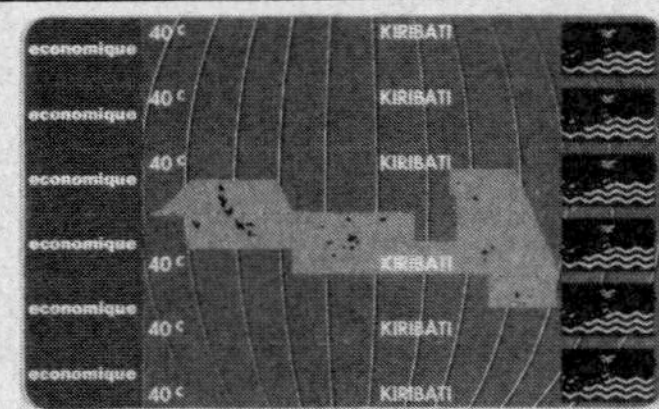

STAMPCARDS. Four Stampcards in the above design, each measuring 85×54 mm, with face values of 40 c., $1, $1.20 and $1.60, were supplied to Kiribati by the Swedish manufacturers in 1993. Each card consists of six self-adhesive stamps, separated by roulettes, with a detachable label, indicating the class of mail for which each value was valid, at left.

The four Kiribati Stampcards were announced as being issued on 1 November 1993, but first day covers, in addition to showing this date on a new type of postmark struck across the stamps, also carry a Betio Post Office Postage Paid mark of 20 December 1993.

It has been reported that Stampcards were only available from the Philatelic Bureau and were not accepted by the ordinary post offices as being valid for postage, although this is contradicted by the Controller of Postal Services. Covers posted by members of the general public at the Philatelic Bureau franked with stamps taken from them show both the special type of postmark and a Betio Postage Paid handstamp.

67 Shepherds and Angels

(Des G. Vasarhelyi. Litho Questa)

1993 (1 Dec). *Christmas. T* **67** *and similar horiz designs showing Pacific Nativity scenes. Multicoloured.* W w **14** (*sideways*). *P* 13½×14.

426 23 c. Type **67** 30 25
427 40 c. Three Kings 55 60
428 60 c. Holy Family .. .. 85 1·00
429 75 c. Virgin and Child .. .. .. 1·10 1·40
426/9 .. .. *Set of* 4 2·50 3·00
MS430 100×81 mm. $3 Virgin and Child (*different*) .. .. 3·75 4·50

68 Group of Dogs

(Des G. Vasarhelyi. Litho Questa)

1994 (18 Feb). *"Hong Kong '94" International Stamp Exhibition. Chinese New Year ("Year of the Dog"). Sheet* 120×90 *mm.* W w **14** (*sideways*). *P* 14.

MS431 **68** $3 multicoloured .. .. .. 4·00 4·50

69 Bryde's Whale and Calf **70** Family silhouetted on Beach

(Des G. Drummond. Litho Questa)

1994 (2 May). *Whales. T* **69** *and similar horiz designs. Multicoloured.* W w **14** (*sideways*). *P* 14×14½.

432 23 c. Type **69** 65 70
a. Horiz pair. Nos. 432/3 .. .. 1·25 1·40
433 23 c. Bryde's Whale with two calves .. 65 70
434 40 c. Blue Whale and calf (face value at left) 80 90
a. Horiz pair. Nos. 434/5 .. .. 1·60 1·75
435 40 c. Blue Whales and calf (face value at right) 80 90
436 60 c. Humpback Whale and calf (face value at left) .. .. 1·40 1·75
a. Horiz pair. Nos. 436/7 .. .. 2·75 3·50
437 60 c. Humpback Whale and calf (face value at right) .. .. 1·40 1·75
438 75 c. Killer Whale and calf .. .. .. 1·40 1·75
a. Horiz pair. Nos. 438/9 .. .. 2·75 3·50
439 75 c. Killer Whale and two calves .. .. 1·40 1·75
432/9 .. .. *Set of* 8 7·50 9·00

The two designs of each value were printed together, *se-tenant*, in horizontal pairs throughout the sheets.

(Des O. Ball. Litho Questa)

1994 (12 July). *15th Anniv of Independence. T* **70** *and similar horiz designs.* W w **14** (*sideways*). *P* 14½.

440 40 c. Type **70** 60 60
441 60 c. Fish and coral .. .. .. 1·00 1·25
442 75 c. Great Frigate Birds in flight .. 1·25 1·50
440/2 .. .. *Set of* 3 2·50 3·00

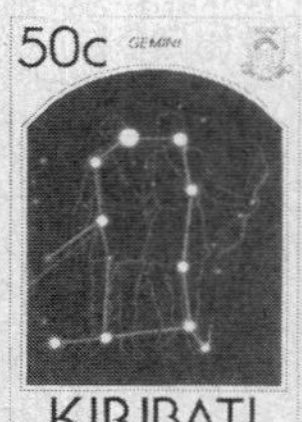

71 *Diaphania indica* **72** *Nerium oleander*

(Des R. Watton. Litho Questa)

1994 (19 Aug). *Butterflies and Moths. T* **71** *and simlar vert designs. Multicoloured.* W w **14**. *P* 14½×14.

443 1 c. Type **71** 10 10
444 5 c. *Herpetogramma licarsisalis* 10 10
445 10 c. *Parotis suralis* 10 10
446 12 c. *Sufetula sunidesalis* 10 10
447 20 c. *Aedia sericea* 15 20
448 23 c. *Anomis vitiensis* 20 25
449 30 c. *Anticarsia irrorata* 25 30
450 35 c. *Spodoptera litura* 30 35
451 40 c. *Mocis frugalis* 35 40
452 45 c. *Agrius convolvuli* 40 45
453 50 c. *Cephonodes picus* 45 50
454 55 c. *Gnathothlibus erotus* 50 55
455 60 c. *Macroglossum hirundo* 50 55
456 75 c. *Badamia exclamationis* 65 70
457 $1 *Precis villida* 90 95
458 $2 *Danaus plexippus* .. .. .. 1·75 1·90
459 $3 *Hypolimnas bolina* (male) .. .. 2·50 2·75
460 $5 *Hypolimnas bolina* (female) .. .. 4·25 4·50
443/60 .. .. .. *Set of* 18 13·50 14·50

For miniature sheet containing No. 457 see No. **MS**527.

(Des N. Shewring. Litho Questa)

1994 (31 Oct). *Seasonal Flowers. T* **72** *and similar vert designs. Multicoloured.* W w **16**. *P* 14.

461 23 c. Type **72** 30 30
462 60 c. *Catharanthus roseus* .. .. .. 80 1·00
463 75 c. *Ipomea pes-caprae* .. .. .. 1·00 1·25
464 $1 *Calophyllum inophyllum* .. .. 1·40 2·00
461/4 .. .. *Set of* 4 3·25 4·00

73 Gemini (The Twins) **74** Church and Traditional Meeting Hut

(Des N. Shewring. Litho Walsall)

1995 (31 Jan). *Night Sky over Kiribati (2nd series). T* **73** *and similar vert designs. Multicoloured.* W w **16**. *P* 14.

465 50 c. Type **73** 75 70
466 60 c. Cancer (The Crab) 85 90
467 75 c. Cassiopeia (The Queen of Ethiopia) .. 1·00 1·25
468 $1 Southern Cross .. .. .. 1·25 1·75
465/8 .. .. *Set of* 4 3·50 4·25

(Des D. Miller. Litho Questa)

1995 (3 Apr). *Tourism. T* **74** *and similar vert designs. Multicoloured. P* 14½. (*a*) W w **16** (*upright*) (*sheets*).

469 30 c. Type **74** 50 55
a. Horiz strip of 5. Nos. 469/73 .. .. 2·25
470 30 c. Fishermen and outrigger canoes .. 50 55
471 30 c. Gun emplacement and map 50 55
472 30 c. Children with marine creatures .. 50 55
473 30 c. Sports 50 55
474 40 c. Local girls in traditional costume .. 55 60
a. Horiz strip of 5. Nos. 474/8 .. .. 2·50
475 40 c. Windsurfing 55 60
476 40 c. Fishermen and wood carver 55 60
477 40 c. Under water sport 55 60
478 40 c. Women weaving 55 60
469/78 .. .. .. *Set of* 10 4·75 5·25

(*b*) W w **16** (*sideways*) (*booklets*)

479 30 c. Type **74** 55 65
a. Booklet pane. Nos. 479/88 plus 5 labels 5·00
480 30 c. Fishermen and outrigger canoes .. 55 65
481 30 c. Gun emplacement and map 55 65
482 30 c. Children with marine creatures .. 55 65
483 30 c. Sports 55 65
484 40 c. Local girls in traditional costume .. 55 65
485 40 c. Windsurfing 55 65

486 40 c. Fishermen and wood carver 55 65
487 40 c. Under water sport 55 65
488 40 c. Women weaving 55 65
479/88 .. .. *Set of* 10 5·00 6·00

Nos. 469/73 and 474/8 were printed together, *se-tenant*, in horizontal strips of 5 throughout the sheets.

Booklet pane No. 479a contains the ten stamps printed together, *se-tenant*, as a block of 10 with each vertical pair separated by half stamp-sized illustrated label.

75 Grumman TBF Avenger

(Des J. Batchelor (Nos. 489/94), R. Watton (No. **MS**495). Litho Cartor (Nos. 489/94) or Questa (No. **MS**495))

1995 (8 May). 50*th Anniv of End of Second World War. American Aircraft. T* **75** *and similar multicoloured designs.* W w **14** (*sideways*). *P* 14×13½.

489 23 c. Type **75** 30 30
490 40 c. Curtiss SOC.3-1 Seagull seaplane .. 50 55
491 50 c. Consolidated B-24 Liberator bomber 60 65
492 60 c. Grumman G-21 Goose amphibian .. 75 80
493 75 c. Martin B-26 Marauder bomber .. 90 1·00
494 $1 Northrop P-61 Black Widow bomber 1·25 1·40
489/94 .. .. *Set of* 6 3·75 4·25
MS495 75×85 mm. $2 Reverse of 1939–45 War Medal (*vert*). Wmk upright. P 14 .. .. 2·50 3·00

76 Eclectus Parrots, Great Frigate Bird and Coconut Crabs **(77)**

(Des N. Shewring. Litho B.D.T.)

1995 (12 July). *Protecting the Environment. T* **76** *and similar horiz designs. Multicoloured.* W w **14** (*sideways*). *P* 14.

496 60 c. Type **76** 85 95
a. Sheetlet. Nos. 496/9 .. .. .. 3·00
497 60 c. Red-tailed Tropic Birds, Common Dolphin and Pantropical Spotted Dolphin 85 95
498 60 c. Blue-striped Snapper ("Yellow and Blue Sea Perch"), Blue-barred Orange Parrotfish and Green Turtle .. 85 95
499 60 c. Red-breasted Wrasse, Pennant Coralfish and Violet Squirrelfish .. 85 95
496/9 .. .. *Set of* 4 3·00 3·50

Nos. 496/9 were printed together, *se-tenant*, in sheetlets of 4 stamps and 4 labels inscribed with details of the species depicted.

1995 (19 Aug). *"Jakarta '95" Stamp Exhibition, Indonesia. Nos. 496/9 optd with T* **77**.

500 60 c. Type **76** .. .. 95 1·10
a. Sheetlet. Nos. 500/3 .. .. .. 3·50
501 60 c. Red-tailed Tropic Birds, Common Dolphin and Pantropical Spotted Dolphin .. .. 95 1·10
502 60 c. Blue-striped Snapper, Blue-barred Orange Parrotfish and Green Turtle .. 95 1·10
503 60 c. Red-breasted Wrasse, Pennant Coralfish and Violet Squirrelfish .. 95 1·10
500/3 .. .. *Set of* 4 3·50 4·00

78 Sow feeding Piglets **79** *Teanoai* (police patrol boat)

(Des D. Miller. Litho Cartor)

1995 (1–14 Sept). *"Singapore '95" International Stamp Exhibition and Beijing International Coin and Stamp Expo '95. Two sheets, each* 113×85 *mm, containing T* **78**. W w **14** (*sideways*). *P* 13.

MS504 $2 multicoloured ("Singapore '95") .. 2·50 3·25
MS505 $2 multicoloured ("Beijing '95") (14 Sept) 2·50 3·25

Nos. **MS**504/5 show the exhibition logos on the sheet margins.

(Des S. Noon. Litho Cartor)

1995 (30 Nov). *Police Maritime Unit. T* **79** *and similar vert design showing* Teanoai. *Multicoloured.* W w **14**. *P* 13.

506 75 c. Type **79** .. .. 1·25 1·40
a. Horiz pair. Nos. 506/7 .. .. 2·50 2·75
507 75 c. *Teanoai* at sea .. .. .. 1·25 1·40

Nos. 506/7 were printed together, *se-tenant*, in horizontal pairs throughout the sheet.

80 Pantropical Spotted Dolphins

(Des R. Watton. Litho Walsall)

1996 (15 Jan). *Dolphins. T* **80** *and similar horiz designs. Multicoloured.* W w **16** (*sideways*). *P* 14.

508 23 c. Type **80** 50 30
509 60 c. Spinner Dolphins .. .. .. 1·00 85
510 75 c. Fraser's Dolphins .. .. .. 1·10 1·00
511 $1 Rough-toothed Dolphins .. .. 1·40 1·40
508/11 .. .. *Set of* 4 3·50 3·25

81 Tap and Top Left Segment of U.N.I.C.E.F. Emblem

(Des N. Shewring. Litho Cartor)

1996 (22 Apr). 50*th Anniv of U.N.I.C.E.F. T* **81** *and similar horiz designs. Multicoloured.* W w **14** (*sideways*). *P* 13.

512 30 c. Type **81** 50 60
a. Block of 4. Nos. 512/15 .. .. 1·75
513 30 c. Documents and top right segment .. 50 60
514 30 c. Syringe and bottom left segment .. 50 60
515 30 c. Open book and bottom right segment 50 60
512/15 .. .. *Set of* 4 1·75 2·25

Nos. 512/15 were printed together, *se-tenant*, throughout the sheet with each block of 4 showing the complete emblem.

82 Chinese Dragon

(Des Jane Evans. Litho B.D.T.)

1996 (30 Apr). *"CHINA '96" 9th Asian International Stamp Exhibition, Peking. Sheet* 110×86 *mm.* W w **16** (*sideways*). *P* 13½.

MS516 **82** 50 c. multicoloured .. .. 90 1·25

83 L.M.S. No. 5609 *Gilbert and Ellice Islands* Locomotive

(Des A. Theobald. Litho Cartor)

1996 (8 June). *"CAPEX '96" International Stamp Exhibition, Toronto. Sheet* 111×80 *mm.* W w **14** (*sideways*). *P* 12.

MS517 **83** $2 multicoloured .. .. .. 2·40 2·75

84 Rathbun Red Crab

(Des G. Drummond. Litho Walsall)

1996 (6 Aug). *Sea Crabs. T* **84** *and similar horiz designs. Multicoloured.* W w **14** (*sideways*). *P* 14.

518 23 c. Type **84** 40 30
519 60 c. Red and White Painted Crab .. 80 80
520 75 c. Red-spotted Crab 95 95
521 $1 Red-spotted White Crab .. .. 1·40 1·75
518/21 .. .. *Set of* 4 3·25 3·50

85 Kiribati Canoe **(86)**

(Des Jane Evans. Litho Questa)

1996 (21 Oct). *"Taipei '96" International Stamp Exhibition, Taiwan. Sheet* 110×86 *mm.* W w **16** (*sideways*). *P* 14½.

MS522 **85** $1.50, multicoloured .. .. 1·75 2·25

(Des E. Nisbet. Litho Walsall)

1996 (2 Dec). *Nautical History (3rd series). Horiz designs as T* **49**. *Multicoloured.* W w **16** (*sideways*). *P* 14½.

523 23 c. *Potomac* (whaling ship), 1843 .. 40 35
524 50 c. *Southern Cross IV* (missionary barquentine), 1891 .. .. .. 70 65
525 60 c. *John Williams III* (missionary barque), 1890 .. .. 85 85
526 $1 H.M.S. *Dolphin* (frigate), 1765 .. 1·25 1·40
523/6 .. .. *Set of* 4 2·75 3·00

(Des D. Miller. Litho Questa)

1997 (12 Feb). *"HONG KONG '97" International Stamp Exhibition. Sheet* 130×90 *mm containing design as No. 457. Multicoloured.* W w **14** (*sideways*). *P* 14½×14.

MS527 $1 *Precis villida* .. .. .. 1·10 1·40

(Des J. Batchelor. Litho Questa)

1997 (29 May). *"Pacific '97" International Stamp Exhibition, San Francisco. Nos. 489/95 optd with T* **86**.

528 23 c. Type **75** 30 25
529 40 c. Curtiss SOC.3-1 Seagull seaplane .. 50 45
530 50 c. Consolidated B-24 Liberator bomber 60 55
531 60 c. Grumman G-21 Goose amphibian .. 70 70
532 75 c. Martin B-26 Marauder bomber .. 80 80
533 $1 Northrop P-61 Black Widow bomber 1·00 1·10
528/33 .. .. *Set of* 6 3·50 3·50
MS534 75×85 mm. $2 Reverse of 1939–45 War Medal (*vert*) .. .. 2·10 2·40

87 Queen Elizabeth II in 1996 **88** Young Rock Dove

(Des N. Shewring (No. **MS**541), D. Miller (others). Litho Questa (No. **MS**541), Cot Printery Ltd, Barbados (others))

1997 (10 July). *Golden Wedding of Queen Elizabeth and Prince Philip. T* **87** *and similar multicoloured designs.* W w **14**. *P* 14½×14.

535 50 c. Type **87** 65 70
a. Horiz pair. Nos. 535/6 .. .. 1·25 1·40
536 50 c. Prince Philip carriage-driving at Windsor Horse Show 65 70
537 60 c. Queen in phaeton at Trooping the Colour 70 75
a. Horiz pair. Nos. 537/8 .. .. 1·40 1·50
538 60 c. Prince Philip on Montserrat, 1993 .. 70 75
539 75 c. Queen Elizabeth and Prince Philip, 1989 .. .. 90 1·00
a. Horiz pair. Nos. 539/40 .. .. 1·75 2·00
540 75 c. Prince Edward on horseback .. 90 1·00
535/40 .. .. *Set of* 6 4·00 4·50
MS541 110×70 mm. $2 Queen Elizabeth and Prince Philip in landau (*horiz*). Wmk sideways. P 14×14½ .. .. 2·40 2·75

Nos. 535/6, 537/8 and 539/40 were each printed together, *se-tenant*, in horizontal pairs throughout the sheets with the backgrounds forming composite designs.

(Litho Walsall)

1997 (1 Dec). *Birds. T* **88** *and similar vert designs. Multicoloured.* W w **16**. *P* 14.

542 50 c. Type **88** 65 70
a. Horiz pair. Nos. 542/3 .. .. 1·25 1·40
543 50 c. Adult Rock Dove 65 70
544 60 c. Adult Pacific Pigeon 70 75
a. Horiz pair. Nos. 544/5 .. .. 1·40 1·50
545 60 c. Young Pacific Pigeon 70 75
546 75 c. Adult Micronesian Pigeon 80 90
a. Horiz pair. Nos. 546/7 .. .. 1·60 1·75
547 75 c. Young Micronesian Pigeon 80 90
542/7 .. .. *Set of* 6 3·50 4·00

Nos. 542/3, 544/5 and 546/7 were each printed together, *se-tenant*, in horizontal pairs throughout the sheets.

(89) **90** Spiny Lobster

1997 (1 Dec). *"ASIA '97" Stamp Exhibition, Bangkok. Nos.* 542/3 *and* 546/7 *optd with T* **89**.

No.	Description		Unused	Used
548	50 c. Type **88**		65	70
	a. Horiz pair. Nos. 548/9		1·25	1·40
549	50 c. Adult Rock Dove		65	70
550	75 c. Adult Micronesian Pigeon		70	80
	a. Horiz pair. Nos. 550/1		1·40	1·60
551	75 c. Young Micronesian Pigeon		70	80
548/51		*Set of* 4	2·40	2·75

(Des Josephine Martin. Litho Cot Printery Ltd, Barbados)

1998 (2 Feb). *Endangered Species. Spiny Lobster. T* **90** *and similar horiz designs. Multicoloured.* W w **14** (*sideways*). *P* 14×14½.

No.	Description		Unused	Used
552	25 c. Type **90**		20	25
	a. Horiz strip of 4. Nos. 552/5		80	
553	25 c. Facing right		20	25
554	25 c. With coral in foreground		20	25
555	25 c. On sponge		20	25
552/5		*Set of* 4	80	85
MS556	69×49 mm. $1.50, Spiny Lobster		1·25	1·40

Nos. 552/5 were printed either in sheets of one design or in *se-tenant* sheets of 16, containing four horizontal strips as No. 552a.

No. **MS**556 does not show the W.W.F. panda emblem.

91 Diana, Princess of Wales, 1992

(Des D. Miller. Litho Questa)

1998 (31 Mar). *Diana, Princess of Wales Commemoration. T* **91** *and similar vert designs. Multicoloured.* W w **16** (*No.* 557). *P* 14½×14.

No.	Description	Unused	Used
557	25 c. Type **91**	20	25
MS558	145×70 mm. 25 c., Type **91**; 50 c., Wearing black evening dress, 1981; 60 c., With scarf over head, 1992; 75 c., Wearing brown jacket, 1993. W w **14** (sideways) (*sold at* $2.10 + 50 c. *charity premium*)	2·40	2·50

STAMP BOOKLETS

1981 (26 Nov). *Royal Wedding. Multicoloured cover,* 105×65 *mm, showing* The Katherine. *Stitched.*

SB1 $1.96, booklet containing eight 12 c. in panes of 4 (No. 156a) and two 50 c. in pane of two (No. 157a) .. 2·00

1983 (8 Aug). *Orange-brown, emerald and cinnamon cover,* 105×64 *mm, showing sea birds. Stitched.*

SB2 $3 booklet containing 25 c. and 50 c. (Nos. 171*a*, 174), each in block of 4 .. 7·50

1987 (31 Mar). *Multicoloured cover,* 105×65 *mm, showing sea birds. Stitched.*

SB3 $3.40, booklet containing 15 c. (No. 170) in block of 8 and 55 c. (No. 175*a*) in block of 4 .. 22·00

1995 (3 Apr). *Tourism. Multicoloured cover showing yacht at sunset. Pane attached by selvedge.*

SB4 $3.50, booklet containing *se-tenant* pane of 10 (No. 479*a*) .. 5·00

POSTAGE DUE STAMPS

D 1 Kiribati Coat of Arms

(Litho Format)

1981 (27 Aug). *P* 14.

No.	Type	Description		Unused	Used
D1	D 1	1 c. black and magenta		10	10
D2		2 c. black and greenish blue		10	10
D3		5 c. black and bright green		10	10
D4		10 c. black and chestnut		10	15
D5		20 c. black and bright blue		15	25
D6		30 c. black and brown-ochre		20	35
D7		40 c. black and purple		25	45
D8		50 c. black and deep blue-green		25	50
D9		$1 black and orange-red		40	75
D1/9			*Set of* 9	1·25	2·25

Nos. D1/9 exist imperforate from stock dispersed by the liquidator of Format International Security Printers Ltd.

OFFICIAL STAMPS

O.K.G.S. (O 1) **O.K.G.S.** (O 2)

1981 (May). *Optd with Type* O **1**. A. *On Nos.* 86, 90/3, 95 *and* 97/9*b*, W w **14** (*sideways**). B. *On Nos.* 121/35. *No wmk.*

No.	Description	A		B	
O 1	1 c. Type **16**	2·00	2·25	10	30
O 2	3 c. M.V. *Tautunu* (inter-island freighter)	†		10	20
O 3	5 c. Hibiscus	†		10	15
O 4	7 c. Catholic Cathedral, Tarawa	†		10	15
O 5	10 c. Maneaba, Bikenibeu	18·00	15·00	10	15
	a. Opt double	†		10·00	—
O 6	12 c. Betio Harbour	5·00	5·00	30	30
O 7	15 c. Eastern Reef Heron	18·00	17·00	90	30
O 8	20 c. Flamboyant Tree	10·00	10·00	20	30
O 9	25 c. Moorish Idol	†		30	30
O10	30 c. Frangipani	5·50	7·00	30	35
	a. Opt double	†		13·00	—
O11	35 c. G.I.P.C. Chapel, Tangintebu	†		35	40
O12	50 c. *Hypolimnas bolina* (butterfly)	5·00	5·00	50	55
	a. Opt double	†		60·00	—
	b. Opt inverted	†		60·00	—
O13	$1 *Tabakea* (Tarawa Lagoon ferry)	13·00	11·00	1·00	75
	w. Wmk Crown to right of CA	50·00	—	†	
O14	$2 Evening scene	15·00	15·00	2·00	1·75
	a. Opt double	†		£110	—
	w. Wmk Crown to right of CA	65·00	—	†	
O15	$5 National flag	3·25	4·00	4·00	4·25
	a. Opt inverted	£150	—	†	
O1A/15A	*Set of* 10	80·00	80·00		
O1B/15B	*Set of* 15			8·00	9·00

*The normal sideways watermark shows Crown to left of CA, *as seen from the back of the stamp.*

1983. *Nos.* 86, 90/3, 95, 97/9 *and* 131 *optd with Type* O **2**.

No.	Description	Unused	Used
O16	1 c. Type **16**	5·50	5·50
O17	10 c. Maneaba, Bikenibeu	12·00	8·00
O18	12 c. Betio Harbour	4·00	4·00
O19	15 c. Eastern Reef Heron	14·00	14·00
O20	20 c. Flamboyant Tree	6·50	6·50
O21	30 c. Frangipani	9·00	5·50
O21*a*	35 c. G.I.P.C. Chapel, Tangintebu	†	—
O22	50 c. *Hypolimnas bolina elliciana* (butterfly)	7·00	4·50
O23	$1 *Tabakea* (Tarawa Lagoon ferry)	10·00	8·00
O24	$2 Evening scene	16·00	10·00

1983 (28 June). *Nos.* 169, 172/3, 175 *and* 177 *optd with Type* O **2**.

No.	Description		Unused	Used
O25	12 c. Polynesian Reed Warbler		40	30
O26	30 c. Brown Booby		70	50
O27	35 c. Audubon's Shearwater		80	60
	a. Opt double			
O28	50 c. Bristle-thighed Curlew		1·00	80
O29	$2 Long-tailed Koel		3·00	2·75
O25/9		*Set of* 5	5·50	4·50

Kuwait

Kuwait, an independent Arab shaikhdom since 1756, placed itself under British protection in 1899 to counter the spread of Ottoman influence in the Arabian Gulf.

The first, somewhat limited, postal service, via Bushire, commenced with the appointment of a Political Agent to Kuwait in August 1904. Because of diplomatic problems this system continued until 21 January 1915 when a regular Indian post office was established.

Limited supplies of Indian stamps were used by the Political Agency postal service, but these became available to the general public from 21 January 1915. Stamps seen postally used from Kuwait before 1923 are usually ½ a., 1 a., 1 r. or 5 r. values, with the occasional Official issue. Much more common are values to 15 r., both postage and Official, used telegraphically.

Before 1910 the name of the shaikhdom was spelt "KOWEIT" and this spelling appears on various circular postmarks used between 1915 and 1923. The more modern version of the name was first used for a postal cancellation in 1923.

1915 "KOWEIT"

1923 "KUWAIT"

On 1 August 1921 responsibility for the Kuwait postal service passed to the Iraq Post Office.

PRICES FOR STAMPS ON COVER TO 1945

Nos. 1/15	*from* × 5
Nos. 16/29	*from* × 3
Nos. 31/51	*from* × 2
Nos. 52/63	*from* × 4
Nos. O1/27	*from* × 10

USED HIGH VALUES. It is necessary to emphasize that used prices quoted for high value stamps are for postally used examples.

(Currency. 16 annas = 1 rupee)

KUWAIT (1) KUWAIT (2)

1923 (1 Apr)–**24.** *Stamps of India (King George V), optd with T* **1** *or* **2** *(rupee values, 15½ mm) by Indian Govt Ptg Wks. W* **34** *(Large Star) of India. P* 14.

1	½ a. pale blue-green (No. 156)	2·00	3·75
	a. Opt double	£190	
	b. Vert pair, one without opt	£475	
2	1 a. chocolate (No. 197)	2·00	2·00
	a. Opt double	£275	
	b. Opt omitted (lower stamp of vert pair)	£800	
3	1½ a. chocolate (A) ("ANNA") (No. 163)	1·25	4·00
4	2 a. violet (No. 168)	3·00	2·00
	a. Bright purple		
5	2 a. 6 p. ultramarine (No. 171)	2·00	8·00
6	3 a. orange-brown (No. 173)	4·25	17·00
7	3 a. ultramarine (No. 200) (1924)	9·00	2·25
8	4 a. deep olive (No. 174)	8·00	24·00
	a. Olive-green		
9	6 a. yellow-bistre (No. 177)	8·50	13·00
10	8 a. purple (No. 179)	8·00	30·00
	a. Mauve		
11	12 a. claret (No. 184)	14·00	35·00
12	1 r. brown and green (No. 185)	16·00	20·00
	a. Red-brown and blue-green	19·00	23·00
13	2 r. carmine and brown (No. 187)	40·00	90·00
14	5 r. ultramarine and violet (No. 188)	80·00	£200
15	10 r. green and scarlet (No. 189)	£120	£450
1/15	*Set of* 15	£275	£750

Essays of the overprint using the obsolete spelling "KOWEIT" were prepared in 1923 and can be found on the original 14 values of the postage stamps and on the 13 stamps of the Official series. (*Price per set of* 27 *unused* £20000).

Nos. 1/4 and 6/7 are all known with inverted overprint and the overprint is also known on examples of India No. 165 ("ANNAS"). It is doubtful if such errors were actually sold at the Kuwait Post Office, although some are known on registered or ordinary covers.

KUWAIT (3) KUWAIT (4)

1929–37. *Stamps of India (King George V, Nasik printing), optd with T* **3** *or* **4** *(rupee values). W* **69** *(Mult Stars) of India. P* 14.

16	½ a. green (No. 202)	2·00	1·40
	aw. Wmk inverted	2·25	2·25
16*b*	½ a. green (No. 232) (1934)	4·50	95
17	1 a. chocolate (No. 203)	7·00	1·40
	aw. Wmk inverted		
17*b*	1 a. chocolate (No. 234) (1934)	4·50	75
18	2 a. purple (No. 206)	2·75	80
19	2 a. vermilion (No. 236)	20·00	75·00
	aw. Wmk inverted	20·00	75·00
19*b*	2 a. vermilion (No. 236*b*) (1934)	16·00	5·50
19*c*	2 a. vermilion (*small die*) (No. 236*c*) (1937)	4·50	1·75
20	3 a. blue (No. 209)	2·75	1·60
21	3 a. carmine (No. 237)	5·50	4·25
22	4 a. sage-green (*wmk inverted*) (No. 211w)	25·00	70·00
22*a*	4 a. pale sage-green (No. 210) (1934)	5·50	11·00
22*b*	6 a. bistre (No. 239) (1937)	22·00	50·00
23	8 a. reddish purple (No. 212)	—	13·00
	w. Wmk inverted	9·00	
24	12 a. claret (*wmk inverted*) (No. 213w) (1933)	19·00	35·00
	w. Wmk inverted	10·00	
25	1 r. chocolate and green (No. 214)	—	26·00
	a. Extended "T"	£275	
	w. Wmk inverted	10·00	
26	2 r. carm & orge (*wmk inverted*) (No. 215w)	10·00	60·00
	a. Extended "T"	£275	£650
27	5 r. ultramarine & purple (No. 216) (1937)	75·00	£190
	a. Extended "T"	£425	
28	10 r. green and scarlet (No. 217) (1934)	£170	£375
	a. Extended "T"	£850	
29	15 r. bl & ol (*wmk inverted*) (No. 218w) (1937)	£475	£750
	a. Extended "T"	£1300	
16/29	*Set of* 20	£800	£1500

The "T" of "KUWAIT" shows a ¾ mm downward extension on R. 3/2, lower left pane.

Nos. 16, 17, 18/19 and 22 are inscribed "INDIA POSTAGE & REVENUE". The remainder are inscribed "INDIA POSTAGE".

No. 19*b* measures 19×22.6 mm and No. 19*c* 18.4×21.8 mm.

Examples of most values are known showing a forged Kuwait postmark dated "11 NOV 37".

1933 (Feb)–**34.** *Air. Nos.* 220/3 *of India optd as T* **2** (16½ *mm*).

31	2 a. deep blue-green	13·00	25·00
	w. Wmk stars to right	13·00	25·00
32	3 a. blue	2·25	2·50
	w. Wmk stars to right	2·25	3·00
33	4 a. olive-green	85·00	£170
34	6 a. bistre (2.34)	2·25	4·50
	w. Wmk stars to right	2·25	4·50
31/4	*Set of* 4	90·00	£180

The normal sideways watermark on Nos. 31/4 shows stars pointing to left, *as seen from the back of the stamp.*

The 3 a. value exists with a most pronounced lithography double print. *Price* £850 *un.,* £650 *used.* Examples of this and other stamps with slight double prints are of little additional value.

1939. *Nos.* 248, 250/1, 253, 255/63 *of India (King George VI) optd with T* **3** *or* **4** *(rupee values).*

36	½ a. red-brown	7·00	1·75
38	1 a. carmine	7·00	1·50
39	2 a. vermilion	7·00	2·50
41	3 a. yellow-green	7·00	2·00
43	4 a. brown	35·00	13·00
44	6 a. turquoise-green	25·00	7·50
45	8 a. slate-violet	28·00	32·00
46	12 a. lake	20·00	42·00
47	1 r. grey and red-brown	5·00	2·50
	a. Extended "T"	£275	
	b. Opt triple, one inverted		
48	2 r. purple and brown	3·75	12·00
	a. Extended "T"	£250	
49	5 r. green and blue	12·00	17·00
	a. Extended "T"	£400	
50	10 r. purple and claret	60·00	70·00
	a. Opt double	£300	
	b. Extended "T"	£550	
51	15 r. brown and green	£120	£190
	a. Extended "T"	£800	
	w. Wmk inverted	85·00	£150
36/51w	*Set of* 13	£275	£300

On later printings the extended "T" variety was corrected in two stages.

Examples of most values are known showing a forged Kuwait postmark dated "17 NOV 39".

Following the rebellion in Iraq control of the Kuwait postal service was assumed by the Indian authorities on 2 June 1941.

Unoverprinted stamps of INDIA were used in Kuwait between 1941 and 1945.

1945. *Nos.* 265/8 *and* 269*a of India (King George VI, on white background) optd with T* **3**.

52	3 p. slate	1·00	2·00
53	½ a. purple	1·00	2·00
54	9 p. green	2·25	6·50
55	1 a. carmine	1·50	1·50
56	1½ a. dull violet	2·75	6·50
57	2 a. vermilion	3·00	2·25
58	3 a. bright violet	3·25	3·00
59	3½ a. bright blue	4·00	6·50
60	4 a. brown	3·25	2·00
60*a*	6 a. turquoise-green	14·00	8·50
61	8 a. slate-violet	7·00	2·50
62	12 a. lake	7·00	2·75
63	14 a. purple	13·00	15·00
52/63	*Set of* 13	55·00	50·00

Following a short period of Pakistani control, from August 1947 the Kuwait postal service passed to British administration on 1 April 1948.

KUWAIT I ANNA (5) KUWAIT 5 RUPEES (6)

NOTE. From 1948 onwards, for stamps with similar surcharges, but without name of country, see British Postal Agencies in Eastern Arabia.

1948 (1 Apr)–**49.** *Nos.* 470, 475, 476*a*/7, 478*a and* 485/90 *of Great Britain (King George VI), surch as T* **5** *or* **6** *(rupee values).*

64	½ a. on ½d. pale green	1·00	90
65	1 a. on 1d. pale scarlet	1·00	90
66	1½ a. on 1½d. pale red-brown	1·25	75
67	2 a. on 2d. pale orange	1·00	90
68	2½ a. on 2½d. light ultramarine	1·25	1·00
69	3 a. on 3d. pale violet	1·00	30
	a. Pair, one surch albino		
70	6 a. on 6d. purple	1·00	50
71	1 r. on 1s. bistre-brown	2·00	85
72	2 r. on 2s. 6d. yellow-green	2·75	3·75
73	5 r. on 5s. red	4·50	4·50
73*a*	10 r. on 10s. ultramarine (4.7.49)	38·00	6·00
64/73*a*	*Set of* 11	48·00	18·00

KUWAIT 2½ ANNAS (7) KUWAIT 15 RUPEES (8)

1948 (1 May). *Royal Silver Wedding. Nos.* 493/4 *of Great Britain surch with T* **7** *or* **8**.

74	2½ a. on 2½d. ultramarine	1·00	50
75	15 r. on £1 blue	30·00	30·00
	a. Short bars (R. 3/4)	£130	

No. 75a has the bars cancelling the original face value 3 mm long instead of the 3½ mm of the normal surcharge.

1948 (29 July). *Olympic Games. Nos.* 495/8 *of Great Britain surch as T* **7**, *but in one line* (6 *a.*) *or two lines (others).*

76	2½ a. on 2½d. ultramarine	1·00	1·50
77	3 a. on 3d. violet	1·00	1·50
78	6 a. on 6d. bright purple	1·25	1·50
79	1 r. on 1s. brown	1·25	1·50
76/9	*Set of* 4	4·00	5·50

1949 (10 Oct). *75th Anniv of U.P.U. Nos.* 499/502 *of Great Britain surch* "KUWAIT" and new values.

80	2½ a. on 2½d. ultramarine	90	1·50
81	3 a. on 3d. violet	1·25	2·00
82	6 a. on 6d. bright purple	1·40	2·00
83	1 r. on 1s. brown	1·60	1·25
80/3	*Set of* 4	4·75	6·00

KUWAIT 2 RUPEES Type I KUWAIT 2 RUPEES Type II (8*a*)

KUWAIT 10 RUPEES Type I KUWAIT 10 RUPEES Type II (8*b*)

2 r. Type I. Type-set surcharge. "2" level with "RUPEES". Surcharge sharp.

Type II. Plate-printed surcharge. "2" raised. Surcharge worn.

10 r. Type I. Type-set surcharge. "1" and "O" spaced. Surcharge sharp and clean.

Type II. Plate-printed surcharge. "1" and "O" closer together. Surcharge appears heavy and worn, see especially "A", "R" and "P".

KUWAIT Extra bar in centre (R. 7/2) KUWAIT Extra bar at top (R. 2/2)

1950 (2 Oct)–**54.** *Nos.* 503/11 *of Great Britain* (*King George VI*) *surch as T* **5** *or* **8***a*/*b* (*rupee values*).

84 ½ a. on ½d. pale orange (3.5.51) .. .. 1·50 1·50
85 1 a. on 1d. light ultramarine (3.5.51) .. 1·50 85
86 1½ a. on 1½d. pale green (3.5.51) .. .. 1·50 2·25
87 2 a. on 2d. pale red-brown (3.5.51) .. 1·50 85
88 2½ a. on 2½d. pale scarlet (3.5.51) .. 1·50 2·25
89 4 a. on 4d. light ultramarine .. .. 1·25 80
90 2 r. on 2s. 6d. yellow-green (I) (3.5.51) .. 15·00 4·50
a. Extra bar in centre £375 £300
b. Type II surch (1954) .. .. .. £180 48·00
91 5 r. on 5s. red (3.5.51) .. .. 21·00 5·00
a. Extra bar at top £250 £190
92 10 r. on 10s. ultramarine (I) (3.5.51) .. 29·00 6·50
a. Type II surch (1952) .. .. .. £225 50·00
84/92 .. .. *Set of* 9 65·00 22·00

No. 92a is known with surch spaced 10 mm apart instead of 9 mm.

W **153** *of Great Britain*

W **165** *of Great Britain*

1952 (10 Dec)–**54.** *Nos.* 515/21, 523 *and* 530/1 *of Great Britain* (*Queen Elizabeth II. W* **153**), *surch as T* **5** (*in two lines only on* 2½ *and* 6 *a.*).

93 ½ a. on ½d. orange-red (31.8.53) 20 40
94 1 a. on 1d. ultramarine (31.8.53) 20 10
95 1½ a. on 1½d. green 15 20
96 2 a. on 2d. red-brown (31.8.53) 35 10
97 2½ a. on 2½d. carmine-red 15 20
98 3 a. on 3d. deep lilac (B.) (18.1.54) .. 40 10
99 4 a. on 4d. ultramarine (2.11.53) .. .. 1·25 75
100 6 a. on 6d. reddish purple (18.1.54) .. 1·25 10
101 12 a. on 1s. 3d. green (2.11.53) .. .. 5·00 2·50
102 1 r. on 1s. 6d. grey-blue (2.11.53) .. .. 4·50 10
93/102 .. .. *Set of* 10 12·00 3·50

1953 (3 June). *Coronation. Nos.* 532/5 *of Great Britain surch* "KUWAIT" *and new values.*

103 2½ a. on 2½d. carmine-red .. .. 2·75 1·75
104 4 a. on 4d. ultramarine .. .. .. 3·00 1·75
105 12 a. on 1s. 3d. deep yellow-green .. .. 4·50 3·00
106 1 r. on 1s. 6d. deep grey-blue .. .. 4·00 80
103/6 .. .. *Set of* 4 13·00 6·50

KUWAIT 2 RUPEES I

KUWAIT 2 RUPEES II

(9)

KUWAIT 5 RUPEES I

KUWAIT 5 RUPEES II

(10)

KUWAIT 10 RUPEES I

KUWAIT 10 RUPEES II

(11)

Type I (**9/11**). Type-set overprints by Waterlow. Bold (generally thicker) letters with sharp corners and straight edges. Bars close together and usually slightly longer than in Type II.

Type II (**9/11**). Plate-printed overprints by Harrison. Thinner letters, rounder corners and rough edges. Bars wider apart.

1955 (23 Sept)–**57.** *Nos.* 536/8 *of Great Britain* (*"Castles" high values*) *surch with T* **9/11.**

		I		II	
107	2 r. on 2s. 6d. black-brown ..	7·00	1·75	55·00	7·00
108	5 r. on 5s. rose-carmine ..	7·50	4·25	85·00	26·00
109	10 r. on 10s. ultramarine ..	8·00	4·50	£140	90·00
107/9	.. .. *Set of* 3	20·00	9·50	£250	£110

Nos. 107II/9II were issued on 10 October 1957.

1956. *Nos.* 540/6, 548 *and* 555/6 *of Great Britain* (*Queen Elizabeth II. W* **165**) *surch as T* **5** (*in two lines only on* 2½ *and* 6 *a.*).

110 ½ a. on ½d. orange-red 30 60
111 1 a. on 1d. ultramarine .. .. .. 50 1·25
112 1½ a. on 1½d. green 40 50
113 2 a. on 2d. red-brown 40 50
114 2½ a. on 2½d. carmine-red .. .. .. 60 1·25
116 4 a. on 4d. ultramarine .. .. .. 4·75 3·25
117 6 a. on 6d. reddish purple .. .. .. 2·25 40
118 12 a. on 1s. 3d. green .. .. .. 9·50 8·00
119 1 r. on 1s. 6d. grey-blue .. .. .. 4·00 30
110/19 .. .. *Set of* 9 20·00 14·50

(New Currency. 100 naye paise = 1 rupee)

KUWAIT NP 1 NP (12)

KUWAIT 3 NP NP (13)

KUWAIT 75 NP (14)

1957 (1 June)–**58.** *Nos.* 540/2, 543*a*/8, 551 *and* 555 *of Great Britain* (*Queen Elizabeth II. W* **165**) *surch as T* **12** (1, 15, 25, 40, 50 *n.p.*), **14** (75 *n.p.*) *or* **13** (*others*).

120 1 n.p. on 5d. brown 10 70
121 3 n.p. on ½d. orange-red .. .. .. 60 2·00
122 6 n.p. on 1d. ultramarine .. .. .. 60 1·25
123 9 n.p. on 1½d. green .. .. .. 60 1·75
124 12 n.p. on 2d. light red-brown .. .. 60 1·75
125 15 n.p. on 2½d. carmine-red (Type I) .. 60 1·00
a. Type II (11.58) .. .. .. 28·00 65·00
126 20 n.p. on 3d. deep lilac (B.) 60 30
127 25 n.p. on 4d. ultramarine .. .. .. 2·25 3·25
128 40 n.p. on 6d. reddish purple .. .. 1·00 30
129 50 n.p. on 9d. bronze-green .. .. 5·50 4·00
130 75 n.p. on 1s. 3d. green .. .. .. 5·50 4·25
120/30 .. .. *Set of* 11 16·00 18·00

20 Shaikh Abdullah as-Salim as-Sabah

(Recess D.L.R.)

1958 (1 Feb). *P* 12½.

131 **20** 5 n.p. bluish green 50 10
132 10 n.p. rose-red 50 10
136 40 n.p. maroon .. .. .. 1·50 55
131/6 .. .. *Set of* 3 2·25 65

Nos. 131/6 were only valid for internal use in Kuwait prior to 1 February 1959. Further values were added to this series following the closure of the British Agency Post Offices on 31 January 1959. Responsibility of the postal service then passed to the Kuwait Government and later issues are listed in Part 19 (*Middle East*) of this catalogue.

OFFICIAL STAMPS

KUWAIT SERVICE (O 1)

KUWAIT SERVICE (O 2)

1923–24. *Stamps of India* (*King George V*), *optd with Type* O **1** *or* O **2** (*rupee values,* 15½–16 *mm*). *W* **34** (*Large Star*) *of India. P* 14.

O 1 ½ a. pale blue-green (No. 156) .. .. 80 18·00
a. Opt double, one albino .. .. 80·00
O 2 1 a. chocolate (No. 197) .. .. .. 1·75 10·00
a. Opt double, one albino .. .. 80·00
O 3 1½ a. chocolate (A) (No. 163) .. .. 2·50 25·00
O 4 2 a. violet (No. 168) .. .. .. 3·75 21·00
a. Bright purple .. .. ..
O 5 2 a. 6 p. ultramarine (No. 171) .. .. 3·50 45·00
O 6 3 a. orange-brown (No. 173) .. .. 3·25 55·00
O 7 3 a. ultramarine (No. 200) (1924) .. 4·50 42·00
O 8 4 a. olive-green (No. 175) .. .. 3·25 50·00
O 9 8 a. purple (No. 179) .. .. .. 4·50 55·00
a. Mauve .. .. ..
O10 1 r. brown and green (No. 185) .. .. 12·00 £110
a. Opt double, one albino £100
O11 2 r. carmine and brown (No. 187) .. 17·00 £160
O12 5 r. ultramarine and violet (No. 188) .. 60·00 £350
a. Opt double, one albino £140
O13 10 r. green and scarlet (No. 189) £110 £350
O14 15 r. blue and olive (No. 190) £180 £475
O1/14 .. .. *Set of* 14 £350 £1600

1929–33. *Nos.* 203, 206, 209 *and* 211/18w *of India* (*King George V, Nasik printing*) *optd as Types* O **1** (*spaced* 10 *mm*) *or* O **2** (14½ *mm*×19–20 *mm wide*). *W* **69** (*Mult Stars*) *of India. P* 14.

O16 1 a. chocolate .. .. .. 3·50 25·00
w. Wmk inverted .. .. ..
O17 2 a. purple .. .. .. 55·00 £150
O19 3 a. blue .. .. .. 3·50 38·00
O20 4 a. sage-green .. .. .. 4·25 65·00
w. Wmk inverted .. .. ..
O21 8 a. reddish purple .. .. .. 4·50 80·00
w. Wmk inverted .. .. .. 4·50
O22 12 a. claret .. .. .. 23·00 £140
w. Wmk inverted .. .. ..
O23 1 r. chocolate and green .. .. 4·00 £160
O24 2 r. carmine and orange (*wmk inverted*) 7·00 £275
O25 5 r. ultramarine & purple (*wmk inverted*) 26·00 £400
O26 10 r. green and scarlet .. .. 50·00 £600
O27 15 r. blue and olive (*wmk inverted*) .. £120 £1100
O16/27 .. .. *Set of* 11 £250 £2750

Labuan

see Malaysia

Lagos

see Nigeria

Leeward Islands

The Federal Colony of the Leeward Islands was constituted in 1871 formalising links between Antigua, British Virgin Islands, Dominica, Montserrat and St. Kitts-Nevis which stretched back to the 1670s. Issues for the individual islands were superseded by those inscribed "LEEWARD ISLANDS", but were in concurrent use with them from 1903. Dominica was transferred to the Windward Islands on 31 December 1939.

PRICES FOR STAMPS ON COVER TO 1945	
Nos. 1/8	*from* × 10
Nos. 9/16	*from* × 12
Nos. 17/19	*from* × 8
Nos. 20/8	*from* × 5
Nos. 29/35	*from* × 4
Nos. 36/45	*from* × 5
Nos. 46/57	*from* × 4
Nos. 58/87	*from* × 5
Nos. 88/91	*from* × 6
Nos. 92/4	*from* × 10
Nos. 95/114	*from* × 5

PRINTERS. All the stamps of Leeward Islands were typographed by De La Rue & Co, Ltd, London, *except where otherwise stated.*

1

2

1890 (31 Oct). *Name and value in second colour. Wmk Crown CA. P* 14.

1 1 ½d. dull mauve and green .. .. 2·75 90
2 1d. dull mauve and rose .. .. 2·50 10
3 2½d. dull mauve and blue .. .. 3·00 15
4 4d. dull mauve and orange .. .. 3·50 7·00
5 6d. dull mauve and brown .. .. 8·50 9·50
6 7d. dull mauve and slate .. .. 2·50 9·50
7 2 1s. green and carmine .. .. 14·00 35·00
8 5s. green and blue £120 £225
1/8 .. .. *Set of* 8 £140 £250
1/8 Optd "Specimen" .. .. *Set of* 8 £200

The colours of this issue are fugitive.

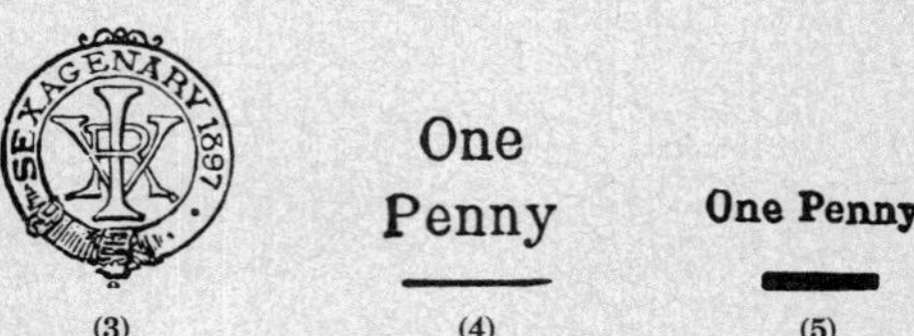

(3) (4) (5)

1897 (22 July). *Queen Victoria's Diamond Jubilee. Handstamped with T* **3**.

9 1 ½d. dull mauve and green .. .. 2·75 8·50
a. Opt double £1200
10 1d. dull mauve and rose .. .. 3·50 9·00
a. Opt double £1000
b. Opt triple £3250
11 2½d. dull mauve and blue .. .. 3·50 9·00
a. Opt double £1200
12 4d. dull mauve and orange .. .. 26·00 65·00
a. Opt double £1200
13 6d. dull mauve and brown .. .. 48·00 85·00
a. Opt double £1400
14 7d. dull mauve and slate .. .. 48·00 85·00
a. Opt double £1400
15 2 1s. green and carmine £120 £190
a. Opt double £1800
16 5s. green and blue £450 £750
a. Opt double £5000
9/16 .. .. *Set of* 8 £600 £1100

Beware of forgeries.

1902 (11 Aug.) *Nos. 4/6 surch.*

17	**4**	1d. on 4d. dull mauve and orange ..	1·10	4·00
		a. Pair, one with tall narrow "O" in "One"	30·00	70·00
		b. Surch double		
18		1d. on 6d. dull mauve and brown ..	2·00	8·00
		a. Pair, one with tall narrow "O" in "One"	45·00	£100
19	**5**	1d. on 7d. dull mauve and slate ..	1·75	3·50
17/19		.. .. *Set of* 3	4·25	14·00

The tall narrow "O" variety occurred on R. 1/1, 5/3, 5/5 and 7/4.

6

7

8

Wide "A" (R. 6/1 of both panes)

Dropped "R" (R. 1/1 of both panes)

1902 (1 Sept–Oct). *Wmk Crown CA. P* 14.

20	**6**	½d. dull purple and green	3·50	60
21		1d. dull purple and carmine	4·50	10
22	**7**	2d. dull purple and ochre (Oct)	2·50	4·00
23	**6**	2½d. dull purple and ultramarine ..	3·50	1·60
		a. Wide "A" in "LEEWARD"	£170	£140
24	**7**	3d. dull purple and black (Oct)	3·00	6·50
25	**6**	6d. dull purple and brown	1·50	7·00
26	**8**	1s. green and carmine	2·00	16·00
		a. Dropped "R" in "LEEWARD" ..	£170	
27	**7**	2s. 6d. green and black (Oct)	25·00	55·00
28	**8**	5s. green and blue (Oct)	48·00	65·00
20/8		.. .. *Set of* 9	80·00	£140
20/8 Optd "Specimen"		.. .. *Set of* 9	£140	

1905 (Apr)–**08**. *Wmk Mult Crown CA. Ordinary paper* (½d., 3d.) *or chalk-surfaced paper* (*others*).

29	**6**	½d. dull purple and green (2.06) ..	2·00	1·75
		a. Chalk-surfaced paper (25.7.08) ..	7·00	6·00
30		1d. dull purple and carmine (29.8.06) ..	4·50	70
31	**7**	2d. dull purple and ochre (25.7.08) ..	3·50	9·00
32	**6**	2½d. dull purple and ultramarine (23.7.06)	48·00	32·00
		a. Wide "A" in "LEEWARD"	£425	£300
33	**7**	3d. dull purple and black	6·50	28·00
		a. Chalk-surfaced paper (18.4.08) ..	22·00	45·00
34	**6**	6d. dull purple and brown (15.7.08) ..	30·00	55·00
35	**8**	1s. green and carmine (15.7.08) ..	38·00	75·00
29/35		.. .. *Set of* 7	£120	£180

1907 (14 Apr)–**11**. *Wmk Mult Crown CA. Chalk-surfaced paper* (*3d. to 5s.*). *P* 14.

36	**7**	¼d. brown ((7.8.09)	1·50	1·00
37	**6**	½d. dull green	1·75	75
38		1d. bright red (7.07)	5·00	70
		a. Rose-carmine	24·00	1·75
39	**7**	2d. grey (3.8.11)	2·25	7·50
40	**6**	2½d. bright blue (5.07)	3·50	3·00
		a. Wide "A" in "LEEWARD"	£170	£150
41	**7**	3d. purple/*yellow* (28.10.10)	2·50	6·00
42	**6**	6d. dull and bright purple (3.8.11) ..	5·50	7·00
43	**8**	1s. black/*green* (3.8.11)	3·00	19·00
44	**7**	2s. 6d. black and red/*blue* (15.9.11) ..	35·00	48·00
45	**8**	5s. green and red/*yellow* (21.11.10) ..	38·00	60·00
36/45		.. .. *Set of* 10	85·00	£140
36/45 Optd "Specimen"		.. .. *Set of* 10	£180	

10

11

12

13

1912 (23 Oct)–**22**. *Die* I (*¼d. to 3d., 6d., 1s., 2s. 6d., 5s.*) *or Die* II (*4d., 2s.*). *Wmk Mult Crown CA. Chalk-surfaced paper* (*3d. to 5s.*). *P* 14.

46	**10**	¼d. brown	90	50
		a. Pale brown	2·25	1·00
47	**11**	½d. yellow-green (12.12)	3·75	1·25
		a. Deep green (1916)	3·50	85
48		1d. red	3·50	60
		a. Bright scarlet (1915)	3·75	70
49	**10**	2d. slate-grey (9.1.13)	3·25	3·75
50	**11**	2½d. bright blue	2·75	7·00
		a. Deep bright blue (1914)	3·50	4·00
51	**10**	3d. purple/*yellow* (9.1.13)	1·00	9·00
		a. White back (Optd S. £40) (11.13) ..	48·00	85·00
		b. On lemon (1914)	3·00	15·00
		c. On buff (Optd S. £40) (1920) ..	35·00	48·00
		d. On orange-buff (1920)	2·50	7·50
		dw. Wmk inverted		
52		4d. blk & red/*pale yell* (Die II) (12.5.22)	2·75	18·00
53	**11**	6d. dull and bright purple (9.1.13) ..	1·75	7·00
54	**12**	1s. black/*green* (9.1.13)	1·50	7·00
		a. White back (Optd S. £42) (11.13) ..	28·00	35·00
		b. On blue-green, olive back (Optd S. £42) (1917)	4·25	6·50
55	**10**	2s. purple & blue/*blue* (Die II) (12.5.22)	5·50	40·00
56		2s. 6d. black and red/*blue* (11.13) ..	11·00	32·00
57	**12**	5s. green and red/*yellow* (9.14) ..	32·00	70·00
		a. White back (Optd S. £45) (11.13) ..	35·00	60·00
		b. On lemon (1915)	13·00	48·00
		c. On orange-buff (1920)	75·00	£120
45/57*b*		.. .. *Set of* 12	45·00	£150
46/57 Optd "Specimen"		.. .. *Set of* 12	£250	

Nos. 51a, 54a, and 57a were only on sale from Montserrat.

HIGH VALUE KEY TYPES. The reign of King Edward VII saw the appearance of the first in a new series of "key type" designs, initially on the issues of Malaya—Straits Settlements and Nyasaland, to be used for high value denominations where a smaller design was felt to be inappropriate. The system was extended during the reign of King George V, using the portrait as Leeward Islands Type **13**, to cover Bermuda, Ceylon, Leeward Islands, Malaya—Straits Settlements, Malta and Nyasaland. A number of these territories continued to use the key type concept for high value King George VI stamps and one, Leeward Islands, for stamps of Queen Elizabeth II.

In each instance the King George V issues were printed in sheets of 60 (12×5) on various coloured papers. The system utilised a common "head" plate used with individual "duty" plates which printed the territory name and face value.

Two major plate flaws occur on the King George V head plate: the break on scroll on R. 1/12 and the broken crown and scroll on R. 2/12. Both of these occur in different states, having been repaired and then damaged once again, perhaps on several occasions. The prices quoted in the listings are for examples approximately as illustrated.

Break in scroll (R. 1/12)

Broken crown and scroll (R. 2/12)

"D I" shaved at foot 1d. R. 7/3 of left pane (all ptgs between Sept 1947 and July 1949. 1s. R. 9/6 of right pane (all ptgs between 1932 and 1938)

1921 (Oct)–**32**. *Wmk Mult Script CA or Mult Crown CA* (£1). *Chalk-surfaced paper* (*3d. to £1*). *P* 14.

(*a*) *Die II* (1921–29)

58	**10**	¼d. brown (1922)	1·50	1·00
59	**11**	½d. blue-green	60	50
60		1d. carmine-red	1·25	20
61		1d. bright violet (1922)	1·75	1·00
62		1d. bright scarlet (1929)	3·50	1·75
63	**10**	1½d. carmine-red (10.9.26)	2·50	1·60
64		1½d. red-brown (1929)	75	10
65		2d. slate-grey (6.22)	1·50	60
		x. Wmk reversed		
66	**11**	2½d. orange-yellow (22.9.23)	5·00	40·00
67		2½d. bright blue (1.3.27)	1·75	60
68	**10**	3d. light ultramarine (22.9.23) ..	3·00	18·00
		a. Deep ultramarine (1925)	38·00	48·00
69		3d. purple/*yellow* (1.7.27)	65	6·00
70		4d. black and red/*pale yellow* (2.24) ..	2·00	17·00
71		5d. dull purple and olive-green (12.5.22)	1·75	4·25
72	**11**	6d. dull and bright purple (17.7.23) ..	7·50	27·00
73	**12**	1s. black/*emerald* (17.7.23)	4·50	8·00
74	**10**	2s. purple and blue/*blue* (12.5.22) ..	16·00	42·00
		a. Red-purple and blue/blue (1926) ..	7·00	42·00
		aw. Wmk inverted	£200	
75		2s. 6d. black and red/*blue* (17.7.23) ..	6·50	23·00
76		3s. bright green and violet (12.5.22) ..	10·00	24·00
77		4s. black and red (12.5.22)	10·00	38·00
78	**12**	5s. green and red/*pale yellow* (17.7.23)	32·00	55·00
79	**13**	10s. green and red/*green* (1928) ..	48·00	70·00
		a. Break in scroll	£150	
		b. Broken crown and scroll	£150	
80		£1 purple and black/*red* (1928) ..	£225	£250
		a. Break in scroll	£375	
		b. Broken crown and scroll	£375	
58/80		.. .. *Set of* 22	£325	£550
58/80 Optd/Perf "Specimen"		.. *Set of* 23	£550	

(*b*) *Reversion to Die* I (*Plate* 23) (1931–32)

81	**10**	¼d. brown	2·25	11·00
82	**11**	½d. blue-green	18·00	23·00
83		1d. bright scarlet	9·00	30
84	**10**	1½d. red-brown	2·25	2·50
85	**11**	2½d. bright blue	4·00	3·50
86		6d. dull and bright purple	12·00	60·00
87	**12**	1s. black/*emerald*	30·00	55·00
		a. "D I" flaw	£225	
81/7		.. .. *Set of* 7	70·00	£140

No. 60 may not have been used locally before January 1923.

No. 68*a* was issued in St. Kitts-Nevis.

Nos. 59, 62 and 82/3 exist in coils, constructed from normal sheets.

Nos. 81/7 result from the use, in error, of Die I which had previously been "retired" in late 1920, to produce Plate 23.

1935 (6 May). *Silver Jubilee. As Nos.* 114/17 *of Jamaica, but printed by Waterlow. P* 11×12.

88	1d. deep blue and scarlet	90	80
89	1½d. ultramarine and grey	1·50	70
90	2½d. brown and deep blue	1·50	3·00
91	1s. slate and purple	5·50	11·00
	k. Kite and vertical log	£160	
	l. Kite and horizontal log	£160	
88/91	.. .. *Set of* 4	8·50	14·00
88/91 Perf "Specimen"	.. .. *Set of* 4	80·00	

For illustrations of plate varieties see Omnibus section following Zimbabwe.

1937 (12 May). *Coronation. As Nos.* 118/20 *of Jamaica.*

92	1d. scarlet	30	15
93	1½d. buff	40	35
94	2½d. bright blue	40	45
92/4	.. .. *Set of* 3	1·00	85
92/4 Perf "Specimen"	.. .. *Set of* 3	60·00	

14

15

(Die A)

(Die B)

In Die B the figure "1" has a broader top and more projecting serif.

"ISI.ANDS" flaw (R. 1/2 of right pane) (Pl. 2 ptgs from November 1942 until corrected in July 1949)

Broken second "E" in "LEEWARD" (R. 4/1 of right pane) (Pl. 3 ptgs from December 1943 until corrected in June 1949)

Broken top right scroll (R. 5/11) (1942 ptg of 10s. only. Corrected on £1 value from same period)

Broken lower right scroll (R. 5/12. 1942 ptgs only)

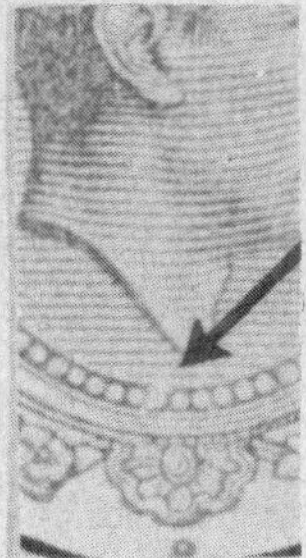
Missing pearl (R. 5/1. 1944 ptgs only)

Gash in chin (R. 2/5. 1942 ptgs only)

1938 (25 Nov)–**51**. *T* **14** *(and similar type, but shaded value tablet,* ½d., 1d., 2½d., 6d.*) and* **15** *(*10s., £1*). Chalk-surfaced paper (*3d. to £1*). P* 14.

(a) Wmk Mult Script CA

95 ¼d. brown 30 85
 a. Chalk-surfaced paper. *Dp brn* (13.6.49) 10 60
96 ½d. emerald 60 60
 a. "ISLANDS" flaw 40·00
97 ½d. slate-grey *(chalk-surfaced paper)* (1.7.49) 30 80
98 1d. scarlet (Die A) 9·00 1·75
99 1d. scarlet (*shades*) (Die B) (1940) 1·50 1·50
 a. "D I" flaw (9.47) £130
 b. *Carmine* (9.42) 1·00 3·75
 c. *Red* (13.9.48) 4·50 2·75
 ca. "D I" flaw £130
100 1d. blue-green *(chalk-surfaced paper)* (1.7.49) 55 15
 a. "D I" flaw £120
101 1½d. chestnut 80 50
102 1½d. yellow-orange and black *(chalk-surfaced paper)* (1.7.49) 50 30
103 2d. olive-grey 2·50 1·00
 a. *Slate-grey* (11.42) 5·50 2·75
104 2d. scarlet *(chalk-surfaced paper)* (1.7.49) 1·40 80
 a. *Vermilion* (24.10.51) 15·00 9·00
105 2½d. bright blue 7·50 2·25
 a. *Light bright blue* (11.42) 60 1·25
106 2½d. black and purple *(chalk-surfaced paper)* (1.7.49) 55 15
107 3d. orange 35·00 2·75
 a. Ordinary paper. *Pale orange* (11.42) 40 85
108 3d. bright blue (1.7.49) 65 15
109 6d. deep dull purple and bright purple 18·00 4·75
 a. Ordinary paper (8.42) 4·50 2·25
 ab. Broken "E" £170
 b. *Purple and deep magenta* (9.47) 4·50 2·75
 ba. Broken "E" £160
110 1s. black/*emerald* 13·00 1·75
 a. "D I" flaw £275
 b. Ordinary paper (3.42) 4·25 90
 ba. Grey and black/emerald (8.42) 23·00 4·00
 bb. Black and grey/emerald (11.42) £130 11·00
111 2s. reddish purple and blue/*blue* 20·00 1·75
 a. Ordinary paper (3.42) 10·00 1·50
 ab. Deep purple and blue/blue (29.9.47) 10·00 1·75
112 5s. green and red/*yellow* 45·00 15·00
 a. Ordinary paper (12.43) 32·00 14·00
 ab. Broken "E" £425
 b. Bright green and red/yellow (24.10.51) 50·00 30·00
113 10s. bluish green and deep red/*green* £190 £120
 a. Ordinary paper. *Pale green and dull red/green* (26.6.44*) £400 £250
 ad. Broken top right scroll
 ae. Broken lower right scroll £2500 £2500
 af. Gash in chin £2250
 b. Ordinary paper. *Green and red/green* (22.2.45*) £150 65·00
 c. Ordinary paper. *Deep green and deep vermilion/green* (17.4.48*) £120 70·00
 ca. Missing pearl £1100

(b) Wmk Mult Crown CA

114 £1 brown-purple and black/*red* £300 £190
 a. Purple and black/carmine (21.9.42*) 80·00 40·00
 ae. Broken lower right scroll £1000 £500
 af. Gash in chin £1000 £500
 b. Brown-purple & black/salmon (5.2.45*) 35·00 24·00
 ba. Missing pearl £900 £600
 c. Perf 13. *Violet & black/scarlet* (4.1.52*) 32·00 35·00
 ca. Wmk sideways £3000
 cw. Wmk inverted £2250
95/114*b* *Set of* 19 £190 £100
95/114 Perf "Specimen" *Set of* 13 £500

*Dates quoted for Nos. 113a/14c are earliest known postmark dates. Nos. 113a and 114a were despatched to the Leeward Islands in March 1942, Nos. 113*b* and 114*b* in December 1943, No. 113*c* in June 1944 and No. 114*c* on 13 December 1951.

Nos. 96, 98/9 and 99b exist in coils constructed from normal sheets.

Printings of the 10s. in March 1942 (No. 113*a*) and of the £1 in February and October 1942 (No. 114*a*) were made by Williams Lea & Co. Ltd. following bomb damage to the De La Rue works in 1940.

For illustrations of Nos. 99a, 99ca, 100a and 110a see above No. 58.

1946 (1 Nov). *Victory. As Nos.* 141/2 *of Jamaica.*

115 1½d. brown 15 10
116 3d. red-orange 15 20
115/16 Perf "Specimen" *Set of* 2 55·00

1949 (2 Jan). *Royal Silver Wedding. As Nos.* 143/4 *of Jamaica.*

117 2½d. ultramarine 10 10
118 5s. green 3·75 2·75

1949 (10 Oct). *75th Anniv of Universal Postal Union. As Nos.* 145/8 *of Jamaica.*

119 2½d. blue-black 15 40
120 3d. deep blue 1·00 80
121 6d. magenta 40 80
122 1s. blue-green 45 80
119/22 *Set of* 4 1·75 2·50

(New Currency. 100 cents = 1 B.W.I. dollar)

1951 (16 Feb). *Inauguration of B.W.I. University College. As Nos.* 149/50 *of Jamaica.*

123 3 c. orange and black 30 50
124 12 c. rose-carmine and reddish violet 60 50

1953 (2 June). *Coronation. As No.* 153 *of Jamaica.*

125 3 c. black and green 30 1·25

16 Queen Elizabeth II **17**

1954. (22 Feb). *Chalk-surfaced paper. Wmk Mult Script CA. P* 14 *(T* **16***) or* 13 *(T* **17***)*

126 **16** ½ c. brown 10 40
127 1 c. grey 30 75
128 2 c. green 30 10
129 3 c. yellow-orange and black 60 75
130 4 c. rose-red 60 10
131 5 c. black and brown-purple 1·25 75
132 6 c. yellow-orange 1·00 30
133 8 c. ultramarine 1·75 10
134 12 c. dull and reddish purple 1·25 10
135 24 c. black and green 1·75 20
136 48 c. dull purple and ultramarine 6·00 2·75
137 60 c. brown and green 6·00 2·25
138 $1.20, yellow-green and rose-red 5·00 2·75
139 **17** $2.40, bluish green and red 6·00 5·00
140 $4.80, brown-purple and black 6·00 6·50
126/40 *Set of* 15 35·00 20·00

The 3 c., 4 c., 6 c., 8 c., 24 c., 48 c., 60 c. and $1.20 have their value tablets unshaded.

The stamps of Leeward Islands were withdrawn and invalidated on 1 July 1956 when the federal colony was dissolved.

Lesotho

(formerly Basutoland)

BASUTOLAND

Stamps of CAPE OF GOOD HOPE were used in Basutoland from about 1876, initially cancelled by upright oval with framed number type postmarks of that colony. Cancellation numbers known to have been used in Basutoland are 133 (Quthing), 156 (Mafeteng), 210 (Mohaleshoek), 277 (Morija), 281 (Maseru), 317 (Thlotse Heights) and 688 (Teyateyaneng).

From 1910 until 1933 the stamps of SOUTH AFRICA were in use. Stamps of the Union provinces are also known used in Basutoland during the early years of this period and can also be found cancelled-to-order during 1932–33.

The following post offices and postal agencies existed in Basutoland before December 1933. Stamps of Cape of Good Hope or South Africa with recognisable postmarks from them are worth a premium. For a few of the smaller offices or agencies there are, as yet, no actual examples recorded. Dates given are those generally accepted as the year in which the office was first opened.

Bokong (1931)
Butha Buthe (1907)
Jonathan's (1927)
Khabos (1927)
Khetisas (1930)
Khukhune (1933)
Kolonyama (1914)
Kueneng (1914)
Leribe (1890)
Mafeteng (1874)
Majara (1912)
Makhoa (1932)
Makoalis (1927)
Mamathes (1919)
Mapoteng (1925)
Marakabeis (1932)
Maseru (1872)
Maseru Rail (1915?)
Mashai (1929)
Matsaile (1930)
Mekading (1914)
Mofokas (1915)
Mohaleshoek (1873)
Mokhotlong (1921)
Morija (1884)
Motsekuoa (1915)
Mount Morosi (1918)
Mphotos (1914)
Peka (1908)
Phamong (1932)
Pitseng (1921)
Qachasnek (1895)
Qalo (1923?)
Quthing (1882)
Rankakalas (1933)
Roma Mission (1913)
Sebapala (1930)
Seforong (1924)
Sehlabathebe (1921)
Sekake (1931)
Teyateyaneng (1886)
Thaba Bosigo (1913)
Thabana Morena (1922)
Thabaneng (1914)
Thaba Tseka (1929)
Thlotse Heights (1872)
Tsepo (1923)
Tsoelike (1927)
Tsoloane (1918)

For further details of the postal history of Basutoland see *The Cancellations and Postal Markings of Basutoland/Lesotho* by A. H. Scott, published by Collectors Mail Auctions (Pty) Ltd, Cape Town, from which the above has been, with permission, extracted.

PRICES FOR STAMPS ON COVER TO 1945

Nos. 1/19	*from* × 5
Nos. 11/14	*from* × 6
Nos. 15/17	*from* × 10
Nos. 18/28	*from* × 6
Nos. 29/31	*from* × 10
Nos. O1/4	*from* × 4
Nos. D1/2	*from* × 25

CROWN COLONY

1 King George V, Nile Crocodile and Mountains

2 King George VI, Nile Crocodile and Mountains

(Recess Waterlow)

1933 (1 Dec). *Wmk Mult Script CA. P* 12½.

1 **1** ½d. emerald 60 1·50
2 1d. scarlet 60 85
3 2d. bright purple 80 35
4 3d. bright blue 70 60
5 4d. grey 2·00 6·50
6 6d. orange-yellow 2·25 1·50
7 1s. red-orange 2·25 4·50
8 2s. 6d. sepia 20·00 45·00
9 5s. violet 42·00 60·00
10 10s. olive-green £100 £110
1/10 *Set of* 10 £150 £190
1/10 Perf "Specimen" *Set of* 10 £250

1935 (4 May). *Silver Jubilee. As Nos.* 114/17 *of Jamaica, but ptd by D.L.R. P* 13½×14.

11 1d. deep blue and carmine 55 25
 f. Diagonal line by turret 60·00
12 2d. ultramarine and grey 65 75
 f. Diagonal line by turret 48·00
 g. Dot to left of chapel 75·00
13 3d. brown and deep blue 3·75 2·25
 g. Dot to left of chapel £120
 h. Dot by flagstaff £120
14 6d. slate and purple 3·75 2·25
 g. Dot to left of chapel £130
 h. Dot by flagstaff £130
 i. Dash by turret £130
11/14 *Set of* 4 8·00 5·00
11/14 Perf "Specimen" *Set of* 4 80·00

For illustrations of plate varieties see Omnibus section following Zimbabwe.

1937 (12 May). *Coronation. As Nos.* 118/20 *of Jamaica. P* 14.

15 1d. scarlet 35 10
16 2d. bright purple 50 85
17 3d. bright blue 60 85
15/17 *Set of* 3 1·25 1·60
15/17 Perf "Specimen" *Set of* 3 55·00

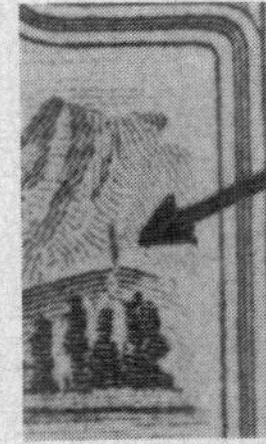
Tower flaw (R. 2/4)

(Recess Waterlow)

1938 (1 Apr). *Wmk Mult Script CA. P* 12½.

18 **2** ½d. green 30 70
19 1d. scarlet 50 40
 a. Tower flaw 70·00
20 1½d. light blue 40 40
21 2d. bright purple 30 40
22 3d. bright blue 30 60
23 4d. grey 1·50 2·75
24 6d. orange-yellow 50 65
25 1s. red-orange 50 90
26 2s. 6d. sepia 8·00 6·00
27 5s. violet 22·00 8·50
28 10s. olive-green 22·00 16·00
18/28 *Set of* 11 50·00 32·00
18/28 Perf "Specimen" *Set of* 11 £190

Basutoland

(3)

1945 (3 Dec). *Victory. Stamps of South Africa, optd with T* **3**, *inscr alternately in English and Afrikaans.*

			Un. pair	*Used pair*	*Used single*
29	**55**	1d. brown and carmine	40	40	10
30	**56**	2d. slate-blue and violet	40	40	10
31	**57**	3d. deep blue and blue	40	70	15
29/31		*Set of* 3	1·10	1·40	30

4 King George VI

5 King George VI and Queen Elizabeth

6 Queen Elizabeth II as Princess, and Princess Margaret

7 The Royal Family

(Recess Waterlow)

1947 (17 Feb). *Royal Visit. Wmk Mult Script CA. P* 12½.

No.	Type	Description	Unused	Used
32	4	1d. scarlet	10	10
33	5	2d. green	10	10
34	6	3d. ultramarine	10	10
35	7	1s. mauve	15	10
32/5		*Set of* 4	40	30
32/5 Perf "Specimen"		*Set of* 4	80·00	

1948 (1 Dec). *Royal Silver Wedding. As Nos.* 143/4 *of Jamaica.*

No.	Description	Unused	Used
36	1½d. ultramarine	20	10
37	10s. grey-olive	30·00	27·00

1949 (10 Oct). *75th Anniv of Universal Postal Union. As Nos.* 145/8 *of Jamaica.*

No.	Description	Unused	Used
38	1½d. blue	30	50
39	3d. deep blue	1·75	1·25
40	6d. orange	1·50	1·25
41	1s. red-brown	1·00	90
38/41	*Set of* 4	4·00	3·50

1953 (3 June). *Coronation. As No.* 153 *of Jamaica.*

No.	Description	Unused	Used
42	2d. black and reddish purple	40	50

8 Qiloane

9 Mohair (Shearing Angora Goats)

(Recess D.L.R.)

1954 (18 Oct)–**58**. *Designs as T* **8/9**. *Wmk Mult Script CA. P* 11½ (10s.) *or* 13½ (*others*).

No.	Description	Unused	Used
43	½d. grey-black and sepia	10	10
44	1d. grey-black and bluish green	10	10
45	2d. deep bright blue and orange	60	10
46	3d. yellow-green and deep rose-red	80	30
	a. Yellow-green and rose (27.11.58)	4·00	75
47	4½d. indigo and deep ultramarine	70	15
48	6d. chestnut and deep grey-green	1·25	15
49	1s. bronze-green and purple	1·25	30
50	1s. 3d. brown and turquoise-green	14·00	4·50
51	2s. 6d. deep ultramarine and crimson	10·00	6·00
	a. Brt ultram & crimson-lake (27.11.58)	28·00	14·00
52	5s. black and carmine-red	5·00	8·50
53	10s. black and maroon	18·00	23·00
43/53	*Set of* 11	45·00	38·00

Designs: *Horiz as T* **8**—1d. Orange River; 2d Mosuto horseman; 3d. Basuto household; 4½d. Maletsunyane Falls; 6d. Herd-boy with Lesiba. 1s. Pastoral scene; 1s. 3d. Aeroplane over Lancers' Gap; 2s. 6d. Old Fort Leribe; 5s. Mission Cave House.

½d. ▬

(19)

20 "Chief Moshoeshoe I" (engraving by Delangle)

1959 (1 Aug). *No.* 45 *surch with T* **19**, *by South African Govt Ptr, Pretoria.*

No.	Description	Unused	Used
54	½d. on 2d. deep bright blue and orange	10	15

(Des from drawings by James Walton. Recess Waterlow)

1959 (15 Dec). *Basutoland National Council. T* **20** *and similar vert designs. W w* **12**. *P* 13 × 13½.

No.	Description	Unused	Used
55	3d. black and yellow-olive	30	10
56	1s. carmine and yellow-green	30	10
57	1s. 3d. ultramarine and red-orange	45	45
55/7	*Set of* 3	95	55

Designs:—1s. Council house; 1s. 3d. Mosuto horseman.

(New Currency. 100 cents = 1 rand)

½c. (23) 1c. (24) 2c (25)

2½c (I) 2½c (II) 3½c (I) 3½c (II)

5c (I) 5c (II) 10c (I) 10c (II)

12½c (I) 12½c (II) 50c (I) 50c (II)

25c (I) 25c (II) 25c (III)

R1 (I) R1 (II) R1 (III)

1961 (14 Feb). *Nos.* 43/53 *surch with T* **23** (½ c.), **24** (1 c.) *or as T* **25** (*others*) *by South African Govt Printer, Pretoria*

No.	Description	Unused	Used
58	½ c. on ½d. grey-black and sepia	10	10
	a. Surch double	£300	
59	1 c. on 1d. grey-black and bluish green	10	10
60	2 c. on 2d. deep bright blue and orange	10	10
	a. Surch inverted	90·00	
61	2½ c. on 3d. yellow-green and rose (Type I)	10	10
	a. Type II	10	10
	b. Type II inverted	—	£1000
62	3½ c. on 4½d. indigo & deep ultram (Type I)	10	10
	a. Type II	2·50	3·50
63	5 c. on 6d. chestnut & dp grey-green (Type I)	10	10
	a. Type II	15	10
64	10 c. on 1s. bronze-green and purple (Type I)	10	10
	a. Type II	70·00	70·00
65	12½ c. on 1s. 3d. brown & turq-green (Type I)	75	20
	a. Type II	75	20
66	25 c. on 2s. 6d. bright ultramarine and crimson-lake (Type I)	30	30
	a. Type II	26·00	7·50
	b. Type III	30	50
67	50 c. on 5s. black and carmine-red (Type I)	1·25	1·40
	a. Type II	90	1·25
68	1 r. on 10s. black and maroon (Type I)	19·00	5·50
	a. Type II	8·50	20·00
	b. Type III	6·00	5·50
58/68b	*Set of* 11	7·50	7·00

There were two printings of the 2½ c. Type II, differing in the position of the surcharge on the stamps.

Examples of the 2 c. surcharge are known in a fount similar to Type **24** (*Price* £140, *unused*).

26 Basuto Household

27 Protein Foods

(Recess D.L.R.)

1961–63. *As Nos.* 43/53 *but values in cents as in T* **26**. *Wmk Mult Script CA. P* 13½ *or* 11½ (1 *r.*).

No.	Description	Unused	Used
69	½ c. grey-black and sepia (as ½d.) (25.9.62)	10	20
	a. Imperf (pair)	£190	
70	1 c. grey-blk & bluish grn (as 1d.) (25.9.62)	10	40
71	2 c. dp brt blue & orange (as 2d.) (25.9.62)	50	1·40
72	2½ c. yellow-green & deep rose-red (14.2.61)	80	20
	a. Pale yellow-green & rose-red (22.5.62)	5·00	40
73	3½ c. indigo & dp ultram (as 4½d.) (25.9.62)	30	1·50
74	5 c. chestnut and deep grey-green (as 6d.) (10.8.62)	30	75
75	10 c. bronze-green & pur (as 1s.) (22.10.62)	30	40
76	12½ c. brown and turquoise-green (as 1s. 3d.) (17.12.62)	11·00	6·50
77	25 c. deep ultramarine and crimson (as 2s. 6d.) (25.9.62)	6·00	6·50
78	50 c. black & carmine-red (as 5s.) (22.10.62)	11·00	13·00
79	1 r. black and maroon (as 10s.) (4.2.63)	22·00	12·00
	a. Black and light maroon (16.12.63)	32·00	18·00
69/79	*Set of* 11	45·00	38·00

(Des M. Goaman. Photo Harrison)

1963 (4 June). *Freedom from Hunger. W w* **12**. *P* 14×14½.

No.	Type	Description	Unused	Used
80	27	12½ c. reddish violet	40	15

1963 (2 Sept). *Red Cross Centenary. As Nos.* 203/4 *of Jamaica.*

No.	Description	Unused	Used
81	2½ c. red and black	20	10
82	12½ c. red and blue	60	60

1964. *As Nos.* 70, 72, 74, 76 *and* 78, *but W w* **12**.

No.	Description	Unused	Used
84	1 c. grey-black and bluish green (11.8.64)	10	20
86	2½ c. pale yellow-green and rose-red (10.3.64)	15	15
88	5 c. chestnut and deep grey-green (10.11.64)	30	40
90	12½ c. brown and turquoise-green (10.11.64)	2·75	1·50
92	50 c. black and carmine-red (29.9.64)	7·25	10·00
84/92	*Set of* 5	9·50	11·00

SELF-GOVERNMENT

28 Mosotho Woman and Child

29 Maseru Border Post

1965 (10 May). *New Constitution. T* **28/9** *and similar horiz designs. Multicoloured. W w* **12**. *P* 14×13½.

No.	Description	Unused	Used
94	2½ c. Type **28**	20	10
	w. Wmk inverted	20·00	
95	3½ c. Type **29**	25	20
96	5 c. Mountain scene	25	20
	w. Wmk inverted	20·00	
97	12½ c. Legislative Buildings	45	70
94/7	*Set of* 4	1·10	1·10

30 I.T.U. Emblem

31 I.C.Y. Emblem

(Des M. Goaman. Litho Enschedé)

1965 (17 May). *I.T.U. Centenary. W w* **12**. *P* 11×11½.

No.	Type	Description	Unused	Used
98	30	1 c. orange-red and bright purple	15	10
99		20 c. light blue and orange-brown	35	30

(Des V. Whiteley. Litho Harrison)

1965 (25 Oct). *International Co-operation Year. W w* **12**. *P* 14½.

No.	Type	Description	Unused	Used
100	31	½ c. reddish purple & turquoise-green	10	10
101		12½ c. deep bluish green and lavender	45	35

32 Sir Winston Churchill and St. Paul's Cathedral in Wartime

(Des Jennifer Toombs. Photo Harrison)

1966 (24 Jan). *Churchill Commemoration. Printed in black, cerise, gold and background in colours stated. W w* **12**. *P* 14.

No.	Type	Description	Unused	Used
102	32	1 c. new blue	15	30
103		2½ c. deep green	35	10
104		10 c. brown	45	30
105		22½ c. bluish violet	70	60
102/5		*Set of* 4	1·50	1·10

Basutoland attained independence on 4 October 1966 as the Kingdom of Lesotho.

LESOTHO

INDEPENDENT KINGDOM

King Moshoeshoe II, 4 October 1966–November 1990 (deposed)

33 Moshoeshoe I and Moshoeshoe II

(Des and photo Harrison)

1966 (4 Oct). *Independence. P* 12½×13.

No.	Type	Description	Unused	Used
106	33	2½ c. light brown, black and red	10	10
107		5 c. light brown, black and new blue	10	10
108		10 c. light brown, black and emerald	15	10
109		20 c. light brown, black & bright purple	20	15
106/9		*Set of* 4	45	30

LESOTHO

(34)

35 "Education Culture and Science"

1966 (1 Nov). *Stamps of Basutoland optd as T* **34**. *A. Nos. 69/71 and 73/9 (Script CA wmk). B. Nos. 84/92 and unissued 1 r. (wmk w* **12**).

No.	Description	A		B	
110	½ c. grey-black and sepia	10	10	†	
111	1 c. grey-blk and bluish grn	10	10	10	10
112	2 c. deep bright blue & orange	80	10	†	
113	2½ c. pale yell-grn & rose-red	†		50	10
114	3½ c. ind & dp ultram	30	10	†	
115	5 c. chestnut & dp grey-grn	20	10	20	10
116	10 c. bronze-green and purple	20	10	†	
117	12½ c. brown & turq-green	4·25	35	30	20
118	25 c. deep ultram & crimson	40	20	†	
119	50 c. black and carmine-red	1·25	65	80	50
120	1 r. black and maroon	1·00	2·50	1·00	75
	a. "LSEOTHO"	60·00	—	40·00	—
	b. Opt double	90·00	—	†	
	ba. Ditto. "LSEOTHO"	—	—	†	
110A/120A	*Set of* 10	7·50	3·50		
111B/120B	*Set of* 6			2·50	1·40

(Des V. Whiteley. Litho D.L.R.)

1966 (1 Dec). *20th Anniv of U.N.E.S.C.O. P* 14½ × 14.

No.	Description		
121 **35**	2½ c. orange-yellow and emerald-green	10	10
122	5 c. light green and olive	15	10
123	12½ c. light blue and red	35	10
124	25 c. red-orange and deep greenish blue	60	25
121/4	*Set of* 4	1·10	40

36 Maize

37 Moshoeshoe II

(Des and photo Harrison)

1967 (1 Apr). *Designs as T* **36/7**. *No wmk. P* 14½×13½ (2 *r*.) *or* 13½×14½ (*others*).

No.	Description		
125	½ c. bluish green and light bluish violet	10	10
126	1 c. sepia and rose-red	10	10
127	2 c. orange-yellow and light green	10	30
128	2½ c. black and ochre	10	10
129	3½ c. chalky blue and yellow	10	20
130	5 c. bistre and new blue	10	10
131	10 c. yellow-brown and bluish grey	10	10
132	12½ c. black and red-orange	20	10
133	25 c. black and bright blue	75	20
134	50 c. black, new blue and turquoise	4·50	45
135	1 r. multicoloured	1·00	75
136	2 r. black, gold and magenta	1·25	1·75
125/36	*Set of* 12	7·00	3·25

Designs: *Horiz as T* **36**—1 c. Cattle; 2 c. Agaves (wrongly inscr "Aloes"); 2½ c. Basotho Hat; 3½ c. Merino Sheep ("Wool"); 5 c. Basotho Pony; 10 c. Wheat; 12½ c. Angora Goat ("Mohair"); 25 c. Maletsunyane Falls; 50 c. Diamonds; 1 r. Arms of Lesotho.

See also Nos. 147/59 and 191/203.

46 Students and University

(Des V. Whiteley. Photo Harrison)

1967 (7 Apr). *First Conferment of University Degrees. P* 14 × 14½.

No.	Description		
137 **46**	1 c. sepia, ultram & light yellow-orange	10	10
138	2½ c. sepia, ultram & light greenish blue	10	10
139	12½ c. sepia, ultramarine and rose	10	10
140	25 c. sepia, ultramarine and light violet	15	15
137/40	*Set of* 4	30	30

47 Statue of Moshoeshoe I

(Des and photo Harrison)

1967 (4 Oct). *First Anniv of Independence. T* **47** *and similar triangular designs. P* 14½ × 14.

No.	Description		
141	2½ c. black and light yellow-green	10	10
142	12½ c. multicoloured	25	15
143	25 c. black, green and light ochre	35	25
141/3	*Set of* 3	65	40

Designs:—12½ c. Lesotho flag; 25 c. Crocodile (national emblem).

50 Lord Baden-Powell and Scout Saluting

(Des V. Whiteley. Photo Harrison)

1967 (1 Nov). *60th Anniv of Scout Movement. P* 14 × 14½.

No.	Description		
144 **50**	15 c. multicoloured	20	10

51 W.H.O. Emblem and World Map

(Des G. Vasarhelyi. Photo Harrison)

1968 (7 Apr). *20th Anniv of World Health Organization. T* **51** *and similar horiz design. P* 14 × 14½.

No.	Description		
145	2½ c. blue, gold and carmine-red	15	10
	a. Gold (emblem) omitted		
146	25 c. multicoloured	45	20

Design:—25 c. Nurse and child.

53 Basotho Hat

54 Sorghum

1968–69. *As Nos. 125/36 and T* **54**, *but wmk* **53** (*sideways on* 2 *r*.).

No.	Description		
147	½ c. bluish green & lt bluish vio (26.11.68)	10	10
	a. Blue-green and violet (30.9.69)	95	95
148	1 c. sepia and rose-red (26.11.68)	10	10
149	2 c. orange-yellow & lt green (26.11.68)	10	10
	a. Orange-yellow & yell-grn (30.9.69)	60	60
150	2½ c. black and ochre (21.10.68)	15	10
	a. Black and yellow-ochre (30.9.69)	60	60
151	3 c. chocolate, green & yell-brn (1.8.68)	15	15
152	3½ c. chalky blue and yellow (26.11.68)	15	10
153	5 c. bistre and new blue (22.7.68)	30	10
154	10 c. yell-brn & pale bluish grey (26.11.68)	15	10
155	12½ c. black and red-orange (30.9.69)	60	35
156	25 c. black and bright blue (30.9.69)	1·50	1·00
157	50 c. black, new blue & turquoise (30.9.69)	11·00	2·50
158	1 r. multicoloured (26.11.68)	2·75	2·75
159	2 r. black, gold and magenta (30.9.69)	9·00	13·00
147/59	*Set of* 13	23·00	18·00

55 Running Hunters

(Des Jennifer Toombs. Photo Harrison)

1968 (1 Nov). *Rock Paintings. T* **55** *and similar designs. W* **53** (*sideways on* 5 *c*., 15 *c*.). *P* 14 × 14½ (5 *c*., 15 *c*.) *or* 14½ × 14 (*others*).

No.	Description		
160	3 c. yellow-brown, lt blue-green & blackish green	25	10
161	3½ c. greenish yellow, yellow-olive and sepia	30	10
162	5 c. Venetian red, yell-ochre & blackish brn	35	10
163	10 c. yellow, rose and deep maroon	45	10
164	15 c. light buff, pale olive-yell & blackish brn	75	30
165	20 c. yellow-grn, greenish yellow & blackish brown	90	55
166	25 c. yellow, orange-brown and black	1·00	75
160/6	*Set of* 7	3·50	1·75

Designs: *Horiz*—3½ c. Baboons; 10 c. Archers; 20 c. Eland; 25 c. Hunting scene. *Vert*—5 c. Javelin throwing; 15 c. Blue Cranes.

62 Queen Elizabeth II Hospital

(Des C. R. Househam and G. Drummond. Litho P.B.)

1969 (11 Mar). *Centenary of Maseru (capital). T* **62** *and similar horiz designs. Multicoloured. W* **53** (*sideways*). *P* 14 × 13½.

No.	Description		
167	2½ c. Type **62**	10	10
168	10 c. Lesotho Radio Station	10	10
169	12½ c. Leabua Jonathan Airport	35	10
170	25 c. Royal Palace	25	15
167/70	*Set of* 4	65	30

66 Rally Car passing Mosotho Horseman

(Des P. Wheeler. Photo Harrison)

1969 (26 Sept). *Roof of Africa Car Rally. T* **66** *and similar horiz designs. W* **53**. *P* 14.

No.	Description		
171	2½ c. yellow, mauve and plum	15	10
172	12½ c. cobalt, greenish yellow and olive-grey	20	10
173	15 c. blue, black and mauve	20	10
174	20 c. black, red and yellow	20	10
171/4	*Set of* 4	65	30

Designs:—12½ c. Rally car on mountain road; 15 c. Chequered flags and mountain scenery; 20 c. Map of rally route and Rally Trophy.

71 Gryponyx and Footprints

75 Moshoeshoe I, when a Young Man

(Des Jennifer Toombs. Photo Harrison)

1970 (5 Jan). *Prehistoric Footprints (1st series). T* **71** *and similar designs. W* **53** (*sideways**). *P* 14×14½ (3 *c*.) *or* 14½×14 (*others*).

No.	Description		
175	3 c. pale brown, yellow-brown and sepia	70	50
176	5 c. dull purple, pink and sepia	85	30
	w. Wmk hat pointing right	3·25	
177	10 c. pale yellow, black and sepia	1·00	35
178	15 c. olive-yellow, black and sepia	1·60	2·00
179	25 c. cobalt and black	2·50	2·00
175/9	*Set of* 5	6·00	4·75

Designs: (60×23 *mm*)—3 c. Dinosaur footprints at Moyeni. (40×24 *mm*)—10 c. Plateosauravus and footprints; 15 c. Tritylodon and footprints; 25 c. Massospondylus and footprints.

*The normal sideways watermark shows the hat pointing left, *when seen from the back of the stamp.*

See also Nos. 596/8.

(Des G. Vasarhelyi. Litho D.L.R.)

1970 (11 Mar). *Death Centenary of King Moshoeshoe I. T* **75** *and similar vert design. W* **53**. *P* 13½.

No.	Description		
180	2½ c. pale green and magenta	10	10
181	25 c. pale blue and chesnut	20	20

Design:—25 c. Moshoeshoe I as an old man.

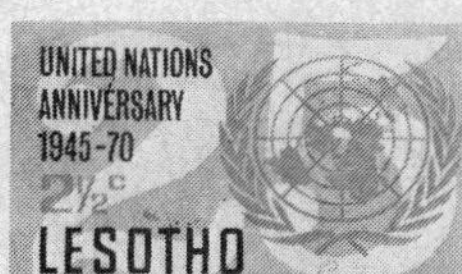

77 U.N. Emblem and "25"

(Des V. Whiteley. Litho Questa)

1970 (26 June). *25th Anniv of United Nations. T* **77** *and similar horiz designs. W* **53** (*sideways*). *P* 14½×14.

No.	Description		
182	2½ c. light pink, light blue and maroon	10	10
183	10 c. multicoloured	10	10
184	12½ c. brown-red, cobalt and drab	10	10
185	25 c. multicoloured	15	15
182/5	*Set of* 4	30	30

Designs:— 10 c. U.N. Building; 12½ c. "People of the World"; 25 c. Symbolic dove.

78 Basotho Hat Gift Shop, Maseru

(Des G. Drummond. Litho Questa)

1970 (27 Oct). *Tourism. T* **78** *and similar horiz designs. Multicoloured. W* **53** (*sideways*). *P* 14.

No.	Description		
186	2½ c. Type **78**	10	10
187	5 c. Trout fishing	20	10
188	10 c. Pony trekking	25	10
189	12½ c. Skiing	50	10
190	20 c. Holiday Inn, Maseru	40	50
186/90	*Set of* 5	1·25	70

79 Maize   80 Lammergeier

(Des Harrison. Litho Questa)

1971 (4 Jan–1 Apr). *As Nos.* 147/58 *but in new format omitting portrait of Moshoeshoe II, as in T* **79**. *4 c. and 2 r. in new designs.* W **53** (*sideways* except 2 r.*). *P* 14.

191 ½ c. blue-green and light bluish violet .. 10 10
192 1 c. brown and orange-red 10 10
193 2 c. yellow and green 10 10
w. Wmk top of hat to right .. ..
194 2½ c. black, olive-green and yellow-ochre 10 10
195 3 c. brown, green and yellow-ochre .. 10 10
196 3½ c. indigo and yellow 10 10
196*a* 4 c. multicoloured (1.4.71) 20 10
aw. Wmk top of hat to right .. ..
197 5 c. yellow-brown and pale blue .. 15 10
198 10 c. orange-brown and grey-blue .. 15 10
199 12½ c. chocolate and yellow-orange .. 25 30
200 25 c. slate and pale bright blue 60 40
201 50 c. black, pale blue and turquoise-green 6·00 4·25
202 1 r. multicoloured .. .. .. 2·25 2·25
203 2 r. yellow-brown and ultramarine .. 2·25 3·00
191/203 .. .. *Set of* 14 11·00 9·50

Designs: *Horiz*—4 c. National flag. *Vert*—2 r. Statue of Moshoeshoe I.

*The normal sideways watermark shows top of hat to left, *as seen from the back of the stamp.*

For 2 r. value without watermark see No. 401

(Des R. Granger Barrett. Litho J.W.)

1971 (1 Mar). *Birds. T* **80** *and similar vert designs. Multicoloured.* W **53**. *P* 14.

204 2½ c. Type **80** .. .. 1·50 10
205 5 c. Bald Ibis .. .. 2·25 1·75
206 10 c. Rufous Rockjumper .. .. .. 3·00 1·75
207 12½ c. Blue Bustard .. .. 3·50 2·75
208 15 c. Painted Snipe .. .. 4·25 4·00
209 20 c. Golden-breasted Bunting .. .. 4·25 4·00
210 25 c. Ground Woodpecker .. .. .. 4·75 4·00
204/10 .. .. *Set of* 7 21·00 16·00

81 Lionel Collett Dam

(Des G. Drummond. Litho J.W.)

1971 (15 July). *Soil Conservation. T* **81** *and similar horiz designs. Multicoloured.* W **53** (*sideways*). *P* 14.

211 4 c. Type **81** 10 10
212 10 c. Contour ridges 10 10
213 15 c. Earth dams 25 10
214 25 c. Beaver dams 35 35
211/14 .. .. *Set of* 4 70 50

82 Diamond Mining

(Des J.W. Litho Questa)

1971 (4 Oct). *Development. T* **82** *and similar horiz designs. Multicoloured.* W **53** (*sideways*). *P* 14.

215 4 c. Type **82** 75 30
216 10 c. Pottery 30 10
217 15 c. Weaving 45 55
218 20 c. Construction 55 95
215/18 .. .. *Set of* 4 1·90 1·75

83 Mail Cart   84 Sprinting

(Des D. B. Picton-Phillips. Litho Questa)

1972 (3 Jan). *Post Office Centenary. T* **83** *and similar designs.* W **53** (*sideways on* 5, 10 *and* 20 *c.*). *P* 14 × 13½ (15 *c.*) *or* 13½ × 14 (*others*).

219 5 c. pale pink and black 15 10
220 10 c. multicoloured 15 10
221 15 c. pale drab, light blue and black 30 15
222 20 c. multicoloured 45 70
219/22 .. .. *Set of* 4 95 80

Designs: *Horiz*—10 c. Postal bus; 20 c. Maseru P.O. *Vert*—15 c. Cape of Good Hope 4d. stamp of 1876.

(Des J. W. Litho Questa)

1972 (1 Sept). *Olympic Games. Munich. T* **84** *and similar vert designs. Multicoloured.* W **53**. *P* 14.

223 4 c. Type **84** 15 10
w. Wmk inverted .. .. ..
224 10 c. Shot putting 20 10
225 15 c. Hurdling 30 10
226 25 c. Long-jumping 35 40
223/6 .. .. *Set of* 4 90 55

85 "Adoration of the Shepherds" (Matthias Stomer)

(Des and litho J.W.)

1972 (1 Dec). *Christmas.* W **53** (*sideways*). *P* 14.

227 **85** 4 c. multicoloured 10 10
228 10 c. multicoloured 10 10
229 25 c. multicoloured 15 20
227/9 .. .. *Set of* 3 30 30

O.A.U.
10th Anniversary
Freedom in Unity

86 W.H.O. Emblem   (87)

(Des. J. Cooter. Litho Questa)

1973 (7 Apr). *25th Anniv of W.H.O.* W **53** (*sideways*). *P* 13½.

230 **86** 20 c. greenish blue and yellow 30 30

1973 (25 May). *Tenth Anniv of O.A.U. Nos.* 194 *and* 196*a*/8 *optd with T* **87** *by Govt Printer, Maseru.*

231 2½ c. black, olive-green and yellow-ochre .. 10 10
232 4 c. multicoloured 10 10
a. Horiz pair, one without opt £150
233 5 c. yellow-brown and pale blue 10 10
234 10 c. orange-brown and grey-blue 15 15
231/4 .. .. *Set of* 4 35 35

88 Basotho Hat and W.F.P. Emblem

(Des locally; adapted J. Cooter. Litho Format)

1973 (1 June). *Tenth Anniv of World Food Programme. T* **88** *and similar horiz designs. Multicoloured.* W **53** (*sideways*). *P* 13½.

235 4 c. Type **88** 10 10
236 15 c. School feeding 20 15
237 20 c. Infant feeding 20 20
a. Imperf (pair) £250
238 25 c. "Food for Work" 25 25
235/8 .. .. *Set of* 4 65 60

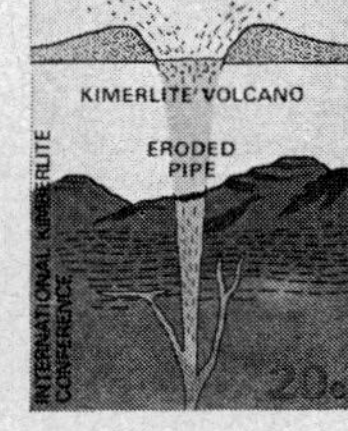

89 *Aeropetes tulbaghia*   90 Kimberlite Volcano

(Des A. McLeod; artwork G. Drummond. Litho Questa)

1973 (3 Sept). *Butterflies. T* **89** *and similar horiz designs. Multicoloured.* W **53** (*sideways*). *P* 14.

239 4 c. Type **89** 65 10
240 5 c. *Papilio demodocus* 75 50
241 10 c. *Cynthia cardui* .. .. .. 1·25 50
242 15 c. *Precis hierta* .. .. .. 2·00 1·75
243 20 c. *Precis oenone* .. .. .. 2·00 1·75
244 25 c. *Danaus chrysippus* .. .. .. 2·25 2·50
245 30 c. *Colotis evenina* .. .. .. 2·25 3·00
239/45 .. .. *Set of* 7 10·00 9·00

(Des PAD Studio. Litho Questa)

1973 (1 Oct). *International Kimberlite Conference. T* **90** *and similar multicoloured designs.* W **53** (*sideways on* 10 *and* 15 *c.*). *P* 13½.

246 10 c. Map of diamond mines (*horiz*) .. .. 2·00 50
247 15 c. Kimberlite-diamond rock (*horiz*) .. 2·25 2·00
248 20 c. Type **90** .. .. 2·25 2·25
249 30 c. Diamond prospecting .. .. .. 3·75 5·00
246/9 .. .. *Set of* 4 9·00 8·75

Type **90** is incorrectly inscribed "KIMERLITE VOLCANO".

91 "Health"   92 Open Book and Wreath

(Des R. Granger Barrett. Litho Questa)

1974 (18 Feb). *Youth and Development. T* **91** *and similar horiz designs. Multicoloured.* W **53** (*sideways*). *P* 13½.

250 4 c. Type **91** 10 10
251 10 c. "Education" 15 10
252 20 c. "Agriculture" 20 10
253 25 c. "Industry" 30 20
254 30 c. "Service" 30 25
250/4 .. .. *Set of* 5 85 55

(Des PAD Studio. Litho Questa)

1974 (8 Apr). *Tenth Anniv of U.B.L.S. T* **92** *and similar vert designs. Multicoloured.* W **53**. *P* 14.

255 10 c. Type **92** 15 10
256 15 c. Flags, mortar-board and scroll .. 20 15
257 20 c. Map of Africa 25 15
258 25 c. King Moshoeshoe II capping a graduate 25 20
255/8 .. .. *Set of* 4 75 45

93 Senqunyane River Bridge, Marakabei

(Des J. Cooter. Litho Questa)

1974 (26 June). *Rivers and Bridges. T* **93** *and similar horiz designs. Multicoloured.* W **53** (*sideways*). *P* 14½.

259 4 c. Type **93** 10 10
260 5 c. Tsoelike River and bridge 10 10
261 10 c. Makhaleng River Bridge 20 10
262 15 c. Seaka Bridge, Orange/Senqu River .. 35 35
263 20 c. Masianokeng Bridge, Phuthiatsana River 40 40
264 25 c. Mahobong Bridge, Hlotse River 45 45
259/64 .. .. *Set of* 6 1·50 1·25

94 U.P.U. Emblem

(Des R. Granger Barrett. Litho Enschedé)

1974 (6 Sept). *Centenary of Universal Postal Union. T* **94** *and similar horiz designs.* W **53** (*sideways*). *P* 13½ × 13.

265 4 c. light emerald and black 10 10
266 10 c. orange, greenish yellow and black .. 15 10
267 15 c. multicoloured 20 40
268 20 c. multicoloured 45 50
265/8 .. .. *Set of* 4 80 90

Designs:—10 c. Map of air-mail routes; 15 c. Post Office H.Q., Maseru; 20 c. Horseman taking rural mail.

On No. 266 the inscriptions for the airstrips at Mokhotlong and Mohlanapeng were transposed in error.

95 Siege of Thaba-Bosiu

(Des Jennifer Toombs. Litho Enschedé)

1974 (25 Nov). *150th Anniv of Establishment of Thaba-Bosiu as Capital. T* **95** *and similar multicoloured designs. W* **53** *(sideways on 4 and 5 c.). P* 12½ × 12 *(4 and 5 c.) or* 12 × 12½ *(others).*

No.	Description	Unused	Used
269	4 c. Type **95**	10	10
270	5 c. The wreath-laying	10	10
271	10 c. Moshoeshoe I (*vert*)	25	10
272	20 c. Makoanyane, the warrior (*vert*)	90	55
269/72	*Set of* 4	1·25	65

96 Mamokhorong

(Des PAD Studio. Litho Questa)

1975 (25 Jan). *Basotho Musical Instruments. T* **96** *and similar horiz designs. Multicoloured. W* **53** *(sideways). P* 14.

No.	Description	Unused	Used
273	4 c. Type **96**	10	10
274	10 c. Lesiba	10	10
275	15 c. Setolotolo	15	20
276	20 c. Meropa	15	20
273/6	*Set of* 4	40	45
MS277	108 × 92 mm. Nos. 273/6	1·00	2·00

97 Horseman in Rock Archway

98 Morena Moshoeshoe I

(Des J. Cooter. Litho Questa)

1975 (15 Apr). *Sehlabathebe National Park. T* **97** *and similar horiz designs. Multicoloured. W* **53** *(sideways). P* 14.

No.	Description	Unused	Used
278	4 c. Type **97**	30	10
279	5 c. Mountain view through arch	30	10
280	15 c. Antelope by stream	50	45
281	20 c. Mountains and lake	50	50
282	25 c. Tourists by frozen waterfall	65	75
278/82	*Set of* 5	2·00	1·60

(Des G. Vasarhelyi. Litho Questa)

1975 (10 Sept). *Leaders of Lesotho. T* **98** *and similar vert designs. W* **53**. *P* 14.

No.	Description	Unused	Used
283	3 c. black and light blue	10	10
284	4 c. black and light mauve	10	10
285	5 c. black and pink	10	10
286	6 c. black and light grey-brown	10	10
287	10 c. black and light claret	10	10
288	15 c. black and light orange-red	20	20
289	20 c. black and dull green	25	30
290	25 c. black and azure	25	40
283/90	*Set of* 8	1·00	1·10

Designs:—4 c. King Moshoeshoe II; 5 c. Morena Letsie I; 6 c. Morena Lerotholi; 10 c. Morena Letsie II; 15 c. Morena Griffith; 20 c. Morena Seeiso Griffith Lerotholi; 25 c. Mofumahali Mantsebo Seeiso, O.B.E.

The 25 c. also commemorates International Women's Year.

99 Mokhibo Dance

(Des PAD Studio. Litho Questa)

1975 (17 Dec). *Traditional Dances. T* **99** *and similar horiz designs. Multicoloured. W* **53** *(sideways). P* 14 × 14½.

No.	Description	Unused	Used
291	4 c. Type **99**	10	10
292	10 c. Ndlamo	15	10
293	15 c. Baleseli	30	45
294	20 c. Mohobelo	35	55
291/4	*Set of* 4	75	1·00
MS295	111 × 100 mm. Nos. 291/94	3·25	3·25

100 Enrolment

(Des L. Curtis. Litho Questa)

1976 (20 Feb). *25th Anniv of the Lesotho Red Cross. T* **100** *and similar horiz designs. Multicoloured. W* **53** *(sideways). P* 14.

No.	Description	Unused	Used
296	4 c. Type **100**	50	10
297	10 c. Medical aid	70	10
298	15 c. Rural service	1·00	1·00
299	25 c. Relief supplies	1·40	1·50
296/9	*Set of* 4	3·25	2·40

101 Tapestry

102 Football

(Des V. Whiteley Studio. Litho Format)

1976 (2 June). *Multicoloured designs as T* **101**. *W* **53** *(sideways* on 2 to 50 c.). P* 14.

No.	Description	Unused	Used
300	2 c. Type **101**	10	30
	w. Wmk top of hat to right		
301	3 c. Mosotho horseman	20	30
302	4 c. Map of Lesotho	55	10
	w. Wmk top of hat to right		
303	5 c. Lesotho Brown diamond	55	45
	w. Wmk top of hat to right		
304	10 c. Lesotho Bank	30	10
305	15 c. Lesotho and O.A.U. flags	80	40
306	25 c. Sehlabathebe National Park	80	35
307	40 c. Pottery	80	90
308	50 c. Prehistoric rock art	1·75	1·75
309	1 r. King Moshoeshoe II (*vert*)	1·40	1·75
300/9	*Set of* 10	6·50	5·75

*The normal sideways watermark shows top of hat to left *when seen from the back of the stamp.*

For 25 c., 40 c. and 50 c. values on unwatermarked paper, see Nos. 398/400

(Des P. Powell. Litho Questa)

1976 (9 Aug). *Olympic Games, Montreal. T* **102** *and similar vert designs. Multicoloured. W* **53**. *P* 14.

No.	Description	Unused	Used
310	4 c. Type **102**	10	10
311	10 c. Weightlifting	10	10
312	15 c. Boxing	20	10
313	25 c. Throwing the discus	35	25
310/13	*Set of* 4	65	40

103 "Rising Sun"

104 Telephones, 1876 and 1976

(Des L. Curtis. Litho Questa)

1976 (4 Oct). *Tenth Anniv of Independence. T* **103** *and similar vert designs. Multicoloured. W* **53**. *P* 14.

No.	Description	Unused	Used
314	4 c. Type **103**	10	10
315	10 c. Open gates	10	10
316	15 c. Broken chains	40	20
317	25 c. Britten Norman Islander aircraft over hotel	50	35
314/17	*Set of* 4	1·00	55

(Des and litho J.W.)

1976 (6 Dec). *Telephone Centenary. T* **104** *and similar horiz designs. Multicoloured. W* **53** *(sideways). P* 13.

No.	Description	Unused	Used
318	4 c. Type **104**	10	10
319	10 c. Early handset and telephone-user, 1976	15	10
320	15 c. Wall telephone and telephone exchange	25	15
321	25 c. Stick telephone and Alexander Graham Bell	45	40
318/21	*Set of* 4	85	55

105 *Aloe striatula*

106 Large-toothed Rock Hyrax

(Des D. Findlay. Litho Walsall)

1977 (14 Feb). *Aloes and Succulents. T* **105** *and similar vert designs. Multicoloured. W* **53** *(inverted). P* 14.

No.	Description	Unused	Used
322	3 c. Type **105**	25	10
323	4 c. *Aloe aristata*	30	10
324	5 c. *Kniphofia caulescens*	35	10
325	10 c. *Euphorbia pulvinata*	50	10
326	15 c. *Aloe saponaria*	1·50	40
327	20 c. *Caralluma lutea*	1·50	65
328	25 c. *Aloe polyphylla*	1·75	90
322/8	*Set of* 7	5·50	2·00

(Des D. Findlay. Litho Questa)

1977 (25 Apr). *Animals. T* **106** *and similar horiz designs. Multicoloured. W* **53** *(sideways). P* 14.

No.	Description	Unused	Used
329	4 c. Type **106**	1·75	10
330	5 c. Cape Porcupine	1·75	10
331	10 c. Zorilla (polecat)	2·00	10
332	15 c. Klipspringer	7·00	1·50
333	25 c. Chacma Baboon	8·00	2·25
329/33	*Set of* 5	18·00	3·50

107 "Rheumatic Man"

108 Small-mouthed Yellowfish

(Des C. Abbott. Litho Questa)

1977 (4 July). *World Rheumatism Year. T* **107** *and similar vert designs showing the "Rheumatic Man". W* **53**. *P* 14.

No.	Description	Unused	Used
334	4 c. yellow and red	10	10
335	10 c. new blue and deep blue	15	10
336	15 c. yellow and blue-green	30	10
337	25 c. orange-red and black	40	40
334/7	*Set of* 4	85	55

Designs:—10 c. Man surrounded by "pain"; 15 c. Man surrounded by "chain"; 25 c. Man supporting globe.

(Des D. Findlay. Litho Questa)

1977 (28 Sept). *Fish. T* **108** *and similar horiz designs. Multicoloured. W* **53** *(sideways). P* 14.

No.	Description	Unused	Used
338	4 c. Type **108**	30	10
339	10 c. Mudfish	45	10
340	15 c. Rainbow Trout	1·00	35
341	25 c. Barnard's Mudfish	1·10	60
338/41	*Set of* 4	2·50	1·00

(109)

110 Black and White Heads

1977 (7 Dec*). *No. 198 surch with T* **109** *by Govt Printer, Maseru.*

No.	Description	Unused	Used
342	3 c. on 10 c. yellow-brn & pale bluish grey	90	90
	a. Top obliterating bar short at left (R.2/5)	14·00	
	b. Top obliterating bar short at right (R.5/5)	14·00	
	w. Wmk top of hat to right		

*Earliest known date of use.

Nos. 342a/b occur on the upper pane.

(Des Jennifer Toombs. Litho Walsall)

1977 (12 Dec). *Decade for Action to Combat Racism. T* **110** *and similar vert designs. W* **53**. *P* 14.

No.	Description	Unused	Used
343	4 c. chocolate and mauve	10	10
344	10 c. chocolate and light new blue	10	10
345	15 c. chocolate and light orange	15	15
346	25 c. chocolate and light turquoise-green	25	25
343/6	*Set of* 4	55	45

Designs:—10 c. Jigsaw pieces; 15 c. Cogwheels; 25 c. Handshake.

(Des D. Findlay. Litho Questa)

1978 (13 Feb). *Flowers. Vert designs similar to T* **105**. *Multicoloured. W* **53**. *P* 14.

No.	Description	Unused	Used
347	2 c. *Papaver aculeatum*	10	20
348	3 c. *Diascia integerrima*	10	20
349	4 c. *Helichrysum trilineatum*	10	10
350	5 c. *Zaluzianskya maritima*	10	10
351	10 c. *Gladiolus natalensis*	20	20
352	15 c. *Chironia krebsii*	30	40
353	25 c. *Wahlenbergia undulata*	50	1·00
354	40 c. *Brunsvigia radulosa*	85	2·00
347/54	*Set of* 8	2·00	3·75

111 Edward Jenner performing Vaccination

112 Tsoloane Falls

(Des G. Hutchins. Litho J.W.)

1978 (8 May). *Global Eradication of Smallpox. T* **111** *and similar vert design. Multicoloured. W* **53.** *P* 13.

355 5 c. Type **111** 20 10
356 25 c. Head of child and W.H.O. emblem .. 60 65
w. Wmk inverted .. .. .. 5·00

(Des Kobus De Beer Art Studio. Litho Questa)

1978 (28 July). *Waterfalls. T* **112** *and similar vert designs. Multicoloured. W* **53.** *P* 14.

357 4 c. Type **112** 15 10
358 10 c. Qiloane Falls 25 10
359 15 c. Tsoelikana Falls 45 60
360 25 c. Maletsunyane Falls .. .. .. 75 1·50
357/60 .. .. *Set of* 4 1·40 2·00

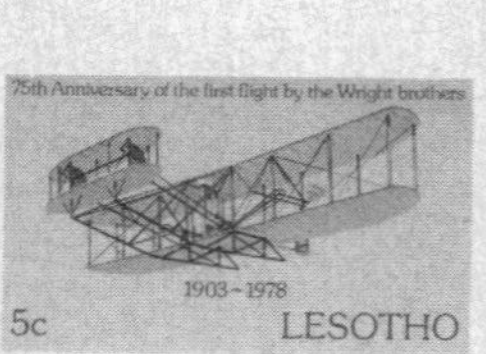

113 Wright Flyer III, 1903

114 *Orthetrum farinosum*

(Des L. Curtis. Litho Harrison)

1978 (9 Oct). *75th Anniv of Powered Flight. T* **113** *and similar horiz design. W* **53** *(sideways). P* 14½ × 14.

361 5 c. black, brown-ochre and new blue .. 15 10
362 25 c. multicoloured 40 55
Design:—25 c. Wilbur and Orville Wright.

(Des D. Findlay. Litho Questa)

1978 (18 Dec). *Insects. T* **114** *and similar vert designs. Multicoloured. W* **53.** *P* 14.

363 4 c. Type **114** 10 10
364 10 c. *Phymateus viridipes* 20 10
365 15 c. *Belonogaster lateritis* 30 40
366 25 c. *Sphodromantis gastrica* 50 80
363/6 .. .. *Set of* 4 1·00 1·25

115 Oudehout Branch in flower

116 Mampharoane

(Des D. Findlay. Litho Questa)

1979 (26 Mar). *Trees. T* **115** *and similar vert designs showing branches in flower. Multicoloured. W* **53.** *P* 14.

367 4 c. Type **115** 15 10
368 10 c. Wild Olive 20 10
369 15 c. Blinkblaar 35 80
370 25 c. Cape Holly .. .. 70 1·50
367/70 .. .. *Set of* 4 1·25 2·25

(New Currency. 100 lisente = 1(má)loti)

(Des D. Findlay. Litho Questa)

1979 (1 June). *Reptiles. T* **116** *and similar horiz designs. Multicoloured. P* 14. *A. No wmk. B. W* **53** *(sideways).*

		A		B	
371	4 s. Type **116**	10	10	10	10
372	10 s. Qoaane	20	10	20	10
373	15 s. Leupa	30	60	30	70
374	25 s. Masumu	60	1·25	60	1·50
371/4	.. .. .. *Set of* 4	1·10	1·75	1·10	2·10

NEW INFORMATION

The editor is always interested to correspond with people who have new information that will improve or correct the Catalogue.

117 Basutoland 1933 1d. Stamp

118 Detail of Painting "Children's Games" by Brueghel

(Des J.W. Litho Format)

1979 (22 Oct). *Death Centenary of Sir Rowland Hill. T* **117** *and similar vert designs showing stamps. P* 14.

375 4 s. multicoloured 10 10
376 15 s. multicoloured 30 20
377 25 s. black, yellow-orange and olive-bistre .. 40 30
375/7 .. .. *Set of* 3 70 50
MS378 118 × 95 mm. 50 s. multicoloured .. 60 80
Designs:—15 s. Basutoland 1962 ½ c. definitive; 25 s. Penny Black; 50 s. 1972 15 c. Post Office Centenary commemorative.

(Des C. Abbott. Litho Questa)

1979 (10 Dec). *International Year of the Child. T* **118** *and similar vert designs showing details of the painting "Children's Games" by Brueghel. W* **53.** *P* 14.

379 4 s. multicoloured 10 10
380 10 s. multicoloured 10 10
381 15 s. multicoloured 15 15
379/81 .. .. *Set of* 3 30 30
MS382 113 × 88 mm. 25 s. multicoloured *(horiz)* (wmk sideways) 55 45

119 Beer Strainer, Broom and Mat

(Des Kobus de Beer Art Studio. Litho Walsall)

1980 (18 Feb). *Grasswork. T* **119** *and similar horiz designs. Multicoloured. W* **53** *(sideways). P* 14.

383 4 s. Type **119** 10 10
384 10 s. Winnowing Basket 10 10
385 15 s. Basotho Hat 20 25
386 25 s. Grain storage 35 40
383/6 .. .. *Set of* 4 60 70

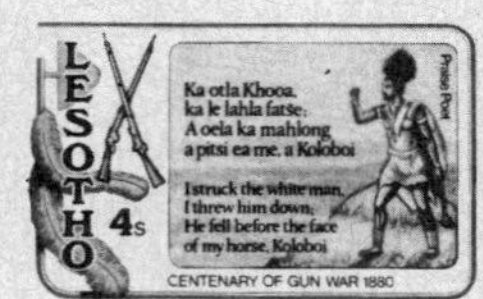

120 Praise Poet

(Des BG Studio. Litho Walsall)

1980 (6 May). *Centenary of Gun War. T* **120** *and similar horiz designs. Multicoloured. P* 14.

387 4 s. Type **120** 15 10
388 5 s. Lerotholi (commander of Basotho Army) 15 10
389 10 s. Ambush at Qalabane 20 10
390 15 s. Snider and Martini-Henry rifles .. 60 45
391 25 s. Map showing main areas of action .. 70 55
387/91 .. .. *Set of* 5 1·60 1·10

121 Olympic Flame, Flags and Kremlin

S
(122)

(Des G. Vasarhelyi. Litho Format)

1980 (20 Sept). *Olympic Games, Moscow. T* **121** *and similar horiz designs. Multicoloured. P* 14½.

392 25 s. Type **121** 25 25
a. Horiz strip of 5. Nos. 392/6 .. .. 1·10
393 25 s. Doves, flame and flags 25 25
394 25 s. Football 25 25
395 25 s. Running 25 25
396 25 s. Opening ceremony 25 25
392/6 .. .. *Set of* 5 1·10 1·10
MS397 110 × 85 mm. 1 m. 40, Ancient and modern athletes carrying Olympic torch .. .. .. 1·10 1·25
Nos. 392/6 were printed together, *se-tenant*, in horizontal strips of 5 throughout the sheet.

1980. *As Nos.* 203 *and* 306/8, *but without wmk.*

398 25 c. Sehlabathebe National Park .. .. 75 1·40
399 40 c. Pottery .. .. 3·00 6·00
400 50 c. Prehistoric rock art .. .. .. 3·00 6·00
401 2 r. Statue of Moshoeshoe I (yellow-brown and ultramarine) .. .. 1·10 3·00
398/401 .. .. *Set of* 4 7·00 15·00

Two opt types of No. 409:
Type I. Cancelling bars centred on depth of "M1" (stamps surcharged in individual panes of 25 and from the righthand panes of those surcharged in sheets of 50 (2 panes 5 × 5)).
Type II. Lower cancelling bar aligns with foot of "M1" (stamps from lefthand panes of those surcharged in sheets of 50).

1980 (20 Oct)–**81**. *As Nos.* 300/5, 309 *and* 398/401 *surch as T* **122** *or with new figures of value* (5 *s.* (*No.* 410A), 6, 75 *s.*, 1 *and* 2 *m.*). A. *By typo (locally).* B. *By litho (London).*

(*a*) *W* **53** *(sideways on* 2, 3, 6, 10, 40, 50 *and* 75 *s.)*

		A		B	
402	2 s. on 2 c. Type **101** ..	10	10	10	10
	w. Wmk top of hat to right	5·50	—	†	
403	3 s. on 3 c. Mosotho horseman	20	10	20	10
404	6 s. on 4 c. Map of Lesotho ..	30	10	30	10
	a. Surch double	†	—	†	
	b. Albino surch	†	—	†	
405	10 s. on 10 c. Lesotho Bank ..	80	10	5·00	5·50
405*a*	25 s. on 25 c. Sehlabathebe National Park	3·25	4·50	†	
406	40 s. on 40 c. Pottery ..	45	50	45	50
407	50 s. on 50 c. Prehistoric rock art	1·50	—	1·00	55
408	75 s. on 15 c. Lesotho and O.A.U. flags	70	75	†	
409	1 m. on 1 r. King Moshoeshoe II (I) (Sil.)	80	1·00	†	
	a. Surch double, one inverted	55·00	—	†	
	b. Opt Type II	3·75	4·00	†	
	(*b*) *No wmk*				
410	5 s. on 5 c. Lesotho Brown diamond	40	10	40	10
	a. Third surch (Basotho hat and "5 s.") double	—	—	†	
	b. Basotho hat and "5 s." surch albino	—	—	†	
	c. Basotho hat and "5 s." omitted	20·00	—	†	
	d. Second surch ("6 s." and bars) albino	22·00	—	†	
411	10 s. on 10 c. Lesotho Bank	†		10	10
412	25 s. on 25 c. Sehlabathebe National Park .. .	25	30	25	30
	a. Surch double	20·00	—	†	
413	40 s. on 40 c. Pottery	4·00	4·25	†	
414	50 s. on 50 c. Prehistoric rock art	1·00	55	†	
415	75 s. on 15 c. Lesotho and O.A.U. flags	†		70	75
416	1 m. on 1 r. King Moshoeshoe II (Blk. and Sil.)	†		80	1·00
417	2 m. on 2 r. Statue of Moshoeshoe I	80	1·40	80	1·40
402/17	.. .. .. *Set of* 12			4·25	4·00

No. 410A is a further surcharge on No. 410B. Initially sheets of No. 410B were locally surcharged "6 s.", but this was later obliterated by a Basotho hat emblem and a further "5 s." surcharge added, both in typography.

The surcharge on No. 416 is similar to that on No. 409 but has the cancelling bars printed in black and the new face value in silver.

On each value except the 5 s. and 1 m. stamps, the design of the surcharge on the local printing is identical to that on the London printing. Stamps from the local printing can easily be identified from those of the London printing as indentations are clearly visible on the reverse of stamps with the typographed surcharge.

It is believed that the local surcharges were not placed on general sale before 1 December 1980. No. 410A did not appear until 20 January 1981.

123 Beer Mug

124 Queen Elizabeth the Queen Mother and Prince Charles

(Des G. Vasarhelyi (No. **MS**422), Kobus de Beer Art Studio (others). Litho Format (No. **MS**422), Questa (others)).

1980 (20 Nov). *Pottery. T* **123** *and similar horiz designs. Multicoloured. W* **53** *(sideways). P* 14.

418 4 s. Type **123** 10 10
419 10 s. Beer brewing pot 10 10
420 15 s. Water pot 15 15
421 25 s. Pot shapes 25 30
418/21 .. .. *Set of* 4 50 50
MS422 150 × 110 mm. 40 s. × 4 Wedgwood plaques of Prince Philip; Queen Elizabeth II; Prince Charles; Princess Anne (*each* 22 × 35 *mm*). P 14 × 14½ 80 90
No. **MS**422 was issued to commemorate the 250th birth anniversary of Josiah Wedgwood.

(Des G. Vasarhelyi. Litho Format)

1980 (1 Dec). *80th Birthday of Queen Elizabeth the Queen Mother. T* **124** *and similar multicoloured designs. P* 14½.

423 5 s. Type **124** .. 25 25
a. Horiz strip of 3. Nos. 423/5 .. 1·25
424 10 s. Queen Elizabeth the Queen Mother .. 25 25
425 1 m. Basutoland 1947 Royal Visit 2d. commemorative and flags (54 × 44 *mm*) 90 90
423/5 .. *Set of* 3 1·25 1·25

Nos. 423/5 were printed together, *se-tenant*, in horizontal strips of 3 throughout small sheets of nine stamps.

125 Lesotho Evangelical Church, Morija

(Des G. Vasarhelyi. Litho Format (75 s., 1 m. 50), Harrison (others))

1980 (8 Dec). *Christmas. T* **125** *and similar horiz designs. Multicoloured. No wmk* (75 s.) *or W* **53** *(others). P* 14 × 14½.

426 4 s. Type **125** .. 10 10
427 15 s. St. Agnes' Anglican Church, Teyateyaneng .. 10 10
428 25 s. Cathedral of Our Lady of Victories, Maseru .. 15 10
429 75 s. University Chapel, Roma .. 45 50
426/9 .. *Set of* 4 65 60
MS430 110 × 85 mm. 1 m. 50, Nativity scene (43 × 29 *mm*). No wmk. P 14½ .. 50 80

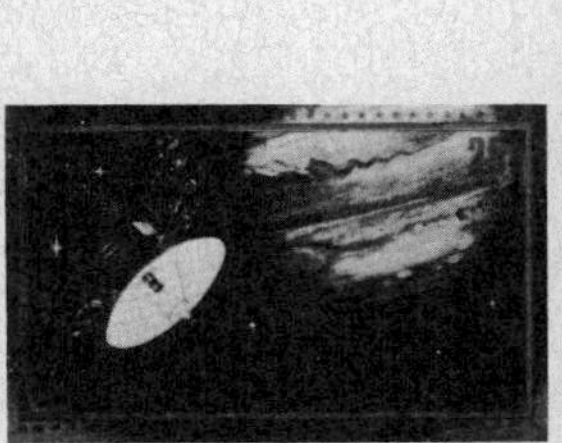

126 "Voyager" Satellite and Jupiter **127** Greater Kestrel

(Des G. Vasarhelyi. Litho Format)

1981 (15 Mar). *Space Exploration. T* **126** *and similar horiz designs. Multicoloured. P* 13½ × 14.

431 25 s. Type **126** .. 30 25
a. Horiz strip of 5. Nos. 431/5 .. 1·40
432 25 s. "Voyager" and Saturn .. 30 25
433 25 s. "Voyager" passing Saturn .. 30 25
434 25 s. "Space Shuttle" releasing satellite .. 30 25
435 25 s. "Space Shuttle" launch .. 30 25
431/5 .. *Set of* 5 1·40 1·10
MS436 111 × 85 mm. 1 m. 40, Saturn .. 1·75 1·00

Nos. 431/5 were printed together, *se-tenant*, in horizontal strips of 5 throughout the sheet.

(Des G. Vasarhelyi. Litho Format)

1981 (20 Apr–Dec). *Birds. Multicoloured designs as T* **127**. *With imprint date. P* 14½.

437 1 s. Type **127** .. 15 20
a. Perf 13 (12.81) .. 55 30
438 2 s. Speckled Pigeon (*horiz*) .. 15 20
a. Perf 13 (12.81) .. 65 30
439 3 s. South African Crowned Crane .. 20 20
440 5 s. Bokmakierie Shrike .. 20 20
a. Perf 13 (12.81) .. 90 30
441 6 s. Cape Robin Chat .. 30 10
442 7 s. Yellow Canary .. 30 10
443 10 s. Red-billed Pintail (*horiz*) .. 40 10
a. Perf 13 (12.81) .. 90 30
444 25 s. Malachite Kingfisher .. 1·00 15
445 40 s. Yellow-tufted Malachite Sunbird (*horiz*) 1·25 40
446 60 s. Cape Longclaw (*horiz*) .. 1·50 65
447 75 s. Hoopoe (*horiz*) .. 2·25 65
448 1 m. Red Bishop (*horiz*) .. 2·50 1·00
449 2 m. Egyptian Goose (*horiz*) .. 3·50 3·00
450 5 m. Lilac-breasted Roller (*horiz*) .. 6·00 7·00
437/50 .. *Set of* 14 18·00 12·00

Imprint dates: "1981", Nos. 437/50; "1982", Nos. 437/41, 443.

Nos. 437/50 exist imperforated and as progressive proofs from stock dispersed by the liquidator of Format International Security Printers Ltd.

For these stamps watermarked w **14** see Nos. 500/13.

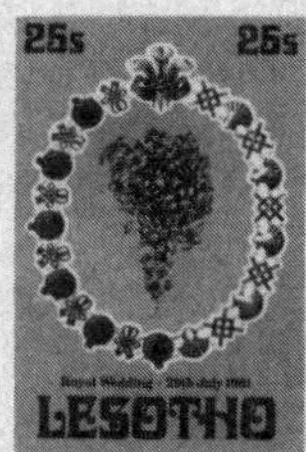

128 Wedding Bouquet from Lesotho

(Des J.W. Litho Format)

1981 (22 July). *Royal Wedding. T* **128** *and similar vert designs. Multicoloured. P* 14.

451 25 s. Type **128** .. 10 10
a. Booklet pane. No. 451 × 3 plus printed label .. 60
b. Booklet pane. Nos. 451/3 plus printed label .. 60
452 50 s. Prince Charles riding .. 20 25
a. Booklet pane. No. 452 × 3 plus printed label .. 70
453 75 s. Prince Charles and Lady Diana Spencer 30 50
a. Booklet pane. No. 453 × 3 plus printed label .. 90
451/3 .. *Set of* 3 55 75

Nos. 451/3 also exist imperforate from a restricted printing (*price for set of* 3 £5.50 *mint*).

Booklet panes Nos. 451a/3a exist part perforated from stock dispersed by the liquidator of Format International Security Printers Ltd.

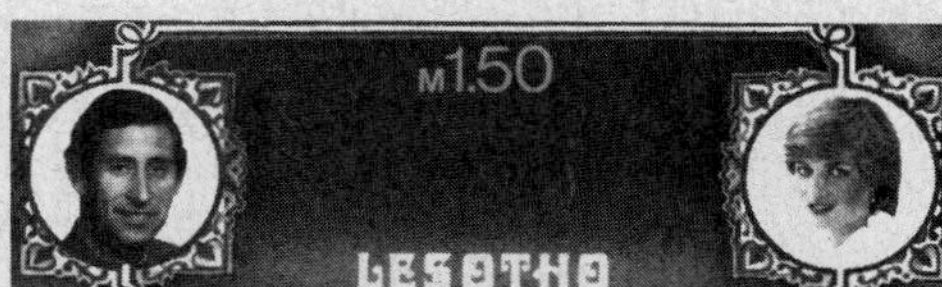

129 Prince Charles and Lady Diana Spencer

(Des G. Vasarhelyi. Litho Format)

1981 (5 Sept). *Royal Wedding* (2nd issue). *Sheet* 115 × 90 *mm. P* 14½.

MS454 **129** 1 m. 50, multicoloured .. 1·50 1·50

No. **MS**454 also exists imperforate from a restricted printing (*price £4 mint*).

130 "Santa planning his Annual Visit" **131** Duke of Edinburgh, Award Scheme Emblem and Flags

(Des G. Vasarhelyi. Litho Format)

1981 (5 Oct). *Christmas. Paintings by Norman Rockwell* (6 *to* 60 *s.*) *or Botticelli* (1 *m.* 25). *T* **130** *and similar multicoloured designs. P* 13½.

455 6 s. Type **130** .. 15 10
456 10 s. "Santa reading his Mail" .. 25 10
457 15 s. "The Little Spooners" .. 30 20
458 20 s. "Raleigh Rockwell Travels" .. 30 25
459 25 s. "Ride 'em Cowboy" .. 30 30
460 60 s. "The Discovery" .. 50 1·00
455/60 .. *Set of* 6 1·60 1·75
MS461 111 × 85 mm. 1 m. 25, "Mystic Nativity" (48 × 31 *mm*). P 13½ × 14 .. 1·50 1·50

(Des G. Vasarhelyi. Litho Format)

1981 (5 Nov). *25th Anniv of Duke of Edinburgh Award Scheme. T* **131** *and similar multicoloured designs. P* 14½.

462 6 s. Type **131** .. 10 10
463 7 s. Tree planting .. 10 10
464 25 s. Gardening .. 25 20
465 40 s. Mountain climbing .. 40 40
466 75 s. Award Scheme emblem .. 70 75
462/6 .. *Set of* 5 1·40 1·40
MS467 111 × 85 mm. 1 m. 40, Duke of Edinburgh (45 × 30 *mm*) .. 1·25 1·25

132 Wild Cat

(Des G. Vasarhelyi. Litho Format)

1981 (16 Nov). *Wildlife. T* **132** *and similar multicoloured designs. P* 13½ (6, 25 *s.*) *or* 14½ *(others)*.

468 6 s. Type **132** .. 1·00 30
469 20 s. Chacma Baboon (44 × 31 *mm*) .. 1·50 70
470 25 s. Eland .. 2·00 75
471 40 s. Cape Porcupine (44 × 31 *mm*) .. 2·50 1·50
472 50 s. Oribi (44 × 31 *mm*) .. 2·50 1·60
468/72 .. *Set of* 5 8·50 4·25
MS473 111 × 85 mm. 1 m. 50, Black-backed Jackal (47 × 31 *mm*). P 13½ × 14 .. 2·75 1·90

133 Scout Bugler

(Des G. Vasarhelyi. Litho Format)

1982 (5 Mar). *75th Anniv of Boy Scout Movement. T* **133** *and similar horiz designs. Multicoloured. P* 13½.

474 6 s. Type **133** .. 50 25
a. Booklet pane. Nos. 474/8 × 2 and **MS**479 8·50
475 30 s. Scouts hiking .. 70 50
476 40 s. Scout sketching .. 75 60
477 50 s. Scout with flag .. 75 65
478 75 s. Scouts saluting .. 80 80
474/8 .. *Set of* 5 3·25 2·50
MS479 117 × 92 mm. 1 m. 50, Lord Baden-Powell 1·50 2·00

Nos. 474/9 exist imperforate from stock dispersed by the liquidator of Format International Security Printers Ltd.

134 Jules Rimet Trophy with Footballers and Flags of 1930 Finalists (Argentina and Uruguay)

(Des G. Vasarhelyi. Litho Format)

1982 (14 Apr). *World Cup Football Championship, Spain. T* **134** *and similar horiz designs showing World Football Cup with players and flags of countries in past finals (Nos. 480/90). Multicoloured. P* 14½.

480 15 s. Type **134** .. 25 25
a. Sheetlet. Nos. 480/91 .. 2·50
481 15 s. Jules Rimet Trophy with Czechoslovakia and Italy, 1934 .. 25 25
482 15 s. Jules Rimet Trophy with Hungary and Italy, 1938 .. 25 25
483 15 s. Jules Rimet Trophy with Brazil and Uruguay, 1950 .. 25 25
484 15 s. Jules Rimet Trophy with Hungary and West Germany, 1954 .. 25 25
485 15 s. Jules Rimet Trophy with Sweden and Brazil, 1958 .. 25 25
486 15 s. Jules Rimet Trophy with Czechoslovakia and Brazil, 1962 .. 25 25
487 15 s. Jules Rimet Trophy with West Germany and England, 1966 .. 25 25
488 15 s. Jules Rimet Trophy with Italy and Brazil, 1970 .. 25 25
489 15 s. World Cup with Holland and West Germany, 1974 .. 25 25
490 15 s. World Cup with Holland and Argentina, 1978 .. 25 25
491 15 s. World Cup and map of World on footballs 25 25
480/91 .. *Set of* 12 2·50 2·50
MS492 118 × 93 mm. 1 m. 25, Bernabeu Stadium, Madrid (47 × 35 *mm*). P 13½ .. 1·10 1·25

Nos. 480/91 were printed together, *se-tenant*, in a sheetlet of 12.

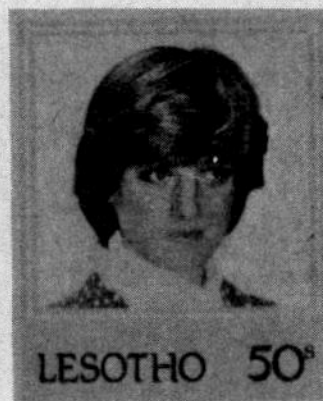

135 Portrait of George Washington **136** Lady Diana Spencer in Tetbury, May 1981

(Des G. Vasarhelyi. Litho Format)

1982 (7 June). *250th Birth Anniv of George Washington. T* **135** *and similar horiz designs. Multicoloured. P* 14 × 13½.

493 6 s. Type **135** .. 10 10
494 7 s. Washington with step-children and dog 10 10
495 10 s. Washington with Indian chief .. 15 10
496 25 s. Washington with troops .. 30 20
497 40 s. Washington arriving in New York 40 40
498 1 m. Washington on parade .. 1·00 1·10
493/8 .. *Set of* 6 1·75 1·75
MS499 117 × 92 mm. 1 m. 25, Washington crossing the Delaware .. 1·50 1·25

1982 (14 June). *As Nos. 437/50 but W w* **14** *(sideways on Nos. 500, 502/5 and 507). "1982" imprint date.*

500 1 s. Type **127** .. 20 50
501 2 s. Speckled Pigeon (*horiz*) .. 20 50
502 3 s. South African Crowned Crane .. 30 50
503 5 s. Bokmakierie Shrike .. 30 40
504 6 s. Cape Robin Chat .. 30 10
505 7 s. Yellow Canary .. 30 10
506 10 s. Red-billed Pintail (*horiz*) .. 30 10
507 25 s. Malachite Kingfisher .. 80 30
508 40 s. Yellow-tufted Malachite Sunbird (*horiz*) 1·00 45
509 60 s. Cape Longclaw (*horiz*) .. 1·25 90
510 75 s. Hoopoe (*horiz*) .. 1·75 90

511 1 m. Red Bishop (*horiz*) .. .. 2·00 2·75
512 2 m. Egyptian Goose (*horiz*) .. .. 2·75 5·00
513 5 m. Lilac-breasted Roller (*horiz*) .. .. .. 5·50 12·00
500/13 .. .. *Set of* 14 15·00 22·00

Nos. 500/13 exist imperforate from stock dispersed by the liquidator of Format International Security Printers Ltd.

(Des Jennifer Toombs. Litho Format)

1982 (1 July). *21st Birthday of Princess of Wales. T* **136** *and similar vert designs. Multicoloured. W* w **14**. A. *P* 14½. B. *P* 14½ × 14.

		A		B	
514	30 s. Lesotho coat of arms ..	40	50	30	30
515	50 s. Type **136**	40	50	75	80
516	75 s. Wedding picture at Buckingham Palace	50	80	70	70
517	1 m. Formal portrait	70	1·25	1·00	1·25
514/17	.. .. *Set of* 4	1·75	2·75	2·40	2·75

Nos. 514/17 exist imperforate from stock dispersed by the liquidator of Format International Security Printers Ltd.

137 Mosotho reading Sesotho Bible

138 Birthday Greetings

(Des G. Vasarhelyi. Litho Format)

1982 (20 Aug). *Centenary of Sesotho Bible, T* **137** *and similar multicoloured designs. P* 14½.

518 6 s. Type **137** 10 10
  a. Horiz strip of 3. Nos. 518/20 65
519 15 s. Sesotho Bible and Virgin Mary holding infant Jesus 20 20
520 1 m. Sesotho Bible and Cathedral (62 × 42 *mm*) 45 65
518/20 .. .. *Set of* 3 65 85

Nos. 518/20 were printed together, *se-tenant*, in horizontal strips of 3 throughout the sheet.

(Des G. Vasarhelyi. Litho Questa)

1982 (30 Sept). *Birth of Prince William of Wales. T* **138** *and similar vert design. Multicoloured. P* 14 × 13½.

521 6 s. Type **138** .. .. 80 1·25
  a. Sheetlet. No. 521 and 522 × 5 .. .. 4·25
522 60 s. Princess Diana and Prince William of Wales 80 80

Nos. 521/2 come from sheetlets of 6 containing one 6 s. and five 60 s. stamps.

139 "A Partridge in a Pear Tree"

(Litho Format)

1982 (1 Dec). *Christmas. "The Twelve Days of Christmas". T* **139** *and similar horiz designs depicting Walt Disney cartoon characters. Multicoloured. P* 11.

523 2 s. Type **139** 10 10
  a. Horiz pair. Nos. 523/4 .. .. .. 10 10
524 2 s. "Two turtle doves" 10 10
525 3 s. "Three French hens" 10 10
  a. Horiz pair. Nos. 525/6 .. .. .. 10 10
526 3 s. "Four calling birds" 10 10
527 4 s. "Five golden rings" 10 10
  a. Horiz pair. Nos. 527/8 .. .. .. 15 15
528 4 s. "Six geese a-laying" 10 10
529 75 s. "Seven swans a-swimming" .. .. 1·40 1·75
  a. Horiz pair. Nos. 529/30 .. .. 2·75 3·50
530 75 s. "Eight maids a-milking" .. .. 1·40 1·75
523/30 .. .. .. *Set of* 8 2·75 3·50
MS531 126 × 101 mm. 1 m. 50, "Nine ladies dancing, ten lords a-leaping, eleven pipers piping, twelve drummers drumming". P 13½ .. .. 2·40 2·75

Nos. 523/4, 525/6, 527/8 and 529/30 were each printed in horizontal *se-tenant* pairs throughout the sheet.

140 *Lepista caffrorum*

(Des G. Vasarhelyi. Litho Format)

1983 (11 Jan). *Fungi. T* **140** *and similar horiz designs. Multicoloured. P* 14½.

532 10 s. Type **140** 15 10
  a. *Tête-bêche* (vert pair) 30 30
  b. Bcoklet pane. Nos. 532/5 .. .. 2·50
  c. Booklet pane. Nos. 532/3 .. .. 3·25
533 30 s. *Broomeia congregata* 30 40
  a. *Tête-bêche* (vert pair) 60 80
534 50 s. *Afroboletus luteolus* 60 90
  a. *Tête-bêche* (vert pair) .. .. 1·10 1·75
535 75 s. *Lentinus tuber-regium* .. .. .. 90 1·40
  a. *Tête-bêche* (vert pair) .. .. 1·75 2·75
532/5 .. .. *Set of* 4 1·75 2·50

Nos. 532/5 were each printed in sheets of 36 stamps plus 4 labels as the fourth horizontal row. The stamps in horizontal rows two, six, eight and ten were inverted, forming vertical *tête-bêche* pairs.

141 Ba-Leseli Dance

(Des J.W. Litho Format)

1983 (14 Mar). *Commonwealth Day. T* **141** *and similar multicoloured designs. P* 14½.

536 5 s. Type **141** 10 10
537 30 s. Tapestry weaving 20 30
538 60 s. Queen Elizabeth II (*vert*) 35 65
539 75 s. King Moshoeshoe II (*vert*) 40 80
536/9 .. .. *Set of* 4 90 1·60

142 "Dancers in a Trance" (rock painting from Ntloana Tsoana)

(Des G. Drummond. Litho Format)

1983 (20 May). *Rock Paintings. T* **142** *and similar multicoloured designs. P* 14½.

540 6 s. Type **142** 20 10
541 25 s. "Baboons", Sehonghong 55 35
542 60 s. "Hunters attacking Mountain Reedbuck", Makhetha .. .. .. 1·10 1·10
543 75 s. "Eland", Lehaha la Likhomo .. .. 1·25 1·60
540/3 .. .. *Set of* 4 2·75 2·75
MS544 166 × 84 mm. Nos. 540/3 and 10 s. "Cattle herding", Sehonghong (52 × 52 *mm*) .. .. 2·40 3·50

No. **MS**544 exists imperforate from stock dispersed by the liquidator of Format International Security Printers Ltd.

143 Montgolfier Balloon, 1783

(Des J.W. Litho Format)

1983 (11 July). *Bicentenary of Manned Flight. T* **143** *and similar multicoloured designs. P* 14½.

545 7 s. Type **143** 15 10
  a. Booklet pane. Nos. 545/8 .. .. 3·00
546 30 s. Wright brothers and Flyer I 40 40
547 60 s. First airmail flight .. .. .. 75 1·00
548 1 m. Concorde .. .. 2·00 2·00
545/8 .. .. *Set of* 4 3·00 2·50
MS549 180×92 mm. Nos. 545/8 and 6 s. Dornier Do-28D Skyservant of Lesotho Airways (60×60 *mm*) .. .. 3·25 2·75

Nos. 545/9 exist imperforate from stock dispersed by the liquidator of Format International Security Printers Ltd.

144 Rev. Eugene Casalis

(Des G. Vasarhelyi. Litho Questa)

1983 (5 Sept). *150th Anniv of Arrival of the French Missionaries. T* **144** *and similar horiz designs. Multicoloured. P* 13½ × 14.

550 6 s. Type **144** 10 10
  a. *Tête-bêche* (vert pair) 10 15
551 25 s. The founding of Morija 10 10
  a. *Tête-bêche* (vert pair) 15 20
552 40 s. Baptism of Libe 10 15
  a. *Tête-bêche* (vert pair) 20 30
553 75 s. Map of Lesotho 20 25
  a. *Tête-bêche* (vert pair) 40 50
550/3 .. .. *Set of* 4 40 60

Nos. 550/3 were each issued in sheets of 20 containing two panes (2 × 5) separated by a vertical gutter. Within these sheets horizontal rows two and four are inverted forming *tête-bêche* vertical pairs.

145 Mickey Mouse and Pluto Greeted by Friends

(Litho Questa)

1983 (18 Oct). *Christmas. T* **145** *and similar horiz designs showing Disney cartoon characters in scenes from "Old Christmas" (Washington Irving's sketchbook). Multicoloured. P* 14 × 13½.

554 1 s. Type **145** 10 10
555 2 s. Donald Duck and Pluto 10 10
556 3 s. Donald Duck with Huey, Dewey and Louie 10 10
557 4 s. Goofy, Donald Duck and Mickey Mouse 10 10
558 5 s. Goofy holding turkey, Donald Duck and Mickey Mouse 10 10
559 6 s. Goofy and Mickey Mouse 10 10
560 75 s. Donald and Daisy Duck .. .. .. 2·00 2·40
561 1 m. Goofy and Clarabell .. .. .. 2·50 2·75
554/61 .. .. *Set of* 8 4·50 5·00
MS562 132 × 113 mm. 1 m. 75, Scrooge McDuck, Pluto and Donald Duck .. .. .. 3·25 4·50

146 *Danaus chrysippus*

(Des and litho Format)

1984 (20 Jan). *Butterflies. T* **146** *and similar horiz designs. Multicoloured. P* 14.

563 1 s. Type **146** 30 40
564 2 s. *Aeropetes tulbaghia* 30 40
565 3 s. *Colotis evenina* 35 40
566 4 s. *Precis oenone* 35 40
567 5 s. *Precis hierta* 35 40
568 6 s. *Catopsilia florella* 35 10
569 7 s. *Phalanta phalantha* 35 10
570 10 s. *Acraea stenobea* 40 10
571 15 s. *Cynthia cardui* 90 10
572 20 s. *Colotis subfasciatus* .. .. .. 1·00 10
573 30 s. *Charaxes jasius* .. .. .. 1·25 30
574 50 s. *Terias brigitta* .. .. .. 1·50 40
575 60 s. *Pontia helice* .. .. 1·60 50
576 75 s. *Colotis regina* .. .. 1·75 50
577 1 m. *Hypolimnas misippus* .. .. .. 2·00 1·50
578 5 m. *Papilio demodocus* .. .. .. 4·50 7·50
563/78 .. .. .. *Set of* 16 15·00 11·50

Nos. 563/73 and 576 exist imperforate and as progressive proofs from stock dispersed by the liquidator of Format International Security Printers Ltd.

147 "Thou Shalt not have Strange Gods before Me"

(Des G. Vasarhelyi. Litho Format)

1984 (30 Mar). *Easter. The Ten Commandments. T* **147** *and similar vert designs. Multicoloured. P* 13½ × 14.

579 20 s. Type **147** 30 30
  a. Sheetlet. Nos. 579/88 .. .. .. 2·75
580 20 s. "Thou shalt not take the name of the Lord thy God in vain" 30 30

581 20 s. "Remember thou keep holy the Lord's Day" 30 30
582 20 s. "Honour thy father and mother" .. 30 30
583 20 s. "Thou shalt not kill" 30 30
584 20 s. "Thou shalt not commit adultery" .. 30 30
585 20 s. "Thou shalt not steal" 30 30
586 20 s. "Thou shalt not bear false witness against thy neighbour" 30 30
587 20 s. "Thou shalt not covet thy neighbour's wife" 30 30
588 20 s. "Thou shalt not covet thy neighbour's goods" 30 30
579/88 .. .. *Set of* 10 2·75 2·75
MS589 102 × 73 mm. 1 m. 50, Moses with Tablets (45 × 28 *mm*). P 14. .. .. 1·25 2·25

Nos. 579/88 were printed together in small sheets of 12 including 2 *se-tenant* stamp-size labels.

148 Torch Bearer

(Des G. Vasarhelyi. Litho Format)

1984 (3 May). *Olympic Games, Los Angeles. T* **148** *and similar horiz designs. Multicoloured. P* 13½ × 14.
590 10 s. Type **148** 10 10
591 30 s. Horse-riding 10 10
592 50 s. Swimming 15 20
593 75 s. Basketball 20 25
594 1 m. Running 25 30
590/4 .. .. *Set of* 5 70 80
MS595 101 × 72 mm. 1 m. 50, Olympic Flame and flags .. .. 1·50 2·50

149 Sauropodomorph Footprints

(Des G. Drummond. Litho Format)

1984 (2 July). *Prehistoric Footprints (2nd series). T* **149** *and similar horiz designs. Multicoloured. P* 13½ × 14.
596 10 s. Type **149** 55 30
597 30 s. Lesothosaurus footprints .. .. 1·25 1·25
598 50 s. Footprint of carnivorous dinosaur .. 1·50 2·00
596/8 .. .. *Set of* 3 3·00 3·25

Nos. 596/8 exist imperforate from stock dispersed by the liquidator of Format International Security Printers Ltd.

150 Wells Fargo Coach, 1852

(Des G. Vasarhelyi. Litho Format)

1984 (5 Sept). *"Ausipex" International Stamp Exhibition, Melbourne, and Bicentenary of First Mail Coach Run. T* **150** *and similar horiz designs. Multicoloured. P* 14.
599 6 s. Type **150** 10 10
a. Sheetlet. Nos. 599 × 4 and No. 603 .. 70
600 7 s. Basotho mail cart, *circa* 1900 .. .. 10 10
a. Sheetlet. No. 600 × 4 and No. 603 .. 80
601 10 s. Bath mail coach, 1784 .. .. .. 10 10
a. Sheetlet. No. 601 × 4 and No. 603 .. 90
602 30 s. Cobb coach, 1853 .. .. 30 35
a. Sheetlet. No. 602 × 4 and No. 603 .. 1·60
603 50 s. Exhibition logo and Royal Exhibition Buildings, Melbourne (82 × 25 *mm*) .. 50 55
599/603 .. .. *Set of* 5 95 1·10
MS604. 147 × 98 mm. 1 m. 75, G.B. Penny Black, Basutoland 1934 "OFFICIAL" optd 6d. and Western Australia 1854 4d. with frame inverted (82 × 25 *mm*) .. .. 2·75 3·75

In addition to the listed sheetlets, Nos. 599/602 also exist in separate sheets of 50. No. 603 only comes from the sheetlets.

151 "The Orient Express" (1900)

(Des Walsall. Litho Format)

1984 (5 Nov). *Railways of the World. T* **151** *and similar horiz designs. Multicoloured. P* 14 × 13½.
605 6 s. Type **151** 40 15
606 15 s. German State Railways Class "05" No. 05001 (1935) 45 30
607 30 s. Caledonian Railway *Cardean* (1906) .. 70 60
608 60 s. Santa Fe "Super Chief" (1940) .. .. 1·00 1·75
609 1 m. L.N.E.R. "Flying Scotsman" (1934) .. 1·25 2·00
605/9 .. .. *Set of* 5 3·50 4·25
MS610 108 × 82 mm. 2 m. South African Railways "The Blue Train" (1972) .. .. 1·00 2·50

No. 607 exists imperforate from stock dispersed by the liquidator of Format International Security Printers Ltd.

152 Eland Calf

153 Crown of Lesotho

(Des G. Drummond. Litho Format)

1984 (20 Dec). *Baby Animals. T* **152** *and similar horiz designs. Multicoloured. P* 14 × 13½ (1 *m.*) *or* 15 (*others*).
611 15 s. Type **152** 35 20
612 20 s. Young Chacma Baboons 40 25
613 30 s. Oribi calf 55 40
614 75 s. Young Natal Red Hares .. .. 1·25 1·60
615 1 m. Black-backed Jackal pups (46 × 27 *mm*) 1·50 2·00
611/15 .. .. *Set of* 5 3·50 4·00

No. 615 exists imperforate from stock dispersed by the liquidator of Format International Security Printers Ltd.

(Des G. Vasarhelyi. Litho Format)

1985 (30 Jan). *Silver Jubilee of King Moshoeshoe II. T* **153** *and similar vert designs. Multicoloured. P* 15.
616 6 s. Type **153** 10 10
617 30 s. King Moshoeshoe in 1960 .. .. 20 30
618 75 s. King Moshoeshoe in traditional dress, 1985 .. .. 50 75
619 1 m. King Moshoeshoe in uniform, 1985 .. 70 1·10
616/19 .. .. *Set of* 4 1·25 2·00

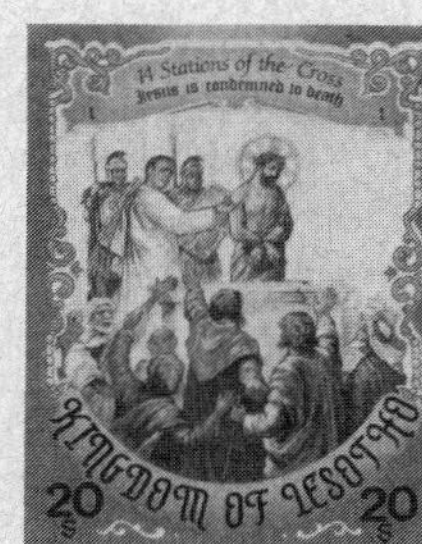

154 Christ condemned to Death

(Des G. Vasarhelyi. Litho Format)

1985 (8 Mar). *Easter. The Stations of the Cross. T* **154** *and similar vert designs. Multicoloured. P* 11.
620 20 s. Type **154** 20 25
a. Sheetlet. Nos. 620/33 .. .. .. 2·25
621 20 s. Christ carrying the Cross 20 25
622 20 s. Falling for the first time 20 25
623 20 s. Christ meets Mary 20 25
624 20 s. Simon of Cyrene helping to carry the Cross 20 25
625 20 s. Veronica wiping the face of Christ .. 20 25
626 20 s. Christ falling a second time 20 25
627 20 s. Consoling the women of Jerusalem .. 20 25
628 20 s. Falling for the third time 20 25
629 20 s. Christ being stripped 20 25
630 20 s. Christ nailed to the Cross 20 25
631 20 s. Dying on the Cross 20 25
632 20 s. Christ taken down from the Cross .. 20 25
633 20 s. Christ being laid in the sepulchre .. 20 25
620/33 .. .. *Set of* 14 2·25 2·75
MS634 138 × 98 mm. 2 m. "The Crucifixion" (Mathias Grünewald). P 13½ × 14 .. .. 2·00 3·50

Nos. 620/33 were printed together, *se-tenant*, in a sheetlet of 14 stamps with one stamp-sized label which appears in the central position.

155 Duchess of York with Princess Elizabeth, 1931

(Des G. Vasarhelyi. Litho Format)

1985 (30 May). *Life and Times of Queen Elizabeth the Queen Mother. T* **155** *and similar multicoloured designs. P* 13½ × 14.
635 10 s. Type **155** 15 10
636 30 s. The Queen Mother in 1975 .. .. 50 50
637 60 s. Queen Mother with Queen Elizabeth and Princess Margaret, 1980 .. .. 60 90
638 2 m. Four generations of Royal Family at Prince Henry's christening, 1984 .. 1·25 2·50
635/8 .. .. *Set of* 4 2·25 3·50
MS639 139 × 98 mm. 2 m. Queen Elizabeth with the Princess of Wales and her children at Prince Henry's christening (37 × 50 *mm*) .. .. 1·90 2·75

156 B.M.W. "732i"

157 American Cliff Swallow

(Litho Format)

1985 (10 June). *Century of Motoring. T* **156** *and similar multicoloured designs. P* 14 × 13½.
640 6 s. Type **156** 25 15
641 10 s. Ford "Crown Victoria" 35 15
642 30 s. Mercedes-Benz "500SE" 75 50
643 90 s. Cadillac "Eldorado Biarritz" .. .. 2·00 2·50
644 2 m. Rolls-Royce "Silver Spirit" .. .. 3·00 4·00
640/4 .. .. *Set of* 5 5·75 6·50
MS645 139 × 98 mm. 2 m. Rolls-Royce "Silver Ghost Tourer", 1907 (37 × 50 *mm*). P 13½ × 14 .. 4·25 6·00

Nos. 640/5 exist imperforate from stock dispersed by the liquidator of Format International Security Printers Ltd.

(Litho Format)

1985 (5 Aug). *Birth Bicentenary of John J. Audubon (ornithologist). T* **157** *and similar multicoloured designs showing original paintings. P* 15.
646 5 s. Type **157** 40 20
647 6 s. Great Crested Grebe (*horiz*) 40 20
648 10 s. Vesper Sparrow (*horiz*) 55 20
649 30 s. Greenshank (*horiz*) .. .. .. 1·25 75
650 60 s. Stilt Sandpiper (*horiz*) .. .. 2·00 2·50
651 2 m. Glossy Ibis (*horiz*) .. .. .. 3·50 5·00
646/51 .. .. *Set of* 6 7·25 8·00

Nos. 646/51 were reissued in February 1986 in sheetlets containing five stamps and one label.

158 Two Youths Rock-climbing

159 U.N. (New York) 1951 1 c. Definitive and U.N. Flag

(Des Walsall. Litho Format)

1985 (26 Sept). *International Youth Year and 75th Anniv of Girl Guide Movement. T* **158** *and similar vert designs. Multicoloured. P* 15.
652 10 s. Type **158** 20 10
653 30 s. Young technician in hospital laboratory 50 40
654 75 s. Three guides on parade .. .. .. 1·00 1·25
655 2 m. Guide saluting .. .. 2·40 3·00
652/5 .. .. *Set of* 4 3·75 4·25
MS656 138 × 98 mm. 2 m. "Olave, Lady Baden-Powell" (Grace Wheatley) (37 × 50 *mm*). P 13½ × 14 .. .. 2·40 2·75

(Des G. Vasarhelyi. Litho Format)

1985 (15 Oct). *40th Anniv of United Nations Organization. T* **159** *and similar designs. P* 15.
657 10 s. multicoloured 25 10
658 30 s. multicoloured 60 35
659 50 s. multicoloured 95 85
660 2 m. black and bronze-green .. .. .. 5·00 6·00
657/60 .. .. *Set of* 4 6·25 6·50

Designs: *Vert*—30 s. Ha Sofonia Earth Satellite Station; 2 m. Maimonides (physician, philosopher and scholar). *Horiz*—50 s. Lesotho Airways Fokker F.27 Friendship at Maseru Airport.

160 Cosmos

160a Mrs. Jumbo and Baby Dumbo

(Des G. Drummond. Litho Format)

1985 (11 Nov). *Wild Flowers. T* **160** *and similar vert designs. Multicoloured. P* 15.

661 6 s. Type **160** 40 15
662 10 s. Small Agapanthus 55 15
663 30 s. Pink Witchweed .. .. 1·10 60
664 60 s. Small Iris .. .. 1·75 1·75
665 90 s. Wild Geranium or Cranesbill .. .. 2·40 2·75
666 1 m. Large Spotted Orchid .. .. .. 3·75 4·50
661/6 .. .. *Set of* 6 9·00 9·00

(Des Walt Disney Productions. Litho Questa)

1985 (2 Dec). *150th Birth Anniv of Mark Twain. T* **160a** *and similar vert designs showing Walt Disney cartoon characters illustrating various Mark Twain quotations. Multicoloured. P* 11.

667 6 s. Type **160a** 40 15
668 50 s. Uncle Scrooge and Goofy reading newspaper .. .. 1·25 1·00
669 90 s. Winnie the Pooh, Tigger, Piglet and Owl .. .. 1·75 2·00
670 1 m. 50, Goofy at ship's wheel .. .. 2·75 3·00
667/70 .. .. *Set of* 4 5·50 5·50
MS671 127 × 102 mm. 1 m. 25, Mickey Mouse as astronaut. P 13½×14 .. .. 4·75 3·75

No. 669 was printed in sheetlets of 8 stamps.

160b Donald Duck as the Tailor

161 Male Lammergeier on Watch

(Des Walt Disney Productions. Litho Format)

1985 (2 Dec). *Birth Bicentenaries of Grimm Brothers (folklorists). T* **160b** *and similar vert designs showing Walt Disney cartoon characters in scenes from "The Wishing Table". Multicoloured. P* 11.

672 10 s. Type **160b** 35 15
673 60 s. The second son (Dewey) with magic donkey and gold coins .. .. 1·25 1·25
674 75 s. The eldest son (Huey) with wishing table laden with food .. .. .. 1·50 1·50
675 1 m. The innkeeper stealing the third son's (Louie) magic cudgel .. .. .. 2·00 2·50
672/5 .. .. *Set of* 4 4·50 4·75
MS676 127 × 102 mm. 1 m. 50, The tailor and eldest son with wishing table. P 13½×14 .. 4·75 5·50

No. 673 was printed in sheetlets of 8 stamps.

(Des G. Drummond. Litho Format)

1986 (20 Jan). *Flora and Fauna of Lesotho. T* **161** *and similar vert designs. Multicoloured. P* 15.

677 7 s. Type **161** 90 30
678 9 s. Prickly Pear 70 20
679 12 s. Stapelia 70 20
680 15 s. Pair of Lammergeiers .. .. .. 1·75 50
681 35 s. Pig's Ears .. .. 1·10 60
682 50 s. Male Lammergeier in flight .. .. 3·00 2·50
683 1 m. Adult and juvenile Lammergeiers .. 3·75 4·50
684 2 m. Columnar cereus .. .. .. 3·75 6·00
677/84 .. .. *Set of* 8 14·00 13·00
MS685 125×106 mm. 2 m. Verreaux's Eagle .. 7·00 9·50

162 Two Players chasing Ball

162a Galileo and 200-inch Hale Telescope at Mt Palomar Observatory, California

(Des Lori Anzalone. Litho Questa)

1986 (17 Mar). *World Cup Football Championship, Mexico. T* **162** *and similar vert designs. Multicoloured. P* 14.

686 35 s. Type **162** .. .. 1·00 50
687 50 s. Goalkeeper saving goal .. .. .. 1·50 1·25
688 1 m. Three players chasing ball .. .. 2·75 2·50
689 2 m. Two players competing for ball .. 4·50 4·50
686/9 .. .. *Set of* 4 8·75 8·00
MS690 104×74 mm. 3 m. Player heading ball .. 8·50 8·50

(Des W. Hanson. Litho Questa)

1986 (5 Apr). *Appearance of Halley's Comet. T* **162a** *and similar horiz designs. Multicoloured. P* 14.

691 9 s. Type **162a** 50 15
692 15 s. Halley's Comet and "Pioneer Venus 2" spacecraft 75 20
693 70 s. Halley's Comet of 684 A.D. (from Nuremberg Chronicle, 1493) .. .. .. 1·60 1·40
694 3 m. Comet and landing of William the Conqueror, 1066 .. .. 4·00 5·50
691/4 .. .. *Set of* 4 6·25 6·50
MS695 101×70 mm. 4 m. Halley's Comet over Lesotho .. .. 6·50 7·00

Nos. 691/3 show the face value followed by "S". Examples of these stamps without this currency abbreviation were prepared, but not issued.

163 International Year of the Child Gold Coin

163a Princess Elizabeth in Pantomime

(Litho Format)

1986 (Apr). *First Anniv of New Currency* (1980). *T* **163** *and similar horiz designs. Multicoloured. P* 13½×14.

696 30 s. Type **163** .. .. 5·00 6·50
a. Horiz strip of 5. Nos. 696/700 .. .. 23·00
697 30 s. Five maloti banknote .. .. .. 5·00 6·50
698 30 s. Fifty lisente coin .. .. .. 5·00 6·50
699 30 s. Ten maloti banknote .. .. .. 5·00 6·50
700 30 s. One sente coin .. .. 5·00 6·50
696/700 .. .. *Set of* 5 23·00 29·00

Nos. 696/700 were printed together, *se-tenant*, in horizontal strips of 5 throughout the sheet.

These stamps were prepared in 1980, but were not issued at that time. Due to increased postal rates a severe shortage of 30 s. stamps occurred in 1986 and Nos. 696/700 were sold for postal purposes from mid-April until early August.

(Des L. Nardo. Litho Questa)

1986 (21 Apr). *60th Birthday of Queen Elizabeth II. T* **163a** *and similar vert designs. P* 14.

701 90 s. black and yellow 50 60
702 1 m. multicoloured 55 65
703 2 m. multicoloured .. .. 90 1·40
701/3 .. .. *Set of* 3 1·75 2·40
MS704 119×85 mm. 4 m. black and grey-brown 1·75 3·25

Designs:— 1 m. Queen at Windsor Horse Show, 1971; 2 m. At Royal Festival Hall, 1971; 4 m. Princess Elizabeth in 1934.

163b Statue of Liberty and Bela Bartok (composer)

(Des J. Iskowitz. Litho Questa)

1986 (5 May). *Centenary of Statue of Liberty. T* **163b** *and similar horiz designs showing the Statue of Liberty and immigrants to the U.S.A. Multicoloured. P* 14.

705 15 s. Type **163b** 85 30
706 35 s. Felix Adler (philosopher) 85 30
707 1 m. Victor Herbert (composer) .. .. 3·00 2·00
708 3 m. David Niven (actor) .. .. .. 4·25 4·00
705/8 .. .. *Set of* 4 8·00 6·00
MS709 103×74 mm. 3 m. Statue of Liberty (*vert*) 3·50 5·00

163c Mickey Mouse and Goofy as Japanese Mail Runners

(Des Walt Disney Productions. Litho Format)

1986 (25 May). *"Ameripex" International Stamp Exhibition, Chicago. T* **163c** *and similar horiz designs showing Walt Disney cartoon characters delivering mail. Multicoloured. P* 11.

710 15 s. Type **163c** 55 20
711 35 s. Mickey Mouse and Pluto with mail sledge 90 30
712 1 m. Goofy as postman riding Harley-Davidson motorcycle .. .. 1·75 1·75
713 2 m. Donald Duck operating railway mail-bag apparatus .. .. 2·25 2·75
710/13 .. .. *Set of* 4 4·75 4·50
MS714 127×101 mm. 4 m. Goofy driving mail to aircraft. P 14×13½ .. .. 6·50 7·00

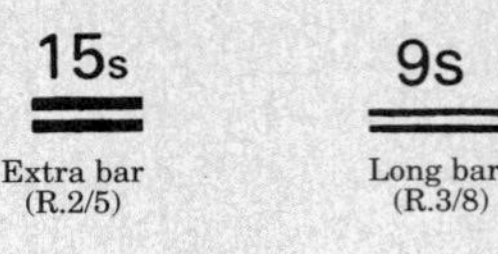

(164) (165) (166) (167) (167a)

15s
Extra bar (R.2/5)

9s
Long bars (R.3/8)

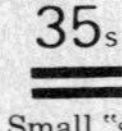

Small "s"

Nos. 720a, 720bb, 721a, 721ca, 730ba. Occurs eleven times in the sheet of 40 on R. 1/5, 1/6, 1/8, 1/9, 2/6, 2/7, 2/8, 3/5, 4/4 4/6 and 4/8 for Nos. 720a, 720bb and 730bc or R. 1/4, 2/4, 4/4, 5/4, 6/4, 7/1, 7/4, 9/1, 9/3, 10/1 and 10/2 for Nos. 721a and 721ca.

No. 728a. Occurs thirteen times in the sheet of 49 on R. 6/2 to 7 and on all positions in Row 7.

9s 35s 20s

(168) (169) (170)

1986 (6 June)–**88.** *Various stamps surch* (*a*) *As T* **164/7a** *by Lesotho Ads, Maseru.* (i) *On Nos.* 440, 447, 500/1, 506/7 *and* 509.

715 9 s. on 10 s. Red-billed Pintail (*horiz*) (No. 506) (Type **164**) .. .. .. 2·00 1·25
a. Surch on No. 443 ("1982" imprint date) 2·25 2·25
b. Surch double .. .. † —
c. Surch double, one inverted .. .. † —
716 15 s. on 1 s. Type **127** (No. 500) (22.8.86) .. 5·00 3·00
a. Extra bar .. ..
b. Surch on No. 437 ("1982" imprint date) £110
c. Surch on No. 437a .. .. .. 5·00 6·00
ca. Extra bar .. ..
cb. Surch double .. ..
717 15 s. on 2 s. Speckled Pigeon (*horiz*) (22.8.86) 4·00 4·50
a. Surch double .. .. 60·00
b. Surch triple .. ..
c. Surch omitted (in horiz pair with normal) .. ..
718 15 s. on 5 s. Bokmakierie Shrike ("1982" imprint date) (2.11.87) .. .. 1·00 35
a. Surch double .. .. 50·00
719 15 s. on 60 s. Cape Longclaw (*horiz*) (No. 509) (22.8.86) 20 10
a. Surch on No. 446 .. .. .. 60 30
720 35 s. on 25 s. Malachite Kingfisher (No. 507) (9.87) .. .. 15·00 20·00
a. Small "s" .. .. 32·00 35·00
b. Surch on No. 444 .. .. .. 50·00 50·00
ba. Surch double £100
bb. Small "s" £100 £100
721 35 s. on 75 s. Hoopoe (*horiz*) (No. 447) (Type **167**) (9.87) .. .. 20·00 18·00
a. Small "s" .. .. 32·00 32·00
b. Surch double .. .. 55·00
c. Surch on No. 510 .. .. .. £110 95·00
ca. Small "s" £200
721*d* 35 s. on 75 s. Hoopoe (*horiz*) (No. 447) (Type **167a**) (1.88) .. .. 75·00

(ii) *On Nos.* 563/5, 567, 573 *and* 575/6

722 9 s. on 30 s. *Charaxes jasius* (Type **164**) (1.7.86) 15 10
a. Surch with Type **165** .. .. 6·50 4·50
ab. Surch double .. .. † —
ac. Surch omitted (in horiz pair with normal) .. ..
723 9 s. on 60 s. *Pontia helice* (Type **165**) (1.7.86) .. .. 4·00 4·00
a. Surch double .. .. 50·00
b. Surch double, one inverted .. .. 50·00
c. Surch inverted .. .. ..
724 15 s. on 1 s. Type **146** (25.6.86) .. .. 2·75 2·75
a. Surch double .. ..
b. Surch omitted (in horiz pair with normal) .. ..
725 15 s. on 2 s. *Aeropetes tulbaghia* (25.6.86) 20 20
726 15 s. on 3 s. *Colotis evenina* (25.6.86) .. 20 20
727 15 s. on 5 s. *Precis hierta* (14.8.87) .. 20 20
a. Surch double .. .. 32·00
b. Surch omitted (in horiz pair with normal) .. .. 30·00
728 35 s. on 75 s. *Colotis regina* (15.8.86) .. 35 35
a. Small "s" .. .. 1·50 1·50

(*b*) *As T* **168/70** *by Epic Printers, Maseru.*
(i) *On Nos.* 440 *and* 444

729 9 s. on 5 s. Bokmakierie Shrike ("1982" imprint date) (30.12.87) 15 20
a. Long bars .. ..

730 16 s. on 25 s. Malachite Kingfisher (No. 444) (3.88) .. 1·75 1·00
a. Surch on No. 507 .. £225
b. Surch on No. 720 ..
ba. Small "s" in surch T **167** ..
731 35 s. on 25 s. Malachite Kingfisher (No. 444) (15.12.87) .. 60 60
a. Surch on No. 507 .. 13·00 10·00

(ii) *On Nos.* 566 *and* 569

732 20 s. on 4 s. *Precis oenone* (30.12.87) .. 10 10
a. Surch double, one inverted .. 12·00 9·00
733 40 s. on 7 s. *Phalanta phalantha* (30.12.87) 15 20

(iii) *On No.* 722

734 3 s. on 9 s. on 30 s. *Charaxes jasius* (2.2.88) 15 15
a. Surch Type **164** double .. † —
735 7 s. on 9 s. on 30 s. *Charaxes jasius* (2.2.88) 25 25
715/35 .. *Set of* 21 48·00 50·00

Some examples of Nos. 722a and 723 show thicker figures due to the method used to construct the artwork for the surcharge.

Nos. 730b/ba show a 16 s. surcharge as T **168** applied to stamps previously surcharged with T **167**.

170a Prince Andrew and Miss Sarah Ferguson

171 Basotho Pony and Rider

(Des D. Miller. Litho Questa)

1986 (23 July). *Royal Wedding. T* **170a** *and similar vert designs. Multicoloured. P* 14.
736 50 s. Type **170a** .. 40 40
737 1 m. Prince Andrew .. 70 70
738 3 m. Prince Andrew piloting helicopter .. 1·90 2·25
736/8 .. *Set of* 3 2·75 3·00
MS739 88 × 88 mm. 4 m. Prince Andrew and Miss Sarah Ferguson (*different*) .. 3·50 4·50

(Des B. Bundock. Litho Format)

1986 (3 Oct). *20th Anniv of Independence. T* **171** *and similar horiz designs. Multicoloured. P* 15.
740 9 s. Type **171** .. 30 10
741 15 s. Basotho woman spinning mohair .. 30 15
742 35 s. Crossing river by rowing boat .. 40 30
743 3 m. Thaba Tseka Post Office .. 1·50 3·00
740/3 .. *Set of* 4 2·25 3·25
MS744 109 × 78 mm. 4 m. King Moshoeshoe I .. 5·50 8·00

171a Chip n'Dale pulling Christmas Cracker

172 Rally Car

(Des Walt Disney Co. Litho Format)

1986 (4 Nov). *Christmas. T* **171a** *and similar vert designs showing Walt Disney cartoon characters. Multicoloured. P* 11.
745 15 s. Type **171a** .. 35 15
746 35 s. Mickey and Minnie Mouse .. 60 30
747 1 m. Pluto pulling Christmas taffy .. 1·50 1·75
748 2 m. Aunt Matilda baking .. 2·00 2·75
745/8 .. *Set of* 4 4·00 4·50
MS749 126 × 102 mm. 5 m. Huey and Dewey with gingerbread house. P 13½ × 14 .. 5·50 7·00

(Litho Questa)

1987 (28 Apr). *Roof of Africa Motor Rally. T* **172** *and similar vert designs. Multicoloured. P* 14.
750 9 s. Type **172** .. 30 10
751 15 s. Motorcyclist .. 35 15
752 35 s. Motorcyclist (*different*) .. 55 35
753 4 m. Rally car (*different*) .. 3·00 4·00
750/3 .. *Set of* 4 3·75 4·25

173 Lawn Tennis

174 Isaac Newton and Reflecting Telescope

(Des Y. Berry. Litho Questa)

1987 (29 May). *Olympic Games, Seoul* (1988) (*1st issue*). *T* **173** *and similar vert designs. Multicoloured. P* 14.
754 9 s. Type **173** .. 30 10
755 15 s. Judo .. 30 15
756 20 s. Athletics .. 35 20
757 35 s. Boxing .. 50 30
758 1 m. Diving .. 1·10 1·40
759 3 m. Ten-pin bowling .. 2·50 4·00
754/9 .. *Set of* 6 4·50 5·50
MS760 Two sheets, each 75 × 105 mm. (a) 2 m. Lawn tennis (*different*). (b) 4 m. Football *Set of* 2 *sheets* 3·75 4·50

Nos. 754/60 incorrectly show the Lesotho flag with white field and emblem at top right.

Similar stamps, with face values of 5, 10, 25, 40, 50 s., 3 m. 50 and a 4 m. miniature sheet showing the correct flag with white field and emblem at top left, were placed on philatelic sale from 30 November 1987. They were not, however, according to the Lesotho Philatelic Bureau, sold through post offices and agencies for postal purposes (*Price for set of* 6 £3, *mint; miniature sheet* £2.75 *mint*).

See also Nos. 838/42.

(Des Mary Walters. Litho Format)

1987 (30 June). *Great Scientific Discoveries. T* **174** *and similar horiz designs. Multicoloured. P* 15.
761 5 s. Type **174** .. 30 10
762 9 s. Alexander Graham Bell and first telephone .. 30 15
763 75 s. Robert Goddard and liquid fuel rocket 80 65
764 4 m. Chuck Yeager and Bell XS-1 rocket plane .. 2·75 3·50
761/4 .. *Set of* 4 3·50 4·00
MS765 98×68 mm. 4 m. "Mariner 10" spacecraft 2·50 3·00

175 Grey Rhebuck

176 Scouts hiking

(Des G. Drummond. Litho Format)

1987 (14 Aug). *Flora and Fauna. T* **175** *and similar multicoloured designs. P* 15.
766 5 s. Type **175** .. 40 15
767 9 s. Cape Clawless Otter .. 40 15
768 15 s. Cape Grey Mongoose .. 55 20
769 20 s. Free State Daisy (*vert*) .. 60 20
770 35 s. River Bells (*vert*) .. 75 30
771 1 m. Turkey Flower (*vert*) .. 1·75 2·25
772 2 m. Sweet Briar (*vert*) .. 2·25 3·50
773 3 m. Mountain Reedbuck .. 2·75 4·50
766/73 .. *Set of* 8 8·50 10·00
MS774 114 × 98 mm. (a) 2 m. Pig-Lily (*vert*). (b) 4 m. Cape Wildebeest .. *Set of* 2 *sheets* 4·25 6·00

(Des Mary Walters. Litho Questa)

1987 (10 Sept). *World Scout Jamboree, Australia. T* **176** *and similar vert designs. Multicoloured. P* 14.
775 9 s. Type **176** .. 40 20
776 15 s. Scouts playing football .. 45 20
777 35 s. Kangaroos .. 60 50
778 75 s. Scout saluting .. 1·25 1·25
779 4 m. Australian scout windsurfing .. 3·50 5·00
775/9 .. *Set of* 5 5·75 6·50
MS780 96 × 66 mm. 4 m. Outline map and flag of Australia .. 3·25 4·00

177 Spotted Trunkfish and Columbus' Fleet

178 "Madonna and Child" (detail)

(Des I. MacLaury. Litho Questa)

1987 (14 Dec). *500th Anniv of Discovery of America by Columbus* (1992). *T* **177** *and similar horiz designs. Multicoloured. P* 14.
781 9 s. Type **177** .. 30 15
782 15 s. Green Turtle and ships .. 40 20
783 35 s. Columbus watching Common Dolphins from ship .. 60 40
784 5 m. White-tailed Tropic Bird and fleet at sea .. 3·75 5·50
781/4 .. *Set of* 4 4·50 5·75
MS785 105 × 76 mm. 4 m. *Santa Maria* and Cuban Amazon in flight .. 3·75 4·00

No. 782 is inscribed "Carribbean" in error.

(Litho Questa)

1987 (21 Dec). *Christmas. T* **178** *and similar vert designs showing religious paintings by Raphael. Multicoloured. P* 14.
786 9 s. Type **178** .. 30 10
787 15 s. "Marriage of the Virgin" .. 45 15
788 35 s. "Coronation of the Virgin" (detail) .. 90 40
789 90 s. "Madonna of the Chair" .. 2·00 3·50
786/9 .. *Set of* 4 3·25 3·75
MS790 75 × 100 mm. 3 m. "Madonna and Child enthroned with Five Saints" (detail) .. 3·00 3·00

179 Lesser Pied Kingfisher (**180**)

(Des G. Drummond. Litho Format)

1988 (5 Apr). *Birds. T* **179** *and similar horiz designs. Multicoloured. "1988" imprint date, but no printer's imprint. P* 15.
791 2 s. Type **179** .. 20 30
792 3 s. Three-banded Plover .. 20 30
793 5 s. Spur-winged Goose .. 20 30
794 10 s. Clapper Lark .. 20 20
795 12 s. Red-eyed Bulbul .. 30 10
796 16 s. Cape Weaver .. 30 10
797 20 s. Paradise Sparrow ("Red-headed Finch") .. 30 10
798 30 s. Mountain Chat .. 35 20
799 40 s. Stonechat .. 40 20
800 55 s. Pied Barbet .. 50 25
801 60 s. Red-shouldered Glossy Starling .. 55 50
802 75 s. Cape Sparrow .. 65 60
803 1 m. Cattle Egret .. 75 80
804 3 m. Giant Kingfisher .. 1·50 2·50
805 10 m. Helmet Guineafowl .. 4·00 7·00
791/805 .. *Set of* 15 9·50 12·00

For these stamps showing Questa imprint at bottom left see Nos. 887/99.

1988 (3 May)*. *Royal Ruby Wedding. Nos.* 701/4 *optd with T* **180** *in silver.*
806 90 s. black and yellow .. 50 65
807 1 m. multicoloured .. 60 80
808 2 m. multicoloured .. 1·00 1·40
806/8 .. *Set of* 3 1·90 2·50
MS809 119×85 mm. 4 m. black and grey-brown 2·50 2·75

*Nos. 806/9 were not available in Lesotho until the middle of 1990.

181 Mickey Mouse and Goofy outside Presidential Palace, Helsinki

(Des Walt Disney Co. Litho Questa)

1988 (2 June). *"Finlandia '88" International Stamp Exhibition, Helsinki. T* **181** *and similar horiz designs showing Walt Disney cartoon characters in Finland. Multicoloured. P* 14×13½.
810 1 s. Type **181** .. 10 10
811 2 s. Goofy and Mickey Mouse in sauna .. 10 10
812 3 s. Goofy and Mickey Mouse fishing in lake .. 10 10
813 4 s. Mickey and Minnie Mouse and Finlandia Hall, Helsinki .. 10 10
814 5 s. Mickey Mouse photographing Goofy at Sibelius Monument, Helsinki .. 10 10
815 10 s. Mickey Mouse and Goofy pony trekking .. 10 10
816 3 m. Goofy, Mickey and Minnie Mouse at Helsinki Olympic Stadium .. 2·75 2·75
817 5 m. Mickey Mouse and Goofy meeting Santa at Arctic Circle .. 3·50 3·50
810/17 .. *Set of* 8 6·25 6·25
MS818 Two sheets, each 127×102 mm. (a) 4 m. Mickey Mouse and nephew as Lapps. (b) 4 m. Daisy Duck, Goofy, Mickey and Minnie Mouse by fountain, Helsinki .. *Set of* 2 *sheets* 5·00 6·50

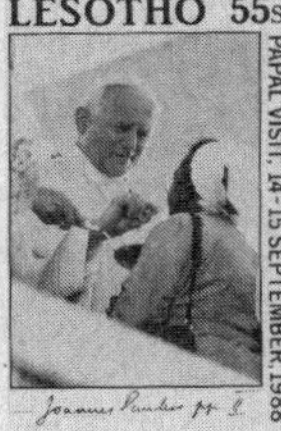

182 Pope John Paul II giving Communion

183 Large-toothed Rock Hyrax

(Litho Questa)

1988 (1 Sept). *Visit of Pope John Paul II. T* **182** *and similar multicoloured designs. P* 14.

819 55 s. Type **182** . . 40 25
820 2 m. Pope leading procession . . 1·25 1·50
821 3 m. Pope at airport . . 1·75 2·00
822 4 m. Pope John Paul II . . 2·25 2·75
819/22 . . *Set of* 4 5·00 6·00
MS823 98×79 mm. 5 m. Archbishop Morapeli (*horiz*) . . 4·50 4·50

(Des L. Watkins. Litho B.D.T.)

1988 (13 Oct). *Small Mammals of Lesotho. T* **183** *and similar vert designs. Multicoloured. P* 14.

824 16 s. Type **183** . . 30 15
825 40 s. Ratel and Black-throated Honeyguide (bird) . . 70 40
826 75 s. Small-spotted Genet . . 90 75
827 3 m. Yellow Mongoose . . 2·75 3·75
824/7 . . *Set of* 4 4·25 4·50
MS828 110×78 mm. 4 m. Meerkat . . 3·25 4·00

184 "Birth of Venus" (detail) (Botticelli)

(Litho Questa)

1988 (17 Oct). *Famous Paintings. T* **184** *and similar vert designs. Multicoloured. P* 13½ × 14.

829 15 s. Type **184** . . 20 15
830 25 s. "View of Toledo" (El Greco) . . 25 20
831 40 s. "Maids of Honour" (detail) (Velasquez) 30 25
832 50 s. "The Fifer" (Manet) . . 40 30
833 55 s. "Starry Night" (detail) (Van Gogh) . . 40 30
834 75 s. "Prima Ballerina" (Degas) . . 55 60
835 2 m. "Bridge over Water Lilies" (Monet) . . 1·50 1·75
836 3 m. "Guernica" (detail) (Picasso) . . 1·75 2·25
829/36 . . *Set of* 8 4·75 5·25
MS837 Two sheets, each 110×95 mm. (a) 4 m. "The Presentation of the Virgin in the Temple" (Titian). (b) 4 m. "The Miracle of the Newborn Infant" (Titian) . . *Set of* 2 *sheets* 4·00 4·50

185 Wrestling

(Des J. Martin. Litho B.D.T.)

1988 (11 Nov). *Olympic Games, Seoul (2nd issue). T* **185** *and similar multicoloured designs. P* 14.

838 12 s. Type **185** . . 10 10
839 16 s. Show jumping (*vert*) . . 10 10
840 55 s. Shooting . . 20 30
841 3 m. 50, As 16 s. (*vert*) . . 1·40 2·00
838/41 . . *Set of* 4 1·50 2·25
MS842 108×77 mm. 4 m. Olympic flame (*vert*) . . 2·75 3·50

186 Yannick Noah and Eiffel Tower, Paris

186a "The Averoldi Polyptych" (detail) (Titian)

(Des J. McDaniels. Litho Questa)

1988 (18 Nov). *75th Anniv of International Tennis Federation. T* **186** *and similar multicoloured designs. P* 14.

843 12 s. Type **186** . . 20 15
844 20 s. Rod Laver and Sydney Harbour Bridge and Opera House . . 25 20
845 30 s. Ivan Lendl and Prague . . 30 25
846 65 s. Jimmy Connors and Tokyo (*vert*) . . 45 40
847 1 m. Arthur Ashe and Barcelona (*vert*) . . 70 60
848 1 m. 55, Althea Gibson and New York (*vert*) 90 90
849 2 m. Chris Evert and Vienna (*vert*) . . 1·25 1·25
850 2 m. 40, Boris Becker and Houses of Parliament, London (*vert*) . . 1·60 1·75
851 3 m. Martina Navratilova and Golden Gate Bridge, San Francisco . . 1·75 2·00
843/51 . . *Set of* 9 6·50 6·75
MS852 98×72 mm. 4 m. Steffi Graf and Berlin 3·00 3·75

No. 844 is inscribed "SIDNEY" in error.

(Litho Questa)

1988 (1 Dec). *Christmas. 500th Birth Anniv of Titian (artist). T* **186a** *and similar multicoloured designs. P* 13½×14.

853 12 s. Type **186a** . . 20 10
854 20 s. "Christ and the Adulteress" (detail) . . 20 10
855 35 s. "Christ and the Adulteress" (different detail) . . 30 20
856 45 s. "Angel of the Annunciation" . . 40 30
857 65 s. "Saint Dominic" . . 55 50
858 1 m. "The Vendramin Family" (detail) . . 75 80
859 2 m. "Mary Magdalen" . . 1·25 1·75
860 3 m. "The Tribute Money" . . 1·75 2·50
853/60 . . *Set of* 8 4·75 5·50
MS861 (a) 94 × 110 mm. 5 m. "Mater Dolorosa". P 13½ × 14. (b) 110 × 94 mm. 5 m. "Christ and the Woman taken in Adultery" (*horiz*). P 14 × 13½ . . *Set of* 2 *sheets* 6·00 8·00

187 Pilatus PC-6 Turbo Porter

(Des K. Gromell. Litho Questa)

1989 (30 Jan). *125th Anniv of International Red Cross. Aircraft. T* **187** *and similar multicoloured designs. P* 14.

862 12 s. Type **187** . . 15 10
863 20 s. Unloading medical supplies from Cessna 208 Caravan I . . 20 15
864 55 s. De Havilland D.H.C.6 Twin Otter 200/300 . . 40 40
865 3 m. Douglas DC-3 . . 2·00 3·00
862/5 . . *Set of* 4 2·50 3·25
MS866 109×80 mm. 4 m. Red Cross logo and Douglas DC-3 (*vert*) . . 3·25 3·25

187a "Dawn Mist at Mishima" (Hiroshige)

(Litho Questa)

1989 (19 June). *Japanese Art. Paintings by Hiroshige. T* **187a** *and similar horiz designs. Multicoloured. P* 14×13½.

867 12 s. Type **187a** . . 30 10
868 16 s. "Night Snow at Kambara" . . 35 10
869 20 s. "Wayside Inn at Mariko Station" . . 35 10
870 35 s. "Shower at Shono" . . 55 20
871 55 s. "Snowfall on the Kisokaido near Oi" . . 65 40
872 1 m. "Autumn Moon at Seba" . . 85 85
873 3 m. 20, "Evening Moon at Ryogoku Bridge" 2·25 3·00
874 5 m. "Cherry Blossoms at Arashiyama" . . 2·75 3·75
867/74 . . *Set of* 8 7·25 7·50
MS875 Two sheets, each 102×76 mm. (a) 4 m. "Listening to the Singing Insects at Dokanyama". (b) 4 m. "Moonlight, Nagakubo" *Set of* 2 *sheets* 6·00 7·00

Nos. 867/74 were each printed in sheetlets of 10 containing two horizontal strips of 5 stamps separated by printed labels commemorating Emperor Hirohito.

188 Mickey Mouse as General

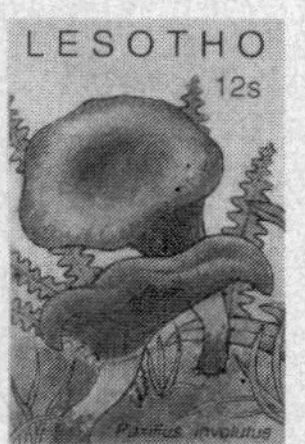

189 *Paxillus involutus*

(Des Walt Disney Company. Litho Questa)

1989 (10 July). *"Philexfrance 89" International Stamp Exhibition, Paris. T* **188** *and similar multicoloured designs showing Walt Disney cartoon characters in French military uniforms of the Revolutionary period. P* 13½×14.

876 1 s. Type **188** . . 10 10
877 2 s. Ludwig von Drake as infantryman . . 10 10
878 3 s. Goofy as grenadier . . 10 10
879 4 s. Horace Horsecollar as cavalryman . . 10 10
880 5 s. Pete as hussar . . 10 10
881 10 s. Donald Duck as marine . . 10 10
882 3 m. Gyro Gearloose as National Guard . . 2·75 3·00
883 5 m. Scrooge McDuck as admiral . . 3·50 3·75
876/83 . . *Set of* 8 6·25 6·50
MS884 Two sheets, each 127×102 mm. (a) 4 m. Mickey and Minnie Mouse as King Louis XVI and Marie Antoinette with Goofy as a National Guard (*horiz*). P 14×13½. (b) 4 m. Mickey Mouse as drummer. P 13½×14 . . *Set of* 2 *sheets* 7·00 8·00

No. 879 is inscribed "CALVARYMAN" in error.

(Litho Questa)

1989 (31 Aug)–**91.** *As Nos.* 793, 795/7 *and* 803/5, *but "1989" imprint date and with printer's imprint at bottom left. P* 14.

887 5 s. Spur-winged Goose (18.1.90) . . 30 40
889 12 s. Red-eyed Bulbul . . 40 15
890 16 s. Cape Weaver (11.11.89) . . 40 15
891 20 s. Paradise Sparrow ("Red-headed Finch") (2.12.89) . . 40 15
897 1 m. Cattle Egret (1991) . . 80 90
898 3 m. Giant Kingfisher (1991) . . 2·00 2·50
899 10 m. Helmet Guineafowl (1991) . . 5·50 7·50
887/99 . . *Set of* 7 9·00 10·50

This issue is also known perforated 12, but there is no evidence that stamps in this perforation were used for postal purposes in Lesotho.

(Des S. Wood. Litho Questa)

1989 (8 Sept). *Fungi. T* **189** *and similar vert designs. Multicoloured. P* 14.

900 12 s. Type **189** . . 20 10
901 16 s. *Ganoderma applanatum* . . 20 15
902 55 s. *Suillus granulatus* . . 45 35
903 5 m. *Stereum hirsutum* . . 3·25 4·50
900/3 . . *Set of* 4 3·75 4·50
MS904 96×69 mm. 4 m. *Scleroderma cepa* ("*flavidum*") . . 3·75 4·50

190 Sesotho Huts

191 Marsh Sandpiper

(Des S. Wood. Litho Questa)

1989 (18 Sept). *Maloti Mountains. T* **190** *and similar vert designs. Multicoloured. P* 14.

905 1 m. Type **190** . . 70 90
a. Horiz strip of 4. Nos. 905/8 . . 2·50
906 1 m. American Aloe and mountains . . 70 90
907 1 m. River valley with waterfall . . 70 90
908 1 m. Sesotho tribesman on ledge . . 70 90
905/8 . . *Set of* 4 2·50 3·25
MS909 86×117 mm. 4 m. Spiral Aloe . . 3·00 4·00

Nos. 905/8 were printed together, *se-tenant*, in horizontal strips of 4 throughout the sheet forming a composite design.

(Des Tracy Pedersen. Litho Questa)

1989 (18 Sept). *Migrant Birds. T* **191** *and similar multicoloured designs. P* 14.

910 12 s. Type **191** . . 55 20
911 65 s. Little Stint . . 1·00 70
912 1 m. Ringed Plover . . 1·40 1·25
913 4 m. Curlew Sandpiper . . 3·25 5·00
910/13 . . *Set of* 4 5·50 6·50
MS914 97×69 mm. 5 m. Ruff (*vert*) . . 6·50 7·50

192 Launch of "Apollo 11"

193 English Penny Post Paid Mark, 1680

(Des G. Welker. Litho Questa)

1989 (6 Nov). *20th Anniv of First Manned Landing on Moon. T* **192** *and similar multicoloured designs. P* 14.

915 12 s. Type **192** . . 25 10
916 16 s. Lunar module *Eagle* landing on Moon (*horiz*) . . 25 15
917 40 s. Neil Armstrong leaving *Eagle* . . 45 25
918 55 s. Edwin Aldrin on Moon (*horiz*) . . 50 30
919 1 m. Aldrin performing scientific experiment (*horiz*) . . 85 85
920 2 m. *Eagle* leaving Moon (*horiz*) . . 1·50 1·75
921 3 m. Command module *Columbia* in Moon orbit (*horiz*) . . 2·00 2·25
922 4 m. Command module on parachutes . . 2·50 2·75
915/22 . . *Set of* 8 7·50 7·50
MS923 81×111 mm. 5 m. Astronaut on Moon 4·00 5·00

(Des U. Purins. Litho B.D.T.)

1989 (17 Nov). *"World Stamp Expo '89" International Stamp Exhibition, Washington* (1st issue). *Stamps and Postmarks. T* **193** *and similar horiz designs. P* 14.

924 75 s. brown-lake, black and stone 55 65
a. Sheetlet. Nos. 924/32 .. .. 4·50
925 75 s. black, grey and rosine 55 65
926 75 s. dull violet, black and cinnamon .. 55 65
927 75 s. red-brown, black and cinnamon .. 55 65
928 75 s. black and olive-yellow 55 65
929 75 s. multicoloured 55 65
930 75 s. black and bright brown-lilac 55 65
931 75 s. black, bright carmine and pale brown 55 65
932 75 s. brt carmine, black & greenish yellow 55 65
924/32 .. .. *Set of* 9 4·50 5·50

Designs:— No. 925, German postal seal and feather, 1807; 926, British Post Offices in Crete 1898 20 pa. stamp; 927, Bermuda 1848 Perot 1d. provisional; 928, U.S.A. Pony Express cancellation, 1860; 929, Finland 1856 5 k. stamp; 930, Fiji 1870 *Fiji Times* 1d. stamp, 1870; 931, Sweden newspaper wrapper handstamp, 1823; 932, Bhor 1879 ½ a. stamp.

Nos. 924/32 were printed together, *se-tenant*, in sheetlets of 9.

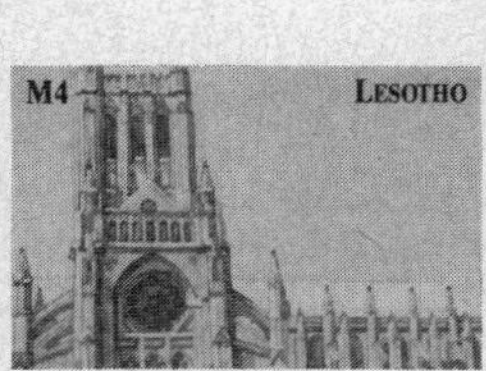

193a Cathedral Church of St. Peter and St. Paul, Washington

193b "The Immaculate Conception" (Velazquez)

(Des Design Element. Litho Questa)

1989 (17 Nov). *"World Stamp Expo '89" International Stamp Exhibition, Washington* (2nd issue). *Sheet* 78×61 *mm. P* 14.

MS933 **193a** 4 m. multicoloured .. .. 2·50 3·00

(Litho Questa)

1989 (18 Dec). *Christmas. Paintings by Velazquez. T* **193b** *and similar vert designs. Multicoloured. P* 14.

934 12 s. Type **193b** 10 10
935 20 s. "St. Anthony Abbot and St. Paul the Hermit" 15 10
936 35 s. "St. Thomas the Apostle" 25 25
937 55 s. "Christ in the House of Martha and Mary" 35 35
938 1 m. "St. John writing The Apocalypse on Patmos" 60 75
939 3 m. "The Virgin presenting the Chasuble to St. Ildephonsus" .. .. .. 1·60 2·25
940 4 m. "The Adoration of the Magi" .. 2·00 2·75
934/40 .. .. *Set of* 7 4·50 6·00
MS941 71×96 mm. 5 m. "The Coronation of the Virgin" .. .. 5·50 6·50

194 Scene from 1966 World Cup Final, England

(Des G. Vasarhelyi. Litho Questa)

1989 (27 Dec). *World Cup Football Championship, Italy. T* **194** *and similar horiz designs showing scenes from past finals. Multicoloured. P* 14.

942 12 s. Type **194** 20 10
943 16 s. 1970 final, Mexico 20 15
944 55 s. 1974 final, West Germany 60 40
945 5 m. 1982 final, Spain .. .. .. 3·25 4·50
942/5 .. .. *Set of* 4 3·75 4·75
MS946 106×85 mm. 4 m. Player's legs and symbolic football .. .. .. 4·00 4·50

16 s (**195**) 16 s (**196**) 16 s Long bars (R. 6/3) 16 s (**196a**)

1990 (22 Feb)–**91**. *Nos.* 795, 798/9 *and* 889 *surch with T* **195/6a** *by Lesotho Ads.*

947 16 s. on 12 s. Red-eyed Bulbul (No. 795) (T **195**) .. .. 1·75 80
948 16 s. on 12 s. Red-eyed Bulbul (No. 889) (T **196**) 40 15
a. Surch inverted .. .. .. 40·00
b. Surch double .. .. .. 60·00
c. Long bars .. .. ..
d. Surch with Type **195** .. ..
948*e* 16 s. on 30 s. Mountain Chat (No. 798) (T **196a**) (18.1.91) 40 15
ea. Surch inverted .. ..
eb. Lower bar omitted .. ..
948*f* 16 s. on 40 s. Stonechat (No. 799) (T **196a**) (18.1.91) 40 15
fa. Lower bar omitted .. ..
947/8*f* .. .. *Set of* 4 2·75 1·10

The lower cancelling bar is frequently completely omitted from Type **196a** on R. 4/4, although on occasions traces of it do remain.

197 *Byblia anvatara*

198 *Satyrium princeps*

(Des L. Nelson. Litho Questa)

1990 (26 Feb). *Butterflies. T* **197** *and similar vert designs. Multicoloured. P* 14.

949 12 s. Type **197** 40 15
950 16 s. *Cynthia cardui* 55 15
951 55 s. *Precis oenone* 80 40
952 65 s. *Pseudacraea boisduvali* 90 65
953 1 m. *Precis orithya* .. .. .. 1·25 1·10
954 2 m. *Precis sophia* .. .. .. 2·25 2·25
955 3 m. *Danaus chrysippus* .. .. 3·00 3·50
956 4 m. *Druryia antimachus* .. .. 4·25 5·50
949/56 .. .. *Set of* 8 12·00 12·00
MS957 105×70 mm. 5 m. *Papilio demodocus* .. 6·50 8·00

(Des B. Tear. Litho Questa)

1990 (12 Mar). *"EXPO 90" International Garden and Greenery Exhibition, Osaka. Local Orchids. T* **198** *and similar horiz designs. Multicoloured. P* 14.

958 12 s. Type **198** 35 15
959 16 s. *Huttonaea pulchra* 40 15
960 55 s. *Herschelia graminifolia* 80 30
961 1 m. *Ansellia gigantea* .. .. .. 1·25 75
962 1 m. 55, *Polystachya pubescens* .. .. 1·50 1·50
963 2 m. 40, *Penthea filicornis* .. .. 1·75 2·00
964 3 m. *Disperis capensis* .. .. .. 2·25 3·00
965 4 m. *Disa uniflora* .. .. .. 3·00 3·75
958/65 .. .. *Set of* 8 10·00 10·50
MS966 95×68 mm. 5 m. *Stenoglottis longifolia* 6·00 7·50

198a Lady Elizabeth Bowes-Lyon and Brother in Fancy Dress

199 King Moshoeshoe II and Prince Mohato wearing Seana-Marena Blankets

(Des Young Phillips Studio. Litho Questa)

1990 (5 July). *90th Birthday of Queen Elizabeth the Queen Mother. T* **198a** *and similar vert portraits,* 1910–1919. *P* 14.

967 1 m. 50, brownish black and bright magenta 80 90
a. Strip of 3. Nos. 967/9 .. .. .. 2·25
968 1 m. 50, brownish black and bright magenta 80 90
969 1 m. 50, brownish black and bright magenta 80 90
967/9 .. .. *Set of* 3 2·25 2·40
MS970 90×75 mm. 5 m. dull orange-brown, brownish black and bright magenta .. .. 2·75 3·50

Designs:—No. 967, Type **198a**; No. 968, Lady Elizabeth Bowes-Lyon in evening dress; No. 969, Lady Elizabeth Bowes-Lyon wearing hat; No. **MS**970, Lady Elizabeth Bowes-Lyon as a child.

Nos. 967/9 were printed together, horizontally and vertically *se-tenant*, in sheetlets of 9 (3×3).

(Litho B.D.T.)

1990 (17 Aug). *Traditional Blankets. T* **199** *and similar multicoloured designs. P* 14.

971 12 s. Type **199** 10 10
972 16 s. Prince Mohato wearing Seana-Marena blanket 10 10
973 1 m. Pope John Paul II wearing Seana-Marena blanket .. .. .. 1·00 80
974 3 m. Basotho horsemen wearing Matlama blankets .. .. 1·75 2·50
971/4 .. .. *Set of* 4 2·75 3·00
MS975 85×104 mm. 5 m. Pope John Paul II wearing hat and Seana-Marena blanket (*horiz*) 3·50 4·00

200 Filling Truck at No. 1 Quarry

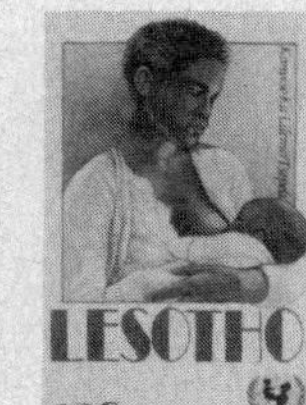

201 Mother breastfeeding Baby

(Litho B.D.T.)

1990 (24 Aug). *Lesotho Highlands Water Project. T* **200** *and similar vert designs. Multicoloured. P* 14.

976 16 s. Type **200** 25 10
977 20 s. Tanker lorry on Pitseng–Malibamatso road 25 10
978 55 s. Piers for Malibamatso Bridge .. 50 30
979 2 m. Excavating Mphosong section of Pitseng–Malibamatso road .. .. 1·75 2·50
976/9 .. .. *Set of* 4 2·50 2·75
MS980 104×85 mm. 5 m. Sinking blasting boreholes on Pitseng–Malibamatso road .. 3·75 4·75

(Litho Questa)

1990 (26 Oct). *U.N.I.C.E.F. Child Survival Campaign. T* **201** *and similar vert designs. Multicoloured. P* 14.

981 12 s. Type **201** 30 10
982 55 s. Baby receiving oral rehydration therapy 60 45
983 1 m. Weight monitoring .. .. .. 90 1·60
981/3 .. .. *Set of* 3 1·60 1·90

King Letsie III, November 1990–25 January 1995 (abdicated)

202 Men's Triple Jump

203 "Virgin and Child" (detail, Rubens)

(Des B. Grout. Litho Questa)

1990 (5 Nov). *Olympic Games, Barcelona* (1992). *T* **202** *and similar multicoloured designs. P* 14.

984 16 s. Type **202** 20 10
985 55 s. Men's 200 metres race 35 25
986 1 m. Men's 5000 metres race 65 80
987 4 m. Show jumping .. .. .. 2·50 3·25
984/7 .. .. *Set of* 4 3·25 4·00
MS988 100×70 mm. 5 m. Olympic flame (*horiz*) 3·75 4·75

(Litho Questa)

1990 (5 Dec). *Christmas. Paintings by Rubens. T* **203** *and similar vert designs. Multicoloured. P* 13½×14.

989 12 s. Type **203** 15 10
990 16 s. "Adoration of the Magi" (detail) .. 15 10
991 55 s. "Head of One of the Three Kings" .. 35 25
992 80 s. "Adoration of the Magi" (different detail) 50 50
993 1 m. "Virgin and Child" (different detail) .. 60 60
994 2 m. "Adoration of the Magi" (different detail) .. .. 1·10 1·25
995 3 m. "Virgin and Child" (different detail) .. 1·75 2·00
996 4 m. "Adoration of the Magi" (different detail) .. .. 1·90 2·50
989/96 .. .. *Set of* 8 6·00 6·50
MS997 71×100 mm. 5 m. "Assumption of the Virgin" (detail) .. .. 3·75 4·75

204 Mickey Mouse at Nagasaki Peace Park

(Des Walt Disney Company. Litho Questa)

1991 (10 June). *"Phila Nippon '91" International Stamp Exhibition, Tokyo. T* **204** *and similar horiz designs showing Walt Disney cartoon characters in Japan. Multicoloured. P* 14×13½.

998 20 s. Type **204** 35 15
999 30 s. Mickey Mouse on Kamakura Beach 40 20
1000 40 s. Mickey and Donald Duck with Bunraku puppet 45 25
1001 50 s. Mickey and Donald eating soba .. 50 35
1002 75 s. Mickey and Minnie Mouse at tea house 75 55
1003 1 m. Mickey running after bullet train .. 90 80
1004 3 m. Mickey Mouse with deer at Todaiji Temple, Nara .. .. .. 2·25 3·00
1005 4 m. Mickey and Minnie outside Imperial Palace .. .. 2·50 3·25
998/1005 .. .. *Set of* 8 7·25 7·75
MS1006 Two sheets, each 127×112 mm. (a) 5 m. Mickey Mouse skiing; (b) 5 m. Mickey and Minnie having a picnic .. .. *Set of* 2 *sheets* 6·50 7·50

205 Stewart Granger (*King Solomon's Mines*)

206 *Satyrus aello*

(Des R. Jung. Litho Questa)

1991 (20 June). *Famous Films with African Themes. T* **205** *and similar vert designs. Multicoloured. P* 14.

No.	Design	Unused	Used
1007	12 s. Type **205**	35	20
1008	16 s. Johnny Weissmuller (*Tarzan the Ape Man*)	35	20
1009	30 s. Clark Gable with Grace Kelly (*Mogambo*)	50	35
1010	55 s. Sigourney Weaver and male gorilla (*Gorillas in the Mist*)	75	55
1011	70 s. Humphrey Bogart and Katharine Hepburn (*The African Queen*)	90	80
1012	1 m. John Wayne and capture of rhinoceros (*Hatari!*)	1·25	1·00
1013	2 m. Meryl Streep and De Havilland D.H.60G Gipsy Moth light aircraft (*Out of Africa*)	2·00	2·25
1014	4 m. Arsenio Hall and Eddie Murphy (*Coming to America*)	2·75	3·50
1007/14	*Set of* 8	8·00	8·00
MS1015	108×77 mm. 5 m. Elsa the lioness (*Born Free*)	3·75	4·50

(Des S. Heimann. Litho Cartor)

1991 (1 Aug)–**92**. *Butterflies. T* **206** *and similar horiz designs. Multicoloured. P* 14×13½. *A. Without imprint date. B. With imprint date* ("1992") *at foot* (4.92).

		A		B	
1016	2 s. Type **206**	†		10	10
	a. Perf 13½	30	30	†	
1017	3 s. *Erebia medusa*	†		10	10
	a. Perf 13½	30	30	†	
1018	5 s. *Melanargia galathea*	30	30	30	30
1019	10 s. *Erebia aethiops*	30	30	10	10
1020	20 s. *Coenonympha pamphilus*	35	30	35	30
	a. Perf 13½	35	30	35	30
1021	25 s. *Pyrameis atalanta*	35	30	10	10
1022	30 s. *Charaxes jasius*	40	30	10	10
	a. Perf 13½	40	30	10	10
1023	40 s. *Colias palaeno*	40	30	10	10
1024	50 s. *Colias cliopatra*	45	40	15	20
1025	60 s. *Colias philodice*	60	60	15	20
1026	70 s. *Rhumni gonepterix*	75	75	25	25
1027	1 m. *Colias caesonia*	†		25	30
	a. Perf 13½	75	75	†	
1028	2 m. *Pyrameis cardui*	1·50	1·50	50	55
	a. Perf 13½	1·50	1·50	†	
1029	3 m. *Danaus chrysippus*	†		80	85
	a. Perf 13½	1·60	1·75	†	
1030	10 m. *Apatura iris*	†		2·50	2·75
	a. Perf 13½	4·50	5·50	†	
1016/30	*Set of* 15	12·00	13·00	5·25	6·00

207 Victim of Drug Abuse

208 Wattled Cranes

(Litho Cartor)

1991 (23 Sept). *"Say No To Drugs" Campaign. P* 13½×14.

No.	Design	Unused	Used
1031	**207** 16 s. multicoloured	50	50

(Litho Cartor)

1991 (10 Oct). *Southern Africa Development Co-ordination Conference Tourism Promotion. T* **208** *and similar horiz designs. Multicoloured. P* 14×13½.

No.	Design	Unused	Used
1032	12 s. Type **208**	50	60
1033	16 s. Butterfly on flowers	50	60
1034	25 s. Zebra and tourist bus at Mukurub (former rock formation), Namibia	60	20
1032/4	*Set of* 3	1·40	1·25
MS1035	75×117 mm. 3 m. Basotho women in ceremonial dress. P 13×12	2·50	3·25

209 De Gaulle in 1939

210 Prince and Princess of Wales

(Des D. Miller. Litho B.D.T.)

1991 (6 Dec). *Birth Centenary of Charles de Gaulle (French statesman). T* **209** *and similar vert designs. P* 14.

No.	Design	Unused	Used
1036	20 s. black and lake-brown	30	15
1037	40 s. black and purple	50	40
1038	50 s. black and yellow-olive	50	25
1039	60 s. black and greenish blue	55	45
1040	4 m. black and dull vermilion	2·00	3·25
1036/40	*Set of* 5	3·50	4·00

Designs:—40 s. General De Gaulle as Free French leader; 50 s. De Gaulle as provisional President of France 1944–46; 60 s. Charles de Gaulle in 1958; 4 m. Pres. De Gaulle, 1969.

(Des D. Miller. Litho B.D.T.)

1991 (9 Dec). *10th Wedding Anniv of Prince and Princess of Wales. T* **210** *and similar horiz designs. Multicoloured. P* 14.

No.	Design	Unused	Used
1041	50 s. Type **210**	45	25
1042	70 s. Prince Charles at polo and Princess Diana holding Prince Henry	55	45
1043	1 m. Prince Charles with Prince Henry and Princess Diana in evening dress	75	65
1044	3 m. Prince William and Prince Henry in school uniform	1·75	2·75
1041/4	*Set of* 4	3·25	3·75
MS1045	68×91 mm. 4 m. Portraits of Prince with Princess and sons	3·75	4·25

211 "St. Anne with Mary and the Child Jesus" (Dürer)

212 Mickey Mouse and Pluto pinning the Tail on the Donkey

(Litho Walsall)

1991 (13 Dec). *Christmas. Drawings by Albrecht Dürer. T* **211** *and similar vert designs. P* 12.

No.	Design	Unused	Used
1046	20 s. black and bright magenta	20	10
1047	30 s. black and new blue	30	20
1048	50 s. black and yellowish green	40	25
1049	60 s. black and vermilion	45	30
1050	70 s. black and lemon	50	35
1051	1 m. black and orange	65	65
1052	2 m. black and bright purple	1·25	1·75
1053	4 m. black and ultramarine	2·00	3·00
1046/53	*Set of* 8	5·25	6·00
MS1054	Two sheets, each 102×127 mm. (a) 5 m. black and carmine-rose. (b) 5 m. black and cobalt. P 14 *Set of* 2 *sheets*	4·25	5·00

Designs:—30 s. "Mary on Grass Bench"; 50 s. "Mary with Crown of Stars"; 60 s. "Mary with Child beside Tree"; 70 s. "Mary with Child beside Wall"; 1 m. "Mary in Halo on Crescent Moon"; 2 m. "Mary breastfeeding Child"; 4 m. "Mary with Infant in Swaddling Clothes"; 5 m. (No. **MS**1054a) "The Birth of Christ"; 5 m. (No. **MS**1054b) "The Holy Family with Dragonfly".

(Des Walt Disney Co. Litho Questa)

1991 (16 Dec). *Children's Games. T* **212** *and similar vert designs showing Walt Disney cartoon characters. Multicoloured. P* 13½×14.

No.	Design	Unused	Used
1055	20 s. Type **212**	30	15
1056	30 s. Mickey playing mancala	35	20
1057	40 s. Mickey rolling hoop	40	20
1058	50 s. Minnie Mouse hula-hooping	45	25
1059	70 s. Mickey and Pluto throwing a frisbee	65	50
1060	1 m. Donald Duck with a diabolo	85	85
1061	2 m. Donald's nephews playing marbles	1·75	2·25
1062	3 m. Donald with Rubik's cube	2·25	2·75
1055/62	*Set of* 8	6·25	6·50
MS1063	Two sheets, each 127×112 mm. (a) 5 m. Donald's and Mickey's nephews playing tug-of-war; (b) 5 m. Mickey and Donald mock fighting *Set of* 2 *sheets*	7·00	8·00

213 Lanner Falcon

214 Queen Elizabeth II and Cooking at a Mountain Homestead

(Des Tracy Pedersen. Litho Questa)

1992 (10 Feb). *Birds. T* **213** *and similar vert designs. Multicoloured. P* 14½×14.

No.	Design	Unused	Used
1064	30 s. Type **213**	40	40
	a. Sheetlet. Nos. 1064/83	7·00	
1065	30 s. Bateleur	40	40
1066	30 s. Paradise Sparrow ("Red-headed Finch")	40	40
1067	30 s. Lesser Striped Swallow	40	40
1068	30 s. Alpine Swift	40	40
1069	30 s. Didric Cuckoo	40	40
1070	30 s. Yellow-tufted Malachite Sunbird	40	40
1071	30 s. Burchell's Gonolek ("Crimson-breasted Shrike")	40	40
1072	30 s. Pin-tailed Whydah	40	40
1073	30 s. Lilac-breasted Roller	40	40
1074	30 s. Little Black Bustard ("Korhaan")	40	40
1075	30 s. Black-collared Barbet	40	40
1076	30 s. Secretary Bird	40	40
1077	30 s. Red-billed Quelea	40	40
1078	30 s. Red Bishop	40	40
1079	30 s. Ring-necked Dove	40	40
1080	30 s. Yellow Canary	40	40
1081	30 s. Cape Longclaw	40	40
1082	30 s. Cordon-bleu ("Blue Waxbill")	40	40
1083	30 s. Golden Bishop	40	40
1064/83	*Set of* 20	7·00	7·00

Nos. 1064/83 were printed together, *se-tenant*, as a sheetlet of 20 with the backgrounds forming a composite design.

(Des D. Miller. Litho Questa)

1992 (2 Mar). *40th Anniv of Queen Elizabeth II's Accession. T* **214** *and similar horiz designs. Multicoloured. P* 14.

No.	Design	Unused	Used
1084	20 s. Type **214**	20	15
1085	30 s. View of the Lowlands	25	20
1086	1 m. Agaves and escarpment	65	65
1087	4 m. Thaba-Bosiu	2·00	2·75
1084/7	*Set of* 4	2·75	3·25
MS1088	75×97 mm. 5 m. Mountains at sunset	2·75	3·50

215 Minnie Mouse as Spanish Lady, 1540–1660

(Des Walt Disney Co. Litho Questa)

1992 (13 Apr). *International Stamp Exhibitions. T* **215** *and similar vert designs showing Walt Disney cartoon characters. Multicoloured. P* 13½×14.

(*a*) *"Granada 92", Spain. Traditional Spanish Costumes.*

No.	Design	Unused	Used
1089	20 s. Type **215**	30	15
1090	50 s. Mickey Mouse as Don Juan at Lepanto, 1571	45	30
1091	70 s. Donald in Galician costume, 1880	60	50
1092	2 m. Daisy Duck in Aragonese costume, 1880	1·50	2·00
1089/92	*Set of* 4	2·50	2·75
MS1093	127×112 mm. 5 m. Goofy the Bullfighter	3·50	4·00

(*b*) *"World Columbian Stamp Expo '92". Red Indian Life.*

No.	Design	Unused	Used
1094	30 s. Donald Duck making arrowheads	30	30
1095	40 s. Goofy playing lacrosse	40	40
1096	1 m. Mickey Mouse and Donald Duck planting corn	70	80
1097	3 m. Minnie Mouse doing bead work	1·60	2·25
1094/7	*Set of* 4	2·75	3·25
MS1098	127×112 mm. 5 m. Mickey paddling canoe	3·50	4·00

216 Stegosaurus

217 Men's Discus

(Des D. Burkhart. Litho Questa)

1992 (9 June). *Prehistoric Animals. T* **216** *and similar horiz designs. Multicoloured. P* 14.

No.	Design	Unused	Used
1099	20 s. Type **216**	30	30
1100	30 s. Ceratosaurus	35	35
1101	40 s. Procompsognathus	45	45
1102	50 s. Lesothosaurus	55	55
1103	70 s. Plateosaurus	70	70
1104	1 m. Gasosaurus	1·00	1·00
1105	2 m. Massospondylus	1·50	1·50
1106	3 m. Archaeopteryx	2·00	2·00
1099/106	*Set of* 8	6·25	6·25
MS1107	Two sheets, each 105×77 mm. (a) 5 m. As 50 s. (b) 5 m. As 3 m. *Set of* 2 *sheets*	7·00	7·00

(Litho Questa)

1992 (5 Aug). *Olympic Games, Albertville and Barcelona. T* **217** *and similar multicoloured designs. P* 14.

1108 20 s. Type **217** 20 15
1109 30 s. Men's long jump 25 15
1110 40 s. Women's 4 × 100 metres relay .. 30 25
1111 70 s. Women's 100 metres 50 50
1112 1 m. Men's parallel bars 70 70
1113 2 m. Men's double luge (*horiz*) .. .. 1·40 1·40
1114 3 m. Women's 30k cross-country skiing (*horiz*) .. .. 1·75 2·00
1115 4 m. Men's biathlon .. .. 2·00 2·25
1108/15 .. .. *Set of* 8 6·50 6·75
MS1116 Two sheets, each 100×70 mm. (a) 5 m. Women's figure skating. (b) 5 m. Ice hockey (*horiz*) .. .. *Set of* 2 *sheets* 6·75 7·50

218 "Virgin and Child" (Sassetta)

219 World Trade Centre, New York

(Litho Questa)

1992 (2 Nov). *Christmas. Religious Paintings. T* **218** *and similar vert designs. Multicoloured. P* $13^{1}/_{2}$×14.

1117 20 s. Type **218** 20 15
1118 30 s. "Coronation of the Virgin" (Master of Bonastre) 25 20
1119 40 s. "Virgin and Child" (Master of SS. Cosmas and Damian) 35 25
1120 70 s. "The Virgin of Great Panagia" (detail) (12th-century Russian school) .. 60 45
1121 1 m. "Madonna and Child" (Vincenzo Foppa) 85 80
1122 2 m. "Madonna and Child" (School of Lippo Memmi) .. .. 1·60 1·75
1123 3 m. "Virgin and Child" (Barnaba da Modena) .. .. 2·00 2·50
1124 4 m. "Virgin and Child with Saints" (triptych) (Simone dei Crocifissi) .. 2·25 2·75
1117/24 .. .. *Set of* 8 7·25 8·00
MS1125 Two sheets, each 76×102 mm. (a) 5 m. "Virgin and Child with Saints" (different detail) (Simone dei Crocifissi). (b) 5 m. "Virgin and Child enthroned and surrounded by Angels" (Cimabue) .. .. .. *Set of* 2 *sheets* 7·00 8·00

(Des Kerri Schiff. Litho Questa)

1992 (17 Nov). *Postage Stamp Mega Event, New York. Sheet* 100×70 *mm. P* 14.

MS1126 **219** 5 m. multicoloured .. .. .. 4·00 4·50

220 Baby Harp Seal (Earth Summit '92, Rio)

(Des L. Birmingham. Litho Questa)

1993 (8 Feb). *Anniversaries and Events. T* **220** *and similar horiz designs. Multicoloured. P* 14.

1127 20 s. Type **220** 30 20
1128 30 s. Giant Panda (Earth Summit '92, Rio) 45 20
1129 40 s. Airship LZ-127 *Graf Zeppelin* over globe (75th death anniv of Count Ferdinand von Zeppelin) 45 20
1130 70 s. Woman grinding maize (International Conference on Nutrition, Rome) .. 45 40
1131 4 m. Lt. Robinson's Royal Aircraft Factory B.E.2C shooting down Schutte Lanz SL-11 airship (75th death anniv of Count Ferdinand von Zeppelin) .. .. 2·00 2·40
1132 5 m. Valentina Tereshkova and "Vostok 6" (30th anniv of first woman in space) 2·25 2·50
1127/32 .. .. *Set of* 6 5·50 5·50
MS1133 Two sheets, each 100×70 mm. (a) 5 m. Dr. Ronald McNair (*Challenger* astronaut) (International Space Year). (b) 5 m. South African Crowned Crane (Earth Summit '92, Rio) *Set of* 2 *sheets* 4·75 5·00

PRICES OF SETS

Set prices are given for many issues, generally those containing three stamps or more. Definitive sets include one of each value or major colour change, but do not cover different perforations, die types or minor shades. Where a choice is possible the set prices are based on the cheapest versions of the stamps included in the listings.

221 "Orpheus and Eurydice" (detail) (Poussin)

222 Aloe

(Litho Walsall)

1993 (19 Mar). *Bicentenary of the Louvre, Paris. T* **221** *and similar vert designs showing paintings. Multicoloured. P* 12.

1134 70 s. Type **221** 55 55
a. Sheetlet. Nos. 1134/41 .. .. 4·00
1135 70 s. "Rape of the Sabine Women" (left detail) (Poussin) 55 55
1136 70 s. "Rape of the Sabine Women" (right detail) (Poussin) 55 55
1137 70 s. "The Death of Sapphira" (left detail) (Poussin) 55 55
1138 70 s. "The Death of Sapphira" (right detail) (Poussin) 55 55
1139 70 s. "Echo and Narcissus" (left detail) (Poussin) 55 55
1140 70 s. "Echo and Narcissus" (right detail) (Poussin) 55 55
1141 70 s. "Self-portrait" (Poussin) 55 55
1134/41 .. .. *Set of* 8 4·00 4·00
MS1142 70×100 mm. 5 m. "The Money Lender and his Wife" (57×89 *mm*) (Metsys). P $14^{1}/_{2}$ .. 3·00 3·50

Nos. 1134/41 were printed together, *se-tenant*, in sheetlets of 8 stamps and one centre label.

(Des Mary Walters. Litho B.D.T.)

1993 (1 June). *Flowers. T* **222** *and similar vert designs. Multicoloured. P* 14.

1143 20 s. Type **222** 20 10
1144 30 s. Calla Lily 25 15
1145 40 s. Bird of Paradise plant 30 15
1146 70 s. Amaryllis 45 30
1147 1 m. Agapanthus 55 50
1148 2 m. Crinum .. .. 1·00 90
1149 4 m. Watsonia .. .. 1·40 1·75
1150 5 m. Gazania .. .. 1·50 2·00
1143/50 .. .. *Set of* 8 5·00 5·25
MS1151 Two sheets, each 98×67 mm. (a) 7 m. Plumbago. (b) 7 m. Desert Rose .. *Set of* 2 *sheets* 5·00 5·50

223 *Precis westermanni*

(Des L. Nelson. Litho B.D.T.)

1993 (30 June). *Butterflies. T* **223** *and similar horiz designs. Multicoloured. P* 14.

1152 20 s. Type **223** 30 15
1153 40 s. *Precis sophia* 40 20
1154 70 s. *Precis terea* 55 40
1155 1 m. *Byblia acheloia* 65 60
1156 2 m. *Papilio antimachus* .. .. .. 1·00 1·00
1157 5 m. *Pseudacraea boisduvali* .. .. 1·50 2·00
1152/7 .. .. *Set of* 6 4·00 4·00
MS1158 Two sheets, each 96×62 mm. (a) 7 m. *Precis oenone*. (b) 7 m. *Precis octavia* *Set of* 2 *sheets* 5·00 5·50

No. 1157 is inscribed "Pesudacraea boisduvali" in error.

224 Queen Elizabeth II at Coronation (photograph by Cecil Beaton)

(Des Kerri Schiff. Litho Questa)

1993 (30 July). *40th Anniv of Coronation. T* **224** *and similar designs. P* $13^{1}/_{2}$×14.

1159 20 s. multicoloured 30 30
a. Sheetlet. Nos. 1159/62×2 .. .. 8·00
1160 40 s. multicoloured 45 45
1161 1 m. black and bottle-green 70 70
1162 5 m. multicoloured .. .. 3·00 3·00
1159/62 .. .. *Set of* 4 4·00 4·00
MS1163 70×100 mm. 7 m. multicoloured ($42^{1}/_{2}$×$28^{1}/_{2}$ *mm*). P 14 .. .. .. 3·50 4·00

Designs: *Vert*—40 s. St. Edward's Crown and Sceptre; 1 m. Queen Elizabeth the Queen Mother; 5 m. Queen Elizabeth II and family. *Horiz*—7 m. "Conversation Piece at Royal Lodge, Windsor" (detail) (Sir James Gunn).

Nos. 1159/62 were printed in sheetlets of 8, containing two *se-tenant* blocks of 4.

225 "Vulcan" Type Locomotive, East African Railways, 1929

226 Court-house

(Des G. Vasarhelyi. Litho B.D.T.)

1993 (31 Aug). *African Railways. T* **225** *and similar horiz designs. Multicoloured. P* 14.

1164 20 s. Type **225** 20 15
1165 30 s. Class "15A" steam locomotive, Zimbabwe Railways, 1952 .. .. 30 20
1166 40 s. Class "25" steam locomotive, South African Railways, 1953 .. .. 35 20
1167 70 s. Class "A 58" Garratt steam locomotive, East African Railways .. 45 35
1168 1 m. Class "9E" electric locomotives, South African Railways 60 55
1169 2 m. Class "87" diesel locomotive, East African Railways, 1971 .. .. 90 90
1170 3 m. Class "92" diesel locomotive, East African Railways, 1971 .. .. 1·25 1·50
1171 5 m. Class "26" steam locomotive, South African Railways, 1982 .. .. 1·75 2·00
1164/71 .. .. *Set of* 8 5·25 5·25
MS1172 Two sheets, each 104×82 mm. (a) 7 m. Class "6E" electric locomotive, South African Railways, 1969. (b) 7 m. Class "231-132BT" steam locomotive, Algerian Railways, 1937 *Set of* 2 *sheets* 6·00 6·25

(Des V. Seatile Nkhomo. Litho Government Printer, Pretoria)

1993 (24 Sept). *Traditional Houses. T* **226** *and similar horiz designs. Multicoloured. P* 14×$14^{1}/_{2}$.

1173 20 s. Type **226** 20 10
1174 30 s. House with reed fence 25 15
1175 70 s. Unmarried girls' house 45 35
1176 4 m. Hut made from branches .. .. 2·25 2·50
1173/6 .. .. *Set of* 4 2·75 2·75
MS1177 81×69 mm. 4 m. Decorated houses .. 2·25 2·50

227 Black and White Shorthair

(Des V. Seatile Nkhomo. Litho Government Printer, Pretoria)

1993 (29 Oct). *Domestic Cats. T* **227** *and similar multicoloured designs. P* 14.

1178 20 s. Type **227** 30 15
1179 30 s. Shorthair Tabby lying down 35 20
1180 70 s. Head of Shorthair Tabby 65 35
1181 5 m. Black and White Shorthair with Shorthair Tabby .. .. 2·50 3·00
1178/81 .. .. *Set of* 4 3·50 3·25
MS1182 113×89 mm. 5 m. Shorthair Tabby with rat (*vert*) .. .. 3·00 3·25

228 Pluto in Chung Cheng Park, Keelung

229 Tseliso "Frisco" Khomari (Lesotho)

(Des Rosemary DeFiglio. Litho Questa)

1993 (15 Nov). *"Taipei '93" Asian International Stamp Exhibition, Taiwan. T* **228** *and similar multicoloured designs showing Walt Disney cartoon characters in Taiwan. P* 14×$13^{1}/_{2}$ (*horiz*) *or* $13^{1}/_{2}$×14 (*vert*).

1183 20 s. Type **228** 20 10
1184 30 s. Donald Duck at Chiao-Tienkung Temple Festival 25 15
1185 40 s. Goofy with lantern figures 30 20
1186 70 s. Minnie Mouse shopping at temple festival 50 35
1187 1 m. Daisy Duck at Queen's Head Rock, Yehliu (*vert*) 65 60

1188 1 m. 20, Mickey and Minnie at National Concert Hall (*vert*) 75 75
1189 2 m. Donald at Chiang Kai-shek Memorial Hall (*vert*) 95 95
1190 2 m. 50, Donald and Daisy at the Grand Hotel, Taipei .. .. .. 1·25 1·40
1183/90 .. .. *Set of* 8 4·25 4·00
MS1191 Two sheets, each 128×102 mm. (a) 5 m. Goofy over National Palace Museum, Taipei. (b) 6 m. Mickey and Minnie at Presidential Palace Museum, Taipei (*vert*) .. .. *Set of 2 sheets* 5·50 6·00

(Des Rosemary DeFiglio. Litho Cartor)

1994 (1 Feb). *World Cup Football Championship* '94, *U.S.A. T* **229** *and similar multicoloured designs. P* 13½×14.
1192 20 s. Type **229** 20 10
1193 30 s. Thato "American Spoon" Mohale (Lesotho) 25 15
1194 40 s. Jozic Davor (Yugoslavia) and Freddy Rincorn (Colombia) 30 20
1195 50 s. Lefika "Mzee" Lekhotla (Lesotho) .. 35 25
1196 70 s. Litsiso "House-on-fire" Khali (Lesotho) 50 35
1197 1 m. Roger Milla (Cameroun) 65 60
1198 1 m. 20, David Platt (England) 75 75
1199 2 m. Karl Heinz Rummenigge (Germany) and Soren Lerby (Denmark) .. 95 95
1192/9 .. .. *Set of* 8 3·50 3·00
MS1200 Two sheets, each 100×70 mm. (a) 6 m. Klaus Lindenberger (Czechoslovakia). (b) 6 m. Franco Baresi (Italy) and Ivan Hasek (Czechoslovakia) (*horiz*). P 13 .. *Set of 2 sheets* 6·00 6·25

230 King Letsie III signing Oath of Office

231 Aquatic River Frog

(Litho Government Printer, Pretoria)

1994 (2 Apr). *1st Anniv of Restoration of Democracy. T* **230** *and similar multicoloured designs. P* 14.
1201 20 s. Type **230** 15 10
1202 30 s. Parliament building (*horiz*) 20 15
1203 50 s. Swearing-in of Dr. Ntsu Mokhehle as Prime Minister (*horiz*) 30 25
1204 70 s. Maj-Gen P. Ramaema handing Instruments of Government to Dr. Ntsu Mokhehle (*horiz*) 50 35
1201/4 .. .. *Set of* 4 1·00 70

(Des V. Seatile Nkhomo (Nos. 1205/8), R. Rundo (No. **MS**1209). Litho Questa)

1994 (16 Aug). *"Philakorea '94" International Stamp Exhibition, Seoul. Frogs and Toads. T* **231** *and similar multicoloured designs. P* 14×14½.
1205 35 s. Type **231** 20 10
1206 50 s. Bubbling Kassina 25 20
1207 1 m. Guttural Toad 45 35
1208 1 m. 50, Common River Frog 60 70
1205/8 .. .. *Set of* 4 1·40 1·25
MS1209 Two sheets, each 102×72 mm. (a) 5 m. Jade frog (sculpture). (b) 5 m. Black Spotted Frog and Oriental White Eye (bird) (*vert*). P 14 *Set of 2 sheets* 6·00 6·25

232 De Havilland D.H.C.6 Twin Otter and Emblem

(Des V. Seatile Nkhomo. Litho Goverment Printer, Pretoria)

1994 (17 Nov). *50th Anniv of International Civil Aviation Organization. T* **232** *and similar horiz designs. Multicoloured. P* 14.
1210 35 s. Type **232** 25 15
1211 50 s. Fokker F.27 Friendship on runway 35 25
1212 1 m. Fokker F.27 Friendship over Moshoeshoe I International Airport 60 55
1213 1 m. 50, Cessna light aircraft over mountains 75 85
1210/13 .. .. *Set of* 4 1·75 1·60

King Moshoeshoe II, 25 January 1995 (restored)–15 January 1996

20s **=**

(233)

234 *Tagetes minuta*

1995 (3 Mar). *No.* 1022aB *surch with T* **233** *by Mazenod Ptg Wks, Lesotho.*
1214 20 s. on 30 s. *Charaxes jasius* (*p* 13½) .. 70 20
a. Perf 14×13½ (No. 1022B) 40 20

(Des V. Seatile Nkhomo. Litho Government Printer, Pretoria)

1995 (22 May). *Medicinal Plants. T* **234** *and similar vert designs. Multicoloured. P* 14.
1215 35 s. Type **234** 10 10
1216 50 s. *Plantago lanceolata* 15 20
1217 1 m. *Amaranthus spinosus* 25 30
1218 1 m. 50, *Taraxacum officinale* 40 45
1215/18 .. .. *Set of* 4 90 1·00
MS1219 120×91 mm. 5 m. *Datura stramonium* 1·25 1·40

235 Pius XII College, 1962

236 Qiloane Pinnacle, Thaba-Bosiu

(Des Sumitra Talukdar (2 m.), D. Ambrose (others). Litho Government Printer, Pretoria)

1995 (26 July). *50th Anniv of University Studies in Lesotho. T* **235** *and similar horiz designs. Multicoloured. P* 14.
1220 35 s. Type **235** 10 10
1221 50 s. Campus, University of Basutoland, Bechuanaland and Swaziland, 1966 15 20
1222 70 s. Campus, University of Botswana, Lesotho and Swaziland, 1970 .. 20 25
1223 1 m. Administration Block, University of Botswana, Lesotho and Swaziland, 1975 .. .. 25 30
1224 1 m. 50, Administration Block, National University of Lesotho, 1988 .. 40 45
1225 2 m. Procession of Vice-Chancellors, National University of Lesotho, 1995 50 55
1220/5 .. .. *Set of* 6 1·60 1·75

(Des M. Phakisi. Litho Government Printer, Pretoria)

1995 (28 Aug). *20th Anniv of World Tourism Organization. T* **236** *and similar multicoloured designs. P* 14.
1226 35 s. Type **236** 10 10
1227 50 s. Ha Mohalenyane rock formation .. 15 20
1228 1 m. Botsoela Falls (*vert*) 25 30
1229 1 m. 50, Backpackers in Makhaleng River Gorge 40 45
1226/9 .. .. *Set of* 4 90 1·10
MS1230 143×88 mm. 4 m. Red Hot Pokers (38×57 *mm*) .. .. 1·00 1·10
No. **MS**1230, which is inscribed "RED HOT PORKERS" in error, was withdrawn in Lesotho on 12 September.

237 "Peace"

238 "Sutter's Gold" Rose

(Des V. Seatile Nkhomo. Litho Government Printer, Pretoria)

1995 (26 Sept). *50th Anniv of United Nations. T* **237** *and similar multicoloured designs. P* 14.
1231 35 s. Type **237** 10 10
1232 50 s. "Justice" (scales) 15 20
1233 1 m. 50, "Reconciliation" (clasped hands) (*horiz*) 40 45
1231/3 .. .. *Set of* 3 65 75

(Des V. Seatile Nkhomo. Litho Government Printer, Pretoria)

1995 (1 Nov). *Christmas. Roses. T* **238** *and similar vert designs. Multicoloured. P* 14.
1234 35 s. Type **238** 10 10
1235 50 s. "Michele Meilland" 15 20
1236 1 m. "J. Otto Thilow" 25 30
1237 2 m. "Papa Meilland" 50 55
1234/7 .. .. *Set of* 4 1·00 1·10

King Letsie III. 15 January 1996 (restored)

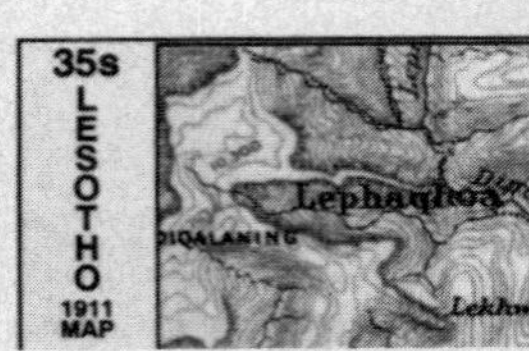

239 Part of 1911 Map showing Lephaqhoa

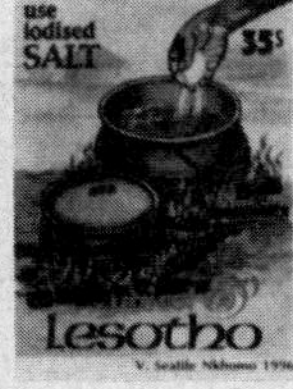

240 Adding Iodised Salt to Cooking Pot

(Des D. Ambrose. Litho Government Printer, Pretoria)

1996 (17 June). *Completion of New Standard Map of Lesotho* (1994). *T* **239** *and similar horiz designs showing map sections of the Malibamatso Valley. Multicoloured. P* 14. (a) *1911 Map*
1238 35 s. Type **239** 10 10
a. Sheetlet. Nos. 1238/47 90
1239 35 s. Boritsa Tsuene 10 10
1240 35 s. Molapo 10 10
1241 35 s. Nkeu 10 10
1242 35 s. Three rivers flowing east 10 10
1243 35 s. Tibedi and Rafanyane 10 10
1244 35 s. Two rivers flowing east 10 10
1245 35 s. Madibatmatso River 10 10
1246 35 s. Bokung River 10 10
1247 35 s. Semena River 10 10

(*b*) *1978 Map*
1248 35 s. Mountains and river valley 10 10
a. Sheetlet. Nos. 1248/57 90
1249 35 s. Pelaneng and Lepaqoa 10 10
1250 35 s. Mamohau 10 10
1251 35 s. Ha Lejone 10 10
1252 35 s. Ha Thoora 10 10
1253 35 s. Ha Mikia 10 10
1254 35 s. Ha Kosetabole 10 10
1255 35 s. Ha Seshote 10 10
1256 35 s. Ha Rapooane 10 10
1257 35 s. Bokong Ha Kennan 10 10

(*c*) *1994 Map*
1258 35 s. Mafika-Lisiu Pass 10 10
a. Sheetlet. Nos. 1258/67 90
1259 35 s. Ha Lesaoana 10 10
1260 35 s. Ha Masaballa 10 10
1261 35 s. Ha Nkisi 10 10
1262 35 s. Ha Rafanyane 10 10
1263 35 s. Laitsoka Pass 10 10
1264 35 s. "Katse Reservoir" 10 10
1265 35 s. Seshote 10 10
1266 35 s. Sephareng 10 10
1267 35 s. Katse Dam 10 10
1238/67 .. .. *Set of* 30 2·75 3·00
Nos. 1238/47, 1248/57 and 1258/67 were printed together, *se-tenant*, in sheetlets, of 10 (2×5) each forming composite designs.
Nos. 1238/67 were issued in conjunction with a schools campaign to promote use and understanding of maps.

(Des V. Seatile Nkhomo. Litho Government Printer, Pretoria)

1996 (30 July). *50th Anniv of U.N.I.C.E.F. T* **240** *and similar multicoloured designs. P* 14.
1268 35 s. Type **240** 10 15
1269 50 s. Herdboys with livestock (*horiz*) .. 15 20
1270 70 s. Children in class (*horiz*) 20 25
1271 1 m. 50, Boys performing traditional dance (*horiz*) 25 30
1268/71 .. .. *Set of* 4 70 90

241 U.S.A. Basketball Team, 1936

(Des J. Puvillard. Litho Questa)

1996 (1 Aug). *Olympic Games, Atlanta. Previous Gold Medal Winners. T* **241** *and similar multicoloured designs. P* 14.
1272 1 m. Type **241** 25 30
1273 1 m. 50, Brandenburg Gate and stadium, Berlin, 1936 .. .. 40 45
1274 1 m. 50, Glen Morris (U.S.A.) (decathlon, 1936) (*vert*) 40 45
a. Sheetlet. Nos. 1274/82 .. .. 3·50
1275 1 m. 50, Saidi Aouita (Morocco) (5000m running, 1984) (*vert*) 40 45
1276 1 m. 50, Arnie Robinson (U.S.A.) (long jump, 1976) (*vert*) 40 45
1277 1 m. 50, Hans Woellke (Germany) (shot put, 1936) (*vert*) 40 45
1278 1 m. 50, Renate Stecher (Germany) (100m running, 1972) (*vert*) 40 45
1279 1 m. 50, Evelyn Ashford (U.S.A.) (100m running, 1984) (*vert*) 40 45
1280 1 m. 50, Willie Davenport (U.S.A.) (110m hurdles, 1968) (*vert*) 40 45
1281 1 m. 50, Bob Beamon (U.S.A.) (long jump, 1968) (*vert*) 40 45
1282 1 m. 50, Heidi Rosendhal (Germany) (long jump, 1972) (*vert*) 40 45
1283 2 m. Jesse Owens (U.S.A.) (track and field, 1936) (*vert*) 50 55

1284 3 m. Speed boat racing 80 85
1272/84 .. .. *Set of* 13 5·50 6·25
MS1285 Two sheets, each 110×80 mm. (a) 8 m. Michael Gross (Germany) (swimming, 1984) (*vert*). (b) 8 m. Kornelia Ender (Germany) (swimming, 1976) (*vert*) .. .. *Set of* 2 *sheets* 3·00 3·25
No. 1273 is inscribed "BRANDEBOURG GATE" in error. No. 1274 incorrectly identifies Glen Morris as the gold medal winner in the 1936 long jump.
Nos. 1274/82 were printed together, *se-tenant*, in sheetlets of 9, the backgrounds forming a composite design.

242 WP Streamlined Locomotive (India)

243 Mothers' Union Member, Methodist Church

(Des G. Bibi. Litho Questa)

1996 (2 Sept). *Trains of the World. T* **242** *and similar horiz designs. Multicoloured. P* 14.
1286 1 m. 50, Type **242** 40 45
a. Sheetlet. Nos. 1286/91 .. .. 2·40
1287 1 m. 50, Canadian Pacific Class 2471 locomotive (Canada) 40 45
1288 1 m. 50, Caledonian Railways locomotive (Scotland) 40 45
1289 1 m. 50, William Mason Type locomotive (U.S.A.) 40 45
1290 1 m. 50, Trans-Siberian Express (Russia) 40 45
1291 1 m. 50, Swiss Federal locomotive (Switzerland) 40 45
1292 1 m. 50, ETR 450 train (Italy) 40 45
a. Sheetlet. Nos. 1292/7 .. .. 2·40
1293 1 m. 50, TGV (France) 40 45
1294 1 m. 50, XPT (Australia) 40 45
1295 1 m. 50, Blue Train (South Africa) .. 40 45
1296 1 m. 50, Inter City 255 (Great Britain) .. 40 45
1297 1 m. 50, Bullet Train (Japan) 40 45
1286/97 .. .. *Set of* 12 4·75 5·25
MS1298 Two sheets, each 98×68 mm. (a) 8 m. Class 52 steam locomotive (Germany) (57×43 *mm*). (b) 8 m. ICE train (Germany) (57×43 *mm*). *Set of* 2 *sheets* 4·00 4·50
Nos. 1286/91 and 1292/7 were each printed together, *se-tenant* in sheetlets of 6.

(Des V. Seatile Nkhomo. Litho Goverment Printer, Pretoria)

1996 (10 Dec). *Christmas. Mothers' Unions. T* **243** *and similar vert designs. Multicoloured. P* 14.
1299 35 s. Type **243** 10 10
1300 50 s. Roman Catholic Church 15 20
1301 1 m. Lesotho Evangelical Church .. 25 30
1302 1 m. 50, Anglican Church 40 45
1299/1302 .. .. *Set of* 4 90 1·00
No. 1302 is inscribed "Anglian" in error.

244 Hand Clasp (Co-operation for Development)

245 Land Reclamation

(Des V. Nkhomo. Litho Government Printer, Pretoria)

1997 (21 Apr). 10*th Anniv of Lesotho Highland Water Project* (1996). *T* **244** *and similar horiz designs. Multicoloured. P* 14.
1303 35 s. Type **244** 10 10
1304 50 s. Bearded Vulture and rock painting (Nature and Heritage) 15 20
1305 1 m. Malibamatso Bridge (Engineering) .. 25 30
1306 1 m. 50, Katse Valley in 1986 and 1996 (75×28 *mm*) 40 45
1303/6 .. .. *Set of* 4 90 1·00
No. 1305 is inscribed "Developement" in error.

(Des V. Nkhomo. Litho Government Printer, Pretoria)

1997 (30 June). *Environment Protection. T* **245** *and similar vert designs. Multicoloured. P* 14.
1307 35 s. Type **245** 10 10
1308 50 s. Throwing rubbish into bin 15 20
1309 1 m. Hands holding globe and tree .. 25 30
1310 1 m. 20, Recycling symbol and rubbish .. 30 35
1311 1 m. 50, Collecting rain water 40 45
1307/11 .. .. *Set of* 5 1·25 1·40

COVER PRICES

Cover factors are quoted at the beginning of each country for most issues to 1945. An explanation of the system can be found on page x. The factors quoted do not, however, apply to philatelic covers.

246 Schmeichel, Denmark

247 *Spialia spio*

(Litho Questa)

1997 (3 Nov). *World Cup Football Championship, France* (1998). *T* **246** *and similar multicoloured designs. P* 13½×14.
1312 1 m. Type **246** 25 30
1313 1 m. 50, Bergkamp, Netherlands .. 40 45
1314 1 m. 50, Argentine players celebrating .. 40 45
a. Sheetlet. Nos. 1314/19 .. .. 2·40
1315 1 m. 50, Argentine and Dutch players competing for ball 40 45
1316 1 m. 50, Players heading ball 40 45
1317 1 m. 50, Goal keeper deflecting ball .. 40 45
1318 1 m. 50, Goalmouth melee 40 45
1319 1 m. 50, Argentine player kicking ball .. 40 45
1320 2 m. Southgate, England 50 55
1321 2 m. 50, Asprilla, Colombia 65 70
1322 3 m. Gascoigne, England 80 85
1323 4 m. Giggs, Wales .. .. .. 1·00 1·10
1312/23 .. .. *Set of* 12 6·00 6·50
MS1324 Two sheets, each 127×102 mm. (a) 8 m. Littbarski, West Germany (*horiz*). P 14×13½. (b) 8 m. Shearer, England. P 13½×14 *Set of* 2 *sheets* 4·00 4·25
Nos. 1314/19 were printed together, *se-tenant*, in sheetlets of 6 and show scenes from the Argentina v Netherlands final of 1978.
Although First Day Covers for Nos. 1312/24 are dated 31 October 1997, the stamps were not available from Lesotho post offices before 3 November.

(Des D. Burkhart. Litho Questa)

1997 (28 Nov). *Butterflies. T* **247** *and similar horiz designs. Multicoloured. P* 14.
1325 1 m. 50, Type **247** 40 45
a. Sheetlet. Nos. 1325/33 .. .. 3·50
1326 1 m. 50, *Leptotes pirithous* 40 45
1327 1 m. 50, *Acratea satis* 40 45
1328 1 m. 50, *Belenois aurota aurota* 40 45
1329 1 m. 50, *Spindasis natalensis* 40 45
1330 1 m. 50, *Torynesis orangica* 40 45
1331 1 m. 50, *Lepidochysops variabilis* .. 40 45
1332 1 m. 50, *Pinacopteryx eriphia* 40 45
1333 1 m. 50, *Anthene butleri livida* 40 45
1325/33 .. .. *Set of* 9 3·50 4·00
MS1334 Two sheets, each 106×76 mm. (a) 8 m. *Bematistes aganice*. (b) 8 m. *Papilio demodocus* *Set of* 2 *sheets* 4·00 4·25
Nos. 1325/33 were printed together, *se-tenant*, in sheetlets of 9 with the backgrounds forming a composite design.
No. 1326 is inscribed "Cyclyrius pirithous", No. 1332 "Pinacopteryx eriphea" and No. **MS**1334(b) "Papalio demodocus", all in error.

248 Rock Paintings and Boy

249 Diana, Princess of Wales

(Des F. Christol, adapted by V. Nkhomo. Litho Government Printer, Pretoria)

1998 (30 Jan). 40*th Anniv of Morija Museum and Archives. T* **248** *and similar multicoloured designs. P* 14½ (*with two elliptical holes on the horiz sides* (45 *s. and* 2 *m.*) *or on the vert sides* (*others*)).
1335 35 s. Type **248** 10 10
1336 45 s. Hippopotamus and bones of lower jaws (*horiz*) 10 15
1337 50 s. Woman and cowhide skirt 15 20
1338 1 m. Drum 25 30
1339 1 m. 50, Breast plate 40 45
1340 2 m. Herders with ox (*horiz*) 50 55
1335/40 .. .. *Set of* 6 1·50 1·75

(Litho Questa)

1998 (16 Mar). *Diana, Princess of Wales Commemoration. T* **249** *and similar vert designs. Multicoloured. P* 13½.
1341 3 m. Type **249** 80 85
a. Sheetlet. Nos. 1341/6 .. .. 4·75
1342 3 m. Wearing grey jacket 80 85
1343 3 m. Wearing white polo-necked jumper 80 85
1344 3 m. Wearing pearl necklace 80 85
1345 3 m. Wearing white evening dress .. 80 85
1346 3 m. Wearing pale blue jacket 80 85
1341/6 .. .. *Set of* 6 4·75 5·00
MS1347 70×100 mm. 9 m. Accepting bouquet 2·40 2·50
Nos. 1341/6 were printed together, *se-tenant*, in sheetlets of 6.

STAMP BOOKLETS

1981 (20 Apr). *Multicoloured cover,* 165×100 *mm, showing Hoopoe (bird) on front and Lesotho village scene on back. Stapled.*
SB1 4 m. 30, booklet containing 5 s., 6 s., 7 s. and 25 s. (Nos. 440, 441/2, 444) in blocks of 10 .. 9·00

1981 (22 July). *Royal Wedding. Multicoloured cover,* 150×100 *mm, showing Prince Charles and Lady Diana Spencer on front and Ba-Leseli dance on back. Stitched.*
SB2 6 m. booklet containing four different panes of 3 stamps and 1 label (Nos. 451a/b, 452a, 453a) 2·75
a. Stapled .. ..

1982 (5 Mar). 75*th Anniv of Boy Scout Movement. Multicoloured cover,* 170×98 *mm, showing Lord Baden-Powell on front and Scout with flag on back. Pane attached by selvedge.*
SB3 5 m. 52, booklet containing *se-tenant* pane of 10 stamps and one miniature sheet (No. 474a) 8·50

1982 (14 Apr). *World Cup Football Championship, Spain. Multicoloured cover,* 170×102 *mm, showing Championship emblems. Stamps attached by selvedge.*
SB4 4 m. 85, booklet containing twenty-four 15 s. (Nos. 480/91) in blocks of 12 and one miniature sheet (No. **MS**492) .. .. 5·50

1982 (14 June). *Multicoloured cover as No.* SB1. *Stapled.*
SB5 4 m. 30, booklet containing 5 s., 6 s., 7 s. and 25 s. (Nos. 503/5, 507) in blocks of 10 .. .. 7·50

1983 (11 Jan). *Fungi. Multicoloured cover,* 155×80 *mm, showing fungi on front and with biography of G. L. Vasarhelyi on back. Panes attached by selvedge.*
SB6 3 m. 70, booklet containing two *se-tenant* panes of 4 stamps and 1 label (No 532b) and one *se-tenant* pane of 2 stamps and 1 label (No. 532c) .. .. 7·50

1983 (11 July). *Bicentenary of Manned Flight. Multicoloured cover,* 211×100 *mm, showing Montgolfier balloon. Panes attached by selvedge.*
SB7 4 m. booklet containing *se-tenant* pane of 4 stamps and 1 label (No. 545a) and one miniature sheet (No. **MS**549) .. .. 6·00

OFFICIAL STAMPS

OFFICIAL

(O 1)

1934 (4 May). *Nos.* 1/3 *and* 6 *optd with Type* O 1.
O1 1 ½d. emerald £3000 £3000
O2 1d. scarlet £1300 £1000
O3 2d. bright purple £750 £550
O4 6d. orange-yellow £9500 £4500
O1/4 .. .. *Set of* 4 £13000 £8000
Collectors are advised to buy these stamps only from reliable sources. They were not sold to the public.

POSTAGE DUE STAMPS

D 1

2d. Normal

2d. Large "d." (R. 9/6, 10/6)

(Typo D.L.R.)

1933 (1 Dec)–**52**. *Wmk Mult Script CA. Ordinary paper. P* 14.
D1 D 1 1d. carmine .. .. 1·75 6·00
a. *Scarlet* (1938) .. .. .. 32·00 38·00
b. Chalk-surfaced paper. *Deep carmine* (24.10.51) .. .. 40 1·00
ba. Error. Crown missing, W9*a* .. £100
bb. Error. St. Edward's Crown, W9*b* .. 60·00
D2 2d. violet .. .. 7·50 12·00
a. Chalk-surfaced paper (6.11.52) .. 30 5·00
ab. Error. Crown missing, W9*a* .. £110
ac. Error. St. Edward's Crown, W9*a* .. 60·00
ad. Large "d" .. .. 4·50
D1/2 Perf "Specimen" .. .. *Set of* 2 42·00

D 2

(Typo D.L.R.)

1956 (1 Dec). *Wmk Mult Script CA. P* 14.
D3 D 2 1d. carmine .. .. 30 2·50
D4 2d. deep reddish violet .. .. .. 30 4·00

5c (I) 5c (II)

1961 (14 Feb). *Surch as T* **24**, *but without stop.*

D5	D **2**	1 c. on 1d. carmine	10	30
D6		1 c. on 2d. deep reddish violet	10	30
D7		5 c. on 2d. deep reddish violet (Type I)	15	30
		a. Type II	15·00	42·00
D5/7		*Set of* 3	30	80

1961 (June). *No.* D2*a surch as T* **24** (*without stop*).

D8	D **1**	5 c. on 2d. violet	1·50	6·50
		a. Error. Missing Crown, W**9***a*	£950	
		b. Error. St. Edward's Crown, W**9***b*	£225	
		c. Large "d"	15·00	

1964. *As No.* D3/4 *but values in cents and W* w **12** (*sideways on* 1 *c.*).

D 9	D **2**	1 c. carmine	1·90	9·50
D10		5 c. deep reddish violet	1·90	9·50

1966 (1 Nov). *Nos.* D9/10 *optd as T* **34** *but smaller.*

D11	D **2**	1 c. carmine	30	75
		a. "LSEOTHO" (R.4/7)	25·00	
D12		5 c. deep reddish violet	30	90
		a. "LSEOTHO" (R.4/7)	45·00	

No. D11 exists with the overprint centred near the foot of the stamp (just above "POSTAGE DUE") (*price* £50 *mint*). It is believed that this comes from a proof sheet which was issued in the normal way. It contains the "LSEOTHO" error, which only occurred in the first printing.

D 1

D 2

(Litho B.W.)

1967 (18 Apr). *No wmk. P* 13½.

D13	D **1**	1 c. blue	15	3·00
D14		2 c. brown-rose	15	3·25
D15		5 c. emerald	20	3·25
D13/15		*Set of* 3	45	8·50

1976 (30 Nov). *W* **53** (*sideways*). *P* 13½.

D17	D **1**	2 c. rose-red	1·50	4·75
D18		5 c. emerald	1·75	5·00

(Des G. Vasarhelyi. Litho Format)

1986. *No wmk. P* 13 × 13½.

D19	D **2**	2 s. light green	10	30
D20		5 s. new blue	10	30
D21		25 s. violet	30	50
D19/21		*Set of* 3	45	1·00

POSTAL FISCAL

In July 1961 the 10s. stamp, T **9**, surcharged "R1 Revenue", was used for postage at one post office at least, but such usage was officially unauthorised.

Appendix

The following stamps have either been issued in excess of postal needs, or have not been made available to the public in reasonable quantities at face value. Miniature sheets, imperforate stamps etc., are excluded from this section.

1981–83

15*th Anniv of Independence. Classic Stamps of the World.* 10 m. × 40, each embossed on gold foil.

Long Island

PRICES FOR STAMPS ON COVER
Most covers from Long Island are philatelic, but these are worth from ×2 (Nos. 1/3) or from ×5 (others).

The Turkish island of Chustan (or Keustan) in the Gulf of Smyrna was occupied by the Royal Navy during April 1916 and renamed Long Island.

The following stamps were provided by the Civil Administrator, Lieut-Cmdr H. Pirie-Gordon, for the postal service inaugurated on 7 May 1916.

USED STAMPS. Stamps of Long Island were cancelled by hand-drawn circular date stamps in blue crayon for the Northend post office ("N") or in red crayon for Nikola post office ("S").

QUANTITIES ISSUED. The figures quoted do not include the remainders subsequently recorded as having been destroyed.

(1)

2

1916 (7 May). *Turkish fiscal stamps surch by typewriter as in T 1. No wmk. P 12.*
1 ½d. on 20 pa. green and buff (new value in red, remainder of surch in black) .. £2250 £4000
2 1d. on 10 pa. carmine and buff £2500 £4000
3 2½d. on 1 pi. violet and buff (R.) £2250 £4000
Quantities issued: ½d. 25; 1d. 20; 2½d. 25.

1916 (7 May). *Typewritten as T 2 in various colours of ribbon and carbon. Each stamp initialled by the Civil Administrator. No gum. Imperf.*

(a) *On pale green paper with horizontal grey lines. No wmk. Sheets of 12 (4×3) or 16 (4×4) with stamps initialled in red ink.*
4 ½d. black £1000 £850
a. "G.R.I." double .. £1800
b. "7" for "&" .. £2750
5 ½d. blue £850
a. "G.R.I." double .. £1800
b. "7" for "&" .. £2750
6 ½d. mauve £400 £450
a. "G.R.I." double .. £1000
b. "7" for "&" .. £2000
Quantity issued: 140 in all.

(b) *On thin horiz laid paper with sheet wmk of* "Silver Linen" *in double-lined letters. Sheets of 20 (4×5) or 16 (some ptgs of 1s.) with stamps initialled in red ink.*
7 ½d. black £350 £425
a. "postage" for "Postage" .. £1500
b. "7" for "&" .. £1500
8 ½d. blue £500 £550
b. "7" for "&" .. £1500
9 ½d. mauve £170 £225
a. "postage" for "Postage" .. £900
b. "7" for "&" .. £1000
10 1d. black £140 £250
a. "7" for "&" .. £1000
b. "Rvevue" for "Revenue" .. £1000
g. "Postagg" for "Postage" .. £1500
11 1d. blue £190 £325
a. "7" for "&" .. £1500
c. "postage" for "Postage" .. £1500
e. "G.R?I?" for "G.R.I." .. £1500
f. "ONR" for "ONE" .. £800
12 1d. mauve £110 £200
a. "7" for "&" .. £1100
b. "Rvevue" for "Revenue" .. £1500
c. "postage" for "Postage" .. £1500
e. "G.R?I?" for "G.R.I." .. † £1600
f. "ONR" for "ONE" .. £600 £850
g. "Postagg" for "Postage" .. £1000
13 1d. red £130 £200
a. "7" for "&" .. £1000
c. "postage" for "Postage" .. £1500
f. "ONR" for "ONE" .. £800 £900
14 2½d. black £700
15 2½d. blue £700 £900
16 2½d. mauve £1300 £850
17 6d. black (inscr "SIX PENCE") .. £900 £1200
b. Without red ink initials .. † £1500
19 6d. mauve (inscr "SIX PENCE") .. £325 £700
a. "SIXPENCE" (one word) .. £1300
20 1s. black £110 £275
a. "ISLANA" for "ISLAND" .. £1500
b. "Postge" for "Postage" .. £850 £1200
c. "Rebenue" for "Revenue" .. £1500
21 1s. blue £900
22 1s. mauve £100 £350
a. "ISLANA" for "ISLAND" .. £1000
b. "Postge" for "Postage" .. £1500
c. "Rebenue" for "Revenue" .. £1500
Quantities issued (all colours); ½d. 237; 1d. 881; 2½d. 80; 6d. 89; 1s. 383.

(c) *On thin wove paper. No wmk. Sheets of 24 with stamps initialled in indelible pencil.*
23 ½d. black £250 £350
25 ½d. mauve £475
26 1d. black £300 £400
27 1d. red £4000 £800
30 2d. black £160 £400
b. Error. 1d. and 2d. *se-tenant* .. £3250
c. Initialled in red ink £750 £850
31 2d. mauve £160 £250
a. Error. 1d. and 2d. *se-tenant* .. £3000
32 2½d. black £350 £450
33 2½d. blue £900
34 2½d. mauve £800 £800
35 6d. black £170 £400
a. "Rvenne &" for "Revenue" .. £1400
b. Error. 2d. and 6d. *se-tenant*, also "ISLND" for "ISLAND" .. £3250 £3250
c. "PENCC" £1100
36 6d. blue £600
a. "Rvenne &" for "Revenue" .. £1800
b. Error. 2d. and 6d. *se-tenant*, also "ISLND" for "ISLAND" .. £3500
c. "PENCC" £1500
Quantities issued (all colours); ½d. 114; 1d. 120; 2d. 249; 2½d. 115; 6d. 200.

TOP SHEETS AND CARBONS. It is believed that the production sequence of the typewritten stamps was as follows:

½d. on pale green (Nos. 4/6)
Two black top sheets of 12 (4×3) and one of 16 (4×4)
Two blue carbon sheets of 12 (4×3) and one of 16 (4×4)
Five mauve carbon sheets of 12, two from one top sheet and three from the other
Varieties: "7" for "&" occurs on an unknown position from one of the sheets of 12 and "G.R.I." double occurs on R. 3/2-4 of the other

½d. on laid paper (Nos. 7/9) in sheets of 20 (4×5)
Three black top sheets
Three blue carbon sheets
Eight mauve carbon sheets, two or three from each top sheet
Varieties: "postage" occurs on R. 3/2 of one top sheet and "7" for "&" on R. 4/2 of another

1d. on laid paper (Nos. 10/13) in sheets of 20 (4×5)
Eleven red top sheets
Fifteen black carbon sheets, three each from five of the top sheets
Six blue carbon sheets, one each from six of the top sheets
Twenty-two mauve carbon sheets, probably two from each top sheet
Varieties: "7" for "&" on R. 3/3, "postage" on R. 3/3, "Rvevue" on R. 1/3 and "Postagg" on R. 2/4, all from different top sheets. The position of "G.R?I?" is not known. "ONR" occurs from three different top sheets on R. 5/1, R. 5/2 & 4 or R. 4/1 and 5/2

2½d. on laid paper (Nos. 14/16) in sheets of 20 (4×5)
One black top sheet
One blue carbon sheet
Two mauve carbon sheets

6d. on laid paper (Nos. 17/19) in sheets of 20 (4×5)
One black top sheet
One blue carbon sheet*
Three mauve carbon sheets
Variety: "SIXPENCE" occurs on R. 1/2-3

1s. on laid paper (Nos. 20/2)
Five black top sheets, four of 20 (4×5) and one of 16 (4×4)
Nine black carbon sheets, three each from two of the top sheets of 20 and three from the top sheet of 16
Two blue carbon sheets, one each from two of the top sheets of 20
Twelve mauve carbon sheets, nine from various top sheets of 20 and three from the top sheet of 16
Varieties: "ISLANA" occurs on R. 1/2 of one of the sheets of 20 and "Postge" on R. 1/3 of the sheet of 16. "Rebenue" comes from one of the other sheets of 20

½d. on wove paper (Nos. 23/5) in sheets of 24 (4×6)
One black top sheet
Three black carbon sheets
One blue carbon sheet*
One mauve carbon sheet

1d. on wove paper (Nos. 26/7) in sheets of 24 (4×6)
One red top sheet
Three black carbon sheets
One blue carbon sheet*
One mauve carbon sheet*

2d. on wove paper (Nos. 30/1) in sheets of 24 (4×6)
Two black top sheets
Six black carbon sheets, three from each top sheet. One initialled in red ink
Four mauve carbon sheets, two from each top sheet
Variety: the "1d." error occurs on R. 5/2 from one top sheet

2½d. on wove paper (Nos. 32/4) in sheets of 24 (4×6)
One black top sheet
Three black carbon sheets
One blue carbon sheet
One mauve carbon sheet

6d. on wove paper (Nos. 35/6) in sheets of 24 (4×6)
Two black top sheets
Six black carbon sheets, three from each top sheet
Two blue carbon sheets, one from each top sheet
Varieties: the "2d." error occurs on R. 5/3 from one top sheet which also showed "PENCC" on R. 3/2, and "Rvenne &" on R. 4/1 of the other

*These carbons are described in written records, but their existence has yet to be confirmed by actual examples.

Madagascar

PRICES FOR STAMPS ON COVER

Nos. 1/47	—
Nos. 50/6	*from* × 50
Nos. 57/62	*from* × 30

BRITISH CONSULAR MAIL

After May 1883 mail from the British community at Antananarivo, the capital, was sent by runner to the British Consulate at Tamatave for forwarding via the French Post Office.

In March of the following year the British Vice-Consul at Antananarivo, Mr. W. C. Pickersgill, reorganised this service and issued stamps for use on both local and overseas mail. Such stamps were only gummed at one of the top corners. This was to facilitate their removal from overseas mail where they were replaced by Mauritius stamps (at Port Louis) or by French issues (at the Vice-Consulate) for transmission via Tamatave and Reunion. Local mail usually had the stamps removed also, being marked with a "PAID" or a Vice-Consular handstamp, although a few covers have survived intact.

CONDITION. Due to the type of paper used, stamps of the British Consular Mail are usually found with slight faults, especially thins. Our prices are for average examples, really fine stamps being worth a premium.

USED STAMPS. Postmarks are not usually found on these issues. Cancellations usually take the form of a manuscript line or cross in crayon, ink or pencil or as five parallel horizontal bars in black or red, approximately 15 mm long. Examples of Nos. 1/3, 5/8 and 11 showing a red diagonal line are believed to be cancelled-to-order.

1

2

1884 (Mar). *Typo locally. Rouletted vertically in colour. No gum, except on one upper corner. With circular consular handstamp reading* "BRITISH VICE-CONSULATE ANTANANARIVO" *around Royal arms in black.*

(a) *Inscr* "LETTER".
1 1 6d. (½ oz) magenta £400 £425
a. Violet handstamp .. £1800
2 1s. (1 oz) magenta £375
3 1s. 6d. (1½ oz) magenta £400
4 2s. (2 oz) magenta £600

(b) *Inscr* "POSTAL PACKET"
5 1 1d. (1 oz) magenta £400 £350
a. Without handstamp .. £3750 £3750
6 2d. (2 oz) magenta £275 £250
7 3d. (3 oz) magenta £275 £250
8 4d. (1 oz amended in ms to "4 oz") magenta £650 £600
a. Without manuscript amendment .. £3000 £3000
ab. Violet handstamp .. £1100
ac. Without handstamp .. £3750 £3750

Nos. 1/8 were printed in horizontal strips of four, each strip containing two impressions of the setting. Each strip contained two stamps with normal stops after "B.C.M." and two with a hollow stop after "B" (1d., 2d., 3d., 4d., 6d. and 2s.) or after "M" (1s. and 1s. 6d.).

Several values are known with the handstamp either inverted or double.

1886. *Manuscript provisionals.*

(a) *No. 2 with* "SHILLING" *erased and* "PENNY" *written above in red ink*
9 1 1d. on 1s. (1 oz) magenta .. ..

(b) *No. 2 surch* "4½d." *and* "W.C.P." *in red ink with a line through the original value*
10 1 4½d. on 1s. (1 oz) magenta .. ..

1886. *As No. 1, but colour changed. Handstamped with circular* "BRITISH VICE-CONSULATE ANTANANARIVO" *in black.*
11 1 6d. (½ oz) rose-red £550 £500

1886. *As No. 8, but handstamped* "BRITISH CONSULAR MAIL ANTANANARIVO" *in black* (B) *or violet* (V)

			B		V	
12 1	4d. (1 oz) magenta ..	..	£1600	—	£3500	—

1886. *Typo locally.* "POSTAGE" *and value in words printed in black. Rouletted vertically in colour. No gum, except on one upper corner.*

I. "POSTAGE" 29½ mm long. *Stops after* "POSTAGE" *and value*

(*a*) *Handstamped* "BRITISH VICE-CONSULATE ANTANANARIVO" *in black* (B) *or violet* (V)

No.	Type	Description	B		V	
14	2	1d. rose	£100	£130	£275	—
15		1½d. rose	£1200	£1000	£850	—
16		2d. rose	£140	—	£275	—
17		3d. rose	£1200	£950	£350	£325
18		4½d. rose	£850	£500	£450	£300
19		8d. rose	£2000	£2000	£1000	£1000
20		9d. rose	£2750	£2500	£950	—

(*b*) *Handstamped* "BRITISH CONSULAR MAIL ANTANANARIVO" *in black*

No.	Type	Description		
21	2	1d. rose	70·00	
22		1½d. rose	70·00	
23		2d. rose	90·00	
24		3d. rose	85·00	£120
		a. Handstamp in red	†	£7500
25		4½d. rose	85·00	£120
		a. Handstamp in red	†	£4500
26		8d. rose	£100	
		a. Handstamp in violet	£1200	
27		9d. rose	£110	£160
		a. Without handstamp	£2750	
		b. Handstamp in violet	£250	

II. "POSTAGE" 29½ mm long. *No stops after* "POSTAGE" *or value*

(*a*) *Handstamped* "BRITISH VICE-CONSULATE ANTANANARIVO" *in violet*

No.	Type	Description	
28	2	1d. rose	£850
29		1½d. rose	£1600
30		3d. rose	£1000
31		4½d. rose	£1500
32		6d. rose	£1200

(*b*) *Handstamped* "BRITISH CONSULAR MAIL ANTANANARIVO" *in black* (B) *or violet* (V)

No.	Type	Description	B		V	
33		1d. rose	70·00	£100	85·00	—
		a. Without handstamp	£1800			
34		1½d. rose	65·00	95·00	£130	—
		a. Without handstamp	£1800			
35		2d. rose	65·00	95·00	£140	—
36		3d. rose	70·00	£100	£120	—
		a. Without handstamp	£2500			
37		4½d. rose	70·00	£100	£120	—
		a. Without handstamp	£2500			
38		6d. rose	70·00	£100	£300	—
		a. Without handstamp	£2750			

III. "POSTAGE" 24½ mm long. *No stop after* "POSTAGE", *but stop after value.*

(*a*) *Handstamped* "BRITISH VICE-CONSULATE ANTANANARIVO" *in violet*

No.	Type	Description	
39	2	4d. rose	£400
40		8d. rose	£500
40*a*		1s. rose	
41		1s. 6d. rose	£3250
42		2s. rose	£1900
		a. Handstamp in black	

(*b*) *Handstamped* "BRITISH CONSULAR MAIL ANTANANARIVO" *in black* (B) *or violet* (V)

No.	Type	Description	B		V	
43		4d. rose	£180	—	£375	—
		a. Without handstamp	£2250			
44		8d. rose	£600	—	£500	—
		a. Without handstamp	£2250			
45		1s. rose	£450	—	£1200	—
		a. Without handstamp	£2250			
46		1s. 6d. rose	£500	—	£1200	—
		a. Without handstamp	£3000			
47		2s. rose	£600	—	£1500	—
		a. Without handstamp	£3000			

The above were also printed in horizontal strips of four.

The stamps of the British Consular Mail were suppressed in 1887, but the postal service continued with the charges paid in cash.

BRITISH INLAND MAIL

In January 1895 the Malagasy government agreed that a syndicate of British merchants at Antananarivo, including the Vice-Consul, should operate an inland postal service during the war with France. Mail was sent by runner to the port of Vatomandry and forwarded via Durban where Natal stamps were added.

Nos. 50/62 were cancelled with dated circular postmarks inscribed "BRITISH MAIL".

4

5 Malagasy Runners

(Typeset London Missionary Society Press, Antananarivo)

1895 (Jan). *Rouletted in black.* (*a*) *Thick laid paper.*

No.	Type	Description		
50	4	4d. black	24·00	12·00
		a. "FUOR" for "FOUR"	—	£800

(*b*) *In black on coloured wove paper*

No.	Type	Description		
51	4	1d. *blue-grey*	24·00	12·00
52		6d. *pale yellow*	24·00	12·00
53		8d. *salmon*	24·00	12·00
54	4	1s. *fawn*	38·00	12·00
55		2s. *bright rose*	38·00	14·00
		a. Italic "2" at left	£130	60·00
56		4s. *grey*	55·00	12·00
50/6		*Set of* 7	£200	75·00

There are six types of each value, printed in blocks of 6 (2×3) separated by gutters, four times on each sheet; the upper and lower blocks being *tête-bêche*.

Nos. 50a and 55a occur in the sixth position in their respective blocks. No. 50a was soon corrected.

(Typo John Haddon & Co, London)

1895 (Mar). *The inscription in the lower label varies for each value. P* 12.

No.	Type	Description		
57	5	2d. blue	5·00	30·00
		a. Imperf between (pair)	£400	
58		4d. rose	5·50	30·00
		a. Imperf between (pair)	£250	
59		6d. green	6·00	30·00
		a. Imperf between (pair)	£475	
60		1s. slate-blue	6·50	40·00
		a. Imperf between (pair)	£400	
61		2s. chocolate	9·00	45·00
		a. Imperf between (pair)	£425	
62		4s. bright purple	14·00	60·00
		a. Imperf between (pair)	£1100	
57/62		*Set of* 6	42·00	£200

This post was suppressed when the French entered Antananarivo on 30 September 1895.

Malawi

(*formerly* Nyasaland)

PRICES FOR STAMPS ON COVER TO 1945

Nos. 1/9*a*	*from* × 15
Nos. 10/19	—
No. 20	*from* × 10
Nos. 21/6	*from* × 5
Nos. 27/31	—
Nos. 32/7	*from* × 6
Nos. 38/42	—
Nos. 43/7	*from* × 12
Nos. 48/52	—
No. 53	*from* × 15
No. 54	*from* × 2
No. 55	*from* × 4
Nos. 55*b*/7*a*	*from* × 7
Nos. 57*d*/63	*from* × 6
Nos. 64/71	—
Nos. 72/9	*from* × 5
Nos. 80/2	—
Nos. 83/95	*from* × 4
Nos. 96/9	—
Nos. 100/57	*from* × 2

By 1891 the territory west of Lake Nyasa was recognised as being under British protection and the southern, eastern and northern borders had been delineated with the Portuguese and German governments.

BRITISH CENTRAL AFRICA

A protectorate under the name "Nyassaland Districts" was declared on 14 May 1891, the title being changed to the "British Central Africa Protectorate" on 22 February 1893. Such a description had been in use for some time previously and the handwritten notice of 20 July 1891, announcing the introduction of postal services, described the area as "British Central Africa".

Until 1895 the British South Africa Company contributed to the revenues of the protectorate administration which, in return governed North-eastern Rhodesia. Stamps of the British South Africa Company overprinted "B.C.A.", in addition to use in British Central Africa, were issued to post offices at Fife, Fort Rosebery, Katwe, Johnston Falls, Rhodesia (later Kalungwisi) and Tanganyika (later Abercorn) in North-eastern Rhodesia from 1893 until 1899.

B.C.A. (1)

B.C.A. FOUR SHILLINGS. (2)

ONE PENNY. (3)

1891 (April)–**1895.** *Stamps of Rhodesia optd as T* **1.** *P* 14, 14½.

No.	Type	Description		
1	1	1d. black	3·00	3·50
2	4	2d. sea-green and vermilion	3·00	3·50
		a. Bisected (1d.) (on cover) (1895)	†	£1800
3		4d. reddish chestnut and black	3·25	4·50
4	1	6d. ultramarine	42·00	20·00
5		6d. deep blue	5·00	8·00
6	4	8d. rose-lake and ultramarine	12·00	28·00
6*a*		8d. red and ultramarine	23·00	45·00
7	1	1s. grey-brown	12·00	11·00
8		2s. vermilion	24·00	48·00
9		2s. 6d. grey-purple	55·00	75·00
9*a*		2s. 6d. lilac	50·00	70·00
10	4	3s. brown and green (1895)	50·00	55·00
11		4s. grey-black and vermilion (2.93)	50·00	80·00
12	1	5s. orange-yellow	55·00	70·00
13		10s. deep green	£110	£160
14	2	£1 deep blue	£475	£500
15		£2 rose-red	£800	
16		£5 sage-green	£1400	
17		£10 brown	£3250	
1/14		*Set of* 13	£750	£950

The overprint varies on values up to 10s. Sets may be made with *thin* or *thick* letters.

The bisected 2d, No. 2a, was authorised for use at Blantyre, Chiromo and Zomba in July and October 1895.

1892 (Aug)–**93.** *Stamps of Rhodesia surch as T* **2.**

No.	Type	Description		
18	4	3s. on 4s. grey-black and vermilion (10.93)	£300	£300
19	1	4s. on 5s. orange-yellow	70·00	80·00

1895. *No.* 2 *surch at Cape Town with T* **3.**

No.	Type	Description		
20	4	1d. on 2d. sea-green and vermilion	6·00	25·00
		a. Surch double	£3000	£2250

Specimens are known with double surcharge, without stop after "PENNY". These are from a trial printing made at Blantyre, but it is believed that they were not issued to the public (*Price* £550 *un.*).

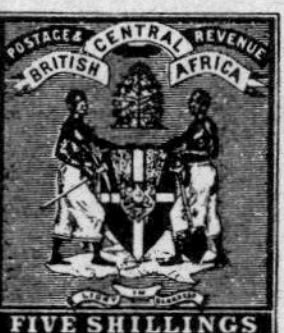

5 Arms of the Protectorate 6

(Des Sir Harry Johnston. Litho D.L.R.)

1895. *No wmk. P* 14.

No.	Type	Description		
21	5	1d. black	10·00	6·00
22		2d. black and green	17·00	11·00
23		4d. black and reddish buff	28·00	26·00
24		6d. black and blue	48·00	6·50
25		1s. black and rose	50·00	23·00
26	6	2s. 6d. black and bright magenta	£140	£200
27		3s. black and yellow	85·00	45·00
28		5s. black and olive	£120	£140
29		£1 black and yellow-orange	£800	£375
30		£10 black and orange-vermilion	£3750	£3250
31		£25 black and blue-green	£6500	
21/8		*Set of* 8	£450	£425
21/9 Optd "Specimen"		*Set of* 9	£375	

Cancellations inscribed "BRITISH CENTRAL AFRICA" within a double-circle and with the name of a town across the centre or at foot were intended for use on stamps presented for the payment of the hut tax. Such marks can be found in black, violet or blue and are without date. Stamps with such fiscal obliterations are of little value. Prices quoted are for postally used.

1896 (Feb). *Wmk Crown CA* (*T* **5**) *or CC* (*sideways*) (*T* **6**), *P* 14.

No.	Type	Description		
32	5	1d. black	3·00	4·50
33		2d. black and green	13·00	5·00
34		4d. black and orange-brown	18·00	17·00
35		6d. black and blue	18·00	9·50
36		1s. black and rose	18·00	11·00
37	6	2s. 6d. black and magenta	£100	£100
38		3s. black and yellow	75·00	48·00
39		5s. black and olive	£100	£130
40		£1 black and blue	£700	£450
41		£10 black and orange (Optd S. £175)	£4250	£3250
42		£25 black and green (Optd S. £325)	£9000	
32/9		*Set of* 8	£300	£300
32/40 Optd "Specimen"		*Set of* 9	£375	

7

8

(Typo D.L.R.)

1897 (Aug). *T* **7** (*wmk Crown CA*) *and* **8** (*wmk Crown CC*). *P* 14.

No.	Type	Description		
43	7	1d. black and ultramarine	1·75	70
44		2d. black and yellow	1·60	1·00
45		4d. black and carmine	5·00	1·50
46		6d. black and green	38·00	4·25
47		1s. black and dull purple	8·00	7·00
48	8	2s. 6d. black and ultramarine	40·00	40·00
49		3s. black and sea-green	£180	£225
50		4s. black and carmine	65·00	75·00
50*a*		10s. black and olive-green	£100	£110
51		£1 black and dull purple	£250	£150
52		£10 black and yellow (Optd S. £200)	£3500	£1700
43/51		*Set of* 10	£600	£550
43/51 Optd "Specimen"		*Set of* 10	£250	

ALTERED CATALOGUE NUMBERS

Any Catalogue numbers altered from the last edition are shown as a list in the introductory pages.

ONE

PENNY

(9)

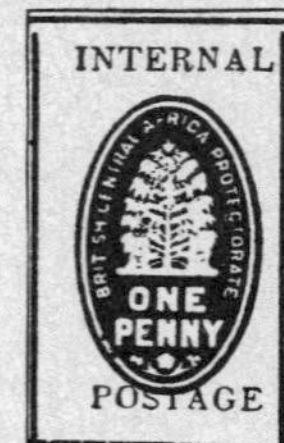

10

1897 (31 Dec). *No. 49 surch with T* **9**, *in red.*

No.	Type	Description	Unused	Used
53	**8**	1d. on 3s. black and sea-green	5·00	8·50
		a. "PNNEY" (R. 4/2)	£1700	£1700
		b. "PENN"	£1100	£900
		c. Surch double	£450	

No. 53b shows an albino impression of the "Y".

1898 (11 Mar). *Imperf.*

(*a*) *Setting I. The vertical frame lines of the stamps cross the space between the two rows of the sheet*

(i) *With the initials "J.G." or "J.T.G." on the back in black ink*

No.	Type	Description	Unused	Used
54	**10**	1d. vermilion and grey-blue	—	£500
		a. Without the initials	£1800	
		b. Without the initials and centre inverted	£8000	

(ii) *With a control number and letter or letters, printed in plain relief at the back*

No.	Type	Description	Unused	Used
55	**10**	1d. vermilion and grey-blue	—	£350

(*b*) *Setting II. The vertical frame lines do not cross the space between the rows except at the extreme ends of the sheet. Control as No.* 55.

No.	Type	Description	Unused	Used
55*b*	**10**	1d. vermilion and pale ultramarine	—	70·00
		c. Control on face	—	£3250
		d. Centre omitted (vert pair with normal)	£9500	
56		1d. vermilion and deep ultramarine	—	70·00
		a. Without Control at back	£1600	£110
		b. Control doubly impressed	—	£350

1898 (June). *Setting II. Control as No.* 55. *P* 12.

No.	Type	Description	Unused	Used
57	**10**	1d. vermilion and pale ultramarine	£1800	15·00
57*a*		1d. vermilion and deep ultramarine	—	24·00
		ab. Without Control at back	£1800	70·00
		ac. Two different Controls on back	—	£500
		ad. Control printed in black	£2250	

The two different settings of these stamps are each in 30 types, issued without gum.

1901. *Wmk Crown CA. P* 14.

No.	Type	Description	Unused	Used
57*d*	**7**	1d. dull purple and carmine-rose	1·60	40
57*e*		4d. dull purple and olive-green	7·00	9·00
58		6d. dull purple and brown	3·50	3·00
57*d*/8		*Set of* 3	11·00	11·00
57*d*/58 Optd "Specimen"		*Set of* 3	60·00	

11

12

(Typo D.L.R.)

1903–4. *T* **11** (*Wmk Crown CA*) *and* **12** (*Wmk Crown CC*). *P* 14.

No.	Type	Description	Unused	Used
59	**11**	1d. grey and carmine	4·25	1·50
60		2d. dull and bright purple	3·25	1·00
61		4d. grey-green and black	2·50	8·00
62		6d. grey and reddish buff	2·50	2·00
		aw. Wmk inverted	75·00	
62*b*		1s. grey and blue	2·50	8·50
63	**12**	2s. 6d. grey-green and green	38·00	50·00
64		4s. dull and bright purple	55·00	75·00
65		10s. grey-green and black	80·00	£160
66		£1 grey and carmine	£190	£160
67		£10 grey and blue (Optd S. £300)	£4000	£3250
59/66		*Set of* 9	£325	£425
59/66 Optd "Specimen"		*Set of* 9	£275	

1907. *Wmk Mult Crown CA. Chalk-surfaced paper. P* 14.

No.	Type	Description	Unused	Used
68	**11**	1d. grey and carmine	3·75	1·75
69		2d. dull and bright purple	£8500	
70		4d. grey-green and black	£8500	
71		6d. grey and reddish buff	26·00	42·00

Nos. 69/70 were not issued in Nyasaland.

NYASALAND PROTECTORATE

The title of the Protectorate was changed again from 6 July 1907.

13

14

POSTAGE

Serif on "G" (R. 4/5. All ptgs of £1 Duty plate)

(Typo D.L.R.)

1908 (22 July)–**11.** *P* 14. (*a*) *Wmk Crown CA. Chalk-surfaced paper.*

No.	Type	Description	Unused	Used
72	**13**	1s. black/*green*	2·50	7·00

(*b*) *Wmk Mult Crown CA. Ordinary paper* (½*d.*, 1*d.*) *or chalk-surfaced paper* (*others*)

No.	Type	Description	Unused	Used
73	**13**	½d. green	1·50	1·50
74		1d. carmine	3·00	80
75		3d. purple/*yellow*	1·25	3·25
		w. Wmk inverted	£110	
76		4d. black and red/*yellow*	1·25	1·50
		w. Wmk inverted	80·00	80·00
77		6d. dull purple and bright purple	3·75	8·50
78	**14**	2s. 6d. brownish black & carm-red/*blue*	42·00	70·00
		a. Brownish black and deep rose-red/pale blue (1911)	£150	£180
79		4s. carmine and black	70·00	90·00
80		10s. green and red/*green*	95·00	£160
81		£1 purple and black/*red*	£400	£450
		c. Serif on "G"	£1400	
82		£10 purple & ultramarine (Optd S. £500)	£7000	£4500
72/81		*Set of* 10	£550	£700
72/81 Optd "Specimen"		*Set of* 10	£400	

15

16

Nick in top right scroll (R. 3/12)

"Bullet holes" flaw (R. 5/2. March 1919 ptgs)

Triangle flaw (R. 3/5. March 1919 ptg of 4s.)

1913 (1 Apr)–**19.** *Wmk Mult Crown CA. Ordinary paper* (½*d. to* 2½*d.*) *or chalk-surfaced paper* (*others*). *P* 14.

No.	Type	Description	Unused	Used
83	**15**	½d. green	50	1·00
84		½d. blue-green (1918)	75	1·00
85		1d. carmine-red	75	1·25
86		1d. scarlet (1916)	1·75	65
87		2d. grey (1916)	1·25	70
88		2d. slate	4·25	2·00
89		2½d. bright blue	2·00	5·00
90		3d. purple/*yellow* (1914)	3·50	3·50
		a. On pale yellow	3·75	8·00
91		4d. black and red/*yellow* (*shades*)	2·00	2·00
		a. On pale yellow	5·50	8·00
92		6d. dull and bright purple	2·50	7·50
92*a*		6d. dull purple and bright violet	8·50	10·00
93		1s. black/*green*	1·75	7·50
		a. On blue-green, olive back	4·25	1·50
		aw. Wmk inverted	70·00	85·00
		b. On emerald back (Optd S. £35)	2·25	5·00
94	**16**	2s. 6d. black and red/*blue*	11·00	10·00
		a. Break in scroll	£100	
		b. Broken crown and scroll	£140	
		d. Nick in top right scroll	£100	
		e. "Bullet-holes" flaw	£150	
95		4s. carmine and black	12·00	42·00
		a. Break in scroll	£110	
		b. Broken crown and scroll	£150	
		d. Nick in top right scroll	£110	
		e. "Bullet-holes" flaw	£160	
		f. Triangle flaw	£160	
96		10s. pale green and deep scarlet/*green*	55·00	75·00
		d. Nick in top right scroll	£250	
		e. Green and deep scarlet/green (1919)	55·00	75·00
		ea. Break in scroll	£250	
		eb. Broken crown and scroll	£250	
		ee. "Bullet holes" flaw	£275	
98		£1 purple and black/*red*	£150	£140
		a. Break in scroll	£425	
		b. Broken crown and scroll	£425	
		c. Serif on "G"	£425	
		d. Nick in top right scroll	£425	
		e. "Bullet holes" flaw	£650	
99		£10 purple & dull ultram (Optd S. £350)	£4000	
		d. Nick in top right scroll		
		e. Purple and royal blue (1919)	£2500	£1700
		eb. Break in scroll		
		ec. Broken crown and scroll		
		ee. "Bullet holes" flaw		
83/98		*Set of* 12	£200	£250
83/98 Optd "Specimen"		*Set of* 12	£350	

For illustrations of the other varieties on Nos. 94/9 see above Leeward Islands No. 58.

For stamps overprinted "N.F." see TANZANIA.

Break through scroll (R. 1/9. Ptgs from June 1929)

Damaged crown (R. 4/1. Ptgs from June 1924)

1921–30. *Wmk Mult Script CA. Ordinary paper* (½*d. to* 2*d.*) *or chalk-surfaced paper* (*others*). *P* 14.

No.	Type	Description	Unused	Used
100	**15**	½d. green	90	30
		w. Wmk inverted	—	75·00
101		1d. carmine	1·25	30
102		1½d. orange	3·25	17·00
103		2d. grey	90	30
105		3d. purple/*pale yellow*	8·00	3·25
106		4d. black and red/*yellow*	2·50	8·00
107		6d. dull and bright purple	3·00	3·25
108		1s. black/*emerald* (1930)	7·00	5·50
109	**16**	2s. purple and blue/*blue* (1926)	13·00	10·00
		a. Break in scroll	80·00	
		b. Broken crown and scroll	80·00	
		c. Break through scroll	£120	
110		2s. 6d. black and red/*blue* (1924)	16·00	15·00
		a. Break in scroll	90·00	
		b. Broken crown and scroll	90·00	
		c. Break through scroll	£130	
		d. Damaged crown	£160	

111 **16** 4s. carmine and black (1927) .. .. 16·00 18·00
a. Break in scroll .. .. .. 90·00
b. Broken crown and scroll .. .. 90·00
112 5s. green and red/*yellow* (1929) .. 32·00 65·00
a. Break in scroll £150
b. Broken crown and scroll £150
113 10s. green and red/*pale emerald* (1926) 70·00 85·00
a. Break in scroll £275
b. Broken crown and scroll £275
c. *Green and scarlet/emerald* (1927) £275 £450
ca. Break in scroll £750
cb. Broken crown and scroll £750
100/13 .. .. *Set of* 13 £150 £200
100/13 Optd/Perf "Specimen" .. *Set of* 13 £350

For illustrations of tbe other varieties on Nos. 109/13 see above Leeward Islands No. 58.

17 King George V and Symbol of the Protectorate

(Des Major H. E. Green. Recess Waterlow)

1934 (June)–**35**. *Wmk Mult Script CA. P* 12½.
114 **17** ½d. green 75 85
115 1d. brown 75 75
116 1½d. carmine .. .. 75 2·00
117 2d. pale grey .. .. 80 1·25
118 3d. blue .. .. 2·25 1·50
119 4d. bright magenta (20.5.35) .. .. 2·25 3·00
120 6d. violet .. .. 2·00 40
121 9d. olive-bistre (20.5.35) .. .. 4·25 9·00
122 1s. black and orange .. .. .. 6·00 11·00
114/22 .. .. .. *Set of* 9 18·00 27·00
114/22 Perf "Specimen" .. .. *Set of* 9 £150

1935 (6 May). *Silver Jubilee. As Nos.* 114/17 *of Jamaica, but ptd by Waterlow. P* 11×12.
123 1d. ultramarine and grey .. .. .. 1·00 1·50
k. Kite and vertical log .. .. .. 70·00
m. "Bird" by turret .. .. .. 85·00
124 2d. green and indigo .. .. .. 1·00 60
m. "Bird" by turret .. .. .. 85·00
125 3d. brown and deep blue .. .. .. 7·00 13·00
k. Kite and vertical log £150
126 1s. slate and purple .. .. .. 16·00 27·00
k. Kite and vertical log £225
123/6 .. .. *Set of* 4 22·00 38·00
123/6 Perf "Specimen" .. .. *Set of* 4 80·00

For illustrations of plate varieties see Omnibus section following Zimbabwe.

1937 (12 May). *Coronation. As Nos.* 118/20 *of Jamaica, but ptd by B.W. P* 11×11½.
127 ½d. green 30 50
128 1d. brown 50 40
129 2d. grey-black 50 90
127/9 .. .. *Set of* 3 1·10 1·60
127/9 Perf "Specimen" .. .. *Set of* 3 55·00

18 Symbol of the Protectorate 19

(T **18** recess Waterlow; T **19** typo D.L.R.)

1938 (1 Jan)–**44**. *Chalk-surfaced paper* (2s. *to* £1). *P* 12½ (T **18**) *or* 14 (T **19**). (*a*) *Wmk Mult Script CA*
130 **18** ½d. green 30 85
130*a* ½d. brown (12.12.42) .. .. .. 10 1·25
131 1d. brown 40 15
131*a* 1d. green (12.12.42) 30 50
132 1½d. carmine .. .. 1·75 4·00
132*a* 1½d. grey (12.12.42) .. .. .. 30 3·25
133 2d. grey .. .. 3·00 90
133*a* 2d. carmine (12.12.42) 30 80
134 3d. blue 60 30
135 4d. bright magenta .. .. .. 1·50 80
136 6d. violet .. .. 1·75 80
137 9d. olive-bistre .. .. .. 2·50 2·25
138 1s. black and orange .. .. .. 2·75 90
139 **19** 2s. purple and blue/*blue* .. .. 10·00 7·50
140 2s. 6d. black and red/*blue* .. .. 12·00 7·50
141 5s. pale green and red/*yellow* .. 40·00 17·00
a. Ordinary paper. *Green and red/pale yellow* (3.44) .. .. 95·00 70·00
142 10s. emerald and deep red/*pale green* 60·00 23·00
a. Ordinary paper. *Bluish green and brown-red/pale green* (1.38) .. £300 £170

(*b*) *Wmk Mult Crown CA*
143 **19** £1 purple and black/*red* .. .. 30·00 23·00
c. Serif on "G" £300
130/43 .. .. *Set of* 18 £150 85·00
130/43 Perf "Specimen" .. *Set of* 18 £600

No. 141a has a yellow surfacing often applied in horizontal lines giving the appearance of laid paper.

The printer's archives record the despatch of No. 142a to Nyasaland in January 1938, but no used examples have been reported before 1945.

20 Lake Nyasa 21 King's African Rifles

(Recess B.W.)

1945 (1 Sept). *T* **20/1** *and similar designs. Wmk Mult Script CA* (*sideways on horiz designs*). *P* 12.
144 ½d. black and chocolate 30 10
145 1d. black and emerald 40 70
146 1½d. black and grey-green 20 50
147 2d. black and scarlet 30 30
148 3d. black and light blue 20 30
149 4d. black and claret .. .. .. 1·00 45
150 6d. black and violet .. .. .. 1·25 40
151 9d. black and olive .. .. .. 1·50 2·50
152 1s. indigo and deep green .. .. .. 1·25 20
153 2s. emerald and maroon .. .. .. 3·75 4·25
154 2s. 6d. emerald and blue .. .. .. 7·50 4·00
155 5s. purple and blue .. .. .. 4·50 6·00
156 10s. claret and emerald .. .. .. 12·00 10·00
157 20s. scarlet and black .. .. .. 17·00 20·00
144/57 .. .. *Set of* 14 45·00 45·00
144/57 Perf "Specimen" .. *Set of* 14 £275

Designs: *Horiz*—1½d., 6d. Tea estate; 2d., 1s., 10s. Map of Nyasaland; 4d., 2s. 6d. Tobacco; 9d. Type **20**; 5s., 20s. Badge of Nyasaland. *Vert*—3d., 2s. Fishing Village.

1946 (16 Dec). *Victory. As Nos.* 141/2 *of Jamaica.*
158 1d. green 10 10
159 2d. red-orange 30 10
158/9 Perf "Specimen" .. .. *Set of* 2 50·00

26 Symbol of the Protectorate 27 Arms in 1891 and 1951

(Recess B.W.)

1947 (20 Oct). *Wmk Mult Script CA. P* 12.
160 **26** 1d. red-brown and yellow-green 50 20
160 Perf "Specimen" .. .. .. 45·00

1948 (15 Dec). *Royal Silver Wedding. As Nos.* 143/4 *of Jamaica.*
161 1d. green 15 10
162 10s. mauve .. .. 15·00 23·00

1949 (21 Nov). *75th Anniv of U.P.U. As Nos.* 145/8 *of Jamaica.*
163 1d. blue-green 50 20
164 3d. greenish blue .. .. 2·00 2·00
165 6d. purple .. .. 1·00 50
166 1s. ultramarine 75 50
163/6 .. .. *Set of* 4 3·75 2·75

(Des C. Twynam. Recess B.W.)

1951 (15 May). *Diamond Jubilee of Protectorate. Wmk Mult Script CA. P* 11 × 12.
167 **27** 2d. black and scarlet .. .. 1·00 75
168 3d. black and turquoise-blue .. 1·00 75
169 6d. black and violet .. .. 1·00 1·25
170 5s. black and indigo .. .. 1·75 6·00
167/70 .. .. *Set of* 4 4·25 8·00

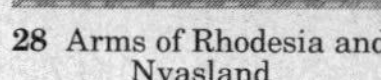

28 Arms of Rhodesia and Nyasaland 29 Grading Cotton

(Recess Waterlow)

1953 (30 May). *Rhodes Centenary Exhibition. Wmk Mult Script CA. P* 14×13½.
171 **28** 6d. violet 20 30

1953 (2 June). *Coronation. As No.* 153 *of Jamaica, but ptd by B.W.*
172 2d. black and brown-orange 50 40

(Recess B.W.)

1953 (1 Sept)–**54**. *Designs previously used for King George VI issue, but with portrait of Queen Elizabeth II as in T* **29**. *Wmk Mult Script CA. P* 12.
173 ½d. black and chocolate 10 85
a. Perf 12 × 12½ (8.3.54) 10 75
174 1d. brown and bright green 65 20
175 1½d. black and deep grey-green .. .. 20 1·90
176 2d. black and yellow-orange 85 30
a. Perf 12 × 12½ (8.3.54) 30 10
177 2½d. green and black 20 50
178 3d. black and scarlet 30 10
179 4½d. black and light blue 30 40
180 6d. black and violet 90 90
a. Perf 12 × 12½ (8.3.54) 90 50
181 9d. black and deep olive .. .. .. 70 2·50
182 1s. deep blue and slate-green .. .. 1·75 50
183 2s. deep green and brown-red .. .. 2·00 3·00
184 2s. 6d. deep emerald and deep blue .. 3·25 4·25
185 5s. purple and Prussian blue .. .. 7·00 4·50
186 10s. carmine and deep emerald .. .. 4·25 11·00
187 20s. red and black .. .. .. 13·00 14·00
173a/87 .. .. .. *Set of* 15 30·00 40·00

Designs: *Horiz*—½d., 9d. Lake Nyasa; 1½d., 6d. Tea estate; 2d., 1s., 10s. Map of Nyasaland; 3d., 2s. 6d. Tobacco; 5s., 20s. Badge of Nyasaland. *Vert*—1d. Symbol of the protectorate; 4½d., 2s. Fishing village.

Stamps perf 12 × 12½ come from sheets comb-perforated 11.8 × 12.25. They were also issued in coils of 480 stamps made up from sheets.

For issues between 1954 and 1963, see RHODESIA AND NYASALAND.

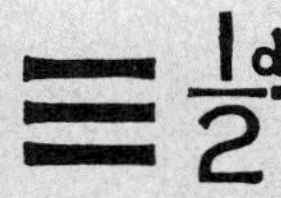

30 (31)

(Recess B.W.)

1963 (1 Nov). *Revenue stamps optd* "POSTAGE", *as in T* **30**, *or additionally surch as T* **31**. *P* 12.
188 ½d. on 1d. greenish blue 30 30
189 1d. green 30 10
190 2d. scarlet 30 30
191 3d. blue 30 10
192 6d. brown-purple 30 10
193 9d. on 1s. cerise 40 25
194 1s. purple 45 10
195 2s. 6d. black .. .. 60 2·00
196 5s. chocolate .. .. 1·25 1·50
197 10s. yellow-olive .. .. 2·50 4·25
a. *Greenish olive* .. .. .. 8·50 13·00
198 £1 deep violet .. .. 3·75 4·25
188/98 .. .. .. *Set of* 11 9·00 12·00

32 Mother and Child 33 Chambo (fish)

34 Tea Industry 35 Nyala

(Des V. Whiteley. Photo Harrison)

1964 (1 Jan). *Designs as T* **32/5**. *P* 14½.
199 ½d. reddish violet 10 30
200 1d. black and green 10 10
201 2d. light red-brown 10 10
202 3d. red-brown, yellow-green & bistre-brown 10 10
203 4d. indigo and orange-yellow 20 30
204 6d. purple, yellow-green and light blue .. 60 30
205 1s. brown, turquoise-blue and pale yellow .. 15 10
206 1s. 3d. bronze-green and chestnut .. 2·25 10
207 2s. 6d. brown and blue .. .. 2·25 50
208 5s. blue, green, yellow and black .. 1·25 1·25
209 10s. green, orange-brown and black .. 1·75 3·00
210 £1 deep reddish purple and yellow .. 7·00 4·25
199/210 .. .. .. *Set of* 12 14·00 9·00

Designs: *As T* **32/3**—2d. Zebu Bull; 3d. Groundnuts; 4d. Fishing. *As T* **34**—1s. Timber; 1s. 3d. Turkish tobacco industry; 2s. 6d. Cotton industry; 5s. Monkey Bay, Lake Nyasa; 10s. Forestry, Afzelia.

Nyasaland attained independence on 5 July 1964 when the country was renamed Malawi.

MALAWI

INDEPENDENT

44 Dr. H. Banda (Prime Minister) and Independence Monument

(Des M. Goaman. Photo Harrison)

1964 (6 July). *Independence. T* **44** *and similar horiz designs. P* 14½.

211	3d. yellow-olive and deep sepia	10	10
212	6d. red, gold, blue, carmine and lake	10	10
213	1s. 3d. red, green, black and bluish violet	35	10
214	2s. 6d. multicoloured	45	75
	a. Blue omitted	£350	
211/14	*Set of* 4	80	85

Designs:—6d. Banda and rising sun. 1s. 3d. Banda and Malawi flag; 2s. 6d. Banda and Malawi coat of arms.

Six examples of No. 214a are known from the top horizontal row of an otherwise normal sheet.

48 Tung Tree

49 Christmas Star and Globe

(Des V. Whiteley. Photo Harrison)

1964 (6 July)–**65.** *As Nos.* 199/210, *but inscr* "MALAWI" *and T* **48** (*9d.*). *No wmk. P* 14½.

215	½d. reddish violet	10	35
216	1d. black and green	10	10
217	2d. light red-brown	10	10
218	3d. red-brown, yellow-green & bistre-brown	15	10
219	4d. black and orange-yellow	60	15
220	6d. bluish violet, yellow-green and light blue	75	10
221	9d. bistre-brown, green and yellow	30	15
222	1s. brown, turquoise-blue and pale yellow	25	10
223	1s. 3d. bronze-green and chestnut	50	60
224	2s. 6d. brown and blue	1·10	1·00
225	5s. blue, green, yellow and sepia	65	2·25
225*a*	5s. blue, green, yellow and sepia (1.6.65)	5·00	90
226	10s. green, orange-brown and black	1·50	2·00
227	£1 deep reddish purple and yellow	7·00	5·50
215/27	*Set of* 14	16·00	11·50

No. 225*a* is inscribed "LAKE MALAWI" instead of "LAKE NYASA".

See also Nos. 252/62.

(Des V. Whiteley. Photo Harrison)

1964 (1 Dec). *Christmas. P* 14½.

228	**49**	3d. blue-green and gold	10	10
		a. Gold (star) omitted	95·00	
229		6d. magenta and gold	10	10
230		1s. 3d. reddish violet and gold	10	10
231		2s. 6d. blue and gold	20	25
228/31		*Set of* 4	30	30
MS231*a*		83 × 126 mm. Nos. 228/31. Imperf	1·00	1·75

No. 228a comes from a sheet on which 41 examples had the gold colour omitted due to a paper fold.

50 Coins

(**51**)

(Des V. Whiteley. Photo Enschedé)

1965 (1 Mar). *Malawi's First Coinage. Coins in black and silver. P* 13½.

232	**50**	3d. green	10	10
233		9d. magenta	20	10
		a. Silver omitted	†	—
234		1s. 6d. purple	25	10
235		3s. blue	35	50
232/5		*Set of* 4	75	65
MS235*a*		126 × 104 mm. Nos. 232/5. Imperf	1·40	1·10

1965 (14 June). *Nos.* 223/4 *surch as T* **51**.

236	1s. 6d. on 1s. 3d. bronze-green and chestnut	10	10
237	3s. on 2s. 6d. brown and blue	20	20

On No. 237 "3/–" occurs below the bars.

52 Chilembwe leading Rebels

(Des M. Goaman. Photo Harrison)

1965 (20 Aug). *50th Anniv of* 1915 *Rising. P* 14 × 14½.

238	**52**	3d. violet and light olive-green	10	10
239		9d. olive-brown and red-orange	10	10
240		1s. 6d. red-brown and grey-blue	15	10
241		3s. turquoise-green and slate-blue	20	25
238/41		*Set of* 4	40	40
MS241*a*		127 × 83 mm. Nos. 238/41	6·50	7·00

53 "Learning and Scholarship"

(Des H. E. Baxter. Photo Harrison)

1965 (6 Oct). *Opening of Malawi University. P* 14½.

242	**53**	3d. black and emerald	10	10
243		9d. black and magenta	10	10
244		1s. 6d. black and reddish violet	10	10
245		3s. black and blue	15	40
242/5		*Set of* 4	30	50
MS246		127 × 84 mm. Nos. 242/5	3·00	3·00

54 *Papilio ophidicephalus*

(Des V. Whiteley. Photo Enschedé)

1966 (15 Feb). *Malawi Butterflies. T* **54** *and similar horiz designs. Multicoloured. P* 13½.

247	4d. Type **54**	80	10
248	9d. *Papilio desmondi* (*magdae*)	1·25	10
249	1s. 6d. *Epamera handmani*	1·75	30
250	3s. *Amauris crawshayi*	2·75	6·00
247/50	*Set of* 4	6·00	6·00
MS251	130×100 mm. Nos. 247/50	16·00	11·00

55 Cockerels

56 Burley Tobacco

57 *Cyrestis camillus* (butterfly)

(New values des V. Whiteley (1s. 6d.), M. Goaman (£2). Photo Harrison)

1966–67. *As Nos.* 215 *etc. but W* **55** (*sideways on* ½*d.,* 2*d.*), *and new values and designs* (*1s. 6d., £2*). *P* 14½.

252	–	½d. reddish violet (1.4.66)	10	10
253	–	1d. black and green (1.4.66)	15	10
254	–	2d. light red-brown (4.6.66)*	15	10
255	–	3d. red-brn, yell-grn & bis-brn (4.3.67)*	20	10
256	–	6d. bluish violet, yell-grn & lt bl (2.7.66)*	1·00	30
257	**48**	9d. bistre-brown, green & yell (5.12.66)*	55	10
258	–	1s. brown, turquoise-bl & pale yell (1.4.66)	25	10
259	**56**	1s. 6d. chocolate & yellow-grn (15.11.66)	30	10
260	–	5s. blue, green, yellow & sepia (6.10.66)*	8·50	2·00
261	–	10s. green, orange-brown & blk (6.10.66)*	17·00	19·00
262	**57**	£2 black, orange-yellow, pale yellow and slate-violet (7.9.66)	25·00	24·00
252/62		*Set of* 11	45·00	40·00

*These are local dates of issue. The Crown Agents, in London, did not distribute these printings until some time later.

No. 260 exists inscribed "LAKE MALAWI".

The 2d. exists with both PVA gum and gum arabic.

58 British Central Africa 6d. Stamp of 1891

59 President Banda

(Des V. Whiteley. Photo Harrison)

1966 (4 May–10 June). *75th Anniv of Postal Services. W* **55**. *P* 14½.

263	**58**	4d. grey-blue and yellow-green	10	10
264		9d. grey-blue and claret	15	10
265		1s. 6d. grey-blue and reddish lilac	20	10
266		3s. grey-blue and new blue	30	30
263/6		*Set of* 4	60	35
MS267		83 × 127 mm. Nos. 263/6 (10 June)	5·00	3·25

REPUBLIC

(Des M. Goaman. Photo Harrison)

1966 (6 July). *Republic Day. W* **55**. *P* 14 × 14½.

268	**59**	4d. brown, silver and emerald	10	10
269		9d. brown, silver and magenta	10	10
270		1s. 6d. brown, silver and violet	15	10
271		3s. brown, silver and blue	25	15
268/71		*Set of* 4	50	30
MS272		83 × 127 mm. Nos. 268/71	2·00	2·25

60 Bethlehem

(Des and photo Harrison)

1966 (12 Oct). *Christmas. W* **55**. *P* 14½.

273	**60**	4d. myrtle-green and gold	10	10
274		9d. brown-purple and gold	10	10
275		1s. 6d. orange-red and gold	15	10
276		3s. blue and gold	40	50
273/6		*Set of* 4	65	55

61 *Ilala I*

(Des Mrs. H. Breggar. Photo Harrison)

1967 (4 Jan). *Lake Malawi Steamers. T* **61** *and similar horiz designs. W* **55**. *P* 14½.

277	4d. black, yellow and bright green	40	10
	a. Yellow omitted	†	£350
278	9d. black, yellow and magenta	45	10
279	1s. 6d., black, red and violet	65	15
280	3s. black, red and bright blue	1·25	1·25
277/80	*Set of* 4	2·50	1·40

Designs:—9d. *Dove*; 1s. 6d. *Chauncy Maples I* (wrongly inscr "Chauncey"); 3s. *Gwendolen*.

No. 277a occurs on first day covers from Blantyre.

62 Golden Mbuna (female)

(Des R. Granger Barrett. Photo Enschedé)

1967 (3 May). *Lake Malawi Cichlids. T* **62** *and similar horiz designs. Multicoloured. W* **55** *(sideways). P* 12½×12.

281	4d. Type **62**	20	10
282	9d. Scraper-mouthed Mbuna	30	10
283	1s. 6d. Zebra Mbuna	40	10
	a. Imperf (pair)	£110	
284	3s. Orange Mbuna	1·25	1·00
	a. Imperf (pair)	£150	
281/4	*Set of* 4	1·90	1·10

63 Rising Sun and Gearwheel

(Des Jennifer Toombs. Litho D.L.R.)

1967 (5 July). *Industrial Development. P* 13½ × 13.

285	**63**	4d. black and emerald	10	10
286		9d. black and carmine	10	10
287		1s. 6d. black and reddish violet	10	10
288		3s. black and bright blue	15	15
285/8		*Set of* 4	30	30
MS289		134 × 108 mm. Nos. 285/8	75	1·40

64 Mary and Joseph beside Crib

(Des Jennifer Toombs. Photo Harrison)

1967 (21 Nov–1 Dec). *Christmas. W* **55**. *P* 14 × 14½.

290	**64**	4d. royal blue and turquoise-green	10	10
291		9d. royal blue and light red	10	10
292		1s. 6d. royal blue and yellow	10	10
293		3s. royal blue and new blue	15	15
290/3		*Set of* 4	30	30
MS294		114 × 100 mm. Nos. 290/3. Wmk sideways. P 14 × 13½ (1 Dec)	1·00	2·50

65 *Calotropis procera*

(Des G. Drummond. Litho D.L.R.)

1968 (24 Apr). *Wild Flowers. T* **65** *and similar horiz designs. Multicoloured. W* **55** *(sideways). P* 13½ × 13.

295	4d. Type **65**	15	10
296	9d. *Borreria dibrachiata*	15	10
297	1s. 6d. *Hibiscus rhodanthus*	15	10
298	3s. *Bidens pinnatipartita*	20	55
295/8	*Set of* 4	60	75
MS299	135 × 91 mm. Nos. 295/8	1·25	2·50

66 Saddleback Steam Locomotive, *Thistle* No. 1

(Des R. Granger Barrett. Photo Harrison)

1968 (24 July). *Malawi Locomotives. T* **66** *and similar horiz designs. W* **55**. *P* 14 × 14½.

300	4d. grey-green, slate-blue and red	40	10
301	9d. red, slate-blue and myrtle-green	50	10
302	1s. 6d. multicoloured	75	25
303	3s. multicoloured	1·40	2·75
300/3	*Set of* 4	2·75	2·75
MS304	120 × 88 mm. Nos. 300/3. P 14½	3·00	6·00

Designs:—9d. Class "G" steam locomotive; 1s. 6d. Diesel locomotive *Zambesi*; 3s. Diesel railcar.

67 "The Nativity" (Piero della Francesca)

(Des and photo Harrison)

1968 (6 Nov). *Christmas. Paintings. T* **67** *and similar horiz designs. Multicoloured. W* **55** *(sideways on 4d.). P* 14 × 14½.

305	4d. Type **67**	10	10
306	9d. "The Adoration of the Shepherds" (Murillo)	10	10
307	1s. 6d. "The Adoration of the Shepherds" (Reni)	10	10
308	3s. "Nativity with God the Father and Holy Ghost" (Pittoni)	15	15
305/8	*Set of* 4	30	30
MS309	115 × 101 mm. Nos. 305/8. P 14 × 13½	35	1·40

68 Scarlet-chested Sunbird

69 Nyasa Lovebird

70 Carmine Bee Eater

(Des V. Whiteley. Photo Harrison)

1968 (13 Nov). *Birds. T* **68/70** *and similar designs. Multicoloured. W* **55** *(sideways on* 1d. *to* 4d. *and* 3s. *to* £1). *P* 14½.

310	1d. Type **68**	15	10
311	2d. Violet Starling	15	10
312	3d. White-browed Robin Chat	20	10
313	4d. Red-billed Fire Finch	35	40
	a. Red omitted	†	—
314	6d. Type **69**	45	15
315	9d. Yellow-rumped Bishop	50	60
316	1s. Type **70**	60	15
317	1s. 6d. Grey-headed Bush Shrike	5·00	7·00
318	2s. Paradise Whydah	5·00	8·00
319	3s. African Paradise Flycatcher	4·50	4·25
320	5s. Bateleur	7·00	4·25
321	10s. Saddle-bill Stork	5·50	7·50
322	£1 Purple Heron	12·00	18·00
323	£2 Knysna Turaco ("Livingstone's Loerie")	38·00	48·00
310/23	*Set of* 14	70·00	85·00

Sizes:—2d. to 4d. as T **68**; 9d. as T **69**; 1s. 6d., 2s., £2 as T **70**; 3s. to £1 as T **70** but vertical.

No. 310 exists in coils, constructed from normal sheets.

An example of No. 313a is known used on local cover from Limbe in September 1970.

71 I.L.O. Emblem

(Des G. Drummond. Photo, emblem die-stamped Harrison)

1969 (5 Feb). *50th Anniv of the International Labour Organization. W* **55** *(sideways on No.* **MS**328). *P* 14.

324	**71**	4d. gold and myrtle-green	10	10
325		9d. gold and chocolate	10	10
326		1s. 6d. gold and blackish brown	10	10
327		3s. gold and indigo	15	15
324/7		*Set of* 4	30	30
MS328		127 × 89 mm. Nos. 324/7	1·75	5·50

72 White-fringed Ground Orchid

73 African Development Bank Emblem

(Des J.W. Litho B.W.)

1969 (9 July). *Orchids of Malawi. T* **72** *and similar horiz designs. Multicoloured. W* **55**. *P* 13½ × 13.

329	4d. Type **72**	15	10
330	9d. Red Ground orchid	20	10
331	1s. 6d. Leopard Tree orchid	30	10
332	3s. Blue Ground orchid	60	1·75
329/32	*Set of* 4	1·10	1·75
MS333	118 × 86 mm. Nos. 329/32	1·10	3·50

(Des G. Vasarhelyi. Litho D.L.R.)

1969 (10 Sept). *Fifth Anniv of African Development Bank. W* **55**. *P* 14.

334	**73**	4d. yellow, yellow-ochre and chocolate	10	10
335		9d. yellow, yellow-ochre & myrtle-green	10	10
336		1s. 6d. yellow, yell-ochre & blackish brn	10	10
337		3s. yellow, yellow-ochre and indigo	15	15
334/7		*Set of* 4	30	30
MS338		102 × 137 mm. Nos. 334/7	50	90

74 Dove over Bethlehem

75 *Zonocerus elegans* (grasshopper)

(Des Jennifer Toombs. Photo Harrison)

1969 (5 Nov). *Christmas. W* **55**. *P* 14½ × 14.

339	**74**	2d. black and olive-yellow	10	10
340		4d. black and deep turquoise	10	10
341		9d. black and scarlet	10	10
342		1s. 6d. black & deep bluish violet	10	10
343		3s. black and ultramarine	15	15
339/43		*Set of* 5	30	30
MS344		130 × 71 mm. Nos. 339/43	1·00	1·75
		a. Ultramarine (background of 3s.) omitted	£450	

(Des V. Whiteley. Litho Format)

1970 (4 Feb). *Insects of Malawi. T* **75** *and similar vert designs. Multicoloured. W* **55**. *P* 14.

345	4d. Type **75**	15	10
346	9d. *Mylabris dicincta* (beetle)	15	10
347	1s. 6d. *Henosepilachna elaterii* (ladybird)	20	10
348	3s. *Sphodromantis speculabunda* (mantid)	35	45
345/8	*Set of* 4	75	55
MS349	86×137 mm. Nos. 345/8	1·25	2·25

Rand Easter Show
1970

(76)

1970 (18 Mar). *Rand Easter Show. No.* 317 *optd with T* **76**.

350	1s. 6d. multicoloured	40	1·50

77 Runner

(Des J. Cooter. Litho B.W.)

1970 (3 June). *Ninth British Commonwealth Games, Edinburgh. W* **55**. *P* 13.

351	**77**	4d. royal blue and blue-green	10	10
352		9d. royal blue and carmine	10	10
353		1s. 6d. royal blue and dull yellow	10	10
354		3s. royal blue and new blue	15	15
351/4		*Set of* 4	30	30
MS355		146 × 96 mm. Nos. 351/4	55	90

(New Currency, 100 tambalas = 1 kwacha)

10t

(78)

79 *Aegocera trimeni*

1970 (2 Sept). *Decimal Currency. Nos.* 316 *and* 318 *surch as T* **78**.

356	10 t. on 1s. multicoloured	1·75	25
	a. Surch double	†	—
357	20 t. on 2s. multicoloured	2·25	2·50

(Des R. Granger Barrett. Litho B.W.)

1970 (30 Sept). *Moths. T* **79** *and similar horiz designs. Multicoloured. W* **55.** *P* 11 × 11½.

358 4d. Type **79** 20 10
359 9d. *Faidherbia bauhiniae* 30 10
360 1s. 6d. *Parasa karschi* 50 20
361 3s. *Teracotona euprepia* .. .. .. 1·25 3·00
358/61 .. .. *Set of* 4 2·00 3·00
MS362 112×92 mm. Nos. 358/61 .. .. 4·00 4·50

80 Mother and Child

30t
Special
United
Kingdom
Delivery
Service

(81)

(Des Brother W. Meyer. Litho J.W.)

1970 (4 Nov). *Christmas. W* **55** *(sideways). P* 14.

363 **80** 2d. black and light yellow 10 10
364 4d. black and emerald 10 10
365 9d. black and orange-red 10 10
366 1s. 6d. black and light purple 10 10
367 3s. black and blue 15 15
363/7 .. .. *Set of* 5 30 30
MS368 166 × 100 mm. Nos. 363/7 .. .. 1·00 1·75

1971 (8 Feb). *No. 319 surch with T* **81.**

369 30 t. on 3s. multicoloured .. .. .. 50 2·00

No. 369 was issued for use on letters carried by an emergency airmail service from Malawi to Great Britain during the British postal strike. The fee of 30 t. was to cover the charge for delivery by a private service, and ordinary stamps to pay the normal airmail fee had to be affixed as well.

The strike ended on 8 March, when private delivery services were withdrawn.

82 Decimal Coinage and Cockerel

(Des V. Whiteley. Litho Format)

1971 (15 Feb). *Decimal Coinage. W* **55** *(sideways). P* 14.

370 **82** 3 t. multicoloured 15 10
371 8 t. multicoloured 20 10
372 15 t. multicoloured 25 15
373 30 t. multicoloured .. .. .. 35 1·00
370/3 .. .. *Set of* 4 85 1·25
MS374 140 × 101 mm. Nos. 370/73 .. .. 1·00 1·75

83 Greater Kudu **84** Eland

(Des and litho J.W.)

1971 (15 Feb)–**75.** *Decimal Currency. Antelopes. Vert designs as T* **83** *(1 t. to 8 t.), or T* **84** *(others). Multicoloured. W* **55** *(sideways* on 1 t. to 8 t.). P* 13½×14 *(1 t to 8 t.) or* 14½ *(others).*

375 1 t. Type **83** 10 10
a. Coil stamp. P 14½×14 .. .. 15 40
b. Perf 14† *(wmk cockerel facing right)* (12.11.74) 45 55
376 2 t. Nyala 15 10
w. Wmk cockerel facing right (5.2.75) .. 30 30
377 3 t. Mountain Reedbuck 20 50
a. Perf 14† *(wmk cockerel facing right)* (12.11.74) 65 75
378 5 t. Puku 40 60
a. Perf 14† *(wmk cockerel facing right)* (12.11.74) 65 90
379 8 t. Impala 45 50
380 10 t. Type **84** 60 10
381 15 t. Klipspringer .. .. .. 1·00 20
w. Wmk inverted .. .. .. † —
382 20 t. Suni .. .. 1·50 90
383 30 t. Roan Antelope .. .. .. 7·00 90
384 50 t. Waterbuck 90 65
w. Wmk inverted (9.5.73) 90 75
385 1 k. Bushbuck .. .. .. 2·00 85
386 2 k. Red Forest Duiker .. .. .. 3·50 1·50
387 4 k. Common Duiker .. .. .. 20·00 17·00
375/87 .. .. *Set of* 13 32·00 21·00

*The normal sideways watermark shows the cockerel's head facing left *as seen from the back of the stamp.*

†These actually gauge 14.2×14 instead of 13.7×14 and are line-perforated; in blocks they can easily be distinguished as in alternate rows across the sheet the horizontal perfs have two holes where they cross the vertical perfs.

No. 387 is incorrectly inscr "Gray Duiker".

85 Christ on the Cross **87** *Holarrhena febrifuga*

(Des G. Drummond. Litho Questa)

1971 (7 Apr). *Easter. Details from Painting "The Small Passion" by Dürer. T* **85** *and similar vert design. W* **55.** *P* 13½.

388 3 t. black and green 10 15
a. Pair. Nos. 388/9 .. .. .. 10 30
389 3 t. black and green 10 15
390 8 t. black and orange-red 10 15
a. Pair. Nos. 390/1 .. .. .. 15 30
391 8 t. black and orange-red 10 15
392 15 t. black and violet 20 25
a. Pair. Nos. 392/3 .. .. .. 40 50
393 15 t. black and violet 20 25
394 30 t. black and bright blue 25 40
a. Pair. Nos. 394/5 .. .. .. 50 80
395 30 t. black and bright blue 25 40
388/95 .. .. *Set of* 8 95 1·75
MS396 Two sheets each 95 × 145 mm (a) Nos. 388, 390, 392 and 394; (b) Nos. 389, 391, 393 and 395 3·25 3·50

Designs:—Nos. 388, 390, 392 and 394, Type **85**; Nos. 389, 391, 393 and 395, The Resurrection.

Nos. 388/9, 390/1, 392/3 and 394/5 were each printed together, *se-tenant,* in pairs throughout the sheet.

(Des G. Drummond. Litho J.W.)

1971 (14 July). *Flowering Shrubs and Trees. T* **87** *and similar vert designs. Multicoloured. W* **55.** *P* 14.

397 3 t. Type **87** 10 10
398 8 t. *Brachystegia spiciformis* 15 10
399 15 t. *Securidaca longepedunculata* 25 10
400 30 t. *Pterocarpus rotundifolius* 40 50
397/400 .. .. *Set of* 4 80 55
MS401 102 × 135 mm. Nos. 397/400 .. .. 1·40 2·00

88 Drum Major **89** "Madonna and Child" (William Dyce)

(Des J.W. Litho Questa)

1971 (5 Oct). *50th Anniv of Malawi Police Force. W* **55.** *P* 14 × 14½.

402 **88** 30 t. multicoloured .. .. .. 65 1·25

(Des J. Cooter. Litho Format)

1971 (10 Nov). *Christmas. T* **89** *and similar vert designs. Multicoloured. W* **55.** *P* 14½.

403 3 t. Type **89** 10 10
404 8 t. "The Holy Family" (M. Schöngauer) .. 15 10
405 15 t. "The Holy Family with St. John" (Raphael) 20 20
406 30 t. "The Holy Family" (Bronzino) .. .. 50 1·00
403/6 .. .. *Set of* 4 85 1·25
MS407 101 × 139 mm. Nos. 403/6 .. .. 1·40 2·50

90 Vickers Viscount 700

(Des R. Granger Barrett. Litho Questa)

1972 (9 Feb). *Air. Malawi Aircraft. T* **90** *and similar horiz designs. Multicoloured. W* **55** *(sideways). P* 13½.

408 3 t. Type **90** 30 10
409 8 t. Hawker Siddeley H.S.748 .. .. 50 10
410 15 t. Britten Norman Islander 75 30
411 30 t. B.A.C. One Eleven .. .. .. 1·25 2·00
408/11 .. .. *Set of* 4 2·50 2·25
MS412 143×94 mm. Nos. 408/11 .. .. 8·00 5·50

91 Figures (Chencherere Hill) **92** Boxing

(Des R. Granger Barrett. Litho Format)

1972 (10 May). *Rock Paintings. T* **91** *and similar horiz designs. W* **55** *(sideways). P* 13½.

413 3 t. apple-green, grey-green and black .. 35 10
414 8 t. red, grey and black 45 10
415 15 t. multicoloured 70 30
416 30 t. multicoloured .. .. .. 1·00 1·00
413/16 .. .. *Set of* 4 2·25 1·25
MS417 121 × 97 mm. Nos. 413/16. P 15 .. .. 3·50 2·75

Designs:—8 t. Lizard and cat (Chencherere Hill); 15 t. Schematics (Diwa Hill); 30 t. Sun through rain (Mikolongwe Hill).

(Des local artist. Litho Harrison)

1972 (9 Aug). *Olympic Games, Munich. W* **55** *(sideways). P* 14 × 14½.

418 **92** 3 t. multicoloured 10 10
419 8 t. multicoloured 10 10
420 15 t. multicoloured 15 10
421 30 t. multicoloured 35 45
418/21 .. .. *Set of* 4 60 55
MS422 110 × 92 mm. Nos. 418/21. P 14 × 13½ .. 1·25 1·75

93 Arms of Malawi **94** "Adoration of the Kings" (Orcagna)

(Des G. Drummond. Litho Questa)

1972 (20 Oct). *Commonwealth Parliamentary Conference. W* **55.** *P* 13½.

423 **93** 15 t. multicoloured 30 35

(Des V. Whiteley. Litho Questa)

1972 (8 Nov). *Christmas. T* **94** *and similar vert designs. Multicoloured. W* **55.** *P* 14½ × 14.

424 3 t. Type **94** 10 10
425 8 t. "Madonna and Child Enthroned" (Florentine School) 10 10
426 15 t. "Virgin and Child" (Crivelli) 20 10
427 30 t. "Virgin and Child with St. Anne" (Flemish School) 45 70
424/7 .. .. *Set of* 4 70 80
MS428 95 × 121 mm. Nos. 424/7 .. .. 1·10 2·00

"MALAŴI". All issues from No. 429 onwards have a circumflex accent over the "W", to give the correct pronunciation of "Malavi".

95 *Charaxes bohemani*

(Des PAD Studio. Litho Questa)

1973 (7 Feb–5 Apr). *Butterflies. T* **95** *and similar horiz designs. Multicoloured. W* **55** *(sideways). P* 13½ × 14.

429 3 t. Type **95** 20 10
430 8 t. *Uranothauma crawshayi* 45 10
431 15 t. *Charaxes acuminatus* 65 30
432 30 t. *Amauris ansorgei* (inscr in error "EUPHAEDRA ZADDACHI") .. .. 3·00 7·50
433 30 t. *Amauris ansorgei* (inscr corrected) (5 Apr) .. .. 3·00 7·50
429/33 .. .. *Set of* 5 6·50 14·00
MS434 145×95 mm. Nos. 429/32 .. .. 7·00 11·50

96 Livingstone and Map

(Des J.W. Litho Format)

1973 (1 May). *Death Centenary of David Livingstone (1st issue). W* **55** *(sideways). P* 13½ × 14.

435	**96** 3 t. multicoloured	.. .. ..	10	10
436	8 t. multicoloured	.. .. ..	15	10
437	15 t. multicoloured	.. .. ..	20	10
438	30 t. multicoloured	.. .. ..	35	60
435/8	.. ..	*Set of* 4	70	70
MS439	144 × 95 mm. Nos. 435/8	.. .. ..	90	1·50

See also Nos. 450/**MS**451.

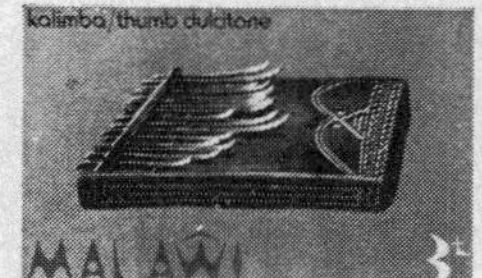

97 Thumb Dulcitone

(Des Jennifer Toombs. Litho Questa)

1973 (8 Aug). *Musical Instruments. T* **97** *and similar multi-coloured designs. W* **55** *(sideways on* 8, 15 *t. and* **MS**444*). P* 14.

440	3 t. Type **97**	.. .. ..	10	10
441	8 t. Hand zither (*vert*)	.. .. ..	15	10
442	15 t. Hand drum (*vert*).	.. .. ..	25	10
443	30 t. One-stringed fiddle	.. .. ..	45	60
440/3	.. ..	*Set of* 4	85	65
MS444	120 × 103 mm. Nos. 440/3	.. .. ..	2·75	2·00

98 The Magi

(Des J.W. Litho Format)

1973 (7 Nov). *Christmas. W* **55** *(sideways). P* 13½.

445	**98** 3 t. greenish blue, dp lilac & dull ultram		10	10
446	8 t. salmon-red, bluish lilac & red-brn		10	10
447	15 t. reddish mve, greenish bl & dp mve		15	10
448	30 t. orange-yell, bluish lilac & lt lake-brn		30	55
445/8	.. ..	*Set of* 4	50	60
MS449	165 × 114 mm. Nos. 445/8	.. .. ..	75	1·40

99 Stained-glass Window, Livingstonia Mission

(Des PAD Studio. Litho Questa)

1973 (12 Dec). *Death Centenary of David Livingstone (2nd issue). W* **55** *(sideways). P* 13½.

450	**99** 50 t. multicoloured	.. .. ..	45	1·00
MS451	71 × 77 mm. No. 450	.. .. ..	80	1·60

100 Large-mouthed Black Bass

(Des Sylvia Goaman. Litho Questa)

1974 (20 Feb). *35th Anniv of Malawi Angling Society. T* **100** *and similar horiz designs. Multicoloured. W* **55** *(sideways). P* 14.

452	3 t. Type **100**	.. .. ..	25	10
453	8 t. Rainbow Trout	.. .. ..	30	10
454	15 t. Silver Alestes ("Lake Salmon")	..	55	20
455	30 t. Tigerfish	.. .. ..	85	75
452/5	.. ..	*Set of* 4	1·75	95
MS456	169×93 mm. Nos. 452/5	.. .. ..	2·25	1·75

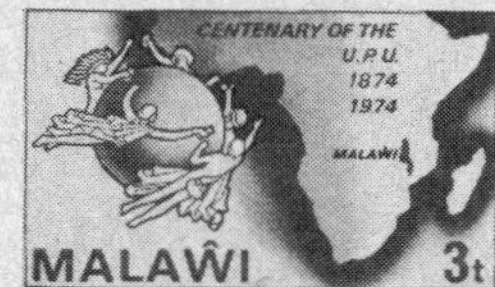

101 U.P.U. Monument and Map of Africa

(Des J. Cooter. Litho J.W.)

1974 (24 Apr). *Centenary of Universal Postal Union. W* **55** *(sideways). P* 13½ *(Nos.* 460/**MS**461*) or* 14½ × 14 *(others).*

457	**101** 3 t. green and ochre	.. .. ..	10	10
	a. Perf 13½ (pair)	.. .. ..	£200	
458	8 t. red and ochre	.. .. ..	10	10
459	15 t. violet and ochre	.. .. ..	15	10
460	30 t. indigo and ochre	.. .. ..	30	70
457/60	.. ..	*Set of* 4	60	80
MS461	115 × 146 mm. Nos. 457/60	.. ..	65	1·75
	a. Perf 14½ × 14	.. .. ..	£550	

No. 457a comes from normal sheets and not No. **MS**461. It can also be identified as a marginal single.

102 Capital Hill, Lilongwe

(Des PAD Studio. Litho Questa)

1974 (3 July). *Tenth Anniv of Independence. W* **55** *(sideways). P* 14.

462	**102** 3 t. multicoloured	.. .. ..	10	10
463	8 t. multicoloured	.. .. ..	10	10
464	15 t. multicoloured	.. .. ..	10	10
465	30 t. multicoloured	.. .. ..	25	35
462/5	.. ..	*Set of* 4	40	40
MS466	120 × 86 mm. Nos. 462/5	.. .. ..	45	1·00

103 "Madonna of the Meadow" (Bellini)

104 Arms of Malawi

(Des Jennifer Toombs. Litho Enschedé)

1974 (4 Dec). *Christmas. T* **103** *and similar horiz designs. Multi-coloured. W* **55** *(sideways). P* 13 × 13½.

467	3 t. Type **103**	.. .. ..	10	10
468	8 t. "The Holy Family with Sts. John and Elizabeth" (Jordaens)	..	10	10
469	15 t. "The Nativity" (Pieter de Grebber)	..	15	10
470	30 t. "Adoration of the Shepherds" (Lorenzo di Credi)	..	30	50
467/70	.. ..	*Set of* 4	50	50
MS471	163 × 107 mm. Nos. 467/70	.. ..	60	1·25

(Des and litho Harrison)

1975 (1 Feb)–**84**. *Coil stamps. W* **55** *(sideways). P* 14½×14.

472	**104** 1 t. deep blue	.. .. ..	20	40
472*a*	5 t. bright carmine (20.9.84)	..	50	85

105 African Snipe

106 Spur-winged Goose

(Des J.W. Litho Questa)

1975 (19 Feb). *Birds. T* **105/6** *and similar multicoloured designs. W* **55** *(sideways on* 2, 3, 8, 50 *t.,* 1 *k.,* 4 *k.). White, ordinary paper.*

(*a*) *Size as T* **105**. *P* 13½ × 14 (1, 5 *t.*) *or* 14 × 13½ *(others)*

473	1 t. Type **105**	.. .. ..	30	1·50
474	2 t. Double-banded Sandgrouse	.. ..	50	1·50
475	3 t. Blue Quail	.. .. ..	1·50	1·50
476	5 t. Bare-throated Francolin	.. ..	3·50	1·25
477	8 t. Harlequin Quail	.. .. ..	4·75	1·00

(*b*) *Size as T* **106**. *P* 14

478	10 t. Type **106**	.. .. ..	8·50	50
479	15 t. Barrow's Bustard	.. .. ..	3·75	3·75
480	20 t. Comb Duck	.. .. ..	1·00	2·25
481	30 t. Helmet Guineafowl	.. .. ..	1·25	70
482	50 t. African Pigmy Goose	.. .. ..	2·00	1·60
483	1 k. Garganey	.. .. ..	3·00	7·00
484	2 k. White-faced Whistling Duck	.. ..	13·00	14·00
485	4 k. African Green Pigeon	.. ..	13·00	16·00
473/85	.. ..	*Set of* 13	50·00	45·00

See also Nos. 501/4

107 M.V. *Mpasa*

108 *Habenaria splendens*

(Des R. Granger Barrett. Litho J.W.)

1975 (12 Mar). *Ships of Lake Malawi (1st series). T* **107** *and similar horiz designs. Multicoloured. W* **55** *(sideways). P* 13½.

486	3 t. Type **107**	.. .. ..	30	10
487	8 t. M.V. *Ilala II*	.. .. ..	40	10
488	15 t. M.V. *Chauncy Maples II*	.. ..	75	30
489	30 t. M.V. *Nkwazi*	.. .. ..	1·00	2·25
486/9	.. ..	*Set of* 4	2·25	2·50
MS490	105 × 142 mm. Nos. 486/9. P 14	.. ..	2·25	3·00

See also Nos. 728/32.

(Des Sylvia Goaman. Litho Questa)

1975 (6 June). *Malawi Orchids. T* **108** *and similar vert designs. Multicoloured. W* **55**. *P* 14.

491	3 t. Type **108**	.. .. ..	35	10
492	10 t. *Eulophia cucullata*	.. .. ..	45	10
493	20 t. *Disa welwitschii*	.. .. ..	70	25
494	40 t. *Angraecum conchiferum*	.. ..	1·00	1·50
491/4	.. ..	*Set of* 4	2·25	1·75
MS495	127 × 111 mm. Nos. 491/4	.. ..	6·00	6·00

109 Thick-tailed Bushbaby

10th ACP
Ministerial
Conference
1975

(110)

(Des R. Granger Barrett. Litho Walsall)

1975 (3 Sept). *Malawi Animals. T* **109** *and similar vert designs. Multicoloured. W* **55** *(inverted). P* 14.

496	3 t. Type **109**	.. .. ..	10	10
497	10 t. Leopard	.. .. ..	35	10
498	20 t. Roan Antelope	.. .. ..	55	35
499	40 t. Common Zebra	.. .. ..	1·00	2·75
496/9	.. ..	*Set of* 4	1·75	3·00
MS500	88×130 mm. Nos. 496/9. W **55** (sideways)		2·50	3·00

1975 (1 Oct). *As Nos.* 473 *etc, but no wmk. Toned, chalk-surfaced paper.*

501	3 t. Blue Quail	.. .. ..	3·00	1·25
502	10 t. Type **106**	.. .. ..	2·00	1·25
503	15 t. Barrow's Bustard	.. .. ..	2·00	1·75
504	2 k. White-faced Whistling Duck	.. ..	6·50	9·50
501/4	.. ..	*Set of* 4	12·00	12·50

Nos. 505/13 vacant.

1975 (9 Dec). *Tenth Africa, Caribbean and Pacific Ministerial Conference. No.* 482 *optd with T* **110**.

514	50 t. African Pygmy Goose	.. ..	85	1·50

111 "A Castle with the Adoration of the Magi"

112 Alexander Graham Bell

(Des PAD Studio. Litho J.W.)

1975 (12 Dec). *Christmas. T* **111** *and similar horiz designs showing religious medallions. Multicoloured. W* **55** *(sideways). P* 13 × 13½.
515 3 t. Type **111** 10 10
516 10 t. "The Nativity" 15 10
517 20 t. "The Adoration of the Magi" 20 10
518 40 t. "The Angel appearing to the Shepherds" 50 1·60
515/18 .. .. *Set of* 4 80 1·60
MS519 98 × 168 mm. Nos. 515/18. P 14 .. .. 1·50 2·75

(Des C. Abbott. Litho Questa)

1976 (24 Mar). *Centenary of the Telephone. W* **55**. *P* 14.
520 **112** 3 t. black and dull green 10 10
w. Wmk inverted .. .. .. 6·00
521 10 t. black and magenta 10 10
522 20 t. black and light reddish violet .. 20 10
523 40 t. black and bright blue 50 70
520/3 .. .. *Set of* 4 80 80
MS524 137×114 mm. Nos. 520/3 .. .. 1·10 1·75

113 President Banda

114 Bagnall Diesel Shunter

(Des PAD Studio. Litho J.W.)

1976 (2 July). *Tenth Anniv of the Republic. Multicoloured; frame colour given. W* **55**. *P* 13.
525 **113** 3 t. green 10 10
526 10 t. magenta 10 10
527 20 t. new blue 20 10
528 40 t. dull ultramarine 50 70
525/8 .. .. *Set of* 4 80 80
MS529 102 × 112 mm. Nos. 524/8. P 13½ .. 95 1·50

(Des G. Drummond. Litho Questa)

1976 (1 Oct). *Malawi Locomotives. T* **114** *and similar horiz designs. Multicoloured. W* **55** *(sideways). P* 14½ × 14.
530 3 t. Type **114** 40 10
531 10 t. "Shire" Class diesel locomotive .. 70 10
532 20 t. Nippon Sharyo diesel locomotive .. 1·40 45
533 40 t. Hunslet diesel locomotive .. .. 2·10 4·25
530/3 .. .. *Set of* 4 4·25 4·50
MS534 130×118 mm. Nos. 530/3 .. .. 4·25 4·50

Blantyre Mission Centenary 1876-1976

(115)

116 Child on Bed of Straw

1976 (22 Oct). *Centenary of Blantyre Mission. Nos.* 503 *and* 481 *optd with T* **115**.
535 15 t. Barrow's Bustard .. .. 1·00 75
536 30 t. Helmet Guineafowl .. .. .. 1·25 2·25

(Des Jennifer Toombs. Litho Walsall)

1976 (6 Dec). *Christmas. W* **55**. *P* 14.
537 **116** 3 t. multicoloured 10 10
538 10 t. multicoloured 10 10
539 20 t. multicoloured 20 10
540 40 t. multicoloured 40 60
537/40 .. .. *Set of* 4 70 70
MS541 135 × 95 mm. Nos. 537/40 .. .. 1·40 1·75

117 Man and Woman

118 Chileka Airport

(Des G. Hutchins. Litho Questa)

1977 (1 Apr). *Handicrafts. T* **117** *and similar multicoloured designs showing wood-carvings. W* **55** *(sideways on 10 and 20 t.). P* 14.
542 4 t. Type **117** 10 10
543 10 t. Elephant (*horiz*) 15 10
544 20 t. Rhino (*horiz*) 20 10
545 40 t. Deer 50 70
542/5 .. .. *Set of* 4 80 80
MS546 153 × 112 mm. Nos. 542/5. Wmk sideways 1·50 2·25

(Des Harrison. Litho Walsall)

1977 (12 July). *Transport. T* **118** *and similar horiz designs. Multicoloured. W* **55** *(sideways). P* 14½ × 14.
547 4 t. Type **118** 40 10
548 10 t. Blantyre-Lilongwe Road 40 10
549 20 t. M.V. *Ilala II* .. .. 1·25 35
550 40 t. Blantyre-Nacala rail line .. .. 2·00 3·25
547/50 .. .. *Set of* 4 3·50 3·50
MS551 127 × 83 mm. Nos. 547/50 .. .. 3·50 3·50

119 Blue-grey Mbuna

120 "Madonna and Child with St. Catherine and the Blessed Stefano Maconi" (Borgognone)

(Des R. Granger Barrett. Litho J.W.)

1977 (4 Oct). *Fish of Lake Malawi. T* **119** *and similar horiz designs. Multicoloured. P* 13½. A. *No wmk*. B. *W* **55** *(sideways).*

		A		B	
552	4 t. Type **119**	50	10	20	10
553	10 t. Livingston's Mbuna ..	60	10	30	20
554	20 t. Zebra Mbuna	1·40	30	—	1·50
555	40 t. Malawi Scale-eater ..	1·40	1·40	1·00	95
552/5	.. .. *Set of* 4	3·50	1·60	†	
MS556	147×99 mm. Nos. 552/5. P 13	3·00	3·25	5·00	6·50

(Des G. Hutchins. Litho Enschedé)

1977 (21 Nov). *Christmas. T* **120** *and similar vert designs. Multicoloured; frame colours given. No wmk. P* 14 × 13½.
557 4 t. deep blue-green 10 10
558 10 t. light vermilion 10 10
559 20 t. dull violet 20 10
560 40 t. blue 50 70
557/60 .. .. *Set of* 4 80 80
MS561 150 × 116 mm. Nos. 557/60 .. .. 2·50 2·50
Designs:—10 t. "Madonna and Child with the Eternal Father and Angels" (Borgognone); 20 t. Bottigella altarpiece (detail, Foppa); 40 t. "Madonna of the Fountain" (van Eyck).

121 "Entry of Christ into Jerusalem" (Giotto)

122 Nyala

(Des G. Hutchins. Litho Cartor)

1978 (1 Mar). *Easter. T* **121** *and similar vert designs showing paintings by Giotto. Multicoloured. P* 12×12½.
562 4 t. Type **121** 10 10
563 10 t. "The Crucifixion" 15 10
564 20 t. "Descent from the Cross" 30 10
565 40 t. "Jesus appears before Mary" 50 55
562/5 .. .. *Set of* 4 90 70
MS566 150 × 99 mm. Nos. 562/5 .. .. 1·90 1·60

(Des G. Hutchins. Litho Enschedé)

1978 (1 June). *Wildlife. T* **122** *and similar multicoloured designs. P* 13½ × 13 (4, 40 *t.*) *or* 13 × 13½ (*others*).
567 4 t. Type **122** .. .. 1·00 10
568 10 t. Lion (*horiz*) .. .. 2·75 30
569 20 t. Common Zebra (*horiz*) .. .. 5·00 80
570 40 t. Mountain Reedbuck .. .. .. 7·00 4·75
567/70 .. .. *Set of* 4 14·00 5·50
MS571 173×113 mm. Nos. 567/70 .. .. 17·00 7·00

123 Malamulo Seventh Day Adventist Church

124 *Vanilla polylepis*

(Des and litho Walsall)

1978 (15 Nov). *Christmas. Churches. T* **123** *and similar horiz designs. Multicoloured. W* **55** *(sideways). P* 13½.
572 4 t. Type **123** 10 10
573 10 t. Likoma Cathedral 10 10
574 20 t. St. Michael's and All Angels', Blantyre .. 20 10
575 40 t. Zomba Catholic Cathedral 40 60
572/5 .. .. *Set of* 4 70 70
MS576 190 × 105 mm. Nos. 572/5 .. .. 70 1·50

(Des G. Drummond. Litho J.W.)

1979 (2 Jan)–**82**. *Orchids. Vert designs as T* **124**. *Multicoloured. W* **55**. *P* 13½.
577 1 t. Type **124** 50 30
578 2 t. *Cirrhopetalum umbellatum* 50 30
w. Wmk inverted .. .. .. 7·50
579 5 t. *Calanthe natalensis* 50 10
580 7 t. *Ansellia gigantea* 50 50
581 8 t. *Tridactyle bicaudata* 50 30
582 10 t. *Acampe pachyglossa* 50 10
w. Wmk inverted (14.6.82) 60 20
583 15 t. *Eulophia quartiniana* 50 15
584 20 t. *Cyrtorchis arcuata (variabilis)* .. 50 50
w. Wmk inverted .. .. ..
585 30 t. *Eulophia tricristata* .. .. .. 1·25 30
586 50 t. *Disa hamatopetala* 85 50
587 75 t. *Cynorchis glandulosa* .. .. .. 2·00 3·50
588 1 k. *Aerangis kotschyana* .. .. .. 1·60 1·25
589 1 k. 50, *Polystachya dendrobiiflora* .. 1·75 2·25
590 2 k. *Disa ornithantha* .. .. .. 1·75 2·00
591 4 k. *Cyrtorchis praetermissa* .. .. 3·00 3·50
577/91 .. .. *Set of* 15 14·50 14·00

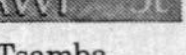

125 Tsamba

126 Train crossing Viaduct

(Des L. Curtis. Litho Questa)

1979 (21 Jan). *National Tree Planting Day. T* **125** *and similar vert designs. Multicoloured. W* **55**. *P* 13½.
592 5 t. Type **125** 20 10
593 10 t. Mulanje Cedar 25 10
594 20 t. Mlombwa 40 20
595 40 t. Mbawa .. .. 70 1·90
592/5 .. .. *Set of* 4 1·40 2·00
MS596 118 × 153 mm. Nos. 592/5 .. .. 1·40 2·00

(Des J.W. Litho Questa)

1979 (17 Feb). *Opening of Salima-Lilongwe Railway. T* **126** *and similar horiz designs. Multicoloured. W* **55** *(sideways) (5 t.) or no wmk (others). P* 14½.
597 5 t. Type **126** 25 10
598 10 t. Diesel railcar at station 40 10
599 20 t. Train rounding bend 60 30
600 40 t. Diesel train passing through cutting .. 85 1·25
597/600 .. .. *Set of* 4 1·90 1·50
MS601 153×103 mm. Nos. 597/600. W **55** (sideways) .. .. 4·00 4·50
Examples of an unissued 4 t. value as Type **126** and of a miniature sheet containing this 4 t. value exist from supplies sent to Malawi before it was decided to increase the internal postage rate to 5 t.

127 Young Child

(Des BG Studio. Litho Questa)

1979 (10 July). *International Year of the Child. T* **127** *and similar horiz designs showing young children. Multicoloured; background colours given. W* **55** *(sideways). P* 13½.
602 5 t. green 10 10
603 10 t. red 10 20
604 20 t. mauve 25 10
605 40 t. blue 45 60
602/5 .. .. *Set of* 4 75 70

128 1964 3d. Independence Commemorative Stamp

(Des J.W. Litho Enschedé)

1979 (17 Sept). *Death Centenary of Sir Rowland Hill. T* **128** *and similar horiz designs showing* 1964 *Independence commemorative stamps. Multicoloured. W* **55** *(sideways*). P* 13×13½.

606 5 t. Type **128** 10 10
607 10 t. 6d. value 10 10
w. Wmk cockerel facing right .. .. 3·00
608 20 t. 1s. 3d. value 20 10
609 40 t. 2s. 6d. value 35 60
606/9 .. .. *Set of* 4 65 70
MS610 163×108mm. Nos. 606/9 .. .. 65 1·40

*The normal sideways watermark has the cockerel facing left, *as seen from the back of the stamp.*

129 River Landscape

130 Limbe Rotary Club Emblem

(Des BG Studio. Litho Format)

1979 (15 Nov). *Christmas. T* **129** *and similar horiz designs showing landscapes. Multicoloured. W* **55** *(sideways). P* 13½ × 14.

611 5 t. Type **129** 10 10
612 10 t. Sunset 10 10
613 20 t. Forest and hill 25 15
614 40 t. Plain and mountain .. .. .. 50 1·40
611/14 .. .. *Set of* 4 85 1·50

(Des L. Curtis. Litho J.W.)

1980 (23 Feb). *75th Anniv of Rotary International. T* **130** *and similar vert designs. W* **55**. *P* 13½.

615 5 t. multicoloured 10 10
616 10 t. multicoloured 10 10
617 20 t. multicoloured 30 15
618 40 t. ultramarine and gold .. .. .. 75 1·60
615/18 .. .. *Set of* 4 1·10 1·75
MS619 105 × 144 mm. Nos. 615/18. P 14 × 14½. 1·25 2·25

Designs:—10 t. Blantyre Rotary Club pennant; 20 t. Lilongwe Rotary Club pennant; 40 t. Rotary International emblem.

131 Mangochi District Post Office

132 Agate Nodule

(Des C. Abbott. Litho Walsall)

1980 (6 May). *"London 1980" International Stamp Exhibition. T* **131** *and similar horiz designs. W* **55** *(sideways). P* 14½ × 14.

620 5 t. black and blue-green 10 10
621 10 t. black and vermilion 10 10
622 20 t. black and violet 15 10
623 1 k. black and deep blue .. .. .. 65 1·10
620/3 .. .. *Set of* 4 80 1·10
MS624 114 × 89 mm. Nos. 620/3 .. .. 1·25 2·25

Designs:–10 t. New Blantyre Sorting Office; 20 t. Mail Transfer Hut, Walala; 1 k. First Nyasaland Post Office, Chiromo.

(Des G. Drummond. Litho J.W.)

1980 (20 Aug). *Gemstones. T* **132** *and similar vert designs. Multicoloured. W* **55**. *P* 13.

625 5 t. Type **132** 60 10
626 10 t. Sunstone 80 10
627 20 t. Smoky Quartz .. .. 1·40 30
628 1 k. Kyanite crystal .. .. 3·50 6·00
625/8 .. .. *Set of* 4 5·75 6·00

133 Elephants

134 Suni

(Des C. Abbott. Litho J.W.)

1980 (10 Nov). *Christmas. Children's Paintings. T* **133** *and similar horiz designs. Multicoloured. W* **55** *(sideways). P* 13.

629 5 t. Type **133** 30 10
630 10 t. Flowers 30 10
631 20 t. "Shire" class diesel train 60 20
632 1 k. Malachite Kingfisher .. .. .. 1·40 2·00
629/32 .. .. *Set of* 4 2·40 2·25

(Des G. Drummond. Litho Questa)

1981 (4 Feb). *Wildlife. T* **134** *and similar horiz designs. Multicoloured. W* **55** *(sideways). P* 14.

633 7 t. Type **134** 15 10
634 10 t. Blue Duiker 20 10
635 20 t. African Buffalo 30 15
636 1 k. Lichtenstein's Hartebeest .. .. 1·25 1·60
633/6 .. .. *Set of* 4 1·75 1·75

135 "Kanjedza II" Standard "A" Earth Station

(Des L. Curtis. Litho Harrison)

1981 (24 Apr). *International Communications. T* **135** *and similar horiz designs. Multicoloured. W* **55** *(sideways). P* 14½.

637 7 t. Type **135** 10 10
638 10 t. Blantyre International Gateway Exchange 15 10
639 20 t. "Kanjedza I" standard "B" earth station 25 15
640 1 k. "Satellite communications" .. .. 1·50 1·90
637/40 .. .. *Set of* 4 1·75 1·90
MS641 101 × 151 mm. Nos. 637/40 .. .. 2·00 3·00

136 Maize

137 "The Adoration of the Shepherds" (Murillo)

(Des Jennifer Toombs. Litho Harrison)

1981 (11 Sept). *World Food Day. Agricultural Produce. T* **136** *and similar horiz designs. Multicoloured. W* **55** *(sideways). P* 14.

642 7 t. Type **136** 15 10
643 10 t. Rice 20 10
644 20 t. Finger-millet 30 20
645 1 k. Wheat .. .. 1·00 1·40
642/5 .. .. *Set of* 4 1·50 1·50

(Des BG Studio. Litho J.W.)

1981 (26 Nov). *Christmas. Paintings. T* **137** *and similar multicoloured designs. W* **55** *(sideways on* 10 *and* 20 *t.). P* 13½ × 13 *(*7 *t.,* 1 *k.) or* 13 × 13½ *(others).*

646 7 t. Type **137** 20 10
647 10 t. "The Holy Family" (Lippi) *(horiz)* .. 25 10
648 20 t. "The Adoration of the Shepherds" (Louis le Nain) *(horiz)* 45 15
649 1 k. "The Virgin and Child, St. John the Baptist and an Angel" (Paolo Morando) 1·10 1·75
646/9 .. .. *Set of* 4 1·75 1·75

138 Impala Herd

(Des A. Theobald. Litho Harrison)

1982 (15 Mar). *National Parks. Wildlife. T* **138** *and similar horiz designs. Multicoloured. W* **55** *(sideways). P* 14½ × 14.

650 7 t. Type **138** 20 10
651 10 t. Lions 35 10
652 20 t. Greater Kudu 50 20
653 1 k. Greater Flamingoes .. .. .. 2·25 4·00
650/3 .. .. *Set of* 4 3·00 4·00

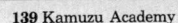

139 Kamuzu Academy

140 Attacker challenging Goalkeeper

(Des PAD Studio. Litho Questa)

1982 (1 July). *Kamuzu Academy. T* **139** *and similar horiz designs showing buildings. W* **55** *(sideways). P* 14½.

654 7 t. multicoloured 15 10
655 20 t. multicoloured 20 10
656 30 t. multicoloured 30 45
657 1 k. multicoloured .. .. 1·00 2·75
654/7 .. .. *Set of* 4 1·50 3·00

(Des and litho Harrison)

1982 (8 Sept). *World Cup Football Championship, Spain. T* **140** *and similar vert designs. Multicoloured. W* **55**. *P* 14 × 15.

658 7 t. Type **140** 55 10
659 20 t. FIFA World Cup trophy .. .. .. 1·25 1·10
660 30 t. Football stadium .. .. 1·50 2·75
658/60 .. .. *Set of* 3 3·00 3·50
MS661 80 × 59 mm. 1 k. Football .. .. 1·50 1·60

141 Blantyre War Memorial, St. Paul's Church

(Des W. Fenton. Litho Format)

1982 (5 Nov). *Remembrance Day. T* **141** *and similar horiz designs. Multicoloured. W* **55** *(sideways). P* 14½ × 14.

662 7 t. Type **141** 10 10
663 20 t. Zomba war memorial 15 10
664 30 t. Chichiri war memorial 20 30
665 1 k. Lilongwe war memorial .. .. .. 65 3·00
662/5 .. .. *Set of* 4 1·00 3·00

142 Kwacha International Conference Centre

143 "Christ and St. Peter"

(Des Walsall. Litho Format)

1983 (14 Mar). *Commonwealth Day. T* **142** *and similar horiz designs. Multicoloured. W* **55** *(sideways). P* 14.

666 7 t. Type **142** 10 10
667 20 t. Tea-picking, Mulanje 20 10
668 30 t. World map showing position of Malawi 25 30
669 1 k. President Dr. H. Kamuzu Banda .. 60 1·50
666/9 .. .. *Set of* 4 1·00 1·75

(Des C. Abbott. Litho Format)

1983 (4 Apr). *500th Birth Anniv of Raphael. Details from the cartoon for "The Miraculous Draught of Fishes" Tapestry. T* **143** *and similar multicoloured designs. W* **55** *(sideways on* 30 *t.). P* 14.

670 7 t. Type **143** 25 10
671 20 t. "Hauling in the Catch" 60 70
672 30 t. "Fishing Village" *(horiz)* .. .. 90 2·25
670/2 .. .. *Set of* 3 1·60 2·75
MS673 110 × 90 mm. 1 k. "Apostle" .. .. 1·60 1·60

144 Pair by Lake

145 Kamuzu International Airport

(Des N. Arlott. Litho Questa)

1983 (11 July). *African Fish Eagle. T* **144** *and similar vert designs. Multicoloured. W* **55**. *P* 14.

674 30 t. Type **144** .. .. 1·10 1·60
a. Horiz strip of 5. Nos. 674/8 .. .. 5·00
675 30 t. Making gull-like call .. .. .. 1·10 1·60
676 30 t. Diving on prey .. .. 1·10 1·60
677 30 t. Carrying fish .. .. 1·10 1·60
678 30 t. Feeding on catch .. .. 1·10 1·60
674/8 .. .. *Set of* 5 5·00 7·00

Nos. 674/8 were printed together, *se-tenant*, in horizontal strips of 5 throughout the sheet, the backgrounds of each design forming a composite picture of Lake Malawi.

(Des A. Theobald. Litho Questa)

1983 (31 Aug). *Bicentenary of Manned Flight*. *T* **145** *and similar horiz designs. Multicoloured. W* **55** *(sideways). P* 14.

679 7 t. Type **145** 10 10
680 20 t. Kamuzu International Airport (*different*) 25 15
681 30 t. B.A.C. One Eleven 40 45
682 1 k. Short S.23 Empire "C" Class flying boat at Cape Maclear .. .. .. 1·10 2·25
679/82 .. .. *Set of* 4 1·75 2·75
MS683 100×121 mm. Nos. 679/82 .. .. 2·00 4·00

146 *Clerodendrum myricoides*

147 Golden Mbuna

(Des R. Reader. Litho J.W.)

1983 (1 Nov). *Christmas. Flowers. T* **146** *and similar vert designs. Multicoloured. P* 13 (20 *t.*) *or* 14 (*others*).

684 7 t. Type **146** 40 10
a. Perf 13 .. .. 15·00
685 20 t. *Gloriosa superba* 90 15
686 30 t. *Gladiolus laxiflorus* .. .. .. 1·25 60
687 1 k. *Aframomum angustifolium* .. .. 3·00 5·50
684/7 .. .. *Set of* 4 5·00 5·75

(Des L. Curtis. Litho Harrison)

1984 (2 Jan). *Fishes. T* **147** *and similar horiz designs. Multicoloured. W* **55** *(sideways). With imprint date. P* 14½×14.

688 1 t. Type **147** 30 60
689 2 t. Malawi Eyebiter 30 60
690 5 t. Blue Mbuna 30 50
691 7 t. Lombardo's Mbuna 30 10
692 8 t. Golden Zebra Mbuna 30 10
693 10 t. Fairy Cichlid 30 10
694 15 t. Crabro Mbuna 30 10
695 20 t. Marbled Zebra Mbuna 30 10
696 30 t. Sky-blue Mbuna 40 20
697 40 t. Venustus Cichlid 60 30
698 50 t. Thumbi Emperor Cichlid .. .. .. 1·50 1·75
699 75 t. Purple Mbuna .. .. 2·00 2·50
700 1 k. Zebra Mbuna .. .. 2·25 3·00
701 2 k. Fairy Cichlid (*different*) .. .. .. 3·25 4·25
702 4 k. Mbenje Emperor Cichlid .. .. .. 4·50 7·00
688/702 .. .. *Set of* 15 15·00 19·00

Imprint dates: "1984", Nos. 688/702; "1986", Nos. 688, 691/7.

148 Smith's Red Hare

149 Running

(Des Garden Studios. Litho Format)

1984 (2 Feb). *Small Mammals. T* **148** *and similar horiz designs. Multicoloured. W* **55** *(sideways). P* 14.

703 7 t. Type **148** 40 10
704 20 t. Gambian Sun Squirrel .. .. .. 1·00 50
705 30 t. South African Hedgehog .. .. .. 1·50 1·10
706 1 k. Large-spotted Genet .. .. .. 1·75 5·50
703/6 .. .. *Set of* 4 4·25 6·50

(Des C. Collins. Litho Harrison)

1984 (1 June). *Olympic Games, Los Angeles. T* **149** *and similar vert designs. Multicoloured. W* **55** *(sideways). P* 14.

707 7 t. Type **149** 15 10
708 20 t. Boxing 35 20
709 30 t. Cycling 75 70
710 1 k. Long jumping .. .. 1·40 3·25
707/10 .. .. *Set of* 4 2·40 3·75
MS711 90 × 128 mm. Nos. 707/10. Wmk upright 2·40 3·75

150 *Euphaedra neophron*

151 "The Virgin and Child" (Duccio)

(Des and photo Courvoisier)

1984 (1 Aug). *Butterflies. T* **150** *and similar vert designs. Granite paper. P* 11½.

712 7 t. multicoloured 95 30
713 20 t. lemon, blackish brown and red .. .. 2·25 45
714 30 t. multicoloured .. .. 2·50 1·10
715 1 k. multicoloured .. .. 4·25 8·00
712/15 .. .. *Set of* 4 9·00 8·75

Designs:—20 t. *Papilio dardanus*; 30 t. *Antanartia schaeneia*; 1 k. *Spindasis nyassae*.

(Des C. Abbott. Litho Harrison)

1984 (22 Oct). *Christmas. Religious Paintings. T* **151** *and similar vert designs. Multicoloured. W* **55**. *P* 14½.

716 7 t. Type **151** 45 10
717 20 t. "Madonna and Child" (Raphael) .. .. 1·25 20
718 30 t. "The Virgin and Child" (ascr to Lippi) .. 1·75 70
719 1 k. "The Wilton Diptych" .. .. .. 3·25 6·25
716/19 .. .. *Set of* 4 6·00 6·50

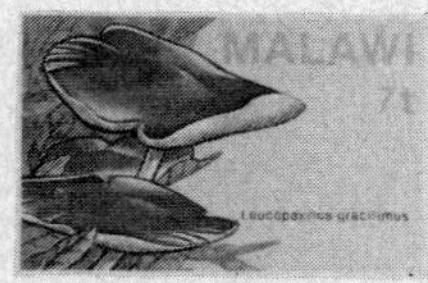

152 *Leucopaxillus gracillimus*

(Des A. Jardine. Litho Harrison)

1985 (23 Jan). *Fungi. T* **152** *and similar horiz designs. Multicoloured. W* **55** *(sideways). P* 14½ × 14.

720 7 t. Type **152** .. .. 1·00 30
721 20 t. *Limacella guttata* .. .. 2·25 45
722 30 t. *Termitomyces eurrhizus* .. .. .. 2·75 1·25
723 1 k. *Cyptotrama asspratum* ("*Kerulina asprata*") .. .. 5·00 7·50
720/3 .. .. *Set of* 4 10·00 8·50

153 Map showing Member States, and Lumberjack (Forestry)

(Des A. Theobald. Litho Harrison)

1985 (1 Apr). *5th Anniv of Southern African Development Co-ordination Conference. T* **153** *and similar horiz designs showing map and aspects of development. W* **55** *(sideways). P* 14.

724 7 t. black, yellowish green and pale green 75 10
725 15 t. black, scarlet-vermilion & salmon pink 1·00 20
726 20 t. blk, bright bluish violet & bright mauve 3·50 1·50
727 1 k. black, bright blue and cobalt .. .. 4·25 7·00
724/7 .. .. *Set of* 4 8·50 8·00

Designs:—15 t. Radio mast (Communications); 20 t. Diesel locomotive (Transport); 1 k. Trawler and net (Fishing).

154 M.V. *Ufulu*

155 Stierling's Woodpecker

(Des L. Curtis. Litho Cartor)

1985 (3 June). *Ships of Lake Malawi* (2*nd series*). *T* **154** *and similar horiz designs. Multicoloured. W* **55** *(sideways). P* 13½×13.

728 7 t. Type **154** 90 10
729 15 t. M.V. *Chauncy Maples II* .. .. .. 1·75 20
730 20 t. M.V. *Mtendere* .. .. 2·25 65
731 1 k. M.V. *Ilala II* .. .. 4·50 6·00
728/31 .. .. *Set of* 4 8·50 6·25
MS732 120 × 84 mm. Nos. 728/31. P 13 × 12 .. 8·00 6·25

(Des M. Stringer. Litho Harrison)

1985 (1 Aug). *Birth Bicentenary of John J. Audubon (ornithologist). T* **155** *and similar vert designs. Multicoloured. W* **55**. *P* 14.

733 7 t. Type **155** .. .. 1·00 20
734 15 t. Lesser Seedcracker .. .. .. 2·00 20
735 20 t. East Coast Akelat .. .. .. 2·25 55
736 1 k. Boehm's Bee Eater .. .. .. 4·25 5·50
733/6 .. .. *Set of* 4 8·50 5·75
MS737 130 × 90 mm. Nos. 733/6. Wmk sideways .. .. 8·50 8·50

156 "The Virgin of Humility" (Jaime Serra)

157 Halley's Comet and Path of *Giotto* Spacecraft

(Photo Courvoisier)

1985 (14 Oct). *Christmas. Nativity Paintings. T* **156** *and similar vert designs. Multicoloured. Granite paper. P* 11½.

738 7 t. Type **156** 30 10
739 15 t. "The Adoration of the Magi" (Stefano da Zevio) 75 15
740 20 t. "Madonna and Child" (Gerard van Honthorst) 85 25
741 1 k. "Virgin of Zbraslav" (Master of Vissy Brod) .. .. 2·25 2·50
738/41 .. .. *Set of* 4 3·75 2·75

(Des N. Shewring. Litho Walsall)

1986 (10 Feb). *Appearance of Halley's Comet. T* **157** *and similar vert designs. Multicoloured. W* **55**. *P* 14½ × 14.

742 8 t. Type **157** 50 10
743 15 t. Halley's Comet above Earth 55 15
w. Wmk inverted 55
744 20 t. Comet and dish aerial, Malawi 80 30
745 1 k. *Giotto* spacecraft .. .. .. 2·00 3·00
742/5 .. .. *Set of* 4 3·50 3·25

158 Two Players competing for Ball

159 President Banda

(Des and photo Courvoisier)

1986 (26 May). *World Cup Football Championship, Mexico. T* **158** *and similar horiz designs. Multicoloured. Granite paper. P* 11½.

746 8 t. Type **158** 60 10
747 15 t. Goalkeeper saving goal 85 20
748 20 t. Two players competing for ball (*different*) .. .. 1·00 35
749 1 k. Player kicking ball .. .. .. 3·50 3·50
746/9 .. .. *Set of* 4 5·50 3·75
MS750 108 × 77 mm. Nos. 746/9 .. .. .. 9·00 10·00

(Des and litho Harrison)

1986 (30 June). *20th Anniv of the Republic. T* **159** *and similar vert designs. Multicoloured. P* 14.

751 8 t. Type **159** .. .. 1·25 1·75
752 15 t. National flag 80 15
753 20 t. Malawi coat of arms 85 25
754 1 k. Kamuzu International Airport and emblem of national airline .. .. 3·25 3·50
751/4 .. .. *Set of* 4 5·50 5·00

It is reported that No. 751 was withdrawn locally five days after issue.

160 "Virgin and Child" (Botticelli)

161 Wattled Crane

(Des and photo Courvoisier)

1986 (15 Dec). *Christmas. T* **160** *and similar vert designs showing paintings. Multicoloured. Granite paper. P* 11½.

755 8 t. Type **160** 45 10
756 15 t. "Adoration of the Shepherds" (Guido Reni) 80 15
757 20 t. "Madonna of the Veil" (Carlo Dolci) .. 1·25 35
758 1 k. "Adoration of the Magi" (Jean Bourdichon) .. .. 3·75 6·00
755/8 .. .. *Set of* 4 5·50 6·00

(Des W. Oliver. Litho Walsall)

1987 (16 Feb)–**88**. *Wattled Crane. T* **161** *and similar horiz designs. Multicoloured. P* 14×14½. (a) *W* **55** *(sideways)*.

759 8 t. Type **161** .. .. 1·25 30
760 15 t. Two cranes .. .. 2·00 40
761 20 t. Cranes at nest .. .. 2·25 70
762 75 t. Crane in lake .. .. 4·50 7·00
759/62 .. .. *Set of* 4 9·00 7·50

(b) W w 14 (sideways) (10.88)

763 8 t. Type **161** .. .. 1·50 30
764 15 t. Two cranes .. .. 2·25 40
765 20 t. Cranes at nest .. .. 2·50 70
766 75 t. Cranes in lake .. .. 4·75 7·00
763/6 .. .. *Set of* 4 10·00 7·50

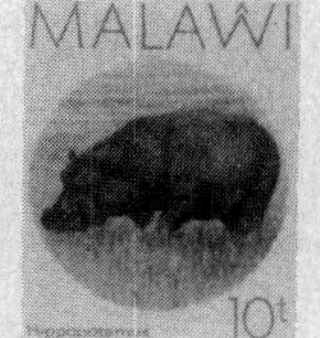

162 Locomotive *Shamrock* No. 2, 1902

163 Hippopotamus grazing

(Des and litho Cartor)

1987 (25 May). *Steam Locomotives. T* **162** *and similar horiz designs. Multicoloured. P* 14×13½.

767 10 t. Type **162**.. .. .. .. 1·50 30
768 25 t. "D" class, No. 8, 1914 .. .. .. 2·00 40
769 30 t. *Thistle* No. 1, 1902 .. .. .. 2·25 75
770 1 k. "Kitson" class, No. 6, 1903 .. .. 4·25 6·50
767/70 .. .. *Set of* 4 9·00 7·00

(Des and photo Courvoisier)

1987 (24 Aug). *Hippopotamus. T* **163** *and similar vert designs. Multicoloured. Granite paper. P* 12½.

771 10 t. Type **163** .. .. 1·25 30
772 25 t. Hippopotami in water .. .. 2·00 40
773 30 t. Female and calf in water .. .. 2·00 70
774 1 k. Hippopotami and Cattle Egret .. 5·50 7·00
771/4 .. .. *Set of* 4 9·75 7·50
MS775 78×101 mm. Nos. 771/4 .. .. 9·75 9·75

164 *Stathmostelma spectabile*

165 African and Staunton Knights

(Des and litho Harrison)

1987 (19 Oct). *Christmas. Wild Flowers. T* **164** *and similar vert designs. Multicoloured. P* 14.

776 10 t. Type **164**.. .. .. .. 65 10
777 25 t. *Pentanisia schweinfurthii* .. .. 1·50 25
778 30 t. *Chironia krebsii*.. .. .. .. 1·75 55
779 1 k. *Ochna macrocalyx* .. .. .. 3·00 6·00
776/9 .. .. *Set of* 4 6·25 6·25

(Des Jennifer Toombs. Litho Walsall)

1988 (8 Feb). *Chess. T* **165** *and similar vert designs showing local and Staunton chess pieces. Multicoloured. W w* **16**. *P* 14½×14.

780 15 t. Type **165** 70 15
781 35 t. Bishops .. .. 1·25 60
782 50 t. Rooks .. .. 1·50 1·50
783 2 k. Queens .. .. 4·75 6·00
780/3 .. .. *Set of* 4 7·50 7·50

166 High Jumping

167 Scrub Warbler

(Des and litho Harrison)

1988 (13 June). *Olympic Games, Seoul. T* **166** *and similar vert designs. Multicoloured. P* 14.

784 15 t. Type **166** 30 10
785 35 t. Javelin throwing 50 20
786 50 t. Tennis 75 50
787 2 k. Shot-putting .. .. 1·60 2·25
784/7 .. .. *Set of* 4 2·75 2·75
MS788 91×121 mm. Nos. 784/7 .. .. 3·25 2·75

(Des N. Arlott (No. 804), Courvoisier (others). Litho Questa (No. 804) or photo Courvoisier (others))

1988 (25 July)–**95**. *Birds. T* **167** *and similar vert designs. Multicoloured. W* w **14** *(sideways) (No. 804) or no wmk (others). Granite paper (1 t. to 4 k.). P* 15×14½ *(No. 804) or* 11½ *(others).*

789 1 t. Type **167** 10 10
790 2 t. Yellow-throated Woodland Warbler .. 10 10
791 5 t. Moustached Green Tinkerbird .. 10 10
792 7 t. Waller's Red-winged Starling .. 10 10
793 8 t. Oriole-Finch 10 10
794 10 t. Starred Robin .. .. 1·25 30
795 15 t. Bar-tailed Trogon 10 10
796 20 t. Green-backed Twin-spot 10 10
797 30 t. African Grey Cuckoo Shrike 10 10
798 40 t. Black-fronted Bush Shrike 10 10
799 50 t. White-tailed Crested Flycatcher .. 2·00 60
800 75 t. Green Barbet 10 10
801 1 k. Lemon Dove ("Cinnamon Dove") .. 10 10
802 2 k. Silvery-cheeked Hornbill 10 15
803 4 k. Crowned Eagle 20 25
804 10 k. Anchieta's Sunbird (3.10.88) .. 3·00 3·25
804*a* 10 k. As 10 t. (1.10.95) 80 85
789/804*a* .. .. *Set of* 17 4·50 2·25

167a Rebuilt Royal Exchange, 1844

168 "Madonna in the Church" (Jan van Eyck)

(Des D. Miller (15 t.), L. Curtis and D. Miller (35 t.), A. Theobald and D. Miller (50 t.), E. Nisbet and D. Miller (2 k.). Litho B.D.T.)

1988 (24 Oct). *300th Anniv of Lloyd's of London. T* **167a** *and similar multicoloured designs. W* w **14** *(sideways on* 35, 50 *t.). P* 14.

805 15 t. Type **167a** 30 10
806 35 t. Opening ceremony, Nkula Falls Hydro-electric Power Station 60 20
807 50 t. Air Malawi B.A.C. One Eleven airliner (*horiz*) .. .. 1·00 50
808 2 k. *Seawise University* (formerly *Queen Elizabeth*) on fire, Hong Kong, 1972 3·00 3·00
805/8 .. .. *Set of* 4 4·50 3·50

(Des and litho Harrison)

1988 (28 Nov). *Christmas. T* **168** *and similar vert designs showing paintings. Multicoloured. P* 14.

809 15 t. Type **168** 40 10
810 35 t. "Virgin, Infant Jesus and St. Anna" (da Vinci).. .. .. 70 25
811 50 t. "Virgin and Angels" (Cimabue) .. 90 70
812 2 k. "Virgin and Child" (Baldovinetti Apenio) .. .. 2·50 4·00
809/12 .. .. *Set of* 4 4·00 4·50

169 Robust Cichlid

(Des and litho Harrison)

1989 (10 Apr). *50th Anniv of Malawi Angling Society. T* **169** *and similar horiz designs. Multicoloured. P* 14.

813 15 t. Type **169** 50 10
814 35 t. Small-scaled Minnow ("Mpasa") .. 95 30
815 50 t. Large-scaled Yellowfish .. .. 1·40 1·40
816 2 k. Tigerfish .. .. 3·75 7·00
813/16 .. .. *Set of* 4 6·00 8·00

170 Independence Arch, Blantyre

(Des and litho Harrison)

1989 (26 June). *25th Anniv of Independence. T* **170** *and similar horiz designs. Multicoloured. P* 14.

817 15 t. Type **170** 50 10
818 35 t. Grain silos 90 30
819 50 t. Capital Hill, Lilongwe .. .. 1·40 1·50
820 2 k. Reserve Bank Headquarters .. .. 3·25 6·00
817/20 .. .. *Set of* 4 5·50 7·00

171 Blantyre Digital Telex Exchange

(Des and litho Harrison)

1989 (30 Oct). *25th Anniv of African Development Bank. T* **171** *and similar horiz designs. Multicoloured. P* 14.

821 15 t. Type **171** 50 10
822 40 t. Dzalanyama steer 90 30
823 50 t. Mikolongwe heifer .. .. .. 1·40 1·50
824 2 k. Zebu bull .. .. 3·25 6·00
821/4 .. .. *Set of* 4 5·50 7·00

172 Rural House with Verandah

(Des and litho Harrison)

1989 (1 Dec). *25th Anniv of Malawi–United Nations Co-operation. T* **172** *and similar horiz designs. Multicoloured. P* 14.

825 15 t. Type **172** 50 10
826 40 t. Rural house 90 30
827 50 t. Traditional hut and modern houses 1·40 1·50
828 2 k. Tea plantation .. .. .. 3·25 6·00
825/8 .. .. *Set of* 4 5·50 7·00

173 St. Michael and All Angels Church

(Des and litho Harrison)

1989 (15 Dec). *Christmas. Churches of Malawi. T* **173** *and similar horiz designs. Multicoloured. P* 14.

829 15 t. Type **173** 50 10
830 40 t. Catholic Cathedral, Limbe 90 30
831 50 t. C.C.A.P. Church, Nkhoma .. .. 1·40 1·50
832 2 k. Cathedral, Likoma Island .. .. 3·25 6·00
829/32 .. .. *Set of* 4 5·50 7·00

174 Ford "Sedan", 1915

175 Player heading Ball into Net

(Des and litho Cartor)

1990 (2 Apr). *Vintage Vehicles. T* **174** *and similar horiz designs. Multicoloured. P* 14×13½.

833 15 t. Type **174** 70 10
834 40 t. Two-seater Ford, 1915 .. .. 1·00 30
835 50 t. Ford pick-up, 1915 .. .. .. 1·40 1·50
836 2 k. Chevrolet bus, 1930 .. .. .. 3·00 6·00
833/6 .. .. *Set of* 4 5·50 7·00
MS837 120×85 mm. Nos. 833/6. P 13×12 .. 8·50 9·50

(Des and litho Questa)

1990 (14 June). *World Cup Football Championship, Italy. T* **175** *and similar vert designs. Multicoloured. P* 14.

838 15 t. Type **175** 70 10
839 40 t. Player tackling .. .. .. 1·00 30
840 50 t. Player scoring goal .. .. .. 1·40 1·50
841 2 k. World Cup .. .. 3·00 6·00
838/41 .. .. *Set of* 4 5·50 7·00
MS842 88×118 mm. Nos. 838/41 .. .. 7·50 9·00

COVER PRICES

Cover factors are quoted at the beginning of each country for most issues to 1945. An explanation of the system can be found on page x. The factors quoted do not, however, apply to philatelic covers.

176 Anniversary Emblem on Map

177 *Aerangis kotschyana*

(Des and litho Questa)

1990 (24 Aug). *Tenth Anniv of Southern Africa Development Co-ordination Conference. T* **176** *and similar horiz designs. Multicoloured. P* 14.
843 15 t. Type **176** 65 10
844 40 t. Tilapia . . . . 1·00 40
845 50 t. Cedar plantation . . . . . . 1·40 1·50
846 2 k. Male Nyala (antelope) . . . . 3·00 6·00
843/6 . . . . *Set of* 4 5·50 7·00
MS847 174×116 mm. Nos. 843/6 . . . . 6·50 7·50

(Litho Cartor)

1990 (26 Nov). *Orchids. T* **177** *and similar vert designs. Multicoloured. P* 13½×14.
848 15 t. Type **177** . . . . 1·00 15
849 40 t. *Angraecum eburneum* . . . . 1·60 55
850 50 t. *Aerangis luteo-alba rhodostica* . . 1·75 1·60
851 2 k. *Cyrtorchis arcuata whytei* . . . . 4·50 6·00
848/51 . . . . *Set of* 4 8·00 7·50
MS852 85×120 mm. Nos. 848/51. P 12×13 . . 8·00 8·50

178 "The Virgin and the Child Jesus" (Raphael)

179 Buffalo

(Litho Cartor)

1990 (7 Dec). *Christmas. Paintings by Raphael. T* **178** *and similar vert designs. Multicoloured. P* 13½×14.
853 15 t. Type **178** 55 10
854 40 t. "Transfiguration" (detail) . . . . 1·00 30
855 50 t. "St. Catherine of Alexandrie" (detail) 1·40 90
856 2 k. "Transfiguration" . . . . . . 3·25 6·00
853/6 . . . . *Set of* 4 5·50 6·50
MS857 85×120 mm. Nos. 853/6. P 12×13 . . 5·50 6·50

(Litho Cartor)

1991 (23 Apr). *Wildlife. T* **179** *and similar horiz designs. Multicoloured. P* 14×13½.
858 20 t. Type **179** 60 15
859 60 t. Cheetah . . . . 1·50 1·00
860 75 t. Greater Kudu . . . . . . 1·50 1·00
861 2 k. Black Rhinoceros . . . . . . 5·00 6·50
858/61 . . . . *Set of* 4 7·75 7·75
MS862 120×85 mm. Nos. 858/61. P 13×12 . . 7·75 8·00

180 Chiromo Post Office, 1891

181 Red Locust

(Litho Cartor)

1991 (2 July). *Centenary of Postal Services. T* **180** *and similar horiz designs. Multicoloured. P* 14×13½.
863 20 t. Type **180** 60 10
864 60 t. Re-constructed mail exchange hut at Walala . . . . 1·10 85
865 75 t. Mangochi post office . . . . . . 1·25 95
866 2 k. Satellite Earth station . . . . 3·50 6·00
863/6 . . . . *Set of* 4 5·75 7·00
MS867 119×83 mm. Nos. 863/6. P 13×12 . . 5·75 7·00

(Litho Cartor)

1991 (26 Sept). *Insects. T* **181** *and similar vert designs. Multicoloured. P* 13½×14.
868 20 t. Type **181** 65 15
869 60 t. Weevil . . . . 1·40 90
870 75 t. Cotton Stainer Bug . . . . . . 1·40 1·25
871 2 k. Pollen Beetle . . . . 4·25 6·50
868/71 . . . . *Set of* 4 7·00 8·00

182 Child in Manger

183 Red Bishop

(Litho Cartor)

1991 (26 Nov). *Christmas. T* **182** *and similar vert designs. Multicoloured. P* 13½×14.
872 20 t. Type **182** 45 10
873 60 t. Adoration of the Kings and Shepherds 1·10 45
874 75 t. Nativity . . . . 1·25 75
875 2 k. Virgin and Child . . . . . . 3·25 5·00
872/5 . . . . *Set of* 4 5·50 5·50

(Des Jennifer Toombs. Litho Questa)

1992 (7 Apr). *Birds. T* **183** *and similar horiz designs. Multicoloured. P* 14.
876 75 t. Type **183** 80 90
a. Sheetlet. Nos. 876/95 . . . . 14·00
877 75 t. Lesser Striped Swallow 80 90
878 75 t. Long-crested Eagle 80 90
879 75 t. Lilac-breasted Roller 80 90
880 75 t. African Paradise Flycatcher 80 90
881 75 t. White-fronted Bee Eater 80 90
882 75 t. White-winged Black Tern 80 90
883 75 t. African Fire Finch 80 90
884 75 t. White-browed Robin Chat 80 90
885 75 t. African Fish Eagle 80 90
886 75 t. Malachite Kingfisher 80 90
887 75 t. Lesser Masked Weaver 80 90
888 75 t. Barn Owl 80 90
889 75 t. Variable Sunbird 80 90
890 75 t. Lesser Flamingo 80 90
891 75 t. South African Crowned Crane . . 80 90
892 75 t. African Pitta 80 90
893 75 t. African Darter 80 90
894 75 t. White-faced Whistling Duck 80 90
895 75 t. African Pied Wagtail 80 90
876/95 . . . . *Set of* 20 14·00 16·00
Nos. 876/95 were printed together, *se-tenant*, as a sheetlet of 20, forming a composite design.

184 Long Jumping

185 "The Angel Gabriel" (detail, "The Annunciation") (Philippe de Champaigne)

(Des G. Vasarhelyi. Litho B.D.T.)

1992 (28 July). *Olympic Games, Barcelona. T* **184** *and similar horiz designs. Multicoloured. P* 13½.
896 20 t. Type **184** 50 10
897 60 t. High Jumping 85 50
898 75 t. Javelin . . . . 1·00 80
899 2 k. Running . . . . 2·25 3·50
896/9 . . . . *Set of* 4 4·25 4·50
MS900 110×100 mm. Nos. 896/9 . . . . 4·25 4·50

(Des D. Miller. Litho Walsall)

1992 (9 Nov). *Christmas. Religious Paintings. T* **185** *and similar vert designs. Multicoloured. P* 14.
901 20 t. Type **185** 40 10
902 75 t. "Virgin and Child" (Bernandino Luini) 85 50
903 95 t. "Virgin and Child" (Sassoferrato) . . 1·25 90
904 2 k. "Virgin Mary" (detail, "The Annunciation") (De Champaigne) . . . . 2·75 3·75
901/4 . . . . *Set of* 4 4·75 4·75

186 "Voyager 2" passing Saturn

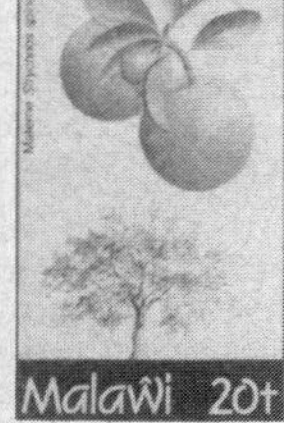

187 *Strychnos spinosa*

(Des A. Theobald. Litho Cartor)

1992 (7 Dec). *International Space Year. T* **186** *and similar horiz designs. Multicoloured. P* 13½.
905 20 t. Type **186** 65 30
906 75 t. Centre of galaxy . . . . . . 1·25 80
907 95 t. Kanjedza II Standard A Earth Station 1·40 1·00
908 2 k. Communications satellite . . . . 2·50 3·75
905/8 . . . . *Set of* 4 5·25 5·25

(Des Jennifer Toombs. Litho Cartor)

1993 (21 Mar). *World Forestry Day. Indigenous Fruit Trees. T* **187** *and similar vert designs. Multicoloured. P* 13½×14.
909 20 t. Type **187** 30 10
910 75 t. *Adansonia digitata* 75 50
911 95 t. *Ximenia caffra* 90 80
912 2 k. *Uapaca kirkiana* . . . . . . 1·75 3·00
909/12 . . . . *Set of* 4 3·25 4·00

188 *Apaturopsis cleocharis*

189 The Holy Family

(Des Leta Marsden-Huggins. Adapted D. Miller. Litho Cartor)

1993 (28 June). *Butterflies. T* **188** *and similar vert designs. Multicoloured. P* 13.
913 20 t. Type **188** 55 20
914 75 t. *Euryphura achlys* . . . . . . 1·00 60
915 95 t. *Cooksonia aliciae* . . . . . . 1·25 95
916 2 k. *Charaxes protoclea azota* . . . . 1·75 3·00
913/16 . . . . *Set of* 4 4·00 4·25

(Des G. Vasarhelyi. Photo Courvoisier)

1993 (30 Nov). *Christmas. T* **189** *and similar vert designs. Multicoloured. Granite paper. P* 11½.
917 20 t. Type **189** 10 10
918 75 t. Shepherds and star 20 20
919 95 t. Three Kings 25 30
920 2 k. Adoration of the Kings . . . . 65 1·25
917/20 . . . . *Set of* 4 1·10 1·60

190 Kentrosaurus

(Des E. Kapitapita and R. Larson. Litho Cartor)

1993 (30 Dec). *Prehistoric Animals. T* **190** *and similar horiz designs. Multicoloured. P* 13.
921 20 t. Type **190** 20 15
922 75 t. Stegosaurus 35 55
923 95 t. Sauropod 45 75
921/3 . . . . *Set of* 3 90 1·25
MS924 157×97 mm. 2 k. Tyrannosaurus; 2 k. Dilophosaurus; 2 k. Brachiosaurus; 2 k. Gallimimus; 2 k. Triceratops; 2 k. Velociraptor 7·50 8·50

191 Socolof's Mbuna

(Des R. Watton. Litho Enschedé)

1994 (21 Mar). *Fishes. T* **191** *and similar horiz designs. Multicoloured. P* 14×15.
925 20 t. Type **191** 10 10
926 75 t. Golden Mbuna 30 30
927 95 t. Lombardo's Mbuna 35 35
928 1 k. Scraper-mouthed Mbuna 40 40
929 2 k. Zebra Mbuna . . . . 80 1·00
930 4 k. Elongate Mbuna . . . . . . 1·50 2·25
925/30 . . . . *Set of* 6 3·00 4·00

MINIMUM PRICE

The minimum price quote is 10p which represents a handling charge rather than a basis for valuing common stamps. For further notes about prices see introductory pages.

192 *Ilala II* (lake vessel)

193 "Virgin and Child" (detail) (Dürer)

(Des N. Shewring. Litho Enschedé)

1994 (19 Oct). *Ships of Lake Malawi. T* **192** *and similar horiz designs. Multicoloured. P* 13½×14.

931 20 t. Type **192** 10 10
932 75 t. *Ufulu* (tanker) 15 15
933 95 t. *Pioneer* (steam launch) 20 20
934 2 k. *Dove* (paddle-steamer) 35 65
931/4 .. .. *Set of* 4 65 1·00
MS935 85×51 mm. 5 k. *Monteith* (lake vessel) 2·50 3·00

(Litho Courvoisier)

1994 (30 Nov). *Christmas. Religious Paintings. T* **193** *and similar multicoloured designs. P* 14½.

936 20 t. Type **193** 10 10
937 75 t. "Wise Men presenting Gifts" (Franco-Flemish Book of Hours) 15 10
938 95 t. "The Nativity" (detail) (Fra Filippo Lippi) (*horiz*) 20 15
939 2 k. "Nativity Scene with Wise Men" (Rogier van der Weyden) (*horiz*) .. 45 70
936/9 .. .. *Set of* 4 80 90

MALAWI 40t

TELECOMMUNICATIONS AND TRAINING

194 Pres. Bakili Muluzi (C.O.M.E.S.A. chairman, 1994–95)

195 Telecommunications Training

(Des and litho Courvoisier)

1995 (10 Apr). *Establishment of C.O.M.E.S.A. (Common Market for Eastern and Southern African States). P* 11½.

940 **194** 40 t. multicoloured 10 10
941 1 k. 40, multicoloured 20 20
942 1 k. 80, multicoloured 25 30
943 2 k. multicoloured 30 50
940/3 .. .. *Set of* 4 75 1·00

(Litho Courvoisier)

1995 (30 Oct). 50*th Anniv of the United Nations. T* **195** *and similar horiz designs. Multicoloured. Granite paper. P* 11½.

944 40 t. Type **195** 10 10
945 1 k. 40, Village women collecting water .. 15 15
946 1 k. 80, Mt Mulanje 15 20
947 2 k. Villagers in field 25 35
944/7 .. .. *Set of* 4 60 70
MS948 123×77mm. As Nos. 944/7, but ordinary paper .. .. 1·00 1·40

196 Teacher and Class

(Photo Courvoisier)

1995 (13 Nov). *Christmas. T* **196** *and similar horiz designs. Multicoloured. Granite paper. P* 11½.

949 40 t. Type **196** 10 10
950 1 k. 40, Dispensing medicine 25 20
951 1 k. 80, Crowd at water pump 30 30
952 2 k. Refugees on ferries 30 40
949/52 .. .. *Set of* 4 80 90

197 *Precis tugela*

198 Children's Party

(Photo Courvoisier)

1996 (5 Dec). *Butterflies. T* **197** *and similar horiz designs. Multicoloured. Granite paper. P* 11½.

953 60 t. Type **197** 10 10
954 3 k. *Papilio pelodorus* 25 30
955 4 k. *Acrea acrita* 30 35
956 10 k. *Melanitis leda* .. .. .. 80 1·25
953/6 .. .. *Set of* 4 1·40 1·75

(Photo Courvoisier)

1996 (12 Dec). *Christmas. T* **198** *and similar vert designs. Multicoloured. Granite paper. P* 11½.

957 10 t. Type **198** 10 10
958 20 t. Nativity play 10 10
959 30 t. Children wearing party hats 15 10
960 60 t. Mother and child 25 30
957/60 .. .. *Set of* 4 40 45

199 Mother and Child

200 The Nativity

(Litho Courvoisier)

1997 (31 Oct). 50*th Anniv of U.N.I.C.E.F. T* **199** *and similar horiz designs. Multicoloured. Granite paper. P* 11½.

961 60 t. Type **199** 10 10
962 3 k. Children in class 15 20
963 4 k. 40, Boy with fish 20 25
964 5 k. Nurse inoculating child 30 35
961/4 .. .. *Set of* 4 75 90

(Litho Courvoisier)

1997 (15 Dec). *Christmas. T* **200** *and similar vert designs. Multicoloured. Granite paper. P* 11½.

965 60 t. Type **200** 10 10
966 3 k. The Nativity (*different*) 15 20
967 4 k. 40, Adoration of the Magi 20 25
968 5 k. The Holy Family 30 35
965/8 .. .. *Set of* 4 75 90

STAMP BOOKLETS

1954 (Jan). *Black on green cover, stitched (No. SB1) or buff cover, stapled (No. SB2). R.W. Gunson (Seeds) Ltd. advertisement on front.*

SB1 2s. 6d. booklet containing four ½d., 1d., and twelve 2d. (Nos. 173/4, 176), each in blocks of 4 27·00
SB2 5s. booklet containing eight ½d., 1d., 6d. and twelve 2d. (Nos. 173/4, 176, 180), each in blocks of 4 .. .. 32·00

POSTAGE DUE STAMPS

D 1

D 2

(Typo D.L.R.)

1950 (1 July). *Wmk Mult Script CA. P* 14.

D1 D **1** 1d. scarlet .. .. 3·50 14·00
D2 2d. ultramarine .. .. 7·50 21·00
D3 3d. green .. .. 8·00 5·50
D4 4d. purple .. .. 15·00 35·00
D5 6d. yellow-orange .. .. .. 22·00 85·00
D1/5 .. .. *Set of* 5 50·00 £140

(Litho Bradbury, Wilkinson)

1967 (1 Sept). *W* **55**. *P* 11½.

D 6 D **2** 1d. carmine .. .. 15 3·00
D 7 2d. sepia .. .. 20 3·00
D 8 4d. reddish violet .. .. .. 25 3·25
D 9 6d. blue .. .. 25 3·50
D10 8d. emerald .. .. 35 3·75
D11 1s. black .. .. 45 4·00
D6/11 .. .. *Set of* 6 1·50 18·00

1971 (15 Feb). *As Nos. D6/11, but values in tambalas. W* **55**. *P* 11½.

D12 D **2** 2 t. greenish drab .. .. .. 30 2·50
D13 4 t. bright mauve .. .. .. 50 2·50
D14 6 t. royal blue .. .. .. 50 2·75
D15 8 t. dull green .. .. .. 50 2·75
D16 10 t. blackish brown .. .. .. 60 2·75
D12/16 .. .. *Set of* 5 2·25 12·00

(Litho Walsall)

1975–84. *Design redrawn, with circumflex accent over "W" of "MALAWI". P* 14. *(a) W* **55** *(sideways).*

D17 D **2** 2 t. chestnut (15.9.75) .. .. 1·25 6·50
D18 2 t. brown (14.6.82) .. .. .. 60 1·75
D19 4 t. deep mauve (14.6.82) .. .. 60 1·75
D20 6 t. royal blue (9.84) .. .. .. 60 1·75
D21 8 t. green (9.84) .. .. .. 60 1·75
D22 10 t. black (14.6.82) .. .. .. 60 1·75
D17/22 .. .. *Set of* 6 3·75 14·00

(b) No wmk

D23 D **2** 2 t. brown (19.10.77) .. .. 4·50 4·50
D24 4 t. mauve (19.10.77) .. .. 4·50 4·50
D25 8 t. green (15.12.78) .. .. .. 2·25 4·50
D26 10 t. brownish grey (19.10.77) .. 4·50 5·00
D23/6 .. .. *Set of* 4 14·00 17·00

(Photo Harrison)

1989. *As Nos. D17/26, but design redrawn smaller,* 17×20½ *mm instead of* 17½×21 *mm. No wmk. P* 15×14.

D27 D **2** 2 t. light brown 30 40
D28 4 t. bright purple 30 40
D29 6 t. bright blue 30 40
D31 10 t. brownish black 40 40
D27/31 .. .. *Set of* 4 1·10 1·40

Malaysia

The Federation of Malaysia was set up on 16 September 1963, and consisted of the former Malayan Federation, the State of Singapore and the two former Crown Colonies in Borneo, Sabah (North Borneo) and Sarawak. Singapore left the federation to become an independent republic on 9 August 1965.

Malaysia now consists of thirteen States (11 in Peninsular Malaysia and two in Borneo), together with the Federal Territories of Kuala Lumpur and Labuan.

The philatelic history of the component parts of the federation is most complex. Under this heading are now listed previous issues made by the present States of the Federation.

The method adopted is to show the general issues for the area first, before dealing with the issues for the individual States. The section is divided as follows:

I. STRAITS SETTLEMENTS
II. FEDERATED MALAY STATES
III. MALAYAN POSTAL UNION
IV. MALAYA (BRITISH MILITARY ADMINISTRATION)
V. MALAYAN FEDERATION
VI. MALAYSIA
VII. MALAYAN STATES—Johore, Kedah, Kelantan, Malacca, Negri Sembilan (with Sungei Ujong), Pahang, Penang, Perak, Perlis, Selangor, Trengganu
VIII. SIAMESE POSTS IN NORTHERN MALAYA 1887–1909
IX. JAPANESE OCCUPATION OF MALAYA
X. THAI OCCUPATION OF MALAYA
XI. LABUAN
XII. SABAH (NORTH BORNEO)
XIII. JAPANESE OCCUPATION OF NORTH BORNEO
XIV. SARAWAK
XV. JAPANESE OCCUPATION OF SARAWAK

I. STRAITS SETTLEMENTS

The three original Settlements, Malacca, Penang (with Province Wellesley) and Singapore (with Christmas Island), were formed into a Crown Colony during 1867. The Cocos (Keeling) Islands were transferred to Straits Settlements on 7 February 1886. Labuan was attached to the Colony in 1896, becoming the fourth Settlement in 1906.

The first known prestamp cover with postal markings from Penang (Prince of Wales Island) is dated March 1806 and from Malacca, under British civil administration, February 1841. The civil post office at Singapore opened on 1 February 1823.

The stamps of India were used at all three post offices from late in 1854 until the Straits Settlements became a separate colony on 1 September 1867.

The Indian stamps were initially cancelled by dumb obliterators and their use in the Straits Settlements can only be identified from complete covers. In 1856 cancellations of the standard Indian octagonal type were issued, numbered "B 109" for Malacca, "B 147" for Penang and "B 172" for Singapore.

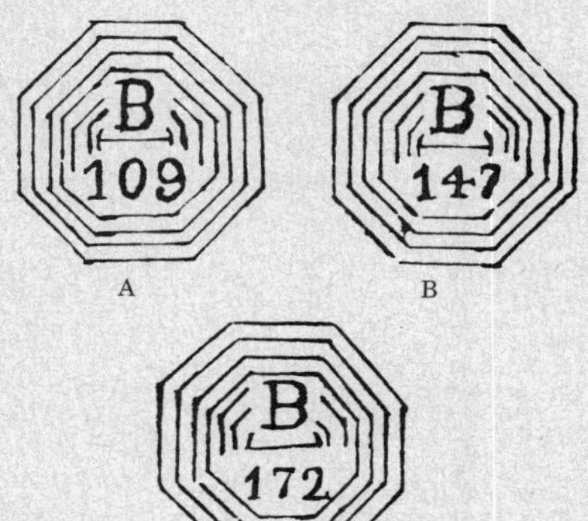

A B C

The Penang and Singapore octagonals were replaced by a duplex type, consisting of a double-ringed datestamp and a diamond-shaped obliterator containing the office number, in 1863 and 1865 respectively.

D E

PRICES. Catalogue prices in this section are for stamps with clearly legible, if partial, examples of the postmarks.

MALACCA

Stamps of INDIA *cancelled with Type* A.

1854. (*Nos.* 2/34).

Z1	½ a. blue (Die I)	£900
Z2	1 a. red (Die I)	£750
Z3	1 a. dull red (Die II)	£800
Z4	2 a. green	£1000
Z4*a*	4 a. blue and pale red (Head Die I) (*cut-to-shape*)	£1100
Z5	4 a. blue and red (Head Die II) (*cut-to-shape*)	£1100
Z5*a*	4 a. blue and red (Head Die III) (*cut-to-shape*)	£1100

1855. (*Nos.* 35/6).

Z6	8 a. carmine (Die I)/*blue glazed*	£275

1856–64. (*Nos.* 37/49).

Z7	½ a. pale blue (Die I)	£160
Z8	1 a. brown	£120
Z8*a*	2 a. dull pink	£180
Z9	2 a. yellow-buff	£130
Z10	2 a. yellow	£140
Z11	4 a. green	£250
Z12	8 a. carmine (Die I)	£160

1860. (*Nos.* 51/3).

Z13	8 p. purple/*bluish*	£450
Z14	8 p. purple/*white*	£200

1865. (*Nos.* 54/65).

Z15	4 a. green	£250

PENANG

Stamps of INDIA *cancelled with Type* B.

1854. (*Nos.* 2/34).

Z20	½ a. blue (Die I)	£250
Z21	1 a. red (Die I)	£130
Z22	2 a. green	£170
Z23	4 a. blue and pale red (Head Die I)	£950
Z24	4 a. blue and red (Head Die II)	£1000
Z25	4 a. blue and red (Head Die III)	£700

1855. (*Nos.* 35/6).

Z26	4 a. black/*blue glazed*	55·00
Z27	8 a. carmine (Die I)/*blue glazed*	48·00
	a. Bisected (4 a.) (1860) (on cover)	£40000

1856–64. (*Nos.* 37/49).

Z28	½ a. pale blue (Die I)	50·00
Z29	1 a. brown	32·00
Z30	2 a. dull pink	45·00
Z31	2 a. yellow-buff	40·00
Z32	2 a. yellow	40·00
Z33	2 a. orange	42·00
Z34	4 a. black	32·00
Z35	8 a. carmine (Die I)	40·00

1860. (*Nos.* 51/3).

Z36	8 p. purple/*white*	90·00

Stamps of INDIA *cancelled with Type* D.

1854. (*Nos.* 2/34).

Z37	½ a. pale blue (Die I)	£130
Z38	1 a. red (Die I)	£1800

1856–64. (*Nos.* 37/49).

Z40	1 a. brown	32·00
Z41	2 a. yellow	40·00
Z42	4 a. black	35·00
Z43	4 a. green	95·00
Z44	8 a. carmine (Die I)	38·00

1860. (*Nos.* 51/3).

Z45	8 p. purple/*white*	55·00
Z46	8 p. mauve	55·00

1865. (*Nos.* 54/65).

Z47	8 p. purple	
Z48	1 a. deep brown	32·00
Z49	2 a. yellow	38·00
Z50	4 a. green	£100
Z51	8 a. carmine (Die I)	

1866–67. (*Nos.* 69/72).

Z52	4 a. green (Die I)	£100

SINGAPORE

Stamps of INDIA *cancelled with Type* C.

1854. (*Nos.* 2/34).

Z60	½ a. blue (Die I)	£140
Z61	1 a. red (Die I)	90·00
Z62	1 a. dull red (Die II)	£120
Z63	1 a. red (Die III)	£800
Z64	2 a. green	75·00
	a. Bisected (1 a.) (1857) (on cover)	£95000
Z65	4 a. blue and pale red (Head Die I)	£850
Z66	4 a. blue and red (Head Die II)	£900
Z67	4 a. blue and red (Head Die III)	£600

1855. (*Nos.* 35/6).

Z68	4 a. black/*blue glazed*	27·00
	a. Bisected (2 a.) (1859) (on cover)	£7500
Z69	8 a. carmine/*blue glazed*	29·00
	a. Bisected (4 a.) (1859) (on cover)	£35000

1856–64. (*Nos.* 37/49).

Z70	½ a. pale blue (Die I)	27·00
Z71	1 a. brown	19·00
	a. Bisected (½ a.) (1859) (on cover)	£50000
Z72	2 a. dull pink	30·00
Z73	2 a. yellow-buff	23·00
Z74	2 a. yellow	26·00
Z75	2 a. orange	30·00
Z76	4 a. black	19·00
	a. Bisected diagonally (2 a.) (1859) (on cover)	£16000
Z77	4 a. green	80·00
Z78	8 a. carmine (Die I)	25·00
	a. Bisected (4 a.) (1859) (on cover)	£38000

1860. (*Nos.* 51/3).

Z79	8 p. purple/*bluish*	£375
Z80	8 p. purple/*white*	45·00
	a. Bisected diagonally (4 p.) (1862) (on cover)	£50000
Z81	8 p. mauve	45·00

1865. (*Nos.* 54/65).

Z82	½ a. blue (Die I)	32·00
Z83	8 p. purple	80·00
Z84	1 a. deep brown	25·00
Z85	2 a. yellow	29·00
Z86	2 a. orange	29·00
Z87	4 a. green	80·00
Z88	8 a. carmine (Die I)	£200

1866–67. (*Nos.* 69/72).

Z89	4 a. green (Die I)	85·00
Z90	6 a. 8 p. slate	£150

OFFICIAL STAMPS

1866–67. (*Nos.* O6/14).

Z91	½ a. pale blue	£225
Z92	2 a. yellow	£350

Stamps of INDIA *cancelled with Type* E.

1856–64. (*Nos.* 37/49).

Z100	1 a. brown	£190
Z101	2 a. yellow	£250
Z102	4 a. black	£250
Z103	8 a. carmine (Die I)	£250

1860. (*Nos.* 51/3).

Z104	8 p. purple/*white*	£275

1865. (*Nos.* 54/65).

Z105	2 a. yellow	£225
Z106	2 a. orange	£225
Z107	4 a. green	£300

PRICES FOR STAMPS ON COVER

Nos. 1/9	*from* × 15
No. 10	—
Nos. 11/19	*from* × 8
Nos. 20/1	*from* × 20
Nos. 22/39	*from* × 10
Nos. 41/6	*from* × 20
No. 47	—
Nos. 48/9	*from* × 10
Nos. 50/62	*from* × 20
Nos. 63/71	*from* × 15
No. 72	—
Nos. 73/8	*from* × 20
No. 80	*from* × 30
Nos. 82/5	*from* × 10
Nos. 86/7	*from* × 20
Nos. 88/94	*from* × 15
Nos. 95/105	*from* × 8
Nos. 106/9	*from* × 20
Nos. 110/21	*from* × 6
No. 122	—
Nos. 123/6	*from* × 5
Nos. 127/38	*from* × 4
Nos. 139/40	—
Nos. 141/51	*from* × 15
Nos. 152/67	*from* × 4
Nos. 168/9	—
Nos. 193/212	*from* × 3
Nos. 213/15	—
Nos. 216/17	*from* × 10
Nos. 218/40*a*	*from* × 3
Nos. 240*b*/*d*	—
Nos. 241/55	*from* × 15
Nos. 256/9	*from* × 4
Nos. 260/98	*from* × 3
Nos. D1/6	*from* × 20

PRINTERS. All Straits Settlements issues were printed in typography by De La Rue & Co, Ltd, London, *unless otherwise stated.*

USED PRICES. The prices quoted for Nos. 1/9 are for fine used examples. Those showing parts of commercial "chops" are worth less.

(Currency. 100 cents = 1 Straits, later Malayan and Malaysian dollar)

THREE-HALF-CENTS (1)

32 CENTS (2)

1867 (1 Sept). *Nos. 54, 59, 61, 64 and 73 of India surch as T* **1** *or* **2** *(24 c., 32 c.) by De La Rue. W* **13** *(Elephant's head) of India. P 14.*

1 1½ c. on ½ a. blue (Die I) (R.) .. .. 75·00 £180
2 2 c. on 1 a. deep brown (R.) .. .. 85·00 65·00
3 3 c. on 1 a. deep brown (B.) .. .. 95·00 70·00
4 4 c. on 1 a. deep brown (Bk.) £180 £200
5 6 c. on 2 a. yellow (P.) £400 £180
6 8 c. on 2 a. yellow (G.) .. .. £130 38·00
7 12 c. on 4 a. green (R.) £650 £250
a. Surch double £1200
8 24 c. on 8 a. rose (Die II) (B.) .. .. £275 70·00
9 32 c. on 2 a. yellow (Bk.) .. .. £250 75·00

The 32 c. was re-issued for postal use in 1884.
No. 7a. is only known unused.

1869 (?). *No.* 1 *with* "THREE HALF" *deleted and* "2" *written above, in black manuscript.*

10 2 on 1½ c. on ½ a. blue £6500 £3500

This stamp has been known from very early days and was apparently used at Penang, but nothing is known of its history.

5 6 7

8 9

1867 (Dec)–**72**. *Wmk Crown CC. P 14. Ornaments in corners differ for each value.*

11 **5** 2 c. brown (6.68) .. .. 18·00 2·75
a. Yellow-brown .. .. 19·00 2·75
b. Deep brown .. .. 55·00 8·00
12 4 c. rose (7.68) .. .. 28·00 5·00
a. Deep rose .. .. 38·00 7·00
13 6 c. dull lilac (1.68) .. .. 55·00 12·00
a. Bright lilac .. .. 60·00 12·00
14 **6** 8 c. orange-yellow .. .. 95·00 7·50
a. Orange .. .. 90·00 8·50
15 12 c. blue .. .. 75·00 5·00
a. Ultramarine .. .. 80·00 8·00
16 **7** 24 c. blue-green .. .. 80·00 4·00
a. Yellow-green .. .. £170 19·00
17 **8** 30 c. claret (12.72) .. .. £140 8·50
18 **9** 32 c. pale red .. .. £325 60·00
19 96 c. grey .. .. £170 32·00
a. Perf 12½ (6.71) £1700 £225

Five Cents. (10)
Seven Cents. (11)

1879 (May). *Nos. 14a and 18 surch with T* **10** *and* **11**.

20 **6** 5 c. on 8 c. orange .. .. 70·00 £100
a. No stop after "Cents" £550 £600
b. "F i" spaced £600 £650
21 **9** 7 c. on 32 c. pale red .. .. 75·00 95·00
a. No stop after "Cents" £700 £750

The no stop error occured once in the setting.

10 cents. (12)

10 (*a*) 10 (*b*) 10 (*c*) 10 (*d*)
10 (*e*) 10 (*f*) 10 (*g*) 10 (*h*)
10 (*i*) 10 (*j*) 10 (*jj*) 10 (*k*) 10 (*l*)

(*a*) "1" thin curved serif and thin foot, "0" narrow.
(*b*) "1" thick curved serif and thick foot; "0" broad. Both numerals heavy.
(*c*) "1" as (*a*); "0" as (*b*)
(*d*) "1" as (*a*) but thicker; "0" as (*a*)
(*e*) As (*a*) but sides of "0" thicker.
(*f*) "1" as (*d*); "0" as (*e*)
(*g*) As (*a*) but "0" narrower.
(*h*) "1" thin, curved serif and thick foot; "0" as (*g*)
(*i*) "1" as (*b*); "0" as (*a*)
(*j*) "1" as (*d*); "0" as (*g*) but raised.
(*jj*) "1" as (*a*) but shorter, and with shorter serif and thicker foot; "0" as (*g*) but level with "1".
(*k*) "1" as (*jj*); "0" as (*a*)
(*l*) "1" straight serif; "0" as (*g*)

1880 (Mar). *No.* 17 *surch with T* **12** *(showing numerals (a) to (jj)).*

22 10 c. on 30 c. claret (*a*) .. .. £200 50·00
23 10 c. on 30 c. claret (*b*) .. .. £190 48·00
24 10 c. on 30 c. claret (*c*) £2000 £400
25 10 c. on 30 c. claret (*d*) £950 £140
26 10 c. on 30 c. claret (*e*) £3250 £750
27 10 c. on 30 c. claret (*f*) £3250 £750
28 10 c. on 30 c. claret (*g*) £1300 £275
29 10 c. on 30 c. claret (*h*) £3250 £750
30 10 c. on 30 c. claret (*i*) £3250 £750
31 10 c. on 30 c. claret (*j*) £3250 £750
32 10 c. on 30 c. claret (*jj*) £3250 £750

Nos. 22/32 come from the same setting of 60 (6 × 10) containing twenty examples of No. 22 (R.1/1-2, 1/4, 1/6, 2/1-6, 3/1, 3/3, 3/5, 4/1, 4/3-4, 10/1, 10/3-5), twenty-two of No. 23 (R.4/6, 5/1-6, 6/1-6, 7/1, 8/2-4, 9/1-5), six of No. 25 (R.1/5, 3/2, 3/4, 4/2, 4/5, 10/2), four of No. 28 (R.7/2-5), two of No. 24 (R.9/6, 10/6) and one each of Nos. 26 (R.3/6), 27 (R.1/3), 29 (R.7/6), 30 (R.8/1), 31 (R.8/6) and 32 (R.8/5).

No. 23 is known with large stop after "cents" and also with stop low.

1880 (April). *No.* 17 *surch as T* **12**, *but without "cents.", showing numerals (a) to (c), (g) to (i), (k) and (l).*

33 10 on 30 c. claret (*a*) .. .. £110 42·00
34 10 on 30 c. claret (*b*) .. .. £120 42·00
35 10 on 30 c. claret (*c*) £375 £100
36 10 on 30 c. claret (*g*) £850 £250
36*a* 10 on 30 c. claret (*h*) .. .. † —
37 10 on 30 c. claret (*i*) £2000 £650
38 10 on 30 c. claret (*k*) £2000 £650
39 10 on 30 c. claret (*l*) £2000 £650

Nos. 33/9 were surcharged from an amended setting of 60 (6×10) of which 59 positions have been identified. Of those known No. 33 occurs on twenty-four (R.6/1–6, 7/1–6, 8/1–6, 9/1–2, 9/6, 10/1–3), No. 34 on twenty-one (R.1/2–6, 2/1–6, 3/1–6, 4/3–5, 5/6), No. 35 on eight (R.1/1, 4/2, 4/6, 5/1–5), No. 36 on three (R.9/3–5) and Nos. 37 (R.10/6), 38 (R.10/4) and 39 (R.10/5) on one each. R.4/1 remains unidentified.

The existence of No. 36*a*, known as a single example from the 6th vertical column, and a stamp in the Royal Collection with "1" as (*b*) and "0" as (*g*) suggests that there may have been another setting.

5 cents. (13)
5 cents. (14)
5 cents. (15)

1880 (Aug). *No. 14a surch with T* **13** *to* **15**.

41 **13** 5 c. on 8 c. orange .. .. 90·00 £110
42 **14** 5 c. on 8 c. orange .. .. 80·00 £100
43 **15** 5 c. on 8 c. orange £275 £350

Surcharged in a setting of 60 (6×10) with T **13** on rows one to four, T **14** on rows five to nine and T **15** on row ten.

10 cents. (16)
5 cents. (17)

1880–81. *Nos. 13, 15/a and 17 surch with T* **16**.

44 10 c. on 6 c. lilac (11.81) .. .. 45·00 6·00
a. Surch double .. .. — £1600
45 10 c. on 12 c. ultramarine (1.81) .. .. 48·00 16·00
a. Blue .. .. 35·00 9·00
46 10 c. on 30 c. claret (12.80) .. .. £250 80·00

A second printing of the 10 c. on 6 c. has the surcharge heavier and the "10" usually more to the left or right of "cents".

1882 (Jan). *No. 12 surch with T* **17**.

47 5 c. on 4 c. rose £225 £250

18 19

1882 (Jan). *Wmk Crown CC. P 14.*

48 **18** 5 c. purple-brown .. .. 65·00 75·00
49 **19** 10 c. slate (Optd S. £250) .. .. £250 60·00

1882. *Wmk Crown CA. P 14.*

50 **5** 2 c. brown (Aug) .. .. £190 30·00
51 4 c. rose (April) .. .. 90·00 4·50
52 **6** 8 c. orange (Sept) .. .. 2·50 75
53 **19** 10 c. slate (Oct) .. .. 3·25 90

For the 4 c. in deep carmine see No. 98.

TWO CENTS **20*a*** "S" wide
TWO CENTS **20*b*** "E" and "S" wide
TWO CENTS **20*c*** "N" wide
TWO CENTS **20*d*** All letters narrow
TWO CENTS **20*e*** "EN" and "S" wide
TWO CENTS **20*f*** "E" wide

1883 (Apr). *Nos. 52 and 18 surch with T* **20*a/f***.

54 **20*a*** 2 c. on 8 c. orange .. .. £140 80·00
55 **20*b*** 2 c. on 8 c. orange .. .. £140 80·00
56 **20*c*** 2 c. on 8 c. orange .. .. £140 80·00
57 **20*d*** 2 c. on 8 c. orange .. .. 80·00 50·00
a. Surch double £2250 £950
58 **20*e*** 2 c. on 8 c. orange £425 £250
59 **20*a*** 2 c. on 32 c. pale red £425 £130
60 **20*f*** 2 c. on 32 c. pale red £475 £140
a. Surch double

The 8 c. was surcharged using one of two triplet settings, either 54 + 55 + 56 or 57 + 57 + 57, applied to rows 2 to 10. A single handstamp, either No. 57 or No. 58, was then used to complete row 1. The 32 c. was surcharged in the same way with a triplet of 59 + 60 + 59 and a single handstamp as No. 60.

2 Cents. (21)
4 Cents (22)
8 Cents (23)

1883 (June–July). *Nos. 51 and 15 surch with T* **21**.

61 2 c. on 4 c. rose .. .. 65·00 75·00
a. "s" of "Cents" inverted £900 £1000
62 2 c. on 12 c. blue (July) .. .. £160 85·00
a. "s" of "Cents" inverted £2250 £1400

The inverted "S" error occurred once in the setting of 60.

Broken oval above "O" of "POSTAGE" (Lower right pane R. 10/5)

1883 (July)–**91**. *Wmk Crown CA. P 14.*

63 **5** 2 c. pale rose .. .. 29·00 2·50
a. Bright rose (1889) .. .. 3·75 40
64 4 c. pale brown .. .. 18·00 1·25
a. Broken oval .. .. £140 32·00
b. Deep brown .. .. 27·00 3·00
ba. Broken oval .. .. £225 48·00
c. Olive-bistre £350 £275
ca. Broken oval
65 **18** 5 c. blue (8.83) .. .. 8·50 80
66 **5** 6 c. lilac (11.84) .. .. 22·00 8·50
a. Violet .. .. 1·60 2·25
67 **6** 12 c. brown-purple .. .. 55·00 8·50
68 **7** 24 c. yellow-green (2.84) .. .. 70·00 5·00
a. Blue-green .. .. 3·25 3·75
69 **8** 30 c. claret (9.91) .. .. 7·00 6·00
70 **9** 32 c. orange-vermilion (1.87) .. .. 6·50 1·75
71 96 c. olive-grey (8.88) .. .. 75·00 38·00
63*a*/71 .. *Set of* 9 £160 55·00
63/65, 67 Optd "Specimen" *Set of* 4 £550

For the 4 c. in deep carmine and 12 c. in claret see Nos. 98 and 102.

1884 (Feb–Aug). *Nos. 65, 15 and 67 surch with T* **22** *or* **23**.

72 **18** 4 c. on 5 c. blue (Aug) £2250 £2750
73 4 c. on 5 c. blue (R.) (Aug) .. .. 90·00 80·00
74 **6** 8 c. on 12 c. blue .. .. £225 95·00
75 8 c. on 12 c. brown-purple (Aug) £190 £120
a. Inverted "8" .. .. † —
b. "s" of "Cents" low (R. 5/1) £1100 £800

1884 (Aug). *No. 65 surch with T* **20*d/f***.

76 **20*d*** 2 c. on 5 c. blue .. .. 95·00 £100
77 **20*e*** 2 c. on 5 c. blue .. .. 95·00 £100
a. Pair, with and without surch
b. Surch double
78 **20*f*** 2 c. on 5 c. blue .. .. 95·00 £100

Surcharged as a triplet, 77 + 76 + 78. On No. 76 "TS" are dropped below the line.

8 (24)
3 CENTS (25)
THREE CENTS (26)

1884 (Sept). *No. 75 additionally surch with large numeral as T* **24** *in red.*

80 **6** 8 on 8 c. on 12 c. dull purple £190 £190
a. Surch T **24** double £3500
b. Surch T **23** in blue £4750
c. "s" of "Cents" low £1100

Examples as No. 75, but with Type **23** in blue, were further surcharged in error.

A similar "4" surcharge in red on No. 73 exists from a trial printing from which seven examples are known, all used on an official's correspondence (*Price* £9500 *used*).

1885. *No. 65 and T* **9** *in new colour, wmk Crown CA, surch with T* **25** *or* **26**.

82 **25** 3 c. on 5 c. blue (Sept) .. .. 90·00 £200
a. Surch double £1600
83 **26** 3 c. on 32 c. pale mag (Dec) (Optd S. £130) 2·50 3·25
a. Deep magenta .. .. 1·25 90

The surcharge on No. 82 was applied locally by a triplet setting. No. 83 was surcharged by De La Rue in complete panes.

3 cents (27) | 2 Cents (28)

1886 (Apr). *No.* 48 *surch with T* **27**.
84 **18** 3 c. on 5 c. purple-brown £150 £160
The surcharge on No. 84 was applied by a triplet setting.

1887 (July). *No.* 65 *surch with T* **28**.
85 **18** 2 c. on 5 c. blue.. .. .. .. 18·00 45·00
a. "C" of "Cents" omitted .. .. — £2000
b. Surch double £600 £500
The surcharge on No. 85 was applied by a triplet setting.

10 CENTS (29) | THIRTY CENTS (30)

1891 (Nov). *Nos.* 68 *and* 70 *surch with T* **29** *and* **30**.
86 **7** 10 c. on 24 c. yellow-green .. .. 2·00 1·25
a. Narrow "0" in "10" (R. 4/6) .. 28·00 28·00
87 **9** 30 c. on 32 c. orange-vermilion .. .. 5·50 3·50
The "R" of "THIRTY" and "N" of "CENTS" are found wide or narrow and in all possible combinations.

ONE CENT (31) | ONE CENT (32)

1892. *Stamps of* 1882–91 (*wmk Crown CA*) *surch with T* **31**.
88 1 c. on 2 c. bright rose (Mar) .. .. 1·50 2·75
89 1 c. on 4 c. brown (Apr) .. .. 3·75 4·00
a. Surch double £800
b. Broken oval .. .. .. 65·00 65·00
90 1 c. on 6 c. lilac (Feb) .. .. 1·00 3·75
a. Surch double, one inverted £900 £800
91 1 c. on 8 c. orange (Jan) .. .. 1·00 60
92 1 c. on 12 c. brown-purple (Mar) .. .. 4·00 9·00
88/92 .. .. .. *Set of* 5 10·00 18·00
The three settings used for Nos. 88/92 contained various combinations of the following varieties: "ON" of "ONE" and "N" of "CENT" wide; "O" wide, "N" of "ONE" narrow and "N" of "CENT" wide; "O" narrow and both letters "N" wide; "ON" narrow, and "N" of "CENT" wide; "O" wide and both letters "N" narrow; "ON" wide and "N" of "CENT" narrow; "ON" and "N" of "CENT" narrow; "O" narrow "N" of "ONE" wide and "N" of "CENT" narrow. Antique "N" and "E" letters also occur.

1892–94. *Colours changed. Wmk Crown CA. P* 14. *Surch with T* **32** *and* **26** *by De la Rue.*
93 **6** 1 c. on 8 c. green (3.92) .. .. 90 1·50
94 **9** 3 c. on 32 c. carmine-rose (6.94) .. 2·25 70
a. Surch omitted £3000
93/94 Optd "Specimen" .. *Set of* 2 85·00
No. 94a comes from a sheet found at Singapore on which all stamps in the upper left pane had the surcharge omitted. Five vertical inter-panneau pairs still exist with the surcharge omitted on the upper stamps (*Price* £22000 *unused*). The only used example of the error is on cover.

33

34

4 cents. (35)

1892 (Mar)–**99.** *Wmk Crown CA. P* 14.
95 **33** 1 c. green (9.92) .. .. .. 1·25 50
a. Malformed "S" .. .. .. £130 55·00
b. Repaired "S" .. .. .. £110 45·00
96 3 c. carmine-rose (2.95) .. .. 9·50 40
a. Malformed "S" .. .. £180 65·00
97 3 c. brown (3.99) .. .. .. 3·50 60
a. Repaired "S" .. .. £160 65·00
b. Yellow-brown .. .. 3·00 60
98 **5** 4 c. deep carmine (7.99) .. .. 3·75 1·25
a. Broken oval .. .. 60·00 35·00
99 **18** 5 c. brown (6.94) .. .. 2·75 1·00
100 5 c. magenta (7.99) .. .. 1·75 2·00
101 **6** 8 c. ultramarine (6.94) .. .. 4·50 50
a. Bright blue .. .. 7·00 80
102 12 c. claret (3.94) .. .. 8·00 8·50
103 **33** 25 c. purple-brown and green .. 17·00 4·75
a. Repaired "S" £275 £120
b. Dull purple and green .. 16·00 4·25
104 50 c. olive-green and carmine .. 18·00 2·50
a. Repaired "S" £325 £120
105 **34** $5 orange and carmine (10.98) .. £300 £250
a. Repaired "S" £1700
95/105 .. .. *Set of* 11 £325 £250
95/101, 103/5 Optd "Specimen" .. *Set of* 10 £300
For illustrations of the Repaired and Malformed "S" varieties see above No. 28 of Seychelles.

1898 (26 Dec). *T* **18** *and* **6** *surch with T* **35** *at Singapore.*
106 4 c. on 5 c. brown (No. 99) .. .. 2·00 4·75
107 4 c. on 5 c. blue (No. 65) .. .. 1·75 8·00
a. Surch double .. .. — £950
108 4 c. on 8 c. ultramarine (No. 101) .. 90 2·75
a. Surch double £800 £700
b. Bright blue (No. 101*a*) 80 90
106/8*b* .. .. *Set of* 3 4·00 12·00
Nos. 107 and 108*b* exist with stop spaced $1^1/_2$ mm from the "S" (R. 10/6).

FOUR CENTS (36)

37

38

1899 (Mar). *T* **18** (*wmk Crown CA. P* 14), *surch with T* **36** *by De La Rue.*
109 4 c. on 5 c. carmine (Optd S. £40) .. 45 30
a. Surch omitted £20000
No. 109a is only known unused.

1902 (Apr)–**03.** *Wmk Crown CA. P* 14.
110 **37** 1 c. grey-green (7.02) .. .. 1·75 2·25
a. Pale green .. .. 3·75 2·50
111 3 c. dull purple and orange .. .. 2·50 15
112 4 c. purple/*red* (9.02) .. .. 4·00 30
113 **38** 5 c. dull purple (8.02) .. .. 3·50 85
114 8 c. purple/*blue* .. .. 3·25 20
115 10 c. purple and black/*yellow* (9.02) .. 17·00 1·50
116 **37** 25 c. dull purple and green (8.02) .. 10·00 4·50
117 **38** 30 c. grey and carmine (7.02) .. 14·00 8·00
118 **37** 50 c. deep green and carmine (9.02) .. 20·00 20·00
a. Dull green and carmine .. 21·00 21·00
119 **38** $1 dull green and black (9.02) .. 22·00 50·00
120 **37** $2 dull purple and black (9.02) .. 55·00 50·00
121 **38** $5 dull green & brown-orange (10.02) £180 £140
122 **37** $100 pur & grn/*yell* (3.03) (Optd S. £300) £7500
110/21 .. .. *Set of* 12 £300 £250
110/21 Optd "Specimen" .. .. *Set of* 12 £250

39

40

41

42

(Des N. Trotter and W. Egerton)

1903 (Dec)–**04.** *Wmk Crown CA. P* 14.
123 **39** 1 c. grey-green .. .. .. 60 6·50
124 **40** 3 c. dull purple (1.04) .. .. 8·00 4·25
125 **41** 4 c. purple/*red* (4.04) .. .. 3·00 30
126 **42** 8 c. purple/*blue* (7.04) .. .. 38·00 1·25
123/6 .. .. .. *Set of* 4 45·00 11·00
123/6 Optd "Specimen" .. .. *Set of* 4 £120

1904 (Aug)–**10.** *Wmk Multiple Crown CA. Ordinary paper* (1 c. *to* $1 *and* $5) *or chalk-surfaced paper* ($2, $25, $100). *P* 14.
127 **39** 1 c. deep green (9.04) .. .. 2·00 10
a. Chalk-surfaced paper (12.05) .. 5·50 1·50
w. Wmk inverted .. .. 60·00 30·00
128 **40** 3 c. dull purple .. .. 1·75 30
a. Chalk-surfaced paper (8.06) .. 6·50 1·25
aw. Wmk inverted .. .. 60·00 40·00
b. Plum (2.08) .. .. 4·00 1·00
129 **41** 4 c. purple/*red* (6.05) .. .. 4·00 65
a. Chalk-surfaced paper (10.05) .. 5·50 1·00
aw. Wmk inverted .. .. 40·00
130 **38** 5 c. dull purple (12.06) .. .. 5·00 2·00
a. Chalk-surfaced paper (12.06) .. 9·50 5·00
131 **42** 8 c. purple/*blue* (8.05) .. .. 17·00 1·25
a. Chalk-surfaced paper (12.05) .. 14·00 2·00
132 **38** 10 c. purple and black/*yellow* (8.05) .. 4·50 60
a. Chalk-surfaced paper (11.05) .. 9·00 2·00
133 **37** 25 c. dull purple and green (1.05) .. 20·00 17·00
a. Chalk-surfaced paper (11.05) .. 24·00 17·00
134 **38** 30 c. grey and carmine (3.05) .. 38·00 2·50
a. Chalk-surfaced paper (3.06) .. 40·00 2·75
135 **37** 50 c. dull green and carmine (10.05) .. 40·00 13·00
a. Chalk-surfaced paper (11.06) .. 25·00 13·00
136 **38** $1 dull green and black (3.05) .. 40·00 16·00
a. Chalk-surfaced paper (3.06) .. 35·00 14·00
137 **37** $2 dull purple and black (10.05) .. 90·00 80·00
138 **38** $5 dull green & brown-orange (10.05) £140 £140
a. Chalk-surfaced paper (1.08) .. £140 £140
139 **37** $25 grey-green and black (7.06) (Optd. S. £150) £1100 £1100
140 $100 purple and green/*yellow* (6.10) .. £8500
127/38 .. .. .. *Set of* 12 £325 £250

STRAITS SETTLEMENTS. (43) | Straits Settlements. (44)

STRAITS SETTLEMENTS.

FOUR CENTS. (45)

1906 (20 Dec)–**07.** *T* **18** *of Labuan* (*Nos.* 117 *etc.*) *optd with T* **43** *or* **44** (10 *c.*), *or additionally surch with T* **45**, *in black* (*No.* 145), *claret* (*No.* 151) *or brown-red* (*others*) *at Singapore. P* $13^1/_2$–14.
141 1 c. black and purple (*p* $14^1/_2$–15) .. 48·00 £130
a. Perf 14 .. .. .. £160
b. Line through "B" £375
142 2 c. black and green £170 £250
a. Perf $14^1/_2$–15 .. .. £150 £250
b. Line through "B" £600
143 3 c. black and sepia (1.07) .. 17·00 85·00
a. Line through "B" £190
144 4 c. on 12 c. black and yellow .. 1·75 6·00
a. No stop after "CENTS" (R.1/8, 6/8) .. £160
b. Line through "B" .. .. 90·00
145 4 c. on 16 c. green and brown (Blk.) .. 2·50 7·50
a. "STRAITS SETTLEMENTS" in both brown-red and black £550 £600
b. Ditto. In vert pair with normal .. £3250
c. Line through "B" .. .. 90·00
146 4 c. on 18 c. black and pale brown .. 2·00 6·00
a. No stop after "CENTS" (R.1/8, 6/8) .. £160
b. "FOUR CENTS" and bar double .. £5000
c. "FOUR CENTS" and bar $1^1/_2$ mm below normal position (pair with normal) £600
d. Line through "B" .. .. 80·00
147 8 c. black and vermilion .. .. 1·75 8·00
a. Line through "B" .. .. 90·00
148 10 c. brown and slate .. .. 5·00 6·00
a. No stop after "Settlements" (R. 1/4, 6/4) £190
b. Line through "B" £130
149 25 c. green and greenish blue (1.07) .. 6·00 28·00
a. Perf $14^1/_2$–15 .. .. 75·00 95·00
b. Perf $13^1/_2$–14 comp $14^1/_2$–15 .. £225
c. Line through "B" £150
150 50 c. dull purple and lilac (1.07) .. 10·00 65·00
a. Line through "B" £200
151 $1 claret and orange (Claret) (1.07) .. 42·00 £100
a. Perf $14^1/_2$–15 .. .. £375
b. Line through "B" £375
141/51 .. .. *Set of* 11 £250 £600
Nos. 141/51 were overprinted by a setting of 50 (10×5) applied twice to the sheets of 100. The "FOUR CENTS" surcharges were applied separately by a similar setting.
No. 145a shows impressions of Type **43** in both brown-red and black. It is known from one complete sheet and the top half of another.
No. 146b occurred on row 5 from one sheet only. No. 146*c* occurred on R.4/10 and 9/10 of the first printing.
The line through "B" flaw occurs on R.5/10 of the basic stamp. For illustration see Labuan.

46

47

1906 (Sept)–**12.** *Wmk Mult Crown CA. Ordinary paper* (1 c. *to* 10 c.) *or chalk-surfaced paper* (21 c. *to* $500). *P* 14.
152 **39** 1 c. blue-green (3.10) .. .. 18·00 95
153 **40** 3 c. red (6.08) .. .. .. 1·50 10
154 **41** 4 c. red (7.07) .. .. .. 5·50 2·50
155 4 c. dull purple (2.08) .. .. 4·00 10
a. Chalk-surfaced paper (1.12) .. 7·50 1·50
156 4 c. claret (9.11) .. .. 1·25 80
157 **38** 5 c. orange (4.09) .. .. 2·75 70
158 **42** 8 c. blue .. .. .. 3·50 40
159 **38** 10 c. purple/*yellow* (7.08) .. .. 4·00 70
a. Chalk-surfaced paper (5.12) .. 11·00 3·75
160 **46** 21 c. dull purple and claret (11.10) .. 6·50 27·00
161 **37** 25 c. dull and bright purple (7.09) .. 9·50 4·25
162 **38** 30 c. purple and orange-yellow (11.09) 27·00 2·50
163 **46** 45 c. black/*green* (11.10) .. .. 2·50 3·75
164 **37** 50 c. black/*green* (4.10) .. .. 4·75 3·25
165 **38** $1 black and red/*blue* (10.10) .. 11·00 4·00
166 **37** $2 green and red/*yellow* (12.09) .. 23·00 20·00
167 **38** $5 green and red/*green* (11.09) .. 90·00 65·00
w. Wmk inverted £400
168 **47** $25 pur & blue/*bl* (5.11) (Optd S. £200) £1000 £800
169 $500 pur & orange (5.10) (Optd S. £900) £60000
152/67 .. .. *Set of* 16 £190 £120
153/67 Optd "Specimen" .. *Set of* 15 £300
Beware of dangerous forgeries of No. 169.

48

49

50

51

52

53

54

1912–23. $25, $100 *and* $500 *as T* **47**, *but with head of King George V. Die* I (5, 10, 25, 30, 50 c., $1, $2, $5). *Wmk Mult Crown CA. Ordinary paper* (*Nos.* 193/6, 198/201, 203) *or chalk-surfaced paper* (*others*). *P* 14.

No.	Type	Description	Unused	Used
193	**48**	1 c. green (9.12)	4·25	1·00
		a. Pale green (1.14)	4·50	80
		b. Blue-green (1917)	6·00	1·50
194		1 c. black (2.19)	50	65
195	**52**	2 c. green (10.19)	50	50
196	**49**	3 c. red (2.13)	2·00	90
		a. Scarlet (2.17)	1·75	10
197	**50**	4 c. dull purple (3.13)	1·00	50
		a. Wmk sideways	†	£1300
198		4 c. rose-scarlet (2.19)	1·50	15
		a. Carmine	1·25	20
199	**51**	5 c. orange (8.12)	1·50	45
		a. Yellow-orange	2·25	70
200	**52**	6 c. dull claret (3.20)	1·75	50
		a. Deep claret	6·00	2·75
201		8 c. ultramarine (3.13)	80	50
202	**51**	10 c. purple/*yellow* (9.12)	1·00	60
		a. White back (1913) (Optd S. £38)	1·00	70
		b. On lemon (1916) (Optd S. £55)	13·00	1·00
203		10 c. deep bright blue (1918)	5·50	30
		a. Bright blue (1919)	4·00	50
204	**53**	21 c. dull and bright purple (11.13)	4·25	8·50
205	**54**	25 c. dull purple and mauve (7.14)	7·00	6·00
		aw. Wmk inverted	60·00	
		b. Dull purple and violet (1919)	45·00	8·50
207	**51**	30 c. dull purple and orange (12.14)	7·00	1·75
208	**53**	45 c. black/*green* (*white back*) (12.14)	6·50	18·00
		a. On blue-green, olive back (7.18) (Optd S. £38)	3·25	15·00
		b. On emerald back (6.22)	3·25	13·00
209	**54**	50 c. black/*green* (7.14)	5·50	2·50
		a. On blue-green, olive back (1918)	15·00	4·75
		b. On emerald back (1921)	12·00	7·00
		c. Die II. *On emerald back* (1922) (Optd S. £38)	3·00	4·00
210	**51**	$1 black and red/*blue* (10.14)	8·50	7·00
		w. Wmk inverted	75·00	
211	**54**	$2 grn & red/*yell, white back* (1914)	6·50	32·00
		a. Green and red/yellow (1915) (Optd. S. £38)	10·00	32·00
		b. On orange-buff (1921)	50·00	65·00
		c. On pale yellow (1921)	50·00	75·00
212	**51**	$5 grn & red/*grn, white back* (11.13)	65·00	42·00
		a. Green and red/green (1915) (Optd S. £55)	70·00	45·00
		b. On blue-green, olive back (1918)	£100	70·00
		c. On emerald back (1920)	£140	80·00
		d. Die II. *On emerald back* (1923) (Optd S. £75)	85·00	50·00
213	–	$25 purple & blue/*blue* (Optd S. £160)	£800	£350
		a. Break in scroll	£1400	
		b. Broken crown and scroll	£1400	
214	–	$100 blk & car/*bl* (8.12) (Optd S. £350)	£4000	
		a. Break in scroll	£6000	
		b. Broken crown and scroll	£6000	
215	–	$500 purple and orange-brown (8.12) (Optd S. £800)	£32000	
		a. Break in scroll	£40000	
		b. Broken crown and scroll	£40000	
193/212		*Set of* 19	£110	£100
193/212 Optd "Specimen"		*Set of* 19	£450	

The 6 c. is similar to T **52**, but the head is in a beaded oval as in T **53**. The 2 c., 6 c. (and 12 c. below) have figures of value on a circular ground while in the 8 c. this is of oval shape.

For illustrations of the varieties on Nos. 213/15 see above No. 58 of Leeward Islands.

RED CROSS

2c.

(55)

MALAYA-
BORNEO
EXHIBITION.

(56)

1917 (1 May). *Surch with T* **55**.

No.	Type	Description	Unused	Used
216	**49**	2 c. on 3 c. scarlet	1·75	22·00
		a. No stop (R. 2/3)	£170	£375
217	**50**	2 c. on 4 c. dull purple	1·75	22·00
		a. No stop (R. 2/3)	£170	£375

Nos. 216a and 217a occur in the first setting only.

Type I

Type II

The duty plate for the 25 c. value was replaced in 1926. In Type II the solid shading forming the back of the figure 2 extends to the top of the curve; the upturned end of the foot of the 2 is short; two background lines above figure 5; c close to 5; STRAITS SETTLEMENTS in taller letters.

1921–33. *Wmk Mult Script CA. Ordinary paper* (1 c. *to* 6 c., 10 c. (*No.* 230), 12 c.) *or chalk-surfaced paper* (*others*). *P* 14.

No.	Type	Description	Unused	Used
218	**48**	1 c. black (3.22)	30	10
219	**52**	2 c. green (5.21)	30	10
		w. Wmk inverted	25·00	
220		2 c. brown (12.25)	7·00	2·25
221	**49**	3 c. green (9.23)	1·50	70
		w. Wmk inverted	25·00	
222	**50**	4 c. carmine-red (10.21)	2·00	3·50
223		4 c. bright violet (8.24)	50	10
		w. Wmk inverted	25·00	
224		4 c. orange (8.29)	1·00	10
225	**51**	5 c. orange (Die I) (5.21)	1·00	15
		a. Wmk sideways	†	£1500
		b. Die II (1922)	2·25	1·25
		w. Wmk inverted	25·00	
226	**51**	5 c. brown (Die II) (1932)	1·75	10
		a. Die I (1933)	5·00	10
227	**52**	6 c. dull claret (10.22)	2·00	15
		w. Wmk inverted	25·00	
228		6 c. rose-pink (2.25)	18·00	8·50
229		6 c. scarlet (1.27)	2·50	10
230	**51**	10 c. bright blue (Die I) (1921)	1·75	95
		w. Wmk inverted	25·00	
231		10 c. purple/*pale yellow* (Die I) (1923)	2·50	5·00
		a. Die II (11.26)	1·75	20
		b. Purple/brt yellow (Die II) (1932)		
		ba. Die I (1933)	4·00	10
232	**52**	12 c. bright blue (1.22)	1·00	10
		w. Wmk inverted	25·00	
233	**53**	21 c. dull and bright purple (2.23)	5·00	40·00
234	**54**	25 c. dull purple and mauve (Die I, Type I) (1921)	24·00	65·00
		a. Die II, Type I (1923)	15·00	3·00
		b. Die II, Type II (1927)	4·00	1·75
235	**51**	30 c. dull purple & orange (Die I) (1921)	16·00	27·00
		a. Die II (1922)	2·00	1·00
236	**53**	35 c. dull purple & orange-yellow (8.22)	12·00	5·00
		a. Dull purple and orange	3·50	5·50
237		35 c. scarlet and purple (4.31)	9·00	7·00
238	**54**	50 c. black/*emerald* (9.25)	1·75	40
239	**51**	$1 black and red/*blue* (Die II) (1921)	6·00	65
240	**54**	$2 grn & red/*pale yell* (Die II) (1923)	10·00	8·00
240*a*	**51**	$5 green and red/*green* (Die II) (1926)	70·00	32·00
240*b*	–	$25 pur & bl/*bl* (5.23) (Optd S. £130)	£475	95·00
		ba. Break in scroll	£800	
		bb. Broken crown and scroll	£800	
240*c*	–	$100 blk & car/*bl* (5.23) (Optd S. £250)	£2500	£1000
		ca. Break in scroll	£4000	
		cb. Broken crown and scroll	£4000	
240*d*	–	$500 purple and orange-brown (4.23) (Optd S. £550)	£22000	
		da. Break in scroll	£29000	
		db. Broken crown and scroll	£29000	
218/40*a*		*Set of* 24	£130	95·00
218/40*a ex* 228 Optd/Perf "Specimen"		*Set of* 23	£475	

Nos. 240*b*/*d* are as Type **47**, but with portrait of George V.

An 8 c. in carmine was prepared but not issued (Optd "Specimen" £225).

The paper of Nos. 231*b*/ba is the normal *pale yellow* at the back, but with a bright yellow surface.

In 1926 new Key and Duty plates were made of 100 (10×10) instead of the usual 60 (6×10).

For illustrations of the varieties on Nos. 240*b*/*d* see above No. 58 of Leeward Islands.

1922 (31 Mar). *Malaya–Borneo Exhibition, Singapore. T* **48** *and T* **50** *to* **54**, *overprinted with T* **56**.

(*a*) *Wmk Mult Crown CA*

No.	Type	Description	Unused	Used
241	**52**	2 c. green	26·00	75·00
242	**50**	4 c. scarlet	6·00	22·00
243	**51**	5 c. orange (Die I)	4·00	16·00
244	**52**	8 c. ultramarine	1·75	6·50
245	**54**	25 c. dull purple and mauve (Die I)	3·00	24·00
246	**53**	45 c. black/*blue-green* (*olive back*)	3·00	20·00
		a. On green (*white back*)	£275	
247	**51**	$1 black and red/*blue* (Die I)	£140	£550
248	**54**	$2 green and red/*orange-buff* (Die I)	25·00	£100
		a. On pale yellow	60·00	£140
249	**51**	$5 green and red/*blue-green* (*ol back*)	£200	£375

(*b*) *Wmk Mult Script CA*

No.	Type	Description	Unused	Used
250	**48**	1 c. black	1·75	9·00
251	**52**	2 c. green	1·40	12·00
252	**50**	4 c. carmine-red	1·75	20·00
253	**51**	5 c. orange (Die II)	2·50	35·00
254		10 c. bright blue (Die I)	2·25	22·00
255		$1 black and red/*blue* (Die II)	15·00	95·00
241/55		*Set of* 11	£225	£650

Nos. 241/55 were overprinted by stereo which repeated a setting of 12 (6×2). The following varieties therefore occur ten times on each sheet of 120: (a) Small second "A" in "MALAYA." (b) No stop. (c) No hyphen. (d) Oval last "O" in "BORNEO," (e) "EXH.BITION".

1935 (6 May). *Silver Jubilee. As Nos.* 114/17 *of Jamaica, but ptd by Waterlow & Sons. P* 11×12.

No.	Description	Unused	Used
256	5 c. ultramarine and grey	2·00	30
	j. Damaged turret	£110	
257	8 c. green and indigo	2·75	2·25
	j. Damaged turret	£140	
258	12 c. brown and deep blue	2·75	2·50
	j. Damaged turret	£140	
259	25 c. slate and purple	3·00	4·50
	j. Damaged turret	£160	
256/9	*Set of* 4	9·50	8·50
256/9 Perf "Specimen"	*Set of* 4	95·00	

57

58

1936 (1 Jan)–**37**. *Chalk-surfaced paper. Wmk Mult Script CA. P* 14.

No.	Type	Description	Unused	Used
260	**57**	1 c. black (1.1.37)	60	20
261		2 c. green (1.2.36)	60	40
262		4 c. orange (15.6.36)	1·25	40
263		5 c. brown (1.8.36)	40	20
264		6 c. scarlet (1.2.36)	90	75
265		8 c. grey	75	40
266		10 c. dull purple (1.7.36)	1·25	30
267		12 c. bright ultramarine (1.9.36)	2·00	2·00
268		25 c. dull purple and scarlet (1.2.36)	1·00	30
269		30 c. dull purple and orange	1·25	2·75
270		40 c. scarlet and dull purple	1·25	2·50
271		50 c. black/*emerald* (1.9.36)	3·00	80
272		$1 black and red/*blue* (1.7.36)	14·00	80
273		$2 green and scarlet (1.4.36)	28·00	10·00
274		$5 green and red/*emerald* (1.1.37)	55·00	10·00
260/74		*Set of* 15	£100	29·00
260/74 Perf "Specimen"		*Set of* 15	£200	

1937 (12 May). *Coronation. As Nos.* 118/20 *of Jamaica.*

No.	Description	Unused	Used
275	4 c. orange	30	10
276	8 c. grey-black	70	10
277	12 c. bright blue	1·25	60
275/7	*Set of* 3	2·00	65
275/7 Perf "Specimen"	*Set of* 3	65·00	

1937–41. *Chalk-surfaced paper. Wmk Mult Script CA. P* 14 *or* 15×14 (15 c.). (*a*) *Die I* (*printed at two operations*).

No.	Type	Description	Unused	Used
278	**58**	1 c. black (1.1.38)	4·00	10
279		2 c. green (6.12.37)	18·00	10
280		4 c. orange (1.1.38)	13·00	20
281		5 c. brown (19.11.37)	23·00	30
282		6 c. scarlet (10.1.38)	10·00	50
283		8 c. grey (26.1.38)	42·00	10
284		10 c. dull purple (8.11.37)	7·50	10
285		12 c. ultramarine (10.1.38)	8·00	30
286		25 c. dull purple and scarlet (11.12.37)	42·00	95
287		30 c. dull purple and orange (1.12.37)	35·00	1·75
288		40 c. scarlet and dull purple (20.12.37)	10·00	2·00
289		50 c. black/*emerald* (26.1.38)	9·00	10
290		$1 black and red/*blue* (26.1.38)	12·00	20
291		$2 green and scarlet (26.1.38)	25·00	4·00
292		$5 green and red/*emerald* (26.1.38)	25·00	3·00

(*b*) *Die II* (*printed at one operation*)

No.	Type	Description	Unused	Used
293	**58**	2 c. green (28.12.38)	50·00	40
294		2 c. orange (6.10.41)	1·75	9·00
295		3 c. green (*ordinary paper*) (5.9.41)	3·25	4·00
296		4 c. orange (29.10.38)	70·00	10
297		5 c. brown (18.2.39)	28·00	10
298		15 c. ultram (*ordinary paper*) (6.10.41)	4·25	10·00
278/98		*Set of* 18	£275	32·00
278/92, 294/5, 298 Perf "Specimen"		*Set of* 18	£350	

Die I. Lines of background outside central oval touch the oval and the foliage of the palm tree is usually joined to the oval frame. The downward-pointing palm frond, opposite the King's eye, has two points.

Die II. Lines of background are separated from the oval by a white line and the foliage of the palm trees does not touch the outer frame. The palm frond has only one point.

Nos. 295 and 298 were printed by Harrison and Sons following bomb damage to the De La Rue works on 29 December 1940.

The 6 c. grey, 8 c. scarlet and $5 purple and orange were only issued with the BMA overprint, but the 8 c. without overprint is known although in this state it was never issued (*Price* £13).

STAMP BOOKLETS

1914–19. *Black on blue* (*No.* SB1) *or grey* (*No.* SB1*b*) *covers. Stapled.*

SB1 $1 booklet containing twenty-five 4 c. dull purple (No. 197) in two blocks of 12 and one single
a. Containing 4 c. rose-scarlet (No. 198) (1919)

SB1*b* $1 booklet containing four 1 c., sixteen 3 c. and twelve 4 c. (Nos. 193, 196/7) in blocks of four

1921. *Black on blue cover. Stapled.*

SB2 $1 booklet containing twenty-five 4 c. (No. 222) in two blocks of 12 and one single
a. Contents as SB2, but four blocks of 6 and one single

1922. *Black on red cover. Stapled.*

SB3 $1 booklet containing 5 c. (No. 225) in block of 8 and 6 c. (No. 227) in block of 10 £900

1925–29. *Black on red cover. Stapled.*

SB4 $1.20, booklet containing thirty 4 c. bright violet (No. 223) in blocks of 10
a. Containing 4 c. orange (No. 224) (1929)

1927. *Black on grey* (*No.* SB5), *green* (*No.* SB6) *or blue* (*No.* SB7) *covers. Stapled.*

SB5 $1 booklet containing 4 c. and 6 c. (Nos. 223, 229) in blocks of 10

SB6 $1.20, booklet containing twenty 6 c. (No. 229) in blocks of 10

SB7 $1.20, booklet containing 2 c., 4 c. and 6 c. (Nos. 219, 223, 229) in blocks of 10

1933. *Black on buff cover. Stapled.*

SB8 $1 booklet containing twenty 5 c. (No. 226a) in blocks of 10

1936. *Stapled.*

SB9 $1 booklet containing twenty 5 c. (No. 263) in blocks of 10

SB10 $1.30, booklet containing 5 c. and 8 c. (Nos. 263, 265) in blocks of 10

1938. *Black on buff* (*No.* SB11) *or black on green* (*No.* SB12) *covers. Stapled.*

SB11 $1 booklet containing twenty 5 c. (No. 281) in blocks of 10 £1100

SB12 $1.30, booklet containing 5 c. and 8 c. (Nos. 281, 283) in blocks of 10 and pane of airmail labels £1400

POSTAGE DUE STAMPS

D 1

1924 (1 Jan)–**26.** *Wmk Mult Script CA. P* 14.

D1 D 1 1 c. violet .. 4·00 5·50
D2 2 c. black .. 3·00 1·25
D3 4 c. green (5.26) .. 2·00 4·75
D4 8 c. scarlet .. 4·50 55
D5 10 c. orange .. 5·50 85
D6 12 c. bright blue .. 7·00 65
D1/6 .. *Set of* 6 23·00 12·00
D1/6 Optd "Specimen" .. *Set of* 6 £200

For later issues of Postage Due stamps, see MALAYAN POSTAL UNION.

The Straits Settlements were occupied by the Japanese in 1942. After the Second World War the stamps of MALAYA (BRITISH MILITARY ADMINISTRATION) were used. In 1946 Singapore became a separate Crown Colony and Labuan was transferred to North Borneo. Separate stamps were issued for Malacca and Penang, which both joined the Malayan Federation on 1 February 1948.

II. FEDERATED MALAY STATES

On 1 July 1896, the States of Negri Sembilan, Pahang, Perak and Selangor were organised on a federal basis to be known as the Federated Malay States. For the time being each State continued with individual issues, but stamps for the use of the Federation replaced these in 1900.

PRICES FOR STAMPS ON COVER	
Nos. 1/13	*from* × 12
No. 14	—
Nos. 15/22	*from* × 10
Nos. 23/5	*from* × 3
No. 26	—
Nos. 27/50	*from* × 6
No. 51	—
Nos. 52/81	*from* × 5
No. 82	—
Nos. D1/6	*from* × 10

PRINTERS. All issues of the Federated Malay States were printed in typography by De La Rue & Co, Ltd, London, *unless otherwise stated.*

FEDERATED MALAY STATES (1)

FEDERATED MALAY STATES (2)

1900. *Optd with T* **1** (*cent values*) *or* **2** (*dollar values*).

(*a*) *Stamps of Negri Sembilan* (*T* **3**)

1 1 c. dull purple and green .. 2·00 4·00
2 2 c. dull purple and brown .. 23·00 48·00
3 3 c. dull purple and black .. 2·00 3·25
4 5 c. dull purple and olive-yellow .. 65·00 £150
5 10 c. dull purple and orange .. 3·50 16·00
6 20 c. green and olive .. 70·00 85·00
7 25 c. green and carmine .. £180 £300
8 50 c. green and black .. 75·00 95·00
1/8 .. *Set of* 8 £375 £600
1/8 Optd "Specimen" .. *Set of* 8 £160

(*b*) *Stamps of Perak* (*T* **44** *and* **45**)

9 5 c. dull purple and olive-yellow .. 11·00 48·00
10 10 c. dull purple and orange .. 60·00 65·00
11 $1 green and pale green .. £130 £170
12 $2 green and carmine .. 90·00 £160
13 $5 green and ultramarine .. £250 £375
14 $25 green and orange (Optd S. £275) .. £6000
11/13 Optd "Specimen" .. *Set of* 3 £120

The Negri Sembilan 3 c. dull purple and black does not exist without overprint Type **1**.

The stamps of STRAITS SETTLEMENTS were used in Federated Malay States from 16 July 1900 until replaced by the 1900–1 issue.

3

4

1900–1. *P* 14. (*a*) *T* **3**. *Wmk Crown CA, sideways* (1901).

15 1 c. black and green .. 3·00 3·00
a. Grey and green .. 1·75 30
b. Grey-brown and green .. 5·00 30
16 3 c. black and brown .. 5·00 2·00
a. Grey and brown .. 2·75 35
b. Grey-brown and brown .. 2·00 20
17 4 c. black and carmine .. 12·00 2·50
a. Grey and carmine .. 4·75 2·25
b. Grey-brown and carmine .. 14·00 1·00
18 5 c. green and carmine/*yellow* .. 1·50 2·00
19 8 c. black and ultramarine .. 38·00 10·00
a. Grey and ultramarine .. 20·00 3·50
b. Grey-brown and ultramarine .. 23·00 3·00
20 10 c. black and claret .. 70·00 16·00
a. Grey and claret .. 50·00 5·00
b. Black and purple .. 85·00 16·00
c. Grey and purple .. 65·00 7·00
d. Grey-brown and purple .. 75·00 4·00
21 20 c. mauve and black .. 17·00 6·50
22 50 c. black and orange-brown .. £100 80·00
a. Grey and orange-brown .. 75·00 35·00
b. Grey-brown and orange-brown .. 75·00 30·00
15/22 .. *Set of* 8 £150 42·00
15/22 Optd "Specimen" .. *Set of* 8 £160

Later printings in 1903–4 show the two upper lines of shading in the background at the corner nearest to the "S" of "STATE" blurred and running into one another, whereas in earlier printings these lines are distinct. Two plates were used for printing the central design of T **3**. In Plate 1 the lines of background are regular throughout, but in Plate 2 they are lighter around the head and back of the tiger. The 5 c. was the only value with single wmk to be printed from Plate 2. Stamps with multiple wmk were printed for a short time from Plate 1, and show the two blurred lines of background near "S" of "STATE," but the majority of these stamps were printed from Plate 2 and later plates.

(*b*) *T* **4**. *Wmk Crown CC* (1900)

23 $1 green and pale green .. 85·00 90·00
24 $2 green and carmine .. 90·00 95·00
25 $5 green and bright ultramarine .. £150 £170
a. Green and pale ultramarine .. £150 £170
26 $25 green and orange (Optd S. £180) .. £1600 £950
23/5 Optd "Specimen" .. *Set of* 3 £110

Two dies for 1 c. green and 4 c. scarlet

Die I. "Head" and duty plates. Thick frame line below "MALAY" and in the 1 c. the "c" is thin whilst in the 4 c. it is thick.

Die II. Single working plate. Thin frame line below "MALAY" and in the 1 c. the "c" is thicker whilst in the 4 c. it is thinner.

1904 (10 Oct)–**22.** *T* **3** *and T* **4** (*dollar values*). *Wmk Mult Crown CA* (*sideways* on T* **3**). *Ordinary paper* (1 c. *to* 50 c.) *or chalk-surfaced paper* ($1 *to* $25).

27 1 c. grey and green .. 50·00 7·00
a. Grey-brown and green .. 21·00 70
28 1 c. green (Die I) (8.7.06) .. 7·50 30
29 1 c. green (Die II) (1908) .. 2·00 20
a. Yellow-green .. 14·00 1·00
aw. Wmk Crown to right of CA .. 25·00 6·00
b. Blue-green .. 18·00 85
30 1 c. deep brown (21.1.19) .. 2·25 90
31 2 c. green (18.2.19) .. 1·00 30
w. Wmk Crown to right of CA .. 25·00 8·00
32 3 c. grey and brown (10.04) .. 35·00 1·00
a. Grey-brown and brown (12.05) .. 23·00 70
ab. Chalk-surfaced paper .. 23·00 1·50
33 3 c. brown (11.7.06) .. 6·00 15
34 3 c. carmine (2.2.09) .. 2·00 10
aw. Wmk Crown to right of CA .. 4·00 30
b. Scarlet (1.17) .. 9·50 40
bw. Wmk Crown to right of CA .. 20·00 4·00
35 3 c. grey (29.10.18) .. 1·25 20
w. Wmk Crown to right of CA .. 20·00 8·00
36 4 c. grey and scarlet .. 27·00 2·25
a. Chalk-surfaced paper. *Grey and rose* .. 10·00 85
b. Grey-brown and scarlet .. 25·00 2·00
c. Black and scarlet .. 22·00 2·25
d. Black and rose .. 4·00 30
dw. Wmk Crown to right of CA .. 6·00 30
e. Black and deep rose (*aniline*) (1909) .. 45·00 5·00
f. Jet black and rose (1914) .. 17·00 1·25
37 4 c. scarlet (Die I) (11.2.19) .. 2·00 3·00
38 4 c. scarlet (Die II) (15.4.19) .. 80 15
aw. Wmk Crown to right of CA .. 25·00 4·00
b. Wmk upright (2.22) .. † £325
39 5 c. green and carmine/*yellow* (5.06) .. 5·50 1·50
aw. Wmk Crown to right of CA .. 35·00 15·00
b. Chalk-surfaced paper .. 16·00 3·50
c. Deep green and carmine/yellow .. 5·50 1·75
d. On orange-buff (1921) .. 11·00 4·00
e. On pale yellow (4.22) .. 5·00 2·50
40 6 c. orange (11.2.19) .. 2·00 1·50
41 8 c. grey and ultramarine (2.05) .. 45·00 15·00
aw. Wmk Crown to right of CA ..
b. Grey-brown and ultramarine (12.05) .. 16·00 3·50
ba. Chalk-surfaced paper .. 30·00 10·00
bb. Wmk upright (3.07) .. 5·00 3·50
42 8 c. ultramarine (8.3.10) .. 13·00 90
aw. Wmk Crown to right of CA .. 40·00 20·00
b. Deep blue (1918) .. 15·00 1·25
43 10 c. grey-brown and claret .. 45·00 3·75
a. Chalk-surfaced paper (1905) .. 55·00 5·00
b. Black and claret .. 15·00 30
bw. Wmk Crown to right of CA .. 25·00 1·00
c. Grey-brown and purple (1905) .. 45·00 2·25
d. Black and purple .. 15·00 1·50
e. Jet-black and bright purple (1914) .. 55·00 3·75
44 10 c. deep blue (3.6.19) .. 6·50 1·00
a. Bright blue .. 6·50 85
ab. Wmk inverted .. † —
aw. Wmk Crown to right of CA .. 30·00 15·00
45 20 c. mauve and black (3.05) .. 4·25 35
a. Chalk-surfaced paper .. 7·50 1·75
w. Wmk Crown to right of CA .. 35·00 15·00
46 35 c. scarlet/*pale yellow* (25.8.22) .. 5·50 12·00
47 50 c. grey and orange (3.05) .. 50·00 5·00
aw. Wmk Crown to right of CA .. £100 30·00
b. Wmk inverted .. † —
c. Grey-brown and orange-brown (1906) 30·00 4·75
ca. Chalk-surfaced paper. *Grey-brown and orange-brown* .. 38·00 4·50
cb. Grey and orange-brown .. 45·00 4·50
cc. Black and orange-brown .. 60·00 9·00
cd. Jet-black and orange-brown (1914) .. 85·00 12·00
48 $1 grey-green and green (11.07) .. 48·00 35·00
a. Green and pale green .. 60·00 38·00
aw. Wmk inverted ..
49 $2 green and carmine (4.12.07) .. 65·00 £100
a. Printed on the gummed side ..
w. Wmk inverted ..
50 $5 green and blue (1.08) .. £110 £120
51 $25 green and orange (12.09) .. £1100 £600
27/50 .. *Set of* 22 £350 £250
28, 30/1, 33/5, 37, 40, 42, 44, 46 Optd "Specimen" *Set of* 11 £350

*The normal sideways watermark shows Crown to left of CA, *as seen from the back of the stamp.*

Nos. 29/*b*, 30, 31, 33, 34/*b* and 35 were printed from single working plates and all the rest from double plates.

Most examples of No. 47b have fiscal cancellations, but at least one is known postally used.

1922–34. *Wmk Mult Script CA* (*sideways* on T* **3**). *Ordinary paper* (1 c. *to* 10 c. (*No.* 66), 12 c., 35 c. (*No.* 72)) *or chalk-surfaced paper* (*others*).

52 **3** 1 c. deep brown (1.8.22) .. 1·50 2·25
w. Wmk Crown to right of CA .. 25·00 25·00
53 1 c. black (12.6.23) .. 60 20
54 2 c. brown (5.8.25) .. 4·00 3·25
55 2 c. green (15.6.26) .. 1·75 10
56 3 c. grey (27.12.22) .. 1·75 6·00
w. Wmk Crown to right of CA .. 30·00 30·00
57 3 c. green (22.1.24) .. 1·25 1·50
58 3 c. brown (31.5.27) .. 70 50
59 4 c. carmine-red (Die II) (27.11.23) .. 2·75 45
w. Wmk Crown to right of CA .. 20·00 10·00
60 4 c. orange (9.11.26) .. 65 10
a. No watermark .. £300 £200
61 5 c. mauve/*pale yellow* (17.3.22) .. 85 20
w. Wmk Crown to right of CA .. 25·00 25·00
62 5 c. brown (1.3.32) .. 2·00 10
63 6 c. orange (2.5.22) .. 55 45
w. Wmk Crown to right of CA ..
64 6 c. scarlet (9.11.26) .. 90 10
65 10 c. bright blue (23.10.23) .. 1·25 7·00
w. Wmk Crown to right of CA ..
66 10 c. black and blue (18.1.24†) .. 2·00 75
67 10 c. purple/*pale yellow* (14.7.31) .. 3·50 40
68 12 c. ultramarine (12.9.22) .. 1·25 10
w. Wmk Crown to right of CA .. 30·00 20·00
69 20 c. dull purple and black (*chalk-surfaced paper*) (3.4.23) .. 4·00 35
a. Ordinary paper (29.12.26) .. 21·00 1·25
70 25 c. purple and bright magenta (3.9.29) 2·50 85
71 30 c. purple and orange-yellow (3.9.29) 3·25 2·25
72 35 c. scarlet/*pale yellow* (6.11.28) .. 3·25 17·00
73 35 c. scarlet and purple (29.9.31) .. 13·00 14·00
74 50 c. black and orange (24.4.24) .. 13·00 6·00
aw. Wmk Crown to right of CA .. 75·00
b. Black and orange-brown .. 20·00 4·50
75 50 c. black/*green* (16.6.31) .. 4·00 1·50
76 **4** $1 pale green and green (2.2.26) .. 19·00 70·00
a. Grey-green and emerald (5.10.26) 13·00 32·00
77 **3** $1 black and red/*blue* (10.3.31) .. 12·00 3·00
78 **4** $2 green and carmine (17.8.26) .. 16·00 65·00
79 **3** $2 green and red/*yellow* (6.2.34) .. 30·00 28·00
80 **4** $5 green and blue (24.2.25) .. 65·00 £140
81 **3** $5 green and red/*green* (7.34) .. £140 £150
82 **4** $25 grn & orge (14.2.28) (Optd S. £120) £800 £500
52/81 .. *Set of* 30 £300 £425
52/81 Optd/Perf "Specimen" .. *Set of* 30 £600

*The normal sideways watermark shows Crown to left of CA, *as seen from the back of the stamp.*

†No. 66 was released in London by the Crown Agents some months earlier but this is the official date of issue in the States.

Nos. 52, 56 and 59 were printed from single working plates and the rest from double plates.

The 5 c. mauve on white Script paper is the result of soaking early printings of No. 61 in water.

STAMP BOOKLETS

1909. *Black on pink* (*Nos.* SB1/2) *or black on buff* (*No.* SB3) *covers. Stapled.*

SB1 25 c. booklet containing twenty-four 1 c. (No. 29) in blocks of 6 .. £2000
a. Black on green cover (1917) ..
b. Black on blue cover .. £2000
SB2 73 c. booklet containing twenty-four 3 c. (No. 34) in blocks of 6 .. £1800
a. Black on red cover (1917) ..
b. Black on blue cover .. £1800
SB3 97 c. booklet containing twenty-four 4 c. (No. 36*d*) in blocks of 6 .. £2000

1919. *Black on green* (*No.* SB4) *or black on pink* (*No.* SB5) *covers. Stapled.*

SB4 49 c. booklet containing twenty-four 2 c. (No. 31) in blocks of 6 ..
SB5 97 c. booklet containing twenty-four 4 c. (No. 37) in blocks of 6 .. £1800

1922. *Black on buff cover* (*No.* SB7). *Stapled.*

SB6 $1. 21, booklet containing twenty-four 5 c. (No. 61) in blocks of 6 ..
SB7 $1. 45, booklet containing twenty-four 6 c. (No. 63) in blocks of 6 .. £2000

1926. *As Nos.* SB4, SB3 *and* SB7, *but sold at face value without premium. Black on green* (*No.* SB8), *black on pink* (*No.* SB9) *or black on buff* (*No.* SB10) *covers. Stapled.*

SB8 48 c. booklet containing twenty-four 2 c. (No. 55) in blocks of 6 ..
SB9 96 c. booklet containing twenty-four 4 c. (No. 60) in blocks of 6 .. £2000
SB10 $1.44 booklet containing twenty-four 6 c. (No. 64) in blocks of 6 .. £2000

1926. *Black on grey cover. Stapled.*

SB11 $1 booklet containing 4 c. and 6 c. (Nos. 60, 64) each in block of 10 ..

1927. *Black on bluish green cover. Stapled.*

SB12 $1.50, booklet containing 2 c., 3 c., 4 c. and 6 c. (Nos. 55, 58, 60, 64) each in block of 10 .. £2000

1927–30. *Black on red cover. Stapled.*
SB13 $1.20, booklet containing thirty 4 c. (No. 60) in blocks of 10 .. £2000
a. Black on orange cover (1930)

1928. *Black on green cover. Stapled.*
SB14 $1.20, booklet containing twenty 6 c. (No. 64) in blocks of 10

1928–30. *Black on blue cover. Stapled.*
SB15 $1.20, booklet containing 2 c., 4 c. and 6 c. (Nos. 55, 60, 64) each in block of 10
a. Black on white cover (1930)

1934.
SB16 $1 booklet containing twenty 5 c. (No. 62) in blocks of 10

POSTAGE DUE STAMPS

D 1

(Typo Waterlow)

1924 (1 Dec)–**26.** *Wmk Mult Script CA* (*sideways**). *P* 15×14.
D1 D 1 1 c. violet 4·25 15·00
w. Wmk Crown to left of CA (1926) 6·00 13·00
D2 2 c. black 1·75 2·50
w. Wmk Crown to left of CA (1926) 2·50 2·50
D3 4 c. green (*wmk Crown to left of CA*) (27.4.26) 2·25 4·50
D4 8 c. red 4·50 16·00
w. Wmk Crown to left of CA (1926) 7·00 14·00
D5 10 c. orange 7·50 13·00
w. Wmk Crown to left of CA (1926) 11·00 11·00
D6 12 c. blue 8·50 18·00
w. Wmk Crown to left of CA (1926) 8·50 14·00
D1/6 *Set of* 6 26·00 50·00
D1/6 Optd "Specimen" *Set of* 6 £150

*The normal sideways watermark shows Crown to right of CA, *as seen from the back of the stamp.*

The issues of the Federated Malay States were replaced by stamps for the individual States from 1935 onwards.

III. MALAYAN POSTAL UNION

The Malayan Postal Union was organised in 1934 and, initially, covered the Straits Settlements and the Federated Malay States. Stamps of the Straits Settlements together with issues for the individual States continued to be used, but Malayan Postal Union postage due stamps were introduced in 1936.

Following the end of the Second World War the use of these postage dues spread throughout Malaya and to Singapore.

PRICES FOR STAMPS ON COVER TO 1945	
Nos. D1/6	*from* × 10
Nos. D7/13	*from* × 4

POSTAGE DUE STAMPS

D 1

10 cents
(D 2)

(Typo Waterlow until 1961, then D.L.R.)

1936 (June)–**38.** *Wmk Mult Script CA. P* 15 × 14.
D1 D 1 1 c. slate-purple (4.38) 4·00 70
D2 4 c. green (9.36) 10·00 1·00
D3 8 c. scarlet 5·00 3·50
D4 10 c. yellow-orange 7·00 30
D5 12 c. pale ultramarine (9.36) 8·00 12·00
D6 50 c. black (1.38) 28·00 5·50
D1/6 *Set of* 6 55·00 21·00
D1/6 Perf "Specimen" *Set of* 6 £130

For use in Negri Sembilan, Pahang, Perak, Selangor and Straits Settlements including Singapore.

1945–49. *New values and colours. Wmk Mult Script CA. P* 15 × 14.
D 7 D 1 1 c. purple 2·75 1·75
D 8 3 c. green 7·00 11·00
D 9 5 c. scarlet 8·00 7·50
D10 8 c. yell-orange (1949) (Perf S. £75) 16·00 16·00
D11 9 c. yellow-orange 50·00 48·00
D12 15 c. pale ultramarine £130 35·00
D13 20 c. blue (1948) (Perf S. £75) 10·00 6·00
D7/13 *Set of* 7 £200 £110

1951 (8 Aug)–**63.** *Wmk Mult Script CA. P* 14.
D14 D 1 1 c. violet (21.8.52) 30 90
D15 2 c. deep slate-blue (16.11.53) 60 1·50
a. Perf 12½ (15.11.60) 40 9·00
ab. Chalk-surfaced paper (10.7.62) 35 6·00
ac. Ditto. Imperf between (vert pair)
D16 3 c. deep green (21.8.52) 17·00 12·00
D17 D 1 4 c. sepia (16.11.53) 45 4·00
a. Perf 12½ (15.11.60) 60 14·00
ab. Chalk-surfaced paper. *Bistre-brown* (10.7.62) 70 11·00
D18 5 c. vermilion 42·00 12·00
D19 8 c. yellow-orange 2·00 3·75
D20 12 c. bright purple (1.2.54) 1·00 5·00
a. Perf 12½. Chalk-surfaced paper (10.7.62) 1·50 20·00
D21 20 c. blue 4·00 6·00
a. Perf 12½. *Deep blue* (10.12.57) 6·00 26·00
ab. Chalk-surfaced paper (15.10.63) 3·00 30·00
D14/21 *Set of* 8 60·00 40·00

Nos. D7 to D21b were for use in the Federation and Singapore, and from 1963 throughout Malaysia.

1964 (14 Apr)–**65.** *Chalk-surfaced paper. Wmk* w **12** (*sideways on* 1 c.). *P* 12½.
D22 D 1 1 c. maroon 30 14·00
a. Perf 12. Wmk upright (4.5.65) 30 14·00
D23 2 c. deep slate-blue 45 13·00
a. Perf 12 (9.3.65) 60 17·00
D24 4 c. bistre-brown 75 13·00
a. Perf 12 (9.3.65) 40 14·00
D25 8 c. yellow-orange (*p* 12) (4.5.65) 2·00 15·00
D27 12 c. bright purple 1·50 18·00
a. Perf 12 (4.5.65) 3·50 28·00
D28 20 c. deep blue 2·50 35·00
a. Perf 12 (4.5.65) 5·50 48·00
D22/8 *Set of* 6 6·25 95·00

1964 (Dec). *As No.* D19 *surch locally with Type* D **2**.
D29 D 1 10 c. on 8 c. yellow-orange 30 2·00

First supplies of this stamp differed from No. D19 in that they had been climatically affected but later a fresh printing of No. D19 was surcharged.

1966. *Unsurfaced paper. Wmk* w **12**. *P* 15×14.
D30 D 1 50 c. black £750 £650

Nos. D22/9 were for use throughout Malaysia and Singapore. They were superseded on 15 August 1966 by the postage dues inscribed "MALAYSIA", but continued in use, together with No. D30, for Singapore until 31 January 1968 when they were replaced by Singapore Postage Dues.

IV. MALAYA (BRITISH MILITARY ADMINISTRATION)

For use throughout all Malay States and in Singapore. From 1948 this general issue was gradually replaced by individual issues for each state. The last usage was in Kelantan where B M A overprints were not withdrawn until 10 July 1951.

B M A
MALAYA
(1)

1945 (19 Oct)–**48.** *T* **58** *of Straits Settlements from Die I (double-plate printing) or Die II (single-plate printing) optd with T* **1**. *Wmk Mult Script CA. Chalk-surfaced paper. P* 14 *or* 15×14 (*No.* 11).
1 1 c. black (I) (R.) 2·00 40
a. Ordinary paper 10 20
2 2 c. orange (II) (8.7.47) 3·50 55
a. Ordinary paper (19.10.45) 20 10
w. Wmk inverted † £1200
3 2 c. orange (I) (*ordinary paper*) (9.46) 12·00 3·25
4 3 c. yellow-green (II) (*ordinary paper*) 30 40
a. *Blue-green* (27.1.47) 3·00 2·50
b. Chalk-surfaced paper. *Blue-grn* (8.7.47) 7·00 50
5 5 c. brown (II) (11.45) 70 60
6 6 c. grey (II) (22.3.48) 7·50 1·75
a. Ordinary paper (19.10.45) 30 20
7 8 c. scarlet (II) (*ordinary paper*) 30 10
8 10 c. purple (I) (12.45) 3·00 50
a. Ordinary paper (19.10.45) 40 10
b. *Slate-purple* (12.45) 2·25 30
c. *Magenta* (22.3.48) 4·25 55
9 10 c. purple (II) (28.7.48) 16·00 2·00
10 12 c. bright ultramarine (I) (11.45) 1·75 4·00
11 15 c. brt ultram (II) (*ordinary paper*) (11.45) 2·25 6·50
12 15 c. bright ultramarine (II) (R.) (22.3.48) 17·00 90
a. Ordinary paper (12.45) 75 20
b. *Blue* (27.11.47) 40·00 85
ba. Ordinary paper (8.7.47) 80·00 12·00
13 25 c. dull purple and scarlet (I) (22.3.48) 6·50 90
a. Ordinary paper (12.45) 1·40 30
ab. Opt double £3750
14 50 c. black/*emerald* (I) (R.) (12.45) 11·00 1·25
a. Ordinary paper 60 10
15 $1 black and red (I) (*ordinary paper*) (12.45) 2·00 10
16 $2 green & scar (I) (*ordinary paper*) (12.45) 2·75 75
17 $5 green and red/*emerald* (I) (11.45) 75·00 70·00
18 $5 pur & orge (I) (*ordinary paper*) (12.45) 3·75 2·75
1/18 *Set of* 15 80·00 70·00
1/11, 13/16, 18 Perf "Specimen" *Set of* 14 £400

The 8 c. grey with "BMA" opt was prepared but not officially issued (*Price £250 unused*).

Nos. 3 and 9 do not exist without the overprint

Initial printings on ordinary paper were produced by Harrison and Sons in 1941 following bomb damage to the De La Rue works on 29 December 1940.

No. 8 with reddish purple medallion and dull purple frame is from a 1947 printing with the head in fugitive ink which discolours with moisture.

Postal forgeries of the 50 c. value exist made by dyeing examples of the 1 c. and then altering the face value to 50 c.

In 1946 8 c. and 15 c. stamps in the Crown Colony Victory design were prepared for the Malayan Union, but not issued. Examples of the 8 c. carmine from this issue exist from unofficial leakages (*Price £250 unused*).

V. MALAYAN FEDERATION

The Malayan Federation, formed on 1 February 1948 by Malacca, Penang, the four Federated Malay States and the five Unfederated States, became an independent member of the British Commonwealth on 31 August 1957.

Commemoratives and a limited series of definitives were issued by the Federation and were used concurrently with the stamps from the individual States.

1 Tapping Rubber

4 Map of the Federation

(Centre recess, frame litho (6 c., 25 c.); centre litho, frame recess (12 c.); recess (30 c.), D.L.R.)

1957 (5 May)–**63.** *T* **1**, **4** *and similar designs. W* w **12**. *P* 13×12½ (*No.* 4) *or* 13 (*others*).
1 6 c. deep blue, red, yellow and grey-blue 50 10
a. *Indigo, red, yellow and grey-blue* (20.6.61) 2·00 30
b. *Indigo, red, yellow & slate-blue* (12.2.63) 2·25 30
c. Yellow (star and crescent) omitted 45·00
2 12 c. red, yellow, blue, black and scarlet 85 30
3 25 c. maroon, red, yellow & dull greenish blue 2·00 10
4 30 c. orange-red and lake 80 20
a. Perf 13. *Orange-red & deep lake* (20.6.61) 60 50
ab. *Orange-red and lake* (10.7.62) 1·50 10
1/4 *Set of* 4 3·50 45

Designs: *Horiz*—12 c. Federation coat of arms; 25 c. Tin dredger.

5 Prime Minister Tunku Abdul Rahman and Populace greeting Independence

(Des A. B. Saman. Recess Waterlow)

1957 (31 Aug). *Independence Day. Wmk Mult Script CA. P* 12½.
5 5 10 c. bistre-brown 10 10

6 United Nations Emblem

7 United Nations Emblem

(Recess D.L.R.)

1958 (5 Mar). *U.N. Economic Commission for Asia and Far East Conference, Kuala Lumpur. W* w **12**. *P* 13½ (12 c.) *or* 12½ (30 c.).
6 6 12 c. carmine-red 30 40
7 7 30 c. maroon 40 40

8 Merdeka Stadium, Kuala Lumpur

9 The Yang di-Pertuan Agong (Tuanku Abdul Rahman)

(Photo Harrison)

1958 (31 Aug). *First Anniv of Independence. W* w **12**. *P* 13½ × 14½ (10 c.) *or* 14½ × 13½ (30 c.).
8 8 10 c. green, yellow, red and blue 15 10
9 9 30 c. red, yellow, violet-blue and green 40 40

10 "Human Rights"

11 Malayan with Torch of Freedom

(Des J. P. Hendroff. Litho (10 c.), photo (30 c.) D.L.R.)

1958 (10 Dec). *Tenth Anniv of Declaration of Human Rights.*

(*a*) *W w* **12.** *P* 12½ × 13

10 **10** 10 c. blue, black, carmine and orange .. 10 10

(*b*) *Wmk Mult Script CA. P* 13 × 12½

11 **11** 30 c. deep green 30 30

12 Mace and Malayan Peoples

(Photo Enschedé)

1959 (12 Sept). *Inauguration of Parliament. No wmk. P* 13 × 14.

12 **12** 4 c. rose-red 10 10
13 10 c. violet 10 10
14 25 c. yellow-green 35 20
12/14 .. .. *Set of* 3 50 30

13 **14**

(Recess D.L.R.)

1960 (7 Apr). *World Refugee Year. W* w **12.** *P* 13½ (12 c.) *or* 12½ × 13 (30 c.).

15 **13** 12 c. purple 10 30
16 **14** 30 c. deep green 10 10

15 Seedling Rubber Tree and Map

16 The Yang di-Pertuan Agong (Tuanku Syed Putra)

(Photo Japanese Govt Ptg Wks)

1960 (19 Sept). *Natural Rubber Research Conference and 15th International Rubber Study Group Meeting, Kuala Lumpur. T* **15** *and similar vert design. No wmk. P* 13.

17 6 c. yellow-green, black, orange & red-brown 20 70
18 30 c. yellow-green, black, orange & bright blue 50 40

No. 18 is inscribed "INTERNATIONAL RUBBER STUDY GROUP 15th MEETING KUALA LUMPUR" at foot.

(Photo Harrison)

1961 (4 Jan). *Installation of Yang di-Pertuan Agong, Tuanku Syed Putra. W* w **12.** *P* 14 × 14½.

19 **16** 10 c. black and blue 10 10

17 Colombo Plan Emblem

18 Malaria Eradication Emblem

(Photo Japanese Govt Ptg Works)

1961 (30 Oct). *Colombo Plan Conference, Kuala Lumpur. P* 13.

20 **17** 12 c. black and magenta .. .. .. 35 2·00
21 25 c. black and apple-green .. .. 80 2·00
22 30 c. black and turquoise-blue 70 30
20/2 .. .. *Set of* 3 1·75 3·75

(Photo Harrison)

1962 (7 Apr). *Malaria Eradication. W* w **13.** *P* 14 × 14½.

23 **18** 25 c. orange-brown 20 35
24 30 c. deep lilac 20 15
25 50 c. ultramarine 40 30
23/5 .. .. *Set of* 3 70 70

19 Palmyra Palm Leaf

20 "Shadows of the Future"

(Photo Harrison)

1962 (21 July). *National Language Month. W* w **13** (*upright or inverted*). *P* 13½.

26 **19** 10 c. light brown and deep reddish violet 15 10
27 20 c. light brown and deep bluish green 25 30
28 50 c. light brown and magenta 45 70
26/8 .. .. *Set of* 3 75 1·00

(Photo Enschedé)

1962 (1 Oct). *Introduction of Free Primary Education. W* w **13.** *P* 13½.

29 **20** 10 c. bright purple 10 10
30 25 c. ochre 30 40
31 30 c. emerald .. .. 1·00 10
29/31 .. .. *Set of* 3 1·25 50

21 Harvester and Fisherman

22 Dam and Pylon

(Photo Courvoisier)

1963 (21 Mar). *Freedom from Hunger. P* 11½.

32 **21** 25 c. carmine and apple-green .. .. 85 2·00
33 30 c. carmine and crimson .. .. 1·50 75
34 50 c. carmine and bright blue .. .. 1·50 2·00
32/4 .. .. *Set of* 3 3·50 4·25

(Photo Harrison)

1963 (26 June). *Cameron Highlands Hydro-Electric Scheme. W* w **13.** *P* 14.

35 **22** 20 c. green and reddish violet 35 10
36 30 c. blue-green and ultramarine 45 60

The definitive general issue for Malaysia and the low value sets for the individual states superseded the stamps of the Malayan Federation by 15 November 1965.

VI. MALAYSIA

On 16 September 1963, the Malayan Federation, Sabah (North Borneo), Sarawak and Singapore formed the Federation of Malaysia. Singapore left the Federation on 9 August 1965, and became an independent republic. Stamps of Singapore continued to be valid in Malaysia, and those of Malaysia in Singapore, until 1 February 1967.

Individual issues for the component States continued, but were restricted to low value definitives and the occasional "State" commemorative. The higher value definitives and the vast majority of commemoratives were issued on a "National" basis.

A. NATIONAL ISSUES

General issues for use throughout the Malaysian Federation.

1 Federation Map

2 Bouquet of Orchids

(Photo Harrison)

1963 (16 Sept). *Inauguration of Federation. W* w **13.** *P* 14½.

1 **1** 10 c. yellow and bluish violet 30 10
a. Yellow omitted .. .. .. 95·00
2 12 c. yellow and deep green 70 60
3 50 c. yellow and chocolate .. .. 1·00 10
1/3 .. .. *Set of* 3 1·75 65

(Photo Enschedé)

1963 (3 Oct). *Fourth World Orchid Conference, Singapore. No wmk. P* 13 × 14.

4 **2** 6 c. multicoloured .. .. .. 1·25 1·25
5 25 c. multicoloured .. .. .. 1·25 25

4 Parliament House, Kuala Lumpur

(Des V. Whiteley. Photo Harrison)

1963 (4 Nov). *Ninth Commonwealth Parliamentary Conference, Kuala Lumpur. W* w **13** (*inverted*). *P* 13½.

7 **4** 20 c. deep magenta and gold 40 40
8 30 c. deep green and gold 40 15

5 "Flame of Freedom" and Emblems of Goodwill, Health and Charity

6 Microwave Tower and I.T.U. Emblem

(Photo Harrison)

1964 (10 Oct). *Eleanor Roosevelt Commemoration. W* w **13.** *P* 14½ × 13½.

9 **5** 25 c. black, red and greenish blue .. 15 10
10 30 c. black, red and deep lilac 15 15
11 50 c. black, red and ochre-yellow .. 15 10
9/11 .. .. *Set of* 3 40 20

(Photo Courvoisier)

1965 (17 May). *I.T.U. Centenary. P* 11½.

12 **6** 2 c. multicoloured 15 80
13 25 c. multicoloured .. .. .. 1·00 50
14 50 c. multicoloured .. .. .. 1·75 10
12/14 .. .. *Set of* 3 2·50 1·25

7 National Mosque

8 Air Terminal

(Photo Harrison)

1965 (27 Aug). *Opening of National Mosque, Kuala Lumpur. W* w **13.** *P* 14 × 14½.

15 **7** 6 c. carmine 10 10
16 15 c. red-brown 20 10
17 20 c. deep bluish green 20 15
15/17 .. .. *Set of* 3 45 30

(Photo Harrison)

1965 (30 Aug). *Opening of International Airport, Kuala Lumpur. W* w **13.** *P* 14½ × 14.

18 **8** 15 c. black, yellow-green and new blue .. 15 10
a. Yellow-green omitted .. .. 20·00
19 30 c. black, yellow-green and magenta .. 30 20

9 Crested Wood Partridge

17 Sepak Raga (ball game) and Football

(Des A. Fraser-Brunner. Photo Harrison)

1965 (9 Sept). *T* **9** *and similar vert designs. Multicoloured. W* w **13.** *P* 14½.

20 25 c. Type **9** 50 10
w. Wmk inverted .. .. .. 2·75
21 30 c. Blue-backed Fairy Bluebird .. 60 10
a. Blue omitted £120
w. Wmk inverted .. .. .. 3·50
22 50 c. Black-naped Oriole 80 10
a. Yellow omitted .. .. .. 75·00
b. Imperf (pair) £200
c. Scarlet (inscr and berries) omitted 50·00
w. Wmk inverted .. .. .. 6·50
23 75 c. Rhinoceros Hornbill 90 10
a. Scarlet omitted* .. .. .. 70·00
24 $1 Zebra Dove .. .. .. 1·50 10
w. Wmk inverted .. .. .. 16·00
25 $2 Great Argus Pheasant .. .. 3·50 30
a. Imperf (pair) £200
w. Wmk inverted .. .. .. 8·50
26 $5 Asiatic Paradise Flycatcher .. 18·00 2·25
w. Wmk inverted .. .. .. 20·00
27 $10 Blue-tailed Pitta .. .. 48·00 9·50
a. Imperf (pair) £275
20/7 .. .. *Set of* 8 65·00 11·00

*The inscription at foot is omitted and the background appears paler.

All values except the 75 c. and $10 exist with PVA gum as well as gum arabic.

(Des E. A. F. Anthony. Litho Japanese Govt Ptg Wks)

1965 (14 Dec). *Third South East Asian Peninsular Games. T* **17** *and similar vert designs. P* 13 × 13½.

28	25 c. black and olive-green		40	90
29	30 c. black and bright purple		40	20
30	50 c. black and light blue		70	30
28/30		*Set of* 3	1·40	1·25

Designs:—30 c. Running; 50 c. Diving.

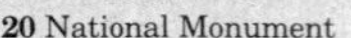

20 National Monument

21 The Yang di-Pertuan Agong (Tuanku Ismail Nasiruddin Shah)

(Photo Harrison)

1966 (8 Feb). *National Monument, Kuala Lumpur. W* w **13.** *P* 13½.

31	**20**	10 c. multicoloured	15	10
		a. Blue omitted	60·00	
32		20 c. multicoloured	25	30

(Photo Japanese Govt Ptg Wks)

1966 (11 Apr). *Installation of Yang di-Pertuan Agong, Tuanku Ismail Nasiruddin Shah. P* 13½.

33	**21**	15 c. black and light yellow	10	10
34		50 c. black and greenish blue	20	20

22 School Building

23 "Agriculture"

(Photo D.L.R.)

1966 (21 Oct). *150th Anniv of Penang Free School. W* w **13** *(sideways). P* 13.

35	**22**	20 c. multicoloured	40	10
36		50 c. multicoloured	60	10

The 50 c. is also inscr "ULANG TAHUN KE-150" at foot and bears a shield at bottom left corner.

(Des Enche Ng Peng Nam. Photo Japanese Govt Ptg Wks)

1966 (1 Dec). *First Malaysia Plan. T* **23** *and similar horiz designs. Multicoloured. P* 13½.

37	15 c. Type **23**		20	10
38	15 c. "Rural Health"		20	10
39	15 c. "Communications"		1·00	15
40	15 c. "Education"		20	10
41	15 c. "Irrigation"		20	10
37/41		*Set of* 5	1·60	50

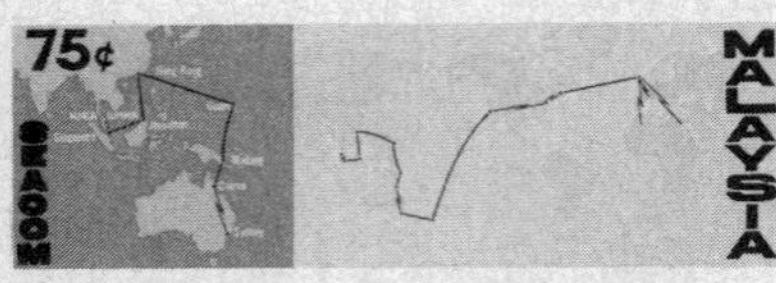

28 Cable Route Maps

(Des Enche Ng Peng Nam. Photo Japanese Govt Ptg Wks)

1967 (31 Aug). *Tenth Anniv of Independence. W* w **13.** *P* 14½.

42	**28**	30 c. multicoloured	80	30
43		75 c. multicoloured	2·50	2·75

29 Hibiscus and Paramount Rulers

(Photo Harrison)

1967 (31 Aug). *Tenth Anniv of Independence. W* w **13.** *P* 14½.

44	**29**	15 c. multicoloured	20	10
		w. Wmk inverted	3·50	
45		50 c. multicoloured	50	50

30 Mace and Shield

31 Straits Settlements 1867 8 c. and Malaysia 1965 25 c. Definitive

(Des Enche Ng Peng Nam. Photo Harrison)

1967 (8 Sept). *Centenary of Sarawak Council. W* w **13.** *P* 14½.

46	**30**	15 c. multicoloured	10	10
47		50 c. multicoloured	30	50

(Des Enche Ng Peng Nam. Photo Japanese Govt Ptg Works)

1967 (2 Dec). *Stamp Centenary. T* **31** *and similar shaped designs. Multicoloured. P* 11½.

48	25 c. Type **31**		1·40	2·25
	a. *Tête-bêche* (horiz pair)		2·75	4·50
49	30 c. Straits Settlements 1867 24 c. and Malaysia 1965 30 c. definitive		1·40	1·50
	a. *Tête-bêche* (horiz pair)		2·75	3·00
50	50 c. Straits Settlements 1867 32 c. and Malaysia 1965 50 c. definitive		2·25	2·00
	a. *Tête-bêche* (horiz pair)		4·50	4·00
48/50		*Set of* 3	4·50	5·25

Nos. 48/50 were each printed in sheets with the stamps arranged horizontally *tête-bêche*.

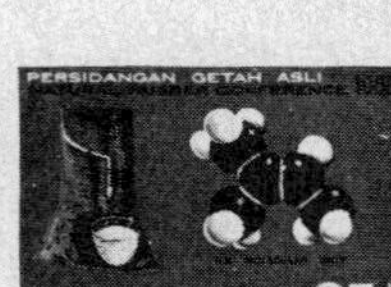

34 Tapping Rubber, and Molecular Unit

37 Mexican Sombrero and Blanket with Olympic Rings

(Litho B.W.)

1968 (29 Aug). *Natural Rubber Conference, Kuala Lumpur. T* **34** *and similar horiz designs. Multicoloured. W* w **13.** *P* 12.

51	25 c. Type **34**		25	10
52	30 c. Tapping rubber, and export consignment		40	20
53	50 c. Tapping rubber, and aircraft tyres		40	10
51/3		*Set of* 3	95	35

(Litho B.W.)

1968 (12 Oct). *Olympic Games, Mexico. T* **37** *and similar vert design. Multicoloured. W* w **13.** *P* 12 × 11½.

54	30 c. Type **37**	20	10
55	75 c. Olympic rings and Mexican embroidery	40	20

39 Tunku Abdul Rahman against background of Pandanus Weave

40

(Photo Japanese Govt Ptg Wks)

1969 (8 Feb). *Solidarity Week. T* **39/40** *and similar multicoloured design. P* 13½.

56	15 c. Type **39**		15	10
57	20 c. Type **40**		20	70
58	50 c. Tunku Abdul Rahman with pandanus pattern *(horiz)*		20	20
56/8		*Set of* 3	50	85

42 Peasant Girl with Sheaves of Paddy

(Des Enche Hoessein Anas. Photo Harrison)

1969 (8 Dec). *National Rice Year. W* w **13.** *P* 13½.

59	**42**	15 c. multicoloured	15	10
60		75 c. multicoloured	55	85

43 Satellite tracking Aerial

44 "Intelsat III" in Orbit

(Photo Enschedé)

1970 (6 Apr). *Satellite Earth Station. W* w **13.** *P* 14 × 13 (15 *c.) or* 13½ × 13 (30 *c.*).

61	**43**	15 c. multicoloured	95	15
		a. *Tête-bêche* (horiz pair)	1·90	2·00
62	**44**	30 c. multicoloured*	95	1·60
63		30 c. multicoloured*	95	1·60
61/3		*Set of* 3	2·50	3·00

No. 61 was issued horizontally *tête-bêche* in the sheets.

*Nos. 62/3 are of the same design, differing only in the lettering colours (No. 62 white; No. 63 gold).

45 *Euploea leucostictus*

46 Emblem

(Des V. Whiteley. Litho B.W. (to 1976) or Harrison)

1970 (31 Aug–16 Nov). *Butterflies. T* **45** *and similar vert designs. Multicoloured. P* 13 × 13½.

64	25 c. Type **45**		1·00	10
65	30 c. *Zeuxidia amethystus*		1·50	10
66	50 c. *Polyura athamas*		1·75	10
67	75 c. *Papilio memnon*		2·00	10
68	$1 *Appias nero* (16.11)		2·50	10
69	$2 *Trogonoptera brookiana* (16.11)		3·50	10
70	$5 *Narathura centaurus* (16.11)		5·00	2·50
71	$10 *Terinos terpander* (16.11)		15·00	5·00
64/71		*Set of* 8	29·00	7·00

See also Nos. 144/5.

(Litho Harrison)

1970 (7 Sept). *50th Anniv of International Labour Organization. P* 14 × 13½.

72	**46**	30 c. grey and new blue	10	20
73		75 c. pink and new blue	20	30

47 U.N. Emblem encircled by Doves

50 The Yang di-Pertuan Agong (Tuanku Abdul Halim Shah)

(Des Enche Ng Peng Nam. Litho D.L.R.)

1970 (24 Oct). *25th Anniv of United Nations. T* **47** *and similar horiz designs. P* 13 × 12½.

74	25 c. gold, black and brown		30	40
75	30 c. multicoloured		30	35
76	50 c. black and dull yellow-green		40	75
74/6		*Set of* 3	90	1·40

Designs:—30 c. Line of doves and U.N. emblem; 50 c. Doves looping U.N. emblem.

(Des Union Art Corp. Photo Harrison)

1971 (20 Feb). *Installation of Yang di-Pertuan Agong (Paramount Ruler of Malaysia). P* 14½ × 14.

77	**50**	10 c. black, gold and lemon	20	30
		a. Gold (value and inscr) omitted	£160	
78		15 c. black, gold and bright mauve	20	30
79		50 c. black, gold and new blue	60	1·60
77/9		*Set of* 3	90	2·00

51 Bank Negara Complex

(Photo Harrison)

1971 (15 May). *Opening of Bank Negara Building. P* 13½ *(and around design).*

80	**51**	25 c. black and silver	80	90
81		50 c. black and gold	80	1·10

52 Aerial view of Parliament Buildings

(Des Union Art Corp. Litho Harrison)

1971 (13 Sept). *17th Commonwealth Parliamentary Association Conference, Kuala Lumpur. T* **52** *and similar multicoloured design. P* 13½ (25 c.) *or* 12½ × 13 (75c.).

82		25 c. Type **52**	1·00	50
83		75 c. Ground view of Parliament Buildings (73 × 23½ *mm*)	2·50	1·75

53 **54** **55**

Malaysian Carnival

(Des locally. Litho Harrison)

1971 (18 Sept). *Visit A.S.E.A.N.* Year. P* 14½.

84	**53**	30 c. multicoloured	1·50	55
		a. Horiz strip of 3. Nos. 84/6	4·00	
85	**54**	30 c. multicoloured	1·50	55
86	**55**	30 c. multicoloured	1·50	55
84/6		.. .. *Set of* 3	4·00	1·50

*A.S.E.A.N. = Association of South East Asian Nations.

Nos. 84/6 were printed together, *se-tenant*, in horizontal strips of 3 throughout the sheet, forming a composite design.

56 Trees, Elephant and Tiger

57 Athletics

(Des from children's drawings. Litho Harrison)

1971 (2 Oct). *25th Anniv of U.N.I.C.E.F. T* **56** *and similar multicoloured designs. P* 12½.

87		15 c. Type **56**	1·75	45
		a. Horiz strip of 5. Nos. 87/91	8·00	
88		15 c. Cat and kittens	1·75	45
89		15 c. Sun, flower and bird (22 × 29 *mm*) ..	1·75	45
90		15 c. Monkey, elephant and lion in jungle ..	1·75	45
91		15 c. Spider and butterflies	1·75	45
87/91		.. .. *Set of* 5	8·00	2·00

Nos. 87/91 were issued in horizontal *se-tenant* strips of 5 throughout the sheet.

(Des Union Art Corp. Litho B.W.)

1971 (11 Dec). *Sixth S.E.A.P.* Games, Kuala Lumpur. T* **57** *and similar horiz designs. Multicoloured. P* 14½ × 14.

92		25 c. Type **57**	45	40
93		30 c. Sepak Raga players	60	50
94		50 c. Hockey	1·50	95
92/4		.. .. *Set of* 3	2·25	1·75

*S.E.A.P. = South East Asian Peninsula.

58 **59** **60**

Map and Tourist Attractions

(Des locally. Litho Harrison)

1972 (31 Jan). *Pacific Area Tourist Association Conference. P* 14 × 14½.

95	**58**	30 c. multicoloured	2·00	70
		a. Horiz strip of 3. Nos. 95/7	5·50	
96	**59**	30 c. multicoloured	2·00	70
97	**60**	30 c. multicoloured	2·00	70
95/7		.. .. *Set of* 3	5·50	1·90

Nos. 95/7 were printed together, *se-tenant*, in horizontal strips of 3 throughout the sheet forming a composite design.

61 Kuala Lumpur City Hall

(Des from colour transparencies. Litho Harrison)

1972 (1 Feb). *City Status for Kuala Lumpur. T* **61** *and similar horiz design. Multicoloured. P* 14½ × 14.

98		25 c. Type **61**	1·25	1·25
99		50 c. City Hall in floodlights	2·00	1·25

62 SOCSO Emblem

63 W.H.O. Emblem

(Des B.W. Litho Harrison)

1973 (2 July). *Social Security Organisation. P* 13½.

100	**62**	10 c. multicoloured	15	15
101		15 c. multicoloured	25	10
102		50 c. multicoloured	60	1·40
100/2		.. .. *Set of* 3	90	1·50

(Des Union Advertising. Litho B.W.)

1973 (1 Aug). *25th Anniv of W.H.O. T* **63** *and similar vert design. P* 13.

103		30 c. multicoloured	60	25
104		75 c. multicoloured	1·40	1·75

64 Fireworks, National Flag and Flower

65 Emblems of Interpol and Royal Malaysian Police

(Des Clover Associates. Litho Harrison)

1973 (31 Aug). *Tenth Anniv of Malaysia. P* 13½.

105	**64**	10 c. multicoloured	30	25
106		15 c. multicoloured	45	15
107		50 c. multicoloured	1·75	1·60
105/7		.. .. *Set of* 3	2·25	1·75

(Des Union Advertising. Litho Harrison)

1973 (15 Sept). *50th Anniv of Interpol. T* **65** *and similar vert design. Multicoloured. P* 13½.

108		25 c. Type **65**	1·00	50
109		75 c. Emblems within "50"	2·00	2·00

66 Boeing 737 and M.A.S. Emblem

(Des Art Dept, Malaysia Airline System. Litho Harrison)

1973 (1 Oct). *Foundation of Malaysia Airline System. P* 14½.

110	**66**	15 c. multicoloured	35	10
111		30 c. multicoloured	65	60
112		50 c. multicoloured	95	1·60
110/12		.. .. *Set of* 3	1·75	2·10

67 Kuala Lumpur

(Des Malaysian Advertising Services. Litho B.W.)

1974 (1 Feb). *Establishment of Kuala Lumpur as Federal Territory. P* 12½ × 13.

113	**67**	25 c. multicoloured	50	85
114		50 c. multicoloured	1·00	1·75

68 Development Projects

69 Scout Badge and Map

(Des Malaysian Advertising Services. Litho Rosenbaum Bros, Vienna)

1974 (25 Apr). *Seventh Annual Meeting of Asian Development Bank's Board of Governors, Kuala Lumpur. P* 13½.

115	**68**	30 c. multicoloured	25	50
116		75 c. multicoloured	80	1·75

(Des Malaysian Advertising Services. Litho Harrison)

1974 (1 Aug). *Malaysian Scout Jamboree. T* **69** *and similar multicoloured designs. P* 13 × 13½ (15 c.) *or* 14 × 13½ (*others*).

117		10 c. Type **69**	30	30
118		15 c. Scouts saluting and flags (46 × 24 *mm*)	35	30
119		50 c. Scout badge	1·25	2·25
117/19		.. .. *Set of* 3	1·75	2·50

70 Coat of Arms and Power Installations

(Des Malaysian Advertising Services. Litho Harrison)

1974 (1 Sept). *25th Anniv of National Electricity Board. T* **70** *and similar multicoloured design. P* 14 (30 c.) *or* 14 × 14½ (75 c.).

120		30 c. Type **70**	30	50
121		75 c. National Electricity Board Building (37 × 27 *mm*)	1·00	2·00

71 U.P.U. and Post Office Emblems within "100"

(Des Clover Associates. Litho Harrison)

1974 (9 Oct). *Centenary of Universal Postal Union. P* 14½ × 14.

122	**71**	25 c. dull yell-grn, brt yell & lt rose-carm	20	35
123		30 c. lt new blue, brt yell & lt rose-carm	25	35
124		75 c. brownish orange, bright yellow and light rose-carmine	65	1·75
122/4		.. .. *Set of* 3	1·00	2·25

72 Gravel Pump in Tin Mine

73 Hockey-players, World Cup and Federation Emblem

(Des Malaysian Advertising Service. Litho D.L.R.)

1974 (31 Oct). *Fourth World Tin Conference, Kuala Lumpur. T* **72** *and similar horiz designs. Multicoloured. P* 13½.

125		15 c. Type **72**	1·75	15
126		20 c. Open-cast mine	2·00	90
127		50 c. Dredger within "ingot"	3·75	4·00
125/7		.. .. *Set of* 3	6·75	4·50

(Des Malaysian Advertising Services. Litho Harrison)

1975 (1 Mar). *Third World Cup Hockey Championships. P* 13½ × 13.

128	**73**	30 c. multicoloured	90	60
129		75 c. multicoloured	2·10	2·25

74 Congress Emblem

75 Emblem of M.K.P.W. (Malayan Women's Organisation)

(Des Malaysian Advertising Services. Litho Harrison)

1975 (1 May). *25th Anniv of Malaysian Trade Union Congress. P* 14 × 14½.

130	**74**	20 c. multicoloured	20	25
131		25 c. multicoloured	30	30
132		30 c. multicoloured	45	60
130/2		*Set of* 3	85	1·00

(Des Malaysian Advertising Services. Litho Harrison)

1975 (25 Aug). *International Women's Year. P* 14.

133	**75**	10 c. multicoloured	15	25
134		15 c. multicoloured	30	25
135		50 c. multicoloured	1·25	2·25
133/5		*Set of* 3	1·50	2·50

76 Ubudiah Mosque, Kuala Kangsar

77 Plantation and Emblem

(Des Malaysian Advertising Services. Litho Harrison)

1975 (22 Sept). *Koran Reading Competition. T* **76** *and similar horiz designs. Multicoloured. P* 14.

136	15 c. Type **76**	1·25	30
	a. Horiz strip of 5. Nos. 136/40	5·75	
137	15 c. Zahir Mosque, Alor Star	1·25	30
138	15 c. National Mosque, Kuala Lumpur	1·25	30
139	15 c. Sultan Abu Bakar Mosque, Johore Bahru	1·25	30
140	15 c. Kuching State Mosque, Sarawak	1·25	30
136/40	*Set of* 5	5·75	1·40

The above were printed together, horizontally *se-tenant* throughout the sheet.

(Des E. Sulaiman bin Haji Hassan and E. Hoh Lian Yong. Litho Harrison)

1975 (22 Oct). *50th Anniv of Malaysian Rubber Research Institute. T* **77** *and similar horiz designs. Multicoloured. P* 14 × 14½.

141	10 c. Type **77**	40	15
142	30 c. Latex cup and emblem	1·10	70
143	75 c. Natural rubber in test-tubes	2·25	2·25
141/3	*Set of* 3	3·25	2·75

77a *Hebomoia glaucippe*

78 Scrub Typhus

(Photo Harrison)

1976 (19 Jan). *Coil Stamps. T* **77a** *and similar horiz design. Multicoloured. P* 13½.

144	10 c. Type **77a**	1·50	4·75
145	15 c. *Precis orithya*	1·50	4·75

(Des Lap Loy Fong (25 c.), Lee Eng Kee (others). Litho Harrison)

1976 (6 Feb). *75th Anniv of the Institute of Medical Research. T* **78** *and similar vert designs. Multicoloured. P* 14.

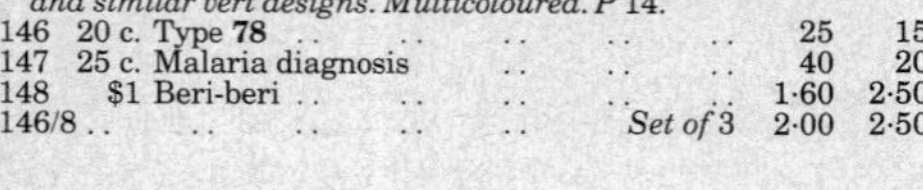

146	20 c. Type **78**	25	15
147	25 c. Malaria diagnosis	40	20
148	$1 Beri-beri	1·60	2·50
146/8	*Set of* 3	2·00	2·50

79 The Yang di-Pertuan Agong (Tuanku Yahya Petra)

80 State Council Complex

(Des Union Advertising. Photo Harrison)

1976 (28 Feb). *Installation of Yang di-Pertuan Agong. P* 14½ × 13½.

149	**79**	10 c. black, bistre and yellow	25	10
150		15 c. black, bistre and bright mauve	40	10
151		50 c. black, bistre and ultramarine	2·25	2·50
149/51		*Set of* 3	2·75	2·50

(Des Aini bin Abdul Rahman. Litho Harrison)

1976 (17 Aug). *Opening of the State Council Complex and Administrative Building, Sarawak. P* 12½.

152	**80**	15 c. grey-green and light yellow	35	10
153		20 c. grey-green and light bright mauve	45	40
154		50 c. grey-green and pale blue	1·00	1·40
152/4		*Set of* 3	1·60	1·75

81 E.P.F. Building

82 Blind People at Work

(Litho Harrison)

1976 (18 Oct). *25th Anniv of Employees' Provident Fund. T* **81** *and similar multicoloured designs. P* 14½ (25 c.) *or* 13½ × 14½ (*others*).

155	10 c. Type **81**	15	10
156	25 c. E.P.F. emblems (27 × 27 *mm*)	25	35
157	50 c. E.P.F. Building at night	60	1·00
155/7	*Set of* 3	90	1·40

(Des Malayan Association for the Blind, Messrs Advertising Sales Promotion and Hexxon Grafic. Litho Harrison)

1976 (20 Nov). *25th Anniv of Malayan Association for the Blind. T* **82** *and similar horiz design. Multicoloured. P* 13½ × 14½.

158	10 c. Type **82**	15	15
159	75 c. Blind man and shadow	1·25	2·40

83 Independence Celebrations, 1957

84 F.E.L.D.A. Village Scheme

(Des Hexxon Grafic. Photo Harrison)

1977 (14 Jan). *First Death Anniversary of Tun Abdul Razak (Prime Minister). T* **83** *and similar horiz designs, each sepia and gold. P* 14.

160	15 c. Type **83**	1·25	40
	a. Horiz strip of 5. Nos. 160/4	5·50	
161	15 c. "Education"	1·25	40
162	15 c. Tun Razak and map ("Development")	1·25	40
163	15 c. "Rukunegara" (National Philosophy)	1·25	40
164	15 c. A.S.E.A.N. meeting	1·25	40
160/4	*Set of* 5	5·50	1·75

The above were printed together, horizontally *se-tenant* throughout the sheet.

(Des Halim Teh and Basyuni Sumrah. Litho Harrison)

1977 (7 July). *21st Anniv of Federal Land Development Authority (F.E.L.D.A.). T* **84** *and similar horiz design. Multicoloured. P* 13½ × 14.

165	15 c. Type **84**	30	10
166	30 c. Oil Palm settlement	80	1·25

85 Figure "10"

86 Games Logos

(Des Hexxon Grafic. Litho Harrison)

1977 (8 Aug). *Tenth Anniv of A.S.E.A.N. (Association of South East Asian Nations). T* **85** *and similar horiz design. Multicoloured. P* 13½ × 14½.

167	10 c. Type **85**	10	10
168	75 c. Flags of members	85	65

(Des PTM Communications & Co. Litho Harrison)

1977 (19 Nov). *9th South East Asia Games, Kuala Lumpur. T* **86** *and similar horiz designs. Multicoloured. P* 13½ × 14½.

169	10 c. Type **86**	15	15
170	20 c. "Ball"	20	15
171	75 c. Symbolic athletes	75	1·50
169/71	*Set of* 3	1·00	1·60

87 Islamic Development Bank Emblem

88 Mobile Post Office

(Des Queen's Advertising. Litho J.W.)

1978 (15 Mar). *Islamic Development Bank Board of Governors Meeting, Kuala Lumpur. P* 14.

172	**87**	30 c. multicoloured	25	15
173		75 c. multicoloured	65	55

(Des Hexxon Grafic. Litho J.W.)

1978 (10 July). *4th Commonwealth Postal Administrations Conference, Kuala Lumpur. T* **88** *and similar horiz designs. Multicoloured. P* 13½ × 13.

174	10 c. Type **88**	30	10
175	25 c. G.P.O., Kuala Lumpur	75	1·00
176	50 c. Postal delivery by motor-cycle	2·00	2·50
174/6	*Set of* 3	2·75	3·25

89 Boy Scout Emblem

90 Dome of the Rock, Jerusalem

(Des Aini bin Abdul Rahman. Litho J.W.)

1978 (26 July). *4th Malaysian Boy Scout Jamboree, Sarawak. T* **89** *and similar horiz design. Multicoloured. P* 13½ × 13.

177	15 c. Type **89**	50	10
178	$1 Bees and honeycomb	2·50	1·75

(Des Union Advertising. Litho Harrison)

1978 (21 Aug). *"Freedom for Palestine". P* 12½.

179	**90**	15 c. multicoloured	50	10
180		30 c. multicoloured	75	1·25

91 Globe and Emblems

92 "Seratus Tahun Getah Asli" and Tapping Knives Symbol

(Litho Harrison)

1978 (30 Sept). *Global Eradication of Smallpox. P* 13½ × 14½.

181	**91**	15 c. black, rosine and new blue	20	20
182		30 c. black, rosine and yellowish green	35	10
183		50 c. black, rosine and rose-pink	55	45
181/3		*Set of* 3	1·00	65

(Des Azmi bin Anuar. Litho J.W.)

1978 (28 Nov). *Centenary of Rubber Industry. T* **92** *and similar horiz designs. P* 13½ × 13.

184	10 c. gold and blue-green	10	10
185	20 c. ultramarine, brown & brt yellow-green	10	10
186	75 c. gold and blue-green	45	65
184/6	*Set of* 3	55	75

Designs:—20 c. Rubber tree seedling and part of "maxi stump"; 75 c. Graphic design of rubber tree, latex cup and globe arranged to form "100".

93 Sultan of Selangor's New Palace

(Des Queen's Advertising. Litho Harrison)

1978 (7 Dec). *Inauguration of Shah Alam New Town as State Capital of Selangor. T* **93** *and similar horiz designs. Multicoloured. P* 13½ × 14½.

187	10 c. Type **93**	10	10
188	30 c. Shah Alam (aerial view)	20	15
189	75 c. Shah Alam	55	1·25
187/9	*Set of* 3	75	1·25

94 Tiger

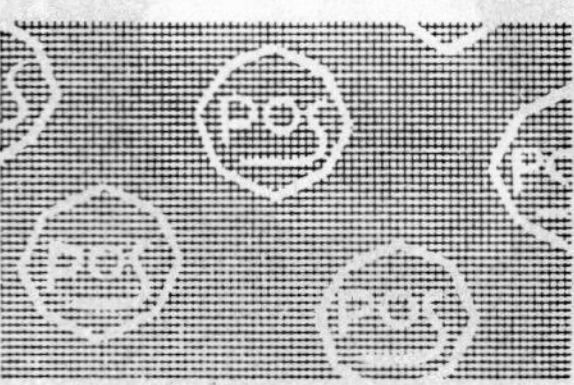

95 Multiple "POS" in Octagon

(Des Ong Soo Keat; adapted Malaysian Advertising Services. Litho Asher and Co, Melbourne)

1979 (4 Jan). *Wildlife. Multicoloured designs as T* **94**. *W* **95** *(inverted on $10 or sideways* on others). P* 14½.

190	30 c. Type **94**	1·50	10
191	40 c. Malayan Flying Lemur (*Cynocephalus variegatus*)	80	10
	w. Wmk top of letters to left		
192	50 c. Lesser Malay Chevrotain (*Tragulus javanicus*)	1·25	10

193 75 c. Leathery Pangolin (*Manis javanicus*) 90 10
194 $1 Malayan Turtle .. .. 1·50 10
195 $2 Malayan Tapir .. .. 1·50 10
196 $5 Gaur .. .. 4·50 1·75
197 $10 Orang-Utan (*vert*) .. .. 7·00 3·25
190/7 .. .. *Set of* 8 17·00 5·00

*The normal sideways watermark shows the top of the letters to right, *as seen from the back of the stamp.*

For these stamps without watermark, see Nos. 272/9.

96 View of Central Bank of Malaysia

97 I.Y.C. Emblem

(Des Union Advertising. Litho J.W.)

1979 (26 Jan). *20th Anniv of Central Bank of Malaysia. T* **96** *and similar vert design showing view of bank building. P* 13.
198 10 c. multicoloured 10 10
199 75 c. multicoloured 40 45

(Des Queen's Advertising. Litho Harrison)

1979 (24 Feb). *International Year of the Child. T* **97** *and similar vert designs. P* 14½ × 14.
200 10 c. gold, blue and salmon 30 10
201 15 c. multicoloured 40 10
202 $1 multicoloured .. .. 1·75 2·75
200/2 .. .. *Set of* 3 2·25 2·75

Designs:—15 c. Children of different races holding hands in front of globe; $1 Children taking part in various activities.

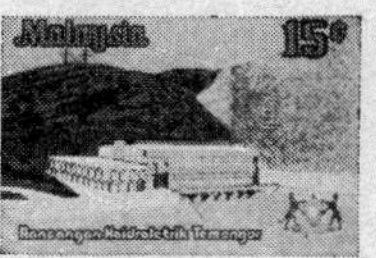

98 Dam and Power Station

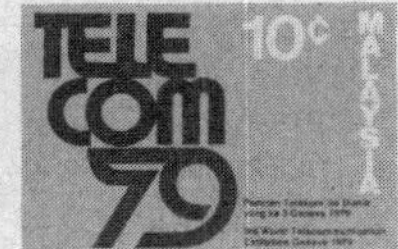

99 Exhibition Emblem

(Des National Electricity Board. Litho Harrison)

1979 (19 Sept). *Opening of Hydro-Electric Power Station, Temengor. T* **98** *and similar horiz designs showing views of power station and dam. P* 13½ × 14½.
203 15 c. multicoloured 20 15
204 25 c. multicoloured 35 50
205 50 c. multicoloured .. .. 55 1·10
203/5 .. .. *Set of* 3 1·00 1·60

(Des Malaysian Advertising Services. Litho J.W.)

1979 (20 Sept). *World Telecommunications Exhibition, Geneva. T* **99** *and similar designs. P* 14 (50 c.) *or* 13 (*others*).
206 10 c. orange, ultramarine and silver 10 20
207 15 c. multicoloured 15 10
208 50 c. multicoloured .. .. 40 1·50
206/8 .. .. *Set of* 3 60 1·60

Designs: (34 × 24 *mm*)—15 c. Telephone receiver joining one half of World to the other. (39 × 28 *mm*)—50 c. Communications equipment.

100 Tuanku Haji Ahmad Shah

101 Pahang and Sarawak Maps within Telephone Dials

(Des Malaysian Advertising Services. Litho Harrison)

1980 (10 July). *Installation of Yang di-Pertuan Agong* (*Tuanku Haji Ahmad Shah*). *P* 14.
209 **100** 10 c. black, gold and yellow 10 20
210 15 c. black, gold and bright purple .. 15 10
211 50 c. black, gold and new blue .. .. 40 1·25
209/11 .. .. *Set of* 3 60 1·40

(Des Malaysian Advertising Services. Litho J.W.)

1980 (31 Aug). *Kuantan-Kuching Submarine Cable Project. T* **101** *and similar horiz designs. Multicoloured. P* 13.
212 10 c. Type **101** 10 25
213 15 c. Kuantan and Kuching views within telephone dials 15 10
214 50 c. Pahang and Sarawak Maps within telephone receiver .. .. 35 1·25
212/14 .. .. *Set of* 3 50 1·40

NEW INFORMATION

The editor is always interested to correspond with people who have new information that will improve or correct the Catalogue.

102 Bangi Campus

103 Mecca

(Des Malaysian Advertising Services. Litho J.W.)

1980 (2 Sept). *10th Anniv of National University of Malaysia. T* **102** *and similar horiz designs. Multicoloured. P* 13.
215 10 c. Type **102** 15 15
216 15 c. Jalan Pantai Baru campus 20 10
217 75 c. Great Hall .. .. 65 2·25
215/17 .. .. *Set of* 3 90 2·25

(Des Malaysian Advertising Services. Litho J.W.)

1980 (9 Nov). *Moslem Year* 1400 *A.H. Commemoration. P* 13.
218 **103** 15 c. multicoloured 10 10
219 50 c. multicoloured 30 90

The 50 c. value is as T **103** but the inscriptions are in Roman lettering and the country name is to the left of the design.

104 Disabled Child learning to Walk

105 Industrial Scene

(Des Malaysian Advertising Services. Litho J.W.)

1981 (14 Feb). *International Year for Disabled Persons. T* **104** *and similar vert designs. Multicoloured. P* 13½ × 13.
220 10 c. Type **104** 30 30
221 15 c. Disabled woman sewing 55 10
222 75 c. Disabled athlete throwing javelin .. 1·50 3·25
220/2 .. .. *Set of* 3 2·10 3·25

(Des Malaysian Advertising Services. Litho J.W.)

1981 (2 May). *"Expo '81" Industrial Training Exposition, Kuala Lumpur and Seminar, Genting Highlands. T* **105** *and similar horiz designs. Multicoloured. P* 13½ × 13.
223 10 c. Type **105** 10 10
224 15 c. Worker and bulldozer 15 10
225 30 c. Workers at ship-building yard 25 35
226 75 c. Agriculture and fishing produce, workers and machinery .. .. 65 1·75
223/6 .. .. *Set of* 4 1·00 2·00

106 "25"

(Des A. Yusof and Malaysian Advertising Services. Litho J.W.)

1981 (17 June). *25th Anniv of Malaysian National Committee for World Energy Conferences. T* **106** *and similar horiz designs. Multicoloured. P* 13½ × 13.
227 10 c. Type **106** 15 15
228 15 c. Drawings showing importance of energy sources in industry 30 10
229 75 c. Symbols of various energy sources .. 1·50 2·50
227/9 .. .. *Set of* 3 1·75 2·50

107 Drawing showing development of Sabah from Village to Urbanised Area

(Des Creative Concepts. Litho J.W.)

1981 (31 Aug). *Centenary of Sabah. T* **107** *and similar horiz design. Multicoloured. P* 12.
230 15 c. Type **107** 50 15
231 80 c. Drawing showing traditional and modern methods of agriculture .. .. 2·00 3·75

108 *Samanea saman*

109 Jamboree Emblem

(Des Yusof bin Hadji Saman. Litho J.W.)

1981 (16 Dec). *Trees. T* **108** *and similar multicoloured designs. P* 14.
232 15 c. Type **108** 55 10
233 50 c. *Dyera costulata* (*vert*) .. .. .. 1·75 1·40
234 80 c. *Dryobalanops aromatica* (*vert*) .. .. 2·00 3·75
232/4 .. .. *Set of* 3 3·75 4·75

(Des P. Lim (15 c.), Datuk Syed Hashim bin Abdullah (others). Litho J.W.)

1982 (10 Apr). *5th Malaysian/7th Asia–Pacific Boy Scout Jamboree. T* **109** *and similar horiz designs. Multicoloured. P* 13½ × 13.
235 15 c. Type **109** 35 10
236 50 c. Malaysian flag and scout emblem .. 80 85
237 80 c. Malaysian and Asia–Pacific scout emblems .. .. 1·25 3·50
235/7 .. .. *Set of* 3 2·25 4·00

110 A.S.E.A.N. Building and Emblem

111 Dome of the Rock, Jerusalem

(Litho J.W.)

1982 (8 Aug). *15th Anniv Ministerial Meeting of A.S.E.A.N.* (*Association of South East Asian Nations*). *T* **110** *and similar horiz design. Multicoloured. P* 14.
238 15 c. Type **110** 15 10
239 $1 Flags of member nations .. .. 60 2·00

(Litho J.W.)

1982 (21 Aug). *"Freedom for Palestine". P* 13½.
240 **111** 15 c. gold, blue-green and black 75 15
241 $1 silver, pale turquoise-green & blk .. 3·00 3·50

112 Views of Kuala Lumpur in 1957 and 1982

(Des Ministry of Information. Litho Rosenbaum Bros, Vienna)

1982 (31 Aug). *25th Anniv of Independence. T* **112** *and similar horiz designs. Multicoloured. P* 14 × 13½.
242 10 c. Type **112** 10 10
243 15 c. Malaysian industries 15 15
244 50 c. Soldiers on parade 40 55
245 80 c. Independence ceremony .. .. .. 70 2·00
242/5 .. .. *Set of* 4 1·25 2·50
MS246 120×190 mm. Nos. 242/5 (with silver frame around centre vignette of 10 c.) .. 13·00 9·00
a. Without silver frame around centre vignette of 10 c. .. .. .. 7·00 8·00

No. **MS**246a is from the second printing. It is without the narrow silver frame around the centre part of the 10 c. design which is shown on Nos. 242 and **MS**246.

113 Shadow Play

(Des N. Ajib. Litho J.W.)

1982 (30 Oct). *Traditional Games. T* **113** *and similar horiz designs. Multicoloured. P* 13.
247 10 c. Type **113** 50 30
248 15 c. Cross Top 50 15
249 75 c. Kite flying .. .. 2·00 3·50
247/9 .. .. *Set of* 3 2·75 3·50

114 Sabah Hats

(Litho Harrison)

1982 (26 Nov). *Malaysian Handicrafts. T* **114** *and similar horiz designs. Multicoloured. P* 13 × 13½.
250 10 c. Type **114** 25 30
251 15 c. Gold-threaded cloth 25 20
252 75 c. Sarawak pottery .. .. 1·25 2·75
250/2 .. .. *Set of* 3 1·60 3·00

115 Gas Exploitation Logo

116 Flag of Malaysia

(Litho Security Printers (M), Malaysia)

1983 (22 Jan). *Export of Liquefied Natural Gas from Bintulu Field, Sarawak. T* **115** *and similar horiz designs. Multicoloured. P* 12.

253	15 c. Type **115**	75	15
	a. Perf 13½	22·00	
254	20 c. *Tenaga Satu* (liquid gas tanker)	1·50	60
	a. Perf 13½	30·00	
255	$1 Gas drilling equipment	3·50	5·00
	a. Perf 13½	50·00	
253/5	*Set of* 3	5·25	5·25

(Litho J.W.)

1983 (14 Mar). *Commonwealth Day. T* **116** *and similar horiz designs. Multicoloured. P* 13½ × 14.

256	15 c. Type **116**	10	10
257	20 c. The King of Malaysia	15	20
258	40 c. Oil palm tree and refinery	25	45
259	$1 Satellite view of Earth	60	2·00
256/9	*Set of* 4	1·00	2·50

117 Nile Mouthbrooder

(Des and litho Security Printers (M), Malaysia)

1983 (15 June). *Freshwater Fishes. T* **117** *and similar horiz designs. Multicoloured. P* 12.

260	20 c. Type **117**	1·00	1·25
	a. Horiz pair. Nos. 260/1	2·00	2·50
	b. Perf 13½×14	6·00	3·25
	ba. Horiz pair. Nos. 260b/1b	12·00	6·50
261	20 c. Common Carp	1·00	1·25
	b. Perf 13½×14	6·00	3·25
262	40 c. Lampan Barb ("*Puntius gonionotus*")	1·75	2·25
	a. Horiz pair. Nos. 262/3	3·50	4·50
	b. Perf 13½×14	2·50	3·25
	ba. Horiz pair. Nos. 262b/3b	5·00	6·50
263	40 c. Grass Carp ("*Ctenopharyngodon idellus*")	1·75	2·25
	b. Perf 13½×14	2·50	3·25
260/3	*Set of* 4	5·00	6·00

Nos. 260/1 and 262/3 were each printed together, *se-tenant*, in horizontal pairs throughout the sheet.

118 Lower Pergau River Bridge

(Des Malaysian Public Works Dept. Litho Security Printers (M), Malaysia)

1983 (11 July). *Opening of East–West Highway. T* **118** *and similar horiz designs. Multicoloured. P* 13½.

264	15 c. Type **118**	80	15
265	20 c. Perak river reservoir bridge	1·00	60
266	$1 Map showing East–West highway	3·25	4·50
264/6	*Set of* 3	4·50	4·75

119 Northrop F-5E Tiger II Fighter

120 Helmeted Hornbill

(Des and litho J.W.)

1983 (16 Sept). *50th Anniv of Malaysian Armed Forces. T* **119** *and similar horiz designs. Multicoloured. P* 13.

267	15 c. Type **119**	1·00	15
268	20 c. Missile boat	1·50	45
269	40 c. Battle of Pasir Panjang	2·00	2·00
270	80 c. Trooping the Colour	3·00	4·00
267/70	*Set of* 4	6·75	6·00
MS271	130×85 mm. Nos. 267/70. P 13½	7·50	8·50

1983 (3 Oct)–**85**.* *As Nos.* 190/7 *but without wmk.*

272	30 c. Type **94** (1984)	2·25	60
273	40 c. Malayan Flying Lemur (6.10.83)	2·00	50
274	50 c. Lesser Malay Chevrotain (10.4.84)	2·25	50
275	75 c. Leathery Pangolin (19.10.85)	4·50	6·50
276	$1 Malayan Turtle (5.10.83)	3·50	50
277	$2 Malayan Tapir	3·25	70
278	$5 Gaur (1985)	14·00	9·00
279	$10 Orang-Utan (*vert*) (3.84)	14·00	11·00
272/9	*Set of* 8	42·00	26·00

*There was no official release date for these stamps. Dates shown are the earliest recorded from postmarks and may be revised should earlier examples be reported.

(Des P. Ket. Litho Security Printers (M), Malaysia)

1983 (26 Oct). *Hornbills of Malaysia. T* **120** *and similar vert designs. Multicoloured. P* 13½.

280	15 c. Type **120**	75	15
281	20 c. Wrinkled Hornbill	1·00	50
282	50 c. Long-crested Hornbill	1·50	1·50
283	$1 Rhinoceros Hornbill	2·50	4·00
280/3	*Set of* 4	5·25	5·50

121 Bank Building, Ipoh

122 Sky-scraper and Mosque, Kuala Lumpur

(Des P. Hoong. Litho Security Printers (M), Malaysia)

1984 (26 Jan). *25th Anniv of Bank Negara. T* **121** *and similar horiz design. Multicoloured. P* 13½ × 14.

284	20 c. Type **121**	40	30
285	$1 Bank building, Alor Setar	2·00	3·25

(Des Mara Institute of Technology. Litho Security Printers (M), Malaysia)

1984 (1 Feb). *10th Anniv of Federal Territory of Kuala Lumpur. T* **122** *and similar multicoloured designs. P* 13½ × 14 (80 c.) *or* 14 × 13½ (*others*).

286	20 c. Type **122**	70	20
287	40 c. Aerial view	1·40	1·40
288	80 c. Gardens and clock-tower (*horiz*)	2·25	3·50
286/8	*Set of* 3	4·00	4·50

123 Map showing Industries

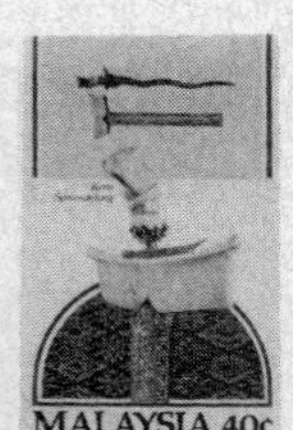

124 Semenanjung Keris

(Litho Security Printers (M), Malaysia)

1984 (16 Apr). *Formation of Labuan Federal Territory. T* **123** *and similar vert design. Multicoloured. P* 13½ × 14.

289	20 c. Type **123**	75	25
290	$1 Flag and map of Labuan	3·00	4·00

(Des P. Ket. Litho Harrison)

1984 (30 May). *Traditional Malay Weapons. T* **124** *and similar vert designs. Multicoloured. P* 13½ × 14.

291	40 c. Type **124**	1·25	1·60
	a. Block of 4. Nos. 291/4	4·50	
292	40 c. Pekakak keris	1·25	1·60
293	40 c. Jawa keris	1·25	1·60
294	40 c. Lada tumbuk	1·25	1·60
291/4	*Set of* 4	4·50	5·50

Nos. 291/4 were printed in *se-tenant* blocks of four throughout the sheet.

125 Map of World and Transmitter

126 Facsimile Service

(Des Dept of Broadcasting. Litho Harrison)

1984 (23 June). *20th Anniv of Asia–Pacific Broadcasting Union. T* **125** *and similar horiz design. Multicoloured. P* 13½ × 14½.

295	20 c. Type **125**	40	25
296	$1 Clasped hands within "20"	2·00	3·50

(Des Mark Johan and Associates. Litho Security Printers (M), Malaysia)

1984 (29 Oct). *Opening of New General Post Office, Kuala Lumpur. T* **126** *and similar horiz designs. Multicoloured. P* 12.

297	15 c. Type **126**	35	20
298	20 c. New G.P.O. building	45	45
299	$1 Mailbag conveyor	2·00	3·50
297/9	*Set of* 3	2·50	3·75

127 Yang di Pertuan Agong (Tuanku Mahmood)

128 White Hibiscus

(Des P. Ket. Litho Security Printers (M), Malaysia)

1984 (15 Nov). *Installation of Yang di Pertuan Agong* (*Tuanku Mahmood*). *T* **127** *and similar design. P* 12.

300	**127**	15 c. multicoloured	40	20
301		20 c. multicoloured	45	20
302	–	40 c. multicoloured	85	1·00
303	–	80 c. multicoloured	2·00	3·25
300/3		*Set of* 4	3·25	4·25

Design: *Horiz* — 40 c., 80 c. Yang di Pertuan Agong and Federal Crest.

(Litho Security Printers (M), Malaysia)

1984 (12 Dec). *Hibiscus. T* **128** *and similar vert designs. Multicoloured. P* 13½.

304	10 c. Type **128**	50	20
305	20 c. Red Hibiscus	1·00	20
306	40 c. Pink Hibiscus	1·75	1·75
307	$1 Orange Hibiscus	2·75	4·50
304/7	*Set of* 4	5·50	6·00

129 Parliament Building

130 Banded Linsang

(Des P. Ket. Litho Security Printers (M), Malaysia)

1985 (30 Mar). *25th Anniv of Federal Parliament. T* **129** *and similar multicoloured design. P* 13½ × 14 (20 c.) *or* 14 × 13½ ($1).

308	20 c. Type **129**	30	15
309	$1 Parliament Building (*different*) (*horiz*)	1·75	1·75

(Des P. Ket. Litho J.W.)

1985 (25 Apr). *Protected Animals of Malaysia* (1*st series*). *T* **130** *and similar multicoloured designs. P* 14.

310	10 c. Type **130**	50	10
311	40 c. Slow Loris (*vert*)	1·40	1·25
312	$1 Spotted Giant Flying Squirrel (*vert*)	3·00	4·00
310/12	*Set of* 3	4·50	4·75

See also Nos. 383/6.

131 Stylised Figures

132 F.M.S.R. "No. 1" Steam Locomotive, 1885

(Des Amir bin Osman. Litho Security Printers (M), Malaysia)

1985 (15 May). *International Youth Year. T* **131** *and similar horiz design. Multicoloured. P* 13.

313	20 c. Type **131**	30	15
314	$1 Young workers	2·75	3·75

(Des AMW Communications Management. Litho Security Printers (M), Malaysia).

1985 (1 June). *Centenary of Malayan Railways. T* **132** *and similar horiz designs. P* 13.

315	15 c. black, carmine-verm & pale orange	1·00	20
316	20 c. multicoloured	1·25	40
317	$1 multicoloured	3·00	4·00
315/17	*Set of* 3	4·75	4·25
MS318	119×59 mm. 80 c. multicoloured. P 13½×13	5·00	6·00

Designs: *Horiz* (*as T* **132**)—20 c. Class "20" diesel locomotive, 1957; $1 Class "23" diesel locomotive, 1983. (48×31 *mm*)— 80 c. Class "56" steam locomotive, 1938.

133 Blue Proton "Saga 1.3s"

134 Penang Bridge

(Des and litho J.W.)

1985 (9 July). *Production of Proton "Saga" (Malaysian national car). T* **133** *and similar horiz designs. Multicoloured. P* 14.
319 20 c. Type **133** 60 15
320 40 c. White Proton "Saga 1.3s" .. .. 1·00 85
321 $1 Red Proton "Saga 1.5s" .. .. .. 2·00 3·25
319/21 .. .. *Set of* 3 3·25 3·75

(Des Kathy's Design. Litho Security Printers (M), Malaysia)

1985 (14 Sept). *Opening of Penang Bridge. T* **134** *and similar horiz designs. Multicoloured. P* 12 ($1) *or* 13 (*others*).
322 20 c. Type **134** 70 15
323 40 c. Penang Bridge and location map .. 1·40 75
324 $1 Symbolic bridge linking Penang to mainland (40 × 24 *mm*) .. .. .. 2·75 3·25
322/4 .. .. *Set of* 3 4·25 3·75

135 Offshore Oil Rig

136 Sultan Azlan Shah and Perak Royal Crest

(Des Andamaz Enterprise. Litho Security Printers (M), Malaysia)

1985 (4 Nov). *Malaysian Petroleum Production. T* **135** *and similar multicoloured designs. P* 12.
325 15 c. Type **135** 75 15
326 20 c. Malaysia's first oil refinery (*horiz*) .. 85 50
327 $1 Map of Malaysian offshore oil and gas fields (*horiz*) .. .. 2·75 3·50
325/7 .. .. *Set of* 3 4·00 3·75

(Des Kathy's Design. Litho J.W.)

1985 (9 Dec). *Installation of the Sultan of Perak. P* 14.
328 **136** 15 c. multicoloured 30 10
329 20 c. multicoloured 40 25
330 $1 multicoloured .. .. 2·25 3·50
328/30 .. .. *Set of* 3 2·75 3·50

137 Crested Fireback Pheasant

139 Two Kadazan Dancers, Sabah

138

(Des P. Ket. Litho Security Printers (M), Malaysia)

1986 (11 Mar). *Protected Birds of Malaysia (1st series). T* **137** *and similar multicoloured designs. W* **138** (*sideways on* 40 c.). *Phosphorised paper. P* 13½.
331 20 c. Type **137** .. .. 2·00 2·25
a. Horiz pair. Nos. 331/2 .. .. .. 4·00 4·50
332 20 c. Malaya Peacock-Pheasant .. .. 2·00 2·25
333 40 c. Bulwer's Pheasant (*horiz*) .. .. 2·50 2·75
a. Horiz pair. Nos. 333/4 .. .. 5·00 5·50
b. Perf 12 .. .. 1·75 2·75
ba. Horiz pair. Nos. 333b/4b .. .. 3·50 5·50
334 40 c. Great Argus Pheasant (*horiz*) .. .. 2·50 2·75
b. Perf 12 .. .. 1·75 2·75
331/4 .. .. *Set of* 4 8·00 9·00

Nos. 331/2 and 333/4 were each printed together, *se-tenant*, in horizontal pairs throughout the sheets.

See also Nos. 394/7.

(Des AMC Advertising Agencies. Litho Questa)

1986 (14 Apr). *Pacific Area Travel Association Conference, Malaysia. T* **139** *and similar vert designs. Multicoloured. P* 15 × 14.
335 20 c. Type **139** 75 85
a. Horiz strip of 3. Nos. 335/7 .. .. 2·00
336 20 c. Dyak dancer and longhouse, Sarawak 75 85
337 20 c. Dancers and fortress, Malacca .. 75 85
338 40 c. Malay dancer and Kuala Lumpur .. 1·10 1·25
a. Horiz strip of 3. Nos. 338/40 .. 3·00
339 40 c. Chinese opera dancer and Penang Bridge .. .. 1·10 1·25
340 40 c. Indian dancer and Batu Caves .. 1·10 1·25
335/40 .. .. *Set of* 6 5·00 5·50

Nos. 335/7 and 338/40 were each printed together, *se-tenant*, in horizontal strips of 3 throughout the sheets.

140 Stylized Competitors

141 Rambutan

141*a*

(Des Design Excelsior. Litho Security Printers (M), Malaysia)

1986 (19 Apr). *Malaysia Games. T* **140** *and similar multi-coloured designs. W* **138** (*sideways on* 20 c.). *Phosphorised paper. P* 12.
341 20 c. Type **140** .. .. 1·25 20
342 40 c. Games emblems (*vert*) .. .. .. 2·25 1·75
343 $1 National and state flags (*vert*) .. .. 5·50 6·00
341/3 .. .. *Set of* 3 8·00 7·25

(Des P. Ket)

1986 (5 June)–**94**. *Fruits of Malaysia. T* **141** *and similar vert designs. Multicoloured.*

(*a*) *Litho Security Printers* (M), *Malaysia. W* **138**. *Phosphorised paper. P* 12
344 40 c. Type **141** 15 20
aw. Wmk inverted .. .. .. 10·00
b. Perf 13½ × 14 (1994) 50 20
345 50 c. Pineapple 15 20
aw. Wmk inverted .. .. ..
b. Perf 13½ × 14 (1994) 50 20
bw. Wmk inverted .. .. ..
346 80 c. Durian 25 30
aw. Wmk inverted .. .. .. 6·00
b. Perf 13½ × 14 (1994) 75 30
347 $1 Mangosteen 30 35
aw. Wmk inverted .. .. .. 7·00
b. Perf 13½ × 14 (1994) 75 35

(*b*) *Photo Harrison. W* **141***a*. *P* 13½.
348 $2 Star Fruit 60 65
349 $5 Banana .. .. 1·60 1·75
350 $10 Mango .. .. 3·25 3·50
351 $20 Papaya .. .. 6·25 6·50
344/51 .. .. *Set of* 8 12·50 13·50

PHOSPHORISED PAPER. From No. 352 onwards all stamps were on phosphorised paper, *unless otherwise stated*.

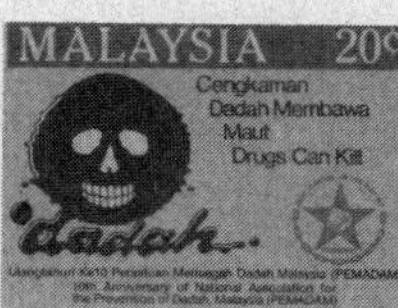

142 Skull and Slogan "Drugs Can Kill"

143 MAS Logo and Map showing Routes

(Des Kathy's Design. Litho Security Printers (M), Malaysia)

1986 (26 June). *10th Anniv of National Association for Prevention of Drug Addiction. T* **142** *and similar multicoloured designs. W* **138** (*sideways on* 20 c., $1). *P* 13.
352 20 c. Type **142** .. .. 1·00 30
353 40 c. Bird and slogan "Stay Free From Drugs" .. .. 1·40 1·10
354 $1 Addict and slogan "Drugs Can Destroy" (*vert*) .. .. 2·25 3·25
352/4 .. .. *Set of* 3 4·25 4·25

(Des PTM Thompson Advertising. Litho Security Printers (M), Malaysia)

1986 (31 July). *Inaugural Flight of Malaysian Airlines Kuala Lumpur–Los Angeles Service. T* **143** *and similar horiz designs. Multicoloured. W* **138** (*sideways*). *P* 14 × 13½.
355 20 c. Type **143** 85 15
356 40 c. Logo, stylized aircraft and route diagram .. .. 1·40 60
357 $1 Logo and stylized aircraft .. .. 2·50 2·00
355/7 .. .. *Set of* 3 4·25 2·50

144 Building Construction

145 Old Seri Menanti Palace, Negri Sembilan

(Des M. Chin. Litho Security Printers (M), Malaysia)

1986 (3 Nov). *20th Anniv of National Productivity Council and 25th Anniv of Asian Productivity Organization* (40 c., $1). *T* **144** *and similar multicoloured designs. W* **138** (*sideways on* 40 c., $1). *P* 13½ × 14 (20 c.) *or* 14 × 13½ (*others*).
358 20 c. Type **144** 85 25
359 40 c. Planning and design (*horiz*) .. .. 1·40 1·00
360 $1 Computer-controlled car assembly line (*horiz*) .. .. 3·75 4·50
358/60 .. .. *Set of* 3 5·50 5·25

(Des P. Ket. Litho Security Printers (M), Malaysia)

1986 (20 Dec). *Historic Buildings of Malaysia (1st series). T* **145** *and similar horiz designs. Multicoloured. W* **138** (*sideways*). *P* 13.
361 15 c. Type **145** 30 15
362 20 c. Old Kenangan Palace, Perak 35 15
363 40 c. Old Town Hall, Malacca 75 60
364 $1 Astana, Kuching, Sarawak .. .. 1·75 2·50
361/4 .. .. *Set of* 4 2·75 3·00

See also Nos. 465/8.

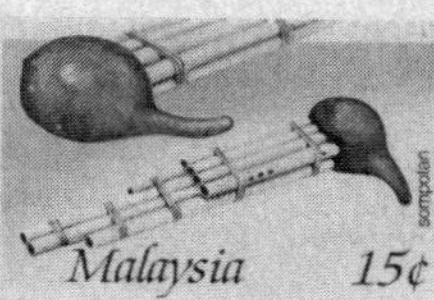

146 Sompotan (bamboo pipes)

(Des Kathy Wong. Litho Security Printers (M), Malaysia)

1987 (7 Mar). *Malaysian Musical Instruments. T* **146** *and similar multicoloured designs. W* **138** (*sideways on* 50, 80 c.). *P* 12.
365 15 c. Type **146** 35 10
366 20 c. Sapih (four-stringed chordophone) .. 45 15
367 50 c. Serunai (pipes) (*vert*) .. .. .. 1·00 35
368 80 c. Rebab (three-stringed fiddle) (*vert*) .. 1·50 65
365/8 .. .. *Set of* 4 3·00 1·10

147 Modern Housing Estate

(Litho Security Printers (M), Malaysia)

1987 (6 Apr). *International Year of Shelter for the Homeless. T* **147** *and similar horiz design. Multicoloured. W* **138**. *P* 12.
369 20 c. Type **147** 20 15
370 $1 Stylised families and houses 80 65

MACHINE LABELS. From 25 May 1987 gummed labels printed in red on yellow paper with an overall design of the postal logo were issued from a machine in Kuala Lumpur. Available face values ranged from 5 c. to $15.

148 Drug Addict and Family

(Des Kathy's Design. Litho Security Printers (M), Malaysia)

1987 (8 June). *International Conference on Drug Abuse, Vienna. T* **148** *and similar horiz designs. Multicoloured. W* **138** (*sideways*). *P* 13.
371 20 c. Type **148** .. .. 1·00 65
a. Vert pair. Nos. 371/2 .. .. .. 2·00 1·25
372 20 c. Hands holding drugs and damaged internal organs .. .. 1·00 65
373 40 c. Healthy boy and broken drug capsule .. 1·50 90
a. Vert pair. Nos. 373/4 .. .. .. 3·00 1·75
374 40 c. Drugs and healthy internal organs .. 1·50 90
371/4 .. .. *Set of* 4 4·50 2·75

Nos. 371/2 and 373/4 were printed together, *se-tenant*, in vertical pairs throughout the sheet, each pair forming a composite design.

149 Spillway and Power Station

(Des Kathy's Design. Litho Security Printers (M), Malaysia)

1987 (13 July). *Opening of Sultan Mahmud Hydro-electric Scheme, Kenyir, Trengganu. T* **149** *and similar horiz design. Multicoloured. W* **138**. *P* 12.
375 20 c. Type **149**. 50 10
376 $1 Dam, spillway and reservoir . . . . 2·50 1·50

150 Crossed Maces and Parliament Building, Kuala Lumpur

151 Dish Aerial, Satellite and Globe

(Des R. Zahabuddin. Litho Security Printers (M), Malaysia)

1987 (1 Sept). *33rd Commonwealth Parliamentary Conference. T* **150** *and similar horiz design. Multicoloured. W* **138**. *P* 12.
377 20 c. Type **150**. 20 10
378 $1 Parliament building and crossed maces emblem 80 75

(Des Mark Design. Litho Security Printers (M), Malaysia)

1987 (26 Oct). *Asia/Pacific Transport and Communications Decade. T* **151** *and similar horiz designs. Multicoloured. W* **138** *(sideways). P* 13.
379 15 c. Type **151** 40 10
380 20 c. Diesel train and car . . . . . . 1·00 55
381 40 c. Container ships and lorry . . . . 1·25 1·25
382 $1 Malaysian Airlines Boeing 747, Kuala Lumpur Airport . . . . . . 2·50 3·00
379/82 . . . . *Set of* 4 4·75 4·25

152 Temminck's Golden Cat

153 Flags of Member Nations and "20"

(Des Ong Soo Keat. Litho Security Printers (M), Malaysia)

1987 (14 Nov). *Protected Animals of Malaysia (2nd series). T* **152** *and similar horiz designs. Multicoloured. W* **138** *(sideways on 15, 20, 40 c.). P* 13.
383 15 c. Type **152**. . . . . 1·00 25
384 20 c. Flatheaded Cat . . . . 1·00 25
385 40 c. Marbled Cat . . . . 2·00 1·50
386 $1 Clouded Leopard . . . . 4·00 4·25
383/6 . . . . *Set of* 4 7·25 5·75

(Des P. Ket. Litho Security Printers (M), Malaysia)

1987 (14 Dec). *20th Anniv of Association of South East Asian Nations. T* **153** *and similar horiz design. Multicoloured. W* **138**. *P* 13.
387 20 c. Type **153**. 15 10
388 $1 Flags of member nations and globe . . 65 1·00

154 Mosque and Portico

155 Aerial View

(Des R. Zahabuddin. Litho Security Printers (M), Malaysia)

1988 (11 Mar). *Opening of Sultan Salahuddin Abdul Aziz Shah Mosque. T* **154** *and similar multicoloured designs. W* **138** *(sideways on 15, 20 c.). P* 12.
389 15 c. Type **154**. 10 10
390 20 c. Dome, minarets and Sultan of Selangor 15 15
391 $1 Interior and dome (*vert*) . . . . 60 1·00
389/91 . . . . *Set of* 3 75 1·10

(Des Azmi bin Kassim. Litho Security Printers (M), Malaysia)

1988 (4 Apr). *Sultan Ismail Hydro-electric Power Station, Paka, Trengganu. T* **155** *and similar horiz design. Multicoloured. W* **138** *(sideways). P* 13.
392 20 c. Type **155**. 15 10
393 $1 Power station and pylons 65 70

156 Black-naped Blue Monarch

157 Outline Map and Products of Sabah

(Des Ong Soo Keat. Litho Security Printers (M), Malaysia)

1988 (30 June). *Protected Birds of Malaysia (2nd series). T* **156** *and similar vert designs. Multicoloured. W* **138**. *P* 13.
394 20 c. Type **156** . . . . 1·25 1·25
a. Horiz pair. Nos. 394/5 . . . . 2·50 2·50
w. Inverted wmk . . . . . . 10·00
wa. Horiz pair. Nos. 394w/5w . . . . 20·00
395 20 c. Scarlet-backed Flowerpecker . . 1·25 1·25
w. Inverted wmk . . . . . . 10·00
396 50 c. Yellow-backed Sunbird . . . . 1·75 1·75
a. Horiz pair. Nos. 396/7 . . . . 3·50 3·50
w. Inverted wmk . . . . . . 5·00
wa. Horiz pair. Nos. 396w/7w . . . . 10·00
397 50 c. Black and Red Broadbill . . . . 1·75 1·75
w. Inverted wmk . . . . . . 5·00
394/7 . . . . *Set of* 4 5·50 5·50

The two designs of each value were printed together, *se-tenant*, in horizontal pairs throughout the sheets.

(Des P. Ket. Litho Security Printers (M), Malaysia)

1988 (31 Aug). *25th Anniv of Sabah and Sarawak as States of Malaysia. T* **157** *and similar vert designs. Multicoloured. W* **138**. *P* 13.
398 20 c. Type **157** 20 40
a. Horiz pair. Nos. 398/9 . . . . 40 80
399 20 c. Outline map and products of Sarawak 20 40
400 $1 Flags of Malaysia, Sabah and Sarawak (30×40 *mm*) . . . . 70 1·25
398/400 . . . . *Set of* 3 1·00 1·75

Nos. 398/9 were printed together, *se-tenant*, in horizontal pairs throughout the sheet.

158 *Glossodoris atromarginata*

159 Sultan's Palace, Malacca

(Litho Security Printers (M), Malaysia)

1988 (17 Dec). *Marine Life (1st series). T* **158** *and similar vert designs. Multicoloured. W* **138**. *P* 12.
401 20 c. Type **158** 45 55
a. Horiz strip of 5. Nos. 401/5 . . 2·00
402 20 c. Ocellate Nudibranch (*Phyllidia ocellata*) 45 55
403 20 c. *Chromodoris annae* 45 55
404 20 c. *Flabellina macassarana* 45 55
405 20 c. Ruppell's Nudibranch (*Reyfria ruppeli*) 45 55
401/5 . . . . *Set of* 5 2·00 2·50
MS406 100×75 mm. $1 Blue-ringed Angelfish (50×40 *mm*). P 14 . . . . . . 1·10 1·10

Nos. 401/5 were printed together, *se-tenant*, in horizontal strips of 5 throughout the sheet, forming a composite background design.

See also Nos. 410/13, 450/3, 492/7 and 559/62.

(Des P. Ket. Litho Security Printers (M), Malaysia)

1989 (15 Apr). *Declaration of Malacca as Historic City. T* **159** *and similar multicoloured designs. W* **138** *(sideways on 20 c.). P* 13.
407 20 c. Type **159** 15 15
408 20 c. Independence Memorial Building . . 15 15
409 $1 Porta De Santiago Fortress (*vert*) . . 75 1·40
407/9 . . . . *Set of* 3 95 1·50

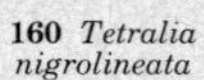

160 *Tetralia nigrolineata*

161 Map of Malaysia and Scout Badge

(Des P. Ket. Litho Security Printers (M), Malaysia)

1989 (29 June). *Marine Life (2nd series). Crustaceans. T* **160** *and similar horiz designs. Multicoloured. W* **138** *(sideways). P* 12.
410 20 c. Type **160** 45 65
a. Horiz pair. Nos. 410/11 . . . . 90 1·25
b. Wmk upright . . . . . .
ba. Horiz pair. Nos. 410b/11b . . . .
411 20 c. *Neopetrolisthes maculatus* (crab) . . 45 65
b. Wmk upright . . . . . .
412 40 c. *Periclimenes holthuisi* (shrimp) . . 55 90
a. Horiz pair. Nos. 412/13 . . . . 1·10 1·75
b. Wmk upright . . . . . .
ba. Horiz pair. Nos. 412b/13b . . . .
413 40 c. *Synalpheus neomeris* (shrimp) . . 55 90
b. Wmk upright . . . . . .
410/13 . . . . *Set of* 4 1·75 2·75

Nos. 410/11 and 412/13 were each printed together, *se-tenant*, in horizontal pairs throughout the sheets.

(Des T. Teh Ching Seng. Litho Security Printers (M), Malaysia)

1989 (26 July). *7th National Scout Jamboree. T* **161** *and similar multicoloured designs. W* **138** *(sideways on* 10, 20 *c.). P* 13.
414 10 c. Type **161** 20 10
415 20 c. Saluting national flag 30 25
416 80 c. Scouts around camp fire (*horiz*) . . 1·10 2·00
w. Wmk inverted . . . . . . 4·00
414/16 . . . . *Set of* 3 1·40 2·00

162 Cycling

163 Sultan Azlan Shah

(Litho Security Printers (M), Malaysia)

1989 (20 Aug). *15th South East Asian Games, Kuala Lumpur. T* **162** *and similar multicoloured designs. W* **138** *(sideways on* 50 *c.,* $1). *P* 13.
417 10 c. Type **162** 15 15
418 20 c. Athletics 25 20
419 50 c. Swimming (*vert*) 50 75
420 $1 Torch bearer (*vert*) . . . . . . 85 1·90
417/20 . . . . *Set of* 4 1·60 2·75

(Des R. Zahabuddin. Litho Security Printers (M), Malaysia)

1989 (18 Sept). *Installation of Sultan Azlan Shah as Yang di Pertuan Agong. W* **138** *(sideways). P* 13.
421 **163** 20 c. multicoloured 15 15
422 40 c. multicoloured 25 35
423 $1 multicoloured . . . . . . 60 1·50
421/3 . . . . *Set of* 3 90 1·75

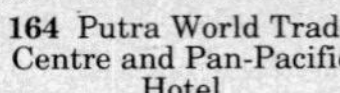

164 Putra World Trade Centre and Pan-Pacific Hotel

165 Clock Tower, Kuala Lumpur City Hall and Big Ben

(Litho Security Printers (M), Malaysia)

1989 (18 Oct). *Commonwealth Heads of Government Meeting, Kuala Lumpur. T* **164** *and similar multicoloured designs. W* **138** *(sideways on* 50 *c.). P* 13.
424 20 c. Type **164** 20 10
a. Wmk sideways . . . . . .
w. Wmk inverted . . . . . . 2·25
425 50 c. Traditional dancers (*vert*) 65 75
a. Wmk upright. . . . . 6·50
426 $1 National flag and map showing Commonwealth countries . . . . 1·25 2·00
a. Wmk sideways . . . . . . 6·50
424/6 . . . . *Set of* 3 1·90 2·50

(Des AMC-Melewar Zecha Communications. Litho Security Printers (M), Malaysia)

1989 (2 Dec). *Inaugural Malaysia Airlines "747" Non-stop Flight to London. T* **165** *and similar horiz designs, each showing Malaysia Airlines Boeing "747-400". Multicoloured. W* **138**. *P* 13.
427 20 c. Type **165** 65 80
a. Horiz pair. Nos. 427/9 . . . . 1·25 1·60
428 20 c. Parliament Buildings, Kuala Lumpur, and Palace of Westminster 65 80
429 $1 World map showing route . . . . 1·75 2·00
427/9 . . . . *Set of* 3 2·75 3·25

Nos. 427/8 were printed together, *se-tenant*, in horizontal pairs throughout the sheet.

166 Sloth and Map of Park

167 Outline Map of South-east Asia and Logo

(Des Jermaine. Litho Security Printers (M), Malaysia)

1989 (28 Dec). *50th Anniv of National Park. T* **166** *and similar vert design. Multicoloured. W* **138**. *P* 12 (20 c.) *or* 13 ($1).

430 20 c. Type **166** 30 15
a. Perf 14½ .. .. 3·25 3·50
431 $1 Pair of Malay Ocellated Pheasants .. 1·25 2·50
a. Perf 14½ .. .. 3·25 4·00

(Des A. Kassim. Litho Security Printers (M), Malaysia)

1990 (1 Jan). *"Visit Malaysia Year". T* **167** *and similar horiz designs. Multicoloured. W* **138** *(sideways). P* 12.

432 20 c. Type **167** 30 15
433 50 c. Traditional drums 65 70
434 $1 Scuba diving, windsurfing and yachting .. .. 1·00 1·75
432/4 .. .. *Set of* 3 1·75 2·40

168 *Dillenia suffruticosa*

169 Monument and Rainbow

(Des T. Teh Chin Seng. Litho Security Printers (M), Malaysia)

1990 (12 Mar). *Wildflowers (1st series). T* **168** *and similar vert designs. Multicoloured. W* **138**. *P* 12.

435 15 c. Type **168** 20 15
436 20 c. *Mimosa pudica* 25 20
437 50 c. *Ipmoea carnea* 50 60
438 $1 *Nymphaea pubescens* .. .. 70 1·50
435/8 .. .. *Set of* 4 1·50 2·25
See also Nos. 505/8.

(Des CD Advertising. Litho Security Printers (M), Malaysia)

1990 (14 May). *Kuala Lumpur, Garden City of Lights. T* **169** *and similar multicoloured designs. W* **138** *(sideways on* 40 c., $1). *P* 12.

439 20 c. Type **169** 15 20
440 40 c. Mosque and skyscrapers at night (*horiz*) 30 45
441 $1 Kuala Lumpur skyline (*horiz*) .. 75 1·75
439/41 .. .. *Set of* 3 1·10 2·25

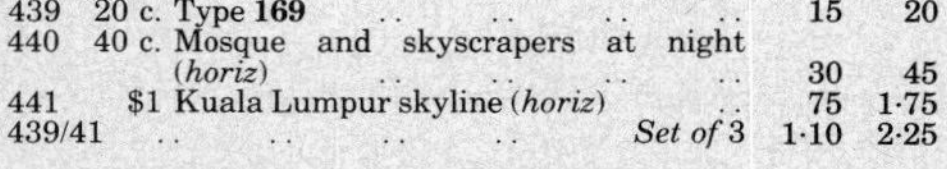

170 Seri Negara Building

171 Alor Setar

(Des T. Teh Chin Seng. Litho Security Printers (M), Malaysia)

1990 (1 June). *1st Summit Meeting of South–South Consultation and Co-operation Group, Kuala Lumpur. T* **170** *and similar horiz design. Multicoloured. W* **138** *(sideways). P* 13.

442 20 c. Type **170** 15 15
443 80 c. Summit logo .. .. 60 1·50

(Des Penerbit Hidayah. Litho Security Printers (M), Malaysia)

1990 (2 June). *250th Anniv of Alor Setar. T* **171** *and similar multicoloured designs. W* **138** *(sideways on* 40 c., $1). *P* 12.

444 20 c. Type **171** 15 20
445 40 c. Musicians and monument (*vert*) .. 25 35
446 $1 Zahir Mosque (*vert*) .. .. .. 70 1·50
444/6 .. .. *Set of* 3 1·00 1·90

172 Sign Language Letters

173 Leatherback Turtle

(Des S. Senika. Litho Security Printers (M), Malaysia)

1990 (8 Sept). *International Literacy Year. T* **172** *and similar multicoloured designs. W* **138** *(sideways on* 20, 40 c.). *P* 13 (40 c.) *or* 12 (*others*).

447 20 c. Type **172** 10 10
a. Perf 13 .. .. 13·00
448 40 c. People reading 25 35
449 $1 Symbolic person reading (*vert*) .. 65 1·50
447/9 .. .. *Set of* 3 90 1·75

(Des Ong Soo Keat. Litho Security Printers (M), Malaysia)

1990 (17 Nov). *Marine Life (3rd series). Sea Turtles. T* **173** *and similar horiz designs. Multicoloured. W* **138** *(sideways). P* 12.

450 15 c. Type **173** 50 10
451 20 c. Common Green Turtle 50 15
452 40 c. Olive Ridley Turtle 90 80
453 $1 Hawksbill Turtle .. .. .. 2·00 2·50
a. Wmk inverted .. .. ..
450/3 .. .. *Set of* 4 3·50 3·00

174 Safety Helmet, Dividers and Industrial Skyline

175 *Eustenogaster calyptodoma*

(Litho Security Printers (M), Malaysia)

1991 (25 Apr). *25th Anniv of MARA (Council of the Indigenous People). T* **174** *and similar horiz designs. Multicoloured. W* **138** *(sideways). P* 12.

454 20 c. Type **174** 15 10
455 40 c. Documents and graph 25 35
456 $1 25th Anniversary logo .. .. 65 1·75
454/6 .. .. *Set of* 3 95 2·00

(Des Loh Wen Kong. Litho Security Printers (M), Malaysia)

1991 (29 July). *Insects. Wasps. T* **175** *and similar vert designs. Multicoloured. W* **138** *(sideways). P* 12.

457 15 c. Type **175** 20 30
a. Wmk upright .. .. 3·25
458 20 c. *Vespa affinis indonensis* 20 20
459 50 c. *Sceliphorn javanum* 50 70
460 $1 *Ampulex compressa* .. .. .. 90 1·50
457/60 .. .. *Set of* 4 1·60 2·40
MS461 130×85 mm. Nos. 457/60. Wmk sideways. P 14½×14 .. .. .. 1·60 2·50
a. Wmk upright. P 12 .. .. .. 8·00 10·00

15 c. stamps from normal sheets (Nos. 457/a) show the wasp's left-hand feeler touching the edge of the design. On stamps of this value from the miniature sheet the feeler stops short of the edge.

176 Tunku Abdul Rahman Putra and Independence Rally

(Des Design Dimension. Litho Security Printers (M), Malaysia)

1991 (30 Aug). *Former Prime Ministers of Malaysia. T* **176** *and similar horiz designs. Multicoloured. W* **138**. *P* 12.

462 $1 Type **176** .. .. 70 1·00
463 $1 Tun Abdul Razak Hussein and jungle village .. .. 70 1·00
464 $1 Tun Hussein Onn and standard-bearers .. .. 70 1·00
462/4 .. .. *Set of* 3 1·90 2·75

177 Maziah Palace, Trengganu

178 Museum Building in 1891, Brass Lamp and Fabric

(Des A. Kassim. Litho Security Printers (M), Malaysia)

1991 (7 Nov). *Historic Buildings of Malaysia (2nd series). T* **177** *and similar horiz designs. Multicoloured. W* **138**. *P* 12.

465 15 c. Type **177** 20 10
466 20 c. Grand Palace, Johore 20 15
467 40 c. Town Palace, Kuala Langat, Selangor 40 50
468 $1 Jahar Palace, Kelantan .. .. 80 1·75
465/8 .. .. *Set of* 4 1·40 2·25

(Des T. Teh Chin Seng. Litho Security Printers (M), Malaysia)

1991 (21 Dec). *Centenary of Sarawak Museum. T* **178** *and similar horiz design. Multicoloured. W* **138**. *P* 12.

469 30 c. Type **178** 20 15
470 $1 Museum building in 1991, vase and fabric .. .. 65 1·10

179 Rural Postman on Cycle

180 Hill Forest and Jelutong Tree

(Des Ismail & Associates. Litho Security Printers (M), Malaysia)

1992 (1 Jan). *Inauguration of Post Office Corporation. T* **179** *and similar vert designs. Multicoloured. W* **138** *(sideways). P* 12.

471 30 c. Type **179** 50 65
a. Horiz strip of 5. Nos. 471/5 .. .. 2·25
472 30 c. Urban postman on motorcycle .. 50 65
473 30 c. Inner city post van 50 65
474 30 c. Industrial post van 50 65
475 30 c. Malaysian Airlines Boeing 747 and globe 50 65
471/5 .. .. *Set of* 5 2·25 3·00

Nos. 471/5 were printed together, *se-tenant*, in horizontal strips of 5 throughout the sheet.

(Des T. Teh Chin Seng. Litho Security Printers (M), Malaysia)

1992 (23 Mar). *Tropical Forests. T* **180** *and similar horiz designs. Multicoloured. W* **138** *(sideways). P* 12.

476 20 c. Type **180** 15 10
477 50 c. Mangrove swamp and Bakau Minyak tree 35 50
478 $1 Lowland forest and Chengal tree .. 75 1·50
476/8 .. .. *Set of* 3 1·10 1·90

181 Tuanku Ja'afar and Coat of Arms

182 Badminton Players

(Des TIARA CDP. Litho Security Printers (M), Malaysia)

1992 (18 Apr). *25th Anniv of Installation of Tuanku Ja'afar as Yang di-Pertuan Besar of Negri Sembilan. T* **181** *and similar horiz design. W* **138** *(sideways). P* 12.

479 30 c. Type **181** 20 20
480 $1 Palace, Negri Sembilan .. .. 80 1·60

(Des T. Teh Chin Seng. Litho Security Printers (M), Malaysia)

1992 (25 July). *Malaysian Victory in Thomas Cup Badminton Championship. T* **182** *and similar multicoloured designs. W* **138**. *P* 12.

481 $1 Type **182** 55 75
482 $1 Thomas Cup and Malaysian flag .. 55 75
MS483 105×80 mm. $2 Winning team (76×28 *mm*). Wmk sideways .. .. .. 1·50 2·25

183 Women in National Costumes

184 Straits Settlements 1867 1½ c. and Malaysian Federation 1957 10 c. Stamps

(Des Image Productions. Litho Security Printers (M), Malaysia)

1992 (8 Aug). *25th Anniv of A.S.E.A.N. (Association of South East Asian Nations). T* **183** *and similar horiz designs. Multicoloured. W* **138** *(sideways). P* 12.

484 30 c. Type **183** 40 30
a. Wmk inverted .. ..
485 50 c. Regional flowers 65 75
486 $1 Traditional architecture .. .. 1·25 2·25
484/6 .. .. *Set of* 3 2·10 3·00

(Des Mega Dot. Litho Security Printers (M), Malaysia)

1992 (1 Sept). *125th Anniv of Postage Stamps and "Kuala Lumpur '92", International Stamp Exhibition. T* **184** *and similar horiz designs. Multicoloured. W* **138** *(sideways). P* 12.

487 30 c. Type **184** 30 50
a. Horiz pair. Nos. 487/8 .. .. 60 1·00
488 30 c. Straits Settlements 1867 2 c. and Malaysia 1963 Federation Inauguration 12 c. 30 50
489 50 c. Straits Settlements 1868 4 c. and Malaysia 1990 Kuala Lumpur 40 c. .. 55 80
a. Horiz pair. Nos. 489/90 .. .. 1·10 1·60
b. Wmk inverted .. .. .. 4·75
ba. Horiz pair. Nos. 489b/90b .. .. 9·50
490 50 c. Straits Settlements 1867 12 c. and Malaysia "Kuala Lumpur '92" $2 .. 55 80
b. Wmk inverted .. .. .. 4·75
487/90 .. .. *Set of* 4 1·50 2·40
MS491 120×92 mm. $2 "Kuala Lumpur '92" logo on Malaysian flag. P 13×13½ .. .. 1·75 2·50
a. Perf 12 .. .. 8·00 10·00

Nos. 487/8 and 489/90 were printed together, *se-tenant*, in horizontal pairs throughout the sheets.

ALTERED CATALOGUE NUMBERS

Any Catalogue numbers altered from the last edition are shown as a list in the introductory pages.

185 *Acropora* **186** Girls smiling

(Des Greenmild Advertising. Litho Security Printers (M), Malaysia)

1992 (21 Dec). *Marine Life (4th series). Corals. T* **185** *and similar multicoloured designs. W* **138**. *P* 12.
492 30 c. Type **185** 65 75
a. Horiz strip of 5. Nos. 492/6 .. .. 3·00
493 30 c. *Dendronephthya* 65 75
494 30 c. *Dendrophyllia* 65 75
495 30 c. *Sinularia* 65 75
496 30 c. *Melithaea* 65 75
492/6 .. .. *Set of* 5 3·00 3·25
MS497 100×70 mm. $2 *Subergorgia* (38×28 *mm*). Wmk sideways .. .. 2·00 2·75
a. Wmk upright .. .. 5·50 7·00
Nos. 492/6 were printed together, *se-tenant*, in horizontal strips of 5 throughout the sheet.

(Des Image Promotions. Litho Security Printers (M), Malaysia)

1993 (24 Apr). *16th Asian–Pacific Dental Congress. T* **186** *and similar horiz designs. Multicoloured. W* **138** *(sideways). P* 12.
498 30 c. Type **186** 50 65
a. Horiz pair. Nos. 498/9 .. .. 1·00 1·25
499 30 c. Girls smiling with Koala Bear .. 50 65
500 50 c. Dentists with Japanese, Malaysian and South Korean flags .. .. .. 80 1·00
a. Horiz pair. Nos. 500/1 .. .. 1·75 2·25
501 $1 Dentists with New Zealand, Thai, Chinese and Indonesian flags .. 1·00 1·25
498/501 .. .. *Set of* 4 2·50 3·25
Nos. 498/9 and 500/1 were each printed together, *se-tenant*, in horizontal pairs throughout the sheets.

187 View of Golf Course **188** *Alpinia rafflesiana*

(Des T. Teh Chin Seng. Litho Security Printers (M), Malaysia)

1993 (24 June). *Centenary of Royal Selangor Golf Club. T* **187** *and similar multicoloured designs. W* **138** *(sideways on* $1). *P* 12.
502 30 c. Type **187** 60 20
503 50 c. Old and new club houses 90 80
w. Wmk inverted .. .. .. 22·00
504 $1 Bunker on course (*horiz*) .. .. 1·75 2·00
502/4 .. .. *Set of* 3 3·00 2·75

(Des TIARA CDP. Litho Security Printers (M), Malaysia)

1993 (2 Aug). *Wildflowers (2nd series). Gingers. T* **188** *and similar vert designs. Multicoloured. W* **138**. *P* 12.
505 20 c. Type **188** 35 10
w. Wmk inverted .. .. .. 12·00
506 30 c. *Achasma megalocheilos* 45 20
507 50 c. *Zingiber spectabile* 70 70
508 $1 *Costus speciosus* .. .. .. 1·40 1·75
w. Wmk inverted .. .. .. 16·00
505/8 .. .. *Set of* 4 2·50 2·50

189 Forest under Magnifying Glass **190** White-breasted Kingfisher

(Des CD Advertising. Litho Security Printers (M), Malaysia)

1993 (13 Sept). *14th Commonwealth Forestry Conference, Kuala Lumpur. T* **189** *and similar multicoloured designs. W* **138** *(sideways on* 30 *c.,* 50 *c.). P* 12.
509 30 c. Type **189** 40 20
510 50 c. Hand holding forest 65 70
511 $1 Forest in glass dome (*vert*) .. .. 1·40 1·90
509/11 .. .. *Set of* 3 2·25 2·50
Nos. 509/11 were re-issued on 1 October 1994 with the Bangkok '93 Stamp Exhibition logo incorporated in the designs. Such stamps were only available from the Malaysia stand at the exhibition and in very limited quantities from the philatelic bureaux.

(Des Ong Soo Keat. Litho Security Printers (M), Malaysia)

1993 (23 Oct). *Kingfishers. T* **190** *and similar vert designs. Multicoloured. W* **138**. *P* 12.
512 30 c. Type **190** 60 80
a. Horiz pair. Nos. 512/13 .. .. 1·10 1·60
513 30 c. Pair of Blue-eared Kingfishers .. 60 80
514 50 c. Chestnut-collared Kingfisher .. 80 1·00
a. Horiz pair. Nos. 514/15 .. .. 1·60 2·00
515 50 c. Pair of Three-toed Kingfishers .. 80 1·00
512/15 .. .. *Set of* 4 2·50 3·25
Nos. 512/13 and 514/15 were printed together, *se-tenant*, in horizontal pairs throughout the sheets.

191 SME MD3-160M Light Aircraft **192** Jeriau Waterfalls

(Des A. Hassan. Litho Security Printers (M), Malaysia)

1993 (7 Dec). *Langkawi International Maritime and Aerospace Exhibition* '93. *T* **191** *and similar horiz designs. Multicoloured. W* **138** *(sideways on* 30 *c.). P* 12.
516 30 c. Type **191** 35 20
a. Wmk inverted .. .. .. 4·25
517 50 c. Eagle X-TS light aircraft 65 70
518 $1 *Kasturi* (frigate) .. .. .. 1·25 1·75
a. Wmk sideways .. .. .. 4·25
516/18 .. .. *Set of* 3 2·00 2·40
MS519 120×80 mm. $2 Map of Langkawi. Wmk upright .. .. 1·25 2·00
a. Wmk sideways .. .. .. 23·00

(Des Mega Dot. Litho Security Printers (M), Malaysia)

1994 (1 Jan). *Visit Malaysia. T* **192** *and similar horiz designs. Multicoloured. W* **138** *(inverted). P* 12.
520 20 c. Type **192** 25 10
521 30 c. Flowers 30 25
522 50 c. Turtle and fishes 45 55
523 $1 Orang-utan and other wildlife .. 90 1·50
520/3 .. .. *Set of* 4 1·60 2·25
Nos. 520/3 were re-issued on 8 November 1994 with the "ASEANPEX '94" Stamp Exhibition logo incorporated in the designs. Such stamps were only available from the Malaysian stand at the exhibition and in very limited quantities from the philatelic bureaux.

193 Planetarium and Planets **194** *Spathoglottis aurea*

(Des CD Advertising and DeArt Forms. Litho Security Printers (M), Malaysia)

1994 (7 Feb). *National Planetarium, Kuala Lumpur. T* **193** *and similar horiz designs. Multicoloured. W* **138** *(inverted on* 30 *c.). P* 12.
524 30 c. Type **193** 50 20
w. Wmk upright .. ..
525 50 c. Static displays 65 65
526 $1 Planetarium auditorium .. .. 1·50 1·75
524/6 .. .. *Set of* 3 2·40 2·40

(Des P. Ket. Litho Security Printers (M), Malaysia)

1994 (17 Feb). *Orchids. T* **194** *and similar multicoloured designs. W* **138** *(sideways). P* 12.
527 20 c. Type **194** 35 10
528 30 c. *Paphiopedilum barbatum* 45 25
529 50 c. *Bulbophyllum lobbii* 75 75
530 $1 *Aerides odorata* .. .. .. 1·25 1·50
527/30 .. .. *Set of* 4 2·50 2·40
MS531 120×82 mm. $2 *Grammatophyllum speciosum* (*horiz*) .. .. 2·25 2·75
No. **MS**531 also commemorates the "Hong Kong '94" International Stamp Exhibition.

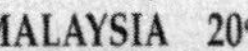

195 Decorative Bowl **196** Flock of Chickens and Vet examining Cat

(Des Assist Ad. Litho Security Printers (M), Malaysia)

1994 (17 June). *World Islamic Civilisation Festival '94, Kuala Lumpur. T* **195** *and similar vert designs. Multicoloured. W* **138**. *P* 12.
532 20 c. Type **195** 15 10
533 30 c. Celestial globe 25 20
534 50 c. Dinar coins 40 55
535 $1 Decorative tile .. .. .. 75 1·25
532/5 .. .. *Set of* 4 1·40 1·90
Nos. 532/5 were re-issued on 16 August 1994 with the "Philakorea '94" Stamp Exhibition logo incorporated in the designs. Such stamps were only available from the Malaysia stand at the exhibition and in very limited quantities from the philatelic bureaux.

(Des TIARA CDP. Litho Security Printers (M), Malaysia)

1994 (26 July). *Centenary of Veterinary Services. T* **196** *and similar vert designs. Multicoloured. W* **138** *(inverted on* 30 *c.). P* 12.
536 30 c. Type **196** 25 20
537 50 c. Vet in abattoir 40 50
538 $1 Herd of cows and veterinary equipment 75 1·25
536/8 .. .. *Set of* 3 1·25 1·75

197 Workers laying Electric Cable **198** Expressway from the Air

(Des Mega Dot. Litho Security Printers (M), Malaysia)

1994 (3 Sept). *Centenary of Electricity Supply. T* **197** *and similar horiz designs. Multicoloured. W* **138** *(sideways). P* 12.
539 30 c. Type **197** 25 45
a. Horiz pair. Nos. 539/40 .. .. 50 90
540 30 c. Illuminated city 25 45
541 $1 City of the future .. .. .. 70 1·10
539/41 .. .. *Set of* 3 1·10 1·75
Nos. 539/40 were printed together, *se-tenant*, in horizontal pairs throughout the sheet.

(Des The Sharper Image. Litho Security Printers (M), Malaysia)

1994 (8 Sept). *Opening of North–South Expressway. T* **198** *and similar horiz designs. Multicoloured. W* **138** *(sideways). P* 12.
542 30 c. Type **198** 20 20
543 50 c. Expressway junction 35 50
544 $1 Expressway bridge .. .. .. 80 1·25
542/4 .. .. *Set of* 3 1·25 1·75

199 Sultan Tuanku Ja'afar **200** Map of Malaysia and Logo

(Des R. Yaacob. Litho Security Printers (M), Malaysia)

1994 (22 Sept). *Installation of Sultan Tuanku Ja'afar as Yang di Pertuan Agong. W* **138**. *P* 12.
545 **199** 30 c. multicoloured 20 20
w. Wmk inverted .. .. .. 2·50
546 50 c. multicoloured 40 50
547 $1 multicoloured .. .. .. 80 1·25
545/7 .. .. *Set of* 3 1·25 1·75

(Des Limkokwing Integrated. Litho Security Printers (M), Malaysia)

1994 (29 Oct). *16th Commonwealth Games, Kuala Lumpur* (1998) (*1st issue*). *T* **200** *and similar vert design. Multicoloured. W* **138**. *P* 12.
548 $1 Type **200** .. .. 80 1·00
a. Horiz pair. Nos. 548/9 .. .. 1·60 2·00
549 $1 Wira (games mascot) holding national flag .. .. 80 1·00
Nos. 548/9 were issued together, *se-tenant*, in sheets of 30 (6×5), showing No. 548 in vertical rows 1 and 4, No. 549 in vertical rows 3 and 6, and a stamp-size label, showing the mascot playing rugby, basketball, cricket and hockey, in vertical rows 2 and 5.
See also Nos. 575/6, 627/30, and 668/71.

201 Tunku Abdul Rahman Putra and National Flag

(Des T. Teh Ching Seng. Litho Leigh-Mardon Ltd, Melbourne, Australia)

1994 (10 Nov). *5th Death Anniv of Tunku Abdul Rahman Putra (former Prime Minister). T* **201** *and simlar horiz design. Multicoloured. P* 14½.
550 30 c. Type **201** 25 20
551 $1 The Residency, Kuala Lumpur . . 75 1·00

202 Library Building

203 *Microporus xanthopus*

(Des Image Promotions. Litho Security Printers (M), Malaysia)

1994 (16 Dec). *Opening of the New National Library Building. T* **202** *and similar horiz designs. Multicoloured.* W **138** (*sideways*). P 12.
552 30 c. Type **202** 25 20
553 50 c. Computer plan on screen 45 50
554 $1 Ancient Koran . . . . . . 1·00 1·40
552/4 . . . . *Set of* 3 1·50 1·90

(Des Greenmild Advertising. Litho Enschedé)

1995 (18 Jan). *Fungi. T* **203** *and similar vert designs. Multicoloured. P* 14½×14.
555 20 c. Type **203** 15 10
556 30 c. *Cookeina tricholoma* 25 20
557 50 c. *Phallus indusiatus* ("*Dictyophora phalloidea*") 45 55
558 $1 *Ramaria* sp. . . . . . . 90 1·50
555/8 . . . . *Set of* 4 1·60 2·00

204 Seafans

(Litho Security Printers (M), Malaysia)

1995 (10 Apr). *Marine Life (5th series). Corals. T* **204** *and similar horiz designs. Multicoloured.* W **138** (*sideways*). *P* 12.
559 20 c. Type **204** 30 45
a. Booklet pane. Nos. 559/60, each × 5 2·75
560 20 c. Feather Stars 30 45
561 30 c. Cup Coral 35 45
a. Booklet pane. Nos. 561/2, each × 5 . . 3·00
562 30 c. Soft Coral 35 45
559/62 . . . . *Set of* 4 1·10 1·60
Nos. 559/60 and 561/2 were only available from $2 and $3 stamp booklets.

205 Clouded Leopard on Branch

(Des A. Robinson. Litho Enschedé)

1995 (18 Apr). *Endangered Species. Clouded Leopard. T* **205** *and similar horiz designs. Multicoloured.* W w **14** (*sideways*). *Ordinary paper. P* 13½.
563 20 c. Type **205** 15 15
a. Strip of 4. Nos. 563/6 . . . . 1·25
564 30 c. With cubs 20 20
565 50 c. Crouched on branch 35 45
566 $1 Climbing tree . . . . . . 65 1·00
563/6 . . . . *Set of* 4 1·25 1·60
In addition to separate sheets of 50 Nos. 563/6 were also available in sheets of 16 (4×4) with the stamps *se-tenant* both vertically and horizontally.

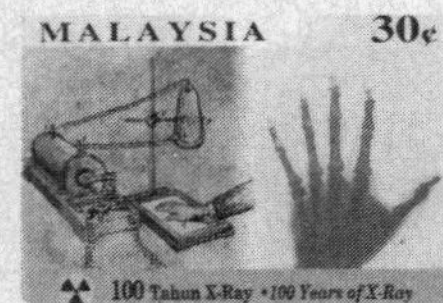

206 Early X-Ray Equipment and X-Ray of Hand

(Des Eka IPR Agensi. Litho Security Printers (M), Malaysia)

1995 (29 May). *Centenary of Discovery of X-Rays by Wilhelm Conrad Röntgen. T* **206** *and similar horiz designs. Multicoloured.* W **138**. *P* 12.
567 30 c. Type **206** 25 40
a. Pair. Nos. 567/8 . . . . . . 50 80
568 30 c. Body scanner and brain scan . . 25 40
569 $1 Chest X-rays . . . . . . 75 1·00
567/9 . . . . *Set of* 3 1·10 1·60
Nos. 567/8 were printed together, *se-tenant*, in horizontal and vertical pairs throughout the sheet.

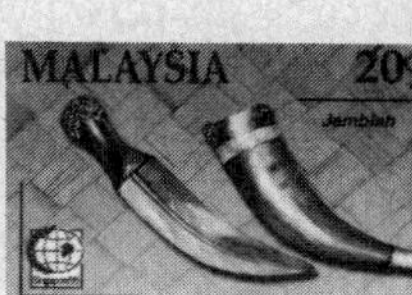

207 Jembiah (curved dagger)

208 Badminton, Cricket, Shooting, Tennis, Hurdling, Hockey and Weightlifting

(Des BJ Image. Litho Questa)

1995 (1 Sept). *"Singapore '95" International Stamp Exhibition. Traditional Malay Weapons. T* **207** *and similar horiz designs. Multicoloured. P* 14.
570 20 c. Type **207** 15 10
571 30 c. Keris panjang (sword) 25 20
572 50 c. Kerambit (curved dagger) 40 50
573 $1 Keris sundang (sword) . . . . 80 1·50
570/3 . . . . *Set of* 4 1·40 2·00
MS574 100×70 mm. $2 Landig terus (dagger) 1·40 2·00

(Des Limkokwing Integrated. Litho Security Printers (M), Malaysia)

1995 (11 Sept). *16th Commonwealth Games, Kuala Lumpur (1998) (2nd issue). T* **208** *and similar vert design. Multicoloured.* W **138**. *P* 14½.
575 $1 Type **208** . . . . . . 70 1·00
a. Horiz pair. Nos. 575/6 . . . . 1·40 2·00
b. Perf 13½ . . . . . .
ba. Horiz pair. Nos. 575b/6b . . . .
576 $1 Cycling, bowls, boxing, basketball, rugby, gymnastics and swimming . . 70 1·00
b. Perf 13½ . . . . . .
Nos. 575/6 were issued together, *se-tenant*, in sheets of 30 (6×5), showing No. 575 in vertical rows 1 and 4, No. 576 in vertical rows 3 and 6, and a stamp-size label, showing the monkey mascot hurdling, boxing and playing badminton, in vertical rows 2 and 5.

209 Leatherback Turtle (*Dermochelys coriacea*)

(Des Choo Beng Teong. Litho Security Printers (M), Malaysia)

1995 (26 Sept). *Turtles. T* **209** *and similar horiz design. Multicoloured.* W **138** (*sideways*). *P* 14½.
577 30 c. Type **209** 30 35
a. Booklet pane. Nos. 577/8 each × 5 . . 2·75
578 30 c. Green Turtle (*Chelonia mydas*) . . 30 35
Nos. 577/8 were only issued in $3 stamp booklets.

210 Anniversary Emblem and Symbolic People around Globe

211 Boeing 747, Globe, Emblem and Malaysian Scenes

(Des PAC Advertising. Litho Southern Colour Print, Dunedin, New Zealand)

1995 (24 Oct). *50th Anniv of United Nations. T* **210** *and similar horiz design. Multicoloured. P* 13½.
579 30 c. Type **210** 15 20
580 $1 United Nations emblem 60 80

(Des ISC Bullseye. Litho Enschedé)

1995 (30 Oct). *50th Anniv of International Air Transport Association. T* **211** *and similar vert designs, each showing Boeing 747 and globe. Multicoloured. P* 14½×14.
581 30 c. Type **211** 25 35
a. Horiz pair. Nos. 581/2 . . . . 50 70
582 30 c. Asian and Australasian scenes . . 25 35
583 50 c. European and African scenes . . 35 55
a. Horiz pair. Nos. 583/4 . . . . 70 1·10
584 50 c. North and South American scenes . . 35 55
581/4 . . . . *Set of* 4 1·10 1·60
Nos. 581/2 and 583/4 were printed together, *se-tenant*, in horizontal pairs throughout the sheets.

212 Proton "Saga 1.5" Saloon, 1985

213 "Ariane 4" Launch Rocket

(Des Long's Creative. Litho Southern Colour Print, Dunedin)

1995 (23 Dec). *10th Anniv of Proton Cars. T* **212** *and similar horiz designs. Multicoloured. P* 14×14½.
585 30 c. Type **212** 20 25
a. Booklet pane. Nos. 585/94 . . . . 1·75
586 30 c. "Iswara 1.5" aeroback, 1992 . . . . 20 25
587 30 c. "Iswara 1.5" saloon, 1992 . . . . 20 25
588 30 c. "Wira 1.6" saloon, 1993 . . . . 20 25
589 30 c. "Wira 1.6" aeroback, 1993 . . . . 20 25
590 30 c. Proton rally car, 1994 . . . . 20 25
591 30 c. "Satria 1.6" hatchback, 1994 . . . . 20 25
592 30 c. "Perdana 2.0" saloon, 1995 . . . . 20 25
593 30 c. "Wira 1.6" aeroback, 1995 . . . . 20 25
594 30 c. "Wira 1.8" saloon, 1995 . . . . 20 25
585/94 . . . . *Set of* 10 1·75 2·25
Nos. 585/94 were only issued in $3 stamp booklets with the horizontal edges of the pane imperforate.

(Des Nerve Centre Associates. Litho Southern Colour Print, Dunedin)

1996 (13 Jan). *Launch of MEASAT I (Malaysia East Asia Satellite). T* **213** *and similar multicoloured designs. P* 13½.
595 30 c. Type **213** 20 20
596 50 c. Satellite over Eastern Asia 30 40
597 $1 Satellite Earth station, Langkawi . . 70 1·10
595/7 . . . . *Set of* 3 1·10 1·50
MS598 100×70 mm. $5 Satellite orbiting Globe (hologram) (*horiz*). P 14×14½ . . . . 2·75 3·50

214 *Nepenthes sanguinea*

215 Brahminy Kite

(Des P. Ket. Litho Security Printers (M), Malaysia)

1996 (6 Apr). *Pitcher Plants. T* **214** *and similar vert designs. Multicoloured.* W **138**. *P* 13½ (30 *c.*) *or* 14½×14 (50 *c.*).
599 30 c. Type **214** 25 35
a. Horiz pair. Nos. 599/600 . . . . 50 70
b. Perf 14½×14 . . . . . .
ba. Horiz pair. Nos. 599b/600b . . . .
600 30 c. *Nepenthes macfarlanei* 25 35
b. Perf 14½×14 . . . . . .
601 50 c. *Nepenthes rajah* 35 50
a. Horiz pair. Nos. 601/2 . . . . 70 1·00
602 50 c. *Nepenthes lowii* 35 50
599/602 . . . . *Set of* 4 1·10 1·50
Nos. 599/600 and 601/2 were each printed together, *se-tenant*, in horizontal pairs throughout the sheets.

(Des Teh Yew Kiang)

1996 (18 May–Dec). *Birds of Prey. T* **215** *and similar multicoloured designs. (a) Litho Security Printers (M), Malaysia.* W **138**. *P* 13½ (30 *c.*) *or* 14½×14 (*others*).
603 20 c. Type **215** 20 15
604 30 c. Crested Serpent Eagle 30 25
aw. Wmk inverted . . . . . .
b. Perf 14×14½ . . . . . . 5·50 70
605 50 c. White-bellied Sea Eagle 45 50
b. Perf 13½ . . . . . .
606 $1 Crested Hawk Eagle . . . . 90 1·25
aw. Wmk inverted . . . . . .
b. Perf 13½ . . . . . .
603/6 . . . . *Set of* 4 1·75 1·90
MS607 100×70 mm. $2 Blyth's Hawk Eagle (*vert*). P 13½×14 . . . . . . 2·25 2·75
a. Perf 13½ . . . . . .
b. Perf 14 . . . . . .

(*b*) *Litho Southern Colour Print, Dunedin. No wmk. P* 13½
607c 20 c. Type **215** (Dec) . . . . 2·50 30
No. **MS**607 also includes the "CHINA '96" 9th Asian International Stamp Exhibition logo on the sheet margin.

216 Family, Globe and Burning Drugs

217 *Graphium sarpedon*

(Des CD Advertising. Litho Security Printers (M), Malaysia)

1996 (26 June). *International Day against Drug Abuse and Illicit Trafficking. T* **216** *and similar horiz designs. Multicoloured. W* 138 *(sideways). P* 14×14½.

608 30 c. Type **216** 25 35
a. Horiz pair. Nos. 608/9 . . . . 50 70
b. Perf 13½ . . . .
ba. Horiz pair. Nos. 608b/9b . . . .
609 30 c. Sporting activities 25 35
b. Perf 13½ . . . . . .
610 $1 Family and rainbow 60 80
608/10 . . . . *Set of* 3 1·00 1·40

Nos. 608/9 were printed together, *se-tenant*, in horizontal pairs throughout the sheet.

(Des P. Chuah. Litho Southern Colour Print, Dunedin)

1996 (27 Sept). *"ISTANBUL '96" International Stamp Exhibition. Butterflies. T* **217** *and similar vert designs. Multicoloured. P* 14½×14.

611 30 c. Type **217** 20 30
a. Booklet pane. Nos. 611/15×2 . . 2·00
612 30 c. *Terinos terpander* 20 30
613 30 c. *Melanocyma faunula* 20 30
614 30 c. *Trogonoptera brookiana* 20 30
615 30 c. *Delias hyparete* 20 30
611/15 . . . . *Set of* 5 90 1·40

Nos. 611/15 were only issued in $3 stamp booklets.

218 Kuala Lumpur Tower

219 C.A.P.A. Logo on Kite

(Des The Sharper Image ($2), Akitek Akiprima (others). Litho Southern Colour Print, Dunedin)

1996 (1 Oct). *Opening of Kuala Lumpur Telecommunications Tower. T* **218** *and similar multicoloured designs. P* 13½.

616 30 c. Type **218** 20 20
617 50 c. Diagram of top of tower 30 35
618 $1 Kuala Lumpur Tower at night . . 80 1·00
616/18 . . . . *Set of* 3 1·10 1·40
MS619 70×100 mm. $2 Top of Kuala Lumpur Tower *(different) (vert)* . . . . . . 1·25 1·75

(Des The Sharper Image. Litho Enschedé)

1996 (7 Oct). *14th Conference of the Confederation of Asian and Pacific Accountants. T* **219** *and similar horiz design. Multicoloured. P* 14×14½.

620 30 c. Type **219** 20 20
621 $1 Globe and C.A.P.A logo 60 70

(Litho Southern Colour Print, Dunedin)

1996 (16 Oct). *"TAIPEI '96" 10th Asian International Stamp Exhibition. As No.* **MS**619, *but with exhibition logo added to bottom right-hand corner of sheet. P* 13½.

MS622 70×100 mm. $2 Top of Kuala Lumpur Tower *(vert)* . . . . 1·25 1·75

220 Model of Atomic Structure

221 Slow Loris

(Des The Sharper Image. Litho Southern Colour Print, Dunedin)

1996 (29 Nov). *National Science Centre. T* **220** *and similar horiz designs. Multicoloured. P* 13½.

623 30 c. Type **220** 20 20
624 50 c. Planetary model and Science Centre 30 35
625 $1 National Science Centre 70 80
623/5 . . . . *Set of* 3 1·10 1·25

(Des Teh Yew Kiang. Litho Southern Colour Print, Dunedin)

1996 (2 Dec). *Stamp Week. Wildlife. Sheet* 165×75 *mm containing T* **221** *and similar multicoloured designs. P* 14.

MS626 20 c. Type **221**; 30 c. Prevost's Squirrel; 50 c. Atlas Moth; $1 Rhinoceros Hornbill (60×30 *mm*); $1 White-handed Gibbon (30×60 *mm*); $2 Banded Palm Civet (60×30 *mm*) . . . . 2·75 3·50

222 Running

223 Pygmy Blue Flycatcher

(Des CD Advertising. Litho Southern Colour Print, Dunedin)

1996 (19 Dec). *16th Commonwealth Games, Kuala Lumpur* (1998) *(3rd issue). T* **222** *and similar horiz designs. Multicoloured. P* 12.

627 30 c. Type **222** 20 20
a. Vert pair. Nos. 627/8 . . . . 40 60
628 30 c. Hurdling 20 30
629 50 c. High jumping 30 40
a. Vert pair. Nos. 629/30 . . . . 60 80
630 50 c. Javelin 30 40
627/30 . . . . *Set of* 4 90 1·25

Nos. 627/8 and 629/30 were each printed together, *se-tenant*, in sheets of 20 (5×4) with the first design in rows 1 and 3 and the second in rows 2 and 4. As there are horizontal gutters between rows 1 and 2 and 3 and 4, Nos. 627a and 629a only occur from rows 2 and 3.

(Des P. Chuah. Litho Enschedé)

1997 (4 Jan). *Highland Birds. T* **233** *and similar vert designs. Multicoloured. P* 13½×14.

631 20 c. Type **223** 20 10
632 30 c. Silver-eared Mesia 25 20
633 50 c. Black-sided Flower-pecker 30 35
634 $1 Scarlet Sunbird 60 70
631/4 . . . . *Set of* 4 1·25 1·25

(Litho Southern Colour Print, Dunedin)

1997 (12 Feb). *"HONG KONG '97" International Stamp Exhibition. As No.* **MS**626, *but with exhibition logo added to top sheet margin. P* 14.

MS635 165×75 mm. 20 c. Type **221**; 30 c. Tree Squirrel; 50 c. *Attacus atlas* (butterfly); $1 Rhinoceros Hornbill (60×30 *mm*); $1 Common Gibbon (30×60 *mm*); $2 Banded Palm Civet (60×30 *mm*) . . . . 2·75 3·50

224 Transit Train leaving Station

225 Bowler

(Des The Sharper Image. Litho Southern Colour Print, Dunedin)

1997 (1 Mar). *Light Rail Transit System. T* **224** *and similar horiz design. Multicoloured. P* 14×14½.

636 30 c. Type **224** 20 20
a. Booklet pane. Nos. 636/7 each × 5 . . 1·60
637 30 c. Trains in central Kuala Lumpur . . 20 20

Nos. 636/7 were only issued in $3 stamp booklets

(Des P. Chuah. Litho Security Printers (M), Malaysia)

1997 (24 Mar). *International Cricket Council Trophy, Kuala Lumpur. T* **225** *and similar vert designs. Multicoloured. W* **138**. *P* 13½ *($1) or* 14½ *(others)*.

638 30 c. Type **225** 20 15
639 50 c. Batsman 30 30
a. Perf 13½ . . . . 4·50
640 $1 Wicket keeper 60 65
a. Perf 14½ . . . . 9·00
638/40 . . . . *Set of* 3 1·00 1·00

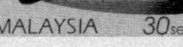

226 Boeing 747-400 over World Map

227 *Schima wallichii*

(Des The Sharper Image. Litho Security Printers (M), Malaysia)

1997 (2 Apr). *50th Anniv of Aviation in Malaysia. T* **226** *and similar horiz designs. Multicoloured. W* **138** *(sideways*). P* 13½ *(30 c.) or* 14½ *(others)*.

641 30 c. Type **226** 20 15
a. Perf 14½ . . . . 1·00
aw. Wmk top of letters to right . . . . 5·00
642 50 c. Boeing 747-400 over Kuala Lumpur 30 30
a. Perf 13½ . . . . 3·00
643 $1 Tail fins of four airliners 60 65
641/3 . . . . *Set of* 3 1·00 1·00

*The normal sideways watermark shows the top of the letters to left, *as seen from the back of the stamp.*

(Des The Sharper Image. Litho Southern Colour Print, Dunedin)

1997 (7 May). *Highland Flowers. T* **227** *and similar vert designs. Multicoloured. P* 14½×14.

644 30 c. Type **227** 20 20
a. Booklet pane. Nos. 644/8 each × 2 . . 1·60
645 30 c. *Aeschynanthus longicalyx* 20 20
646 30 c. *Aeschynanthus speciosa* 20 20
647 30 c. *Phyllagathis tuberculata* 20 20
648 30 c. *Didymocarpus quinquevulnerus* . . 20 20
644/8 . . . . *Set of* 5 90 90

Nos. 644/8 were only issued in $3 stamp booklets showing the outer edges of the pane imperforate.

228 World Youth Football Championship Logo

229 Members of First Conference, 1897

(Litho Harrison (30 c., 50 c.), Security Printers (M), Malaysia ($1))

1997 (16 June). *9th World Youth Football Championship, Malaysia. T* **228** *and similar vert designs. Multicoloured. W* **138** *(sideways) ($1) or no watermark (others). P* 12½ *($1) or* 13½×13 *(others)*.

649 30 c. Type **228** 15 10
650 50 c. Football and players 25 25
651 $1 Map of Malaysia and football . . 50 55
649/51 . . . . *Set of* 3 80 80

(Des R. Zahabuddin. Litho Southern Colour Print, Dunedin)

1997 (31 July). *Centenary of Rulers' Conference. T* **229** *and similar horiz designs. Multicoloured. P* 14.

652 30 c. Type **229** 15 10
653 50 c. State emblems 25 25
654 $1 Seal and press 50 55
652/4 . . . . *Set of* 3 80 80

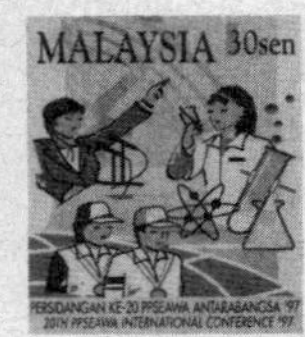

230 *Tubastrea* sp.

231 Women Athletes, Scientist and Politician

(Des The Sharper Image. Litho Southern Colour Print, Dunedin)

1997 (23 Aug). *International Year of the Coral Reefs. T* **230** *and similar multicoloured designs. P* 14½.

655 20 c. Type **230** 10 10
656 30 c. *Melithaea* sp. 10 10
657 50 c. *Aulostomus chinensis* 15 20
658 $1 *Symphillia* sp. 30 35
655/8 . . . . *Set of* 4 60 70
MS659 70×100 mm. $2 Green Turtle *(horiz)* . . 60 65

(Des Eka IPR Agensi. Litho Enschedé)

1997 (25 Aug). *20th International Pan-Pacific and Southeast Asia Women's Association Conference, Kuala Lumpur. T* **231** *and similar vert design. Multicoloured. P* 13×13½.

660 30 c. Type **231** 10 10
a. Booklet pane. Nos. 660/1, each × 5, with margins all round 95
661 30 c. Family and house 10 10

Nos. 660/1 were only available from $3 stamp booklets.

232 Kundang

233 Group of 15 Emblem

(Des Eka IPR Agensi. Litho Southern Colour Print, Dunedin)

1997 (9 Sept). *Fruit. T* **232** *and similar vert designs. Multicoloured. P* 13½.

662 20 c. Type **232** 10 10
663 30 c. Sentul 10 10
664 50 c. Pulasan 15 20
665 $1 Asam Gelugur 60 65
662/5 . . . . *Set of* 4 60 70

(Des P. Khang. Litho Security Printers (M), Malaysia)

1997 (3 Nov). *7th Summit Conference of the Group of* 15. *T* **233** *and similar vert design. Multicoloured. P* 12 (30 *c.*) *or* 13½ ($1).

666	30 c. Type **233**	10	10
667	$1 Flags of member countries	60	65

234 Hockey

(Des CD Advertising. Litho Southern Colour Print, Dunedin)

1997 (15 Nov). *16th Commonwealth Games, Kuala Lumpur* (1998) (4*th issue*). *T* **234** *and similar horiz designs. Multicoloured. P* 12.

668	30 c. Type **234**	10	10
	a. Vert pair. Nos. 668/9	15	
669	30 c. Netball	10	10
670	50 c. Cricket	15	20
	a. Vert pair. Nos. 670/1	30	
671	50 c. Rugby	15	20
668/71	.. .. *Set of* 4	45	50

Nos. 668/9 and 670/1 were each printed together, *se-tenant*, in sheets of 20 (5×4) with the first design in rows 1 and 3 and the second in rows 2 and 4. As there are horizontal gutters between rows 1 and 2 and 3 and 4, Nos 668a and 670a only occur from rows 2 and 3.

235 1867 12 c. on 4 anna with Malacca Postmark

1997 (15 Dec). *"Malpex '97" Stamp Exhibition, Kuala Lumpur. 50th Anniv of Organised Philately. Sheet,* 120×70 *mm, containing T* **235** *and similar diamond-shaped designs. Multicoloured. Litho. P* 12½.

MS672 20 c. Type **235**; 30 c. 1997 Highland Birds set; 50 c. 1996 Wildlife seen through magnifying glass; $1 1867 cover to Amoy .. 60 65

236 False Malayan Gharial

(Des Teh Yew Kiang. Litho Southern Colour Print, Dunedin)

1997 (17 Dec). *Stamp Week '97. Endangered Wildlife. Sheet,* 165×75 *mm, containing T* **236** *and similar multicoloured designs. P* 14½.

MS673 20 c. Type **236**; 30 c. Western Malaysian Tarsier (*vert*); 50 c. Indian Sambar (*vert*); $2 Crested Wood Partridge $2 Malayan Bony-tongue (fish) .. .. 1·60 1·75

STAMP BOOKLETS

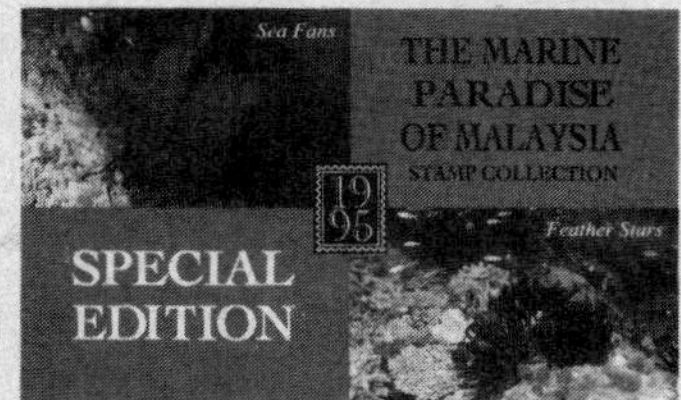

B **1** Seafans and Feather Stars

1995 (10 Apr). *Marine Life (5th series). Corals. Multicoloured covers as Type* B **1**. *Stamps attached by selvedge.*

SB1	$2 booklet containing pane of 10 20 c. stamps (No. 559a) (cover showing Type B 1)	2·75
SB2	$3 booklet containing pane of 10 30 c. stamps (No. 561a) (cover showing Cup Coral and Soft Coral)	3·00

B **2** Turtle swimming Underwater

1995 (26 Sept). *Turtles. Multicoloured cover as Type* B **2**. *Stamps attached by selvedge.*

SB3	$3 booklet containing pane of ten 30 c. stamps (No. 577a)	2·75

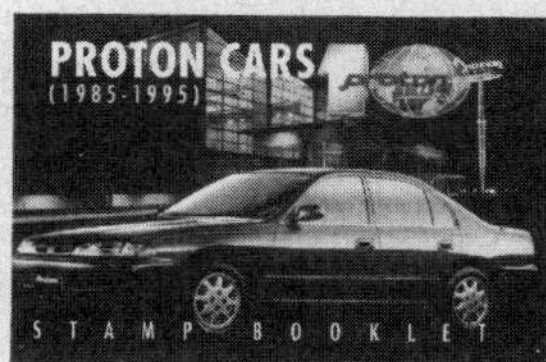

B **3** Proton Saloon Car and Factory

1995 (23 Dec). *10th Anniv of Proton Cars. Multicoloured cover as Type* B **3**. *Stamps attached by selvedge.*

SB4	$3 booklet containing pane of ten 30 c. stamps (No. 585a)	1·75

B **4** *Pachliopta aristolochiae*

1996 (27 Feb). *"ISTANBUL '96" International Stamp Exhibition. Butterflies. Multicoloured cover as Type* B **4**. *Stamps attached by selvedge.*

SB5	$3 booklet containing pane of ten 30 c. stamps (No. 611a)	2·00

B **5** Train leaving Station

1997 (1 Mar). *Light Railway Transit System. Multicoloured cover as Type* B **5**. *Stamps attached by selvedge.*

SB6	$3 booklet containing pane of ten 30 c. stamps (No. 636a)	1·60

B **6** Flowers

1997 (7 May). *Highland Flowers. Multicoloured cover as Type* B **6**. *Stamps attached by selvedge.*

SB7	$3 booklet containing pane of ten 30 c. stamps (No. 644a)	1·60

B **7**

1997 (25 Aug). *20th International Pan-Pacific and Southeast Asia Women's Association Conference, Kuala Lumpur. Multicoloured cover as Type* B **7**. *Stamps attached by selvedge.*

SB8	$3 booklet containing pane of ten 30 c. stamps (No. 660a)	95

POSTAGE DUE STAMPS

Until 15 August 1966 the postage due stamps of MALAYAN POSTAL UNION were in use throughout MALAYSIA.

D 1

D 2

(Litho Harrison)

1966 (15 Aug)–**71**. *Ordinary paper. W* w **13** *(upright). P* 14½ × 14.

D1	D 1	1 c. rose	20	2·50
D2		2 c. indigo	25	2·50
D3		4 c. apple-green	85	3·50
D4		8 c. blue-green	1·25	10·00
		a. Chalk-surfaced paper. *Bright blue-green* (1.6.71)	3·50	10·00
D5		10 c. bright blue	60	2·50
		a. Chalk-surfaced paper (1.6.71)	3·50	10·00
D6		12 c. reddish violet	60	3·50
D7		20 c. red-brown	60	4·75
		a. Chalk-surfaced paper. *Brown-purple* (22.4.69)	2·75	11·00
D8		50 c. brownish bistre	1·25	8·00
		a. Chalk-surfaced paper. *Olive-bistre* (1.6.71)	3·50	12·00
D1/8		*Set of* 8	5·00	32·00

1972 (23 May). *Glazed paper. W* w **13** *(sideways). P* 14½ × 14.

D12	D 1	8 c. turquoise-green	5·00	13·00
D13		10 c. dull ultramarine	5·00	15·00
D15		20 c. pale chocolate	6·50	15·00
D16		50 c. pale olive-bistre	7·00	18·00
D12/16		*Set of* 4	20·00	55·00

1980–86. *No wmk. P* 14½×14.

D17	D 1	2 c. indigo	30	2·00
D18		8 c. blue-green	45	2·25
D19		10 c. dull ultramarine	45	2·00
D19*a*		12 c. reddish lilac (1986)	11·00	14·00
D20		20 c. pale chocolate	55	2·75
D21		50 c. pale olive-bistre	90	3·50
D17/21		*Set of* 6	12·00	24·00

(Des Kathy Wong. Litho Security Printers (M), Malaysia)

1986 (15 Sept). *P* 12×11½.

D22	D 2	5 c. cerise and rose-lilac	10	10
D23		10 c. brownish black & pale olive-grey	10	10
D24		20 c. dull vermilion and cinnamon	10	10
D25		50 c. dp turquoise-green & turq-bl	25	30
D26		$1 ultramarine and cobalt	50	55
D22/6		*Set of* 5	95	1·00

B. FEDERAL TERRITORY ISSUES

Kuala Lumpur, previously part of Selangor state, was established as a Federal Territory on 1 February 1974.

The following stamps were produced for use there, corresponding to the low value definitives provided for the states of the federation.

The island of Labuan, formerly part of Sabah, became the second Federal Territory on 16 April 1984, when Nos. K1/14 replaced the low value definitives of Sabah previously used there.

K 1 *Rafflesia hasseltii*

K 2 Coffee

(Des M. Yusof bin Mohammed; adapted Malaysian Advertising Services. Litho Asher and Co., Melbourne)

1979 (30 Apr). *Flowers. Horiz designs as Type* K **1**. *Multicoloured. W* **95** *(sideways). P* 15 × 14½.

K1	1 c. Type K 1	10	30
K2	2 c. *Pterocarpus indicus*	10	30
K3	5 c. *Lagerstroemia speciosa* (Type I)	10	30
K4	10 c. *Durio zibethinus*	10	10
K5	15 c. *Hibiscus rosa-sinensis*	20	10
	a. Vert pair, top stamp imperf		
K6	20 c. *Rhododendron scortechinii*	20	10
K7	25 c. *Etlingera elatior* (inscr "*Phaeomeria speciosa*")	40	10
K1/7	*Set of* 7	1·00	1·00

For higher values used in conjunction with this series see Nos. 190/7.

I

II

Two types of 5 c.:

Type I. "5" over "i" and "c" to right of "a" in "Malaysia" (Nos. K3 and K10).

Type II. "5" over "s" and "c" aligns on "a" of "Malaysia" (No. K10*a*).

1983–85.* *As Nos.* K3/7 *but without wmk.*

K10	5 c. *Lagerstroemia speciosa* (I) (turquoise-green background) (12.12.84)	9·50	4·00
K10*a*	5 c. *Lagerstroemia speciosa* (II) (turquoise-blue background) (17.12.84)	1·50	1·00
K11	10 c. *Durio zibethinus* (9.84)	35	50
K12	15 c. *Hibiscus rosa-sinensis* (5.11.83)	70	15
K13	20 c. *Rhododendron scortechinii* (blackish brown background) (1983)	14·00	1·25
K13*a*	20 c. *Rhododendron scortechinii* (bronze-green background) (13.11.83)	70	35
K14	25 c. *Etlingera elatior* (inscr "*Phaeomeria speciosa*") (1.85)	5·50	3·00

*There was no official release date for these stamps. Dates shown are the earliest recorded from postmarks and may be revised if earlier examples are reported.

The 10 c., 15 c. and 20 c. (No. K13*a*) are also from redrawn plates and show the inscriptions or the face value in slightly different positions.

(Des Kathy Wong. Litho Security Printers (M), Malaysia)

1986 (25 Oct)–**95**. *Agricultural Products of Malaysia. Vert designs as Type* K **2**. *Multicoloured. W* **138**. *P* 12.

K15	1 c. Type K 2	10	10
K16	2 c. Coconuts	10	10
K17	5 c. Cocoa	10	10
	c. Perf 14×13¾ (1994)	3·25	50
	d. Perf 14		
	f. Perf 14¾×14½ (1995)	1·00	10
K18	10 c. Black Pepper	10	10
	aw. Wmk inverted (1995)		
	b. Perf 13½×13¾	16·00	1·50
	c. Perf 14×13¾ (1994)	3·25	50
	e. Perf 14×14½ (1994)	2·00	35
	f. Perf 14¾×14½ (1994)	2·00	35
K19	15 c. Rubber	10	10
	w. Wmk inverted	5·00	
K20	20 c. Oil palm	10	10
	aw. Wmk inverted	20·00	
	c. Perf 14×13¾ (1994)	1·00	10
	f. Perf 14¾×14½ (1994)	6·50	45
K21	30 c. Rice	15	20
	aw. Wmk inverted	6·50	
	b. Perf 13½×13¾ (1994)		
	c. Perf 14×13¾ (1994)	1·00	20
	d. Perf 14		
	e. Perf 14×14½		
	f. Perf 14¾×14½ (1994)	4·50	45
K15/21	*Set of* 7	50	55

For notes concerning perforation varieties see below Johore Nos. 202/8.

STAMP BOOKLETS

1979 (1 Dec). *Cover as No.* SB5 *of Johore, but inscr* "WILAYAH PERSEKUTUAN". *Stitched.*

KSB1	$3 booklet containing eight 5 c., 10 c., and twelve 15 c., (Nos. K3/5) in blocks of 4	6·50

No. KSB1 exists with two different versions of the back cover.

JABATAN PERKHIDMATAN POS
MALAYSIA
BUKU KECIL INI
MENGANDUNGI
5 SETEM HARGA 20 SEN SATU $1.00

KB 1

1983 (23 May). *Cover as Type* KB **1**. *Stamps attached by selvedge.*

KSB2	$1 booklet containing 20 c. (No. K6) in strip of 5	3·25

JABATAN PERKHIDMATAN POS, MALAYSIA
Buku Kecil ini berisi setem-setem yang berikut:
3 setem harga 20 sen
Harga Jualan – 60 sen

KB 2

1986. *Black on lemon covers as Type* KB **2**. *Stamps attached by selvedge.*

KSB3	60 c. booklet containing 20 c. (No. K13) in strip of 3	28·00
KSB4	$1.50, booklet containing 15 c. (No. K12) in pair and 20 c. (No. K13) in strip of 6	50·00

1987 (1 June). *Cover as Type* B **2** *of Johore, but inscr* "WILAYAH PERSEKUTUAN". *Stapled.*

KSB5	$2 booklet containing 5 c., 10 c., 15 c. and 20 c. (Nos. K17/20), each in block of 4	6·00

1988. *Black on rose cover as Type* B **2**. *Stamps attached by selvedge.*

KSB6	60 c. booklet containing 20 c. (No. K20) in strip of 3	20·00

1992 (1 July). *"Kuala Lumpur '92" International Philatelic Exhibition. Cover as Type* B **3** *of Johore, but inscr* "Wilayah Persekutuan". *Stamps attached by selvedge.*

KSB7	$3 booklet containing 30 c. (No. K21) in block of 10	5·50

1993 (June). *Multicoloured on pale buff covers as Nos.* SB8/9 *of Johore, but inscr* "Wilayah Persekutuan". *Stamps attached by selvedge.*

KSB8	$2 booklet containing 20 c. (No. K20) in block of 10	1·00
KSB9	$3 booklet containing 30 c. (No. K21) in block of 10	1·50

1996. *Black on buff cover as Type* B **2**. *Stamps attached by selvedge.*

KSB10	60 c. booklet containing 10 c. (No. K18) in strip of 3 and 15 c. (No. K19) in pair	

VII. MALAYSIAN STATES

PRINTERS. All Malaysian States stamps were printed in typography by De La Rue and Co, Ltd, London, *unless otherwise stated.*

JOHORE

A British adviser was appointed to Johore in 1914. The state joined the Federation of Malaya on 1 February 1948.

Until 1 January 1899 mail for addresses outside Malaya had the external postage paid by stamps of the STRAITS SETTLEMENTS.

PRICES FOR STAMPS ON COVER TO 1945

Nos. 1/2	—
Nos. 3/5	*from* × 15
No. 6	*from* × 20
Nos. 7/8	—
Nos. 9/15	*from* × 25
No. 16	—
Nos. 17/20	*from* × 15
Nos. 21/31	*from* × 10
Nos. 32/8	*from* × 15
Nos. 39/53	*from* × 8
Nos. 54/60	*from* × 6
Nos. 61/74	*from* × 8
Nos. 75/7	—
Nos. 78/87	*from* × 8
No. 88	*from* × 10
Nos. 89/102	*from* × 6
Nos. 103/25	*from* × 5
Nos. 126/8	—
Nos. 129/30	*from* × 6
Nos. D1/5	*from* × 6

(1)

1876 (July). *No. 11 of Straits Settlements handstamped with T 1.*
1 2 c. brown £8500 £3500
No. 1 is known with the handstamp double.

From September 1878 to August 1884 no overprinted stamps were supplied by Singapore to Johore.

JOHORE (2)

JOHORE (3) ("H" and "E" wide. "J" raised. Opt 16 mm long) — JOHORE (4) ("H" wide, "E" narrow. Opt 16 mm long) — JOHORE (5) ("H" and "E" wide. Opt $16^{3}/_{4}$ mm long)

JOHORE. (6) — JOHORE (7) — JOHORE (8)

1884 (June)–**86**. *No. 63 of Straits Settlements optd with T 2/8.*
2 **2** 2 c. pale rose £3250
3 **3** 2 c. pale rose (8.84) £850 £375
a. Opt double £2000
4 **4** 2 c. pale rose (8.84) £1000 £425
a. Opt double .. .. ..
5 **5** 2 c. pale rose (8.84) £850 £375
a. Opt double .. .. .. — £1200
6 **6** 2 c. pale rose (3.85) £110 £120
a. Opt double .. .. ..
7 **7** 2 c. pale rose (1885) £1900
8 **8** 2 c. pale rose (4.86) .. .. .. 55·00 70·00
Nos. 3 to 7 were from triplet settings, either 3+4+5 or three examples of the same overprint. Nos. 2 and 8 are probably single unit handstamps.

JOHOR (9) (All letters narrow) — JOHOR (10) — JOHOR (11) ("H" wide)

JOHOR (12) — JOHOR (13) — JOHOR. (14)

JOHOR (15) — JOHOR (16)

1884 (Aug)–**91**. *Nos. 63/a of Straits Settlements optd with T 9/16.*
9 **9** 2 c. pale rose .. .. 6·50 11·00
a. Opt double £650
10 **10** 2 c. pale rose (10.84) .. .. .. 4·75 4·50
a. Thin, narrow "J" (R. 6/6) .. .. 80·00 80·00
b. Opt double £650
c. Bright rose (1890) .. .. .. 10·00 12·00
ca. Thin, narrow "J" (R. 6/6) £150 £160
cb. Opt double £750
11 **11** 2 c. pale rose (2.85) .. .. .. 60·00 60·00
12 **12** 2 c. pale rose (1886) .. .. .. 38·00 38·00
a. Opt double £700
13 **13** 2 c. pale rose (1886) .. .. .. 28·00 28·00
14 **14** 2 c. pale rose (1888) .. .. .. 80·00 40·00
a. Thin, narrow "J" £400 £275
b. Opt double £600
15 **15** 2 c. bright rose (9.90) .. .. .. 10·00 9·00
16 **16** 2 c. bright rose (1891) £6500
Settings:
No. 9 — various triplets with the length of the overprint varying from 12 to 15 mm
No. 10 — triplet or 60 (6×10)
No. 11 — triplet 11 + 9 + 9
No. 12 — triplet
No. 13 — triplet
No. 14 — 30 (3×10)
No. 15 — 60 (6×10)
No. 16 — not known. As no used examples are known it is possible that this stamp was not issued.

JOHOR *Two* CENTS (17) — JOHOR *Two* CENTS (18)

JOHOR Two CENTS (19) — JOHOR Two CENTS (20)

1891 (May). *No. 68 of Straits Settlements surch as T 17/20.*
17 **17** 2 c. on 24 c. green .. .. .. 23·00 35·00
a. "CENST" (R. 5/4) £600 £375
18 **18** 2 c. on 24 c. green .. .. .. 95·00 95·00
a. Thin, narrow "J" (R. 6/6) £275 £275
19 **19** 2 c. on 24 c. green .. .. .. 32·00 48·00
20 **20** 2 c. on 24 c. green .. .. .. 90·00 90·00
Nos. 17/20 come from the same setting of 60. Type **17** occurs on horizontal rows 1 to 5, Type **18** on row 6, Type **19** on rows 7, 8 and 9 and Type **20** on row 10.

21 Sultan Aboubakar

3 cents. (22)

KEMAHKOTAAN (23)

1891 (16 Nov)–**94**. *No wmk. P 14.*
21 **21** 1 c. dull purple and mauve (7.94) .. 30 50
22 2 c. dull purple and yellow .. .. 30 1·50
23 3 c. dull purple and carmine (7.94) .. 55 50
24 4 c. dull purple and black .. .. 2·75 10·00
25 5 c. dull purple and green .. .. 7·00 20·00
26 6 c. dull purple and blue .. .. 8·00 20·00
27 $1 green and carmine .. .. 50·00 £110
21/7 .. .. .. *Set of* 7 60·00 £140

1894 (Mar). *Surch with T 22.*
28 **21** 3 c. on 4 c. dull purple and black .. 1·50 50
a. No stop (R. 5/11) .. .. 45·00 45·00
29 3 c. on 5 c. dull purple and green .. 80 2·00
a. No stop (R. 5/11) .. .. 60·00 75·00
30 3 c. on 6 c. dull purple and blue .. 1·75 2·00
a. No stop (R. 5/11) .. .. 85·00 90·00
31 3 c. on $1 green and carmine .. 10·00 45·00
a. No stop (R. 5/11) £225 £400
28/31 .. .. .. *Set of* 4 12·50 45·00
Examples of the 3 c. on 5 c. exist with the surcharge spaced $3^{1}/_{2}$ mm from the bar instead of $7^{1}/_{2}$ mm.

1896 (Mar). *Coronation of Sultan Ibrahim. Optd with T 23.*
32 **21** 1 c. dull purple and mauve 45 85
a. "KETAHKOTAAN" .. .. 3·00 5·00
33 2 c. dull purple and yellow .. .. 45 1·00
a. "KETAHKOTAAN" .. .. 2·75 5·50
34 3 c. dull purple and carmine .. .. 55 1·00
a. "KETAHKOTAAN" .. .. 6·00 7·50
35 4 c. dull purple and black .. .. 80 2·25
a. "KETAHKOTAAN" .. .. 2·75 7·00
36 5 c. dull purple and green .. .. 5·50 7·50
a. "KETAHKOTAAN" .. .. 3·25 7·50
37 6 c. dull purple and blue .. .. 3·50 6·00
a. "KETAHKOTAAN" .. .. 4·50 6·00
38 $1 green and carmine .. .. 40·00 85·00
a. "KETAHKOTAAN" .. .. 27·00 £110
32/8 .. .. .. *Set of* 7 45·00 95·00
32a/8a .. .. .. *Set of* 7 45·00 £130
Stamps overprinted "KETAHKOTAAN" (= We mourn) come from the first overprinting. The overprint was subsequently changed to the intended "KEMAHKOTAAN" (= Coronation), but both were issued together some months after the Coronation of Sultan Ibrahim had taken place.

24 Sultan Ibrahim 25

26

27

1896 (26 Aug)–**99**. *W 27. P 14.*
39 **24** 1 c. green 70 45
40 2 c. green and blue 40 30
41 3 c. green and purple .. .. .. 2·50 1·25
a. Green and dull claret .. .. 2·50 1·25
42 4 c. green and carmine 50 50
43 4 c. yellow and red (1899) 75 65
44 5 c. green and brown .. .. .. 75 1·40
45 6 c. green and yellow .. .. .. 80 2·00
46 **25** 10 c. green and black (1898) .. .. 7·00 45·00
47 25 c. green and mauve (1898) .. .. 9·00 38·00
48 50 c. green and carmine (1898) .. .. 13·00 40·00
49 **24** $1 dull purple and green (1898) .. 26·00 65·00
50 **26** $2 dull purple and carmine (1898) .. 26·00 65·00
51 $3 dull purple and blue (1898) .. 28·00 90·00
52 $4 dull purple and brown (1898) .. 28·00 75·00
53 $5 dull purple and yellow (1898) .. 60·00 £110
39/53 .. .. .. *Set of* 15 £180 £475

3 cents. (28) — 10 cents. (29)

1903 (Apr). *Surch with T 28 or 29.*
54 **24** 3 c. on 4 c. yellow and red .. .. 50 1·10
a. Original value uncancelled .. .. 3·25 13·00
55 10 c. on 4 c. green and carmine .. .. 2·50 6·00
a. Tall "1" in "10" (R. 9/12) .. .. 60·00 90·00
b. Original value uncancelled .. .. 20·00 55·00
ba. As b, with tall "1" in "10" (R. 9/12) .. £750 £900
The bars on these stamps were ruled by hand with pen and ink.

50 Cents. (30) — One Dollar (31)

1903 (Oct). *Surch with T 30 or 31.*
56 **26** 50 c. on $3 dull purple and blue .. .. 25·00 75·00
57 $1 on $2 dull purple and carmine .. .. 55·00 £100
a. "e" of "One" inverted (R. 7/9) .. £1200

10 CENTS. (32)

1904. *Surch as T 32.*
58 **24** 10 c. on 4 c. yellow and red (Apr) .. 20·00 35·00
a. Surcharge double £6500
59 10 c. on 4 c. green and carmine (Aug) .. 9·00 35·00
60 **26** 50 c. on $5 dull purple and yellow (May) 65·00 £130
58/60 .. .. .. *Set of* 3 85·00 £180

33

34

35 Sultan Sir Ibrahim

1904 (Sept)–**10**. *W 27. Ordinary paper. P 14.*
61 **33** 1 c. dull purple and green .. .. 1·25 30
a. Chalk-surfaced paper (10.10) .. 2·50 3·25
62 2 c. dull purple and orange .. .. 1·50 2·50
a. Chalk-surfaced paper (10.10) .. 3·75 6·00
63 3 c. dull purple and olive-black .. .. 2·25 40
64 4 c. dull purple and carmine .. .. 7·50 2·50
65 5 c. dull purple and sage-green .. .. 80 2·75
66 **35** 8 c. dull purple and blue .. .. 3·00 7·00
67 **34** 10 c. dull purple and black .. .. 40·00 9·50
a. Chalk-surfaced paper (1910) .. 50·00 45·00
68 25 c. dull purple and green .. .. 5·00 24·00
69 50 c. dull purple and red .. .. 40·00 14·00
70 **33** $1 green and mauve .. .. 12·00 48·00
71 **35** $2 green and carmine .. .. 17·00 45·00
72 $3 green and blue .. .. 23·00 70·00
73 $4 green and brown .. .. 24·00 90·00
74 $5 green and orange .. .. 32·00 80·00
75 **34** $10 green and black .. .. 48·00 £130
76 $50 green and ultramarine £140 £200
77 $100 green and scarlet £275 £425
61/75 .. .. .. *Set of* 15 £225 £475

1910–19. *Wmk Mult Rosettes (vertical). Chalk-surfaced paper. P 14.*
78 **33** 1 c. dull purple and green (1912) .. 30 15
79 2 c. dull purple and orange (1912) .. 4·50 65
80 3 c. dull purple and olive-black (1912) .. 4·50 65
a. Wmk horizontal (1910) .. .. 10·00 15·00
81 4 c. dull purple and carmine (1912) .. 3·50 90
a. Wmk horizontal (1910) .. .. 20·00 35·00
82 5 c. dull purple and sage-green (1912) .. 2·25 80
83 **35** 8 c. dull purple and blue (1912) .. 4·00 5·00
84 **34** 10 c. dull purple and black (1912) .. 30·00 2·75
a. Wmk horizontal (1911) .. .. 23·00 48·00
85 25 c. dull purple and green (1912) .. 4·50 25·00
86 50 c. dull purple and red (1919) .. 45·00 85·00
87 **33** $1 green and mauve (1918) .. .. 65·00 75·00
78/87 .. .. .. *Set of* 10 £140 £170

(36) 37 Sultan Sir Ibrahim and Sultana

1912 (Mar). *No. 66 surch with T* **36**.
88 3 c. on 8 c. dull purple and blue .. .. 2·25 4·25
a. "T" of "CENTS" omitted £750
b. Bars double .. ..
No. 88b shows the bars printed twice with the upper pair partly erased.

1918–21. *Wmk Mult Crown CA. Chalk-surfaced paper. P* 14.
89 **33** 2 c. dull purple and green (1919) .. 40 80
90 2 c. purple and orange (1921) .. .. 50 2·25
91 4 c. dull purple and red 75 50
92 5 c. dull purple and sage-green (1920) 2·00 4·25
93 **34** 10 c. dull purple and blue .. .. 1·50 1·40
94 21 c. dull purple and orange (1919) .. 2·25 2·50
95 25 c. dull purple and green (1920) .. 8·00 17·00
96 50 c. dull purple and red (1920) .. 19·00 32·00
97 **33** $1 green and mauve .. .. 10·00 55·00
98 **35** $2 green and carmine .. .. 20·00 45·00
99 $3 green and blue .. .. .. 40·00 85·00
100 $4 green and brown .. .. .. 40·00 £100
101 $5 green and orange .. .. .. 60·00 £130
102 **34** $10 green and black £140 £250
89/102 .. .. *Set of* 14 £300 £650
89/102 Optd "Specimen" .. *Set of* 14 £325

1922–40. *Wmk Mult Script CA. Chalk-surfaced paper. P* 14.
103 **33** 1 c. dull purple and black 30 20
104 2 c. purple and sepia (1924) .. .. 85 2·50
105 2 c. green (1928) 40 40
106 3 c. green (1925) .. .. .. 1·50 4·00
107 3 c. purple and sepia (1928) .. .. 1·10 1·50
108 4 c. purple and carmine (1924) .. 2·50 20
109 5 c. dull purple and sage-green .. 30 30
110 6 c. dull purple and claret 40 45
111 **34** 10 c. dull purple and blue .. .. 16·00 28·00
112 10 c. dull purple and yellow 30 25
113 **33** 12 c. dull purple and blue .. .. 1·00 1·25
114 12 c. ultramarine (1940) .. .. 30·00 6·00
115 **34** 21 c. dull purple and orange (1928) .. 2·00 3·00
116 25 c. dull purple and myrtle .. .. 1·75 1·00
117 **35** 30 c. dull purple and orange (1936) .. 4·25 4·00
118 40 c. dull purple and brown (1936) .. 4·25 4·50
119 **34** 50 c. dull purple and red .. .. 3·00 1·60
120 **33** $1 green and mauve .. .. .. 2·25 85
121 **35** $2 green and carmine (1923) .. .. 5·50 3·50
122 $3 green and blue (1925) .. .. 40·00 70·00
123 $4 green and brown (1926) .. .. 70·00 £140
124 $5 green and orange .. .. .. 48·00 48·00
125 **34** $10 green and black (1924) £140 £250
126 $50 green and ultram (Optd S. £150) £550
127 $100 green and scarlet (Optd S. £250) £1200
128 **35** $500 blue and red (1926) (Optd S. £750) £16000
103/25 .. .. *Set of* 23 £325 £500
103/25 Optd/Perf "Specimen" .. *Set of* 23 £450

(Recess Waterlow)

1935 (15 May). *Wmk Mult Script CA (sideways). P* 12½.
129 **37** 8 c. bright violet and slate .. .. 2·50 50
129 Perf "Specimen" .. .. .. 40·00

38 Sultan Sir Ibrahim 39

(Recess D.L.R.)

1940 (Feb). *Wmk Mult Script CA. P* 13½.
130 **38** 8 c. black and pale blue .. .. .. 14·00 30
130 Perf "Specimen" .. .. 40·00

1948 (1 Dec). *Royal Silver Wedding. As Nos.* 143/4 *of Jamaica.*
131 10 c. violet 20 30
132 $5 green .. .. 24·00 35·00

1949 (2 May)–**55.** *Wmk Mult Script CA. Chalk-surfaced paper. P* 17½ × 18.
133 **39** 1 c. black 10 10
134 2 c. orange 10 10
a. Orange-yellow (22.1.52) 10 40
135 3 c. green 35 40
a. Yellow-green (22.1.52) .. .. 6·00 1·75
136 4 c. brown 10 10
136*a* 5 c. bright purple (1.9.52) 30 30
137 6 c. grey 20 10
a. Pale grey (22.1.52) 30 20
ac. Error. St. Edward's Crown W **9***b* .. £900
138 8 c. scarlet .. .. 1·75 90
138*a* 8 c. green (1.9.52) .. .. .. 2·50 1·50
139 10 c. magenta 30 10
aa. Imperf (pair) £1300
139*a* 12 c. scarlet (1.9.52) .. .. .. 2·25 2·75
140 15 c. ultramarine .. .. .. 1·50 10
141 20 c. black and green .. .. .. 45 1·00
141*a* 20 c. bright blue (1.9.52) 80 10
142 25 c. purple and orange 50 10
142*a* 30 c. scarlet and purple (5.9.55) .. 1·75 2·25
142*b* 35 c. scarlet and purple (1.9.52) .. 3·00 1·00
143 40 c. red and purple .. .. .. 2·50 7·00
144 50 c. black and blue 70 10
145 $1 blue and purple .. .. .. 3·50 1·50
146 $2 green and scarlet .. .. .. 14·00 3·50
147 $5 green and brown .. .. .. 40·00 9·00
133/47 .. .. *Set of* 21 70·00 27·00

1949 (10 Oct). *75th Anniv of U.P.U. As Nos.* 145/8 *of Jamaica.*
148 10 c. purple 30 15
149 15 c. deep blue .. .. 1·25 1·00
150 25 c. orange .. .. 65 1·75
151 50 c. blue-black .. .. 1·25 2·00
148/51 .. .. *Set of* 4 3·00 4·50

1953 (2 June). *Coronation. As No.* 153 *of Jamaica.*
152 10 c. black and reddish purple 50 10

40 Sultan Sir Ibrahim 41 Sultan Sir Ismail and Johore Coat of Arms

(Recess D.L.R.)

1955 (1 Nov). *Diamond Jubilee of Sultan. Wmk Mult Script CA. P* 14.
153 **40** 10 c. carmine-red 10 10

(Photo Courvoisier)

1960 (10 Feb). *Coronation of Sultan. No wmk. P* 11½.
154 **41** 10 c. multicoloured 20 20

1960. *As T* **9**/**19** *of Kedah, but with portrait of Sultan Ismail. P* 13½ ($1); *others* 12½ × 13 (*vert*) *or* 13 × 12½ (*horiz*).
155 1 c. black (7.10.60) 10 30
156 2 c. orange-red (7.10.60) 10 30
157 4 c. sepia (19.8.60) 10 10
158 5 c. carmine-lake (7.10.60) 10 10
159 8 c. myrtle-green (9.12.60) .. .. .. 1·50 2·25
160 10 c. deep maroon (10.6.60) 30 10
161 20 c. blue (9.12.60) 60 10
162 50 c. black and bright blue (19.8.60) .. 20 10
163 $1 ultramarine and reddish purple (9.12.60) 1·25 1·50
164 $2 bronze-green and scarlet (9.12.60) .. 6·00 8·50
165 $5 brown and bronze-green (7.10.60) .. 22·00 23·00
155/65 .. .. *Set of* 11 28·00 32·00
In No. 161 there are only two figures in the boat, the steersman being missing. In the 20 c. value for all the other States there are three figures.
The 6, 12, 25 and 30 c. values used with this issue were Nos. 1/4 of Malayan Federation.

42 *Vanda hookeriana* (Inset portrait of Sultan Ismail)

(Des A. Fraser-Brunner. Photo Harrison)

1965 (15 Nov). *T* **42** *and similar horiz designs. W* w **13** (*upright*). *P* 14½.
166 1 c. Type **42** 10 30
a. Black (orchid's name and part of flower) omitted .. .. .. 75·00
w. Wmk inverted .. .. 1·75
167 2 c. *Arundina graminifolia* 10 35
168 5 c. *Paphiopedilum niveum* 10 10
b. Yellow (flower) omitted .. .. 22·00
169 6 c. *Spathoglottis plicata* 40 30
170 10 c. *Arachnis flos-aeris* 40 10
171 15 c. *Rhyncostylis retusa* .. .. .. 1·50 10
b. Green (face value and leaves) omitted £110
172 20 c. *Phalaenopsis violacea* .. .. .. 1·50 40
a. Bright purple (blooms) omitted .. 50·00
166/72 .. .. *Set of* 7 3·50 1·40
The 2 c. to 15 c. exist with both PVA gum and gum arabic.
The 2 c. with black (name of state, arms and head) omitted is listed under Sarawak No. 213a as there is some evidence that a sheet was issued there; if it also exists from any of the other states it would, of course, be identical.
The higher values used with this issue were Nos. 20/27 of Malaysia (National Issues).

1970. *As No.* 166 *and* 170 *but W* w **13** (*sideways*).
173 1 c. multicoloured (20.11) .. .. .. 75 3·00
174 10 c. multicoloured (27.5) .. .. .. 1·25 1·75

44 *Delias ninus* (Inset portrait of Sultan Ismail) 45 *Rafflesia hasseltii* (Inset portrait of Sultan Ismail)

(Des V. Whiteley)

1971 (1 Feb)–**78.** *Butterflies. T* **44** *and similar horiz designs. Multicoloured. No wmk. P* 13½ × 13.

(*a*) *Litho by Bradbury, Wilkinson*
175 1 c. Type **44** 20 80
176 2 c. *Danaus melanippus* 65 80
177 5 c. *Parthenos sylvia* 85 10
178 6 c. *Papilio demoleus* .. .. .. 85 1·10
179 10 c. *Hebomoia glaucippe* 85 10
180 15 c. *Precis orithya* 85 10
181 20 c. *Valeria valeria* 85 30
175/81 .. .. *Set of* 7 4·50 2·75

(*b*) *Photo Harrison* (1977–78)
182 1 c. Type **44** .. .. 1·25 2·50
183 2 c. *Danaus melanippus* .. .. .. 1·25 3·25
184 5 c. *Parthenos sylvia* .. .. .. 3·75 60
185 10 c. *Hebomoia glaucippe* .. .. .. 3·25 30
186 15 c. *Precis orithya* .. .. 3·75 25
187 20 c. *Valeria valeria* .. .. 4·25 1·00
182/7 .. .. *Set of* 6 16·00 7·00
The higher values used with this issue were Nos. 64/71 of Malaysia (National Issues).

DIFFERENCES BETWEEN LITHO AND PHOTO PRINTINGS. Stamps from the photogravure printings can be easily identified by the appearance of certain features. The differences are most easily observed on the face values and inscriptions. Stamps printed by lithography show straight edges to letters and figures, but when those produced by photogravure are examined under a magnifying glass it will be seen that these edges are broken by the photogravure screen.
In addition the backgrounds and portraits of those stamps of this series printed by lithography show a regular screen of dots, a feature not visible on those printed by the photogravure process.
A number of instances have come to light of photogravure stamps which have had the top colour "removed" by means of an eraser.

(Des M. Yusof bin Mohammed; adapted Malaysian Advertising Services. Litho Asher and Co., Melbourne)

1979 (30 Apr). *Flowers. Horiz designs as T* **45**. *Multicoloured. W* **95** *of Malaysia* (*sideways*). *P* 15 × 14½.
188 1 c. Type **45** 10 40
189 2 c. *Pterocarpus indicus* 10 40
190 5 c. *Lagerstroemia speciosa* 10 10
191 10 c. *Durio zibethinus* 15 10
192 15 c. *Hibiscus rosa-sinensis* 15 10
193 20 c. *Rhododendron scortechinii* 20 10
194 25 c. *Etlingera elatior* (inscr "*Phaeomeria speciosa*") 40 10
188/94 .. .. *Set of* 7 1·00 90
For higher values used in conjunction with this series see Nos. 190/7 of Malaysia.

1983 (16 June)–**85.*** *As Nos.* 190/3 *but without wmk.*
197 5 c. *Lagerstroemia speciosa* (20.11.83) .. 80 90
198 10 c. *Durio zibethinus* (11.7.85) 80 90
199 15 c. *Hibiscus rosa-sinensis* (12.83) .. 75 20
200 20 c. *Rhododendron scortechinii* (blackish brown background) .. .. .. 8·50 1·00
200*a* 20 c. *Rhododendron scortechinii* (bronze-green background) (23.9.83) .. .. 1·00 55
*There was no official release date for these stamps. Dates shown are the earliest recorded from postmarks and may be revised if earlier examples are reported.
On Nos. 197/9 and 200a the "Johor" inscription is in rounded instead of square-ended letters.

WATERMARKED AND UNWATERMARKED PRINTINGS. The first printing of the 20 c, value on unwatermarked paper was from the same plates and in the same shades as the original watermarked issue.
Subsequent no watermark printings of the 20 c. and all no watermark printings of the other values were in changed shades and can be readily identified as follows:
5 c. No watermark printing has the frame in turquoise-blue instead of the dull blue of the watermarked version.
10 c. No watermark printing shows a purple-brown background instead of the sepia of the watermarked.
15 c. No watermark printing shows stronger highlights in the design and more detail on the flowers and leaves.
20 c. Later no watermark printings have a bronze-green background instead of the blackish brown shown on the watermarked and first no watermark stamps.
25 c. No watermark printing has a deep background with more detail on the flower. The latin inscription has also been moved downwards to a more central position up the side of the vignette.
Differences also occur in the plates used to apply the state names, rulers' portraits or crests. Notes on these are provided under the individual issues.

46 Coconuts (Inset portrait of Sultan Mahmood)

(Des Kathy Wong. Litho Security Printers (M), Malaysia)

1986 (25 Oct)–**95.** *Agricultural Products of Malaysia. Vert designs as T* **46**. *Multicoloured. W* **138**. *Phosphorised paper. P* 12.
202 1 c. Type **46** 10 10
w. Wmk inverted .. ..
203 2 c. Coconuts 10 10
204 5 c. Cocoa 10 10
aw. Wmk inverted .. ..
c. Perf 14×13¾ (1994) .. .. .. 3·25 30
d. Perf 14 .. ..
f. Perf 14¾×14½ (1995) .. .. .. 1·00 10
205 10 c. Black pepper 10 10
a. Imperf (pair) £160
c. Perf 14×13¾ (1994) .. .. .. 3·25 30
d. Perf 14 .. ..
206 15 c. Rubber 10 10
207 20 c. Oil palm 10 10
c. Perf 14×13¾ (1994) .. .. .. 6·50 30
f. Perf 14¾×14½ (1994) .. .. .. 1·00 10
208 30 c. Rice 15 20
c. Perf 14×13¾ (1994) .. .. .. 3·00 30
cw. Wmk inverted (1995) .. .. .. 12·00
d. Perf 14 .. ..
f. Perf 14¾×14½ (1994) .. .. .. 13·00 1·25
202/8 .. .. *Set of* 7 50 55

PERFORATION VARIETIES. Delays in the production of new definitives to replace the Agricultural Products issue led to an extended series of new printings as the postal authorities in the various states indented, on an annual basis, for fresh stocks of those values which were running short. These annual indents were identified by the plate numbers used so that 1A = 1986, 2A = 1987 etc.

Many of these printings show different perforations from the gauge 12 of the original set. Those perforations known to us have been listed. The order of listing may not show the chronological sequence parts of which remain unclear. Other perforations may well exist on these stamps.

To assist identification the perforations are quoted to the nearest ¼. The exact decimal equivalents are as follows:

13½×13¾ = 13.5×13.75 (used 1991–1993)
14×13¾ = 14.1×13.75 (used 1993–1996)
14 = 14.1×14.1
14×14½ = 14.1×14.4 (used 1994–1996)
14¾×14½ = 14.75×14.4 (used 1994–1996)

STAMP BOOKLETS

1928. *Black on white card. Interleaved with tissue. Stapled.*
SB1 $2 booklet containing ten 1 c. and 2 c. (Nos. 103, 105), twenty 4 c. (No. 108), each in blocks of 10 and eighteen 5 c. (No. 109) in blocks of 6 . .

1929. *Black on pink cover. Stapled.*
SB2 $1 booklet containing 2 c., 3 c. and 5 c. (Nos. 105, 107, 109) in blocks of 10 . . . . . .

1930. *Black on buff cover. Stapled.*
SB3 $1 booklet containing ten 1 c. and 5 c. (Nos. 103, 109) and twenty 2 c. (Nos. 105) in blocks of 10

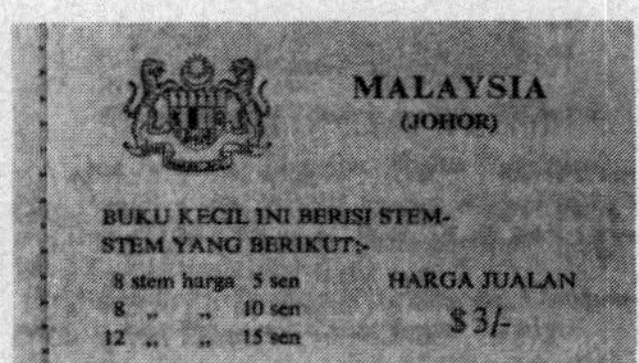

B 1

1973 (8 Dec). *Black on light magenta cover as Type* B **1**. *Stitched.*
SB4 $3 booklet containing eight 5 c., 10 c. and twelve 15 c. (Nos. 177, 179/80) in blocks of 4 . . 18·00

1979 (1 Dec). *Black on pink cover as Type* B **1**, *but* 80×50 *mm.*
SB5 $3 booklet containing eight 5 c., 10 c. and twelve 15 c. (Nos. 190/2) in blocks of 4 . . 7·00

No. SB5 exists with two different versions of the back cover.

B 2 Produce

1987 (1 June). *Black on orange-yellow cover as Type* B **2**. *Stapled.*
SB6 $2 booklet containing 5 c., 10 c., 15 c. and 20 c. (Nos. 204/7) in blocks of 4 . . . . . . 5·00

B 3 Sultan Abdul Samad Building, Kuala Lumpur

1992 (1 July). *"Kuala Lumpur '92" International Philatelic Exhibition. Multicoloured cover as Type* B **3**. *Stamps attached by selvedge.*
SB7 $3 booklet containing 30 c. (No. 208) in block of 10 5·50

1993. *Multicoloured on pale green (No. SB8) or on pale buff (No. SB9) covers as Type* B **3**, *but with face values and "Kuala Lumpur" logo replaced by postal service emblem and face value, both at bottom right. Stamps attached by selvedge.*
SB8 $2 booklet containing 20 c. (No. 207) in block of 10 1·00
SB9 $3 booklet containing 30 c. (No. 208) in block of 10 1·50

POSTAGE DUE STAMPS

D 1

(Typo Waterlow)

1938 (1 Jan). *Wmk Mult Script CA. P* 12½.

D1	D 1	1 c. carmine	12·00	30·00
D2		4 c. green	40·00	38·00
D3		8 c. orange	48·00	£140
D4		10 c. brown	48·00	45·00
D5		12 c. purple	55·00	£110
D1/5		. . . . *Set of* 5	£180	£325
D1/5 Perf "Specimen"		. . . . *Set of* 5	£130	

KEDAH

Suzerainty over Kedah was transferred by Thailand to Great Britain on 15 July 1909. A Treaty of Friendship between Great Britain and Kedah was signed on 1 November 1923.

The state joined the Federation of Malaya on 1 February 1948.

For stamps of THAILAND used in Kedah between 1887 and 1909 see VIII. SIAMESE POSTS IN NORTHERN MALAYA section.

Issues of the FEDERATED MALAY STATES were used in Kedah from 16 July 1909 until 15 June 1912.

PRICES FOR STAMPS ON COVER TO 1945

Nos. 1/14	*from* × 15
Nos. 15/23	*from* × 10
Nos. 24/40	*from* × 8
Nos. 41/8	*from* × 12
Nos. 49/51	—
Nos. 52/9	*from* × 4
Nos. 60/8	*from* × 3
Nos. 68*a*/9	*from* × 4

1 Sheaf of Rice

2 Malay ploughing

3 Council Chamber, Alor Star

1912 (16 June). *Wmk Mult Crown CA (sideways* on 10 c. to $5). P 14.*

1 1 1 c. black and green 30 25
2 3 c. black and red .. .. .. 2·50 30
3 4 c. rose and grey .. .. .. 9·50 25
4 5 c. green and chestnut .. .. .. 2·25 3·00
5 8 c. black and ultramarine .. .. .. 2·25 3·50
6 2 10 c. blue and sepia .. .. .. 1·75 90
w. Wmk inverted .. .. .. † —
7 20 c. black and green .. .. .. 3·25 4·00
8 30 c. black and rose .. .. .. 2·25 10·00
9 40 c. black and purple .. .. .. 3·50 14·00
10 50 c. brown and blue .. .. .. 8·00 13·00
11 3 $1 black and red/*yellow* .. .. 12·00 18·00
w. Wmk Crown to left of CA .. .. 30·00
x. Wmk reversed .. .. ..
y. Wmk Crown to left of CA and reversed .. ..
12 $2 green and brown .. .. .. 16·00 75·00
13 $3 black and blue/*blue* .. .. 50·00 £140
a. "A" of "CA" missing from wmk .. £1000
14 $5 black and red .. .. .. 50·00 £120
1/14 .. .. .. *Set of* 14 £140 £350
1/14 Optd "Specimen" .. .. *Set of* 14 £275

*The normal sideways watermark shows the Crown to right of CA, *as seen from the back of the stamp.*

Due to an increase in postal rates 1 c. and 4 c. stamps of STRAITS SETTLEMENTS were used in Kedah for some months from March 1919.

(i)

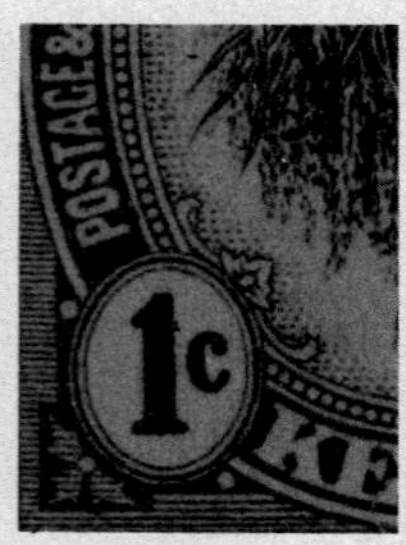
(ii)

DOUBLE AND SINGLE PLATES. (i) Printed from separate plates for frame and centre, with dotted shading extending close to the central sheaf. Soft impression of centre with little clear detail.

(ii) Printed from single plate, with white space around sheaf. Centre more deeply etched with sharp image.

1919 (June)–**21**. *New colours and values. Wmk Mult Crown CA (sideways* on 21 c., 25 c.). P 14.*

15 1 1 c. brown (i) (18.8.19) 55 45
w. Wmk inverted .. .. .. 60·00
y. Wmk inverted and reversed .. .. † £150
18 2 c. green (ii) 50 20
19 3 c. deep purple (i) (1920) 65 70
y. Wmk inverted and reversed .. 50·00 75·00
20 1 4 c. rose (i) .. .. .. 1·50 20
21 4 c. red (ii) (18.8.19) .. .. .. 3·25 30
w. Wmk inverted .. .. ..
22 2 21 c. mauve and purple (18.8.19) .. 5·50 48·00
w. Wmk Crown to left of CA .. .. 85·00
23 25 c. blue and purple (1921) .. .. 1·75 21·00
a. "A" of "CA" missing from wmk .. £275
15/23 .. .. .. *Set of* 6 9·50 65·00
15/23 Optd "Specimen" .. .. *Set of* 6 £140

*The normal sideways watermark shows Crown to right of CA, *as seen from the back of the stamp.*

ONE DOLLAR (4)

MALAYA-BORNEO EXHIBITION. (5)

(Surch by Ribeiro & Co, Penang)

1919 (Mar). *Surch as T* **4**.

24 3 50 c. on $2 green and brown .. .. 50·00 65·00
a. "C" of "CENTS" inserted by hand-stamp (R. 6/4) £1000 £1100
25 $1 on $3 black and blue/*blue* .. .. 20·00 85·00

Nos. 24/5 were surcharged from settings of 30 (5×6).

Two types of centre plate for Type **2** wmkd Mult Script CA:

Type I (Plate 1) (produced by electrotyping)

Type II (Plate 2) (produced by transfer die)

A new common centre plate, 2, was prepared from the original die in 1926. Stamps from Plate 2, produced using a transfer die, show considerably more detail of the ground and have the oxen, ploughman's hat and his clothing much more deeply cut as illustrated in Type II above.

1921–32. *Wmk Mult Script CA (sideways* on 10 c. to $5). P 14.*

26 1 1 c. brown (ii) 40 20
w. Wmk inverted .. .. .. † £150
y. Wmk inverted and reversed .. .. † £150
27 2 c. dull green (ii) (Type I) 75 20
28 3 c. deep purple (ii) 80 70
29 4 c. deep carmine (ii) .. .. .. 5·00 20
30 2 10 c. blue and sepia (I) .. .. .. 2·25 75
ay. Wmk Crown to left of CA and reversed .. .. .. 50·00
b. Type II (*wmk Crown to left of CA*) (1927) .. .. .. 25·00 3·25
31 20 c. black and yellow-green (I) .. .. 3·00 2·00
32 21 c. mauve and purple (I) .. .. 2·00 13·00
33 25 c. blue and purple (I) .. .. .. 2·25 5·50
a. Type II (*wmk Crown to left of CA*) (1932) .. .. .. 38·00 4·00
34 30 c. black and rose (I) (1922) .. .. 3·00 6·00
a. Type II (*wmk Crown to left of CA*) (1927) .. .. .. 26·00 3·00
35 40 c. black and purple (I) .. .. 3·50 35·00
aw. Wmk Crown to left of CA (1924) .. 20·00 27·00
b. Type II (*wmk Crown to left of CA*) (1932) .. .. .. 38·00 20·00
36 50 c. brown and grey-blue (I) .. .. 2·25 9·00
aw. Wmk Crown to left of CA (1924) .. 20·00 12·00
b. Type II (*wmk Crown to left of CA*) (1932) .. .. .. 48·00 4·50
37 3 $1 black and red/*yellow* (1924) .. 50·00 55·00
w. Wmk Crown to left of CA .. .. 6·50 7·50
38 $2 myrtle and brown .. .. .. 13·00 75·00
w. Wmk Crown to left of CA (1924) .. 13·00 75·00
39 $3 black and blue/*blue* .. .. 55·00 75·00
w. Wmk Crown to left of CA (1924) .. 42·00 55·00
40 $5 black and deep carmine .. .. 70·00 £130
w. Wmk Crown to left of CA (1926) .. 50·00 £100
26/40 .. .. .. *Set of* 15 £120 £250
26/40 Optd "Specimen" .. .. *Set of* 15 £275

*The normal sideways watermark shows Crown to right of CA, *as seen from the back of the stamp.*

Nos. 26/40 were produced by De La Rue using the "wet" method of recess-printing during which the stamps contracted when they were dried before gumming. From 1933 the firm adopted the "dry" method, using pre-gummed paper, with the result that stamps were up to 0.5 mm larger in size. Of the low values as Type **1** in this series only the 2 c. was still current when the "dry" method was introduced.

Stamps as Type **1** can be found perforated either comb or line. The 1 c. and 4 c. come comb only, the 3 c. line only and the 2 c. either way.

For the 2 c. Type II see No. 69.

1922 (Apr). *Malaya–Borneo Exhibition, Singapore. Optd as T* **5** *at Singapore.*

I. "BORNEO" 14 *mm. long*

(*a*) *Wmk Mult Crown CA*

41 1 2 c. green (ii) .. .. 3·50 18·00
42 2 21 c. mauve and purple (I) .. .. 24·00 70·00
43 25 c. blue and purple (I) .. .. 24·00 70·00
a. Overprint inverted £800
44 50 c. brown and grey-blue (I) .. .. 24·00 85·00

(*b*) *Wmk Mult Script CA*

45 1 1 c. brown (ii) .. .. 2·25 13·00
46 3 c. purple (ii) .. .. 3·00 35·00
47 4 c. deep carmine (ii) .. .. .. 3·00 25·00
48 2 10 c. blue and sepia (I) .. .. .. 4·50 32·00
41/8 .. .. .. *Set of* 8 80·00 £300

There are setting variations in the size and shape of the letters, stop raised, stop omitted, etc., etc.

II. "BORNEO" 15–15½ *mm long. Wmk Mult Crown CA*

49 2 21 c. mauve and purple (I) .. .. 18·00 90·00
50 25 c. blue and purple (I) .. .. 22·00 £100
51 50 c. brown and grey-blue (I) .. .. 45·00 £150
49/51 .. .. .. *Set of* 3 75·00 £300

1922–40. *New colours, etc. Wmk Mult Script CA (sideways* on 12, 35 c.). P 14.*

52 1 1 c. black (ii) (Type I) 30 10
53 3 c. green (ii) (1924) .. .. .. 1·50 90
54 4 c. violet (ii) (1926) 90 10
55 5 c. yellow (ii) .. .. 1·50 10
w. Wmk inverted .. .. .. 60·00
x. Wmk reversed .. .. .. † £120
y. Wmk inverted and reversed .. .. † £120
56 6 c. carmine (ii) (1926) 70 65
a. Carmine-red (1940) .. .. 22·00 48·00
57 8 c. grey-black (ii) (10.36) .. .. 9·00 10
58 2 12 c. black and indigo (II) (1926) .. 2·25 4·00
59 35 c. purple (II) (1926) .. .. .. 5·00 25·00
52/9 .. .. .. *Set of* 8 19·00 27·00
52/9 Optd/Perf "Specimen" .. *Set of* 8 £160

*The normal sideways watermark shows Crown to left of CA, *as seen from the back of the stamp.*

With the exception of the 6 c. and 8 c. the printing plates for the Type **1** values listed above were, as for the previous issue, produced by electrotyping with the face values added to the plates by pantograph. The plates for the 6 c. and 8 c. values were constructed by the more modern method of using a transfer die to enter each impression.

Printings after November 1933 were normally produced by the "dry" method as described beneath Nos. 26/40. There were late "wet" printings of the 1 c. (No. 68*a*) and 2 c. (No. 27) in August 1938. The 3 c. only exists from a "wet" printing, the 6 c. (No. 56*a*) and 8 c. from dry printings and the remainder from either method.

Stamps as Type **1** can be found perforated either comb or line. The 3 c. and 6 c. (No. 56) come comb only, the 6 c. (No. 56*a*) and 8 c. line only and the 1, 4 and 5 c. either way.

For the 1 c. Type II see No. 68*a*.

6 Sultan Abdul Hamid Halimshah

(Recess Waterlow)

1937 (30 June). *Wmk Mult Script CA. P* 12½.

60 6 10 c. ultramarine and sepia .. .. 3·25 70
61 12 c. black and violet .. .. .. 25·00 12·00
62 25 c. ultramarine and purple .. .. 7·00 4·50
63 30 c. green and scarlet .. .. .. 8·00 10·00
64 40 c. black and purple .. .. .. 3·25 16·00
65 50 c. brown and blue .. .. .. 4·75 4·50
66 $1 black and green .. .. .. 3·25 10·00
67 $2 green and brown .. .. .. £120 85·00
68 $5 black and scarlet .. .. .. 32·00 £120
60/8 .. .. .. *Set of* 9 £190 £225
60/8 Perf "Specimen" .. .. *Set of* 9 £200

I II

I

II

1938 (May)–**40**. *As Nos. 52 and 27, but face values redrawn as Types* II.

68*a* 1 1 c. black .. .. 70·00 3·00
69 2 c. bright green (1940) .. .. .. £140 6·00

1 c. Type II. Figures "1" have square-cut corners instead of rounded, and larger top serif. Larger "C". Line perf. Produced from a new electrotyped Plate 2 with different engraved face values. Printings exist from either the "wet" or "dry" methods.

2 c. Type II. Figures "2" have circular instead of oval drops and the letters "c" are thin and tall instead of thick and rounded. Produced from a new plate, made from a transfer die, and printed by the "dry" method.

1948 (1 Dec). *Royal Silver Wedding. As Nos. 143/4 of Jamaica.*

70 10 c. violet 20 20
71 $5 carmine .. .. 25·00 32·00

1949 (10 Oct). *75th Anniv of U.P.U. As Nos. 145/8 of Jamaica.*

72 10 c. purple 25 20
73 15 c. deep blue .. .. 1·25 1·25
74 25 c. orange .. .. 65 1·25
75 50 c. blue-black .. .. 1·25 2·25
72/5 .. .. .. *Set of* 4 3·00 4·50

7 Sheaf of Rice   8 Sultan Badlishah

1950 (1 June)–**55.** *Wmk Mult Script CA. Chalk-surfaced paper. P* 17½ × 18.

76 **7** 1 c. black 10 30
77 2 c. orange 10 15
78 3 c. green .. .. 70 1·00
79 4 c. brown 50 10
79*a* 5 c. bright purple (1.9.52) 35 80
ab. Bright mauve (24.9.53) 35 30
80 6 c. grey 40 15
81 8 c. scarlet .. .. 65 1·75
81*a* 8 c. green (1.9.52) .. .. .. 75 1·75
ab. Deep green (24.9.53) .. .. 7·00 7·50
82 10 c. magenta 30 10
82*a* 12 c. scarlet (1.9.52) .. .. .. 85 2·50
83 15 c. ultramarine 55 35
84 20 c. black and green .. .. .. 60 2·50
84*a* 20 c. bright blue (1.9.52) 85 10
85 **8** 25 c. purple and orange 55 30
85*a* 30 c. scarlet and purple (5.9.55) .. .. 1·25 1·25
85*b* 35 c. scarlet and purple (1.9.52) .. .. 85 1·50
86 40 c. red and purple .. .. .. 1·25 6·00
87 50 c. black and blue .. .. .. 1·25 20
88 $1 blue and purple .. .. .. 2·75 2·25
89 $2 green and scarlet .. .. .. 20·00 22·00
90 $5 green and brown .. .. .. 42·00 32·00
76/90 .. .. *Set of* 21 65·00 65·00

1953 (2 June). *Coronation. As No.* 153 *of Jamaica.*

91 10 c. black and reddish purple 50 10

9 Copra   10 Pineapples

11 Ricefield   12 Masjid Alwi Mosque, Kangar

13 East Coast Railway   14 Tiger

15 Fishing Prau   16 Aborigines with Blowpipes

17 Government Offices   18 Bersilat

19 Weaving

(Recess D.L.R.)

1957. *Inset portrait of Sultan Badlishah. W w* **12.** *P* 13×12½ (1 c. *to* 8 c.), 12½×13 (10 c., 20 c.), 12½ (50 c., $2, $5) *or* 13½ ($1).

92 **9** 1 c. black (21.8) 10 35
93 **10** 2 c. orange-red (25.7) 10 40
94 **11** 4 c. sepia (21.8) 10 10
95 **12** 5 c. carmine-lake (21.8) 10 20
96 **13** 8 c. myrtle-green (21.8) .. .. .. 2·00 5·00
97 **14** 10 c. deep brown (4.8) 30 10
98 **15** 20 c. blue (26.6) .. .. 1·50 90
99 **16** 50 c. black and blue (25.7) .. .. 1·50 1·75
100 **17** $1 ultramarine & reddish purple (25.7) 3·25 7·00
101 **18** $2 bronze-green and scarlet (21.8) .. 19·00 18·00
102 **19** $5 brown and bronze-green (26.6) .. 35·00 30·00
92/102 .. .. *Set of* 11 55·00 55·00

The 6, 12, 25 and 30 c. values used with this issue were Nos. 1/4 of Malayan Federation.

20 Sultan Abdul Halim Mu'Adzam Shah   21 Sultan Abdul Halim Shah

(Photo Harrison)

1959 (20 Feb). *Installation of the Sultan. W w* **12.** *P* 14 × 14½.

103 **20** 10 c. multicoloured 10 10

1959 (1 July)–**62.** *As Nos.* 92/102 *but with inset portrait of Sultan Abdul Halim Shah as in T* **21.**

104 **21** 1 c. black 10 30
105 **10** 2 c. orange-red 10 30
106 **11** 4 c. sepia 10 10
107 **12** 5 c. carmine-lake 10 10
108 **13** 8 c. myrtle-green .. .. 3·50 1·75
109 **14** 10 c. deep brown 75 10
109*a* 10 c. deep maroon (19.12.61) .. .. 3·50 30
110 **15** 20 c. blue 60 10
111 **16** 50 c. black and blue (*p* 12½) 30 55
a. Perf 12½ × 13 (14.6.60) 30 10
112 **17** $1 ultramarine and reddish purple .. 1·75 2·25
113 **18** $2 bronze-green and scarlet .. .. 13·00 12·00
114 **19** $5 brown and bronze-green (*p* 12½) .. 16·00 17·00
a. Perf 13 × 12½ (26.11.62) .. .. 18·00 11·00
104/14 .. .. *Set of* 12 35·00 25·00

22 *Vanda hookeriana*   23 *Danaus melanippus*

1965 (15 Nov). *As Nos.* 166/72 *of Johore but with inset portrait of Sultan Abdul Halim Shah as in T* **22.** *W w* **13** (*upright*).

115 1 c. multicoloured 10 30
a. Black omitted (orchid's name and part of flower) .. .. 65·00
116 2 c. multicoloured 10 60
b. Yellow (flower) omitted .. .. 55·00
117 5 c. multicoloured 10 10
a. Black (country name and head) omitted .. .. 85·00
118 6 c. multicoloured 15 30
119 10 c. multicoloured 30 10
a. Red omitted £170
b. Green (leaves) omitted £170
120 15 c. multicoloured .. .. 1·50 10
121 20 c. multicoloured .. .. 1·75 50
a. Bright purple (blooms) omitted .. £110
b. Yellow (leaves) omitted .. .. 22·00
115/21 .. .. *Set of* 7 3·50 1·50

The 1 c. to 15 c. exist with PVA gum as well as gum arabic.

The 6 c. value exists with black (country name, arms and head) omitted and is listed under Sarawak where it was issued.

The higher values used with this issue were Nos. 20/27 of Malaysia (National Issues).

1970 (27 May). *As Nos.* 115 *and* 119 *but W w* **13** (*sideways*).

122 **22** 1 c. multicoloured .. .. .. 1·75 4·00
123 – 10 c. multicoloured .. .. .. 75 2·75

1971 (1 Feb)–**78.** *As Nos.* 175/87 *of Johore but with portrait of Sultan Abdul Halim Shah as in T* **23.** (*a*) *Litho by Bradbury, Wilkinson.*

124 1 c. multicoloured 20 65
125 2 c. multicoloured 40 65
126 5 c. multicoloured 80 10
127 6 c. multicoloured 80 80
128 10 c. multicoloured 65 10
129 15 c. multicoloured 80 10
130 20 c. multicoloured .. .. 1·10 45
124/30 .. .. *Set of* 7 4·25 2·50

(*b*) *Photo by Harrison* (1977–78)

130*a* 2 c. multicoloured .. .. 11·00 15·00
131 5 c. multicoloured .. .. 2·75 70
132 10 c. multicoloured .. .. 6·00 40
133 15 c. multicoloured .. .. 2·00 30
134 20 c. multicoloured .. .. 3·00 1·75
130*a*/4 .. .. *Set of* 5 22·00 16·00

The higher values used with this issue were Nos. 64/71 of Malaysia (National Issues).

For differences between litho and photo printings, see after Johore No. 187.

24 *Pterocarpus indicus*   25 Sultan Abdul Halim Shah

1979 (30 Apr). *As Nos.* 188/94 *of Johore but with portrait of Sultan Abdul Halim Shah as in T* **24.**

135 1 c. *Rafflesia hasseltii* 10 40
136 2 c. Type **24** 10 40
137 5 c. *Lagerstroemia speciosa* 10 10
138 10 c. *Durio zibethinus* 15 10
139 15 c. *Hibiscus rosa-sinensis* 15 10
140 20 c. *Rhododendron scortechinii* 20 10
141 25 c. *Etlingera elatior* (inscr "*Phaeomeria speciosa*") 40 10
135/41 .. .. *Set of* 7 1·00 90

For higher values used in conjunction with this series see Nos. 190/7 of Malaysia (National Issues).

(Des and litho Security Printers (M), Malaysia)

1983 (15 July). *Silver Jubilee of Sultan. T* **25** *and similar multicoloured designs. P* 13 × 13½ (20 c.) *or* 13½ × 13 (*others*).

142 20 c. Type **25** 70 30
143 40 c. Paddy fields (*horiz*) .. .. .. 1·50 1·00
144 60 c. Paddy fields and Mount Jerai (*horiz*) .. 2·00 3·25
142/4 .. .. *Set of* 3 3·75 4·00

1983 (22 Feb)–**85.*** *As Nos.* 138/40 *but without wmk.*

148 10 c. *Durio zibethinus* (11.5.85) .. .. 13·00 2·50
149 15 c. *Hibiscus rosa-sinensis* (12.84) 75 50
150 20 c. *Rhododendron scortechinii* (blackish brown background) .. .. .. 13·00 90
150*a* 20 c. *Rhododendron scortechinii* (bronze-green background) (16.12.83) 30 30

*There was no official release date for these stamps. Dates shown are the earliest recorded from postmarks and may be revised if earlier examples are reported.

For details of the shade differences between watermarked and unwatermarked printings see after Johore No. 200*a*.

Nos. 148/9 and 150*a* show "kedah" nearer to "malaysia" than on Nos. 135/41 and 150.

26 Cocoa

1986 (25 Oct)–**96.** *As Nos.* 202/8 *of Johore, but with portrait of Sultan Abdul Halim Shah as in T* **26.** *P* 12.

152 1 c. Coffee 10 10
153 2 c. Coconuts 10 10
154 5 c. Type **26** 10 10
c. Perf 14×13¾ (1996) .. ..
f. Perf 14¾×14½ (1994) .. .. .. 4·50 45
155 10 c. Black pepper 10 10
b. Perf 13½×13¾ .. ..
c. Perf 14×13¾ (1994) .. .. .. 3·25 35
ca. No watermark (1996)
156 15 c. Rubber 10 10
157 20 c. Oil palm 10 10
c. Perf 14×13¾ (1994) .. .. .. 1·00 10
158 30 c. Rice 15 20
c. Perf 14×13¾ (1994) .. .. .. 3·25 30
d. Perf 14 .. ..
e. Perf 14×14½ (1995) .. .. .. 2·25 20
ew. Wmk inverted .. .. .. 13·00
152/8 .. .. *Set of* 7 50 55

STAMP BOOKLETS

1973 (8 Dec). *Cover as Type* B **1** *of Johore, but inscr* "KEDAH". *Stitched.*

SB1 $3 booklet containing eight 5 c., 10 c. and twelve 15 c. (Nos. 126, 128/9) in blocks of 4 .. 18·00

1979 (1 Dec). *Cover as No.* SB5 *of Johore, but inscr* "KEDAH". *Stitched.*

SB2 $3 booklet containing eight 5 c., 10 c., and twelve 15 c. (Nos. 137/9) in blocks of 4 .. .. 7·00

No. SB2 exists with two different versions of the back cover.

1987 (1 June). *Cover as Type* B **2** *of Johore, but inscr* "KEDAH". *Stapled.*

SB3 $2 booklet containing 5 c., 10 c., 15 c. and 20 c. (Nos. 154/7) in blocks of 4 .. .. .. 5·00

1992 (1 July). *"Kuala Lumpur '92" International Philatelic Exhibition. Cover as Type* B **3** *of Johore, but inscr* "Kedah". *Stamps attached by selvedge.*

SB4 $3 booklet containing 30 c. (No. 158) in block of 10 5·50

1993. *Covers as Nos.* SB8/9 *of Johore, but inscr* "Kedah". *Stamps attached by selvedge.*

SB5 $2 booklet containing 20 c. (No. 157) in block of 10 1·00
SB6 $3 booklet containing 30 c. (No. 158) in block of 10 1·50

KELANTAN

Suzerainty over Kelantan was transferred by Thailand to Great Britain on 15 July 1909. A British adviser was appointed in 1923.

The state joined the Federation of Malaya on 1 February 1948.

For stamps of THAILAND used in Kelantan between 1895 and 1909 see VIII. SIAMESE POSTS IN NORTHERN MALAYA section.

From 1909 until the introduction of Kelantan stamps in 1911 the issues of the FEDERATED MALAY STATES to $2 were in use.

PRICES FOR STAMPS ON COVER TO 1945

Nos. 1/11	*from* × 30
No. 12	—
Nos. 14/23	*from* × 30
Nos. 30/8	*from* × 15
Nos. 39/*a*	*from* × 10
Nos. 40/8	*from* × 30
Nos. 49/52	*from* × 20
No. 53	*from* × 3
No. 54	—

1

MALAYA

BORNEO

EXHIBITION

(2)

1911 (Jan)–**15**. *Wmk Mult Crown CA. Ordinary paper* (1 c. *to* 10 c.) *or chalk-surfaced paper* (30 c. *to* $25). *P* 14.

1 1 1 c. yellow-green . . 2·50 90
a. *Blue-green* . . 2·00 30
2 3 c. red . . 3·00 15
3 4 c. black and red . . 1·50 15
4 5 c. green and red/*yellow* . . 7·50 60
5 8 c. ultramarine . . 5·50 1·00
6 10 c. black and mauve . . 24·00 60
7 30 c. dull purple and red . . 10·00 2·50
a. *Purple and carmine* . . 27·00 14·00
8 50 c. black and orange . . 6·00 2·50
9 $1 green and emerald . . 45·00 48·00
9*a* $1 green and brown (5.15) . . 32·00 2·00
10 $2 green and carmine . . 1·00 4·00
11 $5 green and blue . . 4·00 7·50
12 $25 green and orange . . 38·00 75·00
1/12 *Set of* 13 £150 £130
1/12 Optd "Specimen" *Set of* 13 £225

1921 (5 May)–**28**. *Wmk Mult Script CA. Ordinary paper* (1 c. *to* 10 c.) *or chalk-surfaced paper* (30 c. *to* $1). *P* 14.

14 1 1 c. dull green (7.21) . . 4·25 60
15 1 c. black (24.2.23) . . 50 50
16 2 c. brown (29.7.22) . . 4·50 3·75
16*a* 2 c. green (24.7.26) . . 1·00 40
16*b* 3 c. brown (5.3.27) . . 2·75 1·00
ba. "C" of "CA" missing from wmk
17 4 c. black and red (15.7.22) . . 85 10
18 5 c. green and red/*pale yellow* (12.22) . . 70 10
19 6 c. claret (29.7.22) . . 2·50 2·00
19*a* 6 c. scarlet (26.5.28) . . 4·00 5·50
20 10 c. black and mauve . . 2·00 10
21 30 c. purple and carmine (24.7.26) . . 4·00 5·50
22 50 c. black and orange (21.3.25) . . 5·00 40·00
23 $1 green and brown (9.2.24) . . 28·00 65·00
14/23 *Set of* 13 55·00 £110
14/23 Optd "Specimen" *Set of* 13 £275

For the 4 c., 5 c. and 6 c. surcharged, see issues under "Japanese Occupation".

1922 (31 Mar). *Malaya–Borneo Exhibition, Singapore. Optd with T* **2** *by Govt Survey Office, Khota Bharu.*

(*a*) *Wmk Mult Crown CA*

30 1 4 c. black and red . . 2·75 38·00
a. Opt double . . £2500
31 5 c. green and red/*pale yellow* . . 4·50 38·00
32 30 c. dull purple and red . . 4·50 55·00
33 50 c. black and orange . . 7·50 60·00
34 $1 green and brown . . 21·00 80·00
35 $2 green and carmine . . 45·00 £150
36 $5 green and blue . . £130 £300

(*b*) *Wmk Mult Script CA*

37 1 1 c. green . . 2·50 38·00
a. Opt double . . £2500
38 10 c. black and mauve . . 4·75 48·00
30/8 *Set of* 9 £200 £700

Examples of Nos. 30a and 37a show all three lines of the overprint double.

3 Sultan Ismail 4

(Recess Harrison (No. 39) or D.L.R. (No. 39a))

1928–35. *Wmk Mult Script CA. P* 12.

39 3 $1 blue (Perf S. £50) . . 9·50 70·00
a. Perf 14 (1935) . . 32·00 40·00

(Recess B.W.)

1937 (July)–**40**. *Wmk Mult Script CA. P* 12.

40 4 1 c. grey-olive and yellow . . 30 45
41 2 c. green . . 2·50 10
42 4 c. scarlet . . 4·75 55
43 5 c. red-brown . . 4·75 10
44 6 c. lake (10.37) . . 11·00 4·25
45 8 c. grey-olive . . 4·75 10
46 10 c. purple (10.37) . . 22·00 2·75
47 12 c. blue . . 3·25 4·00
48 25 c. vermilion and violet . . 4·75 3·50
49 30 c. violet and scarlet (10.37) . . 40·00 16·00
50 40 c. orange and blue-green . . 8·00 22·00
51 50 c. grey-olive and orange (10.37) . . 55·00 4·75
52 $1 violet and blue-green (10.37) . . 48·00 12·00
53 $2 red-brown and scarlet (3.40) . . £170 £180
54 $5 vermilion and lake (3.40) . . £300 £450
40/54 *Set of* 15 £600 £650
40/54 Perf "Specimen" *Set of* 15 £400

For above issue surcharged see issues under "Japanese Occupation".

1948 (1 Dec). *Royal Silver Wedding. As Nos.* 143/4 *of Jamaica.*

55 10 c. violet . . 60 1·50
56 $5 carmine . . 24·00 48·00

1949 (10 Oct). *75th Anniv of U.P.U. As Nos.* 145/8 *of Jamaica.*

57 10 c. purple . . 25 30
58 15 c. deep blue . . 1·25 90
59 25 c. orange . . 60 2·25
60 50 c. blue-black . . 1·25 2·25
57/60 *Set of* 4 3·00 5·00

5 Sultan Ibrahim

6 Sultan Yahya Petra and Crest of Kelantan

Normal No. 62a

Tiny stop (R. 1/2)

1951 (11 July)–**55**. *Chalk-surfaced paper. Wmk Mult Script CA. P* 17½ × 18.

61 5 1 c. black . . 10 30
62 2 c. orange . . 60 35
a. Tiny stop . . 18·00
b. *Orange-yellow* (11.5.55) . . 1·25 30
63 3 c. green . . 3·25 1·25
64 4 c. brown . . 15 15
65 5 c. bright purple (1.9.52) . . 45 50
a. *Bright mauve* (9.12.53) . . 1·25 50
66 6 c. grey . . 20 20
67 8 c. scarlet . . 95 3·25
68 8 c. green (1.9.52) . . 75 1·75
69 10 c. magenta . . 20 10
70 12 c. scarlet (1.9.52) . . 75 2·25
71 15 c. ultramarine . . 3·00 60
72 20 c. black and green . . 45 5·00
73 20 c. bright blue (1.9.52) . . 80 25
74 25 c. purple and orange . . 65 55
75 30 c. scarlet and purple (5.9.55) . . 1·25 1·75
76 35 c. scarlet and purple (1.9.52) . . 90 1·50
77 40 c. red and purple . . 4·75 11·00
78 50 c. black and blue . . 1·25 40
79 $1 blue and purple . . 6·00 4·00
80 $2 green and scarlet . . 22·00 20·00
81 $5 green and brown . . 48·00 40·00
a. *Green and sepia* (8.12.53) . . 75·00 80·00
61/81 *Set of* 21 85·00 80·00

1953 (2 June). *Coronation. As No.* 153 *of Jamaica.*

82 10 c. black and reddish purple . . 50 70

1957 (26 June)–**63**. *As Nos.* 92/102 *of Kedah but with inset portrait of Sultan Ibrahim.*

83 **9** 1 c. black (21.8.57) . . 10 30
84 **10** 2 c. orange-red (25.7.57) . . 50 40
a. *Red-orange* (17.11.59) . . 5·00 5·50
85 **11** 4 c. sepia (21.8.57) . . 10 10
86 **12** 5 c. carmine-lake (21.8.57) . . 10 10
87 **13** 8 c. myrtle-green (21.8.57) . . 80 2·25
88 **14** 10 c. deep brown (4.8.57) . . 1·00 10
89 10 c. deep maroon (19.4.61) . . 4·50 4·75
90 **15** 20 c. blue . . 70 30
91 **16** 50 c. black and blue (*p* 12½) (25.7.57) . . 50 50
a. Perf 12½ × 13 (28.6.60) . . 1·00 30
92 **17** $1 ultramarine & reddish pur (25.7.57) 4·00 1·50
93 **18** $2 bronze-grn & scar (*p* 12½) (21.8.57) 10·00 6·00
a. Perf 13 × 12½ (9.4.63) . . 14·00 15·00
94 **19** $5 brown and bronze-green (*p* 12½) . . 15·00 12·00
a. Perf 13 × 12½ (13.8.63) . . 19·00 24·00
83/94 *Set of* 12 32·00 25·00

The 6, 12, 25 and 30 c. values used with this issue were Nos. 1/4 of Malayan Federation.

(Photo Harrison)

1961 (17 July). *Coronation of the Sultan. W w* **12**. *P* 15 × 14.

95 **6** 10 c. multicoloured . . 40 30

7 Sultan Yahya Petra

8 *Vanda hookeriana*

(Recess D.L.R.)

1961–63. *As Nos.* 92/8 *of Kedah but with inset portrait of Sultan Yahya Petra as in T* **7**. *W w* **13**. *P* 12½×13 (*vert*) *or* 13×12½ (*horiz*).

96 1 c. black (1.3.62) . . 10 60
97 2 c. orange-red (1.3.62) . . 10 60
98 4 c. sepia (1.3.62) . . 15 10
99 5 c. carmine-lake (1.3.62) . . 15 10
100 8 c. myrtle-green (1.3.62) . . 4·75 5·50
a. *Deep green* (15.1.63) . . 6·00 7·50
101 10 c. deep maroon (2.12.61) . . 50 10
102 20 c. blue (1.3.62) . . 2·75 30
96/102 *Set of* 7 7·50 6·50

1965 (15 Nov). *As Nos.* 166/72 *of Johore but with inset portrait of Sultan Yahya Petra as in T* **8**. *W w* **13** (*upright*).

103 1 c. multicoloured . . 10 40
b. Magenta omitted . . 75·00
104 2 c. multicoloured . . 10 40
105 5 c. multicoloured . . 15 10
106 6 c. multicoloured . . 70 80
107 10 c. multicoloured . . 30 10
a. Red omitted . . 38·00
108 15 c. multicoloured . . 1·50 20
109 20 c. multicoloured . . 1·50 1·25
a. Bright purple (blooms) omitted . . 50·00
b. Yellow (leaves) omitted . . 26·00
103/9 *Set of* 7 3·75 2·75

The 5 c. and 10 c. exist with PVA gum as well as gum arabic.

The higher values used with this issue were Nos. 20/27 of Malaysia (National Issues).

1970 (20 Nov). *As Nos.* 103 *and* 107 *but W w* **13** (*sideways*).

110 **8** 1 c. multicoloured . . 75 5·00
111 – 10 c. multicoloured . . 2·25 3·00

9 *Parthenos sylvia*

10 *Lagerstroemia speciosa*

1971 (1 Feb)–**78**. *As Nos.* 175/87 *of Johore but with portrait of Sultan Yahya Petra and arms, as in T* **9**. (*a*) *Litho by Bradbury, Wilkinson.*

112 1 c. multicoloured . . 20 90
113 2 c. multicoloured . . 40 90
114 5 c. multicoloured . . 90 20
115 6 c. multicoloured . . 90 1·25
116 10 c. multicoloured . . 90 10
117 15 c. multicoloured . . 95 10
a. Black (state inscription, portrait and arms) omitted . . 90·00
118 20 c. multicoloured . . 1·50 90
112/18 *Set of* 7 5·25 3·75

(*b*) *Photo by Harrison* (1977–78)

119 1 c. multicoloured . . 70 3·00
120 5 c. multicoloured . . 5·00 2·75
121 10 c. multicoloured . . 5·50 2·25
122 15 c. multicoloured . . 8·00 75
119/22 *Set of* 4 17·00 8·00

The higher values used with this issue were Nos. 64/71 of Malaysia (National Issues).

For differences between litho and photo printings, see after Johore No. 187.

On No. 117a only the country inscription, portrait and arms are omitted, the remainder of the black printing being as normal. The design was produced using two black plates, one for the main design, value and inscription and the other to apply the state name, head and arms. It is this plate which is omitted from No. 117a.

1979 (30 Apr). *As Nos.* 188/94 *of Johore but with portrait of Sultan Yahya Petra as in T* **10**.

123 1 c. *Rafflesia hasseltii* . . 10 40
124 2 c. *Pterocarpus indicus* . . 10 40
125 5 c. Type **10** . . 10 30
126 10 c. *Durio zibethinus* . . 15 10
127 15 c. *Hibiscus rosa-sinensis* . . 15 10
128 20 c. *Rhododendron scortechinii* . . 20 10
129 25 c. *Etlingera elatior* (inscr "*Phaeomeria speciosa*") . . 40 40
123/9 *Set of* 7 1·00 1·40

For higher values used in conjunction with this series see Nos. 190/7 of Malaysia (National Issues).

11 Sultan Tengku Ismail Petra

12 Black Pepper

(Des M. A. B. bin Saman. Litho Harrison)

1980 (30 Mar). *Coronation of Sultan Tengku Ismail Petra. P* 14.

130	**11**	10 c. multicoloured	40	60
131		15 c. multicoloured	40	15
132		50 c. multicoloured	90	2·25
130/2		*Set of* 3	1·50	2·75

1983–86.* *As Nos.* 125/6 *and* 128 *but without wmk.*

135	5 c. Type **10** (1986)	1·00	1·50
136	10 c. *Durio zibethinus* (18.9.84)	30	50
138	20 c. *Rhododendron scortechinii* (blackish brown background) (1983)	14·00	1·50
138*a*	20 c. *Rhododendron scortechinii* (bronze-green background) (5.10.83)	50	40

*There was no official release date for these stamps. Dates shown are the earliest recorded from postmarks and may be revised if earlier examples are reported.

For details of the shade differences between watermarked and unwatermarked printings see after Johore No. 200*a*.

On Nos. 135/6 and 138*a* the portrait and state arms have been redrawn smaller.

1986 (25 Oct)–**95.** *As Nos.* 202/8 *of Johore, but with portrait of Sultan Ismail Petra as in T* **12**. *P* 12.

140	1 c. Coffee	10	10
141	2 c. Coconuts	10	10
	f. Perf 14¾×14½ (1994)	3·25	50
142	5 c. Cocoa	10	10
143	10 c. Type **12**	10	10
	c. Perf 14×13¾ (1995)	3·25	50
144	15 c. Rubber	10	10
145	20 c. Oil palm	10	10
	c. Perf 14×13¾ (1995)	3·25	50
146	30 c. Rice	15	20
	c. Perf 14×13¾ (1995)	1·00	25
140/6	*Set of* 7	50	55

STAMP BOOKLETS

1927 (June). *Black on white* (No. SB1) *or black on grey* (No. SB2) *covers. Stapled.*

SB1 36 c. booklet containing thirty-six 1 c. (No. 15) in blocks of 6 .. £2000

SB2 96 c. booklet containing twenty-four 4 c. (No. 17) in blocks of 6 .. £2000

1927 (Dec). *Black on white* (No. SB3) *or on grey* (No. SB4) *covers. Stapled.*

SB3 40 c. booklet containing forty 1 c. (No. 15) in blocks of 10 .. £2000

SB4 80 c. booklet containing twenty 4 c. (No. 17) in blocks of 10 .. £2000

1973 (8 Dec). *Cover as Type* B **1** *of Johore, but inscr* "KELANTAN". *Stitched.*

SB5 $3 booklet containing eight 5 c., 10 c. and twelve 15 c. (Nos. 114, 116/17) in blocks of 4 .. 20·00

1979 (1 Dec). *Cover as No.* SB5 *of Johore, but inscr* "KELANTAN". *Stitched.*

SB6 $3 booklet containing eight 5 c., 10 c., and twelve 15 c. (Nos. 125/7) in blocks of 4 .. 7·50

No. SB6 exists with two different versions of the back cover.

1987 (1 June). *Cover as Type* B **2** *of Johore, but inscr* "KELANTAN". *Stapled.*

SB7 $2 booklet containing 5 c., 10 c., 15 c. and 20 c. (Nos. 142/5) in blocks of 4 .. 5·50

1992 (1 July). *"Kuala Lumpur '92" International Philatelic Exhibition. Cover as Type* B **3** *of Johore, but inscr* "Kelantan". *Stamps attached by selvedge.*

SB8 $3 booklet containing 30 c. (No. 146) in block of 10 5·50

1993. *Covers as Nos.* SB8/9 *of Johore, but inscr* "Kelantan". *Stamps attached by selvedge.*

SB9 $2 booklet containing 20 c. (No. 145) in block of 10 .. 1·00

SB10 $3 booklet containing 30 c. (No. 146) in block of 10 .. 1·50

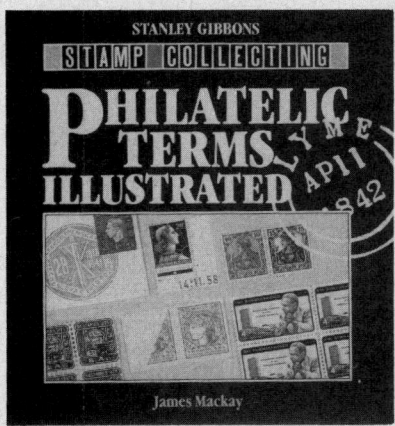

MALACCA

One of the Straits Settlements.
Issues from 1965 are inscribed "MELAKA".

1948 (1 Dec). *Royal Silver Wedding. As Nos.* 143/4 *of Jamaica.*

No.	Type	Description	Unused	Used
1		10 c. violet	30	60
2		$5 brown	26·00	35·00

1949 (1 Mar)–**52**. *As T* **58** *of Straits Settlements, but inscr* "MALACCA" *at foot. Wmk Mult Script CA. Chalk-surfaced paper. P* 17½ × 18.

No.	Type	Description	Unused	Used
3		1 c. black	10	70
4		2 c. orange	60	45
5		3 c. green	30	1·75
6		4 c. brown	15	10
6*a*		5 c. bright purple (1.9.52)	45	1·50
7		6 c. grey	50	85
8		8 c. scarlet	30	5·00
8*a*		8 c. green (1.9.52)	85	4·50
9		10 c. purple	15	10
9*a*		12 c. scarlet (1.9.52)	95	3·50
10		15 c. ultramarine	40	60
11		20 c. black and green	30	5·50
11*a*		20 c. bright blue (1.9.52)	1·50	2·50
12		25 c. purple and orange	30	70
12*a*		35 c. scarlet and purple (1.9.52)	1·00	3·00
13		40 c. red and purple	1·25	11·00
14		50 c. black and blue	65	1·25
15		$1 blue and purple	5·00	15·00
16		$2 green and scarlet	18·00	17·00
17		$5 green and brown	42·00	35·00
3/17		*Set of* 20	65·00	95·00

1949 (10 Oct). *75th Anniv of U.P.U. As Nos.* 145/8 *of Jamaica.*

No.	Type	Description	Unused	Used
18		10 c. purple	20	45
19		15 c. deep blue	1·10	1·75
20		25 c. orange	45	3·75
21		50 c. blue-black	1·00	4·00
18/21		*Set of* 4	2·50	9·00

1953 (2 June). *Coronation. As No.* 153 *of Jamaica.*

No.	Type	Description	Unused	Used
22		10 c. black and reddish purple	40	50

1 Queen Elizabeth II

2 Copra

1954 (9 June)–**57**. *Chalk-surfaced paper. Wmk Mult Script CA. P* 17½×18.

No.	Type	Description	Unused	Used
23	**1**	1 c. black (27.4.55)	10	60
24		2 c. yellow-orange (27.4.55)	30	1·00
25		4 c. brown	40	10
		a. Pale brown (24.4.57)	4·00	2·75
26		5 c. bright purple (12.7.54)	30	1·50
27		6 c. grey	10	30
28		8 c. green (5.1.55)	30	1·50
29		10 c. brown-purple (1.7.54)	40	10
		a. Reddish purple (27.3.57)	80	30
30		12 c. rose-red (5.1.55)	20	1·75
31		20 c. bright blue (5.1.55)	20	70
32		25 c. brown-purple & yellow-orge (27.4.55)	20	80
33		30 c. rose-red and brown-purple (5.9.55)	20	30
34		35 c. rose-red and brown-purple (8.9.54)	20	50
35		50 c. black and bright blue (5.1.55)	30	1·25
36		$1 bright blue and brown-purple (8.9.54)	4·00	5·50
37		$2 emerald and scarlet (27.4.55)	22·00	29·00
38		$5 emerald and brown (27.4.55)	22·00	32·00
23/38		*Set of* 16	45·00	70·00

1957. *As Nos.* 92/102 *of Kedah but with inset portrait of Queen Elizabeth II.*

No.	Type	Description	Unused	Used
39	**9**	1 c. black (21.8)	10	40
40	**10**	2 c. orange-red (25.7)	10	40
41	**11**	4 c. sepia (21.8)	10	10
42	**12**	5 c. carmine-lake (21.8)	10	10
43	**13**	8 c. myrtle-green (21.8)	1·25	2·50
44	**14**	10 c. deep brown (4.8)	30	10
45	**15**	20 c. blue (26.6)	30	40
46	**16**	50 c. black and blue (25.7)	30	50
47	**17**	$1 ultramarine & reddish purple (25.7)	2·25	2·50
48	**18**	$2 bronze-green and scarlet (21.8)	11·00	15·00
49	**19**	$5 brown and bronze-green (26.6)	14·00	24·00
39/49		*Set of* 11	26·00	42·00

The 6, 12, 25 and 30 c. values used with this issue were Nos. 1/4 of Malayan Federation.

(Recess D.L.R.)

1960 (15 Mar)–**62**. *As Nos.* 39/49, *but with inset picture of Melaka tree and Pelandok (mouse deer) as in T* **2**. *W w* **12**. *P* 13 × 12½ (1 *c. to* 8 *c.*, $2, $5), 12½ × 13 (10 *c. to* 50 *c.*) *or* 13½ ($1).

No.	Type	Description	Unused	Used
50		1 c. black	10	30
51		2 c. orange-red	10	30
52		4 c. sepia	10	10
53		5 c. carmine-lake	10	10
54		8 c. myrtle-green	2·50	2·00
55		10 c. deep maroon	30	10
56		20 c. blue	40	40
57		50 c. black and blue	30	40
		a. Black and ultramarine (9.1.62)	90	40
58		$1 ultramarine and reddish purple	1·75	2·50
59		$2 bronze-green and scarlet	4·50	5·50
60		$5 brown and bronze-green	9·00	9·50
50/60		*Set of* 11	17·00	19·00

3 *Vanda hookeriana*

4 *Papilio demoleus*

1965 (15 Nov)–**68**. *As Nos.* 166/72 *of Johore but with Arms of Malacca inset and inscr* "MELAKA" *as in T* **3**. *W w* **13** *(upright).*

No.	Type	Description	Unused	Used
61		1 c. multicoloured	10	60
62		2 c. multicoloured	10	60
63		5 c. multicoloured	10	10
		b. Yellow (flower) omitted	24·00	
		c. Red omitted	35·00	
64		6 c. multicoloured	30	45
65		10 c. multicoloured	20	10
66		15 c. multicoloured	1·75	40
67		20 c. multicoloured (purple-brn background)	2·25	90
		a. Red-brown background (2.4.68)	3·00	1·75
61/7		*Set of* 7	4·00	2·75

The 5 c., 6 c., 10 c. and 20 c. exist with PVA gum as well as gum arabic.

The higher values used with this issue were Nos. 20/27 of Malaysia (National Issues).

1970. *As Nos.* 61 *and* 65 *but W w* **13** *(sideways).*

No.	Type	Description	Unused	Used
68	**3**	1 c. multicoloured (27.5.70)	1·25	5·50
69	–	10 c. multicoloured (20.11.70)	4·50	5·50

1971 (1 Feb)–**78**. *As Nos.* 175/87 *of Johore but with arms of Malacca and inscr* "melaka", *as in T* **4**. (a) *Litho by Bradbury, Wilkinson.*

No.	Type	Description	Unused	Used
70		1 c. multicoloured	30	1·00
71		2 c. multicoloured	50	1·00
72		5 c. multicoloured	85	40
73		6 c. multicoloured	85	1·75
74		10 c. multicoloured	85	30
75		15 c. multicoloured	1·50	10
76		20 c. multicoloured	1·50	1·50
70/6		*Set of* 7	6·00	5·50

(*b*) *Photo by Harrison* (1977–78)

No.	Type	Description	Unused	Used
77		1 c. multicoloured	4·25	6·50
78		5 c. multicoloured	1·50	1·50
79		10 c. multicoloured	4·25	1·50
80		15 c. multicoloured	11·00	50
81		20 c. multicoloured	4·25	3·00
77/81		*Set of* 5	23·00	11·50

The higher values used with this issue were Nos. 64/71 of Malaysia (National Issues).

For differences between litho and photo printings, see after Johore No. 187.

5 *Durio zibethinus*

6 Rubber

1979 (30 Apr). *As Nos.* 188/94 *of Johore but with Arms of Malacca and inscr* "melaka" *as in T* **5**.

No.	Type	Description	Unused	Used
82		1 c. *Rafflesia hasseltii*	10	60
83		2 c. *Pterocarpus indicus*	10	60
84		5 c. *Lagerstroemia speciosa*	10	50
85		10 c. Type **5**	15	10
86		15 c. *Hibiscus rosa-sinensis*	15	10
87		20 c. *Rhododendron scortechinii*	20	10
88		25 c. *Etlingera elatior* (inscr "*Phaeomeria speciosa*")	40	50
82/8		*Set of* 7	1·00	2·00

For higher values used in conjunction with this series see Nos. 190/7 of Malaysia (National Issues).

1983 (26 Oct)–**86**.* *As Nos.* 85/7 *but without wmk.*

No.	Type	Description	Unused	Used
92		10 c. Type **5** (19.4.85)	2·75	3·25
93		15 c. *Hibiscus rosa-sinensis* (9.86)	1·00	55
94		20 c. *Rhododendron scortechinii* (blackish brown background)	13·00	2·75
94*a*		20 c. *Rhododendron scortechinii* (bronze-green background) (13.6.84)	1·00	90

*There was no official release date for these stamps. Dates shown are the earliest recorded from postmarks and may be revised if earlier examples are reported.

For details of the shade differences between watermarked and unwatermarked printings see after Johore No. 200*a*.

On Nos. 92/3 and 94*a* the distance between the coat of arms and the value is greater than on Nos. 85, 87 and 94.

1986 (25 Oct)–**96**. *As Nos.* 202/8 *of Johore, but with Arms of Malacca and inscr* "MELAKA" *as in T* **6**. *P* 12.

No.	Type	Description	Unused	Used
96		1 c. Coffee	10	10
		w. Wmk inverted		
97		2 c. Coconuts	10	10
98		5 c. Cocoa	10	10
		c. Perf 14×13¾ (1995)	1·00	20
99		10 c. Black pepper	10	10
		c. Perf 14×13¾ (1995)	1·00	20
		f. Perf 14¾×14½ (1995)	1·25	10
100		15 c. Type **6**	10	10
101		20 c. Oil palm	10	10
		c. Perf 14×13¾ (1994)	1·00	10
102		30 c. Rice	15	20
		c. Perf 14×13¾ (1994)	3·50	30
		f. Perf 14¾×14½ (1996)	4·75	40
96/102		*Set of* 7	50	55

STAMP BOOKLETS

1973 (8 Dec). *Cover as Type* B **1** *of Johore, but inscr* "MELAKA". *Stitched.*

No.	Description	Price
SB1	$3 booklet containing eight 5 c., 10 c. and twelve 15 c. (Nos. 72, 74/5) in blocks of 4	20·00

1979 (1 Dec). *Cover as No.* SB5 *of Johore, but inscr* "MELAKA". *Stitched.*

No.	Description	Price
SB2	$3 booklet containing eight 5 c., 10 c. and twelve 15 c. (Nos. 84/6) in blocks of 4	7·50

No. SB2 exists with two different versions of the back cover.

1987 (1 June). *Cover as Type* B **2** *of Johore, but inscr* "MELAKA". *Stapled.*

No.	Description	Price
SB3	$2 booklet containing 5 c., 10 c., 15 c. and 20 c. (Nos. 98/101) in blocks of 4	5·50

1992 (1 July). *"Kuala Lumpur '92" International Philatelic Exhibition. Cover as Type* B **3** *of Johore, but inscr* "Melaka". *Stamps attached by selvedge.*

No.	Description	Price
SB4	$3 booklet containing 30 c. (No. 102) in block of 10	5·50

1993. *Covers as Nos.* SB8/9 *of Johore, but inscr* "Melaka". *Stamps attached by selvedge.*

No.	Description	Price
SB5	$2 booklet containing 20 c. (No. 101) in block of 10	1·00
SB6	$3 booklet containing 30 c. (No. 102) in block of 10	1·50

NEGRI SEMBILAN

A federation of smaller states reconstituted in 1886. Sungei Ujong, taken under British protection in 1874, was absorbed into Negri Sembilan by Treaty of 8 August 1895. The Negri Sembilan federation joined the Federated Malay States in 1896.

A. SUNGEI UJONG

Until 1 January 1899, when the Federated Malay States joined the U.P.U., mail for addresses outside Malaya was franked with the stamps of the STRAITS SETTLEMENTS.

PRICES FOR STAMPS ON COVER

Nos. 1/14	—
Nos. 15/27	*from* × 25
Nos. 28/36	*from* × 8
Nos. 37/49	*from* × 10
Nos. 50/5	*from* × 25

(1)

1878. *No. 11 of Straits Settlements handstamped with T* **1**.
1 2 c. brown £1800 £2000
This overprint on India No. 54 is bogus.

SUNGEI (2) (Narrow letters) — SUNGEI (3) ("N" wide) — SUNGEI (4) ("S" wide)

UJONG (5) ("N" wide) — UJONG (6) (Narrow letters, "UJ" close together) — UJONG (7) Narrow letters, evenly spaced)

1881. *No. 11 of Straits Settlements optd with T* **2/7**.
2 **2+5** 2 c. brown £2750 £2500
3 **3+5** 2 c. brown £1700 £1600
4 **2+6** 2 c. brown £150
a. Opt Type **6** double £1200
5 **4+6** 2 c. brown £500
6 **2+7** 2 c. brown £275

The two lines of this surcharge were applied as separate operations. On Nos. 2/3 "SUNGEI" was printed as a triplet, probably 2+3+3, "UJONG" being added by a single unit handstamp. Nos. 4 and 5 come from a similar triplet, 4+4+5, completed by another single unit handstamp. No. 6 comes from a single type triplet with the second line added as a triplet instead of by a single unit handstamp.

The 10 c. slate overprinted Types **2** + **7** is bogus.

SUNGEI (8) ("N" and "E" wide) — SUNGEI (9) ("SUN" and "E" wide) — SUNGEI (10) ("SUN" wide)

SUNGEI (11) ("S" wide) — SUNGEI (12) (Narrow letters)

UJONG (13) ("U" and "NG" wide) — UJONG (14) (Narrow letters)

1881. *No. 11 of Straits Settlements optd with T* **8/14**.
7 **8+13** 2 c. brown £140
8 **9+13** 2 c. brown £170
9 **10+13** 2 c. brown £140
10 **11+14** 2 c. brown £180
a. "S" inverted £2500
11 **12+14** 2 c. brown £120

Nos. 7/11 also had the two lines of the overprint applied at separate operations. "SUNGEI" as a triplet, either 7+8+9 or 10+11+11, and "UJONG" as a single unit.

S.U.

(15)

1882. *Nos. 50/1 of Straits Settlements optd as T* **15**.
12 2 c. brown (with stops) £180
13 2 c. brown (without stops) £200 £250
14 4 c. rose (with stops) £1900 £1900

Each of the above was applied by a triplet setting.

Examples of Straits Settlements No. 11 with a similar overprint, including stops, are trials which were not issued.

SUNGEI (16) ("S" and "E" wide) — SUNGEI (17) ("E" wide) — UJONG (18) ("N" wide)

1882 (Dec)–84. *Nos. 12, 50, 52/3 and 63 of Straits Settlements optd with T* **11/12, 14** *and* **16/18**.
15 **12+14** 2 c. brown £400 £275
16 **11+14** 2 c. brown £600 £400
17 **12+14** 2 c. pale rose (1884) £130 £150
18 **11+14** 2 c. pale rose (1884) £130 £150
a. Opt Type **14** double .. ..
19 **16+14** 2 c. pale rose (1884) .. .. .. 75·00 85·00
20 **17+14** 2 c. pale rose (1884) .. .. .. 85·00 95·00
21 **12+18** 2 c. pale rose (1884) .. .. .. 85·00 95·00
a. Opt Type **18** double .. ..
22 **12+14** 4 c. rose £950 £1000
23 **11+14** 4 c. rose £1700 £1800
24 **12+14** 8 c. orange £1100 £850
25 **11+14** 8 c. orange £2000 £1400
26 **12+14** 10 c. slate £425 £425
27 **11+14** 10 c. slate £650 £650

Nos. 15/27 had the two lines of the overprint applied by separate triplets. Settings so far identified are Nos. 15+16+15, 17+18+19, 19+20+21, 22+23+22, 24+25+24 and 26+27+26.

The 4 c. rose overprinted Types **16**+**14** is now believed to be a trial.

UJONG. (19) (With stop. Narrow letters) — UJONG. (20) (With stop "N" wide) — UJONG (21) (Without stop. Narrow letters)

1883–84. *Nos. 50 and 63/4 of Straits Settlements optd with T* **12, 16/17** *and* **19/21**.
28 **12+19** 2 c. brown .. .. 38·00 90·00
29 **16+19** 2 c. brown .. .. 38·00 90·00
30 **12+20** 2 c. brown .. .. 38·00 90·00
31 **16+21** 2 c. pale rose (1884) .. .. .. 70·00 85·00
32 **17+21** 2 c. pale rose (1884) .. .. .. 70·00 85·00
33 **12+21** 2 c. pale rose (1884) .. .. .. 70·00 85·00
34 **16+21** 4 c. brown (1884) £170 £200
a. Opt Type **16** double .. ..
b. Opt Type **21** double £1100
35 **17+21** 4 c. brown (1884) £170 £200
36 **12+21** 4 c. brown (1884) £170 £200
a. Opt Type **21** double £3500

Nos. 28/36 had the two lines of the overprint applied by separate triplets. Settings were Nos. 28+29+30, 31+32+33 and 34+35+36.

The 8 c. orange overprinted Types **12**+**19** is now believed to be a trial (*Price £650 unused*).

Sungei Ujong (22) — SUNGEI UJONG (23) — SUNGEI UJONG (24)

SUNGEI UJONG (25) — SUNGEI UJONG (26) — SUNGEI UJONG (27)

SUNGEI UJONG (28) — SUNGEI UJONG. (29) — SUNGEI UJONG (30)

1885–90. *Nos. 63/a of Straits Settlements optd with T* **22/30**.
37 **22** 2 c. pale rose .. .. 55·00 65·00
a. Opt double £475 £475
38 **23** 2 c. pale rose .. .. 19·00 55·00
a. Opt double £550
39 **24** 2 c. pale rose (1886) .. .. .. 90·00 £100
40 **25** 2 c. pale rose (1886) £110 £120
a. Opt double .. .. ..
41 **26** 2 c. pale rose (1886) .. .. .. 70·00 80·00
a. Opt double .. .. ..
42 **27** 2 c. pale rose (1887) .. .. .. 8·00 25·00
43 **28** 2 c. pale rose (1889) .. .. .. 4·75 7·50
a. Narrow "E" (2 mm wide) (R. 3/4 and 4/3) .. .. 55·00
c. Opt double £1300
d. Bright rose (1890) .. .. .. 6·50 6·50
da. Narrow "E" (2 mm wide) (R. 3/4 and 4/3) .. .. 65·00
db. Antique "N" in "UJONG" (R. 10/6) .. 90·00
44 **29** 2 c. pale rose (1889) .. .. .. 65·00 65·00
a. "UNJOG" (R. 7/3) £2750 £2500
45 **30** 2 c. bright rose (1890) .. .. .. 20·00 13·00
a. Antique "G" in "SUNGEI" (R. 6/1) .. £150
b. Antique "G" in "UJONG" (R. 8/3) .. £150
c. *Pale rose* .. ..

All the above overprints had both lines applied at the same operation. Nos. 37/42 were from different triplet settings. The first printing of Type **28** was from a triplet (No. 43) but this was followed by two further settings of 60 (6×10), the first containing No. 43a and the second Nos. 43*d*/db. Nos. 44/5 were both from settings of 60.

SUNGEI UJONG Two CENTS (31) — SUNGEI UJONG Two CENTS (32) — SUNGEI UJONG Two CENTS (33)

SUNGEI UJONG Two CENTS (34)

1891. *No. 68 of Straits Settlements surch with T* **31/4**.
46 **31** 2 c. on 24 c. green £425 £450
47 **32** 2 c. on 24 c. green £160 £180
48 **33** 2 c. on 24 c. green £425 £450
49 **34** 2 c. on 24 c. green .. .. 95·00 £120
a. Antique "G" in "SUNGEI" (R. 6/1) .. £550
b. Antique "G" in "UJONG" (R. 8/3) .. £550

Nos. 46/9 come from the same setting of 60 on which "SUNGEI UJONG" was from the same type as No. 45. No. 46 occurs in row 1. No. 47 from rows 2 to 4, No. 48 from row 5 and No. 49 from rows 6 to 10.

35

3 CENTS

(36)

37

1891–94. *Wmk Crown CA. P* 14.
50 **35** 2 c. rose .. .. 24·00 27·00
51 2 c. orange (1894) .. .. 1·40 4·25
52 5 c. blue (1893) .. .. 4·50 5·50
50/2 .. .. *Set of* 3 27·00 32·00
50/2 Optd "Specimen" .. .. *Set of* 3 60·00

1894. *Surch as T* **36** *by De La Rue. Wmk Crown CA. P* 14.
53 **35** 1 c. on 5 c. green 65 70
54 3 c. on 5 c. rose .. .. 2·00 4·75

1895. *Wmk Crown CA. P* 14.
55 **37** 3 c. dull purple and carmine .. .. 6·50 1·50
53/5 Optd "Specimen" .. .. *Set of* 3 60·00

B. NEGRI SEMBILAN

Stamps of the STRAITS SETTLEMENTS were used in Negri Sembilan during 1891, until replaced by the stamps listed below. Until the Federated Malay States joined the U.P.U. On 1 January 1899 Straits Settlements stamps continued to be used for mail to addresses outside Malaya.

PRICES FOR STAMPS ON COVER TO 1945

No. 1	*from* × 200
Nos. 2/4	*from* × 10
Nos. 5/14	*from* × 8
Nos. 15/20	*from* × 10
Nos. 21/49	*from* × 4

(1)

2

3

1891 (Aug?). *No. 63a of Straits Settlements optd with T* **1**.
1 2 c. bright rose .. .. 2·50 4·25

N.SEMBILAN

Short "N" in "SEMBILAN" (Top left pane R. 8/3)

1891–94. *Wmk Crown CA. P* 14.
2 **2** 1 c. green (1893) .. .. 2·75 1·00
3 2 c. rose .. .. 3·25 5·50
a. Short "N" .. .. 65·00
4 5 c. blue (1894) .. .. 27·00 35·00
2/4 .. .. *Set of* 3 30·00 38·00
2/4 Optd "Specimen" .. .. *Set of* 3 70·00

1895–99. *Wmk Crown CA. P* 14.
5 **3** 1 c. dull purple and green (1899) .. 6·00 2·75
6 2 c. dull purple and brown (1898) .. 29·00 £100
7 3 c. dull purple and carmine .. .. 7·00 75
8 5 c. dull purple and orange-yellow (1897) 6·50 5·50
9 8 c. dull purple and ultramarine (1898) .. 28·00 15·00
10 10 c. dull purple and orange (1897) .. 27·00 14·00
11 15 c. green and violet (1896) .. .. 35·00 70·00
12 20 c. green and olive (1897) .. .. 42·00 38·00
13 25 c. green and carmine (1896) .. .. 70·00 90·00
14 50 c. green and black (1896) .. .. 50·00 60·00
5/14 .. .. *Set of* 10 £275 £350
5/14 Optd "Specimen" .. .. *Set of* 10 £160

Four cents. (4) — Four cents. (5)

1898 (Dec)–1900. (*a*) *Surch as T* **4**.
15 **3** 1 c. on 15 c. green and violet (1900) .. 80·00 £170
a. Raised stop (R. 5/1 and R. 10/1 of each pane) £350 £600
16 **2** 4 c. on 1 c. green .. .. 1·25 15·00

17 3 4 c. on 3 c. dull purple and carmine .. 3·00 15·00
a. Horiz pair, one without surch .. £3000 £3000
b. Surch double £1300 £1000
ba. Ditto. "Four cents" albino ..
c. Surch inverted £1000 £1000
d. "cents" repeated at left £1200 £1300
e. "Four" repeated at right £1200 £1300
f. Without bar £600 £475
g. Bar double .. .. † £700
18 2 4 c. on 5 c. blue .. .. .. 1·25 15·00

On Nos. 15 and 17 the bar is at the top of the stamp.
The surcharges were applied as a setting of 30 (6×5).

(b) Surch as T **5**

19 3 4 c. on 8 c. dull purple & ultram (G.) (12.98) 2·25 3·75
a. Vert pair, one without surch .. £3250 £2750
b. Surch double £1500
c. Surch double (G.+R.) £700 £700
20 4 c. on 8 c. dull purple & ultramarine (Bk.) £900 £950

Care should be taken in distinguishing the true black surcharge, No. 20, from very deep shades of the green surcharge, No. 19.

Pending the arrival of the permanent Federated Malay States issue the stamps of SELANGOR, FEDERATED MALAY STATES provisional overprints, STRAITS SETTLEMENTS and PERAK were used at various times between October 1899 and April 1901.
The general issues for FEDERATED MALAY STATES were used in Negri Sembilan from 29 April 1901 until 1935.

6 Arms of Negri Sembilan 7

1935 (2 Dec)–**41**. *Wmk Mult Script CA. Ordinary paper (6 c. grey, 15 c.) or chalk-surfaced paper (others). P* 14.
21 **6** 1 c. black (1.1.36) 75 10
22 2 c. green (1.1.36) 80 20
23 2 c. orange (11.12.41) .. .. .. 2·75 50·00
24 3 c. green (21.8.41) .. .. .. 4·75 8·00
a. Ordinary paper .. .. .. 15·00 8·00
25 4 c. orange 50 10
26 5 c. brown (5.12.35) .. .. .. 1·00 10
27 6 c. scarlet (1.1.37) .. .. .. 8·50 2·25
a. Stop omitted at right (R. 10/4) .. £225 80·00
28 6 c. grey (18.12.41) .. .. .. 3·75 70·00
a. Stop omitted at right (R. 10/4) .. £100 £375
29 8 c. grey .. .. 2·00 10
30 10 c. dull purple (1.1.36) 70 10
31 12 c. bright ultramarine (1.1.36) .. .. 1·40 40
32 15 c. ultramarine (1.10.41) .. .. 7·00 48·00
33 25 c. dull purple and scarlet (1.4.36) .. 90 70
34 30 c. dull purple and orange (1.1.36) .. 3·50 2·00
35 40 c. scarlet and dull purple .. .. 85 2·00
36 50 c. black/*emerald* (1.2.36) .. .. 3·75 1·75
37 $1 black and red/*blue* (1.4.36) .. .. 2·25 2·75
38 $2 green and scarlet (16.5.36) .. .. 24·00 16·00
39 $5 green and red/*emerald* (16.5.36) .. .. 14·00 45·00
21/39 .. .. *Set of* 19 70·00 £225
21/39 Perf "Specimen" .. .. *Set of* 19 £225

The stamps issued in 1941 were printed by Harrison and Sons following bomb damage to the De La Rue works on 29 December 1940.
An 8 c. scarlet was issued but only with opt during Japanese Occupation of Malaya. Unoverprinted specimens result from leakages.

During shortages in 1941 stamps of STRAITS SETTLEMENTS (2 c.), SELANGOR (2 c., 8 c.), PERAK (2 c., 25 c., 50 c.) and PAHANG (8 c.) were issued in Negri Sembilan.

1948 (1 Dec). *Royal Silver Wedding. As Nos.* 143/4 *of Jamaica.*
40 10 c. violet 15 50
41 $5 green .. .. 18·00 28·00

1949 (1 Apr)–**55**. *Chalk-surfaced paper. Wmk Mult Script CA. P* 17½ × 18.
42 **7** 1 c. black 10 10
43 2 c. orange 10 10
44 3 c. green 10 30
45 4 c. brown 10 10
46 5 c. bright purple (1.9.52) 30 50
a. Bright mauve (25.8.53) 30 45
47 6 c. grey 30 10
a. Pale grey (25.8.53) .. .. .. 2·50 10
48 8 c. scarlet 20 75
49 8 c. green (1.9.52) .. .. .. 1·50 1·60
50 10 c. purple 15 10
51 12 c. scarlet (1.9.52) .. .. .. 1·50 2·00
52 15 c. ultramarine .. .. 2·00 10
53 20 c. black and green 25 75
54 20 c. bright blue (1.9.52) 80 10
55 25 c. purple and orange 25 10
56 30 c. scarlet and purple (5.9.55) .. .. 1·25 2·50
57 35 c. scarlet and purple (1.9.52) .. .. 70 1·00
58 40 c. red and purple .. .. .. 80 4·00
59 50 c. black and blue 70 20
60 $1 blue and purple .. .. .. 3·00 1·75
61 $2 green and scarlet .. .. .. 12·00 13·00
62 $5 green and brown .. .. .. 50·00 35·00
42/62 .. .. *Set of* 21 65·00 55·00

1949 (10 Oct). *75th Anniv of U.P.U. As Nos.* 145/8 *of Jamaica.*
63 10 c. purple 20 10
64 15 c. deep blue .. .. 1·10 2·00
65 25 c. orange .. .. 50 2·00
66 50 c. blue-black .. .. 1·00 2·50
63/6 .. .. *Set of* 4 2·50 6·00

1953 (2 June). *Coronation. As No.* 153 *of Jamaica.*
67 10 c. black and reddish purple 50 30

1957 (26 June)–**63**. *As Nos.* 92/102 *of Kedah but with inset Arms of Negri Sembilan.*
68 **9** 1 c. black (21.8.57) 10 10
69 **10** 2 c. orange-red (25.7.57) 10 10
70 **11** 4 c. sepia (21.8.57) 10 10
71 **12** 5 c. carmine-lake (21.8.57) 10 10
72 **13** 8 c. myrtle-green (21.8.57) .. .. 85 1·40
73 **14** 10 c. deep brown (4.8.57) 75 10
74 10 c. deep maroon (10.1.61) .. .. 2·75 10
75 **15** 20 c. blue 60 10
76 **16** 50 c. black and blue (*p* 12½) (25.7.57) .. 30 60
a. Perf 12½ × 13 (19.7.60) 30 10
77 **17** $1 ultramarine & reddish pur (25.7.57) 1·50 1·50
78 **18** $2 bronze-green & scarlet (*p* 12½) (21.8.57) .. .. .. 5·00 10·00
a. Perf 13 × 12½ (15.1.63) .. .. 11·00 16·00
79 **19** $5 brown and bronze-green (*p* 12½) .. 11·00 14·00
a. Perf 13 × 12½ (6.3.62) .. .. 18·00 14·00
ab. Perf 13 × 12½. *Brown and yellow-olive* (13.11.62) .. .. .. £200 70·00
68/79 .. .. *Set of* 12 20·00 24·00

The 6, 12, 25 and 30 c. values used with this issue were Nos. 1/4 of Malayan Federation.

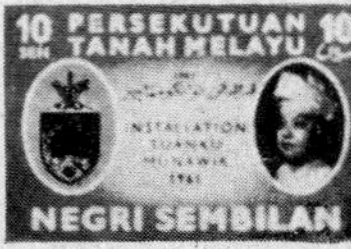

8 Tuanku Munawir

9 *Vanda hookeriana*

(Photo Enschedé)

1961 (17 Apr). *Installation of Tuanku Munawir as Yang di-Pertuan Besar of Negri Sembilan. No wmk. P* 14 × 13.
80 **8** 10 c. multicoloured 20 30

1965 (15 Nov)–**69**. *As Nos.* 166/72 *of Johore but with Arms of Negri Sembilan inset and inscr* "NEGERI SEMBILAN" *as in T* **9**. *W w* **13** *(upright).*
81 1 c. multicoloured 10 50
82 2 c. multicoloured 10 60
w. Wmk inverted .. .. 2·00
83 5 c. multicoloured 40 10
b. Yellow omitted .. .. 28·00
84 6 c. multicoloured 40 40
85 10 c. multicoloured 40 10
86 15 c. multicoloured 80 10
87 20 c. jet-black and multicoloured .. .. 1·25 75
a. Blackish brown & mult (19.12.69) .. 3·00 75
81/7 .. .. *Set of* 7 3·00 2·00

The 2 c., 6 c., 15 c. and 20 c. exist with PVA gum as well as gum arabic.
The higher values used with this issue were Nos. 20/27 of Malaysia (National Issues).
See also No. 90.

10 Negri Sembilan Crest and Tuanku Ja'afar

11 *Hebomoia glaucippe*

(Des Z. Noor. Photo Japanese Govt Ptg Wks)

1968 (8 Apr). *Installation of Tuanku Ja'afar as Yang di-Pertuan Besar of Negri Sembilan. P* 13.
88 **10** 15 c. multicoloured 15 40
89 50 c. multicoloured .. .. .. 30 1·10

1970 (27 May). *As No.* 81 *but with W w* **13** *(sideways).*
90 **9** 1 c. multicoloured .. .. .. 2·00 5·00

1971 (1 Feb)–**78**. *As Nos.* 175/87 *of Johore but with Arms of Negri Sembilan and inscr* "negeri sembilan", *as in T* **11**.

(a) Litho by Bradbury, Wilkinson

91 1 c. multicoloured 30 80
92 2 c. multicoloured 50 80
93 5 c. multicoloured 80 10
94 6 c. multicoloured .. .. 80 1·00
95 10 c. multicoloured 80 10
96 15 c. multicoloured .. .. 1·10 10
97 20 c. multicoloured .. .. 1·10 30
91/7 .. .. *Set of* 7 5·00 2·75

(b) Photo by Harrison (1977–78)

98 2 c. multicoloured .. .. 95 4·50
99 5 c. multicoloured .. .. 95 1·25
100 10 c. multicoloured .. .. 8·50 1·00
101 15 c. multicoloured .. .. 11·00 30
102 20 c. multicoloured .. .. 2·50 1·75
98/102 .. .. *Set of* 5 22·00 8·00

The higher values used with issue were Nos. 64/71 of Malaysia (National Issues).
For differences between litho and photo printings, see after Johore No. 187.

COVER PRICES

Cover factors are quoted at the beginning of each country for most issues to 1945. An explanation of the system can be found on page x. The factors quoted do not, however, apply to philatelic covers.

12 *Hibiscus rosa-sinensis*

13 Oil Palm

1979 (30 Apr). *As Nos.* 188/94 *of Johore but with Arms of Negri Sembilan and inscr* "negeri sembilan" *as in T* **12**.
103 1 c. *Rafflesia hasseltii* 10 50
104 2 c. *Pterocarpus indicus* 10 50
105 5 c. *Lagerstroemia speciosa* 10 10
106 10 c. *Durio zibethinus* 15 10
107 15 c. Type **12** 15 10
108 20 c. *Rhododendron scortechinii* 20 10
109 25 c. *Etlingera elatior* (inscr "*Phaeomeria speciosa*") 40 10
103/9 .. .. *Set of* 7 1·00 1·25

For higher values used in conjunction with this series see Nos. 190/7 of Malaysia (National Issues).

1983 (Oct)–**84**.* *As Nos.* 105/8 *but without wmk.*
112 5 c. *Lagerstroemia speciosa* (25.5.84) .. 1·50 1·75
113 10 c. *Durio zibethinus* (24.10.84) 30 50
114 15 c. Type **12** (11.8.84) .. .. .. 1·00 45
115 20 c. *Rhododendron scortechinii* (blackish brown background) .. .. .. 14·00 1·25
115*a* 20 c. *Rhododendron scortechinii* (bronze-green background) (1983) 30 40

*There was no official release date for these stamps. Dates shown are the earliest recorded from postmarks and may be revised if earlier examples are reported.
For details of the shade differences between watermarked and unwatermarked printings see after Johore No. 200*a*.
Nos. 112/14 and 115*a* show a larger crest, further from the face value than on Nos. 105/8 and 115.

1986 (25 Oct)–**96**. *As Nos.* 202/8 *of Johore, but with Arms of Negri Sembilan and inscr* "NEGERI SEMBILAN" *as in T* **13**. *P* 12.
117 1 c. Coffee 10 10
118 2 c. Coconuts 10 10
119 5 c. Cocoa 10 10
120 10 c. Black pepper 10 10
c. Perf 14×13¾ (1995) .. .. .. 1·00 10
f. Perf 14¾×14½ (1996) .. .. .. 7·00 40
121 15 c. Rubber 10 10
122 20 c. Type **13** 10 10
aw. Wmk inverted .. .. ..
c. Perf 14×13¾ (1994) .. .. .. 2·50 10
123 30 c. Rice 15 20
c. Perf 14×13¾ (1994) .. .. .. 3·25 20
f. Perf 14¾×14½ .. .. ..
117/23 .. .. *Set of* 7 50 55

STAMP BOOKLETS

1935. *Stapled.*
SB1 $1 booklet containing twenty 5 c. (No. 26) in blocks of 10 .. ..
SB2 $1.30, booklet containing 5 c. and 8 c. (Nos. 26, 29), each in block of 10 .. .. ..

1973 (8 Dec). *Cover as Type* B **1** *of Johore, but inscr* "N. SEMBILAN". *Stitched.*
SB3 $3 booklet containing eight 5 c., 10 c. and twelve 15 c. (Nos. 93, 95/6) in blocks of 4 .. .. 18·00

Examples of No. SB3 exist with a white label giving revised postage rates.

1979 (1 Dec). *Cover as No.* SB5 *of Johore, but inscr* "NEGERI SEMBILAN". *Stitched.*
SB4 $3 booklet containing eight 5 c., 10 c., and twelve 15 c. (Nos. 105/7) in blocks of 4 .. .. 7·00

No. SB4 exists with two different versions of the back cover.

1987 (1 June). *Cover as Type* B **2** *of Johore, but inscr* "NEGERI SEMBILAN". *Stapled.*
SB5 $2 booklet containing 5 c., 10 c., 15 c. and 20 c. (Nos. 119/22) in blocks of 4 .. .. .. 5·00

1992 (1 July). *"Kuala Lumpur '92" International Philatelic Exhibition. Cover as Type* B **3** *of Johore, but inscr* "Negeri Sembilan". *Stamps attached by selvedge.*
SB6 $3 booklet containing 30 c. (No. 123) in block of 10 5·50

1993. *Covers as Nos.* SB8/9 *of Johore, but inscr* "Negeri Sembilan". *Stamps attached by selvedge.*
SB7 $2 booklet containing 20 c. (No. 122) in block of 10 1·00
SB8 $3 booklet containing 30 c. (No. 123) in block of 10 1·50

PAHANG

The first British Resident was appointed in 1888. Pahang joined the Federated Malay States in 1896.

Until 1 January 1899, when the Federated Malay States joined the U.P.U., mail for addresses outside Malaya was franked with stamps of the STRAITS SETTLEMENTS.

PRICES FOR STAMPS ON COVER TO 1945

No. 1	*from* × 50
Nos. 2/3	—
No. 4	*from* × 100
No. 5	—
No. 6	*from* × 100
Nos. 7/10	*from* × 8
Nos. 11/13	*from* × 25
Nos. 14/16	*from* × 20
Nos. 17/*a*	—
Nos. 18/*d*	*from* × 6
Nos. 19/24	*from* × 8
No. 25	*from* × 20
Nos. 26/7	—
No. 28	*from* × 15
Nos. 29/46	*from* × 6

PAHANG (1) PAHANG (2) PAHANG (2*a*) (Antique letters)

1889 (Jan). *Nos. 52/3 and 63 of Straits Settlements optd with T* 1.

1	2 c. pale rose	75·00	45·00
2	8 c. orange	£1600	£1400
3	10 c. slate	£225	£250

All three values were overprinted from a triplet setting, but the 2 c. also exists from a similar setting of 30 or 60.

1889. *No. 63 of Straits Settlements optd with T* 2.

4	2 c. pale rose	8·00	11·00
	a. Bright rose	3·75	8·00
	ab. Opt Type 2*a*. Antique letters	£500	

No. 4 was overprinted from a setting of 60. No. 4ab usually occurs on R. 10/1, but has also been found on R. 8/1 as the result of revision of the setting.

PAHANG (3) PAHANG (4)

1890. *No. 63a of Straits Settlements optd.*

5	3	2 c. bright rose	£3000	£900
6	4	2 c. bright rose	70·00	14·00

No. 5 may have been overprinted from a triplet setting. No. 6 was from a setting of 60.

PAHANG Two CENTS (5) PAHANG Two CENTS (6)

PAHANG Two CENTS (7) PAHANG Two CENTS (8)

1891. *No. 68 of Straits Settlements surch with T* 5/8.

7	5	2 c. on 24 c. green	90·00	£100
8	6	2 c. on 24 c. green	£425	£500
9	7	2 c. on 24 c. green	£130	£160
10	8	2 c. on 24 c. green	£425	£500

Nos. 7/10 come from one setting used to surcharge the panes of sixty. No. 7 occurs in rows 1 to 5, No. 8 on row 6, No. 9 on rows 7 to 9 and No. 10 on row 10.

9

10

1891–95. *Wmk Crown CA. P* 14.

11	9	1 c. green (1895)	3·75	2·75
12		2 c. rose	3·75	2·50
13		5 c. blue (1893)	8·50	28·00
11/13		*Set of* 3	14·50	30·00
11/13 Optd "Specimen"		*Set of* 3	60·00	

MINIMUM PRICE

The minimum price quote is 10p which represents a handling charge rather than a basis for valuing common stamps. For further notes about prices see introductory pages.

Following an increase of postage rates on 1 March 1894 1 cent stamps of STRAITS SETTLEMENTS were used in Pahang until the autumn of the following year.

1895–99. *Wmk Crown CA. P* 14.

14	10	3 c. dull purple and carmine	4·25	2·25
15		4 c. dull purple and carmine (1899)	14·00	8·50
16		5 c. dull purple and olive-yellow (1897)	18·00	16·00
14/16		*Set of* 3	32·00	24·00
14/16 Optd "Specimen"		*Set of* 3	60·00	

1897 (2 Aug). *No. 13 bisected, surch in red manuscript at Kuala Lipis and initialled "JFO". (a) Bisected horizontally.*

17	2 c. on half 5 c. blue (surch "2" and bar across "5")	—	£1100
17*a*	3 c. on half of 5 c. blue (surch "3")	£3250	£1100

(b) Bisected diagonally

18	2 c. on half of 5 c. blue (surch "2" and bar across "5")	£950	£300
	a. Unsevered pair. Nos. 18 and 18d	£8000	£3500
	b. *Se-tenant* pair. Nos. 18 and 18d	£3000	£700
	c. Surch in black manuscript	£7000	£2500
18*d*	3 c. on half of 5 c. blue (surch "3")	£950	£300
	dc. Surch in black manuscript	£7000	£2500

The initials are those of John Fortescue Owen, the District Treasurer at Kuala Lipis.

Nos. 17 and 18 only occur on the bottom half of the 5 c. and Nos. 17*a* and 18*d* on the top half. No. 18a is a complete example of No. 13 showing the two surcharges. No. 18b is a *se-tenant* pair of bisects from adjoining stamps.

Pahang. (11) Pahang. (12)

1898–99. *(a) Nos. 72/5 of Perak optd with T* 11.

19	10 c. dull purple and orange	15·00	25·00
20	25 c. green and carmine	75·00	£120
21	50 c. dull purple and greenish black	£200	£225
22	50 c. green and black (1899)	£150	£160

(b) Nos. 76 and 79 of Perak optd with T 12

23	$1 green and pale green	£225	£250
24	$5 green and ultramarine	£700	£850

Pahang Four cents (13) Four cents. (14)

1898. *(a) No. 71 of Perak surch with T* 13.

25	4 c. on 8 c. dull purple and ultramarine	2·50	5·50
	a. Surch inverted	£2250	£1200
	b. Surch double	£650	

(b) T 13 on plain paper (no stamp), but issued for postage. Imperf.

26	4 c. black	—	£1700
27	5 c. black	£1200	

No. 26 also exists pin-perforated.

1899. *No. 16 surch with T* 14.

28	10	4 c. on 5 c. dull purple and olive-yellow	9·00	45·00

Pending the arrival of the permanent Federated Malay States issue the stamps of SELANGOR, FEDERATED MALAY STATES provisional overprints and PERAK were used at various times between November 1899 and July 1902.

The general issues for the FEDERATED MALAY STATES were used in Pahang from July 1902 until 1935.

15 Sultan Sir Abu Bakar

16 Sultan Sir Abu Bakar

1935 (2 Dec)–**41.** *Chalk-surfaced paper. Wmk Mult Script CA. P* 14.

29	15	1 c. black (1.1.36)	15	40
30		2 c. green (1.1.36)	60	50
31		3 c. green (21.8.41)	9·50	11·00
		a. Ordinary paper	18·00	4·25
32		4 c. orange	30	40
33		5 c. brown (5.12.35)	60	10
34		6 c. scarlet (1.1.37)	8·50	2·25
35		8 c. grey	60	10
36		8 c. scarlet (11.12.41)	1·00	42·00
37		10 c. dull purple (1.1.36)	30	10
38		12 c. bright ultramarine (1.1.36)	1·00	1·75
39		15 c. ultram (*ordinary paper*) (1.10.41)	6·50	48·00
40		25 c. dull purple and scarlet (1.4.36)	80	1·40
41		30 c. dull purple and orange (1.1.36)	80	1·10
42		40 c. scarlet and dull purple	75	2·00
43		50 c. black/*emerald* (1.2.36)	2·75	1·75
44		$1 black and red/*blue* (1.4.36)	1·75	7·00
45		$2 green and scarlet (16.5.36)	18·00	26·00
46		$5 green and red/*emerald* (16.5.36)	7·00	50·00
29/46		*Set of* 18	55·00	£170
29/46 Perf "Specimen"		*Set of* 18	£200	

The stamps issued during 1941 were printed by Harrison and Sons following bomb damage to the De La Rue works on 29 December 1940.

A 2 c. orange and a 6 c. grey were prepared but not officially issued. (*Price mint £4 each*).

During shortages in 1941 stamps of STRAITS SETTLEMENTS (2 c.), SELANGOR (2 c., 8 c.) and PERAK (2 c.) were issued in Pahang.

1948 (1 Dec). *Royal Silver Wedding. As Nos. 143/4 of Jamaica.*

47	10 c. violet	15	60
48	$5 green	22·00	40·00

1949 (10 Oct). *75th Anniv of U.P.U. As Nos. 145/8 of Jamaica.*

49	10 c. purple	30	20
50	15 c. deep blue	90	70
51	25 c. orange	35	1·10
52	50 c. blue-black	70	2·00
49/52	*Set of* 4	2·00	3·50

1950 (1 June)–**56.** *Wmk Mult Script CA. Chalk-surfaced paper. P* $17^{1}/_{2}$×18.

53	16	1 c. black	10	10
54		2 c. orange	10	10
55		3 c. green	20	30
56		4 c. brown	15	10
		a. Chocolate (24.3.54)	3·75	1·75
57		5 c. bright purple (1.9.52)	25	60
		a. Bright mauve (10.9.53)	25	15
58		6 c. grey	15	10
59		8 c. scarlet	20	1·00
60		8 c. green (1.9.52)	85	75
61		10 c. magenta	15	10
62		12 c. scarlet (1.9.52)	85	1·25
63		15 c. ultramarine	30	10
64		20 c. black and green	25	2·25
65		20 c. bright blue (1.9.52)	75	10
		a. Ultramarine (8.3.56)	4·00	2·50
66		25 c. purple and orange	30	10
67		30 c. scarlet and brown-purple (5.9.55)	1·25	35
		a. Scarlet and purple (8.3.56)	9·00	3·25
68		35 c. scarlet and purple (1.9.52)	60	25
69		40 c. red and purple	90	7·00
70		50 c. black and blue	1·00	10
71		$1 blue and purple	2·50	2·25
72		$2 green and scarlet	13·00	18·00
73		$5 green and brown	55·00	42·00
		a. Green and sepia (24.3.54)	75·00	75·00
53/73		*Set of* 21	70·00	65·00

1953 (2 June). *Coronation. As No. 153 of Jamaica.*

74	10 c. black and reddish purple	45	10

1957 (26 June)–**62.** *As Nos. 92/102 of Kedah but with inset portrait of Sultan Sir Abu Bakar.*

75	9	1 c. black (21.8.57)	10	10
76	10	2 c. orange-red (25.7.57)	10	10
77	11	4 c. sepia (21.8.57)	10	10
78	12	5 c. carmine-lake (21.8.57)	10	10
79	13	8 c. myrtle-green (21.8.57)	80	1·75
80	14	10 c. deep brown (4.8.57)	40	10
81		10 c. deep maroon (21.2.61)	2·00	20
82	15	20 c. blue	75	10
83	16	50 c. black and blue (*p* $12^{1}/_{2}$) (25.7.57)	20	20
		a. Perf $12^{1}/_{2}$ × 13 (17.5.60)	50	10
84	17	$1 ultramarine & reddish pur (25.7.57)	3·00	1·50
85	18	$2 bronze-grn & scar (*p* $12^{1}/_{2}$) (21.8.57)	3·00	7·50
		a. Perf 13 × $12^{1}/_{2}$ (13.11.62)	4·50	11·00
86	19	$5 brown and bronze-green (*p* $12^{1}/_{2}$)	8·00	9·50
		a. Perf 13 × $12^{1}/_{2}$ (17.5.60)	9·50	9·50
		b. Perf 13 × $12^{1}/_{2}$. Brown and yellow-olive (23.10.62)	25·00	26·00
75/86		*Set of* 12	16·00	19·00

The 6, 12, 25 and 30 c. values used with this issue were Nos. 1/4 of Malayan Federation.

17 *Vanda hookeriana*

18 *Precis orithya*

1965 (15 Nov). *As Nos. 166/72 of Johore but with inset portrait of Sultan Sir Abu Bakar as in T* 17. *W w* 13 *(upright).*

87	1 c. multicoloured	10	40
	c. Grey (flower name, etc) omitted	29·00	
	w. Wmk inverted	4·00	
88	2 c. multicoloured	10	40
89	5 c. multicoloured	15	10
	c. Red (leaves, etc) omitted	35·00	
90	6 c. multicoloured	30	40
91	10 c. multicoloured	20	10
	a. Red omitted	35·00	
92	15 c. multicoloured	1·00	10
93	20 c. multicoloured	1·60	30
87/93	*Set of* 7	3·00	1·50

The 2 c., 5 c. and 6 c. exist with PVA gum as well as gum arabic.

The higher values used with this issue were Nos. 20/27 of Malaysia (National Issues).

1970 (27 May). *As Nos. 87 and 91 but W w 13 (sideways).*

94	17	1 c. multicoloured	1·25	5·50
95	–	10 c. multicoloured	90	3·00

(Litho B.W.)

1971 (1 Feb). *As Nos. 175/81 of Johore but with portrait of Sultan Sir Abu Bakar and arms, as in T* 18.

96	1 c. multicoloured	20	70
97	2 c. multicoloured	40	70
98	5 c. multicoloured	75	40
99	6 c. multicoloured	1·25	85
100	10 c. multicoloured	80	20
101	15 c. multicoloured	90	10
102	20 c. multicoloured	1·50	30
96/102	*Set of* 7	5·25	2·75

The higher values used with this issue were Nos. 64/71 of Malaysia (National Issues).

19 Sultan Haji Ahmad Shah   **20** *Rhododendron scortechinii*

(Des Union Advertising. Litho Harrison)

1975 (8 May). *Installation of the Sultan. P* 14 × 14½.

103	**19**	10 c. slate-green, light lilac and gold ..	50	80
104		15 c. greenish black, yellow & dp green ..	60	10
105		50 c. black, light violet-bl & greenish blk	1·75	3·50
103/5		.. .. *Set of* 3	2·50	4·00

(Photo Harrison)

1977 (5 Sept)–**78.** *As Nos.* 97/8, 100/2 *but with portraits of Sultan Haji Ahmad Shah.*

106	2 c. multicoloured (1978)	35·00	38·00
107	5 c. multicoloured	60	80
108	10 c. multicoloured (10.2.78)	80	40
109	15 c. multicoloured (13.1.78)	80	30
	a. Black (face value, etc.)* omitted.. ..	90·00	
110	20 c. multicoloured (1978)	4·00	1·75
106/10	.. .. *Set of* 5	35·00	38·00

*There were two black cylinders used for No. 109, one to apply the portrait and state details, the other the face value and parts of the main design.

The higher values used with this issue were Nos. 64/71 of Malaysia (National Issues).

1979 (30 Apr). *As Nos.* 188/94 *of Johore but with portrait of Sultan Haji Ahmad Shah as in T* **20**.

111	1 c. *Rafflesia hasseltii*	10	50
112	2 c. *Pterocarpus indicus*	10	50
113	5 c. *Lagerstroemia speciosa*	10	20
114	10 c. *Durio zibethinus*	15	10
115	15 c. *Hibiscus rosa-sinensis*	15	10
116	20 c. Type **20**	20	10
117	25 c. *Etlingera elatior* (inscr "*Phaeomeria speciosa*")	40	40
111/17	.. .. *Set of* 7	75	1·40

For higher values used in conjunction with this series see Nos. 190/7 of Malaysia (National Issues).

1983 (5 Oct)–**85.*** *As Nos.* 113/16 *but without wmk.*

120	5 c. *Lagerstroemia speciosa* (17.11.83) ..	40	40
121	10 c. *Durio zibethinus* (8.1.85)	2·00	1·75
123	20 c. Type **20** (blackish brown background)..	13·00	1·25
123*a*	20 c. Type **20** (bronze-green background) (20.8.84)	50	30

*There was no official release date for these stamps. Dates shown are the earliest recorded from postmarks and may be revised if earlier examples are reported.

For details of the shade differences between watermarked and unwatermarked printings see after Johore No. 200*a*.

On Nos. 120/1 and 123*a* "pahang" is one millimetre nearer "malaysia" than on Nos. 113/16 and 123.

21 Rice

1986 (25 Oct)–**95.** *As Nos.* 202/8 *of Johore, but with portrait of Sultan Ahmad Shah as in T* **21**. *P* 12.

125	1 c. Coffee	10	10
	aw. Wmk inverted	3·50	
	b. Perf 13½×13¾ (1993)	7·00	40
126	2 c. Coconuts	10	10
127	5 c. Cocoa	10	10
128	10 c. Black pepper	10	10
	c. Perf 14×13¾ (1995)	2·00	50
	f. Perf 14¾×14½ (1994)	9·00	60
129	15 c. Rubber	10	10
130	20 c. Oil palm	10	10
	aw. Wmk inverted	†	—
	c. Perf 14×13¾ (1994)	1·00	10
131	30 c. Type **21**	15	20
	aw. Wmk inverted		
	c. Perf 14×13¾ (1994)	3·25	20
	f. Perf 14¾×14½ (1995)	7·00	60
125/31	.. .. *Set of* 7	50	55

STAMP BOOKLETS

1935. *Stapled.*

SB1 $1 booklet containing twenty 5 c. (No. 33) in blocks of 10 .. ..

SB2 $1.30, booklet containing 5 c. and 8 c. (Nos. 33, 35) each in block of 10 .. ..

1973 (8 Dec). *Cover as Type* B **1** *of Johore, but inscr* "PAHANG". *Stitched.*

SB3 $3 booklet containing eight 5 c., 10 c. and twelve 15 c. (Nos. 98, 100/1) in blocks of 4 .. .. 18·00

1979 (1 Dec). *Cover as No.* SB5 *of Johore, but inscr* "PAHANG". *Stitched.*

SB4 $3 booklet containing eight 5 c., 10 c., and twelve 15 c. (Nos. 113/15) in blocks of 4 .. .. 7·00

No. SB4 exists with two different versions of the back cover.

1987 (1 June). *Cover as Type* B **2** *of Johore, but inscr* "PAHANG". *Stapled.*

SB5 $2 booklet containing 5 c., 10 c., 15 c. and 20 c. (Nos. 127/30) in blocks of 4 .. .. 5·00

1992 (1 July). *"Kuala Lumpur '92" International Philatelic Exhibition. Cover as Type* B **3** *of Johore, but inscr* "Pahang". *Stamps attached by selvedge.*

SB6 $3 booklet containing 30 c. (No. 131) in block of 10 5·50

1993. *Covers as Nos.* SB8/9 *of Johore, but inscr* "Pahang". *Stamps attached by selvedge.*

SB7 $2 booklet containing 20 c. (No. 130) in block of 10 1·00

SB8 $3 booklet containing 30 c. (No. 131) in block of 10 1·50

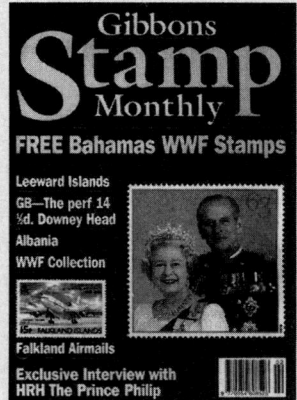

PENANG

One of the Straits Settlements.
Issues from 1965 are inscribed "PULAU PINANG".

1948 (1 Dec). *Royal Silver Wedding. As Nos. 143/4 of Jamaica.*
1 10 c. violet 30 20
2 $5 brown .. .. 30·00 26·00

1949 (21 Feb)–**52**. *As T* **58** *of Straits Settlements, but inscr "PENANG" at foot. Wmk Mult Script CA. Chalk-surfaced paper. P* 17½ × 18.
3 1 c. black 10 10
4 2 c. orange 30 10
5 3 c. green 20 30
6 4 c. brown 20 10
7 5 c. bright purple (1.9.52) .. .. 40 1·25
8 6 c. grey 20 10
9 8 c. scarlet .. .. 30 2·75
10 8 c. green (1.9.52) .. .. 80 1·00
11 10 c. purple 15 10
12 12 c. scarlet (1.9.52) .. .. 80 2·50
13 15 c. ultramarine 20 30
14 20 c. black and green .. .. 20 1·00
15 20 c. bright blue (1.9.52) 55 30
16 25 c. purple and orange 75 10
17 35 c. scarlet and purple (1.9.52) 60 80
18 40 c. red and purple .. .. 75 7·00
19 50 c. black and blue .. .. 1·25 15
20 $1 blue and purple .. .. 11·00 1·50
21 $2 green and scarlet.. .. .. 12·00 1·75
22 $5 green and brown.. .. .. 48·00 1·75
3/22 .. .. *Set of* 20 70·00 20·00

1949 (10 Oct). *75th Anniv of U.P.U. As Nos. 145/8 of Jamaica.*
23 10 c. purple 20 10
24 15 c. deep blue .. .. 1·25 1·00
25 25 c. orange .. .. 45 1·50
26 50 c. blue-black .. .. 1·50 2·00
23/6 .. .. *Set of* 4 3·00 4·00

1953 (2 June). *Coronation. As No. 153 of Jamaica.*
27 10 c. black and reddish purple 50 10

1954 (9 June)–**57**. *As T* **1** *of Malacca (Queen Elizabeth II) but inscr "PENANG" at foot. Chalk-surfaced paper. Wmk Mult Script CA. P* 17½×18.
28 1 c. black (5.1.55) 10 50
29 2 c. yellow-orange (8.9.54) 50 20
30 4 c. brown (1.9.54) 70 10
a. Yellow-brown (17.7.57) .. .. .. 3·50 3·50
31 5 c. bright purple (1.10.54) .. .. 2·00 2·00
a. Bright mauve (17.7.57) .. .. .. 3·50 3·75
32 6 c. grey 15 50
33 8 c. green (5.1.55) .. .. 20 2·50
34 10 c. brown-purple (1.9.54) 20 10
35 12 c. rose-red (5.1.55) .. .. 30 2·50
36 20 c. bright blue (1.9.54) 50 10
37 25 c. brown-purple & yellow-orange (1.12.54) 30 10
38 30 c. rose-red and brown-purple (5.9.55) .. 30 10
39 35 c. rose-red and brown-purple (8.9.54) .. 70 40
40 50 c. black and bright blue (1.12.54) 40 10
41 $1 bright blue and brown-purple (1.10.54) 2·25 10
42 $2 emerald and scarlet (1.10.54) .. .. 6·50 3·00
43 $5 emerald and brown (5.1.55) .. .. 38·00 3·25
28/43 .. .. *Set of* 16 45·00 13·50

1957. *As Nos. 92/102 of Kedah, but with inset portrait of Queen Elizabeth II.*
44 **9** 1 c. black (21.8) 10 60
45 **10** 2 c. orange-red (25.7) 10 60
46 **11** 4 c. sepia (21.8) 10 10
47 **12** 5 c. carmine-lake (21.8).. .. .. .. 10 10
48 **13** 8 c. myrtle-green (21.8).. .. .. .. 1·25 1·75
49 **14** 10 c. deep brown (4.8) 30 10
50 **15** 20 c. blue (26.6) 40 40
51 **16** 50 c. black and blue (25.7) 30 40
52 **17** $1 ultramarine and reddish purple (25.7) .. .. 5·00 40
53 **18** $2 bronze-green and scarlet (21.8) .. 9·00 7·50
54 **19** $5 brown and bronze-green (26.6) .. 16·00 8·00
44/54 .. .. *Set of* 11 29·00 17·00
The note after No. 86 of Pahang also applies here.

1 Copra

2 *Vanda hookeriana*

(Recess D.L.R.)

1960 (15 Mar). *As Nos. 44/54, but with inset Arms of Penang as in T* **1**. *W w* **12**. *P* 13 × 12½ (1 *c. to* 8 *c.*, $2, $5), 12½ × 13 (10 *c. to* 50 *c.*) *or* 13½ ($1).
55 1 c. black 10 60
56 2 c. orange-red 10 60
57 4 c. sepia 10 10
58 5 c. carmine-lake 10 10
59 8 c. myrtle-green .. .. 2·75 3·25
60 10 c. deep maroon 30 10
61 20 c. blue 40 10
62 50 c. black and blue 30 15
a. Imperf (pair) £375
63 $1 ultramarine and reddish purple.. .. .. 3·75 90
64 $2 bronze-green and scarlet.. .. .. .. 4·25 3·50
65 $5 brown and bronze-green .. .. .. 10·00 5·50
55/65 .. .. *Set of* 11 20·00 13·00
No. 62a comes from a sheet purchased at the Penang Post Office which had the upper five horizontal rows imperforate.

1965 (15 Nov)–**68**. *As Nos. 166/72 of Johore but with Arms of Penang inset and inscr "PULAU PINANG" as in T* **2**. *W w* **13** *(upright).*
66 1 c. multicoloured 10 60
67 2 c. multicoloured 10 60
68 5 c. multicoloured 20 10
b. Yellow (flower) omitted .. .. .. 22·00
c. Red omitted .. .. 35·00
d. Blue (background and inscr) omitted 40·00
da. Blue and yellow omitted .. .. .. 85·00
w. Wmk inverted .. .. 1·50
69 6 c. multicoloured 30 60
b. Yellow omitted .. .. 22·00
70 10 c. grey and multicoloured 20 10
a. Jet-black and multicoloured (12.11.68) 20 10
71 15 c. multicoloured .. .. 1·00 10
b. Green (value and leaves) omitted .. 95·00
72 20 c. multicoloured .. .. 1·60 30
a. Bright purple (blooms) omitted .. £130
b. Yellow (leaves) omitted £150
66/72 .. .. *Set of* 7 3·00 2·00
The 2 c., 5 c., 6 c., 10 c. and 20 c. exist with PVA gum as well as gum arabic.
The higher values used with this issue were Nos. 20/27 of Malaysia (National Issues).

1970. *As Nos. 66 and 70 but W w* **13** *(sideways).*
73 **2** 1 c. multicoloured (27.5.70) .. .. 1·00 4·50
74 – 10 c. multicoloured (20.11.70) .. .. 5·00 4·00

3 *Valeria valeria* 4 *Etlingera elatior* (inscr "*Phaeomeria speciosa*")

1971 (1 Feb)–**78**. *As Nos. 175/87 of Johore, but with Arms of Penang and inscr "pulau pinang", as in T* **3**.

(*a*) *Litho by Bradbury Wilkinson*
75 1 c. multicoloured 20 60
76 2 c. multicoloured 50 60
77 5 c. multicoloured 85 20
78 6 c. multicoloured 95 80
79 10 c. multicoloured 95 10
80 15 c. multicoloured 95 10
81 20 c. multicoloured .. .. 1·10 40
75/81 .. .. *Set of* 7 5·00 2·50

(*b*) *Photo by Harrison* (1977–78)
81*a* 1 c. multicoloured .. .. 6·00 7·50
82 5 c. multicoloured .. .. 2·25 60
83 10 c. multicoloured .. .. 4·75 60
84 15 c. multicoloured .. .. 8·50 30
85 20 c. multicoloured .. .. 5·00 1·00
81*a*/5 .. .. *Set of* 5 24·00 9·00
The higher values used with this issue were Nos. 64/71 of Malaysia (National Issues).
For differences between litho and photo printings, see after Johore No. 187.

1979 (30 Apr). *As Nos. 188/94 of Johore but with Arms of Penang and inscr "pulau pinang" as in T* **4**.
86 1 c. *Rafflesia hasseltii* 10 40
87 2 c. *Pterocarpus indicus* 10 40
88 5 c. *Lagerstroemia speciosa* 10 10
89 10 c. *Durio zibethinus* 15 10
90 15 c. *Hibiscus rosa-sinensis* 15 10
91 20 c. *Rhododendron scortechinii* 20 10
92 25 c. Type **4** 40 10
86/92 .. .. *Set of* 7 1·00 90
For higher values used in conjunction with this series see Nos. 190/7 of Malaysia (National Issues).

1983–85.* *As Nos. 88/91, but without wmk.*
95 5 c. *Lagerstroemia speciosa* (1.84) 30 40
96 10 c. *Durio zibethinus* (2.7.85) .. .. 6·00 2·25
97 15 c. *Hibiscus rosa-sinensis* (27.12.83) .. 75 60
98 20 c. *Rhododendron scortechinii* (blackish brown background) (27.6.84) .. .. 22·00 90
98*a* 20 c. *Rhododendron scortechinii* (bronze-green background) (3.84) 40 40
*There was no official release date for these stamps. Dates shown are the earliest recorded from postmarks and may be revised if earlier examples are reported.
For details of the shade differences between watermarked and unwatermarked printings see after Johore No. 200*a*.
On Nos. 95/7 and 98*a* the state arms are larger than on the watermarked printing and No. 98.

5 Cocoa

1986 (25 Oct)–**95**. *As Nos. 202/8 of Johore, but with Arms of Penang and inscr "PULAU PINANG" as in T* **5**. *P* 12.
100 1 c. Coffee 10 10
w. Wmk inverted .. .. 3·00
101 2 c. Coconuts 10 10
102 5 c. Type **5** 10 10
c. Perf 14×13¾ (1994) .. .. 2·50 20
f. Perf 14¾×14½ (1995) .. ..
103 10 c. Black pepper 10 10
aw. Wmk inverted .. ..
c. Perf 14×13¾ (1995) .. .. 1·00 10
e. Perf 14×14½ (1994) .. .. 3·25 20
f. Perf 14¾×14½ (1995) .. .. ..
fw. Wmk inverted .. ..
104 15 c. Rubber 10 10
105 20 c. Oil palm 10 10
aw. Wmk inverted .. .. † —
c. Perf 14×13¾ (1994) .. .. 1·00 10
e. Perf 14×14½ (1994) .. .. 2·00 10
f. Perf 14¾×14½ (1994) .. .. 4·50 20
106 30 c. Rice 15 20
aw. Wmk inverted .. .. 9·00
c. Perf 14×13¾ (1994) .. .. 1·00 10
cw. Wmk inverted (1995) .. .. ..
d. Perf 14 .. ..
e. Perf 14×14½ (1995) .. ..
f. Perf 14¾×14½ (1994) .. .. .. 13·00 30
100/6 .. .. *Set of* 7 50 55

STAMP BOOKLETS

1973 (8 Dec). *Cover as Type* B **1** *of Johore, but inscr* "PULAU PINANG". *Stitched.*
SB1 $3 booklet containing eight 5 c., 10 c. and twelve 15 c. (Nos. 77, 79/80) in blocks of 4 .. .. 18·00

1979 (1 Dec). *Cover as No.* SB5 *of Johore, but inscr* "PULAU PINANG". *Stitched.*
SB2 $3 booklet containing eight 5 c., 10 c., and twelve 15 c. (Nos. 88/90) in blocks of 4 .. .. 7·00
No. SB2 exists with two different versions of the back cover.

1987 (1 June). *Cover as Type* B **2** *of Johore, but inscr* "PULAU PINANG". *Stapled.*
SB3 $2 booklet containing 5 c., 10 c., 15 c. and 20 c. (Nos. 102/5) in blocks of 4 .. .. .. 5·00

1992 (1 July). *"Kuala Lumpur '92" International Philatelic Exhibition. Cover as Type* B **3** *of Johore, but inscr* "Pulau Pinang". *Stamps attached by selvedge.*
SB4 $3 booklet containing 30 c. (No. 106) in block of 10 5·50

1993. *Covers as Nos.* SB8/9 *of Johore, but inscr* "Pulau Pinang". *Stamps attached by selvedge.*
SB5 $2 booklet containing 20 c. (No. 105) in block of 10 1·00
SB6 $3 booklet containing 30 c. (No. 106) in block of 10 1·50

PERAK

Perak accepted a British Resident in 1874, although he was later murdered.
The state joined the Federated Malay States in 1896.

The stamps of the STRAITS SETTLEMENTS were used in Perak during 1877/8.
Until 1 January 1899, when the Federated Malay States joined the U.P.U., mail for addresses outside Malaya was franked with stamps of the STRAITS SETTLEMENTS.

PRICES FOR STAMPS ON COVER TO 1945

No. 1	—
Nos. 2/9	*from* × 60
Nos. 10/13	*from* × 30
Nos. 14/16	*from* × 8
Nos. 17/22	*from* × 20
No. 23	—
Nos. 24/5	—
Nos. 26/8	*from* × 15
No. 29	*from* × 75
No. 30	*from* × 20
Nos. 31/2	—
Nos. 33/40	*from* × 15
Nos. 43/60	*from* × 6
Nos. 61/5	*from* × 20
Nos. 66/79	*from* × 12
No. 80	—
Nos. 81/7	*from* × 8
Nos. 88/102	*from* × 4
Nos. 103/21	*from* × 3

The Official stamps of Perak are rare used on cover.

(1)

1878. *No. 11 of Straits Settlements handstamped with T* **1**.
1 2 c. brown £1300 £950

PERAK (2) (14½ mm long) — PERAK (3) (11 mm long) — PERAK (4) (10¼ mm long)

PERAK (5) (17 mm long) — PERAK (6) ("RA" narrow) — PERAK (7) ("R" narrow)

PERAK (8) ("P" and "K" wide) — PERAK (9) (12 to 13½ mm long)

1880–81. *No. 11 (wmk Crown CC) of Straits Settlements optd with T* **2/9**.
2 **2** 2 c. brown £700 £375
3 **3** 2 c. brown £650 £350
4 **4** 2 c. brown £375 £300
5 **5** 2 c. brown (1881) .. .. 25·00 45·00
6 **6** 2 c. brown (1881) £120 £130
7 **7** 2 c. brown (1881) .. .. 85·00 £100
8 **8** 2 c. brown (1881) £300 £275
9 **9** 2 c. brown (1881) .. .. 85·00 95·00

Of the above No. 2 is from a single unit overprint, No. 5 from a setting of sixty and the remainder from settings applied as horizontal strips of three. Nos. 6/8 come from mixed triplets, either 6 + 7 + 7 or 7 + 7 + 8. No. 4 is believed to come from a single unit overprint in addition to a triplet.

PERAK (10) ("A" wide) — PERAK (11) ("E" wide)

1882–83. *Nos. 50 (wmk Crown CA) and 63 of Straits Settlements optd with T* **9/11**.
10 **9** 2 c. brown .. .. 19·00 32·00
a. Opt double £450
11 2 c. pale rose (1883) .. .. .. 14·00 28·00
a. Opt double £500
12 **10** 2 c. pale rose (1883) .. .. .. 16·00 38·00
13 **11** 2 c. pale rose (1883) .. .. .. 16·00 35·00
a. Opt double £500

The above were all overprinted as triplet settings. Those for the 2 c. rose were 11 + 12 + 13, 13 + 11 + 11 and 13 + 11 + 12.

2 CENTS PERAK (12) — 2 CENTS (13)

1883 (July). *No. 51 (wmk Crown CA) of Straits Settlements surch.*

(*a*) *Surch with T* **12**
14 2 c. on 4 c. rose £1900
a. On Straits Settlements No. 12 (wmk Crown CC) £7000

(*b*) *Optd as T* **9** *or* **11** *and surch with T* **13**
15 **11** 2 c. on 4 c. rose £700 £350
16 **9** 2 c. on 4 c. rose £450 £225

It is believed that No. 14 occurred on the top row of the sheet with the remaining nine rows surcharged with a triplet containing 15 + 16 + 16.
Only one unused example, with defects, of No. 14a is recorded.

PERAK (14) ("E" wide) — PERAK (15) ("E" narrow) — PERAK (16) (12½–13 mm long)

PERAK (17) (12–12½ mm long) — PERAK (18) (10½ mm long) — PERAK (19) (10 mm long)

PERAK (20) (13 mm long)

1884–91. *Nos. 63/a of Straits Settlements optd with T* **14/20**.
17 **14** 2 c. pale rose .. .. 1·25 1·10
a. Opt double £550 £550
b. Opt inverted £325 £425
c. *Bright rose* .. .. 1·50 1·10
18 **15** 2 c. pale rose .. .. 50·00 50·00
b. Opt inverted £900 £1000
c. Opt triple £1000
d. *Bright rose* .. ..
19 **16** 2 c. pale rose (1886) .. .. .. 1·40 5·50
a. Optd "FERAK" £225 £300
20 **17** 2 c. pale rose (1886) .. .. .. 3·50 15·00
a. Opt double £1200
21 **18** 2 c. pale rose (1886) .. .. .. 75·00 90·00
a. *Bright rose* .. ..
22 **19** 2 c. bright rose (1890) .. .. .. 8·50 30·00
23 **20** 2 c. bright rose (1891) £2500

Settings:
Nos. 17/18 – triplets (either 17 + 17 + 17 or 18 + 17 + 17)
– 30 (3 × 10) (containing twenty-eight as No. 17 and two as No. 18)
– 60 (6 × 10) (containing either fifty-seven as No. 17 and three as No. 18 or all as No. 17)
No. 19 – 60 (6 × 10) (No. 19a occurs on one position of the setting, it is often found amended in manuscript)
No. 20 – triplet
No. 21 – triplet
No. 22 – 60 (6 × 10)
No. 23 – not known

1 CENT (21)

1886. *No. 17 surch with T* **21**.
24 **14** 1 c. on 2 c. pale rose £1800 £1800

ONE CENT PERAK (22) — ONE CENT PERAK. (23) — ONE CENT PERAK. (24) ("N" wide in "ONE" and "CENT")

1886. *No. 63 of Straits Settlements surch with T* **22/4**.
25 **22** 1 c. on 2 c. pale rose £425 £450
26 **23** 1 c. on 2 c. pale rose .. .. .. 42·00 60·00
a. Surch double £650
27 **24** 1 c. on 2 c. pale rose .. .. .. 65·00 85·00

Nos. 26/7 are from a triplet setting, 26 + 27 + 26, used on the top nine rows of the sheet. No. 25 may have been used on the bottom row.

1 CENT PERAK (25) — One CENT PERAK (26) — ONE CENT PERAK (27)

1886. *No. 63 of Straits Settlements surch with T* **25**.
28 1 c. on 2 c. pale rose .. .. .. 80·00 90·00
a. Surch double £1500
No. 28 comes from a triplet setting.

1886. *No. 63 of Straits Settlements surch with T* **26**.
29 1 c. on 2 c. pale rose .. .. .. 85 6·00
a. "One" inverted £2250
b. Surch double £900

No. 29 comes from a triplet setting. It is believed that No. 29a occurred when the type was dropped and "One" replaced upside down.

1887. *No. 63 of Straits Settlements surch with T* **27** *in blue.*
30 1 c. on 2 c. pale rose .. .. .. 27·00 38·00
a. Optd in black £1400 £950
No. 30 was printed from a setting of 60.

I CENT PERAK (28) — 1 CENT PERAK (29)

1887. *No. 63 of Straits Settlements surch with T* **28**.
31 1 c. on 2 c. pale rose £350 £375
No. 31 comes from a triplet setting

1887. *No. 63 of Straits Settlements surch with T* **29**.
32 1 c. on 2 c. pale rose £1200 £1300
The size of setting used for No. 32 is not known.

One CENT PERAK (30) — One CENT PERAK (31) — One CENT PERAK (32) — One CENT PERAK (33)

One CENT PERAK (34) — One CENT PERAK (35) — One CENT PERAK (36) — One CENT PERAK (37)

1887–89. *No. 63 of Straits Settlements surch with T* **30/7**.
33 **30** 1 c. on 2 c. pale rose .. .. .. 90 2·50
a. Surch double .. .. ..
b. *Bright rose* .. .. .. 1·25 1·90
34 **31** 1 c. on 2 c. pale rose (1889) .. .. 85·00 95·00
b. *Bright rose* ..
35 **32** 1 c. on 2 c. pale rose (1889) .. .. 8·00 25·00
a. "PREAK" (R. 6/1) £350 £400
b. *Bright rose* .. .. .. 12·00 25·00
ba. "PREAK" (R. 6/1) .. .. ..
36 **33** 1 c. on 2 c. pale rose (1889) .. .. 4·25 6·50
b. *Bright rose* .. .. .. 4·25 6·50
37 **34** 1 c. on 2 c. pale rose (1889) .. .. 4·25 9·50
b. *Bright rose* .. .. .. 4·25 9·50
38 **35** 1 c. on 2 c. bright rose (1889) £450 £550
39 **36** 1 c. on 2 c. bright rose (1889) £180 £200
40 **37** 1 c. on 2 c. pale rose (1889) .. .. 11·00 23·00
b. *Bright rose* .. .. .. 11·00 23·00

Settings. No. 33 originally appeared as a triplet, then as a block of 30 (3 × 10) and, finally, as part of a series of composite settings of 60. Specialists recognise four such composite settings:
Setting I contained No. 33 in Rows 1 to 4, R. 5/1 to 5/5 and Row 7; No. 34 on R. 5/6, 6/1 and 6/2; No. 35 on R. 6/3–6; No. 36 on Row 8; No. 37 on Rows 9 and 10.
Setting II was similar, but had the example of No. 33 on R. 3/5 replaced by No. 38 and those on R. 7/4 and R. 7/6 by No. 39.
Setting III contained No. 33 in Rows 1 to 5; No. 35 in Row 6 with the "PREAK" error on the first position; No. 36 in Row 7; No. 37 in Rows 8 and 9; No. 40 in Row 10.
Setting IV was similar, but showed the "PREAK" error on R. 6/1 corrected.

ONE CENT. (38) — ONE CENT (39)

1889–90. *No. 17 surch with T* **38/9**.
41 **38** 1 c. on 2 c. bright rose £150 £110
42 **39** 1 c. on 2 c. bright rose (1890) .. .. — £190

PERAK Two CENTS (40) — PERAK One CENT (41)

1891. *Nos. 63a, 66 and 68 of Straits Settlements surch.*

(*a*) *As T* **30, 32/4** *and* **37**, *but with "PERAK" at top and a bar through the original value*
43 **30** 1 c. on 6 c. lilac .. .. .. 40·00 25·00
44 **32** 1 c. on 6 c. lilac £130 £130
45 **33** 1 c. on 6 c. lilac £130 £130
46 **34** 1 c. on 6 c. lilac .. .. .. 65·00 65·00
47 **37** 1 c. on 6 c. lilac £130 £130

(*b*) *With T* **40** *and as T* **32/4** *and* **37** *but with "PERAK" at top, all with a bar through the original value*
48 **40** 2 c. on 24 c. green .. .. .. 9·00 9·00
49 **32** 2 c. on 24 c. green .. .. .. 70·00 55·00
50 **33** 2 c. on 24 c. green .. .. .. 70·00 55·00
51 **34** 2 c. on 24 c. green .. .. .. 35·00 24·00
52 **37** 2 c. on 24 c. green .. .. .. 70·00 55·00

(*c*) *With T* **41** *and as T* **30, 34** *and* **37**, *but with "PERAK" at top.*
(i) *Without bar over original value*
53 **30** 1 c. on 2 c. bright rose £160
a. Narrow "O" in "One" (R. 3/3) .. £1700
54 **41** 1 c. on 2 c. bright rose £750
55 **34** 1 c. on 2 c. bright rose £300
56 **37** 1 c. on 2 c. bright rose £750

(ii) *With bar through original value*
57 **30** 1 c. on 2 c. bright rose .. .. .. 55 3·25
a. Narrow "O" in "One" (R. 3/3) .. 16·00 42·00
58 **41** 1 c. on 2 c. bright rose .. .. 4·50 15·00
59 **34** 1 c. on 2 c. bright rose .. .. 85 4·50
60 **37** 1 c. on 2 c. bright rose .. .. 4·50 15·00

Settings. Nos. 43/7 were arranged as Setting IV described under Nos. 33/40.
Nos. 48/52 were similar except that Type **40** replaced Type **30** on the first five rows.
The first printing of the 1 c. on 2 c. was without a bar through the original face value. Both printings, Nos. 53/60, were from the same setting with Type **30** on Rows 1 to 5, **41** on Row 6, **34** on Rows 7 to 9 and **37** on Row 10.

42

3 CENTS
(43)

1892 (1 Jan)–**95.** *Wmk Crown CA. P* 14.
61 **42** 1 c. green 2·25 15
62 2 c. rose 1·75 30
63 2 c. orange (9.9.95) 35 3·25
64 5 c. blue 3·25 7·50
61/4 *Set of* 4 7·00 10·00
61/4 Optd "Specimen" *Set of* 4 75·00

1895 (18 Apr). *Surch with T* **43**. *Wmk Crown CA. P* 14.
65 **42** 3 c. on 5 c. rose (Optd S. £25) 85 1·75

44

45

1895 (2 Sept)–**99.** *P* 14. (*a*) *Wmk Crown CA.*
66 **44** 1 c. dull purple and green 1·00 40
67 2 c. dull purple and brown 75 40
68 3 c. dull purple and carmine 1·50 30
69 4 c. dull purple and carmine (1899) 7·50 4·75
70 5 c. dull purple and olive-yellow 2·75 55
71 8 c. dull purple and ultramarine 35·00 65
72 10 c. dull purple and orange 8·00 45
73 25 c. green and carmine (1897) £110 12·00
74 50 c. dull purple and greenish black 32·00 29·00
75 50 c. green and black (2.99) £130 £130

(*b*) *Wmk Crown CC*
76 **45** $1 green and pale green (1896) 95·00 £100
77 $2 green and carmine (1896) £160 £170
78 $3 green and ochre (1898) £190 £225
79 $5 green and ultramarine (1896) £400 £375
80 $25 green and orange (1899?) (S. £170) £5500 £1700
66/76 *Set of* 11 £375 £250
66/79 Optd "Specimen" *Set of* 14 £250

Pending the arrival of the permanent Federated Malay States issue the stamps of FEDERATED MALAY STATES provisional overprints, SELANGOR and STRAITS SETTLEMENTS were used at various times between June 1900 and February 1901.

The general issues for the FEDERATED MALAY STATES were used in Perak from 1901 until 1935.

One Cent. (46)

ONE CENT. (47)

Three Cent. (48)

Three Cent. (49)

1900. *Stamps of* 1895–99 *surch.*
81 **46** 1 c. on 2 c. dull purple and brown (13 July*) 40 1·75
a. Antique "e" in "One" (R. 5/2) 48·00 £110
b. Antique "e" in "Cent" (R. 9/4) 48·00 £110
82 **47** 1 c. on 4 c. dull purple and carmine 65 7·00
a. Surch double £850
83 **46** 1 c. on 5 c. dull purple & ol-yell (30 June*) 85 8·00
a. Antique "e" in "One" (R. 5/2) 60·00 £180
b. Antique "e" in "Cent" (R. 9/4) 60·00 £180
84 **48** 3 c. on 8 c. dull purple & ultram (26 Sept*) 2·50 5·50
a. Antique "e" in "Cent" (R. 9/4) £100 £160
b. No stop after "Cent" (R. 9/5) £100 £160
c. Surch double £375 £375
85 3 c. on 50 c. green and black (31 Aug*) 1·50 4·75
a. Antique "e" in "Cent" (R. 9/4) 80·00 £150
b. No stop after "Cent" (R. 9/5) 80·00 £150
86 **49** 3 c. on $1 green and pale green (21 Oct*) 55·00 £140
a. Small "t" in "Cent" £275 £475
b. Surch double £1300
87 3 c. on $2 green and carmine (24 Oct*) 28·00 85·00
81/7 *Set of* 7 80·00 £225

*Earliest known postmark date.

With exception of No. 86a, whose sheet position is not known, the remaining surcharge varieties all occur in the left-hand pane.

No. 86b is also known showing the small "t" in "Cent" variety. (*Price* £3500 *unused*).

MINIMUM PRICE

The minimum price quote is 10p which represents a handling charge rather than a basis for valuing common stamps. For further notes about prices see introductory pages.

50 Sultan Iskandar 51

1935 (2 Dec)–**37.** *Chalk-surfaced paper. Wmk Mult Script CA. P* 14.
88 **50** 1 c. black (1.1.36) 30 10
89 2 c. green (1.1.36) 30 10
90 4 c. orange 30 10
91 5 c. brown (5.12.35) 30 10
92 6 c. scarlet (1.1.37) 8·00 3·00
93 8 c. grey 50 10
94 10 c. dull purple (1.1.36) 30 15
95 12 c. bright ultramarine (1.1.36) 70 90
96 25 c. dull purple and scarlet (1.4.36) 85 85
97 30 c. dull purple and orange (1.1.36) 90 1·50
98 40 c. scarlet and dull purple 2·50 4·25
99 50 c. black/*emerald* (1.2.36) 3·50 90
100 $1 black and red/*blue* (1.4.36) 2·00 90
101 $2 green and scarlet (16.5.36) 15·00 8·50
102 $5 green and red/*emerald* (16.5.36) 55·00 28·00
88/102 *Set of* 15 80·00 45·00
88/102 Perf "Specimen" *Set of* 15 £160

No. 91 exists in coils constructed from normal sheets in 1936.

1938 (2 May)–**41.** *Wmk Mult Script CA. Chalk-surfaced paper. P* 14.
103 **51** 1 c. black (4.39) 4·75 10
104 2 c. green (13.1.39) 2·75 10
105 2 c. orange (30.10.41) 1·75 6·00
a. Ordinary paper 2·25 15·00
106 3 c. green (21.8.41) 1·75 4·00
107 4 c. orange (5.39) 30·00 10
108 5 c. brown (1.2.39) 3·75 10
109 6 c. scarlet (12.39) 26·00 10
110 8 c. grey (1.12.38) 22·00 10
111 8 c. scarlet (18.12.41) 1·00 60·00
112 10 c. dull purple (17.10.38) 22·00 10
113 12 c. bright ultramarine (17.10.38) 20·00 2·00
114 15 c. brt ultram (*ordinary paper*) (8.41) 1·75 13·00
115 25 c. dull purple and scarlet (12.39) 70·00 4·25
116 30 c. dull purple and orange (17.10.38) 9·50 3·00
117 40 c. scarlet and dull purple 50·00 2·00
118 50 c. black/*emerald* (17.10.38) 26·00 75
119 $1 black and red/*blue* (7.40) £130 15·00
120 $2 green and scarlet (9.40) £140 55·00
121 $5 green and red/*emerald* (1.41) £190 £250
103/21 *Set of* 19 £650 £375
103/21 Perf "Specimen" *Set of* 19 £300

No. 108 exists in coils constructed from normal sheets.

The stamps issued during 1941 were printed by Harrison and Sons following bomb damage to the De La Rue works on 29 December 1940.

During shortages in 1941 stamps of STRAITS SETTLEMENTS (2 c.), SELANGOR (2 c., 3 c.) and PAHANG (8 c.) were issued in Perak.

1948 (1 Dec). *Royal Silver Wedding. As Nos.* 143/4 *of Jamaica.*
122 10 c. violet 15 10
123 $5 green 20·00 24·00

1949 (10 Oct). *75th Anniv of U.P.U. As Nos.* 145/8 *of Jamaica.*
124 10 c. purple 15 10
125 15 c. deep blue 1·00 80
126 25 c. orange 45 45
127 50 c. blue-black 1·75 2·50
124/7 *Set of* 4 3·00 3·50

52 Sultan Yussuf 'Izzuddin Shah

53 Sultan Idris Shah

1950 (17 Aug)–**56.** *Chalk-surfaced paper. Wmk Mult Script CA. P* 17½×18.
128 **52** 1 c. black 10 10
129 2 c. orange 10 10
130 3 c. green 1·50 10
a. Yellowish green (15.11.51) 4·00 3·75
131 4 c. brown 10 10
a. Yellow-brown (20.6.56) 2·50 10
132 5 c. bright purple (1.9.52) 50 80
a. Bright mauve (10.11.54) 1·25 80
133 6 c. grey 10 10
134 8 c. scarlet 30 75
135 8 c. green (1.9.52) 1·00 60
136 10 c. purple 10 10
a. Brown-purple (20.6.56) 2·75 30
137 12 c. scarlet (1.9.52) 1·00 2·50
138 15 c. ultramarine 30 10
139 20 c. black and green 30 30
140 20 c. bright blue (1.9.52) 75 10
141 25 c. purple and orange 30 10
142 30 c. scarlet and purple (5.9.55) 1·25 20
143 35 c. scarlet and purple (1.9.52) 70 25
144 40 c. red and purple 1·50 4·00
145 50 c. black and blue 70 10
146 $1 blue and purple 7·00 40
147 $2 green and scarlet 13·00 4·50
148 $5 green and brown 38·00 11·00
128/48 *Set of* 21 60·00 23·00

1953 (2 June). *Coronation. As No.* 153 *of Jamaica.*
149 10 c. black and reddish purple 55 10

1957 (26 June)–**61.** *As Nos.* 92/102 *of Kedah but with inset portrait of Sultan Yussuf 'Izzuddin Shah.*
150 1 c. black (21.8.57) 10 20
151 2 c. orange-red (25.7.57) 30 20
a. Red-orange (15.12.59) 75 2·25
152 4 c. sepia (21.8.57) 10 10
153 5 c. carmine-lake (21.8.57) 10 10
154 8 c. myrtle-green (21.8.57) 2·00 2·00
155 10 c. deep brown (4.8.57) 55 10
156 10 c. deep maroon (21.2.61) 90 10
157 20 c. blue 90 10
158 50 c. black and blue (*p* 12½) (25.7.57) 40 10
a. Perf 12½ × 13 (24.5.60) 30 10
159 $1 ultramarine and reddish purple (25.7.57) 5·00 30
160 $2 bronze-green & scar (*p* 12½) (21.8.57) 3·25 2·25
a. Perf 13 × 12½ (21.2.61) 3·25 1·25
161 $5 brown and bronze-green (*p* 12½) 8·00 6·50
a. Perf 13 × 12½ (24.5.60) 8·00 3·75
150/61 *Set of* 12 19·00 7·00

The 6, 12, 25 and 30 c. values used with this issue were Nos. 1/4 of Malayan Federation.

(Photo Harrison)

1963 (26 Oct). *Installation of the Sultan of Perak. W* w **13**. *P* 14½.
162 **53** 10 c. red, black, blue and yellow 10 10

54 *Vanda hookeriana*

55 *Delias ninus*

1965 (15 Nov)–**68.** *As Nos.* 166/72 *of Johore but with inset portrait of Sultan Idris as in T* **54**. *W* w **13** *(upright).*
163 1 c. multicoloured 10 30
w. Wmk inverted 2·25
164 2 c. multicoloured 10 30
w. Wmk inverted 5·00
165 5 c. pale black and multicoloured 10 10
a. Grey-black and multicoloured (2.4.68) 55 30
b. Yellow (flower) omitted 23·00
166 6 c. multicoloured 15 30
167 10 c. multicoloured 15 10
168 15 c. multicoloured 80 10
a. Black (country name and head) omitted £160
c. Magenta (background) omitted £130
169 20 c. multicoloured 1·25 10
a. Bright purple (blooms) omitted 38·00
163/9 *Set of* 7 2·25 1·00

No. 168a comes from a horizontal strip of three, the centre stamp having the black completely omitted. The two outer stamps show the colour partly omitted.

The 2 c. to 15 c. exist with PVA gum as well as gum arabic.

The higher values used with this issue were Nos. 20/27 of Malaysia (National Issues).

1970. *As Nos.* 163 *and* 167, *but W* w **13** *(sideways).*
170 **54** 1 c. multicoloured (27.5.70) 1·75 5·50
171 – 10 c. multicoloured (20.11.70) 5·00 2·50

1971 (1 Feb)–**78.** *As Nos.* 175/87 *of Johore, but with portrait of Sultan Idris and arms, as in T* **55**.

(*a*) *Litho by Bradbury, Wilkinson*
172 1 c. multicoloured 20 80
173 2 c. multicoloured 70 80
174 5 c. multicoloured 80 10
175 6 c. multicoloured 80 80
176 10 c. multicoloured 80 10
177 15 c. multicoloured 80 10
178 20 c. multicoloured 1·25 25
172/8 *Set of* 7 4·75 2·50

(*b*) *Photo by Harrison* (1977–78)
179 1 c. multicoloured 85 2·75
180 5 c. multicoloured 3·50 60
181 10 c. multicoloured 2·50 65
182 15 c. multicoloured 8·00 30
183 20 c. multicoloured 2·75 1·00
179/83 *Set of* 5 16·00 4·75

The higher values used with this issue were Nos. 64/71 of Malaysia (National Issues).

For differences between litho and photo printings, see after Johore, No. 187.

56 *Rafflesia hasseltii*

57 Coffee

1979 (30 Apr). *As Nos.* 188/94 *of Johore but with portrait of Sultan Idris as in T* **56**.
184 1 c. Type **56** 10 30
185 2 c. *Pterocarpus indicus* 10 30
186 5 c. *Lagerstroemia speciosa* 10 10
187 10 c. *Durio zibethinus* 15 10
188 15 c. *Hibiscus rosa-sinensis* 15 10
189 20 c. *Rhododendron scortechinii* 20 10
190 25 c. *Etlingera elatior* (inscr "*Phaeomeria speciosa*") 40 10
184/90 *Set of* 7 1·00 70

For higher values used in conjunction with this series see Nos. 190/7 of Malaysia (National Issues).

1983 (15 Oct)–**84**.* *As Nos.* 186/9 *but without wmk.*

No.	Description	Mint	Used
193	5 c. *Lagerstroemia speciosa* (9.9.83)	30	40
194	10 c. *Durio zibenthinus* (1984)	30	50
195	15 c. *Hibiscus rosa-sinensis* (9.9.83)	1·50	30
196	20 c. *Rhododendron scortechinii* (blackish brown background)	13·00	65
196*a*	20 c. *Rhododendron scortechinii* (bronze-green background) (20.3.84)	50	40

*There was no official release date for these stamps. Dates shown are the earliest recorded from postmarks and may be revised if earlier examples are reported.

For details of the shade differences between watermarked and unwatermarked printings see after Johore No. 200*a*.

On Nos. 193/5 and 196*a* the portrait and arms are redrawn smaller.

1986 (25 Oct)–**96**. *As Nos.* 202/8 *of Johore, but with portrait of Sultan Azlan Shah as in T* **57**. *P* 12.

No.	Description	Mint	Used
198	1 c. Type **57**	10	10
	w. Wmk inverted	4·50	
199	2 c. Coconuts	10	10
	f. Perf 14¾×14½ (1994)	3·25	20
200	5 c. Cocoa	10	10
	c. Perf 14×13¾ (1994)	3·25	20
	f. Perf 14¾×14½ (1996)	2·50	30
201	10 c. Black pepper	10	10
	c. Perf 14×13¾ (1995)	1·00	10
	f. Perf 14¾×14½ (1994)	2·25	20
202	15 c. Rubber	10	10
203	20 c. Oil palm	10	10
	c. Perf 14×13¾ (1994)	1·50	10
	e. Perf 14×14½ (1996)	4·00	40
	f. Perf 14¾×14½ (1996)	5·00	50
204	30 c. Rice	15	20
	aw. Wmk inverted		
	c. Perf 14×13¾ (1994)	8·50	40
	f. Perf 14¾×14½ (1995)	18·00	1·25
198/204	*Set of* 7	50	55

STAMP BOOKLETS

1935.

No.	Description	Price
SB1	$1 booklet containing twenty 5 c. (No. 91) in blocks of 10	
SB2	$1.30, booklet containing 5 c. and 8 c. (Nos. 91, 93), each in block of 10	

1938.

No.	Description	Price
SB3	$1 booklet containing twenty 5 c. (No. 108) in blocks of 10	
SB4	$1.30, booklet containing 5 c. and 8 c. (Nos. 108, 110), each in block of 10	

1973 (8 Dec). *Cover as Type* B **1** *of Johore, but inscr* "PERAK". *Stitched.*

No.	Description	Price
SB5	$3 booklet containing eight 5 c., 10 c. and twelve 15 c. (Nos. 174, 176/7) in blocks of 4	18·00

1979 (1 Dec). *Cover as No.* SB5 *of Johore, but inscr* "PERAK". *Stitched.*

No.	Description	Price
SB6	$3 booklet containing eight 5 c., 10 c. and twelve 15 c. (Nos. 186/8) in blocks of 4	7·00

No. SB6 exists with two different versions of the back cover.

1987 (1 June). *Cover as Type* B **2** *of Johore, but inscr* "PERAK". *Stapled.*

No.	Description	Price
SB7	$2 booklet containing 5 c., 10 c., 15 c. and 20 c. (Nos. 200/3) in blocks of 4	5·00

1992 (1 July). *"Kuala Lumpur '92" International Philatelic Exhibition. Cover as Type* B **3** *of Johore, but inscr* "Perak". *Stamps attached by selvedge.*

No.	Description	Price
SB8	$3 booklet containing 30 c. (No. 204) in block of 10	5·50

1993. *Covers as Nos.* SB8/9 *of Johore, but inscr* "Perak". *Stamps attached by selvedge.*

No.	Description	Price
SB9	$2 booklet containing 20 c. (No. 203) in block of 10	1·00
SB10	$3 booklet containing 30 c. (No. 204) in block of 10	1·50

OFFICIAL STAMPS

P.G.S. (O 1)   Service. (O 2)

1889 (1 Nov). *Stamps of Straits Settlements optd with Type* O **1**. *Wmk Crown CC (Nos. O6 and O8) or Crown CA (others).*

No.	Description	Mint	Used
O1	2 c. bright rose	2·25	3·25
	a. Opt double	£750	£750
	b. Wide space between "G" and "S"	40·00	50·00
	c. No stop after "S"	40·00	50·00
O2	4 c. brown	8·00	16·00
	a. Wide space between "G" and "S"	60·00	75·00
	b. No stop after "S"	85·00	£110
O3	6 c. lilac	18·00	35·00
	a. Wide space between "G" and "S"	90·00	£130
O4	8 c. orange	24·00	65·00
	a. Wide space between "G" and "S"	£110	£170
O5	10 c. slate	75·00	75·00
	a. Wide space between "G" and "S"	£200	£225
O6	12 c. blue (CC)	£160	£170
	a. Wide space between "G" and "S"	£500	
O7	12 c. brown-purple (CA)	£190	£250
	a. Wide space between "G" and "S"	£650	
O8	24 c. green (CC)	£500	£600
	a. Wide space between "G" and "S"	£1700	
O9	24 c. green (CA)	£130	£150
	a. Wide space between "G" and "S"	£450	

Nos. O1/9 were overprinted from a setting of 30 (3×10). The variety "wide space between G and S" occurs on R. 10/3 and R. 10/6 of the original printing. A later printing of the 2 c. and 4 c. values had this variety corrected, but was without a stop after "S" on R. 10/1 and R. 10/4.

1894 (1 June). *No.* 64 *optd with Type* O **2**.

No.	Description	Mint	Used
O10	5 c. blue	42·00	80
	a. Overprint inverted	£650	£450

1897. *No.* 70 *optd with Type* O **2**.

No.	Description	Mint	Used
O11	5 c. dull purple and olive-yellow	1·50	35
	a. Overprint double	£375	£400

PERLIS

Suzerainty over Perlis was transferred by Thailand to Great Britain in 1909. A Treaty of Friendship between Great Britain and Perlis was signed on 28 April 1930.

The State joined the Federation of Malaya on 1 February 1948.

> For stamps of THAILAND used in Perlis between 1894 and 1909 see VIII. SIAMESE POSTS IN NORTHERN MALAYA section.
>
> Issues of the FEDERATED MALAY STATES were in use from 10 July 1909 until 1912 and these were replaced by the stamps of KEDAH between 1912 and 1951.

1948 (1 Dec). *Royal Silver Wedding. As Nos.* 143/4 *of Jamaica.*

1		10 c. violet	30	2·00
2		$5 brown	28·00	42·00

1949 (10 Oct). *75th Anniv of U.P.U. As Nos.* 145/8 *of Jamaica.*

3		10 c. purple	30	60
4		15 c. deep blue	1·25	3·00
5		25 c. orange	65	2·00
6		50 c. blue-black	1·40	3·75
3/6		*Set of* 4	3·25	8·50

1 Raja Syed Putra

2 *Vanda hookeriana*

1951 (26 Mar)–**55**. *Chalk-surfaced paper. Wmk Mult Script CA. P* 17½ × 18.

7	**1**	1 c. black	10	80
8		2 c. orange	15	40
9		3 c. green	50	2·75
10		4 c. brown	70	30
11		5 c. bright purple (1.9.52)	30	2·00
12		6 c. grey	70	1·25
13		8 c. scarlet	1·25	4·00
14		8 c. green (1.9.52)	75	2·25
15		10 c. purple	30	20
16		12 c. scarlet (1.9.52)	75	2·50
17		15 c. ultramarine	1·75	2·75
18		20 c. black and green	80	4·75
19		20 c. bright blue (1.9.52)	85	65
20		25 c. purple and orange	1·25	1·25
21		30 c. scarlet and purple (5.9.55)	1·75	8·00
22		35 c. scarlet and purple (1.9.52)	75	3·25
23		40 c. red and purple	1·50	14·00
24		50 c. black and blue	2·50	3·50
25		$1 blue and purple	4·75	12·00
26		$2 green and scarlet	12·00	20·00
27		$5 green and brown	50·00	60·00
7/27		*Set of* 21	75·00	£130

1953 (2 June). *Coronation. As No.* 153 *of Jamaica.*

28		10 c. black and reddish purple	50	2·25

1957 (26 June)–**62**. *As Nos.* 92/102 *of Kedah but with inset portrait of Raja Syed Putra.*

29	**9**	1 c. black (21.8.57)	10	30
30	**10**	2 c. orange-red (25.7.57)	10	30
31	**11**	4 c. sepia (21.8.57)	10	10
32	**12**	5 c. carmine-lake (21.8.57)	10	10
33	**13**	8 c. myrtle-green (21.8.57)	2·00	1·75
34	**14**	10 c. deep brown (4.8.57)	50	1·00
35		10 c. deep maroon (14.3.61)	3·00	1·75
36	**15**	20 c. blue	1·00	1·75
37	**16**	50 c. black and blue (*p* 12½) (25.7.57)	40	1·75
		a. Perf 12½ × 13 (8.5.62)	1·50	2·00
38	**17**	$1 ultram & reddish purple (25.7.57)	4·25	5·50
39	**18**	$2 bronze-green and scarlet (25.7.57)	4·25	5·00
40	**19**	$5 brown and bronze-green (21.8.57)	8·00	8·50
29/40		*Set of* 12	21·00	25·00

The 6, 12, 25 and 30 c. values used with this issue were Nos. 1/4 of Malayan Federation.

1965 (15 Nov). *As Nos.* 166/72 *of Johore but with inset portrait of Tunku Bendahara Abu Bakar as in T* **2**.

41		1 c. multicoloured	10	60
		w. Wmk inverted	10·00	
42		2 c. multicoloured	10	70
43		5 c. multicoloured	15	15
44		6 c. multicoloured	65	45
45		10 c. multicoloured	65	15
46		15 c. multicoloured	1·00	35
47		20 c. multicoloured	1·00	95
41/7		*Set of* 7	3·25	3·00

The 6 c. exists with PVA gum as well as gum arabic.

The higher values used with this issue were Nos. 20/27 of Malaysia (National Issues).

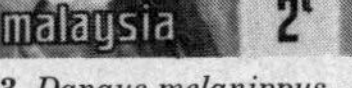

3 *Danaus melanippus*

4 Raja Syed Putra

1971 (1 Feb)–**78**. *As Nos.* 175/87 *of Johore but with portrait of Raja Syed Putra and Arms, as in T* **3**.

(*a*) *Litho by Bradbury, Wilkinson*

48		1 c. multicoloured	20	80
49		2 c. multicoloured	30	90
50		5 c. multicoloured	80	40
51		6 c. multicoloured	80	1·25
52		10 c. multicoloured	80	55
53		15 c. multicoloured	80	25
54		20 c. multicoloured	80	1·00
48/54		*Set of* 7	4·00	4·75

(*b*) *Photo by Harrison* (1977–78)

54*a*		10 c. multicoloured	55·00	6·50
55		15 c. multicoloured	5·50	2·25
55*a*		20 c. multicoloured	25·00	23·00

The higher values used with this issue were Nos. 64/71 of Malaysia (National Issues).

For differences between litho and photo printings, see after Johore No. 187.

(Des Citizen Studio and Engravers. Litho Enschedé)

1971 (28 Mar). *25th Anniv of Installation of Raja Syed Putra. P* 13½ × 13.

56	**4**	10 c. multicoloured	30	1·00
57		15 c. multicoloured	30	50
58		50 c. multicoloured	80	3·00
56/8		*Set of* 3	1·25	4·00

5 *Pterocarpus indicus*

6 Coconuts

1979 (30 Apr). *As Nos.* 188/94 *of Johore but with portrait of Raja Syed Putra as in T* **5**.

59		1 c. *Rafflesia hasseltii*	10	50
60		2 c. Type **5**	10	50
61		5 c. *Lagerstroemia speciosa*	10	45
62		10 c. *Durio zibethinus*	15	10
63		15 c. *Hibiscus rosa-sinensis*	15	10
64		20 c. *Rhododendron scortechinii*	20	10
65		25 c. *Etlingera elatior* (inscr "*Phaeomeria speciosa*")	40	45
59/65		*Set of* 7	1·00	2·00

For higher values used in conjunction with this series see Nos. 190/7 of Malaysia (National Issues).

1983–84*. *As No.* 64 *but without wmk.*

71		20 c. *Rhododendron scortechinii* (blackish brown background)	18·00	4·75
71*a*		20 c. *Rhododendron scortechinii* (bronze-green background) (4.12.84)	75	1·50

*There was no official release date for these stamps. Dates shown are the earliest recorded from postmarks and may be revised if earlier examples are reported.

For details of the shade differences between watermarked and unwatermarked printings see after Johore No. 200*a*.

No. 71*a* shows the Sultan's head larger than on Nos. 64 and 71 and has "perlis" in rounded, instead of square-ended, letters. instead of square-ended, letters.

1986 (25 Oct)–**94**. *As Nos.* 202/8 *of Johore, but with portrait of Raja Syed Putra as in T* **6**. *P* 12.

73		1 c. Coffee	10	10
		w. Wmk inverted	7·00	
74		2 c. Type **6**	10	10
75		5 c. Cocoa	10	10
76		10 c. Black pepper	10	10
		f. Perf 14¾×14½ (1994)	4·50	50
77		15 c. Rubber	10	10
78		20 c. Oil palm	10	10
79		30 c. Rice	15	20
		aw. Wmk inverted		
		c. Perf 14×13¾ (1994)	4·50	30
73/9		*Set of* 7	50	55

7 Raja Syed Putra and Aspects of Perlis

(Des BJ Image Sdn Bhd. Litho Security (M), Malaysia)

1995 (4 Dec). *50th Anniv of Raja Syed Putra's Accession. T* **7** *and similar horiz design. Multicoloured. W* **138** (*sideways*). *P* 14×14½.

80		30 c. Type **7**	20	25
		a. Perf 13½		
81		$1 Raja Syed Putra and Palace	60	1·00
		a. Perf 13½		

STAMP BOOKLETS

1973 (8 Dec). *Cover as Type* B **1** *of Johore, but inscr* "PERLIS". *Stitched.*

SB1	$3 booklet containing eight 5 c., 10 c. and twelve 15 c. (Nos. 50, 52/3) in blocks of 4	20·00

Examples of No. SB1 exist with a white label giving revised postage rates.

1979 (1 Dec). *Cover as No.* SB5 *of Johore, but inscr* "PERLIS". *Stitched.*

SB2	$3 booklet containing eight 5 c., 10 c., and twelve 15 c. (Nos. 61/3) in blocks of 4	8·00

No. SB2 exists with two different versions of the back cover.

1987 (1 June). *Cover as Type* B **2** *of Johore, but inscr* "PERLIS". *Stapled.*

SB3	$2 booklet containing 5 c., 10 c., 15 c. and 20 c. (Nos. 75/8) in blocks of 4	5·50

1992 (1 July). *"Kuala Lumpur '92" International Philatelic Exhibition. Cover as Type* B **3** *of Johore, but inscr* "Perlis". *Stamps attached by selvedge.*

SB4	$3 booklet containing 30 c. (No. 79) in block of 10	5·50

1993. *Covers as Nos.* SB8/9 *of Johore, but inscr* "Perlis". *Stamps attached by selvedge.*

SB5	$2 booklet containing 20 c. (No. 78) in block of 10	1·00
SB6	$3 booklet containing 30 c. (No. 79) in block of 10	1·50

SELANGOR

The first British Resident was appointed in 1874. Selangor joined the Federated Malay States in 1896.

> The stamps of the STRAITS SETTLEMENTS were used in Selangor from 1879 until 1881.
> Until 1 January 1899, when the Federated Malay States joined the U.P.U., mail for addresses outside Malaya was franked with stamps of the STRAITS SETTLEMENTS.

PRICES FOR STAMPS ON COVER TO 1945

Nos. 1/8	—
Nos. 9/19	*from* × 10
Nos. 20/30	*from* × 12
Nos. 31/3	*from* × 25
Nos. 34/6	*from* × 20
Nos. 37/8	*from* × 15
Nos. 38*a*/40	—
Nos. 41/2	*from* × 8
No. 43	—
Nos. 44/8	*from* × 8
Nos. 49/53	*from* × 30
Nos. 54/66	*from* × 10
Nos. 66*a*/7	*from* × 4
Nos. 68/85	*from* × 3
Nos. 86/7	*from* × 4

The Straits Settlements 1867 2 c. brown with Crown CC watermark (No. 11) has been known since 1881 overprinted in black with a crescent and star over a capital S, all within an oval, similar in style to the overprints listed for Perak and Sungei Ujong.

The status of this item remains unclear, but it may well represent the first issue of distinctive stamps for Selangor. This overprint should not be confused with a somewhat similar cancellation used on Selangor stamps of the same period. This cancellation differs in having a circular frame with the capital S shown above the crescent and star. It is usually struck in red.

A similar overprint in red on the Straits Settlements 2 c. brown with Crown CA watermark also exists and may have been produced for sale to collectors.

SELANGOR (1) ("S" inverted and narrow letters)
SELANGOR (2) ("S" wide)
SELANGOR (3) (narrow letters)
SELANGOR (4) ("N" wide)
SELANGOR (5) ("SE" and "AN" wide)
SELANGOR (6) ("SEL" and "N" wide)
SELANGOR (7) ("SELAN" wide)

1881–82. *No. 11 (wmk Crown CC) of Straits Settlements optd with T* **1/7**.

No.	Type	Description	Unused	Used
1	**1**	2 c. brown	£300	£325
2	**2**	2 c. brown	£100	£110
3	**3**	2 c. brown	70·00	75·00
4	**4**	2 c. brown	†	£2000
5	**5**	2 c. brown (1882)	£130	£140
6	**6**	2 c. brown (1882)	£130	£140
7	**7**	2 c. brown (1882)	£130	£140

Nos. 1/3 and 5/7 have been identified as coming from triplet settings, either Nos. 1 + 2 + 3, 2 + 3 + 3 or 5 + 6 + 7. The setting for No. 4 is unknown.

S.
(8)

1882. *No. 50 (wmk Crown CA) of Straits Settlements optd with T* **8**.

No.	Type	Description	Unused	Used
8	**8**	2 c. brown	—	£1900

SELANGOR (9) ("SEL" and "NG" wide)
SELANGOR (10) ("E" and "ANG" wide)
SELANGOR (11) ("ELANG" wide)
SELANGOR (12) ("S" and "L" wide)
SELANGOR (13) ("S" and "A" wide)
SELANGOR (14) ("E" wide)
SELANGOR (15) ("EL" wide)
SELANGOR (16) ("SE" and "N" wide)
SELANGOR (17) ("S" and "N" wide)

1882–83. *No. 50 (wmk Crown CA) of Straits Settlements optd with T* **2/3** *and* **9/17**.

No.	Type	Description	Unused	Used
9	**9**	2 c. brown	£140	£140
10	**10**	2 c. brown	£140	£140
11	**11**	2 c. brown	£140	£140
12	**2**	2 c. brown (1883)	95·00	80·00
13	**3**	2 c. brown (1883)	£170	80·00
14	**12**	2 c. brown (1883)	—	£1800
15	**13**	2 c. brown (1883)	£325	£275
16	**14**	2 c. brown (1883)	£200	£160
17	**15**	2 c. brown (1883)	£200	£160
18	**16**	2 c. brown (1883)	95·00	95·00
19	**17**	2 c. brown (1883)	95·00	95·00

The above were all printed from triplet settings. Those so far identified are Nos. 9 + 10 + 11, 12 (with defective "G") + 13 + 13, 15 + 16 + 17 and 18 + 12 + 19. No. 14 occurs as the first position of a triplet, but the second and third units are not yet known.

SELANGOR (18) ("E" and "A" wide)
SELANGOR (19) ("A" wide)
SELANGOR (20) ("L" wide)
SELANGOR (21) ("L" narrow)
SELANGOR (22) ("A" narrow)
SELANGOR (23) (wide letters)

1883–85. *No. 63 of Straits Settlements optd with T* **2, 4, 12, 14/15** *and* **18/23**.

No.	Type	Description	Unused	Used
20	**12**	2 c. pale rose	£120	£120
21	**14**	2 c. pale rose	80·00	80·00
		a. Opt double		
22	**4**	2 c. pale rose (1884)	£130	£130
23	**15**	2 c. pale rose (1884)	70·00	75·00
		a. Opt double	£700	
		b. Opt triple		
24	**2**	2 c. pale rose (1884)	80·00	80·00
25	**18**	2 c. pale rose (1884)	80·00	80·00
26	**19**	2 c. pale rose (1884)	£180	£140
27	**20**	2 c. pale rose (1884)	£300	£160
28	**21**	2 c. pale rose (1885)	70·00	80·00
29	**22**	2 c. pale rose (1885)	£110	£120
30	**23**	2 c. pale rose (1885)	£225	£160

The above come from triplet settings with Nos. 20 + 21 + 21, 22 + 22 + 23, 23 + 26 (with defective "A") + 26, 24 + 25 + 23 and 28 + 29 + 28 so far identified. The triplets for Nos. 27 and 30 are not known.

SELANGOR (24)
Selangor (25)
SELANGOR (26)
SELANGOR (27)
SELANGOR (28)
SELANGOR (29)
SELANGOR (30)
SELANGOR (31)
SELANGOR (32)
SELANGOR (33)
SELANGOR (34)

1885–91. *Nos. 63/a of Straits Settlements optd with T* **24/34**.

No.	Type	Description	Unused	Used
31	**24**	2 c. pale rose	6·50	13·00
		a. Opt double	£750	£650
32	**25**	2 c. pale rose	£850	£900
33	**26**	2 c. pale rose	23·00	26·00
34	**27**	2 c. pale rose (1886)	45·00	40·00
		a. Opt double	†	£650
35	**28**	2 c. pale rose (horiz opt without stop) (1887)	5·00	2·25
		a. Bright rose	5·00	2·25
36		2 c. pale rose (horiz opt with stop) (1887)	48·00	45·00
		a. Bright rose		
37	**29**	2 c. pale rose (1889)	£140	70·00
38	**30**	2 c. pale rose (vert opt) (1889)	50·00	6·00
		a. Bright rose		
38*b*		2 c. bright rose (horiz opt) (1889)	£3000	
39	**31**	2 c. pale rose (diagonal opt) (1889)	£1400	
40	**32**	2 c. pale rose (1889)	£275	22·00
41	**28**	2 c. brt rose (vert opt without stop) (1890)	12·00	21·00
42	**33**	2 c. bright rose (1890)	95·00	3·00
43	**34**	2 c. bright rose (1891)	£275	£170

Settings:
- Nos. 31/4 – each in triplet containing three examples of the same stamp
- No. 35 – triplet of 60 (6×10)
- No. 36 – 60 (6×10)
- Nos. 37/8 – 60 (6×10) containing both overprints in an unknown combination, but with No. 38 predominating
- Nos. 38*b*/9 – not known
- Nos. 40/3 – each in 60 (6×10)

SELANGOR Two CENTS (35)
SELANGOR Two CENTS (36)
SELANGOR Two CENTS (37)
SELANGOR Two CENTS (38)
SELANGOR Two CENTS (39)

1891. *No. 68 of Straits Settlements, surch with T* **35/9**, *each with bar obliterating old value.*

No.	Type	Description	Unused	Used
44	**35**	2 c. on 24 c. green	18·00	55·00
45	**36**	2 c. on 24 c. green	£120	£180
46	**37**	2 c. on 24 c. green	£120	£180
47	**38**	2 c. on 24 c. green	65·00	£110
		a. "SELANGCR"		
48	**39**	2 c. on 24 c. green	£120	£180

Nos. 44/8 come from the one setting used to surcharge the panes of sixty. No. 44 occurs in rows 1 to 5, No. 45 on row 6, No. 46 on row 7, No. 47 on rows 8 and 9, and No. 48 on row 10.

The error, No. 47a, occurs in the first printing only and is No. 45 (R.8/3) on the pane.

40

3 CENTS
(41)

1891 (Nov)–95. *Wmk Crown CA. P 14.*

No.	Type	Description	Unused	Used
49	**40**	1 c. green (1893)	70	25
50		2 c. rose	3·50	1·00
51		2 c. orange (1895)	1·50	60
52		5 c. blue (1892)	16·00	4·50
49/52		*Set of* 4	20·00	5·75
49/52 Optd "Specimen"		*Set of* 4	70·00	

1894. *Surch with T* **41**. *Wmk Crown CA. P 14.*

No.	Type	Description	Unused	Used
53	**40**	3 c. on 5 c. rose (Optd S. £30)	1·50	40

42

43

Dented frame above "A" of "SELANGOR" (left pane R. 4/5)

1895–99. *Wmk Crown CA or Crown CC (dollar values). P 14.*

No.	Type	Description	Unused	Used
54	**42**	3 c. dull purple and carmine	5·50	30
55		5 c. dull purple and olive-yellow	1·75	30
56		8 c. dull purple and ultramarine (1898)	70·00	7·00
57		10 c. dull purple and orange	8·50	1·50
58		25 c. green and carmine (1896)	80·00	48·00
59		50 c. dull purple and greenish black (1896)	38·00	22·00
		a. Dented frame	£275	
60		50 c. green and black (1898)	£250	£100
		a. Dented frame		
61	**43**	$1 green and yellow-green	45·00	85·00
62		$2 green and carmine (1897)	£140	£140
63		$3 green and ochre (1897)	£350	£225
64		$5 green and blue	£130	£180
65		$10 green and purple (1899) (S. £90)	£400	£475
66		$25 green and orange (1899?) (S. £180)	£1800	
54/62		*Set of* 9	£550	£350
54/64 Optd "Specimen"		*Set of* 11	£225	

> Pending the arrival of the permanent Federated Malay States issue the stamps of STRAITS SETTLEMENTS and PERAK were used at various times between July 1900 and March 1901.
> The general issues for the FEDERATED MALAY STATES were used in Selangor from 1901 until 1935.

One cent.
(44)

Three cents.
(45)

1900 (Oct). *Nos. 55 and 59 surch with T* **44** *or* **45**.

No.	Type	Description	Unused	Used
66*a*	**42**	1 c. on 5 c. dull purple & ol-yell (31 Oct*)	60·00	£100
66*b*		1 c. on 50 c. green and black (22 Oct*)	1·00	17·00
		bc. "cent" repeated at left	£1700	
		bd. Dented frame	50·00	
67		3 c. on 50 c. green and black (30 Oct*)	4·00	17·00
		a. Antique "t" in "cents"	£225	£325
		b. Dented frame	£180	

*Earliest known postmark date.

It is believed that these stamps were surcharged from settings of 30, repeated four times to complete the sheet of 120.

No. 66bc occurred on two separate vertical strips of five stamps where two impressions of the setting overlapped.

The position in the setting of No. 67a is not known.

46 Mosque at Palace, Klang

47 Sultan Suleiman

(Des E. J. McNaughton)

1935 (2 Dec)–41. *Wmk Mult Script CA (sideways on T* **46**). *Chalk-surfaced paper. P 14 or 14×14½ (No. 70).*

No.	Type	Description	Unused	Used
68	**46**	1 c. black (1.1.36)	30	10
69		2 c. green (1.1.36)	60	10
70		2 c. orange (*ordinary paper*) (*p* 14×14½) (21.8.41)	2·50	1·10
		a. Perf 14. Ordinary paper (9.41)	20·00	6·50
		ab. Chalk-surfaced paper	26·00	7·00
71		3 c. green (21.8.41)	12·00	2·75
		a. Ordinary paper	75	7·00
72		4 c. orange	30	10
73		5 c. brown (5.12.35)	60	10
74		6 c. scarlet (1.1.37)	4·50	10

75 46 8 c. grey 50 10
76 10 c. dull purple (1.1.36) 50 10
77 12 c. bright ultramarine (1.1.36) .. 1·00 10
78 15 c. brt ultram (*ordinary paper*) (1.10.41) 8·50 32·00
79 25 c. dull purple and scarlet (1.4.36) .. 1·00 60
80 30 c. dull purple and orange (1.1.36) .. 1·00 85
81 40 c. scarlet and dull purple .. .. 1·25 1·25
82 50 c. black/*emerald* (1.2.36) .. .. 1·00 15
83 47 $1 black and rose/*blue* (1.4.36) .. 5·50 60
84 $2 green and scarlet (16.5.36) .. 20·00 8·00
85 $5 green and red/*emerald* (16.5.36) .. 48·00 23·00
68/85 .. .. *Set of* 18 85·00 60·00
68/85 Perf "Specimen" .. .. *Set of* 18 £250

The stamps issued during 1941 were printed by Harrison and Sons following bomb damage to the De La Rue works on 29 December 1940.

Supplies of an unissued 8 c. scarlet were diverted to Australia in 1941. Examples circulating result from leakages of this supply (*Price* £375).

48 Sultan Hisamud-din Alam Shah 49

1941. *Wmk Mult Script CA. Chalk-surfaced paper. P* 14.
86 48 $1 black and red/*blue* (15.4.41) .. .. 10·00 6·00
87 $2 green and scarlet (7.7.41) (Perf S. £70) 48·00 27·00

A $5 green and red on emerald, T **48**, was issued overprinted during the Japanese occupation of Malaya. Unoverprinted examples are known, but were not issued (*Price* £95).

During shortages in 1941 stamps of STRAITS SETTLEMENTS (2 c.) and PERAK (25 c.) were issued in Selangor.

1948 (1 Dec). *Royal Silver Wedding. As Nos.* 143/4 *of Jamaica.*
88 10 c. violet 20 10
89 $5 green .. .. 23·00 14·00

1949 (12 Sept)–**55.** *Wmk Mult Script CA. Chalk-surfaced paper. P* 17½×18.
90 49 1 c. black 10 20
91 2 c. orange 10 20
92 3 c. green .. .. 30 1·50
93 4 c. brown 10 10
94 5 c. bright purple (1.9.52) 30 90
a. *Bright mauve* (17.9.53) 30 10
95 6 c. grey 10 10
96 8 c. scarlet 25 65
97 8 c. green (1.9.52) 65 80
98 10 c. purple 10 10
99 12 c. scarlet (1.9.52) .. .. .. 80 2·25
w. Wmk inverted £150
100 15 c. ultramarine .. .. .. 1·50 10
101 20 c. black and green 30 10
102 20 c. bright blue (1.9.52) 80 10
103 25 c. purple and orange 75 10
104 30 c. scarlet and purple (5.9.55) .. 1·25 80
105 35 c. scarlet and purple (1.9.52) .. 70 90
106 40 c. scarlet and purple .. .. 3·00 3·00
107 50 c. black and blue 70 10
108 $1 blue and purple .. .. .. 2·75 30
109 $2 green and scarlet .. .. .. 8·50 30
110 $5 green and brown .. .. .. 45·00 1·50
90/110 .. .. *Set of* 21 60·00 11·00

1949 (10 Oct). *75th Anniv of U.P.U. As Nos.* 145/8 *of Jamaica.*
111 10 c. purple 30 10
112 15 c. deep blue .. .. 1·25 75
113 25 c. orange .. .. 50 2·00
114 50 c. blue-black .. .. 1·50 2·00
111/14 .. .. *Set of* 4 3·25 4·25

1953 (2 June). *Coronation. As No.* 153 *of Jamaica.*
115 10 c. black and reddish purple 60 10

1957 (26 June)–**61.** *As Nos.* 92/102 *of Kedah but with inset portrait of Sultan Hisamud-din Alam Shah.*
116 1 c. black (21.8.57) 10 90
117 2 c. orange-red (25.7.57) 10 50
a. *Red-orange* (10.11.59) .. .. 3·75 3·75
118 4 c. sepia (21.8.57) 10 10
119 5 c. carmine-lake (21.8.57) 10 10
120 8 c. myrtle-green (21.8.57) .. .. 1·10 1·50
121 10 c. deep brown (4.8.57) 40 10
122 10 c. deep maroon (9.5.61) .. .. 3·00 10
123 20 c. blue 75 10
124 50 c. black and blue (*p* 12½) (25.7.57) .. 30 10
a. Perf 12½ × 13 (10.5.60) 30 10
125 $1 ultramarine and reddish purple (25.7.57) 2·00 10
126 $2 bronze-green & scarlet (*p* 12½) (21.8.57) 2·50 1·00
a. Perf 13 × 12½ (6.12.60) .. .. 2·25 1·75
127 $5 brown and bronze-green (*p* 12½) .. 7·00 2·00
a. Perf 13 × 12½ (10.5.60) .. .. 4·75 1·00
116/27a .. .. .. *Set of* 12 13·00 4·50

The 6, 12, 25 and 30 c. values used with this issue were Nos. 1/4 of Malayan Federation.

50 Sultan Salahuddin Abdul Aziz Shah 51

(Photo Harrison)

1961 (28 June). *Coronation of the Sultan. W* w **12.** *P* 15 × 14.
128 50 10 c. multicoloured 20 10
a. Black ptg misplaced £150

No. 128a is "The Double-headed Sultan" error, from one sheet where the majority of the stamps showed considerable black printing misplacement.

1961–62. *As Nos.* 92/8 *of Kedah but with inset portrait of Sultan Salahuddin Abdul Aziz as in T* **51.** *W* w **13.** *P* 12½ × 13 (*vert*) *or* 13 × 12½ (*horiz*).
129 1 c. black (1.3.62) 10 75
130 2 c. orange-red (1.3.62) 10 75
131 4 c. sepia (1.3.62) 10 10
132 5 c. carmine-lake (1.3.62) 10 10
133 8 c. myrtle-green (1.3.62) .. .. .. 1·50 2·50
134 10 c. deep maroon (1.11.61) 30 10
135 20 c. blue (1.3.62) .. .. 2·25 20
129/35 .. .. *Set of* 7 3·75 4·00

52 *Vanda hookeriana* 53 *Parthenos sylvia*

1965 (15 Nov). *As Nos.* 166/72 *of Johore but with inset portrait of Sultan Salahuddin Abdul Aziz Shah as in T* **52.**
136 1 c. multicoloured 10 10
b. Magenta omitted .. .. .. 38·00
w. Wmk inverted 50
137 2 c. multicoloured 10 70
b. Yellow (flower) omitted .. .. 22·00
138 5 c. multicoloured 15 10
b. Yellow (flower) omitted .. .. 22·00
c. Red (leaves, etc) omitted .. .. 95·00
139 6 c. multicoloured 15 10
140 10 c. multicoloured 15 10
a. Red omitted .. .. 38·00
141 15 c. multicoloured .. .. 1·25 10
b. Green (value and leaves) omitted .. £140
142 20 c. multicoloured .. .. 1·90 30
a. Bright purple (blooms) omitted .. 38·00
b. Yellow (leaves) omitted .. .. 22·00
136/42 .. .. *Set of* 7 3·25 1·25

The 2 c. to 20 c. values exist with PVA gum as well as gum arabic.

The higher values used with this issue were Nos. 20/27 of Malaysia (National Issues).

1970 (20 Nov). *As Nos.* 136 *etc. but W* w **13** (*sideways*).
143 52 1 c. multicoloured .. .. .. 1·00 4·50
144 10 c. multicoloured .. .. .. 3·50 1·25
145 – 20 c. multicoloured .. .. .. 6·00 6·50
143/5 .. .. *Set of* 3 9·50 11·00

1971 (1 Feb)–**78.** *As Nos.* 175/87 *of Johore but with portrait of Sultan Salahuddin Abdul Aziz Shah and Arms, as in T* **53.**

(*a*) *Litho by Bradbury, Wilkinson*
146 1 c. multicoloured 20 80
147 2 c. multicoloured 75 80
148 5 c. multicoloured 75 10
149 6 c. multicoloured 75 80
150 10 c. multicoloured 75 10
a. Black (state inscr, portrait and arms) omitted .. .. 75·00
151 15 c. multicoloured 75 10
152 20 c. multicoloured .. .. 1·00 30
146/52 .. .. *Set of* 7 4·50 2·50

(*b*) *Photo by Harrison* (1977–78)
153 1 c. multicoloured .. .. 60 3·50
154 5 c. multicoloured .. .. 3·25 1·50
155 10 c. multicoloured .. .. 6·00 1·50
156 15 c. multicoloured .. .. 6·00 30
157 20 c. multicoloured .. .. 3·50 1·00
153/7 .. .. *Set of* 5 17·00 7·00

The higher values used with this issue were Nos. 64/71 of Malaysia (National Issues).

For differences between litho and photo printings see after Johore No. 187.

A used example of No. 150 has been seen with the magenta apparently missing.

For explanation of No. 150a, see note below No. 122 of Kelantan.

54 *Lagerstroemia speciosa*

55 Sultan Salahuddin Abdul Aziz Shah and Royal Crest

1979 (30 Apr). *As Nos.* 188/94 *of Johore but with portrait of Sultan Salahuddin Abdul Aziz Shah as in T* **54.**
158 1 c. *Rafflesia hasseltii* 10 40
159 2 c. *Pterocarpus indicus* 10 40
160 5 c. Type **54** 10 10
161 10 c. *Durio zibethinus* 15 10
162 15 c. *Hibiscus rosa-sinensis* 15 10
163 20 c. *Rhododendron scortechinii* 20 10
164 25 c. *Etlingera elatior* (inscr "*Phaeomeria speciosa*") 40 10
158/64 .. .. *Set of* 7 1·00 90

For higher values used in conjunction with this series see Nos. 190/7 of Malaysia (National Issues).

1983 (6 Oct)–**85.*** *As Nos.* 160/3 *but without wmk.*
166 5 c. Type **54** (20.11.83) 40 50
167 10 c. *Durio zibethinus* (3.85) .. .. 1·50 1·40
168 15 c. *Hibiscus rosa-sinensis* (20.11.83) .. 1·50 60
169 20 c. *Rhododendron scortechinii* (blackish brown background) .. .. .. 13·00 90
169*a* 20 c. *Rhododendron scortechinii* (bronze-green background) (12.12.83) 70 55

*There was no official release date for these stamps. Dates shown are the earliest recorded from postmarks and may be revised if earlier examples are reported.

For details of the shade differences between watermarked and unwatermarked printings see after Johore No. 200*a*.

On Nos. 166/8 and 169*a* the ruler's headdress is bolder than on Nos. 160/3 and 169.

(Des P. Ket. Litho Security Printers (M), Malaysia)

1985 (5 Sept). *Silver Jubilee of Sultan. P* 13.
173 55 15 c. multicoloured 90 10
174 20 c. multicoloured .. .. .. 1·00 15
175 $1 multicoloured .. .. .. 4·00 5·50
173/5 .. .. *Set of* 3 5·50 5·50

56 Black Pepper

1986 (25 Oct)–**95.** *As Nos.* 202/8 *of Johore, but with portrait of Sultan Salahuddin Abdul Aziz Shah as in T* **56.** *P* 12.
176 1 c. Coffee 10 10
w. Wmk inverted .. .. .. 10·00
177 2 c. Coconuts 10 10
178 5 c. Cocoa 10 10
c. Perf 14×13¾ (1994) .. .. .. 1·00 10
f. Perf 14¾×14½ (1994) .. .. .. 4·50 30
179 10 c. Type **56** 10 10
a. Wmk sideways .. .. .. 13·00
bw. Wmk inverted .. .. ..
c. Perf 14×13¾ (1995) .. .. .. 3·50 20
cw. Wmk inverted .. .. .. 10·00
f. Perf 14¾×14½ (1995) .. .. .. 12·00 45
180 15 c. Rubber 10 10
181 20 c. Oil palm 10 10
aw. Wmk inverted .. .. ..
c. Perf 14×13¾ (1994) .. .. .. 1·00 10
d. Perf 14 .. ..
182 30 c. Rice 15 20
aw. Wmk inverted .. .. ..
c. Perf 14×13¾ (1994) .. .. .. 1·00 10
d. Perf 14 .. ..
e. Perf 14×14½ (1994) .. .. ..
f. Perf 14¾×14½ (1995) .. .. .. 4·50 20
176/82 .. .. *Set of* 7 50 55

STAMP BOOKLETS

1935. *Stapled.*
SB1 $1 booklet containing twenty 5 c. (No. 73) in blocks of 10 .. ..
SB2 $1.30, booklet containing 5 c. and 8 c. (Nos. 73, 75), each in block of 10 .. .. ..

1973 (8 Dec). *Cover as Type* B **1** *of Johore, but inscr* "SELANGOR". *Stitched.*
SB3 $3 booklet containing eight 5 c., 10 c. and twelve 15 c. (Nos. 148, 150/1) in blocks of 4 .. 18·00

1979 (1 Dec). *Cover as No.* SB5 *of Johore, but inscr* "SELANGOR". *Stitched.*
SB4 $3 booklet containing eight 5 c., 10 c., and twelve 15 c. (Nos. 160/2) in blocks of 4 .. .. 7·00

No. SB4 exists with two different versions of the back cover.

1986. *Black on lemon cover as Type* B **2** *of Federal Territory. Stamps attached by selvedge.*
SB5 $1.50, booklet containing 15 c. (No. 162) in pair and 20 c. (No. 169*a*) in block of 6 .. 6·50

1986. *Cover as No.* SB5, *but surch with new value and contents. Stamps attached by selvedge.*
SB6 60 c. booklet containing 20 c. (No. 169*a*) in strip of 3 .. .. 8·00

1987. *Black on buff cover as Type* B **2** *of Federal Territory. Stamps attached by selvedge.*
SB7 60 c. booklet containing 20 c. (No. 181) in strip of 3 2·75

1987 (1 June). *Cover as Type* B **2** *of Johore, but inscr* "SELANGOR". *Stapled.*
SB8 $2 booklet containing 5 c., 10 c., 15 c. and 20 c. (Nos. 178/81) in blocks of 4 .. .. .. 5·00

1991. *Black on buff cover as Type* B **2** *of Federal Territory. Stamps attached by selvedge.*
SB9 60 c. booklet containing 10 c. (No. 179) in strip of 3 and 15 c. (No. 180) in pair .. .. .. 1·25

1992 (1 July). *"Kuala Lumpur '92" International Philatelic Exhibition. Cover as Type* B **3** *of Johore, but inscr* "Selangor". *Stamps attached by selvedge.*
SB10 $3 booklet containing 30 c. (No. 182) in block of 10 .. .. 5·50

1993 (June). *Covers as Nos.* SB8/9 *of Johore, but both on pale buff and inscr* "Selangor". *Stamps attached by selvedge.*
SB11 $2 booklet containing 20 c. (No. 181) in block of 10 .. .. 1·00
SB12 $3 booklet containing 30 c. (No. 182) in block of 10 .. .. 1·50

TRENGGANU

Suzerainty over Trengganu was transferred by Thailand to Great Britain in 1909. A British adviser was appointed in 1919. The state joined the Federation of Malaya on 1 February 1948.

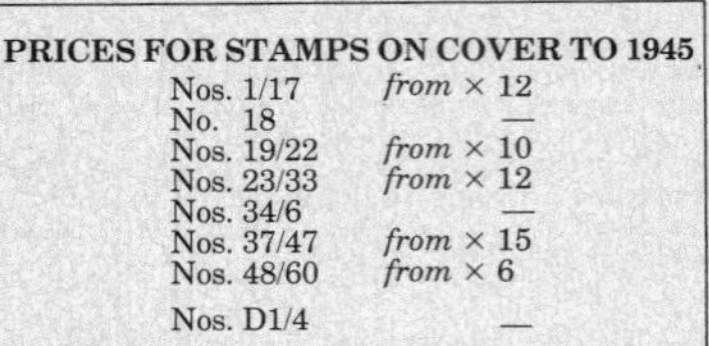

PRICES FOR STAMPS ON COVER TO 1945

Nos. 1/17	*from* × 12
No. 18	—
Nos. 19/22	*from* × 10
Nos. 23/33	*from* × 12
Nos. 34/6	—
Nos. 37/47	*from* × 15
Nos. 48/60	*from* × 6
Nos. D1/4	—

RED CROSS

2c.

1 Sultan Zain ul ab din 2 (3)

1910 (14 Dec)–**19**. *Wmk Mult Crown CA. Ordinary paper (1 c. to 10 c.) or chalk-surfaced paper (20 c. to $25). P 14.*

1	1	1 c. blue-green	50	1·00
		a. Green	2·00	1·00
2		2 c. brown and purple (1915)	40	90
3		3 c. carmine-red	2·00	2·25
4		4 c. orange	3·50	5·50
5		4 c. red-brown and green (1915)	2·00	3·75
5*a*		4 c. carmine-red (1919)	60	1·75
6		5 c. grey	1·25	2·75
7		5 c. grey and brown (1915)	2·25	2·00
8		8 c. ultramarine	1·25	8·00
9		10 c. purple/*yellow*	5·00	10·00
		a. On pale yellow	3·00	3·50
10		10 c. green and red/*yellow* (1915)	1·00	2·25
11		20 c. dull and bright purple	2·50	3·75
12		25 c. green and dull purple (1915)	5·00	25·00
13		30 c. dull purple and black (1915)	6·50	42·00
14		50 c. black/*green*	4·50	6·00
15		$1 black and carmine/*blue*	14·00	17·00
16		$3 green and red/*green* (1915)	£100	£190
17	2	$5 green and dull purple (1912)	£110	£325
18		$25 rose-carmine and green (1912) (Optd S. £160)	£750	
1/17		*Set of* 18	£225	£550
1/17 Optd "Specimen"		*Set of* 18	£400	

The 8 c. is known used bisected at Kretai in December 1918. Such use was not officially authorised.

1917 (June)–**18**. *Surch with T* **3**.

19	1	2 c. on 3 c. carmine-red	30	4·00
		a. Comma after "2 c."	6·50	30·00
		b. "SS" in "CROSS" inverted	£275	£325
		c. "CSOSS for "CROSS"	70·00	£140
		d. "2" in thick block type	19·00	55·00
		e. Surch inverted	£700	£750
		f. Pair, one without surch	£2250	£2000
		g. "RED CROSS" omitted	£225	
		h. "RED CROSS" twice	£300	
		i. "2 c." omitted	£225	
		j. "2 c." twice	£275	
20		2 c. on 4 c. orange	1·00	11·00
		a. Comma after "2 c."	16·00	60·00
		b. "SS" in "CROSS" inverted	£1400	£950
		c. "CSOSS" for "CROSS"	£150	£300
		d. Surch double	£800	
		e. "RED CROSS" omitted	£275	
		f. "RED CROSS" twice	£425	
		g. "2 c." omitted	£275	
		h. "2 c." twice	£375	
21		2 c. on 4 c. red-brown and green (1918)	1·50	25·00
		a. Pair, one without surch	£1600	
22		2 c. on 8 c. ultramarine (1917)	50	25·00
		a. Comma after "2 c."	11·00	80·00
		b. "SS" in "CROSS" inverted	£650	
		c. "CSOSS"" for "CROSS"	£120	£325
		d. "RED CROSS" omitted	£275	
		e. "RED CROSS" twice	£375	
		f. "2 c." omitted	£275	
		g. "2 c." twice	£350	

The surcharges on Nos. 19/22 were arranged in settings of 18 (6×3) applied three times to cover the top nine rows of the sheet with the tenth row completed by a further impression so that "RED CROSS" from the centre row of the setting appears on the bottom sheet margin. Specialists recognise six different settings:

Setting I — Shows comma after "2" on both R.1/3 and 1/5, "SS" inverted on R.1/6 and "CSOSS" for "CROSS" on R.2/1. Used for 4 c. orange and 8 c.

Setting Ia — Inverted "SS" on R.1/6 corrected. Other varieties as Setting I. Used for 3 c., 4 c. orange and 8 c.

Setting II — "CSOSS" on R.2/1 corrected. Comma varieties as Setting I. Used for 3 c., 4 c. orange and 8 c.

Setting III — Both comma varieties now corrected. Used for 3 c., both 4 c. and 8 c.

Setting IIIa — "SS" inverted on R.2/5. Used for 3 c. only

Setting IV — Thick block "2" on R. 2/2. Inverted "SS" on R. 2/5 corrected. Used for 3 c. only.

Nos. 19g/j, 20e/h and 22d/g result from the misplacement of the surcharge.

MINIMUM PRICE

The minimum price quote is 10p which represents a handling charge rather than a basis for valuing common stamps. For further notes about prices see introductory pages.

During a temporary shortage between March and August 1921 2 c., 4 c. and 6 c. stamps of the STRAITS SETTLEMENTS were authorised for use in Trengganu.

2 CENTS

4 Sultan Suleiman 5 (6)

1921–41. *Chalk-surfaced paper. P 14. (a) Wmk Mult Crown CA.*

23	4	$1 purple and blue/*blue*	12·00	18·00
24		$3 green and red/*emerald*	75·00	£160
25	5	$5 green and red/*pale yellow*	75·00	£200
23/5		*Set of* 3	£150	£350
23/5 Optd "Specimen"		*Set of* 3	£100	

(b) Wmk Mult Script CA

26	4	1 c. black (1926)	1·25	80
		a. Ordinary paper (1941)	—	6·00
27		2 c. green	1·25	90
		a. Ordinary paper (1941)	—	6·00
28		3 c. green (1926)	1·50	85
29		3 c. reddish brown (1938)	18·00	9·50
		a. Ordinary paper. *Chestnut* (1941)	—	9·50
30		4 c. rose-red	1·25	30
		a. Ordinary paper. *Scarlet-verm* (1941)	—	15·00
31		5 c. grey and deep brown	2·00	3·75
32		5 c. purple/*yellow* (1926)	1·75	60
33		6 c. orange (1924)	2·75	30
		a. Ordinary paper (1941)	—	8·00
34		8 c. grey (1938)	18·00	3·75
		a. Ordinary paper (1941)	—	12·00
35		10 c. bright blue	2·00	60
36		12 c. bright ultramarine (1926)	4·25	3·50
37		20 c. dull purple and orange	2·00	1·50
38		25 c. green and deep purple	2·25	2·25
39		30 c. dull purple and black	3·25	1·75
40		35 c. carmine/*yellow* (1926)	4·50	8·00
41		50 c. green and bright carmine	5·00	1·75
42		$1 purple and blue/*blue* (1929)	9·00	3·50
43		$3 green and lake/*green* (1926)	55·00	£100
		a. Green and brown-red/green (1938)		
44	5	$5 green and red/*yellow* (1938)	£250	£1300
45		$25 purple and blue (S. £85)	£550	£850
46		$50 green and yellow (S. £170)	£1400	£2250
47		$100 green and scarlet (S. £350)	£4500	£5500
26/44		*Set of* 19	£350	£1300
26/44 Optd/Perf "Specimen"		*Set of* 19	£600	

The used price quoted for No. 44 is for an example with an identifiable cancellation from 1938–41.

Printings of the 2 c. yellow-orange, 3 c. blue-green, 4 c. purple/*yellow*, 6 c. slate-grey, 8 c. rose, 15 c. ultramarine and $1 black and red/*blue* on ordinary paper were despatched to Malaya in late 1941, but did not arrive before the Japanese occupation. Unused examples are known of the 2, 3, 6, 8 and 15 c. (*Price £110 each, unused*).

1922 (31 Mar). *Malaya–Borneo Exhibition, Singapore. Optd "MALAYA–BORNEO EXHIBITION" as T* **56** *of Straits Settlements at Singapore.*

48	4	2 c. green	1·75	25·00
49		4 c. rose-red	4·25	25·00
50	1	5 c. grey and brown	2·50	26·00
51		10 c. green and red/*yellow*	2·75	30·00
52		20 c. dull and bright purple	2·50	35·00
53		25 c. green and dull purple	2·50	35·00
54		30 c. dull purple and black	2·50	35·00
55		50 c. black/*green*	2·50	35·00
56		$1 black and carmine/*blue*	10·00	65·00
57		$3 green and red/*green*	£110	£350
58		$5 green and dull purple	£190	£600
48/58		*Set of* 11	£300	£1100

Minor varieties of this overprint exist as in Straits Settlements.

1941 (1 May). *Nos. 51 and 29 surch as T* **6**.

59	4	2 c. on 5 c. purple/*yellow*	6·50	3·50
60		8 c. on 10 c. bright blue	7·00	3·50

1948 (2 Dec). *Royal Silver Wedding. As Nos. 143/4 of Jamaica.*

61	10 c. violet	15	60
62	$5 carmine	20·00	32·00

1949 (10 Oct). *75th Anniv of U.P.U. As Nos. 145/8 of Jamaica.*

63	10 c. purple	30	35
64	15 c. deep blue	1·10	1·90
65	25 c. orange	55	2·25
66	50 c. blue-black	1·40	2·75
63/6	*Set of* 4	3·00	6·50

7 Sultan Ismail 8 *Vanda hookeriana*

1949 (27 Dec)–**55**. *Wmk Mult Script CA. Chalk-surfaced paper. P* $17\frac{1}{2}\times18$.

67	7	1 c. black	10	30
68		2 c. orange	10	30
69		3 c. green	30	2·25
70		4 c. brown	10	30
71		5 c. bright purple (1.9.52)	30	90
72		6 c. grey	15	30
73	7	8 c. scarlet	20	1·75
74		8 c. green (1.9.52)	65	1·00
		a. Deep green (11.8.53)	3·25	4·50
75		10 c. purple	15	10
76		12 c. scarlet (1.9.52)	65	1·75
77		15 c. ultramarine	30	30
78		20 c. black and green	30	2·25
79		20 c. bright blue (1.9.52)	80	30
80		25 c. purple and orange	40	75
81		30 c. scarlet and purple (5.9.55)	1·25	1·25
82		35 c. scarlet and purple (1.9.52)	70	1·60
83		40 c. red and purple	2·25	11·00
84		50 c. black and blue	50	1·25
85		$1 blue and purple	3·00	4·50
86		$2 green and scarlet	18·00	14·00
87		$5 green and brown	50·00	42·00
67/87		*Set of* 21	70·00	80·00

1953 (2 June). *Coronation. As No. 153 of Jamaica.*

88	10 c. black and reddish purple	50	50

1957 (26 June)–**63**. *As Nos. 92/102 of Kedah, but with inset portrait of Sultan Ismail.*

89	1 c. black (21.8.57)	10	20
90	2 c. orange-red (25.7.57)	70	30
	a. Red-orange (21.2.61)	13·00	11·00
91	4 c. sepia (21.8.57)	10	10
92	5 c. carmine-lake (21.8.57)	10	10
93	8 c. myrtle-green (21.8.57)	4·00	60
94	10 c. deep brown (4.8.57)	30	10
94*a*	10 c. deep maroon (21.2.61)	3·00	10
95	20 c. blue	50	60
96	50 c. black and blue (*p* $12\frac{1}{2}$) (25.7.57)	30	1·25
	a. Perf $12\frac{1}{2}\times13$ (17.5.60)	30	60
	ab. Black and ultramarine (20.3.62)	1·25	80
97	$1 ultramarine and reddish purple (25.7.57)	5·00	3·50
98	$2 bronze-green and scarlet (21.8.57)	8·50	6·00
99	$5 brown and bronze-green	14·00	12·00
	a. Perf $13\times12\frac{1}{2}$ (13.8.63)	15·00	13·00
89/99	*Set of* 12	32·00	21·00

The 6, 12, 25 and 30 c. values used with this issue were Nos. 1/4 of Malayan Federation.

1965 (15 Nov). *As Nos. 166/72 of Johore but with inset portrait of Sultan Ismail Nasiruddin Shah as in T* **8**.

100	1 c. multicoloured	10	70
101	2 c. multicoloured	10	70
102	5 c. multicoloured	10	10
	w. Wmk inverted		
103	6 c. multicoloured	15	70
104	10 c. multicoloured	20	10
105	15 c. multicoloured	1·50	10
106	20 c. multicoloured	1·50	50
	a. Bright purple (blooms) omitted	50·00	
100/6	*Set of* 7	3·25	2·50

The 5 c. value exists with PVA gum as well as gum arabic.

No. 101a, formerly listed here, is now listed as Sarawak No. 213a.

The higher values used with this issue were Nos. 20/27 of Malaysia (National Issues).

9 Sultan of Trengganu 10 *Papilio demoleus*

(Des Enche Nik Zainal Abidin. Photo Harrison)

1970 (16 Dec). *25th Anniv of Installation of H.R.H. Tuanku Ismail Nasiruddin Shah as Sultan of Trengganu. P* $14\frac{1}{2}\times13\frac{1}{2}$.

107	9	10 c. multicoloured	40	1·00
108		15 c. multicoloured	40	80
109		50 c. multicoloured	1·00	1·75
107/9		*Set of* 3	1·60	3·25

1971 (1 Feb)–**78**. *As Nos. 175/87 of Johore but with portrait of Sultan Ismail Nasiruddin Shah and Arms, as in T* **10**.

(a) Litho by Bradbury, Wilkinson

110	1 c. multicoloured	20	1·00
111	2 c. multicoloured	60	1·00
112	5 c. multicoloured	85	40
113	6 c. multicoloured	85	1·25
114	10 c. multicoloured	85	30
115	15 c. multicoloured	95	10
116	20 c. multicoloured	1·10	70
110/16	*Set of* 7	4·75	4·25

(b) Photo by Harrison (1977–78)

116*a*	5 c. multicoloured	18·00	8·50
117	10 c. multicoloured	6·00	2·75
117*a*	15 c. multicoloured	4·25	1·25

The higher values used with this issue were Nos. 64/71 of Malaysia (National Issues).

For differences between litho and photo printings, see after Johore No. 187.

11 *Durio zibethinus* 12 Sultan Mahmud

1979 (30 Apr). *As Nos.* 188/94 *of Johore but with portrait of Sultan Ismail Nasiruddin Shah as in T* **11**.

118	1 c. *Rafflesia hasseltii*	10	50
119	2 c. *Pterocarpus indicus*	10	50
120	5 c. *Lagerstroemia speciosa*	10	20
121	10 c. Type **11**	15	10
122	15 c. *Hibiscus rosa-sinensis*	15	10
123	20 c. *Rhododendron scortechinii*	20	10
124	25 c. *Etlingera elatior* (inscr "*Phaeomeria speciosa*")	40	30
118/24	*Set of* 7	1·00	1·40

For higher values used in conjunction with this series see Nos. 190/7 of Malaysia (National Issues).

(Des Malaysian Advertising Services. Litho Harrison)

1981 (21 Mar). *Installation of Sultan Mahmud. P* 14.

125	**12**	10 c. black, gold and new blue	25	70
126		15 c. black, gold and yellow	30	35
127		50 c. black, gold and bright purple	65	2·25
125/7		*Set of* 3	1·10	3·00

1983 (Oct)–**86.*** *As Nos.* 121/4 *but without wmk.*

131	10 c. Type **11** (1.2.86)	13·00	4·00
132	15 c. *Hibiscus rosa-sinensis* (24.1.85)	1·50	1·00
133	20 c. *Rhododendron scortechinii* (blackish brown background)	16·00	5·00
133*a*	20 c. *Rhododendron scortechinii* (bronze-green background) (2.3.84)	3·50	3·00
134	25 c. *Etlingera elatior* (inscr "*Phaeomeria speciosa*") (13.11.83)	75	1·00

*There was no official release date for these stamps. Dates shown are the earliest recorded from postmarks and may be revised if earlier examples are reported.

For details of the shade differences between watermarked and unwatermarked printings see after Johore No. 200*a*.

On Nos. 131/2, 133*a* and 134 the portrait and state arms have been redrawn smaller.

13 Rubber

1986 (25 Oct)–**95.** *As Nos.* 202/8 *of Johore, but with portrait of Sultan Mahmud and inscr* "TERENGGANU" *as in T* **13**. *P* 12.

135	1 c. Coffee	10	10
	b. Perf $13^1/_2 \times 13^3/_4$ (1993)	4·50	40
136	2 c. Coconuts	10	10
137	5 c. Cocoa	10	10
	w. Wmk inverted	10·00	
138	10 c. Black pepper	10	10
139	15 c. Type **13**	10	10
140	20 c. Oil palm	10	10
	c. Perf $14 \times 13^3/_4$ (1995)	7·00	30
141	30 c. Rice	15	20
	c. Perf $14 \times 13^3/_4$ (1994)		
	f. Perf $14^3/_4 \times 14^1/_2$ (1995)	2·75	30
135/41	*Set of* 7	50	55

STAMP BOOKLETS

1973 (8 Dec). *Cover as Type* B **1** *of Johore but inscr* "TRENGGANU". *Stitched.*

SB1 $3 booklet containing eight 5 c., 10 c. and twelve 15 c. (Nos. 112, 114/15) in blocks of 4 .. 18·00

Examples of No. SB1 exist with a white label giving revised postage rates.

1979 (1 Dec). *Cover as No.* SB5 *of Johore, but inscr* "TRENGGANU". *Stitched.*

SB2 $3 booklet containing eight 5 c., 10 c., and twelve 15 c. (Nos. 120/2) in blocks of 4 .. .. 7·00

No. SB2 exists with two different versions of the back cover.

1987 (1 June). *Cover as Type* SB **2** *of Johore, but inscr* "TERENGGANU". *Stapled.*

SB3 $2 booklet containing 5 c., 10 c., 15 c. and 20 c. (Nos. 137/40) in blocks of 4 .. .. .. 5·00

1992 (1 July). *"Kuala Lumpur '92" International Philatelic Exhibition. Cover as Type* B **3** *of Johore, but inscr* "Terengganu". *Stamps attached by selvedge.*

SB4 $3 booklet containing 30 c. (No. 141) in block of 10 5·50

1993. *Covers as Nos.* SB8/9 *of Johore, but inscr* "Terengganu". *Stamps attached by selvedge.*

SB5 $2 booklet containing 20 c. (No. 140) in block of 10 1·00
SB6 $3 booklet containing 30 c. (No. 141) in block of 10 1·50

POSTAGE DUE STAMPS

D 1

1937 (10 Aug). *Wmk Mult Script CA. P* 14.

D1	D 1	1 c. scarlet	7·50	55·00
D2		4 c. green	8·00	60·00
D3		8 c. yellow	55·00	£275
D4		10 c. brown	£110	95·00
D1/4		*Set of* 4	£160	£425
D1/4 Perf "Specimen"		*Set of* 4	£130	

VIII. SIAMESE POSTS IN NORTHERN MALAYA 1887–1909

The Thai monarchy exercised suzerainty over the northern states of the Malay Peninsula from the 16th century onwards. The extent of Thai involvement in the internal affairs of Kedah, Kelantan, Perlis and Trengganu was very variable, being dependent on the strength, or otherwise, of the Bangkok administration and the degree of co-operation of the local rulers.

The Thai public postal service, which had been inaugurated in 1883, gradually extended into the north of the Malay Peninsula from 1887 onwards and post offices were established in Kedah, Kelantan and Perlis. There is some evidence that Sultan Zainal Abidin III of Trengganu successfully blocked the use of Siamese stamps in his state.

Types of Thailand (Siam)

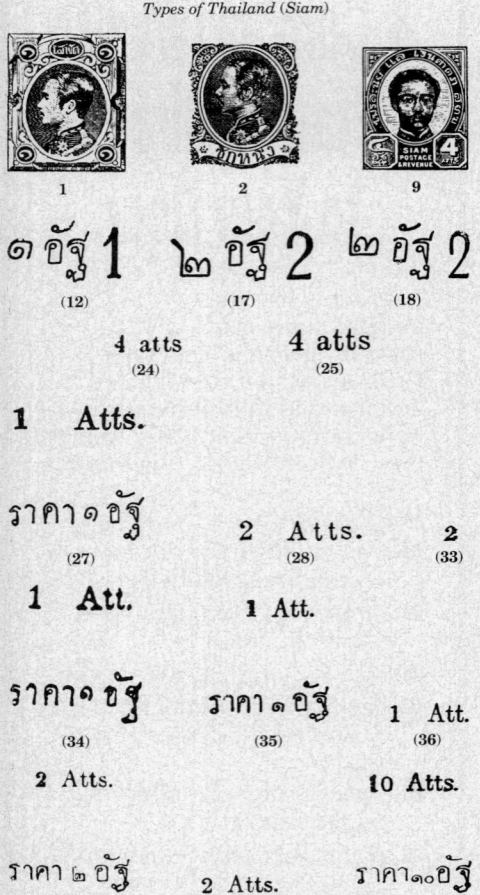

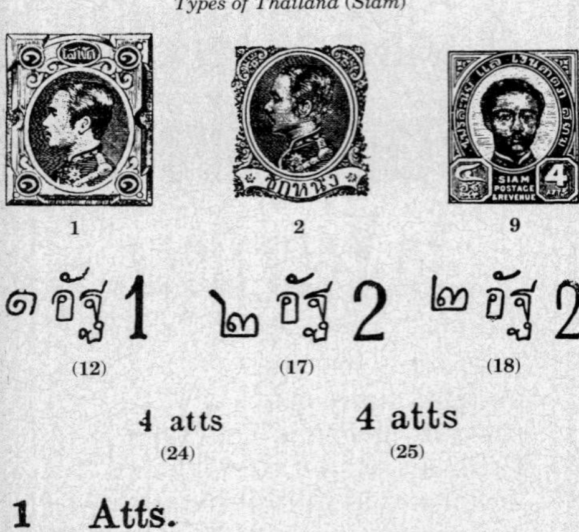

1 2 9

(12) (17) (18)

4 atts (24) 4 atts (25)

1 Atts.

(27) 2 Atts. (28) 2 (33)

1 Att. 1 Att.

(34) (35) 1 Att. (36)

2 Atts. 10 Atts.

(37) 2 Atts. (38) (39)

4 Atts. (40) 4 Atts. (41)

1 Att.

(42) 2 Atts. (44) 3 Atts. (45) 4 Atts. (46)

2 Atts. (48*a*)

49

50

1 Att. (51)

1att. (56) 9 Atts (59)

The following types of postmark were used on Siamese stamps from the Malay tributary states:

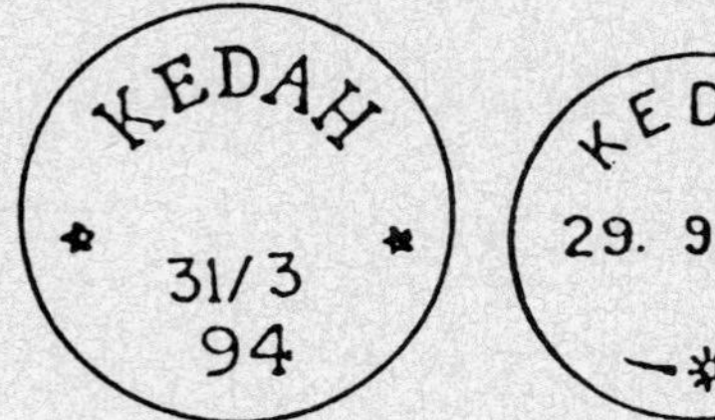

Type A. Single ring with date at foot

Type B. Single ring with date in centre

Type C. Double ring. Bilingual

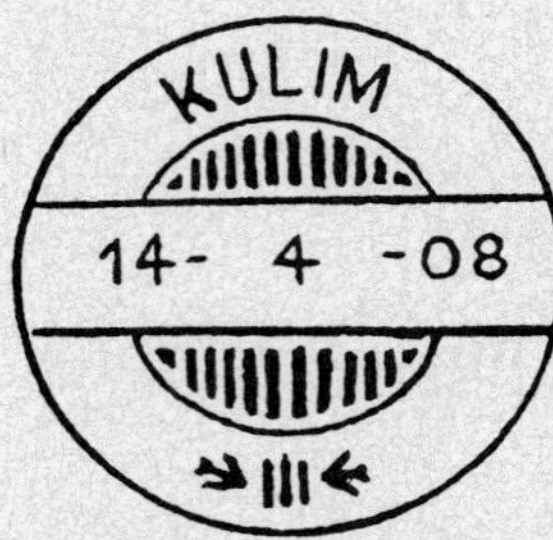

Type D. Double ring. English at top and ornament at foot

Type E. Double ring. English at top and bottom

PRICES are for stamps showing a large part of the postmark with the inscription clearly visible.

KEDAH

The Siamese post office at Alor Star was opened during 1887 with the first known postmark being dated 27 October. Further post offices at Kuala Muda, Kulim and Langkawi followed in 1907.

A straight-line obliteration showing "KEDAH" between short vertical dashes is not believed to be genuine.

Alor Star

Stamps of SIAM *cancelled as Type* A *inscribed* "KEDAH".

1883. (*Nos.* 1/5).
Z2 **1** 1 att. rose-carmine . . £225
Z3 1 sio. red . . £425
Z4 **2** 1 sik. yellow . . £425

1887–91. (*Nos.* 11/18).
Z 6 **9** 1 a. green . . 80·00
Z 7 2 a. green and carmine . . 70·00
Z 8 3 a. green and blue . . 90·00
Z 9 4 a. green and brown . . 80·00
Z10 8 a. green and yellow . . 80·00
Z11 12 a. purple and carmine . . 70·00
Z12 24 a. purple and blue . . 80·00
Z13 64 a. purple and brown . . £130

1889–91. *Surch as T* **12** (*Nos.* Z15, Z19), *T* **17** (*No.* Z21) *or T* **18** (*No.* Z22) (*Nos.* 20/30).
Z15 **9** 1 a. on 2 a. green and carmine . . 90·00
Z19 1 a. on 3 a. green and blue . . £100
Z21 2 a. on 3 a. green and blue . . £130
Z22 2 a. on 3 a. green and blue . . £160

1892. *Surch as T* **24/5** (*with or without stop*) *and Siamese handstamp* (*Nos.* 33/6).
Z28 **9** 4 a. on 24 a. purple and blue (Type **24**) . . 90·00
Z29 4 a. on 24 a. purple and blue (Type **25**) . . £110
Z30 4 a. on 24 a. purple and blue (Type **24** with stop) £110
Z31 4 a. on 24 a. purple and blue (Type **25** with stop) £110

1894. *Surch as T* **27** *with variations of English figures as T* **28** *and* **33** (*Nos.* 37/44).
Z34 **9** 2 a. on 64 a. purple and brown (Type **28**) . . 90·00
Z39 2 a. on 64 a. purple and brown (Type **33**) . . 90·00

1894. *Surch with T* **34** (*No.* 45).
Z41 **9** 1 a. on 64 a. purple and brown . . £110

1894–95. *Surch as T* **35** *with variations of English figures as T* **36/9** (*Nos.* 46/50).
Z42 **9** 1 a. on 64 a. purple and brown (Type **35**) . . 90·00
Z43 1 a. on 64 a. purple and brown (Type **36**) . . 90·00
Z44 2 a. on 64 a. purple and brown (Type **37**) . . 90·00
Z45 2 a. on 64 a. purple and brown (Type **38**) . . 90·00
Z46 10 a. on 24 a. purple and blue (Type **39**) . . 90·00

1896. *Surch as T* **39** (*Siamese*) *and T* **40** (*English*) (*No.* 51).
Z47 **9** 4 a. on 12 a. purple and carmine . . 90·00

1897. *Surch as T* **39** (*Siamese*) *and T* **41** (*English*) (*No.* 52).
Z48 **9** 4 a. on 12 a. purple and carmine . . 90·00

1898–99. *Surch as T* **42** *with variations of English section as T* **44/6** (*Nos.* 53/62).
Z49 **9** 1 a. on 12 a. purple and carmine (Type **42**–11½ mm long) . . £120
Z52 2 a. on 64 a. purple and brown (Type **44**) . . £100
Z53 3 a. on 12 a. purple and carmine (Type **45**–13½ mm long) . . 90·00
Z54 3 a. on 12 a. purple and carmine (Type **45**–11½ to 11¾ mm long) . . 90·00
Z55 4 a. on 12 a. purple & carm (Type **46**–8 mm long) 90·00
Z56 4 a. on 12 a. purple and carmine (Type **46**–8½ to 9 mm long) . . 90·00

1899. *Surch in Siamese and English with T* **48*a*** (*Nos.* 63/6).
Z62 **9** 2 a. on 64 a. purple and brown . . £100

1899–1904. (*Nos.* 67/81).
Z63 **49** 1 a. olive-green (wide Siamese characters in face value) . . 90·00
Z64 2 a. grass-green . . 70·00
Z65 3 a. red and blue . . 75·00
Z66 4 a. carmine . . 70·00
Z67 8 a. deep green and orange . . 70·00
Z69 12 a. brown-purple and carmine . . £110
Z70 24 a. brown-purple and blue . . £160
Z71 64 a. brown-purple and chestnut . . £130

1899. (*Nos.* 82/6).
Z72 **50** 1 a. green . . £275
Z73 2 a. green and red . . £425

Stamps of SIAM *cancelled as Type* B *inscr* "KEDAH".

1887–91. (*Nos.* 11/18).
Z74 **9** 12 a. purple and carmine . . 70·00
Z75 24 a. purple and brown . . 70·00

1898–99. *Surch with T* **42** *with variations of English section as T* **45/6** (*Nos.* 53/62).
Z76 **9** 1 a. on 12 a. pur & carm (Type **42**–11½ mm long) 90·00
Z81 3 a. on 12 a. purple and carmine (Type **45**–11½ to 11¾ mm long) . . 70·00
Z83 4 a. on 12 a. purple and carmine (Type **46**–8½ to 9 mm long) . . 70·00
Z84 4 a. on 24 a. purple and blue (Type **46**) . . 75·00

1899–1904. (*Nos.* 67/81).
Z86 **49** 1 a. olive-green (wide Siamese characters in face value) . . 70·00
a. Narrow Siamese characters in face value 65·00
Z87 2 a. grass-green . . 55·00
Z88 2 a. scarlet and pale blue . . 55·00
Z89 3 a. red and blue . . 65·00
Z90 3 a. deep green . . 65·00
Z91 4 a. carmine . . 55·00
Z92 4 a. chocolate and pink . . 60·00
Z93 8 a. deep green and orange . . 55·00
Z94 10 a. ultramarine . . 55·00
Z95 12 a. brown-purple and carmine . . 65·00
Z96 24 a. brown-purple and blue . . £130
Z97 64 a. brown-purple and chestnut . . £120

1905–09. (*Nos.* 92/105).
Z102 **53** 1 a. green and orange . . 55·00
Z103 2 a. grey and deep violet . . 55·00
Z104 3 a. green . . 65·00
Z105 4 a. pale red and sepia . . 55·00
Z106 5 a. carmine . . 65·00
Z107 8 a. olive-bistre and dull black . . 55·00
Z108 12 a. blue . . 65·00
Z109 24 a. red-brown . . £160
Z110 1 t. bistre and deep blue . . £160

Stamps of SIAM *cancelled as Type* C *inscr* "Kedah" *at foot.*

1887–91. (*Nos.* 11/18).
Z111 **9** 12 a. purple and carmine . . 80·00

1899–1904. (*Nos.* 67/81).

Z112	49	1 a. olive-green (wide Siamese characters in face value)	65·00
		a. Narrow Siamese characters in face value	60·00
Z113		2 a. scarlet and pale blue	55·00
Z114		3 a. red and blue	65·00
Z116		8 a. deep green and orange	65·00
Z117		10 a. ultramarine	60·00
Z118		12 a. brown-purple and carmine	60·00

1905–09. (*Nos.* 95/105).

Z128	53	1 a. green and orange	55·00
Z129		2 a. grey and deep violet	55·00
Z130		3 a. green	65·00
Z131		4 a. pale red and sepia	55·00
Z132		4 a. scarlet	55·00
Z133		5 a. carmine	65·00
Z134		8 a. olive-bistre and dull black	55·00
Z135		9 a. blue	55·00
Z136		18 a. red-brown	90·00
Z137		24 a. red-brown	£160
Z138		1 t. bistre and deep blue	£160

1907. *Surch with T* **56** (*No.* 109).

Z139	9	1 a. on 24 a. purple and blue	65·00

Kuala Muda

Stamps of SIAM *cancelled as Type* B *inscr* "KUALA MUDA".

1887–91. (*Nos.* 11/18).

Z143	9	12 a. purple and carmine	£300

1899–1904. (*Nos.* 67/81).

Z144	49	2 a. scarlet and pale blue	£300
Z145		24 a. brown-purple and blue	£350

1905–09. (*Nos.* 92/105).

Z146	53	1 a. green and orange	£300
Z147		2 a. grey and deep violet	£300
Z148		3 a. green	£325
Z150		5 a. carmine	£325
Z151		8 a. olive-bistre and dull black	£300

Stamps of SIAM *cancelled as Type* C *inscr* "Kuala Muda" *at foot.*

1887–91. (*Nos.* 11/18).

Z155	9	12 a. purple and carmine	£140

1899–1904. (*Nos.* 67/81).

Z156	49	8 a. deep green and orange	£170
Z157		10 a. ultramarine	£170

1905–09. (*Nos.* 92/105).

Z158	53	1 a. green and orange	£170
Z159		2 a. grey and deep violet	£170
Z160		3 a. green	£180
Z161		4 a. pale red and sepia	£170
Z162		4 a. scarlet	£170
Z163		5 a. carmine	£190
Z164		8 a. olive-bistre and dull black	£170
Z165		9 a. blue	£140
Z166		24 a. red-brown	£350

1907. *Surch with T* **56** (*No.* 109).

Z167	9	1 a. on 24 a. purple and blue	£140

Kulim

Stamps of SIAM *cancelled as Type* D *inscr* "KULIM".

1887–91. (*Nos.* 11/18).

Z173	9	12 a. purple and carmine	£300

1899–1904. (*Nos.* 67/81).

Z174	49	8 a. deep green and orange	£300

1905–09. (*Nos.* 92/105).

Z175	53	1 a. green and orange	£325
Z176		2 a. grey and deep violet	£325
Z178		4 a. pale red and sepia	£300
Z179		4 a. scarlet	£300
Z180		5 a. carmine	£325
Z181		8 a. olive-bistre and dull black	£300
Z182		9 a. blue	£300

1907. *Surch with T* **56**. (*No.* 109).

Z184	9	1 a. on 24 a. purple and blue	£300

Stamps of SIAM *cancelled as Type* C *inscr* "Kulim" *at foot.*

1887–91. (*Nos.* 11/18).

Z190	9	12 a. purple and carmine	£120

1899–1904. (*Nos.* 67/81).

Z191	49	8 a. deep green and orange	£120
Z192		10 a. ultramarine	£130

1905–09. (*Nos.* 92/105).

Z196	53	4 a. pale red and sepia	£120
Z197		4 a. scarlet	£120
Z198		5 a. carmine	£130
Z199		9 a. blue	£130
Z200		24 a. red-brown	£300
Z201		1 t. bistre and deep blue	£300

1907. *Surch with T* **56** (*No.* 109).

Z202	9	1 a. on 24 a. purple and blue	£130

Langkawi

Stamps of SIAM *cancelled as Type* D *inscr* "LANGKAWI".

1899–1904. (*Nos.* 67/81).

Z208	49	8 a. deep green and orange	£300
Z209		10 a. ultramarine	£300

1905–09. (*Nos.* 92/105).

Z212	53	3 a. green	£325
Z213		4 a. pale red and sepia	£300
Z215		8 a. olive-bistre and dull black	£300

Stamps of SIAM *cancelled as Type* C *inscr* "Langkawi" *at foot.*

1887–91. (*Nos.* 11/18).

Z219	9	12 a. purple and carmine	£130

1899–1904. (*Nos.* 67/81)

Z220	49	1 a. olive-green (Type B)	£140
Z221		8 a. green and orange	£130

1905–09. (*Nos.* 92/105).

Z222	53	2 a. grey and deep violet	£130
Z223		3 a. green	£180
Z224		4 a. pale red and sepia	£130
Z225		4 a. scarlet	£140
Z226		8 a. olive-bistre and dull black	£130
Z228		24 a. red-brown	£350
Z229		1 t. bistre and deep blue	£350

1907. *Surch with T* **56** (*No.* 109).

Z230	9	1 a. on 24 a. purple and blue	£140

KELANTAN

The first Siamese post office in Kelantan opened at Kota Bharu in 1895. It appears that in the early years this office only accepted letters franked with stamps for delivery within Kelantan.

The initial cancellation, of which no complete example has been discovered, showed Thai characters only. Partial examples have been reported on the 1887–91 8 a. and 1896 4 a. on 12 a.

The operations of the Duff Development Company in Kelantan from 1903 led to a considerable expansion of the postal service based on the company's river steamers. A further post office opened at Batu Mengkebang in 1908, but may have been preceded by manuscript endorsements of "B.M." and date known from early 1907 onwards.

Kota Bharu

Stamps of SIAM *cancelled as Type* B *inscr* "KALANTAN".

1887–91. (*Nos.* 11/18).

Z237	9	2 a. green and carmine	85·00
Z238		3 a. green and blue	90·00
Z239		4 a. green and brown	90·00
Z240		8 a. green and yellow	90·00
Z241		12 a. purple and carmine	80·00
Z242		24 a. purple and blue	85·00

1894. *Surch as T* **27** *with variation of English figures as T* **33** (*Nos.* 37/44).

Z251	9	2 a. on 64 a. purple and brown	£120

1894–95. *Surch as T* **35** *with variation of English figures as T* **36** (*Nos.* 46/50).

Z255	9	1 a. on 64 a. purple and brown	£100

1896. *Surch as T* **39** (*Siamese*) *and T* **40** (*English*) (*No.* 51).

Z259	9	4 a. on 12 a. purple and carmine	£100

1897. *Surch as T* **39** (*Siamese*) *and T* **41** (*English*) (*No.* 52).

Z260	9	4 a. on 12 a. purple and carmine	£100

1898–99. *Surch as T* **42** *with variation of English section as T* **46** (*Nos.* 53/62).

Z267	9	4 a. on 12 a. purple and carmine (8 mm long)	£100

1899–1904. (*Nos.* 67/81).

Z275	49	1 a. olive-green (wide Siamese characters in face value)	85·00
Z276		2 a. grass-green	80·00
Z277		2 a. scarlet and pale blue	80·00
Z278		3 a. red and blue	90·00
Z279		4 a. carmine	80·00
Z280		4 a. chocolate and pink	90·00
Z281	49	8 a. deep green and orange	80·00
Z282		10 a. ultramarine	85·00
Z283		12 a. brown-purple and carmine	85·00
Z284		64 a. brown-purple and chestnut	£180

1905–09. (*Nos.* 92/105).

Z293	53	1 a. green and orange	80·00
Z294		2 a. grey and deep violet	80·00
Z296		4 a. pale red and sepia	80·00
Z297		4 a. scarlet	80·00
Z298		5 a. carmine	95·00
Z299		8 a. olive-bistre and dull black	80·00
Z300		12 a. blue	95·00
Z301		24 a. red-brown	£250
Z302		1 t. bistre and deep blue	£250

1907. *Surch with T* **56** (*No.* 109).

Z303	9	1 a. on 24 a. purple and blue	£100

Stamps of SIAM *cancelled as Type* E *inscr* "Kota Bahru/ Kelantan".

1887–91. (*Nos.* 11/18).

Z307	9	12 a. purple and carmine	80·00
Z308		24 a. purple and blue	£100

1899–1904. (*Nos.* 67/81).

Z309	49	8 a. deep green and orange	85·00
Z310		64 a. brown-purple and chestnut	£120

1905–09. (*Nos.* 92/105).

Z311	53	1 a. green and orange	85·00
Z312		2 a. grey and deep violet	85·00
Z313		2 a. pale yellow-green	85·00
Z314		4 a. pale red and sepia	85·00
Z315		4 a. scarlet	85·00
Z316		8 a. olive-bistre and dull black	80·00
Z317		9 a. blue	80·00
Z318		18 a. red-brown	£140

1907. *Surch with T* **56** (*No.* 109).

Z320	9	1 a. on 24 a. purple and blue	85·00

1908. *Surch as T* **59** (*Nos.* 110/12).

Z326	9	2 a. on 24 a. purple and blue	£120
Z327	53	4 a. on 5 a. carmine	£150
Z328	49	9 a. on 10 a. ultramarine	95·00

Batu Mengkebang

Stamps of SIAM *cancelled as Type* E *inscr* "Batu Menkebang/ Kelantan".

1887–91. (*Nos.* 11/18).

Z329	9	12 a. purple and carmine	£140

1899–1904. (*Nos.* 67/81).

Z330	49	8 a. deep green and orange	£150

1905–09. (*Nos.* 92/105).

Z331	53	1 a. green and orange	£140
Z332		2 a. grey and deep violet	£140
Z333		2 a. pale yellow-green	£150
Z334		4 a. pale red and sepia	£150
Z335		4 a. scarlet	£140
Z336		8 a. olive-bistre and dull black	£120
Z337		9 a. blue	£120
Z338		12 a. blue	£180
Z339		24 a. red-brown	£300
Z340		1 t. bistre and deep blue	£325

1907. *Surch with T* **56** (*No.* 109)

Z341	9	1 a. on 24 a. purple and blue	£120

1908. *Surch as T* **59** (*Nos.* 110/12).

Z347	49	9 a. on 10 a. ultramarine	£180

PERLIS

The Siamese post office at Kangar is recorded as opening during 1894. It is believed that the initial cancellation showed Thai characters only, but no complete example has so far been discovered.

Stamps of SIAM *cancelled as Type* B *inscr* "PERLIS".

1887–91. (*Nos.* 11/18).

Z349	9	12 a. purple and carmine	£120
Z350		24 a. purple and blue	£170

1897. *Surch as T* **39** (*Siamese*) *and T* **41** (*English*) (*No.* 52).

Z351	9	4 a. on 12 a. purple and carmine	£225

1899–1904. (*Nos.* 67/81).

Z352	49	1 a. olive-green (wide Siamese characters in face value)	£150
Z353		2 a. grass-green	£130
Z354		2 a. scarlet and pale blue	£130
Z355		3 a. red and blue	£200
Z356		4 a. carmine	£130

Z357	49	4 a. chocolate and pink	£130
Z358		8 a. deep green and orange	£130
Z359		10 a. ultramarine	£130
Z360		12 a. brown-purple and carmine	£120
Z361		24 a. brown-purple and blue	£250

1905–09. (*Nos.* 97/105).

Z370	53	1 a. green and orange	£120
Z371		2 a. grey and deep violet	£120
Z372		3 a. green	£130
Z373		4 a. pale red and sepia	£120
Z374		5 a. carmine	£130
Z375		8 a. olive-bistre and dull black	£120
Z376		12 a. blue	£140
Z377		24 a. red-brown	£200

Stamps of SIAM *cancelled as Type* C *inscr* "Perlis" *at foot.*

1887–91. (*Nos.* 11/18).

Z379	9	12 a. purple and carmine	£140

1899–1904. (*Nos.* 67/81).

Z380	49	1 a. olive-green (narrow Siamese characters in face value)	£150
Z381		8 a. deep green and orange	£140
Z382		10 a. ultramarine	£150

1905–09. (*Nos.* 92/105).

Z383	53	1 a. green and orange	£150
Z384		2 a. grey and deep violet	£140
Z385		3 a. green	£150
Z386		4 a. pale red and sepia	£140
Z387		4 a. scarlet	£150
Z388		5 a. carmine	£150
Z389		8 a. olive-bistre and dull black	£150
Z390		9 a. blue	£140
Z391		24 a. red-brown	£250

1907. *Surch with T* **56** (*No.* 109).

Z392	9	1 a. on 24 a. purple and blue	£150

Siam transferred suzerainty over the four northern Malay states to Great Britain on 15 July 1909. Use of Siamese stamps in Kelantan and Perlis appears to have extended into early August 1909.

IX. JAPANESE OCCUPATION OF MALAYA

PRICES FOR STAMPS ON COVER

Nos. J1/55	*from* × 10
Nos. J56/76	*from* × 12
Nos. J77/89	*from* × 20
Nos. J90/1	*from* × 15
Nos. J92/115	*from* × 6
Nos. J116/18	—
Nos. J119/32	*from* × 12
Nos. J133/45	*from* × 10
Nos. J146/223	*from* × 6
Nos. J224/58	*from* × 12
No. J259	*from* × 15
Nos. J260/96	*from* × 12
Nos. J297/310	*from* × 20
Nos. J311/17	—
Nos. JD1/10	*from* × 30
Nos. JD11/16	*from* × 12
Nos. JD17/20	*from* × 30
Nos. JD21/7	*from* × 20
Nos. JD28/33	*from* × 30
Nos. JD34/41	*from* × 60

Japanese forces invaded Malaya on 8 December 1941 with the initial landings taking place at Kota Bharu on the east coast. Penang fell, to a force which crossed the border from Thailand, on 19 December, Kuala Lumpur on 11 January 1942 and the conquest of the Malay penisula was completed by the capture of Singapore on 15 February.

During the Japanese Occupation various small Dutch East Indies islands near Singapore were administered as part of Malaya. Stamps of the Japanese Occupation of Malaya were issued to the post offices of Dabo Singkep, Puloe Samboe, Tanjong Balei, Tanjong Batu, Tanjong Pinang and Terempa between 1942 and 1945. The overprinted issues were also used by a number of districts in Northern Sumatra whose postal services were administered from Singapore until the end of March 1943.

Malayan post offices were also opened in October 1943 to serve camps of civilians working on railway construction and maintenance in Thailand. Overprinted stamps of the Japanese Occupation of Malaya were used at these offices between October 1943 and the end of the year after which mail from the camps was carried free. Their postmarks were inscribed in Japanese Katakana characters, and, uniquely, showed the Japanese postal symbol.

MINIMUM PRICE

The minimum price quote is 10p which represents a handling charge rather than a basis for valuing common stamps. For further notes about prices see introductory pages.

JOHORE

The postal service in Johore was reconstituted in mid-April 1942 using Nos. J146/60 and subsequently other general issues. Stamps of Johore overprinted "DAI NIPPON 2602" were, however, only used for fiscal purposes. Overprinted Johore postage due stamps were not issued for use elsewhere in Malaya.

POSTAGE DUE STAMPS

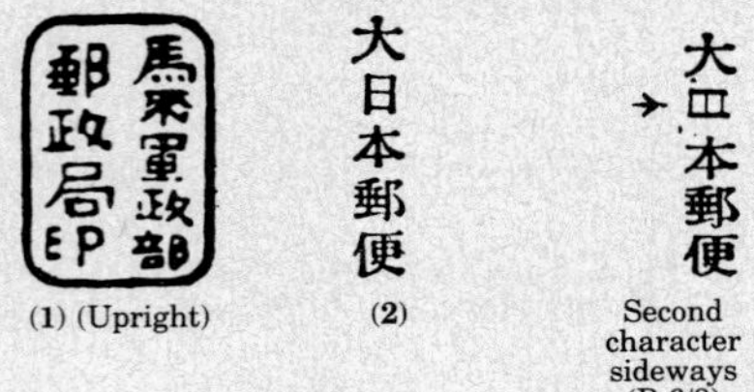

(1) (Upright) (2) Second character sideways (R.6/3)

1942 (Apr). *Nos.* D1/5 *of Johore optd as T* **1**. A. *In brown.* B. *In black.*

			A		B	
JD1	D 1	1 c. carmine	60·00	85·00	30·00	70·00
JD2		4 c. green	80·00	95·00	60·00	80·00
JD3		8 c. orange	£110	£120	75·00	90·00
JD4		10 c. brown	38·00	65·00	15·00	50·00
JD5		12 c. purple	55·00	75·00	27·00	50·00

1943. *Nos.* D1/5 *of Johore optd with T* **2**.

JD 6	D 1	1 c. carmine	3·50	17·00
		a. Second character sideways	£140	£275
JD 7		4 c. green	3·75	18·00
		a. Second character sideways	£150	£275
JD 8		8 c. orange	4·00	19·00
		a. Second character sideways	£180	£325
JD 9		10 c. brown	3·50	23·00
		a. Second character sideways	£180	£350
JD10		12 c. purple	4·50	32·00
		a. Second character sideways	£190	£400

KEDAH

Postal services resumed on 10 February 1942 using unoverprinted Kedah values from 1 c. to 8 c. which were accepted for postage until 13 May 1942.

During the Japanese occupation Perlis was administered as part of Kedah.

DAI NIPPON 2602 (3) DAI NIPPON 2602 (4)

1942 (13 May)–**43**. *Stamps of Kedah (Script wmk) optd with T* **3** (1 *c. to* 8 *c.*) *or* **4** (10 *c. to* \$5), *both in red.*

J 1	1	1 c. black (No. 68*a*)	3·00	4·50
J 2		2 c. bright green (No. 69)	24·00	30·00
J 3		4 c. violet	3·50	4·00
J 4		5 c. yellow	2·50	3·25
		a. Black opt (1943)	£200	£225
J 5		6 c. carmine (No. 56) (Blk.)	1·90	7·00
J 6		8 c. grey-black	2·75	1·75
J 7	6	10 c. ultramarine and sepia	7·00	7·00
J 8		12 c. black and violet	18·00	24·00
J 9		25 c. ultramarine and purple	5·50	9·00
		a. Black opt (1943)	£250	£250
J10		30 c. green and scarlet	65·00	75·00
J11		40 c. black and purple	24·00	35·00
J12		50 c. brown and blue	26·00	38·00
J13		\$1 black and green	£130	£150
		a. Opt inverted	£550	£550
J14		\$2 green and brown	£150	£160
J15		\$5 black and scarlet	60·00	70·00
		a. Black opt (1943)	£750	£750

Nos. J1/15 were gradually replaced by issues intended for use throughout Malaya. Kedah and Perlis were ceded to Thailand by the Japanese on 19 October 1943.

KELANTAN

Postal services resumed on 1 June 1942. Stamps used in Kelantan were overprinted with the personal seals of Sunagawa, the Japanese Governor, and of Handa, the Assistant Governor.

(5) Sunagawa Seal (6) Handa Seal

40 CENTS (7) \$1.00 (8)

1 Cents (9)

1942 (June). *Stamps of Kelantan surch*

(*a*) *As T* **7** *or* **8** (*dollar values*). *Optd with T* **5** *in red*

J16	4	1 c. on 50 c. grey-olive and orange	£225	£180
J17		2 c. on 40 c. orange and blue-green	£375	£250
J18		4 c. on 30 c. violet and scarlet	£1200	£1100
J19		5 c. on 12 c. blue (R.)	£200	£180
J20		6 c. on 25 c. vermilion and violet	£225	£190
J21		8 c. on 5 c. red-brown (R.)	£275	£140
J22		10 c. on 6 c. lake	75·00	£120
J23		12 c. on 8 c. grey-olive (R.)	48·00	£110
J24		25 c. on 10 c. purple (R.)	£1000	£1100
J25		30 c. on 4 c. scarlet	£1700	£1800
J26		40 c. on 2 c. green (R.)	55·00	85·00
J27		50 c. on 1 c. grey-olive and yellow	£1200	£1100
J28	1	\$1 on 4 c. black and red (R., bars Blk.)	50·00	75·00
J29		\$2 on 5 c. green and red/*yellow*	50·00	75·00
J30		\$5 on 6 c. scarlet	50·00	75·00
		a. Surch double	£300	

(*b*) *As T* **7**. *Optd with T* **6** *in red.*

J31	4	12 c. on 8 c. grey-olive	£130	£190

(*c*) *As T* **9**. *Optd with T* **5** *in red.*

J32	4	1 c. on 50 c. grey-olive and orange	£120	85·00
		a. "Cente" for "Cents" (R. 5/1)	£900	£700
J33		2 c. on 40 c. orange and blue-green	£110	90·00
		a. "Cente" for "Cents" (R. 5/1)	£850	
J34		5 c. on 12 c. blue (R.)	95·00	£100
		a. "Cente" for "Cents" (R. 5/1)	£750	
J35		8 c. on 5 c. red-brown (R.)	95·00	70·00
		a. "Cente" for "Cents" (R. 5/1)	£750	£600
J36		10 c. on 6 c. lake	£180	£200
		a. "Cente" for "Cents" (R. 5/1)	£1300	
J37		12 c. on 8 c. grey-olive (R.)	£325	£350
		a. "Cente" for "Cents" (R. 5/1)	£1700	
J38		30 c. on 4 c. scarlet	£1500	£1600
		a. "Cente" for "Cents" (R. 5/1)		
J39		40 c. on 2 c. green (R.)	£350	£375
		a. "Cente" for "Cents" (R. 5/1)	£1800	
J40		50 c. on 1 c. grey-olive and yellow	£900	£950
		a. "Cente" for "Cents" (R. 5/1)		

(*d*) *As T* **9**. *Optd with T* **6** *in red.*

J41	4	1 c. on 50 c. grey-olive and orange	90·00	£130
		a. "Cente" for "Cents" (R. 5/1)	£750	
J42		2 c. on 40 c. orange and blue-green	90·00	£140
		a. "Cente" for "Cents" (R. 5/1)	£750	
J43		8 c. on 5 c. red-brown (R.)	65·00	£120
		a. "Cente" for "Cents" (R. 5/1)	£650	
J44		10 c. on 6 c. lake	85·00	£140
		a. "Cente" for "Cents" (R. 5/1)	£750	

As stamps of the above series became exhausted the equivalent values from the series intended for use throughout Malaya were introduced. Stamps as Nos. J28/30, J32/3 and J35/40, but without Type **5** or **6**, are from remainders sent to Singapore or Kuala Lumpur after the state had been ceded to Thailand (*Price from* £15 *each unused*).

Kelantan was ceded to Thailand by the Japanese on 19 October 1943.

MALACCA

Postal services from Malacca resumed on 21 April 1942, but there were no stamps available for two days.

PRICES. Those quoted are for single stamps. Blocks of four showing the complete handstamp are worth from five times the price of a single stamp.

(**10**) "Military Administration Malacca State Government Seal"

1942 (23 Apr). *Stamps of Straits Settlements handstamped as T* **10**, *in red, each impression covering four stamps.*

			Single Un.	Used
J45	58	1 c. black	75·00	65·00
J46		2 c. orange	55·00	65·00
J47		3 c. green	55·00	65·00
J48		5 c. brown	£100	£100
J49		8 c. grey	£160	£100
J50		10 c. dull purple	65·00	70·00
J51		12 c. ultramarine	90·00	95·00
J52		15 c. ultramarine	65·00	75·00
J53		40 c. scarlet and dull purple	£550	£600
J54		50 c. black/*emerald*	£850	£850
J55		\$1 black and red/*blue*	£900	£850

The 30c., \$2 and \$5 also exist with this overprint, but these values were not available to the public.

POSTAGE DUE STAMPS

1942 (23 Apr). *Postage Due stamps of Malayan Postal Union handstamped as T* **10**, *in red, each impression covering four stamps.*

JD11	D 1	1 c. slate-purple	£160	£160
JD12		4 c. green	£225	£225
JD13		8 c. scarlet	£1600	£1400
JD14		10 c. yellow-orange	£300	£300
JD15		12 c. ultramarine	£500	£475
JD16		50 c. black	£1500	£1300

Nos. J45/55 and JD11/16 were replaced during May 1942 by the overprinted issues intended for use throughout Malaya.

PENANG

Postal services on Penang Island resumed on 30 March 1942 using Straits Settlements stamps overprinted by Japanese seals.

(11) Okugawa Seal

(12) Ochiburi Seal

DAI NIPPON

2602

PENANG

(13)

1942 (30 Mar). *Straits Settlements stamps optd.*

(*a*) *As T* **11** (*three forms of the seal*)

J56 **58** 1 c. black .. 9·50 11·00
J57 2 c. orange .. 24·00 22·00
J58 3 c. green .. 20·00 22·00
J59 5 c. brown .. 24·00 24·00
J60 8 c. grey .. 26·00 26·00
J61 10 c. dull purple .. 48·00 48·00
J62 12 c. ultramarine .. 26·00 32·00
J63 15 c. ultramarine .. 32·00 40·00
J64 40 c. scarlet and dull purple .. 90·00 95·00
J65 50 c. black/*emerald* .. £180 £190
J66 $1 black and red/*blue* .. £190 £200
J67 $2 green and scarlet .. £450 £475
J68 $5 green and red/*emerald* .. £1300 £1300

(*b*) *With T* **12**

J69 **58** 1 c. black .. 95·00 95·00
J70 2 c. orange .. 90·00 85·00
J71 3 c. green .. 80·00 85·00
J72 5 c. brown .. £1000 £1000
J73 8 c. grey .. 55·00 70·00
J74 10 c. dull purple .. 80·00 90·00
J75 12 c. ultramarine .. 75·00 85·00
J76 15 c. ultramarine .. 75·00 85·00

Straits Settlements stamps overprinted with a similar seal impression, but circular and containing four characters, are believed to be fiscal issues.

1942 (15 Apr). *Straits Settlements stamps optd with T* **13**.

J77 **58** 1 c. black (R.) .. 1·75 1·75
a. Opt inverted .. £275 £275
b. Opt double .. £250 £250
J78 2 c. orange .. 4·00 2·75
a. "PE" for "PENANG" .. 85·00 75·00
b. Opt inverted .. £150
c. Opt double .. £300
J79 3 c. green (R.) .. 3·00 1·75
a. Opt double, one inverted .. £275
J80 5 c. brown (R.) .. 1·50 3·25
a. "N PPON" .. £150
b. Opt double .. £275
J81 8 c. grey (R.) .. 2·25 1·40
a. "N PPON" .. 50·00 55·00
b. Opt double, one inverted .. £275
J82 10 c. dull purple (R.) .. 1·50 2·00
a. Opt double .. £300 £300
b. Opt double, one inverted .. £400 £400
J83 12 c. ultramarine (R.) .. 2·50 8·50
a. "N PPON" .. £350
b. Opt double .. £325
c. Opt double, one inverted .. £400 £425
J84 15 c. ultramarine (R.) .. 1·75 2·00
a. "N PPON" .. £100 £110
b. Opt inverted .. £400 £400
c. Opt double .. £425 £425
J85 40 c. scarlet and dull purple .. 3·25 8·50
J86 50 c. black/*emerald* (R.) .. 3·75 16·00
J87 $1 black and red/*blue* .. 6·00 23·00
J88 $2 green and scarlet .. 38·00 75·00
J89 $5 green and red/*emerald* .. £425 £500

Nos. J77/89 were replaced by the overprinted issues intended for use throughout Malaya.

SELANGOR

Postal services resumed in the Kuala Lumpur area on 3 April 1942 and gradually extended to the remainder of the state. Stamps of the general overprinted issue were used, but the following commemorative set was only available in Selangor.

SELANGOR
EXHIBITION
DAI NIPPON
2602
MALAYA

(14)

1942 (3 Nov). *Agri-horticultural Exhibition. Nos.* 294 *and* 283 *of Straits Settlements optd with T* **14**.

J90 **58** 2 c. orange .. 12·00 24·00
a. "C" for "G" in "SELANGOR" (R. 1/9) £250 £300
b. Opt inverted .. £300 £400
J91 8 c. grey .. 13·00 24·00
a. "C" for "G" in "SELANGOR" (R. 1/9) £250 £300
b. Opt inverted .. £300 £400

MINIMUM PRICE

The minimum price quote is 10p which represents a handling charge rather than a basis for valuing common stamps. For further notes about prices see introductory pages.

SINGAPORE

The first post offices re-opened in Singapore on 16 March 1942.

(15) "Malaya Military Government Division Postal Services Bureau Seal"

(Handstamped at Singapore)

1942 (16 Mar). *Stamps of Straits Settlements optd with T* **15** *in red.*

J92 **58** 1 c. black .. 11·00 15·00
J93 2 c. orange .. 11·00 13·00
a. Pair, one without handstamp .. £950
J94 3 c. green .. 48·00 70·00
J95 8 c. grey .. 22·00 18·00
J96 15 c. ultramarine .. 15·00 15·00

The overprint Type **15** has a double-lined frame, although the two lines are not always apparent, as in the illustration. Three chops were used, differing slightly in the shape of the characters, but forgeries also exist. It is distinguishable from Type **1**, used for the general issues, by its extra width, measuring approximately 14 mm against 12½ mm.

The 6, 10, 30, 40, 50 c., $2 and $5 also exist with this overprint, but were not sold to the public.

Nos. J92/6 were replaced on the 3 May 1942 by the stamps overprinted with Type **1** which were intended for use throughout Malaya.

TRENGGANU

Postal services resumed in Trengganu on 5 March 1942 using unoverprinted stamps up to the 35 c. value. These remained in use until September 1942.

1942 (Sept). *Stamps of Trengganu* (*Script wmk*) *optd as T* **1** *at Kuala Lumpur.*

J 97 **4** 1 c. black .. 95·00 85·00
a. Red opt .. £170 £190
b. Brown opt .. £400 £250
J 98 2 c. green (No. 27a) .. £140 £140
a. Red opt .. £190 £200
b. Brown opt .. £425 £300
J 99 2 c. on 5 c. purple/*yellow* (No. 59) .. 60·00 75·00
a. Red opt .. 45·00 70·00
J100 3 c. chestnut (No. 29a) .. 80·00 80·00
a. Brown opt .. £450 £350
J101 4 c. scarlet-vermilion (No. 30a) .. £140 £140
J102 5 c. purple/*yellow* .. 10·00 17·00
a. Red opt .. 20·00
J103 6 c. orange (No. 33a) .. 8·50 23·00
a. Red opt .. 60·00
b. Brown opt .. £375 £375
J104 8 c. grey (No. 34a) .. 9·00 13·00
a. Brown to red opt .. 50·00 65·00
J105 8 c. on 10 c. bright blue (No. 60) .. 13·00 32·00
a. Red opt .. 21·00
J106 10 c. bright blue .. 14·00 25·00
a. Red opt .. 60·00
b. Brown opt .. £375 £375
J107 12 c. bright ultramarine .. 8·00 26·00
a. Red opt .. 27·00
J108 20 c. dull purple and orange .. 8·50 24·00
a. Red opt .. 21·00
J109 25 c. green and deep purple .. 7·50 28·00
a. Red opt .. 22·00
b. Brown opt .. £375 £375
J110 30 c. dull purple and black .. 8·00 24·00
a. Red opt .. 23·00
J111 35 c. carmine/*yellow* .. 20·00 32·00
a. Red opt .. 22·00
J112 50 c. green and bright carmine .. 60·00 70·00
J113 $1 purple and blue/*blue* .. £1900 £1900
J114 $3 green & brown-red/*green* (No. 43*a*) 48·00 80·00
a. Red opt .. 60·00
J115 **5** $5 green and red/*yellow* .. £130 £180
J116 $25 purple and blue .. £900
a. Red opt .. £2500
J117 $50 green and yellow .. £6500
J118 $100 green and scarlet .. £950

DAI NIPPON

2602

MALAYA

(16)

1942 (Sept). *Stamps of Trengganu* (*Script wmk*) *optd with T* **16**.

J119 **4** 1 c. black (No. 26a) .. 12·00 10·00
J120 2 c. green (No. 27a) .. £160 £180
J121 2 c. on 5 c. purple/*yellow* (No. 59) .. 6·00 8·00
J122 3 c. chestnut (No. 29a) .. 9·00 15·00
J123 4 c. scarlet-vermilion (No. 30a) .. 9·00 11·00
J124 5 c. purple/*yellow* .. 5·50 10·00
J125 6 c. orange (No. 33a) .. 5·00 11·00
J126 8 c. grey (No. 34a) .. 70·00 23·00
J127 8 c. on 10 c. bright blue (No. 60) .. 5·50 10·00
J128 12 c. bright ultramarine .. 5·00 17·00
J129 20 c. dull purple and orange .. 9·00 13·00
J130 25 c. green and deep purple .. 7·00 25·00
J131 30 c. dull purple and black .. 7·50 22·00
J132 $3 green & brown-red/*green* (No. 43*a*) 60·00 £110

1943. *Stamps of Trengganu* (*Script wmk*) *optd with T* **2**.

J133 **4** 1 c. black .. 8·00 16·00
J134 2 c. green (No. 27a) .. 7·00 22·00
J135 2 c. on 5 c. purple/*yellow* (No. 59) .. 6·00 18·00
J136 5 c. purple/*yellow* .. 6·50 23·00
J137 6 c. orange (No. 33a) .. 8·00 26·00
J138 8 c. grey (No. 34a) .. 55·00 75·00
J139 8 c. on 10 c. bright blue (No. 60) .. 17·00 38·00
J140 10 c. bright blue .. 75·00 £170
J141 12 c. bright ultramarine .. 11·00 32·00
J142 20 c. dull purple and orange .. 13·00 32·00
J143 25 c. green and deep purple .. 11·00 35·00
J144 30 c. dull purple and black .. 14·00 38·00
J145 35 c. carmine/*yellow* .. 14·00 40·00

POSTAGE DUE STAMPS

1942 (Sept). *Nos.* D1/4 *of Trengganu optd with T* **1** *sideways.*

JD17 **D 1** 1 c. scarlet .. 50·00 80·00
JD18 4 c. green .. 70·00 90·00
a. Brown opt .. 50·00 85·00
JD19 8 c. yellow .. 14·00 50·00
JD20 10 c. brown .. 14·00 50·00

The Trengganu 8 c. postage due also exists overprinted with Type **16**, but this was not issued (*Price* £350 *unused*).

Trengganu was ceded to Thailand by the Japanese on 19 October 1943.

GENERAL ISSUES

The following stamps were produced for use throughout Malaya, except for Trengganu.

1942 (3 Apr). *Stamps optd as T* **1**. (*a*) *On Straits Settlements.*

J146 **58** 1 c. black (R.) .. 3·25 3·25
a. Black opt .. £275 £300
b. Violet opt .. £425 £425
J147 2 c. green (V.) .. £1500 £1500
J148 2 c. orange (R.) .. 3·00 2·25
a. Black opt .. 95·00 £110
b. Violet opt .. £160 £160
c. Brown opt .. £450 £450
J149 3 c. green (R.) .. 2·75 2·25
a. Black opt .. £225 £250
b. Violet opt .. £450 £450
J150 5 c. brown (R.) .. 22·00 28·00
a. Black opt .. £425 £425
J151 8 c. grey (R.) .. 3·50 2·25
a. Black opt .. £200 £225
J152 10 c. dull purple (R.) .. 38·00 40·00
a. Brown opt .. £550 £550
J153 12 c. ultramarine (R.) .. 75·00 95·00
J154 15 c. ultramarine (R.) .. 3·50 3·25
a. Violet opt .. £500 £450
J155 30 c. dull purple and orange (R.) .. £1300 £1400
J156 40 c. scarlet and dull purple (R.) .. 75·00 90·00
a. Brown opt .. £425 £350
J157 50 c. black/*emerald* (R.) .. 45·00 48·00
J158 $1 black and red/*blue* (R.) .. 75·00 75·00
J159 $2 green and scarlet (R.) .. £120 £130
J160 $5 green and red/*emerald* (R.) .. £170 £180

(*b*) *On Negri Sembilan*

J161 **6** 1 c. black (R.) .. 19·00 13·00
a. Violet opt .. 22·00 20·00
b. Brown opt .. 15·00 15·00
c. Black opt .. 45·00 38·00
J162 2 c. orange (R.) .. 17·00 14·00
a. Violet opt .. 38·00 27·00
b. Black opt .. 32·00 28·00
c. Brown opt .. 45·00 42·00
J163 3 c. green (R.) .. 24·00 20·00
a. Violet opt .. 23·00 29·00
b. Violet opt (sideways) .. £200 £200
c. Brown opt .. 75·00 48·00
d. Black opt .. 42·00 40·00
J164 5 c. brown .. 26·00 20·00
a. Pair, one without opt .. £1000
b. Brown opt .. 17·00 15·00
c. Red opt .. 14·00 11·00
d. Violet opt .. 45·00 38·00
J165 6 c. grey .. £130 £120
a. Brown opt .. £325 £325
J166 8 c. scarlet .. 70·00 60·00
J167 10 c. dull purple .. £120 £120
a. Red opt .. £160 £160
b. Brown opt .. £275 £275
J168 12 c. bright ultramarine (Br.) .. £1000 £1000
J169 15 c. ultramarine (R.) .. 18·00 8·00
a. Violet opt .. 45·00 28·00
b. Brown opt .. 25·00 12·00
J170 25 c. dull purple and scarlet .. 28·00 38·00
a. Red opt .. 60·00 75·00
b. Brown opt .. £250 £250
J171 30 c. dull purple and orange .. £160 £150
a. Brown opt .. £700 £700
J172 40 c. scarlet and dull purple .. £750 £750
a. Brown opt .. £800 £800
J173 50 c. black/*emerald* .. £425 £425
J174 $1 black and red/*blue* .. £150 £160
a. Red opt .. £140 £150
b. Brown opt .. £450 £450
J175 $5 green and red/*emerald* .. £400 £425
a. Red opt .. £600 £650

(*c*) *On Pahang*

J176 **15** 1 c. black .. 38·00 35·00
a. Red opt .. 38·00 35·00
b. Violet opt .. £250 £225
c. Brown opt .. £180 £180
J177 3 c. green .. £170 £170
a. Red opt .. £225 £275
b. Violet opt .. £550 £475
J178 5 c. brown .. 12·00 8·50
a. Red opt .. £130 £100
b. Brown opt .. £160 £100
c. Violet opt .. £375 £250
J179 8 c. grey .. £300 £300
J180 8 c. scarlet .. 22·00 10·00
a. Red opt .. 90·00 60·00
b. Violet opt .. 95·00 65·00
c. Brown opt .. £100 85·00

J181 **15** 10 c. dull purple .. .. £120 90·00
 a. Red opt £160 £160
 b. Brown opt £275 £250
J182 12 c. bright ultramarine £1300 £1300
 a. Red opt £1200 £1200
J183 15 c. ultramarine .. .. .. 90·00 90·00
 a. Red opt £180 £180
 b. Violet opt £550 £475
 c. Brown opt £400 £325
J184 25 c. dull purple and scarlet .. .. 18·00 29·00
J185 30 c. dull purple and orange .. .. 12·00 27·00
 a. Red opt £140 £170
J186 40 c. scarlet and dull purple .. .. 16·00 30·00
 a. Brown opt £225 £225
 b. Red opt .. .. 60·00 65·00
J187 50 c. black/*emerald* £425 £425
 a. Red opt £475 £500
J188 $1 black and red/*blue* (R.) £100 £120
 a. Black opt £275 £275
 b. Brown opt £500 £500
J189 $5 green and red/*emerald* £600 £700
 a. Red opt £850 £950

(*d*) *On Perak*

J190 **51** 1 c. black .. .. 45·00 32·00
 a. Violet opt £130 £100
 b. Brown opt .. .. 80·00 80·00
J191 2 c. orange .. .. 25·00 19·00
 a. Violet opt .. .. 70·00 70·00
 b. Red opt .. .. 48·00 38·00
 c. Brown opt .. .. 55·00 55·00
J192 3 c. green .. .. 25·00 27·00
 a. Violet opt £300 £275
 b. Brown opt £160 £150
 c. Red opt £275 £225
J193 5 c. brown .. .. 7·00 6·00
 a. Pair, one without opt £1000
 b. Brown opt .. .. 26·00 24·00
 c. Violet opt £150 £150
 d. Red opt £160 £160
J194 8 c. grey .. .. 45·00 38·00
 a. Red opt £325 £225
 b. Brown opt £275 £225
J195 8 c. scarlet .. .. 24·00 35·00
 a. Violet opt £350 £250
J196 10 c. dull purple .. .. .. 22·00 24·00
 a. Red opt £200 £180
J197 12 c. bright ultramarine £200 £200
J198 15 c. ultramarine .. .. .. 21·00 28·00
 a. Red opt £160 £160
 b. Violet opt £250 £225
 c. Brown opt £250 £225
J199 25 c. dull purple and scarlet .. .. 14·00 23·00
J200 30 c. dull purple and orange .. .. 17·00 32·00
 a. Brown opt £300 £300
 b. Red opt .. .. 32·00 50·00
J201 40 c. scarlet and dull purple £250 £275
 a. Brown opt £425 £425
J202 50 c. black/*emerald* .. .. .. 38·00 48·00
 a. Red opt .. .. 48·00 60·00
 b. Brown opt £250 £250
J203 $1 black and red/*blue* £375 £375
 a. Brown opt £700 £550
J204 $2 green and scarlet £1800 £1800
J205 $5 green and red/*emerald* £475
 a. Brown opt £1300

(*e*) *On Selangor*

J206 **46** 1 c. black, S .. .. 12·00 20·00
 a. Red opt, SU .. .. 24·00 28·00
 b. Violet opt, SU .. .. .. 32·00 32·00
J207 2 c. green, SU £700 £700
 a. Violet opt, U £850 £850
J208 2 c. orange (*p* 14×14½), S .. .. 55·00 45·00
 a. Red opt, U £140 £150
 b. Violet opt, U £200 £150
 c. Brown opt, S .. .. .. 65·00 70·00
J209 2 c. orange (*p* 14), S .. .. .. 75·00 70·00
 a. Red opt, U £140 £150
 b. Violet opt, U £200 £150
J210 3 c. green, SU .. .. 20·00 16·00
 a. Red opt, SU .. .. 18·00 16·00
 b. Violet opt, SU .. .. .. 65·00 50·00
 c. Brown opt, SU .. .. .. 18·00 16·00
J211 5 c. brown, SU .. .. 5·50 5·50
 a. Red opt, S .. .. 11·00 14·00
 b. Violet opt, SU .. .. .. 21·00 25·00
 c. Brown opt, SU .. .. .. 70·00 70·00
J212 6 c. scarlet, S £250 £250
 a. Red opt, S £200 £200
 b. Brown opt, S £450
J213 8 c. grey, S .. .. 17·00 17·00
 a. Red opt, SU .. .. 38·00 30·00
 b. Violet opt, U .. .. .. 35·00 32·00
 c. Brown opt, S .. .. .. 90·00 55·00
J214 10 c. dull purple, S .. .. .. 13·00 21·00
 a. Red opt, S .. .. 48·00 48·00
 b. Brown opt, S .. .. .. £100 60·00
J215 12 c. bright ultramarine, S .. .. 48·00 48·00
 a. Red opt, S £110 £110
 b. Brown opt, S £110 £110
J216 15 c. ultramarine, S .. .. .. 16·00 20·00
 a. Red opt, SU .. .. 45·00 45·00
 b. Violet opt, U .. .. .. £130 90·00
 c. Brown opt, S .. .. .. 70·00 55·00
J217 25 c. dull purple and scarlet, S .. .. 70·00 80·00
 a. Red opt, S .. .. 55·00 75·00
J218 30 c. dull purple and orange, S .. .. 11·00 23·00
 a. Brown opt, S £250 £200
J219 40 c. scarlet and dull purple, S £110 £110
 a. Brown opt, S £250 £180
J220 50 c. black/*emerald*, S .. .. .. 80·00 80·00
 a. Red opt, S .. .. 75·00 80·00
 b. Brown opt, S £250 £250
J221 **48** $1 black and red/*blue* .. .. 30·00 40·00
 a. Red opt £110 £130
J222 $2 green and scarlet .. .. .. 35·00 60·00
 a. Pair, one without opt £1000
 b. Red opt £350 £375
J223 $5 green and red/*emerald* .. .. 60·00 80·00

On T **46** the overprint is normally sideways (with "top" to either right or left), but on T **48** it is always upright.

S=Sideways
U=Upright
SU=Sideways or upright (our prices being for the cheaper).

Specialists recognise nine slightly different chops as Type 1. Initial supplies with the overprint in red were produced at Singapore. Later overprintings took place at Kuala Lumpur in violet, red or brown and, finally, black. No. J155 was from the Kuala Lumpur printing only. Except where noted these overprints were used widely in Malaya and, in some instances, Sumatra.

The following stamps also exist with this overprint, but were not available to the public:

Straits Settlements (in red) 6, 25 c.
Kelantan (in black) 10 c.
Negri Sembilan 2 c. green (Blk. or Brn.), 4 c. (Blk.), 6 c. scarlet (Blk.), 8 c. grey (Blk.), 12 c. (Blk.), $2 (Blk. or Brn.)
Pahang (in black, 2 c. also in brown) 2, 4, 6 c., $2
Perak 2 c. green (R.), 6 c. (Blk.)
Selangor 4 c. (Blk.)

1942 (May). *Optd with T* **16**. (*a*) *On Straits Settlements.*

J224 **58** 2 c. orange 75 50
 a. Opt inverted .. .. .. 8·00 16·00
 b. Opt double, one inverted .. .. 45·00 60·00
J225 3 c. green .. .. 50·00 65·00
J226 8 c. grey .. .. 3·00 1·75
 a. Opt inverted .. .. .. 13·00 27·00
J227 15 c. blue .. .. 8·50 5·50

(*b*) *On Negri Sembilan*

J228 **6** 1 c. black .. .. 1·50 60
 a. Opt inverted .. .. .. 9·00 25·00
 b. Opt double, one inverted .. .. 35·00 50·00
J229 2 c. orange .. .. 3·50 50
J230 3 c. green .. .. 2·25 45
J231 5 c. brown 50 65
J232 6 c. grey .. .. 2·00 1·00
 a. Opt inverted .. .. .. — £950
 b. Stop omitted at right (R. 10/4) .. 65·00 70·00
J233 8 c. scarlet .. .. 2·50 1·25
J234 10 c. dull purple .. .. .. 3·00 2·50
J235 15 c. ultramarine .. .. .. 8·50 2·50
J236 25 c. dull purple and scarlet .. .. 2·25 8·00
J237 30 c. dull purple and orange .. .. 4·25 3·00
J238 $1 black and red/*blue* £100 £110

(*c*) *On Pahang*

J239 **15** 1 c. black .. .. 1·25 1·10
J240 5 c. brown .. .. 1·00 70
J241 8 c. scarlet .. .. 25·00 2·50
J242 10 c. dull purple .. .. .. 8·50 6·00
J243 12 c. bright ultramarine .. .. 1·00 6·50
J244 25 c. dull purple and scarlet .. .. 3·75 12·00
J245 30 c. dull purple and orange .. .. 1·40 6·00

(*d*) *On Perak*

J246 **51** 2 c. orange .. .. 1·25 70
 a. Opt inverted .. .. .. 24·00 26·00
J247 3 c. green 60 60
 a. Opt inverted .. .. .. 10·00 22·00
 b. Opt omitted (in pair with normal) £500
J248 8 c. scarlet 60 40
 a. Opt inverted .. .. .. 4·50 7·00
 b. Opt double, one inverted .. £200 £225
 c. Opt omitted (in horiz pair with normal) £400
J249 10 c. dull purple .. .. .. 7·50 5·00
J250 15 c. ultramarine .. .. .. 3·75 2·00
J251 50 c. black/*emerald* .. .. .. 1·75 2·75
J252 $1 black and red/*blue* £325 £375
J253 $5 green and red/*emerald* .. .. 32·00 65·00
 a. Opt inverted £275 £325

(*e*) *On Selangor*

J254 **46** 3 c. green .. .. 40 1·25
J255 12 c. bright ultramarine .. .. 1·10 8·00
J256 15 c. ultramarine .. .. .. 3·00 1·50
J257 40 c. scarlet and dull purple .. .. 2·00 2·50
J258 **48** $2 green and scarlet .. .. 10·00 27·00

On T **46** the overprint is sideways, with "top" to left or right.

The following stamps also exist with this overprint, but were not available to the public.

Perak 1, 5, 30 c. (*Price for set of* 3 £300 *unused*).
Selangor 1, 5, 10, 30 c., $1, $5 (*Price for set of* 6 £550 *unused*).

DAI NIPPON
2602
MALAYA
2 Cents
(**17**)

DAI NIPPON
YUBIN
2 Cents
(**18**)
"Japanese Postal Service"

1942 (Nov). *No.* 108 *of Perak surch with T* **17**.

J259 **51** 2 c. on 5 c. brown .. .. .. 1·25 1·40

1942 (Nov). *Perak stamps surch or opt only, as in T* **18**.

J260 **51** 1 c. black .. .. 2·00 5·50
 a. Opt inverted .. .. .. 19·00 40·00
J261 2 c. on 5 c. brown .. .. .. 2·00 6·50
 a. "DAI NIPPON YUBIN" inverted 17·00 38·00
 b. Ditto and "2 Cents" omitted .. 45·00 65·00
J262 8 c. scarlet .. .. 3·00 1·75
 a. Opt inverted .. .. .. 11·00 23·00

A similar overprint exists on the Selangor 3 c. but this was not available to the public (*Price* £325 *unused*).

On 8 December 1942 contemporary Japanese 3, 5, 8 and 25 s. stamps were issued without overprint in Malaya and the 1, 2, 4, 6, 7, 10, 30 and 50 s. and 1 y. values followed on 15 February 1943.

大日本郵便
(**19**)

6cts. (**20**) 6 cts. (**21**) 2 Cents (**22**)

6 cts. (**23**) $1.00 (**24**)

1942 (4 Dec)–**44**. *Stamps of various Malayan territories optd "Japanese Postal Service" in Kanji characters as T* **2** *or* **19**, *some additionally surch as T* **20** *to* **24**.

(*a*) *Stamps of Straits Settlements optd with T* **2**

J263 **58** 8 c. grey (Blk.) (1943) .. .. 1·40 50
 a. Opt inverted .. .. .. 32·00 42·00
 b. Opt omitted (in pair with normal) £750
 c. Red opt .. .. 1·25 1·40
J264 12 c. ultramarine (1943) .. .. 55 5·50
J265 40 c. scarlet and dull purple (1943) .. 65 2·50

(*b*) *Stamps of Negri Sembilan optd with T* **2** *or surch also*

J266 **6** 1 c. black 30 50
 a. Opt inverted .. .. .. 8·00 22·00
 b. Sideways second character .. 25·00 26·00
 ba. Opt inverted with sideways second character £500
J267 2 c. on 5 c. brown (surch as T **20**) 40 45
J268 6 c. on 5 c. brown (surch T **21**) (1943) 40 85
 a. Opt Type **2** and surch as Type **21** both inverted £225 £225
J269 25 c. dull purple and scarlet (1943) .. 1·10 8·50

(*c*) *Stamp of Pahang optd with T* **2** *and surch also*

J270 **15** 6 c. on 5 c. brown (surch T **20**) (1943) 50 75
J271 6 c. on 5 c. brown (surch T **21**) (1943) 1·00 1·50

(*d*) *Stamps of Perak optd with T* **2** *or surch also*

J272 **51** 1 c. black 80 60
 a. Sideways second character .. £170 £180
J273 2 c. on 5 c. brown (surch as T **20**) 50 50
 a. Opt Type **2** and surch Type **20** both inverted .. .. 18·00 32·00
 b. Opt Type **2** inverted .. .. 18·00 32·00
 c. Sideways second character .. 50·00 50·00
J274 2 c. on 5 c. brown (surch T **22**) .. 45 45
 a. Surch Type **22** inverted .. 18·00 32·00
 b. Opt Type **2** and surch Type **22** both inverted .. .. 18·00 32·00
 c. Sideways second character .. 25·00 28·00
 ca. Surch Type **22** inverted .. £850
 cb. Opt Type **2** with sideways second character and surch Type **22** both inverted £850
 d. Inverted "s" in Type **22** (R. 3/5) .. 50·00
J275 5 c. brown 45 40
 a. Opt inverted .. .. .. 27·00 35·00
 b. Sideways second character .. £350 £350
J276 8 c. scarlet 55 50
 a. Opt inverted .. .. .. 15·00 26·00
 b. Sideways second character .. 50·00 60·00
 ba. Opt inverted with sideways second character £650
J277 10 c. dull purple (1943) 60 50
J278 30 c. dull purple and orange (1943) .. 1·25 2·50
J279 50 c. black/*emerald* (1943) .. .. 3·00 11·00
J280 $5 green and red/*emerald* (1943) .. 48·00 75·00

(*e*) *Stamps of Selangor optd with T* **2** (*sideways on T* **46**)

J281 **46** 1 c. black (1943) .. .. .. 90 1·00
J282 3 c. green 40 45
 a. Sideways second character .. 17·00 25·00
J283 12 c. bright ultramarine .. .. 45 1·60
 a. Sideways second character .. 28·00 45·00
J284 15 c. ultramarine .. .. .. 2·75 3·00
 a. Sideways second character .. 42·00 48·00
J285 **48** $1 black and red/*blue* .. .. 3·00 14·00
 a. Opt inverted £225 £225
 b. Sideways second character .. £250 £275
J286 $2 green and scarlet (1943) .. .. 10·00 35·00
J287 $5 green and red/*emerald* (1943) .. 22·00 70·00
 a. Opt inverted £225 £225

(*f*) *Stamps of Selangor optd with T* **19** *or surch also*

J288 **46** 1 c. black (R.) (1943) 35 50
J289 2 c. on 5 c. brown (surch as T **21**) (R.) (1943) 30 50
J290 3 c. on 5 c. brown (surch as T **21**) (1943) 30 2·50
 a. "s" in "cts." inverted (R. 4/3) .. 27·00 50·00
 b. Comma after "cts" (R. 9/3) .. 27·00 50·00
J291 5 c. brown (R.) (1944) .. .. 40 2·50
J292 6 c. on 5 c. brown (surch T **21**) (1944) 30 80
J293 6 c. on 5 c. brown (surch T **23**) (1944) 20 70
 a. "6" inverted (R. 7/8) £550
 b. Surch and opt double £300
J294 15 c. ultramarine .. .. .. 4·00 4·00
J295 $1 on 10 c. dull purple (surch T **24**) (18.12.1944) .. .. .. 30 1·00
J296 $1.50 on 30 c. dull purple and orange (surch T **24**) (18.12.1944) .. .. 30 1·00

The error showing the second character in Type **2** sideways occurred on R. 6/3 in the first of four settings only.

The 2 c. orange, 3 c. and 8 c. grey of Perak also exist overprinted with Type **2**, but these stamps were not available to the public (*Price for set of* 3 £100 *unused*).

Examples of No. J275 are known postally used from the Shan States (part of pre-war Burma).

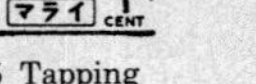

25 Tapping Rubber

26 Fruit

27 Japanese Shrine, Singapore

(Litho Kolff & Co, Batavia)

1943 (29 Apr–1 Oct). *T* **25**/**7** *and similar designs. P* 12½.

J297 **25** 1 c. grey-green (1 Oct) 15 55
J298 **26** 2 c. pale emerald (1 June) 15 15
J299 **25** 3 c. drab (1 Oct) 15 15
J300 – 4 c. carmine-rose 30 15
J301 – 8 c. dull blue 15 15
J302 – 10 c. brown-purple (1 Oct) 15 15

J303 **27** 15 c. violet (1 Oct) .. .. 35 2·00
J304 – 30 c. olive-green (1 Oct) 35 35
J305 – 50 c. blue (1 Oct) .. .. .. 1·00 1·75
J306 – 70 c. blue (1 Oct) .. .. 16·00 10·00
J297/306 .. .. *Set of* 10 17·00 14·00

Designs: *Vert*—4 c. Tin dredger; 8 c. War Memorial, Bukit Batok, Singapore; 10 c. Fishing village; 30 c. Sago palms; 50 c. Straits of Johore. *Horiz*—70 c. Malay Mosque, Kuala Lumpur.

28 Ploughman

29 Rice-planting

1943 (1 Sept). *Savings Campaign. Litho. P* 12½.
J307 **28** 8 c. violet .. .. 7·50 2·75
J308 15 c. scarlet .. .. 6·00 2·75

(Des Hon Chin. Litho)

1944 (15 Feb). *"Re-birth" of Malaya. P* 12½.
J309 **29** 8 c. rose-red .. .. 9·00 2·75
J310 15 c. magenta .. .. 4·00 3·00

大日本
マライ郵便
50 セント
(30)

大日本
マライ郵便
1 ドル
(31)

大日本
マライ郵便
1½ ドル
(32)

1944 (16 Dec). *Stamps intended for use on Red Cross letters. Surch with T* **30/2** *in red. (a) On Straits Settlements.*
J311 **58** 50 c. on 50 c. black/*emerald* .. .. 10·00 23·00
J312 $1 on $1 black and red/*blue* .. .. 18·00 35·00
J313 $1.50 on $2 green and scarlet .. .. 30·00 70·00

(*b*) *On Johore*
J314 **29** 50 c. on 50 c. dull purple and red .. 8·00 18·00
J315 $1.50 on $2 green and carmine .. 5·50 12·00

(*c*) *On Selangor*
J316 **48** $1 on $1 black and red/*blue* .. .. 4·00 12·00
J317 $1.50 on $2 green and scarlet .. .. 6·50 18·00

Nos. J311/17 were issued in Singapore but were withdrawn after one day, probably because supplies of Nos. J295/6 were received and issued on the 18 December.

A similar 6 c surcharge exists on the Straits Settlements 5 c. but this was not available to the public (*Price* £350 *unused*).

POSTAGE DUE STAMPS

Postage Due stamps of the Malayan Postal Union overprinted.

1942 (3 Apr). *Handstamped as T* **1** *in black.*
JD21 D **1** 1 c. slate-purple .. .. .. 12·00 18·00
a. Red opt .. .. 70·00 70·00
b. Brown opt .. .. 85·00 90·00
JD22 3 c. green .. .. 42·00 45·00
a. Red opt .. .. 95·00 £100
JD23 4 c. green .. .. 24·00 24·00
a. Red opt .. .. 40·00 40·00
b. Brown opt .. .. 90·00 £100
JD24 8 c. scarlet .. .. 48·00 48·00
a. Red opt .. .. 80·00 80·00
b. Brown opt £110 £110
JD25 10 c. yellow-orange .. .. .. 20·00 26·00
a. Red opt .. .. 70·00 70·00
b. Brown opt .. .. 48·00 50·00
JD26 12 c. ultramarine .. .. .. 20·00 32·00
a. Red opt £100 £100
JD27 50 c. black .. .. 50·00 60·00
a. Red opt £225 £250

1942. *Optd with T* **16**.
JD28 D **1** 1 c. slate-purple .. .. .. 1·25 7·00
JD29 3 c. green .. .. 8·50 13·00
JD30 4 c. green .. .. 7·00 9·50
JD31 8 c. scarlet .. .. 9·50 12·00
JD32 10 c. yellow-orange .. .. .. 1·60 9·00
JD33 12 c. ultramarine .. .. .. 1·60 21·00

The 9 c. and 15 c. also exist with this overprint, but these were not issued (*Price* £375 *each unused*).

1943–45. *Optd with T* **2**.
JD34 D **1** 1 c. slate-purple .. .. .. 50 2·25
JD35 3 c. green .. .. 50 2·25
a. Opt omitted (in pair with normal) .. £650
JD36 4 c. green .. .. 32·00 35·00
JD37 5 c. scarlet .. .. 50 2·75
JD38 9 c. yellow-orange .. .. .. 60 4·25
a. Opt inverted .. .. .. 20·00 28·00
JD39 10 c. yellow-orange .. .. .. 60 4·00
a. Opt inverted .. .. .. 50·00 50·00
JD40 12 c. ultramarine .. .. .. 60 8·00
JD41 15 c. ultramarine .. .. .. 60 4·50

NEW INFORMATION

The editor is always interested to correspond with people who have new information that will improve or correct the Catalogue.

X. THAI OCCUPATION OF MALAYA

Stamps issued for use in the Malay States of Kedah (renamed Syburi), Kelantan, Perlis and Trengganu, ceded by Japan to Thailand on 19 October 1943. British rule was restored on 9 (Kelantan), 18 (Perlis), 22 (Kedah) and 24 September 1945 (Trengganu). Nos. TM1/6 continued to be used for postage until replaced by the overprinted B.M.A. Malaya issues on 10 October 1945.

PRICES FOR STAMPS ON COVER	
Nos. TK1/5	*from* × 30
Nos. TM1/6	*from* × 25
Nos. TT1/29	*from* × 12

KELANTAN

TK **1**

(Typo Kelantan Ptg Dept, Khota Baru)

1943 (15 Nov). *Handstamped with State arms in violet. No gum. P* 11.
TK1 TK **1** 1 c. black £190 £275
TK2 2 c. black £225 £225
a. Handstamp omitted £700
TK3 4 c. black £225 £275
a. Handstamp omitted £850
TK4 8 c. black £225 £225
a. Handstamp omitted £550
TK5 10 c. black £275 £375

Nos. TK1/5 were printed in sheets of 84 (12×7) and have sheet watermarks in the form of "STANDARD" in block capitals with curved "CROWN" above and "AGENTS" below in double-lined capitals. This watermark occurs four times in the sheet.

Sheets were imperforate at top and left so that stamps exist imperforate at top, left or at top and left.

Similar stamps, but with red handstamps, were for fiscal use.

GENERAL ISSUE

TM **1** War Memorial

(Litho Defence Ministry, Bangkok)

1944 (15 Jan–4 Mar). *Thick opaque, or thin semi-transparent paper. Gummed or ungummed. P* 12½.
TM1 TM **1** 1 c. yellow (4 Mar) .. .. .. 30·00 32·00
TM2 2 c. red-brown .. .. .. 12·00 20·00
a. Imperf (pair) £850
b. Perf 12½×11 .. .. .. 20·00 20·00
TM3 3 c. green (4 Mar) .. .. .. 20·00 38·00
a. Perf 12½×11 .. .. .. 30·00 42·00
TM4 4 c. purple (4 Mar) .. .. .. 14·00 28·00
a. Perf 12½×11 .. .. .. 20·00 35·00
TM5 8 c. carmine (4 Mar) .. .. .. 14·00 20·00
a. Perf 12½×11 .. .. .. 20·00 20·00
TM6 15 c. blue (4 Mar) .. .. .. 38·00 60·00
a. Perf 12½×11 .. .. .. 42·00 60·00

5 c. and 10 c. stamps in this design were prepared, but never issued.

TRENGGANU

TRENGGANU
(TT 1)

(Overprinted at Trengganu Survey Office)

1944 (1 Dec). *Various stamps optd with Type* TT **1**.

(*a*) *On Trengganu without Japanese opt*
TT 1 **4** 1 c. black (26a) .. .. ..
TT 2 30 c. dull purple and black (39) .. ..

(*b*) *On Trengganu stamp optd as T* **1** *of Japanese Occupation*
TT 3 **4** 8 c. grey (J104) £375 £275

(*c*) *On stamps optd with T* **16** *of Japanese Occupation.*
(i) *Pahang*
TT 4 **15** 12 c. bright ultramarine (J243) .. £275 £120

(ii) *Trengganu*
TT 5 **4** 2 c. on 5 c. purple/*yellow* (J121)* £375 £375
TT 6 8 c. on 10 c. brt blue (J127) (inverted) £300 £300
TT 7 12 c. brt ultramarine (J128) (inverted) £300 £300

*This is spelt "TRENGANU" with one "G".

(*d*) *On stamps optd with T* **2** *of Japanese Occupation.*
(i) *Straits Settlements*
TT 8 **58** 12 c. ultramarine (J264) £350 £350
TT 9 40 c. scarlet and dull purple (J265) .. £350 £350

(ii) *Pahang*
TT10 **15** 6 c. on 5 c. brown (J271) .. ..

(iii) *Perak*
TT11 **51** 1 c. black (J272) .. .. ..
TT12 10 c. dull purple (J277) .. .. ..
TT13 30 c. dull purple and orange (J278) .. £600 £350

(iv) *Selangor*
TT14 **46** 3 c. green (J282) £250 £250
TT15 12 c. brt ultramarine (J283) (L. to R.) £150 £110
TT16 12 c. brt ultramarine (J283) (R. to L.) £150 £110
a. Sideways second character .. £1700 £1700

(*e*) *On Selangor stamps optd with T* **19** *of Japanese Occupation*
TT17 **46** 2 c. on 5 c. brown (J289) £350 £350
TT18 3 c. on 5 c. brown (J290) £350 £350

(*f*) *On pictorials of* 1943 (*Nos.* J297/306)
TT19 **25** 1 c. grey-green £275 £275
TT20 **26** 2 c. pale emerald £275 £150
TT21 **25** 3 c. drab £180 £120
TT22 – 4 c. carmine-rose £250 £150
TT23 – 8 c. dull blue £400 £400
TT24 – 10 c. brown-purple £800 £600
TT25 **27** 15 c. violet £250 £150
TT26 – 30 c. olive-green £300 £130
TT27 – 50 c. blue £350 £250
TT28 – 70 c. blue £750 £600

(*g*) *On Savings Campaign stamps (Nos.* J307/8)
TT29 **28** 8 c. violet £400 £400
TT30 15 c. scarlet £275 £160

(*h*) *On stamps of Japan*
TT31 – 3 s. green (No. 319) .. .. ..
TT32 – 5 s. claret (No. 396) £325 £325
TT33 – 25 c. brown and chocolate (No. 329) £170 £110
TT34 – 30 c. blue-green (No. 330) £325 £160

(i) *On Trengganu Postage Due stamp optd with T* **1** *of Japanese Occupation*
TT35 D **1** 1 c. scarlet (JD17) £1200 £1200

XI. LABUAN

CROWN COLONY

The island of Labuan, off the northern coast of Borneo, was ceded to Great Britain by the Sultan of Brunei in December 1846.

Stamps of STRAITS SETTLEMENTS were used from 1867 until 1879. Covers of 1864 and 1865 are known from Labuan franked with stamps of INDIA or HONG KONG.

PRICES FOR STAMPS ON COVER	
Nos. 1/4	—
Nos. 5/10	*from* × 30
Nos. 11/13	—
Nos. 14/21	*from* × 20
Nos. 22/5	—
Nos. 26/35	*from* × 30
Nos. 36/8	—
Nos. 39/47	*from* × 100
Nos. 49/50	*from* × 12
Nos. 51/7	*from* × 60
Nos. 62/74	*from* × 15
Nos. 75/9	*from* × 40
Nos. 80/8	*from* × 20
Nos. 89/97	*from* × 15
Nos. 98/116	*from* × 10
Nos. 117/28	*from* × 30
Nos. 129/37	*from* × 10
Nos. 138/42	—
Nos. D1/9	*from* × 30

1

8
(2)

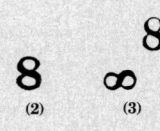

8
8
(3)

(Recess D.L.R.)

1879 (May). *Wmk CA over Crown, sideways. P* 14.
1 **1** 2 c. blue-green £700 £500
2 6 c. orange-brown £150 £140
a. No dot at upper left (R. 2/4) £325 £300
3 12 c. carmine £1200 £475
a. No right foot to second Chinese character (R. 2/3) £2000 £850
4 16 c. blue .. .. 45·00 90·00

This watermark is always found sideways, and extends over two stamps, a single specimen showing only a portion of the Crown or the letters CA, these being tall and far apart. This paper was chiefly used for long fiscal stamps.

1880 (Jan)–**82.** *Wmk Crown CC. P* 14.
5 **1** 2 c. yellow-green .. .. .. 15·00 22·00
6 6 c. orange-brown .. .. .. 70·00 80·00
a. No dot at upper left £150 £160
7 8 c. carmine (4.82) .. .. .. 70·00 75·00
a. No dot at lower left (R. 2/5) £140 £140
8 10 c. brown .. .. 80·00 75·00
9 12 c. carmine £180 £225
a. No right foot to second Chinese character £350 £400
10 16 c. blue (1881) .. .. 65·00 70·00
5/10 .. .. *Set of* 6 £425 £500

1880 (Aug). *(a) No. 9 surch with T* **2** *in black and with the original value obliterated by manuscript bar in red or black.*
11 8 c. on 12 c. carmine £800 £550
a. Type **2** inverted £900 £600
b. "12" not obliterated £1300 £900
c. As b. with Type **2** inverted
d. No right foot to second Chinese character £1300 £900

(b) No. 4 surch with two upright figures and No. 9 surch with two at right angles as T **3**.
12 6 c. on 16 c. blue (R.) £1500 £600
a. With one "6" only
13 8 c. on 12 c. carmine £950 £700
a. Both "8's" upright
b. Upright "8" inverted £1000 £750
c. No right foot to second Chinese character £1500 £1000

EIGHT CENTS
(4)

Eight Cents
(5)

(6)

1881 (Mar). *No. 9 handstamped with T* **4**.
14 8 c. on 12 c. carmine £180 £225
a. No right foot to second Chinese character £350 £425

1881 (June). *No. 9 surch with T* **5**.
15 8 c. on 12 c. carmine 85·00 95·00
a. Surch double £1300 £1300
b. Surch inverted £7500
c. "Eighr" £11000
d. No right foot to second Chinese character £170 £190

The error "Eighr" occurred on R. 2/1 of the first printing, but was soon corrected.

1883. *Wmk Crown CA. P* 14.
17 1 2 c. yellow-green 11·00 20·00
a. Imperf between (horiz pair) £6000
18 8 c. carmine £180 85·00
a. No dot at lower left £350 £150
19 10 c. yellow-brown 22·00 38·00
20 16 c. blue 80·00 £140
21 40 c. amber 11·00 65·00
17/21 *Set of* 5 £275 £300

1883 (May). *No. 10 surch "One Dollar A.S.H." by hand, as T* **6**.
22 1 $1 on 16 c. blue (R.) £2500

The initials are those of the postmaster, Mr. A. S. Hamilton.

2 CENTS
(7)

2 Cents
(8)

2 Cents
(9)

1885 (June). *Nos. 18 and 10 handstamped as T* **7**.
23 1 2 c. on 8 c. carmine £140 £275
a. No dot at lower left £275
24 2 c. on 16 c. blue £750 £750

1885 (July). *No. 20 surch as T* **8**.
25 1 2 c. on 16 c. blue £100 £160
a. Surch double † £3000
b. "2" inserted £1100

No. 25b shows a second "2" applied by a separate handstamp to correct indistinct impressions of Type **8**.

1885 (Sept). *No. 18 handstamped diag as T* **9**.
26 1 2 c. on 8 c. carmine 55·00 90·00
a. No dot at lower left £100 £170

1885 (Sept)–**86**. *Wmk Crown CA. P* 14.
30 1 2 c. rose-red 1·50 7·00
a. Pale rose-red (1886) 1·50 6·00
31 8 c. deep violet 16·00 7·00
a. No dot at lower left 38·00 20·00
b. Mauve (1886) 20·00 8·00
ba. No dot at lower left 45·00 22·00
32 10 c. sepia (1886) 8·00 25·00
33 16 c. grey (1886) 80·00 £140
30/3 *Set of* 4 95·00 £160
30/3 Optd "Specimen" *Set of* 4 £350

ISSUES OF BRITISH NORTH BORNEO COMPANY

From 1 January 1890 while remaining a Crown Colony, the administration of Labuan was transferred to the British North Borneo Co, which issued the following stamps.

6 Cents
(10)

Two CENTS
(11)

Six CENTS
(12)

1891 (July)–**92**. *Handstamped with T* **10**.
34 1 6 c. on 8 c. deep violet (No. 31) 80·00 70·00
a. Surch inverted £130 £120
b. Surch double £425
c. Surch double, one inverted £650
d. "Cents" omitted £350 £350
f. Pair, one without surch, one surch inverted £1000
g. No dot at lower left £160 £150
35 6 c. on 8 c. mauve (No. 31*b*) 6·00 6·00
a. Surch inverted 42·00 42·00
b. Surch double, one inverted £550
c. Surch double, both inverted £550
d. "6" omitted £400
e. Pair, one without surcharge £850 £850
f. Inverted. "Cents" omitted £400
g. Pair, one without surch, one surch inverted £1000
h. Surch double £300
i. No dot at lower left 15·00 15·00
j. Imperf between (horiz pair)
36 6 c. on 8 c. mauve (R.) (No. 31*b*) (2.92) £600 £300
a. Surch inverted £850 £425
37 6 c. on 16 c. blue (No. 4) (3.92) £1500 £1400
a. Surch inverted £5500 £4250
38 6 c. on 40 c. amber (No. 21) £6500 £3500
a. Surch inverted £5500 £5000

There are two different versions of Type **10** with the lines of the surcharge either 1 mm or 2 mm apart.

(Recess D.L.R.)

1892–93. *No wmk. P* 14.
39 1 2 c. rose-lake 3·00 3·50
40 6 c. bright green 5·50 4·50
a. No dot at upper left 16·00 14·00
41 8 c. violet 2·50 6·00
a. Pale violet (1893) 4·00 6·50
43 10 c. brown 6·00 8·00
a. Sepia-brown (1893) 6·00 11·00
45 12 c. bright blue 3·25 6·50
a. No right foot to second Chinese character 10·00 17·00
46 16 c. grey 3·50 7·00
47 40 c. ochre 18·00 32·00
a. Brown-buff (1893) 35·00 25·00
39/47 *Set of* 7 38·00 55·00

The 6 c., 12 c., 16 c. and 40 c. are in sheets of 10, as are all the earlier issues. The other values are in sheets of 30.

1892 (Dec). *Nos. 47 and 46 surch locally as T* **11** *or* **12**.
49 1 2 c. on 40 c. ochre (13 December) £130 90·00
a. Surch inverted £275 £425
50 6 c. on 16 c. grey (20 December) £250 £140
a. Surch inverted £350 £225
b. Surch sideways £350 £225
c. Surch "Six Cents" £1000

There are 10 slightly different versions of each of these surcharges which were applied in settings of 5×2, although instances of single handstamps are known.

A "SIX CENTS" handstamp with Roman "I" in "SIX" (without dot) is a clandestine surcharge, although it can be found with genuine postmarks. It also exists sideways or inverted.

The "Six Cents" surcharge of No. 50c was handstamped onto examples where the Type **12** surcharge had failed to print or where it was partially or completely albino.

CANCELLED-TO-ORDER. Prices are separately indicated, in a third price column, for stamps showing the recognisable black bars remainder cancellation. Earlier issues of the Company administration were also so treated, but, as postal cancellations were used, these cannot be identified.

(Litho D.L.R.)

1894 (Apr). *No wmk. P* 14.
51 1 2 c. carmine-pink 1·10 11·00 30
52 6 c. bright green 7·00 20·00 30
a. Imperf between (horiz pair) £4500
b. No dot at upper left 17·00 45·00 1·25
53 8 c. bright mauve 6·00 18·00 30
54 10 c. brown 23·00 27·00 30
55 12 c. pale blue 16·00 38·00 35
a. No right foot to second Chinese character 35·00 70·00 1·25
56 16 c. grey 21·00 55·00 35
57 40 c. orange-buff 35·00 65·00 35
51/7 *Set of* 7 95·00 £200 2·00
51/7 H/S "Specimen" *Set of* 7 £110

Collectors are warned against forgeries of this issue.

PERFORATION. There are a number of small variations in the perforation of the Waterlow issues of 1894 to 1905 which we believe to be due to irregularity of the pins rather than different perforators.

In the following lists, stamps perf 12, 12½, 13 or compound are described as perf 12–13, stamps perf 13½, 14 or compound are described as perf 13½–14 and those perf 14½, 15 or compound are listed as perf 14½–15. In addition the 13½–14 perforation exists compound with 14½–15 and with 12–13, whilst perf 16 comes from a separate perforator.

13

LABUAN 40 CENTS
(14)

1894 (May)–**96**. *T* **24/32** *of North Borneo (colours changed), with "LABUAN" engraved on vignette plate as T* **13** *(8, 12, 24 c.) or horizontally (others). P* 14½–15.

(a) Name and central part of design in black
62 24 1 c. grey-mauve 1·50 5·50 50
b. Perf 13½–14 6·00 8·50 —
ba. Imperf between (vert pair) £500 — £325
c. Perf 13½–14, comp 14½–15 16·00
d. Perf 13½–14, comp 12–13 14·00 10·00 90
e. Perf 12–13
63 25 2 c. blue 2·50 5·50 50
a. Imperf (pair) £500
b. Perf 13½–14 3·75 6·50 —
c. Perf 13½–14, comp 14½–15 19·00
d. Perf 13½–14, comp 12–13
e. Perf 12–13 55·00
64 26 3 c. ochre 3·75 11·00 50
a. Perf 13½–14 4·75 9·00 —
b. Perf 13½–14, comp 14½–15
c. Perf 13½–14, comp 12–13 20·00
d. Perf 12–13
65 27 5 c. green 22·00 17·00 65
a. Perf 13½–14 24·00 10·00 —
ab. Imperf between (horiz pair)
b. Perf 13½–14, comp 12–13 28·00
c. Perf 12–13 65·00
67 28 6 c. brown-lake 2·50 9·00 50
a. Imperf (pair) £500 † £300
b. Perf 13½–14 — — 1·50
c. Perf 13½–14, comp 14½–15 — — 90
d. Perf 13½–14, comp 12–13
e. Perf 12–13
68 29 8 c. rose-red 14·00 20·00 50
a. Perf 13½–14 18·00 27·00 —
69 8 c. pink (1896) 7·00 23·00 50
a. Perf 13½–14 20·00 25·00 50
70 30 12 c. orange-vermilion 23·00 40·00 50
a. Perf 13½–14 45·00 50·00 2·00
b. Perf 12–13
c. Perf 13½–14, comp 12–13 — 80·00 —
71 31 18 c. olive-brown 22·00 45·00 50
a. Perf 13½–14 42·00
72 18 c. olive-bistre (1896) 42·00 60·00 50
a. Perf 13½–14 26·00 55·00 —
b. Perf 13½–14, comp 12–13
c. Imperf between (vert pair) † † £700

(b) Name and central part in blue
73 32 24 c. pale mauve 18·00 40·00 50
a. Perf 13½–14 16·00 38·00 —
74 24 c. dull lilac (1896) 15·00 40·00 50
a. Perf 13½–14 13·00 38·00 50
62/74 *Set of* 9 85·00 £160 4·00
62/74 Optd "Specimen" *Set of* 9 £140

1895 (June). *No. 83 of North Borneo ($1 inscr* "STATE OF NORTH BORNEO"*) surch as T* **14**.
75 32c 4 c. on $1 scarlet 1·00 1·75 40
76 10 c. on $1 scarlet 1·60 1·40 40
77 20 c. on $1 scarlet 19·00 8·00 40
78 30 c. on $1 scarlet 21·00 27·00 40
79 40 c. on $1 scarlet 18·00 21·00 40
75/9 *Set of* 5 55·00 55·00 1·75
75/9 Optd "Specimen" *Set of* 5 80·00

No. 76 exists with the figures of the surcharge 2½ mm away from "CENTS". The normal setting has a space of 4 mm. Examples of the narrow setting have, so far, only been seen on cancelled-to-order stamps (*Price £16 c.t.o.*).

LABUAN
(15)

1846 JUBILEE 1896
(16)

4 CENTS
(17)

1896. *T* **32a** *to* **32c** *of North Borneo (as Nos. 81 to 83, but colours changed) optd with T* **15**.
80 25 c. green 18·00 22·00 60
a. Opt omitted 15·00 — 1·25
b. Imperf (pair) — — 55·00
ba. Opt omitted 28·00
bb. Stamps ptd double, one inverted 75·00
81 50 c. maroon 18·00 22·00 60
a. Opt omitted 14·00 — 1·25
b. Imperf (pair) — — 55·00
ba. Opt omitted 30·00
bb. Stamps ptd double
82 $1 blue 45·00 38·00 60
a. Opt omitted 18·00 — 1·25
b. Imperf (pair) — — 55·00
ba. Opt omitted 32·00
80/82 Optd "Specimen" *Set of* 3 60·00

Nos. 80bb and 81bb are from waste sheets subsequently sold by the British North Borneo Company to collectors.

1896 (24 Sept). *Jubilee of Cession of Labuan to Gt Britain. Nos. 62 to 68 optd with T* **16**. *P* 14½–15.
83 1 c. black and grey-mauve 17·00 21·00 70
b. Opt in orange £180 £180 20·00
c. "JEBILEE" (R. 8/7) £900 £475 £275
d. "JUBILE" (R. 3/10) £1100
e. Perf 13½–14 17·00 22·00 —
ea. Opt double £250 £275 —
eb. Opt in orange £225 £190 †
f. Perf 13½–14, comp 12–13 23·00 18·00 —
fa. Opt in orange — £190 †
g. Perf 12–13
84 2 c. black and blue 28·00 16·00 70
a. Imperf horiz (vert pair) £475 £550 †
b. "JEBILEE" (R. 8/7) £850 £850 —
c. "JUBILE" (R. 3/10) £1400
d. Perf 13½–14 27·00 14·00 —
e. Perf 13½–14, comp 14½–15 — 32·00 —
f. Perf 13½–14, comp 12–13 35·00

85 3 c. black and ochre .. .. 27·00 22·00 70
c. "JEBILEE" (R. 8/7) .. .. — £1000 £650
d. Perf 13½–14 .. .. 35·00 28·00 80
db. Opt treble £650
e. Perf 13½–14, comp 14½–15 ..
f. Perf 13½–14, comp 12–13 ..
fa. Opt double £300 £300 £150
fb. Opt treble £650
86 5 c. black and green .. .. 48·00 16·00 70
a. Opt double .. .. £375 £375 —
b. Perf 13½–14 .. .. 48·00 18·00 80
c. Perf 13½–14, comp 12–13 ..
87 6 c. black and brown-lake .. .. 22·00 20·00 70
a. Opt double .. .. £475 £400 †
b. "JUBILE" (R. 3/10) .. £1400
c. Perf 13½–14, comp 14½–15 ..
d. Perf 13½–14 .. .. — 50·00 —
88 8 c. black and pink .. .. 35·00 13·00 70
a. Opt double .. .. † £1700 †
b. Perf 13½–14 .. .. 32·00 11·00 70
c. Perf 13½–14, comp 14½–15 .. 45·00 18·00 —
83/8 .. .. *Set of* 6 £160 90·00 3·75
83/8 Optd "Specimen" .. *Set of* 6 £150

The normal overprint on the 1 c. varies in appearance from pure black to brownish black due to a mixing of the inks. The orange overprint on this value is in a clear, bright, unadulterated ink.

No. 84b is known in a vertical strip of 3 imperf horizontally except at the base of the bottom stamp (*Price £4500 unused*).

1897 (Apr)–**1901**. *T* 34/45 *of North Borneo (colours changed), with "LABUAN" engraved on vignette plate as T* 13 (8, 10, 12, 24 c.) *or horizontally (others). Name and central part in black (24 c. in blue). P* 13½–14.

89 **34** 1 c. dull claret (*p* 14½–15) .. 4·00 4·75 40
a. Perf 13½–14, comp 14½–15
b. Brown (1901) .. .. 7·50 11·00 65
ba. Perf 14½–15 .. .. 3·00
bb. Perf 16 .. .. 12·00 13·00 —
90 **35** 2 c. blue .. .. 8·50 4·25 40
a. Imperf between (vert pair) .. † † £425
b. Imperf between (horiz pair) .. † † £450
c. Perf 14½–15 .. .. 15·00 — 75
d. Perf 13½–14, comp 12–13 .. 24·00 16·00 —
e. Perf 16 .. .. — — 6·00
91 **36** 3 c. ochre .. .. 12·00 16·00 40
a. Imperf between (vert pair) .. £550 † £400
b. Perf 14½–15 .. .. 8·50 6·50 40
c. Perf 13½–14, comp 12–13 .. 19·00 23·00
92 **38** 5 c. green .. .. 40·00 40·00 50
a. Perf 14½–15 .. .. 32·00 35·00 —
b. Perf 13½–14, comp 12–13 ..
93 **39** 6 c. brown-lake .. .. 7·50 22·00 40
b. Perf 14½–15 .. .. 4·50 19·00 40
ba. Imperf between (vert pair) .. † † £400
c. Perf 13½–14, comp 12–13 .. — — 4·00
94 **40** 8 c. rose-red .. .. 35·00 — 40
a. Perf 14½–15 .. .. 15·00 12·00 —
b. Perf 13½–14, comp 12–13 .. 23·00 — 2·75
c. Vermilion .. .. 11·00 — 40
ca. Perf 16 .. .. — — 4·00
95 **42** 12 c. vermilion .. .. 50·00 60·00 55
a. Perf 14½–15 .. .. 24·00 40·00 —
96 **44** 18 c. olive-bistre .. .. 38·00 42·00 50
a. Imperf between (vert pair) .. † † —
b. Perf 16 .. .. 15·00 35·00 50
97 **45** 24 c. grey-lilac .. .. 22·00 50·00 60
a. Perf 14½–15 .. .. 10·00 38·00 50
89/97 .. .. *Set of* 9 £110 £180 3·50
89/97 Optd "Specimen" .. *Set of* 9 £160

The 12, 18 and 24 c. above were errors; in the 12 c., "LABUAN" is over the value at the top; the 18 c. has "POSTAL REVENUE" instead of "POSTAGE AND REVENUE", and the 24 c. is without "POSTAGE AND REVENUE".

1897 (Nov)–**98**. (*a*) *Types of North Borneo (colours changed), with "LABUAN" engraved on the vignette plate as in T* 13. *P* 13½–14.

98 **42** 12 c. black and vermilion (3.98) .. † — 1·75
a. Perf 14½–15 .. .. 35·00 42·00 —
b. Perf 13½–14, comp 14½–15 ..
c. Perf 16 .. .. 45·00 48·00 —
99 **46** 18 c. black and olive-bistre
a. Perf 14½–15 .. .. 75·00 60·00 —
b. Perf 16 .. .. † — 7·00
100 **47** 24 c. blue and lilac-brown .. 20·00 48·00 —
a. Perf 14½–15 .. .. 20·00 48·00 —
b. Perf 13½–14, comp 12–13 .. — 55·00 —
c. Perf 16 .. .. 22·00
d. Blue and ochre (*p* 14½–15) .. — — 2·00
98/100 Optd "Specimen" *Set of* 2 40·00

In the 12 c. "LABUAN" is now correctly placed at foot of stamp. The 18 c. and 24 c. have the inscriptions on the stamps corrected, but the 18 c. still has "LABUAN" *over* the value at foot, and was further corrected as follows.

(*b*) *As No.* 99, *but "LABUAN" at top*

101 **46** 18 c. black & olive-bistre (3.98) (Optd S. £27) .. 45·00 48·00 —
a. Perf 14½–15 .. 23·00 55·00 2·50
b. Perf 13½–14, comp 12–13 26·00 45·00 —
c. Perf 12–13 ..

1899 (July). *Surch with T* 17 (*a*) *P* 14½–15.

102 **38** 4 c. on 5 c. (No. 92a) .. .. 27·00 26·00
103 **39** 4 c. on 6 c. (No. 93b) .. .. 17·00 19·00
a. Perf 13½–14 .. .. 24·00 24·00
b. Perf 13½–14, comp 12–13 ..
104 **40** 4 c. on 8 c. (No. 94a) .. .. 38·00 38·00
a. Perf 13½–14 .. .. 19·00 32·00
b. Perf 13½–14, comp 12–13 .. 24·00 32·00
c. Perf 12–13 ..
105 **42** 4 c. on 12 c. (No. 98a) .. .. 32·00 35·00
a. Perf 13½–14 .. .. 32·00
b. Perf 16 .. .. 35·00 40·00
c. Perf 13½–14, comp 12–13 ..
106 **46** 4 c. on 18 c (No. 101a) .. 19·00 17·00
a. Surch double £325 £375
107 **47** 4 c. on 24 c. (No. 100a) .. 18·00 25·00
a. Perf 13½–14 .. .. 16·00 28·00
b. Perf 13½–14, comp 12–13 .. 22·00 23·00
c. Perf 16 .. .. 32·00 40·00

(*b*) *P* 14

108 **32***a* 4 c. on 25 c. (No. 80) .. .. 5·50 7·50
109 **32***b* 4 c. on 50 c. (No. 81) .. .. 5·50 7·50
110 **32***c* 4 c. on $1 (No. 82) .. .. 5·50 7·50
102/10 .. .. *Set of* 9 £130 £150
102/10 Optd "Specimen" .. *Set of* 9 £150

A new setting of the surcharge with closer spacing (2½ mm) between "4" and "CENTS" was used for the Specimen overprints, including unissued surcharges on the 1 c., 2 c. and 3 c. values (*price £130 for the set of three*).

1900–02. *Types of North Borneo with "LABUAN" engraved on the vignette plate as in T* 13, *in green on* 16 *c. P* 13½–14.

111 **35** 2 c. black and green .. 3·75 2·50 30
a. Imperf between (horiz pair) £1600
b. Perf 13½–14, comp 12–13 ..
112 **37** 4 c. black and yellow-brown .. 5·00 28·00 40
a. Imperf between (vert pair) .. £650
b. Perf 13½–14, comp12–13 .. 22·00
113 4 c. black and carmine (8.1900) .. 12·00 2·75 30
a. Perf 14½–15 .. 6·50 6·00 —
b. Perf 13½–14, comp 12–13 .. 22·00 7·00 75
c. Perf 16 ..
114 **38** 5 c. black and pale blue .. 23·00 18·00 65
a. Perf 13½–14, comp 12–13 .. — 60·00 —
115 **41** 10 c. brown & slate-lilac (*p* 14½–15) (1902) .. .. 42·00 65·00 60
116 **43** 16 c. green and chestnut (1902) .. 55·00 75·00 2·50
a. Perf 13½–14, comp 12–13 .. 65·00 75·00 —
b. Perf 12–13 .. £130
c. Perf 14½–15 .. 75·00
111/16 *Set of* 6 £120 £170 4·25
111/16 Optd "Specimen" .. *Set of* 6 £130

No. 112 was printed in an incorrect frame colour and was not issued for postal purposes in Labuan. Used examples come from dealers' stock sent to the island for cancellation.

18

Line through "B" (R.5/10)

(Recess Waterlow)

1902 (Sept)–**03**. *P* 13½–14.

117 **18** 1 c. black and purple (10.03) .. 3·50 6·50 40
a. Perf 14½–15 .. — 7·00 —
b. Perf 13½–14, comp 12–13 65·00
c. Line through "B" .. 38·00 60·00 4·75
118 2 c. black and green .. 3·00 3·75 30
a. Perf 14½–15 .. — 4·75 —
b. Line through "B" .. 38·00 45·00 4·75
119 3 c. black and sepia (10.03) .. 3·00 6·50 30
a. Line through "B" .. 38·00 55·00 4·75
120 4 c. black and carmine .. 3·00 3·00 30
a. Perf 14½–15 .. 4·25 5·50 —
b. Perf 13½–14, comp 12–13 .. 55·00 45·00 —
c. Line through "B" .. 38·00 40·00 4·75
121 8 c. black and vermilion .. 6·50 7·50 40
a. Perf 14½–15 .. 7·00
b. Line through "B" .. 50·00 70·00 4·75
122 10 c. brown and slate-blue .. 3·00 7·50 30
b. Perf 14½–15 .. 3·75
ba. Imperf between (vert pair) .. † † £500
c. Line through "B" .. 38·00 70·00 4·75
123 12 c. black and yellow .. 3·50 10·00 30
a. Imperf between (vert strip of 3) .. † † £2500
b. Perf 16 .. 3·75 12·00 —
c. Line through "B" .. 40·00 80·00 4·75
124 16 c. green and brown .. 4·75 12·00 30
a. Imperf between (vert pair) .. † — —
b. Line through "B" .. 48·00 90·00 4·75
125 18 c. black and pale brown .. 3·25 12·00 30
a. Line through "B" .. 40·00 90·00 4·75
126 25 c. green and greenish blue .. 6·00 15·00 30
a. Perf 14½–15 .. 11·00 22·00
b. Error. Black and greenish blue — † £325
c. Line through "B" .. 60·00 £120 4·75
127 50 c. dull purple and lilac .. 10·00 35·00 50
a. Perf 13½–14, comp 12–13 .. 16·00 38·00 —
b. Line through "B" .. £120 £250 7·00
128 $1 claret and orange .. 8·00 40·00 50
a. Perf 14½–15 .. 10·00
b. Line through "B" .. 85·00 £250 8·00
117/28 .. *Set of* 12 50·00 £140 3·75
117/28 Optd "Specimen" .. *Set of* 12 £170

4
cents

(19)

1904 (Dec). *Issues of* 1895 *and* 1897–8 *surch with T* 19.

(*a*) *P* 14½–15

129 **38** 4 c. on 5 c. (No. 92a) .. 25·00 30·00 11·00
130 **39** 4 c. on 6 c. (No. 93b) .. 12·00 30·00 11·00
131 **40** 4 c. on 8 c. (No. 94a) .. 20·00 32·00 11·00
132 **42** 4 c. on 12 c. (No. 98a) .. 19·00 32·00 11·00
a. Perf 16 .. 21·00 35·00 —
133 **46** 4 c. on 18 c. (No. 101) (*p* 13½–14) 17·00 35·00 11·00
a. Perf 13½–14, comp 12–13 .. 21·00 32·00 —
b. Perf 12–13 ..
134 **47** 4 c. on 24 c. (No. 100a) .. 16·00 35·00 11·00
a. Perf 13½–14 .. 17·00
b. Perf 13½–14, comp 12–13 .. 25·00 38·00 —
c. Perf 16 .. 26·00 32·00 —

(*b*) *P* 14

135 **32***a* 4 c. on 25 c. (No. 80) .. .. 8·50 20·00 11·00
136 **32***b* 4 c. on 50 c. (No. 81) .. .. 8·50 20·00 11·00
a. Surch double £250
137 **32***c* 4 c. on $1 (No. 82) .. .. 8·50 20·00 11·00
129/37 .. .. *Set of* 9 £120 £225

No. 136a usually shows one complete surcharge and parts of two further examples due to the position of the second impression.

The barred cancels can be found used on "philatelic" covers of this issue.

LABUAN (20) **LABUAN** (21)

1904 (12 Oct)–**05**. *Nos.* 81, 83 (*in Labuan colour*), *and* 84/6 *of North Borneo optd locally with T* 20 (25 c., $2) *or* 21 (*others*).

138 **32***a* 25 c. indigo (2.05) .. .. £900 † —
139 **32***c* $1 blue (2.05) .. .. † † £500
140 **32***d* $2 dull green .. .. £2500 £2750 —
141 **14** $5 bright purple (2.05) .. £4750 £4750 £1000
142 **15** $10 brown (11.05) .. .. £15000 † £5500

Dangerous forgeries exist.

The overprint on No. 140 is 12 mm long.

POSTAGE DUE STAMPS

POSTAGE DUE

(D 1)

1901. *Optd with Type* D 1, *reading vertically upwards. P* 13½–14.

D1 **35** 2 c. black and green (111) .. .. 11·00 20·00 40
a. Opt double £275
b. Perf 13½–14, comp 12–13 .. 45·00 55·00 —
D2 **36** 3 c. black and ochre (91) .. .. 16·00 70·00 60
a. Perf 13½–14, comp 12–13 .. 45·00
D3 **37** 4 c. black and carmine (113) .. 23·00 80·00 45
a. Opt double .. .. † † £375
b. Perf 14½–15 .. .. 23·00 70·00 45
D4 **38** 5 c. black and pale blue (114) .. 30·00 80·00 65
a. Perf 14½–15 .. .. 38·00
b. Perf 13½–14, comp 12–13 .. 45·00
D5 **39** 6 c. black and brown-lake (93) .. 16·00 75·00 65
a. Perf 14½–15 .. .. 22·00 70·00 65
b. Perf 16 .. .. 30·00
D6 **40** 8 c. black and vermilion (94c) .. 40·00 75·00 75
a. Frame inverted (*p* 14½–15) † † £6000
b. Perf 14½–15 .. .. 32·00 — 85
c. Perf 16 .. .. 42·00 75·00 —
d. Black and rose-red (94) .. 45·00 85·00 —
da. Perf 14½–15 .. .. — — 6·50
db. Perf 13½–14, comp 12–13 ..
D7 **42** 12 c. black and vermilion (98) .. 60·00 80·00 2·25
a. Opt reading downwards .. † † £375
b. Perf 14½–15 .. .. 60·00 80·00 —
D8 **46** 18 c. blk & ol-bistre (101) (*p* 14½–15) 15·00 75·00 1·25
D9 **47** 24 c. blue and lilac-brown (100) .. 27·00 70·00 1·25
a. Perf 13½–14, comp 12–13 .. 45·00
b. Perf 14½–15 .. .. 25·00
ba. Blue and ochre .. .. 42·00 — 1·25
c. Perf 16 .. .. 30·00 70·00 —
D1/9 .. .. *Set of* 9 £200 £550 7·50

The administration of Labuan reverted to Colonial Office control, as part of an agreement with Brunei, on 1 January 1906. By Letters Patent dated 30 October 1906 Labuan was incorporated with Straits Settlements and ceased issuing its own stamps. In 1946 it became part of the Colony of North Borneo.

XII. SABAH

(*formerly* North Borneo)

NORTH BORNEO

PRICES FOR STAMPS ON COVER TO 1945

No. 1	*from* × 100
Nos. 2/3	*from* × 10
Nos. 4/5	—
Nos. 6/19	*from* × 10
Nos. 19*b*/21*b*	—
Nos. 22/8	*from* × 50
Nos. 29/35	—
Nos. 36/44	*from* × 100
Nos. 45/50	—
Nos. 51/2	*from* × 10
No. 54	—
Nos. 55/65	*from* × 10
Nos. 66/79	*from* × 4
Nos. 81/6	—
Nos. 87/91	*from* × 12
Nos. 92/111	*from* × 4
Nos. 112/26	*from* × 10
Nos. 127/40	*from* × 6
Nos. 141/5	—
Nos. 146/57	*from* × 5
Nos. 158/79	*from* × 8
Nos. 181/5	—
Nos. 186/8	*from* × 10
Nos. 189/230	*from* × 4
Nos. 231/4	—
Nos. 235/49	*from* × 3
Nos. 250/2	—
Nos. 253/75	*from* × 12
Nos. 276/92	*from* × 7
Nos. 293/4	—
Nos. 295/300	*from* × 6
Nos. 301/2	—
Nos. 303/17	*from* × 3
Nos. 318/19	*from* × 20
Nos. 320/34	*from* × 3
Nos. D1/26	*from* × 25
Nos. D27/8	—
Nos. D29/35	*from* × 12
No. D35*a*	—
Nos. D36/65	*from* × 40
Nos. D66/70	*from* × 8

BRITISH NORTH BORNEO COMPANY ADMINISTRATION

PRINTERS. The stamps of this country up to 1894 were designed by T. Macdonald and printed in lithography by Blades, East and Blades, London.

1

8 Cents.
(2)

EIGHT CENTS
(3)

1883 (Mar). *P* 12.

No.	Type	Description	Unused	Used
1	1	2 c. red-brown	22·00	45·00
		a. Imperf between (horiz pair)		

The figure "2" varies in size.

1883 (June). *No.* 1 *surch as T* **2** *or* **3**.

No.	Type	Description	Unused	Used
2	2	8 c. on 2 c. red-brown	£850	£550
3	3	8 c. on 2 c. red-brown	£375	£160
		a. Surch double	†	£3750

Type **2** was handstamped and stamps without stop are generally forgeries. Type **3** was a setting of 50 (10 × 5) providing ten varieties; it normally has a stop which sometimes failed to print.

CANCELLED-TO-ORDER—Prices are separately indicated in a third price column, for stamps showing the recognisable black bars remainder cancellation. The issues since 1916 have not been thus cancelled.

It should be noted, however, that a postmark of this form was in use for postal purposes up to this period, and was used at one or two of the smaller post-offices until 1949. A small oval with five bars was used to mark railway mail during 1945/55 and also as a paquebot mark at Jesselton *c.* 1950.

4

5

and Revenue
(6)

1883. *P* 14.

No.	Type	Description	Unused	Used	CTO
4	4	50 c. violet	85·00	—	18·00
		a. Inverted "L" for first "F" in "FIFTY" (R.5/2)	£600	—	£120
5	5	$1 scarlet	80·00	—	9·50

1883 (July). *P* 12.

No.	Type	Description	Unused	Used
6	1	4 c. pink	32·00	48·00
		a. Imperf (horiz pair)	†	—
7		8 c. green	60·00	50·00

1886. *P* 14.

No.	Type	Description	Unused	Used
8	1	½ c. magenta	70·00	£150
9		1 c. orange	£150	£250
		a. Imperf (pair)	£250	
		b. Imperf horiz (vert pair)		
10		2 c. brown	19·00	20·00
		a. Imperf between (horiz pair)	£550	
11		4 c. pink	17·00	45·00
12		8 c. green	19·00	45·00
		a. Imperf between (horiz pair)	£750	
13		10 c. blue	23·00	42·00
		a. Imperf (pair)	£300	
8/13		*Set of* 6	£275	£500

Imperforate examples of the 4 c. pink are listed under No. 6a.

1886 (Sept). *Nos.* 8 *and* 13 *optd with T* **6**.

No.	Type	Description	Unused	Used
14		½ c. magenta	80·00	£160
15		10 c. blue	£110	£160

3 CENTS
(7)

5 CENTS
(8)

3 CENTS
Small "3" variety (R.3/1, 3/4, 3/7)

(Surchd by *North Borneo Herald*, Sandakan)

1886 (Sept). *T* **1** *surch as T* **7/8**. (*a*) *P* 12.

No.	Type	Description	Unused	Used
16	7	3 c. on 4 c. pink	£110	£170
		a. Small "3"	—	£4250
17	8	5 c. on 8 c. green	£140	£180
		(*b*) *P* 14		
18	7	3 c. on 4 c. pink	60·00	95·00
		a. Small "3"	£1300	
19	8	5 c. on 8 c. green	70·00	95·00
		a. Surch inverted	£1700	

NEW INFORMATION

The editor is always interested to correspond with people who have new information that will improve or correct the Catalogue.

9

10

11

12

13

1886–87. (*a*) *P* 14.

No.	Type	Description	Unused	Used
21*b*	9	½ c. magenta	13·00	40·00
22		½ c. rose	2·50	13·00
		a. Imperf (pair)	20·00	
23		1 c. orange-yellow	6·00	22·00
		a. Imperf between (vert pair)	£300	
		b. Imperf (pair)	25·00	
24		1 c. orange	2·00	8·00
		a. Imperf (pair)	20·00	
25		2 c. brown	2·00	8·50
		a. Imperf (pair)	20·00	
26		4 c. pink	2·25	9·00
		a. Imperf (pair)	20·00	
		b. Imperf between (horiz or vert pair)	£200	
		c. Imperf vert (horiz pair)	£225	
		d. Error. 1 c. pink (R. 2/3) (centre stamp of strip of 3)	£150	£375
		da. Imperf between (pair)		
		db. Imperf (pair)	£2750	
27		8 c. green	6·00	16·00
		a. Imperf (pair)	20·00	
28		10 c. blue	7·00	25·00
		a. Imperf between (vert pair)	£325	
		b. Imperf (pair)	20·00	
29	10	25 c. indigo	£120	10·00
		a. Imperf between (vert pair)		
		b. Imperf (pair)	£180	20·00
30	11	50 c. violet	£150	12·00
		a. Imperf (pair)	£250	20·00
31	12	$1 scarlet	£180	10·00
		a. Imperf (pair)	£250	20·00
32	13	$2 sage-green	£250	17·00
		a. Imperf (pair)	£160	22·00
22/32		*Set of* 10	£650	£120
		(*b*) *P* 12		
34	9	½ c. magenta	£120	£225
35		1 c. orange	95·00	£130

Nos. 21*b*/32 are known to have been sold as cancelled remainders, but these are difficult to distinguish from postally used. Values above 10 c. are infrequently found postally used so that the used prices quoted are for the remainders.

14

15

16

17

18

1888–92. *T* **14** (*as T* **9** *but inscr* "POSTAGE & REVENUE") *and T* **15/18** (*T* **10/13** *redrawn*). *P* 14.

No.	Type	Description	Unused	Used	CTO
36	14	½ c. magenta (1889)	3·50	20·00	2·00
		a. Imperf vert (horiz pair)	†	†	£200
		b. Rose	80	4·00	60
		ba. Imperf between (horiz pair)	£350		
		c. Imperf (pair)	20·00	—	7·00
37		1 c. orange (1892)	1·10	3·25	50
		a. Imperf vert (horiz pair)	£300		
		b. Imperf (pair)	20·00	—	6·00
38		2 c. brown (1889)	6·50	9·00	70
		a. Imperf between (horiz pair)			
		b. Lake-brown	2·00	9·00	50
		c. Imperf (pair)	20·00	—	6·00
39		3 c. violet (1889)	2·50	11·00	50
		a. Printed triple, one inverted			
		b. Imperf (pair)	15·00	—	6·00
40		4 c. rose-pink (1889)	3·75	22·00	50
		a. Imperf between (pair)	—	£120	—
		b. Imperf (pair)	20·00	—	6·00
41		5 c. slate (1889)	2·75	15·00	50
		a. Imperf between (pair)			
		b. Imperf (pair)	20·00	—	6·00
42		6 c. lake (1892)	6·50	17·00	50
		a. Imperf (pair)	20·00	—	7·00
43		8 c. blue-green (1891)	15·00	20·00	75
		a. Yellow-green	13·00	18·00	50
		b. Printed triple, one inverted			
		c. Imperf (pair)	20·00	—	7·00
44		10 c. blue (1891)	8·00	20·00	75
		a. Imperf between (vert pair)	†	†	£200
		b. Dull blue	6·50	16·00	50
		ba. Imperf between (horiz pair)			
		c. Printed double			
		d. Imperf (pair)	20·00	—	7·00
45	15	25 c. indigo	35·00	80·00	75
		a. Imperf (pair)	£150	—	10·00
		b. Imperf vert (horiz pair)	†	†	£250
46	16	50 c. violet	60·00	£120	75
		a. Imperf (pair)	£180	—	10·00
		b. Chalky blue	†	£100	†
47	17	$1 scarlet	27·00	£110	75
		a. Imperf (pair)	£150	—	10·00
48	18	$2 dull green	95·00	£160	1·50
		a. Imperf (pair)	£225	—	12·00
36*b*/48		*Set of* 13	£225	£500	7·50

Nos. 39a, 43b and 44c are from waste sheets subsequently sold by the British North Borneo Company to collectors.

These stamps to the 10 c. value were forged on several occasions. Most forgeries of the ½ c. value can be identified by the presence of a diagonal line joining the top two horizontal strokes of the uppermost Chinese character.

The new 25 c. has the inscription "BRITISH NORTH BORNEO" in taller capitals. In the 50 c. the "0" of the numerals "50" in the two upper corners is square-shaped at the top and bottom instead of being oval. The 1 dollar has 14 pearls instead of 13 at each side, and on the 2 dollars the word "BRITISH" measures 10½ to 11 mm in length in place of 12 mm.

19

20

1889. *P* 14.

No.	Type	Description	Unused	Used	CTO
49	19	$5 bright purple	£120	£130	8·50
		a. Imperf (pair)	£275	—	20·00
50	20	$10 brown	£170	£225	12·00
		a. Imperf (pair)	£400	—	24·00
		b. "DOLLAPS" for "DOLLARS" (R.2/1)	£950	£1200	£325
		ba. Ditto. Imperf (pair)	£1700	—	£700

Two Cents.
(21)

6 cents.
(22)

1 cent.
(23)

1890 (Dec). *Surch as T* **21**, *in red.*

No.	Type	Description	Unused	Used
51	15	2 c. on 25 c. indigo	48·00	70·00
		a. Surch inverted	£325	£325
52		8 c. on 25 c. indigo	75·00	90·00

The first printing of Nos. 51/2 had the two lines of the surcharge 3.5 mm apart. On a second printing of both values this gap widened to 5 mm.

1891–92. *Surch with T* **22**.

No.	Type	Description	Unused	Used
54	9	6 c. on 8 c. green (1892)	£6500	£3500
		a. Large "s" in "cents"	£12000	
55	14	6 c. on 8 c. yellow-green	14·00	9·00
		a. Surch inverted	£250	£300
		b. Inverted "c" in "cents" (R.5/4)	£300	£350
		c. "cetns." for "cents" (R.3/7)	£325	£375
		d. Large "s" in "cents" (R.2/9 or 3/7)	£130	£130
56	9	6 c. on 10 c. blue	48·00	18·00
		a. Surch inverted	£160	£160
		b. Surch double		
		c. Surch treble	£325	
		d. Large "s" in "cents"	£180	£130
57	14	6 c. on 10 c. blue	£100	26·00
		a. Large "s" in "cents"	£375	£160

Unused examples of Nos. 55 and 57 are normally without gum.

There were three settings of the surcharge for No. 55. On the first two the large "s" in "cents" occurred on R.2/9 with the other two listed varieties also included. Nos. 55b/c were corrected on the third setting and the large "s" in cents occurred on R.3/7.

1892 (Mar–Nov). *Surch as T* **23** ("Cents." *with capital* "C" *as in T* **21** *on No.* 65), *in red.*

63 **14** 1 c. on 4 c. rose-pink .. .. .. 18·00 14·00
a. Surch double £850
b. Surch on back and on front .. .. — £550
ba. As b, but with surch double on front
64 1 c. on 5 c. slate (Nov) .. .. .. 6·50 6·00
65 **15** 8 c. on 25 c. indigo (date?) £120 £140

Unused examples of Nos. 63/5 are normally without gum.

24 Dyak Chief

25 Sambar Stag (*Cervus unicolor*)

26 Sago Palm

27 Great Argus Pheasant

28 Arms of the Company

29 Malay Dhow

30 Estuarine Crocodile

31 Mount Kinabalu

32 Arms of the Company with Supporters

PERFORATION. There are a number of small variations in the perforation of the Waterlow issues of 1894 to 1922 which we believe were due to irregularity of the pins rather than different perforators.

In the following lists, stamps perf 12, 12½, 13 or compound are described as perf 12–13, stamps perf 13½, 14 or compound are described as perf 13½–14 and those perf 14½, 15 or compound are listed as perf 14½–15. In addition the 13½–14 perforation exists compound with 14½–15 and with 12–13, whilst perf 15½–16 comes from a separate perforator.

(Recess Waterlow)

1894 (Feb). *P* 14½–15.

66 **24** 1 c. black and olive-bistre .. .. 1·25 8·00 50
a. Imperf between (horiz or vert pair) £500
b. Perf 13½–14 .. .. .. 1·25 8·50 50
c. Perf 13½–14, comp 14½–15 .. 28·00 42·00 —
d. Perf 13½–14, comp 12–13 .. 16·00 35·00 —
e. Perf 12–13 .. .. ..
67 1 c. black and bistre-brown .. 1·50 9·00 50
a. Perf 13½–14 .. .. .. 2·00 9·00 50
b. Perf 13½–14, comp 12–13 .. 18·00 42·00 —
c. Perf 12–13 .. .. ..
68 **25** 2 c. black and rose-lake .. .. 4·50 4·75 50
a. Imperf between (horiz or vert pair) .. .. £425 £475 †
b. Perf 13½–14 .. .. .. 28·00 32·00 —
69 2 c. black and lake .. .. .. 4·50 4·75 50
a. Perf 13½–14 .. .. .. 30·00 32·00 —
b. Perf 13½–14, comp 12–13 .. 24·00 25·00 —
c. Imperf between (horiz pair) ..
70 **26** 3 c. olive-green and dull purple .. 2·25 7·50 50
a. Imperf between (horiz pair) .. — £375 †
b. Bronze-green and dull purple .. 3·75 — 50
c. Perf 13½–14 ..
71 3 c. olive-green & violet (*p* 13½–14) 12·00 38·00 —
a. Imperf between (horiz pair)
72 **27** 5 c. black and vermilion .. .. 10·00 11·00 60
a. Imperf between (horiz or vert pair) £350
b. Perf 13½–14 .. .. .. 40·00 55·00 1·25
c. Perf 13½–14, comp 12–13 .. — 60·00 —
d. Perf 13½–14, comp 14½–15 ..
e. Perf 12–13 .. .. ..
73 **28** 6 c. black and bistre-brown .. 55·00 75·00 60
a. Perf 13½–14 .. .. .. 3·75 15·00 60
b. Perf 13½–14, comp 12–13 .. — 60·00 —
c. Perf 13½–14, comp 14½–15 .. 55·00
d. Imperf between (horiz pair) ..
74 **29** 8 c. black and dull purple .. .. 4·00 9·50 60
a. Imperf between (vert pair) .. £375
b. Perf 13½–14 .. .. .. 8·00 27·00 80
ba. Imperf between (vert pair) .. £375 † £300
d. Perf 13½–14, comp 12–13 ..
75 **30** 12 c. black and blue .. .. .. 25·00 75·00 2·50
a. Perf 13½–14 .. .. .. 25·00 75·00 2·50
b. Imperf between (horiz pair) .. £600 † £425
76 **30** 12 c. black and ultramarine .. .. 38·00 80·00 3·00
a. Perf 13½–14 .. .. .. 35·00 80·00 3·00
b. Imperf between (pair) .. ..
78 **31** 18 c. black and deep green .. .. 20·00 48·00 2·00
a. Perf 13½–14 .. .. .. 25·00 48·00 2·00
79 **32** 24 c. blue and rose-lake .. .. 19·00 65·00 2·00
a. Imperf between (vert pair) .. — — £275
b. Imperf between (vert strip of 3) † † £375
c. Perf 13½–14 .. .. .. 19·00 65·00 2·00
d. Perf 13½–14, comp 14½–15
66/79 .. .. .. *Set of* 9 80·00 £225 9·00

32*a*

32*b*

32*c*

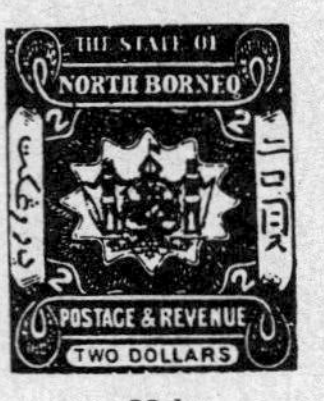
32*d*

(Litho Blades, East & Blades, London)

1894 (Feb). *T* **32*a*** *to* **32*d*** *and T* **19** *and* **20**, *but inscribed* "THE STATE OF NORTH BORNEO". *P* 14.

81 25 c. indigo .. .. 8·50 26·00 90
a. Imperf (pair) .. .. .. 25·00 — 6·00
b. Imperf between (horiz or vert pair) £650 — 85·00
c. Printed double, one inverted .. † † 60·00
82 50 c. deep slate-purple .. .. .. 13·00 48·00 90
a. Imperf (pair) .. .. .. — — 6·00
b. Imperf between (horiz pair) ..
c. Printed double .. .. ..
d. Chalky blue .. .. .. — 50·00 —
83 $1 scarlet .. .. 12·00 24·00 1·00
a. Perf 14 × 11 .. .. .. £180
b. Imperf (pair) .. .. .. 24·00 — 6·00
c. Printed both sides .. .. 28·00
84 $2 dull green .. .. 15·00 70·00 1·25
a. Imperf (pair) .. .. .. — — 8·00
b. Printed double .. .. ..
85 $5 bright purple .. .. .. £160 £200 12·00
a. Imperf (pair) .. .. .. £225 — 25·00
b. Dull purple .. .. .. £130 £170 5·00
86 $10 brown .. .. £170 £225 8·50
a. Imperf (pair) .. .. .. £225 — 25·00
81/6 .. .. .. *Set of* 6 £300 £500 16·00
81/6 Optd "Specimen" .. *Set of* 6 £140

For Nos. 81 to 83 in other colours, see Labuan 80*a*, 81*a* and 82*a*.

Nos. 81*c*, 82*c*, 83*c* and 84*b* are from waste sheets subsequently sold by the British North Borneo Company to collectors.

(**33** (3½ mm between lines of surcharge))

(Surcharged by Waterlow)

1895 (June). *No.* 83 *surch as T* **33**.

87 **32*c*** 4 cents on $1 scarlet .. .. 3·75 1·50 40
a. Surch double, one diagonal £750
88 10 cents on $1 scarlet .. .. 10·00 1·75 40
89 20 cents on $1 scarlet .. .. 27·00 13·00 40
90 30 cents on $1 scarlet .. .. 20·00 19·00 40
91 40 cents on $1 scarlet .. .. 20·00 40·00 40
87/91 .. .. .. *Set of* 5 70·00 65·00 1·75
87/91 Optd "Specimen" .. *Set of* 5 85·00

For 4 c. on $1 with wider spacing see No. 121.

No. 88 exists with the figures of the surcharge 2½ mm away from "CENTS". The normal setting has a space of 3½ mm. Examples of the narrow setting have, so far, only been seen on cancelled-to-order stamps.

34

35

36

37 Orang-Utan

38

39

40

41 Sun Bear

42

43 Borneo Railway Train

44

45

(Recess Waterlow)

1897 (Mar)–**1902.** *T* **34** *to* **45.** *New frames. P* 13½–14.

92 1 c. black and bistre-brown .. 7·50 3·25 40
aa. Perf 16 .. .. ..
a. Perf 14½–15 .. .. .. 6·50 2·50 40
b. Perf 13½–14, comp 12–13 .. 48·00 42·00 —
c. Imperf between (horiz pair) .. † † £375
93 1 c. black and ochre .. .. 35·00 13·00 50
a. Perf 14½–15 .. .. .. 24·00 10·00 50
ab. Imperf between (horiz pair) .. † † £375
b. Perf 13½–14, comp 12–13 ..
94 2 c. black and lake .. .. .. 20·00 3·50 40
a. Perf 14½–15 .. .. .. 14·00 3·00 40
ab. Imperf between (horiz pair) .. † † £375
b. Perf 13½–14, comp 12-13 .. — 14·00 1·25
c. Perf 12–13 .. .. ..
d. Imperf between (vert pair) .. † † £375
95 2 c. black and green (1900) .. .. 35·00 1·50 40
a. Perf 14½–15 .. .. .. 60·00 11·00 —
b. Perf 13½–14, comp 12–13 .. 80·00 22·00 —
c. Perf 12–13 .. .. ..
d. Imperf between (pair) .. .. — £475 †
96 3 c. green and rosy mauve .. .. 30·00 9·00 40
a. Perf 14½–15 .. .. .. 48·00 48·00 1·00
b. Perf 13½–14, comp 12–13 .. 65·00 65·00 —
97 3 c. green & dull mauve (*p* 14½–15) 8·50 3·00 50
98 4 c. black and green (1900) .. .. 8·00 — 1·50
a. Perf 13½–14, comp 12–13 ..
99 4 c. black and carmine (1900) .. 24·00 5·50 50
a. Perf 16 .. .. 50·00 32·00 —
b. Perf 14½–15 .. .. .. 38·00 2·00 50
c. Perf 13½–14, comp 12–13 .. 26·00 28·00 —
d. Perf 12–13 .. .. ..
100 5 c. black and orange-vermilion .. 65·00 3·50 50
a. Perf 14½–15 .. .. .. 65·00 3·00 50
ab. Imperf between (horiz pair) .. † £550 †
b. Perf 13½–14, comp 12–13 .. 65·00 14·00 —
c. Perf 12–13 .. .. ..
101 6 c. black and bistre-brown .. 30·00 15·00 50
a. Perf 14½–15 .. .. .. 11·00 3·25 50
102 8 c. black and brown-purple .. 60·00 48·00 —
a. Perf 16 .. .. 90·00 14·00 70
ab. Imperf between (vert pair) .. £350 £350 —
b. Perf 14½–15 .. .. .. 24·00 2·75 60
103 8 c. black and brown .. .. 7·50 23·00 75
a. Perf 14½–15 .. .. .. 45·00 60·00 —
b. Perf 16 .. ..
104 10 c. brown and slate-lilac (1902) .. 60·00 32·00 1·25
a. Imperf between (vert pair) ..
105 10 c. brown and slate-blue (1902) .. £140 65·00 1·50
106 12 c. black and dull blue .. .. £110 48·00 1·50
a. Imperf between (vert pair) .. † † £375
b. Perf 14½–15 .. .. .. 70·00 28·00 1·50
c. Perf 13½–14, comp 12–13 .. £130 55·00 —
d. Perf 12–13 .. .. ..
107 16 c. green and chestnut (1902) .. £120 85·00 3·00
a. Perf 14½–15 .. .. .. £120 £120 —
108 18 c. black and green (*p* 16) .. .. 16·00 50·00 1·00
a. Imperf vert (horiz pair) .. .. † † 65·00
b. Imperf between (vert pair) .. † † £225
c. Imperf (pair) .. .. .. † † £150
109 24 c. blue and lake .. .. .. 12·00 70·00 1·40
a. Perf 13½–14, comp 12–13 .. 30·00 85·00 1·60
b. Perf 12–13 .. .. .. 85·00
92/109 (*one of each value*) .. *Set of* 12 £350 £250 10·00
92/109 (*excl* 93, 97, 103) Optd "Specimen" *Set of* 14 £200

No. 98 was printed in an incorrect frame colour and it is doubtful if it was issued for postal purposes in North Borneo. Used examples come from dealers' stock sent to the territory for cancellation.

In the above the 18 c. has "POSTAL REVENUE" instead of "POSTAGE AND REVENUE" and the 24 c. has those words omitted. These stamps were replaced by others with corrected inscriptions; see Nos. 110 and 111.

46

47

1897. *Corrected inscriptions. P* 13½–14.
110 **46** 18 c. black and green .. .. 60·00 19·00 1·50
a. Imperf between (horiz pair) † † £375
b. Perf 14½–15 .. .. 50·00 12·00 1·50
c. Perf 13½–14, comp 12–13 ..
111 **47** 24 c. blue and lake .. .. 48·00 35·00 2·00
a. Perf 16 .. .. 90·00 90·00 —
b. Perf 14½–15 .. .. 35·00 48·00 2·00
c. Perf 13½–14, comp 12–13 ..
d. Perf 12–13 .. ..
110/11 Optd "Specimen" .. *Set of* 2 48·00

4 CENTS (48) (4½ mm between lines of surcharge)

BRITISH PROTECTORATE. (49)

4 cents (50)

1899 (22 July–Oct). *Surch with T* **48**. (*a*) *4½ mm between lines of surch. P* 14½–15 (*Nos.* 112/17) *or* 14 (*Nos.* 118/24).
112 4 c. on 5 c. (No. 100a) .. .. .. 35·00 40·00
a. Perf 13½–14 .. .. .. 16·00 10·00
b. Perf 13½–14, comp 12–13 .. .. 28·00 28·00
113 4 c. on 6 c. (No. 101a) (date?) .. .. 17·00 21·00
a. Perf 13½–14 .. .. .. 14·00 38·00
114 4 c. on 8 c. (No. 102b) (Oct) .. .. 14·00 10·00
115 4 c. on 12 c. (No. 106b) (Oct) .. .. 14·00 13·00
a. Imperf between (horiz pair) .. £450
b. Imperf between (vert pair) .. .. — £450
c. Perf 13½–14 .. .. 26·00
d. Perf 12–13 .. ..
e. Perf 13½–14, comp 12–13 .. .. 23·00
116 4 c. on 18 c. (No. 110a) (Oct) .. .. 9·50 13·00
a. Perf 13½–14 .. .. .. 22·00 27·00
117 4 c. on 24 c. (No. 111b) (Oct) .. .. 13·00 13·00
a. Perf 16 .. .. .. 40·00 48·00
b. Perf 13½–14 .. .. .. 13·00 32·00
c. Perf 13½–14, comp 12–13 .. .. 32·00 35·00
d. Perf 12–13 .. .. .. 38·00 48·00
118 4 c. on 25 c. indigo (No. 81) .. .. 5·00 8·50
a. Imperf between (horiz strip of 3) .. £850
119 4 c. on 50 c. deep slate-purple (No. 82) .. 6·00 12·00
a. Chalky blue .. .. .. 25·00 32·00
121 4 c. on $1 scarlet (No. 83) .. .. 5·00 9·00
122 4 c. on $2 dull green (No. 84) .. .. 5·00 12·00
123 4 c. on $5 bright purple (No. 85) £150 £225
a. Dull purple £140 £225
124 4 c. on $10 brown (No. 86) £110 £200
112/24 .. .. .. *Set of* 12 £300 £475
112/24 Optd "Specimen" .. .. *Set of* 12 £160

(*b*) *8½ mm between lines of surch. P* 14
125 4 c. on $5 (No. 85) .. .. .. 5·50 11·00
126 4 c. on $10 (No. 86) .. .. .. 5·50 11·00

No. 121 differs only from No. 87 in having the "4" and "cents" wider apart.

Examples of the Kudat postmark dated "AU 15 1899" struck on Nos. 112/24 are generally considered to be faked.

A new setting of the surcharge, with 2½ mm between "4" and "CENTS" for values to $2 and 3½ mm on the $5 and $10, was used for the Specimen overprints, including unissued surcharges on the 1 c., 2 c. and 3 c. values (*price* £90 *the set of three*).

(Optd by Waterlow)

1901 (8 Oct)–**05**. *Optd as T* **49**. (*a*) *P* 13½–14.
127 1 c. (No. 92) (R.) .. .. .. 3·50 1·50 30
a. Perf 14½–15 .. .. .. 2·00 1·75 30
128 2 c. (No. 95) (R.) .. .. .. 2·50 1·75 30
a. Perf 16 .. .. .. 3·50 7·00 30
b. Perf 14½–15 .. .. .. 7·50 7·50 30
129 3 c. (No. 96) .. .. .. 1·60 3·50 30
a. Imperf between (vert pair) ..
b. Perf 14½–15 .. .. .. 7·00 2·25 30
c. Perf 13½–14, comp 14½–15 .. 42·00
130 4 c. (No. 99) (G.) .. .. .. 6·50 1·50 30
a. Perf 14½–15 .. .. .. 15·00 1·50 30
131 5 c. (No. 100) (G.) .. .. .. 28·00 3·50 30
a. Perf 14½–15 .. .. .. 7·50 2·50 30
132 6 c. (No. 101) (R.) .. .. .. 35·00 48·00 1·25
a. No stop after "Protectorate" .. 70·00 70·00 —
b. Perf 16 .. .. .. 3·00 8·00 70
133 8 c. (No. 103) (B.) .. .. .. 3·00 3·25 50
a. No stop after "Protectorate" .. 3·00 22·00 1·50
b. Perf 13½–14, comp 12–13 .. 42·00 18·00 —
c. Imperf between (vert pair) .. † † £300
134 10 c. (No. 104) (R.) (7.02) .. .. 28·00 5·00 60
a. Perf 14½–15 .. .. .. 70·00 23·00 1·25
c. Perf 13½–14. No stop after "Protectorate" £120
d. Opt double .. .. .. £425 † £250
e. On 10 c. (No. 105) £130
f. Imperf vert (horiz pair) .. † † £350
135 12 c. (No. 106) (R.) .. .. .. 35·00 12·00 1·50
136 16 c. (No. 107) (7.02) .. .. .. 80·00 20·00 2·25
a. Perf 14½–15 .. .. .. 85·00 32·00 2·25
b. Perf 13½–14, comp 12–13 .. £120 48·00 —
137 18 c. (No. 110) (R.) .. .. .. 9·00 25·00 1·25
a. No stop after "Protectorate" ..
b. Perf 13½–14, comp 12–13 ..
138 24 c. (No. 111) .. .. .. 15·00 35·00 1·50
a. Perf 14½–15 .. .. .. 50·00 70·00 1·75
b. Imperf between (horiz pair) ..

(*b*) *P* 14
139 25 c. (No. 81) (R.) .. .. .. 2·00 10·00 50
a. No stop after "Protectorate" £110 £130 20·00
b. Overprints *tête-bêche* (horiz pair)
c. Overprint inverted £375
140 50 c. (No. 82) (R.) .. .. .. 2·75 11·00 55
a. No stop after "Protectorate" . 60·00 £110 —
b. Chalky blue .. ..
141 $1 (No. 83) (R.) (1.04) .. .. 10·00 60·00 —
142 $1 (No. 83) .. .. .. 6·50 35·00 2·50
a. Imperf horiz (vert pair) .. £450
b. Opt double .. .. .. † † £275
c. Opt treble .. .. ..
143 $2 (No. 84) (R.) (1903) .. .. 30·00 95·00 3·50
a. Opt double .. .. .. £1000 — £325
144 $5 (No. 85*b*) (R.) (2.05) .. .. £170 £425 6·00
145 $10 (No. 86) (R.) (2.05) .. .. £275 £500 8·00
a. Opt inverted .. .. .. £1200 † £350
127/45 .. .. .. *Set of* 18 £600 £1100 27·00
127/40 Optd "Specimen" .. *Set of* 14 £275

There was more than one setting of the overprint for some of the values. Full sheets of the 6 c. and 8 c. are known, without stop throughout.

1904–5. *Surch locally with T* **50**. (*a*) *P* 14½–15.
146 4 c. on 5 c. (No. 100a) .. .. 25·00 40·00 6·00
a. Surch omitted (in pair with normal) .. .. ..
147 4 c. on 6 c. (No. 101a) .. .. 7·00 19·00 4·75
a. Surch inverted £180
148 4 c. on 8 c. (No. 102b) .. .. 12·00 26·00 5·00
a. Surch inverted £200
149 4 c. on 12 c. (No. 106b) .. .. 22·00 40·00 5·50
a. Perf 13½–14 .. .. .. 42·00 60·00 5·50
b. Perf 13½–14, comp 12–13 .. 24·00 60·00 —
c. Surch omitted (in pair with normal) .. .. ..
150 4 c. on 18 c. (No. 110b) .. .. 14·00 38·00 5·50
a. Perf 13½–14 .. ..
151 4 c. on 24 c. (No. 111b) .. .. 19·00 48·00 5·50
a. Perf 16 .. .. .. 16·00 48·00 5·50
b. Perf 13½–14 .. .. .. 19·00 48·00 5·50
c. Perf 12–13 .. ..

(*b*) *P* 14
152 4 c. on 25 c. (No. 81) .. .. .. 3·50 25·00 5·50
153 4 c. on 50 c. (No. 82) .. .. .. 3·75 38·00 5·50
154 4 c. on $1 (No. 83) .. .. .. 4·25 48·00 5·50
155 4 c. on $2 (No. 84) .. .. .. 5·50 48·00 6·00
156 4 c. on $5 (No. 85) .. .. .. 11·00 48·00 6·00
a. Surch on No. 85*b* .. .. 30·00 48·00 —
157 4 c. on $10 (No. 86) .. .. .. 11·00 48·00 6·00
a. Surch inverted £1200
b. Surch omitted (in pair with normal) .. .. ..
146/57 .. .. .. *Set of* 12 £110 £425 60·00

51 Malayan Tapir

52 Travellers' Tree

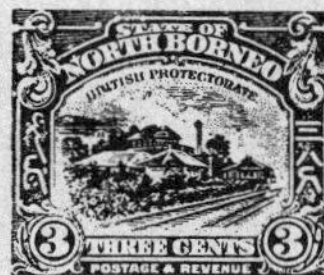

53 Railway at Jesselton

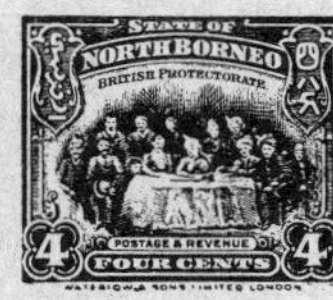

54 The Sultan of Sulu, his staff and W. C. Cowie, Managing Director of the Company

55 Indian Elephant

56 Sumatran Rhinoceros

57 Ploughing with Buffalo

58 Wild Boar

59 Palm Cockatoo

60 Rhinoceros Hornbill

61 Banteng

62 Dwarf Cassowary

(Recess Waterlow)

1909 (1 July)–**23**. *Centres in black. P* 13½–14.
158 **51** 1 c. chocolate-brown .. .. 4·75 1·00 30
a. Perf 14½–15 .. .. 28·00 10·00 40
159 1 c. brown .. .. 11·00 1·60 30
a. Perf 14½–15 .. .. 20·00 3·00 30
b. Imperf between (vert pair) £1000
160 **52** 2 c. green .. .. 1·00 70 30
a. Imperf between (pair) ..
b. Perf 14½–15 .. .. 2·00 70 30
161 **53** 3 c. lake .. .. 3·00 1·75 30
162 3 c. rose-lake .. .. 2·50 1·25 40
a. Perf 14½–15 .. .. 27·00 — 55
163 3 c. green (1923) .. .. 8·00 1·25 —
164 **54** 4 c. scarlet .. .. 2·25 30 30
a. Imperf between (vert pair) ..
b. Perf 14½–15 .. .. 9·00 1·75 35
165 **55** 5 c. yellow-brown .. .. 8·50 4·50 40
a. Perf 14½–15 .. ..
166 5 c. dark brown .. .. 12·00 4·00 —
167 **56** 6 c. olive-green .. .. 6·00 1·75 30
a. Perf 14½–15 .. .. 55·00 6·50 60
168 6 c. apple-green .. .. 20·00 3·00 —
169 **57** 8 c. lake .. .. 2·50 1·75 30
a. Perf 14½–15 .. ..
170 **58** 10 c. greyish blue .. .. 45·00 8·00 50
a. Perf 14½–15 .. .. 65·00 22·00 —
171 10 c. blue .. .. 48·00 3·50 —
172 10 c. turquoise-blue .. .. 18·00 2·00 —
a. Perf 14½–15 .. .. 38·00 5·50 —
173 **59** 12 c. deep blue .. .. 22·00 2·75 50
a. Perf 14½–15 .. ..
b. Imperf between (horiz pair) † † £375
173*c* 12 c. deep bright blue ..
174 **60** 16 c. brown-lake .. .. 18·00 7·00 65
175 **61** 18 c. blue-green .. .. 85·00 30·00 1·00
176 **62** 24 c. deep rose-lilac .. .. 26·00 3·50 60
a. Deep lilac .. .. — 6·00 —
158/76 .. .. *Set of* 13 £180 50·00 —
158/76 Optd "Specimen" .. *Set of* 13 £275

For this issue perf 12½ see Nos. 277, etc.

20 CENTS (63)

64

65

1909 (7 Sept). *No.* 175 *surch with T* **63** *by Waterlow. P* 13½–14.
177 20 c. on 18 c. bl-grn (R.) (Optd S. £38) 6·00 95 20
a. Perf 14½–15 .. .. £160 60·00 —

(Recess Waterlow)

1911 (7 Mar). *P* 13½–14.
178 **64** 25 c. black and yellow-green .. 5·50 3·75 1·50
a. Perf 14½–15 .. .. 9·00 28·00 —
b. Imperf (pair) .. .. 45·00
178*c* 25 c. black and blue-green .. 38·00
179 50 c. black and steel-blue .. 6·50 3·75 1·75
a. Perf 14½–15 .. .. 15·00 19·00 —
ab. Imperf between (horiz pair) £1500
c. Imperf (pair) .. .. 65·00
180 $1 black and chestnut .. .. 15·00 4·00 1·75
a. Perf 14½–15 .. .. 35·00 15·00 —
b. Imperf (pair) .. .. 90·00
181 $2 black and lilac .. .. 40·00 13·00 4·25
182 **65** $5 black and lake .. .. 85·00 90·00 21·00
a. Imperf (pair) £150
183 $10 black and brick-red .. £200 £250 42·00
a. Imperf (pair) £225
178/83 .. .. *Set of* 6 £300 £325 65·00
178/83 Optd "Specimen" .. *Set of* 6 £225

BRITISH PROTECTORATE (66)

2 cents (67)

(68)

1912 (July). *Nos.* 85*b and* 86 *optd with T* **66**.
184 $5 dull purple (R.) .. .. .. £800 — 7·50
185 $10 brown (R.) .. .. .. £1000 — 7·50
a. Opt inverted .. .. .. † † —

1916 (Feb). *Nos.* 162, 167 *and* 173 *surch as T* **67** *by Govt Printing Office, Sandakan. P* 13½–14.
186 **53** 2 c. on 3 c. black and rose-lake .. 17·00 11·00
a. "s" inverted (R. 2/5) .. .. 95·00 95·00
b. Surch double .. ..
187 **56** 4 c. on 6 c. black and olive-green (R.) 14·00 14·00
a. "s" inverted (R. 2/5) .. .. 95·00 95·00
b. "s" inserted by hand .. .. — £600
c. Perf 14½–15 .. .. £120
ca. "s" inverted .. ..
188 **59** 10 c. on 12 c. black and deep blue (R.) 42·00 48·00
a. "s" inverted (R. 2/5) .. £120 £120
b. "s" inserted by hand .. £750
186/8 .. .. *Set of* 3 65·00 65·00
186/8 Optd "Specimen" .. .. *Set of* 3 £110

Nos. 186/8 were surcharged from a setting of 25 (5×5) on which the required face values were inserted.

1916 (May). *Stamps of* 1909–11 *optd with T* **68** *by Waterlow. P* 13½–14. *Centres in black.* (*a*) *Cross in vermilion* (*thick shiny ink*).

189 **51** 1 c. brown .. .. 7·50 30·00
190 **52** 2 c. green .. .. 32·00 75·00
a. Perf 14½–15 .. .. 32·00 80·00
ab. Opt double, one albino £200
191 **53** 3 c. rose-lake .. .. 27·00 45·00
a. Nos. 191 and 204 *se-tenant* (vert pair) £1500
192 **54** 4 c. scarlet .. .. 5·50 28·00
a. Perf 14½–15 .. .. £150 £120
193 **55** 5 c. yellow-brown .. .. .. 30·00 55·00
a. Perf 14½–15 .. ..
194 **56** 6 c. apple-green .. .. .. 50·00 60·00
a. Perf 14½–15 .. .. £160
195 **57** 8 c. lake .. .. 23·00 60·00
196 **58** 10 c. blue .. .. 40·00 70·00
197 **59** 12 c. deep blue .. .. .. 80·00 85·00
198 **60** 16 c. brown-lake .. .. .. 80·00 85·00
199 **61** 20 c. on 18 c. blue-green .. .. 32·00 85·00
200 **62** 24 c. dull mauve .. .. .. 80·00 85·00
a. Imperf between (vert pair)
201 **64** 25 c. green (*p* 14½–15) £275 £350
189/201 .. .. *Set of* 13 £650 £1000

(*b*) *Cross in shades of carmine* (*matt ink*)

202 **51** 1 c. brown .. .. 26·00 65·00
a. Perf 14½–15 .. .. £150
203 **52** 2 c. green .. .. 27·00 45·00
b. Perf 14½–15 .. .. £150
ba. Opt double .. .. † —
204 **53** 3 c. rose-lake .. .. 32·00 65·00
204*a* **54** 4 c. scarlet £450
205 **55** 5 c. yellow-brown .. .. .. 45·00 70·00
206 **56** 6 c. apple-green .. .. .. 38·00 65·00
a. Perf 14½–15 .. .. £160 £180
207 **57** 8 c. lake .. .. 24·00 55·00
208 **58** 10 c. blue .. .. 42·00 65·00
209 **59** 12 c. deep blue .. .. .. 70·00 £100
210 **60** 16 c. brown-lake .. .. .. 70·00 95·00
211 **61** 20 c. on 18 c. blue-green .. .. 60·00 £100
212 **62** 24 c. dull mauve .. .. .. 75·00 £140
213 **64** 25 c. green £650
a. Perf 14½–15 .. .. £425 £475
202/13 (*ex* 4 c.) .. .. .. *Set of* 12 £800 £1200

The British North Borneo Company donated a proportion of the above issue to be sold by the National Philatelic War Fund for the benefit of the Red Cross and St. John's Ambulance Brigade.

RED CROSS ✚

TWO CENTS (69) **FOUR CENTS** (70)

1918 (Aug). *Stamps of* 1909–11 *surch as T* **69**. *P* 13½–14.

(*a*) *Lines of surcharge 9 mm apart*

214 **51** 1 c. + 2 c. brown .. .. .. 3·50 8·00
a. Imperf between (horiz pair) .. £1400
215 **52** 2 c. + 2 c. green .. .. 1·00 8·50
a. Imperf between (horiz or vert pair) £1500
b. Imperf (pair) .. ..
c. Perf 14½–15 .. ..
216 **53** 3 c. + 2 c. rose-red .. .. .. 10·00 15·00
a. Imperf between (horiz pair) .. £1500
b. Perf 14½–15 .. .. 25·00 65·00
217 3 c. + 2 c. dull rose-carmine £140
a. Perf 14½–15 .. .. £170
218 **54** 4 c. + 2 c. scarlet .. .. .. 70 4·00
a. Surch inverted £300
219 **55** 5 c. + 2 c. deep brown .. .. 8·00 22·00
220 5 c. + 2 c. pale brown .. .. 8·50 27·00
221 **56** 6 c. + 2 c. olive-green .. .. 5·00 18·00
a. Perf 14½–15 .. .. £160 £180
221*b* 6 c. + 2 c. apple-green .. .. ..
c. Perf 14½–15 .. .. £275
222 **57** 8 c. + 2 c. lake .. .. 5·50 8·00
a. Inverted figure "3" for "C" in "CENTS" .. ..
223 **58** 10 c. + 2 c. blue .. .. .. 7·50 23·00
224 **59** 12 c. + 2 c. deep bright blue .. .. 18·00 40·00
a. Surch inverted £550
225 **60** 16 c. + 2 c. brown-lake .. .. 20·00 40·00
226 **62** 24 c. + 2 c. mauve .. .. .. 20·00 40·00

(*b*) *Lines of surch* 13–14 *mm apart*

227 **52** 2 c. + 2 c. green .. .. 60·00 £120
228 **56** 6 c. + 2 c. olive-green £300 £600
229 **64** 25 c. + 2 c. green .. .. .. 10·00 38·00
230 50 c. + 2 c. steel-blue .. .. 12·00 38·00
231 $1 + 2 c. chestnut .. .. .. 45·00 48·00
232 $2 + 2 c. lilac .. .. 65·00 95·00
233 **65** $5 + 2 c. lake £300 £400
234 $10 + 2 c. brick-red £300 £400
214/34 .. .. *Set of* 17 £750 £1100

The above stamps were dispatched from London in three consignments, of which two were lost through enemy action at sea.

Only one sheet was found of No. 228.

These stamps were sold at a premium of 2 c. per stamp, which went to the Red Cross Society.

1918 (Oct). *Stamps of* 1909–11 *surch with T* **70**, *in red. P* 13½–14.

235 **51** 1 c. + 4 c. chocolate .. .. .. 60 5·00
a. Imperf between (horiz pair) .. £1400
236 **52** 2 c. + 4 c. green .. .. 65 8·00
237 **53** 3 c. + 4 c. rose-lake .. .. .. 90 3·75
238 **54** 4 c. + 4 c. scarlet .. .. .. 40 4·75
239 **55** 5 c. + 4 c. brown .. .. .. 2·00 18·00
240 **56** 6 c. + 4 c. apple-green .. .. 1·90 12·00
a. Imperf between (vert pair) .. £1300
241 **57** 8 c. + 4 c. lake .. .. 1·25 9·50
242 **58** 10 c. + 4 c. turquoise-blue .. .. 3·75 12·00
242*a* 10 c. + 4 c. greenish blue .. .. 8·00 35·00
243 **59** 12 c. + 4 c. deep blue .. .. .. 9·50 14·00
a. Surch double £750
244 **60** 16 c. + 4 c. brown-lake .. .. .. 7·00 16·00
245 **62** 24 c. + 4 c. mauve .. .. .. 7·00 20·00
246 **64** 25 c. + 4 c. yellow-green .. .. 4·50 48·00
247 25 c. + 4 c. blue-green .. .. .. 24·00 75·00
248 50 c. + 4 c. steel-blue .. .. .. 15·00 42·00
a. Perf 14½–15 .. .. 55·00
249 $1 + 4 c. chestnut .. .. .. 15·00 55·00
a. Perf 14½–15 .. .. 80·00
250 $2 + 4 c. lilac .. .. 45·00 80·00
251 **65** $5 + 4 c. lake £250 £375
252 $10 + 4 c. brick-red £250 £375
235/52 .. .. *Set of* 17 £550 £1000

Nos. 235/52 were sold at face, plus 4 c. on each stamp for Red Cross Funds.

Examples of a double-ring "SANDAKAN N. BORNEO" postmark dated "1 NOV 1918" on these stamps are generally considered to be faked.

MALAYA-BORNEO EXHIBITION 1922. (71) **THREE CENTS** (72)

1922 (31 Mar). *Malaya-Borneo Exhibition, Singapore. Stamps of* 1909–22, *some in different shades, optd as T* **71** *by Govt Printing Office, Sandakan. P* 13½–14.

253 **51** 1 c. brown (R.) .. .. 8·00 48·00
a. "BORHEO" £300 £350
b. "BORNEQ" £450 £500
c. Stop after "EXHIBITION." .. .. 48·00
d. Raised stop after "1922" £400
e. "EXHIBITICN." with stop £450
f. Perf 14½–15 .. .. 19·00 60·00
fa. "BORHEO" £400
fb. "BORNEQ" £650
fc. Raised stop after "1922" £550
fd. "EXHIBITICN." with stop £650
fe. "MHLAYA" and stop after "EXHIBITION" £1900
ff. Stop after "EXHIBITION." .. .. 75·00
253*g* 1 c. brown (B.) (*p* 14½–15) £800
ga. Vert pair, with and without opt .. £3000
gb. Raised stop after "1922." £2250
gc. "BORHEO" £1800
gd. "BORNEQ" £2500
gf. "EXHIBITICN." with stop £2500
gg. "MHLAYA" and stop after "EXHIBITION" .. ..
254 1 c. orange-brown (R.) .. .. .. 18·00 50·00
255 **52** 2 c. green (R.) .. .. 1·60 16·00
a. Stop after "EXHIBITION." .. .. 20·00
256 **53** 3 c. rose-lake (B.) .. .. .. 10·00 38·00
a. Stop after "EXHIBITION." .. .. 48·00
b. "EXHIBITICN." with stop £1900
c. Raised stop after "1922" £1500
257 **54** 4 c. scarlet (B.) .. .. 1·75 26·00
a. Stop after "EXHIBITION." .. .. 21·00
b. Perf 14½–15 .. .. 60·00
ba. Stop after "EXHIBITION." .. ..
258 **55** 5 c. orange-brown (B.) .. .. .. 9·00 48·00
a. Imperf between (vert pair) .. £1000 £1000
b. Stop after "EXHIBITION." .. .. 45·00
c. Opt double £1700
d. Opt double (with stop) £4000
259 5 c. chestnut (B.) .. .. .. 17·00 55·00
a. Stop after "EXHIBITION." .. .. 75·00
260 **56** 6 c. apple-green (R.) .. .. .. 4·00 45·00
a. Stop after "EXHIBITION." .. .. 35·00
b. Opt double £1700
c. Opt double (with stop) £4000
261 **57** 8 c. dull rose (B.) .. .. .. 4·50 42·00
a. Stop after "EXHIBITION." .. .. 42·00
262 8 c. deep rose-lake (B.) .. .. .. 4·50 42·00
a. Stop after "EXHIBITION." .. .. 42·00
263 **58** 10 c. turquoise-blue (R.) .. .. .. 6·00 45·00
a. Stop after "EXHIBITION." .. .. 45·00
b. Perf 14½–15 .. .. 25·00
ba. Stop after "EXHIBITION." £120
264 10 c. greenish blue (R.) .. .. .. 7·00 60·00
a. Stop after "EXHIBITION." .. .. 48·00
265 **59** 12 c. deep blue (R.) .. .. .. 4·50 21·00
a. Stop after "EXHIBITION." .. .. 42·00 £100
266 12 c. deep bright blue (R.) .. .. 30·00
a. Stop after "EXHIBITION." £140
267 **60** 16 c. brown-lake (B.) .. .. .. 11·00 50·00
a. Stop after "EXHIBITION." .. .. 65·00
b. Opt in red £3750
268 **61** 20 c. on 18 c. blue-green (B.) .. .. 12·00 55·00
a. Stop after "EXHIBITION." .. .. 95·00
269 20 c. on 18 c. blue-green (R.) .. .. 20·00 £130
a. Stop after "EXHIBITION." £200 £300
270 **62** 24 c. mauve (R.) .. .. 24·00 50·00
a. Stop after "EXHIBITION." £110
271 24 c. lilac (R.) .. .. 24·00 50·00
a. Stop after "EXHIBITION." £110
272 24 c. reddish lilac (R.) .. .. .. 32·00 65·00
a. Stop after "EXHIBITION." £140
273 **64** 25 c. blue-green (R.) .. .. .. 13·00 60·00
a. Stop after "EXHIBITION." .. .. 48·00
274 25 c. yellow-green (R.) .. .. .. 3·75 50·00
a. Stop after "EXHIBITION." .. .. 42·00
b. Opt double £1800
c. Perf 14½–15 .. .. 13·00 60·00
ca. Stop after "EXHIBITION." £200
cb. Opt double £1800
275 50 c. steel-blue (R.) .. .. .. 7·50 40·00
a. Stop after "EXHIBITION." .. .. 60·00
b. Perf 14½–15 .. .. 20·00 65·00
ba. Stop after "EXHIBITION." £130
253/75 .. .. *Set of* 14 95·00 £500
253/75 Optd "Specimen" .. .. *Set of* 14 £425

These overprints were applied from a number of settings covering 10, 20, 25 or 30 stamps at a time.

Of the ten settings known for the horizontal stamps the earliest were only used for the 1 c. on which most of the varieties occur. Of the others the vast majority come from settings of 20 (10 × 2) with the stop after "EXHIBITION" variety on R. 2/7, or 25 (5 × 5) on which the same variety can be found on R. 5/4. In addition the 3 c. comes from a different setting of 20 (10 × 2) on which there is a raised stop after "1922" on R. 2/8 and "EXHIBITICN." on R. 2/9.

The 1 c. sequence is complicated, but additionally includes a setting of 10 with "BORHEO" on stamps 3 and 10, "BORNEQ" on stamp 4, raised stop on stamp 8 and "EXHIBITICN." on stamp 9. A setting of 20 repeats this sequence on its bottom line as does one of 30, although in this instance "MHLAYA" replaces "EXHIBITICN" as the variety on stamp 9.

For the vertical stamps (2, 6, 10, 12, 16 and 20 c. on 18 c.) the settings were of 20 (10 × 2) or 25 (5 × 5). The stop after "EXHIBITION" occurs on R. 2/7 of the former and R. 5/4 of the latter.

The 25 c. and 50 c. high values were overprinted from a setting of 20 (10 × 2), with the stop after "EXHIBITION" on R. 2/7, or 25 (5 × 5).

1923 (Oct). *T* **54** *surch with T* **72**.

276 3 c. on 4 c. black and scarlet (Optd S. £50) .. 1·00 4·75
a. Surch double £700

1925–28. *Designs as* 1909–22 *issue with centres in black and some frame colours changed. P* 12½.

277 **51** 1 c. chocolate-brown .. .. .. 1·00 70
a. Imperf between (horiz pair) .. £700
278 **52** 2 c. claret 40 60
a. Imperf between (vert pair) .. — £550
b. Imperf between (horiz pair) ..
279 **53** 3 c. green .. .. 2·75 1·40
a. Imperf between (horiz pair) ..
280 **54** 4 c. scarlet 45 10
a. Imperf between (vert pair) .. £275
b. Imperf between (horiz pair) .. £650
c. Imperf between (vert strip of three)
281 **55** 5 c. yellow-brown .. .. .. 4·50 2·75
a. Imperf between (vert pair) .. £650
282 **56** 6 c. olive-green .. .. .. 5·00 90
283 **57** 8 c. carmine .. .. 3·25 50
a. Imperf between (vert pair) .. £375
b. Imperf between (horiz pair) ..
c. Imperf between (vert strip of four) £900
284 **58** 10 c. turquoise-blue .. .. .. 2·50 90
a. Imperf between (horiz pair) .. £600
b. Imperf between (vert pair) ..
285 **59** 12 c. deep blue .. .. 16·00 80
286 **60** 16 c. red-brown .. .. .. 27·00 90·00
287 **61** 20 c. on 18 c. blue-green (R.) .. .. 6·50 3·00
288 **62** 24 c. violet .. .. 48·00 80·00
289 **64** 25 c. green .. .. 7·00 4·25
290 50 c. steel-blue .. .. 9·00 12·00
291 $1 chestnut .. .. 15·00 £140
292 $2 mauve .. .. 50·00 £180
293 **65** $5 lake (1928) £130 £450
294 $10 orange-red (1928) £250 £550
277/94 .. .. *Set of* 18 £500 £1300

Examples of No. 278 were supplied for U.P.U. distribution punched with a 3½ mm diameter hole.

73 Head of a Murut

76 Mount Kinabalu

(Eng J. A. C. Harrison. Recess Waterlow)

1931 (1 Jan). *50th Anniv of British North Borneo Company. T* **73**, **76** *and similar designs. P* 12½.

295 3 c. black and blue-green 80 80
296 6 c. black and orange .. .. .. 16·00 3·25
297 10 c. black and scarlet .. .. .. 3·50 11·00
298 12 c. black and ultramarine .. .. 4·00 8·00
299 25 c. black and violet .. .. .. 38·00 35·00
300 $1 black and yellow-green .. .. 24·00 80·00
301 $2 black and chestnut .. .. .. 48·00 £100
302 $5 black and purple £140 £275
295/302 .. .. *Set of* 8 £250 £450
295/302 Optd "Specimen" .. .. *Set of* 8 £275

Designs: *Vert*—6 c. Orang-Utan; 10 c. Dyak warrior; $1 Badge of the Company; $5 Arms of the Company. *Horiz*—25 c. Clouded Leopard; $2 Arms of the Company.

Examples of all values are known showing a forged Jesselton postmark dated "22 AUG 1931".

81 Buffalo Transport

82 Palm Cockatoo

(Eng J. A. C. Harrison. Recess Waterlow)

1939 (1 Jan). *T* **81/2** *and similar designs. P* 12½.

303 1 c. green and red-brown 75 85
304 2 c. purple and greenish blue .. .. 4·50 85
305 3 c. slate-blue and green .. .. .. 1·50 2·00
306 4 c. bronze-green and violet .. .. 2·75 50
307 6 c. deep blue and claret .. .. .. 2·00 4·00
308 8 c. scarlet .. .. 6·50 1·50

309 10 c. violet and bronze-green 38·00 6·00
310 12 c. green and royal blue 14·00 5·00
a. *Green and blue* 24·00 6·00
311 15 c. blue-green and brown 16·00 6·50
312 20 c. violet and slate-blue 10·00 3·25
313 25 c. green and chocolate 12·00 7·00
314 50 c. chocolate and violet 14·00 6·50
315 $1 brown and carmine 65·00 18·00
316 $2 violet and olive-green 95·00 80·00
317 $5 indigo and pale blue £300 £200
303/17 *Set of* 15 £500 £300
303/17 Perf "Specimen" *Set of* 15 £275

Designs: *Vert*—3 c. Native; 4 c. Proboscis Monkey; 6 c. Mounted Bajaus; 10 c. Orang-Utan; 15 c. Dyak; $1, $2 Badge of the Company. *Horiz*—8 c. Eastern Archipelago; 12 c. Murut with blow-pipe; 20 c. River scene; 25 c. Native boat; 50 c. Mt Kinabalu; $5 Arms of the Company.

WAR TAX (96)   WAR TAX (97)

1941 (24 Feb). *Nos. 303/4 optd at Sandakan with T* **96/7**.
318 1 c. green and red-brown 65 2·00
a. Optd front and back £275
319 2 c. purple and greenish blue 4·25 3·50

The 1 c. was for compulsory use on internal mail and the 2 c. on overseas mail, both in addition to normal postage.

BRITISH MILITARY ADMINISTRATION

North Borneo, including Labuan, was occupied by the Japanese in January 1942. Australian forces landed on Labuan on 10 June 1945 and by the end of the war against Japan on 14 August had liberated much of western North Borneo. The territory was placed under British Military Administration on 5 January 1946.

BMA (98)

(99)

1945 (17 Dec). *Nos. 303/17 optd with T* **98**.
320 1 c. green and red-brown 4·25 1·25
321 2 c. purple and greenish blue 11·00 1·25
a. Opt double £4750
322 3 c. slate-blue and green 1·25 1·25
323 4 c. bronze-green and violet 16·00 13·00
324 6 c. deep blue and claret 1·25 30
325 8 c. scarlet 3·00 55
326 10 c. violet and bronze-green 3·00 30
327 12 c. green and blue 4·75 1·75
a. *Green and royal blue* 6·00 1·00
328 15 c. blue-green and brown 1·50 1·00
329 20 c. violet and slate-blue 2·75 1·25
330 25 c. green and chocolate 4·25 1·25
331 50 c. chocolate and violet 3·00 1·00
332 $1 brown and carmine 38·00 27·00
333 $2 violet and olive-green 38·00 19·00
a. Opt double £2500
334 $5 indigo and pale blue 14·00 9·00
320/34 *Set of* 15 £130 70·00

These stamps and the similarly overprinted stamps of Sarawak were obtainable at all post offices throughout British Borneo (Brunei, Labuan, North Borneo and Sarawak), for use on local and overseas mail.

CROWN COLONY

North Borneo became a Crown Colony on 15 July 1946.

Lower bar broken at right (R. 8/3)

Lower bar broken at left (R. 8/4)

1947 (1 Sept–22 Dec). *Nos. 303 to 317 optd with T* **99** *and bars obliterating words* "THE STATE OF" *and* "BRITISH PROTECTORATE".
335 1 c. green and red-brown (15.12) 15 1·00
b. Lower bar broken at right 14·00
c. Lower bar broken at left 14·00
336 2 c. purple and greenish blue (22.12) 1·50 90
337 3 c. slate-blue and green (R.) (22.12) 15 90
338 4 c. bronze-green and violet 40 40
339 6 c. deep blue and claret (R.) (22.12) 15 20
340 8 c. scarlet 20 20
b. Lower bar broken at right 15·00
341 10 c. violet and bronze-green (15.12) 50 40
342 12 c. green and royal blue (22.12) 2·00 2·25
a. *Green and blue* 2·00 2·50
343 15 c. blue-green and brown (22.12) 2·25 30
344 20 c. violet and slate-blue (22.12) 75 75
b. Lower bar broken at right 25·00
345 25 c. green and chocolate (22.12) 1·75 45
b. Lower bar broken at right 38·00
346 50 c. chocolate and violet (22.12) 1·25 85
b. Lower bar broken at right 38·00
c. Lower bar broken at left 38·00
347 $1 brown and carmine (22.12) 1·40 1·25
348 $2 violet and olive-green (22.12) 5·00 9·00
349 $5 indigo and pale blue (R.) (22.12) 14·00 9·50
b. Lower bar broken at right 90·00
335/49 *Set of* 15 28·00 25·00
335/49 Perf "Specimen" *Set of* 15 £250

1948 (1 Nov). *Royal Silver Wedding. As Nos.* 143/4 *of Jamaica*.
350 8 c. scarlet 30 80
351 $10 mauve 20·00 35·00

1949 (10 Oct). *75th Anniv of U.P.U. As Nos.* 145/8 *of Jamaica*.
352 8 c. carmine 40 30
353 10 c. brown 2·25 1·00
354 30 c. orange-brown 90 1·75
355 55 c. blue 90 2·25
352/5 *Set of* 4 4·00 4·75

100 Mount Kinabalu

102 Coconut Grove

(Photo Harrison)

1950 (1 July)–**52**. *T* **100, 102** *and similar designs. Wmk Mult Script CA. Chalk-surfaced paper. P* 13½ × 14½ (*horiz*), 14½ × 13½ (*vert*).
356 1 c. red-brown 15 70
357 2 c. blue 15 50
358 3 c. green 15 15
359 4 c. bright purple 15 10
360 5 c. violet 15 10
361 8 c. scarlet 75 85
362 10 c. maroon 60 15
363 15 c. ultramarine 1·25 65
364 20 c. brown 1·00 10
365 30 c. olive-brown 1·75 20
366 50 c. rose-carmine ("JESSLETON") 85 3·00
366*a* 50 c. rose-carmine ("JESSELTON") (1.5.52) 6·00 2·00
367 $1 red-orange 1·75 1·00
368 $2 grey-green 2·00 8·00
369 $5 emerald-green 11·00 15·00
370 $10 dull blue 32·00 42·00
356/70 *Set of* 16 55·00 65·00

Designs: *Horiz*—2 c. Native musical instrument; 8 c. Map; 10 c. Log pond; 15 c. Malay prau, Sandakan; 20 c. Bajau Chief; $2 Murut with blowpipe; $5 Net-fishing; $10 Arms of North Borneo. *Vert*—4 c. Hemp drying; 5 c. Cattle at Kota Belud; 30 c. Suluk river canoe, Lahad Datu; 50 c. Clock tower, Jesselton; $1 Bajau horsemen.

1953 (3 June). *Coronation. As No.* 153 *of Jamaica*.
371 10 c. black and bright scarlet 1·00 60

115 Log Pond

(Photo Harrison)

1954 (1 Mar)–**59**. *Designs previously used for King George VI issue, but with portrait of Queen Elizabeth II as in T* **115**. *Chalk-surfaced paper. Wmk Mult Script CA. P* 14½×13½ (*vert*) *or* 13½×14½ (*horiz*).
372 1 c. red-brown (1.10.54) 10 30
373 2 c. blue (1.6.56) 40 15
374 3 c. green (1.2.57) 30 2·00
a. *Deep green* (14.1.59) 2·75 3·50
375 4 c. bright purple (16.5.55) 50 20
376 5 c. reddish violet (1.7.54) 75 10
377 8 c. scarlet (1.10.54) 50 30
378 10 c. maroon 30 10
379 15 c. bright blue (16.5.55) 55 10
380 20 c. brown (3.8.54) 30 15
381 30 c. olive-brown (3.8.54) 2·00 20
382 50 c. rose-carm ("JESSELTON") (10.2.56) 4·50 20
a. *Rose* (9.12.59) 11·00 1·25
aw. Wmk inverted — £180
383 $1 red-orange (1.4.55) 5·00 20
384 $2 deep green (1.10.55) 12·00 1·25
a. *Grey-green* (22.1.58) 18·00 5·00
385 $5 emerald-green (1.2.57) 10·00 23·00
386 $10 deep blue (1.2.57) 23·00 35·00
372/86 *Set of* 15 55·00 55·00

Designs: *Horiz*—1 c. Mount Kinabalu; 2 c. Native musical instrument; 8 c. Map; 15 c. Native prahu, Sandakan; 20 c. Bajau chief; $2 Murut with blowpipe; $5 Net-fishing; $10 Arms of North Borneo. *Vert*—3 c. Coconut grove; 4 c. Hemp drying; 5 c. Cattle at Kota Belud; 30 c. Suluk boat, Lahad Datu; 50 c. Clock Tower, Jesselton; $1 Bajau horseman.

Plate 2 of the 30 c., released 10 August 1960, had a finer, 250 screen, instead of the previous 200 (*price* £3 *mint*).

116 Borneo Railway, 1902

119 Arms of Chartered Company

(Recess Waterlow)

1956 (1 Nov). *75th Anniv of British North Borneo Co. T* **116, 119** *and similar designs. Wmk Mult Script CA. P* 13 × 13½ (*horiz*) *or* 13½ × 13 (*vert*).
387 10 c. black and rose-carmine 1·00 40
388 15 c. black and red-brown 25 30
389 35 c. black and bluish green 30 1·50
390 $1 black and slate 65 2·50
387/90 *Set of* 4 2·00 4·25

Designs: *Horiz*—15 c. Malay prau; 35 c. Mount Kinabalu.

120 Sambar Stag

121 Orang-Utan

(Des Chong Yun Fatt. Recess Waterlow (until 1962), then D.L.R.)

1961 (1 Feb). *Horiz designs as T* **120** *or vert designs as T* **121**. *W w* **12**. *P* 13.
391 1 c. emerald and brown-red 10 10
392 4 c. bronze-green and orange 20 90
393 5 c. sepia and violet 30 10
394 6 c. black and blue-green 40 40
395 10 c. green and red 30 10
396 12 c. brown and grey-green 30 10
397 20 c. blue-green and ultramarine 3·50 10
398 25 c. grey-black and scarlet 70 90
399 30 c. sepia and olive 60 20
400 35 c. slate-blue and red-brown 1·50 90
401 50 c. emerald and yellow-brown 1·50 20
402 75 c. grey-blue and bright purple 7·00 90
403 $1 brown and yellow-green 9·50 80
404 $2 brown and slate 20·00 3·00
405 $5 emerald and maroon 32·00 14·00
406 $10 carmine and blue 24·00 25·00
391/406 *Set of* 16 90·00 42·00

Designs: *Horiz*—4 c. Sun Bear; 5 c. Clouded Leopard; 6 c. Dusun woman with gong; 10 c. Map of Borneo; 12 c. Banteng; 20 c. Butterfly orchid; 25 c. Sumatran Rhinoceros; 30 c. Murut with blow-pipe; 35 c. Mount Kinabalu; 50 c. Dusun and buffalo transport; 75 c. Bajau horsemen. *Vert*—$2 Rhinoceros Hornbill; $5 Crested Wood Partridge; $10 Arms of North Borneo.

1963 (4 June). *Freedom from Hunger. As No.* 80 *of Lesotho*.
407 12 c. ultramarine 1·50 65

North Borneo joined the Federation of Malaysia on 16 September 1963 and was renamed Sabah.

SABAH

STATE OF MALAYSIA

SABAH (136)   SABAH (137)

1964 (1 July)–**65**. *Nos.* 391/406 *of North Borneo* (*D.L.R. printings*), *optd with T* **136** (*Nos.* 408/19) *or T* **137** (*Nos.* 420/3).
408 1 c. emerald and brown-red 10 10
409 4 c. bronze-green and orange 15 50
410 5 c. sepia and violet 15 10
a. *Light sepia and deep violet* (17.8.65) 2·50 1·25
411 6 c. black and blue-green 10 10
412 10 c. green and red 15 10
413 12 c. brown and grey-green 15 10
414 20 c. blue-green and ultramarine 3·50 10
415 25 c. grey-black and scarlet 45 90
416 30 c. sepia and olive 25 10
417 35 c. slate-blue and red-brown 30 20
418 50 c. emerald and yellow-brown 30 10
419 75 c. grey-blue and bright purple 3·25 65
420 $1 brown and yellow-green 5·50 50
421 $2 brown and slate 9·00 2·00
422 $5 emerald and maroon 9·00 12·00
423 $10 carmine and blue 13·00 25·00
408/23 *Set of* 16 40·00 38·00

Old stocks bearing Waterlow imprints of the 4 c., 5 c., 20 c. and 35 c. to $10 were used for overprinting, but in addition new printings of all values by De La Rue using the original plates with the De La Rue imprint replacing the Waterlow imprint were specially made for overprinting.

138 *Vanda hookeriana*

139 *Hebomoia glaucippe*

1965 (15 Nov)–**68**. *As Nos.* 166/72 *of Johore, but with Arms of Sabah inset as in T* **138**. *W w* **13** (*upright*).
424 1 c. multicoloured 10 70
425 2 c. multicoloured 10 80
426 5 c. multicoloured 10 10
427 6 c. multicoloured 30 80
428 10 c. multicoloured 30 10
429 15 c. multicoloured (pale black panel) 2·00 10
a. *Brown-black panel* (20.2.68) 2·25 10
430 20 c. multicoloured 2·75 50
424/30 *Set of* 7 5·00 2·50

The 5 c. to 15 c. exist with PVA gum as well as gum arabic.

The higher values used with this issue were Nos. 20/27 of Malaysia (National Issues).

1970 (20 Nov). *As No. 428, but W w 13 (sideways).*
431 10 c. multicoloured .. .. 4·50 4·25

1971 (1 Feb)–**78.** *As Nos. 175/87 of Johore but with Arms of Sabah, as in T* **139**. *(a) Litho by Bradbury, Wilkinson.*
432 1 c. multicoloured .. .. 30 1·25
433 2 c. multicoloured .. .. 50 1·25
434 5 c. multicoloured 65 20
435 6 c. multicoloured 65 70
436 10 c. multicoloured 65 10
437 15 c. multicoloured 70 10
438 20 c. multicoloured .. .. 1·10 70
432/8 .. .. *Set of* 7 4·00 3·75

(b) Photo by Harrison (1977–78)
439 1 c. multicoloured .. .. 1·75 4·75
440 2 c. multicoloured .. .. 1·75 4·50
441 5 c. multicoloured .. .. 10·00 2·75
442 10 c. multicoloured .. .. 2·50 85
443 15 c. multicoloured .. .. 2·50 30
444 20 c. multicoloured .. .. 32·00 2·75
439/44 .. .. *Set of* 6 45·00 14·50

For differences between litho and photo printings, see after Johore No. 187.

The higher values used with this issue were Nos. 64/71 of Malaysia (National Issues).

140 *Hibiscus rosa-sinensis*

141 Coffee

1979 (30 Apr). *As Nos. 188/94 of Johore but with Arms of Sabah as in T* **140**.
445 1 c. *Rafflesia hasseltii* 10 55
446 2 c. *Pterocarpus indicus* 10 55
447 5 c. *Lagerstroemia speciosa* 15 10
448 10 c. *Durio zibethinus* 30 10
449 15 c. Type **140** 50 10
450 20 c. *Rhododendron scortechinii* 30 10
451 25 c. *Etlingera elatior* (inscr "*Phaeomeria speciosa*") 65 10
445/51 .. .. *Set of* 7 1·75 1·25

For higher values used in conjunction with this series see Nos. 190/7 of Malaysia (National Issues).

1983–85.* *As Nos. 447/50, but without wmk.*
454 5 c. *Lagerstroemia speciosa* (1.85) .. .. 2·50 3·00
455 10 c. *Durio zibethinus* (28.7.84) .. .. 6·00 7·50
456 15 c. Type **140** (5.85) .. .. 5·00 2·75
457 20 c. *Rhododendron scortechinii* (blackish brown background) (1983) .. .. 17·00 2·00
457*a* 20 c. *Rhododendron scortechinii* (bronze-green background) (29.11.83) .. .. 12·00 1·25
454/7*a* .. .. *Set of* 5 38·00 15·00

*There was no official release date for these stamps. Dates shown are the earliest recorded from postmarks and may be revised if earlier examples are reported.

For details of the shade differences between watermarked and unwatermarked printings see after Malaysia–Johore, No. 200*a*.

On Nos. 454/6 and 457*a* the state crest is redrawn larger.

1986 (25 Oct)–**94.** *As Nos. 202/8 of Johore, but with Arms of Sabah as in T* **141**. *P* 12.
459 1 c. Type **141** 10 10
460 2 c. Coconuts 10 10
f. Perf 14³/₄×14¹/₂ (1994) .. .. .. 3·50 40
461 5 c. Cocoa 10 10
462 10 c. Black pepper 10 10
463 15 c. Rubber 10 10
464 20 c. Oil palm 10 10
w. Wmk inverted .. ..
465 30 c. Rice 15 20
c. Perf 14×13³/₄ (1994) .. .. .. 1·00 20
e. Perf 14×14¹/₂ .. ..
f. Perf 14³/₄×14¹/₂ (1994) .. .. .. 4·50 30
459/65 .. .. *Set of* 7 50 55

STAMP BOOKLETS

1973 (8 Dec). *Cover as Type* B **1** *of Johore, but inscr* "SABAH". *Stitched.*
SB1 $3 booklet containing eight 5 c., 10 c. and twelve 15 c. (Nos. 434, 436/7) in blocks of 4 .. 18·00

1979 (1 Dec). *Cover as No. SB5 of Johore, but inscr* "SABAH". *Stitched.*
SB2 $3 booklet containing eight 5 c., 10 c., and twelve 15 c. (Nos. 447/9) in blocks of 4 .. .. 7·00

No. SB2 exists with two different versions of the back cover.

1987 (1 June). *Cover as Type* B **2** *of Johore, but inscr* "SABAH". *Stapled.*
SB3 $2 booklet containing 5 c., 10 c., 15 c. and 20 c. (Nos. 461/4) in blocks of 4 .. .. .. 5·00

1992 (1 July). *"Kuala Lumpur '92" International Philatelic Exhibition. Cover as Type* B **3** *of Johore, but inscr* "Sabah". *Stamps attached by selvedge.*
SB4 $3 booklet containing 30 c. (No. 465) in block of 10 5·50

1993. *Covers as Nos. SB8/9 of Johore, but inscr* "Sabah". *Stamps attached by selvedge.*
SB5 $2 booklet containing 20 c. (No. 464) in block of 10 1·00
SB6 $3 booklet containing 30 c. (No. 465) in block of 10 1·50

POSTAL FISCALS

Three Cents. Revenue

(F 1) (Raised stop)

Ten Cents. Revenue

(F 2)

1886. *Regular issues surch as Type* F **1** *or* F **2**.
F1 1 3 c. on 4 c. pink (No. 6) .. .. .. 80·00 £110
a. Raised stop after "Cents" .. .. 70·00 £100
F2 5 c. on 8 c. green (No. 7) .. .. .. 80·00 £110
a. Raised stop after "Cents" .. .. 70·00 £100
F3 4 10 c. on 50 c. violet (No. 4) £100 £120
a. Surch double .. .. — £800
b. No stop after "Cents" and stop after "Revenue." £300 £350
c. Inverted "L" for first "F" in "FIFTY" (R.5/2) .. .. — £500

It is believed that Nos. F1/2 were each surcharged from a horizontal setting of five so that the raised stop variety occurs on every stamp in the first, second, third, sixth, seventh and eighth vertical columns in the sheets of 50 (10×5).

POSTAGE DUE STAMPS

POSTAGE DUE

(D 1)

1895 (1 Aug). *Stamps of* 1894 *optd with Type* D **1**. *P* 14¹/₂–15.

A. *Vertically (reading upwards)*
D 1 **25** 2 c. black and rose-lake .. 16·00 28·00 2·50
a. Opt double .. .. .. † † £225
b. Opt reading downwards .. † † £275
D 2 2 c. black and lake .. .. 13·00 19·00 1·25
a. Perf 13¹/₂–14 .. .. ..
b. Opt omitted (in vert pair with normal) .. .. † † £1100
D 3 **26** 3 c. olive-green and dull purple .. 4·75 12·00 1·00
a. Bronze-green and dull purple
b. Opt reading downwards ..
D 3*c* 3 c. olive-green and violet ..
ca. Opt double .. .. † † £350
cb. Perf 13¹/₂–14 .. ..
D 4 **27** 5 c. black and vermilion .. 35·00 25·00 2·50
a. Printed double .. .. † — —
b. Stop after "DUE" .. .. 60·00
c. Opt double £450
d. Perf 13¹/₂–14 .. .. — 50·00 —
e. Perf 13¹/₂–14, comp 12–13 .. — 55·00 —
D 5 **28** 6 c. black and bistre-brown .. 35·00 60·00 2·50
a. Perf 13¹/₂–14 .. .. 10·00 35·00 2·50
b. Perf 12–13 .. ..
c. Perf 13¹/₂–14, comp 12–13 ..
d. Opt reading downwards ..
D 6 **31** 18 c. black and deep green .. 60·00 85·00 3·25
a. Opt reading downwards .. £300 £200 †
D3/4 & D6 Optd "Specimen" *Set of* 3 90·00

B. *Horizontally*
D 7 **29** 8 c. black and dull purple .. 32·00 40·00 2·50
a. Opt double .. .. — † £300
b. Perf 13¹/₂–14 .. ..
ba. Opt inverted .. .. † † £150
c. Perf 13¹/₂–14, comp 12–13 .. 50·00
D 8 **30** 12 c. black and blue .. — 45·00 2·50
a. Opt double .. .. † † £300
b. Perf 13¹/₂–14 .. .. 48·00 40·00 2·50
D 9 12 c. black & ultram (*p* 13¹/₂–14) 60·00 55·00 —
D10 **31** 18 c. black and deep green .. 50·00 55·00 4·00
a. Opt inverted .. .. £225 £350 †
b. Perf 13¹/₂–14 .. .. 55·00 70·00 4·00
ba. Opt double .. .. † † £225
D11 **32** 24 c. blue and rose-lake .. 55·00 75·00 4·00
a. Opt double .. .. † † £250
b. Perf 13¹/₂–14 .. .. 21·00 48·00 4·00
c. Perf 13¹/₂–14, comp 14¹/₂–15 ..
D8 & D11 Optd "Specimen" .. *Set of* 2 60·00

1897. *Stamps of* 1897 *optd with Type* D **1**. *P* 14¹/₂–15.

A. *Vertically*
D12 2 c. black and lake .. .. 6·50 8·00 75
a. Perf 13¹/₂–14 .. .. 23·00

B. *Horizontally*
D13 2 c. black and lake .. .. .. 55·00 80·00
D14 8 c. black and brown-purple .. .. 45·00 50·00
a. Stop after "DUE." .. .. 20·00 65·00
D12 & D14 Optd "Specimen" .. *Set of* 2 48·00

1901. *Issue of* 1897–1902 *optd with Type* D **1**. *P* 13¹/₂–14.

A. *Vertically (reading upwards)*
D15 2 c. black and green .. .. 28·00 40·00 70
a. Perf 13¹/₂–14, comp 12–13 .. — 60·00 —
b. Perf 16 .. .. ..
c. Perf 12–13 .. .. ..
d. Opt reading downwards ..
D16 3 c. green and rosy mauve .. 18·00 22·00 70
a. Stop after "DUE" .. .. 42·00 65·00 —
b. Perf 14¹/₂–15 .. .. 9·00 18·00 50
c. Perf 13¹/₂–14, comp 14¹/₂–15 ..
d. Opt double .. ..
e. Opt double. Stop after "DUE" .. £200
D17 3 c. green & dull mauve (*p* 14¹/₂–15) 9·50 25·00 1·25
a. Stop after "DUE" .. .. 42·00 65·00 —
b. Opt double. Stop after "DUE" .. £200 £225 —
D18 4 c. black and carmine .. .. 23·00 24·00 50
a. Perf 14¹/₂–15 .. ..
D19 5 c. black and orange-vermilion .. 18·00 28·00 1·25
a. Perf 14¹/₂–15 .. .. 45·00 45·00 90
b. Stop after "DUE" .. .. 45·00
D20 6 c. black and bistre-brown (Optd "Specimen" £25) .. .. — 25·00 50
a. Perf 14¹/₂–15 .. .. 3·00 20·00 70
b. Perf 13¹/₂–14, comp 12–13 .. — — 2·00
D20*c* 8 c. black and brown-purple (*p* 16) ..
D21 8 c. black and brown .. ..
a. Perf 14¹/₂–15 .. .. 3·50 20·00 50
ab. Opt reading downwards .. † † —
D22 12 c. black and dull blue .. 65·00 £150 4·00
a. Perf 14¹/₂–15 .. ..
D23 18 c. black and green (No. 108) ..
a. Perf 16 .. .. .. † † £400
D24 18 c. black and green (No. 110) .. 32·00 £150 4·00
a. Perf 13¹/₂–14, comp 12–13 .. 65·00 £150 4·00
D25 24 c. blue and lake (No. 109) .. — — £100
D26 24 c. blue and lake (No. 111) ..
a. Perf 14¹/₂–15 .. .. 16·00 £120 2·25

B. *Horizontally*
D27 2 c. black and green .. .. 75·00 85·00 4·00
D28 8 c. black and brown (*p* 14¹/₂–15) .. 85·00 95·00 5·00
a. Stop after "DUE" .. .. £100 £130 —

An example of the 5 c. value, No. D19a, has been seen clearly postmarked 1899.

The stamp showing a stop after "DUE", Nos. D14a, D16a, D17a, D19b and D28a, may well represent a separate local overprint. Such stamps do not come cancelled-to-order.

1902–5. *Stamps of* 1901–5 *optd* "British Protectorate," *further optd with Type* D **1**. *P* 13¹/₂–14. A. *Vertically* (1902).
D29 2 c. black and green (*p* 16) £200 £150
D30 3 c. green and rosy mauve .. .. 70·00 85·00
D31 5 c. black and orange-vermilion (*p* 14¹/₂–15) £110 90·00
D32 8 c. black and brown .. .. .. 95·00 80·00
D33 24 c. blue and lake .. .. .. £120 75·00

B. *Horizontally, at top of stamp* (1904–5)
D34 2 c. black and green (*p* 14¹/₂–15) .. .. 80·00 50·00
a. Perf 16 .. .. .. 60·00 60·00
D35 4 c. black and carmine .. .. 60·00 20·00

C. *Horizontally, at centre of stamp* (1904–5)
D35*a* 1 c. black and bistre-brown .. — — 25·00
b. Perf 14¹/₂–15 .. .. £200 — 25·00
D36 2 c. black and green .. .. 6·50 2·50 20
a. Perf 14¹/₂–15 .. .. 45·00 45·00 —
D37 3 c. green and rosy mauve .. 2·25 2·50 30
a. Perf 14¹/₂–15 .. .. 45·00 30·00 —
ab. "POSTAGE DUE" double ..
D38 4 c. black and carmine .. 4·75 5·00 30
a. "POSTAGE DUE" double .. — † £120
b. Perf 14¹/₂–15 .. .. 4·00 9·00 30
D39 5 c. black and orange-vermilion 12·00 3·75 30
a. No stop after "PROTECTORATE" .. .. 42·00 18·00 —
b. Perf 14¹/₂–15 .. .. 42·00 23·00 —
D40 6 c. black and bistre-brown .. 8·00 8·00 40
a "POSTAGE DUE" inverted .. £350 † 90·00
b. "POSTAGE DUE" double .. † — —
c. No stop after "PROTECTORATE" .. ..
d. Perf 16 .. .. 40·00 29·00 —
D41 8 c. black and brown .. 16·00 4·25 40
a. No stop after "PROTECTORATE" .. .. 40·00 38·00 —
D42 10 c. brown and slate-lilac .. £120 45·00 1·40
a. No stop after "PROTECTORATE" .. ..
D42*b* 10 c. brown and slate-blue .. 55·00 13·00 1·40
D43 12 c. black and blue .. .. 13·00 12·00 1·50
D44 16 c. green and chestnut .. 23·00 17·00 1·50
D45 18 c. black and green .. .. 4·75 16·00 1·50
a. "POSTAGE DUE" double .. £400 † 48·00
b. Imperf between (vert pair) .. — — £350
D46 24 c. blue and lake .. .. 8·50 19·00 1·50
a. Perf 14¹/₂–15 .. ..
b. "POSTAGE DUE" double .. £200 † 75·00

D. *Horizontally. Optd locally, with stop after* "DUE." (1902)
D47 1 c. black and bistre-brown .. 4·00 55·00 —
a. With raised stop after "DUE." .. 4·75 60·00 —

No. D35*a/b* are usually found cancelled-to-order suggesting that they came from remainder stocks which were not issued, but we have also seen one unused example of No. D35a and several of No. D35b.

1919–24. *Stamps of* 1909–23, *optd with Type* D **1**. *P* 13¹/₂–14.

A. *Horizontally at top of stamp*
D48 4 c. black and scarlet (1919) .. .. 75·00 13·00

B. *Horizontally towards foot of stamp*
D49 2 c. black and green (2.24) .. .. 9·50 75·00
a. Perf 14¹/₂–15 .. .. .. 13·00 75·00
D50 3 c. black and green .. .. .. 4·00 30·00
D51 4 c. black and scarlet .. .. .. 80 1·00
D52 5 c. black and yellow-brown .. .. 7·50 15·00
D53 6 c. black and olive-green .. .. 5·50 7·50
D53*a* 6 c. black and apple-green ..
D54 8 c. black and rose-lake .. .. 1·25 1·25
a. Opt double £650
D55 10 c. black and turquoise-blue (7.24) .. 9·50 16·00
a. Perf 14¹/₂–15 .. .. .. 50·00 £110
D56 12 c. black and deep blue (7.24) .. .. 35·00 35·00
a. Horiz pair, one with opt omitted .. £7000
D56*b* 16 c. black and red-brown .. .. 16·00 75·00
ba. Black and brown-lake .. .. 6·50 50·00
D49/56*ba* .. .. .. *Set of* 9 70·00 £200
D49 & D56*b* Optd "Specimen" .. *Set of* 2 48·00

Nos. D51/3 also exist with the overprint towards the centre of the stamp.

1926–31. *Stamps of* 1925 *optd with Type* D **1**. *P* 12¹/₂.
D57 2 c. black and claret .. .. .. 40 1·75
D58 3 c. black and green .. .. .. 3·50 16·00
D59 4 c. black and scarlet .. .. .. 85 1·25
D60 5 c. black and yellow-brown .. .. 6·00 65·00
D61 6 c. black and olive-green .. .. 4·00 2·50
D62 8 c. black and carmine .. .. .. 2·25 12·00
D63 10 c. black and turquoise-blue .. .. 7·00 65·00
D64 12 c. black and deep blue .. .. 23·00 £110
D65 16 c. black and red-brown (1931) .. .. 40·00 £150
D57/65 .. .. .. *Set of* 9 75·00 £375

Nos. D49/65 exist with two types of opt; A. Thick letters; pointed beard to "G". B. Thinner letters; square end to beard and "D" more open. No. D56*b* is Type B and D56*ba*, Type A.

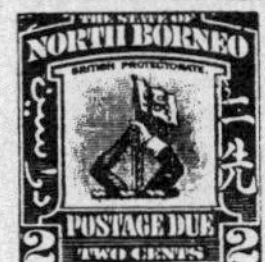

D 2 Crest of the Company

(Recess Waterlow)

1939 (1 Jan). *P* 12½.
D66 **D 2** 2 c. brown .. .. 6·50 70·00
D67 4 c. scarlet .. .. 6·50 90·00
D68 6 c. violet .. .. 19·00 £110
D69 8 c. green .. .. 19·00 £170
D70 10 c. blue .. .. 40·00 £300
D66/70 .. .. .. *Set of* 5 80·00 £650
D66/70 Perf "Specimen" .. .. *Set of* 5 £140

XIII. JAPANESE OCCUPATION OF NORTH BORNEO

Japanese forces landed in Northern Borneo on 15 December 1941 and the whole of North Borneo had been occupied by 19 January 1942.

Brunei, North Borneo, Sarawak and, after a short period, Labuan, were administered as a single territory by the Japanese. Until September–October 1942, previous stamp issues, without overprint, continued to be used in conjunction with existing postmarks. From October 1942 onwards unoverprinted stamps of Japan were made available and examples can be found used from the area for much of the remainder of the War. Japanese Occupation issues for Brunei, North Borneo and Sarawak were equally valid throughout the combined territory but not, in practice, equally available.

PRICES FOR STAMPS ON COVER
Nos. J1/17 *from* × 5
Nos. J18/19 *from* × 6
Nos. J20/32 *from* × 25
Nos. J33/4 *from* × 2
Nos. J35/48 *from* × 12

府政国帝本日大
(1)

2 Mt Kinabalu

3 Borneo Scene

1942 (30 Sept). *Stamps of North Borneo handstamped with* **T 1**.

(*a*) *In violet on Nos.* 303/17
J 1 1 c. green and red-brown £120 £170
a. Black opt £180 £170
J 2 2 c. purple and greenish blue £120 £170
a. Black opt £180 £170
J 3 3 c. slate-blue and green £100 £170
a. Black opt £180 £170
J 4 4 c. bronze-green and violet £100 £170
a. Black opt .. .. .. 48·00 95·00
J 5 6 c. deep blue and claret £110 £170
a. Black opt £180 £170
J 6 8 c. scarlet £110 £150
a. Pair, one without opt £1100
b. Black opt £160 £150
J 7 10 c. violet and bronze-green £120 £170
a. Black opt £180 £170
J 8 12 c. green and bright blue £130 £275
a. Black opt £300 £275
J 9 15 c. blue-green and brown £130 £275
a. Black opt £300 £275
J10 20 c. violet and slate-blue £170 £325
a. Black opt £350 £325
J11 25 c. green and chocolate £170 £325
a. Black opt £350 £325
J12 50 c. chocolate and violet £225 £375
a. Black opt £250 £375
J13 $1 brown and carmine £225 £450
a. Black opt £475 £450
J14 $2 violet and olive-green £325 £600
a. Pair, one without opt £2000
b. Black opt £650 £600
J15 $5 indigo and pale blue £400 £700
a. Black opt £750 £700

(*b*) *In black on Nos.* 318/19 ("WAR TAX")
J16 1 c. green and red-brown £375 £225
a. Pair, one without opt .. .. † £2000
J17 2 c. purple and greenish blue £1000 £325

(Litho Kolff & Co., Batavia)

1943 (29 Apr). *P* 12½.
J18 **2** 4 c. red .. .. 14·00 30·00
J19 **3** 8 c. blue .. .. 14·00 30·00

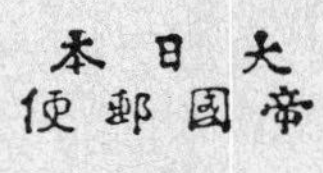

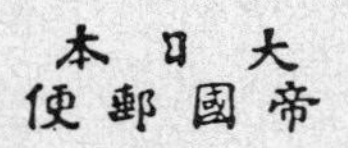

(4)

(5)

("Imperial Japanese Postal Service North Borneo")

1944 (30 Sept). *Nos.* 303/15 *of North Borneo optd as* **T 4**.
J20 1 c. green and red-brown .. .. 4·00 8·50
J21 2 c. purple and greenish blue .. .. 7·50 8·50
a. Optd on No. J2 .. .. .. £400
J22 3 c. slate-blue and green .. .. 3·00 6·00
a. Optd on No. J3 .. .. .. £400
J23 4 c. bronze-green and violet .. .. 4·00 9·00
J24 6 c. deep blue and claret .. .. 3·50 6·00
J25 8 c. scarlet .. .. .. 5·50 17·00
a. Optd on No. J6 .. .. .. £400
J26 10 c. violet and bronze-green .. .. 7·00 13·00
a. Optd on No. J7 .. .. .. £400
b. Optd on No. J7a £180 £350
J27 12 c. green and bright blue .. .. 5·50 13·00
a. Optd on No. J8 .. .. .. £400
J28 15 c. blue-green and brown .. .. 5·00 14·00
a. Optd on No. J9 .. .. .. £400
J29 20 c. violet and slate-blue .. .. 15·00 35·00
J30 25 c. green and chocolate .. .. 15·00 35·00
J31 50 c. chocolate and violet .. .. 50·00 £100
J32 $1 brown and carmine .. .. 80·00 £140
J20/32 .. .. .. *Set of* 13 £180 £350

The spacing between the second and third lines of the overprint is 12 mm on the horizontal stamps, and 15 mm on the upright.

1944 (11 May). *No.* J1 *surch with* **T 5**.
J33 **81** $2 on 1 c. green and red-brown .. £4500 £3750

本 日 大

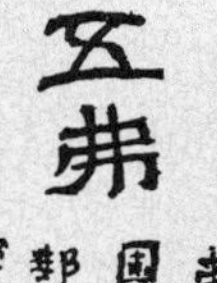

(6)

7 Girl War-worker

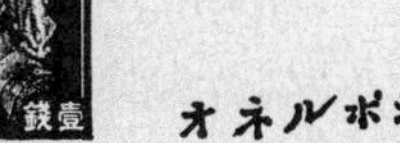

(8) ("North Borneo")

1944 (11 May). *North Borneo No.* 315 *surch with* **T 6**.
J34 $5 on $1 brown and carmine £4000 £2750
a. Surch on No. J13 .. .. ..

1944 (2 Oct)–**45**. *Contemporary stamps of Japan as* **T 7** (*various subjects*) *optd with* **T 8** *at Chinese Press, Kuching.*
J35 1 s. red-brown (No. 391) (1945) .. .. 5·00 13·00
J36 2 s. scarlet (No. 318) (1945) .. .. 5·00 12·00
J37 3 s. emerald-green (No. 319) (12.44) .. 4·25 13·00
J38 4 s. yellow-green (No. 395) (1945) .. 5·00 11·00
J39 5 s. claret (No. 396) (1945) .. .. 6·00 14·00
J40 6 s. orange (No. 322) (1945) .. .. 7·00 15·00
a. Opt double, one inverted £300 £300
J41 8 s. violet (No. 324) (1945) .. .. 4·25 15·00
J42 10 s. carmine and pink (No. 399) (1945) .. 4·50 15·00
J43 15 s. blue (No. 401) (11.44) .. .. 6·50 15·00
J44 20 s. blue-slate (No. 328) (11.44) .. .. 80·00 85·00
J45 25 s. brown and chocolate (No. 329) (1945) 50·00 65·00
J46 30 s. turquoise-blue (No. 330) .. .. £160 95·00
J47 50 s. olive and bistre (No. 331) (1945) .. 55·00 60·00
J48 1 y. red-brown & chocolate (No. 332) (1945) 55·00 75·00
J35/48 .. .. .. *Set of* 14 £400 £450

Designs:—2 s. General Nogi; 3 s. Hydro-electric Works; 4 s. Hyuga Monument and Mt Fuji; 5 s. Admiral Togo; 6 s. Garambi Lighthouse, Formosa; 8 s. Meiji Shrine; 10 s. Palms and map of S.E. Asia; 15 s. Airman; 20 s. Mt Fuji and cherry blossoms; 25 s. Horyu Temple; 30 s. Torii, Itsukushima Shrine at Miyajima; 50 s. Kinkaku Temple; 1 y. Great Buddha, Kamakura.

Examples of some values have been found with hand-painted forged overprints.

XIV. SARAWAK

Sarawak was placed under British protection in 1888. It was ceded to Great Britain on 1 July 1946 and was administered as a Crown Colony until 16 September 1963 when it became a state of the Federation of Malaysia.

From 1859 letters from Sarawak to overseas addresses, other than to other British possessions in Borneo and Singapore, were franked by stamps of INDIA, and subsequently STRAITS SETTLEMENTS, a stock of which was kept by the Sarawak Post Office. The stamps of Sarawak continued to have this limited validity until 1 July 1897 when the country joined the U.P.U.

PRICES FOR STAMPS ON COVER TO 1945
No. 1 —
Nos. 2/7 *from* × 50
Nos. 8/21 *from* × 8
Nos. 22/6 *from* × 6
No. 27 *from* × 40
Nos. 28/35 *from* × 6
Nos. 36/47 *from* × 8
No. 48 †
No. 49 *from* × 10
Nos. 50/61 *from* × 6
No. 62 †
Nos. 63/71 *from* × 4
Nos. 72/3 *from* × 8
Nos. 74/5 —
Nos. 76/90 *from* × 7
Nos. 91/105 *from* × 5
Nos. 106/25 *from* × 3
Nos. 126/45 *from* × 2

BROOKE FAMILY ADMINISTRATION

Sir James Brooke. 1842–11 June 1868
Sir Charles Brooke. 11 June 1868–17 May 1917

UNUSED PRICES. Nos. 1/7, 27 and 32/5 in unused condition are normally found to be without gum. Prices in the unused column are for stamps in this state. Examples of these issues with original gum are worth considerably more.

1 Sir James Brooke

2 Sir Charles Brooke

The initials in the corners of T 1 and 2 stand for "James (Charles) Brooke, Rajah (of) Sarawak".

(T 1 and 2. Die eng Wm. Ridgway. Litho Maclure, Macdonald & Co, Glasgow)

1869 (1 Mar). *P* 11.
1 **1** 3 c. brown/*yellow* .. .. 42·00 £225

Specimens are known printed from the engraved die in orange-brown on orange surface-coloured paper, and perf 12. These were submitted to the Sarawak authorities as examples of the stamps and exist both with and without obliterations.

1871 (1 Jan). *P* 11 (*irregular*).
2 **2** 3 c. brown/*yellow* .. .. .. 1·50 3·00
a. Stop after "THREE". .. .. 40·00 55·00
b. Imperf between (vert pair) £425
c. Imperf between (horiz pair). £600

The "stop" variety, No. 2a, which occurs on R. 10/7 is of no more philatelic importance than any of the numerous other variations, such as narrow first "A" in "SARAWAK" (R. 2/7) and "R" with long tail in left lower corner (R. 9/10), but it has been accepted by collectors for many years, and we therefore retain it. The papermaker's wmk "L N L" appears once or twice in sheets of No. 2.

Specimens are known, recess-printed, similar to those mentioned in the note after No. 1.

TWO CENTS

Copies of No. 2 surcharged as above were first reported in 1876 but following the discovery of dies for forgeries and faked postmarks in 1891 it was concluded that the issue was bogus, especially as the availability of the 2 c. of 1875 made it unnecessary to issue a provisional. It has now been established that a 2 c. postal rate was introduced from 1 August 1874 for the carriage of newspapers. Moreover four examples are known with a stop after "CENTS." and showing other minor differences from the forgery illustrated. This version could be genuine and if others come to light we will reconsider listing it.

1875 (1 Jan). *P* 11½–12.
3 **2** 2 c. mauve/*lilac* (*shades*) .. .. 3·25 15·00
4 4 c. red-brown/*yellow* .. .. 3·25 3·00
a. Imperf between (vert pair) £550
5 6 c. green/*green* .. .. .. 2·75 3·50
6 8 c. bright blue/*blue* .. .. 2·75 3·50
7 12 c. red/*pale rose* .. .. .. 6·50 6·50
3/7 .. .. .. *Set of* 5 17·00 28·00

Nos. 3, 4, 6 and 7 have the watermark "L N L" in the sheet, as No. 2. No. 5 is watermarked "L N T".

All values exist imperf and can be distinguished from the proofs by shade and impression. Stamps rouletted, pin-perf, or roughly perf 6½ to 7 are proofs clandestinely perforated.

The 12 c. "laid" paper, formerly listed, is not on a true laid paper, the "laid" effect being accidental and not consistent.

The lithographic stones for Nos. 3 to 7 were made up from strips of five distinct impressions hence there are five types of each value differing mainly in the lettering of the tablets of value. There are flaws on nearly every individual stamp, from which they can be plated.

4 Sir Charles Brooke

(Typo D.L.R.)

1888 (10 Nov)–**1897**. *No wmk. P* 14.
8 **4** 1 c. purple and black (6.6.92) .. .. 1·00 50
9 2 c. purple and carmine (11.11.88) .. 85 95
a. Purple and rosine (1897) .. .. 7·50 3·25
10 3 c. purple and blue (11.11.88) .. .. 1·75 1·75
11 4 c. purple and yellow .. .. .. 9·50 35·00
12 5 c. purple and green (12.6.91) .. .. 8·00 1·75
13 6 c. purple and brown (11.11.88) .. .. 9·00 45·00
14 8 c. green and carmine (11.11.88) .. .. 5·50 2·50
a. Green and rosine (1897) .. .. 17·00 14·00
15 10 c. green and purple (12.6.91) .. .. 27·00 14·00
16 12 c. green and blue (11.11.88) .. .. 5·50 7·50
17 16 c. green and orange (28.12.97) .. .. 38·00 60·00
18 25 c. green and brown (19.11 88) .. .. 35·00 35·00
19 32 c. green and black (28.12.97) .. .. 25·00 42·00
20 50 c. green (26.7.97) .. .. .. 25·00 75·00
21 $1 green and black (2.11.97) .. .. 48·00 70·00
8/21 .. .. .. *Set of* 14 £200 £350

Prepared for use but not issued
21*a* $2 green and blue £375
21*b* $5 green and violet £375
21*c* $10 green and carmine £375

On No. 21 the value is in black on an uncoloured ground.

The tablet of value in this and later similar issues is in the second colour given.

One Cent. (5) **one cent.** (6)

2c. (7) **5c** (8) **5c.** (9)

1889 (3 Aug)–**92.** *T* 4 *surch. P* 14.
22 5 1 c. on 3 c. (12.1.92) .. 26·00 24·00
a. Surch double .. £450 £350
23 6 1 c. on 3 c. (2.92) .. 2·75 2·75
a. No stop after "cent" (R. 2/6) .. 90·00
24 7 2 c. on 8 c. (3.8.89) .. 2·50 5·00
a. Surch double .. £350
b. Surch inverted .. £2000
c. Surch omitted (in pair with normal) .. £3000
25 8 5 c. on 12 c. (with stop after "C") (17.2.91) .. 19·00 38·00
a. No stop after "C" .. 19·00 35·00
b. "C" omitted .. £325 £325
c. Surch double .. £950
d. Surch double, one vertical .. £2250
e. Surch omitted (in pair with normal) .. £6000
26 9 5 c. on 12 c. (17.2.91) .. 80·00 £120
a. No stop after "C" .. 70·00 85·00
b. "C" omitted .. £400 £350
c. Surch double .. £950

ONE CENT

(10)

1892 (23 May). *No.* 2 *surch with T* **10**.
27 2 1 c. on 3 c. brown/*yellow* .. 60 1·25
a. Stop after "THREE." .. 20·00 28·00
b. Imperf between (vert pair) .. £450
c. Imperf horiz (vert pair) .. £450
d. Bar omitted (1st ptg) .. £140
e. Bar at top and bottom (1st ptg) .. £190
f. Surch double (2nd ptg) .. £325 £350

No. 27 was surcharged with a setting of 100 (10 × 10). It was originally intended that there should be no bar at foot, but this was then added at a second operation before the stamps were issued. Subsequent supplies were surcharged with "ONE CENT" and bar at one operation.

Varieties with part of the surcharge missing are due to gum on the face of the unsurcharged stamps receiving part of the surcharge, which was afterwards washed off.

11 12

13 Sir Charles Brooke 14

(Die eng Wm. Ridgeway. Recess P.B.)

1895 (Feb–Sept). *No wmk. P* 11½–12.
28 11 2 c. brown-red .. 5·50 7·50
a. Imperf between (vert pair) .. £300
b. Imperf between (horiz pair) .. £250
c. Second ptg. Perf 12½ (Sept). .. 6·00 4·50
ca. Perf 12½. Imperf between (horiz pair) £325
29 12 4 c. black .. 5·50 2·50
a. Imperf between (horiz pair) .. £400
30 13 6 c. violet .. 5·50 9·00
31 14 8 c. green .. 20·00 6·00
28/31 .. *Set of* 4 32·00 20·00

Stamps of these types, printed in wrong colours, are trials and these, when surcharged with values in "pence", are from waste sheets that were used by Perkins, Bacon & Co as trial paper when preparing an issue of stamps for British South Africa.

4 CENTS.

(15) 16

1899. *Surch as T* **15**.
32 2 2 c. on 3 c. brown/*yellow* (19.9.99) .. 1·00 1·25
a. Stop after "THREE" .. 38·00 42·00
b. Imperf between (vert pair) .. £750
33 2 c. on 12 c. red/*pale rose* (29.6.99) .. 2·50 3·00
a. Surch inverted .. £750 £1100
34 4 c. on 6 c. green/*green* (R.) (16.11.99) 19·00 48·00
35 4 c. on 8 c. bright blue/*blue* (R.) (29.6.99) 3·25 6·00
32/5 .. *Set of* 4 23·00 55·00

A variety of surcharge with small "S" in "CENTS" may be found in the 2 c. on 12 c. and 4 c. on 8 c. and a raised stop after "CENTS" on the 4 c. on 6 c.

The omission of parts of the surcharge is due to gum on the surface of the stamps (see note after No. 27).

A block of 50 of No. 35 from the right of the pane is known line perforated 12.7 between the stamps and the margins at top and right.

(Typo D.L.R.)

1899 (10 Nov)–**1908.** *Inscribed* "POSTAGE POSTAGE." *No wmk. P* 14.
36 4 1 c. grey-blue and rosine (1.1.01) .. 1·00 1·00
a. Grey-blue and red .. 3·25 1·25
b. Ultramarine and rosine .. 4·50 1·75
c. Dull blue and carmine .. 12·00 4·00
37 2 c. green (16.12.99) .. 1·25 90
38 3 c. dull purple (1.2.08) .. 3·75 50
39 4 c. rose-carmine (10.11.99) .. 6·00 2·50
a. Aniline carmine .. 1·75 15
40 8 c. yellow and black (6.12.99) .. 1·75 80
41 10 c. ultramarine (10.11.99) .. 1·75 80
42 12 c. mauve (16.12.99) .. 3·50 3·50
a. Bright mauve (1905) .. 14·00 7·00
43 16 c. chestnut and green (16.12.99) .. 1·75 1·50
44 20 c. bistre and bright mauve (4.00) .. 4·00 2·75
45 25 c. brown and blue (16.12.99) .. 2·75 4·25
46 50 c. sage-green and carmine (16.12.99) .. 15·00 20·00
47 $1 rose-carmine and green (16.12.99) .. 35·00 75·00
a. Rosine and pale green .. 50·00 80·00
36/47 .. *Set of* 12 65·00 £100

Prepared for use but not issued
48 4 5 c. olive-grey and green .. 12·00

The figures of value in the $1 are in colour on an uncoloured ground.

1902. *Inscribed* "POSTAGE POSTAGE". *W* **16**. *P* 14.
49 4 2 c. green .. 16·00 14·00

Sir Charles Vyner Brooke. 17 May 1917–1 June 1946

17 Sir Charles Vyner Brooke

ONE cent

(18)

(Typo D.L.R.)

1918 (24 Mar–Apr). *No wmk. Chalk-surfaced paper. P* 14.
50 17 1 c. slate-blue and red .. 1·25 1·50
a. Dull blue and carmine .. 1·25 1·75
51 2 c. green .. 1·75 1·25
52 3 c. brown-purple (Apr) .. 3·25 2·50
53 4 c. rose-carmine (Apr) .. 3·25 2·00
a. Rose-red .. 3·25 2·00
54 8 c. yellow and black (Apr) .. 9·50 45·00
55 10 c. blue (*shades*) (Apr) .. 2·75 2·75
56 12 c. purple (Apr) .. 8·50 17·00
57 16 c. chestnut and green (Apr) .. 5·00 6·50
58 20 c. olive and violet (*shades*) (Apr) .. 5·50 6·50
59 25 c. brown and bright blue (Apr) .. 4·00 9·50
60 50 c. olive-green and carmine (Apr) .. 8·00 12·00
61 $1 bright rose and green (Apr) .. 14·00 23·00
50/61 .. *Set of* 12 60·00 £120
50/61 Optd "Specimen" .. *Set of* 12 £190

Prepared for use but not issued
62 17 1 c. slate-blue and slate .. 22·00

On the $1 the figures of value are in colour on an uncoloured ground.

1922 (Jan)–**23.** *New colours and values. No wmk. Chalk-surfaced paper. P* 14.
63 17 2 c. purple (5.3.23) .. 1·75 2·00
64 3 c. dull green (23.3.22) .. 1·00 1·25
65 4 c. brown-purple (10.4.23) .. 1·00 60
66 5 c. yellow-orange .. 1·25 90
67 6 c. claret .. 1·00 1·40
68 8 c. bright rose-red (1922) .. 3·00 25·00
69 10 c. black (1923) .. 2·00 3·25
70 12 c. bright blue (12.22) .. 8·50 16·00
a. Pale dull blue .. 8·50 15·00
71 30 c. ochre-brown and slate .. 3·75 4·25
63/71 .. *Set of* 9 21·00 48·00

1923 (Jan). *Surch as T* **18**. (*a*) *First printing. Bars* 1¼ *mm apart.*
72 17 1 c. on 10 c. dull blue .. 9·00 48·00
a. "cnet" for "cent" (R. 9/5) .. £300 £600
73 2 c. on 12 c. purple .. 6·00 30·00
a. Thick, narrower "W" in "TWO" .. 17·00 70·00
(*b*) *Second printing. Bars* ¾ *mm apart*
74 17 1 c. on 10 c. dull blue
b. "cnet" for "cent" (R. 9/5) .. £9000
c. Bright blue .. £100 £225
ca. "en" of "cent" scratched out and "ne" overprinted (R. 9/5) .. £3500
75 2 c. on 12 c. purple .. 55·00 £140
a. Thick, narrower "W" in "TWO" .. £120

In the 2 c. on 12 c. the words of the surcharge are about 7½ mm from the bars.

The "cnet" error occurred on R.9/5 of all sheets from the first printing of the 1 c. on 10 c. A single example of the error, No. 74b, is known from the second printing, but the error was then corrected, as shown by the evidence of a surviving plate block, only to have the correct spelling scratched out, by a local employee, and "ne" substituted (No. 74ca).

The thick "W" variety occurs on all stamps of the last two horizontal rows of the first printing (12 stamps per sheet), and in the last two vertical rows of the second (20 stamps per sheet).

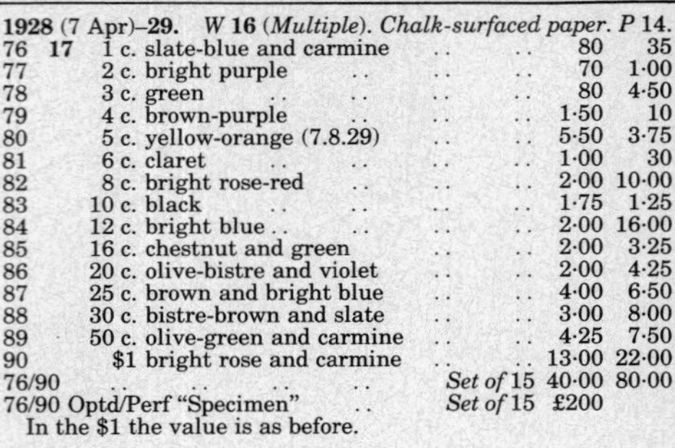

1928 (7 Apr)–**29.** *W* **16** (*Multiple*). *Chalk-surfaced paper. P* 14.
76 17 1 c. slate-blue and carmine .. 80 35
77 2 c. bright purple .. 70 1·00
78 3 c. green .. 80 4·50
79 4 c. brown-purple .. 1·50 10
80 5 c. yellow-orange (7.8.29) .. 5·50 3·75
81 6 c. claret .. 1·00 30
82 8 c. bright rose-red .. 2·00 10·00
83 10 c. black .. 1·75 1·25
84 12 c. bright blue .. 2·00 16·00
85 16 c. chestnut and green .. 2·00 3·25
86 20 c. olive-bistre and violet .. 2·00 4·25
87 25 c. brown and bright blue .. 4·00 6·50
88 30 c. bistre-brown and slate .. 3·00 8·00
89 50 c. olive-green and carmine .. 4·25 7·50
90 $1 bright rose and carmine .. 13·00 22·00
76/90 .. *Set of* 15 40·00 80·00
76/90 Optd/Perf "Specimen" .. *Set of* 15 £200

In the $1 the value is as before.

19 Sir Charles Vyner Brooke 20

(Recess Waterlow)

1932 (1 Jan). *W* **20**. *P* 12½.
91 19 1 c. indigo .. 70 80
92 2 c. green .. 70 80
93 3 c. violet .. 2·25 80
94 4 c. red-orange .. 1·00 45
95 5 c. deep lake .. 3·75 1·00
96 6 c. scarlet .. 5·50 6·50
97 8 c. orange-yellow .. 3·25 7·00
98 10 c. black .. 2·25 2·75
99 12 c. deep ultramarine .. 3·50 6·00
100 15 c. chestnut .. 5·00 6·50
101 20 c. red-orange and violet .. 4·25 7·00
102 25 c. orange-yellow and chestnut .. 8·50 16·00
103 30 c. sepia and vermilion .. 6·00 16·00
104 50 c. carmine-red and olive-green .. 7·50 9·00
105 $1 green and carmine .. 12·00 23·00
91/105 .. *Set of* 15 60·00 90·00
91/105 Perf "Specimen" .. *Set of* 15 £200

21 Sir Charles Vyner Brooke

BMA

(22)

(Recess B.W.)

1934 (1 May)–**41.** *No wmk. P* 12.
106 21 1 c. purple .. 15 10
107 2 c. green .. 15 10
107*a* 2 c. black (1.3.41) .. 1·00 1·60
108 3 c. black .. 15 10
108*a* 3 c. green (1.3.41) .. 2·50 3·50
109 4 c. bright purple .. 20 15
110 5 c. violet .. 50 10
111 6 c. carmine .. 75 60
111*a* 6 c. lake-brown (1.3.41) .. 3·50 8·00
112 8 c. red-brown .. 65 10
112*a* 8 c. carmine (1.3.41) .. 2·50 10
113 10 c. scarlet .. 1·25 40
114 12 c. blue .. 1·50 25
114*a* 12 c. orange (1.3.41) .. 1·75 4·75
115 15 c. orange .. 1·75 5·00
115*a* 15 c. blue (1.3.41) .. 3·75 11·00
116 20 c. olive-green and carmine .. 1·75 70
117 25 c. violet and orange .. 1·75 1·25
118 30 c. red-brown and violet .. 1·75 1·90
119 50 c. violet and scarlet .. 1·75 75
120 $1 scarlet and sepia .. 60 65
121 $2 bright purple and violet .. 7·50 7·50
122 $3 carmine and green .. 22·00 24·00
123 $4 blue and scarlet .. 22·00 28·00
124 $5 scarlet and red-brown .. 22·00 28·00
125 $10 black and yellow .. 18·00 38·00
106/25 .. *Set of* 26 £110 £150
106/25 Perf "Specimen" .. *Set of* 26 £450

For the 3 c. green, wmkd Mult Script CA, see No. 152a.

BRITISH MILITARY ADMINISTRATION

Following the Japanese surrender elements of the British Military Administration reached Kuching on 11 September 1945. From 5 November 1945 current Australian 1d., 3d., 6d. and 1s. stamps were made available for civilian use until replaced by Nos. 126/45. Other Australian stamps were also accepted as valid for postage during this period.

1945 (17 Dec). *Optd with T* **22**.
126 21 1 c. purple .. 40 50
127 2 c. black (R.) .. 40 50
a. Opt double .. † £3750
128 3 c. green .. 40 30
129 4 c. bright purple .. 40 30
130 5 c. violet (R.) .. 40 90
131 6 c. lake-brown .. 70 75
132 8 c. carmine .. 11·00 9·00
133 10 c. scarlet .. 60 70
134 12 c. orange .. 90 3·75
135 15 c. blue .. 1·50 40

136 **21** 20 c. olive-green and carmine 2·25 1·40
137 25 c. violet and orange (R.) 2·25 2·75
138 30 c. red-brown and violet 4·25 2·75
139 50 c. violet and scarlet 1·25 35
140 $1 scarlet and sepia 2·50 1·25
141 $2 bright purple and violet 9·00 6·00
142 $3 carmine and green 17·00 35·00
143 $4 blue and scarlet 25·00 30·00
144 $5 scarlet and red-brown £100 £120
145 $10 black and yellow (R.) £100 £140
126/45 *Set of* 20 £250 £325

These stamps, and the similarly overprinted stamps of North Borneo, were obtainable at all post offices throughout British Borneo (Brunei, Labuan, North Borneo and Sarawak), for use on local and overseas mail.

The administration of Sarawak was returned to the Brooke family on 15 April 1946, but the Rajah, after consulting the inhabitants, ceded the territory to Great Britain on 1 June 1946. Values from the 1934–41 issue were used until replaced by Nos. 150/64.

23 Sir James Brooke, Sir Charles Vyner Brooke and Sir Charles Brooke

(24)

(Recess B.W.)

1946 (18 May). *Centenary Issue. P* 12.
146 **23** 8 c. lake 70 30
147 15 c. blue 70 1·75
148 50 c. black and scarlet 80 1·75
149 $1 black and sepia 1·10 12·00
146/9 *Set of* 4 3·00 14·00
146/9 Perf "Specimen" *Set of* 4 90·00

CROWN COLONY

1947 (16 Apr). *Optd with T* **24**, *typo by B.W. in blue-black or red. Wmk Mult Script CA. P* 12.
150 **21** 1 c. purple 15 30
151 2 c. black (R.) 15 15
152 3 c. green (R.) 15 15
a. Albino opt £3750
153 4 c. bright purple 15 15
154 6 c. lake-brown 20 90
155 8 c. carmine 40 10
156 10 c. scarlet 20 20
157 12 c. orange 20 90
158 15 c. blue (R.) 20 40
159 20 c. olive-green and carmine (R.) 60 50
160 25 c. violet and orange (R.) 40 30
161 50 c. violet and scarlet (R.) 40 40
162 $1 scarlet and sepia 75 90
163 $2 bright purple and violet 1·40 3·25
164 $5 scarlet and red-brown 3·00 3·25
150/64 *Set of* 15 7·25 10·50
150/64 Perf "Specimen" *Set of* 15 £250

No. 152a shows an uninked impression of T **24**.

1948 (25 Oct). *Royal Silver Wedding. As Nos.* 143/4 *of Jamaica.*
165 8 c. scarlet 30 30
166 $5 brown 28·00 28·00

1949 (10 Oct). *75th Anniv of U.P.U. As Nos.* 145/8 *of Jamaica.*
167 8 c. carmine 1·25 50
168 15 c. deep blue 2·50 2·25
169 25 c. deep blue-green 2·00 1·50
170 50 c. violet 2·00 4·00
167/70 *Set of* 4 7·00 7·50

25 *Trogonoptera brookiana*

26 Western Tarsier

(Recess; Arms typo B.W.)

1950 (3 Jan). *T* **25/6** *and similar designs. Wmk Mult Script CA. P* 11½ × 11 (*horiz*) *or* 11 × 11½ (*vert*).
171 1 c. black 30 30
172 2 c. red-orange 20 40
173 3 c. green 10 60
174 4 c. chocolate 10 20
175 6 c. turquoise-blue 10 15
176 8 c. scarlet 10 30
177 10 c. orange 50 3·25
178 12 c. violet 1·75 1·50
179 15 c. blue 1·00 15
180 20 c. purple-brown and red-orange 60 30
181 25 c. green and scarlet 1·00 30
182 50 c. brown and violet 1·25 15
183 $1 green and chocolate 9·50 2·25
184 $2 blue and carmine 21·00 10·00
185 $5 black, yellow, red and purple 19·00 10·00
171/85 *Set of* 15 50·00 27·00

Designs: *Horiz*—8 c. Dayak dancer; 10 c. Malayan Pangolin; 12 c. Kenyah boys; 15 c. Fire-making; 20 c. Kelemantan rice barn; 25 c. Pepper vines; $1 Kelabit smithy; $2 Map of Sarawak; $5 Arms of Sarawak. *Vert*—3 c. Kayan tomb; 4 c. Kayan girl and boy; 6 c. Bead work; 50 c. Iban woman.

40 Map of Sarawak

(Recess B.W.)

1952 (1 Feb). *Wmk Mult Script CA. P* 11½ × 11.
186 **40** 10 c. orange 75 40

1953 (3 June). *Coronation. As No.* 153 *of Jamaica.*
187 10 c. black and deep violet-blue 1·00 1·25

41 Logging

44 Malabar Pied Hornbill

51 Queen Elizabeth II

52 Queen Elizabeth II (after Annigoni)

(Des M. Thoma (1, 2 c.), R. Turrell (4 c.), J. D. Hughes (6, 12 c.), A. Hakim bin Moliti (8 c.), J. Woodcock (10 c.), J. Browning (15 c.), G. Gundersen (20 c.), K. Munich (25 c.). Recess, Arms typo ($5). B.W.)

1955 (1 June)–**59**. *T* **41**, **44**, **51/2** *and similar designs. Wmk Mult Script CA. P* 11×11½ (1 *c.*, 2 *c.*, 4 *c.*), 12×13 (30 *c.*, 50 *c.*, $1, $2) *or* 11½×11 (*others*).
188 **41** 1 c. green (1.10.57) 10 30
189 – 2 c. red-orange (1.10.57) 30 55
190 – 4 c. lake-brown (1.10.57) 45 60
a. Brown-purple (18.3.59) 4·50 4·50
191 **44** 6 c. greenish blue (1.10.57) 3·00 1·25
192 – 8 c. rose-red (1.10.57) 30 30
193 – 10 c. deep green (1.10.57) 20 10
194 – 12 c. plum (1.10.57) 3·75 55
195 – 15 c. ultramarine (1.10.57) 1·00 30
196 – 20 c. olive and brown (1.10.57) 1·00 10
197 – 25 c. sepia and green (1.10.57) 6·50 20
198 **51** 30 c. red-brown and deep lilac 2·50 30
199 50 c. black and carmine (1.10.57) 2·00 30
200 **52** $1 myrtle-green & orange-brn (1.10.57) 4·00 50
201 $2 violet and bronze-green (1.10.57) 12·00 2·75
202 – $5 multicoloured (1.10.57) 16·00 8·00
188/202 *Set of* 15 48·00 14·00

Designs: *Horiz*—8 c. Shield with spears; 10 c. Kenyah ceremonial carving; 12 c. Barong panau (sailing prau); 15 c. Turtles; 20 c. Melanau basket-making; 25 c. Astana, Kuching; $5 Arms of Sarawak. *Vert* (*as T* **41**)—2 c. Young Orang-Utan; 4 c. Kayan dancing.

1963 (4 June). *Freedom from Hunger. As No.* 80 *of Lesotho.*
203 12 c. sepia 1·50 85

STATE OF MALAYSIA

1964–65. *As* 1955–57 *but wmk w* **12**. *Perfs as before.*
204 **41** 1 c. green (8.9.64) 10 50
205 – 2 c. red-orange (17.8.65) 65 7·00
206 **44** 6 c. greenish blue (8.9.64) 4·75 3·25
207 – 10 c. deep green (8.9.64) 1·50 1·00
208 – 12 c. plum (8.9.64) 1·50 7·00
209 – 15 c. ultramarine (17.8.65) 1·25 11·00
210 – 20 c. olive and brown (9.6.64) 50 90
211 – 25 c. deep sepia and bluish green (8.9.64) 2·00 3·75
204/11 *Set of* 8 11·00 30·00

53 *Vanda hookeriana*

54 *Precis orithya*

1965 (15 Nov). *As Nos.* 166/72 *of Johore but with Arms of Sarawak inset as in T* **53**.
212 1 c. multicoloured 10 60
c. Grey omitted 42·00
213 2 c. multicoloured 20 60
a. Black (country name and shield) omitted 85·00
c. Yellow-olive (stems) omitted 75·00
214 5 c. multicoloured 45 10
215 6 c. multicoloured 60 70
a. Black (country name and shield) omitted 85·00
216 10 c. multicoloured 80 10
a. Red omitted 50·00
217 15 c. multicoloured 1·50 10
218 20 c. multicoloured 2·00 50
212/18 *Set of* 7 5·00 2·25

The 1 c., 6 c., 10 c. and 15 c. exist with PVA gum as well as gum arabic.

No. 213a was formerly listed with Trengganu No. 101 but there is evidence that it was issued in Sarawak.

A used example of No. 218 is known with the bright purple (blooms) omitted.

The higher values used with this issue were Nos. 20/7 of Malaysia (National Issues).

(Litho B.W.)

1971 (1 Feb). *As Nos.* 175/81 *of Johore but with Arms of Sarawak inset as in T* **54**.
219 1 c. multicoloured 20 75
220 2 c. multicoloured 40 75
221 5 c. multicoloured 85 10
222 6 c. multicoloured 1·00 1·25
223 10 c. multicoloured 1·00 10
224 15 c. multicoloured 1·50 10
225 20 c. multicoloured 1·75 1·00
219/25 *Set of* 7 6·00 3·50

The higher values used with this issue were Nos. 64/71 of Malaysia (National Issues).

55 *Precis orithya* (different crest at right)

56 *Rhododendron scortechinii*

(Photo Harrison)

1977 (12 Feb)–**78**. *As Nos.* 219/21 *and* 223/5 *but ptd in photogravure showing new State Crest as T* **55**.
226 1 c. multicoloured (1978) 6·50 10·00
227 2 c. multicoloured (1978) 6·00 5·00
228 5 c. multicoloured 80 70
230 10 c. multicoloured (4.4.77) 50 30
231 15 c. multicoloured (19.4.77) 1·25 20
232 20 c. multicoloured (1978) 2·50 2·25
226/32 *Set of* 6 15·00 16·00

1979 (30 Apr). *As Nos.* 188/94 *of Johore but with Arms of Sarawak as in T* **56**.
233 1 c. *Rafflesia hasseltii* 10 40
234 2 c. *Pterocarpus indicus* 10 40
235 5 c. *Lagerstroemia speciosa* 10 10
236 10 c. *Durio zibethinus* 15 10
237 15 c. *Hibiscus rosa-sinensis* 20 10
238 20 c. Type **56** 25 10
239 25 c. *Etlingera elatior* (inscr "*Phaeomeria speciosa*") 40 15
233/9 *Set of* 7 1·10 1·00

For higher values used in conjunction with this series see Nos. 190/7 of Malaysia (National Issues).

1983 (11 Oct)–**86**.* *As Nos.* 235/6 *and* 238 *but without wmk.*
242 5 c. *Lagerstroemia speciosa* (4.4.86) 1·25 1·75
243 10 c. *Durio zibethinus* (9.9.85) 85 1·40
245 20 c. Type **56** (blackish brown background) 13·00 3·00
245*a* 20 c. Type **56** (bronze-green background) (2.8.84) 1·00 1·40
242/5*a* *Set of* 4 14·50 6·75

* There was no official release date for these stamps. Dates shown are the earliest recorded from postmarks and may be revised if earlier examples are reported.

For details of the shade differences between watermarked and unwatermarked printings see after Malaysia–Johore No. 200*a*.

On Nos. 242/3 and 245*a* the crest is closer to the face value than on Nos. 235/6, 238 and 245.

57 Coffee

A

B

Two types of Arms at right.
Type A. Shield divided into three
Type B. Shield with diagonal bars (1.9.93)

1986 (25 Oct)–**95.** *As Nos.* 202/8 *of Johore, but with Arms of Sarawak as in T* **57**. *P* 12.

		A		B	
247	1 c. Type **57**	10	10	10	10
248	2 c. Coconuts	10	10	10	10
	f. Perf 14¾×14½ (1994)	†		3·25	30
249	5 c. Cocoa	10	10	10	10
	w. Wmk inverted	†		—	—
250	10 c. Black pepper	10	10	10	10
	aw. Wmk inverted	†		—	—
	c. Perf 14×13¾ (1995)	†		2·00	20
	f. Perf 14¾×14½ (1995)	†		2·00	20
251	15 c. Rubber	10	10	10	10
252	20 c. Oil palm	10	10	10	10
	w. Wmk inverted	—	—	4·50	—
253	30 c. Rice	15	20	15	20
	aw. Wmk inverted	†		4·00	—
	c. Perf 14×13¾ (1994)	†		1·50	20
	d. Perf 14	†		—	—
	e. Perf 14×14½ (1994)	†		—	—
	f. Perf 14¾×14½ (1994)	†		3·00	30
247/53	*Set of* 7	50	55	50	55

STAMP BOOKLETS

1973 (8 Dec). *Cover as Type* B **1** *of Johore, but inscr* "SARAWAK". *Stitched.*

SB1 $3 booklet containing eight 5 c., 10 c. and twelve 15 c. (Nos. 221, 223/4) in blocks of 4 .. .. 18·00

Examples of No. SB1 exist with a white label giving revised postage rates.

1979 (1 Dec). *Cover as No.* SB5 *of Johore, but inscr* "SARAWAK". *Stitched.*

SB2 $3 booklet containing eight 5 c., 10 c., and twelve 15 c. (Nos. 235/7) in blocks of 4 .. .. 7·00

No. SB2 exists with two different versions of the back cover.

1987 (1 June). *Cover as Type* B **2** *of Johore, but inscr* "SARAWAK". *Stapled.*

SB3 $2 booklet containing 5 c., 10 c., 15 c. and 20 c. (Nos. 249A/52A) in blocks of 4 .. .. 5·00

1992 (1 July). *"Kuala Lumpur '92" International Philatelic Exhibition. Cover as Type* B 3 *of Johore, but inscr* "Sarawak". *Stamps attached by selvedge.*

SB4 $3 booklet containing 30 c. (No. 253A) in block of 10 .. .. 5·50

1993. *Covers as Nos.* SB8/9 *of Johore, but inscr* "Sarawak". *Stamps attached by selvedge.*

SB5 $2 booklet containing 20 c. (No. 252B) in block of 10 .. .. 1·00

SB6 $3 booklet containing 30 c. (No. 253B) in block of 10 .. .. 1·50

XV. JAPANESE OCCUPATION OF SARAWAK

Japanese forces landed in North Borneo on 16 December 1941 and Sarawak was attacked on 23 December 1941.

Brunei, North Borneo, Sarawak and after a short period Labuan, were administered as a single territory by the Japanese. Until September–October 1942, previous stamp issues, without overprint, continued to be used in conjunction with existing postmarks. From 1 October 1942 onwards unoverprinted stamps of Japan were made available and examples can be found used from the area for much of the remainder of the War. Japanese Occupation issues for Brunei, North Borneo and Sarawak were equally valid throughout the combined territory but not, in practice, equally available.

PRICES FOR STAMPS ON COVER	
Nos. J1/21	*from* ×8
Nos. J22/6	—

府政國帝本日大

(1)

("Imperial Japanese Government")

1942 (Oct). *Stamps of Sarawak handstamped with T* **1** *in violet.*

J 1	**21**	1 c. purple	30·00	50·00
		a. Pair, one without opt	£900	
J 2		2 c. green	70·00	£120
		a. Black opt	70·00	
J 3		2 c. black	65·00	75·00
		a. Black opt	80·00	
J 4		3 c. black	£200	£200
J 5		3 c. green	40·00	60·00
		a. Black opt	60·00	
J 6		4 c. bright purple	42·00	60·00
		a. Black opt	60·00	
J 7		5 c. violet	50·00	60·00
		a. Black opt	60·00	
J 8		6 c. carmine	80·00	85·00
J 9		6 c. lake-brown	48·00	60·00
		a. Black opt	60·00	
J10		8 c. red-brown	£170	£180
J11		8 c. carmine	75·00	£110
J12		10 c. scarlet	45·00	65·00
		a. Black opt	60·00	
J13		12 c. blue	£100	£110
		a. Black opt	£130	
J14		12 c. orange	£100	£120
J15		15 c. orange	£200	£200
		a. Black opt	£225	
J16		15 c. blue	70·00	75·00
J17		20 c. olive-green and carmine	40·00	65·00
		a. Black opt	60·00	
J18		25 c. violet and orange	65·00	65·00
		a. Black opt	70·00	
J19		30 c. red-brown and violet	42·00	70·00
		a. Black opt	60·00	
J20		50 c. violet and scarlet	50·00	70·00
J21		$1 scarlet and sepia	65·00	85·00
J22	**21**	$2 bright purple and violet	£140	£170
J23		$3 carmine and green	£750	£850
J24		$4 blue and scarlet	£160	£200
J25		$5 scarlet and red-brown	£160	£200
J26		$10 black and yellow	£160	

The overprint, being handstamped, exists inverted or double on some values.

Stamps of T **21** optd with Japanese symbols within an oval frame are revenue stamps, while the same stamps overprinted with three Japanese characters between two vertical double rules, were used as seals.

Nos. J1/26 have been extensively forged. Recent research indicates that complete or part sets on cover cancelled by Japanese circular postmarks in violet dated "17 11 21" (21 Nov 1942) or "18 3 1" (1 Mar 1943) have forged overprints.

Maldive Islands

PRICES FOR STAMPS ON COVER TO 1945

Nos. 1/6	*from* × 10
Nos. 7/10	*from* × 50
Nos. 11/20	*from* × 20

BRITISH PROTECTORATE

(Currency. 100 cents = 1 Ceylon rupee)

MALDIVES

(1)

2 Minaret, Juma Mosque, Malé

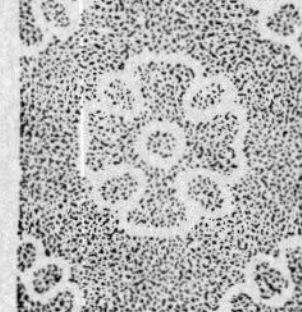

3

1906 (9 Sept). *Nos.* 277/9, 280a *and* 283/4 *of Sri Lanka (Ceylon) optd with T* **1**. *Wmk Mult Crown CA. P* 14.

No.	Type	Description	Unused	Used
1	44	2 c. red-brown	13·00	28·00
2	45	3 c. green	17·00	28·00
3		4 c. orange and ultramarine	32·00	65·00
4	46	5 c. dull purple	4·00	6·50
5	48	15 c. blue	55·00	£110
6		25 c. bistre	65·00	£120
1/6		*Set of* 6	£170	£325

No further supplies of Nos. 1/6 were despatched to the Maldive Islands after 1907 and the stamps of CEYLON were used until 1909. Overseas mail to destinations other than Ceylon or India continued to be franked with Ceylon stamps until 1967 when Maldive Islands joined the U.P.U.

(Recess D.L.R.)

1909 (May). *T* **2** (18½×22½ *mm*). *W* **3**. *P* 14×13½ (2 *c.*, 5 *c.*) *or* 13½×14 (3 *c.*, 10 *c.*).

No.	Type	Description	Unused	Used
7	2	2 c. orange-brown	2·25	2·25
		a. Perf 13½×14	2·50	90
8		3 c. deep myrtle	40	70
9		5 c. purple	40	35
10		10 c. carmine	6·50	80
7/10		*Set of* 4	8·50	2·50

These stamps perforated 14×13½ (14×13.7) are from a line machine and those perforated 13½×14 (13.7×13.9) from a comb machine.

4

(Photo Harrison)

1933. *T* **2** *redrawn (reduced to* 18×21½ *mm). W* **4**. *P* 15×14. A. *Wmk upright.* B. *Wmk sideways.*

No.	Type	Description	A		B	
11	2	2 c. grey	2·75	2·00	3·25	3·25
12		3 c. red-brown	70	1·75	1·75	1·75
13		5 c. claret	†		25·00	25·00
14		5 c. mauve	14·00	10·00	†	
15		6 c. scarlet	1·50	4·00	3·50	4·00
16		10 c. green	75	55	1·75	1·75
17		15 c. black	6·50	10·00	9·50	10·00
18		25 c. brown	6·50	10·00	9·50	10·00
19		50 c. purple	6·50	10·00	9·50	10·00
20		1 r. deep blue	10·00	5·00	10·00	2·75
11/20		*Set of* 9	45·00	48·00	65·00	60·00

(New Currency. 100 larees=1 rupee)

5 Palm Tree and Dhow

(Recess B.W.)

1950 (24 Dec). *P* 13.

No.	Type	Description	Unused	Used
21	5	2 l. olive-green	1·00	40
22		3 l. blue	6·50	40
23		5 l. emerald-green	6·50	50
24		6 l. red-brown	60	30
25		10 l. scarlet	70	30
26		15 l. orange	70	30
27		25 l. purple	60	30
28		50 l. violet	70	30
29		1 r. chocolate	8·00	25·00
21/9		*Set of* 9	23·00	25·00

7 Fish

8 Native Products

(Recess B.W.)

1952. *P* 13.

No.	Type	Description	Unused	Used
30	7	3 l. blue	75	30
31	8	5 l. emerald	50	90

The Maldive Islands became a republic on 1 January 1953, but reverted to a sultanate in 1954.

9 Malé Harbour

10 Fort and Building

(Recess B.W.)

1956 (Feb). *P* 13½ (*T* **9**) *or* 11½ × 11 (*T* **10**).

No.	Type	Description	Unused	Used
32	9	2 l. purple	10	10
33		3 l. slate	10	10
34		5 l. red-brown	10	10
35		6 l. blackish violet	10	10
36		10 l. emerald	10	10
37		15 l. chocolate	10	30
38		25 l. rose-red	10	10
39		50 l. orange	10	10
40	10	1 r. bluish green	15	10
41		5 r. blue	60	30
42		10 r. magenta	1·10	75
32/42		*Set of* 11	2·00	1·40

11 Cycling

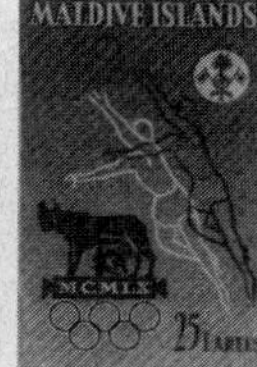

12 Basketball

(Des C. Bottiau. Recess and typo B.W.)

1960 (20 Aug). *Olympic Games. P* 11½ × 11 (*T* **11**) *or* 11 × 11½ (*T* **12**).

No.	Type	Description	Unused	Used
43	11	2 l. purple and green	10	10
44		3 l. greenish slate and purple	10	10
45		5 l. red-brown and ultramarine	10	10
46		10 l. emerald-green and brown	10	10
47		15 l. sepia and blue	10	20
48	12	25 l. rose-red and olive	10	20
49		50 l. orange and violet	15	30
50		1 r. emerald and purple	30	1·10
43/50		*Set of* 8	75	1·60

13 Tomb of Sultan

14 Custom House

(Recess B.W.)

1960 (15 Oct). *T* **13, 14** *and similar horiz designs. P* 11½ × 11.

No.	Type	Description	Unused	Used
51		2 l. purple	10	10
52		3 l. emerald-green	10	10
53		5 l. orange-brown	2·50	2·50
54		6 l. bright blue	10	10
55		10 l. carmine	10	10
56		15 l. sepia	10	10
57		25 l. deep violet	10	10
58		50 l. slate-grey	10	10
59		1 r. orange	15	10
60		5 r. deep ultramarine	2·00	60
61		10 r. grey-green	6·00	1·25
51/61		*Set of* 11	10·00	4·50

Designs:—5 l. Cowrie shells; 6 l. Old Royal Palace; 10 l. Road to Juma Mosque, Malé; 15 l. Council house; 25 l. New Government Secretariat; 50 l. Prime Minister's office; 1 r. Old Ruler's tomb; 5 r. Old Ruler's tomb (distant view); 10 r. Maldivian Port.

Higher values were also issued, intended mainly for fiscal use.

24 "Care of Refugees"

(Recess B.W.)

1960 (15 Oct). *World Refugee Year. P* 11½ × 11.

No.	Type	Description	Unused	Used
62	24	2 l. deep violet, orange and green	10	10
63		3 l. brown, green and red	10	10
64		5 l. deep green, sepia and red	10	10
65		10 l. bluish green, reddish violet and red	10	10
66		15 l. reddish violet, grey-green and red	10	10
67		25 l. blue, red-brown and bronze-green	10	10
68		50 l. yellow-olive, rose-red and blue	10	10
69		1 r. carmine, slate and violet	15	35
62/9		*Set of* 8	30	45

25 Coconuts

26 Map of Malé

(Photo Harrison)

1961 (20 Apr). *P* 14 × 14½ (*Nos.* 70/74) *or* 14½ × 14 (*others*).

No.	Type	Description	Unused	Used
70	25	2 l. yellow-brown and deep green	10	10
71		3 l. yellow-brown and bright blue	10	10
72		5 l. yellow-brown and magenta	10	10
73		10 l. yellow-brown and red-orange	10	10
74		15 l. yellow-brown and black	10	10
75	26	25 l. multicoloured	15	15
76		50 l. multicoloured	15	25
77		1 r. multicoloured	20	40
70/7		*Set of* 8	55	85

27 5 c. Stamp of 1906

30 Malaria Eradication Emblem

(Des M. Shamir. Photo Harrison)

1961 (9 Sept). *55th Anniv of First Maldivian Stamp. T* **27** *and similar horiz designs. P* 14½ × 14.

No.	Type	Description	Unused	Used
78		2 l. brown-purple, ultramarine & lt green	10	10
79		3 l. brown-purple, ultramarine & lt green	10	10
80		5 l. brown-purple, ultramarine & lt green	10	10
81		6 l. brown-purple, ultramarine & lt green	10	10
82		10 l. green, claret and maroon	10	10
83		15 l. green, claret and maroon	10	15
84		20 l. green, claret and maroon	10	20
85		25 l. claret, green and black	10	20
86		50 l. claret, green and black	20	70
87		1 r. claret, green and black	35	1·25
78/87		*Set of* 10	75	2·25
MS87*a*		114 × 88 mm. No. 87 (block of four). Imperf	2·00	3·75

Designs:—2 to 6 l. Type **27**; 10 to 20 l. 1906 3 c. and posthorn; 25 l. to 1 r. 1906 2 c. and olive sprig.

(Recess B.W.)

1962 (7 Apr). *Malaria Eradication. P* 13½ × 13.

No.	Type	Description	Unused	Used
88	30	2 l. chestnut	10	10
89		3 l. emerald	10	10
90		5 l. turquoise-blue	10	10
91		10 l. red	10	10
92	–	15 l. deep purple-brown	15	10
93	–	25 l. deep blue	20	15
94	–	50 l. deep green	25	20
95	–	1 r. purple	55	35
88/95		*Set of* 8	1·25	75

Nos. 92/5 are as T **30**, but have English inscriptions at the side.

31 Children of Europe and America

33 Sultan Mohamed Farid Didi

(Des C. Bottiau. Photo Harrison)

1962 (9 Sept). *15th Anniv of U.N.I.C.E.F. T* **31** *and similar horiz design. Multicoloured. P* 14½ × 14.

No.	Type	Description	Unused	Used
96		2 l. Type **31**	10	10
97		6 l. Type **31**	10	10
98		10 l. Type **31**	10	10
99		15 l. Type **31**	10	10
100		25 l. Children of Middle East and Far East	10	10
101		50 l. As 25 l.	10	10
102		1 r. As 25 l.	10	20
103		5 r. As 25 l.	45	2·50
96/103		*Set of* 8	70	2·75

(Photo Harrison)

1962 (29 Nov). *Ninth Anniv of Enthronement of Sultan. P* 14 × 14½.

No.	Type	Description	Unused	Used
104	33	3 l. orange-brown and bluish green	10	10
105		5 l. orange-brown and indigo	10	10
106		10 l. orange-brown and blue	10	10
107		20 l. orange-brown and olive-green	10	10
108		50 l. orange-brown and deep magenta	15	20
109		1 r. orange-brown and slate-lilac	20	35
104/9		*Set of* 6	45	60

34 Royal Angelfish

(Des R. Hegeman. Photo Enschedé)

1963 (2 Feb). *Tropical Fish. T* **34** *and similar triangular designs. Multicoloured. P* 13½.

No.	Description	Unused	Used
110	2 l. Type **34**	10	10
111	3 l. Type **34**	10	10
112	5 l. Type **34**	10	10
113	10 l. Moorish Idol	15	10
114	25 l. As 10 l.	40	20
115	50 l. Diadem Soldierfish	60	30
116	1 r. Powder-blue Surgeonfish	80	40
117	5 r. Raccoon Butterflyfish	5·50	7·50
110/17	*Set of* 8	6·50	8·00

39 Fishes in Net **40** Handful of Grain

(Photo State Ptg Wks, Vienna)

1963 (21 Mar). *Freedom from Hunger. P* 12.

No.	Type	Description	Unused	Used
118	39	2 l. brown and deep bluish green	30	80
119	40	5 l. brown and orange-red	50	70
120	39	7 l. brown and turquoise	70	70
121	40	10 l. brown and blue	85	70
122	39	25 l. brown and brown-red	3·00	3·25
123	40	50 l. brown and violet	4·75	7·00
124	39	1 r. brown and deep magenta	7·50	11·00
118/24		*Set of* 7	16·00	22·00

41 Centenary Emblem **42** Maldivian Scout Badge

(Photo Harrison)

1963 (Oct). *Centenary of Red Cross. P* 14 × 14½.

No.	Type	Description	Unused	Used
125	41	2 l. red and deep purple	30	90
126		15 l. red and deep bluish green	50	80
127		50 l. red and deep brown	1·25	1·75
128		1 r. red and indigo	2·00	2·00
129		4 r. red and deep brown-olive	6·50	19·00
125/9		*Set of* 5	9·50	22·00

(Photo Enschedé)

1964. *World Scout Jamboree, Marathon* (1963). *P* 13½.

No.	Type	Description	Unused	Used
130	42	2 l. green and violet	10	10
131		3 l. green and bistre-brown	10	10
132		25 l. green and blue	15	15
133		1 r. green and crimson	55	1·50
130/3		*Set of* 4	70	1·60

43 Mosque, Malé **44** Putting the Shot

(Recess B.W.)

1964 (10 Aug). *"Maldives Embrace Islam". W w* **12**. *P* 11½.

No.	Type	Description	Unused	Used
134	43	2 l. purple	10	10
135		3 l. emerald-green	10	10
136		10 l. carmine	10	10
137		40 l. deep dull purple	30	15
138		60 l. blue	50	15
139		85 l. orange-brown	60	20
134/9		*Set of* 6	1·40	60

(Litho Enschedé)

1964 (Oct). *Olympic Games, Tokyo. T* **44** *and similar horiz design. W w* **12**. *P* 14 × 13½.

No.	Description	Unused	Used
140	2 l. deep maroon and turquoise-blue	10	10
141	3 l. crimson and chestnut	10	10
142	5 l. bronze-green and deep green	15	10
143	10 l. slate-violet and reddish purple	20	10
144	15 l. sepia and yellow-brown	30	10
145	25 l. indigo and deep blue	50	10
146	50 l. deep olive-green and yellow-olive	75	20
147	1 r. deep maroon and olive-grey	1·25	40
140/7	*Set of* 8	2·75	70
MS147*a*	126 × 140 mm. Nos. 145/7. Imperf	2·25	2·75

Designs:—2 to 10 l. Type **44**; 15 l. to 1 r. Running.

46 Telecommunications Satellite

(Des M. Shamir. Photo Harrison)

1965 (1 July). *International Quiet Sun Years. P* 14½.

No.	Type	Description	Unused	Used
148	46	5 l. blue	15	15
149		10 l. brown	20	15
150		25 l. green	40	15
151		1 r. deep magenta	90	55
148/51		*Set of* 4	1·50	90

On 26 July 1965, Maldive Islands became independent and left the British Commonwealth.

INDEPENDENT SULTANATE

Sultan Mohamed Farid Didi
29 November 1953–10 November 1968

47 Isis (wall carving, Abu Simbel) **48** President Kennedy and Doves

(Des M. and G. Shamir. Litho Harrison)

1965 (1 Sept). *Nubian Monuments Preservation. T* **47** *and similar vert design. W w* **12**. *P* 14½.

No.	Type	Description	Unused	Used
152	47	2 l. bluish green and brown-purple	10	10
153	–	3 l. lake and deep green	10	10
154	47	5 l. dull green and brown-purple	10	10
155	–	10 l. steel-blue and orange	15	10
156	47	15 l. red-brown and deep violet	25	15
157	–	25 l. reddish purple and deep blue	40	15
158	47	50 l. yellow-green and sepia	55	25
159	–	1 r. ochre and myrtle-green	90	40
152/9		*Set of* 8	2·25	1·00

Design:—3, 10, 25 l., 1 r. Rameses II on throne (wall carving, Abu Simbel).

(Photo State Ptg Wks, Vienna)

1965 (10 Oct). *Second Death Anniv of President Kennedy. T* **48** *and similar horiz design. P* 12.

No.	Type	Description	Unused	Used
160	48	2 l. black and mauve	10	10
161		5 l. bistre-brown and mauve	10	10
162		25 l. indigo and mauve	10	10
163	–	1 r. brt reddish purple, yellow & bl-grn	25	25
164	–	2 r. bronze-green, yellow & blue-green	40	40
160/4		*Set of* 5	75	75
MS164*a*		150 × 130 mm. No. 164 in block of four. Imperf	2·75	3·00

Design:—1 r., 2 r. Pres. Kennedy and hands holding olive-branch.

49 "XX" and U.N. Flag **50** I.C.Y. Emblem

(Des O. Adler. Photo State Ptg Wks, Vienna)

1965 (24 Nov). *20th Anniv of U.N. P* 12.

No.	Type	Description	Unused	Used
165	49	3 l. turquoise-blue and red-brown	10	10
166		10 l. turquoise-blue and violet	10	10
167		1 r. turquoise-blue and bronze-green	35	35
165/7		*Set of* 3	40	40

(Des M. and G. Shamir. Photo State Ptg Wks, Vienna)

1965 (20 Dec). *International Co-operation Year. P* 12.

No.	Type	Description	Unused	Used
168	50	5 l. brown and yellow-bistre	15	10
169		15 l. brown and slate-lilac	20	10
170		50 l. brown and yellow-olive	45	30
171		1 r. brown and orange-red	1·25	1·50
172		2 r. brown and new blue	1·75	3·00
168/72		*Set of* 5	3·50	4·50
MS173		101 × 126 mm. Nos. 170/2. Imperf	6·50	6·50

51 Princely Cone Shells

(Des M. and G. Shamir. Photo State Ptg Wks, Vienna)

1966 (1 June). *T* **51** *and similar multicoloured designs. P* 12.

No.	Description	Unused	Used
174	2 l. Type **51**	20	40
175	3 l. Yellow flowers	20	40
176	5 l. Reticulate Distorsio and Leopard Cone shells	30	15
177	7 l. Camellias	30	15
178	10 l. Type **51**	60	15
179	15 l. Crab Plover and Seagull	2·50	30
180	20 l. As 3 l.	80	30
181	30 l. Type **51**	2·00	35
182	50 l. As 15 l.	4·50	55
183	1 r. Type **51**	3·00	55
184	1 r. As 7 l.	3·00	55
185	1 r. 50, As 3 l.	3·50	2·00
186	2 r. As 7 l.	4·75	2·50
187	5 r. As 15 l.	17·00	10·00
188	10 r. As 5 l.	17·00	14·00
174/88	*Set of* 15	55·00	29·00

The 3 l., 7 l., 20 l., 1 r. (No. 184), 1 r. 50 and 2 r. are diamond-shaped (43½ × 43½ mm); the others are horizontal designs as T **51**.

52 Maldivian Flag

(Des M. and G. Shamir. Litho Harrison)

1966 (26 July). *First Anniv of Independence. P* 14 × 14½.

No.	Type	Description	Unused	Used
189	52	10 l. green, red and turquoise	25	10
190		1 r. green, red, brown & orange-yellow	1·25	40

53 "Luna 9" on Moon

(Des M. and G. Shamir. Litho Harrison)

1966 (1 Nov). *Space Rendezvous and Moon Landing. T* **53** *and similar horiz designs. W w* **12**. *P* 15 × 14.

No.	Description	Unused	Used
191	10 l. light brown, grey-blue and bright blue	15	10
192	25 l. green and carmine	25	10
193	50 l. orange-brown and green	30	15
194	1 r. turquoise-blue and chestnut	60	35
195	2 r. green and violet	1·25	65
196	5 r. rose-pink and deep turquoise-blue	2·00	1·60
191/6	*Set of* 6	4·00	2·50
MS197	108 × 126 mm. Nos. 194/6. Imperf	3·50	4·50

Designs:—25 l., 1 r., 5 r. "Gemini 6" and "7" rendezvous in space; 2 r. "Gemini" spaceship as seen from the other spaceship; 50 l. Type **53**.

54 U.N.E.S.C.O. Emblem, and Owl on Book **55** Sir Winston Churchill and Cortège

(Litho Harrison)

1966 (15 Nov). *20th Anniv of U.N.E.S.C.O. T* **54** *and similar vert designs. W w* **12**. *Multicoloured. P* 15 × 14.

No.	Description	Unused	Used
198	1 l. Type **54**	10	40
199	3 l. U.N.E.S.C.O. emblem, and globe and microscope	10	40
200	5 l. U.N.E.S.C.O. emblem, and mask, violin and palette	15	15

201 50 l. Type **54** 1·25 45
202 1 r. Design as 3 l. 2·00 75
203 5 r. Design as 5 l. 7·00 11·00
198/203 *Set of* 6 9·50 12·00

(Des M. and G. Shamir. Litho Harrison)

1967 (1 Jan). *Churchill Commemoration. T* **55** *and similar horiz design. Flag in red and blue. P* 14½ × 13½.
204 **55** 2 l. olive-brown 15 40
205 – 10 l. turquoise-blue 60 10
206 **55** 15 l. green 85 10
207 – 25 l. violet 1·40 15
208 – 1 r. brown 3·75 75
209 **55** 2 r. 50, crimson 9·00 9·50
204/9 *Set of* 6 14·00 10·00
Design:—10 l., 25 l., 1 r. Churchill and catafalque.

IMPERFORATE STAMPS. From No. 210 onwards some sets and perforated miniature sheets exist imperforate from limited printings.

56 Footballers and Jules Rimet Cup

(Des M. and G. Shamir. Photo Govt Printer, Israel)

1967 (22 Mar). *England's Victory in World Cup Football Championship. T* **56** *and similar horiz designs. Multicoloured. P* 14×13½.
210 2 l. Type **56** 10 40
211 3 l. Player in red shirt kicking ball 10 40
212 5 l. Scoring goal 10 10
213 25 l. As 3 l. 50 10
a. Emerald (face value and inscr) omitted £140
214 50 l. Making a tackle 85 20
215 1 r. Type **56** 1·75 55
216 2 r. Emblem on Union Jack 2·75 3·00
210/16 *Set of* 7 5·50 4·25
MS217 100×121 mm. Nos. 214/16. Imperf 7·50 6·00

57 Ornate Butterflyfish

(Des M. and G. Shamir. Photo Govt Printer, Israel)

1967 (1 May). *Tropical Fishes. T* **57** *and similar horiz designs. Multicoloured. P* 14.
218 2 l. Type **57** 10 30
219 3 l. Black-saddled Pufferfish 10 30
220 5 l. Blue Boxfish 15 10
221 6 l. Picasso Triggerfish 15 20
222 50 l. Semicircle Angelfish 3·00 30
223 1 r. As 3 l. 4·25 75
224 2 r. As 50 l. 8·00 8·00
218/24 *Set of* 7 14·00 9·00

58 Hawker Siddeley H.S.748 over Hulule Airport Building

(Des M. and G. Shamir. Photo Govt Printer, Israel)

1967 (26 July). *Inauguration of Hulule Airport. T* **58** *and similar horiz design. P* 14 × 13½.
225 2 l. reddish violet and yellow-olive 10 40
226 5 l. deep green and lavender 15 10
227 10 l. reddish violet and light turquoise-green 20 10
228 15 l. deep green and yellow-ochre 30 10
229 30 l. deep ultramarine and light blue 80 10
230 50 l. deep brown and magenta 1·25 20
231 5 r. deep ultramarine and yellow-orange 4·25 5·00
232 10 r. deep brown and blue 6·50 8·50
225/32 *Set of* 8 12·00 13·00
Designs:—2 l., 10 l., 30 l., 5 r. T **58**; 5 l., 15 l., 50 l., 10 r. Airport building and Hawker Siddeley H.S.748. Higher values were also issued, intended mainly for fiscal use.

59 "Man and Music" Pavilion

International Tourist Year 1967
(60)

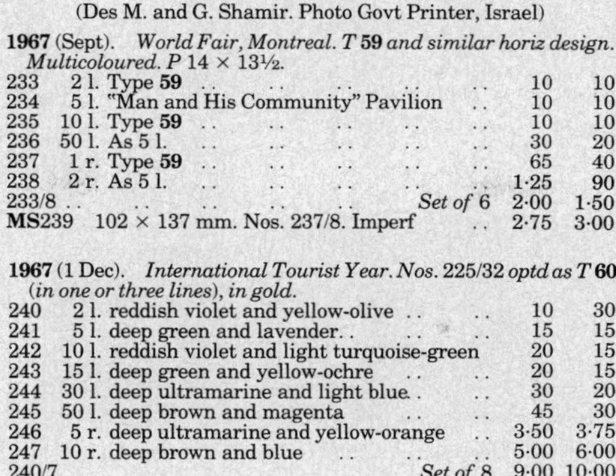

(Des M. and G. Shamir. Photo Govt Printer, Israel)

1967 (Sept). *World Fair, Montreal. T* **59** *and similar horiz design. Multicoloured. P* 14 × 13½.
233 2 l. Type **59** 10 10
234 5 l. "Man and His Community" Pavilion 10 10
235 10 l. Type **59** 10 10
236 50 l. As 5 l. 30 20
237 1 r. Type **59** 65 40
238 2 r. As 5 l. 1·25 90
233/8 *Set of* 6 2·00 1·50
MS239 102 × 137 mm. Nos. 237/8. Imperf 2·75 3·00

1967 (1 Dec). *International Tourist Year. Nos.* 225/32 *optd as T* **60** *(in one or three lines), in gold.*
240 2 l. reddish violet and yellow-olive 10 30
241 5 l. deep green and lavender 15 15
242 10 l. reddish violet and light turquoise-green 20 15
243 15 l. deep green and yellow-ochre 20 15
244 30 l. deep ultramarine and light blue 30 20
245 50 l. deep brown and magenta 45 30
246 5 r. deep ultramarine and yellow-orange 3·50 3·75
247 10 r. deep brown and blue 5·00 6·00
240/7 *Set of* 8 9·00 10·00

61 Cub signalling and Lord Baden-Powell **62** French Satellite "A 1"

(Litho Harrison)

1968 (1 Jan). *Maldivian Scouts and Cubs. T* **61** *and similar vert design. P* 14 × 14½.
248 **61** 2 l. brown, green and yellow 10 30
249 – 3 l. carmine, bright blue and light blue 10 30
250 **61** 25 l. bluish violet, lake and orange-red 1·50 30
251 – 1 r. blackish green, chest & apple-green 3·50 1·60
248/51 *Set of* 4 4·50 2·25
Design:—3 l., 1 r. Scouts and Lord Baden-Powell.

(Des M. and G. Shamir. Photo Govt Printer, Israel)

1968 (27 Jan). *Space Martyrs. Triangular designs as T* **62.** *P* 14.
252 2 l. magenta and ultramarine 10 30
253 3 l. violet and yellow-brown 10 30
254 7 l. olive-brown and lake 15 30
255 10 l. deep blue, pale drab and black 15 15
256 25 l. bright emerald and reddish violet 40 15
257 50 l. blue and orange-brown 75 30
258 1 r. purple-brown and deep bluish green 1·10 50
259 2 r. deep brown, pale blue and black 1·75 1·75
260 5 r. magenta, light drab and black 2·75 3·00
252/60 *Set of* 9 6·50 6·00
MS261 110 × 155 mm. Nos. 258/9. Imperf 3·75 4·00
Designs:—2 l., 50 l. Type **62**; 3 l., 25 l. "Luna 10"; 7 l., 1 r. "Orbiter" and "Mariner"; 10 l., 2 r. Astronauts White, Grissom and Chaffee; 5 r. Cosmonaut V. M. Komarov.

63 Putting the Shot **64** "Adriatic Seascape" (Bonington)

(Des M. Shamir. Litho Harrison)

1968 (Feb). *Olympic Games, Mexico (1st issue). T* **63** *and similar vert design. Multicoloured. P* 14½.
262 2 l. Type **63** 10 15
263 6 l. Throwing the discus 10 15
264 10 l. Type **63** 10 10
265 15 l. As 6 l. 10 10
266 1 r. Type **63** 40 35
267 2 r. 50, As 6 l. 95 1·25
262/7 *Set of* 6 1·40 1·75
See also Nos. 294/7.

(Des M. Shamir. Litho Govt Printer, Israel)

1968 (1 Apr). *Paintings. T* **64** *and similar horiz designs. Multicoloured. P* 14.
268 50 l. Type **64** 60 30
269 1 r. "Ulysses deriding Polyphemus" (Turner) 1·00 45
270 2 r. "Sailing Boat at Argenteuil" (Monet) 1·75 1·60
271 5 r. "Fishing Boats at Les Saintes-Maries" (Van Gogh) 4·00 4·00
268/71 *Set of* 4 6·50 5·75

65 LZ-130 *Graf Zeppelin II* and Montgolfier's Balloon

(Des M. Shamir. Photo Govt Printer, Israel)

1968 (1 June). *Development of Civil Aviation. T* **65** *and similar horiz designs. P* 14 × 13½.
272 2 l. orange-brown, yellow-green & ultram 15 40
273 3 l. turquoise-blue, violet & orange-brown 15 40
274 5 l. slate-green, crimson and turquoise-blue 15 15
275 7 l. bright blue, purple and red-orange 90 55
276 10 l. brown, turquoise-blue and bright purple 35 15
277 50 l. crimson, slate-green and yellow-olive 1·50 20
278 1 r. emerald, blue and vermilion 2·25 50
279 2 r. maroon, bistre and bright blue 14·00 10·00
272/9 *Set of* 8 18·00 11·00
Designs:—3 l., 1 r. Boeing 707-420 and Douglas DC-3; 5 l., 50 l. Wright Type A and Lilienthal's glider; 7 l., 2 r. Projected Boeing 733 and Concorde; 10 l. Type **65**.

66 W.H.O. Building, Geneva

International Boy Scout Jamboree, Farragut Park, Idaho, U.S.A. August 1-9, 1967
(67)

(Litho Harrison)

1968 (15 July). *20th Anniv of World Health Organisation. P* 14½ × 13½.
280 **66** 10 l. violet, turquoise-bl & lt greenish bl 50 10
281 25 l. bronze-green, yell-brn & orge-yell 90 15
282 1 r. deep brown, emerald & brt green 3·00 90
283 2 r. bluish violet, magenta and mauve 4·75 5·00
280/3 *Set of* 4 8·25 5·50

1968 (1 Aug). *First Anniv of Scout Jamboree, Idaho. Nos.* 248/51 *optd with T* **67**.
284 2 l. brown, green and yellow 10 40
285 3 l. carmine, bright blue and light blue 10 40
286 25 l. bluish violet, lake and orange-red 1·25 40
287 1 r. blackish green, chestnut & apple-green 4·25 2·10
284/7 *Set of* 4 5·00 3·00

68 Curlew and Redshank

1968 (24 Sept). *T* **68** *and similar horiz designs. Photo. Multicoloured. P* 14×13½.
288 2 l. Type **68** 50 60
289 10 l. Pacific Grinning Tun and Papal Mitre shells 1·25 20
290 25 l. Oriental Angel Wing and Tapestry Turban shells 1·75 25
291 50 l. Type **68** 6·00 90
292 1 r. As 10 l. 4·50 95
293 2 r. As 25 l. 4·75 4·50
288/93 *Set of* 6 17·00 6·75

69 Throwing the Discus

(Des M. Shamir. Photo Govt Printer, Israel)

1968 (12 Oct). *Olympic Games, Mexico (2nd issue). T* **69** *and similar multicoloured designs. P* 14.
294 10 l. Type **69** 10 10
295 50 l. Running 20 10
296 1 r. Cycling 1·75 35
297 2 r. Basketball 2·50 1·25
294/7 *Set of* 4 4·00 1·60

INDEPENDENT REPUBLIC
11 November 1968

70 Fishing Dhow **71** "The Thinker" (Rodin)

(Photo Harrison)

1968 (11 Nov). *Republic Day. T* **70** *and similar horiz design. P* 14 × 14½.
298 10 l. brown, ultramarine and lt yellow-green .. 75 20
299 1 r. green, red and bright blue .. .. 2·50 80
Design:—1 r. National flag, crest and map.

(Des M. Shamir. Litho Rosenbaum Brothers, Vienna)

1969 (10 Apr). *U.N.E.S.C.O. "Human Rights". T* **71** *and similar vert designs, showing sculptures by Rodin. Multicoloured. P* 13½.
300 6 l. Type **71** 30 15
301 10 l. "Hands" 30 15
302 1 r. 50, "Eve" .. .. 2·00 2·00
303 2 r. 50, "Adam" .. .. 2·50 2·75
300/3 .. .. *Set of* 4 4·75 4·50
MS304 112 × 130 mm. Nos. 302/3. Imperf .. 4·75 5·50

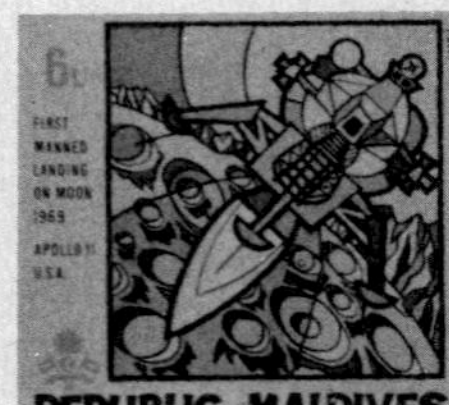

72 Module nearing Moon's Surface

(Des M. Shamir. Litho Govt Printer, Israel)

1969 (25 Sept). *First Man on the Moon. T* **72** *and similar square designs. Multicoloured. P* 14.
305 6 l. Type **72** 15 15
306 10 l. Astronaut with hatchet 15 15
307 1 r. 50, Astronaut and module .. .. 1·60 1·10
308 2 r. 50, Astronaut using camera .. .. 2·00 1·75
305/8 .. .. *Set of* 4 3·50 2·75
MS309 101 × 130 mm. Nos. 305/8. Imperf .. 2·00 3·00

Gold Medal Winner
Mohamed Gammoudi
5000 m. run
Tunisia
REPUBLIC OF MALDIVES

(73)

1969 (1 Dec). *Gold-medal Winners, Olympic Games, Mexico (1968). Nos. 295/6 optd with T* **73**, *or similar inscr honouring P. Trentin (cycling) of France.*
310 50 l. multicoloured 50 50
311 1 r. multicoloured 75 75

74 Raccoon Butterflyfish

(Des M. Shamir. Litho)

1970 (Jan). *Tropical Fish. T* **74** *and similar diamond-shaped designs. Multicoloured. P* 10½.
312 2 l. Type **74** 40 70
313 5 l. Clown Triggerfish 65 40
314 25 l. Broad-barred Lionfish .. .. .. 1·75 40
315 50 l. Long-nosed Butterflyfish .. .. .. 2·50 1·00
316 1 r. Emperor Angelfish .. .. 3·75 1·00
317 2 r. Royal Angelfish .. .. 5·50 6·50
312/17 .. .. *Set of* 6 13·00 9·00

75 Columbia Dauman Victoria, 1899

(Des M. Shamir. Litho)

1970 (1 Feb). *"75 Years of the Automobile". T* **75** *and similar horiz designs. Multicoloured. P* 12.
318 2 l. Type **75** 20 30
319 5 l. Duryea phaeton, 1902 .. .. 25 30
320 7 l. Packard S-24, 1906 .. .. 30 30
321 10 l. Autocar Runabout, 1907 .. .. .. 35 30
322 25 l. Type **75** .. .. 1·00 30
323 50 l. As 5 l. .. .. 2·25 55
324 1 r. As 7 l. .. .. 3·50 90
325 2 r. As 10 l. .. .. 4·50 5·50
318/25 .. .. *Set of* 8 11·00 7·75
MS326 95 × 143 mm. Nos. 324/5. P 11½ .. 4·50 6·50

76 U.N. Headquarters, New York

77 Ship and Light Buoy

(Des M. Shamir. Litho Rosenbaum Brothers, Vienna)

1970 (26 June). *25th Anniv of United Nations. T* **76** *and similar horiz designs. Multicoloured. P* 13½.
327 2 l. Type **76** 10 50
328 10 l. Surgical operation (W.H.O.) 75 15
329 25 l. Student, actress and musician (U.N.E.S.C.O.) .. .. 1·75 30
330 50 l. Children at work and play (U.N.I.C.E.F.) 1·75 60
331 1 r. Fish, corn and farm animals (F.A.O.) .. 1·75 90
332 2 r. Miner hewing coal (I.L.O.) .. .. 4·50 5·00
327/32 .. .. *Set of* 6 9·50 6·75

(Des M. Shamir. Litho)

1970 (26 July). *10th Anniv of Inter-governmental Maritime Consultative Organization. T* **77** *and similar vert design. Multicoloured. P* 13½.
333 50 l. Type **77** 50 40
334 1 r. Ship and lighthouse .. .. 3·00 85

78 "Guitar-player and Masqueraders" (A. Watteau)

EXPO '70
REPUBLIC OF MALDIVES

79 Australian Pavilion

(Des M. Shamir. Litho Govt Printer, Israel)

1970 (1 Aug). *Famous Paintings showing the Guitar. T* **78** *and similar vert designs. Multicoloured. P* 14.
335 3 l. Type **78** 10 30
336 7 l. "Spanish Guitarist" (E. Manet) 10 30
337 50 l. "Costumed Player" (Watteau) 50 35
338 1 r. "Mandoline-player" (Roberti) 85 55
339 2 r. 50, "Guitar-player and Lady" (Watteau) 2·25 2·75
340 5 r. "Mandoline-player" (Frans Hals) .. 4·00 4·50
335/40 .. .. *Set of* 6 7·00 8·00
MS341 132 × 80 mm. Nos. 339/40. Roul .. 6·00 7·00

(Des M. Shamir. Litho Rosenbaum Brothers, Vienna)

1970 (1 Aug). *"EXPO 70" World Fair, Osaka, Japan. T* **79** *and similar vert designs. Multicoloured. P* 13½.
342 2 l. Type **79** 10 40
343 3 l. West German Pavilion 10 40
344 10 l. U.S.A. Pavilion 25 10
345 25 l. British Pavilion 60 15
346 50 l. Soviet Pavilion 90 35
347 1 r. Japanese Pavilion .. .. 1·40 65
342/7 .. .. *Set of* 6 3·00 1·75

80 Learning the Alphabet

(Des M. Shamir. Litho Govt Printer, Israel)

1970 (7 Sept). *International Education Year. T* **80** *and similar horiz designs. Multicoloured. P* 14.
348 5 l. Type **80** 15 15
349 10 l. Training teachers 20 10
350 25 l. Geography lesson 50 15
351 50 l. School inspector 70 45
352 1 r. Education by television .. .. .. 1·00 75
348/52 .. .. *Set of* 5 2·25 1·40

MINIMUM PRICE

The minimum price quote is 10p which represents a handling charge rather than a basis for valuing common stamps. For further notes about prices see introductory pages.

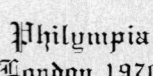

Philympia
London 1970

(81)

82 Footballers

1970 (18 Sept). *"Philympia 1970" Stamp Exhibition, London. Nos. 306/***MS***309 optd with T* **81**, *in silver.*
353 10 l. multicoloured 10 10
354 1 r. 50, multicoloured 65 75
355 2 r. 50, multicoloured .. .. 1·00 1·50
353/5 .. .. *Set of* 3 1·50 2·00
MS356 101 × 130 mm. Nos. 305/8 optd. Imperf .. 6·00 7·00

(Des M. Shamir. Litho Rosenbaum Brothers, Vienna)

1970 (Dec). *World Cup Football Championships, Mexico. T* **82** *and similar vert designs, each showing football scenes and outline of the Jules Rimet Trophy. P* 13½.

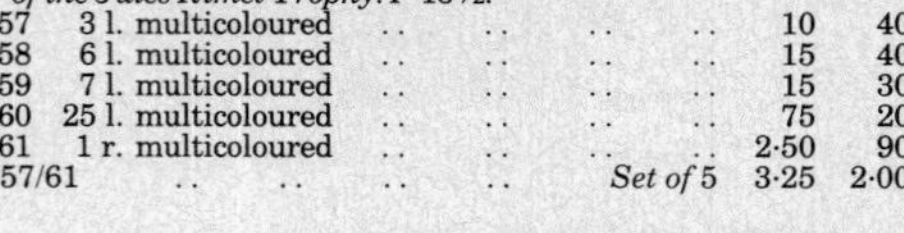
357 3 l. multicoloured 10 40
358 6 l. multicoloured 15 40
359 7 l. multicoloured 15 30
360 25 l. multicoloured 75 20
361 1 r. multicoloured .. .. 2·50 90
357/61 .. .. *Set of* 5 3·25 2·00

83 Little Boy and U.N.I.C.E.F. Flag

84 Astronauts Lovell, Haise and Swigert

(Des M. Shamir. Litho State Printing Works, Budapest)

1971 (1 Apr). *25th Anniv of U.N.I.C.E.F. T* **83** *and similar vert design. Multicoloured. P* 12.
362 5 l. Type **83** 10 15
363 10 l. Little girl with U.N.I.C.E.F. balloon .. 10 15
364 1 r. Type **83** .. .. 1·75 85
365 2 r. As 10 l. .. .. 2·75 3·00
362/5 .. .. *Set of* 4 4·25 3·75

(Des M. Shamir. Litho Govt Printer, Israel)

1971 (27 Apr). *Safe Return of "Apollo 13". T* **84** *and similar vert designs. Multicoloured. P* 14.
366 5 l. Type **84** 15 15
367 20 l. Explosion in Space 30 15
368 1 r. Splashdown 90 50
366/8 .. .. *Set of* 3 1·25 70

85 "Multiracial Flower"

REPUBLIC OF MALDIVES 5L

86 "Mme. Charpentier and her Children" (Renoir)

(Des M. Shamir. Litho)

1971 (3 May). *Racial Equality Year. P* 14.
369 **85** 10 l. multicoloured 10 15
370 25 l. multicoloured 20 15

1971 (Aug). *Famous Paintings showing "Mother and Child". T* **86** *and similar vert designs. Multicoloured. Litho. P* 12.
371 5 l. Type **86** 15 10
372 7 l. "Susanna van Collen and her Daughter" (Rembrandt) 20 10
373 10 l. "Madonna nursing the Child" (Titian) .. 30 10
374 20 l. "Baroness Belleli and her Children" (Degas) 75 15
375 25 l. "The Cradle" (Morisot) 80 15
376 1 r. "Helena Fourment and her Children" (Rubens) .. .. 2·25 85
377 3 r. "On the Terrace" (Renoir) .. .. .. 4·50 5·50
371/7 .. .. *Set of* 7 8·00 6·00

87 Alan Shepard

88 "Ballerina" (Degas)

(Photo State Ptg Works, Vienna)

1971 (11 Nov). *Moon Flight of "Apollo 14". T* **87** *and similar vert designs. Multicoloured. P 12½.*

378 6 l. Type **87** .. 30 10
379 10 l. Stuart Roosa .. 35 10
380 1 r. 50, Edgar Mitchell .. 4·00 2·75
381 5 r. Mission insignia .. 8·50 8·50
378/81 .. *Set of* 4 12·00 10·50

(Litho Rosenbaum Brothers, Vienna)

1971 (19 Nov). *Famous Paintings showing "Dancers". T* **88** *and similar vert designs. Multicoloured. P 14.*

382 5 l. Type **88** .. 15 10
383 10 l. "Dancing Couple" (Renoir) .. 20 10
384 2 r. "Spanish Dancer" (Manet) .. 2·50 2·25
385 5 r. "Ballerinas" (Degas) .. 4·50 4·50
386 10 r. "La Goulue at the Moulin Rouge" (Toulouse-Lautrec) .. 6·50 7·00
382/6 .. *Set of* 5 12·50 12·50

(89) 90 Book Year Emblem

1972 (13 Mar). *Visit of Queen Elizabeth II and Prince Philip. Nos. 382/6 optd with T* **89**.

387 5 l. multicoloured .. 15 10
388 10 l. multicoloured .. 20 10
389 2 r. multicoloured .. 4·50 4·00
390 5 r. multicoloured .. 8·00 8·00
391 10 r. multicoloured .. 9·50 10·00
387/91 .. *Set of* 5 20·00 20·00

(Des M. Shamir. Litho Bradbury, Wilkinson)

1972 (1 May). *International Book Year. P 13 × 13½.*

392 **90** 25 l. multicoloured .. 15 10
393 5 r. multicoloured .. 1·60 2·00

91 Scottish Costume

93 Cross-country Skiing

92 Stegosaurus

(Des M. Shamir. Litho State Printing Works, Budapest)

1972 (15 May). *National Costumes of the World. T* **91** *and similar vert designs. Multicoloured. P 12.*

394 10 l. Type **91** .. 50 10
395 15 l. Netherlands .. 55 15
396 25 l. Norway .. 90 15
397 50 l. Hungary .. 1·75 55
398 1 r. Austria .. 2·25 80
399 2 r. Spain .. 4·00 3·25
394/9 .. *Set of* 6 9·00 4·50

(Des M. Shamir. Litho Rosenbaum Brothers, Vienna)

1972 (31 May). *Prehistoric Animals. T* **92** *and similar horiz designs. Multicoloured. P 14.*

400 2 l. Type **92** .. 50 50
401 7 l. Dimetrodon (inscr "Edaphosaurus") .. 90 40
402 25 l. Diplodocus .. 1·75 40
403 50 l. Triceratops .. 2·00 75
404 2 r. Pteranodon .. 5·00 5·00
405 5 r. Tyrannosaurus .. 9·00 9·50
400/5 .. *Set of* 6 17·00 15·00

An imperforate miniature sheet containing Nos. 404/5 also exists, but was never freely available.

(Des M. Shamir. Litho Rosenbaum Brothers, Vienna)

1972 (June). *Winter Olympic Games, Sapporo, Japan. T* **93** *and similar vert designs. Multicoloured. P 14.*

406 3 l. Type **93** .. 10 30
407 6 l. Bob-sleighing .. 10 30
408 15 l. Speed-skating .. 20 20
409 50 l. Ski-jumping .. 1·00 45
410 1 r. Figure-skating (pair) .. 1·75 70
411 2 r. 50, Ice-hockey .. 5·50 3·25
406/11 .. *Set of* 6 7·50 4·75

94 Scout Saluting

95 Cycling

(Des M. Shamir. Litho Govt Printer, Israel)

1972 (1 Aug). *13th World Scout Jamboree, Asagiri, Japan (1971). T* **94** *and similar vert designs. Multicoloured. P 14.*

412 10 l. Type **92** .. 65 20
413 15 l. Scout signalling .. 85 20
414 50 l. Scout blowing bugle .. 3·00 1·25
415 1 r. Scout beating drum .. 4·50 2·25
412/15 .. *Set of* 4 8·00 3·50

PRINTERS AND PROCESS. *Unless otherwise stated,* all the following issues to No. 1277 were lithographed by Format International Security Printers Ltd, London.

1972 (30 Oct). *Olympic Games, Munich. T* **95** *and similar vert designs. Multicoloured. P 14½ × 14.*

416 5 l. Type **95** .. 30 20
417 10 l. Running .. 20 20
418 25 l. Wrestling .. 30 20
419 50 l. Hurdling .. 50 35
420 2 r. Boxing .. 1·10 1·75
421 5 r. Volleyball .. 2·50 3·25
416/21 .. *Set of* 6 4·50 5·50
MS422 92 × 120 mm. 3 r. As 50 l.; 4 r. As 10 l. P 15 5·25 7·50

96 Globe and Conference Emblem

97 "Flowers" (Van Gogh)

(Litho Harrison)

1972 (15 Nov). *U.N. Environmental Conservation Conference, Stockholm. P 14½.*

423 **96** 2 l. multicoloured .. 10 30
424 3 l. multicoloured .. 10 30
425 15 l. multicoloured .. 30 15
426 50 l. multicoloured .. 75 45
427 2 r. 50, multicoloured .. 3·25 4·00
423/7 .. *Set of* 5 4·00 4·75

(Des M. Shamir)

1973 (Mar). *Floral Paintings. T* **97** *and similar vert designs. Multicoloured. P 13½.*

428 1 l. Type **97** .. 10 30
429 2 l. "Flowers in Jug" (Renoir) .. 10 30
430 3 l. "Chrysanthemums" (Renoir) .. 10 30
431 50 l. "Mixed Bouquet" (Bosschaert) .. 75 20
432 1 r. As 3 l. .. 1·25 40
433 5 r. As 2 l. .. 3·25 4·25
428/33 .. *Set of* 6 4·75 5·25
MS434 120 × 94 mm. 2 r. as 50 l.; 3 r. Type **97**. P 15 6·00 8·00

LEMECHEV
MIDDLE-WEIGHT
GOLD MEDALLIST

(98)

99 Animal Care

1973 (Apr). *Gold-medal Winners, Munich Olympic Games. Nos. 420/***MS***422 optd with T* **98** *or similar commemorative inscr, in blue.*

435 2 r. multicoloured .. 2·75 2·25
436 5 r. multicoloured .. 3·75 3·50
MS437 92 × 120 mm. 3 r. multicoloured; 4 r. multicoloured .. 6·50 8·00

Overprints:—2 r. Type **98**; 5 r. "JAPAN GOLD MEDAL WINNERS" (volleyball). Miniature sheet:—3 r. "EHRHARDT 100 METER HURDLES GOLD MEDALLIST"; 4 r. "SHORTER MARATHON GOLD MEDALLIST".

(Des M. Shamir)

1973 (Aug). *International Scouting Congress, Nairobi and Addis Ababa. T* **99** *and similar horiz designs. Multicoloured. P 14½.*

438 1 l. Type **99** .. 10 20
439 2 l. Lifesaving .. 10 20
440 3 l. Agricultural training .. 10 20
441 4 l. Carpentry .. 10 20
442 5 l. Playing leapfrog .. 10 20
443 1 r. As 2 l. .. 2·75 75
444 2 r. As 4 l. .. 5·00 4·75
445 3 r. Type **99** .. 6·50 7·00
438/45 .. *Set of* 8 13·00 12·00
MS446 101 × 79 mm. 5 r. As 3 l. .. 10·00 14·00

100 Blue Marlin

1973 (Aug). *Fishes. T* **100** *and similar horiz designs. Multicoloured. P 14½.*

447 1 l. Type **100** .. 10 30
448 2 l. Skipjack Tuna .. 10 30
449 3 l. Blue-finned Tuna .. 10 30
450 5 l. Dolphin (fish) .. 10 30
451 60 l. Humpbacked Snapper .. 80 40
452 75 l. As 60 l. .. 1·00 40
453 1 r. 50, Yellow-edged Lyretail .. 1·75 1·75
454 2 r. 50, As 5 l. .. 2·25 2·75
455 3 r. Spotted Coral Grouper .. 2·25 3·00
456 10 r. Spanish Mackerel .. 4·75 8·00
447/56 .. *Set of* 10 11·50 16·00
MS457 119×123 mm. 4 r. As 2 l.; 5 r. Type **100** 15·00 18·00

Nos. 451/2 are smaller, size 29×22 mm.

101 Golden-fronted Leafbird

102 *Lantana camara*

(Des M. Shamir)

1973 (Oct). *Fauna. T* **101** *and similar diamond-shaped designs. Multicoloured. P 14½.*

458 1 l. Type **101** .. 10 30
459 2 l. Indian Flying Fox .. 10 30
460 3 l. Land tortoise .. 10 30
461 4 l. *Kallima inachus* (butterfly) .. 30 30
462 50 l. As 3 l. .. 60 35
463 2 r. Type **101** .. 4·00 4·00
464 3 r. As 2 l. .. 3·50 4·00
458/64 .. *Set of* 7 7·75 8·50
MS465 66 × 74 mm. 5 r. As 4 l. .. 17·00 19·00

(Litho Questa)

1973 (19 Dec). *Flowers of the Maldive Islands. T* **102** *and similar vert designs. Multicoloured. P 14.*

466 1 l. Type **102** .. 10 10
467 2 l. *Nerium oleander* .. 10 10
468 3 l. *Rosa polyantha* .. 10 10
469 4 l. *Hibiscus manihot* .. 10 10
470 5 l. *Bougainvillea glabra* .. 10 10
471 10 l. *Plumera alba* .. 10 10
472 50 l. *Poinsettia pulcherrima* .. 55 25
473 5 r. *Ononis natrix* .. 3·75 4·75
466/73 .. *Set of* 8 4·00 5·00
MS474 110 × 100 mm. 2 r. As 3 l.; 3 r. As 10 l. .. 3·25 5·25

103 "Tiros" Weather Satellite

(Des M. Shamir)

1974 (10 Jan). *Centenary of World Meteorological Organization. T* **103** *and similar horiz designs. Multicoloured. P* 14½.
475 1 l. Type **103** 10 10
476 2 l. "Nimbus" satellite 10 10
477 3 l. *Nomad* (weather ship) 10 10
478 4 l. Scanner, A.P.T. Instant Weather Picture equipment 10 10
479 5 l. Richard's wind-speed recorder 10 10
480 2 r. Type **103** .. .. 2·75 3·00
481 3 r. As 3 l. .. .. 3·00 3·25
475/81 .. .. *Set of* 7 5·50 5·75
MS482 110 × 79 mm. 10 r. As 2 l. .. .. 10·00 14·00

104 "Apollo" Spacecraft and Pres. Kennedy

(Des M. Shamir)

1974 (1 Feb). *American and Russian Space Exploration Projects. T* **104** *and similar horiz designs. Multicoloured. P* 14½.
483 1 l. Type **104** 10 15
484 2 l. "Mercury" capsule and John Glenn .. 10 15
485 3 l. "Vostok 1" and Yuri Gagarin 10 20
486 4 l. "Vostok 6" and Valentina Tereshkova .. 10 20
487 5 l. "Soyuz 11" and "Salyut" space-station .. 10 20
488 2 r. "Skylab" space laboratory .. .. 3·50 3·50
489 3 r. As 2 l. .. .. 4·00 4·00
483/9 .. .. *Set of* 7 7·00 7·50
MS490 103 × 80 mm. 10 r. Type **104** .. .. 9·50 13·00

105 Copernicus and "Skylab" Space Laboratory

106 "Maternity" (Picasso)

(Des G. Vasarhelyi)

1974 (10 Apr). *500th Birth Anniv of Nicholas Copernicus (astronomer). T* **105** *and similar horiz designs. Multicoloured. P* 14½.
491 1 l. Type **105** 10 15
492 2 l. Orbital space-station of the future .. 10 15
493 3 l. Proposed "Space-shuttle" craft 10 15
494 4 l. "Mariner 2" Venus probe 10 20
495 5 l. "Mariner 4" Mars probe 10 20
496 25 l. Type **105** 90 20
497 1 r. 50, As 2 l. .. .. 3·25 3·25
498 5 r. As 3 l. .. .. 8·00 10·00
491/8 .. .. *Set of* 8 11·00 13·00
MS499 106 × 80 mm. 10 r. "Copernicus" orbital observatory .. .. 14·00 17·00

(Des M. Shamir. Litho Questa)

1974 (May). *Paintings by Picasso. T* **106** *and similar vert designs. Multicoloured. P* 14.
500 1 l. Type **106** 10 10
501 2 l. "Harlequin and Friend" 10 10
502 3 l. "Pierrot Sitting" 10 10
503 20 l. "Three Musicians" 25 15
504 75 l. "L'Aficionado" 55 40
505 5 r. "Still Life" .. .. 3·50 4·25
500/5 .. .. *Set of* 6 4·00 4·25
MS506 100 × 101 mm. 2 r. As 20 l.; 3 r. As 5 r. .. 5·50 7·00

107 U.P.U. Emblem, Steam and Diesel Locomotives

108 Footballers

(Des M. Shamir)

1974 (May). *Centenary of Universal Postal Union. T* **107** *and similar horiz designs. Multicoloured. P* 14½.
507 1 l. Type **107** 10 10
508 2 l. Paddle-steamer and modern mailboat 10 10
509 3 l. Airship LZ-127 *Graf Zeppelin* and Boeing 747 airliner 10 10
510 1 r. 50, Mailcoach and motor van 85 85
511 2 r. 50, As 2 l. .. .. 1·40 1·60
512 5 r. Type **107** .. .. 2·75 3·50
507/12 .. .. *Set of* 6 4·50 5·50
MS513 126×105 mm. 4 r. Type **107** .. .. 5·00 6·50

Nos. 507/12 were first issued in sheets of 50, but were later released in small sheets of five stamps and one label. These small sheets were perforated 13½.

(Des M. Shamir)

1974 (June). *World Cup Football Championships, West Germany. T* **108** *and similar vert designs, showing football scenes. P* 14½.
514 1 l. multicoloured 10 15
515 2 l. multicoloured 10 15
516 3 l. multicoloured 10 15
517 4 l. multicoloured 10 15
518 75 l. multicoloured .. .. 1·25 75
519 4 r. multicoloured .. .. 3·50 3·50
520 5 r. multicoloured .. .. 3·75 3·50
514/20 .. .. *Set of* 7 8·00 7·50
MS521 88 × 95 mm. 10 r. multicoloured .. .. 9·00 10·00

109 "Capricorn"

110 Churchill and Avro Type 683 Lancaster

(Des G. Vasarhelyi)

1974 (3 July). *Signs of the Zodiac. T* **109** *and similar horiz designs. Multicoloured. P* 14½.
522 1 l. Type **109** 20 20
523 2 l. "Aquarius" 20 20
524 3 l. "Pisces" 20 20
525 4 l. "Aries" 20 20
526 5 l. "Taurus" 20 20
527 6 l. "Gemini" 20 20
528 7 l. "Cancer" 20 20
529 10 l. "Leo" 30 30
530 15 l. "Virgo" 30 30
531 20 l. "Libra" 30 30
532 25 l. "Scorpio" 30 30
533 5 r. "Sagittarius" .. .. 11·00 11·00
522/33 .. .. *Set of* 12 12·00 12·00
MS534 119 × 99 mm. 10 r. "The Sun" (49 × 37 *mm*). P 13½ .. .. 17·00 19·00

(Des M. Shamir)

1974 (30 Nov). *Birth Centenary of Sir Winston Churchill. T* **110** *and similar horiz designs. Multicoloured. P* 14½.
535 1 l. Type **110** 15 30
536 2 l. Churchill as pilot 15 30
537 3 l. Churchill as First Lord of the Admiralty 20 30
538 4 l. Churchill and H.M.S. *Indomitable* (aircraft carrier) 20 30
539 5 l. Churchill and De Havilland D.H.98 Mosquito bombers 20 30
540 60 l. Churchill and anti-aircraft battery .. 2·75 1·50
541 75 l. Churchill and tank in desert .. 3·00 1·50
542 5 r. Churchill and Short S.25 Sunderland flying boat .. .. 11·00 12·00
535/42 .. .. *Set of* 8 16·00 15·00
MS543 113×83 mm. 10 r. As 4 l. .. .. 17·00 19·00

111 Bullmouth Helmet (*Cypraecassis rufa*)

112 Royal Throne

(Des M. Shamir)

1975 (25 Jan). *Sea Shells and Cowries. T* **111** *and similar multicoloured designs. P* 14×13½ *(60 l., 75 l.) or* 14½ *(others).*
544 1 l. Type **111** 10 30
545 2 l. Venus Comb Murex (*Murex pecten*) .. 10 30
546 3 l. Common or Major Harp (*Harpa major*) 10 30
547 4 l. Chiragra Spider Conch (*Lambis chiragra chiragra*) 10 30
548 5 l. Geography Cone (*Conus geographus*) 10 30
549 60 l. Dawn Cowrie (*Cypraea diluculum*) (22×30 *mm*) .. .. 3·00 2·00
550 75 l. Purplish Clanculus (*Clanculus puniceus*) (22×30 *mm*) .. .. .. 3·50 2·00
551 5 r. Ramose Murex (*Murex ramosus*) .. 8·50 11·00
544/51 .. .. *Set of* 8 14·00 15·00
MS552 152×126 mm. 2 r. As 3 l; 3 r. As 2 l. .. 12·00 15·00

(Des M. Shamir. Litho Questa)

1975 (22 Feb). *Historical Relics and Monuments. T* **112** *and similar multicoloured designs. P* 14.
553 1 l. Type **112** 10 10
554 10 l. Candlesticks 10 10
555 25 l. Lamp-tree 15 10
556 60 l. Royal umbrellas 30 25
557 75 l. Eid-Miskith Mosque (*horiz*) 35 30
558 3 r. Tomb of Al-Hafiz Abu-al Barakath-al Barubari (*horiz*) .. .. 1·60 2·50
553/8 .. .. *Set of* 6 2·25 3·00

113 Guavas

114 *Phyllangia*

(Des M. Shamir)

1975 (Mar). *Fruits. T* **113** *and similar vert designs. Multicoloured. P* 14½.
559 2 l. Type **113** 10 30
560 4 l. Maldive mulberry 15 30
561 5 l. Mountain apples 15 30
562 10 l. Bananas 20 15
563 20 l. Mangoes 40 25
564 50 l. Papaya .. .. 1·00 60
565 1 r. Pomegranates .. .. 1·75 70
566 5 r. Coconut .. .. 8·50 11·00
559/66 .. .. *Set of* 8 11·00 12·00
MS567 136 × 102 mm. 2 r. As 10 l.; 3 r. As 2 l. .. 8·50 12·00

(Des M. Shamir)

1975 (6 June). *Marine Life. T* **114** *and similar triangular designs. Multicoloured. P* 14½.
568 1 l. Type **114** 10 10
569 2 l. *Madrepora oculata* 10 10
570 3 l. *Acropora gravida* 10 10
571 4 l. *Stylotella* 10 10
572 5 l. *Acrophora cervicornis* 10 10
573 60 l. *Strongylocentrotus purpuratus* 75 65
574 75 l. *Pisaster ochraceus* 85 75
575 5 r. *Marthasterias glacialis* .. .. 5·00 6·50
568/75 .. .. *Set of* 8 6·00 7·50
MS576 155 × 98 mm. 4 r. As 1 l. Imperf .. .. 11·00 14·00

115 Clock Tower and Customs Building within "10"

14th Boy Scout Jamboree
July 29 — August 7, 1975
(116)

(Des M. Shamir)

1975 (26 July). *10th Anniv of Independence. T* **115** *and similar horiz designs. Multicoloured. P* 14½.
577 4 l. Type **115** 10 10
578 5 l. Government Offices 10 10
579 7 l. Waterfront 10 10
580 15 l. Mosque and minaret 10 10
581 10 r. Sultan Park and museum .. .. 2·75 6·00
577/81 .. .. *Set of* 5 2·75 6·00

1975 (26 July). *"Nordjamb 75" World Scout Jamboree, Norway. Nos.* 443/5 *and* **MS**446 *optd with T* **116**.
582 1 r. multicoloured 40 40
583 2 r. multicoloured 60 60
584 3 r. multicoloured .. .. 1·25 1·25
582/4 .. .. *Set of* 3 2·00 2·00
MS585 101 × 79 mm. 5 r. multicoloured .. .. 7·00 8·00

117 Madura Prau

118 *Brahmophthalma wallichi* (moth)

(Des M. Shamir)

1975 (Aug). *Ships. T* **117** *and similar multicoloured designs. P* 14½.
586 1 l. Type **117** 10 10
587 2 l. Ganges patela 10 10
588 3 l. Indian palla (*vert*) 10 10
589 4 l. Odhi (dhow) (*vert*) 10 10
590 5 l. Maldivian schooner 10 10
591 25 l. *Cutty Sark* 90 40
592 1 r. Maldivian baggala (*vert*) .. .. 1·50 70
593 5 r. Freighter *Maldive Courage* .. .. 4·00 6·00
586/93 .. .. *Set of* 8 6·00 6·50
MS594 99×85 mm. 10 r. As 1 r. .. .. 9·50 14·00

(Des M. Shamir)

1975 (7 Sept). *Butterflies and Moth. T* **118** *and similar horiz designs. Multicoloured. P* 14½.
595 1 l. Type **118** 15 30
596 2 l. *Teinopalpus imperialis* 15 30
597 3 l. *Cethosia biblis* 15 30
598 4 l. *Idea jasonia* 15 30
599 5 l. *Apatura ilia* 15 30
600 25 l. *Kallima horsfieldi* .. .. .. 1·00 35
601 1 r. 50, *Hebomoia leucippe* .. .. .. 3·00 3·50
602 5 r. *Papilio memnon* .. .. 7·50 9·00
595/602 .. .. *Set of* 8 11·00 13·00
MS603 134×97 mm. 10 r. As 25 l. .. .. 20·00 20·00

119 "The Dying Captive" **120** Beaker and Vase

1975 (9 Oct). *500th Birth Anniv of Michelangelo. T* **119** *and similar vert designs. Multicoloured. P* 14½.

604 1 l. Type **119** 10 10
605 2 l. Detail of "The Last Judgement" 10 10
606 3 l. "Apollo" 10 10
607 4 l. Detail of Sistine Chapel ceiling 10 10
608 5 l. "Bacchus" 10 10
609 1 r. Detail of "The Last Judgement" (*different*) 1·50 40
610 2 r. "David" .. .. 2·50 2·50
611 5 r. "Cumaean Sibyl" .. .. 4·25 5·50
604/11 .. .. *Set of* 8 7·50 8·00
MS612 123 × 113 mm. 10 r. As 2 r. .. .. 8·00 11·00

The 1, 3, 5 l. and 2, 10 r. are sculptures; the other values show details of the frescoes in the Sistine Chapel.

(Des M. Shamir. Litho Questa)

1975 (Dec). *Maldivian Lacquerware. T* **120** *and similar vert designs. Multicoloured. P* 14.

613 2 l. Type **120** 10 30
614 4 l. Boxes 10 30
615 50 l. Jar with lid 40 20
616 75 l. Bowls with covers 50 30
617 1 r. Craftsman at work 65 40
613/17 .. .. *Set of* 5 1·50 1·40

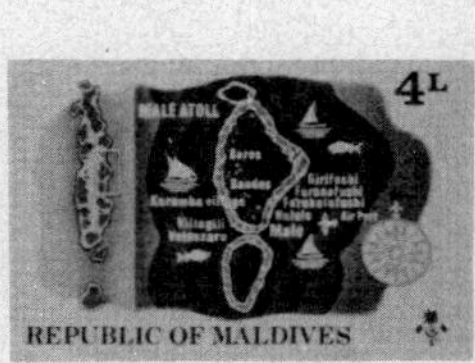

121 Map of Maldives **122** Cross-country Skiing

(Des M. Shamir. Litho Questa)

1975 (25 Dec). *Tourism. T* **121** *and similar horiz designs. Multicoloured. P* 14.

618 4 l. Type **121** 20 20
619 5 l. Motor launch and small craft 20 20
620 7 l. Sailing boats 20 20
621 15 l. Underwater fishing 20 20
622 3 r. Hulule Airport .. .. 2·00 2·00
623 10 r. Motor cruisers .. .. 4·50 6·50
618/23 .. .. *Set of* 6 6·50 8·50

(Des M. Shamir)

1976 (10 Jan). *Winter Olympic Games, Innsbruck, Austria. T* **122** *and similar vert designs. Multicoloured. P* 15.

624 1 l. Type **122** 10 10
625 2 l. Speed ice-skating 10 10
626 3 l. Pairs figure-skating 10 10
627 4 l. Four-man bobsleigh 10 10
628 5 l. Ski-jumping 10 10
629 25 l. Women's figure-skating 35 10
630 1 r. 15, Slalom skiing .. .. 1·00 1·00
631 4 r. Ice-hockey .. .. 3·25 3·50
624/31 .. .. *Set of* 8 4·25 4·50
MS632 93 × 117 mm. 10 r. Downhill skiing .. 9·50 12·00

Nos. 624/31 exist imperforate from stock dispersed by the liquidator of Format International Security Printers Ltd.

123 "General Burgoyne" (Reynolds) **124** Thomas Edison

1976 (15 Feb). *Bicentenary of American Revolution. T* **123** *and similar multicoloured designs. P* 15.

633 1 l. Type **123** 10 10
634 2 l. "John Hancock" (Copley) 10 10
635 3 l. "Death of General Montgomery" (Trumbull) (*horiz*) 10 10
636 4 l. "Paul Revere" (Copley) 10 10
637 5 l. "Battle of Bunker Hill" (Trumbull) (*horiz*) 10 10
638 2 r. "The Crossing of the Delaware" (Sully) (*horiz*) .. .. 2·00 2·25
639 3 r. "Samuel Adams" (Copley) .. .. .. 2·50 2·75
640 5 r. "Surrender of Cornwallis" (Trumbull) (*horiz*) .. .. 3·00 3·25
633/40 .. .. *Set of* 8 7·00 7·50
MS641 147 × 95 mm. 10 r. "Washington at Dorchester Heights" (Stuart) .. .. .. 13·00 16·00

1976 (10 Mar). *Telephone Centenary. T* **124** *and similar horiz designs. Multicoloured. P* 15.

642 1 l. Type **124** 10 20
643 2 l. Alexander Graham Bell 10 20
644 3 l. Telephones of 1919, 1937 and 1972 .. 10 20
645 10 l. Cable entrance into station 20 20
646 20 l. Equaliser circuit assembly 30 20
647 1 r. *Salernum* (cable ship) .. .. .. 1·75 55
648 10 r. "Intelsat IV-A" and Earth Station .. 4·75 7·50
642/8 .. .. *Set of* 7 6·50 8·00
MS649 156 × 105 mm. 4 r. Early telephones .. 7·50 9·00

MAY 29TH–JUNE 6TH
"INTERPHIL" 1976

(125)

126 Wrestling

1976 (29 May). *"Interphil 76" International Stamp Exhibition, Philadelphia. Nos. 638/***MS***641 optd with T* **125**, *in blue (5 r.) or silver (others).*

650 2 r. multicoloured .. .. 1·50 1·75
651 3 r. multicoloured .. .. 2·00 2·25
652 5 r. multicoloured .. .. 2·50 2·75
650/2 .. .. *Set of* 3 5·50 6·00
MS653 147 × 95 mm. 10 r. multicoloured .. 10·00 12·00

(Des M. Shamir)

1976 (June). *Olympic Games, Montreal. T* **126** *and similar vert designs. Multicoloured. P* 15.

654 1 l. Type **126** 10 10
655 2 l. Putting the shot 10 10
656 3 l. Hurdling 10 10
657 4 l. Hockey 10 10
658 5 l. Running 10 10
659 6 l. Javelin-throwing 10 10
660 1 r. 50, Discus-throwing .. .. .. 1·25 1·75
661 5 r. Volleyball .. .. 4·25 5·25
654/61 .. .. *Set of* 8 5·50 6·50
MS662 135 × 106 mm. 10 r. Throwing the hammer 8·50 12·00

Nos. 654/61 exist imperforate from stock dispersed by the liquidator of Format International Security Printers Ltd.

127 *Dolichos lablab* **128** "Viking" approaching Mars

(Des M. Shamir. Litho Questa)

1976 (26 July)–**77**. *Vegetables. T* **127** *and similar vert designs. Multicoloured. P* 14.

663 2 l. Type **127** 10 10
664 4 l. *Moringa pterygosperma* 10 10
665 10 l. *Solanum melongena* 10 10
666 20 l. *Moringa pterygosperma* (1977) .. .. 1·25 1·25
667 50 l. *Cucumis sativus* 80 65
668 75 l. *Trichosanthes anguina* 85 75
669 1 r. *Momordica charantia* 95 85
670 2 r. *Trichosanthes anguina* (1977) .. .. 3·75 5·50
663/70 .. .. *Set of* 8 7·00 8·00

1976 (2 Dec). *"Viking" Space Mission. T* **128** *and similar horiz design. Multicoloured. P* 14.

671 5 r. Type **128** .. .. 2·25 2·75
MS672 121 × 89 mm. 20 r. Landing module on Mars .. .. 10·00 14·00

129 Coronation Ceremony

1977 (6 Feb). *Silver Jubilee of Queen Elizabeth II. T* **129** *and similar horiz designs. Multicoloured. P* 14 × 13½.

673 1 l. Type **129** 10 10
674 2 l. Queen and Prince Philip 10 10
675 3 l. Royal couple with Princes Andrew and Edward 10 10
676 1 r. 15, Queen with Archbishops 35 25
677 3 r. State coach in procession 60 55
678 4 r. Royal couple with Prince Charles and Princess Anne 60 90
673/8 .. .. *Set of* 6 1·50 1·60
MS679 120 × 77 mm. 10 r. Queen and Prince Charles .. .. 3·00 2·75

Nos. 673/8 also exist perf 12 (*Price per set of* 6 £1·50 *mint or used*) from additional sheetlets of five stamps and one label in changed colours.

130 Beethoven and Organ

(Des M. Shamir)

1977 (26 Mar). *150th Death Anniv of Ludwig van Beethoven (composer). T* **130** *and similar horiz designs. Multicoloured. P* 14.

680 1 l. Type **130** 15 20
681 2 l. Portrait and manuscript of *Moonlight Sonata* 15 20
682 3 l. With Goethe at Teplitz 15 20
683 4 l. Portrait and string instruments 15 20
684 5 l. Beethoven's home, Heiligenstadt 15 20
685 25 l. Hands and gold medals 85 20
686 2 r. Portrait and part of *Missa solemnis* .. 2·75 3·00
687 5 r. Portrait and hearing-aids .. .. .. 4·75 5·00
680/7 .. .. *Set of* 8 8·25 8·25
MS688 121 × 92 mm. 4 r. Death mask and room where composer died .. .. 6·00 8·00

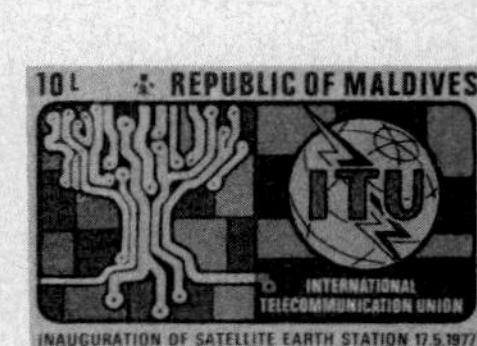

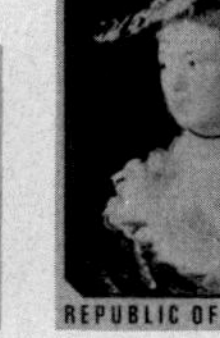

131 Printed Circuit and I.T.U. Emblem **132** "Miss Anne Ford" (Gainsborough)

(Des M. Shamir. Litho Questa)

1977 (17 May). *Inauguration of Satellite Earth Station. T* **131** *and similar horiz designs. Multicoloured. P* 14.

689 10 l. Type **131** 10 10
690 90 l. Central telegraph office 45 45
691 10 r. Satellite Earth station .. .. .. 5·00 7·00
689/91 .. .. *Set of* 3 5·00 7·00
MS692 100×85 mm. 5 r. "Intelsat IV-A" satellite over Maldives .. .. 3·75 5·00

(Des M. Shamir. Litho Questa)

1977 (20 May). *Artists' Birth Anniversaries. T* **132** *and similar vert designs. Multicoloured. P* 14.

693 1 l. Type **132** (250th anniv) 10 10
694 2 l. Group painting by Rubens (400th anniv) 10 10
695 3 l. "Girl with Dog" (Titian) (500th anniv) .. 10 10
696 4 l. "Mrs. Thomas Graham" (Gainsborough) 10 10
697 5 l. "Artist with Isabella Brant" (Rubens) .. 10 10
698 95 l. Portrait by Titian 75 40
699 1 r. Portrait by Gainsborough 75 40
700 10 r. "Isabella Brant" (Rubens) .. .. .. 4·75 7·00
693/700 .. .. *Set of* 8 6·00 7·50
MS701 152 × 116 mm. 5 r. "Self-portrait" (Titian) 3·75 5·50

133 Lesser Frigate Birds **134** Charles Lindbergh

(Des M. Shamir)

1977 (26 July). *Birds. T* **133** *and similar vert designs. Multicoloured. P* 14½.

702 1 l. Type **133** 20 30
703 2 l. Crab Plover 20 30
704 3 l. White-tailed Tropic Bird 20 30
705 4 l. Wedge-tailed Shearwater 20 30
706 5 l. Grey Heron 20 30
707 20 l. White Tern 90 30
708 95 l. Cattle Egret .. .. 2·25 1·60
709 1 r. 25, Black-naped Tern .. .. .. 2·50 2·50
710 5 r. Pheasant Coucal .. .. 6·50 8·00
702/10 .. .. *Set of* 9 12·00 12·50
MS711 124×117 mm. 10 r. Green Heron .. 25·00 25·00

(Des M. Shamir)

1977 (31 Oct). *50th Anniv of Lindbergh's Transatlantic Flight and 75th Anniv of First Navigable Airships. T* **134** *and similar multicoloured designs. P* 14½.

712 1 l. Type **134** 10 10
713 2 l. Lindbergh and Ryan NYP Special *Spirit of St. Louis* 10 10
714 3 l. Lindbergh's Miles Mohawk aircraft (*horiz*) 10 10
715 4 l. Lebaudy-Juillot airship *Morning Post* (*horiz*) 10 10
716 5 l. Airship LZ-127 *Graf Zeppelin* and portrait of Zeppelin 10 10

717 1 r. Airship ZR-3 *Los Angeles* (*horiz*) .. 60 30
718 3 r. Lindbergh and Henry Ford .. .. 1·40 1·75
719 10 r. Vickers airship R-23 .. .. 3·50 5·50
712/19 .. .. *Set of* 8 5·00 7·00
MS720 148×114 mm. 5 r. Ryan NYP Special *Spirit of St. Louis*, Statue of Liberty and Eiffel Tower; 7 r. 50, Airship L-31 over *Ostfriesland* (German battleship) .. .. 15·00 17·00
No. 715 is inscr "Lebaudy I built by H. Juillot 1902".

135 Boat Building

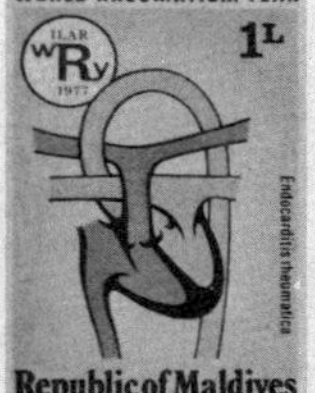

136 Rheumatic Heart

(Des M. Shamir. Litho J.W.)

1977 (11 Nov). *Occupations. T* **135** *and similar multicoloured designs. P* 13½ × 13 (2 r.) *or* 13 × 13½ (*others*).
721 6 l. Type **135** 35 20
722 15 l. Fishing 55 20
723 20 l. Cadjan weaving 65 20
724 90 l. Mat weaving .. .. 1·75 1·40
725 2 r. Lace making (*vert*) .. .. .. 3·00 4·00
721/5 .. .. *Set of* 5 5·75 5·50

(Des M. Shamir. Litho Questa)

1977 (Dec). *World Rheumatism Year. T* **136** *and similar vert designs. Multicoloured. P* 14.
726 1 l. Type **136** 10 30
727 50 l. Rheumatic shoulder 60 30
728 2 r. Rheumatic fingers .. .. .. 1·50 1·50
729 3 r. Rheumatic knee .. .. 1·75 1·75
726/9 .. .. *Set of* 4 3·50 3·50

137 Lilienthal's Biplane Glider

138 Newgate Prison

(Des M. Shamir. Litho Questa)

1978 (27 Feb). *75th Anniv of First Powered Aircraft. T* **137** *and similar horiz designs. Multicoloured. P* 13 × 13½.
730 1 l. Type **137** 20 30
731 2 l. Chanute's glider 20 30
732 3 l. Wright testing glider No. II, 1901 .. 20 30
733 4 l. Roe's Triplane I aircraft 20 30
734 5 l. Wright demonstrating Wright Type A aircraft to King Alfonso of Spain .. 20 30
735 10 l. Roe's second Avro Type D biplane .. 50 30
736 20 l. Wright Brothers and A. G. Bell .. 90 30
737 95 l. Hadley's triplane .. .. .. 2·75 2·00
738 5 r. Royal Aircraft Factory B.E.2A biplanes at Upavon, 1914 .. .. .. 8·00 9·00
730/8 .. .. *Set of* 9 12·00 12·00
MS739 98×82 mm. 10 r. Wright Brothers' Wright Type A .. .. 13·00 16·00
No. 732 is wrongly dated "1900".

1978 (15 Mar). *World Eradication of Smallpox. T* **138** *and similar multicoloured designs. P* 14.
740 15 l. Foundling Hospital, London (*horiz*) .. 75 30
741 50 l. Type **138** .. .. 1·50 60
742 2 r. Edward Jenner .. .. 3·75 4·00
740/2 .. .. *Set of* 3 5·50 4·50

139 Television Set

140 Mas Odi

(Des M. Shamir. Litho J.W.)

1978 (29 Mar). *Inauguration of Television in Maldives. T* **139** *and similar multicoloured designs. P* 13 × 13½ (1 r. 50) *or* 13½ × 13 (*others*).
743 15 l. Type **139** 40 30
744 25 l. Television aerials 55 30
745 1 r. 50, Control desk (*horiz*) .. .. .. 2·25 2·75
743/5 .. .. *Set of* 3 2·75 3·00

(Des M. Shamir)

1978 (27 Apr). *Ships. T* **140** *and similar multicoloured designs. P* 14½.
746 1 l. Type **140** 10 15
747 2 l. Battela 10 15
748 3 l. Bandu odi (*vert*) 10 15
749 5 l. *Maldive Trader* (freighter) 20 20
750 1 r. *Fath-hul Baaree* (brigantine) (*vert*) .. 65 30
751 1 r. 25, Mas dhoni .. .. 1·00 1·00
752 3 r. Baggala (*vert*) .. .. 1·40 2·00
753 4 r. As No. 751 .. .. 1·40 2·00
746/53 .. .. *Set of* 8 4·25 5·50
MS754 152 × 138 mm. 1 r. As No. 747; 4 r. As No. 751 .. .. 3·75 4·25
Nos. 746/8, 750 and 752/4 exist imperforate from stock dispersed by the liquidator of Format International Security Printers Ltd.

141 Ampulla

142 Capt. Cook

(Des M. Shamir. Litho Questa)

1978 (15 May). *25th Anniv of Coronation of Queen Elizabeth II. T* **141** *and similar vert designs. Multicoloured. P* 14.
755 1 l. Type **141** 10 10
756 2 l. Sceptre with dove 10 10
757 3 l. Golden orb 10 10
758 1 r. 15, St. Edward's Crown 15 15
759 2 r. Sceptre with cross 20 25
760 5 r. Queen Elizabeth II 55 70
755/60 .. .. *Set of* 6 80 1·00
MS761 108×106 mm. 10 r. Anointing spoon .. 1·25 2·00
Nos. 755/60 were also each issued in small sheets of three stamps and one label, perf 12, in changed colours.

(Des M. Shamir)

1978 (15 July). *250th Birth Anniv of Capt. James Cook and Bicentenary of Discovery of Hawaii. T* **142** *and similar multi-coloured designs. P* 14½.
762 1 l. Type **142** 10 15
763 2 l. Statue of Kamehameha I of Hawaii .. 10 15
764 3 l. H.M.S. *Endeavour* 10 15
765 25 l. Route of Cook's third voyage 45 45
766 75 l. H.M.S. *Resolution*, H.M.S. *Discovery* and map of Hawaiian Islands (*horiz*) .. 1·25 1·25
767 1 r. 50, Cook meeting Hawaiian islanders on ship (*horiz*) .. .. 2·00 2·25
768 10 r. Death of Cook (*horiz*) .. .. .. 7·50 10·00
762/8 .. .. *Set of* 7 10·50 13·00
MS769 100 × 92 mm. 5 r. H.M.S. *Endeavour* (*different*) .. .. 18·00 20·00
Nos. 763/4 exist imperforate from stock dispersed by the liquidator of Format International Security Printers Ltd.

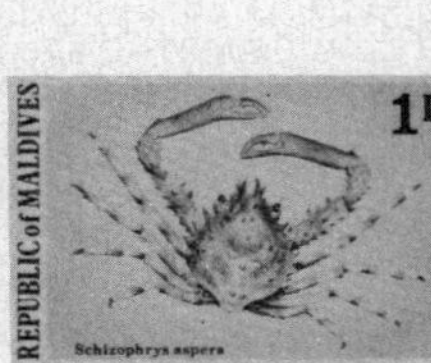

143 *Schizophrys aspera*

144 "Four Apostles"

1978 (30 Aug). *Crustaceans. T* **143** *and similar multicoloured designs. P* 14.
770 1 l. Type **143** 10 10
771 2 l. *Atergatis floridus* 10 10
772 3 l. *Perenon planissimum* 10 10
773 90 l. *Portunus granulatus* 50 40
774 1 r. *Carpilius maculatus* 50 40
775 2 r. *Huenia proteus* .. .. 1·00 1·40
776 25 r. *Etisus laevimanus* .. .. .. 9·00 13·00
770/6 .. .. *Set of* 7 10·00 14·00
MS777 147 × 146 mm. 2 r. *Panulirus longipes* (*vert*) 2·00 2·50

(Des BG Studio. Litho Questa)

1978 (28 Oct). *450th Death Anniv of Albrecht Dürer (artist). T* **144** *and similar designs. P* 14.
778 10 l. multicoloured 10 10
779 20 l. multicoloured 15 10
780 55 l. multicoloured 20 20
781 1 r. black, cinnamon and brown 30 30
782 1 r. 80, multicoloured 45 60
783 3 r. multicoloured .. .. 70 1·25
778/83 .. .. *Set of* 6 1·60 2·25
MS784 141 × 122 mm. 10 r. multicoloured .. 5·00 7·00
Designs: *Vert*—20 l. "Self-portrait at 27", 55 l. "Madonna and Child with a Pear"; 1 r. 80, "Hare"; 3 r. "Great Piece of Turf"; 10 r. "Columbine". *Horiz*— 1 r. "Rhinoceros".

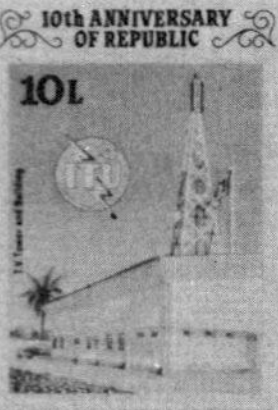

145 T.V. Tower and Building

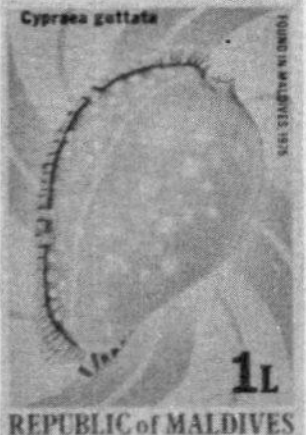

146 Human Rights Emblem

(Des M. Shamir)

1978 (11 Nov). *Tenth Anniv of Republic. T* **145** *and similar horiz designs. Multicoloured. P* 14½.
785 1 l. Fishing boat 10 10
786 5 l. Montessori School 10 10
787 10 l. Type **145** 10 10
788 25 l. Islet 15 15
789 50 l. Boeing "737" 40 15
790 95 l. Beach scene 40 30
791 1 r. 25, Dhow at night 65 55
792 2 r. President's official residence .. .. 85 1·25
793 5 r. Masjidh Afeefuddin (mosque) .. .. 1·25 2·50
785/93 .. .. *Set of* 9 3·50 4·50
MS794 119 × 88 mm. 3 r. Fisherman casting net 2·25 4·00

1978 (10 Dec). *30th Anniv of Declaration of Human Rights. P* 14.
795 **146** 30 l. pale magenta, dp mauve and green 15 15
796 90 l. yellow-ochre, red-brown and green 40 60
797 1 r. 80, lt greenish blue, dp blue & grn .. 70 1·00
795/7 .. .. *Set of* 3 1·10 1·60

147 Great Spotted or Rare Spotted Cowrie (*Cypraea guttata*)

148 Delivery by Bellman

(Des M. Shamir. Litho Questa)

1979 (Jan). *Shells. T* **147** *and similar vert designs. Multicoloured. P* 14.
798 1 l. Type **147** 10 10
799 2 l. Imperial Cone (*Conus imperialis*) .. 10 10
800 3 l. Great Green Turban (*Turbo marmoratus*) 10 10
801 10 l. Giant Spider Conch (*Lambis truncata*) 40 10
802 1 r. White-toothed Cowrie (*Cypraea leucodon*) .. .. 1·50 40
803 1 r. 80, Fig Cone (*Conus figulinus*) .. 2·50 2·25
804 3 r. Glory of the Sea Cone (*Conus gloriamaris*) .. .. 3·25 3·25
798/804 .. .. *Set of* 7 7·00 5·50
MS805 141×110 mm. 5 r. Common Pacific Vase (*Vasum turbinellus*) .. .. 9·00 9·50

(Des M. Shamir. Litho Questa)

1979 (28 Feb). *Death Centenary of Sir Rowland Hill. T* **148** *and similar multicoloured designs. P* 14.
806 1 l. Type **148** 10 10
807 2 l. Mail coach, 1840 (*horiz*) 10 10
808 3 l. First London letter box, 1855 .. .. 10 10
809 1 r. 55, Penny Black stamps and posthorn .. 35 50
810 5 r. Maldives 15 c. stamp, 1906, and carrier pigeon .. .. 90 1·25
806/10 .. .. *Set of* 5 1·25 1·75
MS811 132 × 107 mm. 10 r. Sir Rowland Hill .. 1·75 3·00
Nos. 806/10 were also each issued in small sheets of five stamps and one label, perf 12, in changed colours.

149 Girl with Teddy Bear

150 "White Feathers"

(Des M. Sharmir. Litho Questa)

1979 (10 May). *International Year of the Child* (1st issue). *T* **149** *and similar vert designs. Multicoloured. P* 14.
812 5 l. Type **149** 10 10
813 1 r. 25, Boy with model sailing boat 40 50
814 2 r. Boy with toy rocket 45 55
815 3 r. Boy with toy airship 60 75
812/15 .. .. *Set of* 4 1·40 1·60
MS816 108 × 109 mm. 5 r. Boy with toy train .. 1·60 2·00
See also Nos. 838/**MS**847.

(Des M. Shamir)

1979 (25 June). *25th Death Anniv of Henri Matisse (artist). T* **150** *and similar horiz designs. Multicoloured. P* 14.

No.	Description		
817	20 l. Type **150**	15	15
818	25 l. "Joy of Life"	15	15
819	30 l. "Eggplants"	15	15
820	1 r. 50, "Harmony in Red"	55	65
821	5 r. "Still-life"	1·25	2·25
817/21	*Set of* 5	2·00	3·00
MS822	135 × 95 mm. 4 r. "Water Pitcher"	3·25	4·00

151 Sari with Overdress

152 *Gloriosa superba*

(Des M. Shamir. Litho Questa)

1979 (22 Aug). *National Costumes. T* **151** *and similar vert designs. Multicoloured. P* 14.

No.	Description		
823	50 l. Type **151**	15	15
824	75 l. Sashed apron dress	20	20
825	90 l. Serape	25	25
826	95 l. Ankle-length printed dress	30	30
823/6	*Set of* 4	80	80

(Des M. Shamir. Litho Questa)

1979 (29 Oct). *Flowers. T* **152** *and similar vert designs. Multicoloured. P* 14.

No.	Description		
827	1 l. Type **152**	10	10
828	3 l. *Hibiscus tiliaceus*	10	10
829	50 l. *Barringtonia asiatica*	20	20
830	1 r. *Abutilon indicum*	40	40
831	5 r. *Guettarda speciosa*	1·75	2·25
827/31	*Set of* 5	2·10	2·75
MS832	94 × 85 mm. 4 r. *Pandanus odoratissimus*	1·75	2·75

153 Weaving

(Litho Questa)

1979 (11 Nov). *Handicraft Exhibition. T* **153** *and similar horiz designs. Multicoloured. P* 14.

No.	Description		
833	5 l. Type **153**	10	10
834	10 l. Lacquerwork	10	10
835	1 r. 30, Tortoiseshell jewellery	45	55
836	2 r. Carved woodwork	70	1·00
833/6	*Set of* 4	1·10	1·50
MS837	125 × 85 mm. 5 r. Gold and silver jewellery	1·25	2·25

154 Mickey Mouse attacked by Bird

(Des Walt Disney Productions)

1979 (10 Dec). *International Year of the Child* (2nd issue). *T* **154** *and similar multicoloured designs. P* 11.

No.	Description		
838	1 l. Goofy delivering parcel on motor-scooter (*vert*)	10	10
839	2 l. Type **154**	10	10
840	3 l. Goofy half-covered with letters	10	10
841	4 l. Pluto licking Minnie Mouse's envelopes	10	10
842	5 l. Mickey Mouse delivering letters on roller-skates (*vert*)	10	10
843	10 l. Donald Duck placing letter in mail-box	10	10
844	15 l. Chip and Dale carrying letter	10	10
845	1 r. 50, Donald Duck on monocycle (*vert*)	75	95
846	5 r. Donald Duck with ostrich in crate (*vert*)	2·25	3·25
838/46	*Set of* 9	3·00	4·00
MS847	127 × 102 mm. 4 r. Pluto putting parcel in mail-box. P 13½	5·50	7·00

155 Post-Ramadan Dancing

(Litho Questa)

1980 (19 Jan). *National Day. T* **155** *and similar horiz designs. Multicoloured. P* 14.

No.	Description		
848	5 l. Type **155**	10	10
849	15 l. Musicians and dancer, Eeduu Festival	10	10
850	95 l. Sultan's ceremonial band	30	30
851	2 r. Dancer and drummers, Circumcision Festival	55	85
848/51	*Set of* 4	90	1·25
MS852	131 × 99 mm. 5 r. Swordsmen	1·40	2·50

156 Leatherback Turtle (*Dermochelys coriacea*)

157 Paul Harris (founder)

(Des M. Shamir. Litho Questa)

1980 (17 Feb). *Turtle Conservation Campaign. T* **156** *and similar horiz designs. Multicoloured. P* 14.

No.	Description		
853	1 l. Type **156**	10	20
854	2 l. Flatback turtle (*Chelonia depressa*)	10	20
855	5 l. Hawksbill turtle (*Eretmochelys imbricata*)	15	20
856	10 l. Loggerhead turtle (*Caretta caretta*)	30	20
857	75 l. Olive Ridley turtle (*Lepidochelys olivacea*)	80	45
858	10 r. Atlantic Ridley turtle (*Lepidochelys kempii*)	3·50	4·25
853/8	*Set of* 6	4·25	5·00
MS859	85 × 107 mm. 4 r. Green turtle (*Chelonia mydas*)	1·75	2·50

(Des J.W. Litho Questa)

1980 (7 Apr). *75th Anniv of Rotary International. T* **157** *and similar vert designs. Multicoloured. P* 14.

No.	Description		
860	75 l. Type **157**	35	10
861	90 l. Family (Humanity)	40	20
862	1 r. Wheat (Hunger)	40	25
863	10 r. Caduceus of Hermes (Health)	3·00	4·50
860/3	*Set of* 4	3·75	4·50
MS864	109 × 85 mm. 5 r. Globe	1·50	2·50

LONDON 1980

(**158**)

159 Swimming

1980 (6 May). *"London 1980" International Stamp Exhibition. Nos.* 809/**MS**811 *optd with T* **158**.

No.	Description		
865	1 r. 55, multicoloured	1·75	1·00
866	5 r. multicoloured	3·25	2·75
MS867	132 × 107 mm. 10 r. multicoloured	7·00	8·00

On No. **MS**867 the overprint is horizontal.

(Des J.W. Litho Questa)

1980 (4 June). *Olympic Games, Moscow. T* **159** *and similar horiz designs. Multicoloured. P* 14.

No.	Description		
868	10 l. Type **159**	10	10
869	50 l. Running	20	20
870	3 r. Putting the shot	70	1·10
871	4 r. High jump	80	1·40
868/71	*Set of* 4	1·60	2·50
MS872	105 × 85 mm. 5 r. Weightlifting	1·25	2·25

160 White-tailed Tropic Bird

(Des A. Abbas. Litho Questa)

1980 (10 July). *Birds. T* **160** *and similar horiz designs. Multicoloured. P* 14.

No.	Description		
873	75 l. Type **160**	25	15
874	95 l. Sooty Tern	35	30
875	1 r. Common Noddy	35	30
876	1 r. 55, Curlew	50	70
877	2 r. Wilson's Petrel	60	85
878	4 r. Caspian Tern	1·10	1·60
873/8	*Set of* 6	2·75	3·50
MS879	124 × 85 mm. 5 r. Red-footed Booby and Brown Booby	6·50	8·00

NEW INFORMATION

The editor is always interested to correspond with people who have new information that will improve or correct the Catalogue.

161 Seal of Ibrahim II

(Litho Questa)

1980 (26 July). *Seals of the Sultans. T* **161** *and similar horiz designs. Each purple-brown and black. P* 14.

No.	Description		
880	1 l. Type **161**	10	10
881	2 l. Mohammed Imadudeen II	10	10
882	5 l. Bin Haji Ali	10	10
883	1 r. Kuda Mohammed Rasgefaanu	30	30
884	2 r. Ibrahim Iskander I	50	70
880/4	*Set of* 5	80	1·00
MS885	131 × 95 mm. 3 r. Ibrahim Iskander I (*different*)	85	1·60

162 Queen Elizabeth the Queen Mother

(Des and litho Questa)

1980 (29 Sept). *Queen Mother's 80th Birthday. P* 14.

No.	Description		
886 **162**	4 r. multicoloured	1·00	1·25
MS887	85 × 110 mm. **162** 5 r. multicoloured	1·40	2·25

163 Munnaru

(Des A. Abbas and M. Hassan)

1980 (9 Nov). *1400th Anniv of Hegira. T* **163** *and similar horiz designs. Multicoloured. P* 15.

No.	Description		
888	5 l. Type **163**	15	10
889	10 l. Hukuru Miskiiy mosque	15	10
890	30 l. Medhuziyaaraiy (shrine of saint)	30	30
891	55 l. Writing tablets with verses of Koran	35	35
892	90 l. Mother teaching child Koran	60	70
888/92	*Set of* 5	1·40	1·40
MS893	124 × 101 mm. 2 r. Map of Maldives and coat of arms	80	1·60

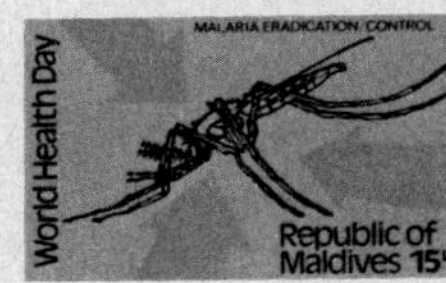

164 Malaria Eradication

(Des J.W. Litho Questa)

1980 (30 Nov). *World Health Day. T* **164** *and similar horiz designs. P* 14.

No.	Description		
894	15 l. black, yellow and vermilion	10	10
895	25 l. multicoloured	10	10
896	1 r. 50, orange-brown, yellow-ochre & black	1·25	1·00
897	5 r. multicoloured	2·25	2·50
894/7	*Set of* 4	3·25	3·25
MS898	68 × 85 mm. 4 r. black, greenish blue and azure	1·25	2·50

Designs:—25 l. Food (Nutrition); 1 r. 50, Molar and toothbrush (Dental health); 4, 5 r. People and medical equipment (Clinics).

165 White Rabbit

(Des Walt Disney Productions)

1980 (22 Dec). *Scenes from Film "Alice in Wonderland". T* **165** *and similar horiz designs. Multicoloured. P* 11.

No.	Description		
899	1 l. Type **165**	10	10
900	2 l. Alice falling into Wonderland	10	10
901	3 l. Alice too big to go through door	10	10
902	4 l. Alice and Tweedledum and Tweedledee	10	10
903	5 l. Alice and the caterpillar	10	10
904	10 l. Cheshire cat	10	10
905	15 l. Alice painting the roses	10	10
906	2 r. 50, Alice and the Queen of Hearts	2·25	2·00
907	4 r. Alice on trial	2·50	2·25
899/907	*Set of* 9	4·75	4·25
MS908	126 × 101 mm. 5 r. Alice at the Mad Hatter's tea-party. P 13½	5·50	6·50

166 Indian Ocean Ridley Turtle **167** Pendant Lamp

(Des A. Abbas and Maniku. Litho Questa)

1980 (29 Dec). *Marine Life. T* **166** *and similar horiz designs. Multicoloured. P* 14.

909 90 l. Type **166** .. .. 2·00 60
910 1 r. 25, Pennant Coralfish .. .. .. 2·25 1·25
911 2 r. Spiny Lobster .. .. 3·00 1·75
909/11 .. .. *Set of* 3 6·50 3·25
MS912 140×94 mm. 4 r. Oriental Sweetlips and Scarlet-finned Squirrelfish .. .. 2·50 3·25

1981 (7 Jan). *National Day. T* **167** *and similar multicoloured designs. P* 14½.

913 10 l. Tomb of Ghaazee Muhammad Thakurufaan (*horiz*) 10 10
914 20 l. Type **167** 15 10
915 30 l. Chair used by Muhammad Thakurufaan 20 10
916 95 l. Muhammad Thakurufaan's palace (*horiz*) 45 45
917 10 r. Cushioned divan .. .. 3·00 4·50
913/17 .. .. *Set of* 5 3·50 4·75

168 Prince Charles and Lady Diana Spencer **169** First Majlis Chamber

(Des and litho J.W.)

1981 (22 June). *Royal Wedding. T* **168** *and similar vert designs. Multicoloured. P* 14.

918 1 r. Type **168** 15 15
919 2 r. Buckingham Palace 25 25
920 5 r. Prince Charles, polo player 40 50
918/20 .. .. *Set of* 3 70 80
MS921 95×83 mm. 10 r. State coach .. .. 1·00 1·10

Nos. 918/20 also exist perforated 12 (*Price for set of* 3 £1 *mint or used*) from additional sheets of five stamps and one label. These stamps have changed background colours.

Nos. 918/21 also exist imperforate from a restricted printing.

(Des I. Azeez)

1981 (27 June). *50th Anniv of Citizens' Majlis (grievance rights). T* **169** *and similar multicoloured designs. P* 14½.

922 95 l. Type **169** 30 30
923 1 r. Sultan Muhammed Shamsuddin III .. 35 35
MS924 137 × 94 mm. 4 r. First written constitution (*horiz*) .. .. 2·50 3·75

170 "Self-portrait with a Palette" **171** Airmail Envelope

(Des J.W. Litho Questa)

1981 (July). *Birth Centenary of Pablo Picasso. T* **170** *and similar vert designs. Multicoloured. P* 13½ × 14.

925 5 l. Type **170** 10 10
926 10 l. "Woman in Blue" 15 10
927 25 l. "Boy with Pipe" 25 10
928 30 l. "Card Player" 25 10
929 90 l. "Sailor" 50 40
930 3 r. "Self-portrait" .. .. 1·25 1·25
931 5 r. "Harlequin" .. .. 1·75 1·75
925/31 .. .. *Set of* 7 3·75 3·25
MS932 106 × 130 mm. 10 r. "Child holding a Dove". Imperf .. .. 3·00 3·50

(Des and litho Questa)

1981 (9 Sept). *75th Anniv of Postal Service. P* 14.

933 **171** 25 l. multicoloured 10 10
934 75 l. multicoloured 20 25
935 5 r. multicoloured .. .. .. 70 1·25
933/5 .. .. *Set of* 3 90 1·40

172 Boeing 737 taking off **173** Homer

(Des A. Abbas. Litho Questa)

1981 (11 Nov). *Male International Airport. T* **172** *and similar horiz designs. Multicoloured. P* 14.

936 5 l. Type **172** 20 20
937 20 l. Passengers leaving Boeing 737 .. 55 20
938 1 r. 80, Refuelling .. .. .. 1·25 1·50
939 4 r. Plan of airport .. .. .. 1·50 2·50
936/9 .. .. *Set of* 4 3·25 4·00
MS940 106×79 mm. 5 r. Aerial view of airport 1·75 2·50

(Des J.W.)

1981 (18 Nov). *International Year of Disabled People. T* **173** *and similar vert designs. Multicoloured. P* 14½.

941 2 l. Type **173** 10 10
942 5 l. Miguel Cervantes 10 10
943 1 r. Beethoven .. .. 2·00 85
944 5 r. Van Gogh .. .. 3·00 5·00
941/4 .. .. *Set of* 4 4·50 5·50
MS945 116 × 91 mm. 4 r. Helen Keller and Anne Sullivan .. .. 4·00 5·50

174 Preparation of Maldive Fish **175** Collecting Bait

(Des Central Art Palace. Litho Questa)

1981 (25 Nov). *Decade for Women. T* **174** *and similar vert designs. Multicoloured. P* 14.

946 20 l. Type **174** 10 10
947 90 l. 16th century Maldive women .. 25 25
948 1 r. Farming 30 30
949 2 r. Coir rope making .. .. .. 55 1·10
946/9 .. .. *Set of* 4 1·10 1·60

(Des I. Azeez. Litho Questa)

1981 (10 Dec). *Fishermen's Day. T* **175** *and similar horiz designs. Multicoloured. P* 14.

950 5 l. Type **175** 35 15
951 15 l. Fishing boats 65 25
952 90 l. Fisherman with catch .. .. 1·25 60
953 1 r. 30, Sorting fish .. .. .. 1·50 1·10
950/3 .. .. *Set of* 4 3·25 1·90
MS954 147 × 101 mm. 3 r. Loading fish for export 1·50 2·50

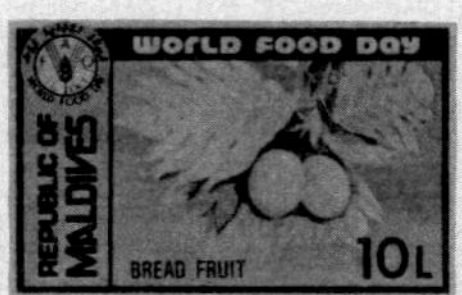

176 Bread Fruit

(Des Design Images. Litho Questa)

1981 (30 Dec). *World Food Day. T* **176** *and similar horiz designs. Multicoloured. P* 14.

955 10 l. Type **176** 25 10
956 25 l. Hen with chicks 60 15
957 30 l. Maize 60 20
958 75 l. Skipjack Tuna .. .. .. 1·75 65
959 1 r. Pumpkin .. .. 2·00 70
960 2 r. Coconuts .. .. 2·25 2·75
955/60 .. .. *Set of* 6 6·75 4·00
MS961 110 × 85 mm. 5 r. Eggplant .. .. 2·50 3·50

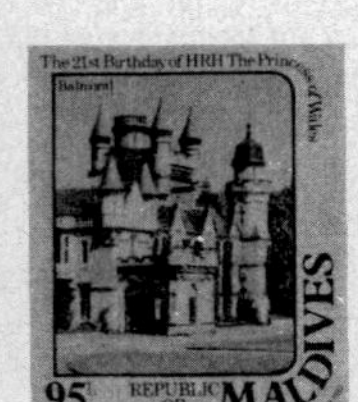

177 Pluto and Cat **178** Balmoral

(Des Walt Disney Productions)

1982 (29 Mar). *50th Anniv of Pluto (Walt Disney cartoon character). T* **177** *and similar multicoloured design. P* 13½.

962 4 r. Type **177** .. .. 3·00 2·75
MS963 127 × 101 mm. 6 r. Pluto (scene from *The Pointer*) .. .. 3·75 4·00

(Des PAD Studio. Litho Questa)

1982 (1 July). *21st Birthday of Princess of Wales. T* **178** *and similar vert designs. Multicoloured. P* 14½ × 14.

964 95 l. Type **178** 20 20
965 3 r. Prince and Princess of Wales .. 50 65
966 5 r. Princess on aircraft steps .. 90 95
964/6 .. .. *Set of* 3 1·40 1·60
MS967 103 × 75 mm. 8 r. Princess of Wales .. 1·25 1·75

Nos. 964/6 also exist in sheetlets of 5 stamps and 1 label.

Nos. 964/7 and the sheetlets exist imperforate from a restricted printing.

COMMONWEALTH MEMBER
9 July 1982

179 Scout saluting and Camp-site **180** Footballer

(Des D. Miller. Litho Questa)

1982 (9 Aug). *75th Anniv of Boy Scout Movement. T* **179** *and similar horiz designs. Multicoloured. P* 14.

968 1 r. 30, Type **179** 40 45
969 1 r. 80, Lighting a fire 50 60
970 4 r. Life-saving .. .. 1·10 1·40
971 5 r. Map-reading .. .. 1·40 1·75
968/71 .. .. *Set of* 4 3·00 3·75
MS972 128 × 66 mm. 10 r. Scout emblem and flag of the Maldives .. .. 2·00 3·00

(Des M. and S. Gerber Studio. Litho Questa)

1982 (4 Oct). *World Cup Football Championship, Spain. T* **180** *and similar square designs. P* 13½.

973 90 l. multicoloured .. .. 1·00 60
974 1 r. 50, multicoloured .. .. .. 1·60 85
975 3 r. multicoloured .. .. 2·25 1·50
976 5 r. multicoloured .. .. 2·75 2·25
973/6 .. .. *Set of* 4 7·00 4·75
MS977 94 × 63 mm. 10 r. multicoloured .. .. 4·50 6·00

1982 (18 Oct). *Birth of Prince William of Wales. Nos.* 964/7 *optd with T* **212***a of Jamaica.*

978 95 l. Type **178** 15 20
979 3 r. Prince and Princess of Wales .. 45 65
980 5 r. Princess on aircraft steps 70 95
978/80 .. .. *Set of* 3 1·10 1·60
MS981 103 × 75 mm. 8 r. Princess of Wales .. 2·25 2·50

Nos. 978/80 also exist in sheetlets of 5 stamps and 1 label.

Nos. 978/81 and the sheetlets exist imperforate from a restricted printing.

181 Basic Education Scheme **182** Koch isolates the Bacillus

(Des and litho Harrison)

1982 (15 Nov). *National Education. T* **181** *and similar horiz designs. Multicoloured. P* 14.

982 90 l. Type **181** 15 25
983 95 l. Primary education 15 25
984 1 r. 30, Teacher training 20 30
985 2 r. 50, Printing educational material .. 40 60
982/5 .. .. *Set of* 4 80 1·25
MS986 100 × 70 mm. 6 r. Thaana typewriter keyboard .. .. 1·00 2·00

(Des Artists International)

1982 (22 Nov). *Centenary of Robert Koch's Discovery of Tubercle Bacillus. T* **182** *and similar multicoloured designs. P* 14.

987 5 l. Type **182** 10 15
988 15 l. Micro-organism and microscope .. 15 15
989 95 l. Dr. Robert Koch in 1905 .. .. 35 45
990 3 r. Dr. Koch and plates from publication .. 85 1·50
987/90 .. .. *Set of* 4 1·25 2·00
MS991 77 × 61 mm. 5 r. Koch in his laboratory (*horiz*) .. .. 80 1·75

No. **MS**991 exists imperforate from stock dispersed by the liquidator of Format International Security Printers Ltd.

183 Blohm and Voss HA 139A Seaplane *Nordsee*

(Des W. Wright. Litho Questa)

1983 (28 July). *Bicentenary of Manned Flight. T* **183** *and similar horiz designs. Multicoloured. P* 14.
992 90 l. Type **183** .. .. 2·00 70
993 1 r. 45, Macchi Castoldi MC-72 seaplane 2·50 1·75
994 4 r. Boeing F4B-3 biplane fighter .. 4·00 3·25
995 5 r. Renard and Kreb's airship *La France* 4·25 3·50
992/5 .. .. *Set of* 4 11·50 8·25
MS996 110×85 mm. 10 r. Nadar's balloon *Le Geant* .. .. 3·00 4·00

184 "Curved Dash" Oldsmobile, 1902

(Des Publishers Graphics Inc)

1983 (Aug). *Classic Motor Cars. T* **184** *and similar horiz designs. Multicoloured. P* 14½.
997 5 l. Type **184** 20 40
998 30 l. Aston Martin "Tourer", 1932 .. .. 60 40
999 40 l. Lamborghini "Muira", 1966 .. .. 60 45
1000 1 r. Mercedes-Benz "300SL", 1945 .. .. 1·00 70
1001 1 r. 45, Stutz "Bearcat", 1913 .. .. 1·25 1·75
1002 5 r. Lotus "Elite", 1958 .. .. .. 2·75 4·25
997/1002 .. .. *Set of* 6 5·75 7·00
MS1003 132 × 103 mm. 10 r. Grand Prix "Sunbeam", 1924. P 14½ .. .. 7·00 10·00
Nos. 997/1002 were each issued in sheets of 9, including one *se-tenant* label.

185 Rough-toothed Dolphin

(Des D. Miller. Litho Questa)

1983 (6 Sept). *Marine Mammals. T* **185** *and similar horiz designs. Multicoloured. P* 14.
1004 30 l. Type **185** .. .. 1·60 60
1005 40 l. Indo-Pacific Hump-backed Dolphin .. 1·60 65
1006 4 r. Finless Porpoise .. .. 5·00 4·00
1007 6 r. Pygmy Sperm Whale .. .. .. 10·00 7·00
1004/7 .. .. *Set of* 4 16·00 11·00
MS1008 82 × 90 mm. 5 r. Striped Dolphin .. 4·50 5·50

186 Dish Aerial

(Des PAD Studio. Litho Questa)

1983 (9 Oct). *World Communications Year. T* **186** *and similar horiz designs. Multicoloured. P* 14.
1009 50 l. Type **186** 40 20
1010 1 r. Land, sea and air communications .. 1·00 60
1011 2 r. Ship-to-shore communication .. .. 1·40 1·50
1012 10 r. Air traffic controller .. .. .. 3·75 6·00
1009/12 .. .. *Set of* 4 6·00 7·50
MS1013 91 × 76 mm. 20 r. Telecommunications 3·75 4·75

187 "La Donna Gravida"

(Des M. Diamond)

1983 (25 Oct). *500th Birth Anniv of Raphael. T* **187** *and similar vert designs showing paintings. Multicoloured. P* 13½.
1014 90 l. Type **187** 25 25
1015 3 r. "Giovanna d'Aragona" (detail) .. 75 1·00
1016 4 r. "Woman with Unicorn" .. .. 1·00 1·40
1017 6 r. "La Muta" .. .. 1·25 2·00
1014/17 .. .. *Set of* 4 3·00 4·25
MS1018 121 × 97 mm. 10 r. "The Knight's Dream" (detail) .. .. 2·75 4·50
Nos. 1014/18 exist imperforate from stock dispersed by the liquidator of Format International Security Printers Ltd.

188 Refugee Camp

(Litho Questa)

1983 (29 Nov). *Solidarity with the Palestinians. T* **188** *and similar horiz designs each showing the Dome of the Rock, Jerusalem. Multicoloured. P* 13½ × 14.
1019 4 r. Type **188** .. .. 1·50 2·00
1020 5 r. Refugee holding dead child .. .. 1·60 2·00
1021 6 r. Child carrying food .. .. .. 1·90 2·50
1019/21 .. .. *Set of* 3 4·50 6·00

189 Education Facilities

190 Baseball

(Des I. Azeez. Litho Questa)

1983 (10 Dec). *National Development Programme. T* **189** *and similar horiz designs. Multicoloured. P* 13½.
1022 7 l. Type **189** 20 10
1023 10 l. Health service and education 30 10
1024 5 r. Growing more food .. .. .. 1·50 1·25
1025 6 r. Fisheries development .. .. .. 2·00 1·50
1022/5 .. .. *Set of* 4 3·50 2·50
MS1026 134 × 93 mm. 10 r. Air transport .. 2·25 2·75

(Des PAD Studio. Litho Questa)

1984 (10 Mar). *Olympic Games, Los Angeles. T* **190** *and similar vert designs. Multicoloured. P* 14.
1027 50 l. Type **190** 25 15
1028 1 r. 55, Backstroke swimming 55 40
1029 3 r. Judo .. .. 1·00 90
1030 4 r. Shot-putting .. .. 1·40 1·40
1027/30 .. .. *Set of* 4 2·75 2·50
MS1031 85 × 105 mm. 10 r. Team Handball .. 2·40 2·75

Rf1.45

19th UPU
CONGRESS HAMBURG

(191) (192)

1984 (19 June). *Universal Postal Union Congress, Hamburg. Nos. 994/6 optd as T* **191**.
1032 4 r. Boeing "F4B-3" .. .. .. 1·40 1·40
1033 5 r. *La France* airship .. .. .. 1·60 1·60
MS1034 110 × 85 mm. 10 r. Nadar's *Le Geant* .. 2·75 4·50

1984 (20 Aug). *Surch as T* **192**. *A. In black. B. In gold.*

(*a*) *On Nos.* 964/7

		A		B	
1035	1 r. 45 on 95 l. Type **178** ..	3·00	2·25	3·00	2·25
1036	1 r. 45 on 3 r. Prince and Princess of Wales	3·00	2·25	3·00	2·25
1037	1 r. 45 on 5 r. Princess on aircraft steps	3·00	2·25	3·00	2·25
1035/7	.. .. .. *Set of* 3	8·00	6·00	8·00	6·00
MS1038	103×75 mm. 1 r. 45 on 8 r. Princess of Wales	2·50	4·25	2·50	4·25

(*b*) *On Nos.* 978/81

		A		B	
1039	1 r. 45 on 95 l. Type **178** ..	3·00	2·25	3·00	2·25
1040	1 r. 45 on 3 r. Prince and Princess of Wales	3·00	2·25	3·00	2·25
1041	1 r. 45 on 5 r. Princess on aircraft steps	3·00	2·25	3·00	2·25
1039/41	.. .. .. *Set of* 3	8·00	6·00	8·00	6·00
MS1042	103×75 mm. 1 r. 45 on 8 r. Princess of Wales	2·50	4·25	2·50	4·25

Nos. 1039A/42A exist imperforate from a restricted printing.
Stamps from the sheetlets of five plus one label were also surcharged, either in black or gold using a slightly different type.

193 Hands breaking Manacles

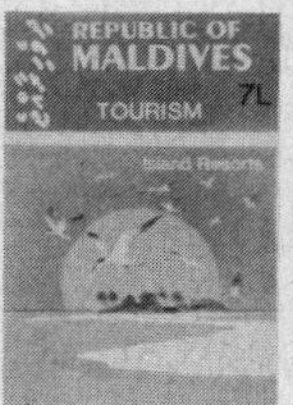

194 Island Resort and Common Terns

1984 (26 Aug). *Namibia Day. T* **193** *and similar horiz designs. Multicoloured. P* 15.
1043 6 r. Type **193** .. .. 1·50 1·60
1044 8 r. Namibia family .. .. 2·00 2·10
MS1045 129 × 104 mm. 10 r. Map of Namibia .. 2·40 2·75

(Litho Questa)

1984 (12 Sept). *Tourism. T* **194** *and similar vert designs. Multicoloured. P* 14.
1046 7 l. Type **194** 30 10
1047 15 l. Dhow 30 10
1048 20 l. Snorkelling 30 10
1049 2 r. Wind-surfing 75 40
1050 4 r. Aqualung diving .. .. .. 1·25 75
1051 6 r. Night fishing .. .. 2·00 1·25
1052 8 r. Game fishing .. .. 2·25 1·50
1053 10 r. Turtle on beach .. .. .. 2·50 1·75
1046/53 .. .. *Set of* 8 8·75 5·25

195 Frangipani

1984 (21 Sept). *"Ausipex" International Stamp Exhibition, Melbourne. T* **195** *and similar horiz designs showing flowers. Multicoloured. P* 15.
1054 5 r. Type **195** .. .. 2·25 1·75
1055 10 r. Cooktown Orchid .. .. .. 4·75 3·75
MS1056 105 × 77 mm. 15 r. Sun Orchid .. .. 9·50 5·50
Nos. 1054/5 exist imperforate from stock dispersed by the liquidator of Format International Security Printers Ltd.

196 Facade of the Malé Mosque

1984 (11 Nov). *Opening of Islamic Centre. T* **196** *and similar multicoloured design. P* 15.
1057 2 r. Type **196** 45 50
1058 5 r. Malé Mosque and minaret (*vert*) .. .. 1·10 1·25

197 Air Maldives Boeing 737

(Des G. Drummond. Litho Questa)

1984 (19 Nov). *40th Anniv of International Civil Aviation Authority. T* **197** *and similar horiz designs. Multicoloured. P* 14.
1059 7 l. Type **197** 40 15
1060 4 r. Air Lanka Lockheed L-1011 TriStar 2·25 1·25
1061 6 r. Alitalia Douglas DC-10-30 .. .. 2·75 1·60
1062 8 r. L.T.U. Lockheed L-1011 TriStar .. 3·00 2·25
1059/62 .. .. *Set of* 4 7·50 4·75
MS1063 110×92 mm. 15 r. Air Maldives Short S.7 Skyvan .. .. 3·75 4·00

PRICES OF SETS

Set prices are given for many issues, generally those containing three stamps or more. Definitive sets include one of each value or major colour change, but do not cover different perforations, die types or minor shades. Where a choice is possible the set prices are based on the cheapest versions of the stamps included in the listings.

198 Daisy Duck

(Litho Questa)

1984 (26 Nov–1 Dec). *50th Anniv of Donald Duck (Walt Disney cartoon character). T* **198** *and similar horiz designs. Multi-coloured. P* 12 (5 r.) *or* 14 × 13½ (*others*).

1064 3 l. Type **198** 10 10
1065 4 l. Huey, Dewey and Louie 10 10
1066 5 l. Ludwig von Drake 10 10
1067 10 l. Gyro Gearloose 10 10
1068 15 l. Uncle Scrooge painting self portrait .. 15 10
1069 25 l. Donald Duck with camera 15 10
1070 5 r. Donald Duck and Gus Goose (1.12) .. 2·25 1·25
1071 8 r. Gladstone Gander .. .. .. 2·50 2·00
1072 10 r. Grandma Duck .. .. .. 3·00 2·50
1064/72 .. .. *Set of* 9 7·50 5·50
MS1073 102 × 126 mm. 15 r. Uncle Scrooge and Donald Duck in front of camera .. .. .. 4·50 5·00
MS1074 126 × 102 mm. 15 r. Uncle Scrooge (1.12) 4·50 5·00

No. 1070 was printed in sheetlets of 8 stamps.

199 "The Day" (detail)

200 "Edmond Iduranty" (Degas)

(Litho Questa)

1984 (10 Dec). *450th Death Anniv of Correggio (artist). T* **199** *and similar vert designs. Multicoloured. P* 14.

1075 5 r. Type **199** .. .. 1·25 1·25
1076 10 r. "The Night" (*detail*) .. .. .. 1·75 2·00
MS1077 60 × 80 mm. 15 r. "Portrait of a Man" .. 3·25 3·25

(Litho Questa)

1984 (15 Dec). *150th Birth Anniv of Edgar Degas (artist). T* **200** *and similar vert designs. P* 14.

1078 75 l. Type **200** 20 20
1079 2 r. "James Tissot" 50 50
1080 5 r. "Achille de Gas in Uniform" .. .. 1·25 1·25
1081 10 r. "Lady with Chrysanthemums" .. 2·50 2·75
1078/81 .. .. *Set of* 4 4·00 4·25
MS1082 100 × 70 mm. 15 r. "Self-portrait" .. 3·25 3·75

201 Pale-footed Shearwater

202 Squad Drilling

(Des I. MacLaury. Litho Questa)

1985 (9 Mar). *Birth Bicentenary of John J. Audubon (ornithologist) (1st issue). T* **201** *and similar multicoloured designs showing original paintings. P* 14.

1083 3 r. Type **201** .. .. 1·75 80
1084 3 r. 50, Little Grebe (*horiz*) .. .. .. 2·00 90
1085 4 r. Common Cormorant .. .. .. 2·00 1·00
1086 4 r. 50, White-faced Storm Petrel (*horiz*) .. 2·00 1·10
1083/6 .. .. *Set of* 4 7·00 3·50
MS1087 108 × 80 mm. 15 r. Red-necked Phalarope (*horiz*) .. .. 3·00 3·25

See also Nos. 1192/200.

(Des and litho Questa)

1985 (6 June). *National Security Service. T* **202** *and similar multicoloured designs. P* 13½ × 14 (*No.* 1092) *or* 14 × 13½ (*others*).

1088 15 l. Type **202** 40 10
1089 20 l. Combat patrol 40 10
1090 1 r. Fire fighting .. .. 1·50 25
1091 2 r. Coastguard cutter .. .. .. 2·00 55
1092 10 r. Independence Day Parade (*vert*) .. 2·75 2·50
1088/92 .. .. *Set of* 5 6·25 3·00
MS1093 128 × 85 mm. 10 r. Cannon on saluting base and National Security Service badge .. 2·25 2·25

GOLD MEDALIST
THERESA ANDREWS
USA

(**203**)

204 Queen Elizabeth the Queen Mother, 1981

1985 (17 July). *Olympic Games Gold Medal Winners, Los Angeles. Nos.* 1027/31 *optd as T* **203** *or in larger capitals* (50 *l.*, 10 *r.*).

1094 50 l. Type **190** (optd "JAPAN") 10 10
1095 1 r. 55, Backstroke swimming (opt T **203**) 30 35
1096 3 r. Judo (Optd "GOLD MEDALIST FRANK WIENEKE USA") 55 60
1097 4 r. Shot-putting (optd "GOLD MEDALIST CLAUDIA LOCH WEST GERMANY") 80 85
1094/7 .. .. *Set of* 4 1·60 1·75
MS1098 85 × 105 mm. 10 r. Team Handball (opt "U.S.A.") .. .. 1·90 2·00

(Des J.W. Litho Questa)

1985 (20 Aug). *Life and Times of Queen Elizabeth the Queen Mother. T* **204** *and similar multicoloured designs. P* 14.

1099 3 r. Type **204** 45 60
1100 5 r. Visiting the Middlesex Hospital (*horiz*) .. .. 65 1·00
1101 7 r. The Queen Mother .. .. .. 85 1·25
1099/101 .. .. *Set of* 3 1·75 2·50
MS1102 56 × 85 mm. 15 r. With Prince Charles at Garter Ceremony .. .. 3·50 3·25

Stamps as Nos. 1099/101, but with face values of 1 r., 4 r. and 10 r., exist from additional sheetlets of 5 plus a label issued 4 January 1986. These also have changed background colours and are perforated 12½ × 12 (4 r.) or 12 × 12½ (others) (*Price for set of 3 stamps £2.50 mint*).

204*a* Liro da Braccio

205 Mas Odi (fishing boat)

(Des Susan David. Litho Questa)

1985 (3 Sept). *300th Birth Anniv of Johann Sebastian Bach (composer). T* **204***a and similar vert designs. P* 14.

1103 15 l. multicoloured 10 10
1104 2 r. multicoloured 50 45
1105 4 r. multicoloured 90 85
1106 10 r. multicoloured .. .. 1·90 2·25
1103/6 .. .. *Set of* 4 3·00 3·25
MS1107 104 × 75 mm. 15 r. black and reddish orange .. .. 3·00 3·50

Designs:—2 r. Tenor oboe; 4 r. Serpent; 10 r. Table organ; 15 r. Johann Sebastian Bach.

(Des H. Afeef. Litho Questa)

1985 (23 Sept). *Maldives Ships and Boats. T* **205** *and similar horiz designs. Multicoloured. P* 14.

1108 3 l. Type **205** 10 10
1109 5 l. Battela (dhow) 10 10
1110 10 l. Addu odi (dhow) 10 10
1111 2 r. 60, Modern dhoni (fishing boat) .. 1·25 1·50
1112 2 r. 70, Mas dhoni (fishing boat) .. .. 1·25 1·50
1113 3 r. Baththeli dhoni .. .. .. 1·40 1·60
1114 5 r. *Inter* 1 (inter-island vessel) .. .. 2·25 2·75
1115 10 r. Dhoni-style yacht .. .. .. 4·00 6·00
1108/15 .. .. *Set of* 8 9·25 12·00

206 Windsurfing

207 United Nations Building, New York

(Des H. Afeef. Litho Questa)

1985 (2 Oct). *10th Anniv of World Tourism Organization. T* **206** *and similar horiz designs. Multicoloured. P* 14.

1116 6 r. Type **206** .. .. 1·75 1·75
1117 8 r. Scuba diving .. .. 2·00 2·00
MS1118 171 × 114 mm. 15 r. Kuda Hithi Resort 2·75 3·00

(Litho Questa)

1985 (24 Oct). *40th Anniv of United Nations Organization and International Year of Peace. T* **207** *and similar multicoloured designs. P* 14.

1119 15 l. Type **207** 10 10
1120 2 r. Hands releasing peace dove 40 45
1121 4 r. U.N. Security Council meeting (*horiz*) 80 1·00
1122 10 r. Lion and lamb .. .. 1·90 2·50
1119/22 .. .. *Set of* 4 2·75 3·50
MS1123 76 × 92 mm. 15 r. U.N. Building and peace dove .. .. 2·75 3·00

208 Maldivian Delegate voting in U.N. General Assembly

(Des BG Studio. Litho Questa)

1985 (24 Oct). *20th Anniv of United Nations Membership. T* **208** *and similar horiz design. Multicoloured. P* 14.

1124 20 l. Type **208** 10 10
1125 15 r. U.N. and Maldivian flags, and U.N. Building, New York .. .. .. 2·75 3·50

209 Youths playing Drums

(Des BG Studio)

1985 (20 Nov). *International Youth Year. T* **209** *and similar multicoloured designs. P* 15.

1126 90 l. Type **209** 15 20
1127 6 r. Tug-of-war .. .. 1·00 1·40
1128 10 r. Community service (*vert*) .. .. 1·60 2·25
1126/8 .. .. *Set of* 3 2·50 3·50
MS1129 85 × 84 mm. 15 r. Raising the flag at youth camp (*vert*) .. .. 2·75 3·00

210 Quotation and Flags of Member Nations

(Litho Questa)

1985 (8 Dec) *1st Summit Meeting of South Asian Association for Regional Co-operation, Dhaka, Bangladesh. P* 14.

1130 **210** 3 r. multicoloured .. .. 1·50 1·25

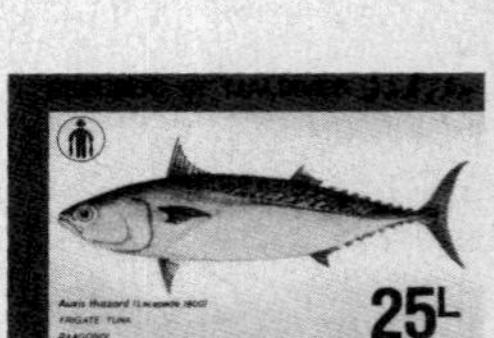

211 Frigate Mackerel

212 Player running with Ball

(Litho Questa)

1985 (10 Dec). *Fishermen's Day. Species of Tuna. T* **211** *and similar horiz designs. Multicoloured. P* 14.

1131 25 l. Type **211** 35 10
1132 75 l. Kawakawa ("Little Tuna") 65 15
1133 3 r. Dog-toothed Tuna .. .. .. 2·00 75
1134 5 r. Yellow-finned Tuna .. .. .. 2·50 1·25
1131/4 .. .. *Set of* 4 5·00 2·00
MS1135 130×90 mm. 15 r. Skipjack Tuna .. 3·50 3·50

(Des Walt Disney Productions. Litho Questa)

1985 (21 Dec). *150th Birth Anniv of Mark Twain. Vert designs as T* **160***a of Lesotho showing Walt Disney cartoon characters illustrating various Mark Twain quotations. Multicoloured. P* 12 (4 *r.*) *or* 13½×14 (*others*).

1136 2 l. Winnie the Pooh 10 10
1137 3 l. Gepetto and Figaro the cat 10 10
1138 4 l. Goofy and basket of broken eggs .. 10 10
1139 20 l. Goofy as doctor scolding Donald Duck 25 10
1140 4 r. Mowgli and King Louis .. .. .. 1·40 1·60
1141 13 r. The wicked Queen and mirror .. 5·00 6·50
1136/41 .. .. *Set of* 6 6·00 7·50
MS1142 126 × 101 mm. 15 r. Mickey Mouse as Tom Sawyer on comet's tail .. .. .. 6·00 6·50

No. 1140 was issued in sheetlets of 8 stamps.

(Des Walt Disney Productions. Litho Questa)

1985 (21 Dec). *Birth Bicentenaries of Grimm Brothers (folklorists). Multicoloured designs as T* **160***b of Lesotho, but horiz, showing Walt Disney cartoon characters in scenes from "Dr. Knowall". P* 12 (3 *r.*) *or* 14×13½ (*others*).

No.	Description	Unused	Used
1143	1 l. Donald Duck as Crabb driving oxcart	10	10
1144	5 l. Donald Duck as Dr. Knowall	10	10
1145	10 l. Dr. Knowall in surgery	10	10
1146	15 l. Dr. Knowall with Uncle Scrooge as a lord	10	10
1147	3 r. Dr. and Mrs. Knowall in pony trap	1·10	1·25
1148	14 r. Dr. Knowall and thief	5·50	6·50
1143/8	*Set of* 6	6·00	7·00
MS1149	126×101 mm. 15 r. Donald and Daisy Duck as Dr. and Mrs. Knowall	6·00	6·50

No. 1147 was printed in sheetlets of 8 stamps.

(Des W. Hanson. Litho Questa)

1986 (29 Apr). *Appearance of Halley's Comet (1st issue). Horiz designs as T* **162***a of Lesotho. Multicoloured. P* 14.

No.	Description	Unused	Used
1150	20 l. N.A.S.A. space telescope and Comet	50	25
1151	1 r. 50, E.S.A. *Giotto* spacecraft and Comet	1·25	1·50
1152	2 r. Japanese *Planet A* spacecraft and Comet	1·50	1·75
1153	4 r. Edmond Halley and Stonehenge	2·75	3·25
1154	5 r. Russian *Vega* spacecraft and Comet	3·00	3·50
1150/4	*Set of* 5	8·00	9·00
MS1155	101×70 mm. 15 r. Halley's Comet	7·50	9·00

See also Nos. 1206/11.

(Des J. Iskowitz. Litho Questa)

1986 (5 May). *Centenary of Statue of Liberty. Multicoloured designs as T* **163***b of Lesotho showing the Statue of Liberty and immigrants to the U.S.A. P* 14.

No.	Description	Unused	Used
1156	50 l. Walter Gropius (architect)	40	30
1157	70 l. John Lennon (musician)	1·50	1·00
1158	1 r. George Balanchine (choreographer)	1·50	1·00
1159	10 r. Franz Werfel (writer)	3·75	6·00
1156/9	*Set of* 4	6·50	7·50
MS1160	100×72 mm. 15 r. Statue of Liberty (*vert*)	5·00	6·00

(Des Walt Disney Productions)

1986 (22 May). *"Ameripex" International Stamp Exhibition, Chicago. Horiz designs as T* **163***c of Lesotho showing Walt Disney cartoon characters and U.S.A. stamps. Multicoloured. P* 11.

No.	Description	Unused	Used
1161	3 l. Johnny Appleseed and 1966 Johnny Appleseed stamp	10	10
1162	4 l. Paul Bunyan and 1958 Forest Conservation stamp	10	10
1163	5 l. Casey and 1969 Professional Baseball Centenary stamp	10	10
1164	10 l. Ichabod Crane and 1974 "Legend of Sleepy Hollow" stamp	10	10
1165	15 l. John Henry and 1944 75th anniv of completion of First Transcontinental Railroad stamp	15	15
1166	20 l. Windwagon Smith and 1954 Kansas Territory Centenary stamp	15	15
1167	13 r. Mike Fink and 1970 Great Northwest stamp	6·50	6·50
1168	14 r. Casey Jones and 1950 Railroad Engineers stamp	7·50	7·50
1161/8	*Set of* 8	13·00	13·00
MS1169	Two sheets, each 127×101 mm. (a) 15 r. Davy Crockett and 1967 Davy Crockett stamp. (b) 15 r. Daisy Duck as Pocahontas saving Captain John Smith (Donald Duck). P 14×13½. *Set of* 2 *sheets*	12·00	15·00

(Litho Questa)

1986 (29 May). *60th Birthday of Queen Elizabeth II. Vert designs as T* **163***a of Lesotho. P* 14.

No.	Description	Unused	Used
1170	1 r. black and chrome-yellow	30	25
1171	2 r. multicoloured	40	55
1172	12 r. multicoloured	2·00	3·00
1170/2	*Set of* 3	2·40	3·50
MS1173	120×85 mm. 15 r. black and grey-brown	3·25	4·25

Designs:—1 r. Royal Family at Girl Guides Rally, 1938; 2 r. Queen in Canada; 12 r. At Sandringham, 1970; 15 r. Princesses Elizabeth and Margaret at Royal Lodge, Windsor, 1940.

Nos. 1170/2 were each issued in sheetlets of five stamps and one stamp-size label.

(Des BG Studio. Litho Questa)

1986 (8 June). *World Cup Football Championship, Mexico. T* **212** *and similar vert designs. Multicoloured. P* 14.

No.	Description	Unused	Used
1174	15 l. Type **212**	75	30
1175	2 r. Player gaining control of ball	2·50	1·75
1176	4 r. Two players competing for ball	4·00	3·50
1177	10 r. Player bouncing ball on knee	7·50	8·00
1174/7	*Set of* 4	13·00	12·00
MS1178	95×114 mm. 15 r. Player kicking ball	3·25	5·00

(Litho Questa)

1986 (1 July). *Royal Wedding. Vert designs as T* **170***a of Lesotho. Multicoloured. P* 14.

No.	Description	Unused	Used
1179	10 l. Prince Andrew and Miss Sarah Ferguson	10	10
1180	2 r. Prince Andrew	60	65
1181	12 r. Prince Andrew in naval uniform	2·75	3·50
1179/81	*Set of* 3	3·00	3·75
MS1182	88×88 mm. 15 r. Prince Andrew and Miss Sarah Ferguson (*different*)	4·00	4·50

NEW INFORMATION

The editor is always interested to correspond with people who have new information that will improve or correct the Catalogue.

213 Moorish Idol and Sea Fan

WINNERS
Argentina 3
W.Germany 2

(**213***a*)

(Des Mary Walters)

1986 (22 Sept). *Marine Wildlife. T* **213** *and similar horiz designs. Multicoloured. P* 15.

No.	Description	Unused	Used
1183	50 l. Type **213**	1·10	30
1184	90 l. Regal Angelfish	1·50	45
1185	1 r. Maldive Anemonefish	1·50	45
1186	2 r. Tiger Cowrie (*Cypraea tigris*) and Stinging Coral	2·00	1·40
1187	3 r. Emperor Angelfish and Staghorn Coral	2·50	1·75
1188	4 r. Black-naped Tern	3·25	2·75
1189	5 r. Fiddler Crab and Staghorn Coral	3·25	2·75
1190	10 r. Hawksbill Turtle	4·00	4·50
1183/90	*Set of* 8	17·00	13·00
MS1191	Two sheets, each 107×76 mm. (a) 15 r. Long-nosed Butterflyfish. (b) 15 r. Oriental Trumpetfish *Set of* 2 *sheets*	10·00	13·00

(Litho Questa)

1986 (9 Oct). *Birth Bicentenary of John J. Audubon (ornithologist) (1985) (2nd issue). Multicoloured designs as T* **201** *showing original paintings. P* 14.

No.	Description	Unused	Used
1192	3 l. Little Blue Heron (*horiz*)	20	30
1193	4 l. White-tailed Kite	20	30
1194	5 l. Greater Shearwater (*horiz*)	20	30
1195	10 l. Magnificent Frigate Bird	30	30
1196	15 l. Black-necked Grebe	55	30
1197	20 l. Goosander	60	30
1198	13 r. Peregrine Falcon (*horiz*)	5·00	6·00
1199	14 r. Prairie Chicken (*horiz*)	5·00	6·00
1192/9	*Set of* 8	10·50	12·50
MS1200	Two sheets, each 74×104 mm. (a) 15 r. Fulmar. (b) 15 r. White-fronted Goose (*horiz*) *Set of* 2 *sheets*	19·00	20·00

Nos. 1192/9 were each issued in sheetlets of five stamps and one stamp-size label, which appears in the centre of the bottom row.

1986 (25 Oct). *World Cup Football Championship Winners, Mexico. Nos. 1174/8 optd with T* **213***a in gold.*

No.	Description	Unused	Used
1201	15 l. Type **212**	20	20
1202	2 r. Player gaining control of ball	85	85
1203	4 r. Two players competing for ball	1·50	1·75
1204	10 r. Player bouncing ball on knee	2·75	3·75
1201/4	*Set of* 4	4·75	6·00
MS1205	95×114 mm. 15 r. Player kicking ball	2·75	4·00

HALLEY'S COMET 1985 OFFICIAL 1986

(**213***b*)

214 Servicing Aircraft

1986 (30 Oct). *Appearance of Halley's Comet (2nd issue). Nos. 1150/5 optd with T* **213***b in silver.*

No.	Description	Unused	Used
1206	20 l. N.A.S.A. space telescope and Comet	50	40
1207	1 r. 50, E.S.A. *Giotto* spacecraft and Comet	1·00	90
1208	2 r. Japanese *Planet A* spacecraft and Comet	1·25	1·25
1209	4 r. Edmond Halley and Stonehenge	1·75	2·00
1210	5 r. Russian *Vega* spacecraft and Comet	1·75	2·00
1206/10	*Set of* 5	5·75	6·00
MS1211	101×70 mm. 15 r. Halley's Comet	3·75	5·00

(Des BG Studio)

1986 (4 Nov). *40th Anniv of U.N.E.S.C.O. T* **214** *and similar vert designs. Multicoloured. P* 15.

No.	Description	Unused	Used
1212	1 r. Type **214**	55	25
1213	2 r. Boat building	75	75
1214	3 r. Children in classroom	85	1·00
1215	5 r. Student in laboratory	1·25	1·75
1212/15	*Set of* 4	3·00	3·25
MS1216	77×100 mm. 15 r. Diving bell on sea bed	2·75	4·00

215 *Hypholoma fasciculare*

216 Ixora

(Des Mary Walters)

1986 (31 Dec). *Fungi of the Maldives. T* **215** *and similar multicoloured designs. P* 15.

No.	Description	Unused	Used
1217	15 l. Type **215**	70	25
1218	50 l. *Kuehneromyces mutabilis* (*vert*)	1·25	45
1219	1 r. *Amanita muscaria* (*vert*)	1·75	60
1220	2 r. *Agaricus campestris*	2·25	1·50
1221	3 r. *Amanita pantherina* (*vert*)	2·25	1·75
1222	4 r. *Coprinus comatus* (*vert*)	2·25	2·25
1223	5 r. *Gymnopilus junonias* ("*Pholiota spectabilis*")	2·40	2·75
1224	10 r. *Pluteus cervinus*	3·75	4·50
1217/24	*Set of* 8	15·00	12·50
MS1225	Two sheets, each 100×70 mm. (a) 15 r. *Armillaria mellea*. (b) 15 r. *Stropharia aeruginosa* (*vert*) *Set of* 2 *sheets*	12·00	14·00

(Des Mary Walters)

1987 (29 Jan). *Flowers. T* **216** *and similar vert designs. Multicoloured. P* 15.

No.	Description	Unused	Used
1226	10 l. Type **216**	10	10
1227	20 l. Frangipani	15	10
1228	50 l. Crinum	90	40
1229	2 r. Pink Rose	75	80
1230	4 r. Flamboyant Flower	1·00	1·50
1231	10 r. Ground Orchid	4·50	5·50
1226/31	*Set of* 6	6·75	7·50
MS1232	Two sheets, each 100×70 mm. (a) 15 r. Gardenia. (b) 15 r. Oleander *Set of* 2 *sheets*	4·75	6·50

Similar 1, 7 and 12 r. stamps were prepared but not issued. They exist from stock dispersed by the liquidator of Format International Security Printers Ltd.

217 Guides studying Wild Flowers

218 *Thespesia populnea*

(Des R. Vigurs)

1987 (4 Apr). *75th Anniv of Girl Guide Movement* (1985). *T* **217** *and similar horiz designs. Multicoloured. P* 15.

No.	Description	Unused	Used
1233	15 l. Type **217**	20	20
1234	2 r. Guides with pet rabbits	60	70
1235	4 r. Guide observing White Spoonbill	1·75	1·75
1236	12 r. Lady Baden-Powell and Guide flag	2·75	4·00
1233/6	*Set of* 4	4·75	6·00
MS1237	104×78 mm. 15 r. Guides in sailing dinghy	2·75	3·75

(Litho Questa)

1987 (22 Apr). *Trees and Plants. T* **218** *and similar multicoloured designs. P* 14.

No.	Description	Unused	Used
1238	50 l. Type **218**	10	10
1239	1 r. *Cocos nucifera*	15	20
1240	2 r. *Calophyllum mophyllum*	30	40
1241	3 r. *Xanthosoma indica* (*horiz*)	45	60
1242	5 r. *Ipomoea batatas* (*horiz*)	80	1·10
1243	7 r. *Artocarpus altilis*	1·10	1·75
1238/43	*Set of* 6	2·50	3·50
MS1244	75×109 mm. 15 r. *Cocos nucifera* (*different*)	2·25	3·25

No. 1241 is inscribed "Xyanthosoma indica" in error.

218*a* *Intrepid*, 1970

219 *Precis octavia*

(Des J. Iskowitz)

1987 (4 May). *America's Cup Yachting Championship. T* **218***a and similar multicoloured designs. P* 15.

No.	Description	Unused	Used
1245	15 l. Type **218***a*	10	10
1246	1 r. *France II*, 1974	20	20
1247	2 r. *Gretel*, 1962	40	60
1248	12 r. *Volunteer*, 1887	2·00	3·00
1245/8	*Set of* 4	2·40	3·50
MS1249	113×83 mm. 15 r. Helmsman and crew on deck of *Defender*, 1895 (*horiz*)	2·25	3·25

1987 (16 Dec). *Butterflies. T* **219** *and similar vert designs. Multicoloured. P* 15.

No.	Description	Unused	Used
1250	15 l. Type **219**	45	30
1251	20 l. *Atrophaneura hector*	45	30
1252	50 l. *Teinopalpus imperialis*	75	40
1253	1 r. *Kallima horsfieldi*	1·00	45
1254	2 r. *Cethosia biblis*	1·60	1·25
1255	4 r. *Idea jasonia*	2·50	2·00
1256	7 r. *Papilio memnon*	3·50	3·50
1257	10 r. *Aeropetes tulbaghia*	4·00	4·50
1250/7	*Set of* 8	13·00	11·50
MS1258	Two sheets, each 135×102 mm. (a) 15 r. *Acraea violae*. (b) 15 r. *Hebomoia leucippe* *Set of* 2 *sheets*	9·00	11·00

220 Isaac Newton experimenting with Spectrum

(Des J. Martin. Litho Questa)

1988 (10 Jan). *Great Scientific Discoveries. T* **220** *and similar multicoloured designs. P* 14.
1259 1 r. 50, Type **220** .. .. 1·25 1·00
1260 3 r. Euclid composing *Principles of Geometry* (*vert*) .. .. 1·60 1·75
1261 4 r. Mendel formulating theory of Genetic Evolution (*vert*) .. .. 1·75 2·00
1262 5 r. Galileo and moons of Jupiter .. .. 3·00 3·00
1259/62 .. .. *Set of* 4 7·00 7·00
MS1263 102×72 mm. 15 r. "Apollo" lunar module (*vert*) .. .. 4·50 5·50

221 Donald Duck and Weather Satellite

(Des Walt Disney Co. Litho Questa)

1988 (15 Feb). *Space Exploration. T* **221** *and similar multicoloured designs showing Walt Disney cartoon characters. P* 14×13½ (*horiz*) *or* 13½×14 (*vert*).
1264 3 l. Type **221** 10 10
1265 4 l. Minnie Mouse and navigation satellite 10 10
1266 5 l. Mickey Mouse's nephews talking via communication satellite 10 10
1267 10 l. Goofy in lunar rover (*vert*) 10 10
1268 20 l. Minnie Mouse delivering pizza to flying saucer (*vert*) 10 10
1269 13 r. Mickey Mouse directing spacecraft docking (*vert*) .. .. .. 5·00 5·00
1270 14 r. Mickey Mouse and "Voyager 2" .. 5·00 5·00
1264/70 .. .. *Set of* 7 9·00 9·00
MS1271 Two sheets, each 127×102 mm. (a) 15 r. Mickey Mouse at first Moon landing, 1969. (b) 15 r. Mickey Mouse and nephews in space station swimming pool (*vert*) .. *Set of* 2 *sheets* 9·00 10·00

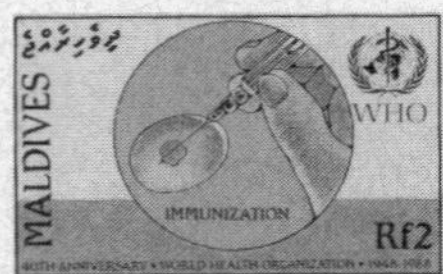

222 Syringe and Bacterium ("Immunization")

(Des Mary Walters. Litho Questa)

1988 (7 Apr). *40th Anniv of World Health Organization. T* **222** *and similar horiz design. Multicoloured. P* 14.
1272 2 r. Type **222** 25 35
1273 4 r. Tap ("Clean Water") 50 65

223 Water Droplet and Atoll **224** Globe, Carrier Pigeon and Letter

(Des I. Rasheed)

1988 (9 May). *World Environment Day* (1987). *T* **223** *and similar multicoloured designs. P* 15.
1274 15 l. Type **223** 10 10
1275 75 l. Coral reef 20 30
1276 2 r. Audubon's Shearwaters in flight .. 75 1·25
1274/6 .. .. *Set of* 3 95 1·50
MS1277 105×76 mm. 15 r. Banyan Tree (*vert*) 2·25 3·50

(Litho Questa)

1988 (31 May). *Transport and Telecommunications Decade. T* **224** *and similar horiz designs, each showing central globe. Multicoloured. P* 14.
1278 2 r. Type **224** 60 65
1279 3 r. Dish aerial and girl using telephone 90 95
1280 5 r. Satellite, television, telephone and antenna tower .. .. 1·75 2·00
1281 10 r. Car, ship and Lockheed L-1011 TriStar airliner .. .. .. 4·50 4·75
1278/81 .. .. *Set of* 4 7·00 7·50

40TH WEDDING ANNIVERSARY
H.M.QUEEN ELIZABETH II
H.R.H. THE DUKE OF EDINBURGH

(**225**)

226 Discus-throwing

1988 (7 July). *Royal Ruby Wedding. Nos.* 1170/3 *optd with T* **225** *in gold.*
1282 1 r. black and chrome-yellow 35 25
1283 2 r. multicoloured 50 60
1284 12 r. multicoloured .. .. .. 2·50 3·50
1282/4 .. .. *Set of* 3 3·00 4·00
MS1285 120×85 mm. 15 r. black and grey-brown 3·50 4·00

(Des B. Bundock. Litho Questa)

1988 (16 July). *Olympic Games, Seoul. T* **226** *and similar multicoloured designs. P* 14.
1286 15 l. Type **226** 10 10
1287 2 r. 100 metres race 40 40
1288 4 r. Gymnastics (*horiz*) 70 80
1289 12 r. Three-day equestrian event (*horiz*) 2·25 3·25
1286/9 .. .. *Set of* 4 3·00 4·00
MS1290 106×76 mm. 20 r. Tennis (*horiz*) .. 3·00 4·00

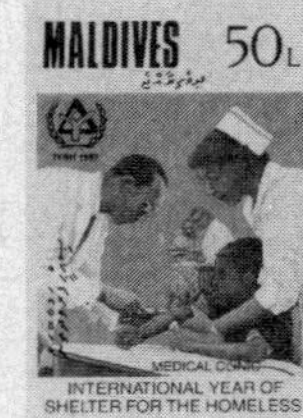

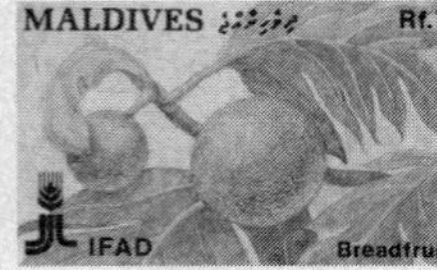

227 Immunization at Clinic **228** Breadfruit

(Des A. DiLorenzo. Litho Questa)

1988 (20 July). *International Year of Shelter for the Homeless. T* **227** *and similar vert designs. Multicoloured. P* 14.
1291 50 l. Type **227** 30 30
1292 3 r. Prefab housing estate .. .. 1·10 1·40
MS1293 63×105 mm. 15 r. Building site .. 1·75 2·25

(Des G. Watkins. Litho Questa)

1988 (30 July). *10th Anniv of International Fund for Agricultural Development. T* **228** *and similar multicoloured designs. P* 14.
1294 7 r. Type **228** .. .. 1·00 1·40
1295 10 r. Mangos (*vert*) .. .. .. 1·50 1·90
MS1296 103×74 mm. 15 r. Coconut palm, fishing boat and Yellowtail Tuna .. .. .. 1·75 2·25

(**229**)

230 Pres. Kennedy and Launch of "Apollo" Spacecraft

1988 (1 Dec). *World Aids Day. Nos.* 1272/3 *optd with T* **229**.
1297 2 r. Type **222** 35 45
1298 4 r. Tap ("Clean Water") 65 80

(Des A. Nahigian. Litho Questa)

1989 (13 Feb). *25th Death Anniv of John F. Kennedy (American statesman)* (1988). *U.S. Space Achievements. T* **230** *and similar vert designs. Multicoloured. P* 14.
1299 5 r. Type **230** .. .. 1·60 1·90
a. Horiz strip of 4. Nos. 1299/1302 .. 5·75
1300 5 r. Lunar module and astronaut on Moon 1·60 1·90
1301 5 r. Astronaut and buggy on Moon .. 1·60 1·90
1302 5 r. President Kennedy and spacecraft .. 1·60 1·90
1299/1302 .. .. .. *Set of* 4 5·75 7·00
MS1303 108 × 77 mm. 15 r. President Kennedy making speech .. .. 2·75 3·50
Nos. 1299/1302 were printed together, *se-tenant*, in horizontal strips of 4 throughout the sheet.

J. SCHULT
DDR

(**231**)

ASIA-PACIFIC
TELECOMMUNITY
10 YEARS

(**232**)

1989 (29 Apr). *Olympic Medal Winners, Seoul. Nos.* 1286/90 *optd as T* **231**.
1304 15 l. Type **226** (optd with T **231**) 15 15
1305 2 r. 100 metres race (optd "C. LEWIS USA") 55 55
1306 4 r. Gymnastics (*horiz*) (optd "MEN'S ALL AROUND V. ARTEMOV USSR") .. 1·10 1·10
1307 12 r. Three-day equestrian event (*horiz*) (optd "TEAM SHOW JUMPING W. GERMANY") .. .. .. 2·50 3·00
1304/7 .. .. *Set of* 4 3·75 4·25
MS1308 106×76 mm. 20 r. Tennis (*horiz*) (optd "OLYMPIC WINNERS MEN'S SINGLES GOLD M. MECIR CZECH. SILVER T. MAYOTTE USA BRONZE B. GILBERT USA") 3·25 4·00
On No. **MS**1308 the overprint appears on the sheet margin and not the 20 r. stamp.

(Litho Questa)

1989 (20 May). *500th Birth Anniv of Titian (artist). Vert designs as T* **186a** *of Lesotho showing paintings. Multicoloured. P* 13½×14.
1309 15 l. "Benedetto Varchi" 10 10
1310 1 r. "Portrait of a Young Man" 20 15
1311 2 r. "King Francis I of France" 40 40
1312 5 r. "Pietro Aretino" .. .. .. 1·10 1·25
1313 15 r. "The Bravo" .. .. 5·00 6·00
1314 20 r. "The Concert" (detail) .. .. 5·50 6·50
1309/14 .. .. *Set of* 6 11·00 13·00
MS1315 Two sheets. (a) 112×96 mm. 20 r. "An Allegory of Prudence" (detail). (b) 96×110 mm. 20 r. "Francesco Maria della Rovere" *Set of* 2 *sheets* 6·00 7·00

1989 (10 July). *10th Anniv of Asia-Pacific Telecommunity. Nos.* 1279/80 *optd with T* **232** *in silver.*
1316 3 r. Dish aerial and girl using telephone 1·00 1·25
1317 5 r. Satellite, television, telephone and antenna tower .. .. .. 1·40 1·75

(Litho Questa)

1989 (2 Sept–16 Oct). *Japanese Art. Paintings by Hokusai. Horiz designs as T* **187a** *of Lesotho. Multicoloured. P* 14×13½.
1318 15 l. "Fuji from Hodogaya" 10 10
1319 50 l. "Fuji from Lake Kawaguchi" .. 15 15
1320 1 r. "Fuji from Owari" 25 25
1321 2 r. "Fuji from Tsukudajima in Edo" .. 50 50
1322 4 r. "Fuji from a Teahouse at Yoshida" .. 90 90
1323 6 r. "Fuji from Tagonoura" .. .. 1·25 1·25
1324 10 r. "Fuji from Mishima-goe" .. .. 3·00 3·25
1325 12 r. "Fuji from the Sumida River in Edo" 3·00 3·25
1318/25 .. .. *Set of* 8 8·25 8·75
MS1326 Two sheets, each 101×77 mm. (a) 18 r. "Fuji from Inume Pass" (2 Sept). (b) 18 r. "Fuji from Fukagawa in Edo" (16 Oct) *Set of* 2 *sheets* 7·50 8·00
Nos. 1318/25 were each printed in sheetlets of 10 containing two horizontal strips of 5 stamps separated by printed labels commemorating Emperor Hirohito.

233 Clown Triggerfish

(Des L. Birmingham. Litho Questa)

1989 (16 Oct). *Tropical Fishes. T* **233** *and similar horiz designs. Multicoloured. P* 14.
1327 20 l. Type **233** 25 20
1328 50 l. Blue-striped Snapper 35 25
1329 1 r. Powder-blue Surgeonfish 45 30
1330 2 r. Oriental Sweetlips 75 65
1331 3 r. Six-barred Wrasse .. .. .. 1·00 85
1332 8 r. Thread-finned Butterflyfish .. 2·00 2·50
1333 10 r. Bicoloured Parrotfish .. .. 2·40 2·75
1334 12 r. Scarlet-finned Squirrelfish .. .. 2·40 2·75
1327/34 .. .. *Set of* 8 8·75 9·25
MS1335 Two sheets, each 101×73 mm. (a) 15 r. Butterfly Perch. (b) 15 r. Semicircle Angelfish *Set of* 2 *sheets* 9·50 11·00

234 Goofy, Mickey and Minnie Mouse with Takuri "Type 3", 1907

(Des Walt Disney Co. Litho Questa)

1989 (17 Nov). *"World Stamp Expo '89" International Stamp Exhibition, Washington (1st issue). T* **234** *and similar horiz designs showing Walt Disney cartoon characters with Japanese cars. Multicoloured. P* 14×13½.

1336 15 l. Type **234** 20 15
1337 50 l. Donald and Daisy Duck in Mitsubishi "Model A", 1917 .. .. 40 30
1338 1 r. Goofy in Datsun "Roadstar", 1935 .. 70 50
1339 2 r. Donald and Daisy Duck with Mazda, 1940 .. .. 1·00 75
1340 4 r. Donald Duck with Nissan "Bluebird 310", 1959 .. .. 1·50 1·25
1341 6 r. Donald and Daisy Duck with Subaru "360", 1958 .. .. 1·75 1·75
1342 10 r. Mickey Mouse and Pluto in Honda "5800", 1966 .. .. 3·25 3·75
1343 12 r. Mickey Mouse and Goofy in Daihatsu "Fellow", 1966 .. .. 3·75 4·25
1336/43 .. .. *Set of* 8 11·50 11·50
MS1344 Two sheets, each 127×102 mm. (a) 20 r. Daisy Duck with Chip n'Dale and Isuzu "Trooper II", 1981 (b) 20 r. Mickey Mouse with tortoise and Toyota "Supra", 1985 .. *Set of* 2 *sheets* 11·00 13·00

(Des Design Element. Litho Questa)

1989 (17 Nov). *"World Stamp Expo '89" International Stamp Exhibition, Washington (2nd issue). Landmarks of Washington. Sheet* 62×78 *mm containing multicoloured designs as T* **193a** *of Lesotho, but vert. P* 14.

MS1345 8 r. Marine Corps Memorial, Arlington National Cemetery .. .. 1·50 2·00

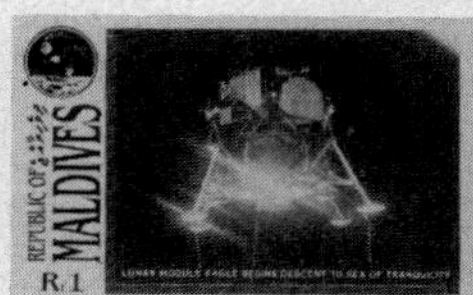

235 Lunar Module *Eagle*

(Des W. Hanson Studio. Litho Questa).

1989 (24 Nov). *20th Anniv of First Manned Landing on Moon. T* **235** *and similar multicoloured designs. P* 14.

1346 1 r. Type **235** 30 20
1347 2 r. Astronaut Aldrin collecting dust samples 50 60
1348 6 r. Aldrin setting up seismometer .. 1·25 1·75
1349 10 r. Pres. Nixon congratulating "Apollo 11" astronauts .. .. 1·90 2·25
1346/9 .. .. *Set of* 4 3·50 4·25
MS1350 107×75 mm. 18 r. Television picture of Armstrong about to step onto Moon (34×47 *mm*). P 13½×14 .. .. .. 3·50 4·00

236 Jawaharlal Nehru with Mahatma Gandhi

237 Sir William van Horne, Locomotive and Map of Canadian Pacific Railway, 1894

(Des Design Element. Litho B.D.T.)

1989 (20 Dec)–**90**. *Anniversaries and Events. T* **236** *and similar multicoloured designs. P* 14.

1351 20 l. Type **236** (birth centenary) 75 45
1352 50 l. Opium poppies and logo (anti-drugs campaign) (*vert*) 75 45
1353 1 r. William Shakespeare (425th birth anniv) (15.2.90) 75 45
1354 2 r. Storming the Bastille (bicent of French Revolution) (*vert*) (15.2.90) .. 75 60
1355 3 r. Concorde (20th anniv of first flight) (15.2.90) .. .. 1·75 1·25
1356 8 r. George Washington (bicent of inauguration) .. .. 1·75 2·00
1357 10 r. William Bligh (bicent of mutiny on the *Bounty*) .. .. 3·50 3·50
1358 12 r. Hamburg Harbour (800th anniv) (*vert*) (15.2.90) .. .. 3·50 3·75
1351/8 .. .. *Set of* 8 13·00 11·00
MS1359 Two sheets. (a) 115×85 mm. 18 r. Baseball players (50th anniv of first televised game) (*vert*). (b) 110×80 mm. 18 r. Franz von Taxis (500th anniv of regular European postal services) (*vert*) (15.2.90) .. .. *Set of* 2 *sheets* 10·00 11·00

(Des A. Fagbohun. Litho Questa)

1989 (26 Dec). *Railway Pioneers. T* **237** *and similar vert designs. Multicoloured. P* 14.

1360 10 l. Type **237** 15 15
1361 25 l. Matthew Murray and Middleton Colliery rack locomotive, 1811 .. 20 20
1362 50 l. Louis Favre and locomotive entering tunnel, 1856 .. .. 25 25
1363 2 r. George Stephenson and *Locomotion*, 1825 .. .. 55 55
1364 6 r. Richard Trevithick and Pen-y-darran locomotive, 1804 .. .. .. 1·50 1·50
1365 8 r. George Nagelmackers and "Orient Express" dining car, 1869 .. .. 1·75 1·75
1366 10 r. William Jessop and horse-drawn line, 1770 .. .. 2·50 2·50
1367 12 r. Isambard Brunel and G.W.R. train, 1833 .. .. 3·00 3·00
1360/7 .. .. *Set of* 8 9·00 9·00
MS1368 Two sheets, each 71×103 mm. (a) 18 r. George Pullman (inventor of sleeping cars), 1864. (b) 18 r. Rudolf Diesel (inventor of diesel engine), 1892 .. .. .. *Set of* 2 *sheets* 7·00 8·00

238 Bodu Thakurufaanu Memorial Centre, Utheemu

239 "Louis XVI in Coronation Robes" (Duplesis)

(Litho B.D.T.)

1990 (1 Jan). *25th Anniv of Independence. T* **238** *and similar horiz designs. Multicoloured. P* 14.

1369 20 l. Type **238** 10 10
1370 25 l. Islamic Centre, Malé 10 10
1371 50 l. National flag and logos of international organizations 10 10
1372 2 r. Presidential Palace, Malé 30 40
1373 5 r. National Security Service .. .. 85 1·25
1369/73 .. .. *Set of* 5 1·25 1·75
MS1374 128×90 mm. 10 r. National emblem .. 1·75 2·25

(Litho Questa)

1990 (11 Jan). *Bicentenary of French Revolution and "Philexfrance 89" International Stamp Exhibition, Paris. French Paintings. T* **239** *and similar multicoloured designs. P* 13½×14.

1375 15 l. Type **239** 15 15
1376 50 l. "Monsieur Lavoisier and his Wife" (David) 25 25
1377 1 r. "Madame Pastoret" (David) 35 35
1378 2 r. "Oath of Lafayette, 14 July 1790" (anon) 55 55
1379 4 r. "Madame Trudaine" (David) .. .. 1·00 1·00
1380 6 r. "Chenard celebrating the Liberation of Savoy" (Boilly) .. .. .. 1·40 1·60
1381 10 r. "An Officer swears Allegiance to the Constitution" (anon) .. .. .. 2·75 3·25
1382 12 r. "Self Portrait" (David) .. .. 3·00 3·50
1375/82 .. .. *Set of* 8 8·50 9·50
MS1383 Two sheets. (a) 104×79 mm. 20 r. "The Oath of the Tennis Court, 20 June 1789" (David) (*horiz*). P 14×13½. (b) 79×104 mm. 20 r. "Rousseau and Symbols of the Revolution" (Jeaurat). P 13½×14 .. .. *Set of* 2 *sheets* 8·00 9·00

239a Donald Duck, Mickey Mouse and Goofy playing Rugby

(Des Walt Disney Co. Litho Questa)

1990 (3 May). *"Stamp World London 90" International Stamp Exhibition. T* **239a** *and similar horiz designs showing Walt Disney cartoon characters playing British sports. Multicoloured. P* 14×13½.

1384 15 l. Type **239a** 15 15
1385 50 l. Donald Duck and Chip-n-Dale curling 25 25
1386 1 r. Goofy playing polo 40 40
1387 2 r. Mickey Mouse and nephews playing soccer 65 65
1388 4 r. Mickey Mouse playing cricket .. 1·25 1·25
1389 6 r. Minnie and Mickey Mouse at Ascot races .. .. 1·60 1·60
1390 10 r. Mickey Mouse and Goofy playing tennis .. .. 3·00 3·00
1391 12 r. Donald Duck and Mickey Mouse playing bowls .. .. 3·00 3·00
1384/91 .. .. *Set of* 8 9·25 9·25
MS1392 Two sheets, each 126×101 mm. (a) 20 r. Minnie Mouse fox-hunting. (b) 20 r. Mickey Mouse playing golf .. .. *Set of* 2 *sheets* 12·00 12·00

240 Silhouettes of Queen Elizabeth II and Queen Victoria

241 Sultan's Tomb

(Des S. Pollard. Litho B.D.T.)

1990 (6 May). *150th Anniv of the Penny Black. T* **240** *and similar horiz designs. P* 15×14.

1393 8 r. black and olive-green .. .. 2·00 2·25
1394 12 r. black and deep dull blue .. .. 2·50 2·75
MS1395 109×84 mm. 18 r. black & yellow-brown 3·50 4·25
Designs:—12 r. As Type **240**, but with position of silhouettes reversed; 18 r. Penny Black.

(Des Young Phillips Studio. Litho Questa)

1990 (8 July). *90th Birthday of Queen Elizabeth the Queen Mother. Vert designs as T* **198a** *of Lesotho showing portraits, 1920–29. P* 14.

1396 6 r. brownish blk, brt mag & turquoise-bl 80 1·10
a. Strip of 3. Nos. 1396/8 .. .. 2·25
1397 6 r. brownish blk, brt mag & turquoise-bl 80 1·10
1398 6 r. brownish blk, brt mag & turquoise-bl 80 1·10
1396/8 .. .. *Set of* 3 2·25 3·00
MS1399 90×75 mm. 18 r. multicoloured .. 2·50 3·25
Designs:—No. 1396, Lady Elizabeth Bowes-Lyon; No. 1397, Lady Elizabeth Bowes-Lyon wearing headband; No. 1398, Lady Elizabeth Bowes-Lyon leaving for her wedding; No. **MS**1399, Lady Elizabeth Bowes-Lyon wearing wedding dress.
Nos. 1396/8 were printed together, horizontally and vertically *se-tenant*, in sheetlets of 9 (3×3).

(Litho Questa)

1990 (21 July). *Islamic Heritage Year. T* **241** *and similar horiz designs, each black and light cobalt. P* 14.

1400 1 r. Type **241** 25 35
a. Block of 6. Nos. 1400/5 .. .. 1·40
1401 1 r. Thakurufaan's Palace 25 35
1402 1 r. Malé Mosque 25 35
1403 2 r. Veranda of Friday Mosque 25 35
1404 2 r. Interior of Friday Mosque 25 35
1405 2 r. Friday Mosque and Monument .. 25 35
1400/5 .. .. *Set of* 6 1·40 1·90
Nos. 1400/5 were printed together, *se-tenant*, in blocks of 6 (3×2) within the sheet of 36.

242 Defence of Wake Island, 1941

(Des W. Wright. Litho Questa)

1990 (9 Aug). *50th Anniv of Second World War. T* **242** *and similar horiz designs. Multicoloured. P* 14.

1406 15 l. Type **242** 15 15
1407 25 l. Stilwell's army in Burma, 1944 .. 20 20
1408 50 l. Normandy offensive, 1944 .. .. 25 25
1409 1 r. Capture of Saipan, 1944 .. .. 40 40
1410 2 r. 50, D-Day landings, 1944 .. .. 70 70
1411 3 r. 50, Allied landings in Norway, 1940 90 90
1412 4 r. Lord Mountbatten, Head of Combined Operations, 1943 .. .. .. 1·10 1·10
1413 6 r. Japanese surrender, Tokyo Bay, 1945 1·50 1·50
1414 10 r. Potsdam Conference, 1945 .. .. 2·50 2·50
1415 12 r. Allied invasion of Sicily, 1943 .. 2·75 2·75
1406/15 .. .. *Set of* 10 9·50 9·50
MS1416 115×87 mm. 18 r. Atlantic convoy .. 5·00 6·00

243 Crested Tern

(Des Mary Walters. Litho Questa)

1990 (9 Aug). *Birds. T* **243** *and similar horiz designs. Multicoloured. P* 14.

1417 25 l. Type **243** 15 15
1418 50 l. Koel 25 25
1419 1 r. White Tern 35 35
1420 3 r. 50, Cinnamon Bittern .. .. 90 1·00
1421 6 r. Sooty Tern .. .. 1·40 1·60
1422 8 r. Audubon's Shearwater .. .. 1·60 2·00
1423 12 r. Common Noddy .. .. .. 2·50 3·00
1424 15 r. Lesser Frigate Bird .. .. .. 2·75 3·25
1417/24 .. .. *Set of* 8 9·00 10·50
MS1425 Two sheets, each 100×69 mm. (a) 18 r. Grey Heron. (b) 18 r. White-tailed Tropic Bird *Set of* 2 *sheets* 8·00 10·00

244 Emblem, Dish Aerial and Sailboards **245** *Spathoglottis plicata*

(Litho Questa)

1990 (21 Nov). *Fifth South Asian Association for Regional Co-operation Summit. T* **244** *and similar horiz designs. P* 14.

1426 75 l. black and brown-orange 20 25
1427 3 r. 50, multicoloured .. .. 90 1·25
MS1428 112×82 mm. 20 r. multicoloured .. 4·25 5·50

Designs:—3 r. 50, Flags of member nations; 20 r. Global warming diagram.

(Des Dot Barlowe. Litho Questa)

1990 (9 Dec). *"EXPO '90" International Garden and Greenery Exhibition, Osaka. Flowers. T* **245** *and similar multicoloured designs. P* 14.

1429 20 l. Type **245** 30 20
1430 75 l. *Hippeastrum puniceum* 50 40
1431 2 r. *Tecoma stans (horiz)* 75 65
1432 3 r. 50 *Catharanthus roseus (horiz)* .. 1·00 1·10
1433 10 r. *Ixora coccinea (horiz)* .. .. 2·25 2·50
1434 12 r. *Clitorea ternatea (horiz)* .. .. 2·50 2·75
1435 15 r. *Caesalpinia pulcherrima* .. .. 2·75 3·00
1429/35 .. .. *Set of* 7 9·00 9·50
MS1436 Four sheets, each 111×79 mm. (a) 20 r. *Plumeria obtusa (horiz).* (b) 20 r. *Jasminum grandiflorum (horiz).* (c) 20 r. *Rosa* sp *(horiz).* (d) 20 r. *Hibiscus tiliaceous (horiz)* .. *Set of* 4 *sheets* 13·00 13·00

246 The Hare and the Tortoise

(Des Walt Disney Co. Litho Questa)

1990 (11 Dec). *International Literacy Year. T* **246** *and similar multicoloured designs showing Walt Disney cartoon characters illustrating fables by Aesop. P* 14×13½.

1437 15 l. Type **246** 20 10
1438 50 l. The Town Mouse and the Country Mouse 35 25
1439 1 r. The Fox and the Crow 45 35
1440 3 r. 50, The Travellers and the Bear .. 1·10 1·10
1441 4 r. The Fox and the Lion .. .. 1·25 1·25
1442 6 r. The Mice Meeting .. .. .. 1·75 1·75
1443 10 r. The Fox and the Goat .. .. 2·00 2·25
1444 12 r. The Dog in the Manger .. .. 2·40 2·75
1437/44 .. .. *Set of* 8 8·50 8·75
MS1445 Two sheets, each 127×102 mm. (a) 20 r. The Miller, his Son and the Ass *(vert).* (b) 20 r. The Miser's Gold *(vert).* P 13½×14 *Set of* 2 *sheets* 10·00 10·00

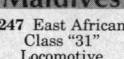

247 East African Class "31" Locomotive **248** Ruud Gullit of Holland

(Des T. Agans. Litho Questa)

1990 (15 Dec). *Steam Railway Locomotives. T* **247** *and similar vert designs. Multicoloured. P* 14.

1446 20 l. Type **247** 45 30
1447 50 l. Sudan Railways Class "Mikado" .. 60 45
1448 1 r. South African Beyer-Garratt Class "GM" 75 60
1449 3 r. Rhodesia Railways Class "7" .. 1·75 1·75
1450 5 r. U.S.A. Central Pacific Class "229" .. 2·00 2·00
1451 8 r. U.S.A. Reading Class "415" .. .. 2·25 2·25
1452 10 r. Canada Porter narrow gauge .. 2·25 2·50
1453 12 r. U.S.A. Great Northern Class "515" .. 2·50 2·75
1446/53 .. .. *Set of* 8 11·50 11·50
MS1454 Two sheets, each 90×65 mm. (a) 20 r. 19th-century standard American locomotive. (b) 20 r. East African Railways locomotive No. 5950 *Set of* 2 *sheets* 10·50 10·50

(Des Young Phillips Studio. Litho Questa)

1990 (27 Dec). *World Cup Football Championship, Italy. T* **248** *and similar multicoloured designs. P* 14.

1455 1 r. Type **248** 75 50
1456 2 r. 50, Paul Gascoigne of England .. 1·25 1·25
1457 3 r. 50, Brazilian challenging Argentine player .. .. 1·60 1·60
1458 5 r. Brazilian taking control of ball .. 2·00 2·00
1459 7 r. Italian and Austrian jumping for header .. .. 2·50 2·50
1460 10 r. Russian being chased by Turkish player .. .. 2·75 3·00
1461 15 r. Andres Brehme of West Germany .. 3·00 3·25
1455/61 .. .. *Set of* 7 12·50 12·50
MS1462 Four sheets, each 77×92 mm. (a) 18 r. Head of an Austrian player *(horiz).* (b) 18 r. Head of a South Korean player *(horiz).* (c) 20 r. Diego Maradonna of Argentina *(horiz).* (d) 20 r. Schilacci of Italy *(horiz)* .. .. *Set of* 4 *sheets* 14·00 15·00

249 Winged Euonymus **250** "Summer" (Rubens)

(Des N. Waldman. Litho Questa)

1991 (29 Jan). *Bonsai Trees and Shrubs. T* **249** *and similar vert designs. Multicoloured. P* 14.

1463 20 l. Type **249** 30 20
1464 50 l. Japanese Black Pine 45 35
1465 1 r. Japanese Five Needle Pine 70 55
1466 3 r. 50, Flowering Quince .. .. 1·60 1·60
1467 5 r. Chinese Elm .. .. .. 2·00 2·00
1468 8 r. Japanese Persimmon .. .. 2·25 2·50
1469 10 r. Japanese Wisteria .. .. .. 2·25 2·50
1470 12 r. Satsuki Azalea .. .. .. 2·50 2·75
1463/70 .. .. *Set of* 8 11·00 11·00
MS1471 Two sheets, each 89×88 mm. (a) 20 r. Trident Maple. (b) 20 r. Sargent Juniper *Set of* 2 *sheets* 8·00 9·00

(Litho Questa)

1991 (7 Feb). *350th Death Anniv of Rubens. T* **250** *and similar horiz designs. Multicoloured. P* 14×13½.

1472 20 l. Type **250** 15 15
1473 50 l. "Landscape with Rainbow" (detail) .. 25 25
1474 1 r. "Wreck of Aeneas" 40 40
1475 2 r. 50, "Chàteau de Steen" (detail) .. 75 75
1476 3 r. 50, "Landscape with Herd of Cows" .. 95 95
1477 7 r. "Ruins on the Palantine" .. .. 1·60 1·60
1478 10 r. "Landscape with Peasants and Cows" 2·00 2·00
1479 12 r. "Wagon fording Stream" .. .. 2·40 2·40
1472/9 .. .. *Set of* 8 7·75 7·75
MS1480 Four sheets, each 100×71 mm. (a) 20 r. "Landscape at Sunset". (b) 20 r. "Peasants with Cattle by a Stream". (c) 20 r. "Shepherd with Flock". (d) 20 r. "Wagon in Stream" *Set of* 4 *sheets* 13·00 14·00

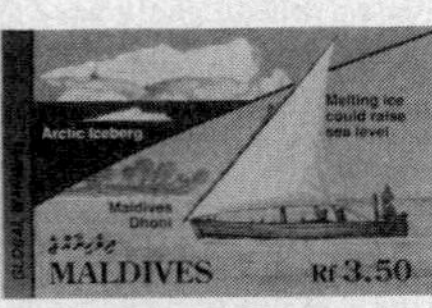

251 Greek Messenger from Marathon, 490 BC (2480th anniv) **252** Arctic Iceberg and Maldives Dhoni

(Des W. Wright. Litho Questa)

1991 (11 Mar). *Anniversaries and Events* (1990). *T* **251** *and similar multicoloured designs. P* 14.

1481 50 l. Type **251** 35 25
1482 1 r. Anthony Fokker in Haarlem Spin monoplane (birth cent) 60 40
1483 3 r. 50, "Early Bird" satellite (25th anniv) 1·25 1·25
1484 7 r. Signing Reunification of Germany agreement *(horiz)* .. .. 1·75 2·25
1485 8 r. King John signing Magna Carta (775th anniv) .. .. .. 2·25 2·50
1486 10 r. Dwight D. Eisenhower (birth cent) .. 2·25 2·50
1487 12 r. Sir Winston Churchill (25th death anniv) .. .. 2·75 3·25
1488 15 r. Pres. Reagan at Berlin Wall (German reunification) *(horiz)* .. .. 2·75 3·25
1481/8 .. .. *Set of* 8 12·50 14·00
MS1489 Two sheets. (a) 180×81 mm. 20 r. German Junkers Ju88 bomber (50th anniv of Battle of Britain) *(horiz).* (b) 160×73 mm. 20 r. Brandenburg Gate (German reunification) *(horiz)* .. .. *Set of* 2 *sheets* 8·50 9·50

(Litho Questa)

1991 (10 Apr). *Global Warming. T* **252** *and similar horiz design. Multicoloured. P* 14.

1490 3 r. 50, Type **252** .. .. 1·25 1·25
1491 7 r. Antarctic iceberg and *Maldive Trader* (freighter) .. .. .. 2·50 2·50

253 S.A.A.R.C. Emblem and Medal **254** Children on Beach

(Litho Questa)

1991 (10 Apr). *Year of the Girl Child. P* 14.

1492 **253** 7 r. multicoloured .. .. .. 1·75 1·75

(Litho Questa)

1991 (14 Apr). *Year of the Maldivian Child. Children's Paintings. T* **254** *and similar horiz designs. Multicoloured. P* 14.

1493 3 r. 50, Type **254** .. .. 1·25 1·25
1494 5 r. Children in a park .. .. .. 1·75 1·75
1495 10 r. Hungry child dreaming of food .. 2·75 3·00
1496 25 r. Scuba diver .. .. 5·00 6·00
1493/6 .. .. *Set of* 4 9·75 11·00

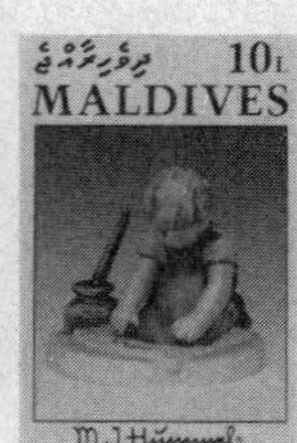

255 "Still Life: Japanese Vase with Roses and Anemones" (Van Gogh) **256** Boy painting

(Litho Walsall)

1991 (6 June). *Death Centenary of Vincent van Gogh (artist)* (1990). *T* **255** *and similar multicoloured designs. P* 13½.

1497 15 l. Type **255** 20 20
1498 20 l. "Still Life: Red Poppies and Daisies" 20 20
1499 2 r. "Vincent's Bedroom in Arles" *(horiz)* 70 70
1500 3 r. 50, "The Mulberry Tree" *(horiz)* .. 1·00 1·00
1501 7 r. "Blossoming Chestnut Branches" *(horiz)* .. .. 1·75 1·75
1502 10 r. "Peasant Couple going to Work" *(horiz)* .. .. 2·25 2·25
1503 12 r. "Still Life: Pink Roses" *(horiz)* .. 2·50 2·50
1504 15 r. "Child with Orange" .. .. 2·75 2·75
1497/1504 .. .. .. *Set of* 8 10·00 10·00
MS1505 Two sheets. (a) 77×101 mm. 25 r. "Houses in Auvers" (70×94 *mm*). (b) 101×77 mm. 25 r. "The Courtyard of the Hospital at Arles" (94×70 *mm*). Imperf .. *Set of* 2 *sheets* 10·50 10·50

(Des D. Miller. Litho Walsall)

1991 (4 July). *65th Birthday of Queen Elizabeth II. Horiz designs as T* **210** *of Lesotho. Multicoloured. P* 14.

1506 2 r. Queen at Trooping the Colour, 1990 75 60
1507 5 r. Queen with Queen Mother and Princess Margaret, 1973 .. .. 1·50 1·50
1508 8 r. Queen and Prince Philip in open carriage, 1986 .. .. .. 2·25 2·50
1509 12 r. Queen at Royal Estates Ball .. .. 2·75 3·25
1506/9 .. .. *Set of* 4 6·50 7·00
MS1510 68×90 mm. 25 r. Separate photographs of Queen and Prince Philip .. .. 5·75 6·50

(Des D. Miller. Litho Walsall)

1991 (4 July). *10th Wedding Anniv of Prince and Princess of Wales. Horiz designs as T* **210** *of Lesotho. Multicoloured. P* 14.

1511 1 r. Prince and Princess skiing, 1986 .. 30 20
1512 3 r. 50, Separate photographs of Prince, Princess and sons .. .. .. 1·00 90
1513 7 r. Prince Henry in Christmas play and Prince William watching polo .. 1·50 1·75
1514 15 r. Princess Diana at Ipswich, 1990, and Prince Charles playing polo .. 2·75 3·00
1511/14 .. .. *Set of* 4 5·00 5·25
MS1515 68×90 mm. 25 r. Prince and Princess of Wales in Hungary, and Princes William and Henry going to school .. .. .. 5·75 6·50

(Litho Questa)

1991 (25 July). *Hummel Figurines. T* **256** *and similar vert designs. Multicoloured. P* 14.
1516 10 l. Type **256** 10 10
1517 25 l. Boy reading at table 15 15
1518 50 l. Boy with school satchel 30 30
1519 2 r. Girl with basket 60 60
1520 3 r. 50, Boy reading .. .. .. 90 1·00
1521 8 r. Girl and young child reading .. 1·75 2·00
1522 10 r. School girls .. .. 2·00 2·25
1523 25 r. School boys .. .. 4·00 5·00
1516/23 .. .. *Set of* 8 9·00 10·00
MS1524 Two sheets, each 97×127 mm. (a) 5 r. As No. 1519; 5 r. As No. 1520; 5 r. As No. 1521; 5 r. As No. 1522; (b) 8 r. As Type **256**; 8 r. As No. 1517; 8 r. As No. 1518; 8 r. As No. 1523 *Set of* 2 *sheets* 9·00 10·00

257 Class "C 57" Steam Locomotive

258 *Salamis temora* and *Vanda caerulea*

(Litho B.D.T.)

1991 (25 Aug). *"Phila Nippon '91" International Stamp Exhibition, Tokyo. Japanese Steam Locomotives. T* **257** *and similar multicoloured designs. P* 14.
1525 15 l. Type **257** 15 15
1526 25 l. Class "6250" locomotive (*horiz*) .. 25 25
1527 1 r. Class "D 51" locomotive 40 40
1528 3 r. 50, Class "8620" locomotive (*horiz*) .. 95 95
1529 5 r. Class "10" locomotive (*horiz*) .. 1·25 1·25
1530 7 r. Class "C 61" locomotive .. .. 1·60 1·60
1531 10 r. Class "9600" locomotive (*horiz*) .. 2·00 2·00
1532 12 r. Class "D 52" locomotive (*horiz*) .. 2·40 2·40
1525/32 .. .. *Set of* 8 8·00 8·00
MS1533 Two sheets, each 118×80 mm. (a) 20 r. Class "C 56" locomotive (*horiz*). (b) 20 r. Class "1080" locomotive (*horiz*) .. *Set of* 2 *sheets* 8·00 8·00

(Litho Questa)

1991 (2 Dec). *Butterflies and Flowers. T* **258** *and similar horiz designs. Multicoloured. P* 14.
1534 10 l. Type **258** 30 30
1535 25 l. *Meneris tulbaghia* and *Incarvillea younghusbandii* 40 25
1536 50 l. *Polyommatus icarus* and *Campsis grandiflora* 55 35
1537 2 r. *Danaus plexippus* and *Thunbergia grandiflora* .. .. 1·00 80
1538 3 r. 50, *Colias interior* and *Medinilla magnifica* .. .. 1·40 1·40
1539 5 r. *Ascalapha ordorata* and *Meconopsis horridula* .. .. 1·75 1·75
1540 8 r. *Papilio memnon* and *Dillenia obovata* 2·00 2·25
1541 10 r. *Precis octavia* and *Thespesia populnea* 2·00 2·25
1534/41 .. .. *Set of* 8 8·50 8·50
MS1542 Two sheets, each 100×70 mm. (a) 20 r. *Bombax ceiba* and *Phyciodes tharos*. (b) 20 r. *Amauris niavius* and *Bombax insigne* *Set of* 2 *sheets* 9·25 9·50

259 "H-II" Rocket

(Des K. Gromell. Litho Questa)

1991 (11 Dec). *Japanese Space Programme. T* **259** *and similar multicoloured designs. P* 14.
1543 15 l. Type **259** 30 20
1544 20 l. Projected "H-II" orbiting plane .. 30 20
1545 2 r. Satellite "GMS-5" 80 60
1546 3 r. 50, Satellite "MOMO-1" .. .. 1·10 1·10
1547 7 r. Satellite "CS-3" .. .. .. 2·00 2·25
1548 10 r. Satellite "BS-2a, 2b" .. .. 2·25 2·50
1549 12 r. "H-I" Rocket (*vert*) .. .. 2·50 2·75
1550 15 r. Space Flier unit and U.S. space shuttle .. .. 2·50 2·75
1543/50 .. .. *Set of* 8 10·50 11·00
MS1551 Two sheets. (a) 116×85 mm. 20 r. Dish aerial, Katsura Tracking Station (*vert*). (b) 85×116 mm. 20 r. "M-3SII" rocket (*vert*) *Set of* 2 *sheets* 8·00 9·00

260 Williams "FW-07"

(Litho B.D.T.)

1991 (28 Dec). *Formula 1 Racing Cars. T* **260** *and similar horiz designs. Multicoloured. P* 14.
1552 20 l. Type **260** 30 20
1553 50 l. Brabham/BMW "BT50" turbo .. 45 30
1554 1 r. Williams/Honda "FW-11" 60 45
1555 3 r. 50, Ferrari "312 T3" .. .. 1·25 1·25
1556 5 r. Lotus/Honda "99T" .. .. .. 1·75 1·75
1557 7 r. Benetton/Ford "B188" .. .. 2·00 2·25
1558 10 r. Tyrrell "P34" six-wheeler .. .. 2·25 2·50
1559 21 r. Renault "RE-30B" turbo .. .. 4·00 5·00
1552/9 .. .. *Set of* 8 11·50 12·50
MS1560 Two sheets, each 84×56 mm. (a) 25 r. Brabham/BMW "BT50" turbo (*different*). (b) 25 r. Ferrari "F189" .. .. *Set of* 2 *sheets* 9·50 10·00

261 "Testa Rossa", 1957 **262** Franklin D. Roosevelt

(Litho Questa)

1991 (28 Dec). *Ferrari Cars. T* **261** *and similar horiz designs. Multicoloured. P* 14.
1561 5 r. Type **261** .. .. 1·50 1·75
a. Sheetlet. Nos. 1561/9 .. .. 12·00
1562 5 r. "275GTB", 1966 .. .. .. 1·50 1·75
1563 5 r. "Aspirarta", 1951 .. .. .. 1·50 1·75
1564 5 r. "Testarossa" .. .. .. 1·50 1·75
1565 5 r. Enzo Ferrari .. .. .. 1·50 1·75
1566 5 r. "Dino 246", 1958 .. .. .. 1·50 1·75
1567 5 r. "Type 375", 1952 .. .. .. 1·50 1·75
1568 5 r. Nigel Mansell's Formula 1 racing car 1·50 1·75
1569 5 r. "312T", 1975 .. .. .. 1·50 1·75
1561/9 .. .. *Set of* 9 12·00 14·00

Nos. 1561/9 were printed together, *se-tenant*, in sheetlets of 9 (3×3).

(Des R. Jung. Litho Questa)

1991 (30 Dec). *50th Anniv of Japanese Attack on Pearl Harbor. American War Leaders. T* **262** *and similar horiz designs. Multicoloured. P* 14½.
1570 3 r. 50, Type **262** .. .. .. 1·00 1·10
a. Sheetlet. Nos. 1570/9 .. .. 9·00
1571 3 r. 50, Douglas MacArthur and map of Philippines .. .. 1·00 1·10
1572 3 r. 50, Chester Nimitz and Pacific island 1·00 1·10
1573 3 r. 50, Jonathan Wainwright and barbed wire .. .. 1·00 1·10
1574 3 r. 50, Ernest King and aircraft carrier 1·00 1·10
1575 3 r. 50, Claire Chennault and Curtiss P-40B Tomahawk II fighters .. 1·00 1·10
1576 3 r. 50, William Halsey and aircraft carrier .. .. 1·00 1·10
1577 3 r. 50, Marc Mitscher and aircraft carrier 1·00 1·10
1578 3 r. 50, James Doolittle and North American B-25B Mitchell bomber .. 1·00 1·10
1579 3 r. 50, Raymond Spruance and Douglas SBD Dauntless dive bomber .. 1·00 1·10
1570/9 .. .. *Set of* 10 9·00 10·00

Nos. 1561/70 were printed together, *se-tenant*, in sheetlets of 10 with the stamps arranged in two horizontal strips of 5 separated by a gutter showing Japanese fighters attacking Pearl Harbor and Admiral Isoroku Yamamoto.

263 Brandenburg Gate and Postcard commemorating Berlin Wall

264 Mickey Mouse on Flying Carpet, Arabia

(Des L. Fried (Nos. 1580, 1583, 1585, 1597, **MS**1599b/d), J. Iskowitz (Nos. 1581/2, 1584, 1586/7, 1589, 1593, 1598, **MS**1599a,f). W. Hanson (Nos. 1594/5, **MS**1599e,h), W. Wright (others). Litho Questa)

1992 (30 Jan). *Anniversaries and Events. T* **263** *and similar multicoloured designs. P* 14.
1580 20 l. Type **263** 10 10
1581 50 l. Schwarzenburg Palace 10 10
1582 1 r. Spa at Baden 15 15
1583 1 r. 75, Berlin Wall and man holding child 30 30
1584 2 r. Royal Palace, Berlin 35 35
1585 4 r. Demonstrator and border guards .. 75 75
1586 5 r. Viennese masonic seal .. .. 1·25 1·25
1587 6 r. De Gaulle and Normandy landings, 1944 (*vert*) .. .. 1·25 1·25
1588 6 r. Lilienthal's signature and *Flugzeug Nr. 16* .. .. 1·25 1·25
1589 7 r. St. Marx .. .. 1·40 1·40
1590 7 r. Modern Trans-Siberian electric locomotive (*vert*) .. .. .. 1·40 1·40
1591 8 r. Kurt Schwitters (artist) and Landesmuseum .. .. 1·40 1·40
1592 9 r. Map of Switzerland and man in Uri traditional costume .. .. .. 1·50 1·50
1593 10 r. De Gaulle in Madagascar, 1958 .. 1·50 1·50
1594 10 r. Scouts exploring coral reef .. .. 1·50 1·50
1595 11 r. Scout salute and badge (*vert*) .. 1·60 1·60
1596 12 r. Steam locomotive .. .. .. 1·90 1·90
1597 15 r. Imperial German badges .. .. 1·90 1·90
1598 20 r. Josepsplatz, Vienna .. .. .. 2·50 2·50
1580/98 .. .. *Set of* 19 20·00 20·00
MS1599 Eight sheets. (a) 76×116 mm. 15 r. General de Gaulle during Second World War (*vert*). (b) 101×72 mm. 18 r. Ancient German helmet. (c) 101×72 mm. 18 r. 19th-century shako. (d) 101×72 mm. 18 r. Helmet of 1939. (e) 90×117 mm. 18 r. Postcard of Lord Baden-Powell carried by rocket, 1937 (brownish grey, black and magenta) (*vert*). (f) 75×104 mm. 20 r. Bust of Mozart (*vert*). (g) 115×85 mm. 20 r. Steam locomotive stopped at signal (57×43 *mm*). (h) 117×90 mm. 20 r. Czechoslovakia 1918 10 h. "Scout Post" stamp (*vert*) .. *Set of* 8 *sheets* 23·00 25·00

Anniversaries and Events:—Nos. 1580, 1583, 1585, 1597, **MS**1599b/d, Bicentenary of Brandenburg Gate, Berlin; Nos. 1581/2, 1584, 1586, 1589, 1598, **MS**1599f, Death bicentenary of Mozart (1991); Nos. 1587, 1593, **MS**1599a, Birth centenary of Charles de Gaulle (French statesman) (1990); No. 1588, Centenary of Otto Lilienthal's first gliding experiments; Nos. 1590, 1596, **MS**1599g, Centenary of Trans-Siberian Railway; No. 1591, 750th anniv of Hannover; No. 1592, 700th anniv of Swiss Confederation; Nos. 1594/5, **MS**1599e,h, 17th World Scout Jamboree, Korea.

(Des Walt Disney Co. Litho B.D.T.)

1992 (4 Feb). *Mickey's World Tour. T* **264** *and similar multicoloured designs showing Walt Disney cartoon characters in different countries. P* 13.
1600 25 l. Type **264** 30 20
1601 50 l. Goofy and Big Ben, Great Britain .. 40 25
1602 1 r. Mickey wearing clogs, Netherlands 50 35
1603 2 r. Pluto eating pasta, Italy 85 65
1604 3 r. Mickey and Donald doing Mexican hat dance .. .. 1·10 1·10
1605 3 r. 50, Mickey, Goofy and Donald as tiki, New Zealand .. .. 1·25 1·25
1606 5 r. Goofy skiing in Austrian Alps .. 1·50 1·50
1607 7 r. Mickey and city gate, Germany .. 1·75 2·00
1608 10 r. Donald as samurai, Japan .. .. 2·00 2·25
1609 12 r. Mickey as heroic statue, Russia .. 2·25 2·50
1610 15 r. Mickey, Donald, Goofy and Pluto as German band .. .. 2·50 2·75
1600/10 .. .. *Set of* 11 13·00 13·00
MS1611 Three sheets, each 83×104 mm. (a) 25 r. Donald chasing leprechaun, Ireland (*horiz*). (b) 25 r. Baby kangaroo surprising Pluto, Australia. (c) 25 r. Mickey and globe .. *Set of* 3 *sheets* 13·00 14·00

265 Whimbrel

266 Powder-blue Surgeonfish

(Des D. Delouise. Litho B.D.T. (6 r. 50 + 50, 30 r., 40 r.) or Questa (others))

1992 (17 Feb)–**94**. *Birds. T* **265** *and similar vert designs. Multicoloured. P* 13 (6 *r.* 50 + 50 *l.*, 30 *r.*, 40 *r.*) *or* 14½ (*others*).
1612 10 l. Type **265** 10 10
1613 25 l. Great Egret 10 10
1614 50 l. Grey Heron 10 10
1615 2 r. Shag 20 25
1616 3 r. 50, Roseate Tern 40 45
1617 5 r. Greenshank 55 60
1617*a* 6 r. 50 + 50 l. Egyptian Vulture (1.1.94) 80 85
1618 8 r. Hoopoe 90 95
1619 10 r. Black-shouldered Kite .. .. 1·10 1·25
1620 25 r. Scarlet Ibis .. .. 2·75 3·00
1620*a* 30 r. Peregrine Falcon (1.1.94) .. .. 3·25 3·50
1620*b* 40 r. Black Kite (1.1.94) .. .. .. 4·50 4·75
1621 50 r. Grey Plover .. .. 5·50 6·00
1612/21 .. .. *Set of* 13 20·00 21·00

Nos. 1617*a* and 1620*a*/*b* are larger, 23×32 mm.

(Des D. Miller. Litho Questa)

1992 (3 Mar). *40th Anniv of Queen Elizabeth II's Accession. Horiz designs as T* **214** *of Lesotho. Multicoloured. P* 14.
1622 1 r. Palm trees on beach 40 25
1623 3 r. 50, Path leading to jetty .. .. 1·25 1·00
1624 7 r. Tropical plant .. .. .. 2·00 2·25
1625 10 r. Palm trees on beach (*different*) .. 2·40 2·75
1622/5 .. .. *Set of* 4 5·50 5·75
MS1626 Two sheets each 74×97 mm. (a) 18 r. Dhow. (b) 18 r. Palm trees on beach (*different*) *Set of* 2 *sheets* 8·00 9·00

(Litho B.D.T.)

1992 (23 Mar). *Fishes. T* **266** *and similar horiz designs. Multicoloured. P* 14.
1627 7 l. Type **266** 30 20
1628 20 l. Catalufa 35 25
1629 50 l. Yellow-finned Tuna 40 30
1630 1 r. Twin-spotted Snapper 55 35
1631 3 r. 50, Hawaiian Squirrelfish .. .. 1·25 1·25
1632 5 r. Picasso Triggerfish .. .. .. 1·75 1·75
1633 8 r. Bennett's Butterflyfish .. .. 2·00 2·25
1634 10 r. Parrotfish .. .. 2·25 2·50
1635 12 r. Coral Hind .. .. 2·50 2·75
1636 15 r. Skipjack Tuna .. .. 2·50 2·75
1627/36 .. .. *Set of* 10 12·50 13·00
MS1637 Four sheets, each 116×76 mm. (a) 20 r. Thread-finned Butterflyfish. (b) 20 r. Oriental Sweetlips. (c) 20 r. Two-banded Anemonefish ("Clownfish"). (d) 20 r. Clown Triggerfish *Set of* 4 *sheets* 13·00 15·00

(Des Walt Disney Co. Litho Questa)

1992 (15 Apr). *International Stamp Exhibitions. Multicoloured designs as T* **215** *of Lesotho, showing Walt Disney cartoon characters. P* 13½×14.

(a) *"Granada '92", Spain. The Alhambra*

1638 2 r. Minnie Mouse in Court of the Lions .. 75 60
1639 5 r. Goofy in Lions Fountain .. .. 1·50 1·50
1640 8 r. Mickey Mouse at the Gate of Justice 2·00 2·25
1641 12 r. Donald Duck serenading Daisy at the Vermilion Towers .. .. .. 2·50 2·75
1638/41 .. .. *Set of* 4 6·00 6·25
MS1642 127×102 mm. 25 r. Goofy pushing Mickey in wheelbarrow .. .. .. 5·00 5·50

(b) *"World Columbian Stamp Expo '92". Chicago Landmarks*

1643 1 r. Mickey meeting Jean Baptiste du Sable (founder) 45 35
1644 3 r. 50, Donald Duck at Old Chicago Post Office .. .. 1·25 1·00
1645 7 r. Donald at Old Fort Dearborn .. 1·75 2·00
1646 15 r. Goofy in Field Museum of Natural History .. .. 2·75 3·00
1643/6 .. .. *Set of* 4 5·75 5·75
MS1647 127×102 mm. 25 r. Mickey and Minnie Mouse at Columbian Exposition, 1893 (*horiz*). P 14×13½ .. .. 5·00 5·50

On No. 1646 the design is wrongly captioned as the Science and Industry Museum.

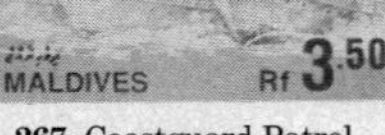

267 Coastguard Patrol Boats

268 Flowers of the United States of America

(Litho Questa)

1992 (21 Apr). *Centenary of National Security Service. T* **267** *and similar horiz designs. Multicoloured. P* 14.

1648 3 r. 50, Type **267** .. .. .. 1·50 1·25
1649 5 r. Infantry in training .. .. .. 1·75 1·75
1650 10 r. Aakoatey fort .. .. .. 2·00 2·25
1651 15 r. Fire Service .. .. 4·00 4·25
1648/51 .. .. *Set of* 4 8·25 8·50
MS1652 100×68 mm. 20 r. Ceremonial procession, 1892 .. .. 5·50 6·00

(Des W. Wright. Litho Questa)

1992 (26 Apr). *National Flowers. T* **268** *and similar multicoloured designs. P* 14½.

1653 25 l. Type **268** 30 20
1654 50 l. Australia 45 30
1655 2 r. England 90 75
1656 3 r. 50, Brazil .. .. 1·25 1·25
1657 5 r. Holland .. .. 1·75 1·75
1658 8 r. France .. .. 2·00 2·25
1659 10 r. Japan .. .. 2·25 2·50
1660 15 r. Africa .. .. 2·50 2·75
1653/60 .. .. *Set of* 8 10·00 10·50
MS1661 Two sheets, each 114×85 mm. (a) 25 r. *Plumieria rubra, Classia fistula* and *Eugenia malaccensis* (57×43 *mm*). (b) 25 r. *Bauhinia variegata, Catharanthus roseus* and *Plumieria alba* (57×43 *mm*). P 14 .. *Set of* 2 *sheets* 9·00 10·00

269 *Laetiporus sulphureus*

270 Hurdling

(Litho Walsall)

1992 (14 May). *Fungi. T* **269** *and similar vert designs. Multicoloured. P* 14.

1662 10 l. Type **269** 20 20
1663 25 l. *Coprinus atramentarius* 25 25
1664 50 l. *Ganoderma lucidum* 40 40
1665 3 r. 50, *Russula aurata* .. .. .. 1·00 1·00
1666 5 r. *Gifola umbellata* ("*Polyporus umbellatus*") .. .. 1·40 1·40
1667 8 r. *Suillus grevillei* .. .. .. 2·00 2·00
1668 10 r. *Clavaria zollingeri* .. .. .. 2·25 2·25
1669 25 r. *Boletus edulis* .. .. .. 4·50 4·50
1662/9 .. .. *Set of* 8 11·00 11·00
MS1670 Two sheets, each 100×70 mm. (a) 25 r. *Marasmius oreades*; (b) 25 r. *Pycnoporus cinnabarinus* ("*Trametes cinnabarina*") *Set of* 2 *sheets* 9·50 10·00

(Litho Questa)

1992 (1 June–5 Oct). *Olympic Games, Albertville and Barcelona* (1*st issue*). *Multicoloured designs as T* **216** *of Lesotho. P* 14.

1671 10 l. Pole vault 20 10
1672 25 l. Men's pommel horse (*horiz*) 25 15
1673 50 l. Men's shot put 30 25
1674 1 r. Men's horizontal bar (*horiz*) 35 30
1675 2 r. Men's triple jump (*horiz*) 80 65
1676 3 r. 50, Table tennis .. .. .. 1·10 1·10
1677 5 r. Two-man bobsled (5 Oct) .. .. 1·40 1·40
1678 7 r. Freestyle wrestling (*horiz*) .. .. 1·75 2·00
1679 8 r. Freestyle ski-jump (5 Oct) .. .. 1·75 2·00
1680 9 r. Baseball .. .. 2·00 2·25
1681 10 r. Women's cross-country Nordic skiing (5 Oct) .. .. 2·00 2·25
1682 12 r. Men's 200 metres backstroke (*horiz*) 2·00 2·25
1671/82 .. .. *Set of* 12 12·50 13·00
MS1683 Three sheets. (a) 100×70 mm. 25 r. Decathlon (*horiz*). (b) 100×70 mm. 25 r. Women's slalom skiing (*horiz*) (5 Oct). (c) 70×100 mm. 25 r. Men's figure skating (5 Oct) *Set of* 3 *sheets* 12·00 13·00

(Litho Walsall)

1992 (1 June). *Olympic Games, Barcelona* (2*nd issue*). *T* **270** *and similar vert designs. Multicoloured. P* 14.

1684 10 l. Type **270** 10 10
1685 1 r. Boxing 30 30
1686 3 r. 50, Women's sprinting 80 70
1687 5 r. Discus .. .. 1·25 1·25
1688 7 r. Basketball .. .. 2·00 1·75
1689 10 r. Long-distance running .. .. 2·00 2·00
1690 12 r. Aerobic gymnastics .. .. .. 2·00 2·25
1691 20 r. Fencing .. .. 2·75 3·25
1684/91 .. .. *Set of* 8 10·00 10·50
MS1692 Two sheets, each 70×100 mm. (a) 25 r. Olympic symbol and national flags. (b) 25 r. Olympic symbol and flame .. *Set of* 2 *sheets* 8·50 9·00

271 Deinonychus

272 Destruction of LZ-129 *Hindenburg* (airship), 1937

(Des D. Ben-Ami. Litho Questa)

1992 (15 Sept). *"Genova '92" International Thematic Stamp Exhibition. Prehistoric Animals. T* **271** *and similar vert designs. Multicoloured. P* 14.

1693 5 l. Type **271** 10 10
1694 10 l. Styracosaurus 10 10
1695 25 l. Mamenchisaurus 10 10
1696 50 l. Stenonychosaurus 10 10
1697 1 r. Parasaurolophus 10 10
1698 1 r. 25, Scelidosaurus 15 20
1699 1 r. 75, Tyrannosaurus 20 25
1700 2 r. Stegosaurus 20 25
1701 3 r. 50, Iguanodon 40 45
1702 4 r. Anatosaurus 45 50
1703 5 r. Monoclonius 55 60
1704 7 r. Tenontosaurus 80 85
1705 8 r. Brachiosaurus 90 95
1706 10 r. Euoplocephalus .. .. .. 1·10 1·25
1707 25 r. Triceratops .. .. 2·75 3·00
1708 50 r. Apatosaurus .. .. 5·50 5·75
1693/1708 .. .. .. *Set of* 16 13·00 14·00
MS1709 Four sheets, each 116×85 mm. (a) 25 r. Hadrosaur hatchling. (b) 25 r. Iguanodon fighting Allosaurus. (c) 25 r. Tyrannosaurus attacking Triceratops. (d) 25 r. Brachiosaurus and Iguanodons .. .. *Set of* 4 *sheets* 11·00 11·50

(Des Kerri Schiff. Litho Questa)

1992 (28 Oct). *Postage Stamp Mega Event, New York. Sheet* 100×70 *mm containing multicoloured design as T* **219** *of Lesotho, but horiz. P* 14.

MS1710 20 r. New York Public Library .. 2·50 2·75

(Des K. Grommell. Litho B.D.T.)

1992 (28 Oct). *Mysteries of the Universe. T* **272** *and similar multicoloured designs, each in separate miniature sheet. P* 14.

MS1711 Sixteen sheets, each 100×71 mm. (a) 25 r. Type **272**. (b) 25 r. Loch Ness Monster. (c) 25 r. Crystal skull. (d) 25 r. Space craft in Black Hole. (e) 25 r. Ghosts (*vert*). (f) 25 r. Flying saucer, 1947 (*vert*). (g) 25 r. Bust of Plato (Atlantis). (h) 25 r. U.F.O, 1973. (i) 25 r. Crop circles. (j) 25 r. Mil Mi-26 Russian helicopter at Chernobyl nuclear explosion. (k) 25 r. Figure from Plain of Nazca. (l) 25 r. Stonehenge (*vert*). (m) 25 r. Yeti footprint (*vert*). (n) 25 r. The Pyramid of Giza. (o) 25 r. *Marie Celeste* (brigantine) (*vert*). (p) 25 r. American Grumman TBF Avenger fighter aircraft (Bermuda Triangle) *Set of* 16 *sheets* 55·00 55·00

273 Zubin Mehta (musical director)

274 Friedrich Schmiedl

(Litho B.D.T.)

1992 (9 Nov). 150*th Anniv of New York Philharmonic Orchestra. Sheet* 100×70 *mm. P* 14.

MS1712 **273** 20 r. multicoloured .. .. 3·00 3·25

(Litho B.D.T.)

1992 (1 Dec). 90*th Birth Anniv of Friedrich Schmiedl* (*rocket mail pioneer*). *Sheet* 104×69 *mm. P* 14½×14.

MS1713 **274** 25 r. multicoloured .. .. 4·00 4·25

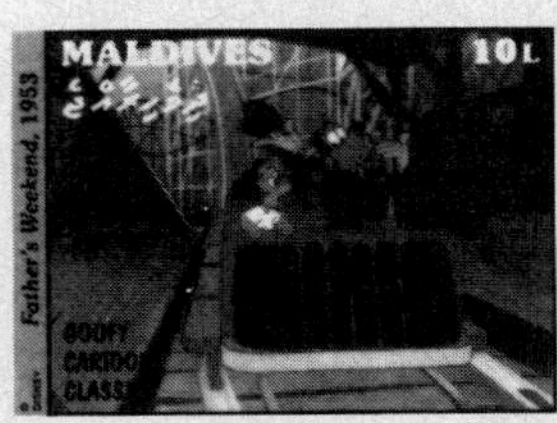

275 Goofy in *Father's Weekend*, 1953

(Des Walt Disney Co. Litho Questa)

1992 (7 Dec). 60*th Anniv of Goofy* (*Disney cartoon character*). *T* **275** *and similar multicoloured designs showing Goofy in various cartoon films. P* 14×13½ (*horiz*) *or* 13½×14 (*vert*).

1714 10 l. Type **275** 10 10
1715 50 l. *Symphony Hour*, 1942 .. .. 25 20
1716 75 l. *Frank Duck Brings 'Em Back Alive*, 1946 .. .. 30 20
1717 1 r. *Crazy with the Heat*, 1947 .. .. 30 20
1718 2 r. *The Big Wash*, 1948 .. .. .. 55 45
1719 3 r. 50, *How to Ride a Horse*, 1950 .. 85 85
1720 5 r. *Two Gun Goofy*, 1952 .. .. 1·25 1·25
1721 8 r. *Saludos Amigos*, 1943 (*vert*) .. 1·60 2·00
1722 10 r. *How to be a Detective*, 1952 .. 1·75 2·00
1723 12 r. *For Whom the Bulls Toil*, 1953 .. 2·00 2·25
1724 15 r. *Double Dribble*, 1946 (*vert*) .. .. 2·00 2·25
1714/24 .. .. *Set of* 11 9·75 10·50
MS1725 Three sheets, each 127×102 mm. (a) 20 r. *Double Dribble*, 1946 (*different*) (*vert*). (b) 20 r. *The Goofy Success Story*, 1955 (*vert*). (c) 20 r. *Mickey and the Beanstalk*, 1947 *Set of* 3 *sheets* 9·00 9·50

276 Minnie Mouse in "Le Missioner" (Toulouse-Lautrec)

(Des Euro-Disney, Paris. Litho Cartor)

1992 (7 Dec). *Opening of Euro-Disney Resort, France. T* **276** *and similar multicoloured designs showing Disney cartoon characters superimposed on Impressionist paintings. P* 14×13½.

1726 5 r. Type **276** .. .. 1·40 1·50
a. Sheetlet. Nos. 1726/34 .. .. 11·00
1727 5 r. Goofy in "The Card Players" (Cezanne) .. .. 1·40 1·50
1728 5 r. Mickey and Minnie Mouse in "The Cafe Terrace, Place du Forum" (Van Gogh) .. .. 1·40 1·50
1729 5 r. Mickey in "The Bridge at Langlois" (Van Gogh) .. .. 1·40 1·50
1730 5 r. Goofy in "Chocolate Dancing" (Toulouse-Lautrec) .. .. .. 1·40 1·50
1731 5 r. Mickey and Minnie in "The Seine at Asnieres" (Renoir) .. .. .. 1·40 1·50
1732 5 r. Minnie in "Ball at the Moulin Rouge" (Toulouse-Lautrec) .. .. .. 1·40 1·50
1733 5 r. Mickey Mouse in "Wheatfield with Cypresses" (Van Gogh) .. .. 1·40 1·50
1734 5 r. Minnie in "When will you Marry?" (Gauguin) .. .. 1·40 1·50
1726/34 .. .. *Set of* 9 11·00 12·00
MS1735 Four sheets. (a) 128×100 mm. 20 r. Minnie as can-can dancer. P 14×13½. (b) 128×100 mm. 20 r. Goofy as cyclist. P 14×13½. (c) 100×128 mm. 20 r. Mickey as artist. P 14×13½. (d) 100×128 mm. 20 r. Donald as Frenchman (*vert*). P 13½×14 .. *Set of* 4 *sheets* 12·00 13·00

Nos. 1726/34 were printed together, *se-tenant*, in sheetlets of 9.

277 Rivers

278 Jürgen Klinsmann (Germany)

(Litho Questa)

1992 (30 Dec). *South Asian Association for Regional Co-operation Year of the Environment. T* **277** *and similar horiz designs showing natural and polluted environments. Multicoloured. P* 14.

1736	25 l. Type **277**	15	10
1737	50 l. Beaches	25	10
1738	5 r. Oceans	80	90
1739	10 r. Weather	1·50	1·75
1736/9	*Set of* 4	2·40	2·50

(Litho Questa)

1993 (7 Jan). *World Cup Football Championship, U.S.A. (1994) (1st issue). T* **278** *and similar multicoloured designs showing German players and officials. P* 14.

1740	10 l. Type **278**	10	10
1741	25 l. Pierre Littbarski	10	10
1742	50 l. Lothar Matthaus	10	10
1743	1 r. Rudi Voller	10	10
1744	2 r. Thomas Hassler	20	25
1745	3 r. 50, Thomas Berthold	40	45
1746	4 r. Jurgen Kohler	45	50
1747	5 r. Berti Vogts	55	60
1748	6 r. Bodo Illgner	65	70
1749	7 r. Klaus Augenthaler	80	85
1750	8 r. Franz Beckenbauer	90	95
1751	10 r. Andreas Brehme	1·10	1·25
1752	12 r. Guido Buchwald	1·40	1·50
1740/52	*Set of* 13	6·50	7·25
MS1753	Two sheets, each 103×73 mm. (a) 35 r. German players celebrating (*horiz*). (b) 35 r. Rudi Voller (*horiz*) *Set of* 2 *sheets*	7·75	8·00

See also Nos. 1990/8 and 2089/101.

279 German Navy Airship L-13 bombing London, 1914–18

280 Elvis Presley

(Des W. Wright and W. Hanson (Nos. 1754, 1766, **MS**1767a), W. Wright (others). Litho B.D.T.)

1993 (7 Jan). *Anniversaries and Events. T* **279** *and similar horiz designs. Multicoloured. P* 14.

1754	1 r. Type **279**	30	20
1755	3 r. 50, Radio telescope	55	60
1756	3 r. 50, Chancellor Adenauer and Pres. De Gaulle	55	60
1757	6 r. Indian Rhinoceros	1·00	1·00
1758	6 r. Columbus and globe	65	70
1759	7 r. Conference emblems	1·00	1·00
1760	8 r. Green Seaturtle	1·40	1·40
1761	10 r. *America* (yacht), 1851	1·75	1·75
1762	10 r. Melvin Jones (founder) and emblem	1·75	1·75
1763	12 r. Columbus landing on San Salvador	1·40	1·50
1764	15 r. "Voyager I" approaching Saturn	2·50	2·50
1765	15 r. Adenauer, N.A.T.O. flag and Lockheed F-104G Starfighter aircraft	2·50	2·50
1766	20 r. *Graf Zeppelin* over New York, 1929	3·00	3·00
1754/66	*Set of* 13	17·00	17·00
MS1767	Five sheets, each 111×80 mm. (a) 20 r. Count Ferdinand von Zeppelin. (b) 20 r. "Landsat" satellite. (c) 20 r. Konrad Adenauer. (d) 20 r. Scarlet Macaw. (e) 20 r. *Santa Maria* *Set of* 5 *sheets*	15·00	16·00

Anniversaries and Events:—Nos. 1754, 1766, **MS**1767a, 75th death anniv of Count Ferdinand von Zeppelin; Nos. 1755, 1764, **MS**1767b, International Space Year; Nos. 1756, 1765, **MS**1767c, 25th death anniv of Konrad Adenauer; Nos. 1757, 1760, **MS**1767d, Earth Summit '92, Rio; Nos. 1758, 1763, **MS**1767e, 500th anniv of Discovery of America by Columbus; No. 1759, International Conference on Nutrition, Rome; No. 1761, Americas Cup Yachting Championship; No. 1762, 75th anniv of International Association of Lions Clubs.

(Des A. Nahigian. Litho Questa)

1993 (7 Jan). *15th Death Anniv of Elvis Presley (singer). T* **280** *and similar vert designs. Multicoloured. P* 14.

1768	3 r. 50, Type **280**	40	45
	a. Strip of 3. Nos. 1768/70	1·10	
1769	3 r. 50, Elvis with guitar	40	45
1770	3 r. 50, Elvis with microphone	40	45
1768/70	*Set of* 3	1·10	1·25

Nos. 1768/70 were printed together, horizontally and vertically *se-tenant*, in sheetlets of 9 (3×3).

(Litho Walsall)

1993 (7 Jan). *Bicentenary of the Louvre, Paris. Multicoloured designs as T* **221** *of Lesotho. P* 12.

1771	8 r. "The Study" (Fragonard)	90	95
	a. Sheetlet. Nos. 1771/8	7·00	
1772	8 r. "Denis Diderot" (Fragonard)	90	95
1773	8 r. "Marie-Mádélaine Guimard" (Fragonard)	90	95
1774	8 r. "Inspiration" (Fragonard)	90	95
1775	8 r. "Waterfalls, Tivoli" (Fragonard)	90	95
1776	8 r. "The Music Lesson" (Fragonard)	90	95
1777	8 r. "The Bolt" (Fragonard)	90	95
1778	8 r. "Blind-man's Buff" (Fragonard)	90	95
1779	8 r. "Self-portrait" (Corot)	90	95
	a. Sheetlet. Nos. 1779/86	7·00	
1780	8 r. "Woman in Blue" (Corot)	90	95
1781	8 r. "Woman with a Pearl" (Corot)	90	95
1782	8 r. "Young Girl at her Toilet" (Corot)	90	95
1783	8 r. "Haydée" (Corot)	90	95
1784	8 r. "Chartres Cathedral" (Corot)	90	95
1785	8 r. "The Belfry of Douai" (Corot)	90	95
1786	8 r. "The Bridge of Mantes" (Corot)	90	95
1787	8 r. "Madame Sériziat" (David)	90	95
	a. Sheetlet. Nos. 1787/94	7·00	
1788	8 r. "Pierre Sériziat" (David)	90	95
1789	8 r. "Madame De Verninac" (David)	90	95
1790	8 r. "Madame Récamier" (David)	90	95
1791	8 r. "Self-portrait" (David)	90	95
1792	8 r. "General Bonaparte" (David)	90	95
1793	8 r. "The Lictors bringing Brutus his Son's Body" (David) (left detail)	90	95
1794	8 r. "The Lictors bringing Brutus his Son's Body" (David) (right detail)	90	95
1771/94	*Set of* 24	21·00	22·00
MS1795	Two sheets, each 100×70 mm. (a) 20 r. "Gardens of the Villa D'Este, Tivoli" (Corot) (85×52 *mm*). (b) 20 r. "Tiger Cub playing with its Mother" (Delacroix) (85×52 *mm*). P 14½ *Set of* 2 *sheets*	4·50	4·75

Nos. 1771/8, 1779/86 and 1787/94 were each printed together, *se-tenant*, in sheetlets of 8 stamps and one centre label.

281 James Stewart and Marlene Dietrich (*Destry Rides Again*)

(Des P. Wolff and D. Lewis. Litho Questa)

1993 (18 Jan). *Famous Western Films. T* **281** *and similar vert designs. Multicoloured. P* 13½×14.

1796	5 r. Type **281**	55	60
	a. Sheetlet. Nos. 1796/1803	4·25	
1797	5 r. Gary Cooper (*The Westerner*)	55	60
1798	5 r. Henry Fonda (*My Darling Clementine*)	55	60
1799	5 r. Alan Ladd (*Shane*)	55	60
1800	5 r. Kirk Douglas and Burt Lancaster (*Gunfight at the O.K. Corral*)	55	60
1801	5 r. Steve McQueen (*The Magnificent Seven*)	55	60
1802	5 r. Robert Redford and Paul Newman (*Butch Cassidy and The Sundance Kid*)	55	60
1803	5 r. Jack Nicholson and Randy Quaid (*The Missouri Breaks*)	55	60
1796/1803	*Set of* 8	4·25	4·75
MS1804	Two sheets, each 134×120 mm. (a) 20 r. John Wayne (*The Searchers*) (French poster). (b) 20 r. Clint Eastwood (*Pale Rider*) (French poster) *Set of* 2 *sheets*	4·50	4·75

Nos. 1796/1803 were printed together, *se-tenant*, in sheetlets of 8.

(Des Kerri Schiff. Litho Questa)

1993 (2 June). *40th Anniv of Coronation. Vert designs as T* **224** *of Lesotho. P* 13½×14.

1805	3 r. 50, multicoloured	40	45
	a. Sheetlet. Nos. 1805/8×2	6·00	
1806	5 r. multicoloured	55	60
1807	10 r. indigo and black	1·10	1·25
1808	10 r. indigo and black	1·10	1·25
1805/8	*Set of* 4	3·00	3·50

Designs:—No. 1805, Queen Elizabeth II at Coronation (photograph by Cecil Beaton); No. 1806, St. Edward's Crown; No. 1807, Guests in the Abbey; No. 1808, Queen Elizabeth II and Prince Philip.

Nos. 1805/8 were printed together in sheetlets of 8, containing two *se-tenant* blocks of 4.

282 Blue Goatfish

(Des S. Barlowe. Litho Cartor)

1993 (30 June). *Fishes. T* **282** *and similar multicoloured designs. P* 14×13½.

1809	3 r. 50, Type **282**	60	70
	a. Sheetlet. Nos. 1809/20	6·50	
1810	3 r. 50, Emperor Angelfish	60	70
1811	3 r. 50, Madagascar Butterflyfish	60	70
1812	3 r. 50, Regal Angelfish	60	70
1813	3 r. 50, Forceps Fish ("Longnose Butterflyfish")	60	70
1814	3 r. 50, Raccoon Butterflyfish	60	70
1815	3 r. 50, Harlequin Filefish	60	70
1816	3 r. 50, Rectangle Triggerfish	60	70
1817	3 r. 50, Yellow-tailed Anemonefish	60	70
1818	3 r. 50, Clown Triggerfish	60	70
1819	3 r. 50, Zebra Lionfish	60	70
1820	3 r. 50, Maldive Anemonefish ("Clownfish")	60	70
1821	3 r. 50, Black-faced Butterflyfish	60	70
	a. Sheetlet. Nos. 1821/32	6·50	
1822	3 r. 50, Bird Wrasse	60	70
1823	3 r. 50, Checkerboard Wrasse	60	70
1824	3 r. 50, Yellow-faced Angelfish	60	70
1825	3 r. 50, Masked Bannerfish	60	70
1826	3 r. 50, Thread-finned Butterflyfish	60	70
1827	3 r. 50, Painted Triggerfish	60	70
1828	3 r. 50, Coral Hind	60	70
1829	3 r. 50, Pennant Coralfish	60	70
1830	3 r. 50, Black-backed Butterflyfish	60	70
1831	3 r. 50, Red-toothed Triggerfish	60	70
1832	3 r. 50, Melon Butterflyfish	60	70
1809/32	*Set of* 24	13·00	15·00
MS1833	Two sheets. (a) 69×96 mm. 25 r. Klein's Butterflyfish (*vert*). (b) 96×69 mm. 25 r. Brown Anemonefish (*vert*). P 12×13 *Set of* 2 *sheets*	8·00	8·50

Nos. 1809/20 and 1821/32 were printed together, *se-tenant*, in sheetlets of 12 with the backgrounds forming composite designs.

283 Gull-billed Tern

284 Precious Wentletrap (*Epitonium scalare*)

(Des S. Barlowe. Litho Cartor)

1993 (5 July). *Birds. T* **283** *and similar multicoloured designs. P* 14×13½ (*horiz*) *or* 13½×14 (*vert*).

1834	3 r. 50, Type **283**	60	70
	a. Sheetlet. Nos. 1834/45	6·50	
1835	3 r. 50, White-tailed Tropic Bird	60	70
1836	3 r. 50, Great Frigate Bird	60	70
1837	3 r. 50, Wilson's Petrel	60	70
1838	3 r. 50, White Tern	60	70
1839	3 r. 50, Brown Booby	60	70
1840	3 r. 50, Marsh Harrier	60	70
1841	3 r. 50, Common Noddy	60	70
1842	3 r. 50, Green Heron ("Little Heron")	60	70
1843	3 r. 50, Turnstone	60	70
1844	3 r. 50, Curlew	60	70
1845	3 r. 50, Crab Plover	60	70
1846	3 r. 50, Pallid Harrier (*vert*)	60	70
	a. Sheetlet. Nos. 1846/57	6·50	
1847	3 r. 50, Cattle Egret (*vert*)	60	70
1848	3 r. 50, Koel (*vert*)	60	70
1849	3 r. 50, Tree Pipit (*vert*)	60	70
1850	3 r. 50, Short-eared Owl (*vert*)	60	70
1851	3 r. 50, Common Kestrel ("European Kestrel") (*vert*)	60	70
1852	3 r. 50, Yellow Wagtail (*vert*)	60	70
1853	3 r. 50, Grey Heron ("Common Heron") (*vert*)	60	70
1854	3 r. 50, Black Bittern (*vert*)	60	70
1855	3 r. 50, Common Snipe (*vert*)	60	70
1856	3 r. 50, Little Egret (*vert*)	60	70
1857	3 r. 50, Little Stint (*vert*)	60	70
1834/57	*Set of* 24	13·00	15·00
MS1858	Two sheets, each 105×75 mm. (a) 25 r. Caspian Tern. (b) 25 r. Audubon's Shearwater. P 13×12 *Set of* 2 *sheets*	7·50	8·00

Nos. 1834/45 and 1846/57 were printed together, *se-tenant*, in sheetlets of 12 with the backgrounds forming composite designs.

(Litho Questa)

1993 (15 July). *Shells. T* **284** *and similar vert designs. Multicoloured. P* 14.

1859	7 l. Type **284**	10	10
1860	15 l. Common Purple Janthina (*Janthina janthina*)	10	10
1861	50 l. Asiatic Arabian Cowrie (*Cypraea arabica asiatica*)	20	15
1862	3 r. 50, Common or Major Harp (*Harpa major*)	70	70
1863	4 r. Amplustre or Royal Paper Bubble (*Aplustrum amplustre*)	80	80
1864	5 r. Sieve Cowrie (*Cypraea cribraria*)	1·00	1·00
1865	6 r. Episcopal Mitre (*Mitra mitra*)	1·25	1·40
1866	7 r. Camp Pitar Venus (*Lioconcha castrensis*)	1·40	1·50
1867	8 r. Spotted or Eyed Auger (*Terebra guttata*)	1·40	1·60
1868	10 r. Exposed Cowrie (*Cypraea succincta*)	1·60	1·75
1869	12 r. Geographic Map Cowrie (*Cypraea mappa geographus*)	1·75	2·00
1870	20 r. Bramble Murex (*Murex tribulus*)	2·50	2·75
1859/70	*Set of* 12	11·50	12·50
MS1871	Three sheets, each 104×75 mm. (a) 25 r. Black-striped Triton (*Cymatium hepaticum*). (b) 25 r. Scorpion Conch (*Lambis scorpio*). (c) 25 r. Bull-mouth Helmet (*Cypraecassis rufa*) *Set of* 3 *sheets*	12·00	13·00

285 Sifaka Lemur

286 Symbolic Heads and Arrows

(Litho Questa)

1993 (20 July). *Endangered Species. T* **285** *and similar vert designs. Multicoloured. P* 14.

1872 7 l. Type **285** 20 10
1873 10 l. Snow Leopard 20 10
1874 15 l. Numbat 20 10
1875 25 l. Gorilla 30 20
1876 2 r. Koala 45 35
1877 3 r. 50, Cheetah 70 70
1878 5 r. Yellow-footed Rock Wallaby .. 90 90
1879 7 r. Orang-Utan .. .. 1·40 1·50
1880 8 r. Black Lemur .. .. 1·40 1·60
1881 10 r. Black Rhinoceros .. .. .. 1·75 2·00
1882 15 r. Humpback Whale .. .. .. 2·00 2·25
1883 20 r. Mauritius Parakeet .. .. 2·50 2·75
1872/83 .. .. *Set of* 12 11·00 11·00
MS1884 Three sheets, each 104×75 mm. (a) 25 r. Giant Panda. (b) 25 r. Tiger. (c) 25 r. Indian Elephant .. .. .. *Set of* 3 *sheets* 11·50 12·00

(Litho Questa)

1993 (25 July). *Productivity Year. T* **286** *and similar vert design. Multicoloured. P* 14.

1885 7 r. Type **286** .. .. 1·00 1·00
1886 10 r. Abstract .. .. 1·40 1·40

287 Early Astronomical Equipment

288 *Limenitis procris* and *Mussaenda*

(Des Kerri Schiff (Nos. 1890, 1894, 1896, 1898, **MS**1899d/e). Litho Questa)

1993 (11 Oct). *Anniversaries and Events. T* **287** *and similar multicoloured designs. P* 14.

1887 3 r. 50, Type **287** 40 45
1888 3 r. 50, "Still Life with Pitcher and Apples" (Picasso) 40 45
1889 3 r. 50, "Zolte Roze" (Menasze Seidenbeurel) 40 45
1890 3 r. 50, Prince Naruhito and engagement photographs (*horiz*) 40 45
1891 5 r. "Bowls and Jug" (Picasso) 55 60
1892 5 r. Krysztofory Palace, Cracow 55 60
1893 8 r. "Jabtka i Kotara" (Waclaw Borowski) 90 95
1894 8 r. Marina Kiehl (Germany) (women's downhill skiing) 90 95
1895 10 r. "Bowls of Fruit and Loaves on a Table" (Picasso) .. .. .. 1·10 1·25
1896 10 r. Masako Owada and engagement photographs (*horiz*) .. .. 1·10 1·25
1897 15 r. American astronaut in space .. 1·60 1·75
1898 15 r. Vegard Ulvang (Norway) (30km cross-country skiing) .. .. 1·60 1·75
1887/98 .. .. *Set of* 12 9·75 10·50
MS1899 Five sheets. (a) 105×75 mm. 20 r. Copernicus. (b) 105×75 mm. 20 r. "Green Still Life" (detail) (Picasso) (*horiz*). (c) 105×75 mm. 25 r. "Pejzaz Morski-Port z Doplywajacym Ststkiem" (detail) (Roman Sielski) (*horiz*). (d) 75×105 mm. 25 r. Masako Owada. (e) 105×75 mm. 25 r. Ice hockey goalkeeper *Set of* 5 *sheets* 12·50 13·00

Anniversaries and Events:—Nos. 1887, 1897, **MS**1899a, 450th death anniv of Copernicus (astronomer); Nos. 1888, 1891, 1895, **MS**1899b, 20th death anniv of Picasso (artist); Nos. 1889, 1892/3, **MS**1899c, "Polska '93" International Stamp Exhibition, Poznań; Nos. 1890, 1896, **MS**1899d, Marriage of Crown Prince Naruhito of Japan; Nos. 1894, 1898, **MS**1899e, Winter Olympic Games '94, Lillehammer.

(Des Tracy Pedersen. Litho B.D.T.)

1993 (25 Oct). *Butterflies and Flowers. T* **288** *and similar multicoloured designs. P* 14.

1900 7 l. Type **288** 15 10
1901 20 l. *Danaus limniace* and *Thevetia neriifolia* 15 10
1902 25 l. *Amblypodia centaurus* and *Clitoria ternatea* 15 10
1903 50 l. *Papilio crino* and *Crossandra infundibuliformis* 20 15
1904 5 r. *Mycalesis patnia* and *Thespesia populnia* .. .. 1·10 1·10
1905 6 r. 50 + 50 l. *Idea jasonia* and *Cassia glauca* .. .. 1·40 1·50
1906 7 r. *Catopsilia pomona* and *Calotropis* .. 1·40 1·50
1907 10 r. *Precis orithyia* and *Thunbergia grandiflora* .. .. .. 1·75 2·00
1908 12 r. *Vanessa cardui* and *Caesalpinia pulcherrima* .. .. .. 2·00 2·25
1909 15 r. *Papilio polymnestor* and *Nerium oleander* .. .. 2·25 2·50
1910 18 r. *Cirrochroa thais* and *Vinca rosea* .. 2·50 2·75
1911 20 r. *Pachliopta hector* and *Ixora coccinea* 2·50 2·75
1900/11 .. .. *Set of* 12 14·00 15·00
MS1912 Three sheets, each 105×72 mm. (a) 25 r. *Cheritra freja* and *Bauhinia purpurea* (*vert*). (b) 25 r. *Rohana parisatis* and *Plumeria acutifolia* (*vert*). (c) 25 r. *Hebomoia glaucippe* and *Punica granatum* (*vert*) .. .. *Set of* 3 *sheets* 12·00 13·00

289 Airship LZ-127 *Graf Zeppelin* in Searchlights

290 Ford Model "T"

(Litho Walsall)

1993 (22 Nov). *Aviation Anniversaries. T* **289** *and similar multicoloured designs. P* 14.

1913 3 r. 50, Type **289** 70 55
1914 5 r. Homing pigeon and message from Santa Catalina mail service, 1894 .. 90 90
1915 10 r. Eckener and airship LZ-127 *Graf Zeppelin* .. .. 1·50 1·60
1916 15 r. Pilot's badge and loading Philadelphia –Washington mail, 1918 .. .. 2·25 2·40
1917 20 r. U.S.S. *Macon* (airship) and mooring mast, 1933 .. .. .. 2·50 2·75
1913/17 .. .. *Set of* 5 7·00 7·50
MS1918 Two sheets. (a) 70×100 mm. 25 r. Santos Dumont's airship *Balloon No. 5* and Eiffel Tower. 1901. (b) 100×70 mm. 25 r. Jean-Pierre Blanchard's balloon, 1793 (*vert*) .. *Set of* 2 *sheets* 6·00 7·00

Anniversaries:—Nos. 1913, 1915, 1917, **MS**1918a, 125th birth anniv of Hugo Eckener (airship pioneer); Nos. 1914, 1916, **MS**1918b, Bicent of First Airmail Flight.

(Litho Questa)

1993 (22 Nov). *Centenaries of Henry Ford's First Petrol Engine (Nos. 1919/30,* **MS***1943a) and Karl Benz's First Four-wheeled Car (others). T* **290** *and similar horiz designs. P* 14.

1919 3 r. 50, multicoloured 40 45
a. Sheetlet. Nos. 1919/30 .. .. 4·75
1920 3 r. 50, multicoloured 40 45
1921 3 r. 50, black and reddish violet 40 45
1922 3 r. 50, multicoloured 40 45
1923 3 r. 50, multicoloured 40 45
1924 3 r. 50, multicoloured 40 45
1925 3 r. 50, multicoloured 40 45
1926 3 r. 50, multicoloured 40 45
1927 3 r. 50, multicoloured 40 45
1928 3 r. 50, multicoloured 40 45
1929 3 r. 50, multicoloured 40 45
1930 3 r. 50, black, light brown & reddish violet 40 45
1931 3 r. 50, multicoloured 40 45
a. Sheetlet. Nos. 1931/42 .. .. 4·75
1932 3 r. 50, multicoloured 40 45
1933 3 r. 50, greenish black, black & reddish vio 40 45
1934 3 r. 50, multicoloured 40 45
1935 3 r. 50, multicoloured 40 45
1936 3 r. 50, multicoloured 40 45
1937 3 r. 50, multicoloured 40 45
1938 3 r. 50, multicoloured 40 45
1939 3 r. 50, multicoloured 40 45
1940 3 r. 50, multicoloured 40 45
1941 3 r. 50, multicoloured 40 45
1942 3 r. 50, black, light brown & reddish violet 40 45
1919/42 .. .. *Set of* 24 9·50 10·50
MS1943 Two sheets, each 100×70 mm. (a) 25 r. multicoloured. (b) 25 r. multicoloured *Set of* 2 *sheets* 5·50 5·75

Designs:—No. 1920, Henry Ford; No. 1921, Plans of first petrol engine; No. 1922, Ford "Probe GT", 1993; No. 1923, Front of Ford "Sportsman", 1947; No. 1924, Back of Ford "Sportsman"; No. 1925, Advertisement of 1915; No. 1926, Ford "Thunderbird", 1955; No. 1927, Ford logo; No. 1928, Ford "Edsel Citation", 1958; No. 1929, Ford half-ton pickup, 1941; No. 1930, Silhouette of early Ford car; No. 1931, Daimler-Benz "Straight 8", 1937; No. 1932, Karl Benz; No. 1933, Mercedes-Benz poster; No. 1934, Mercedes "38-250SS", 1929; No. 1935, Benz "Viktoria", 1893; No. 1936, Benz logo; No. 1937, Plan of Mercedes engine; No. 1938, Mercedes-Benz "300SL Gullwing", 1952; No. 1939, Mercedes-Benz "SL", 1993; No. 1940, Front of Benz 4-cylinder car, 1906; No. 1941, Back of Benz 4-cylinder car and advertisement; No. 1942, Silhouette of early Benz car; No. **MS**1943a, Ford Model "Y", 1933; No. **MS**1943b, Mercedes "300S", 1955.

Nos. 1919/30 and 1931/42 were printed together, *se-tenant*, in sheetlets of 12 each forming a composite design.

291 Ivan, Sonia, Sasha and Peter in the Snow

(Des Rosemary DeFiglio. Litho Questa)

1993 (20 Dec). *Peter and the Wolf. T* **291** *and similar horiz designs showing scenes from Walt Disney's cartoon film. Multicoloured. P* 14×13½.

1944 7 l. Type **291** 10 10
1945 15 l. Grandpa and Peter 10 10
1946 20 l. Peter on bridge 10 10
1947 25 l. Yascha, Vladimir and Mischa .. 10 10
1948 50 l. Sasha on lookout 10 10
1949 1 r. The Wolf 10 10
1950 3 r. 50, Peter dreaming 40 45
a. Sheetlet. Nos. 1950/8 .. .. 3·50
1951 3 r. 50, Peter taking gun 40 45
1952 3 r. 50, Peter with gun in snow 40 45
1953 3 r. 50, Sasha and Peter 40 45
1954 3 r. 50, Sonia and Peter 40 45
1955 3 r. 50, Peter with Ivan and Sasha .. 40 45
1956 3 r. 50, Ivan warning Peter of the Wolf 40 45
1957 3 r. 50, Ivan, Peter and Sasha in tree .. 40 45
1958 3 r. 50, Wolf below tree 40 45
1959 3 r. 50, Wolf and Sonia 40 45
a. Sheetlet. Nos. 1959/67 .. .. 3·50
1960 3 r. 50, Sasha attacking the Wolf .. 40 45
1961 3 r. 50, Sasha walking into Wolf's mouth 40 45
1962 3 r. 50, Peter firing pop gun at Wolf .. 40 45
1963 3 r. 50, Wolf chasing Sonia 40 45
1964 3 r. 50, Ivan tying rope to Wolf's tail .. 40 45
1965 3 r. 50, Peter and Ivan hoisting Wolf .. 40 45
1966 3 r. 50, Sasha and the hunters 40 45
1967 3 r. 50, Ivan and Peter on Wolf hanging from tree 40 45
1944/67 .. .. *Set of* 24 7·25 8·50
MS1968 Two sheets. (a) 102×127 mm. 25 r. Sonia as an angel. (b) 127×102 mm. 25 r. Ivan looking proud .. .. *Set of* 2 *sheets* 5·50 5·75

Nos. 1950/8 and 1959/67 were printed together, *se-tenant*, in sheetlets of 9.

292 "Girl with a Broom" (Rembrandt)

(Des Kerri Schiff. Litho Cartor)

1994 (2 Feb). *Famous Paintings by Rembrandt and Matisse. T* **292** *and similar multicoloured designs. P* 13.

1969 50 l. Type **292** 10 10
1970 2 r. "Girl with Tulips" (Matisse) 20 25
1971 3 r. 50, "Young Girl at half-open Door" (Rembrandt) 40 45
1972 3 r. 50, "Portrait of Greta Moll" (Matisse) 40 45
1973 5 r. "The Prophetess Hannah" (Rembrandt) 55 60
1974 6 r. 50, "The Idol" (Matisse) 75 80
1975 7 r. "Woman with a Pink Flower" (Rembrandt) 80 85
1976 9 r. "Mme Matisse in a Japanese Robe" (Matisse) .. .. 1·00 1·10
1977 10 r. "Portrait of Mme Matisse" (Matisse) 1·10 1·25
1978 12 r. "Lucretia" (Rembrandt) .. .. 1·40 1·50
1979 15 r. "Lady with a Ostrich Feather Fan" (Rembrandt) .. .. 1·60 1·75
1980 15 r. "The Woman with the Hat" (Matisse) 1·60 1·75
1969/80 .. .. *Set of* 12 9·75 10·50
MS1981 Three sheets. (a) 106×132 mm. 25 r. "The Music-makers" (detail) (Rembrandt). (b) 132×106 mm. 25 r. "Married Couple with Three Children" (detail) (Rembrandt) (*horiz*). (c) 132×106 mm. 25 r. "The Painter's Family" (detail) (Matisse) .. .. *Set of* 3 *sheets* 8·25 8·50

No. 1979 is inscribed "The Lady with an Ostich Feather Fan" in error.

293 Hong Kong 1983 $1 Space Museum Stamp and Moon-lantern Festival

294 Vase

(Des W. Hanson. Litho Questa)

1994 (18 Feb). *"Hong Kong '94" International Stamp Exhibition (1st issue). T* **293** *and similar horiz design. Multicoloured. P* 14.

1982 4 r. Type **293** 45 50
a. Horiz pair. Nos. 1982/3 .. .. 90 1·00
1983 4 r. Maldive Islands 1976 5 r. "Viking" space mission stamp and Moon-lantern Festival 45 50

Nos. 1982/3 were printed together, *se-tenant*, in horizontal pairs throughout the sheet with the centre part of each pair forming a composite design.

(Des Kerri Schiff. Litho Questa)

1994 (18 Feb). *"Hong Kong '94" International Stamp Exhibition (2nd issue). Ching Dynasty Cloisonné Enamelware. T* **294** *and similar vert designs. Multicoloured. P* 14.

1984 2 r. Type **294** 20 25
a. Sheetlet. Nos. 1984/9 .. .. 1·00
1985 2 r. Flower holder 20 25

1986 2 r. Elephant with vase on back .. 20 25
1987 2 r. Tibetan style lama's teapot 20 25
1988 2 r. Fo-Dog 20 25
1989 2 r. Teapot with swing handle 20 25
1984/9 .. .. *Set of* 6 1·00 1·50
Nos. 1984/9 were printed, *se-tenant*, in sheetlets of 6.

295 Windischmann (U.S.A.) and Giannini (Italy)

296 Humpback Whale

(Litho Questa)

1994 (28 Feb). *World Cup Football Championship, U.S.A. (2nd issue). T* **295** *and similar multicoloured designs. P* 14.
1990 7 l. Type **295** 10 10
1991 20 l. Carnevale (Italy) and Gascoigne (England) 10 10
1992 25 l. England players congratulating Platt 10 10
1993 3 r. 50, Koeman (Holland) and Klinsmann (Germany) 40 45
1994 5 r. Quinn (Ireland) and Maldini (Italy) 55 60
1995 7 r. Lineker (England) 80 85
1996 15 r. Hassam (Egypt) and Moran (Ireland) 1·60 1·75
1997 18 r. Canniggia (Argentina) .. .. 2·00 2·10
1990/7 .. .. *Set of* 8 5·50 6·00
MS1998 Two sheets, each 103×73 mm. (a) 25 r. Ogris (Austria). (b) 25 r. Conejo (Costa Rica) (*horiz*) .. .. .. *Set of* 2 *sheets* 5·50 5·75

(Litho Questa)

1994 (20 May). *Centenary of Sierra Club (environmental protection society)* (1992). *Endangered Species. T* **296** *and similar multicoloured designs. P* 14.
1999 6 r. 50, Type **296** 75 80
a. Sheetlet. Nos. 1999/2004 .. .. 4·50
2000 6 r. 50, Ocelot crouched in grass .. 75 80
2001 6 r. 50, Ocelot sitting 75 80
2002 6 r. 50, Snow Monkey 75 80
2003 6 r. 50, Prairie Dog 75 80
2004 6 r. 50, Golden Lion Tamarin 75 80
2005 6 r. 50, Prairie Dog eating (*horiz*) .. 75 80
a. Sheetlet. Nos. 2005/10 .. .. 4·50
2006 6 r. 50, Prairie Dog outside burrow (*horiz*) 75 80
2007 6 r. 50, Herd of Woodland Caribou (*horiz*) 75 80
2008 6 r. 50, Woodland Caribou facing left (*horiz*) 75 80
2009 6 r. 50, Woodland Caribou facing right (*horiz*) 75 80
2010 6 r. 50, Pair of Galapagos Penguins (*horiz*) 75 80
2011 6 r. 50, Galapagos Penguin facing right 75 80
a. Sheetlet. Nos. 2011/18 .. .. 6·00
2012 6 r. 50, Galapagos Penguin looking straight ahead 75 80
2013 6 r. 50, Bengal Tiger looking straight ahead 75 80
2014 6 r. 50, Bengal Tiger looking right .. 75 80
2015 6 r. 50, Philippine Tarsier with tree trunk at left 75 80
2016 6 r. 50, Philippine Tarsier with tree trunk at right 75 80
2017 6 r. 50, Head of Philippine Tarsier .. 75 80
2018 6 r. 50, Sierra Club Centennial emblem (black, buff and deep turquoise-green) 75 80
2019 6 r. 50, Golden Lion Tamarin between two branches (*horiz*) 75 80
a. Sheetlet. Nos. 2019/26 .. .. 6·00
2020 6 r. 50, Golden Lion Tamarin on tree trunk (*horiz*) 75 80
2021 6 r. 50, Tail fin of Humpback Whale and coastline (*horiz*) 75 80
2022 6 r. 50, Tail fin of Humpback Whale at night (*horiz*) 75 80
2023 6 r. 50, Bengal Tiger (*horiz*) 75 80
2024 6 r. 50, Ocelot (*horiz*) 75 80
2025 6 r. 50, Snow Monkey in water climbing out of pool (*horiz*) 75 80
2026 6 r. 50, Snow Monkey swimming (*horiz*) 75 80
1999/2026 .. .. .. *Set of* 28 21·00 22·00
Nos. 1999/2004, 2005/10, 2011/18 and 2019/26 were each printed together, *se-tenant*, as two sheetlets of 6 (Nos. 1999/2010) or two sheetlets of 8 (Nos. 2011/26).

297 Dome of the Rock, Jerusalem

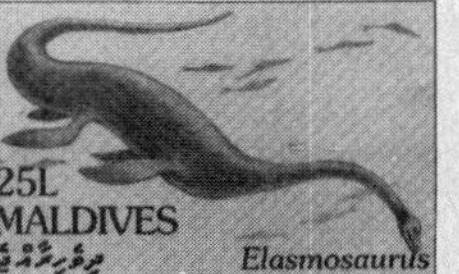

298 Elasmosaurus

(Litho Cartor)

1994 (10 June). *Solidarity with the Palestinians. P* $13^1/_2$×14.
2027 **297** 8 r. multicoloured 90 95

(Des L. Birmingham. Litho B.D.T.)

1994 (20 June). *Prehistoric Animals. T* **298** *and similar multicoloured designs. P* 14.
2028/59 25 l., 50 l., 1 r., 3 r. x 24, 5 r., 8 r., 10 r., 15 r., 20 r. .. .. *Set of* 32 14·50 15·00
MS2060 Two sheets, each 106×76 mm. (a) 25 r. Gallimimus. (b) 25 r. Plateosaurus (*vert*) *Set of* 2 *sheets* 5·50 5·75
Nos. 2031/42 and 2043/54 were each printed together, *se-tenant*, in sheetlets of 12 forming composite designs. The species depicted are, in addition to Type **298**, Dilophosaurus, Avimimus, Dimorphodon, Megalosaurus, Kuehneosaurus, Dryosaurus, Kentrosaurus, Baraposaurus, Tenontosaurus, Elaphrosaurus, Maiasaura, Huayangosaurus, Rutiodon, Pianitzkysaurus, Quetzalcoatlus, Daspletosaurus, Pleurocoelus, Baryonyx, Pentaceratops, Kritosaurus, Microvenator, Nodosaurus, Montanaceratops, Dromiceiomimus, Dryptosaurus, Parkosaurus, Chasmosaurus, Edmontonia, Anatosaurus, Velociraptor and Spinosaurus.

299 Mallet Steam Locomotive, Indonesia

300 Japanese Bobtail

(Des K. Gromell. Litho B.D.T.)

1994 (4 July). *Railway Locomotives of Asia. T* **299** *and similar multicoloured designs. P* 14.
2061 25 l. Type **299** 10 10
2062 50 l. Class "C 62" steam locomotive, Japan 10 10
2063 1 r. Class "D 51" steam locomotive, Japan (*horiz*) 10 10
2064 5 r. Steam locomotive, India (*horiz*) .. 55 60
2065 6 r. 50 + 50 l. Class "W" steam locomotive, India (*horiz*) 80 85
a. Sheetlet. Nos. 2065/70 .. .. 4·75
2066 6 r. 50 + 50 l. Class "C 53" steam locomotive, Indonesia (*horiz*) .. 80 85
2067 6 r. 50 + 50 l. Class "C-10" steam locomotive, Japan (*horiz*) 80 85
2068 6 r. 50 + 50 l. Hanomag steam locomotive, India (*horiz*) 80 85
2069 6 r. 50 + 50 l. Hakari Bullet Train, Japan (*horiz*) 80 85
2070 6 r. 50 + 50 l. Class "C-55" steam locomotive, Japan (*horiz*) 80 85
2071 8 r. Class "485" electric locomotive, Japan (*horiz*) 90 95
2072 10 r. Class "WP" Pacific steam locomotive, India (*horiz*) .. .. .. 1·10 1·25
2073 15 r. "People" Class "RM" steam locomotive, China (*horiz*) .. .. 1·60 1·75
2074 20 r. Class "C 57" steam locomotive, Japan 2·25 2·40
2061/74 .. .. *Set of* 14 11·00 12·00
MS2075 Two sheets, each 110×80 mm. (a) 25 r. Steam locomotive pulling goods train, Indonesia (*horiz*). (b) 25 r. Series "8620" steam locomotive, Japan (*horiz*) .. .. *Set of* 2 *sheets* 5·50 5·75
Nos. 2065/70 were printed together, *se-tenant* in sheetlets of 6.

(Litho Questa)

1994 (11 July). *Cats. T* **297** *and similar multicoloured designs. P* 14.
2076 7 l. Type **297** 10 10
2077 20 l. Siamese (*vert*) 10 10
2078 25 l. Persian Longhair 10 10
2079 50 l. Somali (*vert*) 10 10
2080 3 r. 50, Oriental Shorthair 40 45
2081 5 r. Burmese 55 60
2082 7 r. Bombay carrying kitten 80 85
2083 10 r. Turkish Van (*vert*) .. .. 1·10 1·25
2084 12 r. Javanese (*vert*) .. .. .. 1·40 1·50
2085 15 r. Singapura .. .. 1·60 1·75
2086 18 r. Turkish Angora (*vert*) .. .. 2·00 2·10
2087 20 r. Egyptian Mau (*vert*) .. .. 2·25 2·40
2076/87 .. .. *Set of* 12 10·00 11·00
MS2088 Three sheets. (a) 70×100 mm. 25 r. Birman (*vert*). (b) 70×100 mm. 25 r. Korat (*vert*). (c) 100×70 mm. 25 r. Abyssinian (*vert*) *Set of* 3 *sheets* 8·25 8·50

301 Franco Baresi (Italy) and Stuart McCall (Scotland)

(Litho Questa)

1994 (4 Aug). *World Cup Football Championship, U.S.A. (3rd issue). T* **301** *and similar multicoloured designs. P* 14.

(*a*) *Horiz designs*
2089 10 l. Type **301** 10 10
a. Sheetlet. Nos. 2089/94 .. .. 3·25
2090 25 l. Mick McCarthy (Ireland) and Gary Lineker (England) 10 10
2091 50 l. J. Helt (Denmark) and R. Gordillo (Spain) 10 10
2092 5 r. Martin Vasquez (Spain) and Enzo Scifo (Belgium) 55 60
2093 10 r. Championship emblem .. .. 1·10 1·25
2094 12 r. Tomas Brolin (Sweden) and Gordon Durie (Scotland) .. .. .. 1·40 1·50

(*b*) *Vert designs*
2095 6 r. 50, Bebeto (Brazil) 75 80
a. Sheetlet. Nos. 2095/100 .. .. 4·50
2096 6 r. 50, Lothar Matthaus (Germany) .. 75 80
2097 6 r. 50, Diego Maradona (Argentina) .. 75 80
2098 6 r. 50, Stephane Chapuasti (Switzerland) 75 80
2099 6 r. 50, George Hagi (Rumania) .. 75 80
2100 6 r. 50, Carlos Valderama (Colombia) .. 75 80
2089/100 .. .. *Set of* 12 7·50 8·25
MS2101 100×70 mm. 10 r. Egyptian players 1·10 1·25
Nos. 2089/94 and 2095/100 were each printed together, *se-tenant*, in sheetlets of 6.

302 Crew of "Apollo 11"

303 Linford Christie (Great Britain) (100 metres), 1992

(Des W. Hanson. Litho B.D.T.)

1994 (8 Aug). *25th Anniv of First Moon Landing. T* **302** *and similar multicoloured designs. P* 14.
2102 5 r. Type **302** 55 60
a. Sheetlet. Nos. 2102/7 .. .. 3·25
2103 5 r. "Apollo 11" mission logo 55 60
2104 5 r. Edwin Aldrin (astronaut) and *Eagle* 55 60
2105 5 r. Crew of "Apollo 12" 55 60
2106 5 r. "Apollo 12" mission logo 55 60
2107 5 r. Alan Bean (astronaut) and equipment 55 60
2108 5 r. Crew of "Apollo 16" 55 60
a. Sheetlet. Nos. 2108/13 .. .. 3·25
2109 5 r. "Apollo 16" mission logo 55 60
2110 5 r. Astronauts with U.S. flag 55 60
2111 5 r. Crew of "Apollo 17" 55 60
2112 5 r. "Apollo 17" mission logo 55 60
2113 5 r. Launch of "Apollo 17" 55 60
2102/13 .. .. *Set of* 12 6·50 7·00
MS2114 100×76 mm. 25 r. Launch of Russian rocket from Baikonur (*vert*) .. .. 2·75 3·00
Nos. 2102/7 and 2108/13 were printed together, *se-tenant*, in sheetlets of 6.

(Des Kerri Schiff. Litho Questa)

1994 (8 Aug). *Centenary of International Olympic Committee. Gold Medal Winners. T* **303** *and similar vert designs. Multicoloured. P* 14.
2115 7 r. Type **303** 80 85
2116 12 r. Koji Gushiken (Japan) (gymnastics), 1984 .. .. 1·40 1·50
MS2117 106×71 mm. 25 r. George Hackl (Germany) (single luge), 1994 .. .. 2·75 3·00

304 U.S. Amphibious DUKW

(Des J. Batchelor. Litho Questa)

1994 (8 Aug). *50th Anniv of D-Day. T* **304** *and similar horiz designs. Multicoloured. P* 14.
2118 2 r. Type **304** 20 25
2119 4 r. Landing Craft Tank unloading at Sword Beach 45 50
2120 18 r. Landing Craft Infantry at Omaha Beach .. .. 2·00 2·10
2118/20 .. .. *Set of* 3 2·50 2·75
MS2121 105×76 mm. 25 r. Landing craft with Canadian commandos .. .. .. 2·75 3·00

OMNIBUS ISSUES

Details, together with prices for complete sets, of the various Omnibus issues from the 1935 Silver Jubilee series to date are included in a special section following Zimbabwe at the end of Volume 2.

305 Duckpond, Suwan Folk Village

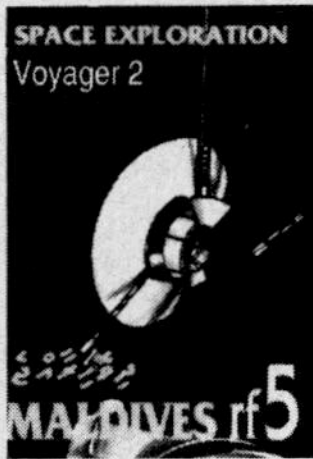

306 U.S. "Voyager 2" Satellite

(Des Kerri Schiff. Litho B.D.T. (3 r.) or Questa (others))

1994 (8 Aug). *"Philakorea '94" International Stamp Exhibition, Seoul. T* **305** *and similar multicoloured designs. P* 13½×14 (*Nos.* 2123/30) *or* 14 (*others*).

2122 50 l. Type **305** .. 10 10
2123 3 r. Pear-shaped bottle .. 35 40
a. Sheetlet. Nos. 2123/30 .. 2·75
2124 3 r. Vase with dragon decoration .. 35 40
2125 3 r. Vase with repaired lip .. 35 40
2126 3 r. Stoneware vase with floral decoration 35 40
2127 3 r. Celadon-glazed vase .. 35 40
2128 3 r. Unglazed stone vase .. 35 40
2129 3 r. Ritual water sprinkler .. 35 40
2130 3 r. Long-necked celadon-glazed vase .. 35 40
2131 3 r. 50, Yongduson Park .. 40 45
2132 20 r. Ploughing with ox, Hahoe .. 2·25 2·40
2122/32 .. *Set of* 11 5·50 6·00
MS2133 70×102 mm. 25 r. "Hunting" (detail from eight-panel painted screen (*vert*) .. 2·75 3·00

Nos. 2123/30, each 24×47 mm, were printed together, *se-tenant*, in sheetlets of 8.

(Des Outsiders Group. Litho Questa)

1994 (8 Aug). *Space Exploration. T* **306** *and similar multicoloured designs. P* 14.

2134 5 r. Type **306** .. 55 60
a. Sheetlet. Nos. 2134/45 .. 6·50
2135 5 r. Russian "Sputnik" satellite .. 55 60
2136 5 r. "Apollo-Soyuz" mission .. 55 60
2137 5 r. "Apollo 10" on parachutes .. 55 60
2138 5 r. "Apollo 11" mission flag .. 55 60
2139 5 r. Hubble space telescope .. 55 60
2140 5 r. Edwin "Buzz" Aldrin (astronaut) .. 55 60
2141 5 r. RCA lunar camera .. 55 60
2142 5 r. Lunar Rover (space buggy) .. 55 60
2143 5 r. Jim Irwin (astronaut) .. 55 60
2144 5 r. "Apollo 12" lunar module .. 55 60
2145 5 r. Astronaut holding equipment .. 55 60
2134/45 .. *Set of* 12 6·50 7·00
MS2146 Two sheets. (a) 70×100 mm. 25 r. David Scott (astronaut) in open hatch of "Apollo 9". (b) 100×70 mm. 25 r. Alan Shepherd Jr. (astronaut) (*horiz*) .. *Set of* 2 *sheets* 5·50 5·75

Nos. 2134/45 were printed together, *se-tenant*, in sheetlets of 12 forming a composite design.

307 Mother, Child, Old Man and Town Skyline

(Litho Questa)

1994 (24 Oct). *United Nations Development Programme. T* **307** *and similar horiz design. Multicoloured. P* 14.

2147 1 r. Type **307** .. 10 10
2148 8 r. Fisherman with son and island .. 90 95

308 School Band

(Litho Questa)

1994 (28 Nov). *50th Anniv of Aminiya School. Children's Paintings. T* **308** *and similar multicoloured designs. P* 14.

2149 15 l. Type **308** .. 10 10
2150 50 l. Classroom .. 10 10
2151 1 r. School emblem and hand holding book (*vert*) .. 10 10
2152 8 r. School girls holding books (*vert*) .. 90 95
2153 10 r. Sporting activities .. 1·10 1·25
2154 11 r. School girls holding crown (*vert*) .. 1·25 1·40
2155 13 r. Science lesson .. 1·50 1·60
2149/55 .. *Set of* 7 4·75 5·25

309 Boeing 747

(Des W. Wright. Litho B.D.T.)

1994 (31 Dec). *50th Anniv of International Civil Aviation Organization. T* **309** *and similar horiz designs. Multicoloured. P* 14.

2156 50 l. Type **309** .. 10 10
2157 1 r. Hawker Siddeley ("de Havilland") Comet 4 .. 10 10
2158 2 r. Male International Airport .. 20 25
2159 3 r. Lockheed L.1649 Super Star .. 35 40
2160 8 r. European Airbus .. 90 95
2161 10 r. Dornier Do-228 .. 1·10 1·25
2156/61 .. *Set of* 6 2·75 3·00
MS2162 100×70mm. 25 r. Concorde .. 2·75 3·00

310 Pintail ("Northern Pintail")

(Des Outsiders Group. Litho Questa)

1995 (27 Feb). *Ducks. T* **310** *and similar multicoloured designs. P* 14.

2163 5 r. Type **310** .. 55 60
a. Sheetlet. Nos. 2163/71 .. 5·00
2164 5 r. Comb Duck .. 55 60
2165 5 r. Ruddy Shelduck .. 55 60
2166 5 r. Garganey .. 55 60
2167 5 r. Indian Whistling Duck ("Lesser Whistling Duck") .. 55 60
2168 5 r. Green-winged Teal .. 55 60
2169 5 r. Fulvous Whistling Duck .. 55 60
2170 5 r. Common Shoveler ("Northern Shoveler") .. 55 60
2171 5 r. Cotton Pygmy Goose .. 55 60
2172 6 r. 50 + 50 l. European Pochard (*vert*) 80 85
a. Sheetlet. Nos. 2172/80 .. 7·25
2173 6 r. 50 + 50 l. Mallard (*vert*) .. 80 85
2174 6 r. 50 + 50 l. European Wigeon (*vert*) .. 80 85
2175 6 r. 50 + 50 l. Common Shoveler ("Northern Shoveler") (*vert*) .. 80 85
2176 6 r. 50 + 50 l. Pintail (*vert*) .. 80 85
2177 6 r. 50 + 50 l. Garganey (*vert*) .. 80 85
2178 6 r. 50 + 50 l. Tufted Duck (*vert*) .. 80 85
2179 6 r. 50 + 50 l. Red-crested Pochard ("Ferruginous Duck") (*vert*) .. 80 85
2180 6 r. 50 + 50 l. Ferruginous Duck ("Red-crested Pochard") (*vert*) .. 80 85
2163/80 .. *Set of* 18 12·00 13·00
MS2181 Two sheets. (a) 100×71 mm. 25 r. Spotbill Duck ("Garganey"). (b) 73×100 mm. 25 r. Cotton Pygmy Goose (*vert*) *Set of* 2 *sheets* 5·50 5·75

Nos. 2163/71 and 2172/80 were printed together, *se-tenant*, in sheetlets of 9, each with enlarged top margin, forming composite designs.

311 Taj Mahal, India

(Litho Questa)

1995 (28 Feb). *Famous Monuments of the World. T* **311** *and similar multicoloured designs. P* 14.

2182 7 l. Type **311** .. 10 10
2183 10 l. Washington Monument, U.S.A. .. 10 10
2184 15 l. Mount Rushmore, U.S.A. .. 10 10
2185 25 l. Arc de Triomphe, Paris (*vert*) .. 10 10
2186 50 l. Sphinx, Egypt (*vert*) .. 10 10
2187 5 r. El Castillo, Toltec pyramid, Yucatan 55 60
2188 8 r. Toltec statue, Tula, Mexico (*vert*) .. 90 95
2189 12 r. Victory Column, Berlin (*vert*) .. 1·40 1·50
2182/9 .. *Set of* 8 3·00 3·25
MS2190 Two sheets, each 112×85 mm. (a) 25 r. Easter Island statue (42×56 *mm*). (b) 25 r. Stonehenge, Wiltshire (85×28 *mm*) *Set of* 2 *sheets* 5·50 5·75

PRICES OF SETS

Set prices are given for many issues, generally those containing three stamps or more. Definitive sets include one of each value or major colour change, but do not cover different perforations, die types or minor shades. Where a choice is possible the set prices are based on the cheapest versions of the stamps included in the listings.

312 Donald Duck driving Chariot

(Des Rosemary DeFiglio. Litho B.D.T.)

1995 (22 Mar). *History of Wheeled Transport. T* **312** *and similar multicoloured designs showing scenes from Disney cartoon film* Donald and the Wheel. *P* 13.

2191 3 l. Type **312** .. 10 10
2192 4 l. Donald with log .. 10 10
2193 5 l. Donald driving early steam locomotive 10 10
2194 10 l. Donald pondering over circle (*vert*) .. 10 10
2195 20 l. Donald in crashed car (*vert*) .. 10 10
2196 25 l. Donald listening to early gramophone 10 10
2197 5 r. Donald on Mammoth .. 55 60
2198 20 r. Donald pushing early car .. 2·25 2·40
2191/8 .. *Set of* 8 2·75 3·00

313 Donald Duck playing Saxophone

314 Islamic Centre, Malé

(Des Alvin White Studios. Litho B.D.T)

1995 (22 Mar). *60th Birthday of Donald Duck. T* **313** *and similar multicoloured designs showing Walt Disney cartoon characters. P* 13.

2199 5 r. Type **313** .. 55 60
a. Sheetlet. Nos. 2199/206 .. 4·25
2200 5 r. Moby Duck playing fiddle .. 55 60
2201 5 r. Feathry Duck with banjo and drum 55 60
2202 5 r. Daisy Duck playing harp .. 55 60
2203 5 r. Gladstone Gander with clarinet .. 55 60
2204 5 r. Huey, Dewey and Louie with bassoon 55 60
2205 5 r. Gus Goose playing flute .. 55 60
2206 5 r. Prof. Ludwig von Drake playing trombone .. 55 60
2207 5 r. Daisy picking flowers .. 55 60
a. Sheetlet. Nos. 2207/14 .. 4·25
2208 5 r. Donald with backpack .. 55 60
2209 5 r. Grandma Duck with kitten .. 55 60
2210 5 r. Gus Goose and pie .. 55 60
2211 5 r. Gyro Gearloose in space .. 55 60
2212 5 r. Huey, Dewey and Louie photographing porcupine .. 55 60
2213 5 r. Prof. Ludwig von Drake .. 55 60
2214 5 r. Scrooge McDuck with money .. 55 60
2199/214 .. *Set of* 16 8·50 9·50
MS2215 Four sheets. (a) 108×130 mm. 25 r. Donald playing banjo. (b) 133×108 mm. 25 r. Donald posing for photo. (c) 108×130 mm. 25 r. Donald conducting (*horiz*). (d) 102×121 mm. 25 r. Huey, Dewey and Louie (*horiz*) *Set of* 4 *sheets* 11·00 11·50

Nos. 2199/206 and 2207/14 were printed together, *se-tenant*, in sheetlets of 8.

(Litho Questa)

1995 (1 May). *Eid Greetings. T* **314** *and similar vert designs. Multicoloured. P* 14.

2216 1 r. Type **314** .. 10 10
2217 1 r. Rose .. 10 10
2218 8 r. Orchid .. 90 95
2219 10 r. Orchid (*different*) .. 1·10 1·25
2216/19 .. *Set of* 4 2·10 2·40

315 Killer Whale

(Des K. Gromell. Litho Questa)

1995 (16 May). *"Singapore '95" International Stamp Exhibition (1st issue). Whales, Dolphins and Porpoises. T* **315** *and similar horiz designs. Multicoloured. P* 14.

2220 1 r. Type **315** .. 10 10
2221 2 r. Bottlenose Dolphins .. 20 25
2222 3 r. Right Whale .. 35 40
a. Sheetlet. Nos. 2222/33 .. 4·25
2223 3 r. Pair of Killer Whales .. 35 40
2224 3 r. Humpback Whale .. 35 40
2225 3 r. Pair of Belugas .. 35 40
2226 3 r. Narwhal .. 35 40

2227 3 r. Head of Blue Whale 35 40
2228 3 r. Bowhead Whale 35 40
2229 3 r. Head of Fin Whale 35 40
2230 3 r. Pair of Pilot Whales 35 40
2231 3 r. Grey Whale 35 40
2232 3 r. Sperm Whale 35 40
2233 3 r. Pair of Goosebeaked Whales .. 35 40
2234 3 r. Hourglass Dolphin 35 40
a. Sheetlet. Nos. 2234/45 .. .. 4·25
2235 3 r. Bottlenose Dolphin (*different*) .. 35 40
2236 3 r. Dusky Dolphin 35 40
2237 3 r. Spectacled Porpoise 35 40
2238 3 r. Fraser's Dolphin 35 40
2239 3 r. Camerson's Dolphin 35 40
2240 3 r. Pair of Spinner Dolphins 35 40
2241 3 r. Pair of Dalls Dolphins 35 40
2242 3 r. Spotted Dolphin 35 40
2243 3 r. Indus River Dolphin 35 40
2244 3 r. Hector's Dolphin 35 40
2245 3 r. Amazon River Dolphin 35 40
2246 8 r. Humpback Whale and calf 90 95
2247 10 r. Common Dolphin .. .. .. 1·10 1·25
2220/47 .. .. *Set of* 28 10·50 12·00
MS2248 Two sheets, each 100×70 mm. (a) 25 r. Sperm Whale (*different*). (b) 25 r. Pair of Hourglass Dolphins .. .. *Set of* 2 *sheets* 5·50 5·75

Nos. 2222/33 and 2234/45 were printed together, *se-tenant*, in sheetlets of 12.

See also Nos. 2302/10.

316 Scout Camp and National Flag

(Des B. Hargreaves. Litho Questa)

1995 (6 July). *18th World Scout Jamboree, Netherlands. T* **316** *and similar multicoloured designs. P* 14.

2249 10 r. Type **316** .. .. 1·10 1·25
a. Horiz strip of 3. Nos. 2249/51 .. 4·00
2250 12 r. Campfire cooking .. .. .. 1·40 1·50
2251 15 r. Scouts erecting tent .. .. 1·60 1·75
2249/51 .. .. *Set of* 3 4·00 4·50
MS2252 102×72 mm. 25 r. Scouts around camp fire (*vert*) .. .. 2·75 3·00

Nos. 2249/51 were printed in sheets of 9 containing three *se-tenant* horizontal strips, each forming a composite design.

317 Soviet Heavy Howitzer Battery

(Des W. Wright. Litho Questa)

1995 (6 July). *50th Anniv of End of Second World War in Europe. T* **317** *and similar horiz designs. Multicoloured. P* 14.

2253 5 r. Type **317** 55 60
a. Sheetlet. Nos. 2253/60 .. .. 4·25
2254 5 r. Ruins of Berchtesgaden 55 60
2255 5 r. U.S. Boeing B-17 Flying Fortress dropping food over the Netherlands 55 60
2256 5 r. Soviet Ilyushin Il-1 bomber .. 55 60
2257 5 r. Liberation of Belsen 55 60
2258 5 r. Supermarine Spitfire and V-1 flying bomb 55 60
2259 5 r. U.S. tanks advancing through Cologne 55 60
2260 5 r. Reichstag in ruins 55 60
2253/60 .. .. *Set of* 8 4·25 4·75
MS2261 107×76 mm. 25 r. Soviet and U.S. troops celebrating .. .. .. 2·75 3·00

Nos. 2253/60 were printed together, *se-tenant*, in sheetlets of 8 with the stamps arranged in two horizontal strips of 4 separated by a gutter showing R.A.F. Lancasters over Dresden.

318 Asian Child and Dove

319 United Nations Emblem

(Des J. Iskowitz. Litho)

1995 (6 July). *50th Anniv of United Nations* (*1st issue*). *T* **318** *and similar vert designs. Multicoloured. P* 14.

2262 6 r. 50 + 50 l. Type **318** 80 85
a. Horiz strip of 3. Nos. 2262/4 .. 2·75
2263 8 r. Globe and dove 90 95
2264 10 r. African child and dove .. .. 1·10 1·25
2262/4 .. .. *Set of* 3 2·75 3·00
MS2265 72×102 mm. 25 r. United Nations emblem and dove .. .. .. 2·75 3·00

Nos. 2262/4 were printed in sheets of 9 containing three *se-tenant* horizontal strips, each forming a composite design.

(Litho Questa)

1995 (6 July). *50th Anniv of United Nations* (*2nd issue*). *T* **319** *and similar horiz designs. P* 14.

2266 30 l. black, bright blue and green .. 10 10
2267 8 r. multicoloured 90 95
2268 11 r. multicoloured .. .. .. 1·25 1·40
2269 13 r. black, grey and rosine .. .. 1·50 1·60
2266/9 .. .. *Set of* 4 3·75 4·00

Designs:—8 r. Symbolic women, flag and map; 11 r. U. N. soldier and symbolic dove; 13 r. Gun barrels, atomic explosion and bomb sight.

320 Asian Child eating Rice

321 Queen Elizabeth the Queen Mother

(Des J. Iskowitz. Litho)

1995 (6 July). *50th Anniv of Food and Agriculture Organization* (*1st issue*). *T* **320** *and similar multicoloured designs. P* 14.

2270 6 r. 50 + 50 l. Type **320** 80 85
a. Horiz strip of 3. Nos. 2270/2 .. 2·75
2271 8 r. F.A.O. emblem 90 95
2272 10 r. African mother and child .. .. 1·10 1·25
2270/2 .. .. *Set of* 3 2·75 3·00
MS2273 72×102 mm. 25 r. African child and symbolic hand holding maize .. .. 2·75 3·00

Nos. 2270/2 were printed in sheets of 9 containing three *se-tenant* horizontal strips.

See also Nos. 2311/12.

(Litho Questa)

1995 (6 July). *95th Birthday of Queen Elizabeth the Queen Mother. T* **321** *and similar vert designs. P* 13½×14.

2274 5 r. orange-brown, pale brown and black 55 60
a. Sheetlet. Nos. 2274/7×2 .. .. 4·25
2275 5 r. multicoloured 55 60
2276 5 r. multicoloured 55 60
2277 5 r. multicoloured 55 60
2274/7 .. .. *Set of* 4 2·10 2·40
MS2278 125×100 mm. 25 r. multicoloured .. 2·75 3·00

Designs:—No. 2274, Queen Elizabeth the Queen Mother (pastel drawing); No. 2275, Without hat; No. 2276, At desk (oil painting); No. 2277, Type **321**; No. **MS**2278, Wearing lilac hat and dress.

Nos. 2274/7 were printed together in sheetlets of 8 containing two *se-tenant* horizontal strips of 4.

(Des J. Batchelor. Litho Questa)

1995 (6 July). *50th Anniv of End of Second World War in the Pacific. Horiz designs as T* **317**. *P* 14.

2279 6 r. 50 + 50 l. Grumman F6F-3 Hellcat aircraft 80 85
a. Sheetlet. Nos. 2279/84 .. .. 4·75
2280 6 r. 50 + 50 l. F4-U1 fighter aircraft attacking beach 80 85
2281 6 r. 50 + 50 l. Douglas SBD Dauntless aircraft 80 85
2282 6 r. 50 + 50 l. American troops in landing craft, Guadalcanal 80 85
2283 6 r. 50 + 50 l. U.S. marines in Alligator tanks 80 85
2284 6 r. 50 + 50 l. U.S. landing ship 80 85
2279/84 .. .. *Set of* 6 4·75 5·00
MS2285 106×74 mm. 25 r. F4-U1 fighter aircraft .. .. 2·75 3·00

Nos. 2279/84 were printed together, *se-tenant*, in sheetlets of 6 with the stamps arranged in two horizontal strips of 3 separated by a gutter showing U.S. marines in landing craft.

322 Students using Library

(Litho Questa)

1995 (12 July). *50th Anniversary of National Library. T* **322** *and similar horiz designs. Multicoloured. P* 14.

2286 2 r. Type **322** 20 25
2287 8 r. Students using library (*different*) .. 90 95
MS2288 105×75 mm. 10 r. Library entrance (*100×70 mm*). Imperf .. .. .. 1·10 1·25

MINIMUM PRICE

The minimum price quote is 10p which represents a handling charge rather than a basis for valuing common stamps. For further notes about prices see introductory pages.

323 Spur-thighed Tortoise

(Des D. Burkhardt. Litho Questa)

1995 (22 Aug). *Turtles and Tortoises. T* **323** *and similar horiz designs. Multicoloured. P* 14.

2289 3 r. Type **323** 35 40
a. Sheetlet. Nos. 2289/96 .. .. 2·75
2290 3 r. Aldabra Turtle 35 40
2291 3 r. Loggerhead Turtle 35 40
2292 3 r. Olive Ridley Turtle 35 40
2293 3 r. Leatherback Turtle 35 40
2294 3 r. Green Turtle 35 40
2295 3 r. Atlantic Ridley Turtle 35 40
2296 3 r. Hawksbill Turtle 35 40
2297 10 r. Hawksbill Turtle on beach .. .. 1·10 1·25
a. Vert strip of 4. Nos. 2297/300 .. 4·25
2298 10 r. Pair of Hawksbill Turtles .. .. 1·10 1·25
2299 10 r. Hawksbill Turtle climbing out of water .. .. 1·10 1·25
2300 10 r. Hawksbill Turtle swimming .. 1·10 1·25
2289/2300 .. .. .. *Set of* 12 7·00 8·00
MS2301 100×70mm. 25 r. Green Turtle .. 2·75 3·00

Nos. 2289/96 were printed together, *se-tenant*, in sheetlets of 8 forming a composite design.

Nos. 2297/2300, which include the W.W.F. Panda emblem, were printed together in sheets of 12 (3×4) containing 3 vertical *se-tenant* strips.

324 *Russula aurata* (fungi) and *Papilio demodocus* (butterfly)

325 Planting Kaashi

(Des L. Nelson. Litho Questa)

1995 (18 Oct). *"Singapore '95" International Stamp Exhibition* (*2nd issue*). *Butterflies and Fungi. T* **324** *and similar multicoloured designs. P* 14.

2302 2 r. Type **324** 20 25
a. Sheetlet. Nos. 2302/5 80
2303 2 r. *Lepista saeva* and *Kallimoides rumia* 20 25
2304 2 r. *Lepista nuda* and *Hypolimnas salmacis* 20 25
2305 2 r. *Xerocomus subtomentosus* ("*Boletus subtomentosus*") and *Precis octavia* .. 20 25
2306 5 r. *Gyroporus castaneus* and *Hypolimnas salmacis* 55 60
a. Sheetlet. Nos. 2306/9 .. .. 3·75
2307 8 r. *Gomphidius glutinosus* and *Papilio dardanus* 90 95
2308 10 r. *Russula olivacea* and *Precis octavia* 1·10 1·25
2309 12 r. *Boletus edulis* and *Prepona praeneste* 1·40 1·50
2302/9 .. .. *Set of* 8 4·75 5·25
MS2310 Two sheets, each 105×76 mm. (a) 25 r. *Amanita muscaria* and *Kallimoides rumia* (*vert*). (b) 25 r. *Boletus rhodoxanthus* and *Hypolimnas salmacis* (*vert*) .. .. *Set of* 2 *sheets* 5·50 5·75

Nos. 2302/5 and 2306/9 were each printed together, *se-tenant*, in sheetlets of 4, forming composite designs.

No. 2304 is inscribed "Lapista" in error.

(Litho Questa)

1995 (2 Nov). *50th Anniv of Food and Agriculture Organization* (*2nd issue*). *T* **325** *and similar vert design. Multicoloured. P* 14.

2311 7 r. Type **325** 80 85
2312 8 r. Fishing boat 90 95

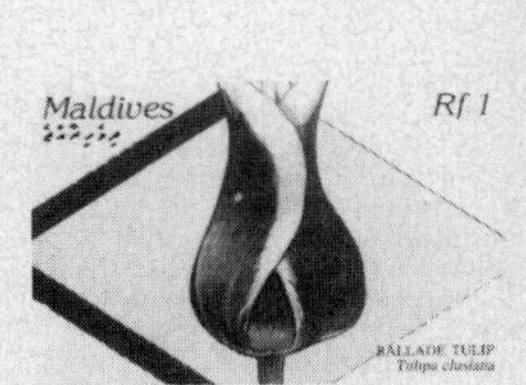

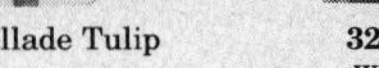

326 Ballade Tulip

327 John Lennon with Microphone

(Des L. Fried. Litho Questa)

1995 (4 Dec). *Flowers. T* **326** *and similar multicoloured designs. P* 14.

2313 1 r. Type **326** 10 10
2314 3 r. White Mallow 35 40
2315 5 r. Regale Trumpet Lily 55 60
2316 5 r. *Dendrobium* "Waipahu Beauty" .. 55 60
a. Sheetlet. Nos. 2316/24 .. .. 4·75
2317 5 r. *Brassocattleya* "Jean Murray" .. 55 60
2318 5 r. *Cymbidium* "Fort George" 55 60
2319 5 r. *Paphiopedilum malipoense* 55 60
2320 5 r. *Cycnoches chlorochilon* 55 60
2321 5 r. *Rhyncholaelia digbgana* 55 60
2322 5 r. *Lycaste deppei* 55 60
2323 5 r. *Masdevallia constricta* 55 60
2324 5 r. *Paphiopedilum* "Clair de Lune" .. 55 60
2325 7 r. Lilactime Dahlia 80 85
2326 8 r. Blue Ideal Iris 90 95
2327 10 r. Red Crown Imperial .. .. .. 1·10 1·25
2313/27 .. .. *Set of* 15 8·50 9·50
MS2328 Two sheets, each 106×76 mm. (a) 25 r. *Encyclia cochleata* (*vert*). (b) 25 r. *Psychopsis kramerina* (*vert*) .. .. .. *Set of* 2 *sheets* 5·50 5·75

Nos. 2316/24 were printed together, *se-tenant*, in sheetlets of 9.

(Litho Questa)

1995 (8 Dec). 15*th Death Anniv of John Lennon* (*musician*). *T* **327** *and similar vert designs. Multicoloured. P* 14.

2329 5 r. Type **327** 90 90
a. Sheetlet. Nos. 2329/34 .. .. 4·75
2330 5 r. With glasses and moustache .. 90 90
2331 5 r. With guitar 90 90
2332 5 r. With guitar and wearing glasses .. 90 90
2333 5 r. Wearing sun glasses and red jacket 90 90
2334 5 r. Wearing headphones 90 90
2329/34 .. .. *Set of* 6 4·75 4·75
MS2335 88×117 mm. 2, 3, 8, 10 r. Different portraits of John Lennon .. .. 4·00 4·00
MS2336 102×72 mm. 25 r. John Lennon performing .. .. 4·25 4·25

Nos. 2329/34 were printed together, *se-tenant*, in sheetlets of 6.

328 Elvis Presley with Microphone

329 Johannes van der Waals (1919 Physics)

(Des R. Martin. Litho Questa)

1995 (8 Dec). 60*th Birth Anniv of Elvis Presley* (*entertainer*). *T* **328** *and similar multicoloured designs. P* 13½×14.

2337 5 r. Type **328** 55 60
a. Sheetlet. Nos. 2337/45 .. .. 4·75
2338 5 r. Wearing red jacket 55 60
2339 5 r. Wearing blue jacket 55 60
2340 5 r. With microphone and wearing blue jacket 55 60
2341 5 r. In army uniform 55 60
2342 5 r. Wearing yellow bow tie 55 60
2343 5 r. In yellow shirt 55 60
2344 5 r. In light blue shirt 55 60
2345 5 r. Wearing red and white high-collared jacket 55 60
2337/45 .. .. *Set of* 9 4·75 5·25
MS2346 80×110 mm. 25 r. Elvis Presley (*horiz*). P 14×13½ .. .. 2·75 3·00

Nos. 2337/45 were printed together, *se-tenant*, in sheetlets of 9.

(Des R. Rundo. Litho Questa)

1995 (28 Dec). *Centenary of Nobel Prize Trust Fund. T* **329** *and similar vert designs. Multicoloured. P* 14.

2347/55 5 r. × 9 (Type **329**; Charles Guillaume (1920 Physics); Sir James Chadwick (1935 Physics); Willem Einthoven (1924 Medicine); Henrik Dam (1943 Medicine); Sir Alexander Fleming (1945 Medicine); Hermann Muller (1946 Medicine); Rodney Porter (1972 Medicine); Werner Arber (1978 Medicine))
a. Sheetlet. Nos. 2347/55 .. .. 5·00
2356/64 5 r. × 9 (Niels Bohr (1922 Physics); Ben Mottelson (1975 Physics); Patrick White (1973 Literature); Elias Canetti (1981 Literature); Theodor Kocher (1909 Medicine); August Krogh (1920 Medicine); William Murphy (1934 Medicine); John Northrop (1946 Chemistry); Luis Leloir (1970 Chemistry))
a. Sheetlet. Nos. 2356/64 .. .. 5·00
2365/73 5 r. × 9 (Dag Hammarskjöld (1961 Peace); Alva Myrdal (1982 Peace); Archbishop Desmond Tutu (1984 Peace); Rudolf Eucken (1908 Literature); Aleksandr Solzhenitsyn (1970 Literature); Gabriel Márquez (1982 Literature); Chen Yang (1957 Physics); Karl Müller (1987 Physics); Melvin Schwartz (1988 Physics))
a. Sheetlet. Nos. 2365/73 .. .. 5·00
2374/82 5 r. × 9 (Robert Millikan (1923 Physics); Louis de Broglie (1929 Physics); Ernest Walton (1951 Physics); Richard Willstätter (1915 Chemistry); Lars Onsager (1968 Chemistry); Gerhard Herzberg (1971 Chemistry); William B. Yeats (1923 Literature); George Bernard Shaw (1925 Literature); Eugene O'Neill (1936 Literature))
a. Sheetlet. Nos. 2374/82 .. .. 5·00
2383/91 5 r. × 9 (Bernardo Houssay (1947 Medicine); Paul Müller (1948 Medicine); Walter Hess (1949 Medicine); Sir MacFarlane Burnet (1960 Medicine); Baruch Blumberg (1976 Medicine); Daniel Nathans (1978 Medicine); Glenn Seaborg (1951 Chemistry); Ilya Prigogine (1977 Chemistry); Kenichi Fukui (1981 Chemistry))
a. Sheetlet. Nos. 2383/91 .. .. 5·00
2392/400 5 r. × 9 (Carl Spitteler (1919 Literature); Henri Bergson (1927 Literature); Johannes Jensen (1944 Literature); Antoine-Henri Becquerel (1903 Physics); Sir William H. Bragg (1915 Physics); Sir William L. Bragg (1915 Physics); Frederik Bajer (1908 Peace); Léon Bourgeois (1920 Peace); Karl Benning (1921 Peace))
a. Sheetlet. Nos. 2392/3000 .. .. 5·00
2347/2400 .. .. *Set of* 54 30·00 32·00
MS2401 Six sheets. (a) 80×110 mm. 25 r. Konrad Bloch (1964 Medicine). (b) 80×110 mm. 25 r. Samuel Beckett (1969 Literature). (c) 80×110 mm. 25 r. Otto Wallach (1910 Chemistry). (d) 110×80 mm. 25 r. Hideki Yukawa (1949 Physics). (e) 110×80 mm. 25 r. Eisaku Sato (1974 Peace). (f) 110×80 mm. 25 r. Robert Koch (1905 Medicine) .. *Set of* 6 *sheets* 16·00 17·00

Nos. 2347/55, 2356/64, 2365/73, 2374/82, 2383/91 and 2392/2400 were printed together, *se-tenant*, in sheetlets of 9.

330 Rhythmic Gymnast and Japanese Fan

(Des L. Fried. Litho Questa)

1996 (25 Jan). *Olympic Games, Atlanta* (1*st issue*). *T* **330** *and similar multicoloured designs. P* 14.

2402 1 r. Type **330** 10 10
2403 3 r. Archer and Moscow Olympics logo .. 35 40
2404 5 r. Diver and Swedish flag 55 60
2405 5 r. Canadian Maple Leaf 55 60
a. Sheetlet. Nos. 2405/13 .. .. 4·75
2406 5 r. Shot putting (Decathlon) 55 60
2407 5 r. Moscow Olympic medal and ribbon .. 55 60
2408 5 r. Fencer 55 60
2409 5 r. Gold medal 55 60
2410 5 r. Equestrian competitor 55 60
2411 5 r. Sydney Opera House 55 60
2412 5 r. Athlete on starting blocks 55 60
2413 5 r. South Korean flag 55 60
2414 7 r. High jumper and Tower Bridge, London 80 85
2415 10 r. Athlete on starting blocks and Brandenburg Gate, Germany .. .. 1·10 1·25
2416 12 r. Hurdler and Amsterdam Olympic logo 1·40 1·50
2402/16 .. .. *Set of* 14 9·00 10·00
MS2417 Two sheets, each 113×80 mm. (a) 25 r. Red Olympic Flame (*vert*). (b) 25 r. Multicoloured Olympic Flame (*vert*) .. .. *Set of* 2 *sheets* 5·50 5·75

Nos. 2405/13 were printed together, *se-tenant*, in sheetlets of 9.

See also Nos. 2469/88.

331 "Self Portrait" (Degas)

(Litho Questa)

1996 (22 Apr). 125*th Anniv of Metropolitan Museum of Art, New York. T* **331** *and similar multicoloured designs. P* 13½×14.

2418/25 4 r. × 8 (Type **331**; "Andromache and Astyanax" (Prud'hon); "René Grenier" (Toulouse-Lautrec); "The Banks of the Biévre near Bicétre" (Rousseau); "The Repast of the Lion" (Rousseau); "Portrait of Yves Gobillard-Morisot" (Degas); "Sunflowers" (Van Gogh); "The Singer in Green" (Degas))
a. Sheetlet. Nos. 2418/25 .. .. 3·50
2426/33 4 r. × 8 ("Still Life" (Fantin-Latour); "Portrait of a Lady in Grey" (Degas); "Apples and Grapes" (Monet); "The Englishman" (Toulouse-Lautrec); "Cypresses" (Van Gogh); "Flowers in a Chinese Vase" (Redon); "The Gardener" (Seurat); "Large Sunflowers I" (Nolde))
a. Sheetlet. Nos. 2426/33 .. .. 3·50
2434/41 4 r. × 8 (All by Manet: "The Spanish Singer"; "Young Man in Costume of Majo"; "Mademoiselle Victorine"; "Boating"; "Peonies"; "Woman with a Parrot"; "George Moore"; "The Monet Family in their Garden")
a. Sheetlet. Nos. 2434/41 .. .. 3·50
2442/9 4 r. × 8 ("Goldfish" (Matisse); "Spanish Woman: Harmony in Blue" (Matisse); "Nasturtiums and the "Dance" II" (Matisse); "The House behind Trees" (Braque); "Mada Primavesi" (Klimt); "Head of a Woman" (Picasso); "Woman in White" (Picasso); "Harlequin" (Picasso))
a. Sheetlet. Nos. 2442/9 .. .. 3·50
2418/49 .. .. *Set of* 32 14·00 15·00
MS2450 Four sheets, each 95×70 mm containing horiz designs, 81×53 mm. P 14. (a) 25 r. "Northeaster" (Homer). (b) 25 r. "The Fortune Teller" (De La Tour). (c) 25 r. "Santo (Sanzio), Ritratto de Andrea Navagero e Agostino Beazzano" (Raphael). (d) 25 r. "Portrait of a Woman" (Rubens) .. .. *Set of* 4 *sheets* 11·00 11·50

Nos. 2418/25, 2426/33, 2434/41 and 2442/9 were each printed together, *se-tenant*, in sheetlets of 8 stamps and one centre label.

332 Mickey Mouse on Great Wall of China

(Des Walt Disney Company Asia Pacific Ltd. Litho Questa)

1996 (10 May). *"CHINA '96" 9th Asian International Stamp Exhibition, Peking. T* **332** *and similar multicoloured designs showing Walt Disney cartoon characters in China. P* 14×13½ (*horiz*) *or* 13½×14 (*vert*).

2451 2 r. Type **332** 20 25
a. Sheetlet. Nos. 2451/6 .. .. 1·25
2452 2 r. Pluto with temple guardian 20 25
2453 2 r. Minnie Mouse with Pandas 20 25
2454 2 r. Mickey windsurfing near junks .. 20 25
2455 2 r. Goofy cleaning Grottoe statue .. 20 25
2456 2 r. Donald and Daisy Duck at Marble Boat 20 25
2457 2 r. Mickey with terracotta warriors .. 20 25
a. Sheetlet. Nos. 2457/62 .. .. 1·25
2458 2 r. Goofy with geese and masks 20 25
2459 2 r. Donald and Goofy on traditional fishing boat 20 25
2460 2 r. Mickey and Minnie in dragon boat .. 20 25
2461 2 r. Donald at Peking opera 20 25
2462 2 r. Mickey and Minnie in Chinese garden 20 25
2463 3 r. Mickey and Minnie at the Ice Pagoda (*vert*) 35 40
a. Sheetlet. Nos. 2463/7 .. .. 1·75
2464 3 r. Donald and Mickey flying Chinese kites (*vert*) 35 40
2465 3 r. Goofy playing anyiwu (*vert*) 35 40
2466 3 r. Paper cutouts of Mickey and Goofy (*vert*) 35 40
2467 3 r. Donald and Mickey in dragon dance (*vert*) 35 40
2451/67 .. .. *Set of* 17 4·25 5·00
MS2468 Three sheets. (a) 108×133 mm. 5 r. Mickey pointing. (b) 133×108 mm. 7 r. Mickey and Minnie watching Moon. (c) 133×108 mm. 8 r. Donald using chopsticks .. *Set of* 3 *sheets* 2·25 2·40

Nos. 2451/6, 2457/62 and 2463/7 were each printed together, *se-tenant*, in sheetlets of 6 (Nos. 2451/6, 2457/62) or 5 stamps and one label (Nos. 2463/7).

333 Stella Walsh (Poland) (10m sprint, 1932) on Medal

(Litho B.D.T.)

1996 (27 May). *Olympic Games, Atlanta* (2*nd issue*). *Previous Gold Medal Winners. T* **333** *and similar multicoloured designs. P* 14.

2469 1 r. Type **333** 10 10
2470 3 r. Emile Zatopek (Czechoslovakia) (10,000m running, 1952) and Olympic torch (*vert*) 35 40
2471 5 r. Yanko Rousseu (Bulgaria) (lightweight, 1980) (*vert*) 55 60
a. Sheetlet. Nos. 2471/9 .. .. 4·75
2472 5 r. Peter Baczako (Hungary) (middle heavyweight, 1980) (*vert*) 55 60

2473 5 r. Leonid Taranenko (Russia) (heavyweight, 1980) (*vert*) 55 60
2474 5 r. Aleksandr Kurlovich (Russia) (heavyweight, 1988) (*vert*) 55 60
2475 5 r. Assen Zlateu (Bulgaria) (middleweight, 1980) (*vert*) 55 60
2476 5 r. Zeng Guoqiang (China) (flyweight, 1984) (*vert*) 55 60
2477 5 r. Yurik Vardanyan (Russia) (heavyweight, 1980) (*vert*) 55 60
2478 5 r. Sultan Rakhmanov (Russia) (super heavyweight, 1980) (*vert*) 55 60
2479 5 r. Vassily Alexeev (Russia) (super heavyweight, 1972) (*vert*) 55 60
2480 5 r. Ethel Catherwood (Canada) (high jump, 1928) 55 60
a. Sheetlet. Nos. 2480/5 .. .. .. 3·25
2481 5 r. Mildred Didrikson (U.S.A.) (javelin, 1932) 55 60
2482 5 r. Francina Blankers-Koen (Netherlands) (80m hurdles, 1948) 55 60
2483 5 r. Tamara Press (Russia) (shot put, 1960) 55 60
2484 5 r. Lia Manoliu (Rumania) (discus, 1968) 55 60
2485 5 r. Rosa Mota (Portugal) (marathon, 1988) 55 60
2486 10 r. Olga Fikotova (Czechoslovakia) (discus, 1956) on medal .. .. 1·10 1·25
2487 12 r. Joan Benoit (U.S.A.) (marathon, 1984) on medal .. .. .. 1·40 1·50
2469/87 .. .. *Set of* 19 10·00 11·00
MS2488 Two sheets. (a) 76×106 mm. 25 r. Naeem Suleymanoglu (Turkey) (weightlifting, 1988) (*vert*). (b) 105×75 mm. 25 r. Irena Szewinska (Poland) (400m running, 1976) on medal .. .. *Set of* 2 *sheets* 5·50 5·75

Nos. 2471/9 (weightlifters) and Nos. 2480/5 (women's track and field as T **333**) were each printed together, *se-tenant*, in sheetlets of 9 or 6.

334 Queen Elizabeth II **335** African Child

(Litho Questa)

1996 (10 July). *70th Birthday of Queen Elizabeth II. T* **334** *and similar vert designs showing different photographs. Multicoloured. P* 13½×14.
2489 8 r. Type **334** 90 95
a. Strip of 3. Nos. 2489/91 .. .. 2·75
2490 8 r. Wearing hat 90 95
2491 8 r. At desk 90 95
2489/91 .. .. *Set of* 3 2·75 3·00
MS2492 125×103 mm. 25 r. Queen Elizabeth and Queen Mother on Buckingham Palace Balcony .. .. 2·75 3·00

Nos. 2489/91 were printed together, *se-tenant*, in horizontal and vertical strips of 3 throughout sheets of 9.

(Litho B.D.T. (No. 2495) or Questa (others))

1996 (10 July). *50th Anniv of U.N.I.C.E.F. T* **335** *and similar vert designs. Multicoloured. P* 14.
2493 5 r. Type **335** 55 60
2494 7 r. European girl 80 85
2495 7 r. Maldivian boy 80 85
2496 10 r. Asian girl .. .. 1·10 1·25
2493/6 .. .. *Set of* 4 3·25 3·50
MS2497 114×74 mm. 25 r. Baby with toy .. 2·75 3·00

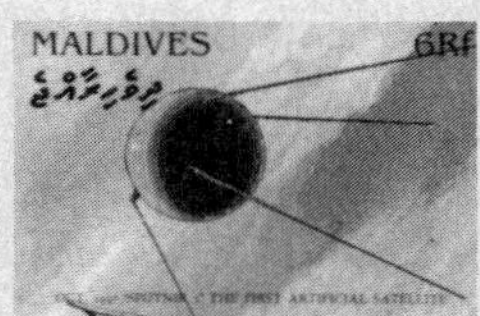

336 "Sputnik 1" Satellite

1996 (10 July). *Space Exploration. T* **336** *and similar multicoloured designs. Litho. P* 14.
2498 6 r. Type **336** 65 70
a. Sheetlet. Nos. 2498/503 .. .. 3·75
2499 6 r. "Apollo 11" command module .. 65 70
2500 6 r. "Skylab" 65 70
2501 6 r. Astronaut Edward White walking in Space 65 70
2502 6 r. "Mariner 9" 65 70
2503 6 r. "Apollo" and "Soyuz" docking .. 65 70
2498/503 .. .. *Set of* 6 3·75 4·00
MS2504 104×74 mm. 25 r. Launch of "Apollo 8" (*vert*) .. .. 2·75 3·00

Nos. 2498/503 were printed together, *se-tenant*, in sheetlets of 6, the background forming a composite design.

337 *Epiphora albida*

1996 (10 July). *Butterflies. T* **337** *and similar multicoloured designs. Litho. P* 14.
2505 7 r. Type **337** 80 85
a. Sheetlet. Nos. 2505/10 .. .. 4·75
2506 7 r. *Satyrus dryas* 80 85
2507 7 r. *Satyrus lena* 80 85
2508 7 r. *Papilio tynderaeus* 80 85
2509 7 r. *Urota suraka* 80 85
2510 7 r. *Satyrus nercis* 80 85
2511 7 r. *Papilio troilus* (*vert*) 80 85
a. Sheetlet. Nos. 2511/18 .. .. 6·25
2512 7 r. *Papilio cresphontes* (*vert*) 80 85
2513 7 r. Lime Swallowtail caterpillar (*vert*) .. 80 85
2514 7 r. *Cynthia virginiensis* (*vert*) 80 85
2515 7 r. Monarch caterpillar (*vert*) 80 85
2516 7 r. *Danaus plexippus* (*vert*) 80 85
2517 7 r. Monarch caterpillar and pupa (*vert*) 80 85
2518 7 r. *Chlosyne harrisii* (*vert*) 80 85
2519 7 r. *Cymothoe coccinata* (*vert*) 80 85
a. Sheetlet. Nos. 2519/22×2 .. .. 6·25
2520 7 r. *Morpho rhetenor* (*vert*) 80 85
2521 7 r. *Callicore lidwina* (*vert*) 80 85
2522 7 r. *Heliconius erato reductimacula* (*vert*) 80 85
2505/22 .. .. *Set of* 18 14·00 15·00
MS2523 Two sheets, each 106×76 mm. (a) 25 r. *Heliconius charitonius* (*vert*). (b) 25 r. *Heliconius cydno* (*vert*) .. .. .. *Set of* 2 *sheets* 5·50 5·75

Nos. 2505/10, 2511/18 and 2519/22 were each printed together, *se-tenant*, in sheetlets of 6 or 8.

338 "F4 OPH" Diesel-electric Locomotive

339 Bongo

1996 (2 Sept). *Trains of the World. T* **338** *and similar horiz designs. Multicoloured. Litho. P* 14.
2524 3 r. Type **338** 35 40
a. Sheetlet. Nos. 2524/32 .. .. 3·00
2525 3 r. Stephenson's *Experiment* 35 40
2526 3 r. Indian-Pacific Intercontinental, Australia 35 40
2527 3 r. Stephenson's locomotive of 1815 .. 35 40
2528 3 r. George Stephenson 35 40
2529 3 r. Stephenson's *Rocket*, 1829 .. .. 35 40
2530 3 r. British Rail "125-HST" 35 40
2531 3 r. First rail passenger coach, 1825 .. 35 40
2532 3 r. Tofac locomotive, U.S.A. 35 40
2533 3 r. Southern Pacific's "Daylight", San Francisco 35 40
a. Sheetlet. Nos. 2533/41 .. .. 3·00
2534 3 r. Timothy Hackworth's *Sans Pareil* .. 35 40
2535 3 r. Chicago and North Western locomotive, U.S.A. 35 40
2536 3 r. Richard Trevithick's *Pen-Y-Darran* locomotive 35 40
2537 3 r. Isambard Kingdom Brunel 35 40
2538 3 r. Great Western locomotive, 1838 .. 35 40
2539 3 r. Express Passenger train, Canada .. 35 40
2540 3 r. Mohawk and Hudson Railroad *Experiment*, 1832 .. .. .. 35 40
2541 3 r. ICE train, Germany 35 40
2542 3 r. Electric container locomotive, Germany 35 40
a. Sheetlet. Nos. 2542/50 .. .. 3·00
2543 3 r. John Blenkinsop's rack locomotive .. 35 40
2544 3 r. Diesel-electric locomotive, Western Australia 35 40
2545 3 r. Timothy Hackworth's *Royal George*, 1827 .. .. 35 40
2546 3 r. Robert Stephenson 35 40
2547 3 r. Trevithick's *Newcastle* 35 40
2548 3 r. Deltic locomotive, British Rail .. 35 40
2549 3 r. Stockton No. 5 locomotive, 1826 .. 35 40
2550 3 r. Channel Tunnel "Le Shuttle" train 35 40
2524/50 .. .. *Set of* 27 9·25 10·50
MS2551 Three sheets, each 96×91 mm. (a) 25 r. *Tom Thumb*, 1830. (b) 25 r. *De Witt Clinton*, 1831. (c) 25 r. *The General*, 1855 *Set of* 3 *sheets* 8·25 8·50

Nos. 2524/32, 2533/41 and 2542/50 were printed together, *se-tenant*, in sheetlets of 9.

1996 (9 Sept). *Wildlife of the World. T* **339** *and similar multicoloured designs. Litho. P* 14.
2552 5 r. Type **339** 55 60
a. Sheetlet. Nos. 2552/9 .. .. 4·25
2553 5 r. Bushbuck 55 60
2554 5 r. Namaqua Dove 55 60
2555 5 r. Hoopoe 55 60
2556 5 r. African Fish Eagle 55 60
2557 5 r. Egyptian Goose 55 60
2558 5 r. Saddle-bill Stork 55 60
2559 5 r. Blue-breasted Kingfisher 55 60
2560 5 r. Yellow Baboon 55 60
a. Sheetlet. Nos. 2560/7 .. .. 4·25
2561 5 r. Banded Duiker ("Zebra Duiker") .. 55 60
2562 5 r. Yellow-backed Duiker 55 60
2563 5 r. Pygmy Hippopotamus 55 60
2564 5 r. Large-spotted Genet 55 60
2565 5 r. African Spoonbill 55 60
2566 5 r. White-faced Whistling Duck .. 55 60
2567 5 r. Helmet Guineafowl 55 60
2568 7 r. Cotton-headed Tamarin (*horiz*) .. 80 85
a. Sheetlet. Nos. 2568/76 .. .. 7·00
2569 7 r. European Bison (*horiz*) 80 85
2570 7 r. Tiger (*horiz*) 80 85
2571 7 r. Capercaillie (*horiz*) 80 85
2572 7 r. Giant Panda (*horiz*) 80 85
2573 7 r. *Trogonoptera brookiana* (butterfly) (*horiz*) 80 85
2574 7 r. American Beaver (*horiz*) 80 85
2575 7 r. *Leiopelma hamiltoni* (frog) (*horiz*) .. 80 85
2576 7 r. Manatee (*horiz*) 80 85
2552/76 .. .. *Set of* 25 15·00 17·00
MS2577 106×76 mm. 25 r. Chimpanzee (*horiz*) 2·75 3·00

Nos. 2552/9, 2560/7 and 2568/76 were each printed together, *se-tenant*, in sheetlets of 8 or 9, the backgrounds forming composite designs.

No. 2553 is inscribed "BUSHBACK" in error.

340 Giant Panda

1996 (9 Sept). *Endangered Species. T* **340** *and similar multicoloured designs. Litho. P* 14.
2578 5 r. Type **340** 55 60
a. Sheetlet. Nos. 2578/83 .. .. 3·25
2579 5 r. Indian Elephant 55 60
2580 5 r. Arrow-poison Frog 55 60
2581 5 r. Mandrill 55 60
2582 5 r. Snow Leopard 55 60
2583 5 r. California Condor 55 60
2584 5 r. Whale-headed Stork ("Shoebill Stork") 55 60
a. Sheetlet. Nos. 2584/9 .. .. 3·25
2585 5 r. Red-billed Hornbill 55 60
2586 5 r. Hippopotamus 55 60
2587 5 r. Gorilla 55 60
2588 5 r. Lion 55 60
2589 5 r. South African Crowned Crane .. 55 60
2578/89 .. .. *Set of* 12 6·50 7·00
MS2590 Two sheets, each 110×80 mm. (a) 25 r. Tiger (*vert*). (b) 25 r. Leopard .. *Set of* 2 *sheets* 5·50 5·75

Nos. 2578/83 and 2584/9 were each printed togther, *se-tenant*, in sheetlets of 6.

341 Mickey Mouse climbing out of Puddle

(Des Alvin White Studio. Litho Questa)

1996 (2 Dec). *Centenary of the Cinema. T* **341** *and similar horiz designs showing a series of cartoon frames from* The Little Whirlwind *(Nos.* 2591/607*) and* Pluto and the Flypaper *(Nos.* 2608/24*). Multicoloured. P* 14×13½.
2591 4 r. Type **341** 45 50
a. Sheetlet. Nos. 2591/8 and 1 label .. 3·50
2592 4 r. Frame 2 .. .. 45 50
2593 4 r. Frame 3 .. .. 45 50
2594 4 r. Frame 4 .. .. 45 50
2595 4 r. Frame 5 .. .. 45 50
2596 4 r. Frame 6 .. .. 45 50
2597 4 r. Frame 7 .. .. 45 50
2598 4 r. Frame 8 .. .. 45 50
2599 4 r. Frame 9 .. .. 45 50
a. Sheetlet. Nos. 2599/607 .. .. 4·00
2600 4 r. Frame 10 .. .. 45 50
2601 4 r. Frame 11 .. .. 45 50
2602 4 r. Frame 12 .. .. 45 50
2603 4 r. Frame 13 .. .. 45 50
2604 4 r. Frame 14 .. .. 45 50
2605 4 r. Frame 15 .. .. 45 50
2606 4 r. Frame 16 (Mickey holding fish above head) 45 50
2607 4 r. Frame 17 (Mickey throwing fish into pool) 45 50
2608 4 r. Frame 1 (Pluto) 45 50
a. Sheetlet. Nos. 2608/15 and 1 label .. 3·50
2609 4 r. Frame 2 .. .. 45 50
2610 4 r. Frame 3 .. .. 45 50
2611 4 r. Frame 4 .. .. 45 50
2612 4 r. Frame 5 .. .. 45 50
2613 4 r. Frame 6 .. .. 45 50
2614 4 r. Frame 7 .. .. 45 50
2615 4 r. Frame 8 .. .. 45 50
2616 4 r. Frame 9 .. .. 45 50
a. Sheetlet. Nos. 2616/24 .. .. 4·00
2617 4 r. Frame 10 .. .. 45 50
2618 4 r. Frame 11 .. .. 45 50
2619 4 r. Frame 12 .. .. 45 50
2620 4 r. Frame 13 .. .. 45 50
2621 4 r. Frame 14 .. .. 45 50
2622 4 r. Frame 15 .. .. 45 50

2623 4 r. Frame 16 .. .. 45 50
2624 4 r. Frame 17 .. .. 45 50
2591/624 .. .. *Set of* 34 15·00 17·00
MS2625 Two sheets, 111×131 mm. (a) 25 r. Frame 18 (*The Little Whirlwind*). (b) 25 r. Frame 18 (*Pluto and the Flypaper*) .. *Set of* 2 *sheets* 5·50 5·75

Nos. 2591/8, 2599/2607, 2608/15 and 2616/24 were printed together, *se-tenant*, in sheets of 8 or 9. It is intended that the stamps should be separated and used as a flip book to produce a moving image.

342 Letter "O" with Chinese Character

343 California Condor

(Des M. Friedman. Litho Questa)

1997 (12 Feb). *"HONG KONG '97" International Stamp Exhibition. T* **342** *and similar multicoloured designs. P* 13½×14.
2626 5 r. Letter "H" and Chinese couple .. 55 60
a. Sheetlet. Nos. 2626/33 .. .. 4·50
2627 5 r. Type **342** 55 60
2628 5 r. Letter "N" and Chinese dragon .. 55 60
2629 5 r. Letter "G" and carnival dragon .. 55 60
2630 5 r. Letter "K" and modern office block 55 60
2631 5 r. Letter "O" and Chinese character (*different*) 55 60
2632 5 r. Letter "N" and Chinese fan cases .. 55 60
2633 5 r. Letter "G" and Chinese junk .. 55 60
2626/33 .. .. *Set of* 8 4·50 4·75
MS2634 106×125 mm. 5 r. "HONG KONG" as on Nos. 2626/33 (76×38 *mm*) .. .. 2·75 3·00

Nos. 2626/33 were printed together, *se-tenant*, in sheetlets of 8.

1997 (12 Feb). *Birds of the World. T* **343** *and similar vert designs. Multicoloured. Litho. P* 14.
2635 5 r. Type **343** 55 60
a. Sheetlet. Nos. 2635/43 .. .. 5·00
2636 5 r. Audouin's Gull 55 60
2637 5 r. Atlantic Puffin 55 60
2638 5 r. Resplendent Quetzal 55 60
2639 5 r. Puerto Rican Amazon 55 60
2640 5 r. Lesser Bird of Paradise 55 60
2641 5 r. Japanese Crested Ibis 55 60
2642 5 r. Mauritius Kestrel 55 60
2643 5 r. Kakapo 55 60
2635/43 .. .. *Set of* 9 5·00 5·50
MS2644 76×106 mm. 25 r. Ivory-billed Woodpecker .. .. 2·75 3·00

Nos. 2635/43 were printed together, *se-tenant*, in sheetlets of 9 with the backgrounds forming a composite design.

344 Ye Qiabo (China) (women's 500/100m speed skating, 1992)

345 Crowned Solitary Eagle

(Litho Questa)

1997 (13 Mar). *Winter Olympic Games, Nagano, Japan* (1998). *T* **344** *and similar vert designs. Multicoloured. P* 14.
2645 2 r. Type **344** 20 25
2646 3 r. Leonhard Stock (Austria) (downhill skiing, 1980) 35 40
2647 5 r. Herma von Szabo-Planck (Austria) (figure skating, 1924) 55 60
a. Sheetlet. Nos. 2647/50×2 .. .. 4·50
2648 5 r. Katarina Witt (Germany) (figure skating, 1988) 55 60
2649 5 r. Natalia Bestemianova and Andrei Bukin (Russia) (pairs ice dancing, 1988) 55 60
2650 5 r. Jayne Torvill and Christopher Dean (Great Britain) (pairs ice dancing, 1984) 55 60
2651 8 r. Bjorn Daehlie (Norway) (cross-country skiing, 1992) 90 95
2652 12 r. Wolfgang Hoppe (Germany) (bobsleigh, 1984) .. .. .. 1·40 1·50
2645/52 .. .. *Set of* 8 5·00 5·50
MS2653 Two sheets, each 76×106 mm. (a) 25 r. Sonja Henie (Norway) (figure skating, 1924). (b) 25 r. Andree Joly and Pierre Brunet (France) (pairs ice dancing, 1932) .. *Set of* 2 *sheets* 5·50 5·75

Nos. 2645/52 were printed together, *se-tenant*, in sheetlets of 8 containing two of each design.

(Litho Questa)

1997 (20 Mar). *Eagles. T* **345** *and similar multicoloured designs. P* 14.
2654 1 r. Type **345** 10 15
2655 2 r. African Hawk Eagle (*horiz*) .. 20 25
2656 3 r. Lesser Spotted Eagle 35 40
2657 5 r. Stellar's Sea Eagle 55 60
2658 5 r. Bald Eagle attacking 55 60
a. Sheetlet. Nos. 2658/63 .. .. 3·25
2659 5 r. Bald Eagle on branch 55 60
2660 5 r. Bald Eagle looking left 55 60
2661 5 r. Bald Eagle looking right 55 60
2662 5 r. Bald Eagle sat on branch with leaves 55 60
2663 5 r. Bald Eagle soaring 55 60
2664 8 r. Spanish Imperial Eagle (*horiz*) .. 90 95
2665 10 r. Harpy Eagle .. .. .. 1·10 1·25
2666 12 r. Crested Serpent Eagle (*horiz*) .. 1·40 1·50
2654/66 .. .. *Set of* 13 7·75 8·75
MS2667 Two sheets. (a) 73×104 mm. 25 r. Bald Eagle. (b) 104×73 mm. 25 r. American Bald Eagle (*horiz*) .. .. .. *Set of* 2 *sheets* 5·50 5·75

Nos. 2658/63 were printed together, *se-tenant*, in sheetlets of 6.

346 Blitzer Benz, 1911

1997 (27 Mar). *Classic Cars. T* **346** *and similar horiz designs. Multicoloured. Litho. P* 14.
2668 5 r. Type **346** 55 60
a. Sheetlet. Nos. 2668/73 .. .. 3·25
2669 5 r. Datsun, 1917 .. .. .. 55 60
2670 5 r. Auburn 8-120, 1929 .. .. 55 60
2671 5 r. Mercedes-Benz C280, 1996 .. 55 60
2672 5 r. Suzuki UR-1 .. .. .. 55 60
2673 5 r. Chrysler Atlantic 55 60
2674 5 r. Mercedes-Benz 190SL, 1961 .. 55 60
a. Sheetlet. Nos. 2674/9 .. .. 3·25
2675 5 r. Kwaishinha D.A.T., 1916 .. .. 55 60
2676 5 r. Rolls-Royce Roadster 20/25 .. 55 60
2677 5 r. Mercedes-Benz SLK, 1997 .. 55 60
2678 5 r. Toyota Camry, 1996 .. .. 55 60
2679 5 r. Jaguar MK 2, 1959 .. .. 55 60
2668/79 .. .. *Set of* 12 6·50 7·25
MS2680 Two sheets, each 100×70 mm. (a) 25 r. Volkswagen, 1939. (b) 25 r. Mazda RX-01 *Set of* 2 *sheets* 5·50 5·75

Nos. 2668/73 and 2674/9 were each printed together, *se-tenant*, in sheetlets of 6.

No. **MS**2680b is inscribed "MAZADA" in error.

347 *Patris II*, Greece (1926)

(Des D. Miller. Litho Questa)

1997 (1 Apr). *Passenger Ships. T* **347** *and similar multicoloured designs. P* 14.
2681 1 r. Type **347** 10 15
2682 2 r. *Infanta Beatriz*, Spain (1928) .. 20 25
2683 3 r. *Vasilefs Constantinos*, Greece (1914) 35 40
a. Sheetlet. Nos. 2683/91 .. .. 3·25
2684 3 r. *Cunene*, Portugal (1911) 35 40
2685 3 r. *Selandia*, Denmark (1912) 35 40
2686 3 r. *President Harding*, U.S.A. (1921) .. 35 40
2687 3 r. *Ulster Monarch*, Great Britain (1929) 35 40
2688 3 r. *Matsonia*, U.S.A. (1913) 35 40
2689 3 r. *France*, France (1911) 35 40
2690 3 r. *Campania*, Great Britain (1893) .. 35 40
2691 3 r. *Klipfontein*, Holland (1922) .. 35 40
2692 3 r. *Eridan*, France (1929) 35 40
a. Sheetlet. Nos. 2692/700 .. .. 3·25
2693 3 r. *Mount Clinton*, U.S.A. (1921) .. 35 40
2694 3 r. *Infanta Isabel*, Spain (1912) .. 35 40
2695 3 r. *Suwa Maru*, Japan (1914) 35 40
2696 3 r. *Yorkshire*, Great Britain (1920) .. 35 40
2697 3 r. *Highland Chieftain*, Great Britain (1929) 35 40
2698 3 r. *Sardinia*, Norway (1920) 35 40
2699 3 r. *San Guuglielmo*, Italy (1911) .. 35 40
2700 3 r. *Avila*, Great Britain (1927) 35 40
2701 8 r. *Stavangerfjord*, Norway (1918) .. 90 95
2702 12 r. *Baloeran*, Netherlands (1929) .. 1·40 1·50
2681/702 .. .. *Set of* 22 9·00 10·00
MS2703 Four sheets. (a) 69×69 mm. 25 r. *Mauritania*, Great Britain (1907). (b) 69×69 mm. 25 r. *United States*, U.S.A. (1952). (c) 69×69 mm. 25 r. *Queen Mary*, Great Britain (1930). (d) 91×76 mm. 25 r. Royal Yacht *Britannia* and Chinese junk, Hong Kong (56×42 *mm*) .. .. *Set of* 4 *sheets* 11·00 11·50

Nos. 2683/91 and 2692/700 were each printed together, *se-tenant*, in sheetlets of 9.

No. **MS**2703d is inscribed "BRITTANIA" in error.

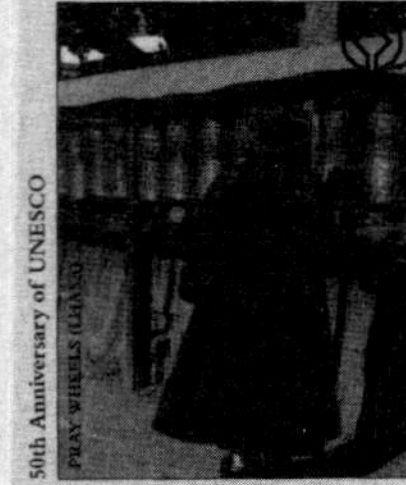

348 Prayer Wheels, Lhasa

(Des M. Freedman and Dena Rubin. Litho Questa)

1997 (7 Apr). *50th Anniv of U.N.E.S.C.O. T* **348** *and similar multicoloured designs. P* 14×13½ (*horiz*) *or* 13½×14 (*vert*).
2704 1 r. Type **348** 10 15
2705 2 r. Ruins of Roman Temple of Diana, Portugal (*horiz*) 20 25
2706 3 r. Santa Maria Cathedral, Hildesheim, Germany (*horiz*) 35 40
2707 5 r. Vivunga National Park, Zaire .. 55 60
a. Sheetlet. Nos. 2707/14 and central label .. .. 4·50
2708 5 r. Valley of Mai Nature Reserve, Seychelles 55 60
2709 5 r. Kandy, Sri Lanka 55 60
2710 5 r. Taj Mahal, India 55 60
2711 5 r. Istanbul, Turkey 55 60
2712 5 r. Sana'a, Yemen 55 60
2713 5 r. Bleinheim Palace, England 55 60
2714 5 r. Grand Canyon National Park, U.S.A. 55 60
2715 5 r. Tombs, Gondar, Ethiopia 55 60
a. Sheetlets. Nos. 2715/22 and central label .. .. 4·50
2716 5 r. Bwindi National Park, Uganda .. 55 60
2717 5 r. Bemaraha National Reserve, Madagascar 55 60
2718 5 r. Buddhist ruins at Takht-I-Bahi, Pakistan 55 60
2719 5 r. Anuradhapura, Sri Lanka 55 60
2720 5 r. Cairo, Egypt 55 60
2721 5 r. Ruins, Petra, Jordan 55 60
2722 5 r. Volcano, Ujung Kulon National Park, Indonesia 55 60
2723 5 r. Terrace, Mount Taishan, China .. 55 60
a. Sheetlet. Nos. 2723/30 and central label .. .. 4·50
2724 5 r. Temple, Mount Taishan, China .. 55 60
2725 5 r. Temple turret, Mount Taishan, China 55 60
2726 5 r. Standing stones, Mount Taishan, China 55 60
2727 5 r. Courtyard, Mount Taishan, China .. 55 60
2728 5 r. Staircase, Mount Taishan, China .. 55 60
2729 5 r. Terracotta Warriors, China .. 55 60
2730 5 r. Head of Terracotta Warrior, China 55 60
2731 7 r. Doorway, Abu Simbal, Egypt .. 80 85
2732 8 r. Mandraki, Rhodes, Greece (*horiz*) 90 95
2733 8 r. Agios Stefanos Monastery, Meteora, Greece (*horiz*) 90 95
a. Sheetlet. Nos. 2733/7 and label .. 4·50
2734 8 r. Taj Mahal, India (*horiz*) 90 95
2735 8 r. Cistercian Abbey of Fontenay, France (*horiz*) 90 95
2736 8 r. Yarushima, Japan (*horiz*) 90 95
2737 8 r. Cloisters, San Gonzalo Convent, Portugal (*horiz*) 90 95
2738 8 r. Olympic National Park, U.S.A. (*horiz*) 90 95
a. Sheetlet. Nos. 2738/42 and label .. 4·50
2739 8 r. Waterfall, Nahanni National Park, Canada (*horiz*) 90 95
2740 8 r. Mountains, National Park, Argentina (*horiz*) 90 95
2741 8 r. Bonfin Salvador Church, Brazil (*horiz*) 90 95
2742 8 r. Convent of the Companions of Jesus, Morelia, Mexico (*horiz*) 90 95
2743 8 r. Two-story Temple, Horyu-ji, Japan (*horiz*) 90 95
a. Sheetlet. Nos. 2743/7 and label .. 4·50
2744 8 r. Summer house, Horyu-ji, Japan (*horiz*) 90 95
2745 8 r. Temple and cloister, Horyu-ji, Japan (*horiz*) 90 95
2746 8 r. Single story Temple, Horyu-ji, Japan (*horiz*) 90 95
2747 8 r. Well, Horyu-ji, Japan (*horiz*) .. 90 95
2748 10 r. Scandola Nature Reserve, France (*horiz*) .. .. 1·10 1·25
2749 12 r. Temple on the Lake, China (*horiz*) .. 1·40 1·50
2704/49 .. .. *Set of* 46 32·00 34·00
MS2750 Four sheets, each 127×102 mm. (a) 25 r. Fatehpur Sikri Monument, India (*horiz*). (b) 25 r. Temple, Chengde, China (*horiz*). (c) 25 r. Serengeti National Park, Tanzania (*horiz*). (d) 25 r. Buddha, Anuradhapura, Sri Lanka (*horiz*) *Set of* 4 *sheets* 11·00 11·50

Nos. 2707/14, 2715/22 and 2723/30 were each printed together, *se-tenant*, in sheetlets of 8 stamps with a central label and Nos. 2733/7, 2738/42 and 2743/7 in sheetlets of 5 stamps with a top left-hand corner label.

No. 2717 is inscribed "MADAGASGAR" and No. 2737 "COVENT", both in error.

349 White Doves and S.A.A.R.C. Logo

(Litho Security Printers (M), Malaysia)

1997 (12 May). *9th South Asian Association for Regional Co-operation Summit, Malé. T* **349** *and similar horiz design. Multicoloured. P* 13.

2751 3 r. Type **349** 35 40
2752 5 r. Flags of member countries 55 60

350 Queen Elizabeth II

(Litho Questa)

1997 (12 June). *Golden Wedding of Queen Elizabeth and Prince Philip. T* **350** *and similar horiz designs. Multicoloured. P* 14.

2753 5 r. Type **350** 55 60
a. Sheetlet. Nos. 2753/8 .. .. 3·25
2754 5 r. Royal coat of arms 55 60
2755 5 r. Queen Elizabeth and Prince Philip at opening of Parliament 55 60
2756 5 r. Queen Elizabeth and Prince Philip with Prince Charles, 1948 .. .. 55 60
2757 5 r. Buckingham Palace from the garden 55 60
2758 5 r. Prince Philip 55 60
2753/8 .. .. *Set of* 6 3·25 3·50
MS2759 100×70 mm. 25 r. Queen Elizabeth II 2·75 3·00

Nos. 2753/8 were printed together, *se-tenant*, in sheetlets of 6.

351 Early Indian Mail Messenger

352 "Dawn at Kanda Myojin Shrine"

(Des J. Iskowitz. Litho Questa)

1997 (12 June). *"Pacific '97 International Stamp Exhibition, San Francisco". Death Centenary of Heinrich von Stephan (founder of the U.P.U.). T* **351** *and similar horiz designs. P* 14.

2760 2 r. turquoise-green and black 20 25
a. Sheetlet. Nos. 2760/2 60
2761 2 r. chestnut and black 20 25
2762 2 r. violet 20 25
2760/2 .. .. *Set of* 3 60 75

Designs:—No. 2760, Type **351**; No. 2761, Von Stephan and Mercury; No. 2762, Autogyro, Washington.

Nos. 2760/2 were printed together, *se-tenant*, in sheetlets of 3 with enlarged right-hand margin.

1997 (12 June). *Birth Bicentenary of Hiroshige (Japanese painter). "One Hundred Famous Views of Edo". T* **352** *and similar vert designs. Multicoloured. Litho. P* 13½×14.

2763 8 r. Type **352** 90 95
a. Sheetlet. Nos. 2763/8 .. .. 5·50
2764 8 r. "Kiyomizu Hall and Shinobazu Pond at Ueno" 90 95
2765 8 r. "Ueno Yamashita" 90 95
2766 8 r. "Moon Pine, Ueno" 90 95
2767 8 r. "Flower Pavilion, Dango Slope, Sendagi" 90 95
2768 8 r. "Shitaya Hirokoji" 90 95
2763/8 .. .. *Set of* 6 5·50 5·75
MS2769 Two sheets, each 102×127 mm. (a) 25 r. "Hilltop View, Yushima Tenjin Shrine". (b) 25 r. "Seido and Kanda River from Shohei Bridge" *Set of* 2 *sheets* 5·50 5·75

Nos. 2763/8 were printed together, *se-tenant*, in sheetlets of 6.

353 Common Noddy

354 *Canarina eminii*

(Des M. Lebouef. Litho B.D.T.)

1997 (17 June). *Birds. T* **353** *and similar vert designs. Multicoloured. P* 14.

2770 30 l. Type **353** 10 10
2771 1 r. Spectacled Owl 10 10
2772 2 r. Malay Fish Owl 20 25
2773 3 r. Peregrine Falcon 35 40
2774 5 r. Golden Eagle 55 60
2775 7 r. Ruppell's Parrot 80 85
a. Sheetlet. Nos. 2775/80 .. .. 4·75
2776 7 r. Blue-headed Parrot 80 85
2777 7 r. St. Vincent Amazon 80 85
2778 7 r. Grey Parrot 80 85
2779 7 r. Masked Lovebird 80 85
2780 7 r. Sun Conure 80 85
2781 8 r. Bateleur 90 95
2782 10 r. Whiskered Tern with chicks .. 1·10 1·25
2783 10 r. Common Caracara .. .. .. 1·10 1·25
2784 15 r. Red-footed Booby .. .. .. 1·60 1·75
2770/84 .. .. *Set of* 15 10·50 11·50
MS2785 Two sheets, each 67×98 mm. (a) 25 r. American Bald Eagle. (b) 25 r. Secretary Bird *Set of* 2 *sheets* 5·50 5·75

Nos. 2775/80 were printed together, *se-tenant*, in sheetlets of 6.

(Litho Questa)

1997 (24 June). *Flowers. T* **354** *and similar multicoloured designs. P* 14½×14 *(vert) or* 14×14½ *(horiz).*

2786 1 r. Type **354** 10 10
2787 2 r. *Delphinium macrocentron* 20 25
2788 3 r. *Leucadendron discolor* 35 40
2789 5 r. *Nymphaea caerulea* 55 60
2790 7 r. *Rosa multiflora polyantha* (20×23 mm) 80 85
2791 8 r. *Bulbophyllum barbigerum* 90 95
2792 8 r. *Acacia seyal (horiz)* 90 95
a. Sheetlet. Nos. 2792/7 .. .. 5·50
2793 8 r. *Gloriosa superba (horiz)* 90 95
2794 8 r. *Gnidia subcordata (horiz)* 90 95
2795 8 r. *Platycelyphium voense (horiz)* .. 90 95
2796 8 r. *Aspilia mossambicensis (horiz)* .. 90 95
2797 8 r. *Adenium obesum (horiz)* 90 95
2798 12 r. *Hibiscus vitifolius* .. .. .. 1·40 1·50
2786/98 .. .. *Set of* 13 9·75 10·50
MS2799 Two sheets, each 105×76 mm. (a) 25 r. *Aerangis rhodosticta (horiz).* (b) 25 r. *Dichrostachys cinerea* and two sailing boats *(horiz)* *Set of* 2 *sheets* 5·50 5·75

Nos. 2792/7 were printed together, *se-tenant*, in sheetlets of 6 with the backgrounds forming a composite design.

Malta

Early records of the postal services under the British Occupation are fragmentary, but it is known that an Island Postmaster was appointed in 1802. A British Packet Agency was established in 1806 and it later became customary for the same individual to hold the two appointments together. The inland posts continued to be the responsibility of the local administration, but the overseas mails formed part of the British G.P.O. system.

The stamps of Great Britain were used on overseas mails from September 1857. Previously during the period of the Crimean War letters franked with Great Britain stamps from the Crimea were cancelled at Malta with a wavy line obliterator. Such postmarks are known between April 1855 and September 1856.

The British G.P.O. relinquished control of the overseas posts on 31 December 1884 when Great Britain stamps were replaced by those of Malta.

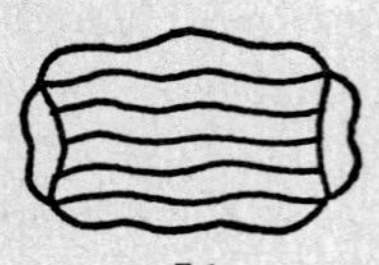

Z 1

Z 2

1855–56. *Stamps of* GREAT BRITAIN *cancelled with wavy lines obliteration, Type* Z **1.**

Z1 1d. red-brown (1854), Die I, *wmk* Small Crown, *perf* 16 .. £800
Z2 1d. red-brown (1855), Die II, *wmk* Small Crown, *perf* 14 .. £800
a. Very blued paper
Z3 1d. red-brown (1855), Die II, *wmk* Large Crown, *perf* 16 .. £800
Z3*a* 1d. red-brown (1855), Die II, *wmk* Large Crown, *perf* 14 .. £800
Z4 2d. blue (1855), *wmk* Large Crown, *perf* 14
Plate No. 5
Z5 6d. (1854) embossed .. £4000
Z6 1s. (1847) embossed .. £4500

It is now established that this obliterator was sent to Malta and used on mail in transit emanating from the Crimea.

1857 (18 Aug)–**59.** *Stamps of* GREAT BRITAIN *cancelled* "M", *Type* Z **2.**

Z 7 1d. red-brown (1841) .. £1200
Z 8 1d. red-brown, Die I, *wmk* Small Crown, *perf* 16 .. 80·00
Z 9 1d. red-brown, Die II, *wmk* Small Crown, *perf* 16 £800
Z10 1d. red-brown, Die II (1855), *wmk* Small Crown, *perf* 14 .. £170
Z11 1d. red-brown, Die II (1855), *wmk* Large Crown, *perf* 14 .. 70·00
Z12 1d. rose-red (1857), *wmk* Large Crown, *perf* 14 .. 20·00
Z13 2d. blue (1841), *imperf* .. £2500
Z14 2d. blue (1854) *wmk* Small Crown, *perf* 16 .. £600
Plate No. 4.
Z15 2d. blue (1855), *wmk* Large Crown, *perf* 14 *From* 45·00
Plate Nos. 5, 6.
Z16 2d. blue (1858), *wmk* Large Crown, *perf* 16 .. £225
Plate No. 6.
Z17 2d. blue (1858) (Plate Nos. 7, 8, 9) .. *From* 35·00
Z18 4d. rose (1857) .. 35·00
a. Thick glazed paper .. £170
Z19 6d. violet (1854), embossed .. £1600
Z20 6d. lilac (1856) .. 40·00
a. Thick paper .. £190
Z21 6d. lilac (1856) (blued *paper*) .. £850
Z22 1s. green (1856) .. £110
a. Thick paper .. £160

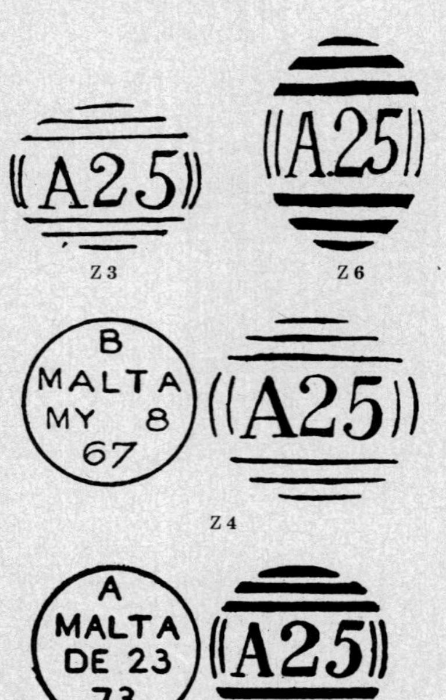

Z 7

1860–84. *Stamps of* GREAT BRITAIN *cancelled* "A 25" *as in Types* Z **3/7.**

Z23 ½d. rose-red (1870–79) .. *From* 18·00
Plate Nos. 4, 5, 6, 8, 9, 10, 11, 12, 13, 14, 15, 19, 20.
Z24 1d. red-brown (1841), *imperf* .. £2000
Z25 1d. red-brown (1854), *wmk* Small Crown, *perf* 16 £225
Z26 1d. red-brown (1855), *wmk* Large Crown, *perf* 14 55·00
Z27 1d. rose-red (1857), *wmk* Large Crown, *perf* 14 .. 7·50
Z28 1d. rose-red (1861), Alphabet IV .. £450
Z30 1d. rose-red (1864–79) .. *From* 12·00
Plate Nos, 71, 72, 73, 74, 76, 78, 79, 80, 81, 82, 83, 84, 85, 86, 87, 88, 89, 90, 91, 92, 93, 94, 95, 96, 97, 98, 99, 100, 101, 102, 103, 104, 105, 106, 107, 108, 109, 110, 111, 112, 113, 114, 115, 116, 117, 118, 119, 120, 121, 122, 123, 124, 125, 127, 129, 130, 131, 132, 133, 134, 135, 136, 137, 138, 139, 140, 141, 142, 143, 144, 145, 146, 147, 148, 149, 150, 151, 152, 153, 154, 155, 156, 157, 158, 159, 160, 161, 162, 163, 164, 165, 166, 167, 168, 169, 170, 171, 172, 173, 174, 175, 176, 177, 178, 179, 180, 181, 182, 183, 184, 185, 186, 187, 188, 189, 190, 191, 192, 193, 194, 195, 196, 197, 198, 199, 200, 201, 202, 203, 204, 205, 206, 207, 208, 209, 210, 211, 212, 213, 214, 215, 216, 217, 218, 219, 220, 221, 222, 223, 224.
Z31 1½d. lake-red (1870–79) (Plate Nos. 1, 3) .. *From* £275
Z32 2d. blue (1841), *imperf* .. £3500
Z33 2d. blue (1855) *wmk* Large Crown *perf* 14 .. 55·00
Z34 2d. blue (1858–69) .. *From* 15·00
Plate Nos. 7, 8, 9, 12, 13, 14, 15.
Z35 2½d. rosy mauve (1875) (blued *paper*) .. *From* 50·00
Plate Nos. 1, 2.
Z36 2½d. rosy mauve (1875–76) (Plate Nos. 1, 2, 3) *From* 27·00
Z37 2½d. rosy mauve (*Error of Lettering*) .. £2250
Z38 2½d. rosy mauve (1876–79) .. *From* 15·00
Plate Nos. 3, 4, 5, 6, 7, 8, 9, 10, 11, 12, 13, 14, 15, 16, 17.
Z39 2½d. blue (1880–81) (Plate Nos. 17, 18, 19, 20) *From* 9·00
Z40 2½d. blue (1881) (Plate Nos. 21, 22, 23) .. *From* 6·00
Z41 3d. carmine-rose (1862) .. £100
Z42 3d. rose (1865) (Plate No. 4) .. 50·00
Z43 3d. rose (1867–73) .. *From* 18·00
Plate Nos. 4, 5, 6, 7, 8, 9, 10.
Z44 3d. rose (1873–76) .. *From* 22·00
Plate Nos. 11, 12, 14, 15, 16, 17, 18, 19, 20.
Z45 3d. rose (1881) (Plate Nos. 20, 21) .. *From* £750
Z46 3d. on 3d. lilac (1883) .. £450
Z47 4d. rose (or rose-carmine) (1857) .. 27·00
a. Thick glazed paper .. £110
Z48 4d. red (1862) (Plate Nos. 3, 4) .. *From* 30·00
Z49 4d. vermilion (1865–73) .. *From* 15·00
Plate Nos. 7, 8, 9, 10, 11, 12, 13, 14.
Z50 4d. vermilion (1876) (Plate No. 15) .. £160
Z51 4d. sage-green (1877) (Plate Nos. 15, 16) .. *From* 85·00
Z52 4d. grey-brown (1880) *wmk* Large Garter .. £120
Plate No. 17.
Z53 4d. grey-brown (1880) *wmk* Crown .. *From* 27·00
Plate Nos. 17, 18.
Z54 6d. violet (1854), embossed .. £1500
Z55 6d. lilac (1856) .. 35·00
a. Thick paper
Z56 6d. lilac (1862) (Plate Nos. 3, 4) .. *From* 30·00
Z57 6d. lilac (1865–67) (Plate Nos. 5, 6) .. *From* 28·00
Z58 6d. lilac (1865–67) (*Wmk error*) .. £1200
Z59 6d. lilac (1867) (Plate No. 6) .. 32·00
Z60 6d. violet (1867–70) (Plate Nos. 6, 8, 9) .. *From* 25·00
Z61 6d. buff (1872–73) (Plate Nos. 11, 12) .. *From* £100
Z62 6d. chestnut (1872) (Plate No. 11) .. 30·00
Z63 6d. grey (1873) (Plate No. 12) .. 70·00
Z64 6d. grey (1873–80) .. *From* 22·00
Plate Nos. 13, 14, 15, 16, 17.
Z65 6d. grey (1881–82) (Plate Nos. 17, 18) .. *From* 30·00
Z66 6d. on 6d. lilac (1883) .. £110
Z67 8d. orange (1876) .. £250
Z68 9d. straw (1862) .. £500
Z69 9d. bistre (1862) .. £475
Z70 9d. straw (1865) .. £475
Z71 9d. straw (1867) .. £600
Z72 10d. red-brown (1867) .. £130
Z73 1s. (1847), embossed .. £1800
Z74 1s. green (1856) .. 70·00
Z75 1s. green (1856) (thick *paper*) .. £250
Z76 1s. green (1862) .. 60·00
Z77 1s. green ("K" *variety*) .. £2250
Z78 1s. green (1865) (Plate No. 4) .. 35·00
Z79 1s. green (1867–73) (Plate Nos. 4, 5, 6, 7) .. *From* 12·00
Z80 1s. green (1873–77) .. *From* 30·00
Plate Nos. 8, 9, 10, 11, 12, 13.
Z81 1s. orange-brown (1880) (Plate No. 13) .. £225
Z82 1s. orange-brown (1881) (Plate Nos. 13, 14) *From* 55·00
Z83 2s. blue (*shades*) (1867) .. *From* 90·00
Z84 2s. brown (1880) .. £1700
Z85 5s. rose (1867–74) (Plate Nos. 1, 2) .. *From* £300
Z86 5s. rose (1882) (Plate No. 4), blue *paper* .. £1100
Z87 5s. rose (1882) (Plate No. 4), white *paper* .. £1000
Z88 10s. grey-green (1878) .. £1600

1880.

Z89 ½d. deep green .. 10·00
Z90 ½d. pale green .. 10·00
Z91 1d. Venetian red .. 9·00
Z92 1½d. Venetian red .. £250
Z93 2d. pale rose .. 30·00
Z94 2d. deep rose .. 30·00
Z95 5d. indigo .. 50·00

1881.

Z96 1d. lilac (14 *dots*) .. 16·00
Z97 1d. lilac (16 *dots*) .. 6·00

1883–84.

Z 98 ½d. slate-blue .. 11·00
Z 99 1½d. lilac
Z100 2d. lilac .. 65·00
Z101 2½d. lilac .. 10·00
Z102 3d. lilac
Z103 4d. dull green .. £110
Z104 5d. dull green .. £110
Z105 6d. dull green
Z106 9d. dull green
Z107 1s. dull green
Z108 5s. rose (*blued paper*) .. £1000
Z109 5s. rose (*white paper*) .. £750

POSTAL FISCALS

Z110 1d. purple (1871) *wmk* Anchor .. £750
Z111 1d. purple (1881) *wmk* Orb .. £600

PRICES FOR STAMPS ON COVER TO 1945	
Nos. 1/3	*from* × 4
Nos. 4/19	*from* × 5
Nos. 20/9	*from* × 6
No. 30	—
Nos. 31/3	*from* × 4
Nos. 34/7	*from* × 10
Nos. 38/88	*from* × 4
Nos. 92/3	*from* × 5
Nos. 97/103	*from* × 3
Nos. 104/5	—
Nos. 106/20	*from* × 3
No. 121	—
Nos. 122/38	*from* × 3
Nos. 139/40	—
Nos. 141/72	*from* × 4
Nos. 173/209	*from* × 3
Nos. 210/31	*from* × 2
Nos. D1/10	*from* × 30
Nos. D11/20	*from* × 15

CROWN COLONY

PRINTERS. Nos. 1/156. Printed by De La Rue; typographed *except where otherwise stated.*

1

Type 1

The first Government local post was established on 10 June 1853 and, as an experiment, mail was carried free of charge. During 1859 the Council of Government decided that a rate of ½d. per ½ ounce should be charged for this service and stamps in Type I were ordered for this purpose. Both the new rate and the stamps were introduced on 1 December 1860. Until 1 January 1885 the ½d. stamps were intended for the local service only; mail for abroad being handled by the British Post Office on Malta, using G.B. stamps.

Specialists now recognise 29 printings in shades of yellow and one in green during the period to 1884. These printings can be linked to the changes in watermark and perforation as follows:

Ptg 1—Blued paper without wmk. P 14.
Ptgs 2 and 3—White paper without wmk. P 14.
Ptgs 4 to 9, 11, 13 to 19, 22 to 24—Crown CC wmk. P 14.
Ptg 10—Crown CC wmk. P 12½ (rough).
Ptg 12—Crown CC wmk. P 12½ (clean-cut).
Ptgs 20 and 21—Crown CC wmk. P 14 × 12½.
Ptgs 25 to 28, 30—Crown CA wmk. P 14.
Ptg 29—In green (No. 20).

(Des E. Fuchs)

1860 (1 Dec)–**63.** *No wmk. P* 14. (*a*) *Blued paper.*

1 ½d. buff (1.12.60) .. £850 £425

(*b*) *Thin, hard white paper*

2 ½d. brown-orange (11.61) .. £800 £325
3 ½d. buff (1.63) .. £550 £275
a. Pale buff .. £550 £275

No. 1 is printed in fugitive ink. It is known imperforate but was not issued in that state (*Price* £9000 *unused*).

The printing on No. 2 gives a very blurred and muddy impression; on Nos. 3/3*a* the impression is clear.

Specks of carmine can often be detected with a magnifying glass on Nos. 2/3*a*, and also on No. 4. Examples also exist on which parts of the design are in pure rose, due to defective mixing of the ink.

1863–81. *Wmk Crown CC.* (*a*) *P* 14.

4 ½d. buff (6.63) .. 80·00 45·00
5 ½d. bright orange (11.64) .. £325 £100
6 ½d. orange-brown (4.67) .. £275 75·00
7 ½d. dull orange (4.70) .. £170 60·00
8 ½d. orange-buff (5.72) .. £130 55·00
9 ½d. golden yellow (aniline) (10.74) .. £250 £300
10 ½d. yellow-buff (9.75) .. 60·00 55·00
11 ½d. pale buff (3.77) .. £140 55·00
12 ½d. bright orange-yellow (4.80) .. £120 65·00
13 ½d. yellow (4.81) .. 80·00 45·00

(*b*) *P* 12½ *rough* (*No.* 14) *or clean-cut* (*No.* 15)

14 ½d. buff-brown (11.68) .. 85·00 75·00
a. Imperf between (vert pair)
15 ½d. yellow-orange (5.71) .. £225 £150

(*c*) *P* 14 × 12½

16 ½d. yellow-buff (7.78) .. £150 85·00
a. Perf 12½ × 14
17 ½d. yellow (2.79) .. £170 90·00

Examples of No. 4 from the 1863 printing are on thin, surfaced

paper; later printings in the same shade were on unsurfaced paper.
The ink used for No. 5 is mineral and, unlike that on No. 9, does not stain the paper.

Some variations of shade on No. 6 may be described as chestnut. The ink of No. 6 is clear and never muddy, although some examples are over-inked. Deeper shades of No. 4, with which examples of No. 6 might be confused, have muddy ink.

1882 (Mar)–**84**. *Wmk Crown CA. P* 14.
18 ½d. orange-yellow .. .. 25·00 35·00
19 ½d. red-orange (9.84) .. .. 17·00 48·00

2

3

4

5

1885 (1 Jan)–**90**. *Wmk Crown CA. P* 14.
20 **1** ½d. green .. .. 1·40 50
21 **2** 1d. rose .. .. 85·00 26·00
22 1d. carmine (*shades*) (1890) .. .. 1·75 35
23 **3** 2d. grey .. .. 4·25 1·25
24 **4** 2½d. dull blue .. .. 48·00 2·00
25 2½d. bright blue .. .. 32·00 1·00
26 2½d. ultramarine .. .. 32·00 90
27 **3** 4d. brown .. .. 10·00 3·00
a. Imperf (pair) £4500 £4500
28 1s. violet .. .. 32·00 9·00
29 1s. pale violet (1890) .. .. .. 50·00 18·00
20/29 .. .. .. *Set of* 6 70·00 14·00
20/28 Optd "Specimen" .. .. *Set of* 6 £2000

Although not valid for postage until 1 January 1885 these stamps were available at the G.P.O., Valletta from 27 December 1884.

Three unused examples of the ½d. green, No. 20, are known line perforated 12. It is believed that these originated from proof books, the stamp not being issued for use with this perforation.

1886 (1 Jan). *Wmk Crown CC. P* 14.
30 **5** 5s. rose (Optd S. £450) .. .. .. £110 80·00

6 Harbour of Valletta

7 Gozo Fishing Boat

8 Galley of Knights of St. John

9 Emblematic figure of Malta

10 Shipwreck of St. Paul

(T **6**/**10** recess)

1899 (4 Feb)–**1901**. *P* 14. (*a*) *Wmk Crown CA* (*sideways on* ¼*d*).
31 **6** ¼d. brown (4.1.01) .. .. .. 2·25 1·75
a. Red-brown 90 40
32 **7** 4½d. sepia .. .. 11·00 9·50
33 **8** 5d. vermilion .. .. 27·00 14·00
(*b*) *Wmk Crown CC*
34 **9** 2s. 6d. olive-grey .. .. .. 40·00 12·00
35 **10** 10s. blue-black .. .. .. 75·00 60·00
31/5 .. .. .. *Set of* 5 £130 85·00
31/5 Optd "Specimen" .. .. *Set of* 5 £225

One
Penny
(11)

12

1902 (4 July). *Nos.* 24 *and* 25 *surch locally at Govt Ptg Office with T* **11**.
36 1d. on 2½d. dull blue (Optd S. £70) 60 80
a. Surch double .. .. — £3750
b. "One Pnney" (R. 9/2) .. .. .. 28·00 55·00
ba. Surch double, with "One Pnney" ..
37 1d. on 2½d. bright blue .. .. .. 60 1·40
a. "One Pnney" (R. 9/2) .. .. .. 30·00 55·00

(Des E. Fuchs)

1903 (12 Mar)–**04**. *Wmk Crown CA. P* 14.
38 **12** ½d. green .. .. 5·50 65
39 1d. blackish brown and red (7.5.03) .. 11·00 30
40 2d. purple and grey .. .. .. 18·00 6·00
41 2½d. maroon and blue (9.03) .. .. 13·00 3·25
42 3d. grey and purple (26.3.03) .. .. 1·25 50
43 4d. blackish brown and brown (19.5.04) 25·00 13·00
44 1s. grey and violet (6.4.03) .. .. 13·00 7·00
38/44 .. .. .. *Set of* 7 75·00 27·00
38/44 Optd "Specimen" .. .. *Set of* 7 £130

1904–14. *Wmk Mult Crown CA* (*sideways* on* ¼*d*.). *P* 14.
45 **6** ¼d. red-brown (10.10.05) .. .. 1·50 20
a. Deep brown (2.4.10†) .. .. 1·10 10
aw. Wmk Crown to left of CA .. .. 5·00 1·50
ax. Wmk reversed .. .. ..
ay. Wmk Crown to left of CA and reversed .. .. ..
47 **12** ½d. green (6.11.04) .. .. .. 2·75 25
aw. Wmk inverted .. .. ..
b. Deep green (1909) .. .. .. 2·00 10
bw. Wmk inverted .. .. ..
48 1d. black and red (24.4.05) .. .. 8·00 10
49 1d. red (2.4.07) .. .. .. 1·25 10
50 2d. purple and grey (22.2.05) .. .. 5·00 1·00
51 2d. grey (4.10.11) .. .. .. 2·25 4·00
52 2½d. maroon and blue (10.04) .. .. 12·00 40
53 2½d. bright blue (15.1.11) .. .. 4·50 2·00
54 4d. black and brown (1.4.06) .. .. 8·50 5·00
w. Wmk inverted .. .. ..
55 4d. black and red/*yellow* (21.11.11) .. 3·75 3·25
57 **7** 4½d. brown (27.2.05) .. .. .. 18·00 5·50
w. Wmk inverted £150 £150
58 4½d. orange (16.3.12†) .. .. .. 3·75 3·25
59 **8** 5d. vermilion (20.2.05) .. .. 22·00 4·25
60 5d. pale sage-green (1909) .. .. 3·75 3·25
a. Deep sage-green (1914) .. .. 11·00 14·00
61 **12** 1s. grey and violet (14.12.04) .. .. 55·00 1·75
62 1s. black/*green* (15.3.11) .. .. 6·00 2·00
63 5s. green and red/*yellow* (22.3.11) .. 60·00 65·00
45/63 .. .. .. *Set of* 17 £200 90·00
45*a*, 47*b*, 49, 51, 53, 55, 58, 60, 62/3 Optd "Specimen" .. .. *Set of* 10 £300

*The normal sideways watermark shows Crown to right of CA, *as seen from the back of the stamp*.
†These are the earliest known dates of use.

13

14

15

1914–21. *Wmk Mult Crown CA. Ordinary paper* (¼*d. to* 2½*d.,* 2*s.* 6*d.*) *or chalk-surfaced paper* (*others*). *P* 14.
69 **13** ¼d. brown (2.1.14) 40 10
a. Deep brown (1919) 40 30
x. Wmk reversed .. .. .. † £350
71 ½d. green (20.1.14) .. .. .. 1·40 15
aa. Wmk sideways .. .. .. † £3500
a. Deep green (1919) .. .. .. 1·00 30
aw. Wmk inverted .. .. .. † £150
73 1d. carmine-red (15.4.14) 60 10
a. Scarlet (1915) .. .. .. 1·25 30
w. Wmk inverted .. .. .. † £150
75 2d. grey (12.8.14) .. .. .. 5·00 2·50
aw. Wmk inverted .. .. .. † £350
b. Deep slate (1919) .. .. .. 8·00 10·00
77 2½d. bright blue (11.3.14) .. .. 1·25 30
w. Wmk inverted .. .. .. † £100
78 **14** 3d. purple/*yellow* (1.5.20) .. .. 2·50 7·00
a. On orange-buff .. .. .. 32·00 40·00
79 **6** 4d. black (21.8.15) .. .. .. 11·00 2·50
a. Grey-black (28.10.16) .. .. 20·00 8·00
80 **13** 6d. dull and bright purple (10.3.14) .. 8·50 14·00
a. Dull purple and magenta (1918) .. 11·00 14·00
w. Wmk inverted .. .. ..
81 **14** 1s. black/*green* (*white back*) (2.1.14) .. 9·00 17·00
a. On grn, grn back (Optd S. £45) (1915) 10·00 13·00
ab. Wmk sideways .. .. .. † £1800
b. On blue-green, olive back (1918) .. 15·00 17·00
c. On emerald surface (1920) .. .. 8·50 20·00
d. On emerald back (1921) .. .. 28·00 45·00
86 **15** 2s. purple and bright blue/*blue* (15.4.14) 50·00 28·00
a. Break in scroll £200
b. Broken crown and scroll £250
c. Dull purple and blue/blue (1921) .. 60·00 42·00
ca. Break in scroll £250
cb. Broken crown and scroll £300
87 **9** 2s. 6d. olive-green (1919) .. .. 50·00 75·00
a. Olive-grey (1920) .. .. .. 50·00 85·00
88 **15** 5s. green and red/*yellow* (21.3.17) .. 70·00 85·00
a. Break in scroll £300
b. Broken crown and scroll £350
69/88 .. .. .. *Set of* 12 £170 £200
69/88 (*excl* 87) Optd "Specimen" .. *Set of* 11 £400

The design of Nos. 79/*a* differs in various details from that of Type **6**.

We have only seen one copy of No. 71aa; it is in used condition.

A 3d. purple on yellow on white back, Type **14**, was prepared for use but not issued. It exists overprinted "Specimen" (*Price* £250).

An example of the 2s. 6d. olive-grey with bottom margin attached exists with the "A" omitted from "CA" in the watermark on the margin.

For illustrations of the varieties on Nos. 86 and 88 see above No. 58 of Leeward Islands.

WAR TAX
(16)

17

18

1917–18. *Optd with T* **16** *by De La Rue*.
92 **13** ½d. deep green (14.12.17*) 40 15
w. Wmk inverted £350
93 **12** 3d. grey and purple (15.2.18*) .. .. 1·25 7·00
92/3 Optd "Specimen" .. .. *Set of* 2 £130

*These are the earliest known dates of use.

(T **17** recess)

1919 (6 Mar). *Wmk Mult Crown CA. P* 14.
96 **17** 10s. black (Optd S. £750) £3000 £3500

Dark flaw on scroll (R. 2/4 1st state)

Lines omitted from scroll (R. 2/4 2nd state)

1921 (16 Feb)–**22**. *Wmk Mult Script CA. Chalk-surfaced paper* (*6d., 2s.*) *or ordinary paper* (*others*). *P* 14.
97 **13** ¼d. brown (12.1.22) .. .. .. 65 23·00
98 ½d. green (19.1.22) .. .. .. 90 15·00
99 1d. scarlet (24.12.21) .. .. .. 65 1·00
w. Wmk inverted £350 £120
100 **18** 2d. grey .. .. 2·50 1·25
101 **13** 2½d. bright blue (15.1.22) .. .. 2·75 21·00
102 6d. dull purple & brt purple (19.1.22) 26·00 65·00
103 **15** 2s. purple and blue/*blue* (19.1.22) .. 60·00 £180
a. Break in scroll £200
b. Broken crown and scroll £200
c. Dark flaw on scroll £1600
d. Lines omitted from scroll £325
104 **17** 10s. black (19.1.22) £300 £550
97/104 .. .. .. *Set of* 8 £350 £750
97/104 Optd "Specimen" .. .. *Set of* 8 £400

For illustrations of other varieties on No. 103 see above No. 58 of Leeward Islands.

Examples of all values are known showing a forged G.P.O. Malta postmark dated "MY 10 22".

SELF-GOVERNMENT
(19)

(20)

1922 (12 Jan–Apr). *Optd with T* **19** *or T* **20** (*large stamps*), *at Govt Printing Office, Valletta.* (*a*) *On No.* 35. *Wmk Crown CC*.
105 **10** 10s. blue-black (R.) £170 £275

(*b*) *On Nos.* 71, 77, 78*a*, 80, 81*d*, 86*c*, 87*a and* 88. *Wmk Mult Crown CA*
106 **13** ½d. green 40 95
w. Wmk inverted .. .. .. 50·00
107 2½d. bright blue .. .. .. 6·00 22·00
108 **14** 3d. purple/*orange-buff* .. .. 1·50 13·00
109 **13** 6d. dull and bright purple .. .. 1·50 13·00
x. Wmk reversed .. .. .. † £500
110 **14** 1s. black/*emerald* .. .. .. 2·75 11·00
111 **15** 2s. purple and blue/*blue* (R.) .. £200 £400
a. Break in scroll £600
b. Broken crown and scroll £600
112 **9** 2s. 6d. olive-grey .. .. .. 19·00 35·00
113 **15** 5s. green and red/*yellow* .. .. 50·00 75·00
a. Break in scroll £200
b. Broken crown and scroll £200
c. Lines omitted from scroll £250
106/13 .. .. .. *Set of* 8 £250 £500

(*c*) *On Nos.* 97/104. *Wmk Mult Script CA*
114 **13** ¼d. brown 10 30
w. Wmk inverted .. .. ..
115 ½d. green (29.4) .. .. .. 60 4·25
116 1d. scarlet 40 15
117 **18** 2d. grey .. .. 1·10 45
118 **13** 2½d. bright blue (15.1) 50 45
119 6d. dull and bright purple (19.4) .. 6·50 23·00
120 **15** 2s. purple and blue/*blue* (R.) (25.1) .. 38·00 75·00
a. Break in scroll £160
b. Broken crown and scroll £160
c. Lines omitted from scroll £225
121 **17** 10s. black (R.) (9.3) £100 £150
114/21 .. .. .. *Set of* 8 £130 £200

Examples of all values are known showing a forged G.P.O. Malta postmark dated "MY 10 22".

One Farthing

(21)

22

23

1922 (15 Apr). *No. 100 surch with T* **21**, *at Govt Printing Office, Valletta.*
122 **18** ¼d. on 2d. grey 30 30

(Des C. Dingli (T **22**) and G. Vella (**23**))

1922 (1 Aug)–**26**. *Wmk Mult Script CA (sideways* on T* **22**, *except No.* 140). *P* 14. (a) *Typo. Chalk-surfaced paper.*
123 **22** ¼d. brown (22.8.22) . . . . . . 1·00 60
a. *Chocolate-brown* . . 1·10 15
w. Wmk Crown to right of CA . . — 50·00
124 ½d. green . . . . . . 1·00 10
w. Wmk Crown to right of CA . . — 50·00
125 1d. orange and purple . . 1·60 15
w. Wmk Crown to right of CA . . — 40·00
126 1d. bright violet (25.4.24) . . 1·60 55
127 1½d. brown-red (1.10.23) . . 1·25 10
128 2d. bistre-brown & turquoise (28.8.22) 1·75 70
w. Wmk Crown to right of CA . . — 75·00
129 2½d. ultramarine (16.2.26) . . 1·25 5·50
130 3d. cobalt (28.8.22) . . . . 2·00 60
a. *Bright ultramarine* . . 2·00 95
131 3d. black/*yellow* (16.2.26) . . 1·25 8·00
132 4d. yellow and bright blue (28.8.22) 1·25 1·75
w. Wmk Crown to right of CA £100
133 6d. olive-green and reddish violet . . 2·00 1·25
134 **23** 1s. indigo and sepia . . . . 4·00 2·50
135 2s. brown and blue . . . . 6·00 8·50
136 2s. 6d. brt magenta & black (28.8.22) 8·00 12·00
137 5s. orange-yell & brt ultram (28.8.22) 17·00 28·00
138 10s. slate-grey and brown (28.8.22) . . 48·00 £120
(*b*) *Recess*
139 **22** £1 black and carmine-red (*wmk sideways*) (28.8.22) . . £110 £250
140 £1 black and bright carmine (*wmk upright*) (14.5.25) . . 90·00 £250
123/39 . . *Set of* 17 £160 £375
123/39 Optd "Specimen" . . *Set of* 17 £450

*The normal sideways watermark shows Crown to left of CA, *as seen from the back of the stamp.*

Two pence halfpenny

(24)

POSTAGE

(25)

1925. *Surch with T* **24**, *at Govt Printing Office, Valletta.*
141 **22** 2½d. on 3d. cobalt (3 Dec) . . 80 1·75
142 2½d. on 3d. bright ultramarine (9 Dec) 1·00 1·75

1926 (1 Apr). *Optd with T* **25** *at Govt Printing Office, Valletta.*
143 **22** ¼d. brown . . . . 15 2·00
144 ½d. green 30 15
w. Wmk Crown to right of CA . . 50·00
145 1d. bright violet . . 40 25
146 1½d. brown-red . . 45 40
147 2d. bistre-brown and turquoise . . 40 20
148 2½d. ultramarine . . 65 40
149 3d. black/*yellow* . . 30 50
a. Opt inverted . . £170 £475
150 4d. yellow and bright blue . . 3·25 11·00
151 6d. olive-green and violet . . 2·00 1·75
152 **23** 1s. indigo and sepia . . 4·50 8·50
153 2s. brown and blue . . 42·00 £130
154 2s. 6d. bright magenta and black . . 9·00 24·00
155 5s. orange-yellow & brt ultramarine 8·00 26·00
156 10s. slate-grey and brown . . 6·00 14·00
143/56 . . *Set of* 14 70·00 £190

26

27 Valletta Harbour

28 St. Publius

33 St. Paul

(T **26** typo, others recess Waterlow)

1926 (6 Apr)–**27**. *T* **26/8**, **33** *and similar designs. Inscr* "POSTAGE". *Wmk Mult Script CA. P* 15×14 (*T* **26**) *or* 12½ (*others*).
157 **26** ¼d. brown 50 15
158 ½d. yellow-green (5.8.26) . . 50 15
a. Printed on the gummed side . .
w. Wmk inverted . .
159 1d. rose-red (1.4.27) . . 1·50 60
160 1½d. chestnut (7.10.26) . . 1·25 10
161 **26** 2d. greenish grey (1.4.27) . . 3·50 7·50
162 2½d. blue (1.4.27) . . 3·00 20
162*a* 3d. violet (1.4.27) . . 3·50 1·75
163 4d. black and red . . 2·75 7·00
164 4½d. lavender and ochre . . 3·00 2·50
165 6d. violet and scarlet (5.5.26) . . 3·25 2·00
166 **27** 1s. black . . 5·50 2·75
167 **28** 1s. 6d. black and green . . 5·50 11·00
168 – 2s. black and purple . . 5·50 13·00
169 – 2s. 6d. black and vermilion . . 12·00 40·00
170 – 3s. black and blue . . 14·00 27·00
171 – 5s. black and green (5.5.26) . . 20·00 55·00
172 **33** 10s. black and carmine (9.2.27) . . 55·00 £100
157/72 . . *Set of* 17 £120 £225
157/72 Optd "Specimen" . . *Set of* 17 £275

Designs: *Vert*—2s. 6d. Gozo fishing boat; 3s. Neptune; *Horiz*—2s. Mdina (Notabile); 5s. Neolithic temple, Mnajdra.

AIR MAIL

(34)

POSTAGE AND REVENUE

(35)

POSTAGE AND REVENUE.

(36)

1928 (1 Apr). *Air. Optd with T* **34**.
173 **26** 6d. violet and scarlet . . 1·25 90

1928 (1 Oct–5 Dec). *As Nos.* 157/72, *optd.*
174 **35** ¼d. brown . . 1·00 10
175 ½d. yellow-green . . 80 10
176 1d. rose-red . . 1·50 2·25
177 1d. chestnut (5.12.28) . . 3·00 10
178 1½d. chestnut . . 1·75 30
179 1½d. rose-red (5.12.28) . . 3·75 10
180 2d. greenish grey . . 3·25 8·00
181 2½d. blue . . 1·50 10
182 3d. violet . . 1·25 30
183 4d. black and red . . 1·25 1·00
184 4½d. lavender and ochre . . 2·25 1·50
185 6d. violet and scarlet . . 2·25 1·00
186 **36** 1s. black (R.) . . 3·75 2·25
187 1s. 6d. black and green (R.) . . 5·00 9·00
188 2s. black and purple (R.) . . 19·00 45·00
189 2s. 6d. black and vermilion (R.) . . 14·00 23·00
190 3s. black and blue (R.) . . 18·00 30·00
191 5s. black and green (R.) . . 26·00 65·00
192 10s. black and carmine (R.) . . 55·00 90·00
174/92 . . *Set of* 19 £130 £250
174/92 Optd "Specimen" . . *Set of* 19 £300

1930 (20 Oct). *As Nos.* 157/172, *but inscr* "POSTAGE (&) REVENUE".
193 ¼d. brown . . 50 10
194 ½d. yellow-green . . 50 10
195 1d. chestnut . . 60 10
196 1½d. rose-red . . 70 10
197 2d. greenish grey . . 1·00 20
198 2½d. blue . . 2·00 10
199 3d. violet . . 1·50 20
200 4d. black and red . . 1·25 3·00
201 4½d. lavender and ochre . . 2·50 1·00
202 6d. violet and scarlet . . 2·00 75
203 1s. black . . 8·00 9·00
204 1s. 6d. black and green . . 5·50 16·00
205 2s. black and purple . . 8·00 16·00
206 2s. 6d. black and vermilion . . 15·00 48·00
207 3s. black and blue . . 22·00 55·00
208 5s. black and green . . 27·00 65·00
209 10s. black and carmine . . 65·00 £120
193/209 . . *Set of* 17 £140 £300
193/209 Perf "Specimen" . . *Set of* 17 £275

1935 (6 May). *Silver Jubilee. As Nos.* 114/17 *of Jamaica.*
210 ½d. black and green . . 40 50
a. Extra flagstaff . . 22·00
b. Short extra flagstaff . . 30·00
c. Lightning conductor . . 28·00
211 2½d. brown and deep blue . . 2·50 3·75
a. Extra flagstaff . . £130
b. Short extra flagstaff . . £130
c. Lightning conductor . . £100
212 6d. light blue and olive-green . . 5·50 3·75
a. Extra flagstaff . . £180
b. Short extra flagstaff . . £160
c. Lightning conductor . . £130
213 1s. slate and purple . . 9·00 14·00
a. Extra flagstaff . . £425
b. Short extra flagstaff . . £350
c. Lightning conductor . . £250
210/13 . . *Set of* 4 16·00 20·00
210/13 Perf "Specimen" . . *Set of* 4 £130

For illustrations of plate varieties see Omnibus section following Zimbabwe.

Sheets from the second printing of the ½d., 6d. and 1s. in November 1935 had the extra flagstaff partially erased from the stamp with a sharp point.

1937 (12 May). *Coronation. As Nos.* 118/20 *of Jamaica.*
214 ½d. green . . 10 10
215 1½d. scarlet . . 50 15
a. *Brown-lake* . . £550 £550
216 2½d. bright blue . . 50 35
214/16 . . *Set of* 3 1·00 50
214/16 Perf "Specimen" . . *Set of* 3 60·00

OMNIBUS ISSUES

Details, together with prices for complete sets, of the various Omnibus issues from the 1935 Silver Jubilee series to date are included in a special section following Zimbabwe at the end of Volume 2.

37 Grand Harbour, Valletta

38 H.M.S. *St. Angelo*

39 Verdala Palace

40 Hypogeum, Hal Saflieni

Broken cross (Right pane R. 5/7)

Extra windows (R. 2/7) (corrected in 1945)

Damaged value tablet (R. 4/9)

Semaphore flaw (R. 2/7)

(Recess Waterlow)

1938 (17 Feb*)–**43**. *T* **37/40** *and similar designs. Wmk Mult Script CA (sideways on No.* 217). *P* 12½.
217 **37** ¼d. brown . . 10 10
218 **38** ½d. green . . 1·75 10
218*a* ½d. red-brown (8.3.43) . . 55 30
219 **39** 1d. red-brown . . 4·25 30
219*a* 1d. green (8.3.43) . . 60 10
220 **40** 1½d. scarlet . . 1·00 15
a. Broken cross . . 55·00
220*b* 1½d. slate-black (8.3.43) . . 30 15
ba. Broken cross . . 45·00
221 – 2d. slate-black . . 40 1·25
a. Extra windows . . 30·00
221*b* – 2d. scarlet (8.3.43) . . 40 10
ba. Extra windows . . 30·00
222 – 2½d. greyish blue . . 75 30
222*a* – 2½d. dull violet (8.3.43) . . 60 10
223 – 3d. dull violet . . 45 70
223*a* – 3d. blue (8.3.43) . . 30 10
224 – 4½d. olive-green and yellow-brown . . 50 10
225 – 6d. olive-green and scarlet . . 75 15
226 – 1s. black . . 75 30
227 – 1s. 6d. black and olive-green . . 7·00 3·50
228 – 2s. green and deep blue . . 3·25 3·50
229 – 2s. 6d. black and scarlet . . 7·00 4·50
a. Damaged value tablet . . £140
230 – 5s. black and green . . 7·00 5·50
a. Semaphore flaw . . 65·00
231 – 10s. black and carmine . . 14·00 14·00
217/31 . . *Set of* 21 45·00 30·00
217/31 Perf "Specimen" . . *Set of* 21 £350

Designs: *Horiz* (*as T* **39**)—2d. Victoria and citadel, Gozo; 2½d. De l'Isle Adam entering Mdina; 4½d. Ruins at Mnajdra; 1s. 6d. St. Publius; 2s. Mdina Cathedral; 2s. 6d. Statue of Neptune. *Vert* (*as T* **40**)—3d. St. John's Co-Cathedral; 6d. Statue of Manoel de Vilhena; 1s. Maltese girl wearing faldetta; 5s. Palace Square, Valletta; 10s. St. Paul.

*This is the local date of issue but the stamps were released in London on 15 February.

1946 (3 Dec). *Victory. As Nos.* 141/2 *of Jamaica, but inscr* "MALTA" *between Maltese Cross and George Cross.*
232 1d. green . . 10 10
233 3d. blue . . 10 20
232/3 Perf "Specimen" . . *Set of* 2 50·00

SELF-GOVERNMENT

(52)

"NT" joined (R. 4/10)

Halation flaw (Pl 2 R. 2/5) (ptg of 8 Jan 1953)

Cracked plate (Pl 2 R. 5/1) (ptg of 8 Jan 1953)

(Optd by Waterlow)

1948 (25 Nov)–**53.** *New Constitution. As Nos.* 217/31 *but optd as T* **52**; *reading up on* ½d. *and* 5s., *down on other values, and smaller on* ¼d. *value.*

234 **37** ¼d. brown 20 20
235 **38** ½d. red-brown 20 10
a. "NT" joined 15·00
236 **39** 1d. green 20 10
236*a* 1d. grey (R.) (8.1.53) 20 10
237 **40** 1½d. blue-black (R.) 75 10
a. Broken cross 48·00
237*b* 1½d. green (8.1.53) 30 10
ba. Albino opt † £10000
238 – 2d. scarlet 75 10
a. Extra windows 30·00
238*b* – 2d. yellow-ochre (8.1.53) 30 10
ba. Halation flaw 95·00
bc. Cracked plate 95·00
239 – 2½d. dull violet (R.) 80 10
239*a* – 2½d. scarlet-vermilion (8.1.53) 30 85
240 – 3d. blue (R.) 30 15
240*a* – 3d. dull violet (R.) (8.1.53) 35 15
241 – 4½d. olive-green and yellow-brown 2·00 1·50
241*a* – 4½d. olive-grn & dp ultram (R.) (8.1.53) 50 90
242 – 6d. olive-green and scarlet 1·25 15
243 – 1s. black 2·25 40
244 – 1s. 6d. black and olive-green 2·50 45
245 – 2s. green and deep blue (R.) 5·00 1·50
246 – 2s. 6d. black and scarlet 14·00 2·50
a. Damaged value tablet £250
247 – 5s. black and green (R.) 19·00 5·50
a. "NT" joined £160 £100
b. Semaphore flaw — £1500
248 – 10s. black and carmine 19·00 19·00
234/48 *Set of* 21 60·00 30·00

1949 (4 Jan). *Royal Silver Wedding. As Nos.* 143/4 *of Jamaica, but inscr* "MALTA" *between Maltese Cross and George Cross and with* £1 *ptd in recess.*

249 1d. green 50 10
250 £1 indigo 38·00 35·00

1949 (10 Oct). *75th Anniv of U.P.U. As Nos.* 145/8 *of Jamaica, but inscr* "MALTA" *in recess.*

251 2½d. violet 30 10
252 3d. deep blue 2·25 50
253 6d. carmine-red 1·50 50
254 1s. blue-black 1·50 1·75
251/4 *Set of* 4 5·00 2·50

53 Queen Elizabeth II when Princess

54 "Our Lady of Mount Carmel" (attrib Palladino)

(T **53/4**. Recess B.W.)

1950 (1 Dec). *Visit of Princess Elizabeth to Malta. Wmk Mult Script CA. P* 12 × 11½.

255 **53** 1d. green 10 10
256 3d. blue 20 10
257 1s. black 55 45
255/7 *Set of* 3 70 55

1951 (12 July). *Seventh Centenary of the Scapular. Wmk Mult Script CA. P* 12 × 11½.

258 **54** 1d. green 10 10
259 3d. violet 20 10
260 1s. black 60 40
258/60 *Set of* 3 80 50

1953 (3 June). *Coronation. As No.* 153 *of Jamaica.*

261 1½d. black and deep yellow-green 30 10

55 St. John's Co-Cathedral

56 "Immaculate Conception" (Caruana) (altar-piece, Cospicua)

(Recess Waterlow)

1954 (3 May). *Royal Visit. Wmk Mult Script CA. P* 12½.

262 **55** 3d. violet 30 10

(Photo Harrison)

1954 (8 Sept). *Centenary of Dogma of the Immaculate Conception. Wmk Mult Script CA. Chalk-surfaced paper. P* 14½ × 14.

263 **56** 1½d. emerald 10 10
264 3d. bright blue 10 10
265 1s. grey-black 35 20
263/5 *Set of* 3 45 30

57 Monument of the Great Siege, 1565

62 Auberge de Castile

(Recess Waterlow (2s. 6d. to £1). B.W. (others))

1956 (23 Jan)–**58.** *T* **57, 62** *and similar designs. Wmk Mult Script CA. P* 14×13½ (2s. 6d. *to* £1) *or* 11½ (*others*).

266 ¼d. violet 20 10
267 ½d. orange 50 10
268 1d. black (9.2.56) 1·25 10
269 1½d. bluish green (9.2.56) 30 10
270 2d. brown (9.2.56) 1·25 10
a. Deep brown (26.2.58) 2·25 10
271 2½d. orange-brown 45 30
272 3d. rose-red (22.3.56) 65 10
w. Wmk inverted † £500
273 4½d. deep blue 85 20
274 6d. indigo (9.2.56) 50 10
w. Wmk inverted 90·00
275 8d. bistre-brown 1·50 1·00
276 1s. deep reddish violet 50 10
277 1s. 6d. deep turquoise-green 7·50 20
278 2s. olive-green 9·00 80
279 2s. 6d. chestnut (22.3.56) 6·50 2·25
280 5s. green (11.10.56) 11·00 2·75
281 10s. carmine-red (19.11.56) 35·00 9·00
282 £1 yellow-brown (5.1.57) 35·00 20·00
266/82 *Set of* 17 95·00 32·00

Designs:—*Vert*—½d. Wignacourt aqueduct horsetrough; 1d. Victory church; 1½d. War memorial; 2d. Mosta dome; 3d. The King's scroll; 4½d. Roosevelt's scroll; 8d. Vedette; 1s. Mdina gate; 1s. 6d. "Les Gavroches" (statue); 2s. Monument of Christ the King; 2s. 6d. Grand Master Cottoner's monument; 5s. Grand Master Perellos's monument; 10s. St. Paul; £1 Baptism of Christ. *Horiz*—6d. Neolithic Temples at Tarxien.

See also Nos. 314/15.

74 "Defence of Malta"

75 Searchlights over Malta

(Des E. Cremona. Photo Harrison)

1957 (15 Apr). *George Cross Commemoration. Cross in silver. T* **74/5** *and similar design. Wmk Mult Script CA. P* 14½ × 14 (3d.) *or* 14 × 14½ (*others*).

283 1½d. deep dull green 15 10
284 3d. vermilion 15 10
285 1s. reddish brown 15 10
283/5 *Set of* 3 40 20

Design: *Vert*—1s. Bombed buildings.

77 "Design"

(Des E. Cremona. Photo Harrison)

1958 (15 Feb). *Technical Education in Malta. T* **77** *and similar designs. W w* **12**. *P* 14 × 14½ (3*d.*) *or* 14½ × 14 (*others*).

286 1½d. black and deep green 10 10
287 3d. black, scarlet and grey 10 10
288 1s. grey, bright purple and black 15 10
286/8 *Set of* 3 30 15

Designs: *Vert*—3d. "Construction". *Horiz*—1s. Technical School, Paola.

ALTERED CATALOGUE NUMBERS

Any Catalogue numbers altered from the last edition are shown as a list in the introductory pages.

80 Bombed-out Family

81 Sea Raid on Grand Harbour, Valletta

(Des E. Cremona. Photo Harrison)

1958 (15 Apr). *George Cross Commemoration. Cross in first colour, outlined in silver. T* **80/1** *and similar design. W w* **12**. *P* 14 × 14½ (3*d.*) *or* 14½ × 14 (*others*).

289 1½d. blue-green and black 15 10
290 3d. red and black 15 10
291 1s. reddish violet and black 15 10
a. Silver (outline) omitted £325
289/91 *Set of* 3 40 15

Design: *Horiz*—1s. Searchlight crew.

83 Air Raid Casualties

84 "For Gallantry"

(Des E. Cremona. Photo Harrison)

1959 (15 Apr). *George Cross Commemoration. T* **83/4** *and similar design. W w* **12**. *P* 14½ × 14 (3*d.*) *or* 14 × 14½ (*others*).

292 1½d. grey-green, black and gold 20 10
293 3d. reddish violet, black and gold 20 10
294 1s. blue-grey, black and gold 70 65
292/4 *Set of* 3 1·00 65

Design: *Vert*—1s. Maltese under bombardment.

86 Shipwreck of St. Paul (after Palombi)

87 Statue of St. Paul, Rabat, Malta

(Des E. Cremona. Photo Harrison)

1960 (9 Feb). *19th Centenary of the Shipwreck of St. Paul. T* **86/7** *and similar designs. W w* **12**. *P* 13 (1½*d.*, 3*d.*, 6*d.*) *or* 14×14½ (*others*).

295 1½d. blue, gold and yellow-brown 15 10
a. Gold (dates and crosses) omitted 55·00
296 3d. bright purple, gold and blue 15 10
a. Printed on the gummed side
297 6d. carmine, gold and pale grey 25 10
298 8d. black and gold 30 50
299 1s. maroon and gold 25 10
300 2s. 6d. blue, deep bluish green and gold 1·00 2·00
a. Gold omitted £325
295/300 *Set of* 6 1·90 2·50

Designs: *Vert as T* **86**—3d. Consecration of St. Publius (first Bishop of Malta) (after Palombi); 6d. Departure of St. Paul (after Palombi). *Diamond shaped as T* **87**—1s. Angel with *Acts of the Apostles*; 2s. 6d. St. Paul with *Second Epistle to the Corinthians*.

92 Stamp of 1860

(Centre litho; frame recess. Waterlow)

1960 (1 Dec). *Stamp Centenary. W w* **12**. *P* 13½.

301 **92** 1½d. buff, pale blue and green 25 10
a. Buff, pale bl & myrtle (white paper) 3·00 1·75
302 3d. buff pale blue and deep carmine 30 10
a. Blank corner £140
303 6d. buff, pale blue and ultramarine 40 55
301/3 *Set of* 3 85 60

Examples of the 1½d. apparently with the blue omitted are from sheets with a very weak printing of this colour.

No. 302a shows the right-hand bottom corner of the 1860 stamp blank. It occurs on R. 4/7 from early trial plates and sheets containing the error should have been destroyed, but some were sorted into good stock and issued at a post ofice.

93 George Cross

(Photo Harrison)

1961 (15 Apr). *George Cross Commemoration. T* **93** *and similar designs showing medal. W* w **12**. *P* 15 × 14.

304 1½d. black, cream and bistre 15 10
305 3d. olive-brown and greenish blue 30 10
306 1s. olive-green, lilac & dp reddish violet .. 60 1·25
304/6 .. .. *Set of* 3 95 1·25

96 "Madonna Damascena"

(Photo Harrison)

1962 (7 Sept). *Great Siege Commemoration. T* **96** *and similar vert designs. W* w **12**. *P* 13 × 12.

307 2d. bright blue 10 10
308 3d. red 10 10
309 6d. bronze-green 20 10
310 1s. brown-purple 20 20
307/10 .. .. *Set of* 4 45 30

Designs:—3d. Great Siege Monument; 6d. Grand Master La Valette; 1s. Assault on Fort St. Elmo.

1963 (4 June). *Freedom from Hunger. As No.* 80 *of Lesotho.*

311 1s. 6d. sepia .. .. 2·00 2·50

1963 (2 Sept). *Red Cross Centenary. As Nos.* 203/4 *of Jamaica.*

312 2d. red and black 25 15
313 1s. 6d. red and blue .. .. 3·00 3·75

1963 (15 Oct)–**64**. *As Nos.* 268 *and* 270, *but wmk* w **12**.

314 **59** 1d. black 50 30
315 **61** 2d. deep brown (11.7.64*) .. .. 1·50 2·25

*This is the earliest known date recorded in Malta.

100 Bruce, Zammit and Microscope

101 Goat and Laboratory Equipment

(Des E. Cremona. Photo Harrison)

1964 (14 April). *Anti-Brucellosis Congress. W* w **12**. *P* 14.

316 **100** 2d. light brown, black and bluish green 10 10
a. Black (microscope, etc) omitted .. £250
317 **101** 1s. 6d. black and maroon 65 20

102 "Nicola Cotoner tending Sick Man" (M. Preti)

105 Maltese Cross (*Upright*)

In this illustration the points of the crosses meet in a vertical line. When the watermark is sideways they meet in a horizontal line.

(Des E. Cremona. Photo Harrison)

1964 (5 Sept). *First European Catholic Doctors' Congress, Vienna. T* **102** *and similar horiz designs. W* **105** *(sideways). P* 13½ × 11½.

318 2d. red, black, gold and grey-blue 20 10
319 6d. red, black, gold and bistre 50 15
320 1s. 6d. red, black, gold and reddish violet .. 1·10 1·60
318/20 .. .. *Set of* 3 1·60 1·60

Designs:—6d. St. Luke and Hospital; 1s. 6d. Sacra Infermeria, Valletta.

INDEPENDENT

106 Dove and British Crown

109 "The Nativity"

(Des E. Cremona. Photo Harrison)

1964 (21 Sept). *Independence. T* **106** *and similar vert designs. W* **105**. *P* 14½ × 13½.

321 2d. olive-brown, red and gold 30 10
a. Gold omitted .. .. .. 70·00
322 3d. brown-purple, red and gold 30 10
a. Gold omitted .. .. .. 70·00
323 6d. slate, red and gold 70 15
324 1s. blue, red and gold 70 15
325 1s. 6d. indigo, red and gold .. .. 2·00 1·00
326 2s. 6d. deep violet-blue, red and gold .. 2·00 2·25
321/6 .. .. *Set of* 6 5·50 3·25

Designs:—2d., 1s. Type **106**; 3d., 1s. 6d. Dove and Pope's Tiara; 6d., 2s. 6d. Dove and U.N. emblem.

(Des E. Cremona. Photo D.L.R.)

1964 (3 Nov). *Christmas. W* **105** *(sideways). P* 13 × 13½.

327 **109** 2d. bright purple and gold 10 10
328 4d. bright blue and gold 20 15
329 8d. deep bluish green and gold 45 45
327/9 .. .. *Set of* 3 65 60

110 Neolithic Era

117 Galleys of Knights of St. John

119 British Rule

(Des E. Cremona. Photo Harrison)

1965 (7 Jan)–**70**. *Chalk-surfaced paper. T* **110**, **117**, **119** *and similar designs. W* **105**. *P* 14×14½ *(vert) or* 14½ *(horiz).*

330 ½d. multicoloured 10 10
a. "½d" (white) printed twice† .. 10·00
b. Rose-pink ("MALTA") printed twice 10·00
c. White (face value) omitted .. 40·00
331 1d. multicoloured 10 10
a. Gold (ancient lettering) omitted .. 50·00
b. White (Greek lettering and "PUNIC") omitted .. .. .. 50·00
c. White ptg double .. .. 20·00
d. "PUNIC" omitted .. .. 85·00
332 1½d. multicoloured 30 10
333 2d. multicoloured 10 10
a. Gold omitted .. .. .. 22·00
b. Imperf (pair) £275
334 2½d. multicoloured 40 10
a. Orange omitted* .. .. 70·00
b. Gold ("SARACENIC") omitted .. 55·00
c. Salmon printed twice† .. .. 60·00
335 3d. multicoloured 10 10
a. Gold (windows) omitted .. .. 75·00
b. "MALTA" (silver) omitted .. .. 26·00
c. "MALTA" (silver) printed twice .. £275
d. Bright lilac ("SICULO NORMAN") omitted .. .. ..
e. Imperf (pair) £300
336 4d. multicoloured 30 10
a. "KNIGHTS OF MALTA" (silver) omitted .. .. .. 50·00
b. "MALTA" (silver) omitted .. .. 55·00
c. Black (shield surround) omitted .. 55·00
d. Imperf (pair) £200
337 4½d. multicoloured 70 40
a. Silver ("MALTA", etc) omitted .. £300
337*b* 5d. multicoloured (1.8.70) 30 20
ba. "FORTIFICATIONS" (gold) omitted 70·00
338 6d. multicoloured 20 10
a. "MALTA" (silver) omitted .. .. 42·00
b. Black omitted .. .. .. 75·00
339 8d. multicoloured 40 10
a. Gold (centre) omitted .. .. 35·00
b. Gold (frame) omitted .. .. 60·00
339*c* 10d. multicoloured (1.8.70) .. .. 45 1·40
ca. "NAVAL ARSENAL" (gold) omitted £120
340 1s. multicoloured 30 10
a. Gold (centre) omitted £120
b. Gold (framework) omitted .. .. 42·00
341 1s. 3d. multicoloured .. .. .. 2·00 1·40
a. Gold (centre) omitted .. .. 50·00
b. Gold (framework) omitted £100
c. Imperf (pair) £350
342 1s. 6d. multicoloured 60 10
a. Head (black) omitted £225
b. Gold (centre) omitted .. .. 40·00
c. Gold (frame) omitted .. .. 70·00
343 2s. multicoloured 70 10
a. Gold (centre) omitted £120
b. Gold (framework) omitted .. .. 48·00
344 2s. 6d. multicoloured 70 50
345 3s. multicoloured .. .. .. 1·50 75
a. Gold (framework) omitted .. .. 30·00
346 5s. multicoloured .. .. .. 5·50 1·00
a. Gold (HAFMED emblem) omitted .. 80·00
b. Gold (framework) omitted .. .. 70·00
347 10s. multicoloured .. .. .. 3·50 3·00
a. Gold (centre) omitted £110
348 £1 multicoloured .. .. .. 3·75 5·00
a. Pink omitted .. .. .. 26·00
330/48 .. .. *Set of* 21 19·00 12·50

Designs: *Vert*—1d. Punic era; 1½d. Roman era; 2d. Proto Christian era; 2½d. Saracenic era; 3d. Siculo Norman era; 4d. Knights of Malta; 5d. Fortifications; 6d. French occupation. *Horiz*—10d. Naval arsenal; 1s. Maltese corps of the British army; 1s. 3d. International Eucharistic congress, 1913; 1s. 6d. Self-government, 1921; 2s. Gozo civic council; 2s. 6d. State of Malta; 3s. Independence, 1964; 5s. HAFMED (Allied forces, Mediterranean); 10s. The Maltese Islands (map); £1 Patron saints.

*The effect of this is to leave the Saracenic pattern as a pink colour.

†On the ½d. the second impression is 6½ mm lower or 3 mm to the left, and on the 2½d. 1 mm lower so that it falls partly across "MALTA" and "2½d". Stamps with almost coincidental double impression are common.

The ½d. and 1d. had white printing plates. Two silver plates were used on the 4d., one for "KNIGHTS OF MALTA" and the other for "MALTA". Two gold plates were used for the 8d. to 10s., one for the framework and the other for the gold in the central part of the designs.

No. 337a comes from a sheet on which the silver printing was so misplaced that it missed the top horizontal row entirely.

The ½d. to 4d., 1s. and 1s. 6d. to 5s. values exist with PVA gum as well as gum arabic and the 5d. and 10d. have PVA gum only.

129 "Dante" (Raphael)

(Des E. Cremona. Photo Govt Ptg Works, Rome)

1965 (7 July). *700th Birth Anniv of Dante. P* 14.

349 **129** 2d. indigo 10 10
350 6d. bronze-green 25 10
351 2s. chocolate .. .. .. 1·10 90
349/51 .. .. *Set of* 3 1·25 1·00

130 Turkish Camp

131 Turkish Fleet

(Des E. Cremona. Photo Harrison)

1965 (1 Sept). *400th Anniv of Great Siege. T* **130/1** *and similar designs. W* **105** *(sideways). P* 13 *(6d., 1s.) or* 14½×14 *(others).*

352 2d. olive-green, red and black 30 10
353 3d. olive-green, red, black and light drab .. 30 10
354 6d. multicoloured 50 10
a. Gold (framework and dates) omitted .. £200
b. Black (on hulls) omitted £200
355 8d. red, gold, indigo and blue 90 90
a. Gold (flag and dates) omitted .. £100
356 1s. red, gold and deep grey-blue 50 10
357 1s. 6d. ochre, red and black .. .. 1·25 30
358 2s. 6d. sepia, black, red and yellow-olive .. 1·50 2·50
352/8 .. .. *Set of* 7 4·75 3·50

Designs: *Square (as T* **130**)—3d. Battle scene; 8d. Arrival of relief force; 1s. 6d. "Allegory of Victory" (from mural by M. Preti); 2s. 6d. Victory medal. *Vert (as T* **131**)—1s. Grand Master J. de La Valette's arms.

NEW INFORMATION

The editor is always interested to correspond with people who have new information that will improve or correct the Catalogue.

137 "The Three Kings" **138** Sir Winston Churchill

(Des E. Cremona. Photo Enschedé)

1965 (7 Oct). *Christmas. W* **105** *(sideways). P* 11 × 11½.
359 **137** 1d. slate-purple and red 10 10
360 4d. slate-purple and blue 30 25
361 1s. 3d. slate-purple and bright purple 30 30
359/61 .. .. *Set of* 3 60 50

(Des E. Cremona. Photo Harrison)

1966 (24 Jan). *Churchill Commemoration. T* **138** *and similar square design. W* **105** *(sideways). P* 14½ × 14.
362 **138** 2d. black, red and gold.. .. .. 20 10
363 – 3d. bronze-green, yellow-olive and gold 20 10
364 **138** 1s. maroon, red and gold 25 10
a. Gold (shading) omitted £150
365 – 1s. 6d. chalky blue, violet-blue and gold 35 40
362/5 .. .. *Set of* 4 90 55
Design:—3d., 1s. 6d. Sir Winston Churchill and George Cross.

140 Grand Master La Valette **145** President Kennedy and Memorial

(Des E. Cremona. Photo State Ptg Works, Vienna)

1966 (28 Mar). *400th Anniv of Valletta. T* **140** *and similar square designs. Multicoloured. W* **105** *(sideways). P* 12.
366 2d. Type **140** 10 10
367 3d. Pope Pius V 10 10
a. Gold omitted £275
368 6d. Map of Valletta 15 10
369 1s. Francesco Laparelli (architect) .. 15 10
370 2s. 6d. Girolamo Cassar (architect) .. 35 50
366/70 .. .. *Set of* 5 65 65

(Des E. Cremona. Photo Harrison)

1966 (28 May). *President Kennedy Commemoration. W* **105** *(sideways). P* 15 × 14.
371 **145** 3d. olive, gold and black 10 10
a. Gold inscr omitted £150
372 1s. 6d. Prussian blue, gold and black 10 10

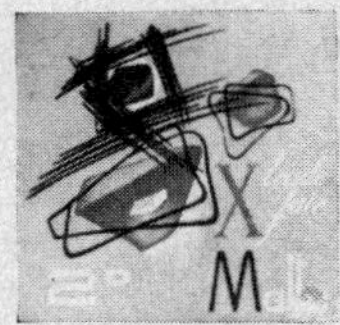

146 "Trade"

(Des E. Cremona. Photo D.L.R.)

1966 (16 June). *Tenth Malta Trade Fair. W* **105** *(sideways). P* 13½.
373 **146** 2d. multicoloured 10 10
374 8d. multicoloured 30 25
375 2s. 6d. multicoloured 30 25
373/5 .. .. *Set of* 3 65 50

147 "The Child in the Manger" **148** George Cross

(Des E. Cremona. Photo D.L.R.)

1966 (7 Oct). *Christmas. W* **105**. *P* 13½.
376 **147** 1d. black, gold, turquoise-bl & slate-pur 10 10
377 4d. black, gold, ultramarine & slate-pur 10 10
378 1s. 3d. black, gold, brt pur & slate-pur 10 10
a. Gold omitted .. .. 60·00
376/8 .. .. *Set of* 3 15 10

(Des E. Cremona. Photo Harrison)

1967 (1 Mar). *25th Anniv of George Cross Award to Malta. W* **105** *(sideways). P* 14½ × 14.
379 **148** 2d. multicoloured 10 10
380 4d. multicoloured 10 10
381 3s. multicoloured 15 15
379/81 .. .. *Set of* 3 15 15

149 Crucifixion of St. Peter

150 Open Bible and Episcopal Emblems

(Des E. Cremona. Photo Harrison)

1967 (28 June). *1900th Anniv of Martyrdom of Saints Peter and Paul. T* **149/50** *and similar design. W* **105** *(sideways). P* 13½ × 14½ *(8d.) or* 14½ *(others).*
382 2d. chestnut, orange and black 10 10
383 8d. yellow-olive, gold and black 15 10
384 3s. blue, light blue and black 20 15
382/4 .. .. *Set of* 3 30 20
Design:—*Square as T* **149**—3s. Beheading of St. Paul.

152 "St. Catherine of Siena" **156** Temple Ruins, Tarxien

(Des E. Cremona. Photo Enschedé)

1967 (1 Aug). *300th Death Anniv of Melchior Gafa (sculptor). T* **152** *and similar horiz designs. Multicoloured. W* **105** *(sideways). P* 13½ × 13.
385 2d. Type **152** 10 10
386 4d. "St. Thomas of Villanova" 10 10
387 1s. 6d. "Baptism of Christ" (detail) 10 10
388 2s. 6d. "St. John the Baptist" (from "Baptism of Christ") 10 10
385/8 .. .. *Set of* 4 20 15

(Des E. Cremona. Photo Harrison)

1967 (12 Sept). *15th International Historical Architecture Congress, Valletta. T* **156** *and similar square designs. Multicoloured. W* **105**. *P* 15 × 14½.
389 2d. Type **156** 10 10
390 6d. Facade of Palazzo Falzon, Notabile .. 10 10
391 1s. Parish Church, Birkirkara 10 10
392 3s. Portal, Auberge de Castille 15 15
389/92 .. .. *Set of* 4 20 20

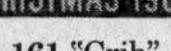

160 "Angels" **161** "Crib" **162** "Angels"

(Des E. Cremona. Photo D.L.R.)

1967 (20 Oct). *Christmas. W* **105** *(sideways). P* 14.
393 **160** 1d. multicoloured 10 10
a. Horiz strip of 3. Nos. 393/5 .. 20 20
b. White stars (red omitted) .. 70·00
394 **161** 8d. multicoloured 10 10
395 **162** 1s. 4d. multicoloured 10 10
393/5 .. .. *Set of* 3 20 20
Nos. 393/5 were issued in sheets of 60 of each value (arranged *tête-bêche*), and also in sheets containing the three values *se-tenant*, thus forming a triptych of the Nativity.

163 Queen Elizabeth II and Arms of Malta

(Des E. Cremona. Photo Harrison)

1967 (13 Nov). *Royal Visit. T* **163** *and similar designs. W* **105** *(sideways on 2d., 3s.). P* 14 × 15 *(4d.) or* 15 × 14 *(others).*
396 2d. multicoloured 10 10
a. Cream omitted* .. ..
397 4d. black, brown-purple and gold 10 10
398 3s. multicoloured 20 25
396/8 .. .. *Set of* 3 30 30
Designs: *Vert*—4d. Queen in Robes of Order of St. Michael and St. George. *Horiz*—3s. Queen and outline of Malta.
*This affects the Queen's face.

166 Human Rights Emblem and People **167**

(Des E. Cremona. Photo Harrison)

1968 (2 May). *Human Rights Year. W* **105**. *P* 12½ *(6d.) or* 14½ *(others).*
399 **166** 2d. multicoloured 10 10
400 **167** 6d. multicoloured 10 10
401 – 2s. multicoloured 10 10
399/401 .. .. *Set of* 3 15 10
The design of the 2s. value is a reverse of Type **166.**

169 Fair "Products"

(Des E. Cremona. Photo Harrison)

1968 (1 June). *Malta International Trade Fair. W* **105** *(sideways). P* 14½ × 14.
402 **169** 4d. multicoloured 10 10
403 8d. multicoloured 10 10
404 3s. multicoloured 15 10
402/4 .. .. *Set of* 3 20 15

170 Arms of the Order of St. John and La Valette **171** "La Valette" (A. de Favray)

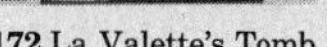

172 La Valette's Tomb **173** Angels and Scroll bearing Date of Death

(Des E. Cremona. Photo Govt Printer, Israel)

1968 (1 Aug). *Fourth Death Centenary of Grand Master La Valette. W* **105** *(upright, 1s. 6d.; sideways, others). P* 13 × 14 *(1d., 1s. 6d.) or* 14 × 13 *(others).*
405 **170** 1d. multicoloured 10 10
406 **171** 8d. multicoloured 15 10
407 **172** 1s. 6d. multicoloured 15 10
408 **173** 2s. 6d. multicoloured 20 20
405/8 .. .. *Set of* 4 45 30

174 Star of Bethlehem and Angel waking Shepherds **177** "Agriculture"

(Des E. Cremona. Photo Harrison)

1968 (3 Oct). *Christmas. T* **174** *and similar shaped designs. Multicoloured.* W **105** *(sideways). P* 14½ × 14.

409	1d. Type **174**		10	10
410	8d. Mary and Joseph with shepherd watching over cradle		10	10
411	1s. 4d. Three Wise Men and Star of Bethlehem		10	10
409/11		*Set of* 3	15	15

The shortest side at top and the long side at the bottom both gauge 14½, the other three sides are 14. Nos. 409/11 were issued in sheets of 60 arranged in ten strips of six, alternately upright and inverted.

(Des E. Cremona. Photo Enschedé)

1968 (21 Oct). *Sixth Food and Agricultural Organization Regional Conference for Europe. T* **177** *and similar vert designs. Multicoloured.* W **105** *(sideways). P* 12½ × 12.

412	4d. Type **177**		10	10
413	1s. F.A.O. emblem and coin		10	10
414	2s. 6d. "Agriculture" sowing seeds		10	15
412/14		*Set of* 3	15	20

180 Mahatma Gandhi

181 I.L.O. Emblem

(Des E. Cremona. Photo Enschedé)

1969 (24 Mar). *Birth Centenary of Mahatma Gandhi.* W **105**. *P* 12 × 12½.

415	**180**	1s. 6d. blackish brown, black and gold	15	10

(Des E. Cremona. Photo Harrison)

1969 (26 May). *50th Anniv of International Labour Organization.* W **105** *(sideways). P* 13½ × 14½.

416	**181**	2d. indigo, gold and turquoise	10	10
417		6d. sepia, gold and chestnut	10	10

182 Robert Samut

(Des E. Cremona. Photo D.L.R.)

1969 (26 July). *Birth Centenary of Robert Samut (composer of Maltese National Anthem).* W **105** *(sideways). P* 13.

418	**182**	2d. multicoloured	10	10

183 Dove of Peace, U.N. Emblem and Sea-Bed

(Des E. Cremona. Photo D.L.R.)

1969 (26 July). *United Nations Resolution on Oceanic Resources.* W **105** *(sideways). P* 13.

419	**183**	5d. multicoloured	10	10

184 "Swallows" returning to Malta

(Des E. Cremona. Photo D.L.R.)

1969 (26 July). *Maltese Migrants' Convention.* W **105** *(sideways). P* 13.

420	**184**	10d. black, gold and yellow-olive	10	10

185 University Arms and Grand Master de Fonseca (founder)

(Des E. Cremona. Photo D.L.R.)

1969 (26 July). *Bicentenary of University of Malta.* W **105** *(sideways). P* 13.

421	**185**	2s. multicoloured	10	20

186 1919 Monument

187 Flag of Malta and Birds

(Des E. Cremona. Photo Enschedé)

1969 (20 Sept). *Fifth Anniv of Independence. T* **186/7** *and similar designs.* W **105** *(upright on 5d., sideways others). P* 13½ × 12½ *(2d.),* 12 × 12½ *(5d.), or* 12½ × 12 *(others).*

422	2d. multicoloured		10	10
423	5d. black, red and gold		10	10
424	10d. black, turquoise-blue and gold		10	10
425	1s. 6d. multicoloured		15	30
426	2s. 6d. black, olive-brown and gold		20	35
422/6		*Set of* 5	40	75

Designs:—*Vert as T* **187**—10d. "Tourism"; 1s. 6d. U.N. and Council of Europe emblems; 2s. 6d. "Trade and Industry".

191 Peasants playing Tambourine and Bagpipes

(Des E. Cremona. Litho D.L.R.)

1969 (8 Nov). *Christmas. Children's Welfare Fund. T* **191** *and similar horiz designs. Multicoloured.* W **105** *(sideways). P* 12½.

427	1d. + 1d. Type **191**		10	20
	a. Gold omitted		90·00	
	b. Horiz strip of 3. Nos. 427/9		30	75
428	5d. + 1d. Angels playing trumpet and harp		15	20
429	1s. 6d. + 3d. Choir boys singing		15	45
427/9		*Set of* 3	30	75

Nos. 427/9 were issued in sheets of 60 of each value, and also in sheets containing the three values *se-tenant*, thus forming the triptych No. 427b.

194 "The Beheading of St. John" (Caravaggio)

(Des E. Cremona. Photo Enschedé)

1970 (21 Mar). *13th Council of Europe Art Exhibition. T* **194** *and similar multicoloured designs.* W **105** *(upright, 10d., 2s.; sideways, others). P* 14 × 13 *(1d., 8d.),* 12 *(10d., 2s.) or* 13 × 13½ *(others).*

430	1d. Type **194**		10	10
431	2d. "St. John the Baptist" (M. Preti) (45 × 32 *mm*)		10	10
432	5d. Interior of St. John's Co-Cathedral, Valletta (39 × 39 *mm*)		10	10
433	6d. "Allegory of the Order" (Neapolitan School) (45 × 32 *mm*)		10	10
434	8d. "St. Jerome" (Caravaggio)		15	20
435	10d. Articles from the Order of St. John in Malta (63 × 21 *mm*)		15	10
436	1s. 6d. "The Blessed Gerard receiving Godfrey de Bouillon" (A. de Favray) (45 × 35 *mm*)		15	25
437	2s. Cape and Stolone (16th-century) (63 × 21 *mm*)		20	35
430/37		*Set of* 8	70	85

202 Artist's Impression of Fujiyama

(Des E. Cremona. Photo D.L.R.)

1970 (29 May). *World Fair, Osaka.* W **105** *(sideways). P* 15.

438	**202**	2d. multicoloured	10	10
439		5d. multicoloured	10	10
440		3s. multicoloured	15	15
438/40		*Set of* 3	15	15

203 "Peace and Justice"

204 Carol-Singers, Church and Star

(Des J. Casha. Litho Harrison)

1970 (30 Sept). *25th Anniv of United Nations.* W **105**. *P* 14 × 14½.

441	**203**	2d. multicoloured	10	10
442		5d. multicoloured	10	10
443		2s. 6d. multicoloured	15	15
441/3		*Set of* 3	15	15

(Des E. Cremona. Photo Govt Printer, Israel)

1970 (7 Nov). *Christmas. T* **204** *and similar vert designs. Multicoloured.* W **105** *(sideways). P* 14 × 13.

444	1d. + ½d. Type **204**		10	10
445	10d. + 2d. Church, star and angels with Infant		10	20
446	1s. 6d. + 3d. Church, star and nativity scene		15	35
444/6		*Set of* 3	20	60

207 Books and Quill

208 Dun Karm, Books, Pens and Lamp

(Des H. Alden (1s. 6d.), A. Agius (2s.). Litho D.L.R.)

1971 (20 Mar). *Literary Anniversaries. Death Bicentenary* (1970) *of De Soldanis (historian)* (1s. 6d.) *and Birth Centenary of Dun Karm (poet)* (2s.). W **105** *(sideways). P* 13 × 13½.

447	**207**	1s. 6d. multicoloured	10	10
448	**208**	2s. multicoloured	10	15

209 Europa "Chain"

(Des H. Haflidason; adapted E. Cremona. Litho Harrison)

1971 (3 May). *Europa.* W **105** *(sideways). P* 13½ × 14½.

449	**209**	2d. orange, black and yellow-olive	10	10
450		5d. orange, black and vermilion	10	10
451		1s. 6d. orange, black and slate	45	90
449/51		*Set of* 3	55	90

210 "St. Joseph, Patron of the Universal Church" (G. Cali)

211 *Centaurea spathulata*

(Des E. Cremona. Litho D.L.R.)

1971 (24 July). *Centenary of Proclamation of St. Joseph as Patron Saint of Catholic Church, and 50th Anniv of the Coronation of the Statue of "Our Lady of Victories". T* **210** *and similar horiz design. Multicoloured.* W **105** *(sideways). P* 13 × 13½.

452	2d. Type **210**		10	10
453	5d. Statue of "Our Lady of Victories" and galley		10	10
454	10d. Type **210**		10	10
455	1s. 6d. As 5d.		20	40
452/5		*Set of* 4	30	50

(Des Reno Psaila. Litho Harrison)

1971 (18 Sept). *National Plant and Bird of Malta. T* **211** *and similar horiz design. Multicoloured.* W **105** *(sideways on 5d. and 10d.). P* 14½ × 14.

456	2d. Type **211**		10	10
457	5d. Blue Rock Thrush		10	10
458	10d. As 5d.		25	15
459	1s. 6d. Type **211**		25	1·25
456/9		*Set of* 4	60	1·40

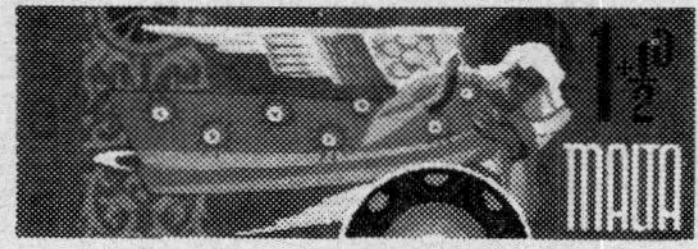

212 Angel

(Des E. Cremona. Litho Format)

1971 (8 Nov). *Christmas. T* **212** *and similar horiz designs. Multicoloured. W* **105** *(sideways). P* 13½ × 14.

No.	Description	Unused	Used
460	1d. + ½d. Type **212**	10	10
461	10d. + 2d. Mary and the Child Jesus.. ..	15	20
462	1s. 6d. + 3d. Joseph lying awake	20	30
460/2	.. .. *Set of* 3	35	55
MS463	131 × 113 mm. Nos. 460/2. P 15	75	2·50

213 Heart and W.H.O. Emblem **214** Maltese Cross

(Des A. Agius. Litho Format)

1972 (20 Mar). *World Health Day. W* **105**. *P* 13½ × 14.

No.	Description	Unused	Used
464	**213** 2d. multicoloured	10	10
465	10d. multicoloured	15	10
466	2s. 6d. multicoloured	40	80
464/6	.. .. *Set of* 3	55	85

(New Currency. 10 mils = 1 cent; 100 cents = 1 Maltese pound)

(Des G. Pace. Litho Format)

1972 (16 May). *Decimal Currency. T* **214** *and similar vert designs showing decimal coins. Multicoloured. W* **105**. *P* 14 *(2 m., 3 m., 2 c.),* 14½ × 14 *(5 m., 1 c., 5 c.) or* 13½ *(10 c., 50 c.).*

No.	Description	Unused	Used
467	2 m. Type **214**	10	10
468	3 m. Bee on honeycomb	10	10
469	5 m. Earthen lampstand	10	10
470	1 c. George Cross	10	10
471	2 c. Classical head	10	10
472	5 c. Ritual altar	10	10
473	10 c. Grandmaster's galley	20	10
474	50 c. Great Siege Monument	1·25	1·25
467/74	.. .. *Set of* 8	1·60	1·25

Sizes:—2 m., 3 m. and 2 c. as T **214**; 5 m., 1 c. and 5 c. 22 × 27 mm; 10 c. and 50 c. 27 × 35 mm.

No. 467 exists imperforate from stock dispersed by the liquidator of Format International Security Printers Ltd.

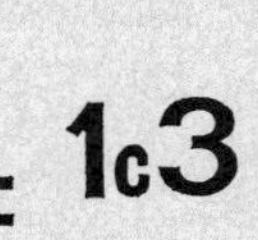

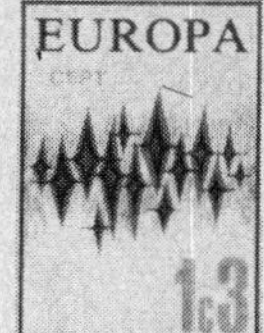

(215) **216** "Communications"

1972 (30 Sept). *Nos.* 337*a*, 339 *and* 341 *surch as T* **215**, *by Govt. Printing Works, Valletta.*

No.	Description	Unused	Used
475	1 c. 3 on 5d. multicoloured	10	10
476	3 c. on 8d. multicoloured	15	10
	a. Surch inverted	55·00	
	b. Gold (frame) omitted	60·00	
477	5 c. on 1s. 3d. multicoloured	15	20
	a. Surch double	55·00	
	b. Surch inverted	30·00	
	c. Gold (centre) omitted	45·00	
475/7	.. .. *Set of* 3	30	35

PRINTERS. All stamps from No. 478 onwards were printed in lithography by Printex Ltd, Malta.

(Des P. Huovinen; adapted G. Pace)

1972 (11 Nov). *Europa. W* **105** *(sideways). P* 13.

No.	Description	Unused	Used
478	**216** 1 c. 3, multicoloured	10	10
479	3 c. multicoloured	10	10
480	5 c. multicoloured	15	35
481	7 c. 5, multicoloured	20	75
478/81	.. .. *Set of* 4	50	1·10

Nos. 478/81 were each printed in sheets including two *se-tenant* stamp-size labels in the second and third positions of the top row.

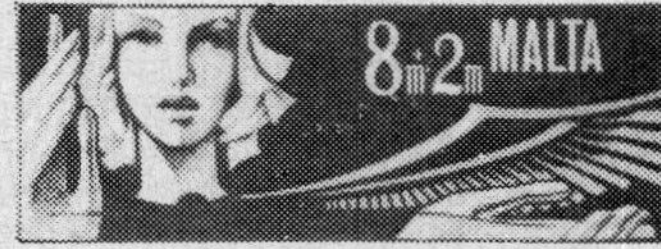

217 Angel

(Des E. Cremona)

1972 (9 Dec). *Christmas. T* **217** *and similar horiz designs. W* **105** *(sideways). P* 13½.

No.	Description	Unused	Used
482	8 m. + 2 m. dull sepia, brownish grey & gold	10	10
483	3 c. + 1 c. plum, lavender and gold ..	15	40
484	7 c. 5 + 1 c. 5, indigo, azure and gold ..	20	50
482/4	.. .. *Set of* 3	35	85
MS485	137×113 mm. Nos. 482/4	2·25	4·25

Designs:—No. 483, Angel with tambourine; No. 484, Singing angel.

See also Nos. 507/10.

218 Archaeology **219** Europa "Posthorn"

(Des E. Cremona)

1973 (31 Mar)–**76**. *T* **218** *and similar designs. Multicoloured. W* **105** *(sideways). P* 13½ × 14 *(Nos. 500/a) or* 13½ *(others).*

No.	Description	Unused	Used
486	2 m. Type **218**	10	10
487	4 m. History	10	10
	a. Gold (inscr and decoration) omitted ..	75·00	
	b. Imperf (pair)	£325	
488	5 m. Folklore	10	10
489	8 m. Industry	10	10
490	1 c. Fishing industry	10	10
491	1 c. 3, Pottery	10	10
492	2 c. Agriculture	10	10
493	3 c. Sport	10	10
494	4 c. Yacht marina	15	10
495	5 c. Fiesta	15	10
496	7 c. 5, Regatta	25	10
497	10 c. Voluntary service	25	10
498	50 c. Education	75	1·00
499	£1 Religion	2·00	2·75
500	£2 Coat of arms *(horiz)*	12·00	17·00
	a. Gold omitted		
500*b*	£2 National Emblem *(horiz)* (28.1.76)	8·00	14·00
486/500*b*	.. .. .. *Set of* 16	21·00	32·00

Nos. 500/*b* are larger, 32 × 27 mm.

(Des L. Anisdahl; adapted G. Pace)

1973 (2 June). *Europa. W* **105**. *P* 14.

No.	Description	Unused	Used
501	**219** 3 c. multicoloured	15	10
502	5 c. multicoloured	15	35
503	7 c. 5, multicoloured	25	60
501/3	.. .. *Set of* 3	50	95

Nos. 501/3 were each printed in sheets containing two *se-tenant* stamp-size labels.

220 Emblem, and Woman holding Corn **221** Girolamo Cassar (architect)

(Des H. Alden)

1973 (6 Oct). *Anniversaries. T* **220** *and similar vert designs showing emblem and allegorical figures. W* **105** *(sideways). P* 13½.

No.	Description	Unused	Used
504	1 c. 3, multicoloured	10	10
505	7 c. 5, multicoloured	25	40
506	10 c. multicoloured	30	50
504/6	.. .. *Set of* 3	55	85

Anniversaries:—1 c. 3, Tenth Anniv of World Food Programme; 7 c. 5, 25th Anniv of W.H.O.; 10 c. 25th Anniv of Universal Declaration of Human Rights.

(Des E. Cremona)

1973 (10 Nov). *Christmas. Horiz designs as T* **217**. *Multicoloured. W* **105** *(sideways). P* 13½.

No.	Description	Unused	Used
507	8 m. + 2 m. Angels and organ pipes	15	10
508	3 c. + 1 c. Madonna and Child	25	55
509	7 c. 5 + 1 c. 5, Buildings and Star ..	45	1·00
507/9	.. .. *Set of* 3	75	1·50
MS510	137 × 112 mm. Nos. 507/9	5·50	7·00

(Des E. Cremona)

1974 (12 Jan). *Prominent Maltese. T* **221** *and similar vert designs. W* **105**. *P* 14.

No.	Description	Unused	Used
511	1 c. 3, dull myrtle-grn, dull grey-grn & gold..	10	10
512	3 c. deep turquoise, grey-blue and gold ..	15	10
513	5 c. dull sepia, deep slate-green and gold ..	20	15
514	7 c. 5, slate-blue, light slate-blue and gold ..	20	30
515	10 c. purple, dull purple and gold	20	40
511/15	.. .. *Set of* 5	70	85

Designs:—3 c. Giuseppe Barth (ophthalmologist); 5 c. Nicolo' Isouard (composer); 7 c. 5, John Borg (botanist); 10 c. Antonio Sciortino (sculptor).

222 "Air Malta" Emblem

(Des E. Cremona)

1974 (30 Mar). *Air. T* **222** *and similar horiz design. Multicoloured. W* **105** *(sideways). P* 13½.

No.	Description	Unused	Used
516	3 c. Type **222**	15	10
517	4 c. Boeing 720B	15	10
518	5 c. Type **222**	20	10
519	7 c. 5, As 4 c.	25	10
520	20 c. Type **222**	70	60
521	25 c. As 4 c.	70	60
522	35 c. Type **222**	1·00	1·40
516/22	.. .. *Set of* 7	2·75	2·50

223 Prehistoric Sculpture

(Des E. Cremona)

1974 (13 July). *Europa. T* **223** *and similar designs. W* **105** *(sideways on Nos.* 523 *and* 525*). P* 13½.

No.	Description	Unused	Used
523	1 c. 3, slate-blue, grey-black and gold ..	15	10
524	3 c. light bistre-brown, grey-black and gold	20	15
525	5 c. purple, grey-black and gold	25	50
526	7 c. 5, dull green, grey-black and gold ..	35	1·00
523/6	.. .. *Set of* 4	85	1·60

Designs: *Vert*—3 c. Old Cathedral Door, Mdina; 7 c. 5, "Vetlina" (sculpture by A. Sciortino). *Horiz*—5 c. Silver Monstrance.

Nos. 523/6 were each printed in sheets including two *se-tenant* stamp-size labels.

224 Heinrich von Stephan (founder) and Land Transport **225** Decorative Star and Nativity Scene

(Des S. and G. Sullivan)

1974 (20 Sept). *Centenary of Universal Postal Union. T* **224** *and similar horiz designs. W* **105**. *P* 13½ × 14.

No.	Description	Unused	Used
527	1 c. 3, blue-green, lt violet-blue & yell-orge ..	30	10
528	5 c. brown, dull vermilion and yellow-green	30	10
529	7 c. 5, dp dull blue, lt violet-blue & yell-grn ..	35	20
530	50 c. purple, dull vermilion and yellow-orange	1·00	1·25
527/30	.. .. *Set of* 4	1·75	1·50
MS531	126 × 91 mm. Nos. 527/30	4·50	6·50

Designs (each containing portrait as T **224**):—5 c. *Washington* (paddle-steamer) and *Royal Viking Star* (liner); 7 c. 5, Balloon and Boeing 747-100; 50 c. U.P.U. Buildings, 1874 and 1974.

(Des E. Cremona)

1974 (22 Nov). *Christmas. T* **225** *and similar vert designs, each with decorative star. Multicoloured. W* **105** *(sideways). P* 14.

No.	Description	Unused	Used
532	8 m. + 2 m. Type **225**	10	10
533	3 c. + 1 c. "Shepherds"	15	20
534	5 c. + 1 c. "Shepherds with gifts"	20	35
535	7 c. 5 + 1 c. 5, "The Magi"	30	40
532/5	.. .. *Set of* 4	65	95

REPUBLIC

226 Swearing-in of Prime Minister

(Des E. Cremona)

1975 (31 Mar). *Inauguration of Republic. T* **226** *and similar horiz designs. W* **105** *(sideways). P* 14.

No.	Description	Unused	Used
536	1 c. 3, multicoloured	10	10
537	5 c. rose-red and grey-black	20	10
538	25 c. multicoloured	60	1·00
536/8	.. .. *Set of* 3	75	1·10

Designs:—5 c. National flag; 25 c. Minister of Justice, President and Prime Minister.

227 Mother and Child ("Family Life")

(Des D. Friggieri)

1975 (30 May). *International Women's Year. T* **227** *and similar horiz design. W* **105**. *P* 13½ × 14.

No.	Description	Unused	Used
539	**227** 1 c. 3, light violet and gold	15	10
540	– 3 c. light blue and gold	20	10
541	**227** 5 c. dull olive-sepia and gold	40	20
542	– 20 c. chestnut and gold	1·50	3·00
539/42	.. .. *Set of* 4	2·00	3·00

Design:—3 c., 20 c. Office secretary ("Public Life").

228 "Allegory of Malta" (Francesco de Mura)

(Des E. Cremona)

1975 (15 July). *Europa. T* **228** *and similar horiz design. Multicoloured. W* **105**. *P* 14 × 13½.
543 5 c. Type **228** 30 10
544 15 c. "Judith and Holofernes" (Valentin de Boulogne) 50 75

The 15 c. is a smaller design than the 5 c. (47 × 23 mm), though the perforated area is the same.

Nos. 543/4 were each printed in sheets including two *se-tenant* stamp-size labels.

229 Plan of Ggantija Temple

(Des R. England)

1975 (16 Sept). *European Architectural Heritage Year. T* **229** *and similar horiz designs. W* **105** *(sideways). P* 13½.
545 1 c. 3, brownish black and light orange-red 10 10
546 3 c. dull purple, lt orange-red & blackish brn 20 10
547 5 c. blackish brown and light orange-red 40 35
548 25 c. dull grey-olive, light orange-red and brownish black 1·40 3·25
545/8 *Set of* 4 1·75 3·50

Designs:—3 c. Mdina skyline; 5 c. View of Victoria, Gozo; 25 c. Silhouette of Fort St. Angelo.

230 Farm Animals

231 "The Right to Work"

(Des E. Cremona)

1975 (4 Nov). *Christmas. T* **230** *and similar multicoloured designs. W* **105** *(sideways). P* 13½.
549 8 m. + 2 m. Type **230** 30 25
a. Horiz strip of 3. Nos. 549/51 1·60 4·00
550 3 c. + 1 c. Nativity scene (50×23 *mm*) 60 75
551 7 c. 5 + 1 c. 5, Approach of the Magi 90 1·40
549/51 *Set of* 3 1·60 2·25

Nos. 549/51 were issued in sheets of 50 of each value, and also in sheets containing the three values horizontally *se-tenant*, thus forming the triptych No. 549a which is a composite design of "The Nativity" by Master Alberto.

(Des A. de Giovanni)

1975 (12 Dec). *First Anniv of Republic. T* **231** *and similar vert designs. W* **105**. *P* 14.
552 1 c. 3, multicoloured 10 10
553 5 c. multicoloured 20 10
554 25 c. deep rose, light steel-blue and black 70 1·10
552/4 *Set of* 3 80 1·10

Designs:—5 c. "Safeguarding the Environment"; 25 c. National Flag.

232 "Festa Tar-Rahal"

233 Water Polo

(Des M. Camilleri)

1976 (26 Feb). *Maltese Folklore. T* **232** *and similar multicoloured designs. W* **105** *(sideways on* 5 c. *and* 7 c. 5*). P* 14.
555 1 c. 3, Type **232** 10 10
556 5 c. "L-Imnarja" (*horiz*) 15 10
557 7 c. 5, "Il-Karnival" (*horiz*) 35 70
558 10 c. "Il-Gimgha L-Kbira" 55 1·40
555/8 *Set of* 4 1·00 2·00

(Des H. Alden)

1976 (28 Apr). *Olympic Games, Montreal. T* **233** *and similar horiz designs. Multicoloured. W* **105**. *P* 13½ × 14.
559 1 c. 7, Type **233** 10 10
560 5 c. Sailing 25 10
561 30 c. Athletics 85 1·50
559/61 *Set of* 3 1·10 1·50

234 Lace-making

(Des F. Portelli)

1976 (8 July). *Europa. T* **234** *and similar horiz design. Multicoloured. W* **105** *(sideways). P* 13½ × 14.
562 7 c. Type **234** 20 35
563 15 c. Stone carving 25 60

Nos. 562/3 were each printed in sheets including two *se-tenant* stamp-size labels.

235 Nicola Cotoner

(Des E. Cremona)

1976 (14 Sept). *300th Anniv of School of Anatomy and Surgery. T* **235** *and similar horiz designs. Multicoloured. W* **105** *(sideways). P* 13½.
564 2 c. Type **235** 10 10
565 5 c. Arm 10 10
566 7 c. Giuseppe Zammit 15 10
567 1 c. Sacra Infermeria 25 65
564/7 *Set of* 4 50 75

236 St. John the Baptist and St. Michael

237 Jean de la Valette's Armour

1c7

(238)

(Des E. Cremona)

1976 (23 Nov). *Christmas. Designs showing portions of "Madonna and Saints" by Domenico di Michelino. Multicoloured. W* **105** *(sideways on No.* 571*). P* 13½ × 14 *(No.* 571*) or* 13½ *(others).*
568 1 c. + 5 m. Type **236** 15 20
569 5 c. + 1 c. Madonna and Child 20 60
570 7 c. + 1 c. 5, St. Christopher and St. Nicholas 30 80
571 10 c. + 2 c. Complete painting (32 × 27 *mm*) 40 1·25
568/71 *Set of* 4 95 2·50

(Des J. Briffa)

1977 (20 Jan). *Suits of Armour. T* **237** *and similar vert designs. Multicoloured. W* **105**. *P* 13½.
572 2 c. Type **237** 10 10
573 7 c. Aloph de Wignacourt's armour 20 10
574 11 c. Jean Jacques de Verdelin's armour 25 50
572/4 *Set of* 3 45 60

1977 (24 Mar). *No.* 336 *surch with T* **238** *by Govt Printing Press, Malta.*
575 **116** 1 c. 7 on 4d. multicoloured 25 25
a. "KNIGHTS OF MALTA" (silver) omitted 70·00

239 "Annunciation"

240 Map and Radio Aerial

(Des E. Cremona)

1977 (30 Mar). *400th Birth Anniversary of Rubens. Flemish tapestries (1st series) showing his paintings as T* **239**. *Multicoloured. W* **105** *(sideways). P* 14.
576 2 c. Type **239** 10 10
577 7 c. "Four Evangelists" 25 10
578 11 c. "Nativity" 45 45
579 20 c. "Adoration of the Magi" 80 1·00
576/9 *Set of* 4 1·40 1·50

See also Nos. 592/5, 615/18 and 638/40.

(Des H. Borg)

1977 (17 May). *World Telecommunication Day. T* **240** *and similar design. W* **105** *(sideways on* 1 *and* 6 c.*). P* 14 × 13½ *(*1 *and* 6 c.*) or* 13½ × 14 *(others).*
580 **240** 1 c. black, green and vermilion 10 10
581 6 c. black, grey-blue and vermilion 20 10
582 – 8 c. black, chestnut and vermilion 25 10
583 – 17 c. black, dull mauve and vermilion 40 40
580/3 *Set of* 4 80 55

Design: *Horiz*—8 and 17 c. Map, aerial and aeroplane tail-fin.

241 Ta' L-Isperanza

242 "Aid to Handicapped Workers" (detail from Workers' Monument)

(Des G. French)

1977 (5 July). *Europa. T* **241** *and similar horiz design. Multicoloured. W* **105** *(sideways). P* 13½.
584 7 c. Type **241** 30 15
585 20 c. Is-Salini 35 1·00

Nos. 584/5 were each printed in sheets including two *se-tenant* stamp-size labels.

(Des A. Agius)

1977 (12 Oct). *Maltese Worker Commemoration. T* **242** *and similar designs. W* **105** *(sideways on* 20 c.*). P* 13½.
586 2 c. orange-brown and light brown 10 10
587 7 c. chestnut and brown 15 10
588 20 c. multicoloured 40 60
586/8 *Set of* 3 55 60

Designs: *Vert*—7 c. "Stoneworker, modern industry and shipbuilding" (monument detail). *Horiz*—20 c. "Mother with Dead Son" and Service Medal.

243 The Shepherds

244 "Young Lady on Horseback and Trooper"

(Des E. Cremona)

1977 (16 Nov). *Christmas. T* **243** *and similar horiz designs. Multicoloured. W* **105** *(sideways). P* 13½×14.
589 1 c. + 5 m. Type **243** 10 20
a. Horiz strip of 3. Nos. 589/91 40
590 7 c. + 1 c. The Nativity 15 30
591 11 c. + 1 c. 5, Flight into Egypt 20 45
589/91 *Set of* 3 40 85

Nos. 589/91 were issued in sheets of 50 of each value, and also in sheets containing the three values *se-tenant*, thus forming the triptych No. 589a.

(Des E. Cremona)

1978 (26 Jan). *Flemish Tapestries (2nd series). Horiz designs similar to T* **239**. *Multicoloured. W* **105** *(sideways). P* 14.
592 2 c. "The Entry into Jerusalem" (artist unknown) 10 10
593 7 c. "The Last Supper" (after Poussin) 25 10
594 11 c. "The Raising of the Cross" (after Rubens) 30 25
595 25 c. "The Resurrection" (after Rubens) 70 80
592/5 *Set of* 4 1·25 1·10

(Des A. Camilleri)

1978 (7 Mar). *450th Death Anniv of Albrecht Dürer. T* **244** *and similar vert designs. W* **105**. *P* 14.
596 1 c. 7, black, vermilion and deep blue 10 10
597 8 c. black, vermilion and slate 15 10
598 17 c. black, vermilion and deep slate 40 45
a. Vermilion (monogram) omitted 75·00
596/8 *Set of* 3 55 55

Designs:—8 c. "The Bag-piper"; 17 c. "The Virgin and Child with a Monkey".

PRICES OF SETS

Set prices are given for many issues, generally those containing three stamps or more. Definitive sets include one of each value or major colour change, but do not cover different perforations, die types or minor shades. Where a choice is possible the set prices are based on the cheapest versions of the stamps included in the listings.

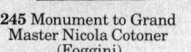

245 Monument to Grand Master Nicola Cotoner (Foggini)

246 Goalkeeper

(Des E. Cremona)

1978 (26 Apr). *Europa. Monuments. T* **245** *and similar vert design. Multicoloured. W* **105**. *P* 14 × 13½.

599 7 c. Type **245** 15 10
600 25 c. Monument to Grand Master Ramon Perellos (Mazzuoli) 35 90

Nos. 599/600 were each printed in sheets including two *se-tenant* stamp-size labels.

(Des A. de Giovanni)

1978 (6 June). *World Cup Football Championship, Argentina. T* **246** *and similar vert designs. Multicoloured. W* **105** *(sideways). P* 14 × 13½.

601 2 c. Type **246** 10 10
602 11 c. Players heading ball 15 10
603 15 c. Tackling 25 35
601/3 .. .. *Set of* 3 45 45
MS604 125 × 90 mm. Nos. 601/3 .. .. .. 1·75 2·75

247 Boeing 707 over Megalithic Temple

(Des R. Caruana)

1978 (3 Oct). *Air. Horiz designs as T* **247**. *Multicoloured. W* **105** *(sideways). P* 13½.

605 5 c. Type **247** 20 10
606 7 c. Air Malta Boeing 720B 20 10
607 11 c. Boeing 747 taking off from Luqa Airport 35 10
608 17 c. Type **247** 45 30
609 20 c. As 7 c. 60 40
610 75 c. As 11 c. .. .. 1·75 2·75
605/10 .. .. *Set of* 6 3·25 3·25

248 Folk Musicians and Village Church

249 Luzzu and Aircraft Carrier

(Des E. Cremona)

1978 (9 Nov). *Christmas. T* **248** *and similar multicoloured designs. W* **105** *(sideways). P* 13½ *(11 c.) or* 14 *(others)*.

611 1 c. + 5 m. Type **248** 10 10
612 5 c. + 1 c. Choir of Angels 15 20
613 7 c. + 1 c. 5, Carol singers 20 25
614 11 c. + 3 c. Folk musicians, church, angels and carol singers (58 × 23 *mm*) 25 35
611/14 .. .. *Set of* 4 60 80

The 1, 5 and 7 c. values depict details of the complete design shown on the 11 c. value.

(Des E. Cremona)

1979 (24 Jan). *Flemish Tapestries (3rd series). Horiz designs as T* **239** *showing paintings by Rubens. Multicoloured. W* **105** *(sideways). P* 14.

615 2 c. "The Triumph of the Catholic Church" .. 10 10
616 7 c. "The Triumph of Charity" 20 10
617 11 c. "The Triumph of Faith" 30 25
618 25 c. "The Triumph of Truth" 95 80
615/18 .. .. *Set of* 4 1·40 1·10

(Des E. Cremona)

1979 (31 Mar). *End of Military Facilities Agreement. T* **249** *and similar vert designs. Multicoloured. W* **105** *(sideways). P* 13½.

619 2 c. Type **249** 10 10
620 5 c. Raising the flag ceremony 10 10
621 7 c. Departing soldier and olive sprig .. 15 10
622 8 c. Type **249** 40 40
623 17 c. As 5 c. 55 60
624 20 c. As 7 c. 55 60
619/24 .. .. *Set of* 6 1·60 1·60

250 Speronara (fishing boat) and Tail of Air Malta Airliner

251 Children on Globe

(Des E. Cremona)

1979 (9 May). *Europa. Communications. T* **250** *and similar vert design. Multicoloured. W* **105** *(sideways). P* 14.

625 7 c. Type **250** 20 10
626 25 c. Coastal watch tower and radio link towers 40 50

Nos. 625/6 were each printed in sheets including two *se-tenant* stamp-size labels.

(Des A. Bonnici (2 c.), A. Pisani (7 c.), M. French (11 c.))

1979 (13 June). *International Year of the Child. T* **251** *and similar multicoloured designs. W* **105** *(sideways). P* 14 × 13½ *(2 c.) or* 14 *(others)*.

627 2 c. Type **251** 10 10
628 7 c. Children flying kites (27 × 33 *mm*) .. 15 10
629 11 c. Children in circle (27 × 33 *mm*). 20 35
627/9 .. .. *Set of* 3 35 45

252 Shells (*Gibbula nivosa*)

(Des R. Pitré)

1979 (10 Oct). *Marine Life. T* **252** *and similar horiz designs. Multicoloured. W* **105**. *P* 13½.

630 2 c. Type **252** 10 10
631 5 c. Loggerhead Turtle (*Garetta garetta*) 20 10
632 7 c. Dolphin (fish) (*Coryphaena hippurus*) 25 10
633 25 c. Noble Pen Shell (*Pinna nobilis*) .. 90 1·25
630/3 .. .. *Set of* 4 1·25 1·25

253 "The Nativity" (detail)

(Des E. Cremona)

1979 (14 Nov). *Christmas. Paintings by G. Cali. T* **253** *and similar horiz designs. Multicoloured. W* **105**. *P* 14 × 13½.

634 1 c. + 5 m. Type **253** 10 10
635 5 c. + 1 c. "The Flight into Egypt" (detail) .. 10 15
636 7 c. + 1 c. 5, "The Nativity" 15 20
637 11 c. + 3 c. "The Flight into Egypt" 25 50
634/7 .. .. *Set of* 4 50 85

(Des E. Cremona)

1980 (30 Jan). *Flemish Tapestries (4th series). Horiz designs as T* **239** *taken from paintings. Multicoloured. W* **105** *(sideways). P* 14.

638 2 c. "The Institution of Corpus Domini" (Rubens) 10 10
639 8 c. "The Destruction of Idolatry" (Rubens) .. 20 20
MS640 114 × 86 mm. 50 c. "Grand Master Perellos with St. Jude and St. Simon" (unknown Maltese artist) (*vert*) .. .. 80 1·60

254 Hal Saflieni Hypogeum, Paola

255 Dun Gorg Preca

1980 (15 Feb). *International Restoration of Maltese Monuments Campaign. T* **254** *and similar multicoloured designs. W* **105** *(sideways on* 8 *and* 12 *c.). P* 14.

641 2 c. 5, Type **254** 10 15
642 6 c. Vilhena Palace, Mdina 25 20
643 8 c. Victoria Citadel, Gozo (*horiz*) 30 40
644 12 c. Fort St. Elmo, Valletta (*horiz*) 40 60
641/4 .. .. *Set of* 4 95 1·25

(Des R. Pitré)

1980 (12 Apr). *Birth Centenary of Dun Gorg Preca (founder of Society of Christian Doctrine). W* **105** *(sideways). P* 14 × 13½.

645 **255** 2 c. 5, black and grey 10 10

256 Ruzar Briffa (poet)

257 "Annunciation"

(Des V. Apap)

1980 (29 Apr). *Europa. Personalities. T* **256** *and similar horiz design. W* **105** *(sideways). P* 13½ × 14.

646 8 c. black, brown-ochre and bronze-green .. 20 10
647 30 c. brown, brown-olive and brown-lake .. 55 1·10

Design:—30 c. Nikiol Anton Vassalli (scholar and patriot).

Nos. 646/7 were each printed in sheets including two *se-tenant* stamp-size labels.

(Des R. Pitré)

1980 (7 Oct). *Christmas. Paintings by A. Inglott. T* **257** *and similar multicoloured designs. W* **105** *(sideways on* 12 *c.). P* 14 *(*12 *c.) or* 13½ *(others)*.

648 2 c. + 5 m. Type **257** 10 10
649 6 c. + 1 c. "Conception" 20 15
650 8 c. + 1 c. 5, "Nativity" 25 30
651 12 c. + 3 c. "Annunciation", "Conception" and "Nativity" (47 × 38 *mm*) 30 40
648/51 .. .. *Set of* 4 75 85

The paintings from the 2, 6 and 8 c. values are united to form the triptych on the 12 c. value.

258 Rook and Pawn

259 Barn Owl (*Tyto alba*)

(Des H. Borg)

1980 (20 Nov). *24th Chess Olympiad and International Chess Federation Congress, Malta. T* **258** *and similar multicoloured designs. W* **105** *(sideways on* 30 *c.) P* 14×13½ *(*30 *c.) or* 13½×14 *(others)*.

652 2 c. 5, Type **258** 25 10
653 8 c. Bishop and Pawn 85 15
654 30 c. King, Queen and Pawn (*vert*) .. 1·00 80
652/4 .. .. *Set of* 3 1·75 95

(Des M. Burlò)

1981 (20 Jan). *Birds. T* **259** *and similar vert designs. Multicoloured. W* **105** *(sideways). P* 13½.

655 3 c. Type **259** 30 15
656 8 c. Sardinian Warbler (*Sylvia melanocephala*) 50 20
657 12 c. Woodchat Shrike (*Lanius senator*) .. 60 70
658 23 c. British Storm Petrel (*Hydrobates pelagicus*) .. .. 1·10 1·50
655/8 .. .. *Set of* 4 2·25 2·25

260 Traditional Horse Race

261 Stylised "25"

(Des H. Borg)

1981 (28 Apr). *Europa. Folklore. T* **260** *and similar vert design. Multicoloured. W* **105** *(sideways). P* 14.

659 8 c. Type **260** 20 10
660 30 c. Attempting to retrieve flag from end of "gostra" (greasy pole) 40 65

The two values were each printed in sheets including two *se-tenant* stamp-size labels.

(Des A. de Giovanni)

1981 (12 June). *25th Maltese International Trade Fair. W* **105** *(sideways). P* 13½.

661 **261** 4 c. multicoloured 15 15
662 25 c. multicoloured 50 60

OMNIBUS ISSUES

Details, together with prices for complete sets, of the various Omnibus issues from the 1935 Silver Jubilee series to date are included in a special section following Zimbabwe at the end of Volume 2.

262 Disabled Artist at Work **263** Wheat Ear in Conical Flask

(Des A. Camilleri)

1981 (17 July). *International Year for Disabled Persons. T* **262** *and similar vert design. Multicoloured. W* **105** (*sideways*). *P* 13½.
663 3 c. Type **262** 20 10
664 35 c. Disabled child playing football 65 75

(Des R. Caruana)

1981 (16 Oct). *World Food Day. W* **105** (*sideways*). *P* 14.
665 **263** 8 c. multicoloured 15 15
666 23 c. multicoloured 60 50

264 Megalithic Building **265** Children and Nativity Scene

(Des F. Portelli)

1981 (31 Oct). *History of Maltese Industry. Horiz designs as T* **264**. *Multicoloured. W* **105**. *P* 14.
667 5 m. Type **264** 10 20
668 1 c. Cotton production 10 10
669 2 c. Early ship-building 60 10
670 3 c. Currency minting 30 10
671 5 c. "Art" 30 25
672 6 c. Fishing 80 25
673 7 c. Agriculture 30 70
674 8 c. Stone quarrying 45 35
675 10 c. Grape pressing 35 50
676 12 c. Modern ship-building . . . . 1·25 1·25
677 15 c. Energy . . . . 70 1·25
678 20 c. Telecommunications 70 75
679 25 c. "Industry" . . . . 90 1·60
680 50 c. Drilling for water . . . . 1·75 2·50
681 £1 Sea transport . . . . 6·00 7·00
682 £3 Air transport . . . . 11·00 17·00
667/82 . . . . *Set of* 16 23·00 30·00

(Des A. Bugeja)

1981 (18 Nov). *Christmas. T* **265** *and similar multicoloured designs. W* **105** (*sideways*). *P* 14.
683 2 c. + 1 c. Type **265** 15 10
684 8 c. + 2 c. Christmas Eve procession (*horiz*) . . 25 20
685 20 c. + 3 c. Preaching midnight sermon . . 50 60
683/5 . . . . *Set of* 3 80 80

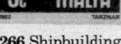

266 Shipbuilding **267** Elderly Man and Has-Serh (home for elderly)

(Des N. Attard)

1982 (29 Jan). *Shipbuilding Industry. T* **266** *and similar vert designs showing different scenes. W* **105** (*sideways*). *P* 13½.
686 3 c. multicoloured 15 10
687 8 c. multicoloured 30 30
688 13 c. multicoloured 55 55
689 27 c. multicoloured . . . . 1·25 1·25
686/9 . . . . *Set of* 4 2·00 2·00

(Des R. Pitré)

1982 (16 Mar). *Care of Elderly. T* **267** *and similar horiz design. Multicoloured. W* **105**. *P* 14 × 13½.
690 8 c. Type **267** 40 20
691 30 c. Elderly woman and Has-Zmien (hospital for elderly) . . . . 1·40 1·40

268 Redemption of Islands by Maltese, 1428

(Des F. Portelli)

1982 (29 Apr). *Europa. Historical Events. T* **268** *and similar horiz design. Multicoloured. W* **105**. *P* 14 × 13½.
692 8 c. Type **268** 40 20
693 30 c. Declaration of rights by Maltese, 1802 . . 1·00 1·40
Nos. 692/3 were each printed in sheets containing 2 *se-tenant* stamp-size labels.

269 Stylised Footballer

(Des R. Caruana)

1982 (11 June). *World Cup Football Championship, Spain. T* **269** *and similar horiz designs showing stylised footballers. W* **105**. *P* 14.
694 3 c. multicoloured 20 10
695 12 c. multicoloured 60 55
696 15 c. multicoloured 70 65
694/6 . . . . *Set of* 3 1·40 1·25
MS697 125 × 90 mm. Nos. 694/6 . . . . 2·50 3·25

270 Angel appearing to Shepherds

(Des J. Mallia)

1982 (8 Oct). *Christmas. T* **270** *and similar multicoloured designs. W* **105** (*sideways*). *P* 14 (*No.* 700) *or* 13½ (*others*).
698 2 c. + 1 c. Type **270** 15 15
699 8 c. + 2 c. Nativity and Three Wise Men bearing gifts 50 50
700 20 c. + 3 c. Nativity scene (*larger* 45 × 37 *mm*) 1·00 1·00
698/700 . . . . *Set of* 3 1·50 1·50
The designs from the 2 and 8 c. values are united to form the design of the 20 c. stamp.

271 *Ta' Salvo Serafino* (oared brigantine), 1531

(Des N. Attard)

1982 (13 Nov). *Maltese Ships* (1*st series*). *T* **271** *and similar horiz designs. Multicoloured. W* **105**. *P* 14 × 13½.
701 3 c. Type **271** 40 10
702 8 c. *La Madonna del Rosaria* (tartane), 1740 . . . . 80 30
703 12 c. *San Paulo* (xebec), 1743 . . . . 1·25 55
704 20 c. *Ta' Pietro Saliba* (xprunara), 1798 . . 1·60 90
701/4 . . . . *Set of* 4 3·50 1·60
See also Nos. 725/8, 772/5, 792/5 and 809/12.

272 *Manning Wardle*, 1883

(Des R. Caruana)

1983 (21 Jan). *Centenary of Malta Railway. T* **272** *and similar horiz designs. Multicoloured. W* **105**. *P* 14 × 13½.
705 3 c. Type **272** 45 15
706 13 c. *Black Hawthorn*, 1884 . . . . 1·00 1·00
707 27 c. *Beyer Peacock*, 1895 . . . . 2·00 3·25
705/7 . . . . *Set of* 3 3·00 4·00

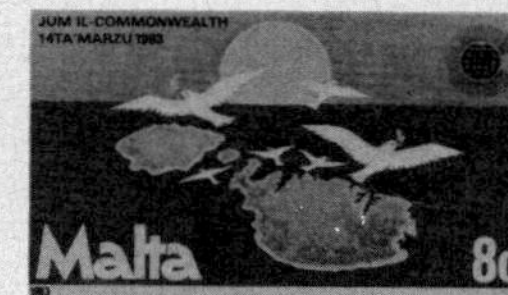

273 Peace Doves leaving Malta

(Des C. Cassar)

1983 (14 Mar). *Commonwealth Day. T* **273** *and similar multicoloured designs. W* **105** (*sideways on vert designs*). *P* 14 × 13½ (8, 12 c.) *or* 13½ × 14 (*others*).
708 8 c. Type **273** 25 30
709 12 c. Tourist landmarks 40 60
710 15 c. Holiday beach (*vert*) 45 75
711 23 c. Ship-building (*vert*) . . . . 70 1·00
708/11 . . . . *Set of* 4 1·60 2·40

274 Ggantija Megalithic Temples, Gozo

(Des T. Bugeja (8 c.), R. Caruana (30 c.))

1983 (5 May). *Europa. T* **274** *and similar horiz design. Multicoloured. W* **105**. *P* 14 × 13½.
712 8 c. Type **274** 65 40
713 30 c. Fort St. Angelo . . . . 1·75 2·40
Nos. 712/13 were each printed in sheets including two *se-tenant* stamp-size labels.

275 Dish Aerials (World Communications Year)

(Des D. Friggieri)

1983 (14 July). *Anniversaries and Events. T* **275** *and similar horiz designs. Multicoloured. W* **105** (*sideways*). *P* 13½ × 14.
714 3 c. Type **275** 45 15
715 7 c. Ships' prows and badge (25th anniv of I.M.O. Convention) 70 55
716 13 c. Container lorries and badge (30th anniv of Customs Co-operation Council) . . 90 90
717 20 c. Stadium and emblem (9th Mediterranean Games) . . . . 1·00 2·25
714/17 . . . . *Set of* 4 2·75 3·50

276 Monsignor Giuseppe de Piro **277** Annunciation

(Des E. Barthet)

1983 (1 Sept). *50th Death Anniv of Monsignor Giuseppe de Piro. W* **105** (*sideways*). *P* 14.
718 **276** 3 c. multicoloured 15 15

(Des N. Attard)

1983 (6 Sept). *Christmas. T* **277** *and similar vert designs. Multicoloured. W* **105** (*sideways*). *P* 13½ × 14.
719 2 c. + 1 c. Type **277** 30 15
720 8 c. + 2 c. The Nativity 75 60
721 20 c. + 3 c. Adoration of the Magi . . . . 1·40 2·00
719/21 . . . . *Set of* 3 2·25 2·50

278 Workers at Meeting

(Des F. Portelli)

1983 (5 Oct). *40th Anniv of General Workers' Union. T* **278** *and similar horiz designs. Multicoloured. W* **105**. *P* 14 × 13½.
722 3 c. Type **278** 25 10
723 8 c. Worker with family 50 40
724 27 c. Union H.Q. Building . . . . 1·50 1·75
722/4 . . . . *Set of* 3 2·00 2·00

(Des N. Attard)

1983 (17 Nov). *Maltese Ships* (2*nd series*). *Horiz designs as T* **271**. *Multicoloured. W* **105**. *P* 14 × 13½.
725 2 c. *Strangier* (full-rigged ship), 1813 . . 30 25
726 12 c. *Tigre* (topsail schooner), 1839 . . 1·25 1·25
727 13 c. *La Speranza* (brig), 1844 . . 1·25 1·25
728 20 c. *Wignacourt* (barque), 1844 . . 1·75 2·75
725/8 . . . . *Set of* 4 4·00 5·00

279 Boeing 737

(Des R. Caruana)

1984 (26 Jan). *Air. T* **279** *and similar horiz designs. Multicoloured.* W **105**. *P* 14 × 13½.

729	7 c. Type **279**	50	30
730	8 c. Boeing 720B	60	35
731	16 c. Vickers 953 Vanguard	1·25	70
732	23 c. Vickers Viscount 700	1·50	70
733	27 c. Douglas DC-3	1·75	80
734	38 c. Armstrong Whitworth A.W.15 Atalanta *Artemis*	2·25	2·75
735	75 c. Marina Fiat MF.5 flying boat	3·25	5·00
729/35	*Set of* 7	10·00	9·50

280 C.E.P.T. 25th Anniversary Logo **281** Early Policeman

(Des J. Larrivière and L. Borg)

1984 (27 Apr). *Europa.* W **105**. *P* 13½.

736 **280**	8 c. green, black and gold	35	35
737	30 c. carmine-lake, black and gold	1·25	1·25

Nos. 736/7 were each printed in sheets including two *se-tenant* stamp-size labels.

(Des T. Bugeja)

1984 (14 June). 170*th Anniv of Malta Police Force. T* **281** *and similar vert designs. Multicoloured.* W **105**. *P* 14 × 13½.

738	3 c. Type **281**	65	15
739	8 c. Mounted police	1·50	65
	a. Pale Venetian red (background) omitted	£110	
740	11 c. Motorcycle policeman	1·75	1·75
741	25 c. Policeman and fireman	2·75	3·25
738/41	*Set of* 4	6·00	5·25

282 Running **283** "The Visitation" (Pietru Caruana)

(Des L. Micallef)

1984 (26 July). *Olympic Games, Los Angeles. T* **282** *and similar vert designs. Multicoloured.* W **105** (*sideways*). *P* 14.

742	7 c. Type **282**	25	30
743	12 c. Gymnastics	50	70
744	23 c. Swimming	85	1·25
742/4	*Set of* 3	1·50	2·00

(Des L. Micallef)

1984 (5 Oct). *Christmas. Paintings from Church of Our Lady of Porto Salvo, Valletta. T* **283** *and similar multicoloured designs.* W **105** (*sideways on horiz designs*). *P* 14.

745	2 c. + 1 c. Type **283**	55	55
746	8 c. + 2 c. "The Epiphany" (Rafel Caruana) (*horiz*)	1·00	1·25
747	20 c. + 3 c. "Jesus among the Doctors" (Rafel Caruana) (*horiz*)	2·00	3·75
745/7	*Set of* 3	3·25	5·00

284 Dove on Map **285** 1885 ½d. Green Stamp

(Des L. Micallef)

1984 (12 Dec). 10*th Anniv of Republic. T* **284** *and similar vert designs. Multicoloured.* W **105** (*sideways*). *P* 14.

748	3 c. Type **284**	40	20
749	8 c. Fort St. Angelo	75	65
750	30 c. Hands	2·50	4·75
748/50	*Set of* 3	3·25	5·00

(Des N. Attard)

1985 (2 Jan). *Centenary of Malta Post Office. T* **285** *and similar vert designs showing stamps of* 1885. *Multicoloured.* W **105**. *P* 14.

751	3 c. Type **285**	45	15
752	8 c. 1885 1d. rose	65	45
753	12 c. 1885 2½d. dull blue	90	1·40
754	20 c. 1885 4d. brown	1·40	3·00
751/4	*Set of* 4	3·00	4·50
MS755	165 × 90 mm. Nos. 751/4. Wmk sideways	3·25	5·00

286 Boy, and Hands planting Vine

(Des T. Bugeja)

1985 (7 Mar). *International Youth Year. T* **286** *and similar multicoloured designs.* W **105** (*sideways on* 13 *c.*). *P* 14.

756	2 c. Type **286**	15	15
757	13 c. Young people and flowers (*vert*)	75	60
758	27 c. Girl holding flame in hand	1·50	1·40
756/8	*Set of* 3	2·25	1·90

287 Nicolo Baldacchino (tenor) **288** Guzeppi Bajada and Manwel Attard (victims)

(Des L. Micallef)

1985 (25 Apr). *Europa. European Music Year. T* **287** *and similar vert design. Multicoloured.* W **105**. *P* 14.

759	8 c. Type **287**	2·00	50
760	30 c. Francesco Azopardi (composer)	3·00	4·50

Nos. 759/60 were each printed in sheets including two *se-tenant* stamp-size labels.

(Des L. Micallef)

1985 (7 June). 66*th Anniv of* 7 *June* 1919 *Demonstrations. T* **288** *and similar multicoloured designs.* W **105** (*sideways on* 3 *c.*, 7 *c.*). *P* 14.

761	3 c. Type **288**	35	15
762	7 c. Karmnu Abela and Wenzu Dyer (victims)	75	35
763	35 c. Model of projected Demonstration monument by Anton Agius (*vert*)	2·50	2·00
761/3	*Set of* 3	3·25	2·25

289 Stylized Birds **290** Giorgio Mitrovich (nationalist) (Death Centenary)

(Des D. Friggieri)

1985 (26 July). 40*th Anniv of United Nations Organization. T* **289** *and similar horiz designs. Multicoloured.* W **105** (*sideways*). *P* 13½ × 14.

764	4 c. Type **289**	25	15
765	11 c. Arrow-headed ribbons	85	1·25
766	31 c. Stylized figures	2·00	3·25
764/6	*Set of* 3	2·75	4·25

(Des R. Pitre)

1985 (3 Oct). *Celebrities' Anniversaries. T* **290** *and similar vert design. Multicoloured.* W **105** (*sideways*). *P* 14.

767	8 c. Type **290**	80	35
768	12 c. Pietru Caxaru (poet and administrator) (400th death anniv)	1·60	2·50

COVER PRICES

Cover factors are quoted at the beginning of each country for most issues to 1945. An explanation of the system can be found on page x. The factors quoted do not, however, apply to philatelic covers.

291 The Three Wise Men **292** John XXIII Peace Laboratory and Statue of St. Francis of Assisi

(Des G. Bonnici)

1985 (10 Oct). *Christmas. T* **291** *and similar vert designs showing details of terracotta relief by Ganni Bonnici. Multicoloured.* W **105** (*sideways*). *P* 14.

769	2 c. + 1 c. Type **291**	55	75
770	8 c. + 2 c. Virgin and Child	1·25	1·75
771	20 c. + 3 c. Angels	2·50	4·00
769/71	*Set of* 3	3·75	6·00

(Des N. Attard)

1985 (27 Nov). *Maltese Ships* (3*rd series*). *Steamships. Horiz designs as T* **271**. *Multicoloured.* W **105**. *P* 14.

772	3 c. *Scotia* (paddle-steamer), 1844	75	20
773	7 c. *Tagliaferro* (screw steamer), 1882	1·40	1·00
774	15 c. *Gleneagles* (screw steamer), 1885	2·00	3·25
775	23 c. *L'Isle Adam* (screw steamer), 1886	2·75	4·00
772/5	*Set of* 4	6·25	7·50

(Des A. Agius (8 c.), T. Bugeja (11, 27 c.))

1986 (28 Jan). *International Peace Year. T* **292** *and similar horiz designs. Multicoloured.* W **105** (*sideways*). *P* 14 (8, 27 *c.*) *or* 13½ × 14 (11 *c.*).

776	8 c. Type **292**	1·00	50
777	11 c. Dove and hands holding olive branch (40 × 19 *mm*)	1·50	2·50
778	27 c. Map of Africa, dove and two heads	3·00	4·75
776/8	*Set of* 3	5·00	7·00

293 Symbolic Plant and *Cynthia cardui, Vanessa atalanta* and *Polyommatus icarus* (butterflies) **294** Heading the Ball

(Des M. Burló)

1986 (3 Apr). *Europa. Environmental Conservation. T* **293** *and similar vert design. Multicoloured.* W **105**. *P* 14.

779	8 c. Type **293**	1·75	50
780	35 c. Island, Neolithic frieze, sea and sun	3·25	6·00

Nos. 779/80 were each printed in sheets including two *se-tenant* stamp-size labels.

(Des T. Bugeja)

1986 (30 May). *World Cup Football Championship, Mexico. T* **294** *and similar horiz designs. Multicoloured.* W **105**. *P* 14.

781	3 c. Type **294**	60	20
782	7 c. Saving a goal	1·25	1·00
783	23 c. Controlling the ball	4·00	6·50
781/3	*Set of* 3	5·25	7·00
MS784	125 × 90 mm. Nos. 781/3. Wmk sideways	6·50	8·00

295 Father Diegu **296** "Nativity"

(Des L. Micallef)

1986 (28 Aug). *Maltese Philanthropists. T* **295** *and similar vert designs. Multicoloured.* W **105**. *P* 14.

785	2 c. Type **295**	40	30
786	3 c. Adelaide Cini	50	30
787	8 c. Alfonso Maria Galea	1·25	60
788	27 c. Vincenzo Bugeja	3·25	6·00
785/8	*Set of* 4	5·00	6·50

(Des L. Micallef)

1986 (10 Oct). *Christmas. T* **296** *and similar multicoloured designs showing paintings by Giuseppe D'Arena. W* **105** *(sideways on horiz designs). P* 14.

789 2 c.+1 c. Type **296** 80 90
790 8 c.+2 c. "Nativity" (detail) (*vert*) .. .. 2·25 2·75
791 20 c.+3 c. "Epiphany" .. .. .. 3·50 5·00
789/91 .. .. *Set of* 3 6·00 7·75

(Des N. Attard)

1986 (19 Nov). *Maltese Ships (4th series). Horiz designs as T* **271**. *Multicoloured. W* **105**. *P* 14.

792 7 c. *San Paul* (freighter), 1921 .. .. 1·25 50
793 10 c. *Knight of Malta* (mail steamer), 1930 1·50 1·75
794 12 c. *Valetta City* (freighter), 1948 .. 1·75 2·75
795 20 c. *Saver* (freighter), 1959 .. .. 3·00 4·50
792/5 .. .. *Set of* 4 6·75 8·50

297 European Robin

(Des R. Caruana)

1987 (26 Jan). *25th Anniv of Malta Ornithological Society. T* **297** *and similar multicoloured designs. W* **105** *(sideways on* 3, 23 *c.). P* 14.

796 3 c. Type **297** 75 50
797 8 c. Peregrine Falcon (*vert*) .. .. .. 1·75 1·00
798 13 c. Hoopoe (*vert*) .. .. 2·50 3·50
799 23 c. Cory's Shearwater .. .. .. 3·25 5·50
796/9 .. .. *Set of* 4 7·50 9·50

298 Aquasun Lido **299** 16th-century Pikeman

(Des R. England)

1987 (15 Apr). *Europa. Modern Architecture. T* **298** *and similar vert design. Multicoloured. W* **105**. *P* 14.

800 8 c. Type **298** .. .. 1·25 75
801 35 c. Church of St. Joseph, Manikata .. 3·50 6·25

Nos. 800/1 were each printed in sheets including two *se-tenant* stamp-size labels.

(Des L. Micallef)

1987 (10 June). *Maltese Uniforms (1st series). T* **299** *and similar vert designs. Multicoloured. W* **105** *(sideways). P* 14.

802 3 c. Type **299** 65 40
803 7 c. 16th-century officer .. .. .. 1·25 90
804 10 c. 18th-century standard bearer .. .. 1·50 2·25
805 27 c. 18th-century General of the Galleys .. 3·25 4·75
802/5 .. .. *Set of* 4 6·00 7·50

See also Nos. 832/5, 851/4, 880/3 and 893/6.

300 Maltese Scenes, Wheat Ears and Sun (European Environment Year)

(Des A. Camilleri)

1987 (18 Aug). *Anniversaries and Events. T* **300** *and similar horiz designs. Multicoloured. W* **105** *(sideways). P* 14.

806 5 c. Type **300** .. .. 1·00 50
807 8 c. Esperanto star as comet (Centenary of Esperanto) .. .. 1·25 60
808 23 c. Family at house door (International Year of Shelter for the Homeless) .. 3·00 3·00
806/8 .. .. *Set of* 3 4·75 3·75

(Des N. Attard)

1987 (16 Oct). *Maltese Ships (5th series). Horiz designs as T* **271**. *Multicoloured. W* **105**. *P* 14.

809 2 c. *Medina* (freighter), 1969 .. .. 60 60
810 11 c. *Rabat* (container ship), 1974 .. .. 2·25 2·50
811 13 c. *Ghawdex* (passenger ferry), 1979 .. 2·50 2·75
812 20 c. *Pinto* (car ferry), 1987 .. .. 3·50 4·00
809/12 .. .. *Set of* 4 8·00 9·00

301 "The Visitation"

(Des R. Caruana)

1987 (6 Nov). *Christmas. T* **301** *and similar horiz designs, each showing illuminated illustration, score and text from 16th-century choral manuscript. Multicoloured. W* **105** *(sideways). P* 14.

813 2 c. + 1 c. Type **301** 50 50
814 8 c. + 2 c. "The Nativity" .. .. .. 1·75 2·75
815 20 c. + 3 c. "The Adoration of the Magi" .. 3·00 4·50
813/15 .. .. *Set of* 3 4·75 7·00

302 Dr. Arvid Pardo (U.N. representative) **303** Ven. Nazju Falzon (Catholic catechist)

(Des S. Mallia)

1987 (18 Dec). *20th Anniv of United Nations Resolution on Peaceful Use of the Seabed. T* **302** *and similar vert design. Multicoloured. W* **105**. *P* 14.

816 8 c. Type **302** .. .. 1·00 75
817 12 c. U.N. emblem and sea .. .. .. 1·75 3·00
MS818 125×90 mm. Nos. 816/17. Wmk sideways. P 13×13½ .. .. 2·75 3·50

(Des E. Barthet)

1988 (23 Jan). *Maltese Personalities. T* **303** *and similar vert designs. Multicoloured. W* **105**. *P* 14.

819 2 c. Type **303** 25 30
820 3 c. Mgr. Sidor Formosa (philanthropist) .. 25 30
821 4 c. Sir Luigi Preziosi (ophthalmologist) .. 30 30
822 10 c. Fr. Anastasju Cuschieri (poet) .. 70 85
823 25 c. Mgr. Pietru Pawl Saydon (Bible translator) .. .. 2·00 3·25
819/23 .. .. *Set of* 5 3·25 4·50

304 "St. John Bosco with Youth" (statue) (Death Centenary) **305** Bus, Ferry and Airliner

(Des F. Portelli)

1988 (5 Mar). *Religious Anniversaries. T* **304** *and similar vert designs. Multicoloured. W* **105** *(sideways). P* 14.

824 10 c. Type **304** .. .. 1·00 1·00
825 12 c. "Assumption of Our Lady" (altarpiece by Perugino, Ta' Pinu, Gozo) (Marian Year) .. .. 1·25 1·50
826 14 c. "Christ the King" (statue by Sciortino) (75th anniv of International Eucharistic Congress, Valletta) .. 1·75 2·50
824/6 .. .. *Set of* 3 3·50 4·50

(Des F. Fenech)

1988 (9 Apr). *Europa. Transport and Communications. T* **305** *and similar vert design. Multicoloured. W* **105** *(sideways). P* 13½.

827 10 c. Type **305** .. .. 1·25 75
828 35 c. Control panel, dish aerial and pylons 2·75 4·50

Nos. 827/8 were each printed in sheets including two *se-tenant* stamp-size labels.

NEW INFORMATION

The editor is always interested to correspond with people who have new information that will improve or correct the Catalogue.

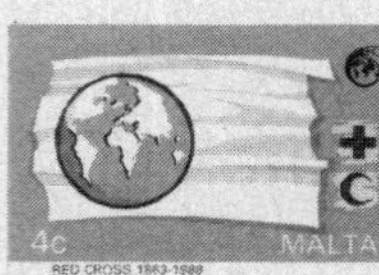

306 Globe and Red Cross Emblems (125th anniv of International Red Cross) **307** Athletics

(Des M. Cremona)

1988 (28 May). *Anniversaries and Events. T* **306** *and similar horiz designs. Multicoloured. W* **105**. *P* 13½.

829 4 c. Type **306** 40 50
830 18 c. Divided globe (Campaign for North-South Interdependence and Solidarity) 1·75 2·50
831 19 c. Globe and symbol (40th anniv of World Health Organization) .. .. .. 1·75 2·50
829/31 .. .. *Set of* 3 3·50 5·00

(Des L. Micallef)

1988 (23 July). *Maltese Uniforms (2nd issue). Vert designs as T* **299**. *Multicoloured. W* **105** *(sideways). P* 14.

832 3 c. Private, Maltese Light Infantry, 1800 30 30
833 4 c. Gunner, Malta Coast Artillery, 1802 .. 35 35
834 10 c. Field Officer, 1st Maltese Provincial Battalion, 1805 .. .. .. 85 1·25
835 25 c. Subaltern, Royal Malta Regiment, 1809 .. .. 2·25 4·25
832/5 .. .. *Set of* 4 3·25 5·50

(Des R. Gauci)

1988 (17 Sept). *Olympic Games, Seoul. T* **307** *and similar vert designs. Multicoloured. W* **105** *(sideways). P* 14×13½.

836 4 c. Type **307** 30 30
837 10 c. Diving .. .. 70 1·00
838 35 c. Basketball .. .. 2·00 3·25
836/8 .. .. *Set of* 3 2·75 4·00

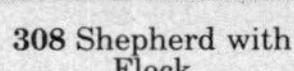

308 Shepherd with Flock **309** Commonwealth Emblem

(Des R. Gauci)

1988 (5 Nov). *Christmas. T* **308** *and similar vert designs. Multicoloured. W* **105**. *P* 14.

839 3 c. + 1 c. Type **308** 30 30
840 10 c. + 2 c. The Nativity .. .. .. 70 1·25
841 25 c. + 3 c. Three Wise Men .. .. 1·75 2·50
839/41 .. .. *Set of* 3 2·50 3·50

(Des F. Portelli)

1989 (28 Jan). *25th Anniv of Independence. T* **309** *and similar multicoloured designs. W* **105** *(sideways). P* 14 (25 *c.*) *or* 13½ *(others).*

842 2 c. Type **309** 25 35
843 3 c. Council of Europe flag 25 35
844 4 c. U.N. flag 30 35
845 10 c. Workers hands gripping ring and national flag 75 95
846 12 c. Scales and allegorical figure of Justice 90 1·40
847 25 c. Prime Minister Borg Olivier with Independence constitution (42 × 28 *mm*) .. 1·90 3·25
842/7 .. .. *Set of* 6 4·00 6·00

310 New State Arms **311** Two Boys flying Kite

(Des F. Portelli)

1989 (25 Mar). *W* **105**. *P* 14.

848 **310** £1 multicoloured .. .. .. 4·00 4·50

(Des R. Gauci)

1989 (6 May). *Europa. Children's Games. T* **311** *and similar vert design. Multicoloured. W* **105** *(sideways). P* 13½.

849 10 c. Type **311** .. .. 1·25 75
850 35 c. Two girls with dolls .. .. .. 3·25 4·50

Nos. 849/50 were each printed in sheets including two *se-tenant* stamp-size labels.

(Des L. Micallef)

1989 (24 June). *Maltese Uniforms* (*3rd series*). *Vert designs as T* **299**. *Multicoloured. W* **105** (*sideways*). *P* 14.

851 3 c. Officer, Maltese Veterans, 1815 .. 45 45
852 4 c. Subaltern, Royal Malta Fencibles, 1839 50 50
853 10 c. Private, Malta Militia, 1856 .. .. 1·50 1·50
854 25 c. Colonel, Royal Malta Fencible Artillery, 1875 .. .. .. 2·75 3·75
851/4 .. .. *Set of* 4 4·75 5·50

312 Human Figures and Buildings

313 Angel and Cherub

(Des L. Casha)

1989 (17 Oct). *Anniversaries and Commemorations. T* **312** *and similar horiz designs showing logo and stylized human figures. Multicoloured. W* **105** (*sideways*). *P* 14.

855 3 c. Type **312** (20th anniv of U.N. Declaration on Social Progress and Development) 30 30
856 4 c. Workers and figure in wheelchair (Malta's Ratification of European Social Charter) 35 35
857 10 c. Family (40th anniv of Council of Europe) .. .. 80 1·25
858 14 c. Teacher and children (70th anniv of Malta Union of Teachers) .. .. 1·00 1·75
859 25 c. Symbolic knights (Knights of the Sovereign Military Order of Malta Assembly) .. .. .. 2·25 3·50
855/9 .. .. *Set of* 5 4·25 6·50

(Des J. Mallia)

1989 (11 Nov). *Christmas. T* **313** *and similar horiz designs showing vault paintings by Mattia Preti from St. John's Co-Cathedral, Valletta. Multicoloured. W* **105**. *P* 13½.

860 3 c. + 1 c. Type **313** 50 50
861 10 c. + 2 c. Two angels .. .. .. 1·25 1·75
862 20 c. + 3 c. Angel blowing trumpet .. 1·75 3·00
860/2 .. .. *Set of* 3 3·25 4·75

314 Presidents Bush and Gorbachev

315 General Post Office, Auberge d'Italie, Valletta

1989 (2 Dec). *U.S.A.–U.S.S.R. Summit Meeting, Malta. W* **105**. *P* 14.

863 **314** 10 c. multicoloured .. .. .. 1·00 1·25

(Des R. Caruana)

1990 (9 Feb). *Europa. Post Office Buildings. T* **315** *and similar multicoloured design. W* **105** (*sideways on* 10 *c.*). *P* 14.

864 10 c. Type **315** 75 50
865 35 c. Branch Post Office, Zebbug (*horiz*) 2·25 3·50

Nos. 864/5 were each printed in sheets including two *se-tenant* stamp-size labels.

316 Open Book and Letters from Different Alphabets (International Literacy Year)

317 Samuel Taylor Coleridge (poet) and Government House

(Des T. Bugeja)

1990 (7 Apr). *Anniversaries and Events. T* **316** *and similar multicoloured designs. W* **105** (*sideways on* 4, 19 *c.*). *P* 14.

866 3 c. Type **316** 25 25
867 4 c. Count Roger of Sicily and Norman soldiers (900th anniv of Sicilian rule) (*horiz*) 30 30
868 19 c. Communications satellite (25th anniv of International Telecommunication Union membership) (*horiz*) .. 1·50 2·50
869 20 c. Football and map of Malta (Union of European Football Associations 20th Ordinary Congress, Malta) .. .. 1·50 2·50
866/9 .. .. *Set of* 4 3·25 5·00

(Des A. Grech)

1990 (3 May). *British Authors. T* **317** *and similar horiz designs. Multicoloured. W* **105** (*sideways*). *P* 13½.

870 4 c. Type **317** 30 30
871 10 c. Lord Byron (poet) and map of Valletta 60 70
872 12 c. Sir Walter Scott (novelist) and Great Siege 70 95
873 25 c. William Makepeace Thackeray (novelist) and Naval Arsenal .. .. 1·40 2·25
870/3 .. .. *Set of* 4 2·75 3·75

318 St. Paul

319 Flags and Football

(Des N. Bason)

1990 (25 May). *Visit of Pope John Paul II. T* **318** *and similar vert design showing bronze bas-reliefs. W* **105** (*sideways*). *P* 14.

874 4 c. brownish black, flesh and carmine .. 50 1·50
a. Pair. Nos. 874/5 .. .. .. 2·00 3·25
875 25 c. brownish black, flesh and carmine .. 1·50 1·75

Design:—25 c. Pope John Paul II.

Nos. 874/5 were printed together in a sheet of 12 (4×3) containing 10 stamps, *se-tenant* horizontally or vertically, and two stamp-size labels on R. 2/1 and 2/4.

(Des T. Bugeja)

1990 (8 June). *World Cup Football Championship, Italy. T* **319** *and similar horiz designs. Multicoloured. W* **105**. *P* 14.

876 5 c. Type **319** 35 30
877 10 c. Football in net .. .. .. 65 1·00
878 14 c. Scoreboard and football .. .. 1·00 1·75
876/8 .. .. *Set of* 3 1·75 2·75
MS879 123×90 mm. Nos. 876/8. Wmk sideways 2·00 3·00

(Des L. Micallef)

1990 (25 Aug). *Maltese Uniforms* (*4th series*). *Vert designs as T* **299**. *Multicoloured. W* **105** (*sideways*). *P* 14.

880 3 c. Captain, Royal Malta Militia, 1889 .. 55 55
881 4 c. Field officer, Royal Malta Artillery, 1905 .. .. 60 60
882 10 c. Labourer, Malta Labour Corps, 1915 1·50 1·50
883 25 c. Lieutenant, King's Own Malta Regiment of Militia, 1918 .. .. 2·50 3·00
880/3 .. .. *Set of* 4 4·75 5·00

320 Innkeeper

321 1919 10s. Stamp under Magnifying Glass

(Des J. Smith)

1990 (10 Nov). *Christmas. Figures from Crib by Austin Galea, Marco Bartolo and Rosario Zammit. T* **320** *and similar multicoloured designs. W* **105** (*sideways*). *P* 14×14½ (10 *c.*) *or* 13½×14 (*others*).

884 3 c. + 1 c. Type **320** 30 40
885 10 c. + 2 c. Nativity (41×28 *mm*) .. .. 70 1·25
886 25 c. + 3 c. Shepherd with sheep .. 1·60 2·25
884/6 .. .. *Set of* 3 2·40 3·50

(Des J. Mallia)

1991 (6 Mar). *25th Anniv of Philatelic Society of Malta. W* **105** (*sideways*). *P* 14.

887 **321** 10 c. multicoloured 60 70

322 "Eurostar" Satellite and V.D.U. Screen

323 St. Ignatius Loyola (founder of Jesuits) (500th birth anniv)

(Des R. Caruana)

1991 (16 Mar). *Europa. Europe in Space. T* **322** *and similar vert design. Multicoloured. W* **105** (*sideways*). *P* 14.

888 10 c. Type **322** .. .. 1·25 70
889 35 c. "Ariane 4" rocket and projected HOTOL aerospaceplane .. .. 2·25 2·75

Nos. 888/9 were each printed in sheets including two *se-tenant* stamp-size labels.

(Des J. Mallia)

1991 (29 Apr). *Religious Commemorations. T* **323** *and similar multicoloured designs. W* **105** (*sideways on* 3, 30 *c.*). *P* 14.

890 3 c. Type **323** 30 20
891 4 c. Abbess Venerable Maria Adeodata Pisani (185th birth anniv) (*vert*) .. 35 25
892 30 c. St. John of the Cross (400th death anniv) .. .. 2·00 2·25
890/2 .. .. *Set of* 3 2·40 2·40

(Des L. Micallef)

1991 (13 Aug). *Maltese Uniforms* (*5th series*). *Vert designs as T* **299**. *Multicoloured. W* **105** (*sideways*). *P* 14.

893 3 c. Officer with colour, Royal Malta Fencibles, 1860 .. .. 30 25
894 10 c. Officer with colour, Royal Malta Regiment of Militia, 1903 .. .. 70 60
895 19 c. Officer with Queen's colour, King's Own Malta Regiment, 1968 .. .. 1·40 1·75
896 25 c. Officer with colour, Malta Armed Forces, 1991 .. .. 1·75 2·00
893/6 .. .. *Set of* 4 3·75 4·25

324 Interlocking Arrows

325 Honey Buzzard

(Des N. Attard)

1991 (23 Sept). *25th Anniv of Union Haddiema Maghqudin* (*public services union*). *W* **105** (*sideways*). *P* 13½.

897 **324** 4 c. multicoloured 30 30

(Des H. Borg)

1991 (3 Oct). *Endangered Species. Birds. T* **325** *and similar vert designs. Multicoloured. W* **105**. *P* 14.

898 4 c. Type **325** .. .. 1·40 1·40
a. Horiz strip of 4. Nos. 898/901 .. 5·00
899 4 c. Marsh Harrier .. .. .. 1·40 1·40
900 10 c. Eleonora's Falcon .. .. .. 1·40 1·40
901 10 c. Lesser Kestrel .. .. .. 1·40 1·40
898/901 .. .. *Set of* 4 5·00 5·00

Nos. 898/901 were printed together, *se-tenant*, in horizontal strips of 4 throughout the sheet.

326 Three Wise Men

327 Ta' Hagrat Neolithic Temple

(Des H. Borg)

1991 (6 Nov). *Christmas. T* **326** *and similar vert designs. Multicoloured. W* **105**. *P* 14.

902 3 c. + 1 c. Type **326** 25 25
903 10 c. + 2 c. Holy Family 65 85
904 25 c. + 3 c. Two shepherds .. .. 1·25 2·00
902/4 .. .. *Set of* 3 2·00 2·75

(Des F. Portelli)

1991 (9 Dec). *National Heritage of the Maltese Islands. T* **327** *and similar multicoloured designs. W* **105** (*sideways on* £2). *P* 13½.

905 1 c. Type **327** 10 10
906 2 c. Cottoner Gate 10 10
907 3 c. St. Michael's Bastion, Valletta .. 10 10
908 4 c. Spinola Palace, St. Julian's 10 15
909 5 c. Birkirkara Church 15 20
910 10 c. Mellieha Bay 30 35
911 12 c. Wied iz-Zurrieq 35 40
912 14 c. Mgarr harbour, Gozo 40 45
913 20 c. Yacht marina 60 65
914 50 c. Gozo Channel .. .. .. 1·50 1·60
915 £1 "Arab Horses" (sculpture by Antonio Sciortino) .. .. 3·00 3·25
916 £2 Independence Monument (Ganni Bonnici) (*vert*) .. .. .. 6·00 6·25
905/16 .. .. *Set of* 12 12·50 13·50

MINIMUM PRICE

The minimum price quote is 10p which represents a handling charge rather than a basis for valuing common stamps. For further notes about prices see introductory pages.

328 Aircraft Tailfins and Terminal

(Des. H. Borg)

1992 (8 Feb). *Opening of International Air Terminal. T* **328** *and similar horiz design. W* **105** *(sideways). P* 14.
917 4 c. Type **328** 45 30
918 10 c. National flags and terminal 65 65

329 Ships of Columbus

330 George Cross and Anti-aircraft Gun Crew

(Des H. Borg)

1992 (20 Feb). *Europa. 500th Anniv of Discovery of America by Columbus. T* **329** *and similar horiz design. W* **105** *(sideways). P* 14.
919 10 c. Type **329** 55 55
920 35 c. Columbus and map of Americas . . 2·00 2·25
Nos. 919/20 were each printed in sheets including two *se-tenant* stamp-size labels.

(Des H. Borg)

1992 (15 Apr). *50th Anniv of Award of George Cross to Malta. T* **330** *and similar vert designs. Multicoloured. W* **105**. *P* 14.
921 4 c. Type **330** 40 25
922 10 c. George Cross and memorial bell . . 1·00 80
923 50 c. Tanker *Ohio* entering Grand Harbour 4·00 5·50
921/3 . . . . *Set of* 3 4·75 6·00

331 Running

332 Church of the Flight into Egypt

(Des H. Borg)

1992 (24 June). *Olympic Games, Barcelona. T* **331** *and similar horiz designs. Multicoloured. W* **105** *(sideways). P* 14.
924 3 c. Type **331** 45 20
925 10 c. High jumping 95 70
926 30 c. Swimming . . . . 2·25 3·25
924/6 . . . . *Set of* 3 3·25 3·75

(Des N. Attard)

1992 (5 Aug). *Rehabilitation of Historical Buildings. T* **332** *and similar designs. W* **105** *(sideways on 4, 25 c.). P* 14.
927 3 c. black, pale stone and bluish grey . . 25 15
928 4 c. black, pale stone and flesh . . 30 20
929 19 c. black, pale stone and pale rose-lilac . . 1·50 1·75
930 25 c. black, pale stone and pale grey-olive 1·75 1·75
927/30 . . . . *Set of* 4 3·50 3·50
Designs: *Horiz*—4 c. St. John's Co-Cathedral; 25 c. Auberge de Provence. *Vert*—19 c. Church of Madonna del Pillar.

333 "The Nativity" (Giuseppe Cali)

334 Malta College Building, Valletta

(Des L. Buttigieg)

1992 (22 Oct). *Christmas. Religious Paintings by Giuseppe Cali from Mosta Church. T* **333** *and similar horiz designs. Multicoloured. W* **105** *(sideways). P* 14.
931 3 c. + 1 c. Type **333** 50 50
932 10 c. + 2 c. "Adoration of the Magi" . . 1·25 1·50
933 25 c. + 3 c. "Christ with the Elders in the Temple" . . . . 2·50 3·00
931/3 . . . . *Set of* 3 3·75 4·50

(Des L. Buttigieg)

1992 (12 Nov). *400th Anniv of University of Malta. T* **334** *and similar multicoloured design. W* **105** *(sideways on 30 c.). P* 14.
934 4 c. Type **334** 40 25
935 30 c. Modern University complex, Tal-Qroqq (*horiz*) . . . . 2·00 2·75

335 Lions Club Emblem

336 Untitled Painting by Paul Carbonaro

(Des H. Borg)

1993 (4 Feb). *75th Anniv of International Association of Lions Club. T* **335** *and similar horiz design. Multicoloured. W* **105**. *P* $13^{1}/_{2}$.
936 4 c. Type **335** 50 20
937 50 c. Eye (Sight First Campaign) . . . . 2·50 2·75

1993 (7 Apr). *Europa. Contemporary Art. T* **336** *and similar multicoloured design. W* **105** *(sideways on 35 c.). P* 14.
938 10 c. Type **336** 75 50
939 35 c. Untitled painting by Alfred Chircop (*horiz*) . . . . 2·25 3·25
Nos. 938/9 were each printed in sheets including two stamp-size labels.

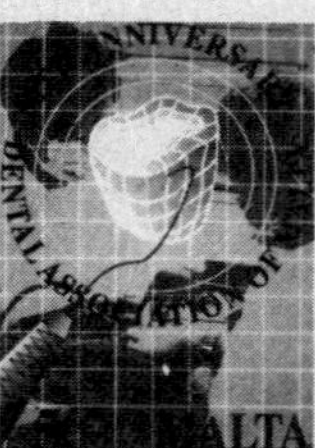

337 Mascot holding Flame

338 Learning First Aid

(Des R. Caruana)

1993 (4 May). *5th Small States of Europe Games. T* **337** *and similar horiz designs. Multicoloured. W* **105**. *P* $13^{1}/_{2}\times14$.
940 3 c. Type **337** 20 20
941 4 c. Cycling 40 30
942 10 c. Tennis . . . . 1·00 90
943 35 c. Yachting . . . . 2·25 3·00
940/3 . . . . *Set of* 4 3·50 4·00
MS944 120×80 mm. Nos. 940/3. Wmk sideways 3·50 3·50

(Des L. Micallef)

1993 (21 July). *50th Anniv of Award of Bronze Cross to Maltese Scouts and Guides. T* **338** *and similar vert designs. Multicoloured. W* **105**. *P* 14.
945 3 c. Type **338** 20 15
946 4 c. Bronze Cross 20 20
947 10 c. Scout building camp fire 70 65
948 35 c. Governor Lord Gort presenting Bronze Cross, 1943 . . . . 2·00 2·40
945/8 . . . . *Set of* 4 2·75 3·00

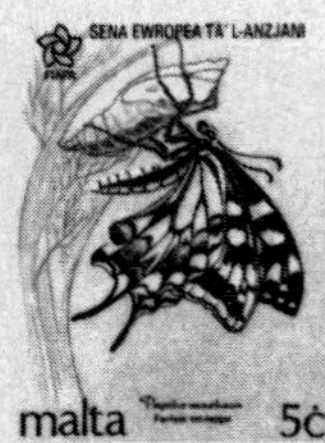
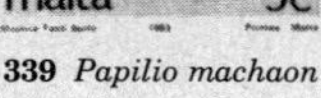

339 *Papilio machaon*

340 G.W.U. Badge and Interlocking "50"

(Des M. Burlo)

1993 (23 Sept). *European Year of the Elderly. Butterflies. T* **339** *and similar vert design. Multicoloured. W* **105**. *P* 14.
949 5 c. Type **339** 35 20
950 35 c. *Vanessa atalanta* . . . . . . 1·75 2·25

(Des H. Borg)

1993 (5 Oct). *50th Anniv of General Workers Union. W* **105** *(sideways). P* $13^{1}/_{2}$.
951 **340** 4 c. multicoloured 35 40

341 Child Jesus and Star

(Des H. Borg)

1993 (5 Nov). *Christmas. T* **341** *and similar vert designs. Multicoloured. W* **105**. *P* 14.
952 3 c. + 1 c. Type **341** 30 30
953 10 c. + 2 c. Christmas tree 85 95
954 25 c. + 3 c. Star in traditional window . . 1·60 2·25
952/4 . . . . *Set of* 3 2·50 3·25

342 Council Arms (face value top left)

(Des J. Mizzi)

1993 (20 Nov). *Inauguration of Local Community Councils. Sheet* 110×93 *mm. containing T* **342** *and similar horiz designs showing different Council Arms. Multicoloured. W* **105** *(sideways). P* 14.
MS955 5 c. Type **342**; 5 c. Face value top right; 5 c. Face value bottom left; 5 c. Face value bottom right . . . . 1·50 2·25

343 Symbolic Tooth and Probe

344 Sir Themistocles Zammit (discoverer of Brucella microbe)

(Des F. Ancilleri)

1994 (12 Feb). *50th Anniv of Maltese Dental Association. T* **343** *and similar vert design. Multicoloured. W* **105**. *P* 14.
956 5 c. Type **343** 35 30
957 44 c. Symbolic mouth and dental mirror . . 2·75 2·75

(Des H. Borg)

1994 (29 Mar). *Europa. Discoveries. T* **344** *and similar vert design. Multicoloured. W* **105**. *P* 14.
958 14 c. Type **344** 50 30
959 30 c. Bi-lingually inscribed candelabrum of 2nd century B.C. (deciphering of ancient Phoenician language) . . 1·90 2·75
Nos. 958/9 were each printed in sheets including two *se-tenant* stamp-size labels.

345 Family in Silhouette (International Year of the Family)

346 Football and Map

(Des F. Ancilleri)

1994 (10 May). *Anniversaries and Events. T* **345** *and similar multicoloured designs. W* **105** *(sideways on* 25 *c.). P* 14.

960	5 c. Type **345**	25	20
961	9 c. Stylised Red Cross (International Recognition of Malta Red Cross Society)	50	40
962	14 c. Animals and crops (150th anniv of Agrarian Society)	85	80
963	20 c. Worker in silhouette (75th anniv of International Labour Organization)	1·25	1·40
964	25 c. St. Paul's Anglican Cathedral (155th anniv) (*vert*)	1·40	1·60
960/4	*Set of* 5	3·75	4·00

(Des F. Ancilleri)

1994 (9 June). *World Cup Football Championship, U.S.A. T* **346** *and similar horiz designs. Multicoloured. W* **105**. *P* 14.

965	5 c. Type **346**	30	20
966	14 c. Ball and goal	85	80
967	30 c. Ball and pitch superimposed on map	2·25	2·00
965/7	*Set of* 3	3·00	2·75
MS968	123×88 mm. Nos. 965/7. Wmk sideways	3·00	3·00

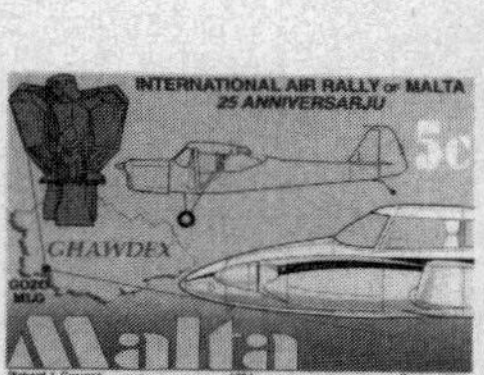

347 Falcon Trophy, Twin Comanche and Auster (25th anniv of Malta International Rally)

348 National Flags and Astronaut on Moon

(Des R. Caruana)

1994 (2 July). *Aviation Anniversaries and Events. T* **347** *and similar horiz designs. Multicoloured. W* **105** *(sideways). P* 14.

969	5 c. Type **347**	40	20
970	14 c. Alouette helicopter, display teams and logo (Malta International Airshow)	1·10	85
971	20 c. De Havilland Dove *City of Valetta* and Avro York aircraft with logo (50th anniv of International Civil Aviation Organization)	1·60	1·40
972	25 c. Airbus 320 *Nicolas Cottoner* and De Havilland Comet aircraft with logo (50th anniv of I.C.A.O.)	1·75	1·75
969/72	*Set of* 4	4·25	3·75

After printing it was found that all examples of the 20 c. were inscribed "Anniverarju" in error. These were withdrawn before issue and replaced by stock showing the word correctly spelt as "Anniversarju". It is reported that all sheets of the incorrect printing were destroyed.

(Des R. Caruana)

1994 (20 July). *25th Anniv of First Moon Landing. W* **105**. *P* 14.

973	**348**	14 c. multicoloured	90	95

349 Virgin Mary and Child with Angels

350 Helmet-shaped Ewer

(Des H. Borg)

1994 (26 Oct). *Christmas. T* **349** *and similar multicoloured designs. W* **105** *(sideways on* 5 *c.). P* 13½ (5 *c.) or* 14 *(others).*

974	5 c. Type **349**	20	10
975	9 c. + 2 c. Angel in pink (*vert*)	55	60
976	14 c. + 3 c. Virgin Mary and Child (*vert*)	80	1·10
977	20 c. + 3 c. Angel in green (*vert*)	1·40	2·00
974/7	*Set of* 4	2·75	3·50

Nos. 975/7 are larger, 28×41 mm, and depict details from Type **349**.

(Des M. Burlo)

1994 (12 Dec). *Maltese Antique Silver Exhibition. T* **350** *and similar vert designs. Multicoloured. W* **105**. *P* 14.

978	5 c. Type **350**	25	20
979	14 c. Balsamina	70	80
980	20 c. Coffee pot	1·25	1·40
981	25 c. Sugar box	1·50	1·75
978/81	*Set of* 4	3·25	3·75

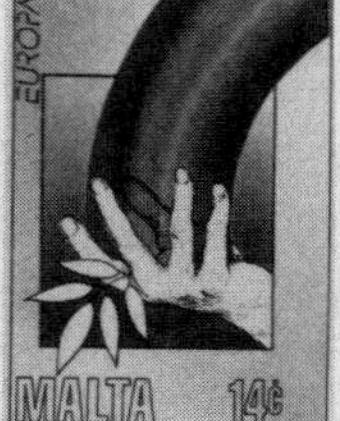

351 "60 plus" and Hands touching

352 Hand holding Leaf and Rainbow

(Des Anna Grima)

1995 (27 Feb). *Anniversaries and Events. T* **351** *and similar vert designs. Multicoloured. W* **105** *(sideways). P* 14.

982	2 c. Type **351** (25th anniv of National Association of Pensioners)	15	15
983	5 c. Child's drawing (10th anniv of National Youth Council)	25	20
984	14 c. Conference emblem (4th World Conference on Women, Peking, China)	70	80
985	20 c. Nurse and thermometer (50th anniv of Malta Memorial District Nursing Association)	1·25	1·40
986	25 c. Louis Pasteur (biologist) (death centenary)	1·50	1·75
982/6	*Set of* 5	3·50	3·75

(Des H. Borg)

1995 (29 Mar). *Europa. Peace and Freedom. T* **352** *and similar multicoloured design. W* **105** *(sideways on* 30 *c.). P* 14.

987	14 c. Type **352**	75	55
988	30 c. Peace doves (*horiz*)	1·50	2·00

Nos. 987/8 were each printed in sheets including two stamp-size labels.

353 Junkers Ju 87B "Stuka" Dive Bombers over Valletta and Anti-aircraft Gun

354 Light Bulb

(Des F. Ancilleri)

1995 (21 Apr). *Anniversaries. T* **353** *and similar multicoloured designs. W* **105** *(sideways on horiz designs). P* 14.

989	5 c. Type **353** (50th anniv of end of Second World War)	25	25
990	14 c. Silhouetted people holding hands (50th anniv of United Nations)	70	80
991	35 c. Hands holding bowl of wheat (50th anniv of Food and Agriculture Organization) (*vert*)	2·00	2·25
989/91	*Set of* 3	2·75	3·00

(Des M. Burlo)

1995 (15 June). *Maltese Electricity and Telecommunications. T* **354** *and similar vert designs. Multicoloured. W* **105** *(sideways). P* 13½.

992	2 c. Type **354**	15	15
993	5 c. Symbolic owl and binary codes	25	25
994	9 c. Dish aerial	45	50
995	14 c. Sun and rainbow over trees	70	80
996	20 c. Early telephone, satellite and Moon's surface	1·25	1·50
992/6	*Set of* 5	2·50	2·75

355 Rock Wall and Girna

356 Pinto's Turret Clock

(Des M. Burlo)

1995 (26 July). *European Nature Conservation Year. T* **355** *and similar horiz designs. W* **105** *(sideways). P* 14.

997	5 c. Type **355**	25	25
998	14 c. Maltese Wall Lizards	70	80
999	44 c. Aleppo Pine	2·75	3·00
997/9	*Set of* 3	3·25	3·50

(Des F. Ancilleri)

1995 (5 Oct). *Treasures of Malta. Antique Maltese Clocks. T* **356** *and similar vert designs. Multicoloured. W* **105**. *P* 14.

1000	1 c. Type **356**	10	10
1001	5 c. Michelangelo Sapiano (horologist) and clocks	25	25
1002	14 c. Arlogg tal-lira clock	70	80
1003	25 c. Sundials	1·40	1·60
1000/3	*Set of* 4	2·25	2·00

357 Children's Christmas Eve Procession

(Des H. Borg)

1995 (15 Nov). *Christmas. T* **357** *and simlar multicoloured designs. W* **105** *(sideways on* 5 *c.). P* 14×13½.

1004	5 c. Type **357**	25	10
1005	5 c. + 2 c. Children with crib (*vert*)	30	35
1006	14 c. + 3 c. Children with lanterns (*vert*)	75	85
1007	25 c. + 3 c. Boy with lantern and balustrade (*vert*)	1·40	1·40
1004/7	*Set of* 4	2·40	2·40

Nos. 1005/7 are 27×32 mm and depict details from Type **357**.

358 Silhouetted Children and President's Palace, San Anton

(Des F. Ancilleri)

1996 (29 Feb). *Anniversaries. T* **358** *and similar horiz designs. Multicoloured. W* **105** *(sideways). P* 14.

1008	5 c. Type **358** (35th anniv of the President's Award)	25	25
1009	14 c. Father Nazzareno Camilleri and St. Patrick's Church, Salesjani (90th birth anniv)	65	65
1010	20 c. St. Mary Euphrasia and convent (Birth bicentenary)	1·00	1·10
1011	25 c. Silhouetted children and fountain (50th anniv of U.N.I.C.E.F.)	1·25	1·40
1008/11	*Set of* 4	2·75	3·00

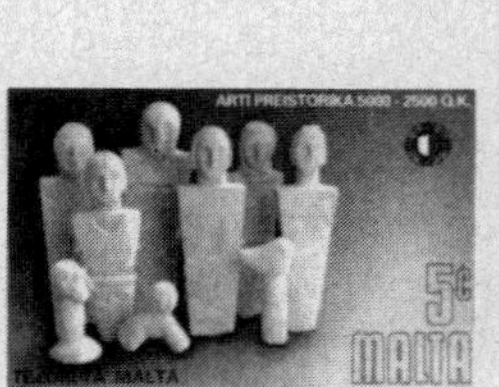

359 Carved Figures from Skorba

360 Mabel Strickland (politician and journalist)

(Des H. Borg)

1996 (29 Mar). *Maltese Prehistoric Art Exhibition. T* **359** *and similar multicoloured designs. W* **105** *(sideways on horiz designs). P* 14.

1012	5 c. Type **359**	30	20
1013	14 c. Temple carving, Gozo	80	85
1014	20 c. Carved figure of a woman, Skorba (*vert*)	1·10	1·25
1015	35 c. Ghar Dalam pot (*vert*)	1·90	2·25
1012/15	*Set of* 4	3·75	4·00

(Des Catherine Cavallo)

1996 (24 Apr). *Europa. Famous Women. T* **360** *and similar vert design. Multicoloured. W* **105**. *P* 14.

1016	14 c. Type **360**	70	55
1017	30 c. Inez Soler (artist, musician and writer)	1·75	2·00

PRICES OF SETS

Set prices are given for many issues, generally those containing three stamps or more. Definitive sets include one of each value or major colour change, but do not cover different perforations, die types or minor shades. Where a choice is possible the set prices are based on the cheapest versions of the stamps included in the listings.

361 Face and Emblem (United Nations Decade against Drug Abuse)

362 Judo

(Des D. Nicolas)

1996 (5 June). *Anniversaries and Events. T* **361** *and similar vert designs. Multicoloured.* W **105**. *P* 14.

1018 5 c. Type **361** 25 25
1019 5 c. "Fi" and emblem (50th anniv of Malta Federation of Industry) 25 25
1020 14 c. Commemorative plaque and national flag (75th anniv of Self-government) 80 80
1021 44 c. Guglielmo Marconi and early radio equipment (Centenary of radio) . . 2·25 2·50
1018/21 . . . . *Set of* 4 3·25 3·50

(Des L. Micallef)

1996 (10 July). *Olympic Games, Atlanta. T* **362** *and similar horiz designs. Multicoloured.* W **105** (*sideways*). *P* 14.

1022 2 c. Type **362** 10 10
1023 5 c. Athletics 25 25
1024 14 c. Diving 70 70
1025 25 c. Rifle-shooting . . . . . . 1·25 1·40
1022/5 . . . . *Set of* 4 2·00 2·10

363 "Harvest Time" (Cali)

(Des Debbie Dingli)

1996 (22 Aug). 150*th Birth Anniv of Guiseppe Cali (painter). T* **363** *and similar multicoloured designs.* W **105** (*sideways on* 5, 14 *c.*). *P* 14.

1026 5 c. Type **363** 25 25
1027 14 c. "Dog" (Cali) 70 70
1028 20 c. "Countrywoman in a Field" (Cali) (*vert*) . . . . 1·00 1·00
1029 25 c. "Cali at his Easel" (Edward Dingli) (*vert*) . . . . 1·10 1·10
1026/9 . . . . *Set of* 4 2·75 2·75

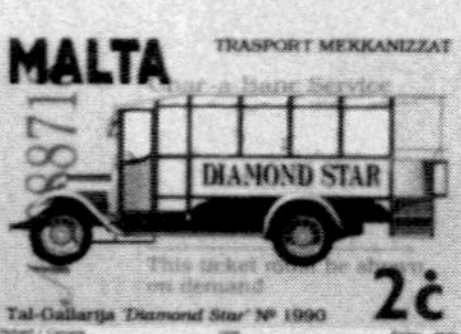

364 Bus No. 1990 *Diamond Star*, 1920s

(Des R. Caruana)

1996 (26 Sept). *Buses. T* **364** *and similar horiz designs. Multicoloured.* W **105** (*sideways*). *P* 14.

1030 2 c. Type **364** 10 10
1031 5 c. No. 434 *Tom Mix*, 1930s 25 25
1032 14 c. No. 1764 *Verdala*, 1940s 70 70
1033 30 c. No. 3495, 1960s . . . . . . 1·40 1·40
1030/3 . . . . *Set of* 4 2·25 2·25

365 Stained Glass Window

(Des H. Borg)

1996 (1 Nov). *Christmas. T* **365** *and similar multicoloured designs.* W **105** (*sideways on* 5 *c.*). *P* 14×13½.

1034 5 c. Type **365** 30 10
1035 5 c. + 2 c. Madonna and Child (29×35 *mm*) 35 30
1036 14 c. + 3 c. Angel facing right (29×35 *mm*) 70 70
1037 25 c. + 3 c. Angel facing left (29×35 *mm*) 1·00 1·25
1034/7 . . . . *Set of* 4 2·10 2·10

Nos. 1035/7 show details from Type **365**.

366 Hompesch Arch and Arms, Zabbar

367 Captain-General of the Galleys' Sedan Chair

(Des R. Caruana)

1997 (20 Feb). *Bicentenary of Maltese Cities. T* **366** *and similar vert designs. Multicoloured.* W **105**. *P* 14.

1038 6 c. Type **366** 30 25
1039 16 c. Statue, church and arms, Siggiewi . . 70 70
1040 26 c. Seated statue and arms, Zejtun . . 1·10 1·10
1038/40 . . . . *Set of* 3 1·90 1·90
MS1041 125×90 mm. As Nos. 1038/40. Wmk sideways . . . . 1·90 1·90

1997 (11 Apr). *Treasures of Malta. Sedan Chairs. T* **367** *and similar multicoloured designs.* W **105** (*sideways on horiz designs*). *P* 14.

1042 2 c. Type **367** 15 15
1043 6 c. Cotoner Grandmasters' chair . . 30 30
1044 16 c. Chair from Cathedral Museum, Mdina (*vert*) 70 70
1045 27 c. Chevalier D'Arezzo's chair (*vert*) . . 1·10 1·10
1042/5 . . . . *Set of* 4 2·00 2·00

368 Gahan carrying Door

369 Modern Sculpture (Antonio Sciortino)

(Des J. Mallia)

1997 (5 May). *Europa. Tales and Legends. T* **368** *and similar vert design. Multicoloured.* W **105** (*sideways*). *P* 14.

1046 16 c. Type **368** 75 75
1047 35 c. St. Dimitrius appearing from painting 1·25 1·50

Nos. 1046/7 were each printed in sheets of 10 and two stamp-size labels.

1997 (10 July). *Anniversaries. T* **369** *and similar multi-coloured designs.* W **105** (*sideways on horiz designs*). *P* 14.

1048 1 c. Type **369** 10 10
1049 6 c. Joseph Calleia and film reel (*horiz*) 30 30
1050 6 c. Gozo Cathedral (*horiz*) 30 30
1051 11 c. City of Gozo (*horiz*) 50 50
1052 16 c. Sculpture of head (Sciortino) . . 70 70
1053 22 c. Joseph Calleia and film camera (*horiz*) 1·00 1·00
1048/53 . . . . *Set of* 6 2·50 2·50

Anniversaries; 1 c., 16 c. 50th death anniv of Antonio Sciortino (sculptor); 6 c. (No. 1049), 22 c., Birth centenary of Joseph Calleia (actor); 6 c. (No. 1050), 11 c. 300th anniv of construction of Gozo Cathedral

370 Dr. Albert Laferla

371 The Nativity

(Des Debbie Dingli)

1997 (24 Sept). *Pioneers of Education. T* **370** *and similar vert designs. Multicoloured.* W **105**. *P* 14.

1054 6 c. Type **370** 30 25
1055 16 c. Sister Emilie de Vialar 70 70
1056 19 c. Mgr. Paolo Pullicino 80 80
1057 26 c. Mgr. Tommaso Gargallo . . . . 1·00 1·10
1054/7 . . . . *Set of* 4 2·50 2·50

(Des H. Borg)

1997 (12 Nov). *Christmas. T* **371** *and similar multicoloured designs.* W **105** (*sideways on* 6 *c.*). *P* 14.

1058 6 c. Type **371** 20 25
1059 6 c. + 2 c. Mary and baby Jesus (*vert*) . . 25 30
1060 16 c. + 3 c. Joseph with donkey (*vert*) . . 60 65
1061 26 c. + 3 c. Shepherd with lamb (*vert*) . . 90 95
1058/61 . . . . *Set of* 4 1·90 2·10

Nos. 1059/61 show details from Type **371**.

372 Plan of Fort and Soldiers in Victoria Lines

373 "Maria Amelia Grognet" (Antoine de Favray)

1997 (5 Dec). *Anniversaries. T* **372** *and similar horiz designs. Multicoloured (except* 6 *c.).* W **105** (*sideways*). *P* 14.

1062 2 c. Type **372** 10 10
1063 6 c. Sir Paul Boffa making speech (black and scarlet) 20 25
1064 16 c. Plan of fort and gun crew 50 55
1065 37 c. Queue of voters . . . . . . 1·10 1·25
1062/5 . . . . *Set of* 4 1·90 2·10

Anniversaries; 2 c., 16 c. Centenary of Victoria Lines; 6 c., 37 c. 50th anniv of 1947 Self-Government Constitution

(Des F. Ancilleri)

1998 (26 Feb). *Treasures of Malta. Costumes and Paintings. T* **373** *and similar vert designs.* W **105**. *P* 14.

1066 6 c. Type **373** 20 25
1067 6 c. Gentleman's waistcoat, *c.* 1790–1810 20 25
1068 16 c. Lady's dinner dress, *c.* 1880 . . 50 55
1069 16 c. "Veneranda, Baroness Abela, and her Grandson" (De Favray) 50 55
1066/9 . . . . *Set of* 4 1·40 1·60
MS1070 123×88 mm. 26 c. City of Valletta from old print (39×47 *mm*). Wmk sideways. P 13×13½ 75 80

STAMP BOOKLETS

B 1

1970 (16 May). *Brownish black on brownish grey cover as Type* B **1** *depicting G.P.O. Palazzo Parisio, Valletta. Stitched.*

SB1	2s. 6d. booklet containing six 1d. and twelve 2d. (Nos. 331, 333) in blocks of 6	4·50

1970 (18 May). *Black on pink cover as Type* B **1** *depicting Magisterial Palace, Valletta. Stitched.*

SB2	2s. 6d. booklets containing six 1d. and twelve 2d. (Nos. 331, 333) in blocks of 6	4·00

1971 (29 May). *Black on green cover as Type* B **1** *depicting Auberge d'Aragon, Valletta. Stitched.*

SB3	2s. 6d. booklet containing six 1d. and twelve 2d. (Nos. 331, 333) in blocks of 6	10·00

1971 (3 July). *Black on white cover as Type* B **1** *depicting Fort St. Angelo. Stitched.*

SB4	5s. booklet containing twelve 5d. (No. 337*b*) in blocks of 6	9·00

B 2

1994 (2 Nov). *Multicoloured covers as Type* B **2**. *Stamps attached by selvedge.*

SB5	50 c. booklet containing 5 c. (No. 909) in block of 10, (cover showing Malta 1926 2s. Mdina (Notabile) stamp)	1·75
SB6	70 c. booklet containing 14 c. (No. 912) in strip of 5 with 6 airmail labels (cover showing Malta 1926 1s. Valleta Harbour stamp)	2·50

POSTAGE DUE STAMPS

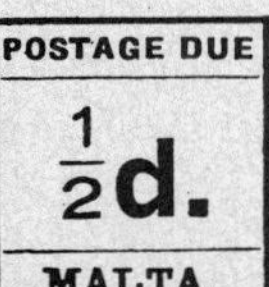

D 1

D 2

D 3 Maltese Lace

1925 (16 Apr). *Type-set by Govt Printing Office, Valletta. Imperf.*

D 1	D 1	½d. black	1·25	4·00
		a. *Tête-bêche* (horiz pair)	5·00	15·00
D 2		1d. black	3·00	2·50
		a. *Tête-bêche* (horiz pair)	10·00	11·00
D 3		1½d. black	3·00	3·50
		a. *Tête-bêche* (horiz pair)	10·00	14·00
D 4		2d. black	4·75	9·00
		a. *Tête-bêche* (horiz pair)	15·00	30·00
D 5		2½d. black	2·75	2·75
		a. "2" of "½" omitted	£900	£1200
		b. *Tête-bêche* (horiz pair)	12·00	14·00
D 6		3d. black/*grey*	9·00	11·00
		a. *Tête-bêche* (horiz pair)	30·00	40·00
D 7		4d black/*buff*	5·00	9·00
		a. *Tête-bêche* (horiz pair)	17·00	35·00
D 8		6d. black/*buff*	5·00	13·00
		a. *Tête-bêche* (horiz pair)	17·00	48·00
D 9		1s. black/*buff*	7·50	17·00
		a. *Tête-bêche* (horiz pair)	25·00	55·00
D10		1s. 6d. black/*buff*	13·00	50·00
		a. *Tête-bêche* (horiz pair)	40·00	£130
D1/10		. . . . *Set of* 10	48·00	£110

Nos. D1/10 were each issued in sheets containing 4 panes (6×7) printed separately, the impressions in the two right-hand panes being inverted. Fourteen horizontal *tête-bêche* pairs occur from the junction of the left and right-hand panes.

No. D5a occurred on R. 4/4 of the last 2½d. pane position to be printed. Forgeries exist, but can be detected by comparison with a normal example under ultra-violet light. They are often found in pair with normal, showing forged cancellations of "VALLETTA AP20 25" or "G.P.O" MY 7 25".

(Typo B.W.)

1925 (20 July). *Wmk Mult Script CA (sideways). P* 12.

D11	D 2	½d. green	1·25	60
D12		1d. violet	1·25	45
D13		1½d. brown	1·50	1·25
D14		2d. grey	11·00	1·50
D15		2½d. orange	2·00	1·25
		x. Wmk reversed	75·00	
D16		3d. blue	3·25	1·25
D17		4d. olive-green	12·00	14·00
D18		6d. purple	3·00	3·25
D19		1s. black	6·50	10·00
D20		1s. 6d. carmine	8·50	22·00
D11/20		. . . . *Set of* 10	45·00	50·00
D11/20 Optd "Specimen"		. . . . *Set of* 10	£200	

1953 (5 Nov)–**63**. *Wmk Mult Script CA (sideways). Chalk-surfaced paper. P* 12.

D21	D 2	½d. emerald	70	1·75
D22		1d. purple	70	1·25
		a. Deep purple (17.9.63)	75	3·00
D23		1½d. yellow-brown	3·00	8·50
D24		2d. grey-brown (20.3.57)	5·00	8·00
		a. Blackish brown (3.4.62)	17·00	13·00
D25		3d. deep slate-blue	1·50	2·00
D26		4d. yellow-olive	4·50	8·00
D21/6		. . . . *Set of* 6	14·00	26·00

1966 (Oct). *As No.* D24, *but wmk* w **12** *(sideways).*

D27	D 2	2d. grey-brown	16·00	25·00

1967–70. *Ordinary paper.* W **105** *(sideways).*

(a) P 12, line (9.11.67)

D28	D 2	½d. emerald	4·00	9·00
D29		1d. purple	4·00	9·00
D30		2d. blackish brown	4·00	9·00
D31		4d. yellow-olive	50·00	£100
D28/31		. . . . *Set of* 4	55·00	£120

(b) P 12½, *comb* (30.5.68–70)

D32	D 2	½d. emerald	35	1·50
D33		1d. purple	30	1·00
D34		1½d. yellow-brown	35	2·75
		a. Orange-brown (23.10.70)	90	3·00
D35		2d. blackish brown	85	70
		a. Brownish black (23.10.70)	1·50	3·00
D36		2½d. yellow-orange	60	70
D37		3d. deep slate-blue	60	60
D38		4d. yellow-olive	1·00	80
D39		6d. purple	75	1·00
D40		1s. black	90	1·50
D41		1s. 6d. carmine	2·25	5·50
D32/41		. . . . *Set of* 10	7·00	14·00

The above are the local release dates. In the 12½ perforation the London release dates were 21 May for the ½d. to 4d. and 4 June for the 6d. to 1s. 6d.

Nos. D34*a* and D35*a* are on glazed paper.

(Des G. Pace. Litho Printex Ltd, Malta)

1973 (28 Apr). W **105**. *P* 13 × 13½.

D42	D 3	2 m. grey-brown and reddish brown . .	10	10
D43		3 m. dull orange and Indian red . .	10	15
D44		5 m. rose and bright scarlet . .	15	20
D45		1 c. turquoise and bottle green . .	30	35
D46		2 c. slate and black . .	30	35
D47		3 c. light yellow-brown and red-brown	30	35
D48		5 c. dull blue and royal blue	55	70
D49		10 c. reddish lilac and plum	75	1·00
D42/9		. . . . *Set of* 8	2·25	2·75

D 4

(Des M. Bonavia. Litho Printex Ltd, Malta)

1993 (4 Jan). W **105** *(sideways). P* 14.

D50	D 4	1 c. magenta and pale magenta . .	10	10
D51		2 c. new blue and pale blue	10	10
D52		5 c. blue-green & pale turquoise-green	15	20
D53		10 c. yellow-orange and greenish yellow	30	35
D50/3		. . . . *Set of* 4	55	65

Mauritius

GREAT BRITAIN STAMPS USED IN MAURITIUS. We no longer list the Great Britain stamps with obliteration "B 53" as there is no evidence that British stamps were available from the Mauritius Post Office.

See under SEYCHELLES for stamps of Mauritius used at Victoria with "B 64" cancellations between 1861 and 1890.

A similar "B 65" cancellation was used on the island of Rodrigues, a dependency of Mauritius, from 11 December 1861 onwards.

PRICES FOR STAMPS ON COVER TO 1945

Nos. 1/5	*from* × 2
Nos. 6/9	*from* × 3
Nos. 10/15	*from* × 4
Nos. 16/25	*from* × 5
Nos. 26/9	*from* × 3
Nos. 30/1	*from* —
Nos. 32/5	*from* × 4
Nos. 36/44	*from* × 5
Nos. 46/72	*from* × 3
Nos. 76/82	*from* × 5
Nos. 83/91	*from* × 6
Nos. 92/100	*from* × 4
Nos. 101/11	*from* × 3
Nos. 117/24	*from* × 8
Nos. 127/32	*from* × 7
No. 133	*from* × 4
Nos. 134/5	*from* × 10
No. 136	*from* × 8
Nos. 137/56	*from* × 6
Nos. 157/63	*from* × 5
Nos. 164/221	*from* × 3
No. 222	—
Nos. 223/41	*from* × 3
Nos. 242/4	*from* × 10
Nos. 245/8	*from* × 3
Nos. 249/63	*from* × 2
Nos. E1/6	*from* × 10
Nos. D1/7	*from* × 40
Nos. R1/3	*from* × 15

CROWN COLONY

Nos. 1/25*b* and 36/44 were printed in Mauritius.

1
("POST OFFICE")

2
("POST PAID")

(Engraved on copper by J. O. Barnard)

1847 (21 Sept). *Head of Queen on groundwork of diagonal and perpendicular lines. Imperf.*

1 1 1d. orange-red .. .. — £450000
2 2d. deep blue .. .. — £550000

A single plate contained one example of each value.

It is generally agreed that fifteen examples of No. 1 have survived (including two unused) and twelve of No. 2 (including four unused). Most are now in permanent museum collections.

NOTE. Our prices for early Mauritius are for stamps in very fine condition. Exceptional copies are worth more, poorer copies considerably less.

(Engraved on copper by J. O. Barnard)

1848 (June)–**59.** *Imperf.*

A. *Earliest impressions. Design deep, sharp and clear. Diagonal lines predominate. Thick paper (Period of use: 1d. 1853–54, 2d. 1848–49)*

3 2 1d. orange-vermilion/*yellowish* £35000 £13000
4 2d. indigo-blue/*grey to bluish* £30000 £15000
a. "PENOE" for "PENCE" (R. 3/1) .. £60000 £23000
5 2d. deep blue/*grey to bluish* £30000 £15000
a. "PENOE" for "PENCE" (R. 3/1) .. £60000 £26000

B. *Early impressions. Design sharp and clear but some lines slightly weakened. Paper not so thick, grey to yellowish white or bluish (Period of use: 1d. 1853–55, 2d. 1849–54).*

6 2 1d. vermilion £15000 £5500
7 1d. orange-vermilion £16000 £5000
8 2d. blue £17000 £6000
a. "PENOE" for "PENCE" (R. 3/1) .. £27000 £9500
9 2d. deep blue £21000 £6500

C. *Intermediate impressions. White patches appear where design has worn. Paper yellowish white, grey or bluish, of poorish quality (Period of use: 1d and 2d. 1854–57)*

10 2 1d. bright vermilion £7500 £2000
11 1d. dull vermilion £7500 £2000
12 1d. red £7500 £2000
13 2d. deep blue £10000 £3000
14 2d. blue £7500 £2250
a. "PENOE" for "PENCE" (R. 3/1) *from* £13000 £4750
15 2d. light blue £7500 £2250

D. *Worn impressions. Much of design worn away but some diagonal lines distinct. Paper yellowish, grey or bluish, of poorish quality (Period of use: 1d. 1857–59, 2d. 1855–58)*

16 2 1d. red/*yellowish or grey* £2250 £425
17 1d. red-brown/*yellowish or grey* £2250 £425
18 1d. red/*bluish* £1700 £375
a. Doubly printed .. ..
19 1d. red-brown/*bluish* £1700 £375
20 2d. blue (*shades*)/*yellowish or grey* .. £2500 £800
a. "PENOE" for "PENCE" (R. 3/1) .. *from* — £1300
21 2d. grey-blue/*yellowish or grey* £2750 £750
22 2d. blue (*shades*)/*bluish* £2500 £750
a. Doubly printed .. ..

E. *Latest impressions. Almost none of design showing except part of Queen's head and frame. Paper yellowish, grey or bluish, of poorish quality (Period of use: 1d. 1859, 2d. 1856–58)*

23 2 1d. red £1400 £375
24 1d. red-brown £1400 £375
25 2d. grey-blue/*bluish* £1800 £475
a. "PENOE" for "PENCE" (R. 3/1) .. £3250 £900

Earliest known use of the 2d. value is on 19 June 1848, but the 1d. value is not known used before 27 September 1853.

There were separate plates for the 1d. and 2d. values, each of 12 (3×4).

3

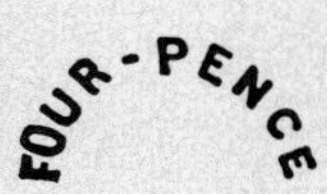

(4)

5

(Eng G. Fairman. Recess P.B.)

1858*. *Surch with T 4. Imperf.*

26 3 4d. green £750 £375

*Although originally gazetted for use from 8 April 1854, research into the archives indicates that No. 26 was not actually issued until 1858, when the stamps were mentioned in an ordinance of 30 April. The earliest dated postmark known is 27 March 1858.

1858–62. *No value expressed. Imperf.*

27 3 (4d.) green £425 £200
28 (6d.) vermilion .. .. 25·00 35·00
29 (9d.) dull magenta (1859) £500 £200
a. Reissued as (1d.) value (11.62) .. † £160

Use of the dull magenta as a 1d. value can be confirmed by the presence of the "B 53" cancellation which was first introduced in 1861.

Prepared for use, but not issued

30 3 (No value), red-brown .. .. .. 9·00
31 (No value), blue .. .. 2·75

Remainders of these were overprinted "L.P.E. 1890" in red, perforated at the London Philatelic Exhibition and sold as souvenirs.

(Recess P.B.)

1859–61. *Imperf.*

32 5 6d. blue .. .. £500 30·00
33 6d. dull purple-slate (1861) .. .. 18·00 26·00
34 1s. vermilion .. .. £2000 45·00
35 1s. yellow-green (1861) .. .. .. £375 85·00

The 1859 printings had the colours transposed by mistake.

6

7

8

(Engraved on copper by J. Lapirot)

1859 (Mar–Nov). *Imperf. (a) Early impressions.*

36 6 2d. deep blue £4750 £1800
37 2d. blue £3750 £1600

(*b*) *Intermediate prints. Lines of background, etc, partly worn away* (July)

38 6 2d. blue £2500 £600

(*c*) *Worn impressions, bluish-paper* (Oct)

39 6 2d. blue £1100 £400

(*d*) *Retouched impression* (Nov)

39*a* 6 2d. blue .. .. † —
ab. "MAURITUIS" (R.2/4) .. .. .. † —
ac. "MAURITUS" (R.3/1) .. .. .. † —

Nos. 36/9*a* were printed from a plate of 12 (4×3). The plate became worn through use, and was eventually extensively re-engraved. Only two pairs (one on cover) have been recorded from this retouched impression. The errors made in the re-engraving of the inscriptions probably resulted in it being withdrawn from use.

(1848 plate re-engraved by R. Sherwin)

1859 (Oct). *Bluish paper. Imperf.*

40 7 2d. deep blue £100000 £4000

The 1d. plate was also re-engraved, but was not put into use. Reprints in black were made in 1877 from both 1d. and 2d. re-engraved plates. Coloured autotype illustrations were prepared from these reprints and 600 were included in the R.P.S.L. handbook on *British Africa* in 1900. Further reprints in black were made in 1911 after the plates had been presented to the R.P.S.L. and defaced.

(Lithographed by L. A. Dardenne)

1859 (12 Dec). *White laid paper. Imperf.*

41 8 1d. deep red £5000 £1500
41*a* 1d. red £4000 £850
42 1d. dull vermilion £3000 £750
43 8 2d. slate-blue £3250 £700
43*a* 2d. blue £1600 £450
44 2d. pale blue £1500 £350
a. Heavy retouch on neck .. .. .. — £1100
b. Retouched below "TWO" .. .. .. — £600

The neck retouch shows a prominent curved white line running from the base of the chignon to the nape of the neck. No. 44*b* shows several diagonal lines in the margin below "TWO".

9

10

(Typo D.L.R.)

1860 (Apr)–**63.** *No wmk. P 14.*

46 9 1d. purple-brown .. .. £120 17·00
47 2d. blue .. .. £160 26·00
48 4d. rose .. .. £160 21·00
49 6d. green (1862) £600 £100
50 6d. slate (1863) .. .. £170 75·00
51 9d. dull purple .. .. 80·00 35·00
52 1s. buff (1862) .. .. £225 60·00
53 1s. green (1863) £550 £140

1862. *Intermediate perf* 14 *to* 16.

54 5 6d. slate .. .. 15·00 35·00
a. Imperf between (horiz pair) £4250
55 1s. deep green £1800 £325

1863–72. *Wmk Crown CC. P* 14.

56 9 1d. purple-brown .. .. 48·00 8·00
57 1d. brown .. .. 60·00 5·50
58 1d. bistre (1872) .. .. 85·00 6·00
59 2d. pale blue .. .. 65·00 6·50
60 2d. bright blue .. .. 65·00 6·50
a. Imperf (pair) £1300 £1800
61 3d. deep red .. .. £120 22·00
61*a* 3d. dull red .. .. 40·00 8·50
62 4d. rose .. .. 75·00 2·50
63 6d. dull violet .. .. £140 23·00
64 6d. yellow-green (1865) .. .. .. £120 11·00
65 6d. blue-green .. .. 90·00 3·75
66 9d. yellow-green (1872) £100 £160
67 10 10d. maroon (1872) .. .. £160 29·00
68 9 1s. yellow .. .. £140 15·00
69 1s. blue (1866) .. .. £130 18·00
70 1s. orange (1872) .. .. £130 12·00
71 5s. rosy mauve .. .. £150 45·00
72 5s. bright mauve (1865) .. .. .. £180 45·00

HALF PENNY
(11)

½ d
HALF PENNY
(12)

1876. (*a*) *Nos. 51 and 67 surch with T* **11** *locally.*

76 9 ½d. on 9d. dull purple .. .. .. 6·00 8·50
a. Surch inverted £350
b. Surch double .. .. — £1100
77 10 ½d. on 10d. maroon .. .. .. 1·25 12·00

(*b*) *Prepared for use, but not issued. No. 51 surch with T* **12.**

78 9 ½d. on 9d. dull purple (R.) £700
a. "PRNNY" .. ..
b. Black surch £950

HALF PENNY
(13)

One Penny
(14)

One Shilling
(15)

Shill
Wrong fount "S"

1877 (Apr–Dec). *Nos. 62, 67 (colour changed) and 71/2 surch with T* **13/15** *locally.*

79 10 ½d. on 10d. rose .. .. 2·50 25·00
80 9 1d. on 4d. rose-carmine (6 Dec) .. .. 7·50 12·00
81 1s. on 5s. rosy mauve (6 Dec) .. .. £200 85·00
82 1s. on 5s. bright mauve (6 Dec) £200 £100
a. Wrong fount "S" .. .. ..

(New Currency. 100 cents = 1 rupee)

"CANCELLED" OVERPRINTS. Following the change of currency in 1878 various issues with face values in sterling were overprinted "CANCELLED" in serifed type and sold as remainders. The stamps involved were Nos. 51, 56/62, 65, 67/8, 71/2, 76, 78/*b*, 79 and 81/2.

Examples of such overprints on stamps between Nos. 51 and 72 are worth about the same as the prices quoted for used, on Nos. 78/*b* they are worth 12% of the unused price, on No. 79 65% and on Nos. 81/2 20%.

2 CENTS
(16)

2 Rs. 50 C.
(17)

1878 (3 Jan). *Surch as T* **16** *or* **17** *(No.* 91*). Wmk Crown CC. P* 14.
83 **10** 2 c. dull rose (lower label blank) .. 5·50 4·50
84 **9** 4 c. on 1d. bistre .. 7·50 4·00
85 8 c. on 2d. blue .. 65·00 1·00
86 13 c. on 3d. orange-red .. 7·50 22·00
87 17 c. on 4d. rose .. £130 1·50
88 25 c. on 6d. slate-blue .. £160 4·75
89 38 c. on 9d. pale violet .. 18·00 48·00
90 50 c. on 1s. green .. 85·00 2·50
91 2 r. 50 on 5s. bright mauve .. 12·00 12·00
83/91 .. *Set of* 9 £450 90·00

18 19 20

21 22 23

24 25 26

(Typo D.L.R.)

1879 (Mar)–**80**. *Wmk Crown CC. P* 14.
92 **18** 2 c. Venetian red (1.80) .. 30·00 11·00
93 **19** 4 c. orange .. 65·00 3·50
94 **20** 8 c. blue (1.80) .. 13·00 1·75
95 **21** 13 c. slate (1.80) .. £120 £160
96 **22** 17 c. rose (1.80) .. 45·00 4·75
97 **23** 25 c. olive-yellow .. £225 8·00
98 **24** 38 c. bright purple (1.80) .. £150 £180
99 **25** 50 c. green (1.80) .. 3·50 2·25
100 **26** 2 r. 50, brown-purple (1.80) .. 28·00 50·00
92/100 .. *Set of* 9 £600 £375

27

(Typo D.L.R.)

1883–94. *Wmk Crown CA. P* 14.
101 **18** 1 c. pale violet (1893) .. 1·25 45
102 2 c. Venetian red .. 29·00 4·75
103 2 c. green (1885) .. 1·75 55
104 **19** 4 c. orange .. 65·00 2·50
105 4 c. carmine (1885) .. 2·50 60
106 **20** 8 c. blue (1891) .. 1·50 80
107 **27** 15 c. chestnut (1893) .. 3·25 90
108 15 c. blue (1894) .. 5·50 65
109 16 c. chestnut (1885) .. 3·25 80
110 **23** 25 c. olive-yellow .. 4·25 1·75
111 **25** 50 c. orange (1887) .. 28·00 8·00
101/11 .. *Set of* 11 £130 19·00
101, 103, 105, 107/9, 111 Optd "Specimen" *Set of* 7 £350

16 CENTS — (28)

SIXTEEN CENTS — (29)

(*a*) Surcharge 14 mm long and 3 high.
(*b*) Surcharge 15 mm long and 3½ high.
(*c*) Surcharge 15 mm long and 2½ high.

1883 (26 Feb). *No.* 96 *surch as T* **28** *locally.*
112 **22** 16 c. on 17 c. rose (*a*) .. £120 50·00
a. Surch double
113 16 c. on 17 c. rose (*b*) .. £130 50·00
114 16 c. on 17 c. rose (*c*) .. £275 £100

1883 (14 July). *Surch with T* **29** *by D.L.R. Wmk Crown CA. P* 14.
115 **22** 16 c. on 17 c. rose .. 55·00 80

MINIMUM PRICE

The minimum price quote is 10p which represents a handling charge rather than a basis for valuing common stamps. For further notes about prices see introductory pages.

2 CENTS — (30)

2 CENTS — (31)

1885 (11 May). *No.* 98 *surch with T* **30** *locally.*
116 **24** 2 c. on 38 c. bright purple .. 85·00 32·00
a. Without bar .. — £110
b. Surch inverted .. £400 £400
c. Surch double .. £450

1887 (6 July). *No.* 95 *surch with T* **31** *locally.*
117 **21** 2 c. on 13 c. slate (R.) .. 35·00 60·00
a. Surch inverted .. £120 £140
b. Surch double .. — £425
c. Surch double, one on back of stamp £475

TWO CENTS — (32)

TWO CENTS — (33)

1891 (10–16 Sept). *Nos.* 88, 96, 98 *and* 105 *surch locally as T* **32** *(Nos.* 118/19, 121*) or T* **33** *(No.* 120*).*
118 **19** 2 c. on 4 c. carmine (No. 105) (12 Sept) 1·00 40
a. Surch inverted .. 65·00
b. Surch double .. 70·00 65·00
c. Surch double, one inverted .. 70·00 65·00
119 **22** 2 c. on 17 c. rose (No. 96) (16 Sept) .. 85·00 85·00
a. Surch inverted .. £225
b. Surch double .. £425 £425
120 **9** 2 c. on 38 c. on 9d. pale violet (No. 89) (16 Sept) .. 1·40 3·50
a. Surch inverted .. £180
b. Surch double .. £425 £425
c. Surch double, one inverted .. 90·00
121 **24** 2 c. on 38 c. bright purple (No. 98) .. 2·00 3·50
a. Surch inverted .. £425
b. Surch double .. £100
c. Surch double, one inverted .. £100

Minor varieties are also known with portions of the surcharge missing, due to defective printing.

ONE CENT — (34)

ONE CENT — (35)

1893 (1–7 Jan). *Surch with T* **34** *by D.L.R. or T* **35** *locally. Wmk Crown CA. P* 14.
123 **18** 1 c. on 2 c. pale violet (Optd S. £28) .. 80 50
124 **27** 1 c. on 16 c. chestnut (7 Jan) .. 80 2·25

36

37

(Typo D.L.R.)

1895–9. *Wmk Crown CA. P* 14.
127 **36** 1 c. dull purple and ultramarine (8.7.97) 75 90
128 2 c. dull purple and orange (8.7.97) .. 2·00 50
129 3 c. dull purple and deep purple .. 60 50
130 4 c. dull purple and emerald (8.7.97) .. 3·75 50
131 6 c. green and rose-red (1899) .. 3·50 3·50
132 18 c. green and ultramarine (8.7.97) .. 6·50 5·00
127/32 .. *Set of* 6 15·00 9·75
127/32 Optd "Specimen" .. *Set of* 6 80·00

(Des L. Duvergé. Typo D.L.R.)

1898 (15 Apr). *Diamond Jubilee. Wmk CA over Crown (sideways). P* 14.
133 **37** 36 c. orange and ultramarine (Optd S. £42) 9·50 14·00

6 CENTS — (38)

15 CENTS — (39)

1899 (23–28 May). *Nos.* 132/3 *surcharged with T* **38/9** *locally.*
134 **36** 6 c. on 18 c. green and ultramarine (R.) 70 75
a. Surch inverted .. £275 £160
135 **37** 15 c. on 36 c. orge & ultram (B.) (28 May) 1·00 1·60
a. Bar of surch omitted .. £200

The space between "6" and "CENTS" varies from 2½ to 4 mm.

40 Admiral Mahé de Labourdonnais, Governor of Mauritius, 1735–46

4 Cents — (41)

(Recess D.L.R.)

1899 (13 Dec). *Birth Bicentenary of Labourdonnais. Wmk Crown CC. P* 14.
136 **40** 15 c. ultramarine (Optd S. £65) .. 10·00 2·75

1900. *No.* 109 *surch with T* **41** *locally.*
137 **27** 4 c. on 16 c. chestnut .. 2·00 6·50

42

12 CENTS — (43)

(Typo D.L.R.)

1900–05. *Wmk Crown CC (1 r.) or Crown CA (others) (sideways on 2 r. 50, 5 r.). Ordinary paper. P* 14.
138 **36** 1 c. grey and black (1901) .. 50 10
139 2 c. dull purple and bright purple (4.01) 60 20
140 3 c. green and carmine/*yellow* (1902) 3·00 80
141 4 c. purple and carmine/*yellow* .. 1·50 40
w. Wmk inverted
142 4 c. grey-green and violet (1903) .. 60 1·50
w. Wmk inverted
143 4 c. black and carmine/*blue* (14.10.04) 4·00 60
w. Wmk inverted .. 15·00 15·00
144 5 c. dull purple & brt pur/*buff* (8.10.02) 4·50 50·00
145 5 c. dull purple and black/*buff* (2.03) 1·75 2·50
146 6 c. purple and carmine/*red* (1902) .. 1·25 60
w. Wmk inverted .. 20·00 15·00
147 8 c. green and black/*buff* (16.7.02) .. 1·40 5·00
148 12 c. grey-black and carmine (16.7.02) 1·50 1·60
149 15 c. green and orange .. 7·50 6·00
150 15 c. black and blue/*blue* (1905) .. 45·00 1·25
151 25 c. green and carmine/*green* (1902) .. 6·00 15·00
a. Chalk-surfaced paper .. 2·50 10·00
152 50 c. dull green & dp green/*yellow* (1902) 11·00 26·00
153 **42** 1 r. grey-black and carmine (1902) .. 48·00 38·00
w. Wmk inverted .. 80·00
154 2 r. 50, green and black/*blue* (1902) .. 14·00 70·00
155 5 r. purple and carmine/*red* (1902) .. 50·00 75·00
138/55 .. *Set of* 18 £180 £250
138/55 Optd "Specimen" .. *Set of* 18 £250

1902. *No.* 132 *surch with T* **43**.
156 **36** 12 c. on 18 c. green and ultramarine .. 1·25 5·00

The bar cancelling the original value seems in some cases to be one thick bar and in others two thin ones.

Postage & Revenue. — (44)

1902 (7 July). *Various stamps optd with T* **44** *locally.*
157 **36** 4 c. purple and carmine/*yellow* (No. 141) 30 20
158 6 c. green and rose-red (No. 131) .. 35 2·50
159 15 c. green and orange (No. 149) .. 1·25 30
160 **23** 25 c. olive-yellow (No. 110) .. 1·50 2·25
161 **25** 50 c. green (No. 99) .. 3·75 2·00
162 **26** 2 r. 50, brown-purple (No. 100) .. 70·00 85·00
157/62 .. *Set of* 6 70·00 85·00

Nos. 157/62 were overprinted to make surplus stocks of postage stamps available for revenue (fiscal) purposes also.

1902 (22 Sept). *No.* 133 *surch as T* **43**, *but with longer bar.*
163 **37** 12 c. on 36 c. orange and ultramarine .. 1·25 1·25
a. Surch inverted .. £375 £275

The note below No. 156 also applies to No. 163.

Forged double surcharge errors show a straight, instead of a curved, serif to the "1" of "12".

1904–7. *Wmk Mult Crown CA. Ordinary paper (2 c., 4 c., 6 c.) or chalk-surfaced paper (others). P* 14.
164 **36** 1 c. grey and black (1907) .. 8·00 2·75
165 2 c. dull and bright purple (1905) .. 16·00 2·00
a. Chalk-surfaced paper .. 16·00 1·00
166 3 c. green and carmine/*yellow* .. 20·00 7·50
167 4 c. black and carmine/*blue* .. 7·00 90
a. Chalk-surfaced paper .. 1·00 10
168 6 c. purple and carmine/*red* .. 4·25 10
a. Chalk-surfaced paper .. 1·50 10
171 15 c. black and blue/*blue* (1907) .. 4·00 35
174 50 c. green and deep green/*yellow* .. 1·50 2·25
175 **42** 1 r. grey-black and carmine (1907) .. 19·00 42·00
164/75 .. *Set of* 8 65·00 50·00

46

47

(Typo D.L.R.)

1910 (17 Jan). *Wmk Mult Crown CA. Ordinary paper* (1 c. *to* 15 c.) *or chalk-surfaced paper* (25 c. *to* 10 r.). *P* 14.

181 **46** 1 c. black .. .. 2·00 30
182 2 c. brown .. .. 2·25 10
183 3 c. green .. .. 2·25 10
w. Wmk inverted .. .. .. 20·00
184 4 c. pale yellow-green and carmine .. 2·50 10
w. Wmk inverted .. .. .. — 30·00
185 **47** 5 c. grey and carmine .. .. 1·75 2·25
186 **46** 6 c. carmine-red .. .. .. 1·50 10
a. Pale red .. .. 2·50 85
ab. "A" of "CA" missing from wmk .. † —
187 8 c. orange .. .. 2·25 1·25
188 **47** 12 c. greyish slate .. .. .. 1·25 2·00
189 **46** 15 c. blue .. .. 13·00 10
190 **47** 25 c. black and red/*yellow* .. .. 1·75 9·50
191 50 c. dull purple and black .. .. 1·75 16·00
192 1 r. black/*green* .. .. .. 5·00 9·50
193 2 r. 50, black and red/*blue* .. .. 8·50 55·00
194 5 r. green and red/*yellow* .. .. 25·00 80·00
195 10 r. green and red/*green* .. .. 85·00 £170
181/95 .. .. *Set of* 15 £140 £300
181/95 Optd "Specimen" .. .. *Set of* 15 £225

On Nos. 188, 190 and 195 the value labels are as in T **49**.

48

49

(Typo D.L.R.)

1913–22. *Die I. Wmk Mult Crown CA. Ordinary paper* (5 c., 12 c.) *or chalk-surfaced paper* (*others*). *P* 14.

196 **48** 5 c. grey and carmine (1913) .. 1·25 3·00
a. Slate-grey and carmine .. .. 9·50 8·50
198 **49** 12 c. greyish slate (1914) .. .. 3·25 40
199 25 c. black and red/*yellow* (1913) .. 40 1·40
a. White back (1914) .. .. 50 13·00
aw. Wmk inverted and reversed .. 25·00
b. On orange-buff (1920) .. .. 32·00 60·00
c. On pale yellow (1921) (Optd S. £28) 32·00 40·00
cw. Wmk inverted .. .. .. 75·00
d. Die II. *On pale yellow* (1921) (Optd S. £28) .. .. 60 14·00
200 **48** 50 c. dull purple and black (1920) .. 27·00 50·00
201 1 r. black/*blue-green* (*ol back*) (1917) 2·00 15·00
a. On emerald (*olive back*) (1921) .. 7·50 48·00
b. Die II. *On emerald* (*emerald back*) (1921) (Optd S. £26) .. .. 1·25 6·50
202 2 r. 50, black and red/*blue* (1916) .. 16·00 40·00
203 5 r. green and red/*orange-buff* (1921) 55·00 90·00
a. On pale yellow (1921) .. .. 50·00 90·00
b. Die II. *On pale yellow* (1922) .. 40·00 £110
204 **49** 10 r. grn & red/*grn* (*bl-grn back*) (1913) 50·00 95·00
a. On blue-green (*olive back*) (1919) £750
b. On emerald (*olive back*) (1921) .. 55·00 95·00
c. On emerald (*emerald back*) (1921) 40·00 95·00
d. Die II. *On emerald* (*emerald back*) (1922) (Optd S. £35) .. .. 25·00 80·00
196/204 .. .. *Set of* 8 £100 £250
196/204 (5 r. 203*a*) Optd "Specimen" .. *Set of* 8 £160

1921–26. *Wmk Mult Script CA. Chalk-surfaced paper* (50 *r.*). *P* 14.

205 **46** 1 c. black 80 90
w. Wmk inverted .. .. ..
206 2 c. brown 80 10
w. Wmk inverted .. .. ..
207 2 c. purple/*yellow* (1926) 60 20
w. Wmk inverted .. .. .. 15·00
208 3 c. green (1926) .. .. .. 2·50 1·00
209 4 c. pale olive-green and carmine .. 1·50 1·75
x. Wmk reversed .. .. ..
210 4 c. green (1922) .. .. .. 1·00 10
w. Wmk inverted .. .. ..
x. Wmk reversed .. .. ..
211 4 c. brown (1926) .. .. .. 2·00 1·25
212 6 c. carmine .. .. 11·00 6·50
x. Wmk reversed .. .. .. 50·00
213 6 c. bright mauve (1922) .. .. 1·25 10
214 8 c. orange (1925) .. .. .. 2·25 14·00
215 10 c. grey (1922) .. .. .. 2·00 3·25
216 10 c. carmine-red (1926) .. .. 2·75 1·25
217 12 c. carmine-red (1922) .. .. 1·25 40
218 12 c. grey (1926) .. .. .. 1·00 2·50
219 15 c. blue .. .. 5·50 4·00
ax. Wmk reversed .. .. ..
b. Cobalt (1926) 75 25
220 20 c. blue (1922) .. .. .. 2·00 70
221 20 c. purple (1926) .. .. .. 8·00 10·00
222 – 50 r. dull purple and green (1924) (Optd S. £190) £700 £1300
205/21 .. .. *Set of* 17 38·00 38·00
205/21 Optd "Specimen" .. .. *Set of* 17 £250

No. 222 is as Type **46**, but measures 25×35 mm.

Normal

Open "C" (R. 9/6 of right pane)

A

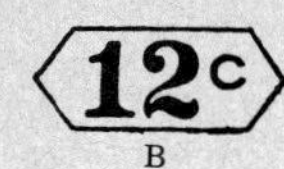

B

Two types of duty plate in the 12 c. In Type B the letters of "MAURITIUS" are larger; the extremities of the downstroke and the tail of the "2" are pointed, instead of square, and the "c" is larger.

1921–34. *Die II. Wmk Mult Script CA. Chalk-surfaced paper* (25 *c. to* 10 *r.*). *P* 14.

223 **49** 1 c. black (1926) 70 80
224 2 c. brown (1926) 55 10
225 3 c. green (1926) 60 30
226 4 c. sage-green and carmine (1926) .. 45 30
a. Open "C" .. ..
b. Die I (1932) .. .. .. 5·50 28·00
ba. Open "C" .. ..
226*c* 4 c. green (Die I) (1932) .. .. 3·50 45
ca. Open "C" .. ..
227 **48** 5 c. grey and carmine (1922) 80 10
a. Die I (1932) .. .. .. 4·00 4·00
228 **49** 6 c. sepia (1927) 60 60
229 8 c. orange (1926) .. .. .. 60 8·00
230 10 c. carmine-red (1926) .. .. 1·00 20
a. Die I (1932) .. .. .. 4·75 6·00
231 12 c. grey (Type A) (1922) .. .. 60 9·00
232 12 c. carmine-red (Type A) (1922) .. 30 3·00
232*a* 12 c. pale grey (Type A) (1926) (Optd S £28) .. .. 80 9·00
232*b* 12 c. grey (Type B) (1934) .. .. 3·00 20
233 15 c. Prussian blue (1926) 70 20
234 20 c. purple (1926) 45 40
235 20 c. Prussian blue (Die I) (1932) .. 9·50 80
a. Die II (1934) .. .. .. 11·00 30
236 25 c. black and red/*pale yellow* (1922) 30 15
a. Die I (1932) .. .. .. 2·75 25·00
237 **48** 50 c. dull purple and black (1921) .. 7·50 3·50
238 1 r. black/*emerald* (1924) .. .. 2·25 40
a. Die I (1932) .. .. .. 11·00 23·00
239 2 r. 50, black and red/*blue* (1922) .. 16·00 6·00
240 5 r. green and red/*yellow* (1924) .. 25·00 60·00
241 **49** 10 r. green and red/*emerald* (1924) .. 55·00 £130
223/41 .. .. *Set of* 20 £110 £190
223/41 Optd/Perf "Specimen" .. *Set of* 20 £325

3
Cents

(50)

51

1925 (25 Nov). *Nos.* 210, 217 *and* 220 *surch locally as T* **50**.

242 **46** 3 c. on 4 c. green .. .. .. 2·50 3·75
243 10 c. on 12 c. carmine-red 30 20
244 15 c. on 20 c. blue 55 20
242/4 .. .. *Set of* 3 3·00 3·75
242/4 Optd "Specimen" .. .. *Set of* 3 70·00

1935 (6 May). *Silver Jubilee. As Nos.* 114/17 *of Jamaica but ptd by D.L.R. P* 13½×14.

245 5 c. ultramarine and grey 50 10
f. Diagonal line by turret .. .. 35·00
g. Dot to left of chapel .. .. 50·00
h. Dot by flagstaff .. .. .. 50·00
246 12 c. green and indigo .. .. .. 4·00 10
f. Diagonal line by turret .. .. 70·00
g. Dot to left of chapel £100
247 20 c. brown and deep blue .. .. 4·00 20
g. Dot to left of chapel £110
248 1 r. slate and purple .. .. .. 28·00 38·00
h. Dot by flagstaff £275
245/8 .. .. *Set of* 4 32·00 38·00
245/8 Perf "Specimen" .. .. *Set of* 4 80·00

For illustrations of plate varieties see Omnibus section following Zimbabwe.

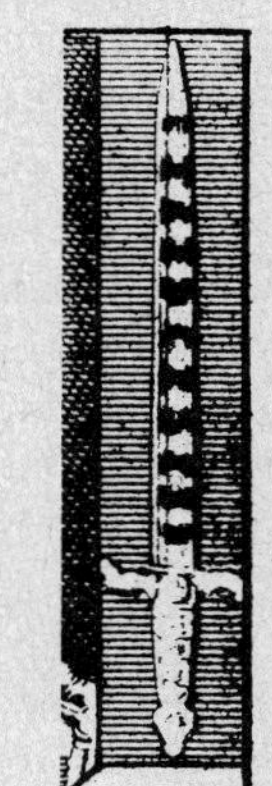
Line through sword (R. 2/2)

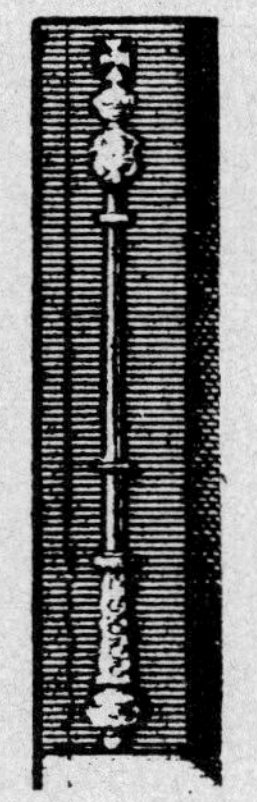
Line by sceptre (R. 5/3)

1937 (12 May). *Coronation. As Nos.* 118/20 *of Jamaica.*

249 5 c. violet 40 10
250 12 c. scarlet .. .. 40 1·50
251 20 c. bright blue 40 10
a. Line through sword .. .. .. 50·00
b. Line by sceptre .. .. .. 50·00
249/51 .. .. *Set of* 3 1·10 1·50
249/51 Perf "Specimen" .. .. *Set of* 3 50·00

Sliced "S" at right (R. 2/2, 3/2, right pane)

Sliced "S" at top (R. 4/1, left pane and R. 8/4, right pane)

Broken frame under "A" of "MAURITIUS" (R. 9/3 left pane, Key Plate 2)

"IJ" flaw (R. 3/6 of right pane)

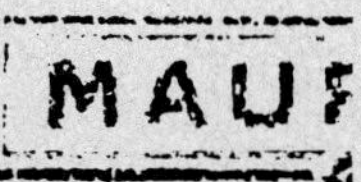

Battered "A" (R. 6/1 of right pane)

(Typo D.L.R.)

1938–49. *T* **51** *and similar types. Wmk Mult Script CA. Chalk-surfaced paper* (25 *c. to* 10 *r.*). *P* 14.

252 2 c. olive-grey (9.3.38) 30 10
a. Perf 15×14 (1942) .. .. .. 1·00 10
253 3 c. reddish purple and scarlet (27.10.38) 2·00 1·25
a. Sliced "S" at right .. .. .. 65·00
b. Reddish lilac and red (4.43) .. .. 2·25 2·25
ba. Sliced "S" at right .. .. .. 70·00
254 4 c. dull green (26.2.38) .. .. .. 2·25 1·25
a. Open "C" .. ..
b. Deep dull green (4.43) .. .. .. 1·00 1·25
ba. Open "C" .. ..
255 5 c. slate-lilac (23.2.38) .. .. .. 6·00 50
a. Pale lilac (*shades*) (4.43) .. .. 2·25 20
b. Perf 15×14 (1942) .. .. .. 35·00 10
256 10 c. rose-red (9.3.38) .. .. .. 2·25 20
a. Sliced "S" at top .. .. .. 80·00
b. Deep reddish rose (*shades*) (4.43) .. 2·25 10
ba. Sliced "S" at top .. .. .. 80·00
c. Perf 15×14. *Pale reddish rose* (1942) 27·00 85
ca. Sliced "S" at top £250
257 12 c. salmon (*shades*) (26.2.38) .. .. 1·00 20
a. Perf 15×14 (1942) .. .. .. 50·00 75
258 20 c. blue (26.2.38) .. .. 1·00 10
a. Broken frame £100
259 25 c. brown-purple (2.3.38) .. .. .. 6·00 20
a. "IJ" flaw £170
b. Ordinary paper (8.4.43) .. .. 3·50 10
ba. "IJ" flaw £100
260 1 r. grey-brown (2.3.38) .. .. .. 19·00 1·50
a. Battered "A" £250
b. Ordinary paper (8.4.43) .. .. 14·00 70
ba. Battered "A" £180
c. Drab (4.49) .. .. 20·00 3·75
ca. Battered "A" £250
261 2 r. 50, pale violet (2.3.38) .. .. 38·00 10·00
a. Ordinary paper (8.4.43) .. .. 25·00 8·00
b. Slate-violet (4.48) .. .. .. 38·00 20·00
262 5 r. olive-green (2.3.38) .. .. .. 48·00 22·00
a. Ordinary paper. *Sage-green* (8.4.43) 27·00 22·00
263 10 r. reddish purple (*shades*) (2.3.38) .. 42·00 26·00
a. Ordinary paper (8.4.43) .. .. 10·00 19·00
252/63*a* .. .. *Set of* 12 80·00 45·00
252/63 Perf "Specimen" .. .. *Set of* 12 £160

The stamps perf 15 × 14 were printed by Bradbury, Wilkinson from De La Rue plates and issued only in the colony in 1942. De La Rue printings of the 2 c. to 20 c. in 1943–45 were on thin, whiter paper. 1943–45 printings of the 25 c. to 10 r. were on unsurfaced paper.

1946 (20 Nov). *Victory. As Nos.* 141/2 *of Jamaica.*

264 5 c. lilac 10 10
265 20 c. blue 10 10
264/5 Perf "Specimen" .. .. *Set of* 2 50·00

52 1d. "Post Office" Mauritius and King George VI

(Recess B.W.)

1948 (22 Mar). *Centenary of First British Colonial Postage Stamp. Wmk Mult Script CA. P* 11½×11.

266 **52** 5 c. orange and magenta 10 30
267 12 c. orange and green 10 10
268 – 20 c. blue and light blue 10 10
269 – 1 r. blue and red-brown 15 30
266/9 .. .. *Set of* 4 40 60
266/9 Perf "Specimen" .. .. *Set of* 4 90·00

Design:—20 c., 1 r. As T **52** but showing 2d. "Post Office" Mauritius.

1948 (25 Oct). *Royal Silver Wedding. As Nos.* 143/4 *of Jamaica.*

270 5 c. violet 10 10
271 10 r. magenta .. .. 9·00 19·00

1949 (10 Oct). *75th Anniv of U.P.U. As Nos.* 145/8 *of Jamaica.*

272 12 c. carmine 60 65
273 20 c. deep blue .. .. 1·25 1·25
274 35 c. purple 60 65
275 1 r. sepia 60 20
272/5 .. .. *Set of* 4 2·75 2·50

53 Labourdonnais Sugar Factory

55 Aloe Plant

(Photo Harrison)

1950 (1 July). *T* **53, 55** *and similar designs. Wmk Mult Script CA. Chalk surfaced paper. P* 13½ × 14½ *(horiz)*, 14½ × 13½ *(vert)*.

276 1 c. bright purple .. 10 50
277 2 c. rose-carmine .. 15 10
278 3 c. yellow-green .. 60 2·25
279 4 c. green .. 20 95
280 5 c. blue .. 15 10
281 10 c. scarlet .. 30 75
282 12 c. olive-green .. 1·25 1·50
283 20 c. ultramarine .. 60 15
284 25 c. brown-purple .. 1·25 40
285 35 c. violet .. 30 10
286 50 c. emerald-green .. 2·00 50
287 1 r. sepia .. 4·25 10
288 2 r. 50, orange .. 12·00 5·50
289 5 r. red-brown .. 13·00 13·00
290 10 r. dull blue .. 14·00 15·00
276/290 .. *Set of* 15 45·00 35·00

Designs: *Horiz*—2 c. Grand Port; 5 c. Rempart Mountain; 10 c. Transporting cane; 12 c. Mauritius Dodo and map; 35 c. Government House, Reduit; 1 r. Timor Deer; 2 r. 50, Port Louis; 5 r. Beach scene; 10 r. Arms of Mauritius. *Vert*—4 c. Tamarind Falls; 20 c. Legend of Paul and Virginie (inscr "VIRGINIA"); 25 c. Labourdonnais statue; 50 c. Pieter Both Mountain.

The latitude is incorrectly shown on No. 282. This was corrected before the same design was used for No. 302*a*.

1953 (2 June). *Coronation. As No.* 153 *of Jamaica*.

291 10 c. black and emerald .. 70 15

68 Tamarind Falls

69 Historical Museum, Mahebourg

(Photo Harrison)

1953 (3 Nov)–**58**. *Designs previously used for King George VI issue, but with portrait of Queen Elizabeth II as in T* **68/9**. *Wmk Mult Script CA. Chalk-surfaced paper. P* 13½×14½ *(horiz) or* 14½×13½ *(vert)*.

293 2 c. bright carmine (1.6.54) .. 10 10
294 3 c. yellow-green (1.6.54) .. 30 40
295 4 c. bright purple .. 10 60
w. Wmk inverted .. 22·00
296 5 c. Prussian blue (1.6.54) .. 10 10
297 10 c. bluish green .. 20 10
a. Yellowish green (9.2.55) .. 20 10
298 15 c. scarlet .. 10 10
299 20 c. brown-purple .. 15 20
w. Wmk inverted .. 6·00
300 25 c. bright ultramarine .. 1·25 10
a. Bright blue (19.6.57) .. 2·25 30
301 35 c. reddish violet (1.6.54) .. 20 10
w. Wmk inverted
302 50 c. bright green .. 55 65
302*a* 60 c. deep green (2.8.54) .. 10·00 10
ab. Bronze-green (27.8.58) .. 11·00 10
303 1 r. sepia .. 30 10
a. Deep grey-brown (19.6.57) .. 1·50 65
w. Wmk inverted .. £110
304 2 r. 50, orange (1.6.54) .. 13·00 6·50
305 5 r. red-brown (1.6.54) .. 13·00 7·50
a. Orange-brown (19.6.57) .. 22·00 9·00
306 10 r. deep grey-blue (1.6.54) .. 13·00 65
293/306 .. *Set of* 15 48·00 15·00

Designs: *Horiz*—2 c. Grand Port; 4 c. Sugar factory; 5 c. Rempart Mountain; 35 c. Government House; 60 c. Mauritius Dodo and map; 1 r. Timor Deer; 2 r. 50, Port Louis; 5 r. Beach scene; 10 r. Arms of Mauritius. *Vert*—3 c. Aloe plant; 20 c. Labourdonnais statue; 25 c. Legend of Paul and Virginie; 50 c. Pieter Both Mountain.

Nos. 296 and 300 exist in coils, constructed from normal sheets.

See also Nos. 314/16.

70 Queen Elizabeth II and King George III (after Lawrence)

(Litho Enschedé)

1961 (11 Jan). *150th Anniv of British Post Office in Mauritius. W* **w 12**. *P* 13½ × 14.

307 **70** 10 c. black and brown-red .. 10 10
w. Wmk inverted .. 65·00 15·00
308 20 c. ultramarine and light blue .. 25 25
w. Wmk inverted .. 35·00
309 35 c. black and yellow .. 35 25
310 1 r. deep maroon and green .. 40 25
w. Wmk inverted
307/10 .. *Set of* 4 1·00 70

1963 (4 June). *Freedom from Hunger. As No.* 80 *of Lesotho*.

311 60 c. reddish violet .. 40 10

1963 (2 Sept). *Red Cross Centenary. As Nos.* 203/4 *of Jamaica*.

312 10 c. red and black .. 15 10
313 60 c. red and blue .. 60 20

1963 (12 Nov)–**65**. *As Nos.* 297, 302*ab and* 304 *but wmk* **w 12**.

314 **68** 10 c. bluish green (1964) .. 15 10
a. Yellowish green (21.1.65) .. 25 10
315 – 60 c. bronze-green (28.5.64) .. 1·75 10
316 – 2 r. 50, orange .. 3·75 7·50
314/16 .. *Set of* 3 5·00 7·50

71 Bourbon White Eye

(Des D. M. Reid-Henry. Photo Harrison)

1965 (16 Mar). *Horiz designs as T* **71**. *W* **w 12** *(upright). Multicoloured; background colours given. P* 14½×14.

317 2 c. lemon .. 30 15
a. Grey (leg) omitted .. 90·00
w. Wmk inverted .. 9·00
318 3 c. brown .. 90 15
a. Black (eye and beak) omitted .. 85·00
w. Wmk inverted .. 22·00
319 4 c. light reddish purple .. 15 15
a. Mauve-pink omitted* .. 35·00
b. Pale grey omitted .. 85·00
c. Orange omitted .. £140
w. Wmk inverted .. 4·00
320 5 c. grey-brown .. 2·50 10
w. Wmk inverted .. 40·00
321 10 c. light grey-green .. 30 10
w. Wmk inverted .. 6·00
322 15 c. pale grey .. 1·75 40
a. Red (beak) omitted .. 70·00
w. Wmk inverted .. 24·00
323 20 c. light yellow-bistre .. 1·75 10
w. Wmk inverted .. 8·00
324 25 c. bluish grey .. 2·00 30
w. Wmk inverted .. 7·50
325 35 c. greyish blue .. 2·25 10
w. Wmk inverted .. 45·00
326 50 c. light yellow-buff .. 50 40
w. Wmk inverted .. 35·00
327 60 c. light greenish yellow .. 50 10
w. Wmk inverted .. 1·50
328 1 r. light yellow-olive .. 4·25 10
a. Pale orange omitted .. £110
b. Light grey (ground) omitted .. £130
329 2 r. 50, pale stone .. 4·50 6·00
330 5 r. pale grey-blue .. 13·00 8·50
a. Brown-red omitted .. £110
331 10 r. pale bluish green .. 24·00 15·00
317/31 .. *Set of* 15 48·00 28·00

Designs:—3 c. Rodriguez Fody; 4 c. Mauritius Olive White Eye; 5 c. Mascarene Paradise Flycatcher; 10 c. Mauritius Fody; 15 c. Mauritius Parakeet; 20 c. Mauritius Greybird; 25 c. Mauritius Kestrel; 35 c. Pink Pigeon; 50 c. Reunion Bulbul; 60 c. Mauritius Blue Pigeon (extinct); 1 r. Mauritius Dodo (extinct); 2 r. 50, Rodriguez Solitaire (extinct); 5 r. Mauritius Red Rail (extinct); 10 r. Broad-billed Parrot (extinct).

*On the 4 c. the background is printed in two colours so that in No. 319a the background colour is similar to that of the 5 c.

On No. 317*a* it is the deep grey which is missing, affecting the leg, beak and part of the branch. On No. 319*c* the missing orange affects the under breast of the bird, which appears much paler. On No. 328*a* the omission affects the legs and part of the body and on No. 330*a* the whole of the bird appears in the same colour as the legs.

The 50 c. and 2 r. 50 exist with PVA gum as well as gum arabic.

Nos. 320 and 324 exist in coils, constructed from normal sheets.

See also Nos. 340/1 and 370/5.

1965 (17 May). *I.T.U. Centenary. As Nos.* 98/9 *of Lesotho*.

332 10 c. red-orange and apple-green .. 15 10
333 60 c. yellow and bluish violet .. 40 20

1965 (25 Oct). *International Co-operation Year. As Nos.* 100/1 *of Lesotho*.

334 10 c. reddish purple and turquoise-green .. 15 10
335 60 c. deep bluish green and lavender .. 30 20

1966 (24 Jan). *Churchill Commemoration. As Nos.* 102/5 *of Lesotho*.

336 2 c. new blue .. 10 1·75
w. Wmk inverted .. 27·00
337 10 c. deep green .. 25 10
w. Wmk inverted .. 20·00
338 60 c. brown .. 1·10 20
w. Wmk inverted .. 8·00
339 1 r. bluish violet .. 1·25 20
336/9 .. *Set of* 4 2·40 2·00

1966–67. *As Nos.* 320, 325 *but wmk* **w 12** *sideways**.

340 5 c. grey-brown (1966) .. 10 15
w. Wmk Crown to right of CA .. 27·00
341 35 c. greyish blue (27.6.67) .. 20 15

*The normal sideways watermark shows Crown to left of CA, *as seen from the back of the stamp.*

No. 340 exists in coils, constructed from normal sheets.

72 "Education"

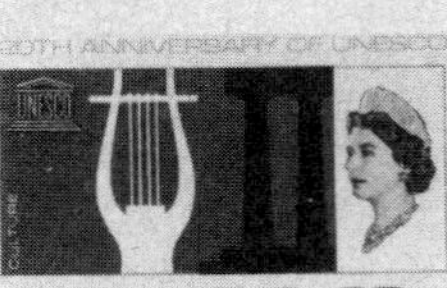

73 "Science"

74 "Culture"

(Des Jennifer Toombs. Litho Harrison)

1966 (1 Dec). *20th Anniv of U.N.E.S.C.O. W* **w 12** *(sideways). P* 14.

342 **72** 5 c. slate-violet, red, yellow and orange 15 30
343 **73** 10 c. orange-yellow, violet and deep olive 25 10
344 **74** 60 c. black, bright purple and orange .. 70 15
342/4 .. *Set of* 3 1·00 45

SELF-GOVERNMENT

86 Red-tailed Tropic Bird

(Des D. M. Reid-Henry. Photo Harrison)

1967 (1 Sept). *Self-Government. T* **86** *and similar horiz designs. Multicoloured. W* **w 12**. *P* 14½.

345 2 c. Type **86** .. 15 60
w. Wmk inverted .. 8·00
346 10 c. Rodriguez Brush Warbler .. 40 10
347 60 c. Rose-ringed Parakeet (extinct) .. 50 10
348 1 r. Grey-rumped Swiftlet .. 50 10
345/8 .. *Set of* 4 1·40 70

SELF GOVERNMENT 1967

(90)

1967 (1 Dec). *Self-Government. As Nos.* 317/31 *but wmk sideways* on Nos.* 352/3 *and* 357. *Optd with T* **90**. *P* 14×14½.

349 2 c. lemon .. 10 50
w. Wmk inverted .. 6·00
350 3 c. brown .. 10 50
w. Wmk inverted .. 9·00
351 4 c. light reddish purple .. 10 50
a. Orange omitted .. 60·00
352 5 c. grey-brown .. 10 10
353 10 c. light grey-green .. 10 10
w. Wmk Crown to right of CA .. 7·50
354 15 c. pale grey .. 10 30
355 20 c. light yellow-bistre .. 15 10
w. Wmk inverted .. 6·50
356 25 c. bluish grey .. 15 10
357 35 c. greyish blue .. 20 10
w. Wmk Crown to right of CA .. 35·00
358 50 c. light yellow-buff .. 30 15
359 60 c. light greenish yellow .. 30 10
w. Wmk inverted .. 2·75
360 1 r. light yellow-olive .. 35 10
361 2 r. 50, pale stone .. 1·00 2·25
362 5 r. pale grey-blue .. 5·00 3·25
363 10 r. pale bluish green .. 7·00 11·00
349/63 .. *Set of* 15 13·00 17·00

*The normal sideways watermark shows Crown to left of CA, *as seen from the back of the stamp.*

INDEPENDENT

91 Flag of Mauritius

(Litho D.L.R.)

1968 (12 Mar). *Independence. T* **91** *and similar horiz design. P* 13½ × 13.
364 **91** 2 c. multicoloured 10 95
365 – 3 c. multicoloured 15 95
366 **91** 15 c. multicoloured 15 10
367 – 20 c. multicoloured 30 10
368 **91** 60 c. multicoloured 50 10
369 – 1 r. multicoloured 60 10
364/9 .. .. *Set of* 6 1·60 2·00
Design:—3 c., 20 c. and 1 r. Arms and Mauritius Dodo emblem.

1968 (12 July). *As Nos.* 317/18, 322/3 *and* 327/8 *but background colours changed as below.*
370 2 c. olive-yellow .. .. 20 1·60
a. Black printed double .. ..
b. Grey printed double .. .. 65·00
371 3 c. cobalt .. .. 1·75 3·25
w. Wmk inverted .. .. 55·00
372 15 c. cinnamon 55 20
a. Greenish blue omitted £140
373 20 c. buff .. .. 3·50 2·25
374 60 c. rose .. .. 1·25 15
w. Wmk inverted .. .. 30·00
375 1 r. reddish purple .. .. 2·25 1·00
370/5 .. .. *Set of* 6 8·50 7·50

93 Dominique rescues Paul and Virginie

(Des V. Whiteley, from prints. Litho Format)

1968 (2 Dec). *Bicentenary of Bernardin de St. Pierre's Visit to Mauritius. Multicoloured designs as T* **93**. *P* 13½.
376 2 c. Type **93** 10 50
377 15 c. Paul and Virginie crossing the river .. 20 10
378 50 c. Visit of Labourdonnais to Madame de la Tour (*horiz*) 30 10
379 60 c. Meeting of Paul and Virginie in Confidence (*vert*) 30 10
380 1 r. Departure of Virginie for Europe (*horiz*) 40 20
381 2 r. 50, Bernardin de St. Pierre (*vert*) .. 1·10 3·00
376/81 .. .. *Set of* 6 2·25 3·50

99 Black-spotted Emperor

(Des J. Vinson (3 c., 20 c., 1 r.), R. Granger Barrett (others). Photo Harrison)

1969 (12 Mar)–**73**. *W* w **12** (*sideways** *on* 2, 3, 4, 5, 10, 15, 60 *and* 75 *c*). *Chalk-surfaced paper. P* 14.
382 2 c. multicoloured .. .. 10 1·25
a. Pale green printed double** .. .. 42·00
383 3 c. multicoloured .. .. 10 2·00
w. Wmk Crown to right of CA .. ..
384 4 c. multicoloured .. .. 1·40 2·25
w. Wmk Crown to right of CA .. .. 9·00
385 5 c. multicoloured 30 10
386 10 c. scarlet, black and flesh .. .. 1·00 10
w. Wmk Crown to right of CA .. .. 7·00
387 15 c. ochre, black and cobalt 30 10
w. Wmk Crown to right of CA .. .. 1·75
388 20 c. multicoloured 65 70
a. Glazed ordinary paper (20.2.73) .. 45 4·25
389 25 c. red, black and pale apple-green .. 30 1·50
a. Glazed ordinary paper (22.1.71) .. 3·75 4·50
w. Wmk inverted .. .. 4·00
390 30 c. multicoloured .. .. 1·50 1·50
a. Glazed, ordinary paper (20.3.73) .. 6·50 8·00
391 35 c. multicoloured .. .. 1·50 1·00
a. Glazed ordinary paper (3.2.71) .. 90 1·75
aw. Wmk inverted .. .. 3·50
392 40 c. multicoloured .. .. 35 1·25
a. Glazed ordinary paper (20.2.73) .. 6·50 8·00
aw. Wmk inverted .. .. 10·00
393 50 c. multicoloured .. .. 1·00 10
a. Red omitted .. .. 75·00
b. Glazed ordinary paper (22.1.71) .. 1·50 20
ba. Red printed double .. .. ..
bw. Wmk inverted .. .. 1·50 20
394 60 c. black, rose and ultramarine .. .. 1·50 10
395 75 c. multicoloured .. .. 1·50 2·25
w. Wmk Crown to right of CA .. .. 17·00
396 1 r. multicoloured 60 10
a. Glazed ordinary paper (22.1.71) .. 2·25 15
aw. Wmk inverted .. .. 45·00
397 2 r. 50, multicoloured .. .. .. 2·75 7·00
a. Glazed ordinary paper (20.2.73) .. 2·00 9·00
398 5 r. multicoloured .. .. 8·00 8·00
a. Glazed ordinary paper (22.1.71) .. 12·00 5·50
aw. Wmk inverted .. .. 21·00
399 10 r. multicoloured .. .. 2·50 4·50
w. Wmk inverted (26.1.72) .. .. 2·50 4·00
382/99 .. .. *Set of* 18 22·00 30·00
388a/98a .. .. *Set of* 9 32·00 38·00
Designs:—3 c. Red Reef Crab; 4 c. Episcopal Mitre (*Mitra mitra*); 5 c. Black-saddled Pufferfish ("Bourse"); 10 c. Starfish; 15 c. Sea Urchin; 20 c. Fiddler Crab; 25 c. Spiny Shrimp; 30 c. Single Harp Shells and Double Harp Shell; 35 c. Common Paper Nautilus (*Argonauta argo*); 40 c. Spanish Dancer (*Hexabranchus sanguineus*); 50 c. Orange Spider Conch (*Lambis crocata*) and Violet Spider Conch (*Lambis violacea*); 60 c. Blue Marlin; 75 c. *Conus clytospira*; 1 r. Dolphin (fish); 2 r. 50, Spiny Lobster; 5 r. Ruby Snapper ("Sacré Chien Rouge"); 10 r. Yellow-edged Lyretail ("Croissant Queue Jaune").
*The normal sideways watermark shows Crown to left of CA, *as seen from the back of the stamp.*
**No. 382a occurs from a sheet on which a second printing of the pale green appears above the normal.
Nos. 385/6 and 389 exist in coils constructed from normal sheets.
See also Nos. 437/54 and475/91.

117 Gandhi as Law Student

124 Frangourinier Cane-crusher (18th cent)

(Des J. W. Litho Format)

1969 (1 July). *Birth Centenary of Mahatma Gandhi. T* **117** *and similar vert designs. Multicoloured. W* w **12**. *P* 13½.
400 2 c. Type **117** 10 10
401 15 c. Gandhi as stretcher-bearer during Zulu Revolt 25 10
402 50 c. Gandhi as Satyagrahi in South Africa .. 30 20
403 60 c. Gandhi at No. 10 Downing Street, London 30 10
404 1 r. Gandhi in Mauritius, 1901 .. .. 40 10
405 2 r. 50, Gandhi, the "Apostle of Truth and Non-Violence" .. .. 90 1·25
400/5 .. .. *Set of* 6 2·00 1·50
MS406 153 × 153 mm. Nos. 400/5 .. .. 3·00 7·50

(Des V. Whiteley. Photo Enschedé)

1969 (22 Dec).* *150th Anniv of Telfair's Improvements to the Sugar Industry. T* **124** *and similar multicoloured designs. W* w **12** (*sideways on* 2 *c. to* 1 *r.*), *P* 11½ × 11 (2 *r.* 50) *or* 11 × 11½ (*others*).
407 2 c. Three-roller Vertical Mill 10 20
408 15 c. Type **124** 10 10
409 60 c. Beau Rivage Factory, 1867 .. .. 10 10
410 1 r. Mon Désert-Alma Factory, 1969 .. 10 10
411 2 r. 50, Dr. Charles Telfair (*vert*) 25 80
407/11 .. .. *Set of* 5 45 60
MS412 159 × 88 mm. Nos. 407/11†. Wmk sideways. P 11 × 11½ .. .. 1·25 2·25
*This was the local release date but the Crown Agents issued the stamps on 15 December.
† In the miniature sheet the 2 r. 50 is perf 11 at the top and imperf on the other three sides.

EXPO '70'
OSAKA
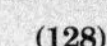
(128)

129 Morne Plage, Mountain and Boeing 707

1970 (7 Apr). *World Fair, Osaka. Nos.* 394 *and* 396 *optd with T* **128** *by Harrison & Sons.*
413 60 c. black, rose and ultramarine 10 10
w. Wmk Crown to right of CA .. .. 45·00
414 1 r. multicoloured 10 10

(Des H. Rose. Litho G. Gehringer, Kaiserslautern, Germany)

1970 (2 May). *Inauguration of Lufthansa Flight, Mauritius-Frankfurt. T* **129** *and similar multicoloured design. P* 14.
415 25 c. Type **129** 10 10
416 50 c. Boeing 707 and Map (*vert*) 10 10

131 Lenin as a Student

133 2d. "Post Office" Mauritius and original Post Office

(Photo State Ptg Works, Moscow)

1970 (15 May). *Birth Centenary of Lenin. T* **131** *and similar vert design. P* 12 × 11½.
417 15 c. blackish green and silver 10 10
418 75 c. blackish brown and gold 20 20
Design:—75 c. Lenin as Founder of U.S.S.R.

(Des and litho D.L.R.)

1970 (15 Oct). *Port Louis, Old and New. T* **133** *and similar horiz designs. Multicoloured. W* w **12** (*sideways*). *P* 14.
419 5 c. Type **133** 10 10
420 15 c. G.P.O. Building (built 1870) 10 10
421 50 c. Mail Coach (*c.* 1870) 40 10
422 75 c. Port Louis Harbour (1970) 55 10
423 2 r. 50, Arrival of Pierre A. de Suffren (1783) 70 70
419/23 .. .. *Set of* 5 1·60 80
MS424 165 × 95 mm. Nos. 419/23 .. .. 2·75 6·50

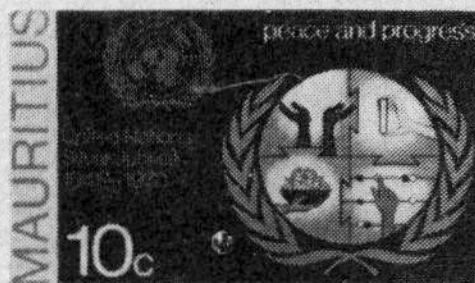

138 U.N. Emblem and Symbols

(Des Jennifer Toombs. Litho Format)

1970 (24 Oct). *25th Anniv of United Nations. W* w **12** (*sideways*). *P* 14½.
425 **138** 10 c. multicoloured 10 10
426 60 c. multicoloured 40 10

139 Rainbow over Waterfall

(Des R. Granger Barrett from local ideas (60 c.), R. Granger Barrett from local ideas and adapted by N. Mossae (others). Litho Format)

1971 (12 Apr). *Tourism. T* **139** *and similar horiz designs. Multicoloured. W* w **12** (*sideways**). *P* 14.
427 10 c. Type **139** 35 10
428 15 c. Trois Mamelles Mountains 35 10
w. Wmk Crown to right of CA .. .. 11·00
429 60 c. Beach scene 55 10
430 2 r. 50, Marine life .. .. 1·50 1·50
427/30 .. .. *Set of* 4 2·50 1·50
*The normal sideways watermark shows Crown to left of CA, *as seen from the back of the stamp.*
Nos. 427/30 are inscribed on the reverse with details of tourist attractions in Mauritius.

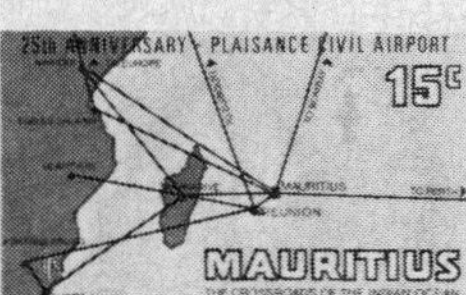

140 "Crossroads" of Indian Ocean

(Des R. Granger Barrett (60 c.) or V. Whiteley (others). Litho Harrison)

1971 (23 Oct). *25th Anniv of Plaisance Airport. T* **140** *and similar horiz designs. Multicoloured. W* w **12** (*sideways* on* 15 *c.*). *P* 14.
431 15 c. Type **140** 20 10
w. Wmk Crown to right of CA .. .. 20·00
432 60 c. Boeing 707 and Terminal Buildings .. 40 10
w. Wmk inverted .. .. 2·50
433 1 r. Air hostesses on gangway 45 10
w. Wmk inverted .. .. 2·75 90
434 2 r. 50, Farman F.190 *Roland Garros* airplane, Choisy Airfield, 1937 .. 1·75 3·75
431/4 .. .. *Set of* 4 2·50 3·75
*The normal sideways watermark shows Crown to left of CA, *as seen from the back of the stamp.*

141 Princess Margaret Orthopaedic Centre

(Des and litho Harrison)

1971 (2 Nov). *Third Commonwealth Medical Conference. T* **141** *and similar horiz design. Multicoloured. W* w **12**. *P* 14 × 13½.
435 10 c. Type **141** 10 10
w. Wmk inverted .. .. 6·00
436 75 c. Operation Theatre in National Hospital 20 20

1972–74. *As Nos.* 382/99 *but W* w **12** *upright* (2, 3, 4, 5, 10, 15, 60, 75 *c.*) *or sideways** (*others*).

A. Glazed, ordinary paper. B. Chalk-surfaced paper.

		A		B	
437	2 c. multicoloured	30	2·00	1·50	3·50
438	3 c. multicoloured	3·75	5·00	40	1·75
439	4 c. multicoloured	†		8·50	8·50
440	5 c. multicoloured	4·00	30	30	10
	w. Wmk inverted	60	—	†	
441	10 c. scarlet, black and flesh	4·25	30	8·50	2·00
	w. Wmk inverted	†		22·00	—
442	15 c. ochre, black and cobalt	50	90	35	30
	w. Wmk inverted	35·00	—	†	

443 20 c. multicoloured † 35 1·50
c. Printed on the gummed side † 40·00 †
444 25 c. red, black & apple-green † 35 1·75
w. Wmk Crown to right of CA † 35·00 —
445 30 c. multicoloured † 3·50 7·00
446 35 c. multicoloured † 6·00 75
a. Orange-brown omitted † 85·00 —
w. Wmk Crown to right of CA † 9·00 —
447 40 c. multicoloured † 6·50 9·00
448 50 c. multicoloured † 45 10
a. Red omitted † 80·00 —
w. Wmk Crown to right of CA † † 30·00
449 60 c. black, rose & ultramarine 60 60 65 10
a. Rose omitted † 55·00 —
w. Wmk inverted 16·00 — †
450 75 c. multicoloured 1·75 9·00 3·00 1·25
451 1 r. multicoloured † 1·25 30
452 2 r. 50, multicoloured † 2·00 3·75
453 5 r. multicoloured † 3·00 2·00
a. Greenish blue printed double † 45·00 —
454 10 r. multicoloured † 5·00 8·00
437/50A *Set of* 7 13·50 16·00
437/54B *Set of* 18 45·00 45·00

*The normal sideways watermark shows Crown to left of CA, *as seen from the back of the stamp.*

Nos. 440B and 444B exist in coils, constructed from normal sheets.

Dates of issue:

Glazed paper—10.1.72, 5 c., 10 c.; 20.2.73, 2 c., 3 c., 15 c., 60 c., 75 c.

Chalk-surfaced paper—8.11.73, 10 c., 20 c., 30 c., 35 c., 40 c., 75 c., 1 r., 10 r.; 12.12.73, 25 c., 50 c., 2 r. 50, 5 r.; 25.2.74, 5 c., 15 c., 60 c.; 13.6.74, 2 c., 3 c., 4 c.

142 Queen Elizabeth and Prince Philip

(Des and photo Harrison)

1972 (24 Mar). *Royal Visit. T* **142** *and similar multicoloured design. W* w **12**. *P* 14.
455 15 c. Type **142** 15 10
456 2 r. 50, Queen Elizabeth II (*vert*) 2·50 2·50

143 Theatre Façade

(Des and litho Harrison)

1972 (26 June). *150th Anniversary of Port Louis Theatre. T* **143** *and similar horiz design. Multicoloured. W* w **12**. *P* 14.
457 10 c. Type **143** 10 10
w. Wmk inverted 3·50
458 1 r. Theatre Auditorium 40 20
w. Wmk inverted 4·50

144 Pirate Dhow

(Des and litho Harrison)

1972 (17 Nov). *Pirates and Privateers. T* **144** *and similar multicoloured designs. W* w **12** (*sideways on* 60 c. *and* 1 r.). *P* 14½ × 14 (60 c., 1 r.) *or* 14 × 14½ (*others*).
459 15 c. Type **144** 65 15
460 60 c. Treasure chest (*vert*) 1·00 20
461 1 r. Lemene and *L'Hirondelle* (*vert*) 1·25 20
462 2 r. 50, Robert Surcouf 4·50 7·50
459/62 *Set of* 4 6·75 7·50

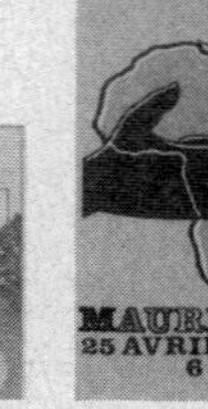

145 Mauritius University **146** Map and Hands

(Des and litho Harrison)

1973 (10 Apr). *Fifth Anniv of Independence. T* **145** *and similar horiz designs. Multicoloured. W* w **12** (*sideways**). *P* 14.
463 15 c. Type **145** 10 10
w. Wmk Crown to right of CA 28·00
464 60 c. Tea Development 15 15
465 1 r. Bank of Mauritius 15 15
463/5 *Set of* 3 30 30

*The normal sideways watermark shows Crown to left of CA, *as seen from the back of the stamp.*

(Des and litho Harrison)

1973 (25 Apr). *O.C.A.M.* Conference. T* **146** *and similar multi-coloured design. W* w **12** (*sideways on* 10 *c.*). *P* 14½ × 14 (10 *c.*) *or* 14 × 14½ (2 *r.* 50).
466 10 c. O.C.A.M. emblem (*horiz*) 10 10
467 2 r. 50, Type **146** 40 45

*O.C.A.M. = Organisation Commune Africaine Malgache et Mauricienne.

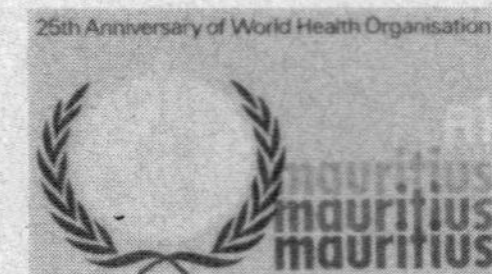

147 W.H.O. Emblem

(Des and litho Harrison)

1973 (20 Nov). *25th Anniv of W.H.O. W* w **12**. *P* 14.
468 **147** 1 r. multicoloured 10 10
a. Wmk sideways 20 10

148 Meteorological Station, Vacoas.

(Des and litho Harrison)

1973 (27 Nov). *I.M.O./W.M.O. Centenary. W* w **12** (*sideways*). *P* 14.
469 **148** 75 c. multicoloured 30 60

149 Capture of the *Kent*, 1800 **150** P. Commerson (naturalist)

(Des and litho Harrison)

1974 (21 Mar). *Birth Bicent of Robert Surcouf* (*privateer*). *W* w **12** (*sideways*). *P* 14.
470 **149** 60 c. multicoloured 50 85

(Des and litho Harrison)

1974 (18 Apr). *Death Bicent of Philibert Commerson* (1973). *W* w **12**. *P* 14½.
471 **150** 2 r. 50, multicoloured 30 40

151 Cow being Milked

(Des and litho Harrison)

1974 (23 Oct). *Eighth F.A.O. Regional Conference for Africa, Mauritius. W* w **12** (*sideways*). *P* 14.
472 **151** 60 c. multicoloured 20 20

152 Mail Train

(Des and litho Harrison)

1974 (4 Dec). *Centenary of Universal Postal Union. T* **152** *and similar horiz design. Multicoloured. W* w **12**. *P* 14.
473 15 c. Type **152** 40 15
474 1 r. New G.P.O., Port Louis 40 20

1975–77. *As Nos.* 382/99 *but W* w **14** (*sideways** *on* 2 *to* 15 *c.*, 60 *c. and* 75 *c.*). *Chalk-surfaced paper.*
475 2 c. multicoloured (16.8.77) 6·00 1·50
476 3 c. multicoloured (16.8.77) 6·00 1·50
w. Wmk Crown to right of CA 24·00
477 4 c. multicoloured (16.8.77) 7·50 1·50
478 5 c. multicoloured (19.3.75) 1·00 40
w. Wmk Crown to right of CA 5·50
479 15 c. ochre, black and cobalt (21.1.75) 2·25 1·25
480 20 c. multicoloured (19.3.76) 70 30
a. Grey (background) omitted £170
481 25 c. red, black and apple-green (19.3.75) 1·00 5·00
482 30 c. multicoloured (21.1.75) 35 6·50
a. Yellow omitted 85·00
483 35 c. multicoloured (19.3.76) 1·00 15
a. Orange-brown omitted 55·00
484 40 c. multicoloured (19.3.76) 1·00 60
485 50 c. multicoloured (19.3.76) 1·00 10
w. Wmk inverted 16·00
486 60 c. black, rose and ultramarine (16.8.77) 7·50 25
487 75 c. multicoloured (19.4.77) 1·25 1·50
488 1 r. multicoloured (19.3.76) 1·00 20
a. Deep bluish green (fin and tail markings) omitted £110
489 2 r. 50, multicoloured (16.8.77) 16·00 4·00
w. Wmk inverted 19·00
490 5 r. multicoloured (21.1.75) 5·00 15·00
w. Wmk inverted 60·00
491 10 r. multicoloured (21.1.75) 7·50 12·00
475/91 *Set of* 17 60·00 45·00

No. 492 is vacant.

153 "Cottage Life" (F. Leroy)

(Des and litho Harrison)

1975 (6 Mar). *Aspects of Mauritian Life. T* **153** *and similar multicoloured designs showing paintings. W* w **14** (*sideways** *on* 15 *c.*, 60 *c. and* 2 *r.* 50). *P* 14.
493 15 c. Type **153** 10 10
w. Wmk Crown to right of CA
494 60 c. "Milk Seller" (A. Richard) (*vert*) 35 10
a. Brown and stone (ornaments and frame) double
495 1 r. "Entrance of Port Louis Market" (Thuillier) 35 10
496 2 r. 50, "Washerwoman" (Max Boulleé) (*vert*) 95 80
w. Wmk Crown to right of CA 5·00
493/6 *Set of* 4 1·60 85

*The normal sideways watermark shows Crown to left of CA, *as seen from the back of the stamp.*

154 Mace across Map

(Des Harrison. Litho Questa)

1975 (21 Nov). *French-speaking Parliamentary Assemblies Conference. Port Louis. W* w **14** (*sideways*). *P* 14.
497 **154** 75 c. multicoloured 30 80

155 Woman with Lamp ("The Light of the World")

(Des A. H. Abdoolah; adapted Harrison. Litho Questa)

1975 (5 Dec). *International Women's Year. W* w **14** (*sideways*). *P* 14½.
498 **155** 2 r. 50, multicoloured 35 1·00

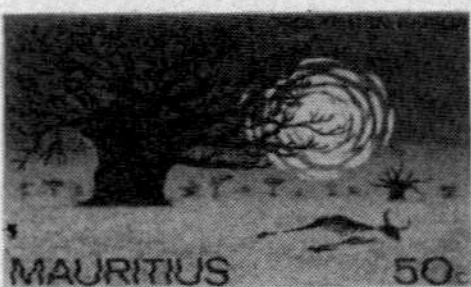

156 Parched Landscape

(Des Harrison (50 c.), J.W. Ltd (60 c.) Litho Questa)

1976 (26 Feb). *Drought in Africa. T* **156** *and similar design. Multicoloured. W* w **14** (*sideways on* 50 *c.*). *P* 14.
499 50 c. Type **156** 15 15
500 60 c. Map of Africa and carcass (*vert*) 15 15

157 *Pierre Loti*, 1953–70

(Des J. W. Litho Questa)

1976 (2 July). *Mail Carriers to Mauritius. T* **157** *and similar horiz designs. Multicoloured. W w* **14** (*sideways**). *P* 14½×14.

501	10 c. Type **157**	45	10
502	15 c. *Secunder*, 1907	65	10
	w. Wmk Crown to right of CA	35·00	
503	50 c. *Hindoostan*, 1842	1·10	15
504	60 c. *St. Geran*, 1740	1·25	15
505	2 r. 50, *Maën*, 1638	3·00	6·50
501/5	*Set of* 5	5·75	6·50
MS506	115×138 mm. Nos. 501/5	6·00	8·00

*The normal sideways watermark shows Crown to left of CA, *as seen from the back of the stamp.*

158 "The Flame of Hindi carried across the Seas"

159 Conference Logo and Map of Mauritius

(Des N. Nagalingum (Type **158**), C. R. Prakashi and R. B. Kailash (1 r. 20); adapted J. W. Litho Questa)

1976 (28 Aug). *Second World Hindi Convention. T* **158** *and similar horiz design. Multicoloured. W w* **14** (*sideways*). *P* 14.

507	10 c. Type **158**	10	10
508	75 c. Type **158**	10	15
509	1 r. 20, Hindi script	20	50
507/9	*Set of* 3	30	60

(Des J. W. Litho Questa)

1976 (22 Sept). *22nd Commonwealth Parliamentary Association Conference. T* **159** *and similar vert design. Multicoloured. W w* **14**. *P* 14.

510	1 r. Type **159**	35	10
511	2 r. 50, Conference logo	65	1·00

160 King Priest and Breastplate

161 Sega Scene

(Des J. W. Litho Walsall)

1976 (15 Dec). *Moenjodaro Excavations, Pakistan. T* **160** *and similar vert designs. Multicoloured. W w* **14**. *P* 14.

512	60 c. Type **160**	30	10
513	1 r. House with well and goblet	50	10
514	2 r. 50, Terracotta figurine and necklace	1·25	65
512/14	*Set of* 3	1·75	70

(Des BG Studio. Litho J.W.)

1977 (20 Jan). *Second World Black and African Festival of Arts and Culture, Nigeria. W w* **14** (*sideways*). *P* 13.

515	**161**	1 r. multicoloured	30	15

162 The Queen with Sceptre and Rod

163 *Hugonia tomentosa*

(Des L. Curtis. Litho Harrison)

1977 (7 Feb). *Silver Jubilee. T* **162** *and similar vert designs. Multicoloured. W w* **14** (*sideways*). *P* 14½ × 14.

516	50 c. The Queen at Mauritius Legislative Assembly, 1972	15	10
517	75 c. Type **162**	20	10
518	5 r. Presentation of Sceptre and Rod	55	75
516/18	*Set of* 3	80	75

(Des Jennifer Toombs. Litho Questa)

1977 (22 Sept). *Indigenous Flowers. T* **163** *and similar multi-coloured designs. W w* **14** (*sideways on* 20 *c. and* 1 *r.* 50). *P* 14.

519	20 c. Type **163**	20	10
520	1 r. *Ochna mauritiana* (*vert*)	40	10
521	1 r. 50, *Dombeya acutangula*	50	20
522	5 r. *Trochetia blackburniana* (*vert*)	1·10	1·25
519/22	*Set of* 4	2·00	1·40
MS523	130 × 130 mm. Nos. 519/22. Wmk sideways	3·00	6·00

164 De Havilland D.H.C.6 Twin Otter 200/300

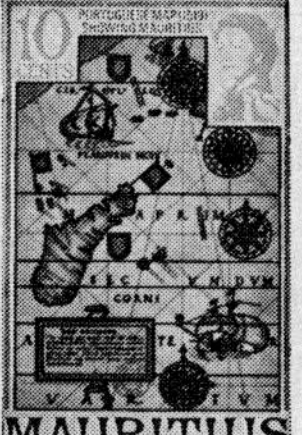

165 Portuguese Map of Mauritius, 1519

(Des A. Theobald. Litho Questa)

1977 (31 Oct). *Inaugural International Flight of Air Mauritius. T* **164** *and similar horiz designs. Multicoloured. W w* **14** (*sideways**). *P* 14½×14.

524	25 c. Type **164**	60	10
	w. Wmk Crown to right of CA	3·25	
525	50 c. De Havilland D.H.C.6 Twin Otter 200/300 and Air Mauritius emblem	80	10
	w. Wmk Crown to right of CA	3·75	
526	75 c. Piper PA-31 Navajo and Boeing 747-100	95	10
	w. Wmk Crown to right of CA	4·00	
527	5 r. Boeing 707	3·00	2·50
	w. Wmk Crown to right of CA	8·50	
524/7	*Set of* 4	4·75	2·50
MS528	110×152 mm. Nos. 524/7	5·50	5·50

*The normal sideways watermark shows Crown to left of CA, *as seen from back of the stamp.*

(Des Harrison. Litho J.W.)

1978 (12 Mar)–**85**. *Designs as T* **165** *in light brown, chestnut and black* (25 *r.*) *or multicoloured* (*others*). *W w* **14** (*sideways* on horiz designs*). *P* 13½. *A. Without imprint. B. With imprint date at foot.*

		A		B	
529	10 c. Type **165**	50	90	75	90
530	15 c. Dutch Occupation, 1638–1710 (*horiz*)	1·25	1·75	†	
531	20 c. Van Keulen's map, *c.* 1700 (*horiz*)	80	1·75	†	
532	25 c. Settlement on Rodriguez, 1691	60	60	1·25	40
	w. Wmk inverted	4·00	—	†	
533	35 c. French charter, 1715	30	85	1·00	20
	w. Wmk inverted	13·00	—	†	
534	50 c. Construction of Port Louis, *c.* 1736 (*horiz*)	50	60	1·25	20
535	60 c. Pierre Poivre, *c.* 1767	60	1·25	†	
536	70 c. Bellin's map, 1763 (*horiz*)	2·25	2·50	†	
537	75 c. First coinage, 1794	2·00	2·00	1·25	1·50
538	90 c. Battle of Grand Port, 1810 (*horiz*)	2·25	2·50	†	
539	1 r. British landing, 1810 (*horiz*)	60	40	1·25	20
540	1 r. 20, Government House, *c.* 1840 (*horiz*)	1·75	2·25	†	
541	1 r. 25, Lady Gomm's ball, 1847	1·50	40	1·25	20
542	1 r. 50, Indian immigration, 1835 (*horiz*)	1·00	1·00	†	
543	2 r. Race course, *c.* 1870 (*horiz*)	60	40	1·25	30
	w. Wmk Crown to left of CA	3·00	—	†	
544	3 r. Place d'Armes, *c.* 1880 (*horiz*)	60	40		
545	5 r. Royal Visit postcard, 1901 (*horiz*)	60	1·00	4·00	4·00
	w. Wmk Crown to left of CA	20·00	—	†	
546	10 r. Royal College, 1914 (*horiz*)	1·00	1·00	†	
547	15 r. Unfurling Mauritian flag, 1968	1·50	2·25	†	
548	25 r. First Mauritian Prime Minister and Governor-General (*horiz*)	2·00	3·00	†	
529A/48A	*Set of* 20	20·00	24·00		
529B/45B	*Set of* 9			12·00	7·00

*The normal sideways watermark shows Crown to right of CA, *as seen from the back of the stamp.*

Dates of issue:—12.3.78, Nos. 529A/48A; 15.6.83, Nos. 537B, 541B, 543B; 1.84, No. 533B; 11.84, Nos. 529B, 532B, 534B; 4.85, No. 539B; 8.5.85, No. 545B.

Imprint dates: "1983", Nos. 533B, 537B, 541B, 543B; "1985", Nos. 529B, 532B/4B, 537B, 539B, 541B, 543B, 545B.

For 35 c. as No. 533B, but perforated 14½ see No. 737 and for values watermarked w **16** see Nos. 740/57.

166 Mauritius Dodo

167 Problem of Infection, World War I

(Des Jennifer Toombs. Litho Questa)

1978 (21 Apr). *25th Anniv of Coronation. T* **166** *and similar vert designs. P* 15.

549	3 r. grey-blue, black and new blue	25	45
	a. Sheetlet, Nos. 549/51, each × 2	1·75	
550	3 r. multicoloured	25	45
551	3 r. grey-blue, black and new blue	25	45
549/51	*Set of* 3	65	1·25

Designs:—No. 549, Antelope of Bohun; 550, Queen Elizabeth II.

Nos. 549/51 were printed together in small sheets of 6, containing two *se-tenant* strips of 3 with horizontal gutter margin between.

(Des Jennifer Toombs. Litho Enschedé)

1978 (3 Aug). *50th Anniv of Discovery of Penicillin. T* **167** *and similar horiz designs. W w* **14** (*sideways*). *P* 13½ × 14.

552	20 c. multicoloured	50	10
553	1 r. multicoloured	1·10	10
554	1 r. 50, black, olive-bistre & dp bluish grn	1·50	1·00
555	5 r. multicoloured	2·25	4·50
552/5	*Set of* 4	4·75	5·25
MS556	150 × 90 mm. Nos. 552/5	4·75	6·00

Designs:—1 r. First mould-growth, 1928; 1 r. 50, *Penicillium chrysogenum* ("*notatum*"); 5 r. Sir Alexander Fleming.

168 *Papilio manlius* (butterfly)

169 Ornate Table

(Des G. Drummond. Litho Walsall)

1978 (21 Sept). *World Wildlife. T* **168** *and similar horiz designs. Multicoloured. W w* **14** (*sideways*). *P* 13½ × 14.

557	20 c. Type **168**	1·25	10
558	1 r. Geckos	90	10
559	1 r. 50 Greater Mascarene Flying Fox	1·25	55
560	5 r. Mauritius Kestrel	10·00	5·50
557/60	*Set of* 4	12·00	5·50
MS561	154 × 148 mm. Nos. 557/60	20·00	12·00

(Des C. Abbott. Litho Questa)

1978 (21 Dec). *Bicentenary of Reconstruction of Chateau Le Réduit. T* **169** *and similar vert designs. Multicoloured. W w* **14**. *P* 14½ × 14.

562	15 c. Type **169**	10	10
563	75 c. Chateau Le Réduit	10	10
564	3 r. Le Réduit gardens	30	45
562/4	*Set of* 3	40	50

170 Whitcomb Diesel Locomotive "65H.P.", 1949

171 Father Laval and Crucifix

(Des G. Hutchins. Litho Questa)

1979 (1 Feb). *Railway Locomotives. T* **170** *and similar horiz designs. Multicoloured. W w* **14** (*sideways*). *P* 14½.

565	20 c. Type **170**	20	10
566	1 r. *Sir William*, 1922	40	10
567	1 r. 50, Kitson type, 1930	60	45
568	2 r. Garratt type, 1927	75	85
565/8	*Set of* 4	1·75	1·25
MS569	128 × 128 mm. Nos. 565/8	2·00	3·50

(Des J. W. Litho Questa)

1979 (30 Apr). *Beatification of Father Laval* (*missionary*). *T* **171** *and similar multicoloured designs. W w* **14** (*sideways on* 5 *r*). *P* 14.

570	20 c. Type **171**	10	10
571	1 r. 50, Father Laval	10	10
572	5 r. Father Laval's tomb (*horiz*)	35	50
570/2	*Set of* 3	40	55
MS573	150 × 96 mm. Nos. 570/2 (wmk upright)	90	1·40

172 Astronaut descending from Lunar Module **173** Great Britain 1855 4d. Stamp and Sir Rowland Hill

(Manufactured by Walsall)

1979 (20 July). *10th Anniv of Moon Landing. T* **172** *and similar vert designs. Multicoloured. Imperf × roul 5*. Self-adhesive (from booklets).*

574 20 c. Type **172** .. 25 30
a. Booklet pane. Nos. 574/6 .. 3·00
b. Booklet pane. Nos. 574/5, each × 3 .. 2·50
575 3 r. Astronaut performing experiment on Moon .. 70 90
576 5 r. Astronaut on Moon .. 2·50 4·50
574/6 .. *Set of* 3 3·00 5·00

*Nos. 574/6 are separated by various combinations of rotary-knife (giving a straight edge) and roulette.

(Des J. W. Litho Questa)

1979 (27 Aug). *Death Centenary of Sir Rowland Hill. T* **173** *and similar vert designs showing stamps and Sir Rowland Hill. Multicoloured.* W w **14**. *P* 14.

577 25 c. Type **173** .. 10 10
578 2 r. 1954 60 c. definitive .. 55 50
579 5 r. 1847 1d. "POST OFFICE" .. 1·00 1·25
577/9 .. *Set of* 3 1·50 1·60
MS580 120 × 89 mm. 3 r. 1847 2d. "POST OFFICE" .. 1·10 1·25

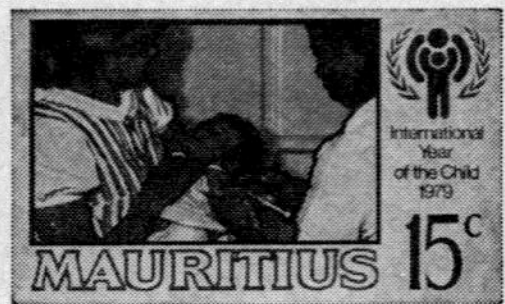

174 Young Child being Vaccinated

(Des V. Whiteley Studio. Litho Questa)

1979 (11 Oct). *International Year of the Child. T* **174** *and similar designs in black, ultramarine and bright blue (1 r.) or multicoloured (others).* W w **14** *(sideways on 15, 25 c., 1 r. 50, and 3 r.). P* 14½ × 14.

581 15 c. Type **174** .. 10 10
582 25 c. Children playing .. 10 10
583 1 r. I.Y.C. emblem (*vert*) .. 15 10
584 1 r. 50, Girls in chemistry laboratory .. 30 20
585 3 r. Boy operating lathe .. 50 50
581/5 .. *Set of* 5 1·00 75

175 The Liénard Obelisk **176** *Emirne* (French steam packet)

(Des L. Curtis. Litho Questa)

1980 (24 Jan). *Pamplemousses Botanical Gardens. T* **175** *and similar horiz designs. Multicoloured.* W w **14** *(sideways*). P* 14 × 14½.

586 20 c. Type **175** .. 10 10
587 25 c. Poivre Avenue .. 10 10
w. Wmk Crown to right of CA .. 18·00
588 1 r. Varieties of Vacoas .. 20 10
589 2 r. Giant Water Lilies .. 35 55
590 5 r. Mon Plaisir (mansion) .. 60 2·00
586/90 .. *Set of* 5 1·25 2·50
MS591 152×105mm. Nos. 586/90 .. 2·75 3·50

*The normal watermark shows Crown to left of CA, *as seen from the back of the stamp.*

(Des J.W. Litho Walsall)

1980 (6 May). *"London 1980" International Stamp Exhibition. Mail-carrying Ships. T* **176** *and similar horiz designs. Multicoloured.* W w **14** *(sideways*). P* 14½×14.

592 25 c. Type **176** .. 25 10
w. Wmk Crown to right of CA .. 8·50
593 1 r. *Boissevain* (cargo liner) .. 40 10
594 2 r. *La Boudeuse* (Bougainville) .. 60 50
595 5 r. *Sea Breeze* (English clipper) .. 80 1·75
592/5 .. *Set of* 4 1·90 2·25

*The normal sideways watermark shows Crown to left of CA, *as seen from the back of the stamp.*

NEW INFORMATION

The editor is always interested to correspond with people who have new information that will improve or correct the Catalogue.

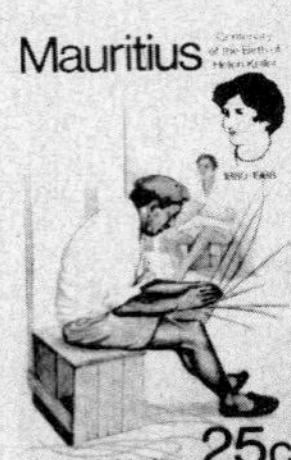

177 Blind Person Basket-making **178** Prime Minister Sir Seewoosagur Ramgoolam

(Des J. W. Litho Harrison)

1980 (27 June). *Birth Centenary of Helen Keller (campaigner for the handicapped). T* **177** *and similar vert designs. Multicoloured.* W w **14**. *P* 14.

596 25 c. Type **177** .. 15 10
597 1 r. Deaf child under instruction .. 35 10
598 2 r. 50, Helen reading braille .. 55 35
599 5 r. Helen at graduation, 1904 .. 1·00 90
596/9 .. *Set of* 4 1·90 1·25

(Des Walsall. Litho and gold foil embossed Questa)

1980 (18 Sept). *80th Birthday and 40th Year in Parliament of Prime Minister Sir Seewoosagur Ramgoolam.* W w **14**. *P* 13½.

600 **178** 15 r. multicoloured .. 1·00 1·40

No. 600 was printed in sheets of 4 stamps.

179 Headquarters, Mauritius Institute

(Des BG Studio. Litho J.W.)

1980 (1 Oct). *Centenary of Mauritius Institute. T* **179** *and similar horiz designs. Multicoloured.* W w **14** *(sideways). P* 13.

601 25 c. Type **179** .. 15 10
602 2 r. Rare copy of Veda .. 40 15
603 2 r. 50, Glory of India Cone shell .. 55 20
604 5 r. "Le Torrent" (painting by Harpignies) .. 65 60
601/4 .. *Set of* 4 1·60 90

180 *Hibiscus liliiflorus* **181** Beau-Bassin/Rose Hill

(Des Jennifer Toombs. Litho Questa)

1981 (15 Jan). *Flowers. T* **180** *and similar vert designs. Multicoloured.* W w **14**. *P* 14.

605 25 c. Type **180** .. 20 10
606 2 r. *Erythrospermum monticolum* .. 70 65
607 2 r. 50, *Chasalia boryana* .. 80 1·00
608 5 r. *Hibiscus columnaris* .. 1·40 2·50
605/8 .. *Set of* 4 2·75 3·75

(Des. L. Curtis. Litho J.W.)

1981 (10 Apr). *Coats of Arms of Mauritius Towns. T* **181** *and similar vert designs. Multicoloured.* W w **14**. *P* 13½ × 13.

609 25 c. Type **181** .. 10 10
610 1 r. 50, Curepipe .. 30 20
611 2 r. Quatre-Bornes .. 35 25
612 2 r. 50, Vacoas/Phoenix .. 40 30
613 5 r. Port Louis .. 75 75
609/13 .. *Set of* 5 1·75 1·40
MS614 130×130 mm. Nos. 609/13. P 14 .. 2·75 5·00
w. Wmk inverted .. £120

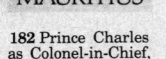

182 Prince Charles as Colonel-in-Chief, Royal Regiment of Wales **183** Emmanuel Anquetil and Guy Rozemont

(Des J. W. Litho Questa)

1981 (22 July). *Royal Wedding. T* **182** *and similar vert designs. Multicoloured.* W w **14**. *P* 14.

615 25 c. Wedding bouquet from Mauritius .. 10 10
616 2 r. 50, Type **182** .. 40 15
617 10 r. Prince Charles and Lady Diana Spencer 80 90
615/17 .. *Set of* 3 1·10 1·00

(Des G. Vasarhelyi. Litho Questa)

1981 (27 Aug). *Famous Politicians and Physician (5 r.). T* **183** *and similar horiz designs.* W w **14** *(sideways). P* 14½.

618 20 c. black and carmine .. 10 10
619 25 c. black and lemon .. 10 10
620 1 r. 25, black and emerald .. 30 15
621 1 r. 50, black and rose-red .. 35 15
622 2 r. black and ultramarine .. 45 20
623 2 r. 50, black and orange-brown .. 50 30
624 5 r. black and turquoise-blue .. 1·25 90
618/24 .. *Set of* 7 2·75 1·60

Designs:—25 c. Remy Ollier and Sookdeo Bissoondoyal; 1 r. 25, Maurice Curé and Barthélemy Ohsan; 1 r. 50, Sir Guy Forget and Renganaden Seeneevassen; 2 r. Sir Abdul Razak Mohamed and Jules Koenig; 2 r. 50, Abdoollatiff Mahomed Osman and Dazzi Rama (Pandit Sahadeo); 5 r. Sir Thomas Lewis and electrocardiogram.

184 Drummer and Piper **185** "Skills"

(Des Jennifer Toombs. Litho Format)

1981 (16 Sept). *Religion and Culture. T* **184** *and similar multicoloured designs.* W w **14** *(sideways on 20 c. and 5 r.). P* 14 × 13½ *(20 c.),* 13½ × 14 *(2 r.) or* 13½ *(5 r.).*

625 20 c. Type **184** .. 10 10
626 2 r. Swami Sivananda (*vert*) .. 1·00 1·00
627 5 r. Chinese Pagoda .. 1·25 3·00
625/7 .. *Set of* 3 2·00 3·50

The 20 c. value commemorates the World Tamil Culture Conference (1980).

(Des BG Studio. Litho Questa)

1981 (15 Oct). *25th Anniv of Duke of Edinburgh Award Scheme. T* **185** *and similar vert designs. Multicoloured.* W w **14**. *P* 14.

628 25 c. Type **185** .. 10 10
629 1 r. 25, "Service" .. 10 10
w. Wmk inverted .. 12·00
630 5 r. "Expeditions" .. 20 30
631 10 r. Duke of Edinburgh .. 40 70
628/31 .. *Set of* 4 60 1·00

186 Ka'aba (sacred shrine, Great Mosque of Mecca) **187** Scout Emblem

(Des Jennifer Toombs. Litho Questa)

1981 (26 Nov). *Moslem Year 1400A.H. Commemoration. T* **186** *and similar vert designs. Multicoloured.* W w **14**. *P* 14½ × 14.

632 25 c. Type **186** .. 30 10
633 2 r. Mecca .. 80 80
634 5 r. Mecca and Ka'aba .. 1·40 2·50
632/4 .. *Set of* 3 2·25 3·00

(Des C. Abbott. Litho Walsall)

1982 (22 Feb). *75th Anniv of Boy Scout Movement and 70th Anniv of Scouting in Mauritius. T* **187** *and similar horiz designs.* W w **14** *(sideways). P* 14 × 14½.

635 25 c. deep lilac and light green .. 10 10
636 2 r. deep brown and brown-ochre .. 30 30
637 5 r. deep green and yellow-olive .. 70 1·00
638 10 r. deep green and new blue .. 1·25 2·00
635/8 .. *Set of* 4 2·00 3·00

Designs:—2 r. Lord Baden-Powell and Baden-Powell House; 5 r. Grand Howl; 10 r. Ascent of Pieter Both.

188 Charles Darwin **189** Bride and Groom at Buckingham Palace

(Des L. Curtis. Litho Questa)

1982 (19 Apr). *150th Anniv of Charles Darwin's Voyage. T* **188** *and similar horiz designs. Multicoloured. W w* **14** *(sideways). P* 14.

639 25 c. Type **188** 10 10
a. Yellow (background to side panels) omitted .. ..
640 2 r. Darwin's telescope 30 45
641 2 r. 50, Darwin's elephant ride 35 55
642 10 r. H.M.S. *Beagle* beached for repairs .. 1·40 2·75
639/42 .. .. *Set of* 4 1·90 3·50

(Des Jennifer Toombs. Litho J. W.)

1982 (1 July). *21st Birthday of Princess of Wales. T* **189** *and similar vert designs. Multicoloured. W w* **14**. *P* 13.

643 25 c. Mauritius coat of arms 10 10
644 2 r. 50, Princess Diana in Chesterfield, November 1981 .. .. 50 35
645 5 r. Type **189** 75 80
646 10 r. Formal portrait .. .. 2·00 1·75
643/6 .. .. *Set of* 4 3·00 2·75

190 Prince and Princess of Wales with Prince William **191** Bois Fandamane Plant

(Des Harrison. Litho Walsall)

1982 (22 Sept). *Birth of Prince William of Wales. W w* **14** *(sideways). P* 14 × 14½.

647 **190** 2 r. 50, multicoloured 75 30

(Des Harrison. Litho Format)

1982 (15 Dec). *Centenary of Robert Koch's Discovery of Tubercle Bacillus. T* **191** *and similar vert designs. Multicoloured. W w* **14**. *P* 14.

648 25 c. Type **191** 10 10
649 1 r. 25, Central market, Port Louis 40 40
650 2 r. Bois Banane plant 65 75
651 5 r. Platte de Lézard plant .. .. .. 1·00 2·25
652 10 r. Dr. Robert Koch .. .. 1·75 3·75
648/52 .. .. *Set of* 5 3·50 6·50

192 Arms and Flag of Mauritius **193** Early Wall-mounted Telephone

(Des and litho J.W.)

1983 (14 Mar). *Commonwealth Day. T* **192** *and similar horiz designs. Multicoloured. W w* **14** *(sideways). P* 13.

653 25 c. Type **192** 10 10
654 2 r. 50, Satellite view of Mauritius 15 30
655 5 r. Harvesting sugar cane 30 75
656 10 r. Port Louis harbour .. .. .. 70 1·50
653/6 .. .. *Set of* 4 1·10 2·40

(Des G. Vasarhelyi. Litho Format)

1983 (24 June). *World Communications Year. T* **193** *and similar multicoloured designs. W w* **14** *(sideways on* 1 *r.* 25 *and* 10 *r.). P* 14.

657 25 c. Type **193** 10 10
658 1 r. 25, Early telegraph apparatus (*horiz*) .. 40 20
659 2 r. Earth satellite station 70 50
660 10 r. First hot-air balloon in Mauritius, 1784 (*horiz*) .. .. 1·75 2·75
657/60 .. .. *Set of* 4 2·50 3·25

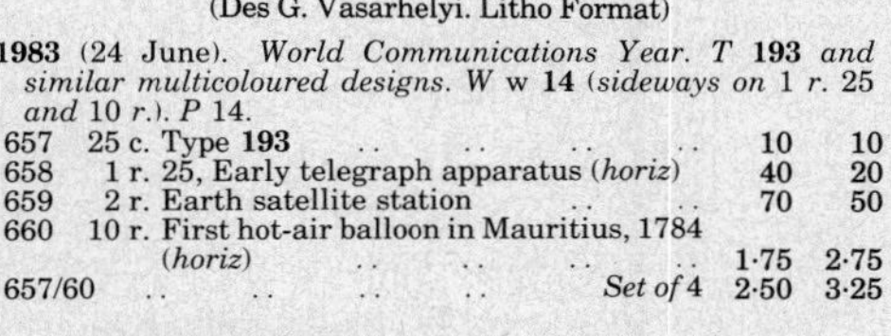

194 Map of Namibia **195** Fish Trap

(Des J. W. Litho Questa)

1983 (26 Aug). *Namibia Day. T* **194** *and similar vert designs. Multicoloured. W w* **14**. *P* 14.

661 25 c. Type **194** 45 10
662 2 r. 50, Hands breaking chains .. .. 1·50 75
663 5 r. Family and settlement .. .. .. 2·00 2·25
664 10 r. Diamond mining .. .. 3·75 3·75
661/4 .. .. *Set of* 4 7·00 6·00

(Des Walsall. Litho Format)

1983 (25 Sept). *Fishery Resources. T* **195** *and similar multicoloured designs. W w***14** *(sideways on* 1 *r. and* 10 *r.). P* 14.

665 25 c. Type **195** 15 10
666 1 r. Fishing boat (*horiz*) 55 15
667 5 r. Game fishing .. .. 1·25 2·50
668 10 r. Octopus drying (*horiz*) .. .. .. 1·75 4·00
665/8 .. .. *Set of* 4 3·25 6·00

196 Swami Dayananda **197** Adolf von Plevitz

(Des A. Theobald. Litho Questa)

1983 (3 Nov). *Death Centenary of Swami Dayananda. T* **196** *and similar vert designs. Multicoloured. W w* **14**. *P* 14.

669 25 c. Type **196** 10 10
670 35 c. Last meeting with father 10 10
671 2 r. Receiving religious instruction 50 65
672 5 r. Swami demonstrating strength .. .. 90 2·25
673 10 r. At a religious gathering .. .. .. 1·40 3·50
669/73 .. .. *Set of* 5 2·75 6·00

(Des L. Curtis. Litho Harrison)

1983 (8 Dec). *125th Anniv of the Arrival in Mauritius of Adolf von Plevitz (social reformer). T* **197** *and similar horiz designs. Multicoloured. W w* **14** *(sideways). P* 14 × 14½.

674 25 c. Type **197** 10 10
675 1 r. 25, La Laura Government school 30 30
676 5 r. Von Plevitz addressing 1872 Commission of Enquiry .. .. 1·00 2·25
677 10 r. Von Plevitz with Indian farm workers .. 1·75 3·50
674/7 .. .. *Set of* 4 2·75 5·50

198 Courtship Chase **199** Wreck of S.S. *Tayeb*

(Des N. Arlott. Litho Format)

1984 (26 Mar). *Mauritius Kestrel. T* **198** *and similar multicoloured designs. W w* **14** *(sideways on* 25 *c. and* 2 *r.). P* 14.

678 25 c. Type **198** 65 30
679 2 r. Kestrel in tree (*vert*) .. .. .. 1·50 1·10
680 2 r. 50, Young Kestrel .. .. 1·75 2·00
681 10 r. Head (*vert*) .. .. 3·25 6·50
678/81 .. .. *Set of* 4 6·50 9·00

(Des M. Joyce. Litho Questa)

1984 (23 May). *250th Anniv of "Lloyd's List" (newspaper). T* **199** *and similar vert designs. Multicoloured. W w* **14**. *P* 14½ × 14.

682 25 c. Type **199** 30 10
683 1 r. S.S. *Taher* 95 15
684 5 r. East Indiaman *Triton* .. .. .. 2·50 3·25
685 10 r. M.S. *Astor* .. .. 3·00 5·50
682/5 .. .. *Set of* 4 6·00 8·00

200 Blue Latan Palm **201** Slave Girl

(Des Jennifer Toombs. Litho Format)

1984 (23 July). *Palm Trees. T* **200** *and similar vert designs. Multicoloured. W w* **14**. *P* 14½.

686 25 c. Type **200** 10 10
687 50 c. *Hyophorbe vaughanii* 20 20
688 2 r. 50, *Tectiphiala ferox* .. .. .. 1·25 1·50
689 5 r. Round Island Bottle-palm .. .. 2·00 3·00
690 10 r. *Hyophorbe amaricaulis* .. .. .. 3·25 5·25
686/90 .. .. *Set of* 5 6·25 9·00

(Des C. Abbott. Litho Walsall)

1984 (20 Aug). *150th Anniv of the Abolition of Slavery and of the Introduction of Indian Immigrants. T* **201** *and similar designs. W w* **14** *(sideways on* 2 *r.,* 10 *r.). P* 14½.

691 25 c. deep rose-lilac, rose-lilac and bistre .. 15 10
692 1 r. deep rose-lilac, rose-lilac and bistre .. 70 10
693 2 r. deep rose-lilac and rose-lilac .. .. 1·50 90
694 10 r. deep rose-lilac and rose-lilac .. .. 5·00 6·50
691/4 .. .. *Set of* 4 6·50 6·75

Designs: *Vert*—1 r. Slave market. *Horiz*—2 r. Indian immigrant family; 10 r. Arrival of Indian immigrants.

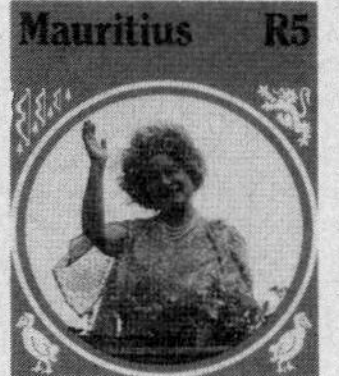

202 75th Anniversary Production of *Faust* and Leoville L'Homme **203** The Queen Mother on Clarence House Balcony, 1980

(Des Walsall. Litho Questa)

1984 (10 Sept). *Centenary of Alliance Francaise (cultural organization). T* **202** *and similar horiz designs. Multicoloured. W w* **14** *(sideways). P* 14½ × 14.

695 25 c. Type **202** 20 10
696 1 r. 25, Prize-giving ceremony and Aunauth Beejadhur 70 50
697 5 r. First headquarters and Hector Clarenc .. 2·00 3·00
698 10 r. Lion Mountain and Labourdonnais .. 2·50 5·00
695/8 .. .. *Set of* 4 4·75 7·75

(Des A. Theobald (15 r.), C. Abbott (others). Litho Questa)

1985 (7 June). *Life and Times of Queen Elizabeth the Queen Mother. T* **203** *and similar vert designs. Multicoloured. W w* **16**. *P* 14½ × 14.

699 25 c. The Queen Mother in 1926 .. .. 10 10
700 2 r. With Princess Margaret at Trooping the Colour 30 30
701 5 r. Type **203**. .. .. 60 1·40
702 10 r. With Prince Henry at his christening (from photo by Lord Snowdon).. .. 1·10 2·25
699/702 .. .. *Set of* 4 1·90 3·50
MS703 91 × 73 mm. 15 r. Reopening the Stratford Canal, 1964. Wmk sideways .. .. .. 3·25 3·00

204 High Jumping **205** Adult and Fledgling Pink Pigeons

(Des Joan Thompson. Litho Walsall)

1985 (24 Aug). *2nd Indian Ocean Islands Games. T* **204** *and similar vert designs. Multicoloured. W w* **14**. *P* 14½.

704 25 c. Type **204**. 20 10
705 50 c. Javelin-throwing 45 30
706 1 r. 25, Cycling .. .. 2·00 1·25
707 10 r. Wind surfing .. .. 4·50 6·50
704/7 .. .. *Set of* 4 6·50 7·25

(Des N. Arlott. Litho Walsall)

1985 (2 Sept). *Pink Pigeon. T* **205** *and similar vert designs. Multicoloured. W w* **16**. *P* 14.

708 25 c. Type **205**. .. .. 1·50 30
709 2 r. Pink Pigeon displaying at nest .. .. 3·50 1·75
710 2 r. 50, On nest .. .. 4·00 3·25
711 5 r. Pair preening .. .. 7·50 7·50
708/11 .. .. *Set of* 4 15·00 11·50

206 Caverne Patates, Rodrigues

(Des D. Miller. Litho Walsall)

1985 (27 Sept). *10th Anniv of World Tourism Organization T* **206** *and similar horiz designs. Multicoloured. W w* **16** *(sideways). P* 14½.

712 25 c. Type **206**. 50 10
713 35 c. Coloured soils, Chamarel 50 30
714 5 r. Serpent Island .. .. 3·50 4·00
715 10 r. Coin de Mire Island .. .. .. 5·50 7·00
712/15 .. .. *Set of* 4 9·00 10·00

207 Old Town Hall, Port Louis

(Des Jennifer Toombs. Litho J.W.)

1985 (22 Nov). *250th Anniv of Port Louis. T* **207** *and similar horiz designs. Multicoloured. W w* **16** (*sideways*). *P* 13 × 13½.
716 25 c. Type **207** 10 10
717 1 r. Al-Aqsa Mosque (180th anniv) .. 90 10
718 2 r. 50, Vase and trees (250th anniv of settlement of Tamil-speaking Indians) 1·25 1·50
719 10 r. Port Louis Harbour .. .. .. 5·00 6·50
716/19 .. .. *Set of* 4 6·50 7·25

208 Edmond Halley and Diagram

209 Maize (World Food Day)

(Des D. Hartley. Litho Walsall)

1986 (21 Feb). *Appearance of Halley's Comet. T* **208** *and similar horiz designs. Multicoloured. W w* **16** (*sideways*). *P* 14.
720 25 c. Type **208** 40 10
721 1 r. 25, Halley's Comet (1682) and Newton's Reflector 90 50
722 3 r. Halley's Comet passing Earth .. .. 1·40 1·50
723 10 r. *Giotto* spacecraft .. .. .. 3·25 4·50
720/3 .. .. *Set of* 4 5·50 6·00

(Des A. Theobald. Litho Harrison)

1986 (21 Apr). *60th Birthday of Queen Elizabeth II. Vert designs as T* **230a** *of Jamaica. Multicoloured. W w* **16**. *P* 14½×14.
724 25 c. Princess Elizabeth wearing badge of Grenadier Guards, 1942 .. .. 10 10
725 75 c. Investiture of Prince of Wales, 1969 .. 10 10
726 2 r. With Prime Minister of Mauritius, 1972 20 25
727 3 r. In Germany, 1978 .. .. .. 30 40
728 15 r. At Crown Agents Head Office, London, 1983 .. .. 1·25 2·00
724/8 .. .. *Set of* 5 1·60 2·50

(Des O. Bell. Litho Walsall)

1986 (25 July). *International Events. T* **209** *and similar vert designs. Multicoloured. W w* **16**. *P* 14.
729 25 c. Type **209** 10 10
w. Wmk inverted .. .. 23·00
730 1 r. African Regional Industrial Property Organization emblem (10th anniv) .. 35 10
731 1 r. 25, International Peace Year emblem 55 40
732 10 r. Footballer and Mauritius Football Association emblem (World Cup Football Championship, Mexico) .. 4·75 5·50
729/32 .. .. *Set of* 4 5·25 5·50

210 *Cryptopus elatus*

211 Hesketh Bell Bridge

(Des Harrison. Litho Walsall)

1986 (3 Oct). *Orchids. T* **210** *and similar vert designs. Multicoloured. W w* **16**. *P* 14½ × 14.
733 25 c. Type **210** 40 10
734 2 r. *Jumellea recta* .. .. 1·10 45
735 2 r. 50, *Angraecum mauritianum* .. .. 1·25 60
736 10 r. *Bulbophyllum longiflorum* .. .. 2·25 3·00
733/6 .. .. *Set of* 4 4·50 3·75

1986 (Nov). *As No.* 533B *but printed litho by Questa.* "1986" *imprint date. P* 14½.
737 35 c. French charter, 1715 .. .. 1·75 1·50

(Litho Questa)

1987 (11 Jan)–**89**. *As Nos.* 531/2, 534, 543/5 *and* 548 *but W w* **16** (*sideways on horiz designs*). *Imprint date. P* 14½.
740 20 c. Van Keulen's map, *c.* 1700 (*horiz*) .. 1·25 60
741 25 c. Settlement on Rodriguez, 1691 .. 1·40 80
743 50 c. Construction of Port Louis, *c.* 1736 (*horiz*) (16.1.89) .. .. .. 1·40 30
752 2 r. Race course, *c.* 1870 (*horiz*) .. .. 1·40 30
753 3 r. Place d'Armes, *c.* 1880 (*horiz*) (16.1.89) 2·00 2·25
754 5 r. Royal Visit postcard, 1901 (*horiz*) (16.1.89) .. .. 3·00 3·50
757 25 r. First Mauritian Governor-General and Prime Minister (*horiz*) (16.1.89) .. 4·00 7·00
740/57 .. .. .. *Set of* 7 13·00 13·00
Imprint dates: "1987", Nos. 740/1, 752; "1989", Nos. 743, 752/3, 754, 757.

(Des D. Hartley. Litho Format)

1987 (22 May). *Mauritius Bridges. T* **211** *and similar horiz designs. Multicoloured. W w* **16** (*sideways*). *P* 14½.
758 25 c. Type **211** 25 10
759 50 c. Sir Colville Deverell Bridge 35 20
760 2 r. 50, Cavendish Bridge .. .. .. 1·10 75
761 5 r. Tamarin Bridge .. .. 1·75 2·00
762 10 r. Grand River North West Bridge .. 2·50 2·50
758/62 .. .. *Set of* 5 5·50 5·00

212 Supreme Court, Port Louis

213 Dodo Mascot

(Des N. Shewring. Litho Walsall)

1987 (2 June). *Bicentenary of the Mauritius Bar. T* **212** *and similar horiz designs. Multicoloured. W w* **16** (*sideways*). *P* 14 × 14½.
763 25 c. Type **212** 10 10
764 1 r. District Court, Flacq 40 10
765 1 r. 25, Statue of Justice 50 20
766 10 r. Barristers of 1787 and 1987 .. .. 2·00 2·00
763/6 .. .. *Set of* 4 2·75 2·00

(Des O. Bell. Litho Format)

1987 (5 Sept). *International Festival of the Sea. T* **213** *and similar multicoloured designs. W w* **16** (*sideways on* 25 c., 5 r.). *P* 14 × 14½ (*vert*) *or* 14½ × 14 (*horiz*).
767 25 c. Type **213** 20 10
768 1 r. 50, Yacht regatta (*horiz*) .. .. 1·00 90
769 3 r. Water skiing (*horiz*) .. .. .. 2·00 2·50
770 5 r. *Svanen* (barquentine) .. .. .. 2·75 4·00
767/70 .. .. *Set of* 4 5·50 6·75

214 Toys

215 Maison Ouvriere (Int Year of Shelter for the Homeless)

(Des G. Vasarhelyi. Litho Walsall)

1987 (30 Oct). *Industrialisation. T* **214** *and similar horiz designs. Multicoloured. W w* **14** (*sideways*). *P* 14.
771 20 c. Type **214** 10 10
772 35 c. Spinning factory 10 10
773 50 c. Rattan furniture 10 10
774 2 r. 50, Spectacle factory 85 80
775 10 r. Stone carving .. .. 2·50 2·75
771/5 .. .. *Set of* 5 3·25 3·25

(Des D. Miller. Litho Walsall)

1987 (30 Dec). *Art and Architecture. T* **215** *and similar horiz designs. W w* **16** (*sideways*). *P* 14 × 14½.
776 25 c. multicoloured 10 10
777 1 r. black and brownish grey 25 10
778 1 r. 25, multicoloured 30 30
779 2 r. multicoloured 55 55
780 5 r. multicoloured .. .. 1·00 1·25
776/80 .. .. *Set of* 5 2·00 2·00
Designs:—1 r. "Paul et Virginie" (lithograph); 1 r. 25, Chateau de Rosnay; 2 r. "Vielle Ferme" (Boulle); 5 r. "Trois Mamelles".

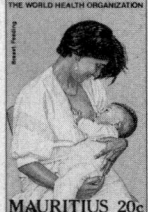

216 University of Mauritius

217 Breast Feeding

(Des A. Theobald. Litho B.D.T.)

1988 (11 Mar). *20th Anniv of Independence. T* **216** *and similar horiz designs. Multicoloured. W w* **14** (*sideways*). *P* 13½.
781 25 c. Type **216** 10 10
782 75 c. Anniversary gymnastic display 20 10
783 2 r. 50, Hurdlers and aerial view of Sir Maurice Rault Stadium 70 55
784 5 r. Air Mauritius aircraft at Sir Seewoosagur Ramgoolam International Airport 1·40 1·60
785 10 r. Governor-General Sir Veerasamy Ringadoo and Prime Minister Anerood Jugnauth .. .. 2·25 2·75
781/5 .. .. *Set of* 5 4·25 4·50

(Des D. Ashby. Litho B.D.T.)

1988 (1 July). *40th Anniv of World Health Organization. T* **217** *and similar vert designs. Multicoloured. W w* **14**. *P* 13½.
786 20 c. Type **217** 15 10
787 2 r. Baby under vaccination umbrella and germ droplets .. .. 1·25 70
788 3 r. Nutritious food .. .. 1·40 1·25
789 10 r. W.H.O. logo .. .. 2·75 3·25
786/9 .. .. *Set of* 4 5·00 4·75

218 Modern Bank Building

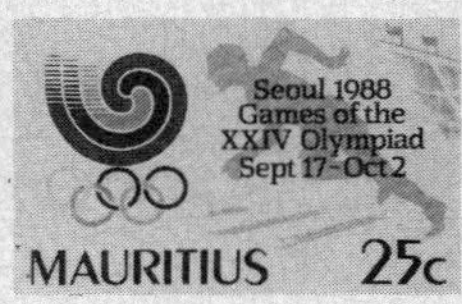

219 Olympic Rings and Athlete

(Des N. Shewring (25 r.). Litho B.D.T.)

1988 (1 Sept). *150th Anniv of Mauritius Commercial Bank Ltd. T* **218** *and similar multicoloured designs. W w* **14** (*sideways on* 1, 25 *r.*). *P* 13½.
790 25 c. black, blue-green and new blue .. 10 10
791 1 r. black and brown-lake 15 10
792 1 r. 25, multicoloured 30 30
793 25 r. multicoloured .. .. 6·50 7·00
790/3 .. .. *Set of* 4 6·50 7·00
Designs: *Horiz*—1 r. Mauritius Commercial Bank, 1897; 25 r. Fifteen dollar bank note of 1838. *Vert*—1 r. 25, Bank arms.

(Des P. Broadbent. Litho B.D.T.)

1988 (1 Oct). *Olympic Games, Seoul. T* **219** *and similar horiz designs. Multicoloured. W w* **14** (*sideways*). *P* 14.
794 25 c. Type **219** 10 10
795 35 c. Wrestling 15 15
796 1 r. 50, Long distance running 75 60
797 10 r. Swimming .. .. 2·50 3·75
794/7 .. .. *Set of* 4 3·25 4·00

220 Nature Park

221 La Tour Sumeire, Port Louis

(Des D. Miller. Litho Harrison (40 c. (No. 809), 3 r., 4r., (No. 804), 6 r., 10 r.) or B.D.T. (others))

1989 (11 Mar)–**96**. *Protection of the Environment. T* **220** *and similar multicoloured designs. P* 14.

(*a*) *W w* **14** (*sideways on horiz designs*). A. *Without imprint date.* B. *With imprint date.*

No.	Value	Design	A		B	
798	15 c.	View beneath the sea ..	40	10	10	10
799	20 c.	As 15 c.	†		10	10
800	30 c.	Greenshank	†		10	10
801	40 c.	Type **220**	†		10	10
801*a*	60 c.	As 50 c.	†		10	10
802	1 r.	50, Whimbrel	10	10	†	
803	3 r.	Marine life	15	20	†	
804	4 r.	Fern Tree (*vert*) ..	40	40	20	25
805	6 r.	Ecological scenery (*vert*)	35	40	†	
806	10 r.	*Phelsuma ornata* (gecko) on plant (*vert*)	†		55	60
807	25 r.	Migratory birds and map (*vert*)	1·40	1·50	†	

(*b*) *W w* **16** (*sideways on horiz designs*). A. *Without imprint date.* B. *With imprint date.*

No.	Value	Design	A		B	
808	30 c.	Greenshank	50	15	†	
809	40 c.	Type **220**	50	30	†	
810	50 c.	Round Island (*vert*) ..	10	10	†	
811	75 c.	Bassin Blanc	10	10	†	
812	1 r.	Mangrove (*vert*) ..	10	10	†	
813	2 r.	Le Morne	10	15	†	
814	5 r.	Rivière du Poste estuary	30	35	†	
815	10 r.	*Phelsuma ornata* (gecko) on plant (*vert*) ..	55	60	†	
816	15 r.	Benarès waves	80	85	†	
817	25 r.	Migratory birds and map (*vert*)	†		1·40	1·50
798/817		.. .. *Set of* 21			6·75	7·00

Dates of issue: 11.3.89, Nos. 803A/5A, 809A, 815A; 29.11.90, Nos. 798A, 802A, 807A/8A; 19.2.91, No. 801B; 4.10.91, Nos. 810A/11A, 813A/14A, 816A; 26.7.94, Nos. 798B, 804B; 10.95, Nos. 800B, 806B; 1.96, No. 817B; 3.96, Nos. 799B, 801*a*B.

Imprint dates: "1991", No. 801B; "1993", No. 801B; "1994" Nos. 798B, 800B/1B, 804B; "1995", Nos. 798B, 800B, 806B; "1996", Nos. 799B, 801*a*B, 817B; "1997" Nos. 801B, 801*a*B, 806B, 817B.

(Des A. Theobald. Litho B.D.T.)

1989 (14 July). *Bicentenary of the French Revolution. T* **221** *and similar vert designs. W w* **14**. *P* 14.
818 30 c. black, emerald & pale greenish yellow 10 10
819 1 r. black, orange-brown and cinnamon .. 20 10
820 8 r. multicoloured .. .. 1·50 1·50
821 15 r. multicoloured .. .. 2·00 2·25
818/21 .. .. *Set of* 4 3·50 3·50
Designs:—1 r. Salle de Spectacle du Jardin; 8 r. Portrait of Comte de Malartic; 15 r. Bicentenary logo.

222 Cardinal Jean Margeot   223 Nehru

(Des L. Curtis. Litho B.D.T.)

1989 (13 Oct). *Visit of Pope John Paul II. T* **222** *and similar vert designs. Multicoloured. W* w **14**. *P* 14×13½.

822 30 c. Type **222** 30 10
823 40 c. Pope John Paul II and Prime Minister Jugnauth, Vatican, 1988 .. .. 50 25
824 3 r. Mère Marie Magdeleine de la Croix and Chapelle des Filles de Marie, Port Louis, 1864 .. .. 1·25 1·00
825 6 r. St. Francois d'Assise Church, Pamplemousses, 1756 .. .. 1·75 2·50
826 10 r. Pope John Paul II .. .. .. 3·25 3·75
822/6 .. .. *Set of* 5 6·25 6·75

(Des K. Clarkson. Litho B.D.T.)

1989 (14 Nov). *Birth Centenary of Jawaharlal Nehru (Indian statesman). T* **223** *and similar horiz designs. Multicoloured. W* w **16** (*sideways*). *P* 14.

827 40 c. Type **223** 50 20
828 1 r. 50, Nehru with daughter, Indira, and grandsons .. .. 1·00 60
829 3 r. Nehru and Gandhi .. .. .. 2·00 2·00
830 4 r. Nehru with Presidents Nasser and Tito 2·00 2·25
831 10 r. Nehru with children .. .. .. 4·00 5·00
827/31 .. .. *Set of* 5 8·50 9·00

224 Cane cutting   225 Industrial Estate

(Des D. Miller. Litho B.D.T.)

1990 (10 Jan). *350th Anniv of Introduction of Sugar Cane to Mauritius. T* **224** *and similar horiz designs. Multicoloured. W* w **16** (*sideways*). *P* 13½.

832 30 c. Type **224** 10 10
833 40 c. Sugar factory, 1867 .. .. .. 15 10
834 1 r. Mechanical loading of cane 30 10
835 25 r. Modern sugar factory .. .. .. 6·50 7·50
832/5 .. .. *Set of* 4 6·50 7·50

(Des L. Curtis. Litho B.D.T.)

1990 (29 Mar). *60th Birthday of Prime Minister Sir Anerood Jugnauth. T* **225** *and similar horiz designs. Multicoloured. W* w **14** (*sideways*). *P* 13½.

836 35 c. Type **225** 10 10
837 40 c. Sir Anerood Jugnauth at desk 10 10
838 1 r. 50, Mauritius Stock Exchange symbol 25 25
839 4 r. Jugnauth with Governor-General Sir Seewoosagur Ramgoolam .. .. 1·25 1·75
840 10 r. Jugnauth greeting Pope John Paul II 3·75 5·00
836/40 .. .. *Set of* 5 4·75 6·50

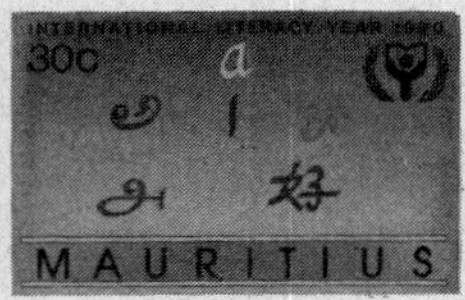

226 Desjardins (naturalist) (150th death anniv)   227 Letters from Alphabets

(Des D. Miller. Litho B.D.T.)

1990 (5 July). *Anniversaries. T* **226** *and similar multicoloured designs. W* w **14** (*sideways on* 35 c., 8 *r.*). *P* 14.

841 30 c. Type **226** 20 10
842 35 c. Logo on TV screen (25th anniv of Mauritius Broadcasting Corporation) (*horiz*) 20 10
843 6 r. Line Barracks (now Police Headquarters) (250th anniv) .. .. 3·00 3·25
844 8 r. Town Hall, Curepipe (centenary of municipality) (*horiz*) .. .. 3·00 3·50
841/4 .. .. *Set of* 4 5·75 6·25

(Des G. Vasarhelyi. Litho B.D.T.)

1990 (28 Sept). *International Literacy Year. T* **227** *and similar horiz designs. Multicoloured. W* w **14** (*sideways*). *P* 14.

845 30 c. Type **227** 15 10
846 1 r. Blind child reading Braille 60 15
847 3 r. Open book and globe .. .. .. 1·40 1·40
848 10 r. Book showing world map with quill pen 3·50 5·00
845/8 .. .. *Set of* 4 5·00 6·00

(Des D. Miller. Litho Questa)

1991 (17 June). *65th Birthday of Queen Elizabeth II and 70th Birthday of Prince Philip. Vert designs as T* **58** *of Kiribati. Multicoloured. W* w **16** (*sideways*). *P* 14½×14.

849 8 r. Queen Elizabeth II .. .. .. 1·40 2·00
a. Horiz pair. Nos. 849/50 separated by label .. .. 2·75 4·00
850 8 r. Prince Philip in Grenadier Guards ceremonial uniform .. .. .. 1·40 2·00

Nos. 849/50 were printed together in a similar sheet format to Nos. 366/7 of Kiribati.

228 City Hall, Port Louis (25th anniv of City status)   229 *Euploea euphon*

(Des G. Vasarhelyi. Litho Questa)

1991 (18 Aug). *Anniversaries and Events. T* **228** *and similar multicoloured designs. W* w **14** (*sideways on* 40 *c.*, 10 *r.*). *P* 14.

851 40 c. Type **228** 10 10
852 4 r. Colonel Draper (race course founder) (150th death anniv) (*vert*) .. .. 1·50 1·50
853 6 r. Joseph Barnard (engraver) and "POST PAID" 2d. stamp (175th birth anniv) (*vert*) .. .. 1·75 2·00
854 10 r. Supermarine Spitfire *Mauritius II* (50th anniv of Second World War) 4·00 4·50
851/4 .. .. *Set of* 4 6·50 7·25

(Des I. Loe. Litho Walsall)

1991 (15 Nov). *"Phila Nippon '91" International Stamp Exhibition, Tokyo. Butterflies. T* **229** *and similar horiz designs. W* w **14** (*sideways*). *P* 14×14½.

855 40 c. Type **229** 40 20
856 3 r. *Hypolimnas misippus* (female) .. 1·40 90
857 8 r. *Papilio manlius* .. .. .. 2·50 3·00
858 10 r. *Hypolimnas misippus* (male) .. 2·50 3·25
855/8 .. .. *Set of* 4 6·00 6·50

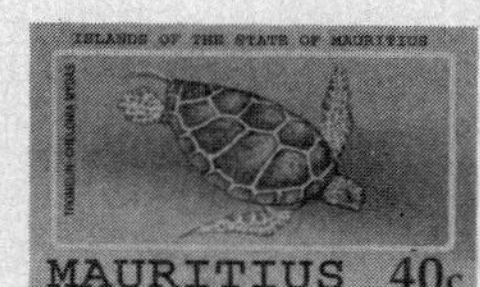

230 Green Turtle, Tromelin

(Des G. Vasarhelyi. Litho Walsall)

1991 (13 Dec). *Indian Ocean Islands. T* **230** *and similar horiz designs. Multicoloured. W* w **14** (*sideways*). *P* 14.

859 40 c. Type **230** 40 20
860 1 r. Glossy Ibis, Agalega .. .. .. 1·10 30
861 2 r. Takamaka flowers, Chagos Archipelago .. .. 1·40 1·10
862 15 r. Violet Spider Conch (*Lambis violacea*) sea shell, St. Brandon .. .. 5·00 6·50
859/62 .. .. *Set of* 4 7·00 7·25

231 Pres. Veerasamy Ringadoo and President's Residence   232 Ticolo (mascot)

(Des G. Vasarhelyi. Litho Walsall)

1992 (12 Mar). *Proclamation of Republic. T* **231** *and similar horiz designs. W* w **14** (*sideways*). *P* 13½×14.

863 40 c. Type **231** 10 10
864 4 r. Prime Minister Anerood Jugnauth and Government House .. .. .. 80 1·00
865 8 r. Children and rainbow .. .. .. 1·75 2·50
866 10 r. Presidential flag .. .. .. 2·00 2·75
863/6 .. .. *Set of* 4 4·25 5·75

(Des G. Vasarhelyi. Litho B.D.T.)

1992 (25 June). *8th African Athletics Championships, Port Louis. T* **232** *and similar multicoloured designs. W* w **14** (*sideways on* 4, 5 *r.*). *P* 13½.

867 40 c. Type **232** 10 10
868 4 r. Sir Anerood Jugnauth Stadium (*horiz*) 65 95
869 5 r. High jumping (*horiz*) .. .. .. 75 1·10
870 6 r. Championships emblem .. .. .. 90 1·60
867/70 .. .. *Set of* 4 2·10 3·25

233 Bouquet (25th anniv of Fleurir Maurice)   234 Bank of Mauritius Headquarters

(Des D. Miller. Litho B.D.T.)

1992 (13 Aug). *Local Events and Anniversaries. T* **233** *and similar multicoloured designs. W* w **14** (*sideways on* 2, 3, 15 *r.*). *P* 13½.

871 40 c. Type **233** 10 10
872 1 r. Swami Krishnanandji Maharaj (25th anniv of arrival) 40 10
873 2 r. Boy with dog (humane education) (*horiz*) 85 60
874 3 r. Commission Headquarters (10th anniv of Indian Ocean Commission) (*horiz*) 85 90
875 15 r. Radio telescope antenna, Bras d'Eau (project inauguration) (*horiz*) .. 3·50 4·50
871/5 .. .. *Set of* 5 5·00 5·50

(Des D. Miller. Litho Walsall)

1992 (29 Oct). *25th Anniv of Bank of Mauritius. T* **234** *and similar multicoloured designs. W* w **14** (*sideways on horiz designs*). *P* 14½.

876 40 c. Type **234** 10 10
877 4 r. Dodo gold coin (*horiz*) 80 70
878 8 r. First bank note issue (*horiz*) .. 1·75 2·25
879 15 r. Graph of foreign exchange reserves, 1967–92 (*horiz*) .. .. .. 2·75 3·75
876/9 .. .. *Set of* 4 4·75 6·00

REPUBLIC OF MAURITIUS
Bell 206 B Jet Ranger 40cs

235 Housing Development   236 Bell 206B JetRanger Helicopter

(Des G. Vasarhelyi. Litho B.D.T.)

1993 (12 Mar). *25th Anniv of National Day. T* **235** *and similar vert designs. Multicoloured. W* w **14**. *P* 15×14.

880 30 c. Type **235** 10 10
881 40 c. Gross domestic product graph on computer screen 10 10
882 3 r. National colours on map of Mauritius 40 50
883 4 r. Ballot box 45 60
884 15 r. Grand Commander's insignia for Order of Star and Key of the Indian Ocean 1·75 3·00
880/4 .. .. *Set of* 5 2·50 3·75

(Des N. Shewring. Litho B.D.T.)

1993 (14 June). *25th Anniv of Air Mauritius Ltd. T* **236** *and similar horiz designs. Multicoloured. W* w **14** (*sideways*). *P* 14.

885 40 c. Type **236** 45 20
886 3 r. Boeing 747SP 80 80
887 4 r. Aerospatiale/Aeritalia ATR 42 .. 90 1·00
888 10 r. Boeing 767-200ER .. .. .. 2·00 3·00
885/8 .. .. *Set of* 4 3·75 4·50
MS889 150×91 mm. Nos. 885/8 .. .. 4·25 5·00

40cs ═

(**237**)

1993 (15 Sept). *No.* 811A *surch with T* **237**

890 40 c. on 75 c. Bassin Blanc 30 30

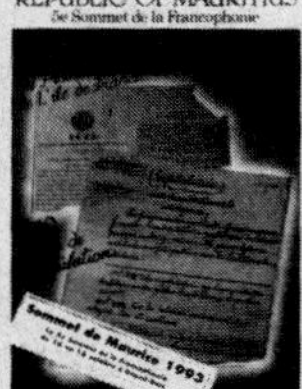

238 French Royal Charter, 1715, and Act of Capitulation, 1810   239 *Scotia* (cable ship) and Map of Cable Route

(Des D. Miller. Litho B.D.T.)

1993 (16 Oct). *5th Summit of French-speaking Nations. T* **238** *and similar vert designs. Multicoloured.* W w **14**. *P* 14.

891 1 r. Type **238** 25 10
892 5 r. Road signs .. .. 1·25 1·10
893 6 r. Code Napoléon .. .. 1·25 1·40
894 7 r. Early Mauritius newspapers .. 1·50 1·75
891/4 .. .. *Set of* 4 3·75 3·75

(Des N. Shewring. Litho Cartor)

1993 (25 Nov). *Centenary of Telecommunications. T* **239** *and similar horiz designs. Multicoloured.* W w **14** (*sideways*). *P* 13.

895 40 c. Type **239** 20 10
896 3 r. Morse key and code 60 70
897 4 r. Signal Mountain Earth station .. 75 1·00
898 8 r. Communications satellite .. .. 1·40 2·00
895/8 .. .. *Set of* 4 2·75 3·50

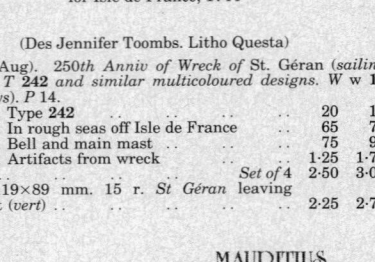

240 Indian Mongoose

241 Dr. Edouard Brown-Séquard (physiologist) (death cent)

(Des A. Robinson. Litho Questa)

1994 (9 Mar). *Mammals. T* **240** *and similar horiz designs. Multicoloured.* W w **16** (*sideways*). *P* $14^1/_2$.

899 40 c. Type **240** 20 10
900 2 r. Indian Black-naped Hare 45 35
901 8 r. Pair of Crab-eating Macaque .. 1·50 2·25
902 10 r. Adult and infant Common Tenrec .. 1·75 2·50
899/902 .. .. *Set of* 4 3·50 4·75

(Des N. Shewring. Litho B.D.T.)

1994 (16 June). *Anniversaries and Events. T* **241** *and similar vert designs. Multicoloured.* W w **14**. *P* 14.

903 40 c. Type **241** 10 10
904 4 r. Family in silhouette (International Year of the Family) 45 55
905 8 r. World Cup and map of U.S.A. (World Cup Football Championship, U.S.A.) 1·00 1·50
906 10 r. Control tower, SSR International Airport (50th anniv of Civil Aviation Organization) .. .. .. 1·25 1·75
903/6 .. .. *Set of* 4 2·50 3·50

242 *St. Géran* leaving L'Orient for Isle de France, 1744

(Des Jennifer Toombs. Litho Questa)

1994 (18 Aug). *250th Anniv of Wreck of* St. Géran *(sailing packet). T* **242** *and similar multicoloured designs.* W w **16** (*sideways*). *P* 14.

907 40 c. Type **242** 20 10
908 5 r. In rough seas off Isle de France .. 65 70
909 6 r. Bell and main mast 75 90
910 10 r. Artifacts from wreck .. .. 1·25 1·75
907/10 .. .. *Set of* 4 2·50 3·00
MS911 119×89 mm. 15 r. *St Géran* leaving L'Orient (*vert*) .. .. 2·25 2·75

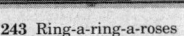

243 Ring-a-ring-a-roses

244 Nutmeg

(Des G. Vasarhelyi. Litho B.D.T.)

1994 (25 Oct). *Children's Games and Pastimes. T* **243** *and similar horiz designs showing children's paintings. Multicoloured.* W w **14** (*sideways*). *P* $13^1/_2$.

912 30 c. Type **243** 10 10
913 40 c. Skipping and ball games 10 10
914 8 r. Water sports .. .. 1·25 1·60
915 10 r. Blind man's buff .. .. .. 1·25 1·75
912/15 .. .. *Set of* 4 2·40 3·00

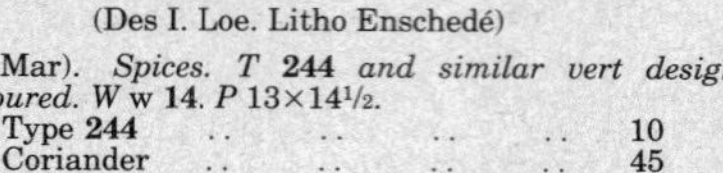

(Des I. Loe. Litho Enschedé)

1995 (10 Mar). *Spices. T* **244** *and similar vert designs. Multicoloured.* W w **14**. *P* 13×$14^1/_2$.

916 40 c. Type **244** 10 10
917 4 r. Coriander 45 55
918 5 r. Cloves 50 65
919 10 r. Cardamom .. .. 1·00 1·75
916/19 .. .. *Set of* 4 1·90 2·75

(Des A. Theobald. Litho B.D.T)

1995 (8 May). *50th Anniv of End of Second World War. Designs as T* **75** *of Kiribati, but* 35×28 *mm. Multicoloured.* W w **14** (*sideways*). *P* $13^1/_2$.

920 5 r. H.M.S. *Mauritius* (cruiser) .. .. 80 1·00
921 5 r. Mauritian soldiers and map of North Africa .. .. 80 1·00
922 5 r. Consolidated PBY-5 Catalina flying boat, Tombeau Bay .. .. .. 80 1·00
920/2 .. .. *Set of* 3 2·25 2·75

245 Mare Longue Reservoir

246 Ile Plate Lighthouse

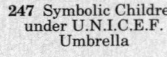

(Des A. Theobald. Litho B.D.T.)

1995 (8 May). *Anniversaries. T* **245** *and similar horiz designs. Multicoloured.* W w **14** (*sideways*). *P* $13^1/_2$.

923 40 c. Type **245** (50th anniv of construction) 10 10
924 4 r. Mahebourg to Curepipe road (bicentenary of construction) 50 65
925 10 r. Buildings on fire (centenary of Great Fire of Port Louis) .. .. .. 1·10 1·60
923/5 .. .. *Set of* 3 1·50 2·00

(Des N. Shewring. Litho Enschedé)

1995 (28 Aug). *Lighthouses. T* **246** *and similar vert designs. Multicoloured.* W w **14**. *P* 13×$14^1/_2$.

926 30 c. Type **246** 20 10
927 40 c. Pointe aux Caves 20 10
928 8 r. Ile aux Fouquets .. .. .. 1·25 1·60
929 10 r. Pointe aux Canonniers .. .. 1·40 1·75
926/9 .. .. *Set of* 4 2·75 3·00
MS930 130×100 mm. Nos. 926/9 .. .. 2·75 3·25

247 Symbolic Children under U.N.I.C.E.F. Umbrella

248 C.O.M.E.S.A. Emblem

(Des E. Nisbet. Litho B.D.T.)

1995 (24 Oct). *50th Anniv of United Nations. T* **247** *and similar horiz designs. Multicoloured.* W w **14** (*sideways*). *P* $13^1/_2$.

931 40 c. Type **247** 10 10
932 4 r. Hard hat and building construction (I.L.O.) 35 45
933 8 r. Satellite picture of cyclone (W.M.O.) 70 1·10
934 10 r. Bread and grain (F.A.O.) .. .. 90 1·40
931/5 .. .. *Set of* 4 1·90 2·75

(Des E. Nisbet. Litho Cartor)

1995 (8 Dec). *Inauguration of Common Market for Eastern and Southern Africa.* W w **14**. *P* 13×$13^1/_2$.

935 **248** 60 c. black and rose 10 10
936 4 r. black and cobalt 35 45
937 8 r. black and lemon .. .. .. 70 1·10
938 10 r. black and bright emerald .. .. 90 1·40
935/8 .. .. *Set of* 4 1·90 2·75

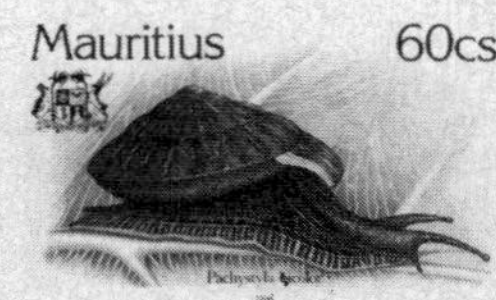

249 *Pachystyla bicolor*

(Des I. Loe. Litho Cartor)

1996 (11 Mar). *Snails. T* **249** *and similar horiz designs. Multicoloured.* W w **14** (*sideways*). *P* 14×$13^1/_2$.

939 60 c. Type **249** 15 10
940 4 r. *Gonidomus pagodus* 45 50
941 5 r. *Harmogenanina implicata* 45 60
942 10 r. *Tropidophora eugeniae* .. .. 85 1·25
939/42 .. .. *Set of* 4 1·75 2·25

250 Boxing

(Des R. Watton. Litho B.D.T.)

1996 (26 June). *Centenary of Modern Olympic Games. T* **250** *and similar horiz designs. Multicoloured.* W w **16** (*sideways*). *P* $13^1/_2$.

943 60 c. Type **250** 10 10
944 4 r. Badminton 45 50
945 5 r. Basketball 60 65
946 10 r. Table tennis .. .. 1·00 1·50
943/6 .. .. *Set of* 4 1·90 2·40

251 *Zambezia* (freighter)

(Des J. Batchelor. Litho B.D.T.)

1996 (30 Sept). *Ships. T* **251** *and similar horiz designs. Multicoloured.* W w **14** (*sideways*). *P* 14.

947 60 c. Type **251** 15 10
948 4 r. *Sir Jules* (coastal freighter) 45 50
949 5 r. *Mauritius* (cargo liner) 50 60
950 10 r. *Mauritius Pride* (container ship) .. 1·00 1·50
947/50 .. .. *Set of* 4 1·90 2·40
MS951 125×91 mm. Nos. 947/50 .. .. 1·90 2·40

252 Posting a Letter

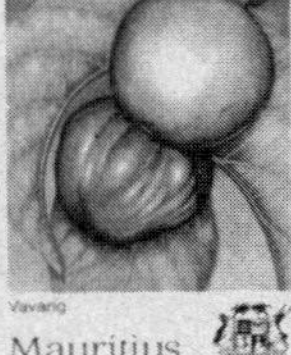

253 Vavang

(Des D. Miller. Litho B.D.T.)

1996 (2 Dec). *150th Anniv of the Post Office Ordinance. T* **252** *and similar horiz designs. Multicoloured.* W w **16** (*sideways*). *P* $13^1/_2$.

952 60 c. Type **252** 10 10
953 4 r. "B53" duplex postmark 35 45
954 5 r. Modern mobile post office 45 55
955 10 r. Carriole (19th-century horse-drawn postal carriage) .. .. .. 85 1·25
952/5 .. .. *Set of* 4 1·50 2·00

(Des I. Loe. Litho Cartor)

1997 (10 Mar). *Fruits. T* **253** *and similar vert designs. Multicoloured.* W w **14**. *P* 13×$13^1/_2$.

956 60 c. Type **253** 10 10
957 4 r. Pom Zako 35 40
958 5 r. Zambos 45 55
959 10 r. Sapot Negro .. .. 85 1·25
956/9 .. .. *Set of* 4 1·50 2·00

254 Governor Mahé de la Bourdonnais and Map

(Des G. Vasarhelyi. Litho B.D.T.)

1997 (9 June). *Aspects of Mauritius History. T* **254** *and similar horiz designs. Multicoloured.* W w **14** (*sideways*). *P* $13^1/_2$.

960 60 c. Type **254** 10 10
961 1 r. La Pérouse and map of Pacific .. 15 10
961 4 r. Governor Sir William Gomm and Lady Gomm's Ball, 1847 .. .. .. 30 30
962 6 r. George Clark discovering skeleton of dodo, 1865 .. .. 45 45
964 10 r. Professor Brian Abel-Smith and Social Policies report of 1960 .. .. 70 80
960/4 .. .. *Set of* 5 1·50 1·60

255 1d. "POST OFFICE" Mauritius

(Des D. Miller. Litho B.D.T.)

1997 (22 Sept). *150th Anniv of* "POST OFFICE" *Stamps. T* **255** *and similar horiz designs. Multicoloured. W* w **14** *(sideways). P* 13½.

965 60 c. Type **255** 10 10
 a. Sheetlet. Nos. 965×7 and 966×5 .. 1·75
 b. Booklet pane of 10 with margins all round .. .. 1·00
966 4 r. 2d. "POST OFFICE" Mauritius .. 20 25
 a. Booklet pane of 10 with margins all round .. .. 2·00
967 5 r. "POST OFFICE" 1d. and 2d. on gold background 30 35
 a. Booklet pane of 10 with margins all round .. .. 3·00
968 10 r. "POST OFFICE" 2d. and 1d. on silver background 55 60
 a. Booklet pane of 10 with margins all round .. .. 5·50
965/8 .. .. *Set of* 4 1·10 1·25
MS969 127×90 mm. 20 r. "POST OFFICE" stamps on cover to Bordeaux .. .. .. 1·10 1·25

Nos. 965/8 were issued in separate sheets, but Nos. 965/6 also exist as a sheetlet of 12 (3×4), containing seven 60 c. and four 4 r.

256 Wheelwright

(Des N. Shewring. Litho Walsall)

1997 (1 Dec). *Small Businesses. T* **256** *and similar horiz designs. Multicoloured. W* w **14** *(sideways). P* 14½.

970 60 c. Type **256** 10 10
971 4 r. Laundryman 20 25
972 5 r. Shipwright 30 35
973 15 r. Quarryman 80 85
970/3 .. .. *Set of* 4 1·40 1·50

257 *Phelsuma guentheri* (gecko)

(Des W. Oliver. Litho B.D.T.)

1998 (11 Mar). *Geckos. T* **257** *and similar horiz designs. Multicoloured. W* w **14** *(sideways). P* 13½.

974 1 r. Type **257** 10 10
975 6 r. *Nactus serpensinsula durrelli* 35 40
976 7 r. *Nactus coindemirensis* 40 45
977 8 r. *Phelsuma edwardnewtonii* 45 50
974/7 .. .. *Set of* 4 1·25 1·40

STAMP BOOKLETS

1953 (10 Oct). *Black on white cover. Stapled.*
SB1 5 r. booklet containing four 5 c., eight 10 c. and 50 c. (Nos. 280, 286, 291) in blocks of 4 and one pane of 4 air mail labels £180

1954 (23 Sept). *Black on white or grey cover. Stapled.*
SB2 5 r. booklet containing four 5 c., eight 10 c. and 50 c. (Nos. 296/7, 302) in blocks of 4 and one pane of 4 air mail labels .. .. .. 35·00

1955. *Black on grey cover. Stapled.*
SB3 5 r. booklet containing four 5 c., eight 10 c. and 50 c. (Nos. 296, 297*a*, 302) in block of 4 and one pane of 4 air mail labels .. .. .. 40·00

1979 (20 July). *Tenth Anniv of Moon Landing. Multicoloured cover, 165×92 mm, showing astronauts on front and Lunar Module above Moon on back. Stitched.*
SB4 17 r. 80, booklet containing *se-tenant* panes of 3 or 6 (Nos. 574a/b) .. .. 5·50

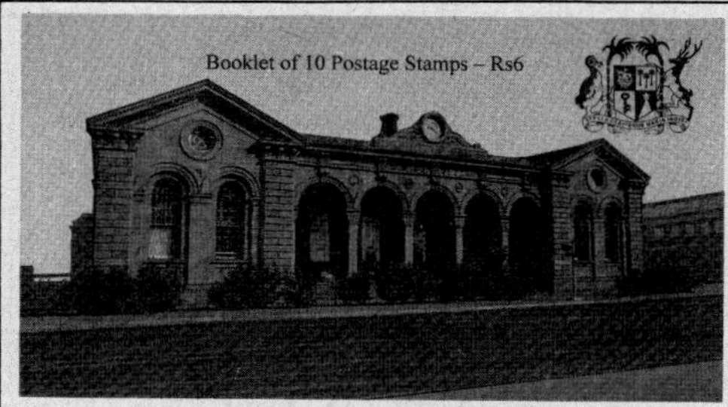

B 1 Port Louis Post Office
(Illustration reduced. Actual size 125×71 mm)

1997 (22 Sept). *150th Anniv of* "POST OFFICE" *Stamps. Covers as Type* B **1**. *Panes attached by selvedge.*
SB5 6 r. booklet containing pane of ten 60 c. (No. 965b) .. .. 1·00
SB6 40 r. booklet containing pane of ten 4 r. (No. 966a) .. .. 2·00
SB7 50 r. booklet containing pane of ten 5 r. (No. 967a) .. .. 3·00
SB8 100 r. booklet containing pane of ten 10 r. (No. 968a) .. .. 5·50

EXPRESS DELIVERY STAMPS

EXPRESS DELIVERY 15c.
(E 1)

EXPRESS DELIVERY (INLAND) 15c.
(E 2)

EXPRESS DELIVERY (INLAND) 15 c.
(E 3)

EXPRESS DELIVERY (INLAND) 15 c
(E 4)

Type E 2. "(INLAND)" was inserted at a second printing on stamps already surcharged with Type E 1 (No. E1).
Type E 3. New setting made at one printing. More space above and below "(INLAND)".
Type E 4. New setting with smaller "15 c" and no stop.

1903 (10 Aug)–**04.** *No. 136 surch locally in red.*
E1 E 1 15 c. on 15 c. ultramarine .. .. 5·00 16·00
E2 E 2 15 c. on 15 c. ultramarine (28.3.04) .. 26·00 29·00
 a. "A" inverted £450 £350
 b. "(INLAND)" inverted .. .. † —
E3 E 3 15 c. on 15 c. ultramarine (4.04) .. 5·50 1·75
 a. Surch and wmk inverted .. .. — £300
 b. Surch double, both inverted ..
 c. Imperf between (vert pair) .. £2500
 w. Wmk inverted .. .. ..
E4 E 4 15 c. on 15 c. ultramarine (1904) .. £275 £275
 a. Surch inverted .. .. ..
 b. Surch double .. .. ..
 c. Surch double, both inverted ..
 d. "c" omitted .. .. .. — £1000

(FOREIGN) EXPRESS DELIVERY 18 CENTS
(E 5)

1904. *T* **42** *(without value in label), surch with Type* E **5** *locally. Wmk Crown CC. P* 14.
E5 18 c. green .. .. 1·50 17·00
 a. Exclamation mark for "I" in "FOREIGN" £350

1904. *T* **42** *(without value in label) surch with Type* E **3** *locally.*
E6 15 c. grey-green (R.) .. .. .. 2·50 2·50
 a. Surch inverted £375 £375
 b. Surch double £275
 c. Surch double, one "LNIAND" £300 £300

POSTAGE DUE STAMPS

D 1

POSTAGE DUE 10c
(D 2)

(Typo Waterlow)

1933–54. *Wmk Mult Script CA. P* 15 × 14.
D1 D 1 2 c. black 50 50
D2 4 c. violet 40 65
D3 6 c. scarlet 40 80
D4 10 c. green 40 70
D5 20 c. bright blue 50 90
D6 50 c. deep magenta (1.3.54) .. .. 55 12·00
D7 1 r. orange (1.3.54) .. .. .. 70 14·00
D1/7 .. .. .. *Set of* 7 3·00 27·00
D1/5 Perf "Specimen" .. .. *Set of* 5 65·00

(Typo D.L.R.)

1966–72. *Wmk* w **12**. *Chalk-surfaced paper. P* 13½×14 (2 c.) *or* 15×14 *(others).*
D 8 D 1 2 c. black (11.7.67) .. .. .. 2·00 2·50
D 9 4 c. slate-lilac (7.1.69) .. .. 1·75 5·50
D10 6 c. red-orange (7.1.69) .. .. 6·00 15·00
 a. Perf 13½×14 .. .. .. 22·00 32·00
D11 10 c. yellow-green (16.2.67) .. .. 30 1·50
D12 20 c. blue (3.1.66) .. .. .. 2·25 4·00
 a. Deep blue (7.1.69) .. .. 2·25 8·00
D13 50 c. deep magenta (7.1.69) .. .. 75 9·00
 a. Magenta (10.1.72) .. .. 1·75 14·00
D8/13 .. .. .. *Set of* 6 11·50 35·00

1982 (25 Oct). *Nos.* 530A/1A, 535A, 540A, 542A *and* 547A *optd as Type* D **2**, *by J. W. Dunn Printers Ltd.*
D14 10 c. on 15 c. Dutch Occupation, 1638–1710 .. 20 30
D15 20 c. on 20 c. Van Keulen's map, *circa* 1700 .. 30 30
D16 50 c. on 60 c. Pierre Poivre, *circa* 1767 .. 30 30
D17 1 r. on 1 r. 20, Government House, *circa* 1840 40 30
D18 1 r. 50 on 1 r. 50, Indian immigration, 1835 50 75
D19 5 r. on 15 r. Unfurling Mauritian flag, 1968 1·00 2·00
D14/19 .. .. .. *Set of* 6 2·40 3·50

FISCALS USED FOR POSTAGE

INLAND REVENUE
(F 1)

INLAND REVENUE
(F 2)

F 3

1889. *T* **19**, *wmk Crown CA, optd. P* 14.
R1 F 1 4 c. carmine .. .. 8·50 5·00
R2 F 2 4 c. lilac .. .. 2·50 10·00

(Typo D.L.R.)

1896. *Wmk Crown CA. P* 14.
R3 F 3 4 c. dull purple .. .. 18·00

MINIMUM PRICE

The minimum price quote is 10p which represents a handling charge rather than a basis for valuing common stamps. For further notes about prices see introductory pages.

Montserrat

A local post office operated on Montserrat from some time early in the 18th century, although the first recorded postal marking does not occur until 1791. A branch of the British G.P.O. was established at Plymouth, the island capital, in 1852.

The stamps of Great Britain were used from 1858 until the overseas postal service reverted to local control on 1 April 1860.

In the interim period between 1860 and the introduction of Montserrat stamps in 1876 No. CC1 and a similar "uncrowned" handstamp were again used.

PLYMOUTH

CROWNED-CIRCLE HANDSTAMPS

C 1

CC1 C **1** MONTSERRAT (R.) (15.7.1852) *Price on cover* £2500

No. CC1 was used as an emergency measure, struck in black, during 1886.

Stamps of GREAT BRITAIN *cancelled* "A 08" *as Type* Z **1** *of Jamaica.*

1858 (8 May) *to* **1860.**

No.	Description	Price
Z1	1d. rose-red (1857), *perf* 14	£1100
Z2	4d. rose (1857)	
Z3	6d. lilac (1856)	£450
Z4	1s. green (1856)	

PRICES FOR STAMPS ON COVER TO 1945

Nos. 1/2	*from* × 40
No. 3	†
Nos. 4/5	*from* × 8
Nos. 6/13	*from* × 12
Nos. 14/22	*from* × 4
No. 23	—
Nos. 24/33	*from* × 4
Nos. 35/47	*from* × 3
No. 48	—
Nos. 49/59	*from* × 3
Nos. 60/2	*from* × 15
Nos. 63/83	*from* × 3
Nos. 84/93	*from* × 4
Nos. 94/7	*from* × 3
Nos. 98/100	*from* × 8
Nos. 101/12	*from* × 5

1

MONTSERRAT

(2)

3 (Die I)

(T **1** recess D.L.R.)

1876 (Sept). *Stamps of Antigua optd with T* **2**. *Wmk Crown CC. P* 14.

No.	Type	Description	Unused	Used
1	**1**	1d. red	20·00	15·00
		a. Bisected (½d.) (on cover)	†	£1400
		b. Inverted "S"	£1000	£750
2		6d. green	55·00	40·00
		a. Bisect (used as 2½d.) (on cover)	†	£5000
		b. Inverted "S"	£1300	£1000
3		6d. blue-green	£1000	
		a. Inverted "S"	£6000	

Nos. 1/3 were overprinted either from a setting of 120 (12×10) or from a setting of 60 (6×10) applied twice to each sheet. This setting of 60 had an inverted "S" on R. 3/3. The same setting was subsequently used for some sheets of Nos. 7 and 13.

No. 1 was bisected and used for a ½d. in 1883. This bisected stamp is found surcharged with a small "½" in *black* and also in *red*; both were unofficial and they did not emanate from the Montserrat P.O.

The 6d. in blue-green is only known unused.

(T **3** typo D.L.R.)

1880 (Jan). *Wmk Crown CC. P* 14.

No.	Type	Description	Unused	Used
4	**3**	2½d. red-brown	£250	£180
5		4d. blue	£140	40·00

Top left triangle detached
(Pl 2 R.3/3 of right pane)

1884–85. *Wmk Crown CA. P* 14.

No.	Type	Description	Unused	Used
6	**3**	½d. dull green	1·00	6·50
		a. Top left triangle detached	42·00	
7	**1**	1d. red	14·00	18·00
		a. Inverted "S"	£850	£850
		b. Rose-red (1885)	15·00	14·00
		ba. Bisected vert (½d.) (on cover)	†	£1300
		bb. Inverted "S"	£950	£950
9	**3**	2½d. red-brown	£225	65·00
10		2½d. ultramarine (1885)	17·00	16·00
		a. Top left triangle detached	£180	
11		4d. blue	£1800	£250
12		4d. mauve (1885)	4·00	3·00
		a. Top left triangle detached	85·00	
10, 12 Optd "Specimen"		*Set of* 2	£300	

1884 (May). *Wmk Crown CA. P* 12.

No.	Type	Description	Unused	Used
13	**1**	1d. red	70·00	50·00
		a. Inverted "S"	£1800	£1300
		b. Bisected (½d.) (on cover)	†	£1600

The stamps for Montserrat were superseded by the general issue for Leeward Islands in November 1890, but the following issues were in concurrent use with the stamps inscribed "LEEWARD ISLANDS" until 1 July 1956, when Leeward Islands stamps were withdrawn and invalidated.

4 Device of the Colony

5

(Typo D.L.R.)

1903 (Aug). (*a*) *Wmk Crown CA. P* 14.

No.	Type	Description	Unused	Used
14	**4**	½d. grey-green and green	75	11·00
15		1d. grey-black and red	75	40
		w. Wmk inverted		
16		2d. grey and brown	5·00	20·00
17		2½d. grey and blue	1·50	1·75
18		3d. dull orange and deep purple	4·00	22·00
19		6d. dull purple and olive	4·00	35·00
20		1s. green and bright purple	10·00	16·00
21		2s. green and brown-orange	23·00	16·00
22		2s. 6d. green and black	17·00	30·00
		(*b*) *Wmk Crown CC. P* 14		
23	**5**	5s. black and scarlet	85·00	£150
14/23		*Set of* 10	£130	£275
14/23 Optd "Specimen"		*Set of* 10	£160	

1904–08. *Wmk Mult Crown CA. Ordinary paper (½d., 2d., 3d., 6d.) or chalk-surfaced paper (others). P* 14.

No.	Type	Description	Unused	Used
24	**4**	½d. grey-green and green	2·00	1·00
		a. Chalk-surfaced paper (3.06)	40	75
25		1d. grey-black and red (1905)	12·00	21·00
26		2d. grey and brown	65	3·50
		a. Chalk-surfaced paper (5.06)	1·75	1·00
27		2½d. grey and blue (1905)	2·50	6·50
28		3d. dull orange and deep purple	5·00	4·50
		a. Chalk-surfaced paper (1908)	5·00	2·50
29		6d. dull purple and olive	3·25	14·00
		a. Chalk-surfaced paper (1908)	5·00	5·00
30		1s. green and bright purple (1908)	8·50	7·00
31		2s. green and orange (1908)	29·00	40·00
32		2s. 6d. green and black (1908)	40·00	42·00
33	**5**	5s. black and red (1907)	75·00	£110
24/33		*Set of* 10	£160	£200

1908 (June)–**14.** *Wmk Mult Crown CA. Ordinary paper (½d. to 2½d.) or chalk-surfaced paper (3d. to 5s.). P* 14.

No.	Type	Description	Unused	Used
35	**4**	½d. deep green (4.10)	4·00	1·00
36		1d. rose-red	1·40	30
38		2d. greyish slate (9.09)	1·75	12·00
39		2½d. blue	2·25	3·50
40		3d. purple/*yellow* (9.09)	1·00	16·00
		a. White back (1.14) (Optd S. £25)	3·00	25·00
43		6d. dull and deep purple (9.09)	6·50	42·00
		a. Dull and bright purple (1914)	9·00	42·00
44		1s. black/*green* (9.09)	7·50	40·00
45		2s. purple and bright blue/*blue* (9.09)	24·00	48·00
46		2s. 6d. black and red/*blue* (9.09)	30·00	60·00
47	**5**	5s. red and green/*yellow* (9.09)	48·00	60·00
35/47		*Set of* 10	£100	£250
35/47 Optd "Specimen"		*Set of* 10	£190	

Examples of most values are known showing forged Montserrat postmarks dated "OC 16 1909" or "NO 26 1910".

7

8

WAR STAMP

(**9**)

(T **7/8** typo D.L.R.)

1914. *Wmk Mult Crown CA. Chalk-surfaced paper. P* 14.

No.	Type	Description	Unused	Used
48	**7**	5s. red and green/*yellow*	55·00	85·00
48 Optd "Specimen"			75·00	

1916 (10 Oct)–**23.** *Wmk Mult Crown CA. Ordinary paper (½d. to 2½d.) or chalk-surfaced paper (3d. to 5s.). P* 14.

No.	Type	Description	Unused	Used
49	**8**	½d. green	30	2·25
50		1d. scarlet	35	75
		a. Carmine-red	14·00	6·00
51		2d. grey	1·25	4·00
52		2½d. bright blue	1·50	14·00
53		3d. purple/*yellow*	75	6·50
		a. On pale yellow (1922) (Optd S. £20)	75	9·00
54		4d. grey-black and red/*pale yellow* (1923)	5·50	27·00
55		6d. dull and deep purple	2·75	18·00
56		1s. black/*blue-green* (*olive back*)	3·00	17·00
57		2s. purple and blue/*blue*	13·00	22·00
58		2s. 6d. black and red/*blue*	22·00	42·00
59		5s. green and red/*yellow*	38·00	48·00
49/59		*Set of* 11	75·00	£180
49/59 Optd "Specimen"		*Set of* 11	£160	

1917 (Oct)–**18.** *No.* 49 *optd with T* **9**.

No.	Type	Description	Unused	Used
60	**8**	½d. green (R.)	10	1·00
		a. Short opt (right pane R. 10/1)	10·00	
		y. Wmk inverted and reversed		
61		½d. green (Blk.) (6.18)	15	1·60
		a. Short opt (right pane R. 10/1)	10·00	
		b. Deep green (10.18)	15	1·25
		ba. "C" and "A" missing from wmk		
		bb. Short opt (right pane R. 10/1)	10·00	
		w. Wmk inverted		

Nos. 60a, 61a, and 61bb show the overprint 2 mm high instead of 2½ mm.

No. 61ba shows the "C" omitted from one impression and the "A" missing from the next.

1919 (Mar). *T* **8**. *Special printing in orange. Value and* "WAR STAMP" *as T* **9** *inserted in black at one printing.*

No.	Type	Description	Unused	Used
62		1½d. black and orange	10	30
60/2 Optd "Specimen"		*Set of* 3	80·00	

1922 (13 July)–**29.** *Wmk Mult Script CA. Ordinary paper (¼d. to 3d. (No. 73) or chalk-surfaced paper (others). P* 14.

No.	Type	Description	Unused	Used
63	**8**	¼d. brown	15	4·50
64		½d. green (5.4.23)	20	30
65		1d. bright violet (5.4.23)	30	50
66		1d. carmine (1929)	75	1·00
67		1½d. orange-yellow	1·75	9·50
68		1½d. carmine (5.4.23)	30	2·50
69		1½d. red-brown (1929)	70	50
70		2d. grey	45	1·25
71		2½d. deep bright blue	8·00	16·00
		a. Pale brt blue (17.8.26) (Optd S. £30)	60	90
72		2½d. orange-yellow (5.4.23)	1·25	18·00
73		3d. dull blue (5.4.23)	50	14·00
74		3d. purple/*yellow* (2.1.27)	1·10	4·75
75		4d. black and red/*pale yellow*	60	8·50
76		5d. dull purple and olive	2·50	10·00
77		6d. pale and bright purple (5.4.23)	2·00	6·00
78		1s. black/*emerald* (5.4.23)	3·00	7·00
79		2s. purple and blue/*blue*	5·50	13·00
80		2s. 6d. black and red/*blue* (5.4.23)	11·00	45·00
81		3s. green and violet	12·00	18·00
82		4s. black and scarlet	14·00	27·00
83		5s. green and red/*pale yellow* (6.23)	21·00	32·00
63/83		*Set of* 21	70·00	£200
63/83 Optd/Perf "Specimen"		*Set of* 21	£275	

10 Plymouth

(Recess D.L.R.)

1932 (18 April). *Tercentenary. Wmk Mult Script CA. P* 14.

No.	Type	Description	Unused	Used
84	**10**	½d. green	75	5·00
85		1d. scarlet	75	4·50
86		1½d. red-brown	1·25	2·25
87		2d. grey	1·25	13·00
88		2½d. ultramarine	1·25	11·00
89		3d. orange	1·50	12·00
90		6d. violet	2·25	24·00
91		1s. olive-brown	11·00	30·00
92		2s. 6d. purple	48·00	65·00
93		5s. chocolate	£100	£150
84/93		*Set of* 10	£150	£275
84/93 Perf "Specimen"		*Set of* 10	£225	

Examples of all values are known showing a forged G.P.O. Plymouth postmark dated "MY 13 32".

1935 (6 May). *Silver Jubilee. As Nos.* 114/17 *of Jamaica, but ptd by Waterlow & Sons. P* 11×12.

No.	Description	Unused	Used
94	1d. deep blue and scarlet	85	2·75
95	1½d. ultramarine and grey	75	2·75
96	2½d. brown and deep blue	2·25	2·75
97	1s. slate and purple	3·00	12·00
94/7	*Set of* 4	6·25	18·00
94/7 Perf "Specimen"	*Set of* 4	75·00	

1937 (12 May). *Coronation. As Nos.* 118/20 *of Jamaica.*

No.	Description	Unused	Used
98	1d. scarlet	30	40
99	1½d. yellow-brown	40	25
100	2½d. bright blue	40	60
98/100	*Set of* 3	1·00	1·10
98/100 Perf "Specimen"	*Set of* 3	50·00	

11 Carr's Bay

12 Sea Island Cotton

13 Botanic Station

(Recess D.L.R.)

1938 (2 Aug)–**48.** *Wmk Mult Script CA. P* 12 (10*s.*, £1) *or* 13 (*others*).

101 **11** ½d. blue-green .. .. 2·00 1·25
 a. Perf 14 (1942) 15 20
102 **12** 1d. carmine .. .. 1·75 40
 a. Perf 14 (1943) 30 30
103 1½d. purple .. .. 9·50 50
 a. Perf 14 (1942) 30 50
 ab. "A" of "CA" missing from wmk ..
104 **13** 2d. orange .. .. 8·00 60
 a. Perf 14 (1942) 85 70
105 **12** 2½d. ultramarine 65 60
 a. Perf 14 (1943) 40 30
106 **11** 3d. brown .. .. 1·50 40
 a. Perf 14, *Red-brown* (1942) .. .. 1·75 40
 ab. Deep brown (1943) .. .. .. 4·00 4·75
107 **13** 6d. violet .. .. 6·50 80
 a. Perf 14 (1943) .. .. 2·50 60
108 **11** 1s. lake .. .. 8·00 70
 a. Perf 14 (1942) .. .. 2·00 30
109 **13** 2s. 6d. slate-blue .. .. 17·00 80
 a. Perf 14 (1943) .. .. 17·00 2·50
110 **11** 5s. rose-carmine .. .. 24·00 8·00
 a. Perf 14 (1942) .. .. 21·00 3·00
111 **13** 10s. pale blue (1948) .. .. .. 13·00 17·00
112 **11** £1 black (1948) .. .. .. 13·00 27·00
101a/12 .. .. *Set of* 12 65·00 45·00
101/12 Perf "Specimen" .. .. *Set of* 12 £250

1946 (1 Nov). *Victory. As Nos.* 141/2 *of Jamaica.*

113 1½d. purple 10 10
114 3d. chocolate 10 10
113/14 Perf "Specimen" .. .. *Set of* 2 55·00

1949 (3 Jan). *Royal Silver Wedding. As Nos.* 143/4 *of Jamaica.*

115 2½d. ultramarine 10 10
116 5s. carmine .. .. 4·50 5·50

1949 (10 Oct). *75th Anniv of U.P.U. As Nos.* 145/8 *of Jamaica.*

117 2½d. ultramarine 20 30
118 3d. brown .. .. 1·50 30
119 6d. purple 40 30
120 1s. purple 40 30
117/20 .. .. *Set of* 4 2·25 1·10

(New Currency. 100 cents = 1 West Indies, later Eastern Caribbean dollar)

1951 (16 Feb). *Inauguration of B.W.I. University College. As Nos.* 149/50 *of Jamaica.*

121 3 c. black and purple 20 50
122 12 c. black and violet 20 50

14 Government House

18 Badge of Presidency

(Recess B.W.)

1951 (17 Sept). *T* **14**, **18** *and similar horiz designs. Wmk Mult Script CA. P* 11½ × 11.

123 **14** 1 c. black .. .. 10 1·25
124 – 2 c. green 15 70
125 – 3 c. orange-brown 30 70
126 – 4 c. carmine 30 40
127 – 5 c. reddish violet 30 70
128 **18** 6 c. olive-brown 30 30
129 – 8 c. deep blue 35 20
130 – 12 c. blue and chocolate 35 30
131 – 24 c. carmine and yellow-green 85 30
132 – 60 c. black and carmine .. .. .. 5·50 2·50
133 – $1.20, yellow-green and blue .. .. 5·50 3·75
134 – $2.40, black and green .. .. .. 4·50 12·00
135 **18** $4.80, black and purple .. .. .. 16·00 16·00
123/135 .. .. *Set of* 13 30·00 32·00

Designs:—2 c., $1.20, Sea Island cotton: cultivation; 3 c. Map of colony; 4, 24 c. Picking tomatoes; 5, 12 c. St. Anthony's Church; 8, 60 c. Sea Island cotton: ginning; $2.40, Government House.

1953 (2 June). *Coronation. As No.* 153 *of Jamaica.*

136 2 c. black and deep green 40 15

19 Government House

20 Shakespeare and Memorial Theatre, Stratford-upon-Avon

Two Types of ½ c., 3 c., 6 c. and $4.80: I. Inscr "PRESIDENCY". II. Inscr "COLONY".

(Recess B.W.)

1953 (15 Oct)–**62.** *As King George VI issue, but with portrait of Queen Elizabeth II as in T* **19.** *Wmk Mult Script CA. P* 11½×11.

136*a* – ½ c. deep violet (I) (3.7.56) 50 10
136*b* – ½c. deep violet (II) (1.9.58) 70 10
137 **19** 1 c. black 10 10
138 – 2 c. green 15 10
139 – 3 c. orange-brown (I) 50 10
139*a* – 3 c. orange-brown (II) (1.9.58) 70 70
140 – 4 c. carmine-red (1.6.55) 30 20
141 – 5 c. reddish lilac (1.6.55) 30 30
142 **18** 6 c. deep bistre-brown (I) (1.6.55) .. 30 10
142*a* 6 c. deep bistre-brown (II) (1.9.58) .. 40 15
 ab. Deep sepia-brown (30.7.62) .. 5·50 4·25
143 – 8 c. deep bright blue (1.6.55) .. .. 1·00 10
144 – 12 c. blue and red-brown (1.6.55) .. 1·50 10
145 – 24 c. carmine-red and green (1.6.55) .. 1·50 20
145*a* – 48 c. yellow-olive and purple (15.10.57) 12·00 2·25
146 – 60 c. black and carmine (1.6.55) .. 7·00 2·00
147 – $1.20, green and greenish blue (1.6.55) 14·00 4·25
148 – $2.40, black and bluish green (1.6.55) 12·00 10·00
149 **18** $4.80, black & deep purple (I) (1.6.55) 6·00 10·00
149*a* $4.80, black & deep purple (II) (1.9.58) 10·00 7·50
136*a*/49 .. .. *Set of* 15 50·00 24·00

Extra designs:—½, 3 c. Map of colony; 48 c. Sea Island cotton cultivation.

See also No. 157.

1958 (22 Apr). *Inauguration of British Caribbean Federation. As Nos.* 175/7 *of Jamaica.*

150 3 c. deep green 55 20
151 6 c. blue 75 45
152 12 c. scarlet 90 15
150/2 .. .. *Set of* 3 2·00 70

1963 (8 July). *Freedom from Hunger. As No.* 80 *of Lesotho.*

153 12 c. reddish violet 30 15

1963 (2 Sept). *Red Cross Centenary. As Nos.* 203/4 *of Jamaica.*

154 4 c. red and black 10 20
155 12 c. red and blue 25 50

(Des R. Granger Barrett. Photo Harrison)

1964 (23 Apr). *400th Birth Anniv of William Shakespeare. W w* **12.** *P* 14×14½.

156 **20** 12 c. indigo 10 10

1964 (29 Oct). *As No.* 138 *but wmk w* **12.**

157 2 c. green 40 20

1965 (17 May). *I.T.U. Centenary. As Nos.* 98/9 *of Lesotho.*

158 4 c. vermilion and violet 15 10
159 48 c. light emerald and carmine 30 20

21 Pineapple

22 Avocado

(Des Sylvia Goaman. Photo Harrison)

1965 (16 Aug). *T* **21/2** *and similar vert designs showing vegetables, fruit or plants. Multicoloured. W w* **12** (*upright*). *P* 15×14.

160 1 c. Type **21** 10 10
 w. Wmk inverted .. .. 1·00 1·25
161 2 c. Type **22** 10 10
162 3 c. Soursop 10 10
163 4 c. Pepper 10 10
164 5 c. Mango 10 10
165 6 c. Tomato 10 10
166 8 c. Guava 10 10
167 10 c. Ochro 10 10
168 12 c. Lime 15 10
 w. Wmk inverted .. .. — 28·00
169 20 c. Orange 20 10
170 24 c. Banana 20 10
171 42 c. Onion 75 60
172 48 c. Cabbage .. .. 1·50 75
173 60 c. Pawpaw .. .. 2·25 90
174 $1.20, Pumpkin .. .. 2·00 2·00
175 $2.40, Sweep potato .. .. .. 6·00 4·25
176 $4.80, Egg plant .. .. 6·00 7·50
160/76 .. .. *Set of* 17 17·00 15·00

See also Nos. 213/22

1965 (25 Oct). *International Co-operation Year. As Nos.* 100/1 *of Lesotho.*

177 2 c. reddish purple and turquoise-green .. 10 20
178 12 c. deep bluish green and lavender .. 25 10

1966 (26 Jan). *Churchill Commemoration. As Nos.* 102/5 *of Lesotho.*

179 1 c. new blue 10 10
 a. Cerise (sky) omitted £250
180 2 c. deep green 10 10
181 24 c. brown 15 10
182 42 c. bluish violet 20 15
179/82 .. .. *Set of* 4 40 30

23 Queen Elizabeth II and Duke of Edinburgh

(Des H. Baxter. Litho B.W.)

1966 (4 Feb). *Royal Visit. W w* **12.** *P* 11×12.

183 **23** 14 c. black and ultramarine 40 15
184 24 c. black and magenta 60 15

24 W.H.O. Building

(Des M. Goaman. Litho Harrison)

1966 (20 Sept). *Inauguration of W.H.O. Headquarters, Geneva. W w* **12** (*sideways*). *P* 14.

185 **24** 12 c. black, yellow-green and light blue .. 10 10
186 60 c. black, light purple and yellow-brown 25 20

1966 (1 Dec). *20th Anniv of U.N.E.S.C.O. As Nos.* 342/4 *of Mauritius.*

187 4 c. slate-violet, red, yellow and orange .. 10 10
 a. Orange omitted .. .. 65·00
188 60 c. orange-yellow, violet and deep olive .. 30 10
189 $1.80, black, bright purple and orange .. 1·25 70
187/9 .. .. *Set of* 3 1·40 75

On No. 187a the omission of the orange only affects the squares of the lower case letters so that they appear yellow, the same as the capital squares.

25 Yachting

$1.00

(26)

(Des and photo Harrison)

1967 (29 Dec). *International Tourist Year. T* **25** *and similar multicoloured designs. W w* **12** (*sideways on* 15 *c.*). *P* 14.

190 5 c. Type **25** 15 10
191 15 c. Waterfall near Chance Mountain (*vert*) 20 10
192 16 c. Fishing, skin-diving and swimming .. 20 30
193 24 c. Playing golf .. .. 1·10 35
190/3 .. .. *Set of* 4 1·50 70

1968 (6 May). *Nos.* 168, 170, 172 *and* 174/6 *surch as T* **26.** *W w* **12** (*upright*).

194 15 c. on 12 c. Lime 20 15
195 25 c. on 24 c. Banana 25 15
196 50 c. on 48 c. Cabbage 45 15
197 $1 on $1.20, Pumpkin 80 40
198 $2.50 on $2.40, Sweet potato .. .. 1·25 3·25
199 $5 on $4.80, Egg plant .. .. .. 1·40 3·75
194/9 .. .. *Set of* 6 4·00 7·00

See also Nos. 219 etc.

27 Sprinting

28 Sprinting, and Aztec Pillars

(Des G. Vasarhelyi. Photo Harrison)

1968 (31 July). *Olympic Games, Mexico. T* **27/8** *and similar designs. W w* **12** (*sideways on* $1). *P* 14.

200 15 c. deep claret, emerald and gold 10 10
201 25 c. blue, orange and gold 15 10
202 50 c. green, red and gold 20 10
203 $1 multicoloured 30 20
200/3 .. .. *Set of* 4 60 30

Designs: *Horiz as T* **27**—25 c. Weightlifting; 50 c. Gymnastics.

31 Alexander Hamilton

(Des and photo Harrison)

1968 (6 Dec*). *Human Rights Year. T* **31** *and similar horiz designs. Multicoloured. W* w **12**. *P* 14 × 14½.
204 5 c. Type **31** 10 10
205 15 c. Albert T. Marryshow 10 10
206 25 c. William Wilberforce 10 10
207 50 c. Dag Hammarskjöld 10 10
208 $1 Dr. Martin Luther King 25 30
204/8 .. .. *Set of* 5 40 45
*Although first day covers were postmarked 2 December, these stamps were not put on sale in Montserrat until 6 December.

32 "The Two Trinities" (Murillo)

33 "The Adoration of the Kings" (detail, Botticelli)

(Des and photo Harrison)

1968 (16 Dec). *Christmas. W* w **12** (*sideways*). *P* 14½ × 14.
209 **32** 5 c. multicoloured 10 10
210 **33** 15 c. multicoloured 10 10
211 **32** 25 c. multicoloured 10 10
212 **33** 50 c. multicoloured 25 20
209/12 .. .. *Set of* 4 40 30

1969–70. *As Nos.* 160/4, 167, 167 *and* 194/6 *but wmk* w **12** *sideways**.
213 1 c. Type **21** (24.6.69) 10 10
214 2 c. Type **22** (23.4.70) 70 75
215 3 c. Soursop (24.6.69) 30 15
w. Wmk Crown to right of CA .. .. 15·00
216 4 c. Pepper (24.6.69) 60 15
217 5 c. Mango (23.4.70) .. .. .. 1·00 85
218 10 c. Ochro (24.6.69) 50 15
w. Wmk Crown to right of CA .. .. 60·00
219 15 c. on 12 c. Lime (24.6.69) 60 30
220 20 c. Orange (17.3.69) 75 30
221 25 c. on 24 c. Banana (24.6.69) 90 60
222 50 c. on 48 c. Cabbage (24.6.69) .. .. 4·50 8·50
213/22 .. .. *Set of* 10 9·00 10·50
*The normal sideways watermark shows Crown to left of CA, *as seen from the back of the stamp.*

The 1 c., 3 c., 4 c., 10 c., 15 c. and 20 c. exist with PVA gum as well as gum arabic, but the 2 c. and 5 c. exist with PVA gum only.

34 Map showing "CARIFTA" Countries

35 "Strength in Unity"

(Des J. Cooter. Photo Harrison)

1969 (27 May). *First Anniv of CARIFTA (Caribbean Free Trade Area). W* w **12** (*sideways* on T* **34**). *P* 14.
223 **34** 15 c. multicoloured 10 10
224 20 c. multicoloured 10 10
w. Wmk Crown to right of CA .. 1·60
225 **35** 35 c. multicoloured 10 10
226 30 c. multicoloured 15 15
223/6 .. .. *Set of* 4 30 30
*The normal sideways watermark shows Crown to left of CA, *as seen from the back of the stamp.*

36 Telephone Receiver and Map of Montserrat

40 Dolphin (fish)

(Des R. Reid, adapted by V. Whiteley. Litho P.B.)

1969 (29 July). *Development Projects. T* **36** *and similar vert designs. Multicoloured. W* w **12**. *P* 13½.
227 15 c. Type **36** 10 10
228 25 c. School symbols and map 10 10
229 50 c. Hawker Siddeley H.S.748 aircraft and map 15 10
230 $1 Electricity pylon and map 25 20
227/30 .. .. *Set of* 4 35 30

(Des Harrison. Photo Enschedé)

1969 (1 Nov). *Game Fish. T* **40** *and similar horiz designs. Multicoloured. P* 13 × 13½.
231 5 c. Type **40** 35 10
232 15 c. Atlantic Sailfish 50 10
233 25 c. Black-finned Tuna 60 10
234 40 c. Spanish Mackerel 80 55
231/4 .. .. *Set of* 4 2·00 75

41 King Caspar before the Virgin and Child (detail) (Norman 16th-cent stained glass window)

42 "Nativity" (Leonard Limosin)

(Des J. Cooter. Litho D.L.R.)

1969 (10 Dec). *Christmas. Paintings multicoloured; frame colours given. W* w **12** (*sideways on* 50 c.). *P* 13.
235 **41** 15 c. black, gold and violet 10 10
236 25 c. black and vermilion 10 10
237 **42** 50 c. black, ultramarine & yellow-orange 15 15
235/7 .. .. *Set of* 3 30 30

43 "Red Cross Sale"

(Des and litho J.W.)

1970 (13 Apr). *Centenary of British Red Cross. T* **43** *and similar horiz designs. Multicoloured. W* w **12** (*sideways*). *P* 14½ × 14.
238 3 c. Type **43** 10 10
239 4 c. School for deaf children 10 10
240 15 c. Transport services for disabled .. 10 20
241 20 c. Workshop 10 60
238/41 .. .. *Set of* 4 30 80

44 Red-footed Booby

45 "Madonna and Child with Animals" (Brueghel the Elder, after Dürer)

(Des V. Whiteley. Photo Harrison)

1970 (2 July)–**74.** *Birds. T* **44** *and similar multicoloured designs. W* w **12** (*sideways* on vert designs and upright on horiz designs*). *P* 14×14½ (*horiz*) *or* 14½×14 (*vert*). A. *Chalk-surfaced paper* (2.7.70). B. *Glazed, ordinary paper* (30.10.74, $10; 22.1.71, *others*).

		A		B	
242	1 c. Type **44**	10	10	†	
	w. Wmk inverted	12·00	—	†	
243	2 c. American Kestrel ..	15	15	1·25	3·00
244	3 c. Magnificent Frigate Bird	15	15	†	
	w. Wmk Crown to right of CA	—	—	†	
245	4 c. Great Egret	1·00	15	†	
246	5 c. Brown Pelican	2·00	10	1·50	2·00
	w. Wmk Crown to right of CA	2·50	—	—	—
247	10 c. Bananaquit	40	10	1·50	2·00
248	15 c. Smooth-billed Ani ..	30	15	4·50	5·00
	w. Wmk inverted	†		4·50	—
249	20 c. Red-billed Tropic Bird ..	35	15	1·50	2·00
250	25 c. Montserrat Oriole ..	50	50	5·00	6·00
251	50 c. Green-throated Carib ..	5·00	1·00	4·00	4·50
252	$1 Antillean Crested Hummingbird	6·50	1·00	4·25	5·00
	w. Wmk inverted	18·00	—	†	
253	$2.50, Little Blue Heron ..	5·00	8·00	8·00	10·00
254	$5 Purple-throated Carib ..	7·50	10·00	13·00	18·00
254*c*	$10 Forest Thrush	†		15·00	15·00
242A/54A	.. .. *Set of* 13	25·00	19·00		
243B/54*c*B	.. .. *Set of* 11			55·00	65·00

The 1 c., 15 c., 20 c., 25 c., $1, $5 and $10 are horizontal, and the remainder are vertical designs.
*The normal sideways watermark shows Crown to left of CA, *as seen from the back of the stamp.*
See also Nos. 295/302.

(Des G. Drummond. Litho D.L.R.)

1970 (1 Oct).* *Christmas. T* **45** *and similar multicoloured design. W* w **12**. *P* 13½ × 14.
255 5 c. Type **45** 10 10
w. Wmk inverted .. .. .. 18·00
256 15 c. "The Adoration of the Shepherds" (Domenichino) 10 10
257 20 c. Type **45** 10 10
w. Wmk inverted .. .. .. 4·00
258 $1 As 15 c. 35 90
255/8 .. .. *Set of* 4 55 1·00
*This was the local date of issue but the stamps were released by the Crown Agents on 21 September.

46 War Memorial

47 Girl Guide and Badge

(Des V. Whiteley. Litho J.W.)

1970 (30 Nov). *Tourism. T* **46** *and similar horiz designs. Multicoloured. W* w **12** (*sideways**). *P* 14½×14.
259 5 c. Type **46** 10 10
260 15 c. Plymouth from Fort St. George .. 10 10
261 25 c. Carr's Bay 15 10
262 50 c. Golf Fairway .. .. 1·00 60
w. Wmk Crown to right of CA .. 5·50
259/62 .. .. *Set of* 4 1·25 75
MS263 135×109mm. Nos. 259/62 .. .. 2·50 2·00
*The normal sideways watermark shows Crown to left of CA, *as seen from the back of the stamp.*

(Des V. Whiteley. Litho Questa)

1970 (31 Dec). *Diamond Jubilee of Montserrat Girl Guides. T* **47** *and similar vert design. Multicoloured. W* w **12**. *P* 14.
264 10 c. Type **47** 10 10
265 15 c. Brownie and Badge 10 10
266 25 c. As 15 c. 15 10
267 40 c. Type **47** 20 20
264/7 .. .. *Set of* 4 50 30

48 "Descent from the Cross" (Van Hemessen)

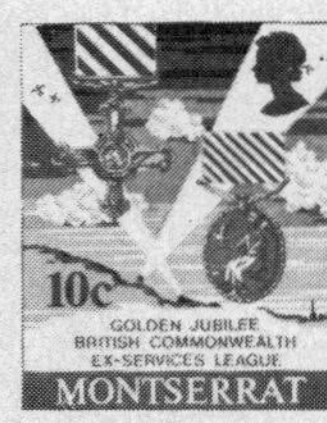

49 D.F.C. and D.F.M. in Searchlights

(Des J.W. Photo Enschedé)

1971 (22 Mar). *Easter. T* **48** *and similar vert design. Multicoloured. W* w **12**. *P* 13½.
268 5 c. Type **48** 10 10
269 15 c. "Noli me tangere" (Orcagna) 10 10
270 20 c. Type **48** 10 10
271 40 c. As 15 c. 15 15
268/71 .. .. *Set of* 4 30 30

(Des Col. A. Maynard. Litho Questa)

1971 (8 July). *Golden Jubilee of Commonwealth Ex-Services League. T* **49** *and similar vert designs. Multicoloured. W* w **12**. *P* 14.
272 10 c. Type **49** 10 10
273 20 c. M.C., M.M. and jungle patrol 15 10
274 40 c. D.S.C., D.S.M. and submarine action .. 20 15
275 $1 V.C. and soldier attacking bunker .. 50 70
272/5 .. .. *Set of* 4 85 85

50 "The Nativity with Saints" (Romanino)

51 Piper PA-23 Apache

(Des G. Drummond. Litho Questa)

1971 (16 Sept). *Christmas. T* **50** *and similar vert design. Multicoloured. W* w **12**. *P* 14 × 13½.
276 5 c. Type **50** 10 10
277 15 c. "Choir of Angels" (Simon Marmion) .. 10 10
278 20 c. Type **50** 10 10
279 $1 As 15 c. 35 40
276/9 .. .. *Set of* 4 50 50

(Des and litho J.W.)

1971 (16 Dec). *14th Anniv of Inauguration of L.I.A.T. (Leeward Islands Air Transport). T* **51** *and similar horiz designs. Multicoloured. P* 13½.
280 5 c. Type **51** 10 10
281 10 c. Beech 50 Twin Bonanza 15 15
282 15 c. De Havilland D.H.114 Heron 2 .. 30 15
283 20 c. Britten Norman Islander 35 15
284 40 c. De Havilland D.H.C.6 Twin Otter 100 65 45
285 75 c. Hawker Siddeley H.S.748 .. .. 2·00 2·25
280/5 .. .. *Set of* 6 3·25 3·00
MS286 203×102 mm. Nos. 280/5 .. .. 10·00 13·00

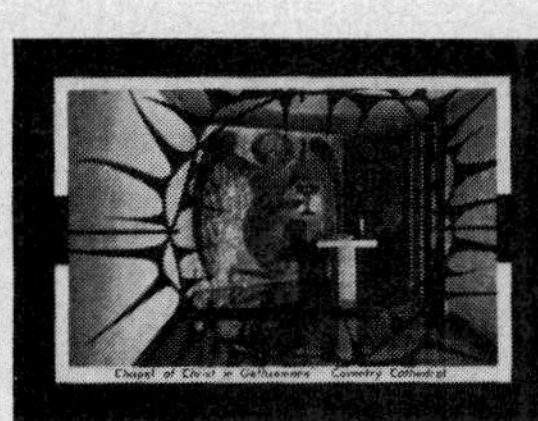

52 "Chapel of Christ in Gethsemane", Coventry Cathedral

53 Lizard

(Des G. Drummond. Litho A. & M.)

1972 (9 Mar). *Easter. T* **52** *and similar horiz design. Multicoloured. W* w **12**. *P* 13.

287 5 c. Type **52** 10 10
288 10 c. "The Agony in the Garden" (Bellini) .. 10 10
289 20 c. Type **52** 10 10
290 75 c. As 10 c. 35 50
287/90 .. .. *Set of* 4 45 60

(Des G. Drummond. Litho Questa)

1972 (20 July). *Reptiles. T* **53** *and similar multicoloured designs. W* w **12** *(sideways on* 40 *c. and* $1*). P* 14½.

291 15 c. Type **53** 15 10
292 20 c. Mountain Chicken (frog) 20 10
293 40 c. Iguana (*horiz*) 35 20
294 $1 Tortoise (*horiz*) .. .. 2·00 2·00
291/4 .. .. *Set of* 4 2·40 2·00

1972 (21 July)–**74**. *As No.* 242 *etc., but W* w **12**, *sideways* on horiz designs* (1, 15, 20, 25 *c.*) *and upright on vert designs (others). Glazed, ordinary paper.*

295 1 c. Type **44** .. .. 1·25 45
 a. Chalk-surfaced paper (4.2.74) 80 45
296 2 c. American Kestrel .. .. 1·50 45
 aw. Wmk inverted .. .. 11·00
 b. Chalk-surfaced paper (4.2.74) .. .. 3·25 45
297 3 c. Magnificent Frigate Bird .. .. 12·00 10·00
298 4 c. Great Egret (*chalk-surfaced paper*) (4.2.74) .. .. 1·00 3·00
 w. Wmk inverted .. .. 7·50
299 5 c. Brown Pelican (8.3.73) .. .. .. 1·50 30
 a. Chalk-surfaced paper (4.2.74) 60 55
300 15 c. Smooth-billed Ani (8.3.73) 50 45
 a. Chalk-surfaced paper (2.10.73) .. .. 85 1·00
 aw. Wmk Crown to left of CA (17.5.74) .. 1·75 1·90
301 20 c. Red-billed Tropic Bird (*chalk-surfaced paper*) (2.10.73) .. .. 1·40 1·50
302 25 c. Montserrat Oriole (*chalk-surfaced paper*) (17.5.74) .. .. 3·25 3·50
295/302 .. .. *Set of* 8 19·00 18·00

*The normal sideways watermark shows Crown to left of CA on 1 c and 20 c., and to right on 15 c. and 25 c., *as seen from the back of the stamp*.

In 1973–74, during shortages of the 5 c. value, letters can be found posted unstamped and franked with a "postage paid" mark. Other covers exist with the word "paid" in manuscript.

54 "Madonna of the Chair" (Raphael)

(Des J. Cooter. Litho Format)

1972 (18 Oct). *Christmas. T* **54** *and similar horiz designs. Multicoloured. W* w **12**. *P* 13½.

303 10 c. Type **54** 10 10
304 35 c. "Virgin and Child with Cherub" (Fungai) 20 10
305 50 c. "Madonna of the Magnificat" (Botticelli) 30 30
306 $1 "Virgin and Child with St. John and an Angel" (Botticelli) 40 65
303/6 .. .. *Set of* 4 80 90

55 Lime, Tomatoes and Pawpaw

56 *Passiflora herbertiana*

(Des (from photographs by D. Groves) and photo Harrison)

1972 (20 Nov). *Royal Silver Wedding. Multicoloured; background colour given. W* w **12**. *P* 14 × 14½.

307 **55** 35 c. rose 10 10
308 $1 bright blue 20 20
 w. Wmk inverted .. .. 38·00

(Des J. Cooter. Litho Walsall)

1973 (9 Apr). *Easter. T* **56** *and similar vert designs showing passion-flowers. Multicoloured. W* w **12**. *P* 13½.

309 20 c. Type **56** 25 10
310 35 c. *P. vitifolia* 35 10
311 75 c. *P. amabilis* .. .. 1·00 1·00
312 $1 *P. alata-caerulea* .. .. 1·10 1·10
309/12 .. .. *Set of* 4 2·40 2·00

Nos. 309/12 are inscribed on the reverse with information about the passion-flower.

57 Montserrat Monastery, Spain

58 "Virgin and Child" (School of Gerard David)

(Des J. Cooter. Litho Format)

1973 (9 July). *480th Anniv of Columbus's Discovery of Montserrat. T* **57** *and similar horiz designs. Multicoloured. W* w **12**. *P* 13½.

313 10 c. Type **57** 15 10
314 35 c. Columbus sighting Montserrat 30 15
315 60 c. Columbus's ship off Montserrat .. .. 1·10 1·10
316 $1 Colony badge and map of voyage .. 1·25 1·10
313/16 .. .. *Set of* 4 2·50 2·25
MS317 126×134 mm. Nos. 313/16. Wmk inverted 11·00 13·00
 w. Wmk upright .. .. 75·00

(Des J. Cooter. Litho Questa)

1973 (22 Oct). *Christmas. T* **58** *and similar vert designs. Multicoloured. W* w **12** *(sideways). P* 13½.

318 20 c. Type **58** 25 10
319 35 c. "The Holy Family with St. John" (Jordaens) 30 10
320 50 c. "Virgin and Child" (Bellini) 45 50
321 90 c. "Virgin and Child with Flowers" (Dolci) 65 1·00
318/21 .. .. *Set of* 4 1·50 1·40

58*a* Princess Anne and Captain Mark Phillips

59 Steel Band

(Des PAD Studio. Litho Questa)

1973 (14 Nov). *Royal Wedding. Centre multicoloured. W* w **12** *(sideways). P* 13½.

322 **58*a*** 35 c. sage-green 10 10
323 $1 violet-blue 20 20

(Des J. W. Litho Questa)

1974 (8 Apr). *25th Anniv of University of West Indies. T* **59** *and similar designs. Multicoloured. W* w **12** *(sideways on* 20 *c.*, $1 *and* **MS**328*).*

324 20 c. Type **59** 15 10
325 35 c. Masqueraders (*vert*) 15 10
326 60 c. Student weaving (*vert*) 35 60
 w. Wmk inverted .. .. † £100
327 $1 University Centre, Montserrat 45 70
324/7 .. .. *Set of* 4 1·00 1·25
MS328 130×89 mm. Nos. 324/7 .. .. 2·00 6·50

60 Hands with Letters

02¢

(61)

(Des P. Powell. Litho Walsall)

1974 (3 July). *Centenary of Universal Postal Union. T* **60** *and similar horiz design. W* w **12**. *P* 14½ × 14.

329 **60** 1 c. multicoloured 10 10
330 – 2 c. lt rose-red, orange-verm & blk .. 10 10
331 **60** 3 c. multicoloured 10 10
332 – 5 c. lt yellow-orange, reddish orge & blk 10 10
333 **60** 50 c. multicoloured 20 20
334 – $1 pale blue, turquoise-blue and black 40 65
329/34 .. .. *Set of* 6 75 90

Designs:—2 c., 5 c., $1 Figures from U.P.U. Monument.

1974 (2 Oct). *Various stamps surch as T* **61**.

335 2 c. on $1 (No. 252B) .. .. .. 30 1·25
 w. Wmk inverted .. .. 40·00
336 5 c. on 50 c. (No. 333) 40 60
337 10 c. on 60 c. (No. 326) .. .. .. 90 1·75
338 20 c. on $1 (No. 252B) .. .. .. 30 1·00
 a. "2" with serifs (Pl 1B R. 3/1) .. .. 13·00
 b. Bottom bar of surch omitted (Pl 1B R. 5/1-5) .. .. 4·25
339 35 c. on $1 (No. 334) .. .. .. 60 1·25
335/9 .. .. *Set of* 5 2·25 5·25

62 Churchill and Houses of Parliament

63 Carib "Carbet"

(Des R. Granger Barrett. Litho D.L.R.)

1974 (30 Nov). *Birth Centenary of Sir Winston Churchill. T* **62** *and similar vert design. Multicoloured. No wmk. P* 13 × 13½.

340 35 c. Type **62** 15 10
341 70 c. Churchill and Blenheim Palace 20 20
MS342 81 × 85 mm. Nos. 340/1 .. .. .. 50 70

(Des C. Abbott. Litho Walsall)

1975 (3 Mar). *Carib Artefacts. T* **63** *and similar horiz designs.*

(*a*) *W* w **12** *(sideways). From sheets. P* 14

343 5 c. lake-brown, yellow and black 10 10
344 20 c. black, lake-brown and yellow 10 10
345 35 c. black, yellow and lake-brown 15 10
346 70 c. yellow, lake-brown and black 45 40
343/6 .. .. *Set of* 4 70 60

(*b*) *No wmk. Self-adhesive with advertisements on the reverse. From booklets. Rouletted*

347 5 c. lake-brown, yellow and black 15 25
 a. Booklet pane. Nos. 347/50 *se-tenant* .. 90
348 20 c. black, lake-brown and yellow 15 25
 a. Booklet pane. Nos. 348 × 3 and No. 349 × 3 90
349 35 c. black, yellow and lake-brown 15 25
350 70 c. yellow, lake-brown and black 55 80
347/50 .. .. *Set of* 4 90 1·40

Designs:—20 c. "Caracoli"; 35 c. Club or mace; 70 c. Canoe.

64 One-Bitt Coin

(Des J. Cooter. Litho Questa)

1975 (1 Sept). *Local Coinage,* 1785–1801. *T* **64** *and similar diamond-shaped designs. W* w **14** *(sideways). P* 13½.

351 5 c. black, light violet-blue and silver .. 10 10
352 10 c. black, salmon and silver 15 10
353 35 c. black, light blue-green and silver .. 20 15
354 $2 black, bright rose and silver .. .. 90 1·50
351/4 .. .. *Set of* 4 1·25 1·60
MS355 142 × 142 mm. Nos. 351/4 .. .. 1·25 2·75

Designs:—10 c. Eighth dollar; 35 c. Quarter dollar; $2 One dollar.

No. **MS**355 has details of the coins depicted printed on the reverse side, beneath the gum.

65 1d. and 6d. Stamps of 1876

66 "The Trinity"

(Des J. Cooter. Litho J. W.)

1976 (5 Jan). *Centenary of First Montserrat Postage Stamp. T* **65** *and similar horiz designs. W* w **12** *(sideways). P* 13.

356 5 c. deep carmine, yellowish green and black 15 10
357 10 c. light yellow-ochre, scarlet and black .. 20 10
358 40 c. multicoloured 50 40
359 55 c. deep mauve, yellowish green and black 60 50
360 70 c. multicoloured 70 70
361 $1.10, yellowish green, brt blue & grey-blk .. 1·00 1·00
356/61 .. .. *Set of* 6 2·75 2·50
MS362 170 × 159 mm. Nos. 356/61. P 13½ .. 3·75 5·50

Designs:—10 c. G.P.O. and bisected 1d. stamp; 40 c. Bisects on cover; 55 c. G.B. 6d. used in Montserrat and local 6d. of 1876; 70 c. Stamps for 2½d. rate, 1876; $1.10, Packet boat *Antelope* and 6d. stamp.

(Des J. Cooter. Litho Questa)

1976 (5 Apr). *Easter. Unissued stamps prepared for Easter* 1975 *with values and date obliterated by black bars. T* **66** *and similar vert designs showing paintings by Orcagna. Multicoloured.* W w **14**. *P* 13½.

363 15 c. on 5 c. Type **66** 10 10
a. Surch omitted .. .. 40·00
364 40 c. on 35 c. "The Resurrection" 15 15
a. Surch omitted .. .. 40·00
365 55 c. on 70 c. "The Ascension" 15 15
a. Surch omitted .. .. 40·00
366 $1.10 on $1 "Pentecost" 30 40
a. Surch omitted .. .. 40·00
363/6 .. .. *Set of* 4 55 65
MS367 160 × 142 mm. Nos. 363/6 .. .. .. 1·25 2·25
a. Surch omitted £160

For No. 363 the "1" was added to the original 5 c. to make 15 c.

2¢
(67)

68 White Frangipani

1976 (12 Apr). *Nos.* 244A, 246A *and* 247A *surch as T* **67**.

368 2 c. on 5 c. Brown Pelican 10 15
369 30 c. on 10 c. Bananaquit 30 20
370 45 c. on 3 c. Magnificent Frigate Bird 40 25
a. Surch triple .. ..
b. Surch double .. .. 32·00
368/70 .. .. *Set of* 3 70 55

(Des J. Cooter. Litho Questa)

1976 (5 July)–**80**. *Various horiz designs showing Flowering Trees as T* **68**. *Multicoloured. Ordinary paper.* W w **14** (*sideways**). *P* 13½.

371 1 c. Type **68** 10 10
372 2 c. Cannon-ball Tree 10 10
w. Wmk Crown to right of CA .. .. 60·00
373 3 c. Lignum vitae 10 10
374 5 c. Malay apple 15 10
w. Wmk Crown to right of CA .. .. 22·00
375 10 c. Jacaranda 30 10
376 15 c. Orchid Tree 30 10
a. Chalk-surfaced paper (8.80) .. .. 1·25 2·00
377 20 c. Manjak 30 10
a. Chalk-surfaced paper (8.80) .. .. 1·25 2·00
378 25 c. Tamarind 40 20
379 40 c. Flame of the Forest 40 30
380 55 c. Pink Cassia 50 30
381 70 c. Long John 50 30
382 $1 Saman 65 50
383 $2.50, Immortelle .. .. 1·25 1·50
384 $5 Yellow Poui .. .. 1·75 2·25
w. Wmk Crown to right of CA .. .. 10·00
385 $10 Flamboyant .. .. 2·75 4·25
371/85 .. .. *Set of* 15 8·00 9·00

*The normal sideways watermark shows Crown to left of CA, *as seen from the back of the stamp.*

69 Mary and Joseph

70 Hudson River Review, 1976

(Des L. Curtis. Litho Format)

1976 (4 Oct). *Christmas. T* **69** *and similar vert designs. Multicoloured.* W w **14**. *P* 14.

386 15 c. Type **69** 10 10
387 20 c. The Shepherds 10 10
388 55 c. Mary and Jesus 15 15
389 $1.10, The Magi 30 50
386/9 .. .. *Set of* 4 50 65
MS390 95 × 135 mm. Nos. 386/9 .. .. .. 60 1·75

(Des and litho J.W.)

1976 (13 Dec). *Bicentenary of American Revolution. T* **70** *and similar vert designs. Multicoloured.* W w **14**. *P* 13.

391 15 c. Type **70** 40 20
a. Horiz pair. Nos. 391 and 394 .. .. 1·75 80
392 40 c. *Raleigh* (American frigate), 1777* .. 70 40
a. Horiz pair. Nos. 392/3 .. .. .. 1·40 80
393 75 c. H.M.S. *Druid* (frigate), 1777* 70 40
394 $1.25, Hudson River Review .. .. .. 1·25 60
391/4 .. .. *Set of* 4 2·75 1·40
MS395 95×145 mm. Nos. 391/4. *P* 13½ .. .. 2·75 2·75

*The date is wrongly given on the stamps as "1776".

Nos. 392/3 and 391 with 394 were each printed in horizontal *se-tenant* pairs throughout the sheets, the pairs forming composite designs.

71 The Crowning

72 *Ipomoea alba*

(Des G. Vasarhelyi. Litho J.W.)

1977 (7 Feb). *Silver Jubilee. T* **71** *and similar horiz designs. Multicoloured.* W w **14** (*sideways*). *P* 13.

396 30 c. Royal Visit, 1966.. .. .. .. 10 10
397 45 c. Cannons firing salute 15 10
398 $1 Type **71** 25 50
396/8 .. .. *Set of* 3 45 60

(Des J. Cooter. Litho Questa)

1977 (1 June). *Flowers of the Night. T* **72** *and similar multicoloured designs.* W w **14** (*sideways on* 40 *and* 55 *c.*). *P* 14.

399 15 c. Type **72** 20 10
400 40 c. *Epiphyllum hookeri* (*horiz*) 55 30
401 55 c. *Cereus hexagonus* (*horiz*) 55 45
402 $1.50, *Cestrum nocturnum* .. .. .. 1·75 1·25
399/402 .. .. *Set of* 4 2·75 1·90
MS403 126 × 130 mm. Nos. 399/402. Wmk sideways .. .. 2·75 3·75

73 Princess Anne laying Foundation Stone of Glendon Hospital

(Des BG Studio. Litho Questa)

1977 (3 Oct). *Development. T* **73** *and similar horiz designs. Multicoloured.* W w **14** (*sideways**). *P* 14½×14.

404 20 c. Type **73** 15 10
405 40 c. *Statesman* (freighter) at Plymouth .. 35 15
406 55 c. Glendon Hospital 35 20
w. Wmk Crown to right of CA .. .. 30·00
407 $1.50, Jetty at Plymouth Port .. .. 90 1·00
404/7 .. .. *Set of* 4 1·60 1·25
MS408 146×105 mm. Nos. 404/7 .. .. .. 2·00 2·50

*The normal sideways watermark shows Crown to left of CA, *as seen from the back of the stamp.*

$1.00
SILVER JUBILEE 1977
ROYAL VISIT
TO THE CARIBBEAN
(74)

1977 (28 Oct). *Royal Visit. Nos.* 380/1 *and* 383 *surch locally with T* **74**.

409 $1 on 55 c. Pink Cassia 30 45
410 $1 on 70 c. Long John 30 45
411 $1 on $2.50, Immortelle 30 45
a. Surch double .. ..
b. Surch omitted (top stamp of vert pair)
409/11 .. .. *Set of* 3 80 1·25

On No. 411b the lower stamp in the pair also shows the surcharge bars omitted.

75 The Stable at Bethlehem

76 Four-eyed Butterflyfish

(Des L. Curtis. Litho Walsall)

1977 (14 Nov). *Christmas. T* **75** *and similar vert designs. Multicoloured.* W w **14**. *P* 14 × 14½.

412 5 c. Type **75** 10 10
413 40 c. The Three Kings.. .. .. .. 15 10
414 55 c. Three Ships 20 10
415 $2 Three Angels 65 75
412/15 .. .. *Set of* 4 90 85
MS416 119 × 115 mm. Nos. 412/15 .. .. 1·00 2·00

(Des J.W. Litho Walsall)

1978 (15 Mar). *Fish. T* **76** *and similar horiz designs. Multicoloured.* W w **14** (*sideways*). *P* 14.

417 30 c. Type **76** 45 10
418 40 c. French Angelfish 50 15
419 55 c. Blue Tang 65 15
420 $1.50, Queen Triggerfish .. .. .. 1·10 1·25
417/20 .. .. *Set of* 4 2·40 1·40
MS421 152 × 102 mm. Nos. 417/20 .. .. 2·75 3·00

77 St. Paul's Cathedral

78 *Alpinia speciosa*

(Des G. Drummond. Litho J.W.)

1978 (2 June). *25th Anniv of Coronation. T* **77** *and similar horiz designs. Multicoloured.* W w **14** (*sideways*). *P* 13.

422 40 c. Type **77** 10 10
423 55 c. Chichester Cathedral 10 10
424 $1 Lincoln Cathedral 20 25
425 $2.50, Llandaff Cathedral 40 50
422/5 .. .. *Set of* 4 65 75
MS426 130 × 102 mm. Nos. 422/5. *P* 13½ × 14 .. 70 1·25

Nos. 422/5 were each printed in sheets including two *se-tenant* stamp-size labels.

(Des J. Cooter. Litho J.W.)

1978 (18 Sept). *Flowers. T* **78** *and similar vert designs. Multicoloured.* W w **14**. *P* 13½ × 13.

427 40 c. Type **78** 20 10
428 55 c. *Allamanda cathartica* 25 15
429 $1 *Petrea volubilis* 45 45
430 $2 *Hippeastrum puniceum* 70 80
427/30 .. .. *Set of* 4 1·40 1·40

79 Private, 21st (Royal North British Fusiliers), 1796

80 Cub Scouts

(Des J.W. Litho Questa)

1978 (20 Nov). *Military Uniforms* (1*st series*). *T* **79** *and similar vert designs showing soldiers from British infantry regiments. Multicoloured.* W w **14**. *P* 14 × 14½.

431 30 c. Type **79** 15 15
432 40 c. Corporal, 86th (Royal County Down), 1831 .. .. 20 15
433 55 c. Sergeant, 14th (Buckinghamshire) 1837 30 20
434 $1.50, Officer, 55th (Westmorland), 1784 .. 75 80
431/4 .. .. *Set of* 4 1·25 1·10
MS435 140 × 89 mm. Nos. 431/4 .. .. .. 2·00 2·75

See also Nos. 441/5.

(Des J. W. Litho Walsall)

1979 (2 Apr). *50th Anniv of Boy Scout Movement on Montserrat. T* **80** *and similar multicoloured designs.* W w **14** (*sideways on* 40 *and* 55 *c*). *P* 14.

436 40 c. Type **80** 25 10
437 55 c. Scouts with signalling equipment .. 35 20
438 $1.25, Camp fire (*vert*) 60 55
439 $2 Oath ceremony (*vert*) .. .. .. 1·00 1·00
436/9 .. .. *Set of* 4 2·00 1·75
MS440 120 × 110 mm. Nos. 436/9 .. .. .. 2·25 2·25

(Des J.W. Litho Questa)

1979 (4 June). *Military Uniforms* (2*nd series*). *Vert designs as T* **79** *showing soldiers from infantry regiments. Multicoloured.* W w **14**. *P* 14 × 14½.

441 30 c. Private, 60th (Royal American), 1783 .. 15 15
442 40 c. Private, 1st West India, 1819 .. .. 20 15
443 55 c. Officer, 5th (Northumberland), 1819 .. 30 25
444 $2.50, Officer, 93rd (Sutherland Highlanders), 1830 .. .. 1·00 1·10
441/4 .. .. *Set of* 4 1·50 1·50
MS445 139 × 89 mm. Nos. 441/4 .. .. .. 2·00 2·50

81 Child reaching out to Adult

(Des G. Vasarhelyi. Litho Questa)

1979 (17 Sept). *International Year of the Child. W* w **14** (*sideways*). *P* 13½ × 14.
446 **81** $2 black, orange-brown and flesh .. 50 55
MS447 85 × 99 mm. No. 446 .. .. .. 50 1·10

82 Sir Rowland Hill with Penny Black and Montserrat 1876 1d. Stamp **83** Plume Worm

(Des G. Vasarhelyi. Litho Questa)

1979 (1 Oct). *Death Centenary of Sir Rowland Hill and Centenary of U.P.U. Membership. T* **82** *and similar horiz designs. Multicoloured. W* w **14** (*sideways*). *P* 14.
448 40 c. Type **82** 20 10
449 55 c. U.P.U. emblem and notice announcing Leeward Islands entry into Union .. 20 15
450 $1 1883 Letter following U.P.U. membership 30 50
451 $2 Great Britain Post Office Regulations notice and Sir Rowland Hill 40 80
448/51 .. .. *Set of* 4 1·00 1·40
MS452 135 × 154 mm. Nos. 448/51 .. .. 1·60 2·25

(Des G. Drummond. Litho Walsall)

1979 (26 Nov). *Marine Life. T* **83** *and similar vert designs. Multicoloured. W* w **14**. *P* 14.
453 40 c. Type **83** 30 15
454 55 c. Sea Fans 40 20
455 $2 Coral and Sponge .. .. .. 1·00 1·75
453/5 .. .. *Set of* 3 1·50 1·90

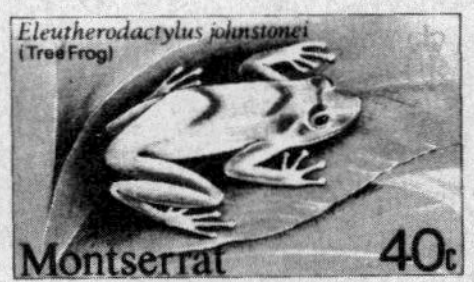

84 Tree Frog

(Des J. Cooter. Litho Rosenbaum Bros, Vienna)

1980 (4 Feb). *Reptiles and Amphibians. T* **84** *and similar horiz designs. Multicoloured. W* w **14** (*sideways**). *P* 13½.
456 40 c. Type **84** 20 15
w. Wmk Crown to right of CA 20
457 55 c. Tree Lizard 25 25
w. Wmk Crown to right of CA 30
458 $1 Crapaud 45 50
w. Wmk Crown to right of CA 55
459 $2 Wood Slave 80 90
w. Wmk Crown to right of CA 90
456/9 .. .. *Set of* 4 1·50 1·60
*The normal sideways watermark shows Crown to left of CA, *as seen from the back of the stamp.*

75th Anniversary of Rotary International

85 *Marquess of Salisbury* and 1838 Handstamps **(86)**

(Des BG Studio. Litho Questa)

1980 (14 Apr). *"London 1980" International Stamp Exhibition. T* **85** *and similar horiz designs. Multicoloured. W* w **14** (*sideways*). *P* 14.
460 40 c. Type **85** 20 15
461 55 c. Hawker Siddeley H.S.748 aircraft and 1976 55 c. definitive 25 25
462 $1.20, *La Plata* (liner) and 1903 5s. stamp 30 45
463 $1.20, *Lady Hawkins* (packet steamer) and 1932 Tercentenary 5s. commemorative 30 45
464 $1.20, *Avon* (paddle-steamer) and Penny Red stamp with "A 08" postmark .. 30 45
465 $1.20, Aeronca Champion 17 airplane and 1953 $1.20 definitive 30 45
460/5 .. .. *Set of* 6 1·50 2·00
MS466 115×110 mm. Nos. 460/5. P 12 .. 1·60 2·50
Nos. 460/5 were each printed in sheets of 4 stamps and two *se-tenant* stamp-size labels.
Some sheets of No. 462 showed the red colour omitted from the map in the right-hand label.

1980 (7 July). *75th Anniv of Rotary International. No.* 383 *optd with T* **86**.
467 $2.50, Immortelle 55 85

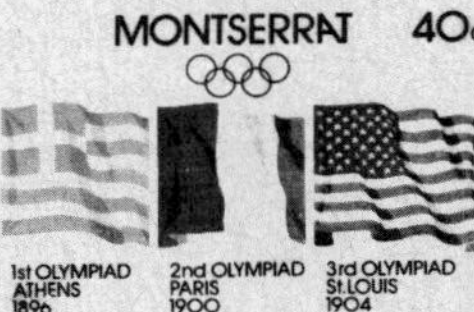

87 Greek, French and U.S.A. Flags

(Des A. Theobald. Litho Questa)

1980 (7 July). *Olympic Games, Moscow. T* **87** *and similar horiz designs. Multicoloured. W* w **14** (*sideways*). *P* 13½ × 14.
468 40 c. Type **87** 20 15
469 55 c. Union, Swedish and Belgian flags .. 20 15
470 70 c. French, Dutch and U.S.A. flags .. 30 20
471 $1 German, Union and Finnish flags .. 35 25
472 $1.50, Australian, Italian and Japanese flags 45 50
473 $2 Mexican, West German and Canadian flags 50 65
474 $2.50, "The Discus Thrower" (sculpture by Miron) 55 90
468/74 .. .. *Set of* 7 2·25 2·50
MS475 150 × 100 mm. Nos. 468/74 .. .. 2·25 3·00
a. Bottom row of stamps in miniature sheet imperf on 3 sides £475
Nos. 468/74 were each printed in small sheets of 4 including one *se-tenant* stamp-size label.
No. **MS**475a shows the three stamps in the bottom row of the miniature sheet imperforate vertically and with no perforations between the stamps and the bottom margin.

XX 5¢

(88) **89** *Lady Nelson*, 1928

1980 (30 Sept). *Nos.* 371, 373, 376 *and* 379 *surch as T* **88**.
476 5 c. on 3 c. Lignum vitae 10 10
a. Surch double, one inverted .. .. 35·00
477 35 c. on 1 c. Type **68** 15 15
a. Surch omitted (in vert pair with normal) .. .. 35·00
478 35 c. on 3 c. Lignum vitae 15 15
479 35 c. on 15 c. Orchid Tree 15 15
480 55 c. on 40 c. Flame of the Forest 15 15
a. Surch inverted .. .. 50·00
481 $5 on 40 c. Flame of the Forest .. .. 85 2·00
476/81 .. .. *Set of* 6 1·40 2·25
The surcharge omitted error, No. 477a, occurs on the lower stamp of a vertical pair. On the upper stamp the surcharge is at the foot of the design.
For 30 c. on 15 c. and $2.50 on 40 c. see Nos. O33a and O39a.

(Des J.W. Litho Walsall)

1980 (3 Nov). *Mail Packet Boats* (*1st series*). *T* **89** *and similar horiz designs. Multicoloured. W* w **14** (*sideways*). *P* 14.
482 40 c. Type **89** 30 15
483 55 c. *Chignecto*, 1913 .. .. 40 25
484 $1 *Solent II*, 1878 .. .. 80 60
485 $2 *Dee*, 1841 .. .. 1·10 1·25
482/5 .. .. *Set of* 4 2·40 2·00
See also Nos. 615/19.

90 *Heliconius charithonia* **91** Atlantic Spadefish

(Des J.W. Litho Questa)

1981 (2 Feb). *Butterflies. T* **90** *and similar square designs. Multicoloured. W* w **14** (*inverted*). *P* 14.
486 50 c. Type **90** 60 40
w. Wmk upright .. .. 1·75
487 65 c. *Pyrgus oileus* 70 45
488 $1.50, *Phoebis agarithe* 90 85
489 $2.50, *Danaus plexippus* .. .. .. 1·25 1·10
486/9 .. .. *Set of* 4 3·00 2·50
Nos. 486/9 were each printed in sheets including two *se-tenant* stamp-size labels.

(Des G. Drummond. Litho J.W.)

1981 (20 Mar). *Fishes. Vert designs as T* **91**. *Multicoloured. W* w **14**. *No imprint date. P* 13½×13.
490 5 c. Type **91** 70 30
491 10 c. Hogfish and Neon Goby 70 30
492 15 c. Creole Wrasse 80 30
493 20 c. Three-spotted Damselfish 90 30
494 25 c. Sergeant Major 90 30
495 35 c. Fin-spot Wrasse 80 30
496 45 c. Schoolmaster 80 40
497 55 c. Striped Parrotfish .. .. .. 1·10 45
498 65 c. Bigeye 80 60
499 75 c. French Grunt 80 60
w. Wmk inverted .. .. 11·00
500 $1 Rock Beauty .. .. 1·00 70
501 $2 Blue Chromis .. .. 1·75 1·10
502 $3 Royal Gramma ("Fairy Basslet") and Blueheads .. .. 1·90 1·75
503 $5 Cherub Angelfish .. .. 2·75 2·75
w. Wmk inverted .. .. 13·00
504 $7.50, Long-jawed Squirrelfish .. .. 5·50 4·75
505 $10 Caribbean Long-nosed Butterflyfish .. 6·50 6·50
490/505 .. .. *Set of* 16 25·00 19·00
For stamps watermarked with W w **15** see Nos. 555/70.

92 Fort St. George

(Des J. Cooter. Litho Format)

1981 (18 May). *Montserrat National Trust. T* **92** *and similar horiz designs. Multicoloured. W* w **14** (*sideways*). *P* 13½ × 14.
506 50 c. Type **92** 25 20
507 65 c. Bird sanctuary, Fox's Bay 45 35
508 $1.50, Museum 50 65
509 $2.50, Bransby Point Battery, *circa* 1780 .. 60 1·10
506/9 .. .. *Set of* 4 1·60 2·10

(Des D. Shults. Litho Questa)

1981 (17 July–19 Nov). *Royal Wedding. Horiz designs as T* **26/27** *of Kiribati. Multicoloured.* (a) *W* w **15**. *P* 14.
510 90 c. *Charlotte* 25 25
aw. Wmk inverted .. .. 12·00
b. Sheetlet. No. 510×6 and No. 511 .. 2·10
bw. Wmk inverted .. .. 80·00
511 90 c. Prince Charles and Lady Diana Spencer 85 85
aw. Wmk inverted .. .. 38·00
512 $3 *Portsmouth* 60 60
aw. Wmk inverted .. .. 8·50
b. Sheetlet. No. 512×6 and No. 513 .. 4·50
bw. Wmk inverted .. .. 60·00
513 $3 As No. 511 .. .. 1·50 1·50
aw. Wmk inverted .. .. 28·00
514 $4 *Britannia* 75 75
aw. Wmk inverted .. .. 9·50
b. Sheetlet. No. 514×6 and No. 515 .. 5·50
bw. Wmk inverted .. .. 75·00
515 $4 As No. 511 .. .. 1·75 1·75
aw. Wmk inverted .. .. 30·00
510/15 .. .. *Set of* 6 5·25 5·25
MS516 120×109 mm. $5 As No. 511. Wmk sideways. P 12 (19 Nov) .. .. .. 1·00 1·00
(*b*) *Booklet stamps. No wmk. P* 12 (19 Nov)
517 90 c. As No. 510 .. .. 30 45
a. Booklet pane. No. 517×4 with margins all round .. .. 1·10
518 $3 As No. 513 .. .. 1·40 1·75
a. Booklet pane. No. 518×2 with margins all round .. .. 2·75
Nos. 510/15 were printed in sheetlets of seven stamps of the same face value, each containing six of the "Royal Yacht" design and one of the larger design showing Prince Charles and Lady Diana.
Nos. 517/18 come from $13.20 stamp booklets.

93 H.M.S. *Dorsetshire* and Fairey IIIF Firefly Seaplane **94** Methodist Church, Bethel

(Des Court House Advertising Ltd. Litho Questa)

1981 (31 Aug). *50th Anniv of Montserrat Airmail Service. T* **93** *and similar horiz designs. Multicoloured. W* w **14** (*sideways*). *P* 14.
519 50 c. Type **93** 50 30
520 65 c. Beech 50 Twin Bonanza 65 50
521 $1.50, De Havilland D.H.89 Dragon Rapide *Lord Shaftesbury* .. .. 1·10 1·75
522 $2.50, Hawker Siddeley H.S.748 and maps of Montserrat and Antigua .. .. 1·40 2·75
519/22 .. .. *Set of* 4 3·25 4·75

(Des J. Cooter. Litho Walsall)

1981 (16 Nov). *Christmas. Churches. T* **94** *and similar vert designs. Multicoloured. W* w **14**. *P* 14 × 13½.
523 50 c. Type **94** 20 15
524 65 c. St George's Anglican Church, Harris .. 25 15
525 $1.50, St Peter's Anglican Church, St Peters 60 60
526 $2.50, St Patrick's R.C. Church, Plymouth 75 1·00
523/6 .. .. *Set of* 4 1·75 1·75
MS527 176 × 120 mm. Nos. 523/6 .. .. 3·00 3·75

95 Rubiaceae (*Rondeletia buxifolia*) **96** Plymouth

(Des local artist. Litho Questa)

1982 (18 Jan). *Plant Life. T* **95** *and similar multicoloured designs. W* w **14** (*sideways on* 65 c. *and* $2.50). *P* 14½.
528 50 c. Type **95** 30 30
529 65 c. Boraginaceae (*Heliotropium ternatum*) (*horiz*) 40 40
530 $1.50, Simarubaceae (*Picramnia pentandra*) 85 85
531 $2.50, Ebenaceae (*Diospyrus revoluta*) (*horiz*) 1·25 1·25
528/31 . . . . . . *Set of* 4 2·50 2·50

(Litho Format)

1982 (17 Apr). *350th Anniv of Settlement of Montserrat by Sir Thomas Warner. W* w **14** (*sideways*). *P* 14½.
532 **96** 40 c. green 30 30
533 55 c. red 35 35
534 65 c. chestnut 40 50
535 75 c. olive-grey 45 60
536 85 c. bright blue 50 75
537 95 c. bright orange 55 80
538 $1 bright reddish violet 55 80
539 $1.50, brown-olive . . . . . . 65 1·50
540 $2 deep claret . . . . . . 80 1·75
541 $2.50, bistre-brown . . . . . . 1·00 2·00
532/41 . . . . . . *Set of* 10 5·00 8·50
Nos. 532/41 are based on the 1932 Tercentenary set.

97 Catherine of Aragon, Princess of Wales, 1501

98 Local Scout

(Des D. Shults and J. Cooter. Litho Format)

1982 (16 June). *21st Birthday of Princess of Wales. T* **97** *and similar vert designs. Multicoloured. W* w **15**. *P* 13½ × 14.
542 75 c. Type **97** 15 15
543 $1 Coat of arms of Catherine of Aragon 15 15
w. Wmk inverted . . . . . . 14·00
544 $5 Diana, Princess of Wales . . . . 80 1·25
542/4 . . . . . . *Set of* 3 1·00 1·40

(Des D. Shults. Litho Format)

1982 (13 Sept). *75th Anniv of Boy Scout Movement. T* **98** *and similar vert design. Multicoloured. W* w **15**. *P* 14.
545 $1.50, Type **98** 75 70
546 $2.50, Lord Baden-Powell . . . . 1·00 1·10
Nos. 545/6 exist imperforate from stock dispersed by the liquidator of Format International Security Printers Ltd.

99 Annunciation

(Des Jennifer Toombs. Litho Walsall)

1982 (18 Nov). *Christmas. T* **99** *and similar horiz designs. Multicoloured. W* w **14** (*sideways*). *P* 14.
547 35 c. Type **99** 20 15
548 75 c. Shepherd's Vision 35 35
549 $1.50, The Stable 75 85
550 $2.50, Flight into Egypt . . . . 95 1·10
547/50 . . . . . . *Set of* 4 2·00 2·25

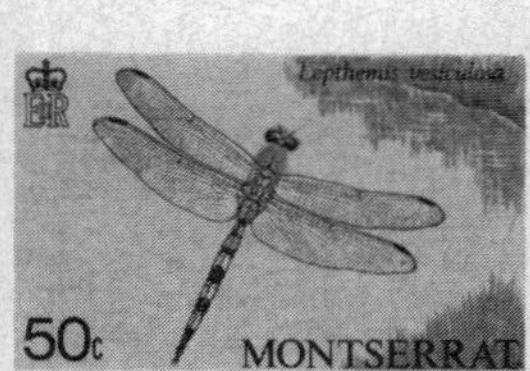

100 *Lepthemis vesiculosa*

101 Blue-headed Hummingbird

(Des J. Cooter. Litho Walsall)

1983 (19 Jan). *Dragonflies. T* **100** *and similar horiz designs. Multicoloured. W* w **14** (*sideways*). *P* 13½ × 14.
551 50 c. Type **100** 40 20
552 65 c. *Orthemis ferruginea* 50 25
553 $1.50, *Triacanthagyna trifida* . . . . 1·00 1·00
554 $2.50, *Erythrodiplax umbrata* . . . . 1·40 1·60
551/4 . . . . . . *Set of* 4 3·00 2·75

1983 (12 Apr). *As Nos.* 490/505, *but W* w **15** *and imprint date* "1983" *added. P* 13½ × 13.
555 5 c. Type **91** 20 10
556 10 c. Hogfish and Neon Goby 25 10
559 25 c. Sergeant Major 35 20
560 35 c. Fin-spot Wrasse 45 30
564 75 c. French Grunt 75 55
565 $1 Rock Beauty 85 65
568 $5 Cherub Angelfish . . . . . . 2·75 3·00
570 $10 Caribbean Long-nosed Butterflyfish . . 5·50 6·00
555/70 . . . . . . *Set of* 8 10·00 10·00

(Des G. Drummond. Litho Format)

1983 (24 May). *Hummingbirds. T* **101** *and similar vert designs. Multicoloured. W* w **14**. *P* 14.
571 35 c. Type **101** . . . . . . 1·50 35
572 75 c. Green-throated Carib . . . . 1·75 85
573 $2 Antillean Crested Hummingbird . . 2·75 2·50
574 $3 Purple-throated Carib . . . . 3·00 3·50
571/4 . . . . . . *Set of* 4 8·00 6·50

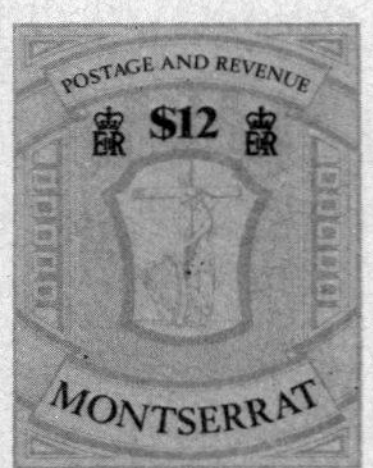

102 Montserrat Emblem

40¢

(103)

(Litho Harrison)

1983 (25 July). *W* w **14**. *P* 14½.
575 **102** $12 royal blue and rose . . . . 4·25 5·00
576 $30 rose and royal blue . . . . 11·00 12·00

1983 (15 Aug). *Various stamps surch as T* **103**. (*a*) *Nos.* 491, 498, 501 (*all W* w 14), 559, 564 (*both W* w **15**).
577 40 c. on 25 c. Sergeant Major (No. 559) . . 30 30
a. Surch inverted . . . . . . 20·00
b. Surch on No. 494 . . . . . . 5·00 10·00
c. Error. Surch on 10 c. (No. 491) . . 14·00
d. Surch double . . . . . . 40·00
578 70 c. on 10 c. Hogfish and Neon Goby (No. 491) 45 45
a. Surch inverted . . . . . . 20·00
b. Surch on No. 556 . . . . . . 24·00 24·00
c. Surch omitted (in pair with normal) . . £130
d. Surch double . . . . . . 24·00
579 90 c. on 65 c. Bigeye (No. 498) . . 55 60
a. Error. Surch on 10 c. (No. 491) . . 80·00
b. Error. Surch on 75 c. (No. 499) . . 80·00
c. Surch double . . . . . . 40·00
580 $1.15 on 75 c. French Grunt (No. 564) . . 65 70
a. Surch on No. 499 . . . . . . 9·50 11·00
b. Error. Surch on 25 c. (No. 559) . . 40·00
c. Surch inverted . . . . . . 25·00
581 $1.50 on $2 Blue Chromis (No. 501) . . 85 90
a. Surch inverted . . . . . . 60·00
b. Error. Surch on 75 c. (No. 499) . . 80·00
c. Error. Surch on 75 c. (No. 564) . .

(*b*) *Nos.* 512/15
582 70 c. on $3 *Portsmouth* 65 85
aw. Wmk inverted . . . . . . 15·00
b. Sheetlet. No. 582×6 and No. 583 . . 4·50
bw. Wmk inverted £120
c. Surch double . . . . . . 5·00
d. Surch inverted . . . . . . 17·00
e. Surch inverted (horiz pair) . . 35·00
583 70 c. on $3 Prince Charles and Lady Diana Spencer . . . . . . 1·50 2·25
aw. Wmk inverted . . . . . . 55·00
b. Surch double . . . . . . 32·00
c. Surch inverted . . . . . . 90·00
584 $1.15 on $4 *Britannia* . . . . 1·10 1·25
aw. Wmk inverted . . . . . . 15·00
b. Sheetlet. No. 584×6 and No. 585 . . 7·50
bw. Wmk inverted £120
c. Surch double . . . . . . 20·00
d. Surch inverted . . . . . . 11·00
e. Surch inverted (horiz pair) . . 22·00
f. Error. Surch on $3 (No. 512) . . 5·50
585 $1.15 on $4 As No. 583 . . . . 1·75 2·50
aw. Wmk inverted . . . . . . 55·00
b. Surch double . . . . . . 30·00
c. Surch inverted . . . . . . 65·00
f. Error. Surch on $3 (No. 513) . . 70·00
577/85 . . . . . . *Set of* 9 7·00 8·75
Nos. 582e and 584e show the long surcharge intended for Nos. 583 or 585 inverted across horizontal pairs of the smaller design. Nos. 583c and 585c show two examples of the smaller surcharge inverted.

104 Montgolfier Balloon, 1783

105 Boys dressed as Clowns

(Des A. Theobald. Litho Format)

1983 (19 Sept). *Bicentenary of Manned Flight. T* **104** *and similar multicoloured designs. W* w **14** (*sideways** on 75 c. *to* $2). *P* 14.
586 35 c. Type **104** 15 15
587 75 c. De Havilland D.H.C.6 Twin Otter 200/300 (*horiz*) 30 30
588 $1.50, Lockheed Vega V (*horiz*) . . 60 75
w. Wmk Crown to right of CA . . 35·00
589 $2 Beardmore airship R-34 (*horiz*) . . 85 1·25
586/9 . . . . . . *Set of* 4 1·75 2·25
MS590 109×145 mm. Nos. 586/9. Wmk sideways 1·50 2·75
*The normal sideways watermark shows Crown to left of CA, *as seen from the back of the stamp.*
Nos. 586/9 were re-issued on 15 December 1983 overprinted "INAUGURAL FLIGHT Montserrat–Nevis–St. Kitts". It is understood that all but approximately 100 sets were used on Flown First Flight/Day Covers (*Price for set of 4 on First Flight Cover* £30).

(Des Jennifer Toombs. Litho Format)

1983 (18 Nov). *Christmas. Carnival. T* **105** *and similar horiz designs. Multicoloured. W* w **15** (*sideways*). *P* 14.
591 55 c. Type **105** 10 10
592 90 c. Girls dressed as silver star bursts . . 15 20
593 $1.15, Flower girls 20 35
594 $2 Masqueraders 35 80
591/4 . . . . . . *Set of* 4 70 1·25

106 Statue of Discus-thrower

107 Cattle Egret

(Des Court House Studio. Litho Questa)

1984 (26 Mar). *Olympic Games, Los Angeles. T* **106** *and similar vert designs. Multicoloured. W* w **15** (*sideways**). *P* 14.
595 90 c. Type **106** 30 35
w. Wmk POST OFFICE reading upwards 3·00
596 $1 Olympic torch 35 45
w. Wmk POST OFFICE reading upwards
597 $1.15, Olympic Stadium, Los Angeles . . 40 50
w. Wmk POST OFFICE reading upwards 4·50
598 $2.50, Olympic and American flags . . 65 1·00
w. Wmk POST OFFICE reading upwards 7·00
595/8 . . . . . . *Set of* 4 1·50 2·10
MS599 110×110 mm. Nos. 595/8. Wmk upright 1·50 2·25
w. Wmk inverted . . . . . . 20·00
*The normal sideways watermark shows "POST OFFICE" reading downwards.

(Des G. Drummond. Litho Walsall)

1984 (28 May). *Birds of Montserrat. T* **107** *and similar multicoloured designs. W* w **15** (*sideways** on 5 c. *to* 90 c.). *P* 14.
600 5 c. Type **107** 30 30
601 10 c. Carib Grackle 30 30
a. Printed on the gummed side . . 75·00
602 15 c. Moorhen ("Common Gallinule") . . 30 30
w. Wmk POST OFFICE reading upwards 2·75
603 20 c. Brown Booby 40 30
604 25 c. Black-whiskered Vireo 40 40
605 40 c. Scaly-breasted Thrasher 60 50
606 55 c. Laughing Gull 75 30
607 70 c. Glossy Ibis 90 45
608 90 c. Green Heron . . . . . . 1·00 60
609 $1 Belted Kingfisher (*vert*) . . . . 1·25 70
610 $1.15, Bananaquit (*vert*) . . . . 1·50 1·40
w. Wmk inverted . . . . . . 4·50
611 $3 American Kestrel ("Sparrow Hawk") (*vert*) . . . . . . 3·25 5·00
612 $5 Forest Thrush (*vert*) . . . . 4·50 7·00
613 $7.50, Black-crowned Night Heron (*vert*) 6·00 12·00
614 $10 Bridled Quail Dove (*vert*) . . . . 7·00 13·00
600/14 . . . . . . *Set of* 15 26·00 38·00
*The normal sideways watermark shows "POST OFFICE" reading downwards.

(Des J.W. Litho Format)

1984 (9 July). *Mail Packet Boats* (*2nd series*). *Multicoloured designs as T* **89**. *W* w **15** (*sideways*). *P* 14.
615 55 c. *Tagus II*, 1907 . . . . . . 20 40
616 90 c. *Cobequid*, 1913 . . . . . . 30 50
617 $1 *Lady Drake*, 1942 . . . . . . 40 70
618 $2 *Factor*, 1948 . . . . . . 60 1·25
615/18 . . . . . . *Set of* 4 1·40 2·50
MS619 152×100 mm. Nos. 615/18 . . . . 2·00 5·00
No. **MS**619 also commemorates the 250th anniversary of *Lloyd's List* (newspaper).

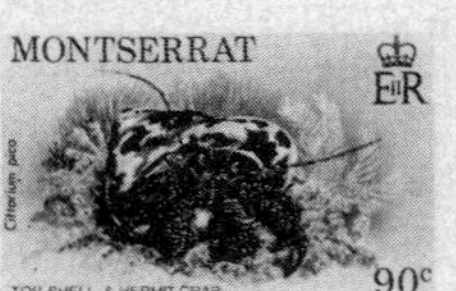

108 Hermit Crab and West Indian Top Shell (*Cittarium pica*)

(Des G. Drummond. Litho Questa)

1984 (24 Sept). *Marine Life. T* **108** *and similar horiz designs. Multicoloured. W* w **15** (*sideways*). *P* 14.
620 90 c. Type **108** . . . . . . 1·50 1·00
621 $1.15, Rough File Shell (*Lima scabra*) . . 1·75 1·40

622 $1.50, True Tulip (*Fasciolaria tulipa*) .. 2·50 3·00
623 $2.50, Queen or Pink Conch (*Strombus gigas*) .. .. 3·25 4·75
620/3 .. .. *Set of* 4 8·00 9·00

109 "Bull Man"

110 Mango

(Des Jennifer Toombs. Litho Questa)

1984 (12 Nov). *Christmas. Carnival Costumes. T* **109** *and similar horiz designs. Multicoloured.* W w **15** (*sideways*). *P* 14.
624 55 c. Type **109** 50 25
625 $1.15, Masquerader Captain .. .. 1·50 1·25
626 $1.50, "Fantasy" Carnival Queen .. 1·75 2·25
627 $2.30, "Ebony and Ivory" Carnival Queen .. 2·50 4·00
624/7 .. .. *Set of* 4 5·75 7·00

(Des G. Drummond. Litho Format)

1985 (8 Feb). *National Emblems. T* **110** *and similar vert designs. Multicoloured.* W w **15**. *P* 14.
628 $1.15, Type **110** 30 60
629 $1.50, Lobster Claw .. .. 40 1·00
630 $3 Montserrat Oriole .. .. 60 2·00
628/30 .. .. *Set of* 3 1·10 3·25

IMPERFORATES AND MISSING COLOURS. Various issues between Nos. 631 and 695 exist either imperforate or with colours omitted. Such items are not listed as there is no evidence that they fulfil the criteria outlined on page xi of this catalogue.

111 *Oncidium urophyllum*

112 Queen Elizabeth the Queen Mother

(Des J. Cooter. Litho Format)

1985 (9 May). *Orchids of Montserrat. T* **111** *and similar vert designs. Multicoloured.* W w **15**. *P* 14.
631 90 c. Type **111** 45 55
632 $1.15, *Epidendrum difforme* 55 80
633 $1.50, *Epidendrum ciliare* .. .. .. 60 1·10
634 $2.50, *Brassavola cucullata* .. .. 1·00 2·50
631/4 .. .. *Set of* 4 2·40 4·50
MS635 120×140 mm. Nos. 631/4 .. .. 4·25 6·50

(Des D. Ewart ($2), Maxine Marsh (others). Litho Format)

1985 (7 Aug). *Life and Times of Queen Elizabeth the Queen Mother. Various vertical portraits as T* **112**. *P* 12½.
636 55 c. multicoloured 25 40
a. Horiz pair. Nos. 636/7 .. .. .. 50 80
637 55 c. multicoloured 25 40
638 90 c. multicoloured 25 60
a. Horiz pair. Nos. 638/9 .. .. .. 50 1·10
639 90 c. multicoloured 25 60
640 $1.15, multicoloured 25 60
a. Horiz pair. Nos. 640/1 .. .. .. 50 1·10
641 $1.15, multicoloured 25 60
642 $1.50, multicoloured 30 60
a. Horiz pair. Nos. 642/3 .. .. .. 60 1·10
643 $1.50, multicoloured 30 60
636/43 .. .. *Set of* 8 1·90 3·75
MS644 85×113 mm. $2 multicoloured; $2 multicoloured .. .. 65 1·90

The two designs of each value were issued, *se-tenant*, in horizontal pairs within the sheets. Each *se-tenant* pair shows a floral pattern across the bottom of the portraits which stops short of the left-hand edge on the left-hand stamp and of the right-hand edge on the right-hand stamp.

Designs as Nos. 636/7 and 642/3 but with face values of $6×2 and $3.50×2, also exist in additional miniature sheets from a restricted printing issued 10 January 1986.

Nos. 636/43 and an unissued 15 c. also exist in separate miniature sheets, combining the two designs for each value, from stock dispersed by the liquidator of Format International Security Printers Ltd.

113 Cotton Plants

(Des G. Drummond. Litho Format)

1985 (18 Oct). *Montserrat Sea Island Cotton Industry. T* **113** *and similar horiz designs. Multicoloured.* W w **15**. *P* 15.
645 90 c. Type **113** 25 45
646 $1 Operator at carding machine 25 50
647 $1.15, Threading loom 25 65
648 $2.50, Weaving with hand loom .. .. 50 2·25
645/8 .. .. *Set of* 4 1·10 3·50
MS649 148×103 mm. Nos. 645/8. Wmk sideways .. .. 3·00 3·75

CARIBBEAN ROYAL VISIT 1985

(114)

115 Black-throated Blue Warbler

1985 (25 Oct). *Royal Visit. Nos.* 514/15, 543, 587/8 *and* 640/1 *optd as T* **114** *or surch also.*
650 75 c. multicoloured (No. 587) .. .. 2·75 2·50
651 $1 multicoloured (No. 543) .. .. 4·25 3·50
652 $1.15, multicoloured (No. 640) .. .. 4·25 5·00
a. Horiz pair. Nos. 652/3 .. .. .. 8·50 10·00
653 $1.15, multicoloured (No. 641) .. .. 4·25 5·00
654 $1.50, multicoloured (No. 588) .. .. 6·00 6·00
655 $1.60 on $4 multicoloured (No. 514) .. 3·00 3·75
a. Sheetlet. No. 655×6 and No. 656 .. 28·00
ab. Sheetlet No. 655×6 and No. 656a .. 35·00
656 $1.60 on $4 multicoloured (No. 515) (surch $1.60 only) .. .. 12·00 16·00
a. Additionally optd "CARIBBEAN ROYAL VISIT—1985" .. .. .. 20·00 24·00
650/6 .. .. *Set of* 7 32·00 38·00

No. 656 shows a new face value only; "CARIBBEAN ROYAL VISIT" being omitted from the surcharge. No. 656a is the corrected version issued subsequently.

(Des R. Vigurs. Litho Format)

1985 (29 Nov). *Leaders of the World. Birth Bicentenary of John J. Audubon (ornithologist). T* **115** *and similar vert designs showing original paintings. Multicoloured. P* 12½.
657 15 c. Type **115** 15 20
a. Horiz pair. Nos. 657/8 .. .. .. 30 40
658 15 c. Palm Warbler 15 20
659 30 c. Bobolink 20 30
a. Horiz pair. Nos. 659/60 .. .. .. 40 60
660 30 c. Lark Sparrow 20 30
661 55 c. Chipping Sparrow 30 40
a. Horiz pair. Nos. 661/2 .. .. .. 60 80
662 55 c. Northern Oriole 30 40
663 $2.50, American Goldfinch .. .. .. 50 1·25
a. Horiz pair. Nos. 663/4 .. .. 1·00 2·50
664 $2.50, Blue Grosbeak .. .. .. 50 1·25
657/64 .. .. *Set of* 8 2·10 4·00

Nos. 657/8, 659/60, 661/2 and 663/4 were printed together, *se-tenant*, in horizontal pairs throughout the sheets.

116 Herald Angel appearing to Goatherds

117 Lord Baden-Powell

(Des Jennifer Toombs. Litho Format)

1985 (2 Dec). *Christmas. T* **116** *and similar horiz designs showing a Caribbean Nativity. Multicoloured. P* 15.
665 70 c. Type **116** 15 15
666 $1.15, Three Wise Men following the Star 25 40
667 $1.50, Carol singing around War Memorial, Plymouth 30 70
668 $2.30, Praying to "Our Lady of Montserrat" Church of Our Lady, St. Patrick's Village .. .. 45 1·60
665/8 .. .. *Set of* 4 1·00 2·50

(Des G. Vasarhelyi. Litho Format)

1986 (11 Apr). *50th Anniv of Montserrat Girl Guide Movement. T* **117** *and similar vert designs. Multicoloured.* W w **15** (*sideways*). *P* 15.
669 20 c. Type **117** 15 40
a. Horiz pair. Nos. 669/70 .. .. .. 30 80
670 20 c. Girl Guide saluting 15 40
671 75 c. Lady Baden-Powell 30 75
a. Horiz pair. Nos. 671/2 .. .. .. 60 1·50
672 75 c. Guide assisting in old people's home .. 30 75
673 90 c. Lord and Lady Baden-Powell 40 75
a. Horiz pair. Nos. 673/4 .. .. .. 80 1·50
674 90 c. Guides serving meal in old people's home 40 75
675 $1.15, Girl Guides of 1936 .. .. .. 55 80
a. Horiz pair. Nos. 675/6 .. .. 1·10 1·60
676 $1.15, Two Guides saluting 55 80
669/76 .. .. *Set of* 8 2·50 4·75

Nos. 669/70, 671/2, 673/4 and 675/6 were each printed together, *se-tenant*, in horizontal pairs throughout the sheets.

117*a* Queen Elizabeth II

(Des Court House Studio. Litho Format)

1986 (21 Apr). *60th Birthday of Queen Elizabeth II. T* **117*a*** *and similar multicoloured designs. P* 12½.
677 10 c. Type **117*a*** 10 10
678 $1.50, Princess Elizabeth in 1928 .. 25 50
679 $3 In Antigua, 1977 .. .. .. 40 85
680 $6 In Canberra, 1982 (*vert*) .. .. 65 1·75
677/80 .. .. *Set of* 4 1·25 2·75
MS681 85×115 mm. $8 Queen with bouquet .. 3·25 5·50

The 10 c., $1.50 and $3 also exist watermarked w **16** (sideways), but no examples of these used from Montserrat have been seen.

Nos. 677/80 also exist in individual miniature sheets from stock dispersed by the liquidator of Format International Security Printers Ltd.

118 King Harold and Halley's Comet, 1066 (from Bayeux Tapestry)

(Des Court House Studio. Litho Format)

1986 (9 May). *Appearance of Halley's Comet. T* **118** *and similar horiz designs. Multicoloured. P* 14×13½.
682 35 c. Type **118** 25 25
683 50 c. Comet of 1301 (from Giotto's "Adoration of the Magi") 30 30
684 70 c. Edmond Halley and Comet of 1531 .. 40 40
685 $1 Comets of 1066 and 1910 .. .. 50 50
686 $1.15, Comet of 1910 .. .. .. 60 60
687 $1.50, E.S.A. *Giotto* spacecraft and Comet 60 1·10
688 $2.30, U.S. Space Telescope and Comet .. 70 2·00
689 $4 Computer reconstruction of 1910 Comet 1·10 3·25
682/9 .. .. *Set of* 8 4·00 7·50
MS690 Two sheets, each 140×115 mm. (a) 40 c. Type **118**; $1.75, As No. 683; $2 As No. 684; $3 As No. 685. (b) 55 c. As No. 686; 60 c. As No. 687; 80 c. As No. 688; $5 As No. 689 *Set of* 2 *sheets* 6·00 9·00

118*a* Prince Andrew

119 *Antelope* being attacked by *L'Atalante*

(Des Court House Studio. Litho Format)

1986 (23 July–15 Oct). *Royal Wedding* (1st issue). *T* **118*a*** *and similar multicoloured designs. P* 12½.
691 70 c. Type **118*a*** 25 35
a. Pair. Nos. 691/2 .. .. 50 70
692 70 c. Miss Sarah Ferguson 25 35
693 $2 Prince Andrew wearing stetson (*horiz*) 40 80
a. Pair. Nos. 693/4 .. .. 80 1·60
694 $2 Miss Sarah Ferguson on skiing holiday (*horiz*) 40 80
691/4 .. .. *Set of* 4 1·10 2·10
MS695 115×85 mm. $10 Duke and Duchess of York on Palace balcony after wedding (*horiz*) (15.10) .. .. 3·00 4·50

Nos. 691/2 and 693/4 were printed together, *se-tenant*, in horizontal and vertical pairs throughout the sheets.

Nos. 691/4 imperforate come from souvenir stamp booklets.

See also Nos. 705/8.

A set of eight was prepared for the 1986 World Cup Football Championships, but was not issued. Examples exist from stock dispersed by the liquidator of Format International Security Printers Ltd.

(Des T. Hadler. Litho Questa)

1986 (29 Aug). *Mail Packet Sailing Ships. T* **119** *and similar horiz designs. Multicoloured. W* w **15**. *P* 14.
696 90 c. Type **119** . . . . 2·00 1·50
697 $1.15, *Montagu* (1810) . . . . . . 2·25 2·00
698 $1.50, *Little Catherine* being pursued by *L'Etoile* (1813) . . . . . . 2·75 2·75
699 $2.30, *Hinchingbrook I* (1813) . . . . 3·50 5·00
696/9 . . . . *Set of* 4 9·50 10·00
MS700 165×123 mm. Nos. 696/9, Wmk sideways 10·00 11·00

120 Radio Montserrat Building, Dagenham

(Des G. Vasarhelyi. Litho Questa)

1986 (29 Sept). *Communications. T* **120** *and similar horiz designs. Multicoloured. W* w **15**. *P* 14.
701 70 c. Type **120**. . . . . 1·00 70
702 $1.15, Radio Gem dish aerial, Plymouth . . 1·50 1·50
703 $1.50, Radio Antilles studio, O'Garro's . . 1·75 2·00
704 $2.30, Cable and Wireless building, Plymouth . . . . . . 2·25 4·00
701/4 . . . . *Set of* 4 6·00 7·50

Congratulations to
T.R.H. The Duke
& Duchess of York

(**121**) **121*a*** Statue of Liberty

1986 (14 Nov). *Royal Wedding (2nd issue). Nos.* 691/4 *optd as T* **121** *in silver.*
705 70 c. Type **118*a*** . . . . 70 1·00
a. Pair. Nos. 705/6 . . . . . . 1·40 2·00
706 70 c. Miss Sarah Ferguson . . . . . . 70 1·00
707 $2 Prince Andrew wearing stetson (*horiz*) 1·25 1·75
a. Pair. Nos. 707/8. . . . . . 2·50 3·50
708 $2 Miss Sarah Ferguson on skiing holiday (*horiz*) . . . . 1·25 1·75
705/8 . . . . *Set of* 4 3·50 5·00

(Des Court House Studio. Litho Format)

1986 (18 Nov). *Centenary of Statue of Liberty. Vert views of Statue as T* **121*a*** *in separate miniature sheets. Multicoloured. P* 14×13½.
MS709 Three sheets, each 85×115 mm. $3; $4.50; $5 . . . . . . *Set of* 3 *sheets* 6·00 9·00

122 Sailing and Windsurfing **123** Christmas Rose

(Des J. Cooter. Litho Format)

1986 (10 Dec). *Tourism. T* **122** *and similar horiz designs. Multicoloured. P* 15.
710 70 c. Type **122**. 40 70
711 $1.15, Golf . . . . 80 1·50
712 $1.50, Plymouth market . . . . . . 80 2·00
713 $2.30, Air Recording Studios . . . . 1·25 3·00
710/13 . . . . *Set of* 4 3·00 6·50

(Des Jennifer Toombs. Litho Questa)

1986 (12 Dec). *Christmas. Flowering Shrubs. T* **123** *and similar vert designs. Multicoloured. P* 14.
714 70 c. Type **123**. 70 40
715 $1.15, Candle Flower 95 85
716 $1.50, Christmas Tree Kalanchoe . . 1·50 1·50
717 $2.30, Snow on the Mountain . . . . 2·00 4·00
714/17 . . . . *Set of* 4 4·75 6·00
MS718 150×110 mm. Nos. 714/17. P 12 . . 7·00 7·50

MINIMUM PRICE

The minimum price quote is 10p which represents a handling charge rather than a basis for valuing common stamps. For further notes about prices see introductory pages.

5c ▬

124 Tiger Shark (**125**)

(Des M. Hillier. Litho Questa)

1987 (2 Feb). *Sharks. T* **124** *and similar horiz designs. Multicoloured. W* w **15**. *P* 14.
719 40 c. Type **124** . . . . 1·50 55
720 90 c. Lemon Shark . . . . 2·50 1·50
721 $1.15, Great White Shark . . . . 2·75 2·00
722 $3.50, Whale Shark . . . . . . 5·50 8·00
719/22 . . . . *Set of* 4 11·00 11·00
MS723 150×102 mm. Nos. 719/22. Wmk sideways. P 12 . . . . 12·00 13·00

1987 (6 Apr). *Nos.* 601, 603, 607/8 *and* 611 *surch as T* **125**.
724 5 c. on 70 c. Glossy Ibis 40 50
725 $1 on 20 c. Brown Booby . . . . . . 1·50 90
726 $1.15 on 10 c. Carib Grackle . . . . 1·75 1·25
727 $1.50 on 90 c. Green Heron. . . . . . 2·00 2·25
728 $2.30 on $3 American Kestrel (*vert*) . . 3·00 4·50
724/8 . . . . *Set of* 5 7·75 8·50

(**126**) **127** *Phoebis trite*

1987 (13 June). *"Capex '87" International Stamp Exhibition, Toronto. No.* **MS**690 *optd with T* **126** *in black and red.*
MS729 Two sheets. As No. **MS**690
Set of 2 *sheets* 6·50 9·00

No. **MS**729 also carries an overprint commemorating the exhibition on the lower sheet margins.

(Des M. Hillier. Litho Questa)

1987 (10 Aug). *Butterflies. T* **127** *and similar square designs. Multicoloured. W* w **15**. *P* 14.
730 90 c. Type **127** . . . . 2·00 1·10
731 $1.15, *Biblis hyperia* . . . . . . 2·50 1·60
732 $1.50, *Polygonus leo* . . . . . . 3·00 2·50
733 $2.50, *Hypolimnas misippus* . . . . 4·50 6·50
730/3 . . . . *Set of* 4 11·00 10·50

128 *Oncidium variegatum*

(Des R. Vigurs. Litho Questa)

1987 (13 Nov). *Christmas. Orchids. T* **128** *and similar multicoloured designs. P* 14×13½ (90 c., $1.50) *or* 13½×14 (*others*).
734 90 c. Type **128**. 60 45
735 $1.15, *Vanilla planifolia* (*horiz*) . . 85 55
736 $1.50, *Gongora quinquenervis* . . . . 1·10 1·00
737 $3.50, *Brassavola nodosa* (*horiz*) . . 2·00 3·50
734/7 . . . . *Set of* 4 4·00 5·00
MS738 100×75 mm. $5 *Oncidium lanceanum* (*horiz*) . . . . 8·00 9·00

(**129**) **130** Free-tailed Bat

1987 (29 Nov). *Royal Ruby Wedding. Nos* 601, 604/5 *and* 608 *surch as T* **129**. *A. Surch "Edingburgh". B. Surch "Edinburgh".*

		A		B	
739	5 c. on 90 c. Green Heron . .	1·50	1·75	30	40
740	$1.15 on 10 c. Carib Grackle . .	3·25	3·25	1·00	1·00
741	$2.30 on 25 c. Black-whiskered Vireo . .	6·00	7·00	1·75	2·00
742	$5 on 40 c. Scaly-breasted Thrasher . .	9·00	10·00	3·50	4·00
739/42 . .	*Set of* 4	18·00	20·00	6·00	6·75

Nos. 739A/42A were from the first printing using Type **129**. After the spelling mistake was noticed it was corrected on sheets subsequently surcharged.

(Des M. Pollard. Litho Questa)

1988 (8 Feb). *Bats. T* **130** *and similar vert designs. Multicoloured. W* w **15** (*sideways*). *P* 14.
743 55 c. Type **130**. 80 40
744 90 c. *Chiroderma improvisum* (fruit bat) . . 1·25 90
745 $1.15, Fisherman Bat . . . . . . 1·60 1·50
746 $2.30, *Brachyphylla cavernarum* (fruit bat) 3·00 5·00
743/6 . . . . *Set of* 4 6·00 7·00
MS747 133×110 mm. $2.50, Funnel-eared Bat. Wmk upright . . . . 4·50 5·50

131 Magnificent Frigate Bird **132** Discus throwing

(Des R. Vigurs. Litho Questa)

1988 (2 Apr). *Easter. Birds. T* **131** *and similar vert designs. Multicoloured. P* 14×13½.
748 90 c. Type **131** 60 45
749 $1.15, Caribbean Elaenia 80 75
750 $1.50, Glossy Ibis . . . . . . 1·00 1·50
751 $3.50, Purple-throated Carib . . . . 2·00 3·50
748/51 . . . . *Set of* 4 4·00 5·50
MS752 100 × 75 mm. $5 Brown Pelican . . 2·50 3·50

(Des R. Vigurs. Litho Questa)

1988 (29 July). *Olympic Games, Seoul. T* **132** *and similar horiz designs. Multicoloured. P* 13½×14.
753 90 c. Type **132** 50 50
754 $1.15, High jumping 60 60
755 $3.50, Athletics . . . . 2·00 3·00
753/5 . . . . *Set of* 3 2·75 3·75
MS756 103×77 mm. $5 Rowing . . . . 2·75 2·75

133 Golden Tulip (*Pleuroploca aurantiaca*) **134** University Crest

(Des R. Vigurs. Litho Questa)

1988 (30 Aug). *Sea Shells. T* **133** *and similar horiz designs. Multicoloured. P* 14.
757 5 c. Type **133** 30 30
758 10 c. Little Knobbed Scallop (*Chlamys imbricata*) 40 40
759 15 c. Sozoni's Cone (*Conus delessertii*) . . 40 40
760 20 c. Globular Coral Shell (*Coralliophila aberrans*) 50 40
761 25 c. American or Common Sundial (*Architectonica nobilis*) 50 40
762 40 c. King Helmet (*Cassis tuberosa*) . . 60 40
763 55 c. Channelled Turban (*Turbo canaliculatus*) 80 40
764 70 c. True Tulip (*Fasciolaria tulipa*) . . 1·00 75
765 90 c. Music Volute (*Voluta musica*) . . 1·25 75
766 $1 Flame Auger (*Terebra taurina*) . . 1·40 80
767 $1.15, Rooster-tail Conch (*Strombus gallus*) . . . . 1·50 90
768 $1.50, Queen or Pink Conch (*Strombus gigas*) . . . . 1·60 1·40
769 $3 Teramachi's Slit Shell (*Perotrochus teramachii*) . . . . 2·75 3·50
770 $5 Common or Florida Crown Conch (*Melongena corona*) . . . . . . 4·50 6·00
771 $7.50, Beau's Murex (*Murex beauii*) . . 6·50 8·50
772 $10 Atlantic Trumpet Triton (*Charonia variegata*) . . . . 7·50 10·00
757/72 . . . . *Set of* 16 27·00 32·00

(Des R. Vigurs. Litho Questa)

1988 (14 Oct). *40th Anniv of University of West Indies. P* 14×13½.
773 **134** $5 multicoloured . . . . . . 2·40 3·25

=
HRH PRINCESS
ALEXANDRA'S VISIT
NOVEMBER 1988
40¢

(**135**)

1988 (4 Nov). *Princess Alexandra's Visit. Nos.* 763, 766 *and* 769/70 *surch as T* **135**.
774 40 c. on 55 c. Channelled Turban (*Turbo canaliculatus*) 45 45
775 90 c. on $1 Flame Auger (*Terebra taurina*) 70 80
776 $1.15 on $3 Teramachi's Slit Shell (*Perotrochus teramachii*) 85 95
a. Surch double .. .. 55·00
777 $1.50 on $5 Common or Florida Crown Conch (*Melongena corona*) .. .. 1·10 1·50
774/7 .. .. *Set of* 4 2·75 3·25

136 Spotted Sandpiper

(Des R. Vigurs. Litho Questa)

1988 (4 Dec). *Christmas. Sea Birds. T* **136** *and similar horiz designs. Multicoloured. P* 13½×14.
778 90 c. Type **136** 70 55
779 $1.15, Turnstone 85 70
780 $3.50, Red-footed Booby .. .. .. 2·00 3·50
778/80 .. .. *Set of* 3 3·25 4·25
MS781 105×79 mm. $5 Audubon's Shearwater 2·75 3·75

137 Handicapped Children in Classroom

(Des R. Vigurs. Litho Questa)

1988 (16 Dec). 125*th Anniv of International Red Cross. P* 13½ × 14.
782 **137** $3.50, multicoloured .. .. .. 1·50 2·25

138 Drum Major in Ceremonial Uniform

139 Amazon Lily

(Des R. Vigurs. Litho Questa)

1989 (24 Feb). 75*th Anniv of Montserrat Defence Force* (1988). *Uniforms. T* **138** *and similar vert designs. Multicoloured. P* 14×13½.
783 90 c. Type **138** 70 55
784 $1.15, Field training uniform 85 75
785 $1.50, Cadet in ceremonial uniform .. 1·25 1·75
786 $3.50, Gazetted Police Officer in ceremonial uniform .. .. .. 2·50 3·50
783/6 .. .. *Set of* 4 4·75 6·00
MS787 102×76 mm. $5 Island Girl Guide Commissioner and Brownie .. .. .. 3·50 4·25

(Litho Questa)

1989 (21 Mar). *Easter. Lilies. T* **139** *and similar multicoloured designs. P* 13½×14 (90 *c.*) *or* 14×13½ (*others*).
788 90 c. Type **139** 50 50
789 $1.15, Salmon Blood Lily (*vert*) 70 70
790 $1.50, Amaryllis (*Hippeastrum vittatum*) (*vert*) .. .. 85 1·25
791 $3.50, Amaryllis (*Hippeastrum* hybrid) (*vert*) .. .. 1·90 2·75
788/91 .. .. *Set of* 4 3·50 4·75
MS792 103×77 mm. $5 Resurrection Lily (*vert*) 3·75 5·50

140 *Morning Prince* (schooner), 1942

141 The Scarecrow

(Des R. Vigurs. Litho Questa)

1989 (30 June). *Shipbuilding in Montserrat. T* **140** *and similar horiz designs. Multicoloured. P* 13½×14.
793 90 c. Type **140** 90 60
794 $1.15, *Western Sun* (inter-island freighter) 1·40 1·10
795 $1.50, *Kim G* (inter-island freighter) under construction .. .. .. 1·75 1·75
796 $3.50, *Romaris* (island ferry), *c.* 1942 2·75 3·75
793/6 .. .. *Set of* 4 6·00 6·50

(Litho Questa)

1989 (22 Sept). 50*th Anniv of* The Wizard of Oz *(film). T* **141** *and similar multicoloured designs. P* 14.
797 90 c. Type **141** 40 45
798 $1.15, The Lion 55 60
799 $1.50, The Tin Man 70 85
800 $3.50, Dorothy .. .. 1·60 2·25
797/800 .. .. *Set of* 4 3·00 3·75
MS801 113×84 mm. $5 Characters from film (*horiz*) .. .. 2·40 3·50

Hurricane Hugo
Relief Surcharge $2.50

(**142**)

1989 (20 Oct). *Hurricane Hugo Relief Fund. Nos.* 795/6 *surch with T* **142**.
802 $1.50 + $2.50, *Kim G* (inter-island freighter) under construction .. 2·25 3·00
803 $3.50 + $2.50, *Romaris* (island ferry), *c.* 1942 .. .. 2·50 4·00

143 "Apollo 11" above Lunar Surface

(Litho Questa)

1989 (19 Dec). 20*th Anniv of First Manned Landing on Moon. T* **143** *and similar multicoloured designs. P* 13½×14.
804 90 c. Type **143** 35 40
805 $1.15, Astronaut alighting from lunar module *Eagle* 45 50
806 $1.50, *Eagle* and astronaut conducting experiment 60 80
807 $3.50, Opening "Apollo 11" hatch after splashdown .. .. 1·40 2·25
804/7 .. .. *Set of* 4 2·50 3·50
MS808 101×76 mm. $5 Astronaut on Moon. P 14 ×13½ .. .. 3·75 5·00

144 *Yamato* (Japanese battleship)

145 The Empty Tomb

(Litho Questa)

1990 (12 Feb). *World War II Capital Ships. T* **144** *and similar horiz designs. Multicoloured. P* 14.
809 70 c. Type **144** .. .. 1·25 70
810 $1.15, U.S.S. *Arizona* at Pearl Harbour .. 1·75 95
811 $1.50, *Bismarck* (German battleship) in action .. .. 2·25 2·25
812 $3.50, H.M.S. *Hood* (battle cruiser) .. 3·50 5·00
809/12 .. .. *Set of* 4 8·00 8·00
MS813 118×90 mm. $5 *Bismarck* and map of North Atlantic .. .. 5·50 7·00

(Des R. Vigurs. Litho Questa)

1990 (12 Apr). *Easter. T* **145** *and similar vert designs showing stained glass windows from St. Michael's Parish Church, Bray, Berkshire. Multicoloured. P* 14×15.
814 $1.15, Type **145** .. .. 75 1·00
a. Horiz strip of 3. Nos. 814/16 .. .. 3·00
815 $1.50, The Ascension .. .. .. 1·00 1·40
816 $3.50, The Risen Christ with Disciples .. 1·60 2·00
814/16 .. .. *Set of* 3 3·00 4·00
MS817 65×103 mm. $5 The Crucifixion .. 3·50 4·50
Nos. 814/16 were printed together, *se-tenant*, in sheets of 6 (3×2).

70¢

(**146**)

1990 (3 May). *"Stamp World London 90" International Stamp Exhibition. Nos.* 460/4 *surch as T* **146** *in bright purple.*
818 70 c. on 40 c. Type **85** 50 50
819 90 c. on 55 c. Hawker Siddeley H.S.748 aircraft and 1976 55 c. definitive .. 70 70
820 $1 on $1.20, *La Plata* (liner) and 1903 5s. stamp 80 90
821 $1.15 on $1.20, *Lady Hawkins* (packet steamer) and 1932 Tercentenary 5s. commemorative .. .. 90 1·10
822 $1.50 on $1.20, *Avon* (paddle-steamer) and Penny Red stamp with "A 08" postmark .. .. 1·25 1·75
818/22 .. .. *Set of* 5 3·75 4·50
Nos. 818/22 also show the "Stamp World London 90" emblem overprinted on one of the *se-tenant* labels.

147 General Office, Montserrat, and 1884 ½d. Stamp

(Litho Questa)

1990 (1 June). 150*th Anniv of the Penny Black. T* **147** *and similar multicoloured designs. P* 13½×14 (*horiz*) *or* 14×13½ (*vert*).
823 90 c. Type **147** 65 65
824 $1.15, Sorting letters and Montserrat 1d. stamp of 1876 (*vert*) 85 90
825 $1.50, Posting letters and Penny Black (*vert*) .. .. 1·25 1·75
826 $3.50, Postman delivering letters and 1840 Twopence Blue .. .. .. 3·00 4·00
823/6 .. .. *Set of* 4 5·25 6·50
MS827 102×75 mm. $5 Montserrat soldier's letter of 1836 and Penny Black .. .. 5·00 6·00

148 Montserrat v. Antigua Match

(Litho Questa)

1990 (8 July). *World Cup Football Championship, Italy. T* **148** *and similar multicoloured designs. P* 14.
828 90 c. Type **148** 55 55
829 $1.15, U.S.A v. Trinidad match 75 75
830 $1.50, Montserrat team .. .. .. 1·00 1·25
831 $3.50, West Germany v. Wales match .. 2·00 2·75
828/31 .. .. *Set of* 4 3·75 4·75
MS832 77×101 mm. $5 World Cup trophy (*vert*) 3·75 5·00

149 Spinner Dolphin

(Des Jennifer Toombs. Litho Questa)

1990 (25 Sept). *Dolphins. T* **149** *and similar horiz designs. Multicoloured. P* 14.
833 90 c. Type **149** .. .. 1·25 85
834 $1.15, Common Dolphin .. .. .. 1·50 1·25
835 $1.50, Striped Dolphin .. .. .. 2·25 2·25
836 $3.50, Atlantic Spotted Dolphin .. .. 3·50 4·50
833/6 .. .. *Set of* 4 7·75 8·00
MS837 103×76 mm. $5 Atlantic White-sided Dolphin .. .. 5·00 6·00

150 Spotted Goatfish

5c

(**151**)

(Litho Questa)

1991 (7 Feb). *Tropical Fishes. T* **150** *and similar horiz designs. Multicoloured. P* 13½×14.
838 90 c. Type **150** 1·25 85
839 $1.15, Cushion Star 1·50 1·25
840 $1.50, Rock Beauty 2·25 2·25
841 $3.50, French Grunt 3·50 4·50
838/41 *Set of* 4 7·75 8·00
MS842 103×76 mm. $5 Buffalo Trunkfish 4·75 6·00

1991 (27 Feb). *Nos.* 760/1, 768 *and* 771 *surch as T* **151.**
843 5 c. on 20 c. Globular Coral Shell (*Corallio-phila aberrans*) 50 75
844 5 c. on 25 c. American or Common Sundial (*Architectonica nobilis*) 50 75
845 $1.15 on $1.50, Queen or Pink Conch (*Strombus gigas*) 2·50 3·00
846 $1.15 on $7.50, Beau's Murex (*Murex beauii*) 2·50 3·00
843/6 *Set of* 4 5·50 6·75

152 Duck

153 *Panaeolus antillarum*

(Des K. West. Litho Questa)

1991 (29 May). *Domestic Birds. T* **152** *and similar horiz designs. Multicoloured. P* 14.
847 90 c. Type **152** 60 60
848 $1.15, Hen and chicks 80 90
849 $1.50, Red Junglefowl 1·10 1·50
850 $3.50, Helmet Guineafowl 2·40 3·50
847/50 *Set of* 4 4·50 6·00

(Des M. Pollard. Litho Questa)

1991 (13 June). *Fungi. T* **153** *and similar square designs. P* 14.
851 90 c. olive-grey 1·00 90
852 $1.15, rosine 1·25 1·10
853 $1.50, yellow-brown 2·00 2·00
854 $2 maroon 2·25 3·00
855 $3.50, dull ultramarine 3·50 4·50
851/5 *Set of* 5 9·00 10·50
Designs:—$1.15, *Cantharellus cinnabarinus*; $1.50, *Gymnopilus chrysopellus*; $2, *Psilocybe cubensis*; $3.50, *Leptonia caeruleocapitata.*

154 Red Water Lily

155 Tree Frog

(Des M. Pollard. Litho Questa)

1991 (8 Aug). *Lilies. T* **154** *and similar vert designs. Multicoloured. P* 14.
856 90 c. Type **154** 65 65
857 $1.15, Shell Ginger 75 85
858 $1.50, Early Day Lily 1·00 1·60
859 $3.50, Anthurium 2·50 3·50
856/9 *Set of* 4 4·50 6·00

(Des M. Pollard. Litho B.D.T.)

1991 (9 Oct). *Frogs and Toad. T* **155** *and similar multi-coloured designs. P* 14.
860 $1.15, Type **155** 2·00 1·25
861 $2 Crapaud Toad 2·75 3·25
862 $3.50, Mountain Chicken (frog) 4·75 5·50
860/2 *Set of* 3 8·50 9·00
MS863 110×110 mm. $5 Tree Frog, Crapaud Toad and Mountain Chicken (76½×44 *mm*). P 15×14 5·50 6·50

156 Black British Shorthair Cat

(Des M. Pollard. Litho B.D.T.)

1991 (5 Dec). *Cats. T* **156** *and similar horiz designs. Multicoloured. P* 14.
864 90 c. Type **156** 1·25 90
865 $1.15, Seal Point Siamese 1·50 1·10
866 $1.50, Silver Tabby Persian 2·00 2·00
867 $2.50, Birman Temple Cat 2·75 3·50
868 $3.50, Egyptian Mau 3·50 4·50
864/8 *Set of* 5 10·00 11·00

157 Navigational Instruments

158 Runner with Olympic Flame

(Des M. Pollard. Litho Questa)

1992 (16 Jan). *500th Anniv of Discovery of America by Columbus. T* **157** *and similar horiz designs. Multicoloured. P* 14.
869 $1.50, Type **157** 1·25 1·50
a. Sheetlet. Nos. 869/75 8·50
870 $1.50, Columbus and coat of arms 1·25 1·50
871 $1.50, Landfall on the Bahamas 1·25 1·50
872 $1.50, Petitioning Queen Isabella 1·25 1·50
873 $1.50, Tropical birds 1·25 1·50
874 $1.50, Tropical fruits 1·25 1·50
875 $3 Ships of Columbus (81×26 *mm*) 1·75 2·00
869/75 *Set of* 7 8·50 10·00
Nos. 869/75 were printed together, *se-tenant*, in sheetlets of 7 with decorative margins.
For these designs, some with different face values, inscr "500TH ANNIVERSARY DISCOVERY OF MONTSERRAT", see Nos. 915/21.

(Des M. Pollard. Litho B.D.T.)

1992 (10 Apr). *Olympic Games, Barcelona. T* **158** *and similar square designs. Multicoloured. P* 14.
876 $1 Type **158** 70 60
877 $1.15, Montserrat, Olympic and Spanish flags 1·25 90
878 $2.30, Olympic flame on map of Montserrat 2·00 2·25
879 $3.60, Olympic events 2·50 3·50
876/9 *Set of* 4 5·75 6·50

159 Tyrannosaurus

(Des M. Pollard. Litho Questa)

1992 (1 May). *Death Centenary of Sir Richard Owen (zoologist). T* **159** *and similar multicoloured designs. P* 14.
880 $1 Type **159** 1·50 1·10
881 $1.15, Diplodocus 1·75 1·40
882 $1.50, Apatosaurus 2·25 2·25
883 $3.45, Dimetrodon 4·50 6·25
880/3 *Set of* 4 9·00 10·00
MS884 114×84 mm. $4.60, Sir Richard Owen and dinosaur bone (*vert*) 7·50 8·50

160 Male Montserrat Oriole

(Des R. Vigurs. Litho Questa)

1992 (30 June). *Montserrat Oriole. T* **160** *and similar horiz designs. Multicoloured. P* 14.
885 $1 Type **160** 1·10 1·10
886 $1.15, Male and female Orioles 1·40 1·40
887 $1.50, Female Oriole with chicks 1·75 2·00
888 $3.60, Map of Montserrat and male Oriole 3·50 5·00
885/8 *Set of* 4 7·00 8·50

161 *Psophus stridulus* (grasshopper)

(Des M. Pollard. Litho B.D.T.)

1992 (20 Aug). *Insects. T* **161** *and similar horiz designs. Multicoloured. P* 15×14.
889 5 c. Type **161** 30 40
890 10 c. *Gryllus campestris* (field cricket) 35 40
891 15 c. *Lepthemis vesiculosa* (dragonfly) 40 40
892 20 c. *Orthemis ferruginea* (red skimmer) 45 45
893 25 c. *Gerris lacustris* (pond skater) 45 45
894 40 c. *Byctiscus betulae* (leaf weevil) 60 50
895 55 c. *Atta texana* (leaf-cutter ants) 60 40
896 70 c. *Polistes fuscatus* (paper wasp) 70 60
897 90 c. *Sparmopolius fulvus* (bee fly) 80 60
898 $1 *Chrysopa carnea* (lace wing) 1·10 65
899 $1.15, *Phoebis philea* (butterfly) 1·50 90
900 $1.50, *Cynthia cardui* (butterfly) 1·75 1·75
901 $3 *Utetheisa bella* (moth) 2·50 3·25
902 $5 *Alucita pentadactyla* (moth) 3·50 4·00
903 $7.50, *Anartia jatropha* (butterfly) 4·50 6·50
904 $10 *Heliconius melpomene* (butterfly) 5·00 7·00
889/904 *Set of* 16 22·00 25·00

162 Adoration of the Magi

(Des M. Pollard. Litho Questa)

1992 (26 Nov). *Christmas. T* **162** *and similar horiz design. Multicoloured. P* 13½×14.
905 $1.15, Type **162** 1·25 75
906 $4.60, Appearance of angel to shepherds 3·75 5·00

163 $1 Coin and $20 Banknote

164 Columbus meeting Amerindians

(Des R. Vigurs. Litho Questa)

1993 (10 Feb). *East Caribbean Currency. T* **163** *and similar vert designs. Multicoloured. P* 14.
907 $1 Type **163** 80 70
908 $1.15, 10 c. and 25 c. coins with $10 banknote 1·00 85
909 $1.50, 5 c. coin and $5 banknote 1·50 1·75
910 $3.60, 1 c. and 2 c. coins with $1 banknote 3·75 5·00
907/10 *Set of* 4 6·25 7·50

(Des M. Pollard. Litho Questa)

1993 (10 Mar). *Organization of East Caribbean States. 500th Anniv of Discovery of America by Columbus. T* **164** *and similar square design. Multicoloured. P* 14.
911 $1 Type **164** 1·10 90
912 $2 Ships approaching island 1·75 2·50

165 Queen Elizabeth II on Montserrat with Chief Minister W. H. Bramble, 1966

(Des M. Pollard. Litho Questa)

1993 (2 June). *40th Anniv of Coronation. T* **165** *and similar horiz design. Multicoloured. P* 14.
913 $1.15, Type **165** 1·50 75
914 $4.60, Queen Elizabeth II in State Coach, 1953 4·00 5·00

1993 (5 Oct). *500th Anniv of Discovery of Montserrat. Designs as Nos.* 869/75, *some with new values, each showing* "500th ANNIVERSARY DISCOVERY OF MONTSERRAT" *at foot and with additional historical inscr across the centre. P* 14.
915 $1.15, multicoloured (As Type **157**) 1·10 1·40
a. Sheetlet. Nos. 915/21 9·00
916 $1.15, multicoloured (As No. 870) 1·10 1·40
917 $1.15, multicoloured (As No. 871) 1·10 1·40
918 $1.50, multicoloured (As No. 872) 1·40 1·75
919 $1.50, multicoloured (As No. 873) 1·40 1·75
920 $1.50, multicoloured (As No. 874) 1·40 1·75
921 $3.45, multicoloured (As No. 875) 2·40 3·00
915/21 *Set of* 7 9·00 11·00
Additional inscriptions:—No. 915, "PRE-COLUMBUS CARIB NAME OF ISLAND ALLIOUGANA"; No. 916, "COLUMBUS NAMED ISLAND SANTA MARIA DE MONTSERRATE"; No. 917, "COLUMBUS SAILED ALONG COASTLINE 11th NOV. 1493"; No. 918, "ISLAND OCCUPIED BY FRENCH BRIEFLY IN 1667"; No. 919, "ISLAND DECLARED ENGLISH BY TREATY OF BREDA 1667"; No. 920, "AFRICAN SLAVES BROUGHT IN DURING 1600's"; No. 921, "IRISH CATHOLICS FROM ST. KITTS AND VIRGINIA SETTLED ON ISLAND BETWEEN 1628–1634".
Nos. 915/21 were printed together, *se-tenant*, in sheetlets of 7, with decorative margins.

166 Boeing E-3 Sentry, 1993

(Des A. Theobald. Litho Questa)

1993 (17 Nov). *75th Anniv of Royal Air Force. T* **166** *and similar horiz designs. Multicoloured. W* w **14** (*sideways*). *P* 14.

922 15 c. Type **166** .. 30 20
923 55 c. Vickers Valiant B Mk 1, 1962 .. 45 40
924 $1.15, Handley Page H.P.67 Hastings C Mk 2, 1958 .. 1·00 75
925 $3 Lockheed PV-1 Ventura, 1943 .. 2·50 3·75
922/5 .. *Set of* 4 3·75 4·50
MS926 117×78 mm. $1.50, Felixstowe F5, 1921; $1.50, Armstrong Whitworth Atlas, 1934; $1.50, Fairey Gordon, 1935; $1.50, Boulton & Paul Overstrand, 1936 .. 4·50 5·50

167 Ground Beetle

168 *Gossypium barbadense*

(Des M. Pollard. Litho B.D.T.)

1994 (21 Jan). *Beetles. T* **167** *and similar horiz designs. Multicoloured. P* 15×14.

927 $1 Type **167** .. 65 65
928 $1.15, Click Beetle .. 80 80
929 $1.50, Harlequin Beetle .. 1·25 1·50
930 $3.45, Leaf Beetle .. 3·00 4·25
927/30 .. *Set of* 4 5·25 6·50
MS931 68×85 mm. $4.50, Scarab Beetle .. 3·50 3·50

(Des R. Vigurs. Litho Questa)

1994 (22 Mar). *Flowers. T* **168** *and similar vert designs. Multicoloured. P* 14×13½.

932 90 c. Type **168** .. 1·00 80
933 $1.15, *Hibiscus sabdariffa* .. 1·25 1·00
934 $1.50, *Hibiscus esculentus* .. 1·60 1·75
935 $3.50, *Hibiscus rosa-sinensis* .. 3·50 5·00
932/5 .. *Set of* 4 6·50 7·75

169 Coaching Young Players and Logo

(Litho Questa)

1994 (20 Apr). *World Cup Football Championship, U.S.A. T* **169** *and similar horiz designs. Multicoloured. P* 14×14½.

936 90 c. Type **169** .. 1·25 1·75
a. Vert strip of 4. Nos. 936/9 .. 6·00
937 $1 United States scoring against England, 1950 .. 1·25 1·75
938 $1.15, Rose Bowl stadium, Los Angeles, and trophy .. 1·25 1·75
939 $3.45, German players celebrating with trophy, 1990 .. 2·75 3·25
936/9 .. *Set of* 4 6·00 7·75
MS940 114×85 mm. $2 Jules Rimet (founder) and Jules Rimet Trophy; $2 Bobby Moore (England) holding trophy, 1966; $2 Lew Jaschin (U.S.S.R); $2 Sepp Herberger (Germany) and German players celebrating, 1990 .. 7·00 8·00

Nos. 936/9 were printed together, *se-tenant*, in vertical strips of 4, each sheet containing two such strips separated by a gutter of 4 stamp-size labels showing Montserrat flag, championship mascot and logos.

170 Elasmosaurus

(Des M. Pollard. Litho B.D.T.)

1994 (6 May). *Aquatic Dinosaurs. T* **170** *and similar horiz designs. Multicoloured. P* 15×14.

941 $1 Type **170** .. 1·60 1·75
a. Horiz strip of 4. Nos. 941/4 .. 7·00
942 $1.15, Plesiosaurus .. 1·60 1·75
943 $1.50, Nothosaurus .. 1·90 2·00
944 $3.45, Mosasaurus .. 2·75 3·50
941/4 .. *Set of* 4 7·00 8·00

Nos. 941/4 were printed together, *se-tenant*, in horizontal strips of 4 throughout the sheet.

Space Anniversaries
Columbia
First Space Shuttle
April 12, 1981
$2 30

(171)

1994 (20 July). *Space Anniversaries. Nos.* 804/7 *surch in black and red or optd in red only as T* **171**, *each including* "Space Anniversaries".

945 40 c. on 90 c. Type **143** .. 75 60
946 $1.15, Astronaut alighting from lunar module *Eagle* .. 1·50 1·25
947 $1.50, *Eagle* and astronaut conducting experiment .. 2·00 2·00
948 $2.30 on $3.50, Opening "Apollo 11" hatch after splashdown .. 3·00 4·00
945/8 .. *Set of* 4 6·50 7·00

Surcharges and overprints:—No. 945, "Juri Gagarin First man in space April 12, 1961"; No. 946, "First Joint US Soviet Mission July 15, 1975"; No. 947 "25th Anniversary First Moon Landing Apollo XI – July 20, 1994".

Nos. 945 and 948 show the face value obliterated in black and the rest of the surcharge in red.

172 1969 Festival Logo

173 Sea Fan

(Des A. Skolnick and Barbara Pensoy. Litho The Mansfield Press)

1994 (20 Oct). *25th Anniv of Woodstock Music Festival. T* **172** *and similar vert design. Multicoloured. P* 12½.

949 $1.15, Type **172** .. 1·00 1·00
950 $1.50, 1994 anniversary festival logo .. 1·25 1·25

(Des M. Pollard. Litho B.D.T.)

1995 (14 Feb). *Marine Life. T* **173** *and simlar vert designs. Multicoloured. P* 14×15.

951 $1 Type **173** .. 60 50
952 $1.15, Sea Lily .. 70 60
953 $1.50, Sea Pen .. 90 1·00
954 $3.45, Sea Fern .. 2·00 2·75
951/4 .. *Set of* 4 3·75 4·25
MS955 88×96 mm. $4.50, Sea Rose .. 3·00 3·50

174 Marilyn Monroe

175 Jesse Owens (U.S.A.)

(Des S. Bickel (No. **MS**965), Lisa Egeli (others). Litho)

1995 (13 June). *Centenary of Cinema. T* **174** *and similar vert designs showing portraits of Marilyn Monroe (film star). Multicoloured. P* 12½.

956 $1.15, Type **174** .. 90 1·00
a. Sheetlet. Nos. 956/64 .. 7·00
957 $1.15, Puckering lips .. 90 1·00
958 $1.15, Laughing in brown evening dress and earrings .. 90 1·00
959 $1.15, Wearing red earrings .. 90 1·00
960 $1.15, In brown dress without earrings .. 90 1·00
961 $1.15, With white boa .. 90 1·00
962 $1.15, In red dress .. 90 1·00
963 $1.15, Wearing white jumper .. 90 1·00
964 $1.15, Looking over left shoulder .. 90 1·00
956/64 .. *Set of* 9 7·00 8·00
MS965 102×132 mm. $6 With Elvis Presley (50×56 *mm*) .. 4·50 4·75

Nos. 956/64 were printed together, *se-tenant*, in sheetlets of 9.

(Des M. Morck. Litho B.D.T.)

1995 (3 Aug). *5th International Amateur Athletic Federation Games, Göteborg. Sheet* 181×103 *mm, containing T* **175** *and similar vert designs. P* 14.

MS966 $1.50, black and pink (Type **175**); $1.50, black and pale orange (Eric Lemming (Sweden)); $1.50, black and chrome-yellow (Rudolf Harbig (Germany)); $1.50, black and bright yellow-green (young Montserrat athletes) .. 4·50 5·50

176 Atmospheric Sounding Experiments using V2 Rockets

177 Ears of Wheat ("Food")

(Des M. Pollard. Litho Cot Printery Ltd, Barbados)

1995 (15 Aug). *50th Anniv of End of Second World War. Scientific Achievements. T* **176** *and similar horiz designs. Multicoloured. P* 14.

967 $1.15, Type **176** .. 80 90
a. Horiz pair. Nos. 967/8 .. 1·60 1·75
968 $1.15, American Space Shuttle *Challenger* 80 90
969 $1.15, Nuclear experiment, Chicago, 1942 80 90
a. Horiz pair. Nos. 969/70 .. 1·60 1·75
970 $1.15, Calder Hall Atomic Power Station, 1956 .. 80 90
971 $1.50, Radar-equipped Ju 88G 7a night-fighter .. 1·00 1·25
a. Horiz pair. Nos. 971/2 .. 2·00 2·50
972 $1.50, Boeing E6 A.W.A.C.S. aircraft .. 1·00 1·25
973 $1.50, Gloster G.41 Meteor Mk III jet fighter .. 1·00 1·25
a. Horiz pair. Nos. 973/4 .. 2·00 2·50
974 $1.50, Concorde (airliner) .. 1·00 1·25
967/74 .. *Set of* 8 6·50 7·50

Nos. 967/8, 969/70, 971/2 and 973/4 were each printed together, *se-tenant*, in horizontal pairs throughout the sheets.

(Des M. Pollard. Litho Cot Printery Ltd, Barbados)

1995 (14 Sept). *50th Anniv of United Nations. T* **177** *and similar vert designs. Multicoloured. P* 14.

975 $1.15, Type **177** .. 90 75
976 $1.50, Open book ("Education") .. 1·25 1·00
977 $2.30, P.T. class ("Health") .. 1·75 2·25
978 $3 Dove ("Peace") .. 2·25 3·00
975/8 .. *Set of* 4 5·50 6·25
MS979 105×75 mm. $6 Scales ("Justice") .. 3·50 4·50

178 Headquarters Building

(Litho Cot Printery Ltd, Barbados)

1995 (15 Nov). *25th Anniv of Montserrat National Trust. T* **178** *and similar multicoloured designs. P* 14.

980 $1.15, Type **178** .. 80 75
981 $1.50, 17th-century cannons, Bransby Point 1·25 1·00
982 $2.30, Impression of Galways Sugar Mill (*vert*) .. 2·00 2·25
983 $3 Great Alps Falls (*vert*) .. 3·00 4·00
980/3 .. *Set of* 4 6·25 7·25

+$5⁰⁰

(179)

1995 (29 Dec). *25th Anniv of Air Recording Studios. No.* 713 *surch with T* **179** *in red.*

984 $2.30 + $5 Air Recording Studios .. 4·25 4·75

The $5 premium on No. 984 was for relief following a volcanic eruption.

180 Bull Shark

(Des M. Pollard. Litho B.D.T.)

1996 (14 Feb). *Scavengers of the Sea. T* **180** *and similar horiz designs. Multicoloured. P* 15×14.

985 $1 Type **180** .. 80 70
986 $1.15, Sea Mouse .. 90 80
987 $1.50, Bristleworm .. 1·25 1·25
988 $3.45, Prawn *Xiphocaris* .. 2·50 3·00
985/8 .. *Set of* 4 5·00 5·25
MS989 69×95 mm. $4.50, Man of War Fish .. 3·00 3·50

181 Marconi and Radio Equipment, 1901

(Des M. Pollard. Litho Cot Printery Ltd, Barbados)

1996 (19 Mar). *Centenary of Radio. T* **181** *and similar horiz designs. Multicoloured. P* 14.

990 $1.15, Type **181** .. 90 80
991 $1.50, Marconi's steam yacht *Elettra* .. 1·25 1·00
992 $2.30, Receiving first Transatlantic radio message, Newfoundland, 1901 .. 1·75 2·00
993 $3 Imperial Airways airplane at Croydon Airport, 1920 .. 2·25 2·75
990/3 .. *Set of* 4 5·50 6·00
MS994 74×105 mm. $4.50, Radio telescope, Jodrell Bank .. 3·00 3·50

182 Paul Masson (France) (Cycling)

(Litho B.D.T.)

1996 (24 June). *Olympic Games, Atlanta. Gold Medal Winners of* 1896. *T* **182** *and similar diamond-shaped designs. Multicoloured. P* 14.

995 $1.15, Type **182** .. 80 80
996 $1.50, Robert Garrett (U.S.A.) (Discus) .. 1·00 1·00
997 $2.30, Spyridon Louis (Greece) (Marathon) 1·50 1·75
998 $3 John Boland (Great Britain) (Tennis) 2·00 2·50
995/8 .. *Set of* 4 4·75 5·50

183 James Dean **184** Leprechaun

(Des T. Kelly. Litho)

1996 (28 June). *James Dean (film star) Commemoration. T* **183** *and similar designs. Multicoloured. P* 12½.

999 $1.15, Type **183** .. 80 80
a. Sheetlet. Nos. 999/1007 .. 6·50
1000 $1.15, Wearing stetson facing right .. 80 80
1001 $1.15, Wearing blue sweater .. 80 80
1002 $1.15, Wearing black sweater .. 80 80
1003 $1.15, Full face portrait wearing stetson 80 80
1004 $1.15, Wearing fawn jacket .. 80 80
1005 $1.15, Wearing red wind-cheater .. 80 80
1006 $1.15, Smoking a cigarette .. 80 80
1007 $1.15, In open-necked shirt and green jumper .. 80 80
999/1007 .. *Set of* 9 6·50 6·50
MS1008 169×133 mm. $6 As No. 1000 (51×57 *mm*) .. 4·50 5·00

Nos. 999/1007 were printed together, *se-tenant*, in sheetlets of 9.

(Litho Cot Printery Ltd, Barbados)

1996 (15 Aug). *Mythical Creatures. T* **184** *and similar vert designs. Multicoloured. P* 14.

1009 5 c. Type **184** .. 10 10
1010 10 c. Pegasus .. 10 10
1011 15 c. Griffin .. 10 10
1012 20 c. Unicorn .. 10 10
1013 25 c. Gnomes .. 10 15
1014 40 c. Mermaid .. 20 25
1015 55 c. Cockatrice .. 25 30
1016 70 c. Fairy .. 35 40
1017 90 c. Goblin .. 40 45
1018 $1 Faun .. 45 50
1019 $1.15, Dragon .. 50 55
1020 $1.50, Giant .. 70 75
1021 $3 Elves .. 1·40 1·50
1022 $5 Centaur .. 2·25 2·40
1023 $7.50, Phoenix .. 3·50 3·75
1024 $10 Erin .. 4·50 4·75
1009/24 .. *Set of* 16 15·00 16·00

185 Blue and Green Teddybears **186** Turkey Vulture

1996 (21 Oct). *Jerry Garcia and the Grateful Dead (rock group) Commemoration. T* **185** *and similar vert designs. Multicoloured. Litho. P* 12½.

1025 $1.15, Type **185** .. 90 1·00
a. Horiz strip of 3. Nos. 1025/7 .. 2·40
1026 $1.15, Green and yellow teddybears .. 90 1·00
1027 $1.15, Brown and pink teddybears .. 90 1·00
1028 $6 Jerry Garcia (37×50 *mm*) .. 5·00 5·50
1025/8 .. *Set of* 4 7·00 7·75

Nos. 1025/7 were printed together, *se-tenant*, in horizontal strips of 3 throughout the sheet, each strip forming a composite design.

(Des M. Pollard. Litho B.D.T.)

1997 (28 Jan). *Scavengers of the Sky. T* **186** *and similar horiz designs. Multicoloured. P* 15×14.

1029 $1 Type **186** .. 65 60
1030 $1.15, American Crow .. 80 70
1031 $1.50, Great Skua .. 1·00 1·00
1032 $3.45, Kittiwake .. 1·90 2·00
1029/32 .. *Set of* 4 4·00 4·00
MS1033 74×95 mm. $4.50, King Vulture .. 2·10 2·25

HONG KONG '97

(187)

(Litho Cambridge Security Press Ltd)

1997 (26 Mar). *"HONG KONG '97" International Stamp Exhibition. Nos.* 1025/7 *overprinted with T* **187** *in deep blue across horizontal strips of three.*

1034 $1.15, Type **185** .. 70 80
a. Horiz strip of 3. Nos. 1034/6 .. 1·90
1035 $1.15, Green and yellow teddybears .. 70 80
1036 $1.15, Brown and pink teddybears .. 70 80
1034/6 .. *Set of* 3 1·90 2·25

Type **187** falls across the three stamps with "HO" on No. 1034, "NG KONG" on No. 1035 and "'97" on No. 1036.

(188) **189** Heavy Ash Eruption over Plymouth, 1995

1997 (2 June). *"Pacific '97" International Stamp Exhibition, San Francisco. Nos.* 999/1007 *optd with T* **188** *with each impression falling across two stamps.*

1037 $1.15, Type **183** .. 80 90
a. Sheetlet. Nos. 1037/45 .. 6·50
1038 $1.15, Wearing stetson facing right .. 80 90
1039 $1.15, Wearing blue sweater .. 80 90
1040 $1.15, Wearing black sweater .. 80 90
1041 $1.15, Full face portrait wearing stetson 80 90
1042 $1.15, Wearing fawn jacket .. 80 90
1043 $1.15, Wearing red wind-cheater .. 80 90
1044 $1.15, Smoking a cigarette .. 80 90
1045 $1.15, In open-necked shirt and green jumper .. 80 90
1037/45 .. *Set of* 9 6·50 7·25

(Des M. Pollard. Litho Cot Printery, Barbados)

1997 (23 June). *Eruption of Soufriere Volcano. T* **189** *and similar vert designs. Multicoloured. P* 14½×14.

1046 $1.50, Type **189** .. 1·10 1·10
a. Sheetlet. Nos. 1046/54 .. 9·00
1047 $1.50, Burning rock flow entering sea .. 1·10 1·10
1048 $1.50, Double venting at Castle Peak .. 1·10 1·10
1049 $1.50, Mangrove Cuckoo .. 1·10 1·10
1050 $1.50, Lava flow at night, 1996 .. 1·10 1·10
1051 $1.50, Antillean Crested Hummingbird .. 1·10 1·10
1052 $1.50, Ash cloud over Plymouth .. 1·10 1·10
1053 $1.50, Lava spine, 1996 .. 1·10 1·10
1054 $1.50, Burning rock flows forming new land .. 1·10 1·10
1046/54 .. *Set of* 9 9·00 9·00

Nos. 1046/54 were printed together, *se-tenant*, in sheetlets of 9.

190 Elvis Presley **191** Untitled Painting by Frama

(Litho Cambridge Security Press Ltd)

1997 (29 Aug). *Rock Legends. T* **190** *and similar vert designs. Multicoloured. P* 12½.

1055 $1.15, Type **190** .. 75 80
1056 $1.15, Jimi Hendrix .. 75 80
1057 $1.15, Jerry Garcia .. 75 80
1058 $1.15, Janis Joplin .. 75 80
1055/8 .. *Set of* 4 2·75 3·00

Nos. 1055/8 were each printed in sheets of 8 containing two blocks of four separated by a vertical gutter.

(Litho Cambridge Security Press Ltd)

1997 (29 Aug). *Frama Exhibition at Guggenheim Museum, New York. P* 12½.

1059 **191** $1.50, multicoloured .. 85 95
a. Sheetlet. No. 1059×8 .. 6·00

No. 1059 was printed in sheetlets of 8 stamps, containing two blocks of four separated by an illustrated margin.

STAMP BOOKLETS

1975 (3 Mar). *Carib Artefacts. Multicoloured cover. Stitched.*
SB1 $2.95, booklet containing *se-tenant* panes of 4 and 6 (Nos. 347a/8a) .. .. 1·90

1977 (7 Feb). *Silver Jubilee. Black on white cover. Stapled.*
SB2 $7 booklet containing 30 c., 45 c. and $1 (Nos. 396/8), each in block of 4 .. .. .. 6·50

1978 (2 June). *25th Anniv of Coronation. Multicoloured cover, 82×52 mm, showing Coronation ceremony on the front and Westminster Abbey on the reverse. Stapled.*
SB3 $8.90, booklet containing 40 c., 55 c., $1 and $2.50 (Nos. 422/5), each in pair .. .. .. 1·25

1981. *Black and blue cover, 102×64 mm, showing stylized fishes design. Stitched.*
SB4 $5.80, booklet containing 35 c., 45 c. and 65 c. (Nos. 495/6, 498), each in block of 4 .. .. 4·50

1981 (19 Nov). *Royal Wedding. Multicoloured cover, 105×65 mm, showing* The Charlotte. *Stitched.*
SB5 $13.20, booklet containing eight 90 c. in panes of 4 (No. 517a) and two $3 in pane of 2 (No. 518a) 4·25

1986 (23 July). *Royal Wedding. Gold* (*No.* SB6) *or silver* (*No.* SB7) *on greenish yellow covers. Stapled.*
SB6 $8.40, booklet (Westminster Abbey) containing twelve 70 c. (Nos. 691/2) in blocks of 4 .. 3·25
SB7 $10.80, booklet (State Coach) containing 70 c. and $2 (Nos. 691/4, but imperf), each value in block of 4 .. .. 4·75

OFFICIAL STAMPS

O.H.M.S. (O 1) — **O.H.M.S.** (O 2)

1976 (12 Apr). *Various stamps, some already surcharged, optd locally with Type* O **1**.
O1 5 c. multicoloured (No. 246A) .. .. † 65
O2 10 c. multicoloured (No. 247A) .. .. † 75
a. Opt double .. .. .. † 14·00
b. Horiz pair, one stamp without opt .. † £250
O3 30 c. on 10 c. multicoloured (No. 369) .. † 1·50
a. Opt double .. .. .. † 40·00
w. Wmk Crown to right of CA .. .. † 25·00
O4 45 c. on 3 c. multicoloured (No. 370) .. † 2·00
O5 $5 multicoloured (No. 254A) .. .. † £100
O6 $10 multicoloured (No. 254aB) .. .. † £550
O1/6 .. .. *Set of* 6 † £600
These stamps were issued for use on mail from the Montserrat Philatelic Bureau. They were not available for sale in either unused or used condition.

1976 (1 Oct)–**80**. *Nos.* 374/8, 380/2 *and* 384/5 *optd with Type* O **2** *locally*.
O 7 5 c. Malay Apple .. .. .. † 15
a. Opt inverted .. .. .. † —
b. Missing stop after "S" .. .. † 1·50
O 8 10 c. Jacaranda .. .. .. † 20
a. Missing stop after "S" .. .. † 1·50
O 9 15 c. Orchid Tree .. .. .. † 25
a. Opt inverted .. .. .. † 70·00
b. Missing stop after "S" .. .. † 1·50
w. Wmk Crown to right of CA .. .. † 25·00
O10 20 c. Manjak .. .. .. † 30
a. Opt inverted .. .. .. † 70·00
b. Missing stop after "S" .. .. † 1·50
c. Chalk-surfaced paper (1980) .. .. † —
O11 25 c. Tamarind .. .. .. † 35
a. Missing stop after "S" .. .. † 1·50
O12 55 c. Pink Cassia .. .. .. † 55
a. Opt inverted .. .. .. † —
b. Opt double .. .. .. † —
c. Missing stop after "S" .. .. † 2·50
O13 70 c. Long John .. .. .. † 60
a. Missing stop after "S" .. .. † 3·50
O14 $1 Saman .. .. .. † 75
a. Opt inverted .. .. .. † —
b. Missing stop after "S" .. .. † 5·00
O15 $5 Yellow Poui .. .. .. † 2·00
a. Missing stop after "S" .. .. † 11·00
w. Wmk Crown to right of CA .. .. † 10·00
O16 $10 Flamboyant (14.4.80) .. .. † 3·75
a. Missing stop after "S" .. .. † 20·00
O7/16 .. .. *Set of* 10 † 8·00
Nos. O7/16 were not available in an unused condition, but were sold to the public cancelled-to-order.
The missing stop after "S" variety occurs on R. 1/3 and 3/5.

O.H.M.S. (O 3) — O.H.M.S. (O 4) — O.H.M.S. 45¢ (O 5)

1980 (7 July). *Nos.* 374/8, 380/2 *and* 384/5 *optd with Type* O **3** *in Great Britain*.
O17 5 c. Malay Apple .. .. .. † 10
a. Opt double .. .. .. † —
O18 10 c. Jacaranda .. .. .. † 10
O19 15 c. Orchid Tree .. .. .. † 10
O20 20 c. Manjak .. .. .. † 10
a. Opt double .. .. .. † 70·00
O21 25 c. Tamarind .. .. .. † 15
O22 55 c. Pink Cassia .. .. .. † 35
a. Opt double .. .. .. † 13·00
O23 70 c. Long John .. .. .. † 45
O24 $1 Saman .. .. .. † 60
O25 $5 Yellow Poui .. .. .. † 2·00
O26 $10 Flamboyant .. .. .. † 3·00
O17/26 .. .. *Set of* 10 † 6·00
Nos. O17/26 were not available in an unused condition, but were sold to the public cancelled-to-order. At least two values, the 20 c. and $1 are, however, known uncancelled.
These stamps were originally intended for issue on 3 November 1980, but certain values were placed on sale from 7 July onwards to meet shortages. Bulk supplies did not arrive on the island until early December 1980.

O.H. M.S.
Spaced "H" and "M" (R. 3/4)

1980 (30 Sept). *Nos.* 374/82, 384/5 *and* 476, *together with surcharges on Nos.* 372, 376 *and* 379, *optd as Type* O **4** *locally*.
O27 5 c. Malay Apple .. .. .. † 30
O28 5 c. on 3 c. Lignum vitae .. .. † 30
O29 10 c. Jacaranda .. .. .. † 30
O30 15 c. Orchid Tree .. .. .. † 30
a. Opt double .. .. .. † —
O31 20 c. Manjak .. .. .. † 40
a. Opt double .. .. .. † 12·00
O32 25 c. Tamarind .. .. .. † 40
O33 30 c. on 15 c. Orchid Tree .. .. † 40
a. "O.H.M.S." opt omitted .. .. † —
O34 35 c. on 2 c. Cannon-ball Tree .. .. † 40
a. Spaced "H" and "M" .. .. † 3·50
O35 40 c. Flame of the Forest .. .. † 50
O36 55 c. Pink Cassia .. .. .. † 45
O37 70 c. Long John .. .. .. † 80
O38 $1 Saman .. .. .. † 80
O39 $2.50 on 40 c. Flame of the Forest .. † 2·25
a. "O.H.M.S." opt omitted £160
O40 $5 Yellow Poui .. .. .. † 2·50
O41 $10 Flamboyant .. .. .. † 4·00
a. Opt double .. .. .. † 75·00
O27/41 .. .. *Set of* 15 † 12·50
Nos. O27/41 were not available in an unused condition, but were sold to the public cancelled-to-order. No. O39a was, however, found amongst supplies of the postage series.

1981 (20 Mar). *Nos.* 490/4, 496, 498, 500, 502/3 *and* 505 *optd with Type* O **4**.
O42 5 c. Type **91** 10 10
a. Opt inverted .. .. .. 15·00
O43 10 c. Hogfish and Neon Goby 10 10
O44 15 c. Creole Wrasse 10 10
a. Opt double .. .. .. † —
O45 20 c. Three-spotted Damselfish 15 15
O46 25 c. Sergeant Major 15 15
O47 45 c. Schoolmaster 25 20
a. Opt double .. .. .. 16·00
ab. Opt double, one on reverse .. .. 11·00
b. Opt inverted .. .. .. 20·00
O48 65 c. Bigeye 35 30
a. Opt inverted .. .. .. 65·00
O49 $1 Rock Beauty 65 65
O50 $3 Royal Gramma ("Fairy Basslet") and Blueheads .. .. .. 1·75 1·75
O51 $5 Cherub Angelfish .. .. .. 3·00 3·00
w. Wmk inverted .. .. .. 30·00
O52 $10 Caribbean Long-nosed Butterflyfish 5·50 3·00
w. Wmk inverted .. .. .. 32·00
O42/52 .. .. .. *Set of* 11 11·00 8·50

1982 (17 Nov). *Nos.* 510/15 *surch as Type* O **5** (*in one line on Nos.* O54, O56 *and* O58).
O53 45 c. on 90 c. *Charlotte* 15 30
a. Sheetlet. No. O53×6 and No. O54 .. 1·25
b. Surch double .. .. .. 21·00
c. Surch inverted .. .. .. 12·00
d. Surch inverted (horiz pair) .. .. 32·00
e. Horiz pair, one without surch .. .. 70·00
O54 45 c. on 90 c. Prince Charles and Lady Diana Spencer 50 60
b. Surch double .. .. .. 70·00
c. Surch inverted .. .. .. 50·00
O55 75 c. on $3 *Portsmouth* 25 35
aw. Wmk inverted .. .. .. 10·00
b. Sheetlet. No. O55×6 and No. O56 .. 1·90
bw. Wmk inverted .. .. .. 80·00
c. Surch double .. .. .. 27·00
d. Surch inverted .. .. .. 13·00
e. Surch inverted (horiz pair) .. .. 23·00
f. Horiz pair, one without surch .. .. 70·00
g. Error. Surch on $4 (No. 514) .. .. 12·00
ga. Sheetlet. No. O55g×6 and No. O56g £130
O56 75 c. on $3 Prince Charles and Lady Diana Spencer 60 80
aw. Wmk inverted .. .. .. 40·00
c. Surch double .. .. .. 75·00
d. Surch inverted .. .. .. 22·00
g. Error. Surch on $4 (No. 515) .. .. 70·00
O57 $1 on $4 *Britannia* 35 50
aw. Wmk inverted .. .. .. 10·00
b. Sheetlet. No. O57×6 and No. O58 .. 2·50
bw. Wmk inverted .. .. .. 80·00
c. Surch double .. .. .. 32·00
d. Surch inverted .. .. .. 7·50
e. Surch inverted (horiz pair) .. .. 21·00
f. Horiz pair, one without surch
O58 $1 on $4 Prince Charles and Lady Diana Spencer 75 90
aw. Wmk inverted .. .. .. 40·00
c. Surch double .. .. .. 80·00
d. Surch inverted .. .. .. 23·00
O53/8 .. .. .. *Set of* 6 2·40 3·00
Nos. O53d, O55e and O57e show the long surcharge, intended for Nos. O54, O56 or O58, inverted across horizontal pairs of the smaller design. Nos. O54c, O56d and O58d show two examples as Type O **5** inverted on the same stamp.

NEW INFORMATION

The editor is always interested to correspond with people who have new information that will improve or correct the Catalogue.

70¢ (O 6) — O.H.M.S. — O H M S (O 7) — O H M S (O 8)

1983 (19 Oct). *Nos.* 542/4 *surch as Type* O **6** *or optd only* ($1).
O59 70 c. on 75 c. Type **97** 60 40
O60 $1 Coat of Arms of Catherine of Aragon .. 70 50
a. Opt inverted .. .. .. 40·00
O61 $1.50 on $5 Diana, Princess of Wales .. 1·00 80
O59/61 .. .. .. *Set of* 3 2·10 1·60

1985 (12 Apr). *Nos.* 600/12 *and* 614 *opt with Type* O **7** (*horizontally on Nos.* O71/5).
O62 5 c. Type **107** 50 50
O63 10 c. Carib Grackle 50 50
O64 15 c. Moorhen 55 50
O65 20 c. Brown Booby 60 50
O66 25 c. Black-whiskered Vireo 60 50
O67 40 c. Scaly-breasted Thrasher 75 55
a. Opt double .. .. .. † —
O68 55 c. Laughing Gull 90 50
O69 70 c. Glossy Ibis .. .. .. 1·10 70
O70 90 c. Green Heron .. .. .. 1·40 70
O71 $1 Belted Kingfisher .. .. .. 1·50 60
O72 $1.15, Bananaquit .. .. .. 2·00 90
O73 $3 American Kestrel .. .. .. 3·25 3·50
O74 $5 Forest Thrush .. .. .. 4·25 3·50
O75 $10 Bridled Quail Dove .. .. .. 6·00 3·50
O62/75 .. .. .. *Set of* 14 22·00 15·00

1989 (9 May). *Nos.* 757/70 *and* 772 *optd with Type* O **8**.
O76 5 c. Type **133** 20 20
O77 10 c. Little Knobbed Scallop (*Chlamys imbricata*) 20 20
O78 15 c. Sozoni's Cone (*Conus delessertii*) .. 20 20
O79 20 c. Globular Coral Shell (*Coralliophila aberrans*) 20 20
O80 25 c. American or Common Sundial (*Architectonica nobilis*) 25 25
O81 40 c. King Helmet (*Cassis tuberosa*) .. 30 30
O82 55 c. Channelled Turban (*Turbo canaliculatus*) 40 40
O83 70 c. True Tulip (*Fasciolaria tulipa*) .. 50 50
a. Horiz pair, left-hand stamp without opt
O84 90 c. Music Volute (*Voluta musica*) .. 65 65
O85 $1 Flame Auger (*Terebra taurina*) .. 70 70
O86 $1.15, Rooster-tail Conch (*Strombus gallus*) 80 80
O87 $1.50, Queen or Pink Conch (*Strombus gigas*) 95 95
O88 $3 Teramachi's Slit Shell (*Perotrochus teramachii*) .. .. .. 1·75 1·75
O89 $5 Common or Florida Crown Conch (*Melongena corona*) .. .. .. 3·00 3·00
O90 $10 Atlantic Trumpet Triton (*Charonia variegata*) .. .. .. 5·50 5·50
O76/90 .. .. .. *Set of* 15 14·00 14·00

70¢ — OHMS

OHMS (O 9) — 70¢ (O 10)

1989 (26 May). *Nos.* 578 *and* 580/1 *surch with Type* O **9**.
O91 70 c. on 10 c. Hogfish and Neon Goby .. 1·25 1·25
O92 $1.15 on 75 c. French Grunt .. .. 1·75 1·50
O93 $1.50 on $2 Blue Chromis .. .. 2·00 2·25
O91/3 .. .. .. *Set of* 3 4·50 4·50

1992 (3 July–Nov). *Nos.* 838/41, 847/50 *and* 856/9 *surch or optd only as Type* O **10** ("OHMS" *vert on Nos.* O96, O98/9, O102/3 *and* O105) *by Benjies Printery, Antigua*.
O94 70 c. on 90 c. Type **150** .. .. 1·00 1·00
O95 70 c. on 90 c. Type **152** .. .. 1·00 1·00
a. Vert opt (11.92) .. .. ..
O96 70 c. on 90 c. Type **154** .. .. 1·00 1·00
O97 70 c. on $3.50, French Grunt .. .. 1·00 1·00
O98 $1 on $3.50, Helmet Guineafowl .. 1·25 1·25
O99 $1 on $3.50, Anthurium .. .. 1·25 1·25
O100 $1.15, Cushion Star .. .. .. 1·25 1·25
a. Vert opt (11.92) .. .. ..
O101 $1.15, Hen and Chicks .. .. 1·25 1·25
O102 $1.15, Shell Ginger .. .. .. 1·25 1·25
O103 $1.50, Rock Beauty .. .. .. 1·50 1·50
O104 $1.50, Red Junglefowl .. .. 1·50 1·50
O105 $1.50, Early Day Lily .. .. 1·50 1·50
O94/105 .. .. .. *Set of* 12 13·00 13·00

OHMS (O 11)

1993 (14 Apr). *Nos. 889/902 and 904 optd with Type* O **11** *in red.*

O106	5 c. Type **161**	30	40
O107	10 c. *Gryllus campestris* (field cricket)	30	40
O108	15 c. *Lepthemis vesiculosa* (dragonfly)	40	40
O109	20 c. *Orthemis ferruginea* (Red Skimmer)	40	40
O110	25 c. *Gerris lacustris* (pond skater)	40	40
O111	40 c. *Byctiscus betulae* (leaf weevil)	50	40
O112	55 c. *Atta texana* (Leaf-cutter Ants)	55	30
O113	70 c. *Polistes fuscatus* (Paper Wasp)	60	55
O114	90 c. *Sparmopolius fulvus* (Bee Fly)	70	60
O115	$1 *Chrysopa carnea* (lace wing)	75	60
O116	$1.15, *Phoebis philea* (butterfly)	1·00	80
O117	$1.50, *Cynthia cardui* (butterfly)	1·25	1·50
O118	$3 *Utetheisa bella* (moth)	2·00	2·50
O119	$5 *Alucita pentadactyla* (moth)	2·75	3·00
O120	$10 *Heliconius melpomene* (butterfly)	4·75	5·50
O106/20	*Set of* 15	15·00	16·00

Morocco Agencies

(British Post Offices)

With the growth of trade and commerce during the 19th century European powers opened post offices or postal agencies in various ports along the Moroccan coast from the early 1850's onwards. French and, in the north, Spanish influence eventually became predominant, leading to the protectorates of 1912. The British, who had inaugurated a regular postal service between Gibraltar and Tangier or Tetuan in May 1778, established their first postal agency in 1857. German offices followed around the turn of the century.

Before 1892 there was no indigenous postal service and those towns where there was no foreign agency were served by a number of private local posts which continued to flourish until 1900. In November 1892 the Sultan of Morocco established the Cherifian postal service, but this was little used until after its reorganization at the end of 1911. The Sultan's post was absorbed by the French postal service on 1 October 1913. Issues of the local posts and of the Sultan's post can occasionally be found used on cover in combination with stamps of Gibraltar or the Morocco Agencies.

In 1857 the first British postal agency was established at Tangier within the precincts of the Legation and was run by the official interpreter. From 1 March 1858 all letters for Great Britain sent via the British mail packets from Gibraltar required franking with Great Britain stamps.

In 1872 the Tangier office was relocated away from the Legation and the interpreter was appointed British Postal Agent. At the same time the agency was placed under the control of the Gibraltar postmaster. When the colonial posts became independent of the British G.P.O. on 1 January 1886 Gibraltar retained responsibility for the Morocco Agencies. Further offices, each under the control of the local Vice-Consul, were opened from 1886 onwards.

I. GIBRALTAR USED IN MOROCCO

Details of the various agencies are given below. Type C, the "A26" killer, is very similar to postmarks used at Gibraltar during this period. In addition to the town name postmarks as Types A, B and D from Fez, Mazagan, Saffi and Tetuan were also inscribed "MOROCCO".

Postmark Types used on Gibraltar issues.

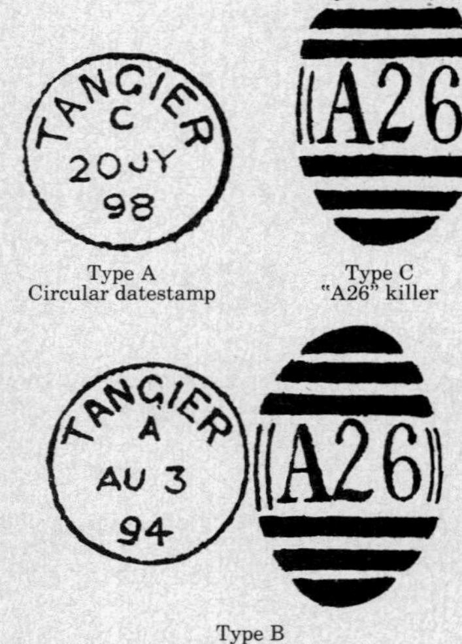

Type A
Circular datestamp

Type C
"A26" killer

Type B
Duplex cancellation

Type D
Registered oval

BISECTS. The 10 c., 40 c. and 50 c. values of the 1889 surcharges and of the 1889–96 issue are known bisected and used for half their value from various of the Morocco Agencies. These bisects were never authorised by the Gibraltar Post Office.

CASABLANCA

The British postal agency opened on 1 January 1887 and was initially supplied with ½d., 4d. and 6d. stamps from the Gibraltar 1886 overprinted on Bermuda issue and 1d., 2d. and 2½d. values from the 1886–87 set.

Stamps of GIBRALTAR *cancelled with Types* A (*without code or code* "C"), B (*without code or code* "A") *or* D.

1886. *Optd on Bermuda* (*Nos.* 1/7).

Z1	½d. dull green	48·00
Z2	4d. orange-brown	£250
Z3	6d. deep lilac	£250

1886–87. *Queen Victoria £sd issue* (*Nos.* 8/14).

Z 4	½d. dull green	24·00
Z 5	1d. rose	26·00
Z 6	2d. brown-purple	55·00
Z 7	2½d. blue	35·00
Z 8	4d. orange-brown	85·00
Z10	1s. bistre	£250

1889. *Surch in Spanish currency* (*Nos.* 15/21).

Z11	5 c. on ½d. green	40·00
Z12	10 c. on 1d. rose	35·00
Z13	25 c. on 2d. brown-purple	45·00
Z14	25 c. on 2½d. bright blue	30·00
Z15	40 c. on 4d. orange-brown	90·00
Z16	50 c. on 6d. bright lilac	85·00
Z17	75 c. on 1s. bistre	£110

1889–96. *Queen Victoria Spanish currency issue* (*Nos.* 22/33).

Z18	5 c. green	11·00
Z19	10 c. carmine	11·00
Z20	20 c. olive-green and brown	25·00
Z22	25 c. ultramarine	11·00
Z23	40 c. orange-brown	28·00
Z24	50 c. bright lilac	22·00
Z25	75 c. olive-green	65·00
Z26	1 p. bistre	55·00
Z28	1 p. bistre and ultramarine	28·00
Z29	2 p. black and carmine	42·00

FEZ

The British postal agency in this inland town opened on 24 February 1892 and was initially supplied with stamps up to the 50 c. value from the Gibraltar 1889–96 issue.

Stamps of GIBRALTAR *cancelled with Types* A (*without code*) *or* D.

1889–96. *Queen Victoria Spanish currency issue* (*Nos.* 22/33).

Z31	5 c. green	24·00
Z32	10 c. carmine	26·00
Z33	20 c. olive-green and brown	45·00
Z35	25 c. ultramarine	38·00
Z36	40 c. orange-brown	65·00
Z37	50 c. bright lilac	48·00

LARAICHE

The British postal agency at Laraiche opened in March 1886, although the first postmark, an "A26" killer, was not supplied until May.

Stamps of GIBRALTAR *cancelled with Types* B (*without code*) *or* D.

1886. *Optd on Bermuda* (*Nos.* 1/7).

Z39	½d. dull green	
Z40	1d. rose-red	
Z41	2½d. ultramarine	

1886–87. *Queen Victoria £sd issue* (*Nos.* 8/14).

Z42	½d. dull green	75·00
Z43	1d. rose	75·00
Z45	2½d. blue	80·00

1889. *Surch in Spanish currency* (*Nos.* 15/21).

Z47	5 c. on ½d. green	50·00
Z48	10 c. on 1d. rose	
Z49	25 c. on 2½d. bright blue	

It is believed that the other surcharges in this series were not supplied to Laraiche.

1889–96. *Queen Victoria Spanish currency issue* (*Nos.* 22/33).

Z50	5 c. green	24·00
Z51	10 c. carmine	32·00
Z52	20 c. olive-green and brown	
Z54	25 c. ultramarine	32·00
Z55	40 c. orange-brown	
Z56	50 c. bright-lilac	70·00
Z57	1 p. bistre and ultramarine	

MAZAGAN

This was the main port for the inland city of Marrakesh. The British postal agency opened on 1 March 1888 and was initially supplied with stamps from the Gibraltar 1886–87 series.

Stamps of GIBRALTAR *cancelled with Types* A (*codes* "A" *or* "C") *or* D (*without code, code* "A" *or code* "C").

1886–87. *Queen Victoria £sd issue* (*Nos.* 8/14).

Z58	½d. dull green	22·00
Z59	1d. rose	22·00
Z60	2d. brown-purple	
Z61	2½d. blue	28·00
Z62	4d. orange-brown	90·00
Z63	6d. lilac	£110

1889. *Surch in Spanish currency* (*Nos.* 15/21).

Z64	5 c. on ½d. green	
Z65	10 c. on 1d. rose	
Z66	25 c. on 2½d. bright blue	

It is believed that the other surcharges in this series were not supplied to Mazagan.

1889–96. *Queen Victoria Spanish currency issue* (*Nos.* 22/33).

Z67	5 c. green	17·00
Z68	10 c. carmine	15·00
Z69	20 c. olive-green and brown	45·00
Z70	25 c. ultramarine	38·00
Z71	40 c. orange-brown	65·00
Z72	50 c. bright lilac	
Z74	1 p. bistre and ultramarine	
Z75	2 p. black and carmine	

MOGADOR

The British postal agency at this port opened in May 1887 and was initially supplied with stamps from the Gibraltar 1886–87 series.

Stamps of GIBRALTAR *cancelled with Types* A (*code* "C"), B (*code* "C") *or* D.

1886–87. *Queen Victoria £sd issue* (*Nos.* 8/14).

Z76	½d. dull green	24·00
Z77	1d. rose	32·00
Z78	2d. brown-purple	55·00
Z79	2½d. blue	32·00

1889. *Surch in Spanish currency* (*Nos.* 15/21).

Z80	5 c. on ½d. green	38·00
Z81	10 c. on 1d. rose	38·00
Z82	25 c. on 2½d. bright blue	38·00

It is believed that the other surcharges in this series were not supplied to Mogador.

1889–96. *Queen Victoria Spanish currency issue* (*Nos.* 22/33).

Z83	5 c. green	11·00
Z84	10 c. carmine	13·00
Z85	20 c. olive-green and brown	
Z87	25 c. ultramarine	17·00
Z88	40 c. orange-brown	27·00
Z89	50 c. bright lilac	27·00

RABAT

The British postal agency at this port on the north-west coast of Morocco opened in March 1886, although the first cancellation, an "A26" killer, was not supplied until May. The initial stock of stamps was from the Gibraltar 1886 overprinted on Bermuda issue.

Stamps of GIBRALTAR *cancelled with Types* B (*code* "O") *or* D.

1886. *Optd on Bermuda* (*Nos.* 1/7).

Z92	½d. dull green	
Z93	1d. rose-red	
Z94	2½d. ultramarine	£110

1886–87. *Queen Victoria £sd issue* (*Nos.* 8/14).

Z 95	½d. dull green	24·00
Z 96	1d. rose	24·00
Z 97	2d. brown-purple	60·00
Z 98	2½d. blue	35·00
Z101	1s. bistre	£300

1889. *Surch in Spanish currency* (*Nos.* 15/21).

Z102	5 c. on ½d. green	42·00
Z103	10 c. on 1d. rose	38·00
Z104	25 c. on 2½d. bright blue	42·00

It is believed that the other surcharges in this series were not supplied to Rabat.

1889–96. *Queen Victoria Spanish currency issue* (*Nos.* 22/33).

Z105	5 c. green	16·00
Z106	10 c. carmine	16·00
Z107	20 c. olive-green and brown	35·00
Z108	25 c. ultramarine	17·00
Z109	40 c. orange-brown	38·00
Z110	50 c. bright lilac	35·00

SAFFI

The British postal agency at this port opened on 1 July 1891 and was supplied with stamps from the Gibraltar 1889–96 series.

Stamps of GIBRALTAR *cancelled with Types* B (*code* "C") *or* D (*code* "C").

1889–96. *Queen Victoria Spanish currency issue* (*Nos.* 22/33).

Z111	5 c. green	16·00
Z112	10 c. carmine	16·00
Z113	20 c. olive-green and brown	38·00
Z115	25 c. ultramarine	18·00
Z116	40 c. orange-brown	65·00
Z117	50 c. bright lilac	45·00
Z118	1 p. bistre and ultramarine	50·00
Z119	2 p. black and carmine	60·00

TANGIER

The British postal agency in Tangier opened on 1 April 1857 and from 1 March of the following year letters from it sent via the packet service to Great Britain required franking with Great Britain stamps.

No identifiable postmark was supplied to Tangier until 1872 and all earlier mail was cancelled with one of the Gibraltar marks. In April 1872 a postmark as Type A was supplied on which the "N" of "TANGIER" was reversed. A corrected version, with code letter "A", followed in 1878, but both were used as origin or arrival marks and the Great Britain stamps continued to be cancelled with Gibraltar obliterators. The Type A postmarks generally fell into disuse after 1880 and very few identifiable marks occur on mail from Tangier until the introduction of Gibraltar stamps in 1886.

Stamps of GIBRALTAR *cancelled with Types* A (*codes* "A" *or* "C"), B (*code* "A") *or* D.

1886. *Optd on Bermuda* (*Nos.* 1/7).
Z120 ½d. dull green .. .. 40·00
Z121 1d. rose-red .. .. 50·00
Z122 2d. purple-brown £130
Z123 2½d. ultramarine .. .. 40·00
Z124 4d. orange-brown £160
Z125 6d. deep lilac £200
Z126 1s. yellow-brown £500

1886–87. *Queen Victoria £sd issue* (*Nos.* 8/14).
Z127 ½d. dull green .. .. 15·00
Z128 1d. rose .. .. 15·00
Z129 2d. brown-purple .. .. 40·00
Z130 2½d. blue .. .. 25·00
Z131 4d. orange-brown .. .. 70·00
Z132 6d. lilac £100
Z133 1s. bistre £225

1889. *Surch in Spanish currency* (*Nos.* 15/21).
Z134 5 c. on ½d. green .. .. 24·00
Z135 10 c. on 1d. rose .. .. 17·00
Z136 25 c. on 2d. brown-purple .. .. 30·00
Z137 25 c. on 2½d. bright blue .. .. 25·00
Z138 40 c. on 4d. orange-brown .. .. 85·00
Z139 50 c. on 6d. bright lilac .. .. 80·00
Z140 75 c. on 1s. bistre £100

1889–96. *Queen Victoria Spanish currency issue* (*Nos.* 22/33).
Z141 5 c. green .. .. 5·00
Z142 10 c. carmine .. .. 5·00
Z143 20 c. olive-green and brown .. .. 18·00
Z144 20 c. olive-green .. .. 45·00
Z145 25 c. ultramarine .. .. 8·00
Z146 40 c. orange-brown .. .. 10·00
Z147 50 c. bright lilac .. .. 9·00
Z148 75 c. olive-green .. .. 45·00
Z149 1 p. bistre .. .. 50·00
Z150 1 p. bistre and ultramarine .. .. 15·00
Z151 2 p. black and carmine .. .. 35·00
Z152 5 p. slate-grey .. .. 95·00

TETUAN

The British postal agency in this northern town was opened in 1890 and was supplied with stamps from the Gibraltar 1889–96 series.

Stamps of GIBRALTAR *cancelled with Types* A (*code* "C"), B (*code* "C" *often inverted*) *or* D (*code* "C").

1889–96. *Queen Victoria Spanish currency issue* (*Nos.* 22/33).
Z153 5 c. green .. .. 18·00
Z154 10 c. carmine .. .. 25·00
Z155 20 c. olive-green and brown .. .. 42·00
Z157 25 c. ultramarine .. .. 28·00
Z158 40 c. orange-brown .. .. 45·00
Z159 50 c. bright lilac .. .. 48·00
Z161 1 p. bistre and ultramarine .. ..

PRICES FOR STAMPS ON COVER TO 1945

Nos. 1/16	*from* × 7
Nos. 17/30	*from* × 3
Nos. 31/74	*from* × 3
Nos. 75/6	*from* × 4
Nos. 112/24	*from* × 4
No. 125	—
Nos. 126/35	*from* × 5
Nos. 136/42	*from* × 2
Nos. 143/59	*from* × 3
Nos. 160/75	*from* × 8
Nos. 191/9	*from* × 5
Nos. 200/1	*from* × 3
Nos. 202/11	*from* × 4
Nos. 212/15	*from* × 5
Nos. 216/24	*from* × 8
Nos. 225/6	*from* × 2
Nos. 227/30	*from* × 8
Nos. 231/52	*from* × 6

The above prices apply to stamps used on cover from Morocco. Examples of Nos. 31/76 and 231/52 used on cover in Great Britain after 1950 have little additional value.

II. GIBRALTAR ISSUES OVERPRINTED

With the reversion of Gibraltar to sterling in 1898 it became necessary to provide separate issues for the Morocco Agencies which continued to use Spanish currency.

The following were used in all the British postal agencies.

Morocco Agencies (1) **Morocco Agencies** (2)

Agencies — Inverted "V" for "A" (Right-hand pane R.6/6)

Agencies — Long tail to "S" (Right-hand pane R.8/2)

Broken "M" (Pl 2 R. 4/5)

Flat top to "C" (Pl 2 R. 4/4)

1898 (1 June)–**1900.** *Nos.* 22/8 *and* 31/2 (*Queen Victoria*) *of Gibraltar optd with T* 1 (*wide* "M" *and ear of* "g" *projecting upwards*), *in black at* Gibraltar Chronicle *office.*
1 5 c. green .. .. 1·00 90
a. Inverted "V" for "A" .. .. .. 21·00 24·00
b. Long tail to "S" .. .. .. 21·00 24·00
c. Broken "M" in "CENTIMOS" .. .. 25·00
2 10 c. carmine .. .. 1·50 20
b. Bisected (5 c.) (on cover) .. .. † £1100
c. Inverted "V" for "A" £225 £275
d. Long tail to "S" £225
e. Lines of opt 5 mm apart (6.00) .. .. 2·75 1·75
ea. Opt double £500
3 20 c. olive-green and brown .. .. .. 3·00 1·25
a. Inverted "V" for "A" .. .. .. 30·00 30·00
b. Long tail to "S" .. .. .. 30·00 30·00
3*c* 20 c. olive-green .. .. 4·00 4·50
ca. Opt double £450
cb. Inverted "V" for "A" .. .. .. 35·00 40·00
cc. Long tail to "S" .. .. .. 35·00 40·00
cd. Flat top to "C" in "CENTIMOS" .. 40·00
4 25 c. ultramarine .. .. 2·00 60
a. Inverted "V" for "A" £100 £120
b. Long tail to "S" £100 £120
5 40 c. orange-brown (2.6.98) .. .. .. 3·25 3·25
a. Inverted "V" for "A" £150 £180
b. Long tail to "S" £150 £180
c. Blue opt (7.98) .. .. .. 30·00 32·00
6 50 c. bright blue (2.6.98) .. .. .. 14·00 23·00
a. Inverted "V" for "A" £250 £275
b. Long tail to "S" £250 £275
c. Blue opt (7.98) .. .. .. 9·50 12·00
7 1 p. bistre and ultramarine (2.6.98) .. 9·50 22·00
a. Inverted "V" for "A" £180 £250
b. Long tail to "S" £180 £250
c. Blue opt (7.98) £140 £180
8 2 p. black and carmine (4.6.98) .. .. 9·50 23·00
a. Inverted "V" for "A" £225 £275
b. Long tail to "S" £225 £275
1/8 .. .. *Set of* 8 35·00 60·00

The blue overprint can be easily distinguished by looking through the stamp in front of a strong light.

The listed varieties of overprint occur from the first setting. They were corrected on the second setting of July 1898, which produced Nos. 5c, 6c, 7c and further supplies of No. 8. The corrected type was subsequently used to produce additional stocks of Nos. 1/2. Numerous more minor varieties exist from these settings.

No. 2e comes from two further printings in 1900 using a third setting on which the two lines of the overprint were 5 mm apart instead of the 4 mm space used previously.

Agencies — "CD" sideways flaw (Left-hand pane R.1/5)

Morocco — Broad top to "M" (Left-hand pane R.7/3)

Agencies — Hyphen between "nc" (Right-hand pane R.3/5)

1899 (Feb)–**1902.** *Nos.* 22/3, 25/8 *and* 31/2 (*Queen Victoria*) *of Gibraltar optd with T* 2 (*narrow* "M" *and ear of* "g" *horizontal*), *in black by D.L.R., London.*
9 5 c. green (4.99) 30 20
a. "CD" sideways .. .. .. 11·00 11·00
b. Broad top to "M" .. .. .. 8·00 8·00
c. Hyphen between "nc" .. .. .. 8·00 8·00
d. Broken "M" in "CENTIMOS" .. .. 10·00
10 10 c. carmine 35 20
a. "CD" sideways .. .. .. 11·00 11·00
b. Broad top to "M" .. .. .. 8·00 8·00
c. Hyphen between "nc" .. .. .. 8·00 8·00
d. Opt double £700 £700
11 20 c. olive-green (5.02) .. .. .. 3·00 70
b. Broad top to "M" .. .. .. 24·00 24·00
c. Hyphen between "nc" .. .. .. 24·00 24·00
d. Flat top to "C" in "CENTIMOS" .. 27·00
12 25 c. ultramarine (10.99) .. .. .. 4·75 90
a. "CD" sideways .. .. .. 35·00 35·00
b. Broad top to "M" .. .. .. 30·00 30·00
c. Hyphen between "nc" .. .. .. 30·00 30·00
13 40 c. orange-brown (3.02) .. .. .. 32·00 20·00
b. Broad top to "M" £160 £160
c. Hyphen between "nc" £160 £160
14 50 c. bright lilac (4.99) .. .. .. 5·50 3·50
b. Broad top to "M" .. .. .. 90·00 £110
c. Hyphen between "nc" .. .. .. 90·00 £110
15 1 p. bistre and ultramarine (4.99) .. .. 19·00 26·00
b. Broad top to "M" £120 £150
c. Hyphen between "nc" £120 £150
16 2 p. black and carmine (3.01) .. .. 30·00 45·00
b. Broad top to "M" £250 £325
c. Hyphen between "nc" £250 £325
9/16 .. .. *Set of* 8 85·00 85·00
9/16 Optd "Specimen" .. .. *Set of* 8 £180

1903–5. *As Nos.* 46/51 (*King Edward VII*) *of Gibraltar, but with value in Spanish currency, optd with T* 2. *Wmk Crown CA. P* 14.
17 5 c. grey-green and green (1.03) .. .. 4·75 1·75
a. "CD" sideways .. .. .. 32·00 32·00
b. Broad top to "M" .. .. .. 32·00 32·00
c. Hyphen between "nc" .. .. .. 32·00 32·00
18 10 c. dull purple/*red* (8.03) .. .. .. 4·25 30
a. "CD" sideways .. .. .. 30·00 30·00
b. Broad top to "M" .. .. .. 30·00 30·00
c. Hyphen between "nc" .. .. .. 30·00 30·00
w. Wmk inverted .. .. ..
19 20 c. grey-green and carmine (9.04) .. 9·00 42·00
a. "CD" sideways .. .. .. 65·00 £130
b. Broad top to "M" .. .. .. 65·00 £130
c. Hyphen between "nc" .. .. .. 65·00 £130
20 25 c. purple and black/*blue* (1.7.03) .. 3·50 15
a. "CD" sideways .. .. .. 35·00 35·00
b. Broad top to "M" .. .. .. 35·00 35·00
c. Hyphen between "nc" .. .. .. 35·00 35·00
21 50 c. purple and violet (3.7.05) .. .. 75·00 £150
a. "CD" sideways £300 £475
b. Broad top to "M" £300 £475
c. Hyphen between "nc" £300 £475
22 1 p. black and carmine (19.11.05) .. .. 45·00 £150
a. "CD" sideways £225 £450
b. Broad top to "M" £225 £450
c. Hyphen between "nc" £225 £450
23 2 p. black and blue (19.11.05) .. .. 50·00 £120
a. "CD" sideways £250 £425
b. Broad top to "M" £250 £425
c. Hyphen between "nc" £250 £425
17/23 .. .. *Set of* 7 £170 £425
17/23 Optd "Specimen" .. .. *Set of* 7 £180

Examples of Nos. 19 and 21/3 are known showing a forged Registered Mazagan postmark dated "15 SP 10".

1905 (Jan)–**06.** *As Nos.* 17/23 *but wmk Mult Crown CA. Ordinary paper* (5, 10, 20 *c.*) *or chalk-surfaced paper* (*others*).
24 5 c. grey-green and green (4.05) .. .. 3·50 2·50
a. "CD" sideways .. .. .. 30·00 30·00
b. Broad top to "M" .. .. .. 30·00 30·00
c. Hyphen between "nc" £600 £650
d. Chalk-surfaced paper (1.06) .. .. 3·50 2·50
da. "CD" sideways .. .. .. 30·00 30·00
db. Broad top to "M" .. .. .. 30·00 30·00
25 10 c. dull purple/*red* .. .. .. 4·25 70
a. "CD" sideways .. .. .. 30·00 23·00
b. Broad top to "M" .. .. .. 30·00 23·00
cw. Wmk inverted .. .. ..
d. Chalk-surfaced paper (12.05) .. .. 1·50 70
da. "CD" sideways .. .. .. 20·00 20·00
db. Broad top to "M" .. .. .. 20·00 20·00
26 20 c. grey-green and carmine (1.06) .. .. 2·50 25·00
a. "CD" sideways .. .. .. 32·00 95·00
b. Broad top to "M" .. .. .. 32·00 95·00
27 25 c. purple and black/*blue* (6.06) .. .. 25·00 5·50
a. "CD" sideways £160 £110
b. Broad top to "M" £160 £110
28 50 c. purple and violet (7.06) .. .. 6·00 29·00
a. "CD" sideways £130 £200
b. Broad top to "M" £130 £200
29 1 p. black and carmine (11.05) .. .. 23·00 75·00
a. "CD" sideways £180 £300
b. Broad top to "M" £180 £300
30 2 p. black and blue (11.05) .. .. 15·00 32·00
a. "CD" sideways £160 £225
b. Broad top to "M" £160 £225
24/30 .. .. *Set of* 7 65·00 £150

Examples of Nos. 26 and 28/30 are known showing a forged Registered Mazagan postmark dated "15 SP 10".

Control of the British postal agencies in Morocco returned to the G.P.O., London, from 1 January 1907.

All the following issues are overprinted on Great Britain

III. BRITISH CURRENCY

Stamps overprinted "MOROCCO AGENCIES" only were primarily intended for use on parcels (and later, air-mail correspondence), and were on sale at British P.Os throughout Morocco including Tangier, until 1937.

PRICES. Our prices for used stamps with these overprints are for specimens used in Morocco. These stamps could be used in the United Kingdom, with official sanction, from the summer of 1950 onwards with U.K. postmarks are worth about 50 per cent less.

MOROCCO AGENCIES (4) **MOROCCO AGENCIES** (5) **MOROCCO AGENCIES** (6)

1907 (30 Apr)–**13.** *King Edward VII optd as T* 4 *or* 5 (2*s.* 6*d.*).

(*a*) *De La Rue printings. Ordinary paper* (½*d.*, 1*d.*, 4*d.* (*No.* 35) *or chalk-surfaced paper* (*others*)
31 ½d. pale yellowish green (1.6.07) .. .. 1·25 6·50
32 1d. scarlet (5.5.07) .. .. .. 5·50 3·75
33 2d. pale grey-green and carmine-red .. 4·50 4·50
34 4d. green and chocolate-brown (29.10.07) 3·75 3·25
35 4d. pale orange (3.12) .. .. .. 6·50 6·50
a. Orange-red .. .. .. 6·50 6·50
36 6d. pale dull purple (5.5.07) .. .. 10·00 12·00
a. Dull purple .. .. .. 10·00 12·00
37 1s. dull green and carmine (5.5.07) .. 22·00 16·00
38 2s. 6d. pale dull purple (5.5.07) .. .. 60·00 95·00
a. Dull purple .. .. .. 60·00 £100
31/8 .. .. *Set of* 8 £100 £130
37/8 Optd "Specimen" .. .. *Set of* 2 £140

(*b*) *Harrison printing. Ordinary paper*
40 4d. bright orange (No. 286) (1913) .. 11·00 18·00

(*c*) *Somerset House printing. Ordinary paper*
41 2s. 6d. dull greyish purple (No. 315) (1913) 80·00 £140

1914–31. *King George V.*

(*a*) *W* 100 (*Simple Cypher*). *Optd with T* 4
42 ½d. green .. .. 1·50 45
43 1d. scarlet 60 10
44 1½d. red-brown (1921) .. .. .. 1·75 11·00
45 2d. orange (Die I) .. .. 1·50 35
46 3d. bluish violet (1921) .. .. .. 1·00 35
47 4d. grey-green (1921) .. .. .. 1·75 70

48 6d. reddish purple (*chalk-surfaced paper*) (1921) .. .. 3·50 13·00
49 1s. bistre-brown (1917) .. .. 5·00 75
a. Opt triple, two albino .. .. .. 95·00

(*b*) *W* **110** (*Single Cypher*). *Optd with T* **6**.

50 2s. 6d. sepia-brown (*Waterlow ptg*) (No. 400) (1914) .. .. 38·00 48·00
a. Re-entry (R. 2/1) £550 £550
b. Opt double, one albino £150
51 2s. 6d. yellow-brown (*D.L.R. ptg*) (No. 406) (1917) .. .. 40·00 28·00
a. Opt double £1500 £1000
b. Pale brown (No. 407) .. .. .. 28·00 48·00
53 2s. 6d. chocolate-brown (*B.W. ptg*) (No. 414) 32·00 25·00
a. Opt double, one albino* £150
54 5s. rose-red (*B.W. ptg*) (No. 416) (1931) 48·00 75·00
a. Opt triple, two albino
42/54 .. .. *Set of* 10 85·00 £110
49/50, 54 Optd "Specimen" .. *Set of* 3 £200

*The albino overprint is quite clear, with the "MOROCCO" appearing just below "AGENCIES" of the normal overprint and a little to the right as seen from the back. There is also a second faint albino impression just below the normal overprint.

MOROCCO AGENCIES (7) S (A) MOROCCO AGENCIES (8) S (B)

(A) Opt 14 mm long; ends of "s" cut off diagonally.
(B) Opt 15½ mm long; ends of "s" cut off horizontally

1925–36. *King George V* (*W* **111** (*Block Cypher*)) *optd with T* **7** (A) *or T* **8** (B).

		A		B	
55	½d. green	60	30	3·50	26·00
	w. Wmk inverted	75·00	—		†
56	1½d. chestnut (1931)	9·00	13·00		†
57	2d. orange	2·00	1·00		†
58	2½d. blue	2·00	5·00	£100	30·00
59	4d. grey-green (1.36)		†	4·25	30·00
60	6d. purple (1931)	2·00	8·50	55	60
61	1s. bistre-brown	15·00	5·00	50·00	55·00
55/61 (*cheapest*)	*Set of* 7	29·00	50·00		
61A Optd "Specimen"		60·00			

1935 (8 May). *Silver Jubilee* (*Nos.* 453/6) *optd* "MOROCCO AGENCIES" *only, as in T* **17**.

62 ½d. green (B.) .. .. 1·25 4·00
63 1d. scarlet (B.) .. .. 1·25 4·50
64 1½d. red-brown (B.) .. .. .. 1·50 9·00
65 2½d. blue (R.) .. .. 1·50 2·50
62/5 .. .. *Set of* 4 5·00 18·00

1935–37. *King George V.* (*a*) *Harrison photo ptgs* (*Nos.* 440/5 *and* 449). *W* **111** (*Block Cypher*). *Optd with T* **8**.

66 1d. scarlet (4.35) .. .. .. 3·25 6·00
67 1½d. red-brown (28.4.36) .. .. 2·25 10·00
68 2d. orange (1.5.36) .. .. .. 40 3·50
69 2½d. ultramarine (11.2.36) .. .. 1·75 4·25
70 3d. violet (2.3.36) 40 20
71 4d. deep grey-green (14.5.36) 40 20
72 1s. bistre-brown (31.8.36) .. .. 80 1·25

(*b*) *Waterlow re-engraved ptgs. W* **110** (*Single Cypher*) *optd with T* **6**

73 2s. 6d. chocolate-brown (No. 450) .. 35·00 42·00
74 5s. bright rose-red (No. 451) (2.3.37) .. 23·00 80·00
66/74 .. .. *Set of* 9 60·00 £130
72/3 Optd "Specimen" .. *Set of* 2 £130

1936 (26 Oct)–**37**. *King Edward VIII, optd* "MOROCCO AGENCIES" *only, as in T* **18**.
A. MOROCCO 14½ mm long.
B. MOROCCO 15¼ mm long (5.1.37)

		A		B	
75	1d. scarlet	10	30	4·50	9·50
76	2½d. bright blue	10	15	80	4·25

The first two printings of both values showed all the stamps with the short overprint, Nos. 75A/6A.

On 5 January 1937 a further printing of both values was placed on sale in London which had 24 stamps, 24 in all, from the bottom two horizontal rows (Rows 19 and 20) with the long overprint, Nos. 75B/6B. Subsequent printings increased the number of long overprints in the sheet to 25 by the addition of R. 8/9, and, finally, to 31 (R. 1/7, R. 7/1, R. 8/1, R. 13/3, 4 and 10, R 14/6, but without R. 8/9).

For the 1d. value all sheets from cylinder 2 show the first setting. Sheets from cylinder 6 were also used for the first, and for all subsequent settings. The 2½d. value was overprinted on sheets from cylinder 2 throughout.

From 3 June 1937 unoverprinted stamps of Great Britain were supplied to the post offices at Tangier and Tetuan (Spanish Zone) as local stocks of issues overprinted "MOROCCO AGENCIES" were exhausted.

Type E Type F

Stamps of GREAT BRITAIN *cancelled as Types* E *or* F *at Tangier.*

1937. *King George V photo and re-engraved issues.*

Z170 1½d. red-brown (No. 441) .. .. ..
Z171 2d. orange (No. 442) .. .. ..
Z172 3d. violet (No. 444) .. .. ..
Z173 4d. deep grey-green (No. 445) .. .. 8·00
Z174 6d. purple (No. 426*a*) .. .. .. 8·00
Z175 1s. bistre-brown (No. 449) .. .. 30·00
Z176 2s. 6d. chocolate-brown (No. 450) .. 60·00
Z177 5s. bright rose-red (No. 451) .. ..

1937–39. *King George VI* (*Nos.* 462/75).

Z178 ½d. green .. .. ..
Z179 1d. scarlet .. .. ..
Z180 1½d. red-brown .. .. ..
Z181 2d. orange .. .. ..
Z182 2½d. ultramarine .. .. ..
Z183 3d. violet .. .. .. 8·00
Z184 4d. grey-green .. .. .. 8·00
Z185 5d. brown .. .. ..
Z186 6d. purple .. .. .. 5·00
Z187 7d. emerald-green .. .. ..
Z188 8d. bright carmine .. .. ..
Z189 9d. deep olive-green .. .. 10·00
Z190 10d. turquoise-blue .. .. ..
Z191 1s. bistre-brown .. .. .. 5·00

1939–42. *King George VI* (*Nos.* 476/8*a*).

Z192 2s. 6d. brown .. .. .. 35·00
Z193 2s. 6d. yellow-green .. .. 12·00
Z194 5s. red .. .. .. 18·00
Z195 10s. dark blue .. .. .. 70·00
Z196 10s. ultramarine .. .. .. 30·00

1941–42. *King George VI pale colours* (*Nos.* 485/90).

Z197 ½d. pale green .. .. ..
Z198 1d. pale scarlet .. .. ..
Z199 1½d. pale red-brown .. .. ..
Z200 2d. pale orange .. .. ..
Z201 2½d. light ultramarine .. .. ..
Z202 3d. pale violet .. .. .. 5·00

1946. *Victory* (*Nos.* 491/2).

Z203 2½d. ultramarine .. .. .. 7·00
Z204 3d. violet .. .. .. 7·00

Type G

Stamps of GREAT BRITAIN *cancelled as Type* G *at Tetuan.*

1937. *King George V.*

Z209 6d. purple (No. 426*a*) .. .. ..
Z210 1s. bistre-brown (No. 449) .. .. ..

1937–39. *King George VI* (*Nos.* 465/75)

Z211 2d. orange .. .. ..
Z212 2½d. ultramarine .. .. ..
Z213 3d. violet .. .. ..
Z214 4d. grey-green .. .. ..
Z215 6d. purple .. .. .. 10·00
Z216 9d. deep olive-green .. .. ..
Z217 1s. bistre-brown .. .. .. 10·00

1939–42. *King George VI* (*Nos.* 476/7).

Z218 2s. 6d. brown .. .. ..
Z219 2s. 6d. yellow-green .. .. 30·00
Z220 5s. red .. .. .. 40·00

1941. *King George VI pale colours* (*Nos.* 485/90).

Z221 ½d. pale green .. .. ..
Z222 2d. pale orange .. .. ..
Z223 2½d. light ultramarine .. .. ..
Z224 3d. pale violet .. .. .. 10·00

Other unoverprinted stamps of Great Britain are known with Morocco Agencies postmarks during this period, but it is believed that only Nos. Z170/224 were sold by the local post offices.

The use of unoverprinted stamps in Tangier ceased with the issue of Nos. 261/75 on 1 January 1949. Stamps overprinted "MOROCCO AGENCIES" replaced the unoverprinted values at Tetuan on 16 August 1949.

MOROCCO AGENCIES (9) MOROCCO AGENCIES (10)

1949 (16 Aug). *King George VI, optd with T* **9** *or* **10** (2*s.* 6*d.*, 5*s.*).

77 ½d. pale green .. .. .. 1·75 5·00
78 1d. pale scarlet .. .. .. 2·75 7·00
79 1½d. pale red-brown .. .. .. 2·75 6·50
80 2d. pale orange .. .. .. 3·00 7·00
81 2½d. light ultramarine .. .. 3·25 8·00
82 3d. pale violet .. .. .. 1·50 1·10
83 4d. grey-green 45 70
84 5d. brown .. .. .. 3·00 13·00
85 6d. purple .. .. .. 1·50 1·00
86 7d. emerald-green .. .. .. 40 14·00
87 8d. bright carmine .. .. .. 3·00 5·00
88 9d. deep olive-green .. .. .. 40 9·50
89 10d. turquoise-blue .. .. .. 40 4·50
90 11d. plum .. .. .. 70 4·50
91 1s. bistre-brown .. .. .. 2·75 4·50
92 2s. 6d. yellow-green .. .. 10·00 26·00
93 5s. red .. .. .. 28·00 48·00
77/93 .. .. *Set of* 17 60·00 £150

1951 (3 May). *King George VI* (*Nos.* 503/7, 509/10), *optd with T* **9** *or* **10** (2*s.* 6*d.*, 5*s.*).

94 ½d. pale orange .. .. .. 1·75 40
95 1d. light ultramarine .. .. 1·75 50
96 1½d. pale green .. .. .. 1·75 1·00
97 2d. pale red-brown .. .. .. 1·75 2·75
98 2½d. pale scarlet .. .. .. 1·75 2·25
99 2s. 6d. yellow-green (H.M.S. *Victory*) .. 11·00 16·00
100 5s. red (Dover) .. .. .. 11·00 17·00
94/100 .. .. .. *Set of* 7 28·00 35·00

1952–55. *Queen Elizabeth II. W* **153** (*Tudor Crown*). *Optd with T* **9**.

101 ½d. orange-red (31.8.53) 10 10
102 1d. ultramarine (31.8.53) 15 80
103 1½d. green (5.12.52) 15 20
104 2d. red-brown (31.8.53) 20 90
105 2½d. carmine-red (5.12.52) 15 40
106 4d. ultramarine (1.3.55) .. .. 85 3·00
107 5d. brown (6.7.53) 65 60
108 6d. reddish purple (1.3.55) .. .. 85 3·00
109 8d. magenta (6.7.53) .. .. 70 1·00
110 1s. bistre-brown (6.7.53) 70 60
101/10 .. .. .. *Set of* 10 4·00 9·50

1956 (10 Sept). *Queen Elizabeth II. W* **165** (*St. Edward's Crown*). *Optd with T* **9**.

111 2½d. carmine-red (No. 544) .. .. 55 2·50

Stamps overprinted "MOROCCO AGENCIES" were withdrawn from sale on 31 December 1956.

IV. SPANISH CURRENCY

Stamps surcharged in Spanish currency were sold at British P.Os. throughout Morocco until the establishment of the French Zone and the Tangier International Zone, when their use was confined to the Spanish Zone.

During this period further British postal agencies were opened at Alcazar (1907–1916), Fez–Mellah (Jewish quarter) (1909), Marrakesh (1909), Marrakesh–Mellah (Jewish quarter) (1909–17) and Mequinez (1907–1916).

MOROCCO AGENCIES 5 CENTIMOS (11) MOROCCO AGENCIES 6 PESETAS (12)

1907 (1 Jan)–**12**. *King Edward VII surch as T* **11** (5 *c. to* 1 *p.*) *or* **12** (3 *p. to* 12 *p.*).

(*a*) *De La Rue printings. Ordinary paper* (*Nos.* 112/13, 116, 118, 122/3) *or chalk-surfaced paper* (*others*)

112 5 c. on ½d. pale yellowish green .. 2·00 15
a. Yellowish green .. .. .. 2·00 15
113 10 c. on 1d. scarlet .. .. .. 4·50 10
a. Bright scarlet .. .. .. 4·50 10
114 15 c. on 1½d. pale dull purple and green .. 2·00 15
a. Slate-purple and bluish green .. 1·25 15
b. "1" of "15" omitted £3250
115 20 c. on 2d. pale grey-green and carmine-red 80 15
a. Pale grey-green and scarlet .. 1·10 15
116 25 c. on 2½d. ultramarine .. .. 1·25 15
a. Pale ultramarine .. .. 1·00 15
117 40 c. on 4d. green & chocolate-brn (29.10.07) 90 1·75
a. Deep green and chocolate-brown .. 1·00 1·75
118 40 c. on 4d. pale orange (12.5.10) .. 1·00 60
a. Orange-red 60 60
119 50 c. on 5d. dull purple and ultramarine .. 2·50 1·60
a. Slate-purple and ultramarine .. 1·25 80
120 1 p. on 10d. dull purple and carmine .. 14·00 8·00
a. Slate-purple and carmine .. 14·00 7·00
b. No cross on crown .. ..
121 3 p. on 2s. 6d. pale dull purple .. 18·00 24·00
a. Dull purple .. .. .. 18·00 24·00
122 6 p. on 5s. bright carmine .. .. 35·00 45·00
a. Deep bright carmine .. .. 35·00 45·00
123 12 p. on 10s. ultramarine (30.4.07) .. 75·00 75·00
112/23 .. .. .. *Set of* 12 £140 £140
117, 123 Optd "Specimen" .. *Set of* 2 £140

(*b*) *Harrison printing. Ordinary paper*

124 25 c. on 2½d. bright blue (No. 283) (1912) 20·00 19·00
a. Dull blue .. .. .. 20·00 19·00

(*c*) *Somerset House printing. Ordinary paper*

125 12 p. on 10s. blue (No. 319) (1912) .. £150 £200

No. 114b occurred on stamps from the first vertical row of one sheet.

1912. *King George V* (*W* **49** (*Imperial Crown*)) *surch as T* **11**.

126 5 c. on ½d. green (No. 339) .. .. 1·75 10
127 10 c. on 1d. scarlet (No. 342) 50 10
a. No cross on crown .. .. £110 55·00

MOROCCO AGENCIES 3 CENTIMOS (13) MOROCCO AGENCIES 10 CENTIMOS (14)

MOROCCO AGENCIES 15 CENTIMOS (15)

MOROCCO AGENCIES 6 PESETAS (16)

1914–26. *King George V. (a) W* **100** *(Simple Cypher). Surch as T* **11** *(5 c.),* **13** *(3 c. and 40 c.)*,* **15** *(15 c.) and* **14** *(remainder).*

No.	Description	Unused	Used
128	3 c. on ½d. green (1917)	30	3·25
129	5 c. on ½d. green	30	10
130	10 c. on 1d. scarlet	40	10
	y. Wmk inverted and reversed		
131	15 c. on 1½d. red-brown (1915)	40	10
	a. Surch double, one albino	80·00	
132	20 c. on 2d. orange (Die I)	40	25
	a. Surch double, one albino	80·00	
133	25 c. on 2½d. blue (*shades*)	90	25
	w. Wmk inverted		
134	40 c. on 4d. grey-green (1917)	1·50	4·00
	a. Surch double, one albino		
135	1 p. on 10d. turquoise-blue	1·50	3·75

*The surcharge on Nos. 134, 148 and 158 is as T **13** for the value and T **15** for "MOROCCO AGENCIES".

(b) W **110** *(Single Cypher). Surch as T* **16**. *(i) Waterlow printings*

No.	Description	Unused	Used
136	6 p. on 5s. rose-carmine	27·00	48·00
	a. Surch double, one albino	£120	
	b. Surch triple, two albino	£130	
137	6 p. on 5s. pale rose-carmine	£130	£180
	a. Surch double, one albino	£160	
138	12 p. on 10s. indigo-blue (R.)	£110	£160
	a. Surch double, one albino	£200	£180
	b. Surch triple, two albino		
136, 138	Optd "Specimen" *Set of* 2	£180	
	(ii) De La Rue printings		
139	3 p. on 2s. 6d. grey-brown (1918)	30·00	85·00
	a. Surch double, one albino		
140	3 p. on 2s. 6d. yellow-brown	26·00	£100
	a. Surch double, one albino		
141	12 p. on 10s. blue (R.)	£110	£160
	a. Surch double, one albino	£250	
	(iii) Bradbury Wilkinson printings		
142	3 p. on 2s. 6d. chocolate-brown (1926)	23·00	65·00
128/42	*Set of* 11	£140	£250

1925–31. *King George V (W* **111** *(Block Cypher)), surch as T* **11, 13, 14** *or* **15.**

No.	Description	Unused	Used
143	5 c. on ½d. green (1931)	75	9·00
144	10 c. on 1d. scarlet (1929)	11·00	18·00
145	15 c. on 1½d. red-brown	7·00	17·00
146	20 c. on 2d. orange (1931)	3·00	6·50
	a. Surch double, one albino	85·00	
147	25 c. on 2½d. blue	1·00	1·00
	w. Wmk inverted	50·00	
148	40 c. on 4d. grey-green (1930)	1·00	1·00
	a. Surch double, one albino		
143/8	*Set of* 6	21·00	48·00

MOROCCO AGENCIES 10 CENTIMOS (17)

MOROCCO 10 AGENCIES CENTIMOS (18)

1935 (8 May). *Silver Jubilee (Nos. 453/6). Surch as T* **17**.

No.	Description	Unused	Used
149	5 c. on ½d. green (B.)	1·00	55
150	10 c. on 1d. scarlet (B.)	2·75	2·25
	a. Pair, one with "CENTIMES"	£1200	£1300
151	15 c. on 1½d. red-brown (B.)	3·00	13·00
152	25 c. on 2½d. blue (R.)	5·00	2·25
149/52	*Set of* 4	10·50	16·00

No. 150a occurred on R. 5/4 of a small second printing made in June 1935. The error can only be identified when *se-tenant* with a normal No. 150. Beware of forgeries.

1935–37. *King George V Harrison photo ptgs (Nos. 439/43, 445 and 448). W* **111** *(Block Cypher). Surch as T* **11, 13, 14** *or* **15.**

No.	Description	Unused	Used
153	5 c. on ½d. green (9.6.36)	75	12·00
154	10 c. on 1d. scarlet (11.36)	2·50	4·00
155	15 c. on 1½d. red-brown (4.35)	3·00	3·25
156	20 c. on 2d. orange (26.10.36)	40	25
157	25 c. on 2½d. ultramarine (8.9.36)	1·25	3·75
158	40 c. on 4d. deep grey-green (18.5.37)	45	3·00
159	1 p. on 10d. turquoise-blue (14.4.37)	3·00	30
153/9	*Set of* 7	10·00	24·00

1936 (26 Oct)–**37.** *King Edward VIII, surch as T* **18**.
A. "MOROCCO" 14¼ mm long.
B. "MOROCCO" 15¼ mm long (5.1.37)

No.	Description	A Unused	A Used	B Unused	B Used
160	5 c. on ½d. green	10	10	†	
161	10 c. on 1d. scarlet	50	1·25	3·00	7·00
162	15 c. on 1½d. red-brown	10	10	†	
163	25 c. on 2½d. bright blue	10	10	†	
160/3	*Set of* 4	65	1·40		

The first three printings of the 10 c. on 1d. (from cyls 4, 5 and 6) showed all stamps with the short surcharge (No. 161A).

On 5 January 1937 a further printing was placed on sale in London which had 49 stamps in the sheet (R. 1/2 to 11, R. 2/1, 5 and 6, 8 and 9, R. 3/5, R. 4/5, R. 5/4 and 5, 10, R. 6/6 and 7, R. 7/8, R. 8/8, R. 9/8, R. 11/7, 9, R.13/2 to 5, 7 and 8, R. 14/1, 7, R. 15/7, 11, R. 16/5, 10, R. 17/4, 10 and 11, R. 18/1, R. 19/2, R. 20/1 and 2, 3, 7, 9) with the long surcharge (No. 161B). The next printing increased the number of long surcharges in the sheet to 50 (R. 10/2), but the final version, although retaining 50 long surcharges, showed them on R. 1/2 to 11, R. 17/5 to 8 and the entire rows 18, 19 and 20. The first two printings with long surcharges were from cylinder 6 and the last from cylinder 13.

MOROCCO 15 CENTIMOS AGENCIES (19)

1937 (13 May). *Coronation (No. 461), surch as T* **19**.

No.	Description	Unused	Used
164	15 c. on 1½d. maroon (B.)	50	30

MOROCCO AGENCIES 10 CENTIMOS (20)

MOROCCO AGENCIES 10 CENTIMOS (21)

1937 (June)–**52.** *King George VI (Nos. 462/4, 466, 468, 471 and 474), surch as T* **20**.

No.	Description	Unused	Used
165	5 c. on ½d. green (B.)	55	15
166	10 c. on 1d. scarlet	50	10
167	15 c. on 1½d. red-brown (B.) (4.8.37)	55	25
168	25 c. on 2½d. ultramarine	60	50
169	40 c. on 4d. grey-green (9.40)	22·00	9·00
170	70 c. on 7d. emerald-green (9.40)	50	8·00
171	1 p. on 10d. turquoise-blue (16.6.52)	70	3·50
165/71	*Set of* 7	23·00	19·00

1940 (6 May). *Centenary of First Adhesive Postage Stamps (Nos. 479/81 and 483), surch as T* **21**.

No.	Description	Unused	Used
172	5 c. on ½d. green (B.)	30	1·25
173	10 c. on 1d. scarlet	2·10	1·75
174	15 c. on 1½d. red-brown (B.)	30	1·50
175	25 c. on 2½d. ultramarine	30	50
172/5	*Set of* 4	2·75	4·50

25 CENTIMOS MOROCCO AGENCIES (22)

45 PESETAS MOROCCO AGENCIES (23)

1948 (26 Apr). *Silver Wedding (Nos. 493/4), surch with T* **22** *or* **23.**

No.	Description	Unused	Used
176	25 c. on 2½d. ultramarine	40	15
177	45 p. on £1 blue	17·00	22·00

1948 (29 July). *Olympic Games (Nos. 495/8), variously surch as T* **22**.

No.	Description	Unused	Used
178	25 c. on 2½d. ultramarine	40	50
179	30 c. on 3d. violet	40	50
180	60 c. on 6d. bright purple	40	50
181	1 p. 20 c. on 1s. brown	55	50
	a. Surch double	£600	
178/81	*Set of* 4	1·60	1·75

1951 (3 May)–**52.** *King George VI (Nos. 503/5 and 507/8), surch as T* **20**.

No.	Description	Unused	Used
182	5 c. on ½d. pale orange	2·00	1·50
183	10 c. on 1d. light ultramarine	3·25	3·00
184	15 c. on 1½d. pale green	1·75	11·00
185	25 c. on 2½d. pale scarlet	1·75	3·00
186	40 c. on 4d. light ultramarine (26.5.52)	60	9·00
182/6	*Set of* 5	8·50	25·00

1954–55. *Queen Elizabeth II. W* **153** *(Tudor Crown). Surch as T* **20.**

No.	Description	Unused	Used
187	5 c. on ½d. orange-red (1.9.54)	20	1·75
188	10 c. on 1d. ultrammarine (1.3.55)	50	75

1956. *Queen Elizabeth II. W* **165** *(St. Edward's Crown). Surch as T* **20.**

No.	Description	Unused	Used
189	5 c. on ½d. orange-red (June)	15	50
190	40 c. on 4d. ultramarine (15 Aug)	70	1·75

The British postal agency at Laraiche closed on 30 June 1938. Stamps surcharged in Spanish currency were withdrawn from sale when the Tetuan agency closed on 31 December 1956.

PRICES OF SETS

Set prices are given for many issues, generally those containing three stamps or more. Definitive sets include one of each value or major colour change, but do not cover different perforations, die types or minor shades. Where a choice is possible the set prices are based on the cheapest versions of the stamps included in the listings.

V. FRENCH CURRENCY

For use in the British postal agencies at Casablanca (closed 14.8.37), Fez (closed 8.1.38), Fez–Mellah (closed after 1930), Marrakesh (closed 14.8.37), Mazagan (closed 14.8.37), Mogador (closed 31.10.33), Rabat (closed 8.1.38) and Saffi (closed 14.8.37).

MOROCCO AGENCIES 25 CENTIMES (24)

MOROCCO AGENCIES 1 FRANC (25)

1917–24. *King George V (W* **100** *(Simple Cypher)), surch as T* **24** *or* **25** *(1 f.).*

No.	Description	Unused	Used
191	3 c. on ½d. green (R.)	50	2·50
192	5 c. on ½d. green	30	10
193	10 c. on 1d. scarlet	2·00	15
194	15 c. on 1½d. red-brown	1·75	15
195	25 c. on 2½d. blue	1·00	15
196	40 c. on 4d. slate-green	1·75	60
197	50 c. on 5d. yellow-brown (1923)	70	2·75
198	75 c. on 9d. olive-green (1924)	50	75
199	1 f. on 10d. turquoise-blue	4·00	1·25
	a. Surch double, one albino	85·00	
191/9	*Set of* 9	11·00	7·50

1924–32. *King George V (B. W. ptg). W* **110** *(Single Cypher), surch as T* **25**, *but closer vertical spacing.*

No.	Description	Unused	Used
200	3 f. on 2s. 6d. chocolate-brown	7·50	2·00
	b. Major re-entry (R. 1/2)	£350	£350
	b. Surch double, one albino		
	c. Reddish brown	13·00	10·00
201	6 f. on 5s. rose-red (1932)	38·00	42·00
200/1	Optd "Specimen" *Set of* 2	£120	

1925–34. *King George V (W* **111** *(Block Cypher)), surch as T* **24** *or* **25** *(1 f.).*

No.	Description	Unused	Used
202	5 c. on ½d. green	30	6·50
203	10 c. on 1d. scarlet	30	60
204	15 c. on 1½d. red-brown	85	1·75
205	25 c. on 2½d. blue	30	40
206	40 c. on 4d. grey-green	50	80
207	50 c. on 5d. yellow-brown	50	10
	w. Wmk inverted	75·00	
208	75 c. on 9d. olive-green	1·50	15
	w. Wmk inverted		
209	90 c. on 9d. olive-green	8·50	4·00
210	1 f. on 10d. turquoise-blue	70	10
211	1 f. 50 on 1s. bistre-brown (Optd S. £50)	5·50	2·25
202/11	*Set of* 10	17·00	15·00

1935 (8 May). *Silver Jubilee (Nos. 453/6), surch as T* **17**, *but in French currency.*

No.	Description	Unused	Used
212	5 c. on ½d. green (B.)	15	15
213	10 c. on 1d. scarlet (B.)	1·50	50
214	15 c. on 1½d. red-brown (B.)	20	50
215	25 c. on 2½d. blue (R.)	30	15
212/15	*Set of* 4	1·90	1·10

1935–37. *King George V (Harrison photo ptgs. W* **111** *(Block Cypher)), surch as T* **24** *or* **25** *(1 f.).*

No.	Description	Unused	Used
216	5 c. on ½d. green (10.35)	45	3·00
217	10 c. on 1d. scarlet (2.3.36)	35	30
218	15 c. on 1½d. red-brown	2·25	2·75
219	25 c. on 2½d. ultramarine (25.9.36)	30	15
220	40 c. on 4d. deep grey-green (2.12.36)	30	15
221	50 c. on 5d. yellow-brown (15.9.36)	30	15
222	90 c. on 9d. deep olive-green (15.2.37)	35	1·00
223	1 f. on 10d. turquoise-blue (10.2.37)	30	30
224	1 f. 50 on 1s. bistre-brown (20.7.37) (Optd S. £50)	40	1·75

1935–36. *King George V (Waterlow re-engraved ptgs. W* **100** *(Single Cypher)), surch as T* **25**, *but closer vertical spacing.*

No.	Description	Unused	Used
225	3 f. on 2s. 6d. chocolate-brown (No. 450)	4·75	12·00
226	6 f. on 5s. bright rose-red (No. 451) (17.6.36)	6·00	20·00
216/26	*Set of* 11	14·00	38·00
225/6	Optd "Specimen" *Set of* 2	£120	

1936 (26 Oct). *King Edward VIII, surch as T* **18**, *but in French currency.*

No.	Description	Unused	Used
227	5 c. on ½d. green	10	15
	a. Bar through "POSTAGE"	£425	
228	15 c. on 1½d. red-brown	10	15

1937 (13 May). *Coronation (No. 461), surch as T* **19**, *but in French currency.*

No.	Description	Unused	Used
229	15 c. on 1½d. maroon (B.)	30	20

1937 (June). *King George VI, surch as T* **20**, *but in French currency.*

No.	Description	Unused	Used
230	5 c. on ½d. green (B.)	70	1·25

Stamps surcharged in French currency were withdrawn from sale on 8 January 1938.

VI. TANGIER INTERNATIONAL ZONE

By an agreement between Great Britain, France and Spain Tangier was declared an international zone in 1924. Stamps overprinted "Morocco Agencies" or surcharged in Spanish currency were used there until replaced by Nos. 231/4.

PRICES. Our note *re* U.K. usage (at beginning of Section III) also applies to "TANGIER" optd stamps.

TANGIER (26) TANGIER (27)

1927. *King George V (W* **111** *(Block Cypher)), optd with T* **26.**

231 ½d. green 80 10
 a. Opt double, one albino
232 1d. scarlet 1·00 10
 a. Inverted "Q" for "O" (R. 20/3) £800
233 1½d. chestnut 3·25 2·00
234 2d. orange 3·25 10
 a. Opt double, one albino 80·00
231/4 *Set of* 4 7·50 2·00

1934 (Dec)–**35.** *King George V (Harrison photo ptgs. W* **111** *(Block Cypher)), optd with T* **26.**

235 ½d. green (2.35) 1·00 1·40
236 1d. scarlet 1·40 70
237 1½d. red-brown 15 10
235/7 *Set of* 3 2·25 2·00

1935 (8 May). *Silver Jubilee (Nos.* 453/5*), optd with T* **27.**

238 ½d. green (B.) 1·00 1·75
239 1d. scarlet 11·00 7·50
240 1½d. red-brown (B.) 1·25 30
238/40 *Set of* 3 12·00 8·50

1936 (26 Oct). *King Edward VIII, optd with T* **26.**

241 ½d. green 10 15
242 1d. scarlet 10 10
243 1½d. red-brown 15 10
241/3 *Set of* 3 30 30

TANGIER (28) TANGIER (29)

1937 (13 May). *Coronation (No.* 461*), optd with T* **28.**

244 1½d. maroon (B.) 40 30

1937. *King George VI (Nos.* 462/4*), optd with T* **29.**

245 ½d. green (B.) (June) 70 30
246 1d. scarlet (June) 2·50 30
247 1½d. red-brown (B.) (4 Aug) 60 10
245/7 *Set of* 3 3·50 60

TANGIER (30) TANGIER (31)

1940 (6 May). *Centenary of First Adhesive Postage Stamps (Nos.* 479/81*), optd with T* **30.**

248 ½d. green (B.) 30 2·75
249 1d. scarlet 45 40
250 1½d. red-brown (B.) 2·00 2·00
248/50 *Set of* 3 2·50 4·75

1944. *King George VI pale colours (Nos.* 485/6*), optd with T* **29.**

251 ½d. pale green (B.) 5·50 2·00
252 1d. pale scarlet 5·50 1·75

1946 (11 June). *Victory (Nos.* 491/2*), optd as T* **31.**

253 2½d. ultramarine 30 20
254 3d. violet 30 30

The opt on No. 254 is smaller (23×2½ mm).

1948 (26 Apr). *Royal Silver Wedding (Nos.* 493/4*), optd with T* **30.**

255 2½d. ultramarine 30 15
 a. Opt omitted (in vert pair with stamp optd at top) £2500
256 £1 blue 25·00 25·00

No. 255a comes from a sheet on which the overprint is misplaced downwards resulting in the complete absence of the opt from the six stamps of the top row. On the rest of the sheet the opt falls at the top of each stamp instead of at the foot (*Price £250, unused*).

1948 (29 July). *Olympic Games (Nos.* 495/8*), optd with T* **30.**

257 2½d. ultramarine 65 90
258 3d. violet 65 75
259 6d. bright purple 65 90
260 1s. brown 65 40
257/60 *Set of* 4 2·40 2·75

1949 (1 Jan). *King George VI, optd with T* **29.**

261 2d. pale orange 3·25 3·00
262 2½d. light ultramarine 35 2·25
263 3d. pale violet 35 40
264 4d. grey-green 5·00 8·50
265 5d. brown 2·50 7·50
266 6d. purple 35 30
267 7d. emerald-green 80 8·50
268 8d. bright carmine 2·50 7·00
269 9d. deep olive-green 50 10·00
270 10d. turquoise-blue 50 10·00
271 11d. plum 50 7·00
272 1s. bistre-brown 60 1·25
273 2s. 6d. yellow-green 4·00 8·50
274 5s. red 10·00 30·00
275 10s. ultramarine 35·00 85·00
261/75 *Set of* 15 60·00 £170

1949 (10 Oct). *75th Anniv of U.P.U. (Nos.* 499/502*), optd with T* **30.**

276 2½d. ultramarine 50 1·00
277 3d. violet 50 85
278 6d. bright purple 50 85
279 1s. brown 50 1·75
276/9 *Set of* 4 1·75 4·00

1950 (2 Oct)–**51.** *King George VI, optd with T* **29** *or* **30** *(shilling values).*

280 ½d. pale orange (3.5.51) 45 75
281 1d. light ultramarine (3.5.51) 70 2·00
282 1½d. pale green (3.5.51) 70 12·00
283 2d. pale red-brown (3.5.51) 70 1·40
284 2½d. pale scarlet (3.5.51) 70 2·25
285 4d. light ultramarine 1·00 2·25
286 2s. 6d. yell-grn (H.M.S. *Victory*) (3.5.51) 7·00 4·00
287 5s. red (Dover) (3.5.51) 12·00 14·00
288 10s. ultramarine (St. George) (3.5.51) 16·00 14·00
280/8 *Set of* 9 35·00 48·00

1952–54. *Queen Elizabeth II (W* **153** *(Tudor Crown)), optd with T* **29.**

289 ½d. orange-red (31.8.53) 10 30
290 1d. ultramarine (31.8.53) 15 30
291 1½d. green (5.12.52) 10 30
292 2d. red-brown (31.8.53) 20 30
293 2½d. carmine-red (5.12.52) 10 30
294 3d. deep lilac (B.) (18.1.54) 20 30
295 4d. ultramarine (2.11.53) 45 2·25
296 5d. brown (6.7.53) 60 90
297 6d. reddish purple (18.1.54) 45 15
298 7d. bright green (18.1.54) 80 2·00
299 8d. magenta (6.7.53) 60 1·50
300 9d. bronze-green (8.2.54) 1·40 75
301 10d. Prussian blue (8.2.54) 1·40 2·75
302 11d. brown-purple (8.2.54) 1·40 3·25
303 1s. bistre-brown (6.7.53) 50 30
304 1s. 3d. green (2.11.53) 65 1·50
305 1s. 6d. grey-blue (2.11.53) 1·00 1·75
289/305 *Set of* 17 9·00 17·00

1953 (3 June). *Coronation (Nos.* 532/5*), optd with T* **30.**

306 2½d. carmine-red 50 30
307 4d. ultramarine 1·00 30
308 1s. 3d. deep yellow-green 1·25 1·25
309 1s. 6d. deep grey-blue 1·25 60
306/9 *Set of* 4 3·50 2·25

1955 (23 Sept). *Queen Elizabeth II, Castle high values (W* **165** *(St. Edward's Crown)), optd with T* **30.**

310 2s. 6d. black-brown 3·25 5·50
311 5s. rose-red 5·50 10·00
312 10s. ultramarine 19·00 20·00
310/12 *Set of* 3 25·00 32·00

1956. *Queen Elizabeth II (W* **165** *St. Edward's Crown)), optd with T* **29.**

313 ½d. orange-red (21 March) 10 20
314 1d. ultramarine (13 April) 20 30
315 1½d. green (22 Oct) 40 90
316 2d. red-brown (25 July) 1·25 1·75
317 2d. light red-brown (10 Dec) 70 30
318 2½d. carmine-red (19 Dec) 40 30
319 3d. deep lilac (B.) (22 Oct) 40 1·00
320 4d. ultramarine (25 June) 65 2·00
321 6d. reddish purple (22 Oct) 50 1·00
322 1s. 3d. green (26 Nov) 1·75 12·00
313/22 *Set of* 10 5·50 17·00

1857-1957 TANGIER (32) 1857-1957 TANGIER (33)

1957 (1 Apr). *Centenary of British Post Office in Tangier.*

(*a*) *Nos.* 540/2 *and* 543*b*/56 *(W* **165** *(St. Edward's Crown)), optd as T* **32** *or* **33** *(7d)*

323 ½d. orange-red 10 10
324 1d. ultramarine 10 10
325 1½d. green 10 10
326 2d. light red-brown 10 10
327 2½d. carmine-red 15 40
328 3d. deep lilac (B.) 15 10
329 4d. ultramarine 30 20
330 5d. brown 30 35
331 6d. reddish purple 30 15
332 7d. bright green 30 30
333 8d. magenta 30 70
334 9d. bronze-green 30 30
 a. "TANGIER" omitted £3750
335 10d. Prussian blue 30 30
336 11d. brown-purple 30 30
337 1s. bistre-brown 30 30
338 1s. 3d. green 45 1·50
339 1s. 6d. grey-blue 50 85

(*b*) *Nos.* 536/8 *(W* **165** *(St. Edward's Crown)), optd as T* **32.**

340 2s. 6d. black-brown 2·00 3·00
 a. Hyphen omitted 60·00
 b. Hyphen inserted 20·00
341 5s. rose-red 2·75 3·25
 a. Hyphen omitted 60·00
 b. Hyphen inserted 10·00
342 10s. ultramarine 5·50 4·50
 a. Hyphen omitted 75·00
 b. Hyphen inserted 15·00
323/42 *Set of* 20 13·00 15·00

Nos. 340a/b, 341a/b and 342a/b occur on R.9/2 in the sheet of 40 (4×10). They are best collected in marginal blocks of four from the bottom left corner of the sheet. Specialists recognise two forms of No. 340b; one where the hyphen on R.9/2 was inserted separately to correct the error, No. 340a; the other from a later printing where a new and corrected overprinting plate was used. (*Price £12 un.*)

All stamps overprinted "TANGIER" were withdrawn from sale on 30 April 1957.

Mosul
see Iraq

Mozambique

The Republic of Mozambique joined the Commonwealth on 12 November 1995. Stamps issued after this date will appear in the *Part 1* catalogue.

(Currency. 100 centavos = 1 metical)

PRINTERS. All stamps are printed in lithography by the State Printing Works, Maputo, *unless otherwise stated.*

267 Child wearing Blue Cloak

268 Player scoring Goal

(Des F. Jofane)

1995 (22 Nov). *20th Anniv of U.N.I.C.E.F. in Mozambique. P* 11½×11.

1417 **267** 5000 m. multicoloured 60 65

(Des F. Jofane)

1996 (5 Apr). *Football. T* **268** *and similar horiz designs. Multicoloured. P* 11×11½.

1418 1000 m. Type **268** 10 15
1419 2000 m. Goalkeeper holding ball 20 25
1420 4000 m. Referee admonishing players 40 45
1421 6000 m. Two players tackling for ball 60 65
1418/21 *Set of* 4 1·25 1·50

269 Mask

270 "Mae Africa" (De Malangatana)

1996 (2 July). *Local Masks. T* **269** *and similar vert designs showing different local masks. P* 11½×11.

1422 1000 m. Type **269** 10 15
1423 2000 m. multicoloured 20 25
1424 4000 m. multicoloured 40 45
1425 6000 m. multicoloured 60 65
1422/5 *Set of* 4 1·25 1·50

1996 (10 July). *15th Anniv of Mozambique Red Cross. P* 11½×11.

1426 **270** 5000 m. multicoloured 50 55

271 African Elephant

272 Mine Field

1996 (3 Sept). *Wild Animals. T* **271** *and similar vert designs. Multicoloured. P* 11½×11.

1427 1000 m. Type **271** 10 15
1428 2000 m. White Rhinoceros 20 25
1429 4000 m. Leopard 40 45
1430 6000 m. Pel's Fishing Owl 60 65
1427/30 *Set of* 4 1·25 1·50

1996 (9 Nov). *Land Mine Clearance Campaign. T* **272** *and similar vert designs. Multicoloured. P* 11½×11.

1431	2000 m. Type **272**	20	25
1432	6000 m. Warning sign	60	65
1433	8000 m. Soldier with mine detector	80	85
1434	10000 m. Soldier lifting mine	1·00	1·10
1431/4	*Set of* 4	2·50	2·75

273 City Street

274 5 r. Stamp of 1876 and Magnifying Glass

1996 (16 Dec). *"Keeping the City Clean". P* 11½×11.

1435	**273**	2000 m. multicoloured	20	25

(Des F. Jofane)

1996 (16 Dec). 120*th Anniv of Mozambique Stamps. P* 11½×11.

1436	**274**	2000 m. multicoloured	20	25

275 Mitumbui

276 Village Scene

1997 (10 Apr). *Local Boats. T* **275** *and similar horiz designs. Multicoloured. P* 11×11½.

1437	2000 m. Type **275**	20	25
1438	6000 m. Muterere	60	65
1439	8000 m. Lancha	80	85
1440	10000 m. Dhow	1·00	1·10
1437/40	*Set of* 4	2·50	2·75

1997 (1 June). *International Children's Day. P* 11×11½.

1441	**276**	2000 m. multicoloured	20	25

277 Yellow-billed Stork

1997 (16 July). *Aquatic Birds. T* **277** *and similar multicoloured designs. P* 11½×11 *(vert) or* 11×11½ *(horiz)*.

1442	2000 m. Type **277**	20	25
1443	4000 m. Black-winged Stilt	40	45
1444	8000 m. Long-toed Stint (*horiz*)	80	85
1445	10000 m. Eastern White Pelican	1·00	1·10
1442/5	*Set of* 4	2·50	2·75

Muscat

An independent Arab Sultanate in Eastern Arabia with an Indian postal administration.

The Indian post office at Muscat town is officially recorded as having opened on 1 May 1864. Stamps of India were provided for its use, most surviving examples being of the ½ a. value, although others to the 8 a. are known.

The office was initially included in the Bombay Postal Circle and the first postmark, so far only recorded on stampless covers, was a single circle, 21½ mm in diameter, broken at the top by "MUSCAT" and with the date in two lines across the centre. This was followed by a cancellation showing the post office number, "309", within a diamond of 13, later 16, bars. It is believed that this was used in conjunction with a single ring date stamp inscribed "MUSCAT".

1864 Diamond

In 1869 the office was transferred to the Sind Circle, assigned a new number, "23", and issued with a duplex cancellation. Major reorganisation of the postal service in 1873 resulted in Muscat becoming office "K-4". For ten years from 1873 the cancellations do not, very confusingly, carry any indication of the year of use.

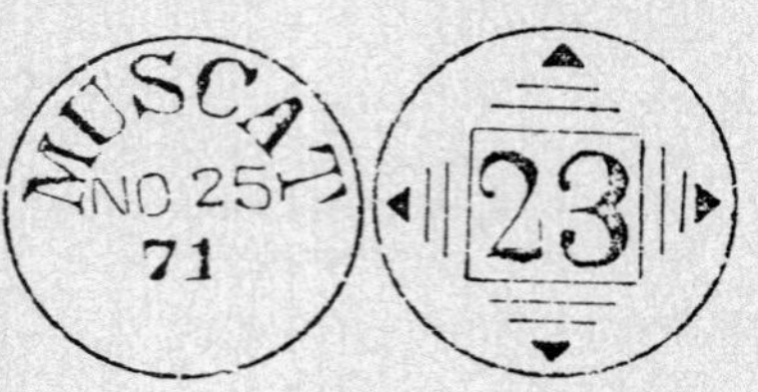

1869 Duplex

1873 Duplex

Muscat rejoined the Bombay Circle in 1879 and was issued with a cancellation showing a "B" within a square of horizontal bars. The date stamp used at this time was unique in that it carried the inscription "MASKAT", although the spelling reverted to the more usual form by 1882. The square cancellation had been replaced by a similar circular mark by 1884.

Subsequent postmarks were of various circular types, all inscribed "MUSCAT".

There was only one Indian post office in Muscat, but a further office did exist, from 12 April 1868, at the Muscat dependency of Guadur, a port on the Mekran coast of Baluchistan.

No cancellations have been reported from Guadur before its transfer to the Sind Circle in 1869. Cancellations are all similar in style to those for Muscat, Guadur being initially assigned number "24", although an office in Southern India is also known to have used this numeral. The 1869 duplex is interesting in that it is inscribed "GWADUR". Under the 1873 reorganisation the office became "4/K-1", this postmark using the "GUADUR" spelling.

1869 Duplex

PRICES FOR STAMPS ON COVER

Nos. 1/15	*from* ×50
Nos. O1/10	*from* ×75

(Currency 12 pies = 1 anna; 16 annas = 1 Indian rupee)

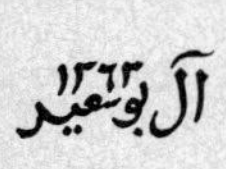

(1)

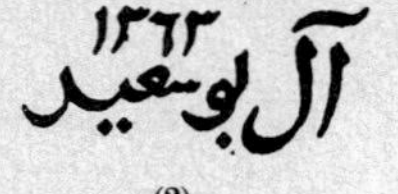

(2)

1944 (20 Nov). *Bicentenary of Al-Busaid Dynasty. Nos.* 259/60, 265/8 *and* 269*a*/77 (*King George VI*) *of India optd* ("AL BUSAID 1363" *in Arabic script*) *as T* **1** *or* **2** (*rupee values*).

1	3 p. slate	30	4·50
2	½ a. purple	30	4·50
3	9 p. green	30	4·50
4	1 a. carmine	30	4·50
5	1½ a. dull violet	30	4·50
6	2 a. vermilion	30	4·50
7	3 a. bright violet	50	4·50
8	3½ a. bright blue	50	4·50
9	4 a. brown	50	4·50
10	6 a. turquoise-green	65	4·50
11	8 a. slate-violet	65	4·75
12	12 a. lake	80	5·00
13	14 a. purple	1·25	7·00
14	1 r. grey and red-brown	50	9·00
15	2 r. purple and brown	1·10	15·00
1/15	*Set of* 15	7·50	75·00

OFFICIAL STAMPS

1944 (20 Nov). *Bicentenary of Al-Busaid Dynasty. Nos.* O138, O143, O144*a*/6 *and* 146*b*/50 *of India optd as T* **1** *or* **2** (1 *r.*).

O 1	3 p. slate	50	9·00
O 2	½ a. purple	50	9·00
O 3	9 p. green	50	9·00
O 4	1 a. carmine	50	9·00
O 5	1½ a. dull violet	50	9·00
O 6	2 a. vermilion	50	9·00
O 7	2½ a. bright violet	1·25	9·00
O 8	4 a. brown	1·00	9·00
O 9	8 a. slate-violet	1·40	9·50
O10	1 r. grey and red-brown	2·25	18·00
O1/10	*Set of* 10	8·00	90·00

From December 1947 there was a Pakistani postal administration and stamps of Pakistan were used until 31 March 1948. The subsequent British administration operated from 1 April 1948 to 29 April 1966 when the stamps of the BRITISH POSTAL AGENCIES IN EASTERN ARABIA were used.

Later issues for this area will be found listed under OMAN in Part 19 (*Middle East*) of this catalogue.

Nagaland

Labels inscribed "NAGALAND" with currency in cents and chaplees are considered to be propaganda labels.

Namibia

(*formerly* South West Africa)

SOUTH WEST AFRICA

The stamps of Germany were used in the colony from July 1886 until the introduction of issues for GERMAN SOUTH-WEST AFRICA in May 1897. Following occupation by South African forces in 1914–15 the issues of SOUTH AFRICA were used, being replaced by the overprinted issues in 1923.

Walvis (or Walfish) Bay, the major anchorage on the South West Africa coast, was claimed by Great Britain as early as 1796. In 1878 the 430 sq mile area around the port, together with a number of offshore islands, was annexed to Cape Province, passing to the Union of South Africa in 1910.

Stamps of the Cape of Good Hope and South Africa were used at Walfish Bay, often cancelled with numeral obliterator 300, until the enclave was transferred to the South West Africa administration on 1 October 1922.

The Walfish Bay territory reverted to South Africa on 30 August 1977 and from that date the stamps of South Africa were, once again, in use.

PRICES FOR STAMPS ON COVER TO 1945

Nos. 1/40*a*	*from* × 6
Nos. 41/133	*from* × 2
Nos. D1/5	*from* × 10
Nos. D6/51	*from* × 20
Nos. O1/4	*from* × 3
Nos. O5/20	*from* × 15
No. O21	*from* × 2
No. O22	*from* × 15

INSCRIPTIONS. Most of the postage stamps up to No. 140 are inscribed alternately in English and Afrikaans throughout the sheets and the same applies to all the Official stamps and to Nos. D30/33.

PRICES for Nos. 1/140 are for unused horizontal pairs, used horizontal pairs or used singles (either inscr), *unless otherwise indicated.*

OVERPRINT SETTINGS. Between 1923 and 1928 the King George V definitives of South Africa, Types **2** and **3**, and the various postage due stamps were issued overprinted for use in South West Africa. A number of overprint settings were used:

- Setting I – Overprint Types **1** and **2** ("Zuid-West Afrika"). 14 mm between lines of overprint. See Nos. 1/12 and D1/9
- Setting II – As Setting I, but 10 mm between lines of overprint. See Nos. 13/15 and D10/13
- Setting III – Overprint Types **3** ("Zuidwest Afrika") and **4**. "South West" 14 mm long. "Zuidwest" 11 mm long. 14 mm between lines of overprint. See Nos. 16/27 and D14/17
- Setting IV – As Setting III, but "South West" 16 mm long, "Zuidwest" 12 mm long and 14 mm between lines of overprint. See Nos. 28 and D17*a*/20
- Setting V – As Setting IV, but 12 mm between lines of overprint. See Nos. D21/4
- Setting VI – As Setting IV, but 9½ mm between lines of overprint. See Nos. 29/40 and D25/32.

South West Africa. (1)	Zuid-West Afrika. (2)

1923 (1 Jan–17 June). *Nos.* 3/4, 6 *and* 9/17 *of South Africa optd alternately with T* **1** *and* **2** *by typography.*

		Un pair	*Us pair*	*Us single*
	(*a*) *Setting* I (14 *mm between lines of opt*)			
1	½d. green	2·00	7·00	1·00
	a. "Wes" for "West" (R. 20/8)	80·00	£110	
	b. "Afr ica" (R. 20/2)	£120		
	c. Litho opt in shiny ink (17 June)	8·50	40·00	4·50
2	1d. rose-red	2·50	7·00	1·00
	a. Opt inverted	£450		
	b. "Wes" for "West" (R. 12/2)	£150		
	c. "Af.rica" for "Africa" (R. 20/6)	£140	£160	
	d. Opt double	£750		
	e. "Afr ica" (R. 20/2)	£120		
	f. "Afrika" without stop (R. 17/8)	£225		
3	2d. dull purple	3·50	9·50	1·50
	a. Opt inverted	£500	£550	
	b. "Wes" for "West" (R. 20/8)	£225		
	c. Litho opt in shiny ink (30 Mar)	35·00	80·00	10·00
4	3d. ultramarine	7·50	16·00	2·75
5	4d. orange-yellow and sage-green	13·00	45·00	4·00
	a. Litho opt in shiny ink (19 Apr)	35·00	65·00	8·00
6	6d. black and violet	8·00	38·00	4·00
	a. Litho opt in shiny ink (19 Apr)	35·00	65·00	7·50
7	1s. orange-yellow	23·00	48·00	5·00
	a. Litho opt in shiny ink (19 Apr)	60·00	95·00	11·00
8	1s. 3d. pale violet	30·00	55·00	5·50
	a. Opt inverted	£300		
	b. Litho opt in shiny ink (19 Apr)	75·00	£120	14·00
9	2s. 6d. purple and green	70·00	£130	18·00
	a. Litho opt in shiny ink (19 Apr)	£150	£250	35·00
10	5s. purple and blue	£160	£325	50·00
11	10s. blue and olive-green	£1600	£2500	£400
12	£1 green and red	£900	£1600	£250
1/12	*Set of* 12	£2500	£4250	£650
1/12 Optd "Specimen"	*Set of* 12 *singles*	£1500		

Nos. 1/12 were overprinted in complete sheets of 240 (4 panes 6×10).

No. 3b shows traces of a type spacer to the right of where the "t" should have been. This spacer is not visible on Nos. 1a and 2b.

Minor varieties, such as broken "t" in "West", were caused by worn type. Stamps showing one line of overprint only or with the lower line above the upper line due to overprint misplacement may also be found. All values exist showing a faint stop after "Afrika" on R.17/8, but only the 1d. has been confirmed as existing with it omitted.

	(*b*) *Setting* II (10 *mm between lines of opt*) (31 Mar)			
13	5s. purple and blue	£140	£250	45·00
	a. "Afrika" without stop (R.6/1)	£1200	£1300	
14	10s. blue and olive-green	£500	£850	£140
	a. "Afrika" without stop (R.6/1)	£2250	£2750	
15	£1 green and red	£1000	£1400	£200
	a. "Afrika" without stop (R.6/1)	£5000	£5000	£900
13/15	*Set of* 3	£1500	£2250	£350

Nos. 13/15 were overprinted in separate panes of 60 (6×10).

Zuidwest Afrika. (3)	South West Africa. (4)

1923 (15 July)–**26**. *Nos.* 3/4, 6 *and* 9/17 *of South Africa optd as T* **3** (*"Zuidwest" in one word, without hyphen*) *and* **4** *alternately.*

	(*a*) *Setting* III ("South West" 14 *mm long*, "Zuidwest" 11 *mm long*, 14 *mm between lines of opt*)			
16	½d. green (5.9.24)	4·50	28·00	3·50
	a. "outh" for "South" (R. 1/1)	£1300		
17	1d. rose-red (28.9.23)	4·25	7·50	1·40
	a. "outh" for "South" (R. 1/1)	£1300		
18	2d. dull purple (28.9.23)	4·50	7·00	1·25
	a. Opt double	£850		
19	3d. ultramarine	4·75	7·00	1·25
20	4d. orange-yellow and sage-green	5·50	18·00	2·75
	w. Wmk inverted	†	†	—
21	6d. black and violet (28.9.23)	12·00	38·00	4·00
22	1s. orange-yellow	14·00	42·00	5·00
23	1s. 3d. pale violet	29·00	45·00	5·50
24	2s. 6d. purple and green	45·00	80·00	10·00
25	5s. purple and blue	70·00	£130	18·00

26 10s. blue and olive-green . . . . £200 £300 50·00
27 £1 green and red (28.9.23) . . £350 £475 70·00
16/27 . . . . . . *Set of* 12 £650 £1000 £150

Nos. 16/27 were overprinted in complete sheets of 240 (4 panes 6×10).

Two sets may be made with this overprint, one with bold lettering, and the other from September 1924, with thinner lettering and smaller stops.

(*b*) *Setting* IV ("South West" 16 *mm long*, "Zuidwest" 12 *mm long*, 14 *mm between lines of opt*)

28 2s. 6d purple and green (29.6.24) . . 80·00 £150 28·00

No. 28 was overprinted on two panes of 60 horizontally side by side.

(*c*) *Setting* VI ("South West" 16 *mm long*, "Zuidwest" 12 *mm long*, 9½ *mm between lines of opt*)

29 ½d. green (16.12.25) . . . . 6·50 40·00 5·00
30 1d. rose-red (9.12.24) . . . . 3·00 8·50 1·40
a. Opt omitted (in pair with normal) £1000
31 2d. dull purple (9.12.24) . . . . 4·50 17·00 1·75
32 3d. ultramarine (31.1.26) . . . . 4·50 26·00 2·75
a. Deep bright blue (20.4.26) . . 55·00 90·00 12·00
33 4d. orge-yellow & sage-grn (9.12.24) 6·50 38·00 4·00
34 6d. black and violet (9.12.24) . . 7·50 45·00 5·00
35 1s. orange-yellow (9.12.24) . . 11·00 45·00 5·00
36 1s. 3d. pale violet (9.12.24) . . 15·00 45·00 5·00
37 2s. 6d. purple and green (9.12.24) . . 35·00 70·00 10·00
38 5s. purple and blue (31.1.26) . . 55·00 £100 14·00
39 10s. blue and olive-green (9.12.24) . . 85·00 £130 20·00
40 £1 green and red (9.1.26) . . £300 £450 70·00
a. Pale olive-green and red (8.11.26) £250 £450 90·00
29/40*a* . . . . . . *Set of* 12 £425 £850 £140
35, 39/40 H/S "Specimen" . . *Set of* 3 £500

Nos. 29/40 were overprinted in complete sheets of 240 (4 panes of 6×10) with, initially, "South West Africa" 16½ mm long on the upper two panes and 16 mm long on the lower two. This order was subsequently reversed. For printings from 8 November 1926 all four panes showed the 16½ mm measurement. No. 40*a* only comes from this printing.

Suidwes Afrika. (5)

South West Africa. (6)

1926 (1 Jan–1 May). *Nos. 30/2 of South Africa optd with T* **5** (*on stamps inscr in Afrikaans*) *and* **6** (*on stamps inscr in English*) *sideways, alternately in black.*

41 ½d. black and green . . . . 3·75 8·50 1·00
42 1d. black and carmine . . . . 3·00 7·50 80
43 6d. green and orange (1 May) . . 28·00 48·00 7·00
41/3 . . . . . . *Set of* 3 32·00 55·00 8·00

SOUTH WEST AFRICA (7)

SUIDWES-AFRIKA (8)

1926. *No. 33 of South Africa, imperf, optd with T* **7** (E.) *or T* **8** (A.).

Single stamps E A
44 4d. grey-blue . . . . . . 65 2·50 65 2·50

1927. *As Nos. 41/3, but Afrikaans opt on stamp inscr in English and vice versa.*

45 ½d. black and green . . . . 1·60 5·50 80
a. "Africa" without stop (R.13/8) . . £150
46 1d. black and carmine . . . . 1·60 2·50 50
a. "Africa" without stop (R.13/8) . . £225
47 6d. green and orange . . . . 14·00 25·00 3·00
a. "Africa" without stop (R.13/8) . . £170
45/7 . . . . . . *Set of* 3 15·00 30·00 3·75

SOUTH WEST AFRICA (9)

S.W.A. (10)

S.W.A. (11)

1927. *As No. 44E, but overprint T* **9**.

Single stamps
48 4d. grey-blue (H/S S. £70) . . . . 7·50 19·00

1927 (Apr). *Nos. 34/9 of South Africa optd alternately as T* **5** *and* **6**, *in blue, but with lines of overprint spaced 16 mm.*

49 2d. grey and purple . . . . 4·00 15·00 1·75
50 3d. black and red . . . . 4·00 24·00 2·50
51 1s. brown and blue . . . . 15·00 32·00 4·00
52 2s. 6d. green and brown . . 45·00 80·00 13·00
53 5s. black and green . . . . 75·00 £150 20·00
54 10s. blue and bistre-brown . . 85·00 £130 20·00
49/54 . . . . *Set of* 6 £200 £375 50·00
49/51, 54 H/S "Specimen" . . *Set of* 4 £350

A variety of Nos. 49, 50, 51 and 54, with spacing 16½ mm between lines of overprint, occurs in the third vertical row of each sheet.

1927. *As No. 44, but perf* 11½ *by John Meinert, Ltd, Windhoek.*

Single stamps E A
55 4d. grey-blue . . . . . . 80 4·00 80 4·00
a. Imperf between (pair) . . 32·00 70·00 32·00 70·00
55 H/S "Specimen" . . . . 70·00 70·00

1927 (Aug)–**30**. *Optd with T* **10**. (*a*) *On Nos. 13 and 17a of South Africa.*

Single stamps
56 1s. 3d. pale violet (H/S S. £70) . . 1·25 6·00
a. Without stop after "A" (R.3/4) . . 90·00
57 £1 pale olive-green and red . . £120 £180
a. Without stop after "A" (R.3/4) . . £1800 £2500

(*b*) *On Nos. 30/2 and 34/9 of South Africa*

Un pair *Us pair* *Us single*
58 ½d. black and green . . . . 1·75 5·50 75
a. Without stop after "A" . . 50·00 75·00
b. "S.W.A." opt above value . . 2·75 14·00 2·25
c. As b, in vert pair, top stamp without opt . . £475
59 1d. black and carmine . . . . 1·25 3·25 55
a. Without stop after "A" . . 50·00 75·00
b. "S.W.A." opt at top (30.4.30) . . 1·75 12·00 1·60
c. As b, in vert pair, top stamp without opt . . £375
60 2d. grey and maroon . . . . 6·00 18·00 1·50
c. Perf 14×13½ . . . . 15·00 27·00
ca. Without stop after "A" . . 75·00 £110
cb. Opt double, one inverted . . £650 £850
61 3d. black and red . . . . 6·00 23·00 3·25
a. Without stop after "A" . . 75·00 £120
b. Perf 14×13½ . . . . 11·00 35·00
ba. Without stop after "A" . . 75·00 £120
62 4d. brown (4.28) . . . . 18·00 48·00 7·00
a. Without stop after "A" . . 85·00 £130
b. Perf 14×13½ . . . . 20·00 48·00
63 6d. green and orange . . . . 13·00 22·00 2·75
a. Without stop after "A" . . £110
64 1s. brown and deep blue . . 24·00 48·00 5·00
b. Perf 14×13½ . . . . 50·00 75·00
ba. Without stop after "A" . . £1700
65 2s. 6d. green and brown . . 45·00 80·00 11·00
a. Without stop after "A" . . £160 £250
b. Perf 14×13½ . . . . 65·00 £100
ba. Without stop after "A" . . £180 £275
66 5s. black and green . . . . 65·00 £120 18·00
a. Without stop after "A" . . £225 £350
b. Perf 14×13½ . . . . 85·00 £140
ba. Without stop after "A" . . £225 £350
67 10s. bright blue and brown . . £120 £190 28·00
a. Without stop after "A" . . £325 £500
58/67 . . . . *Set of* 10 £250 £500 70·00
58/61, 63/7 H/S "Specimen" *Set of* 9 £550

On the ½d., 1d. and 6d. the missing stop variety occurs three times on each sheet, R.1/7, 13/4 and one position not yet identified. For the other values it comes on R.2/3 of the right pane and, for the 2s. 6d., 5s. and 10s., on R.8/1 of the left pane.

The overprint is normally found at the base of the ½d., 1d., 6d., 1s. 3d. and £1 values and at the top on the remainder.

1930–31. *Nos. 42 and 43 of South Africa (rotogravure printing) optd with T* **10**.

68 ½d. black and green (1931) . . 8·00 25·00 2·75
69 1d. black and carmine . . . . 6·00 24·00 2·75

1930 (27 Nov–Dec). *Air. Nos. 40/1 of South Africa optd.*

(*a*) *As T* **10**.

Un single *Us single*
70 4d. green (*first printing*) . . 12·00 25·00
a. No stop after "A" of "S.W.A." . . 80·00 £110
b. Later printings . . . . 7·00 27·00
71 1s. orange (*first printing*) . . 70·00 £120
a. No stop after "A" of "S.W.A." . . £400 £500
b. Later printings . . . . 15·00 50·00

First printing: Thick letters, blurred impression. Stops with rounded corners.

Later printings: Thinner letters, clear impression. Clean cut, square stops.

(*b*) *As T* **11** (12.30)

72 4d. green . . . . . . 1·25 6·00
a. Opt double £140
b. Opt inverted £130
73 1s. orange . . . . . . 3·25 15·00
a. Opt double £500

12 Kori Bustard

13 Cape Cross

14 Bogenfels

15 Windhoek

16 Waterberg

17 Luderitz Bay

18 Bush Scene

19 Elands

20 Mountain Zebra and Blue Wildebeests

21 Herero Huts

22 Welwitschia Plant

23 Okuwahaken Falls

24 Monoplane over Windhoek

25 Biplane over Windhoek

(Recess B.W.)

1931 (5 Mar). *T* **12** *to* **25** (*inscr alternately in English and Afrikaans*). *W* **9** *of South Africa. P* 14 × 13½. (*a*) *Postage.*

74 ½d. black and emerald . . . . 1·75 1·50 10
75 1d. indigo and scarlet . . . . 1·60 2·00 10
76 2d. blue and brown . . . . 50 3·25 15
w. Wmk inverted £350
77 3d. grey-blue and blue . . . . 50 3·50 15
78 4d. green and purple . . . . 1·25 6·00 20
79 6d. blue and brown . . . . 75 7·00 20
80 1s. chocolate and blue . . . . 1·00 7·00 25
81 1s. 3d. violet and yellow . . 9·50 11·00 50
82 2s. 6d. carmine and grey . . 22·00 22·00 1·75
83 5s. sage-green and red-brown . . 20·00 40·00 2·75
84 10s. red-brown and emerald . . 55·00 60·00 7·00
85 20s. lake and blue-green . . £110 £110 12·00

(*b*) *Air*

86 3d. brown and blue . . . . 32·00 40·00 3·50
87 10d. black and purple-brown . . 55·00 85·00 9·00
74/87 . . . . . . *Set of* 14 £275 £350 32·00

26

(Recess B.W.)

1935 (1 May). *Silver Jubilee. Inscr bilingually. W* **9** *of South Africa. P* 14 × 13½.

Un single *Us single*
88 **26** 1d. black and scarlet . . . . 1·00 25
89 2d. black and sepia . . . . 1·00 25
90 3d. black and blue . . . . 13·00 16·00
91 6d. black and purple . . . . 6·00 8·00
88/91 . . . . . . *Set of* 4 19·00 22·00

1935–36. *Voortrekker Memorial Fund. Nos. 50/3 of South Africa optd with T* **10**.

92 ½d. + ½d. black and green . . 1·00 5·50 75
a. Opt inverted £250
93 1d. + ½d. grey-black and pink . . 1·50 3·25 40
94 2d. + 1d. grey-green and purple . . 5·50 6·00 80
a. Without stop after "A" . . £190
b. Opt double £180
95 3d. + 1½d. grey-green and blue . . 16·00 32·00 4·00
a. Without stop after "A" . . £200 £250
92/5 . . . . . . *Set of* 4 22·00 42·00 5·50

27 Mail Train

28

(Recess B.W.)

1937 (1 Mar). *W* **9** *of South Africa. P* 14 × 13½.

96 **27** 1½d. purple-brown . . . . 14·00 3·00 25

(Recess B.W.)

1937 (12 May). *Coronation. W* **9** *of South Africa (sideways). P* 13½ × 14.

97 **28** ½d. black and emerald . . 50 15 10
98 1d. black and scarlet . . 50 15 10
99 1½d. black and orange . . 50 15 10
100 2d. black and brown . . 50 15 10
101 3d. black and blue . . 50 15 10
102 4d. black and purple . . 50 20 10
103 6d. black and yellow . . 80 2·00 20
104 1s. black and grey-black . . 1·25 2·50 25
97/104 . . . . . . *Set of* 8 4·50 5·00 65

1938 (14 Dec). *Voortrekker Centenary Memorial. Nos.* 76/9 *of South Africa optd as T* **11**.
105 ½d. + ½d. blue and green .. .. 8·00 13·00 1·75
106 1d. + 1d. blue and carmine .. .. 18·00 7·00 1·00
107 1½d. + 1½d. chocolate & blue-green 22·00 18·00 2·75
108 3d. + 3d. bright blue .. .. 42·00 45·00 6·50
105/8 .. .. .. *Set of* 4 80·00 75·00 11·00

1938 (14 Dec). *Voortrekker Commemoration. Nos.* 80/1 *of South Africa optd as T* **11**.
109 1d. blue and carmine .. .. 10·00 12·00 1·50
a. Three bolts in wheel rim .. 30·00
110 1½d. greenish blue and brown .. 12·00 13·00 1·75

1939 (17 July). *250th Anniv of Landing of Huguenots in South Africa and Huguenot Commemoration Fund. Nos.* 82/4 *of South Africa optd as T* **11**.
111 ½d. + ½d. brown and green .. 10·00 10·00 1·10
112 1d. + 1d. green and carmine .. 15·00 11·00 1·25
113 1½d. + 1½d. blue-green and purple .. 18·00 11·00 1·25
111/13 .. .. .. *Set of* 3 38·00 28·00 3·25

SWA (29) SWA (30) SWA (31) S W A (32)

1941 (1 Oct)–**43**. *War Effort. Nos.* 88/96 *of South Africa optd with T* **29** *or* **30** (3d. *and* 1s.). (a) *Inscr alternately.*
114 ½d. green (1.12.41) .. .. 75 2·25 15
a. Blue-green (1942) .. .. 65 1·50 15
115 1d. carmine (1.11.41) .. .. 55 1·75 15
a. "Stain" on uniform .. .. 6·00
116 1½d. myrtle-green (21.1.42) .. .. 55 1·75 15
117 3d. blue .. .. .. 22·00 15·00 1·00
a. Cigarette flaw .. .. 55·00
118 4d. orange-brown .. .. 6·50 11·00 1·00
a. Red-brown .. .. 17·00 23·00 3·00
119 6d. red-orange .. .. 2·50 3·00 50
120 1s. 3d. olive-brown (15.1.43) .. 11·00 13·00 1·25

(*b*) *Inscr bilingually*
Un single *Us single*
121 2d. violet 50 40
122 1s. brown (17.11.41) 60 40
114/22 *Set of 7 pairs and 2 singles* 40·00 42·00

1943–44. *War Effort (reduced sizes). Nos.* 97/104 *of South Africa, optd with T* **29** (1½d. *and* 1s., *No.* 130), *or T* **31** (*others*).

(*a*) *Inscr alternately*
Un unit *Us unit* *Us single*
123 ½d. blue-green (T) .. .. 40 2·50 10
a. Green .. .. 3·25 3·75 15
b. Greenish blue .. .. 3·25 3·75 10
124 1d. carmine-red (T) .. .. 90 2·50 10
a. Bright carmine .. .. 2·25 3·50 10
125 1½d. red-brown (P) 45 50 10
126 2d. violet (P) .. .. 4·50 2·75 10
a. Reddish violet .. .. 5·50 3·00 10
b. Apostrophe flaw .. .. 15·00
127 3d. blue (T) .. .. 3·25 11·00 45
128 6d. red-orange (P) .. .. 4·50 2·50 30
a. Opt inverted £425

(*b*) *Inscr bilingually*
129 4d. slate-green (T) .. .. 2·00 13·00 45
a. Opt inverted .. .. £425 £275 50·00
130 1s. brown (opt T **29**) (P) .. 11·00 22·00 2·00
a. Opt inverted £425 £300
b. Opt T **31** (1944) .. .. 4·00 4·00 30
c. Opt T **31** inverted .. .. £375 £275 40·00
d. "Bursting shell" .. .. 25·00
123/30*b* .. .. *Set of* 8 18·00 35·00 1·75

The "units" referred to above consist of pairs (P) or triplets (T).
No. 128 exists with another type of opt as Type **31**, but with broader "s", narrower "w" and more space between the letters.

1945. *Victory. Nos.* 108/10 *of South Africa optd with T* **30**.
131 1d. brown and carmine 25 50 10
a. Opt inverted £225 £250
132 2d. slate-blue and violet 30 55 10
133 3d. deep blue and blue .. .. 1·25 90 10
131/3 .. .. .. *Set of* 3 1·60 1·75 20

1947 (17 Feb). *Royal Visit. Nos.* 111/13 *of South Africa optd as T* **31**, *but* 8½ × 2 *mm.*
134 1d. black and carmine 10 10 10
135 2d. violet 10 20 10
a. "Bird" on "2" .. .. 5·50
136 3d. blue 15 20 10
134/6 .. .. .. *Set of* 3 30 45 15

1948 (26 Apr). *Royal Silver Wedding. No.* 125 *of South Africa, optd as T* **31**, *but* 4 × 2 *mm.*
137 3d. blue and silver .. .. 1·50 35 10

1949 (1 Oct). *75th Anniv of U.P.U. Nos.* 128/30 *of South Africa optd as T* **30**, *but* 13 × 4 *mm.*
138 ½d. blue-green .. .. 1·00 2·00 25
139 1½d. brown-red .. .. 1·00 1·00 15
140 3d. bright blue .. .. 1·50 1·50 25
a. Serif on "C" .. .. 20·00
b. "Lake" in East Africa .. .. 25·00
138/40 .. .. .. *Set of* 3 3·25 4·00 60

1949 (1 Dec). *Inauguration of Voortrekker Monument, Pretoria. Nos.* 131/3 *of South Africa optd with T* **32**.
Un single *Us single*
141 1d. magenta 10 10
142 1½d. blue-green 10 10
143 3d. blue 15 25
141/3 .. .. .. *Set of* 3 30 30

1952 (14 Mar). *Tercentenary of Landing of Van Riebeeck. Nos.* 136/40 *of South Africa optd as T* **30**, *but* 8 × 3½ *mm* (1d., 4½d.) *or* 11 × 4 *mm* (*others*).
144 ½d. brown-purple and olive-grey .. 10 40
145 1d. deep blue-green 10 10
146 2d. deep violet 50 10
147 4½d. blue .. .. .. 30 2·50
148 1s. brown .. .. .. 1·25 20
144/8 .. .. .. *Set of* 5 2·00 3·00

PRINTERS. The following stamps were printed by the Government Printer, Pretoria, in photogravure (Nos. 149/234) or lithography (subsequent issues), *unless stated otherwise.*

33 Queen Elizabeth II and *Catophracies Alexandri*

1953 (2 June). *Coronation. T* **33** *and similar horiz designs. W* **9** *of South Africa. P* 14.
149 1d. bright carmine 60 10
150 2d. deep bluish green 60 10
151 4d. magenta .. .. .. 1·10 55
152 6d. dull ultramarine .. .. 1·10 1·25
153 1s. deep orange-brown .. .. 1·10 40
149/53 .. .. .. *Set of* 5 4·00 2·25

Designs:—2d. *Bauhinia macrantha*, 4d. *Caralluma nebrownii*, 6d. *Gloriosa virescens*, 1s. *Rhigozum tricholotum*.

34 "Two Bucks" (rock painting)

36 "Rhinoceros Hunt" (rock painting)

38 Karakul Lamb

39 Ovambo Woman blowing Horn

(Des O. Schroeder (1d. to 4d.), M. Vandenschen (4½d. to 10s.))

1954 (15 Nov). *T* **34**, **36**, **38/9** *and similar designs. W* **9** *of South Africa (sideways* on vert designs). P* 14.
154 1d. brown-red 30 10
w. Wmk head of springbok to right .. 15·00 7·00
155 2d. deep brown 35 10
156 3d. dull purple .. .. .. 2·25 10
157 4d. blackish olive .. .. .. 2·50 10
158 4½d. deep blue .. .. .. 1·25 20
159 6d. myrtle-green .. .. .. 1·25 50
w. Wmk head of springbok to right .. 60·00 32·00
160 1s. deep mauve .. .. .. 1·25 50
161 1s. 3d. cerise .. .. .. 6·00 80
162 1s. 6d. purple .. .. .. 6·00 50
163 2s. 6d. bistre-brown .. .. 10·00 70
164 5s. deep bright blue .. .. 15·00 2·75
165 10s. deep myrtle-green .. .. 48·00 15·00
154/65 .. .. .. *Set of* 12 85·00 19·00

Designs: *Vert* (*as T* **34**)—2d. "White Lady" (rock painting). (*As T* **38**)—2s. 6d. Lioness; 5s. Gemsbok; 10s. African Elephant. (*As T* **39**)—1s. Ovambo woman; 1s. 3d. Herero woman; 1s. 6d. Ovambo girl. *Horiz* (*as T* **36**)—4d. "White Elephant and Giraffe" (rock painting).

*The normal sideways watermark shows springbok heads pointing left, *as seen from the back of the stamp.*

1960 *As Nos.* 154/7, 162, *but W* **102** *of South Africa (sideways on vert designs). P* 14.
166 1d. brown-red .. .. .. 55 1·25
167 2d. deep brown .. .. .. 70 1·25
168 3d. dull purple .. .. .. 1·40 4·00
169 4d. blackish olive .. .. .. 4·25 4·75
170 1s. 6d. purple .. .. .. 26·00 15·00
166/70 .. .. .. *Set of* 5 30·00 23·00

(New Currency. 100 cents = 1 South African rand)

46 G.P.O. Windhoek

47 Finger Rock

48 Mounted Soldier Monument

49 Quivertree

50 S.W.A. House, Windhoek

50a Greater Flamingoes and Swakopmund Lighthouse

51 Fishing Industry

52 Greater Flamingo

53 German Lutheran Church, Windhoek

54 Diamond

55 Fort Namutoni

55a Hardap Dam

56 Topaz

57 Tourmaline

58 Heliodor

1961 (14 Feb)–**63**. *Unsurfaced paper. W* **102** *of South Africa (sideways on vert designs). P* 14.
171 **46** ½ c. brown and pale blue 60 10
172 **47** 1 c. sepia and reddish lilac 15 10
173 **48** 1½ c. slate-violet and salmon 20 10
174 **49** 2 c. deep green and yellow 75 50
175 **50** 2½ c. red-brown and light blue 35 10
176 **50a** 3 c. ultramarine and rose-red (1.10.62) 4·25 40
177 **51** 3½ c. indigo and blue-green 70 15
178 **52** 5 c. scarlet and grey-blue .. .. 6·50 10
179 **53** 7½ c. sepia and pale lemon 70 15
180 **54** 10 c. blue and greenish yellow .. .. 1·75 15
181 **55** 12½ c. indigo and lemon 85 30
182 **55a** 15 c. chocolate and light blue (16.3.63) 14·00 3·25
183 **56** 20 c. brown and red-orange .. .. 8·00 30
184 **57** 50 c. deep bluish green & yellow-orge 11·00 1·50
185 **58** 1 r. yellow, maroon and blue .. 22·00 15·00
171/185 .. .. .. *Set of* 15 60·00 19·00

See also Nos. 186/91, 202/16, 224/6 and 240.

1962–66. *As No.* 171, *etc., but without watermark.*
186 **46** ½ c. brown and pale blue (8.62) .. 50 1·75
187 **48** 1½ c. slate-violet and salmon (9.62) .. 6·00 35
188 **49** 2 c. deep green and yellow (5.62) .. 3·50 4·00
189 **50** 2½ c. red-brown and light blue (1964) .. 5·00 5·00
190 **51** 3½ c. indigo and blue-green (1966) .. 12·00 4·50
191 **52** 5 c. scarlet and grey-blue (9.62) .. 7·00 75
186/91 .. .. .. *Set of* 6 30·00 14·50

59 "Agricultural Development"

60 Centenary Emblem and Map

61 Centenary Emblem and part of Globe

1963 (16 Mar). *Opening of Hardap Dam. W* **102** *of South Africa (sideways). P* 14.
192 **59** 3 c. chocolate and light green 30 15

1963 (30 Aug). *Centenary of Red Cross. P* 14.
193 **60** 7½ c. red, black and light blue .. .. 7·00 6·00
194 **61** 15 c. red, black and orange-brown .. 11·00 9·00

62 Interior of Assembly Hall

63 Calvin

1964 (14 May). *Opening of Legislative Assembly Hall, Windhoek. W* **102** *of South Africa. P* 14.
195 **62** 3 c. ultramarine and salmon 50 30

1964 (1 Oct). 400*th Death Anniv of Calvin (Protestant reformer). P* 14.
196 **63** 2½ c. brown-purple and gold 50 15
197 15 c. deep bluish green and gold .. .. 2·75 3·25

64 Mail Runner of 1890

65 Kurt von François (founder)

66 Dr. H. Vedder

(Des D. Aschenborn)

1965 (18 Oct). 75*th Anniv of Windhoek. Chalk-surfaced paper. W* **127** *of South Africa (sideways). P* 14.
198 **64** 3 c. sepia and scarlet 50 15
199 **65** 15 c. red-brown and blue-green .. .. 1·25 2·25

1966 (4 July). 90*th Birth Anniv of Dr. H. Vedder (philosopher and writer). Chalk-surfaced paper. W* **127** *of South Africa (sideways). P* 14.
200 **66** 3 c. blackish green and salmon 50 15
201 15 c. deep sepia and light blue .. .. 1·25 65

Nos. 200/1 exist on Swiss-made paper with *tête-bêche* watermark from a special printing made for use in presentation albums for delegates to the U.P.U. Congress in Tokyo in 1969, as supplies of the original Harrison paper were by then exhausted (*Set of 2 price £22 mint*).

1966–72. *As 1961–66 but chalk-surfaced paper and W* **127** *of South Africa* (sideways† on vert designs).*
202 **46** ½ c. brown and pale blue (1967) .. 1·25 10
203 **47** 1 c. sepia and light reddish lilac (1967) 1·50 10
a. Grey-brown and lilac (9.72) .. 3·00 10
204 **48** 1½ c. slate-violet and salmon (1968) .. 7·00 30
205 **49** 2 c. deep bluish green and yellow .. 4·00 10
206 **50** 2½ c. dp red-brown & lt turquoise-blue 2·50 30
a. Dp red-brown & pale blue (1967) 70 10
207 **50a** 3 c. ultramarine and rose-red (1970) 8·50 50
208 **51** 3½ c. indigo and blue-green (1967) .. 4·00 4·00
209 **50** 4 c. dp red-brown & lt turq-bl (1.4.71) 1·50 2·50
210 **52** 5 c. scarlet and grey-blue (1968) .. 4·00 10
211 **53** 6 c. sepia & greenish yellow (31.8.71) 8·50 11·00
212 7½ c. sepia and pale lemon (1967) .. 3·50 30
w. Wmk top of triangle to right .. 3·50 30
213 **55** 9 c. indigo & greenish yellow (1.7.71) 8·50 11·00
214 **54** 10 c. brt blue & greenish yellow (6.70) 18·00 1·50
a. Whiter background** (9.72) .. 18·00 2·25
215 **55a** 15 c. chocolate and light blue (1.72) 20·00 6·50
216 **56** 20 c. brown and red-orange (1968) .. 18·00 1·75
202/16 .. .. *Set of* 15 95·00 35·00

*The watermark in this issue is indistinct but the stamps can be distinguished from the stamps without watermark by their shades and the chalk-surfaced paper which is appreciably thicker and whiter. The 1, 1½, 3, 4, 5, 6, 9, 10, 15 and 20 c. are known only with the watermark *tête-bêche* but the ½ c. and 2½ c. exist with both forms, the remainder being as illustrated.

†The normal sideways watermark shows top of triangle pointing to left, *as seen from the back of the stamp.*

**No. 214a, printed from sheets, has a much whiter background around the value and behind "SOUTH WEST AFRICA" compared with No. 214, which was issued in coils only.

See also Nos. 224/6 and 240.

67 Camelthorn Tree

(Des D. Aschenborn (2½ c., 3 c.), Govt Printer, Pretoria (15 c.))

1967 (6 Jan). *Verwoerd Commemoration. Chalk-surfaced paper. T* **67** *and similar designs. W* **127** *of South Africa (sideways on vert designs). P* 14.
217 2½ c. black and emerald-green 20 10
218 3 c. brown and new blue 30 10
219 15 c. blackish brown and reddish purple 1·10 45
217/19 .. .. *Set of* 3 1·40 60

Designs: *Vert.*—3 c. Waves breaking against rock; 15 c. Dr. H. F. Verwoerd.

COVER PRICES

Cover factors are quoted at the beginning of each country for most issues to 1945. An explanation of the system can be found on page x. The factors quoted do not, however, apply to philatelic covers.

70 President Swart   71 President and Mrs. Swart

1968 (2 Jan). *Swart Commemoration. Chalk-surfaced paper. W* **127** *of South Africa (tête-bêche, sideways). P* 14 × 15.
220 **70** 3 c. orange-red, black & turquoise-blue
G. Inscribed in German 45 15
A. Inscribed in Afrikaans 45 15
E. Inscribed in English 45 15
221 **71** 15 c. red, blackish olive and dull green
G. Inscribed in German .. .. 1·50 1·75
A. Inscribed in Afrikaans .. .. 1·50 1·75
E. Inscribed in English .. .. 1·50 1·75
a. Red, brownish olive & bronze-green
G. Inscribed in German .. .. 3·00 2·25
A. Inscribed in Afrikaans .. .. 3·00 2·25
E. Inscribed in English .. .. 3·00 2·25
220/1 .. .. *Set of 2 values in strips of three* 12·00
Set of 6 singles 5·00 5·00

The three languages appear, *se-tenant*, both horizontally and vertically, throughout the sheet.

1970 (14 Feb). *Water 70 Campaign. As Nos.* 299/300 *of South Africa, but without phosphor band and inscr* "SWA".
222 2½ c. green, bright blue and chocolate .. 75 30
223 3 c. Prussian blue, royal blue and buff .. 75 30

72 G.P.O., Windhoek

73 "Red Sand-dunes, Eastern South West Africa"

1970–71. *As Nos.* 202 *and* 204/5 *but* "POSGELD INKOMSTE" *omitted and larger figure of value as in T* **72**. *W* **127** *of South Africa (tête-bêche, sideways on* 1½ *and* 2 *c.).*
224 **72** ½ c. brown and pale blue (6.70).. .. 1·50 30
225 – 1½ c. slate-violet and salmon (1.6.71) .. 13·00 16·00
226 – 2 c. deep bluish green and lemon (11.70) 5·00 40
224/6 .. .. *Set of* 3 18·00 16·00

1970 (24 Aug). 150*th Anniv of Bible Society of South Africa. As Nos.* 301/2 *of South Africa, but inscr* "SWA".
228 2½ c. multicoloured .. .. .. 1·50 10
229 12½ c. gold, black and blue .. .. 8·00 7·50

No. 228 has a phosphor frame, probably added in error.

A mint example of No. 229 exists with a second, blind, impression of the die-stamped features.

1971 (31 May). *"Interstex" Stamp Exhibition, Cape Town. As No.* 303A *of South Africa, but without phosphor frame and inscr* "SWA".
230 5 c. light greenish blue, black and pale yellow 4·75 1·50

1971 (31 May). *Tenth Anniv of Antarctic Treaty. As No.* 304 *of South Africa, but without phosphor frame, and inscr* "SWA".
231 12½ c. blue-black, greenish blue & orge-red 32·00 21·00

1971 (31 May). *Tenth Anniv of the South African Republic. As Nos.* 305/6 *of South Africa, but without phosphor frame, and inscr* "SWA".
232 2 c. pale flesh and brown-red.. .. .. 3·25 75
233 4 c. green and black .. .. .. 3·25 75

1972 (19 Sept). *Centenary of S.P.C.A. As No.* 312 *of South Africa, but inscr* "SWA".
234 5 c. multicoloured .. .. 3·50 55

WATERMARK. All issues from this date are on unwatermarked paper.

(Lettering by E. de Jong)

1973 (1 May). *Scenery. T* **73** *and similar multicoloured designs showing paintings by Adolph Jentsch. P* 11½ × 12½ (10 *and* 15 *c.) or* 12½ × 11½ *(others).*
235 2 c. Type **73** 75 75
236 4 c. "After the Rain" .. .. .. 1·25 1·25
237 5 c. "Barren Country" .. .. .. 1·50 1·50
238 10 c. "Schaap River" (*vert*) .. .. 2·75 2·75
239 15 c. "Namib Desert" (*vert*) .. .. 4·00 4·00
235/9 .. .. *Set of* 5 9·00 9·00

1973 (28 May). *As Nos.* 207 *but without wmk. Phosphorised paper.*
240 **50a** 3 c. ultramarine and rose-red .. .. 2·50 1·25

No. 240 is also distinguishable in that the lettering of "SOUTH WEST AFRICA" is whiter.

74 *Sarcocaulon rigidum*

75 *Euphorbia virosa*

(Des D. Findlay)

1973 (1 Sept)–**79**. *Succulents. Various multicoloured designs as T* **74/5**. *Phosphorised glossy paper (original printing of all values) or ordinary paper* (1, 2, 3, 4, 5, 9, 10, 15, 20, 30, 50 *c.*).

(*a*) *As T* **74**. *P* 12½.
241 1 c. Type **74** 15 10
a. Black (face value, etc.) omitted .. £200
242 2 c. *Lapidaria margaretae* 90 50
a. Perf 14 × 13½ (4.8.79) 20 10
243 3 c. *Titanopsis schwantesii* 20 10
a. Black (face value, etc.) omitted .. 80·00
b. Perf 14 × 13½ (8.8.79) 30 15
244 4 c. *Lithops karasmontana* 25 10
245 5 c. *Caralluma lugardii* 40 30
a. Black (face value, etc.) omitted .. £140
b. Perf 14 × 13½ (12.12.79) 50 20
246 6 c. *Dinteranthus microspermus* .. 1·25 1·25
247 7 c. *Conophytum gratum* .. .. 75 1·25
248 9 c. *Huernia oculata* .. .. .. 65 1·50
249 10 c. *Gasteria pillansii* 80 45
a. Black (face value, etc.) omitted .. £200
b. Perf 14 × 13½ (13.8.79) 40 30
250 14 c. *Stapelia pedunculata* .. .. 1·50 2·00
251 15 c. *Fenestraria aurantiaca* 65 30
252 20 c. *Decabelone grandiflora* .. .. 4·50 2·25
253 25 c. *Hoodia bainii* .. .. .. 3·00 1·75

(*b*) *As T* **75**. *P* 11½×12½ (30 *c.*, 1 *r.*) *or* 12½×11½ (50 *c.*)
254 30 c. Type **75** .. .. 1·00 80
a. Perf 13½×14 (27.12.79) 90 90
255 50 c. *Pachypodium namaquanum* (*vert*) .. 1·25 2·25
a. Perf 14×13½ (18.12.79) .. .. 1·25 1·25
256 1 r. *Welwitschia bainesii* .. .. 2·00 5·00
241/56 .. .. *Set of* 16 16·00 16·00

1973 (1 Sept)–**80**. *Coil stamps. As Nos.* 241/2 *and* 245 *but photo, colours changed. P* 14.
257 1 c. black and light mauve 70 60
a. Chalk-surfaced paper (7.76?) .. 1·00 40
b. Imperf × perf 14. Chalk-surfaced paper (1980) .. .. 4·75 5·00
258 2 c. black and yellow 50 50
a. Chalk-surfaced paper (7.76?) .. 1·00 50
b. Imperf × perf 14. Chalk-surfaced paper (1.79) .. .. 1·00 40
259 5 c. black and light rose-red .. .. 1·75 60
a. Imperf × perf 14. Chalk-surfaced paper (8.2.78) .. .. 1·25 60
257/9 .. .. *Set of* 3 2·25 1·25

Coils of Nos. 257b, 258b and 259a come with every fifth stamp numbered on the reverse.

76 Chat-shrike

77 Giraffe, Antelope and Spoor

(Des D. Findlay)

1974 (13 Feb). *Rare Birds. T* **76** *and similar vert designs. Multicoloured. P* 12½ × 11½.
260 4 c. Type **76** .. .. 3·25 1·00
261 5 c. Peach-faced Lovebirds .. .. 4·25 1·50
262 10 c. Damaraland Rock Jumper .. .. 11·00 5·50
263 15 c. Rüppell's Parrots .. .. .. 15·00 9·50
260/3 .. .. *Set of* 4 30·00 16·00

(Des O. Schröder)

1974 (10 Apr). *Twyfelfontein Rock-engravings. T* **77** *and similar multicoloured designs. P* 11½ × 12½ (15 *c.*) *or* 12½ (*others*).
264 4 c. Type **77** .. .. 1·50 50
265 5 c. Elephant, hyena, antelope and spoor .. 1·50 80
a. Black (value and "SWA") omitted .. £1000
266 15 c. Kudu Cow (38 × 21 *mm*) .. .. 7·00 7·50
264/6 .. .. *Set of* 3 9·00 8·00

78 Cut Diamond

79 Wagons and Map of the Trek

(Des M. Barnett)

1974 (30 Sept). *Diamond Mining. T* **78** *and similar vert design. Multicoloured. P* 12½ × 11½.

267	10 c. Type **78**	6·00	6·00
268	15 c. Diagram of shore workings	6·00	6·00

(Des K. Esterhuysen)

1974 (13 Nov). *Centenary of Thirstland Trek. P* 11½ × 12½.

269	**79** 4 c. multicoloured	1·00	1·00

80 Peregrine Falcon **81** Kolmannskop (ghost town)

(Des D. Findlay)

1975 (19 Mar). *Protected Birds of Prey. T* **80** *and similar vert designs. Multicoloured. P* 12½ × 11½.

270	4 c. Type **80**	2·00	1·25
271	5 c. Verreaux's Eagle	2·25	1·75
272	10 c. Martial Eagle	6·00	5·50
273	15 c. Egyptian Vulture	7·50	8·00
270/3	*Set of* 4	16·00	15·00

(Des A. H. Barrett)

1975 (23 July). *Historic Monuments. T* **81** *and similar horiz designs. Multicoloured. P* 11½ × 12½.

274	5 c. Type **81**	30	15
275	9 c. "Martin Luther" (steam tractor)	50	60
276	15 c. Kurt von François and Old Fort, Windhoek	1·00	1·00
274/6	*Set of* 3	1·60	1·60

82 "View of Lüderitz"

(Des J. Hoekstra)

1975 (15 Oct). *Otto Schröder. T* **82** *and similar horiz designs showing his paintings. Multicoloured. P* 11½ × 12½.

277	15 c. Type **82**	60	60
	a. Block of 4. Nos. 277/80	2·25	
278	15 c. "View of Swakopmund"	60	60
279	15 c. "Harbour Scene"	60	60
280	15 c. "Quayside, Walvis Bay"	60	60
277/80	*Set of* 4	2·25	2·25
MS281	122 × 96 mm. Nos. 277/80	2·25	4·50

Nos. 277/80 were printed together, in *se-tenant* blocks of four within the sheet.

83 Elephants

(Des H. Pager)

1976 (31 Mar). *Prehistoric Rock Paintings. T* **83** *and similar horiz designs. Multicoloured. P* 11½ × 12½.

282	4 c. Type **83**	50	15
283	10 c. Rhinoceros	75	60
284	15 c. Antelope	90	70
285	20 c. Man with bow and arrow	1·25	1·10
282/5	*Set of* 4	3·00	2·25
MS286	121 × 95 mm. Nos. 282/5	3·00	4·00

84 Schwerinsburg

(Des H. Pager)

1976 (14 May). *Castles. T* **84** *and similar horiz designs. Multicoloured. P* 11½ × 12½.

287	10 c. Type **84**	40	30
288	15 c. Schloss Duwisib	55	50
289	20 c. Heynitzburg	75	80
287/9	*Set of* 3	1·50	1·40

NEW INFORMATION

The editor is always interested to correspond with people who have new information that will improve or correct the Catalogue.

85 Large-toothed Rock Hyrax

(Des D. Findlay)

1976 (16 July). *Fauna Conservation. T* **85** *and similar horiz designs. Multicoloured. P* 11½ × 12½.

290	4 c. Type **85**	50	20
291	10 c. Kirk's Dik-Dik	1·25	90
292	15 c. Kuhl's Tree Squirrel	2·00	2·25
290/2	*Set of* 3	3·25	3·00

86 The Augustineum, Windhoek

(Des H. Pager)

1976 (17 Sept). *Modern Buildings. T* **86** *and similar horiz design. P* 11½ × 12½.

293	15 c. black and yellow	50	65
294	20 c. black and light yellow	60	75

Design:—20 c. Katutura Hospital, Windhoek.

87 Ovambo Water Canal System

(Des A. H. Barrett)

1976 (19 Nov). *Water and Electricity Supply. T* **87** *and similar horiz design. Multicoloured. P* 11½ × 12½.

295	15 c. Type **87**	40	40
296	20 c. Ruacana Falls Power Station	50	50

88 Coastline near Pomona

(Des A. H. Barrett)

1977 (29 Mar). *Namib Desert. T* **88** *and similar horiz designs. Multicoloured. P* 12½.

297	4 c. Type **88**	20	15
298	10 c. Bush and dunes, Sossusvlei	30	30
299	15 c. Plain near Brandberg	50	50
300	20 c. Dunes, Sperr Gebiet	60	60
297/300	*Set of* 4	1·40	1·40

89 Kraal

(Des A. H. Barrett)

1977 (15 July). *The Ovambo People. T* **89** *and similar horiz designs. P* 11½ × 12½.

301	4 c. multicoloured	10	10
302	10 c. black, dull orange and cinnamon	30	20
303	15 c. multicoloured	30	25
304	20 c. multicoloured	35	45
301/4	*Set of* 4	95	90

Designs—10 c. Grain baskets; 15 c. Pounding grain; 20 c. Women in tribal dress.

90 Terminal Buildings

(Des H. Pager and A. H. Barrett)

1977 (22 Aug). *J. G. Strijdom Airport, Windhoek. P* 12½.

305	**90** 20 c. multicoloured	40	30

91 Drostdy, Lüderitz **92** Side-winding Adder

(Des A. H. Barrett)

1977 (4 Nov). *Historic Houses. T* **91** *and similar horiz designs. Multicoloured. P* 12 × 12½.

306	5 c. Type **91**	15	10
307	10 c. Woermannhaus, Swakopmund	30	30
308	15 c. Neu-Heusis, Windhoek	35	35
309	20 c. Schmelenhaus, Bethanie	55	40
306/9	*Set of* 4	1·25	1·10
MS310	122 × 96 mm. Nos. 306/9	1·50	2·25

(Des D. Findlay)

1978 (6 Feb). *Small Animals. T* **92** *and similar horiz designs. Multicoloured. P* 12½.

311	4 c. Type **92**	15	10
312	10 c. Grant's Desert Golden Mole	30	30
313	15 c. Palmato Gecko	50	30
314	20 c. Namaqua Chameleon	65	40
311/14	*Set of* 4	1·40	1·00

93 Ostrich Hunting

(Des A. H. Barrett)

1978 (14 Apr). *The Bushmen. T* **93** *and similar horiz designs in light grey-brown, stone and black. P* 12 × 12½.

315	4 c. Type **93**	30	10
316	10 c. Woman carrying ostrich eggs	30	20
317	15 c. Hunters kindling fire	45	30
318	20 c. Woman with musical instrument	55	40
315/18	*Set of* 4	1·40	90

94 Lutheran Church, Windhoek

ALGEMENE
STEMREG

(95)

(Des A. H. Barrett)

1978 (16 June). *Historic Churches. T* **94** *and similar horiz designs. P* 12½.

319	4 c. grey-black and cinnamon	10	10
320	10 c. grey-black and ochre	15	20
321	15 c. grey-black and light brown-rose	20	25
322	20 c. grey-black and light grey-blue	30	35
319/22	*Set of* 4	65	80
MS323	125 × 90 mm. Nos. 319/22	1·00	1·75

Designs:—10 c. Lutheran Church, Swakopmund; 15 c. Rhenish Mission Church, Otjimbingwe; 20 c. Rhenish Missionary Church, Keetmanshoop.

1978 (1 Nov). *Universal Suffrage. Designs as Nos.* 244/5, 249 *and* 251/3 *optd with T* **95** *(or similar inscr in English or German).*

324	4 c. *Lithops karasmontana*		
	A. Opt in Afrikaans	10	10
	E. Opt in English	10	10
	G. Opt in German	10	10
325	5 c. *Caralluma lugardii*		
	A. Opt in Afrikaans	10	10
	E. Opt in English	10	10
	G. Opt in German	10	10
326	10 c. *Gasteria pillansii*		
	A. Opt in Afrikaans	10	10
	E. Opt in English	10	10
	G. Opt in German	10	10
327	15 c. *Fenestraria aurantiaca*		
	A. Opt in Afrikaans	15	15
	E. Opt in English	15	15
	G. Opt in German	15	15
328	20 c. *Decabelone grandiflora*		
	A. Opt in Afrikaans	20	20
	E. Opt in English	20	20
	G. Opt in German	20	20
329	25 c. *Hoodia bainii*		
	A. Opt in Afrikaans	25	25
	E. Opt in English	25	25
	G. Opt in German	25	25
324/9	*Set of* 18 (6 *strips of* 3)	2·40	2·40

Nos. 324A/G, 325A/G, 326A/G, 327A/G, 328A/G and 329A/G were each printed together, *se-tenant*, in horizontal and vertical strips of 3 throughout the sheets.

OMNIBUS ISSUES

Details, together with prices for complete sets, of the various Omnibus issues from the 1935 Silver Jubilee series to date are included in a special section following Zululand at the end of the catalogue.

96 Greater Flamingo **97** Silver Topaz

(Des D. Findlay)

1979 (5 Apr). *Water Birds. T* **96** *and similar vert designs. Multicoloured. P* 14.

330 4 c. Type **96** .. 20 10
331 15 c. White-breasted Cormorant .. 45 25
332 20 c. Chestnut-banded Sand Plover .. 50 35
333 25 c. Eastern White Pelican .. 55 40
330/3 .. *Set of* 4 1·50 1·00

(Des H. Botha)

1979 (26 Nov). *Gemstones. T* **97** *and similar horiz designs. Multicoloured. P* 14.

334 4 c. Type **97** .. 30 10
335 15 c. Aquamarine .. 65 20
336 20 c. Malachite .. 70 25
337 25 c. Amethyst .. 70 30
334/7 .. *Set of* 4 2·10 75

98 Killer Whale **99** Impala

(Des A. H. Barrett)

1980 (25 Mar). *Whales. T* **98** *and similar multicoloured designs. P* 14.

338 4 c. Type **98** .. 35 20
339 5 c. Humpback Whale (38 × 22 *mm*) .. 40 20
340 10 c. Black Right Whale (38 × 22 *mm*) .. 55 30
341 15 c. Sperm Whale (58 × 22 *mm*) .. 1·00 75
342 20 c. Fin Whale (58 × 22 *mm*) .. 1·25 90
343 25 c. Blue Whale (88 × 22 *mm*) .. 1·60 1·25
338/43 .. *Set of* 6 4·50 3·25
MS344 202 × 95 mm. Nos. 338/43 .. 5·50 6·00

(Des P. Bosman)

1980 (25 June). *25th Anniv of Division of Nature Conservation and Tourism. Antelopes. T* **99** *and similar horiz designs. Multicoloured. P* 14.

345 5 c. Type **99** .. 15 10
346 10 c. Topi .. 20 10
347 15 c. Roan Antelope .. 40 15
348 20 c. Sable Antelope .. 50 20
345/8 .. *Set of* 4 1·10 45

100 Black-backed Jackal **101** Meerkat

(Des Sheila Nowers (11, 12, 14, 16 c.), P. Bosman (others))

1980 (1 Oct)–**89**. *Wildlife. Multicoloured designs as T* **100**. *Ordinary paper. P* 14.

349 1 c. Type **100** .. 15 10
a. Chalk-surfaced paper (11.6.85) .. 1·00 1·00
350 2 c. Hunting Dog .. 30 10
a. Chalk-surfaced paper (4.6.86) .. 1·25 1·25
351 3 c. Brown Hyena .. 20 10
a. Chalk-surfaced paper (10.2.88) .. 80 90
352 4 c. Springbok .. 20 10
a. Chalk-surfaced paper (29.7.87) .. 80 90
353 5 c. Gemsbok .. 20 10
a. Chalk-surfaced paper (11.6.85) .. 1·75 1·75
354 6 c. Greater Kudu .. 20 10
a. Chalk-surfaced paper (8.8.88) .. 1·75 1·75
355 7 c. Mouuntain Zebra (*horiz*) .. 40 20
a. Chalk-surfaced paper (19.3.86) .. 2·00 2·00
356 8 c. Cape Porcupine (*horiz*) .. 30 10
a. Chalk-surfaced paper (11.6.85) .. 2·00 2·00
357 9 c. Ratel (*horiz*) .. 30 10
a. Chalk-surfaced paper (10.2.88) .. 2·00 2·00
358 10 c. Cheetah (*horiz*) .. 30 10
358*a* 11 c. Blue Wildebeest (2.4.84) .. 40 30
358*b* 12 c. African Buffalo (*horiz*) (1.4.85) .. 70 1·25
ba. Booklet pane of 10 with margins all round (1.8.85) .. 4·50
358*c* 14 c. Caracal (*horiz*) (*chalk-surfaced paper*) (1.4.86) .. 3·00 2·25
359 15 c. Hippopotamus (*horiz*) .. 30 10
a. Chalk-surfaced paper (10.2.88) .. 80 1·10
359*b* 16 c. Warthog (*horiz*) (*chalk-surfaced paper*) (1.4.87) .. 1·75 1·75
ba. Ordinary paper (15.2.89) .. 3·00 3·00
360 20 c. Eland (*horiz*) .. 30 10
a. Chalk-surfaced paper (11.6.85) .. 80 1·25
361 25 c. Black Rhinoceros (*horiz*) .. 50 20
a. Chalk-surfaced paper (11.6.85) .. 80 1·25
362 30 c. Lion (*horiz*) .. 80 20
a. Chalk-surfaced paper (4.6.86) .. 1·75 1·75
363 50 c. Giraffe .. 50 30
a. Chalk-surfaced paper (21.4.88) .. 1·25 1·75
364 1 r. Leopard .. 1·00 55
a. Chalk-surfaced paper (4.6.86) .. 2·25 2·50
365 2 r. African Elephant .. 1·00 90
a. Chalk-surfaced paper (10.2.88) .. 3·00 3·25
349/65 .. *Set of* 21 11·50 8·00

Some printings of the 4, 15 and 25 c. from 1983/4 were on phosphorescent paper. The same paper was used for printings of the 1, 2, 3, 8, 9, 10, 16 c. (No. 359ba), 20, 30 c. and 1 r. during 1989.

For $1.20 design as No. 359*b* see No. **MS**675 and for $1.30 as No. 358*c* see No. **MS**685.

(Des P. Bosman. Photo)

1980 (1 Oct). *Coil stamps. Wildlife. Vert designs as T* **101**. *Imperf × perf* 14.

366 1 c. yellow-brown .. 20 20
367 2 c. deep dull blue .. 20 20
368 5 c. yellow-olive .. 30 30
366/8 .. *Set of* 3 65 65

Designs:—2 c. Savanna Monkey; 5 c. Chacma Baboon.

102 Von Bach

(Des A. H. Barrett)

1980 (25 Nov). *Water Conservation. Dams. T* **102** *and similar horiz designs. Multicoloured. P* 14.

369 5 c. Type **102** .. 10 10
370 10 c. Swakoppoort .. 15 10
371 15 c. Naute .. 20 20
372 20 c. Hardap .. 25 25
369/72 .. *Set of* 4 60 60

103 View of Fish River Canyon **104** *Aloe erinacea*

(Des A. H. Barrett)

1981 (20 Mar). *Fish River Canyon. T* **103** *and similar horiz designs showing various views of canyon. P* 14.

373 5 c. multicoloured .. 10 10
374 15 c. multicoloured .. 20 20
375 20 c. multicoloured .. 25 25
376 25 c. multicoloured .. 30 30
373/6 .. *Set of* 4 75 70

(Des D. Findlay)

1981 (14 Aug). *Aloes. T* **104** *and similar vert designs. Multicoloured. P* 14 × 13½.

377 5 c. Type **104** .. 15 10
378 15 c. *Aloe viridiflora* .. 35 25
379 20 c. *Aloe pearsonii* .. 40 25
380 25 c. *Aloe littoralis* .. 50 30
377/80 .. *Set of* 4 1·25 75

105 Paul Weiss-Haus

(Des A. H. Barrett)

1981 (16 Oct). *Historic Buildings of Lüderitz. T* **105** *and similar horiz designs. Multicoloured. P* 14.

381 5 c. Type **105** .. 10 10
382 15 c. Deutsche Afrika Bank .. 20 20
383 20 c. Schroederhaus .. 30 30
384 25 c. Altes Postamt .. 30 35
381/4 .. *Set of* 4 75 80
MS385 125 × 90 mm. Nos. 381/4 .. 85 90

106 Salt Pan **107** Kalahari Starred Tortoise (*Psammobates oculifer*)

(Des A. H. Barrett)

1981 (4 Dec). *Salt Industry. T* **106** *and similar horiz designs. Multicoloured. P* 14.

386 5 c. Type **106** .. 10 10
387 15 c. Dumping and washing .. 20 20
388 20 c. Loading by conveyor .. 25 30
389 25 c. Dispatch to refinery .. 30 35
386/9 .. *Set of* 4 70 80

(Des A. H. Barrett)

1982 (12 Mar). *Tortoises. T* **107** *and similar horiz designs. Multicoloured. P* 14.

390 5 c. Type **107** .. 15 10
391 15 c. Leopard Tortoise (*Geochelone pardalis*) .. 25 25
392 20 c. Angulate Tortoise (*Chersina angulata*) .. 30 35
393 25 c. Speckled Padloper (*Homopus signatus*) .. 40 45
390/3 .. *Set of* 4 1·00 1·00

108 Mythical Sea-monster

(Des Sheila Nowers)

1982 (28 May). *Discoverers of South West Africa.* (*1st series*). *Bartolomeu Dias. T* **108** *and similar horiz designs. Multicoloured. P* 14.

394 15 c. Type **108** .. 20 20
395 20 c. Bartolomeu Dias and map of Africa showing voyage .. 30 30
396 25 c. Dias' caravel .. 55 40
397 30 c. Dias erecting commemorative cross, Angra das Voltas, 25 July 1488 .. 55 45
394/7 .. *Set of* 4 1·40 1·25

See also Nos. 455/8.

109 Brandberg **110** Otjikaeva Head-dress of Herero Woman

(Des A. H. Barrett)

1982 (3 Aug). *Mountains of South West Africa. T* **109** *and similar horiz designs. Multicoloured. P* 13½ × 14.

398 6 c. Type **109** .. 10 10
399 15 c. Omatako .. 20 20
400 20 c. Die Nadel .. 25 30
401 25 c. Spitzkuppe .. 30 35
398/401 .. *Set of* 4 75 85

(Des A. H. Barrett)

1982 (15 Oct). *Traditional Head-dresses of South West Africa.* (*1st series*). *T* **110** *and similar vert designs. Multicoloured. P* 14.

402 6 c. Type **110** .. 10 10
403 15 c. Ekori head-dress of Himba .. 25 35
404 20 c. Oshikoma hair-piece and iipando plaits of Ngandjera .. 35 45
405 25 c. Omhatela head-dress of Kwanyama .. 35 60
402/5 .. *Set of* 4 95 1·40

See also Nos. 427/30.

111 Fort Vogelsang **112** Searching for Diamonds, Kolmanskop, 1908

(Des J. van Ellinckhuijzen)

1983 (16 Mar). *Centenary of Lüderitz. T* **111** *and similar designs. P* 14.

406 6 c. brownish black and deep carmine-red .. 10 10
407 20 c. brownish black and yellow-brown .. 25 30
408 25 c. brownish black and chestnut .. 30 35
409 30 c. brownish black and brown-purple .. 35 40
410 40 c. brownish black and bright green .. 50 55
406/10 .. *Set of* 5 1·40 1·50

Designs: *Vert* (23 × 29 *mm*)—20 c. Chief Joseph Fredericks; 30 c. Heinrich Vogelsang (founder); 40 c. Adolf Lüderitz (colonial promoter). *Horiz* (*As T* **111**)—25 c. Angra Pequena.

(Des J. van Ellinckhuijzen)

1983 (8 June). *75th Anniv of Discovery of Diamonds. T* **112** *and similar designs. P* 13½ × 14 (10, 20 *c.*) *or* 14 × 13½ (*others*).

411 10 c. deep brown and pale stone 15 15
412 20 c. maroon and pale stone 30 30
413 25 c. Prussian blue and pale stone 35 35
414 40 c. brownish black and pale stone 55 55
411/14 .. .. *Set of* 4 1·25 1·25

Designs: *Horiz* (34 × 19 *mm*)—20 c. Digging for diamonds, Kolmanskop, 1908. *Vert* (19 × 26 *mm*)—25 c. Sir Ernest Oppenheimer (industrialist); 40 c. August Stauch (prospector).

113 "Common Zebras drinking" (J. van Ellinckhuijzen)

114 The Rock Lobster

1983 (1 Sept). *Painters of South West Africa. T* **113** *and similar horiz designs. Multicoloured. P* 13½ × 14.

415 10 c. Type **113** 15 15
416 20 c. "Rossing Mountain" (H. Henckert) .. 25 30
417 25 c. "Stampeding African Buffalo" (F. Krampe) 30 35
418 40 c. "Erongo Mountains" (J. Blatt) 50 55
415/18 .. .. *Set of* 4 1·10 1·25

(Des J. van Ellinckhuijzen)

1983 (23 Nov). *Lobster Industry. T* **114** *and similar horiz designs. Multicoloured. P* 13½ × 14.

419 10 c. Type **114** 15 15
420 20 c. Mother ship and fishing dinghies .. 25 30
421 25 c. Netting lobsters from dinghy 30 35
422 40 c. Packing lobsters 50 55
419/22 .. .. *Set of* 4 1·10 1·25

115 Hohenzollern House

(Des A. H. Barrett)

1984 (8 Mar). *Historic Buildings of Swakopmund. T* **115** *and similar horiz designs. P* 14.

423 10 c. grey-black and orange-brown 15 15
424 20 c. grey-black and new blue 30 25
425 25 c. grey-black and yellow-green 30 30
426 30 c. grey-black and ochre 35 30
423/6 .. .. *Set of* 4 1·00 90

Designs:—20 c. Railway Station; 25 c. Imperial District Bureau; 30 c. Ritterburg.

(Des A. H. Barrett)

1984 (25 May). *Traditional Head-dresses of South West Africa (2nd series). Multicoloured designs as T* **110**. *P* 14.

427 11 c. Eendjushi head-dress of Kwambi .. 25 15
428 20 c. Bushman woman 40 25
429 25 c. Omulenda head-dress of Kwaluudhi .. 45 30
430 30 c. Mbukushu women 45 30
427/30 .. .. *Set of* 4 1·40 90

116 Map and German Flag

117 Sweet Thorn

(Des J. van Ellinckhuijzen)

1984 (7 Aug). *Centenary of German Colonisation. T* **116** *and similar horiz designs. Multicoloured. P* 14 × 14½.

431 11 c. Type **116** 25 15
432 25 c. Raising the German flag, 1884 .. .. 50 50
433 30 c. German Protectorate boundary marker 50 60
434 45 c. *Elizabeth* and *Leipzig* (German corvettes) .. .. 1·25 1·75
431/4 .. .. *Set of* 4 2·25 2·75

(Des Eva-Maria Linsmayer)

1984 (22 Nov). *Spring in South West Africa. T* **117** *and similar vert designs. Multicoloured. P* 14.

435 11 c. Type **117** 25 15
436 25 c. Camel Thorn 50 35
437 30 c. Hook Thorn 55 45
438 45 c. Candle-pod Acacia 70 70
435/8 .. .. *Set of* 4 1·75 1·50

NEW INFORMATION

The editor is always interested to correspond with people who have new information that will improve or correct the Catalogue.

118 Head of Ostrich

(Des J. van Ellinckhuijzen)

1985 (15 Mar). *Ostriches. T* **118** *and similar horiz designs. Multicoloured. P* 14.

439 11 c. Type **118** 40 10
440 25 c. Ostrich on eggs 70 30
441 30 c. Newly-hatched chick and eggs 80 50
442 50 c. Mating dance .. .. 1·10 75
439/42 .. .. *Set of* 4 2·75 1·50

119 Kaiserstrasse

(Des A. H. Barrett)

1985 (6 June). *Historic Buildings of Windhoek. T* **119** *and similar horiz designs. P* 14.

443 12 c. black and brown-ochre 25 10
444 25 c. black and grey-olive 45 25
445 30 c. black and brown 45 30
446 50 c. black and yellow-brown 90 70
443/6 .. .. *Set of* 4 1·90 1·25

Designs:—25 c. Turnhalle; 30 c. Old Supreme Court Building; 50 c. Railway Station.

120 Zwilling Locomotive

121 Lidumu-dumu (keyboard instrument)

(Des J. van Ellinckhuijzen)

1985 (2 Aug). *Narrow-gauge Railway Locomotives. T* **120** *and similar horiz designs. Multicoloured. P* 14.

447 12 c. Type **120** 30 10
448 25 c. Feldspur side-tank locomotive 60 25
449 30 c. Jung and Henschel side-tank locomotive 70 35
450 50 c. Henschel Hd locomotive 90 60
447/50 .. .. *Set of* 4 2·25 1·10

(Des J. van Ellinckhuijzen)

1985 (17 Oct). *Traditional Musical Instruments. T* **121** *and similar horiz designs. Multicoloured. P* 14.

451 12 c. Type **121** 10 10
452 25 c. Ngoma (drum) 20 20
453 30 c. Okambulumbumbwa (stringed instrument) 25 25
454 50 c. // Gwashi (stringed instrument) 35 35
451/4 .. .. *Set of* 4 80 80

122 Erecting Commemorative Pillar at Cape Cross, 1486

123 Ameib, Erongo Mountains

(Des J. van Ellinckhuijzen)

1986 (24 Jan). *Discoverers of South West Africa (2nd series). Diogo Cao. T* **122** *and similar horiz designs. P* 14.

455 12 c. black, brownish grey & deep dull green 35 10
456 20 c. black, brownish grey & pale red-brown 55 25
457 25 c. black, brownish grey and dull blue .. 70 35
458 30 c. black, brownish grey & dull reddish pur 85 60
455/8 .. .. *Set of* 4 2·25 1·10

Designs:—20 c. Diogo Cao's coat of arms; 25 c. Caravel; 30 c. Diogo Cao.

(Des J. van Niekerk)

1986 (24 Apr). *Rock Formations. T* **123** *and similar horiz designs. Multicoloured. P* 14.

459 14 c. Type **123** 60 15
460 20 c. Vingerklip, near Outjo 70 25
461 25 c. Petrified sand dunes, Kuiseb River .. 85 40
462 30 c. Orgelpfeifen, Twyfelfontein 95 55
459/62 .. .. *Set of* 4 2·75 1·25

PHILATELIC FOUNDATION MINIATURE SHEETS. These miniature sheets were issued by the Philatelic Foundation of Southern Africa and not the postal administration. They could be purchased by post or from a limited number of philatelic offices, mainly in South Africa, at a premium in aid of various national and international stamp exhibitions.

124 Model wearing Swakara Coat

125 Pirogue, Lake Liambezi

(Des J. van Ellinckhuijzen)

1986 (10 July). *Karakul Industry. T* **124** *and similar vert designs. Multicoloured. P* 14.

463 14 c. Type **124** 35 15
464 20 c. Weaving karakul wool carpet 55 30
465 25 c. Flock of karakul ewes on veld 55 45
466 30 c. Karakul rams 75 60
463/6 .. .. *Set of* 4 2·00 1·40

The 30 c. value exists as a Philatelic Foundation miniature sheet.

1986 (6 Nov). *Life in the Caprivi Strip. T* **125** *and similar horiz designs. Multicoloured. P* 14.

467 14 c. Type **125** 50 15
468 20 c. Ploughing with oxen 80 80
469 25 c. Settlement in Eastern Caprivi .. .. 1·00 1·25
470 30 c. Map of Caprivi Strip .. .. .. 1·25 2·00
467/70 .. .. *Set of* 4 3·25 3·75

126 "Gobabis Mission Station", 1863

127 *Garreta nitens* (beetle)

1987 (19 Feb). *Paintings by Thomas Baines. T* **126** *and similar horiz designs. Multicoloured. P* 14.

471 14 c. Type **126** 50 15
472 20 c. "Outspan at Koobie", 1861 .. .. 90 90
473 25 c. "Outspan under Oomahaama Tree", 1862 .. .. 1·25 1·50
474 30 c. "Swakop River", 1861 .. .. .. 1·50 2·50
471/4 .. .. *Set of* 4 3·75 4·50

The 25 c. value exists as a Philatelic Foundation miniature sheet.

(Des E. Holm)

1987 (7 May). *Useful Insects. T* **127** *and similar horiz designs. Multicoloured. P* 14.

475 16 c. Type **127** 60 15
476 20 c. *Alcimus stenurus* (fly) 95 95
477 25 c. *Anthophora caerulea* (bee) .. .. 1·25 1·75
478 30 c. *Hemiempusa capensis* (mantid) .. .. 1·60 2·50
475/8 .. .. *Set of* 4 4·00 4·75

128 Okaukuejo

(Des J. van Niekerk)

1987 (23 July). *Tourist Camps. T* **128** *and similar horiz designs. Multicoloured. P* 14½ × 14.

479 16 c. Type **128** 55 15
480 20 c. Daan Viljoen 70 75
481 25 c. Ai-Ais .. .. 80 1·40
482 30 c. Hardap .. .. 85 1·60
479/82 .. .. *Set of* 4 2·50 3·50

129 Wreck of *Hope* (Dutch whaling schooner), 1804

130 Bartolomeu Dias

(Des Sheila Nowers)

1987 (15 Oct). *Shipwrecks. T* **129** *and similar horiz designs. Multicoloured. P* 14.

483 16 c. Type **129** 60 15
484 30 c. *Tilly* (brig), 1885 .. .. 1·00 1·00
485 40 c. *Eduard Bohlen* (steamer), 1909 .. 1·25 2·25
486 50 c. *Dunedin Star* (liner), 1942 .. .. 1·50 2·75
483/6 .. .. *Set of* 4 4·00 5·50

(Des Sheila Nowers)

1988 (7 Jan). *500th Anniv of Discovery of Cape of Good Hope by Bartolomeu Dias. T* **130** *and similar vert designs. Multicoloured. P* 14.

487	16 c. Type **130**	45	15
488	30 c. Caravel	85	55
489	40 c. Map of South West Africa, *c.* 1502	1·00	70
490	50 c. King João II of Portugal	1·00	75
487/90	*Set of* 4	3·00	2·00

131 Sossusvlei

(Des J. van Niekerk)

1988 (3 Mar). *Landmarks of South West Africa. T* **131** *and similar horiz designs. Multicoloured. P* 14.

491	16 c. Type **131**	45	15
492	30 c. Sesriem Canyon	80	65
493	40 c. Hoaruseb "clay castles"	95	90
494	50 c. Hoba meteorite	1·00	1·00
491/4	*Set of* 4	2·75	2·40

MACHINE LABELS. From 30 March 1988 gummed labels in the above design numbered "PT01", ranging in value from 1 c. to 99 r. 99, were available from a machine located at the Windhoek Post Office. During March 1989 three further machines at Windhoek Ausspanplatz (PT02), Swakopmund (PT03) and Keepmanshoop (PT04) were added. All machines were withdrawn in November 1990. A commemorative design, without code number, was used at the "OTYIMBINGUE 100" philatelic exhibition, Windhoek, between 7 and 9 July 1988.

132 First Postal Agency, Otyimbingue, 1888

133 Herero Chat

(Des H. Pulon)

1988 (7 July). *Centenary of Postal Service in South West Africa. T* **132** *and similar horiz designs. Multicoloured. P* 14.

495	16 c. Type **132**	45	15
496	30 c. Post Office, Windhoek, 1904	80	55
497	40 c. Mail-runner and map	90	70
498	50 c. Camel mail, 1904	1·00	75
495/8	*Set of* 4	2·75	2·00

The 50 c. value exists as a Philatelic Foundation miniature sheet.

(Des G. Arnott)

1988 (3 Nov). *Birds of South West Africa. T* **133** *and similar vert designs. Multicoloured. P* 14.

499	16 c. Type **133**	55	15
500	30 c. Gray's Lark	85	60
501	40 c. Rüppell's Bustard	1·10	75
502	50 c. Monteiro's Hornbill	1·25	80
499/502	*Set of* 4	3·25	2·10

134 Dr. C. H. Hahn and Gross-Barmen Mission

135 Beech Commuter 1900

(Des H. Pulon)

1989 (16 Feb). *Missionaries. T* **134** *and similar horiz designs. Multicoloured. P* 14.

503	16 c. Type **134**	30	10
504	30 c. Revd. J. G. Krönlein and Berseba Mission	60	50
505	40 c. Revd. F. H. Kleinschmidt and Rehoboth Mission	70	65
506	50 c. Revd. J. H. Schmelen and Bethanien Mission	70	70
503/6	*Set of* 4	2·10	1·75

(Des M. Botha)

1989 (18 May). *75th Anniv of Aviation in South West Africa. T* **135** *and similar horiz designs. Multicoloured. P* 14.

507	18 c. Type **135**	40	15
508	30 c. Ryan Navion	70	50
509	40 c. Junkers F-13	80	55
510	50 c. Pfalz Otto biplane	90	70
507/10	*Set of* 4	2·50	1·75

The 50 c. value exists as a Philatelic Foundation miniature sheet.

136 Barchan Dunes

(Des A. H. Barrett)

1989 (14 Aug). *Namib Desert Sand Dunes. T* **136** *and similar horiz designs. Multicoloured. P* 14.

511	18 c. Barchan dunes	35	15
512	30 c. Star dunes (36×20 *mm*)	65	40
513	40 c. Transverse dunes	75	60
514	50 c. Crescentic dunes (36×20 *mm*)	1·00	80
511/14	*Set of* 4	2·50	1·75

137 Ballot Box and Outline Map of South West Africa

1989 (24 Aug). *South West Africa Constitutional Election. P* 14.

515 **137**	18 c. purple-brown and salmon	30	15
516	35 c. deep grey-blue and pale emerald	50	40
517	45 c. plum and lemon	70	60
518	60 c. dull green and deep yellow-ochre	80	80
515/18	*Set of* 4	2·10	1·75

138 Gypsum

139 Oranjemund Alluvial Diamond Field

(Des J. van Niekerk)

1989 (16 Nov)–**90**. *Minerals. T* **138/9** *and similar multicoloured designs. Phosphorised paper* (25 *c.*) *or chalk-surfaced paper* (30, 35, 50 *c.*, 1 *r.*). *P* 14.

519	1 c. Type **138**	10	10
520	2 c. Fluorite	15	10
521	5 c. Mimetite	20	10
522	7 c. Cuprite	20	10
523	10 c. Azurite	25	10
524	18 c. Boltwoodite (inscr "K (H3O) (UO2) (SiO4)")	25	10
	a. Formula corrected to "K2 (UO2) 2 (SiO3) 2 (OH) 2 5 H2O" (25.10.90)	11·00	2·00
525	20 c. Dioptase	40	15
526	25 c. Type **139**	50	15
527	30 c. Tsumeb lead and copper complex	65	20
528	35 c. Rosh Pinah zinc mine	65	20
529	40 c. Diamonds	85	30
530	45 c. Wulfenite	85	30
531	50 c. Uis tin mine	1·00	40
532	1 r. Rössing uranium mine	1·75	1·00
533	2 r. Gold	2·75	2·00
519/33	*Set of* 15	9·50	4·50

The 1, 2, 5, 7, 10, 18, 20, 40, 45 c. and 2 r. are vertical as T **138**, and the 25, 30, 35, 50 c. and 1 r. horizontal as T **139**.

140 Arrow Poison

(Des Eva-Maria Linsmayer)

1990 (1 Feb). *Flora. T* **140** *and similar vert designs. Multicoloured. P* 14.

534	18 c. Type **140**	45	10
535	35 c. Baobab flower	85	40
536	45 c. Sausage Tree flowers	95	50
537	60 c. Devil's Claw	1·10	90
534/7	*Set of* 4	3·00	1·75

The 60 c. value exists as a Philatelic Foundation miniature sheet.

NAMIBIA

South West Africa became independent, as Namibia, on 21 March 1990.

The Walvis Bay Territory was ceded by South Africa to Namibia on 1 March 1994.

PRINTERS. The following stamps were printed in lithography by the Government Printer, Pretoria, South Africa.

141 Pres. Sam Nujoma, Map of Namibia and National Flag

142 Fish River Canyon

(Des T. Marais)

1990 (21 Mar). *Independence. T* **141** *and similar multicoloured designs. P* 14.

538	18 c. Type **141**	30	15
539	45 c. Hands releasing dove and map of Namibia (*vert*)	70	1·00
540	60 c. National flag and map of Africa	1·25	1·75
538/40	*Set of* 3	2·00	2·50

(Des J. van Ellinckhuijzen)

1990 (26 Apr). *Namibia Landscapes. T* **142** *and similar horiz designs. Multicoloured. P* 14.

541	18 c. Type **142**	35	20
542	35 c. Quiver-tree forest, Keetmanshoop	65	35
543	45 c. Tsaris Mountains	75	55
544	60 c. Dolerite boulders, Keetmanshoop	85	65
541/4	*Set of* 4	2·40	1·60

The 60 c. value exists as a Philatelic Foundation miniature sheet.

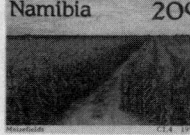

143 Stores on Kaiser Street, *c.* 1899

144 Maizefields

(Des J. van Ellinckhuijzen)

1990 (26 July). *Centenary of Windhoek. T* **143** *and similar horiz designs. Multicoloured. P* 14.

545	18 c. Type **143**	25	20
546	35 c. Kaiser Street, 1990	45	35
547	45 c. City Hall, 1914	55	55
548	60 c. City Hall, 1990	70	85
545/8	*Set of* 4	1·75	1·75

1990 (11 Oct). *Farming. T* **144** *and similar horiz designs. Multicoloured. P* 14.

549	20 c. Type **144**	25	20
550	35 c. Sanga bull	45	35
551	50 c. Damara ram	60	45
552	65 c. Irrigation in Okavango	75	60
549/52	*Set of* 4	1·90	1·40

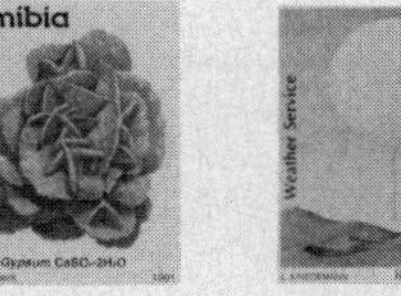

145 Gypsum

146 Radiosonde Weather Balloon

(Des J. van Niekerk)

1991 (2 Jan–14 June). *Minerals. Designs as Nos.* 519/21 *and* 523/33, *some with values changed, and new design* (5 *r.*), *inscr "Namibia" as T* **145**. *Multicoloured. Chalk-surfaced paper* (25, 30, 35, 50 *c.*, 1 *r.*). *P* 14.

553	1 c. Type **145**	10	10
554	2 c. Fluorite	15	10
555	5 c. Mimetite	20	10
556	10 c. Azurite	30	10
557	20 c. Dioptase	35	10
558	25 c. Type **139**	35	15
	a. Ordinary paper (14 June)	35	15
559	30 c. Tsumeb lead and copper complex	50	20
560	35 c. Rosh Pinah zinc mine	50	20
561	40 c. Diamonds	65	25
562	50 c. Uis tin mine	65	25
563	65 c. Boltwoodite	65	35
564	1 r. Rössing uranium mine	70	50
565	1 r. 50, Wulfenite	1·00	70
566	2 r. Gold	1·50	1·10
567	5 r. Willemite (vert as T **145**)	3·00	2·75
553/67	*Set of* 15	9·50	6·00

Printings of the 5 c. and 10 c. in 1992 were on phosphorescent paper.

(Des L. Kriedemann)

1991 (1 Feb). *Centenary of Weather Service. T* **146** *and similar horiz designs. Multicoloured. P* 14.

568	20 c. Type **146**	30	20
569	35 c. Sunshine recorder	45	30
570	50 c. Measuring equipment	60	50
571	65 c. Meteorological station, Gobabeb	70	60
568/71	*Set of* 4	1·90	1·40

147 Herd of Zebras **148** Karas Mountains

1991 (18 Apr). *Endangered Species. Mountain Zebra. T* **147** *and similar horiz designs. Multicoloured. P* 14.
572 20 c. Type **147** 90 60
573 25 c. Mare and foal .. .. 1·00 65
574 45 c. Zebras and foal .. .. 1·50 1·50
575 60 c. Two zebras .. .. 2·00 2·25
572/5 .. .. *Set of* 4 4·75 4·50
The 45 c. value exists as a Philatelic Foundation miniature sheet.

(Des A. H. Barrett)

1991 (18 July). *Mountains of Namibia. T* **148** *and similar horiz designs. Multicoloured. P* 14.
576 20 c. Type **148** 35 20
577 25 c. Gamsberg Mountains 40 30
578 45 c. Mount Brukkaros 70 70
579 60 c. Erongo Mountains .. .. 80 1·00
576/9 .. .. *Set of* 4 2·00 2·00

149 Bernabe de la Bat Camp **150** Artist's Pallet

(Des J. van Niekerk)

1991 (24 Oct). *Tourist Camps. T* **149** *and similar horiz designs. Multicoloured. P* 14.
580 20 c. Type **149** 35 30
581 25 c. Von Bach Dam Recreation Resort .. 40 35
582 45 c. Gross Barmen Hot Springs 65 55
583 60 c. Namutoni Rest Camp 80 70
580/3 .. .. *Set of* 4 2·00 1·75

(Des H. Pulon)

1992 (30 Jan). *21st Anniv of Windhoek Conservatoire. T* **150** *and similar horiz designs. Multicoloured. P* 14.
584 20 c. Type **150** 20 15
585 25 c. French horn and cello 25 20
586 45 c. Theatrical masks 50 45
587 60 c. Ballet dancers 65 75
584/7 .. .. *Set of* 4 1·40 1·40

151 Mozambique Mouthbrooder **152** Old Jetty

(Des B. Jackson)

1992 (16 Apr). *Freshwater Angling. T* **151** *and similar horiz designs. Multicoloured. P* 14.
588 20 c. Type **151** 40 20
589 25 c. Large-mouthed Yellowfish 45 20
590 45 c. Common Carp 85 50
591 60 c. Sharp-toothed Catfish 95 65
588/91 .. .. *Set of* 4 2·40 1·40
The 45 c. value exists as a Philatelic Foundation miniature sheet.

1992 (2 July). *Centenary of Swakopmund. T* **152** *and similar horiz designs. Multicoloured. P* 14.
592 20 c. Type **152** 25 25
593 25 c. Recreation centre 25 25
594 45 c. State House and lighthouse 80 60
595 60 c. Sea front 85 75
592/5 .. .. *Set of* 4 1·90 1·60
MS596 118×93 mm. Nos. 592/5 .. .. .. 2·25 2·50

153 Running **154** Wrapping English Cucumbers

(Des B. Jackson)

1992 (24 July). *Olympic Games, Barcelona. T* **153** *and similar horiz designs. Multicoloured. P* 14.
597 20 c. Type **153** 25 20
598 25 c. Map of Namibia, Namibian flag and Olympic rings 30 20
599 45 c. Swimming 50 40
600 60 c. Olympic Stadium, Barcelona 65 55
597/600 .. .. *Set of* 4 1·50 1·25
MS601 115×75 mm. Nos. 597/600 (*sold at* 2 *r.*) 2·25 2·75

1992 (10 Sept). *Integration of the Disabled. T* **154** *and similar horiz designs. Multicoloured. P* 14.
602 20 c. Type **154** 15 15
603 25 c. Weaving mats 15 15
604 45 c. Spinning thread 30 30
605 60 c. Preparing pot plants 40 50
602/5 .. .. *Set of* 4 90 1·00

155 Elephants in Desert **156** Herd of Simmentaler Cattle

(Des D. Murphy)

1993 (25 Feb). *Namibia Nature Foundation. Rare and Endangered Species. T* **155** *and similar horiz designs. Multicoloured. P* 14.
606 20 c. Type **155** 40 20
607 25 c. Sitatunga in swamp 30 20
608 45 c. Black Rhinoceros 65 50
609 60 c. Hunting Dogs 65 60
606/9 .. .. *Set of* 4 1·75 1·40
MS610 217×59 mm. Nos. 606/9 (*sold at* 2 r. 50) 2·50 2·50

(Des Carola Kronsbein-Goldbeck)

1993 (16 Apr). *Centenary of Simmentaler Cattle in Namibia. T* **156** *and similar horiz designs. Multicoloured. P* 14.
611 20 c. Type **156** 25 10
612 25 c. Cow and calf 25 15
613 45 c. Bull 50 40
614 60 c. Cattle on barge 75 75
611/14 .. .. *Set of* 4 1·60 1·25
The 45 c. value exists as a Philatelic Foundation miniature sheet.

157 Sand Dunes, Sossusvlei **158** Smiling Child

(Des J. van Ellinckhuijzen)

1993 (4 June). *Namib Desert Scenery. T* **157** *and similar horiz designs. Multicoloured. P* 14.
615 30 c. Type **157** 25 20
616 40 c. Blutkuppe 25 20
617 65 c. River Kuiseb, Homeb 40 45
618 85 c. Desert landscape 60 65
615/18 .. .. *Set of* 4 1·40 1·40

(Des J. van Ellinckhuijzen)

1993 (6 Aug). *S.O.S. Child Care in Namibia. T* **158** *and similar horiz designs. Multicoloured. P* 14.
619 30 c. Type **158** 30 20
620 40 c. Family 35 20
621 65 c. Modern house 60 55
622 85 c. Young artist with mural 80 80
619/22 .. .. *Set of* 4 1·90 1·60

(New Currency. 100 cents = 1 Namibia dollar)

159 *Charaxes jasius* **160** White Seabream

(Des A. Ainslie)

1993 (1 Oct). *Butterflies. T* **159** *and similar vert designs. Multicoloured. P* 14.
623 5 c. Type **159** 20 20
624 10 c. *Acraea anemosa* 20 20
625 20 c. *Papilio nireus* 30 10
626 30 c. *Junonia octavia* 30 10
627 40 c. *Hypolimnus misippus* 30 10
628 50 c. *Physcaeneura panda* 40 20
629 65 c. *Charaxes candiope* 40 30
630 85 c. *Junonia hierta* 50 40
631 90 c. *Colotis cellmene* 50 40
632 $1 *Cacyreus dicksoni* 55 35
633 $2 *Charaxes bohemani* 80 80
634 $2.50, *Stugeta bowkeri* .. .. .. 1·00 1·10
635 $5 *Byblia anvatara* .. .. 1·50 1·75
623/35 .. .. *Set of* 13 6·25 5·50
For similar design inscribed "STANDARDISED MAIL" see No. 648.
For 5 c. and 50 c. with elliptical perforations see Nos. 707/8.

(Des B. Jackson)

1994 (4 Feb). *Coastal Angling. T* **160** *and similar horiz designs. Multicoloured. P* 14.
636 30 c. Type **160** 25 25
637 40 c. Kob 25 25
638 65 c. West Coast Steenbras 40 40
639 85 c. Galjoen 60 60
636/9 .. .. *Set of* 4 1·40 1·40
MS640 134×89 mm. Nos. 636/9 (*sold at* $2.50) .. 2·00 2·50

161 Container Ship at Wharf **162** *Adenolobus pechuelii*

(Des Liza van der Wal (85 c.))

1994 (1 Mar). *Incorporation of Walvis Bay Territory into Namibia. T* **161** *and similar vert designs. Multicoloured. P* 14.
641 30 c. Type **161** 30 30
642 65 c. Aerial view of Walvis Bay 50 60
643 85 c. Map of Namibia 75 90
641/3 .. .. *Set of* 3 1·40 1·60

(Des Auriol Batten)

1994 (8 Apr). *Flowers. T* **162** *and similar vert designs. Multicoloured. P* 14.
644 35 c. Type **162** 30 25
645 40 c. *Hibiscus elliottiae* 30 25
646 65 c. *Pelargonium cortusifolium* 55 40
647 85 c. *Hoodia macrantha* 75 60
644/7 .. .. *Set of* 4 1·60 1·40

1994 (8 Apr). *Butterflies. Vert design as T* **159**, *but inscr* "STANDARDISED MAIL". *Multicoloured. P* 14.
648 (–) *Graphium antheus* 15 20
No. 648 was initially sold at 35 c., but this was subsequently increased to reflect changes in postal rates.

163 Yellow-billed Stork **164** Steam Railcar, 1908

(Des A. Barrett)

1994 (3 June). *Storks. T* **163** *and similar vert designs. Multicoloured. P* 14.
649 35 c. Type **163** 30 30
650 40 c. Abdim's Stork 30 30
651 80 c. African Open-bill Stork 50 50
652 $1.10, White Stork 65 65
649/52 .. .. *Set of* 4 1·60 1·60

(Des H. Botha)

1994 (5 Aug). *Steam Locomotives. T* **164** *and similar horiz designs. Multicoloured. P* 14.
653 35 c. Type **164** 45 30
654 70 c. Krauss narrow-gauge side-tank locomotive No. 106, 1904 .. .. .. 70 50
655 80 c. Class "24" locomotive, 1948 .. .. 75 55
656 $1.10, Class "7C" locomotive, 1914 .. 1·10 80
653/6 .. .. *Set of* 4 2·75 1·90
The 80 c. value exists as a Philatelic Foundation miniature sheet.

165 No. 84 *Prince Edward* Steam Locomotive, Cape Cross, 1895 **166** National Arms

(Des H. Botha)

1995 (8 Mar–1 Nov). *Centenary of Railways in Namibia. T* **165** *and similar horiz designs. Multicoloured. P* 14.
657 35 c. Type **165** 45 25
658 70 c. German South West Africa steam locomotive 70 35
659 80 c. Class "8" steam locomotive of South African Railways 75 40

660 $1.10, Class "33-400" diesel-electric locomotive of Transnamib Railways .. 1·10 55
657/60 .. .. *Set of* 4 2·75 1·40
MS661 101×94 mm. Nos. 657/60 .. .. 2·75 1·75
a. Optd "November 1995" on sheet margin (1 Nov) .. .. .. 2·75 2·25

(Des B. Wepener)

1995 (21 Mar). *5th Anniv of Independence. P* 14.
662 **166** (–) multicoloured 30 30
No. 662 is inscribed "STANDARDISED MAIL" and was initially sold for 35 c., but this was subsequently increased to reflect changes in postal rates.

167 Living Tortoise and *Geochelone stromeri* (fossil)

168 Martii Rautanen and Church

(Des L. Kriedemann)

1995 (24 May). *Fossils. T* **167** *and similar vert designs. Multicoloured. P* 14.
663 40 c. Type **167** 40 25
664 80 c. Ward's Diamond Bird and *Diamantornis wardi* (fossil eggs) 70 60
665 90 c. Hyraxes and *Prohyrax hendeyi* skull 80 70
666 $1.20, Crocodiles and *Crocodylus lloydi* skull .. .. 1·10 90
663/6 .. .. *Set of* 4 2·75 2·25
The 80 c. value exists as a Philatelic Foundation miniature sheet.

(Des H. Pulon)

1995 (10 July). *125th Anniv of Finnish Missionaries in Namibia. T* **168** *and similar horiz designs. Multicoloured. P* 14.
667 40 c. Type **168** 25 20
668 80 c. Albin Savola and hand printing press 50 50
669 90 c. Karl Weikkolin and wagon 60 65
670 $1.20, Dr. Selma Rainio and Onandjokwe Hospital 85 95
667/70 .. .. *Set of* 4 2·00 2·10

169 Ivory Buttons

170 U.N. Flag

(Des H. Pulon)

1995 (16 Aug). *Personal Ornaments. T* **169** *and similar vert designs. Multicoloured. P* 14.
671 40 c. Type **169** 20 20
672 80 c. Conus shell pendant 45 45
673 90 c. Cowrie shell headdress 55 55
674 $1.20, Shell button pendant 85 95
671/4 .. .. *Set of* 4 1·90 2·00

(Des Sheila Nowers)

1995 (1 Sept). *"Singapore '95" International Stamp Exhibition. Sheet, 110×52 mm, containing designs as No. 359b with altered face value and inscription. P* 14.
MS675 $1.20, multicoloured .. .. .. 90 1·00
No. MS675 shows the exhibition emblem printed on the sheet margin.

(Des J. van Niekerk)

1995 (24 Oct). *50th Anniv of the United Nations. P* 14.
676 **170** 40 c. new blue and black 20 20

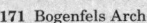

171 Bogenfels Arch

172 Sister Leoni Kreitmeier and Döbra Education and Training Centre

(Des Christine Marais. Litho Harrison)

1996 (1 Apr). *Tourism. T* **171** *and similar horiz designs. Multicoloured. P* 15×14.
677 (–) Type **171** 15 15
678 90 c. Ruacana Falls 30 30
679 $1 Epupa Falls 30 30
680 $1.30, Herd of wild horses 35 50
677/80 .. .. *Set of* 4 1·00 1·10
No. 677 is inscribed "Standardised Mail" and was initially sold at 45 c.

(Des J. van Niekerk. Litho Harrison)

1996 (27 May). *Centenary of Catholic Missions in Namibia. T* **172** *and similar horiz designs. Multicoloured. P* 15×14.
681 50 c. Type **172** 20 20
682 95 c. Father Johann Malinowski and Heirachabis Mission 30 35
683 $1 St. Mary's Cathedral, Windhoek .. 30 35
684 $1.30, Archbishop Joseph Gotthardt and early church, Ovamboland 35 65
681/4 .. .. *Set of* 4 1·00 1·40

(Des Sheila Nowers)

1996 (8 June). *"CAPEX '96" International Stamp Exhibition, Toronto. Sheet, 105×45 mm, containing design similar to No. 358c with new face value and inscription. P* 14½×14.
MS685 $1.30, multicoloured 85 90

173 Children and U.N.I.C.E.F. Volunteer

(Des A. Ainslie. Litho Harrison)

1996 (14 June). *50th Anniv of U.N.I.C.E.F. T* **173** *and similar horiz design. Multicoloured. P* 15×14.
686 (–) Type **173** 10 15
687 $1.30, Girls in school 35 40
No. 686 is inscribed "STANDARD POSTAGE" and was initially sold at 50 c.

174 Boxing

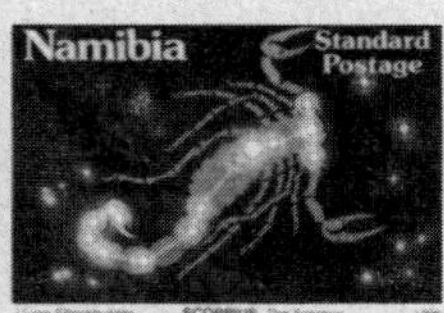

175 Scorpius

(Des B. Jackson. Litho Harrison)

1996 (27 June). *Centennial Olympic Games, Atlanta. T* **174** *and similar horiz designs. Multicoloured. P* 15×14.
688 (–) Type **174** 15 15
689 90 c. Cycling 30 40
690 $1 Swimming 30 40
691 $1.30, Running 35 55
688/91 .. .. *Set of* 4 1·00 1·40
No. 688 is inscribed "Standard Postage" and was initially sold at 50 c.

(Des J. van Ellinckhuijzen. Litho Harrison)

1996 (12 Sept). *Stars in the Namibian Sky. T* **175** *and similar horiz designs. Multicoloured. P* 15×14.
692 (–) Type **175** 15 15
693 90 c. Sagittarius 25 30
694 $1 Southern Cross 30 30
695 $1.30, Orion 35 50
692/5 .. .. *Set of* 4 95 1·10
MS696 100×80 mm. No. 694 .. .. .. 1·00 1·10
No. 692 is inscribed "Standard Postage" and was initially sold at 50 c.
For No. **MS**696 revalued to $3.50 see No. **MS**706

176 Urn-shaped Pot

177 Khauxa!nas Ruins

(Des Sheila Nowers. Litho Harrison)

1996 (17 Oct). *Early Pottery. T* **176** *and similar vert designs. Multicoloured. P* 14×15.
697 (–) Type **176** 15 15
698 90 c. Decorated storage pot 25 35
699 $1 Reconstructed cooking pot 30 35
700 $1.30, Storage pot 35 50
697/700 .. .. *Set of* 4 95 1·25
No. 697 is inscribed "Standard Postage" and was initially sold at 50 c.

(Des J. van Ellinckhuijzen. Litho Harrison)

1997 (6 Feb). *Khaux!nas Ruins. T* **177** *and similar horiz designs showing different views. P* 15×14.
701 (–) multicoloured 20 20
702 $1 multicoloured 35 40
703 $1.10, multicoloured 35 40
704 $1.50, multicoloured 50 60
701/4 .. .. *Set of* 4 1·25 1·40
No. 701 is inscribed "Standard postage" and was initially sold at 50 c.

178 Ox

179 Heinrich von Stephan

(Des J. van Ellinckhuijzen. Litho Harrison)

1997 (12 Feb). *"HONG KONG '97" International Stamp Exhibition and Chinese New Year ("Year of the Ox"). Sheet 103×67 mm. P* 15×14.
MS705 **178** $1.30, multicoloured .. .. 1·10 1·10

1997 (17 Feb). *Support for Organised Philately. No.* **MS**696 *with margin additional inscr* "Reprint February 17 1997. *Sold in aid of organized Philately* N$3.50".
MS706 $1 Southern Cross (*sold at* $3.50) .. 1·40 1·50

(Litho Harrison)

1997 (26 Mar). *As Nos. 623 and 628, but P* 14½ (*with two elliptical holes on each vertical side*).
707 5 c. Type **159** 10 10
708 50 c. *Physcaeneura panda* 15 20

(Des J. van Ellinckhuijzen. Litho Harrison)

1997 (8 Apr). *Death Centenary of Heinrich von Stephan (founder of U.P.U.). P* 14×15.
709 **179** $2 multicoloured 60 65

180 Cinderella Waxbill

181 Helmet Guineafowl

(Des Julia Birkhead. Litho Harrison)

1997 (6 May). *Booklet Stamps. Waxbills. T* **180** *and similar horiz design. Multicoloured. P* 14×14½ (*with one elliptical hole on each horizontal side*).
710 50 c. Type **180** 15 20
a. Booklet pane. Nos. 710/11, each ×5 1·50
711 60 c. Black-cheeked Waxbill 15 20
Nos. 710/11 were only available from $5.50 stamp booklets.

(Des Isabel van der Ploeg. Litho Enschedé)

1997 (6 May). *Greetings Stamp. P* 15×14.
712 **181** $1.20, multicoloured 30 35
For similar designs see Nos. 743/6

182 Jackass Penguins calling

183 Caracal

(Des D. Thorpe. Litho Harrison)

1997 (15 May). *Endangered Species. Jackass Penguin. T* **182** *and similar vert designs. Multicoloured. P* 14×15.
713 (–) Type **182** 25 30
714 $1 Incubating egg 40 40
715 $1.10, Adult with chick 50 50
716 $1.50, Penguins swimming 55 60
713/16 .. .. *Set of* 4 1·50 1·50
MS717 101×92 mm. As Nos. 713/16, but without the WWF symbol (*sold at* $5) .. .. 1·50 1·50
No. 713 is inscribed "STANDARD POSTAGE" and was initially sold for 50 c.

(Des Sheila Nowers. Litho Harrison)

1997 (12 June). *Wildcats. T* **183** *and similar horiz designs. Multicoloured. P* 15×14.
718 (–) Type **183** 20 20
719 $1 *Felis lybica* 30 30
720 $1.10, Serval 35 40
721 $1.50, Black-footed Cat 50 55
718/21 .. .. *Set of* 4 1·25 1·25
MS722 100×80 mm. $5 As No. 721 .. .. 1·25 1·40
No. 718 is inscribed "STANDARD POSTAGE" and was initially sold at 50 c.
No. **MS**722 was sold in aid of organised philately in Southern Africa.

184 *Catophractes alexndri* **185** Collecting Bag

(Des T. Breckwoldt (Nos 723/7), Isabel van der Ploeg (others). Litho Enschedé)

1997 (27 June). *Greeting Stamps. Flowers and Helmet Guineafowl. T* **184** *and similar horiz designs. Multicoloured. P* 14×13½.

723 (–) Type **184** 15 20
a. Booklet pane. Nos. 723/7, each × 2, and 10 labels . . . . 1·50
724 (–) *Crinum paludosum* 15 20
725 (–) *Gloriosa superba* 15 20
726 (–) *Tribulus zeyheri* 15 20
727 (–) *Aptosimum pubescens* 15 20
728 50 c. Helmet Guineafowl raising hat . . 15 20
a. Booklet pane. Nos. 728/32, each × 2, and 10 labels . . . . 1·50
729 50 c. Holding bouquet 15 20
730 50 c. Ill in bed 15 20
731 $1 With heart round neck 25 20
732 $1 With suitcase and backpack 25 20
723/32 . . . . *Set of* 10 1·75 2·25

These stamps only come from $5 (Nos. 723/7) or $7 (Nos. 728/32) stamp booklets where they occur in panes of 10 (5×2) with margins all round and greetings labels at top and bottom.

Nos. 723/7 are inscribed "Standard Postage" and were initially sold at 50 c. each.

(Des J. van Niekerk. Litho Harrison)

1997 (8 July). *Basket Work. T* **185** *and similar vert designs. Multicoloured. P* 14×15.

733 50 c. Type **185** 20 20
734 90 c. Powder basket 30 30
735 $1.20, Fruit basket 35 35
736 $2 Grain basket 70 75
733/6 . . . . *Set of* 4 1·40 1·40

186 Veterinary Association Coat of Arms

(Des C. Marais. Litho Harrison)

1997 (12 Sept). *50th Anniv of Namibian Veterinary Association. P* 14×14½.

737 **186** $1.50, multicoloured 50 50
a. *Tête-bêche* pair . . . . . . 1·00 1·00

No. 737 was issued in sheets of 10 containing one row of *tête-bêche* pairs.

187 Head of Triceratops **188** German South West Africa Postman

(Des J. van Ellinckhuijzen. Litho Enschedé)

1997 (27 Sept). *Youth Philately. Dinosaurs. Sheet* 82×56 *mm. P* 12½×13.

MS738 **187** $5 multicoloured . . . . . . 1·25 1·40

(Des J. Madisia. Litho Enschedé)

1997 (9 Oct). *World Post Day. P* 14×15

739 **188** (–) multicoloured 15 20

No. 739 is inscribed "STANDARD POSTAGE" and was initially sold at 50 c.

189 False Mopane **190** Flame Lily

(Des Auriol Batten. Litho Enschedé)

1997 (10 Oct). *Trees. T* **189** *and similar vert designs. Multicoloured. P* 14×15.

740 (–) Type **189** 15 20
741 $1 Ana Tree 25 30
742 $1.10, Shepherd's Tree 30 35
740/2 . . . . *Set of* 3 70 85

No. 740 is inscribed "STANDARD POSTAGE" and was initially sold at 50 c.

1997 (3 Nov). *Christmas. Multicoloured designs as T* **181** *showing Helmet Guineafowl, each with festive frame. P* 13×12½.

743 (–) Guineafowl facing right 15 20
744 $1 Guineafowl in grass 25 30
745 $1.10, Guineafowl on rock 30 35
746 $1.50, Guineafowl in desert 40 45
743/6 . . . . *Set of* 4 1·10 1·25
MS747 110×80 mm. $5 Helmet Guineafowl (*vert*). P 12½×13 . . . . . . 1·25 1·40

No. 743 is inscribed "standard postage" and was initially sold at 50 c.

(Des D. Murphy. Litho Enschedé)

1997 (3 Nov). *Flora and Fauna. T* **190** *and similar vert designs. Multicoloured.* (a) *P* 13½.

748 5 c. Type **190** 10 10
a. Booklet pane. Nos. 748/65 with margins all round . . . . . . 7·75
749 10 c. Bushman Poison 10 10
750 20 c. Camel's Foot 10 10
751 30 c. Western Rhigozum 10 10
752 40 c. Blue-cheeked Bee-eater 10 10
753 50 c. Laughing Dove 15 20
754 (–) Peach-faced Lovebird 15 20
a. Booklet pane. No. 754×10 with margins all round . . . . . . 1·25
755 60 c. Lappet-faced Vulture 15 20
756 90 c. Yellow-billed Hornbill 25 30
757 $1 Lilac-brested Roller 25 30
758 $1.10, Hippopotamus 30 35
759 $1.20, Giraffe 30 35
760 (–) Leopard 30 35
a. Booklet pane. No. 760×10 with margins all round . . . . . . 3·00
761 $1.50, Elephant 40 45
762 $2 Lion 50 55
763 $4 Buffalo . . . . 1·00 1·10
764 $5 Black Rhinoceros . . . . . . 1·25 1·40
765 $10 Cheetah . . . . 2·50 2·75
748/65 . . . . *Set of* 18 7·75 8·50

(*b*) *Self-adhesive. P* 12×12½

766 (–) As No. 754 . . . . 15 20
767 $1 As No. 757 . . . . 25 30
768 (–) As No. 760 . . . . 30 35
766/8 . . . . *Set of* 3 70 85

Nos. 754 and 766 are inscribed "standard postage" and were each initially sold at 50 c., Nos. 760 and 768 are inscribed "postcard rate" and were each initially sold at $1.20.

191 John Muafangejo

(Des J. van Ellinckhuijzen. Litho Harrison)

1997 (27 Nov). *10th Death Anniv of John Muafangejo. P* 14×15.

769 **191** (–) multicoloured 15 20

No. 769 is inscribed "STANDARD POSTAGE" and was initially sold at 50 c.

STAMP BOOKLETS

B 1 Buffalo

(*Illustration further reduced. Actual size* 125×74 *mm*)

1985 (1 Aug). *Multicoloured cover as Type* B 1. *Pane attached by selvedge.*

SB1 1 r. 20, booklet containing pane of 10 12 c. (No. 358ba) . . . . 4·50

1986 (Feb). *Multicoloured cover as Type* B 1 *but smaller,* 125×70 *mm, showing herd of buffaloes. Pane attached by selvedge.*

SB2 1 r. 20, booklet containing pane of 10 12 c. (No. 358ba) . . . . 4·50

B 2

1997 (1 Feb). *Multicoloured cover as Type* B 2. *Stamps attached by selvedge.*

SB3 ($5) booklet containing block of 10 "STANDARDISED MAIL" (No. 648) . . 1·25
SB4 $5 booklet containing two strips of 5 "STANDARDISED MAIL" (No. 662) . . 1·25

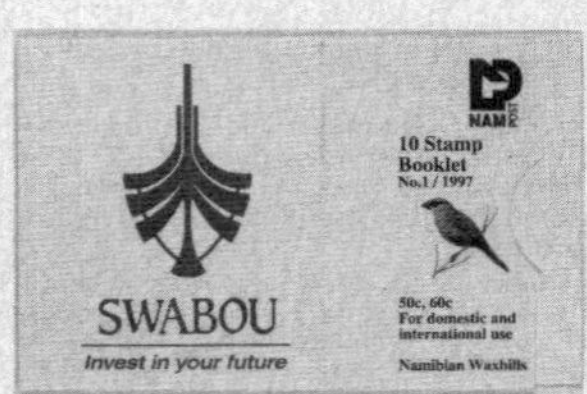

B 3

1997 (6 May). *Waxbills. Multicoloured cover as Type* B 3. *Stamps attached by selvedge.*

SB5 $5.50, booklet containing block of 10 (2×5) (No. 710a) . . . . 1·40

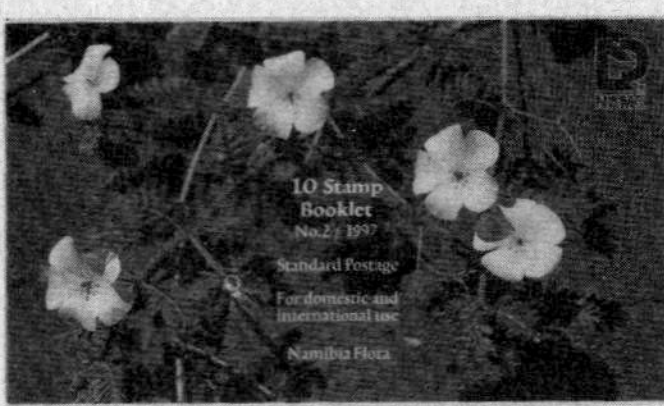

B 4 *Tribulus zeyheri*

(*Illustration further reduced. Actual size* 132×80 *mm*)

1997 (27 June). *Greetings Stamps. Multicoloured covers as Type* B 4. *Panes attached by selvedge.*

SB6 ($5) booklet containing pane of 10 (5×2) (No. 723a) (Type B 4) . . . . . . 1·25
SB7 $7 booklet containing pane of 10 (5×2) (No. 728a) (cover showing Helmet Guineafowl and chicks) . . . . 1·75

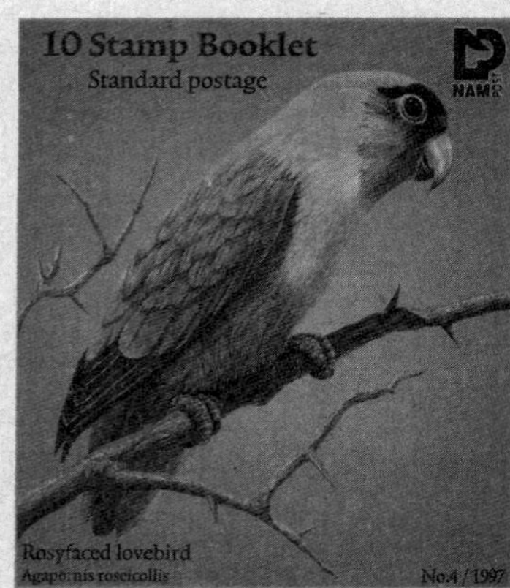

B 5 Peach-faced Lovebird

1997 (3 Nov). *Flora and Fauna. Multicoloured covers as Type* B 5. *Panes attached by selvedge.*

SB8 ($5) booklet containing pane of 10 (5×2) (No. 754a) (cover showing Peach-faced Lovebird) 1·25
SB9 ($12) booklet containing pane of 10 (5×2) (No. 760a) (cover showing Leopard) . . . . 3·00
SB10 ($30.55) booklet containing pane of 18 (9×2) (No. 748a) (cover showing animals and birds) 7·75

AFFIX
STAMP
HERE

Stanley Gibbons
Mail Order Department
399 Strand
LONDON
ENGLAND
WC2R 0LX

AFFIX
STAMP
HERE

Stanley Gibbons Publications
5 Parkside
Christchurch Road
Ringwood
HAMPSHIRE
ENGLAND
BH24 3SH

AFFIX
STAMP
HERE

Stanley Gibbons
Postal Auctions Deoartment
399 Strand
LONDON
ENGLAND
WC2R 0LX

STANLEY
GIBBONS

Complimentary
Perforation
Gauge

20 millimetres

17 · 16½ · 16 · 15½ · 15 · 14½ · 14 · 13½ · 13 · 12½ · 12 · 11½ · 11 · 10½ · 10 · 9½ · 9 · 8½ · 8 · 7

20 millimetres

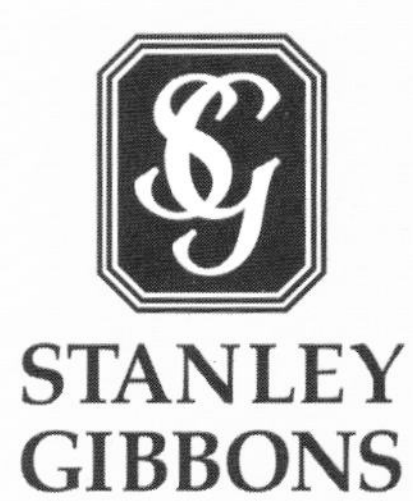

STANLEY
GIBBONS

399 Strand
London
WC2R 0LX

Tel: 0171 836 8444
Fax: 0171 836 7342

e.mail
sales@stangib.demon.co.uk

POSTAGE DUE STAMPS

PRICES for Nos. D1/39 are for unused horizontal pairs, used horizontal pairs and used singles.

1923 (1 Jan–July). *Optd with T* **1** *and* **2** *alternately.*

(*a*) *Setting* I (*14 mm between lines of overprint*) (i) *On Nos.* D5/6 *of Transvaal*

D1 5d. black and violet .. .. 4·00 42·00 10·00
a. "Wes" for "West" (R. 8/6, 10/2 left pane) £130
b. "Afrika" without stop (R. 6/1) 80·00
D2 6d. black and red-brown .. .. 17·00 42·00 11·00
a. "Wes" for "West" (R. 10/2) .. £225
b. "Afrika" without stop (R. 6/1, 7/2) £140

(ii) *On Nos.* D3/4 *and* D6 *of South Africa* (*De La Rue printing*)

D3 2d. black and violet .. .. 20·00 40·00 10·00
a. "Wes" for "West" (R. 10/2) .. £150 £200
b. "Afrika" without stop (R. 6/1, 7/2) £150
D4 3d. black and blue .. .. 9·00 40·00 10·00
a. "Wes" for "West" (R. 10/2) .. £120
D5 6d. black and slate (20 Apr) .. 24·00 48·00 13·00
a. "Wes" for "West" (R. 8/6) .. £150

(iii) *On Nos.* D9/10, D11 *and* D14 *of South Africa* (*Pretoria printings*)

D6 ½d. black and green (*p* 14) .. 5·50 23·00 5·50
a. Opt inverted £400
b. Opt double £750 £800
c. "Wes" for "West" (R. 10/2) .. 75·00
d. "Afrika" without stop (R. 6/1, 7/2) .. .. .. 75·00
D7 1d. black and rose (*roul*) .. 7·00 24·00 6·00
a. "Wes" for "West" (R. 10/2) .. 85·00
b. "Afrika" without stop (R. 6/1) 85·00
c. Imperf between (horiz pair) .. £950
D8 1½d. black and yellow-brown (*roul*) 1·00 12·00 2·75
a. "Wes" for "West" (R. 8/6, 10/2) 70·00
b. "Afrika" without stop (R. 6/1) 70·00
D9 2d. black and violet (*p* 14) (21 June) 3·25 22·00 5·00
a. "Wes" for "West" (R. 8/6) .. 85·00
b. "Afrika" without stop (R. 6/1) £100

Nos. D1/9 were initially overprinted as separate panes of 60, but some values were later done as double panes of 120.

A variety of Nos. D1, D4/5 and D9 with 15 mm between the lines of overprint occurs on four positions in each pane from some printings.

(*b*) *Setting* II (*10 mm between lines of overprint*). (i) *On No.* D5 *of Transvaal*

D10 5d. black and violet (20 Apr) .. 55·00 £130

(ii) *On Nos.* D3/4 *of South Africa* (*De La Rue printing*)

D11 2d. black and violet (20 Apr) .. 15·00 35·00 9·00
a. "Afrika" without stop (R.6/1) .. £130
D12 3d. black and blue (20 Apr) .. 7·50 23·00 5·50
a. "Afrika" without stop (R.6/1) 80·00

(iii) *On No.* D9 *of South Africa* (*Pretoria printing*). *Roul*

D13 1d. black and rose (July) .. £8500 — £1500

1923 (30 July)–**26**. *Optd as T* **3** ("Zuidwest" *in one word without hyphen*) *and* **4**.

(*a*) *Setting* III ("South West" *14 mm long*, "Zuidwest" *11 mm long and 14 mm between lines of overprint*).

(i) *On No.* D6 *of Transvaal*

D14 6d. black and red-brown.. .. 20·00 75·00 20·00

(ii) *On Nos.* D9 *and* D11/12 *of South Africa* (*Pretoria printing*)

D15 ½d. black and green (*p* 14) .. 9·00 23·00 5·00
D16 1d. black and rose (*roul*) .. 3·00 23·00 5.00
D17 1d. black and rose (*p* 14) (2.8.23) 9·00 23·00 5·00

(*b*) *Setting* IV ("South West" *16 mm long*, "Zuidwest" *12 mm long and 14 mm between lines of overprint*).

(i) *On No.* D5 *of Transvaal*

D17*a* 5d. black and violet (1.7.24) .. £425 £850

(ii) *On Nos.* D11/12 *and* D16 *of South Africa* (*Pretoria printing*). *P* 14

D18 ½d. black and green (1.7.24) .. 5·50 23·00 5·00
D19 1d. black and rose (1.7.24) .. 5·00 23·00 5·00
D20 6d. black and slate (1.7.24) .. 2·25 35·00 9·00
a. "Africa" without stop (R.9/5) £100

(*c*) *Setting* V (*12 mm between lines of overprint*).

(i) *On No.* D5 *of Transvaal*

D21 5d. black and violet (6.8.24) .. 3·25 35·00 8·50

(ii) *On No.* D4 *of South Africa* (*De La Rue printing*)

D22 3d. black and blue (6.8.24) .. 13·00 42·00 11·00

(iii) *On Nos.* D11 *and* D13 *of South Africa* (*Pretoria printing*). *P* 14

D23 ½d. black and green (6.8.24) .. 2·50 25·00 6·50
D24 1½d. black & yellow-brown (6.8.24) 4·50 27·00 7·00

(*d*) *Setting* VI (*9½ mm between lines of overprint*).

(i) *On No.* D5 *of Transvaal*

D25 5d. black and violet (7.9.24) .. 2·50 15·00 3·50
a. "Africa" without stop (R. 9/5) 65·00

(ii) *On No.* D4 *of South Africa* (*De La Rue printing*)

D26 3d. black and blue (3.2.26) .. 6·50 45·00 11·00

(iii) *On Nos.* D11/16 *of South Africa* (*Pretoria printing*). *P* 14

D27 ½d. black and green (1.3.26) .. 7·00 28·00 7·50
D28 1d. black and rose (16.3.25) .. 2·00 8·00 1·60
a. "Africa" without stop (R. 9/5 right pane) .. .. .. 75·00
D29 1½d. black & yellow-brown (1.10.26) 3·75 25·00 6·00
a. "Africa" without stop (R. 9/5 right pane) .. .. .. 80·00
D30 2d. black and violet (7.9.24) .. 2·50 15·00 3·25
a. "Africa" without stop (R. 9/5) right pane) .. .. .. 65·00
D31 3d. black and blue (6.5.26) .. 4·00 16·00 3·50
a. "Africa" without stop (R. 9/5) right pane) .. .. .. 70·00
D32 6d. black and slate (1.10.26) .. 9·00 48·00 14·00
a. "Africa" without stop (R. 9/5 right pane) £120
D27/32 .. .. .. *Set of* 6 25·00 £130 32·00

For Setting VI the overprint was applied to sheets of 120 (2 panes of 60) of the 1d., 3d. and 6d., and to individual panes of 60 for the other values. The two measurements of "South West", as detailed under No. 40, also occur on the postage dues. Nos. D25 and D31/2 show it 16 mm long, No. 27 16½ mm long and the other stamps can be found with either measurement. In addition to the complete panes the 16½ mm long "South West" also occurs on R.2/4 in the 16 mm left pane for Nos. D28 and D30/2.

Suidwes South West

Afrika. Africa.

(D 1) (D 2)

1927 (14 May–27 Sept). *Optd as Types* D **1** *and* D **2**, *alternately, 12 mm between lines of overprint.* (*a*) *On No.* D5 *of Transvaal.*

D33 5d. black and violet (27 Sept) .. 19·00 85·00 23·00

(*b*) *On Nos.* D13/16 *of South Africa* (*Pretoria printing*). *P* 14

D34 1½d. black and yellow-brown .. 80 13·00 3·25
D35 2d. black and pale violet (27 Sept) 3·75 13·00 3·25
a. Black and deep violet .. 5·50 14·00 3·50
D37 3d. black and blue (27 Sept) .. 13·00 40·00 11·00
D38 6d. black and slate (27 Sept) .. 7·50 30·00 8·50

(*c*) *On No.* D18 *of South Africa* (*Pretoria printing*). *P* 14

D39 1d. black and carmine .. 1·00 9·00 2·25
D33/9 .. .. *Set of* 6 40·00 £160 45·00

No. D33 was overprinted in panes of 60 and the remainder as complete sheets of 120.

Examples of all values can be found with very small or very faint stops from various positions in the sheet.

1928–29. *Optd with T* **10**. (*a*) *On Nos.* D15/16 *of South Africa*

			Single	Single
D40	3d. black and blue	.. ..	1·25	12·00
	a. Without stop after "A" (R.3/6)	..	25·00	
D41	6d. black and slate	.. ..	6·00	24·00
	a. Without stop after "A" (R.3/6)	..	£120	
	(*b*) *On Nos.* D17/21 *of South Africa*			
D42	½d. black and green	.. ..	40	7·00
D43	1d. black and carmine	.. ..	40	3·25
	a. Without stop after "A" (R.3/6)	..	40·00	
D44	2d. black and mauve	.. ..	40	4·00
	a. Without stop after "A" (R.3/6)	..	55·00	
D45	3d. black and blue	.. ..	2·25	22·00
D46	6d. black and slate	.. ..	1·50	18·00
	a. Without stop after "A" (R.3/6)	..	45·00	
D42/6	.. .. ..	*Set of* 5	4·50	48·00

D 3

D 4

D 5

(Litho B.W.)

1931 (23 Feb). *Inscribed bilingually.* W **9** *of South Africa. P* 12.

D47 D **3** ½d. black and green .. .. .. 70 8·00
D48 1d. black and scarlet .. .. .. 70 1·25
D49 2d. black and violet .. .. .. 70 2·50
D50 3d. black and blue .. .. .. 3·25 15·00
D51 6d. black and slate .. .. .. 13·00 25·00
D47/51 .. .. *Set of* 5 16·00 45·00

PRINTER. The following issues have been printed by the South African Government Printer, Pretoria.

1959 (18 May). *Centre typo; frame roto.* W **9** *of South Africa. P* 15 × 14.

D52 D **4** 1d. black and scarlet .. .. .. 1·50 14·00
D53 2d. black and reddish violet .. .. 1·50 14·00
D54 3d. black and blue .. .. .. 1·50 14·00
D52/4 .. .. *Set of* 3 4·00 38·00

1960 (Dec). *As Nos.* D52 *and* D54 *but* W **102** *of South Africa.*

D55 1d. black and scarlet.. .. .. .. 2·25 4·50
D56 3d. black and blue .. .. 2·25 6·50

1961 (14 Feb). *As Nos.* D52 *etc, but whole stamp roto, and value in cents.* W **102** *of South Africa.*

D57 1 c. black and blue-green .. .. .. 70 3·25
D58 2 c. black and scarlet.. .. .. .. 70 3·25
D59 4 c. black and reddish violet .. .. .. 70 3·25
D60 5 c. black and light blue .. .. .. 1·00 3·75
D61 6 c. black and green .. .. .. 1·25 5·50
D62 10 c. black and yellow .. .. .. 3·25 7·00
D57/62 .. .. .. *Set of* 6 7·00 23·00

1972 (22 Mar). W **127** (*sideways tête-bêche*). *Phosphorised chalk-surfaced paper. P* 14 × 13½.

D63 D **5** 1 c. emerald .. .. .. 75 4·00
D64 8 c. ultramarine .. .. .. 3·00 8·00

The use of Postage Due stamps ceased in April 1975.

NEW INFORMATION

The editor is always interested to correspond with people who have new information that will improve or correct the Catalogue.

OFFICIAL STAMPS

OFFICIAL OFFISIEEL

South West Africa. Suidwes Afrika.

(O 1) (O 2)

1926 (Dec). *Nos.* 30, 31, 6 *and* 32 *of South Africa optd with Type* O **1** *on English stamp and* O **2** *on Afrikaans stamp alternately.*

			Un pair	*Us pair*	*Us single*
O1	½d. black and green ..	.. ..	70·00	£160	30·00
O2	1d. black and carmine	.. ..	70·00	£160	30·00
O3	2d. dull purple	.. ..	£160	£250	45·00
O4	6d. green and orange	.. ..	90·00	£150	30·00
O1/4	.. .. ..	*Set of* 4	£350	£650	£120

OFFICIAL OFFISIEEL

S.W.A. S.W.A.

(O 3) (O 4)

1929 (May). *Nos.* 30, 31, 32 *and* 34 *of South Africa optd with Type* O **3** *on English stamp and* O **4** *on Afrikaans stamp.*

O5 ½d. black and green .. .. 1·00 13·00 2·75
O6 1d. black and carmine .. .. 1·00 13·00 2·75
O7 2d. grey and purple .. .. 1·50 17·00 3·50
a. Pair, stamp without stop after "OFFICIAL" .. .. 5·50 38·00
b. Pair, stamp without stop after "OFFISIEEL" .. .. 5·50 38·00
c. Pair, comprising a and b .. 16·00 75·00
O8 6d. green and orange .. .. 3·00 18·00 3·75
O5/8 .. .. .. *Set of* 4 6·00 55·00 11·50

Types O **3** and O **4** are normally spaced 17 mm between lines on all except the 2d. value, which is spaced 13 mm.

Except on No. O7, the words "OFFICIAL" or "OFFISIEEL" normally have no stops after them.

OFFICIAL S.W.A. OFFISIEEL S.W.A.

(O 5) (O 6)

OFFICIAL. S.W.A. OFFISIEEL. S.W.A.

(O 7) (O 8)

1929 (Aug). *Nos.* 30, 31 *and* 32 *of South Africa optd with Types* O **5** *and* O **6**, *and No.* 34 *with Types* O **7** *and* O **8**, *languages to correspond.*

O 9 ½d. black and green .. .. 65 13·00 2·75
O10 1d. black and carmine .. .. 75 13·00 2·75
O11 2d. grey and purple .. .. 90 13·00 3·25
a. Pair, one stamp without stop after "OFFICIAL" .. 3·75 35·00
b. Pair, one stamp without stop after "OFFISIEEL" .. .. 3·75 35·00
c. Pair, comprising a and b .. 18·00 75·00
O12 6d. green and orange .. .. 3·00 27·00 6·50
O9/12 .. .. .. *Set of* 4 4·75 60·00 13·50

OFFICIAL OFFISIEEL

(O 9) (O 10)

1931. *English stamp optd with Type* O **9** *and Afrikaans stamp with Type* O **10** *in red.*

O13 **12** ½d. black and emerald .. .. 10·00 17·00 3·50
O14 **13** 1d. indigo and scarlet .. .. 75 17·00 3·50
O15 **14** 2d. blue and brown .. .. 1·60 10·00 2·25
O16 **17** 6d. blue and brown .. .. 2·25 14·00 3·25
O13/16 .. .. *Set of* 4 13·00 50·00 11·50

OFFICIAL OFFISIEEL

(O 11) (O 12)

1938 (1 July). *English stamp optd with Type* O **11** *and Afrikaans with Type* O **12** *in red.*

O17 **27** 1½d. purple-brown .. .. 24·00 42·00 6·00

OFFICIAL OFFISIEEL

(O 13) (O 14)

1945–50. *English stamp optd with Type* O **13**, *and Afrikaans stamp with Type* O **14** *in red.*

O18 **12** ½d. black and emerald .. .. 11·00 26·00 5·00
O19 **13** 1d. indigo and scarlet (1950) .. 4·00 15·00 3·25
a. Opt double £425
O20 **27** 1½d. purple-brown .. .. 45·00 35·00 6·[illegible]
O21 **14** 2d. blue and brown (1947?) .. £450 £600 £[illegible]00
O22 **17** 6d. blue and brown .. .. 10·00 40·00 7·00
O18/20, O22 .. .. *Set of* 4 60·00 £100 20·00

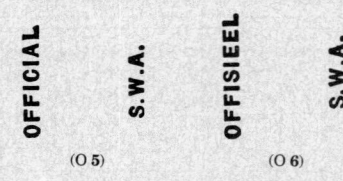

OFFICIAL (O 15) **OFFISIEEL** (O 16)

1951 (16 Nov)–**52**. *English stamp optd with Type* O **15** *and Afrikaans stamp with Type* O **16**, *in red.*

O23	**12**	½d. black and emerald (1952) ..	12·00	20·00	4·50
O24	**13**	1d. indigo and scarlet	3·50	12·00	1·75
		a. Opts transposed	65·00	95·00	
O25	**27**	1½d. purple-brown	24·00	24·00	5·00
		a. Opts transposed	70·00	80·00	
O26	**14**	2d. blue and brown	1·25	15·00	3·50
		a. Opts transposed	42·00	£100	
O27	**17**	6d. blue and brown	2·75	35·00	7·50
		a. Opts transposed	22·00	£110	
O23/7		.. .. .. *Set of* 5	38·00	95·00	20·00

The above errors refer to stamps with the English overprint on Afrikaans stamp and *vice versa.*

The use of official stamps ceased in January 1955.

Natal
see South Africa

Nauru

Stamps of MARSHALL ISLANDS were used in Nauru from the opening of the German Colonial Post Office on 14 July 1908 until 8 September 1914.

Following the occupation by Australian forces the "N.W. PACIFIC ISLANDS" overprints on Australia (see NEW GUINEA) were used from the early months of 1915.

PRICES FOR STAMPS ON COVER TO 1945

Nos. 1/12	*from* ×10
Nos. 13/16	*from* ×4
Nos. 17/25	—
Nos. 26/39	*from* × 6
Nos. 40/3	*from* × 10
Nos. 44/7	*from* × 15

BRITISH MANDATE

NAURU (1) NAURU (2) NAURU (3)

1916 (2 Sept)–**23**. *Stamps of Great Britain* (1912–22) *overprinted at Somerset House.*

(a) With T **1** (12½ *mm long) at foot*

1	½d. yellow-green	1·25	6·00
	a. "NAUP.U"	£350	
	b. Double opt, one albino	60·00	
2	1d. bright scarlet	1·25	3·75
	a. "NAUP.U"	£600	
2*b*	1d. carmine-red	10·00	
	bb. Double opt, one albino	£200	
3	1½d. red-brown (1923)	55·00	80·00
4	2d. orange (Die I)	2·00	9·00
	a. "NAUP.U"	£350	£400
	b. Double opt, one albino	£100	
5	2d. orange (Die II) (1923)	70·00	£100
6	2½d. blue	2·75	7·00
	a. "NAUP.U"	£400	£450
	b. Double opt, one albino	£200	
7	3d. bluish violet	2·00	3·50
	a. "NAUP.U"	£425	£475
	b. Double opt, one albino	£200	
8	4d. slate-green	2·00	8·50
	a. "NAUP.U"	£550	£650
	b. Double opt, one albino	£200	
9	5d. yellow-brown	2·25	8·50
	a. "NAUP.U"	£750	
	b. Double opt, one albino	£140	
10	6d. purple (*chalk-surfaced paper*) ..	3·25	10·00
	a. "NAUP.U"	£700	
	b. Double opt, one albino	£225	
11	9d. agate	8·50	19·00
	a. Double opt, one albino	£225	
12	1s. bistre-brown (Optd S. £130)	7·00	19·00
	a. Double opt, one albino	£250	
1/12	.. .. *Set of* 11	75·00	£150

(b) With T **2** (13½ *mm long) at centre* (1923)

13	½d. green	4·50	40·00
14	1d. scarlet	18·00	30·00
15	1½d. red-brown	23·00	40·00
	a. Double opt, one albino	£140	
16	2d. orange (Die II)	30·00	60·00
13/16	.. .. *Set of* 4	65·00	£150

The "NAUP.U" errors occur on R.6/2 from Control I 16 only. The ink used on this batch of overprints was shiny jet-black.

There is a constant variety consisting of short left stroke to "N" which occurs on Nos. 1, 2, 2*b*, 4 (£30 *each*); 3 (£175); 5 (£200); 6, 7 (£40 *each*); 8, 9, 10 (£60 *each*); 11, 12 (£85 *each*). All unused prices.

(c) With T **3**. (i) *Waterlow printing*

17	5s. rose-carmine	£2250	£1600
18	10s. indigo-blue (R.) (Optd S. £1200) ..	£6000	£4500
	a. Double opt, one albino	£7000	£7000

(ii) *De La Rue printing*

19	2s. 6d. deep brown (Optd S. £275) ..	£550	£650
	a. Double opt, one albino	£1200	
	b. Treble opt, two albino	£1300	
20	2s. 6d. yellow-brown	65·00	90·00
21	2s. 6d. pale brown (worn plate) (Optd S. £250)	70·00	85·00
	a. Re-entry (R. 2/1)		
22	5s. bright carmine (*shades*) (Optd S. £250)	£100	£140
	a. Treble opt, two albino	£550	
23	10s. pale blue (R.)	£250	£325
	a. Treble opt (Blk. + R. + albino) ..	£2000	
	b. Double opt, one albino	£850	
23*c*	10s. deep bright blue (R.)	£500	£550

(iii) *Bradbury, Wilkinson printing* (1919)

24	2s. 6d. chocolate-brown	75·00	£100
	a. Major re-entry (R. 1/2)		
	b. Double opt, one albino	£325	
25	2s. 6d. pale brown	60·00	85·00
	a. Double opt, one albino	£300	

Examples of most values between Nos. 1 and 25 are known showing a forged P.O. Pleasant Island postmark dated "NO 2 21".

AUSTRALIAN MANDATE

4 *Century* (freighter)

(Des R. A. Harrison. Eng T. S. Harrison. Recess Note Printing Branch of the Treasury, Melbourne and from 1926 by the Commonwealth Bank of Australia)

1924–48. *T* **4**. *No wmk. P* 11.
I. Rough surfaced, greyish paper (1924–34).
II. Shiny surfaced, white paper (1937–48).

		I		II	
26	½d. chestnut	1·25	2·75	8·00	13·00
	a. Perf 14 (1947)	†		1·40	9·00
27	1d. green	2·75	2·75	2·50	3·00
28	1½d. scarlet	3·25	3·75	90	1·50
29	2d. orange	3·25	9·00	1·75	8·00
30	2½d. slate-blue	4·25	18·00	†	
30*a*	2½d. greenish blue (1934) ..	4·25	12·00	†	
30*b*	2½d. dull blue (1948) ..	†		1·50	3·75
	ba. Imperf between (vert pair)	†		£4250	£4250
	bb. Imperf between (horiz pair)	†		£4250	£4250
31	3d. pale blue	2·50	11·00	†	
31*a*	3d. greenish grey (1947) ..	†		2·25	9·50
32	4d. olive-green	5·00	14·00	4·25	10·00
33	5d. brown	3·00	6·50	3·50	4·00
34	6d. dull violet	3·50	12·00	3·25	4·50
35	9d. olive-brown	8·00	19·00	7·50	20·00
36	1s. brown-lake	6·00	13·00	5·50	2·75
37	2s. 6d. grey-green	26·00	45·00	25·00	35·00
38	5s. claret	50·00	90·00	35·00	50·00
39	10s. yellow	£110	£140	£100	£120
26I/39I	.. .. *Set of* 14	£200	£350	†	
26II/39II	.. .. *Set of* 14	†		£170	£250

HIS MAJESTY'S JUBILEE.

1910 - 1935

(5)

6

1935 (12 July). *Silver Jubilee. T* **4** (*shiny surfaced, white paper*) *optd with T* **5**.

40	1½d. scarlet	75	80
41	2d. orange	1·25	4·00
42	2½d. dull blue	1·50	1·50
43	1s. brown-lake	5·00	3·50
40/3	.. .. *Set of* 4	7·75	9·00

(Recess John Ash, Melbourne)

1937 (10 May). *Coronation. P* 11.

44	**6**	1½d. scarlet	45	1·00
45		2d. orange	45	1·50
46		2½d. blue	45	40
47		1s. purple	65	90
44/7		.. .. *Set of* 4	1·75	3·50

Japanese forces invaded Nauru on 26 August 1942 and virtually all the inhabitants were removed to Truk in the Caroline Islands.

The Australian army liberated Nauru on 13 September 1945. After an initial period without stamps Australian issues were supplied during October 1945 and were used from Nauru until further supplies of Nos. 26/39 became available. The deportees did not return until early in 1946.

COVER PRICES

Cover factors are quoted at the beginning of each country for most issues to 1945. An explanation of the system can be found on page x. The factors quoted do not, however, apply to philatelic covers.

7 Nauruan Netting Fish

8 Anibare Bay

15 Map of Nauru

(Recess Note Printing Branch, Commonwealth Bank, Melbourne, and from 1960 by Note Ptg Branch, Reserve Bank of Australia, Melbourne)

1954 (6 Feb)–**65**. *T* **7/8**, **15** *and similar designs. Toned paper. P* 13½×14½ (*horiz*) *or* 14½×13½ (*vert*).

48	½d. deep violet	20	30
	a. Violet (8.5.61)	20	30
49	1d. bluish green	30	50
	a. Emerald-green (8.5.61)	20	40
	b. Deep green (1965)	85	50
50	3½d. scarlet	1·50	60
	a. Vermilion (1958)	2·75	60
51	4d. grey-blue	1·50	1·50
	a. Deep blue (1958)	5·00	2·50
52	6d. orange	70	20
53	9d. claret	60	20
54	1s. deep purple	30	20
55	2s. 6d. deep green	2·75	80
56	5s. magenta	9·00	2·50
48/56	.. .. *Set of* 9	15·00	6·00

Designs: *Horiz*—3½d. Loading phosphate from cantilever; 4d. Great Frigate Bird; 6d. Nauruan canoe; 9d. Domaneab (meeting-house); 2s. 6d. Buada lagoon. *Vert*—1s. Palm trees.

Nos. 48*a*, 49*a*/*b*, 50*a* and 51*a* are on white paper.

16 Micronesian Pigeon

17 Poison Nut

20 Capparis

21 White Tern

(Recess (10d., 2s. 3d.) or photo (others) Note Ptg Branch, Reserve Bank of Australia, Melbourne)

1963–65. *T* **16/17**, **20/1** *and similar designs. P* 13½ × 13 (5*d.*), 13 × 13½ (8*d.*), 14 × 13½ (10*d.*), 15 × 14½ (1*s.* 3*d.*) *or* 13½ (*others*).

57	2d. black, blue, red-brn & orge-yell (3.5.65)	1·00	2·25
58	3d. multicoloured (16.4.64)	75	35
59	5d. multicoloured (22.4.63)	75	75
60	8d. black and green (1.7.63)	2·50	80
61	10d. black (16.4.64)	50	30
62	1s. 3d. blue, black & yellow-green (3.5.65) ..	4·50	3·50
63	2s. 3d. ultramarine (16.4.64)	3·50	55
64	3s. 3d. multicoloured (3.5.65)	4·50	2·75
57/64	.. .. *Set of* 8	16·00	10·00

Designs: *Vert*—5d. "Iyo" (*calophyllum*). *Horiz*—8d. Black Lizard; 2s. 3d. Coral pinnacles; 3s. 3d. Finsch's Reed Warbler.

22 "Simpson and his Donkey"

(Des C. Andrew (after statue, Shrine of Remembrance, Melbourne. Photo Note Ptg Branch, Reserve Bank of Australia, Melbourne)

1965 (14 Apr). *50th Anniv of Gallipoli Landing. P* 13½.

65	**22**	5d. sepia, black and emerald	15	10

(New Currency. 100 cents = 1 Australian dollar)

24 Anibare Bay 25 "Iyo" (*calophyllum*)

(Recess (1, 2, 3, 5, 8, 19, 25 c. and $1) or photo (others))

1966 (14 Feb–25 May). *Decimal Currency. Various stamps with values in cents and dollars as T* **24/5** *and some colours changed. Recess printed stamps on helecon paper.*

66	**24**	1 c. deep blue	15	10
67	**7**	2 c. brown-purple (25 May)	15	40
68	–	3 c. bluish green (as 3½d.) (25 May)	30	90
69	**25**	4 c. multicoloured	25	10
70	–	5 c. deep ultramarine (as 1s.) (25 May)	25	60
71	–	7 c. black and chestnut (as 8d.)	30	10
72	**20**	8 c. olive-green	30	10
73	–	10 c. red (as 4d.)	40	10
74	**21**	15 c. blue, black and yellow-green (25 May)	80	1·50
75	–	25 c. deep brown (as 2s. 3d.) (25 May)	45	60
76	**17**	30 c. multicoloured	70	30
77	–	35 c. multicoloured (as 3s. 3d.) (25 May)	1·25	35
78	**16**	50 c. multicoloured	2·50	80
79	–	$1 magenta (as 5s.)	2·00	1·00
66/79		*Set of* 14	8·50	6·00

The 25 c. is as No. 63, but larger, 27½×24½ mm.

REPUBLIC

Nauru became independent on 31 January 1968 and was later admitted into special membership of the Commonwealth.

REPUBLIC OF NAURU

(26)

1968 (31 Jan–15 May). *Nos. 66/79 optd with T* **26**.

80	**24**	1 c. deep blue (R.)	10	30
81	**7**	2 c. brown-purple	10	10
82	–	3 c. bluish green	15	10
83	**25**	4 c. multicoloured (15.5.68)	15	10
84	–	5 c. deep ultramarine (R.)	15	10
85	–	7 c. black and chestnut (R.) (15.5.68)	25	10
86	**20**	8 c. olive-green (R.)	25	10
87	–	10 c. red	30	15
88	**21**	15 c. blue, black and yellow-green	2·75	2·50
89	–	25 c. deep brown (R.)	30	15
90	**17**	30 c. multicoloured (15.5.68)	55	15
91	–	35 c. multicoloured (15.5.68)	1·50	30
92	**16**	50 c. multicoloured	2·00	50
93		$1 magenta	1·25	75
80/93		*Set of* 14	8·00	4·50

27 "Towards the Sunrise" 28 Planting Seedling, and Map

(Des H. Fallu (5 c.), Note Ptg Branch (10 c.). Photo Note Ptg Branch, Reserve Bank of Australia, Melbourne)

1968 (11 Sept). *Independence. P* 13½.

94	**27**	5 c. black, slate-lilac, orange-yellow and yellow-green	10	10
95	**28**	10 c. black, yellow-green and new blue	10	10

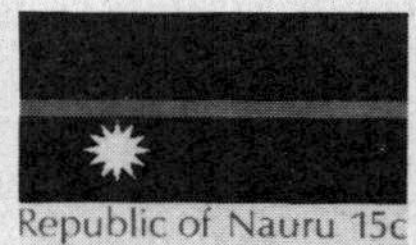

29 Flag of Independent Nauru 30 Island, "C" and Stars

(Des J. Mason. Photo Note Ptg Branch, Reserve Bank of Australia, Melbourne)

1969 (31 Jan). *P* 13½.

96	**29**	15 c. yellow, orange and royal blue	40	15

This is a definitive issue which was put on sale on the first anniversary of Independence.

(Des R. Brooks, Litho Format)

1972 (7 Feb). *25th Anniv of South Pacific Commission. P* 14½ × 14.

97	**30**	25 c. multicoloured	30	25

Independence 1968-1973

(31)

1973 (31 Jan). *Fifth Anniv of Independence. No. 96 optd with T* **31** *in gold.*

98	**29**	15 c. yellow, orange and royal blue	20	30

32 Denea 33 Artefacts and Map

(Des locally; adapted G. Vasarhelyi. Litho Format)

1973 (28 Mar*–25 July). *Various multicoloured designs as T* **32** *(1 to 5 c.) or T* **33** *(others). P 14 (1 to 5 c.), 14½ × 14 (7, 8, 10, 30, 50 c.) or 14 × 14½ (others).*

99	1 c. Ekwenababae	50	20
100	2 c. Kauwe Iud	65	20
101	3 c. Rimone	65	20
102	4 c. Type **32**	65	40
103	5 c. Erekogo	65	40
104	7 c. Raccoon Butterflyfish ("Ikimago") (25.7)	30	40
105	8 c. Catching flying-fish (23.5)	30	20
106	10 c. Itsibweb (ball game) (23.5)	30	20
107	15 c. Nauruan wrestling (23.5)	35	20
108	20 c. Snaring Great Frigate Birds (23.5)	50	30
109	25 c. Nauruan girl (25.7)	50	30
110	30 c. Catching Common Noddy Birds (25.7)	85	40
111	50 c. Great Frigate Birds (25.7)	1·25	75
112	$1 Type **33**	1·25	75
99/112	*Set of* 14	8·00	4·50

*This is the local release date but the Crown Agents issued the stamps on 21 March.

The 1 to 5 c. show flowers, and the 7, 8, 10, 30, 50 c. are horiz designs.

Nos. 99/112 exist imperforate from stock dispersed by the liquidator of Format International Security Printers Ltd.

34 Co-op Store 35 Phosphate Mining

(Des G. Vasarhelyi. Litho Format)

1973 (20 Dec). *50th Anniv of Nauru Co-operative Society. T* **34** *and similar multicoloured designs. P 14 × 14½ (50 c.) or 14½ × 14 (others).*

113	5 c. Type **34**	20	30
114	25 c. Timothy Detudamo (founder)	20	15
115	50 c. N.C.S. trademark (*vert*)	45	55
113/15	*Set of* 3	75	90

(Des G. Vasarhelyi (7 c. from original by J. Mason; 10 c. from original by K. Depaune). Litho Format)

1974 (21 May). *175th Anniv of First Contact with the Outside World. T* **35** *and similar horiz designs. Multicoloured. P 13 × 13½ (7, 35, 50 c.) or 13½ × 13 (others).*

116	7 c. *Eigamoiya* (bulk carrier) (70×22 *mm*)	1·25	90
117	10 c. Type **35**	1·00	25
118	15 c. Fokker F.28 Fellowship *Nauru Chief*	1·00	30
119	25 c. Nauruan chief in early times	1·25	35
120	35 c. Capt. Fearn and H.M.S. *Hunter* (70×22 *mm*)	5·50	2·50
121	50 c. H.M.S. *Hunter* off Nauru (70×22 *mm*)	2·50	1·40
116/21	*Set of* 6	11·00	5·25

36 Map of Nauru 37 Rev. P. A. Delaporte

(Des G. Vasarhelyi. Litho Format)

1974 (23 July). *Centenary of Universal Postal Union. T* **36** *and similar multicoloured designs. P 13½ × 14 (5 c.), 13 × 13½ ($1) or 13½ × 13 (others).*

122	5 c. Type **36**	20	20
123	8 c. Nauru Post Office	20	20
124	20 c. Nauruan postman	20	10
125	$1 U.P.U. Building and Nauruan flag	50	60
122/5	*Set of* 4	1·00	1·00
MS126	157 × 105 mm. Nos. 122/5. Imperf	2·50	5·50

The 8 and 20 c. are horiz (33 × 21 mm), and the $1 is vert (21 × 33 mm).

(Des J.W. Litho Format)

1974 (10 Dec). *Christmas and 75th Anniv of Rev. Delaporte's Arrival. P* 14½.

127	**37**	15 c. multicoloured	20	20
128		20 c. multicoloured	30	30

NEW INFORMATION

The editor is always interested to correspond with people who have new information that will improve or correct the Catalogue.

38 Map of Nauru, Lump of Phosphate Rock and Albert Ellis 39 Micronesian Outrigger

(Des M. and Sylvia Goaman. Litho Format)

1975 (23 July). *Phosphate Mining Anniversaries. T* **38** *and similar horiz designs. Multicoloured. P* 14½ × 14.

129	5 c. Type **38**	30	40
130	7 c. Coolies and mine	40	40
131	15 c. Electric railway, barges and ship	1·25	1·40
132	25 c. Modern ore extraction	1·50	1·50
129/32	*Set of* 4	3·00	3·25

Anniversaries:—5 c. 75th Anniv of discovery; 7 c. 70th Anniv of Mining Agreement; 15 c. 55th Anniv of British Phosphate Commissioners; 25 c. 5th Anniv of Nauru Phosphate Corporation.

(Des M. and Sylvia Goaman. Litho Format)

1975 (1 Sept). *South Pacific Commission Conference, Nauru (1st issue). T* **39** *and similar horiz designs. Multicoloured. P* 13½ × 14.

133	20 c. Type **39**	75	40
	a. Block of 4. Nos. 133/6	2·75	
134	20 c. Polynesian double-hull	75	40
135	20 c. Melanesian outrigger	75	40
136	20 c. Polynesian outrigger	75	40
133/6	*Set of* 4	2·75	1·40

Nos. 133/6 were printed in *se-tenant* blocks of four throughout the sheet.

40 New Civic Centre 41 "Our Lady" (Yaren Church)

(Des M. and Sylvia Goaman. Litho Format)

1975 (29 Sept). *South Pacific Commission Conference, Nauru (2nd issue). T* **40** *and similar horiz design. Multicoloured. P* 14.

137	30 c. Type **40**	15	15
138	50 c. Domaneab (meeting-house)	30	30

(Des M. and Sylvia Goaman. Litho Format)

1975 (7 Nov). *Christmas. T* **41** *and similar vert design showing stained-glass window. Multicoloured. P* 14½ × 14.

139	5 c. Type **41**	15	15
140	7 c. "Suffer little children. . ." (Orro Church)	15	15
141	15 c. As 7 c.	30	45
142	25 c. Type **41**	45	55
139/42	*Set of* 4	95	1·10

42 Flowers floating towards Nauru

(Des M. and Sylvia Goaman. Litho Format)

1976 (31 Jan*). *30th Anniv of the Return from Truk. T* **42** *and similar horiz designs. Multicoloured. P* 14½.

143	10 c. Type **42**	10	10
144	14 c. Nauru encircled by garland	15	10
145	25 c. Finsch's Reed Warbler and maps	35	25
146	40 c. Return of the islanders	45	35
143/6	*Set of* 4	95	65

*This is the local date of issue; the Crown Agents released the stamps one day earlier.

Nos. 143/6 exist imperforate from sets of progressive proofs.

43 3d. and 9d. Stamps of 1916

(Des M. and Sylvia Goaman. Litho Format)

1976 (6 May). *60th Anniv of Nauruan Stamps. T* **43** *and similar horiz designs. Multicoloured. P* 13½.
147 10 c. Type **43** 15 15
148 15 c. 6d. and 1s. stamps 20 15
149 25 c. 2s. 6d. stamp 30 25
150 50 c. 5s. "Specimen" stamp 40 35
147/50 .. .. *Set of* 4 95 80
Nos. 147/8 show stamps with errors; the 3d. "Short N" and the 6d. "P" for "R".
Nos. 147/50 exist imperforate from sets of progressive proofs.

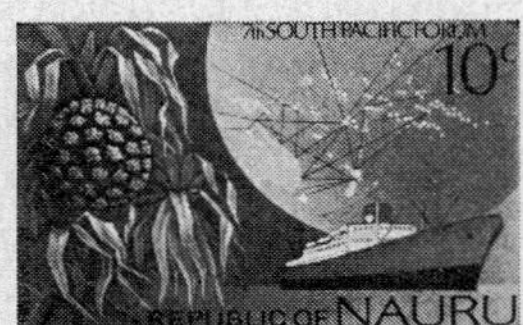

44 *Pandanus mei* and *Enna G* (cargo liner)

(Des M. and Sylvia Goaman. Litho Format)

1976 (26 July). *South Pacific Forum, Nauru. T* **44** *and similar horiz designs. Multicoloured. P* 13½.
151 10 c. Type **44** 15 10
152 20 c. *Tournefortia argentea* with Boeing 737 and Fokker F.28 Fellowship aircraft 20 15
153 30 c. *Thespesia populnea* and Nauru Tracking Station 25 15
154 40 c. *Cordia subcordata* and produce .. 35 25
151/4 .. .. .. *Set of* 4 85 60
Nos. 151/4 exist imperforate from sets of progressive proofs.

45 Nauruan Choir **46** Nauru House and Coral Pinnacles

(Des G. Vasarhelyi. Litho Format)

1976 (17 Nov). *Christmas. T* **45** *and similar vert designs. Multicoloured. P* 13½.
155 15 c. Type **45** 10 10
a. Horiz pair. Nos. 155/6 .. .. .. 20 20
156 15 c. Nauruan choir 10 10
157 20 c. Angel in white dress 15 15
a. Horiz pair. Nos. 157/8 .. .. .. 30 30
158 20 c. Angel in red dress 15 15
155/8 .. .. *Set of* 4 50 50
Nos. 155/6 and 157/8 were printed horizontally *se-tenant* throughout the sheet, both forming composite designs.

(Des D. Gentleman. Photo Harrison)

1977 (25 Apr*). *Opening of Nauru House, Melbourne. T* **46** *and similar vert design. Multicoloured. P* 14.
159 15 c. Type **46** 15 15
160 30 c. Nauru House and Melbourne skyline .. 25 25
*This is the local release date. The London agency released the stamps on 14 April.

47 Cable Ship *Anglia* **48** Father Kayser and First Catholic Church

(Des D. Gentleman. Photo Harrison)

1977 (7 Sept). *75th Anniv of First Trans-Pacific Cable and 20th Anniv of First Artificial Earth Satellite. T* **47** *and similar vert designs. P* 14 × 14½.
161 7 c. multicoloured 30 10
162 15 c. light blue, grey and black 40 15
163 20 c. light blue, grey and black 40 20
164 25 c. multicoloured 45 20
161/4 .. .. *Set of* 4 1·40 60
Designs:—15 c. Tracking station, Nauru; 20 c. Stern of *Anglia*; 25 c. Dish aerial.

(Des D. Gentleman. Photo Harrison)

1977 (28 Nov). *Christmas. T* **48** *and similar vert designs. Multicoloured. P* 14½.
165 15 c. Type **48** 10 10
166 25 c. Congregational Church, Orro 15 15
167 30 c. Catholic Church, Arubo 15 15
165/7 .. .. *Set of* 3 30 30
No. 165 also commemorates the 75th anniversary of the Catholic Church on Nauru.

49 Arms of Nauru

=
4c
(50)

(Des G. Vasarhelyi. Litho Format)

1978 (31 Jan). *Tenth Anniv of Independence. P* 14½.
168 **49** 15 c. multicoloured 20 15
169 60 c. multicoloured 35 30

1978 (29 Mar). *Nos. 159/60 surch as T* **50** *by Format.*
170 4 c. on 15 c. Type **46** .. .. 90 2·00
171 5 c. on 15 c. Type **46** .. .. 90 2·00
172 8 c. on 30 c. No. 160 .. .. 90 2·00
173 10 c. on 30 c. No. 160 .. .. 90 2·25
170/3 .. .. *Set of* 4 3·25 7·50

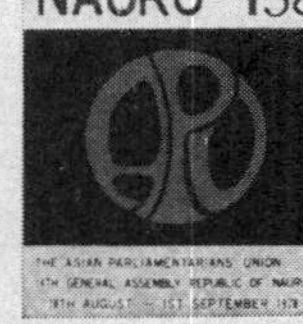

51 Collecting Shellfish **52** A.P.U. Emblem

(Des D. Gentleman. Photo Harrison)

1978 (17 May)–**79**. *Horiz designs as T* **51** *in brown, blue and black (4 c.), grey, black and light blue (20 c., $5) or multicoloured (others). P* 14½.
174 1 c. Type **51** 50 30
175 2 c. Coral outcrop (6.6.79) 50 30
176 3 c. Reef scene (6.6.79) 70 30
177 4 c. Girl with fish (6.6.79) 50 30
178 5 c. Eastern Reef Heron (6.6.79) .. .. 1·50 30
179 7 c. Catching fish, Buada Lagoon 30 40
180 10 c. Ijuw Lagoon 30 20
181 15 c. Girl framed by coral 40 30
182 20 c. Pinnacles, Anibare Bay reef 30 30
183 25 c. Pinnacle at Meneng 30 30
184 30 c. Head of Great Frigate Bird .. .. 1·50 45
185 32 c. White-capped Noddy in coconut palm .. 2·00 65
186 40 c. Wandering Tattler .. .. .. 1·50 1·25
187 50 c. Great Frigate Birds on perch 85 75
188 $1 Old coral pinnacles at Topside 70 55
189 $2 New pinnacles at Topside .. .. .. 95 1·00
190 $5 Blackened pinnacles at Topside .. .. 1·75 2·25
174/90 .. .. *Set of* 17 13·00 9·00

(Litho Toppan Ptg Co, Ltd)

1978 (28 Aug). *14th General Assembly of Asian Parliamentarians' Union. T* **52** *and similar vert design. P* 13.
191 15 c. multicoloured 20 25
192 20 c. black, deep ultramarine and gold .. 20 25
Design:—20 c. As T **52** but different background.

53 Virgin and Child **54** Baden-Powell and Cub Scout

(Des R. Vigurs. Litho Format)

1978 (1 Nov). *Christmas. T* **53** *and similar multicoloured design. P* 14.
193 7 c. Type **53** 10 10
194 15 c. Angel in sun-rise scene (*horiz*) 10 10
195 20 c. As 15 c. 15 15
196 30 c. Type **53** 20 20
193/6 .. .. *Set of* 4 40 40

(Des J. Charles. Litho Format)

1978 (1 Dec). *70th Anniv of Boy Scout Movement. T* **54** *and similar horiz designs. Multicoloured. P* 13½.
197 20 c. Type **54** 20 15
198 30 c. Baden-Powell and Boy Scout 25 20
199 50 c. Baden-Powell and Rover Scout 35 30
197/9 .. .. *Set of* 3 70 60

COVER PRICES

Cover factors are quoted at the beginning of each country for most issues to 1945. An explanation of the system can be found on page x. The factors quoted do not, however, apply to philatelic covers.

55 Wright Flyer I over Nauru

(Des D. Gentleman. Litho Format)

1979 (24 Jan). *Flight Anniversaries. T* **55** *and similar horiz designs. Multicoloured. P* 14.
200 10 c. Type **55** 15 15
201 15 c. Fokker F.VIIa/3m *Southern Cross* superimposed on nose of Boeing 737 25 20
a. Pair. Nos. 201/2 .. .. .. 50 40
202 15 c. Fokker F.VIIa/3m *Southern Cross* and Boeing 737 (front view) 25 20
203 30 c. Wright Flyer I over Nauru airfield .. 35 30
200/3 .. .. *Set of* 4 90 75
Commemorations:—10, 30 c. 75th anniversary of powered flight; 15 c. 50th anniversary of Kingsford-Smith's Pacific flight.
Nos. 201/2 were printed together, *se-tenant*, in horizontal and vertical pairs throughout the sheet.
No. 203 exists with black (inscription) omitted from stock dispersed by the liquidator of Format International Security Printers Ltd.

56 Sir Rowland Hill and Marshall Islands 10 pf. Stamp of 1901

(Des R. Granger Barrett. Litho Format)

1979 (27 Feb). *Death Centenary of Sir Rowland Hill. T* **56** *and similar horiz designs showing stamps and Sir Rowland Hill. Multicoloured. P* 14½.
204 5 c. Type **56** 15 10
a. Imperf (pair) £100
205 15 c. "NAURU" opt on Great Britain 10s. "Seahorse" of 1916–23 .. .. .. 25 20
a. Imperf (pair) £100
206 60 c. 1978 10th Anniversary of Independence 60 c. commemorative 55 40
a. Imperf (pair) £100
204/6 .. .. *Set of* 3 85 60
MS207 159 × 101 mm. Nos. 204/6 .. .. 85 1·25
a. Error. Imperf £250

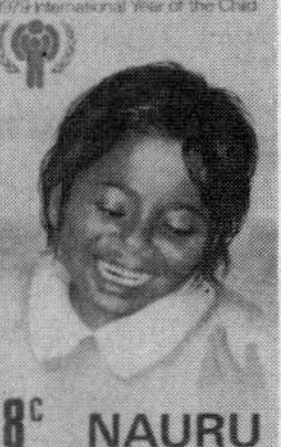

57 Dish Antenna, Transmitting Station and Radio Mast **58** Smiling Child

(Des G. Vasarhelyi. Litho Format)

1979 (22 Aug). *50th Anniv of International Consultative Radio Committee. T* **57** *and similar horiz designs. Multicoloured. P* 14½.
208 7 c. Type **57** 15 10
209 32 c. Telex operator 35 25
210 40 c. Radio operator 40 25
208/10 .. .. *Set of* 3 80 55

(Des G. Vasarhelyi. Litho Format)

1979 (3 Oct). *International Year of the Child. T* **58** *and similar vert designs showing smiling children. P* 14½.
211 8 c. multicoloured 10 10
a. Horiz strip of 5. Nos. 211/15 70
212 15 c. multicoloured 15 15
213 25 c. multicoloured 20 20
214 32 c. multicoloured 20 20
215 50 c. multicoloured 25 25
211/15 .. .. *Set of* 5 70 70
Nos. 211/15 were printed together, *se-tenant*, in horizontal strips of 5 throughout the sheet, forming a composite design.

59 Ekwenababae (flower), Scroll inscribed "Peace on Earth" and Star

(Des G. Vasarhelyi. Litho Format)

1979 (14 Nov). *Christmas. T* **59** *and similar horiz designs. Multicoloured. P* 14½.
216 7 c. Type **59** 10 10
217 15 c. *Thespia populnea* (flower), scroll inscribed "Goodwill toward Men" and star .. 10 10

218 20 c. Denea (flower), scroll inscribed "Peace on Earth" and star 10 10
219 30 c. Erekogo (flower), scroll inscribed "Good-will toward Men" and star 20 20
216/19 . . . . *Set of* 4 40 40
Nos. 216/19 exist imperforate from sets of progressive proofs.

60 Dassault Bregeut Mystère Falcon 50 over Melbourne

(Des G. Vasarhelyi. Litho Format)

1980 (28 Feb). *10th Anniv of Air Nauru. T* **60** *and similar horiz designs. Multicoloured. P* 14½.
220 15 c. Type **60** 35 15
221 20 c. Fokker F.28 Fellowship over Tarawa 40 15
222 25 c. Boeing 727-100 over Hong Kong . . 40 15
223 30 c. Boeing 737 over Auckland . . 40 15
220/3 . . . . *Set of* 4 1·40 55
No. 222 exists imperforate from stock dispersed by the liquidator of Format International Security Printers Ltd.

61 Steam Locomotive

(Des G. Vasarhelyi. Litho Format)

1980 (6 May). *10th Anniv of Nauru Phosphate Corporation. Railway Locomotives. T* **61** *and similar horiz designs. Multicoloured. P* 14½.
224 8 c. Type **61** 10 10
225 32 c. Electric locomotives 20 20
226 60 c. Diesel locomotive 35 35
224/6 . . . . *Set of* 3 60 60
MS227 168 × 118 mm. Nos. 224/6. P 13 . . . . 2·00 2·50
No. **MS**227 also commemorates the "London 1980" International Stamp Exhibition.

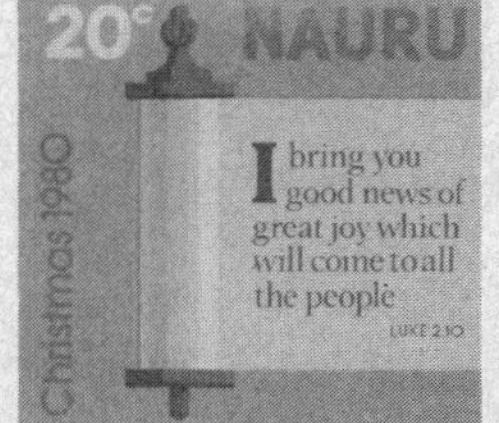

62 Verse 10 from Luke, Chapter 2 in English

(Des C. Abbott. Litho Format)

1980 (24 Sept). *Christmas. T* **62** *and similar square designs showing verses from Luke, chapter 2. Multicoloured. P* 14½.
228 20 c. Type **62** 10 10
a. Horiz pair. Nos. 228/9 . . . . 20 20
229 20 c. Verse 10 in Nauruan 10 10
230 30 c. Verse 14 in English 15 15
a. Horiz pair. Nos. 230/1 . . . . 30 30
231 30 c. Verse 14 in Nauruan 15 15
228/31 . . . . *Set of* 4 50 50
Nos. 228/9 and 230/1 were each printed together, *se-tenant*, in horizontal pairs throughout the sheet.
See also Nos. 248/51.

63 Nauruan, Australian, Union and New Zealand Flags on Aerial View of Nauru

(Des H. Woods. Litho Format)

1980 (3 Dec)–**81**. *20th Anniv of U.N. Declaration on the Granting of Independence to Colonial Countries and Peoples. T* **63** *and similar multicoloured designs. P* 14½ *(25 c.) or* 13½ *(others)*.
232 25 c. Type **63** 15 15
233 30 c. U.N. Trusteeship Council (72 × 23 *mm*) (11.2.81) 15 15
234 50 c. Nauru independence ceremony, 1968 (72 × 23 *mm*) 25 25
232/4 . . . . *Set of* 3 50 50
The 25 c. value was printed in sheets including 5 *se-tenant* stamp-size labels; the other two values were each printed in sheets including 5 *se-tenant* half stamp-size labels.
Nos. 233/4 exist imperforate from stock dispersed by the liquidator of Format International Security Printers Ltd.

64 Timothy Detudamo

(Des R. Granger Barrett. Litho Format)

1981 (11 Feb). *30th Anniv of Nauru Local Government Council. Head Chiefs. T* **64** *and similar horiz designs. Multicoloured. P* 14½.
235 20 c. Type **64** 15 15
236 30 c. Raymond Gadabu 15 15
237 50 c. Hammer DeRoburt 25 25
235/7 . . . . *Set of* 3 50 50
Nos. 235/7 exist imperforate from stock dispersed by the liquidator of Format International Security Printers Ltd.

65 Casting Net by Hand

(Litho Questa)

1981 (22 May). *Fishing. T* **65** *and similar horiz designs. Multicoloured. P* 12 × 11½.
238 8 c. Type **65** 10 10
239 20 c. Outrigger canoe 20 15
240 32 c. Outboard motor boat 25 20
241 40 c. Trawler 30 25
238/41 . . . . *Set of* 4 75 60
MS242 167 × 116 mm. No. 241 × 4. P 14 . . . . 2·25 2·00
No. **MS**242 was issued to commemorate the "WIPA 1981" International Stamp Exhibition, Vienna.

66 Bank of Nauru Emblem and Building 67 Inaugural Speech

(Des H. Woods. Litho Harrison)

1981 (21 July). *Fifth Anniv of Bank of Nauru. P* 14 × 14½.
243 **66** $1 multicoloured 60 60

(Des G. Vasarhelyi. Litho Questa)

1981 (24 Oct). *U.N. Day. E.S.C.A.P. (United Nations Economic and Social Commission for Asia and the Pacific) Events. T* **67** *and similar square designs. Multicoloured. P* 14 × 14½.
244 15 c. Type **67** 15 15
245 20 c. Presenting credentials 15 15
246 25 c. Unveiling plaque 20 20
247 30 c. Raising U.N. flag 25 25
244/7 . . . . *Set of* 4 65 65

(Des C. Abbott. Litho Format)

1981 (14 Nov). *Christmas. Bible Verses. Square designs as T* **62**. *Multicoloured. P* 14½.
248 20 c. Matthew 1, 23 in English 15 15
a. Horiz pair. Nos. 248/9 . . . . 30 30
249 20 c. Matthew 1, 23 in Nauruan 15 15
250 30 c. Luke 2, 11 in English 20 20
a. Horiz pair. Nos. 250/1 . . . . 40 40
251 30 c. Luke 2, 11 in Nauruan 20 20
248/51 . . . . *Set of* 4 70 70
Nos. 248/9 and 250/1 were each printed together, *se-tenant*, in horizontal pairs throughout the sheet.

68 Earth Satellite Station

(Des M. Rickards. Litho Format)

1981 (9 Dec). *Tenth Anniv of South Pacific Forum. T* **68** *and similar horiz designs. Multicoloured. P* 13½ × 14.
252 10 c. Type **68** 30 20
253 20 c. *Enna G* (cargo liner) 35 25
254 30 c. Boeing 737 airliner 35 30
255 40 c. Local produce 45 40
252/5 . . . . *Set of* 4 1·25 1·00

69 Nauru Scouts leaving for 1935 Frankston Scout Jamboree

(Des C. Abbott. Litho Format)

1982 (23 Feb). *75th Anniv of Boy Scout Movement. T* **69** *and similar multicoloured designs. P* 14.
256 7 c. Type **69** 15 15
257 8 c. Two Nauru scouts on *Nauru Chief*, 1935 (*vert*) 15 15
258 15 c. Nauru scouts making pottery, 1935 (*vert*) 15 20
259 20 c. Lord Huntingfield addressing Nauru scouts, Frankston Jamboree, 1935 . . 20 25
260 25 c. Nauru cub and scout, 1982 . . 20 30
261 40 c. Nauru cubs, scouts and scouters, 1982 . . 30 45
256/61 . . . . *Set of* 6 1·00 1·40
MS262 152 × 114 mm. Nos. 256/61. Imperf . . 1·25 2·25
No. **MS**262 also commemorates Nauru's participation in the "Stampex" National Stamp Exhibition, London.
Nos. 256/61 were each printed in sheets including four *se-tenant* stamp-size labels.

70 100kw Electricity Generating Plant under Construction (left side)

(Litho Irish Security Stamp Printing Ltd)

1982 (10 June). *Ocean Thermal Energy Conversion. T* **70** *and similar horiz designs. Multicoloured. P* 13½.
263 25 c. Type **70** 50 30
a. Horiz pair. Nos. 263/4 . . . . 1·00 60
264 25 c. 100kw Electricity Generating Plant under construction (right side) 50 30
265 40 c. Completed plant (left) 70 40
a. Horiz pair. Nos. 265/6 . . . . 1·40 80
266 40 c. Completed plant (right) 70 40
263/6 . . . . *Set of* 4 2·25 1·25
Nos. 263/4 and 265/6 were printed together, *se-tenant*, in horizontal pairs forming composite designs throughout sheets which also included two stamp-size and twelve half stamp-size labels.

71 S.S. *Fido* 72 Queen Elizabeth II on Horseback

(Des R. Littleford (5 c.), Debbie Ryder (10, 30 c.), Cecilia Eales (60 c.), Jane Evans ($1). Litho Format)

1982 (11 Oct). *75th Anniv of Phosphate Shipments. T* **71** *and similar horiz designs. Multicoloured. P* 14.
267 5 c. Type **71** 50 10
268 10 c. Steam locomotive *Nellie* 70 20
269 30 c. Modern "Clyde" class diesel loco . . 80 50
270 60 c. M.V. *Eigamoiya* (bulk carrier) . . 85 80
267/70 . . . . *Set of* 4 2·50 1·40
MS271 165×107 mm. $1 *Eigamoiya, Rosie-D* and *Kolle-D* (bulk carriers) (67 × 27 *mm*) . . 1·50 2·25
No. **MS**271 was issued to commemorate "ANPEX 82" National Stamp Exhibition, Brisbane.
Nos. 268/71 exist imperforate from stock dispersed by the liquidator of Format International Security Printers Ltd.

(Des G. Vasarhelyi. Litho Format)

1982 (21 Oct). *Royal Visit. T* **72** *and similar multicoloured designs. P* 14½.
272 20 c. Type **72** 40 30
273 50 c. Prince Philip, Duke of Edinburgh . . 50 60
274 $1 Queen Elizabeth II and Prince Philip (*horiz*) . . . . 80 1·25
272/4 . . . . *Set of* 3 1·50 1·90

73 Father Bernard Lahn 74 Speaker of the Nauruan Parliament

(Des G. Vasarhelyi. Litho Format)

1982 (17 Nov). *Christmas. T* **73** *and similar horiz designs. Multicoloured. P* 14½.
275 20 c. Type **73** 30 30
276 30 c. Reverend Itubwa Amram 35 45
277 40 c. Pastor James Aingimen 40 70
278 50 c. Bishop Paul Mea . . . . 40 1·00
275/8 . . . . *Set of* 4 1·25 2·25
Nos. 275/8 were printed in sheets of 25 including 5 *se-tenant*, stamp-size, labels.

(Des G. Vasarhelyi. Litho Walsall)

1983 (23 Mar). *15th Anniv of Independence. T* **74** *and similar multicoloured designs.* W w **14** *(sideways on* 30, 50 c.). *P* 14.

279	15 c. Type **74**	15	15
280	20 c. Family Court in session	20	20
281	30 c. Law Courts building *(horiz)*	25	25
282	50 c. Parliamentary chamber *(horiz)*	40	40
279/82	*Set of* 4	90	90

75 Nauru Satellite Earth Station

(Des C. Abbott. Litho Questa)

1983 (11 May). *World Communications Year. T* **75** *and similar horiz designs. Multicoloured.* W w **14** *(sideways). P* 14.

283	5 c. Type **75**	15	10
284	10 c. Omni-directional range installation	20	15
285	20 c. Emergency short-wave radio	25	25
286	25 c. Radio Nauru control room	35	30
287	40 c. Unloading air mail	70	45
283/7	*Set of* 5	1·50	1·10

76 Return of Exiles from Truk on M.V. *Trienza*, 1946

77 "The Holy Virgin, the Holy Child and St. John" (School of Raphael)

(Des D. Slater. Litho Format)

1983 (14 Sept). *Angam Day. T* **76** *and similar multicoloured designs.* W w **14** *(sideways on* 15 c.). *P* 13½ (15 c.) *or* 14 *(others).*

288	15 c. Type **76**	20	25
289	20 c. Mrs. Elsie Agio (exile community leader)	20	25
290	30 c. Child on scales	35	40
291	40 c. Nauruan children	45	50
288/91	*Set of* 4	1·10	1·25

Nos. 289/91 are vertical designs, each 25 × 41 mm.

(Des L. Curtis. Litho Questa)

1983 (16 Nov). *Christmas. T* **77** *and similar multicoloured designs.* W w **14** *(sideways on* 50 c.). *P* 14 × 14½ (50 c.) *or* 14½ × 14 *(others).*

292	5 c. Type **77**	10	10
293	15 c. "Madonna on the Throne surrounded by Angels" (School of Seville)	20	15
294	50 c. "The Mystical Betrothal of St. Catherine with Jesus" (School of Veronese) *(horiz)*	60	40
292/4	*Set of* 3	75	55

78 S.S. *Ocean Queen*

79 1974 U.P.U. $1 Stamp

(Des Beverley Barnard and L. Curtis. Litho Questa)

1984 (23 May). *250th Anniv of "Lloyd's List" (newspaper). T* **78** *and similar vert designs. Multicoloured.* W w **14**. *P* 14½ × 14.

295	20 c. Type **78**	50	30
296	25 c. M.V. *Enna G*	55	35
297	30 c. M.V. *Baron Minto*	60	40
298	40 c. Sinking of M.V. *Triadic*, 1940	85	55
295/8	*Set of* 4	2·25	1·40

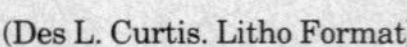

(Des L. Curtis. Litho Format)

1984 (4 June). *Universal Postal Union Congress, Hamburg.* W w **14**. *P* 14.

299	**79**	$1 multicoloured	1·25	1·25

80 *Hypolimnas bolina* (female)

(Des I. Loe. Litho B.D.T.)

1984 (24 July). *Butterflies. T* **80** *and similar horiz designs. Multicoloured.* W w **14** *(sideways). P* 14.

300	25 c. Type **80**	50	40
301	30 c. *Hypolimnas bolina* (male)	55	55
302	50 c. *Danaus plexippus*	70	85
300/2	*Set of* 3	1·60	1·60

81 Coastal Scene

82 Buada Chapel

(Des A. Theobald. Litho Enschedé)

1984 (21 Sept). *Life in Nauru. T* **81** *and similar multicoloured designs.* W w **14** *(sideways on horiz designs). P* 13½ × 14 (1, 5, 10, 25, 40 c., $2) *or* 14 × 13½ *(others).*

303	1 c. Type **81**	10	40
304	3 c. Nauruan woman *(vert)*	15	40
305	5 c. Modern trawler	40	50
306	10 c. Golfer on the links	90	50
307	15 c. Excavating phosphate *(vert)*	90	65
308	20 c. Surveyor *(vert)*	65	55
309	25 c. Air Nauru Boeing 727 airliner	80	55
310	30 c. Elderly Nauruan *(vert)*	50	50
311	40 c. Loading hospital patient on to Boeing 727 aircraft	90	55
312	50 c. Skin-diver with fish *(vert)*	1·00	80
313	$1 Tennis player *(vert)*	2·50	3·25
314	$2 Anabar Lagoon	2·50	3·75
303/14	*Set of* 12	10·00	11·00

Nos. 303/14 were each issued in sheets of 9 with decorative margins.

(Des L. Curtis. Litho Format)

1984 (14 Nov). *Christmas. T* **82** *and similar multicoloured designs.* W w **14** *(sideways on* 50 c.). *P* 14.

315	30 c. Type **82**	60	50
316	40 c. Detudamo Memorial Church	80	65
317	50 c. Candle-light service, Kayser College *(horiz)*	90	70
315/17	*Set of* 3	2·10	1·75

83 Air Nauru Boeing 737 Jet on Tarmac

(Des L. Curtis. Litho Walsall)

1985 (26 Feb). *15th Anniv of Air Nauru. T* **83** *and similar multicoloured designs.* W w **14** *(sideways on* 20 c., 40 c.). *P* 14.

318	20 c. Type **83**	65	35
319	30 c. Stewardess on Boeing 727 aircraft steps *(vert)*	85	60
320	40 c. Fokker F.28 Fellowship over Nauru	1·10	75
321	50 c. Freight being loaded onto Boeing 727 *(vert)*	1·25	85
318/21	*Set of* 4	3·50	2·25

84 Open Cut Mining

85 Mother and Baby on Beach

(Des L. Curtis. Litho B.D.T.)

1985 (31 July). *15th Anniv of Nauru Phosphate Corporation. T* **84** *and similar horiz designs. Multicoloured.* W w **14** *(sideways). P* 14.

322	20 c. Type **84**	80	60
323	25 c. Locomotive hauling crushed ore	1·50	1·00
324	30 c. Phosphate drying plant	1·50	1·00
325	50 c. Early steam locomotive	2·25	1·75
322/5	*Set of* 4	5·50	4·00

(Des A. Theobald. Litho Questa)

1985 (15 Nov). *Christmas. T* **85** *and similar vert design. Multicoloured.* W w **16** *(sideways). P* 14.

326	50 c. Beach scene	1·40	2·00
	a. Horiz pair. Nos. 326/7	2·75	4·00
327	50 c. Type **85**	1·40	2·00

Nos. 326/7 were printed in sheets of 16 made up of two strips of four *se-tenant* pairs, each pair forming a composite design. The two strips were divided by a horizontal gutter.

86 Adult Common Noddy with Juvenile

(Des N. Arlott. Litho Questa)

1985 (31 Dec). *Birth Bicentenary of John J. Audubon (ornithologist). Common "Brown" Noddy. T* **86** *and similar horiz designs. Multicoloured.* W w **16**. *P* 14.

328	10 c. Type **86**	35	35
	w. Wmk inverted	25·00	
329	20 c. Adult and immature birds in flight	50	70
	w. Wmk inverted	25·00	
330	30 c. Adults in flight	65	85
	w. Wmk inverted	25·00	
331	50 c. "Brown Noddy" (John J. Audubon)	80	1·00
328/31	*Set of* 4	2·10	2·75

87 Douglas Motor Cycle

(Des M. Joyce. Litho Questa)

1986 (5 Mar). *Early Transport on Nauru. T* **87** *and similar horiz designs. Multicoloured.* W w **16**. *P* 14.

332	15 c. Type **87**	80	70
333	20 c. Primitive lorry	95	95
334	30 c. German 2 ft gauge locomotive (1910)	1·50	1·50
335	40 c. "Baby" Austin car	1·75	1·75
332/5	*Set of* 4	4·50	4·50

88 Island and Bank of Nauru

89 *Plumeria rubra*

(Des G. Vasarhelyi. Litho Format)

1986 (21 July). *10th Anniv of Bank of Nauru. Children's Paintings. T* **88** *and similar horiz designs. Multicoloured.* W w **16** *(sideways). P* 14.

336	20 c. Type **88**	30	30
337	25 c. Borrower with notes and coins	35	35
338	30 c. Savers	40	40
339	40 c. Customers at bank counter	55	55
336/9	*Set of* 4	1·40	1·40

(Des Doreen McGuinness. Litho Questa)

1986 (30 Sept). *Flowers. T* **89** *and similar horiz designs. Multicoloured.* W w **16**. *P* 14.

340	20 c. Type **89**	55	70
341	25 c. *Tristellateia australis*	65	85
342	30 c. *Bougainvillea cultivar*	75	1·00
343	40 c. *Delonix regia*	1·00	1·25
340/3	*Set of* 4	2·75	3·50

90 Carol Singers

91 Young Girls Dancing

(Des M. Joyce. Litho Questa)

1986 (8 Dec). *Christmas. T* **90** *and similar horiz design. Multicoloured.* W w **16** *(sideways). P* 14.

344	20 c. Type **90**	45	30
345	$1 Carol singers and hospital patient	2·00	3·00

(Des Joan Thompson. Litho Questa)

1987 (31 Jan). *Nauruan Dancers. T* **91** *and similar multicoloured designs.* W w **16** *(sideways on* 20, 30 c.). *P* 14.

346	20 c. Type **91**	80	80
347	30 c. Stick dance	1·00	1·25
348	50 c. Boy doing war dance *(vert)*	1·75	2·50
346/8	*Set of* 3	3·25	4·00

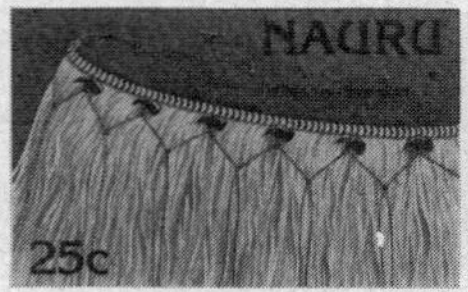

92 Hibiscus Fibre Skirt

93 U.P.U. Emblem and Air Mail Label

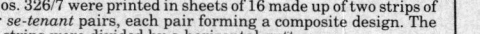

(Des L. Curtis. Litho B.D.T.)

1987 (30 July). *Personal Artifacts. T* **92** *and similar horiz designs. Multicoloured.* W w **16** (*sideways*). P 14.
349 25 c. Type **92** 75 75
350 30 c. Headband and necklets 85 85
351 45 c. Decorative necklets . . . . . . 1·10 1·10
352 60 c. Pandanus leaf fan . . . . . . 1·60 1·60
349/52 . . . . *Set of* 4 3·75 3·75

(Des D. Miller. Litho Format)

1987 (20 Oct). *World Post Day. T* **93** *and similar multicoloured design.* W w **16**. P 14½ × 14.
353 40 c. Type **93** 90 75
w. Wmk inverted . . . . 14·00
MS354 122×82mm. $1 U.P.U. emblem and map of Pacific showing mail routes (114×74 *mm*). Wmk sideways. Imperf . . . . . . 2·25 3·00

94 Open Bible

95 Nauruan Children's Party

(Des Janet Boschen. Litho Walsall)

1987 (5 Nov). *Centenary of Nauru Congregational Church.* W w **14**. P 13 × 13½.
355 **94** 40 c. multicoloured . . . . . . 75 1·00

(Des M. Joyce. Litho Format)

1987 (27 Nov). *Christmas. T* **95** *and similar horiz design. Multicoloured.* W w **16** (*sideways*). P 14.
356 20 c. Type **95** 75 50
357 $1 Nauruan Christmas dinner . . . . 2·75 3·25

96 Loading Phosphate on Ship

97 Map of German Marshall Is. and 1901 5 m. Yacht Definitive

(Des B. Clinton. Litho CPE Australia Ltd, Melbourne)

1988 (31 Jan). *20th Anniv of Independence. T* **96** *and similar multicoloured designs.* P 13½ × 14 (25 c.), 14 × 13½ (40, 55 c.) or 13 ($1).
358 25 c. Type **96** 80 80
359 40 c. Tomano flower (*vert*) . . . . 1·50 1·50
360 55 c. Great Frigate Bird (*vert*) . . . . 2·00 2·25
361 $1 Arms of Republic (35×35 *mm*) . . 2·25 3·25
358/61 . . . . *Set of* 4 6·00 7·00

(Des O. Bell. Litho Format)

1988 (29 July). *80th Anniv of Nauru Post Office. T* **97** *and similar horiz designs. Multicoloured.* W w **16** (*sideways*). P 14.
362 30 c. Type **97** 75 75
363 50 c. Letter and post office of 1908 . . . . 1·00 1·25
364 70 c. Nauru Post Office and airmail letter . . 1·25 1·50
362/4 . . . . *Set of* 3 2·75 3·25

98 "Itubwer" (mat)

99 U.P.U. Emblem and National Flag

(Des Jennifer Toombs. Litho CPE Australia Ltd, Melbourne)

1988 (1 Aug). *String Figures. T* **98** *and similar horiz designs. Multicoloured.* P 13½ × 14.
365 25 c. Type **98** 25 30
366 40 c. "Etegerer–the Pursuer" 40 50
367 55 c. "Holding up the Sky" 50 65
368 80 c. "Manujie's Sword" . . . . . . 75 1·00
365/8 . . . . *Set of* 4 1·75 2·25

(Des Elisabeth Innes. Litho CPE Australia Ltd, Melbourne)

1988 (1 Oct). *Centenary of Nauru's Membership of Universal Postal Union.* P 13½ × 14.
369 **99** $1 multicoloured . . . . 95 1·00

100 "Hark the Herald Angels"

101 Logo (15th anniv of Nauru Insurance Corporation)

(Des Elisabeth Innes. Litho CPE Australia Ltd, Melbourne)

1988 (28 Nov). *Christmas. T* **100** *and similar square designs showing words and music from "Hark the Herald Angels Sing".* P 13.
370 20 c. black, orange-vermilion and lemon . . 40 30
371 60 c. black, orange-vermilion and mauve . . 1·00 85
372 $1 black, orange-vermilion & bright green 1·60 1·40
370/2 . . . . *Set of* 3 2·75 2·25

(Litho Note Ptg Branch, Reserve Bank of Australia)

1989 (19 Nov). *Anniversaries and Events. T* **101** *and similar vert designs. Multicoloured.* P 14×15.
373 15 c. Type **101** 30 30
374 50 c. Logos (World Telecommunications Day and 10th anniv of Asian Pacific Telecommunity) 75 85
375 $1 Photograph of island scene (150 years of photography) . . . . . . 1·75 2·00
376 $2 Capitol and U.P.U. emblem (20th U.P.U. Congress, Washington) . . 2·75 3·25
373/6 . . . . *Set of* 4 5·00 5·75

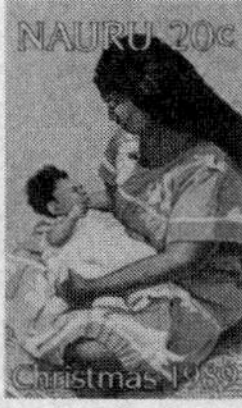

102 Mother and Baby

103 Eigigu working while Sisters play

(Des Robin White. Litho Note Ptg Branch, Reserve Bank of Australia)

1989 (15 Dec). *Christmas. T* **102** *and similar vert design. Multicoloured.* P 14×15.
377 20 c. Type **102** 50 30
378 $1 Children opening presents . . . . 2·25 3·00

(Des Anita Cecil. Litho Note Ptg Branch, Reserve Bank of Australia)

1989 (22 Dec). *20th Anniv of First Manned Landing on Moon. Legend of Eigigu, the Girl in the Moon. T* **103** *and similar vert designs. Multicoloured.* P 14×15.
379 25 c. Type **103** . . . . 2·50 2·50
380 30 c. Eigigu climbing tree . . . . . . 2·75 2·75
381 50 c. Eigigu stealing toddy from blind woman . . . . 4·75 4·75
382 $1 Eigigu on Moon . . . . 7·00 7·00
379/82 . . . . *Set of* 4 15·00 15·00

104 Early Mining by Hand

105 Sunday School Class

(Des Robin White. Litho Note Ptg Branch. Reserve Bank of Australia)

1990 (3 July). *20th Anniv of Nauru Phosphate Corporation. T* **104** *and similar vert design. Multicoloured.* P 14×15.
383 50 c. Type **104** . . . . 1·50 1·50
384 $1 Modern mining by excavator . . . . 2·25 2·25

(Litho Note Ptg Branch, Reserve Bank of Australia)

1990 (26 Nov). *Christmas. T* **105** *and similar vert design. Multicoloured.* P 14×15.
385 25 c. Type **105** . . . . 1·25 1·25
a. Horiz pair. Nos. 385/6 . . . . 2·50 2·50
386 25 c. Teacher telling Christmas story . . 1·25 1·25
Nos. 385/6 were printed together, *se-tenant*, in horizontal pairs throughout the sheet, each pair forming a composite design.

106 Eoiyepiang laying Baby on Mat

107 Oleander

(Des Robin White. Litho Note Ptg Branch, Reserve Bank of Australia)

1990 (24 Dec). *Legend of "Eoiyepiang, the Daughter of Thunder and Lightning". T* **106** *and similar vert designs. Multicoloured.* P 14×15.
387 25 c. Type **106** 85 60
388 30 c. Eoiyepiang making floral decoration . . 90 70
389 50 c. Eoiyepiang left on snow-covered mountain . . . . 1·50 1·75
390 $1 Eoiyepiang and warrior . . . . 2·25 2·75
387/90 . . . . *Set of* 4 5·00 5·25

(Litho Leigh-Mardon Ltd, Melbourne)

1991 (22 July). *Flowers. T* **107** *and similar multicoloured designs.* P 14½.
391 15 c. Type **107** 15 20
392 20 c. Lily 15 20
393 25 c. Passion Flower 25 30
394 30 c. Lily (*different*) 25 30
395 35 c. Caesalpinia 30 35
396 40 c. Clerodendron 35 40
397 45 c. *Baubina pinnata* 40 45
398 50 c. Hibiscus (*vert*) 45 50
399 75 c. Apocymaceae 65 70
400 $1 Bindweed (*vert*) 90 95
401 $2 Tristellateia (*vert*) . . . . . . 1·75 1·90
402 $3 Impala Lily (*vert*) . . . . . . 2·50 2·75
391/402 . . . . *Set of* 12 8·00 9·00

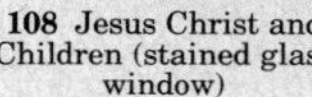

108 Jesus Christ and Children (stained glass window)

109 Star and Symbol of Asian Development Bank

(Des R. Varma. Litho Leigh-Mardon Ltd, Melbourne)

1991 (12 Dec). *Christmas. Sheet* 124×82 *mm.* P 14.
MS403 **108** $2 multicoloured . . . . . . 3·50 4·00

(Des R. Varma. Litho Leigh-Mardon Ltd, Melbourne)

1992 (4 May). *25th Annual Meeting of Asian Development Bank.* P 14×14½.
404 **109** $1.50, multicoloured . . . . . . 2·00 2·50

110 Gifts under Christmas Tree

111 Hammer DeRoburt

(Des B. Clinton. Litho Printset Cambec Pty Ltd, Australia)

1992 (23 Nov). *Christmas. Children's Paintings. T* **110** *and similar horiz design. Multicoloured.* P 14½×14.
405 45 c. Type **110** 75 75
406 60 c. Father Christmas in sleigh . . . . 1·00 1·25

(Des B. Clinton. Litho McPherson's Ptg Group. Mulgrave)

1993 (31 Jan). *25th Anniv of Independence and Hammer DeRoburt (former President) Commemoration.* P 14×14½.
407 **111** $1 multicoloured . . . . 2·00 2·50

112 Running, Constitution Day Sports

(Des B. Clinton. Litho McPherson's Ptg Group, Mulgrave)

1993 (17 May). *15th Anniv of Constitution Day. T* **112** *and similar vert design. Multicoloured. P* 14×14½.
408 70 c. Type **112** . . . . 1·00 1·00
409 80 c. Part of Independence Proclamation . . 1·25 1·50

113 Great Frigate Birds, Flying Fish and Island

(Litho McPherson's Printing Group, Mulgrave)

1993 (9 Aug). *24th South Pacific Forum Meeting, Nauru. T* **113** *and similar horiz designs. Multicoloured. P* 14½×14.
410 60 c. Type **113** . . . . 1·40 1·50
a. Block of 4. Nos. 410/13 . . . . 5·00
411 60 c. Red-tailed Tropic Bird, Great Frigate Bird, dolphin and island . . . . 1·40 1·50
412 60 c. Raccoon Butterflyfish ("Ikimago"), coral and sea urchins . . . . 1·40 1·50
413 60 c. Three different types of fish with corals 1·40 1·50
410/13 . . . . *Set of* 4 5·00 5·50
MS414 140×130 mm. Nos. 410/13 . . . . 5·50 6·50
Nos. 410/13 were printed together, *se-tenant*, in blocks of 4 throughout the sheet with each block forming a composite design.

114 "Peace on Earth, Goodwill to Men" and Star

(Litho Leigh-Mardon Ltd, Melbourne)

1993 (29 Nov). *Christmas. T* **114** *and similar horiz design. Multicoloured. P* 14½×14.
415 55 c. Type **114** 85 85
416 65 c. "Hark the Herald Angels Sing" and star 90 90
Nos. 415/16 were printed in sheets containing the two values in blocks of 9 (3×3) separated by a horizontal gutter.

115 Girls with Dogs

116 Weightlifting

(Des B. Clinton. Litho McPherson's Ptg Group, Mulgrave)

1994 (10 Feb). *"Hong Kong '94" International Stamp Exhibition. Chinese New Year ("Year of the Dog"). T* **115** *and similar vert designs. Multicoloured. P* 14×14½.
417 $1 Type **115** . . . . 1·50 1·75
a. Horiz pair. Nos. 417/18 . . . . 3·00 3·50
418 $1 Boys with dogs . . . . 1·50 1·75
MS419 100×75 mm. Nos. 417/18 . . . . 3·00 3·75
a. Optd with exhibition logo on margin at bottom right . . . . 3·00 3·75
Nos. 417/18 were printed together, *se-tenant*, in horizontal pairs throughout the sheet of 12.

1994 (31 Aug). *"Singpex '94" National Stamp Exhibition, Singapore. No.* **MS**419 *optd "SINGPEX '94" and emblem in gold on sheet margin.*
MS420 100×75 mm. Nos. 417/18 . . . . 3·00 3·75

(Des R. Innes. Litho Printset Cambec Pty Ltd, Melbourne)

1994 (8 Sept). *15th Commonwealth Games, Victoria, Canada. P* 14×14½.
421 **116** $1.50, multicoloured . . . . . . 1·40 1·50

117 Peace Dove and Star over Island

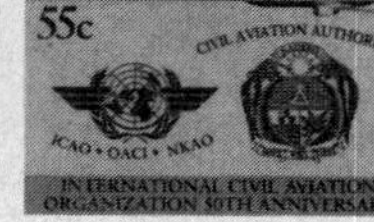

118 Air Nauru Airliner and Emblems

(Des Passmore Design. Litho McPherson's Ptg Group, Mulgrave)

1994 (20 Nov). *Christmas. T* **117** *and similar vert design. Multicoloured. P* 14½×14.
422 65 c. Type **117** 60 65
423 75 c. Star over Bethlehem 70 75

(Litho Printset Cambec Pty Ltd, Melbourne)

1994 (14 Dec). *50th Anniv of International Civil Aviation Organization. T* **118** *and similar horiz designs. Multicoloured. P* 14×14½.
424 55 c. Type **118** 50 55
425 65 c. Control tower, Nauru International Airport 60 65
426 80 c. D.V.O.R. equipment 70 75
427 $1 Crash tenders 90 95
424/7 . . . . *Set of* 4 2·50 2·75
MS428 165×127 mm. Nos. 424/7 . . . . 3·50 4·00

119 Emblem and Olympic Rings

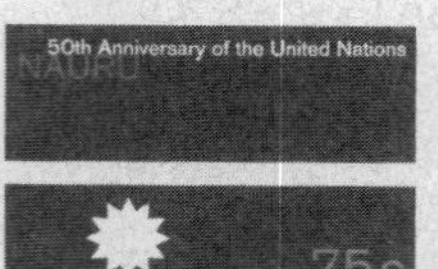

120 Nauruan Flag

(Des D. Sharma. Litho McPherson's Ptg Group, Mulgrave)

1994 (27 Dec). *Nauru's Entry into International Olympic Committee. P* 14×14½.
429 **119** 50 c. multicoloured 45 50

(Litho McPherson's Ptg Group, Mulgrave)

1995 (1 Jan). *50th Anniv of United Nations (1st issue). T* **120** *and similar horiz designs. Multicoloured. P* 14×14½.
430 75 c. Type **120** 80 90
a. Block of 4. Nos. 430/3 . . . . 3·00
431 75 c. Arms of Nauru 80 90
432 75 c. Outrigger canoe on coastline . . 80 90
433 75 c. Airliner over phosphate freighter . . 80 90
430/3 . . . . *Set of* 4 3·00 3·25
MS434 110×85 mm. Nos. 430/3 . . . . 3·75 4·50
Nos. 430/3 were printed together, *se-tenant*, in blocks of 4 with Nos. 432/3 forming a composite design.
See also Nos. 444/5.

121 Signing Phosphate Agreement, 1967

at Beijing

50c

(**122**)

(Des B. Clinton. Litho Printset Cambec Pty Ltd, Melbourne)

1995 (1 July). *25th Anniv of Nauru Phosphate Corporation. T* **121** *and similar horiz designs. Multicoloured. P* 14×14½.
435 60 c. Type **121** 80 90
a. Horiz pair. Nos. 435/6 . . . . 1·60 1·75
436 60 c. Pres. Bernard Dowiyogo and Prime Minister Keating of Australia shaking hands 80 90
MS437 120×80 mm. $2 Excavating phosphate 2·75 3·25
Nos. 435/6 were printed together, *se-tenant*, in horizontal pairs throughout the sheet.

1995 (19 Aug). *International Stamp Exhibitions. No. 309 surch as T* **122**.
438 50 c. on 25 c. mult (surch with T **122**) . . 1·00 1·10
a. Horiz strip of 3. Nos. 438/40 . . 3·25
439 $1 on 25 c. mult (surch "at Jakarta") . . 1·25 1·40
440 $1 on 25 c. mult (surch "at Singapore") . . 1·25 1·40
438/40 . . . . *Set of* 3 3·25 3·50
Nos. 438/40 were surcharged together, *se-tenant*, as horizontal strips of 3 on the sheets of 9.

123 Sea Birds (face value at top right)

124 Children playing on Gun

(Litho Southern Colour Print, Dunedin)

1995 (1 Sept). *Olympic Games, Atlanta. Sheet* 140×121 *mm, containing T* **123** *and similar vert designs. Multicoloured. P* 12.
MS441 60 c. + 15 c. Type **123**; 60 c. + 15 c. Sea birds (face value at top left); 60 c. + 15 c. Four dolphins; 60 c. + 15 c. Pair of dolphins . . 4·00 4·50
The premiums on No. **MS**441 were for Nauru sport development.

(Des Passmore Design. Litho Questa)

1995 (13 Sept). *50th Anniv of Peace. T* **124** *and similar horiz design. Multicoloured. P* 14×13½.
442 75 c. Type **124** . . . . 1·25 1·50
a. Horiz pair. Nos. 442/3 and label . . 3·00
b. Vert pair. Nos. 442/3 . . 3·00
443 $1.50, Children making floral garlands 1·75 2·00
Nos. 442/3 were printed together, *se-tenant*, in sheets of 12 (3×4) containing 8 stamps and 4 labels. The labels, which show a dove or a war memorial, occur in the centre vertical row.
Nos. 442/3 were reissued on 23 February 1996 with the centre labels overprinted in gold with the "HONGPEX '96" logo or a mouse.

125 Nauru Crest, Coastline and U.N. Anniversary Emblem

126 Young Girl praying

(Des and litho Courvoisier)

1995 (24 Oct). *50th Anniv of United Nations (2nd issue). T* **125** *and similar horiz design. Multicoloured. P* 14½×14.
444 75 c. Type **125** . . . . 90 1·00
445 $1.50, Aerial view of Nauru and U.N. Headquarters, New York . . . . 1·60 2·00

(Litho Questa)

1995 (7 Dec). *Christmas. T* **126** *and similar vert design. Multicoloured. P* 14½.
446 60 c. Type **126** . . . . 90 1·00
a. Horiz pair. Nos. 446/7 . . . . 1·75 2·00
447 70 c. Man praying . . . . . . 90 1·00
Nos. 446/7 were printed together, *se-tenant*, in horizontal pairs throughout the sheet.

127 Returning Refugees and Head Chief Timothy Detudamo

(Des P. Arnold. Litho Southern Colour Print, Dunedin)

1996 (31 Jan). *50th Anniv of Nauruans' Return from Truk. P* 12.
448 **127** 75 c. multicoloured . . . . . . 90 1·00
449 $1.25, multicoloured . . . . 1·60 2·00
MS450 120×80 mm. Nos. 448/9 . . . . 2·50 3·00

128 Nanjing Stone Lion

129 Symbolic Athlete

(Litho Southern Colour Print, Dunedin)

1996 (20 Mar). *"CHINA '96" 9th Asian International Stamp Exhibition, Peking. Sheet* 130×110 *mm. P* 12.

MS451 **128** 45 c. multicoloured 70 85

(Des and litho Courvoisier)

1996 (21 July). *Centenary of Modern Olympic Games. T* **129** *and similar multicoloured designs. P* 14.

452 40 c. Type **129** 60 60
453 50 c. Symbolic weightlifter 70 80
454 60 c. Weightlifter (*horiz*) 80 90
455 $1 Athlete (*horiz*) .. .. .. 1·25 1·75
452/5 .. .. *Set of* 4 3·00 3·50

130 The Nativity and Angel

131 Dolphin (fish)

(Des G. Vasarhelyi. Litho Courvoisier)

1996 (16 Dec). *Christmas. T* **130** *and similar horiz design. Multicoloured. P* 14.

456 50 c. Type **130** 60 60
457 70 c. Angel, world map and wild animals .. 80 80

(Des and litho Courvoisier)

1997 (12 Feb). *Endangered Species. Fishes. T* **131** *and similar horiz designs. Multicoloured. P* 11½.

458 20 c. Type **131** 45 45
a. Strip of 4. Nos. 458/61 .. .. 2·10
459 30 c. Wahoo 55 55
460 40 c. Sailfish 60 60
461 50 c. Yellow-finned Tuna 70 70
458/61 .. .. *Set of* 4 2·10 2·10

Nos. 458/61 were printed together, *se-tenant*, as horizontal or vertical strips of 4 in sheets of 16.

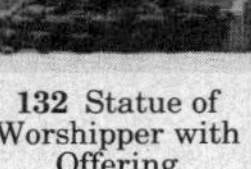

132 Statue of Worshipper with Offering

133 Princess Elizabeth and Lieut. Philip Mountbatten, 1947

(Litho Southern Colour Print, Dunedin)

1997 (12 Feb). *"HONG KONG '97" International Stamp Exhibition. T* **132** *and similar vert designs showing statues of different worshippers* (1 c. *to* 15 c.) *or Giant Buddha of Hong Kong* (25 c.). *P* 14.

462 1 c. multicoloured 10 10
a. Sheetlet. Nos. 462/8 .. .. .. 1·50
463 2 c. multicoloured 15 15
464 5 c. multicoloured 25 25
465 10 c. multicoloured 30 30
466 12 c. multicoloured 30 30
467 15 c. multicoloured 30 30
468 25 c. multicoloured 40 40
462/8 .. .. *Set of* 7 1·50 1·50

No. 468 is larger, 59×79 mm, and was printed with Nos. 462/7 in *se-tenant* sheetlets of 7.

(Des Colleen Corlett. Litho and embossed Southern Colour Print, Dunedin)

1997 (15 July). *Golden Wedding of Queen Elizabeth and Prince Philip. T* **133** *and similar vert design. P* 13½.

469 80 c. black and gold 80 85
470 $1.20, multicoloured .. .. .. 1·25 1·40
MS471 150×110 mm. Nos. 469/70 (*sold at* $3) 3·00 3·25

Design:—$1.20, Queen Elizabeth and Prince Philip, 1997.

134 Conference Building

(Des Patricia Altman. Litho Southern Colour Print, Dunedin)

1997 (24 July). *28th Parliamentary Conference of Presiding Officers and Clerks. Sheet* 150×100 *mm. P* 14.

MS472 **134** $2 multicoloured .. .. .. 1·75 1·90

135 Commemorative Pillar

(Des Audrey Bascand. Litho Southern Colour Print, Dunedin)

1997 (5 Nov). *Christmas. 110th Anniv of Nauru Congregational Church. T* **135** *and similar horiz design. Multicoloured. P* 13½.

473 60 c. Type **135** 50 55
474 80 c. Congregational Church 70 75

Nevis
see St. Kitts-Nevis

New Brunswick
see Canada

Newfoundland
see Canada

New Guinea
see Papua New Guinea

New Hebrides
see Vanuatu

New Republic
see South Africa

New South Wales
see Australia

New Zealand

From 1831 mail from New Zealand was sent to Sydney, New South Wales, routed through an unofficial postmaster at Kororareka.

The first official post office opened at Kororareka in January 1840 to be followed by others at Auckland, Britannia, Coromandel Harbour, Hokianga, Port Nicholson, Russell and Waimate during the same year. New South Wales relinquished control of the postal service when New Zealand became a separate colony on 3 May 1841.

The British G.P.O. was responsible for the operation of the overseas mails from 11 October 1841 until the postal service once again passed under colonial control on 18 November 1848.

CC 1

CC 2

AUCKLAND

CROWNED-CIRCLE HANDSTAMPS

CC1 CC 1 AUCKLAND NEW ZEALAND (R.) (31.10.1846) .. .. *Price on cover* £250

NELSON

CROWNED-CIRCLE HANDSTAMPS

CC2 CC 1 NELSON NEW ZEALAND (R.) (31.10.1846) *Price on cover* £900

NEW PLYMOUTH

CROWNED-CIRCLE HANDSTAMPS

CC3 CC 1 NEW PLYMOUTH NEW ZEALAND (R. *or* Black) (31.10.1846) .. *Price on cover* £1500

CC3*a* CC 2 NEW PLYMOUTH NEW ZEALAND (R. *or* Black) (1854) .. *Price on cover* £2000

OTAGO

CROWNED-CIRCLE HANDSTAMPS

CC4 CC 2 OTAGO NEW ZEALAND (R.) (1851) *Price on cover* £1500

PETRE

CROWNED-CIRCLE HANDSTAMPS

CC5 CC 1 PETRE NEW ZEALAND (R.) (31.10.1846) *Price on cover* £1200

PORT VICTORIA

CROWNED-CIRCLE HANDSTAMPS

CC6 CC 2 PORT VICTORIA NEW ZEALAND (R.) (1851) .. .. .. *Price on cover* £1000

RUSSELL

CROWNED-CIRCLE HANDSTAMPS

CC7 CC 1 RUSSELL NEW ZEALAND (R.) (31.10.1846) *Price on cover* £3000

WELLINGTON

CROWNED-CIRCLE HANDSTAMPS

CC8 CC 1 WELLINGTON NEW ZEALAND (R.) (31.10.1846) .. .. *Price on cover* £300

A similar mark for Christchurch as Type CC **2** is only known struck, in black, as a cancellation after the introduction of adhesive stamps.

No. CC3*a* is a locally-cut replacement with the office name around the circumference, but a straight "PAID AT" in the centre.

PRICES FOR STAMPS ON COVER TO 1945

Nos. 1/125	*from* × 2
Nos. 126/36	*from* × 3
Nos. 137/9	*from* × 2
No. 140	—
No. 141	*from* × 2
No. 142	—
Nos. 143/8	*from* × 2
Nos. 149/51	*from* × 10
Nos. 152/84	*from* × 2
Nos. 185/6	—
Nos. 187/203	*from* × 3
Nos. 205/7*e*	—
Nos. 208/13	*from* × 2
Nos. 214/16*j*	—
Nos. 217/58	*from* × 3
No. 259	—
Nos. 260/9	*from* × 3
No. 270	—
Nos. 271/6	*from* × 3
Nos. 277/307	*from* × 2
Nos. 308/16	*from* × 3
No. 317	—
Nos. 318/28	*from* × 3
Nos. 329/48	—
No. 349	*from* × 5
Nos. 350/1	—
No. 352	*from* × 5
Nos. 353/69	—
Nos. 370/86	*from* × 2
No. 387	*from* × 4
Nos. 388/99	*from* × 3
Nos. 400/666	*from* × 2
Nos. E1/5	*from* × 5
No. E6	*from* × 10
Nos. D1/8	*from* × 3
Nos. D9/16	*from* × 5
Nos. D17/20	*from* × 3
Nos. D21/47	*from* × 6
Nos. O1/24	*from* × 12
Nos. O59/66	*from* × 4
Nos. O67/8	—
Nos. O69/81	*from* × 5
Nos. O82/7	—
Nos. O88/93	*from* × 20
Nos. O94/9	*from* × 12
Nos. O100/11	*from* × 5
Nos. O112/13	—
Nos. O115/19	*from* × 15
Nos. O120/33	*from* × 10
Nos. O134/51	*from* × 4
Nos. P1/7	*from* × 8
Nos. L1/9	*from* × 10
Nos. L9*a*/12	—
Nos. L13/20	*from* × 15
Nos. L21/3	—
Nos. L24/41	*from* × 12
No. F1	—
No. F2	*from* × 5
Nos. F3/144	—
Nos. F145/58	*from* × 3
Nos. F159/68	—
Nos. F169/79	*from* × 3
Nos. F180/6	—
Nos. F187/90	*from* × 2
Nos. F191/203	*from* × 3
Nos. F204/11	—
Nos. F212/18	*from* × 2
Nos. A1/3	*from* × 2

CROWN COLONY

1

2

(Eng by Humphreys. Recess P.B.)

1855 (18 July). *Wmk Large Star, W w* **1.** *Imperf.*

1 1 1d. dull carmine (*white paper*) .. £30000 £9000
2 2d. dull blue (*blued paper*) £14000 £550
3 1s. pale yellow-green (*blued paper*) .. £25000 £5000
a. Bisected (6d.) (on cover) .. .. † £22000

The 2d. and 1s. on white paper formerly listed are now known to be stamps printed on blued paper which have had the bluing washed out.

Nos. 3a and 6a were used at Dunedin between March 1857, when the rate for ½ oz. letters to Great Britain was reduced to 6d., and August 1859. All known examples are bisected vertically.

(Printed by J. Richardson, Auckland, N.Z.)

1855 (Dec). *First printing. Wmk Large Star. White paper. Imperf.*

3*b* 1 1d. orange £15000

1855 (Dec)–**57.** *No wmk. Blue paper. Imperf.*

4 1 1d. red £6500 £1500
5 2d. blue (3.56) £2250 £300
a. Without value .. .. ..
6 1s. green (9.57) £19000 £3500
a. Bisected (6d.) (on cover) .. . † £15000

These stamps on blue paper may occasionally be found watermarked double-lined letters, being portions of the paper-maker's name.

1857 (Jan). *Wmk Large Star. White paper similar to the issue of July* 1855.

7 1 1d. dull orange .. .. — £12000

This stamp is in the precise shade of the 1d. of the 1858 printing by Richardson on *no wmk* white paper. An unsevered pair is known with Dunedin cancellation on a cover front showing an Auckland arrival postmark of 19.1.1857.

1857–63. *Hard or soft white paper. No wmk.* (*a*) *Imperf.*

8 1 1d. dull orange (1858) £1700 £475
8*a* 2d. deep ultramarine (1858) £1600 £800
9 2d. pale blue £750 £180
10 2d. blue (12.57) £750 £180
11 2d. dull deep blue £1100 £250
12 6d. bistre-brown (8.59) £2250 £500
13 6d. brown £1200 £300
14 6d. pale brown £1200 £300
15 6d. chestnut £2500 £550
16 1s. dull emerald-green (1858) .. £7000 £1200
17 1s. blue-green £7000 £1200

(*b*) *Pin-roulette, about* 10 *at Nelson* (1860)

18 1 1d. dull orange .. .. — £4500
19 2d. blue .. .. — £3000
20 6d. brown .. .. — £3750
21 1s. blue-green .. .. — £5500

(*c*) *Serrated perf about* 16 *or* 18 *at Nelson* (1862)

22 1 1d. dull orange .. .. — £3500
23 2d. blue .. .. — £2750
24 6d. brown .. .. — £2750
25 6d. chestnut .. .. — £5500
26 1s. blue-green .. .. — £4750

(*d*) *Rouletted* 7 *at Auckland* (April 1859)

27 1 1d. dull orange £5000 £3750
28 2d. blue £5500 £2750
29 6d. brown £4000 £2250
a. Imperf between (pair) £12000 £9000
30 1s. dull emerald-green £6000 £3500
31 1s. blue-green £7000 £3500

(*e*) *P* 13 *at Dunedin* (1863)

31*a* 1 1d. dull orange .. .. — £3750
31*b* 2d. pale blue £2750 £1800
32 6d. pale brown .. .. — £5000

(*f*) "H" *roulette* 16 *at Nelson*

32*a* 1 2d. blue .. .. — £3500
32*b* 6d. brown .. .. — £3750

(*g*) "Y" *roulette* 18 *at Nelson*

32*c* 1 1d. dull orange .. .. .. — £4000
32*d* 2d. blue .. .. — £3250
32*e* 6d. brown .. .. — £3750
32*f* 6d. chestnut .. .. — £3750
32*g* 1s. blue-green .. .. .. — £6000

(*h*) *Oblique roulette* 13 *at Wellington*

32*h* 1 1d. dull orange .. .. .. — £4000

The various separations detailed above were all applied by hand to imperforate sheets. The results were often poorly cut and badly aligned. Nos. 32*a*/*b* and 32*c*/*g* were produced using roulette wheels fitted with cutting edges in the shape of "H" or "Y".

(Printed by John Davies at the G.P.O., Auckland, N.Z.)

1862 (Feb–Dec). *Wmk Large Star.* (*a*) *Imperf.*

33 1 1d. orange-vermilion £450 £180
34 1d. vermilion £425 £180
35 1d. carmine-vermilion £375 £200

No.	Type	Description	Unused	Used
36	1	2d. deep blue (Plate I)	£350	65·00
		a. Double print	—	£2500
37		2d. slate-blue (Plate I)	£1500	£180
37*a*		2d. milky blue (Plate I, worn)	—	£225
38		2d. pale blue (Plate I, worn)	£275	70·00
39		2d. blue (*to* deep) (Plate I, very worn)	£250	70·00
40		3d. brown-lilac (Dec 1862)	£325	£120
41		6d. black-brown	£800	90·00
42		6d. brown	£750	90·00
43		6d. red-brown	£600	80·00
44		1s. green	£900	£200
45		1s. yellow-green	£800	£200
46		1s. deep green	£950	£250

The 2d. in a distinctive deep bright blue on white paper wmkd. Large Star is believed by experts to have been printed by Richardson in 1861 or 1862. This also exists doubly printed and with serrated perf.

No. 37 shows traces of plate wear to the right of the Queen's head. This is more pronounced on Nos. 37*a*/8 and quite extensive on No. 39.

(*b*) *Rouletted* 7 *at Auckland* (5.62)

No.	Type	Description	Unused	Used
47	1	1d. orange-vermilion	£3500	£700
48		1d. vermilion	£2000	£650
48*a*		1d. carmine-vermilion	£3500	£800
49		2d. deep blue	£2000	£400
50		2d. slate-blue	£3000	£750
51		2d. pale blue	£1700	£500
52		3d. brown-lilac	£2000	£650
53		6d. black-brown	£2250	£400
54		6d. brown	£2000	£500
55		6d. red-brown	£2000	£400
56		1s. green	£2250	£550
57		1s. yellow-green	£3250	£550
58		1s. deep green	£3250	£650

(*c*) *Serrated perf* 16 *or* 18 *at Nelson* (8.62)

No.	Type	Description	Unused	Used
59	1	1d. orange-vermilion	—	£1400
60		2d. deep blue	—	£950
		a. Imperf between (pair)	£6000	£3000
61		2d. slate-blue		
62		3d. brown-lilac	£2750	£1500
63		6d. black-brown	—	£1500
64		6d. brown	—	£1600
65		1s. yellow-green	—	£2500

(*d*) *Pin-perf* 10 *at Nelson* (8.62)

No.	Type	Description	Unused	Used
66	1	2d. deep blue	—	£2000
67		6d. black-brown	—	£3000

(*e*) "H" *roulette* 16 *at Nelson*

No.	Type	Description	Unused	Used
67*a*	1	2d. deep blue (Plate I)	—	£1700
67*b*		6d. black-brown	—	£1600
67*c*		1s. green	—	£1900

(*f*) "Y" *roulette* 18 *at Nelson*

No.	Type	Description	Unused	Used
67*d*	1	1d. orange-vermilion	—	£1500
67*e*		2d. deep blue (Plate I)	—	£1700
67*f*		2d. slate-blue (Plate I)	—	£1700
67*g*		3d. brown-lilac	—	£1800
67*h*		6d. black-brown	—	£1600
67*i*		6d. brown	—	£1600
67*j*		1s. yellow-green	—	£1900

(*g*) *Oblique roulette* 13 *at Wellington*

No.	Type	Description	Unused	Used
67*k*	1	2d. deep blue (Plate I)	—	£1700
67*l*		2d. slate-blue (Plate I)		
67*m*		3d. brown-lilac	—	£1900
67*n*		6d. black-brown	—	£1600

(*h*) *Square roulette* 14 *at Auckland*

No.	Type	Description	Unused	Used
67*o*	1	1d. orange-vermilion	—	£1500
67*p*		2d. deep blue (Plate I)	—	£1700
67*q*		3d. brown-lilac	—	£1900
67*r*		6d. black-brown	—	£1600

(*i*) *Serrated perf* 13 *at Dunedin*

No.	Type	Description	Unused	Used
67*s*	1	1d. orange-vermilion	—	£1900
67*t*		2d. deep blue (Plate I)	—	£1700
67*u*		3d. brown-lilac	—	£1600
67*v*		6d. black-brown	—	£1600
67*w*		1s. yellow-green	—	£2250

The dates put to above varieties are the earliest that have been met with.

1862. *Wmk Large Star. P* 13 (*at Dunedin*).

No.	Type	Description	Unused	Used
68	1	1d. orange-vermilion	£750	£225
69		1d. carmine-vermilion	£750	£225
70		2d. deep blue (Plate I)	£300	70.00
71		2d. slate-blue (Plate I)	—	£600
72		2d. blue (Plate I)	£225	48·00
72*a*		2d. milky blue (Plate I)	—	£500
73		2d. pale blue (Plate I)	£225	50·00
74		3d. brown-lilac	£750	£225
75		6d. black-brown	£800	£150
		a. Imperf between (horiz pair)		
76		6d. brown	£650	70·00
77		6d. red-brown	£600	60·00
78		1s. dull green	£800	£250
79		1s. deep green	£850	£225
80		1s. yellow-green	£850	£200

See also Nos. 110/125 and the note that follows these.

1862–63. *Pelure paper. No wmk.* (*a*) *Imperf.*

No.	Type	Description	Unused	Used
81	1	1d. orange-vermilion (1863)	£6000	£1700
82		2d. ultramarine	£3500	£750
83		2d. pale ultramarine	£3250	£750
84		3d. lilac	£25000	†
85		6d. black-brown	£1400	£250
86		1s. deep green	£6000	£900

The 3d. is known only unused.

(*b*) *Rouletted* 7 *at Auckland*

No.	Type	Description	Unused	Used
87	1	1d. orange-vermilion	—	£4000
88		6d. black-brown	£2000	£450
89		1s. deep green	£6500	£1400

(*c*) *P* 13 *at Dunedin*

No.	Type	Description	Unused	Used
90	1	1d. orange-vermilion	£9500	£3000
91		2d. ultramarine	£4500	£600
92		2d. pale ultramarine	£4500	£600
93		6d. black-brown	£3500	£325
94		1s. deep green	£7000	£1200

(*d*) *Serrated perf* 16 *at Nelson*

No.	Type	Description	Unused	Used
95	1	6d. black-brown	—	£4000

(*e*) *Serrated perf* 13 *at Dunedin*

No.	Type	Description	Unused	Used
95*a*	9	1d. orange-vermilion	—	£6000

1863 (early). *Thick soft white paper. No wmk.* (*a*) *Imperf.*

No.	Type	Description	Unused	Used
96	1	2d. dull deep blue (*shades*)	£2250	£800

(*b*) *P* 13

No.	Type	Description	Unused	Used
96*a*	1	2d. dull deep blue (*shades*)	£1600	£475

These stamps show slight beginnings of wear of the printing plate in the background to right of the Queen's ear, as one looks at the stamps. By the early part of 1864, the wear of the plate had spread, more or less, all over the background of the circle containing the head. The major portion of the stamps of this printing appears to have been consigned to Dunedin and to have been there perforated 13.

1864. *Wmk* "N Z", *W* **2**. (*a*) *Imperf.*

No.	Type	Description	Unused	Used
97	1	1d. carmine-vermilion	£700	£225
98		2d. pale blue (Plate I worn)	£750	£200
99		6d. red-brown	£2750	£500
100		1s. green	£950	£250

(*b*) *Rouletted* 7 *at Auckland*

No.	Type	Description	Unused	Used
101	1	1d. carmine-vermilion	£4500	£2750
102		2d. pale blue (Plate I worn)	£1400	£750
103		6d. red-brown	£4250	£2750
104		1s. green	£2750	£1000

(*c*) *P* 13 *at Dunedin*

No.	Type	Description	Unused	Used
104*a*	1	1d. carmine-vermilion	£6000	£4000
105		2d. pale blue (Plate I worn)	£550	£160
106		1s. green	£1100	£450
		a. Imperf between (horiz pair)	£7500	

(*d*) "Y" *roulette* 18 *at Nelson*

No.	Type	Description	Unused	Used
106*b*	1	1d. carmine-vermilion	—	£3500

(*e*) *P* 12½ *at Auckland*

No.	Type	Description	Unused	Used
106*c*	1	1d. carmine-vermilion	£5500	£3000
107		2d. pale blue (Plate I worn)	£225	50·00
108		6d. red-brown	£225	30·00
109		1s. yellow-green	£4000	£2000

1864–67. *Wmk Large Star. P* 12½ (*at Auckland*).

No.	Type	Description	Unused	Used
110	1	1d. carmine-vermilion (1864)	£100	23·00
111		1d. pale orange-vermilion	£130	23·00
		a. Imperf (pair)	£2000	£1500
112		1d. orange	£300	70·00
113		2d. pale blue (Plate I worn) (1864)	£130	17·00
114		2d. deep blue (Plate II) (1866)	£100	17·00
		a. Imperf vert (horiz pair)	—	£2750
115		2d. blue (Plate II)	£100	17·00
		a. Retouched (Plate II) (1867)	£150	38·00
		c. Imperf (pair) (Plate II)	£1400	£1400
		d. Retouched. Imperf (pair)	£2250	£2500
116		3d. brown-lilac (1864)	£1000	£500
117		3d. lilac	85·00	25·00
		a. Imperf (pair)	£3000	£1500
118		3d. deep mauve	£375	60·00
		a. Imperf (pair)	£2750	£1500
119		4d. deep rose (1865)	£2250	£250
120		4d. yellow (1865)	£120	75·00
121		4d. orange	£1200	£800
122		6d. red-brown (1864)	£130	23·00
122*a*		6d. brown	£150	29·00
		b. Imperf (pair)	£1400	£1400
123		1s. deep green (1864)	£550	£225
124		1s. green	£275	90·00
125		1s. yellow-green	£130	70·00

The above issue is sometimes difficult to distinguish from Nos. 68/80 because the vertical perforations usually gauge 12¾ and sometimes a full 13. However stamps of this issue invariably gauge 12½ horizontally, whereas the 1862 stamps measure a full 13.

Nos. 111a, 115c/d, 117a, 118a and 122b were issued during problems with the perforation machine which occurred in 1866–67, 1869–70 and 1871–73. Imperforate sheets of the 1s. were also released, but these stamps are very similar to Nos. 44/6.

The new plate of the 2d. showed signs of deterioration during 1866 and thirty positions in rows 13 and 16 to 20 were retouched by a local engraver.

The 1d., 2d. and 6d. were officially reprinted imperforate, without gum, in 1884 for presentation purposes. They can be distinguished from the errors listed by their shades which are pale orange, dull blue and dull chocolate-brown respectively, and by the worn state of the plates from which they were printed (*Prices £60 each unused*).

1871. *Wmk Large Star.* (*a*) *P* 10.

No.	Type	Description	Unused	Used
126	1	1d. brown	£425	75·00

(*b*) *P* 12½ × 10

No.	Type	Description	Unused	Used
127	1	1d. deep brown	—	£900

(*c*) *P* 10 × 12½

No.	Type	Description	Unused	Used
128	1	1d. brown	£150	28·00
		a. Perf 12½ comp 10 (1 side)	£275	75·00
129		2d. deep blue (Plate II)	—	£6000
		a. Perf 10*		†£10000
130		2d. vermilion	£140	22·00
		a. Retouched	£200	38·00
		b. Perf 12½ comp 10 (1 side)	—	£325
		c. Perf 10*		†£10000
131		6d. deep blue	£1200	£600
		a. Blue	£800	£325
		b. Imperf between (vert pair)	—	£4750
		c. Perf 12½ comp 10 (1 side)	£700	£275
		ca. Imperf vert (horiz pair)		

(*d*) *P* 12½

No.	Type	Description	Unused	Used
132	1	1d. red-brown	£100	22·00
		a. Brown (shades, worn plate)	95·00	22·00
		b. Imperf horiz (vert pair)	—	£3250
133		2d. orange	75·00	20·00
		a. Retouched	£120	40·00
134		2d. vermilion	£100	23·00
		a. Retouched	£160	50·00
135		6d. blue	£140	42·00
136		6d. pale blue	95·00	42·00

*Only one used copy each of Nos. 129a and 130c have been reported.

1872. *No wmk. P* 12½.

No.	Type	Description	Unused	Used
137	1	1d. brown	£400	75·00
138		2d. vermilion	70·00	38·00
		a. Retouched	£150	60·00
139		4d. orange-yellow	£140	£600

1872. *Wmk* "N Z", *W* **2**. *P* 12½.

No.	Type	Description	Unused	Used
140	1	1d. brown	—	£3750
141		2d. vermilion	£400	£120
		a. Retouched	£700	£200

In or about 1872 1d., 2d. and 4d. stamps were printed on paper showing sheet watermarks of either "W. T. & Co." (Wiggins Teape & Co.) in script letters or "T. H. Saunders" in double-lined capitals; portions of these letters are occasionally found on stamps.

1872. *Wmk Lozenges, with* "INV!CTA" *in double-lined capitals four times in the sheet. P* 12½.

No.	Type	Description	Unused	Used
142	1	2d. vermilion	£2750	£500
		a. Retouched	£4000	£750

3

4

(Des John Davies. Die eng on wood in Melbourne. Printed from electrotypes at Govt Ptg Office, Wellington)

1873 (1 Jan). (*a*) *Wmk* "NZ", *W* **2**.

No.	Type	Description	Unused	Used
143	3	½d. pale dull rose (*p* 10)	70·00	30·00
144		½d. pale dull rose (*p* 12½)	£180	65·00
145		½d. pale dull rose (*p* 12½ × 10)	£110	65·00

(*b*) *No wmk*

No.	Type	Description	Unused	Used
146	3	½d. pale dull rose (*p* 10)	£100	42·00
147		½d. pale dull rose (*p* 12½)	£200	75·00
148		½d. pale dull rose (*p* 12½ × 10)	£150	70·00

As the paper used for Nos. 143/5 was originally intended for fiscal stamps which were more than twice as large, about one-third of the impressions fall on portions of the sheet showing no watermark, giving rise to varieties Nos. 146/8. In later printings of No. 151 a few stamps in each sheet are without watermark. These can be distinguished from No. 147 by the shade.

1875 (Jan). *Wmk Star, W* **4**.

No.	Type	Description	Unused	Used
149	3	½d. pale dull rose (*p* 12½)	12·00	1·00
		a. Imperf horiz (vert pair)	£600	£325
		b. Imperf between (horiz pair)	†	£500
150		½d. dull pale rose (*p nearly* 12)	60·00	11·00

1892 (May). *Wmk* "*NZ and Star*". *W* **12***b*. *P* 12½.

No.	Type	Description	Unused	Used
151	3	½d. bright rose (*shades*)	7·00	60
		a. No wmk	12·00	7·50

5  6  7

8  9  10

11  12  12*a* 6 mm

12*b* 7 mm  12*c* 4 mm

(T **5**/**10** eng De La Rue. T **11** and **12** des, eng & plates by W. R. Bock. Typo Govt Ptg Office, Wellington)

1874 (2 Jan)–**78**. *W* **12***a*. *A. White paper.* (*a*) *P* 12½.

No.	Type	Description	Unused	Used
152	5	1d. lilac	45·00	3·75
		a. Imperf	£400	
153	6	2d. rose	45·00	1·75
154	7	3d. brown	£100	55·00
155	8	4d. maroon	£250	60·00
156	9	6d. blue	£180	10·00
157	10	1s. green	£650	27·00

(b) *Perf nearly* 12

158	6	2d. rose (1878)	£600	£180

(c) *Perf compound of* 12½ *and* 10

159	5	1d. lilac	£150	40·00
160	6	2d. rose	£350	75·00
161	7	3d. brown	£160	60·00
162	8	4d. maroon	£350	£100
163	9	6d. blue	£225	45·00
164	10	1s. green	£650	£110
		aa. Imperf between (vert pair)	†	—

(d) *Perf nearly* 12 × 12½

164*a*	5	1d. lilac (1875)	£650	£250
165	6	2d. rose (1878)	£650	£190

B. *Blued paper.* (a) *P* 12½

166	5	1d. lilac	80·00	29·00
167	6	2d. rose	£100	29·00
168	7	3d. brown	£225	80·00
169	8	4d. maroon	£425	£100
170	9	6d. blue	£325	48·00
171	10	1s. green	£1000	£190

(b) *Perf compound of* 12½ *and* 10

172	5	1d. lilac	£180	50·00
173	6	2d. rose	£500	80·00
174	7	3d. brown	£200	75·00
175	8	4d. maroon	£475	£120
176	9	6d. blue	£300	90·00
177	10	1s. green	£1000	£225

1875. *Wmk Large Star, W* w **1.** *P* 12½.

178	5	1d. deep lilac	£600	£110
179	6	2d. rose	£300	17·00

1878. *W* **12***a*. *P* 12 × 11½ *(comb).*

180	5	1d. mauve-lilac	35·00	3·00
181	6	2d. rose	35·00	1·40
182	8	4d. maroon	£140	40·00
183	9	6d. blue	80·00	10·00
184	10	1s. green	£110	32·00
185	11	2s. deep rose (1 July)	£325	£275
186	12	5s. grey (1 July)	£350	£275

This perforation is made by a horizontal "comb" machine, giving a gauge of 12 horizontally and about 11¾ vertically. Single specimens can be found apparently gauging 11½ all round or 12 all round, but these are all from the same machine. The perforation described above as "nearly 12" was from a single-line machine.

13 14 15 16 17 18 19 20 21

22

Description of Watermarks

W12*a*. 6 mm between "N Z" and star; broad irregular star; comparatively wide "N"; "N Z" 11½ mm wide.

W12*b*. 7 mm between "N Z" and star; narrower star; narrow "N"; "N Z" 10 mm wide.

W12*c*. 4 mm between "N Z" and star; narrow star; wide "N"; "N Z" 11½ mm wide.

Description of Papers

1882–88.	Smooth paper with horizontal mesh. W **12***a*.
1888–98.	Smooth paper with vertical mesh. *W* **12***b*.
1890–91.	Smooth paper with vertical mesh. *W* **12***c*.
1898.	Thin yellowish toned, coarse paper with clear vertical mesh. *W* **12***b*. Perf 11 only.

In 1899–1900 stamps appeared on medium to thick white coarse paper but we do not differentiate these (except where identifiable by shade) as they are more difficult to distinguish.

PAPER MESH. This shows on the back of the stamp as a series of parallel grooves, either vertical or horizontal. It is caused by the use of a wire gauze conveyor-belt during paper-making.

Description of Dies

1d.

Die 1

Die 2

Die 3

1882. Die 1.	Background shading complete and heavy.
1886. Die 2.	Background lines thinner. Two lines of shading weak or missing left of Queen's forehead.
1889. Die 3.	Shading on head reduced; ornament in crown left of chignon clearer, with unshaded "arrow" more prominent.

2d.

Die 1

Die 2

Die 3

1882. Die 1.	Background shading complete and heavy.
1886. Die 2.	Weak line of shading left of forehead and missing shading lines below "TA".
1889. Die 3.	As Die 2 but with comma-like white notch in hair below "&".

6d.

Die 1

Die 2

1882. Die 1.	Shading heavy. Top of head merges into shading.
1892. Die 2.	Background lines thinner. Shading on head more regular with clear line of demarcation between head and background shading.

STAMPS WITH ADVERTISEMENTS. During November 1891 the New Zealand Post Office invited tenders for the printing of advertisements on the reverse of the current 1d. to 1s. stamps. The contract was awarded to Messrs Miller, Truebridge & Reich and the first sheets with advertisements on the reverse appeared in February 1893.

Different advertisements were applied to the backs of the individual stamps within the sheets of 240 (four panes of 60).

On the first setting those in a vertical format were inverted in relation to the stamps and each of the horizontal advertisements had its base at the left-hand side of the stamp when seen from the back. For the second and third settings the vertical advertisements were the same way up as the stamps and the bases of those in the horizontal format were at the right as seen from the back. The third setting only differs from the second in the order of the individual advertisements.

The experiment was not, however, a success and the contract was cancelled at the end of 1893.

(Des F. W. Sears (½d.), A. E. Cousins (2½d.), A. W. Jones (5d.); others adapted from 1874 issue by W. H. Norris. Dies eng A. E. Cousins (½d., 2½d., 5d.), W. R. Bock (others). Typo Govt Ptg Office)

1882–1900. *Inscr* "POSTAGE & REVENUE".

A. *W* **12***a*. *Paper with horiz mesh* (1.4.82–86). (a) *P* 12 × 11½

187	14	1d. rose *to* rose-red (Die 1)	35·00	4·75
		a. Imperf (pair)	£325	
		b. Imperf between (vert pair)	£350	
		c. Die 2. *Pale rose to carmine-rose* (1886)	30·00	5·00
188	15	2d. lilac *to* lilac-purple (Die 1)	40·00	4·00
		a. Imperf (pair)	£350	
		b. Imperf between (vert pair)	£350	
		c. Die 2. *Lilac* (1886)	50·00	7·00
189	17	3d. yellow (1884)	50·00	5·50
190	18	4d. blue-green	70·00	5·00
191	20	6d. brown (Die 1)	80·00	3·75
192	21	8d. blue (1885)	70·00	45·00
193	22	1s. red-brown	85·00	12·00

(b) *P* 12½ (1884?)

193*a*	14	1d. rose *to* rose-red (Die 1)	£170	85·00

B. *W* **12***b*. *Paper with vert mesh* (1888–95)

(a) *P* 12×11½ (1888–95)

194	13	½d. black (1.4.95)	25·00	75·00
195	14	1d. rose *to* rosine (Die 2)	35·00	3·50
		a. Die 3. *Rose to carmine* (1889)	35·00	3·50
		ab. Red-brn advert (1st setting) (2.93)	50·00	11·00
		ac. Red advert (1st setting) (3.93)	50·00	11·00
		ad. Blue advert (2nd setting) (4.93)	65·00	35·00
		ae. Mauve advert (2nd setting) (5.93)	40·00	6·50
		af. Green advert (2nd setting) (6.93)		
		ag. Brn-red advert (3rd setting) (9.93)	40·00	6·50
196	15	2d. lilac (Die 2)	40·00	4·25
		a. Die 3. *Lilac to purple* (1889)	40·00	4·25
		ab. Red advert (1st setting) (3.93)	60·00	15·00
		ac. Mauve advert (2nd setting) (5.93)	50·00	15·00
		ad. Sepia advert (2nd setting) (5.93)	50·00	20·00
		ae. Green advert (2nd setting) (6.93)	—	75·00
		af. Brn-red advert (3rd setting) (9.93)	50·00	15·00
197	16	2½d. pale blue (1891)	55·00	5·50
		a. Brn-red advert (2nd setting) (4.93)	70·00	15·00
		b. *Ultramarine* (green advert. 2nd setting) (6.93)	70·00	17·00
198	17	3d. yellow	40·00	6·50
		a. Brn-red advert (2nd setting) (4.93)	70·00	17·00
		b. Sepia advert (2nd setting) (5.93)		
199	18	4d. green *to* bluish green	50·00	3·00
		a. Sepia advert (2nd setting) (5.93)	65·00	11·00
200	19	5d. olive-black (1.2.91)	42·00	9·00
		a. Imperf (pair)	£350	
		b. Brn-pur advert (3rd setting) (9.93)	60·00	30·00
201	20	6d. brown (Die 1)	70·00	2·25
		a. Die 2 (1892)	£110	50·00
		ab. Sepia advert (2nd setting) (5.93)		
		ac. Brn-red advert (3rd setting) (9.93)	£150	70·00
202	21	8d. blue	65·00	45·00
203	22	1s. red-brown	80·00	6·00
		a. Black advert (2nd setting) (5.93)	£300	£150
		b. Brn-pur advert (3rd setting) (9.93)	£110	16·00

(b) *P* 12×12½ (1888–91)

204	14	1d. rose (Die 2)	£190	85·00
		a. Die 3 (1889)		

(c) *P* 12½ (1888–89)

205	14	1d. rose (Die 3) (1889)	£160	95·00
		a. Mauve advert (2nd setting) (5.93)		
206	15	2d. lilac (Die 2)	£120	85·00
		a. Die 3. *Deep lilac* (1889)	90·00	65·00
		ab. Brn-red advert (3rd setting) (9.93)	£160	85·00
207	16	2½d. blue (1891)	£170	95·00

(d) *Mixed perfs* 12×11½ *and* 12½ (1891–93)

207*a*	14	1d. rose (Die 3) (brn-red advert. 3rd setting)	—	50·00
207*b*	15	2d. lilac (Die 3)		
		ba. Brn-red advert (3rd setting) (9.93)		
207*c*	18	4d. green	—	50·00
207*d*	19	5d. olive-black	—	95·00
207*e*	20	6d. brown (Die I)	—	£100
		ea. Die 2	—	£150

C. *W* **12***c*. *Paper with vert mesh* (1890). (a) *P* 12 × 11½

208	14	1d. rose (Die 3)	70·00	6·50
209	15	2d. purple (Die 3)	70·00	6·50
210	16	2½d. ultramarine (27.12)	65·00	11·00
211	17	3d. yellow	70·00	14·00
		a. *Lemon-yellow*	70·00	16·00
212	20	6d. brown (Die 1)	£120	24·00
213	22	1s. deep red-brown	£130	55·00

(b) *P* 12½

214	14	1d. rose (Die 3)	£170	£100
215	15	2d. purple (Die 3)	£150	£100
216	16	2½d. ultramarine	£200	£100

(c) *P* 12×12½

216*a*	20	6d. brown (Die 1)	£180	£140

D. *Continuation of W* **12***b*. *Paper with vert mesh* (1891–1900)

(a) *P* 10×12½ (1891–94)

216*b*	14	1d. rose (Die 3)	£180	90·00
		ba. Perf 12½×10	£200	90·00
		bb. Red-brn advert (1st setting) (2.93)	£250	£120
		bc. Brn-red advert (2nd setting) (4.93)	£250	£100
		bd. Mauve advert (2nd setting) (5.93)	£250	£100
		be. Green advert (2nd setting) (6.93)	£250	£140
216*c*	15	2d. lilac (Die 3)	£150	60·00
216*d*	16	2½d. blue (1893)	£130	65·00
216*e*	17	3d. yellow	£150	75·00
216*f*	18	4d. green	£170	£140
216*g*	19	5d. olive-black (1894)	£180	£170
		ga. Perf 12½×10		

No.	Type	Description	Un	Used
216h	20	6d. brown (Die II)	£190	£190
		i. Die 2 (1892)	£150	£150
		ia. Brown-purple advert (3rd setting) (9.93)	£200	£180
216j	22	1s. red-brown	£170	£170
		ja. Perf 12½×10	†	—
		(b) P 10 (1891–95)		
217	13	½d. black (1895)	3·50	40
218	14	1d. rose (Die 3)	4·00	10
		a. Carmine	8·50	1·25
		b. Imperf (pair)	£275	£275
		c. Imperf between (pair)	£325	
		d. Imperf horiz (vert pair)	£250	
		e. Mixed perfs 10 and 12½	£250	£120
		f. Red-brown advert (1st setting) (2.93)	14·00	4·00
		g. Red advert (1st setting) (3.93)	14·00	5·00
		h. Brown-red advert (2nd and 3rd settings) (4.93)	8·00	2·50
		i. Blue advert (2nd setting) (4.93)	60·00	25·00
		j. Mauve advert (2nd setting) (5.93)	8·00	2·50
		k. Green advert (2nd setting) (6.93)	50·00	16·00
		l. Brown-purple advert (3rd setting) (9.93)	8·00	2·50
219	15	2d. lilac (Die 3)	9·00	40
		a. Purple	10·00	40
		b. Imperf between (pair)	£300	
		c. Mixed perfs 10 and 12½	—	90·00
		d. Red-brown advert (1st setting) (2.93)	22·00	6·00
		e. Red advert (1st setting) (3.93)	22·00	5·00
		f. Brown-red advert (2nd and 3rd settings) (4.93)	12·00	2·50
		g. Sepia advert (2nd setting) (5.93)	15·00	3·00
		h. Green advert (2nd setting) (6.93)	32·00	8·00
		i. Brown-purple advert (3rd setting) (9.93)	12·00	2·50
220	16	2½d. blue (1892)	48·00	3·50
		a. Ultramarine	48·00	4·00
		b. Mixed perfs 10 and 12½	£170	90·00
		c. Mauve advert (2nd setting) (5.93)	65·00	8·00
		d. Green advert (2nd setting) (6.93)	75·00	9·00
		e. Brown-purple advert (3rd setting) (9.93)	65·00	8·00
221	17	3d. pale orange-yellow	40·00	8·50
		a. Orange	40·00	9·50
		b. Lemon-yellow	40·00	12·00
		c. Mixed perfs 10 and 12½	£160	£120
		d. Brown-red advert (2nd and 3rd settings) (4.93)	65·00	12·00
		e. Sepia advert (2nd setting) (5.93)	75·00	24·00
		f. Brown-purple advert (3rd setting) (9.93)	65·00	10·00
222	18	4d. green (1892)	45·00	2·50
		a. Blue-green	50·00	3·75
		b. Mixed perfs 10 and 12½	£190	80·00
		c. Brown-red advert (2nd setting) (4.93)	65·00	4·00
		d. Brown-purple advert (3rd setting) (9.93)	65·00	4·00
223	19	5d. olive-black (1893)	42·00	11·00
		a. Brown-purple advert (3rd setting) (9.93)	65·00	15·00
224	20	6d. brown (Die 1)	85·00	19·00
		a. Mixed perfs 10 and 12½		
		b. Die 2 (1892)	45·00	5·50
		ba. Black-brown	50·00	6·00
		bb. Imperf (pair)	£325	
		bc. Mixed perfs 10 and 12½	90·00	50·00
		bd. Sepia advert (2nd setting) (4.93)	85·00	9·50
		be. Brown-red advert (3rd setting) (9.93)	85·00	9·50
		bf. Brown-purple advert (3rd setting) (9.93)	85·00	9·50
225	21	8d. blue (brown-purple advert. 3rd setting) (9.93)	65·00	45·00
226	22	1s. red-brown	75·00	5·50
		a. Imperf between (pair)	£550	
		b. Mixed perfs 10 and 12½	£150	£110
		c. Sepia advert (2nd setting) (5.93)	£100	15·00
		d. Black advert (2nd setting) (5.93)	£180	£110
		e. Brown-red advert (3rd setting) (9.93)	£100	15·00
		f. Brown-purple advert (3rd setting) (9.93)	£100	15·00
		(c) P 10×11 (1895–97)		
227	13	½d. black (1896)	3·25	50
		a. Mixed perfs 10 and 11	85·00	28·00
		b. Perf 11×10	28·00	11·00
228	14	1d. rose (Die 3)	4·75	15
		a. Mixed perfs 10 and 11	85·00	50·00
		b. Perf 11×10	55·00	7·50
229	15	2d. purple (Die 3)	8·50	30
		a. Mixed perfs 10 and 11	60·00	50·00
230	16	2½d. blue (1896)	45·00	3·75
		a. Ultramarine	45·00	4·50
		b. Mixed perfs 10 and 11	—	65·00
231	17	3d. lemon-yellow (1896)	60·00	8·00
232	18	4d. pale green (1896)	70·00	11·00
		a. Mixed perfs 10 and 11	—	85·00
233	19	5d. olive-black (1897)	48·00	10·00
234	20	6d. deep brown (Die 2) (1896)	65·00	4·50
		a. Mixed perfs 10 and 11		
		b. Perf 11×10	£160	50·00
235	22	1s. red-brown (1896)	75·00	8·50
		a. Mixed perfs 10 and 11	£140	70·00
		(d) P 11 (1895–1900)		
236	13	½d. black (1897)	3·00	15
		a. Thin coarse toned paper (1898)	22·00	1·75
		b. Ditto. Wmk sideways	—	£150
237	14	1d. rose (Die 3)	3·75	10
		a. Deep carmine	5·50	1·40
		b. Imperf between (pair)	£350	
		c. Deep carmine/thin coarse toned (1898)	8·00	1·25
		d. Ditto. Wmk sideways	—	£200
238	15	2d. mauve (Die 3)	7·50	30
		a. Purple	8·50	30
		b. Deep purple/thin coarse toned (1898)	8·50	1·75
		c. Ditto. Wmk sideways	—	£180
239	16	2½d. blue (1897)	38·00	3·75
		a. Thin coarse toned paper (1898)	50·00	12·00
240	17	3d. pale yellow (1897)	48·00	4·75
		a. Pale dull yellow/thin coarse toned (1898)	60·00	9·50
		b. Orange (1899)	40·00	8·00
		c. Dull orange-yellow (1900)	48·00	10·00
241	18	4d. yellowish green	48·00	3·50
		a. Bluish green (1897)	48·00	3·25
242	19	5d. olive-black/*thin coarse toned* (1899)	50·00	21·00
243	20	6d. brown (Die 2) (1897)	65·00	3·00
		a. Black-brown	65·00	3·00
		b. Brown/thin coarse toned (1898)	80·00	4·75
244	21	8d. blue (1898)	65·00	45·00
245	22	1s. red-brown (1897)	75·00	6·50

Only the more prominent shades have been included.

Stamps perf compound of 11 and 12½ exist but we do not list them as there is some doubt as to whether they are genuine.

For the ½d. and 2d. with double-lined watermark, see Nos. 271/2.

23 Mount Cook or Aorangi — 24 Lake Taupo and Mount Ruapehu — 25 Pembroke Peak, Milford Sound

26 Lake Wakatipu and Mount Earnslaw, inscribed "WAKITIPU" — 27 Lake Wakatipu and Mount Earnslaw, inscribed "WAKATIPU"

28 Sacred Huia Birds — 29 White Terrace, Rotomahana — 30 Otira Gorge and Mount Ruapehu

31 Brown Kiwi — 32 Maori War Canoe

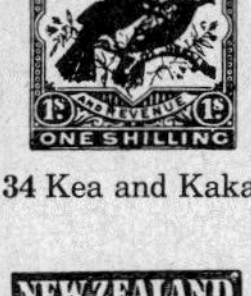

33 Pink Terrace, Rotomahana — 34 Kea and Kaka

35 Milford Sound — 36 Mount Cook

(Des H. Young (½d.), J. Gaut (1d.), W. Bock (2d., 3d., 9d., 1s.), E. Howard (4d., 6d., 8d.), E. Luke (others). Eng A. Hill (2½d., 1s.), J. A. C. Harrison (5d.), Rapkin (others). Recess Waterlow)

1898 (5 Apr). *No wmk. P* 12 *to* 16.

No.	Type	Description	Un	Used
246	23	½d. purple-brown	4·00	60
		a. Imperf between (pair)	£650	£650
		b. Purple-slate	4·50	60
		c. Purple-black	7·00	2·00
247	24	1d. blue and yellow-brown	3·25	20
		a. Imperf between (pair)	£650	
		b. Imperf vert (horiz pair)	£450	£500
		c. Imperf horiz (vert pair)	£450	£500
		d. Blue and brown	3·50	80
		da. Imperf between (pair)	£650	
248	25	2d. lake	26·00	20
		a. Imperf vert (horiz pair)	£400	
		b. Rosy lake	26·00	20
		ba. Imperf between (pair)	£550	
		bb. Imperf vert (horiz pair)	£400	
249	26	2½d. sky-blue (inscr "WAKITIPU")	6·50	22·00
		a. Blue	6·50	22·00
250	27	2½d. blue (inscr "WAKATIPU")	21·00	1·75
		a. Deep blue	21·00	1·75
251	28	3d. yellow-brown	23·00	7·00
252	29	4d. bright rose	12·00	15·00
		a. Lake-rose	14·00	17·00
		b. Dull rose	12·00	16·00
253	30	5d. sepia	55·00	£140
		a. Purple-brown	35·00	12·00
254	31	6d. green	48·00	25·00
		a. Grass-green	55·00	45·00
255	32	8d. indigo	38·00	35·00
		a. Prussian blue	38·00	26·00
256	33	9d. purple	40·00	24·00
257	34	1s. vermilion	55·00	19·00
		a. Dull red	55·00	19·00
		ab. Imperf between (pair)	£1600	
258	35	2s. grey-green	£100	85·00
		a. Imperf between (vert pair)	£1600	£1600
259	36	5s. vermilion	£170	£275
246/59		*Set of* 13	£500	£450

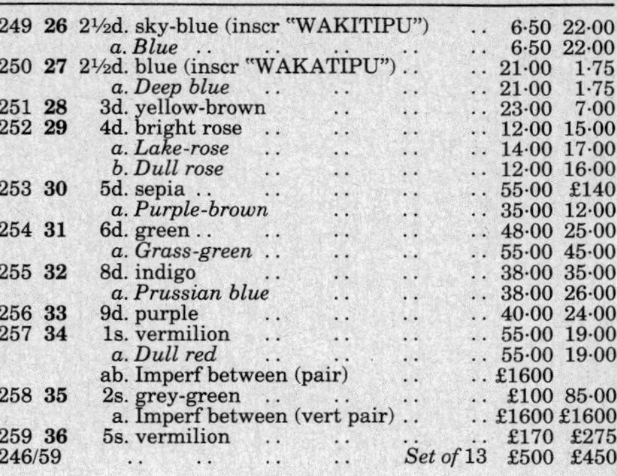

37 Lake Taupo and Mount Ruapehu

(Recess Govt Printer, Wellington)

1899 (May)–**03**. *Thick, soft ("Pirie") paper. No wmk. P* 11.

No.	Type	Description	Un	Used
260	27	2½d. blue (6.99)	12·00	2·50
		a. Imperf between (pair)	£550	
		b. Imperf horiz (vert pair)	£350	
		c. Deep blue	12·00	2·50
261	28	3d. yellow-brown (5.00)	27·00	2·00
		a. Imperf between (pair)	£750	
		b. Imperf vert (horiz pair)	£425	
		c. Deep brown	27·00	2·00
		ca. Imperf between (pair)	£750	
262	37	4d. indigo and brown (8.99)	5·50	2·25
		a. Bright blue and chestnut	5·50	2·25
		b. Deep blue and bistre-brown	5·50	2·25
263	30	5d. purple-brown (6.99)	23·00	2·50
		a. Deep purple-brown	23·00	2·50
		ab. Imperf between (pair)	£850	
264	31	6d. deep green	55·00	55·00
		a. Yellow-green	70·00	85·00
265		6d. pale rose (5.5.00)	35·00	3·50
		a. Imperf vert (horiz pair)	£375	
		b. Rose-red	35·00	3·50
		ba. Printed double	£375	
		bb. Imperf between (pair)	£500	
		bc. Imperf vert (horiz pair)	£225	
		bd. Showing part of sheet wmk (7.02)*	75·00	42·00
		c. Scarlet	50·00	12·00
		ca. Imperf vert (horiz pair)	£400	
266	32	8d. indigo	27·00	12·00
		a. Prussian blue	27·00	11·00
267	33	9d. deep purple (8.99)	45·00	25·00
		a. Rosy purple	35·00	9·50
268	34	1s. red (5.00)	48·00	8·50
		a. Dull orange-red	48·00	3·00
		b. Dull brown-red	48·00	8·50
		c. Bright red	60·00	26·00
269	35	2s. blue-green (7.99)	75·00	30·00
		a. Laid paper (1.03)	£180	£200
		b. Grey-green	75·00	40·00
270	36	5s. vermilion (7.99)	£170	£190
		a. Carmine-red	£250	£300
260/70		*Set of* 11	£425	£275

*No. 265bd is on paper without general watermark, but showing the words "LISBON SUPERFINE" wmkd once in the sheet; the paper was obtained from Parsons Bros, an American firm with a branch at Auckland.

38

1900. *Thick, soft ("Pirie") paper. Wmk double-lined "NZ" and Star, W* **38** *(sideways). P* 11.

No.	Type	Description	Un	Used
271	13	½d. black	7·50	7·50
272	15	2d. bright purple	15·00	8·00

39 White Terrace, Rotomahana — 41

40 Commemorative of the New Zealand Contingent in the South African War

(Des J. Nairn (1½d.). Recess Govt Printer, Wellington)

1900 (Mar–Dec). *Thick, soft ("Pirie") paper.* W **38**. *P* 11.
273 **23** ½d. pale yellow-green (7.3.00) .. .. 8·00 3·25
a. Yellow-green .. .. 5·50 60
b. Green .. .. 4·75 30
ba. Imperf between (pair) £300
c. Deep green .. .. 4·75 30
274 **39** 1d. crimson (7.3.00) .. .. .. 13·00 10
a. Rose-red .. .. 13·00 10
ab. Imperf between (pair) £600 £600
ac. Imperf vert (horiz pair) £325
b. Lake .. .. 25·00 3·00
275 **40** 1½d. khaki (7.12.00) £750 £500
a. Brown .. .. 50·00 50·00
ab. Imperf vert (horiz pair) £500
ac. Imperf (pair) £600
b. Chestnut .. .. 8·50 4·00
ba. Imperf vert (horiz pair) £500
bb. Imperf horiz (vert pair) £600
c. Pale chestnut .. .. 8·50 4·00
ca. Imperf (pair) £600
276 **41** 2d. dull violet (3.00) .. .. .. 7·00 65
a. Imperf between (pair) £700
b. Mauve .. .. 8·00 1·50
c. Purple .. .. 7·00 65
ca. Imperf between (pair) £550

The above ½d. stamps are slightly smaller than those of the previous printing. A new plate was made to print 240 stamps instead of 120 as previously, and to make these fit the watermarked paper the border design was redrawn and contracted, the centre vignette remaining as before. The 2d. stamp is also from a new plate providing smaller designs.

42

(Des G. Bach and G. Drummond. Eng J. A. C. Harrison. Recess Waterlow)

1901 (1 Jan). *Universal Penny Postage. No wmk. P* 12 *to* 16.
277 **42** 1d. carmine .. .. 4·00 2·50

All examples of No. 277 show a small dot above the upper left corner of the value tablet which is not present on later printings.

(Recess Govt Printer, Wellington)

1901 (Feb–Dec). *Thick, soft ("Pirie") paper.* W **38**. (a) *P* 11.
278 **42** 1d. carmine .. .. 6·00 15
a. Imperf vert (horiz pair) £250
b. Deep carmine .. .. .. 6·00 15
ba. Imperf vert (horiz pair) £250
c. Carmine-lake .. .. .. 20·00 8·00

(*b*) *P* 14
279 **23** ½d. green (11.01) .. .. .. 11·00 3·00
280 **42** 1d. carmine .. .. 40·00 9·00
a. Imperf vert (horiz pair) £225

(*c*) *P* 14×11
281 **23** ½d. green .. .. 8·00 5·00
a. Deep green .. .. 8·00 5·00
b. Perf 11×14 .. .. 10·00 11·00
282 **42** 1d. carmine .. .. £250 75·00
a. Perf 11×14 .. .. £1100 £275

(*d*) *P* 11 *and* 14 *mixed**
283 **23** ½d. green .. .. 38·00 42·00
284 **42** 1d. carmine .. .. £250 75·00

*The term "mixed" is applied to stamps from sheets which were at first perforated 14, or 14×11, and either incompletely or defectively perforated. These sheets were patched on the back with strips of paper, and re-perforated 11 in those parts where the original perforation was defective.

Nos. 278/84 were printed from new plates supplied by Waterlow. These were subsequently used for Nos. 285/307 with later printings on Cowan paper showing considerable plate wear.

(Recess Govt Printer, Wellington)

1901 (Dec). *Thin, hard ("Basted Mills") paper.* W **38**. (a) *P* 11.
285 **23** ½d. green .. .. 48·00 55·00
286 **42** 1d. carmine .. .. 65·00 70·00

(*b*) *P* 14
287 **23** ½d. green .. .. 24·00 16·00
a. Imperf vert (horiz pair) £325
288 **42** 1d. carmine .. .. 13·00 2·50
a. Imperf vert (horiz pair) £250
b. Imperf horiz (vert pair) £250

(*c*) *P* 14×11
289 **23** ½d. green .. .. 20·00 38·00
a. Deep green .. .. 20·00 38·00
b. Perf 11×14 .. .. 20·00 38·00
290 **42** 1d. carmine .. .. 17·00 5·00
a. Perf 11×14 .. .. 12·00 3·25

(*d*) *Mixed perfs*
291 **23** ½d. green .. .. 50·00 60·00
292 **42** 1d. carmine .. .. 75·00 60·00

(Recess Govt Printer, Wellington)

1902 (Jan). *Thin, hard ("Cowan") paper. No wmk.* (a) *P* 11.
293 **23** ½d. green .. .. 90·00 £150

(*b*) *P* 14
294 **23** ½d. green .. .. 9·00 3·75
295 **42** 1d. carmine .. .. 12·00 1·50

(*c*) *P* 14×11
296 **23** ½d. green .. .. 65·00 £110
a. Perf 11×14 .. .. 75·00 £120
297 **42** 1d. carmine £110 £110
a. Perf 11×14 .. .. £110 £130

(*d*) *Mixed perfs*
298 **23** ½d. green .. .. 90·00 £120
299 **42** 1d. carmine £120 £120

43 "Single" Wmk

SIDEWAYS WATERMARKS. In its sideways format the single NZ and Star watermark, W **43**, exists indiscriminately sideways, sideways inverted, sideways reversed and sideways inverted plus reversed.

(Recess Govt Printer, Wellington)

1902 (Apr). *Thin, hard ("Cowan") paper.* W **43**. (a) *P* 11.
300 **23** ½d. green .. .. 65·00 85·00
301 **42** 1d. carmine £600 £450

(*b*) *P* 14
302 **23** ½d. green .. .. 5·00 40
a. Imperf vert (horiz pair) £180
b. Deep green .. .. 5·50 60
ba. Imperf vert (horiz pair) £180
c. Yellow-green .. .. 5·50 60
d. Pale yellow-green .. .. .. 12·00 2·50
w. Wmk inverted .. .. .. 20·00 10·00
x. Wmk reversed .. .. .. 30·00 18·00
y. Wmk inverted and reversed .. 40·00 24·00
303 **42** 1d. carmine .. .. 3·00 10
a. Imperf horiz (vert pair) £170
b. Booklet pane of 6 (21.8.02) .. £200
c. Pale carmine .. .. 3·00 10
ca. Imperf horiz (vert pair) £170
cb. Booklet pane of 6 .. .. .. £200
*d. Deep carmine** .. .. .. 32·00 4·00
w. Wmk inverted .. .. .. 60·00 35·00
x. Wmk reversed .. .. .. 60·00 35·00
y. Wmk inverted and reversed .. 35·00 15·00

(*c*) *P* 14×11
304 **23** ½d. green .. .. 17·00
a. Deep green .. .. 24·00
b. Perf 11×14 .. .. 15·00
305 **42** 1d. carmine .. .. £100 80·00
a. Perf 11×14 .. .. £120 90·00
*ab. Deep carmine** £400 £300

(*d*) *Mixed perfs*
306 **23** ½d. green .. .. 24·00 38·00
a. Deep green .. .. 30·00
307 **42** 1d. carmine .. .. 24·00 30·00
a. Pale carmine .. .. 24·00 30·00
*b. Deep carmine** £250 £250
y. Wmk inverted and reversed

*Nos. 303*d*, 305*a* and 307*b* were printed from a plate made by Waterlow & Sons, known as the "Reserve" plate. The stamps do not show evidence of wearing and the area surrounding the upper part of the figure is more deeply shaded. This plate was subsequently used to produce Nos. 362, 364, and 366/9.

A special plate, made by W. R. Royle & Sons, showing a minute dot between the horizontal rows, was introduced in 1902 to print the booklet pane, No. 303b. A special characteristic of the booklet pane was that the pearl in the top left-handed corner was large. Some panes exist with the outer edges imperforate.

(Recess Govt Printer, Wellington)

1902 (28 Aug)–**09**. *Thin, hard ("Cowan") paper.* W **43** (*sideways on 3d., 5d., 6d., 8d., 1s. and 5s.*). (a) *P* 11
308 **27** 2½d. blue (5.03) .. .. .. 11·00 12·00
a. Deep blue .. .. 13·00 12·00
w. Wmk inverted .. .. .. — 50·00
x. Wmk reversed .. .. ..
309 **28** 3d. yellow-brown .. .. .. 23·00 1·00
a. Bistre-brown .. .. .. 23·00 1·00
b. Pale bistre .. .. .. 35·00 3·25
310 **37** 4d. dp blue & dp brn/*bluish* (27.11.02) 7·50 55·00
a. Imperf vert (horiz pair) £450
311 **30** 5d. red-brown (4.03) .. .. .. 22·00 6·50
a. Deep brown .. .. 20·00 4·00
b. Sepia .. .. 38·00 15·00
312 **31** 6d. rose (9.02) .. .. 35·00 4·50
a. Rose-red .. .. 35·00 5·50
ab. Wmk upright £500 £350
b. Rose-carmine .. .. .. 40·00 5·50
ba. Imperf vert (horiz pair) £425
bb. Imperf horiz (vert pair)
c. Bright carmine-pink .. .. 50·00 6·50
d. Scarlet .. .. 55·00 16·00
313 **32** 8d. blue (2.03) .. .. 27·00 7·00
a. Steel-blue .. .. 27·00 7·00
ab. Imperf vert (horiz pair) £650
ac. Imperf horiz (vert pair) £650
314 **33** 9d. purple (5.03) .. .. .. 40·00 11·00
w. Wmk inverted .. .. .. 60·00 40·00
x. Wmk reversed .. .. .. 75·00 75·00
y. Wmk inverted and reversed .. 60·00 40·00
315 **34** 1s. brown-red (11.02) .. .. .. 48·00 7·50
a. Bright red .. .. 48·00 8·50
b. Orange-red .. .. 48·00 3·75
ba. Error. Wmk W 12*b* (inverted) .. † £1400
c. Orange-brown .. .. .. 60·00 10·00
316 **35** 2s. green (4.03) .. .. 75·00 48·00
a. Blue-green .. .. 70·00 40·00
w. Wmk inverted .. .. .. £200 55·00
317 **36** 5s. deep red (6.03) £170 £200
a. Wmk upright £200 £250
b. Vermilion £170 £200
ba. Wmk upright £200 £250
w. Wmk inverted

(*b*) *P* 14
318 **40** 1½d. chestnut (2.07) .. .. .. 15·00 45·00
319 **41** 2d. grey-purple (12.02) .. .. .. 5·50 1·25
a. Purple .. .. 5·50 1·25
ab. Imperf vert (horiz pair) £350
ac. Imperf horiz (vert pair) £350
b. Bright reddish purple .. .. 6·50 2·00
320 **27** 2½d. blue (1906) .. .. .. 8·50 2·00
a. Deep blue .. .. 8·50 2·00
x. Wmk reversed .. .. ..
321 **28** 3d. bistre-brown (1906) .. .. .. 27·00 2·50
a. Imperf vert (horiz pair) £550
b. Bistre .. .. 27·00 2·50
c. Pale yellow-bistre .. .. .. 48·00 9·50
322 **37** 4d. dp blue & dp brown/*bluish* (1903) 6·00 2·75
a. Imperf vert (horiz pair) £400
b. Imperf horiz (vert pair) £400
c. Centre inverted .. .. .. † £55000
d. Blue and chestnut/bluish .. .. 4·00 1·25
e. Blue and ochre-brown/bluish .. 4·00 1·25
w. Wmk inverted .. .. .. 20·00 7·00
x. Wmk reversed .. .. .. 15·00 5·00
y. Wmk inverted and reversed .. 40·00 12·00
323 **30** 5d. black-brown (1906) .. .. .. 50·00 17·00
a. Red-brown .. .. 24·00 6·50
324 **31** 6d. bright carmine-pink (1906) .. 50·00 7·00
a. Imperf vert (horiz pair) £475
b. Rose-carmine .. .. .. 50·00 8·00
325 **32** 8d. steel-blue (1907) .. .. .. 26·00 6·50
326 **33** 9d. purple (1906) .. .. .. 25·00 6·00
w. Wmk inverted .. .. .. 60·00 20·00
327 **34** 1s. orange-brown (1906) .. .. .. 60·00 5·50
a. Orange-red .. .. 55·00 5·50
b. Pale red .. .. 80·00 32·00
328 **35** 2s. green (1.06) .. .. 65·00 22·00
a. Blue-green .. .. 70·00 26·00
aw. Wmk inverted .. .. .. £200 60·00
ax. Wmk reversed .. .. ..
329 **36** 5s. deep red (1906) £170 £180
a. Wmk upright £200 £225
b. Dull red £170 £180
ba. Wmk upright £180 £200

(*c*) *Perf compound of* 11 *and* 14
330 **40** 1½d. chestnut (1907) £650
331 **41** 2d. purple (1903) £275
332 **28** 3d. bistre-brown (1906) £550 £450
333 **37** 4d. blue and yellow-brown (1903) .. £300 £300
334 **30** 5d. red-brown (1906) £475 £500
335 **31** 6d. rose-carmine (1907) £325 £200
336 **32** 8d. steel-blue (1907) £600
337 **33** 9d. purple (1906) £900 £900
338 **36** 5s. deep red (1906) £1800

(*d*) *Mixed perfs*
339 **40** 1½d. chestnut (1907) £650
340 **41** 2d. purple (1903) £150
341 **28** 3d. bistre-brown (1906) £550 £450
342 **37** 4d. blue and chestnut/*bluish* (1904) £250 £250
a. Blue and yellow-brown/bluish .. £250 £250
343 **30** 5d. red-brown (1906) £425 £425
344 **31** 6d. rose-carmine (1907) £275 £200
a. Bright carmine-pink £300 £200
345 **32** 8d. steel-blue (1907) £600
346 **33** 9d. purple (1906) £800 £800
347 **35** 2s. blue-green (1906) £950 £950
348 **36** 5s. vermilion (*wmk upright*) (1906) .. £1600
w. Wmk inverted

Two sizes of paper were used for the above stamps:—

(1) A sheet containing 240 wmks, with a space of 9 mm between each.

(2) A sheet containing 120 wmks, with a space of 24 mm between each vertical row.

Size (1) was used for the ½d., 1d., 2d., and 4d., and size (2) for 2½d., 5d., 9d., and 2s. The paper in each case exactly fitted the plates, and had the watermark in register, though in the case of the 4d., the plate of which contained only 80 stamps, the paper was cut up to print it. The 3d., 6d., 8d., and 1s. were printed on variety (1), but with watermark sideways: by reason of this, specimens from the margins of the sheets show parts of the words "NEW ZEALAND POSTAGE" in large letters, and some copies have no watermark at all. For the 1½d. and 5s. stamps variety (1) was also used, but two watermarks appear on each stamp.

(Recess Govt Printer, Wellington)

1904 (Feb). *Printed from new "dot" plates made by W.R. Royle & Sons. Thin, hard ("Cowan") paper.* W **43**. (a) *P* 14.
349 **42** 1d. rose-carmine .. .. .. 7·50 40
a. Pale carmine .. .. 7·50 40
w. Wmk inverted .. .. .. 75·00 25·00
y. Wmk inverted and reversed .. 85·00 35·00

(*b*) *P* 11×14
350 **42** 1d. rose-carmine £120 £110

(*c*) *Mixed perfs*
351 **42** 1d. rose-carmine .. .. .. 24·00 25·00
a. Pale carmine .. .. 24·00 25·00

These plates have a minute dot in the horizontal margins between the rows, centred under each stamp, but it is frequently cut out by the perforations. However, they can be further distinguished by the notes below.

In 1906 fresh printings were made from four new plates, two of which, marked in the margin "W1" and "W2", were supplied by Waterlow Bros and Layton, and the other two, marked "R1" and "R2", by W. R. Royle & Son. The intention was to note which pair of plates wore the best and produced the best results. They can be distinguished as follows:—

(*a*)

(*b*)

(*c*)

(d)

(e)

(f)

(a) Four o'clock flaw in rosette at top right corner. Occurs in all these plates but not in the original Waterlow plates.
(b) Pearl at right strong.
(c) Pearl at right weak.
(d) Dot at left and S-shaped ornament unshaded.
(e) S-shaped ornament with one line of shading within.
(f) As (e) but with line from left pearl to edge of stamp.
"Dot" plates comprise (a) and (d).
Waterlow plates comprise (a), (b) and (e).
Royle plates comprise (a), (c) and (e) and the line in (f) on many stamps but not all.

(Recess Govt Printer, Wellington)

1906. *Thin, hard ("Cowan") paper. W* **43**.

(a) Printed from new Waterlow plates. (i) *P* 14
352 **42** 1d. deep rose-carmine .. .. .. 24·00 1·00
a. Imperf horiz (vert pair) £200
b. Aniline carmine .. .. .. 23·00 1·00
ba. Imperf vert (horiz pair) £200
c. Rose-carmine .. .. .. 23·00 1·00
y. Wmk inverted and reversed ..

(ii) *P* 11
353 **42** 1d. aniline carmine £550 £650

(iii) *P* 11×14
354 **42** 1d. rose-carmine £425
a. Perf 14×11 .. .. .. — £750

(iv) *Mixed perfs*
355 **42** 1d. deep rose-carmine £400

(b) Printed from new Royle plates. (i) *P* 14
356 **42** 1d. rose-carmine .. .. .. 10·00 1·25
a. Imperf horiz (vert pair) £225 £225
b. Bright rose-carmine .. .. .. 12·00 1·40
w. Wmk inverted .. ..
y. Wmk inverted and reversed ..

(ii) *P* 11
357 **42** 1d. bright rose-carmine £100 £150

(iii) *P* 11×14
358 **42** 1d. rose-carmine £100
a. Perf 14×11 .. .. £100

(iv) *Mixed perfs*
359 **42** 1d. rose-carmine £100

(v) *P* 14×14½ *(comb)*
360 **42** 1d. bright rose-carmine .. .. .. 60·00 45·00
a. Rose-carmine .. .. 60·00 45·00

Nos. 360/a are known both with and without the small dot. See also No. 386.

1905 (15 June)**–06.** *Stamps supplied to penny-in-the-slot machines.*

(i) *"Dot" plates of* 1904. (ii) *Waterlow "reserve" plate of* 1902

(a) Imperf top and bottom; zigzag roulette 9½ on one or both sides, two large holes at sides
361 **42** 1d. rose-carmine (i) £120
362 1d. deep carmine (ii) £140

(b) As last but rouletted 14½ (8.7.05)
363 **42** 1d. rose-carmine (i) £140
364 1d. deep carmine (ii) £250

(c) Imperf all round, two large holes each side (6.3.06)
365 **42** 1d. rose-carmine (i) £110
366 1d. deep carmine (ii) £110

(d) Imperf all round (21.6.06)
367 **42** 1d. deep carmine (ii) £130

(e) Imperf all round. Two small indentations on back of stamp (1.06)
368 **42** 1d. deep carmine (ii) £160 £140

(f) Imperf all round; two small pin-holes in stamp (21.6.06)
369 **42** 1d. deep carmine (ii) £140 £140

No. 365 *only* exists from strips of Nos. 361 or 363 (resulting from the use of successive coins) which have been separated by scissors. Similarly strips of Nos. 362 and 364 can produce single copies of No. 366 but this also exists in singles from a different machine.

Most used copies of Nos. 361/7 are forgeries and they should only be collected on cover.

44 Maori Canoe, *Te Arawa*

(Des L. J. Steele. Eng W. R. Bock. Typo Govt Printer, Wellington)

1906 (1–17 Nov). *New Zealand Exhibition, Christchurch. T* **44** *and similar horiz designs. W* **43** *(sideways). P* 14.
370 ½d. emerald-green .. .. 17·00 27·00
371 1d. vermilion .. .. 14·00 16·00
a. Claret £6000 £8000
372 3d. brown and blue .. .. .. 45·00 75·00
373 6d. pink and olive-green (17.11) .. £160 £250
370/3 .. .. *Set of* 4 £200 £325

Designs:—1d. Maori art; 3d. Landing of Cook; 6d. Annexation of New Zealand.

The 1d. in claret was the original printing, which was considered unsatisfactory.

47 (T **28** reduced)

48 (T **31** reduced)

49 (T **34** reduced)

(New plates (except 4d.), supplied by Perkins Bacon. Recess Govt Printer, Wellington).

1907–8. *Thin, hard ("Cowan") paper. W* **43**. *(a) P 14 (line).*
374 **23** ½d. green (1907) .. .. 24·00 8·00
a. Imperf (pair) £130
b. Yellow-green .. .. 17·00 2·75
c. Deep yellow-green .. .. .. 15·00 2·50
375 **47** 3d. brown (6.07) .. .. 45·00 22·00
376 **48** 6d. carmine-pink (3.07) .. .. .. 45·00 6·00
a. Red .. .. 60·00 35·00

(b) P 14×13, 13½ *(comb)*
377 **23** ½d. green (1907) .. .. 17·00 8·50
a. Yellow-green .. .. 8·00 1·75
378 **47** 3d. brown (2.08) .. .. 45·00 24·00
a. Yellow-brown .. .. 45·00 26·00
379 **37** 4d. blue and yellow-brown/*bluish* (6.08) 28·00 24·00
380 **48** 6d. pink (2.08) .. .. £275 95·00
381 **49** 1s. orange-red (12.07) .. .. .. £130 48·00

(c) P 14×15 *(comb)*
382 **23** ½d. yellow-green (1907) .. .. .. 8·00 85
y. Wmk inverted and reversed .. .. — £150
383 **47** 3d. brown (8.08) .. .. 35·00 8·00
a. Yellow-brown .. .. 35·00 8·00
384 **48** 6d. carmine-pink (8.08) .. .. .. 40·00 10·00
385 **49** 1s. orange-red (8.08) .. .. .. £120 24·00
a. Deep orange-brown £325 £475

The ½d. stamps of this 1907–8 issue have a minute dot in the margin between the stamps, where not removed by the perforation. (See note after No. 351*a*). Those perforated 14 can be distinguished from the earlier stamps, Nos. 302/*d*, by the absence of plate wear. This is most noticeable on the 1902 printings as a white patch at far left, level with the bottom of the "P" in "POSTAGE". Such damage is not present on the new plates used for Nos. 374/*c*.

Stamps of T **47, 48** and **49** also have a small dot as described in note after No. 351*a*.

TYPOGRAPHY PAPERS. 1908–30. De La Rue paper is chalk-surfaced and has a smooth finish. The watermark is as illustrated. The gum is toned and strongly resistant to soaking. **Jones paper** is chalk-surfaced and has a coarser texture, is poorly surfaced and the ink tends to peel. The outline of the watermark commonly shows on the surface of the stamp. The gum is colourless or only slightly toned and washes off readily. **Cowan paper** is chalk-surfaced and is white and opaque. The watermark is usually smaller than in the "Jones" paper and is often barely visible

Wiggins Teape paper is chalk-surfaced and is thin and hard. It has a vertical mesh with a narrow watermark, whereas the other papers have a horizontal mesh and a wider watermark.

50

(Typo Govt Printer, Wellington, from Perkins Bacon plate).

1908 (1 Dec). *De La Rue chalk-surfaced paper. W* **43**. *P* 14×15 *(comb).*
386 **50** 1d. carmine .. .. 22·00 50
w. Wmk inverted .. .. — 50·00

The design of Type **50** differs from Type **42** by alterations in the corner rosettes and by the lines on the globe which are diagonal instead of vertical.

51

52

53

(Eng. P.B. Typo Govt Printer, Wellington)

1909 (8 Nov)**–12.** *De La Rue chalk-surfaced paper with toned gum. W* **43**. *P* 14×15 *(comb).*
387 **51** ½d. yellow-green .. .. .. 3·50 10
aa. Deep green .. .. .. 3·50 20
a. Imperf (pair) £160
b. Booklet pane. Five stamps plus label in position 1 (4.10) £500
c. Ditto, but label in position 6 (4.10) £500
d. Booklet pane of 6 (4.10) £150
e. Ditto, but with coloured bars on selvedge (5.12) £140
w. Wmk inverted .. .. .. † —

Stamps with blurred and heavy appearance are from booklets.

(Eng W. R. Royle & Son, London. Recess Govt Printer, Wellington)

1909 (8 Nov)**–16.** *T* **52** *and similar portraits.*

(a) W **43**. *P* 14×14½ *(comb)*
388 2d. mauve .. .. 14·00 6·50
a. Deep mauve .. .. 18·00 6·50
w. Wmk inverted .. .. † —
389 3d. chestnut .. .. 22·00 40
390 4d. orange-red .. .. 24·00 25·00
a. Orange-yellow (1912) .. .. .. 7·00 3·50
aw. Wmk inverted .. .. £250 75·00
391 5d. brown (1910) .. .. 17·00 1·50
a. Red-brown .. .. 15·00 1·50
w. Wmk inverted .. .. † —
392 6d. carmine (1910) .. .. 40·00 80
a. Deep carmine (29.10.13) .. .. 40·00 2·50
393 8d. indigo-blue .. .. 10·00 65
a. Deep bright blue .. .. .. 13·00 65
w. Wmk inverted .. .. 35·00 20·00
394 1s. vermilion (1910) .. .. .. 48·00 1·75
w. Wmk inverted .. .. £150 50·00
388/94 .. .. *Set of* 8 £160 35·00

(b) W **43**. *P* 14 *(line)**
395 3d. chestnut (1910) .. .. .. 40·00 5·00
396 4d. orange (1910) .. .. .. 17·00 9·00
397 5d. brown .. .. 23·00 3·75
a. Red-brown (15.9.11) .. .. .. 25·00 4·25
w. Wmk inverted .. .. ..
398 6d. carmine .. .. 45·00 9·00
399 1s. vermilion .. .. 48·00 9·00
395/9 .. .. *Set of* 5 £160 32·00

(c) W **43** *(sideways) (paper with widely spaced watermark as used for Nos.* 308 *and* 320 *– see note below No.* 348*). P* 14 *(line)**
400 8d. indigo-blue (8.16) .. .. .. 15·00 48·00
a. No wmk .. .. 60·00 £140

(d) W **43**. *P* 14×13½ *(comb)†*
401 3d. chestnut (1915) .. .. .. 60·00 75·00
a. Vert pair. P 14×13½ and 14×14½ .. £225 £275
w. Wmk inverted £120 £120
402 5d. red-brown (1916) .. .. .. 19·00 2·00
a. Vert pair. P 14×13½ and 14×14½ .. 50·00 70·00
403 6d. carmine (1915) .. .. .. 70·00 75·00
a. Vert pair. P 14×13½ and 14×14½ .. £225 £275
404 8d. indigo-blue (3.16) .. .. .. 24·00 2·50
a. Vert pair. P 14×13½ and 14×14½ .. 50·00 70·00
b. Deep bright blue .. .. .. 25·00 2·50
ba. Vert pair. P 14×13½ and 14×14½ .. 50·00 70·00
w. Wmk inverted .. .. 35·00 20·00
401/4 .. .. *Set of* 4 £150 £140

*In addition to showing the usual characteristics of a line perforation, these stamps may be distinguished by their vertical perforation which measures 13.8. Nos. 388/94 generally measure vertically 14 to 14.3. An exception is 13.8 one vertical side but 14 the other.

†The 3d. and 6d. come in full sheets perf 14×13½. The 3d., 5d. and 6d. values also exist in two combinations: (*a*) five top rows perf 14×13½ with five bottom rows perf 14×14½ and (*b*) four top rows perf 14×13½ with six bottom rows perf 14×14½. The 8d. perf 14×13½ only exists from combination (*b*).

(Eng P.B. Typo Govt Printer, Wellington)

1909 (8 Nov)**–26.** *P* 14×15 *(comb).*

(a) W **43**. *De La Rue chalk-surfaced paper with toned gum*
405 **53** 1d. carmine .. .. 1·25 10
a. Imperf (pair) £250
b. Booklet pane of 6 (4.10) £140
c. Ditto, but with coloured bars on selvedge (5.12) £110
w. Wmk inverted .. .. .. 25·00 20·00
y. Wmk inverted and reversed ..

(b) W **43**. *Jones chalk-surfaced paper with white gum*
406 **53** 1d. deep carmine (1924) .. .. 12·00 4·75
a. On unsurfaced paper. *Pale carmine* £325
b. Booklet pane of 6 with bars on selvedge (1.12.24) £100
w. Wmk inverted .. .. .. 35·00 25·00

(c) W **43**. *De La Rue unsurfaced medium paper with toned gum*
407 **53** 1d. rose-carmine (4.25) .. .. 26·00 65·00

(d) W **43** *(sideways). De La Rue chalk-surfaced paper with toned gum*
408 **53** 1d. bright carmine (4.25) .. .. 6·50 27·00
a. No wmk .. .. 20·00 55·00
b. Imperf (pair) .. .. .. 50·00

(e) No wmk, but bluish "NZ" and Star lithographed on back. Art paper
409 **53** 1d. rose-carmine (1925) .. .. 2·25 2·00
a. "NZ" and Star in black .. .. 13·00
b. "NZ" and Star colourless .. .. 24·00

(f) W **43**. *Cowan thick, opague, chalk-surfaced paper with white gum*
410 **53** 1d. deep carmine (8.25) .. .. 4·25 1·00
a. Imperf (pair) .. .. .. 65·00 70·00
b. Booklet pane of 6 with bars and adverts on selvedge £100
w. Wmk inverted .. .. .. 30·00 20·00
x. Wmk reversed (1926) .. .. 6·00 1·50
y. Wmk inverted and reversed (1926) 30·00 20·00

(g) W **43**. *Wiggins Teape thin, hard, chalk-surfaced paper with white gum*
411 **53** 1d. rose-carmine (6.26) .. .. 24·00 11·00
w. Wmk inverted .. .. .. 35·00 20·00

Examples of No. 405 with a blurred and heavy appearance are from booklets.

No. 406a comes from a sheet on which the paper coating was missing from the right-hand half.

Many stamps from the sheets of No. 408 were without watermark or showed portions of "NEW ZEALAND POSTAGE" in double-lined capitals.

AUCKLAND
EXHIBITION,
1913.
(59)

60

1913 (1 Dec). *Auckland Industrial Exhibition. Nos. 387aa, 389, 392 and 405 optd with T* **59** *by Govt Printer, Wellington.*
412 **51** ½d. deep green .. .. 13·00 38·00
413 **53** 1d. carmine .. .. 19·00 38·00
414 **52** 3d. chestnut £130 £225
415 6d. carmine £140 £250
412/15 .. .. *Set of* 4 £275 £500
These overprinted stamps were only available for letters in New Zealand and to Australia.

(Des H. L. Richardson. Recess Govt Printer, Wellington, from plates made in London by P.B.)

1915 (30 July)–**30.** (a) *W* **43**, *Cowan unsurfaced paper. P* 14×13½ *(comb) (see notes below).*
416 **60** 1½d. grey-slate .. .. 2·00 1·50
a. Perf 14×14½ (1915) .. .. .. 3·50 1·50
aw. Wmk inverted .. .. ..
b. Vert pair. Nos. 416/a .. .. .. 35·00 55·00
417 2d. bright violet .. .. 7·00 23·00
a. Perf 14×14½ .. .. .. 7·00 25·00
b. Vert pair. Nos. 417/a .. .. .. 24·00 £110
418 2d. yellow (15.1.16) .. .. .. 5·00 16·00
a. Perf 14×14½ .. .. .. 5·00 18·00
b. Vert pair. Nos. 418/a .. .. .. 18·00 £110
419 2½d. blue .. .. 3·25 3·50
a. Perf 14×14½ (1916) .. .. .. 9·50 14·00
b. Vert pair. Nos. 419/a .. .. .. 35·00 70·00
420 3d. chocolate .. .. 9·00 1·25
aw. Wmk inverted .. .. .. £100 60·00
ax. Wmk reversed .. .. ..
b. Perf 14×14½ .. .. .. 9·00 1·40
bw. Wmk inverted .. .. .. £100 60·00
bx. Wmk reversed .. .. .. 75·00
c. Vert pair. Nos. 420 and 420b .. 35·00 70·00
cw. Wmk inverted .. .. ..
cx. Wmk reversed .. .. ..
421 4d. yellow .. .. 4·25 42·00
a. Re-entry (Pl 20 R. 1/6) .. .. 30·00
b. Re-entry (Pl 20 R. 4/10) .. .. 35·00
c. Perf 14×14½ .. .. .. 4·25 45·00
d. Vert pair. Nos. 421 and 421c .. 26·00 £130
422 4d. bright violet (7.4.16) .. .. 7·00 30
a. Imperf (horiz pair) £750
b. Re-entry (Pl 20 R. 1/6) .. .. 35·00
c. Re-entry (Pl 20 R. 4/10) .. .. 40·00
dx. Wmk reversed .. .. ..
e. Perf 14×14½ .. .. .. 7·00 30
ew. Wmk inverted .. .. .. † —
ex. Wmk reversed .. .. .. — 90·00
f. Vert pair. Nos. 422 and 422e .. 35·00 70·00
fx. Wmk reversed .. .. ..
423 4½d. deep green .. .. 12·00 11·00
a. Perf 14×14½ (1915) .. .. .. 22·00 25·00
b. Vert pair. Nos. 423/a .. .. .. 48·00 75·00
424 5d. light blue (4.22) .. .. .. 6·50 1·00
a. Imperf (pair) £120 £150
bw. Wmk inverted .. .. .. — 90·00
c. Perf 14×14½ .. .. .. 18·00 35·00
d. *Pale ultramarine* (5.30) .. .. 8·00 5·50
da. Perf 14×14½ .. .. .. 12·00 15·00
db. Vert pair. Nos. 424d/da .. .. 55·00 £100
425 6d. carmine .. .. 7·00 40
a. Imperf three sides (top stamp of vert pair) £1200
bw. Wmk inverted .. .. .. £100 60·00
bx. Wmk reversed .. .. .. — 90·00
by. Wmk inverted and reversed ..
c. *Carmine-lake* (11.27) £500 £275
d. Perf 14×14½ (1915) .. .. 8·50 60
dw. Wmk inverted .. .. .. 50·00 40·00
e. Vert pair. Nos. 425 and 425d .. 65·00 £110
426 7½d. red-brown .. .. 13·00 23·00
a. Perf 14×14½ (10.20) .. .. 30·00 48·00
b. Vert pair. Nos. 426/a .. .. 50·00 £110
427 8d. indigo-blue (19.4.21) .. .. 17·00 45·00
a. Perf 14×14½ .. .. .. 18·00 45·00
b. Vert pair. Nos. 427/a .. .. 38·00 £130
428 8d. red-brown (3.22) .. .. .. 18·00 1·50
429 9d. sage-green .. .. 17·00 2·00
a. Imperf (pair) £800
b. Imperf three sides (top stamp of vert pair) £1300
c. *Yellowish olive* (12.25) .. .. 28·00 8·50
d. Perf 14×14½ .. .. .. 19·00 9·00
e. Vert pair. Nos. 429 and 429d .. 70·00 £120
430 1s. vermilion .. .. 13·00 2·25
a. Imperf (pair) £2250
bw. Wmk inverted £200 £120
c. Perf 14×14½ (1915) .. .. 14·00 50
ca. *Pale orange-red* (4.24) .. .. 30·00 12·00
cb. Imperf (pair) £325
cc. *Orange-brown* (1.2.28) £500 £250
cw. Wmk inverted £300
d. Vert pair. Nos. 430 and 430c .. 75·00 £130
dw. Wmk inverted .. .. ..
416/30 .. .. *Set of* 15 £120 £150

(b) *W* **43** *(sideways on 2d., 3d. and 6d.). Thin paper with widely spaced watermark as used for Nos. 308 and 320 (see note below No. 348). P* 14×13½ *(comb) (see notes below)* (1½d.) *or* 14 *(line) (others)*
431 **60** 1½d. grey-slate (3.16) .. .. .. 1·50 4·75
a. No wmk .. .. .. 2·50 10·00
b. Perf 14×14½ .. .. .. 1·50 4·75
ba. No wmk .. .. .. 2·50 10·00
by. Wmk inverted and reversed ..
c. Vert pair. Nos. 431 and 431b .. 20·00 55·00
ca. Vert pair. Nos. 431a and 431ba .. 38·00 85·00
432 2d. yellow (6.16) .. .. .. 4·50 42·00
a. No wmk .. .. .. 32·00 85·00
433 3d. chocolate (6.16) .. .. .. 6·00 20·00
a. No wmk .. .. .. 28·00 70·00
434 6d. carmine (6.16) .. .. .. 8·00 48·00
a. No wmk .. .. .. 60·00 £130
431/4 .. .. *Set of* 4 18·00 £100

The 1½d., 2½d., 4½d. and 7½d. have value tablets as shown in Type **60**. For the other values the tablets are shortened and the ornamental border each side of the crown correspondingly extended.

With the exception of Nos. 432/4 stamps in this issue were comb-perforated 14×13½, 14×14½ or a combination of the two.

The 1½d. (No. 416), 2½d., 4d. (both), 4½d., 5d., 6d., 7½d., 8d. red-brown, 9d. and 1s. are known to have been produced in sheets perforated 14×13½ throughout with the 4d. bright violet, 5d., 6d. and 1s. known perforated 14×14½ throughout.

On the sheets showing the two perforations combined the top four rows are usually perforated 14×13½ and the bottom six 14×14½. Combination sheets are known to have been produced in this form for the 1½d. (Nos. 416 and 431), 2d. (both), 2½d., 3d., 4d. (both), 4½d., 6d., 7½d., 8d. indigo-blue, 9d. and 1s. On a late printing of the 4d. bright violet and 5d. pale ultramarine the arrangement is different with the top five rows perforated 14×14½ and the bottom five 14×13½.

With the exception of Nos. 432/4 any with perforations measuring 14×14 or nearly must be classed as 14×14½, this being an irregularity of the comb machine, and not a product of the 14-line machine.

During the laying-down of plate 20 for the 4d., from the roller-die which also contained dies of other values, an impression of the 4½d. value was placed on R. 1/6 and of the 2½d. on R. 4/10. These errors were subsequently corrected by re-entries of the 4d. impression, but on R. 1/6 traces of the original impression can be found in the right-hand value tablet and above the top frame line, while on R. 4/10 the foot of the "2" is visible in the left-hand value tablet with traces of "½" to its right.

61

62

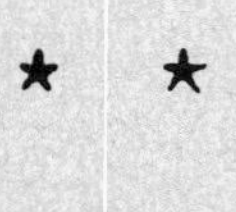

(63)

Type **62** (from local plates) can be identified from Type **61** (prepared by Perkins Bacon) by the shading on the portrait. This is diagonal on Type **62** and horizontal on Type **61**.

(Die eng W. R. Bock. Typo Govt Printer, Wellington, from plates made by P.B. (T **61**) or locally (T **62**))

1915 (30 July)–**34.** *P* 14×15.
(a) *W* **43**. *De La Rue chalk-surfaced paper with toned gum.*
435 **61** ½d. green 80 10
a. Booklet pane of 6 with bars on selvedge £110
b. *Yellow-green* .. .. .. 3·75 90
ba. Booklet pane of 6 with bars on selvedge .. .. 90·00
c. Very thick, hard, highly surfaced paper with white gum (12.15) .. 12·00 30·00
w. Wmk inverted .. .. .. 30·00 60·00
x. Wmk reversed .. .. .. — 50·00
y. Wmk inverted and reversed .. — 50·00
436 **62** 1½d. grey-black (4.16) .. .. .. 5·50 85
a. *Black* .. .. .. 6·50 95
y. Wmk inverted and reversed .. — £110
437 **61** 1½d. slate (5.9.16) .. .. .. 6·50 10
w. Wmk inverted .. .. .. — £110
438 1½d. orange-brown (9.18) .. .. 2·25 10
w. Wmk inverted .. .. .. 75·00 60·00
x. Wmk reversed .. .. .. † —
y. Wmk inverted and reversed .. £100 80·00
439 2d. yellow (9.16) .. .. .. 1·75 10
a. *Pale yellow* .. .. .. 3·75 60
w. Wmk inverted .. .. .. 75·00
440 3d. chocolate (5.19) .. .. .. 7·00 40
435/40 .. .. *Set of* 6 21·00 1·40

(b) *W* **43**. *Jones chalk-surfaced paper with white gum*
441 **61** ½d. green (10.24) .. .. .. 6·50 6·50
a. Booklet pane of 6 with bars on selvedge (1.12.24) £100
w. Wmk inverted .. .. .. 40·00
442 2d. dull yellow (7.24) .. .. .. 4·50 22·00
w. Wmk inverted .. .. .. 30·00
443 3d. deep chocolate (3.25) .. .. 18·00 9·00
441/3 .. .. *Set of* 3 26·00 35·00

(c) *No wmk, but bluish "NZ" and Star lithographed on back. Art paper*
444 **61** ½d. apple-green (4.25) .. .. .. 1·50 1·75
a. "NZ" and Star almost colourless .. 4·25
445 2d. yellow (7.25) .. .. .. 6·50 48·00

(d) *W* **43**. *Cowan thick, opaque, chalk-surfaced paper with white gum*
446 **61** ½d. green (8.25) 50 10
a. Booklet pane of 6 with bars and adverts on selvedge .. .. .. 90·00
ab. Booklet pane of 6 with bars on selvedge (1934) £250
bw. Wmk inverted .. .. .. 35·00 25·00
bx. Wmk reversed (1926) .. .. 3·50 1·50
by. Wmk inverted and reversed (1926) 35·00 20·00
c. Perf 14 (1927) 60 20
ca. Booklet pane of 6 with bars on selvedge (1928) .. .. .. 85·00
cb. Booklet pane of 6 with bars and adverts on selvedge (1928) .. 85·00
cw. Wmk inverted .. .. .. 40·00 25·00
447 1½d. orange-brown (*p* 14) (8.29) .. 8·50 15·00
a. Perf 14×15 (7.33) .. .. 40·00 60·00
448 2d. yellow (8.25) .. .. .. 4·25 20
ax. Wmk reversed (1927) .. .. 10·00 40·00
ay. Wmk inverted and reversed (1927) £100
b. Perf 14 (1929) .. .. .. 2·75 10
bw. Wmk inverted .. .. .. 35·00 20·00
449 3d. chocolate (8.25) .. .. .. 7·00 20
aw. Wmk inverted .. .. .. 60·00
b. Perf 14 (1929) .. .. .. 7·50 2·50
446/9 .. .. *Set of* 4 17·00 15·00

(e) *W* **43**. *Wiggins Teape thin, hard, chalk-surfaced paper*
450 **61** 1½d. orange-brown (*p* 14) (1930) .. 30·00 60·00
451 2d. yellow (5.26) .. .. .. 7·50 16·00
aw. Wmk inverted .. .. .. 24·00
b. Perf 14 (10.27) .. .. .. 6·50 16·00
bw. Wmk inverted .. .. .. 30·00 30·00

The designs of these stamps also differ as described beneath No. 434.

Stamps from booklet panes often have blurred, heavy impressions. Different advertisements can be found on the listed booklet panes.

1915 (24 Sept). *No. 435 optd with T* **63**.
452 **61** ½d. green .. .. 1·60 30

64 "Peace" and Lion 65 "Peace" and Lion

(Des and typo D.L.R. from plates by P.B., Waterlow and D.L.R.)

1920 (27 Jan). *Victory. T* **64/5** *and similar designs. W* **43** *(sideways on* ½d., 1½d., 3d. *and* 1s.). *De La Rue chalk-surfaced paper. P* 14.
453 ½d. green .. .. 2·25 2·25
a. *Pale yellow-green* .. .. .. 25·00 23·00
454 1d. carmine-red .. .. 4·00 40
a. *Bright carmine* .. .. .. 6·00 50
w. Wmk inverted .. .. .. 15·00 4·00
x. Wmk reversed .. .. .. 48·00 10·00
455 1½d. brown-orange .. .. 3·50 30
456 3d. chocolate .. .. 13·00 11·00
457 6d. violet .. .. 14·00 14·00
a. Wmk sideways .. .. .. † £300
x. Wmk inverted .. .. .. — £110
458 1s. orange-red .. .. 24·00 48·00
453/8 .. .. *Set of* 6 55·00 70·00

Designs: *Horiz (as T* **65**)—1½d. Maori chief. *(As T* **64**)—3d. Lion; 1s. King George V. *Vert (as T* **64**)—6d. "Peace" and "Progress".

The above stamps were placed on sale in London in November, 1919.

2d. 2d.
TWOPENCE
(68)

69

1922 (Mar). *No. 453 surch with T* **68**.
459 **64** 2d. on ½d. green (R.) .. .. .. 3·00 1·00

(Des and eng W. R. Bock. Typo Govt Printer, Wellington)

1923 (1 Oct)–**25.** *Restoration of Penny Postage. W* **43**. *P* 14×15.
(a) *De La Rue chalk-surfaced paper with toned gum.*
460 **69** 1d. carmine .. .. 2·25 30
(b) *Jones chalk-surfaced paper with white gum*
461 **69** 1d. carmine (3.24) .. .. .. 5·00 3·50
w. Wmk inverted .. .. .. 50·00 40·00
(c) *Cowan unsurfaced paper with very shiny gum*
462 **69** 1d. carmine-pink (4.25) .. .. .. 27·00 26·00
The paper used for No. 462 is similar to that of Nos. 416/30.

70 Exhibition Buildings

(Des H. L. Richardson. Eng and typo Govt Printer, Wellington)

1925 (17 Nov). *Dunedin Exhibition. W* **43**. *Cowan chalk-surfaced paper. P* 14×15.
463 **70** ½d. yellow-green/*green* .. .. .. 2·75 11·00
w. Wmk inverted £225 £100
464 1d. carmine/*rose* .. .. .. 3·00 5·50
w. Wmk inverted £225 £100
465 4d. mauve/*pale mauve* .. .. .. 40·00 70·00
a. "POSTAGF" at right (R. 1/2, R 10/1) £120 £170
463/5 .. .. *Set of* 3 42·00 80·00

71

72

(Des H. L. Richardson; plates by B.W. (1d. from sheets), P.B. (1d. from booklets), Royal Mint, London (others). Typo Govt Printer, Wellington)

1926 (12 July)–**34.** *W* **43**. *P* 14. (a) *Jones chalk-surfaced paper with white gum.*
466 **72** 2s. deep blue .. .. 48·00 55·00
w. Wmk inverted .. .. .. 48·00 55·00
467 3s. mauve .. .. 70·00 £130
w. Wmk inverted .. .. .. 70·00 £130

(b) *Cowan thick, opaque, chalk-surfaced paper with white gum*
468 **71** 1d. rose-carmine (15.11.26) 40 10
a. Imperf (pair) .. .. .. 90·00
b. Booklet pane of 6 with bars on selvedge (1928) .. .. .. 75·00
c. Booklet pane of 6 with bars and adverts on selvedge (1928) .. 75·00
dw. Wmk inverted .. .. .. 20·00 10·00
e. Perf 14×15 (3.27) 45 10
ea. Booklet pane of 6 with bars and adverts on selvedge (1934) .. 85·00
ew. Wmk inverted .. .. .. 20·00 10·00
ex. Wmk reversed .. .. .. 10·00

469	72	2s. light blue (5.27)	48·00	18·00
470		3s. pale mauve (9.27)	80·00	£110
468/70		*Set of* 3	£120	£120

(c) *Wiggins Teape thin, hard, chalk-surfaced paper with white gum*

471	71	1d. rose-carmine (6.30)	15·00	7·00
		w. Wmk inverted	30·00	15·00

No. 468ex exists in a range of colours including scarlet and deep carmine to magenta but we have insufficient evidence to show that these were issued.

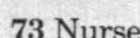
73 Nurse

74 Smiling Boy

(Typo Govt Printing Office, Wellington)

1929–30. *Anti-Tuberculosis Fund. T* **73** *and similar design. W* **43**. *P* 14.

(a) *Inscribed* "HELP STAMP OUT TUBERCULOSIS".

544		1d. + 1d. scarlet (11.12.29)	11·00	17·00
		w. Wmk inverted	£180	£180

(b) *Inscribed* "HELP PROMOTE HEALTH"

545		1d. + 1d. scarlet (29.10.30)	20·00	28·00

(Des L. C. Mitchell. Dies eng and plates made Royal Mint, London (1d.), Govt Ptg Office, Wellington from W. R. Bock die (2d.). Typo Govt Ptg Office, Wellington)

1931 (31 Oct). *Health Stamps. W* **43** *(sideways). P* 14½×14.

546	74	1d. + 1d. scarlet	75·00	75·00
547		2d. + 1d. blue	75·00	65·00

75 New Zealand Lake Scenery

FIVE PENCE
(76)

(Des L. C. Mitchell. Plates, Royal Mint, London. Typo Govt Ptg Office)

1931 (10 Nov)–**35**. *Air. W* **43**. *P* 14×14½.

548	75	3d. chocolate	23·00	13·00
		a. Perf 14×15 (4.35)	£130	£425
549		4d. blackish purple	23·00	15·00
550		7d. brown-orange	26·00	7·50
548/50		*Set of* 3	65·00	32·00

1931 (18 Dec). *Air. Surch with T* **76**. *W* **43**. *P* 14×14½.

551	75	5d. on 3d. green (R.)	11·00	7·50

77 Hygeia, Goddess of Health

78 The Path to Health

(Des R. E. Tripe and W. J. Cooch. Eng H. T. Peat. Recess Govt Printing Office, Wellington)

1932 (18 Nov). *Health Stamp. W* **43**. *P* 14.

552	77	1d. + 1d. carmine	23·00	26·00
		w. Wmk inverted	£200	£110
		x. Wmk reversed	†	£250

(Des J. Berry. Eng H. T. Peat. Recess Govt Printing Office, Wellington)

1933 (8 Nov). *Health Stamp. W* **43**. *P* 14.

553	78	1d. + 1d. carmine	12·00	15·00
		w. Wmk inverted	£130	

TRANS-TASMAN
AIR MAIL
"FAITH IN AUSTRALIA."
(79)

80 Crusader

1934 (17 Jan). *Air. T* **75** *in new colour optd with T* **79**. *W* **43**. *P* 14×14½.

554	75	7d. light blue (B.)	35·00	40·00

(Des J. Berry. Recess D.L.R.)

1934 (25 Oct). *Health Stamp. W* **43** *(sideways). P* 14×13½.

555	80	1d. + 1d. carmine	8·50	13·00

81 Collared Grey Fantail

82 Brown Kiwi

83 Maori Woman

84 Maori Carved House

85 Mt Cook

86 Maori Girl

87 Mitre Peak

88 Striped Marlin

89 Harvesting

90 Tuatara Lizard

91 Maori Panel

92 Tui

93 Capt. Cook at Poverty Bay

94 Mt Egmont

Die I Die II

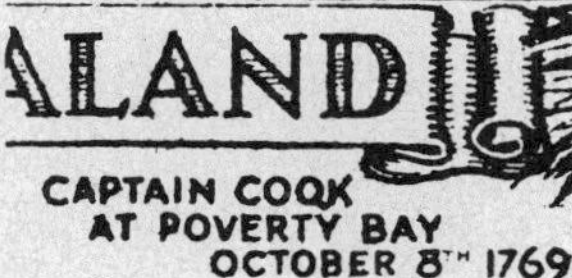

"Captain Coqk"
(R. 1/4)

(Des J. Fitzgerald (½d., 4d.), C. H. and R. J. G. Collins (1d.), M. Matthews (1½d.), H. W. Young (2d.), L. C. Mitchell (2½d., 3d., 8d., 1s., 3s.), W. J. Cooch and R. E. Tripe (5d.), T. I. Archer (6d.), I. F. Calder (9d.) and I. H. Jenkins (2s.). Litho Waterlow (9d.). Recess D.L.R. (remainder))

1935 (1 May)–**36**. *W* **43** *(sideways on 8d.)*.

556	81	½d. bright green, *p* 14×13½	1·50	40
		w. Wmk inverted	2·00	1·50
557	82	1d. scarlet (Die I), *p* 14×13½	1·50	30
		aw. Wmk inverted	1·75	1·25
		b. Perf 13½×14 (1936)	70·00	38·00
		c. Die II. Perf 14×13½ (1935)	5·00	2·75
		ca. Booklet pane of 6 with adverts on selvedge	38·00	
		w. Wmk inverted	12·00	3·00
558	83	1½d. red-brown, *p* 14×13½	4·75	7·50
		a. Perf 13½×14 (1935)	4·25	4·50
		ay. Wmk inverted and reversed (2.36)	18·00	22·00

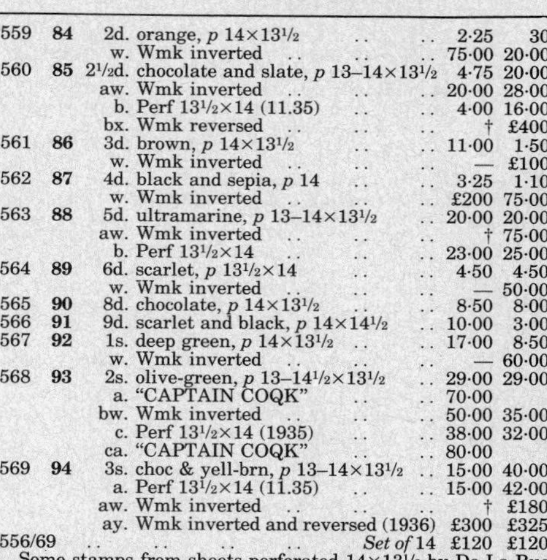

559	84	2d. orange, *p* 14×13½	2·25	30
		w. Wmk inverted	75·00	20·00
560	85	2½d. chocolate and slate, *p* 13–14×13½	4·75	20·00
		aw. Wmk inverted	20·00	28·00
		b. Perf 13½×14 (11.35)	4·00	16·00
		bx. Wmk reversed	†	£400
561	86	3d. brown, *p* 14×13½	11·00	1·50
		w. Wmk inverted	—	£100
562	87	4d. black and sepia, *p* 14	3·25	1·10
		w. Wmk inverted	£200	75·00
563	88	5d. ultramarine, *p* 13–14×13½	20·00	20·00
		aw. Wmk inverted	†	75·00
		b. Perf 13½×14	23·00	25·00
564	89	6d. scarlet, *p* 13½×14	4·50	4·50
		w. Wmk inverted	—	50·00
565	90	8d. chocolate, *p* 14×13½	8·50	8·00
566	91	9d. scarlet and black, *p* 14×14½	10·00	3·00
567	92	1s. deep green, *p* 14×13½	17·00	8·50
		w. Wmk inverted	—	60·00
568	93	2s. olive-green, *p* 13–14½×13½	29·00	29·00
		a. "CAPTAIN COQK"	70·00	
		bw. Wmk inverted	50·00	35·00
		c. Perf 13½×14 (1935)	38·00	32·00
		ca. "CAPTAIN COQK"	80·00	
569	94	3s. choc & yell-brn, *p* 13–14×13½	15·00	40·00
		a. Perf 13½×14 (11.35)	15·00	42·00
		aw. Wmk inverted	†	£180
		ay. Wmk inverted and reversed (1936)	£300	£325
556/69		*Set of* 14	£120	£120

Some stamps from sheets perforated 14×13½ by De La Rue sometimes show the horizontal perforations nearer 13½.

In the 2½d., 5d., 2s. and 3s. perf 13–14×13½ the horizontal perforations of each stamp are in two sizes, one half of each horizontal side measuring 13 and the other 14.

See also Nos. 577/90 and 630/1.

95 Bell Block Aerodrome

96 King George V and Queen Mary

(Des J. Berry. Eng Stamp Printing Office, Melbourne. Recess Govt Printing Office, Wellington)

1935 (4 May). *Air. W* **43**. *P* 14.

570	95	1d. carmine	75	50
		w. Wmk inverted	60·00	40·00
571		3d. violet	4·00	3·00
		w. Wmk inverted	75·00	40·00
572		6d. blue	7·50	2·00
		w. Wmk inverted	85·00	60·00
570/2		*Set of* 3	11·00	5·00

(Frame by J. Berry. Recess B.W.)

1935 (7 May). *Silver Jubilee. W* **43**. *P* 11 × 11½.

573	96	½d. green	75	70
574		1d. carmine	1·25	60
575		6d. red-orange	18·00	20·00
573/5		*Set of* 3	18·00	20·00

97 "The Key to Health"

98 "Multiple Wmk"

(Des S. Hall. Recess John Ash, Melbourne)

1935 (30 Sept). *Health Stamp. W* **43**. *P* 11.

576	97	1d. + 1d. scarlet	2·00	2·50

WATERMARKS. In W **43** the wmk units are in vertical columns widely spaced and the sheet margins are unwatermarked or wmkd "NEW ZEALAND POSTAGE" in large letters.

In W **98** the wmk units are arranged alternately in horizontal rows closely spaced and are continued into the sheet margins.

Stamps with W **98** sideways show the star to the left of NZ, *as seen from the back*. Sideways inverted varieties have the star to right *as seen from the back*.

(Litho Govt Ptg Office, Wellington (9d). Recess Waterlow or D.L.R. (others))

1936–42. *W* **98**.

577	81	½d. bright green, *p* 14×13½	2·50	10
		w. Wmk inverted	4·50	1·50
578	82	1d. scarlet (Die II), *p* 14×13½ (4.36)	2·00	10
		w. Wmk inverted	6·50	2·25
579	83	1½d. red-brown, *p* 14×13½ (6.36)	7·50	4·50
580	84	2d. orange, *p* 14×13½ (3.36)	30	10
		aw. Wmk inverted	80·00	27·00
		b. Perf 12½† (6.41)	3·50	10
		bw. Wmk inverted		
		c. Perf 14 (6.41)	23·00	80
		d. Perf 14×15 (6.41)	38·00	16·00
581	85	2½d. chocolate and slate, *p* 13–14×13½	3·00	12·00
		aw. Wmk inverted	20·00	28·00
		b. Perf 14 (11.36)	3·75	1·25
		bw. Wmk inverted	13·00	16·00
		c. Perf 14×13½ (11.42)	50	3·50

582 **86** 3d. brown, *p* 14×13½ .. .. 30·00 20
w. Wmk inverted .. .. .. 60·00 25·00
583 **87** 4d. black and sepia, *p* 14×13½ .. 4·50 30
aw. Wmk inverted .. .. .. 14·00 7·00
b. Perf 12½* (1941) .. .. 26·00 8·00
bw. Wmk inverted .. .. ..
c. Perf 14, line (1941) .. .. 65·00 90·00
d. Perf 14×14½ comb (7.42) .. 90 10
dw. Wmk inverted .. .. .. 90·00
584 **88** 5d. ultramarine, *p* 13–14×13½ (8.36) 11·00 1·90
aw. Wmk inverted .. .. .. 30·00 13·00
b. Perf 12½*† (7.41) .. .. 20·00 1·75
c. Perf 14×13½ (11.42) .. .. 3·00 65
cw. Wmk inverted .. .. .. 90·00 65·00
585 **89** 6d. scarlet, *p* 13½×14 (8.36) .. 10·00 70
aw. Wmk inverted .. .. .. 35·00 5·00
b. Perf 12½* (10.41) .. .. 3·00 3·25
c. Perf 14½×14 (6.42) 75 10
cw. Wmk inverted .. .. .. £225 60·00
586 **90** 8d. choc, *p* 14×13½ (*wmk sideways*) 9·00 2·50
aw. Wmk sideways inverted .. .. 25·00 8·00
b. Wmk upright (7.39) .. .. 4·00 2·75
bw. Wmk inverted .. .. ..
c. Perf 12½* (*wmk sideways*) (7.41) 3·50 1·50
d. Perf 14×14½ (*wmk sideways*) (7.42) .. .. 3·50 50
dw. Wmk sideways inverted .. .. — 35·00
587 **91** 9d. red and grey, *p* 14×15 (*wmk sideways*) .. .. 40·00 3·25
aw. Wmk sideways inverted .. .. — 75·00
b. Wmk upright. *Red and grey-black*, *p* 13½×14 (1.3.38).. .. 65·00 3·25
bw. Wmk inverted .. .. .. 90·00 24·00
588 **92** 1s. deep green, *p* 14×13½ .. .. 2·50 60
aw. Wmk inverted .. .. .. 55·00 10·00
b. Perf 12½* (11.41) .. .. 65·00 14·00
589 **93** 2s. olive-green, *p* 13–14×13½ (8.36) 30·00 4·00
a. "CAPTAIN COQK" .. .. 55·00
bw. Wmk inverted .. .. .. £100 28·00
c. Perf 13½×14 (3.39) .. .. £250 2·50
ca. "CAPTAIN COQK" £250
d. Perf 12½*† (7.41) .. .. 38·00 6·00
da. "CAPTAIN COQK" .. .. 60·00
e. Perf 14×13½ (10.42) .. .. 10·00 1·50
ea. "CAPTAIN COQK" .. .. 75·00
ew. Wmk inverted .. .. .. — 85·00
590 **94** 3s. chocolate & yell-brn, *p* 13–14×13½ 42·00 6·00
aw. Wmk inverted .. .. .. 65·00 16·00
b. Perf 12½* (1941) .. .. 75·00 48·00
c. Perf 14×13½ (1942) .. .. 5·00 2·00
577/90c .. .. *Set of* 14 95·00 12·50

*†Stamps indicated with an asterisk were printed and perforated by Waterlow; those having a dagger were printed by D.L.R. and perforated by Waterlow. No. 580d was printed by D.L.R. and perforated by Harrison and No. 583c was printed by Waterlow and perforated by D.L.R. These are all known as "Blitz perfs" because De La Rue were unable to maintain supplies after their works were damaged by enemy action. All the rest, except the 9d., were printed and perforated by D.L.R.

On stamps printed and perforated by De La Rue the perf 14×13½ varies in the sheet and is sometimes nearer 13½. 2d. perf 14×15 is sometimes nearer 14×14½.

2½d., 5d., 2s. and 3s. In perf 13–14×13½ one half the length of each horizontal perforation measures 13 and the other 14. In perf 14×13½ the horizontal perforation is regular.

4d. No. 583c. is line-perf measuring 14 exactly and has a blackish sepia frame. No. 583d is a comb-perf measuring 14×14.3 or 14×14.2 and the frame is a warmer shade.

2s. No. 589c is comb-perf and measures 13.5×13.75.

For 9d. typographed, see Nos. 630/1.

99 N.Z. Soldier at Anzac Cove

100 Wool

(Des L. C. Mitchell. Recess John Ash, Melbourne)

1936 (27 Apr). *Charity. 21st Anniv of "Anzac" Landing at Gallipoli. W* **43**. *P* 11.
591 **99** ½d. + ½d. green .. .. .. 40 1·60
592 1d. + 1d. scarlet .. .. .. 40 1·25

(Des L. C. Mitchell. Recess John Ash, Melbourne)

1936 (1 Oct). *Congress of British Empire Chambers of Commerce, Wellington. Industries Issue. T* **100** *and similar horiz designs. W* **43** (*sideways*). *P* 11½.
593 ½d. emerald-green 30 30
594 1d. scarlet 30 20
595 2½d blue .. .. .. 1·00 7·00
596 4d. violet .. .. .. 80 4·75
597 6d. red-brown .. .. .. 1·40 4·00
593/7 .. .. *Set of* 5 3·50 14·50

Designs:—1d. Butter; 2½d. Sheep; 4d. Apples; 6d. Exports.

105 Health Camp

106 King George VI and Queen Elizabeth

(Des J. Berry. Recess John Ash, Melbourne)

1936 (2 Nov). *Health Stamp. W* **43** (*sideways*). *P* 11.
598 **105** 1d. + 1d. scarlet .. .. .. 1·00 3·50

(Recess B.W.)

1937 (13 May). *Coronation. W* **98**. *P* 14 × 13½.
599 **106** 1d. carmine 30 10
600 2½d. Prussian blue .. .. .. 1·25 2·00
601 6d. red-orange .. .. .. 1·75 1·75
599/601 .. .. .. *Set of* 3 3·00 3·25

107 Rock climbing

108 King George VI

108a

(Des G. Bull and J. Berry. Recess John Ash, Melbourne)

1937 (1 Oct). *Health Stamp. W* **43**. *P* 11.
602 **107** 1d. + 1d. scarlet .. .. .. 2·00 2·75

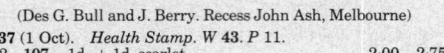

Broken ribbon flaw (R. 6/6 of Pl 8)

(Des W. J. Cooch. Recess B.W.)

1938–44. *W* **98**. *P* 14×13½.
603 **108** ½d. green (1.3.38) .. .. 6·50 10
w. Wmk inverted .. .. 11·00 2·50
604 ½d. orange-brown (10.7.41) .. 20 10
w. Wmk inverted .. .. ..
605 1d. scarlet (1.7.38) .. .. 5·00 10
a. Broken ribbon .. .. 45·00
w. Wmk inverted .. .. 11·00 2·50
606 1d. green (21.7.41) 20 10
w. Wmk inverted .. .. 28·00 18·00
607 **108a** 1½d. purple-brown (26.7.38) .. 26·00 1·60
w. Wmk inverted .. .. 38·00 3·75
608 1½d. scarlet (1.2.44) 20 30
w. Wmk inverted .. .. — 60·00
609 3d. blue (26.9.41) 20 10
w. Wmk inverted .. .. — 45·00
603/9 .. .. .. *Set of* 7 35·00 1·90

For other values see Nos. 680/9.

109 Children playing

110 Beach Ball

(Des J. Berry. Recess B.W.)

1938 (1 Oct). *Health Stamp. W* **98**. *P* 14 × 13½.
610 **109** 1d. + 1d. scarlet .. .. .. 3·50 2·00

(Des S. Hall. Recess Note Printing Branch, Commonwealth Bank of Australia, Melbourne)

1939 (16 Oct). *Health Stamps. Surcharged with new value. W* **43**. *P* 11.
611 **110** 1d. on ½d. + ½d. green .. .. 3·00 3·25
612 2d. on 1d. + 1d. scarlet.. .. .. 3·50 3·25

111 Arrival of the Maoris, 1350

115 Signing Treaty of Waitangi, 1840

(Des L. C. Mitchell (½d., 3d., 4d.); J. Berry (others). Recess B.W.)

1940 (2 Jan–8 Mar). *Centenary of Proclamation of British Sovereignty. T* **111**, **115** *and similar designs. W* **98**. *P* 14 × 13½ (2½d.), 13½ × 14 (5d.) *or* 13½ (*others*).
613 ½d. blue-green 30 10
614 1d. chocolate and scarlet .. .. 2·75 10
615 1½d. light blue and mauve 30 20
616 2d. blue-green and chocolate .. 1·50 10
617 2½d. blue-green and blue .. .. 1·75 55
618 3d. purple and carmine .. .. 3·00 50
619 4d. chocolate and lake .. .. 16·00 90
620 5d. pale blue and brown .. .. 6·00 3·00
621 6d. emerald-green and violet .. 13·00 70
622 7d. black and red .. .. 1·50 3·75
623 8d. black and red (8.3) .. .. 13·00 2·25
624 9d. olive-green and orange .. .. 7·50 1·50
625 1s. sage-green and deep green .. 17·00 3·00
613/25 .. .. .. *Set of* 13 75·00 14·50

Designs: *Horiz* (*as T* **111**)—1d. *Endeavour*, Chart of N.Z., and Capt. Cook; 1½d. British Monarchs; 2d. Tasman with his ship and chart; 3d. Landing of immigrants, 1840; 4d. Road, Rail, Sea and Air Transport; 6d. *Dunedin* and "Frozen Mutton Route" to London; 7d., 8d. Maori council; 9d. Gold mining in 1861 and 1940. (*As T* **115**)—5d. H.M.S. *Britomar* at Akaroa, 1840. *Vert* (*as T* **111**)—1s. Giant Kauri tree.

1940 (1 Oct). *Health Stamps. As T* **110**, *but without extra surcharge. W* **43**. *P* 11.
626 **110** 1d. + ½d. blue-green .. .. 12·00 12·00
627 2d. + 1d. brown-orange .. .. 12·00 12·00

1ᴰ 1ᴰ ■ ■
(**123**)

2ᴰ
Inserted "2"

1941
(**124**)

1941. *Nos.* 603 *and* 607 *surch as T* **123**.
628 **108** 1d. on ½d. green (1.5.41) 80 10
629 **108a** 2d. on 1½d. purple-brown (4.41) .. 80 10
a. Inserted "2" £550 £300

The surcharge on No. 629 has only one figure, at top left, and there is only one square to obliterate the original value at bottom right.

The variety "Inserted 2" occurs on the 10th stamp, 10th row. It is identified by the presence of remnants of the damaged "2", and by the spacing of "2" and "D" which is variable and different from the normal.

(Typo Govt Printing Office, Wellington)

1941. *As T* **91**, *but smaller* (17½×20½ *mm*). *Chalk-surfaced paper*. *P* 14×15. (*a*) *W* **43**.
630 **91** 9d. scarlet and black (5.41) .. .. 90·00 24·00
w. Wmk inverted .. .. .. † —

(*b*) *W* **98**
631 **91** 9d. scarlet and black (29.9.41) .. 3·25 2·25
w. Wmk inverted .. .. .. £120 75·00

1941 (4 Oct). *Health Stamps. Nos.* 626/7 *optd with T* **124**.
632 **110** 1d. + ½d. blue-green .. .. 25 1·75
633 2d. + 1d. brown-orange .. .. 25 1·75

125 Boy and Girl on Swing

126 Princess Margaret

(Des S. Hall. Recess Note Printing Branch, Commonwealth Bank of Australia, Melbourne)

1942 (1 Oct). *Health Stamps. W* **43**. *P* 11.
634 **125** 1d. + ½d. blue-green 15 65
635 2d. + 1d. orange-red 15 60

(Des J. Berry. Recess B.W.)

1943 (1 Oct). *Health Stamps. T* **126** *and similar triangular design. W* **98**. *P* 12.
636 1d. + ½d. green 15 70
a. Imperf between (vert pair) £4750
637 2d. + 1d. red-brown.. .. .. 15 15
a. Imperf between (vert pair) £4750 £4750

Design:—2d. Queen Elizabeth II as Princess.

(**128**)

1944 (1 May). *No.* 615 *surch with T* **128**.
662 10d. on 1½d. light blue and mauve .. 10 10

129 Queen Elizabeth II as Princess and Princess Margaret

130 Statue of Peter Pan, Kensington Gardens

(Recess B.W.)

1944 (9 Oct). *Health Stamps. W* **98**. *P* 13½.
663 **129** 1d. + ½d. green 20 20
664 2d. + 1d. blue 20 20

(Des J. Berry. Recess B.W.)

1945 (1 Oct). *Health Stamps.* *W* **98**. *P* 13½.
665 **130** 1d. + ½d. green and buff 10 15
w. Wmk inverted .. .. .. 50·00 35·00
666 2d. + 1d. carmine and buff 10 15
w. Wmk inverted .. .. .. 60·00 45·00

131 Lake Matheson

132 King George VI and Parliament House, Wellington

133 St. Paul's Cathedral

139 "St. George" (Wellington College War Memorial Window)

Printer's guide mark (R. 12/3)

Completed rudder (R. 2/4 of Pl 42883 and R. 3/2 of Pl 42796)

(Des J. Berry. Photo Harrison (1½d. and 1s.). Recess B.W. (1d. and 2d.) and Waterlow (others))

1946 (1 Apr). *Peace issue. T* **131/3, 139** *and similar designs. W* **98** *(sideways on* 1½*d.). P* 13 *(1d., 2d.),* 14×14½ *(*1½*d., 1s.),* 13½ *(others).*
667 ½d. green and brown 15 20
a. Printer's guide mark .. .. 5·50
w. Wmk inverted .. .. .. 55·00 38·00
668 1d. green 10 10
w. Wmk inverted .. .. .. 38·00 23·00
669 1½d. scarlet 10 10
w. Wmk sideways inverted 10 10
670 2d. purple 15 10
671 3d. ultramarine and grey 30 15
a. Completed rudder .. .. 5·50
672 4d. bronze-green and orange 20 20
w. Wmk inverted .. .. .. 90·00 40·00
673 5d. green and ultramarine 30 40
674 6d. chocolate and vermilion 15 10
675 8d. black and carmine 15 10
676 9d. blue and black 15 10
677 1s. grey-black 15 15
667/77 .. .. .. *Set of* 11 1·60 1·40

Designs: *Horiz (as T* **132**)—2d. The Royal Family. *(As T* **131**) —3d. R.N.Z.A.F. badge and airplanes; 4d. Army badge, tank and plough; 5d. Navy badge, H.M.N.Z.S. *Achilles* (cruiser) and *Dominion Monarch* (liner); 6d. N.Z. coat of arms, foundry and farm; 9d. Southern Alps and Franz Josef Glacier. *Vert (as T* **139**)—1s. National Memorial Campanile.

142 Soldier helping Child over Stile

(Des J. Berry. Recess Waterlow)

1946 (24 Oct). *Health Stamps. W* **98**. *P* 13½.
678 **142** 1d. + ½d. green and orange-brown .. 10 10
a. Yellow-green and orange-brown .. 4·50 5·00
w. Wmk inverted .. .. .. 13·00 13·00
679 2d. + 1d. chocolate and orange-brown 10 10

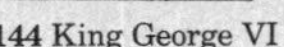
144 King George VI

145 Statue of Eros

Plate 1

Plate 2

(Des W. J. Cooch. Recess T **108a**, B.W.; T **144**, D.L.R.)

1947–52. *W* **98** *(sideways on "shilling" values). (a) P* 14×13½.
680 **108a** 2d. orange 15 10
w. Wmk inverted .. .. .. 80·00
681 4d. bright purple 60 30
682 5d. slate 50 55
683 6d. carmine 40 10
w. Wmk inverted .. .. .. 70·00 14·00
684 8d. violet 65 30
685 9d. purple-brown .. .. .. 1·50 30
w. Wmk inverted .. .. .. 35·00 10·00

(b) P 14
686 **144** 1s. red-brown and carmine (Plate 1) 1·40 60
aw. Wmk sideways inverted .. 12·00 7·50
b. Wmk upright (Plate 1) 50 50
c. Wmk upright (Plate 2) .. .. 2·25 60
cw. Wmk inverted .. .. .. 55·00 20·00
687 1s. 3d. red-brown and blue (Plate 2) 1·00 70
aw. Wmk sideways inverted .. 7·50 5·00
b. Wmk upright (14.1.52) .. .. 2·25 3·25
bw. Wmk inverted .. .. .. †
688 2s. brown-orange and green (Plate 1) 2·75 1·50
aw. Wmk sideways inverted .. 15·00 9·50
b. Wmk upright (Plate 1) .. .. 2·50 4·50
689 3s. red-brown and grey (Plate 2) .. 3·25 3·00
w. Wmk sideways inverted .. 29·00 13·00
680/9 .. .. .. *Set of* 10 10·00 6·50

In head-plate 2 the diagonal lines of the background have been strengthened and result in the upper corners and sides appearing more deeply shaded.

(Des J. Berry. Recess Waterlow)

1947 (1 Oct). *Health Stamps. W* **98** *(sideways). P* 13½.
690 **145** 1d. + ½d. green 10 10
w. Wmk sideways inverted .. .. 25·00 25·00
691 2d. + 1d. carmine 10 10
w. Wmk sideways inverted .. .. 38·00 38·00

146 Port Chalmers, 1848

148 First Church, Dunedin

(Des J. Berry. Recess B.W.)

1948 (23 Feb). *Centennial of Otago. T* **146, 148** *and similar designs. W* **98** *(sideways on 3d.). P* 13½.
692 1d. blue and green 10 20
w. Wmk inverted .. .. .. 30·00 30·00
693 2d. green and brown 10 20
694 3d. purple 15 20
695 6d. black and rose 15 20
w. Wmk inverted .. .. .. – £170
692/5 .. .. .. *Set of* 4 40 70

Designs: *Horiz*—2d. Cromwell, Otago; 6d. University of Otago.

150 Boy Sunbathing and Children Playing

151 Nurse and Child

(Des E. Linzell. Recess B.W.)

1948 (1 Oct). *Health Stamps. W* **98**. *P* 13½.
696 **150** 1d. + ½d. blue and green 10 10
w. Wmk inverted .. .. .. 20·00 20·00
697 2d. + 1d. purple and scarlet 10 10

1949 ROYAL VISIT ISSUE. Four stamps were prepared to commemorate this event: 2d. Treaty House, Waitangi; 3d. H.M.S. *Vanguard*; 5d. Royal portraits; 6d. Crown and sceptre. The visit did not take place and the stamps were destroyed, although a few examples of the 3d. later appeared on the market. A similar set was prepared in 1952, but was, likewise, not issued.

(Des J. Berry. Photo Harrison)

1949 (3 Oct). *Health Stamps. W* **98**. *P* 14 × 14½.
698 **151** 1d. + ½d. green 15 15
699 2d. + 1d. ultramarine 15 15
a. No stop below "D" of "1D." (R.1/2) 6·50 15·00

1½d.

POSTAGE

(**152**)

153 Queen Elizabeth II and Prince Charles

1950 (28 July). *As Type* **F 6**, *but without value, surch with T* **152**. *W* **98** *(inverted). Chalk-surfaced paper. P* 14.
700 **F 6** 1½d. carmine 10 10
w. Wmk upright .. .. .. 2·50 3·00

(Des J. Berry and R. S. Phillips. Photo Harrison)

1950 (2 Oct). *Health Stamps. W* **98**. *P* 14×14½.
701 **153** 1d. +½d. green 15 10
w. Wmk inverted .. .. .. 4·75 4·75
702 2d. +1d. plum 15 10
w. Wmk inverted .. .. .. 16·00 16·00

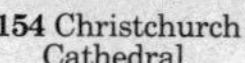
154 Christchurch Cathedral

155 Cairn on Lyttleton Hills

(Des L. C. Mitchell (2d.), J. A. Johnstone (3d.) and J. Berry (others). Recess B.W.)

1950 (20 Nov). *Centennial of Canterbury, N.Z. T* **154/5** *and similar designs. W* **98** *(sideways on 1d. and 3d.). P* 13½.
703 1d. green and blue 15 30
704 2d. carmine and orange 15 30
705 3d. dark blue and blue 20 40
706 6d. brown and blue 20 45
707 1s. reddish purple and blue 20 60
703/7 .. .. .. *Set of* 5 80 1·90

Designs: *Vert (as T* **154**)—3d. John Robert Godley. *Horiz (as T* **155**)—6d. Canterbury University College; 1s. Aerial view of Timaru.

159 "Takapuna" class Yachts

(Des J. Berry and R. S. Phillips. Recess B.W.)

1951 (1 Nov). *Health Stamps. W* **98**. *P* 13½.
708 **159** 1½d. + ½d. scarlet and yellow .. 15 60
709 2d. + 1d. deep green and yellow .. 15 10
w. Wmk inverted .. .. .. 45·00 45·00

160 Princess Anne

161 Prince Charles

3D

(**162**)

(From photographs by Marcus Adams. Photo Harrison)

1952 (1 Oct). *Health Stamps. W* **98**. *P* 14 × 14½.
710 **160** 1½d. + ½d. carmine-red 15 10
711 **161** 2d. + 1d. brown 15 10

1952–53. *Nos. 604 and 606 surch as T* **162**.
712 **108** 1d. on ½d. brown-orange (11.9.53) 20 60
a. "D" omitted .. .. .. † —
713 3d. on 1d. green (12.12.52*) 10 10
*Earliest known date used.

163 Buckingham Palace

164 Queen Elizabeth II

(Des L. C. Mitchell (1s. 6d.), J. Berry (others). Recess D.L.R. (2d., 4d.), Waterlow (1s. 6d.) Photo Harrison (3d., 8d.))

1953 (25 May). *Coronation. T* **163/4** *and similar designs.* **W 98.** *P* 13 (2*d.*, 4*d.*), 13½ (1*s.* 6*d.*) *or* 14 × 14½ (3*d.*, 8*d.*).

714 2d. deep bright blue 30 30
715 3d. brown 30 10
716 4d. carmine .. .. 1·25 2·25
717 8d. slate-grey .. .. 80 1·00
718 1s. 6d. purple and ultramarine .. .. 2·00 2·25
714/18 .. .. *Set of* 5 4·25 5·25

Designs: *Horiz (as T* **163**)—4d. Coronation State Coach; 1s. 6d. St. Edward's Crown and Royal Sceptre. *Vert (as T* **164**)—8d. Westminster Abbey.

168 Girl Guides

169 Boy Scouts

(Des J. Berry. Photo Harrison)

1953 (7 Oct). *Health Stamps.* **W 98.** *P* 14 × 14½.

719 **168** 1½d. + ½d. blue 15 10
720 **169** 2d. + 1d. deep yellow-green 15 30
a. Imperf 3 sides (block of 4) .. £1500

No. 720a shows the left-hand vertical pair imperforate at right and the right-hand pair imperforate at left, top and bottom.

170 Queen Elizabeth II

171 Queen Elizabeth II and Duke of Edinburgh

(Des L. C. Mitchell. Recess Waterlow)

1953 (9 Dec). *Royal Visit.* **W 98.** *P* 13×14 (3*d.*) *or* 13½ (4*d.*).

721 **170** 3d. dull purple 10 10
w. Wmk inverted .. .. — 38·00
722 **171** 4d. deep ultramarine 10 40

172 **173** Queen Elizabeth II **174**

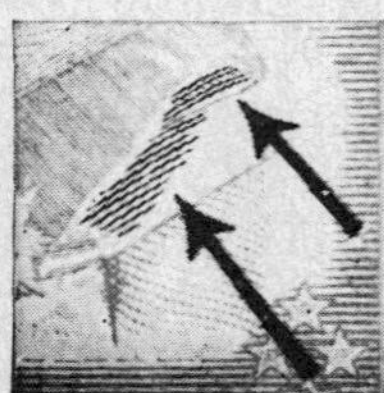

Die I

Die II

(Des L. C. Mitchell (T **172/3**), J. Berry (T **174**). Recess D.L.R. (T **173**), B.W. (others))

1953 (15 Dec)–**59.** **W 98.** *P* 14×13½ (*T* **172**), 14 (*T* **173**) *or* 13½ (*T* **174**).

723 **172** ½d. slate-black (1.3.54) 15 30
724 1d. orange (1.3.54) 15 10
w. Wmk inverted 30 60
725 1½d. brown-lake 20 10
w. Wmk inverted .. .. .. — £300
726 2d. bluish green (1.3.54) 20 10
w. Wmk inverted .. .. .. — £300
727 3d. vermilion (1.3.54) 20 10
w. Wmk inverted 40 60
728 4d. blue (1.3.54) 40 40
729 6d. purple (1.3.54) .. .. .. 70 1·40
w. Wmk inverted £250
730 8d. carmine (1.3.54) 60 60
w. Wmk inverted .. .. .. — £300
731 **173** 9d. brown and bright green (1.3.54) 60 30
w. Wmk inverted £250 £150
732 1s. black & carm-red (Die I) (1.3.54) 65 10
aw. Wmk inverted .. .. .. — £200
b. Die II (1958) .. .. .. 70·00 17·00
733 1s. 6d. black and bright blue (1.3.54) 1·75 50
aw. Wmk inverted £250
733*b* 1s. 9d. black and red-orange (1.7.57) 8·50 1·00
bw. Wmk inverted .. .. .. — £250
c. White opaque paper (2.2.59) .. 7·00 1·00
733*d* **174** 2s. 6d. brown (1.7.57) .. .. 27·00 7·50
734 3s. bluish green (1.3.54) .. .. 12·00 30
w. Wmk inverted .. .. .. — £300
735 5s. carmine (1.3.54) .. .. .. 20·00 3·25
736 10s. deep ultramarine (1.3.54) .. 45·00 16·00
723/36 .. .. *Set of* 16 £100 28·00

1s. Dies I and II. The two dies of the Queen's portrait differ in the shading on the sleeve at right. The long lines running upwards from left to right are strong in Die I and weaker in Die II. In the upper part of the shading the fine cross-hatching is visible in Die I only between the middle two of the four long lines, but in Die II it extends clearly across all four lines.

In the lower part of the shading the strength of the long lines in Die I makes the cross-hatching appear subdued, whereas in Die II the weaker long lines make the cross-hatching more prominent.

Centre plates 1A, 1B and 2B are Die I; 3A and 3B are Die II.

For stamps as T **172** but with larger figures of value see Nos. 745/51.

WHITE OPAQUE PAPER. A new white opaque paper first came into use in August 1958. It is slightly thicker than the paper previously used, but obviously different in colour (white, against cream) and opacity (the previous paper being *relatively* transparent).

175 Young Climber and Mts Aspiring and Everest

(Des J. Berry. Recess; vignette litho B.W.)

1954 (4 Oct). *Health Stamps.* **W 98.** *P* 13½.

737 **175** 1½d. + ½d. sepia and deep violet .. 15 20
738 2d. + 1d. sepia and blue-black .. 15 20

176 Maori Mail-carrier

177 Queen Elizabeth II

178 Douglas DC-3 Airliner

(Des R. M. Conly (2d.), J. Berry (3d.), A. G. Mitchell (4d.). Recess D.L.R.)

1955 (18 July). *Centenary of First New Zealand Postage Stamps.* **W 98.** *P* 14 (2*d.*), 14 × 14½ (3*d.*) *or* 13 (4*d.*).

739 **176** 2d. sepia and deep green 10 10
w. Wmk inverted .. .. .. — £100
740 **177** 3d. brown-red 10 10
741 **178** 4d. black and bright blue 25 55
739/41 .. .. *Set of* 3 40 65

179 Children's Health Camps Federation Emblem

180

(Des E. M. Taylor. Recess B.W.)

1955 (3 Oct). *Health Stamps.* **W 98** (*sideways*). *P* 13½ × 13.

742 **179** 1½d. + ½d. sepia and orange-brown .. 10 35
743 2d. + 1d. red-brown and green .. 10 15
744 3d. + 1d. sepia and deep rose-red .. 15 10
a. Centre omitted .. .. ..
742/4 .. .. *Set of* 3 30 55

1955–59. *As Nos.* 724/30 *but larger figures of value with stars omitted from lower right corner and new colour* (8*d.*).

745 **180** 1d. orange (12.7.56) 50 10
aw. Wmk inverted .. .. .. 1·25 1·00
b. White opaque paper (2.6.59) .. 50 10
bw. Wmk inverted 80 80
746 1½d. brown-lake (1.12.55) 60 60
747 2d. bluish green (19.3.56) 40 10
a. White opaque paper (10.11.59) .. 55 10
748 **180** 3d. vermilion (1.5.56) .. .. 1·50 60
aw. Wmk inverted .. .. .. 1·50 80
b. White opaque paper (20.6.59) .. 75 10
bw. Wmk inverted .. .. .. 1·75 1·25
749 4d. blue (3.2.58) .. .. .. 1·50 55
a. White opaque paper (9.9.59) .. 2·00 70
750 6d. purple (20.10.55) .. .. .. 9·50 10
751 8d. chestnut (*white opaque paper*) (1.12.59) .. .. .. 6·50 7·00
745/51 .. .. *Set of* 7 18·00 7·50

See note *re* white opaque paper after No. 736.

181 "The Whalers of Foveaux Strait"

183 Takahe

(Des E. R. Leeming (2d.), L. C. Mitchell (3d.), M. R. Smith (8d.). Recess D.L.R.)

1956 (16 Jan). *Southland Centennial. T* **181, 183** *and similar design.* **W 98.** *P* 13½ × 13 (8*d.*) *or* 13 × 12½ (*others*).

752 2d. deep blue-green 30 15
753 3d. sepia 10 10
w. Wmk inverted .. .. — 80·00
754 8d. slate-violet and rose-red .. .. 1·10 1·25
752/4 .. .. *Set of* 3 1·25 1·25

Design: *Horiz*—3d. "Farming".

184 Children picking Apples

(Des L. C. Mitchell, after photo by J. F. Louden. Recess B.W.)

1956 (24 Sept). *Health Stamps.* **W 98.** *P* 13 × 13½.

755 **184** 1½d. + ½d. purple-brown 15 40
a. *Blackish brown* .. .. 75 6·00
756 2d. + 1d. blue-green 15 30
757 3d. + 1d. claret 15 15
755/7 .. .. *Set of* 3 40 75

185 New Zealand Lamb and Map

186 Lamb, *Dunedin* and *Port Brisbane* (refrigerated freighter)

(Des M. Goaman. Photo Harrison)

1957 (15 Feb). *75th Anniv of First Export of N.Z. Lamb.* **W 98** (*sideways inverted on* 4*d.*). *P* 14×14½ (4*d.*) *or* 14½×14 (8*d.*).

758 **185** 4d. blue 40 90
w. Wmk sideways .. .. .. 8·00 12·00
759 **186** 8d. deep orange-red .. .. .. 60 1·00

187 Sir Truby King

(Des M. R. Smith. Recess B.W.)

1957 (14 May). *50th Anniv of Plunket Society.* **W 98.** *P* 13.

760 **187** 3d. bright carmine-red 10 10
w. Wmk inverted .. .. .. 65·00

188 Life-savers in Action

189 Children on Seashore

(Des L. Cutten (2d.), L. C. Mitchell (3d.). Recess Waterlow)

1957 (25 Sept). *Health Stamps.* **W 98** (*sideways*). *P* 13½.

761 **188** 2d. + 1d. black and emerald 15 40
762 **189** 3d. + 1d. ultramarine and rose-red .. 15 10
MS762*b* Two sheets each 112 × 96 mm with Nos. 761 and 762 in blocks of 6 (2 × 3) .. *Per pair* 12·00 19·00
MS762*c* As last but with wmk upright *Per pair* 16·00 40·00

2d

(190)

191 Girls' Life Brigade Cadet

192 Boys' Brigade Bugler

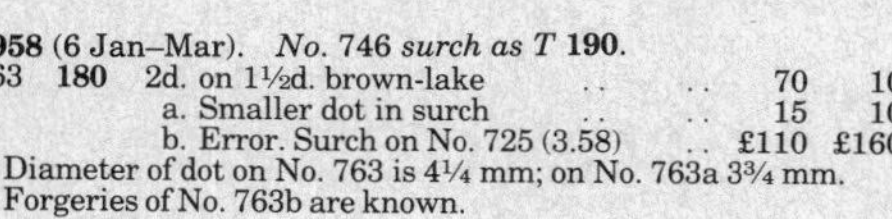

1958 (6 Jan–Mar). *No. 746 surch as T* **190**.
763 **180** 2d. on 1½d. brown-lake 70 10
a. Smaller dot in surch 15 10
b. Error. Surch on No. 725 (3.58) .. £110 £160
Diameter of dot on No. 763 is 4¼ mm; on No. 763a 3¾ mm.
Forgeries of No. 763b are known.

(Des J. Berry. Photo Harrison)

1958 (20 Aug). *Health Stamps. W* **98**. *P* 14 × 14½.
764 **191** 2d. + 1d. green 20 25
765 **192** 3d. + 1d. blue 20 25
MS765*a* Two sheets each 104 × 124 mm with Nos. 764/5 in blocks of 6 (3 × 2) .. .. *Per pair* 14·00 12·00

193 Sir Charles Kingsford-Smith and Fokker F.VIIa/3m *Southern Cross*

194 Seal of Nelson

(Des J. E. Lyle. Eng F. D. Manley. Recess Commonwealth Bank of Australia Note Ptg Branch)

1958 (27 Aug). *30th Anniv of First Air Crossing of the Tasman Sea. W* **98** *(sideways). P* 14 × 14½.
766 **193** 6d. deep ultramarine 30 40

(Des M. J. Macdonald. Recess B.W.)

1958 (29 Sept). *Centenary of City of Nelson. W* **98**. *P* 13½×13.
767 **194** 3d. carmine 10 10

195 "Pania" Statue, Napier

196 Australian Gannets on Cape Kidnappers

(Des M. R. Smith (2d.), J. Berry (3d.), L. C. Mitchell (8d.). Photo Harrison)

1958 (3 Nov). *Centenary of Hawke's Bay Province. T* **195/6** *and similar design. W* **98** *(sideways on 3d.). P* 14½×14 *(3d.) or* 13½×14½ *(others)*.
768 2d. yellow-green 10 10
769 3d. blue 20 10
770 8d. red-brown .. .. 55 1·25
768/70 .. .. *Set of* 3 75 1·25
Design:—*Vert* 8d. Maori sheep-shearer.

197 "Kiwi" Jamboree Badge

198 Careening H.M.S. *Endeavour* at Ship Cove

(Des Mrs. S. M. Collins. Recess B.W.)

1959 (5 Jan). *Pan-Pacific Scout Jamboree, Auckland. W* **98**. *P* 13½×13.
771 **197** 3d. sepia and carmine 20 10

(Des G. R. Bull and G. R. Smith. Photo Harrison)

1959 (2 Mar). *Centenary of Marlborough Province. T* **198** *and similar horiz designs. W* **98** *(sideways). P* 14½ × 14.
772 2d. green 30 10
773 3d. deep blue 30 10
774 8d. light brown .. .. 1·00 1·75
772/4 .. .. *Set of* 3 1·40 1·75
Designs:—3d. Shipping wool, Wairau Bar, 1857; 8d. Salt industry, Grassmere.

201 Red Cross Flag

(Photo Harrison)

1959 (3 June). *Red Cross Commemoration. W* **98** *(sideways). P* 14½ × 14.
775 **201** 3d. + 1d. red and ultramarine 20 10
a. Red Cross omitted £1100

202 Grey Teal

203 New Zealand Stilt

(Des Display Section, G.P.O. Photo Harrison)

1959 (16 Sept). *Health Stamps. W* **98** *(sideways). P* 14×14½.
776 **202** 2d. + 1d. greenish yellow, ol & rose-red 40 40
777 **203** 3d. + 1d. black, pink and light blue .. 40 40
a. Pink omitted £100
bw. Wmk sideways inverted .. .. 16·00 16·00
MS777*c* Two sheets, each 95×109 mm. with Nos. 776/7 in blocks of 6 (3×2) .. .. *Per pair* 6·50 15·00

204 "The Explorer"

205 "The Gold Digger"

(Des G. R. Bull and G. R. Smith. Photo Harrison)

1960 (16 May). *Centenary of Westland Province. T* **204/5** *and similar vert design. W* **98**. *P* 14 × 14½.
778 2d. deep dull green 20 10
779 3d. orange-red 20 10
780 8d. grey-black .. .. 60 2·50
778/80 .. .. *Set of* 3 90 2·50
Design:—8d. "The Pioneer Woman".

207 Manuka (Tea Tree)

214 National Flag

216 Rainbow Trout

219 Taniwha (Maori Rock Drawing)

220 Butter Making

221 Tongariro National Park and Château

221*a* Tongariro National Park and Château

(Des Harrison (½d.), G. F. Fuller (1d., 3d., 6d.), A. G. Mitchell (2d., 4d., 5d., 8d., 3s., 10s., £1), P.O. Public Relations Division (7d.), P.O. Publicity Section (9d.), J. Berry (1s., 1s. 6d.), R. E. Barwick (1s. 3d.), J. C. Boyd (1s. 9d.), D. F. Kee (2s.), L. C. Mitchell (2s. 6d., 5s.). Photo D.L.R. (½d., 1d., 2d., 3d., 4d., 6d., 8d.) or Harrison (others))

1960 (11 July)–**66**. *T* **207**, **214**, **216**, **219/21***a* *and similar designs. Chalk-surfaced paper* (2½*d.*, 5*d.*, 7*d.*, 1*s.* 9*d.* (*No.* 795), 3*s.* (*No.* 799). *W* **98** (*sideways on* 5*d.*, 1*s.* 3*d.*, 1*s.* 6*d.*, 2*s.* 6*d.*, 3*s. and* 10*s. or sideways inverted* (2½*d.*)). *P* 14×14½ (1*s.* 3*d.*, 1*s.* 6*d.*, 2*s.*, 5*s.*, £1) *or* 14½×14 (*others*).
781 **207** ½d. grey, green and cerise (1.9.60) 10 10
a. Grey omitted .. .. .. 80·00
b. Green omitted £140
782 – 1d. orge, green, lake & brn (1.9.60) 10 10
a. Orange omitted £200
b. Coil. Perf 14½×13. Wmk sideways (11.63) .. .. 1·25 2·50
c. Chalk-surfaced paper (1965?) 10 60
783 – 2d. carmine, black, yellow & green 10 10
a. Black omitted £200
b. Yellow omitted £250
784 – 2½d. red, yellow, blk & grn (1.11.61) 70 10
a. Red omitted £350
b. Yellow omitted £120
c. Green omitted £140
d. Red and green omitted .. £450
w. Wmk sideways .. .. — 40·00
785 – 3d. yellow, green, yellow-brown and deep greenish blue (1.9.60) .. 30 10
a. Yellow omitted £110
b. Green omitted £110
c. Yellow-brown omitted .. £110
e. Coil. Perf 14½×13. Wmk sideways (3.10.63) .. .. 1·25 2·25
f. Chalk-surfaced paper (1965?) 30 80
786 – 4d. purple, buff, yellow-green & lt bl 40 10
a. Purple omitted £200
b. Buff omitted £250
d. Chalk-surfaced paper (1965?) £550 10·00
787 – 5d. yell, dp grn, blk & vio (14.5.62) 85 10
a. Yellow omitted £190
w. Wmk sideways inverted .. — 45·00
788 – 6d. lilac, green and deep bluish green (1.9.60) 60 10
a. No wmk .. .. .. 30·00
ab. Lilac omitted £190
ac. Green omitted £170
c. Chalk-surfaced paper (1966?) 65 2·50
788*d* – 7d. red, green, yellow and pale red (16.3.66) .. .. .. 35 1·00
dw. Wmk inverted .. .. 3·50 4·50
789 – 8d. rose-red, yellow, green and grey (1.9.60) 40 10
790 **214** 9d. red and ultramarine (1.9.60) .. 40 10
a. Red omitted £275
791 – 1s. brown and deep green .. 30 10
792 **216** 1s. 3d. carmine, sepia & bright blue 3·25 50
a. Carmine omitted £300
b. Carmine, sepia and greyish blue 1·50 10
w. Wmk sideways inverted .. £200 £110
793 – 1s. 6d. olive-green & orange-brown 80 10
794 – 1s. 9d. bistre-brown .. .. 18·00 15
795 – 1s. 9d. orange-red, blue, green and yellow (4.11.63) .. .. 8·50 75
a. Wmk sideways £375
w. Wmk inverted £500
796 **219** 2s. black and orange-buff .. 3·50 10
a. Chalk-surfaced paper (1966) .. 2·25 2·25
797 **220** 2s. 6d. yellow and light brown .. 1·75 85
a. Yellow omitted £350
798 **221** 3s. blackish brown .. .. 40·00 65
799 **221***a* 3s. bistre, blue and green (1.4.64) 6·50 1·75
w. Wmk sideways inverted .. 28·00 30·00
800 – 5s. blackish green .. .. 5·50 80
a. Chalk-surfaced paper (1966) .. 2·25 4·75
801 – 10s. steel-blue .. .. .. 9·00 3·00
a. Chalk-surfaced paper (1966) .. 4·50 11·00
802 – £1 deep magenta .. .. .. 13·00 6·00
781/802 .. .. *Set of* 23 90·00 13·00
Designs: *Vert* (*as T* **207**)—1d. Karaka; 2d. Kowhai Ngutu–kaka (Kaka Beak); 2½d. Titoki; 3d. Kowhai; 4d. Puarangi (Hibiscus); 5d. Matua Tikumu (Mountain Daisy); 6d. Pikiarero (Clematis); 7d. Koromiko; 8d. Rata. (*As T* **216**)—1s. 6d. Tiki. (*As T* **219**)—5s. Sutherland Falls; £1 Pohutu Geyser. *Horiz* (*as T* **214**)—1s. Timber industry—1s. 9d. Aerial top dressing. (*As T* **221**)—10s. Tasman Glacier.
Nos. 782b and 785e were replaced by coils with upright watermark perf 14½ × 14 in 1966.

CHALKY PAPER. The chalk-surfaced paper is not only whiter but also thicker, making the watermark difficult to see. Examples of the 4d. value can be found on a thick surfaced paper. These should not be confused with the rare chalk-surfaced printing, No. 786d, which can be identified by its positive reaction to the silver test.

225 Sacred Kingfisher

226 New Zealand Pigeon

(Des Display Section, G.P.O. Recess B.W.)

1960 (10 Aug). *Health Stamps. W* **98**. *P* 13½.
803 **225** 2d. + 1d. sepia and turquoise-blue .. 75 50
804 **226** 3d. + 1d. deep purple-brown and orange 75 50
MS804*b* Two sheets each 95 × 107 mm with Nos. 803 and 804 in blocks of 6. *P* 11½ × 11 *Per pair* 30·00 32·00

227 "The Adoration of the Shepherds" (Rembrandt)

(Photo Harrison)

1960 (1 Nov). *Christmas.* W **98**. P 12.
805 **227** 2d. red and deep brown/*cream* 15 10
a. Red omitted.. .. .. .. £225

228 Great Egret

229 New Zealand Falcon

(Des Display Section, G.P.O. Recess B.W.)

1961 (2 Aug). *Health Stamps.* W **98**. P 13½.
806 **228** 2d. + 1d. black and purple 50 50
807 **229** 3d. + 1d. deep sepia and yellow-green 50 50
MS807*a* Two sheets each 97 × 121 mm with Nos. 806/7 in blocks of 6 (3 × 2) .. *Per pair* 25·00 25·00

2½d

(**230**)

2½d

(**231**)

232 "Adoration of the Magi" (Dürer)

1961 (1 Sept). *No.* 748 *surch with T* **230** (*wide setting*).
808 **180** 2½d. on 3d. vermilion 15 15
a. Narrow setting (T **231**) 15 15
b. Pair, wide and narrow .. .. 16·00 26·00
The difference in the settings is in the overall width of the new value, caused by two different spacings between the "2", "½" and "d".

(Photo Harrison)

1961 (16 Oct). *Christmas.* W **98** (*sideways*). P 14½×14.
809 **232** 2½d. multicoloured 10 10
w. Wmk sideways inverted .. 45·00 14·00

233 Morse Key and Port Hills, Lyttleton

(Des A. G. Mitchell (3d.) and L. C. Mitchell (8d.). Photo Harrison)

1962 (1 June). *Telegraph Centenary.* T **233** *and similar horiz design.* W **98** (*sideways*). P 14½ × 14.
810 3d. sepia and bluish green 10 10
a. Bluish green omitted £475
811 8d. black and brown-red 45 55
a. Imperf (pair) £900
b. Black omitted £400
Design:—8d. Modern teleprinter.
No. 811a comes from a sheet with the two top rows imperforate and the third row imperforate on three sides.

235 Red-fronted Parakeet

236 Tieke Saddleback

(Des Display Section, G.P.O. Photo D.L.R.)

1963 (3 Oct). *Health Stamps.* W **98**. P 15×14.
812 **235** 2½d. + 1d. multicoloured 40 40
a. Orange omitted .. ..
b. Printed on the gummed side .. £250
w. Wmk inverted .. .. 48·00 65·00
813 **236** 3d. + 1d. multicoloured 40 40
a. Orange omitted £1100
MS813*b* Two sheets, each 96×101 mm with Nos. 812/13 in blocks of 6 (3×2) .. .. *Per pair* 45·00 50·00
No. 812b comes from a miniature sheet.

237 "Madonna in Prayer" (Sassoferrato)

(Photo Harrison)

1962 (15 Oct). *Christmas.* W **98**. P 14½ × 14.
814 **237** 2½d. multicoloured 10 10

238 Prince Andrew **239**

(Design after photographs by Studio Lisa, London. Recess D.L.R.)

1963 (7 Aug). *Health Stamps.* W **98**. P 14.
815 **238** 2½d. + 1d. dull ultramarine .. 30 50
a. Ultramarine 40 60
b. Deep blue 30 40
816 **239** 3d. + 1d. carmine 30 10
MS816*a* Two sheets each 93×100 mm with Nos. 815/16 in blocks of 6 (3 × 2) .. *Per pair* 26·00 27·00

240 "The Holy Family" (Titian)

(Photo Harrison)

1963 (14 Oct). *Christmas.* W **98** (*sideways*). P 12½.
817 **240** 2½d. multicoloured 10 10
a. Imperf (pair) £200
b. Yellow omitted £250
w. Wmk sideways inverted .. 40 40

241 Steam Locomotive *Pilgrim* and "DG" Diesel Electric Loco

242 Diesel Express and Mt Ruapehu

(Des Commercial Art Section, N.Z. Railways. Photo D.L.R.)

1963 (25 Nov). *Railway Centenary.* W **98** (*sideways*). P 14.
818 **241** 3d. multicoloured 40 10
a. Blue (sky) omitted £275
819 **242** 1s. 9d. multicoloured .. .. .. 2·25 1·50
a. Red (value) omitted £1000

243 "Commonwealth Cable"

(Des P. Morriss. Photo Note Printing Branch, Reserve Bank of Australia)

1963 (3 Dec). *Opening of COMPAC (Trans-Pacific Telephone Cable). No wmk.* P 13½.
820 **243** 8d. red, blue and yellow .. .. .. 50 1·25

244 Road Map and Car Steering-wheel

245 Silver Gulls

(Des L. C. Mitchell. Photo Harrison)

1964 (1 May). *Road Safety Campaign.* W **98**. P 15 × 14.
821 **244** 3d. black, ochre-yellow and blue .. 20 10

(Des Display Section G.P.O., after Miss T. Kelly. Photo Harrison)

1964 (5 Aug). *Health Stamps.* T **245** *and similar horiz design. Multicoloured.* W **98**. P 14½.
822 2½d. + 1d. Type **245** 30 20
a. Red (beak and legs) omitted £160
w. Wmk inverted .. .. .. † £225
823 3d. + 1d. Little Penguin 30 20
aw. Wmk inverted £100
MS823*b* Two sheets each 171×84 mm with Nos 822/3 in blocks of 8 (4×2) .. .. *Per pair* 48·00 48·00
bw. Wmk inverted (No. 823 only) ..

246 Rev. S. Marsden taking first Christian service at Rangihoua Bay, 1814

7D
POSTAGE

(**247**)

(Des L. C. Mitchell. Photo Harrison)

1964 (12 Oct). *Christmas.* W **98** (*sideways*). P 14 × 13½.
824 **246** 2½d. multicoloured 10 10

1964 (14 Dec). *As Type* F **6**, *but without value, surch with T* **247**. W **98**. *Unsurfaced paper.* P 14 × 13½.
825 F **6** 7d. carmine-red 60 90

248 Anzac Cove

(Des R. M. Conly. Photo Harrison)

1965 (14 Apr). *50th Anniv of Gallipoli Landing.* T **248** *and similar horiz design.* W **98**. P 12½.
826 4d. yellow-brown 10 10
827 5d. green and red 10 30
Design:—5d. Anzac Cove and poppy.

249 I.T.U. Emblem and Symbols

250 Sir Winston Churchill

(Photo Harrison)

1965 (17 May). *I.T.U. Centenary.* W **98**. P 14½×14.
828 **249** 9d. blue and pale chocolate 40 35

(Des P. Morriss from photograph by Karsh. Photo Note Ptg Branch, Reserve Bank of Australia)

1965 (24 May). *Churchill Commemoration.* P 13½.
829 **250** 7d. black, pale grey and light blue .. 15 50

251 Wellington Provincial Council Building

(Des from painting by L. B. Temple (1867). Photo Harrison)

1965 (26 July). *Centenary of Government in Wellington.* W **98** (*sideways*). P 14½ × 14.
830 **251** 4d. multicoloured 10 10

252 Kaka

253 Collared Grey Fantail (after Miss T. Kelly)

(Des Display Section, G.P.O. Photo Harrison)

1965 (4 Aug). *Health Stamps. W* **98**. *P* 14×14½.

831 **252** 3d. + 1d. multicoloured 30 20
w. Wmk inverted .. .. ..
832 **253** 4d. + 1d. multicoloured 30 20
a. Green ("POSTAGE HEALTH" and on leaves) omitted £275
MS832*b* Two sheets each 100×109 mm with Nos. 831/2 in blocks of 6 (3×2) .. .. *Per pair* 40·00 50·00
bw. Wmk inverted (No. 831 only) ..

254 I.C.Y. Emblem

255 "The Two Trinities" (Murillo)

(Litho D.L.R.)

1965 (28 Sept). *International Co-operation Year. W* **98** *(sideways). P* 14.

833 **254** 4d. carmine-red and light yellow-olive 15 10
w. Wmk sideways inverted .. .. 4·00 1·75

(Photo Harrison)

1965 (11 Oct). *Christmas. W* **98**. *P* 13½ × 14.

834 **255** 3d. multicoloured 10 10
a. Gold (frame) omitted £600

256 Arms of New Zealand

259 "Progress" Arrowhead

(Des Display Section, G.P.O. Photo D.L.R.)

1965 (30 Nov). *11th Commonwealth Parliamentary Conference. T* **256** *and similar horiz designs. Multicoloured. P* 14.

835 4d. Type **256** 25 20
a. Blue (incl value) omitted £350
b. Printed on the gummed side .. ..
836 9d. Parliament House, Wellington and Badge .. .. 55 1·25
837 2s. Wellington from Mt Victoria .. .. 4·00 5·50
a. Carmine omitted £325
835/7 .. .. *Set of* 3 4·25 6·25

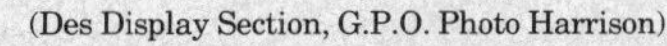

(Des Display Section, G.P.O. Photo Harrison)

1966 (5 Jan). *Fourth National Scout Jamboree, Trentham. W* **98**. *P* 14 × 15.

838 **259** 4d. gold and myrtle-green 10 10
a. Gold (arrowhead) omitted .. £475

260 New Zealand Bell Bird

262 "The Virgin with Child" (Maratta)

(Des Display Section, G.P.O. Photo Harrison)

1966 (3 Aug). *Health Stamps. T* **260** *and similar vert design. Multicoloured. W* **98** *(sideways). P* 14 × 14½.

839 3d. + 1d. Type **260** 30 40
w. Wmk sideways inverted .. .. 80·00
840 4d. + 1d. Weka Rail 30 40
a. Deep brown (values and date) omitted £1000
w. Wmk sideways inverted .. .. 50·00
MS841 Two sheets each 107×91 mm. Nos. 839/40 in blocks of 6 (3×2) .. .. *Per pair* 20·00 45·00

In No. 840a besides the value, "1966" and "Weka" are also omitted and the bird, etc. appears as light brown.

(Photo Harrison)

1966 (3 Oct). *Christmas. W* **98** *(sideways). P* 14½.

842 **262** 3d. multicoloured 10 10
a. Red omitted £150

263 Queen Victoria and Queen Elizabeth II

264 Half-sovereign of 1867 and Commemorative Dollar Coin

(Des Display Section, G.P.O. Photo Harrison)

1967 (3 Feb). *Centenary of New Zealand Post Office Savings Bank. W* **98** *(sideways on 4d.). P* 14 × 14½.

843 **263** 4d. black, gold and maroon 10 10
w. Wmk sideways inverted .. .. 45·00 16·00
844 **264** 9d. gold, silver, black, lt blue & dp grn 10 20
w. Wmk inverted .. .. ..

(New Currency. 100 cents = 1 New Zealand Dollar)

265 Manuka (Tea Tree)

266 Pohutu Geyser

1967 (10 July). *Decimal Currency. Designs as 1960–66 issue, but with values inscr in decimal currency as T* **265/6**. *Chalky paper. W* **98** *(sideways on 8 c., 10 c., 20 c., 50 c. and $2). P 13½×14 (½ c. to 3 c., 5 c. and 7 c.), 14½×14 (4 c., 6 c., 8 c., 10 c., 25 c. and $1) or 14×14½ (15 c., 20 c., 50 c. and $2).*

845 **265** ½ c. pale blue, yellow-green & cerise 10 10
846 – 1 c. yellow, carmine, green and light brown (as 1d.) 10 10
a. Booklet pane. Five stamps plus one printed label .. .. 2·25
847 – 2 c. carmine, black, yellow, and green (as 2d.) 10 10
848 – 2½ c. yellow, green, yellow-brown, and deep bluish green (as 3d.) .. 10 10
a. Deep bluish green omitted* .. £475
b. Imperf (pair)† £100
849 – 3 c. purple, buff, yellow-green and light greenish blue (as 4d.) .. 10 10
850 – 4 c. yellow, deep green, black and violet (as 5d.) 30 10
851 – 5 c. lilac, yellow-olive and bluish green (as 6d.) 65 10
852 – 6 c. red, green, yell & lt pink (as 7d.) 70 20
853 – 7 c. rose-red, yell, grn & grey (as 8d.) 85 20
w. Wmk inverted .. .. ..
854 **214** 8 c. red and ultramarine 85 10
a. Red omitted £325
855 – 10 c. brown and deep green (as 1s.) 90 10
w. Wmk sideways inverted .. ..
856 – 15 c. olive-grn & orge-brn (as 1s. 6d.) 80 60
w. Wmk inverted .. .. .. 6·00 7·50
857 **219** 20 c. black and buff .. .. .. 2·50 10
858 **220** 25 c. yellow and light brown .. .. 4·25 1·75
859 **221a** 30 c. olive-yellow, green & greenish bl 4·00 25
w. Wmk inverted .. .. .. 90·00 42·00
860 – 50 c. blackish green (as 5s.) .. .. 4·25 75
861 – $1 Prussian blue (as 10s.) .. .. 16·00 1·25
w. Wmk inverted £170 £100
862 **266** $2 deep magenta .. .. .. 9·00 12·00
845/62 .. .. *Set of* 18 38·00 15·00

*This occurred on one horizontal row of ten, affecting the background colour so that the value is also missing. In the row above and the row below, the colour was partially omitted. The price is for a vertical strip.

The 2½ c. value has been seen with the yellow omitted, but only on a used example.

†This comes from a sheet of which the six right-hand vertical rows were completely imperforate and the top, bottom and left-hand margins had been removed.

The 4 c., 30 c. and 50 c. exist with PVA gum as well as gum arabic. No. 859a exists with PVA gum only.

For $4 to $10 in the "Arms" type, see under Postage Fiscal stamps.

For other versions of 15 c., 30 c., and $2 see Nos. 870/9.

268 Running with Ball

(Des L. C. Mitchell. Photo Harrison)

1967 (2 Aug). *Health Stamps. Rugby Football. T* **268** *and similar multicoloured design. W* **98** *(sideways on 2½ c.). P 14½ × 14 (2½ c.) or 14 × 14½ (3 c.).*

867 2½ c. + 1 c. Type **268** 15 10
868 3 c. + 1 c. Positioning for a place-kick (*horiz*) 15 10
MS869 Two sheets; (*a*) 76 × 130 mm (867); (*b*) 130 × 76 mm (868). Containing blocks of six .. .. *Per pair* 23·00 35·00

270 *Kaita* (trawler) and Catch

271 Brown Trout

276 Dairy Farm, Mt Egmont and Butter Consignment

277 Fox Glacier, Westland National Park

(Des Display Section, G.P.O. (7, 8, 10, 18, 20, 25 c. and 28 c. from photo), R. M. Conly (7½ c.). Litho B.W. (7, 8, 18, 20 c.) or photo D.L.R. (7½ c.) and Harrison (10, 25, 28 c.). Others (15 c., 30 c., $2) as before)

1967–70. *T* **270/1**, **276/7** *and similar designs. Chalky paper (except 7, 8, 18, 20 c.). No wmk (7, 8, 20, 30 c.) or W* **98** *(sideways inverted on 7½ c., sideways on 10, 15, 25 c., upright on 18, 28 c., $2). P 13½ (7, 7½ c.), 13×13½ (8, 18, 20 c.), 14½×14 (10, 25, 30 c.) or 14×14½ (15, 28 c., $2).*

870 **270** 7 c. multicoloured (3.12.69) .. 1·50 90
871 **271** 7½ c. multicoloured* (29.8.67) .. 30 70
a. Wmk upright (10.68) .. 50 90
872 – 8 c. multicoloured (8.7.69) .. 75 70
873 – 10 c. multicoloured (2.4.68) .. 50 10
a. Green (background) omitted £375
w. Wmk sideways inverted .. † —
874 – 15 c. apple-green, myrtle-green and carm (as No. 856†) (19.3.68) 1·25 70
w. Wmk sideways inverted ..
875 – 18 c. multicoloured (8.7.69) .. 1·40 55
a. Printed on the gummed side
876 – 20 c. multicoloured (8.7.69) .. 1·40 20
877 **276** 25 c. multicoloured (10.12.68) .. 4·50 2·00
878 **277** 28 c. multicoloured (30.7.68) .. 60 10
aw. Wmk inverted .. ..
878*b* **221a** 30 c. olive-green, green & greenish blue (as No. 859) (2.6.70) .. 3·50 3·75
879 **266** $2 black, ochre and pale blue (as No. 862) (10.12.68) .. 27·00 19·00
870/9 .. .. *Set of* 11 38·00 25·00

Designs: *Horiz*—8 c. Apples and orchard; 10 c. Forest and timber; 18 c. Sheep and the "Woolmark"; 20 c. Consignments of beef and herd of cattle.

*No. 871 was originally issued to commemorate the introduction of the brown trout into New Zealand.

† No. 874 is slightly larger than No. 856, measuring 21 × 25 mm and the inscriptions and numerals differ in size.

278 "The Adoration of the Shepherds" (Poussin)

279 Mount Aspiring, Aurora Australis and Southern Cross

280 Sir James Hector (founder)

(Photo Harrison)

1967 (3 Oct). *Christmas. W* **98** *(sideways). P* 13½ × 14.

880 **278** 2½ c. multicoloured 10 10

(Des J. Berry. Litho D.L.R.)

1967 (10 Oct). *Centenary of the Royal Society of New Zealand. W* **98** *(sideways on 4 c.). P* 14 (4 c) *or* 13 × 14 (8 c.).

881	**279**	4 c. multicoloured	25	20
		w. Wmk sideways inverted	7·50	7·00
882	**280**	8 c. multicoloured	25	60

281 Open Bible

282 Soldiers and Tank

(Des Display Section, G.P.O. Litho D.L.R.)

1968 (23 Apr). *Centenary of Maori Bible. W* **98**. *P* 13½.

883	**281**	3 c. multicoloured	10	10
		a. Gold (inscr etc.) omitted	£140	
		w. Wmk inverted	27·00	

(Des L. C. Mitchell. Litho D.L.R.)

1968 (7 May). *New Zealand Armed Forces. T* **282** *and similar horiz designs. Multicoloured. W* **98** *(sideways). P* 14 × 13½.

884	4 c. Type **282**	30	15
	w. Wmk sideways inverted	9·00	11·00
885	10 c. Airmen, Fairey Firefly and English Electric Canberra aircraft	50	60
886	28 c. Sailors and H.M.N.Z.S. *Achilles*, 1939, and H.M.N.Z.S. *Waikato*, 1968 ..	70	2·00
	w. Wmk sideways inverted	5·00	7·50
884/6	.. .. *Set of* 3	1·40	2·50

285 Boy breasting Tape, and Olympic Rings

287 Placing Votes in Ballot Box

(Des L. C. Mitchell. Photo Harrison)

1968 (7 Aug). *Health Stamps. T* **285** *and similar horiz design. Multicoloured. P* 14½ × 14.

887	2½ c. + 1 c. Type **285**	20	15
888	3 c. + 1 c. Girl swimming and Olympic rings	20	15
	a. Red (ring) omitted	£800	
	b. Blue (ring) omitted	£425	
MS889	Two sheets each 145×95 mm. Nos. 887/8 in blocks of six .. .. .. *Per pair*	15·00	38·00

No. 888a occurred in one miniature sheet. Six examples are known, one being used. No. 888b occurred from a second miniature sheet.

(Des J. Berry. Photo Japanese Govt Ptg Bureau, Tokyo)

1968 (19 Sept). *75th Anniv of Universal Suffrage in New Zealand. P* 13.

890	**287**	3 c. ochre, olive-green and light blue ..	10	10

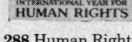

288 Human Rights Emblem

289 "Adoration of the Holy Child" (G. van Honthorst)

(Photo Japanese Govt Ptg Bureau, Tokyo)

1968 (19 Sept). *Human Rights Year. P* 13.

891	**288**	10 c. scarlet, yellow and deep green ..	10	30

(Photo Harrison)

1968 (1 Oct). *Christmas. W* **98** *(sideways). P* 14 × 14½.

892	**289**	2½ c. multicoloured	10	10

290 I.L.O. Emblem

(Photo Harrison)

1969 (11 Feb). *50th Anniv of International Labour Organization. W* **98** *(sideways). P* 14½ × 14.

893	**290**	7 c. black and carmine-red	15	30

291 Supreme Court Building, Auckland

292 Law Society's Coat of Arms

(Des R. M. Conly. Litho B.W.)

1969 (8 Apr). *Centenary of New Zealand Law Society. T* **291/2** *and similar design. P* 13½ × 13 (3 c.) *or* 13 × 13½ *(others)*.

894	3 c. multicoloured *(shades)*	10	10
895	10 c. multicoloured	35	55
896	18 c. multicoloured *(shades)*	45	1·00
894/6	.. .. *Set of* 3	80	1·50

Design:—*Vert*—18 c. "Justice" (from Memorial Window in University of Canterbury, Christchurch).

295 Student being conferred with Degree

(Des R. M. Conly. Litho B.W.)

1969 (3 June). *Centenary of Otago University T* **295** *and similar multicoloured design. P* 13 × 13½ (3 c.) *or* 13½ × 13 (10 c.).

897	3 c. Otago University *(vert)*	10	10
898	10 c. Type **295**	20	25

296 Boys playing Cricket

298 Dr. Elizabeth Gunn (founder of First Children's Health Camp)

(Des R. M. Conly (4 c.); L. C. Mitchell (others). Litho B.W.)

1969 (6 Aug). *Health Stamps. T* **296** *and similar horiz design and T* **298**. *P* 12½ × 13 *(No. 901) or* 13 × 12½ *(others)*.

899	2½ c. + 1 c. multicoloured	40	50
900	3 c. + 1 c. multicoloured	40	50
901	4 c. + 1 c. brown and ultramarine ..	40	1·75
899/901	.. .. .. *Set of* 3	1·10	2·50
MS902	Two sheets each 144 × 84 mm. Nos. 899/900 in blocks of six .. .. *Per pair*	20·00	48·00

Design:—3 c. Girls playing cricket.

299 Oldest existing House in New Zealand, and Old Stone Mission Store, Kerikeri

(Litho D.L.R.)

1969 (18 Aug). *Early European Settlement in New Zealand, and 150th Anniv of Kerikeri. T* **299** *and similar horiz design. Multicoloured. W* **98** *(sideways). P* 13 × 13½.

903	4 c. Type **299**	20	25
904	6 c. View of Bay of Islands	30	1·75

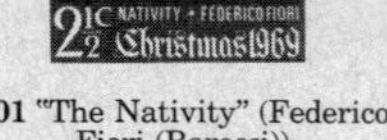

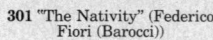

301 "The Nativity" (Federico Fiori (Barocci))

302 Captain Cook, Transit of Venus and "Octant"

(Photo Harrison)

1969 (1 Oct). *Christmas. P* 13×14. A. *W* **98**. B. *No wmk.*

			A		B	
905	**301**	2½ c. multicoloured ..	10	10	10	15

(Des Eileen Mayo. Photo; portraits embossed Harrison)

1969 (9 Oct). *Bicentenary of Captain Cook's Landing in New Zealand. T* **302** *and similar horiz designs. P* 14½ × 14.

906	4 c. black, cerise and blue	1·00	35
907	6 c. slate-green, purple-brown & black ..	1·25	2·75
908	18 c. purple-brown, slate-green & black	2·75	2·75
909	28 c. cerise, black and blue	4·50	4·75
906/9	.. .. .. *Set of* 4	8·50	9·50
MS910	109 × 90 mm. Nos. 906/9	18·00	32·00

Designs:—6 c. Sir Joseph Banks (naturalist) and outline of H.M.S. *Endeavour*; 18 c. Dr. Daniel Solander (botanist) and his plant; 28 c. Queen Elizabeth II and Cook's chart, 1769.

The miniature sheet exists additionally inscribed on the selvedge at bottom. "A SOUVENIR FROM NEW ZEALAND STAMP EXHIBITION, NEW PLYMOUTH 6TH–11TH OCTOBER. 1969". These were not sold from Post Offices.

306 Girl, Wheat Field and C.O.R.S.O. Emblem

307 Mother feeding her Child, Dairy Herd and C.O.R.S.O. Emblem

(Des L. C. Mitchell. Photo Japanese Govt Printing Bureau, Tokyo)

1969 (18 Nov). *25th Anniv of C.O.R.S.O. (Council of Organizations for Relief Services Overseas). P* 13.

911	**306**	7 c. multicoloured	55	1·25
912	**307**	8 c. multicoloured	55	1·25

308 "Cardigan Bay" (champion trotter)

(Des L. C. Mitchell. Photo Courvoisier)

1970 (28 Jan). *Return of "Cardigan Bay" to New Zealand. P* 11½.

913	**308**	10 c. multicoloured	30	30

309 *Vanessa gonerilla* (butterfly)

310 Queen Elizabeth II and New Zealand Coat of Arms

(Des Enid Hunter (½ c., 1 c., 2 c., 18 c., 20 c.), Eileen Mayo (2½ c. to 7 c.), D. B. Stevenson (7½ c., 8 c.), M. Cleverley (10 c., 15 c., 25 c., 30 c., $1, $2), M. V. Askew (23 c., 50 c.). Photo Harrison (½ c. to 20 c.), Enschedé (23 c., 50 c.), Courvoisier ($1, $2) or Litho B.W. (25 c., 30 c.))

1970 (12 Mar)–**76**. *Various designs at T* **309/10**. *W* **98** *(sideways on 10 c., or sideways inverted on 15 c., 20 c.) or No wmk (23 c. to $2).*

(a) Size as T **309**. *P* 13½×13

914	½ c. multicoloured (2.9.70)	10	20
	w. Wmk inverted	—	£110
915	1 c. multicoloured (2.9.70)	10	10
	aw. Wmk inverted	40·00	27·00
	b. Wmk sideways inverted (booklets) (6.7.71)	80	1·50
	ba. Booklet pane. No. 915b×3 with three *se-tenant* printed labels	2·25	
916	2 c. multicoloured (2.9.70)	10	10
	a. Black (inscr, etc) omitted	£200	
	w. Wmk inverted	2·75	1·50
917	2½ c. multicoloured (2.9.70)	40	10
918	3 c. black, brown and orange (2.9.70) ..	15	10
	aw. Wmk inverted	2·50	2·75
	b. Wmk sideways inverted (booklets) (6.7.71)	55	1·25
	bw. Wmk sideways	24·00	24·00
919	4 c. multicoloured (2.9.70)	15	10
	aw. Wmk inverted	3·00	1·75
	b. Wmk sideways inverted (booklets) (6.7.71)	55	1·25
	bw. Wmk sideways	70·00	60·00
920	5 c. multicoloured (4.11.70)	45	10
	w. Wmk inverted		
921	6 c. blackish grn, yell-grn & carm (4.11.70)	45	20
922	7 c. multicoloured (4.11.70)	55	45
	w. Wmk inverted	—	50·00
923	7½ c. multicoloured (4.11.70)	1·00	1·50
	w. Wmk inverted		
924	8 c. multicoloured (4.11.70)	65	60

(b) Size as T **310**. *Various Perfs*

925	10 c. multicoloured (*p* 14½×14)	40	15
	w. Wmk sideways inverted	6·00	3·00
926	15 c. black, flesh & pale brown (*p* 13½×13) (20.1.71)	1·50	50
	w. Wmk sideways	35·00	27·00

927 18 c. chestnut, blk & apple-grn (*p* 13×13½)
(20.1.71) .. .. 1·50 40
w. Wmk inverted .. .. 35·00 25·00
928 20 c. black & yell-brn (*p* 13½×13) (20.1.71) 1·50 15
929 23 c. multicoloured (*p* 13½×12½) (1.12.71) 80 30
930 25 c. multicoloured (*p* 13×13½) (1.9.71) .. 1·50 40
b. Perf 14 (11.76?) 70 40
ba. Printed on the gummed side .. £400
931 30 c. multicoloured (*p* 13×13½) (1.9.71) .. 1·25 15
a. Perf 14 (9.76?) .. .. 1·75 2·00
932 50 c. multicoloured (*p* 13½×12½) (1.9.71) 80 20
a. Apple green (hill) omitted .. .. 28·00
b. Buff (shore) omitted .. .. .. 55·00
933 $1 multicoloured (*p* 11½) (14.4.71) .. 2·25 85
934 $2 multicoloured (*p* 11½) (14.4.71) .. 3·75 1·25
914/34 .. .. *Set of* 21 17·00 6·75

Designs: *Vert*—½ c. *Lycaena salustius* (butterfly); 2 c. *Argyrophenga antipodum* (butterfly); 2½ c. *Nyctemera annulata* (moth); 3 c. *Detunda egregia* (moth); 4 c. *Charagia virescens* (moth); 5 c. Scarlet Wrasse ("Scarlet Parrot Fish"); 6 c. Big-bellied Sea Horses; 7 c. Leather-jacket (fish); 7½ c. Intermediate Halfbeak ("Garfish"); 8 c. John Dory (fish); 18 c. Maori club; 25 c. Hauraki Gulf Maritime Park; 30 c. Mt Cook National Park. *Horiz*—10 c. Type **310**: 15 c. Maori fish hook; 20 c. Maori tattoo pattern; 23 c. Egmont National Park; 50 c. Abel Tasman National Park; $1 Geothermal Power; $2 Agricultural Technology.

Although issued as a definitive No. 925 was put on sale on the occasion of the Royal Visit to New Zealand.

See also Nos. 1008, etc.

311 Geyser Restaurant

312 U.N. H.Q. Building

(Des M. Cleverley. Photo Japanese Govt Printing Bureau, Tokyo)

1970 (8 Apr). *World Fair, Osaka. T* **311** *and similar horiz designs. Multicoloured. P* 13.
935 7 c. Type **311** .. .. 40 1·00
936 8 c. New Zealand Pavilion .. .. .. 40 1·00
937 18 c. Bush Walk .. .. 60 1·00
935/7 .. .. *Set of* 3 1·25 2·75

(Des R. M. Conly (3 c.), L. C. Mitchell (10 c.). Litho D.L.R.)

1970 (24 June). *25th Anniv of United Nations. T* **312** *and similar vert design. P* 13½.
938 3 c. multicoloured 10 10
939 10 c. scarlet and yellow 20 20
Design:—10 c. Tractor on horizon.

313 Soccer

(Des L. C. Mitchell. Litho D.L.R.)

1970 (5 Aug). *Health Stamps. T* **313** *and similar multicoloured design. P* 13½.
940 2½ c. + 1 c. Netball (*vert*) 20 40
941 3 c. + 1 c. Type **313** 20 40
MS942 Two sheets: (a) 102×125 mm (940); (b) 125×102 mm (941), containing blocks of six
Per pair 17·00 38·00

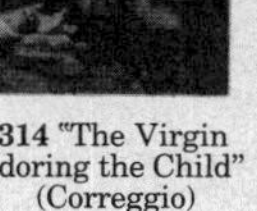

314 "The Virgin adoring the Child" (Correggio)

315 "The Holy Family" (stained glass window, Invercargill Presbyterian Church)

(Litho D.L.R.)

1970 (1 Oct). *Christmas. T* **314/15** *and similar design. P* 12½.
943 2½ c. multicoloured 10 10
944 3 c. multicoloured 10 10
a. Green (inscr and value) omitted .. £225
945 10 c. black, orange and silver 30 75
943/5 .. .. *Set of* 3 35 75

Design: *Horiz*—10 c. Tower of Roman Catholic Church, Sockburn.

No. 943 exists as an imperforate proof with the country inscription and face value omitted.

316 Chatham Islands Lily

(Des Eileen Mayo. Photo Japanese Govt Printing Bureau, Tokyo)

1970 (2 Dec). *Chatham Islands. T* **316** *and similar horiz design. Multicoloured. P* 13.
946 1 c. Type **316** 10 25
947 2 c. Shy Albatross 30 35

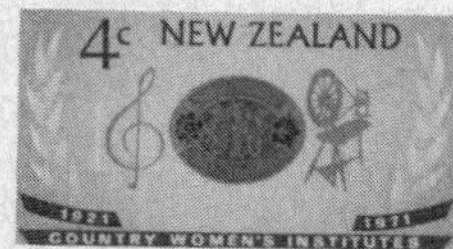

317 Country Women's Institute Emblem

(Des L. C. Mitchell. Photo Japanese Govt Ptg Bureau, Tokyo)

1971 (10 Feb). *50th Anniversaries of Country Women's Institutes and Rotary International in New Zealand. T* **317** *and similar horiz design. Multicoloured. P* 13.
948 4 c. Type **317** 10 10
949 10 c. Rotary emblem and map of New Zealand 10 30

318 *Rainbow II* (yacht)

(Des J. Berry (5 c.), G. F. Fuller (8 c.). Litho B.W.)

1971 (3 Mar). *One Ton Cup Racing Trophy. T* **318** *and similar horiz design. Multicoloured. P* 13½ × 13.
950 5 c. Type **318** 20 25
951 8 c. One Ton Cup .. .. 30 1·00

319 Civic Arms of Palmerston North

(Des R. M. Conly. Photo Japanese Govt Ptg Bureau, Tokyo)

1971 (12 May). *City Centenaries. T* **319** *and similar horiz designs. Multicoloured. P* 13.
952 3 c. Type **319** 10 10
953 4 c. Arms of Auckland 10 10
954 5 c. Arms of Invercargill 15 60
952/4 .. .. *Set of* 3 30 70

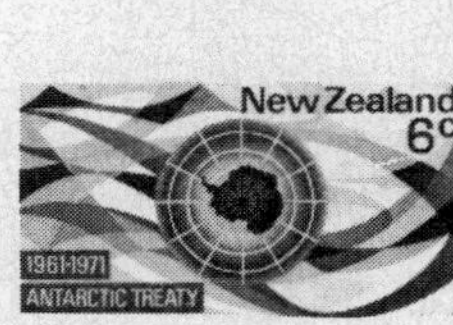

320 Antarctica on Globe

321 Child on Swing

(Des Eileen Mayo. Photo Japanese Govt Ptg Bureau, Tokyo)

1971 (9 June). *Tenth Anniv of Antarctic Treaty. P* 13.
955 **320** 6 c. multicoloured .. .. 1·00 1·00

(Des Eileen Mayo. Photo Japanese Govt Ptg Bureau, Tokyo)

1971 (9 June). *25th Anniv of U.N.I.C.E.F. P* 13.
956 **321** 7 c. multicoloured 50 70

4c 4c 4c

= = =

(**322**) (**322***a*) (**322***b*)

T **322**. Photo, showing screening dots; thin bars, wide apart.
T **322***a*. Typo, without screening dots; thick bars, closer together.
T **322***b*. Typo; bars similar to T **322**.

1971–73. *No.* 917 *surcharged.*

(*a*) *In photogravure, by Harrison* (23.6.71*)
957 **322** 4 c. on 2½ c. multicoloured 15 10

(*b*) *Typographically, by Harrison* (13.7.72*)
957*a* **322***a* 4 c. on 2½ c. multicoloured 45 10
ab. Albino surch £110
ac. Surch double, one albino .. .. 15·00

(*c*) *Typographically, locally* (18.6.73*)
957*b* **322***b* 4 c. on 2½ c. multicoloured 15 10
*Earliest known postmarks.

323 Satellite-tracking Aerial

(Des M. Cleverley. Photo Courvoisier)

1971 (14 July). *Opening of Satellite Earth Station. T* **323** *and similar horiz design. P* 11½.
958 8 c. black, drab-grey and vermilion .. .. 60 1·25
959 10 c. black, turquoise-grn & pale bluish vio .. 65 1·00
Design:—10 c. Satellite.

324 Girls playing Hockey

(Des L. C. Mitchell. Litho Harrison)

1971 (4 Aug). *Health Stamps. T* **324** *and similar horiz designs. Multicoloured. W* **98** (*sideways on* 5 c.). *P* 13½ × 13.
960 3 c. + 1 c. Type **324** 45 50
961 4 c. + 1 c. Boys playing hockey 45 50
962 5 c. + 1 c. Dental Health .. .. .. 1·10 2·00
960/2 .. .. *Set of* 3 1·75 2·75
MS963 Two sheets, each 122×96 mm. Nos. 960/1 in blocks of six .. .. *Per pair* 19·00 38·00

325 "Madonna bending over the Crib" (Maratta)

326 "Tiffany" Rose

(Des Enid Hunter (10 c.), D. A. Hatcher (others). Photo Harrison)

1971 (6 Oct). *Christmas. T* **325** *and similar vert designs. Multicoloured. P* 13 × 13½.
964 3 c. Type **325** 10 10
965 4 c. "The Annunciation" (stained-glass window) (21½ × 38 *mm*) 10 10
966 10 c. "The Three Kings" (21½ × 38 *mm*) .. 70 1·25
964/6 .. .. *Set of* 3 80 1·25

(Des A. G. Mitchell. Photo Courvoisier)

1971 (3 Nov). *First World Rose Convention, Hamilton. T* **326** *and similar vert designs showing roses. Multicoloured. P* 11½.
967 2 c. Type **326** 15 30
968 5 c. "Peace" 35 35
969 8 c. "Chrysler Imperial" .. .. 60 1·10
967/9 .. .. *Set of* 3 1·00 1·60

327 Lord Rutherford and Alpha Particles

328 Benz (1895)

(Des M. Cleverley. Litho B.W.)

1971 (1 Dec). *Birth Centenary of Lord Rutherford (scientist). T* **327** *and similar horiz design. Multicoloured. P* 13½ × 13.
970 1 c. Type **327** 25 40
971 7 c. Lord Rutherford and formula .. .. 85 1·40

(Des A. G. Mitchell. Litho B.W.)

1972 (2 Feb). *International Vintage Car Rally. T* **328** *and similar horiz designs. Multicoloured. P* 14.
972 3 c. Type **328** 20 10
973 4 c. Oldsmobile (1904) 25 10
974 5 c. Ford "Model T" (1914) 25 10
975 6 c. Cadillac Service car (1915) 40 45
976 8 c. Chrysler (1924) .. .. 1·00 1·60
977 10 c. Austin "7" (1923) .. .. 1·00 1·40
972/7 .. .. *Set of* 6 2·75 3·25

329 Coat of Arms of Wanganui　**330** Black Scree Cotula

(Des M. Cleverley. Litho Harrison)

1972 (5 Apr). *Anniversaries. T* **329** *and similar designs. P* 13 × 13½ (3, 5 *and* 8 c.) *or* 13½ × 13 (*others*).

No.	Description		
978	3 c. multicoloured	15	10
979	4 c. red-orange, brown-bistre and black	15	10
980	5 c. multicoloured	25	10
981	8 c. multicoloured	90	1·40
982	10 c. multicoloured	90	1·40
978/82	*Set of* 5	2·10	2·75

Designs and Events: *Vert*—3 c. Type **329** (centenary of Wanganui Council govt); 5 c. De Havilland D.H.89 Dragon Rapide and Boeing 737 (25th anniv of National Airways Corp); 8 c. French frigate and Maori palisade (bicent of landing by Marion du Fresne). *Horiz*—4 c. Postal Union symbol (10th anniv of Asian-Oceanic Postal Union); 10 c. Stone cairn (150th anniv of New Zealand Methodist Church).

(Des Eileen Mayo. Litho Harrison)

1972 (7 June). *Alpine Plants. T* **330** *and similar vert designs. Multicoloured. P* 13½.

No.	Description		
983	4 c. Type **330**	30	10
984	6 c. North Island Edelweiss	60	60
985	8 c. Haast's Buttercup	90	1·25
986	10 c. Brown Mountain Daisy	1·25	1·75
983/6	*Set of* 4	2·75	3·25

331 Boy playing Tennis

332 "Madonna with Child" (Murillo)

(Des L. C. Mitchell. Litho Harrison)

1972 (2 Aug). *Health Stamps. T* **331** *and similar vert design. P* 13 × 13½.

No.	Description		
987	3 c. + 1 c. light grey and chestnut	30	45
988	4 c. + 1 c. light red-brown, grey and lemon	30	45
MS989	Two sheets each 107 × 123 mm. Nos. 987/8 in blocks of six *Per pair*	18·00	35·00

Design:—No. 988, Girl playing tennis.

(Des D. A. Hatcher. Photo Courvoisier)

1972 (4 Oct). *Christmas. T* **332** *and similar vert designs. Multicoloured. P* 11½.

No.	Description		
990	3 c. Type **332**	10	10
991	5 c. "The Last Supper" (stained-glass window, St. John's Church, Levin)	15	10
992	10 c. Pohutukawa flower	55	1·00
990/2	*Set of* 3	70	1·00

333 Lake Waikaremoana

334 Old Pollen Street

(Des D. A. Hatcher. Photo Courvoisier)

1972 (6 Dec). *Lake Scenes. T* **333** *and similar vert designs. Multicoloured. P* 11½.

No.	Description		
993	6 c. Type **333**	1·00	1·25
994	8 c. Lake Hayes	1·10	1·25
995	18 c. Lake Wakatipu	1·50	2·25
996	23 c. Lake Rotomahana	1·75	2·75
993/6	*Set of* 4	4·75	6·75

(Des Miss V. Jepsen (3 c.), B. Langford (others). Litho Harrison)

1973 (7 Feb). *Commemorations. T* **334** *and similar horiz designs. Multicoloured* (*except* 8 c.). *P* 13½ × 13.

No.	Description		
997	3 c. Type **334**	10	10
998	4 c. Coal-mining and pasture	15	10
999	5 c. Cloister	15	15
1000	6 c. Forest, birds and lake	60	80
1001	8 c. Rowers (light grey, indigo and gold)	50	80
1002	10 c. Graph and people	70	1·25
997/1002	*Set of* 6	2·00	2·75

Events:—3 c. Centennial of Thames Borough; 4 c. Centennial of Westport Borough; 5 c. Centennial of Canterbury University; 6 c. 50th Anniv of Royal Forest and Bird Protection Society; 8 c. Success of N.Z. Rowers in 1972 Olympics; 10 c. 25th Anniv of E.C.A.F.E.

335 Class "W" Locomotive

336 "Maori Woman and Child"

(Des R. M. Conly. Litho Harrison)

1973 (4 Apr). *New Zealand Steam Locomotives. T* **335** *and similar horiz designs. Multicoloured. P* 14 × 14½.

No.	Description		
1003	3 c. Type **335**	40	10
1004	4 c. Class "X"	40	10
1005	5 c. Class "Ab"	40	10
1006	10 c. Class "Ja"	2·25	1·75
1003/6	*Set of* 4	3·00	1·75

1973–76. *As Nos.* 915 *etc., but no wmk.*

No.	Description		
1008	1 c. multicoloured (7.9.73)	90	1·10
	a. Booklet pane. No. 1008 × 3 with three *se-tenant* printed labels (8.74)	2·40	
	b. Red (wing markings) omitted	£180	
	c. Blue (spots on wings) omitted	£120	
1009	2 c. multicoloured (6.73?)	30	10
1010	3 c. black, light brown and orange (1974)	2·25	1·50
1011	4 c. multicoloured (7.9.73)	70	10
	a. Bright green (wing veins) inverted	£325	
	b. Purple-brown omitted	£190	
	c. Orange-yellow omitted	£250	
	d. Greenish blue (background) omitted	£200	
	e. Bright green (wing veins) omitted	6·00	
	f. Apple green (wings) omitted	£180	
1012	5 c. multicoloured (1973)	2·00	1·75
1013	6 c. blackish green, yellow-green and rose-carmine (7.9.73)	40	30
	a. Yellow-grn (part of sea horse) omitted	£200	
1014	7 c. multicoloured (1974)	3·75	2·50
1015	8 c. multicoloured (1974)	5·00	1·50
	a. Blue-green (background) omitted	£300	
1017	10 c. multicoloured, *p* 13½×13 (6.73?)	1·00	10
	a. Silver (Arms) omitted	£130	
	b. Imperf (vert pair)	£190	
	c. Deep blue (Queen's head, face value etc.) omitted	£225	
	d. Red (hair ribbon) omitted	17·00	
1018	15 c. black, flesh & pale brown, *p* 13½×13 (2.8.76)	2·25	10
1019	18 c. chestnut, black & apple-green (1974)	1·00	1·10
	a. Black (inscr, etc.) omitted	£190	
1020	20 c. black and yellow-brown (1974)	80	40
1008/20	*Set of* 12	18·00	9·00

(Des and photo Courvoisier)

1973 (6 June). *Paintings by Frances Hodgkins. T* **336** *and similar vert designs. Multicoloured. P* 11½.

No.	Description		
1027	5 c. Type **336**	40	15
1028	8 c. "Hilltop"	60	75
1029	10 c. "Barn in Picardy"	80	1·25
1030	18 c. "Self Portrait Still Life"	1·25	2·50
1027/30	*Set of* 4	2·75	4·25

337 Prince Edward

338 "Tempi Madonna" (Raphael)

(Des and litho Harrison)

1973 (1 Aug). *Health Stamps. P* 13 × 13½.

No.	Description		
1031	**337** 3 c. + 1 c. dull yellowish green and reddish brown	30	30
1032	4 c. + 1 c. rose-red and blackish brown	30	30
MS1033	Two sheets each 96 × 121 mm with Nos. 1031/2 in blocks of 6 (3 × 2) *Per pair*	16·00	30·00

(Des A. G. Mitchell. Photo Enschedé)

1973 (3 Oct). *Christmas. T* **338** *and similar vert designs. Multicoloured. P* 12½ × 13½.

No.	Description		
1034	3 c. Type **338**	10	10
1035	5 c. "Three Kings" (stained-glass window, St. Theresa's Church, Auckland)	10	10
1036	10 c. Family entering church	25	50
1034/6	*Set of* 3	40	50

339 Mitre Peak　**340** Hurdling

(Des D. A. Hatcher. Photo Enschedé)

1973 (5 Dec). *Mountain Scenery. T* **339** *and similar multicoloured designs. P* 13 × 13½ (6, 8 c.) *or* 13½ × 13 (*others*).

No.	Description		
1037	6 c. Type **339**	70	80
1038	8 c. Mt Ngauruhoe	80	1·25
1039	18 c. Mt Sefton (*horiz*)	1·40	2·50
1040	23 c. Burnett Range (*horiz*)	1·50	2·75
1037/40	*Set of* 4	4·00	6·50

(Des M. Cleverley. Litho Harrison)

1974 (9 Jan). *Tenth British Commonwealth Games, Christchurch. T* **340** *and similar vert designs.* 5 c. *black and violet-blue, others multicoloured. P* 13 × 14.

No.	Description		
1041	4 c. Type **340**	10	10
1042	5 c. Ball-player	15	10
1043	10 c. Cycling	20	15
1044	18 c. Rifle-shooting	25	50
1045	23 c. Bowls	35	70
1041/5	*Set of* 5	85	1·40

No. 1042 does not show the Games emblem, and commemorates the Fourth Paraplegic Games, held at Dunedin.

341 Queen Elizabeth II

342 "Spirit of Napier" Fountain

(Des D. A. Hatcher and A. G. Mitchell. Litho Harrison)

1974 (5 Feb). *New Zealand Day. Sheet* 131 × 74 mm. *containing T* **341** *and similar horiz designs, size* 37 × 20 *mm. Multicoloured. P* 13.

No.	Description		
MS1046	4 c. × 5 Treaty House, Waitangi; Signing Waitangi Treaty; Type **341**; Parliament Buildings Extensions; Children in Class	70	2·25

(Des Miss V. Jepsen. Photo Courvoisier)

1974 (3 Apr). *Centenaries of Napier and U.P.U. T* **342** *and similar vert designs. Multicoloured. P* 11½.

No.	Description		
1047	4 c. Type **342**	10	10
1048	5 c. Clock Tower, Berne	15	25
1049	8 c. U.P.U. Monument, Berne	65	1·40
1047/9	*Set of* 3	80	1·60

343 Boeing Seaplane, 1919　**344** Children, Cat and Dog

(Des R. M. Conly. Litho Harrison)

1974 (5 June). *History of New Zealand Airmail Transport. T* **343** *and similar horiz designs. Multicoloured. P* 14 × 13.

No.	Description		
1050	3 c. Type **343**	30	10
1051	4 c. Lockheed 10 Electra *Kauha*, 1937	35	10
1052	5 c. Bristol Type 170 Freighter Mk 31, 1958	40	30
1053	23 c. Short S.30 modified "G" Class flying-boat *Aotearoa*, 1940	1·75	2·50
1050/3	*Set of* 4	2·50	2·75

(Des B. Langford. Litho Harrison)

1974 (7 Aug). *Health Stamps. P* 13 × 13½.

No.	Description		
1054	**344** 3 c. + 1 c. multicoloured	20	35
1055	— 4 c. + 1 c. multicoloured	25	35
1056	— 5 c. + 1 c. multicoloured	1·00	1·50
1054/6	*Set of* 3	1·25	2·00
MS1057	145 × 123 mm. No. 1055 in block of ten	21·00	32·00

Nos. 1055/6 are as T **344**, showing children and pets.

345 "The Adoration" of the Magi" (Konrad Witz)

346 Great Barrier Island

(Des Eileen Mayo. Photo Courvoisier)

1974 (2 Oct). *Christmas. T* **345** *and similar horiz designs. Multicoloured. P* 11½.
1058 3 c. Type **345** 10 10
1059 5 c. "The Angel Window" (stained-glass window, Old St. Pauls Church, Wellington) 10 10
1060 10 c. Madonna Lily 30 60
1058/60 .. .. *Set of* 3 40 65

(Des D. A. Hatcher. Photo Enschedé)

1974 (4 Dec). *Off-shore Islands. T* **346** *and similar horiz designs. Multicoloured. P* 13½ × 13.
1061 6 c. Type **346** 30 40
1062 8 c. Stewart Island .. .. 50 1·25
1063 18 c. White Island .. .. 70 1·25
1064 23 c. The Brothers .. .. 75 1·50
1061/4 .. .. *Set of* 4 2·00 4·00

347 Crippled Child

(Des Miss V. Jepsen (3 c., 5 c.), A. G. Mitchell (10 c., 18 c.). Litho Harrison)

1975 (5 Feb). *Anniversaries and Events. T* **347** *and similar horiz designs. Multicoloured. P* 13½.
1065 3 c. Type **347** 10 10
1066 5 c. Farming family 15 10
1067 10 c. I.W.Y. symbols 20 65
1068 18 c. Medical School Building, Otago University .. .. 55 1·25
1065/8 .. .. *Set of* 4 90 1·75

Commemorations:—3 c. 40th Anniv of N.Z. Crippled Children Society; 5 c. 50th Anniv of Women's Division, Federated Farmers of N.Z.; 10 c. International Women's Year; 18 c. Centenary of Otago Medical School.

348 Scow *Lake Erie*

(Des R. M. Conly. Litho Harrison)

1975 (2 Apr). *Historic Sailing Ships. T* **348** *and similar horiz designs. P* 13½ × 13.
1069 4 c. black and red 30 10
1070 5 c. black and turquoise-blue 30 10
1071 8 c. black and yellow 55 60
1072 10 c. black and olive-yellow 60 60
1073 18 c. black and light brown .. .. .. 1·00 1·50
1074 23 c. black and slate-lilac .. .. .. 1·10 1·50
1069/74 .. .. *Set of* 6 3·50 3·75

Ships:—5 c. Schooner *Herald*; 8 c. Brigantine *New Zealander*; 10 c. Topsail schooner *Jessie Kelly*; 18 c. Barque *Tory*; 23 c. Full-rigged clipper *Rangitiki*.

349 Lake Sumner Forest Park

(Des and photo Enschedé)

1975 (4 June). *Forest Park Scenes. T* **349** *and similar horiz designs. Multicoloured. P* 13.
1075 6 c. Type **349** 50 70
1076 8 c. North-west Nelson .. .. 60 1·00
1077 18 c. Kaweka .. .. 1·00 1·75
1078 23 c. Coromandel .. .. 1·25 2·00
1075/8 .. .. *Set of* 4 3·00 5·00

COVER PRICES

Cover factors are quoted at the beginning of each country for most issues to 1945. An explanation of the system can be found on page x. The factors quoted do not, however, apply to philatelic covers.

350 Girl feeding Lamb

351 "Virgin and Child" (Zanobi Machiavelli)

(Des Margaret Chapman. Litho Harrison)

1975 (6 Aug). *Health Stamps. T* **350** *and similar horiz designs. Multicoloured. P* 13½ × 13.
1079 3 c. + 1 c. Type **350** 20 30
1080 4 c. + 1 c. Boy with hen and chicks 20 30
1081 5 c. + 1 c. Boy with duck and duckling .. 60 1·25
1079/81 .. .. *Set of* 3 90 1·60
MS1082 123 × 146 mm. No. 1080 × 10 .. .. 14·00 35·00

(Des Enid Hunter. Photo Harrison)

1975 (1 Oct). *Christmas. T* **351** *and similar horiz designs. Multicoloured. P* 13 × 13½ (3 c.) *or* 13½ × 13 (*others*).
1083 3 c. Type **351** 10 10
a. Red omitted* £200
1084 5 c. "Cross in Landscape" (stained-glass window, Greendale Church) 10 10
a. Brown (face value) omitted £170
1085 10 c. "I saw three ships . . ." (carol) 35 65
1083/5 .. .. *Set of* 3 60 65

*This occurred in the last two vertical rows of the sheet with the red partially omitted on the previous row.

Used copies of No. 1083 have been seen with the orange ("Christmas 1975") omitted.

352 "Sterling Silver"

353 Queen Elizabeth II (photograph by W. Harrison)

353*a* Maripi (knife)

353*b* Rainbow Abalone or Paua

353*c* "Beehive" (section of Parliamentary Buildings, Wellington)

(Des A. G. Mitchell (1 to 14 c.), I. Hulse (20 c. to $2), R. Conly ($5). Photo Harrison (1 to 10 c.), Courvoisier (11 to 14 c.), Heraclio Fournier (20 c. to $5))

1975 (26 Nov)–**81**. (*a*) *Vert designs as T* **352** *showing garden roses. Multicoloured. P* 14½ (6 *to* 8 *c.*) *or* 14½ × 14 (*others*).
1086 1 c. Type **352** 10 10
1087 2 c. "Lilli Marlene" 10 10
1088 3 c. "Queen Elizabeth" 60 10
a. Perf 14½ (6.79) 85 10
1089 4 c. "Super Star" 10 10
1090 5 c. "Diamond Jubilee" 10 10
1091 6 c. "Cresset" .. .. 90 1·00
a. Perf 14½ × 14 (8.76?) 40 70
1092 7 c. "Michele Meilland" .. .. .. 1·25 50
a. Perf 14½ × 14 (6.76?) 40 10
1093 8 c. "Josephine Bruce" .. .. .. 1·25 90
a. Perf 14½ × 14 (8.76?) 65 10
1094 9 c. "Iceberg" 30 40

(*b*) *Type* **353**. *P* 14½ × 14 (7.12.77)
1094*a* 10 c. multicoloured 65 20
ab. Perf 14½ (2.79) 30 10

(*c*) *Vert designs as T* **353***a* *showing Maori artefacts. P* 11½ (24.11.76)
1095 11 c. reddish brown, lemon & blackish brown 45 50
1096 12 c. reddish brown, lemon & blackish brown 30 15
1097 13 c. reddish brown, greenish blue and blackish brown 60 65
1098 14 c. reddish brown, lemon & blackish brown 30 20

Designs:—12 c. Putorino (flute); 13 c. Wahaika (club); 14 c. Kotiate (club).

(*d*) *Horiz designs as T* **353***b* *showing sea shells. Multicoloured. P* 13
1099 20 c. Type **353***b* (29.11.78) 15 20
1100 30 c. Toheroa Clam (29.11.78) 25 30
1101 40 c. Old Woman or Coarse Dosina (29.11.78) 30 35
1102 50 c. New Zealand or Spiny Murex (29.11.78) 40 45
1103 $1 New Zealand Scallop (26.11.79) .. 70 85
a. Imperf between (vert pair) .. £450
1104 $2 Circular Saw (26.11.79) .. .. 1·00 1·75

(*e*) *Type* **353***c*. *P* 13 (2.12.81)
1105 $5 multicoloured .. .. 3·00 2·00
a. Imperf (vert pair)
1086/105 .. .. *Set of* 21 9·00 7·50

Faked "missing colour errors" exist of No. 1094a, involving parts of the portrait.

Used examples of No. 1099 exists with the black colour omitted so that the body of the shell appears in blue instead of green.

No. 1103a occurs on the top two rows of the sheet; the lower stamp being imperforate on three edges except for two perforation holes at the foot of each vertical side.

354 Family and League of Mothers Badge

(Des A. P. Derrick. Litho J.W.)

1976 (4 Feb). *Anniversaries and Metrication. T* **354** *and similar horiz designs. Multicoloured. P* 13½ × 14.
1110 6 c. Type **354** 10 10
1111 7 c. Weight, temperature, linear measure and capacity 10 10
1112 8 c. *William Bryan* (immigrant ship), mountain and New Plymouth 15 10
1113 10 c. Two women shaking hands and Y.W.C.A. badge 15 50
1114 25 c. Map of the world showing cable links .. 30 1·25
1110/14 .. .. *Set of* 5 70 1·75

Anniversaries:—6 c. League of Mothers, 50th Anniv; 7 c. Metrication; 8 c. Centenary of New Plymouth; 10 c. 50th Anniv of New Zealand Y.W.C.A.; 25 c. Centenary of link with International Telecommunications Network.

355 Gig

356 Purakaunui Falls

(Des G. F. Fuller. Litho Harrison)

1976 (7 Apr). *Vintage Farm Transport. T* **355** *and similar horiz designs. Multicoloured. P* 13½ × 13.
1115 6 c. Type **355** 15 40
1116 7 c. Thornycroft lorry 20 10
1117 8 c. Scandi wagon 40 20
1118 9 c. Traction engine 30 50
1119 10 c. Wool wagon 30 50
1120 25 c. Cart .. .. 85 2·25
1115/20 .. .. *Set of* 6 2·00 3·50

(Des and photo Courvoisier)

1976 (2 June). *Waterfalls. T* **356** *and similar vert designs. Multicoloured. P* 11½.
1121 10 c. Type **356** 35 10
1122 14 c. Marakopa Falls 60 75
1123 15 c. Bridal Veil Falls 65 85
1124 16 c. Papakorito Falls .. .. 70 1·00
1121/4 .. .. *Set of* 4 2·10 2·40

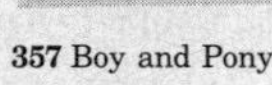

357 Boy and Pony

358 "Nativity" (Spanish carving)

(Des Margaret Chapman. Litho Harrison)

1976 (4 Aug). *Health Stamps. T* **357** *and similar vert designs. Multicoloured. P* 13 × 13½.
1125 7 c. + 1 c. Type **357** 20 30
1126 8 c. + 1 c. Girl and calf 20 30
1127 10 c. + 1 c. Girls and bird 40 90
1125/7 .. .. *Set of* 3 70 1·40
MS1128 96 × 121 mm. Nos. 1125/7 × 2 .. .. 4·50 8·00

(Des Margaret Chapman (18 c.), D. A. Hatcher (others). Photo Harrison)

1976 (6 Oct). *Christmas. T* **358** *and similar horiz designs. Multicoloured. P* 14 × 14½ (7 c.) *or* 14½ × 14 (*others*).
1129 7 c. Type **358** 15 10
1130 11 c. "Resurrection" (stained-glass window, St. Joseph's Catholic Church, Grey Lynn) 25 30
1131 18 c. Angels 40 90
1129/31 .. .. *Set of* 3 70 1·10

359 Arms of Hamilton **360** Queen Elizabeth II

(Des P. L. Blackie. Litho Harrison)

1977 (19 Jan). *Anniversaries. T* **359** *and similar vert designs. Multicoloured. P* 13 × 13½.

1132 8 c. Type **359** .. 15 10
a. Horiz strip of 3, Nos. 1132/4 .. 45
1133 8 c. Arms of Gisborne .. 15 10
1134 8 c. Arms of Masterton .. 15 10
1135 10 c. A.A. emblem .. 15 40
a. Horiz pair. Nos. 1135/6 .. 30 1·00
1136 10 c. Arms of the College of Surgeons .. 15 40
1132/6 .. *Set of* 5 75 1·00

Events:—Nos. 1132/4, City Centenaries; No. 1135, 75th Anniv of the Automobile Association in New Zealand; No. 1136, 50th Anniv of Royal Australasian College of Surgeons.

Designs of each value were printed in the same sheet horizontally *se-tenant*.

(Des and photo Harrison from photographs by Warren Harrison)

1977 (23 Feb). *Silver Jubilee. Sheet* 178 × 82 *mm containing T* **360** *and similar vert designs showing different portraits. P* 14 × 14½.

MS1137 8 c. × 5 multicoloured .. 65 1·40
a. Imperf .. £1200
ab. Ditto, and silver omitted .. £2000
b. Silver omitted .. £800
c. Indian red omitted .. £300

361 Physical Education and Maori Culture **(362)**

(Des A. G. Mitchell. Litho Harrison)

1977 (6 Apr). *Education. T* **361** *and similar vert designs. Multicoloured. P* 13 × 13½.

1138 8 c. Type **361** .. 40 70
a. Horiz strip of 5, Nos. 1138/42 .. 1·75
1139 8 c. Geography, science and woodwork .. 40 70
1140 8 c. Teaching the deaf, kindergarten and woodwork .. 40 70
1141 8 c. Tertiary and language classes .. 40 70
1142 8 c. Home science, correspondence school and teacher training .. 40 70
1138/42 .. *Set of* 5 1·75 3·25

Nos. 1138/42 were printed horizontally *se-tenant* throughout the sheet.

1977 (Apr). *Coil Stamps. Nos.* 1010/11 *surch as T* **362** *by Govt Printer, Wellington.*

1143 7 c. on 3 c. *Detunda egregia* (moth) (19.4) 40 70
1144 8 c. on 4 c. *Charagia virescens* (moth) (21.4) 40 70
a. Bright green (wing veins) omitted .. £250

Forged "7 c." surcharges, similar to No. 1143, but in smaller type, are known applied to Nos. 918 and 1010.

363 Karitane Beach **364** Girl with Pigeon

(Des D. A. Hatcher. Photo Heraclio Fournier)

1977 (1 June). *Seascapes. T* **363** *and similar horiz designs. Multicoloured. P* 14½.

1145 10 c. Type **363** .. 15 10
1146 16 c. Ocean Beach, Mount Maunganui .. 30 30
1147 18 c. Piha Beach .. 30 30
1148 30 c. Kaikoura Coast .. 35 40
1145/8 .. *Set of* 4 1·00 1·00

(Des A. P. Derrick. Litho Harrison)

1977 (3 Aug). *Health Stamps. T* **364** *and similar vert designs. Multicoloured. P* 13 × 13½.

1149 7 c. + 2 c. Type **364** .. 20 30
1150 8 c. + 2 c. Boy with frog .. 25 40
1151 10 c. + 2 c. Girl with butterfly .. 45 80
1149/51 .. *Set of* 3 80 1·40
MS1152 97 × 120 mm. Nos. 1149/51 × 2 .. 3·00 7·50

Stamps from the miniature sheet are without white border and together form a composite design.

365 "The Holy Family" (Correggio)

(Des Margaret Chapman (23 c.), graphics for all values produced by printer. Photo Courvoisier)

1977 (5 Oct). *Christmas. T* **365** *and similar vert designs. Multicoloured. P* 11½.

1153 7 c. Type **365** .. 15 10
1154 16 c. "Madonna and Child" (stained-glass window, St. Michael's and All Angels, Dunedin) .. 25 25
1155 23 c. "Partridge in a Pear Tree" .. 40 75
1153/5 .. *Set of* 3 70 95

366 Merryweather Manual Pump, 1860 **367** Town Clock and Coat of Arms, Ashburton

(Des R. M. Conly. Litho Harrison)

1977 (7 Dec). *Fire Fighting Appliances. T* **366** *and similar horiz designs. Multicoloured. P* 14 × 13.

1156 10 c. Type **366** .. 15 10
1157 11 c. 2-wheel hose, reel and ladder, 1880 .. 15 25
1158 12 c. Shand Mason steam fire engine, 1873 .. 20 30
1159 23 c. Chemical fire engine, 1888 .. 30 50
1156/9 .. *Set of* 4 70 1·00

(Des P. L. Blackie (No. 1162), Harrison (No. 1163), P. J. Durrant (others), Litho Harrison)

1978 (8 Mar). *Centenaries. T* **367** *and similar multicoloured designs. P* 14.

1160 10 c. Type **367** .. 15 10
a. Horiz pair. Nos. 1160/1 .. 30 50
1161 10 c. Stratford and Mt Egmont .. 15 10
1162 12 c. Early telephone .. 15 15
1163 20 c. Bay of Islands (*horiz*) .. 20 30
1160/3 .. *Set of* 4 60 60

Centenaries commemorated are those of the towns of Ashburton and Stratford, of the telephone in New Zealand, and of the Bay of Islands County.

The 10 c. values were printed together, *se-tenant*, in horizontal pairs throughout the sheet.

368 Students and Ivey Hall, Lincoln College **369** **370** Maui Gas Drilling Platform

(Des A. P. Derrick. Litho Harrison)

1978 (26 Apr). *Land Resources and Centenary of Lincoln College of Agriculture. T* **368** *and similar vert designs. Multicoloured. P* 14½.

1164 10 c. Type **368** .. 15 10
1165 12 c. Sheep grazing .. 15 25
1166 15 c. Fertiliser ground spreading .. 15 30
1167 16 c. Agricultural Field Days .. 15 30
1168 20 c. Harvesting grain .. 20 40
1169 30 c. Dairy farming .. 30 70
1164/9 .. *Set of* 6 1·00 1·90

(Photo Harrison)

1978 (3 May–9 June). *Coil Stamps. P* 14½ × 14 (10 c.) *or* 14 × 13 (*others*).

1170 **369** 1 c. bright purple (9.6) .. 10 30
1171 2 c. bright orange (9.6) .. 10 30
1172 5 c. red-brown (9.6) .. 10 35
1173 10 c. bright blue .. 30 70
1170/3 .. *Set of* 4 45 1·50

(Des R. M. Conly. Litho Harrison)

1978 (7 June). *Resources of the Sea. T* **370** *and similar vert designs. Multicoloured. P* 13 × 14.

1174 12 c. Type **370** .. 20 15
1175 15 c. Trawler .. 25 30
1176 20 c. Map of 200 mile fishing limit .. 30 40
1177 23 c. Humpback Whale and Bottle-nosed Dolphins .. 40 50
1178 35 c. Kingfish, snapper, grouper and squid .. 60 75
1174/8 .. *Set of* 5 1·60 1·90

371 First Health Charity Stamp **372** "The Holy Family" (El Greco) **373** Sir Julius Vogel

(Des A. G. Mitchell. Litho Harrison)

1978 (2 Aug). *Health Stamps. Health Services Commemorations. T* **371** *and similar vert design. P* 13 × 14.

1179 10 c. + 2 c. black, red and gold .. 30 35
1180 12 c. + 2 c. multicoloured .. 30 40
MS1181 97 × 124 mm. Nos. 1179/80 × 3 .. 2·50 4·00

Designs and commemorations:—10 c. Type **371** (50th anniversary of health charity stamps); 12 c. Heart operation (National Heart Foundation).

(Des R. M. Conly. Photo Courvoisier)

1978 (4 Oct). *Christmas. T* **372** *and similar multicoloured designs. P* 11½.

1182 7 c. Type **372** .. 10 10
1183 16 c. All Saints' Church, Howick (*horiz*) .. 25 35
1184 23 c. Beach scene (*horiz*) .. 30 50
1182/4 .. *Set of* 3 60 80

(Des A. G. Mitchell. Litho J.W.)

1979 (7 Feb). *Statesmen. T* **373** *and similar vert designs in sepia and drab. P* 13 × 13½.

1185 10 c. Type **373** .. 30 65
a. Horiz strip of 3, Nos. 1185/7 .. 90
1186 10 c. Sir George Grey .. 30 65
1187 10 c. Richard John Seddon .. 30 65
1185/7 .. *Set of* 3 90 1·75

Nos. 1185/7 were printed together, *se-tenant*, in horizontal strips of 3 throughout the sheet.

Nos. 1185/7 have matt, almost invisible gum.

374 Riverlands Cottage, Blenheim **375** Whangaroa Harbour

(Des P. Leitch. Litho Enschedé)

1979 (4 Apr). *Architecture* (1*st series*). *T* **374** *and similar horiz designs. P* 13½ × 13.

1188 10 c. black, new blue and deep blue .. 10 10
1189 12 c. black, pale green and bottle green .. 15 25
1190 15 c. black and grey .. 20 30
1191 20 c. black, yellow-brown and sepia .. 25 30
1188/91 .. *Set of* 4 65 90

Designs:—12 c. The Mission House, Waimate North; 15 c. "The Elms", Tauranga; 20 c. Provincial Council Buildings, Christchurch.

See also Nos. 1217/20 and 1262/5.

(Photo Heraclio Fournier)

1979 (6 June). *Small Harbours. T* **375** *and similar multicoloured designs. P* 13.

1192 15 c. Type **375** .. 20 10
1193 20 c. Kawau Island .. 25 35
1194 23 c. Akaroa Harbour (*vert*) .. 30 40
1195 35 c. Picton Harbour (*vert*) .. 45 55
1192/5 .. *Set of* 4 1·10 1·25

376 Children with Building Bricks

(Des W. Kelsall. Litho J.W.)

1979 (6 June). *International Year of the Child. P* 14.

1196 **376** 10 c. multicoloured .. 15 10

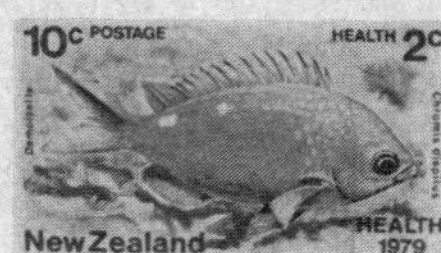

4c

377 Two-spotted Chromis (**378**)

(Des P. Blackie (12 c.), G. Fuller (others). Litho Harrison)

1979 (25 July). *Health Stamps. Marine Life. T* **377** *and similar multicoloured designs. P* 13 × 13½ (12 *c.*) *or* 13½ × 13 (*others*).
1197 10 c. + 2 c. Type **377** 40 60
a. Horiz pair. Nos. 1197/8 .. .. 80 1·10
1198 10 c. + 2 c. Sea Urchin 40 60
1199 12 c. + 2 c. Red Goatfish and underwater cameraman (*vert*) 40 60
1197/9 .. .. *Set of* 3 1·10 1·60
MS1200 144×72 mm. Nos. 1197/9, each × 2. P 14×14½ (12 c.) or 14½×14 (others) .. 2·25 4·50
Nos. 1197/8 were printed together, *se-tenant*, in horizontal pairs throughout the sheet.

1979 (31 Aug)–**80**. *Nos.* 1091a, 1092a, 1093a *and* 1094ab *surch as T* **378** *by Govt Printer, Wellington.*
1201 4 c. on 8 c. "Josephine Bruce" (24.9.79) 10 20
a. Surch double .. .. .. 35·00
1202 14 c. on 10 c. Type **353** 30 20
a. Surch double, one albino £140
1203 17 c. on 6 c. "Cresset" (9.10.79) 30 70
1203*a* 20 c. on 7 c. "Michele Meilland" (29.9.80) 30 10
1201/3*a* .. .. *Set of* 4 80 1·10
Neither of the impressions of the surcharge on No. 1201a are properly inked.

379 "Madonna and Child" (sculpture by Ghiberti) **380** Chamber, House of Representatives

(Des D. Hatcher. Photo Courvoisier)

1979 (3 Oct). *Christmas. T* **379** *and similar vert designs. Multicoloured. P* 11½.
1204 10 c. Type **379** 15 10
1205 25 c. Christ Church, Russell 30 40
1206 35 c. Pohutukawa (tree) 40 55
1204/6 .. .. *Set of* 3 75 90

(Des D. Hatcher. Litho J.W.)

1979 (26 Nov). *25th Commonwealth Parliamentary Conference, Wellington. T* **380** *and similar vert designs. Multicoloured. P* 13½.
1207 14 c. Type **380** 15 10
1208 20 c. Mace and Black Rod 20 30
1209 30 c. Wall hanging from the "Beehive" .. 30 60
1207/9 .. .. *Set of* 3 60 85

381 1855 1d. Stamp

(Des D. Hatcher (14 c. (all designs)), R. Conly (others). Litho Harrison)

1980 (7 Feb). *Anniversaries and Events. T* **381** *and similar designs. P* 13½×13 (14 *c.* (*all designs*)) *or* 14 (*others*).
1210 14 c. black, brown-red and yellow 20 30
a. Horiz strip of 3. Nos. 1210/12 60
ab. Black (inscription) omitted (*strip of* 3) .. £250
1211 14 c. black, deep turquoise-blue and yellow .. 20 30
1212 14 c. black, dull yellowish green and yellow .. 20 30
1213 17 c. multicoloured 20 30
1214 25 c. multicoloured 25 35
1215 30 c. multicoloured 25 40
1210/15 .. .. *Set of* 6 1·10 1·75
MS1216 146×96 mm. Nos. 1210/12 (as horiz strip). P 14½×14 (*sold at* 52 *c.*) .. 2·00 4·25
Designs and commemorations; (38 × 22 *mm*)—No. 1210, Type **381**; No. 1211, 1855 2d. stamp; No. 1212, 1855 1s. stamp (125th anniversary of New Zealand stamps). (40 × 23 *mm*)—No. 1213, Geyser, wood-carving and building (centenary of Rotorua (town)); No. 1214, *Earina autumnalis* and *thelymitra venosa* (International Orchid Conference, Auckland); No. 1215; Ploughing and Golden Plough Trophy (World Ploughing Championships, Christchurch).
The premium on No. **MS**1216 was used to help finance the "Zeapex 80" International Stamp Exhibition, Auckland.
Nos. 1210/12 were printed together, *se-tenant*, in horizontal strips of 3 throughout the sheet.

382 Ewelme Cottage, Parnell **383** Auckland Harbour

(Des P. Leitch. Litho Enschedé)

1980 (2 Apr). *Architecture (2nd series). T* **382** *and similar horiz designs. Multicoloured. P* 13½ × 12½.
1217 14 c. Type **382** 15 10
1218 17 c. Broadgreen, Nelson 25 35
1219 25 c. Courthouse, Oamaru 30 45
1220 30 c. Government Buildings, Wellington .. 35 45
1217/20 .. .. *Set of* 4 95 1·25

(Des D. Hatcher. Photo Heraclio Fournier)

1980 (4 June). *Large Harbours. T* **383** *and similar horiz designs. Multicoloured. P* 13.
1221 25 c. Type **383** 25 20
1222 30 c. Wellington Harbour 30 30
1223 35 c. Lyttelton Harbour 30 35
1224 50 c. Port Chalmers 50 65
1221/4 .. .. *Set of* 4 1·25 1·40

384 Surf-fishing **385** "Madonna and Child with Cherubim" (sculpture by Andrea della Robbia)

(Des Margaret Chapman. Litho Enschedé)

1980 (6 Aug). *Health Stamps. Fishing. T* **384** *and similar horiz designs. Multicoloured. P* 13 × 12½.
1225 14 c. + 2 c. Type **384** 45 70
a. Horiz pair. Nos. 1225/6 .. .. 90 1·40
1226 14 c. + 2 c. Wharf-fishing 45 70
1227 17 c. + 2 c. Spear-fishing 45 55
1225/7 .. .. *Set of* 3 1·25 1·75
MS1228 148 × 75 mm. Nos. 1225/7 each × 2. P 13½ × 13 .. .. .. 2·00 3·00
Nos. 1225/6 were printed together, *se-tenant*, in horizontal pairs throughout the sheet.

(Des P. Durrant. Photo Courvoisier)

1980 (1 Oct). *Christmas. T* **385** *and similar vert designs. Multicoloured. P* 11½.
1229 10 c. Type **385** 15 10
1230 25 c. St. Mary's Church, New Plymouth .. 25 25
1231 35 c. Picnic scene 40 55
1229/31 .. .. *Set of* 3 70 80

386 Te Heu Heu (chief) **387** Lt.-Col. the Hon W. H. A. Feilding and Borough of Feilding Crest

(Des R. Conly. Litho Heraclio Fournier)

1980 (26 Nov). *Maori Personalities. Vert designs as T* **386**. *Multicoloured. P* 12½ × 13.
1232 15 c. Type **386** 10 10
1233 25 c. Te Hau (chief) 15 15
1234 35 c. Te Puea (princess) 20 10
1235 45 c. Ngata (politician) 30 20
1236 60 c. Te Ata-O-Tu (warrior) 35 20
1232/6 .. .. *Set of* 5 1·00 60

(Des R. Conly. Litho Harrison)

1981 (4 Feb). *Commemorations. T* **387** *and similar horiz design. P* 14½.
1237 20 c. multicoloured 20 20
1238 25 c. black and brown-ochre 25 25
Designs and Commemorations:—20 c. Type **387** (Centenary of Feilding (town)); 25 c. I.Y.D. emblem and cupped hands (International Year of the Disabled).

388 The Family at Play **389** Kaiauai River

(Des A. Derrick. Litho J.W.)

1981 (1 Apr). *"Family Life." T* **388** *and similar vert designs. Multicoloured. P* 13½ × 13.
1239 20 c. Type **388** 20 10
1240 25 c. The family, young and old 25 30
1241 30 c. The family at home 30 40
1242 35 c. The family at church 35 55
1239/42 .. .. *Set of* 4 1·00 1·25

(Des D. Hatcher. Photo Heraclio Fournier)

1981 (3 June). *River Scenes. T* **389** *and similar multicoloured designs. P* 13½ × 13 (30, 35 *c.*) *or* 13 × 13½ (*others*).
1243 30 c. Type **389** 25 25
1244 35 c. Mangahao 30 30
1245 40 c. Shotover (*horiz*) 35 40
1246 60 c. Cleddau (*horiz*) 55 65
1243/6 .. .. *Set of* 4 1·25 1·40

390 St. Paul's Cathedral **391** Girl with Starfish

(Des and litho Harrison)

1981 (29 July). *Royal Wedding. T* **390** *and similar horiz design. Multicoloured. P* 14½.
1247 20 c. Type **390** 20 30
a. Pair. Nos. 1247/8 .. .. .. 40 60
ab. Deep grey (inscriptions and date) omitted £800
1248 20 c. Prince Charles and Lady Diana Spencer 20 30
Nos. 1247/8 were printed together, *se-tenant*, in horizontal and vertical pairs throughout the sheet.

(Des P.O. Litho Harrison)

1981 (5 Aug). *Health Stamps. Children playing by the Sea. T* **391** *and similar vert designs. Multicoloured. P* 14½.
1249 20 c. + 2 c. Type **391** 25 50
a. Horiz pair. Nos. 1249/50 .. .. 50 1·00
1250 20 c. + 2 c. Boy fishing 25 50
1251 25 c. + 2 c. Children exploring rock pool .. 25 35
1249/51 .. .. *Set of* 3 70 1·25
MS1252 100 × 125 mm. Nos. 1249/51, each × 2 .. 1·60 2·75
The 20 c. values were printed together, *se-tenant*, in horizontal pairs throughout the sheet, forming a composite design.
The stamps from No. **MS**1252 were printed together, *se-tenant*, in two horizontal strips of 3, each forming a composite design.

392 "Madonna Suckling the Child" (painting, d'Oggiono) **393** Tauranga Mission House

(Des Margaret Chapman. Photo Courvoisier)

1981 (7 Oct). *Christmas. T* **392** *and similar vert designs. Multicoloured. P* 11½.
1253 14 c. Type **392** 15 10
1254 30 c. St. John's Church, Wakefield 35 25
1255 40 c. Golden Tainui (flower) 45 35
1253/5 .. .. *Set of* 3 85 60

(Des A. Derrick. Litho Walsall)

1982 (3 Feb). *Commemorations. T* **393** *and similar vert designs. Multicoloured. P* 14½.
1256 20 c. Type **393** 25 10
a. Horiz pair. Nos. 1256/7 .. .. 50 60
1257 20 c. Water tower, Hawera 25 10
1258 25 c. Cat 35 35
1259 30 c. *Dunedin* (refrigerated sailing ship) .. 35 40
1260 35 c. Scientific research equipment 40 45
1256/60 .. .. *Set of* 5 1·40 1·25
Commemorations:—No. 1256, Centenary of Tauranga (town); No. 1257, Centenary of Hawera (town); No. 1258, Centenary of S.P.C.A. (Society for the Prevention of Cruelty to Animals in New Zealand); No. 1259, Centenary of Frozen Meat Exports; No. 1260, International Year of Science.
The 20 c. values were printed together, *se-tenant*, in horizontal pairs throughout the sheet.

394 Map of New Zealand **395** Alberton, Auckland

(Des A. G. Mitchell. Litho Leigh-Mardon Ltd, Melbourne)

1982 (1 Apr–13 Dec). *P* 12½.
1261 **394** 24 c. pale yellowish green and ultram .. 30 10
a. Perf 14½ × 14 (13.12.82) .. 35 10

(Des P. Leitch. Litho Walsall)

1982 (7 Apr). *Architecture* (3rd series). *T* **395** *and similar horiz designs. Multicoloured. P* 14 × 14½.
1262 20 c. Type **395** 20 15
1263 25 c. Caccia Birch, Palmerston North .. 25 25
1264 30 c. Railway station, Dunedin 50 30
1265 35 c. Post Office, Ophir 40 40
1262/5 .. .. *Set of* 4 1·25 1·00

396 Kaiteriteri Beach, Nelson (Summer)

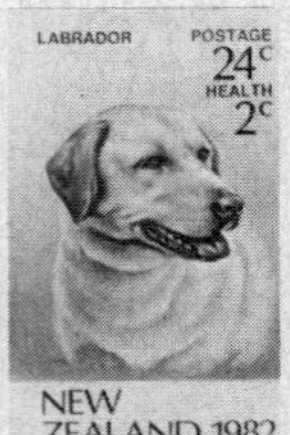

397 Labrador

(Des D. Hatcher. Photo Heraclio Fournier)

1982 (2 June). *"The Four Seasons". New Zealand Scenes. T* **396** *and similar horiz designs. Multicoloured. P* 13 × 13½.
1266 35 c. Type **396** 30 30
1267 40 c. St. Omer Park, Queenstown (Autumn) 35 35
1268 45 c. Mt Ngauruhoe, Tongariro National Park (Winter) 40 40
1269 70 c. Wairarapa farm (Spring) 60 60
1266/9 .. .. *Set of* 4 1·50 1·50

(Des R. Conly. Litho Enschedé)

1982 (4 Aug). *Health Stamps. Dogs. T* **397** *and similar vert designs. Multicoloured. P* 13 × 13½.
1270 24 c. + 2 c. Type **397** .. .. .. 80 1·00
a. Horiz pair. Nos. 1270/1 .. .. .. 1·60 2·00
1271 24 c. + 2 c. Border Collie .. .. .. 80 1·00
1272 30 c. + 2 c. Cocker Spaniel .. .. .. 80 1·00
1270/2 .. .. *Set of* 3 2·25 2·75
MS1273 98 × 125 mm. Nos. 1270/2, each × 2. P 14 × 13½ .. .. 4·25 6·00

The 24 c. values were printed together, *se-tenant*, in horizontal pairs throughout the sheet.

398 "Madonna with Child and Two Angels" (painting by Piero di Cosimo)

(Des Margaret Chapman. Photo Heraclio Fournier)

1982 (6 Oct). *Christmas. T* **398** *and similar vert designs. Multicoloured. P* 14 × 13½.
1274 18 c. Type **398** 20 10
1275 35 c. Rangiatea Maori Church, Otaki .. 35 30
1276 45 c. Surf life-saving 50 40
1274/6 .. .. *Set of* 3 95 65

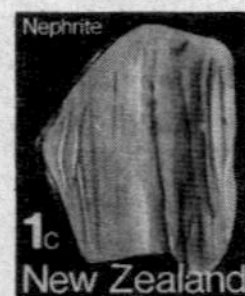

399 Nephrite

399a Grapes

399b Kokako

(Des P. Durrant (Nos. 1277/82), D. Little (Nos. 1283/7), Janet Marshall (Nos. 1288/97). Litho Leigh-Mardon Ltd. Melbourne)

1982 (1 Dec)–**89**. *Multicoloured. P* 14½×14 (*Nos.* 1277/87) *or* 14½ (*Nos.* 1288/97).

(*a*) *Minerals. T* **399** *and similar vert designs*
1277 1 c. Type **399** 10 10
a. Perf 12½ 65 20
1278 2 c. Agate 10 10
a. Perf 12½ .. .. 1·75 1·50
1279 3 c. Iron Pyrites 10 10
1280 4 c. Amethyst 10 10
1281 5 c. Carnelian 10 10
1282 9 c. Native Sulphur 20 10

(*b*) *Fruits. T* **399a** *and similar vert designs*
1283 10 c. Type **399a** (7.12.83) 50 10
1284 20 c. Citrus Fruit (7.12.83) 35 10
1285 30 c. Nectarines (7.12.83) 30 10
1286 40 c. Apples (7.12.83) 35 10
1287 50 c. Kiwifruit (7.12.83) 40 10

(*c*) *Native Birds. T* **399b** *and similar vert designs*
1288 30 c. Kakapo (1.5.86) 50 25
1289 40 c. Mountain ("Blue") Duck (2.2.87) .. 60 35
1290 45 c. New Zealand Falcon (1.5.86) .. 1·00 35
1291 60 c. New Zealand Teal (2.2.87) .. .. 1·00 40
1292 $1 Type **399b** (24.4.85) .. .. .. 1·00 30
1293 $2 Chatham Island Robin (24.4.85) .. 1·75 50
1294 $3 Stitchbird (23.4.86) .. .. .. 2·00 1·40
1295 $4 Saddleback (23.4.86) .. .. .. 2·25 2·50
1296 $5 Takahe (20.4.88) .. .. 3·00 3·00
1297 $10 Little Spotted Kiwi (19.4.89) .. 6·00 6·75
1277/97 .. .. *Set of* 21 20·00 15·00
1292/7 Optd "Specimen" .. .. .. *Set of* 6 7·50

Nos. 1292/7 overprinted "Specimen" come from a special "NEW ZEALAND 1990" Presentation Pack issued on 19 April 1989.

A miniature sheet containing No. 1293 was only available from the New Zealand stand at "PHILEXFRANCE '89" International Stamp Exhibition or the Philatelic Bureau at Wanganui.

Versions of the $3 with narrow face value and of the $4 in horizontal format were prepared, but not issued for postal purposes.

For No. 1297 in a miniature sheet for "POST X 95" Postal History Exhibition see No. **MS**1854.

400 Old Arts Building, Auckland University

401 Queen Elizabeth II

(Des G. Emery (35 c.), P. Durrant (others). Litho Cambec Press, Melbourne (35 c.), J.W. (others))

1983 (2 Feb). *Commemorations. T* **400** *and similar vert designs. Multicoloured. P* 13 × 13½ (35 c.) *or* 14 × 13½ (*others*).
1303 24 c. Salvation Army Centenary logo .. 20 10
1304 30 c. Type **400** 30 35
1305 35 c. Stylised Kangaroo and Kiwi 35 35
1306 40 c. Rainbow Trout 40 45
1307 45 c. Satellite over Earth 45 50
1303/7 .. .. *Set of* 5 1·50 1·50

Commemorations:—24 c. Centenary of Salvation Army; 30 c. Centenary of Auckland University; 35 c. Closer Economic Relationship agreement with Australia; 40 c. Centenary of introduction of Rainbow Trout into New Zealand; 45 c. World Communications Year.

(Des P. Durrant. Litho Harrison)

1983 (14 Mar). *Commonwealth Day. T* **401** *and similar horiz designs. Multicoloured. P* 13½.
1308 24 c. Type **401** 30 10
1309 35 c. Maori rock drawing 40 50
1310 40 c. Woolmark and wool-scouring symbols .. 45 80
1311 45 c. Coat of arms 55 80
1308/11 .. .. *Set of* 4 1·50 2·00

402 "Boats, Island Bay" (Rita Angus)

403 Mt Egmont

(Des D. Hatcher. Litho Leigh-Mardon Ltd, Melbourne)

1983 (6 Apr). *Paintings by Rita Angus. T* **402** *and similar vert designs. Multicoloured. P* 14½.
1312 24 c. Type **402** 35 10
1313 30 c. "Central Otago Landscape" 40 45
1314 35 c. "Wanaka Landscape" 50 50
1315 45 c. "Tree" 70 70
1312/15 .. .. *Set of* 4 1·75 1·60

(Des P. Durrant. Photo Heraclio Fournier)

1983 (1 June). *Beautiful New Zealand. T* **403** *and similar multicoloured designs. P* 13.
1316 35 c. Type **403** 30 35
1317 40 c. Cooks Bay 35 40
1318 45 c. Lake Matheson (*horiz*) 40 45
1319 70 c. Lake Alexandrina (*horiz*) 65 70
1316/19 .. .. *Set of* 4 1·50 1·75

404 Tabby

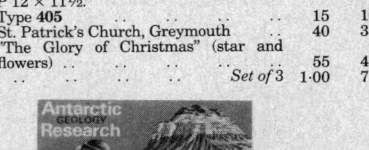

405 "The Family of the Holy Oak Tree" (Raphael)

(Des R. Conly. Litho Harrison)

1983 (3 Aug). *Health Stamps. Cats. T* **404** *and similar vert designs. Multicoloured. P* 14.
1320 24 c. + 2 c. Type **404** 40 40
a. Horiz pair. Nos. 1320/1 .. .. .. 80 80
1321 24 c. + 2 c. Siamese 40 40
1322 30 c. + 2 c. Persian 75 75
1320/2 .. .. *Set of* 3 1·40 1·40
MS1323 100 × 126 mm. Nos. 1320/2, each × 2 .. 2·25 2·25

The 24 c. values were printed together, *se-tenant*, in horizontal pairs throughout the sheet.

(Des R. Conly (45 c.), M. Wyatt (others). Photo Courvoisier)

1983 (5 Oct). *Christmas. T* **405** *and similar vert designs. Multicoloured. P* 12 × 11½.
1324 18 c. Type **405** 15 10
1325 35 c. St. Patrick's Church, Greymouth .. 40 35
1326 45 c. "The Glory of Christmas" (star and flowers) 55 45
1324/6 .. .. *Set of* 3 1·00 75

406 Geology

(Des R. Conly. Litho Cambec Press, Melbourne)

1984 (1 Feb). *Antarctic Research. T* **406** *and similar horiz designs. Multicoloured. P* 13½ × 13.
1327 24 c. Type **406** 35 10
1328 40 c. Biology 45 40
1329 58 c. Glaciology 60 55
1330 70 c. Meteorology 70 70
1327/30 .. .. *Set of* 4 1·90 1·60
MS1331 126 × 110 mm. Nos. 1327/30 .. .. 1·90 3·25

407 *Mountaineer*, Lake Wakatipu

408 Mount Hutt

(Des M. Wyatt. Litho Cambec Press, Melbourne)

1984 (4 Apr). *New Zealand Ferry Boats. T* **407** *and similar horiz designs. Multicoloured. P* 13½ × 13.
1332 24 c. Type **407** 25 10
1333 40 c. *Waikana*, Otago 30 40
1334 58 c. *Britannia*, Waitemata .. .. .. 40 1·00
1335 70 c. *Wakatere*, Firth of Thames 55 75
1332/5 .. .. *Set of* 4 1·40 2·00

(Des D. Little. Litho Cambec Press, Melbourne)

1984 (6 June). *Ski-slope Scenery. T* **408** *and similar horiz designs. Multicoloured. P* 13½ × 13.
1336 35 c. Type **408** 40 40
1337 40 c. Coronet Park 45 45
1338 45 c. Turoa 50 50
1339 70 c. Whakapapa 75 75
1336/9 .. .. *Set of* 4 1·90 1·90

409 Hamilton's Frog

(Des A. G. Mitchell. Litho Cambec Press, Melbourne)

1984 (11 July). *Amphibians and Reptiles. T* **409** *and similar horiz designs. Multicoloured. P* 13½.
1340 24 c. Type **409** 30 30
a. Horiz pair. Nos. 1340/1 .. .. .. 60 60
1341 24 c. Great Barrier Skink 30 30
1342 30 c. Harlequin Gecko 35 35
1343 58 c. Otago Skink 70 70
1344 70 c. Gold-striped Gecko 75 75
1340/4 .. .. *Set of* 5 2·25 2·25

Nos. 1340/1 were printed together, *se-tenant*, in horizontal pairs throughout the sheet.

410 Clydesdales ploughing Field

(Des Margaret Chapman. Litho Harrison)

1984 (1 Aug). *Health Stamps. Horses. T* **410** *and similar horiz designs. Multicoloured. P* 14½.

1345 24 c. + 2 c. Type **410** 30 50
a. Horiz pair. Nos. 1345/6 .. .. .. 60 1·00
1346 24 c. + 2 c. Shetland ponies 30 50
1347 30 c. + 2 c. Thoroughbreds 45 50
1345/7 .. .. *Set of* 3 1·00 1·40
MS 1348 148 × 75 mm. Nos. 1345/7, each × 2 .. 1·60 2·00

Nos. 1345/6 were printed together, *se-tenant*, in horizontal pairs throughout the sheet.

MACHINE LABELS. An automatic machine dispensing labels, ranging in value from 1 c. to $99.99, was installed at the Queen Street Post Office, Auckland, on 3 September 1984 for a trial period. The oblong designs, framed by simulated perforations at top and bottom and vertical rules at the sides, showed the "Southern Cross", face value and vertical column of six horizontal lines between the "NEW ZEALAND" and "POSTAGE" inscriptions. The trial period ended abruptly on 16 October 1984.

Similar labels, with the face value and inscriptions within a plain oblong, were introduced on 12 February 1986 and from 22 August 1988 they were printed on paper showing New Zealand flags. On 12 September 1990 the design printed on the paper was changed to show seaplanes and on 12 August 1992 to a Maori pattern. A further Maori pattern, taken from rafters, in green and grey appeared on 21 February 1996.

A commemorative label was available at "NEW ZEALAND '90" held at Auckland between 24 August and 2 September 1990.

411 "Adoration of the Shepherds" (Lorenzo di Credi)

(Des R. Conly (45 c.), P. Durrant (others). Photo Heraclio Fournier)

1984 (26 Sept). *Christmas. T* **411** *and similar multicoloured designs. P* 13½ × 14 (18 *c.*) *or* 14 × 13½ (*others*).

1349 18 c. Type **411** 20 10
1350 35 c. Old St. Paul's, Wellington (*vert*) .. 40 40
1351 45 c. "The Joy of Christmas" (*vert*) 50 65
1349/51 .. .. *Set of* 3 1·00 1·00

412 Mounted Riflemen, South Africa, 1901

(Des R. Conly. Litho Harrison)

1984 (7 Nov). *New Zealand Military History. T* **412** *and similar horiz designs. Multicoloured. P* 15 × 14.

1352 24 c. Type **412** 25 10
1353 40 c. Engineers, France, 1917 .. .. 35 45
1354 58 c. Tanks of 2nd N.Z. Divisional Cavalry, North Africa, 1942 .. .. .. 50 60
1355 70 c. Infantryman in jungle kit, and 25-pounder gun, Korea and South-East Asia, 1950–72 .. .. .. 60 75
1352/5 .. .. *Set of* 4 1·50 1·75
MS1356 122 × 106 mm. Nos. 1352/5 .. .. 1·25 1·90

413 St. John Ambulance Badge

(Des Lindy Fisher. Litho J.W.)

1985 (16 Jan). *Centenary of St. John Ambulance in New Zealand. P* 14.

1357 **413** 24 c. black, gold and bright rosine .. 25 15
1358 30 c. black, sil & bright ultram .. 35 45
1359 40 c. black and grey 40 90
1357/9 .. .. *Set of* 3 90 1·25

The colours of the badge depicted are those for Bailiffs and Dames Grand Cross (24 c.), Knights and Dames of Grace (30 c.) and Serving Brothers and Sisters (40 c.).

414 Nelson Horse-drawn Tram, 1862

415 Shotover Bridge

(Des. R. Conly. Litho Cambec Press, Melbourne)

1985 (6 Mar). *Vintage Trams. T* **414** *and similar horiz designs. Multicoloured. P* 13½.

1360 24 c. Type **414** 40 10
1361 30 c. Graham's Town steam tram, 1871 .. 50 60
1362 35 c. Dunedin cable car, 1881 .. .. 50 70
1363 40 c. Auckland electric tram, 1902 .. .. 50 70
1364 45 c. Wellington electric tram, 1904 .. .. 60 90
1365 58 c. Christchurch electric tram, 1905 .. 70 1·50
1360/5 .. .. *Set of* 6 2·75 4·00

TARAPEX '86. To support this National Philatelic Exhibition the New Zealand Post Office co-operated with the organisers in the production of a set of "postage imprint labels". Five of the designs showed drawings of Maoris, taken from originals by Arthur Herbert Messenger and the sixth the Exhibition logo.

The sheetlets of 6 gummed and perforated labels were released by the Exhibition organisers on 3 April 1985. Although such labels were valid for postage, and could be so used by the general public, the sheetlets were not available from any New Zealand post office or from the Philatelic Bureau.

(Des R. Freeman. Photo Courvoisier)

1985 (12 June). *Bridges of New Zealand. T* **415** *and similar multicoloured designs. Granite paper. P* 11½.

1366 35 c. Type **415** 60 60
1367 40 c. Alexandra Bridge 65 60
1368 45 c. South Rangitikei Railway Bridge (*vert*) 70 1·25
1369 70 c. Twin Bridges (*vert*) .. .. .. 90 1·25
1366/9 .. .. *Set of* 4 2·50 3·25

416 Queen Elizabeth II (from photo by Camera Press)

417 Princess of Wales and Prince William

(Des B. Clinton. Litho Leigh-Mardon Ltd, Melbourne)

1985 (1 July). *Multicoloured, background colours given. P* 14½ × 14.

1370 **416** 25 c. rosine 50 10
1371 35 c. new blue 90 10

Examples of the 25 c. value exist with the orders on the sash omitted. These are believed to originate from unissued sheets sent for destruction in March 1986.

(Des D. Little. Litho Cambec Press, Melbourne)

1985 (31 July). *Health Stamps. T* **417** *and similar vert designs showing photographs by Lord Snowdon. Multicoloured. P* 13½.

1372 25 c. + 2 c. Type **417** 50 75
a. Horiz pair. Nos. 1372/3 .. .. 1·00 1·50
1373 25 c. + 2 c. Princess of Wales and Prince Henry 50 75
1374 35 c. + 2 c. Prince and Princess of Wales with Princes William and Henry .. 55 75
1372/4 .. .. *Set of* 3 1·40 2·00
MS1375 118 × 84 mm. Nos. 1372/4, each × 2 .. 2·50 4·00

Nos. 1372/3 were printed together, *se-tenant*, in horizontal pairs throughout the sheet.

418 The Holy Family in the Stable

419 H.M.N.Z.S. *Philomel* (1914–47)

(Des Eileen Mayo. Photo Enschedé)

1985 (18 Sept). *Christmas. T* **418** *and similar vert designs. Multicoloured. P* 13½ × 12½.

1376 18 c. Type **418** 20 10
1377 40 c. The shepherds 40 85
1378 50 c. The angels .. .. 45 1·00
1376/8 .. .. *Set of* 3 95 1·75

Examples of the 18 c. and 50 c. stamps exist showing the spelling error "CRISTMAS". These are believed to originate from unissued sheets sent for destruction in March 1986. The New Zealand Post Office has stated that no such stamps were issued and that existing examples "were removed unlawfully during the destruction process".

(Des P. Durrant. Litho Cambec Press, Melbourne)

1985 (6 Nov). *New Zealand Naval History. T* **419** *and similar horiz designs. Multicoloured. P* 13½.

1379 25 c. Type **419** 70 15
1380 45 c. H.M.N.Z.S. *Achilles* (1936–46) .. 1·10 1·40
1381 60 c. H.M.N.Z.S. *Rotoiti* (1949–65) .. .. 1·40 2·00
1382 75 c. H.M.N.Z.S. *Canterbury* (from 1971) .. 1·75 2·25
1379/82 .. .. *Set of* 4 4·50 5·25
MS1383 124 × 108 mm. Nos. 1379/82 .. .. 4·50 5·25

420 Police Computer Operator

421 Indian "Power Plus" 1000cc Motor Cycle (1920)

(Des A. Mitchell. Litho Leigh-Mardon Ltd, Melbourne)

1986 (15 Jan). *Centenary of New Zealand Police. T* **420** *and similar vert designs, each showing historical aspects above modern police activities. Multicoloured. P* 14½ × 14.

1384 25 c. Type **420** 35 50
a. Horiz strip of 5. Nos. 1384/8 .. .. 1·60
1385 25 c. Detective and mobile control room .. 35 50
1386 25 c. Policewoman and badge 35 50
1387 25 c. Forensic scientist, patrol car and policeman with child 35 50
1388 25 c. Police College, Porirua, Patrol boat *Lady Elizabeth II* and dog handler .. 35 50
1384/8 .. .. *Set of* 5 1·60 2·25

Nos. 1384/8 were printed together, *se-tenant*, in horizontal strips of 5 throughout the sheet.

(Des M. Wyatt. Litho J.W.)

1986 (5 Mar). *Vintage Motor Cycles. T* **421** *and similar horiz designs. Multicoloured. P* 13 × 12½.

1389 35 c. Type **421** 50 45
1390 45 c. Norton "CS1" 500cc (1927) 60 65
1391 60 c. B.S.A. "Sloper" 500cc (1930) .. .. 75 1·10
1392 75 c. Triumph "Model H" 550cc (1915) .. 85 1·10
1389/92 .. .. *Set of* 4 2·40 3·00

422 Tree of Life

423 Knights Point

(Des Margaret Clarkson. Litho J.W.)

1986 (5 Mar). *International Peace Year. T* **422** *and similar horiz design. Multicoloured. P* 13 × 12½.

1393 25 c. Type **422** 30 30
a. Horiz pair. Nos. 1393/4 .. .. 60 60
1394 25 c. Peace dove 30 30

Nos. 1393/4 were printed together, *se-tenant*, in horizontal pairs throughout the sheet.

(Des P. Durrant. Photo Heraclio Fournier)

1986 (11 June). *Coastal Scenery. T* **423** *and similar horiz designs. Multicoloured. P* 14.

1395 55 c. Type **423** 55 60
1396 60 c. Becks Bay 55 70
1397 65 c. Doubtless Bay 60 70
1398 80 c. Wainui Bay 75 95
1395/8 .. .. *Set of* 4 2·25 2·75
MS1399 124 × 99 mm. No. 1398 (*sold at* $1.20) .. 1·10 90

The 40 c. premium on No. **MS**1399 was to support "New Zealand 1990" International Stamp Exhibition, Auckland.

No. **MS**1399 exists overprinted for "Stockholmia". Such miniature sheets were only available at this International Stamp Exhibition in Stockholm and were not placed on sale in New Zealand.

424 "Football" (Kylie Epapara)

425 "A Partridge in a Pear Tree"

(Litho Leigh-Mardon Ltd, Melbourne)

1986 (30 July). *Health Stamps. Children's Paintings (1st series). T* **424** *and similar multicoloured designs. P* 14½×14 (30 *c.) or* 14×14½ (45 *c.).*

1400 30 c. + 3 c. Type **424** 40 40
a. Horiz pair. Nos. 1400/1 .. .. .. 80 80
1401 30 c. + 3 c. "Children at Play" (Philip Kata) 40 40
1402 45 c. + 3 c. "Children Skipping" (Mia Flannery) (*horiz*) 50 50
1400/2 .. .. *Set of* 3 1·10 1·10
MS1403 144×81 mm. Nos. 1400/2, each×2 .. 2·25 2·25

Nos. 1400/1 were printed together, *se-tenant*, in horizontal pairs throughout the sheet.

No. **MS**1403 exists overprinted for "Stockholmia". Such miniature sheets were only available at this International Stamp Exhibition in Stockholm and were not placed on sale in New Zealand.

See also Nos. 1433/6.

(Des Margaret Halcrow-Cross. Photo Heraclio Fournier)

1986 (17 Sept). *Christmas. "The Twelve Days of Christmas" (carol). T* **425** *and similar vert designs. Multicoloured. P* 14½.

1404 25 c. Type **425** 20 10
1405 55 c. "Two turtle doves" 45 45
1406 65 c. "Three French hens" 50 50
1404/6 .. .. *Set of* 3 1·00 95

426 Conductor and Orchestra

427 Jetboating

(Des R. Freeman. Litho Leigh-Mardon Ltd, Melbourne)

1986 (5 Nov). *Music in New Zealand. T* **426** *and similar vert designs. P* 14½×14.

1407 30 c. multicoloured 25 10
1408 60 c. black, new blue and yellow-orange .. 45 60
1409 80 c. multicoloured .. .. 70 1·25
1410 $1 multicoloured .. .. 80 1·10
1407/10 .. .. *Set of* 4 2·00 2·75

Designs:—60 c. Cornet and brass band; 80 c. Piper and Highland pipe band; $1 Guitar and country music group.

(Des M. Wyatt. Litho Leigh-Mardon Ltd, Melbourne)

1987 (14 Jan). *Tourism. T* **427** *and similar vert designs. Multicoloured. P* 14½×14.

1411 60 c. Type **427** 50 50
1412 70 c. Sightseeing flights 60 60
1413 80 c. Camping 70 75
1414 85 c. Windsurfing 70 75
1415 $1.05, Mountaineering .. .. .. 90 1·00
1416 $1.30, River rafting .. .. .. 1·10 1·25
1411/16 .. .. *Set of* 6 4·00 4·25

428 Southern Cross Cup

(Des R. Proud. Litho Leigh-Mardon Ltd, Melbourne)

1987 (2 Feb). *Yachting Events. T* **428** *and similar horiz designs showing yachts. Multicoloured. P* 14×14½.

1417 40 c. Type **428** 35 15
1418 80 c. Admiral's Cup 70 80
1419 $1.05, Kenwood Cup .. .. 85 1·25
1420 $1.30, America's Cup .. .. .. 1·10 1·40
1417/20 .. .. *Set of* 4 2·75 3·25

429 Hand writing Letter and Postal Transport

(Des Communication Arts Ltd. Litho C.P.E. Australia Ltd, Melbourne)

1987 (1 Apr). *New Zealand Post Ltd Vesting Day. T* **429** *and similar horiz design. Multicoloured. P* 13½.

1421 40 c. Type **429** .. .. 1·00 1·40
a. Horiz pair. Nos. 1421/2 .. .. .. 2·00 2·75
1422 40 c. Posting letter, train and mailbox .. 1·00 1·40

Nos. 1421/2 were printed together, *se-tenant*, in horizontal pairs throughout the sheet.

430 Avro Type 626 and Wigram Airfield, 1937

431 Urewera National Park and Fern Leaf

(Des P. Leitch. Litho Leigh-Mardon Ltd, Melbourne)

1987 (15 Apr). *50th Anniv of Royal New Zealand Air Force. T* **430** *and similar horiz designs. Multicoloured. P* 14×14½.

1423 40 c. Type **430** 60 15
1424 70 c. Curtiss P-40E Kittyhawk I over World War II Pacific airstrip .. .. .. 80 1·25
1425 80 c. Short S.25 Sunderland flying boat and Pacific lagoon .. .. 90 1·25
1426 85 c. Douglas A-4F Skyhawk and Mt Ruapehu .. .. 95 1·25
1423/6 .. .. *Set of* 4 3·00 3·50
MS1427 115×105 mm. Nos. 1423/6 .. .. 4·50 3·25

No. **MS**1427 overprinted on the selvedge with the "CAPEX" logo was only available from the New Zealand stand at this International Philatelic Exhibition in Toronto.

(Des Tracey Purkis. Litho Leigh-Mardon Ltd, Melbourne)

1987 (17 June). *Centenary of National Parks Movement. T* **431** *and similar vert designs. Multicoloured. P* 14½.

1428 70 c. Type **431** 70 55
1429 80 c. Mt Cook and buttercup 75 60
1430 85 c. Fiordland and pineapple shrub 80 65
1431 $1.30, Tongariro and tussock .. .. 1·40 95
1428/31 .. .. *Set of* 4 3·25 2·50
MS1432 123×99 mm. No. 1431 (*sold at* $1.70) .. 1·75 1·75

The 40 c. premium on No. **MS**1432 was to support "New Zealand 1990" International Stamp Exhibition, Auckland.

No. **MS**1432 overprinted on the selvedge with the "CAPEX" logo was only available from the New Zealand stand at this International Philatelic Exhibition in Toronto.

432 "Kite Flying" (Lauren Baldwin)

433 "Hark the Herald Angels Sing"

(Adapted D. Little. Litho Leigh-Mardon Ltd, Melbourne)

1987 (29 July). *Health Stamps. Children's Paintings (2nd series). T* **432** *and similar multicoloured designs. P* 14½.

1433 40 c. + 3 c. Type **432** .. .. .. 80 1·25
a. Horiz pair. Nos. 1433/4 .. .. 1·60 2·50
1434 40 c. + 3 c. "Swimming" (Ineke Schoneveld) 80 1·25
1435 60 c. + 3 c. "Horse Riding" (Aaron Tylee) (*vert*) .. .. 1·25 1·50
1433/5 .. .. *Set of* 3 2·50 3·50
MS1436 100×117 mm. Nos. 1433/5, each×2 .. 5·00 6·50

Nos. 1433/4 were printed together, *se-tenant*, in horizontal pairs throughout the sheet.

(Des Ellen Giggenbach. Litho Leigh-Mardon Ltd, Melbourne)

1987 (16 Sept). *Christmas. T* **433** *and similar vert designs. Multicoloured. P* 14½.

1437 35 c. Type **433** 45 10
1438 70 c. "Away in a Manger" 90 55
1439 85 c. "We Three Kings of Orient Are" .. 1·10 65
1437/9 .. .. *Set of* 3 2·25 1·25

434 Knot ("Pona")

435 "Geothermal"

(Des Nga Puna Waihanga. Litho Security Printers (M), Malaysia)

1987 (4 Nov). *Maori Fibre-work. T* **434** *and similar vert designs. Multicoloured. W* **138** *of Malaysia. P* 12.

1440 40 c. Type **434** 35 10
1441 60 c. Binding ("Herehere") 45 45
1442 80 c. Plait ("Whiri") 60 65
1443 85 c. Cloak weaving ("Korowai") with flax fibre ("Whitau") 65 70
1440/3 .. .. *Set of* 4 1·90 1·75

(Des Fay McAlpine. Litho Leigh-Mardon Ltd, Melbourne)

1988 (13 Jan). *Centenary of Electricity. T* **435** *and similar horiz designs, each showing radiating concentric circles representing energy generation. P* 14×14½.

1444 40 c. multicoloured 30 35
1445 60 c. black, rosine and brownish black .. 40 45
1446 70 c. multicoloured 50 55
1447 80 c. multicoloured 55 60
1444/7 .. .. *Set of* 4 1·60 1·75

Designs:—60 c. "Thermal"; 70 c. "Gas"; 80 c. "Hydro".

436 Queen Elizabeth II and 1882 Queen Victoria 1d. Stamp

437 "Mangopare"

(Des A. G. Mitchell (40 c.), M. Conly and M. Stanley ($1). Litho Leigh-Mardon Ltd, Melbourne)

1988 (13 Jan). *Centenary of Royal Philatelic Society of New Zealand. T* **436** *and similar multicoloured designs. P* 14×14½.

1448 40 c. Type **436** 35 50
a. Horiz pair. Nos. 1448/9 .. .. 70 1·00
1449 40 c. As Type **436**, but 1882 Queen Victoria 2d. 35 50
MS1450 107×160 mm. $1 "Queen Victoria" (Chalon) (*vert*). P 14½×14 .. .. 2·75 2·75

Nos. 1448/9 were printed together, *se-tenant*, in horizontal pairs throughout the sheet.

No. **MS**1450 overprinted on the selvedge with the "SYDPEX" logo was only available from the New Zealand stand at this International Philatelic Exhibition in Sydney and from the Philatelic Bureau at Wanganui.

(Des S. Adsett. Litho Leigh-Mardon Ltd, Melbourne)

1988 (2 Mar). *Maori Rafter Paintings. T* **437** *and similar vert designs. Multicoloured. P* 14½.

1451 40 c. Type **437** 40 40
1452 40 c. "Koru" 40 40
1453 40 c. "Raupunga" 40 40
1454 60 c. "Koiri" 55 65
1451/4 .. .. *Set of* 4 1·60 1·75

438 "Good Luck"

439 Paradise Shelduck

(Des Communication Arts Ltd. Litho CPE Australia Ltd, Melbourne)

1988 (18 May). *Greetings Booklet Stamps. T* **438** *and similar multicoloured designs. P* 13½.

1455 40 c. Type **438** 55 55
a. Booklet pane. Nos. 1455/9 .. .. 2·50
1456 40 c. "Keeping in touch" 55 55
1457 40 c. "Happy birthday" 55 55
1458 40 c. "Congratulations" (41 × 27 *mm*) .. 55 55
1459 40 c. "Get well soon" (41 × 27 *mm*) .. 55 55
1455/9 .. .. *Set of* 5 2·50 2·50

Nos. 1455/9 only exist from $2 stamp booklets.

(Des Pauline Morse. Litho Southern Colour Print, Dunedin (Nos. 1467ab/ac) or Leigh-Mardon Ltd, Melbourne (others))

1988 (7 June)–**95**. *Native Birds. T* **439** *and similar vert designs. Multicoloured. P* 14½×14.

1459*a* 5 c. Sooty Crake (1.7.91) 10 10
1460 10 c. Double-banded Plover ("Banded Dotterel") (2.11.88) 10 10
1461 20 c. Yellowhead (2.11.88) 15 20
a. Perf 13½ (22.9.95) 45 30
1462 30 c. Grey-backed White Eye ("Silvereye") (2.11.88) 25 30
1463 40 c. Brown Kiwi (2.11.88) 35 40
a. Perf 13½×13 (8.11.89) .. .. 90 1·25
ab. Pack pane. No. 1463a×10 with margins all round .. .. .. 8·50
1463*b* 45 c. Rock Wren (1.7.91) 40 45
ba. Booklet pane. No. 1463*b*×10 with horiz sides of pane imperf (1.10.91) 4·50
1464 50 c. Sacred Kingfisher (2.11.88) 40 45
1465 60 c. Spotted Cormorant ("Spotted Shag") (2.11.88) 50 55
a. Perf 13½ (22.9.95) 70 70
1466 70 c. Type **439** 55 60
1467 80 c. Fiordland Crested Penguin (2.11.88) .. 70 70
1467*a* 80 c. New Zealand Falcon (31.3.93) 70 70
ab. Perf 12 (7.94) 65 70
ac. Booklet pane. No. 1467ab×10 .. 7·50
1468 90 c. New Zealand Robin (2.11.88) 75 80
1459*a*/68 .. .. *Set of* 12 4·50 4·75

No. 1463a was only issued in panes of ten with margins on all four sides. These panes were initially included in "Stamp Pads" of 50 such panes, but subsequently appeared in $4 stamp packs.

A miniature sheet containing No. 1466 was only available from the New Zealand stand at "WORLD STAMP EXPO '89" International Stamp Exhibition or the Philatelic Bureau, Wanganui. It was subsequently overprinted with the "New Zealand 1990" emblem.

No. 1467a was originally issued in $8 booklets on 31 March 1993, but appeared in sheets on 18 February 1994.

No. 1467ab was only issued in $8 stamp booklets and shows the vertical edges of the pane imperforate.

For 40 c. and 45 c. stamps in similar designs, but self-adhesive, see Nos. 1589/*a*.

For Nos. 1459*a*/65 in miniature sheet for the "Philakorea '94" International Stamp Exhibition see No. **MS**1830.

440 Milford Track

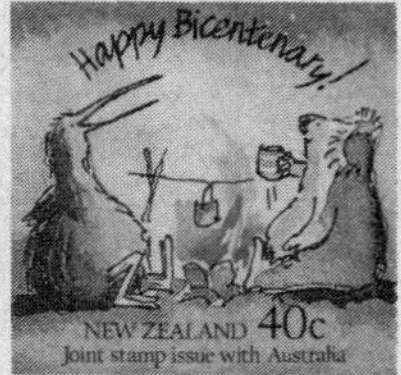

441 Kiwi and Koala at Campfire

(Des H. Thompson. Litho Leigh-Mardon Ltd, Melbourne)

1988 (8 June). *Scenic Walking Trails. T* **440** *and similar vert designs. Multicoloured. P* 14½.

1469 70 c. Type **440** . . 50 60
1470 80 c. Heaphy Track . . 55 70
1471 85 c. Copland Track . . 60 75
1472 $1.30, Routeburn Track . . 90 1·10
1469/72 *Set of* 4 2·25 2·75
MS1473 124 × 99 mm. No. 1472 (*sold at* $1.70) 1·50 1·50

The 40 c. premium on No. **MS**1473 was to support "New Zealand 1990" International Stamp Exhibition, Auckland.

(Des R. Harvey. Litho Leigh-Mardon Ltd, Melbourne)

1988 (21 June). *Bicentenary of Australian Settlement. P* 14½.

1474 **441** 40 c. multicoloured . . 60 35

A stamp in a similar design was also issued by Australia.

442 Swimming

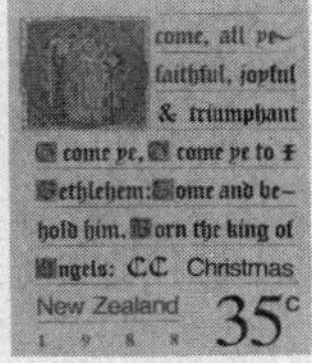

443 "O Come All Ye Faithful"

(Des R. Proud. Litho Leigh-Mardon Ltd, Melbourne)

1988 (27 July). *Health Stamps. Olympic Games, Seoul. T* **442** *and similar horiz designs. Multicoloured. P* 14½.

1475 40 c. + 3 c. Type **442** . . 40 60
1476 60 c. + 3 c. Athletics . . 60 90
1477 70 c. + 3 c. Canoeing . . 70 1·00
1478 80 c. + 3 c. Show-jumping . . 90 1·25
1475/8 *Set of* 4 2·40 3·25
MS1479 120 × 90 mm. Nos. 1475/8 . . 3·25 3·75

(Des Fay McAlpine. Litho Leigh-Mardon Ltd, Melbourne)

1988 (14 Sept). *Christmas. Carols. T* **443** *and similar vert designs, each showing illuminated verses. Multicoloured. P* 14½.

1480 35 c. Type **443** . . 35 30
1481 70 c. "Hark the Herald Angels Sing" . . 65 65
1482 80 c. "Ding Dong Merrily on High" . . 70 70
1483 85 c. "The First Nowell" . . 80 80
1480/3 *Set of* 4 2·25 2·25

444 "Lake Pukaki" (John Gully)

445 Brown Kiwi

(Litho Leigh-Mardon Ltd, Melbourne)

1988 (5 Oct). *New Zealand Heritage (1st issue). The Land. T* **444** *and similar horiz designs showing 19th-century paintings. Multicoloured. P* 14 × 14½.

1484 40 c. Type **444** . . 35 35
1485 60 c. "On the Grass Plain below Lake Arthur" (William Fox) . . 45 45
1486 70 c. "View of Auckland" (John Hoyte) . . 55 55
1487 80 c. "Mt. Egmont from the Southward" (Charles Heaphy) . . 60 60
1488 $1.05, "Anakiwa, Queen Charlotte Sound" (John Kinder) . . 80 80
1489 $1.30, "White Terraces, Lake Rotomahana" (Charles Barraud) . . 95 95
1484/9 *Set of* 6 3·25 3·25

See also Nos. 1505/10, 1524/9, 1541/6, 1548/53 and 1562/7.

(Des A. Mitchell. Eng. G. Prosser of B.A.B.N. Recess Leigh-Mardon Ltd, Melbourne)

1988 (19 Oct)–**93**. *P* 14½ (*and* 13 *around design*).

1490 **445** $1 bronze-green . . 2·00 2·75
a. Booklet pane. No. 1490×6 . . 11·00
1490*b* $1 bright scarlet (17.4.91) . . 1·00 1·40
1490*c* $1 blue (9.6.93) . . 90 1·25
1490/*c* *Set of* 3 3·50 4·75

Nos. 1490/*c* were each printed within a square margin, perforated vertically for No. 1490 and on all four sides for Nos. 1490*b*/*c*, and with a further circular perforation around the design.

No. 1490 was only issued in $6 stamp booklets with the horizontal edges of the booklet pane imperforate.

Nos. 1490*b*/*c* were printed in sheets of 24 (6×4).

For miniature sheets containing similar stamps, some printed in lithography, see Nos. **MS**1745 and **MS**1786.

For $1 violet printed in lithography see No. 2090.

446 Humpback Whale and Calf

447 Clover

(Des Lindy Fisher. Litho Govt Ptg Office, Wellington)

1988 (2 Nov). *Whales. T* **446** *and similar horiz designs. Multicoloured. P* 13½.

1491 60 c. Type **446** . . 80 85
1492 70 c. Killer Whales . . 1·00 1·10
1493 80 c. Southern Right Whale . . 1·10 1·25
1494 85 c. Blue Whale . . 1·25 1·50
1495 $1.05, Southern Bottlenose Whale and calf . . 1·50 2·00
1496 $1.30, Sperm Whale . . 1·60 2·00
1491/6 *Set of* 6 6·50 8·00

Although inscribed "ROSS DEPENDENCY" Nos. 1491/6 were available from post offices throughout New Zealand.

(Des Heather Arnold. Litho Leigh-Mardon Ltd, Melbourne)

1989 (18 Jan). *Wild Flowers. T* **447** *and similar horiz designs. Multicoloured. P* 14½.

1497 40 c. Type **447** . . 40 35
1498 60 c. Lotus . . 50 55
1499 70 c. Montbretia . . 60 65
1500 80 c. Wild Ginger . . 70 75
1497/1500 *Set of* 4 2·00 2·10

448 Katherine Mansfield

449 Moriori Man and Map of Chatham Islands

(Des A. G. Mitchell. Litho Harrison)

1989 (1 Mar). *New Zealand Authors. T* **448** *and similar vert designs. Multicoloured. P* 12½.

1501 40 c. Type **448** . . 30 35
1502 60 c. James K. Baxter . . 40 50
1503 70 c. Bruce Mason . . 50 60
1504 80 c. Ngaio Marsh . . 55 70
1501/4 *Set of* 4 1·60 1·90

(Des D. Gunson. Litho Leigh-Mardon Ltd, Melbourne)

1989 (17 May). *New Zealand Heritage (2nd issue). The People. T* **449** *and similar horiz designs. P* 14×14½.

1505 40 c. multicoloured . . 45 35
1506 60 c. orge-brn, brownish grey & reddish brn 60 70
1507 70 c. yellow-grn, brownish grey & dp olive 65 75
1508 80 c. bright greenish blue, brownish grey and deep dull blue . . 75 85
1509 $1.05, grey, brownish grey & grey-black 1·00 1·10
1510 $1.30, bright rose-red, brownish grey, and lake-brown . . 1·25 1·40
1505/10 *Set of* 6 4·25 4·50

Designs:—60 c. Gold prospector; 70 c. Settler ploughing; 80 c. Whaling; $1.05, Missionary preaching to Maoris; $1.30, Maori village.

450 White Pine (Kahikatea)

451 Duke and Duchess of York with Princess Beatrice

(Des D. Gunson. Litho Questa)

1989 (7 June). *Native Trees. T* **450** *and similar vert designs. Multicoloured. P* 14×14½.

1511 80 c. Type **450** . . 75 80
1512 85 c. Red Pine (Rimu) . . 80 85
1513 $1.05, Totara . . 1·00 1·10
1514 $1.30, Kauri . . 1·25 1·40
1511/14 *Set of* 4 3·50 3·75
MS1515 102×125 mm. No. 1514 (*sold at* $1.80) 1·75 1·75

The 50 c. premium on No. **MS**1515 was to support "New Zealand 1990" International Stamp Exhibition, Auckland.

(Des and litho Leigh-Mardon Ltd, Melbourne)

1989 (26 July). *Health Stamps. T* **451** *and similar vert designs. Multicoloured. P* 14½.

1516 40 c. + 3 c. Type **451** . . 80 1·00
a. Horiz pair. Nos. 1516/17 . . 1·60 2·00
1517 40 c. + 3 c. Duchess of York with Princess Beatrice . . 80 1·00
1518 80 c. + 3 c. Princess Beatrice . . 1·40 1·75
1516/18 *Set of* 3 2·75 3·25
MS1519 120×89 mm. Nos. 1516/18, each ×2 . . 5·50 7·00

Nos. 1516/17 were printed together, *se-tenant*, in horizontal pairs throughout the sheet.

No. **MS**1519 overprinted on the selvedge with the "WORLD STAMP EXPO '89" logo was only available from the New Zealand stand at this International Stamp Exhibition and from the Philatelic Bureau at Wanganui.

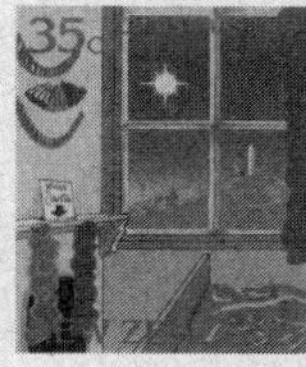

452 One Tree Hill, Auckland, through Bedroom Window

453 Windsurfing

(Des H. Chapman. Litho Leigh-Mardon Ltd, Melbourne)

1989 (13 Sept). *Christmas. T* **452** *and similar vert designs showing Star of Bethlehem. Multicoloured. P* 14½.

1520 35 c. Type **452** . . 40 30
1521 65 c. Shepherd and dog in mountain valley 75 70
1522 80 c. Star over harbour . . 95 90
1523 $1 Star over globe . . 1·25 1·40
1520/3 *Set of* 4 3·00 3·00

(Des M. Bailey. Litho Leigh-Mardon Ltd, Melbourne)

1989 (11 Oct). *New Zealand Heritage (3rd issue). The Sea. T* **453** *and similar horiz designs. Multicoloured. P* 14×14½.

1524 40 c. Type **453** . . 40 35
1525 60 c. Fishes of many species . . 70 70
1526 65 c. Striped Marlin and game fishing launch . . 75 75
1527 80 c. Rowing boat and yachts in harbour 85 85
1528 $1 Coastal scene . . 1·10 1·10
1529 $1.50, *Rotoiti* (container ship) and tug 1·50 1·60
1524/9 *Set of* 6 4·75 4·75

454 Games Logo

(Des Heather Arnold. Litho Leigh-Mardon Ltd, Melbourne)

1989 (8 Nov)–**90**. *14th Commonwealth Games. Auckland. T* **454** *and similar horiz designs. Multicoloured. P* 14½.

1530 40 c. Type **454** . . 40 35
1531 40 c. Goldie (games kiwi mascot) . . 40 35
1532 40 c. Gymnastics . . 40 35
1533 50 c. Weightlifting . . 50 55
1534 65 c. Swimming . . 65 70
1535 80 c. Cycling . . 80 90
1536 $1 Lawn bowling . . 1·00 1·25
1537 $1.80, Hurdling . . 1·75 1·90
1530/7 *Set of* 8 5·50 5·75
MS1538 Two sheets, each 105×92 mm. with different margin designs. (a) Nos. 1530/1 (horiz pair). (b) Nos. 1530/1 (vert pair) (24.1.90) *Set of* 2 *sheets* 5·00 3·50

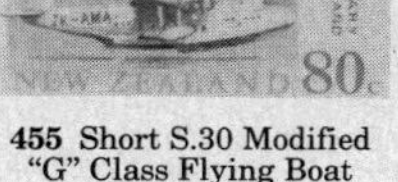

455 Short S.30 Modified "G" Class Flying Boat *Aotearoa* and Boeing 747-200

456 Chief Kawiti signing Treaty

(Des R. Proud. Litho Enschedé)

1990 (17 Jan). *50th Anniv of Air New Zealand. P* 13×14½.

1539 **455** 80 c. multicoloured . . 1·40 80

(Des A. G. Mitchell from painting by L. C. Mitchell. Litho Enschedé)

1990 (17 Jan). *150th Anniv of Treaty of Waitangi. Sheet 80×118 mm, containing T* **456** *and similar multicoloured design. P* 13½.

MS1540 40 c. Type **456**; 40 c. Chief Hone Heke (first signatory) and Lieut-Governor Hobson (*horiz*) . . 3·25 3·25

457 Maori Voyaging Canoe **458** *Thelymitra pulchella*

(Des G. Fuller. Litho Leigh-Mardon Ltd, Melbourne)

1990 (7 Mar). *New Zealand Heritage (4th issue). The Ships. T* **457** *and similar horiz designs. Multicoloured. P* 14×14½.
1541 40 c. Type **457** 60 35
1542 50 c. H.M.S. *Endeavour* (Cook), 1769 .. 75 65
1543 60 c. *Tory* (barque), 1839 .. .. .. 85 70
1544 80 c. *Crusader* (full-rigged immigrant ship), 1871 .. .. 1·25 95
1545 $1 *Edwin Fox* (full-rigged immigrant ship), 1873 .. .. 1·40 1·25
1546 $1.50, *Arawa* (steamer), 1884 .. .. 2·00 1·75
1541/6 .. .. *Set of* 6 6·25 5·00

A miniature sheet containing No. 1542 was only available from the New Zealand stand at "Stamp World London '90" International Stamp Exhibition or from the Philatelic Bureau, Wanganui.

(Des Lindy Fisher. Litho Leigh-Mardon Ltd, Melbourne)

1990 (18 Apr). *"New Zealand 1990" International Stamp Exhibition, Auckland. Native Orchids. Sheet* 179×80 *mm. containing T* **458** *and similar vert designs. Multicoloured. P* 14½.
MS1547 40 c. Type **458**; 40 c. *Corybas macranthus*; 40 c. *Dendrobium cunninghamii*; 40 c. *Pterostylis banksii*; 80 c. *Aporostylis bifolia* (*sold at* $4.90) .. .. 4·50 4·50

The stamps in No. **MS**1547 form a composite design.
The $2.50 premium on No. **MS**1547 was used to support the Exhibition.
Miniature sheets as No. **MS**1547, but imperforate are from a limited printing distributed to those purchasing season tickets for the exhibition.

459 Grace Neill (social reformer) and Maternity Hospital, Wellington **460** Akaroa

(Des Elspeth Williamson. Litho Leigh-Mardon Ltd, Melbourne)

1990 (16 May). *New Zealand Heritage (5th issue). Famous New Zealanders. T* **459** *and similar horiz designs. Multicoloured. P* 14×14½.
1548 40 c. Type **459** 55 30
1549 50 c. Jean Batten (pilot) and Percival P.3 Gull Six aircraft 65 75
1550 60 c. Katherine Sheppard (suffragette) and 19th-century women .. .. .. 85 1·25
1551 80 c. Richard Pearse (inventor) and early flying machine .. .. 1·10 1·25
1552 $1 Lt.-Gen. Sir Bernard Freyberg and tank .. .. 1·25 1·25
1553 $1.50, Peter Buck (politician) and Maori pattern .. .. 1·50 2·00
1548/53 .. .. *Set of* 6 5·50 6·25

(Des Lindy Fisher. Litho Leigh-Mardon Ltd, Melbourne)

1990 (13 June). *150th Anniversary of European Settlements. T* **460** *and similar vert designs. Multicoloured. P* 14½.
1554 80 c. Type **460** 75 75
1555 $1 Wanganui 95 95
1556 $1.50, Wellington .. .. 1·40 1·90
1557 $1.80, Takapuna Beach, Auckland .. 1·60 2·00
1554/7 .. .. *Set of* 4 4·25 5·00
MS1558 125×100 mm. No. 1557 (*sold at* $2.30) 3·50 3·50

The 50 c. premium on No. **MS**1558 was to support "New Zealand 1990" International Stamp Exhibition, Auckland.

461 Jack Lovelock (athlete) and Race **462** Creation Legend of Rangi and Papa

(Des T. Crilley. Litho Questa)

1990 (25 July). *Health Stamps. Sportsmen (1st series). T* **461** *and similar horiz design. Multicoloured. P* 14½×13½.
1559 40 c. + 5 c. Type **461** 50 65
1560 80 c. + 5 c. George Nepia (rugby player) and match .. .. 75 1·10
MS1561 115×96 mm. Nos. 1559/60, each × 2 2·50 2·75

See also Nos. 1687/9.

(Des K. Hall. Litho Leigh-Mardon Ltd, Melbourne)

1990 (24 Aug). *New Zealand Heritage (6th issue). The Maori. T* **462** *and similar horiz designs. Multicoloured. P* 14×14½.
1562 40 c. Type **462** 40 30
a. Violet-blue (face value) omitted .. £275
1563 50 c. Pattern from Maori feather cloak .. 55 65
1564 60 c. Maori women's choir 60 70
1565 80 c. Maori facial tattoos 75 85
1566 $1 War canoe prow (detail) .. .. 90 1·10
1567 $1.50, Maori haka .. .. 1·40 2·25
1562/7 .. .. *Set of* 6 4·25 5·25

463 Queen Victoria **464** Angel

(Des A. G. Mitchell. Recess Leigh-Mardon Ltd, Melbourne)

1990 (29 Aug). *150th Anniv of the Penny Black. Sheet* 169×70 *mm containing T* **463** *and similar vert designs. P* 14½×14.
MS1568 40 c.×6 indigo (Type **463**, King Edward VII, King George V, King Edward VIII, King George VI, Queen Elizabeth II) .. .. 3·75 4·00

(Des Sally Simons. Litho Leigh-Mardon Ltd, Melbourne)

1990 (12 Sept). *Christmas. T* **464** *and similar vert designs showing angels. P* 14½.
1569 40 c. purple, dp greenish bl & dp yellow-brn 40 30
1570 $1 purple, blue-green & dp yellow-brown 80 80
1571 $1.50, pur, brt crimson & dp yellow-brn 1·40 1·60
1572 $1.80, purple, red and deep yellow-brown 1·60 1·75
1569/72 .. .. *Set of* 4 3·75 4·00

465 Antarctic Petrel **466** Coopworth Ewe and Lambs

(Des Janet Luxton. Litho Heraclio Fournier)

1990 (7 Nov). *Antarctic Birds. T* **465** *and similar vert designs. Multicoloured. P* 13½×13.
1573 40 c. Type **465** 60 30
1574 50 c. Wilson's Petrel 70 50
1575 60 c. Snow Petrel 85 60
1576 80 c. Southern Fulmar 90 75
1577 $1 Chinstrap Penguin .. .. 1·10 85
1578 $1.50, Emperor Penguin .. .. .. 1·60 1·75
1573/8 .. .. *Set of* 6 5·25 4·25

Although inscribed "Ross Dependency" Nos. 1573/8 were available from post offices throughout New Zealand.

(Des Lindy Fisher. Litho Leigh-Mardon Ltd, Melbourne)

1991 (23 Jan). *New Zealand Farming and Agriculture. Sheep Breeds. T* **466** *and similar vert designs. Multicoloured. P* 14½×14.
1579 40 c. Type **466** 40 40
1580 60 c. Perendale 55 75
1581 80 c. Corriedale 70 85
1582 $1 Drysdale 85 90
1583 $1.50, South Suffolk .. .. 1·25 2·00
1584 $1.80, Romney .. .. 1·50 2·00
1579/84 .. .. *Set of* 6 4·75 6·25

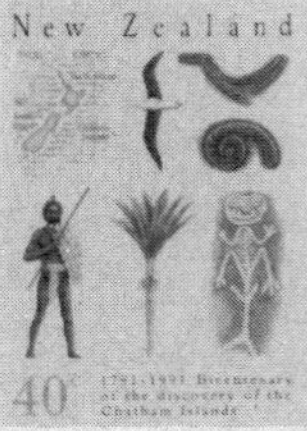

467 Moriori, Royal Albatross, Nikau Palm and Artefacts **468** Goal and Footballers

(Des K. Hall. Litho Southern Colour Print Ltd, Dunedin)

1991 (6 Mar). *Bicentenary of Discovery of Chatham Islands. T* **467** *and similar vert design. Multicoloured. P* 13½.
1585 40 c. Type **467** 50 50
1586 80 c. Carvings, H.M.S. *Chatham*, Moriori house of 1870, and Tommy Solomon 1·25 1·60

(Des T. Crilley. Litho Southern Colour Print Ltd, Dunedin)

1991 (6 Mar). *Centenary of New Zealand Football Association. T* **468** *and similar horiz design. Multicoloured. P* 13½.
1587 80 c. Type **468** .. .. 1·00 1·40
a. Horiz pair. Nos. 1587/8 .. .. 2·00 2·75
1588 80 c. Five footballers and referee .. .. 1·00 1·40

Nos. 1587/8 were printed together, *se-tenant*, in horizontal pairs throughout the sheet, each pair forming a composite design.

(Des Pauline Morse. Litho Printset-Cambec Pty Ltd, Melbourne (40 c., 45 c. (No. 1589a) or Leigh-Mardon Ltd, Melbourne (45 c. (No. 1589ab))

1991 (17 Apr–Dec). *As Nos.* 1463/*b, but self-adhesive. P* 11½.
1589 40 c. Brown Kiwi 45 60
1589*a* 45 c. Rock Wren (1 July) 30 45
ab. Perf 11 (Dec) 30 45

Nos. 1589/*a* were only available in coils of 100, each stamp, with die-cut perforations, being separate on the imperforate backing paper. Initially the 45 c. showed the surplus surface paper removed, but from December 1991 supplies of No. 1589ab had the stamps surrounded by white selvedge. The format was changed again in March 1992 when the coils again appeared without the white selvedge. Part of the March 1992 printing, and all subsequent supplies, had the stamps interlocked with no backing paper visible between them.

A limited quantity of the 45 c. (No. 1589a) in sheets of 200 (8×25) was produced for use on official first day covers. It is reported that a small number of such sheets were subsequently sold by a few post offices.

469 Tuatara on Rocks **470** Clown

(Des Pauline Morse. Litho Leigh-Mardon Ltd, Melbourne)

1991 (17 Apr). *Endangered Species. The Tuatara. T* **469** *and similar horiz designs. Multicoloured. P* 14½.
1590 40 c. Type **469** 40 55
1591 40 c. Tuatara in crevice 40 55
1592 40 c. Tuatara with foliage 40 55
1593 40 c. Tuatara in dead leaves 40 55
1590/3 .. .. *Set of* 4 1·40 2·00

(Des Helen Crawford. Litho Leigh-Mardon Ltd, Melbourne)

1991 (15 May–1 July). *Booklet Stamps. "Happy Birthday". T* **470** *and similar multicoloured designs. P* 13½.
1594 40 c. Type **470** 45 60
a. Booklet pane. Nos. 1594/8 .. .. 2·00
1595 40 c. Balloons 45 60
1596 40 c. Party hat 45 60
1597 40 c. Birthday present (41×27 *mm*) 45 60
1598 40 c. Birthday cake (41×27 *mm*) 45 60
1599 45 c. Type **470** (1 July) 45 60
a. Booklet pane. Nos. 1599/1603 .. 2·00
1600 45 c. As No. 1595 (1 July) 45 60
1601 45 c. As No. 1596 (1 July) 45 60
1602 45 c. As No. 1597 (1 July) 45 60
1603 45 c. As No. 1598 (1 July) 45 60
1594/1603 .. .. .. *Set of* 10 4·00 5·50

The above were only issued in $2 (Nos. 1594/8) or $2.25 (Nos. 1599/1603) stamp booklets.

471 Cat at Window **472** Punakaiki Rocks

(Des Jennifer Lautusi. Litho Leigh-Mardon Ltd, Melbourne)

1991 (15 May–1 July). *Booklet Stamps. "Thinking of You". T* **471** *and similar multicoloured designs. P* 13½.
1604 40 c. Type **471** 45 60
a. Booklet pane. Nos. 1604/8 .. .. 2·00
1605 40 c. Cat playing with slippers 45 60
1606 40 c. Cat with alarm clock 45 60
1607 40 c. Cat in window (41×27 *mm*) 45 60
1608 40 c. Cat at door (41×27 *mm*) 45 60
1609 45 c. Type **471** (1 July) 45 60
a. Booklet pane. Nos. 1609/13 .. .. 2·00
1610 45 c. As No. 1605 (1 July) 45 60
1611 45 c. As No. 1606 (1 July) 45 60
1612 45 c. As No. 1607 (1 July) 45 60
1613 45 c. As No. 1608 (1 July) 45 60
1604/13 .. .. *Set of* 10 4·00 5·50

The above were only issued in $2 (Nos. 1604/8) or $2.25 (Nos. 1609/13) stamp booklets.

(Des H. Thompson. Litho Leigh-Mardon Ltd, Melbourne)

1991 (12 June). *Scenic Landmarks. T* **472** *and similar horiz designs. Multicoloured. P* 14½.
1614 40 c. Type **472** 40 30
1615 50 c. Moeraki Boulders 55 55
1616 80 c. Organ Pipes 85 85
1617 $1 Castle Hill 95 95
1618 $1.50, Te Kaukau Point .. .. .. 1·50 1·60
1619 $1.80, Ahuriri River Clay Cliffs .. .. 1·75 1·90
1614/19 .. .. *Set of* 6 5·50 5·50

473 Dolphins Underwater

474 Children's Rugby

(Des Heather Arnold. Litho Leigh-Mardon Ltd, Melbourne)

1991 (24 July). *Health Stamps. Hector's Dolphin.* T **473** *and similar horiz design. Multicoloured.* P 14½.

1620 45 c. + 5 c. Type **473** 75 90
1621 80 c. + 5 c. Dolphins leaping .. .. 1·00 1·40
MS1622 115×100 mm. Nos. 1620/1, each × 2 4·00 4·00

(Des A.G. Mitchell. Litho Leigh-Mardon Ltd, Melbourne)

1991 (21 Aug). *World Cup Rugby Championship.* T **474** *and similar vert designs. Multicoloured.* P 14½×14.

1623 80 c. Type **474** .. .. 85 1·00
1624 $1 Women's rugby 95 95
1625 $1.50, Senior rugby .. .. .. 1·60 2·25
1626 $1.80, "All Blacks" (national team) .. 1·90 2·25
1623/6 .. .. *Set of* 4 4·75 5·75
MS1627 113×90 mm. No. 1626 (*sold at* $2.40) 2·00 2·25

No. **MS**1627 additionaly inscribed "PHILA NIPPON '91" was available, at $1·80, from the New Zealand stand at this International Stamp Exhibition in Tokyo and from the Philatelic Bureau at Wanganui.

475 Three Shepherds

476 *Dodonidia helmsii*

(Des Designworks Communications. Litho Southern Colour Print, Dunedin)

1991 (18 Sept). *Christmas.* T **475** *and similar vert designs. Multicoloured.* P 13½.

1628 45 c. Type **475** 55 65
a. Block of four. Nos 1628/31 .. .. 2·00
1629 45 c. Two Kings on camels 55 65
1630 45 c. Mary and Baby Jesus 55 65
1631 45 c. King with gift 55 65
1632 65 c. Star of Bethlehem 70 80
1633 $1 Crown 85 95
1634 $1.50, Angel .. .. 1·40 1·75
1628/34 .. .. *Set of* 7 4·50 5·50

Nos. 1628/31 were printed together, *se-tenant,* in blocks of four throughout the sheet.

(Des Pauline Morse)

1991 (6 Nov)–**97.** *Butterflies.* T **476** *and similar vert designs. Multicoloured. (a) Litho Leigh-Mardon Ltd, Melbourne.* P 14½.

1635 $1 Type **476** 85 60
1636 $2 *Zizina otis oxleyi* .. .. .. 1·75 1·25
1637 $3 *Vanessa itea* .. .. 2·50 2·50
1638 $4 *Lycaena salustius* (25.1.95) .. .. 3·50 3·75
1639 $5 *Bassaris gonerilla* (25.1.95) .. .. 4·25 4·50
1635/9 .. .. *Set of* 5 13·00 11·50

(*b*) *Litho Questa.* P 13½×14

1640 $1 As Type **476** (6.11.96) 75 80
1641 $2 As No. 1636 (6.11.96) .. .. 1·50 1·60
1642 $3 As No. 1637 (8.96) .. .. .. 2·25 2·40
a. Grey (inscrs) and apple-green (frame) omitted .. ..
1643 $4 As No. 1638 (10.97) .. .. .. 3·00 3·25
1644 $5 As No. 1639 (9.10.96) .. .. 3·75 4·00
1640/4 .. .. *Set of* 5 11·00 12·00

(*c*) *Booklet stamps. Litho Southern Colour Print, Dunedin.* P 14×14½

1645 $1 Type **476** (1.9.95) .. .. .. 2·25 2·75
a. Booklet pane. No. 1645×5 and five "airPOST" labels .. .. .. 11·00

Nos. 1640/2 are from the 3 kiwi printings and Nos. 1643/4 from the 1 kiwi. The designs of Nos. 1640/1 are redrawn.

No. 1645 only exists imperforate at foot and was issued in $5 stamp booklets in which the airmail labels were vertically *se-tenant* with the stamps.

A miniature sheet containing No. 1637 was only available from the New Zealand stand at "PHILA NIPPON '91" International Stamp Exhibition, Tokyo, or the Philatelic Bureau, Wanganui.

479 Yacht *Kiwi Magic,* 1987

480 *Heemskerk*

(Des R. Proud. Litho Leigh-Mardon Ltd, Melbourne)

1992 (22 Jan). *New Zealand Challenge for America's Cup.* T **479** *and similar horiz designs. Multicoloured.* P 14.

1655 45 c. Type **479** 45 35
1656 80 c. Yacht *New Zealand,* 1988 .. .. 80 70
1657 $1 Yacht *America,* 1851 .. .. 95 85
1658 $1.50, "America's Cup" Class yacht, 1992 1·40 1·40
1655/8 .. .. *Set of* 4 3·25 3·00

(Des G. Fuller. Litho Enschedé)

1992 (12 Mar). *Great Voyages of Discovery.* T **480** *and similar horiz designs. Multicoloured.* P 13×14½.

1659 45 c. Type **480** 50 35
1660 80 c. *Zeehan* 80 70
1661 $1 *Santa Maria* .. .. 1·00 85
1662 $1.50, *Pinta* and *Nina* .. .. .. 1·50 1·40
1659/62 .. .. *Set of* 4 3·50 3·00

Nos. 1659/60 commemorate the 350th anniversary of Tasman's discovery of New Zealand and Nos. 1661/2 the 500th anniversary of discovery of America by Columbus.

A miniature sheet containing stamps as Nos. 1661/2, but perforated 14, was only available from the New Zealand stand at "World Columbian Stamp Expo '92", Chicago, and from the Philatelic Bureau at Wanganui.

481 Sprinters

482 Weddell Seal and Pup

(Des Sheryl McCammon. Litho Southern Colour Print, Dunedin)

1992 (3 Apr). *Olympic Games, Barcelona (1st issue).* P 13½.

1663 **481** 45 c. multicoloured 50 40

See also Nos. 1670/4.

(Des Lindy Fisher. Litho Southern Colour Print, Dunedin)

1992 (8 Apr). *Antarctic Seals.* T **482** *and similar horiz designs. Multicoloured.* P 13½.

1664 45 c. Type **482** 65 35
1665 50 c. Crabeater Seals swimming 75 35
1666 65 c. Leopard Seal and Adelie Penguins .. 85 70
1667 80 c. Ross Seal .. .. 1·00 85
1668 $1 Southern Elephant Seal and harem 1·10 95
1669 $1.80, Hooker's Sea Lion and pup .. 2·00 1·90
1664/9 .. .. *Set of* 6 5·75 4·75

Although inscribed "ROSS DEPENDENCY" Nos. 1664/9 were available from post offices throughout New Zealand.

483 Cycling

484 Ice Pinnacles, Franz Josef Glacier

(Des M. Bailey. Litho Southern Colour Print, Dunedin)

1992 (13 May). *Olympic Games, Barcelona (2nd issue).* T **483** *and similar horiz designs.* P 13½.

1670 45 c. Type **483** 55 35
1671 80 c. Archery 80 70
1672 $1 Equestrian three-day eventing .. 95 85
1673 $1.50, Sailboarding .. .. .. 1·40 1·40
1670/3 .. .. *Set of* 4 3·25 3·00
MS1674 125×100 mm. Nos. 1670/3. P 14×14½ 3·50 3·50

No. **MS**1674 exists overprinted with the emblem of the "World Columbian, Stamp Expo '92" and was only available from the New Zealand stand at this International Stamp Exhibition in Chicago and from the Philatelic Bureau at Wanganui.

(Des A. Hollows. Litho Southern Colour Print, Dunedin)

1992 (12 June). *Glaciers.* T **484** *and similar horiz designs. Multicoloured.* P 13½.

1675 45 c. Type **484** 40 35
1676 50 c. Tasman Glacier 50 45
1677 80 c. Snowball glacier, Marion Plateau .. 70 70
1678 $1 Brewster Glacier 85 85
1679 $1.50, Fox Glacier .. .. .. 1·40 1·40
1680 $1.80, Franz Josef Glacier .. .. 1·50 1·60
1675/80 .. .. *Set of* 6 4·75 4·75

485 "Grand Finale" Camellia

486 Tree and Hills

(Des Patricia Altman. Litho Leigh-Mardon Ltd, Melbourne)

1992 (8 July). *Camellias.* T **485** *and similar vert designs. Multicoloured.* P 14½.

1681 45 c. Type **485** 40 35
1682 50 c. "Showa-No-Sakae" 50 45
1683 80 c. "Sugar Dream" 70 70
1684 $1 "Night Rider" 85 85
1685 $1.50, "E.G. Waterhouse" .. .. 1·40 1·40
1686 $1.80, "Dr. Clifford Parks" .. .. 1·50 1·50
1681/6 .. .. *Set of* 6 4·75 4·75

(Des T. Crilley. Litho Southern Colour Print, Dunedin)

1992 (12 Aug). *Health Stamps. Sportsmen (2nd series). Horiz designs as* T **461.** *Multicoloured.* P 13½.

1687 45 c. + 5 c. Anthony Wilding (tennis player) and match 55 60
1688 80 c. + 5 c. Stewie Dempster (cricketer) and batsman 70 80
MS1689 115×96 mm. Nos. 1687/8, each × 2. P 14 .. .. 3·50 3·50

(Des Van de Roer Design. Litho Leigh-Mardon Ltd, Melbourne)

1992 (1 Sept). *Booklet Stamps. Landscapes.* T **486** *and similar horiz designs. Multicoloured.* P 14×14½.

1690 45 c. Type **486** 40 50
a. Booklet pane. Nos. 1690/9 .. .. 3·75
1691 45 c. River and hills 40 50
1692 45 c. Hills and mountain 40 50
1693 45 c. Glacier 40 50
1694 45 c. Hills and waterfall 40 50
1695 45 c. Tree and beach 40 50
1696 45 c. Estuary and cliffs 40 50
1697 45 c. Fjord 40 50
1698 45 c. River delta 40 50
1699 45 c. Ferns and beach 40 50
1690/9 .. .. *Set of* 10 3·75 4·50

Nos. 1690/9 were only issued in $4.50 stamp booklets with the pane forming a composite design.

487 Reindeer over Houses

488 1920s Fashions

(Des K. Hall. Litho Leigh-Mardon Ltd, Melbourne)

1992 (16 Sept). *Christmas.* T **487** *and similar vert designs. Multicoloured.* P 14½.

1700 45 c. Type **487** 60 65
a. Block of 4. Nos. 1700/3 .. .. 2·25
1701 45 c. Santa Claus on sleigh over houses .. 60 65
1702 45 c. Christmas tree in window .. 60 65
1703 45 c. Christmas wreath and children at window 60 65
1704 65 c. Candles and fireplace 70 70
1705 $1 Family going to church 90 90
1706 $1.50, Picnic under Pohutukawa tree 1·50 1·50
1700/6 .. .. *Set of* 7 5·00 5·25

Nos. 1700/3 were printed together, *se-tenant,* in blocks of four throughout the sheet.

(Des T. Crilley. Litho Southern Colour Print, Dunedin)

1992 (4 Nov). *New Zealand in the 1920s.* T **488** *and similar vert designs. Multicoloured.* P 13½.

1707 45 c. Type **488** 45 35
1708 50 c. Dr. Robert Jack and early radio announcer 50 50
1709 80 c. "All Blacks" rugby player, 1924 .. 75 75
1710 $1 Swaggie and dog 85 85
1711 $1.50, Ford "Model A" car and young couple .. .. 1·50 1·50
1712 $1.80, Amateur aviators and biplane .. 1·90 2·00
1707/12 .. .. *Set of* 6 5·50 5·50

489 "Old Charley" Toby Jug

490 Women's Fashions of the 1930s

(Des Brand New Ltd. Litho Leigh-Mardon Ltd, Melbourne)

1993 (20 Jan). *Royal Doulton Ceramics Exhibition, New Zealand.* T **489** *and similar vert designs. Multicoloured.* P 13.

1713 45 c. Type **489** 45 35
1714 50 c. "Bunnykins" nursery plate 50 50
1715 80 c. "Maori Art" tea set 75 75
1716 $1 "Ophelia" handpainted plate 90 90
1717 $1.50, "St. George" figurine .. .. 1·50 1·50
1718 $1.80, "Lambeth" saltglazed stoneware vase .. .. 1·75 2·00
1713/18 .. .. *Set of* 6 5·25 5·50
MS1719 125×100 mm. No. 1718 .. .. 1·60 1·60

(Des R. Jones. Litho Leigh-Mardon Ltd, Melbourne)

1993 (17 Feb). *New Zealand in the 1930s. T* **490** *and similar vert designs. Multicoloured. P* 14½×14.

1720 45 c. Type **490** 45 40
1721 50 c. Unemployed protest march 50 65
1722 80 c. "Phar Lap" (racehorse) 75 80
1723 $1 State housing project 90 95
1724 $1.50, Boys drinking free school milk .. 1·50 1·75
1725 $1.80, Cinema queue .. .. .. 1·75 1·75
1720/5 .. .. *Set of* 6 5·25 5·75

491 Women signing Petition

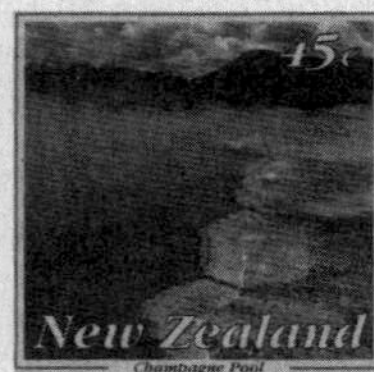

492 Champagne Pool

(Des Lindy Fisher. Litho Southern Colour Print, Dunedin)

1993 (31 Mar). *Centenary of Women's Suffrage. T* **491** *and similar vert designs. Multicoloured. P* 13½.

1726 45 c. Type **491** 45 35
1727 80 c. Aircraft propeller and woman on tractor 75 75
1728 $1 Housewife with children 90 95
1729 $1.50, Modern women .. .. .. 1·50 1·60
1726/9 .. .. *Set of* 4 3·25 3·25

(Des A. Hollows. Litho Southern Colour Print, Dunedin)

1993 (5 May). *Thermal Wonders, Rotorua. T* **492** *and similar square designs. Multicoloured. P* 12.

1730 45 c. Type **492** 50 40
1731 50 c. Boiling mud 50 40
1732 80 c. Emerald Pool 75 70
1733 $1 Hakereteke Falls 85 80
1734 $1.50, Warbrick Terrace .. .. .. 1·40 1·50
1735 $1.80, Pohutu Geyser .. .. .. 1·50 1·75
1730/5 .. .. *Set of* 6 5·00 5·00

For miniature sheet containing $1.80 see No. **MS**1770.

493 Yellow-eyed Penguin, Hector's Dolphin and New Zealand Fur Seal

494 Boy with Puppy

(Des Donna McKenna. Litho Southern Colour Print, Dunedin (No. 1740) or Leigh-Mardon Ltd, Melbourne (others))

1993 (9 June). *Endangered Species Conservation. T* **493** *and similar horiz designs. Multicoloured. P* 13½ (*No.* 1740) *or* 14×14½ (*others*).

1736 45 c. Type **493** 45 45
a. Block of 4. Nos. 1736/9 .. .. 1·60
1737 45 c. Chatham Island Taiko (bird), Mount Cook Lily and Mountain Duck .. 45 45
1738 45 c. Giant Snail, Rock Wren and Hamilton's Frog 45 45
1739 45 c. Kaka (bird), New Zealand Pigeon and Giant Weta 45 45
1740 45 c. Tusked Weta (23×28 *mm*) 45 45
1736/40 .. .. *Set of* 5 2·00 2·00

Nos. 1736/9 were issued either in sheets of one design or in sheets containing *se-tenant* blocks of four, as No. 1736a, each forming a composite design.

No. 1740 was only issued in $4.50 stamp booklets.

(Des Karen Odiam. Litho Southern Colour Print, Dunedin)

1993 (21 July). *Health Stamps. Children's Pets. T* **494** *and similar vert design. Multicoloured. P* 13½.

1741 45 c. + 5 c. Type **494** 50 60
1742 80 c. + 5 c. Girl with kitten .. .. .. 75 1·00
MS1743 115×96 mm. Nos. 1741/2, each × 2. P 14½ .. .. 2·50 3·00

No. **MS**1743 exists surcharged "STAMPEX '93 NATIONAL YOUTH PHILATELIC EXHIBITION CHRISTCHURCH 19TH–21ST AUGUST 1993 $6·00" in ultramarine. Such miniature sheets were prepared by the organisers and sold at the Exhibition P.O. philatelic counter.

(Recess and litho Leigh-Mardon Ltd, Melbourne (No. **MS**1745))

1993 (14 Aug). *"Taipei '93" Asian International Stamp Exhibition, Taiwan.*

(*a*) *No.* **MS**1743 *optd* "TAIPEI '93" *and emblem on sheet margin*

MS1744 Nos. 1741/2, each × 2 .. .. .. 6·50 7·50

(*b*) *Sheet* 125×100 *mm containing No.* 1490*c* (*recess*) *and two similar designs as Nos.* 1490/*b*, *but litho. P* 13 (*around design*)

MS1745 **445** $1 deep green, $1 blue, $1 rosine 4·50 4·50

Unlike previous miniature sheets produced by New Zealand Post for international stamp exhibitions overseas Nos. **MS**1744/5, and all subsequent issues of this type, were supplied to collectors in New Zealand and abroad by standing order.

495 Christmas Decorations (value at left)

496 Rainbow Abalone or Paua

(Des Kristine Cotton. Litho Southern Colour Print, Dunedin (Nos. 1746b/9b) or Leigh-Mardon Ltd, Melbourne (others))

1993 (1 Sept–3 Nov). *Christmas. T* **495** *and similar vert designs. Multicoloured. P* 14½×14.

1746 45 c. Type **495** 50 60
a. Block of 4. Nos. 1746/9 .. .. 2·00
b. Perf 12 (3 Nov) .. .. .. 1·00 1·25
ba. Booklet pane. Nos. 1746b/7a, each × 3, and 1748a/9a, each × 2 .. 8·50
1747 45 c. Christmas decorations (value at right) 50 60
a. Perf 12 (3 Nov) .. .. .. 1·00 1·25
1748 45 c. Sailboards, gifts and Christmas pudding (value at left) 50 60
a. Perf 12 (3 Nov) .. .. .. 1·00 1·25
1749 45 c. Sailboards, gifts and Christmas pudding (value at right) 50 60
a. Perf 12 (3 Nov) .. .. .. 1·00 1·25
1750 $1 Sailboards, baubles and Christmas cracker .. .. 1·25 1·25
1751 $1.50, Sailboards, present and wreath 1·75 2·25
1746/51 .. .. *Set of* 6 4·50 5·50

Nos. 1746/9 were printed together, *se-tenant*, in blocks of four throughout the sheet.

Booklet pane No. 1746ba contains two *se-tenant* blocks of 4 and a horizontal pair.

(Des R. Youmans. Litho Southern Colour Print, Dunedin)

1993 (1 Sept). *Booklet Stamps. Marine Life. T* **496** *and similar horiz designs. Multicoloured. P* 13½.

1752 45 c. Type **496** 50 50
a. Booklet pane. Nos. 1752/61 and two stamp-size labels .. .. .. 4·50
1753 45 c. Green Mussels 50 50
1754 45 c. Tarakihi 50 50
1755 45 c. Salmon 50 50
1756 45 c. Southern Blue-finned Tuna, Yellow-finned Tuna and Kahawai 50 50
1757 45 c. Rock Lobster 50 50
1758 45 c. Snapper 50 50
1759 45 c. Grouper 50 50
1760 45 c. Orange Roughy 50 50
1761 45 c. Squid, Hoki and Black Oreo 50 50
1752/61 .. .. *Set of* 10 4·50 4·50

Nos. 1752/61 were only issued in $4.50 stamp booklets with the *se-tenant* pane, which includes two inscribed labels at left, forming a composite design.

497 Sauropod

498 Soldiers, National Flag and Pyramids

(Des G. Cox. Litho Southern Colour Print, Dunedin)

1993 (1 Oct). *Prehistoric Animals. T* **497** *and similar multicoloured designs. P* 12 (*No.* 1763) *or* 13½ (*others*).

1762 45 c. Type **497** 45 45
1763 45 c. Carnosaur and Sauropod (30×25 *mm*) 45 45
a. Booklet pane of 10 and two labels .. 4·25
1764 80 c. Pterosaur 85 85
1765 $1 Ankylosaur 95 95
1766 $1.20, Mauisaurus .. .. .. 1·40 1·40
1767 $1.50, Carnosaur .. .. .. 1·50 1·50
1762/7 .. .. *Set of* 6 5·00 5·00
MS1768 125×100 mm. $1.50, As No. 1767. P 14½×14 .. .. 1·75 1·75

No. 1763 was only issued in $4.50 stamp booklets.

A used example of No. 1762 is known with the yellow omitted.

(Des A. Hollows (No. **MS**1770). Litho Southern Colour Print, Dunedin)

1993 (1 Oct). *"Bangkok '93" International Stamp Exhibition, Thailand.*

(*a*) *No.* **MS**1768 *optd* "BANGKOK '93" *and emblem on sheet margin*

MS1769 $1.50, As No. 1767 .. .. .. 1·40 2·00

(*b*) *Sheet* 115×100 *mm. containing No.* 1735

MS1770 $1.80, multicoloured .. .. .. 1·75 2·25

(Des P. Andrews. Litho Questa)

1993 (3 Nov). *New Zealand in the 1940s. T* **498** *and similar vert designs. Multicoloured. P* 14.

1771 45 c. Type **498** 45 40
1772 50 c. Aerial crop spraying 50 50
1773 80 c. Hydro-electric scheme 80 80
1774 $1 Marching majorettes 90 90
1775 $1.50, American troops .. .. .. 1·50 1·50
1776 $1.80, Crowd celebrating victory .. 1·60 1·60
1771/6 .. .. *Set of* 6 5·25 5·25

499 Bungy Jumping

500 *New Zealand Endeavour* (yacht)

(Des G. Taylor. Litho Southern Colour Print, Dunedin)

1994 (19 Jan). *Tourism. T* **499** *and similar multicoloured designs. P* 12.

1777 45 c. Type **499** 50 40
1778 45 c. White water rafting (25×25 *mm*) .. 50 55
a. Booklet pane of 10 plus 4 half stamp-size greetings labels .. .. 4·50
1779 80 c. Trout fishing 70 70
1780 $1 Jet boating (*horiz*) 80 80
1781 $1.50, Tramping .. .. 1·40 1·40
1782 $1.80, Heli-skiing .. .. .. 1·90 2·00
1777/82 .. .. *Set of* 6 5·25 5·25

No. 1778 was only issued in $4.50 stamp booklets.

For miniature sheet containing the $1.80 see No. **MS**1785.

(Des B. Hall. Litho Leigh-Mardon Ltd, Melbourne)

1994 (19 Jan). *Round the World Yacht Race. P* 14½ (*and* 13 *around design*).

1783 **500** $1 multicoloured .. .. .. 1·40 1·40

No. 1783 was printed in sheets of 24 (6×4) with each stamp within a square perforated margin and with a further circular perforation around the design..

501 Mt Cook and New Zealand Symbols

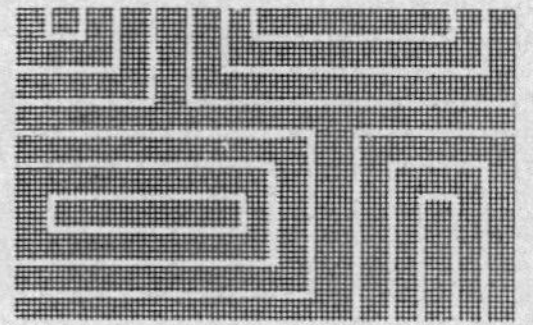

502

(Des Heather Arnold. Engraved C. Slania. Recess and die-stamped (gold) Leigh-Mardon Ltd, Melbourne)

1994 (18 Feb). *W* **502**. *P* 14½×15.

1784 **501** $20 deep violet-blue and gold .. 15·00 16·00

No. 1784 shows a fluorescent security pattern of "New Zealand Post" printed beneath the design.

(Des G. Taylor (No. **MS**1785), Karen Odiam (No. **MS**1786). Litho Southern Colour Print, Dunedin (No. **MS**1785) or Leigh-Mardon Ltd, Melbourne (No. **MS**1786))

1994 (18 Feb). *"Hong Kong '94" International Stamp Exhibition. P* 12 (*No.* **MS**1785) *or* 13 (*No.* **MS**1786).

MS1785 95×115 mm. $1.80, mult (No. 1782) .. 2·25 2·25
MS1786 100×125 mm. $1 deep green, $1 rosine, $1 blue (As Nos. 1490/*c*, but all printed litho) 3·75 3·75

503 Rock and Roll Dancers

504 Mt Cook and Mt Cook Lily ("Winter")

(Des Karen Odiam. Litho Leigh-Mardon Ltd, Melbourne)

1994 (23 Mar). *New Zealand in the 1950s. T* **503** *and similar vert designs. Multicoloured. P* 14½×14.

1787 45 c. Type **503** 45 40
1788 80 c. Sir Edmund Hillary on Mt Everest 75 75
1789 $1 Aunt Daisy (radio personality) .. 85 85
1790 $1.20, Queen Elizabeth II during 1953 royal visit .. .. 1·25 1·25
1791 $1.50, Children playing with Opo the dolphin .. .. 1·60 1·60
1792 $1.80, Auckland Harbour Bridge .. 1·90 2·00
1787/92 .. .. *Set of* 6 6·25 6·25

(Des R. Youmans. Litho Southern Colour Print, Dunedin)

1994 (27 Apr). *The Four Seasons. T* **504** *and similar horiz designs. Multicoloured. P* 12.
1793 45 c. Type **504** 45 40
a. Horiz strip of 4. Nos. 1793/6 .. 3·75
1794 70 c. Lake Hawea and Kowhai ("Spring") 65 65
1795 $1.50, Opononi Beach and Pohutukawa ("Summer") .. .. 1·40 1·40
1796 $1.80, Lake Pukaki and Puriri ("Autumn") .. .. 1·75 1·75
1793/6 .. .. *Set of* 4 3·75 3·75
In addition to separate sheets of 100 (10×10) Nos. 1793/6 were also printed together, *se-tenant*, in horizontal strips of 4 throughout sheets of 80 (8×10).

505 Rainbow Abalone or Paua Shell

506 Maui pulls up Te Ika

(Des D. Gunson. Litho Southern Colour Print, Dunedin)

1994 (27 Apr). *Booklet Stamps. New Zealand Life. T* **505** *and similar multicoloured designs. P* 12.
1797 45 c. Type **505** (25×20 *mm*) 35 40
a. Booklet pane. Nos. 1797/1806 .. 3·50
1798 45 c. Pavlova dessert (35×20 *mm*) .. 35 40
1799 45 c. Hokey pokey ice cream (25×20 *mm*) 35 40
1800 45 c. Fish and chips (35×20 *mm*) .. 35 40
1801 45 c. Jandals (30×20 *mm*) 35 40
1802 45 c. Bush shirt (25×30½ *mm*) 35 40
1803 45 c. Buzzy Bee (toy) (35×30½ *mm*) .. 35 40
1804 45 c. Gumboots and black singlet (25×30½ *mm*) 35 40
1805 45 c. Rugby boots and ball (35×30½ *mm*) 35 40
1806 45 c. Kiwifruit (30×30½ *mm*) 35 40
1797/1806 .. .. *Set of* 10 3·50 4·00
Nos. 1797/1806 were only issued in $4.50 stamp booklets.

(Des Manu Kopere Society. Litho Leigh-Mardon Ltd, Melbourne)

1994 (8 June). *Maori Myths. T* **506** *and similar vert designs. Multicoloured. P* 13.
1807 45 c. Type **506** 45 40
1808 80 c. Rona snatched up by Marama .. 75 85
1809 $1 Maui attacking Tuna .. .. 90 1·00
1810 $1.20, Tane separating Rangi and Papa 1·25 1·60
1811 $1.50, Matakauri slaying the Giant of Wakatipu .. .. 1·40 1·75
1812 $1.80, Panenehu showing crayfish to Tangaroa .. .. 1·60 1·75
1807/12 .. .. *Set of* 6 5·75 6·50

507 1939 2d. on 1d. + 1d. Health Stamp and Children playing with Ball

508 Astronaut on Moon (hologram)

(Des D. Gunson. Litho Leigh-Mardon Ltd, Melbourne)

1994 (20 July). *Health Stamps. 75th Anniv of Children's Health Camps. T* **507** *and similar vert designs. Multicoloured. P* 14½.
1813 45 c. + 5 c. Type **507** 50 70
1814 45 c. + 5 c. 1949 1d. + ½d. stamp and nurse holding child 50 70
1815 45 c. + 5 c. 1969 4 c. + 1 c. stamp and children reading 50 70
1816 80 c. + 5 c. 1931 2d. + 1d. stamp and child in cap 75 90
1813/16 .. .. *Set of* 4 2·00 2·75
MS1817 130×90 mm. Nos. 1813/16 .. .. 2·00 2·75

(Des Brand New Ltd, Wellington. Litho Southern Colour Print, Dunedin (hologram by Woodmansterne Ltd, Watford))

1994 (20 July). *25th Anniv of First Moon Landing. P* 12.
1818 **508** $1.50, multicoloured .. .. .. 1·10 1·25

509 "people reaching people"

510 African Elephants

Two types of Type **509**:
Type I: "w" of "new" partly in blue. "i" of "reaching" without dot.
Type II: "w" of "new" all in magenta. "i" of "reaching" with dot.

(Des Van de Roer Designs. Litho Leigh-Mardon Ltd, Melbourne (Nos. 1818a, 1819) or SNP Cambec (Nos. 1818ab, 1819a))

1994 (20 July)–**96**. *Self-adhesive. P* 11.
1818*a* **509** 40 c. multicoloured (I) (2.10.95) .. 1·50 1·50
ab. Perf 11½. Type II (1996) .. 35 40
1819 45 c. multicoloured (I) 45 45
a. Perf 11½. Type II (1995) .. 50 40
Nos. 1818*a*/19*a* were each available in coils of 100. On Nos. 1818a and 1819 the vertical die-cut perforations interlock, but on No. 1818ab and 1819a the stamps are separate on the backing paper.

(Des Denise Durkin. Litho Leigh-Mardon Ltd, Melbourne)

1994 (16 Aug). *Stamp Month. Wild Animals. T* **510** *and similar horiz designs. Multicoloured. P* 14×14½.
1820 45 c. Type **510** 45 45
a. Block of 10. Nos. 1820/9 .. .. 4·00
1821 45 c. White Rhinoceros 45 45
1822 45 c. Lions 45 45
1823 45 c. Common Zebras 45 45
1824 45 c. Giraffe and calf 45 45
1825 45 c. Siberian Tiger 45 45
1826 45 c. Hippopotami 45 45
1827 45 c. Spider Monkey 45 45
1828 45 c. Giant Panda 45 45
1829 45 c. Polar Bear and cub 45 45
1820/9 .. .. *Set of* 10 4·00 4·00
Nos. 1820/9 were printed together, *se-tenant*, in sheets of 100 so arranged as to provide horizontal or vertical strips of 10 or blocks of 10 (5×2) showing all the designs.

(Des Pauline Morse (No. **MS**1830), Denise Durkin (No. **MS**1831). Litho Leigh-Mardon Ltd, Melbourne)

1994 (16 Aug). *"Philakorea '94" International Stamp Exhibition, Seoul. Multicoloured. P* 14½×14 *(No.* **MS**1830) *or* 14×14½ *(No.* **MS**1831).
MS1830 125×100 mm. Nos. 1459a/65 .. 3·50 3·25
MS1831 125×100 mm. Nos. 1820, 1822, 1824/5 and 1828/9 .. .. 3·00 3·50

511 Children with Crib

512 Batsman

(Des Karen Odiam. Litho Southern Colour Print, Dunedin (No. 1832) or Leigh-Mardon Ltd, Melbourne (others))

1994 (21 Sept). *Christmas. T* **511** *and similar horiz designs. Multicoloured. P* 12 *(No.* 1832) *or* 14½ *(others)*.
1832 45 c. Father Christmas and children (30×25 *mm*) 35 40
1833 45 c. Type **511** 35 40
1834 70 c. Man and toddler with crib 55 70
1835 80 c. Three carol singers 60 75
1836 $1 Five carol singers 80 90
1837 $1.50, Children and candles .. .. 1·10 1·50
1838 $1.80, Parents with child .. .. 1·40 1·75
1832/8 .. .. *Set of* 7 5·00 5·75
MS1839 125×100 mm. Nos. 1833/6 .. .. 2·75 2·75
No. 1832 was only issued in $4.50 stamp booklets.

(Des M. Bailey (Nos. 1840/9), P. Andrews (others). Litho Southern Colour Print, Dunedin)

1994 (2 Nov). *Centenary of New Zealand Cricket Council.*

(*a*) *Horiz designs, each 30×25 mm. Multicoloured. P* 12
1840 45 c. Bathers catching balls 40 50
a. Booklet pane of 10. Nos. 1840/9 .. 3·50
1841 45 c. Child on surf board at top 40 50
1842 45 c. Young child with rubber ring at top 40 50
1843 45 c. Man with beach ball at top 40 50
1844 45 c. Woman with cricket bat at right .. 40 50
1845 45 c. Boy in green cap with bat 40 50
1846 45 c. Man in spotted shirt running .. 40 50
1847 45 c. Woman in striped shorts with bat .. 40 50
1848 45 c. Boy in wet suit with surf board at right 40 50
1849 45 c. Sunbather with newspaper at right 40 50

(*b*) *T* **512** *and similar vert designs. Multicoloured. P* 13½
1850 45 c. Type **512** 45 40
1851 80 c. Bowler 80 80
1852 $1 Wicket keeper .. .. .. 1·00 1·00
1853 $1.80, Fielder .. .. 1·75 1·75
1840/53 .. .. *Set of* 14 7·25 8·00
Nos. 1840/9 were only issued in $4.50 stamp booklets.

(Litho Leigh-Mardon Ltd, Melbourne)

1995 (3 Feb). *"POST X '95" Postal History Exhibition, Auckland. Sheet 130×90 mm, containing No.* 1297 *and a reproduction of No.* 557 *optd "SPECIMEN". P* 14½.
MS1854 $10 multicoloured .. .. .. 15·00 15·00

COVER PRICES

Cover factors are quoted at the beginning of each country for most issues to 1945. An explanation of the system can be found on page x. The factors quoted do not, however, apply to philatelic covers.

513 Auckland

514 The 15th Hole, Waitangi

(Des Red Cactus Design. Litho Southern Colour Print, Dunedin)

1995 (22 Feb). *New Zealand by Night. T* **513** *and similar horiz designs. Multicoloured. P* 12.
1855 45 c. Type **513** 35 40
1856 80 c. Wellington 60 65
1857 $1 Christchurch 80 85
1858 $1.20, Dunedin .. .. 95 1·00
1859 $1.50, Rotorua .. .. 1·10 1·25
1860 $1.80, Queenstown .. .. .. 1·40 1·50
1855/60 .. .. *Set of* 6 5·00 5·50
See also No. **MS**1915.

(Des R. Jones. Litho Leigh-Mardon Ltd, Melbourne)

1995 (22 Mar). *New Zealand Golf Courses. T* **514** *and similar vert designs. Multicoloured. P* 14½×14.
1861 45 c. Type **514** 50 40
1862 80 c. The 6th hole, New Plymouth .. 80 80
1863 $1.20, The 9th hole, Rotorua .. .. 1·25 1·25
1864 $1.80, The 5th hole, Queenstown .. 2·10 2·25
1861/4 .. .. *Set of* 4 4·25 4·25

515 New Zealand Pigeon and Nest

516 Teacher with Guitar and Children

(Des Niki Hill. Litho Southern Colour Print, Dunedin)

1995 (22 Mar). *Booklet Stamps. Environment. T* **515** *and similar horiz designs. Multicoloured. P* 12.
1865 45 c. Type **515** 60 60
a. Booklet pane. Nos. 1865/74 .. 5·50
1866 45 c. Planting sapling 60 60
1867 45 c. Dolphins and whales 60 60
1868 45 c. Thunder storm 60 60
1869 45 c. Backpackers 60 60
1870 45 c. Animal pests 60 60
1871 45 c. Noxious plants 60 60
1872 45 c. Undersized fish and shellfish .. 60 60
1873 45 c. Pollution from factories 60 60
1874 45 c. Family at picnic site 60 60
1865/74 .. .. *Set of* 10 5·50 5·50
Nos. 1865/74 were only issued in $4.50 stamp booklets with the vertical edges of the pane imperforate. Each vertical pair forms a composite design.

(Des M. Kopere. Litho Southern Colour Print, Dunedin)

1995 (3 May). *Maori Language Year. T* **516** *and similar vert designs. Multicoloured. P* 13½.
1875 45 c. Type **516** 50 45
1876 70 c. Singing group 75 75
1877 80 c. Mother and baby 85 85
1878 $1 Women performing traditional welcome .. .. 1·10 1·10
1879 $1.50, Grandfather reciting family genealogy .. .. 1·75 1·75
1880 $1.80, Tribal orator .. .. .. 2·00 2·00
1875/80 .. .. *Set of* 6 6·25 6·25
In addition to sheets containing stamps of one value Nos. 1875/80 also exist in sheetlets of 24 containing four of each value *se-tenant*. These sheetlets were only available from Limited Edition Collectors Packs costing NZ$135.

517 Map of Australasia and Asia

518 *Black Magic* (yacht)

(Des Cue Design. Litho Southern Colour Print, Dunedin)

1995 (3 May). *Meetings of Asian Development Bank Board of Governors and International Pacific Basin Economic Council, Auckland. T* **517** *and similar horiz design. Multicoloured. P* 13½.
1881 $1 Type **517** .. .. 1·00 1·00
1882 $1.50, Map of Australasia and Pacific .. 1·50 2·00

(Des A. Hollows. Litho Southern Colour Print, Dunedin)

1995 (16 May). *New Zealand's Victory in 1995 America's Cup. P* 12.
1883 **518** 45 c. multicoloured 55 55
No. 1883 was issued in small sheets of 10 with a seascape printed on the margins. This sheetlet also exists numbered and overprinted in gold foil from a Limited Edition Collectors Pack costing NS$25.

519 Boy on Skateboard **520** Lion Red Cup and Players

(Des P. Martinson. Litho Leigh-Mardon Ltd, Melbourne)

1995 (21 June). *Health Stamps. Children's Sports. T* **519** *and similar triangular design. Multicoloured. P* 14½.
1884 45 c. + 5 c. Type **519** 50 55
a. *Tête-bêche* (pair) .. .. 1·00 1·10
1885 80 c. + 5 c. Girl on bicycle .. .. .. 90 1·00
a. *Tête-bêche* (pair) .. .. 1·75 2·00
MS1886 130×90 mm. Nos. 1884/5, each × 2 .. 3·75 3·75
Nos. 1884/5 were each printed in sheets with the horizontal rows made up of *tête-bêche* pairs.

1995 (1 July). *"Stampex '95" National Stamp Exhibition, Wellington. No.* **MS**1886 *additionally inscr with* "Stampex '95" *and emblem on sheet margin.*
MS1887 130×90 mm. Nos. 1884/5, each × 2 .. 3·75 4·00

(Des Heather Arnold. Litho Southern Colour Print, Dunedin (No. 1888) or Enschedé (others))

1995 (26 July). *Centenary of Rugby League. T* **520** *and similar horiz designs. Multicoloured. P* 12 *(No.* 1888) *or* 14×14½ *(others).*
1888 45 c. Trans Tasman test match (30×25 *mm*) 50 45
a. Booklet pane. No. 1888×10 .. 4·00
1889 45 c. Type **520** 50 45
1890 $1 Children's rugby and mascot .. 1·10 1·10
1891 $1.50, George Smith, Albert Baskerville and early match .. .. .. 1·75 1·75
1892 $1.80, Courtney Goodwill Trophy and match against Great Britain .. 2·00 2·10
1888/92 .. .. *Set of* 5 5·25 5·25
MS1893 125×100 mm. No. 1892 .. .. 2·25 2·25
No. 1888 was only issued in $4.50 stamp booklets and has the vertical edges of the pane imperforate.
No. **MS**1893 imperforate comes from a Limited Edition Collectors Pack costing NZ$135.

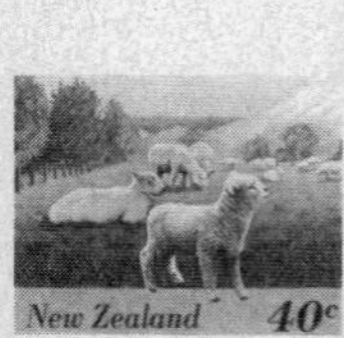

521 Sheep and Lamb **522** Archangel Gabriel

(Des Joanne Kreyl. Litho Southern Colour Print, Dunedin)

1995 (1 Sept–2 Oct). *Booklet Stamps. Farmyard Animals. T* **521** *and similar horiz designs. P* 14×14½.
1894 40 c. Type **521** (2 Oct) 35 40
a. Booklet pane. Nos. 1894/1903 .. 3·50
1895 40 c. Deer (2 Oct) 35 40
1896 40 c. Mare and foal (2 Oct) 35 40
1897 40 c. Cow with calf (2 Oct) 35 40
1898 40 c. Goats and kid (2 Oct) 35 40
1899 40 c. Common Turkey (2 Oct) 35 40
1900 40 c. Ducks (2 Oct) 35 40
1901 40 c. Red Junglefowl (2 Oct) 35 40
1902 40 c. Sow with piglets (2 Oct) 35 40
1903 40 c. Border Collie (2 Oct) 35 40
1904 45 c. Type **521** 50 55
a. Booklet pane. Nos. 1904/13 .. 4·50
1905 45 c. As No. 1895 .. .. .. 50 55
1906 45 c. As No. 1896 .. .. .. 50 55
1907 45 c. As No. 1897 .. .. .. 50 55
1908 45 c. As No. 1898 .. .. .. 50 55
1909 45 c. As No. 1899 .. .. .. 50 55
1910 45 c. As No. 1900 .. .. .. 50 55
1911 45 c. As No. 1901 .. .. .. 50 55
1912 45 c. As No. 1902 .. .. .. 50 55
1913 45 c. As No. 1903 .. .. .. 50 55
1894/1913 .. .. .. *Set of* 20 7·75 8·50
Nos. 1894/1903 and 1904/13 were only issued in $4 (Nos. 1894/1903) and $4.50 (Nos. 1904/13) stamp booklets in which the horizontal edges of the booklet panes are imperforate.

(Des Joanne Kreyl (No. **MS**1914), Red Cactus Design (No. **MS**1915). Litho Southern Colour Print, Dunedin)

1995 (1 Sept). *"Singapore '95" International Stamp Exhibition. P* 12.
MS1914 170×70 mm. Nos. 1909/13 .. .. 2·40 2·40
MS1915 148×210 mm. Nos. 1855/60 .. .. 6·50 6·50
No. **MS**1915 also includes the "JAKARTA '95" logo.

(Des K. Hall. Litho Southern Colour Print, Dunedin)

1995 (1 Sept–9 Nov). *Christmas. Stained Glass Windows from St. Mary's Anglican Church, Merivale (Nos.* 1916/18), *The Lady Chapel of St. Luke's Anglican Church, Christchurch (Nos.* 1919/22) *or St. John the Evangelist Church, Cheviot (No.* 1923). *Multicoloured. (a) As T* **522**. *P* 12
1916 40 c. Type **522** (2 Oct) 45 40
1917 45 c. Type **522** 55 45
1918 70 c. Virgin Mary 80 80
1919 80 c. Shepherds 90 90
1920 $1 Virgin and Child .. .. .. 1·10 1·10
1921 $1.50, Two Wise Men .. .. .. 1·75 2·00
1922 $1.80, Wise Man kneeling .. .. 2·00 2·25

(b) Smaller design, 25×30 *mm. P* 14½×14
1923 40 c. Angel with Trumpet (9 Nov) .. 40 45
a. Booklet pane. No. 1923×10 .. 4·00
1916/23 .. .. *Set of* 8 7·00 7·50
No. 1923 was only issued in $4 stamp booklets which show the outer edges of the pane imperforate.
Nos. 1916 and 1918/22 also exist as a miniature sheet, only available as part of a joint Phone Card and Stamp Collectors Pack produced in a limited quantity and costing NZ$115.

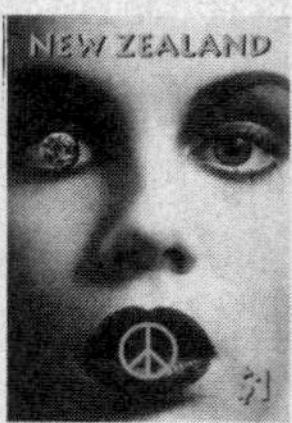

523 Face and Nuclear Disarmament Symbol **524** Mount Cook

(Des C. Martin. Litho Southern Colour Print, Dunedin)

1995 (1 Sept). *Nuclear Disarmament. P* 13½.
1924 **523** $1 multicoloured .. .. .. 1·00 90

(Des Red Cactus Design. Litho Enschedé ($10) or Southern Colour Print, Dunedin (others))

1995 (2 Oct)–**97**. *New Zealand Scenery. T* **524** *and similar multicoloured designs. P* 13½×14 *($10) or* 13½ *(others).*
1925 5 c. Type **524** (27.3.96) 10 10
1926 10 c. Champagne Pool (27.3.96) 10 10
1927 20 c. Cape Reinga (27.3.96) 15 20
1928 30 c. Mackenzie Country (27.3.96) .. 20 25
1929 40 c. Mitre Peak *(vert)* 30 35
1930 50 c. Mount Ngauruhoe (27.3.96) .. 35 40
1931 60 c. Lake Wanaka *(vert)* (27.3.96) .. 45 50
1932 70 c. Giant Kauri tree *(vert)* (27.3.96) .. 55 60
1933 80 c. Doubtful Sound *(vert)* (27.3.96) .. 60 65
1934 90 c. Waitomo Limestone Cave *(vert)* (27.3.96) 65 70
1935 $10 Mt Ruapehu (40×34 *mm*) (12.2.97) 7·25 7·50
1925/35 .. .. .. *Set of* 11 11·00 11·50
For miniature sheets containing some of these designs see Nos. **MS**1978, **MS**1998 and **MS**2005.
For similar self-adhesive designs see Nos. 1984/91.

525 Dame Kiri te Kanawa (opera singer) **526** National Flags, Peace Dove and "50"

(Des Karen Odiam. Litho Southern Colour Print, Dunedin)

1995 (4 Oct). *Famous New Zealanders. T* **525** *and similar horiz designs. Multicoloured. P* 12.
1936 40 c. Type **525** 55 40
1937 80 c. Charles Upham, V.C. (war hero) .. 80 85
1938 $1 Barry Crump (author) .. .. 1·00 1·00
1939 $1.20, Sir Brian Barratt-Boyes (surgeon) 1·25 1·25
1940 $1.50, Dame Whina Cooper (Maori leader) .. .. 1·50 1·75
1941 $1.80, Sir Richard Hadlee (cricketer) .. 2·25 2·25
1936/41 .. .. .. *Set of* 6 6·50 6·75
Nos. 1936/41 were issued in sheets with each stamp *se-tenant* horizontally with a 10×30 mm label inscribed "STAMP MONTH October 1995".

(Des S. Fuller. Litho Leigh-Mardon Ltd, Melbourne)

1995 (4 Oct). *50th Anniv of United Nations. P* 15.
1942 **526** $1.80, multicoloured .. .. .. 1·90 1·90

NEW INFORMATION

The editor is always interested to correspond with people who have new information that will improve or correct the Catalogue.

527 Fern and Globe

(Des Red Cactus Design. Litho Leigh-Mardon Ltd, Melbourne)

1995 (9 Nov). *Commonwealth Heads of Government Meeting, Auckland. T* **527** *and similar horiz design. Multicoloured. P* 14.
1943 40 c. Type **527** 50 40
1944 $1.80, Fern and New Zealand flag .. 2·00 2·00

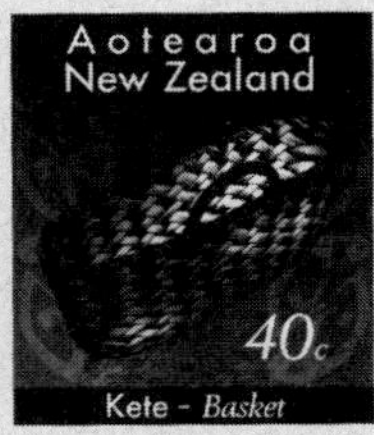

528 "Kiwi" **529** Kete (basket)

(Des Communication Arts Ltd. Litho Enschedé)

1996 (24 Jan). *Famous Racehorses. T* **528** *and similar horiz designs. Multicoloured. P* 14×14½.
1945 40 c. Type **528** 55 40
1946 80 c. "Rough Habit" 95 95
1947 $1 "Blossom Lady" .. .. .. 1·25 1·25
1948 $1.20, "Il Vicolo" .. .. .. 1·60 1·60
1949 $1.50, "Horlicks" .. .. .. 1·75 1·75
1950 $1.80, "Bonecrusher" .. .. .. 2·50 2·50
1945/50 .. .. .. *Set of* 6 7·75 7·75
MS1951 Seven sheets, each 162×110 mm. (a) No. 1945. (b) No. 1946. (c) No. 1947. (d) No. 1948. (e) No. 1949. (f) No. 1950. (g) Nos. 1945/50 *Set of* 7 *sheets* 15·00 17·00
Nos. **MS**1951a/g were only available from $13.70 stamp booklets, with each miniature sheet showing a line of roulettes at left.
An overprinted and numbered miniature sheet containing Nos. 1945/50 comes from a Limited Edition Collectors Pack costing NZ$135.

"BEST OF '96". Sets of three miniature sheets with this inscription and containing Nos. 1950, 1957, 1983, 1997, 2012, 2017, 2025, 2033 and 2042 were distributed by the Philatelic Bureau to customers who had purchased a certain amount of philatelic material from them during the year. These miniature sheets were printed in lithography by Southern Colour Print, Dunedin, and a number of the stamps they contain show different perforations from the examples in normal sheets. They could not be purchased by the general public at post offices.

(Des G. Hubbard. Litho Enschedé)

1996 (21 Feb). *Maori Crafts. T* **529** *and similar vert designs. Multicoloured. P* 14×13½.
1952 40 c. Type **529** 50 40
1953 80 c. Head of Taiaha (spear) 90 90
1954 $1 Taniko (embroidery) .. .. 1·25 1·25
1955 $1.20, Pounamu (greenstone) .. .. 1·50 1·50
1956 $1.50, Hue (gourd) .. .. .. 1·75 1·75
1957 $1.80, Korowai (feather cloak) .. 2·00 2·25
1952/7 .. .. .. *Set of* 6 7·25 7·25
For miniature sheet containing some of these designs see No. **MS**2049.

530 Black-backed Gulls **531** Fire and Ambulance Services

(Des Sue Wickison)

1996 (21 Feb–7 Aug). *Booklet Stamps. Seaside Environment. T* **530** *and similar horiz designs. Multicoloured.*

(a) Litho Southern Colour Print, Dunedin. P 14×14½.
1958 40 c. Type **530** 45 50
a. Booklet pane of 10. Nos. 1958/67 .. 4·25
1959 40 c. Children, Sea Cucumber and Spiny Starfish 45 50
1960 40 c. Yacht, gull and Common Shrimps .. 45 50
1961 40 c. Gaudy Nudibranch 45 50
1962 40 c. Large Rock Crab and Clingfish .. 45 50
1963 40 c. Snake Skin Chiton and Red Rock Crab 45 50
1964 40 c. Estuarine Triplefin and Cat's-eye shell 45 50
1965 40 c. Cushion Star and Sea Horses .. 45 50

1966 40 c. Blue-eyed Triplefin and Yaldwyn's Triplefin 45 50
1967 40 c. Common Octopus 45 50
1958/67 .. .. *Set of* 10 4·25 4·50

Nos. 1958/67 were only issued in $4 stamp booklets in which the horizontal edges of the pane are imperforate.

(*b*) *Litho SNP Cambec, Australia. Self-adhesive. P* $11^1/_2$ (7 Aug)

1968 40 c. Type **530** 45 50
a. Booklet pane of 10. Nos. 1968/77 .. 4·25
1969 40 c. Children, Sea Cucumber and Spiny Starfish 45 50
1970 40 c. Yacht, gull and Common Shrimps .. 45 50
1971 40 c. Gaudy Nudibranch 45 50
1972 40 c. Large Rock Crab and Clingfish .. 45 50
1973 40 c. Snake Skin Chiton and Red Rock Crab 45 50
1974 40 c. Estuarine Triplefin and Cat's-eye shell 45 50
1975 40 c. Cushion Star and Sea Horses .. 45 50
1976 40 c. Blue-eyed Triplefin and Yaldwyn's Triplefin 45 50
1977 40 c. Common Octopus 45 50
1968/77 .. .. *Set of* 10 4·25 4·50

Nos. 1958/67 were only issued in $4 stamp booklets in which the horizontal edges of the pane are imperforate.

Nos. 1968/77 were only issued in $4 self-adhesive stamp booklets, containing No. 1968a on which the surplus self-adhesive paper around each stamp was retained.

The phosphor, which shows pink under U.V. light, forms an irregular frame on two sides of each design.

(Litho Southern Colour Print, Dunedin)

1996 (15 Mar). *"SOUTHPEX '96" Stamp Show, Invercargill. Sheet* 100×215 *mm, containing No.* 1929×10. *P* 12.

MS1978 40 c. × 10 multicoloured .. .. 4·50 5·00

(Des Dave Clark Design Associates. Litho Southern Colour Print, Dunedin)

1996 (27 Mar). *Rescue Services. T* **531** *and similar vert designs. Multicoloured. P* $14^1/_2$×15.

1979 40 c. Type **531** 50 40
1980 80 c. Civil Defence 90 90
1981 $1 Air-sea rescue .. .. 1·10 1·10
1982 $1.50, Air ambulance and rescue helicopter .. .. 1·60 1·60
1983 $1.80 Mountain rescue and Red Cross .. 2·25 2·40
1979/83 .. .. *Set of* 5 5·75 5·75

532 Mt Egmont, Taranaki

533 Yellow-eyed Penguin

(Des Red Cactus Design. Litho Southern Colour Print, Dunedin (Nos. 1984b/9b) or SNP Cambec, Australia (others))

1996 (1 May)–**98**. *New Zealand Scenery. Self-adhesive. T* **532** *and similar multicoloured designs. Phosphor frame. P* $11^1/_2$.

1984 40 c. Type **532** 30 35
a. Sheetlet of 10. Nos. 1984/9 (one each of two designs and two each of the remainder) .. .. 20·00
b. Perf 10 (14.1.98) 30 35
ba. Booklet pane Nos. 1984b×2, 1985b, 1986b×2, 1987b and 1988b/9b each × 2 .. .. 1·75
1985 40 c. Piercy Island, Bay of Islands .. 30 35
b. Perf 10 (14.1.98) 30 35
1986 40 c. Tory Channel, Marlborough Sounds 30 35
b. Perf 10 (14.1.98) 30 35
ba. "Marlborough Sounds" inscr omitted 20·00
1987 40 c. *Earnslaw* (ferry), Lake Wakatipu .. 30 35
b. Perf 10 (14.1.98) 30 35
1988 40 c. Lake Matheson 30 35
b. Perf 10 (14.1.98) 30 35
1989 40 c. Fox Glacier 30 35
b. Perf 10 (14.1.98) 30 35
1990 80 c. Doubtful Sound (as No. 1933) (*vert*) (13.11.96) 60 65
a. Booklet pane. No. 1990×10 .. .. 6·00
1991 $1 Pohutukawa tree (33×22 *mm*) (7.8.96) 90 95
a. Booklet pane. No. 1991×5 .. .. 4·50
1984/91 .. .. *Set of* 8 3·50 4·00

Nos. 1984/9 occur in rolls of 100, with the surplus self-adhesive paper around each stamp removed.

No. 1984a comes from the residue of special sheet stock used to prepare first day covers and subsequently sold as $4 "hang-sell" sheetlets.

Nos. 1984b/9b come from $4 stamp booklets, containing No. 1984ba, on which the surplus self-adhesive paper was retained.

No. 1986ba occurs on one example of this design from a proportion of the booklet pane No. 1984ba.

Nos. 1990/1 come from stamp booklets on which the surplus self-adhesive paper around each stamp was retained.

The phosphor, which shows pink under U.V. light, appears as an irregular frame to each design.

(Des Sea Sky Design. Litho Southern Colour Print, Dunedin)

1996 (1 May). *Marine Wildlife. T* **533** *and similar multicoloured designs. P* 14.

1992 40 c. Type **533** 50 50
a. Block of 6. Nos. 1992/7 .. .. 6·75
1993 80 c. Royal Albatross (*horiz*) 90 90
1994 $1 White Herons (*horiz*) .. .. .. 1·10 1·10
1995 $1.20, Flukes of Sperm Whale (*horiz*) .. 1·40 1·40
1996 $1.50, Fur Seals .. .. 1·60 1·60
1997 $1.80, Bottlenose Dolphin .. .. .. 2·00 2·00
1992/7 .. .. *Set of* 6 6·75 6·75

In addition to separate sheets of 100 Nos. 1992/7 were also issued in *se-tenant* blocks of 6 which also contained two irregular-shaped labels.

For miniature sheets containing these designs see Nos. **MS**1999 and **MS**2037.

(Des Diane Prosser (No. **MS**1998), Sea Sky Design (No. **MS**1999). Litho Southern Colour Print, Dunedin)

1996 (18 May). *"CHINA '96" 9th International Stamp Exhibition, Peking. Multicoloured. P* $13^1/_2$ (*No.* **MS**1998) *or* 14 (*No.* **MS**1999).

MS1998 180×80 mm. Nos. 1926/8 and 1930 .. 1·40 1·60
MS1999 140×90 mm. Nos. 1994 and 1996 .. 2·75 3·00

No. **MS**1999 also shows designs as Nos. 1992/3, 1995 and 1997, but without face values.

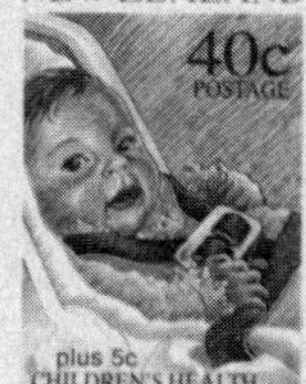

534 Baby in Car Seat

(Des Helen Casey)

1996 (5 June). *Health Stamps. Child Safety. T* **534** *and similar vert design. Multicoloured. (a) Litho Southern Colour Print, Dunedin (No.* 2000*), Enschedé (Nos.* 2000a, 2001*) or SNP Cambec (No.* **MS**2002*). P* $13^1/_2$.

2000 40 c. + 5 c. Type **534** 40 45
a. As Type **534**, but teddy bear at top right and face value at bottom left £350
2001 80 c. + 5 c. Child and adult on zebra crossing 75 80
MS2002 130×90 mm. Nos. 2000/1, each × 2. P 14×$14^1/_2$ .. .. 2·75 2·75

(*b*) *Litho SNP Cambec. Self-adhesive. Phosphor frame on three sides. P* $11^1/_2$

2003 40 c. + 5 c. Type **534** 40 45
a. As Type **534**, but teddy bear at top right and face value at bottom left .. £500

The original versions (Nos. 2000a and 2003a) of the 40 c. + 5 c. showed a teddy bear at top right and the face value above the inscription at bottom left. As depicted the design breached New Zealand safety guidelines and both versions were redrawn as shown in Type **534**. All the original versions should have been withdrawn from post office stocks before the release date, but examples were sold from at least two New Zealand Post outlets and used for postal purposes.

Stamps from No. **MS**2002 are slightly larger with "NEW ZEALAND" and the face values redrawn.

No. 2003 is smaller, $21^1/_2$×38 mm, and occurs in rolls of 100 with the surplus self-adhesive paper around each stamp removed. The phosphor shows pink under U.V. light.

(Des Diane Prosser (No. **MS**2005). Litho SNP Cambec (No. **MS**2004) or Southern Colour Print, Dunedin (No. **MS**2005))

1996 (8 June). *"CAPEX '96" International Stamp Exhibition, Toronto.*

(*a*) *No.* **MS**2002 *optd* "CAPEX '96" *and emblem on sheet margin*

MS2004 Nos. 2000/1, each × 2 .. .. .. 3·25 2·75

(*b*) *Sheet* 180×80 *mm, containing Nos.* 1931/4. *P* $13^1/_2$

MS2005 $3 multicoloured .. .. 3·25 3·25

535 Violin

(Des M. Bailey. Litho and gold die-stamped Southern Colour Print, Dunedin)

1996 (10 July). *50th Anniv of New Zealand Symphony Orchestra. T* **535** *and similar horiz design. Multicoloured. P* 15×$14^1/_2$.

2006 40 c. Type **535** 35 40
2007 80 c. French horn 70 75

536 Swimming

537 *Hinemoa*

(Des S. Fuller. Litho Southern Colour Print, Dunedin)

1996 (10 July). *Centennial Olympic Games, Atlanta. T* **536** *and similar circular designs. Multicoloured. P* $14^1/_2$ *(and* 14 *around design).*

2008 40 c. Type **536** 45 40
2009 80 c. Cycling 90 85
2010 $1 Running .. .. 1·00 1·00
2011 $1.50, Rowing .. .. 1·50 1·75
2012 $1.80, Yachting .. .. 1·60 1·75
2008/12 .. .. *Set of* 5 5·00 5·25
MS2013 120×80 mm. Nos. 2008/12 .. .. 6·00 6·00

A miniature sheet containing Nos. 2008/12 both perforated and imperforate comes from a Limited Edition Collectors Pack costing NZ$135.

(Des Eyework Design and Production. Litho Southern Colour Print, Dunedin (prize labels printed by Sabre Print))

1996 (7 Aug). *Centenary of New Zealand Cinema. T* **537** *and similar vert designs. Multicoloured. P* $14^1/_2$.

2014 40 c. Type **537** 45 40
2015 80 c. *Broken Barrier* 80 80
2016 $1.50, *Goodbye Pork Pie* .. .. .. 1·50 1·75
2017 $1.80, *Once Were Warriors* .. .. .. 1·75 2·00
2014/17 .. .. *Set of* 4 4·00 4·50

Nos. 2014/17 were printed in sheets of 25, each stamp being *se-tenant* with a "Scratch and Win" stamp-size label.

538 Danyon Loader (swimmer) and Blyth Tait (horseman)

539 Beehive Ballot Box

(Des Red Cactus Design. Litho Southern Colour Print, Dunedin)

1996 (28 Aug). *New Zealand Olympic Gold Medal Winners, Atlanta. P* $14^1/_2$ *(and* 14 *around design).*

2018 **538** 40 c. multicoloured 35 40

No. 2018 was printed in sheets of 36 (6×6) with each stamp within a square perforated margin showing a pattern of Olympic rings and fern leaves.

(Des Gatehaus Design. Litho Southern Colour Print, Dunedin)

1996 (4 Sept). *New Zealand's First Mixed Member Proportional Representation Election. P* 12.

2019 **539** 40 c. black, scarlet and pale yellow 35 40

No. 2019 was printed in sheets of 10 (2×5) with decorated margins.

540 King following Star

541 Adzebill

(Des Lindy Fisher)

1996 (4 Sept). *Christmas. T* **540** *and similar horiz designs. Multicoloured. (a) Litho Questa. Designs* 35×35 *mm. P* 14.

2020 40 c. Type **540** 45 40
2021 70 c. Shepherd and Baby Jesus 70 75
2022 80 c. Angel and shepherd 80 80
2023 $1 Mary, Joseph and Baby Jesus .. 1·00 1·00
2024 $1.50, Mary and Joseph with donkey .. 1·40 1·75
2025 $1.80, The Annunciation .. .. .. 1·60 1·90
2020/5 .. .. *Set of* 6 5·50 6·00

(*b*) *Litho SNP Cambec, Australia. Smaller designs,* 30×24 *mm. Self-adhesive. P* $11^1/_2$

2026 40 c. Angels with trumpets 35 50
2027 40 c. King with gift 45 50
a. Booklet pane. No. 2027×10 .. .. 4·25

No. 2026 comes from rolls of 100, on which the surplus self-adhesive paper around each stamp was removed, and No. 2027 from $4 booklets, containing No. 2027a on which the surplus paper was retained.

The phosphor, which shows pink under U.V. light, appears as a three-sided frame on stamps from both rolls and booklets.

(Des G. Cox)

1996 (2 Oct). *Extinct Birds. T* **541** *and similar horiz designs. Multicoloured. (a) Litho Southern Colour Print, Dunedin. Designs* 40×28 *mm. P* 13½.

2028 40 c. Type **541** 45 40
2029 80 c. South Island Whekau ("Laughing Owl") 80 85
2030 $1 Piopio .. .. 1·00 1·10
2031 $1.20, Huia .. .. 1·25 1·40
2032 $1.50, Giant Eagle .. .. 1·50 1·75
2033 $1.80, Giant Moa .. .. 1·60 1·75
2028/33 .. .. *Set of* 6 6·00 6·50
MS2034 105×92 mm. No. 2033. P 14 .. .. 2·00 2·00

(b) Litho SNP Cambec, Australia. Smaller design, 30×24 *mm. Self-adhesive. P* 11½

2035 40 c. Stout-legged Wren 45 50
a. Booklet pane. No. 2035×10 .. .. 4·25

No. 2035 comes from $4 booklets, containing No. 2035a on which the surplus self-adhesive paper was retained.

The phosphor, which shows orange under U.V. light, appears as a vertical band at the right of the stamp.

(Des G. Cox (No. **MS**2036), Sea Sky Design (No. **MS**2037). Litho Southern Colour Print, Dunedin)

1996 (21 Oct). *"TAIPEI '96" 10th Asian International Stamp Exhibition, Taiwan. (a) No.* **MS**2034 *overprinted with* "TAIPEI '96" *logo on sheet margin.*

MS2036 105×92 mm. No. 2033 .. .. .. 2·75 2·75

(b) Sheet 140×90 *mm containing Nos.* 1993 *and* 1997. *Multicoloured. P* 14.

MS2037 Nos. 1993 and 1997 .. .. .. 2·75 2·75

No. **MS**2037 also shows designs as Nos. 1992 and 1994/6, but without face values

542 Seymour Square, Blenheim

543 Holstein Friesian Cattle

(Des H. Thompson. Litho Walsall)

1996 (13 Nov). *Scenic Gardens. T* **542** *and similar vert designs. Multicoloured. P* 13½.

2038 40 c. Type **542** 45 40
2039 80 c. Pukekura Park, New Plymouth .. 80 80
2040 $1 Wintergarden, Auckland .. .. 1·00 1·10
2041 $1.50, Botanic Garden, Christchurch .. 1·60 1·75
2042 $1.80, Marine Parade Gardens, Napier 1·75 1·75
2038/42 .. .. *Set of* 5 5·00 5·25

(Des Lindy Fisher. Litho Questa)

1997 (15 Jan). *Cattle Breeds. T* **543** *and similar vert designs. Multicoloured. P* 14×14½.

2043 40 c. Type **543** 45 40
2044 80 c. Jersey 80 80
2045 $1 Simmental .. .. 1·00 1·00
2046 $1.20, Ayrshire .. .. 1·25 1·40
2047 $1.50, Angus .. .. 1·40 1·75
2048 $1.80, Hereford .. .. 1·60 1·90
2043/8 .. .. *Set of* 6 6·00 6·00

(Des Red Cactus Design (No. **MS**2049), Lindy Fisher (No. **MS**2050) Litho Southern Colour Print, Dunedin (**MS**2049) or Questa (**MS**2050))

1997 (12 Feb). *"HONG KONG '97" International Stamp Exhibition. P* 13 *(No.* **MS**2049) *or* 14×14½ *(No.* **MS**2050).

MS2049 130×110 mm. Nos. 1952/3 and 1956 3·00 3·00
MS2050 101×134 mm. Nos. 2044/5 and 2047 3·50 3·50

No. **MS**2050 is also inscribed for the Chinese New Year ("Year of the Ox").

544 James Cook and Sextant

(Des Red Cactus Design. Litho Southern Colour Print, Dunedin)

1997 (12 Feb). *Millennium Series (1st issue). Discoverers of New Zealand. T* **544** *and similar multicoloured designs. P* 14½×14 *($1, $1.20) or* 14×14½ *(others).*

2051 40 c. Type **544** 55 45
2052 80 c. Kupe and ocean-going canoe .. 80 80
2053 $1 Carved panel depicting Maui *(vert)* .. 1·00 1·00
2054 $1.20, Anchor and Jean de Surville's ship *(vert)* .. .. 1·25 1·40
2055 $1.50, Dumont d'Urville, crab and ship 1·40 1·75
2056 $1.80, Abel Tasman and illustration from journal .. .. 1·60 1·75
2051/6 .. .. *Set of* 6 6·00 6·50

545 Rippon Vineyard, Central Otago

546 Cottage Letterbox

(Des Dianne Prosser from paintings by Nancy Tichborne. Litho Southern Colour Print, Dunedin)

1997 (19 Mar). *New Zealand Vineyards. T* **545** *and similar horiz designs. Multicoloured. P* 14.

2057 40 c. Type **545** 45 40
2058 80 c. Te Mata Estate, Hawke's Bay .. 80 80
2059 $1 Cloudy Bay Vineyard, Marlborough 1·00 1·00
2060 $1.20, Pegasus Bay Vineyard, Waipara 1·25 1·40
2061 $1.50, Milton Vineyard, Gisborne .. 1·40 1·75
2062 $1.80, Goldwater Estate, Waiheke Island 1·60 1·90
2057/62 .. .. *Set of* 6 6·00 6·50
MS2063 Seven sheets, each 150×110 mm. (a) No. 2057; (b) No. 2058; (c) No. 2059; (d) No. 2060; (e) No. 2061; (f) No. 2062; (g) Nos. 2057/62 *Set of* 7 *sheets* 12·00 13·00

Nos. **MS**2063a/g were only available from $13.40 stamp booklets with each miniature sheet showing a line of roulettes at left.

An overprinted and numbered miniature sheet containing Nos. 2057/62 comes from a Limited Edition Collectors Pack costing NZ$135.

For a further miniature sheet containing Nos. 2057, 2059 and 2061 see No. **MS**2081.

(Des Communication Arts. Litho SNP Cambec, Australia)

1997 (19 Mar). *Curious Letterboxes. Self-adhesive Booklet Stamps. T* **546** *and similar vert designs. Multicoloured. Phosphor frame. P* 11½.

2064 40 c. Type **546** 45 50
a. Booklet pane of 10. Nos. 2064/73 .. 4·25
b. Sheetlet of 10. Nos. 2064/73 .. 18·00
2065 40 c. Owl letterbox 45 50
2066 40 c. Blue whale letterbox 45 50
2067 40 c. "Kilroy is Back" letterbox 45 50
2068 40 c. Nesting box letterbox 45 50
2069 40 c. Piper letterbox 45 50
2070 40 c. Diver's helmet letterbox 45 50
2071 40 c. Aircraft letterbox 45 50
2072 40 c. Water tap letterbox 45 50
2073 40 c. Indian palace letterbox 45 50
2064/73 .. .. *Set of* 10 4·25 4·50

The phosphor, which shows orange under U.V. light, appears as a frame on two adjacent sides of each design.

The booklet pane No. 2064a shows the surplus self-adhesive paper around each stamp retained.

No. 2064b comes from the residue of special sheet stock used to prepare first day covers and subsequently sold as $4 "hang-sell" sheetlets. The stamps are on plain backing paper with the surplus self-adhesive paper around each stamp removed.

547 "The Promised Land", 1948 (Colin McCahon)

(Des H. Thompson. Litho Southern Colour Print, Dunedin)

1997 (7 May). *Contemporary Paintings by Colin McCahon. T* **547** *and similar horiz designs. Multicoloured. P* 14.

2074 40 c. Type **547** 40 35
2075 $1 "Six Days in Nelson and Canterbury", 1950 .. .. 90 90
2076 $1.50, "Northland Panels" (detail), 1958 1·40 1·50
2077 $1.80, "Moby Dick is sighted off Muriwai Beach", 1972 .. .. 1·60 1·75
2074/7 .. .. *Set of* 4 3·75 4·00

548 Carrier Pigeon (based on 1899 "Pigeon-gram" local stamp)

(Des S. Fuller. Litho Southern Colour Print, Dunedin)

1997 (7 May). *Centenary of Great Barrier Island Pigeon Post. P* 14×13½.

2078 **548** 40 c. scarlet 45 50
a. *Tête-bêche* pair .. .. .. 90 1·00
2079 80 c. deep dull blue 85 90
a. *Tête-bêche* pair .. .. .. 1·60 1·75

Nos. 2078/9 were each issued in sheets of 50 on which the stamps were arranged both horizontally and vertically *tête-bêche*.

(Des S. Fuller (No. **MS**2080), Dianne Prosser (No. **MS**2081). Litho Southern Colour Print, Dunedin)

1997 (29 May). *"Pacific '97" International Stamp Exhibition, San Francisco. P* 14×13½ *(No.* **MS**2080) *or* 14 *(No.* **MS**2081).

MS2080 137×120 mm. Nos. 2078/9, each × 2 2·25 2·50
MS2081 140×100 mm. Nos. 2057, 2059 and 2061 2·50 2·75

No. **MS**2080 is in a triangular format.

549 Rainbow Trout and Red Setter Fly

(Des Joanne Kreyl. Litho Southern Colour Print, Dunedin)

1997 (18 June). *Fly Fishing. T* **549** *and similar horiz designs. Multicoloured. P* 13.

2082 40 c. Type **549** 40 35
2083 $1 Sea-run Brown Trout and Grey Ghost fly 90 90
2084 $1.50, Brook Charr and Twilight Beauty fly .. .. 1·40 1·50
2085 $1.80, Brown Trout and Hare and Cooper fly .. .. 1·60 1·75
2082/5 .. .. *Set of* 4 3·75 4·00

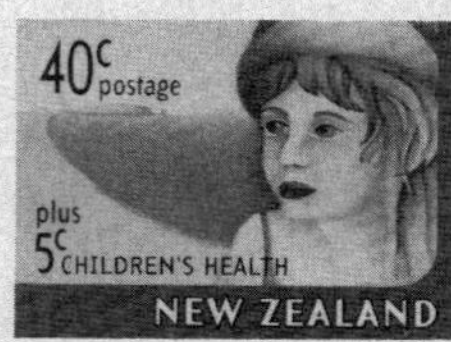

550 "Beach Scene" (Fern Petrie)

(Adapted Communication Arts Ltd. Litho Southern Colour Print, Dunedin)

1997 (18 June). *Children's Health. T* **550** *and similar multicoloured designs showing children's paintings. (a) P* 14.

2086 40 c. + 5 c. Type **550** 45 45
2087 80 c. + 5 c. "Horse-riding on the Water-front" (Georgia Dumergue) 80 85
MS2088 130×90 mm. Nos. 2086/7 and 40 c. + 5 c. As No. 2089 (25×36 *mm*). P 14½ (as No. 2089) or 14 (others) .. .. 1·75 1·75

(b) Self-adhesive. P 10×10½

2089 40 c. + 5 c. "Picking Fruit" (Anita Pitcher) 45 45
2086/9 .. .. *Set of* 3 1·60 1·75

No. 2089 comes from rolls of 100 on which the surplus self-adhesive paper around each stamp was removed. This design with traditional gum was only available as part of No. **MS**2088

(Des A. Mitchell. Litho Southern Colour Print, Dunedin)

1997 (6 Aug). *P* 14½ *(and* 14 *around design).*

2090 **445** $1 violet 75 80

No. 2090 was printed in sheets of 36 with each stamp within a square margin perforated on all four sides and with a further circular perforation around the design.

551 Paremata, Wellington ("The Overlander")

552 Samuel Marsden's *Active*, Bay of Islands

(Des R. Jones. Litho Southern Colour Print, Dunedin)

1997 (6 Aug). *Scenic Railway Services. T* **551** *and similar horiz designs. Multicoloured. P* 14×14½.

2091 40 c. Type **551** 40 35
2092 80 c. Southern Alps ("The Tranz Alpine") 80 80
2093 $1 Canterbury ("The Southerner") .. 90 90
2094 $1.20, Kaikoura Coast ("The Coastal Pacific") .. .. 1·25 1·40
2095 $1.50, Central Hawke's Bay ("The Bay Express") .. .. 1·40 1·60
2096 $1.80, Tauranga Harbour ("The Kaimai Express") .. .. 1·60 1·75
2091/6 .. .. *Set of* 6 5·75 6·25

A miniature sheet containing Nos. 2091/3 comes from a Limited Edition Collectors Pack costing NZ$135.

(Des Fifi Colston. Litho Southern Colour Print, Dunedin)

1997 (3 Sept). *Christmas. T* **552** *and similar vert designs. Multicoloured. (a) P* 14.

2097 40 c. Type **552** 40 40
a. Block of 6. Nos. 2097/102 .. .. 5·00
2098 70 c. Revd. Marsden preaching 65 65
2099 80 c. Marsden and Maori chiefs 75 75

2100 $1 Maori family 90 90
2101 $1.50, Handshake and cross 1·40 1·60
2102 $1.80, Pohutukawa (flower) and Rangihoua Bay 1·60 1·75

(b) *Self-adhesive. Smaller design, 29×24 mm. P* 10
2103 40 c. Memorial cross, Pohutukawa and Bay of Islands 35 35
a. Booklet pane of 10 3·50
2097/103 *Set of* 7 6·00 6·25

In addition to separate sheets Nos. 2097/102 were also issued as *se-tenant* blocks of 6.

No. 2103 comes from either rolls of 100, on which the surplus adhesive paper was removed, or from $4 booklets on which the surplus paper was retained.

553 Huhu Beetle

554 *Rosa rugosa*

(Des D. Gunson. Litho SNP Cambec, Australia)

1997 (1 Oct). *Insects. Self-adhesive Booklet Stamps. T* **553** *and similar horiz designs. Multicoloured. Two phosphor bands. P* 11½.
2104 40 c. Type **553** 30 35
a. Booklet pane. Nos. 2104/13 3·00
b. Sheetlet of 10. Nos. 2104/13 10·00
2105 40 c. Giant Land Snail 30 35
2106 40 c. Giant Weta 30 35
2107 40 c. Giant Dragonfly 30 35
2108 40 c. Peripatus 30 35
2109 40 c. Cicada 30 35
2110 40 c. Puriri Moth 30 35
2111 40 c. Veined Slug 30 35
2112 40 c. Katipo 30 35
2113 40 c. Flax Weevil 30 35
2104/13 *Set of* 10 3·00 3·50

The phosphor, which shows pink under U.V. light, appears as horizontal bands across the top and bottom of each design.

The booklet pane, No. 2104a, shows the surplus self-adhesive paper around each stamp retained.

No. 2104b comes from the residue of special sheet stock used to prepare first day covers and subsequently sold as $4 "hang-sell" sheetlets. The stamps are on plain backing paper, with the surplus self-adhesive paper around each stamp removed.

(Des Z. Guizheng. Litho Southern Colour Print, Dunedin)

1997 (9 Oct). *New Zealand–China Joint Issue. Roses. T* **554** *and similar vert design. Multicoloured. P* 14.
2114 40 c. Type **554** 35 40
a. Horiz pair. Nos. 2114/15 70 80
2115 40 c. Aotearoa 35 40
MS2116 115×95 mm. 80 c. Nos. 2114/15 75 85

Nos. 2114/15 were printed together, *se-tenant*, in horizontal pairs throughout the sheet.

Stamps in similar designs were also issued by China.

555 Queen Elizabeth II and Prince Philip

556 Cartoon Kiwi on Busy-bee

(Des Red Cactus Design. Litho Southern Colour Print, Dunedin)

1997 (12 Nov). *Golden Wedding of Queen Elizabeth and Prince Philip. P* 12.
2117 **555** 40 c. multicoloured 30 35

No. 2117 was printed in sheets of 10 (2×5) with decorated margins.

(Des G. Tremain (40 c.), J. Hubbard ($1), E. Heath ($1.50), B. Silver ($1.80). Litho Southern Colour Print, Dunedin)

1997 (12 Nov). *New Zealand Cartoons. "Kiwis taking on the World". T* **556** *and similar horiz designs. Multicoloured. P* 14.
2118 40 c. Type **556** 30 35
2119 $1 "Let's have 'em for Breakfast" 75 80
2120 $1.50, Kiwi dinghy winning race 1·10 1·25
2121 $1.80, "CND" emblem cut in forest 1·25 1·40
2118/21 *Set of* 4 3·50 3·75

(Des S. Fuller. Litho Southern Colour Print, Dunedin)

1997 (13 Nov). *"Aupex '97" National Stamp Exhibition, Auckland. Sheet* 140×120 *mm. P* 14×13½.
MS2122 Nos. 2078/9, each × 2 2·10 2·10

No. **MS**2122 is in a triangular format

1997 (19 Nov). *International Stamp and Coin Exhibition* 1997, *Shanghai. Sheet as No.* **MS**2116 *but redrawn to include* "Issued by New Zealand Post to commemorate the International Stamp and Coin Expo. Shanghai, China. 19–23 November 1997" *inscr in English and Chinese with additional die-stamped gold frame and logo.*
MS2123 115×95 mm. Nos. 2114/15 70 70

557 Modern Dancer

(Des N. Childs. Litho Southern Colour Print, Dunedin)

1998 (14 Jan). *Performing Arts. T* **557** *and similar vert designs. Multicoloured. P* 13½.
2124 40 c. Type **557** 30 35
2125 80 c. Trombone player 60 65
a. Perf 14
2126 $1 Opera singer 75 80
2127 $1.20, Actor 90 95
2128 $1.50, Singer 1·10 1·25
2129 $1.80, Ballet dancer 1·25 1·40
a. Perf 14
2124/9 *Set of* 6 5·00 5·50
MS2130 Seven sheets, each 150×110 mm. (a) No. 2124; (b) No. 2125; (c) No. 2126; (d) No. 2127; (e) No. 2128; (f) No. 2129; (g) Nos. 2124/9. P 12 (Nos. **MS**2130c, **MS**2130g) or 13½ (others) *Set of* 7 *sheets* 10·00 10·50

Nos. 2130a/g were only available from $13.40 stamp booklets, with each miniature sheet showing a line of roulettes at left.

558 Museum of New Zealand

(Des Joanne Kreyl. Litho Southern Colour Print, Dunedin)

1998 (11 Feb). *Opening of Museum of New Zealand, Wellington. T* **558** *and similar diamond-shaped design. Multicoloured. P* 14½.
2131 40 c. Type **558** 30 35
2132 $1.80, Museum and seabirds 1·25 1·40

559 Domestic Cat

560 Maoris and Canoe

(Des Julie Grieg. Litho Southern Colour Print, Dunedin)

1998 (11 Feb). *Cats. T* **559** *and similar vert designs. Multicoloured. P* 13½.
2133 40 c. Type **559** 30 35
2134 80 c. Burmese 60 65
2135 $1 Birman 75 80
2136 $1.20, British Blue 90 95
2137 $1.50, Persian 1·10 1·25
2138 $1.80, Siamese 1·25 1·40
2133/8 *Set of* 6 5·00 5·50

(Des Julie Grieg. Litho Southern Colour Print, Dunedin)

1998 (11 Feb). *Chinese New Year ("Year of the Tiger"). P* 13½.
MS2139 100×135 mm. Nos. 2133, 2135 and 2138 2·25 2·40

(Des T. Crilley. Litho Southern Colour Print, Dunedin)

1998 (18 Mar). *Millennium Series (2nd issue). Immigrants. T* **560** *and similar vert designs. Multicoloured. P* 14½×14.
2140 40 c. Type **560** 30 35
2141 80 c. 19th-century European settlers and immigrant ship 60 65
2142 $1 Gold miners and mine 75 80
2143 $1.20, Post 1945 European migrants and liner 90 95
2144 $1.50, Pacific islanders and church 1·10 1·25
2145 $1.80, Asian migrant and jumbo jet 1·25 1·40
2140/5 *Set of* 6 5·00 5·25

561 "With Great Respect to the Mehmetcik" Statue, Gallipoli

(Des Dianne Prosser. Litho Southern Colour Print, Dunedin)

1998 (18 Mar). *Joint Issue New Zealand–Turkey. Memorial Statues. T* **561** *and similar vert design. Multicoloured. P* 13½.
2146 40 c. Type **561** 30 35
2147 $1.80, "Mother with Children", National War Memorial, Wellington 1·25 1·40

Index to New Zealand Stamp Designs from 1946

The following index is intended to facilitate the identification of all New Zealand stamps from 1946 onwards. Portrait stamps are usually listed under surnames only, views under the name of the town or city and other issues under the main subject or a prominent word and date chosen from the inscription. Simple abbreviations have occasionally been resorted to and when the same design or subject appears on more than one stamp, only the first of each series is indicated.

STAMP BOOKLETS

Nos. SB1 to SB24 are stapled.
Nos. SB1/5 were sold at ½d. above the face value of the stamps to cover the cost of manufacture.

1901 (1 Apr). *White card covers with postage rates.*
SB1 1s. ½d. booklet containing twelve 1d. (No. 278) in blocks of 6 . . . . £1800
SB2 2s. 6½d. booklet containing thirty 1d. (No. 278) in blocks of 6 . . . . £2250

Original printings of Nos. SB1/2 showed the face value on the cover in small figures. Subsequent printings show large figures of value on the covers and the prices quoted are for this type.

1902 (21 Aug)–**05.** *White card covers with postage rates.*
SB3 1s. ½d. booklet containing twelve 1d. in panes of 6 (Nos. 303b or 303cb) £1500
SB4 2s. ½d. booklet containing twenty-four 1d. in panes of 6 (Nos. 303b or 303cb) (21.3.05) . . £1700
SB5 2s. 6½d. booklet containing thirty 1d. in panes of 6 (Nos. 303b or 303cb) £2250

1910 (Apr). *White card cover with postage rates.*
SB6 2s. booklet containing eleven ½d. in pane of 5 with 1 label (Nos. 387b or 387c) and pane of 6 (No. 387d), and eighteen 1d. in three panes of 6 (No. 405b) £3250

1912 (May). *White card cover.*
SB7 2s. booklet containing twelve ½d. and eighteen 1d. in panes of 6 with bars on the selvedge (Nos. 387e, 405c) £2250

1915 (Feb). *Red card cover.*
SB8 2s. booklet containing twelve ½d. and eighteen 1d. in panes of 6 with bars on the selvedge (Nos. 435a or 435ba, 405c) £1000
a. Grey cover . . . . . .
b. Blue cover . . . . . .
c. Yellow-buff cover . . . . . .
d. Purple-buff cover . . . . . .

1924 (1 Dec)–**25.** *Cover inscription within frame.*
SB9 2s. booklet containing twelve ½d. and eighteen 1d. in panes of 6 with bars on the selvedge (Nos. 441a, 406b) (lilac cover) £1100
a. Grey cover . . . . . .
SB10 2s. booklet containing twelve ½d. and eighteen 1d. in panes of 6 with bars and advertisements on the selvedge (Nos. 446a, 410b) (yellow-buff cover) (1925) £1200
a. Grey-green cover £1200
b. Grey-buff cover . . . .
c. Grey-pink cover £1600

1928–34.
SB11 2s. booklet containing twelve ½d. and eighteen 1d. in panes of 6 with bars on the selvedge (Nos. 446ca, 468b) £1000
a. As No. SB11 but panes with bars and advertisements on the selvedge (Nos. 446cb, 468c) £1000
SB12 2s. booklet containing twenty-four 1d. in panes of 6 with bars and advertisements on the selvedge (No. 468c) (1930) £1000
SB13 2s. booklet containing twelve ½d. and eighteen 1d. in panes of 6 with bars on the selvedge (Nos. 446ab, 468b) (1934) £1700
SB14 2s. booklet containing twenty-four 1d. in panes of 6 with bars and advertisements on the selvedge (No. 468ea) (1934) £900

1935.
SB15 2s. booklet containing twenty-four 1d. in panes of 6 with advertisements on the selvedge (No. 557ca) £300

1936.
SB16 2s. booklet containing twenty-four 1d. (No. 578) in blocks of 6 . . . . £200

B 1

1938 (1 July). *Cream cover as Type* B **1**.
SB17 2s. booklet containing twenty-four 1d. (No. 605) in blocks of 6 . . . . £225

1938 (Nov). *Cream* (*No.* SB18) *or blue* (*No.* SB19) *covers as Type* B **1**.
SB18 2s. booklet containing twelve ½d. and eighteen 1d. (Nos. 603, 605) in blocks of 6 . . . . £250
SB19 2s. 3d. booklet containing eighteen 1½d. (No. 607) in blocks of 6 . . . . £225

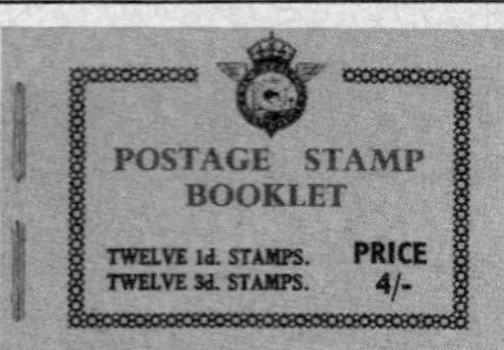

B 2

1954 (Apr). *Black and green on cream cover as Type* B **2**.
SB20 4s. booklet containing twelve 1d. and 3d (Nos. 724, 727), each in blocks of 6 . . . . 6·00
a. Contents as SB20 but with one pane of airmail labels . . . . 18·00

1956 (1 May). *Black and green on cream cover as Type* B **2**.
SB21 4s. booklet containing twelve 1d. and 3d. (Nos. 724, 748), each in blocks of 6, and one pane of air mail labels . . . . 13·00

1957 (5 Sept). *Black and green on cream cover as Type* B **2**.
SB22 4s. booklet containing twelve 1d. and 3d. (Nos. 745, 748), each in blocks of 6, and one pane of air mail labels . . . . 12·00

B 3

1960 (1 Sept). *Black and red on cream cover as Type* B **3**.
SB23 4s. booklet containing twelve 1d. and 3d. (Nos. 782, 785), each in blocks of 6, and one pane of air mail labels . . . . 15·00

1962 (21 May). *Black and red on cream cover as Type* B **3**.
SB24 4s. 6d. booklet containing twelve ½d., 1d. and 3d. (Nos. 781, 782, 785), each in blocks of 6, and one pane of air mail labels . . . . . . 45·00

1964. *Black and carmine on cream cover as Type* B **3**. *Stitched.*
SB25 4s. 3d. booklet containing six ½d. and twelve 1d. and 3d. (Nos. 781/2, 785), each in blocks of 6, and one pane of air mail labels . . . . 20·00

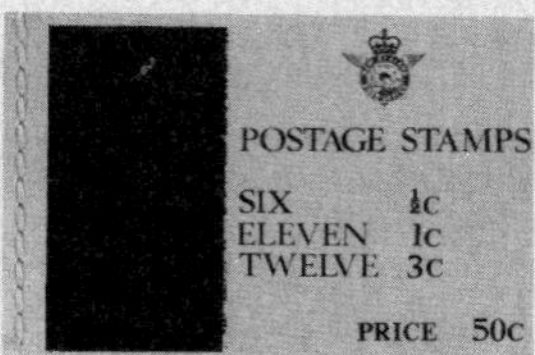

B 4 Maori Art

1967 (10 July). *Black and carmine on pale lemon cover as Type* B **4**. *Stitched.*
SB26 50 c. booklet containing ½ c. (No. 845) in block of 6, eleven 1 c. in block of 6 (No. 846) and pane of 5 stamps and 1 label (No. 846a), and twelve 3 c. (No. 849) in blocks of 6 . . 10·00

B 5 Native Trees

1971 (6 July). *Multicoloured cover as Type* B **5**. *Stitched.*
SB27 75 c. booklet containing nine 1 c. (No. 915b) in block of 6 and in pane of 3 stamps and three labels (No. 915ba), six 3 c. (No. 918b) and twelve 4 c. (No. 919b), each in blocks of 6 with sideways inverted or sideways watermarks . . . . 12·00

1974 (Aug). *Multicoloured cover as Type* B **5**. *Stitched.*
SB28 75 c. booklet. As No. SB27 but containing stamps without watermark (Nos. 1008/a, 1010/11) 12·00

All booklets from No. SB29 onwards have their panes attached by the selvedge, *unless otherwise stated.*

B 6 Garden Rose "Josephine Bruce"

1977 (Apr). *Multicoloured cover as Type* B **6**.
SB29 80 c. booklet containing 8 c. (No. 1093a) in block of 10 . . . . 5·00

B 7

1977 (Apr). *Blue and black printed cover as Type* B **7**.
SB30 $1 booklet containing 10 c. (No. 1017) in block of 10 . . . . 7·50

B 8

Two Settings of Booklet Cover for No. SB31:
Setting I. Inscription at foot. "c" aligned at top of "10" (similar to Type B **8**).
Setting II. Inscription at top. "c" aligned on bottom of "10".

1978 (Aug)–**79.** *Black and ultramarine printed cover as Type* B **8**.
SB31 $1 booklet containing 10 c. (No. 1094a) in block of 10 (Cover Setting I) . . . . . . 9·00
a. Cover Setting II . . . . . . 15·00
b. Containing 10 c. (No. 1094ab) (Cover Setting I) (1979) . . . . 12·00

1978 (Aug). *Black and orange cover as Type* B **8**
SB32 $1.20, booklet containing 12 c. (No. 1096) in block of 10 . . . . 5·00

1980 (Mar). *Black and red cover as Type* B **8**
SB33 $1.40, booklet containing 14 c. (No. 1098) in block of 10 . . . . 5·00

B 9

1980 (12 May). *Black and green cover as Type* B **9**.
SB34 $1.40, booklet containing 14 c. (No. 1098) in block of 10 . . . . 4·00

The cover of No. SB34 is inscribed "$1.54" which included a premium payable when purchased from commercial outlets authorized to sell booklets. It was available at $1.40 (value of contents) from the Post Office Philatelic Bureau.

B 10

1981. *Black and blue cover as Type* B **10**.
SB35 $2 booklet containing 20 c. (No. 1099) in block of 10 .. .. 4·00

B 11

1981. *Black and green cover as Type* B **11**.
SB36 $2 booklet containing 20 c. (No. 1099) in block of 10 .. .. 3·50
The cover of No. SB36 is inscribed "$2.20". See note below No. SB34.

1982 (1 Apr)–**83**. *Black and green cover as Type* B **8**.
SB37 $2.40, booklet containing 24 c. (*p* 12½) (No. 1261) in block of 10 .. .. 4·25
a. Containing 24 c. (*p* 14½×14) (No. 1261a) (1983) .. .. 9·00

1982 (1 Apr)–**84**. *Black and blue cover as Type* B **9**.
SB38 $2.40, booklet containing 24 c. (*p* 12½) (No. 1261) in block of 10 .. .. 4·50
a. Containing 24 c. (*p* 14½×14) (No. 1261a) (1984) .. .. 13·00
The covers of Nos. SB38/a are inscribed "$2.64". See note below No. SB34.

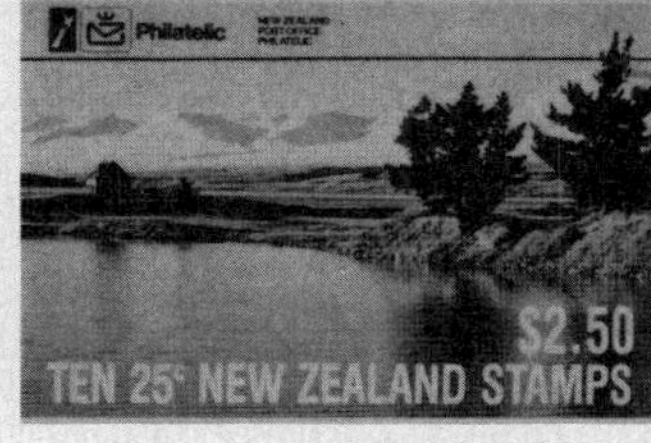

B 12 Lake Tekapo, South Island

1985 (2 July). *Multicoloured cover as Type* B **12** *with design continuing on back cover.*
SB39 $2.50, booklet (Type B **12**) containing 25 c. (No. 1370) in block of 10 .. .. 6·00
SB40 $2.50, booklet (Tongariro Park, North Island) containing 25 c. (No. 1370) in block of 10 .. 7·00
The cover of No. SB40 is inscribed "$2.75". See note below No. SB34.

1986 (1 May). *Multicoloured covers as Type* B **12**, *but* 115×60 *mm, with the design continuing on back cover.*
SB41 $3 booklet (Matukituki Valley, Otago) containing 30 c. (No. 1288) in block of 10 .. .. 8·00
SB42 $3 booklet (Stream and native bush, Canterbury) containing 30 c. (No. 1288) in block of 10 8·00
The cover of No. SB42 is inscribed "$3.30". See note below No. SB34.
Nos. SB41/2 exist overprinted on the front cover with the "Stockholmia" logo for sale at the International Philatelic Exhibition in Sweden.

1987 (2 Feb–June). *Multicoloured covers as Type* B **12**, *but* 115×60 *mm, with the design continuing on back cover.*
SB43 $4 booklet (Ahuriri Valley, Otago) containing 40 c. (No. 1289) in block of 10 .. .. 10·00
a. Revised "NZ POST" logo without crown (June) 10·00
SB44 $4 booklet (Totaranui Beach, Abel Tasman National Park, Nelson) containing 40 c. (No. 1289) in block of 10 .. .. 10·00
a. Revised "NZ POST" logo without crown (June) 16·00
The covers of booklets Nos. SB44/a are inscribed "$4.40". See note below No. SB34.
Nos. SB43a and SB44a exist overprinted on the front cover with the "CAPEX" logo for sale at the International Philatelic Exhibition in Toronto.

1987 (Nov). *Multicoloured covers as Type* B **12**, *but* 115×60 *mm, with the design continuing on back cover. New "NZ POST" logo as shown on Type* B **14**.
SB45 $4 booklet (Wellington by night) containing 40 c. (No. 1289) in block of 10 .. .. 8·00
SB46 $4 booklet (Katiki Point) containing 40 c. (No. 1289) in block of 10 .. .. 27·00
The cover of No. SB46 is inscribed "$4.40". See note below No. SB34.

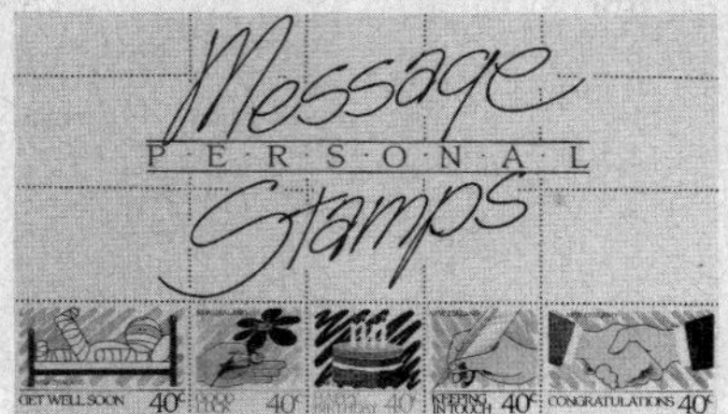

B 13

1988 (18 May). *"Personal Message Stamps". Multicoloured cover as Type* B **13**.
SB47 $2 booklet containing pane of 5 different 40 c. (No. 1455a) .. .. 2·50
No. SB47 exists overprinted on the front cover with the "WORLD STAMP EXPO '89" logo for sale at the International Stamp Exhibition in Washington, U.S.A.

B 14

1988 (7 June). *"Fast Post" Service. Black, bright scarlet and new blue cover as Type* B **14**.
SB48 $7 booklet containing 70 c. (No. 1466) in block of 10 .. .. 6·50

B 15

1988 (14 Sept). *Christmas. Multicoloured cover as Type* B **15**.
SB49 $3.50, booklet containing 35 c. (No. 1480) in block of 10 .. .. 4·00

B 16

1988 (19 Oct). *Multicoloured cover as Type* B **16**.
SB50 $6 booklet containing pane of 6 $1 (No. 1490a) 11·00

B **17** Mt Cook from the Hooker Valley, South Canterbury

1988 (2 Nov). *Multicoloured cover as Type* B **17** *with design continuing on back cover.*
SB51 $4 booklet containing 40 c. (No. 1463) in block of 10 .. .. 5·50
No. SB51 exist overprinted on the front cover with the "Stamp World London'90" logo for sale at the International Stamp Exhibition in Great Britain.

1989 (13 Sept). *Christmas. Multicoloured cover as Type* B **17**.
SB52 $3.50, booklet containing 35 c. (No. 1520) in block of 10 .. .. 5·50

B 18

1990 (Aug). *Black and white cover as Type* B **18** *showing multicoloured stamp No.* 1463.
SB53 $4 booklet containing 40 c. (No. 1463) in block of 10 with three fastPOST labels .. .. 7·00
No. SB53 has a slot in the cover for hanging display. Booklets in this format were produced for self-service sales.

B 19

1991 (15 May). *"Happy Birthday". Multicoloured cover as Type* B **19**.
SB54 $2 booklet containing pane of 5 different 40 c. (No. 1594a) .. .. 2·00

B 20

1991 (15 May). *"Thinking of You". Multicoloured cover as Type* B **20**.
SB55 $2 booklet containing pane of 5 different 40 c. (No. 1604a) .. .. 2·00

1991 (1 July). *Blue and white cover as Type* B **18** *showing multicoloured stamp No.* 1463*b*.
SB56 $4.50, booklet containing 45 c. (No. 1463*b*) in block of 10 .. .. 4·00

1991 (1 July). *"Happy Birthday". Multicoloured vert cover as Type* B **19**, *but in hanging display format as Type* B **18**.
SB57 $2.25, booklet containing pane of 5 different 45 c. (No. 1599a) .. .. 2·00

1991 (1 July). *"Thinking of You". Multicoloured cover as Type* B **20**, *but in hanging display format as Type* B **18**.
SB58 $2.25, booklet containing pane of 5 different 45 c. (No. 1609a) .. .. 2·00

BARCODES. All booklets from No. SB59 show a barcode on the reverse, *unless indicated otherwise.*

B 21

1991 (1 Oct). *Bright red and black cover as Type* B **21** *showing multicoloured stamp No. 1463b. Roman "I" on back.*
SB59 $4.50, booklet containing 45 c. (No. 1463*b*) in block of 10 .. .. 4·00
a. Roman "II" on back .. .. 4·50
b. With additional slotted tab at right. Containing 45 c. in pane of 10 (No. 1463ba) ("I" on back) .. .. 4·50
ba. Containing 45 c. (No. 1463b) in block of 10 ("II" on back) .. .. 4·50

1992 (May–8 June). *Bright blue and black cover as Type* B **21**, *but without stamp design. No barcode on reverse.*
SB60 $4 booklet containing 80 c. (No. 1467) in strip of 5 and pane of six fastPOST labels .. .. 4·00
SB61 $8 booklet containing 80 c. (No. 1467) in block of 10 and pane of ten fastPOST labels .. 20·00
a. Barcode on back (8 June) .. .. .. 8·00

1992 (1 Sept). *Landscapes. Bright red and black cover as Type* B **21** *showing multicoloured stamp No. 1690. Roman "I" on back.*
SB62 $4.50, booklet containing pane of 10 different 45 c. (No. 1690a) .. .. 3·75
a. Roman "II" on back .. .. 7·50
b. Roman "III" on back .. .. .. 14·00
c. With additional slotted tab at right ("I" on back) .. .. 3·75
ca. Roman "II" on back .. .. 7·50
cb. Roman "III" on back .. .. .. 14·00

1993 (31 Mar)–**94**. *Bright blue and black cover as Type* B **21**, *but without stamp design.*
SB63 $8 booklet containing 80 c. (No. 1467*a*) in block of 10 and block of 10 fastPOST labels .. 5·75
a. Containing pane No. 1467ab (*p* 12) (7.94) .. 8·00

1993 (9 June). *Endangered Species Conservation. Cover as Type* B **21** *showing multicoloured illustration of Tusked Weta.*
SB64 $4.50, booklet containing 45 c. (No. 1740) in block of 10 .. .. 4·50
a. With additional slotted tab at right .. 4·50

1993 (1 Sept). *Marine Life. Bright red and black cover as Type* B **21** *showing multicoloured illustration of Groper (fish).*
SB65 $4.50, booklet containing pane of 10 different 45 c. (No. 1752a) .. .. 4·50
a. With additional slotted tab at right .. 5·50

1993 (1 Oct). *Prehistoric Animals. Cover as Type* B **21** *showing multicoloured illustration of Carnosaur.*
SB66 $4.50, booklet containing pane of ten 45 c. plus two labels (No. 1763a) .. .. .. 4·25
a. With additional slotted tab at right .. 4·25

1993 (3 Nov). *Christmas. Bright red and black cover as Type* B **21** *showing multicoloured illustration of Christmas Pudding.*
SB67 $4.50, booklet containing pane of ten 45 c. (No. 1746ba) .. .. 8·50
a. With additional slotted tab at right .. 8·50

1994 (19 Jan). *Tourism. Bright red and black cover as Type* B **21** *showing multicoloured illustration of White Water Rafting.*
SB68 $4.50, booklet containing pane of ten 45 c. and four half stamp-size greetings labels (No. 1778a) (horiz format) .. .. .. 4·50
a. Roman "II" on back .. .. 5·00
b. Vert format with additional slotted tab at top 5·00
ba. Roman "II" on back .. .. 5·00

1994 (27 Apr). *New Zealand Life. Bright red and black cover as Type* B **21** *showing multicoloured illustration of Buzzy Bee.*
SB69 $4.50, booklet containing pane of ten different 45 c. (No. 1797a) (horiz format) .. .. 3·50
a. Vert format with additional slotted tab at right .. .. 3·50

1994 (21 Sept). *Christmas. Multicoloured covers as Type* B **21** *showing illustration of Father Christmas and children.*
SB70 $4.50, booklet containing 45 c. (No. 1832) in block of 10 (horiz format) .. .. .. 3·50
a. Vert format with additional slotted tab at top 4·00

1994 (2 Nov). *Centenary of New Zealand Cricket Council. Multicoloured covers as Type* B **21** *showing illustration of father and son playing cricket.*
SB71 $4.50, booklet containing pane of ten 45 c. (No. 1840a) (horiz format) .. .. 3·50
a. Vert format with additional slotted tab at top 4·00

B 22

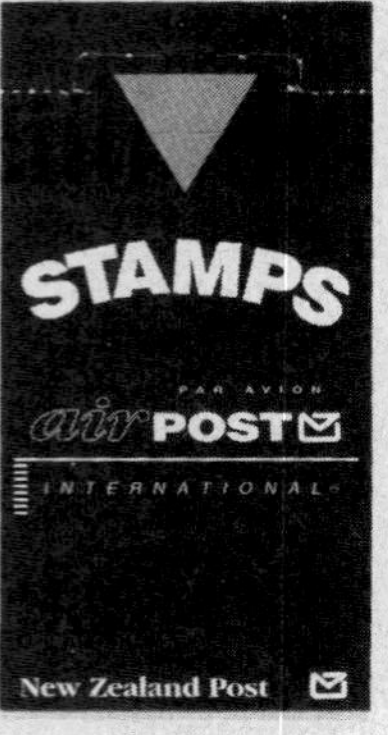

B 23

1995 (22 Mar). *Environment. Bright red and black cover as Type* B **22** *showing multicoloured illustration of backpackers.*
SB72 $4.50, booklet containing pane of ten 45 c. (No. 1865a) inserted sideways in the vertical cover 5·50

1995 (26 July). *Centenary of Rugby League. Multicoloured cover as Type* B **21** *showing New Zealand and Australian Players.*
SB73 $4.50, booklet containing pane of ten 45 c. (No. 1889) .. .. 4·75

1995 (1 Sept). *Black and bright royal blue cover as Type* B **23** *inscribed* "airPOST INTERNATIONAL".
SB74 $5 booklet containing pane of five $1 and five labels (No. 1645a) inserted sideways in the cover .. .. 11·00

1995 (1 Sept–2 Oct). *Farmyard Animals. Multicoloured covers as Type* B **22** *showing illustration of sow and piglets.*
SB75 $4 booklet containing pane of ten 40 c. (No. 1894a) inserted sideways in the cover (2 Oct) 3·50
SB76 $4.50, booklet containing pane of ten 45 c. (No. 1904a) inserted sideways in the cover .. 4·50

1995 (9 Nov). *Christmas. Multicoloured cover as Type* B **22** *showing illustration of Angel holding trumpet.*
SB77 $4 booklet containing pane of ten 40 c. (No. 1923a) .. .. 4·00

B 24
(Illustration reduced. Actual size 166×110 *mm)*

1996 (24 Jan). *Famous Racehorses. Multicoloured cover as Type* B **24** *showing illustrations of harness and horse races.*
SB78 $13.40, booklet containing seven miniature sheets (Nos. **MS**1951a/g) .. .. .. 15·00

1996 (21 Feb). *Seaside Environment. Multicoloured cover as Type* B **21**, *but vert, showing illustration of sea shore.*
SB79 $4 booklet containing pane of ten 40 c. (No. 1958a) .. .. 4·25

1996 (7 Aug). *Seaside Environment. Multicoloured cover as No.* SB79, *but* 58×78 *mm. Self-adhesive.*
SB80 $4 booklet containing pane of ten 40 c. (No. 1968a) .. .. 4·25

B 25

1996 (7 Aug). *Multicoloured cover as Type* B **25** *showing illustration of Pohutukawa tree. Self-adhesive.*
SB81 $5 booklet containing pane of five $1 (No. 1991a) 4·50

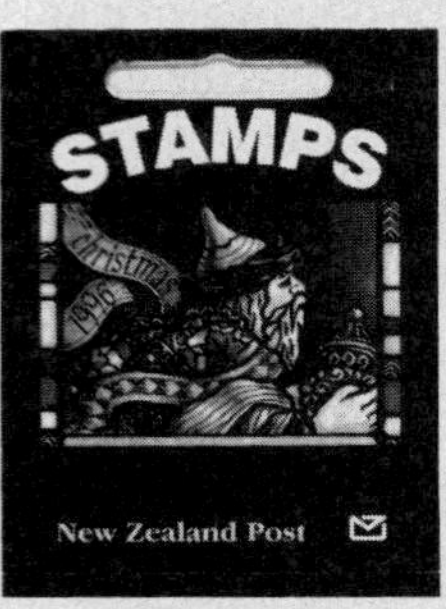

B 26

1996 (4 Sept). *Christmas. Multicoloured cover as Type* B **26** *showing illustration of King. Self-adhesive.*
SB82 $4 booklet containing pane of ten 40 c. (No. 2027a) .. .. 4·25

1996 (2 Oct). *Extinct Birds. Multicoloured cover as Type* B **26** *showing illustration of Stout-legged Wren. Self-adhesive.*
SB83 $4 booklet containing pane of ten 40 c. (No. 2035a) .. .. 4·25

1996 (13 Nov). *Multicoloured cover as Type* B **25** *but smaller,* 59×78 *mm, inscr* "fastPOST" *with illustration of Doubtful Sound. Self-adhesive.*
SB84 $8 booklet containing pane of ten 80 c. (No. 1990a) .. .. 7·00

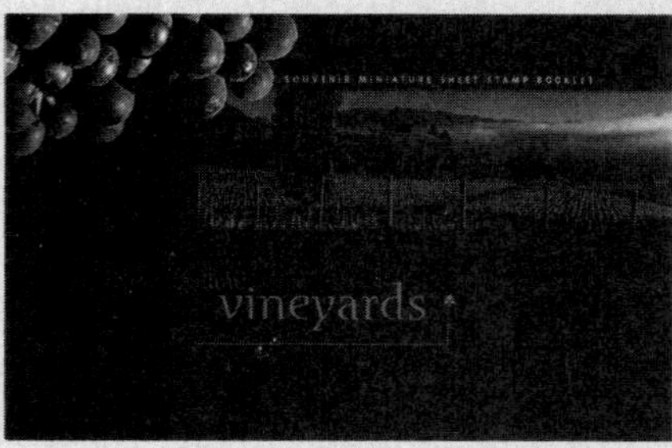

B 27
(Illustration reduced. Actual size 116×110 *mm)*

1997 (19 Mar). *New Zealand Vineyards. Multicoloured cover as Type* B **27**.
SB85 $13.40, booklet containing seven miniature sheets (Nos. **MS**2063a/g) .. .. .. 12·00

1997 (19 Mar). *Curious Letterboxes. Multicoloured cover as Type* B **26** *showing letterbox. Self-adhesive.*
SB86 $4 booklet containing pane of ten 40 c. (No. 2064a) .. .. 4·25

1997 (3 Sept). *Christmas. Multicoloured cover as Type* B **26** *showing illustration as No. 2103. Self-adhesive.*
SB87 $4 booklet containing pane of ten 40 c. (No. 2103a) .. .. 3·50

1997 (1 Oct). *Insects. Multicoloured cover as Type* B **26** *showing illustration of Grasshopper's head. Self-adhesive.*
SB88 $4 booklet containing pane of ten 40 c. (No. 2104a) .. .. 3·50

1998 (14 Jan). *Multicoloured cover as Type* B **26** *showing New Zealand scenery. Self-adhesive.*
SB89 $4 booklet containing pane of ten 45 c. (No. 1984ba) .. .. 3·00

B 28
(Illustration reduced. Actual size 164×110 *mm)*

1998 (14 Jan). *Performing Arts. Multicoloured cover as Type* B **28** *showing illustration of performers.*
SB90 $13.40, booklet containing seven miniature sheets (Nos. **MS**2130a/g) .. .. .. 9·75

EXPRESS DELIVERY STAMPS

E 1

(Typo Govt Printing Office, Wellington)

1903 (9 Feb). *Value in first colour. W* **43** *(sideways). P* 11.
E1 E 1 6d. red and violet .. .. .. 35·00 22·00

1926–36. *Thick, white, opaque chalk-surfaced "Cowan" paper. W* **43**.
(*a*) *P* 14×14½
E2 E 1 6d. vermilion and bright violet .. 40·00 24·00
w. Wmk inverted £100
(*b*) *P* 14×15 (1936)
E3 E 1 6d. carmine and bright violet .. 45·00 48·00

1937–39. *Thin, hard, chalk-surfaced "Wiggins Teape" paper.*
(*a*) *P* 14 × 14½
E4 E 1 6d. carmine and bright violet .. .. 85·00 48·00
(*b*) *P* 14 × 15 (1939)
E5 E 1 6d. vermilion and bright violet .. £130 £180

E 2 Express Mail Delivery Van

(Des J. Berry. Eng Stamp Ptg Office, Melbourne Recess Govt Ptg Office, Wellington)

1939 (16 Aug). *W* **43**. *P* 14.
E6 E 2 6d. violet .. .. 1·50 1·75
w. Wmk inverted .. .. .. 70·00

POSTAGE DUE STAMPS

D 1

(I)

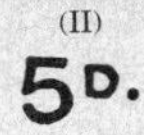

(II)

3D. (*a*) Large "D"   5D. (*b*) Small "D"

(Typo Govt Printing Office, Wellington)

1899 (1 Dec). *W* **12***b*. *Coarse paper. P* 11.

I. Type I. *Circle of* 14 *ornaments,* 17 *dots over* "N.Z.", "N.Z." *large.*
(*a*) *Large* "D"
D1 D 1 ½d. carmine and green .. .. 12·00 24·00
a. No stop after "D" (Right pane R. 2/3) 85·00 £140
D2 8d. carmine and green .. .. 60·00 75·00
D3 1s. carmine and green .. .. 65·00 80·00
D4 2s. carmine and green £120 £140
D1/4 .. .. *Set of* 4 £225 £275

To avoid further subdivision the 1s. and 2s. are placed with the *pence* values, although the two types of "D" do not apply to the higher values.

(*b*) *Small* "D"
D6 D 1 5d. carmine and green .. .. .. 21·00 21·00
D7 6d. carmine and green .. .. .. 27·00 23·00
D8 10d. carmine and green .. .. .. 70·00 85·00
D6/8 .. .. *Set of* 3 £100 £110

II. Type II. *Circle of* 13 *ornaments,* 15 *dots over* "N.Z.", "N.Z." *small.*
(*a*) *Large* "D"
D 9 D 1 ½d. vermilion and green .. .. 2·50 16·00
a. No stop after "D" (Right pane R. 2/3) .. .. .. 55·00 95·00
D10 1d. vermilion and green .. .. 9·50 1·00
D11 2d. vermilion and green .. .. 48·00 9·00
D12 3d. vermilion and green .. .. 13·00 3·50
D9/12 .. .. *Set of* 4 65·00 26·00
(*b*) *Small* "D"
D14 D 1 1d. vermilion and green .. .. 14·00 1·50
D15 2d. vermilion and green .. .. 42·00 4·75
D16 4d. vermilion and green .. .. 29·00 9·00
D14/16 .. .. *Set of* 3 75·00 14·00

Nos. D9/16 were printed from a common frame plate of 240 (4 panes of 60) used in conjunction with centre plates of 120 (2 panes of 60) for the ½d. and 4d. or 240 for the other values. Sheets of the 1d. and 2d. each contained two panes with large "D" and two panes with small "D".

D 2

D 3

(Des W. R. Bock. Typo Govt Printing Office)

1902 (28 Feb). *No wmk. P* 11.
D17 D 2 ½d. red and deep green .. .. 1·50 6·00

1904–08. *"Cowan" unsurfaced paper. W* **43** *(sideways). (a) P* 11.
D18 D 2 ½d. red and green (4.04) .. .. 1·50 1·50
a. Imperf between (horiz pair) .. £600
D19 1d. red and green (5.12.05) .. 8·50 3·50
D20 2d. red and green (5.4.06) .. 90·00 95·00
D18/20 .. .. .. *Set of* 3 90·00 95·00
(*b*) *P* 14
D21 D 2 1d. carmine and green (12.06) .. 12·00 1·50
a. Rose-pink and green (9.07) .. 11·00 1·50
D22 2d. carmine and green (10.06) .. 9·00 5·50
a. Rose-pink and green (6.08) .. 5·00 1·50

1919 (Jan)–**20.** *"De La Rue" chalky paper. Toned gum. W* **43**. *P* 14 × 15.
D23 D 2 ½d. carmine and green (6.19) .. 3·25 3·75
w. Wmk inverted .. .. .. † —
D24 1d. carmine and green .. .. 7·00 30
D25 2d. carmine and green (8.20) .. 11·00 2·50
D23/5 .. .. *Set of* 3 19·00 6·00

1925 (May). *"Jones" chalky paper. White gum. W* **43**. *P* 14 × 15.
D26 D 2 ½d. carmine and green .. .. 35·00 38·00

1925 (July). *No wmk, but bluish "N Z" and Star lithographed on back. P* 14 × 15.
D27 D 2 ½d. carmine and green .. .. 2·00 23·00
D28 2d. carmine and green .. .. 3·50 19·00

1925 (Nov)–**35.** *"Cowan" thick, opaque chalky paper. W* **43**.
(*a*) *P* 14 × 15
D29 D 2 ½d. carmine and green (12.26) .. 1·75 8·00
D30 1d. carmine and green .. .. 3·75 80
D31 2d. carmine and green (6.26) .. 18·00 4·25
D32 3d. carmine and green (6.35) .. 48·00 55·00
D29/32 .. .. *Set of* 4 65·00 60·00
(*b*) *P* 14
D33 D 2 ½d. carmine and green (10.28) .. 35·00 30·00
D34 1d. rose and pale yellow-green (6.28) .. 4·00 1·25
D35 2d. carmine and green (10.29) .. 7·00 3·00
D36 3d. carmine and green (5.28) .. 15·00 42·00
D33/6 .. .. *Set of* 4 55·00 70·00

1937–38. *"Wiggins Teape" thin, hard chalky paper. W* **43**. *P* 14 × 15.
D37 D 2 ½d. carmine and yellow-green (2.38) .. 18·00 32·00
D38 1d. carmine and yellow-green (1.37) .. 11·00 3·75
D39 2d. carmine and yellow-green (6.37) .. 30·00 13·00
D40 3d. carmine and yellow-green (11.37) 85·00 55·00
D37/40 .. .. *Set of* 4 £130 95·00

(Des J. Berry. Typo Govt Printing Office, Wellington)

1939–49. *P* 15×14. (*a*) *W* **43** *(sideways inverted)* (16.8.39).
D41 D 3 ½d. turquoise-green .. .. 5·00 5·00
D42 1d. carmine .. .. 2·75 30
w. Wmk sideways .. .. — 1·50
D43 2d. bright blue .. .. 6·00 2·75
D44 3d. orange-brown .. .. 22·00 24·00
w. Wmk sideways
D41/4 .. .. *Set of* 4 32·00 29·00
(*b*) *W* **98** *(sideways (1d.) or sideways inverted (2d.))*
D45 D 3 1d. carmine (4.49) .. .. 16·00 5·50*
D46 2d. bright blue (12.46) .. 7·50 1·00
w. Wmk sideways (4.49) .. 2·75 8·00
D47 3d. orange-brown (1943) .. 40·00 32·00
a. Wmk sideways inverted (6.45) 15·00 5·00
aw. Wmk sideways (28.11.49) .. 9·00 8·00
D45/7 .. .. *Set of* 3 25·00 10·00*

*The use of Postage Due stamps ceased on 30 September 1951, our used price for No. D45 being for stamps postmarked after this date (*price for examples clearly cancelled* 1949–51, £27).

OFFICIAL STAMPS

1891 (Dec)–**1906.** *Contemporary issues handstamped* "O.P. S.O." *diagonally. (a) Stamps of* 1873 *type. W* **12***b*. *P* 12½.
O 1 3 ½d. rose (V.) .. .. .. — £450
(*b*) *Stamps of* 1882–97 *optd in rose or magenta. W* **12***b*.
O 2 13 ½d. black (*p* 10) .. .. .. — £180
a. Violet opt .. .. .. — £225
O 3 ½d. black (*p* 10 × 11) .. .. — £180
O 4 14 1d. rose (*p* 12 × 11½) .. .. — £180
O 5 1d. rose (*p* 11) .. .. .. — £180
O 6 15 2d. purple (*p* 11) .. .. .. — £325
O 7 2d. mauve-lilac (*p* 10) .. .. — £325
a. Violet opt .. .. ..
O 8 16 2½d. blue (*p* 11) .. .. .. — £225
O 9 2½d. ultramarine (*p* 10) .. .. — £225
O10 2½d. ultramarine (*p* 10 × 11) .. — £225
O11 19 5d. olive-black (*p* 12 × 11½) .. — £375
O12 20 6d. brown (*p* 12 × 11½) .. .. — £500
(*c*) *Stamps of* 1898–1903 *optd in violet. P* 11. (i) *No wmk*
O13 23 ½d. green (*p* 14) (No. 294) .. — £180
O14 26 2½d. blue (*p* 12–16) (No. 249*a*) .. — £400
O15 27 2½d. blue (No. 260) .. .. — £325
O16 37 4d. indigo and brown (No. 262) .. — £375
O17 30 5d. purple-brown (No. 263) .. — £400
a. Green opt .. .. .. — £375
O18 32 8d. indigo (No. 266) .. .. — £475
(ii) *W* **38**
O19 42 1d. carmine (No. 278) .. .. — £180
(iii) *W* **43** *(sideways on* 3d., 1s.)
O20 42 1d. carmine (*p* 14) (No. 303) .. — £180
a. Green opt .. .. .. — £180
O21 27 2½d. blue (No. 308) .. .. — £275
O22 28 3d. yellow-brown (No. 309) .. — £400
O23 34 1s. orange-red (No. 315*b*) .. — £800
O24 35 2s. green (No. 316) .. .. — £1200

The letters signify "On Public Service Only", and stamps so overprinted were used by the Post Office Department on official correspondence between the department and foreign countries.

OFFICIAL.

(O 3)

1907. *Stamps of* 1902–6 *optd with Type* O **3** *(vertically upwards). W* **43** *(sideways on* 3d., 6d., 1s. *and* 5s.). *P* 14.
O59 23 ½d. yellow-green .. .. .. 8·00 50
a. Perf 11×14 .. .. .. 85·00
b. Mixed perfs .. .. .. 85·00
O60 42 1d. carmine (No. 303) (1.7.07*) .. 7·00 10·00
a. Booklet pane of 6 .. .. 42·00
O60*b* 1d. rose-carmine (Waterlow) (No. 352) 8·00 30
ba. Perf 11×14 .. .. .. — £250
bb. Mixed perfs .. .. .. — £250
O60*c* 1d. carmine (Royle) .. .. .. 14·00 30
ca. Perf 11×14 .. .. .. £225
cb. Mixed perfs £225
O61 41 2d. purple .. .. .. 9·00 1·60
a. Bright reddish purple .. .. 8·50 1·25
ab. Mixed perfs £180 £180
O63 28 3d. bistre-brown .. .. .. 42·00 1·75
O64 31 6d. bright carmine-pink .. .. £130 18·00
a. Imperf vert (horiz pair) £800
b. Mixed perfs £450 £400
O65 34 1s. orange-red .. .. .. 85·00 15·00
O66 35 2s. blue-green .. .. .. 70·00 48·00
a. Imperf between (pair) £1400
b. Imperf vert (horiz pair) £1000
w. Wmk inverted £250
O67 36 5s. deep red £150 £170
a. Wmk upright £700 £750

*Though issued in 1907, a large quantity of booklets was mislaid and not utilized until they were found in 1930.

1908–09. *Optd as Type* O **3**. *W* **43**.
O69 23 ½d. green (*p* 14 × 15) .. .. 7·50 1·50
O70 50 1d. carmine (*p* 14 × 15) .. .. 65·00 2·25
O71 48 6d. pink (*p* 14 × 13, 13½) .. .. £140 45·00
O72 6d. pink (*p* 14 × 15) (1909) .. .. £110 35·00
O72*a* F 4 £1 rose-pink (*p* 14) (No. F89) .. £500 £400

1910. *No.* 387 *optd with Type* O **3**.
O73 51 ½d. yellow-green .. .. .. 4·25 30
a. Opt inverted (reading downwards) † £1200

1910–16. *Nos.* 389 *and* 392/4 *optd with Type* O **3**. *P* 14×14½.
O74 52 3d. chestnut .. .. .. 14·00 80
a. Perf 14×13½ (1915) .. .. 60·00 70·00
ab. Vert pair. Nos. O74/a £300 £350
O75 – 6d. carmine .. .. .. 19·00 4·00
a. Perf 14 (line) (No. 398) .. .. † —
b. Deep carmine .. .. .. 25·00 4·25
w. Wmk inverted .. .. ..
O76 – 8d. indigo-blue (R.) (5.16) .. 14·00 18·00
aw. Wmk inverted .. .. .. 30·00 30·00
b. Perf 14×13½ .. .. .. 14·00 18·00
ba. Vert pair. Nos. O76 and O76b .. 45·00 70·00
bw. Wmk inverted .. .. .. 30·00 30·00
O77 – 1s. vermilion .. .. .. 48·00 12·00
O74/7 .. .. *Set of* 4 85·00 30·00

1910–25. *Optd with Type* O **3**. (*a*) *W* **43**. *De La Rue chalk-surfaced paper with toned gum.*
O78 53 1d. carmine (No. 405) .. .. 3·25 10
y. Wmk inverted and reversed ..
(*b*) *W* **43**. *Jones chalk-surfaced paper with white gum*
O79 53 1d. deep carmine (No. 406) (1925) .. 10·00 6·00
(*c*) *No wmk, but bluish "NZ" and Star lithographed on back. Art paper*
O80 53 1d. rose-carmine (No. 409) (1925) .. 6·00 14·00
(*d*) *W* **43**. *Cowan thick, opaque, chalk-surfaced paper with white gum*
O81 53 1d. deep carmine (No. 410) (1925) .. 8·00 1·25

1913–25. *Postal Fiscal stamps optd with Type* O **3**.
(i) *Chalk-surfaced De La Rue paper.* (*a*) *P* 14 (1913–14)
O82 F 4 2s. blue (30.9.14) .. .. .. 48·00 35·00
O83 5s. yellow-green (13.6.13) .. .. 75·00 90·00
O84 £1 rose-carmine (1913) £550 £450
O82/4 .. .. *Set of* 3 £600 £500
(*b*) *P* 14½ × 14, *comb* (1915)
O85 F 4 2s. deep blue (Aug) .. .. 55·00 35·00
a. No stop after "OFFICIAL" .. £120 90·00
O86 5s. yellow-green (Jan) .. .. 65·00 65·00
a. No stop after "OFFICIAL" .. £200 £200
(ii) *Thick, white, opaque chalk-surfaced Cowan paper. P* 14½ × 14 (1925)
O87 F 4 2s. blue .. .. .. 80·00 70·00
a. No stop after "OFFICIAL" .. £180 £180

The overprint on these last, and on Nos. O69 and O72*a*, is from a new set of type, giving a rather sharper impression than Type O 3, but otherwise resembling it closely.

1915 (12 Oct)–**34.** *Optd with Type* O **3**. *P* 14 × 15. (*a*) *On Nos.* 435/40 *(De La Rue chalk-surfaced paper with toned gum).*
O88 61 ½d. green .. .. .. 1·25 10
O89 62 1½d. grey-black (6.16) .. .. 6·50 2·50
O90 61 1½d. slate (12.16) .. .. .. 4·25 65
O91 1½d. orange-brown (4.19) .. .. 4·25 30
O92 2d. yellow (4.17) .. .. .. 4·25 10
O93 3d. chocolate (11.19) .. .. 11·00 90
O88/93 .. .. *Set of* 6 28·00 4·00
(*b*) *On Nos.* 441 *and* 443 *(Jones chalk-surfaced paper with white gum)*
O94 61 ½d. green (1924) .. .. .. 4·50 3·00
O95 3d. deep chocolate (1924) .. .. 35·00 8·00

(c) *On Nos. 446/7 and 448a/9 (Cowan thick, opaque, chalk-surfaced paper with white gum)*

O96 **61** ½d. green (1925) 80 10
ax. Wmk reversed (1927) .. .. 8·00 10·00
ay. Wmk inverted and reversed (1927) .. .. 30·00 20·00
b. Perf 14 (1929) .. .. 3·50 35
ba. No stop after "OFFICIAL" .. 23·00 32·00
O97 1½d. orange-brown (*p* 14) (1929) .. 9·50 11·00
a. No stop after "OFFICIAL" .. 48·00 60·00
b. Perf 14×15 (1934) .. .. 22·00 28·00
O98 2d. yellow (*p* 14) (1931) .. 2·00 40
a. No stop after "OFFICIAL" .. 35·00 38·00
O99 3d. chocolate (1925) .. .. 4·00 40
a. No stop after "OFFICIAL" .. 65·00 45·00
b. Perf 14 (1930) .. .. 35·00 1·75
ba. No stop after "OFFICIAL" .. £120 50·00
O96/9 .. .. *Set of* 4 14·50 11·00

1915 (Dec)–**27**. *Optd with Type* O 3. *P* 14×13½. (a) *Nos.* 420, 422, 425, 428 *and* 429/30 (*Cowan unsurfaced paper*).

O100 **60** 3d. chocolate .. .. .. 4·00 1·25
aw. Wmk inverted .. .. 10·00 4·00
b. Perf 14×14½ .. .. 4·00 1·25
bw. Wmk inverted .. .. 10·00 4·00
c. Vert pair, Nos. O100 and O100b 35·00 50·00
cw. Wmk inverted .. .. 65·00
O101 4d. bright violet (4.25) .. .. 14·00 3·00
a. Re-entry (Pl 20 R. 1/6) .. .. 40·00
b. Re-entry (Pl 20 R. 4/10) .. .. 45·00
c. Perf 14×14½ (4.27) .. .. 27·00 1·00
O102 6d. carmine (6.16) .. .. 5·00 75
aw. Wmk inverted .. .. 85·00
b. Perf 14×14½ .. .. 6·00 85
c. Vert pair, Nos. O102 and O102b 50·00 60·00
O103 8d. red-brown (8.22) .. .. 70·00 90·00
O104 9d. sage-green (4.25) .. .. 38·00 32·00
O105 1s. vermilion (9.16) .. .. 17·00 13·00
aw. Wmk inverted £180 £120
b. Perf 14×14½ .. .. 7·00 2·00
ba. *Pale orange-red* .. .. 28·00 20·00
bw. Wmk inverted £180 £120
c. Vert pair. Nos. O105 and O105b 65·00 90·00
cw. Wmk inverted £400
O100/5 .. .. *Set of* 6 £120 £110

(b) *No.* 433 (*Thin paper with widely spaced sideways wmk*)

O106 **60** 3d. chocolate (*p* 14) (7.16) .. .. 3·00 6·50
a. No wmk .. .. .. 35·00 55·00

1927–33. *Optd with Type* O 3. W 43. *P* 14.

O111 **71** 1d. rose-carmine (No. 468) .. .. 2·00 10
a. No stop after "OFFICIAL" .. 22·00 26·00
bw. Wmk inverted .. .. † 25·00
c. Perf 14×15 .. .. 1·50 10
O112 **72** 2s. light blue (No. 469) (2.28) .. 70·00 £100
O113 **F 6** 5s. green (1933) £250 £300
O111/13 .. .. *Set of* 3 £300 £350

Official (O 4)   Official (O 5)

1936–61. *Pictorial issue optd horiz or vert (2s.) with Type* O 4.

(a) *W* **43** (*Single* "N Z" *and Star*)

O115 **82** 1d. scarlet (Die I) (*p* 14×13½) .. 2·25 70
a. Perf 13½×14 .. .. 75·00 60·00
O116 **83** 1½d. red-brown (*p* 13½×14) .. 20·00 24·00
a. Perf 14×13½ £5000
O118 **92** 1s. deep green (*p* 14×13½) .. 24·00 35·00
w. Wmk inverted .. .. † 75·00
O119 **F 6** 5s. green (*p* 14) (12.38) .. £130 38·00
O115/19 .. .. *Set of* 4 £160 85·00

The watermark of No. O119 is almost invisible.

Only four examples of No. O116a exist. The error occurred when a sheet of No. 558a was found to have a block of four missing. This was replaced by a block of No. 558 and the sheet was then sent for overprinting.

(b) *W* **98** (*Mult* "N Z" *and Star*)

O120 **81** ½d. bright green, *p* 14×13½ (7.37) 5·50 3·75
O121 **82** 1d. scar (Die II), *p* 14×13½ (11.36) 3·50 30
w. Wmk inverted .. .. 7·50 4·00
O122 **83** 1½d. red-brown, *p* 14×13½ (7.36) .. 13·00 4·00
O123 **84** 2d. orange, *p* 14×13½ (1.38) .. 2·00 10
aw. Wmk inverted .. .. — £110
b. Perf 12½ (1942) .. .. £190 55·00
c. Perf 14 (1942) .. .. 48·00 15·00
O124 **85** 2½d. chocolate & slate, *p* 13–14×13½ (26.7.38) .. .. 48·00 70·00
a. Perf 14 (1938) .. .. 14·00 20·00
O125 **86** 3d. brown, *p* 14×13½ (1.3.38) .. 48·00 3·00
w. Wmk inverted .. .. — 27·00
O126 **87** 4d. black and sepia, *p* 14×13½ (8.36) 8·50 95
a. Perf 14 (8.41) .. .. 7·50 3·50
b. Perf 12½ (1941) .. .. 5·00 4·50
c. Perf 14×14½ (10.42) .. .. 3·50 65
cw. Wmk inverted .. .. — 45·00
O127 **89** 6d. scarlet, *p* 13½×14 (12.37) .. 15·00 50
aw. Wmk inverted .. ..
b. Perf 12½ (1941) .. .. 13·00 5·00
c. Perf 14½×14 (7.42) .. .. 7·50 30
O128 **90** 8d. chocolate, *p* 12½ (*wmk sideways*) (1942) .. .. .. 14·00 15·00
a. Perf 14×14½ (*wmk sideways*) (1945) .. .. .. 8·00 14·00
b. Perf 14×13½ .. .. † £1600
O129 **91** 9d. red & grey-black (G.) (No. 587*a*), *p* 13½×14 (1.3.38) .. 55·00 38·00
O130 9d. scar & blk (*chalk-surfaced paper*) (Blk.) (No. 631), *p* 14×15 (1943) 20·00 22·00
O131 **92** 1s. deep green, *p* 14×13½ (2.37) 45·00 1·50
aw. Wmk inverted .. .. — 85·00
b. Perf 12½ (1942) .. .. 22·00 85
O132 **93** 2s. olive-green, *p* 13–14×13½ (5.37) 80·00 28·00
a. "CAPTAIN COQK" .. .. 95·00
b. Perf 13½×14 (1939) .. .. £160 6·00
ba. "CAPTAIN COQK" £170
c. Perf 12½ (1942) .. .. 90·00 26·00
ca. "CAPTAIN COQK" £110
d. Perf 14×13½ (1944) .. .. 42·00 7·00
da. "CAPTAIN COQK" £200

O133 **F 6** 5s. green (*chalk-surfaced paper*), *p* 14 (3.43) .. .. .. 35·00 5·00
aw. Wmk inverted .. .. 35·00 5·00
b. Perf 14×13½. *Yellow-green (ordinary paper)* (10.61) .. 17·00 30·00
O120/33 .. .. *Set of* 14 £250 £110

The opt on No. O127a was sometimes applied at the top of the stamp, instead of always at the bottom, as on No. O127.

All examples of No. O128b were used by a government office in Whangerei.

The 5s. value on ordinary paper perforated 14×13½ does not exist without the "Official" overprint.

See notes on perforations after No. 590b.

1938–51. *Nos.* 603 *etc., optd with Type* O 4.

O134 **108** ½d. green (1.3.38) .. .. 14·00 2·00
O135 ½d. brown-orange (1946) .. .. 1·60 2·50
O136 1d. scarlet (1.7.38) .. .. 15·00 15
O137 1d. green (10.7.41) .. .. 2·25 10
O138 **108a** 1½d. purple-brown (26.7.38) .. .. 75·00 18·00
O139 1½d. scarlet (2.4.51) .. .. 9·00 5·00
O140 3d. blue (16.10.41) .. .. 2·25 10
O134/40 .. .. *Set of* 7 £110 24·00

1940 (2 Jan–8 Mar). *Centennial. Nos.* 613, *etc., optd with Type* O 5.

O141 ½d. blue-green (R.) .. .. 1·50 35
a. "ff" joined, as Type O 4 .. 50·00 60·00
O142 1d. chocolate and scarlet .. .. 4·00 10
a. "ff" joined, as Type O 4 .. 60·00 60·00
O143 1½d. light blue and mauve .. .. 2·50 2·00
O144 2d. blue-green and chocolate .. 4·00 10
a. "ff" joined, as Type O 4 .. 60·00 60·00
O145 2½d. blue-green and ultramarine .. 3·75 2·75
a. "ff" joined, as Type O 4 .. 60·00 65·00
O146 3d. purple and carmine (R.) .. 8·00 90
a. "ff" joined, as Type O 4 .. 42·00 48·00
O147 4d. chocolate and lake .. .. 48·00 2·00
a. "ff" joined, as Type O 4 .. £140 80·00
O148 6d. emerald-green and violet .. 25·00 2·00
a. "ff" joined, as Type O 4 .. 70·00 70·00
O149 8d. black and red (8.3) .. .. 32·00 17·00
a. "ff" joined, as Type O 4 .. 75·00 £100
O150 9d. olive-green and vermilion .. 11·00 7·00
O151 1s. sage-green and deep green .. 48·00 4·00
O141/51 .. .. .. *Set of* 11 £160 35·00

For this issue the Type O 4 overprint occurs on R.4/3 of the 2½d. and on R.1/10 of the other values.

1947–49. *Nos.* 680, *etc., optd with Type* O 4.

O152 **108a** 2d. orange .. .. .. 1·75 10
O153 4d. bright purple .. .. 4·25 1·25
O154 6d. carmine .. .. .. 11·00 40
O155 8d. violet .. .. .. 8·00 6·50
O156 9d. purple-brown .. .. 9·00 6·50
O157 **144** 1s. red-brown and carmine (*wmk upright*) (Plate 1) .. .. 17·00 95
a. Wmk sideways (Plate 1) (1949) 8·50 8·50
aw. Wmk sideways inverted .. 35·00
b. Wmk upright (Plate 2) .. 24·00 7·00
bw. Wmk inverted .. .. 65·00 28·00
O158 2s. brown-orange and green (*wmk sideways*) (Plate 1) .. .. 23·00 16·00
a. Wmk upright (Plate 1) .. 32·00 38·00
O152/8 .. .. *Set of* 7 60·00 28·00

OFFICIAL 2d NEW ZEALAND 2d
O 6
Queen Elizabeth II

6d
(O 7)

(Des J. Berry. Recess B.W.)

1954 (1 Mar)–**63**. *W* **98**. *P* 14×13½.

O159 **O 6** 1d. orange 60 30
a. White opaque paper (8.7.59) .. 50 20
O160 1½d. brown-lake .. .. 2·50 3·50
O161 2d. bluish green 40 15
a. White opaque paper (11.12.58) 40 15
O162 2½d. olive (*white opaque paper*) (1.3.63) .. .. .. 4·25 1·50
O163 3d. vermilion 50 10
a. White opaque paper (1960) .. 40 10
aw. Wmk inverted .. .. 17·00 15·00
O164 4d. blue .. .. .. 1·25 20
a. Printed on the gummed side .. £120
b. White opaque paper (1.9.61) .. 1·00 50
O165 9d. carmine .. .. .. 5·50 75
O166 1s. purple .. .. .. 1·00 10
a. White opaque paper (2.10.61) .. 2·50 75
O167 3s. slate (*white opaque paper*) (1.3.63) .. .. .. 35·00 48·00
O159/67 .. .. *Set of* 9 45·00 48·00

See note *re* white opaque paper after No. 736.

1959 (1 Oct). *No.* O160 *surch with Type* O 7.

O168 **O 6** 6d. on 1½d. brown-lake .. .. 40 1·10

1961 (1 Sept). *No.* O161 *surch as Type* O 7.

O169 **O 6** 2½d. on 2d. bluish green .. .. 75 1·50

Owing to the greater use of franking machines by Government Departments, the use of official stamps was discontinued on 31 March 1965, but they remained on sale at the G.P.O. until 31 December 1965.

STAMP BOOKLET

1907 (1 July). *White card cover.*

OB1 10s. booklet containing one hundred and twenty 1d. in panes of 6 (No. O60a) £900

PROVISIONALS ISSUED AT REEFTON AND USED BY THE POLICE DEPARTMENT

1907 (Jan). *Current stamps of* 1906, *overwritten* "Official," *in red ink, and marked* "Greymouth—PAID—3" *inside a circular postmark stamp. P* 14.

P1 **23** ½d. green £700 £900
P2 **40** 1d. carmine £700 £950
P3 **38a** 2d. purple £950 £1000
P4 **28** 3d. bistre £950 £1100
P5 **31** 6d. pink £1200 £1300
P6 **34** 1s. orange-red £1600 £1800
P7 **35** 2s. green .. .. .. — £5500

LIFE INSURANCE DEPARTMENT

L 1 Lighthouse L 2

(Des W. B. Hudson and J. F. Rogers; eng A. E. Cousins. Typo Govt Printing Office, Wellington)

1891 (2 Jan)–**98**. A. *W* **12c**. *P* 12×11½.

L 1 **L 1** ½d. bright purple .. .. 55·00 6·00
L 2 1d. blue .. .. .. 55·00 4·00
a. Wmk **12b** .. .. 90·00 20·00
L 3 2d. brown-red .. .. 85·00 7·00
a. Wmk **12b** .. .. 95·00 13·00
L 4 3d. deep brown .. .. £160 20·00
L 5 6d. green .. .. .. £275 60·00
L 6 1s. rose £500 £120
L1/6 .. .. *Set of* 6 £1000 £200

B. *W* **12b** (1893–98). (a) *P* 10 (1893)

L 7 **L 1** ½d. bright purple .. .. 55·00 8·50
L 8 1d. blue .. .. .. 55·00 1·25
L 9 2d. brown-red .. .. 75·00 3·75
L7/9 .. .. *Set of* 3 £160 12·00

(b) *P* 11×10

L10 **L 1** ½d. bright purple (1896) .. .. 90·00 26·00
a. Perf 10×11 .. .. — 60·00
L11 1d. blue (1897) .. ..
a. Perf 10×11 .. .. 55·00 12·00

(c) *Mixed perfs* 10 *and* 11 (1897)

L12 **L 1** 2d. brown-red £550 £550

(d) *P* 11 (1897–98)

L13 **L 1** ½d. bright purple .. .. 55·00 2·75
a. Thin coarse toned paper (1898) .. 65·00 5·50
L14 1d. blue .. .. .. 55·00 75
a. Thin coarse toned paper (1898) .. 65·00 1·50
L15 2d. brown-red .. .. .. 70·00 3·50
a. *Chocolate* .. .. £110 24·00
b. Thin coarse toned paper (1898) .. 80·00 3·50
L13/15 .. .. *Set of* 3 £160 6·25

1902–04. *W* **43** (*sideways*). (a) *P* 11.

L16 **L 1** ½d. bright purple (1903) .. .. 55·00 4·50
L17 1d. blue (1902) .. .. 55·00 1·00
L18 2d. brown-red (1904) .. .. 90·00 6·50
L16/18 .. .. *Set of* 3 £180 11·00

(b) *P* 14×11

L19 **L 1** ½d. bright purple (1903) £1300
L20 1d. blue (1904) .. .. 95·00 11·00

Nos. L16/17 and L20 are known without watermark from the margins of the sheet.

1905–6. *Redrawn, with* "V.R." *omitted. W* **43** (*sideways*). (a) *P* 11.

L21 **L 2** 2d. brown-red (12.05) .. .. £1000 80·00

(b) *P* 14

L22 **L 2** 1d. blue (1906) .. .. .. £150 30·00

(c) *P* 14×11

L23 **L 2** 1d. blue (1906) £475 £150
a. Mixed perfs .. .. — £375

Between January 1907 and the end of 1912 the Life Insurance Department used ordinary Official stamps.

1913 (2 Jan)–**37**. *New values and colours. W* **43**.

(a) *"De La Rue" paper. P* 14×15

L24 **L 2** ½d. green .. .. .. 9·50 80
a. *Yellow-green* .. .. 9·50 80
L25 1d. carmine .. .. .. 8·00 1·00
a. *Carmine-pink* .. .. 15·00 1·40
L26 1½d. black (1917) .. .. 40·00 6·50
L27 1½d. chestnut-brown (1919) .. 1·50 2·25
L28 2d. bright purple .. .. 48·00 26·00
w. Wmk inverted .. .. † 75·00
L29 2d. yellow (1920) .. .. 4·00 2·00
L30 3d. yellow-brown .. .. 45·00 24·00
L31 6d. carmine-pink .. .. 35·00 22·00
L24/31 .. .. *Set of* 8 £170 75·00

(b) *"Cowan" paper.* (i) *P* 14×15

L31*a* **L 2** ½d. yellow-green (1925) .. .. 26·00 4·00
L31*b* 1d. carmine-pink (1925) .. .. 26·00 3·50
bw. Wmk inverted .. .. 35·00 5·00

(ii) *P* 14

L32 **L 2** ½d. yellow-green (1926) .. .. 9·00 1·50
w. Wmk inverted .. .. † 8·00
L33 1d. scarlet (1931) .. .. 7·00 1·50
w. Wmk inverted .. .. 12·00 2·50
L34 2d. yellow (1937) .. .. 5·00 4·50
w. Wmk inverted .. .. 30·00 25·00
L35 3d. brown-lake (1931) .. .. 18·00 22·00
L36 6d. pink (1925) .. .. 32·00 35·00
L32/6 .. .. *Set of* 5 65·00 55·00

(c) *"Wiggins Teape" paper. P* 14×15

L36*a* **L 2** ½d. yellow-green (3.37) .. .. 6·50 9·00
L36*b* 1d. scarlet (3.37) .. .. 14·00 3·25
L36*c* 6d. pink (7.37) .. .. 30·00 38·00
L36*a/c* .. .. *Set of* 3 45·00 45·00

For descriptions of the various types of paper, see after No. 385.

In the 1½d. the word "POSTAGE" is in both the side-labels instead of at left only.

1944–47. *W* **98.** *P* 14 × 15.
L37 L 2 ½d. yellow-green (7.47) .. .. .. 4·25 7·50
L38 1d. scarlet (6.44) .. .. .. 2·25 2·00
L39 2d. yellow (1946) .. .. .. 9·50 12·00
L40 3d. brown-lake (10.46) .. .. .. 14·00 26·00
L41 6d. pink (7.47) .. .. .. 11·00 30·00
L37/41 .. .. *Set of* 5 38·00 70·00

L 3 Castlepoint Lighthouse

L 6 Cape Campbell Lighthouse

(Des J. Berry. Recess B.W.).

1947 (1 Aug)–**65.** *Type* **L 3, L 6** *and similar designs.* **W 98** *(sideways on 1d., 2d., 2½d.). P* 13½.
L42 ½d. grey-green and orange-red .. .. 1·00 60
L43 1d. olive-green and pale blue .. .. 1·00 65
L44 2d. deep blue and grey-black 70 30
L45 2½d. black and bright blue (*white opaque paper*) (4.11.63) .. .. 9·50 13·00
L46 3d. mauve and pale blue .. .. 2·50 35
L47 4d. brown and yellow-orange .. .. 3·00 95
a. Wmk sideways (*white opaque paper*) (13.10.65) .. .. 5·00 13·00
L48 6d. chocolate and blue .. .. 3·50 1·25
L49 1s. red-brown and blue .. .. 3·50 2·25
L42/49 .. .. *Set of* 8 22·00 17·00
Designs: *Horiz (as Type* **L 3**)–1d Taiaroa lighthouse; 2d. Cape Palliser lighthouse; 6d. The Brothers lighthouse. *Vert (as Type* **L 6**)–3d. Eddystone lighthouse; 4d. Stephens Island lighthouse; 1s. Cape Brett lighthouse.

(L 11) (L 12)

1967 (10 July)–**68.** *Decimal currency. Stamps of* 1947–65, *surch as Type* **L 12** *or* **L 11** (2 c.).
L50 1 c. on 1d. (No. L43) .. .. .. 2·25 4·25
a. Wmk upright (*white opaque paper*) (10.5.68) .. .. 1·75 4·00
L51 2 c. on 2½d. (No. L45) .. .. .. 10·00 12·00
L52 2½ c. on 3d. (No. L46) .. .. .. 2·00 4·50
a. Horiz pair, one without surcharge £1800
b. Wmk sideways (*white opaque paper*) (4.68?) .. .. 2·40 4·75
L53 3 c. on 4d. (No. L47a) .. .. .. 4·50 5·50
w. Wmk sideways inverted .. .. † —
L54 5 c. on 6d. (No. L48) .. .. .. 1·50 7·00
a. White opaque paper .. .. 2·00 7·50
L55 10 c. on 1s. (No. L49) .. .. .. 2·50 11·00
a. Wmk sideways (*white opaque paper*) 1·00 4·00
aw. Wmk sideways inverted .. .. † —
L50/5a .. .. *Set of* 6 19·00 32·00
See note *re* white paper below No. 736.

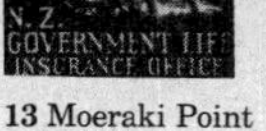

L 13 Moeraki Point Lighthouse

L 14 Puysegur Point Lighthouse

(Des J. Berry. Litho B.W.)

1969 (27 Mar)–**77.** *Types* **L 13/14** *and similar designs. No wmk. Chalk-surfaced paper* (8, 10 c.), *ordinary paper (others). P* 14 (8, 10 *c.*) *or* 13½ (*others*).
L56 ½ c. greenish yellow, red and deep blue 1·50 2·25
L57 2½ c. ultramarine, green and pale buff .. 75 1·25
L58 3 c. reddish brown and yellow 75 75
a. Chalk-surfaced paper (16.6.77) .. 80 2·25
L59 4 c. lt new blue, yellowish grn & apple-grn 1·00 1·00
a. Chalk-surfaced paper (16.6.77) .. 65 2·25
L60 8 c. multicoloured (17.11.76) .. .. 45 2·50
L61 10 c. multicoloured (17.11.76) .. .. 45 2·50
L62 15 c. black, light yellow and ultramarine 60 2·00
a. Chalk-surfaced paper (3.75) .. 20·00 20·00
ab. Perf 14 (24.12.76) .. .. .. 1·50 2·25
L56/62 .. .. *Set of* 7 4·50 11·00
Designs: *Horiz*–4 c. Cape Egmont Lighthouse; *Vert*–3c. Baring Head Lighthouse; 8 c. East Cape; 10 c. Farewell Spit; 15 c. Dog Island Lighthouse.

(L 16)

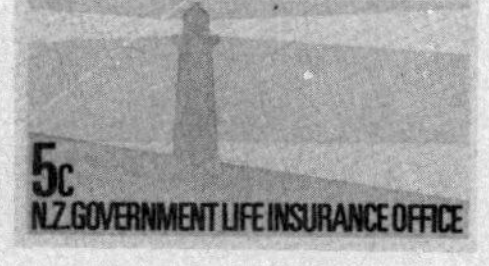

L 17

1978 (8 Mar). *No.* L 57 *surch with Type* **L 16.** *Chalky paper.*
L63 L 14 25 c. on 2½ c. ultramarine, grn & buff 75 1·75

(Des A. G. Mitchell. Litho Harrison)

1981 (3 June). *P* 14½.
L64 L 17 5 c. multicoloured 10 10
L65 10 c. multicoloured 10 10
L66 20 c. multicoloured 15 15
L67 30 c. multicoloured 25 25
L68 40 c. multicoloured 35 30
L69 50 c. multicoloured 45 35
L64/9 .. .. *Set of* 6 1·25 1·00
Issues for the Government Life Insurance Department were withdrawn on 1 December 1989 when it became the privatised Tower Corporation.

POSTAL FISCAL STAMPS

As from 1 April 1882 fiscal stamps were authorised for postal use and conversely postage stamps became valid for fiscal use. Stamps in the designs of 1867 with "STAMP DUTY" above the Queen's head were withdrawn and although some passed through the mail quite legitimately they were mainly "philatelic" and we no longer list them. The issue which was specifically authorised in 1882 was the one which had originally been put on sale for fiscal use in 1880.

Although all fiscal stamps were legally valid for postage only values between 2s. and £1 were stocked at ordinary post offices. Other values could only be obtained by request from the G.P.O., Wellington or from offices of the Stamp Duties Department. Later the Arms types above £1 could also be obtained from the head post offices in Auckland, Christchurch, Dunedin and also a branch post office at Christchurch North where there was a local demand for them.

It seems sensible to list under Postal Fiscals the Queen Victoria stamps up to the £1 value and the Arms types up to the £5 because by 1931 the higher values were genuinely needed for postal purposes. Even the £10 was occasionally used on insured airmail parcels.

Although 2s. and 5s. values were included in the 1898 pictorial issue, it was the general practice for the Postal Department to limit the postage issues to 1s. until 1926 when the 2s. and 3s. appeared. These were then dropped from the fiscal issues and when in turn the 5s. and 10s. were introduced in 1953 and the £1 in 1960 no further printings of these values occurred in the fiscal series.

FORGED POSTMARKS. Our prices are for stamps with genuine postal cancellations. Beware of forged postmarks on stamps from which fiscal cancellations have been cleaned off.

Many small post offices acted as agents for government departments and it was the practice to use ordinary postal date-stamps on stamps used fiscally, so that when they are removed from documents they are indistinguishable from postally used specimens unless impressed with the embossed seal of the Stamp Duties Department.

Date-stamps very similar to postal date-stamps were sometimes supplied to offices of the Stamp Duties Department and it is not clear when this practice ceased. Prior to the Arms types the only sure proof of the postal use of off-cover fiscal stamps is when they bear a distinctive duplex, registered or parcel post cancellation, but beware of forgeries of the first two.

F 1

F 2

F 3

(Die eng W. R. Bock. Typo Govt Ptg Office)

1882 (Feb). *W* **12a.** *P* 12 × 11½.
F1 F 1 1d. lilac £170 £300
F2 1d. blue .. .. 80·00 25·00
The 1d. fiscal was specifically authorised for postal use in February 1882 owing to a shortage of the 1d. Type **5** and pending the introduction of the 1d. Type **14** on 1 April.

The 1d. lilac fiscal had been replaced by the 1d. blue in 1878 but postally used copies with 1882 duplex postmarks are known although most postally used examples are dated from 1890 and these must have been philatelic.

(Des and dies eng W. R. Bock. Typo Govt Ptg Office)

1882 (early). *W* **12a.** *P* 12 × 11½.
F3 F 2 1s. grey green .. ..
F4 F 3 1s. grey-green and red .. .. ..
Copies of these are known postally used in 1882 and although not specifically authorised for postal use it is believed that their use was permitted where there was a shortage of the 1s. postage stamp.

The 2s. value Type F **3** formerly listed is not known with 1882–83 postal date-stamps.

WMK TYPE F 5. The balance of the paper employed for the 1867 issue was used for early printings of Type F **4** introduced in 1880 before changing over to the "N Z" and Star watermark. The values we list with this watermark are known with 1882–83 postal date stamps. Others have later dates and are considered to be philatelic but should they be found with 1882–83 postal dates we would be prepared to add them to the list.

In the following list the 4d., 6d., 8d. and 1s. are known with early 1882 postal date-stamps and, like Nos. F3/4, it is assumed that they were used to meet a temporary shortage of postage stamps.

OMNIBUS ISSUES

Details, together with prices for complete sets, of the various Omnibus issues from the 1935 Silver Jubilee series to date are included in a special section following Zimbabwe at the end of Volume 2.

F 4

F 5

The 12s. 6d. value has the head in an oval (as Type **10**), and the 15s. and £1 values have it in a broken circle (as Type **7**).

(Dies eng W. R. Bock. Typo Govt Ptg Office)

1882 (1 Apr). *Type* F **4** *and similar types. "De La Rue" paper.*

A. *W* **12a** (6 *mm*). (a) *P* 12 (1882)
F 5 4d. orange-red (*Wmk* F **5**) .. .. .. — £150
F 6 6d. lake-brown .. .. — £150
F 7 8d. green (*Wmk* F **5**) .. .. ..
F 8 1s. pink .. ..
F 9 2s. blue .. .. 50·00 4·50
F10 2s. 6d. grey-brown .. .. .. 85·00 4·50
a. Wmk F **5** .. .. ..
F11 3s. mauve .. .. £110 5·50
F12 4s. brown-rose .. .. £110 11·00
F13 5s. green .. .. £140 11·00
a. *Yellow-green* .. .. .. £140 11·00
F14 6s. rose .. .. £150 27·00
F15 7s. ultramarine .. .. £160 48·00
F16 7s. 6d. bronze-grey .. .. .. £160 60·00
F17 8s. deep blue .. .. £160 60·00
F18 9s. orange .. .. £150 50·00
F19 10s. brown-red .. .. £140 15·00
a. Wmk F **5** .. .. ..
F20 15s. green .. .. £190 60·00
F21 £1 rose-pink .. .. £190 45·00

(*b*) *P* 12½ (1886)
F22 2s. blue .. .. 50·00 4·50
F23 2s. 6d. grey-brown .. .. .. 85·00 4·50
F24 3s. mauve .. .. £110 5·50
F25 4s. purple-claret .. .. .. £110 11·00
a. *Brown-rose* .. .. .. £110 11·00
F26 5s. green .. .. £140 11·00
a. *Yellow-green* .. .. .. £140 11·00
F27 6s. rose .. .. £150 27·00
F28 7s. ultramarine .. .. £160 48·00
F29 8s. deep blue .. .. £160 60·00
F30 9s. orange .. .. £150 50·00
F31 10s. brown-red .. .. £140 15·00
F32 15s. green .. .. £190 60·00
F33 £1 rose-pink .. .. £190 45·00

B. *W* **12b** (7 *mm*). *P* 12½ (1888)
F34 2s. blue .. .. 45·00 4·50
F35 2s. 6d. grey-brown .. .. .. 80·00 4·50
F36 3s. mauve .. .. £100 5·50
F37 4s. brown-rose .. .. £100 11·00
a. *Brown-red* .. .. .. £100 11·00
F38 5s. green .. .. £130 11·00
a. *Yellow-green* .. .. .. £130 11·00
F39 6s. rose .. .. £150 27·00
F40 7s. ultramarine .. .. £160 48·00
F41 7s. 6d. bronze-grey .. .. .. £160 60·00
F42 8s. deep blue .. .. £160 60·00
F43 9s. orange .. .. £150 50·00
F44 10s. brown-red .. .. £140 13·00
a. *Maroon* .. .. .. £140 13·00
F45 £1 pink .. .. £190 45·00

C. *W* **12c** (4 *mm*). *P* 12½ (1890)
F46 2s. blue .. .. 75·00 11·00
F47 3s. mauve .. .. £150 27·00
F48 4s. brown-red .. .. £120 15·00
F49 5s. green .. .. £140 12·00
F50 6s. rose .. .. £160 27·00
F51 7s. ultramarine .. .. £170 48·00
F52 8s. deep blue .. .. £170 60·00
F53 9s. orange .. .. £160 60·00
F54 10s. brown-red .. .. £140 14·00
F55 15s. green .. .. £250 85·00

D. *Continuation of W* **12b.** *P* 11 (1895–1901)
F56 2s. blue .. .. 27·00 5·50
F57 2s. 6d. grey-brown .. .. .. 80·00 4·50
a. Inscr "COUNTERPART" (1901)* .. £150 £120
F58 3s. mauve .. .. £100 5·50
F59 4s. brown-red .. .. £100 10·00
F60 5s. yellow-green .. .. .. £130 12·00
F61 6s. rose .. .. £140 27·00
F62 7s. pale blue .. .. £160 48·00
F63 7s. 6d. bronze-grey .. .. .. £160 60·00
F64 8s. deep blue .. .. £160 60·00
F65 9s. orange .. .. £150 50·00
a. Imperf between (horiz pair) .. £800
F66 10s. brown-red .. .. £140 13·00
a. *Maroon* .. .. .. £140 13·00
F67 15s. green .. .. £190 60·00
F68 £1 rose-pink .. .. £190 45·00
*The plate normally printed in yellow and inscribed "COUNTERPART" just above the bottom value panel, was for use on the counterparts of documents but was issued in error in the colour of the normal fiscal stamp and accepted for use.

E. *W* **43** (*sideways*)
(i) *Unsurfaced "Cowan" paper.* (*a*) *P* 11 (1903)
F69 2s. 6d. grey-brown .. .. .. 80·00 4·50
F70 3s. mauve .. .. £100 5·50
F71 4s. orange-red .. .. £100 10·00
F72 6s. rose .. .. £140 27·00
F73 7s. pale blue .. .. £160 48·00
F74 8s. deep blue .. .. £150 60·00
F75 10s. brown-red .. .. £130 15·00
a. *Maroon* .. .. .. £130 15·00
F76 15s. green .. .. £190 60·00
F77 £1 rose-pink .. .. £170 45·00

(*b*) *P* 14 (1906)

F78 2s. 6d. grey-brown .. 80·00 4·50
F79 3s. mauve .. £100 5·50
F80 4s. orange-red .. £100 7·50
F81 5s. yellow-green .. 70·00 7·50
F82 6s. rose .. £140 27·00
F83 7s. pale blue .. £150 48·00
F84 7s. 6d. bronze-grey .. £150 60·00
F85 8s. deep blue .. £150 60·00
F86 9s. orange .. £140 50·00
F87 10s. maroon .. £130 13·00
F88 15s. green .. £190 60·00
F89 £1 rose-pink .. £170 48·00

(*c*) *P* 14½ × 14, *comb* (*clean-cut*) (1907)

F90 2s. blue .. 25·00 4·00
F91 2s. 6d. grey-brown .. 80·00 4·50
F92 3s. mauve .. £100 5·50
F93 4s. orange-red .. 90·00 7·50
F94 6s. rose .. £140 27·00
F95 10s. maroon .. £130 13·00
F96 15s. green .. £170 60·00
F97 £1 rose-pink .. £170 45·00

(ii) *Chalk-surfaced "De La Rue" paper.* (*a*) *P* 14 (1913)

F 98 2s. blue .. 25·00 4·00
F 99 2s. 6d. grey-brown .. 27·00 4·50
F100 3s. purple .. 70·00 5·50
F101 4s. orange-red .. 70·00 7·00
F102 5s. yellow-green .. 70·00 7·50
F103 6s. rose .. £100 14·00
F104 7s. pale blue .. £100 22·00
F105 7s. 6d. bronze-grey .. £150 60·00
F106 8s. deep blue .. £130 29·00
F107 9s. orange .. £140 50·00
F108 10s. maroon .. £130 13·00
F109 15s. green .. £170 60·00
F110 £1 rose-carmine .. £170 45·00

(*b*) *P* 14½ × 14, *comb* (1913–21)

F111 2s. deep blue .. 25·00 4·00
F112 2s. 6d. grey-brown .. 27·00 4·50
F113 3s. purple .. 70·00 5·50
F114 4s. orange-red .. 70·00 7·00
F115 5s. yellow-green .. 70·00 7·50
F116 6s. rose .. £100 14·00
F117 7s. pale blue .. £100 22·00
F118 8s. deep blue .. £130 29·00
F119 9s. orange .. £130 50·00
F120 10s. maroon .. £130 13·00
F121 12s. 6d. deep plum (1921) .. £2500 £950
F122 15s. green .. £170 55·00
F123 £1 rose-carmine .. £170 45·00

The "De La Rue" paper has a smooth finish and has toned gum which is strongly resistant to soaking.

(iii) *Chalk-surfaced "Jones" paper. P* 14½ × 14, *comb* (1924)

F124 2s. deep blue .. 30·00 5·00
F125 2s. 6d. deep grey-brown .. 32·00 5·50
F126 3s. purple .. 80·00 6·50
F127 5s. yellow-green .. 80·00 8·50
F128 10s. brown-red .. £140 14·00
F129 12s. 6d deep purple .. £2500 £950
F130 15s. green .. £200 65·00

The "Jones" paper has a coarser texture, is poorly surfaced and the ink tends to peel. The outline of the watermark commonly shows on the surface of the stamp. The gum is colourless or only slightly toned and washes off readily.

(iv) *Thick, opaque, chalk-surfaced "Cowan" paper. P* 14½×14, *comb* (1925–30)

F131 2s. blue .. 27·00 5·00
F132 2s. 6d. deep grey-brown .. 30·00 5·50
F133 3s. mauve .. £100 10·00
F134 4s. orange-red .. 70·00 9·00
F135 5s. yellow-green .. 70·00 10·00
x. Wmk reversed (1927) .. £100 20·00
F136 6s. rose .. £100 16·00
F137 7s. pale blue .. £100 20·00
F138 8s. deep blue .. £130 29·00
a. Error. Blue (as 2s.) (1930) .. £500
F139 10s. brown-red .. £130 14·00
x. Wmk reversed (1927) .. £200 £150
F140 12s. 6d. blackish purple .. £2500 £950
F141 15s. green .. £200 65·00
F142 £1 rose-pink .. £170 48·00

The "Cowan" paper is white and opaque and the watermark, which is usually smaller than in the "Jones" paper, is often barely visible.

(v) *Thin, hard, chalk-surfaced "Wiggins Teape" paper. P* 14½ × 14, *comb* (1926)

F143 4s. orange-red .. 80·00 12·00
F144 £1 rose-pink .. £180 90·00

The "Wiggins Teape" paper has a vertical mesh with narrow watermark, whereas other chalk-surfaced papers with this perforation have a horizontal mesh and wider watermark.

F 6

35/-

(F 7)

(Des H. L. Richardson. Typo Govt Ptg Office)

1931–40. *As Type* F **6** (*various frames*). W **43**. *P* 14.

(i) *Thick, opaque, chalk-surfaced "Cowan" paper, with horizontal mesh* (1931–35)

F145 1s. 3d. lemon (4.31) .. 10·00 35·00
F146 1s. 3d. orange-yellow .. 4·50 4·75
F147 2s. 6d. deep brown .. 13·00 4·00
F148 4s. red .. 14·00 4·75
F149 5s. green .. 17·00 7·00
F150 6s. carmine-rose .. 32·00 12·00
F151 7s. blue .. 27·00 18·00
F152 7s. 6d. olive-grey .. 55·00 80·00
F153 8s. slate-violet .. 28·00 26·00
F154 9s. brown-orange .. 30·00 26·00
F155 10s. carmine-lake .. 24·00 8·00
F156 12s. 6d. deep plum (9.35) .. £140 £140
F157 15s. sage-green .. 60·00 30·00
F158 £1 pink .. 60·00 17·00
F159 25s. greenish blue .. £250 £375
F160 30s. brown (1935) .. £250 £140
F161 35s. orange-yellow .. £2250 £2750
F162 £2 bright purple .. £300 60·00
F163 £2 10s. red .. £225 £300
F164 £3 green .. £300 £170
F165 £3 10s. rose (1935) .. £1200 £1000
F166 £4 light blue (1935) .. £325 £130
F167 £4 10s. deep olive-grey (1935) .. £1100 £1100
F168 £5 indigo-blue .. £325 90·00

(ii) *Thin, hard "Wiggins Teape" paper with vertical mesh* (1936–40)

(*a*) *Chalk-surfaced* (1936–39)

F169 1s. 3d. pale orange-yellow .. 10·00 2·75
F170 2s. 6d. dull brown .. 40·00 3·00
F171 4s. pale red-brown .. 50·00 5·50
F172 5s. green .. 60·00 6·00
w. Wmk inverted
F173 6s. carmine-rose .. 60·00 23·00
F174 7s. pale blue .. 70·00 26·00
F175 8s. slate-violet .. 95·00 42·00
F176 9s. brown-orange .. £100 60·00
F177 10s. pale carmine-lake .. £100 6·50
F178 15s. sage-green .. £160 48·00
F179 £1 pink .. £120 23·00
F180 30s. brown (1.39) .. £350 £140
F181 35s. orange-yellow .. £3000 £3000
F182 £2 bright purple (1937) .. £425 80·00
w. Wmk inverted
F183 £3 green (1937) .. £450 £190
F184 £5 indigo-blue (1937) .. £650 £160

(*b*) *Unsurfaced* (1940)

F185 7s. 6d. olive-grey .. £140 90·00

Not all values listed above were stocked at ordinary post offices as some of them were primarily required for fiscal purposes but all were valid for postage.

1939. *No.* F161 *surch with Type* F **7**.

F186 35/- on 35s. orange-yellow .. £400 £225

Because the 35s. orange-yellow could so easily be confused with the 1s. 3d. in the same colour it was surcharged.

1940 (June). *New values surch as Type* F **7**. W **43**. *"Wiggins Teape" chalk-surfaced paper. P* 14.

F187 3/6 on 3s. 6d. grey-green .. 45·00 14·00
F188 5/6 on 5s. 6d. lilac .. 75·00 42·00
F189 11/- on 11s. yellow .. £130 95·00
F190 22/- on 22s. scarlet .. £325 £225
F187/90 .. *Set of* 4 £500 £325

These values were primarily needed for fiscal use.

1940–58. *As Type* F **6** (*various frames*). W **98**.

(i) *P* 14. *"Wiggins Teape" chalk-surfaced paper with vertical mesh* (1940–56)

F191 1s. 3d. orange-yellow .. 6·50 1·50
w. Wmk inverted
F192 1s. 3d. yellow and black (*wmk inverted*) (14.6.55) .. 1·00 70
aw. Wmk upright (9.9.55) .. 25·00 25·00
b. Error. Yellow and blue (*wmk inverted*) (7.56) .. 3·00 5·50
F193 2s. 6d. deep brown .. 6·50 30
w. Wmk inverted (3.49) .. 8·00 30
F194 4s. red-brown .. 11·00 70
w. Wmk inverted (3.49) .. 13·00 70
F195 5s. green .. 17·00 80
w. Wmk inverted (1.5.50) .. 22·00 80
F196 6s. carmine-rose .. 30·00 3·25
w. Wmk inverted (1948) .. 30·00 2·50
F197 7s. pale blue .. 30·00 4·25
F198 7s. 6d. ol-grey (*wmk inverted*) (21.12.50) 60·00 50·00
F199 8s. slate-violet .. 48·00 17·00
w. Wmk inverted (6.12.50) .. 45·00 17·00
F200 9s. brown-orange (1.46) .. 22·00 35·00
w. Wmk inverted (9.1.51) .. 42·00 35·00
F201 10s. carmine-lake .. 28·00 2·25
w. Wmk inverted (4.50) .. 28·00 2·50
F202 15s. sage-green .. 42·00 18·00
w. Wmk inverted (8.12.50) .. 55·00 25·00
F203 £1 pink .. 26·00 3·50
w. Wmk inverted (1.2.50) .. 38·00 4·00
F204 25s. greenish blue (1946) .. £325 £350
w. Wmk inverted (7.53) .. £350 £375
F205 30s. brown (1946) .. £225 £100
w. Wmk inverted (9.49) .. £200 £100
F206 £2 bright purple (1946) .. 80·00 18·00
w. Wmk inverted (17.6.52) .. 80·00 18·00
F207 £2 10s. red (*wmk inverted*) (9.8.51) .. £225 £225
F208 £3 green (1946) .. £110 48·00
w. Wmk inverted (17.6.52) .. £100 45·00
F209 £3 10s. rose (11.48) .. £1400 £1000
w. Wmk inverted (5.52) .. £1400 £1000
F210 £4 light blue (*wmk inverted*) (12.2.52) .. £120 80·00
w. Wmk upright .. † —
F211 £5 indigo-blue .. £225 48·00
w. Wmk inverted (11.9.50) .. £160 45·00
F191/211 .. *Set of* 21 £2500 £1700

THREE SHILLINGS I.

THREE SHILLINGS II.

3s. 6d.

Type I. Broad serifed capitals

Type II. Taller capitals, without serifs

Surcharged as Type F **7**

F212 3/6 on 3s. 6d. grey-green (I) (1942) .. 20·00 6·50
w. Wmk inverted (12.10.50) .. 26·00 7·00
F213 3/6 on 3s. 6d. grey-green (II) (6.53) .. 12·00 35·00
w. Wmk inverted (6.53) .. 30·00 35·00
F214 5/6 on 5s. 6d. lilac (1944) .. 40·00 17·00
w. Wmk inverted (13.9.50) .. 40·00 17·00
F215 11/- on 11s. yellow (1942) .. 75·00 48·00
F216 22/- on 22s. scarlet (1945) .. £250 £130
w. Wmk inverted (1.3.50) .. £250 £130
F212/16 .. *Set of* 5 £350 £200

(ii) *P* 14×13½. *"Wiggins Teape" unsurfaced paper with horizontal mesh* (1956–58)

F217 1s. 3d. yellow and black (11.56) .. 1·50 1·50
w. Wmk inverted .. 17·00 17·00
F218 £1 pink (20.10.58) .. 32·00 12·00

No. F192b had the inscription printed in blue in error but as many as 378,000 were printed.

From 1949–53 inferior paper had to be used and for technical reasons it was necessary to feed the paper into the machine in a certain way which resulted in whole printings with the watermark inverted for most values.

F 8

1967 (10 July)–**68.** *Decimal currency.* W **98** (*sideways inverted*). *Unsurfaced paper. P* 14.

F219 F **8** $4 deep reddish violet .. 10·00 7·00
w. Wmk sideways (17.9.68) .. 3·00 1·50
F220 $6 emerald .. 12·00 11·00
w. Wmk sideways (17.9.68) .. 4·50 2·50
F221 $8 light greenish blue .. 17·00 16·00
w. Wmk sideways (20.6.68) .. 6·00 4·50
F222 $10 deep ultramarine .. 25·00 20·00
w. Wmk sideways (20.6.68) .. 7·50 4·50
F219/22 .. *Set of* 4 60·00 48·00
F219w/22w .. *Set of* 4 19·00 11·50

The original printings were line perforated on paper with the sideways watermark inverted ("N Z" to right of star when viewed from the front). In 1968 the stamps appeared comb perforated with the normal sideways watermark. A further comb perforated printing in July 1984 showed the watermark sideways inverted.

1986 (Apr). *As Nos.* F220/2 *but without wmk. Chalk-surfaced paper.*

F223 F **8** $6 bright green .. 5·50 4·75
F224 $8 light greenish blue .. 7·00 13·00
F225 $10 deep ultramarine .. 8·00 6·50
F223/5 .. *Set of* 3 18·00 22·00

ANTARCTIC EXPEDITIONS

VICTORIA LAND

These issues were made under authority of the New Zealand Postal Department and, while not strictly necessary, they actually franked correspondence to New Zealand. They were sold to the public at a premium.

1908 (15 Jan). *Shackleton Expedition.* T **42** *of New Zealand* (*p* 14), *optd* "King Edward VII Land", *in two lines, reading up, by Coulls, Culling and Co., Wellington.*

A1 1d. rose-carmine (No. 356 Royle) (G.) .. £400 35·00
a. Opt double .. † £1500
A1*b* 1d. rose-carmine (No. 352*c* Waterlow) (G.) .. £1300 £800

Nos. A1/1*b* were used on board the expedition ship, *Nimrod*, and at the Cape Royds base in McMurdo Sound. Due to adverse conditions Shackleton landed in Victoria Land rather than King Edward VII Land the intended destination.

1911 (9 Feb)–**13.** *Scott Expedition. Stamps of New Zealand optd* "VICTORIA LAND.", *in two lines by Govt Printer, Wellington.*

A2 **51** ½d. deep green (No. 387*aa*) (18.1.13) £550 £650
A3 **53** 1d. carmine (No. 405) .. 45·00 85·00
a. No stop after "LAND" (R. 7/5) .. £275 £600

Nos. A2/3 were used at the Cape Evans base on McMurdo Sound or on the *Terra Nova*.

ROSS DEPENDENCY

This comprises a sector of the Antarctic continent and a number of islands. It was claimed by Great Britain on 30 July 1923 and soon afterward put under the jurisdiction of New Zealand.

1 H.M.S. *Erebus*

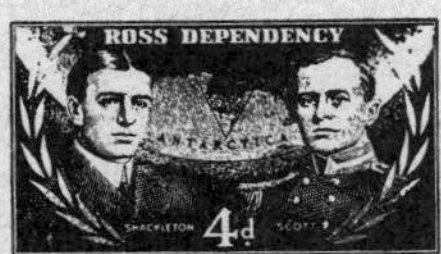

2 Shackleton and Scott

3 Map of Ross Dependency and New Zealand

4 Queen Elizabeth II

(Des E. M. Taylor (3d.), L. C. Mitchell (4d.), R. Smith (8d.), J.Berry (1s. 6d.). Recess D.L.R.)

1957 (11 Jan). *W* **98** *of New Zealand (Mult* N Z *and Star). P* 13 (1s. 6d.) *or* 14 (*others*).

1	1	3d. indigo	2·00	1·00
2	2	4d. carmine-red	2·00	75
3	3	8d. bright carmine-red and ultramarine	2·00	1·00
		a. Bright carmine-red and blue	7·50	6·00
4	4	1s. 6d. slate-purple	2·00	1·25
1/4		*Set of* 4	7·25	3·50

(New Currency. 100 cents = 1 New Zealand dollar)

5 H.M.S. *Erebus*

1967 (10 July). *Decimal currency. As Nos.* 1/4 *but with values inscr in decimal currency as T* **5**. *Chalky paper (except* 15 *c.). W* **98** *of New Zealand (sideways on* 7 *c.). P* 13 (15 *c.) or* 14 (*others*).

5	5	2 c. indigo	12·00	4·75
		a. Deep blue	16·00	7·00
6	2	3 c. carmine-red	8·00	4·75
		w. Wmk inverted	65·00	
7	3	7 c. bright carmine-red and ultramarine	11·00	7·50
8	4	15 c. slate-purple	11·00	12·00
		w. Wmk inverted	85·00	
5/8		*Set of* 4	38·00	26·00

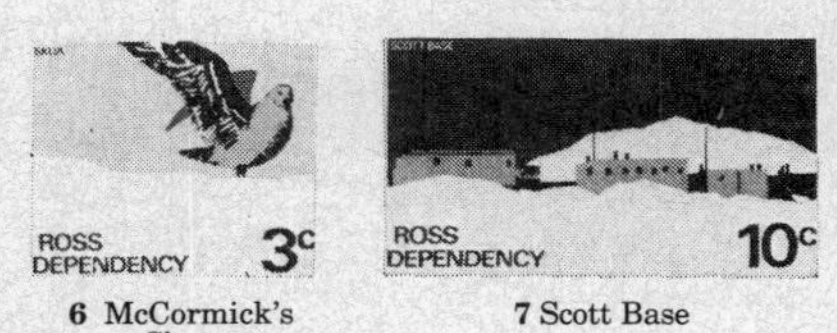

6 McCormick's Skua — 7 Scott Base

(Des M. Cleverley. Litho B.W.)

1972 (18 Jan)–**79**. *Horiz design as T* **6** (3 *to* 8 *c.) or* **7** (10, 18 *c.*). *Ordinary paper. P* 14½ × 14 (10, 18 *c.) or* 13 (*others*).

9		3 c. black, brownish grey and pale blue	1·25	1·40
		a. Chalk-surfaced paper (2.79)	1·10	1·60
10		4 c. black, royal blue and violet	65	1·40
		a. Chalk-surfaced paper (2.79)	40	1·60
11		5 c. black, brownish grey and rose-lilac	60	1·40
		a. Chalk-surfaced paper (2.79)	30	1·60
12		8 c. black, yellow-brown and brownish grey	60	1·40
		a. Chalk-surfaced paper (2.79)	30	1·60
13		10 c. black, turquoise-green and slate-green	80	1·50
		a. Perf 13½ × 13. Chalk-surfaced paper (2.79)	30	1·60
14		18 c. black, violet and bright violet	1·75	2·50
		a. Perf 13½ × 13. Chalk-surfaced paper (2.79)	40	1·60
9/14		*Set of* 6	5·00	8·50
9a/14a		*Set of* 6	2·50	8·50

Designs:—4 c. Lockheed C-130 Hercules airplane at Williams Field; 5 c. Shackleton's Hut; 8 c. Supply ship H.M.N.Z.S. *Endeavour*; 18 c. Tabular ice floe.

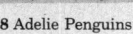

8 Adelie Penguins

9 McCormick's Skua

(Des R. Conly. Litho Asher and Co, Melbourne)

1982 (20 Jan). *Horiz designs as T* **8**. *Multicoloured. P* 15½.

15	5 c. Type **8**	1·00	1·00
16	10 c. Tracked vehicles	40	40
17	20 c. Scott Base	40	40
18	30 c. Field party	40	40
19	40 c. Vanda Station	40	40
20	50 c. Scott's hut, Cape Evans	40	40
15/20	*Set of* 6	2·75	2·75

The post office at Scott Base closed on 30 September 1987 and Nos. 15/20 were withdrawn from sale at philatelic counters in New Zealand on 31 December 1987. Local stamps were subsequently issued by the Armed Forces Canteen Council to cover the cost of mail carriage from Scott Base to New Zealand. These are not listed as they had no national or international validity.

Sets of stamps, showing whales, Antarctic birds and seals, inscribed "NEW ZEALAND ROSS DEPENDENCY", were issued in 1988, 1990 and 1992. These were available from post offices throughout New Zealand, but not in the Ross Dependency.

Separate issues for Ross Dependency were resumed in November 1994. Such stamps were only valid on mail from Scott Base, but were not postmarked until arrival at the New Zealand Post Ross Dependency Agency situated at Christchurch.

(Des G. Millen. Litho Southern Colour Print, Dunedin)

1994 (2 Nov)–**95**. *Wildlife. T* **9** *and similar horiz designs. Multicoloured. P* 13½.

21	5 c. Type **9**	10	10
22	10 c. Snow Petrel chick	10	10
23	20 c. Black-browed Albatross	20	25
24	40 c. Emperor Penguins (2.10.95)	35	40
25	45 c. As 40 c.	40	45
26	50 c. Chinstrap Penguins	45	50
27	70 c. Adelie Penguin	60	65
28	80 c. Elephant Seals	70	75
29	$1 Leopard Seal	90	95
30	$2 Weddell Seal	1·75	1·90
31	$3 Crabeater Seal pup	2·75	3·00
21/31	*Set of* 11	8·25	9·00

10 Capt. James Cook with H.M.S. *Resolution* and H.M.S. *Adventure*

11 Inside Ice Cove

(Des G. Fuller. Litho Questa)

1995 (9 Nov). *Antarctic Explorers. T* **10** *and similar horiz designs. Multicoloured. P* 14½.

32	40 c. Type **10**	55	55
33	80 c. James Clark Ross with H.M.S. *Erebus* and H.M.S. *Terror*	95	95
34	$1 Roald Amundsen and *Fram*	1·10	1·10
35	$1.20, Robert Scott with *Terra Nova*	1·40	1·40
36	$1.50, Ernest Shackleton with *Endurance*	1·75	1·75
37	$1.80, Richard Byrd with Ford 4-AT-B Trimotor *Floyd Bennett* (airplane)	2·00	2·00
32/7	*Set of* 6	7·00	7·00

(Des Diane Prosser. Litho Enschedé)

1996 (13 Nov). *Antarctic Landscapes. T* **11** *and similar multicoloured designs. P* 14½×14 (*vert*) *or* 14×14½ (*horiz*).

38	40 c. Type **11**	30	35
39	80 c. Base of glacier	60	65
40	$1 Glacier ice fall	75	80
41	$1.20, Climbers on crater rim (*horiz*)	90	95
42	$1.50, Pressure ridges (*horiz*)	1·10	1·25
43	$1.80, Fumarole ice tower (*horiz*)	1·25	1·40
38/43	*Set of* 6	5·00	5·50

12 Snow Petrel

(Des P. Martinson. Litho Southern Colour Print, Dunedin)

1997 (12 Nov). *Antarctic Seabirds. T* **12** *and similar vert designs. Multicoloured. P* 14. (*a*) *With* "WWF" *panda emblem.*

44	40 c. Type **12**	30	35
45	80 c. Cape Petrel	60	65
46	$1.20, Antarctic Fulmar	90	95
47	$1.50, Antarctic Petrel	1·10	1·25
	(*b*) *Without* "WWF" *panda emblem*		
48	40 c. Type **12**	30	35
	a. Block of 6. Nos. 48/53	4·75	
49	80 c. Cape Petrel	60	65
50	$1 Antarctic Prion	75	80
51	$1.20, Antarctic Fulmar	90	95
52	$1.50, Antarctic Petrel	1·10	1·25
53	$1.80, Antarctic Tern	1·25	1·40
44/53	*Set of* 10	7·75	8·50

Nos. 44/7 were printed in sheets containing stamps of one value.

Nos. 48/53 were printed in sheets containing the six values together, *se-tenant*, with the backgrounds forming a composite design. In addition the $1 and $1.80 were also produced in separate sheets.

TOKELAU

Formerly known as the Union Islands, and administered as part of the Gilbert & Ellice Islands Colony, they were transferred to New Zealand on 4 November 1925 and then administered by Western Samoa. The islands were finally incorporated in New Zealand on 1 January 1949 and became a dependency. The name Tokelau was adopted on 7 May 1946.

> Stamps of GILBERT AND ELLICE ISLANDS were used in Tokelau from February 1911 until June 1926 when they were replaced by those of SAMOA. These were current until 1948.
> The post office on Atafu opened in 1911, but the cancellations for the other two islands, Fakaofo and Nukunono, did not appear until 1926.

1 Atafu Village and Map

(Des J. Berry from photographs by T. T. C. Humphrey. Recess B.W.)

1948 (22 June). *T* **1** *and similar horiz designs. Wmk T* **98** *of New Zealand (Mult N Z and Star). P* 13½.
1 ½d. red-brown and purple . . 15 40
2 1d. chestnut and green . . 15 30
w. Wmk inverted . . £275
3 2d. green and ultramarine . . 15 30
1/3 . . *Set of* 3 40 90
Designs:—1d. Nukunono hut and map; 2d. Fakaofo village and map.
Covers are known postmarked 16 June 1948, but this was in error for 16 July.

1953 (15 June*). *Coronation. As No.* 715 *of New Zealand, but inscr* "TOKELAU ISLANDS".
4 **164** 3d. brown . . 2·00 2·00
*This is the date of issue in Tokelau. The stamps were released in New Zealand on 25 May.

ONE SHILLING
(4)

6D
TOKELAU
ISLANDS
(5)

1956 (27 Mar). *No.* 1 *surch with T* 4 *by Govt Printer, Wellington.*
5 **1** 1s. on ½d. red-brown and purple . . 2·00 2·00

1966 (8 Nov). *Postal fiscal stamps of New Zealand (Type* F **6**), *but without value, surch as T* **5** *by Govt Printer, Wellington. W* **98** *of New Zealand. P* 14.
6 6d. light blue . . 50 1·00
7 8d. light emerald . . 60 1·00
8 2s. light pink . . 70 1·10
6/8 . . *Set of* 3 1·60 2·75

(New Currency. 100 cents = 1 New Zealand dollar)

1c
(6)

5c
TOKELAU
ISLANDS
(7)

1967 (4 Sept*). *Decimal currency.*
(*a*) *Nos.* 1/3 *surch in decimal currency as T* **6** *by Govt Printer, Wellington*
9 1c. on 1d. . . 50 60
10 2 c. on 2d. . . 75 1·00
11 10 c. on ½d. . . 1·50 2·00
(*b*) *Postal Fiscal stamps of New Zealand (Type* F **6**), *but without value, surch as T* **7** *by Govt Printer, Wellington. W* **98** *of New Zealand (sideways). P* 14 (*line or comb*)
12 **F 6** 3 c. reddish lilac . . 30 30
13 5 c. light blue . . 30 30
14 7 c. light emerald . . 30 30
15 20 c. light pink . . 30 40
9/15 . . *Set of* 7 3·50 4·50
*This is the date of issue in Tokelau. The stamps were released in New Zealand on 10 July.

8 British Protectorate (1877)

12 H.M.S. *Dolphin*, 1765

(Des New Zealand P.O. artists from suggestions by Tokelau Administration. Litho B.W.)

1969 (8 Aug). *History of Tokelau. T* **8** *and similar horiz designs. W* **98** *of New Zealand. P* 13 × 12½.
16 5 c. ultramarine, yellow and black . . 25 10
17 10 c. vermilion, yellow and black . . 30 10
18 15 c. green, yellow and black . . 35 15
19 20 c. yellow-brown, yellow and black . . 40 15
16/19 . . *Set of* 4 1·10 45
Designs:—10 c. Annexed to Gilbert and Ellice Islands, 1916: 15 c. New Zealand Administration, 1925; 20 c. New Zealand Territory, 1948.

1969 (1 Oct). *Christmas. As T* **301** *of New Zealand, but inscr* "TOKELAU ISLANDS". *W* **98** *of New Zealand. P* 13½ × 14½.
20 **301** 2 c. multicoloured . . 10 15

1970 (1 Oct). *Christmas. As T* **314** *of New Zealand but inscr* "TOKELAU ISLANDS". *P* 12½.
21 **341** 2 c. multicoloured . . 10 20

(Des D. B. Stevenson. Litho B.W.)

1970 (9 Dec). *Discovery of Tokelau. T* **12** *and similar multicoloured designs. P* 13½.
22 5 c. Type **12** . . 1·00 35
23 10 c. H.M.S. *Pandora*, 1791 . . 1·00 35
24 25 c. *General Jackson* (American whaling ship), 1835 (*horiz*) . . 2·50 70
22/4 . . *Set of* 3 4·00 1·25

13 Fan

14 Windmill Pump

(Des Enid Hunter. Litho Harrison)

1971 (20 Oct). *Various horiz designs as T* **13** *showing handicrafts. Multicoloured. P* 14.
25 1 c. Type **13** . . 20 20
26 2 c. Hand-bag . . 30 30
27 3 c. Basket . . 30 40
28 5 c. Hand-bag . . 35 65
29 10 c. Shopping-bag . . 35 80
30 15 c. Fishing box . . 50 1·50
31 20 c. Canoe . . 50 1·75
32 25 c. Fishing hooks . . 50 1·75
25/32 . . *Set of* 8 2·75 6·50

(Des A. G. Mitchell. Litho Questa)

1972 (6 Sept). *25th Anniversary of South Pacific Commission. T* **14** *and similar vert designs. Multicoloured. P* 14 × 13½.
33 5 c. Type **14** . . 40 60
34 10 c. Community well . . 50 75
35 15 c. Pest eradication . . 70 1·25
36 20 c. Flags of member nations . . 75 1·25
33/6 . . *Set of* 4 2·10 3·50
On No. 35 "PACIFIC" is spelt "PACFIC".

15 Horny Coral

16 Hump-back Cowrie

(Des Eileen Mayo. Litho B.W.)

1973 (12 Sept). *Coral. T* **15** *and similar vert designs. Multicoloured P.* 13.
37 3 c. Type **15** . . 80 80
38 5 c. Soft Coral . . 80 90
39 15 c. Mushroom Coral . . 1·25 1·50
40 25 c. Staghorn Coral . . 1·50 1·75
37/40 . . *Set of* 4 4·00 4·50

(Des G. F. Fuller. Litho Questa)

1974 (13 Nov). *"Shells of the Coral Reef". T* **16** *and similar horiz designs. Multicoloured. P* 14.
41 3 c. Type **16** . . 1·00 1·25
42 5 c. Tiger Cowrie . . 1·10 1·50
43 15 c. Mole Cowrie . . 1·75 3·00
44 25 c. Eyed Cowrie . . 2·25 3·25
41/4 . . *Set of* 4 5·50 8·00

17 Moorish Idol

18 Canoe Building

(Des Eileen Mayo. Litho Questa)

1975 (19 Nov). *Fishes. T* **17** *and similar vert designs. Multicoloured. P* 14.
45 5 c. Type **17** . . 40 1·00
46 10 c. Long-nosed Butterflyfish . . 60 1·25
47 15 c. Lined Butterflyfish . . 70 1·50
48 25 c. Lionfish ("Red Fire Fish") . . 80 1·75
45/8 . . *Set of* 4 2·25 5·00

(Des F. Paulo. Litho Questa)

1976 (27 Oct)–**81**. *T* **18** *and similar multicoloured designs showing local life. P* 14 × 13½ (9 *c. to* $1) *or* 13½ × 14 (*others*).
49 1 c. Type **18** . . 40 1·25
a. Perf 14½ × 15 (15.7.81) . . 10 15
50 2 c. Reef fishing . . 30 1·60
51 3 c. Weaving preparation . . 25 75
a. Perf 14½ × 15 (15.7.81) . . 10 15
52 5 c. Umu (kitchen) . . 30 75
a. Perf 14½ × 15 (15.7.81) . . 10 15
53 9 c. Carving (*vert*) . . 10 1·00
a. Perf 15 × 14½ (15.7.81) . . 10 15
54 20 c. Husking coconuts (*vert*) . . 15 80
a. Perf 15 × 14½ (15.7.81) . . 15 20
55 50 c. Wash day (*vert*) . . 20 90
a. Perf 15 × 14½ (15.7.81) . . 20 20
56 $1 Meal time (*vert*) . . 35 2·00
a. Perf 15 × 14½ (15.7.81) . . 30 30
49/56 . . *Set of* 8 1·60 8·00
49a/56a . . *Set of* 7 95 1·10

19 White Tern

20 Westminster Abbey

(Des F. Paulo. Litho Questa)

1977 (16 Nov). *Birds of Tokelau. T* **19** *and similar horiz designs. Multicoloured. P* 14½.
57 8 c. Type **19** . . 40 50
58 10 c. Turnstone . . 45 55
59 15 c. White-capped Noddy . . 70 1·00
60 30 c. Common Noddy . . 90 1·60
57/60 . . *Set of* 4 2·25 3·25

(Des Eileen Mayo. Litho Questa)

1978 (28 June). *25th Anniv of Coronation. T* **20** *and similar vert designs. Multicoloured. P* 14.
61 8 c. Type **20** . . 20 20
62 10 c. King Edward's Chair . . 20 20
63 15 c. Coronation regalia . . 30 35
64 30 c. Queen Elizabeth II . . 50 60
61/4 . . *Set of* 4 1·10 1·25

21 Canoe Race

22 Rugby

(Des F. Paulo. Photo Heraclio Fournier)

1978 (8 Nov). *Canoe Racing. T* **21** *and similar horiz designs showing races. P* 13½ × 14.
65 8 c. multicoloured . . 20 25
66 12 c. multicoloured . . 25 30
67 15 c. multicoloured . . 30 35
68 30 c. multicoloured . . 50 60
65/8 . . *Set of* 4 1·10 1·40

(Des F. Paulo. Photo Heraclio Fournier)

1979 (7 Nov). *Sports. T* **22** *and similar horiz designs. Multicoloured. P* 13½.
69 10 c. Type **22** . . 20 25
70 15 c. Cricket . . 55 75
71 20 c. Rugby (*different*) . . 55 80
72 30 c. Cricket (*different*) . . 70 1·00
69/72 . . *Set of* 4 1·75 2·50

23 Surfing

24 Pole Vaulting

(Des F. Paulo. Litho J.W.)

1980 (5 Nov). *Water Sports. T* **23** *and similar horiz designs. Multicoloured. P* 13.
73 10 c. Type **23** . . 10 10
74 20 c. Surfing (*different*) . . 15 15
75 30 c. Swimming . . 20 25
76 50 c. Swimming (*different*) . . 25 35
73/6 . . *Set of* 4 60 75

(Des F. Paulo. Photo Heraclio Fournier)

1981 (4 Nov). *Sports. T* **24** *and similar vert designs. Multicoloured. P* 14 × 13½.

77 10 c. Type **24** .. 10 10
78 20 c. Volleyball .. 20 20
79 30 c. Running .. 25 30
80 50 c. Volleyball (*different*) .. 30 35
77/80 .. *Set of* 4 75 85

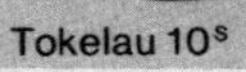

25 Wood Carving

26 Octopus Lure

(Des R. Conly. Litho Enschedé)

1982 (5 May). *Handicrafts. T* **25** *and similar vert designs. Multicoloured. P* 14 × 13½.

81 10 s. Type **25** .. 10 15
82 22 s. Bow-drilling sea shell .. 15 30
83 34 s. Bowl finishing .. 20 40
84 60 s. Basket weaving .. 35 70
81/4 .. *Set of* 4 70 1·40

(Des R. Conly. Litho Questa)

1982 (3 Nov). *Fishing Methods. T* **26** *and similar vert designs. Multicoloured. P* 14.

85 5 s. Type **26** .. 15 10
86 18 s. Multiple-hook fishing .. 35 20
87 23 s. Ruvettus fishing .. 40 25
88 34 s. Netting flyingfish .. 45 30
89 63 s. Noose fishing .. 55 40
90 75 s. Bonito fishing .. 60 45
85/90 .. *Set of* 6 2·25 1·50

27 Outrigger Canoe

28 Javelin Throwing

(Des R. Conly. Litho Cambec Press, Melbourne)

1983 (4 May). *Transport. T* **27** *and similar horiz designs. Multicoloured. P* 13 × 13½.

91 5 s. Type **27** .. 10 10
92 18 s. Wooden whaleboat .. 15 15
93 23 s. Aluminium whaleboat .. 15 20
94 34 s. *Alia* (fishing catamaran) .. 25 25
95 63 s. *Frysna* (freighter) .. 35 40
96 75 s. Grumman MacKinnon G-21C Goose flying boat .. 45 50
91/6 .. *Set of* 6 1·25 1·40

(Des R. Conly. Litho Questa)

1983 (2 Nov). *Traditional Pastimes. T* **28** *and similar horiz designs. Multicoloured. P* 14.

97 5 s. Type **28** .. 10 10
98 18 s. String game .. 15 15
99 23 s. Fire making .. 15 20
100 34 s. Shell throwing .. 25 25
101 63 s. Hand-ball game .. 35 40
102 75 s. Mass wrestling .. 45 50
97/102 .. *Set of* 6 1·25 1·40

29 Planting and Harvesting

30 Convict Tang ("Manini")

(Des R. Conly. Litho J.W.)

1984 (2 May). *Copra Industry. T* **29** *and similar vert designs. Multicoloured. P* 13½ × 13.

103 48 s. Type **29** .. 40 45
a. Horiz strip of 5. Nos. 103/7 .. 1·90
104 48 s. Husking and splitting .. 40 45
105 48 s. Drying .. 40 45
106 48 s. Bagging .. 40 45
107 48 s. Shipping .. 40 45
103/7 .. *Set of* 5 1·90 2·00

Nos. 103/7 were printed together, *se-tenant*, in horizontal strips of 5 throughout the sheet.

(Des R. Conly. Litho B.D.T.)

1984 (5 Dec). *Fishes. T* **30** *and similar horiz designs. Multicoloured. P* 15 × 14.

108 1 s. Type **30** .. 15 10
109 2 s. Flyingfish ("Hahave") .. 15 10
110 5 s. Surge Wrasse ("Uloulo") .. 15 10
111 9 s. Unicornfish ("Ume ihu") .. 20 10
112 23 s. Wrasse ("Lafilafi") .. 40 20
113 34 s. Red Snapper ("Fagamea") .. 50 25
114 50 s. Yellow-finned Tuna ("Kakahi") .. 70 40
115 75 s. Oilfish ("Palu po") .. 1·00 55
116 $1 Grey Shark ("Mokoha") .. 1·25 70
117 $2 Black Marlin ("Hakula") .. 1·75 1·40
108/17 .. *Set of* 10 5·50 3·25

Examples of Nos. 108/17 are known postmarked at Nukunonu on 23 November 1984.

The 50 s., No. 114 was sold at the "STAMPEX 86" Stamp Exhibition, Adelaide, overprinted "STAMPEX 86 4–10 AUGUST 1986" in three lines. These overprinted stamps were not available from post offices in Tokelau. Used examples come from dealers' stocks subsequently sent to the islands for cancellation.

31 *Ficus tinctoria* ("Mati")

32 Administration Centre, Atafu

(Des R. Conly. Litho Wyatt and Wilson Ltd, Christchurch, N.Z.)

1985 (26 June). *Native Trees. T* **31** *and similar vert designs. Multicoloured. P* 13.

118 5 c. Type **31** .. 10 10
119 18 c. *Morinda citrifolia* ("Nonu") .. 15 15
120 32 c. Breadfruit Tree ("Ulu") .. 20 25
121 48 c. *Pandanus tectorius* ("Fala") .. 35 40
122 60 c. *Cordia subcordata* ("Kanava") .. 40 45
123 75 c. Coconut Palm ("Niu") .. 50 55
118/23 .. *Set of* 6 1·50 1·60

Nos. 118/23 were issued with matt, almost invisible PVA gum.

(Des R. Conly. Litho Questa)

1985 (4 Dec). *Tokelau Architecture* (1*st series*). *Public Buildings. T* **32** *and similar horiz designs. Multicoloured. P* 14.

124 5 c. Type **32** .. 10 10
125 18 c. Administration Centre, Nukunonu .. 15 15
126 32 c. Administration Centre, Fakaofo .. 20 25
127 48 c. Congregational Church, Atafu .. 35 40
128 60 c. Catholic Church, Nukunonu .. 40 45
129 75 c. Congregational Church, Fakaofo .. 50 55
124/9 .. *Set of* 6 1·50 1·60

33 Atafu Hospital

(Des R. Conly. Litho Cambec Press, Melbourne)

1986 (7 May). *Tokelau Architecture* (2*nd series*). *Hospitals and Schools. T* **33** *and similar horiz designs. Multicoloured. P* 13½.

130 5 c. Type **33** .. 20 15
131 18 c. St. Joseph's Hospital, Nukunonu .. 20 15
132 32 c. Fenuafala Hospital, Fakaofo .. 30 30
133 48 c. Matauala School, Atafu .. 45 45
134 60 c. Matiti School, Nukunonu .. 50 60
135 75 c. Fenuafala School, Fakaofo .. 80 90
130/5 .. *Set of* 6 2·25 2·25

34 Coconut Crab

(Des R. Conly. Litho Questa)

1986 (3 Dec). *Agricultural Livestock. T* **34** *and similar horiz designs. Multicoloured. P* 14.

136 5 c. Type **34** .. 10 10
137 18 c. Pigs .. 15 15
138 32 c. Chickens .. 25 25
139 48 c. Reef Hawksbill Turtle .. 40 40
140 60 c. Goats .. 45 45
141 75 c. Ducks .. 60 60
136/41 .. *Set of* 6 1·75 1·75

35 *Scaevola taccada* ("Gahu")

(Des R. Conly. Litho Questa)

1987 (6 May). *Tokelau Flora. T* **35** *and similar horiz designs. Multicoloured. P* 14.

142 5 c. Type **35** .. 45 50
143 18 c. *Hernandia nymphaeifolia* ("Puka") .. 70 80
144 32 c. *Pandanus tectorius* ("Higano") .. 1·00 1·10
145 48 c. *Gardenia taitensis* ("Tialetiale") .. 1·25 1·40
146 60 c. *Pemphis acidula* ("Gagie") .. 1·60 1·75
147 75 c. *Guettarda speciosa* ("Puapua") .. 1·75 1·90
142/7 .. *Set of* 6 6·00 6·75

36 Javelin-throwing

(Des F. Paulo. Litho Leigh-Mardon Ltd, Melbourne)

1987 (2 Dec). *Tokelau Olympic Sports. T* **36** *and similar horiz designs. Multicoloured. P* 14 × 14½.

148 5 c. Type **36** .. 25 30
149 18 c. Shot-putting .. 45 50
150 32 c. Long jumping .. 70 90
151 48 c. Hurdling .. 85 1·10
152 60 c. Sprinting .. 1·25 1·75
153 75 c. Wrestling .. 1·50 1·90
148/53 .. *Set of* 6 4·50 5·75

37 Small Boat Flotilla in Sydney Harbour

38 Island Maps and Ministerial Representatives

(Des and litho CPE Australia Ltd, Melbourne)

1988 (30 July). *Bicentenary of Australian Settlement and "Sydpex '88" National Stamp Exhibition, Sydney. T* **37** *and similar square designs. Multicoloured. P* 13.

154 50 c. Type **37** .. 1·60 1·75
a. Horiz strip of 5. Nos. 154/8 .. 7·25
155 50 c. Sailing ships and liners .. 1·60 1·75
156 50 c. Sydney skyline and Opera House .. 1·60 1·75
157 50 c. Sydney Harbour Bridge .. 1·60 1·75
158 50 c. Sydney waterfront .. 1·60 1·75
154/8 .. *Set of* 5 7·25 8·00

Nos. 154/8 were printed together, *se-tenant*, in horizontal strips of five throughout the sheet, forming a composite aerial view of the re-enactment of First Fleet's arrival.

(Des F. Paulo. Litho Leigh-Mardon Ltd, Melbourne)

1988 (10 Aug). *Political Development. T* **38** *and similar horiz designs. Multicoloured. P* 14½.

159 5 c. Type **38** (administration transferred to N.Z. Foreign Affairs Ministry, 1975) .. 20 25
160 18 c. General Fono (island assembly) meeting, 1977 .. 25 30
161 32 c. Arms of New Zealand (first visit by New Zealand Prime Minister, 1985) .. 50 60
162 48 c. U.N. logo (first visit by U.N. representative, 1976) .. 65 75
163 60 c. Canoe and U.N. logo (first Tokelau delegation to U.N., 1987) .. 80 90
164 75 c. Secretary and N.Z. flag (first islander appointed as Official Secretary, 1987) .. 90 1·00
159/64 .. *Set of* 6 3·00 3·50

39 Three Wise Men in Canoe and Star

(Des F. Paulo. Litho Govt Ptg Office, Wellington)

1988 (7 Dec). *Christmas. T* **39** *and similar horiz designs showing Christmas in Tokelau. Multicoloured. P* 13½.

165 5 c. Type **39** .. 20 20
166 20 c. Tokelau Nativity .. 25 25
167 40 c. Flight to Egypt by canoe .. 55 55
168 60 c. Children's presents .. 70 80
169 70 c. Christ child in Tokelauan basket .. 80 90
170 $1 Christmas parade .. 1·00 1·25
165/70 .. *Set of* 6 3·25 3·50

40 Launching Outrigger Canoe

41 Basketwork

(Des F. Paulo. Litho Leigh-Mardon Ltd, Melbourne)

1989 (28 June). *Food Gathering. T* **40** *and similar horiz designs. Multicoloured. P* 14×14½.

171	50 c. Type **40**	1·25	1·40
	a. Horiz strip of 3. Nos. 171/3	3·25	
172	50 c. Paddling canoe away from shore	1·25	1·40
173	50 c. Fishing punt and sailing canoe	1·25	1·40
174	50 c. Canoe on beach	1·25	1·40
	a. Horiz strip of 3. Nos. 174/6	3·25	
175	50 c. Loading coconuts into canoe	1·25	1·40
176	50 c. Tokelauans with produce	1·25	1·40
171/6	*Set of* 6	6·50	7·50

Nos. 171/3 and 174/6 were each printed together, *se-tenant*, in horizontal strips of three throughout the sheets, forming composite designs.

A $3 miniature sheet commemorating the 150th anniversary of the Penny Black and "Stamp World London 90" International Stamp Exhibition exists, but was not issued or used by the New Zealand Post offices on the islands. Examples were subsequently offered to collectors in January 1994.

(Litho Leigh-Mardon Ltd, Melbourne)

1990 (2 May). *Women's Handicrafts. T* 41 *and similar horiz designs. Multicoloured. P* 14½.

177	5 c. Type **41**	45	45
178	20 c. Preparing cloth	85	85
179	40 c. Tokelau fabrics	1·25	1·25
180	60 c. Mat weaving	1·75	2·00
181	80 c. Weaving palm fronds	2·50	2·75
182	$1 Basket making	2·75	3·25
177/82	*Set of* 6	8·50	9·50

42 Man with Adze and Wood Blocks

43 Swimming

(Des F. Paulo. Litho Wyatt & Wilson, Christchurch)

1990 (1 Aug). *Men's Handicrafts. T* **42** *and similar horiz designs. Multicoloured. P* 13½.

183	50 c. Type **42**	1·50	1·75
	a. Horiz strip of 3. Nos. 183/5	4·00	
184	50 c. Making fishing boxes	1·50	1·75
185	50 c. Fixing handles to fishing boxes	1·50	1·75
186	50 c. Two men decorating fishing boxes	1·50	1·75
	a. Horiz strip of 3. Nos. 186/8	4·00	
187	50 c. Canoe building (two men)	1·50	1·75
188	50 c. Canoe building (three men)	1·50	1·75
183/8	*Set of* 6	8·00	9·50

Nos. 183/5 and 186/8 were each printed together, *se-tenant*, in horizontal strips of 3 throughout the sheets, and have matt, almost invisible, gum.

Under the terms of the Tokelau Post Office Regulations which came into force on 1 March 1991 the responsibility for providing postage stamps for the islands passed from New Zealand Post to the Administrator of Tokelau, based at the Ministry of External Relations, Wellington.

(Des R. Roberts. Litho Southern Colour Print, Dunedin)

1992 (8 July). *Olympic Games, Barcelona. T* **43** *and similar vert designs. Multicoloured. P* 13½.

189	40 c. Type **43**	60	60
190	60 c. Longjumping	80	90
191	$1 Volleyball	1·60	1·75
192	$1.80, Running	2·25	2·75
189/92	*Set of* 4	4·75	5·50

44 *Santa Maria*

45 Queen Elizabeth II in 1953

(Des R. Roberts. Litho Southern Colour Print, Dunedin)

1992 (18 Dec). *500th Anniv of Discovery of America by Columbus. T* **44** *and similar horiz designs. Multicoloured. P* 13½.

193	40 c. Type **44**	60	60
194	60 c. Christopher Columbus	90	1·00
195	$1.20, Fleet of Columbus	2·00	2·25
196	$1.80, Columbus landing in the New World	3·00	3·25
193/6	*Set of* 4	6·00	6·50

(Des M. Conly. Litho Southern Colour Print, Dunedin)

1993 (8 July). *40th Anniv of Coronation. T* **45** *and similar horiz designs. Multicoloured. P* 13½.

197	25 c. Type **45**	50	45
198	40 c. Prince Philip	70	70
199	$1 Queen Elizabeth II in 1993	1·25	1·40
200	$2 Queen Elizabeth II and Prince Philip	2·25	2·50
197/200	*Set of* 4	4·25	4·50

46 Bristle-thighed Curlew

(Des M. Conly. Litho Southern Colour Print, Dunedin)

1993 (15 Dec). *Birds of Tokelau. T* **46** *and similar horiz designs. Multicoloured. P* 13½.

201	25 c. Type **46**	45	45
202	40 c. Red-tailed Tropic Bird	65	70
203	$1 Eastern Reef Heron	1·25	1·50
204	$2 American Golden Plover	2·00	2·75
201/4	*Set of* 4	4·00	4·75

(Des M. Conly. Litho Southern Colour Print, Dunedin)

1994 (18 Feb). *"Hong Kong '94" International Stamp Exhibition. Multicoloured. P* 14×14½.

MS205	125×100 mm. As Nos. 201/4 (*sold at* $5)	5·00	6·00

47 Great Egret ("White Heron")

(Des M. Conly. Litho Southern Colour Print, Dunedin)

1994 (16 Aug). *"Philakorea '94" International Stamp Exhibition, Seoul. P* 12.

206 **47**	$2 multicoloured	2·25	2·50
MS207	110×76 mm. No. 206	2·50	3·00

48 Model Outrigger Canoe

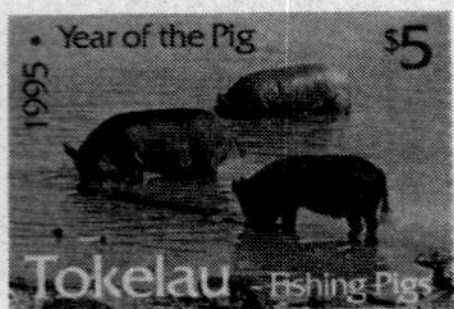

49 Fishing Pigs

(Des M. Conly. Litho Southern Colour Print, Dunedin)

1994 (19 Dec). *Handicrafts. T* **48** *and similar horiz designs. Multicoloured. P* 13½.

208	5 c. Type **48**	10	10
209	25 c. Plaited fan	20	25
210	40 c. Plaited baskets	30	35
211	50 c. Fishing box	35	40
212	80 c. Water bottle	60	65
213	$1 Fishing hook	75	80
214	$2 Coconut gourds	1·50	1·60
215	$5 Shell necklace	3·75	4·00
208/15	*Set of* 8	7·50	8·00

(Litho Southern Colour Print, Dunedin)

1995 (3 Feb). *Chinese New Year ("Year of the Pig"). Sheet* 100×75 *mm. P* 14×14½.

MS218 **49**	$5 multicoloured	6·00	6·50

1995 (3 Feb). *"PostX '95" National Stamp Exhibition, Auckland. No.* **MS**218 *optd with "PostX '95" emblem on sheet margin in red.*

MS219 **49**	$5 multicoloured	6·50	7·00

50 Pacific Pigeon on Branch

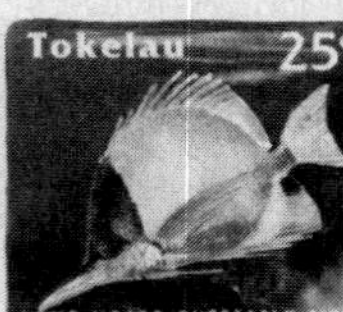

51 Long-nosed Butterflyfish

(Des Patricia Altman. Litho Southern Colour Print, Dunedin)

1995 (27 Apr). *Endangered Species. Pacific Pigeon. T* **50** *and similar horiz designs. Multicoloured. P* 13½.

220	25 c. Type **50**	45	45
221	40 c. On branch (*different*)	70	70
222	$1 On branch with berries	1·40	1·60
223	$2 Chick in nest	2·40	2·75
220/3	*Set of* 4	4·50	5·00

(Des R. Youmans. Litho Southern Colour Print, Dunedin)

1995 (1 Sept). *Reef Fishes. T* **51** *and similar horiz designs. Multicoloured. P* 12.

224	25 c. Type **51**	45	45
225	40 c. Emperor Angelfish	70	70
226	$1 Moorish Idol	1·40	1·60
227	$2 Lined Butterflyfish	2·40	2·75
224/7	*Set of* 4	4·50	5·00
MS228	130×90 mm. Lionfish (39×34 *mm*)	3·25	3·75

No. **MS**228 includes the "Singapore '95" International Stamp Exhibition logo on the sheet margin.

1995 (1 Sept). *"Singapore '95" International Stamp Exhibition. No.* **MS**218 *optd with exhibition emblem in red on sheet margin.*

MS229 **49**	$5 multicoloured	5·50	6·50

52 *Danaus plexippus*

53 Hawksbill Turtle

(Des Patricia Altman. Litho Southern Colour Print, Dunedin)

1995 (16 Oct). *Butterflies and Moths. T* **52** *and similar vert designs. Multicoloured. P* 12.

230	25 c. Type **52**	45	45
231	40 c. *Precis villida samoensis*	70	70
232	$1 *Hypolimnas bolina*	1·60	1·75
233	$2 *Euploea lewenii*	2·75	3·00
230/3	*Set of* 4	5·00	5·50

(Des Patricia Altman. Litho Southern Colour Print, Dunedin)

1995 (27 Nov). *Year of the Sea Turtle. T* **53** *and similar horiz designs. Multicoloured. P* 12.

234	25 c. Type **53**	45	45
235	40 c. Leatherback Turtle	70	70
236	$1 Green Turtle	1·60	1·75
237	$2 Loggerhead Turtle	2·75	3·00
234/7	*Set of* 4	5·00	5·50
MS238	130×90 mm. $3 As $2 (50×40 *mm*)	4·00	4·50

54 Pacific Rat

(Des Patricia Altman. Litho Southern Colour Print, Dunedin)

1996 (19 Feb). *Chinese New Year ("Year of the Rat"). Sheet* 128×97 *mm. P* 12.

MS239 **54**	$3 multicoloured	3·00	3·50

55 Queen Elizabeth II and Nukunonu

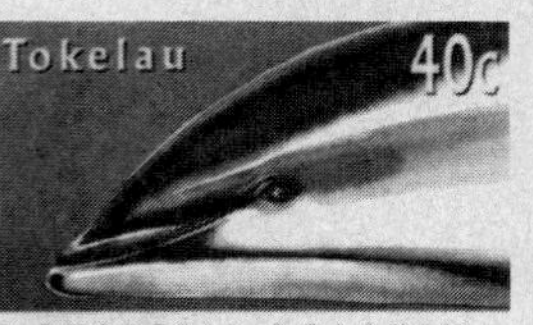

56 Fraser's Dolphin

(Des D. Miller. Litho Enschedé)

1996 (22 Apr). *70th Birthday of Queen Elizabeth II. T* **55** *and similar vert designs, each incorporating a different photograph of the Queen. Multicoloured. P* 13½.

240	40 c. Type **55**	50	50
241	$1 Atafu at night	1·40	1·50
242	$1.25, Atafu	1·60	1·75
243	$2 Atafu village	2·00	2·50
240/3	*Set of* 4	5·00	5·75
MS244	64×66 mm. $3 Queen Elizabeth II	3·25	3·75

1996 (18 May). *"CHINA '96" 9th Asian International Stamp Exhibition, Peking. No.* **MS**239 *optd with exhibition emblem on sheet margin in red.*

MS245	128×97 mm. $3 Type **54**	3·50	4·00

(Des R. Youmans. Litho Southern Colour Print, Dunedin)

1996 (15 July). *Dolphins. T* **56** *and similar horiz designs. Multicoloured. P* 14.

246 40 c. Type **56** 70 70
247 $1 Common Dolphin .. .. .. 1·75 1·75
248 $1.25, Striped Dolphin .. .. .. 2·00 2·00
249 $2 Spotted Dolphin .. .. .. 3·25 3·25
246/9 .. .. *Set of* 4 7·00 7·00

57 Mole Cowrie

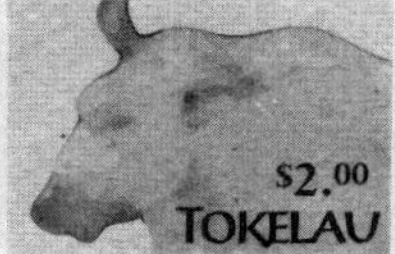

58 Ox

(Des Patricia Altman. Litho Southern Colour Print, Dunedin)

1996 (16 Oct). *Sea Shells. T* **57** *and similar horiz designs. Multicoloured. P* 12.

250 40 c. Type **57** 60 60
251 $1 Humpback Cowrie .. .. .. 1·50 1·50
252 $1.25, Eyed Cowrie .. .. .. 1·60 1·75
253 $2 Tiger Cowrie .. .. 2·25 2·75
250/3 .. .. *Set of* 4 5·50 6·00
MS254 123×83 mm. $3 Humpback Cowrie *(different)* (50×40 *mm)* .. .. .. 3·25 3·75

1996 (16 Oct). *"TAIPEI '96" 10th Asian International Stamp Exhibition, Taiwan. No.* **MS**239 *optd with exhibition emblem on sheet margin in red.*

MS255 128×97 mm. $3 Type **54** .. .. 3·25 3·75

(Des Patricia Altman. Litho Southern Colour Print, Dunedin)

1997 (12 Feb). *Chinese New Year ("Year of the Ox"). Sheet* 120×78 *mm. P* 15×14½.

MS256 **58** $2 multicoloured .. .. .. 2·00 2·25

1997 (12 Feb). *"HONG KONG '97" International Stamp Exhibition. No.* **MS**256 *optd with* "HONG KONG '97 STAMP EXHIBITION" *in gold on sheet margin.*

MS257 120×78 mm. **58** $2 multicoloured .. 2·00 2·25

1997 (29 May). *"Pacific '97" International Stamp Exhibtion, San Francisco. No.* **MS**256 *optd with exhibition emblem in red on sheet margin.*

MS258 120×78 mm. **58** $2 multicoloured .. 1·90 2·25

59 Humpback Whale

60 Church by Lagoon

(Des Patricia Altman. Litho Southern Colour Print, Dunedin)

1997 (10 June). *Humpback Whales. T* **59** *and similar horiz designs. Multicoloured. P* 12.

259 40 c. Type **59** 50 45
260 $1 Family of Humpback Whales .. 1·00 1·00
261 $1.25, Humpback Whale feeding .. 1·40 1·50
262 $2 Humpback whale and calf .. .. 2·00 2·25
259/62 .. .. *Set of* 4 4·50 4·75
MS263 135×87 mm. $3 Head of Humpback Whale 2·75 3·00

(Des R. Youmans. Litho Southern Colour Print, Dunedin)

1997 (17 Sept). *50th Anniv of South Pacific Commission. T* **60** *and similar horiz designs showing views of Tokelau. Multicoloured. P* 14.

264 40 c. Type **60** 45 45
265 $1 Boy looking across lagoon 90 90
266 $1.25, Bungalow on small island .. 1·25 1·40
267 $2 Tokelau from the air .. .. .. 1·90 2·00
264/7 .. .. *Set of* 4 4·00 4·25

61 Gorgonian Coral and Emperor Angelfish

62 Tiger

(Des Patricia Altman. Litho Southern Colour Print, Dunedin)

1997 (20 Oct). *Pacific Year of the Coral Reef. T* **61** *and similar horiz designs. Multicoloured. P* 13½.

268 $1 Type **61** 75 80
a. Horiz strip of 5. Nos. 268/72 .. .. 3·75
269 $1 Soft Coral 75 80
270 $1 Mushroom Coral 75 80
271 $1 Staghorn Coral 75 80
272 $1 Staghorn Coral and Moorish Idols .. 75 80
268/72 .. .. *Set of* 5 3·75 4·00

Nos. 268/72 were printed together, *se-tenant*, in horizontal strips of five with the backgrounds forming a composite design.

(Des Patricia Altman. Litho Southern Colour Print, Dunedin)

1997 (13 Nov). *"Aupex '97" National Stamp Exhibition, Auckland. No.* **MS**263 *optd* "AUPEX '97 13–16 NOVEMBER NZ NATIONAL STAMP EXHIBITION" *on sheet margin in black. P* 12.

MS273 135×87 mm. $3 Head of Humpback Whale 2·75 2·40

(Des S. Chan. Litho Southern Colour Print, Dunedin)

1998 (28 Jan). *Chinese New Year ("Year of the Tiger"). Sheet* 130×95 *mm. P* 14×14½.

MS274 **62** $2 multicoloured .. .. .. 1·50 1·60

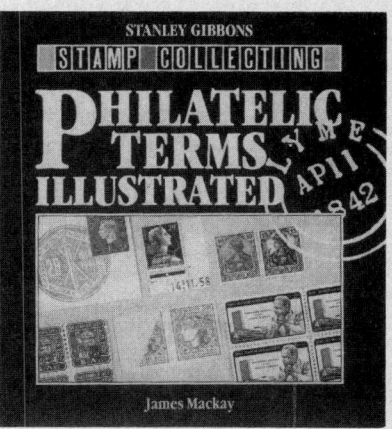

Nigeria

LAGOS

A British Consul was established at Lagos during 1853 as part of the anti-slavery policy, but the territory was not placed under British administration until occupied by the Royal Navy in August 1861. From 19 February 1866 Lagos was administered with Sierra Leone and from July 1874 as part of Gold Coast. It became a separate colony on 13 January 1886.

Although a postal service had been established by the British G.P.O. in April 1852 no postal markings were supplied to Lagos until 1859. The British G.P.O. retained control of the postal service until June 1863, when it became the responsibility of the colonial authorities.

CROWNED-CIRCLE HANDSTAMPS

CC 1

CC1 CC 1 LAGOS (19.12.1859) .. .. *Price on cover* £1600

First recorded use of No. CC1 is 12 December 1871. It is later known used as a cancellation.

PRICES FOR STAMPS ON COVER

Nos. 1/9	*from* × 10	
Nos. 10/26	*from* × 8	
Nos. 27/9	—	
Nos. 30/8	*from* × 10	
Nos. 39/41	—	
No. 42	*from* × 20	
Nos. 44/50	*from* × 8	
Nos. 51/3	—	
Nos. 54/60	*from* × 8	
Nos. 61/3	—	

PRINTERS. All the stamps of Lagos were typographed by D.L.R.

1

1874 (10 June)–**75.** *Wmk Crown CC. P* 12½.
1 1 1d. lilac-mauve .. 50·00 29·00
2 2d. blue .. 50·00 26·00
3 3d. red-brown (2.75) .. 90·00 42·00
4 3d. red-brown and chestnut .. 75·00 48·00
5 4d. carmine .. 60·00 40·00
6 6d. blue-green .. 80·00 11·00
8 1s. orange (value 15½ mm) (2.75) .. £325 £140
9 1s. orange (value 16½ mm) (7.75) .. £250 60·00
1/9 .. *Set of* 6 £500 £180

1876–79. *Wmk Crown CC. P* 14.
10 1 1d. lilac-mauve .. 35·00 16·00
11 2d. blue .. 35·00 12·00
12 3d. red-brown .. 90·00 18·00
13 3d. chestnut .. £110 32·00
14 4d. carmine .. £160 11·00
a. Wmk sideways .. £850 £130
15 6d. green .. 80·00 6·00
16 1s. orange (value 16½ mm long) (1879) .. £450 70·00
10/16 .. *Set of* 6 £750 £120

1882 (June). *Wmk Crown CA. P* 14.
17 1 1d. lilac-mauve .. 17·00 10·00
18 2d. blue .. £120 4·75
19 3d. chestnut .. 13·00 5·00
20 4d. carmine .. £110 12·00
17/20 .. *Set of* 4 £225 29·00

1884 (Dec)–**86.** *New values and colours. Wmk Crown CA. P* 14.
21 1 ½d. dull green (1885) .. 1·75 60
22 1d. rose-carmine .. 1·75 60
23 2d. grey .. 50·00 5·00
24 4d. pale violet .. 90·00 8·50
25 6d. olive-green .. 7·00 28·00
26 1s. orange (3.85) .. 6·00 17·00
27 2s. 6d. olive-black (1886) .. £275 £250
28 5s. blue (1886) .. £475 £400
29 10s. purple-brown (1886) .. £1200 £800
21/9 .. *Set of* 9 £1800 £1300
27/9 Optd "Specimen" .. *Set of* 3 £400

We would warn collectors against clever forgeries of Nos. 27 to 29 on genuinely watermarked paper.

A

B

1887 (Mar)–**1902.** *Wmk Crown CA. P* 14.
30 1 2d. dull mauve and blue .. 2·25 1·50
31 2½d. ultramarine (A) (1891) .. 2·50 1·75
a. Larger letters of value (B) .. 21·00 17·00
b. *Blue* (A) .. 80·00 50·00
32 3d. dull mauve and chestnut (4.91) .. 2·50 3·25
33 4d. dull mauve and black .. 2·25 1·75
34 5d. dull mauve and green (2.94) .. 2·00 11·00
35 6d. dull mauve and mauve .. 4·50 3·00
a. *Dull mauve and carmine* (10.02) .. 4·50 12·00
36 7½d. dull mauve and carmine (2.94) .. 2·00 26·00
37 10d. dull mauve and yellow (2.94) .. 3·25 13·00
38 1s. yellow-green and black .. 4·25 20·00
a. *Blue-green and black* .. 4·25 22·00
39 2s. 6d. green and carmine .. 22·00 75·00
40 5s. green and blue .. 38·00 £130
41 10s. green and brown .. 65·00 £170
30/41 .. *Set of* 12 £130 £400
30/41 Optd "Specimen" .. *Set of* 12 £225

HALF PENNY

(2)

3

1893 (2 Aug). *No.* 33 *surch with T* 2 *locally.*
42 1 ½d. on 4d. dull mauve and black .. 3·75 2·50
a. Surch double .. 55·00 55·00
b. Surch treble .. £100
c. Error. ½d. on 2d. (No. 30) .. — £11000

There were two separate settings of No. 42. The most common, of which there were five separate printings, shows "HALF PENNY" 16 mm long and was applied as a horizontal pair or triplet. The scarcer setting, also applied as a triplet, shows "HALF PENNY" 16½ mm long.

Three examples of No. 42c are known, two unused and one used. Only the latter is in private hands.

1904 (22 Jan–Nov). *Wmk Crown CA. P* 14.
44 3 ½d. dull green and green .. 1·50 5·50
45 1d. purple and black/*red* .. 1·00 15
46 2d. dull purple and blue .. 6·00 10·00
47 2½d. dull purple and blue/*blue* (B) .. 1·00 1·50
aw. Wmk inverted .. — 50·00
b. Smaller letters of value as A .. 4·25 8·50
bw. Wmk inverted ..
48 3d. dull purple and brown .. 1·50 2·25
49 6d. dull purple and mauve .. 35·00 10·00
50 1s. green and black .. 35·00 38·00
51 2s. 6d. green and carmine .. 80·00 £180
52 5s. green and blue .. £150 £275
53 10s. green and brown (Nov) .. £275 £750
44/53 .. *Set of* 10 £500 £1100
44/53 Optd "Specimen" .. *Set of* 10 £180

1904–06. *Wmk Mult Crown CA. Ordinary paper. P* 14.
54 3 ½d. dull green and green (30.10.04) .. 7·50 2·50
a. Chalk-surfaced paper (12.3.06) .. 9·00 1·75
w. Wmk inverted ..
55 1d. purple and black/*red* (22.10.04) .. 5·00 10
a. Chalk-surfaced paper (21.9.05) .. 1·25 10
aw. Wmk inverted .. — 50·00
56 2d. dull purple and blue (2.05) .. 2·00 1·40
a. Chalk-surfaced paper (25.9.06) .. 11·00 5·00
aw. Wmk inverted .. 75·00
57 2½d. dull purple and blue/*blue* (B) (*chalk-surfaced paper*) (13.10.05) .. 1·75 16·00
a. Smaller letters of value as A .. 55·00 £120
58 3d. dull purple and brown (27.4.05) .. 3·50 90
a. Chalk-surfaced paper (2.8.06) .. 14·00 1·75
w. Wmk inverted ..
59 6d. dull purple and mauve (31.10.04) .. 6·00 2·00
a. Chalk-surfaced paper (1.3.06) .. 4·25 1·25
60 1s. green and black (15.10.04) .. 9·00 12·00
a. Chalk-surfaced paper (4.06) .. 17·00 2·25
w. Wmk inverted ..
61 2s. 6d. green and carmine (3.12.04) .. 12·00 35·00
a. Chalk-surfaced paper (21.10.06) .. 28·00 35·00
62 5s. green and blue (1.05) .. 22·00 90·00
a. Chalk-surfaced paper (21.10.06) .. 45·00 £110
63 10s. green and brown (3.12.04) .. 48·00 £160
a. Chalk-surfaced paper (12.3.06) .. 70·00 £160
54/63 .. *Set of* 10 £100 £275

Lagos was incorporated into the Colony and Protectorate of Southern Nigeria, previously formed from Niger Coast Protectorate and part of the Niger Company territories, on 16 February 1906. Stamps of Lagos were then authorised for use throughout Southern Nigeria.

NIGER COAST PROTECTORATE

OIL RIVERS PROTECTORATE

A British consulate for the Bights of Benin and Biafra was established in 1849 on the off-shore Spanish island of Fernando Po. In 1853 the appointment was divided with a consul for the Bight of Benin at Lagos. The consulate for the Bight of Biafra was transferred to Old Calabar in 1882.

A British protectorate was proclaimed over the coastal area, with the exceptions of the colony of Lagos and the centre of the Niger delta, on 5 June 1885. It was not, however, until July 1891 that steps were taken to set up an administration with a consul-general at Old Calabar and vice-consuls at some of the river ports.

The consulate-general at Old Calabar and the vice-consulates at Benin, Bonny, Brass, Forcados and Opobo acted as collection and distribution centres for mail from November 1891, but were not recognised as post offices until 20 July 1892.

For a few months from July 1892 local administrative handstamps, as Type Z 1, were in use either as obliterators or in conjunction with the c.d.s.

Z 1

These oval handstamps are usually found on the 1892 overprinted issue, but the following are known on unoverprinted stamps of Great Britain:

1892

BENIN

Stamps of GREAT BRITAIN *cancelled with oval postmark, Type* Z 1, *inscribed* "BENIN".
Z1 2½d. purple/*blue* (V.) .. £1000

BONNY

Stamps of GREAT BRITAIN *cancelled with oval postmark, Type* Z 1, *inscribed* "BONNY".
Z2 2½d. purple/*blue* (V.) .. £1000

BRASS RIVER

Stamps of GREAT BRITAIN *cancelled with oval postmark, Type* Z 1, *inscribed* "BRASS".
Z3 2½d. purple/*blue* (Blk.) .. £750

OLD CALABAR RIVER

Stamps of GREAT BRITAIN *cancelled with oval postmark, Type* Z 1, *inscribed* "OLD CALABAR".
Z4 2½d. purple/*blue* (Blk.) .. £750

Stamps of GREAT BRITAIN *cancelled* "BRITISH VICE-CONSULATE OLD CALABAR" *within double-lined circle.*
Z5 2½d. purple/*blue* (V.) .. £450
Z6 5d. dull purple and blue (V.) ..

For later use of Type Z 1 and the circular Vice-Consulate marks see note beneath No. 6.

Z 2.

Unoverprinted stamps of Great Britain remained officially valid for postage in the Protectorate until 30 September 1892, but were available from post offices in the Niger Company Territories up to the end of 1899. The two areas were so closely linked geographically that offices in the Protectorate continued to accept letters franked with Great Britain stamps until the reorganisation of 1900. The listing below covers confirmed examples, known on cover or piece, the prices quoted being for the latter.

1892 *to* **1899**

Stamps of GREAT BRITAIN *cancelled with circular postmarks as Type* Z 2.

BENIN RIVER

Z 7 2d. green and carmine ..
Z 8 2½d. purple/*blue* .. £500
Z 9 3d. purple/*yellow* .. £500
Z10 5d. dull purple and blue ..
Z11 1s. green ..

BONNY RIVER

Z12 ½d. vermilion .. £350
Z12*a* 1d. lilac .. £300
Z13 2½d. purple/*blue* .. £250
Z14 5d. dull purple and blue .. £350
Z15 6d. deep purple/*red* .. £350

BRASS RIVER

Z16 1½d. dull purple and green .. £750
Z17 2½d. purple/*blue* .. £650
Z17*a* 2½d. purple/*blue* (squared-circle cancellation) .. £850
Z18 6d. purple/*red* .. £700

FORCADOS RIVER

Z19 1d. lilac .. £550
Z20 2½d. purple/*blue* ..
Z21 5d. dull purple and blue (m/s cancellation)
Z22 10d. dull purple and carmine ..

OLD CALABAR RIVER

Z23 ½d. vermilion .. £300
Z24 1d. lilac .. £250
Z25 1½d. dull purple and green .. £350
Z26 2d. green and vermilion .. £350
Z27 2½d. purple/*blue* .. £250
Z28 5d. dull purple and blue .. £350
Z29 6d. purple/*red* .. £350
Z30 1s. green .. £450

OPOBO RIVER

Z31 2½d. purple/*blue* £300
Z32 10d. dull purple and carmine £600

Some later covers are known franked with G.B. stamps, but the origin of the stamps involved is uncertain.

PRICES FOR STAMPS ON COVER

Nos. 1/6	*from* × 12
Nos. 7/36	*from* × 4
Nos. 37/44	—
Nos. 45/50	*from* × 10
Nos. 51/6	*from* × 12
Nos. 57/65	*from* × 3
Nos. 66/73	*from* × 12

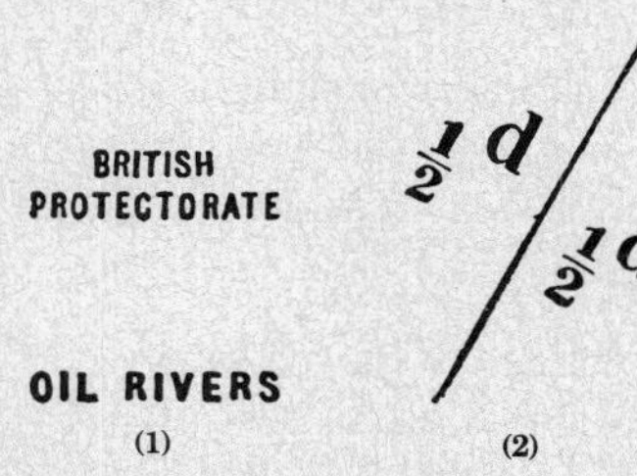

½d ½d

(1) (2)

1892 (20 July)–**94**. *Nos.* 172, 197, 200/1, 207*a and* 211 *of Great Britain optd by D.L.R. with T* **1**.

1 ½d. vermilion .. .. 8·00 4·50
2 1d. lilac .. .. 5·50 5·50
a. Opt reversed "OIL RIVERS" at top .. £4000
b. Bisected (½d.) (on cover) .. .. † £2500
3 2d. grey-green and carmine .. .. 17·00 8·00
a. Bisected (1d.) (on cover) .. .. † £2500
4 2½d. purple/*blue* .. .. 6·50 2·25
5 5d. dull purple and blue (Die II (No. 207*a*)) 7·50 7·50
a. On Die I (No. 207) .. ..
6 1s. dull green .. .. 50·00 70·00
1/6 .. .. *Set of* 6 85·00 85·00
1/6 H/S "Specimen" .. .. *Set of* 6 £250

Nos. 2b and 3a were used at Bonny River during August and September 1894.

Die II of the 5d. shows thin vertical lines to the right of "5d.". On Die I there are square dots in this position.

OVAL HANDSTAMPS. In addition to Nos. Z1/4 postmarks as Type Z 1 are also known used on the 1892–94 overprinted issue from the following offices:

Bakana (Nos. 2, 4/6)
Benin (Nos. 1/6)
Bonny (No. 2)
Brass (Nos. 3/5)
Buguma (Nos. 4 and 6)
Old Calabar (No. 4)
Opobo (Nos. 1/3)
Sombreiro River (Nos. 1/6)

The Vice-Consulate marks, as Nos. Z5/6, are also known struck on examples of No. 4 from Bonny, Forcados or Old Calabar.

Nos. 2 to 6 surcharged locally

1893 (3 Sept). *Issued at Old Calabar. Surch with T* **2** *and then bisected.*

7 ½d. on half of 1d. (R.) £150 £140
a. Unsevered pair £450 £425
ab. Surch inverted and dividing line reversed (unsevered pair) .. — £7500
b. Surch reversed (dividing line running from left to right) (unsevered pair) .. — £7500
c. Straight top to "1" in ½ £350 £350
d. "½" omitted .. .. ..
e. Surch double (unsevered pair with normal) .. .. .. — £1600
f. Vert *se-tenant* pair. Nos. 7a/8a .. — £9500
8 ½d. on half of 1d. (V.) £3500 £3250
a. Unsevered pair £8000 £7500
b. Surch double (pair) £13000

The surcharge was applied in a setting covering one horizontal row at a time. Violet ink was used for the top row in the first sheet, but was then replaced with red.

HALF PENNY. (3) HALF PENNY. (4)

In T **3** "HALF" measures 9½ mm and "PENNY" 12½ mm with space 1½ mm between the words. Bar 14½ mm ending below the stop. The "F" is nearly always defective.

In T **4** "HALF" is 8½ mm, "PENNY" 12½ mm, spacing 2½ mm, and bar 16 mm, extending beyond the stop.

HALF PENN.Y — **5** (Stop after "N")
HALF PENNY — **6** (No stop after "N")

In T **5** the "P" and "Y" are raised, and the space between the words is about 4 mm. Bar is short, approx 13½ mm. T **6** is similar but without the stop after "N".

Half Penny (7) Half Penny (8)

In T **7** the "a" and "e" are narrow and have a short upward terminal hook. The "l" has a very small hook. The letters "nny" have curved serifs, and the distance between the words is 5½ mm.

In T **8** the "a" and "e" are wider. The "l" has a wider hook. The letters "nny" have straight serifs, and the distance between the words is 4¼ mm.

HALF PENNY. (9) HALF PENNY (10)

1893 (Dec). *Issued at Old Calabar. Nos. 3/4 handstamped.*

(*a*) *With T* **3**

9 ½d. on 2d. (V.) £500 £300
a. Surch inverted £3750
b. Surch diagonal (up or down) .. £2250
c. Surch vertical (up or down) .. £2750
10 ½d. on 2½d. (Verm.) £8000
10*a* ½d on 2½d. (C.) £20000

(*b*) *With T* **4**

11 ½d. on 2½d. (G.) £225 £225
a. Surch double £2000 £2000
b. Surch diagonally inverted .. £2750
12 ½d. on 2½d. (Verm.) £500 £300
13 ½d. on 2½d. (C.) £300 £300
a. Surch omitted (in pair) .. ..
14 ½d. on 2½d. (B.) £300 £350
15 ½d. on 2½d. (Blk.) £3000
a. Surch inverted £4750
b. Surch diagonal inverted (up or down) £3750
16 ½d. on 2½d. (B.-Blk.) £3000

(*c*) *With T* **5**

17 ½d. on 2½d. (Verm.) £500 £200
a. Surch double .. .. .. — £1300
b. Surch vertical (up) .. .. — £2750

(*d*) *With T* **6**

18 ½d. on 2d. (V.) £550 £350
19 ½d. on 2½d. (Verm.) £225 £250
a. Surch inverted £2000
b. Surch double .. .. .. — £1600
c. Surch diagonal (up or down) .. £1400
d. Surch omitted (in strip of 3) .. £9500
e. Surch vertical (up or down) .. £1800
f. Surch diagonal, inverted (up or down) £1800

(*e*) *With T* **7**

20 ½d. on 2d. (V.) £275 £225
a. Surch double .. .. .. — £5500
b. Surch vertical (up or down) .. £2500
c. Surch diagonal (up or down) .. £2000
d. Surch diagonal (inverted) .. £3250
e. Surch inverted .. .. ..
21 ½d. on 2½d. (Verm.) £225 £180
a. Surch double £4000
b. Surch vertical (up or down) .. £1800
c. Surch inverted £2000
d. Surch diagonal (up or down) .. £1300
e. Surch diagonal, inverted (up) .. £3250
22 ½d. on 2½d. (B.) £7500 £7500
23 ½d. on 2½d. (C.) £7000
24 ½d. on 2½d. (V.) £3750

(*f*) *With T* **8**

25 ½d. on 2½d. (Verm.) £375 £475
a. Surch diagonal (up) £1900
26 ½d. on 2½d. (B.) £20000
27 ½d. on 2½d. (G.) £300 £400
a. Surch double £5000
28 ½d. on 2½d. (C.) £15000 £15000

(*g*) *With T* **9**

29 ½d. on 2d. (V.) £300 £325
30 ½d. on 2d. (B.) £1100 £550
a. Surch double .. .. ..
31 ½d. on 2½d. (Verm.) £425 £500
a. Surch double .. .. ..
32 ½d. on 2½d. (B.) £300 £300
33 ½d. on 2½d. (G.) £300 £300
a. Surch double (G.) £1600
b. Surch double (G. + Verm.) ..
34 ½d. on 2½d. (V.) £3250

(*h*) *With T* **10**

35 ½d. on 2½d. (G.) £400 £450
36 ½d. on 2½d. (Verm.) £4750

Various types of surcharges on Nos. 9 to 36 were printed on the same sheet, and different types in different colours may be found *se-tenant* (*Prices, from £1600 per pair, unused*).

One Shilling (11) 5/- (12)

1893 (Dec). *Issued at Old Calabar Nos.* 3 *and* 5/6 *handstamped.*

(*a*) *With T* **11**

37 1s. on 2d. (V.) £400 £350
a. Surch inverted £4000
b. Surch vertical (up or down) .. £3500
c. Surch diagonal (up or down) .. £2500
d. Surch diagonal, inverted (up or down) £3750
e. Pair, Nos. 37 and 38 .. .. £1800
38 1s. on 2d. (Verm.) £550 £3250
a. Surch inverted £5500
b. Surch diagonal (up or down) .. £4000
c. Surch vertical (up or down) .. £5500
39 1s. on 2d. (Blk.) £5500
a. Surch inverted £10000
b. Surch vertical (up or down) .. £8500
c. Surch diagonal (up) £6500

(*b*) *As T* **12**

40 5s. on 2d. (V.) £7500 £8500
a. Surch inverted £13000
b. Surch vertical (up or down) .. £13000 £13000
c. Surch diagonal (down) £13000
41 10s. on 5d. (Verm.) £6000 £8000
a. Surch inverted £13000
b. Surch vertical (up or down) .. £13000
c. Surch diagonal (down) .. ..
42 20s. on 1s. (V.) £70000
a. Surch inverted £85000
43 20s. on 1s. (Verm.) £70000
44 20s. on 1s. (Blk.) £70000

There are two main settings of the "One Shilling" surcharge:—

Type A. The "O" is over the "hi" of "Shilling" and the downstrokes on the "n" in "One", if extended, would meet the "ll" of "Shilling". The "g" is always raised. Type A is known in all three colours from one sheet of 120.

Type B. The "O" is over the first "i" of "Shilling" and the downstrokes of the "n" would meet the "li" of "Shilling". Type B is known in violet (two sheets) and vermilion (one sheet).

NIGER COAST PROTECTORATE

The protectorate was extended into the interior and the name changed to Niger Coast Protectorate on 12 May 1893.

PERFORATION. There are a number of small variations in the perforation of the Waterlow issues of 1893 to 1898 which were due to irregularity of the pins rather than different perforators.

In the following lists, stamps perf 12, 12½, 13 or compound are described as perf 12–13, stamps perf 13½, 14 or compound are described as perf 13½–14 and those perf 14½, 15 or compound are listed as perf 14½–15. In addition the 13½–14 perforation exists compound with 14½–15 and with 12–13, whilst perf 15½–16 comes from a separate perforator.

13

14

(Des G. D. Drummond. Recess Waterlow)

1894 (1 Jan). *T* **13** (*with* "OIL RIVERS" *obliterated and* "NIGER COAST" *in top margin*). *Various frames. No wmk. Thick and thin papers. P* 14½–15.

45 ½d. vermilion .. .. 4·00 3·75
a. Perf 13½–14 .. .. 6·00
46 1d. pale blue .. .. 5·00 3·25
a. Bisected (½d.) (on cover) .. .. † £550
b. Dull blue .. .. 3·75 3·25
ba. Bisected (½d.) (on cover) .. .. † £450
c. Perf 13½–14 .. .. 4·00
d. Perf 13½–14, comp 12–13 .. ..
47 2d. green .. .. 21·00 17·00
a. Imperf between (horiz pair) .. † £3750
b. Bisected (1d.) (on cover) .. .. † £700
c. Perf 14½–15, comp 12–13 .. ..
d. Perf 13½–14 .. .. 17·00 13·00
e. Perf 13½–14, comp 12–13 .. .. 27·00 24·00
d. Perf 12–13 .. ..
48 2½d. carmine-lake .. .. 6·50 3·50
a. Perf 13½–14 .. .. 9·00 7·00
b. Perf 13½–14, comp 12–13 .. ..
c. Perf 12–13 .. ..
49 5d. grey-lilac .. .. 14·00 12·00
a. Lilac (1894) .. .. 12·00 15·00
b. Perf 13½–14 .. .. 12·00
50 1s. black .. .. 14·00 12·00
a. Perf 14½–15, comp 12–13 .. ..
b. Perf 13½–14 .. .. 22·00
c. Perf 13½–14, comp 12–13 .. .. 26·00
45/50 .. .. *Set of* 6 50·00 42·00

There were three printings of each value, in November 1893, Jan 1894 and March 1894.

Nos. 46a, 46ba and 47b were used at Bonny River during August and September 1894.

(Recess Waterlow)

1894 (May). *T* **14** (*various frames*). *No wmk. P* 14½–15.

51 ½d. yellow-green .. .. 3·25 3·50
a. Deep green .. .. 3·75 4·50
b. Perf 14½–15, comp 13½–14 .. ..
c. Perf 13½–14 .. .. 5·00 6·00
d. Perf 13½–14, comp 12–13 .. .. 14·00
52 1d. orange-vermilion .. .. .. 12·00 8·50
a. Vermilion .. .. 9·00 5·50
b. Bisected diagonally (½d.) (on cover) .. † £500
c. Perf 15½–16 .. ..
d. Perf 13½–14 .. .. 13·00
e. Perf 13½–14, comp 12–13 .. ..
53 2d. lake .. .. 19·00 5·50
a. Bisected diagonally (1d.) (on cover)
b. Perf 13½–14 .. .. 20·00 5·50
54 2½d. blue .. .. 12·00 3·75
a. Pale blue .. .. 8·50 6·50
b. Perf 13½–14 .. .. 15·00
55 5d. purple .. .. 6·00 5·50
a. Deep violet .. .. 6·00 5·50
56 1s. black .. .. 25·00 13·00
a. Perf 13½–14 .. .. 25·00 7·00
b. Perf 13½–14, comp 12–13 .. .. 32·00
51/6 .. .. *Set of* 6 65·00 28·00

Nos. 52b and 53a were used at Bonny River during August and September 1894.

½ (15) 1 (16) ONE = = HALF PENNY (17)

1894. *Provisionals. Issued at Opobo.*

(a) *Nos.* 46*b and* 46 *bisected vertically and surch with T* 15 (May–June)

57 "½" on half of 1d dull blue (R.) (May) .. £900 £325
a. Surch inverted (in strip of 3 with normals) £8000
58 "½" on half of 1d. pale blue (R.) (June) .. £600 £250
a. Surch *tête-bêche* (pair)
b. Surcharge inverted .. £3000

(b) *No. 3 bisected vertically and surch*

(i) *With T* **16** (12 *mm high*) (June-Oct)

59 "1" on half of 2d. (Verm.) .. £1400 £250
a. Surch double .. £2500 £1200
b. Surch inverted .. — £1500

(ii) *Smaller* "1" (4¾ *mm high*)

60 "1" on half of 2d. (C.) .. — £3750

(iii) *Smaller* "1" (3¾ *mm high*)

61 "1" on half of 2d. (C.)

Nos. 60 and 61 exist *se-tenant*. (*Price* £20000 *used*)

(c) *No. 52a bisected, surch with T* 15 (Aug–Sept)

62 ½ on half of 1d. vermilion (Blk.) .. £2500 £650
63 ½ on half of 1d. vermilion (V.) .. £1800 £400
64 ½ on half of 1d. vermilion (B.) .. £1500 £325
a. "½" double .. — £2250

The stamp is found divided down the middle and also diagonally.

1894 (10 Aug). *Issued at Old Calabar. No.* 54 *surch with T* **17** *and two bars through value at foot.*

65 ½d. on 2½d. blue .. £300 £200
a. Surch double .. £2250 £1400
b. "OIE" for "ONE" .. £1400 £1000
c. Ditto. Surch double .. — £3250

There are eight types in the setting of Type **17**, arranged as a horizontal row. No. 65b occurred on No. 8 in the setting at some point during surcharging.

(Recess Waterlow)

1897 (Mar)–**98**. *As T* 14 (*various frames*). *Wmk Crown CA. P* 14½–15.

66 ½d. green (7.97) .. 2·75 1·50
a. Sage-green .. 3·50 2·25
b. Perf 13½–14 .. 2·50 2·50
c. Perf 15½–16 .. 12·00 6·50
d. Perf 13½–14, comp 12–13 .. 15·00
67 1d. orange-vermilion .. 3·25 1·50
a. Vermilion .. 3·25 1·50
b. Imperf vert (horiz pair) .. £3500
c. Perf 15½–16 .. 8·00
d. Perf 13½–14 .. 2·50 2·25
e. Perf 13½–14, comp 12–13 .. — 10·00
68 2d. lake (7.97) .. 1·75 1·25
a. Perf 15½–16 .. 4·00 2·25
b. Perf 13½–14 .. 4·00 2·75
c. Perf 13½–14, comp 12–13 .. 18·00
69 2½d. slate-blue (8.97) .. 5·00 2·00
a. Deep bright blue .. 5·50 1·50
b. Perf 13½–14 .. 6·00 3·25
70 5d. red-violet (*p* 13½–14) (1898) .. 8·50 55·00
a. Purple .. 8·50 60·00
b. Perf 13½–14, comp 12–13 .. 18·00
71 6d. yellow-brown (6.98) .. 7·00 6·50
a. Perf 13½–14 .. 8·50
b. Perf 15½–16 .. — 13·00
72 1s. black (1898) .. 15·00 24·00
a. Perf 13½–14 .. 14·00 24·00
b. Perf 13½–14, comp 12–13 .. 28·00
73 2s. 6d. olive-bistre (6.98) .. 40·00
a. Perf 15½–16 .. 40·00
b. Perf 13½–14 .. 22·00 75·00
74 10s. deep violet (6.98) .. 85·00 £160
a. Bright violet .. 85·00 £160
b. Perf 13½–14 .. 80·00 £160
66/74 .. *Set of* 9 £120 £275
71, 73/4 Optd "Specimen" .. *Set of* 3 £225

Owing to temporary shortages in Southern Nigeria, the above issue was again in use at various times from 1902 until 1907.

On 1 January 1900 the Niger Coast Protectorate together with the southern portion of the Niger Company Territories became the protectorate of Southern Nigeria.

NIGER COMPANY TERRITORIES

Following the development of trade along the Niger, British commercial interests formed the United African Company in 1879 which became the National African Company in 1882 and the Royal Niger Company in 1886. A charter was granted to the Company in the same year to administer territory along the Rivers Niger and Benue over which a British protectorate had been proclaimed in June 1885. The Company's territories extended to the Niger delta to provide access to the interior.

Post Offices were opened at Akassa (1887), Burutu (1896), Lokoja (1899) and Abutshi (1899). The stamps of Great Britain were used from 1888.

On the establishment of postal services in 1887 the Company arranged with the British G.P.O. that unstamped mail marked with their handstamps would be delivered in Great Britain, the recipients only being charged the normal rate of postage from West Africa. This system was difficult to administer, however, so the British authorities agreed in 1888 to the supply of G.B. stamps for use at the Company post offices.

Initially the stamps on such covers were left uncancelled until the mail arrived in the United Kingdom, the Company handstamp being struck elsewhere on the address side. This method continued to be used until early 1896, although a number of covers from the twelve months prior to that date do show the Company handstamp cancelling the stamps. Some of these covers were later recancelled on arrival in Great Britain. From May 1896 the postage stamps were cancelled in the Niger Territories.

In the following listings no attempt has been made to cover the use of the Company marks on the reverse of envelopes.

Dates given are those of earliest known postmarks. Colour of postmarks in brackets. Where two or more colours are given, price is for cheapest. Illustrations are reduced to two-thirds linear of the actual size.

Stamps of GREAT BRITAIN *cancelled as indicated below.*

ABUTSHI

1899. *Cancelled as T* 8, *but inscribed* "THE ROYAL NIGER CO. C. & L. ABUTSHI" *with* "CUSTOMS (date) OFFICE" *in central oval.*

Z1 ½d. vermilion (V.) .. £475
Z2 1d. lilac (V.) .. £350
Z3 2½d. purple/*blue* (V.) .. £475
Z4 5d. dull purple and blue (V.) .. £500
Z5 10d. dull purple and carmine (V.) .. £600
Z6 2s. 6d. deep lilac (V.) .. £650

AKASSA

The listings for Nos. Z7/15*a* are for *covers* on which the Akassa handstamp appears on the front, but is *not* used as a cancellation for the G.B. stamps. Examples of Nos. Z16/26 occur, from 1895–96, with the handstamp struck on the front of the cover away from the stamps, or, from 1896, used as a cancellation. The prices quoted are for *single stamps* showing the cancellation; covers from either period being worth considerably more. On Nos. Z29/42*b* the handstamp was used as a cancellation and the prices quoted are for *single stamps*.

1

THE ROYAL NIGER COMPANY CHARTERED & LIMITED POST 3 OCT 94 OFFICE AKASSA

2

1888–90. *Cancelled as T* 3, *but with Maltese cross each side of* "AKASSA". *Size* 36×22 *mm.*

Z7 6d. deep purple/*red* (V.) .. £1000

1889–94. *Size* 39×24 *mm.*

Z 8 1 2½d. purple/*blue* (V.) .. £600
Z 9 3d. purple/*yellow* (V.)
Z10 5d. dull purple and blue (V.)
Z11 6d. deep purple/*red* (V.) .. £400
Z12 10d. dull purple and carmine (V.)
Z12*a* 1s. green (V.)
Z13 2s. 6d. lilac (V.)

1894–95.

Z14 2 1d. lilac (V.) .. £300
Z15 2½d. purple/*lilac* (V.)
Z15*a* 2s. 6d. lilac (V.)

3

THE ROYAL NIGER COMPANY CHARTERED & LIMITED. 7- AUG. 98 POST OFFICE AKASSA.

4

1895. *Size* 39×25 *mm.*

Z16 3 2½d. purple/*blue* (V.)

1895–99.

Z17 4 ½d. vermilion (V.) .. 60·00
Z18 1d. lilac (V.) .. 50·00
Z19 2d. green and vermilion (V.) .. £300
Z20 2½d. purple/*blue* (V.) .. 35·00
Z21 3d. purple/*yellow* (V.) .. £200
Z22 5d. dull purple and blue (V.) .. 45·00
Z23 6d. deep purple/*red* (V.) .. £200
Z24 9d. dull purple and blue (V.) .. £250
Z25 10d. dull purple and carmine (V.) .. 80·00
Z26 2s. 6d. deep lilac (V.) .. £170

THE ROYAL NIGER COMPANY, CHARTERED & LIMITED. 4 NOV. 1899 POST OFFICE, AKASSA.

5

1897–99.

Z29 5 ½d. vermilion (V.) .. 48·00
Z30 1d. lilac (V.) .. 40·00
a. "RECD" for year in postmark .. £500
Z31 2d. green and vermilion (V.) .. £160
Z32 2½d. purple/*blue* (V.) .. 45·00
a. "RECD" for year in postmark (1898) .. £1000
Z33 3d. purple/*yellow* (V.) .. £170
Z34 4d. green and brown (V.) .. £170
Z35 4½d. green and carmine (V.) .. £650
Z36 5d. dull purple and blue (V.) .. 60·00
Z37 6d. deep purple/*red* (V.) .. £180
Z38 9d. dull purple and blue (V.) .. £275
Z39 10d. dull purple and carmine (V.) .. £150
Z40 1s. green (V.) .. £500
Z41 2s. 6d. deep lilac (V.) .. £225

1899. *Cancelled as T* 7, *but inscribed* "AKASSA".

Z42 5d. dull purple and blue (V.) .. £1000

1899. *Cancelled as T* 4, *but* "CUSTOMS DEPT" *in place of* "POST OFFICE".

Z42*a* 1d. lilac (V.) .. £600
Z42*b* 2½d. purple/*blue* (V.) .. £600

BURUTU

THE ROYAL NIGER COMPANY CHARTERED & LIMITED. 31 MAR 1898 POST OFFICE. BURUTU.

6

1896–99. *Cancelled as T* 6, "BURUTU" *in sans-serif caps. Size* 44×24 *mm.*

Z43 6 ½d. vermilion (V., Blk.) .. 80·00
Z44 1d. lilac (V.) .. 70·00
Z45 1½d. dull purple and green (V.) .. £250
Z46 2d. green and carmine (V.) .. £160
Z47 2½d. purple/*blue* (V., Blk.) .. 35·00
Z48 3d. purple/*yellow* (V., Blk.) .. £160
Z49 4d. green and brown (V.) .. £160
Z50 5d. dull purple and blue (V., Blk.) .. 60·00
Z51 6d. deep purple/*red* (V.) .. £180
Z52 9d. dull purple and blue (V.) .. £275
Z53 10d. dull purple and carmine (V., Blk.) .. £100
Z54 1s. green (V.) .. £475
Z55 2s. 6d. lilac (V.) .. £190

1898–99. *Cancelled as T* 4, *but inscribed* "BURUTU" *in serifed caps. Size* 44×27 *mm.*

Z56 ½d. vermilion (V., Blk.) .. 60·00
Z57 1d. lilac (V., Blk.) .. 48·00
Z58 2d. green and vermilion (V.) .. £200
Z59 2½d. purple/*blue* (V., Blk.) .. 42·00
Z60 3d. purple/*yellow* (V.) .. £180
Z61 4d. green and brown (V.) .. £180
Z62 4½d. green and carmine (V.) .. £650
Z63 5d. dull purple and blue (V.) .. 65·00
Z64 6d. deep purple/*red* (V.) .. £200
Z65 9d. dull purple and blue (V.) .. £300
Z66 10d. dull purple and carmine (V., Blk.) .. £100
Z67 2s. 6d. lilac (V., Blk.) .. £225

7

1898–99.

Z68 7 1d. lilac (V.)
Z69 2½d. purple/*blue* (V.) .. £300

1899. *Cancelled as T* 4, *but inscribed* "CUSTOM DEPT. BURUTU".

Z70 1d. lilac (V.)

LOKOJA

8

1899.

Z71 8 ½d. vermilion (V.) .. 95·00
Z72 1d. lilac (V.) .. 75·00
Z73 2½d. purple/*blue* (V.) .. £250
Z74 5d. dull purple and blue (V.) .. £325
Z75 10d. dull purple and carmine (V.) .. £350
Z76 2s. 6d. deep lilac (V.) .. £400

AGENT GENERAL NIGER TERRITORIES

The listings for Nos. Z78/9 are for covers showing a handstamp struck on the address side, but *not* used as a cancellation for the G.B. stamp.

1894–99. *Cancelled as T* 8, *but inscribed* "AGENT GENERAL NIGER TERRITORIES".

Z77 1d. lilac (V.)
Z78 2½d. purple/*blue* (V.) .. £1000

1895–96. *Cancelled as T* 7, *but inscribed as Nos.* Z77/8.

Z79 2½d. purple/*blue* (V.) .. £1000
Z80 5d. dull purple and blue (V.)
Z81 10d. dull purple and carmine (V.)
Z82 2s. 6d. deep lilac (V.)

It is now believed that these cancellations may have been used at Asaba. They all occur on covers with Akassa handstamps, often of different dates.

The British Government purchased the Royal Niger Company territories and from 1 January 1900 they were incorporated into the protectorates of Northern and Southern Nigeria. Of the post offices listed above only Lokoja was then situated in Northern Nigeria, the remainder joining Niger Coast in forming Southern Nigeria.

Issues for Northern Nigeria did not reach Lokoja until sometime in March 1900 and the post office there continued to use unoverprinted stamps of Great Britain until these supplies arrived.

NORTHERN NIGERIA

The protectorate of Northern Nigeria was formed on 1 January 1900 from the northern part of the Niger Company Territories. Only one post office existed in this area, at Lokoja, and this continued to use unoverprinted stamps of GREAT BRITAIN until the arrival of Nos. 1/9 during April 1900.

PRICES FOR STAMPS ON COVER

Nos. 1/7	*from* × 6
Nos. 8/9	—
Nos. 10/16	*from* × 5
Nos. 17/19	—
Nos. 20/6	*from* × 5
No. 27	—
Nos. 28/37	*from* × 5
Nos. 38/9	—
Nos. 40/9	*from* × 5
Nos. 50/2	—

PRINTERS. All issues were typographed by De La Rue & Co.

1

2

1900 (Apr). *Wmk Crown CA. P* 14.

No.	Type	Description	Unused	Used
1	1	½d. dull mauve and green	1·50	8·50
2		1d. dull mauve and carmine	2·25	3·00
3		2d. dull mauve and yellow	7·00	28·00
4		2½d. dull mauve and ultramarine	6·50	28·00
5	2	5d. dull mauve and chestnut	14·00	29·00
6		6d. dull mauve and violet	13·00	23·00
7	1	1s. green and black	16·00	50·00
8		2s. 6d. green and ultramarine	70·00	£325
9		10s. green and brown	£180	£425
1/9		*Set of* 9	£275	£800
1/9 Optd "Specimen"		*Set of* 9	£180	

Examples of all values are known showing a forged Northern Nigeria postmark dated "AU 14 1900".

3

4

1902 (1 July). *Wmk Crown CA. P* 14.

No.	Type	Description	Unused	Used
10	3	½d. dull purple and green	1·50	70
11		1d. dull purple and carmine	1·50	30
12		2d. dull purple and yellow	1·50	2·25
13		2½d. dull purple and ultramarine	1·25	5·50
14	4	5d. dull purple and chestnut	1·50	4·75
15		6d. dull purple and violet	3·75	4·50
16	3	1s. green and black	2·75	4·75
17		2s. 6d. green and ultramarine	8·00	30·00
18		10s. green and brown	45·00	48·00
10/18		*Set of* 9	55·00	90·00
10/18 Optd "Specimen"		*Set of* 9	£150	

1904 (Apr). *Wmk Mult Crown CA. P* 14.

No.	Type	Description	Unused	Used
19	4	£25 green and carmine	£35000	

No. 19, although utilising the "POSTAGE & REVENUE" Key type, was intended to pay the fiscal fee for liquor licences.

1905 (Aug)–**07**. *Wmk Mult Crown CA. Ordinary paper. P* 14.

No.	Type	Description	Unused	Used
20	3	½d. dull purple and green (10.05)	9·50	6·00
		a. Chalk-surfaced paper (1906)	4·50	4·50
21		1d. dull purple and carmine	7·50	50
		a. Chalk-surfaced paper (1906)	3·00	90
22		2d. dull purple and yellow (10.05)	8·50	24·00
		a. Chalk-surfaced paper (1907)	14·00	18·00
23		2½d. dull purple and ultramarine (10.05)	5·00	6·50
24	4	5d. dull purple and chestnut (10.05)	17·00	42·00
		a. Chalk-surfaced paper (1907)	25·00	42·00
25		6d. dull purple and violet (10.05)	18·00	32·00
		a. Chalk-surfaced paper (1906)	25·00	25·00
26	3	1s. green and black (10.05)	45·00	70·00
		a. Chalk-surfaced paper (1906)	20·00	42·00
27		2s. 6d. green and ultramarine (10.05)	48·00	48·00
		a. Chalk-surfaced paper (1906)	30·00	48·00
20/7		*Set of* 8	95·00	£170

1910 (30 Jan)–**11**. *Wmk Mult Crown CA. Ordinary paper* (½*d. to* 2½*d.*) *or chalk-surfaced paper* (*others*). *P* 14.

No.	Type	Description	Unused	Used
28	3	½d. green (15.4.10)	1·40	80
29		1d. carmine	1·50	75
30		2d. grey (26.10.11)	2·75	2·25
31		2½d. blue (10.10.)	1·00	5·50
32	4	3d. purple/*yellow* (10.9.11)	2·75	50
34		5d. dull purple and olive-green (26.2.11)	3·50	6·50
35		6d. dull purple and purple (10.11.10)	5·50	13·00
		a. Dull and bright purple (1911)	2·75	5·50
36	3	1s. black/*green* (10.11.10)	1·50	65
37		2s. 6d. black and red/*blue* (15.3.11)	9·50	23·00
38	4	5s. green and red/*yellow* (10.9.11)	23·00	65·00
39	3	10s. green and red/*green* (15.3.11)	42·00	45·00
28/39		*Set of* 11	80·00	£140
28/39 Optd "Specimen"		*Set of* 11	£190	

5

6

1912. *Wmk Mult Crown CA. Ordinary paper* (½*d.*, 1*d.*, 2*d.*) *or chalk-surfaced paper* (*others*). *P* 14.

No.	Type	Description	Unused	Used
40	5	½d. deep green	60	50
41		1d. red	60	50
42		2d. grey	2·50	4·00
43	6	3d. purple/*yellow*	1·75	1·25
44		4d. black and red/*yellow*	60	1·75
45		5d. dull purple and olive-green	3·50	4·75
46		6d. dull and bright purple	3·00	3·75
47		9d. dull purple and carmine	1·75	10·00
48	5	1s. black/*green*	3·25	1·75
49		2s. 6d. black and red/*blue*	7·00	28·00
50	6	5s. green and red/*yellow*	17·00	65·00
51	5	10s. green and red/*green*	35·00	45·00
52	6	£1 purple and black/*red*	£170	£110
40/52		*Set of* 13	£225	£250
40/52 Optd "Specimen"		*Set of* 13	£200	

Examples of most values are known showing forged postmarks of Lokoja dated "MR 22 12" or Minna dated "JN 16 1913". These forged postmarks have also been seen on examples of earlier issues.

On 1 January 1914 Northern Nigeria became part of Nigeria.

SOUTHERN NIGERIA

The Colony and Protectorate of Southern Nigeria was formed on 1 January 1900 by the amalgamation of Niger Coast Protectorate with the southern part of the Niger Territories. Lagos was incorporated into the territory on 1 May 1906.

The stamps of NIGER COAST PROTECTORATE were used in Southern Nigeria until the introduction of Nos. 1/9, and also during a shortage of these values in mid-1902. The issues of LAGOS were utilized throughout Southern Nigeria after 1 May 1906 until supplies were exhausted.

PRICES FOR STAMPS ON COVER

Nos. 1/7	*from* × 8
Nos. 8/9	—
Nos. 10/18	*from* × 4
Nos. 19/20	—
Nos. 21/30	*from* × 4
Nos. 31/2	—
Nos. 33/42	*from* × 4
Nos. 43/4	—
Nos. 45/53	*from* × 4
Nos. 55/6	—

PRINTERS. All issues of Southern Nigeria were typographed by De La Rue & Co, Ltd, London.

1

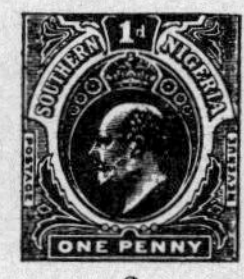

2

3

1901 (Mar)–**02**. *Wmk Crown CA. P* 14.

No.	Type	Description	Unused	Used
1	1	½d. black and pale green	1·40	1·75
		a. Sepia and green (1902)	1·75	1·50
2		1d. black and carmine	1·40	1·00
		a. Sepia and carmine (1902)	1·75	1·00
3		2d. black and red-brown	2·50	3·50
4		4d. black and sage-green	2·00	9·50
5		6d. black and purple	2·00	5·50
6		1s. green and black	7·00	22·00
7		2s. 6d. black and brown	38·00	70·00
8		5s. black and orange-yellow	42·00	85·00
9		10s. black and purple/*yellow*	75·00	£130
1/9		*Set of* 9	£150	£275
1/9 Optd "Specimen"		*Set of* 9	£130	

1903 (Mar)–**04**. *Wmk Mult Crown CA. P* 14.

No.	Type	Description	Unused	Used
10	2	½d. grey-black and pale green	70	15
		w. Wmk inverted		
11		1d. grey-black and carmine	1·25	40
12		2d. grey-black and chestnut	5·00	90
13		2½d. grey-black and blue (1904)	2·00	75
14		4d. grey-black and olive-green	2·00	4·50
15		6d. grey-black and purple	3·50	8·00
16		1s. green and black	24·00	17·00
17		2s. 6d. grey-black and brown	18·00	45·00
18		5s. grey-black and yellow	48·00	95·00
19		10s. grey-black and purple/*yellow*	26·00	75·00
20		£1 green and violet	£250	£450
10/20		*Set of* 11	£325	£650
10/20 Optd "Specimen"		*Set of* 11	£180	

Two Dies of Head Plate:

A

B

In Head A the fifth line of shading on the king's cheek shows as a line of dots and the lines of shading up to the king's hair are broken in places. In Head B the lines of shading are more regular, especially the fifth line.

1904 (June)–**09**. *Head Die A. Wmk Mult Crown CA. Ordinary paper. P* 14.

No.	Type	Description	Unused	Used
21	2	½d. grey-black and pale green	50	10
		a. Chalk-surfaced paper (1905)	65	60
22		1d. grey-black and carmine	8·00	20
		a. Chalk-surfaced paper (1905)	9·00	10
23		2d. grey-black and chestnut (1905)	2·50	45
		a. Pale grey and chestnut (Head Die B) (1907)	3·25	40
24		2½d. grey-black and bright blue (9.09)	1·00	95
25		3d. orange-brown and bright purple (*chalk-surfaced paper*) (Head Die B) (18.8.07) (Optd S. £20)	9·00	1·25
26		4d. grey-black and olive-green (12.05)	14·00	23·00
		a. Chalk-surfaced paper (1906)	23·00	25·00
		ab. Grey-black and pale olive-green (Head Die B) (1907)	25·00	23·00
27		6d. grey-black and bright purple (12.05)	9·00	2·25
		a. Chalk-surfaced paper (1906)	10·00	2·50
		ab. Head Die B (1907)	14·00	1·50
28		1s. grey-green and black (19.9.07)	3·00	2·75
		a. Chalk-surfaced paper (Head Die B) (1907)	19·00	2·50
29		2s. 6d. grey-black and brown (30.4.06)	18·00	13·00
		a. Chalk-surfaced paper (1906)	28·00	11·00
		ab. Head Die B (1907)	23·00	11·00
30		5s. grey-black and yellow (10.12.07)	35·00	65·00
		a. Chalk-surfaced paper (Head Die B) (1908)	42·00	65·00
31		10s. grey-black and purple/*yellow* (*chalk-surfaced paper*) (Head Die B) (9.08)	85·00	£140
32		£1 green and violet (19.3.06)	£150	£180
		a. Chalk-surfaced paper (1906)	£160	£180
		ab. Head Die B (1907)	£120	£160
21/32		*Set of* 12	£275	£375

I

II

Die I. Thick "1", small "d". (double working plate).
Die II. Thinner "1", larger "d" (single working plate).

1907–11. *Colours changed. Head Die B. Ordinary paper* (½*d. to* 2½*d.*) *or chalk-surfaced paper* (*others*). *Wmk Mult Crown CA. P* 14.

No.	Type	Description	Unused	Used
33	2	½d. pale green (1907)	80	20
		a. Head Die A	3·75	30
		b. Blue-green (1910)	80	20
34		1d. carmine (I) (12.8.07)	1·75	60
		a. Head Die A	4·50	30
		ab. Die II. *Carmine-red* (1910)	50	10
35		2d. greyish slate (9.09)	1·50	70
36		2½d. blue (9.09)	1·25	3·75
37		3d. purple/*yellow* (7.09)	1·25	30
38		4d. black and red/*yellow* (9.09)	1·40	80
39		6d. dull purple and purple (9.09)	18·00	3·25
		a. Dull purple and bright purple (1911)	22·00	3·25
		aw. Wmk inverted		
40		1s. black/*green* (7.09)	7·00	40
41		2s. 6d. black and red/*blue* (9.09)	4·50	90
42		5s. green and red/*yellow* (9.09)	30·00	48·00
43		10s. green and red/*green* (9.09)	55·00	85·00
44		£1 purple and black/*red* (9.09)	£160	£170
33/44		*Set of* 12	£250	£275
33/44 Optd "Specimen"		*Set of* 12	£225	

1912. *Wmk Mult Crown CA. P* 14.

No.	Type	Description	Unused	Used
45	3	½d. green	1·00	10
46		1d. red	80	10
47		2d. grey	60	85
48		2½d. bright blue	2·50	2·75
49		3d. purple/*yellow*	75	30
50		4d. black and red/*yellow*	70	2·00
51		6d. dull and bright purple	75	1·25
52		1s. black/*green*	2·75	75
53		2s. 6d. black and red/*blue*	7·50	22·00
54		5s. green and red/*yellow*	16·00	55·00
55		10s. green and red/*green*	38·00	75·00
56		£1 purple and black/*red*	£150	£160
45/56		*Set of* 12	£200	£275
45/56 Optd "Specimen"		*Set of* 12	£200	

STAMP BOOKLETS

1904. *Black on red cover. Stapled.*

SB1 2s. 1d. booklet containing twenty-four 1d (No. 11) in blocks of 6

1905 (1 June)–**06**. *Black on red cover. Stapled.*

SB2 2s. 1d. booklet containing twenty-four 1d. (No. 22) in blocks of 6
a. As No. SB2 but containing No. 22a (1906) £850

1907 (7 Oct). *Black on red cover. Stapled.*

SB3 2s. 1d. booklet containing twenty-four 1d (No. 34) in blocks of 6 £1700

1910 (19 Sept). *Black on red cover. Stapled.*

SB4 2s. booklet containing eleven ½d. and eighteen 1d. (Nos. 33*b*, 34ab) in blocks of 6 or 5

1912 (Oct). *Black on red cover. Stapled.*

SB5 2s. booklet containing twelve ½d. and eighteen 1d. (Nos. 45/6) in blocks of 6

On 1 January 1914 Southern Nigeria became part of Nigeria.

COVER PRICES

Cover factors are quoted at the beginning of each country for most issues to 1945. An explanation of the system can be found on page x. The factors quoted do not, however, apply to philatelic covers.

NIGERIA

Nigeria was formed on 1 January 1914 from the former protectorates of Northern and Southern Nigeria.

PRICES FOR STAMPS ON COVER TO 1945	
Nos. 1/10	*from* × 3
Nos. 11/12	—
Nos. 15/28	*from* × 3
Nos. 29/a	—
Nos. 30/3	*from* × 3
Nos. 34/59	*from* × 2

CROWN COLONY

1

2

(Typo D.L.R.)

1914 (1 June)–**29.** *Die I. Wmk Mult Crown CA. Ordinary paper (½d. to 2½d.) or chalk-surfaced paper (others). P 14.*

1 1 ½d. green .. .. 2·75 70
2 1d. carmine-red .. 3·50 10
a. Scarlet (1916) .. 4·50 15
w. Wmk inverted .. 50·00
3 2d. grey .. 5·00 1·25
a. Slate-grey (1918) .. 6·00 75
4 2½d. bright blue .. 3·25 1·75
a. Dull blue (1915) .. 6·00 2·25
5 2 3d. purple/*yellow* (*white back*) .. 3·25 7·50
a. Lemon back (1915) .. 1·50 2·25
b. On deep yellow (*yellow back*) (*thick paper*) (1915) (Optd S. £35) .. 23·00 7·50
c. On orange-buff (1920) .. 8·50 21·00
d. On buff (1920) .. 10·00
e. On pale yellow (1921) .. 10·00 15·00
6 4d. black and red/*yellow* (*white back*) .. 1·40 7·50
a. Lemon back (1915) .. 1·00 4·25
b. On deep yellow (*yellow back*) (*thick paper*) (1915) (Optd S. £35) .. 23·00 6·50
c. On orange-buff (1920) .. 10·00 8·50
d. On buff (1920) .. 10·00
e. On pale yellow (1921) .. 10·00 17·00
7 6d. dull purple and bright purple .. 7·00 7·00
8 1 1s. black/*blue-green* (*white back*) .. 1·00 14·00
a. On yellow-green (*white back*) (1915) £100
b. Yellow-green back (1915) .. 24·00 27·00
c. Blue-green back (1915) (Optd S. £35) 1·00 7·50
d. Pale olive back (1917) .. 18·00 19·00
dw. Wmk inverted
e. On emerald (*pale olive back*) (1920) 6·50 24·00
f. On emerald (*emerald back*) (1920) .. 1·25 12·00
9 2s. 6d. black and red/*blue* .. 11·00 5·00
10 2 5s. green and red/*yellow* (*white back*) .. 9·50 35·00
a. Lemon back (1915) .. 16·00 48·00
b. On deep yellow (*yellow back*) (*thick paper*) (1915) (Optd S. £40) .. 38·00 60·00
c. On orange-buff (1920) .. 32·00 75·00
d. On buff (1920) .. 40·00
e. On pale yellow (1921) .. 50·00 £100
11 1 10s. green and red/*blue-green* (*white back*) 45·00 £120
a. Blue-green back (1915) (Optd S. £45) 48·00 80·00
b. Pale olive back (1917) .. £600 £1100
c. On emerald (*pale olive back*) (1920) .. 90·00 £120
d. On emerald (*emerald back*) (1921) .. 38·00 85·00
12 2 £1 deep purple and black/*red* .. £150 £190
a. Purple and black/red (1917) .. £150 £180
b. Die II. *Dp purple & black/red* (19.1.27) £160 £225
ba. *Purple and black/red* (1929) .. £170 £225
1/12 .. *Set of* 12 £200 £275
1/12 Optd "Specimen" *Set of* 12 £300

The ½d. and 1d. were printed in sheets of 240 using two plates one above the other.

1921–32. *Wmk Mult Script CA. Ordinary paper (½d. to 3d.) or chalk-surfaced paper (others). P 14.*

15 1 ½d. green (Die I) (1921) .. 1·00 40
aw. Wmk inverted .. 50·00
b. Die II (1925) .. 3·75 85
c. Vert gutter pair. Die I and Die II. Nos. 15/b (1925) .. £120
16 1d. rose-carmine (Die I) (1921) .. 2·50 30
aw. Wmk inverted .. 50·00 50·00
b. Die II (1925) .. 1·75 55
c. Vert gutter pair. Die I and Die II. Nos. 16/b (1925) .. £120
17 2 1½d. orange (Die II) (1.4.31) .. 3·25 15
18 1 2d. grey (Die I) (1921) .. 1·50 3·25
a. Die II (1924) .. 7·00 40
19 2d. chestnut (Die II) (1.10.27) .. 3·50 1·00
20 2d. chocolate (Die II) (1.7.28) .. 1·25 15
a. Die I (1932) .. 5·50 75
21 2½d. bright blue (Die I) (1921) .. 1·00 4·00
22 2 3d. bright violet (Die I) (1924) .. 5·00 3·25
a. Die II (1925) .. 10·00 1·50
23 3d. bright blue (Die II) (1.4.31) .. 4·50 2·00
24 4d. black & red/*pale yellow* (Die II) (1923) 65 55
a. Die I (1932) .. 5·50 7·00
25 6d. dull purple & brt purple (Die I) (1921) 11·00 12·00
a. Die II (1923) .. 7·00 8·00
aw. Wmk inverted .. 60·00
26 1 1s. black/*emerald* (Die II) (1924) .. 1·25 1·50
27 2s. 6d. black and red/*blue* (Die II) (1925) 6·50 20·00
a. Die I (1932) .. 38·00 50·00
28 2 5s. green & red/*pale yellow* (Die II) (1926) 14·00 60·00
a. Die I (1932) .. 60·00 £130
29 1 10s. green and red/*green* (Die II) (1925) 55·00 £150
a. Die I (1932) .. £100 £300
15/29 .. *Set of* 15 95·00 £225
15/19, 21/9 Optd/Perf "Specimen" *Set of* 14 £325

The ½d. and 1d., together with the 1½d. from 1932, were printed in sheets of 240 using two plates one above the other. Nos. 15c and 16c come from printings in November 1924 which combined Key Plate No. 7 (Die I) above Key Plate No. 12 (Die II).

1935 (6 May). *Silver Jubilee. As Nos. 114/17 of Jamaica, but ptd by Waterlow. P* 11×12.

30 1½d. ultramarine and grey .. 80 50
31 2d. green and indigo .. 1·50 50
k. Kite and vertical log .. 60·00
32 3d. brown and deep blue .. 3·00 8·00
33 1s. slate and purple .. 3·00 21·00
30/3 .. *Set of* 4 7·50 27·00
30/3 Perf "Specimen" *Set of* 4 75·00

For illustration of plate variety see Omnibus section following Zimbabwe.

3 Apapa Wharf

4 Fishing Village

5 Victoria-Buea Road

(Recess D.L.R.)

1936 (1 Feb). *Designs as T* 3/5. *Wmk Mult Script CA.*

(*a*) *P* 11½ × 13

34 ½d. green .. 1·00 1·40
35 1d. carmine .. 40 40
36 1½d. brown .. 85 40
a. Perf 12½ × 13½ .. 38·00 2·75
37 2d. black .. 40 80
38 3d. blue .. 1·00 1·25
a. Perf 12½ × 13½ .. 80·00 24·00
39 4d. red-brown .. 1·25 2·00
40 6d. dull violet .. 40 60
41 1s. sage-green .. 1·10 4·50

(*b*) *P* 14

42 2s. 6d. black and ultramarine .. 3·50 18·00
43 5s. black and olive-green .. 6·00 23·00
44 10s. black and grey .. 45·00 65·00
45 £1 black and orange .. 75·00 £140
34/45 .. *Set of* 12 £120 £225
34/45 Perf "Specimen" *Set of* 12 £225

Designs: *Vert as T* 3/4—1d. Cocoa; 1½d. Tin dredger; 2d. Timber industry; 4d. Cotton ginnery; 6d. Habe minaret; 1s. Fulani Cattle. *Horiz as T* 5—5s. Oil Palms; 10s. River Niger at Jebba; £1, Canoe pulling.

1937 (12 May). *Coronation. As Nos. 118/20 of Jamaica, but ptd by B.W. & Co. P* 11×11½.

46 1d. carmine .. 30 1·50
47 1½d. brown .. 1·25 2·00
48 3d. blue .. 1·40 2·00
46/8 .. *Set of* 3 2·75 5·00
46/8 Perf "Specimen" *Set of* 3 55·00

15 King George VI — 16 Victoria-Buea Road

(Recess B.W. (T **15**), D.L.R. (others))

1938 (1 May)–**51.** *Designs as T* **15/16.** *Wmk Mult Script CA. P* 12 (*T* **15**) *or* 13×11½ (*others*).

49 15 ½d. green .. 10 10
a. Perf 11½ (15.2.50) .. 30 10
50 1d. carmine .. 19·00 2·50
a. Rose-red (*shades*) (1940) .. 75 30
50*b* 1d. bright purple (1.12.44) .. 10 20
ba. Perf 11½ (15.2.50) .. 20 50
51 1½d. brown .. 20 10
a. Perf 11½ (15.11.50) .. 10 10
52 2d. black .. 10 1·00
52*a* 2d. rose-red (1.12.44) .. 10 80
ab. Perf 11½ (15.2.50) .. 10 40
52*b* 2½d. orange (4.41) .. 10 70
53 3d. blue .. 10 10
a. Wmk sideways .. † £2500
53*b* 3d. black (1.12.44) .. 10 40
54 4d. orange .. 48·00 2·75
54*a* 4d. blue (1.12.44) .. 15 1·75
55 6d. blackish purple .. 40 10
a. Perf 11½ (17.4.51) .. 40 60
56 1s. sage-green .. 60 10
a. Perf 11½ (15.2.50) .. 15 10
57 1s. 3d. light blue (1940) .. 90 30
a. Perf 11½ (14.6.50) .. 80 70
ab. Wmk sideways .. † £2250
58 16 2s. 6d. black and blue .. 60·00 12·00
a. Perf 13½ (6.42) .. 3·75 4·25
ab. Black and deep blue (1947) .. 55·00 45·00
b. Perf 14 (1942) .. 2·00 2·75
c. Perf 12 (15.8.51) .. 1·75 3·00
59 – 5s. black and orange .. £110 12·00
a. Perf 13½ (8.42) .. 5·50 4·50
b. Perf 14 (1948) .. 6·00 3·00
c. Perf 12 (19.5.49) .. 5·50 4·00
49/59c .. *Set of* 16 50·00 12·00
49/52*a*, 53/9 Perf "Specimen" *Set of* 15 £200

Design: *Horiz as T* **16**—5s. R. Niger at Jebba.

The 1d., No. 50ba, exists in coils constructed from normal sheets.

1946 (21 Oct). *Victory. As Nos. 141/2 of Jamaica.*

60 1½d. chocolate .. 20 10
61 4d. blue .. 20 90
60/1 Perf "Specimen" .. *Set of* 2 55·00

1948 (20 Dec). *Royal Silver Wedding. As Nos. 143/4 of Jamaica.*

62 1d. bright purple .. 35 30
63 5s. brown-orange .. 5·00 8·00

1949 (10 Oct). *75th Anniv of U.P.U. As Nos. 145/8 of Jamaica.*

64 1d. bright reddish purple .. 20 10
65 3d. deep blue .. 1·25 1·75
66 6d. purple .. 70 2·00
67 1s. olive .. 80 1·75
64/7 .. *Set of* 4 2·75 5·00

1953 (2 June). *Coronation. As No. 153 of Jamaica, but ptd by B.W.*

68 1½d. black and emerald .. 40 10
w. Wmk inverted .. † —

18 Old Manilla Currency

21 "Tin"

Die I Flat-bed — Die Ia Rotary

Two types of 1d.:

The Belgian rotary printings have thicker lines of shading giving blotches of black colour instead of fine lines, particularly in the stirrups.

Major re-entry showing duplication of steps of the terraces (Pl 3, R. 1/5)

Type A
Gap in row of dots

Type B
Unbroken row of dots

Two types of 2d. slate-violet:

Nos. 72c/cc. The original cylinder used was Type A (July 1956); later Type B (Sept 1957). The above illustrations will help classification, but two stamps per sheet of 60 of Type A show faint dots. However, one of these has the "2d." re-entry which does not exist in Type B sheets, and shades are distinctive.

Die I Flat-bed

Die 1a Rotary

Two types of 3d.:

As in the 1d. the Belgian rotary printings have thicker lines of shading and this is particularly noticeable in the dark hills in the background.

24 Ife Bronze **26** Victoria Harbour

29 New and Old Lagos

(Des M. Fievet. Recess Waterlow)

1953 (1 Sept)–**58**. *T* **18, 21, 24, 26, 29** *and similar designs. Wmk Mult Script CA. P* 14.

69	**18**	½d. black and orange	15	30
70	–	1d. black and bronze-green (Die I)	20	10
		a. Die Ia (1.9.58)	20	10
71	–	1½d. blue-green	50	40
72	**21**	2d. black and yellow-ochre	4·00	30
		a. Black and ochre (18.8.54)	4·25	30
		b. Re-entry	80·00	
72*c*		2d. slate-violet (Type A) (23.7.56)	3·00	1·50
		ca. Slate-blue (shades) (Type A)	7·00	30
		cb. Bluish grey (Type B) (25.9.57)	3·50	40
		cc. Grey (shades) (Type B)	4·25	30
73	–	3d. black and purple (Die I)	55	10
		a. Die Ia. *Black & reddish pur* (1.9.58)	55	10
		b. Imperf (pair)	£200	
74	–	4d. black and blue	2·50	20
75	**24**	6d. orange-brown and black	30	10
		a. Chestnut and black (18.8.54)	90	10
76	–	1s. black and maroon	40	10
77	**26**	2s. 6d. black and green	5·50	40
		a. Black and deep green (18.8.54)	7·50	40
78	–	5s. black and red-orange	3·50	85
79	–	10s. black and red-brown	12·00	2·50
80	**29**	£1 black and violet	21·00	6·50
69/80		*Set of* 13	48·00	11·00

Designs: *Horiz* (*as T* **18**)—1d. Bornu horsemen; 1½d. "Groundnuts"; 3d. Jebba Bridge and R. Niger; 4d. "Cocoa"; 1s. "Timber". (*As T* **26**)—5s. "Palm-oil"; 10s. "Hides and skins".

Nos. 70a, 72*c/cc* and 73a were printed on rotary machines by a subsidiary company, Imprimerie Belge de Securité, in Belgium.

Nos. 72ca and 72cc were only available in Nigeria.

The ½d. and 1d. (Die I) exist in coils constructed from sheets. Coils containing the 1d. (Die Ia) and 2d. (Type A) appeared in 1958 from continuously printed reels.

(30)

31 Victoria Harbour

1956 (28 Jan). *Royal Visit. No.* 72*a optd with T* **30**.

81	**21**	2d. black and ochre	40	20
		a. Opt inverted	£180	

(Recess Waterlow)

1958 (1 Dec). *Centenary of Victoria. W* w **12**. *P* 13½ × 14.

82	**31**	3d. black and purple	20	20

32 Lugard Hall

(Recess Waterlow)

1959 (14 Mar). *Attainment of Self-Government, Northern Region of Nigeria. T* **32** *and similar horiz design. W* w **12**. *P* 13½ (3*d*.) *or* 13½ × 14 (1*s*.).

83	3d. black and purple	15	10
84	1s. black and green	55	65

Design:—1s. Kano Mosque.

INDEPENDENT FEDERATION

34

35 Legislative Building **38** Dove, Torch and Map

(Des L. J. Wittington (1d.), R. Crawford (3d.), R. D. Baxter (6d.), J. White (1s. 3d.), Photo Waterlow)

1960 (1 Oct). *Independence. T* **35, 38** *and similar horiz designs. W* **34**. *P* 13½ (1*s*. 3*d*.) *or* 14 (*others*).

85	1d. black and scarlet	10	10
86	3d. black and greenish blue	15	10
87	6d. green and red-brown	20	20
88	1s. 3d. bright blue and yellow	40	20
85/8	*Set of* 4	70	50

Designs: (As *T* **35**)—3d. African paddling canoe; 6d. Federal Supreme Court.

39 Groundnuts **48** Central Bank

1961 (1 Jan). *T* **39, 48**, *and similar designs. W* **34**. *P* 15 × 14 (½*d. to* 1*s* 3*d*.) *or* 14½ (*others*).

89	½d. emerald	10	50
90	1d. reddish violet	80	10
91	1½d. carmine-red	60	2·00
92	2d. deep blue	30	10
93	3d. deep green	40	10
94	4d. blue	40	55
95	6d. yellow and black	80	10
	a. Yellow omitted	—	£550
96	1s. yellow-green	4·25	10
97	1s. 3d. orange	90	10
98	2s. 6d. black and yellow	2·25	15
99	5s. black and emerald	50	55
100	10s. black and ultramarine	1·50	2·00
101	£1 black and carmine-red	7·50	8·50
	w. Wmk inverted		
89/101	*Set of* 13	18·00	13·00

Designs: *Vert* (*as T* **39**)—1d. Coal mining; 1½d. Adult education; 2d. Pottery; 3d. Oyo carver; 4d. Weaving; 6d. Benin mask; 1s. Yellow-casqued Hornbill; 1s. 3d. Camel train. *Horiz* (*as T* **48**)—5s. Nigeria Museum; 10s. Kano airport; £1 Lagos railway station.

PRINTERS. The above and all following issues to No. 206 were printed in photogravure by Harrison & Sons, *except where otherwise stated*.

52 Globe and Railway Locomotive **56** Coat of Arms

(Des M. Goaman)

1961 (25 July). *Admission of Nigeria into U.P.U. T* **52** *and similar horiz designs. W* **34**. *P* 14½.

102	1d. red-orange and blue	20	10
103	3d. olive-yellow and black	20	10
104	1s. 3d. blue and carmine-red	70	20
105	2s. 6d. deep green and blue	85	1·40
102/5	*Set of* 4	1·75	1·60

Designs:—3d. Globe and mail-van; 1s. 3d. Globe and Bristol 175 Britannia aircraft; 2s. 6d. Globe and liner.

(Des S. Bodo (3d.), R. Hopeman (4d.), C. Adesina (6d.), M. Shamir (1s. 6d.), B. Enweonwu (2s. 6d.))

1961 (1 Oct). *First Anniv of Independence. T* **56** *and similar designs. W* **34**. *P* 14½.

106	3d. multicoloured	10	10
107	4d. yellow-green and yellow-orange	20	10
108	6d. emerald-green	30	10
109	1s. 3d. grey, emerald and blue	35	10
110	2s. 6d. green and grey-blue	40	1·25
106/10	*Set of* 5	1·25	1·40

Designs: *Horiz*—4d. Natural resources and map; 6d. Nigerian Eagle; 1s. 3d. Eagles in flight; 2s. 6d. Nigerians and flag.

A used copy of No. 106 has been seen with both the silver (large "Y" appearing grey) and the yellow (appearing white) omitted.

61 "Health" **66** Malaria Eradication Emblem and Parasites

(Des M. Shamir)

1962 (25 Jan). *Lagos Conference of African and Malagasy States. T* **61** *and similar vert designs. W* **34**. *P* 14 × 14½.

111	1d. yellow-bistre	10	10
112	3d. deep reddish purple	10	10
113	6d. deep green	15	10
114	1s. brown	20	10
115	1s. 3d. blue	25	20
111/15	*Set of* 5	65	40

Designs:—3d. "Culture"; 6d. "Commerce"; 1s. "Communications"; 1s. 3d. "Co-operation".

1962 (7 Apr). *Malaria Eradication. T* **66** *and similar horiz designs. W* **34**. *P* 14½.

116	3d. green and orange-red	10	10
117	6d. blue and bright purple	15	10
118	1s. 3d. magenta and violet-blue	20	10
119	2s. 6d. blue and yellow-brown	30	40
116/19	*Set of* 4	65	50

Designs:—6d. Insecticide spraying; 1s. 3d. Aerial spraying; 2s. 6d. Mother, child and microscope.

70 National Monument **71** Benin Bronze

(Des S. Bodo (3d.), B. Enweonwu (5s.))

1962 (1 Oct). *Second Anniv of Independence. W* **34**. *P* 14½ × 14 (3*d*.) *or* 14 × 14½ (5*s*.).

120	**70**	3d. emerald and blue	10	10
		a. Emerald omitted		
121	**71**	5s. red, emerald and violet	1·00	55

72 Fair Emblem **73** "Cogwheels of Industry"

(Des M. Goaman (1d., 2s. 6d.), J. O. Gbagbeolu and M. Goaman (6d.), R. Hegeman (1s.))

1962 (27 Oct). *International Trade Fair, Lagos. W* **34**. *T* **72/3** *and similar designs. P* 14½.

122	1d. olive-brown and orange-red	10	10
123	6d. carmine-red and black	15	10
124	1s. orange-brown and black	15	10
125	2s. 6d. ultramarine and yellow	60	20
122/5	*Set of* 4	85	30

Designs: *Horiz as T* **73**—1s. "Cornucopia of Industry; 2s. 6d. Oilwells and tanker.

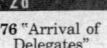

76 "Arrival of Delegates"

77 Mace as Palm Tree

(Des S. Akosile (2½d.), M. Goaman (others))

1962 (5 Nov). *Eighth Commonwealth Parliamentary Conference, Lagos. T* **76/77** *and similar design.* W **34**. *P* 14½.

126 2½d. greenish blue .. 15 15
127 4d. indigo and rose-red .. 15 10
128 1s. 3d. sepia and lemon .. 20 20
126/8 .. *Set of* 3 45 35

Design: *Horiz*—4d. National Hall.

80 Tractor and Maize

81 Mercury Capsule and Kano Tracking Station

(Des M. Goaman)

1963 (21 Mar). *Freedom from Hunger. T* **80** *and similar design.* W **34**. *P* 14.

129 3d. olive-green .. 1·00 20
130 6d. magenta .. 1·50 20

Design: *Vert*—3d. Herdsman.

(Des R. Hegeman)

1963 (21 June). *"Peaceful Use of Outer Space". T* **81** *and similar vert design.* W **34**. *P* 14½ × 14.

131 6d. blue and yellow-green .. 25 10
132 1s. 3d. black and blue-green .. 35 20

Design:—1s. 3d. Satellite and Lagos Harbour.

83 Scouts shaking Hands

(Des S. Apostolou (3d.), G. Okiki (1s.))

1963 (1 Aug). *11th World Scout Jamboree, Marathon. T* **83** *and similar triangular-shaped design.* W **34**. *P* 14.

133 3d. red and bronze-green .. 30 15
134 1s. black and red .. 95 65
MS134*a* 93 × 95 mm. Nos. 133/4 .. 1·75 1·75
ab. Red omitted (on 3d. value) .. £275

Design:—1s. Campfire.

85 Emblem and First Aid Team

88 President Azikiwe and State House

(Des M. Goaman)

1963 (1 Sept). *Red Cross Centenary. T* **85** *and similar horiz designs.* W **34**. *P* 14½.

135 3d. red and deep ultramarine .. 75 10
136 6d. red and deep green .. 1·25 10
137 1s. 3d. red and deep sepia .. 1·75 70
135/7 .. *Set of* 3 3·25 80
MS137*a* 102 × 102 mm. No. 137 (block of four) .. 8·50 10·00

Designs:—6d. Emblem and "Hospital Services"; 1s. 3d. Patient and emblem.

(Des M. Shamir. Photo Govt Printer, Israel)

1963 (1 Oct). *Republic Day. T* **88** *and similar vert designs showing administrative buildings and President Azikiwe.* *P* 14 × 13.

138 3d. yellow-olive and grey-green .. 10 10
139 1s. 3d. yellow-brown and sepia .. 10 10
a. Yellow-brown (portrait) omitted
140 2s. 6d. turquoise-blue and deep violet-blue .. 15 15
138/40 .. *Set of* 3 30 30

Designs:—1s. 3d. Federal Supreme Court Building; 2s. 6d. Parliament Building.

89 Charter and Broken Whip

90 "Freedom of Worship"

(Des S. Apostolou (3d.), Mrs. F. P. Effiong (others). Photo D.L.R.)

1963 (10 Dec). *15th Anniv of Declaration of Human Rights. T* **89/90** *and similar designs.* W **34**. *P* 13.

141 3d. vermilion .. 10 10
142 6d. blue-green .. 15 10
143 1s. 3d. ultramarine .. 30 10
144 2s. 6d. bright purple .. 45 30
141/4 .. *Set of* 4 85 35

Designs: *Vert as T* **90**—1s. 3d. "Freedom from want"; 2s. 6d. "Freedom of speech".

93 Queen Nefertari

94 Rameses II

(Des M. Shamir)

1964 (8 Mar). *Nubian Monuments Preservation.* W **34**. *P* 14½.

145 **93** 6d. yellow-olive and emerald .. 50 10
146 **94** 2s. 6d. brown, deep olive and emerald 2·00 1·75

95 President Kennedy

(Des M. Shamir (1s. 3d.), M. Goaman (2s. 6d.), Mr. Bottiau (5s.). Photo Govt Printer, Israel (1s. 3d.); litho Lewin-Epstein, Bat Yam, Israel (others))

1964 (27 Aug). *President Kennedy Memorial Issue. T* **95** *and similar horiz designs. P* 13 × 14 (1s. 3d.) *or* 14 (*others*).

147 1s. 3d. light violet and black .. 50 15
148 2s. 6d. black, red, blue and green .. 70 55
149 5s. black, deep blue, red and green .. 1·25 1·60
147/9 .. *Set of* 3 2·25 2·10
MS149*a* 154 × 135 mm. No. 149 (block of four). Imperf .. 10·00 12·00

Designs:—2s. 6d. President Kennedy and flags; 5s. President Kennedy (U.S. coin head) and flags.

98 President Azikiwe

99 Herbert Macaulay

(Des S. Apostolou (3d.), W. H. Irvine (others). Photo Govt Printer, Israel (3d.); Harrison (others))

1964 (1 Oct). *First Anniv of Republic. T* **98** *or* **99** *and similar vert design. P* 14 × 13 (3d.) *or* 14½ (*others*).

150 3d. red-brown .. 10 10
151 1s. 3d. green .. 35 10
152 2s. 6d. deep grey-green .. 70 50
150/2 .. *Set of* 3 1·00 60

Design:—2s. 6d. King Jaja of Opobo.

101 Boxing Gloves

102 Hurdling

(Des A. Adalade (3d.), S. Medahunsi (6d.), M. Shamir (1s. 3d.), M. Goaman (2s. 6d.))

1964 (10 Oct). *Olympic Games, Tokyo. T* **101** *and similar designs, and T* **102**. W **34**. *P* 14 (2s. 6d.) *or* 14½ (*others*).

153 3d. sepia and olive-green .. 45 10
154 6d. emerald and indigo .. 60 10
155 1s. 3d. sepia and yellow-olive .. 1·00 15
156 2s. 6d. sepia and chestnut .. 2·00 3·00
153/6 .. *Set of* 4 3·50 3·00
MS156*a* 102 × 102 mm. No. 156 (block of four). Imperf .. 3·00 4·25

Designs: *Horiz*—6d. High-jumping. *Vert*—1s. 3d. Running.

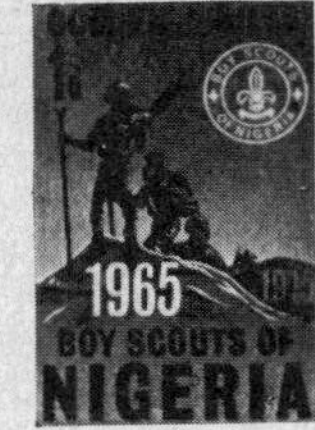

105 Scouts on Hill-top

(Des S. Apostolou (1d., 1s. 3d.), H. N. G. Cowham and Eagle Scout N. A. Lasisi (3d.), W. H. Irvine (6d.))

1965 (1 Jan). *50th Anniv of Nigerian Scout Movement. T* **105** *and similar vert designs. P* 14 × 14½.

157 1d. brown .. 10 10
158 3d. red, black and emerald .. 15 10
159 6d. red, sepia and yellow-green .. 25 20
160 1s. 3d. bistre-brown, greenish yellow and black-green .. 40 85
157/60 .. *Set of* 4 75 1·10
MS160*a* 76 × 104 mm. No. 160 (block of four). Imperf .. 5·00 8·50

Designs:—3d. Scout badge on shield; 6d. Scout badges; 1s. 3d. Chief Scout and Nigerian scout.

109 "Telstar"

110 Solar Satellite

(Des M. Shamir. Photo Govt Printer, Israel)

1965 (1 Apr). *International Quiet Sun Years. P* 14 × 13.

161 **109** 6d. reddish violet and turquoise-blue .. 15 15
162 **110** 1s. 3d. green and reddish lilac .. 15 15

111 Native Tom-tom and Modern Telephone

(Des C. Botham (5s.), H. N. G. Cowham (others). Photo Enschedé)

1965 (2 Aug). *I.T.U. Centenary. T* **111** *and similar designs. P* 11½ × 11 (1s. 3d.) *or* 11 × 11½ (*others*).

163 3d. black, carmine and yellow-brown .. 15 10
164 1s. 3d. black, blue-green and chalky blue .. 1·50 1·00
165 5s. black, carmine, blue & brt greenish blue 4·25 5·50
163/5 .. *Set of* 3 5·50 6·00

Designs: *Vert*—1s. 3d. Microwave aerial. *Horiz*—5s. Telecommunications satellite and part of globe.

114 I.C.Y. Emblem and Diesel Locomotive

117 Carved Frieze

(Des W. H. Irvine. Photo D.L.R.)

1965 (1 Sept). *International Co-operation Year. T* **114** *and similar horiz designs.* W **34**. *P* 14 × 15.

166 3d. green, red and orange .. 3·00 20
167 1s. black, bright blue and lemon .. 3·00 40
168 2s. 6d. green, bright blue and yellow .. 9·00 5·50
166/8 .. *Set of* 3 13·50 5·50

Designs:—1s. Students and Lagos Teaching Hospital; 2s. 6d. Kainji (Niger) Dam.

(Des S. Apostolou (3d.), W. H. Irvine (others). Photo D.L.R.)

1965 (1 Oct). *2nd Anniv of Republic. T* **117** *and similar designs. P* 14 × 15 (*3d.*) *or* 15 × 14 (*others*).

169 3d. black, red and orange-yellow 10 10
170 1s. 3d. red-brown, dp green & lt ultramarine 65 10
171 5s. brown, blackish brown and light green .. 1·50 1·50
169/71 .. .. *Set of* 3 2·00 1·50

Designs: *Vert*—1s. 3d. Stone images at Ikom; 5s. Tada bronze.

120 Lion and Cubs **121** African Elephants

132 Hippopotamus **133** African Buffalo

(Des M. Fievet. Photo Harrison (1d., 2d., 3d., 4d. (No. 177a), 9d.) or Delrieu (others))

1965 (1 Nov)–**66**. *T* **120/1, 132/3** *and similar designs. Without printer's imprint. Chalk-surfaced paper* (*1d., 2d., 3d., 4d., 9d.*). *P* 12 × 12½ (*½d., 6d.*), 12½ × 12 (*1½d., 4d.*), 14 × 13½ (*1d., 2d., 3d., 9d.*) *or* 12½ (*others*).

172 ½d. multicoloured (1.11.65) .. .. .. 80 1·75
173 1d. multicoloured (1.11.65) 40 15
174 1½d. multicoloured (2.5.66) .. .. .. 5·50 6·50
175 2d. multicoloured (1.4.66) .. .. .. 3·00 15
176 3d. multicoloured (17.10.66) .. .. .. 1·25 30
177 4d. multicoloured (2.5.66) .. .. .. 50 2·75
 a. Perf 14 × 13½ (1966) 30 10
178 6d. multicoloured (2.5.66) .. .. .. 2·00 40
179 9d. Prussian blue and orange-red (17.10.66) 3·00 60
180 1s. multicoloured (2.5.66) .. .. .. 2·50 60
181 1s. 3d. multicoloured (2.5.66) .. .. .. 8·50 90
182 2s. 6d. orange-brown, buff and brown (2.5.66) 75 85
183 5s. chestnut, light yellow and brown (2.5.66) 1·75 2·25
 a. Pale chestnut, yellow and brown-purple (1966) .. .. 2·00 2·25
184 10s. multicoloured (2.5.66) .. .. .. 6·50 3·00
185 £1 multicoloured (2.5.66) .. .. .. 15·00 9·00
172/85 .. .. *Set of* 14 45·00 24·00

Designs: *Horiz* (*as T* **121**)—1½d. Splendid Sunbird; 2d. Village Weaver and Red-headed Malimbe; 3d. Cheetah; 4d. Leopards; 9d. Grey Parrots. (*As T* **133**)—1s. Blue-breasted Kingfishers; 1s. 3d. Crowned Cranes; 2s. 6d. Kobs; 5s. Giraffes. *Vert* (*as T* **120**)—6d. Saddle-bill Stork.

The 2d. and 3d. exist with PVA gum as well as gum arabic.

See also Nos. 220, etc.

The 1d., 3d., 4d. (No. 177a), 1s., 1s. 3d., 2s. 6d., 5s. and £1 values exist overprinted "F.G.N." (Federal Government of Nigeria) twice in black. They were prepared during 1968 at the request of one of the State Governments for use as official stamps, but the scheme was abandoned and meter machines were used instead. Some stamps held at Lagos Post Office were sold over the counter in error and passed through the post in October 1968. The Director of Posts made limited stocks of all values, except the 1s., available from the Philatelic Bureau from 11 April 1969 "in order not to create an artificial scarcity", but they had no postal validity. Covers do, however, exist showing the 4d. value used by Lagos Federal Income Tax Office in April 1969 and others from the Office of the Secretary to the Military Government in 1973 carry the 3d., 4d. and 2s. 6d. values.

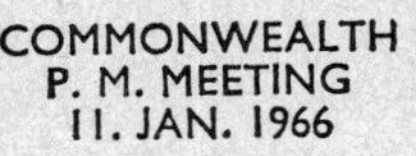

(**134**) **135** Y.M.C.A. Emblem and H.Q., Lagos

1966 (11 Jan). *Commonwealth Prime Ministers' Meeting, Lagos. No* 98 *optd with T* **134** *by the Nigerian Security Printing and Minting Co, Lagos, in red.*

186 **48** 2s. 6d. black and yellow 30 30

(Des S. B. Ajayi. Litho Nigerian Security Printing & Minting Co Ltd)

1966 (1 Sept). *Nigerian Y.W.C.A.'s Diamond Jubilee. P* 14.

187 **135** 4d. yellow-orange, ultramarine, orange-brown and yellow-green 15 10
188 9d. yellow-orange, ultramarine, brown and turquoise-green 15 60

137 Telephone Handset and Linesman **139** "Education, Science and Culture"

(Des S. B. Ajayi (4d.), N. Lasisi (1s. 6d.), B. Enweonwu (2s. 6d))

1966 (1 Oct). *Third Anniv of Republic. T* **137** *and similar designs. W* **34**. *P* 14½ × 14.

189 4d. green 10 10
190 1s. 6d. black, brown and reddish violet .. 45 50
191 2s. 6d. indigo, blue, yellow and green .. 1·25 2·25
189/91 .. .. *Set of* 3 1·60 2·50

Designs: *Vert*—4d. Dove and flag. *Horiz*—2s. 6d. Niger Bridge, Jebba.

(Des V. Whiteley from sketch by B. Salisu)

1966 (4 Nov). *20th Anniv of U.N.E.S.C.O. W* **34** (*sideways*). *P* 14½ × 14.

192 **139** 4d. black, lake and orange-yellow .. 40 10
193 1s. 6d. black, lake and turquoise-green 1·75 2·50
194 2s. 6d. black, lake and rose-pink .. 2·75 5·00
192/4 .. .. *Set of* 3 4·50 7·00

140 Children drinking

(Des V. Whiteley, after M. O. Afamefuna (4d.), I. U. Anawanti (1s. 6d.) and S. Adeyemi (2s. 6d.))

1966 (1 Dec). *Nigerian Red Cross. T* **140** *and similar designs. W* **34**. *P* 14 × 14½ (*1s. 6d.*) *or* 14½ × 14 (*others*).

195 4d. + 1d. black, reddish violet and red .. 40 30
196 1s. 6d. + 3d. multicoloured .. .. .. 1·00 3·75
197 2s. 6d. + 3d. multicoloured .. .. .. 1·10 4·25
195/7 .. .. *Set of* 3 2·25 7·50

Designs: *Vert*—1s. 6d. Tending patient. *Horiz*—2s. 6d. Tending casualties, and badge.

143 Surveying

(Des M. Goaman)

1967 (1 Feb). *International Hydrological Decade. T* **143** *and similar multicoloured design. W* **34**. *P* 14½ × 14 (*4d.*) *or* 14 × 14½ (*2s. 6d.*).

198 4d. Type **143** 10 10
199 2s. 6d. Water gauge on dam (*vert*) 25 80

145 Globe and Weather Satellite **147** Eyo Masqueraders

(Des M. Shamir (4d.), S. Bodo (1s. 6d.))

1967 (23 Mar). *World Meteorological Day. T* **145** *and similar horiz design. W* **34**. *P* 14½ × 14.

200 4d. magenta and blue 15 10
201 1s. 6d. black, yellow and blue 65 65

Design:—1s. 6d. Passing storm and sun.

(Des G. A. Okiki (4d.), A. B. Saka Lawal (1s. 6d.), S. Bodo (2s. 6d.). Photo Enschedé)

1967 (1 Oct). *4th Anniv of Republic. T* **147** *and similar multicoloured designs. P* 11½ × 11 (*2s. 6d.*) *or* 11 × 11½ (*others*).

202 4d. Type **147** 15 10
203 1s. 6d. Crowd watching acrobat .. .. 65 1·50
204 2s. 6d. Stilt dancer (*vert*) .. .. 90 3·00
202/4 .. .. *Set of* 3 1·50 4·25

150 Tending Sick Animal **151** Smallpox Vaccination

(Des G. Drummond)

1967 (1 Dec). *Rinderpest Eradication Campaign. P* 14½ × 14.

205 **150** 4d. multicoloured 15 10
206 1s. 6d. multicoloured .. .. .. 55 1·25

PRINTERS AND PROCESS. Nos. 207/89 were printed in photogravure by the Nigerian Security Printing and Minting Co Ltd, *unless otherwise stated.*

(Des J. Owei. Litho)

1968 (7 Apr). *20th Anniv of World Health Organization. T* **151** *and similar horiz design. P* 14.

207 4d. magenta and black 15 10
208 1s. 6d. orange, lemon and black 55 40

Design:—1s. 6d. African and mosquito.

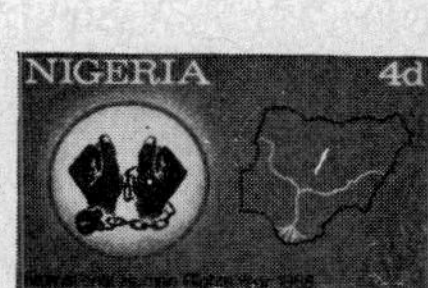

153 Chained Hands and Outline of Nigeria **155** Hand grasping at Doves of Freedom

(Des Jennifer Toombs)

1968 (1 July). *Human Rights Year. T* **153** *and similar design. P* 14.

209 4d. greenish blue, black and yellow 10 10
210 1s. 6d. myrtle-green, orange-red and black .. 20 30

Design: *Vert*—1s. 6d. Nigerian flag and Human Rights emblem.

(Des G. Vasarhelyi)

1968 (1 Oct). *5th Anniv of Federal Republic. P* 13½ × 14

211 **155** 4d. multicoloured 10 10
212 1s. 6d. multicoloured 20 20

156 Map of Nigeria and Olympic Rings **158** G.P.O., Lagos

(Des J. Owei)

1968 (14 Oct). *Olympic Games, Mexico. T* **156** *and similar horiz design. P* 14.

213 4d. black, green and scarlet 10 10
214 1s. 6d. multicoloured 20 20

Design:—1s. 6d. Nigerian athletes, flag and Olympic rings.

(Des D.L.R.)

1969 (11 Apr). *Inauguration of Philatelic Service. P* 14.

215 **158** 4d. black and green 10 10
216 1s. 6d. black and blue 20 20

159 Yakubu Gowon and Victoria Zakari

(Des adapted from photo by Jackie Phillips. Litho)

1969 (20 Sept). *Wedding of General Gowon. P* 13 × 13½.

217 **159** 4d. chocolate and emerald 10 10
218 1s. 6d. black and emerald 50 20

1969–72. (*a*) *As No. 173 etc, but printed by Nigerian Security Printing and Minting Co Ltd. With printer's imprint* "N.S.P. & M. CO. LTD." *P* 13½ (*6d.*) *or P* 13 × 13½ (*others*).

220 1d. multicoloured .. .. .. 2·75 2·00
222 2d. multicoloured .. .. .. 1·50 90
 a. Smaller imprint* (13.1.71) .. .. 1·25 1·75
223 3d. multicoloured (7.71) 65 90
 a. Larger imprint* (22.10.71) .. .. 1·00 1·50
224 4d. multicoloured .. .. .. 8·00 30
 a. Smaller imprint† .. .. .. 50·00
225 6d. multicoloured (1971) .. .. .. 1·75 50
226 9d. Prussian blue and orange-red (1970) 6·00 1·25
 a. "TD" of "LTD" omitted from imprint (Pl. 1B, R. 10/2) .. .. .. 40·00
227 1s. multicoloured (8.71) .. .. .. 2·00 60
228 1s. 3d. multicoloured (1971) .. .. 11·00 3·75
229 2s. 6d. multicoloured (1972) .. .. 8·00 7·00
230 5s. multicoloured (1972) .. .. .. 3·00 12·00
220/30 .. .. *Set of* 10 40·00 26·00

*On No. 222a the designer's name measures 4¾ mm. On No. 223a the imprints measure 9 and 8½ mm respectively. The normal imprints on Nos. 222/3 both measure 5½ mm.

The date given for Nos. 222a and 223a are for the earliest known used copies.

†No. 224 has the left-hand imprint 6 mm long and the right-hand 5½ mm. On No. 224a the imprints are 5½ mm and 4½ mm respectively. The width of the design is also ½ mm smaller.

Postal forgeries of the 2s. 6d. exist printed by lithography and roughly perforated 11–12.

Imperforate proofs of similar 10s. and £1 values are known.

(*b*) *As Nos. 222 and 224, but redrawn, and printed by Enschedé. No printer's imprint; designer's name at right. P* 14½ × 13.

231 2d. multicoloured (9.70) .. .. .. 29·00 4·00
232 4d. multicoloured (3.71) .. .. .. 1·00 70

In the 2d. the face value is white instead of yellow, and in the 4d. the white lettering and value are larger.

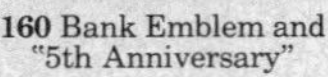

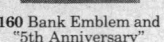

160 Bank Emblem and "5th Anniversary"

161 Bank Emblem and Rays

(Des J. Owei (4d.), B. Salisu (1s. 6d.). Litho)

1969 (18 Oct). *Fifth Anniv of African Development Bank. P* 14.
233 **160** 4d. orange, black and blue 10 10
234 **161** 1s. 6d. lemon, black and plum .. 20 20

162 I.L.O. Emblem

164 Olumo Rock

(Des D. West)

1969 (15 Nov). *50th Anniv of International Labour Organisation. T* **162** *and similar horiz design. P* 14.
235 4d. black and bright reddish violet 10 10
236 1s. 6d. emerald and black 60 70
Design:—1s. 6d. World map and I.L.O. emblem.

(Des A. Onwudimegwu)

1969 (30 Dec). *International Year of African Tourism. T* **164** *and similar designs. P* 14.
237 4d. multicoloured 10 10
238 1s. black and bright emerald 20 10
239 1s. 6d. multicoloured 80 35
237/9 .. .. *Set of* 3 1·00 45
Designs: *Vert*—1s. Traditional musicians; 1s. 6d. Assob Falls.

167 Symbolic Tree

168 U.P.U. H.Q. Building

(Des E. Emokpae (4d., 1s., 2s.), B. Onobrakpeya (1s. 6d.). Photo Enschedé)

1970 (28 May). *"Stamp of Destiny"; End of Civil War. T* **167** *and similar designs. P* 11 × 11½ (2s.) *or* 11½ × 11 (*others*).
240 4d. gold, new blue and black 10 10
241 1s. multicoloured 10 10
242 1s. 6d. yellow-green and black 15 10
243 2s. multicoloured 20 20
240/3 .. .. *Set of* 4 40 30
Designs: *Vert*—1s. Symbolic Wheel; 1s. 6d. United Nigerians supporting Map. *Horiz*—2s. Symbolic Torch.

(Des A. Onwudimegwu)

1970 (29 June). *New U.P.U. Headquarters Building. P* 14.
244 **168** 4d. reddish violet and greenish yellow .. 10 10
245 1s. 6d. light greenish blue and deep blue 40 20

169 Scroll

170 Oil Rig

(Des A. Onwudimegwu)

1970 (1 Sept). *25th Anniv of United Nations. T* **169** *and similar vert design. P* 14.
246 4d. orange-brown, buff and black 10 10
247 1s. 6d. steel-blue, cinnamon and gold .. 30 20
Design:—1s. 6d. U.N. Building.

(Des E. Emokpae. Litho Enschedé)

1970 (30 Sept). *Tenth Anniv of Independence. T* **170** *and similar vert designs. Multicoloured. P* 13½ × 13.
248 2d. Type **170** 25 10
249 4d. University Graduate 15 10
250 6d. Durbar Horsemen 30 10
251 9d. Servicemen raising Flag 40 10
252 1s. Footballer 40 10
253 1s. 6d. Parliament Building 40 40
254 2s. Kainji Dam 70 90
255 2s. 6d. Agricultural Produce .. .. 70 1·00
248/55 .. .. *Set of* 8 3·00 2·40

171 Children and Globe

172 Ibibio Face Mask

(Des E. Emokpae and A. Onwudimegwu. Photo Enschedé)

1971 (21 Mar). *Racial Equality Year. T* **171** *and similar multi-coloured designs. P* 13 × 13½ (4d., 2s.) *or* 13½ × 13 (*others*).
256 4d. Type **171** 10 10
257 1s. Black and white men uprooting "Racism" (*vert*) 10 10
258 1s. 6d. The world in black and white (*vert*) .. 15 60
259 2s. Black and white men united 15 85
256/9 .. .. *Set of* 4 35 1·50

(Des A. Onwudimegwu)

1971 (30 Sept). *Antiquities of Nigeria. T* **172** *and similar vert designs. P* 13½ × 14.
260 4d. black and pale blue 10 10
261 1s. 3d. blackish brown and ochre 15 30
262 1s. 9d. emerald, sepia and olive-yellow .. 20 80
260/2 .. .. *Set of* 3 35 1·00
Designs:—1s. 3d. Benin bronze; 1s. 9d. Ife bronze.

173 Children and Symbol

174 Mast and Dish Aerial

(Des E. Emokpae)

1971 (11 Dec). *25th Anniv of U.N.I.C.E.F. T* **173** *and similar vert designs, each incorporating the U.N.I.C.E.F. symbol. P* 13½ × 14.
263 4d. multicoloured 10 10
264 1s. 3d. yellow-orange, orge-red & carm-lake 15 40
265 1s. 9d. pale greenish blue & dp greenish blue 15 85
263/5 .. .. *Set of* 3 30 1·25
Designs:—1s. 3d. Mother and child; 1s. 9d. Mother carrying child.

(Des A. Onwudimegwu)

1971 (30 Dec). *Opening of Nigerian Earth Satellite Station. T* **174** *and similar horiz designs. P* 14.
266 **174** 4d. multicoloured 15 10
267 – 1s. 3d. green, blue and black 30 50
268 – 1s. 9d. brown, orange and black .. 40 1·00
269 – 3s. mauve, black and magenta .. 85 2·00
266/9 .. .. *Set of* 4 1·50 3·25
Designs:—Nos. 267/9, as T **174**, but showing different views of the Satellite Station.
The 4d. has been seen on a cover from Ilorin, postmarked 23.12.71.

175 Trade Fair Emblem

176 Traffic

(Des E. Emokpae (4d.), A. Onwudimegwu (others). Litho D.L.R.)

1972 (23 Feb). *All-Africa Trade Fair. T* **175** *and similar designs. P* 13.
270 4d. multicoloured 10 10
271 1s. 3d. deep lilac, lemon and gold 15 35
272 1s. 9d. yellow-orange, orange-yellow & black 15 90
270/2 .. .. *Set of* 3 30 1·25
Designs: *Horiz*—1s. 3d. Map of Africa with pointers to Nairobi. *Vert*—1s. 9d. Africa on globe.

(Des A. Onwudimegwu (4d., 3s.), E. Emokpae (1s. 3d.), J. Owei (1s. 9d.). Litho D.L.R.)

1972 (23 June). *Change to Driving on the Right. T* **176** *and similar horiz designs. Multicoloured (except 4d.). P* 13.
273 4d. Type **176** (yellow-orge, dp chest & black) 50 10
274 1s. 3d. Roundabout .. .. 1·25 70
275 1s. 9d. Highway .. .. 1·40 1·25
276 3s. Road junction .. .. 2·25 3·00
273/6 .. .. *Set of* 4 4·75 4·50

177 Nok Style Terracotta Head

178 Hides and Skins

(Des G. Okiki (1s. 3d.), A. Aiyegbusi (others). Litho D.L.R.)

1972 (1 Sept). *All-Nigeria Arts Festival. T* **177** *and similar multi-coloured designs. P* 13.
277 4d. Type **177** 10 10
278 1s. 3d. Bronze pot from Igbo-Ukwu 25 60
279 1s. 9d. Bone harpoon (*horiz*) .. .. 30 1·50
277/9 .. .. *Set of* 3 60 2·00

(New Currency. 100 kobo = 1 naira)

(Des E. Emokpae (8, 25, 30, 50 k., 1 n.), A. Onwudimegwu (others))

1973–74. *T* **178** *and similar designs. P* 14.

(*a*) *Photo. Left-hand imprint* 5¼ *mm long* (2 Jan–2 Apr)
280 1 k. multicoloured (deep green foliage) .. 90 70
*a. Light emerald foliage** (2.4.73) 20 10
281 2 k. black, pale turquoise-blue and bright purple 35 10
282 5 k. multicoloured (emerald hills) 60 60
*a. Bright yellow-green hills** (2.4.73) .. 50 10
283 10 k. black, orange-yellow and lilac 70 80
284 12 k. black, pale emerald and deep cobalt .. 11·00 8·00
285 18 k. multicoloured .. .. 11·00 2·00
286 20 k. multicoloured .. .. 12·00 3·00
287 30 k. black, chrome-yellow and new blue .. 12·00 7·00
288 50 k. multicoloured (black background and figure) .. .. 4·00 2·75
*a. Deep chocolate background and figure** (2.4.73) .. .. 1·50 90
289 1 n. multicoloured .. .. 4·50 8·50
280/9 .. .. *Set of* 10 48·00 27·00

(*b*) *Litho. Left-hand imprint* 6 *mm long* (2 Apr 1973†–74)
290 1 k. multicoloured (8.73) 10 20
291 2 k. black, pale turquoise-blue and bright purple (27.6.74)** .. .. .. 3·00 90
292 3 k. multicoloured 15 10
293 5 k. multicoloured (*shades*) (2.74) .. .. 3·75 1·00
294 7 k. multicoloured .. .. 30 1·25
295 8 k. multicoloured 40 10
296 10 k. black, orange-yellow and lilac (8.73) .. 4·50 20
297 12 k. black, green and cobalt (*shades*) .. 30 2·00
298 15 k. multicoloured 30 60
299 18 k. multicoloured 50 30
300 20 k. multicoloured 65 30
301 25 k. multicoloured 85 45
302 30 k. black, chrome-yellow and new blue .. 40 1·00
303 35 k. multicoloured .. .. 6·00 4·25
305 1 n. multicoloured (*shades*) .. .. 1·00 1·10
306 2 n. multicoloured (*shades*) .. .. 2·50 3·75
290/306 .. .. *Set of* 16 22·00 15·00

Designs: *Horiz*—2 k. Natural gas tanks; 3 k. Cement works; 5 k. Cattle-ranching; 7 k. Timber mill; 8 k. Oil refinery; 10 k. Cheetahs, Yankari Game Reserve; 12 k. New Civic Building; 15 k. Sugar-cane harvesting; 20 k. Vaccine production; 25 k. Modern wharf; 35 k. Textile machinery; 1 n. Eko Bridge; 2 n. Teaching Hospital, Lagos. *Vert*—18 k. Palm oil production; 30 k. Argungu Fishing Festival; 50 k. Pottery.

*On Nos. 280*a*, 282*a* and 288*a* other colours also differ, but the shades can best be identified by the distinctive features noted.

†Although First Day Covers of Nos. 290/306 were dated 1 April the stamps were not placed on sale until 2 April. Later, post-dated, covers included No. 291.

**This is the earliest known postmark date. No. 291 was not released by the Crown Agents in London until 11 September 1975.

Differences between printings:

1 k. In photogravure printings the stretched hide at left is in brownish black; on the litho stamps this hide is brown and yellow.

2 k. On the litho stamp the line of division between the black and pale blue colours of the gas tanks is a regular curve; on the photogravure printing it is horizontal and irregular. The litho stamp also has a wider mauve border at top.

5 k. The litho printing differs from the photogravure (Nos. 282/*a*) in having brown on the herdsman, instead of black.

10 k. The litho version has much less black on the cheetahs and tree trunk. It also shows black details at the left-hand end of the trunk, which do not appear on the photogravure version.

12 k. No. 284 is much darker than the litho version, especially within the building and amongst the trees at right.

18 k. The lithographed printing shows two oildrums in the fore-ground which are not present on the photogravure stamp.

20 k. The lithographed printing includes a brown plate not present on the photogravure version and this shows on the chemist. The liquid in the flasks is grey-blue instead of black. On the watermarked version, No. 348, the liquid is turquoise-blue.

30 k. No. 287 is much darker, with greater use of black in the design.

50 k. The litho version (No. 352) has solid shading on the potter's upper arm and lacks a black inner frame-line beneath the potter's wheel. No. 352 has a green printer's imprint at foot (instead of black) and its background is similar to that of No. 288*a*.

1 n. On the photogravure stamp the traffic is shown driving on the left. For the litho version the traffic is corrected to show it driving on the right.

Used copies of No. 282*a* have been seen with orange omitted.

Postal forgeries of the 10 k. Yankari Game Reserve design exist crudely printed by lithography on unwatermarked paper and roughly perforated 11–12.

See also Nos. 338/54.

PROCESS. From No. 307 onwards all stamps were lithographed by the Nigerian Security Printing and Minting Co Ltd.

179 Athlete

1973 (8 Jan). *Second All-African Games. Lagos. T* **179** *and similar multicoloured designs (except 5 k.). P* 13.
307 5 k. Type **179** (lt lilac, lt greenish bl & blk) .. 15 10
308 12 k. Football 25 50
309 18 k. Table-tennis .. .. 60 1·00
310 25 k. National Stadium (*vert*) .. .. .. 70 1·50
307/10 .. .. *Set of* 4 1·50 2·75

180 All-Africa House, Addis Ababa **181** Dr. Hansen

1973 (25 May). *Tenth Anniv of O.A.U. T* **180** *and similar vert designs. Multicoloured. P* 14.
311 5 k. Type **180** 10 10
312 18 k. O.A.U. flag 30 40
313 30 k. O.A.U. emblem and symbolic flight of ten stairs 50 80
311/13 .. .. *Set of* 3 70 1·10

(Des A. Onwudimegwu)

1973 (30 July). *Centenary of Discovery of Leprosy Bacillus. P* 14.
314 **181** 5 k. + 2 k. lt red-brown, flesh & black .. 30 70

182 W.M.O. Emblem and Weather-vane **183** University Complex

(Des O. I. Oshiga)

1973 (4 Sept). *I.M.O./W.M.O. Centenary. P* 14.
315 **182** 5 k. multicoloured 30 10
316 30 k. multicoloured .. .. 1·50 2·25

(Des A. Onwudimegwu (5, 18 k.), C. Okechukwu (12 k.), O. I. Oshiga (30 k.))

1973 (17 Nov). *25th Anniv of Ibadan University. T* **183** *and similar multicoloured designs. P* 13½ × 14 (12 *k.*) *or* 14 × 13½ (*others*).
317 5 k. Type **183** 10 10
318 12 k. Students' population growth (*vert*) .. 25 30
319 18 k. Tower and students 35 55
320 30 k. Teaching Hospital 50 85
317/20 .. .. *Set of* 4 1·10 1·50

184 Lagos 1d. Stamp of 1874

(Des A. Onwudimegwu (30 k.), S. Eluare (others))

1974 (10 June). *Stamp Centenary. T* **184** *and similar horiz designs. P* 14 × 13½.
321 5 k. light emerald, yellow-orange and black 20 10
322 12 k. multicoloured 60 60
323 18 k. light yellowish green, mauve and black 80 1·00
324 30 k. multicoloured .. .. 2·25 2·50
321/4 .. .. *Set of* 4 3·50 3·75
Designs:—5 k. Graph of mail traffic growth; 12 k. Northern Nigeria £25 stamp of 1904; 30 k. Forms of mail transport.

185 U.P.U. Emblem on Globe **186** Starving and Well-fed Children

(Des S. Eluare (5 k.). A. Onwudimegwu (18 k.), O. I. Oshiga (30 k.))

1974 (9 Oct). *Centenary of Universal Postal Union. T* **185** *and similar horiz designs. P* 14.
325 5 k. lt greenish blue, yellow-orange & black 15 10
326 18 k. multicoloured .. .. 2·00 60
327 30 k. bistre-brown, lt greenish blue & black .. 1·75 1·75
325/7 .. .. *Set of* 3 3·50 3·25
Designs:—18 k. World transport map; 30 k. U.P.U. emblem and letters.

(Des A. Onwudimegwu (12 k.), S. Eluare (others))

1974 (25 Nov). *Freedom from Hunger Campaign. T* **186** *and similar designs. P* 14.
328 5 k. apple-green, buff and grey-black .. 10 10
329 12 k. multicoloured 40 50
330 30 k. multicoloured .. .. 1·10 1·75
328/30 .. .. *Set of* 3 1·40 2·00
Designs: *Horiz*—12 k. Poultry battery. *Vert*—30 k. Water-hoist.

187 Telex Network and Teleprinter **188** Queen Amina of Zaria

(Des S. Eluare)

1975 (3 July). *Inauguration of Telex Network. T* **187** *and similar vert designs. P* 13½ × 14.
331 5 k. black, yellow-orange & light olive-green 10 10
332 12 k. black, lemon and orange-brown 20 20
333 18 k. multicoloured 30 30
334 30 k. multicoloured 50 50
331/4 .. .. *Set of* 4 1·00 1·00
Nos. 332/4 are as T **187** but have the motifs arranged differently.

(Des A. Onwudimegwu)

1975 (18 Aug). *International Women's Year. P* 14.
335 **188** 5 k. deep olive, light yellow and azure .. 20 10
336 18 k. purple, pale blue and light mauve .. 80 80
337 30 k. multicoloured .. .. 95 1·60
335/7 .. .. *Set of* 3 1·75 2·25

WATERMARK VARIETIES. Issues printed by Nigerian Security Printing and Minting Co. Ltd. on W **189** show the horizontal stamps with the watermark upright or inverted and the vertical stamps with it reading up or down.

189

1975–82*. *As Nos.* 290 *etc., but W* **189** (*sideways on* 18, 50 *k.*).
338 1 k. multicoloured (6.4.77) 75 90
339 2 k. black, pale turq-bl & bright purple (9.75) 1·00 10
340 3 k. multicoloured (10.75) 15 10
341 5 k. multicoloured (1.76) .. .. .. 1·25 10
342 7 k. multicoloured (16.5.80) .. .. .. 2·00 1·50
343 8 k. multicoloured (12.76) .. .. .. 2·00 90
344 10 k. blk, orange-yell & lilac (*shades*) (7.4.76) 1·00 20
346 15 k. multicoloured (5.82) .. .. .. — 1·75
347 18 k. multicoloured (12.78) .. .. .. 2·75 2·50
348 20 k. multicoloured (9.79) .. .. .. 3·00 2·75
349 25 k. multicoloured (21.3.77) .. .. .. 3·25 30
352 50 k. multicoloured (2.9.77) .. .. .. 4·25 3·50
354 2 n. multicoloured (11.77) .. .. .. 7·00 7·00
*Earliest known dates of issue.
Some values of this series, including the 50 k., were re-issued in 1992 during shortages of the current definitive set.

190 Alexander Graham Bell **191** Child Writing

(Des A. Onwudimegwu)

1976 (10 Mar). *Telephone Centenary. T* **190** *and similar designs. W* **189** (*sideways on* 5 *and* 25 *k.*). *P* 13½.
355 5 k. multicoloured 10 10
356 18 k. multicoloured 40 55
357 25 k. royal blue, pale blue and blackish brown 70 1·00
a. No wmk .. .. 10·00
355/7 .. .. *Set of* 3 1·10 1·50
Designs: *Horiz*—18 k. Gong and modern telephone system. *Vert*—25 k. Telephones, 1876 and 1976.

(Des A. Onwudimegwu (5 k.), S. Eluare (18 k.), N. Lasisi (25 k.))

1976 (20 Sept). *Launching of Universal Primary Education. T* **191** *and similar designs. W* **189** (*sideways on* 18 *and* 25 *k.*). *P* 14.
358 5 k. lemon, light violet and bright mauve .. 10 10
359 18 k. multicoloured 45 60
360 25 k. multicoloured 70 85
358/60 .. .. *Set of* 3 1·10 1·40
Designs: *Vert*—18 k. Children entering school; 25 k. Children in class.

192 Festival Emblem

(Des O. I. Oshiga (5 k., 30 k.), A. Onwudimegwu (10 k., 12 k.), N. Lasisi (18 k.))

1976–77. *Second World Black and African Festival of Arts and Culture, Nigeria. T* **192** *and similar horiz designs. W* **189**. *P* 14.
361 5 k. gold and blackish brown (1.11.76) .. 25 10
362 10 k. lt red-brown, lt yellow & black (15.1.77) 35 40
363 12 k. multicoloured (15.1.77) 60 55
364 18 k. chrome-yellow, lt brown & blk (1.11.76) 80 80
365 30 k. magenta and black (15.1.77) .. .. 1·00 1·50
361/5 .. .. *Set of* 5 2·75 3·00
Designs:—10 k. National Arts Theatre; 12 k. African hair styles; 18 k. Musical instruments; 30 k. "Nigerian arts and crafts".

193 General Murtala Muhammed and Map of Nigeria **194** Scouts Saluting

(Des A. Onwudimegwu (5, 18 k.), O. I. Oshiga (30 k.))

1977 (13 Feb). *First Death Anniv of General Muhammed (Head of State). T* **193** *and similar vert designs. Multicoloured. W* **189** (*sideways on* 18 *and* 30 *k.*). *P* 14.
366 5 k. Type **193** 10 10
367 18 k. General in dress uniform 20 35
368 30 k. General in battle dress 30 70
366/8 .. .. *Set of* 3 50 1·00

(Des N. Lasisi (18 k.), A. Onwudimegwu (others))

1977 (2 Apr). *First All-Africa Scout Jamboree, Jos, Nigeria. T* **194** *and similar horiz designs. Multicoloured. W* **189** (*sideways on* 5 *k.*). *P* 14.
369 5 k. Type **194** 15 10
370 18 k. Scouts cleaning street 70 70
371 25 k. Scouts working on farm .. .. .. 85 1·25
372 30 k. Jamboree emblem and map of Africa .. 1·10 2·00
369/72 .. .. *Set of* 4 2·50 3·50

195 Trade Fair Complex

(Des S. Eluare (5 k.), A. Onwudimegwu (others))

1977 (27 Nov). *1st Lagos International Trade Fair. T* **195** *and similar horiz designs. W* **189**. *P* 14.
373 5 k. black, new blue and yellow-green .. 10 10
374 18 k. black, new blue and magenta 20 25
375 30 k. multicoloured 30 45
373/5 .. .. *Set of* 3 50 70
Designs:—18 k. Globe and Trade Fair emblem; 30 k. Weaving and basketry.

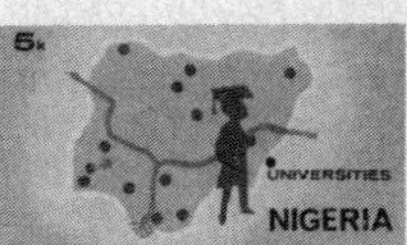

196 Map showing Nigerian Universities

(Des M. O. Shadare (5 k.), C. Okechukwu (12 k.), A. Onwudimegwu (18 k.), N. Lasisi (30 k.))

1978 (28 Apr). *Global Conference on Technical Co-operation between Developing Countries, Buenos Aires. T* **196** *and similar horiz designs. W* **189**. *P* 14.
376 5 k. multicoloured 10 10
377 12 k. multicoloured 15 15
378 18 k. multicoloured 25 25
379 30 k. yellow, bluish violet and black 45 60
376/9 .. .. *Set of* 4 80 1·00
Designs:—12 k. Map of West African highways and telecommunications; 18 k. Technologists undergoing training; 30 k. World map.

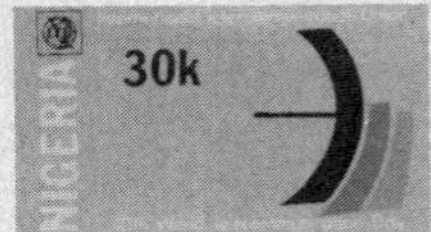

197 Microwave Antenna

1978 (17 May). *10th World Telecommunications Day. W* **189**. *P* 14.
380 **197** 30 k. multicoloured 50 60

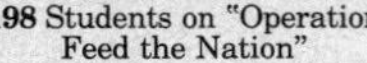

198 Students on "Operation Feed the Nation" 199 Mother with Infected Child

(Des J. Salisu (5 k.), N. Lasisi (18 k.), A. Onwudimegwu (30 k.))

1978 (7 July). *"Operation Feed the Nation" Campaign. T* **198** *and similar multicoloured designs. W* **189** *(sideways on 30 k.). P* 14.
381 5 k. Type **198** 10 10
382 18 k. Family backyard farm 20 20
383 30 k. Plantain farm (*vert*) 35 60
381/3 .. .. *Set of* 3 55 75

(Des G. Osuji (30 k.), N. Lasisi (others))

1978 (31 Aug). *Global Eradication of Smallpox. T* **199** *and similar designs. W* **189** *(sideways on 30 k.). P* 14.
384 5 k. black, orange-brown and rose-lilac .. 20 10
385 12 k. multicoloured 30 20
386 18 k. black, lake-brown and greenish yellow .. 55 40
387 30 k. black, silver and rose-pink 70 70
384/7 .. .. *Set of* 4 1·60 1·25
Designs: *Horiz*—12 k. Doctor and infected child; 18 k. Group of children being vaccinated. *Vert*—30 k. Syringe.

200 Nok Terracotta Human Figure, Bwari (900 B.C.–200 A.D.) 201 Anti-Apartheid Emblem

(Des local artists)

1978 (27 Oct). *Antiquities. T* **200** *and similar designs. W* **189** *(sideways on 5, 18 and 30 k.). P* 14.
388 5 k. black, new blue and carmine-red .. 10 10
389 12 k. multicoloured 15 10
390 18 k. black, greenish blue and carmine-red .. 20 15
391 30 k. multicoloured 25 20
388/91 .. .. *Set of* 4 60 45
Designs: *Horiz*—12 k. Igbo-Ukwu bronze snail shell, Igbo Isaiah (9th-century A.D.). *Vert*—18 k. Ife bronze statue of king (12th–15th century A.D.); 30 k. Benin bronze equestrian figure (about 1700 A.D.).

(Des A. Onwudimegwu)

1978 (10 Dec). *International Anti-Apartheid Year. W* **189** *(sideways). P* 14.
392 **201** 18 k. black, greenish yellow & vermilion 15 15

202 Wright Brothers and Wright Type A 203 Murtala Muhammed Airport

(Des A. Onwudimegwu)

1978 (28 Dec). *75th Anniv of Powered Flight. T* **202** *and similar horiz design. W* **189**. *P* 14.
393 5 k. multicoloured 25 10
394 18 k. black, ultramarine and light blue .. 1·00 20
Design:—18 k. Nigerian Air Force formation.

(Des A. Onwudimegwu)

1979 (15 Mar). *Opening of Murtala Muhammed Airport. W* **189**. *P* 14.
395 **203** 5 k. black, grey-blk & brt greenish blue 40 30

MINIMUM PRICE

The minimum price quote is 10p which represents a handling charge rather than a basis for valuing common stamps. For further notes about prices see introductory pages.

204 Child with Stamp Album 205 Mother and Child

1979 (11 Apr). *10th Anniv of National Philatelic Service. W* **189**. *P* 14.
396 **204** 5 k. multicoloured 10 10

1979 (28 June). *International Year of the Child. T* **205** *and similar multicoloured designs. W* **189** *(sideways on 25 k.). P* 14.
397 5 k. Type **205** 15 10
398 18 k. Children studying 50 30
399 25 k. Children playing (*vert*) 60 50
397/9 .. .. *Set of* 3 1·10 80

206 Trainee Teacher making Audio Visual Aid Materials 207 Necom House

(Des M. Shadare and O. Oshiga)

1979 (25 July). *50th Anniv of International Bureau of Education. T* **206** *and similar vert design. Multicoloured. W* **189** *(sideways). P* 14.
400 10 k. Type **206** 10 10
401 30 k. Adult education class 25 30

(Des A. Onwudimegwu)

1979 (20 Sept). *50th Anniv of Consultative Committee of International Radio. W* **189** *(sideways). P* 14.
402 **207** 10 k. multicoloured 15 20

208 Trainees of the Regional Aerial Survey School, Ile-Ife

(Des A. Onwudimegwu)

1979 (12 Dec). *21st Anniv of the Economic Commission for Africa. W* **189**. *P* 14.
403 **208** 10 k. multicoloured 20 20

209 Football, Cup and Map of Nigeria 210 Wrestling

(Des G. Akinola (10 k.), Mrs. O. Adeyeye (30 k.)

1980 (8 Mar). *African Cup of Nations Football Competition, Nigeria. T* **209** *and similar multicoloured design. W* **189** *(sideways on 30 k.). P* 14.
404 10 k. Type **209** 20 10
405 30 k. Footballer (*vert*) 60 50

(Des M. Shadare (10 k.), Mrs. O. Adeyeye (others))

1980 (19 July). *Olympic Games, Moscow. T* **210** *and similar designs. W* **189** *(sideways on 10, 20 and 45 k.). P* 14.
406 10 k. multicoloured 10 10
407 20 k. black and bright yellow-green 10 10
408 30 k. black, reddish orange and blue 15 15
409 45 k. multicoloured 20 20
406/9 .. .. *Set of* 4 45 45
Designs: *Vert*—20 k. Long jump; 45 k. Netball. *Horiz*—30 k. Swimming.

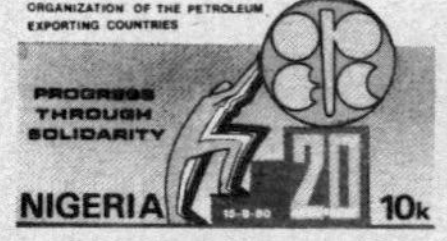

211 Figures supporting O.P.E.C. Emblem 212 Steam Locomotive

(Des G. Oluwasegun)

1980 (15 Sept). *20th Anniv of O.P.E.C. (Organization of Petroleum Exporting Countries). T* **211** *and similar design. W* **189** *(sideways on 45 k.). P* 14.
410 10 k. black, ultramarine and greenish yellow 25 10
411 45 k. black, deep turquoise-blue and magenta 1·00 60
Design: *Vert*—45 k. O.P.E.C. emblem on globe.

1980 (2 Oct). *25th Anniv of Nigerian Railway Corporation. T* **212** *and similar horiz designs. Multicoloured. W* **189**. *P* 14.
412 10 k. Type **212** 75 10
413 20 k. Loading goods train .. .. .. 1·50 85
414 30 k. Freight train .. .. 2·00 1·25
412/14 .. .. *Set of* 3 3·75 2·00

213 Metric Scales 214 "Communications" Symbols and Map of West Africa

(Des G. Akinola (10 k.), M. Shadare (30 k.))

1980 (14 Oct). *World Standards Day. T* **213** *and similar design. W* **189** *(sideways on 10 k.). P* 14.
415 10 k. red and black 10 10
416 30 k. multicoloured 35 40
Design: *Horiz*—30 k. Quality control.

1980 (5 Nov). *5th Anniv of E.C.O.W.A.S. (Economic Community of West African States). T* **214** *and similar horiz designs showing symbols of economic structure and map of West Africa. W* **189**. *P* 14.
417 10 k. black, yellow-orange and grey-olive .. 10 10
418 25 k. black, emerald and bright rose 30 10
419 30 k. black, greenish yellow and yellow-brown 20 15
420 45 k. black, turquoise-blue and bright blue .. 25 25
417/20 .. .. *Set of* 4 70 50
Designs:—25 k. "Transport"; 30 k. "Agriculture"; 45 k. "Industry".

215 Disabled Woman Sweeping 216 President launching "Green Revolution" (food production campaign)

(Des N. Lasisi (10 k.), G. Akinola (30 k.))

1981 (25 June). *International Year for Disabled Persons. T* **215** *and similar vert design. W* **189** *(sideways). P* 14.
421 10 k. multicoloured 20 10
422 30 k. black, chestnut and new blue 65 65
Design:—30 k. Disabled man filming.

(Des Mrs. A. Adeyeye (10 k.), G. Akinola (30 k.), S. Eluare (others))

1981 (16 Oct). *World Food Day. T* **216** *and similar designs. W* **189** *(sideways on 25 and 30 k.). P* 14.
423 10 k. multicoloured 10 10
424 25 k. black, greenish yellow and emerald .. 20 50
425 30 k. multicoloured 25 55
426 45 k. black, yellow-brown and orange-yellow 45 85
423/6 .. .. *Set of* 4 85 1·75
Designs: *Vert*—25 k. Food crops; 30 k. Harvesting tomatoes. *Horiz*—45 k. Pig farming.

217 Rioting in Soweto 218 "Preservation of Wildlife"

(Des G. Osuji)

1981 (10 Dec). *Anti-Apartheid Movement. T* **217** *and similar design. W* **189** *(sideways on 45 k.). P* 14.
427 30 k. multicoloured 35 45
428 45 k. black, vermilion and light green .. 50 80
Design: *Vert*—45 k. "Police brutality".

(Des G. Akinola)

1982 (22 Feb). *75th Anniv of Boy Scout Movement. T* **218** *and similar horiz design. Multicoloured. W* **189**. *P* 14.
429 30 k. Type **218** 75 55
430 45 k. Lord Baden-Powell taking salute .. 1·00 95

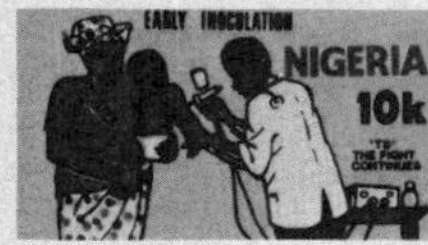

219 Early Inoculation

220 "Keep Your Environment Clean"

(Des G. Osuji (10 k.), C. Ogbebor (30 k.), N. Lasisi (45 k.))

1982 (24 Mar). *Centenary of Robert Koch's Discovery of Tubercle Bacillus. T* **219** *and similar designs. W* **189** (*sideways on* 45 *k.*). *P* 14.
431 10 k. multicoloured 30 15
432 30 k. grey-black, brown and turquoise-green .. 80 65
433 45 k. grey-black, light brown and bright green 1·10 1·40
431/3 .. .. *Set of* 3 2·00 2·00
Designs: *Horiz*—30 k. Technician and microscope. *Vert*—45 k. Patient being X-rayed.

(Des C. Ogbebor (10 k.), N. Lasisi (others))

1982 (10 June). *10th Anniv of U.N. Conference on Human Environment. T* **220** *and similar horiz designs. W* **189**. *P* 14.
434 10 k. multicoloured 15 10
435 20 k. yellow-orange, greenish grey and black .. 30 40
436 30 k. multicoloured 45 60
437 45 k. multicoloured 65 85
434/7 .. .. *Set of* 4 1·40 1·75
Designs:—20 k. "Check air pollution"; 30 k. "Preserve natural environment"; 45 k. "Reafforestation concerns all".

221 *Salamis parhassus*

222 Carving of "Male and Female Twins"

(Des G. Akinola)

1982 (15 Sept). *Nigerian Butterflies. T* **221** *and similar horiz designs. Multicoloured. W* **189**. *P* 14.
438 10 k. Type **221** 15 10
439 20 k. *Iterus zalmoxis* 30 30
440 30 k. *Cymothoe beckeri* 40 40
441 45 k. *Papilio hesperus* 70 70
438/41 .. .. *Set of* 4 1·40 1·40

(Des C. Ogbebor (10 k.), G. Akinola (20 k.), S. Eluare (30 k.), N. Lasisi (45 k.))

1982 (18 Nov). *25th Anniv of National Museum. T* **222** *and similar multicoloured designs. W* **189** (*sideways on* 10, 30, 45 *k.*). *P* 14.
442 10 k. Type **222** 20 10
443 20 k. Royal bronze leopard (*horiz*) 40 55
444 30 k. Soapstone seated figure .. .. .. 60 1·25
445 45 k. Wooden helmet mask .. .. .. 90 2·00
442/5 .. .. *Set of* 4 1·90 3·50

223 Three Generations

224 Satellite View of Globe

(Des G. Akinola)

1983 (8 Mar). *Family Day. T* **223** *and similar multicoloured design. W* **189** (*sideways on* 30 *k.*). *P* 14.
446 10 k. Type **223** 15 10
447 30 k. Parents with three children (*vert*) .. 50 65

(Des N. Lasisi (30 k.), C. Ogbebor (others))

1983 (14 Mar). *Commonwealth Day. T* **224** *and similar designs. W* **189** (*sideways on* 30, 45 *k.*). *P* 14.
448 10 k. yellow-brown and black 10 10
449 25 k. multicoloured 20 30
450 30 k. black, magenta and pale grey 55 35
451 45 k. multicoloured 35 45
448/51 .. .. *Set of* 4 1·10 1·10
Designs: *Horiz*—25 k. National Assembly Buildings. *Vert*—30 k. Drilling for oil; 45 k. Athletics.

225 Corps Members on Building Project

226 Postman on Bicycle

(Des Mrs. A. Adeyeye (25 k.), G. Akinola (others))

1983 (25 May). *10th Anniv of National Youth Service Corps. T* **225** *and similar multicoloured designs. W* **189** (*sideways on* 25, 30 *k.*). *P* 14.
452 10 k. Type **225** 15 10
453 25 k. On the assault-course (*vert*) 30 30
454 30 k. Corps members on parade (*vert*) .. 40 40
452/4 .. .. *Set of* 3 75 70

(Des N. Lasisi (25 k.), O. Ogunfowora (30 k.), Mrs. A. Adeyeye (others))

1983 (20 July). *World Communications Year. T* **226** *and similar multicoloured designs. W* **189** (*sideways on* 10 *k.*). *P* 14.
455 10 k. Type **226** 15 10
456 25 k. Newspaper kiosk (*horiz*) 30 40
457 30 k. Town crier blowing elephant tusk (*horiz*) 35 45
458 45 k. T.V. newsreader (*horiz*) 45 55
455/8 .. .. *Set of* 4 1·10 1·25

227 Pink Shrimp

228 On Parade

(Des Hilda Woods (10 k.), G. Osuji (25 k.), Mrs. A. Adeyeye (30 k.), O. Ogunfowora (45 k.))

1983 (22 Sept). *World Fishery Resources. T* **227** *and similar horiz designs. W* **189**. *P* 14.
459 10 k. rose, new blue and black 15 10
460 25 k. multicoloured 30 40
461 30 k. multicoloured 30 45
462 45 k. multicoloured 40 70
459/62 .. .. *Set of* 4 1·00 1·40
Designs:—25 k. Long-necked Croaker; 30 k. Barracuda; 45 k. Fishing techniques.

(Des F. Nwaije (10 k.), Mrs A. Adeyeye (30 k.), G. Osuji (45 k.))

1983 (14 Oct). *Boys' Brigade Centenary and 75th Anniv of Movement in Nigeria. T* **228** *and similar multicoloured designs. W* **189** (*sideways on* 10 *k.*). *P* 14.
463 10 k. Type **228** 40 10
464 30 k. Members working on cassava plantation (*horiz*) .. .. 1·50 1·50
465 45 k. Skill training (*horiz*) .. .. .. 2·25 2·75
463/5 .. .. *Set of* 3 3·75 4·00

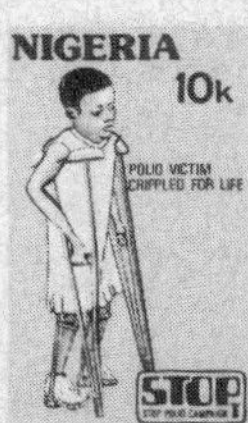

229 Crippled Child

230 Waterbuck

(Des S. Eluare (10 k.), G. Osuji (others))

1984 (29 Feb). *Stop Polio Campaign. T* **229** *and similar designs. W* **189** (*sideways on* 10 *k. and* 30 *k.*). *P* 14.
466 10 k. light blue, black and light brown .. 25 15
467 25 k. pale orange, black and greenish yellow 55 75
468 30 k. carmine-rose, black and orange-brown 70 1·10
466/8 .. .. *Set of* 3 1·40 1·75
Designs: *Horiz*—25 k. Child receiving vaccine. *Vert*—30 k. Healthy child.

(Des O. Ogunfowora (30 k.), Mrs. A. Adeyeye (45 k.), N. Lasisi (others))

1984 (25 May). *Nigerian Wildlife. T* **230** *and similar designs. W* **189** (*inverted on* 30 *k.*, *sideways on* 10 *k.*, 45 *k.*). *P* 14.
469 10 k. light green, light brown and black .. 20 10
470 25 k. multicoloured 50 50
471 30 k. yellow-brown, black and light green .. 60 90
472 45 k. new blue, pale orange and black .. 80 1·25
469/72 .. .. *Set of* 4 1·90 2·50
Designs: *Horiz*—25 k. Hartebeest; 30 k. African Buffalo. *Vert*—45 k. Diademed Monkey ("African Golden Monkey").

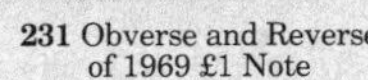

231 Obverse and Reverse of 1969 £1 Note

232 Boxing

1984 (2 July). *25th Anniv of Nigerian Central Bank. T* **231** *and similar horiz designs. W* **189** (*inverted on* 30 *k.*). *P* 14.
473 10 k. multicoloured 20 10
474 25 k. deep cinnamon, black and light green .. 45 50
475 30 k. light rose, black and grey-olive 55 60
473/5 .. .. *Set of* 3 1·10 1·10
Designs:—25 k. Central Bank; 30 k. Obverse and reverse of 1959 £5 note.

1984 (20 July). *Olympic Games, Los Angeles. T* **232** *and similar vert designs. Multicoloured. W* **189** (*sideways*). *P* 14.
476 10 k. Type **232** 15 10
477 25 k. Discus-throwing 35 50
478 30 k. Weightlifting 40 60
479 45 k. Cycling 60 90
476/9 .. .. *Set of* 4 1·40 1·90

233 Irrigation Project, Lesotho

234 Pin-tailed Whydah

(Des Mrs. A. Adeyeye (10 k.), S. Eluare (25 k.), Hilda Woods (30 k.), O. Ogunfowora (45 k.))

1984 (10 Sept). *20th Anniv of African Development Bank. T* **233** *and similar designs. W* **189** (*sideways on* 10 *k.*). *P* 14.
480 10 k. multicoloured 20 10
481 25 k. multicoloured 50 50
482 30 k. black, chrome yell & bright greenish bl 60 60
483 45 k. black, orange-brn & bright greenish bl .. 2·00 90
480/3 .. .. *Set of* 4 3·00 1·90
Designs: *Horiz*—25 k. Bomi Hills Road, Liberia; 30 k. School building project, Seychelles; 45 k. Coal mining, Niger.

(Des S. Eluare (25 k.), O. Ogunfowora (45 k.), F. Isibor (others))

1984 (24 Oct). *Rare Birds. T* **234** *and similar vert designs. Multicoloured. W* **189** (*sideways*). *P* 14.
484 10 k. Type **234** 75 20
485 25 k. Spur-winged Plover .. .. .. 1·50 70
486 30 k. Red Bishop .. .. 1·50 1·75
487 45 k. Double-spurred Francolin .. .. 1·75 2·50
484/7 .. .. *Set of* 4 5·00 4·75

235 Boeing 747 Airliner taking-off

236 Office Workers and Clocks ("Punctuality")

(Des. F. Isibor (10 k.), O. Ogunfowora (45 k.))

1984 (7 Dec). *40th Anniv of International Civil Aviation Organization. T* **235** *and similar horiz design. Multicoloured. W* **189** (*inverted on* 45 *k.*). *P* 14.
488 10 k. Type **235** 50 10
489 45 k. Boeing 707 airliner circling globe .. 2·00 2·25

(Des O. Ogunfowora)

1985 (27 Feb). *"War against Indiscipline". T* **236** *and similar horiz design. Multicoloured. W* **189** (*inverted on* 20 *k.*). *P* 14.
490 20 k. Type **236** 40 35
491 50 k. Cross over hands passing banknotes ("Discourage Bribery") 85 75

237 Footballers receiving Flag from Major-General Buhari

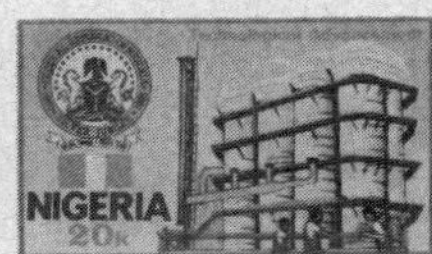

238 Rolling Mill

(Des F. Isibor (50 k.), G. Akinola (others))

1985 (5 June). *International Youth Year. T* **237** *and similar multicoloured designs. W* **189** (*sideways on* 50, 55 *k.*). *P* 14.
492 20 k. Type **237** 30 35
493 50 k. Girls of different tribes with flag (*vert*) 80 80
494 55 k. Members of youth organizations with flags (*vert*) 90 90
492/4 .. .. *Set of* 3 1·75 1·90

(Des O. Ogunfowora (50 k.), Mrs. A. Adeyeye (others))

1985 (2 Sept). *25th Anniv of Independence. T* **238** *and similar horiz designs. Multicoloured. W* **189**. *P* 14.
495 20 k. Type **238** 40 10
496 50 k. Map of Nigeria 60 35
497 55 k. Remembrance Arcade 60 40
498 60 k. Eleme, first Nigerian oil refinery .. 1·25 50
495/8 .. .. *Set of* 4 2·50 1·25
MS499 101×101 mm. Nos. 495/8. Wmk sideways 5·00 6·00

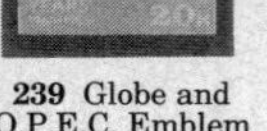
239 Globe and O.P.E.C. Emblem

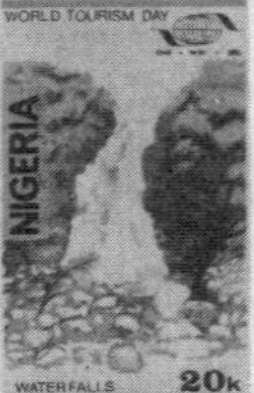
240 Waterfall

1985 (15 Sept). *25th Anniv of Organization of Petroleum Exporting Countries. T* **239** *and similar design.* W **189** (*sideways on 20 k.*). *P* 14.
500 20 k. greenish blue and orange-vermilion .. 1·00 35
501 50 k. black and ultramarine .. .. 1·75 75
Design: *Horiz*—50 k. World map and O.P.E.C. emblem.

(Des S. Eluare (55 k.), F. Isibor (60 k.), Mrs. A. Adeyeye (others))

1985 (27 Sept). *World Tourism Day. T* **240** *and similar multicoloured designs.* W **189** (*sideways on 20, 55, 60 k., inverted on 50 k.*). *P* 14.
502 20 k. Type **240** 45 10
503 50 k. Pottery, carved heads and map of Nigeria (*horiz*) 55 50
504 55 k. Calabash carvings and Nigerian flag .. 55 50
505 60 k. Leather work 55 55
502/5 .. .. *Set of* 4 1·90 1·50

241 Map of Nigeria and National Flag

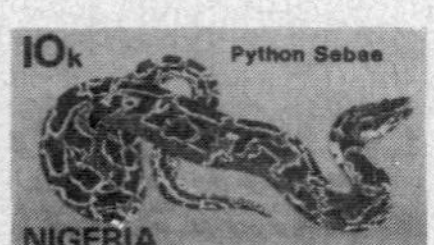
242 Rock Python

(Des N. Lasisi (20 k.), Mrs. A. Adeyeye (50 k.), O. Ogunfowora (55 k.))

1985 (7 Oct). *40th Anniv of United Nations Organization and 25th Anniv of Nigerian Membership. T* **241** *and similar designs.* W **189** (*sideways on 20 k., inverted on 50 k.*). *P* 14.
506 20 k. black, light green and pale blue .. 25 10
507 50 k. black, dull ultramarine and cerise .. 50 50
508 55 k. black, new blue and carmine .. 50 60
506/8 .. .. *Set of* 3 1·10 1·10
Designs: *Horiz*—50 k. United Nations Building, New York; 55 k. United Nations logo.

IMPERFORATE STAMPS. Nos. 509/12, 528/38, 543/6, 555/7, 560/79, 582/94, 599/603, 607/16, 619/37, 642/64 and 667/70 exist imperforate from restricted printings. Such printings may also exist for other issues.

(Des Hilda Woods (10, 30 k.), G. Akinola (20 k.), F. Isibor (25 k.))

1986 (15 Apr). *African Reptiles. T* **242** *and similar horiz designs.* W **189**. *P* 14.
509 10 k. multicoloured 35 10
510 20 k. black, orange-brown and pale new blue 65 85
511 25 k. multicoloured .. .. 70 1·00
512 30 k. multicoloured .. .. 70 1·00
509/12 .. .. *Set of* 4 2·25 2·75
Designs:—20 k. Long Snouted Crocodile; 25 k. Gopher Tortoise; 30 k. Chameleon.

243 Social Worker with Children

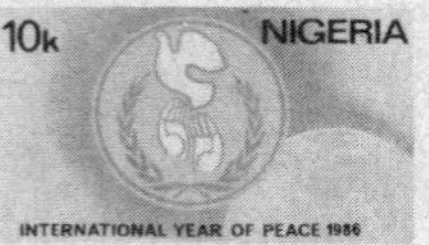
244 Emblem and Globe

(Des G. Akinola (1, 35 k.), S. Eluare (5 k., 20 n.), O. Ogunfowora (10, 15 k.), Mrs. A. Adeyeye (40, 45 k., 50 n.), G. Osuji (50 k.), Hilda Woods (10 n.), F. Abdul (500 n.), C. Ogbebor (all other values except 100 n.))

1986 (16 June)–**97**. *Nigerian Life. T* **243** *and similar multicoloured designs.* W **189** (*sideways on 1, 10, 20, 40 k., 100 n.*). *P* 14.
513 1 k. Type **243** 10 20
514 2 k. Volkswagen motor assembly line (*horiz*) 10 20
515 5 k. Modern housing estate (*horiz*) .. 10 20
516 10 k. Harvesting oil palm fruit 10 10
517 15 k. Unloading freighter (*horiz*) .. 10 10
518 20 k. *Tecoma stans* (flower) 10 10
519 25 k. Hospital ward (*horiz*) 10 10
519*a* 30 k. Birom dancers (*horiz*) 10 10
520 35 k. Telephonists operating switchboard (*horiz*) 10 10
521 40 k. Nkpokiti dancers 10 10
522 45 k. Hibiscus (*horiz*) 10 10
523 50 k. Post Office counter (*horiz*) .. 30 20
a. No wmk (1992) 10 10
524 1 n. Stone quarry (*horiz*) 10 10
a. No wmk (1993) 10 10
525 2 n. Students in laboratory (*horiz*) .. 30 30
a. No wmk (1993) 10 10
525*b* 10 n. Lekki Beach (*horiz*) (1.92) .. .. 2·00 1·25
ba. No wmk (1992) 55 60
525*c* 20 n. Ancient wall, Kano (*horiz*) (5.90) .. 4·00 1·50
525*d* 50 n. Rock bridge (*horiz*) (5.90) .. 2·75 3·00
da. No wmk (1997?) .. .. ..
525*e* 100 n. Ekpe masquerader (5.90) .. .. 5·50 5·75
525*f* 500 n. National Theatre (*horiz*) (5.90) .. 27·00 28·00
513/25*f* .. .. *Set of* 19 35·00 38·00
Nos. 513/25 were originally scheduled for issue during 1984, but were delayed. The 5 k., 10 k. and 20 k. appear to have been released earlier for postal purposes and are known postmarked from 2 November 1984 (5 k.), 14 October 1985 (10 k.) or December 1983 (20 k.). The 30 k. value, No. 519a, was not included in the 1986 philatelic release.
By 1997 the plates of those higher values still in use had deteriorated to such an extent that some examples are difficult to recognise. The perforations on such examples are in a very rough gauge.

(Des Mrs. A. Adeyeye)

1986 (20 June). *International Peace Year. T* **244** *and similar horiz design. Multicoloured.* W **189**. *P* 14.
526 10 k. Type **244** 20 10
527 20 k. Hands of five races holding globe .. 60 1·00

245 *Goliathus goliathus* (beetle)

246 Oral Rehydration Therapy

(Des Hilda Woods (25 k.), S. Eluare (others))

1986 (14 July). *Nigerian Insects. T* **245** *and similar horiz designs. Multicoloured.* W **189**. *P* 14.
528 10 k. Type **245** 40 10
529 20 k. *Vespa vulgaris* (wasp) 55 60
530 25 k. *Acheta domestica* (cricket) 65 90
531 30 k. *Anthrenus verbasci* (beetle) .. .. 95 1·40
528/31 .. .. *Set of* 4 2·25 2·75
MS532 119×101 mm. Nos. 528/31. Wmk sideways .. .. 5·50 6·50

(Des N. Lasisi (10 k.), F. Isibor (30 k.), Mrs. A. Adeyeye (others))

1986 (11 Nov). *40th Anniv of United Nations Children's Fund. T* **246** *and similar vert designs.* W **189** (*sideways*). *P* 14.
533 10 k. multicoloured 35 10
534 20 k. black, reddish brown & greenish yellow 60 55
535 25 k. multicoloured 70 75
536 30 k. multicoloured .. .. 90 1·10
533/6 .. .. *Set of* 4 2·25 2·25
Designs:—20 k. Immunisation; 25 k. Breast feeding; 30 k. Mother and child.

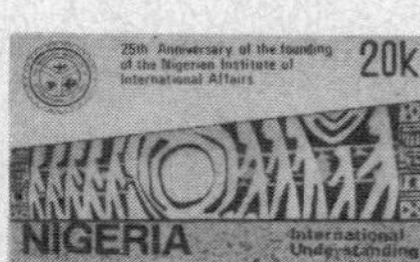
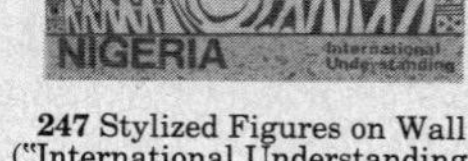
247 Stylized Figures on Wall ("International Understanding")

248 Freshwater Clam

(Des S. Eluare (20 k.), Hilda Woods (30 k.))

1986 (12 Dec). *25th Anniv of Nigerian Institute of International Affairs. T* **247** *and similar design.* W **189** (*sideways on 30 k.*). *P* 14.
537 20 k. black, greenish blue and light green .. 70 65
538 30 k. multicoloured .. .. 1·10 1·60
Design: *Vert*—30 k. "Knowledge" (bronze sculpture).

(Des G. Osuji (20 k.), F. Isibor (others))

1987 (31 Mar). *Shells. T* **248** *and similar horiz designs.* W **189** (*inverted on 10, 25 k.*). *P* 14.
539 10 k. multicoloured 80 10
540 20 k. black, reddish brown & pale rose-pink 1·50 1·75
541 25 k. multicoloured .. .. 2·00 2·00
542 30 k. multicoloured .. .. 2·25 2·50
539/42 .. .. *Set of* 4 6·00 5·50
Design:—20 k. Periwinkle; 25 k. Bloody Cockle (inscr "BLOODY COCKLE"); 30 k. Mangrove Oyster.

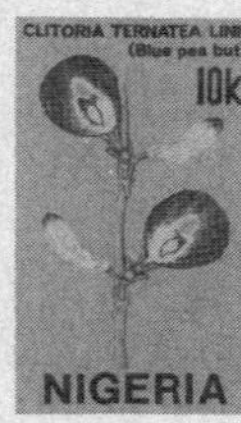

249 *Clitoria ternatea*

250 Doka Hairstyle

(Des S. Eluare (10 k.), Hilda Woods (20 k.), Mrs. A. Adeyeye (others))

1987 (28 May). *Nigerian Flowers. T* **249** *and similar vert designs.* W **189** (*sideways*). *P* 14.
543 10 k. multicoloured 10 10
544 20 k. lake-brown, greenish yellow & emerald 15 10
545 25 k. multicoloured 15 15
546 30 k. multicoloured 20 30
543/6 .. .. *Set of* 4 55 55
Designs:—20 k. *Hibiscus tiliaceus*; 25 k. *Acanthus montanus*; 30 k. *Combretum racemosum*.

(Des G. Akinola (25 k.), S. Eluare (30 k.), Mrs. A. Adeyeye (others))

1987 (15 Sept). *Women's Hairstyles. T* **250** *and similar vert designs.* W **189** (*sideways*). *P* 14.
547 10 k. black, orange-brown and olive-grey .. 10 10
548 20 k. multicoloured 15 20
549 25 k. black, brown and vermilion 20 30
550 30 k. multicoloured 20 30
547/50 .. .. *Set of* 4 60 75
Designs:—20 k. Eting; 25 k. Agogo; 30 k. Goto.

251 Family sheltering under Tree

252 Red Cross Worker distributing Food

(Des S. Nwasike (20 k.), Mrs. A. Adeyeye (30 k.))

1987 (10 Dec). *International Year of Shelter for the Homeless. T* **251** *and similar vert design. Multicoloured.* W **189** (*sideways*). *P* 14.
551 20 k. Type **251** 15 10
552 30 k. Family and modern house 15 20

(Des G. Osuji)

1988 (17 Feb). *125th Anniv of International Red Cross. T* **252** *and similar vert design. Multicoloured.* W **189** (*sideways*). *P* 14.
553 20 k. Type **252** 65 30
554 30 k. Carrying patient to ambulance .. 65 95

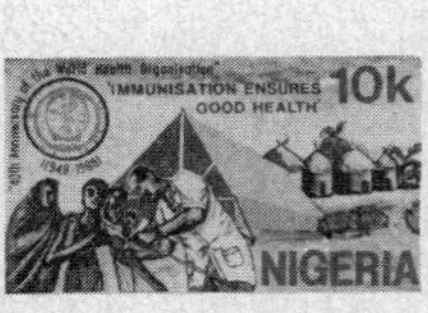
253 Doctor vaccinating Baby

254 O.A.U. Logo

(Des C. Ogbebor (10 k.), G. Osuji (others))

1988 (7 Apr). *40th Anniv of World Health Organization. T* **253** *and similar horiz designs. Multicoloured.* W **189** (*inverted*). *P* 14.
555 10 k. Type **253** 25 10
556 20 k. W.H.O. logo and outline map of Nigeria 60 60
557 30 k. Doctor and patients at mobile clinic .. 60 60
555/7 .. .. *Set of* 3 1·25 1·10

(Des O. Ojo (10 k.), Mrs. A. Adeyeye (20 k.))

1988 (25 May). *25th Anniv of Organization of African Unity. T* **254** *and similar vert design.* W **189** (*sideways*). *P* 14.
558 10 k. olive-bistre, emerald and bright orange 15 15
559 20 k. multicoloured 15 15
Design:—20 k. Four Africans supporting map of Africa.

255 Pink Shrimp

256 Weightlifting

(Des S. Eluare)

1988 (2 June). *Shrimps. T* **255** *and similar horiz designs.* W **189**. *P* 14.
560 10 k. multicoloured 25 10
561 20 k. black and pale yellow-olive 40 15
562 25 k. black, orange-vermilion & yell-brown 45 25
563 30 k. reddish orange, olive-bistre and black 55 50
560/3 .. .. *Set of* 4 1·50 90
MS564 120 × 101 mm. Nos. 560/3. Wmk sideways .. .. 1·50 2·00
Designs:—20 k. Tiger Shrimp; 25 k. Deepwater Roseshrimp; 30 k. Estuarine Prawn.

(Des G. Osuji (30 k.), Mrs. A. Adeyeye (others))

1988 (6 Sept). *Olympic Games, Seoul. T* **256** *and similar multicoloured designs.* W **189** (*sideways on 30 k.*). *P* 14.
565 10 k. Type **256** 25 10
566 20 k. Boxing 35 35
567 30 k. Athletics (*vert*) 45 55
565/7 .. .. *Set of* 3 95 90

257 Banknote Production Line

(Des Mrs. A. Adeyeye (25 k.), G. Akinola (30 k.), O. Ojo (others))

1988 (28 Oct). *25th Anniv of Nigerian Security Printing and Minting Co Ltd. T* **257** *and similar designs. W* **189** *(inverted on 10 k.). P* 14.

568	10 k. multicoloured	10	10
569	20 k. black, silver and emerald	20	20
570	25 k. multicoloured	30	30
571	30 k. multicoloured	45	45
568/71	*Set of* 4	95	95

Designs: *Horiz (as T* **257**)—20 k. Coin production line. *Vert* (37 × 44 *mm*)—25 k. Montage of products; 30 k. Anniversary logos.

258 Tambari **259** Construction of Water Towers, Mali

(Des S. Nwasike (10 k.), N. Lasisi (20 k.), S. Eluare (others))

1989 (29 June). *Nigerian Musical Instruments. T* **258** *and similar horiz designs. W* **189** *(inverted). P* 14.

572	10 k. multicoloured	10	10
573	20 k. multicoloured	20	20
574	25 k. chestnut, bronze-green and black	30	30
575	30 k. red-brown and black	45	45
572/5	*Set of* 4	95	95

Designs:—20 k. Kundung, 25 k. Ibid; 30 k. Dundun.

(Des Hilda Woods (10 k.), F. Abdul (20, 25 k.), S. Eluare (30 k.))

1989 (10 Sept). *25th Anniv of African Development Bank. T* **259** *and similar multicoloured designs. W* **189** *(inverted on 10, 25 k. and sideways on 30 k.). P* 14.

576	10 k. Type **259**	10	10
577	20 k. Paddy field, Gambia	15	15
578	25 k. Bank Headquarters, Abidjan, Ivory Coast	25	25
579	30 k. Anniversary logo (*vert*)	35	35
576/9	*Set of* 4	75	75

260 Lighting Campfire **261** Etubom Costume

(Des F. Abdul (10 k.), Mrs. A. Adeyeye (20 k.))

1989 (16 Sept). *70th Anniv of Nigerian Girl Guides Association. T* **260** *and similar multicoloured design. W* **189** *(inverted on 10 k. and sideways on 20 k.). P* 14.

580	10 k. Type **260**	30	10
581	20 k. Guide on rope bridge (*vert*)	60	60

(Des S. Eluare (10 k.), Mrs. A. Adeyeye (20 k.), F. Abdul (others))

1989 (26 Oct). *Traditional Costumes. T* **261** *and similar vert designs. Multicoloured. W* **189** *(sideways). P* 14.

582	10 k. Type **261**	15	10
583	20 k. Fulfulde	25	25
584	25 k. Aso-Ofi	35	40
585	30 k. Fuska Kura	45	60
582/5	*Set of* 4	1·10	1·25

262 Dove with Letter and Map of Africa **263** Oil Lamps

1990 (18 Jan). *10th Anniv of Pan African Postal Union. T* **262** *and similar vert design. Multicoloured. W* **189** *(sideways). P* 14.

586	10 k. Type **262**	25	10
587	20 k. Parcel and map of Africa	50	50

1990 (24 May). *Nigerian Pottery. T* **263** *and similar horiz designs. W* **189** *(inverted on 10 k.). P* 14.

588	10 k. brownish black, orange-brn & slate-vio	10	10
589	20 k. brownish black, red-brown & slate-vio	20	20
590	25 k. reddish brown and slate-violet	25	25
591	30 k. multicoloured	35	35
588/91	*Set of* 4	75	75
MS592	120×100 mm. Nos. 588/91. Wmk sideways	80	90

Designs:—20 k. Water pots; 25 k. Musical pots; 30 k. Water jugs.

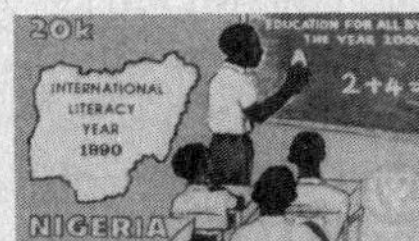

264 Teacher and Class

(Des Mrs. A. Adeyeye (20 k.), G. Osuji (30 k.))

1990 (8 Aug). *International Literacy Year. T* **264** *and similar horiz design. W* **189** *(inverted). P* 14.

593	20 k. multicoloured	20	10
594	30 k. blackish brn, greenish bl & orange-yell	30	30

Design:—30 k. Globe and book.

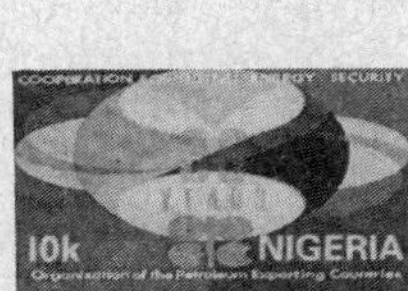

265 Globe and OPEC Logo **266** Grey Parrot

1990 (14 Sept). *30th Anniv of the Organisation of Petroleum Exporting Countries. T* **265** *and similar multicoloured designs. W* **189** *(inverted on 10, 25 k. and sideways on others). P* 14.

595	10 k. Type **265**	10	10
596	20 k. Logo and flags of member countries (*vert*)	20	20
597	25 k. World map and logo	25	25
598	30 k. Logo within inscription "Co-operation for Global Energy Security" (*vert*)	35	35
595/8	*Set of* 4	75	75

(Des C. Ogbebor (20 k.), G. Osuji (30 k, 2 n. 50), S. Eluare (1 n. 50))

1990 (8 Nov). *Wildlife. T* **266** *and similar vert designs. Multicoloured. W* **189** *(sideways). P* 14.

599	20 k. Type **266**	20	10
600	30 k. Roan Antelope	20	10
601	1 n. 50, Grey-necked Bald Crow ("Rock-fowl")	60	80
602	2 n. 50, Mountain Gorilla	85	1·25
599/602	*Set of* 4	1·75	2·00
MS603	118×119 mm. Nos. 599/602. Wmk inverted	1·75	2·00

267 Eradication Treatment **268** Hand holding Torch (Progress)

(Des C. Ogbebor (20 k.), G. Osuji (others))

1991 (20 Mar). *National Guineaworm Eradication Day. T* **267** *and similar multicoloured designs. W* **189** *(sideways on 10, 30 k.). P* 14.

604	10 k. Type **267**	15	10
605	20 k. Women collecting water from river (*horiz*)	25	25
606	30 k. Boiling pot of water	25	25
604/6	*Set of* 3	60	55

1991 (26 May). *Organization of African Unity Heads of State and Governments Meeting, Abuja. T* **268** *and similar vert designs each showing outline map of Africa. Multicoloured. W* **189** *(sideways). P* 14.

607	20 k. Type **268**	15	10
608	30 k. Cogwheel (Unity)	20	25
609	50 k. O.A.U. flag (Freedom)	20	45
607/9	*Set of* 3	50	70

MINIMUM PRICE

The minimum price quote is 10p which represents a handling charge rather than a basis for valuing common stamps. For further notes about prices see introductory pages.

269 National Flags **270** Electric Catfish

(Des G. Osuji)

1991 (4 July). *Economic Community of West African States Summit Meeting, Abuja. T* **269** *and similar horiz design. Multicoloured. W* **189** *(inverted). P* 14.

610	20 k. Type **269**	15	10
611	50 k. Map showing member states	30	45

(Des R. Adeyemi (10 k.), C. Ogbebor (20 k.), N. Lasisi (others))

1991 (30 July). *Nigerian Fishes. T* **270** *and similar horiz designs. Multicoloured. W* **189** *(inverted on 20 k.). P* 14.

612	10 k. Type **270**	15	10
613	20 k. Nile Perch	25	25
614	30 k. Nile Mouthbrooder ("Talapia")	35	35
615	50 k. Sharp-toothed Catfish	50	55
612/15	*Set of* 4	1·10	1·10
MS616	121×104 mm. Nos. 612/15. Wmk sideways	1·25	1·40

Postal forgeries of the 50 k. value exist crudely printed by lithography and roughly perforated 11–12.

271 Telecom '91 Emblem **272** Boxing

(Des S. Eluare)

1991 (7 Oct). *"Telecom '91" 6th World Telecommunication Exhibition, Geneva. T* **271** *and similar design. W* **189** *(sideways on 50 k.). P* 14.

617	20 k. black, deep green and deep violet	30	10
618	50 k. multicoloured	40	30

Design: *Vert*—50 k. Emblem and patchwork.

(Des G. Akinola (2 n.), G. Osuji (others))

1992 (24 Jan). *Olympic Games, Barcelona (1st issue). T* **272** *and similar horiz designs. W* **189** *(2 n.) or no wmk (others). Multicoloured. P* 14.

619	50 k. Type **272**	15	15
620	1 n. Nigerian athlete winning race	25	25
621	1 n. 50, Table tennis	35	35
622	2 n. Taekwondo	45	45
619/22	*Set of* 4	1·10	1·10
MS623	120×117 mm. Nos. 619/22. W **189** (sideways)	1·40	1·75

273 Football **274** Blood Pressure Gauge

(Des A. Olusola)

1992 (3 Apr). *Olympic Games, Barcelona (2nd issue). W* **189** *(sideways). P* 14.

624 **273**	1 n. 50, multicoloured	50	50

(Des Mrs. A. Adeyeye (50 k., 1 n.), G. Osuji (others))

1992 (7 Apr). *World Health Day. T* **274** *and similar vert designs. No wmk. Multicoloured. P* 14.

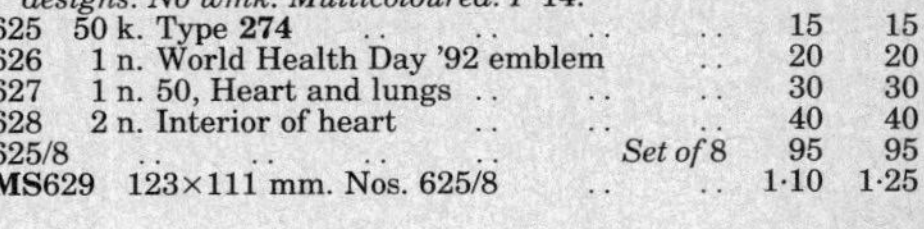

625	50 k. Type **274**	15	15
626	1 n. World Health Day '92 emblem	20	20
627	1 n. 50, Heart and lungs	30	30
628	2 n. Interior of heart	40	40
625/8	*Set of* 8	95	95
MS629	123×111 mm. Nos. 625/8	1·10	1·25

275 Map of World and Stamp on Globe **276** Gathering Plantain Fruit

(Des Mrs. A. Adeyeye)

1992 (3 July). *"Olymphilex '92" Olympic Stamp Exhibition, Barcelona. T* **275** *and similar horiz design. Multicoloured. W* **189**. *P* 14.

630 50 k. Type **275** 20 10
631 1 n. 50, Examining stamps 40 40
MS632 120×109 mm. Nos. 630/1. No wmk . . 1·40 1·60

(Des S. Eluare (50 k., 1 n.), N. Lasisi (1 n. 50), G. Osuji (2 n.))

1992 (17 July). *25th Anniv of International Institute of Tropical Agriculture. T* **276** *and similar designs. P* 14.

633 50 k. multicoloured 10 10
634 1 n. multicoloured 15 15
635 1 n. 50, black, reddish brown and emerald 20 20
636 2 n. multicoloured 25 25
633/6 . . . . . . *Set of* 4 60 60
MS637 121×118 mm. Nos. 633/6 . . . . 1·25 1·50

Designs: *Vert*—1 n. 50, Harvesting cassava tubers; 2 n. Stacking yams. *Horiz*—1 n. Tropical foods

277 Centre Emblem

278 Healthy Food and Emblem

(Des Mrs. A. Adeyeye (50 k., 2 n.), G. Osuji (others))

1992 (16 Oct). *Commissioning of Maryam Babangida National Centre for Women's Development. T* **277** *and similar designs. P* 14.

638 50 k. gold, emerald and blue-green . . 10 10
639 1 n. multicoloured 15 15
640 1 n. 50, multicoloured 20 20
641 2 n. multicoloured 30 30
638/41 . . . . . . *Set of* 4 65 65

Designs: *Vert*—1 n. Women working in fields; 2 n. Woman at loom. *Horiz*—1 n. 50, Maryam Babangida National Centre.

All examples of No. 641 are without a "NIGERIA" inscription.

1992 (1 Dec). *International Conference on Nutrition, Rome. T* **278** *and similar multicoloured designs. P* 14.

642 50 k. Type **278** 10 10
643 1 n. Child eating 15 15
644 1 n. 50, Fruit (*vert*) 20 20
645 2 n. Vegetables 25 25
642/5 . . . . . . *Set of* 4 60 60
MS646 120×100 mm. Nos. 642/5 . . . . 1·50 1·75

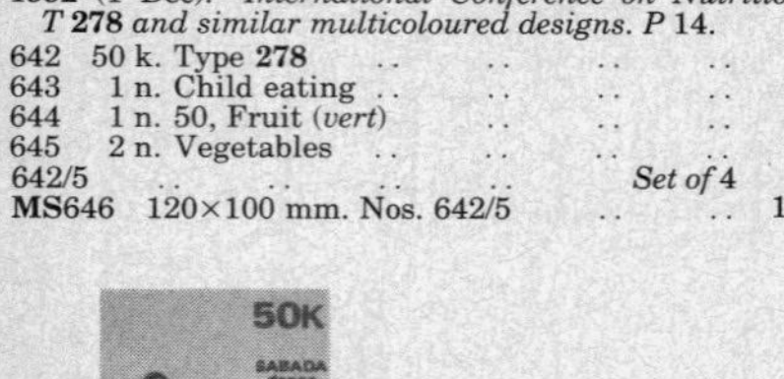

279 Sabada Dance

280 African Elephant

(Des S. Eluare (50 k.), Mrs A. Adeyeye (1 n.), G. Osuji (1 n. 50), G. Akinola (2 n.))

1992 (15 Dec). *Traditional Dances. T* **279** *and similar vert designs. Multicoloured. P* 14.

647 50 k. Type **279** 10 10
648 1 n. Sato 15 15
649 1 n. 50, Asian Ubo Ikpa 20 20
650 2 n. Dundun 25 25
647/50 . . . . . . *Set of* 4 60 60
MS651 126×107 mm. Nos. 647/50 . . . . 1·50 1·75

(Des G. Osuji (1 n. 50), S. Eluare (5 n.), D. Ogunfowora (20 n.), F. Abdul (30 n.))

1993 (Feb). *Wildlife. T* **280** *and similar multicoloured designs. P* 14.

652 1 n. 50, Type **280** 20 10
653 5 n. Stanley Crane (*vert*) 60 25
654 20 n. Roan Antelope . . . . . . 2·50 1·40
655 30 n. Lion . . . . 4·00 2·00
652/5 . . . . . . *Set of* 4 7·25 3·75

Postal forgeries have been reported of the 30 n. used in 1994.

281 Suburban Garden

282 Oni Figure

(Des A. Lasisi (1 n., 1 n. 50), S. Eluare (5 n.), Mrs. A. Adeyeye (10 n.))

1993 (4 June). *World Environment Day. T* **281** *and similar horiz designs. Multicoloured. P* 14.

656 1 n. Type **281** 10 10
657 1 n. 50, Water pollution 15 10
658 5 n. Forest road 50 50
659 10 n. Rural house 90 90
656/9 . . . . . . *Set of* 4 1·50 1·40

(Des G. Osuji (1 n.), O. Ogunfowora (others))

1993 (28 July). *50th Anniv of National Museums and Monuments Commission. T* **282** *and similar multicoloured designs. P* 14.

660 1 n. Type **282** 10 10
661 1 n. 50, Bronze head of Queen Mother . . 10 10
662 5 n. Bronze pendant (*horiz*) 30 35
663 10 n. Nok head 70 75
660/3 . . . . . . *Set of* 4 1·10 1·10

283 *Bulbophyllum distans*

284 Children in Classroom and Adults carrying Food

1993 (28 Oct). *Orchids. T* **283** *and similar vert designs. Multicoloured. P* 14.

664 1 n. Type **283** 10 10
a. Booklet pane. Nos. 664/7 with margins all round . . . . 1·10
665 1 n. 50, *Eulophia cristata* 15 10
666 5 n. *Eulophia horsfalli* 45 45
667 10 n. *Eulophia quartiniana* . . . . 1·00 1·10
664/7 . . . . . . *Set of* 4 1·50 1·50
MS668 103×121 mm. Nos. 664/7 . . . . 1·75 2·00

1994 (30 Mar). *International Year of the Family. T* **284** *and similar horiz design. Multicoloured. P* 14.

669 1 n. 50, Type **284** 10 10
670 10 n. Market . . . . 1·00 1·00

285 Hand with Tweezers holding 1969 4d. Philatelic Service Stamp

286 "I Love Stamps"

1994 (11 Apr). *25th Anniv of National Philatelic Service. T* **285** *and similar horiz designs. Multicoloured. P* 14.

671 1 n. Type **285** 10 10
672 1 n. 50, Philatelic Bureau 15 10
673 5 n. Stamps forming map of Nigeria . . 45 45
674 10 n. Philatelic counter . . . . 1·00 1·10
671/4 . . . . . . *Set of* 4 1·50 1·50

1994 (10 June). *120th Anniv of First Postage Stamps in Nigeria. T* **286** *and similar horiz designs. Multicoloured. P* 14.

675 1 n. Type **286** 10 10
676 1 n. 50, "I Collect Stamps" 15 10
677 5 n. 19th-century means of communication 45 45
678 10 n. Lagos stamp of 1874 . . . . 1·00 1·10
675/8 . . . . . . *Set of* 4 1·50 1·50

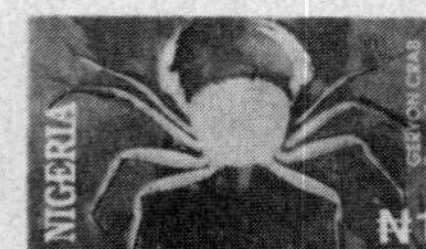

287 Magnifying Glass over Globe

288 Geryon Crab

1994 (16 Aug). *"Philakorea '94" International Stamp Exhibition. Seoul. P* 14.

679 **287** 30 n. multicoloured . . . . 2·25 2·40
MS680 127×115 mm. **287** 30 n. multicoloured. Roul 9 . . . . 3·75 4·00

1994 (12 Aug). *Crabs. T* **288** *and similar horiz designs. Multicoloured. P* 14.

681 1 n. Type **288** 10 10
682 1 n. 50, Spider Crab 10 10
683 5 n. Red Spider Crab 45 45
684 10 n. Geryon Maritae Crab 90 90
681/4 . . . . . . *Set of* 4 1·40 1·40

289 Sewage Works

290 Letterbox

1994 (16 Sept). *30th Anniv of African Development Bank. T* **289** *and similar horiz design. Multicoloured. P* 14.

685 1 n. 50, Type **289** 15 10
686 30 n. Development Bank emblem and flowers . . . . 2·25 2·40

1995 (1 Jan). *10th Anniv of Nigerian Post and Telecommunication Corporations. T* **290** *and similar multicoloured designs. P* 14.

687 1 n. Type **290** 10 10
688 1 n. 50, Letter showing "1 JAN 1985" postmark (*horiz*) 10 10
689 5 n. Nipost and Nitel emblems (*horiz*) . . 30 35
690 10 n. Mobile telephones 60 65
687/90 . . . . . . *Set of* 4 1·10 1·25

291 Woman preparing Food

292 "Candlestick" Telephone

(Des F. Abdul (1 n. 50), S. Eluare (5 n), G. Osuji (1, 10 n))

1995 (20 July). *Family Support Programme. T* **291** *and similar horiz designs. Multicoloured. P* 14.

691 1 n. Type **291** 10 10
692 1 n. 50, Mother teaching children . . 10 10
693 5 n. Family meal 30 35
694 10 n. Agricultural workers and tractor . . 60 65
691/4 . . . . . . *Set of* 4 1·10 1·25

1995 (9 Oct). *Centenary of First Telephone in Nigeria. T* **292** *and similar vert design. Multicoloured. P* 14.

695 1 n. 50, Type **292** 10 10
696 10 n. Early equipment 60 65

293 F.A.O. Emblem

294 "Justice" and 50th Anniversary Emblem

1995 (16 Oct). *50th Anniv of Food and Agriculture Organization. T* **293** *and similar horiz design. Multicoloured. P* 14.

697 1 n. 50, Type **293** 10 10
698 30 n. Fishing canoes . . . . . . 1·90 2·00

1995 (24 Oct). *50th Anniv of United Nations. T* **294** *and similar multicoloured designs. P* 14.

699 1 n. Type **294** 10 10
700 1 n. 50, Toxic waste (*horiz*) 10 10
701 5 n. Tourist hut (*horiz*) 30 35
702 10 n. Nigerian armoured car on U.N. duty (*horiz*) 90 95
699/702 . . . . . . *Set of* 4 1·25 1·25

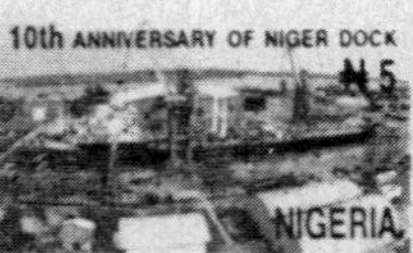

295 Container Ship in Dock

296 Scientist and Crops

1996 (29 Apr). *10th Anniv of Niger Dock. T* **295** *and similar horiz designs. Multicoloured. P* 14.

703 5 n. Type **295** 35 30
704 10 n. *Badagri* (tourist launch) on crane . . 65 60
705 20 n. Shipping at dock . . . . . . 1·50 1·50
706 30 n. *Odoragushin* (ferry) . . . . 2·50 2·50
703/6 . . . . . . *Set of* 4 4·50 4·50

(Des O. Ogunfowora (5 n.), S. Eluare (30 n.))

1996 (28 May). *21st Anniv of E.C.O.W.A.S. (Economic Community of West African States). T* **296** *and similar horiz design. Multicoloured. P* 14.

707	5 n. Type **296**	40	30
708	30 n. Queue at border crossing	2·00	2·00

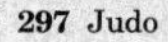

297 Judo

298 Nigerian Flag and Exhibition Emblem

1996 (28 June). *Olympic Games, Atlanta. T* **297** *and similar vert designs. Multicoloured. P* 14.

709	5 n. Type **297**	35	30
710	10 n. Tennis	80	60
711	20 n. Relay race	1·50	1·50
712	30 n. Football	2·25	2·25
709/12	*Set of* 4	4·50	4·25

1996 (10 Oct). *"ISTANBUL '96" International Stamp Exhibition. P* 14.

713	**298** 30 n. cerise, light green and black	2·00	2·00

299 *Volvariella esculenta*

300 Boy with Toys

1996 (19 Nov). *Fungi. T* **299** *and similar horiz designs. Multicoloured. P* 14.

714	5 n. Type **299**	45	30
715	10 n. *Lentinus subnudus*	90	60
716	20 n. *Tricholoma lobayensis*	1·50	1·50
717	30 n. *Pleurotus tuber-regium*	2·00	2·25
714/17	*Set of* 4	4·25	4·25

1996 (10 Dec). *50th Anniv of U.N.I.C.E.F. T* **300** *and similar multicoloured design. P* 14.

718	5 n. Type **300**	40	30
719	30 n. Girl reading book (*horiz*)	2·00	2·00

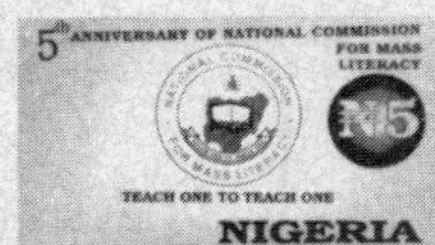

301 Literacy Logo

1996 (30 Dec). *5th Anniv of Mass Literacy Commission. T* **301** *and similar horiz design. P* 14.

720	5 n. emerald, light green and black	40	30
721	30 n. emerald, light green and black	2·00	2·00

Design—30 n. Hands holding book and literacy logo.

STAMP BOOKLETS

1915. *Crimson cover.*
SB1 2s. booklet containing twelve $\frac{1}{2}$d. and eighteen 1d. (Nos. 1/2) in blocks of 6

1921. *Crimson cover.*
SB2 4s. booklet containing twelve 1d. and eighteen 2d. (Nos. 16, 18) in blocks of 6

1924. *Scarlet cover.*
SB3 4s. booklet containing twelve 1d. and eighteen 2d. (Nos. 16, 18a) in blocks of 6

1926.
SB4 4s. booklet containing twelve 1d. and eighteen 2d. (Nos. 16a, 18a) in blocks of 6

1928. *Crimson cover.*
SB5 4s. booklet containing twelve 1d. and eighteen 2d. (Nos. 16a, 19) in blocks of 6

1929.
SB6 4s. booklet containing twelve 1d. and eighteen 2d. (Nos. 16a, 20) in blocks of 6

1931 (Jan).
SB7 4s. booklet containing twelve 1d. and twenty-four $1\frac{1}{2}$d. (Nos. 16a, 17) in blocks of 6

1957 (Aug). *Black on green cover. Stitched.*
SB8 2s. booklet containing four 1d. and eight $\frac{1}{2}$d. and 2d. (Nos. 69/70, 72c) in blocks of 4 .. 24·00
a. Contents as No. SB8, but containing No. 72*cb* 38·00

1957 (Oct). *Black on buff cover. Stitched.*
SB9 10s. booklet containing eight 3d. and 1s. (Nos. 73, 76) in blocks of 4 and a pane of air mail labels 26·00

1963. *Black on green (No.* SB10*) or buff (No.* SB11*) covers. Stitched.*
SB10 2s. booklet containing 1d. and 3d. (Nos. 90, 93) in blocks of 6 .. 5·50
SB11 10s. 6d. booklet containing six 1s. 3d. and twelve 3d. (Nos. 93, 97) in blocks of 6 and two panes of air mail labels .. 15·00

1966. *Black on green cover. Stitched.*
SB12 3s. booklet containing four 1d. and 4d. and eight 2d. (Nos. 173, 175, 177a) in blocks of 4 .. 30·00

1993 (28 Oct). *Orchids. Multicoloured cover. Stapled.*
SB13 35 n. booklet containing pane No. 664a×2 .. 2·10

POSTAGE DUE STAMPS

D 1

(Litho B.W.)

1959 (4 Jan). *Wmk Mult Script CA. P* $14\frac{1}{2}$ × 14.

D1	D 1	1d. red-orange	10	65
D2		2d. red-orange	15	80
D3		3d. red-orange	20	1·25
D4		6d. red-orange	20	4·00
D5		1s. grey-black	45	5·50
D1/5		*Set of* 5	1·00	11·00

1961 (1 Aug). *W* **34**. *P* $14\frac{1}{2}$ × 14.

D 6	D 1	1d. red	10	25
D 7		2d. light blue	10	30
D 8		3d. emerald	15	50
D 9		6d. yellow	30	70
D10		1s. blue (*shades*)	45	1·75
D6/10		*Set of* 5	1·00	3·25

(Litho Nigerian Security Printing & Minting Co)

1973 (3 May)–**94.** *New Currency. No wmk. P* $12\frac{1}{2}$×$13\frac{1}{2}$.

D11	D 1	2 k. red	10	10
		a. Roul 9 (1990)	1·50	
D12		3 k. blue (*shades*)	10	10
D13		5 k. orange-yellow (*shades*)	10	10
		a. Roul 9 (1994)		
D14		10 k. light apple-green (*shades*)	10	10
		a. Roul 9. *Emerald* (1987)	4·00	
D11/14		*Set of* 4	20	20

Nos. D11a and D14a are known postally used at Ibadan in January 1990 and August 1987.

BIAFRA

The following stamps were issued by Biafra (the Eastern Region of Nigeria) during the civil war with the Federal Government, 1967–70.

They were in regular use within Biafra from the time when supplies of Nigerian stamps were exhausted; and towards the end of the conflict they began to be used on external mail carried by air via Libreville.

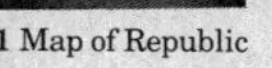
1 Map of Republic

2 Arms, Flag and Date of Independence

3 Mother and Child

(Typo and litho Mint, Lisbon)

1968 (5 Feb). *Independence. P* 12½.

1	**1**	2d. multicoloured	10	55
2	**2**	4d. multicoloured	10	55
3	**3**	1s. multicoloured	15	1·40
1/3		*Set of* 3	30	2·25

(4)

1968 (Apr). *Nos.* 172/5 *and* 177/85 *of Nigeria optd as T* **4** (*without* "SOVEREIGN" *on* 10s.).

4	½d. multicoloured (No. 172)	1·25	2·75
5	1d. multicoloured (No. 173)	1·50	4·00
	a. Opt double	£200	
	b. Opt omitted (in pair with normal)	£400	
6	1½d. multicoloured (No. 174)	5·00	8·50
7	2d. multicoloured (No. 175)	19·00	45·00
8	4d. multicoloured (No. 177a)	17·00	45·00
9	6d. multicoloured (No. 178)	4·50	8·50
10	9d. Prussian blue and orange-red (No. 179)	2·50	2·50
11	1s. multicoloured (Blk. + R.) (No. 180)	55·00	£100
12	1s. 3d. multicoloured (Blk. + R.) (No. 181)	32·00	50·00
	a. Black opt omitted	£300	
	b. Red opt omitted	£300	
13	2s. 6d. orange-brown, buff and brown (Blk. + R.) (No. 182)	1·75	8·50
	a. Red opt omitted	£200	
14	5s. chestnut, light yellow and brown (Blk. + R.) (No. 183)	2·25	7·50
	a. Red opt omitted	£200	
	b. Black opt omitted	£200	
	c. Red opt double	£300	
	d. Pale chestnut, yell & brn-pur (No. 183*a*)	2·25	7·50
15	10s. multicoloured (No. 184)	10·00	30·00
16	£1 multicoloured (Blk. + R.) (No. 185)	10·00	30·00
	a. Black ("SOVEREIGN BIAFRA") opt omitted	£200	
	b. Red (coat of arms) opt omitted	£200	
4/16	*Set of* 13	£130	£300

Nos. 172/3 of Nigeria also exist surcharged "BIAFRA – FRANCE FRIENDSHIP 1968 SOVEREIGN BIAFRA", clasped hands and "+5/-" (½d.) or "+£1" (1d.). There is no evidence that these two surcharges were used for postage within Biafra (*Price for set of* 2 £20 *mint*).

5 Weapon Maintenance

8 Biafran Arms and Banknote

9 Orphaned Child

(Litho Mint, Lisbon)

1968 (30 May). *First Anniv of Independence. T* **5, 8/9** *and similar vert designs. P* 12½.

17	4d. multicoloured	15	10
18	1s. multicoloured	20	20
19	2s. 6d. multicoloured	45	2·00
20	5s. multicoloured	60	2·75
	a. Indigo (banknote) omitted	60·00	
	b. Red (from flag) omitted	50·00	
21	10s. multicoloured	1·00	3·25
	a. Bright green (from flag) omitted	35·00	
17/21	*Set of* 5	2·10	7·50

Designs:—1s. Victim of atrocity; 2s. 6d. Nurse and refugees.

Nos. 17/21 also exist surcharged "HELP BIAFRAN CHILDREN" and different charity premium ranging from 2d. on the 4d. to 2s. 6d. on the 10s. There is no evidence that these surcharges were used for postage within Biafra (*Price for set of* 5 £2 *mint*).

In late 1968 a set of four values, showing butterflies and plants, was offered for sale outside Biafra. The same stamps also exist overprinted "MEXICO OLYMPICS 1968" and Olympic symbol. There is no evidence that either of these issues were used for postage within Biafra (*Price for set of* 4 £4 (*Butterflies and Plants*) or £3.50 (*Olympic overprints*), *both mint*).

CANCELLED-TO-ORDER. Many issues of Biafra, including the three unissued sets mentioned above, were available cancelled-to-order with a special "UMUAHIA" handstamp. This was the same diameter as postal cancellations, but differed from them by having larger letters, 3 mm. high, and the year date in full. Where such cancellations exist on issued stamps the used prices quoted are for c-t-o examples. Postally used stamps are worth considerably more.

16 Child in Chains and Globe

17 Pope Paul VI, Map of Africa and Papal Arms

1969 (30 May). *Second Anniv of Independence. Multicoloured; frame colours given. Litho. P* 13 × 13½.

35	**16**	2d. yellow-orange	1·00	3·50
36		4d. red-orange	1·00	3·50
		a. Green (wreath) and orange (Sun) omitted	£190	
37		1s. new blue	1·50	5·50
38		2s. 6d. emerald	2·00	10·00
35/8		*Set of* 4	5·00	20·00

A miniature sheet with a face value of 10s. was also released.

1969 (1 Aug). *Visit of Pope Paul to Africa. T* **17** *and similar vert designs. Multicoloured. Litho. P* 13×13½.

39	4d. Type **17**	40	2·50
40	6d. Pope Paul VI, Map of Africa and arms of the Vatican	55	5·50
41	9d. Pope Paul VI, map of Africa and St. Peter's Basilica, Vatican	75	7·50
42	3s. Pope Paul VI, map of Africa and Statue of St. Peter	2·25	12·00
39/42	*Set of* 4	3·50	25·00

A miniature sheet with a face value of 10s. was also released.

No. 42 has a magenta background. This value is also known with the background in brown-red or brown.

Biafra was overrun by Federal troops on 10 January 1970 and surrender took place on 15 January.

On 17 December the French Agency released a Christmas issue consisting of Nos. 39/42 overprinted "CHRISTMAS 1969 PEACE ON EARTH AND GOODWILL TO ALL MEN" together with the miniature sheet overprinted "CHRISTMAS 1969" and surcharged £1. Later Nos. 35/38 were released overprinted in red "SAVE BIAFRA 9TH JAN 1970" with a premium of 8d., 1s. 4d., 4s., and 10s. respectively together with the miniature sheet with a premium of £1. We have no evidence that these issues were actually put on sale in Biafra before the collapse, but it has been reported that the 4d. Christmas issue and 2d. + 8d. Save Biafra exist genuinely used before capitulation.

Nos. 40/41 have been seen surcharged "+ 10/–HUMAN RIGHTS" and the United Nations emblem but it is doubtful if they were issued.

No. 81 of Nigeria has also been reported with the original "ROYAL VISIT 1956" overprint, together with "NIGERIA" from the basic stamp, obliterated and a "SERVICE" overprint added. Such stamps were not used for official mail in Biafra, although an example is known with the "UMUAHIA" c-t-o mark.

Niue

Niue became a British Protectorate on 20 April 1900 and was transferred to New Zealand control on 11 June 1901. There was considerable local resentment at attempts to incorporate Niue into the Cook Islands and, in consequence, the island was recognised as a separate New Zealand dependency from 1902.

PRICES FOR STAMPS ON COVER TO 1945	
No. 1	*from* × 3
Nos. 2/5	*from* × 8
Nos. 6/7	—
Nos. 8/9	*from* × 30
Nos. 10/12	—
Nos. 13/31	*from* × 3
Nos. 32/7c	—
Nos. 38/47	*from* × 5
Nos. 48/9	—
No. 50	*from* × 15
Nos. 51/4	—
Nos. 55/61	*from* × 8
Nos. 62/8	*from* × 12
Nos. 69/71	*from* × 3
Nos. 72/4	*from* × 10
Nos. 75/8	*from* × 8
Nos. 79/88	—
Nos. 89/97	*from* × 2

NEW ZEALAND DEPENDENCY

Stamps of New Zealand overprinted

NIUE

(1)

1902 (4 Jan). *Handstamped with T* **1**, *in green or bluish green. Pirie paper. Wmk double-lined "N Z" and Star, W* **38** *of New Zealand. P* 11.

1	**42**	1d. carmine	£300	£300

A few overprints were made with a *greenish violet* ink. These occurred only in the first vertical row and part of the second row of the first sheet overprinted owing to violet ink having been applied to the pad (*Price* £1400 *un*).

NIUE. ½ PENI. **(2)** NIUE. TAHA PENI. **(3)** 1d. NIUE. 2½ PENI. **(4)**

1902 (4 Apr). *Type-set surcharges. T* **2, 3,** *and* **4**.

(*i*) *Pirie paper. No wmk. P* 11.

2	**27**	2½d. blue (R.)	1·25	3·75
		a. No stop after "PENI"	25·00	48·00
		b. Surch double	£2000	

(ii) *Basted Mills paper. Wmk double-lined* "N Z" *and Star,* *W* **38** *of New Zealand.*

(*a*) *P* 14

3	**23**	½d. green (R.)	1·75	4·00
		a. Spaced "U" and "E" (R. 3/3, 3/6, 8/3, 8/6)	8·50	15·00
		b. Surch inverted	£275	£450
		c. Surch double	£750	
4	**42**	1d. carmine (B.)	13·00	15·00
		a. Spaced "U" and "E" (R. 3/3, 3/6, 8/6)	80·00	90·00
		b. No stop after "PENI" (R. 9/3)	£190	£200
		c. Varieties a. and b. on same stamp (R. 8/3)	£190	£200

(*b*) *P* 11×14

5	**42**	1d. carmine (B.)	1·75	2·00
		b. Spaced "U" and "E" (R. 3/3, 3/6, 8/6)	11·00	12·00
		c. No stop after "PENI" (R. 9/3)	30·00	38·00
		d. Varieties b. and c. on same stamp (R. 8/3)	30·00	38·00

(*c*) *Mixed perfs*

6	**23**	½d. green (R.)	£900	
7	**42**	1d. carmine (B.)	£650	

1902 (2 May). *Type-set surcharges, T* **2, 3**. *Cowan paper. Wmk single-lined "N Z" and Star, W* **43** *of New Zealand.* (*a*) *P* 14..

8	**23**	½d. green (R.)	75	80
		a. Spaced "U" and "E" (R. 3/3, 3/6, 8/3, 8/6)	5·50	6·50
9	**42**	1d. carmine (B.)	50	70
		a. Surch double	£950	
		b. Spaced "U" and "E" (R. 3/3, 3/6, 8/6)	9·00	12·00
		c. No stop after "PENI" (R. 5/3, 7/3, 9/3, 10/3, 10/6)	9·00	12·00
		d. Varieties b. and c. on same stamp (R. 8/3)	28·00	38·00
		e. "I" of "NIUE" omitted (R. 6/5 from end of last ptg)		

(*b*) *P* 14×11

10	**23**	½d. green (R.)		

(*c*) *Mixed perfs*

11	**23**	½d. green (R.)	£900	
12	**42**	1d. carmine (B.)	£180	
		a. Spaced "U" and "E" (R. 3/3, 3/6, 8/3, 8/6)	£475	
		b. No stop after "PENI" (R. 5/3, 7/3, 9/3, 10/3, 10/6)	£475	

NIUE. **(5)** Tolu e Pene. **(6)** 3d.

Ono e Pene. **(7)** 6d. Taha e Sileni. **(8)** 1s.

1903 (2 July). *Optd with name at top, T* **5**, *and values at foot, T* **6/8**, *in blue. W* **43** *of New Zealand (sideways). P* 11.

13	**28**	3d. yellow-brown	8·50	5·00
14	**31**	6d. rose-red	11·00	11·00
15	**34**	1s. brown-red ("Tahae" joined)	£650	
16		1s. bright red	32·00	32·00
		a. Orange-red	42·00	45·00
13/16		*Set of* 3	45·00	42·00

NIUE. ½ PENI. **(9)** NIUE. 2½ PENI. **(9*a*)** NIUE. **(10)**

1911 (30 Nov). *½d. surch with T* **9**, *others optd at top as T* **5** *and values at foot as T* **7, 8**. *W* **43** *of New Zealand. P* 14×15 (*½d.*) *or* 14×14½ (*others*).

17	**51**	½d. green (C.)	45	40
18	**52**	6d. carmine (B.)	2·00	7·00
19		1s. vermilion (B.)	6·50	45·00
17/19		*Set of* 3	8·00	48·00

1915 (Sept). *Surch with T* **9a**. *W* **43** *of New Zealand. P* 14.

20	**27**	2½d. deep blue (C.)	14·00	25·00

1917 (Aug). *1d. surch as T* **3**, *3d. optd as T* **5** *with value as T* **6**. *W* **43** *of New Zealand.*

21	**53**	1d. carmine (*p* 14×15) (Br.)	7·00	5·50
		a. No stop after "PENI" (R.10/16)	£225	
22	**60**	3d. chocolate (*p* 14×14½) (B.)	48·00	80·00
		a. No stop after "PENE" (R.10/4)	£500	
		b. Perf 14×13½	60·00	90·00
		c. Vert pair, Nos. 22/b	£180	

1917–21. *Optd with T* **10**. *W* **43** *of New Zealand.* (a) *P* 14×15.

23 **61** ½d. green (R.) (2.20) .. 60 1·75
24 **53** 1d. carmine (B.) (10.17) .. 6·00 6·50
25 **61** 1½d. slate (R.) (11.17) .. 80 2·00
26 1½d. orange-brown (R.) (2.19) .. 70 3·25
27 3d. chocolate (B.) (6.19) .. 1·40 22·00

(b) *P* 14×13½

28 **60** 2½d. blue (R.) (10.20) .. 2·00 4·50
a. Perf 14×14½ .. 1·00 3·50
b. Vert pair, Nos. 28/a .. 18·00 42·00
29 3d. chocolate (B.) (10.17) .. 1·60 2·00
a. Perf 14×14½ .. 1·25 1·50
b. Vert pair, Nos. 29/a .. 27·00 40·00
30 6d. carmine (B.) (8.21) .. 5·00 19·00
a. Perf 14×14½ .. 4·75 19·00
b. Vert pair, Nos. 30/a .. 38·00 75·00
31 1s. vermilion (B.) (10.18) .. 8·50 19·00
a. Perf 14×14½ .. 5·50 19·00
b. Vert pair, Nos. 31/a .. 42·00 75·00
23/31 .. *Set of* 9 20·00 70·00

1918–29. *Postal Fiscal stamps as Type* F **4** *of New Zealand optd with T* **10**. *W* **43** *of New Zealand (sideways).*

(i) *Chalk-surfaced "De La Rue" paper.* (a) *P* 14

32 5s. yellow-green (R.) (7.18) .. £100 £110

(b) *P* 14½ × 14, *comb*

33 2s. deep blue (R.) (9.18) .. 15·00 32·00
34 2s. 6d. grey-brown (B.) (2.23) .. 20·00 48·00
35 5s. yellow-green (R.) (10.18) .. 23·00 50·00
36 10s. maroon (B.) (2.23) .. 85·00 95·00
37 £1 rose-carmine (B.) (2.23) .. £130 £150
33/7 .. *Set of* 5 £250 £325

(ii) *Thick, opaque, white chalk-surfaced "Cowan" paper.* *P* 14½ × 14

37*a* 5s. yellow-green (R.) (10.29) .. 25·00 48·00
37*b* 10s. brown-red (B.) (2.27) .. 75·00 90·00
37*c* £1 rose-pink (B.) (2.28) .. £130 £150
37*a/c* .. *Set of* 3 £200 £250

11 Landing of Captain Cook

12 Landing of Captain Cook

R.2/8 R.3/6 R.5/2

Double derrick flaws

(Des, eng and recess P.B.)

1920 (23 Aug). *T* **11** *and similar designs. No wmk. P* 14.

38 ½d. black and green .. 3·75 3·75
39 1d. black and dull carmine .. 2·00 1·25
a. Double derrick flaw (R.2/8, 3/6 or 5/2) 6·50
40 1½d. black and red .. 2·50 5·50
41 3d. black and blue .. 60 9·50
42 6d. red-brown and green .. 1·75 16·00
43 1s. black and sepia .. 1·75 16·00
38/43 .. *Set of* 6 11·00 45·00

Designs: *Vert*—1d. Wharf at Avarua; 1½d. "Capt Cook (Dance)"; 3d. Palm tree. *Horiz*—6d. Huts at Arorangi; 1s. Avarua Harbour.

Examples of the 6d. with inverted centre were not supplied to the Post Office.

1925–27. *As Nos.* 38/9 *and new values. W* **43** *of New Zealand. P* 14.

44 ½d. black and green (1927) .. 1·50 6·50
45 1d. black and deep carmine (1925) .. 1·75 75
a. Double derrick flaw (R.2/8, 3/6 or 5/2) 5·50
46 2½d. black and blue (10.27) .. 3·50 9·00
47 4d. black and violet (10.27) .. 6·50 15·00
44/7 .. *Set of* 4 12·00 28·00

Designs: *Vert*—2½d. Te Po, Rarotongan chief. *Horiz*—4d. Harbour, Rarotonga, and Mount Ikurangi.

1927–28. *Admiral type of New Zealand optd as T* **10**. *W* **43** *of New Zealand. P* 14.

(a) *"Jones" paper*

48 **72** 2s. deep blue (2.27) (R.) .. 18·00 45·00
w. Wmk inverted .. 15·00 45·00

(b) *"Cowan" paper*

49 **72** 2s. light blue (R.) (2.28) .. 18·00 32·00

1931 (Apr). *No.* 40 *surch as T* **18** *of Cook Is.*

50 2d. on 1½d. black and red .. 2·00 1·00

1931 (12 Nov). *Postal Fiscal stamps as Type* F **6** *of New Zealand optd as T* **10**. *W* **43** *of New Zealand. Thick, opaque, chalk-surfaced "Cowan" paper. P* 14.

51 2s. 6d. deep brown (B.) .. 4·00 11·00
52 5s. green (R.) .. 26·00 55·00
53 10s. carmine-lake (B.) .. 35·00 85·00
54 £1 pink (B.) .. 55·00 £120
51/4 .. *Set of* 4 £110 £250

See also Nos. 79/82 for different type of overprint.

(Des L. C. Mitchell. Recess P.B.)

1932 (16 Mar). *T* **12** *and similar designs inscr* "NIUE" *and* "COOK ISLANDS". *No wmk. P* 13.

55 ½d. black and emerald .. 8·50 19·00
a. Perf 13×14×13×13 .. £250
56 1d. black and deep lake .. 1·00 30
57 2d. black and red-brown .. 1·50 3·50
a. Perf 14×13×13×13 .. £100 £160
58 2½d. black and slate-blue .. 7·00 55·00
59 4d. black and greenish blue .. 13·00 45·00
a. Perf 14 .. 13·00 38·00
60 6d. black and orange-vermilion .. 2·25 2·00
61 1s. black and purple (*p* 14) .. 2·00 5·00
55/61 .. *Set of* 7 32·00 £110

Designs: *Vert*—1d. Capt. Cook; 1s. King George V. *Horiz*—2d. Double Maori canoe; 2½d. Islanders working cargo; 4d. Port of Avarua; 6d. R.M.S. *Monowai.*

Examples of the 2½d. with inverted centre were not supplied to the Post Office.

Nos. 55a and 57a are mixed perforations, each having one side perforated 14 where the original perforation, 13, was inadequate.

(Recess from Perkins, Bacon's plates at Govt Ptg Office, Wellington, N.Z.)

1932–36. *As Nos.* 55/61, *but W* **43** *of New Zealand. P* 14.

62 ½d. black and emerald .. 50 2·00
63 1d. black and deep lake .. 50 75
w. Wmk inverted .. 45·00
64 2d. black and yellow-brown (1.4.36) .. 40 80
w. Wmk inverted .. 25·00
65 2½d. black and slate-blue .. 40 3·50
w. Wmk inverted .. 45·00
66 4d. black and greenish blue .. 1·75 2·00
w. Wmk inverted ..
67 6d. black and red-orange (1.4.36) .. 70 65
68 1s. black and purple (1.4.36) .. 6·50 19·00
62/8 .. *Set of* 7 9·50 26·00

Imperforate proofs of No. 65 are known used on registered mail from Niue postmarked 30 August 1945 or 29 October 1945.

See also Nos. 89/97.

SILVER JUBILEE
OF
KING GEORGE V.
1910-1935.

(13)

Normal letters

B K E N
B K E N

Narrow letters

1935 (7 May). *Silver Jubilee. Designs as Nos.* 63, 65 *and* 67 *(colours changed) optd with T* **13** *(wider vertical spacing on 6d.). W* **43** *of New Zealand. P* 14.

69 1d. red-brown and lake .. 60 2·00
a. Narrow "K" in "KING" .. 2·75 8·00
b. Narrow "B" in JUBILEE .. 2·75 8·00
70 2½d. dull and deep blue (R.) .. 3·25 4·50
a. Narrow first "E" in "GEORGE" .. 4·00 13·00
71 6d. green and orange .. 3·25 5·50
a. Narrow "N" in "KING" .. 15·00 35·00
69/71 .. *Set of* 3 6·50 11·00

Examples of No. 70 imperforate horizontally are from proof sheets not issued through the Post and Telegraph Department (*Price £350 for vert pair*).

NIUE

(14)

15 King George VI

16 Tropical Landscape

1937 (13 May). *Coronation. Nos.* 599/601 *of New Zealand optd with T* **14**.

72 1d. carmine .. 30 10
73 2½d. Prussian blue .. 40 30
74 6d. red-orange .. 40 20
72/4 .. *Set of* 3 1·00 50

1938 (2 May). *T* **15** *and similar designs inscr* "NIUE COOK ISLANDS". *W* **43** *of New Zealand. P* 14.

75 1s. black and violet .. 4·75 5·50
76 2s. black and red-brown .. 12·00 15·00
77 3s. light blue and emerald-green .. 30·00 16·00
75/7 .. *Set of* 3 42·00 32·00

Designs: *Vert*—2s. Island village. *Horiz*—3s. Cook Islands canoe.

1940 (2 Sept). *Unissued stamp surch as in T* **16**. *W* **98** *of New Zealand. P* 13½×14.

78 3d. on 1½d. black and purple .. 30 10

NIUE.

(17)

1941–67. *Postal Fiscal stamps as Type* F **6** *of New Zealand with thin opt, T* **17**. *P* 14.

(i) *Thin, hard, chalk-surfaced "Wiggins Teape" paper with vertical mesh* (1941–43). (a) *W* **43** *of New Zealand*

79 2s. 6d. deep brown (B.) (4.41) .. 55·00 60·00
80 5s. green (R.) (4.41) .. £200 £170
81 10s. pale carmine-lake (B.) (6.42) .. £100 £170
82 £1 pink (B.) (2.43?) .. £170 £250
79/82 .. *Set of* 4 £475 £600

(b) *W* **98** *of New Zealand* (1944–54)

83 2s. 6d. deep brown (B.) (3.45) .. 3·50 7·50
w. Wmk inverted (11.51) .. 6·50 10·00
84 5s. green (R.) (11.44) .. 7·50 10·00
w. Wmk inverted (19.5.54) .. 7·50 10·00
85 10s. carmine-lake (B.) (11.45) .. 55·00 90·00
w. Wmk inverted .. 55·00 90·00
86 £1 pink (B.) (6.42) .. 42·00 50·00
83/6 .. *Set of* 4 95·00 £140

(ii) *Unsurfaced "Wiggins Teape" paper with horizontal mesh. W* **98** *of New Zealand* (1957–67)

87 2s. 6d. deep brown (*p* 14 × 13½) (1.11.57) .. 6·50 9·00
88 5s. pale yellowish green (*wmk sideways*) (6.67) .. 42·00 75·00

No. 88 came from a late printing made to fill demands from Wellington, but no supplies were sent to Niue. It exists in both line and comb perf.

1944–46. *As Nos.* 62/7 *and* 75/7, *but W* **98** *of New Zealand (sideways on ½d., 1d., 1s. and 2s.).*

89 **12** ½d. black and emerald .. 50 1·75
90 – 1d. black and deep lake .. 50 70
91 – 2d. black and red-brown .. 5·00 6·00
92 – 2½d. black and slate-blue (1946) .. 60 95
93 – 4d. black and greenish blue .. 2·75 90
w. Wmk inverted and reversed .. 16·00
94 – 6d. black and red-orange .. 90 1·40
95 **14** 1s. black and violet .. 1·25 85
96 – 2s. black and red-brown (1945) .. 8·50 2·75
97 – 3s. light blue and emerald-green (1945) 14·00 7·00
89/97 .. *Set of* 9 30·00 20·00

1946 (4 June). *Peace. Nos.* 668, 670, 674/5 *of New Zealand optd as T* **17** *without stop (twice, reading up and down on 2d.).*

98 1d. green (Blk.) .. 15 10
99 2d. purple (B.) .. 15 10
100 6d. chocolate and vermilion (Blk.) .. 20 30
a. Opt double, one albino .. £200
101 8d. black and carmine (B.) .. 20 30
98/101 .. *Set of* 4 60 60

Nos. 102/112 are no longer used.

18 Map of Niue

19 H.M.S. *Resolution*

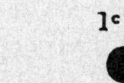

23 Bananas

24 Matapa Chasm

(Des J. Berry. Recess B.W.)

1950 (3 July). *T* **18/19, 23/24** *and similar designs. W* **98** *of New Zealand (sideways inverted on 1d., 2d., 3d., 4d., 6d. and 1s.). P* 13½×14 *(horiz) or* 14×13½ *(vert).*

113 ½d. orange and blue .. 10 30
114 1d. brown and blue-green .. 2·25 1·50
115 2d. black and carmine .. 20 30
116 3d. blue and violet-blue .. 10 15
117 4d. olive-green and purple-brown .. 10 15
118 6d. green and brown-orange .. 60 40
119 9d. orange and brown .. 10 40
120 1s. purple and black .. 10 15
121 2s. brown-orange and dull green .. 1·00 3·50
122 3s. blue and black .. 4·50 4·00
113/22 .. *Set of* 10 8·00 9·50

Designs: *Horiz (as T* **19**)—2d. Alofi landing; 3d. Native hut; 4d. Arch at Hikutavake; 6d. Alofi bay; 1s. Cave, Makefu. *Vert (as T* **18**)—9d. Spearing fish.

1953 (25 May). *Coronation. As Nos.* 715 *and* 717 *of New Zealand, but inscr* "NIUE".

123 3d. brown .. 65 40
124 6d. slate-grey .. 95 40

(New Currency. 100 cents = 1 New Zealand dollar)

1c

(25)

26

1967 (10 July–7 Aug). *Decimal currency.* (a) *Nos.* 113/22 *surch as T* **25**.

125 ½ c. on ½d. .. 10 10
126 1 c. on 1d. .. 1·10 15
127 2 c. on 2d. .. 10 10
128 2½ c. on 3d. .. 10 10
129 3 c. on 4d. .. 10 10
130 5 c. on 6d. .. 10 10
131 8 c. on 9d. .. 10 10
132 10 c. on 1s. .. 10 10
133 20 c. on 2s. .. 50 1·00
134 30 c. on 3s. .. 1·00 1·50
125/34 .. *Set of* 10 2·50 2·50

(b) *Arms type of New Zealand without value, surch as in T* **26**. *W* **98** *of New Zealand (sideways). P* 14.

135 **26** 25 c. deep yellow-brown .. 55 55
a. Rough perf 11 .. 6·00 13·00
136 50 c. pale yellowish green .. 80 80
a. Rough perf 11 .. 7·00 14·00
137 $1 magenta .. 60 1·25
a. Rough perf 11 .. 9·00 13·00

138 **26** $2 light pink .. .. 90 2·00
a. Rough perf 11 .. .. .. 11·00 14·00
135/8 .. .. *Set of 4* 2·50 4·25
135a/8a .. .. *Set of 4* 30·00 48·00

The 25 c., $1 and $2 perf 14 exist both line and comb perforated. The 50 c. is comb perforated only. The perf 11 stamps resulted from an emergency measure in the course of printing.

1967 (3 Oct). *Christmas. As T* **278** *of New Zealand, but inscr* "NIUE". *W* **98** *(sideways) of New Zealand. P* 13½×14.
139 2½ c. multicoloured 10 10
w. Wmk sideways inverted 15 30

1969 (1 Oct). *Christmas. As T* **301** *of New Zealand, but inscr* "NIUE". *W* **98** *of New Zealand. P* 13½ × 14½.
140 2½ c. multicoloured 10 10

27 "Pua" 37 Kalahimu

(Des Mrs. K. W. Billings. Litho Enschedé)

1969 (27 Nov). *T* **27** *and similar vert designs. Multicoloured. P* 12½ × 13½.
141 ½ c. Type **27** 10 10
142 1 c. "Golden Shower" 10 10
143 2 c. Flamboyant 10 10
144 2½ c. Frangipani 10 10
145 3 c. Niue Crocus 10 10
146 5 c. Hibiscus 10 10
147 8 c. "Passion Fruit" 10 10
148 10 c. "Kampui" 10 10
149 20 c. Queen Elizabeth II (after Anthony Buckley) .. .. 1·00 1·25
150 30 c. Tapeu Orchid .. .. 1·75 1·75
141/150 .. .. *Set of 10* 3·00 3·00

For 20 c. design as 5 c. see No. 801.

(Des G. F. Fuller. Photo Enschedé)

1970 (19 Aug). *Indigenous Edible Crabs. T* **37** *and similar horiz designs. Multicoloured. P* 13½ × 12½.
151 3 c. Type **37** 10 10
152 5 c. Kalavi 10 10
153 30 c. Unga 30 25
151/3 .. .. *Set of 3* 45 40

1970 (1 Oct). *Christmas. As T* **314** *of New Zealand, but inscr* "NIUE".
154 2½ c. multicoloured 10 10

38 Outrigger Canoe and Fokker F.27 Friendship Aircraft over Jungle 39 Spotted Triller

(Des L. C. Mitchell. Litho B.W.)

1970 (9 Dec). *Opening of Niue Airport. T* **38** *and similar horiz designs. Multicoloured. P* 13½.
155 3 c. Type **38** 10 10
156 5 c. *Tofua II* (cargo liner) and Fokker F.27 Friendship over harbour 15 10
157 8 c. Fokker F.27 Friendship over Airport 15 20
155/7 .. .. *Set of 3* 35 35

(Des A. G. Mitchell. Litho B.W.)

1971 (23 June). *Birds. T* **39** *and similar horiz designs. Multicoloured. P* 13½.
158 5 c. Type **39** 15 10
159 10 c. Purple-capped Fruit Dove 70 15
160 20 c. Blue-crowned Lory 80 20
158/60 .. .. *Set of 3* 1·50 40

1971 (6 Oct). *Christmas. As T* **325** *of New Zealand, but inscr* "Niue".
161 3 c. multicoloured 10 10

40 Niuean Boy 41 Octopus Lure

(Des L. C. Mitchell. Litho Harrison)

1971 (17 Nov). *Niuean Portraits. T* **40** *and similar vert designs. Multicoloured. P* 13 × 14.
162 4 c. Type **40** 10 10
163 6 c. Girl with garland 10 10
164 9 c. Man 10 20
165 14 c. Woman with garland 15 40
162/5 .. .. *Set of 4* 35 65

(Des A. G. Mitchell. Litho B.W.)

1972 (3 May). *South Pacific Arts Festival, Fiji. T* **41** *and similar multicoloured designs. P* 13½.
166 3 c. Type **41** 10 10
167 5 c. War weapons 15 10
168 10 c. Sika throwing (*horiz*) 20 10
169 25 c. Vivi dance (*horiz*) 30 20
166/9 .. .. *Set of 4* 65 40

42 Alofi Wharf

(Des A. G. Mitchell. Litho Questa)

1972 (6 Sept). *25th Anniversary of South Pacific Commission. T* **42** *and similar horiz designs. Multicoloured. P* 14.
170 4 c. Type **42** 10 10
171 5 c. Medical Services 15 10
172 6 c. Schoolchildren 15 10
173 18 c. Dairy cattle 25 20
170/3 .. .. *Set of 4* 60 40

1972 (4 Oct). *Christmas. As T* **332** *of New Zealand but inscr* "NIUE".
174 3 c. multicoloured 10 10

43 Silver Sweeper 44 "Large Flower Piece" (Jan Brueghel)

(Des G. F. Fuller. Litho Harrison)

1973 (27 June). *Fishes. T* **43** *and similar horiz designs. Multicoloured. P* 14 × 13½.
175 8 c. Type **43** 25 25
176 10 c. Peacock Hind ("Loi") 30 30
177 15 c. Yellow-edged Lyretail ("Malau") .. 40 40
178 20 c. Ruby Snapper ("Palu") 45 45
175/8 .. .. *Set of 4* 1·25 1·25

(Des and litho Enschedé)

1973 (21 Nov). *Christmas. T* **44** *and similar vert designs showing flower studies by the artists listed. Multicoloured. P* 14 × 13½.
179 4 c. Type **44** 10 10
180 5 c. Bollongier 10 10
181 10 c. Ruysch 20 20
179/81 .. .. *Set of 3* 30 30

45 Capt. Cook and Bowsprit 46 King Fataaiki

(Des A. G. Mitchell. Litho Questa)

1974 (20 June). *Bicentenary of Capt. Cook's Visit. T* **45** *and similar horiz designs each showing Cook's portrait. Multicoloured. P* 13½ × 14.
182 2 c. Type **45** 20 20
183 3 c. Niue landing place 20 20
184 8 c. Map of Niue 35 30
185 20 c. Ensign of 1774 and Administration Building 55 65
182/5 .. .. *Set of 4* 1·10 1·25

SELF-GOVERNMENT

(Des A. G. Mitchell. Litho Questa)

1974 (19 Oct). *Self-Government. T* **46** *and similar multicoloured designs. P* 14 × 13½ (4 *and* 8 c.) *or* 13½ × 14 (*others*).
186 4 c. Type **46** 10 10
187 8 c. Annexation Ceremony, 1900 .. .. 10 10
188 10 c. Legislative Assembly Chambers (*horiz*) 10 10
189 20 c. Village meeting (*horiz*) 15 15
186/9 .. .. *Set of 4* 35 30

47 Decorated Bicycles 48 Children going to Church

(Des B. C. Strong. Litho D.L.R.)

1974 (13 Nov). *Christmas. T* **47** *and similar vert designs. P* 12½.
190 3 c. multicoloured 10 10
191 10 c. multicoloured 10 10
192 20 c. dull red-brown, slate and black .. 20 30
190/2 .. .. *Set of 3* 30 40

Designs:—10 c. Decorated motorcycles; 20 c. Motor transport to church.

(Des Enid Hunter. Litho Questa)

1975 (29 Oct). *Christmas. T* **48** *and similar horiz designs. Multicoloured. P* 14.
193 4 c. Type **48** 10 10
194 5 c. Child with balloons on bicycle 10 10
195 10 c. Balloons and gifts on tree 20 20
193/5 .. .. *Set of 3* 30 30

49 Hotel Buildings 50 Preparing Ground for Taro

(Des B. C. Strong. Litho Harrison)

1975 (19 Nov). *Opening of Tourist Hotel. T* **49** *and similar horiz design. Multicoloured. P* 13½ × 13.
196 8 c. Type **49** 10 10
197 20 c. Ground-plan and buildings 20 20

(Des A. G. Mitchell. Litho Questa)

1976 (3 Mar). *T* **50** *and similar horiz designs showing food gathering. Multicoloured. P* 13½ × 14.
198 1 c. Type **50** 10 10
199 2 c. Planting taro 10 10
200 3 c. Banana gathering 10 10
201 4 c. Harvesting taro 10 10
202 5 c. Gathering shell fish 30 10
203 10 c. Reef fishing 20 10
204 20 c. Luku gathering 20 15
205 50 c. Canoe fishing 30 60
206 $1 Coconut husking 35 80
207 $2 Uga gathering .. .. 60 1·40
198/207 .. .. *Set of 10* 1·75 2·75

See also Nos. 249/58 and 264/73.

51 Water 52 Christmas Tree, Alofi

(Des A. G. Mitchell. Litho Questa)

1976 (7 July). *Utilities. T* **51** *and similar vert designs. Multicoloured. P* 14.
208 10 c. Type **51** 10 10
209 15 c. Telecommunications 15 15
210 20 c. Power 15 15
208/10 .. .. *Set of 3* 30 30

(Des A. G. Mitchell. Litho Questa)

1976 (15 Sept). *Christmas. T* **52** *and similar horiz design. Multicoloured. P* 14.
211 9 c. Type **52** 15 15
212 15 c. Church Service, Avatele 15 15

53 Queen Elizabeth II and Westminster Abbey

(Des and photo Heraclio Fournier)

1977 (7 June). *Silver Jubilee. T* **53** *and similar horiz design. Multicoloured. P* 13½.
213 $1 Type **53** 75 50
214 $2 Coronation regalia .. .. .. 1·00 75
MS215 72 × 104 mm. Nos. 213/14 .. .. 1·10 1·60

Stamps from the miniature sheet have a blue border.

OMNIBUS ISSUES

Details, together with prices for complete sets, of the various Omnibus issues from the 1935 Silver Jubilee series to date are included in a special section following Zimbabwe at the end of Volume 2.

54 Child Care **55** "The Annunciation"

(Des R. M. Conly. Litho Questa)

1977 (29 June). *Personal Services. T* **54** *and similar horiz designs. Multicoloured. P* 14½.

216	10 c. Type **54**	15	10
217	15 c. School dental clinic	20	20
218	20 c. Care of the aged	20	20
216/18	.. .. *Set of* 3	50	45

(Des and photo Heraclio Fournier)

1977 (15 Nov). *Christmas. T* **55** *and similar vert designs showing paintings by Rubens. Multicoloured. P* 13.

219	10 c. Type **55**	20	10
220	12 c. "Adoration of the Magi"	20	15
221	20 c. "Virgin in a Garland	35	40
222	35 c. "The Holy Family"	55	90
219/22	.. .. *Set of* 4	1·10	1·40
MS223	82 × 129 mm. Nos. 219/22	1·50	2·25

(**56**)

1977 (15 Nov). *Nos.* 198 *etc.,* 214, 216 *and* 218 *surch as T* **56** *by New Zealand Govt Printer.*

224	12 c. on 1 c. Type **50**	25	25
225	16 c. on 2 c. Planting taro	30	30
226	30 c. on 3 c. Banana gathering	40	40
227	35 c. on 4 c. Harvesting taro	45	45
228	40 c. on 5 c. Gathering shell fish	45	50
229	60 c. on 20 c. Luku gathering	45	55
230	70 c. on $1 Coconut husking	45	55
231	85 c. on $2 Uga gathering	45	60
232	$1.10 on 10 c. Type **54**	45	60
233	$2.60 on 20 c. Care of the aged	50	70
234	$3.20 on $2 Coronation regalia (Gold) ..	60	80
224/34	.. .. *Set of* 11	4·25	5·00

57 "An Island View in Atooi"

(Photo Heraclio Fournier)

1978 (18 Jan). *Bicentenary of Discovery of Hawaii. T* **57** *and similar horiz designs showing paintings by John Webber. Multicoloured. P* 13.

235	12 c. Type **57**	85	40
236	16 c. "View of Karakaooa, in Owhyhee" ..	95	50
237	20 c. "Offering before Capt. Cook in the Sandwich Islands"	1·25	60
238	30 c. "Tereoboo, King of Owhyhee bringing presents to Capt. Cook"	1·40	70
239	35 c. "Canoe in the Sandwich Islands, the rowers masked"	1·50	80
235/9	.. .. *Set of* 5	5·50	2·75
MS240	121 × 121 mm. Nos. 235/9	5·50	2·75

Nos. 235/9 were each printed in small sheets of 6, including 1 *se-tenant* stamp-size label.

58 "The Deposition of Christ" (Caravaggio) **59** Flags of Niue and U.K.

(Photo Heraclio Fournier)

1978 (15 Mar). *Easter. Paintings from the Vatican Galleries. T* **58** *and similar vert design. Multicoloured. P* 13.

241	10 c. Type **58**	30	10
242	20 c. "The Burial of Christ" (Bellini)	60	25
MS243	102 × 68 mm. Nos. 241/2	90	75

1978 (15 Mar). *Easter. Children's Charity. Designs as Nos.* 241/2 *in separate miniature sheets* 64 × 78 *mm, each with a face value of* 70 *c.* + 5 *c. P* 13.

MS244	As Nos. 241/2 .. .. *Set of* 2 *sheets*	1·25	2·00

(Photo Heraclio Fournier)

1978 (26 June). *25th Anniv of Coronation. T* **59** *and similar horiz designs. Multicoloured. A. White border. B. Turquoise-green border. P* 13.

		A		B	
245	$1.10 Type **59**	75	1·00	75	1·00
246	$1.10 Coronation portrait by Cecil Beaton	75	1·00	75	1·00
247	$1.10 Queen's personal flag for New Zealand	75	1·00	75	1·00
245/7	.. .. .. *Set of* 3	2·00	2·75	2·00	2·75
MS248	87 × 98 mm. Nos. 245/7	3·00	2·00	†	

Nos. 245/7 were printed together in small sheets of 6, containing two *se-tenant* strips of 3, with horizontal gutter margin between. The upper strip has white borders, the lower turquoise-green.

(Litho Questa)

1978 (27 Oct). *Designs as Nos.* 198/207 *but margin colours changed and silver frame. P* 13½ × 14.

249	12 c. Type **50**	20	20
250	16 c. Planting taro	20	20
251	30 c. Banana gathering	30	25
252	35 c. Harvesting taro	30	30
253	40 c. Gathering shell fish	40	40
254	60 c. Reef fishing	40	35
255	75 c. Luku gathering	40	40
256	$1.10, Canoe fishing	50	80
257	$3.20, Coconut husking	60	90
258	$4.20, Uga gathering	65	95
249/58	.. .. *Set of* 10	3·50	4·25

See also Nos. 264/73.

60 "Festival of the Rosary"

(Des and photo Heraclio Fournier)

1978 (30 Nov). *Christmas. 450th Death Anniv of Dürer. T* **60** *and similar horiz designs. Multicoloured. P* 13.

259	20 c. Type **60**	40	20
260	30 c. "The Nativity"	50	30
261	35 c. "Adoration of the Magi"	60	35
259/61	.. .. *Set of* 3	1·40	75
MS262	143 × 82 mm. Nos. 259/61	1·50	1·75

Nos. 259/61 were each printed in small sheets of 6.

1978 (30 Nov). *Christmas. Children's Charity. Designs as Nos.* 259/61 *in separate miniature sheets* 74 × 66 *mm., each with a face value of* 60 *c.* + 5 *c. P* 13.

MS263	As Nos. 259/61 .. .. *Set of* 3 *sheets*	1·25	2·00

(Litho Questa)

1979 (26 Feb–28 May). *Air. Designs as Nos.* 249/58 *but gold frames and additionally inscr* "AIRMAIL". *P* 13½ × 14.

264	15 c. Planting taro	20	15
265	20 c. Banana gathering	25	15
266	23 c. Harvesting taro	30	15
267	50 c. Canoe fishing	70	20
268	90 c. Reef fishing	85	35
269	$1.35, Type **50** (30.3)	90	1·50
270	$2.10, Gathering shell fish (30.3)	90	2·25
271	$2.60, Luku gathering (30.3)	90	2·25
272	$5.10, Coconut husking (28.5)	1·00	2·25
273	$6.35, Uga gathering (28.5)	1·00	2·25
264/73	.. .. *Set of* 10	6·25	10·00

PRINTERS. The following stamps were printed in photogravure by Heraclio Fournier, Spain, *except where otherwise stated.*

61 "Pietà" (Gregorio Fernandez) **62** "The Nurse and Child" (Franz Hals)

1979 (2 Apr). *Easter. Paintings. T* **61** *and similar horiz design. Multicoloured. P* 13.

274	30 c. Type **61**	30	25
275	35 c. "Burial of Christ" (Pedro Roldan) ..	35	25
MS276	82 × 82 mm. Nos. 274/5	1·25	1·25

1979 (2 Apr). *Easter. Children's Charity. Designs as Nos.* 274/5 *in separate miniature sheets* 86 × 69 *mm., each with a face value of* 70 *c.* + 5 *c. P* 13.

MS277	As Nos. 274/5 .. .. *Set of* 2 *sheets*	1·10	1·75

1979 (31 May). *International Year of the Child. Details of Paintings. T* **62** *and similar vert designs. Multicoloured. P* 14 × 13½.

278	16 c. Type **62**	30	15
279	20 c. "Child of the Duke of Osuna" (Goya) ..	35	20
280	30 c. "Daughter of Robert Strozzi" (Titian) ..	55	35
281	35 c. "Children eating Fruit" (Murillo) ..	60	40
278/81	.. .. *Set of* 4	1·60	1·00
MS282	80 × 115 mm. Nos. 278/81. P 13	1·60	2·25

1979 (31 May). *International Year of the Child. Children's Charity. Designs as Nos.* 278/81 *in separate miniature sheets* 99 × 119 *mm, each with a face value of* 70 *c.* + 5 *c. P* 13.

MS283	As Nos. 278/81 .. .. *Set of* 4 *sheets*	1·25	1·75

63 Penny Black Stamp **64** Cook's Landing at Botany Bay

1979 (3 July). *Death Centenary of Sir Rowland Hill. T* **63** *and similar vert designs. Multicoloured. P* 14 × 13½.

284	20 c. Type **63**	20	15
285	20 c. Sir Rowland Hill and original Bath mail coach	20	15
286	30 c. Basel 1845 2½ r. stamp	30	20
287	30 c. Rowland Hill and Alpine village coach	30	20
288	35 c. U.S.A. 1847 5 c. stamp	35	25
289	35 c. Sir Rowland Hill and *Washington* (first Transatlantic U.S.A. mail vessel) ..	35	25
290	50 c. France 1849 20 c. stamp	40	35
291	50 c. Sir Rowland Hill and French Post Office railway van, 1849	40	35
292	60 c. Bavaria 1849 1 k. stamp	40	40
293	60 c. Sir Rowland Hill and Bavarian coach with mail	40	40
284/93	.. .. *Set of* 10	3·00	2·50
MS294	143×149 mm. Nos. 284/93	3·50	3·75

Nos. 284/5, 286/7, 288/9, 290/1 and 292/3 were each printed together, *se-tenant,* in horizontal pairs throughout the sheet forming composite designs.

1979 (30 July). *Death Bicentenary of Captain Cook. T* **64** *and similar horiz designs. Multicoloured. P* 14.

295	20 c. Type **64**	55	30
296	30 c. Cook's men during a landing on Erromanga	75	40
297	35 c. H.M.S. *Resolution* and H.M.S. *Discovery* in Queen Charlotte's Sound	85	45
298	75 c. Death of Captain Cook, Hawaii	1·50	70
295/8	.. .. *Set of* 4	3·25	1·75
MS299	104 × 80 mm. Nos. 295/8. P 13½	3·75	3·00

65 Launch of "Apollo 11" **66** "Virgin of Tortosa" (P. Serra)

1979 (27 Sept). *10th Anniv of First Moon Landing. T* **65** *and similar vert designs. Multicoloured. P* 13½.

300	30 c. Type **65**	35	20
301	35 c. Lunar module on Moon	45	25
302	60 c. Sikorsky S-61B SH-3 Sea King helicopter, recovery ship and command module after splashdown	60	40
300/2	.. .. *Set of* 3	1·25	75
MS303	120×82 mm. Nos. 300/2	1·25	1·60

Stamps from No. **MS**303 have the inscription in gold on a blue panel.

1979 (29 Nov). *Christmas. Paintings. T* **66** *and similar vert designs. Multicoloured. P* 13.

304	20 c. Type **66**	10	10
305	25 c. "Virgin with Milk" (R. di Mur)	15	15
306	30 c. "Virgin and Child" (S. di G. Sassetta) ..	20	20
307	50 c. "Virgin and Child" (J. Huguet)	25	25
304/7	.. .. *Set of* 4	60	60
MS308	95 × 113 mm. Nos. 304/7	75	1·25

1979 (29 Nov). *Christmas. Children's Charity. Designs as Nos.* 304/7 *in separate miniature sheets,* 49 × 84 *mm, each with a face value of* 85 *c.* + 5 *c. P* 13.

MS309	As Nos. 304/7 .. .. *Set of* 4 *sheets*	1·25	2·00

HURRICANE
RELIEF
Plus 2c

(**67**)

68 "Pietà" (Bellini)

1980 (25 Jan). *Hurricane Relief. Various stamps surch as T* **67** *in black (Nos.* 310/19) *or silver* (320/30).

(*a*) *Nos.* 284/93 (*Death Centenary of Sir Rowland Hill*)

310	20 c. + 2 c. Type **63**	30	30
311	20 c. + 2 c. Sir Rowland Hill and original Bath mail coach	30	30
312	30 c. + 2 c. Basel 1845 2½ r. stamp	35	35
313	30 c. + 2 c. Sir Rowland Hill and Alpine village coach	35	35
314	35 c. + 2 c. U.S.A. 1847 5 c. stamp	40	40

No.	Description	Unused	Used
315	35 c. + 2 c. Sir Rowland Hill and *Washington* (first Transatlantic U.S.A. mail vessel)	40	40
316	50 c. + 2 c. France 1849 20 c. stamp ..	55	55
317	50 c. + 2 c. Sir Rowland Hill and French Post Office railway van, 1849	55	55
318	60 c. + 2 c. Bavaria 1849 1 k. stamp ..	65	65
319	60 c. + 2 c. Sir Rowland Hill and Bavarian coach with mail	65	65
	(b) Nos. 295/8 (Death Bicentenary of Captain Cook)		
320	20 c. + 2 c. Type **64**	40	40
321	30 c. + 2 c. Cook's men during a landing on Erromanga	50	50
322	35 c. + 2 c. H.M.S. *Resolution* and H.M.S. *Discovery* in Queen Charlotte's Sound ..	55	55
323	75 c. + 2 c. Death of Captain Cook, Hawaii ..	1·00	1·00
	(c) Nos. 300/2 (10th Anniv of First Moon Landing)		
324	30 c. + 2 c. Type **65**	35	35
325	35 c. + 2 c. Lunar module on Moon ..	40	40
326	60 c. + 2 c. Sikorsky S-61B SH-3 Sea King helicopter, recovery ship and command module after splashdown	65	65
	(d) Nos. 304/7 (Christmas)		
327	20 c. + 2 c. Type **66**	25	25
328	25 c. + 2 c. "Virgin with Milk" (R. de Mur) ..	30	30
329	30 c. + 2 c. "Virgin and Child" (S. di G. Sassetta)	35	35
330	50 c. + 2c. "Virgin and Child" (J. Huguet) ..	55	55
310/30	.. .. *Set of* 21	9·00	9·00

On Nos. 310/19 "HURRICANE RELIEF" covers the two designs of each value.

1980 (2 Apr). *Easter. Paintings. T* **68** *and similar horiz designs showing "Pietà" paintings by various artists. Multicoloured. P* 13½ × 13.

No.	Description	Unused	Used
331	25 c. Type **68**	30	15
332	30 c. Botticelli	35	20
333	35 c. Antony van Dyck	35	20
331/3	.. .. *Set of* 3	90	50
MS334	75 × 104 mm. As Nos. 331/3, but each with additional premium of "+ 2 c."	55	90

The premiums on No. **MS**334 were used to support Hurricane Relief.

1980 (2 Apr). *Easter. Hurricane Relief. Designs as Nos.* 331/3 *in separate miniature sheets,* 75 × 52 *mm, each with a face value of* 85 c. + 5 c. *P* 13 × 14.

No.	Description	Unused	Used
MS335	As Nos. 331/3 .. .. *Set of 3 sheets*	1·25	1·75

69 Ceremonial Stool, New Guinea

1980 (30 July). *South Pacific Festival of Arts, New Guinea. T* **69** *and similar vert designs. Multicoloured. P* 13.

No.	Description	Unused	Used
336	20 c. Type **69**	15	15
337	20 c. Ku-Tagwa plaque, New Guinea	15	15
338	20 c. Suspension hook, New Guinea	15	15
339	20 c. Ancestral board, New Guinea	15	15
340	25 c. Platform post, New Hebrides	15	15
341	25 c. Canoe ornament, New Ireland	15	15
342	25 c. Carved figure, Admiralty Islands ..	15	15
343	25 c. Female with child, Admiralty Islands ..	15	15
344	30 c. The God A'a, Rurutu (Austral Islands) ..	15	15
345	30 c. Statue of Tangaroa, Cook Islands ..	15	15
346	30 c. Ivory pendant, Tonga	15	15
347	30 c. Tapa (Hiapo) cloth, Niue	15	15
348	35 c. Feather box (Waka), New Zealand ..	20	20
349	35 c. Hei-Tiki amulet, New Zealand	20	20
350	35 c. House post, New Zealand	20	20
351	35 c. Feather image of god Ku, Hawaii ..	20	20
336/51	.. .. *Set of* 16	2·40	2·40
MS352	Four sheets, each 86 × 124 mm. (a) Nos. 336, 340, 344, 348; (b) Nos. 337, 341, 345, 349; (c) Nos. 338, 342, 346, 350; (d) Nos. 339, 343, 347, 351. Each stamp with an additional premium of 2 c. .. .. .. *Set of 4 sheets*	2·25	2·50

Nos. 336/9, 340/3, 344/7 and 348/51 were each printed together, *se-tenant*, in horizontal strips of 4 throughout the sheet.

NEW ZEALAND STAMP EXHIBITION

ZEAPEX'80 AUCKLAND

(70) (71)

1980 (22 Aug). *"Zeapex '80" International Stamp Exhibition, Auckland. Nos.* 284, 286, 288, 290 *and* 292 *optd with T* **70** *and Nos.* 285, 287, 289, 291 *and* 293 *optd with T* **71**, *both in black on silver background.*

No.	Description	Unused	Used
353	20 c. Type **63**	30	20
354	20 c. Sir Rowland Hill and original Bath mail coach	30	20
355	30 c. Basel 1845 2½ r. stamp	40	25
356	30 c. Sir Rowland Hill and Alpine village coach	40	25
357	35 c. U.S.A. 1847 5 c. stamp	40	25
358	35 c. Sir Rowland Hill and *Washington* (first Transatlantic U.S.A. mail vessel) ..	40	25
359	50 c. France 1849 20 c. stamp	40	30
360	50 c. Sir Rowland Hill and French Post Office railway van, 1849	40	30
361	60 c. Bavaria 1849 1 k. stamp	40	35
362	60 c. Sir Rowland Hill and Bavarian coach with mail	40	35
353/62	.. .. *Set of* 10	3·50	2·50
MS363	143 × 149 mm. Nos. 353/62, each additionally surcharged "+ 2 c."	4·00	3·25

72 Queen Elizabeth the Queen Mother

73 100 Metre Dash

1980 (15 Sept). *80th Birthday of Queen Elizabeth the Queen Mother. P* 13.

No.	Description	Unused	Used
364	**72** $1.10 multicoloured	80	1·50
MS365	55 × 80 mm. **72** $3 multicoloured	1·00	1·75

No. 364 was printed in small sheets of 6 including one *se-tenant* stamp-size label.

1980 (30 Oct). *Olympic Games, Moscow. T* **73** *and similar horiz designs. Multicoloured. P* 14 × 13½.

No.	Description	Unused	Used
366	20 c. Type **73**	20	15
367	20 c. Allen Wells, Great Britain (winner of 100 metre dash)	20	15
368	25 c. } 400 metre freestyle (winner, Ines Diers,	20	20
369	25 c. } D.D.R.)	20	20
370	30 c. } "Soling" Class Yachting (winner,	25	20
371	30 c. } Denmark)	25	20
372	35 c. } Football (winner, Czechoslovakia)	25	25
373	35 c. }	25	25
366/73	.. .. *Set of* 8	1·60	1·40
MS374	119 × 128 mm. Nos. 366/73, each stamp including premium of 2 c.	1·25	1·50

Nos. 366/7, 368/9, 370/1 and 372/3 were each printed together, *se-tenant*, in horizontal pairs throughout the sheet, forming composite designs. On the 25 c. and 35 c. stamps the face value is at right on the first design and at left on the second in each pair. For the 30 c. No. 370 has a yacht with a green sail at left and No. 371 a yacht with a red sail.

74 "The Virgin and Child"

75 *Phalaenopsis sp.*

1980 (28 Nov). *Christmas and 450th Death Anniv of Andrea del Sarto (painter). T* **74** *and similar vert designs showing different "The Virgin and Child" works. P* 13.

No.	Description	Unused	Used
375	20 c. multicoloured	15	15
376	25 c. multicoloured	15	15
377	30 c. multicoloured	20	20
378	35 c. multicoloured	20	20
375/8	.. .. *Set of* 4	60	60
MS379	87 × 112 mm. Nos. 375/8	85	1·25

1980 (28 Nov). *Christmas. Children's Charity. Designs as Nos.* 375/8 *in separate miniature sheets* 62 × 84 *mm, each with a face value of* 80 c. + 5 c. *P* 13.

No.	Description	Unused	Used
MS380	As Nos. 375/8 .. .. *Set of 4 sheets*	1·50	2·00

1981 (2 Apr)–**82**. *Flowers (1st series). Horiz designs as T* **75**. *Multicoloured. P* 13.

No.	Description	Unused	Used
381	2 c. Type **75**	10	10
382	2 c. Moth Orchid	10	10
383	5 c. *Euphorbia pulcherrima*	10	10
384	5 c. Poinsettia	10	10
385	10 c. *Thunbergia alata*	10	10
386	10 c. Black-eyed Susan	10	10
387	15 c. *Cochlospermum hibiscoides*	15	15
388	15 c. Buttercup Tree	15	15
389	20 c. *Begonia sp.*	20	20
390	20 c. Begonia	20	20
391	25 c. *Plumeria sp.*	25	25
392	25 c. Frangipani	25	25
393	30 c. *Strelitzia reginae* (26 May)	30	30
394	30 c. Bird of Paradise (26 May)	30	30
395	35 c. *Hibiscus syriacus* (26 May)	30	30
396	35 c. Rose of Sharon (26 May)	30	30
397	40 c. *Nymphaea sp.* (26 May)	35	35
398	40 c. Water Lily (26 May)	35	35
399	50 c. *Tibouchina sp.* (26 May)	45	45
400	50 c. Princess Flower (26 May)	45	45
401	60 c. *Nelumbo sp.* (26 May)	55	55
402	60 c. Lotus (26 May)	55	55
403	80 c. *Hybrid hibiscus* (26 May)	75	75
404	80 c. Yellow Hibiscus (26 May)	75	75
405	$1 Golden Shower Tree (*Cassia fistula*) (9.12.81)	1·25	1·00
406	$2 *Orchid var.* (9.12.81)	3·50	2·50
407	$3 *Orchid sp.* (9.12.81)	4·50	3·50
408	$4 *Euphorbia pulcherrima poinsettia* (15.1.82)	3·50	4·00
409	$6 *Hybrid hibiscus* (15.1.82)	5·50	6·00
410	$10 Scarlet Hibiscus (*Hibiscus rosasinensis*) (12.3.82)	8·50	9·00
381/410	.. .. *Set of* 30	30·00	30·00

The two designs of the 2 c. to 80 c. show different drawings of the same flower, one inscribed with its name in Latin, the other giving the common name. These were printed together, *se-tenant*, in horizontal and vertical pairs throughout the sheet.

Nos. 405/10 are larger, 47 × 33 mm.

See also Nos. 527/36.

76 "Jesus Defiled" (El Greco)

77 Prince Charles

1981 (10 Apr). *Easter. Details of Paintings. T* **76** *and similar horiz designs. Multicoloured. P* 14.

No.	Description	Unused	Used
425	35 c. Type **76**	40	30
426	50 c. "Pietà" (Fernando Gallego)	60	50
427	60 c. "The Supper of Emmaus" (Jacopo da Pontormo)	65	55
425/7	.. .. *Set of* 3	1·50	1·25
MS428	69 × 111 mm. As Nos. 425/7, but each with charity premium of 2 c. P 13½	1·75	1·75

1981 (10 Apr). *Easter. Children's Charity. Designs as Nos.* 425/7 *in separate miniature sheets* 78 × 86 *mm, each with a face value of* 80 c. + 5 c. *P* 13½ × 14.

No.	Description	Unused	Used
MS429	As Nos. 425/7 .. .. *Set of 3 sheets*	1·50	2·00

1981 (26 June). *Royal Wedding. T* **77** *and similar vert designs. Multicoloured. P* 14.

No.	Description	Unused	Used
430	75 c. Type **77**	35	60
431	95 c. Lady Diana Spencer	60	70
432	$1.20, Prince Charles and Lady Diana ..	65	80
430/2	.. .. *Set of* 3	1·40	1·90
MS433	78 × 85 mm. Nos. 430/2	2·00	2·50

Nos. 430/2 were each printed in small sheets of 6, including one *se-tenant* stamp-size label.

+5c

78 Footballer Silhouettes (**79**)

1981 (16 Oct). *World Cup Football Championship, Spain* (1982). *T* **78** *and similar horiz designs showing footballer silhouettes. P* 13.

No.	Description	Unused	Used
434	30 c. blue-green, gold & new blue (Type **78**) ..	20	20
435	30 c. blue-green, gold and new blue (gold figure 3rd from left of stamp)	20	20
436	30 c. blue-green, gold and new blue (gold figure 4th from left)	20	20
437	35 c. new blue, gold and reddish orange (gold figure 3rd from left)	25	25
438	35 c. new blue, gold and reddish orange (gold figure 4th from left)	25	25
439	35 c. new blue, gold and reddish orange (gold figure 2nd from left)	25	25
440	40 c. reddish orange, gold and blue-green (gold figure 3rd from left, displaying close control)	25	25
441	40 c. reddish orange, gold and blue-green (gold figure 2nd from left)	25	25
442	40 c. reddish orange, gold and blue-green (gold figure 3rd from left, heading)	25	25
434/42	.. .. *Set of* 9	1·90	1·90
MS443	162 × 122 mm. 30 c. + 3 c., 35 c. + 3 c., 40 c. + 3 c. (each × 3). As Nos. 434/42	1·60	2·00

The three designs of each value were printed together, *se-tenant*, in horizontal strips of 3 throughout the sheets.

1981 (3 Nov). *International Year for Disabled Persons. Nos.* 430/3 *surch as T* **79**.

No.	Description	Unused	Used
444	75 c. + 5 c. Type **77**	80	1·25
445	95 c. + 5 c. Lady Diana Spencer	1·00	1·50
446	$1.20 + 5 c. Prince Charles and Lady Diana	1·25	1·75
444/6	.. .. *Set of* 3	2·75	4·00
MS447	78×85 mm. As Nos. 444/6, with each surcharged "+ 10 c."	2·75	5·00

Nos. 444/6 have a commemorative inscription overprinted on the sheet margins.

OMNIBUS ISSUES

Details, together with prices for complete sets, of the various Omnibus issues from the 1935 Silver Jubilee series to date are included in a special section following Zimbabwe at the end of Volume 2.

80 "The Holy Family with Angels" (detail)

81 Prince of Wales

1981 (11 Dec). *Christmas and 375th Birth Anniv of Rembrandt. T* **80** *and similar vert designs. Multicoloured. P* 14 × 13.
448 20 c. Type **80** 65 45
449 35 c. "Presentation in the Temple" 85 55
450 50 c. "Virgin and Child in Temple" .. .. 95 1·10
451 60 c. "The Holy Family" .. .. .. 1·25 1·50
448/51 .. .. *Set of* 4 3·25 3·25
MS452 79 × 112 mm. Nos. 448/51 .. .. .. 3·25 3·50

1982 (22 Jan). *Christmas. Children's Charity. Designs as Nos. 448/51 in separate miniature sheets 66 × 80 mm, each with a face value of* 80 c. + 5 c. *P* 14 × 13.
MS453 As Nos. 448/51 .. .. *Set of* 4 *sheets* 2·00 2·50

1982 (1 July). *21st Birthday of Princess of Wales. T* **81** *and similar horiz designs. Multicoloured. P* 14.
454 50 c. Type **81** 40 55
455 $1.25, Prince and Princess of Wales .. 60 90
456 $2.50, Princess of Wales .. .. .. 1·50 1·40
454/6 .. .. *Set of* 3 2·25 2·50
MS457 81 × 101 mm. Nos. 454/6 .. .. .. 4·00 3·50
Nos. 454/6 were each printed in small sheets of 6 including one *se-tenant* stamp-size label.
The stamps from No. **MS**457 are without white borders.

(82)

83 Infant

1982 (23 July). *Birth of Prince William of Wales (1st issue). Nos. 430/3 optd as T* **82**.
458 75 c. Type **77** (optd with T **82**).. .. .. 2·25 2·00
a. Pair. Nos. 458/9 .. .. .. 4·50 4·00
459 75 c. Type **77** (optd "BIRTH OF PRINCE WILLIAM OF WALES 21 JUNE 1982") 2·25 2·00
460 95 c. Lady Diana Spencer (optd with T **82**) .. 3·50 2·50
a. Pair. Nos. 460/1 .. .. .. 7·00 5·00
461 95 c. Lady Diana Spencer (optd "BIRTH OF PRINCE WILLIAM OF WALES 21 JUNE 1982") .. .. .. 3·50 2·50
462 $1.20, Prince Charles and Lady Diana Spencer (optd with T **82**) .. .. 3·50 2·75
a. Pair. Nos. 462/3 .. .. .. 7·00 5·50
463 $1.20, Prince Charles and Lady Diana Spencer (optd "BIRTH OF PRINCE WILLIAM OF WALES 21 JUNE 1982") 3·50 2·75
458/63 .. .. *Set of* 6 17·00 13·00
MS464 78 × 85 mm. Nos. 430/2 each optd "PRINCE WILLIAM OF WALES 21 JUNE 1982" .. .. 7·00 6·00
Nos. 458/9, 460/1 and 462/3 were each printed *se-tenant* in small sheets of 6, containing three stamps overprinted with Type **82**, two with "BIRTH OF PRINCE WILLIAM OF WALES 21 JUNE 1982" and one stamp-size label.

1982 (10 Sept). *Birth of Prince William of Wales (2nd issue). Designs as Nos. 454/7 but with changed inscriptions. Multicoloured. P* 14.
465 50 c. Type **81** 45 55
466 $1.25, Prince and Princess of Wales .. 85 1·00
467 $2.50, Princess of Wales .. .. .. 2·00 1·75
465/7 .. .. *Set of* 3 3·00 3·00
MS468 81 × 101 mm. As Nos. 465/7 .. .. 5·00 5·00
Nos. 465/7 were each printed in small sheets of 6 including one *se-tenant*, stamp-size, label.

1982 (3 Dec). *Christmas. Paintings of Infants by Bronzino, Murillo and Boucher. T* **83** *and similar horiz designs. P* 13 × 14½.
469 40 c. multicoloured 80 35
470 52 c. multicoloured 90 45
471 83 c. multicoloured .. .. 1·75 1·00
472 $1.05, multicoloured .. .. 1·90 1·10
469/72 .. .. *Set of* 4 4·75 2·50
MS473 110 × 76 mm. Designs as Nos. 469/72 (*each* 31 × 27 *mm*), but without portrait of Princess and Prince William. P 13½ .. .. 2·75 2·75

MINIMUM PRICE

The minimum price quote is 10p which represents a handling charge rather than a basis for valuing common stamps. For further notes about prices see introductory pages.

84 Prince and Princess of Wales with Prince William

85 Prime Minister Robert Rex

1982 (3 Dec). *Christmas. Children's Charity. Sheet* 72 × 58 *mm. P* 13 × 13½.
MS474 **84** 80 c. + 5 c. multicoloured .. .. 1·25 1·25
No. **MS**474 occurs with four different designs in the sheet margin.

1983 (14 Mar). *Commonwealth Day. T* **85** *and similar horiz designs. Multicoloured. P* 13.
475 70 c. Type **85** 65 70
476 70 c. H.M.S. *Resolution* and H.M.S. *Adventure* off Niue, 1774 .. .. .. 65 70
477 70 c. Passion flower 65 70
478 70 c. Limes 65 70
475/8 .. .. *Set of* 4 2·40 2·50
Nos. 475/8 were issued together, *se-tenant*, in blocks of four throughout the sheet.

86 Scouts signalling

XV WORLD JAMBOREE CANADA
(87)

1983 (28 Apr). *75th Anniv of Boy Scout Movement and 125th Birth Anniv of Lord Baden-Powell. T* **86** *and similar vert designs. Multicoloured. P* 13.
479 40 c. Type **86** 35 40
480 50 c. Planting sapling 45 50
481 83 c. Map-reading 85 90
479/81 .. .. *Set of* 3 1·50 1·60
MS482 137 × 90 mm. As Nos. 479/81, but each with premium of 3 c. .. .. 1·60 1·75

1983 (14 July). *15th World Scout Jamboree, Alberta, Canada. Nos. 479/82 optd with T* **87**, *in black on silver background.*
483 40 c. Type **86** 35 40
484 50 c. Planting sapling 45 50
485 83 c. Map-reading 85 90
483/5 .. .. *Set of* 3 1·50 1·60
MS486 137 × 90 mm. As Nos. 483/5, but each with premium of 3 c. .. .. 1·60 1·75

88 Black Right Whale

1983 (15 Aug). *Protect the Whales. T* **88** *and similar horiz designs. Multicoloured. P* 13 × 14.
487 12 c. Type **88** 75 65
488 25 c. Fin Whale 95 80
489 35 c. Sei Whale .. .. 1·50 1·25
490 40 c. Blue Whale .. .. 1·75 1·50
491 58 c. Bowhead Whale .. .. 1·90 1·60
492 70 c. Sperm Whale .. .. 2·25 1·75
493 83 c. Humpback Whale .. .. 2·50 2·25
494 $1.05, Minke Whale ("Lesser Rorqual") .. 3·00 2·50
495 $2.50, Grey Whale .. .. 4·25 4·00
487/95 .. .. *Set of* 9 17·00 15·00

89 Montgolfier Balloon, 1783

90 "The Garvagh Madonna"

1983 (14 Oct). *Bicentenary of Manned Flight. T* **89** *and similar horiz designs. Multicoloured. (a) Postage. P* 13½.
496 25 c. Type **89** 35 25
497 40 c. Wright Brothers Flyer 1, 1903 .. .. 65 45
498 58 c. Airship LZ-127 *Graf Zeppelin*, 1928 .. 80 60
499 70 c. Boeing 247, 1933 .. .. 1·00 75
500 83 c. "Apollo 8", 1968 .. .. 1·25 90
501 $1.05, Space shuttle *Columbia*, 1982 .. 1·40 1·10
496/501 .. .. *Set of* 6 5·00 3·50
(*b*) *Air. Inscr* "AIRMAIL"
MS502 118 × 130 mm. Nos. 496/501. P 13 .. 3·00 3·25

1983 (25 Nov). *Christmas. 500th Birth Anniv of Raphael. T* **90** *and similar vert designs. Multicoloured. P* 14 × 13½.
503 30 c. Type **90** 30 30
504 40 c. "Madonna of the Granduca" 35 35
505 58 c. "Madonna of the Goldfinch" 55 50
506 70 c. "The Holy Family of Francis I" 70 60
507 83 c. "The Holy Family with Saints" 85 70
503/7 .. .. *Set of* 5 2·50 2·25
MS508 120 × 114 mm. As Nos. 503/7 but each with a premium of 3 c. .. .. 3·00 2·75

83c
=
(90a)

1983 (30 Nov). *Various stamps surch as T* **90a**.
(*a*) *Nos.* 393/4, 399/404 *and* 407
509 52 c. on 30 c. *Strelitzia reginae* 60 45
510 52 c. on 30 c. Bird of Paradise 60 45
511 58 c. on 50 c. *Tibouchina sp.* 70 55
512 58 c. on 50 c. Princess Flower 70 55
513 70 c. on 60 c. *Nelumbo sp.* 75 60
514 70 c. on 60 c. Lotus 75 60
515 83 c. on 80 c. *Hybrid hibiscus* 90 75
516 83 c. on 80 c. Yellow Hibiscus 90 75
517 $3.70 on $3 *Orchid sp.* .. .. .. 5·00 3·25
(*b*) *Nos.* 431/2 *and* 455/6
518 $1.10 on 95 c. Lady Diana Spencer .. 2·50 2·25
a. Error. Surch on No. 458 .. .. 6·00 6·00
ab. Pair. Nos. 518a/b .. .. .. 13·00 13·00
b. Error. Surch on No. 459 .. .. 7·00 7·00
519 $1.10 on $1.25, Prince and Princess of Wales (Gold on Blk.) .. .. .. 2·00 2·00
520 $2.60 on $1.20, Prince Charles and Lady Diana .. .. 4·00 3·50
a. Error. Surch on No. 462 .. .. 6·00 6·00
ab. Pair. Nos. 520a/b .. .. .. 13·00 13·00
b. Error. Surch on No. 463 .. .. 7·00 7·00
521 $2.60 on $2.50, Princess of Wales (Gold on Blk.) .. .. 2·75 3·25
509/21 .. .. *Set of* 13 20·00 17·00

1983 (29 Dec). *Christmas. 500th Birth Anniv of Raphael. Children's Charity. Designs as Nos. 503/7 in separate miniature sheets, 65 × 80 mm, each with face value of* 85 c. + 5 c. *P* 13½.
MS522 As Nos. 503/7 .. .. *Set of* 5 *sheets* 2·25 2·75

91 Morse Key Transmitter

92 *Phalaenopsis sp.*

1984 (23 Jan). *World Communications Year. T* **91** *and similar vert designs. Multicoloured. P* 13 × 13½.
523 40 c. Type **91** 30 35
524 52 c. Wall-mounted phone 40 45
525 83 c. Communications satellite 60 65
523/5 .. .. *Set of* 3 1·10 1·25
MS526 114 × 90 mm. Nos. 523/5 .. .. .. 1·10 1·50

1984 (20 Feb–23 July). *Flowers (2nd series). Designs as Nos. 381 etc., but with gold frames and redrawn inscr as in T* **92**. *Multicoloured. P* 13 (*Nos.* 537/42) *or* 13 × 13½ (*others*).
527 12 c. Type **92** 25 15
528 25 c. *Euphorbia pulcherrima* 35 20
529 30 c. *Cochlospermum hibiscoides* 40 25
530 35 c. *Begonia sp.* 40 25
531 40 c. *Plumeria sp.* 50 30
532 52 c. *Strelitzia reginae* 65 40
533 58 c. *Hibiscus syriacus* 70 45
534 70 c. *Tibouchina sp.* .. .. .. 1·00 60
535 83 c. *Nelumbo sp.* .. .. 1·10 70
536 $1.05, *Hybrid hibiscus* .. .. .. 1·25 85
537 $1.75, *Cassia fistula* (10.5) .. .. 2·00 1·50
538 $2.30, *Orchid var.* (10.5) .. .. .. 3·50 2·00
539 $3.90, *Orchid sp.* (10.5) .. .. .. 5·00 4·00
540 $5 *Euphorbia pulcherrima poinsettia* (18.6) 6·50 4·50
541 $6.60, *Hybrid hibiscus* (18.6) .. .. 7·00 6·00
542 $8.30, *Hibiscus rosasinensis* (23.7) .. 8·00 7·00
527/42 .. .. *Set of* 16 35·00 26·00
Nos. 537/42 are larger, 39 × 31 mm.

93 Discus-throwing

94 Koala

1984 (15 Mar). *Olympic Games, Los Angeles. T* **93** *and similar multicoloured designs showing ancient Greek sports. P* 14.

547 30 c. Type **93** 25 30
548 35 c. Sprinting (*horiz*) 30 35
549 40 c. Horse racing (*horiz*) 35 40
550 58 c. Boxing (*horiz*) 50 55
551 70 c. Javelin-throwing 60 65
547/51 *Set of* 5 1·75 2·00

1984 (24 Aug). *"Ausipex" International Stamp Exhibition, Melbourne* (1*st issue*). *P* 14. (*a*) *Postage. Vert designs as T* **94** *showing Koala Bears.*

552 25 c. multicoloured 60 30
553 35 c. multicoloured 65 35
554 40 c. multicoloured 70 40
555 58 c. multicoloured 90 65
556 70 c. multicoloured 1·10 75

(*b*) *Air. Vert designs showing Red Kangaroos*

557 83 c. multicoloured 1·25 85
558 $1.05, multicoloured 1·50 1·25
559 $2.50, multicoloured 3·00 3·50
552/9 *Set of* 8 8·75 7·25
MS560 110 × 64 mm. $1.75, Wallaby; $1.75, Koala Bear. P 13½ 4·00 4·00
See also Nos. **MS**566/7.

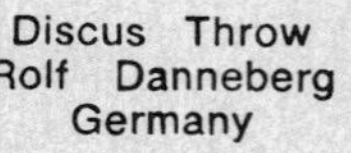

(**95**)

96 Niue National Flag and Premier Sir Robert Rex

1984 (7 Sept). *Olympic Gold Medal Winners, Los Angeles. Nos.* 547/51 *optd as T* **95** *in red* (35 *c.*) *or gold* (*others*).

561 30 c. Type **93** (opt T **95**) 25 30
562 35 c. Sprinting (optd "1,500 Metres Sebastian Coe Great Britain") 30 35
563 40 c. Horse racing (optd "Equestrian Mark Todd New Zealand") 30 35
564 58 c. Boxing (optd "Boxing Tyrell Biggs United States") 45 50
565 70 c. Javelin-throwing (optd "Javelin Throw Arto Haerkoenen Finland") 55 60
561/5 *Set of* 5 1·75 1·90

1984 (20 Sept). *"Ausipex" International Stamp Exhibition, Melbourne* (2*nd issue*). *Designs as Nos.* 552/60 *in miniature sheets of six or four. Multicoloured. P* 13½.

MS566 109 × 105 mm. Nos. 552/6 and $1.75, Koala Bear (as No. **MS**560) 4·50 3·50
MS567 80 × 105 mm. Nos. 557/9 and $1.75, Wallaby (as No. **MS**560) 6·00 4·75

1984 (19 Oct). 10*th Anniv of Self-Government. T* **96** *and similar horiz designs. Multicoloured. P* 13.

568 40 c. Type **96** 40 35
569 58 c. Map of Niue and Premier Rex 60 50
570 70 c. Premier Rex receiving proclamation of self-government 65 60
568/70 *Set of* 3 1·50 1·25
MS571 110 × 83 mm. Nos. 568/70 1·50 1·75
MS572 100 × 74 mm. $2.50, As 70 c. (50 × 30 *mm*) 1·75 1·90

$2
Prince Henry
IIII
IIII
15. 9. 84

(**97**)

98 "The Nativity" (A. Vaccaro)

1984 (22 Oct). *Birth of Prince Henry. Nos.* 430 *and* 454 *optd as T* **97**.

573 $2 on 50 c. Type **81** (Sil.) 2·50 1·75
574 $2 on 75 c. Type **77** (R.) 2·50 1·75

1984 (23 Nov). *Christmas. T* **98** *and similar vert designs. Multicoloured. P* 13 × 13½.

575 40 c. Type **98** 30 35
576 58 c. "Virgin with Fly" (anon, 16th-century) 45 50
577 70 c. "The Adoration of the Shepherds" (B. Murillo) 55 60
578 83 c. "Flight into Egypt" (B. Murillo) 65 70
575/8 *Set of* 4 1·75 1·90
MS579 115 × 111 mm. As Nos. 575/8 but each stamp with a 5 c. premium 2·25 2·25
MS580 Four sheets, each 66 × 98 mm. As Nos. 575/8, but each stamp 30 × 42 mm. with a face value of 95 c. + 10 c. P 13½ *Set of 4 sheets* 2·75 3·00

99 House Wren

1985 (15 Apr). *Birth Bicentenary of John J. Audubon* (*ornithologist*). *T* **99** *and similar horiz designs showing original paintings. Multicoloured. P* 14.

581 40 c. Type **99** 2·50 85
582 70 c. Veery 2·75 1·40
583 83 c. Grasshopper Sparrow 3·00 1·75
584 $1.05, Henslow's Sparrow 3·25 1·75
585 $2.50, Vesper Sparrow 4·50 3·50
581/5 *Set of* 5 14·50 8·25
MS586 Five sheets, each 54 × 60 mm. As Nos. 581/5 but each stamp 34 × 26 mm with a face value of $1.75 and without the commemorative inscription *Set of 5 sheets* 10·00 8·50

100 The Queen Mother in Garter Robes

1985 (14 June). *Life and Times of Queen Elizabeth the Queen Mother. T* **100** *and similar horiz designs. Multicoloured. P* 13.

587 70 c. Type **100** 55 60
588 $1.15, In open carriage with the Queen 80 95
589 $1.50, With Prince Charles during 80th birthday celebrations 90 1·25
587/9 *Set of* 3 2·00 2·50
MS590 70 × 70 mm. $3 At her desk in Clarence House (38 × 35 *mm*) 2·75 2·50
Nos. 587/9 were each issued in sheetlets of five stamps and one stamp-size label at top left, showing the Queen Mother's arms.
For Nos. 587/9 in miniature sheet see No. **MS**627.

52
c

(**101**)

1985 (26 July). *South Pacific Mini Games, Rarotonga. Nos.* 547/8 *and* 550/1 *surch as T* **101** *in black and gold.*

591 52 c. on 70 c. Javelin-throwing 40 45
592 83 c. on 58 c. Boxing 65 70
593 95 c. on 35 c. Sprinting 75 80
594 $2 on 30 c. Type **93** 1·50 1·60
591/4 *Set of* 4 3·00 3·25
On Nos. 591/4 the new face values and inscriptions are surcharged in black on gold panels. The Games emblem is in gold only.

PACIFIC ISLANDS CONFERENCE, RAROTONGA

(**102**)

103 "R. Strozzi's Daughter" (Titian)

1985 (26 July). *Pacific Islands Conference, Rarotonga. Nos.* 475/8 *optd with T* **102** *in black on silver.*

595 70 c. Type **85** 55 60
596 70 c. *Resolution* and *Adventure* off Niue, 1774 55 60
597 70 c. Passion flower 55 60
598 70 c. Limes 55 60
595/8 *Set of* 4 2·00 2·25
No. 595 also shows an overprinted amendment to the caption which now reads "Premier Sir Robert Rex K.B.E.".

1985 (11 Oct). *International Youth Year. T* **103** *and similar vert designs. Multicoloured. P* 13.

599 58 c. Type **103** 1·00 90
600 70 c. "The Fifer" (E. Manet) 1·25 1·00
601 $1.15, "Portrait of a Young Girl" (Renoir) 1·90 1·90
602 $1.50, "Portrait of M. Berard" (Renoir) 2·25 2·50
599/602 *Set of* 4 5·75 5·75
MS603 Four sheets, each 63 × 79 mm. As Nos. 599/602 but each with a face value of $1.75 + 10 c. *Set of 4 sheets* 10·00 10·00

104 "Virgin and Child"

1985 (29 Nov). *Christmas. Details of Paintings by Correggio. T* **104** *and similar vert designs. Multicoloured. P* 13 × 13½.

604 58 c. Type **104** 1·25 85
605 85 c. "Adoration of the Magi" 1·60 1·25
606 $1.05, "Virgin with Child and St. John" 2·00 2·25
607 $1.45, "Virgin and Child with St. Catherine" 2·50 3·00
604/7 *Set of* 4 6·50 6·50
MS608 83 × 123 mm. As Nos. 604/7, but each stamp with a face value of 60 c. + 10 c. 3·00 2·75
MS609 Four sheets, each 80 × 90 mm. 65 c. Type **104**; 95 c. As No. 605; $1.20, As No. 606; $1.75, As No. 607 (each stamp 49 × 59 mm). Imperf *Set of 4 sheets* 4·00 4·00

105 "The Constellations" (detail)

106 Queen Elizabeth II and Prince Philip

1986 (24 Jan). *Appearance of Halley's Comet. T* **105** *and similar horiz designs showing details from ceiling painting "The Constellations" by Giovanni de Vecchi. Nos.* 611/13 *show different spacecraft at top left. P* 13½.

610 60 c. multicoloured 50 50
611 75 c. multicoloured (*Vega* spacecraft) 65 65
612 $1.10, multicoloured (*Planet A* spacecraft) 90 90
613 $1.50, multicoloured (*Giotto* spacecraft) 1·25 1·25
610/13 *Set of* 4 3·00 3·00
MS614 125 × 91 mm. As Nos. 610/13 but each stamp with a face value of 95 c. 4·25 4·25
Stamps from No. **MS**614 are without borders.

1986 (28 Apr). 60*th Birthday of Queen Elizabeth II. T* **106** *and similar vert designs. Multicoloured. P* 14½ × 13.

615 $1.10, Type **106** 70 1·00
616 $1.50, Queen and Prince Philip at Balmoral 90 1·25
617 $2 Queen at Buckingham Palace 1·25 1·75
615/17 *Set of* 3 2·50 3·50
MS618 110 × 70 mm. As Nos. 615/17, but each stamp with a face value of 75 c. 2·75 3·25
MS619 58 × 89 mm. $3 Queen and Prince Philip at Windsor Castle 3·50 4·25

107 U.S.A. 1847 Franklin 5 c. Stamp and Washington Sculpture, Mt. Rushmore, U.S.A.

108 "Statue under Construction, Paris, 1883" (Victor Dargaud)

1986 (22 May). *"Ameripex '86" International Stamp Exhibition, Chicago. T* **107** *and similar vert design. Multicoloured. P* 14.
620 $1 Type **107** .. .. 2·50 2·50
a. Horiz pair. Nos. 620/1 .. .. .. 5·00 5·00
621 $1 Flags of Niue and U.S.A. and Mt. Rushmore sculptures .. .. 2·50 2·50
Nos. 620/1 were printed together, *se-tenant*, in horizontal pairs, within sheetlets of 8 stamps, each pair forming a composite design.

1986 (4 July). *Centenary of Statue of Liberty (1st issue). T* **108** *and similar vert design. Multicoloured. P* 13 × 13½.
622 $1 Type **108** .. .. 2·00 2·00
623 $2.50, "Unveiling of the Statue of Liberty" (Edmund Morand).. .. .. .. 2·75 2·75
MS624 107 × 73 mm. As Nos. 622/3, but each stamp with a face value of $1.25 .. .. 2·50 3·00
See also No. **MS**648.

109 Prince Andrew, Miss Sarah Ferguson and Westminster Abbey

1986 (23 July). *Royal Wedding. T* **109** *and similar horiz design. Multicoloured. P* 13½ × 13.
625 $2.50, Type **109** .. .. 2·75 3·00
MS626 106 × 68 mm. $5 Prince Andrew and Miss Sarah Ferguson (43 × 30 *mm*) .. .. .. 7·50 7·50

1986 (4 Aug). *86th Birthday of Queen Elizabeth the Queen Mother. Nos. 587/9 in miniature sheet,* 109 × 83 *mm. P* 13.
MS627 Nos. 587/9 .. .. 7·50 8·50

110 Great Egret

111 "Virgin and Child" (Perugino)

1986 (4 Aug). *"Stampex '86" Stamp Exhibition, Adelaide. Australian Birds. T* **110** *and similar multicoloured designs. P* 13 × 13½ (40, 75 *c.*, $1, $2.20) *or* 13½ × 13 (*others*).
628 40 c. Type **110** .. .. 2·50 1·75
629 60 c. Painted Finch (*horiz*) .. .. .. 2·75 2·00
630 75 c. Australian King Parrot .. .. .. 3·00 2·25
631 80 c. Variegated Wren (*horiz*) .. .. .. 3·25 2·50
632 $1 Peregrine Falcon .. .. 3·75 2·75
633 $1.65, Azure Kingfisher (*horiz*) .. .. .. 5·00 4·00
634 $2.20, Budgerigars.. .. .. 6·00 6·00
635 $4.25, Emu (*horiz*) .. .. 7·50 7·50
628/35 .. .. *Set of* 8 30·00 26·00

1986 (14 Nov). *Christmas. Paintings from the Vatican Museum. T* **111** *and similar vert designs. Multicoloured. P* 14.
636 80 c. Type **111**.. .. .. 2·00 1·75
637 $1.15, "Virgin of St. N. dei Frari" (Titian) 2·25 2·00
638 $1.80, "Virgin with Milk" (Lorenzo di Credi) .. .. 3·25 3·50
639 $2.60, "Madonna of Foligno" (Raphael) .. 4·00 4·50
636/9 .. .. *Set of* 4 10·50 10·50
MS640 87 × 110 mm. As Nos. 636/9, but each stamp with a face value of $1.50. P 13½ .. 7·50 5·50
MS641 70 × 100 mm. $7.50, As No. 639, but 27 × 43 mm. P 14½ × 13 .. .. 7·50 8·50

+10c

(112)

1986 (21 Nov). *Visit of Pope John Paul II to South Pacific. Nos. 636/41 surch as T* **112** *in black on silver.*
642 80 c. + 10 c. Type **111** .. .. 2·25 2·25
643 $1.15 + 10 c. "Virgin of St. N. dei Frari" (Titian) .. .. 2·75 2·75
644 $1.80 + 10 c. "Virgin with Milk" (Lorenzo di Credi).. .. .. 3·75 3·75
645 $2.60 + 10 c. "Madonna of Foligno" (Raphael) .. .. 4·50 4·50
642/5 .. .. *Set of* 4 12·00 12·00
MS646 87 × 110 mm. As Nos. 642/5, but each stamp with a face value of $1.50 + 10 c.. .. 9·50 10·00
MS647 70 × 100 mm. $7.50 + 50 c. As No. 645, but 27 × 43 mm .. .. 9·50 10·00

1987 (20 May). *Centenary of Statue of Liberty (1986) (2nd issue). Two sheets, each* 122 × 122 *mm, containing multicoloured designs as T* **63** *of Cook Islands (Penrhyn). Litho. P* 13½ × 14 (*horiz*) *or* 14 × 13½ (*vert*).
MS648 Two sheets. (a) 75 c. Sailing ship under Brooklyn Bridge; 75 c. Restoring Statue's flame; 75 c. Steam-cleaning Statue's torch; 75 c. *Esmerelda* (Chilean cadet barquentine) off Manhattan; 75 c. Cadet barque at dusk. (b) 75 c. Statue of Liberty at night (*vert*); 75 c. Statue at night (side view) (*vert*); 75 c. Cleaning Statue's crown (*vert*); 75 c. Statue at night (rear view) (*vert*); 75 c. Cleaning a finial (*vert*) *Set of* 2 *sheets* 4·25 5·50

113 Boris Becker, Olympic Rings and Commemorative Coin

(Des G. Vasarhelyi. Litho Questa)

1987 (25 Sept). *Olympic Games, Seoul (1988). Tennis (1st issue). T* **113** *and similar horiz designs showing Boris Becker in play. P* 13½ × 14.
649 80 c. multicoloured .. .. 1·75 1·75
650 $1.15, multicoloured .. .. 2·00 2·00
651 $1.40, multicoloured .. .. 2·25 2·25
652 $1.80, multicoloured .. .. 2·75 2·75
649/52 .. .. *Set of* 4 8·00 8·00

(Des G. Vasarhelyi. Litho Questa)

1987 (20 Oct). *Olympic Games, Seoul (1988). Tennis (2nd issue). Horiz designs as T* **113**, *but showing Steffi Graf. P* 13½ × 14.
653 85 c. multicoloured .. .. 1·25 1·25
654 $1.05, multicoloured .. .. 1·50 1·50
655 $1.30, multicoloured .. .. 1·75 1·75
656 $1.75, multicoloured .. .. 2·00 2·00
653/6 .. .. *Set of* 4 6·00 6·00

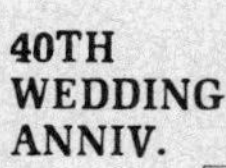

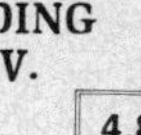

(114)

115 "The Nativity"

1987 (20 Nov). *Royal Ruby Wedding. Nos. 616/17 optd with T* **114**.
657 $4.85 on $1.50, Queen and Prince Philip at Balmoral .. .. 3·50 4·50
658 $4.85 on $2 Queen at Buckingham Palace .. 3·50 4·50
On Nos. 657/8 the original values are obliterated in gold.

1987 (4 Dec). *Christmas. Religious Paintings by Dürer. T* **115** *and similar horiz designs. Multicoloured. P* 13½.
659 80 c. Type **115**.. .. .. 1·50 1·25
660 $1.05, "Adoration of the Magi" .. .. 1·75 1·75
661 $2.80, "Celebration of the Rosary" .. 3·25 3·50
659/61 .. .. *Set of* 3 6·00 6·00
MS662 100 × 140 mm. As Nos. 659/61, but each size 48 × 37 mm with a face value of $1.30 .. 4·50 4·25
MS663 90 × 80 mm. $7.50, As No. 661, but size 51 × 33 mm .. .. 6·50 7·00
Nos. 659/61 each include a detail of an angel with lute as in T **115**. Stamps from the miniature sheets are without this feature.

116 Franz Beckenbauer in Action

(Des G. Vasarhelyi. Litho Questa)

1988 (20 June). *West German Football Victories. T* **116** *and similar horiz designs. Multicoloured. P* 13½ × 14.
664 20 c. Type **116** 70 70
665 40 c. German "All Star" team in action .. 90 90
666 60 c. Bayern Munich team with European Cup, 1974 .. .. 1·10 1·10
667 80 c. World Cup match, England, 1966 .. 1·40 1·40
668 $1.05, World Cup match, Mexico, 1970 .. 1·60 1·60
669 $1.30, Beckenbauer with pennant, 1974 2·00 2·00
670 $1.80, Beckenbauer and European Cup, 1974 .. .. 2·25 2·25
664/70 .. .. *Set of* 7 9·00 9·00

NEW INFORMATION

The editor is always interested to correspond with people who have new information that will improve or correct the Catalogue.

Australia 24 Jan 88
French Open 4 June 88

(117)

118 Angels

1988 (14 Oct). *Steffi Graf's Tennis Victories. Nos. 653/6 optd as T* **117**.
671 85 c. multicoloured (optd with T **117**) .. 1·25 1·25
672 $1.05, mult (optd "Wimbledon 2 July 88 U S Open 10 Sept. 88") .. .. 1·50 1·50
673 $1.30, mult (optd "Women's Tennis Grand Slam: 10 September 88") .. .. 1·75 1·75
674 $1.75, multicoloured (optd "Seoul Olympic Games Gold Medal Winner") .. .. 1·90 1·90
671/4 .. .. *Set of* 4 5·75 5·75

1988 (28 Oct). *Christmas. T* **118** *and similar vert designs showing details from "The Adoration of the Shepherds" by Rubens. Multicoloured. P* 13½.
675 60 c. Type **118** .. .. 1·25 1·25
676 80 c. Shepherds .. .. 1·60 1·60
677 $1.05, Virgin Mary .. .. 2·25 2·25
678 $1.30, Holy Child .. .. 2·50 2·50
675/8 .. .. *Set of* 4 7·00 7·00
MS679 83 × 103 mm. $7.20, The Nativity (38 × 49 *mm*) .. .. 6·00 7·00

119 Astronaut and "Apollo 11" Emblem

(Des G. Vasarhelyi)

1989 (20 July). *20th Anniv of First Manned Landing on Moon. T* **119** *and similar horiz designs. Multicoloured. P* 14.
680 $1.50, Type **119** .. .. 3·25 3·25
a. Horiz strip of 3. Nos. 680/2 .. .. 8·75
681 $1.50, Earth and Moon .. .. .. 3·25 3·25
682 $1.50, Astronaut and "Apollo 1" emblem 3·25 3·25
680/2 .. .. *Set of* 3 8·75 8·75
MS683 160 × 64 mm. As Nos. 680/2, but each stamp with a face value of $1.15. P 13 .. 4·25 4·25
Nos. 680/2 were printed together, *se-tenant*, in horizontal strips of 3 throughout the sheet.

120 Priests

1989 (22 Nov). *Christmas. T* **120** *and similar multicoloured designs showing details from "Presentation in the Temple" by Rembrandt. P* 13.
684 70 c. Type **120** .. .. 1·75 1·75
685 80 c. Virgin and Christ Child in Simeon's arms .. .. 1·75 1·75
686 $1.05, Joseph .. .. 2·25 2·25
687 $1.30, Simeon and Christ Child .. .. 2·50 2·50
684/7 .. .. *Set of* 4 7·50 7·50
MS688 84 × 110 mm. $7.20, "Presentation in the Temple" (39 × 49 *mm*). P 13½ .. .. .. 9·50 10·00

121 Fritz Walter

1990 (5 Feb). *World Cup Football Championship, Italy. German Footballers. T* **121** *and similar horiz designs. Multicoloured. P* 13½ × 13.
689 80 c. Type **121** .. .. 2·25 2·25
690 $1.15, Franz Beckenbauer .. .. .. 2·50 2·50
691 $1.40, Uwe Seeler .. .. 2·75 2·75
692 $1.80, German team emblem and signatures of former captains .. .. .. 3·50 3·50
689/92 .. .. *Set of* 4 10·00 10·00

122 "Merchant Maarten Looten" (Rembrandt)

123 Queen Elizabeth the Queen Mother

1990 (2 May). *150th Anniv of the Penny Black. T* **122** *and similar vert designs showing Rembrandt paintings. Multicoloured. P* 13½.

693 80 c. Type **122** .. .. 2·00 2·00
694 $1.05, "Rembrandt's Son Titus with Pen in Hand" .. .. 2·25 2·25
695 $1.30, "The Shipbuilder and his Wife" .. 2·50 2·50
696 $1.80, "Bathsheba with King David's Letter" .. .. 2·75 2·75
693/6 .. .. .. *Set of* 4 8·50 8·50
MS697 82×143 mm. As Nos. 693/6, but each with a face value of $1.50 .. .. .. 7·50 7·50

1990 (23 July). *90th Birthday of Queen Elizabeth the Queen Mother. P* 13×13½.

698 **123** $1.25, multicoloured .. .. .. 3·50 3·75
MS699 84×64 mm. **123** $7 multicoloured .. 11·00 11·00

124 "Adoration of the Magi" (Dirk Bouts)

(125)

(Litho Questa)

1990 (27 Nov). *Christmas. Religious Paintings. T* **124** *and similar vert designs. Multicoloured. P* 14.

700 70 c. Type **124** .. .. 1·75 1·50
701 80 c. "Holy Family" (Fra Bartolommeo) .. 2·00 1·75
702 $1.05, "Nativity" (Memling) .. .. 2·25 2·25
703 $1.30, "Adoration of the Kings" (Bruegel the Elder) .. .. .. 2·50 3·00
700/3 .. .. .. *Set of* 4 7·75 7·75
MS704 100×135 mm. $7.20, "Virgin and Child Enthoned" (detail, Cosimo Tura) .. .. 8·50 10·00

1990 (5 Dec). *"Birdpex '90" Stamp Exhibition, Christchurch, New Zealand. No.* 410 *optd with T* **125** *in silver.*

705 $10 Scarlet Hibiscus .. .. .. 11·00 12·00

SIXTY FIFTH BIRTHDAY
QUEEN ELIZABETH II

(126)

1991 (22 Apr). *65th Birthday of Queen Elizabeth II. No.* 409 *optd with T* **126**.

706 $6 *Hybrid hibiscus* .. .. .. 8·00 9·00

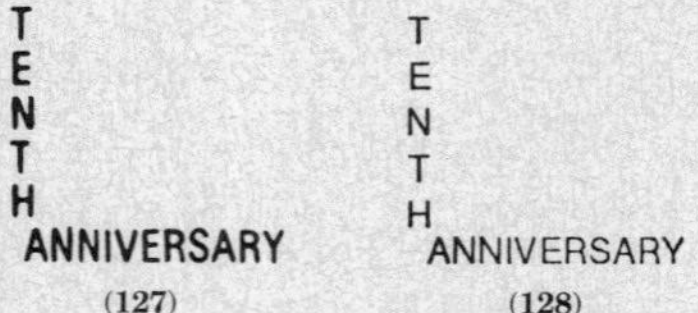

(127) (128)

1991 (26 June). *10th Wedding Anniv of Prince and Princess of Wales. Nos.* 430/2 *optd. A. With T* **127** *in typography* (75 c. *in silver*). *B. With T* **128** *in lithography* (75 c. *in black*).

		A		B	
707	75 c. Type **77**	1·50	1·50	1·50	1·50
708	95 c. Lady Diana Spencer ..	2·50	2·50	2·50	2·50
709	$1.20, Prince Charles and Lady Diana	2·50	2·50	2·50	2·50
707/9	.. *Set of* 3	6·00	6·00	6·00	6·00

Nos. 707A/9A come from small sheets of 6, including one *se-tenant* stamp-size label, and Nos. 707B/9B from uncut sheets containing four such small sheets.

MINIMUM PRICE

The minimum price quote is 10p which represents a handling charge rather than a basis for valuing common stamps. For further notes about prices see introductory pages.

129 "The Virgin and Child with Sts Jerome and Dominic" (Lippi)

130 Banded Rail

(Des G. Vasarhelyi. Litho Questa)

1991 (11 Nov). *Christmas. Religious Paintings. T* **129** *and similar vert designs. Multicoloured. P* 14.

710 20 c. Type **129** 50 50
711 50 c. "The Isenheim Altarpiece" (M. Grunewald) .. .. 1·00 1·00
712 $1 "The Nativity" (G. Pittoni) .. .. 1·75 2·00
713 $2 "Adoration of the Kings" (J. Brueghel the Elder) .. .. .. 2·50 2·75
710/13 .. .. .. *Set of* 4 5·00 5·50
MS714 79×104 mm. $7 "Adoration of the Shepherds" (G. Reni) .. .. .. 7·50 8·50

(Litho B.D.T.)

1992 (19 Feb)–**93**. *Birds. T* **130** *and similar vert designs. Multicoloured. P* 13 ($7, $10, $15) *or* 14 (*others*).

718 20 c. Type **130** 40 40
719 50 c. Red-tailed Tropic Bird 70 70
720 70 c. Purple Swamphen 90 90
721 $1 Pacific Pigeon .. .. .. 1·40 1·40
722 $1.50, White-collared Kingfisher (20.3.92) 2·00 2·00
723 $2 Blue-crowned Lory (20.3.92) .. .. 2·50 2·50
724 $3 Purple-capped Fruit Dove (16.4.92) .. 3·25 3·25
726 $5 Barn Owl (15.5.92) .. .. .. 5·50 5·50
727 $7 Longtailed Koel ("Cockoo") (26.3.93) 6·25 6·50
728 $10 Eastern Reef Heron (16.4.93) .. 8·75 9·00
729 $15 Spotted Triller ("Polynesian Triller") (10.8.93) .. .. 13·00 13·50
718/29 .. .. .. *Set of* 11 40·00 42·00

Nos. 727/9 are larger, 48½×35 mm, and show a silhouette portrait of Queen Elizabeth II at right.

131 Columbus before King Ferdinand and Queen Isabella

(Des G. Vasarhelyi. Litho B.D.T.)

1992 (22 May). *500th Anniv of Discovery of America by Columbus. T* **131** *and similar horiz designs. Multicoloured. P* 13½×13.

731 $2 Type **131** .. .. 2·75 2·75
732 $3 Fleet of Columbus .. .. .. 4·50 4·50
733 $5 Claiming the New World for Spain .. 6·00 6·00
731/3 .. .. .. *Set of* 3 12·00 12·00

132 Tennis and $10 Commemorative Coin

(Des G. Vasarhelyi. Litho B.D.T.)

1992 (22 July). *Olympic Games, Barcelona. T* **132** *and similar horiz designs. Multicoloured. P* 13.

734 $2.50, Type **132** .. .. .. 4·00 4·00
a. Horiz strip of 3. Nos. 734/6 .. .. 11·00
735 $2.50, Olympic flame and national flags 4·00 4·00
736 $2.50, Gymnastics and different $10 coin 4·00 4·00
734/6 .. .. .. *Set of* 3 11·00 11·00
MS737 152×87 mm. $5 Water polo .. 6·50 7·00

Nos. 734/6 were printed together, *se-tenant*, in horizontal strips of 3 throughout the sheet.

$1 =

(133)

134 "St. Catherine's Mystic Marriage" (detail) (Memling)

1992 (30 Sept). *6th Festival of Pacific Arts, Rarotonga. Nos.* 336/51 *surch with T* **133**.

738 $1 on 20 c. Type **69** .. .. .. 1·00 1·00
739 $1 on 20 c. Ku-Tagwa plaque, New Guinea 1·00 1·00
740 $1 on 20 c. Suspension hook, New Guinea 1·00 1·00
741 $1 on 20 c. Ancestral board, New Guinea 1·00 1·00
742 $1 on 25 c. Platform post, New Hebrides 1·00 1·00
743 $1 on 25 c. Canoe ornament, New Ireland 1·00 1·00
744 $1 on 25 c. Carved figure, Admiralty Islands .. .. 1·00 1·00
745 $1 on 25 c. Female with child, Admiralty Islands .. .. 1·00 1·00
746 $1 on 30 c. The God A'a, Rurutu (Austral Islands) .. .. 1·00 1·00
747 $1 on 30 c. Statue of Tangaroa, Cook Islands .. .. 1·00 1·00
748 $1 on 30 c. Ivory pendant, Tonga .. 1·00 1·00
749 $1 on 30 c. Tapa (Hiapo) cloth, Niue .. 1·00 1·00
750 $1 on 35 c. Feather box (Waka), New Zealand .. .. 1·00 1·00
751 $1 on 35 c. Hei-Tiki amulet, New Zealand 1·00 1·00
752 $1 on 35 c. House post, New Zealand .. 1·00 1·00
753 $1 on 35 c. Feather image of god Ku, Hawaii .. .. 1·00 1·00
738/53 .. .. .. *Set of* 16 14·50 14·50

1992 (18 Nov). *Christmas. Different details from "St. Catherine's Mystic Marriage" by Hans Memling. T* **134** *and similar vert designs. Litho. P* 13½.

754 20 c. Type **134** 35 30
755 50 c. multicoloured 70 70
756 $1 multicoloured .. .. .. 1·25 1·25
757 $2 multicoloured .. .. .. 2·25 2·75
754/7 .. .. .. *Set of* 4 4·00 4·50
MS758 87×101 mm. $7 multicoloured (as 50 c., but larger (36×47 *mm*)) .. .. .. 7·00 8·00

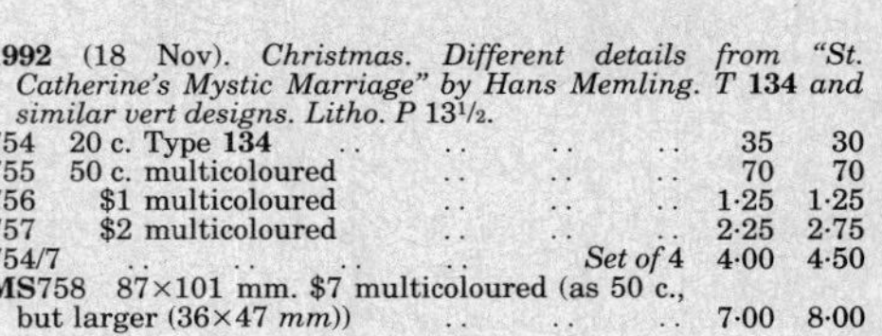

135 Queen on Official Visit

136 Rough-toothed Dolphin

(Litho B.D.T.)

1992 (7 Dec). *40th Anniv of Queen Elizabeth II's Accession. T* **135** *and similar vert designs. Multicoloured. P* 14.

759 70 c. Type **135** .. .. 1·25 1·25
760 $1 Queen in green evening dress .. 1·75 1·75
761 $1.50, Queen in white embroidered evening dress .. .. .. 2·50 2·50
762 $2 Queen with bouquet .. .. .. 2·75 2·75
759/62 .. .. .. *Set of* 4 7·50 7·50

(Des G. Drummond. Litho B.D.T.)

1993 (13 Jan). *Endangered Species. South Pacific Dolphins. T* **136** *and similar horiz designs. Multicoloured. P* 14.

763 20 c. Type **136** 80 70
764 50 c. Fraser's Dolphin .. .. .. 1·50 1·25
765 75 c. Pantropical Spotted Dolphin .. .. 2·00 2·00
766 $1 Risso's Dolphin .. .. .. 2·40 2·75
763/6 .. .. .. *Set of* 4 6·00 6·00

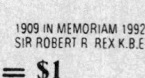

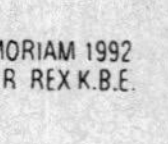

= $1

(137)

138 Queen Elizabeth II in Coronation Robes and St. Edward's Crown

1993 (15 Mar). *Premier Sir Robert Rex Commemoration. Nos.* 568/70 *optd or surch as T* **137**.

767 40 c. Type **96** 85 85
768 58 c. Map of Niue and Premier Rex .. 1·00 1·00
769 70 c. Premier Rex receiving proclamation of self-government .. .. .. 1·25 1·25
770 $1 on 40 c. Type **96** .. .. .. 1·60 1·60
771 $1 on 58 c. Map of Niue and Premier Rex 1·60 1·60
772 $1 on 70 c. Premier Rex receiving proclamation of self-government .. 1·60 1·60
767/72 .. .. .. *Set of* 6 7·00 7·00

(Litho B.D.T.)

1993 (2 June). *40th Anniv of Coronation. P* 14.

773 **138** $5 multicoloured .. .. .. 6·00 6·50

139 "Virgin of the Rosary" (detail) (Guido Reni)

(Litho Fournier)

1993 (29 Oct). *Christmas. Different details of "Virgin of the Rosary" (Reni). T* **139** *and similar vert designs. P* 13½ ($3) *or* 14 (*others*).

774 20 c. multicoloured 55 45
775 70 c. multicoloured .. .. .. 1·25 1·00
776 $1 multicoloured .. .. .. 1·40 1·25
777 $1.50, multicoloured .. .. .. 2·25 2·50
778 $3 multicoloured (32×47 *mm*) .. .. 3·75 4·50
774/8 .. .. *Set of* 5 8·25 8·75

140 World Cup and Globe with Flags of U.S.A. and Previous Winners

(Des G. Vasarhelyi. Litho B.D.T.)

1994 (17 June). *World Cup Football Championship, U.S.A. P* 14.

779 **140** $4 multicoloured .. .. .. 5·50 6·00

141 "Apollo 11" and Astronaut on Moon

(Litho B.D.T.)

1994 (20 July). *25th Anniv of First Moon Landing. T* **141** *and similar horiz designs. Multicoloured. P* 14.

780 $2.50, Type **141** .. .. .. 4·50 4·50
a. Horiz strip of 3. Nos. 780/2 .. .. 12·00
781 $2.50, Astronaut and flag .. .. 4·50 4·50
782 $2.50, Astronaut and equipment .. .. 4·50 4·50
780/2 .. .. *Set of* 3 12·00 12·00

Nos. 780/2 were printed together, *se-tenant*, in horizontal strips of 3 throughout the sheet.

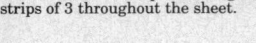

142 "The Adoration of the Kings" (Jan Gossaert)

143 Long John Silver and Jim Hawkins (*Treasure Island*)

(Litho B.D.T.)

1994 (28 Nov). *Christmas. Religious Paintings. T* **142** *and similar horiz designs. Multicoloured. P* 14.

783 70 c. Type **142** .. .. .. 1·00 1·25
a. Block of 4. Nos. 783/6 .. .. 3·50
784 70 c. "Madonna and Child with Sts. John and Catherine" (Titian) .. .. 1·00 1·25
785 70 c. "The Holy Family and Shepherd" (Titian) .. .. .. 1·00 1·25
786 70 c. "The Virgin and Child with Saints" (Gerard David) .. .. .. 1·00 1·25
787 $1 "The Adoration of the Shepherds" (cherubs detail) (Poussin) .. .. 1·25 1·50
a. Block of 4. Nos. 787/90 .. .. 4·50
788 $1 "The Adoration of the Shepherds" (Holy Family detail) (Poussin) .. .. 1·25 1·50
789 $1 "Madonna and Child with Sts. Joseph and John" (Sebastiano) .. .. 1·25 1·50
790 $1 "The Adoration of the Kings" (Veronese) .. .. 1·25 1·50
783/90 .. .. *Set of* 8 8·00 10·00

Nos. 783/6 and 787/90 were printed together, *se-tenant*, on blocks of 4 throughout the sheets.

(Des G. Vasarhelyi. Litho B.D.T.)

1994 (14 Dec). *Death Centenary of Robert Louis Stevenson (author). T* **143** *and similar vert designs. Multicoloured. P* 15×14.

791 $1.75, Type **143** .. .. .. 2·50 2·50
a. Block of 4. Nos. 791/4 .. .. 9·00
792 $1.75, Transformation of Dr. Jekyll (*Dr. Jekyll and Mr. Hyde*) .. .. 2·50 2·50
793 $1.75, Attack on David Balfour (*Kidnapped*) 2·50 2·50
794 $1.75, Robert Louis Stevenson, tomb and inscription .. .. .. 2·50 2·50
791/4 .. .. *Set of* 4 9·00 9·00

Nos. 791/4 were printed together, *se-tenant*, in blocks of 4 throughout the sheet.

XXX
50c
(144)

145 Tapeu Orchid

1996 (19 Feb). *Nos. 720 and 722 surch as T* **144** *by Tonga Govt Printers.*

795 50 c. on 70 c. Purple Swamphen .. .. 2·00 1·50
796 $1 on $1.50, White-collared Kingfisher .. 3·00 2·50

(Litho Questa)

1996 (10 May). *Flowers. T* **145** *and similar vert designs. Multicoloured. P* 14½.

797 70 c. Type **145** 80 80
798 $1 Frangipani .. .. 1·00 1·00
799 $1.20, "Golden Shower" .. .. .. 1·40 1·60
800 $1.50, "Pua" .. .. 1·90 2·25
797/800 .. .. *Set of* 4 4·50 5·00

(Litho Photopress International, Norfolk Island)

1996 (22 Aug). *Booklet Stamp. Redrawn design as No.* 146. *Roul* 7.

801 20 c. rosine and green 15 20
a. Booklet pane of 10 with margins all round .. .. 1·75

146 *Jackfish* (yacht)

147 *Desert Star* (ketch)

(Des Mary Butterfield. Litho Questa)

1996 (30 Sept). *Sailing Ships. T* **146** *and similar square designs. Multicoloured. P* 14½.

802 70 c. Type **146** 90 90
803 $1 *Jennifer* (yacht) .. .. .. 1·40 1·40
804 $1.20, *Mikeva* (yacht) .. .. .. 1·75 2·00
805 $2 *Eye of the Wind* (cadet brig) .. .. 2·25 2·50
802/5 .. .. *Set of* 4 5·50 6·00

(Litho Southern Colour Print, Dunedin)

1996 (31 Oct). *"Taipei '96" International Philatelic Exhibition, Taiwan. Sheet* 90×80 *mm. P* 14.

MS806 **147** $1.50, multicoloured .. .. 1·50 1·75

148 *Acropora gemmifera*

149 Ox

(Des Sue Wickison. Litho Southern Colour Print, Dunedin)

1996 (20 Dec). *Corals. T* **148** *and similar horiz designs. Multicoloured. P* 14.

807 20 c. Type **148** 15 20
808 50 c. *Acropora nobilis* 35 40
809 70 c. *Goniopora lobata* 50 55
810 $1 *Stylaster* sp. 75 80
811 $1.20, *Alveopora catalai* 90 95
812 $1.50, *Fungia scutaria* .. .. .. 1·10 1·25
813 $2 *Porites solida* .. .. .. 1·50 1·60
814 $3 *Millepora* sp. .. .. 2·25 2·40
815 $4 *Pocillopora eydouxi* .. .. .. 3·00 3·25
816 $5 *Platygyra pini* .. .. .. 3·75 4·00
807/16 .. .. *Set of* 10 14·00 15·00

(Des Tracey Yager. Litho Southern Colour Print, Dunedin)

1997 (10 Feb). *"HONG KONG '97" International Stamp Exhibition. Chinese New Year ("Year of the Ox"). Sheet* 120×90 *mm. P* 13.

MS817 **149** $1.50, multicoloured .. .. 1·50 1·75

150 Steps to Lagoon

(Des M. Cross. Litho Questa)

1997 (18 Apr). *Island Scenes. T* **150** *and similar horiz designs. Multicoloured. P* 13½×14.

818 $1 Type **150** .. .. 1·00 1·10
a. Block of 4. Nos. 818/21 .. .. 3·75
819 $1 Islands in lagoon .. .. .. 1·00 1·10
820 $1 Beach with rocks in foreground .. 1·00 1·10
821 $1 Over-hanging rock on beach .. .. 1·00 1·10
818/21 .. .. *Set of* 4 3·75 4·00

Nos. 818/21 were printed together, *se-tenant*, in blocks of 4 forming a composite design.

151 Humpback Whale

(Des Sue Wickison. Litho Southern Colour Print, Dunedin)

1997 (29 May). *Whales* (*1st issue*). *T* **151** *and similar multicoloured designs. P* 14.

822 20 c. Type **151** 30 25
823 $1 Humpback Whale and calf (*vert*) .. 1·10 1·10
824 $1.50, Humpback Whale surfacing (*vert*) 1·60 1·75
822/4 .. .. *Set of* 3 3·00 3·00
MS825 120×90 mm. Nos. 822/4 .. .. 2·00 2·25

No. **MS**825 shows the "Pacific '97" International Stamp Exhibition, San Francisco emblem on the margin.

See also Nos. 827/9

152 Niue 1902 Ovpt on New Zealand 1d.

153 Niue 1918–29 Overprint on New Zealand £1

1997 (9 June). *"Aupex '97" Stamp Exhibition, Auckland* (*1st issue*). *Sheet* 136×90 *mm. Litho. P* 14×15.

MS826 **152** $2+20 c. multicoloured .. .. 2·10 2·25

(Des Sue Wickison. Litho Southern Colour Print, Dunedin)

1997 (3 Sept). *Whales* (*2nd series*). *Multicoloured designs as T* **151**, *but vert. P* 14.

827 50 c. Killer Whale 50 50
828 70 c. Minke Whale 70 70
829 $1.20, Sperm Whale .. .. .. 1·00 1·00
827/9 .. .. *Set of* 3 2·00 2·00

1997 (13 Nov). *"Aupex '97" Stamp Exhibition, Auckland* (*2nd issue*). *Sheet* 90×135 *mm. Litho. P* 14½×15.

MS830 **153** $2 + 20 c. multicoloured .. .. 1·60 1·75

154 Floral Display in Woven Basket

(Des Neline Pasisi. Litho Southern Colour Print, Dunedin)

1997 (26 Nov). *Christmas. Floral Displays. T* **154** *and similar vert designs. Multicoloured. P* 14.

831	20 c. Type **154**	25	20
832	50 c. Display in white pot	50	50
833	70 c. Display in white basket	70	70
834	$1 Display in purple vase	80	85
831/4	*Set of* 4	2·00	2·00

(Des D. Miller. Litho Questa)

1998 (31 Mar). *Diana, Princess of Wales Commemoration. Sheet* 145×70 *mm, containing vert designs as T* **91** *of Kiribati. Multicoloured. P* 14½×14.

MS835	20 c. Wearing white jacket, 1992; 50 c. Wearing pearl-drop earrings, 1988; $1 In raincoat, 1990; $2 With Mother Theresa, 1992 (*sold at* $3.70 + 50 c. *charity premium*)	3·00	3·25

STAMP BOOKLETS

1982 (June). *Royal Wedding. Multicoloured cover,* 129×74 *mm, showing Prince and Princess of Wales. Stitched.*

SB1	$8.50, booklet containing 75 c. and 95 c. (Nos. 430/1), each in block of 5 stamps and 1 label	7·00

B 2

(*Illustration reduced. Actual size* 170×80 *mm*)

1996 (22 Aug). *Flowers. Multicoloured cover as Type* B **2**. *Stamps attached by selvedge.*

SB2	$2 booklet containing pane of ten 20 c. (No. 801a)	1·75

OFFICIAL STAMPS

O.H.M.S. (O 1) **O.H.M.S.** (O 2)

1985 (1 July)–**87**. *Nos.* 408/10 *optd with Type* O **2** *in gold and Nos.* 527/42 *optd with Type* O **1** *in blue, all by foil embossing.*

O 1	12 c. Type **92**	20	20
O 2	25 c. *Euphorbia pulcherrima*	25	25
O 3	30 c. *Cochlospermum hibiscoides*	25	25
O 4	35 c. *Begonia sp.*	30	30
O 5	40 c. *Plumeria sp.*	35	35
O 6	52 c. *Strelitzia reginae*	40	40
O 7	58 c. *Hibiscus syriacus*	45	45
O 8	70 c. *Tibouchina sp.*	60	60
O 9	83 c. *Nelumbo sp.*	70	70
O10	$1.05, *Hybrid hibiscus*	90	90
O11	$1.75, *Cassia fistula*	1·50	1·50
O12	$2.30, *Orchid var.* (29.11.85)	3·75	2·25
O13	$3.90, *Orchid sp.* (29.11.85)	4·50	3·50
O14	$4 *Euphorbia pulcherrima poinsettia* (1.4.86)	4·00	3·75
O15	$5 *Euphorbia pulcherrima poinsettia* (1.4.86)	4·25	4·50
O16	$6 *Hybrid hibiscus* (29.4.87)	5·50	6·00
O17	$6.60, *Hybrid hibiscus* (15.9.86)	6·00	6·50
O18	$8.30, *Hibiscus rosasinensis* (15.9.86)	7·00	7·50
O19	$10 Scarlet Hibiscus (29.4.87)	8·00	8·50
O1/19	*Set of* 19	42·00	42·00

O.H.M.S. (O 3)

1993 (10 Dec)–**94**. *Nos.* 718/29 *optd with Type* O **3** *(larger,* 25×4 *mm, on Nos.* 727/9*) in gold by foil embossing.*

O20	20 c. Type **130**	20	25
O21	50 c. Red-tailed Tropic Bird	45	50
O22	70 c. Purple Swamphen	60	65
O23	$1 Pacific Pigeon	90	95
O24	$1.50, White-collared Kingfisher	1·40	1·50
O25	$2 Blue-crowned Lory	1·75	2·00
O26	$3 Crimson-crowned Fruit Dove (27.4.94)	2·75	3·00
O27	$5 Barn Owl (27.4.94)	4·50	4·75
O28	$7 Longtailed Cuckoo (48½×35 *mm*) (1.9.94)	6·25	6·50
O29	$10 Eastern Reef Heron (48½×35 *mm*) (1.9.94)	8·75	9·00
O30	$15 Spotted Triller ("Polynesian Triller") (48½×35 *mm*) (30.9.94)	13·00	13·00
O20/30	*Set of* 11	40·00	42·00

Norfolk Island
see after Australia

North Borneo
see Malaysia

Northern Nigeria
see Nigeria

Northern Rhodesia
see Zambia

North-West Pacific Islands
see Papua New Guinea

Nova Scotia
see Canada

Nyasaland Protectorate
see Malawi

Orange Free State
see South Africa

Pakistan

(Currency. 12 pies = 1 anna; 16 annas = 1 rupee)

DOMINION

PAKISTAN (1) **PAKISTAN** (2)

1947 (1 Oct). *Nos. 259/68 and 269a/77 (King George VI) of India optd by litho at Nasik, as T* **1** *(3 p. to 12 a.) or* **2** *(14 a. and rupee values).*

No.	Value	Description	Unused	Used
1	3 p.	slate	10	10
2	½ a.	purple	10	10
3	9 p.	green	10	10
4	1 a.	carmine	10	10
5	1½ a.	dull violet	10	10
	w.	Wmk inverted		
6	2 a.	vermilion	10	20
7	3 a.	bright violet	10	20
8	3½ a.	bright blue	65	2·25
9	4 a.	brown	20	10
10	6 a.	turquoise-green	1·00	75
11	8 a.	slate-violet	30	60
12	12 a.	lake	1·00	20
13	14 a.	purple	2·50	75
14	1 r.	grey and red-brown	1·75	60
15	2 r.	purple and brown	3·25	85
16	5 r.	green and blue	4·00	3·25
17	10 r.	purple and claret	4·00	2·00
18	15 r.	brown and green	48·00	75·00
19	25 r.	slate-violet and purple	55·00	38·00
1/19		*Set of* 19	£110	£110

Numerous provisional "PAKISTAN" overprints, both hand-stamped and machine-printed, in various sizes and colours, on Postage and Official stamps, also exist.

These were made under authority of Provincial Governments, District Head Postmasters or Local Postmasters and are of considerable philatelic interest.

The 1 a. 3 p. (India No. 269) exists only as a local issue (*Price*, Karachi opt 90*p. unused*; £1.75 *used*).

The 12 a., as No. 12 but overprinted at Karachi, exists with overprint inverted (*Price* £60 *unused*).

The 1 r. value with local overprint exists with overprint inverted (*Price* £150 *unused*) or as a pair with one stamp without overprint (*Price* £600 *unused*).

3 Constituent Assembly Building, Karachi

6 Crescent and Stars

(Des A. R. Chughtai (1 r.). Recess D.L.R.)

1948 (9 July). *Independence. T* **3, 6** *and similar horiz designs. P* 13½ × 14 *or* 11½ *(1 r.).*

No.	Value	Description	Unused	Used
20	1½ a.	ultramarine	70	50
21	2½ a.	green	70	10
22	3 a.	purple-brown	70	20
23	1 r.	scarlet	70	50
	a.	Perf 14 × 13½	4·25	12·00
20/3		*Set of* 4	2·50	1·10

Designs:—2½ a. Karachi Airport entrance; 3 a. Gateway to Lahore Fort.

7 Scales of Justice

8 Star and Crescent

9 Lloyds Barrage

10 Karachi Airport

13 Khyber Pass

(Des M. M. A. Suharwardi (T **8**). Recess Pakistan Security Ptg Corp Ltd, Karachi (P 13 and 13½), D.L.R. (others))

1948 (14 Aug)–**56**?. *T* **7/10, 13** *and similar designs.*

No.	Type	Value	Description	Unused	Used
24	**7**	3 p.	red (*p* 12½)	10	10
		a.	Perf 13½ (1954?)	20	20
25		6 p.	violet (*p* 12½)	80	10
		a.	Perf 13½ (1954?)	1·50	75
26		9 p.	green (*p* 12½)	50	10
		a.	Perf 13½ (1954?)	60	40
27	**8**	1 a.	blue (*p* 12½)	10	40
28		1½ a.	grey-green (*p* 12½)	10	10
29		2 a.	red (*p* 12½)	40	40
30	**9**	2½ a.	green (*p* 14×13½)	2·75	5·50
31	**10**	3 a.	green (*p* 14)	7·50	50
32	**9**	3½ a.	bright blue (*p* 14×13½)	3·50	3·75
33		4 a.	reddish brown (*p* 12½)	50	10
34	–	6 a.	blue (*p* 14×13½)	50	50
35	–	8 a.	black (*p* 12½)	50	40
36	**10**	10 a.	scarlet (*p* 14)	4·50	6·50
37	–	12 a.	scarlet (*p* 14×13½)	6·50	60
38	–	1 r.	ultramarine (*p* 14)	5·50	10
		a.	Perf 13½ (1954?)	13·00	1·75
39	–	2 r.	chocolate (*p* 14)	20·00	30
		a.	Perf 13½ (1954?)	22·00	85
40	–	5 r.	carmine (*p* 14)	15·00	50
		a.	Perf 13½ (7.53)	9·00	20
41	**13**	10 r.	magenta (*p* 14)	9·00	13·00
		a.	Perf 12	65·00	4·50
		b.	Perf 13 (1951)	17·00	30
42		15 r.	blue-green (*p* 12)	16·00	9·50
		a.	Perf 14	13·00	30·00
		b.	Perf 13 (1956?)	17·00	12·00
43		25 r.	violet (*p* 14)	55·00	70·00
		a.	Perf 12	25·00	30·00
		b.	Perf 13 (1954)	35·00	18·00
24/43			*Set of* 20	95·00	42·00

Designs: *Vert (as T* **7**)—6 a., 8 a., 12 a. Karachi Port Trust. (*As T* **10**)—1 r., 2 r., 5 r. Salimullah Hostel, Dacca.

For 25 r. with W **98**, see No. 210.

14 Star and Crescent

15 Karachi Airport

(Recess Pakistan Security Ptg Corp (P 13½), D.L.R. (others).

1949 (Feb)–**53**? *Redrawn. Crescent moon with points to left as T* **14/15**.

No.	Type	Value	Description	Unused	Used
44	**14**	1 a.	blue (*p* 12½)	3·75	50
		a.	Perf 13½ (1953?)	3·25	10
45		1½ a.	grey-green (*p* 12½)	3·75	50
		a.	Perf 13½ (1952?)	3·00	10
		ab.	Printed on the gummed side	50·00	
46		2 a.	red (*p* 12½)	3·75	10
		a.	Perf 13½ (1953?)	3·25	10
47	**15**	3 a.	green (*p* 14)	6·00	65
48	–	6 a.	blue (as No. 34) (*p* 14×13½)	8·50	30
49	–	8 a.	black (as No. 35) (*p* 12½)	4·00	85
50	**15**	10 a.	scarlet (*p* 14)	12·00	1·25
51	–	12 a.	scarlet (as No. 37) (*p* 14×13½)	17·00	30
44/51			*Set of* 8	50·00	3·00

16

(Recess D.L.R.)

1949 (11 Sept). *First Death Anniv of Mohammed Ali Jinnah. T* **16** *and similar design. P* 14.

No.	Type	Value	Description	Unused	Used
52	**16**	1½ a.	brown	1·25	75
53		3 a.	green	1·25	75
54	–	10 a.	black	4·00	5·25
52/4			*Set of* 3	6·00	6·00

Design:—10 a. Similar inscription reading "QUAID-I-AZAM/ MOHAMMAD ALI JINNAH" etc.

17 Pottery

18 Aeroplane and Hour-glass

Two Types of 3½ a.:

I 

 II

19 Saracenic Leaf Pattern

20 Archway and Lamp

(Des A. R. Chughtai. Recess D.L.R., later printings, Pakistan Security Ptg Corp)

1951 (14 Aug)–**56.** *Fourth Anniv of Independence. P* 13.

No.	Type	Value	Description	Unused	Used
55	**17**	2½ a.	carmine	1·00	40
56	**18**	3 a.	purple	50	10
57	**17**	3½ a.	blue (I)	75	2·50
57*a*		3½ a.	blue (II)(12.56)	3·25	2·00
58	**19**	4 a.	green	35	10
59		6 a.	brown-orange	45	10
60	**20**	8 a.	sepia	4·00	10
61		10 a.	violet	80	70
62	**18**	12 a.	slate	90	10
55/62			*Set of* 9	11·00	5·00

The above and the stamps issued on the 14 August 1954, 1955 and 1956, are basically definitive issues, although issued on the Anniversary date of Independence.

21 "Scinde Dawk" stamp and Ancient and Modern Transport

(Recess D.L.R.)

1952 (14 Aug). *Centenary of "Scinde Dawk" Issue of India. P* 13.

No.	Type	Value	Description	Unused	Used
63	**21**	3 a.	deep olive/*yellow-olive*	75	60
64		12 a.	deep brown/*salmon*	1·00	15

PRINTERS. All issues up to No. 219 were recess-printed by the Pakistan Security Printing Corporation, *unless otherwise stated.*

22 Kaghan Valley

23 Mountains, Gilgit

24 Tea Plantation, East Pakistan

1954 (14 Aug). *Seventh Anniv of Independence. T* **22/4** *and similar designs. P* 13½ (14 *a.*, 1 *r.*, 2 *r.*) *or* 13 (*others*).

65 6 p. reddish violet 10 10
66 9 p. blue .. .. 3·25 1·50
67 1 a. carmine 10 10
68 1½ a. red 10 10
69 14 a. deep green 55 10
70 1 r. green .. .. 11·00 10
71 2 r. red-orange .. .. 2·75 10
65/71 .. .. *Set of* 7 16·00 1·50

Designs: *As T* **22**—1½ a. Mausoleum of Emperor Jehangir, Lahore. *As T* **23**—1 a. Badshahi Mosque, Lahore. *As T* **24**—1 r. Cotton plants, West Pakistan; 2 r. Jute fields and river, East Pakistan.

29 View of K 2

1954 (25 Dec). *Conquest of K 2 (Mount Godwin-Austen). P* 13.

72 **29** 2 a. deep violet 30 30

30 Karnaphuli Paper Mill, Type I (Arabic fraction on left)

Type II (Arabic fraction on right)

1955 (14 Aug)–**56**. *Eighth Anniv of Independence. T* **30** *and similar horiz designs. P* 13.

73 2½ a. scarlet (I) 50 70
73*a* 2½ a. scarlet (II) (12.56) 30 70
74 6 a. deep ultramarine .. .. 1·00 10
75 8 a. deep reddish violet .. .. 3·75 10
76 12 a. carmine and orange .. .. 4·00 10
73/6 .. .. *Set of* 5 8·50 1·40

Designs:—6 a. Textile mill, West Pakistan; 8 a. Jute mill, East Pakistan; 12 a. Main Sui gas plant.

TENTH
ANNIVERSARY
UNITED NATIONS

24.10.55.

(34)

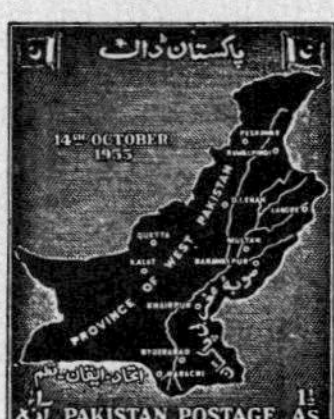
35 Map of West Pakistan

TENTH
ANNIVERSARY
UNITED NATIONS

24.10.55.

"UNITED NATIONS" shifted 1 mm to left (1½ a. R. 7/10; 12 a. R. 1/8, 3/8, 5/8, 7/8, 9/8)

1955 (24 Oct). *Tenth Anniv of United Nations. Nos.* 68 *and* 76 *optd as T* **34**.

77 1½ a. red (B.) .. .. 1·75 5·00
a. "UNITED NATIONS" 1 mm to left 3·75 7·00
78 12 a. carmine and orange (B.) .. .. 75 4·50
a. "UNITED NATIONS" 1 mm to left 3·75 7·00

Forgeries exist of the overprint on No. 77. These are in very uneven thin type and measure 20×18 mm instead of the genuine 19½×19 mm.

1955 (7 Dec). *West Pakistan Unity. P* 13½.

79 **35** 1½ a. myrtle-green 15 10
80 2 a. sepia 15 10
81 12 a. deep rose-red 75 15
79/81 .. .. *Set of* 3 95 30

REPUBLIC

36 Constituent Assembly Building, Karachi

(Litho D.L.R.)

1956 (23 Mar). *Republic Day. P* 13.

82 **36** 2 a. myrtle-green 80 10

37

38 Map of East Pakistan

1956 (14 Aug). *Ninth Anniv of Independence. P* 13½.

83 **37** 2 a. scarlet 65 10
a. Printed on the gummed side .. 6·50

1956 (15 Oct). *First Session of National Assembly of Pakistan at Dacca. P* 13½.

84 **38** 1½ a. myrtle-green .. .. 30 1·00
85 2 a. sepia 30 10
86 12 a. deep rose-red 30 45
84/6 .. .. *Set of* 3 80 1·40

39 Karnaphuli Paper Mill, East Bengal

40 Pottery

41 Orange Tree

1957 (23 Mar). *First Anniv of Republic. P* 13.

87 **39** 2½ a. scarlet 20 10
88 **40** 3½ a. blue 30 10
89 **41** 10 r. myrtle-green and yellow-orange .. 80 20
87/9 .. .. *Set of* 3 1·10 30

The above and No. 95 are primarily definitive issues, although issued on the Anniversary of Republic Day.

For 10 r. with W **98**, see No. 208.

42 Pakistani Flag

43 Pakistani Industries

(Litho D.L.R.)

1957 (10 May). *Centenary of Struggle for Independence (Indian Mutiny). P* 13.

90 **42** 1½ a. bronze-green 50 10
91 12 a. light blue .. .. 1·25 10

(Litho D.L.R.)

1957 (14 Aug). *Tenth Anniv of Independence. P* 14.

92 **43** 1½ a. ultramarine 20 30
93 4 a. orange-red 40 50
94 12 a. mauve 40 50
92/4 .. .. *Set of* 3 90 1·10

44 Coconut Tree

45

1958 (23 Mar). *Second Anniv of Republic. P* 13.

95 **44** 15 r. red and deep reddish purple .. 4·25 3·00

This is a definitive issue, see note below No. 89.

See No. 209 for this stamp with W **98**.

(Photo Harrison)

1958 (21 Apr). *20th Death Anniv of Mohammed Iqbal (poet). P* 14½ × 14.

96 **45** 1½ a. yellow-olive and black 55 10
97 2 a. orange-brown and black 55 10
98 14 a. turquoise-blue and black 90 10
96/8 .. .. *Set of* 3 1·75 20

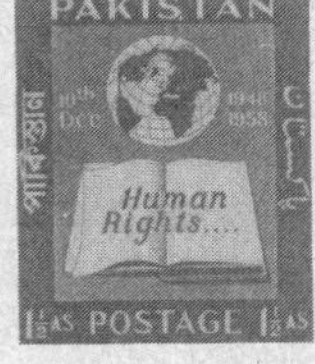
46 U.N. Charter and Globe

PAKISTAN
BOY SCOUT
2nd NATIONAL
JAMBOREE

CHITTAGONG
Dec. 58—Jan. 59

(47)

1958 (10 Dec). *Tenth Anniv of Declaration of Human Rights. P* 13.

99 **46** 1½ a. turquoise-blue 10 10
100 14 a. sepia 65 10

1958 (28 Dec). *Second Pakistan Boy Scouts National Jamboree, Chittagong. Nos.* 65 *and* 75 *optd with T* **47**.

101 6 p. reddish violet 30 10
102 8 a. deep reddish violet 65 10

REVOLUTION
DAY
Oct. 27, 1959

(48)

49 "Centenary of An Idea"

1959 (27 Oct). *Revolution Day. No.* 74 *optd with T* **48** *in red.*

103 6 a. deep ultramarine 80 10

1959 (19 Nov). *Red Cross Commemoration. Recess; cross typo. P* 13.

104 **49** 2 a. red and green 30 10
105 10 a. red and deep blue 55 10

50 Armed Forces Badge

51 Map of Pakistan

(Litho D.L.R.)

1960 (10 Jan). *Armed Forces Day. P* 13½ × 13.

106 **50** 2 a. red, ultramarine and blue-green .. 60 10
107 14 a. red and bright blue .. .. .. 1·50 10

1960 (23 Mar). *P* 13×13½.

108 **51** 6 p. deep purple 40 10
109 2 a. brown-red 60 10
110 8 a. deep green .. .. 1·25 10
111 1 r. blue .. .. 2·00 10
a. Printed on the gummed side ..
108/11 .. .. *Set of* 4 3·75 20

52 Uprooted Tree

53 Punjab Agricultural College

1960 (7 Apr). *World Refugee Year. P* 13.

112 **52** 2 a. rose-carmine 20 10
113 10 a. green 30 10

1960 (10 Oct). *Golden Jubilee of Punjab Agricultural College, Lyallpur. T* **53** *and similar horiz design. P* 12½ × 14.
114 2 a. slate-blue and carmine-red 10 10
115 8 a. bluish green and reddish violet 20 10
Design:—8 a. College arms.

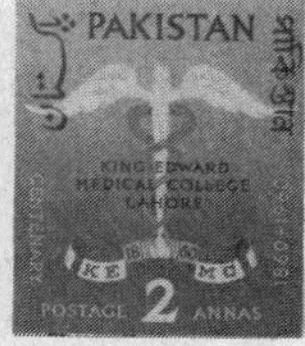

55 "Land Reforms, Rehabilitation and Reconstruction" **56** Caduceus

(Des M. H. Hanjra. Photo D.L.R.)

1960 (27 Oct). *Revolution Day. P* 13 × 13½.
116 **55** 2 a. green, pink and brown 10 10
a. Green and pink omitted . . . . 12·00
b. Pink omitted . . . . 5·00
117 14 a. green, yellow and ultramarine . . 50 40

(Photo D.L.R.)

1960 (16 Nov). *Centenary of King Edward Medical College, Lahore. P* 13.
118 **56** 2 a. yellow, black and blue 50 10
119 14 a. emerald, black and carmine . . 1·75 40

57 "Economic Co-operation" **58** Zam-Zama Gun, Lahore ("Kim's Gun," after Rudyard Kipling)

1960 (5 Dec). *International Chamber of Commerce C.A.F.E.A. Meeting, Karachi. P* 13.
120 **57** 14 a. orange-red 30 10

(Centre typo, background recess Pakistan Security Ptg Corp)

1960 (24 Dec). *Third Pakistan Boy Scouts National Jamboree, Lahore. P* 12½ × 14.
121 **58** 2 a. carmine, yellow & dp bluish green 70 10

(New Currency. 100 paisa=1 rupee)

I PAISA
(59)

1961 (1 Jan–14 Feb). *Nos.* 24a, 67/8, 83 *and* 108/9, *surch as T* **59**. *Nos.* 123/4 *and* 126 *surch by Pakistan Security Ptg Corp and others by the Times Press, Karachi.*
122 1 p. on 1½ a. red (10.1) 30 10
a. Printed and surch on the gummed side
123 2 p. on 3 p. red 10 10
124 3 p. on 6 p. deep purple 10 10
a. "PASIA" for "PAISA" . . . . 3·50
125 7 p. on 1 a. carmine (14.2) 30 10
126 13 p. on 2 a. brown-red (14.2) 30 10
a. "PAIS" for "PAISA" . . . . 3·50
127 13 p. on 2 a. scarlet (14.2) 20 10
122/7 . . . . *Set of* 6 1·00 30
No. 122. Two settings were used, the first with figure "1" 2½ mm. tall and the second 3 mm.
On the 1 p. with tall "1" and the 13 p. (No. 127), the space between the figures of value and "P" of "PAISA" varies between 1½ mm and 3 mm.
See also Nos. 262/4.

ERRORS. In the above issue and the corresponding official stamps we have listed errors in the stamps surcharged by the Pakistan Security Printing Corp but have not included the very large number of errors which occurred in the stamps surcharged by the less experienced Times Press. This was a very hurried job and there was no time to carry out the usual checks. It is also known that some errors were not issued to the public but came on the market by other means.

NOTE. Stamps in the old currency were also *handstamped* with new currency equivalents and issued in various districts but these local issues are outside the scope of this catalogue.

60 Khyber Pass **61** Shalimar Gardens, Lahore

62 Chota Sona Masjid (gateway)

(a) (b) (c)

Types (*a*) and (*b*) show the first letter in the top right-hand inscription; (*a*) wrongly engraved, "SH" (*b*) corrected to "P".
On Nos. 131/2 and 134 the corrections were made individually on the plate, so that each stamp in the sheet may be slightly different.
Type (*c*) refers to No. 133a only.

1961–63. *No wmk. P* 13 (*T* **62**) *or* 14 (*others*).

(*a*) *Inscribed* "SHAKISTAN" *in Bengali*
128 **60** 1 p. violet (1.1.61) . . . . . . 1·25 10
129 2 p. rose-red (12.1.61) . . . . . . 1·25 10
130 5 p. ultramarine (23.3.61) . . . . 2·00 10

(*b*) *Inscribed* "PAKISTAN" *in Bengali*
131 **60** 1 p. violet 55 10
a. Printed on the gummed side . .
132 2 p. rose-red 55 10
133 3 p. reddish purple (27.10.61) 30 10
a. Re-engraved. First letter of Bengali inscription as Type (*c*) (1963) . . 2·75 3·00
134 5 p. ultramarine . . . . . . 2·50 10
a. Printed on the gummed side . .
135 7 p. emerald (23.3.61) . . . . 1·25 10
136 **61** 10 p. brown (14.8.61) 20 10
137 13 p. slate-violet (14.8.61) 15 10
138 25 p. deep blue (1.1.62) . . . . 4·75 10
139 40 p. deep purple (1.1.62) 90 10
140 50 p. deep bluish green (1.1.62) 35 10
141 75 p. carmine-red (23.3.62) 40 10
142 90 p. yellow-green (1.1.62) 50 10
143 **62** 1 r. vermilion (7.1.63) . . . . 2·00 10
a. Imperf (pair) . . . .
144 1 r. 25, reddish violet (27.10.61) . . 75 45
144*a* 2 r. orange (7.1.63) . . . . 5·50 15
144*b* 5 r. green (7.1.63) . . . . 6·00 2·00
128/44*b* . . . . *Set of* 19 28·00 3·00
See also Nos. 170/81 and 204/7.

(63) **64** Warsak Dam and Power Station

1961 (12 Feb). *Lahore Stamp Exhibition. No.* 110 *optd with T* **63**.
145 **51** 8 a. deep green (R.) . . . . . . 90 1·50

1961 (1 July). *Completion of Warsak Hydro-Electric Project. P* 12½ × 14.
146 **64** 40 p. black and blue 60 10

65 Narcissus **66** Ten Roses

1961 (2 Oct). *Child Welfare Week. P* 14.
147 **65** 13 p. turquoise-blue 40 10
148 90 p. bright purple . . . . . . 1·10 20

1961 (4 Nov). *Co-operative Day. P* 13.
149 **66** 13 p. rose-red and deep green 50 10
150 90 p. rose-red and blue . . . . 1·25 40

67 Police Crest and "Traffic Control" **68** Locomotive *Eagle* of 1861

(Photo D.L.R.)

1961 (30 Nov). *Police Centenary. P* 13.
151 **67** 13 p. silver, black and blue 50 10
152 40 p. silver, black and red . . . . 1·00 20

(Des M. Thoma. Photo D.L.R.)

1961 (31 Dec). *Railway Centenary. T* **68** *and similar horiz design. P* 14.
153 13 p. green, black and yellow . . . . 1·00 80
154 50 p. yellow, black and green . . . . 1·25 1·00
Design:—50 p. Diesel locomotive and tracks forming "1961".

FIRST JET FLIGHT
KARACHI-DACCA 13 Paisa

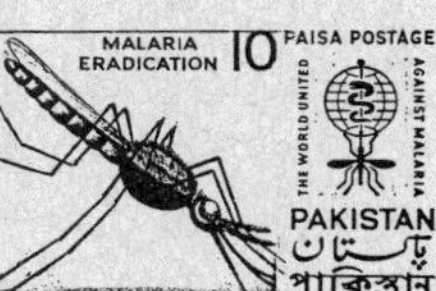

(70) **71** *Anopheles* sp (mosquito)

1962 (6 Feb). *First Karachi–Dacca Jet Flight. No.* 87 *surch with T* **70**.
155 **39** 13 p. on 2½ a. scarlet (R.) . . . . 1·25 80

(Photo D.L.R.)

1962 (7 Apr). *Malaria Eradication. T* **71** *and similar horiz design. P* 14.
156 10 p. black, yellow and red 50 10
157 13 p. black, greenish yellow and red 50 10
Design:—13 p. Mosquito pierced by blade.

73 Pakistan Map and Jasmine

(Photo Courvoisier)

1962 (8 June). *New Constitution. P* 12.
158 **73** 40 p. yellow-green, bluish green and grey 1·00 10

74 Football **78** Marble Fruit Dish and Bahawalpuri Clay Flask

1962 (14 Aug). *Sports. T* **74** *and similar horiz designs. P* 12½ × 14.
159 7 p. black and blue 10 10
160 13 p. black and green 60 40
161 25 p. black and purple 20 10
162 40 p. black and orange-brown . . . . 2·00 2·25
159/62 . . . . *Set of* 4 2·50 2·50
Designs:—13 p. Hockey; 25 p. Squash; 40 p. Cricket.

1962 (10 Nov). *Small Industries. T* **78** *and similar vert designs. P* 13.
163 7 p. brown-lake 10 10
164 13 p. deep green . . . . . . 4·00 1·75
165 25 p. reddish violet 10 10
166 40 p. yellow-green 10 10
167 50 p. deep red 10 10
163/7 . . . . *Set of* 5 4·00 1·90
Designs:—13 p. Sports equipment; 25 p. Camel-skin lamp and brassware; 40 p. Wooden powderbowl and basket-work; 50 p. Inlaid cigarette-box and brassware.

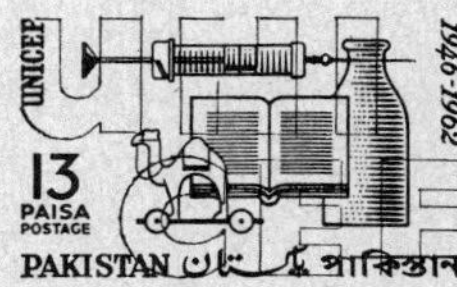

83 "Child Welfare"

(Des M. Thoma. Photo D.L.R.)

1962 (11 Dec). *16th Anniv of U.N.I.C.E.F. P* 14.
168 **83** 13 p. black, light blue and maroon . . 30 10
169 40 p. black, yellow and turquoise-blue . . 30 10

Nos. 170, etc. Nos. 131/42

1962–70. *As T* **60/1** *but with redrawn Bengali inscription at top right. No wmk.*
170 **60** 1 p. violet (1963) 10 10
171 2 p. rose-red (1964) 75 10
a. Imperf (pair) . . . . 3·00
172 3 p. reddish purple (1970) . . . . 4·00 2·75
173 5 p. ultramarine (1963) 10 10
a. Printed on the gummed side . . 12·00
174 7 p. emerald (1964) . . . . 5·00 2·75
175 **61** 10 p. brown (1963) 10 10
a. Printed on the gummed side . . 12·00
176 13 p. slate-violet 10 10
176*a* 15 p. bright purple (31.12.64) 15 10
ab. Imperf (pair) . . . . 4·50
ac. Printed on the gummed side . .
176*b* 20 p. myrtle-green (26.1.70) 30 10
ba. Imperf (pair) . . . . 3·50
bb. Printed on the gummed side . . 15·00
177 25 p. deep blue (1963) . . . . 6·50 10
a. Imperf (pair) . . . .
178 40 p. deep purple (1964) 15 15
a. Imperf (pair) . . . . 6·50
179 50 p. deep bluish green (1964) 15 10
a. Printed on the gummed side . .
180 75 p. carmine-red (1964) 30 70
a. Printed on the gummed side . . 12·00
181 90 p. yellow-green (1964) 30 90
170/81 . . . . *Set of* 14 16·00 7·00
Other values in this series and the high values (Nos. 204/10) are known imperforate but we are not satisfied as to their status.

U.N. FORCE W. IRIAN

(84)

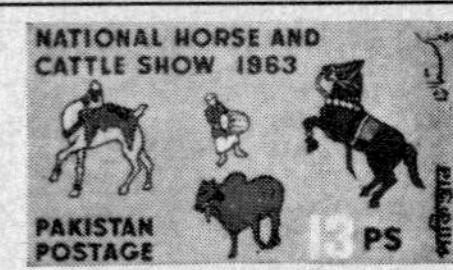

85 "Dancing" Horse, Camel and Bull

1963 (15 Feb). *Pakistan U.N. Force in West Irian. No. 176 optd with T* **84**.
182 **61** 13 p. slate-violet (R.) 10 20

(Des S. Jahangir. Photo Courvoisier)

1963 (13 Mar). *National Horse and Cattle Show. P* 11½.
183 **85** 13 p. blue, sepia and cerise 10 10

86 Wheat and Tractor

1963 (21 Mar). *Freedom from Hunger. T* **86** *and similar horiz design. P* 12½ × 14.
184 13 p. orange-brown . . . . 2·00 10
185 50 p. bistre-brown . . . . 3·50 55
Design:—50 p. Rice.

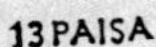

INTERNATIONAL DACCA STAMP EXHIBITION 1963

(88)

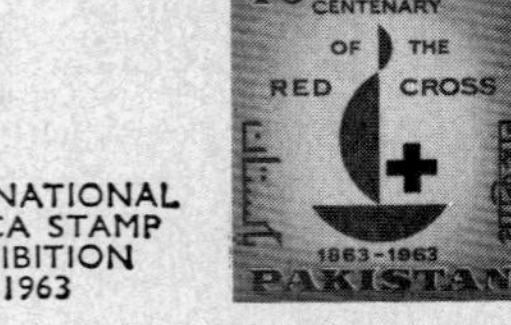

89 Centenary Emblem

1963 (23 Mar). *2nd International Stamp Exhibition, Dacca. No. 109 surch with T* **88**.
186 **51** 13 p. on 2 a. brown-red 75 10

1963 (25 June). *Centenary of Red Cross. Recess; cross typo. P* 13.
187 **89** 40 p. red and deep olive . . . . 2·00 15

90 Paharpur

100 YEARS OF P.W.D.
OCTOBER, 1963
13

(94)

1963 (16 Sept). *Archaeological Series. T* **90** *and similar designs. P* 14 × 12½ (13 *p.*) *or* 12½ × 15 (*others*).
188 7 p. ultramarine 45 10
189 13 p. sepia 45 10
190 40 p. carmine 80 10
191 50 p. deep reddish violet 85 10
188/91 . . . . . . *Set of* 4 2·25 30
Designs: *Vert*—13 p. Moenjodaro; *Horiz*—40 p. Taxila; 50 p. Mainamati.

1963 (7 Oct). *Centenary of Public Works Department. No.* 133 *surch with T* **94** *by typography*.
192 **60** 13 p. on 3 p. reddish purple 10 10
Forged surcharges applied in *lithography* exist.

95 Ataturk's Mausoleum

1963 (10 Nov). *25th Death Anniv of Kemal Atatürk. P* 13½.
193 **95** 50 p. red 80 10

96 Globe and U.N.E.S.C.O. Emblem

(Photo D.L.R.)

1963 (10 Dec). *15th Anniv of Declaration of Human Rights. P* 14.
194 **96** 50 p. brown, red and ultramarine . . 70 10

97 Thermal Power Installations

1963 (25 Dec). *Completion of Multan Thermal Power Station. P* 12½ × 14.
195 **97** 13 p. ultramarine 10 10

98 Multiple Star and Crescent

99 Temple of Thot, Queen Nefertari and Maids

1963–79. *As Nos.* 43*b*, 89, 95 *and* 143/4*b*, *but W* **98** (*sideways* on* 15 *r.*).
204 **62** 1 r. vermilion 30 10
a. Printed on the gummed side . .
b. Imperf (pair) . . . . . . 7·50
w. Wmk inverted . . . . . . 1·25
205 1 r. 25, reddish violet (1964) . . 1·25 10
aw. Wmk inverted . . . . . . 2·25
b. Purple (1975?) . . . . . . 1·25 10
ba. Imperf (pair) . . . . . . 6·00
206 2 r. orange (1964) 55 15
a. Imperf (pair) . . . . . . 8·00
w. Wmk inverted . . . . . . 1·75
207 5 r. green (1964) . . . . . . 4·00 55
a. Imperf (pair) . . . . . . 11·00
w. Wmk inverted . . . . . . 4·00
208 **41** 10 r. myrtle-green & yellow-orge (1968) 3·00 3·50
a. Imperf (pair) . . . . . .
bw. Wmk inverted . . . . . .
c. Wmk sideways . . . . . . 1·25 1·25
209 **44** 15 r. red & deep reddish purple (20.3.79) 1·25 1·75
a. Imperf (pair) . . . . . . 13·00
w. Wmk tips of crescent pointing downwards . . . . . .
210 **13** 25 r. violet (1968) . . . . . . 6·00 9·00
aw. Wmk inverted . . . . . . 13·00
b. Wmk sideways . . . . . . 3·00 4·00
ba. Imperf (pair) . . . . . . 15·00
204/10b . . . . . . *Set of* 7 10·50 7·00
*The normal sideways watermark shows the tips of the crescent pointing upwards, *when viewed from the back of the stamp*.

1964 (30 Mar). *Nubian Monuments Preservation. T* **99** *and similar horiz design. P* 13 × 13½.
211 13 p. turquoise-blue and red 75 10
212 50 p. bright purple and black . . . . . . 1·25 10
Design:—50 p. Temple of Abu Simbel.

101 "Unisphere" and Pakistan Pavilion

103 Shah Abdul Latif's Mausoleum

1964 (22 Apr). *New York World's Fair. T* **101** *and similar design. P* 12½ × 14 (13 *p.*) *or* 14 × 12½ (1 *r.* 25).
213 13 p. ultramarine 10 10
214 1 r. 25, ultramarine and red-orange 40 20
Design: *Vert*—1 r. 25, Pakistan Pavilion on "Unisphere".

1964 (25 June). *Death Bicentenary of Shah Abdul Latif of Bhit. P* 13½ × 13.
215 **103** 50 p. bright blue and carmine-lake . . 80 10

104 Mausoleum of Quaid-i-Azam

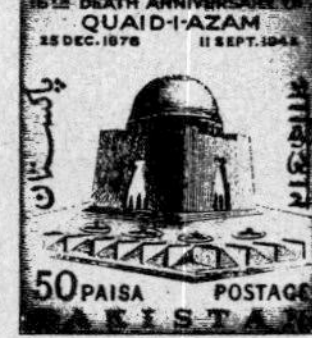

105 Mausoleum

1964 (11 Sept). *16th Death Anniv of Mohammed Ali Jinnah (Quaid-i-Azam). P* 13½ (15 *p.*) *or* 13 (50 *p.*).
216 **104** 15 p. emerald-green 75 10
217 **105** 50 p. bronze-green . . . . . . 1·75 10

106 Bengali and Urdu Alphabets

ENGINEERING UNIVERSITY LAHORE
107 University Building

1964 (5 Oct). *Universal Children's Day. P* 13.
218 **106** 15 p. brown 10 10

1964 (21 Dec). *First Convocation of the West Pakistan University of Engineering and Technology, Lahore. P* 12½ × 14.
219 **107** 15 p. chestnut 10 10

PROCESS. All the following issues were lithographed by the Pakistan Security Printing Corporation, *unless otherwise stated*.

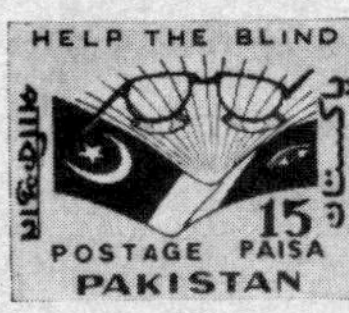

108 "Help the Blind"

109 "I.T.U. Emblem and Symbols

(Des A. Chughtai)

1965 (28 Feb). *Blind Welfare. P* 13.
220 **108** 15 p. ultramarine and yellow 20 10

1965 (17 May). *I.T.U. Centenary. Recess. P* 12½ × 14.
221 **109** 15 p. reddish purple . . . . . . 1·50 30

110 I.C.Y. Emblem

1965 (26 June). *International Co-operation Year. P* 13 × 13½.
222 **110** 15 p. black and light blue 50 15
223 50 p. green and yellow . . . . . . 1·00 40

111 "Co-operation"

112 Globe and Flags of Turkey, Iran and Pakistan

1965 (21 July). *First Anniv of Regional Development Co-operation Pact. P* 13½ × 13 (15 *p.*) *or* 13 (50 *p.*).
224 **111** 15 p. multicoloured 20 10
225 **112** 50 p. multicoloured . . . . . . 1·10 10

113 Soldier and Tanks

1965 (25 Dec). *Pakistan Armed Forces. T* **113** *and similar horiz designs. Multicoloured. P* 13½ × 13.
226 7 p. Type **113** 75 30
227 15 p. Naval officer and *Tughril* (destroyer) 1·50 10
228 50 p. Pilot and Lockheed F-104C Star-fighters . . . . 2·50 30
226/8 . . . . . . *Set of* 3 4·25 60

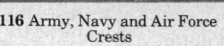

ARMED FORCES DAY
FEBRUARY, 1966
15 PAISA POSTAGE
PAKISTAN
116 Army, Navy and Air Force Crests

117 Atomic Reactor, Islamabad

1966 (13 Feb). *Armed Forces Day. P* 13½ × 13.
229 **116** 15 p. royal blue, dull grn, brt blue & buff 55 10

1966 (30 Apr). *Inauguration of Pakistan's First Atomic Reactor. Recess. P* 13.
230 **117** 15 p. black 10 10

118 Bank Crest — **119** Children

1966 (25 Aug). *Silver Jubilee of Habib Bank. P* 12½ × 14.
231 **118** 15 p. blue-green, yellow-orange & sepia 10 10

1966 (3 Oct). *Universal Children's Day. P* 13½.
232 **119** 15 p. black, red and pale yellow 10 10

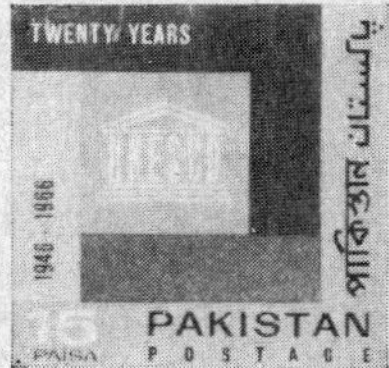

120 U.N.E.S.C.O. Emblem

1966 (24 Nov). *20th Anniv of U.N.E.S.C.O. P* 14.
233 **120** 15 p. multicoloured . . . . . . 2·75 30

121 Flag, Secretariat Building and President Ayub

1966 (29 Nov). *Islamabad (new capital). P* 13.
234 **121** 15 p. deep bluish green, chestnut, light blue and bistre-brown 25 10
235 50 p. deep bluish green, chestnut, light blue and black 60 10

122 Avicenna — **123** Mohammed Ali Jinnah

1966 (3 Dec). *Foundation of Health and Tibbi Research Institute. P* 13 × 13½.
236 **122** 15 p. dull green and salmon 40 10
a. Imperf (pair) . . . . . . 65·00

1966 (25 Dec). *90th Birth Anniv of Mohammed Ali Jinnah. T* **123** *and similar design bearing same portrait but in different frame. Litho and recess. P* 13.
237 **123** 15 p. black, orange and greenish blue . . 20 10
238 – 50 p. black, purple and ultramarine . . 50 10

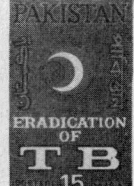

124 Tourist Year Emblem — **125** Emblem of Pakistan T.B. Association

1967 (1 Jan). *International Tourist Year. P* 13½ × 13.
239 **124** 15 p. black, light blue and yellow-brown 10 10

1967 (10 Jan). *Tuberculosis Eradication Campaign. P* 13½ × 13.
240 **125** 15 p. red, sepia and chestnut 10 10

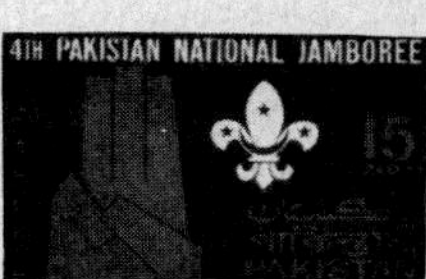

126 Scout Salute and Badge — **127** "Justice"

1967 (29 Jan). *4th National Scout Jamboree. Photo. P* 12½ × 14.
241 **126** 15 p. light orange-brown and maroon . . 15 10

1967 (17 Feb). *Centenary of West Pakistan High Court. P* 13.
242 **127** 15 p. black, slate, light red and slate-blue 10 10

128 Dr. Mohammed Iqbal (philosopher)

1967 (21 Apr). *Iqbal Commemoration. P* 13.
243 **128** 15 p. sepia and light red 15 10
244 1 r. sepia and deep green 60 10

129 Hilal-i-Isteqlal Flag

1967 (15 May). *Award of Hilal-i-Isteqlal (for Valour) to Lahore, Sialkot, and Sargodha. P* 13.
245 **129** 15 p. multicoloured 10 10

130 "20th Anniversary"

1967 (14 Aug). *20th Anniv of Independence. Photo. P* 13.
246 **130** 15 p. red and deep bluish green 10 10

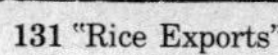

131 "Rice Exports" — **132** Cotton Plant, Yarn and Textiles

1967 (26 Sept). *Pakistan Exports. T* **131/2** *and similar design. Photo. P* 13 × 13½.
247 10 p. yellow, deep bluish green and deep blue 10 15
248 15 p. multicoloured 10 10
a. Pale orange (top panel) omitted . . . . 10·00
249 50 p. multicoloured 20 15
247/9 . . . . *Set of* 3 30 30
Design: *Vert as T* **132**—50 p. Raw jute, bale and bags.

134 Clay Toys

1967 (2 Oct). *Universal Children's Day. P* 13.
250 **134** 15 p. multicoloured 10 10

135 Shah and Empress of Iran and Gulistan Palace, Teheran

1967 (26 Oct). *Coronation of Shah Mohammed Riza Pahlavi and Empress Farah of Iran. Recess and litho. P* 13.
251 **135** 50 p. purple, blue and light yellow-ochre 70 10

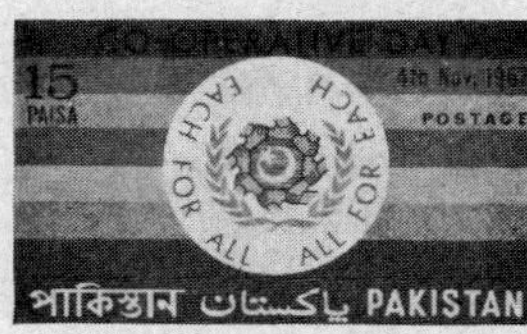

136 "Each For All–All For Each"

1967 (4 Nov). *Co-operative Day. P* 13.
252 **136** 15 p. multicoloured 10 10

137 Mangla Dam

1967 (23 Nov). *Indus Basin Project. P* 13.
253 **137** 15 p. multicoloured 10 10

138 Crab pierced by Sword — **139** Human Rights Emblem

1967 (26 Dec). *The Fight Against Cancer. P* 13.
254 **138** 15 p. red and black 70 10

1968 (31 Jan). *Human Rights Year. Photo. P* 14 × 13.
255 **139** 15 p. red and deep turquoise-blue . . 10 15
256 50 p. red, yellow and silver-grey 10 15

140 Agricultural University, Mymensingh — **141** W.H.O. Emblem

1968 (28 Mar). *First Convocation of East Pakistan Agricultural University. Photo. P* 13½ × 13.
257 **140** 15 p. multicoloured 10 10

1968 (7 Apr). *20th Anniv of World Health Organization. Photo. P* 14 × 13.
258 **141** 15 p. green and orange-red 10 15
a. "PAIS" for "PAISA" (R.4/5) . . 1·50
259 50 p. red-orange and indigo 10 15

142 Kazi Nazrul Islam (poet, composer and patriot)

1968 (25 June). *Nazrul Islam Commemoration. Recess and litho. P* 13.
260 **142** 15 p. sepia and pale yellow 30 15
261 50 p. sepia and pale rose-red 60 15
Nos. 260/1 with a two-line inscription giving the wrong date of birth ("1889") were prepared but not issued. Some are known to have been released in error.

4 PAISA

(143)

1968 (18 July–Aug). *Nos.* 56, 74 *and* 61 *surch as T* **143**.

262 4 p. on 3 a. purple .. .. 65 1·25
263 4 p. on 6 a. deep ultramarine (R.) (Aug) .. 1·00 1·25
264 60 p. on 10 a. violet (R.) 50 35
a. Surch in black 30 70
b. Surch triple .. .. 30·00
262/4 .. .. *Set of* 3 1·90 2·50

144 Children running with Hoops

1968 (7 Oct). *Universal Children's Day. P* 13.

265 **144** 15 p. multicoloured 10 10

145 "National Assembly"

1968 (27 Oct). *"A Decade of Development". T* **145** *and similar horiz designs. P* 13.

266 10 p. multicoloured 10 10
267 15 p. multicoloured 15 10
268 50 p. multicoloured .. .. 2·25 20
269 60 p. light blue, dull purple and vermilion .. 1·00 35
266/9 .. .. *Set of* 4 3·00 65

Designs:—15 p. Industry and agriculture; 50 p. Army, Navy and Air Force; 60 p. Minaret and atomic reactor plant.

149 Chittagong Steel Mill

1969 (7 Jan). *Pakistan's First Steel Mill, Chittagong. P* 13.

270 **149** 15 p. grey, light blue & pale yellow-olive 10 10

150 "Family"

151 Olympic Gold Medal and Hockey Player

1969 (14 Jan). *Family Planning. P* 13½ × 13.

271 **150** 15 p. bright purple & pale greenish blue 10 10

1969 (30 Jan). *Olympic Hockey Champions. Photo. P* 13½.

272 **151** 15 p. black, gold, deep green & pale blue 1·00 50
273 1 r. black, gold, dp green & flesh-pink .. 2·50 1·00

152 Mirza Ghalib and Lines of Verse

1969 (15 Feb). *Death Centenary of Mirza Ghalib (poet). P* 13.

274 **152** 15 p. multicoloured 20 15
275 50 p. multicoloured 50 15

The lines of verse on No. 275 are different from those in T **152**.

153 Dacca Railway Station

1969 (27 Apr). *First Anniv of New Dacca Railway Station. P* 13.

276 **153** 15 p. multicoloured 30 10

154 I.L.O. Emblem and "1919–1969"

155 "Lady on Balcony" (18th-cent Mogul)

1969 (15 May). *50th Anniv of International Labour Organisation. P* 13½.

277 **154** 15 p. buff and bluish green 10 10
278 50 p. cinnamon and cerise 40 10

1969 (21 July). *Fifth Anniv of Regional Co-operation for Development. T* **155** *and similar vert designs showing miniatures. Multicoloured. P* 13.

279 20 p. Type **155** 15 10
280 50 p. "Kneeling Servant" (17th-cent Persian) 15 10
281 1 r. "Suleiman the Magnificent holding Audience" (16th-cent Turkish) .. 20 10
279/81 .. .. *Set of* 3 45 30

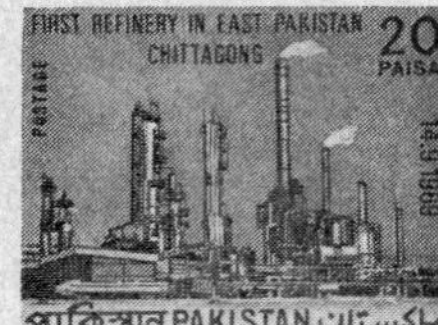

158 Eastern Refinery, Chittagong

1969 (14 Sept). *First Oil Refinery in East Pakistan. Photo. P* 13½ × 13.

282 **158** 20 p. multicoloured 10 10

159 Children playing Outside "School"

1969 (6 Oct). *Universal Children's Day. Photo. P* 13.

283 **159** 20 p. multicoloured 10 10

160 Japanese Doll and P.I.A. Air Routes

1969 (1 Nov). *Inauguration of P.I.A. Pearl Route, Dacca–Tokyo. P* 13½ × 13.

284 **160** 20 p. multicoloured 60 10
a. Yellow and pink omitted .. .. 8·00
285 50 p. multicoloured 90 40
a. Yellow and pink omitted .. .. 8·00

161 "Reflection of Light" Diagram

1969 (4 Nov). *Millenary Commemorative of Ibn-al-Haitham (physicist). Photo. P* 13.

286 **161** 20 p. black, lemon and light blue .. 10 10

172 Vickers Vimy and Karachi Airport

163 Flags, Sun Tower and Expo Site Plan

1969 (2 Dec). *50th Anniv of First England–Australia Flight. Photo. P* 13½ × 13.

287 **162** 50 p. multicoloured .. .. .. 1·00 35

1970 (15 Mar). *World Fair, Osaka. P* 13.

288 **163** 50 p. multicoloured 20 30

164 New U.P.U. H.Q. Building

1970 (20 May). *New U.P.U. Headquarters Building. P* 13½ × 13.

289 **164** 20 p. multicoloured 15 10
290 50 p. multicoloured 25 25

The above, in a miniature sheet, additionally inscr "U.P.U. Day 9th Oct, 1971", were put on sale on that date in very limited numbers.

165 U.N. H.Q. Building

1970 (26 June). *25th Anniv of United Nations. T* **165** *and similar horiz design. Multicoloured. P* 13 × 13½.

291 20 p. Type **165** 15 10
292 50 p. U.N. emblem 15 20

167 I.E.Y. Emblem, Book and Pen

1970 (6 July). *International Education Year. P* 13.

293 **167** 20 p. multicoloured 10 10
294 50 p. multicoloured 20 20

168 Saiful Malook Lake (Pakistan)

1970 (21 July). *Sixth Anniv of Regional Co-operation for Development. T* **168** *and similar square designs. Multicoloured. P* 13.

295 20 p. Type **168** 15 10
296 50 p. Seeyo-Se-Pol Bridge, Esfahan (Iran) .. 20 10
297 1 r. View from Fethiye (Turkey) 20 15
295/7 .. .. *Set of* 3 50 30

171 Asian Productivity Symbol

172 Dr. Maria Montessori

1970 (18 Aug). *Asian Productivity Year. Photo. P* 12½ × 14.
298 **171** 50 p. multicoloured 20 20

1970 (31 Aug). *Birth Centenary of Dr. Maria Montessori (educationist). P* 13.
299 **172** 20 p. multicoloured 15 10
300 50 p. multicoloured 15 30

173 Tractor and Fertilizer Factory

1970 (12 Sept). *Tenth Near East F.A.O. Regional Conference, Islamabad. P* 13.
301 **173** 20 p. bright green, and orange-brown 15 20

174 Children and Open Book

175 Pakistan Flag and Text

1970 (5 Oct). *Universal Children's Day. Photo. P* 13.
302 **174** 20 p. multicoloured 15 10

1970 (7 Dec). *General Elections for National Assembly. P* 13½ × 13.
303 **175** 20 p. green and bluish violet 15 10

1970 (17 Dec). *General Elections for Provincial Assemblies. As No.* 303, *but inscr* "PROVINCIAL ASSEMBLIES 17TH DEC., 1970".
304 **175** 20 p. green and pale magenta 15 10

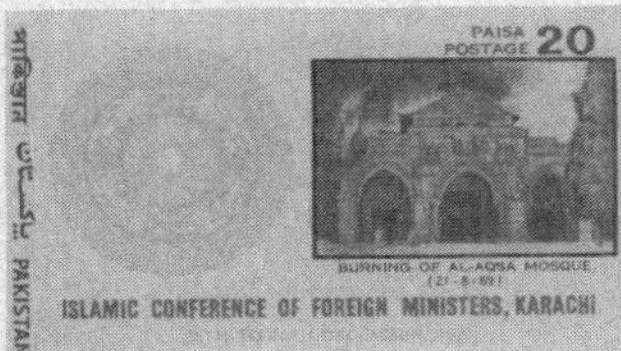

176 Conference Crest and burning Al-Aqsa Mosque

1970 (26 Dec). *Conference of Islamic Foreign Ministers. Karachi. P* 13.
305 **176** 20 p. multicoloured 15 15

177 Coastal Embankments

1971 (25 Feb). *Coastal Embankments in East Pakistan Project. P* 13.
306 **177** 20 p. multicoloured 15 15

178 Emblem and United Peoples of the World

180 Chaharbagh School (Iran)

179 Maple Leaf Cement Factory, Daudkhel

1971 (21 Mar). *Racial Equality Year. P* 13.
307 **178** 20 p. multicoloured 10 15
308 50 p. multicoloured 20 45

1971 (1 July). *20th Anniv of Colombo Plan. P* 13.
309 **179** 20 p. brown, black and reddish violet .. 10 10

1971 (21 July). *Seventh Anniv of Regional Co-operation for Development. T* **180** *and similar horiz designs. Multicoloured. P* 13.
310 10 p. Selimiye Mosque (Turkey) 10 15
311 20 p. Badshahi Mosque (Lahore) 20 25
312 50 p. Type **180** 30 35
310/12 .. .. *Set of* 3 55 65

181 Electric Locomotive and Boy with Toy Train

1971 (4 Oct). *Universal Children's Day. P* 13.
313 **181** 20 p. multicoloured .. .. .. 1·75 50

182 Horseman and Symbols

1971 (15 Oct). *2500th Anniv of Persian Monarchy. P* 13.
314 **182** 10 p. multicoloured 35 30
315 20 p. multicoloured 45 40
316 50 p. multicoloured 55 75
314/16 .. .. *Set of* 3 1·25 1·25
The above exist in a miniature sheet, but only a very limited quantity was placed on sale.

183 Hockey-player and Trophy

1971 (24 Oct). *World Cup Hockey Tournament, Barcelona. P* 13.
317 **183** 20 p. multicoloured .. .. .. 1·75 65

184 Great Bath, Moenjodaro

1971 (4 Nov). *25th Anniv of U.N.E.S.C.O. and Campaign to save the Moenjodaro Excavations. P* 13.
318 **184** 20 p. multicoloured 20 30

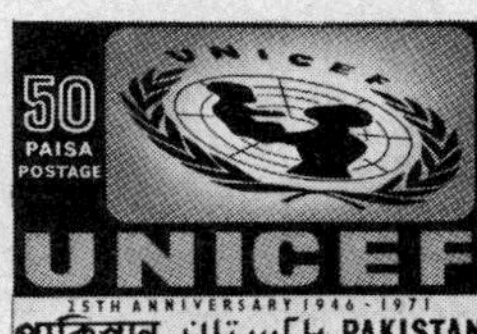

185 U.N.I.C.E.F. Symbol

1971 (11 Dec). *25th Anniv of U.N.I.C.E.F. P* 13.
319 **185** 50 p. multicoloured 30 60

186 King Hussein and Jordanian Flag

1971 (25 Dec). *50th Anniv of Hashemite Kingdom of Jordan. P* 13.
320 **186** 20 p. multicoloured 15 20

187 Badge of Hockey Federation and Trophy

188 Reading Class

1971 (31 Dec). *Hockey Championships Victory. P* 13.
321 **187** 20 p. multicoloured .. .. .. 2·50 90

1972 (15 Jan). *International Book Year. P* 13½.
322 **188** 20 p. multicoloured 20 30

OUTSIDE THE COMMONWEALTH

On 30 January 1972 Pakistan left the Commonwealth.

189 View of Venice

1972 (7 Feb). *U.N.E.S.C.O. Campaign to Save Venice. P* 13.
323 **189** 20 p. multicoloured 30 30

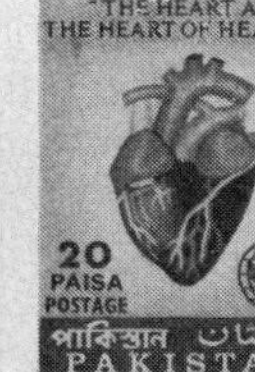

190 E.C.A.F.E. Emblem and Discs

191 Human Heart

1972 (28 Mar). *25th Anniv of E.C.A.F.E. (Economic Commission for Asia and the Far East). P* 13.
324 **190** 20 p. multicoloured 15 30

1972 (7 Apr). *World Health Day. P* 13 × 13½.
325 **191** 20 p. multicoloured 20 30

192 "Only One Earth"

193 "Fisherman" (Cevat Dereli)

1972 (5 June). *U.N. Conference on the Human Environment, Stockholm. P* 13 × 13½.
326 **192** 20 p. multicoloured 20 30

1972 (21 July). *Eighth Anniv of Regional Co-operation for Development. T* **193** *and similar vert designs. Multicoloured. P* 13.
327 10 p. Type **193** 20 20
328 20 p. "Iranian Woman" (Behzad) 35 25
329 50 p. "Will and Power" (A. R. Chughtai) .. 55 70
a. Brown-ochre (border) omitted .. .. 17·00
327/9 .. .. *Set of* 3 1·00 1·00

194 Mohammed Ali Jinnah and Tower   **195** Donating Blood

1972 (14 Aug). *25th Anniv of Independence. T* **194** *and similar horiz designs. Multicoloured. P* 13 (10 *and* 60 *p.*) *or* 14 × 12½ (20 *p.*).
330 10 p. Type **194** 10 10
331 20 p. "Land Reform" (74×23½ *mm*) .. 15 25
a. Vert strip of 4. Nos. 331/4 55
332 20 p. "Labour Reform" (74×23½ *mm*) .. 15 25
333 20 p. "Education Policy" (74×23½ *mm*) .. 15 25
334 20 p. "Health Policy" (74×23½ *mm*) .. 15 25
335 60 p. National Assembly Building (46×28 *mm*) 25 35
330/5 .. .. *Set of* 6 80 1·25
Nos. 331/4 were printed vertically *se-tenant* throughout the sheet.

1972 (6 Sept). *National Blood Transfusion Service. P* 13½×12½.
336 **195** 20 p. multicoloured 20 30

196 People and Squares

1972 (16 Sept). *Centenary of Population Census. P* 13½.
337 **196** 20 p. multicoloured 20 20

197 Children from Slums

1972 (2 Oct). *Universal Children's Day. P* 13.
338 **197** 20 p. multicoloured 20 30

198 People and Open Book

1972 (23 Oct). *Education Week. P* 13.
339 **198** 20 p. multicoloured 20 30

199 Nuclear Power Plant

1972 (28 Nov). *Inauguration of Karachi Nuclear Power Plant. P* 13.
340 **199** 20 p. multicoloured 20 30

200 Copernicus in Observatory

1973 (19 Feb). *500th Birth Anniv of Nicholas Copernicus (astronomer). P* 13.
341 **200** 20 p. multicoloured 20 30

201 Moenjodaro Excavations   **202** Elements of Meteorology

1973 (23 Feb). *50th Anniv of Moenjodaro Excavations. P* 13 × 13½.
342 **201** 20 p. multicoloured 20 30

1973 (23 Mar). *I.M.O./W.M.O. Centenary. P* 13.
343 **202** 20 p. multicoloured 20 30

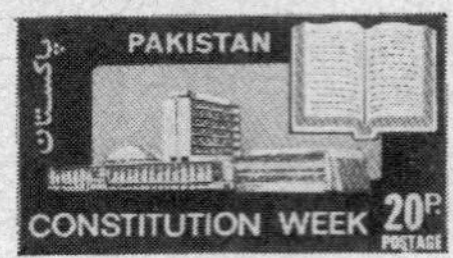

203 Prisoners-of-war

1973 (18 Apr). *Prisoners-of-war in India. P* 13.
344 **203** 1 r. 25, multicoloured .. .. 1·50 2·25

204 National Assembly Building and Constitution Book

1973 (21 Apr). *Constitution Week. P* 12½ × 13½.
345 **204** 20 p. multicoloured 40 40

205 Badge and State Bank Building

1973 (1 July). *25th Anniv of Pakistan State Bank. P* 13.
346 **205** 20 p. multicoloured 15 30
347 1 r. multicoloured 30 50

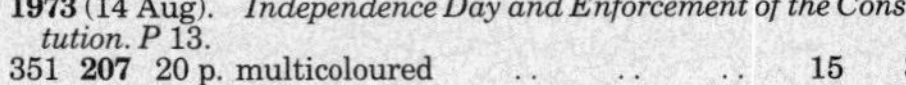

206 Lut Desert Excavations (Iran)   **207** Constitution Book and Flag

1973 (21 July). *9th Anniv of Regional Co-operation for Development. T* **206** *and similar vert designs. Multicoloured. P* 13 × 13½.
348 20 p. Type **206** 30 20
349 60 p. Main Street, Moenjodaro (Pakistan) .. 55 50
350 1 r. 25, Mausoleum of Antiochus I (Turkey) 75 1·25
348/50 .. .. *Set of* 3 1·40 1·75

1973 (14 Aug). *Independence Day and Enforcement of the Constitution. P* 13.
351 **207** 20 p. multicoloured 15 30

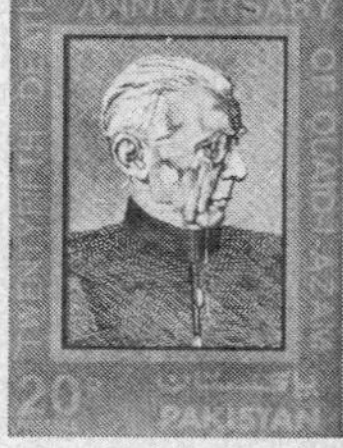

208 Mohammed Ali Jinnah (Quaid-i-Azam)   **209** Wallago

1973 (11 Sept). *25th Death Anniv of Mohammed Ali Jinnah. P* 13.
352 **208** 20 p. light emerald, pale yellow and black 15 30

1973 (24 Sept). *Fishes. T* **209** *and similar horiz designs. Multicoloured. P* 13½.
353 10 p. Type **209** .. .. 1·10 1·10
a. Horiz strip of 4. Nos. 353/6 .. .. 4·75
354 20 p. Rohu .. .. 1·25 1·25
355 60 p. Mozambique Mouthbrooder .. .. 1·40 1·40
356 1 r. Catla .. .. 1·40 1·40
353/6 .. .. *Set of* 4 4·75 4·75
Nos. 353/6 were printed within one sheet, horizontally *se-tenant*.

210 Children's Education

1973 (1 Oct). *Universal Children's Day. P* 13.
357 **210** 20 p. multicoloured 15 30

211 Harvesting

1973 (15 Oct). *Tenth Anniv of World Food Programme. P* 13.
358 **211** 20 p. multicoloured 60 40

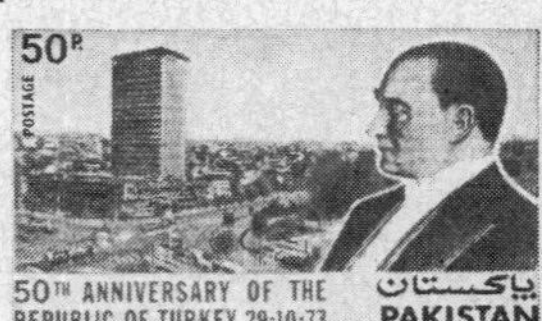

212 Ankara and Kemal Atatürk

1973 (29 Oct). *50th Anniv of Turkish Republic. P* 13.
359 **212** 50 p. multicoloured 45 35

213 Boy Scout   **214** "Basic Necessities"

1973 (11 Nov). *National Silver Jubilee Scout Jamboree. P* 13.
360 **213** 20 p. multicoloured .. .. .. 1·75 50

1973 (16 Nov). *25th Anniv of Declaration of Human Rights. P* 13.
361 **214** 20 p. multicoloured 30 30

215 Al-Biruni and Nandana Hill   **216** Dr. Hansen, Microscope and Bacillus

1973 (26 Nov). *Al-Biruni Millennium Congress. P* 13.
362 **215** 20 p. multicoloured 40 20
363 1 r. 25, multicoloured 85 75

1973 (29 Dec). *Centenary of Hansen's Discovery of Leprosy Bacillus. P* 13.
364 **216** 20 p. multicoloured .. .. .. 1·00 60

217 Family and Emblem   **218** Conference Emblem

1974 (1 Jan). *World Population Year. P* 13.
365 **217** 20 p. multicoloured 10 10
366 1 r. 25, multicoloured 30 40

1974 (22 Feb). *Islamic Summit Conference, Lahore. T* **218** *and similar design. P* 14 × 12½ (20 *p.*) *or* 13 (65 *p.*).
367 20 p. Type **218** 10 10
368 65 p. Emblem on "Sun" (42 × 30 *mm*) 25 60
MS369 102 × 102 mm. Nos. 367/8. Imperf .. 2·50 5·50

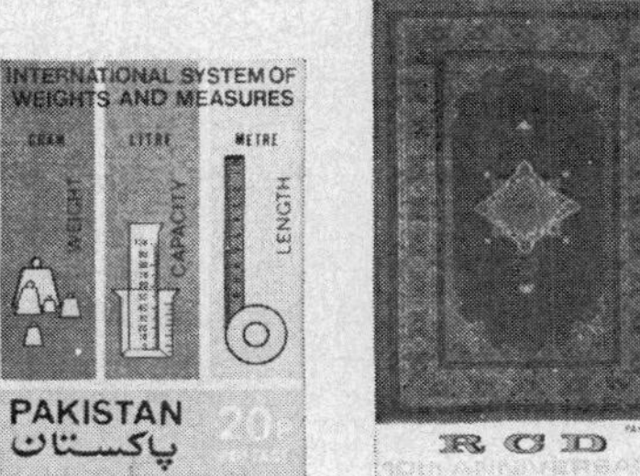

219 Units of Weight and Measurement **220** "Chand Chauthai" Carpet, Pakistan

1974 (1 July). *Adoption of International Weights and Measures System. P* 13.
370 **219** 20 p. multicoloured 15 25

1974 (21 July). *Tenth Anniv of Regional Co-operation for Development. Vert designs as T* **220** *showing carpets from member countries. Multicoloured. P* 13.
371 20 p. Type **220** 20 15
372 60 p. Persian carpet, 16th-century 55 55
373 1 r. 25, Anatolian carpet, 15th-century .. 90 1·25
371/3 .. .. *Set of* 3 1·50 1·75

221 Hands protecting Sapling **222** Torch and Map

1974 (9 Aug). *Tree Planting Day. P* 13.
374 **221** 20 p. multicoloured 50 50

1974 (26 Aug). *Namibia Day. P* 13.
375 **222** 60 p. multicoloured 35 60

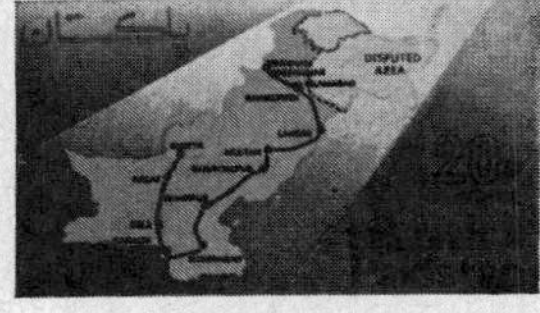

223 Highway Map

1974 (23 Sept). *Shahrah-e-Pakistan (Pakistan Highway). P* 13.
376 **223** 20 p. multicoloured 90 60

224 Boy at Desk **225** U.P.U. Emblem

1974 (7 Oct). *Universal Children's Day. P* 13.
377 **224** 20 p. multicoloured 30 30

1974 (9 Oct). *Centenary of Universal Postal Union. T* **225** *and similar vert design. Multicoloured. P* 13 × 13½ (20 *p.*) *or* 13 (2 *r.* 25).
378 20 p. Type **225** 20 20
379 2 r. 25, U.P.U. emblem, Boeing 707 and mail-wagon (30×41 *mm*) .. .. 55 1·40
MS380 100×101 mm. Nos. 378/9. Imperf .. 4·00 8·50

226 Liaquat Ali Khan **227** Dr. Mohammed Iqbal (poet and philosopher)

1974 (16 Oct). *Liaquat Ali Khan (First Prime Minister of Pakistan). P* 13 × 13½.
381 **226** 20 p. black and light vermilion 30 30

1974 (9 Nov). *Birth Centenary of Dr. Iqbal* (1977) (*1st issue*). *P* 13.
382 **227** 20 p. multicoloured 30 30
See also Nos. 399, 433 and 445/9.

228 Dr. Schweitzer and River Scene

1975 (14 Jan). *Birth Centenary of Dr. Albert Schweitzer. P* 13.
383 **228** 2 r. 25, multicoloured .. .. .. 2·75 3·25

229 Tourism Year Symbol

1975 (15 Jan). *South East Asia Tourism Year. P* 13.
384 **229** 2 r. 25, multicoloured 55 80

230 Assembly Hall, Flags and Prime Minister Bhutto

(Des A. Salahuddin)

1975 (22 Feb). *First Anniv of Islamic Summit Conference, Lahore. P* 13.
385 **230** 20 p. multicoloured 45 35
386 1 r. multicoloured .. .. .. 1·10 1·40

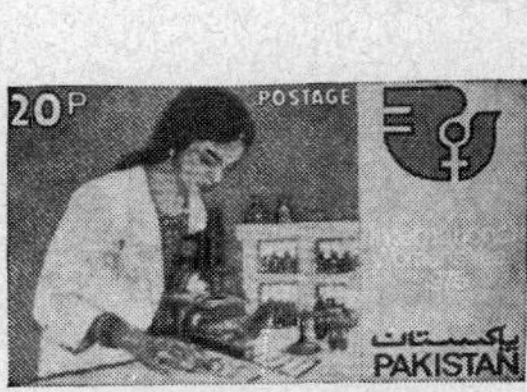

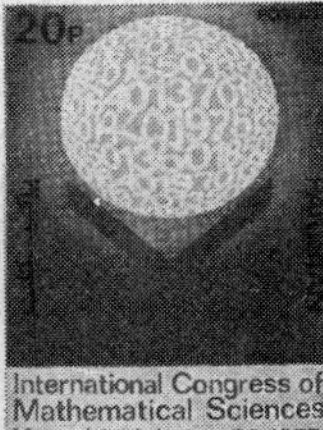

231 "Scientific Research" **232** "Globe" and Algebraic Symbol

(Des A. Salahuddin (20 p.), M. Ahmed (2 r. 25))

1975 (15 June). *International Women's Year. T* **231** *and similar horiz design. Multicoloured. P* 13.
387 20 p. Type **231** 20 25
388 2 r. 25, Girl teaching woman ("Adult Education") .. .. 1·10 2·00

1975 (14 July). *International Congress of Mathematical Sciences, Karachi. P* 13.
389 **232** 20 p. multicoloured 50 50

233 Pakistani Camel-skin Vase **234** Sapling and Dead Trees

(Des I. Gilani)

1975 (21 July). *Eleventh Anniv of Regional Co-operation for Development. T* **233** *and similar multicoloured designs. P* 13.
390 20 p. Type **233** 25 30
391 60 p. Iranian tile (*horiz*) .. .. .. 50 1·00
392 1 r. 25, Turkish porcelain vase .. .. 75 1·50
390/2 .. .. *Set of* 3 1·40 2·50

1975 (9 Aug). *Tree Planting Day. P* 13 × 13½.
393 **234** 20 p. multicoloured 35 40

235 Black Partridge **236** "Today's Girls"

(Des A. Salahuddin)

1975 (30 Sept). *Wildlife Protection* (*1st series*). *P* 13.
394 **235** 20 p. multicoloured .. .. .. 1·25 35
395 2 r. 25, multicoloured .. .. .. 4·00 4·25
See also Nos. 400/1, 411/12, 417/18, 493/6, 560, 572/3, 581/2, 599, 600, 605, 621/2, 691, 702, 752, 780/3 and 853.

1975 (6 Oct). *Universal Children's Day. P* 13.
396 **236** 20 p. multicoloured 30 30

237 Hazrat Amir Khusrau, Sitar and Tabla

(Des A. Salahuddin)

1975 (24 Oct). *700th Birth Anniv of Hazrat Amir Khusrau (poet and musician). P* 13½ × 12½.
397 **237** 20 p. multicoloured 20 45
398 2 r. 25, multicoloured .. .. .. 75 1·60

238 Dr. Mohammed Iqbal **239** Urial (wild sheep)

(Des A. Salahuddin)

1975 (9 Nov). *Birth Centenary of Dr. Iqbal* (1977) (*2nd issue*). *P* 13.
399 **238** 20 p. multicoloured 30 30

(Des M. Ahmed)

1975 (31 Dec). *Wildlife Protection* (*2nd series*). *P* 13.
400 **239** 20 p. multicoloured 40 30
401 3 r. multicoloured .. .. .. 2·50 3·25

240 Moenjodaro Remains **241** Dome and Minaret of Rauza-e-Mubarak

(Des A. Salahuddin)

1976 (29 Feb). *"Save Moenjodaro"* (*1st series*). *T* **240** *and similar vert designs. Multicoloured. P* 13.
402 10 p. Type **240** 65 75
a. Horiz strip of 5. Nos. 402/6 .. .. 3·25
403 20 p. Remains (*different*) 75 85
404 65 p. The Citadel 75 85
405 3 r. Well inside a house 75 85
406 4 r. The "Great Bath" 85 95
402/6 .. .. *Set of* 5 3·25 3·75
Nos. 402/6 were printed horizontally *se-tenant* within the sheet, the five stamps forming a composite design of the excavations.
See also Nos. 414 and 430.

(Des A. Ghani. Photo)

1976 (3 Mar). *International Congress on Seerat. P* 13 × 13½.

407 **241** 20 p. multicoloured 20 20
408 3 r. multicoloured 70 90

242 Alexander Graham Bell and Telephone Dial

(Des M. M. Saeed. Photo)

1976 (10 Mar). *Telephone Centenary. P* 13.

409 **242** 3 r. multicoloured . . . . . . 1·25 2·00

243 College Arms within "Sun"

(Des A. Salahuddin)

1976 (15 Mar). *Centenary of National College of Arts, Lahore. P* 13.

410 **243** 20 p. multicoloured 30 40

244 Common Peafowl

(Des A. Salahuddin)

1976 (31 Mar). *Wildlife Protection* (3*rd series*). *P* 13.

411 **244** 20 p. multicoloured . . . . . . 1·00 35
412 3 r. multicoloured . . . . . . 3·50 4·50

245 Human Eye

(Des M. M. Saeed)

1976 (7 Apr). *Prevention of Blindness. P* 13.

413 **245** 20 p. multicoloured 70 70

246 Unicorn and Ruins

(Des I. Gilani)

1976 (31 May). *"Save Moenjodaro"* (2*nd series*). *P* 13.

414 **246** 20 p. multicoloured 30 35

247 Jefferson Memorial **248** Ibex

(Des I. Gilani (90 p.), A. Salahuddin (4 r.))

1976 (4 July). *Bicentenary of American Revolution. T* **247** *and similar horiz design. Multicoloured. P* 13 (90 *p.*) *or* 13½ (4 *r.*).

415 90 p. Type **247** . . . . . . 1·00 60
416 4 r. "Declaration of Independence" (47 × 36 *mm*) . . . . . . 3·75 5·00

(Des M. Ahmed)

1976 (12 July). *Wildlife Protection* (4*th series*). *P* 13.

417 **248** 20 p. multicoloured 30 35
418 3 r. multicoloured . . . . . . 1·75 2·50

249 Mohammed Ali Jinnah

(Des A. Salahuddin)

1976 (21 July). *Twelfth Anniv of Regional Co-operation for Development. T* **249** *and similar diamond-shaped designs. Multicoloured. P* 14.

419 20 p. Type **249** 80 80
a. Vert strip of 3. Nos. 419/21 . . . . 2·25
420 65 p. Reza Shah the Great (Iran) 80 80
421 90 p. Kemal Atatürk (Turkey) 80 80
419/21 . . . . . . *Set of* 3 2·25 2·25

Nos. 419/21 were printed vertically *se-tenant* throughout the sheet.

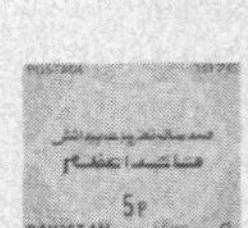

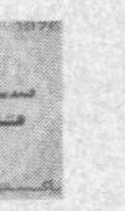

250 Urdu Text **251** Mohammed Ali Jinnah and Wazir Mansion

1976 (14 Aug). *Birth Centenary of Mohammed Ali Jinnah* (1*st issue*). *P* 13. (*a*) *Type* **250**.

422 5 p. black, new blue and yellow 20 25
a. Block of 8. Nos. 422/9 . . . . 1·75
423 10 p. black, yellow and magenta 20 25
424 15 p. black and violet-blue 20 25
425 1 r. black, yellow and new blue 30 30

(*b*) *Multicoloured designs as T* **251**, *different buildings in the background*

426 20 p. Type **251** 20 25
427 40 p. Sind Madressah 20 25
428 50 p. Minar Qarardad-e-Pakistan 20 25
429 3 r. Mausoleum 45 50
422/9 . . . . . . *Set of* 8 1·75 2·10

Nos. 422/9 were printed in *se-tenant* blocks of 8 throughout the sheet.

See also No. 436.

252 Dancing-girl, Ruins and King Priest

(Des A. Salahuddin)

1976 (31 Aug). *"Save Moenjodaro"* (3*rd series*). *P* 14.

430 **252** 65 p. multicoloured 35 60

253 U.N. Racial Discrimination Emblem

(Des A. Salahuddin)

1976 (15 Sept). *U.N. Decade to Combat Racial Discrimination. P* 12½ × 13½.

431 **253** 65 p. multicoloured 30 60

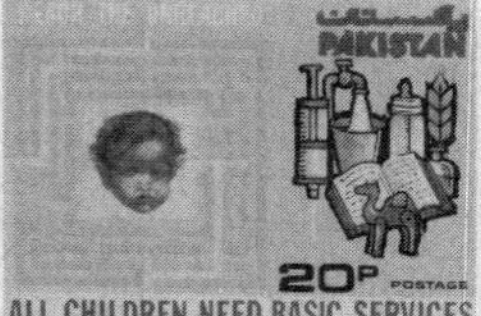

254 Child in Maze and Basic Services

(Des M. Ahmed)

1976 (4 Oct). *Universal Children's Day. P* 13.

432 **254** 20 p. multicoloured 30 30

Stamps commemorating the visit of King Khalid of Saudi Arabia and showing the Islamabad Mosque were prepared for release on 11 October 1976, but withdrawn before issue. Some are known to have been released in error.

255 Verse from "Allama Iqbal" **256** Mohammed Ali Jinnah giving Scout Salute

(Des M. A. Javed)

1976 (9 Nov). *Birth Centenary of Dr. Iqbal* (1977) (3*rd issue*). *P* 13.

433 **255** 20 p. multicoloured 15 30

(Des I. Gilani)

1976 (20 Nov). *Quaid-i-Azam Centenary Jamboree. P* 13½.

434 **256** 20 p. multicoloured 55 30

257 Children Reading **258** Mohammed Ali Jinnah

(Des M. Ahmed)

1976 (15 Dec). *Children's Literature. P* 13.

435 **257** 20 p. multicoloured 20 30

(Litho and embossed Cartor S.A., France)

1976 (25 Dec). *Birth Centenary of Mohammed Ali Jinnah* (2*nd issue*). *P* 12½.

436 **258** 10 r. emerald and gold . . . . . . 2·50 3·50

259 Rural Family **260** Turkish Vase, 1800 B.C.

(Des M. Ahmed)

1977 (14 Apr). *Social Welfare and Rural Development Year. P* 13.

437 **259** 20 p. multicoloured 15 10

(Des A. Salahuddin)

1977 (21 July). 13*th Anniv of Regional Co-operation for Development. T* **260** *and similar horiz designs. P* 13.

438 20 p. red-orange, violet-blue and black . . 35 10
439 65 p. multicoloured 55 40
440 90 p. multicoloured . . . . . . 80 1·25
438/40 . . . . . . *Set of* 3 1·50 1·50

Designs:—60 p. Pakistani toy bullock cart, Moenjodaro; 90 p. Pitcher with spout, Sialk Hill, Iran.

261 Forest **262** Desert Scene

(Des A. Ahmed)

1977 (9 Aug). *National Tree Plantation Campaign. P* 13.
441 **261** 20 p. multicoloured 10 30

(Des M. A. Javed)

1977 (5 Sept). *U.N. Conference on Desertification, Nairobi. P* 13.
442 **262** 65 p. multicoloured 40 30

263 "Water for the Children of the World"
264 Aga Khan III

(Des A. Salahuddin)

1977 (3 Oct). *Universal Children's Day. P* 13½ × 12½.
443 **263** 50 p. multicoloured 40 30

(Des A. Rauf)

1977 (2 Nov). *Birth Centenary of Aga Khan III. P* 13.
444 **264** 2 r. multicoloured 55 85

265 Iqbal and Spirit of the Poet Roomi (from painting by Behzad)
266 The Holy "Khana-Kaaba" (House of God, Mecca)

(Des A. Ahmed)

1977 (9 Nov). *Birth Centenary of Dr. Mohammed Iqbal (4th issue). T* **265** *and similar vert designs. Multicoloured. P* 13.
445 20 p. Type **265** 30 40
a. Horiz strip of 5. Nos. 445/9 .. .. 1·75
446 65 p. Iqbal looking at Jamaluddin Afghani and Saeed Haleem Pasha at prayer (Behzad) 30 40
447 1 r. 25, Urdu verse 35 45
448 2 r. 25, Persian verse 45 55
449 3 r. Iqbal 50 60
445/9 .. .. *Set of* 5 1·75 2·25
Nos. 445, 448/9, 447 and 446 (in that order) were issued in horizontal *se-tenant* strips of 5.

(Des I. Gilani)

1977 (21 Nov). *Haj (pilgrimage to Mecca). P* 14.
450 **266** 65 p. multicoloured 30 30

267 Rheumatic Patient and Healthy Man
268 Woman in Costume of Rawalpindi-Islamabad

(Des T. Hameed)

1977 (19 Dec). *World Rheumatism Year. P* 13.
451 **267** 65 p. turquoise-blue, black and yellow .. 30 20

(Des A. Salahuddin)

1978 (5 Feb). *Indonesia–Pakistan Economic and Cultural Co-operation Organization. P* 12½ × 13½.
452 **268** 75 p. multicoloured 30 20

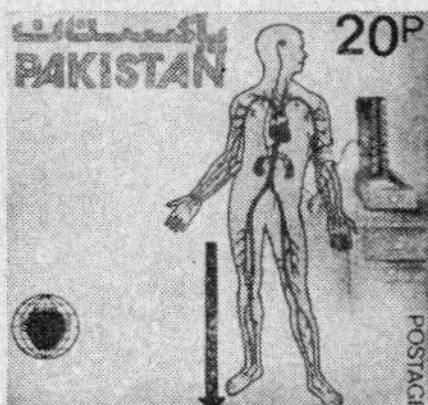

269 Human Body and Sphygmomanometer
270 Henri Dunant

(Des A. Salahuddin)

1978 (20 Apr). *World Hypertension Month. P* 13.
453 **269** 20 p. multicoloured 15 10
454 – 2 r. multicoloured 60 75
The 2 r. value is as T **269**, but has the words "Down with high blood pressure" instead of the Urdu inscription at bottom left.

(Des A. Salahuddin)

1978 (8 May). *150th Birth Anniv of Henri Dunant (founder of Red Cross). P* 14.
455 **270** 1 r. black, new blue and vermilion .. 1·00 20

271 Red Roses (Pakistan)
272 "Pakistan, World Cup Hockey Champions"

(Des A. Salahuddin)

1978 (21 July). *14th Anniv of Regional Co-operation for Development. T* **271** *and similar vert designs. Multicoloured. P* 13½.
456 20 p. Type **271** 35 20
a. Horiz strip of 3. Nos. 456/8 .. .. 1·40
457 90 p. Pink roses (Iran) 50 20
458 2 r. Yellow rose (Turkey) 75 25
456/8 .. .. *Set of* 3 1·40 60
Nos. 456/8 were printed together, *se-tenant*, in horizontal strips of 3 throughout the sheet.

(Des M. Munawar)

1978 (26 Aug). *"Riccione '78" International Stamp Fair. T* **272** *and similar vert design. Multicoloured. P* 13.
459 1 r. Type **272** .. .. 1·50 25
460 2 r. Fountain at Piazza Turismo .. .. 1·25 35

273 Cogwheels within Globe Symbol
274 St. Patrick's Cathedral

(Des A. Salahuddin)

1978 (3 Sept). *U.N. Technical Co-operation amongst Developing Countries Conference. P* 13.
461 **273** 75 p. multicoloured 15 10

(Des A. Salahuddin)

1978 (29 Sept). *Centenary of St. Patrick's Cathedral, Karachi. T* **274** *and similar vert design. Multicoloured. P* 13.
462 1 r. Type **274** 10 10
463 2 r. Stained glass window 25 25

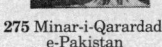

275 Minar-i-Qarardad-e-Pakistan
276 Tractor

276a Mausoleum of Ibrahim Khan Makli, Thatta

Two Dies of 75 p. value:

Die I
Die II

Die I. Size of design 26½ × 21½ mm. Figures of value large; "p" small. Plough does not touch left-hand frame.
Die II. Size of design 25½ × 21 mm. Smaller figures; larger "p". Plough touches left-hand frame.

(Des A. Salahuddin. Litho (10, 25, 40, 50, 90 p.), recess (others))

1978 (7 Nov)–**81**. *No wmk (2 to 90 p.) or W* **98** *(1 to 5 r.). P* 14×13½ *(2 to 5 p.),* 13½×14 *(10 to 90 p.) or* 13 *(1 to 5 r.).*
464 **275** 2 p. deep grey-green 10 10
a. Printed on the gummed side ..
465 3 p. black 10 10
a. Imperf (pair) .. .. .. 5·00
b. Printed on the gummed side ..
466 5 p. deep ultramarine 10 10
a. Printed on the gummed side .. 8·00
467 **276** 10 p. new blue & greenish bl (7.10.79) 10 10
468 20 p. deep yellow-green (25.3.79) .. 50 10
469 25 p. dp green & dull mag (19.3.79) .. 80 10
470 40 p. new blue and magenta (16.12.78) 10 10
471 50 p. slate-lilac & turq-green (19.3.79) 30 10
a. Printed on the gummed side .. 6·00
472 60 p. black (16.12.78) 10 10
a. Imperf (pair) .. .. .. 5·00
473 75 p. dull vermilion (I) (16.12.78) .. 60 10
a. Imperf (pair) .. .. .. 16·00
b. Die II (1980) 55 10
ba. Imperf (pair) .. .. .. 6·00
bb. Printed on the gummed side ..
474 90 p. magenta and new blue (16.12.78) 20 10
a. Printed on the gummed side .. 18·00
475 **276a** 1 r. bronze-green (2.8.80) 10 10
a. Imperf (pair) .. .. .. 14·00
476 1 r. 50, red-orange (17.11.79) .. 10 10
a. Imperf (pair) .. .. .. 6·00
w. Wmk inverted .. .. ..
477 2 r. carmine-red (17.11.79) 10 10
a. Imperf (pair) .. .. .. 7·00
b. Printed on the gummed side .. 10·00
w. Wmk inverted .. .. ..
478 3 r. blue-black (4.6.80) 15 10
a. Imperf (pair) .. .. .. 9·00
479 4 r. black (1.1.81) 15 10
a. Imperf (pair) .. .. .. 9·00
480 5 r. sepia (1.1.81) 20 10
a. Imperf (pair) .. .. .. 9·00
w. Wmk inverted .. .. ..
464/80 .. .. *Set of* 17 3·25 75
The remaining values as Type **276** printed in recess, are from Die II.
Postal forgeries exist of the 2 r. and 3 r. values. These are poorly printed with perforations which do not match those of the genuine stamps.

GUM. Later printings of the 10 p., 20 p., 25 p., 4 r. and 5 r. values (Nos. 467/9 and 479/80) occur with matt, almost invisible gum of a PVA type, instead of the gum arabic used previously.

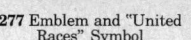

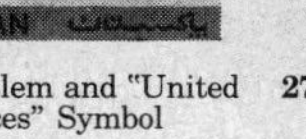

277 Emblem and "United Races" Symbol
278 Maulana Mohammad Ali Jauhar

(Des M. Munawar)

1978 (20 Nov). *International Anti-Apartheid Year. P* 13.
481 **277** 1 r. multicoloured 15 15

(Des A. Salahuddin)

1978 (10 Dec). *Birth Centenary of Maulana Mohammad Ali Jauhar (patriot). P* 13.
482 **278** 50 p. multicoloured 40 20

279 Panavia MRCA Tornado, De Havilland D.H.89 Dragon Rapide and Wright Flyer I

(Des A. Salahuddin)

1978 (24 Dec). *75th Anniv of Powered Flight. T* **279** *and similar diamond-shaped designs. Multicoloured. P* 13.
483 65 p. Type **279** .. .. 1·50 1·75
a. Block of 4. Nos. 483/6 .. .. 6·00
484 1 r. McDonnell Douglas F-4A Phantom II, Lockheed L-1011 TriStar 500 and Wright Flyer I .. .. .. 1·60 1·75
485 2 r. North American X-15, Tupolev Tu-104 and Wright Flyer I .. .. .. 1·75 2·00
486 2 r. 25, Mikoyan Gurevich MiG-15, Concorde and Wright Flyer I .. 2·00 2·25
483/6 .. .. *Set of* 4 6·00 7·00
Nos. 483/6 were printed together, *se-tenant*, in blocks of 4 throughout the sheet.

280 "Holy Koran illuminating Globe" and Raudha-e-Mubarak (mausoleum) **281** "Aspects of A.P.W.A."

(Des A. Salahuddin)

1979 (10 Feb). *"12th Rabi-ul-Awwal" (Prophet Mohammed's birthday). P* 13.
487 **280** 20 p. multicoloured 30 15

(Des M. Saeed)

1979 (25 Feb). *30th Anniv of A.P.W.A. (All Pakistan Women's Association). P* 13.
488 **281** 50 p. multicoloured 60 15

282 Tippu Sultan Shaheed of Mysore

(Des A. Rauf)

1979 (23 Mar). *Pioneers of Freedom (1st series). T* **282** *and similar diamond-shaped designs. Multicoloured. W* **98**. *P* 14.
490 10 r. Type **282** .. .. 75 1·25
a. Horiz strip of 3. Nos. 490/2 .. .. 3·00
491 15 r. Sir Syed Ahmad Khan .. .. .. 1·00 1·75
492 25 r. Altaf Hussain Hali .. .. .. 1·50 2·00
490/2 .. .. *Set of* 3 3·00 4·50
Nos. 490/2 were printed together, *se-tenant* in the same sheet; there being ten horizontal strips of 3 values and ten additional 10 r. stamps.
See also Nos. 757, 801/27, 838/46, 870/2, 904/6, 921/8, 961/2 and 1007.

283 Himalayan Monal Pheasant

(Des M. Ahmed)

1979 (17 June). *Wildlife Protection (5th series). Pheasants. T* **283** *and similar horiz designs. Multicoloured. P* 13.
493 20 p. Type **283** .. .. 1·25 60
494 25 p. Kalij .. .. 1·25 80
495 40 p. Koklass .. .. 1·60 1·75
496 1 r. Cheer .. .. 3·00 2·00
493/6 .. .. *Set of* 4 6·25 4·75

284 "Pakistan Village Scene" (Ustad Bakhsh)

(Des A. Rauf)

1979 (21 July). *15th Anniv of Regional Co-operation for Development. Paintings. T* **284** *and similar horiz designs. Multicoloured. P* 14 × 12½.
497 40 p. Type **284** 20 25
a. Vert strip of 3. Nos. 497/9 60
498 75 p. "Iranian Goldsmith" (Kamal al Molk) .. 20 25
499 1 r. 60, "Turkish Harvest" (Namik Ismail) .. 25 30
497/9 .. .. *Set of* 3 60 70
Nos. 497/9 were printed together, *se-tenant*, in vertical strips of 3 throughout the sheet.

285 Guj Embroidered Shirt (detail)

1979 (23 Aug). *Handicrafts (1st series). T* **285** *and similar horiz designs. Multicoloured. P* 14 × 12½.
500 40 p. Type **285** 20 20
a. Block of 4. Nos. 500/3 .. .. .. 1·00
501 1 r. Enamel inlaid brass plate 25 25
502 1 r. 50, Baskets 30 30
503 2 r. Chain-stitch embroidered rug (detail) .. 40 40
500/3 .. .. *Set of* 4 1·00 1·00
Nos. 500/3 were printed together, *se-tenant*, in blocks of 4 throughout the sheet.
See also Nos. 578/9, 595/6 and 625/8.

286 Children playing on Climbing Frame

(Des A. Rauf)

1979 (10 Sept). *S.O.S. Children's Village, Lahore (orphanage). P* 13.
504 **286** 50 p. multicoloured 40 40

287 "Island" (Z. Maloof)

(Des A. Salahuddin)

1979 (22 Oct). *International Year of the Child. Children's Paintings. T* **287** *and similar horiz designs. Multicoloured. P* 14 × 12½.
505 40 p. Type **287** 15 15
a. Block of 4. Nos. 505/8 85
506 75 p. "Playground" (R. Akbar) 25 25
507 1 r. "Fairground" (M. Azam) 25 25
508 1 r. 50, "Hockey Match" (M. Tayyab) .. 30 30
505/8 .. .. *Set of* 4 85 85
MS509 79 × 64 mm. 2 r. "Child looking at Faces in the Sky" (M. Mumtaz) (*vert*). Imperf .. 1·40 2·00
Nos. 505/8 were printed together, *se-tenant*, in blocks of 4 throughout the sheet.
Examples of No. **MS**509 are known overprinted in gold for the "PHILEXFRANCE" International Stamp Exhibition in 1982. The Pakistan Post Office has declared such overprints to be bogus.

288 Warrior attacking Crab **289** Pakistan Customs Emblem

(Des A. Salahuddin)

1979 (12 Nov). *Fight Against Cancer. P* 14.
510 **288** 40 p. black, greenish yellow and magenta 70 70

(Des A. Salahuddin)

1979 (10 Dec). *Centenary of Pakistan Customs Service. P* 13 × 13½.
511 **289** 1 r. multicoloured 30 30

290 Boeing 747-200 and Douglas DC-3 Airliners **291** Islamic Pattern

(Des A. Salahuddin)

1980 (10 Jan). *25th Anniv of Pakistan International Air Lines. P* 13.
512 **290** 1 r. multicoloured .. .. .. 1·75 90

(Des and litho Secura, Singapore)

1980 (15 Jan–10 Mar). *Matt, almost invisible PVA gum. P* 12.
513 **291** 10 p. slate-green and orange-yellow .. 10 10
514 15 p. slate-green & bright yellow-green 10 10
515 25 p. violet and brown-red (10.3) .. 10 30
516 35 p. carmine & brt yellow-green (10.3) 10 30
517 – 40 p. rosine and olive-sepia .. 15 10
a. Printed on the gummed side ..
518 – 50 p. violet and dull yellow-green (10.3) 10 30
519 – 80 p. bright yellow-green & black (10.3) 15 40
513/19 .. .. *Set of* 7 70 1·25
The 40 to 80 p. values also show different Islamic patterns, the 40 p. being horizontal and the remainder vertical.

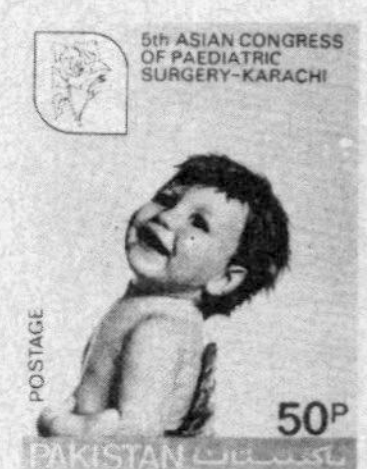

292 Young Child **293** Conference Emblem

(Des M. Saeed)

1980 (16 Feb). *5th Asian Congress of Paediatric Surgery, Karachi. P* 13.
530 **292** 50 p. multicoloured .. .. .. 1·00 1·50

(Des A. Salahuddin)

1980 (17 May). *11th Islamic Conference of Foreign Ministers, Islamabad. P* 13.
531 **293** 1 r. multicoloured 50 50

294 Karachi Port

(Des A. Salahuddin)

1980 (15 July). *Centenary of Karachi Port Authority. P* 13 × 13½.
532 **294** 1 r. multicoloured .. .. .. 1·75 1·40

PRICES OF SETS

Set prices are given for many issues, generally those containing three stamps or more. Definitive sets include one of each value or major colour change, but do not cover different perforations, die types or minor shades. Where a choice is possible the set prices are based on the cheapest versions of the stamps included in the listings.

RICCIONE 80

(295)

296 College Emblem with Old and New Buildings

1980 (30 Aug). *"Riccione 80" International Stamp Exhibition. Nos.* 505/8 *optd with T* **295** *in red.*

533 40 p. Type **287** 40 60
a. Block of 4. Nos. 533/6 .. .. 1·90
534 75 p. "Playground" (R. Akbar) 50 70
535 1 r. "Fairground" (M. Azam) 55 75
536 1 r. 50, "Hockey Match" (M. Tayyab) .. 70 90
533/6 .. .. *Set of* 4 1·90 2·75

(Des M. Munawar)

1980 (18 Sept). *75th Anniv of Command and Staff College, Quetta. P* 13.

537 **296** 1 r. multicoloured 10 15

WORLD TOURISM CONFERENCE
MANILA 80

(297)

1980 (27 Sept). *World Tourism Conference, Manila. No.* 496 *optd with T* **297**.

538 1 r. Cheer 75 30

298 Birth Centenary Emblem

(Des A. Salahuddin)

1980 (5 Oct). *Birth Centenary of Hafiz Mahmood Shairani. P* 13.

539 **298** 40 p. multicoloured 30 75

299 Shalimar Gardens, Lahore

(Des A. Salahuddin)

1980 (23 Oct). *Aga Khan Award for Architecture. P* 13.

540 **299** 2 r. multicoloured 40 75

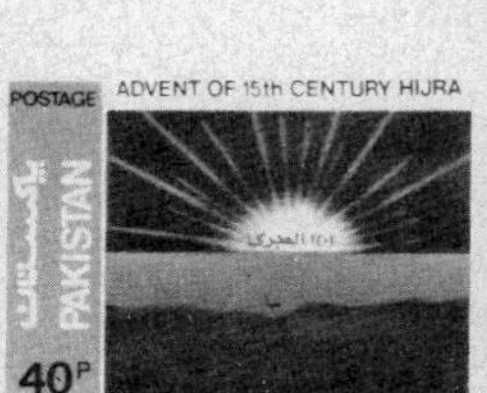

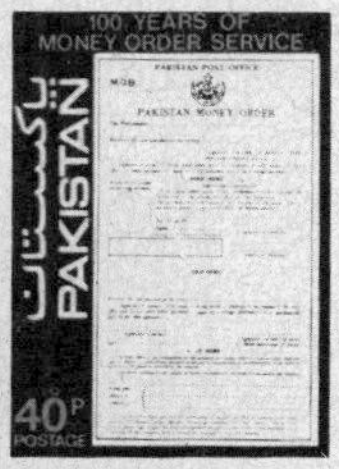

300 Rising Sun

301 Money Order Form

(Des S. Ahmed (40 p.), J. Sultana (2 r.), A. Salahuddin (others))

1980 (10 Nov). *1400th Anniv of Hegira (1st issue). T* **300** *and similar multicoloured designs. P* 14 (2 *r.*) *or* 13 (*others*).

541 40 p. Type **300** 10 10
542 2 r. Ka'aba and symbols of Moslem achievement (34 × 34 *mm*) 25 40
543 3 r. Holy Koran illuminating World (31 × 54 *mm*) 30 60
541/3 .. .. *Set of* 3 55 95
MS544 106 × 84 mm. 4 r. Candles. Imperf .. 45 1·00

See also No. 549.

(Des A. Ahmed)

1980 (20 Dec). *Centenary of Money Order Service. P* 13.

545 **301** 40 p. multicoloured 20 60

302 Postcards encircling Globe

303 Heinrich von Stephan and U.P.U. Emblem

(Des A. Ahmed)

1980 (27 Dec). *Centenary of Postcard Service. P* 13.

546 **302** 40 p. multicoloured 20 60

(Des J. Sultana)

1981 (7 Jan). *150th Birth Anniv of Heinrich von Stephan (founder of U.P.U.). P* 13.

547 **303** 1 r. multicoloured 30 20

304 Aircraft and Airmail Letters

(Des J. Sultana)

1981 (15 Feb). *50th Anniv of Airmail Service. P* 13.

548 **304** 1 r. multicoloured 60 20

305 Mecca

306 Conference Emblem and Afghan Refugees

1981 (7 Mar). *1400th Anniv of Hegira (2nd issue). P* 13.

549 **305** 40 p. multicoloured 20 60

(Des Z. Akhlaq (Nos. 550 and 552), A. Ahmed (Nos. 551 and 553), M. Jafree (No. 554))

1981 (29 Mar). *Islamic Summit Conference (1st issue). T* **306** *and similar multicoloured designs. P* 13.

550 40 p. Type **306** 30 10
551 40 p. Conference emblem encircled by flags and Afghan refugees (28 × 58 *mm*) .. 30 10
552 1 r. Type **306** 50 10
553 1 r. As No. 551 .. .. 50 10
554 2 r. Conference emblem and map showing Afghanistan (48 × 32 *mm*) 65 50
550/4 .. .. *Set of* 5 2·00 75

307 Conference Emblem

308 Kemal Atatürk

(Des A. Salahuddin (Nos. 555, 557), A. Irani (Nos. 556, 558))

1981 (20 Apr). *Islamic Summit Conference (2nd issue). T* **307** *and similar multicoloured design. P* 13.

555 40 p. Type **307** 10 10
556 40 p. Conference emblem and flags (28 × 46 *mm*) 10 10
557 85 p. Type **307** 20 30
558 85 p. As No. 556 .. .. 20 30
555/8 .. .. *Set of* 4 55 70

(Des A. Salahuddin)

1981 (19 May). *Birth Centenary of Kemal Atatürk (Turkish statesman). P* 13.

559 **308** 1 r. multicoloured 50 15

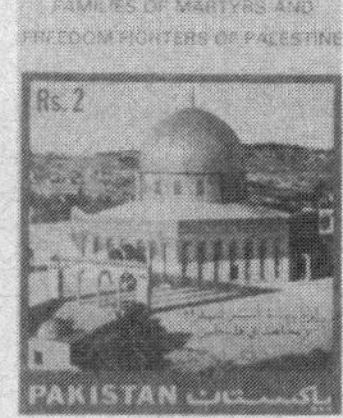

309 Green Turtle

310 Dome of the Rock

(Des Jamal. Litho Secura, Singapore)

1981 (20 June). *Wildlife Protection (6th series). Matt, almost invisible PVA gum. P* 12 × 11½.

560 **309** 40 p. multicoloured .. .. .. 1·25 40

(Des A. Salahuddin)

1981 (25 July). *Palestinian Welfare. P* 13.

561 **310** 2 r. multicoloured 35 35

311 Malubiting West

(Litho Secura, Singapore)

1981 (20 Aug). *Mountain Peaks (1st series). Karakoram Range. T* **311** *and similar multicoloured designs. Matt, almost invisible PVA gum. P* 14 × 13½.

562 40 p. Type **311** 40 40
a. Horiz pair. Nos. 562/3 .. .. 80 80
563 40 p. Malubiting West (24 × 31 *mm*) .. 40 40
564 1 r. Haramosh 75 75
a. Horiz pair. Nos. 564/5 .. .. 1·50 1·50
565 1 r. Haramosh (24 × 31 *mm*) 75 75
566 1 r. 50, K6 .. .. 90 1·00
a. Horiz pair. Nos. 566/7 .. .. 1·75 2·00
567 1 r. 50, K6 (24 × 31 *mm*) .. .. 90 1·00
568 2 r. K2, Broad Peak, Gasherbrum 4 and Gasherbrum 2 .. .. 1·00 1·40
a. Horiz pair. Nos. 568/9 .. .. 2·00 2·75
569 2 r. K2 (24 × 31 *mm*) .. .. .. 1·00 1·40
562/9 .. .. *Set of* 8 5·50 6·50

The two designs of each value were printed together, *se-tenant*, in horizontal pairs throughout the sheet.

See also Nos. 674/5.

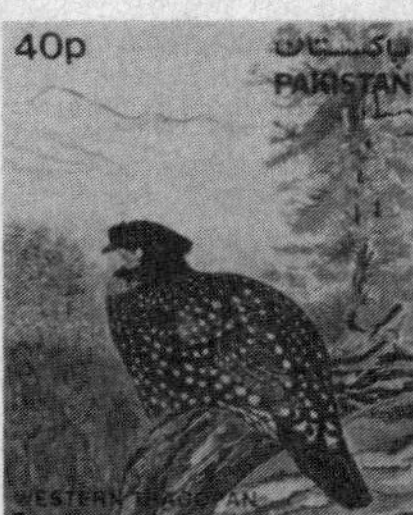

312 Pakistan Steel "Furnace No. 1"

313 Western Tragopan

(Des A. Ahmed)

1981 (31 Aug). *First Firing of Pakistan Steel "Furnace No. 1", Karachi. P* 13.

570 **312** 40 p. multicoloured 25 10
571 2 r. multicoloured .. .. .. 65 1·00

(Litho Secura, Singapore)

1981 (15 Sept). *Wildlife Protection (7th series). Matt, almost invisible PVA gum. P* 14.

572 **313** 40 p. multicoloured .. .. .. 1·50 75
573 – 2 r. multicoloured .. .. .. 3·50 4·25

The 2 r. value is as Type **313** but the background design shows a winter view.

314 Disabled People and I.Y.D.P. Emblem

315 World Hockey Cup below flags of participating Countries

(Des M. Saeed)

1981 (12 Dec). *International Year for Disabled Persons. P* 13.
574 **314** 40 p. multicoloured 40 50
575 2 r. multicoloured .. .. 1·40 1·75

(Des A. Salahuddin)

1982 (31 Jan). *Pakistan—World Cup Hockey Champions. T* **315** *and similar vert design. Multicoloured. P* 13.
576 1 r. Type **315** .. .. 2·00 1·50
577 1 r. World Hockey Cup above flags of participating countries .. .. 2·00 1·50

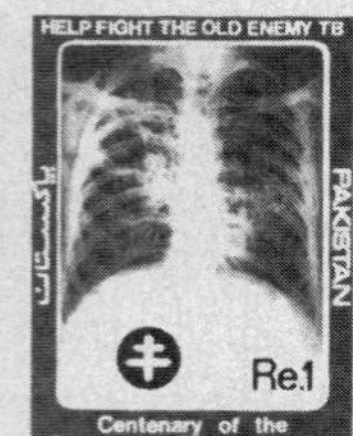

316 Camel Skin Lamp

317 Chest X-Ray of Infected Person

(Des A. Salahuddin. Litho Secura, Singapore)

1982 (20 Feb). *Handicrafts* (2*nd series*). *T* **316** *and similar vert design. Multicoloured. P* 14.
578 1 r. Type **316** 70 70
579 1 r. Hala pottery 70 70
See also Nos. 595/6.

(Des A. Ahmed)

1982 (24 Mar). *Centenary of Robert Koch's Discovery of Tubercle Bacillus. P* 13.
580 **317** 1 r. multicoloured .. .. 1·75 90

318 Indus Dolphin

(Des A. Salahuddin. Litho Secura, Singapore)

1982 (24 Apr). *Wildlife Protection* (8*th series*). *P* 12 × 11½.
581 **318** 40 p. multicoloured .. .. 1·50 1·00
582 – 1 r. multicoloured .. .. 3·00 2·25
The 1 r. value is as Type **318** but the design is reversed.

319 "Apollo–Soyuz" Link-up, 1975

(Des A. Salahuddin)

1982 (7 June). *Peaceful Uses of Outer Space. P* 13.
583 **319** 1 r. multicoloured .. .. 2·50 1·25

320 Sukkur Barrage

(Des A. Salahuddin)

1982 (17 July). *50th Anniv of Sukkur Barrage. P* 13.
584 **320** 1 r. multicoloured 30 30

321 Pakistan National Flag and Stylised Sun

RICCIONE — 82 —
(322)

(Des A. Ahmed)

1982 (14 Aug). *Independence Day. T* **321** *and similar vert design. Multicoloured. P* 13.
585 40 p. Type **321** 10 30
586 85 p. Map of Pakistan and stylised torch .. 20 50

1982 (28 Aug). *"Riccione 82" International Stamp Exhibition. No.* 584 *optd with T* **322**.
587 **320** 1 r. multicoloured 20 20

323 Arabic Inscription and University Emblem

(Des Syed Tanwir Rizvi)

1982 (14 Oct). *Centenary of the Punjab University. P* 13½ × 13.
588 **323** 40 p. multicoloured 75 30

324 Scout Emblem and Tents

325 Laying Pipeline

(Des M. Saeed)

1982 (23 Dec). *75th Anniv of Boy Scout Movement. P* 13.
589 **324** 2 r. multicoloured 50 45

(Des A. Salahuddin)

1983 (6 Jan). *Inauguration of Quetta Natural Gas Pipeline Project. P* 13.
590 **325** 1 r. multicoloured 30 20

326 *Papilio polyctor*

(Litho Secura, Singapore)

1983 (15 Feb). *Butterflies. T* **326** *and similar horiz designs. Multicoloured. Matt, almost invisible PVA gum. P* 13½.
591 40 p. Type **326** .. .. 1·25 20
592 50 p. *Atrophaneura aristolochiae* .. .. 1·50 20
593 60 p. *Danaus chrysippus* .. .. .. 1·75 60
594 1 r. 50, *Papilio demoleus* .. .. .. 2·50 2·25
591/4 .. .. *Set of* 4 6·25 3·00

(Litho Secura, Singapore)

1983 (9 Mar). *Handicrafts* (3*rd series*). *Vert designs as T* **316**. *Multicoloured. Matt, almost invisible PVA gum. P* 14.
595 1 r. Five flower motif needlework, Sind .. 15 15
596 1 r. Straw mats 15 15

ALTERED CATALOGUE NUMBERS

Any Catalogue numbers altered from the last edition are shown as a list in the introductory pages.

327 School of Nursing and University Emblem

(Des A. Salahuddin)

1983 (16 Mar). *Presentation of Charter to Aga Khan University, Karachi. P* 13½ × 13.
597 **327** 2 r. multicoloured 40 30
No. 597 was issued in sheets of 8 (2 × 4), each horizontal pair being separated by a different *se-tenant* label showing views of the University.

328 Yak Caravan crossing Zindiharam-Darkot Pass, Hindu Kush

(Des A. Salahuddin)

1983 (28 Apr). *Trekking in Pakistan. P* 13.
598 **328** 1 r. multicoloured .. .. 1·50 60

329 Marsh Crocodile

(Litho Secura, Singapore)

1983 (19 May). *Wildlife Protection* (9*th series*). *Matt, almost invisible PVA gum. P* 13½.
599 **329** 3 r. multicoloured .. .. 3·50 2·00

330 Goitred Gazelle

331 Floral Design

(Litho Secura, Singapore)

1983 (20 June). *Wildlife Protection* (10*th series*). *Matt, almost invisible PVA gum. P* 14 × 13½.
600 **330** 1 r. multicoloured .. .. 2·75 2·00

(Des A. Ahmed)

1983 (14 Aug). *36th Anniv of Independence. T* **331** *and similar vert design. Multicoloured. P* 13.
601 60 p. Type **331** 10 10
602 4 r. Hand holding flaming torch 40 45

332 Traditional Weaving, Pakistan

(Des A. Salahuddin)

1983 (19 Aug). *Indonesian–Pakistan Economic and Cultural Co-operation Organization, 1969–1983. T* **332** *and similar horiz design. Multicoloured. P* 13.
603 2 r. Type **332** 20 25
604 2 r. Traditional weaving, Indonesia 20 25

333 "Siberian Cranes" (Great White Cranes) (Sir Peter Scott)

1983 (8 Sept). *Wildlife Protection (11th series). P* 13.
605 **333** 3 r. multicoloured .. .. 3·00 3·00

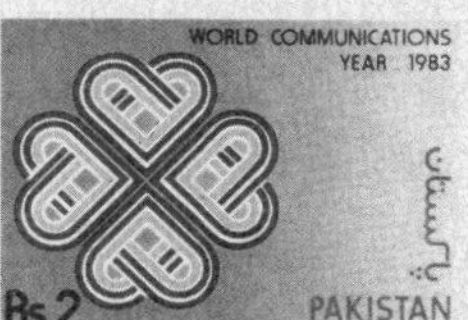

334 W.C.Y. Emblem

1983 (9 Oct). *World Communications Year. T* **334** *and similar multicoloured design. P* 13 (2 *r.*) *or* 14 (3 *r.*).
606 2 r. Type **334** 20 25
607 3 r. W.C.Y. emblem (*different*) (33 × 33 *mm*) 30 35

335 Farm Animals

336 Agricultural Produce and Fertiliser Factory

(Des A. Salahuddin)

1983 (24 Oct). *World Food Day. T* **335** *and similar horiz designs. Multicoloured. P* 13.
608 3 r. Type **335** .. .. 1·50 1·50
a. Horiz strip of 4. Nos. 608/11 .. .. 5·50
609 3 r. Fruit .. .. 1·50 1·50
610 3 r. Crops .. .. 1·50 1·50
611 3 r. Sea food .. .. 1·50 1·50
608/11 .. .. *Set of* 4 5·50 5·50
Nos. 608/11 were printed together, *se-tenant*, in horizontal strips of four throughout the sheet.

(Des J. Sultana)

1983 (24 Oct). *National Fertiliser Corporation. P* 13 × 13½.
612 **336** 60 p. multicoloured 15 30

337 Lahore, 1852

338 Winner of "Enterprise" Event

(Des A. Salahuddin)

1983 (13 Nov). *National Stamp Exhibition, Lahore. T* **337** *and similar vert designs showing panoramic view of Lahore in 1852. Multicoloured. P* 13 × 13½.
613 60 p. Musti Durwaza Dharmsala 60 70
a. Horiz strip of 6. Nos. 613/18 .. .. 3·25
614 60 p. Khabgha 60 70
615 60 p. Type **337** 60 70
616 60 p. Summan Burj Hazuri 60 70
617 60 p. Flower Garden, Samadhi Northern Gate 60 70
618 60 p. Budda Darya, Badshahi Masjid 60 70
613/18 .. .. *Set of* 6 3·25 3·75
Nos. 613/18 were printed together, *se-tenant* in sheets of twelve, containing two horizontal strips of six.

(Des J. Sultana)

1983 (31 Dec). *Yachting Champions, Asian Games, Delhi. T* **338** *and similar vert design. Multicoloured. P* 13.
619 60 p. Type **338** .. .. 1·75 1·75
620 60 p. Winner of "OK" Dinghy event .. .. 1·75 1·75

339 Snow Leopard

(Litho Secura, Singapore)

1984 (21 Jan). *Wildlife Protection (12th series). Matt, almost invisible PVA gum. P* 14.
621 **339** 40 p. multicoloured .. .. .. 1·75 90
622 1 r. 60, multicoloured .. .. .. 4·75 6·00

340 Jahangir Khan (World Squash Champion)

341 P.I.A. Boeing 707 Airliner

1984 (17 Mar). *Squash. P* 13.
623 **340** 3 r. multicoloured .. .. 2·25 1·75

(Des A. Salahuddin)

1984 (29 Apr). *20th Anniv of Pakistan International Airways' Service to China. P* 13.
624 **341** 3 r. multicoloured .. .. 5·00 4·50

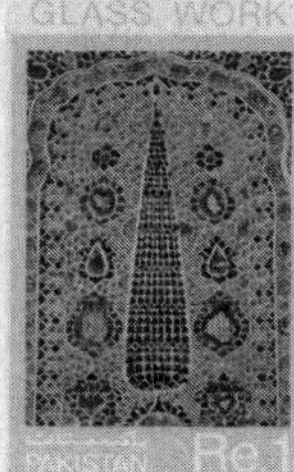

342 Glass-work

343 Attock Fort

(Des A. Salahuddin. Litho Secura, Singapore)

1984 (31 May). *Handicrafts (4th series). T* **342** *and similar designs showing glass-work in Sheesh Mahal, Lahore Fort. P* 13½.
625 1 r. multicoloured (blue frame) 25 15
626 1 r. multicoloured (red frame) 25 15
627 1 r. multicoloured (green frame) (*horiz*) .. 25 15
628 1 r. multicoloured (violet frame) (*horiz*) .. 25 15
625/8 .. .. *Set of* 4 90 55

(Des J. Sultana)

1984 (16 June)–**86**. *Forts. T* **343** *and similar horiz designs. P* 11.
629 5 p. brownish black & brown-pur (1.11.84) 10 10
630 10 p. brownish black and rose-red (25.9.84) 10 10
631 15 p. reddish violet & bistre-brown (1.12.86) 10 10
632 20 p. black and bright reddish violet .. 10 10
a. Black ptd double .. ..
633 50 p. sepia and Venetian red (10.4.86) 15 10
634 60 p. blackish brown and light brown .. 20 10
635 70 p. greenish blue (3.8.86) 20 10
636 80 p. bistre-brown and dull scarlet (1.7.86) 20 10
629/36 .. .. *Set of* 8 1·00 40
Designs:—5 p. Kot Diji Fort; 10 p. Rohtas Fort; 15 p. Bala Hissar Fort; 50 p. Hyderabad Fort; 60 p. Lahore Fort; 70 p. Sibi Fort; 80 p. Ranikot Fort.
No. 632a appears to have received two distinct impressions of the black plate rather than an offset from the litho "blanket".

344 Shah Rukn i Alam's Tomb, Multan

1984 (26 June). *Aga Khan Award for Architecture. P* 13.
647 **344** 60 p. multicoloured .. .. 1·50 1·50

345 Radio Mast and Map of World

1984 (1 July). *20th Anniv of Asia–Pacific Broadcasting Union. P* 13.
648 **345** 3 r. multicoloured 80 60

346 Wrestling

(Des A. Salahuddin)

1984 (31 July). *Olympic Games, Los Angeles. T* **346** *and similar horiz designs. Multicoloured. P* 13.
649 3 r. Type **346** .. .. 1·50 1·50
650 3 r. Boxing .. .. 1·50 1·50
651 3 r. Athletics .. .. 1·50 1·50
652 3 r. Hockey .. .. 1·50 1·50
653 3 r. Yachting .. .. 1·50 1·50
649/53 .. .. *Set of* 5 6·75 6·75

347 Jasmine (National flower) and Inscription

348 Gearwheel Emblem and Flags of Participating Nations

(Des M. Munawar)

1984 (14 Aug). *Independence Day. T* **347** *and similar horiz design. Multicoloured. P* 13.
654 60 p. Type **347** 10 10
655 4 r. Symbolic torch 45 50

(Des A. Zafar)

1984 (1 Sept). *Pakistan International Trade Fair. P* 13.
656 **348** 60 p. multicoloured 60 30

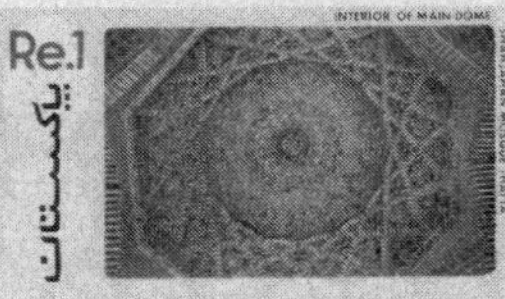

349 Interior of Main Dome

1984 (5 Nov). *Tourism Convention. Shahjahan Mosque, Thatta. T* **349** *and similar horiz designs. Multicoloured. P* 13½.
657 1 r. Type **349** 50 50
a. Horiz strip of 5. Nos. 657/61 .. .. 2·25
658 1 r. Brick and glazed tile work 50 50
659 1 r. Gateway 50 50
660 1 r. Symmetrical archways 50 50
661 1 r. Interior of a dome 50 50
657/61 .. .. *Set of* 5 2·25 2·25
Nos. 657/61 were printed together, *se-tenant*, in horizontal strips of 5 throughout the sheet

350 Bank Emblem in Floral Pattern

(Des A. Zafar)

1984 (7 Nov). *25th Anniv of United Bank Ltd. P* 13½.
662 **350** 60 p. multicoloured 70 70

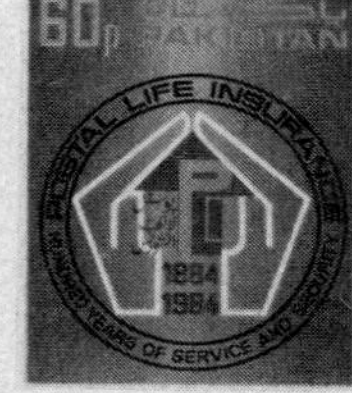

351 Conference Emblem   **352** Postal Life Insurance Emblem within Hands

(Des A. Salahuddin)

1984 (24 Dec). *20th United Nations Conference on Trade and Development. P* 14.
663 **351** 60 p. multicoloured 70 40

(Des A. Zafar and J. Sultana)

1984 (29 Dec). *Centenary of Postal Life Insurance. T* **352** *and similar vert design. Multicoloured. P* 13½.
664 60 p. Type **352** 45 15
665 1 r. "100" and Postal Life Insurance emblem 55 15

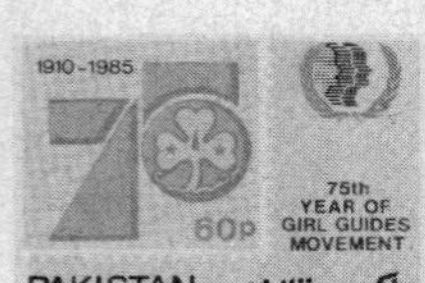

353 Bull (Wall painting)   **354** International Youth Year Emblem and "75"

(Des A. Salahuddin and M. Munawar)

1984 (31 Dec). *U.N.E.S.C.O. Save Moenjadoro Campaign. T* **353** *and similar vert design. Multicoloured. P* 13½.
666 2 r. Type **353** .. .. 1·40 1·00
a. Horiz pair. Nos. 666/7 .. .. 2·75 2·00
667 2 r. Bull (seal).. .. .. 1·40 1·00
Nos. 666/7 were printed together, *se-tenant*, in horizontal pairs throughout the sheet.

(Des A. Salahuddin)

1985 (6 Jan). *75th Anniv of Girl Guide Movement. P* 13½.
668 **354** 60 p. multicoloured .. .. .. 2·25 1·00

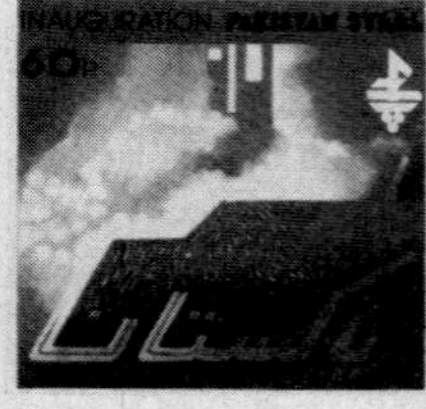

355 Smelting Ore   **356** Map of Pakistan and Rays of Sun

1985 (15 Jan). *Inauguration of Pakistan Steel Corporation. T* **355** *and similar multicoloured design. P* 13.
669 60 p. Type **355** 65 25
670 1 r. Pouring molten steel from ladle (28 × 46 *mm*) .. .. 1·10 25

(Des A. Salahuddin)

1985 (20 Mar). *Presidential Referendum of* 19 *December* 1984. *P* 13.
671 **356** 60 p. multicoloured 80 40

357 Ballot Box and Voting Paper

(Des A. Salahuddin (No. 672), Sultana Shamim Haider (No. 673))

1985 (23 Mar). *March Elections. T* **357** *and similar multi-coloured design. P* 13.
672 1 r. Type **357** 65 15
673 1 r. Minar-e-Qarardad-e-Pakistan Tower, and word "Democracy" (31 × 43 *mm*) .. 65 15

(Des and litho Secura, Singapore)

1985 (27 May). *Mountain Peaks (2nd series). Horiz designs as T* **311**. *Multicoloured. Matt, almost invisible PVA gum. P* 14 × 13½.
674 40 p. Rakaposhi (Karakoram Range) .. 1·75 75
675 2 r. Nangaparbat (Western Himalayas) .. 3·75 5·00

358 Trophy and Medals from Olympic Games 1984, Asia Cup 1985 and World Cup 1982

(Des A. Salahuddin)

1985 (5 July). *Pakistan Hockey Team "Grand Slam" Success. P* 13.
676 **358** 1 r. multicoloured .. .. .. 2·50 1·50

359 King Edward Medical College

(Des Sultana Shamim Haider)

1985 (28 July). *125th Anniv of King Edward Medical College, Lahore. P* 13.
677 **359** 3 r. multicoloured .. .. .. 1·75 65

360 Illuminated Inscription in Urdu

(Des A. Salahuddin)

1985 (14 Aug). *Independence Day. T* **360** *and similar horiz design. Multicoloured. P* 13.
678 60 p. Type **360** 20 20
a. Sheetlet. Nos. 678/9 × 2 70
679 60 p. Illuminated "XXXVIII" (inscr in English).. .. .. 20 20
Nos. 678/9 were issued *se-tenant*, both horizontally and vertically, in sheetlets of four stamps and four stamp-size labels inscribed in Urdu.

361 Sind Madressah-tul-Islam, Karachi

(Des A. Salahuddin)

1985 (1 Sept). *Centenary of Sind Madressah-tul-Islam (theological college), Karachi. P* 13.
680 **361** 2 r. multicoloured .. .. .. 1·75 70

362 Jamia Masjid Mosque by Day

(Des A. Salahuddin)

1985 (14 Sept). *Inauguration of New Jamia Masjid Mosque, Karachi. T* **362** *and similar horiz design. Multicoloured. P* 13.
681 1 r. Type **362** 90 35
682 1 r. Jamia Masjid illuminated at night .. 90 35

363 Lawrence College, Murree

(Des A. Salahuddin)

1985 (21 Sept). *125th Anniv of Lawrence College, Murree. P* 13.
683 **363** 3 r. multicoloured .. .. .. 2·00 65

364 United Nations Building, New York

(Des A. Salahuddin)

1985 (24 Oct). *40th Anniv of United Nations Organization. T* **364** *and similar diamond-shaped design. Multicoloured. P* 14.
684 1 r. Type **364** 30 15
685 2 r. U.N. Building and emblem 40 25

365 Tents and Jamboree Emblem

(Des A. Salahuddin)

1985 (8 Nov). *10th National Scout Jamboree. P* 13.
686 **365** 60 p. multicoloured .. .. .. 2·25 2·25

366 Islamabad   **367** Map of S.A.A.R.C. Countries and National Flags

(Des H. Durrani)

1985 (30 Nov). *25th Anniv of Islamabad. P* 14½ × 14.
687 **366** 3 r. multicoloured .. .. .. 1·75 45

(Des A. Salahuddin)

1985 (8 Dec). *1st Summit Meeting of South Asian Association for Regional Cooperation, Dhaka, Bangladesh. T* **367** *and similar multicoloured design. P* 13½ × 13 (1 *r*.) *or* 13 (2 *r*.).
688 1 r. Type **367** .. .. 2·25 4·00
689 2 r. National flags (39 × 39 *mm*) .. .. 1·75 2·00
No. 688 is reported to have been withdrawn on 9 December 1985.

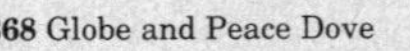
368 Globe and Peace Dove   **369** Peregrine Falcon

(Des A. Salahuddin)

1985 (14 Dec). *25th Anniv of U.N. General Assembly's Declaration on Independence for Colonial Territories. P* 13.
690 **368** 60 p. multicoloured .. .. .. 1·00 60

(Des and litho Secura, Singapore)

1986 (20 Jan). *Wildlife Protection* (13*th series*). *Peregrine Falcon. Matt, almost invisible PVA gum. P* 13½.
691 **369** 1 r. 50, multicoloured .. .. .. 4·25 4·25

370 A.D.B.P. Building, Islamabad

(Des A. Salahuddin)

1986 (18 Feb). *25th Anniv of Agricultural Development Bank of Pakistan. P* 13.
692 **370** 60 p. multicoloured 90 50

371 Government S.E. College **372** Emblem and Bar Graph

(Des Sultana Shamim Haider)

1986 (25 Apr). *Centenary of Government Sadiq Egerton College, Bahawalpur. P* 13.
693 **371** 1 r. multicoloured .. .. .. 1·50 40

(Des Sultana Shamim Haider)

1986 (11 May). *25th Anniv of Asian Productivity Organization. P* 13½.
694 **372** 1 r. multicoloured .. .. .. 1·00 30

373 "1947 1986" **374** Open Air Class

(Des A. Salahuddin (80 p.), M. Munawar (1 r.))

1986 (14 Aug). *39th Anniv of Independence. T* **373** *and similar vert design. Multicoloured. P* 14.
695 80 p. Type **373**.. .. .. 40 15
696 1 r. Illuminated inscription in Urdu .. 40 15

(Des Sultana Shamim Haider)

1986 (8 Sept). *International Literacy Day. P* 13.
697 **374** 1 r. multicoloured 60 30

375 Mother and Child **376** Aitchison College

1986 (28 Oct). *U.N.I.C.E.F. Child Survival Campaign. P* 13½×13.
698 **375** 80 p. multicoloured .. .. .. 1·25 30

(Des A. Salahuddin)

1986 (3 Nov). *Centenary of Aitchison College, Lahore. P* 13½.
699 **376** 2 r. 50, multicoloured 45 30

377 Two Doves carrying Olive Branches **378** Table Tennis Players

(Des Sultana Shamim Haider)

1986 (20 Nov). *International Peace Year. P* 13.
700 **377** 4 r. multicoloured 50 50

(Des A. Salahuddin)

1986 (25 Nov). *4th Asian Cup Table Tennis Tournament, Karachi. P* 14.
701 **378** 2 r. multicoloured .. .. .. 2·00 65

379 Argali

(Des M. Jamal. Litho Secura, Singapore)

1986 (4 Dec). *Wildlife Protection* (14*th series*). *Argali. Matt, almost invisible PVA gum. P* 14.
702 **379** 2 r. multicoloured .. .. .. 3·00 3·00

380 Selimiye Mosque, Edirne, Turkey

(Des A. Salahuddin)

1986 (20 Dec). *"Ecophilex '86" International Stamp Exhibition, Islamabad. T* **380** *and similar vert designs. Multicoloured. P* 13.
703 3 r. Type **380** .. .. 1·40 1·60
a. Horiz strip of 3. Nos. 703/5 .. .. 3·75
704 3 r. Gawhar Shad Mosque, Mashhad, Iran .. 1·40 1·60
705 3 r. Grand Mosque, Bhong, Pakistan .. 1·40 1·60
703/5 .. .. *Set of* 3 3·75 4·25

Nos. 703/5 were printed together, *se-tenant*, in horizontal strips of three, within sheetlets of 12.

381 St. Patrick's School

(Des A. Salahuddin)

1987 (29 Jan). *125th Anniv of St. Patrick's School, Karachi. P* 13.
706 **381** 5 r. multicoloured .. .. .. 1·75 90

382 Mistletoe Flowerpecker and Defence Symbols

(Des A. Salahuddin)

1987 (21 Feb). *Post Office Savings Bank Week. T* **382** *and similar vert designs, each showing a different bird. Multicoloured. P* 13.
707 5 r. Type **382** .. .. 1·10 70
a. Block of 4. Nos. 707/10 .. .. .. 4·00
708 5 r. Spotted Pardalote and laboratory apparatus .. .. 1·10 70
709 5 r. Black-throated Blue Warbler and agriculture symbols .. .. 1·10 70
710 5 r. Red-capped Manakin and industrial skyline .. .. 1·10 70
707/10 .. .. *Set of* 4 4·00 2·50

Nos. 707/10 were printed together, *se-tenant*, in blocks of four throughout the sheet of 32 which contained six blocks of four and eight labels in the left and right-hand vertical columns.

383 New Parliament House, Islamabad

(Des A. Salahuddin)

1987 (23 Mar). *Inauguration of New Parliament House, Islamabad. P* 13.
711 **383** 3 r. multicoloured 30 30

384 Opium Poppies and Flames

(Des A. Salahuddin)

1987 (30 June). *Campaign against Drug Abuse. P* 13.
712 **384** 1 r. multicoloured 45 20

385 Flag and National Anthem Score

(Des A. Salahuddin)

1987 (14 Aug). *40th Anniv of Independence. T* **385** *and similar horiz design. Multicoloured. P* 13.
713 80 p. Type **385**.. .. .. 20 10
714 3 r. Text of speech by Mohammed Ali Jinnah, Minar-e-Qardad-e-Pakistan Tower and arms 55 25

386 Hawker Tempest Mk II

(Des M. Hussaini and A. Salahuddin)

1987 (7 Sept). *Air Force Day. T* **386** *and similar horiz designs showing military aircraft. Multicoloured. P* 13½.
715 3 r. Type **386** .. .. 1·25 1·25
a. Sheetlet. Nos. 715/24 .. .. 11·00
716 3 r. Hawker Fury .. .. .. 1·25 1·25
717 3 r. Supermarine Attacker .. .. 1·25 1·25
718 3 r. North American F-86 Sabre .. .. 1·25 1·25
719 3 r. Lockheed F-104C Starfighter .. 1·25 1·25
720 3 r. Lockheed C-130 Hercules .. .. 1·25 1·25
721 3 r. Shenyang/Tianjin F-6 .. .. 1·25 1·25
722 3 r. Dassault Mirage III .. .. .. 1·25 1·25
723 3 r. North American A-5A Vigilante .. 1·25 1·25
724 3 r. General Dynamics F-16 Fighting Falcon .. .. 1·25 1·25
715/24 .. .. *Set of* 10 11·00 11·00

Nos. 715/24 were printed together, *se-tenant*, in sheetlets of 10.

387 Pasu Glacier

(Des A. Salahuddin)

1987 (1 Oct). *Pakistan Tourism Convention. T* **387** *and similar horiz designs showing views along Karakoram Highway. Multicoloured. P* 13.

725 1 r. 50, Type **387** 60 40
 a. Block of 4. Nos. 725/8 .. .. .. 2·25
726 1 r. 50, Apricot trees 60 40
727 1 r. 50, Karakoram Highway 60 40
728 1 r. 50, View from Khunjerab Pass 60 40
725/8 .. .. *Set of* 4 2·25 1·40

Nos. 725/8 were printed together, *se-tenant*, in blocks of four throughout the sheet of 24.

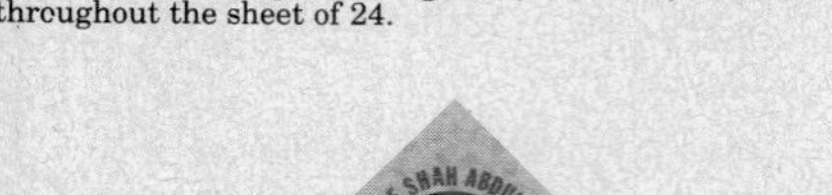

388 Shah Abdul Latif Bhitai Mausoleum

(Des A. Salahuddin)

1987 (8 Oct). *Shah Abdul Latif Bhitai (poet) Commemoration. P* 13.

729 **388** 80 p. multicoloured 20 20

389 D. J. Sind Science College, Karachi

(Des Sultana Shamim Haider)

1987 (7 Nov). *Centenary of D. J. Sind Science College, Karachi. P* 13.

730 **389** 80 p. multicoloured 20 20

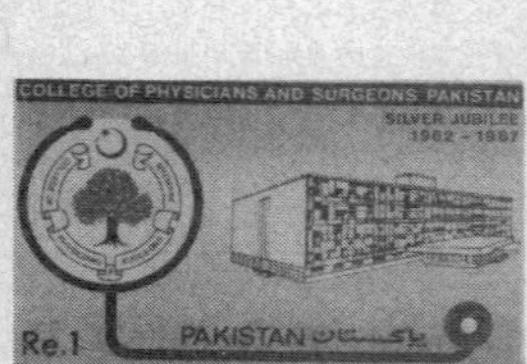

390 College Building

391 Homeless People, Houses and Rising Sun

(Des Sultana Shamim Haider)

1987 (9 Dec). *25th Anniv of College of Physicians and Surgeons. P* 13.

731 **390** 1 r. multicoloured 30 20

(Des Sultana Shamim Haider)

1987 (15 Dec). *International Year of Shelter for the Homeless. P* 13.

732 **391** 3 r. multicoloured 30 30

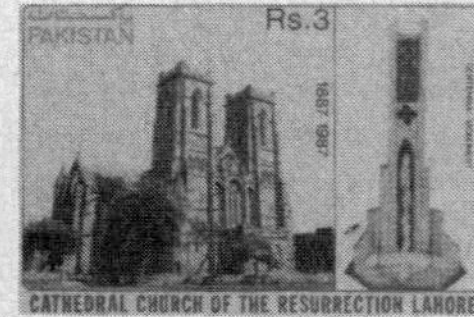

392 Cathedral Church of the Resurrection, Lahore

(Des A. Salahuddin)

1987 (20 Dec). *Centenary of Cathedral Church of the Resurrection, Lahore. P* 13.

733 **392** 3 r. multicoloured 30 30

393 Honeycomb and Arms

(Des A. Salahuddin)

1987 (28 Dec). *40th Anniv of Pakistan Post Office. P* 13.

734 **393** 3 r. multicoloured 30 30

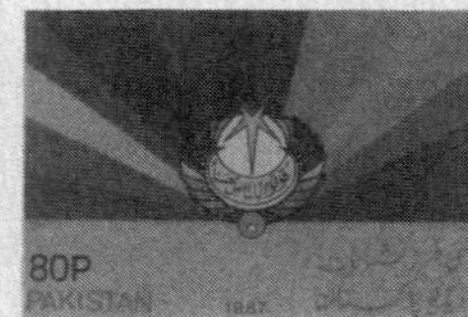

394 Corporation Emblem

(Des A. Salahuddin)

1987 (31 Dec). *Radio Pakistan's New Programme Schedules. P* 13.

735 **394** 80 p. multicoloured 15 15

395 Jamshed Nusserwanjee Mehta and Karachi Municipal Corporation Building

396 Leprosy Symbols within Flower

(Des A. Salahuddin)

1988 (7 Jan). *Birth Centenary* (1986) *of Jamshed Nusserwanjee Mehta (former President of Karachi Municipal Corporation). P* 13.

736 **395** 3 r. multicoloured 30 30

(Des Sultana Shamim Haider)

1988 (31 Jan). *World Leprosy Day. P* 13.

737 **396** 3 r. multicoloured 75 30

397 W.H.O. Building, Geneva

(Des A. Salahuddin)

1988 (7 Apr). *40th Anniv of World Health Organization. P* 13.

738 **397** 4 r. multicoloured 35 35

398 Globe

399 Crescent, Leaf Pattern and Archway

1988 (8 May). *125th Anniv of International Red Cross and Crescent. P* 13.

739 **398** 3 r. multicoloured 30 30

(Des A. Salahuddin)

1988 (14 Aug). *Independence Day. P* $13^{1}/_{2}$.

740 **399** 80 p. multicoloured 10 10
741 4 r. multicoloured 25 30

400 Field Events

(Des A. Salahuddin)

1988 (17 Sept). *Olympic Games, Seoul. T* **400** *and similar horiz designs. Multicoloured. P* 13.

742 10 r. Type **400** .. .. 1·10 1·10
 a. Sheetlet. Nos. 742/51 .. .. .. 10·00
743 10 r. Track events .. .. 1·10 1·10
744 10 r. Jumping and pole vaulting .. .. 1·10 1·10
745 10 r. Gymnastics .. .. 1·10 1·10
746 10 r. Table tennis, tennis, hockey and baseball .. .. 1·10 1·10
747 10 r. Volleyball, football, basketball and handball .. .. 1·10 1·10
748 10 r. Wrestling, judo, boxing and weightlifting .. .. 1·10 1·10
749 10 r. Shooting, fencing and archery .. 1·10 1·10
750 10 r. Water sports .. .. 1·10 1·10
751 10 r. Equestrian events and cycling .. 1·10 1·10
742/51 .. .. *Set of* 10 10·00 10·00

Nos. 742/51 were issued, *se-tenant*, in sheetlets of ten stamps and thirty-six half stamp-size labels.

401 Markhor

(Litho Secura, Singapore)

1988 (29 Oct). *Wildlife Protection (15th series). Markhor. Matt, almost invisible PVA gum. P* 14.

752 **401** 2 r. multicoloured 40 40

402 Islamia College, Peshawar

(Des A. Salahuddin)

1988 (22 Dec). *75th Anniv of Islamia College, Peshawar. P* $13^{1}/_{2}$.

753 **402** 3 r. multicoloured 30 30

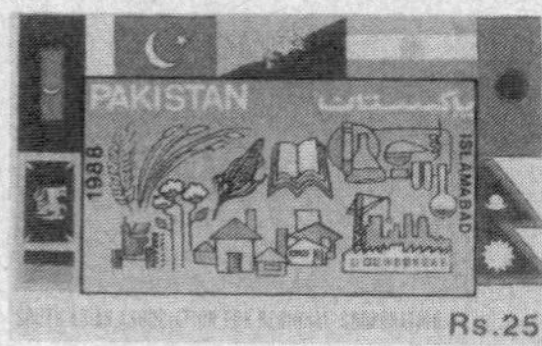

403 Symbols of Agriculture, Industry and Education with National Flags

(Des Sultana Shamim Haider (25 r.), G. M. Shaikh (50 r.), A. Salahuddin (75 r.))

1988 (29 Dec). *South Asian Association for Regional Co-operation, 4th Summit Meeting, Islamabad. T* **403** *and similar multicoloured designs. P* 13 (25 *r.*), 14 (50 *r.*) *or* $13^{1}/_{2}$×13 (75 *r.*).

754 25 r. Type **403** .. .. 1·50 1·50
755 50 r. National flags on globe and symbols of communications (33×33 *mm*) .. 3·25 3·25
756 75 r. Stamps from member countries (52×29 *mm*) .. .. 4·50 4·50
754/6 .. .. *Set of* 3 8·25 8·25

No. 755 was printed in sheets of eight stamps and one stamp-size label, showing the S.A.A.R.C. emblem, in the central position.

(Des A. Salahuddin)

1989 (23 Jan). *Pioneers of Freedom (2nd series). Diamond-shaped design as T* **282**. *Multicoloured. W* **98**. *P* 14.

757 3 r. Maulana Hasrat Mohani 15 20

404 Logo **405** Zulfikar Ali Bhutto

(Des A. Salahuddin)

1989 (18 Feb). *"Adasia 89" 16th Asian Advertising Congress, Lahore. P* 13.

758 **404** 1 r. mult ("Pakistan" in yellow) .. 65 65
a. Sheetlet. Nos. 758/60, each × 3 5·25
759 1 r. mult ("Pakistan" in turquoise-bl) 65 65
760 1 r. mult ("Pakistan" in white) .. 65 65
758/60 .. .. *Set of* 3 1·75 1·75

Nos. 758/60 were printed together, *se-tenant*, in horizontal and vertical strips of three within the sheetlets of nine.

(Des A. Munir (1 r.), A. Salahuddin (2 r.))

1989 (4 Apr). *10th Death Anniv of Zulfikar Ali Bhutto (statesman). T* **405** *and similar vert design. Multicoloured. P* 13.

761 1 r. Type **405** 15 10
762 2 r. Zulfikar Ali Bhutto (*different*) .. 20 20

406 "Daphne" Class Submarine

(Des A. Salahuddin)

1989 (1 June). *25 Years of Pakistan Navy Submarine Operations. T* **406** *and similar horiz designs. Multicoloured. P* 13½.

763 1 r. Type **406** .. .. .. 1·10 1·10
a. Vert strip of 3. Nos. 763/5 .. .. 3·00
764 1 r. "Fleet Snorkel" class submarine .. 1·10 1·10
765 1 r. "Agosta" class submarine .. 1·10 1·10
763/5 .. .. *Set of* 3 3·00 3·00

Nos. 763/5 were printed together, *se-tenant*, in vertical strips of three throughout the sheet.

407 "The Oath of the Tennis Court" (David)

(Des A. Salahuddin)

1989 (24 June). *Bicentenary of French Revolution. P* 13½.

766 **407** 7 r. multicoloured .. .. .. 1·75 90

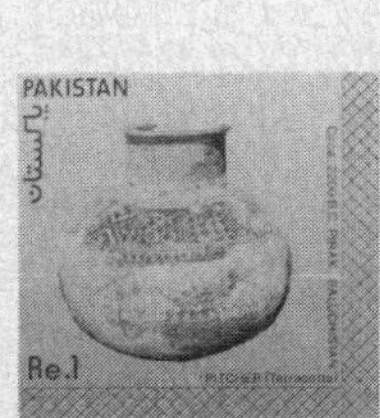

408 Pitcher, *c.* 2200 B.C. **409** Satellites and Map of Asian Telecommunications Network

(Des A. Salahuddin)

1989 (28 June). *Archaeological Artifacts. T* **408** *and similar square designs showing terracotta pottery from Baluchistan Province. Multicoloured. P* 14.

767 1 r. Type **408** 15 15
a. Block of 4. Nos. 767/70 55
768 1 r. Jar, *c.* 2300 B.C. 15 15
769 1 r. Vase, *c.* 3600 B.C. 15 15
770 1 r. Jar, *c.* 2600 B.C. 15 15
767/70 .. .. *Set of* 4 55 55

Nos. 767/70 were printed together, *se-tenant*, in blocks of four throughout the sheet.

(Des G. Shaikh)

1989 (1 July). *10th Anniv of Asia-Pacific Telecommunity. P* 13½.

771 **409** 3 r. multicoloured 30 30

410 Container Ship at Wharf **411** Mohammed Ali Jinnah

(Des A. Salahuddin)

1989 (5 Aug). *Construction of Integrated Container Terminal, Port Qasim. P* 14.

772 **410** 6 r. multicoloured .. .. .. 3·00 3·25

(Des A. Salahuddin. Eng A. Munir. Recess and litho)

1989 (14 Aug). *W* **98**. *P* 13.

773 **411** 1 r. multicoloured 20 10
774 1 r. 50, multicoloured 20 20
775 2 r. multicoloured 30 30
a. Head omitted .. .. ..
776 3 r. multicoloured 40 40
777 4 r. multicoloured 45 45
778 5 r. multicoloured 50 60
773/8 .. .. *Set of* 6 1·90 1·90

No. 775a occurs on the last vertical row of a sheet and shows the sepia head completely omitted together with almost all the oval frame.

Examples of Nos. 773/8 overprinted "NATIONAL SEMINAR ON PHILATELY MULTAN 1992" as a continuous pattern were available at this event on 15 and 16 April 1992.

Details of authorisation by the Pakistan Post Offices and of availability at Multan are disputed, but, even if officially sanctioned, these overprints do not fulfil the criteria for catalogue listing due to their limited availability. They were not available from any post office other than Multan and, it is reported, only forty-five sheets of each of the three higher values were overprinted.

412 Mausoleum of Shah Abdul Latif Bhitai **413** Asiatic Black Bear

(Des A. Salahuddin)

1989 (16 Sept). *300th Birth Anniv of Shah Abdul Latif Bhitai (poet). P* 13.

779 **412** 2 r. multicoloured 20 20

COMMONWEALTH MEMBER

Pakistan rejoined the Commonwealth on 1 October 1989.

(Des A. McCoy)

1989 (7 Oct). *Wildlife Protection (16th series). Asiatic Black Bear. T* **413** *and similar horiz designs. Multicoloured. P* 13½.

780 4 r. Type **413** .. .. .. 90 1·00
a. Block of 4. Nos. 780/3 .. .. 3·25
781 4 r. Bear among boulders .. .. 90 1·00
782 4 r. Standing on rock .. .. 90 1·00
783 4 r. Sitting by trees .. .. 90 1·00
780/3 .. .. *Set of* 4 3·25 3·50

Nos. 780/3 were printed together, *se-tenant*, in blocks of 4 throughout the sheet.

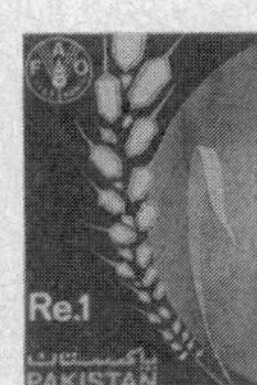

414 Ear of Wheat encircling Globe **415** Games Emblem and Flags of Member Countries

(Des A. Salahuddin)

1989 (16 Oct). *World Food Day. P* 14×12½.

784 **414** 1 r. multicoloured 35 35

(Des A. Salahuddin)

1989 (20 Oct). *4th South Asian Sports Federation Games, Islamabad. P* 13.

785 **415** 1 r. multicoloured 35 35

416 Patchwork Kamblee (cloth) entering Gate of Heaven

(Des Farah and Fareeda Batul)

1989 (20 Oct). *800th Birth Anniv of Baba Farid (Muslim spiritual leader). P* 13.

786 **416** 3 r. multicoloured 30 30

417 Pakistan Television Logo **418** Family of Drug Addicts in Poppy Bud

(Des A. Salahuddin)

1989 (26 Nov). *25th Anniv of Television Broadcasting in Pakistan. P* 13½.

787 **417** 3 r. multicoloured 30 30

(Des M. Munawar)

1989 (8 Dec). *South Asian Association for Regional Co-operation Anti-Drugs Campaign. P* 13.

788 **418** 7 r. multicoloured .. .. .. 1·10 85

419 Murray College, Sialkot

(Des A. Salahuddin)

1989 (18 Dec). *Centenary of Murray College, Sialkot. P* 14.

789 **419** 6 r. multicoloured 50 70

420 Government College, Lahore

(Des N. Sheikh)

1989 (21 Dec). *125th Anniv of Government College, Lahore. P* 13.

790 **420** 6 r. multicoloured 50 80

421 Fields, Electricity Pylons and Rural Buildings

(Des A. Salahuddin)

1989 (31 Dec). *10th Anniv of Centre for Asia and Pacific Integrated Rural Development. P* 13.
791 **421** 3 r. multicoloured 30 40

422 Emblem and Islamic Patterns

(Des A. Salahuddin)

1990 (9 Feb). *20th Anniv of Organization of the Islamic Conference. P* 13.
792 **422** 1 r. multicoloured 40 20

423 Hockey Match

(Des M. Khan)

1990 (12 Feb). *7th World Hockey Cup, Lahore. P* 13½.
793 **423** 2 r. multicoloured . . . . . . 3·00 3·00

424 Mohammed Iqbal addressing Crowd and Liaquat Ali Khan taking Oath

(Des A. Zafar (1 r.), A. Salahuddin (7 r.))

1990 (23 Mar). *50th Anniv of Passing of Pakistan Resolution. T* **424** *and similar multicoloured designs. P* 13 (1 *r.*) *or* 13½ (7 *r.*).
794 1 r. Type **424** 80 80
a. Horiz strip of 3. Nos. 794/6 . . . . 2·25
795 1 r. Maulana Mohammad Ali Jauhar and Mohammed Ali Jinnah with banner . . 80 80
796 1 r. Women with Pakistan flag, and Mohammed Ali Jinnah taking Governor-General's oath, 1947 . . 80 80
797 7 r. Minar-i-Qarardad-e-Pakistan Monument and Resolution in Urdu and English (86×42 *mm*) . . . . 1·40 1·40
794/7 . . . . *Set of* 4 3·50 3·50
Nos. 794/6 were printed together, *se-tenant*, in horizontal strips of 3 throughout the sheet, each strip forming a composite design.

425 Pregnant Woman resting

(Des Family Planning Association of Pakistan)

1990 (24 Mar). *"Safe Motherhood" South Asia Conference, Lahore. P* 13½.
798 **425** 5 r. multicoloured 75 75

PRICES OF SETS

Set prices are given for many issues, generally those containing three stamps or more. Definitive sets include one of each value or major colour change, but do not cover different perforations, die types or minor shades. Where a choice is possible the set prices are based on the cheapest versions of the stamps included in the listings.

426 "Decorated Verse by Ghalib" (Shakir Ali)

(Des A. Salahuddin)

1990 (19 Apr). *Painters of Pakistan* (1*st series*). *Shakir Ali. P* 13½×13.
799 **426** 1 r. multicoloured 75 65
See also Nos. 856/7.

427 Satellite in Night Sky

(Des A. Salahuddin)

1990 (26 July). *Launch of* "Badr 1" *Satellite. P* 13.
800 **427** 3 r. multicoloured . . . . . . 1·40 1·40

428 Allama Mohammed Iqbal

1990 (14 Aug). *Pioneers of Freedom* (3*rd series*). *T* **428** *and similar vert designs. Each brown and green. P* 13.
801 1 r. Type **428** 25 25
a. Sheetlet. Nos. 801/9 . . . . 2·00
802 1 r. Mohammed Ali Jinnah 25 25
803 1 r. Sir Syed Ahmad Khan 25 25
804 1 r. Nawab Salimullah 25 25
805 1 r. Mohtarma Fatima Jinnah 25 25
806 1 r. Aga Khan III 25 25
807 1 r. Nawab Mohammad Ismail Khan . . 25 25
808 1 r. Hussain Shaheed Suhrawardy . . 25 25
809 1 r. Syed Ameer Ali 25 25
810 1 r. Nawab Bahadur Yar Jung 25 25
a. Sheetlet. Nos. 810/18 . . . . 2·00
811 1 r. Khawaja Nazimuddin 25 25
812 1 r. Maulana Obaidullah Sindhi 25 25
813 1 r. Sahibzada Abdul Qaiyum Khan . . 25 25
814 1 r. Begum Jahanara Shah Nawaz . . 25 25
815 1 r. Sir Ghulam Hussain Hidayatullah . . 25 25
816 1 r. Qazi Mohammad Isa 25 25
817 1 r. Sir M. Shahnawaz Khan Mamdot . . 25 25
818 1 r. Pir Sahib of Manki Sharif 25 25
819 1 r. Liaquat Ali Khan 25 25
a. Sheetlet. Nos. 819/27 . . . . 2·00
820 1 r. Maulvi A. K. Fazl-ul-Haq 25 25
821 1 r. Allama Shabbir Ahmad Usmani . . 25 25
822 1 r. Sadar Abdur Rab Nishtar 25 25
823 1 r. Bi Amma 25 25
824 1 r. Sir Abdullah Haroon 25 25
825 1 r. Chaudhry Rahmat Ali 25 25
826 1 r. Raja Sahib of Mahmudabad 25 25
827 1 r. Hassanally Effendi 25 25
801/27 . . . . . . *Set of* 27 6·00 6·00
Nos. 801/9, 810/18 and 819/27 were printed together, *se-tenant*, in sheetlets of nine.
See also Nos. 838/46, 870/2, 904/6, 921/8, 961/2 and 1007.

429 Cultural Aspects of Indonesia and Pakistan

(Des J. Engineer)

1990 (19 Aug). *Indonesia–Pakistan Economic and Cultural Cooperation Organization. P* 13.
828 **429** 7 r. multicoloured 60 60

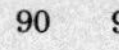

430 Globe, Open Book and Pen

(Des S. Afar)

1990 (8 Sept). *International Literacy Year. P* 13
829 **430** 3 r. multicoloured 90 90

431 College Crests **432** Children and Globe

(Des I. Gilani)

1990 (22 Sept). *Joint Meeting between Royal College of Physicans, Edinburgh, and College of Physicians and Surgeons, Pakistan. P* 13.
830 **431** 2 r. multicoloured 60 45

(Des A. Salahuddin)

1990 (29 Sept). *U. N. World Summit for Children, New York. P* 13.
831 **432** 7 r. multicoloured 55 65

433 Girl within Members' Flags

(Des A. Salahuddin)

1990 (21 Nov). *South Asian Association for Regional Co-operation Year of Girl Child. P* 13½.
832 **433** 2 r. multicoloured 70 75

434 Paper passing over Rollers **435** Civil Defence Worker protecting Islamabad

(Des I. Jillani)

1990 (8 Dec). *25th Anniv of Security Papers Limited. P* 13.
833 **434** 3 r. multicoloured 75 80
a. Red ("25 YEARS OF SECURITY PAPERS LTD") omitted . . . . 60·00

(Des I. Jillani)

1991 (1 Mar). *International Civil Defence Day. P* 13.
834 **435** 7 r. multicoloured . . . . . . 1·25 1·50

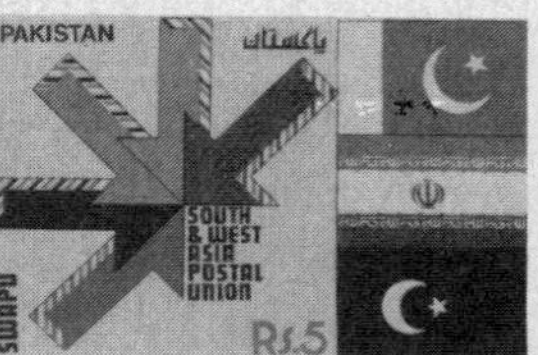

436 Logo and Flags of Member Countries

(Des A. Salahuddin)

1991 (12 Mar). *South and West Asia Postal Union Commemoration. P* 13.
835 **436** 5 r. multicoloured . . . . . . 1·60 1·60

437 Globe and Figures

(Des S. Afsar)

1991 (11 July). *World Population Day. P* 13.
836 **437** 10 r. multicoloured . . . . . . 1·90 2·00

438 Mentally Handicapped Athlete

439 Habib Bank Headquarters and Emblem

(Des A. Salahuddin)

1991 (19 July). *Pakistan Participation in Special Olympic Games. P* 13.
837 **438** 7 r. multicoloured . . . . . . 1·75 2·00

1991 (14 Aug). *Pioneers of Freedom* (4*th series*). *Vert designs as T* **428**. *Each brown and green. P* 13.

838	1 r. Maulana Zafar Ali Khan	25	25
	a. Sheetlet. Nos. 838/46	2·00	
839	1 r. Maulana Mohamed Ali Jauhar	25	25
840	1 r. Chaudhry Khaliquzzaman	25	25
841	1 r. Hameed Nizami	25	25
842	1 r. Begum Ra'ana Liaquat Ali Khan	25	25
843	1 r. Mirza Abol Hassan Ispahani	25	25
844	1 r. Raja Ghazanfar Ali Khan	25	25
845	1 r. Malik Barkat Ali	25	25
846	1 r. Mir Jaffer Khan Jamali	25	25
838/46	*Set of* 9	2·00	2·00

Nos. 838/46 were printed together, *se-tenant*, as a sheetlet of nine.

(Des I. Jillani)

1991 (25 Aug). 50*th Anniv of Habib Bank. P* 13.
847 **439** 1 r. multicoloured 30 10
848 5 r. multicoloured . . . . . . 1·75 2·00

440 St. Joseph's Convent School

(Des A. Salahuddin)

1991 (8 Sept). 130*th Anniv* (1992) *of St. Joseph's Convent School, Karachi. P* 13.
849 **440** 5 r. multicoloured . . . . . . 1·50 1·75

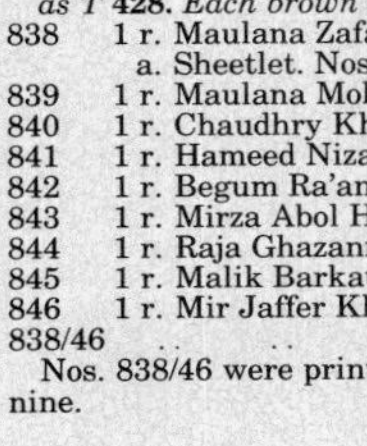

441 Emperor Sher Shah Suri

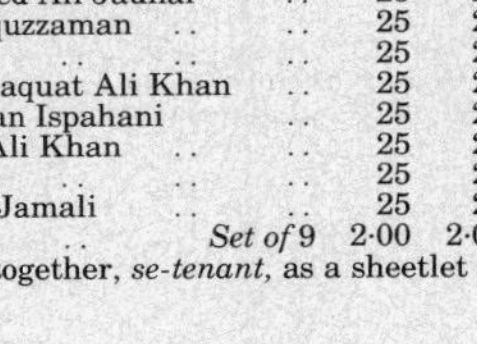

442 Jinnah Antarctic Research Station

(Des S. Akhtar)

1991 (5 Oct). *Emperor Sher Shah Suri* (*founder of road network*) *Commemoration. Multicoloured. P* 13.
850 5 r. Type **441** . . . . . . 1·50 1·75
MS851 92×80 mm. 7 r. Emperor on horseback and portrait as Type **441**. Imperf . . 1·40 2·00

(Des I. Jillani)

1991 (28 Oct). *Pakistan Scientific Expedition to Antarctica. P* 13.
852 **442** 7 r. multicoloured . . . . . . 2·50 2·25

443 Houbara Bustard

444 Mosque

1991 (4 Nov). *Wildlife Protection* (17*th series*). *P* 13.
853 **443** 7 r. multicoloured . . . . . . 2·00 2·00

1991 (22 Nov). 300*th Death Anniv of Hazrat Sultan Bahoo. P* 13.
854 **444** 7 r. multicoloured 70 80

445 Development Symbols and Map of Asia

1991 (19 Dec). 25*th Anniv of Asian Development Bank. P* 13.
855 **445** 7 r. multicoloured 85 85

1991 (24 Dec). *Painters of Pakistan* (2*nd series*). *Horiz designs as T* **426**. *Multicoloured. P* 13½×13.
856 1 r. "Procession" (Haji Muhammad Sharif) 90 90
857 1 r. "Women harvesting" (Ustad Allah Bux) 90 90

446 American Express Travellers Cheques of 1891 and 1991

1991 (26 Dec). *Centenary of American Express Travellers Cheques. P* 13½.
858 **446** 7 r. multicoloured . . . . . . 1·75 2·00

447 Flag, Banknote and Banking Equipment

1992 (8 Apr). 1*st Anniv of Muslim Commercial Bank Privatisation. T* **447** *and similar horiz design. Multicoloured. P* 13.
859 1 r. Type **447** 10 10
860 7 r. Flag with industrial and commercial scenes 45 60

448 Imran Khan (team captain) and Trophy

449 "Rehber-1" Rocket and Satellite View of Earth

(Des I. Jillani (2 r.), A. Salahuddin (5 r.), M. Ahmed (7 r.))

1992 (27 Apr). *Pakistan's Victory in World Cricket Championship. T* **448** *and similar multicoloured designs. P* 13.
861 2 r. Type **448** 70 70
862 5 r. Trophy and national flags (*horiz*) . . 1·50 1·50
863 7 r. Pakistani flag, trophy and symbolic cricket ball . . . . . . 1·75 1·75
861/3 . . . . *Set of* 3 3·50 3·50

(Des I. Jillani (1 r.), S. Afsar (2 r.))

1992 (7 June). *International Space Year. T* **449** *and similar horiz design. Multicoloured. P* 13.
864 1 r. Type **449** 15 10
865 2 r. Satellite orbiting Earth and logo . . 20 20

450 Surgical Instruments

451 Globe and Symbolic Family

(Des S. Afsar)

1992 (5 July). *Industries. T* **450** *and similar horiz designs. Multicoloured. P* 13½.
866 10 r. Type **450** 60 70
a. Horiz strip of 3. Nos. 866/8 . . . . 2·40
867 15 r. Leather goods 75 80
868 25 r. Sports equipment . . . . . . 1·25 1·40
866/8 . . . . *Set of* 3 2·40 2·50
Nos. 866/8 were printed together, *se-tenant*, in horizontal strips of three throughout the sheet.

(Des S. Afsar)

1992 (25 July). *Population Day. P* 13.
869 **451** 6 r. multicoloured 80 90

(Des S. Akhtar)

1992 (14 Aug). *Pioneers of Freedom* (5*th series*). *Vert designs as T* **428**. *Each brown and green. P* 13.
870 1 r. Syed Suleman Nadvi 40 40
a. Horiz strip of 3. Nos. 870/2 . . . . 1·10
871 1 r. Nawab Iftikhar Hussain Khan Mamdot 40 40
872 1 r. Maulana Muhammad Shibli Naumani 40 40
870/2 . . . . *Set of* 3 1·10 1·10
Nos. 870/2 were printed together, *se-tenant*, in horizontal strips of three throughout a sheetlet of nine.

452 Scout Badge and Salute

453 College Building

(Des I. Jillani)

1992 (23 Aug). 6*th Islamic Scout Jamboree and* 4*th Islamic Scouts Conference. T* **452** *and similar vert design. Multicoloured. P* 14×13.
873 6 r. Type **452** 50 60
874 6 r. Conference centre and scout salute . . 50 60

1992 (1 Nov). *Centenary of Islamia College, Lahore. P* 13.
875 **453** 3 r. multicoloured 35 40

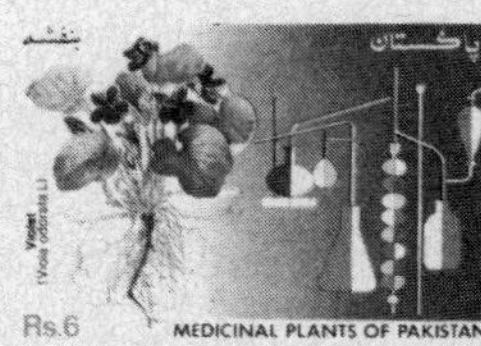

454 *Viola odorata* (flower) and Symbolic Drug Manufacture

(Des S. Afsar)

1992 (22 Nov). *Medicinal Plants* (1*st series*). *P* 13.
876 **454** 6 r. multicoloured 70 70
See also Nos. 903, 946 and 1010.

455 Emblem

(Des A. Salahuddin)

1992 (28 Nov). *Extraordinary Ministerial Council Session of Economic Co-operation Organization, Islamabad. P* 13.
877 **455** 7 r. multicoloured 70 80

456 Emblems and Field

457 Alhambra Palace, Granada, Spain

(Des A. Salahuddin)

1992 (5 Dec). *International Conference on Nutrition, Rome. P* 14.
878 **456** 7 r. multicoloured 70 80

(Des A. Salahuddin)

1992 (14 Dec). *Cultural Heritage of Muslim Granada. P* 13.
879 **457** 7 r. multicoloured 70 80

458 Mallard

459 Baluchistan Costume

Four different versions of designs as T **458**:
Type A. "Rs.5" at right with rainbow 8 mm beneath "P" of "PAKISTAN"
Type B. "Rs.5" at right with rainbow 2 mm beneath "P"
Type C. "Rs.5" at left with rainbow 2 mm beneath "N" of "PAKISTAN"
Type D. "Rs.5" at left with rainbow 8 mm beneath "N"

1992 (31 Dec). *Water Birds. T* **458** *and similar vert designs. Multicoloured. P* 14×13.
880 5 r. Type **458** (A) 60 60
a. Sheetlet. Nos. 880/95 .. .. 8·50
881 5 r. Type **458** (B) 60 60
882 5 r. Type **458** (C) 60 60
883 5 r. Type **458** (D) 60 60
884 5 r. Greylag Goose (A) 60 60
885 5 r. As No. 884 (B) 60 60
886 5 r. As No. 884 (C) 60 60
887 5 r. As No. 884 (D) 60 60
888 5 r. Gadwall (A) 60 60
889 5 r. As No. 888 (B) 60 60
890 5 r. As No. 888 (C) 60 60
891 5 r. As No. 888 (D) 60 60
892 5 r. Common Shelduck (A) 60 60
893 5 r. As No. 892 (B) 60 60
894 5 r. As No. 892 (C) 60 60
895 5 r. As No. 892 (D) 60 60
880/95 .. .. *Set of* 16 8·50 8·50

Nos. 880/95 were printed together, *se-tenant*, in sheetlets of 16 (4×4). Stamps in the first two vertical rows show the face value at right and those in the last two show it at left. Each horizontal row shows a rainbow which curves across the tops of the designs. The four different bird designs are repeated in different positions on each horizontal row. Row 1 contains Nos. 880 (A), 885 (B), 890 (C) and 895 (D). Row 2 commences with No. 884 (A) and ends with No. 883 (D) and the sequence continues on the other rows.

(Des S. Rahman)

1993 (10 Mar). *Women's Traditional Costumes. T* **459** *and similar vert designs. Multicoloured. P* 13.
896 6 r. Type **459** .. .. 1·25 1·25
897 6 r. Punjab .. .. 1·25 1·25
898 6 r. Sindh .. .. 1·25 1·25
899 6 r. North-west Frontier Province .. 1·25 1·25
896/9 .. .. *Set of* 4 4·50 4·50

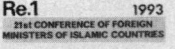

460 Clasped Hands and Islamic Symbols

461 I.T.U. Emblem

(Des I. Jilani)

1993 (25 Apr). *21st Conference of Islamic Foreign Ministers, Karachi. P* 13.
900 **460** 1 r. multicoloured 25 10
901 6 r. multicoloured 70 80

(Des Pakistan Telecommunication Corporation, Islamabad)

1993 (17 May). *25th Anniv of World Telecommunication Day. P* 13.
902 **461** 1 r. multicoloured 40 20

(Des S. Afsar)

1993 (20 June). *Medicinal Plants (2nd series). Horiz design as T* **454**. *Multicoloured. P* 13.
903 6 r. Fennel and symbolic drug manufacture 90 90

(Des S. Akhtar)

1993 (14 Aug). *Pioneers of Freedom (6th series). Vert designs as T* **428**. *Each brown and vermilion. P* 13.
904 1 r. Ghulam Mohammad Bhurgri .. 40 40
a. Horiz strip of 3. Nos. 904/6 .. .. 1·10
905 1 r. Ahmed Yar Khan 40 40
906 1 r. Mohammad Pir Sahib Zakori Sharif 40 40
904/6 .. .. *Set of* 3 1·10 1·10

Nos. 904/6 were printed together, *se-tenant*, in horizontal strips of three throughout a sheetlet of nine.

462 College Building and Arms

(Des Nargis Munir)

1993 (1 Sept). *Centenary of Gordon College, Rawalpindi. P* 13.
907 **462** 2 r. multicoloured 40 40

463 Juniper Forest

464 Globe, Produce and Emblem

(Des A. Salahuddin)

1993 (30 Sept)–**95**. *Campaign to Save the Juniper Forest, Ziarat. P* 13.
907*a* **463** 1 r. multicoloured (14.2.95) 30 20
908 7 r. multicoloured .. .. .. 1·25 1·25

(Des Jawaiduddin)

1993 (16 Oct). *World Food Day. P* 14.
909 **464** 6 r. multicoloured 65 65

465 Burn Hall Institution, Abbottabad

466 Peace Dove carrying Letter and National Flags

(Des I. Jilani)

1993 (28 Oct). *50th Anniv of Burn Hall Institutions. P* 13.
910 **465** 7 r. multicoloured 75 80

(Des F. Amir)

1993 (18 Nov). *South and West Asia Postal Union Commemoration. P* 13.
911 **466** 7 r. multicoloured 80 90

467 Congress Emblem

468 Wazir Mansion (birthplace)

1993 (10 Dec). *Pakistan College of Physicians and Surgeons International Medical Congress. P* 13.
912 **467** 1 r. multicoloured 40 20

1993 (25 Dec). *45th Death Anniv of Mohammed Ali Jinnah.* W **98**. *P* 13½×13.
913 **468** 1 r. multicoloured 40 20

469 Emblem and National Flag

(Des A. Salahuddin)

1994 (11 Apr). *75th Anniv of International Labour Organization.* W **98**. *P* 13.
914 **469** 7 r. multicoloured 50 60

470 Ratan Jot (flower)

471 Silhouette of Family and Emblem

(Des I. Jillani)

1994 (20 Apr). *Ratification of International Biological Diversity Convention. T* **470** *and similar horiz designs. Multicoloured.* W **98** (*sideways*). *P* 13½.
915 6 r. Type **470** 35 35
a. Horiz strip of 4. Nos. 915/18 .. .. 1·25
916 6 r. Wetlands habitat 35 35
917 6 r. Golden Mahseer (*Tor puttitora*) (fish) 35 35
918 6 r. Brown Bear 35 35
915/18 .. .. *Set of* 4 1·25 1·25

Nos. 915/18 were printed together, *se-tenant*, in horizontal strips of 4 throughout the sheet.

(Des Nargis Munir)

1994 (15 May). *International Year of the Family.* W **98** (*sideways*). *P* 13.
919 **471** 7 r. multicoloured 40 40

472 Symbolic Globe and Logo

1994 (11 July). *World Population Day.* W **98** (*sideways*). *P* 13.
920 **472** 7 r. multicoloured 40 40

1994 (14 Aug). *Pioneers of Freedom (7th series). Vert designs as T* **428**. *Each brown and green. No wmk. P* 13.

921 1 r. Nawab Mohsin-Ul-Mulk 10 10
a. Sheetlet. Nos. 921/8 80
922 1 r. Sir Shahnawaz Bhutto 10 10
923 1 r. Nawab Viqar-Ul-Mulk 10 10
924 1 r. Pir Ilahi Bux 10 10
925 1 r. Sheikh Abdul Qadir 10 10
926 1 r. Dr. Sir Ziauddin Ahmed 10 10
927 1 r. Jam Mir Ghulam Qadir Khan .. 10 10
928 1 r. Sardar Aurangzeb Khan 10 10
921/8 .. .. Set of 8 80 80

Nos. 921/8 were printed together, *se-tenant*, in sheetlets of 8 stamps and one centre label showing the Pakistan flag.

473 Hala Pottery, Pakistan

474 Boy writing and Globe

(Des A. Siddique (No. 929))

1994 (19 Aug). *Indonesia-Pakistan Economic and Cultural Co-operation Organization. T* **473** *and similar vert design. Multicoloured. W* **98**. *P* 13.

929 10 r. Type **473** 45 50
a. Horiz pair. Nos. 929/30 .. .. 90 1·00
930 10 r. Lombok pottery, Indonesia 45 50

Nos. 929/30 were printed together, *se-tenant*, in horizontal pairs throughout the sheet.

(Des Nargis Manir)

1994 (8 Sept). *International Literacy Day. W* **98**. *P* $13^1/_2$.

931 **474** 7 r. multicoloured 30 35

475 Mohammed Ali Jinnah and Floral Pattern

476 Gateway and Emblem

(Recess and litho)

1994 (11 Sept). *W* **98**. *P* 13.

932 **475** 1 r. multicoloured 10 10
933 2 r. multicoloured 10 10
934 3 r. multicoloured 10 10
935 4 r. multicoloured 15 20
936 5 r. multicoloured 20 25
937 7 r. multicoloured 25 30
938 10 r. multicoloured 40 45
939 12 r. multicoloured 45 50
940 15 r. multicoloured 55 60
941 20 r. multicoloured 75 80
942 25 r. multicoloured .. .. .. 95 1·00
943 30 r. multicoloured .. .. .. 1·10 1·25
932/43 .. .. Set of 12 5·00 5·50

(Des Nargis Munir)

1994 (22 Sept). *2nd South Asian Association for Regional Co-operation and 12th National Scout Jamborees, Quetta. W* **98** *(sideways). P* 13.

944 **476** 7 r. multicoloured 30 35

477 Engraver

478 Henbane

1994 (7 Oct). *First International Festival of Islamic Artisans at Work. W* **98**. *P* $13^1/_2$.

945 **477** 2 r. multicoloured 40 30

(Des F. Amir)

1994 (18 Oct). *Medicinal Plants (3rd series). W* **98**. *P* 13.

946 **478** 6 r. multicoloured 55 60

479 Abu-I Kasim Firdausi (poet)

480 Museum Building

(Des F. Amir)

1994 (27 Oct). *Millenary of Shahnama (poem). W* **98**. *P* 13.

947 **479** 1 r. multicoloured 15 15

(Des A. Siddique)

1994 (27 Dec). *Centenary of Lahore Museum. W* **98** *(sideways). P* 13.

948 **480** 4 r. multicoloured 40 40

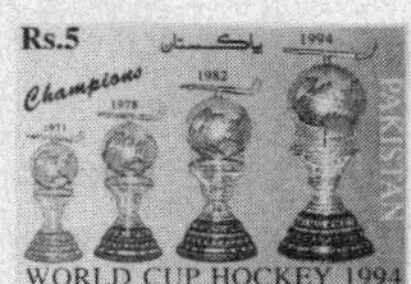

481 World Cup Trophies for 1971, 1978, 1982 and 1994

(Des Jawaiduddin)

1994 (31 Dec). *Victory of Pakistan in World Cup Hockey Championship. W* **98** *(sideways). P* $13^1/_2$×13.

949 **481** 5 r. multicoloured 50 50

482 Tourist Attractions

(Des Nargis Munir)

1995 (2 Jan). *20th Anniv of World Tourism Organization. W* **98**. *P* 13.

950 **482** 4 r. multicoloured 40 40

483 Khan Khushal of Khattak and Army

484 E.C.O. Emblem

(Des S. Afsar)

1995 (28 Feb). *Khan Khushal of Khattak (poet) Commemoration. W* **98**. *P* 13.

951 **483** 7 r. multicoloured 65 65

1995 (14 Mar). *3rd Economic Co-operation Organization Summit, Islamabad. W* **98**. *P* 14.

952 **484** 6 r. multicoloured 55 55

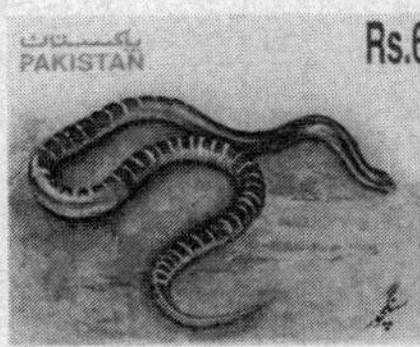

485 Common Indian Krait

486 Globe and Environments

(Des M-ur Rehman (Nos. 953, 955), A. Siddique (Nos. 954, 956))

1995 (15 Apr). *Snakes. T* **485** *and similar horiz designs. Multicoloured. P* $13^1/_2$.

953 6 r. Type **485** 70 70
a. Block of 4. Nos. 953/6 .. .. 2·50
954 6 r. Indian Cobra 70 70
955 6 r. Indian Python 70 70
956 6 r. Russell's Viper 70 70
953/6 .. .. Set of 4 2·50 2·50

Nos. 953/6 were printed together, *se-tenant*, in blocks of 4 throughout the sheet.

(Des A. Siddique)

1995 (20 Apr). *Earth Day. W* **98**. *P* 13.

957 **486** 6 r. multicoloured 55 55

487 Victoria Carriage, Karachi

(Des F. Amir)

1995 (22 May). *Traditional Transport. W* **98**. *P* 13.

958 **487** 5 r. multicoloured 50 50

488 Prime Minister Tansu Ciller of Turkey and Rose

(Des J. Siddique)

1995 (1 Aug). *First Muslim Women Parliamentarians' Conference, Islamabad. T* **488** *and similar horiz design. Multicoloured. P* 13.

959 5 r. Type **488** 40 50
a. Horiz pair. Nos. 959/60 .. .. 80 1·00
960 5 r. Prime Minister Benazir Bhutto and jasmine 40 50

Nos. 959/60 were printed together, *se-tenant*, in horizontal pairs throughout the sheet.

1995 (14 Aug). *Pioneers of Freedom (8th series). Vert designs as T* **428**. *Each brown and myrtle-green. P* 13.

961 1 r. Maulana Shaukat Ali 25 25
a. Pair. Nos. 961/2 .. .. .. 50 50
962 1 r. Chaudhry Ghulam Abbas 25 25

Nos. 961/2 were printed together, *se-tenant*, in sheetlets of 8 stamps and one centre label showing the Pakistani flag.

489 Oil Sardine

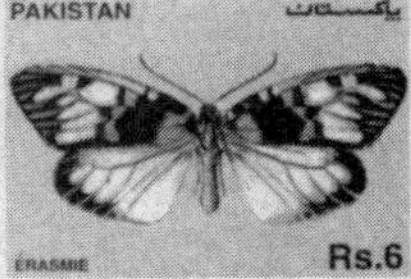

490 *Erasmia pulchella*

1995 (1 Sept). *Fishes. T* **489** *and similar horiz designs. Multicoloured. W* **98**. *P* $13^1/_2$.

963 6 r. Type **489** 45 45
a. Horiz strip of 4. Nos. 963/6 .. 1·60
964 6 r. Mozambique Mouthbrooder ("Tilapia") 45 45
965 6 r. Brown Trout 45 45
966 6 r. Rohu 45 45
963/6 .. .. Set of 4 1·60 1·60

Nos. 963/6 were printed together, *se-tenant*, in horizontal strips of 4 throughout the sheet.

1995 (1 Sept). *Butterflies. T* **490** *and similar horiz designs. Multicoloured. W* **98**. *P* $13^1/_2$.

967 6 r. Type **490** 45 45
a. Horiz strip of 4. Nos. 967/70 .. 1·60
968 6 r. *Callicore astarte* (inscr "CATOGRAMME") 45 45
969 6 r. *Ixias pyrene* 45 45
970 6 r. *Heliconius* 45 45
967/70 .. .. Set of 4 1·60 1·60

Nos. 967/70 were printed together, *se-tenant*, in horizontal strips of 4 throughout the sheet.

OMNIBUS ISSUES

Details, together with prices for complete sets, of the various Omnibus issues from the 1935 Silver Jubilee series to date are included in a special section following Zimbabwe at the end of Volume 2.

491 Major Raja Aziz Bhatti Shaheed and Medal

1995 (6 Sept). *Defence Day.* W **98** (*inverted*). *P* 13.
971 **491** 1 r. 25, multicoloured 40 40

492 Presentation Convent School, Rawalpindi
493 Women Soldiers, Golfer and Scientist

1995 (8 Sept). *Centenary of Presentation Convent School, Rawalpindi.* W **98**. *P* 13½.
972 **492** 1 r. 25, multicoloured 20 10

1995 (15 Sept). *4th World Conference on Women, Peking. T* **493** *and similar vert designs. Multicoloured.* W **98** (*sideways*). *P* 13.
973 1 r. 25, Type **493** 20 20
a. Horiz strip of 4. Nos. 973/6 70
974 1 r. 25, Women graduates, journalist, computer operator and technicians .. 20 20
975 1 r. 25, Sewing machinist and women at traditional crafts 20 20
976 1 r. 25, Army officer and women at traditional tasks 20 20
973/6 .. .. *Set of* 4 70 70
Nos. 973/6 were printed together, *se-tenant*, in horizontal strips of 4 throughout the sheet.

494 "Louis Pasteur in Laboratory" (Edelfelt)
495

1995 (28 Sept). *Death Centenary of Louis Pasteur (chemist).* W **98** (*sideways*). *P* 13.
977 **494** 5 r. multicoloured 45 50

1995 (28 Sept)–**96**. *P* 13½.
978 **495** 5 p. blue, yellow-orange and reddish brown (10.10.95) 10 10
979 15 p. yellow-orange, dull violet and reddish brown (10.10.95) .. 10 10
980 25 p. cobalt, cerise and purple .. 10 10
981 75 p. bright green, red-brown and reddish brown (15.5.96) 10 10
978/81 .. .. *Set of* 4 10 10

496 Liaquat Ali Khan

1995 (1 Oct). *Birth Centenary (1995) of Liaquat Ali Khan (statesman).* W **98**. *P* 13.
987 **496** 1 r. 25, multicoloured 20 10

497 Village and Irrigated Fields

1995 (16 Oct). *50th Anniv of Food and Agriculture Organization.* W **98**. *P* 13.
988 **497** 1 r. 25, multicoloured 20 10

498 Pakistani Soldier treating Somali Refugees
499 Education Emblem

1995 (24 Oct). *50th Anniv of United Nations.* W **98**. *P* 13½.
989 **498** 7 r. multicoloured 50 50

1995 (3 Nov). *80th Anniv (1993) of Kinnaird College for Women, Lahore.* W **98** (*sideways*). *P* 14×13.
990 **499** 1 r.25, multicoloured 20 10

500 Hand holding Book, Eye and Pen Nib
501 Children holding Hands and S.A.A.R.C. Logo

1995 (30 Nov). *International Conference of Writers and Intellectuals, Islamabad.* W **98** (*sideways*). *P* 14.
991 **500** 1 r. 25, multicoloured 20 10

1995 (8 Dec). *10th Anniv of South Asian Association for Regional Co-operation.* W **98** (*sideways*). *P* 13.
992 **501** 1 r. 25, multicoloured 20 10

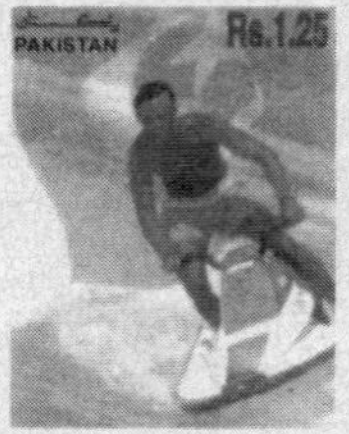

502 Jet Skier

1995 (14 Dec). *National Water Sports Gala, Karachi. T* **502** *and similar vert designs. Multicoloured.* W **98** (*sideways*). *P* 13.
993 1 r. 25, Type **502** 20 20
a. Block of 4. Nos. 993/6 70
994 1 r. 25, Local punts 20 20
995 1 r. 25, Wind surfers 20 20
996 1 r. 25, Water skier 20 20
993/6 .. .. *Set of* 4 70 70
Nos. 993/6 were printed together, *se-tenant*, in blocks of four throughout the sheet.

503 Mortar Board and Books

1995 (16 Dec). *20th Anniv of Allama Iqbal Open University.* W **98**. *P* 13.
997 **503** 1 r. 25, multicoloured 20 10

504 Balochistan Quetta University Building
505 Zulfikar Ali Bhutto, Flag and Crowd

1995 (31 Dec). *25th Anniv of Balochistan Quetta University.* W **98**. *P* 13.
998 **504** 1 r. 25, multicoloured 20 10

1996 (4 Apr). *17th Death Anniv of Zulfikar Ali Bhutto (former Prime Minister). T* **505** *and similar multicoloured designs.* W **98** (*sideways on 4 r.*). *P* 13.
999 1 r. 25, Type **505** 20 10
1000 4 r. Zulfikar Ali Bhutto and flag (53×31 *mm*) 70 70
MS1001 118×74 mm. 8 r. Zulfikar Ali Bhutto and crowd (118×74 *mm*). Wmk sideways. Imperf 1·40 1·40

506 Wrestling

1996 (3 Aug). *Olympic Games, Atlanta. T* **506** *and similar horiz designs. Multicoloured.* W **98** (*sideways*). *P* 13.
1002 5 r. Type **506** 40 40
1003 5 r. Boxing 40 40
1004 5 r. Pierre de Coubertin 40 40
1005 5 r. Hockey 40 40
1002/5 .. .. *Set of* 4 1·40 1·40
MS1006 112×100 mm. 25 r. Designs as Nos. 1002/5, but without face values. Imperf .. 2·00 2·25

1996 (14 Aug). *Pioneers of Freedom (9th series). Vert design as T* **428** *showing Allama Abdullah Yousuf Ali. P* 13.
1007 1 r. brown and myrtle-green 10 10

507 G.P.O. Building, Lahore
508 Symbolic Open Book and Text

1996 (21 Aug). *Restoration of G.P.O. Building, Lahore.* W **98**. *P* 14.
1008 **507** 5 r. multicoloured 30 35

1996 (8 Sept). *International Literacy Day.* W **98**. *P* 13.
1009 **508** 2 r. multicoloured 20 15

509 Yarrow

1996 (25 Nov). *Medicinal Plants (4th series).* W **98** (*sideways*). *P* 13.
1010 **509** 3 r. multicoloured 10 15

STAMP BOOKLETS

1956 (23 Mar). *Black on green cover. Stapled.*
SB1 1 r. 08, booklet containing twelve 6 p. and 1½ a. (Nos. 65, 68) in blocks of 4 .. .. .. 9·00

1994 (1 Feb). *Maroon on bright greenish blue cover with "window" showing contents. Stamps affixed by selvedge.*
SB2 15 r. booklet containing fourteen 1 r. (No. 913) in block of 14 50

OFFICIAL STAMPS

PAKISTAN

(O 1)

1947. *Nos.* O138/41 *and* O143/50 (*King George VI*) *of India, optd as Type* O **1** (*Nos.* O1/9) *or as T* **2** (*Nos.* O10/13) *both in litho by Nasik.*
O 1 3 p. slate 80 10
O 2 ½ a. purple 30 10
O 3 9 p. green .. .. 3·75 2·50
O 4 1 a. carmine 30 10
O 5 1½ a. dull violet 30 10
O 6 2 a. vermilion 30 10
O 7 2½ a. bright violet .. .. 5·50 7·00
O 8 4 a. brown .. .. 1·25 30
O 9 8 a. slate-violet .. .. 1·50 90
O10 1 r. grey and red-brown 80 85
O11 2 r. purple and brown .. .. .. 3·50 2·50
O12 5 r. green and blue .. .. 14·00 24·00
O13 10 r. purple and claret .. .. 35·00 80·00
O1/13 .. .. *Set of* 13 60·00 £110
See note after No. 19. The 1 a. 3 p. (India No. O146*a*) exists as a local issue (*Price*, Karachi opt, £4.25 *mint*, £11 *used*).

SERVICE (O 2) **SERVICE** (O 3) **SERVICE** (O 4)

NOTE. Apart from a slight difference in size, Types O **2** and O **3** can easily be distinguished by the difference in the shape of the "c". Type O **4** is taller and thinner in appearance.

PRINTERS. Type O **2** was overprinted by De La Rue and Types O **3** and O **4** by the Pakistan Security Ptg Corp.

1948 (14 Aug)–**54?** *Optd with Type* O **2**.
O14 **7** 3 p. red (No. 24) 10 10
O15 6 p. violet (No. 25) (R.) 10 10
O16 9 p. green (No. 26) (R.) 10 10
O17 **8** 1 a. blue (No. 27) (R.) .. .. 3·75 10
O18 1½ a. grey-green (No. 28) (R.) .. .. .. 3·50 10
O19 2 a. red (No. 29) .. .. 1·50 10
O20 **10** 3 a. green (No. 31) .. .. 18·00 4·75
O21 **9** 4 a. reddish brown (No. 33) 80 10
O22 – 8 a. black (No. 35) (R.) .. .. 1·25 5·00
O23 – 1 r. ultramarine (No. 38) .. .. 1·00 10
O24 – 2 r. chocolate (No. 39) .. .. 13·00 5·50
O25 – 5 r. carmine (No. 40) .. .. 20·00 5·50
O26 **13** 10 r. magenta (No. 41) .. .. 13·00 38·00
a. Perf 12 (10.10.51) .. .. 15·00 35·00
b. Perf 13 (1954?) .. .. 13·00 45·00
O14/26 .. .. *Set of* 13 70·00 50·00

1949. *Optd with Type* O **2**.
O27 1 a. blue (No. 44) (R.) .. .. 1·00 10
O28 1½ a. grey-green (No. 45) (R.) 30 10
a. Opt inverted .. .. £250 40·00
O29 2 a. red (No. 46) .. .. 1·00 10
a. Opt omitted (in pair with normal) .. .. — £120
O30 3 a. green (No. 47) .. .. 15·00 3·75
O31 8 a. black (No. 49) (R.) .. .. 25·00 12·00
O27/31 .. .. *Set of* 5 38·00 14·00

1951 (14 Aug). *4th Anniv of Independence. As Nos.* 56, 58 *and* 60, *but inscr* "SERVICE" *instead of* "PAKISTAN POSTAGE".
O32 **18** 3 a. purple .. .. 5·00 6·50
O33 **19** 4 a. green .. .. 1·50 10
O34 **20** 8 a. sepia .. .. 6·00 2·25
O32/4 .. .. *Set of* 3 11·00 8·00

1953. *Optd with Type* O **3**.
O35 3 p. red (No. 24a) 10 10
O36 6 p. violet (No. 25a) (R.) 10 10
O37 9 p. green (No. 26a) (R.) 10 10
O38 1 a. blue (No. 44a) (R.) 10 10
O39 1½ a. grey-green (No. 45a) (R.) 10 10
O40 2 a. red (No. 46a) (1953?) 15 10
O41 1 r. ultramarine (No. 38a) .. .. 7·00 2·25
O42 2 r. chocolate (No. 39a) .. .. 3·50 10
O43 5 r. carmine (No. 40a) .. .. 20·00 9·50
O44 10 r. magenta (No. 41b) (date?) .. .. .. 20·00 48·00
O35/44 .. .. *Set of* 10 45·00 55·00

1954 (14 Aug). *Seventh Anniv of Independence. Nos.* 65/71 *optd with Type* O **3**.
O45 6 p. reddish violet (R.) .. .. 10 1·75
O46 9 p. blue (R.) .. .. 80 6·00
O47 1 a. carmine .. .. 15 1·50
O48 1½ a. red .. .. 15 1·50
O49 14 a. deep green (R.) .. .. 60 5·00
O50 1 r. green (R.) 75 10
O51 2 r. red-orange .. .. 1·50 15
O45/51 .. .. *Set of* 7 3·50 14·50

1955 (14 Aug). *Eighth Anniv of Independence. No.* 75 *optd with Type* O **3**.
O52 8 a. deep reddish violet (R.) 30 10

1957 (Jan)–**59**. *Nos.* 65/71 *optd with Type* O **4**.
O53 6 p. reddish violet (R.) 10 10
a. Opt inverted .. .. † —
O54 9 p. blue (R.) (1.59) 10 10
a. Opt inverted .. .. 23·00
O55 1 a. carmine 10 10
a. Opt inverted .. .. — 60·00
b. Printed on the gummed side .. .. ..
O56 1½ a. red 10 10
a. Opt double .. ..
b. Printed on the gummed side .. .. ..
O57 14 a. deep green (R.) (2.59) .. .. .. 40 3·25
O58 1 r. green (R.) (4.58) 40 10
O59 2 r. red-orange (4.58) .. .. 5·00 10
O53/9 .. .. *Set of* 7 5·50 3·25

1958 (Jan)–**61**. *Optd with Type* O **4**.
O60 **7** 3 p. red (No. 24a) 10 10
O61 – 5 r. carmine (No. 40a) (7.59) .. .. .. 5·00 15
O62 **41** 10 r. myrtle-green and yellow-orange (No. 89) (R.) (1961) .. .. .. 6·50 8·00
a. Opt inverted .. .. 15·00
O60/2 .. .. *Set of* 3 10·50 8·00

1958 (Jan)–**61**. *Nos.* 74/5 *optd with Type* O **4**.
O63 6 a. deep ultramarine (R.) (4.61) 15 10
O64 8 a. deep reddish violet (R.) 15 10

1959 (Aug). *No.* 83 *optd with Type* O **4**.
O65 **37** 2 a. scarlet 10 10

1961 (Apr). *Nos.* 110/11 *optd with Type* O **4**.
O66 **51** 8 a. deep green 20 10
O67 1 r. blue 20 10
a. Opt inverted .. .. 7·50

NEW CURRENCY. In addition to the local *handstamped* surcharges mentioned in the note above No. 122, the following *typographed* surcharges were made at the Treasury at Mastung and issued in the Baluchi province of Kalat: 6 p. on 1 a. (No. O55), 9 p. on 1½ a. (No. O56) and 13 p. on 2 a. (No. O65). They differ in that the surcharges are smaller and "PAISA" is expressed as "Paisa". Being locals they are outside the scope of this catalogue.

1961. *Optd with Type* O **4**.
O68 1 p. on 1½ a. (No. 122) 10 10
a. Optd with Type O **3** .. .. 2·75 95
O69 2 p. on 3 p. (No. 123) (1.1.61) 10 10
a. Surch double .. ..
b. Optd with Type O **3** .. .. 4·00 3·00
O70 3 p. on 6 p. (No. 124) 10 10
O71 7 p. on 1 a. (No. 125) 10 10
a. Optd with Type O **3** .. .. 4·00 4·00
O72 13 p. on 2 a. (No. 126) 10 10
O73 13 p. on 2 a. (No. 127) 10 10
O68/73 .. .. *Set of* 6 30 30
No. O68 exists with small and large "1" (see note below Nos. 122/7, etc.).

ERRORS. See note after No. 127.

SERVICE (O 5) **SERVICE** (O 6)

1961–63. *Nos.* 128/44*b optd with Type* O **4** (*rupee values*) *or* O **5** (*others*). (*a*) *Inscribed* "SHAKISTAN".
O74 1 p. violet (R.) (1.1.61) 10 10
O75 2 p. rose-red (R.) (12.1.61) 10 10
O76 5 p. ultramarine (R.) (23.3.61) 15 10

(*b*) *Inscribed* "PAKISTAN"
O77 1 p. violet (R.) .. .. 1·75 10
a. Printed on the gummed side .. .. ..
O78 2 p. rose-red (R.) 10 10
a. Printed on the gummed side .. .. ..
O79 3 p. reddish purple (R.) (27.10.61) 10 10
O80 5 p. ultramarine (R.) .. .. 4·50 10
O81 7 p. emerald (R.) (23.3.61) 10 10
O82 10 p. brown (R.) 10 10
a. Opt inverted .. ..
O83 13 p. slate-violet (R.) (14.2.61) 10 10
O85 40 p. deep purple (R.) (1.1.62) 10 10
O86 50 p. deep bluish green (R.) (1.1.62) 15 10
a. Opt double .. .. † —
O87 75 p. carmine-red (R.) (23.3.62) 20 10
a. Opt double .. ..
O88 1 r. vermilion (7.1.63) 35 10
a. Opt double .. .. 10·00
b. Opt as Type O **3** .. .. 8·50 8·50
c. Opt inverted .. .. 8·50
O89 2 r. orange (7.1.63) .. .. 1·50 20
O90 5 r. green (R.) (7.1.63) .. .. 4·25 6·00
O74/90 .. .. *Set of* 16 12·00 6·50

1963–78? *Nos.* 170, *etc., optd with Type* O **5**, *in red.*
O 91 1 p. violet 10 10
O 92 2 p. rose-red (1965) 10 10
a. Opt inverted .. .. 2·25
b. Albino opt .. ..
c. Opt double, one albino .. .. ..
O 93 3 p. reddish purple (1967) .. .. 1·75 70
a. Opt double .. .. 5·00
b. Opt inverted .. .. 2·50
c. Printed on the gummed side .. .. ..
O 94 5 p. ultramarine 10 10
a. Opt inverted .. .. 1·75
ab. Vert pair, top stamp without opt, lower with opt inverted .. .. ..
O 95 7 p. emerald (date?) .. .. 8·00 7·00
O 96 10 p. brown (1965) 10 10
a. Opt inverted .. .. 2·50
O 97 13 p. slate-violet 10 10
O 98 15 p. bright purple (31.12.64) 10 50
O 99 20 p. myrtle-green (26.1.70) 10 30
a. Opt double .. .. 22·00
O100 25 p. deep blue (1977) .. .. 5·50 1·75
O101 40 p. deep purple (1972?) .. .. 9·00 3·75
O102 50 p. deep bluish green (1965) 10 15
O103 75 p. carmine-red (date?) .. .. 7·50 7·50
O104 90 p. yellow-green (5.78?) .. .. 3·50 3·50
O91/104 .. .. *Set of* 14 30·00 23·00

1968–(?). *Nos.* 204, 206 *and* 207 *optd with Type* O **4**.
O105 **62** 1 r. vermilion .. .. 1·50 30
a. Opt inverted .. .. 9·00
b. Printed and overprinted on the gummed side .. .. 9·00
w. Wmk inverted .. .. 9·00
O107 2 r. orange (date?) .. .. 8·00 85
a. Opt inverted .. .. 9·50
O108 5 r. green (R.) (date?) .. .. 12·00 4·50
a. Opt inverted .. .. 13·00
O105/8 .. .. *Set of* 3 19·00 5·00

1979–85. *Nos.* 464/72, 473*b and* 475/80 *optd as Type* O **5** *in black* (2 *r.*) *or in red* (*reading vertically downwards on* 2, 3 *and* 5 *p.*) (*others*).
O109 **275** 2 p. deep grey-green 10 10
a. Opt reading upwards .. .. ..
ab. Horiz pair, one with opt reading upwards, the other with opt omitted .. .. ..
b. Printed on the gummed side .. ..
O110 3 p. black 10 10
a. Opt reading upwards .. .. .. 3·00 90
O111 5 p. deep ultramarine 10 10
a. Opt reading upwards .. .. .. 1·50 1·50
b. Vert pair, top stamp without opt .. .. 3·00
O112 **276** 10 p. new blue and greenish blue 10 10
O113 20 p. deep yellow-green 10 10
O114 25 p. deep green and dull magenta 10 10
O115 40 p. new blue and magenta 30 10
a. Opt inverted .. .. 8·00
b. Albino opt .. .. 10·00
O116 50 p. slate-lilac and turquoise-green .. 10 10
O117 60 p. black .. .. 1·00 10
a. Printed on the gummed side .. ..
O118 75 p. dull vermilion (Die II) (1980) .. .. 1·00 10
O119 **276a** 1 r. bronze-green (1980) .. .. .. 2·25 10
O120 1 r. 50, red-orange (1979) 10 10
w. Wmk inverted .. ..
O121 2 r. carmine-red (1979) 15 10
w. Wmk inverted .. ..
O122 3 r. blue-black (1980) 20 20
O123 4 r. black (1985) 90 25
O124 5 r. sepia (1985) .. .. 1·00 30
O109/24 .. .. *Set of* 16 6·50 1·50

(Des and litho Secura, Singapore)

1980 (15 Jan–10 Mar). *As Nos.* 513/19 *but inscr* "SERVICE". *P* 12.
O125 **291** 10 p. slate-green and orange-yellow .. 80 10
O126 15 p. slate-green & brt yellow-green .. 80 10
O127 25 p. violet and brown-red (10 Mar) .. 15 10
O128 35 p. carmine & brt yell-grn (10 Mar) .. 20 10
O129 – 40 p. rosine and olive-sepia 85 10
O130 – 50 p. violet & dull yell-green (10 Mar) 20 10
O131 – 80 p. brt yellow-green & blk (10 Mar) .. 30 40
O125/31 .. .. *Set of* 7 3·00 70

1984 (25 Sept)–**89**. *Nos.* 629/30 *and* 632/6 *optd with Type* O **6** *in red.*
O132 – 5 p. brownish blk & brn-pur (1989?) 10 10
O133 – 10 p. brownish black and rose-red .. 10 10
O135 **343** 20 p. black and bright reddish violet (opt at right) (20.11.84) 10 10
a. Opt at left 10 10
O136 – 50 p. sepia and Venetian red (1988?) 10 10
O137 – 60 p. lt brown & blackish brown (1985) 10 10
O138 – 70 p. greenish blue (1988?) 10 10
O139 – 80 p. bistre-brown & dull scar (1988) 10 10
O132/9 .. .. *Set of* 7 35 35

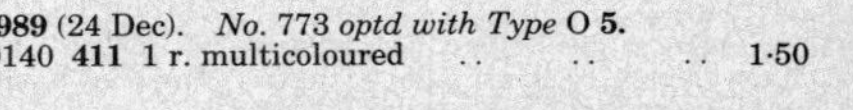

1989 (24 Dec). *No.* 773 *optd with Type* O **5**.
O140 **411** 1 r. multicoloured .. .. 1·50 60

O **7** State Bank of Pakistan Building, Islamabad

1990 (12 Apr). *W* **98** (*sideways**). *P* 13½.
O141 O **7** 1 r. carmine and dull green 10 10
w. Wmk tips of crescent pointing downwards
O142 2 r. carmine and rose-carmine 10 10
O143 3 r. carmine and ultramarine 10 10
O144 4 r. carmine and red-brown 15 20
O145 5 r. carmine and reddish purple (*wmk tips of crescent pointing downwards*) .. ..
O141/5 .. .. *Set of* 5 65 75
*The normal sideways watermark shows the tips of the crescent pointing upwards, *when viewed from the back of the stamp.*

BAHAWALPUR

Bahawalpur, a former feudatory state situated to the west of the Punjab, was briefly independent following the partition of India on 15 August 1947 before acceding to Pakistan on 3 October of the same year.

East India Company and later Indian Empire post offices operated in Bahawalpur from 1854. By a postal agreement of 1879 internal mail from the state administration was carried unstamped, but this arrangement was superseded by the issue of Official stamps in 1945.

These had been preceded by a series of pictorial stamps prepared in 1933–34 on unwatermarked paper. It was intended that these would be used as state postage stamps, but permission for such use was withheld by the Indian Government so they were used for revenue purposes. The same designs were utilised for the 1945 Official series, Nos. O1/6, on paper watermarked Star and Crescent. Residual stocks of the unwatermarked 1 a., 8 a., 1 r. and 2 r. were used for the provisional Officials, Nos. O7 and O11/13.

A commemorative 1 a. Receipt stamp was produced to mark the centenary of the alliance with Great Britain. This may not have been ready until 1935, but an example of this stamp is known used on cover from Deh Rawal to Sadiq Garh and postmarked 14 August 1933. Both this 1 a. and the same value from the unwatermarked set also exist with Official Arabic overprint in black. These were not issued for postal purposes although one used example of the latter has been recorded postmarked 22 February 1933 also from Deh Rawal.

Stamps of India were overprinted in the interim period between 15 August and 3 October 1947. After the state joined Pakistan postage stamps were issued for internal use until 1953.

PRICES FOR STAMPS ON COVER

The postage and Official stamps of Bahawalpur are rare used on cover.

Nawab (from 1947 Amir) Sadiq Mohammad Khan Abbasi V, 1907–1966

(1)

1947 (15 Aug). *Nos. 265/8, 269a/77 and 259/62 (King George VI) of India optd locally with T* **1**.

1 3 p. slate (R.) .. .. 12·00
2 ½ a. purple .. .. 12·00
3 9 p. green (R.) .. .. 12·00
4 1 a. carmine .. .. 12·00
5 1½ a. dull violet (R.) .. .. 12·00
6 2 a. vermilion .. .. 12·00
a. Opt double £750
7 3 a. bright violet (R.) .. .. 12·00
8 3½ a. bright blue (R.) .. .. 12·00
9 4 a. brown .. .. 12·00
10 6 a. turquoise-green (R.) .. .. .. 12·00
a. Opt double £750
11 8 a. slate-violet (R.) .. .. 12·00
12 12 a. lake .. .. 12·00
13 14 a. purple .. .. 45·00
14 1 r. grey and red-brown .. .. .. 18·00
15 2 r. purple and brown (R.) £750
16 5 r. green and blue (R.) £750
17 10 r. purple and claret £750
1/17 .. .. *Set of* 17 £2250

Nos. 1/17 were issued during the interim period, following the implementation of the Indian Independence Act, during which time Bahawalpur was part of neither of the two Dominions created. The Amir acceded to the Dominion of Pakistan on 3 October 1947 and these overprinted stamps of India were then withdrawn.

The stamps of Bahawalpur only had validity for use within the state. For external mail Pakistan stamps were used.

PRINTERS. All the following issues were recess-printed by De La Rue & Co, Ltd, London.

2 Amir Muhammad Bahawal Khan I Abbasi

3

1947 (1 Dec). *Bicentenary Commemoration. W* **3** *(sideways). P* 12½×11½.

18 **2** ½ a. black and carmine .. .. .. 1·00 1·25

4 H.H. the Amir of Bahawalpur

5 The Tombs of the Amirs

6 Mosque in Sadiq-Garh

7 Fort Derawar from the Lake

8 Nur-Mahal Palace

9 The Palace, Sadiq-Garh

10 H.H. the Amir of Bahawalpur

11 Three Generations of Rulers; H.H. the Amir in centre

1948 (1 Apr). *W* **3** *(sideways on vert designs). P* 12½ *(T* **4**), 11½ × 12½ *(T* **5**, **7**, **8** *and* **9**), 12½ × 11½ *(T* **6** *and* **10**) *or* 13½ × 14 *(T* **11**).

19 **4** 3 p. black and blue .. .. .. 50 14·00
20 ½ a. black and claret .. .. .. 50 14·00
21 9 p. black and green .. .. .. 50 14·00
22 1 a. black and carmine .. .. .. 50 14·00
23 1½ a. black and violet .. .. .. 50 11·00
24 **5** 2 a. green and carmine .. .. .. 70 15·00
25 **6** 4 a. orange and brown .. .. .. 80 15·00
26 **7** 6 a. violet and blue .. .. .. 90 15·00
27 **8** 8 a. carmine and violet .. .. .. 90 15·00
28 **9** 12 a. green and carmine .. .. .. 1·00 21·00
29 **10** 1 r. violet and brown .. .. .. 15·00 30·00
30 2 r. green and claret .. .. .. 28·00 45·00
31 5 r. black and violet .. .. .. 30·00 60·00
32 **11** 10 r. scarlet and black .. .. .. 30·00 75·00
19/32 .. .. *Set of* 14 £100 £325

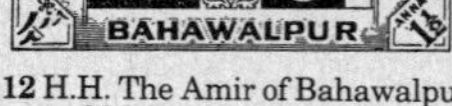

12 H.H. The Amir of Bahawalpur and Mohammed Ali Jinnah

13 Soldiers of 1848 and 1948

1948 (3 Oct). *First Anniv of Union of Bahawalpur with Pakistan. W* **3**. *P* 13.

33 **12** 1½ a. carmine and blue-green .. .. 60 1·25

1948 (15 Oct). *Multan Campaign Centenary. W* **3**. *P* 11½.

34 **13** 1½ a. black and lake .. .. .. 70 6·50

1948. *As Nos. 29/32, but colours changed.*

35 **10** 1 r. deep green and orange .. .. 60 14·00
36 2 r. black and carmine .. .. .. 70 17·00
37 5 r. chocolate and ultramarine .. .. 80 29·00
38 **11** 10 r. red-brown and green .. .. 90 35·00
35/8 .. .. *Set of* 4 2·75 85·00

14 Irrigation

17 U.P.U. Monument, Berne

1949 (3 Mar). *Silver Jubilee of Accession of H.H. the Amir of Bahawalpur. T* **14** *and similar horiz designs. W* **3**. *P* 14.

39 3 p. black and ultramarine .. .. .. 10 8·00
40 ½ a. black and brown-orange .. .. .. 10 8·00
41 9 p. black and green .. .. .. 10 8·00
42 1 a. black and carmine .. .. .. 10 8·00
39/42 .. .. *Set of* 4 30 29·00

Designs:—½ a. Wheat; 9 p. Cotton; 1 a. Sahiwal bull.

Nos. 39/42 exist imperforate (*Prices, £15 per pair, unused*).

1949 (10 Oct). *75th Anniv of Universal Postal Union. W* **3**. *P* 13.

43 **17** 9 p. black and green .. .. .. 20 2·00
a. Perf 17½ × 17 .. .. .. 2·50 14·00
44 1 a. black and magenta .. .. .. 20 2·00
a. Perf 17½ × 17 .. .. .. 2·50 14·00
45 1½ a. black and orange .. .. .. 20 2·00
a. Perf 17½ × 17 .. .. .. 2·50 14·00
46 2½ a. black and blue .. .. .. 20 2·00
a. Perf 17½ × 17 .. .. .. 2·50 14·00
43/6 .. .. *Set of* 4 70 7·00
43a/6a .. .. *Set of* 4 9·00 50·00

Nos. 43/6 exist imperforate (*Prices, £10 per pair, unused*).

OFFICIAL STAMPS

O 1 Panjnad Weir

O 2 Dromedary and Calf

O 3 Blackbuck

O 4 Eastern White Pelicans

O 5 Friday Mosque, Fort Derawar

O 6 Temple at Pattan Munara

1945 (1 Mar). *Various horizontal pictorial designs, with red Arabic opt. W* **3**. *P* 14.

O1 **O 1** ½ a. black and green .. .. .. 2·75 8·50
O2 **O 2** 1 a. black and carmine .. .. .. 3·75 5·50
a. Opt omitted .. .. .. † £650
O3 **O 3** 2 a. black and violet .. .. .. 3·25 8·50
O4 **O 4** 4 a. black and olive-green .. .. 7·50 19·00
O5 **O 5** 8 a. black and brown .. .. .. 16·00 10·00
O6 **O 6** 1 r. black and orange .. .. .. 17·00 10·00
O1/6 .. .. *Set of* 6 45·00 55·00

Permission for the introduction of Nos. O1/6 was granted by the Imperial Government as from 1 January 1945, but the stamps were not used until 1 March. First Day covers exist showing the January date.

Examples of No. O2a come from a sheet used at Rahimya Khan.

O 7 Baggage Camels

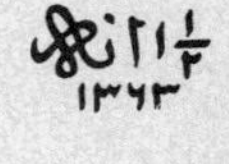

(O 8)

1945 (10 Mar). *Revenue stamp with red Arabic opt. No wmk. P* 14.

O7 **O 7** 1 a. black and brown .. .. .. 26·00 48·00

1945 (Mar–June). *Surch as Type* **O 8** *(at Security Printing Press, Nasik) instead of red Arabic opt. No wmk. P* 14.

O11 **O 5** ½ a. on 8 a. black and purple .. .. 4·25 3·25
O12 **O 6** 1½ a. on 1 r. black and orange .. .. 28·00 8·50
O13 **O 1** 1½ a. on 2 r. black and blue (1 June) .. £100 9·50
O11/13 .. .. *Set of* 3 £120 19·00

The stamps used as a basis for Nos. O7 and O11/13 were part of the Revenue series issued in 1933–34.

SERVICE

(O 9)

O 10 H.H. the Amir of Bahawalpur

1945. *Optd with Type* O **9** (*by D.L.R.*) *instead of red Arabic opt. No wmk. P* 14.

No.	Type	Description	Unused	Used
O14	O 1	½ a. black and carmine	1·25	9·00
O15	O 2	1 a. black and carmine	2·00	12·00
O16	O 3	2 a. black and orange	3·25	35·00
O14/16		*Set of* 3	6·00	50·00

1945. *P* 14.

No.	Type	Description	Unused	Used
O17	O 10	3 p. black and blue	2·25	6·00
O18		1½ a. black and violet	12·00	6·00

O 11 Allied Banners

(Des E. Meronti. Recess, background litho)

1946 (1 May). *Victory. P* 14.

No.	Type	Description	Unused	Used
O19	O 11	1½ a. green and grey	1·75	2·50

1948. *Nos.* 19, 22, 24/5 *and* 35/8 *optd as Nos.* O1/6.

No.	Type	Description	Unused	Used
O20	4	3 p. black and blue (R.)	60	8·50
O21		1 a. black and carmine (Blk.)	60	7·50
O22	5	2 a. green and carmine (Blk.)	60	9·00
O23	6	4 a. orange and brown (Blk.)	60	12·00
O24	10	1 r. deep green and orange (R.)	60	14·00
O25		2 r. black and carmine (R.)	60	16·00
O26		5 r. chocolate and ultramarine (R.)	60	32·00
O27	11	10 r. red-brown and green (R.)	60	35·00
O20/7		*Set of* 8	4·25	£120

1949 (10 Oct). *75th Anniv of Universal Postal Union. Nos.* 43/6 *optd as Nos.* O1/6.

No.	Type	Description	Unused	Used
O28	17	9 p. black and green	15	4·50
		aw. Wmk inverted	†	£100
		b. Perf 17½×17	2·00	24·00
O29		1 a. black and magenta	15	4·50
		b. Perf 17½×17	2·00	24·00
O30		1½ a. black and orange	15	4·50
		b. Perf 17½×17	2·00	24·00
O31		2½ a. black and blue	15	4·50
		b. Perf 17½×17	2·00	24·00
O28/31		*Set of* 4	55	16·00
O28b/31b		*Set of* 4	7·50	85·00

Nos. O28/31 exist imperforate (*Prices, £10 per pair, unused*)

From 1947 stamps of Pakistan were used on all external mail. Bahawalpur issues continued to be used on internal mail until 1953.

Palestine

The stamps of TURKEY were used in Palestine from 1865.
In addition various European Powers, and Egypt, maintained post offices at Jerusalem (Austria, France, Germany, Italy, Russia), Jaffa (Austria, Egypt, France, Germany, Russia) and Haifa (Austria, France) using their own stamps or issues specially prepared for Levant post offices. All foreign post offices had closed by the time of the British Occupation.

PRICES FOR STAMPS ON COVER TO 1945

No. 1	*from* × 6
No. 2	*from* × 4
Nos. 3/4	*from* × 5
Nos. 5/15	*from* × 4
Nos. 16/29	*from* × 3
Nos. 30/42	*from* × 2
No. 43	—
Nos. 44/57	*from* × 2
Nos. 58/9	—
Nos. 60/8	*from* × 3
Nos. 69/70	—
Nos. 71/89	*from* × 3
Nos. 90/103	*from* × 4
Nos. 104/11	*from* × 8
Nos. D1/5	*from* × 30
Nos. D6/20	*from* × 10

BRITISH MILITARY OCCUPATION

British and allied forces invaded Palestine in November 1917 capturing Gaza (7 November), Jaffa (16 November) and Jerusalem (9 December). The front line then stabilised until the second British offensive of September 1918.

Nos. 1/15 were issued by the British military authorities for use by the civilian population in areas they controlled previously part of the Ottoman Empire. Before the issue of Nos. 1/2 in February 1918 civilian mail was carried free. In addition to Palestine the stamps were available from E.E.F. post offices in Syria (including what subsequently became Transjordan) from 23 September 1918 to 23 February 1922, Lebanon from 21 October 1918 to September 1920 and Cilicia from 2 September 1919 to 16 July 1920. Use in the following post offices outside Palestine is recorded in *British Empire Campaigns and Occupations in the Near East, 1914–1924* by John Firebrace:

Adana, Cilicia
Akkari ("Akkar"), Syria
Aleppo ("Alep, Halep"), Syria
Aleih ("Alie"), Lebanon
Alexandretta, Syria
Antakie, Syria
Ba'abda, Lebanon
Baalbek, Lebanon
Bab, Syria
Babitoma, Syria
Behamdoun, Lebanon
Beit ed Dine, Lebanon
Bekaa, Lebanon
Beyrouth, Lebanon
Beit Mery, Beyrouth Lebanon
Bouzanti, Syria
Broumana, Lebanon
Damascus ("Damas"), Syria
Damour ("Damor"), Lebanon
Der'a ("Deraa"), Syria
Deurt-Yol, Syria
Djey Han, Syria
Djezzin ("Djezzine"), Lebanon
Djon, Lebanon
Djounie, Lebanon
Djubeil, Lebanon
Douma, Syria
Edleb, Syria
Feke, Turkey
Habib Souk, Syria
Hajjin ("Hadjin"), Cilicia
Hama, Syria
Hasbaya, Lebanon
Hasine, Cilicia
Hommana, Lebanon
Homs, Syria
Kozan, Cilicia
Lattakia ("Laskie, Lattaquie"), Syria
Massel el Chouf ("Moussalc"), Lebanon
Merdjajoun, Lebanon
Mersina ("Mersine"), Cilicia
Mounboudje, Syria
Nabatti, Lebanon
Nebk ("Nebik"), Syria
Payass, Syria
Racheya, Lebanon
Safita, Syria
Savour, Tyre, Lebanon
Selimie, Syria
Sidan ("Saida (Echelle)"), Lebanon
Suweidiya ("Suvedie"), Syria
Talia, Syria
Tarsous, Cilicia
Tartous, Syria
Tibnin, Lebanon
Tripoli, Syria
Zahle, Lebanon
Zebdani, Syria

This information is reproduced here by permission of the publishers, Robson Lowe Publications.

(Currency. 10 milliemes = 1 piastre)

1

(2)

3

"E.E.F." = Egyptian Expeditionary Force

W **100** of Great Britain

(Des G. Rowntree. Litho Typographical Dept, Survey of Egypt, Giza, Cairo)

1918 (10 Feb). *Wmk Royal Cypher in column* (W **100** *of Great Britain*). *Ungummed. Roul* 20.

No.	Type	Description	Unused	Used
1	1	1 p. indigo (Optd S. £300)	£200	£130
		a. Deep blue	£180	£120
		b. Blue	£180	£120

Control: A 18 (*Prices, corner block of* 4; No. 1 £850. No. 1*a*, £750. No. 1*b*, £850).

1918 (16 Feb). *As last* (*ungummed*) *surch with T* **2**.

No.	Type	Description	Unused	Used
2	1	5 m. on 1 p. cobalt-blue (Optd S. £300)	£100	£575
		a. "MILLILMES" (No. 10 in sheet)	£3250	£9000
		w. Wmk inverted		

Control: B 18 A (*Corner block*, £1100).

1918 (5 Mar). *As No.* 1 *but colour changed. With gum.*

No.	Type	Description	Unused	Used
3	1	1 p. ultramarine (*shades*)	2·50	2·50
		w. Wmk inverted	£160	£150

Control: C 18. (*Corner block*, £70).

1918 (5 Mar *and* 13 May). *No.* 3 *surch with T* **2**.

No.	Type	Description	Unused	Used
4	1	5 m. on 1 p. ultramarine	5·00	4·00
		a. Arabic surch wholly or partly missing (No. 11 in sheet)	£400	£400
		w. Wmk inverted	£250	

Controls: C 18 B (Mar). (*Corner block*, £800).
D 18 C (May). (*Corner block*, £200).

(Typo Stamping Dept, Board of Inland Revenue, Somerset House, London)

1918 (16 July–27 Dec). *Wmk Royal Cypher in column* (W **100** *of Great Britain*). *P* 15×14.

No.	Type	Description	Unused	Used
5	3	1 m. sepia	30	40
		a. Deep brown	40	40
6		2 m. blue-green	30	45
		a. Deep green	70	70
7		3 m. yellow-brown (17 Dec)	35	35
		a. Chestnut	10·00	6·00
8		4 m. scarlet	35	40
9		5 m. yellow-orange (25 Sept)	60	30
		a. Orange	65	45
		w. Wmk inverted	—	£1500
10		1 p. deep indigo (9 Nov)	35	25
		w. Wmk inverted	£150	£150
11		2 p. pale olive	60	60
		a. Olive	1·50	1·10
12		5 p. purple	1·75	2·25
13		9 p. ochre (17 Dec)	2·25	4·50
14		10 p. ultramarine (17 Dec)	2·25	3·00
		w. Wmk inverted	£400	
15		20 p. pale grey (27 Dec)	11·00	16·00
		a. Slate-grey	15·00	22·00
5/15		*Set of* 11	18·00	25·00

There are two sizes of the design of this issue:
19 × 23 mm. 1, 2, and 4 m., and 2 and 5 p.
18 × 21½ mm. 3 and 5 m., and 1, 9, 10 and 20 p.
There are numerous minor plate varieties in this issue, such as stops omitted in "E.E.F.", malformed Arabic characters, etc.

CIVIL ADMINISTRATION UNDER BRITISH HIGH COMMISSIONER

Palestine was placed under civil administration by a British High Commissioner on 1 July 1920.

فلسطين
PALESTINE
פלשתינה א״י
(4)

فلسطين
PALESTINE
פלשתינה א״י
(5)

فلسطين
PALESTINE
פלשתינה א״י
(6)

Differences:—
T **5**. 20 mm vert and 7 mm between English and Hebrew.
T **6**. 19 mm and 6 mm respectively.

(Optd at Greek Orthodox Convent, Jerusalem)

1920 (1 Sept). *Optd with T* **4** (*Arabic* 8 *mm long*). (*a*) *P* 15×14.

No.	Type	Description	Unused	Used
16	3	1 m. sepia	1·75	1·90
17		2 m. blue-green	6·00	4·50
18		3 m. chestnut	4·00	4·75
		a. Opt inverted	£450	£600
19		4 m. scarlet	1·00	1·25
20		5 m. yellow-orange	11·00	4·25
21		1 p. deep indigo (Sil.)	1·00	80
		w. Wmk inverted	60·00	60·00
22		2 p. deep olive	1·75	1·90
23		5 p. deep purple	9·00	17·00
24		9 p. ochre	8·00	20·00
25		10 p. ultramarine	10·00	17·00
26		20 p. pale grey	18·00	42·00
		(*b*) *P* 14		
27	3	2 m. blue-green	1·40	1·40
28		3 m. chestnut	42·00	42·00
29		5 m. orange	1·40	90
16/29		*Set of* 14	£100	£140

Two settings of T 4 are known to specialists, the first, of 24, being used for all values perforated 15×14 (but only on one sheet of the 1 p.) and the second, of 12, for all values in both perforations.

Apart from minor varieties due to broken type, there are three major errors which are rare in some values. These are (*a*) two Hebrew characters at left transposed (all values of first setting only); (*b*) diamond-shaped dot over the Arabic "t" making the word read "Faleszin" for "Falestin" (2 p. to 20 p. of first setting and 1 m. and 3 m. perf 15 × 14, and 5 m. perf 14 of second setting); (*c*) "B" for final "E" of "PALESTINE" (2 p. to 20 p. of first setting and all values of second setting except 3 m. perf 14).

Faulty registration of the overprint in this issue has resulted in numerous misplaced overprints, either vertically or horizontally, which are not of great importance with the exception of Nos. 21 and 29 which exist with the overprint out of sequence, i.e. Hebrew/Arabic/English or English/Arabic/Hebrew or English/Hebrew only. Also all values are known with Arabic/English only.

1920 (22 Sept)–**21**. *Optd with T* **5*** (*Arabic* 10 *mm long*).

No.	Type	Description	Unused	Used
		(*a*) *P* 15×14		
30	3	1 m. sepia (27.12.20)	85	1·00
		a. Opt inverted	£400	†
31		2 m. blue-green (27.12.20)	5·50	4·00
		a. Opt double		
32		3 m. yellow-brown (27.12.20)	1·00	1·00
33		4 m. scarlet (27.12.20)	1·00	1·25
34		5 m. yellow-orange	2·25	75
35		1 p. deep indigo (Silver) (21.6.21)	£500	25·00
36		2 p. olive (21.6.21)	60·00	25·00
37		5 p. deep purple (21.6.21)	25·00	9·50
		(*b*) *P* 14		
38	3	1 m. sepia	£600	£750
39		2 m. blue-green	2·50	4·00
40		4 m. scarlet	55·00	75·00
41		5 m. orange	£100	9·00
		a. Yellow-orange	2·50	1·10
42		1 p. deep indigo (Silver)	30·00	1·25
43		5 p. purple	£225	£500

*In this setting the Arabic and Hebrew characters are badly worn and blunted, the Arabic "S" and "T" are joined (i.e. there is no break in the position indicated by the arrow in our illustration); the letters of "PALESTINE" are often irregular or broken; and the space between the two groups of Hebrew characters varies from 1 mm to over 1¾ mm. The " character in the left-hand Hebrew word extends above the remainder of the line (*For clear, sharp overprint, see Nos.* 47/59.)

The dates of issue given are irrespective of the perforations, i.e. one or both perfs could have been issued on the dates shown.

Nos. 31 and 39 exist with any one line of the overprint partly missing.

1920 (6 Dec). *Optd with T* **6**. (*a*) *P* 15 × 14.

No.	Type	Description	Unused	Used
44	3	3 m. yellow-brown	32·00	32·00
44*a*		5 m. yellow-orange	£14000	£12000
		(*b*) *P* 14		
45	3	1 m. sepia	32·00	32·00
46		5 m. orange	£350	30·00

فلسطين
PALESTINE
פלשתינה א״י
(6*a*)

فلسطين
PALESTINE
פלשתינה א״י
(7)

فلسطين
PALESTINE
פלשתינה א״י
(8)

1921 (29 May–4 Aug). *Optd as T* **6***a*. (*a*) *P* 15×14.

No.	Type	Description	Unused	Used
47	3	1 m. sepia (23.6)	7·00	3·50
48		2 m. blue-green (23.6)	11·00	5·50
49		3 m. yellow-brown (23.6)	24·00	3·00
		a. "PALESTINE" omitted	£2500	

No.	Type	Description	Mint	Used
50	**3**	4 m. scarlet (23.6)	22·00	3·50
51		5 m. yellow-orange	25·00	1·00
52		1 p. deep indigo (Silver) (July)	18·00	75
53		2 p. olive (4.8)	21·00	6·00
54		5 p. purple (4.8)	25·00	8·00
55		9 p. ochre (4.8)	40·00	90·00
56		10 p. ultramarine (4.8)	42·00	14·00
57		20 p. pale grey (4.8)	75·00	50·00
47/57		*Set of* 11	£275	£160
		(*b*) *P* 14		
58	**3**	1 m. sepia	—	£2000
59		20 p. pale grey	£12000	£2500

In this setting the Arabic and Hebrew characters are sharp and pointed and there is usually a break between the Arabic "S" and "T", though this is sometimes filled with ink. The space between the two groups of Hebrew characters is always $1^3/_4$ mm. The top of the " character in the Hebrew aligns with the remainder of the word.

1921 (Sept–Oct). *Optd with T* **7** ("PALESTINE" *in sans-serif letters*) *by Stamping Dept, Board of Inland Revenue, Somerset House, London. Wmk Royal Cypher in column* (*W* **100** *of Great Britain*). *P* 15×14.

No.	Type	Description	Mint	Used
60	**3**	1 m. sepia	65	30
61		2 m. blue-green	70	30
62		3 m. yellow-brown	90	30
63		4 m. scarlet	90	60
64		5 m. yellow-orange	90	30
65		1 p. bright turquoise-blue	90	35
66		2 p. olive	1·40	40
67		5 p. deep purple	5·50	5·00
68		9 p. ochre	14·00	14·00
69		10 p. ultramarine	19·00	£500
70		20 p. pale grey	50·00	£1200
60/70		*Set of* 11	85·00	

(Printed and optd by Waterlow & Sons from new plates)

1922 (Sept–Nov). *T* **3** (*redrawn*), *optd with T* **8**. *Wmk Mult Script CA.* (*a*) *P* 14.

No.	Type	Description	Mint	Used
71	**3**	1 m. sepia	30	30
		a. Deep brown	60	30
		b. Opt inverted	—	£12000
		c. Opt double	£225	£425
		w. Wmk inverted	15·00	10·00
72		2 m. yellow	45	30
		a. Orange-yellow	2·00	50
		b. Wmk sideways	†	—
73		3 m. greenish blue	45	15
		w. Wmk inverted	30·00	30·00
74		4 m. carmine-pink	40	20
		w. Wmk inverted	38·00	38·00
75		5 m. orange	55	50
		w. Wmk inverted	50·00	38·00
76		6 m. blue-green	80	30
		w. Wmk inverted	40·00	40·00
77		7 m. yellow-brown	80	30
		w. Wmk inverted	£150	£150
78		8 m. scarlet	80	30
		w. Wmk inverted	45·00	50·00
79		1 p. grey	80	30
		w. Wmk inverted	50·00	50·00
80		13 m. ultramarine	75	15
		w. Wmk inverted	30·00	20·00
81		2 p. olive	1·50	35
		a. Opt inverted	£300	£500
		b. Ochre	£120	6·50
		w. Wmk inverted	£150	£120
82		5 p. deep purple	4·75	1·25
		aw. Wmk inverted		£400
82*b*		9 p. ochre	£900	£200
83		10 p. light blue	30·00	8·50
		a. "E.F.F." for "E.E.F." in bottom panel	£600	£400
84		20 p. bright violet	£120	90·00
		(*b*) *P* 15×14		
86	**3**	5 p. deep purple	35·00	4·00
87		9 p. ochre	9·00	9·00
88		10 p. light blue	7·50	2·50
		a. "E.F.F." for "E.E.F." in bottom panel	£400	£275
89		20 p. bright violet	9·00	5·50
71/89 Optd "Specimen"		*Set of* 15	£400	

Most values can be found on thin paper.

In this issue the design of all denominations is the same size, 18 mm × $21^1/_2$ mm. Varieties may be found with one or other of the stops between "E.E.F." missing.

BRITISH MANDATE TO THE LEAGUE OF NATIONS

The League of Nations granted a mandate to Great Britain for the administration of Palestine on 29 September 1923.

(New Currency. 1,000 mils = 1 Palestine pound)

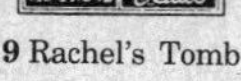

9 Rachel's Tomb

10 Dome of the Rock

11 Citadel, Jerusalem

12 Sea of Galilee

(Des F. Taylor. Typo Harrison)

1927 (1 June)–**45**. *Wmk Mult Script CA. P* $13^1/_2 \times 14^1/_2$ (*2 m. to 20 m.*) *or* 14.

No.	Type	Description	Mint	Used
90	**9**	2 m. greenish blue (14.8.27)	30	10
		w. Wmk inverted	—	£400
91		3 m. yellow-green	40	10
		w. Wmk inverted	—	£200
92	**10**	4 m. rose-pink (14.8.27)	3·25	1·25
93	**11**	5 m. orange (14.8.27)	65	10
		a. From coils. Perf $14^1/_2$×14 (1935)	14·00	18·00
		b. Yellow (12.44)	65	15
		c. Yellow. From coils. Perf $14^1/_2$×14 (1945)	30·00	27·00
		w. Wmk inverted	15·00	18·00
94	**10**	6 m. pale green (14.8.27)	3·00	1·75
		a. Deep green	50	20
95	**11**	7 m. scarlet (14.8.27)	4·00	60
96	**10**	8 m. yellow-brown (14.8.27)	12·00	6·00
97	**9**	10 m. slate (14.8.27)	40	10
		a. Grey. From coils. Perf $14^1/_2$×14 (11.38)	20·00	24·00
		aw. Wmk inverted		
		b. Grey (1944)	75	10
98	**10**	13 m. ultramarine	4·00	30
99	**11**	20 m. dull olive-green (14.8.27)	1·00	15
		a. Bright olive-green (12.44)	1·00	15
		w. Wmk inverted	—	£275
100	**12**	50 m. deep dull purple (14.8.27)	1·00	30
		a. Bright purple (12.44)	1·25	30
		w. Wmk inverted		
101		90 m. bistre (14.8.27)	60·00	65·00
102		100 m. turquoise-blue (14.8.27)	2·00	70
103		200 m. deep violet (14.8.27)	8·00	5·00
		a. Bright violet (1928)	27·00	16·00
		b. Blackish violet (12.44)	6·00	3·50
90/103*b*		*Set of* 14	85·00	65·00
90/103 H/S "Specimen"		*Set of* 14	£325	

Three sets may be made of the above issue; one on thin paper, one on thicker paper with a ribbed appearance, and another on thick white paper without ribbing.

2 m. stamps in the grey colour of the 10 m., including an example postmarked in 1935, exist as do 50 m. stamps in blue, but it has not been established whether they were issued.

Nos. 90/1 and 93 exist in coils, constructed from normal sheets.

1932 (1 June)–**44**. *New values and colours. Wmk Mult Script CA. P* $13^1/_2 \times 14^1/_2$ (*4 m. to 15 m.*) *or* 14.

No.	Type	Description	Mint	Used
104	**10**	4 m. purple (1.11.32)	65	10
		w. Wmk inverted	—	£400
105	**11**	7 m. deep violet	45	10
106	**10**	8 m. scarlet	60	20
		w. Wmk inverted	—	£500
107		13 m. bistre (1.8.32)	70	10
108		15 m. ultramarine (1.8.32)	1·50	10
		a. Grey-blue (12.44)	1·00	40
		b. Greenish blue	1·10	40
		w. Wmk inverted	—	£500
109	**12**	250 m. brown (15.1.42)	3·75	1·75
110		500 m. scarlet (15.1.42)	4·50	3·00
111		£P1 black (15.1.42)	5·00	3·50
104/11		*Set of* 8	15·00	8·00
104/11 Perf "Specimen"		*Set of* 8	£375	

No. 108 exists in coils, constructed from normal sheets.

STAMP BOOKLETS

1929. *Blue cover inscr* "PALESTINE POSTAGE STAMP BOOKLET" *and contents in English. Without advertisements on front. Stitched.*

SB1	150 m. booklet containing twelve 2 m., 3 m. and eighteen 5 m. (Nos. 90/1, 93) in blocks of 6	£2000
	a. As No. SB1, but stapled	£1600

1930. *Blue cover inscr* "PALESTINE POSTS & TELEGRAPHS POSTAGE STAMP BOOKLET" *and contents all in English, Arabic and Hebrew. Without advertisements on front. Stapled.*

SB2	150 m. booklet. Contents as No. SB1	

1937–38. *Red cover inscr* "POSTAGE STAMP BOOKLET" *and contents in English, Hebrew and Arabic. With advertisements on front. Stapled.*

SB3	150 m. booklet containing 2 m., 3 m., 5 m. and 15 m. (Nos. 90/1, 93, 108) in blocks of 6	£1600
	a. Blue cover (1938)	£1600

1939. *Pink cover inscr* "POSTAGE STAMP BOOKLET" *and contents in English, Hebrew and Arabic. With advertisements on front. Stapled.*

SB4	120 m. booklet containing six 10 m. and twelve 5 m. (Nos. 93, 97) in blocks of 6	£1500

POSTAL FISCALS

Type-set stamps inscribed "O.P.D.A." (= Ottoman Public Debt Administration) or "H.J.Z." (Hejaz Railway); British 1d. stamps of 1912–24 and Palestine stamps overprinted with one or other of the above groups of letters, or with the word "Devair", with or without surcharge of new value, are fiscal stamps. They are known used as postage stamps, alone, or with other stamps to make up the correct rates, and were passed by the postal authorities, although they were not definitely authorised for postal use.

POSTAGE DUE STAMPS

D 1

D 2 (MILLIEME)

D 3 (MIL)

(Typo Greek Orthodox Convent Press, Jerusalem)

1923 (1 Apr). *P* 11.

No.	Type	Description	Mint	Used
D1	D **1**	1 m. yellow-brown	25·00	38·00
		a. Imperf (pair)	£300	
		b. Imperf between (horiz pair)	£1100	
D2		2 m. blue-green	18·00	27·00
		a. Imperf (pair)	£400	
D3		4 m. scarlet	22·00	35·00
D4		8 m. mauve	15·00	26·00
		a. Imperf (pair)	£120	
		b. Imperf between (horiz pair)	—	£1800
D5		13 m. steel blue	15·00	26·00
		a. Imperf between (horiz pair)	£850	
D1/5		*Set of* 5	85·00	£140

Perfectly centred and perforated stamps of this issue are worth considerably more than the above prices, which are for average specimens.

(Types D **2**/**3**. Typo D.L.R.)

1924 (1 Dec). *Wmk Mult Script CA. P* 14.

No.	Type	Description	Mint	Used
D 6	D **2**	1 m. deep brown	90	2·00
D 7		2 m. yellow	1·40	1·75
		w. Wmk inverted	—	£400
D 8		4 m. green	1·50	1·25
D 9		8 m. scarlet	3·00	90
D10		13 m. ultramarine	2·75	2·50
D11		5 p. violet	7·50	1·75
D6/11		*Set of* 6	16·00	9·00
D6/11 Optd "Specimen"		*Set of* 6	£275	

1928 (1 Feb)–**45**. *Wmk Mult Script CA. P* 14.

No.	Type	Description	Mint	Used
D12	D **3**	1 m. brown	45	85
		a. Perf 15×14 (1944)	32·00	60·00
D13		2 m. yellow	55	60
		w. Wmk inverted	†	£400
D14		4 m. green	80	1·60
		a. Perf 15×14 (1945)	55·00	75·00
D15		6 m. orange-brown (10.33)	11·00	8·50
D16		8 m. carmine	1·75	90
D17		10 m. pale grey	1·25	60
D18		13 m. ultramarine	1·50	1·75
D19		20 m. pale olive-green	1·60	1·25
D20		50 m. violet	2·50	1·25
D12/20		*Set of* 9	18·00	16·00
D12/20 Perf (D15) or Optd (others) "Specimen"		*Set of* 9	£300	

Nos. D12a and D14a were printed and perforated by Harrison and Sons following bomb damage to the De La Rue works on 29 December 1940.

The British Mandate terminated on 14 May 1948. Later issues of stamps and occupation issues will be found listed under Gaza, Israel and Jordan in Part 19 (*Middle East*) of this catalogue.

Papua New Guinea

NEW GUINEA

Stamps of Germany and later of GERMAN NEW GUINEA were used in New Guinea from 1888 until 1914.

During the interim period between the "G.R.I." surcharges and the "N.W. PACIFIC ISLANDS" overprints, stamps of AUSTRALIA perforated "OS" were utilised.

PRICES FOR STAMPS ON COVER

Nos. 1/30	*from* × 3
Nos. 31/2	—
Nos. 33/49	*from* × 3
Nos. 50/9	*from* × 2
Nos. 60/2	—
Nos. 63/4	*from* × 2
Nos. 64*c*/*q*	—
Nos. 65/81	*from* × 5
Nos. 83/5	—
Nos. 86/97	*from* × 5
No. 99	—
Nos. 100/16	*from* × 4
Nos. 117/18	—
Nos. 119/24	*from* × 4
Nos. 125/203	*from* × 2
Nos. 204/5	—
Nos. 206/11	*from* × 8
Nos. 212/25	*from* × 2
Nos. O1/33	*from* × 8

AUSTRALIAN OCCUPATION

Stamps of German New Guinea surcharged

G.R.I. 2d.	G.R.I. 1s.	G.R.I. 1d.
(1)	(2)	(3)

SETTINGS. The "G.R.I" issues of New Guinea were surcharged on a small hand press which could only accommodate one horizontal row of stamps at a time. In addition to complete sheets the surcharges were also applied to multiples and individual stamps which were first lightly affixed to plain paper backing sheets. Such backing sheets could contain a mixture of denominations, some of which required different surcharges.

Specialists recognise twelve settings of the low value surcharges (1d. to 8d.):

Setting 1 (Nos. 1/4, 7/11) shows the bottom of the "R" 6 mm from the top of the "d"

Setting 2 (Nos. 16/19, 22/6) shows the bottom of the "R" 5 mm from the top of the "d"

Setting 3 was used for the Official stamps (Nos. O1/2)

Setting 4, which included the 2½d. value for the first time, and Setting 5 showed individual stamps with either 6 mm or 5 mm spacing.

These five settings were for rows of ten stamps, but the remaining seven, used on odd stamps handed in for surcharging, were applied as strips of five only. One has, so far, not been reconstructed, but of the remainder three show the 6 mm spacing, two the 5 mm and one both.

On the shilling values the surcharges were applied as horizontal rows of four and the various settings divide into two groups, one with 3½ to 4½ mm between the bottom of the "R" and the top of numeral, and the second with 5½ mm between the "R" and numeral. The first group includes the very rare initial setting on which the space is 4 to 4½ mm.

G.R.I. 2d. — "1" for "I" (Setting 1)
G.R.I. 1d. — Short "1" (Setting 1)
G.R.I. 1s. — Large "S" (Setting 1)

1914 (17 Oct)–**15**. *Stamps of* 1901 *surch.*

(*a*) *As T* **1**. "G.R.I." *and value* 6 mm *apart*

1 1d. on 3 pf. brown .. £300 £300
a. "1" for "I" .. £700
b. Short "1" .. £700
c. "1" with straight top serif (Setting 6) £700
d. "I" for "1" (Setting 12) .. £900
2 1d. on 5 pf. green .. 38·00 50·00
a. "1" for "I" .. £180 £225
b. Short "1" .. £180 £225
c. "1" with straight top serif (Settings 6 and 9) .. £275 £325
3 2d. on 10 pf. carmine .. 42·00 65·00
a. "1" for "I" .. £225 £250
4 2d. on 20 pf. ultramarine .. 42·00 50·00
a. "1" for "I" .. £180 £225
e. Surch double, one "G.R.I." albino .. £2250
f. Surch inverted .. £4250
5 2½d. on 10 pf. carmine (27.2.15) .. 65·00 £140
a. Fraction bar omitted (Setting 9) .. £1200 £1300
6 2½d. on 20 pf. ultramarine (27.2.15) .. 70·00 £140
a. Fraction bar omitted (Setting 9) ..
7 3d. on 25 pf. black and red/*yellow* .. £180 £225
a. "1" for "I" .. £550 £600
8 3d. on 30 pf. black and orange/*buff* .. £200 £225
a. "1" for "I" .. £600
e. Surch double .. £4000 £3750
9 4d. on 40 pf. black and carmine .. £225 £275
a. "1" for "I" .. £750
e. Surch double .. £950 £1400
f. Surch inverted .. £4250
10 5d. on 50 pf. black and purple/*buff* .. £425 £600
a. "1" for "I" .. £1100 £1400
e. Surch double .. £4250
11 8d. on 80 pf. black and carmine/*rose* .. £600 £800
a. "1" for "I" .. £1600
d. No stop after "d" .. £1900
e. Error. Surch "G.R.I. 4d." .. £3500

(*b*) *As T* **2**. "G.R.I." *and value* 3½ *to* 4 mm *apart*

12 1s. on 1 m. carmine .. £1500 £2000
a. Large "s" .. £4500 £4500
13 2s. on 2 m. blue .. £1600 £2500
a. Large "s" .. £4500 £6000
c. Error. Surch "G.R.I. 5s." .. £12000
d. Error. Surch "G.R.I. 2d." corrected by handstamped "S" .. £12000
14 3s. on 3 m. violet-black .. £3250 £4250
a. Large "s" .. £6000
b. No stop after "I" (Setting 3) .. £6500 £6500
15 5s. on 5 m. carmine and black .. £6000 £7500
a. Large "s" .. £12000
b. No stop after "I" (Setting 3) .. £9500 £12000
c. Error. Surch "G.R.I. 1s." .. £18000

G.R.I. 3d. — Thick "3" (Setting 2)
G.R.I. 5d. — Thin "5" (Setting 2)

1914 (16 Dec)–**15**. *Stamps of* 1901 *surch.*

(*a*) *As T* **1**. "G.R.I." *and value* 5 mm *apart*

16 1d. on 3 pf. brown .. 40·00 50·00
a. "I" for "1" (Setting 11) .. £350
b. Short "1" (Setting 2) .. £190
c. "1" with straight top serif (Settings 2 and 6) .. 75·00 90·00
e. Surch double .. £400 £550
f. Surch double, one inverted .. £1700
g. Surch inverted .. £1000 £1400
h. Error. Surch "G.R.I. 4d." .. £4000
17 1d. on 5 pf. green .. 16·00 26·00
b. Short "1" (Setting 2) .. £110 £160
c. "1" with straight top serif (Setting 2) 35·00 60·00
e. "d" inverted .. † £900
f. "1d" inverted .. † £3000
g. "G.R.I." without stops or spaces .. £3000
ga. "G.R.I." without stops, but with normal spaces .. — £3000
h. "G.I.R." instead of "G.R.I." .. £4000 £4250
i. Surch double .. £1100
18 2d. on 10 pf. carmine .. 20·00 32·00
e. No stop after "d" (Setting 2) .. £120 £170
f. Stop before, instead of after, "G" (Settings 4 and 5) .. £3000
g. Surch double .. £4250 £4250
h. Surch double, one inverted .. — £2500
i. In vert pair with No. 20 .. £9500
j. In horiz pair with No. 20 .. £9500
k. Error. Surch ".GRI. 1d." .. £3000 £2500
l. Error. Surch "G.I.R. 3d." .. £4000
19 2d. on 20 pf. ultramarine .. 26·00 38·00
e. No stop after "d" (Setting 2) .. 95·00 £130
f. No. stop after "I" (Setting 11) .. £700
g. "R" inverted (Settings 4 and 5) .. — £2750
h. Surch double .. £900 £1600
i. Surch double, one inverted .. £1400 £1700
j. Surch inverted .. £2500 £3000
k. Albino surch (in horiz pair with normal) .. £7000
l. In vert pair with No. 21 .. £6000 £7500
m. Error. Surch "G.R.I. 1d." .. £4000 £4000
20 2½d. on 10 pf. carmine (27.2.15) .. £140 £250
21 2½d. on 20 pf. ultramarine (27.2.15) .. £1400 £1700
22 3d. on 25 pf. black and red/*yellow* .. 90·00 £120
e. Thick "3" .. £500
f. Surch double .. £3000 £3750
g. Surch inverted .. £3000 £3750
h. Surch omitted (in horiz pair with normal) .. £7000
i. Error. Surch "G.R.I. 1d." .. £7000
23 3d. on 30 pf. black and orange/*buff* .. 75·00 £100
e. No stop after "d" (Setting 2) .. £550
f. Thick "3" .. £475
g. Surch double .. £1000 £1500
h. Surch double, one inverted .. £1300 £1700
i. Surch double, both inverted .. £3000 £3750
j. Surch inverted .. £2500
k. Albino surch .. £5500
l. Surch omitted (in vert pair with normal) .. £3750
m. Error. Surch "G.R.I. 1d." .. £3000 £4000
24 4d. on 40 pf. black and carmine .. 90·00 £120
e. Surch double .. £900
f. Surch double, one inverted .. £1700
g. Surch double, both inverted .. £3500
h. Surch inverted .. £1900
i. Error. Surch "G.R.I. 1d." .. £1800
ia. Surch "G.R.I. 1d." inverted .. £3500
j. Error. Surch "G.R.I. 3d." double .. £5500
k. No stop after "I" (Setting 11) .. £1700
25 5d. on 50 pf. black and purple/*buff* .. £130 £160
e. Thin "5" .. £750 £1300
f. Surch double .. £1300
g. Surch double, one inverted .. £2500 £3750
h. Surch double, both inverted .. £3000 £3750
i. Surch inverted .. £1900
j. Error. Surch "G.I.R. 3d." .. £6000
26 8d. on 80 pf. black and carmine/*rose* .. £325 £400
e. Surch double .. £1900 £2250
f. Surch double, one inverted .. £1900 £2250
g. Surch triple .. £2000 £2500
h. Surch inverted .. £3250 £3750
i. Error. Surch "G.R.I. 3d." .. £6500

(*b*) *As T* **2**. "G.R.I." *and value* 5½ *mm apart*

27 1s. on 1 m. carmine .. £2500 £3500
a. No stop after "I" (Setting 7) .. £4750
28 2s. on 2 m. blue .. £2750 £4250
a. No stop after "I" (Setting 7) .. £4750
29 3s. on 3 m. violet-black .. £4000 £6500
a. G.R.I." double .. £13000
30 5s. on 5 m. carmine and black .. £14000 £16000

1915 (Jan.). *Nos.* 18 *and* 19 *further surch as in T* **3**.

31 "1" on 2d. on 10 pf. .. £13000 £13000
32 "1" on 2d. on 20 pf. .. £12000 £7500

OFFICIAL STAMPS

O. S.
G.R.I.
1d.
(O 3*a*)

1915 (27 Feb). *Stamps of* 1901 *surch as Type* O **3***a*. "G.R.I." *and value* 3½ *mm apart.*

O1 1d. on 3 pf. brown .. 25·00 70·00
a. "1" and "d" spaced .. 75·00 £150
b. Surch double .. £2250
O2 1d. on 5 pf. green .. 75·00 £130
a. "1" and "d" spaced .. £150 £250

German New Guinea Registration Labels surcharged

4

4*a*

G.R.I.
3d.
Sans serif "G" and different "3"

1915 (Jan). *Registration Labels surch* "G.R.I. 3d." *in settings of five or ten and used for postage. Each black and red on buff. Inscr* "(Deutsch Neuguinea)" *spelt in various ways as indicated. P* 14 (*No.* 43) *or* 11½ (*others*).

I. *With name of town in sans-serif letters as T* **4**

33 Rabaul "(Deutsch Neuguinea)" .. £140 £190
a. "G.R.I. 3d." double .. £1800 £2000
b. No bracket before "Deutsch" .. £650 £850
ba. No bracket and surch double .. £4250
d. "(Deutsch-Neuguinea)" .. £225 £325
da. "G.R.I. 3d." double .. £4250 £4250
db. No stop after "I" .. £650
dc. "G.R.I. 3d" inverted .. £4250
dd. No bracket before "Deutsch" .. £950
de. No bracket after "Neuguinea" .. £950 £1300
34 Deulon "(Deutsch Neuguinea)" .. £12000
35 Friedrich-Wilhelmshafen "(Deutsch Neuguinea)" .. £160 £400
a. No stop after "d" .. £325
b. "G" omitted .. £2500
c. Sans-serif "G" .. £4500
d. Sans-serif "G" and different "3" .. £4000
e. Surch inverted .. † £4250
f. "(Deutsch-Neuguinea)" .. £170 £400
fa. No stop after "d" .. £350
36 Herbertshöhe "(Deutsch Neuguinea)" .. £190 £450
a. No stop after "d" .. £400
b. No stop after "I" .. £700
c. "G" omitted .. £2750
d. Surch omitted (in horiz pair with normal) .. £5500
e. "(Deutsch Neu-Guinea)" .. £325
37 Käwieng "(Deutsch-Neuguinea)" .. £500
a. No bracket after "Neuguinea" .. £2250
b. "Deutsch Neu-Guinea" .. £225 £425
ba. No stop after "d" .. £425
bb. "G.R.I." double .. £1900
bc. "3d." double .. £1900
bd. "G" omitted .. £3250
38 Kieta "(Deutsch-Neuguinea)" .. £325 £550
a. No bracket before "Deutsch" .. £1100 £1700
b. No stop after "d" .. £650
c. Surch omitted (righthand stamp of horiz pair) .. £5500
e. No stop after "I" .. £950
f. "G" omitted .. £3000
39 Manus "(Deutsch Neuguinea)" .. £190 £475
a. "G.R.I. 3d." double .. £2250
b. No bracket before "Deutsch" .. £850 £1300
40 Stephansort "(Deutsch Neu-Guinea)" .. † £1700
a. No stop after "d" .. † £3750

II. *With name of town in letters with serifs as T* **4a**

41 Friedrich Wilhelmshafen "(Deutsch-Neuguinea)" .. £160 £375
b. No stop after "d" .. £325 £650
c. No stop after "I" .. £650 £1000
d. No bracket before "Deutsch" .. £900 £1400
e. No bracket after "Neuguinea" .. £900 £1400
42 Käwieng "(Deutsch Neuguinea)" .. £150 £350
a. No stop after "d" .. £375
43 Manus "(Deutsch-Neuguinea)" .. £1800 £2500
a. No stop after "I" .. £3000 £3000

Stamps of Marshall Islands surcharged

SETTINGS. The initial supply of Marshall Islands stamps, obtained from Nauru, was surcharged with Setting 2 (5 mm between "R" and "d") on the penny values and with the 3½ to 4 setting on the shilling stamps.

Small quantities subsequently handed in were surcharged, often on the same backing sheet as German New Guinea values, with Settings 6, 7 or 12 (all 6 mm between "R" and "d") for the penny values and with a 5½ mm setting for the shilling stamps.

1914 (16 Dec). *Stamps of* 1901 *surch.*

(*a*) *As T* **1**. "G.R.I." *and value* 5 *mm apart*

50 1d. on 3 pf. brown .. 42·00 70·00
c. "1" with straight top serif (Setting 2) £100 £160
d. ".GRI." and "1" with straight top serif (Settings 4 and 5) .. † £4000
e. Surch inverted .. £2000
51 1d. on 5 pf. green .. 45·00 50·00
c. "1" with straight top serif (Settings 2 and 11) .. £100 £120
d. "I" for "1" (Setting 11) .. £550
e. "1" and "d" spaced .. £325 £350
f. Surch double .. £950 £1600
g. Surch inverted .. £1200
52 2d. on 10 pf. carmine .. 15·00 24·00
e. No stop after "G" (Setting 2) .. £550
f. Surch double .. £950 £1600
g. Surch double, one inverted .. £1200 £1600
h. Surch inverted .. £1700
i. Surch sideways .. £3250
53 2d. on 20 pf. ultramarine .. 16·00 27·00
e. No stop after "d" (Setting 2) .. 42·00 80·00
g. Surch double .. £1200 £1700
h. Surch double, one inverted .. £2000 £2500
i. Surch inverted .. £2750 £2750
54 3d. on 25 pf. black and red/*yellow* .. £250 £350
e. No stop after "d" (Settings 2 and 11) £500 £700
f. Thick "3" .. £750
g. Surch double .. £1200 £1700
h. Surch double, one inverted .. £1200
i. Surch inverted .. £2750
55 3d. on 30 pf. black and orange/*buff* .. £300 £400
e. No stop after "d" (Setting 2) .. £550 £700
f. Thick "3" .. £800
g. Surch inverted .. £1900 £2250
h. Surch double .. £1800
56 4d. on 40 pf. black and carmine .. 90·00 £120
e. No stop after "d" (Setting 2) .. £250 £400
f. "d" omitted (Setting 2) .. † £3500
g. Surch double .. £1800 £2250
h. Surch triple .. £3500
i. Surch inverted .. £2250
j. Error. Surch "G.R.I. 1d." .. £4750
k. Error. Surch "G.R.I. 3d." .. £4750

57 5d. on 50 pf. black and purple/*buff* .. £130 £170
e. Thin "5" £2500
f. "d" omitted (Setting 2) £1400
g. Surch double £2750
h. Surch inverted £3500
58 8d. on 80 pf. black and carmine/*rose* .. £375 £475
e. Surch double £2250
f. Surch double, both inverted £3000 £3500
g. Surch triple £3750
h. Surch inverted £2750

(*b*) *As T* **2**. "G.R.I." *and value* 3½–4 *mm apart*
59 1s. on 1 m. carmine £1700 £2750
b. No stop after "I" £3000 £4250
e. Surch double £9000
60 2s. on 2 m. blue £1200 £1900
b. No stop after "I" £2500 £3500
e. Surch double £9000
f. Surch double, one inverted £8500 £8500
61 3s. on 3 m. violet-black £3000 £4250
b. No stop after "I" £4250
e. Surch double £9500 £13000
62 5s. on 5 m. carmine and black £6000 £7500
e. Surch double, one inverted .. .. † £16000

1915 (Jan.) *Nos.* 52 *and* 53 *further surch as in T* **3**.
63 "1" on 2d. on 10 pf. carmine £140 £170
a. "1" double £7500
b. "1" inverted £7500 £7500
64 "1" on 2d. on 20 pf. ultramarine £3000 £2000
a. On No 53e. £5000 £2750
b. "1" inverted £8000 £8000

1915. *Stamps of* 1901 *surch.*

(*a*) *As T* **1**. "G.R.I." *and value* 6 *mm apart*
64*c* 1d. on 3 pf. brown £850
cc. "1" with straight top serif (Setting 6) .. ..
cd. "I" for "1" (Setting 12) £1200
ce. Surch inverted £3750
64*d* 1d. on 5 pf. green £900
dc. "1" with straight top serif (Setting 6) £1200
dd. "I" for "1" (Setting 12) £1200
de. Surch inverted £3750
df. Surch double £3750
64*e* 2d. on 10 pf. carmine £1300
ea. Surch sideways £4250
64*f* 2d. on 20 pf. ultramarine £1100
fe. Surch inverted £3750
64*g* 2½d. on 10 pf. carmine £6000
64*h* 2½d. on 20 pf. ultramarine £9000
64*i* 3d. on 25 pf. black and red/*yellow* .. £1500
64*j* 3d. on 30 pf. black and orange/*buff* .. £1500
je. Error. Surch "G.R.I. 1d." £4750
64*k* 4d. on 40 pf. black and carmine £1500
ke. Surch double £4000
kf. Surch inverted £4000
64*l* 5d. on 50 pf. black and purple/*buff* .. £1300
le. Surch double £4000
64*m* 8d. on 80 pf. black and carmine/*rose* .. £1900
me. Surch inverted £4500

(*b*) *As T* **2**. "G.R.I." *and value* 5½ *mm apart*
64*n* 1s. on 1 m. carmine £6000
na. Large "s" (Setting 5) £7500
nb. No stop after "I" (Setting 7) .. £7500
64*o* 2s. on 2 m. blue £4750
oe. Surch double, one inverted .. £16000
64*p* 3s. on 3 m. violet-black £8500
pa. Large "s" (Setting 5) £11000
pb. No stop after "I" (Setting 7) .. £11000
pe. Surch inverted £16000
64*q* 5s. on 5 m. carmine and black .. £14000
qa. Large "s" (Setting 5) £17000

Stamps of Australia overprinted

T **1** *of Australia*

T **5a** *of Australia*

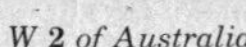

W **2** *of Australia*

W **5** *of Australia*

W **6** *of Australia*

N. W. PACIFIC ISLANDS.	N. W. PACIFIC ISLANDS.	N. W. PACIFIC ISLANDS.
(*a*)	(*b*)	(*c*)

(6)

1915–16. *Stamps of Australia optd in black as T* **6** (*a*), (*b*) *or* (*c*).

(i) *T* **5a**. *W* **5** *of Australia. P* 14 (4 Jan–15 March 1915)
65 ½d. green .. .. 2·00 7·00
a. Bright green .. .. 2·50 7·50
aw. Wmk inverted .. .. ..
67 1d. pale rose (Die I) (4.1) .. .. .. 6·00 5·50
a. Dull red .. .. 7·00 6·00
b. Carmine-red .. .. 6·50 5·50
ba. Substituted cliché (Pl 2 rt pane R. 6/5) £1200 £750
c. Die II. *Carmine-red* £180 £140
ca. Substituted cliché (Pl 2 rt pane R. 6/4) £1200 £750
70 4d. yellow-orange .. .. .. 4·00 12·00
a. Pale orange-yellow .. .. .. 17·00 26·00
b. Chrome-yellow £250 £275
c. Line through "FOUR PENCE" (Pl 2 rt pane R. 2/6) (*all shades*) .. *from* £350 £550
72 5d. brown .. .. 3·25 15·00

(ii) *T* **1**. *W* **2** *of Australia. P* 12 (4 Jan 1915–March 1916)
73 2d. grey (Die I) .. .. 18·00 38·00
74 2½d. indigo (Die II) (4.1.15) .. .. 2·75 16·00
76 3d. yellow-olive (Die I) .. .. .. 20·00 45·00
a. Die II £300 £400
ab. In pair with Die I £500 £700
c. Greenish olive £190 £275
ca. Die II £1300
cb. In pair with Die I £2250
78 6d. ultramarine (Die II) .. .. .. 38·00 55·00
a. Retouched "E" £5000
w. Wmk inverted .. .. .. 75·00
79 9d. violet (Die II) .. .. 38·00 55·00
81 1s. green (Die II) .. .. 40·00 55·00
83 5s. grey and yellow (Die II) (3.16) .. £750 £1100
84 10s. grey and pink (Die II) (12.15) .. £110 £160
85 £1 brown and ultramarine (Die II) (12.15) £400 £600

(iii) *T* **1**. *W* **5** *of Australia. P* 12 (Oct 1915–July 1916)
86 2d. grey (Die I) .. .. .. 13·00 15·00
87 2½d. indigo (Die II) (7.16) £10000 £10000
88 6d. ultramarine (Die II) .. .. 10·00 12·00
89 9d. violet (Die II) (12.15) .. .. 14·00 18·00
90 1s. emerald (Die II) (12.15) .. 11·00 24·00
91 2s. brown (Die II) (12.15) .. 80·00 £100
92 5s. grey and yellow (Die II) (12.15) 70·00 £100

(iv) *T* **1**. *W* **6** *of Australia. P* 12 (Dec 1915–1916)
94 2d. grey (Die I) .. .. 5·00 11·00
a. In pair with Die IIA £250
96 3d. yellow-olive (Die I) .. .. .. 5·00 11·00
a. Die II .. .. 75·00 £120
ab. In pair with Die I £160
97 2s. brown (Die II) (8.16) .. .. .. 27·00 45·00
w. Wmk inverted .. .. .. 35·00
99 £1 chocolate and dull blue (Die II) (8.16) £250 £400

Dates for Nos. 67 and 74 are issue dates. All other dates are those of despatch. Nos. 65/6, 68/73, 76/81 were despatched on 15 March 1915.

For Die IIA of 2d. see note below Australia No. 45.

SETTINGS. Type **6** exists in three slightly different versions, illustrated above as (*a*), (*b*), *and* (*c*). These differ in the letters "S" of "ISLANDS" as follows:

(*a*) Both "SS" normal.
(*b*) First "S" with small head and large tail and second "S" normal.
(*c*) Both "SS" with small head and large tail.

Type **11**, which also shows the examples of "S" as the normal version, can be identified from Type **6**(a) by the relative position of the second and third lines of the overprint. On Type **6***a* the "P" of "PACIFIC" is exactly over the first "S" of "ISLANDS". On Type **11** the "P" appears over the space between "I" and "S".

It has been established, by the study of minor variations, that there are actually six settings of the "N.W. PACIFIC ISLANDS" overprint, including that represented by T **11**, but the following are the different arrangements of Type **6**(*a*), (*b*), and (*c*) which occur.

A. Horizontal rows 1 and 2 all Type (*a*). Row 3 all Type (*b*). Rows 4 and 5 all Type (*c*).

B. (½d. green only). As A, except that the types in the bottom row run (*c*) (*c*) (*c*) (*c*) (*b*) (*c*).

C. As A, but bottom row now shows types (*a*) (*c*) (*c*) (*c*) (*b*) (*c*).

Horizontal strips and pairs showing varieties (*a*) and (*c*), or (*b*) and (*c*) *se-tenant* are scarce.

The earliest printing of the 1d. and 2½d. values was made on sheets with margin attached on two sides, the later printings being on sheets from which the margins had been removed. In this printing the vertical distances between the overprints are less than in later printings, so that in the lower horizontal rows of the sheet the overprint is near the top of the stamp.

The settings used on King George stamps and on the Kangaroo type are similar, but the latter stamps being smaller the overprints are closer together in the vertical rows.

PURPLE OVERPRINTS. We no longer differentiate between purple and black overprints in the above series. In our opinion the two colours are nowadays insufficiently distinct to warrant separation.

PRICES. The prices quoted for Nos. 65 to 101 apply to stamps with opts Types **6** (*a*) or **6** (*c*). Stamps with opt Type **6** (*b*) are worth a 25 per cent premium. Vertical strips of three, showing (*a*), (*b*) and (*c*), are worth from four times the prices quoted for singles as Types **6** (*a*) or **6** (*c*).

One Penny	N. W. PACIFIC ISLANDS.
(10)	**(11)**

1918 (23 May). *Nos.* 72 *and* 81 *surch locally with T* **10**.
100 1d. on 5d. brown .. .. 90·00 80·00
101 1d. on 1s. green .. .. 90·00 75·00

Types **6** (*a*), (*b*), (*c*) occur on these stamps also.

1918–23. *Stamps of Australia optd with T* **11** ("P" *of* "PACIFIC" *over space between* "I" *and* "S" *of* "ISLANDS").

(i) *T* **5a**. *W* **5** *of Australia. P* 14
102 ½d. green .. .. 1·00 3·50
103 1d. carmine-red (Die I) .. .. .. 2·50 1·60
a. Substituted cliché (Pl 2 rt pane R. 6/5) £650 £375
b. Die II .. .. £110 48·00
ba. Substituted cliché (Pl 2 rt pane R. 6/4) £650 £375
104 4d. yellow-orange (1919) .. .. 3·25 16·00
a. Line through "FOUR PENCE" (Pl 2 rt pane R. 2/6) £800 £1200
105 5d. brown (1919) .. .. .. 1·75 12·00

(ii) *T* **1**. *W* **6** *of Australia. P* 12
106 2d. grey (Die I) (1919) .. .. .. 6·00 16·00
a. Die II .. .. 10·00 38·00
107 2½d. indigo (Die II) (1919) .. .. 3·00 15·00
a. "1" of "½" omitted £5500 £7000
b. Blue (1920) .. .. 7·00 24·00
109 3d. greenish olive (Die I) (1919) .. 19·00 22·00
a. Die II .. .. 48·00 60·00
ab. In pair with Die I £325 £400
b. Light olive (Die IIB) (1923) .. .. 19·00 25·00
110 6d. ultramarine (Die II) (1919) .. .. 4·50 14·00
a. Greyish ultramarine (1922) .. .. 42·00 65·00
112 9d. violet (Die IIB) (1919) .. .. 7·50 35·00
113 1s. emerald (Die II) .. .. .. 6·50 28·00
a. Pale blue-green .. .. .. 14·00 28·00
115 2s. brown (Die II) (1919) .. .. 24·00 38·00
116 5s. grey and yellow (Die II) (1919) .. 60·00 65·00
117 10s. grey and bright pink (Die II) (1919) £150 £200
118 £1 bistre-brown & grey-bl (Die II) (1922) £2750 £4000

(iii) *T* **5a**. *W* **5** *of Australia. Rough, unsurfaced paper, locally gummed. P* 14
118*a* 1d. rosine (Die I) £400 £120
ab. Substituted cliché (Pl 2 rt pane R. 6/5)
b. Die II .. .. — £400
ba. Substituted cliché (Pl 2 rt pane R. 6/4)

(iv) *T* **5a**. *W* **6a** *of Australia* (*Mult Crown A*). *P* 14
119 ½d. green (1919) .. .. .. 75 3·50
w. Wmk inverted .. .. .. 35·00

(v) *T* **5a**. *W* **5** *of Australia. Colour changes and new value*
120 1d. violet (*shades*) (1922) .. .. 1·00 6·50
121 2d. orange (1921) .. .. .. 4·50 3·75
122 2d. rose-scarlet (1922) .. .. .. 7·50 5·50
123 4d. violet (1922) .. .. 28·00 48·00
a. "FOUR PENCE" in thinner letters (Pl 2 rt pane R. 2/6) £750 £1000
124 4d. ultramarine (1922) .. .. .. 11·00 50·00
a. "FOUR PENCE" in thinner letters (Pl 2 rt pane R. 2/6) £750
120/4 .. .. *Set of* 5 45·00 £100

Type **11** differs from Type **6** (*a*) in the position of the "P" of "PACIFIC", which is further to the left in Type **11**.

Nos. 118*a*/ba only exist perforated "O S".

MANDATED TERRITORY OF NEW GUINEA

PRINTERS. See note at the beginning of Australia.

12 Native Village

(13)

(Des R. Harrison. Eng T. Harrison. Recess Note Printing Branch, Treasury, Melbourne, from 1926 Note Ptg Branch, Commonwealth Bank of Australia, Melbourne).

1925–28. *P* 11.
125 **12** ½d. orange .. .. 2·25 4·75
126 1d. green .. .. 2·25 4·75
126*a* 1½d. orange-vermilion (1926) .. .. 2·75 2·25
127 2d. claret .. .. 2·25 4·50
128 3d. blue .. .. 4·50 4·00
129 4d. olive-green .. .. 13·00 16·00
130 6d. dull yellow-brown .. .. .. 20·00 48·00
a. Olive-bistre (1927) .. .. .. 6·00 48·00
b. Pale yellow-bistre (1928) .. .. 4·50 48·00
131 9d. dull purple (*to* violet) .. .. 13·00 42·00
132 1s. dull blue-green .. .. .. 15·00 22·00
133 2s. brown-lake .. .. 30·00 42·00
134 5s. olive-bistre .. .. 48·00 65·00
135 10s. dull rose £100 £160
136 £1 dull olive-green £180 £250
125/36 .. .. *Set of* 13 £375 £550

1931 (8 June). *Air. Optd with T* **13**. *P* 11.
137 **12** ½d. orange .. .. 1·00 4·00
138 1d. green .. .. 1·60 4·50
139 1½d. orange-vermilion .. .. .. 1·00 5·00
140 2d. claret .. .. 1·00 7·00
141 3d. blue .. .. 1·75 13·00
142 4d. olive-green .. .. 1·25 8·50
143 6d. pale yellow-bistre .. .. .. 1·75 13·00
144 9d. violet .. .. 3·00 17·00
145 1s. dull blue-green .. .. .. 3·00 17·00
146 2s. brown-lake .. .. 7·00 35·00
147 5s. olive-bistre .. .. 20·00 65·00
148 10s. bright pink .. .. 65·00 £100
149 £1 olive-grey £110 £180
137/49 .. .. *Set of* 13 £200 £425

14 Raggiana Bird of Paradise (Dates either side of value)

AIR
MAIL

(15)

(Recess John Ash, Melbourne)

1931 (2 Aug). *Tenth Anniv of Australian Administration. T* **14** *(with dates). P* 11.

150 **14** 1d. green .. 2·25 60
151 1½d. vermilion .. 4·00 10·00
152 2d. claret .. 4·00 2·25
153 3d. blue .. 4·00 4·50
154 4d. olive-green .. 5·50 14·00
155 5d. deep blue-green .. 4·00 15·00
156 6d. bistre-brown .. 4·00 15·00
157 9d. violet .. 7·00 15·00
158 1s. pale blue-green .. 5·00 15·00
159 2s. brown-lake .. 9·00 27·00
160 5s. olive-brown .. 35·00 48·00
161 10s. bright pink .. 75·00 £120
162 £1 olive-grey .. £160 £225
150/62 .. *Set of* 13 £275 £450

1931 (2 Aug). *Air. Optd with T* **15**.

163 **14** ½d. orange .. 2·00 2·75
164 1d. green .. 2·75 3·75
165 1½d. vermilion .. 2·50 8·00
166 2d. claret .. 1·50 2·75
167 3d. blue .. 4·25 4·25
168 4d. olive-green .. 4·25 6·00
169 5d. deep blue-green .. 4·50 8·50
170 6d. bistre-brown .. 7·00 24·00
171 9d. violet .. 8·00 15·00
172 1s. pale blue-green .. 7·00 15·00
173 2s. dull lake .. 14·00 48·00
174 5s. olive-brown .. 38·00 65·00
175 10s. bright pink .. 60·00 £110
176 £1 olive-grey .. £100 £190
163/76 .. *Set of* 14 £200 £450

1932 (30 June)–**1934**. *T* **14** *(redrawn without dates). P* 11.

177 1d. green .. 60 20
178 1½d. claret .. 70 9·00
179 2d. vermilion .. 75 20
179*a* 2½d. green (14.9.34) .. 5·00 14·00
180 3d. blue .. 1·25 80
180*a* 3½d. aniline carmine (14.9.34) .. 11·00 9·00
181 4d. olive-green .. 75 4·00
182 5d. deep blue-green .. 85 70
183 6d. bistre-brown .. 1·75 3·00
184 9d. violet .. 8·00 18·00
185 1s. blue-green .. 4·00 10·00
186 2s. dull lake .. 4·00 17·00
187 5s. olive .. 27·00 45·00
188 10s. pink .. 48·00 70·00
189 £1 olive-grey .. 95·00 £100
177/89 .. *Set of* 15 £190 £250

1932 (30 June)–**34**. *Air. T* **14** *(redrawn without dates), optd with T* **15**. *P* 11.

190 ½d. orange .. 50 1·50
191 1d. green .. 60 1·50
192 1½d. claret .. 80 4·75
193 2d. vermilion .. 80 30
193*a* 2½d. green (14.9.34) .. 3·75 2·25
194 3d. blue .. 1·75 1·75
194*a* 3½d. aniline carmine (14.9.34) .. 3·75 3·25
195 4d. olive-green .. 3·50 8·00
196 5d. deep blue-green .. 6·50 7·50
197 6d. bistre-brown .. 3·50 12·00
198 9d. violet .. 6·00 9·00
199 1s. pale blue-green .. 6·00 7·50
200 2s. dull lake .. 7·50 40·00
201 5s. olive-brown .. 45·00 55·00
202 10s. pink .. 75·00 75·00
203 £1 olive-grey .. 75·00 55·00
190/203 .. *Set of* 16 £200 £225

The ½d. orange redrawn without dates exists without overprint, but it is believed that this was not issued (*Price* £125 *un*).

16 Bulolo Goldfields

(Recess John Ash, Melbourne)

1935 (1 May). *Air. P* 11.

204 **16** £2 bright violet .. £225 £130
205 £5 emerald-green .. £550 £400

HIS MAJESTY'S
JUBILEE.
1910 — 1935

(17)

18

1935 (27 June). *Silver Jubilee. As Nos.* 177 *and* 179, *but shiny paper. Optd with T* **17**.

206 1d. green .. 45 35
207 2d. vermilion .. 1·25 35

(Recess John Ash, Melbourne)

1937 (18 May). *Coronation. P* 11.

208 **18** 2d. scarlet .. 50 30
209 3d. blue .. 60 45
210 5d. green .. 50 45
a. Red-entry (design completely duplicated) (Pl 2a R. 5/2) .. 65·00 80·00
211 1s. purple .. 80 35
208/11 .. *Set of* 4 2·25 1·40

(Recess John Ash, Melbourne)

1939 (1 Mar). *Air. Inscr* "AIR MAIL POSTAGE" *at foot. P* 11.

212 **16** ½d. orange .. 2·25 4·50
213 1d. green .. 3·25 3·50
214 1½d. claret .. 2·25 6·50
215 2d. vermilion .. 7·50 3·00
216 3d. blue .. 9·50 16·00
217 4d. yellow-olive .. 8·00 7·50
218 5d. deep green .. 7·00 2·25
219 6d. bistre-brown .. 16·00 13·00
220 9d. violet .. 16·00 19·00
221 1s. pale blue-green .. 17·00 17·00
222 2s. dull lake .. 48·00 42·00
223 5s. olive-brown .. £100 90·00
224 10s. pink .. £300 £200
225 £1 olive-green .. £100 £110
212/25 .. *Set of* 14 £550 £475

OFFICIAL STAMPS

Australian stamps perforated "O S" exist with overprint Type 11 for use in New Guinea. We do not list such varieties.

O S (O 1) **o s** (O 2)

1925–31. *Optd with Type* O **1**. *P* 11.

O3 **12** 1d. green .. 1·00 4·50
O4 1½d. orange-vermilion (1931) .. 5·50 17·00
O5 2d. claret .. 1·60 3·75
O6 3d. blue .. 3·25 5·50
O7 4d. olive-green .. 4·00 8·50
O8 6d. olive-bistre .. 17·00 35·00
a. Pale yellow-bistre (1931) .. 7·00 35·00
O9 9d. violet .. 3·75 35·00
O10 1s. dull blue-green .. 5·00 35·00
O11 2s. brown-lake .. 27·00 60·00
O3/11 .. *Set of* 9 50·00 £180

1931 (2 Aug). *Optd with Type* O **2**. *P* 11.

O12 **14** 1d. green .. 3·00 13·00
O13 1½d. vermilion .. 3·25 12·00
O14 2d. claret .. 6·50 7·00
O15 3d. blue .. 4·00 6·00
O16 4d. olive-green .. 3·25 8·50
O17 5d. deep blue-green .. 8·00 12·00
O18 6d. bistre-brown .. 11·00 17·00
O19 9d. violet .. 14·00 28·00
O20 1s. pale blue-green .. 14·00 28·00
O21 2s. brown-lake .. 35·00 65·00
O22 5s. olive-brown .. 90·00 £150
O12/22 .. *Set of* 11 £170 £325

1932 (30 June)–**34**. *T* **14** *(redrawn without dates), optd with Type* O **2**. *P* 11.

O23 1d. green .. 3·50 3·75
O24 1½d. claret .. 4·00 12·00
O25 2d. vermilion .. 4·25 2·75
O26 2½d. green (14.9.34) .. 3·00 6·00
O27 3d. blue .. 6·00 18·00
O28 3½d. aniline carmine (14.9.34) .. 3·00 9·00
O29 4d. olive-green .. 5·00 14·00
O30 5d. deep blue-green .. 5·00 14·00
O31 6d. bistre-brown .. 7·00 32·00
O32 9d. violet .. 10·00 40·00
O33 1s. pale blue-green .. 15·00 28·00
O34 2s. dull lake .. 35·00 75·00
O35 5s. olive-brown .. £120 £160
O23/35 .. *Set of* 13 £190 £375

Civil Administration in New Guinea was suspended in 1942, following the Japanese invasion.

Various New Guinea stamps exist overprinted with an anchor and three Japanese characters in a style similar to the Japanese Naval Control Area overprints found on the stamps of Netherlands Indies. These overprints on New Guinea are bogus and are believed to have originated in Japan during 1947.

On resumption, after the Japanese defeat in 1945, Australian stamps were used until the appearance of the issue for the combined territories of Papua & New Guinea.

PRICES OF SETS

Set prices are given for many issues, generally those containing three stamps or more. Definitive sets include one of each value or major colour change, but do not cover different perforations, die types or minor shades. Where a choice is possible the set prices are based on the cheapest versions of the stamps included in the listings.

PAPUA (BRITISH NEW GUINEA)

Stamps of QUEENSLAND were used in British New Guinea (Papua) from at least 1885 onwards. Post Offices were opened at Daru (1894), Kulumadau (Woodlarks) (1899), Nivani (1899), Port Moresby (1885), Samarai (1888), Sudest (1899) and Tamata (1899). Stamps were usually cancelled "N.G." (at Port Moresby from 1885) or "BNG" (without stops at Samarai or with stops at the other offices) from 1888. Queensland stamps were replaced in Papua by the issue of 1901.

PRICES FOR STAMPS ON COVER

Nos. 1/7	*from* × 15
No. 8	—
Nos. 9/15	*from* × 20
No. 16	—
Nos. 17/27	*from* × 6
No. 28	—
Nos. 39/45a	*from* × 5
Nos. 47/71	*from* × 8
Nos. 72/4	—
Nos. 75/92*a*	*from* × 8
Nos. 93/103	*from* × 6
Nos. 104/5	—
Nos. 106/11	*from* × 10
Nos. 112/14	*from* × 6
No. 115	—
Nos. 116/28	*from* × 5
Nos. 130/53	*from* × 4
Nos. 154/7	*from* × 12
Nos. 158/67	*from* × 4
No. 168	*from* × 3
Nos. O1/54	*from* × 10
Nos. O55/66*a*	*from* × 7

1 Lakatoi (trading canoe) with Hanuabada Village in Background

2 (Horizontal)

Deformed "d" at left (R. 4/3)

(Recess D.L.R.)

1901 (1 July)–**05**. *Wmk Mult Rosettes, W* **2**. *P* 14.

A. *Wmk horizontal. Thick paper. Line perf*

1 **1** ½d. black and yellow-green .. 8·00 12·00
a. Thin paper .. £170 £140
2 1d. black and carmine .. 6·00 8·00
3 2d. black and violet .. 7·00 7·00
4 2½d. black and ultramarine .. 14·00 10·00
a. Thin paper .. £225 £160
ab. Black and dull blue .. £500 £350
5 4d. black and sepia .. 45·00 35·00
a. Deformed "d" at left .. £250 £200
6 6d. black and myrtle-green .. 42·00 35·00
7 1s. black and orange .. 60·00 65·00
8 2s. 6d. black and brown (1.1.05) .. £600 £550

B. *Wmk vertical. Medium to thick paper. Line or comb perf*

9 **1** ½d. black and yellow-green .. 4·50 3·75
a. Thin paper (*comb perf*) (1905) .. 14·00 23·00
10 1d. black and carmine .. 3·50 2·00
11 2d. black and violet .. 9·00 4·00
a. Thin paper (*comb perf*) (1905) .. 48·00 16·00
12 2½d. black and ultramarine (*shades*) .. 9·00 12·00
13 4d. black and sepia .. 32·00 48·00
a. Deformed "d" at left .. £200 £275
b. Thin paper (*comb perf*) (1905) .. £190
ba. Deformed "d" at left .. £750
14 6d. black and myrtle-green .. 48·00 70·00
a. Thin paper (*comb perf*) (1905) .. £600
15 1s. black and orange .. 55·00 80·00
a. Thin paper (*comb perf*) (1905) .. £550
16 2s. 6d. black and brown (1905) .. £3000 £250
a. Thin paper (*comb perf*) .. £550 £1000
1/16 .. *Set of* 8 £650 £650

The paper used for Nos. 1/8 is white, of consistent thickness and rather opaque. The thin paper used for the horizontal watermark printings is of variable thickness, readily distinguishable from the thick paper by its greater transparency and by the gum which is thin and smooth.

Nos. 9/16 were initially printed on the same thick paper as the stamps with horizontal watermark and were line perforated. Values from ½d. to 2½d. were subsequently printed on medium paper on which the watermark was more visible. These were comb perforated. The thin paper with vertical watermark, produced in 1905. is much more transparent and has smooth gum. Printings were made on this paper for all values except the 2½d., but only the ½d. and 2d. were issued in Papua although used examples of the 2s. 6d. are also known. The entire printing of the 1d. on thin paper with vertical watermark was used for subsequent overprints.

The sheets of the ½d., 2d. and 2½d. show a variety known as "white leaves" on R. 4/5 while the 2d. and 2½d. (both R. 6/2) and the ½d. and 1s. (both R. 6/3) show what is known as the "unshaded leaves" variety.

Papua. (3) **Papua.** (4)

1906–07. I. *Optd with T* **3** (*large opt*), *at Port Moresby* (8 Nov 1906).

A. *Wmk horizontal. Thick paper. Line perf*

17 **1** 4d. black and sepia £180 £150
a. Deformed "d" at left £550
18 6d. black and myrtle-green .. .. 38·00 40·00
19 1s. black and orange .. .. 20·00 38·00
20 2s. 6d. black and brown £140 £150

B. *Wmk vertical. Thin paper* (½d., 1d., 2d.) *or medium to thick paper* (*others*). *Comb perf* (½d. *to* 2½d.) *or line perf* (*others*)

21 **1** ½d. black and yellow-green .. .. 4·50 20·00
22 1d. black and carmine .. .. 8·00 16·00
23 2d. black and violet .. .. 4·75 3·00
24 2½d. black and ultramarine .. .. 3·75 15·00
25 4d. black and sepia £160 £130
a. Deformed "d" at left £500
26 6d. black and myrtle-green .. .. 28·00 55·00
27 1s. black and orange £1100 £850
28 2s. 6d. black and brown £7500 £5500
17/28 .. .. *Set of* 8 £325 £375

II. *Optd with T* **4** (*small opt*), *at Brisbane* (May–June 1907)

A. *Wmk horizontal. Thick paper. Line perf*

34 **1** ½d. black and yellow-green .. ..
a. Thin paper .. .. .. 60·00 80·00
35 2½d. black and ultramarine .. ..
a. Thin paper .. .. .. 30·00 60·00
ac. Black and dull blue £130 £140
36 1s. black and orange £140 £180
37 2s. 6d. black and brown .. .. 32·00 45·00
a. Opt reading downwards £3750
c. Opt double (horiz) .. .. .. † £2750
d. Opt triple (horiz) .. .. .. † £2500

B. *Wmk vertical. Thin paper* (½d., 1d., 2d., 4d., 6d.) *or medium to thick paper* (2½d., 1s., 2s. 6d.). *Line or comb perf* (2½d.), *line perf* (1s., 2s. 6d.) *or comb perf* (*others*)

38 **1** ½d. black and yellow-green .. .. 5·50 7·00
a. Opt double £1700
39 1d. black and carmine .. .. 3·50 5·00
a. Opt reading upwards £1900 £1200
40 2d. black and violet .. .. 4·50 2·25
41 2½d. black and ultramarine .. .. 8·00 18·00
42 4d. black and sepia .. .. 25·00 48·00
a. Deformed "d" at left £170 £275
43 6d. black and myrtle-green .. .. 23·00 35·00
a. Opt double £2250 £4000
44 1s. black and orange .. .. 60·00 75·00
b. Thin paper (*comb perf*) .. .. 27·00 40·00
ba. Opt double, one diagonal £6000 £3500
45 2s. 6d. black and brown £5500 £4250
a. Thin paper (*comb perf*) .. .. 38·00 48·00
34/45 (*cheapest*) .. .. .. *Set of* 8 £110 £180

In the setting of this overprint Nos. 10, 16, and 21 have the "p" of "Papua" with a defective foot or inverted "d" for "p", and in No. 17 the "pua" of "Papua" is a shade lower than the first "a".

No. 37a comes from a single sheet on which the overprints were sideways. Examples exist showing one, two or four complete or partial overprints.

PRINTERS. All the following issues were printed at Melbourne by the Stamp Ptg Branch (to 1928) or Note Ptg Branch.

WATERMARK VARIETIES. When printing the lithographed issues, Nos. 47/83, little attention was paid to the position of the watermark. Nos. 47, 49/58 and 75/83 all come either upright or inverted while Nos. 48 and 59/71 all occur with watermark sideways to left or right. Nos. 51/2 are known with watermark reversed and others may well exist.

5 Large "PAPUA"

B

C

Three types of the 2s. 6d.:—

A. Thin top to "2" and small ball. Thin "6" and small ball. Thick uneven stroke.

B. Thin top to "2" and large, well shaped ball. Thin "6" and large ball. Very thick uneven stroke.

C. Thick top to "2" and large, badly shaped ball. Thick "6" and uneven ball. Thin even line.

Type A is not illustrated as the stamp is distinguishable by perf and watermark.

The litho stones were prepared from the engraved plates of the 1901 issue, value for value except the 2s. 6d. for which the original plate was mislaid. No. 48 containing Type A was prepared from the original ½d. plate with the value inserted on the stone and later a fresh stone was prepared from the 1d. plate and this contained Type B. Finally, the original plate of the 2s. 6d. was found and a third stone was prepared from this, and issued in 1911. These stamps show Type C.

6 Small "PAPUA"

(Litho Stamp Ptg Branch, Melbourne, from transfers taken from original engraved plates)

1907–10. *Wmk Crown over A, W w* **11**.

A. *Large "PAPUA". (a) Wmk upright. P* 11

47 **5** ½d. black and yellow-green (11.07) .. 1·25 3·50

(*b*) *Wmk sideways. P* 11

48 **5** 2s. 6d. black and chocolate (A) (12.09) .. 48·00 60·00
a. "POSTAGIE" at left (R. 1/5) .. £550 £650

B. *Small "PAPUA"*

I. *Wmk upright.* (*a*) *P* 11 (1907–8)

49 **6** 1d. black and rose (6.08) .. .. 4·75 3·75
50 2d. black and purple (10.08) .. .. 6·50 4·50
51 2½d. black and bright ultramarine (7.08) 15·00 23·00
a. Black and pale ultramarine .. 5·50 6·50
52 4d. black and sepia (20.11.07) .. .. 4·25 7·50
a. Deformed "d" at left .. .. 26·00 38·00
53 6d. black and myrtle-green (4.08) .. 11·00 16·00
54 1s. black and orange (10.08) .. .. 17·00 20·00

(*b*) *P* 12½ (1907–9)

55 **6** 2d. black and purple (10.08) .. .. 14·00 6·50
56 2½d. black and bright ultramarine (7.08) £120 £130
b. Black and pale ultramarine .. 48·00 75·00
57 4d. black and sepia (20.11.07) .. .. 8·00 8·00
a. Deformed "d" at left .. .. 42·00 42·00
58 1s. black and orange (1.09) .. .. 60·00 85·00

II. *Wmk sideways.* (*a*) *P* 11 (1909–10)

59 **6** ½d. black and yellow-green (12.09) .. 2·25 2·75
a. Black and deep green (1910) .. 28·00 42·00
60 1d. black and carmine (1.10) .. .. 8·50 7·00
61 2d. black and purple (1.10) .. .. 6·00 6·50
62 2½d. black and dull blue (1.10) .. .. 4·25 17·00
63 4d. black and sepia (1.10) .. .. 4·00 7·50
a. Deformed "d" at left .. .. 20·00 35·00
64 6d. black and myrtle-green (11.09) .. 10·00 14·00
65 1s. black and orange (3.10) .. .. 40·00 60·00

(*b*) *P* 12½ (1909–10)

66 **6** ½d. black and yellow-green (12.09) .. 1·60 3·25
a. Black and deep green (1910) .. 30·00 38·00
67 1d. black and carmine (12.09) .. .. 6·00 9·00
68 2d. black and purple (1.10) .. .. 3·50 3·75
69 2½d. black and dull blue (1.10) .. .. 8·00 27·00
70 6d. black and myrtle-green (11.09) .. £2750 £3750
71 1s. black and orange (3.10) .. .. 12·00 27·00

(*c*) *Perf compound of* 11 *and* 12½

72 **6** ½d. black and yellow-green £2250 £2250
73 2d. black and purple £850

(*d*) *Mixed perfs* 11 *and* 12½

74 **6** 4d. black and sepia £4750

Compound perforations on the 4d. are fakes.

The only known examples of No. 74 come from the top row of a sheet perforated 11 and with an additional line perf 12½ in the top margin.

(Litho Stamp Ptg Branch, Melbourne, by J. B. Cooke, from new stones made by fresh transfers)

1910 (Sept)–**11.** *Large "PAPUA". W w* **11** (*upright*). *P* 12½.

75 **5** ½d. black and green (12.10) .. .. 3·50 11·00
76 1d. black and carmine .. .. 9·00 6·50
77 2d. black & dull purple (*shades*) (12.10) 4·00 5·00
a. "C" for "O" in "POSTAGE" (R. 4/3) 60·00 60·00
78 2½d. black and blue-violet (10.10) .. 4·50 17·00
79 4d. black and sepia (10.10) .. .. 3·75 10·00
a. Deformed "d" at left .. .. 20·00 50·00
80 6d. black and myrtle-green .. .. 7·50 7·50
81 1s. black and deep orange (12.10) .. 5·50 16·00
82 2s. 6d. black and brown (B) .. .. 35·00 50·00
83 2s. 6d. black and brown (C) (1911) .. 42·00 60·00
75/82 .. .. *Set of* 8 65·00 £110

A variety showing a white line or "rift" in clouds occurs on R. 5/3 in Nos. 49/74 and the "white leaves" variety mentioned below No. 22 occurs on the 2d. and 2½d. values in both issues. They are worth about three times the normal price.

8

ONE PENNY

(9)

(Eng S. Reading. Typo J. B. Cooke)

1911–15. *Printed in one colour. W* **8** (*sideways**).

(*a*) *P* 12½ (1911–12)

84 **6** ½d. yellow-green .. .. .. 1·00 3·50
a. Green .. .. 40 2·25
w. Wmk Crown to right of A .. .. 10·00
85 1d. rose-pink 70 75
w. Wmk Crown to right of A .. .. 20·00 20·00
86 2d. bright mauve 70 75
w. Wmk Crown to right of A .. .. — 40·00
87 2½d. bright ultramarine .. .. .. 4·75 8·50
a. Dull ultramarine .. .. .. 5·50 8·50
aw. Wmk Crown to right of A .. .. 50·00
88 4d. pale olive-green .. .. .. 2·25 11·00
w. Wmk Crown to right of A .. .. — 40·00
89 6d. orange-brown .. .. .. 3·75 5·00
90 1s. yellow .. .. .. 9·00 15·00
w. Wmk Crown to right of A .. .. 75·00
91 2s. 6d. rose-carmine .. .. .. 32·00 38·00
w. Wmk Crown to right of A £170
84/91 .. .. *Set of* 8 48·00 70·00

(*b*) *P* 14

92 **6** 1d. rose-pink (6.15) .. .. .. 22·00 6·00
a. Pale scarlet .. .. .. 6·50 2·00
w. Wmk Crown to right of A .. .. — 40·00

*The normal sideways watermark shows Crown to left of A, *as seen from the back of the stamp.*

(Typo J. B. Cooke (1916–18), T. S. Harrison (1918–26), A. J. Mullett (No. 95*b* only) (1926–27), or John Ash (1927–31))

1916 (Aug)–**31.** *Printed in two colours. W* **8** (*sideways**). *P* 14.

93 **6** ½d. myrtle and apple green (Harrison and Ash) (1919) .. .. .. 80 1·00
a. Myrtle and pale olive-green (1927) 1·75 1·75
w. Wmk Crown to right of A .. 5·00 5·00
94 1d. black and carmine-red .. .. 1·40 1·25
a. Grey-black and red (1918) .. 1·60 1·00
aw. Wmk Crown to right of A .. 2·75 40
b. Intense black and red (Harrison) (*wmk Crown to right of A*) (1926) 2·50 2·50
95 1½d. pale grey-blue (*shades*) & brn (1925) 2·00 80
aw. Wmk Crown to right of A .. 15·00 5·00
b. Cobalt and light brown (Mullett) (*wmk Crown to right of A*) (1927) 6·00 3·25
c. Bright blue and bright brown (1929) 2·75 2·00
d. "POSTACE" at right (R. 1/1) (all printings) .. .. .. *From* 38·00 38·00
96 2d. brown-purple & brown-lake (1919) 1·75 75
a. Deep brown-purple and lake (1931) 25·00 1·75
aw. Wmk Crown to right of A .. 30·00 1·75
b. Brown-purple and claret (1931) .. 2·00 75
97 2½d. myrtle and ultramarine (1919) .. 4·75 12·00
98 3d. black and bright blue-green (12.16) 1·25 1·75
a. Error. Black and deep greenish Prussian blue† £500 £500
b. Sepia-black & brt bl-grn (Harrison) 22·00 19·00
c. Black and blue-green (1927) .. 4·50 8·00
99 4d. brown and orange (1919) .. .. 2·50 5·00
a. Light brown and orange (1927) .. 7·50 14·00
aw. Wmk Crown to right of A .. 7·50 14·00
100 5d. bluish slate and pale brown (1931) 4·25 16·00
101 6d. dull and pale purple (*wmk Crown to right of A*) (1919) .. .. 3·25 9·50
aw. Wmk Crown to left of A .. 10·00
b. Dull purple and red-purple (*wmk Crown to left of A*) (1927) .. 10·00 16·00
c. "POSTACE" at left (R. 6/2) (all printings) .. .. .. *From* 70·00 £100
102 1s. sepia and olive (1919) .. .. 3·50 6·50
a. Brown and yellow-olive (1927) .. 6·50 13·00
103 2s. 6d. maroon and pale pink (1919) .. 18·00 40·00
a. Maroon & brt pink (*shades*) (1927) 19·00 50·00
104 5s. black and deep green (12.16) .. 40·00 48·00
105 10s. green and pale ultramarine (1925) £140 £180
93/105 .. .. *Set of* 13 £200 £250

*The normal sideways watermark shows Crown to left of A, *as seen from the back of the stamp.*

†Beware of similar shades produced by removal of yellow pigment. No. 98a is a colour trial, prepared by Cooke, of which, it is believed, five sheets were sold in error.

The printers of various shades can be determined by their dates of issue. The Ash printings are on whiter paper.

For 9d. and 1s. 3d. values, see Nos. 127/8.

1917 (Oct). *Nos.* 84, 86/9 *and* 91 *surch with T* **9** *by Govt Ptg Office, Melbourne.*

106 **6** 1d. on ½d. yellow-green .. .. 1·25 1·60
a. Green .. .. 50 1·25
w. Wmk Crown to right of A .. .. 4·00 4·00
107 1d. on 2d. bright mauve .. .. 12·00 15·00
108 1d. on 2½d. ultramarine .. .. 1·25 3·75
109 1d. on 4d. pale olive-green .. .. 1·75 4·50
w. Wmk Crown to right of A .. .. — 40·00
110 1d. on 6d. orange-brown .. .. 8·00 17·00
111 1d. on 2s. 6d. rose-carmine .. .. 1·50 6·00
106/11 .. .. *Set of* 6 22·00 42·00

AIR MAIL

(10)

(11)

1929 (Oct)–**30.** *Air. Optd with T* **10** *by Govt Printer, Port Moresby.*

(*a*) *Cooke printing. Yellowish paper*

112 **6** 3d. black and bright blue-green .. 1·25 9·00
a. Opt omitted in vert pair with normal £2750

(*b*) *Harrison printing. Yellowish paper*

113 **6** 3d. sepia-black and bright blue-green 50·00 60·00

(*c*) *Ash printing. White paper*

114 **6** 3d. black and blue-green .. .. 90 7·00
a. Opt omitted (in horiz pair with normal) £3250
b. Ditto, but vert pair £2750
c. Opt vertical, on back £3000
d. Opts *tête-bêche* (vert pair) .. £2750

1930 (15 Sept). *Air. Optd with T* **11**, *in carmine by Govt Printer, Port Moresby.* (*a*) *Harrison printings. Yellowish paper.*

115 **6** 3d. sepia-black and bright blue-green £1500 £2750
116 6d. dull and pale purple .. .. 3·00 16·00
a. "POSTACE" at left (R. 6/2) .. 65·00 £110
117 1s. sepia and olive .. .. 8·00 23·00
a. Opt inverted £4000

(*b*) *Ash printings. White paper*

118 **6** 3d. black and blue-green .. .. 90 6·00
119 6d. dull purple and red-purple .. .. 7·00 10·00
a. "POSTACE" at left (R. 6/2) .. 70·00 £100
120 1s. brown and yellow-olive .. .. 4·25 15·00
118/20 .. .. *Set of* 3 11·00 28·00

The rare Harrison printing with this overprint, No. 115, should not be confused with examples of the Ash printing, No. 118, which have been climatically toned.

5d.

TWO PENCE (12) **FIVE PENCE** (13)

1931 (1 Jan). *Surch with T 12 by Govt Printer, Port Moresby.*

(a) Mullett printing

121 **6** 2d. on 1½d. cobalt and light brown .. 12·00 24·00
a. "POSTACE" at right (R. 1/1) .. £140 £225

(b) Ash printing

122 **6** 2d. on 1½d. bright blue and bright brown .. .. 1·00 2·00
a. "POSTACE" at right (R. 1/1) .. 30·00 48·00

1931. *Surch as T 13 by Govt Printer, Port Moresby.*

(a) Cooke printing

123 **6** 1s. 3d. on 5s. black and deep green .. 4·00 9·00

(b) Harrison printing. Yellowish paper

124 **6** 9d. on 2s. 6d. maroon and pale pink (Dec) 6·00 17·00

(c) Ash printings. White paper

125 **6** 5d. on 1s. brown and yellow-olive (26.7) 75 1·75
126 9d. on 2s. 6d. maroon and bright pink 5·50 8·50

(Typo J. Ash)

1932. *W 15 of Australia (Mult "C of A"). P 11.*

127 **5** 9d. lilac and violet .. .. 4·50 27·00
128 1s. 3d. lilac and pale greenish blue .. 7·50 32·00
127/8 Optd "Specimen" .. .. *Set of* 2. £450

15 Motuan Girl

18 Raggiana Bird of Paradise

20 Native Mother and Child

22 Papuan Motherhood

(Des F. E. Williams (2s., £1 and frames of other values), E. Whitehouse (2d., 4d., 6d., 1s., and 10s.); remaining centres from photos by Messrs F. E. Williams and Gibson. Recess J. Ash (all values) and W. C. G. McCracken (½d., 1d., 2d., 4d.))

1932 (14 Nov). *T 15, 18, 20, 22 and similar designs. No wmk. P 11.*

130 ½d. black and orange .. .. .. 85 3·25
a. Black and buff (McCracken) .. .. 13·00 21·00
131 1d. black and green .. .. .. 1·50 60
132 1½d. black and lake .. .. .. 70 6·00
133 2d. red .. .. 8·00 30
134 3d. black and blue .. .. .. 2·50 6·00
135 4d. olive-green .. .. .. 4·00 7·50
136 5d. black and slate-green .. .. .. 2·00 3·00
137 6d. bistre-brown .. .. .. 5·50 5·50
138 9d. black and violet .. .. .. 8·00 18·00
139 1s. dull blue-green .. .. .. 3·00 8·50
140 1s. 3d. black and dull purple .. .. 12·00 22·00
141 2s. black and slate-green .. .. .. 13·00 21·00
142 2s. 6d. black and rose-mauve .. .. 24·00 38·00
143 5s. black and olive-brown .. .. .. 55·00 50·00
144 10s. violet .. .. 75·00 75·00
145 £1 black and olive-grey £170 £130
130/145 .. .. .. *Set of* 16 £325 £325

Designs: *Vert (as T 15)*—1d. A Chieftain's son; 1½d. Tree-houses; 3d. Papuan dandy; 5d. Masked dancer; 9d. Papuan shooting fish; 1s. 3d. Lakatoi; 2s. Papuan art; 2s. 6d. Pottery making; 5s. Native policeman; £1 Delta house. *(As T 18)*—1s. *Dubu*—or ceremonial platform. *Horiz (as T 20)*—10s. Lighting a fire.

31 Hoisting the Union Jack

32 Scene on H.M.S. *Nelson*

(Recess J. Ash)

1934 (6 Nov). *50th Anniv of Declaration of British Protectorate. P 11.*

146 **31** 1d. green .. .. 1·00 2·75
147 **32** 2d. scarlet .. .. 1·75 2·75
148 **31** 3d. blue .. .. 1·75 3·00
149 **32** 5d. purple .. .. 11·00 12·00
146/9 .. .. *Set of* 4 14·00 18·00

HIS MAJESTY'S JUBILEE.

1910 1935

(33)

HIS MAJESTY'S
JUBILEE.
1910 — 1935

(34)

MAJESTY'S MAJESTY'S

Normal "Accent" flaw (R. 5/4)

1935 (9 July). *Silver Jubilee. Nos. 131, 133/4 and 136 optd with T 33 or 34 (2d.).*

150 1d. black and green .. .. .. 75 1·75
a. "Accent" flaw .. .. .. 27·00 45·00
151 2d. scarlet .. .. 2·00 1·75
152 3d. black and blue .. .. .. 1·75 2·50
a. "Accent" flaw .. .. .. 45·00 70·00
153 5d. black and slate-green .. .. 2·50 2·75
a. "Accent" flaw .. .. .. 60·00 80·00
150/3 .. .. .. *Set of* 4 6·25 8·00

35

36 Port Moresby

(Recess J. Ash)

1937 (14 May). *Coronation. P 11.*

154 **35** 1d. green 55 15
155 2d. scarlet 55 30
156 3d. blue 55 45
157 5d. purple .. .. 55 1·00
154/7 .. .. .. *Set of* 4 2·00 1·60

Some covers franked with these stamps and posted on 2 June 1937 were postmarked 2 April 1937 in error.

(Recess J. Ash)

1938 (6 Sept). *Air. 50th Anniv of Declaration of British Possession. P 11.*

158 **36** 2d. rose-red .. .. 3·75 2·25
159 3d. bright blue .. .. 3·75 2·25
160 5d. green .. .. 3·75 3·25
161 8d. brown-lake .. .. 11·00 14·00
162 1s. mauve .. .. 30·00 15·00
158/62 .. .. .. *Set of* 5 48·00 32·00

37 Natives poling Rafts

(Recess J. Ash)

1939 (6 Sept). *Air. P 11.*

163 **37** 2d. rose-red .. .. 6·00 3·75
164 3d. bright blue .. .. 6·00 6·50
165 5d. green .. .. 8·00 1·50
166 8d. brown-lake .. .. 10·00 2·50
167 1s. mauve .. .. 13·00 6·00

(Recess W. C. G. McCracken)

1941 (2 Jan). *Air. P 11½.*

168 **37** 1s. 6d. olive-green .. .. .. 40·00 32·00
163/168 .. .. .. *Set of* 6 75·00 45·00

OFFICIAL STAMPS

1908 (Oct). *Punctured* "OS".

O1 **1** 2s. 6d. black and brown (No. 37) .. £600 35·00
O2 2s. 6d. black and brown (No. 45) .. £2250 £2000
a. Thin paper (No. 45a) £700 £550

1909–10. *Nos. 49/71 punctured* "OS". I. *Wmk upright. (a) P 11.*

O 4 **6** 1d. black and rose .. .. .. 13·00 4·75
O 5 2d. black and purple .. .. .. 14·00 4·50
O 6 2½d. black and bright ultramarine .. 28·00 21·00
a. Black and pale ultramarine .. 11·00 4·25
O 7 4d. black and sepia .. .. .. 15·00 4·50
a. Deformed "d" at left .. .. 75·00 22·00
O 8 6d. black and myrtle-green .. .. 26·00 15·00
O 9 1s. black and orange .. .. .. 28·00 16·00
O4/9 .. .. .. *Set of* 6 95·00 45·00

(b) P 12½

O10 **6** 2d. black and purple .. .. .. 22·00 6·00
O11 2½d. black and bright ultramarine .. 85·00 70·00
b. Black and pale ultramarine .. 65·00 55·00
O12 4d. black and sepia .. .. .. 23·00 9·00
a. Deformed "d" at left .. .. £100 45·00
O13 1s. black and orange .. .. .. 85·00 45·00
O10/13 .. .. .. *Set of* 4 £180 £100

II. *Wmk sideways. (a) P 11*

O14 **6** ½d. black and yellow-green .. .. 11·00 4·50
a. Black and deep green .. .. 45·00 30·00
O15 1d. black and carmine .. .. .. 25·00 8·00
O16 2d. black and purple .. .. .. 14·00 2·00
O17 2½d. black and dull blue .. .. 16·00 5·00
O18 4d. black and sepia .. .. .. 14·00 6·50
a. Deformed "d" at left .. .. 70·00 28·00
O19 6d. black and myrtle-green .. .. 30·00 5·00
O20 1s. black and orange .. .. .. 80·00 28·00
O14/20 .. .. .. *Set of* 7 £170 50·00

(b) P 12½

O21 **6** ½d. black and yellow-green .. .. 8·00 1·50
a. Black and deep green .. .. 48·00 30·00
O22 1d. black and carmine .. .. .. 20·00 4·00
O23 2d. black and purple .. .. .. 14·00 3·00
O24 2½d. black and dull blue .. .. 30·00 14·00
O25 6d. black and myrtle-green .. .. — £1100
O26 1s. black and orange .. .. .. 38·00 14·00

1910. *Nos. 47/8 punctured* "OS".

O27 **5** ½d. black & yellow-green *(wmk upright)* 11·00 11·00
O28 2s. 6d. black & chocolate *(wmk sideways)* £110 85·00

1910–11. *Nos. 75/83 punctured* "OS".

O29 **5** ½d. black and green .. .. .. 11·00 4·50
O30 1d. black and carmine .. .. .. 18·00 4·50
O31 2d. black and dull purple .. .. 11·00 4·50
a. "C" for "O" in "POSTAGE" .. £110 60·00
O32 2½d. black and blue-violet .. .. 16·00 6·50
O33 4d. black and sepia .. .. .. 16·00 6·00
a. Deformed "d" at left .. .. 75·00 27·00
O34 6d. black and myrtle-green .. .. 16·00 6·00
O35 1s. black and deep orange .. .. 26·00 9·00
O36 2s. 6d. black and brown (B) .. .. 75·00 30·00
O37 2s. 6d. black and brown (C) .. .. 90·00 60·00
O29/36 .. .. .. *Set of* 8 £170 65·00

1911–12. *Nos. 84/91 punctured* "OS".

O38 **6** ½d. yellow-green .. .. .. 5·00 2·00
O39 1d. rose-pink .. .. .. 6·50 1·25
O40 2d. bright mauve .. .. .. 6·50 1·25
w. Wmk Crown to right of A .. .. — 20·00
O41 2½d. bright ultramarine .. .. 13·00 7·50
O42 4d. pale olive-green .. .. .. 15·00 15·00
O43 6d. orange-brown .. .. .. 13·00 6·00
O44 1s. yellow .. .. .. 18·00 11·00
O45 2s. 6d. rose-carmine .. .. .. 55·00 60·00
O38/45 .. .. .. *Set of* 8 £120 95·00

1930. *Nos. 93/6a and 98c/103 punctured* "OS".

O46 **6** ½d. myrtle and apple green .. .. 3·25 5·50
O47 1d. intense black and red .. .. 7·50 3·25
O48 1½d. bright blue and bright brown .. 5·00 6·00
a. "POSTACE" at right .. .. 65·00 75·00
O49 2d. deep brown-purple and lake .. 20·00 22·00
O50 3d. black and blue-green .. .. 30·00 40·00
O51 4d. light brown and orange .. .. 16·00 22·00
O52 6d. dull purple and pale purple .. 12·00 18·00
a. "POSTACE" at left £120 £140
O53 1s. brown and yellow-olive .. .. 17·00 28·00
O54 2s. 6d. maroon and pale pink .. .. 60·00 75·00
O46/54 .. .. .. *Set of* 9 £150 £200

O S

(O 1)

(Typo T. S. Harrison (1d. and 2s. 6d.) and J. Ash)

1931 (29 July)–**32.** *Optd with Type O 1. W 8 or W 15 of Australia (9d., 1s. 3d.). P 14 or 11 (9d., 1s. 3d.).*

O55 **6** ½d. myrtle and apple-green .. .. 1·00 4·75
O56 1d. grey-black and red .. ..
a. Intense black and red .. .. 3·75 7·00
O57 1½d. bright blue and bright brown .. 1·40 12·00
a. "POSTACE" at right .. .. 45·00 £120
O58 2d. brown-purple and claret .. .. 2·50 9·00
O59 3d. black and blue-green .. .. 2·50 17·00
O60 4d. light brown and orange (No. 99aw) 2·50 15·00
O61 5d. bluish slate and pale brown .. 6·00 38·00
O62 6d. dull purple and red-purple .. 4·00 8·50
a. "POSTACE" at left .. .. 80·00 £160
O63 9d. lilac and violet (1932) .. .. 40·00 55·00
O64 1s. brown and yellow-olive .. .. 9·00 27·00
O65 1s. 3d. lilac & pale greenish blue (1932) 40·00 55·00
O66 2s. 6d. maroon & pale pink (Harrison) 40·00 85·00
a. Maroon and bright pink (Ash) .. 40·00 85·00
O55/66 .. .. .. *Set of* 12 £130 £275

Civil Administration, in Papua, was suspended in 1942; on resumption, after the Japanese defeat in 1945, Australian stamps were used until the appearance of the issue of the combined territories of Papua & New Guinea.

PAPUA NEW GUINEA

AUSTRALIAN TRUST TERRITORY

The name of the combined territory was changed from "Papua and New Guinea" to "Papua New Guinea" at the beginning of 1972.

SPECIMEN OVERPRINTS. These come from specimen sets in which the lower values were cancelled-to-order, but stamps above the value of 10s. were overprinted "Specimen". These overprints are listed as they could be purchased from the Post Office.

1 Matschie's Tree Kangaroo

2 Buka Head-dresses

3 Native Youth

14 Map of Papua and New Guinea

15 Papuan shooting Fish

(Recess Note Printing Branch, Commonwealth Bank, Melbourne)

1952 (30 Oct)–**58**. *T* **1/3, 14/15** *and similar designs. P* 14.

1		½d. emerald	30	10
2		1d. deep brown	20	10
3		2d. blue	35	10
4		2½d. orange	2·00	40
5		3d. deep green	80	10
6		3½d. carmine-red	60	10
6*a*		3½d. black (2.6.58)	9·50	2·25
7		6½d. dull purple	2·00	10
		a. Maroon (1956)	6·50	15
8		7½d. blue	4·50	1·75
9		9d. brown	5·00	60
10		1s. yellow-green	2·75	10
11		1s. 6d. deep green	10·00	80
12		2s. indigo	8·00	10
13		2s. 6d. brown-purple	7·50	40
14		10s. blue-black	45·00	12·00
15		£1 deep brown	48·00	13·00
1/15		*Set of* 16	£130	28·00
14/15 Optd "Specimen"		*Set of* 2	£120	

Designs: *Vert* (*as T* 1/3)—2½d. Greater Bird of Paradise; 3d. Native policeman; 3½d. Papuan head-dress. (*As T* 15)—6½d. Kiriwina Chief House; 7½d. Kiriwina yam house; 1s. 6d. Rubber tapping; 2s. Sepik dancing masks. *Horiz* (*as T* 14)—9d. Copra making; 1s. Lakatoi; 2s. 6d. Native shepherd and flock.

(16) (17)

1957 (29 Jan). *Nos.* 4 *and* 10 *surch with T* **16** *or T* **17**.

16	4d. on 2½d. orange	70	10
17	7d. on 1s. yellow-green	40	10

18 Cacao Plant

19 Klinki Plymill

20 Cattle

21 Coffee Beans

(Recess Note Ptg Branch, Commonwealth Bank, Melbourne)

1958 (2 June)–**60**. *New values. P* 14.

18	**18**	4d. vermilion	1·50	10
19		5d. green (10.11.60)	1·50	10
20	**19**	7d. bronze-green	9·00	10
21		8d. deep ultramarine (10.11.60)	1·50	1·75
22	**20**	1s. 7d. red-brown	20·00	12·00
23		2s. 5d. vermilion (10.11.60)	4·75	2·25
24	**21**	5s. crimson and olive-green	12·00	1·50
18/24		*Set of* 7	45·00	16·00

(22)

23 Council Chamber, Port Moresby

1959 (1 Dec). *No.* 1 *surch with T* **22**.

25	**1**	5d. on ½d. emerald	1·00	10

(Photo Harrison)

1961 (10 Apr). *Reconstitution of Legislative Council. P* 15 × 14.

26	**23**	5d. deep green and yellow	1·50	25
27		2s. 3d. deep green and light salmon	4·50	1·50

24 Female, Goroka, New Guinea

26 Female Dancer

28 Traffic Policeman

(Des Pamela M. Prescott, Recess Note Ptg Branch, Reserve Bank of Australia, Melbourne)

1961 (26 July)–**62**. *T* **24, 26, 28** *and similar designs. P* 14½ × 14 (*1d., 3d., 3s.*) *or* 14 × 14½ (*others*).

28	1d. lake	1·25	10
29	3d. indigo	30	10
30	1s. bronze-green	4·00	15
31	2s. maroon	45	15
32	3s. deep bluish green (5.9.62)	2·25	1·00
28/32	*Set of* 5	7·50	1·25

Designs: *Vert* (*as T* **24**)—3d. Tribal elder, Tari, Papua. (*As T* **26**)—2s. Male dancer.

29 Campaign Emblem

30 Map of South Pacific

(Recess Note Ptg Branch, Reserve Bank of Australia, Melbourne)

1962 (7 Apr). *Malaria Eradication. P* 14.

33	**29**	5d. carmine-red and light blue	45	15
34		1s. red and sepia	1·00	25
35		2s. black and yellow-green	1·40	70
33/5		*Set of* 3	2·50	1·00

(Des Pamela M. Prescott. Recess Note Ptg Branch, Reserve Bank of Australia, Melbourne)

1962 (9 July). *Fifth South Pacific Conference, Pago Pago. P* 14½ × 14.

36	**30**	5d. scarlet and light green	65	15
37		1s. 6d. deep violet and light yellow	2·00	60
38		2s. 6d. deep green and light blue	2·00	1·25
36/8		*Set of* 3	4·25	1·75

31 Throwing the Javelin

33 Runners

(Des G. Hamori. Photo Courvoisier)

1962 (24 Oct). *Seventh British Empire and Commonwealth Games, Perth. T* **31, 33** *and similar design. P* 11½.

39	5d. brown and light blue	25	10
	a. Pair. Nos. 39/40	50	50
40	5d. brown and orange	25	10
41	2s. 3d. brown and light green	1·50	75
39/41	*Set of* 3	1·75	85

Design: (*As T* **31**)—5d. High jump.

Nos. 39/40 are arranged together *se-tenant* in sheets of 100.

34 Raggiana Bird of Paradise

35 Common Phalanger

36 Rabaul

37 Queen Elizabeth II

(Des S. T. Cham (10s.), A. Buckley (photo) (£1). Photo Harrison (£1), Courvoisier (others)).

1963. *P* 14½ (£1) *or* 11½ (*others*).

42	**34**	5d. yellow, chestnut and sepia (27 Mar)	1·50	10
43	**35**	6d. red, yellow-brown and grey (27 Mar)	75	90
44	**36**	10s. multicoloured (13 Feb)	17·00	8·50
45	**37**	£1 sepia, gold and blue-green (3 July)	5·00	2·50
		a. Gold ptd double		
42/5		*Set of* 4	22·00	11·00
44/5 Optd "Specimen"		*Set of* 2	90·00	

38 Centenary Emblem

39 Waterfront, Port Moresby

(Des G. Hamori. Photo Note Ptg Branch, Reserve Bank of Australia, Melbourne)

1963 (1 May). *Red Cross Centenary. P* 13½×13.

46	**38**	5d. red, grey-brown and bluish green	60	10

(Des J. McMahon (8d.), Pamela M. Prescott (2s. 3d.). Recess Note Ptg Branch, Reserve Bank of Australia, Melbourne)

1963 (8 May). *T* **39** *and similar horiz design. P* 14×13½.

47	**39**	8d. green	50	15
48	–	2s. 3d. ultramarine	75	30

Design:—2s. 3d. Piaggio P-166B Portofino aircraft landing at Tapini.

40 Games Emblem

41 Watam Head

(Des Pamela M. Prescott. Recess Note Ptg Branch, Reserve Bank of Australia, Melbourne)

1963 (14 Aug). *First South Pacific Games, Suva. P* 13½ × 14½.

49	**40**	5d. bistre	10	10
50		1s. deep green	30	20

(Des Pamela M. Prescott. Photo Courvoisier)

1964 (5 Feb). *Native Artefacts. T* **41** *and similar vert designs. Multicoloured. P* 11½.

51	11d. Type **41**	60	10
52	2s. 5d. Watam Head (*different*)	60	75
53	2s. 6d. Bosmun Head	60	10
54	5s. Medina Head	80	15
51/4	*Set of* 4	2·40	90

45 Casting Vote

46 "Health Centres"

(Photo Courvoisier)

1964 (4 Mar). *Common Roll Elections. P* 11½.

55	**45**	5d. brown and drab	10	10
56		2s. 3d. brown and pale blue	20	25

(Recess Note Ptg Branch, Reserve Bank of Australia, Melbourne)

1964 (5 Aug). *Health Services. T* **46** *and similar vert designs. P* 14.

57	5d. violet	10	10
58	8d. bronze-green	15	10
59	1s. blue	15	10
60	1s. 2d. brown-red	35	35
57/60	*Set of* 4	65	50

Designs:—8d. "School health"; 1s. "Infant, child and maternal health"; 1s. 2d. "Medical training".

50 Striped Gardener Bowerbird

51 Emperor of Germany Bird of Paradise

(Photo Courvoisier)

1964 (28 Oct)–**65**. *Vert designs as T* **50** *(1d. to 8d.) or* **51** *(others). Multicoloured; background colours given. P* 11½ *(1d. to 8d.) or* 12 × 11½ *(1s. to 10s.).*

61 1d. pale olive-yellow (20.1.65) 40 10
62 3d. light grey (20.1.65) 50 10
63 5d. pale red (20.1.65) 55 10
64 6d. pale green 75 10
65 8d. lilac 1·50 20
66 1s. salmon 1·50 10
67 2s. light blue (20.1.65) 1·00 40
68 2s. 3d. light green (20.1.65) 1·00 85
69 3s. pale yellow (20.1.65) 1·00 1·25
70 5s. cobalt (20.1.65) 15·00 2·50
71 10s. pale drab (Optd S. £120) 8·00 10·00
61/71 *Set of* 11 27·00 14·00

Designs:—3d. Adelbert Bowerbird; 5d. Blue Bird of Paradise; 6d. Lawes's Parotia; 8d. Black-billed Sicklebill; 2s. Brown Sicklebill; 2s. 3d. Lesser Bird of Paradise; 3s. Magnificent Bird of Paradise; 5s. Twelve-wired Bird of Paradise; 10s. Magnificent Riflebird.

61 Canoe Prow

(Des Pamela M. Prescott. Photo Courvoisier)

1965 (24 Mar). *Sepik Canoe Prows in Port Moresby Museum. T* **61** *and similar horiz designs showing carved prows. P* 11½.

72 4d. multicoloured 50 10
73 1s. 2d. multicoloured 2·25 1·50
74 1s. 6d. multicoloured 50 10
75 4s. multicoloured 1·00 30
72/5 *Set of* 4 3·75 1·75

1965 (14 Apr). *50th Anniv of Gallipoli Landing. As T* **22** *of Nauru. P* 13½.

76 2s. 3d. sepia, black and emerald 20 10

65 Urban Plan and Native House

(Des G. Hamori. Photo Courvoisier)

1965 (7 July). *Sixth South Pacific Conference, Lae. T* **65** *and similar horiz design. P* 11½.

77 6d. multicoloured 10 10
78 1s. multicoloured 10 10

No. 78 is similar to T **65** but with the plan on the right and the house on the left. Also "URBANISATION" reads downwards.

66 Mother and Child

67 Globe and U.N. Emblem

(Photo Courvoisier)

1965 (13 Oct). *20th Anniv of U.N.O. T* **66/7** *and similar vert design. P* 11½.

79 6d. sepia, blue and pale turquoise-blue 10 10
80 1s. orange-brown, blue & dp reddish violet 10 10
81 2s. blue, blue-green and light yellow-olive 15 10
79/81 *Set of* 3 30 20

Design:—2s. U.N. Emblem and globes.

(New Currency. 100 cents = 1 Australian dollar)

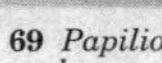

69 *Papilio ulysses*

71 *Ornithoptera priamus*

(Photo Courvoisier)

1966 (14 Feb–12 Oct). *Decimal Currency. Butterflies. Vert designs as T* **69** *(1 to 5 c.), or horiz as T* **71** *(others). Multicoloured. P* 11½.

82 1 c. Type **69** 40 50
83 3 c. *Cyrestis acilia* 40 60
84 4 c. *Graphium weiskei* 40 50
85 5 c. *Terinos alurgis* 40 10
86 10 c. Type **71** 50 30
86*a* 12 c. *Euploea callithoe* (12.10) 2·25 2·25
87 15 c. *Papilio euchenor* 2·50 80
88 20 c. *Parthenos sylvia* 1·00 25
89 25 c. *Delias aruna* 2·25 90
90 50 c. *Apaturina erminea* 12·00 1·25
91 $1 *Doleschallia dascylus* 4·00 1·50
92 $2 *Ornithoptera paradisea* 7·00 8·00
82/92 *Set of* 12 30·00 15·00

80 "Molala Harai"

84 Throwing the Discus

(Des Rev. H. A. Brown. Photo Courvoisier)

1966 (8 June). *Folklore. Elema Art (1st series). T* **80** *and similar vert designs. P* 11½.

93 2 c. black and carmine 10 10
94 7 c. black, light yellow and light blue 10 10
95 30 c. black, carmine and apple-green 15 10
96 60 c. black, carmine and yellow 40 30
93/6 *Set of* 4 65 45

Designs:—7 c. "Marai"; 30 c. "Meavea Kivovia"; 60 c. "Toivita Tapaivita".

Nos. 93/6 were supplementary values to the decimal currency definitive issue.

See also Nos. 152/5 and 342/5.

(Photo Courvoisier)

1966 (31 Aug). *South Pacific Games, Nouméa. T* **84** *and similar vert designs. Multicoloured. P* 11½.

97 5 c. Type **84** 10 10
98 10 c. Football 10 10
99 20 c. Tennis 15 10
97/9 *Set of* 3 30 20

87 *Mucuna novoguineensis*

91 "Fine Arts"

(Des Mrs. D. Pearce. Photo Courvoisier)

1966 (7 Dec). *Flowers. T* **87** *and similar vert designs. Multicoloured. P* 11½.

100 5 c. Type **87** 15 10
101 10 c. *Tecomanthe dendrophila* 15 10
102 20 c. *Rhododendron macgregoriae* 35 10
103 60 c. *Rhododendron konori* 1·00 1·75
100/3 *Set of* 4 1·50 1·75

(Des G. Hamori. Photo Courvoisier)

1967 (8 Feb). *Higher Education. T* **91** *and similar horiz designs. Multicoloured. P* 12½ × 12.

104 1 c. Type **91** 10 10
105 3 c. "Surveying" 10 10
106 4 c. "Civil Engineering" 10 10
107 5 c. "Science" 10 10
108 20 c. "Law" 10 10
104/8 *Set of* 5 30 30

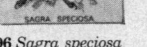

96 *Sagra speciosa*

100 Laloki River

(Des Pamela M. Prescott. Photo Courvoisier)

1967 (12 Apr). *Fauna Conservation (Beetles). T* **96** *and similar vert designs. Multicoloured. P* 11½.

109 5 c. Type **96** 20 10
110 10 c. *Eupholus schoenherri* 30 10
111 20 c. *Sphingnotus albertisi* 50 10
112 25 c. *Cyphogastra albertisi* 55 10
109/12 *Set of* 4 1·40 30

(Des G. Wade. Photo Courvoisier)

1967 (28 June). *Laloki River Hydro-Electric Scheme, and "New Industries". T* **100** *and similar vert designs. Multicoloured. P* 12½.

113 5 c. Type **100** 10 10
114 10 c. Pyrethrum 10 10
115 20 c. Tea Plant 15 10
116 25 c. Type **100** 15 10
113/16 *Set of* 4 40 30

103 Air Attack at Milne Bay

107 Papuan Lory

(Des R. Hodgkinson (2 c.), F. Hodgkinson (5 c.), G. Wade (20 c., 50 c.). Photo Courvoisier)

1967 (30 Aug). *25th Anniv of the Pacific War. T* **103** *and similar multicoloured designs. P* 11½.

117 2 c. Type **103** 10 30
118 5 c. Kokoda Trail (*vert*) 10 10
119 20 c. The Coast Watchers 25 15
120 50 c. Battle of the Coral Sea 80 60
117/20 *Set of* 4 1·00 1·00

(Des T. Walcot. Photo Courvoisier)

1967 (29 Nov). *Christmas. Territory Parrots. T* **107** *and similar vert designs. Multicoloured. P* 12½.

121 5 c. Type **107** 25 10
122 7 c. Pesquet's Parrot 30 75
123 20 c. Dusky Lory 70 10
124 25 c. Edward's Fig Parrot 70 10
121/4 *Set of* 4 1·75 90

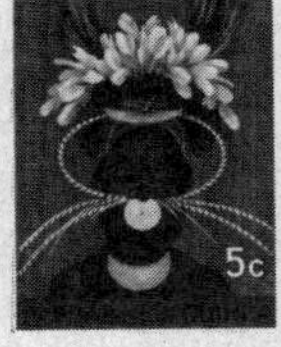

111 Chimbu Head-dresses **112**

(Des P. Jones. Photo Courvoisier)

1968 (21 Feb). *"National Heritage". T* **111/12** *and similar multicoloured designs. P* 12 × 12½ *(5, 60 c.) or* 12½ × 12 *(10, 20 c.).*

125 5 c. Type **111** 10 10
126 10 c. Southern Highlands Head-dress (*horiz*) 15 10
127 20 c. Western Highlands Head-dress (*horiz*) 20 10
128 60 c. Type **112** 70 30
125/8 *Set of* 4 1·00 50

115 *Hyla thesaurensis*

119 Human Rights Emblem and Papuan Head-dress (abstract)

(Des and photo Courvoisier)

1968 (24 Apr). *Fauna Conservation (Frogs). T* **115** *and similar horiz designs. Multicoloured. P* 11½.

129 5 c. Type **115** 15 30
130 10 c. *Hyla iris* 15 10
131 15 c. *Ceratobatrachus guentheri* 15 10
132 20 c. *Nyctimystes narinosa* 20 30
129/32 *Set of* 4 60 60

(Des G. Hamori. Litho Enschedé)

1968 (26 June). *Human Rights Year. T* **119** *and similar horiz design. Multicoloured. P* 13½ × 12½.

133 5 c. Type **119** 10 10
134 10 c. Human Rights in the World (abstract) 10 10

121 Leadership (abstract)

123 Common Egg Cowrie (*Ovula ovum*)

(Des G. Hamori. Litho Enschedé)

1968 (26 June). *Universal Suffrage. T* **121** *and similar horiz design. Multicoloured. P* 13½ × 12½.

135 20 c. Type **121** 15 15
136 25 c. Leadership of the Community (abstract) 15 15

(Des P. Jones. Photo Courvoisier)

1968–69. *Sea Shells. Multicoloured designs as T* **123**. *P* 12×12½ *($2),* 12½×12 *(1 c. to 20 c.) or* 11½ *(others).*

137 1 c. Type **125** (29.1.69) 10 10
138 3 c. Laciniate Conch (*Strombus sinuatus*) (30.10.68) 30 40
139 4 c. Lithograph Cone (*Conus litoglyphus*) (29.1.69) 20 40
140 5 c. Marbled Cone (*Conus marmoreus marmoreus*) (28.8.68) 25 10
141 7 c. Episcopal Mitre (*Mitra mitra*) (29.1.69) 35 10
142 10 c. *Cymbiola rutila ruckeri* (30.10.68) 45 10

143 12 c. Checkerboard Bonnet (*Phalium areola*) (29.1.69) .. 1·25 1·25
144 15 c. Scorpion Conch (*Lambis scorpius*) (30.10.68) .. 60 50
145 20 c. Fluted Giant Clam or Scale Tridacna (*Tridacna sqamosa*) (28.8.68) .. 70 10
146 25 c. Camp Pitar Venus (*Lioconcha castrensis*) (28.8.68) .. 70 30
147 30 c. Ramose Murex (*Murex ramosus*) (28.8.68) .. 90 75
148 40 c. Chambered or Pearly Nautilus (*Nautilus pompilius*) (30.10.68) .. 75 65
149 60 c. Trumpet Triton (*Charonia tritonis*) (28.8.68) .. 80 30
150 $1 Manus Green Papuina (*Papuina pulcherrima*) (30.10.68) .. 2·00 70
151 $2 Glory of the Sea Cone (*Conus gloriamaris*) (*vert*) (29.1.69) .. 18·00 6·50
137/51 .. *Set of* 15 24·00 11·00

The 1, 5, 7, 15, 40, 60 c. and $1 exist with PVA gum as well as gum arabic.

138 Tito Myth

140 Luvuapo Myth

139 Iko Myth

141 Miro Myth

(Des from native motifs by Revd. H. A. Brown. Litho Enschedé)

1969 (9 Apr). *Folklore. Elema Art (2nd series). P* 12½ × 13½ × *Roul* 9 *between se-tenant pairs.*
152 **138** 5 c. black, yellow and red .. 10 40
a. Pair. Nos. 152/3 .. 20 80
153 **139** 5 c. black, yellow and red .. 10 40
154 **140** 10 c. black, grey and red .. 15 40
a. Pair. Nos. 154/5 .. 30 80
155 **141** 10 c. black, grey and red .. 15 40
152/5 .. *Set of* 4 50 1·60

Nos. 152/3 and 154/5 were issued in vertical *se-tenant* pairs, separated by a line of roulette.

142 "Fireball" Class Yacht

145 *Dendrobium ostrinoglossum*

(Des J. Fallas. Recess Note Ptg Branch, Reserve Bank of Australia)

1969 (25 June). *Third South Pacific Games, Port Moresby. T* **142** *and similar designs. P* 14 × 14½ (5 c.) *or* 14½ × 14 (*others*).
156 5 c. black .. 10 10
157 10 c. deep bluish violet .. 10 10
158 20 c. myrtle-green .. 15 15
156/8 .. *Set of* 3 30 30

Designs: *Horiz*—10 c. Swimming pool, Boroko; 20 c. Games arena, Konedobu.

(Des P. Jones. Photo Courvoisier)

1969 (27 Aug). *Flora Conservation (Orchids). T* **145** *and similar vert designs. Multicoloured. P* 11½.
159 5 c. Type **145** .. 25 10
160 10 c. *Dendrobium lawesii* .. 35 70
161 20 c. *Dendrobium pseudofrigidum* .. 55 90
162 30 c. *Dendrobium conanthum* .. 70 70
159/62 .. *Set of* 4 1·75 2·25

149 Bird of Paradise

150 Native Potter

(Des G. Hamori. Photo Note Ptg Branch, Reserve Bank of Australia)

1969 (24 Sept)–71. *Coil stamps. P* 15 × *imperf.*
162*a* **149** 2 c. blue, black and red (1.4.71) .. 10 15
163 5 c. bright green, brown and red-orange 10 10

(Des G. Hamori. Photo Courvoisier)

1969 (24 Sept). *50th Anniv of International Labour Organization. P* 11½.
164 **150** 5 c. multicoloured .. 10 10

151 Tareko

155 Prehistoric Ambun Stone

(Des G. Hamori. Photo Courvoisier)

1969 (29 Oct). *Musical Instruments. T* **151** *and similar horiz designs. P* 12½ × 12.
165 5 c. multicoloured .. 10 10
166 10 c. black, olive-green and pale yellow .. 10 10
167 25 c. black, yellow and brown .. 15 15
168 30 c. multicoloured .. 25 15
165/8 .. *Set of* 4 55 45

Designs:—10 c. Garamut; 25 c. Iviliko; 30 c. Kundu.

(Des R. Bates. Photo Courvoisier)

1970 (11 Feb). *"National Heritage". T* **155** *and similar horiz designs. Multicoloured. P* 12½ × 12.
169 5 c. Type **155** .. 15 10
170 10 c. Masawa canoe of Kula Circuit .. 20 15
171 25 c. Torres' Map, 1606 .. 55 15
172 30 c. H.M.S. *Basilisk* (paddle-sloop), 1873 .. 75 20
169/72 .. *Set of* 4 1·50 50

159 King of Saxony Bird of Paradise

(Des T. Walcot. Photo Courvoisier)

1970 (13 May). *Fauna Conservation (Birds of Paradise). T* **159** *and similar vert designs. Multicoloured. P* 12.
173 5 c. Type **159** .. 1·00 15
174 10 c. King Bird of Paradise .. 1·25 60
175 15 c. Raggiana Bird of Paradise .. 2·00 1·00
176 25 c. Sickle-crested Bird of Paradise .. 2·25 70
173/6 .. *Set of* 4 6·00 2·25

163 Douglas DC-6B and Mt Wilhelm

164 Lockheed L.188 Electra and Mt Yule

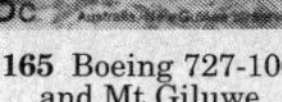

165 Boeing 727-100 and Mt Giluwe

166 Fokker F.27 Friendship and Manam Island

(Des D. Gentleman. Photo Harrison)

1970 (8 July). *Australian and New Guinea Air Services. T* **163/6** *and similar horiz designs. Multicoloured. P* 14½ × 14.
177 5 c. Type **163** .. 30 10
a. Block of 4. Nos. 177/80 .. 1·10
178 5 c. Type **164** .. 30 10
179 5 c. Type **165** .. 30 10
180 5 c. Type **166** .. 30 10
181 25 c. Douglas DC-3 and Matupi Volcano .. 70 40
182 30 c. Boeing 707 and Hombrom's Bluff .. 70 60
177/82 .. *Set of* 6 2·40 1·25

Nos. 177/80 were issued together, *se-tenant*, in blocks of 4 throughout the sheet.

ALTERED CATALOGUE NUMBERS

Any Catalogue numbers altered from the last edition are shown as a list in the introductory pages.

169 N. Miklouho-Maclay (scientist) and Effigy

170 Wogeo Island Food Bowl

(Des D. Gentleman. Photo Courvoisier)

1970 (19 Aug). *42nd ANZAAS (Australian-New Zealand Association for the Advancement of Science) Congress, Port Moresby. T* **169** *and similar horiz designs. P* 11½.
183 5 c. multicoloured .. 10 10
184 10 c. multicoloured .. 20 10
185 15 c. multicoloured .. 90 25
186 20 c. multicoloured .. 60 25
183/6 .. *Set of* 4 1·60 55

Designs:—10 c. B. Malinowski (anthropologist) and native hut; 15 c. T. Salvadori (ornithologist) and Double-wattled Cassowary; 20 c. F.R.R. Schlechter (botanist) and flower.

(Des P. Jones. Photo Courvoisier)

1970 (28 Oct). *Native Artefacts. T* **170** *and similar multicoloured designs. P* 12½ × 12 (30 *c.*) *or* 12 × 12½ (*others*).
187 5 c. Type **170** .. 10 10
188 10 c. Lime Pot .. 20 10
189 15 c. Aibom Sago Storage Pot .. 20 10
190 30 c. Manus Island Bowl (*horiz*) .. 25 30
187/90 .. *Set of* 4 70 50

171 Eastern Highlands Dwelling

172 Spotted Phalanger

(Des G. Wade. Photo Courvoisier)

1971 (27 Jan). *Native Dwellings. T* **171** *and similar vert designs showing dwellings from the places given. Multicoloured. P* 11½.
191 5 c. Type **171** .. 15 10
192 7 c. Milne Bay .. 15 20
193 10 c. Purari Delta .. 15 10
194 40 c. Sepik .. 35 70
191/4 .. *Set of* 4 70 95

(Des R. Bates. Photo Courvoisier)

1971 (31 Mar). *Fauna Conservation. T* **172** *and similar multicoloured designs. P* 11½.
195 5 c. Type **172** .. 30 10
196 10 c. Long-fingered Possum .. 60 15
197 15 c. Feather-tailed Possum .. 1·25 1·00
198 25 c. Long-nosed Echidna (*horiz*) .. 1·75 1·00
199 30 c. Ornate Tree Kangaroo (*horiz*) .. 1·75 70
195/9 .. *Set of* 5 5·00 2·50

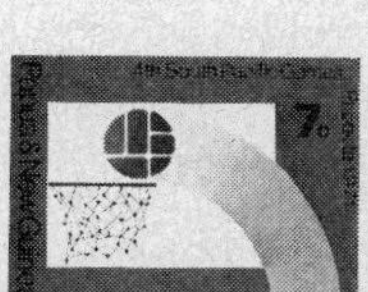

173 "Basketball"

174 Bartering Fish for Vegetables

(Des G. Hamori, Litho D.L.R.)

1971 (9 June). *Fourth South Pacific Games, Papeete, Tahiti. T* **173** *and similar horiz designs. Multicoloured. P* 13½ × 14.
200 7 c. Type **173** .. 10 10
201 14 c. "Sailing" .. 15 20
202 21 c. "Boxing" .. 15 30
203 28 c. "Athletics" .. 15 40
200/3 .. *Set of* 4 50 85

(Des G. Wade. Photo Courvoisier)

1971 (18 Aug). *Primary Industries. T* **174** *and similar vert designs. Multicoloured. P* 11½.
204 7 c. Type **174** .. 10 10
205 9 c. Man stacking yams .. 15 30
206 14 c. Vegetable market .. 25 10
207 30 c. Highlanders cultivating garden .. 45 65
204/7 .. *Set of* 4 85 1·00

175 Sia Dancer — **176** Papuan Flag over Australian Flag

(Des Bette Hays. Photo Courvoisier)

1971 (27 Oct). *Native Dancers. T* **175** *and similar multicoloured designs. P* 11½.

208 7 c. Type **175** .. 20 10
209 9 c. Urasena dancer .. 25 20
210 20 c. Siassi Tubuan dancers (*horiz*) .. 60 75
211 28 c. Sia dancers (*horiz*) .. 80 90
208/11 .. *Set of* 4 1·60 1·75

(Des R. Bates. Photo Courvoisier)

1972 (26 Jan). *Constitutional Development. T* **176** *and similar horiz design. P* 12½ × 12.

212 **176** 7 c. multicoloured .. 30 10
a. Pair. Nos. 212/13 .. 60 90
213 – 7 c. multicoloured .. 30 10

Design:—No. 213, Crest of Papua New Guinea and Australian coat of arms.

Nos. 212/13 were printed vertically *se-tenant* within the sheet.

177 Map of Papua New Guinea and Flag of South Pacific Commission — **178** Turtle

(Des R. Bates. Photo Courvoisier)

1972 (26 Jan). *25th Anniv of South Pacific Commission. T* **177** *and similar horiz design. P* 12½ × 12.

214 **177** 15 c. multicoloured .. 45 55
a. Pair. Nos. 214/15 .. 90 1·75
215 – 15 c. multicoloured .. 45 55

Design:—No. 215, Man's face and flag of the Commission.

Nos. 214/15 were printed vertically *se-tenant* within the sheet.

(Des R. Bates. Photo Courvoisier)

1972 (17 Mar). *Fauna Conservation (Reptiles). T* **178** *and similar horiz designs. Multicoloured. P* 11½.

216 7 c. Type **178** .. 40 10
217 14 c. Rainforest Dragon .. 1·00 1·25
218 21 c. Green Python .. 1·25 1·50
219 30 c. Salvador's Monitor .. 1·75 1·25
216/19 .. *Set of* 4 4·00 3·50

179 Curtiss MF-6 Seagull Aircraft and *Eureka* (schooner) — **180** New National Flag

(Des Major L. G. Halls. Photo Courvoisier)

1972 (7 June). *50th Anniv of Aviation. T* **179** *and similar horiz designs. Multicoloured. P* 11½.

220 7 c. Type **179** .. 50 10
221 14 c. De Havilland D.H.37 and native porters .. 1·00 1·25
222 20 c. Junkers G.31 and gold dredger .. 1·25 1·25
223 25 c. Junkers F-13 and mission church .. 1·25 1·25
220/3 .. *Set of* 4 3·50 3·50

(Des R. Bates. Photo Courvoisier)

1972 (16 Aug). *National Day. T* **180** *and similar vert designs. Multicoloured. P* 11½.

224 7 c. Type **180** .. 20 10
225 10 c. Native drum .. 25 25
226 30 c. Trumpet Triton .. 45 50
224/6 .. *Set of* 3 80 70

181 Rev. Copland King — **182** Mt Tomavatur Station

(Des G. Wade. Photo Courvoisier)

1972 (25 Oct). *Christmas (Missionaries). T* **181** *and similar horiz designs. Multicoloured. P* 11½.

227 7 c. Type **181** .. 25 40
228 7 c. Rev. Dr. Flierl .. 25 40
229 7 c. Bishop Verjus .. 25 40
230 7 c. Pastor Ruatoka .. 25 40
227/30 .. *Set of* 4 90 1·40

(Des R. Bates. Photo Courvoisier)

1973 (24 Jan). *Completion of Telecommunications Project, 1968–72. T* **182** *and similar horiz designs. Multicoloured. P* 12½ *(Nos.* 231/4) *or* 11½ *(others).*

231 7 c. Type **182** .. 35 20
a. Block of 4. Nos. 231/4 .. 1·25
232 7 c. Mt Kerigomma Station .. 35 20
233 7 c. Sattelburg Station .. 35 20
234 7 c. Wideru Station .. 35 20
235 9 c. Teleprinter (36 × 26 *mm*) .. 35 55
236 30 c. Network Map (36 × 26 *mm*) .. 1·00 1·50
231/6 .. *Set of* 6 2·50 2·50

Nos. 231/4 were printed in *se-tenant* blocks of four within the sheet.

183 Queen Carola's Parotia — **184** Wood Carver

(Des W. Cooper. Photo Courvoisier)

1973 (30 Mar). *Birds of Paradise. T* **183** *and similar vert designs. Multicoloured. P* 11½.

237 7 c. Type **183** .. 1·25 35
238 14 c. Goldie's Bird of Paradise .. 2·75 1·25
239 21 c. Ribbon-tailed Bird of Paradise (18 × 49 *mm*) .. 3·00 2·00
240 28 c. Princess Stephanie's Bird of Paradise (18 × 49 *mm*) .. 4·25 2·50
237/40 .. *Set of* 4 10·00 5·50

(Des R. Bates. Photo Courvoisier)

1973 (13 June)–**74**. *T* **184** *and similar horiz designs. Multicoloured. P* 11½.

241 1 c. Type **184** .. 10 10
242 3 c. Wig-makers (23.1.74) .. 40 10
243 5 c. Mt Bagana (22.8.73) .. 55 10
244 6 c. Pig Exchange (7.8.74) .. 70 90
245 7 c. Coastal village .. 30 10
246 8 c. Arawe mother (23.1.74) .. 35 30
247 9 c. Fire dancers .. 30 20
248 10 c. Tifalmin hunter (23.1.74) .. 55 10
249 14 c. Crocodile hunters (22.8.73) .. 45 70
250 15 c. Mt Elimbari .. 50 30
251 20 c. Canoe-racing, Manus (23.1.74) .. 1·50 40
252 21 c. Making sago (22.8.73) .. 50 80
253 25 c. Council House .. 50 45
254 28 c. Menyamya bowmen (22.8.73) .. 65 75
255 30 c. Shark-snaring (22.8.73) .. 65 75
256 40 c. Fishing canoes, Madang .. 70 60
257 60 c. Tapa cloth-making (23.1.74) .. 80 80
258 $1 Asaro Mudmen (23.1.74) .. 1·40 1·75
259 $2 Enga "Sing Sing" (7.8.74) .. 4·00 6·00
241/59 .. *Set of* 19 13·00 13·50

185 Stamps of German New Guinea, 1897

(Des R. Bates. Photo (1 c.), litho and recess (6 c.) or litho (7 c.) State Printing Works, Berlin. Photo and recess D.L.R. (9 c.). Recess and typo Reserve Bank of Australia (25 and 30 c.))

1973 (24 Oct). *75th Anniv of Papua New Guinea Stamps. T* **185** *and similar horiz designs. Chalky paper* (25, 30 *c.*). *P* 13½ (1, 6, 7 *c.*), 14 × 13½ (9 *c.*) *or* 14 × 14½ (25, 30 *c.*).

260 1 c. multicoloured .. 15 15
261 6 c. indigo, new blue and silver .. 25 35
262 7 c. multicoloured .. 25 35
263 9 c. multicoloured .. 25 45
264 25 c. orange and gold .. 50 1·00
265 30 c. plum and silver .. 55 1·25
260/65 .. *Set of* 6 1·75 3·25

Designs: *As T* **185**—6 c. 2 mark stamp of German New Guinea, 1900; 7 c. Surcharged registration label of New Guinea, 1914. 46 × 35 *mm*.—9 c. Papua 1s. stamp, 1901. 45 × 38 *mm*—25 c. ½d. stamp of New Guinea, 1925; 30 c. Papua 10s. stamp, 1932.

SELF-GOVERNMENT

186 Native Carved Heads — **187** Queen Elizabeth II (from photograph by Karsh)

(Des G. Wade. Photo Courvoisier)

1973 (5 Dec). *Self-Government. P* 11½.

266 **186** 7 c. multicoloured .. 30 15
267 10 c. multicoloured .. 50 65

(Des and photo Harrison)

1974 (22 Feb). *Royal Visit. P* 14 × 14½.

268 **187** 7 c. multicoloured .. 25 15
269 30 c. multicoloured .. 75 1·50

188 Blyth's Hornbill — **189** *Dendrobium bracteosum*

(Des T. Nolan. Photo Courvoisier)

1974 (12 June). *Birds' Heads. T* **188** *and similar multicoloured designs. P* 11½ (10 *c.*) *or* 12 (*others*).

270 7 c. Type **188** .. 2·00 70
271 10 c. Double-wattled Cassowary (33 × 49 *mm*) 3·00 3·25
272 30 c. New Guinea Harpy Eagle .. 7·00 8·50
270/2 .. *Set of* 3 11·00 11·00

(Des T. Nolan. Photo Courvoisier)

1974 (20 Nov). *Flora Conservation. T* **189** *and similar vert designs. Multicoloured. P* 11½.

273 7 c. Type **189** .. 50 10
274 10 c. *D. anosmum* .. 80 50
275 20 c. *D. smillieae* .. 1·00 1·25
276 30 c. *D. insigne* .. 1·25 1·75
273/6 .. *Set of* 4 3·25 3·25

190 Motu Lakatoi — **191** 1-toea Coin

(Des G. Wade. Photo Courvoisier)

1975 (26 Feb). *National Heritage—Canoes. T* **190** *and similar horiz designs. Multicoloured. P* 11½.

277 7 c. Type **190** .. 30 10
278 10 c. Tami two-master morobe .. 50 70
279 25 c. Aramia racing canoe .. 1·25 2·50
280 30 c. Buka Island canoe .. 1·25 1·25
277/80 .. *Set of* 4 3·00 4·00

(New Currency. 100 toea = 1 kina)

(Des G. Wade. Photo Courvoisier)

1975 (21 Apr). *New Coinage. T* **191** *and similar multicoloured designs. P* 11½.

281 1 t. Type **191** .. 10 10
282 7 t. New 2 t. and 5 t. coins (45 × 26 *mm*) .. 50 10
283 10 t. New 10 t. coin .. 50 30
284 20 t. New 20 t. coin .. 90 80
285 1 k. New 1 k. coin (45 × 26 *mm*) .. 2·75 4·00
281/5 .. *Set of* 5 4·25 4·50

192 *Ornithoptera alexandrae* — **193** Boxing

(Des R. Bates. Photo Courvoisier)

1975 (11 June). *Fauna Conservation (Birdwing Butterflies). T* 192 *and similar vert designs. Multicoloured. P* 11½.

286	7 t. Type **192**	50	10
287	10 t. *O. victoriae*	60	65
288	30 t. *O. allottei*	1·00	2·00
289	40 t. *O. chimaera*	1·50	3·25
286/9	*Set of* 4	3·25	5·50

(Des R. Bates. Photo Courvoisier)

1975 (2 Aug). *Fifth South Pacific Games, Guam. T* **193** *and similar vert designs. Multicoloured. P* 11½.

290	7 t. Type **193**	15	10
291	20 t. Running	25	30
292	25 t. Basketball	30	45
293	30 t. Swimming	35	50
290/3	*Set of* 4	95	1·10

INDEPENDENT

194 Map and National Flag

(Des and photo Courvoisier)

1975 (10 Sept). *Independence. T* **194** *and similar horiz design. Multicoloured. P* 11½.

294	7 t. Type **194**	20	10
295	30 t. Map and National emblem	40	65
MS296	116 × 58 mm. Nos. 294/5	1·10	1·75

195 M.V. *Bulolo*

196 Rorovana Carvings

(Des R. Bates. Photo Courvoisier)

1976 (21 Jan). *Ships of the 1930s. T* **195** *and similar horiz designs. Multicoloured. P* 11½.

297	7 t. Type **195**	35	10
298	15 t. M.V. *Macdhui*	55	30
299	25 t. M.V. *Malaita*	75	65
300	60 t. S.S. *Montoro*	1·75	2·50
297/300	*Set of* 4	3·00	3·25

(Des R. Bates. Photo Courvoisier)

1976 (17 Mar). *Bougainville Art. T* **196** *and similar horiz designs. Multicoloured. P* 11½.

301	7 t. Type **196**	20	10
302	20 t. Upe hats	40	75
303	25 t. Kapkaps	50	85
304	30 t. Canoe paddles	55	90
301/4	*Set of* 4	1·50	2·25

197 Rabaul House

198 Landscouts

(Des G. Wade. Photo Courvoisier)

1976 (9 June). *Native Dwellings. T* **197** *and similar horiz designs. Multicoloured. P* 11½.

305	7 t. Type **197**	15	10
306	15 t. Aramia house	25	30
307	30 t. Telefomin house	50	75
308	40 t. Tapini house	55	1·25
305/8	*Set of* 4	1·25	2·10

(Des R. Bates. Photo Courvoisier)

1976 (18 Aug). *50th Anniversaries of Survey Flight and Scouting in Papua New Guinea. T* **198** *and similar horiz designs. Multicoloured. P* 11½.

309	7 t. Type **198**	30	10
310	10 t. De Havilland D.H.50A seaplane	40	30
311	15 t. Seascouts	50	65
312	60 t. De Havilland D.H.50A seaplane on water	1·25	2·50
309/12	*Set of* 4	2·25	3·25

199 Father Ross and New Guinea Highlands

(Des R. Bates. Photo Courvoisier)

1976 (28 Oct). *William Ross Commemoration. P* 11½.

313	**199** 7 t. multicoloured	40	15

200 Picture Wrasse

(Des P. Jones. Photo Courvoisier)

1976 (28 Oct). *Fauna Conservation (Tropical Fish). T* **200** *and similar horiz designs. Multicoloured. P* 11½.

314	5 t. Type **200**	30	10
315	15 t. Emperor Angelfish	60	45
316	30 t. Six-blotched Hind	1·10	80
317	40 t. Thread-finned Butterflyfish	1·40	1·10
314/17	*Set of* 4	3·00	2·25

201 Man from Kundiawa

202 Headdress, Wasara Tribe

(Des R. Bates. Litho Questa (1, 2 k.) or photo Courvoisier (others))

1977 (12 Jan)–**78**. *T* **201/2** *and similar multicoloured designs showing headdresses. P* 14 (1, 2 *k.*) *or* 11½ (*others*).

318	1 t. Type **201** (29.3.78)	10	10
319	5 t. Masked dancer, Abelam area of Maprik (29.3.78)	10	10
320	10 t. Headdress from Koiari (7.6.78)	30	15
321	15 t. Woman with face paint, Hanuabada (29.3.78)	30	20
322	20 t. Orokaiva dancer (7.6.78)	50	30
323	25 t. Haus Tambaran dancer, Abelam area of Maprik (29.3.78)	40	30
324	30 t. Asaro Valley headdress (29.3.78)	45	35
325	35 t. Singsing costume, Garaina (7.6.78)	70	45
326	40 t. Waghi Valley headdress (29.3.78)	60	35
327	50 t. Trobriand Island dancer (7.6.78)	1·00	60
328	1 k. Type **202**	1·00	1·50
329	2 k. Headdress, Mekeo tribe	1·75	3·00
318/29	*Set of* 12	6·50	6·50

Sizes—1, 5, 20 t. 25×31 *mm*; 35, 40 t. 23×38 *mm*; 1 k. 28×35 *mm*; 2 k. 33×23 *mm*; others 26×26 *mm*.

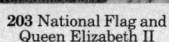

203 National Flag and Queen Elizabeth II

204 White-breasted Ground Pigeon

(Des and photo Harrison)

1977 (16 Mar). *Silver Jubilee. Horiz designs showing Queen Elizabeth as T* **203**. *Multicoloured. P* 14½ × 14.

330	7 t. Type **203**	20	10
	a. Silver (face value and inscr) omitted	£450	
331	15 t. National emblem	25	35
332	35 t. Map of P.N.G.	40	70
330/2	*Set of* 3	75	1·00

(Des W. Cooper. Photo Courvoisier)

1977 (8 June). *Fauna Conservation (Birds). T* **204** *and similar horiz designs. Multicoloured. P* 11½.

333	5 t. Type **204**	35	10
334	7 t. Victoria Crowned Pigeon	35	10
335	15 t. Pheasant Pigeon	65	65
336	30 t. Orange-fronted Fruit Dove	1·00	1·10
337	50 t. Banded Imperial Pigeon	1·60	3·50
333/7	*Set of* 5	3·50	4·75

205 Guides and Gold Badge

206 Kari Marupi Myth

(Des R. Bates. Litho Questa)

1977 (10 Aug). *50th Anniv of Guiding in Papua New Guinea. Horiz designs showing badge as T* **205**. *Multicoloured. P* 14½.

338	7 t. Type **205**	20	10
339	15 t. Guides mapping	35	20
340	30 t. Guides washing	55	50
341	35 t. Guides cooking	60	60
338/41	*Set of* 4	1·50	1·25

(Des Revd. H. A. Brown. Litho Enschedé)

1977 (19 Oct). *Folklore. Elema Art (3rd series). T* **206** *and similar vert designs. P* 13½ × 13.

342	7 t. multicoloured	20	10
343	20 t. multicoloured	45	35
344	30 t. orange-red, light blue and black	50	75
345	35 t. orange-red, yellow and black	50	75
342/5	*Set of* 4	1·50	1·75

Designs:—20 t. Savoripi clan myth; 30 t. Oa-Laea myth; 35 t. Oa-Iriarapo myth.

207 Blue-tailed Skink

208 *Roboastra arika*

(Des T. Nolan. Photo Courvoisier)

1978 (25 Jan). *Fauna Conservation (Skinks). T* **207** *and similar horiz designs. Multicoloured. P* 11½.

346	10 t. Type **207**	25	10
347	15 t. Green Tree Skink	30	25
348	35 t. Crocodile Skink	45	70
349	40 t. New Guinea Blue-tongued Skink	60	85
346/9	*Set of* 4	1·40	1·75

(Des B. Twigden. Photo Courvoisier)

1978 (29 Aug). *Sea Slugs. T* **208** *and similar horiz designs. Multicoloured. P* 11½.

350	10 t. Type **208**	25	10
351	15 t. *Chromodoris fidelis*	30	30
352	35 t. *Flabellina macassarana*	60	85
353	40 t. *Chromodoris marginata*	60	1·00
350/3	*Set of* 4	1·60	2·00

209 Present Day Royal Papua New Guinea Constabulary

210 Ocarina

(Des R. Bates. Photo Harrison)

1978 (26 Oct). *History of Royal Papua New Guinea Constabulary. T* **209** *and similar horiz designs showing uniformed police and constabulary badges. Multicoloured. P* 14½.

354	10 t. Type **209**	20	10
355	15 t. Mandated New Guinea Constabulary, 1921–1941	30	15
356	20 t. British New Guinea Armed Constabulary, 1890–1906	35	40
357	25 t. German New Guinea Police, 1899–1914	35	40
358	30 t. Royal Papua and New Guinea Constabulary, 1906–1964	40	60
354/8	*Set of* 5	1·40	1·50

(Des R. Bates. Litho Questa)

1979 (24 Jan). *Musical Instruments. T* **210** *and similar multicoloured designs. P* 14½ × 14 (7, 28 *t.*) *or* 14 × 14½ (*others*).

359	7 t. Type **210**	10	10
360	20 t. Musical bow (*horiz*)	20	20
361	28 t. Launut	25	30
362	35 t. Nose flute (*horiz*)	30	45
359/62	*Set of* 4	75	90

211 East New Britain Canoe

212 Katudababila (waist belt)

(Des G. Wade. Litho Questa)

1979 (28 Mar). *Traditional Canoe Prows and Paddles. T* **211** *and similar vert designs. Multicoloured. P* 14½.

363	14 t. Type **211**	20	15
364	21 t. Sepik war canoe	30	25
365	25 t. Trobriand Island canoe	30	30
366	40 t. Milne Bay canoe	40	60
363/6	*Set of* 4	1·10	1·10

(Des R. Bates. Photo Courvoisier)

1979 (6 June). *Traditional Currency. T* **212** *and similar horiz designs. Multicoloured. P* 12½ × 12.

367	7 t. Type **212**	10	10
368	15 t. Doga (chest ornament)	20	30
369	25 t. Mwali (armshell)	35	55
370	35 t. Soulava (necklace)	45	75
367/70	*Set of* 4	1·00	1·50

213 *Aenetus cyanochlora* 214 "The Right to Affection and Love"

(Des T. Nolan. Photo Courvoisier)

1979 (29 Aug). *Fauna Conservation. Moths. T* **213** *and similar multicoloured designs. P* 11½.

371 7 t. Type **213** 20 10
372 15 t. *Celerina vulgaris* 30 35
373 20 t. *Alcidis aurora (vert)* 40 65
374 25 t. *Phyllodes conspicillator* 45 80
375 30 t. *Lyssa patroclus (vert)* 55 90
371/5 .. .. *Set of* 5 1·75 2·50

(Des G. Wade. Litho Enschedé)

1979 (24 Oct). *International Year of the Child. T* **214** *and similar vert designs. Multicoloured. P* 13½ × 13.

376 7 t. Type **214** 10 10
377 15 t. "The right to adequate nutrition and medical care" 15 15
378 30 t. "The right to play" 20 20
379 60 t. "The right to a free education" 45 60
376/9 .. .. *Set of* 4 80 90

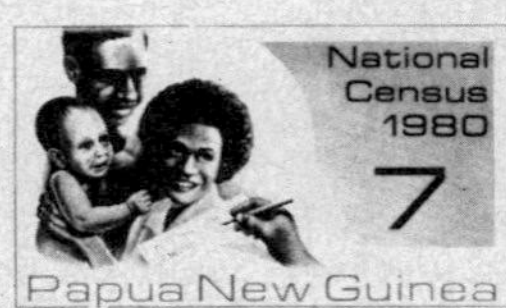

215 "Post Office Service" 216 Detail from Betrothal Ceremony Mural, Minj District, Western Highlands Province

(Des G. Wade. Litho Enschedé)

1980 (23 Jan). *Admission to U.P.U.* (1979). *T* **215** *and similar horiz designs. Multicoloured. P* 13 × 13½.

380 7 t. Type **215** 10 10
381 25 t. "Wartime mail" 25 25
382 35 t. U.P.U. emblem 35 40
383 40 t. "Early postal services" 40 50
380/3 .. .. *Set of* 4 1·00 1·10

(Des W. Tubun. Photo Courvoisier)

1980 (26 Mar). *South Pacific Festival of Arts. T* **216** *and similar vert designs showing different details from mural of betrothal ceremony, Minj District, Western Highlands Province. P* 11½.

384 20 t. black, greenish yellow and pale orange .. 25 35
a. Strip of 5. Nos. 384/8 .. .. .. 1·10
385 20 t. multicoloured (two figures—left-hand black and yellow; right-hand black, yellow and red) 25 35
386 20 t. multicoloured (two figures—left-hand black and orange; right-hand black) .. 25 35
387 20 t. multicoloured (two figures, one behind the other) 25 35
388 20 t. multicoloured (one figure) 25 35
384/8 .. .. *Set of* 5 1·10 1·60

Nos. 384/8 were printed together, *se-tenant*, in horizontal strips of 5 throughout the sheet.

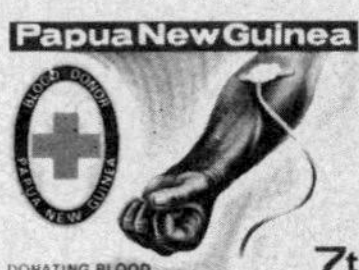

218 Donating Blood 219 Dugong

(Des R. Bates. Litho Questa)

1980 (27 Aug). *Red Cross Blood Bank. T* **218** *and similar horiz designs. Multicoloured. P* 14½.

393 7 t. Type **218** 15 10
394 15 t. Receiving transfusion 20 20
395 30 t. Map of Papua New Guinea showing blood transfusion centres 25 25
396 60 t. Blood and its components 40 60
393/6 .. .. *Set of* 4 90 1·00

(Des Dr. E. Lindgren (35 t.), T. Nolan (others). Photo Courvoisier)

1980 (29 Oct). *Mammals. T* **219** *and similar multicoloured designs. P* 11½.

397 7 t. Type **219** 10 10
398 30 t. New Guinea Marsupial Cat *(vert)* 40 45
399 35 t. Tube-nosed Bat *(vert)* 40 45
400 45 t. Rufescent Bandicoot ("Mumut") 50 55
397/400 .. .. *Set of* 4 1·25 1·40

220 White-headed Kingfisher 221 Native Mask

(Des W. Peckover. Photo Courvoisier)

1981 (21 Jan). *Kingfishers. T* **220** *and similar multicoloured designs. P* 11½.

401 3 t. Type **220** 20 50
402 7 t. Forest Kingfisher 20 10
403 20 t. Sacred Kingfisher 60 50
404 25 t. White-tailed Kingfisher (26 × 46 *mm*) .. 70 85
405 60 t. Blue-winged Kookaburra .. .. .. 1·40 2·75
401/5 .. .. *Set of* 5 2·75 4·25

(Des R. Bates. Photo Note Ptg Branch, Reserve Bank of Australia)

1981 (21 Jan). *Coil stamps. Vert designs as T* **221**. *P* 15 × *imperf*.

406 2 t. reddish violet and orange 10 20
407 5 t. cerise and blue-green 10 20

Design:—5 t. Hibiscus flower.

222 Mortar Team 223 M.A.F. (Missionary Aviation Fellowship) Cessna 205 Super Skywagon

(Des T. Reilly (15 t.), R. Bates (others). Litho Enschedé)

1981 (25 Mar). *Defence Force. T* **222** *and similar horiz designs. Multicoloured. P* 13 × 13½.

408 7 t. Type **222** 15 10
409 15 t. Douglas DC-3 and aircrew 25 25
410 40 t. *Aitape* (patrol boat) and seamen 45 65
411 50 t. Medical team examining children 50 75
408/11 .. .. *Set of* 4 1·25 1·50

(Des G. Wade. Litho Questa)

1981 (17 June). *"Mission Aviation". T* **223** *and similar vert designs. Multicoloured. P* 14.

412 10 t. Type **223** 25 10
413 15 t. Catholic mission British Aircraft Swallow *St. Paulus* 30 25
414 20 t. S.I.L. (Summer Institute of Linguistics) Hiller 12E helicopter 35 35
415 30 t. Lutheran mission Junkers F-13 .. .. 50 55
416 35 t. S.D.A. (Seventh Day Adventist Church) Piper PA-23 Aztec 55 65
412/16 .. .. *Set of* 5 1·75 1·75

(Des G. Wade. Litho Questa)

1981 (26 Aug). *Fishing. T* **224** *and similar horiz designs. Multicoloured. P* 14.

417 10 t. Type **224** 15 10
418 15 t. Kite fishing 20 30
419 30 t. Rod fishing 30 50
420 60 t. Scissor net fishing 55 85
417/20 .. .. *Set of* 4 1·10 1·60

(Des P. Jones. Photo Courvoisier)

1981 (28 Oct). *Land Snail Shells. T* **225** *and similar horiz designs. Multicoloured. P* 11½ × 12.

421 5 t. Type **225** 10 10
422 15 t. Yellow Naninia (*Naninia citrina*) .. 20 25
423 20 t. Adonis Papuina (*Papuina adonis*) and Hermione Papuina (*Papuina hermione*) 25 35
424 30 t. Hinde's Papuina (*Papuina hindei*) and New Pommeranian Papuina (*Papuina novaepommeraniae*) 35 50
425 40 t. *Papuina strabo* 50 80
421/5 .. .. *Set of* 5 1·25 1·75

226 Lord Baden-Powell and Flag-raising Ceremony 227 Yangoru and Boiken Bowls, East Sepik

(Des G. Wade. Photo Courvoisier)

1982 (20 Jan). *75th Anniv of Boy Scout Movement. T* **226** *and similar horiz designs. Multicoloured. P* 11½.

426 15 t. Type **226** 30 25
427 25 t. Scout leader and camp 35 50
428 35 t. Scout, and hut building 45 65
429 50 t. Percy Chaterton, and Scouts administering first aid 60 85
426/9 .. .. *Set of* 4 1·50 2·00

(Des R. Bates. Litho Questa)

1982 (24 Mar). *Native Pottery. T* **227** *and similar multicoloured designs. P* 14 (10, 20 *t.*) *or* 14½ *(others)*.

430 10 t. Type **227** 10 10
431 20 t. Utu cooking pot and small Gumalu pot, Madang 20 30
432 40 t. Wanigela pots, Northern District (37 × 23 *mm*) 40 55
433 50 t. Ramu Valley pots, Madang (37 × 23 *mm*) 45 80
430/3 .. .. *Set of* 4 1·00 1·60

228 "Eat Healthy Foods" 229 *Stylophora sp*

(Des G. Wade, Litho J.W.)

1982 (21 May). *Food and Nutrition. T* **228** *and similar horiz designs. Multicoloured. P* 14½ × 14.

434 10 t. Type **228** 10 10
435 15 t. Protein foods 20 30
436 30 t. Protective foods 40 55
437 40 t. Energy foods 45 70
434/7 .. .. *Set of* 4 1·00 1·50

(Des Courvoisier or W. Peckover (5 k.). Photo Courvoisier)

1982 (21 July)—**85**. *Granite paper. (a) Corals. Multicoloured designs as T* **229**. *P* 11½.

438 1 t. Type **229** 10 20
439 3 t. *Dendrophyllia sp. (vert)* (12.1.83) .. 60 40
440 5 t. *Acropora humilis* 15 10
441 10 t. *Dendronephthya sp. (vert)* (12.1.83) .. 80 30
442 12 t. As 10 t. (29.5.85) .. .. 4·00 4·50
443 15 t. *Distichopora sp* 30 20
444 20 t. *Isis sp. (vert)* (9.11.83) 90 25
445 25 t. *Acropora sp. (vert)* (9.11.83) 40 50
446 30 t. *Dendronephthya sp. (diff) (vert)* (12.1.83) 1·50 90
447 35 t. *Stylaster elegans (vert)* (9.11.83) .. .. 1·40 50
448 40 t. *Antipathes sp. (vert)* (12.1.83) .. .. 2·00 75
449 45 t. *Turbinarea sp. (vert)* (9.11.83) .. .. 2·50 50
450 1 k. *Xenia sp* .. .. 1·25 85
451 3 k. *Distichopora sp. (vert)* (12.1.83) .. .. 3·75 3·50

(b) Bird of Paradise. Multicoloured square design, 33×33 mm

452 5 k. Raggiana Bird of Paradise (7.8.84) .. 7·00 9·00
438/52 .. .. *Set of* 15 24·00 20·00

230 Missionaries landing on Beach 231 Athletics

224 Scoop Net Fishing 225 Bühler's Papuina (*Forcartia buehleri*)

National Census 1980 7 Papua New Guinea

217 Family being Interviewed

(Des R. Bates. Litho Questa)

1980 (4 June). *National Census. T* **217** *and similar horiz designs. Multicoloured. P* 14 × 13½.

389 7 t. Type **217** 10 10
390 15 t. Population symbol 15 15
391 40 t. Figures and map of Papua New Guinea 30 40
392 50 t. Heads symbolising population growth .. 35 50
389/92 .. .. *Set of* 4 80 1·00

NEW INFORMATION

The editor is always interested to correspond with people who have new information that will improve or correct the Catalogue.

(Des B. To Una. Photo Courvoisier)

1982 (15 Sept). *Centenary of Catholic Church in Papua New Guinea. Mural on wall of Nordup Catholic Church, East New Britain. T* **230** *and similar vert designs. Multicoloured. P* 11½.

457 10 t. Type **230** 30 30
 a. Horiz strip of 3. Nos. 457/9 80
458 10 t. Missionaries talking to natives 30 30
459 10 t. Natives with slings and spears ready to attack 30 30
457/9 .. .. *Set of* 3 80 80

Nos. 457/9 come in *se-tenant* strips of 3 horizontally throughout the sheet, each strip forming a composite design.

(Des R. Bates. Litho Questa)

1982 (6 Oct). *Commonwealth Games and "Anpex 82" Stamp Exhibition, Brisbane. T* **231** *and similar horiz designs. Multicoloured. P* 14½.

460 10 t. Type **231** 15 10
461 15 t. Boxing 20 25
462 45 t. Rifle-shooting 40 70
463 50 t. Bowls 45 75
460/3 .. .. *Set of* 4 1·10 1·60

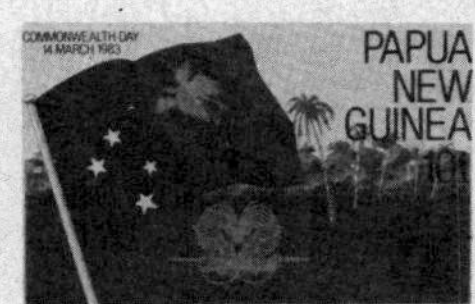

232 National Flag

(Des Walsall. Litho Harrison)

1983 (9 Mar). *Commonwealth Day. T* **232** *and similar horiz designs. Multicoloured. P* 14.

464 10 t. Type **232** 15 10
465 15 t. Basket-weaving and cabbage-picking .. 20 30
466 20 t. Crane hoisting roll of material 25 35
467 50 t. Lorries and ships 60 75
464/7 .. .. *Set of* 4 1·10 1·40

233 Transport Communications   234 *Chelonia depressa*

(Des G. Wade. Litho J.W.)

1983 (7 Sept). *World Communications Year. T* **233** *and similar horiz designs. Multicoloured. P* 14.

468 10 t. Type **233** 30 10
469 25 t. "Postal service" 70 45
470 30 t. "Telephone service" 80 50
471 60 t. "Transport service" .. .. 1·50 90
468/71 .. .. *Set of* 4 3·00 1·75

(Des R. Bates. Photo Courvoisier)

1984 (8 Feb). *Turtles. T* **234** *and similar horiz designs. Multicoloured. P* 11½.

472 5 t. Type **234** 20 10
473 10 t. *Chelonia mydas* 35 10
474 15 t. *Eretmochelys imbricata* 50 30
475 20 t. *Lepidochelys olivacea* 65 35
476 25 t. *Caretta caretta* 70 50
477 40 t. *Dermochelys coriacea* 95 75
472/7 .. .. *Set of* 6 3·00 1·75

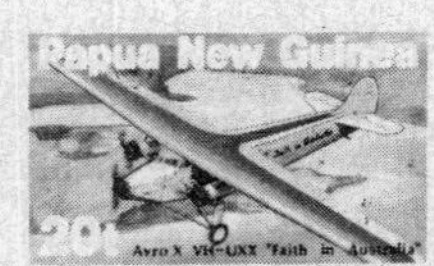

235 Avro Type 618 Ten *Faith in Australia*

(Des T. Reilly. Litho Format)

1984 (9 May). *50th Anniv of First Airmail Australia-Papua New Guinea. T* **235** *and similar horiz designs. Multicoloured. P* 14½ × 14.

478 20 t. Type **235** 40 30
479 25 t. De Havilland D.H.86B Dragon Express *Carmania* 40 45
480 40 t. Westland Widgeon 65 80
481 60 t. Consolidated PBY-5 Catalina flying boat *Guba* .. .. 1·00 1·25
478/81 .. .. *Set of* 4 2·25 2·50

236 Parliament House   237 Ceremonial Shield and Club, Central Province

(Des A. Brennan, adapted G. Vasarhelyi. Litho Harrison)

1984 (7 Aug). *Opening of New Parliament House. P* 13½ × 14.

482 **236** 10 t. multicoloured 30 30

(Des Revd. A. H. Brown. Photo Courvoisier)

1984 (21 Sept). *Ceremonial Shields. T* **237** *and similar vert designs. Multicoloured. Granite paper. P* 11½.

483 10 t. Type **237** 30 10
484 20 t. Ceremonial shield, West New Britain .. 50 50
485 30 t. Ceremonial shield, Madang Province .. 75 1·00
486 50 t. Ceremonial shield, East Sepik .. .. 1·25 2·75
483/6 .. .. *Set of* 4 2·50 3·75

238 H.M.S. *Nelson* at Port Moresby, 1884   239 Fergusson Island

(Des R. Bates, Litho Format)

1984 (6 Nov). *Centenary of Protectorate Proclamations for British New Guinea and German New Guinea. T* **238** *and similar horiz designs. Multicoloured. P* 14½ × 14.

487 10 t. Type **238** 35 55
 a. Horiz pair. Nos. 487/8 .. .. .. 70 1·10
488 10 t. Papua New Guinea flag and Port Moresby, 1984 .. .. 35 55
489 45 t. Papua New Guinea flag and Rabaul, 1984 .. .. 1·00 1·90
 a. Horiz pair. Nos. 489/90 .. .. .. 2·00 3·75
490 45 t. German warship *Elisabeth* at Rabaul, 1884 .. .. 1·00 1·90
487/90 .. .. *Set of* 4 2·40 4·50

as horizontal pairs throughout the sheets, each pair forming a composite picture.

(Des R. Bates. Photo Courvoisier)

1985 (6 Feb). *Tourist Scenes. T* **239** *and similar multicoloured designs. Granite paper. P* 11½.

491 10 t. Type **239** 30 10
492 25 t. Sepik River 65 60
493 40 t. Chimbu Gorge (*horiz*) .. .. .. 95 1·25
494 60 t. Dali Beach, Vanimo (*horiz*) .. .. 1·40 1·75
491/4 .. .. *Set of* 4 3·00 3·25

12t

(240)

241 Dubu Platform, Central Province

1985 (1 Apr). *No. 408 surch with T* **240**.

495 12 t. on 7 t. Type **222** 60 75
 a. Surch omitted (in horiz pair with normal) £110
 b. Surch inverted .. .. † —

At least one sheet of No. 495 exists with the surcharge completely omitted on five positions of the sheet and poorly printed on the remainder.

(Des G. Wade. Photo Heraclio Fournier)

1985 (1 May). *Ceremonial Structures. T* **241** *and similar vert designs. Multicoloured. P* 13.

496 15 t. Type **241** 45 15
497 20 t. Tamuniai house, West New Britain .. 60 50
498 30 t. Traditional yam tower, Trobriand Island 85 80
499 60 t. Huli grave, Tari .. .. 1·25 1·75
496/9 .. .. *Set of* 4 2·75 3·00

Imperforate examples of Nos. 496/9 and similar designs, each 26×33 mm, perforated and with face values shown as "10", "20", "30", or "60", are reported by the Papua New Guinea Philatelic Bureau as having been removed from their archives without authority.

242 Head of New Britain Sparrow Hawk   243 National Flag and Parliament House

(Des P. Slater. Litho Format)

1985 (26 Aug). *Birds of Prey. T* **242** *and similar vert designs, Multicoloured. P* 14 × 14½.

500 12 t. Type **242** .. .. 70 1·25
 a. Horiz pair. Nos. 500/1 .. .. .. 1·40 2·50
501 12 t. New Britain Sparrow Hawk in flight .. 70 1·25
502 30 t. Doria's Goshawk .. .. 1·00 1·50
 a. Horiz pair. Nos. 502/3 .. .. .. 2·00 3·00
503 30 t. Doria's Goshawk in flight .. .. .. 1·00 1·50
504 60 t. Long-tailed Honey Buzzard .. .. .. 1·50 2·25
 a. Horiz pair. Nos. 504/5 .. .. .. 3·00 4·50
505 60 t. Long-tailed Honey Buzzard in flight .. 1·50 2·25
500/5 .. .. *Set of* 6 5·75 9·00

Nos. 500/1, 502/3 and 504/5 were each printed together, *se-tenant*, in horizontal pairs throughout the sheets.

(Des R. Bates. Litho B.D.T.)

1985 (11 Sept). *10th Anniv of Independence. P* 14 × 15.

506 **243** 12 t. multicoloured 60 70

244 Early Postcard, Aerogramme, Inkwell and Spectacles   245 Figure with Eagle

(Des R. Bates. Litho Walsall)

1985 (9 Oct). *Centenary of the Papua New Guinea Post Office. T* **244** *and similar horiz designs. Multicoloured. P* 14½ × 14.

507 12 t. Type **244** 45 10
508 30 t. Queensland 1897 1d. die with proof and modern press printing stamps .. .. 1·10 1·00
509 40 t. Newspaper of 1885 announcing shipping service and loading mail into aircraft .. .. 1·75 2·00
510 60 t. Friedrich-Wilhelmshafen postmark of 1892 and Port Moresby F.D.C. postmark of 9 Oct 1985 .. .. .. 2·00 3·50
507/10 .. .. *Set of* 4 4·75 6·00
MS511 90×79 mm. As Nos. 507/10, but designs continue on sheet margins .. .. .. 5·50 6·00

(Des R. Bates. Photo Courvoisier)

1985 (13 Nov). *Nombowai Wood Carvings. T* **245** *and similar vert designs. Multicoloured. Granite paper. P* 11½.

512 12 t. Type **245** 50 10
513 30 t. Figure with clamshell .. .. .. 1·25 75
514 60 t. Figure with dolphin .. .. .. 2·00 2·75
515 80 t. Figure of woman with cockerel .. .. 2·50 4·25
512/15 .. .. *Set of* 4 5·75 7·00

246 Valentine or Prince Cowrie (*Cypraea valentia*)   247 Rufous Fantail

(Des R. Bates. Photo Courvoisier)

1986 (12 Feb). *Seashells. T* **246** *and similar horiz designs. Multicoloured. Granite paper. P* 11½.

516 15 t. Type **246** 75 15
517 35 t. Bulow's Olive (*Oliva buelowi*) .. .. 1·60 1·40
518 45 t. Parkinson's Olive (*Oliva parkinsoni*) .. 2·00 2·00
519 70 t. Golden Cowrie (*Cypraea aurantium*) .. 2·50 4·75
516/19 .. .. *Set of* 4 6·00 7·50

(Des A. Theobald. Litho Harrison)

1986 (21 Apr). *60th Birthday of Queen Elizabeth II. Vert designs as T* **230a** *of Jamaica. Multicoloured. P* 14½×14.

520 15 t. Princess Elizabeth in A.T.S. uniform, 1945 .. .. 20 15
521 35 t. Silver Wedding Anniversary photograph (by Patrick Lichfield), Balmoral, 1972 .. .. 50 55
522 50 t. Queen inspecting guard of honour, Port Moresby, 1982 .. .. 70 75
523 60 t. On board Royal Yacht *Britannia*, Papua New Guinea, 1982 .. .. 85 90
524 70 t. At Crown Agents' Head Office, London, 1983 .. .. 95 1·10
520/4 .. .. *Set of* 5 3·00 3·00

(Des W. Peckover. Photo Courvoisier)

1986 (22 May). *"Ameripex '86" International Stamp Exhibition, Chicago. Small Birds (1st series). T* **247** *and similar multicoloured designs. Granite paper. P* 12½.

525 15 t. Type **247** 90 20
526 35 t. Streaked Berrypecker .. .. .. 1·75 1·25
527 45 t. Red-breasted Pitta .. .. 1·90 1·25
528 70 t. Olive-yellow Robin (*vert*) .. .. .. 2·50 5·00
525/8 .. .. *Set of* 4 6·25 7·00

The scientific name on the 15 t. value refers to the 45 t. design, and vice versa.

See also Nos. 597/601.

248 Martin Luther nailing Theses to Cathedral Door, Wittenberg, and Modern Lutheran Pastor

249 *Dendrobium vexillarius*

(Des local artist. Litho Questa)

1986 (3 July). *Centenary of Lutheran Church in Papua New Guinea. T* **248** *and similar vert design. Multicoloured. P* 14×15.

529 15 t. Type **248** 75 15
530 70 t. Early church, Finschhafen, and modern Martin Luther Chapel, Lae Seminary .. 2·25 3·25

(Des Harrison. Litho B.D.T.)

1986 (4 Aug). *Orchids. T* **249** *and similar vert designs. Multicoloured. P* 13½.

531 15 t. Type **249** 95 15
532 35 t. *Dendrobium lineale* .. .. .. 2·00 75
533 45 t. *Dendrobium johnsoniae* .. .. 2·00 1·10
534 70 t. *Dendrobium cuthbertsonii* .. .. 2·75 3·00
531/4 .. .. *Set of* 4 7·00 4·50

250 Maprik Dancer

251 Whitebonnet Anemonefish

(Des R. Bates. Litho B.D.T.)

1986 (12 Nov). *Papua New Guinea Dancers. T* **250** *and similar vert designs. Multicoloured. P* 14.

535 15 t. Type **250** 65 15
536 35 t. Kiriwina .. .. 1·40 80
537 45 t. Kundiawa .. .. 1·50 95
538 70 t. Fasu .. .. 2·40 2·50
535/8 .. .. *Set of* 4 5·50 4·00

(Des Harrison. Litho Format)

1987 (15 Apr). *Anemonefish. T* **251** *and similar horiz designs. Multicoloured. P* 15.

539 17 t. Type **251** 70 25
540 30 t. Orange-finned Anemonefish .. .. 1·40 1·10
541 35 t. Fire Anemonefish ("Tomato Clown-fish") .. .. 1·50 1·40
542 70 t. Spine-cheeked Anemonefish .. .. 2·50 5·00
539/42 .. .. *Set of* 4 5·50 7·00

252 *Roebuck* (Dampier), 1700 (253)

(Des R. Bates. Photo Courvoisier)

1987 (15 June)–**88**. *Ships. T* **252** *and similar square designs. Multicoloured. Granite paper. P* 11½.

543 1 t. *La Boudeuse* (De Bougainville), 1768 (16.11.88) 50 80
544 5 t. Type **252** 70 80
545 10 t. H.M.S. *Swallow* (Philip Carteret), 1767 (16.11.88) .. .. 1·00 80
546 15 t. H.M.S. *Fly* (Blackwood), 1845 (17.2.88) 1·00 60
547 17 t. As 15 t. (16.3.88) .. .. .. 1·00 40
548 20 t. H.M.S. *Rattlesnake* (Owen Stanley), 1849 (17.2.88) .. .. 1·10 90
549 30 t. *Vitiaz* (Maclay), 1871 (16.11.88) .. 1·40 1·50
550 35 t. *San Pedrico* (Torres) and zabra, 1606 .. 70 60
551 40 t. *L'Astrolabe* (d'Urville), 1827 (17.2.88) .. 1·75 1·50
552 45 t. *Neva* (D'Albertis), 1876 .. .. 75 1·00
553 60 t. Spanish galleon (Jorge de Meneses), 1526 (17.2.88) .. .. 2·50 3·00
554 70 t. *Eendracht* (Schouten and Le Maire), 1616 .. .. 1·75 2·25
555 1 k. H.M.S. *Blanche* (Simpson), 1872 (16.3.88) .. .. 2·50 2·75
556 2 k. *Merrie England* (steamer), 1889 .. 3·25 2·75
557 3 k. *Samoa* (German colonial steamer), 1884 (16.11.88) .. .. 4·00 5·50
543/57 .. .. *Set of* 15 21·00 23·00

A printing by lithography of a 45 t. (as issued 70 t.), 70 t. (as 45 t.), 80 t. (as 35 t.) and 2 k. was originally produced, but such stamps were not issued for postal purposes. Examples in circulation are from a small quantity sold by the U.S.A. philatelic agent in error.

(Des Revd. A. H. Brown. Photo Courvoisier)

1987 (19 Aug). *War Shields. Vert designs as T* **237**. *Multicoloured. Granite paper. P* 11½.

558 15 t. Gulf Province 20 25
559 35 t. East Sepik 45 50
560 45 t. Madang Province 55 60
561 70 t. Telefomin 85 90
558/61 .. .. *Set of* 4 1·90 2·00

1987 (23 Sept). *No. 442 surch with T* **253**.

562 15 t. on 12 t. *Dendronephthya sp.* 65 65

For similar 20 t. surcharge see No. 602.

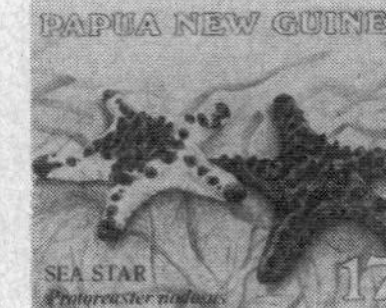

254 *Protoreaster nodosus*

255 Cessna 206 Stationair 6 taking off, Rabaraba

(Des Harrison. Litho B.D.T.)

1987 (30 Sept). *Starfish. T* **254** *and similar horiz designs. Multicoloured. P* 13½.

563 17 t. Type **254** 55 25
564 35 t. *Gomophia egeriae* .. .. .. 1·10 70
565 45 t. *Choriaster granulatus* .. .. .. 1·25 80
566 70 t. *Neoferdina ocellata* .. .. .. 1·75 2·25
563/6 .. .. *Set of* 4 4·25 3·50

(Des A. Theobald. Litho Questa)

1987 (11 Nov). *Aircraft in Papua New Guinea. T* **255** *and similar horiz designs. Multicoloured. P* 14.

567 15 t. Type **255** 80 25
568 35 t. Britten-Norman Islander over Hombrum Bluff .. .. 1·50 75
569 45 t. De Havilland D.H.C.6 Twin Otter 100 over Highlands .. .. 1·50 90
570 70 t. Fokker F.28 Fellowship over Madang 2·50 3·00
567/70 .. .. *Set of* 4 5·75 4·00

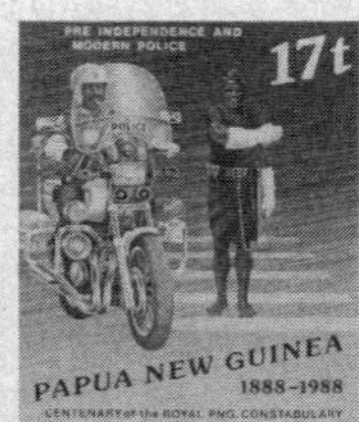

256 Pre-Independence Policeman on Traffic Duty and Present-day Motorcycle Patrol

(Des R. Bates. Litho Questa)

1988 (15 June). *Centenary of Royal Papua New Guinea Constabulary. T* **256** *and similar vert designs. Multicoloured. P* 14 × 15.

571 17 t. Type **256** 45 25
572 35 t. British New Guinea Armed Constabulary, 1890, and Governor W. MacGregor 80 50
573 45 t. Police badges 90 65
574 70 t. German New Guinea Police, 1888, and Dr. A. Hahl (founder) .. .. .. 1·50 1·75
571/4 .. .. *Set of* 4 3·25 2·75

257 Lakatoi (canoe) and Sydney Opera House

(Des R. Bates. Litho Harrison)

1988 (30 July). *"Sydpex '88" National Stamp Exhibition, Sydney. P* 14.

575 **257** 35 t. multicoloured 80 50

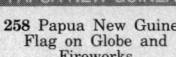

258 Papua New Guinea Flag on Globe and Fireworks

259 Male and Female Butterflies in Courtship

(Des R. Bates. Litho CPE Australia Ltd, Melbourne)

1988 (30 July). *Bicentenary of Australian Settlement. T* **258** *and similar horiz design. Multicoloured. P* 13½.

576 35 t. Type **258** 55 65
a. Horiz pair. Nos. 576/7 .. .. 1·10 1·25
577 35 t. Australian flag on globe and fireworks 55 65
MS578 90 × 50 mm. Nos. 576/7 .. .. 1·10 1·25

Nos. 576/7 were printed together, *se-tenant*, in horizontal pairs throughout the sheet, each pair forming a composite design.

(Des M. Parsons, adapted D. Miller. Litho Walsall)

1989 (19 Sept). *Endangered Species.* Ornithoptera alexandrae *(Queen Alexandra's Birdwing butterfly). T* **259** *and similar multicoloured designs. P* 14½.

579 5 t. Type **259** 85 20
580 17 t. Female laying eggs and mature larva (*vert*) .. .. 1·75 40
581 25 t. Male emerging from pupa (*vert*) .. 2·50 2·25
582 35 t. Male feeding .. .. 3·00 2·75
579/82 .. .. *Set of* 4 7·50 5·00

260 Athletics

(Des G. Wade. Litho CPE Australia Ltd, Melbourne)

1988 (19 Sept). *Olympic Games, Seoul. T* **260** *and similar horiz design. Multicoloured. P* 13½.

583 17 t. Type **260** 20 25
584 45 t. Weightlifting 60 65

261 *Rhododendron zoelleri*

263 Writing Letter

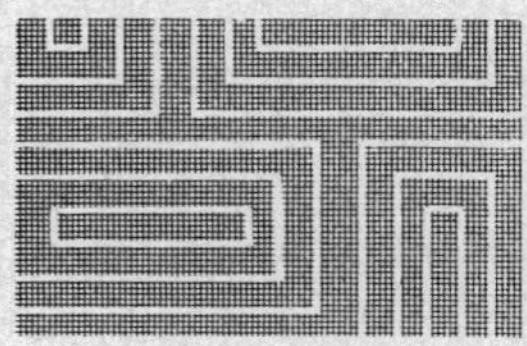

262

(Des N. Cruttwell and I. Loe. Litho Leigh-Mardon Ltd, Melbourne)

1989 (25 Jan). *Rhododendrons. T* **261** *and similar vert designs. Multicoloured. W* **262**. *P* 14½.

585 3 t. Type **261** 10 10
586 20 t. *Rhododendron cruttwellii* 50 30
587 60 t. *Rhododendron superbum* .. .. 1·25 1·25
588 70 t. *Rhododendron christianae* .. .. 1·50 1·50
585/8 .. .. *Set of* 4 3·00 2·75

(Des R. Bates. Litho Leigh-Mardon Ltd, Melbourne)

1989 (22 Mar). *International Letter Writing Week. T* **263** *and similar square designs. Multicoloured. W* **262**. *P* 14½.

589 20 t. Type **263** 30 30
590 35 t. Stamping letter 55 50
591 60 t. Posting letter .. .. 90 1·10
592 70 t. Reading letter .. .. 1·10 1·40
589/92 .. .. *Set of* 4 2·50 3·00

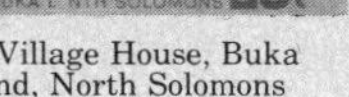

264 Village House, Buka Island, North Solomons

265 Tit Berrypecker (female)

(Des G. Wade. Litho Leigh-Mardon Ltd, Melbourne)

1989 (17 May). *Traditional Dwellings. T* **264** *and similar horiz designs. Multicoloured.* W **262**. *P* 15.

593 20 t. Type **264** 40 35
594 35 t. Koiari tree house, Central Province .. 70 60
595 60 t. Longhouse, Lauan, New Ireland .. 1·25 1·40
596 70 t. Decorated house, Basilaki, Milne Bay 1·50 1·60
593/6 .. .. *Set of* 4 3·50 3·50

(Des W. Peckover. Litho Questa)

1989 (12 July). *Small Birds (2nd issue). T* **265** *and similar vert designs. Multicoloured. P* 14½.

597 20 t. Type **265** 90 90
a. Horiz pair. Nos. 597/8 .. .. 1·75 1·75
598 20 t. Tit Berrypecker (male) 90 90
599 35 t. Blue-capped Babbler .. .. .. 1·25 75
600 45 t. Black-throated Robin .. .. 1·40 1·00
601 70 t. Large Mountain Sericornis .. .. 2·00 2·25
597/601 .. .. *Set of* 5 5·75 5·25

Nos. 597/8 were printed together, *se-tenant*, in horizontal pairs throughout the sheet.

1989 (12 July). *No.* 539 *surch as T* **253**.

602 20 t. on 17 t. Type **251** 60 70
a. Surch double .. .. .. † £170

266 Motu Motu Dancer, Gulf Province

267 Hibiscus, People going to Church and Gope Board

(Des G. Wade. Litho Leigh-Mardon Ltd, Melbourne)

1989 (6 Sept). *Traditional Dancers. T* **266** *and similar vert designs. Multicoloured.* W **262**. *P* 14×14½.

603 20 t. Type **266** 65 35
604 35 t. Baining, East New Britain .. .. 1·10 90
605 60 t. Vailala River, Gulf Province .. .. 2·00 2·25
606 70 t. Timbunke, East Sepik Province .. 2·00 2·50
603/6 .. .. *Set of* 4 5·25 5·50

(Des R. Bates. Litho Leigh-Mardon Ltd, Melbourne)

1989 (8 Nov). *Christmas. T* **267** *and similar horiz designs showing flowers and carved panels. Multicoloured. P* 14×14½.

607 20 t. Type **267** 40 35
608 35 t. Rhododendron, Virgin and Child and mask 60 60
609 60 t. D'Albertis Creeper, Christmas candle and warshield .. .. .. 1·25 1·60
610 70 t. Pacific Frangapani, peace dove and flute mask .. .. 1·40 1·90
607/10 .. .. *Set of* 4 3·25 4·00

268 Guni Falls

269 Boys and Census Form

(Des A. Theobald. Litho Questa)

1990 (1 Feb). *Waterfalls. T* **268** *and similar vert designs. Multicoloured. P* 14.

611 20 t. Type **268** 60 35
612 35 t. Rouna Falls 85 75
613 60 t. Ambua Falls .. .. 1·40 1·50
614 70 t. Wawoi Falls .. .. 1·60 1·75
611/14 .. .. *Set of* 4 4·00 4·00

MACHINE LABELS. From 7 March 1990 gummed labels inscribed "PAPUA NEW GUINEA BOROKO" with values from 1 t. to 99 k. 99 were available from an automatic machine installed at Boroko Post Office. This machine was withdrawn on 6 March 1991. A second machine was operational at Rabaul Post Office from 8 February 1991. Labels from this machine do not carry an indication of its location.

(Des R. Bates. Litho Questa)

1990 (2 May). *National Census. T* **269** *and similar horiz design. Multicoloured. P* 14½×15.

615 20 t. Type **269** 40 30
616 70 t. Family and census form .. .. 1·50 2·00

270 Gwa Pupi Dance Mask

271 Sepik and Maori Kororu Masks

(Des G. Vasarhelyi. Litho Leigh-Mardon Ltd, Melbourne)

1990 (11 July). *Gogodala Dance Masks. T* **270** *and similar vert designs. Multicoloured. P* 13½.

617 20 t. Type **270** 80 30
618 35 t. Tauga paiyale .. .. 1·25 70
619 60 t. A: ga .. .. 2·00 2·50
620 70 t. Owala .. .. 2·00 3·00
617/20 .. .. *Set of* 4 5·50 6·00

(Des R. Bates. Litho Leigh-Mardon Ltd, Melbourne)

1990 (24 Aug). *"New Zealand 1990" International Stamp Exhibition, Auckland. P* 14½.

621 **271** 35 t. multicoloured 75 75

272 Dwarf Cassowary and Great Spotted Kiwi

273 Whimbrel

(Des R. Bates. Litho Leigh-Mardon Ltd, Melbourne)

1990 (24 Aug). 150*th Anniv of Treaty of Waitangi. T* **272** *and similar square design. Multicoloured. P* 14½.

622 20 t. Type **272** .. .. 1·00 40
623 35 t. Double-wattled Cassowary and Brown Kiwi .. .. 1·25 1·25

(Des L. Curtis. Litho Questa)

1990 (26 Sept). *Migratory Birds. T* **273** *and similar horiz designs. Multicoloured. P* 14½×13½.

624 20 t. Type **273** 85 30
625 35 t. Sharp-tailed Sandpiper .. .. 1·25 80
626 60 t. Turnstone .. .. 2·25 2·75
627 70 t. Terek Sandpiper .. .. .. 2·50 2·75
624/7 .. .. *Set of* 4 6·25 6·00

274 Jew's Harp

275 Weigman's Papuina (*Papuina weigmani*)

(Des R. Bates. Litho Leigh-Mardon Ltd, Melbourne)

1990 (31 Oct). *Musical Instruments. T* **274** *and similar square designs. Multicoloured. P* 13.

628 20 t. Type **274** 60 30
629 35 t. Musical bow 90 50
630 60 t. Wantoat drum .. .. 1·75 2·25
631 70 t. Gogodala rattle .. .. .. 1·75 2·50
628/31 .. .. *Set of* 4 4·50 5·00

(Des P. Schouter. Litho Leigh-Mardon Ltd, Melbourne)

1991 (6 Mar). *Land Shells. T* **275** *and similar horiz designs. Multicoloured. P* 14×14½.

632 21 t. Type **275** 65 30
633 40 t. *Papuina globula* and *Papuina azonata* 1·00 85
634 50 t. *Planispira deaniana* .. .. .. 1·40 1·60
635 80 t. Chance's Papuina (*Papuina chancei*) and Golden-mouth Papuina (*Papuina xanthochila*) .. .. 2·00 2·75
632/5 .. .. *Set of* 4 4·50 5·00

276 Magnificent Riflebird

277 Cricket

(Des W. Peckover (10 k.), R. Bates (others). Litho Leigh-Mardon Ltd, Melbourne)

1991 (1 May)–**93**. *Birds of Paradise. T* **276** *and similar multicoloured designs with imprint date at foot (except* 10 *k.). P* 13 (10 *k.) or* 14½ *(others).*

(*a*) *Face values shown as "t" or "K"*

636 1 t. Type **276** (20.1.93) 15 30
637 5 t. Loria's Bird of Paradise (2.9.92) .. 20 30
638 10 t. Sickle Crested Bird of Paradise (20.1.93) 20 30
639 20 t. Wahnes' Parotia (20.1.93) 50 30
640 21 t. Crinkle-collared Manucode (25.3.92) 70 30
641 30 t. Goldie's Bird of Paradise (20.1.93) .. 30 40
642 40 t. Wattle-billed Bird of Paradise (2.9.92) 40 50
643 45 t. King Bird of Paradise (25.3.92) .. 2·25 65
644 50 t. Short-tailed Paradigalla Bird of Paradise (2.9.92) 50 55
645 60 t. Queen Carola's Parotia (25.3.92) .. 3·50 2·25
646 90 t. Emperor of Germany Bird of Paradise (25.3.92) .. .. 3·75 3·25
647 1 k. Magnificent Bird of Paradise (2.9.92) 1·75 1·75
648 2 k. Superb Bird of Paradise (2.9.92) .. 1·90 2·00
649 5 k. Trumpet Bird (20.1.93) .. .. 8·50 9·00
650 10 k. Lesser Bird of Paradise (32×32 *mm*) 11·50 12·00
636/50 .. .. *Set of* 15 32·00 30·00

(*b*) *Face values shown as "T"* (1.7.93)

650*a* 21 t. Crinkle-collared Manucode 90 40
650*b* 45 t. King Bird of Paradise .. .. 2·00 1·00
650*c* 60 t. Queen Carola's Parotia .. .. 2·25 2·25
650*d* 90 t. Emperor of Germany Bird of Paradise 2·75 3·50
650*a/d* .. .. *Set of* 4 7·00 6·50

It was originally intended that the 21, 45, 60 and 90 t. values should appear on 19 February 1992, but, when it was noticed that the "T" used for the currency abbreviation on Nos. 650*a/d* did not match the remainder of the set, the stamps were withdrawn before issue and replaced by Nos. 640, 643 and 645/6. Some examples from the original printing escaped the withdrawal notice, however, and were soon on the market at substantial prices. The postal authorities subsequently decided to release the stock of stamps showing the "T" on 1 July 1993.

Imprint dates: "1992", Nos. 637, 640, 642/8, 650*a/d*; "MAY 1992", Nos. 640, 643; "1993", Nos. 636, 638/41, 643, 649.

For 40 t., 50 t., 1 k. and 2 k. in these designs, but without "1992 BIRD OF PARADISE" at foot, see Nos. 704/7.

(Des D.D.S. Associates and T. Sipa. Litho Leigh-Mardon Ltd, Melbourne)

1991 (26 June). 9*th South Pacific Games. T* **277** *and similar horiz designs. Multicoloured. P* 13.

651 21 t. Type **277** .. .. 1·25 40
652 40 t. Athletics .. .. 1·50 1·00
653 50 t. Baseball .. .. 1·75 2·25
654 80 t. Rugby Union .. .. 2·25 3·50
651/4 .. .. *Set of* 4 6·00 6·50

278 Cathedral of St. Peter and St. Paul, Dogura

279 Rambusto Headdress, Manus Province

(Des G. Wade. Litho Questa)

1991 (7 Aug). *Centenary of Anglican Church in Papua New Guinea. T* **278** *and similar horiz designs. Multicoloured. P* 14½.

655 21 t. Type **278** 70 30
656 40 t. Missionaries landing, 1891, and Kaieta shrine .. .. 1·40 1·40
657 80 t. First church and Modawa tree .. 2·25 3·50
655/7 .. .. *Set of* 3 4·00 5·50

(Des D.D.S. Associates and T. Sipa. Litho Leigh-Mardon Ltd, Melbourne)

1991 (16 Oct). *Tribal Headdresses. T* **279** *and similar vert designs. Multicoloured. P* 13.

658 21 t. Type **279** 60 30
659 40 t. Marawaka, Eastern Highlands .. 1·10 1·40
660 50 t. Tufi, Oro Province .. .. .. 1·25 1·60
661 80 t. Sina Sina, Simbu Province .. .. 2·00 3·25
658/61 .. .. *Set of* 4 4·50 6·00

280 *Nina*

281 Canoe Prow Shield, Bamu

(Des G. Wade. Litho Leigh-Mardon Ltd, Melbourne)

1992 (15 Apr). *500th Anniv of Discovery of America by Columbus and "EXPO '92" World's Fair, Seville. T* **280** *and similar horiz designs. Multicoloured. P* 14.
662 21 t. Type **280** 60 30
663 45 t. *Pinta* .. .. 1·25 1·00
664 60 t. *Santa Maria* .. .. 1·75 2·00
665 90 t. Christopher Columbus and ships .. 2·25 3·00
662/5 .. .. *Set of* 4 5·25 5·75

(Des G. Wade. Litho Leigh-Mardon Ltd, Melbourne)

1992 (22 May). *"World Columbian Stamp Expo '92", Chicago. Sheet, 110×80 mm, containing Nos.* 664/5. *P* 14.
MS666 60 t. *Santa Maria*; 90 t. Christopher Columbus and ships (*sold at* 1 *k.* 70) .. .. 3·75 4·50

(Des I. Giles. Litho Leigh-Mardon Ltd, Melbourne)

1992 (3 June). *Papuan Gulf Artifacts. T* **281** *and similar vert designs. Multicoloured. P* 14.
667 21 t. Type **281** 40 30
668 45 t. Skull rack, Kerewa 85 80
669 60 t. Ancestral figure, Era River .. .. 1·25 1·50
670 90 t. Gope (spirit) board, Urama .. .. 1·60 2·50
667/70 .. .. *Set of* 4 3·75 4·50

282 Papuan Infantryman

283 *Hibiscus tiliāceus*

(Des G. Wade. Litho Leigh-Mardon Ltd, Melbourne)

1992 (22 July). *50th Anniv of Second World War Campaigns in Papua New Guinea. T* **282** *and similar vert designs. Multicoloured. P* 14.
671 21 t. Type **282** 60 30
672 45 t. Australian militiaman .. .. .. 1·25 90
673 60 t. Japanese infantryman .. .. .. 1·75 2·25
674 90 t. American infantryman .. .. .. 2·50 3·50
671/4 .. .. *Set of* 4 5·50 6·25

(Des T. Sipa. Litho Leigh-Mardon Ltd, Melbourne)

1992 (28 Oct). *Flowering Trees. T* **283** *and similar vert designs. Multicoloured. P* 14.
675 21 t. Type **283** 65 30
676 45 t. *Castanospermum australe* .. .. 1·50 1·00
677 60 t. *Cordia subcordata* .. .. .. 2·50 2·75
678 90 t. *Acacia auriculiformis* .. .. .. 2·75 4·00
675/8 .. .. *Set of* 4 6·75 7·25

284 Three-striped Dasyure

285 Rufous Wren Warbler

(Des R. Bates. Litho Leigh-Mardon Ltd, Melbourne)

1993 (7 Apr). *Mammals. T* **284** *and similar horiz designs. Multicoloured. P* 14.
679 21 t. Type **284** 40 30
680 45 t. Striped Bandicoot 90 80
681 60 t. Dusky Black-eared Giant Rat .. .. 1·25 1·50
682 90 t. Painted Ringtail Possum .. .. .. 1·75 2·50
679/82 .. .. *Set of* 4 3·75 4·50

(Des G. Vasarhelyi. Litho Leigh-Mardon Ltd, Melbourne)

1993 (9 June). *Small Birds. T* **285** *and similar vert designs. Multicoloured. P* 14.
683 21 t. Type **285** 45 30
684 45 t. Superb Pitta 90 80
685 60 t. Mottled Whistler .. .. 1·25 1·50
686 90 t. Slaty-chinned Longbill .. .. .. 1·60 2·50
683/6 .. .. *Set of* 4 3·75 4·50

(**286**)

287 Thread-finned Rainbowfish

1993 (13 Aug). *"Taipei '93" Asian International Stamp Exhibition, Taiwan. Nos.* 683/6 *optd with T* **286** *in greenish yellow, bright green and greenish blue.*
687 21 t. Type **285** 55 30
688 45 t. Superb Pitta .. .. 1·00 80
689 60 t. Mottled Whistler .. .. 1·40 2·00
690 90 t. Slaty-chinned Longbill .. .. .. 2·00 2·75
687/90 .. .. *Set of* 4 4·50 5·25

(Des I. Giles. Litho Leigh-Mardon Ltd, Melbourne)

1993 (29 Sept). *Freshwater Fishes. T* **287** *and similar horiz designs. Multicoloured. P* 14×14½.
691 21 t. Type **287** 60 30
692 45 t. Peacock Gudgeon .. .. 1·25 80
693 60 t. Northern Rainbowfish .. .. .. 1·60 1·90
694 90 t. Popondetta Blue-eye .. .. .. 2·25 2·75
691/4 .. .. *Set of* 4 5·25 5·25

288 Blue Bird of Paradise

(Litho Leigh-Mardon Ltd, Melbourne)

1993 (29 Sept). *"Bangkok '93" Asian International Stamp Exhibition, Thailand. Sheet* 100×65 *mm. P* 14.
MS695 **288** 2 k. multicoloured .. .. .. 5·00 6·00

289 Douglas DC-3

290 Girl holding Matschie's Tree Kangaroo

(Des G. Vasarhelyi. Litho Leigh-Mardon Ltd, Melbourne)

1993 (27 Oct). *20th Anniv of Air Niugini. T* **289** *and similar horiz designs. Multicoloured. P* 14.
696 21 t. Type **289** 65 25
697 45 t. Fokker F.27 Friendship .. .. .. 1·50 70
698 60 t. De Havilland D.H.C.7 Dash Seven .. 1·90 2·00
699 90 t. Airbus Industrie A310 .. .. .. 2·50 3·25
696/9 .. .. *Set of* 4 6·00 5·50

(Des R. Bates. Litho Leigh-Mardon Ltd, Melbourne)

1994 (19 Jan). *Matschie's (Huon Gulf) Tree Kangaroo. T* **290** *and similar vert designs. Multicoloured. P* 14½.
700 21 t. Type **290** 35 25
701 45 t. Adult male 90 60
702 60 t. Female with young in pouch .. .. 1·25 1·75
703 90 t. Adolescent on ground .. .. .. 1·90 2·75
700/3 .. .. *Set of* 4 4·00 4·75

(Des R. Bates. Litho Leigh-Mardon Ltd, Melbourne)

1994 (18 Feb). *"Hong Kong '94" International Stamp Exhibition. Designs as Nos.* 642, 644 *and* 647/8, *but without* "1992 BIRD OF PARADISE" *at foot. Multicoloured. P* 14½.
704 40 t. Yellow-breasted Bird of Paradise .. 85 1·25
 a. Horiz strip of 4. Nos. 704/7 plus centre label .. .. 6·50
705 50 t. Short-tailed Paradigalla Bird of Paradise .. .. 1·25 1·50
706 1 k. Magnificent Bird of Paradise .. .. 2·00 2·50
707 2 k. Superb Bird of Paradise .. .. .. 3·00 3·25
704/7 .. .. *Set of* 4 6·50 7·50

Nos. 704/7 were printed together, *se-tenant*, in horizontal strips of 4 stamps and one centre label with each strip being sold at 4 k.

(**291**)

1994 (16 Mar). *Nos.* 541 *and* 551 *surch as T* **291**.
708 21 t. on 35 t. Fire Anemonefish .. .. 11·00 50
709 1 k. 20 on 40 t. *L'Astrolabe* (d'Urville), 1827 3·00 1·50

COVER PRICES

Cover factors are quoted at the beginning of each country for most issues to 1945. An explanation of the system can be found on page x. The factors quoted do not, however, apply to philatelic covers.

292 Hagen Axe, Western Highlands

293 Ford Model "T", 1920

(Des R. Bates. Litho Leigh-Mardon Ltd, Melbourne)

1994 (23 Mar)–**95**. *Artifacts. T* **292** *and similar vert designs. Multicoloured. P* 14×14½.
710 1 t. Type **292** (29.6.94) 10 10
711 2 t. Telefomin shield, West Sepik (29.6.94) 10 10
712 20 t. Head mask, Gulf Province (29.6.94) .. 30 25
713 21 t. Kanganaman stool, East Sepik .. 30 25
714 45 t. Trobriand lime gourd, Milne Bay .. 55 45
715 60 t. Yuat River flute stopper, East Sepik 80 60
716 90 t. Tami Island dish, Morobe .. .. 1·40 1·25
717 1 k. Kundu (drum), Ramu River estuary (12.4.95) .. .. 1·75 1·60
723 5 k. Gogodala dance mask, Western Province (29.6.94) .. .. .. 3·50 3·75
724 10 k. Malanggan mask, New Ireland (12.4.95) .. .. 7·00 7·25
710/24 .. .. *Set of* 10 14·00 14·00

(Des G. Wade. Litho Leigh-Mardon Ltd, Melbourne)

1994 (11 May). *Historical Cars. T* **293** *and similar horiz designs. Multicoloured. P* 14.
725 21 t. Type **293** 35 25
726 45 t. Chevrolet "490", 1915 .. .. .. 90 60
727 60 t. Austin "7", 1931 .. .. 1·25 1·75
728 90 t. Willys Jeep, 1942 .. .. 1·90 2·75
725/8 .. .. *Set of* 4 4·00 4·75

294 Grizzled Tree Kangaroo

(Des R. Bates. Litho Leigh-Mardon Ltd, Melbourne)

1994 (10 Aug). *"Phila Korea '94" International Stamp Exhibition, Seoul. Tree Kangaroos. Sheet* 106×70 *mm, containing T* **294** *and similar vert design. Multicoloured. P* 14.
MS729 90 t. Type **294**; 1 k. 20, Doria's Tree Kangaroo .. .. 4·00 4·50

5t

(**295**) (**296**)

1994 (23 Aug–28 Nov). *Surch as T* **295** *or with T* **296** (*No.* 737).
730 – 5 t. on 35 t. mult (No. 604) (6 Oct) .. 1·00 75
731 – 5 t. on 35 t. mult (No. 629) (3 Oct) .. 18·00 13·00
 a. "5 t." omitted
732 **271** 10 t. on 35 t. multicoloured (3 Oct) .. 25·00 8·00
733 – 10 t. on 35 t. multicoloured (No. 623) 13·00 5·00
734 – 21 t. on 80 t. mult (No. 635) (28 Aug) .. 45·00 1·00
735 – 50 t. on 35 t. mult (No. 612) (28 Nov) 35·00 18·00
736 – 50 t. on 35 t. mult (No. 618) (28 Nov) 90·00 25·00
 a. Surch inverted .. ..
737 – 65 t. on 70 t. mult (No. 542) (28 Nov) 2·75 1·40
738 – 65 t. on 70 t. mult (No. 616) (28 Nov) 2·75 1·40
739 – 1 k. on 70 t. mult (No. 614) (28 Nov) 20·00 6·00
740 – 1 k. on 70 t. mult (No. 620) (28 Nov) 2·75 3·00
730/40 .. .. *Set of* 11 £225 75·00

297 *Daphnis hypothous pallescens*

298 Peter To Rot

(Des G. Vasarhelyi. Litho Leigh-Mardon Ltd, Melbourne)

1994 (26 Oct). *Moths. T* **297** *and similar horiz designs. Multicoloured. P* 14.
741 21 t. Type **297** 35 25
742 45 t. *Tanaorhinus unipuncta* 80 65
743 60 t. *Neodiphthera sciron* .. .. .. 1·10 1·50
744 90 t. *Parotis marginata* .. .. .. 1·60 2·00
741/4 .. .. *Set of* 4 3·50 4·00

(Des R. Bates. Litho Leigh-Mardon Ltd, Melbourne)

1995 (11 Jan). *Beatification of Peter To Rot (catechist) and Visit of Pope John Paul II. T* **298** *and similar vert design. P* 14½×14.

745	21 t. Type **298**	50	50
	a. Horiz pair. Nos. 745/6	1·75	2·00
746	1 k. on 90 t. Pope John Paul II	1·25	1·50
	a. Surch omitted	£120	

Nos. 745/6 were issued together, *se-tenant*, in sheets of 30 (6×5), showing No. 745 in vertical rows 1 and 4, No. 746 in vertical rows 3 and 6, and a stamp-size label, showing emblem, in vertical rows 2 and 5.

299 Airliner over Holiday Village

(Des G. Wade. Litho Leigh-Mardon Ltd, Melbourne)

1995 (11 Jan). *Tourism. T* **299** *and similar horiz designs. Multicoloured. P* 14.

747	21 t. *Melanesian Discoverer* (cruise ship) and launch	50	50
	a. Horiz pair. Nos. 747/8	1·00	1·00
748	21 t. Tourist taking photo of traditional mask	50	50
749	50 t. on 45 t. Type **299**	1·25	1·25
	a. Horiz pair. Nos. 749/50	2·50	2·50
750	50 t. on 45 t. Holiday homes	1·25	1·25
751	65 t. on 60 t. Tourists and guide crossing river	1·50	1·50
	a. Horiz pair. Nos. 751/2	3·00	3·00
	b. "65 t" omitted (R. 8/3)	27·00	
752	65 t. on 60 t. White water rafting	1·50	1·50
753	1 k. on 90 t. Scuba diver and launch	2·00	2·00
	a. Horiz pair. Nos. 753/4	4·00	4·00
754	1 k. on 90 t. Divers and wreck of aircraft	2·00	2·00
747/54	*Set of* 8	9·50	9·50

Nos. 747/8, 749/50, 751/2 and 753/4 were printed together, *se-tenant*, in horizontal pairs throughout the sheets. Nos. 749/54 were not issued without surcharge.

21t ■ (300) 21t ■ 300*a*

1995 (27 Mar–4 Aug). *Nos.* 643, 646, 650*b and* 650*d surch as T* **300**. (*a*) *Original face values shown as* "t"

755	21 t. on 45 t. King Bird of Paradise (16 May)	2·00	1·00
	b. Surch as Type **300***a* (4 Aug)	6·00	
756	21 t. on 90 t. Emperor of Germany Bird of Paradise	2·00	1·00
	b. Surch Type **300***a* (4 Aug)	6·00	
	(*b*) *Original face values shown as* "T"		
757	21 t. on 45 t. King Bird of Paradise (16 May)	4·75	3·00
	b. Surch as Type **300***a* (4 Aug)	42·00	
758	21 t. on 90 t. Emperor of Germany Bird of Paradise (25 Apr)	6·00	1·00
	a. Surch double	†	£200
	b. Surch Type **300***a* (4 Aug)	42·00	

Nos. 755b/8b come from a second setting on which the "t" in the surcharge is the same height as the figures. On the 45 t. values these second setting surcharges show a smaller obliterating oblong than on the first setting, but for the 90 t. the oblong on the second setting is much larger.

Nos. 755b/6b occur on stamps with either "1992" or "1993" imprint dates.

■ 21t (301)

1995 (20 June). *Nos.* 692/4 *surch with T* **301**.

759	21 t. on 45 t. Peacock Gudgeon	55	40
760	21 t. on 60 t. Northern Rainbowfish	2·00	2·00
	a. Surch double	†	—
761	21 t. on 90 t. Popondetta Blue-eye	55	60
759/61	*Set of* 3	2·75	2·75

302 *Lentinus umbrinus* **302***a*

(Des J. Cooter)

1995 (21 June–Sept). *Fungi. T* **302** *and similar vert designs. Multicoloured.* (*a*) *Litho Leigh-Mardon Ltd, Melbourne. P* 14.

762	25 t. Type **302**	35	30
763	50 t. *Amanita hemibapha*	70	80
764	65 t. *Boletellus emodensis*	85	1·00
765	1 k. *Ramaria zippelli*	1·40	1·75
762/5	*Set of* 4	3·00	3·50
	(*b*) *Litho Southern Colour Print, Dunedin. P* 12		
765*a*	25 t. Type **302***a* (Sept)	35	35

On Type **302a** the fungi illustration is larger, 26×32 mm instead of 27×30½ mm, face value and inscriptions are in a different type and there is no imprint date at foot.

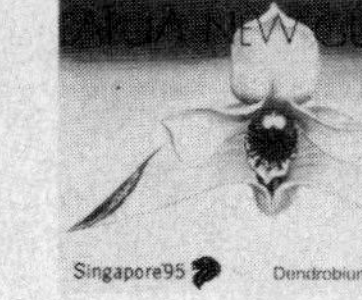

303 Anniversary Emblem and Map of Papua New Guinea

304 *Dendrobium rigidifolium*

(Des B. Masiboda. Litho Leigh-Mardon Ltd, Melbourne)

1995 (30 Aug). *20th Anniv of Independence. T* **303** *and similar vert design. Multicoloured. P* 14.

766	21 t. Type **303**	30	25
767	50 t. Emblem and lines on graph	70	80
768	1 k. As 50 t.	1·40	2·00
766/8	*Set of* 3	2·25	2·75

(Des G. Wade. Litho Leigh-Mardon Ltd, Melbourne)

1995 (30 Aug). *"Singapore '95" International Stamp Exhibition. Orchids. Sheet* 150×95 *mm, containing T* **304** *and similar horiz designs. Multicoloured. P* 14.

MS769	21 t. Type **304**; 45 t. *Dendrobium convolutum*; 60 t. *Dendrobium spectabile*; 90 t. *Dendrobium tapiniense* (*sold at* 3 *k*)	3·75	4·50

305 Pig

306 Volcanic Eruption, Tavurvur

(Litho Leigh-Mardon Ltd, Melbourne)

1995 (14 Sept). *Chinese New Year ("Year of the Pig"). Sheet* 150×95 *mm. P* 14½×14.

MS770	**305** 3 k. multicoloured	3·75	4·00

No. **MS**770 is also inscribed "BEIJING '95" on the sheet margin.

(Des B. Masiboda. Litho Leigh-Mardon Ltd, Melbourne)

1995 (19 Sept). *1st Anniv of Volcanic Eruption, Rabaul. P* 14.

771	**306** 2 k. multicoloured	2·75	2·75

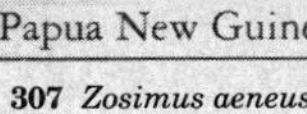

307 *Zosimus aeneus*

308 Pesquet's Parrot

(Des Jane Moore. Litho Leigh-Mardon Ltd, Melbourne)

1995 (25 Oct). *Crabs. T* **307** *and similar horiz designs. Multicoloured. P* 14.

772	21 t. Type **307**	30	25
773	50 t. *Cardisoma carnifex*	60	60
774	65 t. *Uca tetragonon*	75	95
775	1 k. *Eriphia sebana*	1·10	1·50
772/5	*Set of* 4	2·40	3·00

(Des V. Pascoe. Litho Southern Colour Print, Dunedin)

1996 (17 Jan). *Parrots. T* **308** *and similar vert designs. Multicoloured. P* 12.

776	25 t. Type **308**	50	30
777	50 t. Rainbow Lory	85	65
778	65 t. Papuan King Parrot	1·00	1·00
779	1 k. Red-winged Parrot	1·40	2·00
776/9	*Set of* 4	3·25	3·50

309 *Lagriomorpha indigacea*

(Des J. Cooter. Litho Southern Colour Print, Dunedin)

1996 (20 Mar). *Beetles. T* **309** *and similar vert designs. Multicoloured. P* 12.

780	25 t. Type **309**	45	25
781	50 t. *Eupholus geoffroyi*	80	65
782	65 t. *Promechus pulcher*	95	1·00
783	1 k. *Callistola pulchra*	1·10	1·60
780/3	*Set of* 4	3·00	3·25

310 Guang Zhou Zhong Shang Memorial Hall

(Des Stamps World Co. Litho Southern Colour Print, Dunedin)

1996 (22 Apr). *"CHINA '96" 9th Asian International Stamp Exhibition, Peking. Sheet* 105×70 *mm. P* 14.

MS784	**310** 70 t. multicoloured	85	1·10

311 Rifle-shooting

(Des Danbury Studio. Litho Southern Colour Print, Dunedin)

1996 (24 July). *Olympic Games, Atlanta. T* **311** *and similar horiz designs. Multicoloured. P* 12.

785	25 t. Type **311**	50	25
786	50 t. Athletics	1·00	70
787	65 t. Weightlifting	1·25	1·25
788	1 k. Boxing	1·50	1·75
785/8	*Set of* 4	3·75	3·50

312 Air Traffic Controller

313 Dr. Sun Yat-sen

(Des G. Wade. Litho Southern Colour Print, Dunedin)

1996 (11 Sept). *Centenary of Radio. T* **312** *and similar horiz designs. Multicoloured. P* 12.

789	25 t. Type **312**	35	25
790	50 t. Radio disc-jockey	70	65
791	65 t. Dish aerials	85	1·00
792	1 k. Early radio transmitter	1·25	1·60
789/92	*Set of* 4	2·75	3·25

(Des B. Masiboda. Litho Southern Colour Print, Dunedin)

1996 (16 Oct). *"TAIPEI '96" 10th Asian International Stamp Exhibition, Taiwan. Sheet* 105×70 *mm, containing T* **313** *and similar vert design. Multicoloured. P* 14.

MS793	65 t. Type **313**; 65 t. Dr. John Guise (former speaker of Papau New Guinea House of Assembly)	1·90	2·25

OMNIBUS ISSUES

Details, together with prices for complete sets, of the various Omnibus issues from the 1935 Silver Jubilee series to date are included in a special section following Zimbabwe at the end of Volume 2.

314 *Hibiscus rosa-sinensis* **315** Ox and National Flag

(Des B. Masiboda (1, 5, 65 t., 1 k.), J. Kipong (others). Litho Southern Colour Print, Dunedin)

1996 (27 Nov)–**97.** *Flowers. T* **314** *and similar multicoloured designs. P* 14 (1, 5, 65 *t.,* 1 *k*) *or* 12 (*others*).

794	1 t. Type **314**	10	10
795	5 t. *Bougainvillea spectabilis*	10	10
796	10 t. *Thunbergia fragrans* (*vert*) (26.11.97)	10	10
797	20 t. *Caesalpinia pulcherrima* (*vert*) (26.11.97)	15	20
798	25 t. *Hoya* sp. (*vert*) (26.11.97)	15	20
799	30 t. *Heliconia* spp. (*vert*) (26.11.97)	20	25
800	50 t. *Amomun goliathensis* (*vert*) (26.11.97)	35	40
801	65 t. *Plumeria rubra*	45	50
802	1 k. *Mucuna novo-guineensis*	70	75
794/802	*Set of* 9	2·00	2·50

(Des G. Vasarhelyi. Litho Questa)

1997 (3 Feb). *"HONG KONG '97" International Stamp Exhibition. Sheet* 130×90 *mm. P* 14.

MS808 **315** 1 k. 50, multicoloured .. .. 1·50 1·75

316 Gogodala Canoe Prow

(Des T. Sipa. Litho Questa)

1997 (19 Mar). *Canoe Prows. T* **316** *and similar horiz designs. Multicoloured. P* 14½×14.

809	25 t. Type **316**	25	25
810	50 t. East New Britain	50	60
811	65 t. Trobriand Island	70	80
812	1 k. Walomo	1·00	1·40
809/12	*Set of* 4	2·25	2·75

(Des N. Shewring (No. **MS**819), D. Miller (others). Litho Questa (No. **MS**819), Enschedé (others))

1997 (25 June). *Golden Wedding of Queen Elizabeth and Prince Philip. Multicoloured designs as T* **87** *of Kiribati. P* 14×13½.

813	25 t. Prince Philip on polo pony, 1972	30	30
	a. Horiz pair. Nos. 813/14	60	60
814	25 t. Queen Elizabeth at Windsor Polo Club	30	30
815	50 t. Prince Philip carriage-driving, 1995	55	55
	a. Horiz pair. Nos. 815/16	1·10	1·10
816	50 t. Queen Elizabeth and Prince Edward on horseback	55	55
817	1 k. Prince Philip waving and Peter and Zara Phillips on horseback	1·10	1·10
	a. Horiz pair. Nos. 817/18	2·10	2·10
818	1 k. Queen Elizabeth waving and Prince Harry on horseback	1·10	1·10
813/18	*Set of* 6	3·50	3·50
MS819	105×71 mm. 2 k. Queen Elizabeth and Prince Philip in landau (*horiz*). P 14×14½	2·00	2·25

Nos. 813/14, 815/16 and 818/19 were each printed together, *se-tenant*, in horizontal pairs throughout the sheets with the backgrounds forming composite designs.

317 Air Niugini Airliner over Osaka

(Des B. Masiboda. Litho Southern Colour Print, Dunedin)

1997 (19 July). *Inaugural Air Niugini Port Moresby to Osaka Flight. Sheet* 110×80 *mm. P* 12.

MS820 **317** 3 k. multicoloured .. .. .. 3·25 3·50

318 *Pocillopora woodjonesi* **319** Sooty Owl

(Des Citi Studio. Litho Southern Colour Print, Dunedin)

1997 (27 Aug). *Pacific Year of the Coral Reef. Corals. T* **318** *and similar horiz designs. Multicoloured. P* 12.

821	25 t. Type **318**	25	20
822	50 t. *Subergorgia mollis*	65	55
823	65 t. *Oxypora glabra*	85	80
824	1 k. *Turbinaria reinformis*	1·50	1·75
821/4	*Set of* 4	3·00	3·00

(Des T. Nolan. Litho Southern Colour Print, Dunedin)

1998 (28 Jan). *Birds. T* **319** *and similar horiz designs. Multicoloured. P* 12.

825	25 t. Type **319**	15	20
826	50 t. Wattled Brush Turkey	35	40
827	65 t. New Guinea Grey-headed Goshawk	45	50
828	1 k. Forest Bittern	70	75
825/8	*Set of* 4	1·60	1·75

STAMP BOOKLETS

POSTAGE STAMP
BOOKLET
TERRITORY OF PAPUA AND NEW GUINEA
10 5-Cent Stamps 50c

B 1

1970 (28 Jan). *Green on olive-yellow cover as Type* B **1**, *but "POSTAGE STAMP" in seriffed type. Stamps attached by selvedge.*

SB1 50 c. booklet containing 5 c. (No. 140) in block of 10 £350

1970 (25 May). *Green on cream cover as Type* B **1** *with "POSTAGE STAMP" without serifs. Stamps attached by selvedge.*

SB2 50 c. booklet containing 5 c. (No. 140) in block of 10 13·00

No. SB2 shows "GP-P&NG/B1112" imprint on reverse.

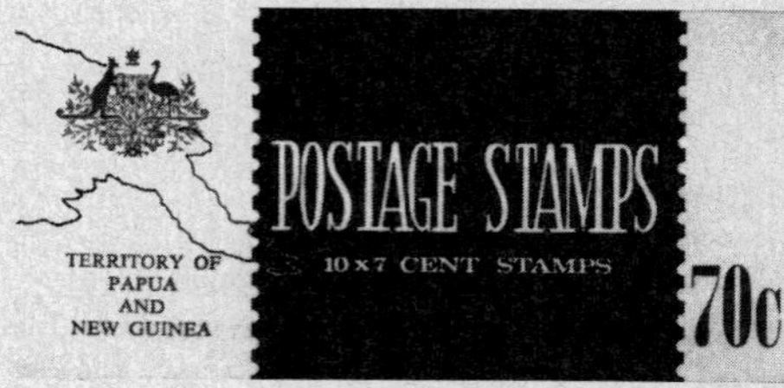

B 2

1971 (1 Apr). *Red and green printed cover as Type* B **2**. *Stamps attached by selvedge.*

SB3 70 c. booklet containing 7 c. (No. 141) in block of 10 9·50

B 3

1972 (14 Feb). *Orange and black printed cover as Type* B **3**. *Stamps attached by selvedge.*

SB4 70 c. booklet containing 7 c. (Nos. 212/13) in block of 10 .. 12·00

1973 (16 Feb). *Orange and black printed cover as Type* B **3**. *Stamps attached by selvedge.*

SB5 70 c. booklet containing 7 c. (Nos. 231/4) in block of 10 .. 10·00
a. Cover optd for "INTERPEX" Stamp Exhibition .. £120

An example of No. SB5 has been reported containing No. 229 in block of 10.

B 4

1993 (15 Apr). *Birds of Paradise. Multicoloured covers as Type* B **4**. *Stamps attached by selvedge.*

SB6 2 k. 10, booklet containing 21 t. (No. 640) in block of 10 .. 7·50
a. With additional slotted tab at right .. 7·50
SB7 4 k. 50, booklet containing 45 t. (No. 643) in block of 10 .. 8·50
a. With additional slotted tab at right .. 8·50

Nos. SB6a and SB7a were intended for self-service sales.

1993 (9 June). *Small Birds. Multicoloured covers as Type* B **4**. *Stamps attached by selvedge.*

SB8 6 k. booklet containing 60 t.(No. 685) in block of 10 11·00
a. With additional slotted tab at right .. 11·00
SB9 9 k. booklet containing 90 t.(No. 686) in block of 10 15·00
a. With additional slotted tab at right .. 15·00

Nos. SB8a and SB9a were intended for self-service sales.

B 5

1994 (11 May). *Historical Cars. Multicoloured covers as Type* B **5**. *Stamps attached by selvedge.*

SB10	2 k. 10, booklet containing 21 t. (No. 725) in block of 10	4·75
SB11	4 k. 50, booklet containing 45 t. (No. 726) in block of 10	9·00

1995 (21 June). *Fungi. Multicoloured covers as Type* B **5**. *Stamps attached by selvedge.*

SB12	2 k. 50, booklet containing 25 t. (No. 762) in block of 10	4·25
SB13	5 k. booklet containing 50 t. (No. 763) in block of 10	7·50

POSTAGE DUE STAMPS

POSTAL
CHARGES

6d.

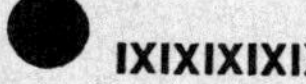

IXIXIXIXIX

(D 1)

POSTAL
CHARGES

3s.

(D 2)

1960 (1 Mar). *Postage stamps surcharged. (a) No.* 8 *with Type* D 1

D1	6d. on 7½d. blue (R.)	£800	£425
	a. Surch double	£3250	£1800

(b) Nos. 1, 4, 6*a*, 7/8 *as Type* D 2

D2	1d. on 6½d. maroon	6·00	6·00
D3	3d. on ½d. emerald (B.)	7·50	4·50
	a. Surch double	£600	
D4	6d. on 7½d. blue (R.)	30·00	11·00
	a. Surch double	£600	
D5	1s. 3d. on 3½d. black (O.)	8·50	8·50
D6	3s. on 2½d. orange	25·00	14·00
D2/6	*Set of* 5	70·00	40·00

D 3

(Typo Note Ptg Branch, Reserve Bank of Australia, Melbourne)

1960 (2 June). *W* **15** *of Australia. P* 14.

D 7	D 3	1d. orange	65	75
D 8		3d. yellow-brown	70	75
D 9		6d. blue	75	40
D10		9d. deep red	75	1·75
D11		1s. light emerald	75	50
D12		1s. 3d. violet	1·40	2·00
D13		1s. 6d. pale blue	5·50	6·00
D14		3s. yellow	6·00	1·25
D7/14		*Set of* 8	15·00	12·00

The use of Postal Charge stamps was discontinued on 12 February 1966, but they remained on sale at the Philatelic Bureau until 31 August 1966.

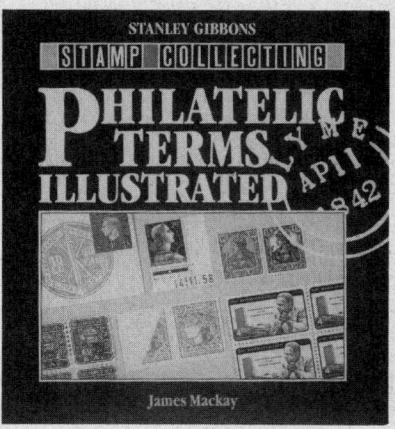

Pitcairn Islands

CROWN COLONY

The settlement of Pitcairn Island by the *Bounty* mutineers in 1790 was not discovered until the American whaler *Topaz*, Capt. Mayhew Folger, called there in 1808. A visit by two Royal Navy frigates followed in 1814 and reports from their captains resulted in considerable interest being taken in the inhabitants' welfare by religious and philanthropic circles in Great Britain.

Due to overcrowding the population was resettled on Tahiti in 1831, but many soon returned to Pitcairn which was taken under British protection in 1838. The island was again evacuated in 1856, when the inhabitants were moved to Norfolk Island, but a number of families sailed back to their original home in 1859 and 1864.

The earliest surviving letter from the island is dated 1849. Before 1921 the mail service was irregular, as it depended on passing ships, and mail for the island was often sent via Tahiti. Some covers, purportedly sent from Pitcairn between 1883 and 1890 are known handstamped "Pitcairn Island" or "PITCAIRN ISLAND", but these are now believed to be forgeries.

In 1921 a regular mail service was introduced. As there were no stamps available letters were allowed free postage as long as they carried a cachet, or manuscript endorsement, indicating their origin. Illustrations of Cachets I/VI, VIII, X, XIII and XIV are taken from *Pitcairn Islands Postal Markings 1883–1991*, published by the Pitcairn Islands Study Group, and are reproduced by permission of the author, Mr. Cy Kitching. Cachets I to XIV are shown three-quarter size.

POSTED IN PITCAIRN
NO STAMPS AVAILABLE

Cachet I

Cat No. — *Value on cover*

C1 **1921–25** Cachet I (62×8 *mm*) (*violet*) £2500

POSTED AT PITCAIRN ISLAND
NO STAMPS AVAILABLE.

Cachet II

C2 **1921–25.** Cachet II (*violet or red*) £2000

POSTED AT PITCAIRN ISLAND
NO STAMPS AVAILABLE.

Cachet III

C3 **1922–28.** Cachet III (49×8½*mm*) (*vio, pur or blk*) £1500

POSTED IN PITCAIRN ISLAND
1923 NO STAMPS AVAILABLE

Cachet IV

C4 **1923.** Cachet IV (*black*) £2250

Posted at Pitcairn
Island no Stamps
Available

Cachet IVa

C4*a* **1923** Cachet IVa (73½×22 *mm*) (*red*) .. ..

POSTED AT PITCAIRN ISLAND
NO STAMPS AVAILABLE

Cachet V

C5 **1923–28** (Aug). Cachet V (47×9 *mm*) (*red, violet or black*) £1500

C5*a* **1925–26.** As Cachet V, but second line shown as "No Stamps Available" (*black*) .. ..

POSTED AT PITCAIRN ISLAND.
NO STAMPS AVAILABLE.
NOT TO BE SURCHARGED.

Cachet VI

C6 **1923.** Cachet VI (*blue-green*) .. .. ..

C7 **1923.** As Cachet V, but in three lines (*red*) .. ..

POSTED AT PITCAIRN ISLAND
NO STAMPS AVAILABLE.

Cachet VII

C8 **1923–27.** Cachet VII (*violet*) £1500

C9 **1924.** As Cachet IV, but dated "1924" (*black*) .. £1600

POSTED AT PITCAIRN ISLAND.
NO STAMPS AVAILABLE.

Cachet VIII

C10 **1924.** Cachet VIII (36×8 *mm*) (*violet*) £2000

POSTED AT PITCAIRN ISLAND
NO STAMPS AVAILABLE.

Cachet IX

C11 **1924** (Feb)–**25.** Cachet IX (63×7 *mm*) (*vio or blk*)

POSTED·IN·PITCAIRN·
NO·STAMPS·AVAILABLE

Cachet IXa

C11*a* **1924–28.** Cachet IXa (58×8½ *mm*) (*vio or blk*)

C12 **1925** (Sept). As Cachet IV, but dated "1925" (*blk*) £2000

POSTED IN PITCAIRN
NO STAMPS AVAILABLE.

Cachet X

C13 **1925.** Cachet X (48×5 *mm*) £1700

POSTED AT PITCAIRN ISLAND,
NO STAMPS AVAILABLE.

Cachet XI

C14 **1925** Cachet XI (50×10 *mm*) (*violet or blk*) .. £2000

Posted at PITCAIRN ISLAND
No Stamps Available

Cachet XII

C15 **1925** Cachet XII (55×7½ *mm*) (*violet*) .. ..

POSTED IN PITCAIRN
NO STAMPS AVAILABLE.

Cachet XIII

C16 **1926** (Jan). Cachet XIII (64×8 *mm*) (*pur or blk*)

POSTED AT PITCAIRN
NO STAMPS AVAILABLE

Cachet XIV

C17 **1926.** Cachet XIV (36×3¾ *mm*) £1600

The New Zealand Government withdrew the free postage concession on 12 May 1926, but after representations from the islanders opened a postal agency on Pitcairn using New Zealand stamps cancelled with Type Z 1. Some impressions of this postmark appear to show a double ring, but this is the result of heavy or uneven use of the handstamp. The postal agency operated from 7 June 1927 until 14 October 1940.

PRICES. Those quoted for Nos. Z1/47 are for examples showing a virtually complete strike of Type Z 1. Due to the size of the cancellation such examples will usually be on piece.

Z 1

Stamps of New Zealand cancelled with Type Z 1.

1915–29. *King George V* (*Nos.* 419, 422/6, 431 *and* 446/8).

Z1	½d. green	22·00
Z2	1½d. grey-slate	45·00
Z3	1½d. orange-brown	38·00
Z4	2d. yellow	32·00
Z5	2½d. blue	60·00
Z6	4d. bright violet	60·00
Z6*a*	4½d. deep green	75·00
Z7	5d. light blue	60·00
Z7*a*	6d. carmine	75·00
Z8	7½d. red-brown	80·00

1926. *King George V in Admiral's uniform* (*No.* 468).

Z9	1d. rose-carmine	22·00

1931. *Air* (*No.* 548).

Z10	3d. chocolate	£150

1935. *Pictorials* (*Nos.* 556/7, 560*a and* 567). *W* **43**.

Z11	½d. bright green	48·00
Z12	1d. scarlet	30·00
Z13	2½d. chocolate and slate	60·00
Z13*a*	1s. deep green	75·00

1935. *Silver Jubilee* (*Nos.* 573/5).

Z14	½d. green	32·00
Z15	1d. carmine	32·00
Z16	6d. red-orange	60·00

1935. *Health* (*No.* 576).

Z17	1d. + 1d. scarlet	50·00

1936. *Pictorials* (*Nos.* 577/82).

Z18	½d. bright green	38·00
Z19	1d. scarlet	13·00
Z20	1½d. red-brown	60·00
Z21	2d. orange	48·00
Z22	2½d. chocolate and slate	50·00
Z23	3d. brown	55·00

1936. *21st Anniv of "Anzac" Landing at Gallipoli* (*Nos.* 591/2).

Z24	½d. + ½d. green	35·00
Z25	1d. + 1d. scarlet	35·00

1936. *Congress of British Empire Chambers of Commerce* (*Nos.* 593/7)

Z26	½d. emerald-green	32·00
Z27	1d. scarlet	32·00
Z28	2½d. blue	38·00
Z28*a*	4d. violet	55·00
Z28*b*	6d. red-brown	55·00

1936. *Health* (*No.* 598).

Z29	1d. + 1d. scarlet	50·00

1937. *Coronation* (*Nos.* 599/601).

Z30	1d. carmine	26·00
Z31	2½d. Prussian blue	28·00
Z32	6d. red-orange	28·00

1937. *Health* (*No.* 602).

Z33	1d. + 1d. scarlet	50·00

1938. *King George VI* (*Nos.* 603, 605, 607).

Z34	½d. green	50·00
Z35	1d. scarlet	50·00
Z35*a*	1½d. purple-brown	

1940. *Centenary of British Sovereignty* (*Nos.* 613/22, 624/5).

Z36	½d. blue-green	27·00
Z37	1d. chocolate and scarlet	30·00
Z38	1½d. light blue and mauve	32·00
Z39	2d. blue-green and chocolate	32·00
Z40	2½d. blue-green and blue	35·00
Z41	3d. purple and carmine	35·00
Z42	4d. chocolate and lake	50·00
Z43	5d. pale blue and brown	55·00
Z44	6d. emerald-green and violet	55·00
Z45	7d. black and red	75·00
Z46	9d. olive-green and orange	75·00
Z47	1s. sage-green and deep green	75·00

PRICES FOR STAMPS ON COVER TO 1945
Nos. 1/8 — *from* × 10

1 Cluster of Oranges

2 Christian on *Bounty* and Pitcairn Island

(Recess B.W. (1d., 3d., 4d., 8d. and 2s. 6d.), and Waterlow (others))

1940 (15 Oct)–**51.** *T* **1**/**2** *and similar horiz designs. Wmk Mult Script CA. P* 11½×11 (1*d.*, 3*d.*, 4*d.*, 8*d. and* 2*s.* 6*d.*) *or* 12½ (*others*).

1	½d. orange and green	40	60
2	1d. mauve and magenta	55	70
3	1½d. grey and carmine	55	50
4	2d. green and brown	1·75	1·40
5	3d. yellow-green and blue	1·25	1·40
	aw. Wmk inverted	£3250	
5*b*	4d. black and emerald-green (1.9.51)	15·00	8·00
6	6d. brown and grey-blue	5·00	2·25
6*a*	8d. olive-green and magenta (1.9.51)	16·00	7·00
7	1s. violet and grey	3·00	2·25
8	2s. 6d. green and brown	7·50	4·25
1/8	*Set of* 10	45·00	25·00
1/5, 6, 7/8	Perf "Specimen" *Set of* 8	£800	

Designs:—1½d. John Adams and his house; 2d. Lt. Bligh and H.M.S. *Bounty*; 3d. Pitcairn Islands and Pacific Ocean; 4d. *Bounty* Bible; 6d. H.M.S. *Bounty*; 8d. School, 1949; 1s. Fletcher Christian and Pitcairn Island; 2s. 6d. Christian on H.M.S. *Bounty* and Pitcairn Coast.

Flagstaff flaw
(R. 8/2)

1946 (2 Dec). *Victory. As Nos.* 141/2 *of Jamaica.*
9 2d. brown 50 15
10 3d. blue 50 15
a. Flagstaff flaw . . . . 25·00
9/10 Perf "Specimen" . . . . *Set of* 2 £140

1949 (1 Aug). *Royal Silver Wedding. As Nos.* 143/4 *of Jamaica.*
11 1½d. scarlet . . . . 2·00 1·00
12 10s. mauve . . . . 48·00 50·00

1949 (10 Oct). *75th Anniv of U.P.U. As Nos.* 145/8 *of Jamaica.*
13 2½d. red-brown . . . . 2·00 3·50
14 3d. deep blue . . . . 12·00 4·00
15 6d. deep blue-green . . . . . . 10·00 5·00
16 1s. purple . . . . 10·00 5·00
13/16 . . . . *Set of* 4 30·00 16·00

1953 (2 June). *Coronation. As No.* 153 *of Jamaica, but ptd by B.W.*
17 4d. black and deep bluish green . . . . 2·00 3·25

9 *Cordyline terminalis* 10 Pitcairn Island Map

(Recess D.L.R.)

1957 (2 July)–**63**. *T* **9/10** *and similar designs. Wmk Mult Script CA. P* 13×12½ *(horiz) or* 12½×13 *(vert).*
18 ½d. green and reddish lilac . . . . 80 1·25
a. Green and reddish purple (9.3.63) . . 1·75 3·25
19 1d. black and olive-green . . . . 2·50 1·00
a. Black and yellow-olive (19.2.59) . . 11·00 16·00
b. Black and light olive-green (24.2.60) 16·00 12·00
20 2d. brown and greenish blue 75 60
21 2½d. deep brown and red-orange 50 40
22 3d. emerald and deep ultramarine 80 40
23 4d. scarlet and deep ultramarine (I) . . 90 40
23*a* 4d. carmine-red & dp ultram (II) (5.11.58) 5·00 1·50
24 6d. pale buff and indigo . . . . 1·25 55
25 8d. deep olive-green and carmine-lake . . 60 40
26 1s. black and yellowish brown . . . . 1·50 40
27 2s. green and red-orange . . . . 22·00 10·00
28 2s. 6d. ultramarine and lake . . . . 17·00 9·00
a. Blue and deep lake (10.2.59) . . 32·00 11·00
18/28 . . . . *Set of* 12 48·00 23·00
Designs: *Vert*—2d. John Adams and *Bounty* Bible; 2s. Island wheelbarrow. *Horiz*—2½d. Handicrafts: Bird model; 3d. Bounty Bay; 4d. Pitcairn School; 6d. Pacific Ocean map; 8d. Inland scene; 1s. Handicrafts: Ship model; 2s. 6d. Launching new whaleboat.
Nos. 23/a. Type I is inscribed "PITCAIRN SCHOOL"; Type II "SCHOOLTEACHER'S HOUSE".
See also No. 33

20 Pitcairn Island and Simon Young

(Des H. E. Maud. Photo Harrison)

1961 (15 Nov). *Centenary of Return of Pitcairn Islanders from Norfolk Island. T* **20** *and similar horiz designs. W* w **12**. *P* 14½ × 13½.
29 3d. black and yellow 40 30
30 6d. red-brown and blue 90 80
31 1s. red-orange and blue-green 90 85
29/31 . . . . *Set of* 3 2·00 1·75
Designs:—6d. Norfolk Island and Pitcairn Islands; 1s. Migrant brigantine *Mary Ann.*

1963 (4 June). *Freedom from Hunger. As No.* 80 *of Lesotho.*
32 2s. 6d. ultramarine . . . . . . 14·00 3·00

1963 (4 Dec). *As No.* 18*a, but wmk* w **12**.
33 **9** ½d. green and reddish purple 45 60

1963 (9 Dec). *Red Cross Centenary. As Nos.* 203/4 *of Jamaica.*
34 2d. red and black . . . . 2·50 1·00
35 2s. 6d. red and blue . . . . . . 8·50 5·50

23 Pitcairn Is Longboat **24** Queen Elizabeth II (after Anthony Buckley)

(Des M. Farrar Bell. Photo Harrison)

1964 (5 Aug)–**65**. *T* **23/4** *and similar horiz designs. Multicoloured. W* w **12**. *P* 14 × 14½.
36 ½d. Type **23** 10 30
37 1d. H.M.S. *Bounty* 30 30
38 2d. "Out from Bounty Bay" 30 30
39 3d. Great Frigate Bird 75 30
40 4d. White Tern 75 30
41 6d. Pitcairn Warbler 75 30
42 8d. Red-footed Booby 75 30
a. Pale blue (beak) omitted £225
43 10d. Red-tailed Tropic Birds 60 30
44 1s. Henderson Island Crake 60 30
45 1s. 6d. Stephen's Lory . . . . . . 5·50 1·25
46 2s. 6d. Murphy's Petrel . . . . . . 5·00 1·50
47 4s. Henderson Island Fruit Dove . . 7·00 1·75
48 8s. Type **24** (5.4.65) . . . . . . 2·75 1·75
36/48 . . . . *Set of* 13 22·00 8·00

1965 (17 May). *I.T.U. Centenary. As Nos.* 98/9 *of Lesotho.*
49 1d. mauve and orange-brown . . . . 1·00 40
50 2s. 6d. turquoise-green and bright blue . . 14·00 3·50
w. Wmk inverted . . . . 85·00

1965 (25 Oct). *International Co-operation Year. As Nos.* 100/1 *of Lesotho.*
51 1d. reddish purple and turquoise-green . . 1·00 40
a. "TRISTAN DA CUNHA" offset on back in reddish purple £110
52 1s. 6d. deep bluish green and lavender . . 12·00 4·50
No. 51a was caused by the back of one sheet of stamps coming into contact with the blanket plate used for applying the Tristan da Cunha inscription to the same basic design.

1966 (24 Jan). *Churchill Commemoration. As Nos.* 102/5 *of Lesotho.*
53 2d. new blue . . . . 1·50 75
54 3d. deep green . . . . 4·50 90
55 6d. brown . . . . 5·50 1·75
56 1s. bluish violet . . . . 7·50 2·75
53/6 . . . . *Set of* 4 17·00 5·50

25 Footballer's Legs, Ball and Jules Rimet Cup

(Des V. Whiteley. Litho Harrison)

1966 (1 Aug). *World Cup Football Championships. W* w **12** *(sideways). P* 14.
57 **25** 4d. violet, yellow-green, lake & yellow-brn 1·75 1·00
58 2s. 6d. chocolate, blue-grn, lake & yell-brn 4·25 1·75

1966 (20 Sept). *Inauguration of W.H.O. Headquarters, Geneva. As Nos.* 185/6 *of Montserrat.*
59 8d. black, yellow-green and light blue . . 5·00 2·75
60 1s. 6d. black, light purple and yellow-brown 9·00 3·25

1966 (1 Dec). *20th Anniv of U.N.E.S.C.O. As Nos.* 342/4 *of Mauritius.*
61 ½d. slate-violet, red, yellow and orange . . 20 40
62 10d. orange-yellow, violet and deep olive . . 4·50 2·00
63 2s. black, bright purple and orange . . 9·00 3·00
61/3 . . . . *Set of* 3 12·50 4·75

36 Mangarevan Canoe, *circa* 1325

(Des V. Whiteley. Photo Harrison)

1967 (1 Mar). *Bicentenary of Discovery of Pitcairn Islands. T* **36** *and similar horiz designs. Multicoloured. W* w **12**. *P* 14½.
64 ½d. Type **36** 10 10
65 1d. P. F. de Quiros and *San Pedro y Pablo*, 1606 . . . . 20 10
66 8d. *San Pedro y Pablo* and *Los Tres Reyes*, 1606 . . . . 40 15
67 1s. Carteret and H.M.S. *Swallow*, 1767 . . 40 15
68 1s. 6d. *Hercules*, 1819 . . . . . . 40 15
64/8 . . . . *Set of* 5 1·25 50

MINIMUM PRICE

The minimum price quote is 10p which represents a handling charge rather than a basis for valuing common stamps. For further notes about prices see introductory pages.

(New Currency. 100 cents = 1 New Zealand dollar)

½c

(**41** *Bounty* Anchor)

1967 (10 July). *Decimal currency. Nos.* 36/48 *surch in decimal currency by die-stamping in gold as T* **41**.
69 ½ c. on ½d. multicoloured 10 10
a. Deep brown omitted £550
b. Surch double, one albino £110
70 1 c. on 1d. multicoloured 30 40
71 2 c. on 2d. multicoloured 25 40
72 2½ c. on 3d. multicoloured 25 40
73 3 c. on 4d. multicoloured 25 15
74 5 c. on 6d. multicoloured 30 40
75 10 c. on 8d. multicoloured 30 30
a. "10 c." omitted £600
b. Pale blue (beak) omitted £250
76 15 c. on 10d. multicoloured . . . . 1·25 40
77 20 c. on 1s. multicoloured . . . . 1·25 55
78 25 c. on 1s. 6d. multicoloured . . . . 2·75 1·25
79 30 c. on 2s. 6d. multicoloured . . . . 3·25 1·25
80 40 c. on 4s. multicoloured . . . . 4·50 1·25
81 45 c. on 8s. multicoloured . . . . 4·25 1·50
69/81 . . . . *Set of* 13 17·00 7·50
On No. 75a the anchor emblem is still present. Several examples of this variety have been identified as coming from R. 9/1.
The ½ c. and 1 c. exist with PVA gum as well as gum arabic.

42 Bligh and *Bounty*'s Launch

(Des Jennifer Toombs. Litho D.L.R.)

1967 (7 Dec). *150th Death Anniv of Admiral Bligh. T* **42** *and similar horiz designs. P* 13½ × 13.
82 1 c. turq-blue, black and royal blue (*shades*) 10 10
83 8 c. black, yellow and magenta 30 50
84 20 c. black, brown and pale buff 35 60
82/4 . . . . *Set of* 3 65 1·00
Designs:—8 c. Bligh and followers cast adrift; 20 c. Bligh's tomb.

45 Human Rights Emblem

(Des G. Hamori. Litho D.L.R.)

1968 (4 Mar). *Human Rights Year. P* 13½ × 13.
85 **45** 1 c. multicoloured 10 10
86 2 c. multicoloured 10 10
87 25 c. multicoloured 20 20
85/7 . . . . *Set of* 3 30 30

46 Miro Wood and Flower

(Des Jennifer Toombs. Photo Harrison)

1968 (19 Aug). *Handicrafts (1st series). T* **46** *and similar designs. W* w **12** *(sideways* on vert designs). P* 14×13½ *(5, 10 c.) or* 13½×14 *(others).*
88 5 c. multicoloured 25 20
89 10 c. bronze-green, brown and orange . . 30 30
90 15 c. deep bluish violet, chocolate and salmon 35 30
91 20 c. multicoloured 40 30
w. Wmk Crown to right of CA £120
88/91 . . . . *Set of* 4 1·10 1·00
Designs: *Horiz*—10 c. Flying Fish model. *Vert*—15 c. "Hand" vases; 20 c. Woven baskets.
*The normal sideways watermark shows Crown to left of CA, *as seen from the back of the stamp.*
See also Nos. 207/10.

50 Microscope and Slides

(Des Jennifer Toombs. Litho D.L.R.)

1968 (25 Nov). *20th Anniv of World Health Organisation. T* **50** *and similar horiz design.* W w **12** *(sideways). P* 14.

92 2 c. black, turquoise-blue and ultramarine .. 10 10
93 20 c. black, orange and bright purple .. 40 20

Design:—20 c. Hypodermic syringe and jars of tablets.

52 Pitcairn Island

62 "Flying Fox" Cable System

(Des Jennifer Toombs. Litho Questa (50 c., $1), D.L.R. (others))

1969 (17 Sept)–**75.** *T* **52, 62** *and similar designs. Chalk-surfaced paper.* W w **12** *(upright on 3 c., 25 c., sideways* on $1 and horiz designs). P* 14½×14 (50 c.), 14 ($1) *or* 13 *(others).*

94 1 c. multicoloured 50 30
a. Glazed, ordinary paper (9.8.71) .. 1·25 1·00
aw. Wmk Crown to right of CA .. .. 3·00
95 2 c. multicoloured 25 15
96 3 c. multicoloured 25 15
97 4 c. multicoloured 40 15
98 5 c. multicoloured 30 15
99 6 c. multicoloured 30 20
100 8 c. multicoloured 50 20
101 10 c. multicoloured .. .. 2·00 85
a. Glazed, ordinary paper (9.8.71) .. 2·00 2·75
aw. Wmk Crown to right of CA .. .. 6·00
102 15 c. multicoloured 60 50
a. Queen's head omitted £500
103 20 c. multicoloured 60 40
104 25 c. multicoloured 70 40
105 30 c. multicoloured 55 45
106 40 c. multicoloured 75 60
106*a* 50 c. multicoloured *(glazed, ordinary paper)* (2.1.73) .. .. 10·00 11·00
106*b* $1 multicoloured *(glazed, ordinary paper)* (21.4.75) .. .. 13·00 16·00
94/106*b* .. .. *Set of* 15 27·00 28·00

Designs: *Horiz*—2 c. Captain Bligh and *Bounty* chronometer; 4 c. Plans and drawing of *Bounty*; 5 c. Breadfruit containers and plant; 6 c. Bounty Bay; 8 c. Pitcairn longboat; 10 c. Ship landing point; 15 c. Fletcher Christian's Cave; 20 c. Thursday October Christian's House; 30 c. Radio Station, Taro Ground; 40 c. *Bounty* Bible; 50 c. Pitcairn Coat of Arms. *Vert*—3 c. *Bounty* anchor; $1 Queen Elizabeth II.

*The normal sideways watermark shows Crown to left of CA, *as seen from the back of the stamp.*

See also No. 133.

65 Lantana

69 Band-tailed Hind

(Des Jennifer Toombs. Litho D.L.R.)

1970 (23 Mar). *Flowers. T* **65** *and similar vert designs. Multi-coloured.* W w **12**. *P* 14.

107 1 c. Type **65** 20 50
108 2 c. "Indian Shot" 35 65
109 5 c. Pulau 60 75
110 25 c. Wild Gladiolus .. .. 1·25 2·00
107/10 .. .. *Set of* 4 2·25 3·50

(Des Jennifer Toombs. Photo Harrison)

1970 (12 Oct). *Fishes. T* **69** *and similar horiz designs. Multi-coloured.* W w **12**. *P* 14.

111 5 c. Type **69** .. .. 2·75 70
w. Wmk inverted .. .. 6·00
112 10 c. High-finned Rudderfish .. .. 2·75 85
w. Wmk inverted .. .. 7·00
113 15 c. Elwyn's Wrasse .. .. .. 3·25 1·00
w. Wmk inverted .. .. 7·00
114 20 c. Yellow Wrasse ("Whistling Daughter") 3·50 1·25
w. Wmk inverted .. .. 15·00
111/14 .. .. *Set of* 4 11·00 3·50

PRICES OF SETS

Set prices are given for many issues, generally those containing three stamps or more. Definitive sets include one of each value or major colour change, but do not cover different perforations, die types or minor shades. Where a choice is possible the set prices are based on the cheapest versions of the stamps included in the listings.

ROYAL VISIT 1971
(70)

71 Polynesian Rock Carvings

1971 (22 Feb). *Royal Visit. No.* 101 *optd with T* **70**, *in silver.*

115 10 c. multicoloured .. .. 1·75 2·50

(Des Jennifer Toombs. Litho A & M)

1971 (3 May). *Polynesian Pitcairn. T* **71** *and similar multi-coloured designs.* W w **12** *(sideways* on* 10 *and* 15 *c.). P* 13½.

116 5 c. Type **71** .. .. 2·00 1·00
w. Wmk inverted .. .. 3·00
117 10 c. Polynesian artefacts *(horiz)* .. .. 2·50 1·25
w. Wmk Crown to right of CA .. .. 3·50
118 15 c. Polynesian stone fish-hook *(horiz)* .. 2·75 1·25
w. Wmk Crown to right of CA .. .. 3·75
119 20 c. Polynesian stone deity .. .. 2·75 1·50
w. Wmk inverted .. .. 4·00
116/19 .. .. *Set of* 4 9·00 4·50

*The normal sideways watermark shows Crown to left of CA, *as seen from the back of the stamp.*

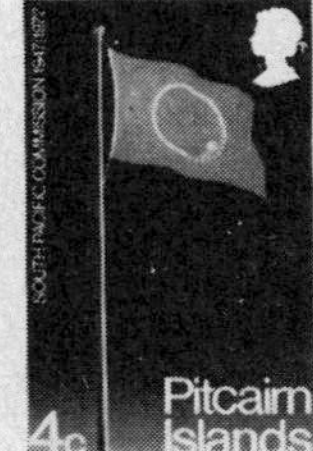

72 Commission Flag

73 Red-tailed Tropic Birds and Longboat

(Des Jennifer Toombs. Litho Questa)

1972 (4 Apr). *25th Anniv of South Pacific Commission. T* **72** *and similar horiz designs. Multicoloured (except* 4 *c.).* W w **12** *(sideways on* 4 *c.). P* 14.

120 4 c. dp blue, blue-violet & brt yellow (T **72**) 75 75
121 8 c. Young and elderly (Health) 75 75
122 18 c. Junior School (Education) .. .. 80 1·10
w. Wmk inverted .. .. 3·00
123 20 c. Goods store (Economy) .. .. 1·50 1·75
120/3 .. .. *Set of* 4 3·50 4·00

(Des (from photographs by D. Groves) and photo Harrison)

1972 (20 Nov). *Royal Silver Wedding. Multicoloured; background colour given.* W w **12**. *P* 14 × 14½.

124 **73** 4 c. slate-green 30 60
w. Wmk inverted .. .. .. 75·00
125 20 c. bright blue 45 90
w. Wmk inverted .. .. .. 16·00

74 Rose-apple

75 Obelisk Vertagus (*Rhinoclavis sinensis*) and Episcopal Mitre (*Mitra mitra*) Shells

(Des Jennifer Toombs. Litho J.W.)

1973 (25 June). *Flowers. T* **74** *and similar vert designs. Multi-coloured.* W w **12** *(sideways). P* 14.

126 4 c. Type **74** .. .. 1·25 55
127 8 c. Mountain-apple .. .. 1·75 75
128 15 c. "Lata" .. .. 3·00 1·00
129 20 c. "Dorcas-flower" .. .. 3·25 1·25
130 35 c. Guava .. .. 4·00 1·75
126/30 .. .. *Set of* 5 12·00 4·75

1973 (14 Nov). *Royal Wedding. As Nos.* 322/3 *of Montserrat. Centre multicoloured.* W w **12** *(sideways). P* 13½.

131 10 c. bright mauve 20 15
132 25 c. emerald 25 30

1974 (4 Feb). *As No.* 94a, *but wmk upright. Glazed, ordinary paper.*

133 **52** 1 c. multicoloured .. .. .. 3·75 5·00

134/46 Catalogue numbers vacant.

(Des Jennifer Toombs. Litho Questa)

1974 (15 Apr). *Shells. T* **75** *and similar horiz designs. Multi-coloured.* W w **12**. *P* 14.

147 4 c. Type **75** .. .. 1·50 70
148 10 c. Turtle Dove shell (*Pyrene testudinaria tylerae*) .. .. 1·75 90
149 18 c. Indo-Pacific Limpet (*Cellana radiata*), Fringed False Limpet (*Siphonaria laciniosa*) and *Siphonaria normalis* .. 2·00 1·25
150 50 c. *Ctena divergens* .. .. .. 2·75 1·75
147/50 .. .. *Set of* 4 7·00 4·25
MS151 130×121 mm. Nos. 147/50 .. .. 8·00 14·00

76 Island Post Office

(Des Jennifer Toombs. Litho Questa)

1974 (22 July). *Centenary of Universal Postal Union. T* **76** *and similar horiz designs.* W w **12** *(sideways). P* 14.

152 4 c. multicoloured 25 35
153 20 c. bright purple, light cinnamon and black 40 60
154 35 c. multicoloured 50 70
152/4 .. .. *Set of* 3 1·00 1·50

Designs:—20 c. Pre-stamp letter, 1922; 35 c. Mailship and Pitcairn longboat.

77 Churchill and Text "Lift up your Hearts . . ."

(Des Jennifer Toombs. Litho Questa)

1974 (30 Nov). *Birth Centenary of Sir Winston Churchill. T* **77** *and similar horiz design.* W w **14** *(sideways). P* 14½.

155 20 c. blackish olive, apple-green & dp slate .. 40 85
156 35 c. sepia, greenish yellow and deep slate .. 60 90

Design:—35 c. Text "Give us the tools . . .".

78 H.M.S. *Seringapatam* (frigate), 1830

(Des Jennifer Toombs. Litho Walsall)

1975 (22 July). *Mailboats. T* **78** *and similar horiz designs. Multicoloured.* W w **14** *(sideways*). P* 14.

157 4 c. Type **78** 40 60
158 10 c. *Pitcairn* (missionary schooner), 1890 50 85
159 18 c. *Athenic* (liner), 1904 .. .. .. 60 1·40
160 50 c. *Gothic* (liner), 1948 .. .. .. 1·25 2·25
157/60 .. .. *Set of* 4 2·50 4·50
MS161 145×110 mm. Nos. 157/60 .. .. 10·00 15·00
w. Wmk Crown to right of CA .. .. 42·00

*The normal watermark shows Crown to left of CA, *as seen from the back of the stamp.*

79 *Polistes jadwigae* (wasp)

80 Fletcher Christian

(Des Jennifer Toombs. Litho Questa)

1975 (9 Nov). *Pitcairn Insects. T* **79** *and similar horiz designs. Multicoloured.* W w **12** *(sideways). P* 14.

162 4 c. Type **79** 40 45
163 6 c. *Euconocephalus* sp (grasshopper) .. 50 55
164 10 c. *Anomis flavia* and *Chasmina tibialis* (moths) 60 70
165 15 c. *Pantala flavescens* (skimmer) .. .. 80 1·25
166 20 c. *Gnathothlibus erotus* (Banana moth) .. 1·10 1·50
162/6 .. .. *Set of* 5 3·00 4·00

(Des Jennifer Toombs. Litho J.W.)

1976 (4 July). *Bicentenary of American Revolution. T* **80** *and similar vert designs. Multicoloured.* W w **14**. *P* 13½.

167 5 c. Type **80** 30 65
a. Horiz pair. Nos. 167 and 169 .. .. 80 1·60
168 10 c. H.M.S. *Bounty* 40 80
a. Horiz pair. Nos. 168 and 170 .. .. 1·10 2·25

169 30 c. George Washington 50 95
170 50 c. *Mayflower*, 1620 .. .. 70 1·50
167/70 .. .. *Set of* 4 1·75 3·50

The 5 and 30 c. and 10 and 50 c. values were each printed together, *se-tenant*, in horizontal pairs throughout the sheets.

81 Chair of Homage

82 The Island's Bell

(Des Jennifer Toombs. Litho J.W.)

1977 (6 Feb). *Silver Jubilee. T* **81** *and similar vert designs. Multi-coloured. W* w **14**. *P* 13.

171 8 c. Prince Philip's visit, 1971 .. .. .. 10 15
172 20 c. Type **81** 20 25
173 50 c. Enthronement 40 50
171/3 .. .. *Set of* 3 60 80

(Des Jennifer Toombs. Litho Walsall)

1977 (12 Sept)–**81**. *Various multicoloured designs as T* **82**. *W* w **14** (*sideways* on horiz designs*). *P* 14.

174 1 c. Type **82** 30 50
175 2 c. Building a longboat (*horiz*) 30 50
176 5 c. Landing cargo (*horiz*) 35 50
177 6 c. Sorting supplies (*horiz*) 30 50
178 9 c. Cleaning wahoo (fish) 30 50
w. Wmk inverted .. .. 70·00 25·00
179 10 c. Cultivation (*horiz*) 30 50
179*a* 15 c. Sugar Mill (*horiz*) (1.10.81) .. .. 1·25 1·00
180 20 c. Grating coconut and bananas (*horiz*) 30 50
181 35 c. The Island church (*horiz*) 35 70
w. Wmk Crown to right of CA 70
182 50 c. Fetching miro logs, Henderson Is (*horiz*) 35 80
aw. Wmk Crown to right of CA .. .. 2·00
182*b* 70 c. Burning obsolete stamp issues (1.10.81) 1·25 1·25
183 $1 Prince Philip, Bounty Bay and Royal Yacht *Britannia* (*horiz*) .. .. .. 50 1·10
184 $2 Queen Elizabeth II (photograph by Reginald Davis) .. .. 90 1·75
174/84 .. .. *Set of* 13 6·00 9·00

*The normal sideways watermark shows Crown to left of CA, *as seen from the back of the stamp.*

83 Building a *Bounty* Model

84 Coronation Ceremony

(Des E. W. Roberts. Litho Questa)

1978 (9 Jan). *"Bounty Day". T* **83** *and similar horiz designs. Multicoloured. W* w **14** (*sideways**). *P* 14½.

185 6 c. Type **83** 35 35
186 20 c. The model at sea 45 60
187 35 c. Burning the model 60 70
185/7 .. .. *Set of* 3 1·25 1·50
MS188 166×122 mm. Nos. 185/7 .. .. 5·50 9·00
w. Wmk Crown to right of CA .. ..

*The normal sideways watermark shows Crown to left of CA, *as seen from the back of the stamp.*

(Des Jennifer Toombs. Litho Cartor)

1978 (9 Oct). *25th Anniv of Coronation. Sheet* 94×78 *mm. W* w **14**. *P* 12.

MS189 **84** $1.20, multicoloured .. .. .. 80 1·75
w. Wmk inverted .. .. .. 4·75

85 Harbour before Development

(Des J.W. Litho Bruder Rosenbaum, Vienna)

1978 (18 Dec). *"Operation Pallium" (Harbour Development Project). T* **85** *and similar horiz designs. Multicoloured. W* w **14** (*sideways**). *P* 13½.

190 15 c. Type **85** 30 50
w. Wmk Crown to left of CA 75
191 20 c. Unloading R.F.A. *Sir Geraint* 40 60
w. Wmk Crown to left of CA 85
192 30 c. Work on the jetty 45 70
w. Wmk Crown to left of CA 95
193 35 c. Harbour after development 50 80
w. Wmk Crown to left of CA .. .. 1·00
190/3 .. .. *Set of* 4 1·50 2·40

*The normal sideways watermark shows Crown to right of CA, *as seen from the back of the stamp.*

86 John Adams and Diary Extract

(Des Jennifer Toombs. Litho Questa)

1979 (5 Mar). *150th Death Anniv of John Adams (mutineer from the "Bounty"). T* **86** *and similar horiz design. Multicoloured. W* w **14** (*sideways*). *P* 14.

194 35 c. Type **86** 30 70
195 70 c. John Adams' grave and diary extract .. 45 90

87 Pitcairn's Island sketched from H.M.S. *Amphitrite*

(Des Jennifer Toombs. Litho Questa)

1979 (12 Sept). *19th-century Engravings. T* **87** *and similar horiz designs. W* w **14** (*sideways*). *P* 14.

196 6 c. black, brown-ochre and stone 15 20
197 9 c. black, violet and pale violet 15 25
198 20 c. black, brt green & pale yellowish green 15 40
199 70 c. black, scarlet and pale rose .. .. 50 1·00
196/9 .. .. *Set of* 4 85 1·75

Designs:—9 c. Bounty Bay and Village of Pitcairn; 20 c. Lookout Ridge; 70 c. Church and School House.

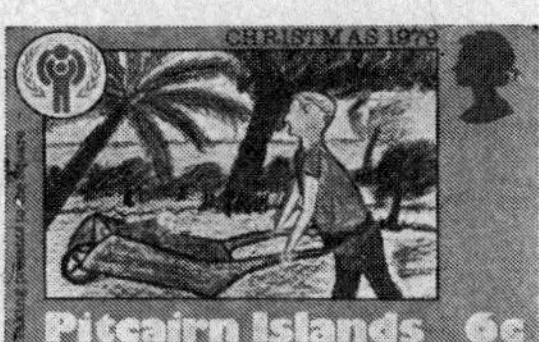

88 Taking Presents to the Square

(Des and litho J.W.)

1979 (28 Nov). *Christmas and International Year of the Child. T* **88** *and similar horiz designs. Multicoloured. W* w **14** (*sideways*). *P* 13.

200 6 c. Type **88** 10 20
201 9 c. Decorating trees with the presents .. 10 25
202 20 c. Chosen men distribute the gifts 20 40
203 35 c. Carrying presents home 25 50
200/3 .. .. *Set of* 4 55 1·25
MS204 198×73 mm. Nos. 200/3. P 13½×14 .. 1·10 1·40

89 Loading Mail from Supply Ship to Longboats

(Des Jennifer Toombs. Litho Format)

1980 (6 May). *"London 1980" International Stamp Exhibition. Sheet* 120×135 *mm containing T* **89** *and similar horiz designs. Multicoloured. W* w **14** (*sideways**). *P* 14½.

MS205 35 c. Type **89**; 35 c. Mail being conveyed by "Flying Fox" (hoisting mechanism) to the Edge; 35 c. Tractor transporting mail from the Edge to Adamstown; 35 c. Mail being off-loaded at Post Office .. .. 75 1·50
w. Wmk Crown to right of CA .. ..

*The normal sideways watermark shows Crown to left of CA, *as seen from the back of the miniature sheet.*

90 Queen Elizabeth the Queen Mother at Henley Regatta

(Des Harrison. Litho Questa)

1980 (4 Aug). *80th Birthday of Queen Elizabeth the Queen Mother. W* w **14** (*sideways*). *P* 14.

206 **90** 50 c. multicoloured 40 70

(Des Jennifer Toombs. Litho Questa)

1980 (29 Sept). *Handicrafts* (*2nd series*). *Multicoloured designs as T* **46**. *W* w **14** (*sideways* on* 9 *and* 20 *c.*). *P* 14.

207 9 c. Turtles (wood carvings) 10 10
208 20 c. Pitcairn wheelbarrow (wood carving) 10 15
w. Wmk Crown to right of CA .. .. 80·00
209 35 c. Gannet (wood carving) (*vert*) .. 15 25
210 40 c. Woven bonnet and fan (*vert*) .. 15 25
w. Wmk inverted .. .. 90·00
207/10 .. .. *Set of* 4 40 65

*The normal sideways watermark shows Crown to left of CA, *as seen from the back of the stamp.*

91 Part of Adamstown

(Des BG Studio. Litho Rosenbaum Bros, Vienna)

1981 (22 Jan). *Landscapes. T* **91** *and similar horiz designs. Multicoloured. W* w **14** (*sideways**). *P* 13½.

211 6 c. Type **91** 10 10
w. Wmk Crown to right of CA .. .. 10·00
212 9 c. Big George 10 15
w. Wmk Crown to right of CA .. .. 10·00
213 20 c. Christian's Cave, Gannets Ridge .. 15 20
w. Wmk Crown to right of CA .. .. 7·00
214 35 c. Radio Station from Pawala Valley Ridge 20 30
w. Wmk Crown to right of CA .. .. 3·50
215 70 c. Tatrimoa 30 45
211/15 .. .. *Set of* 5 75 1·10

*The normal sideways watermark shows Crown to left of CA, *as seen from the back of the stamp.*

92 Islanders preparing for Departure

93 Prince Charles as Colonel-in-Chief, Cheshire Regiment

(Des Jennifer Toombs. Litho Heraclio Fournier)

1981 (3 May). *125th Anniv of Pitcairn Islanders' Migration to Norfolk Island. T* **92** *and similar horiz designs. Multicoloured. P* 13 × 14.

216 9 c. Type **92** 30 30
217 35 c. View of Pitcairn Island from *Morayshire* 50 50
218 70 c. *Morayshire* 80 80
216/18 .. .. *Set of* 3 1·40 1·40

(Des J.W. Litho Format)

1981 (22 July). *Royal Wedding. T* **93** *and similar vert designs. Multicoloured. W* w **14**. *P* 14.

219 20 c. Wedding bouquet from Pitcairn Islands 20 20
220 35 c. Type **93** 25 20
221 $1.20, Prince Charles and Lady Diana Spencer 75 60
w. Wmk inverted .. .. .. 60·00
219/21 .. .. *Set of* 3 1·10 90

94 Lemon

95 Pitcairn Islands Coat of Arms

(Des Daphne Padden. Litho Harrison)

1982 (23 Feb). *Fruit. T* **94** *and similar horiz designs. Multicoloured.* W w **14** *(sideways)*. P 14½.

222	9 c. Type **94**	10	10
223	20 c. Pomegranate	15	20
224	35 c. Avocado	25	30
225	70 c. Pawpaw	50	65
222/5	*Set of* 4	90	1·10

(Des Jennifer Toombs. Litho Harrison)

1982 (1 July). *21st Birthday of Princess of Wales. T* **95** *and similar vert designs. Multicoloured.* W w **14**. P 14½ × 14.

226	6 c. Type **95**	10	20
227	9 c. Princess at Royal Opera House, Covent Garden, December 1981	30	20
228	70 c. Balcony Kiss	70	60
229	$1.20, Formal portrait	1·25	80
226/9	*Set of* 4	2·10	1·60

96 Raphael's Angels

(Des Leslie McCombie. Litho Walsall)

1982 (19 Oct). *Christmas. T* **96** *and similar designs showing Raphael's Angels.* W w **14** *(sideways* on 15 c. and 20 c.)*. P 13½×14 *(15 c., 20 c.) or* 14×13½ *(others)*.

230	15 c. black, silver and pink	15	15
	w. Wmk Crown to right of CA	25·00	
231	20 c. black, silver and pale lemon	15	15
232	50 c. yellow-brown, silver and stone	30	30
233	$1 black, silver and cobalt	40	40
230/3	*Set of* 4	90	90

The 50 c. and $1 are vertical designs.

*The normal sideways watermark shows Crown to left of CA, *as seen from the back of the stamp.*

97 Radio Operator

(Des Jennifer Toombs. Litho Harrison)

1983 (14 Mar). *Commonwealth Day. T* **97** *and similar horiz designs. Multicoloured.* W w **14** *(sideways*)*. P 13½.

234	6 c. Type **97**	10	10
235	9 c. Postal clerk	10	10
236	70 c. Fisherman	35	65
	w. Wmk Crown to right of CA	16·00	
237	$1.20, Artist	60	1·10
	w. Wmk Crown to right of CA	45·00	
234/7	*Set of* 4	1·00	1·60

*The normal sideways watermark shows Crown to left of CA, *as seen from the back of the stamp.*

98 *Topaz* sights Smoke on Pitcairn

(Des Jennifer Toombs. Litho B.D.T.)

1983 (14 June). *175th Anniv of Folger's Discovery of the Settlers. T* **98** *and similar horiz designs. Multicoloured.* W w **14** *(sideways)*. P 14.

238	6 c. Type **98**	30	20
239	20 c. Three islanders approach the *Topaz*	45	30
240	70 c. Capt. Mayhew Folger welcomed by John Adams	85	75
241	$1.20, Folger presented with *Bounty* chronometer	1·25	1·10
238/41	*Set of* 4	2·50	2·10

99 Hattie-Tree

(Des Jennifer Toombs. Litho B.D.T.)

1983 (6 Oct). *Trees of Pitcairn Islands (1st series). T* **99** *and similar horiz designs. Multicoloured.* W w **14** *(sideways)*. P 13½.

242	35 c. Type **99**	30	55
	a. Pair. Nos. 242/3	60	1·10
243	35 c. Leaves from Hattie-Tree	30	55
244	70 c. Pandanus	50	90
	a. Pair. Nos. 244/5	1·00	1·75
245	70 c. Pandanus and basket weaving	50	90
242/5	*Set of* 4	1·40	2·50

The two designs of each value were printed together, *se-tenant,* in horizontal and vertical pairs throughout the sheet.

See also Nos. 304/7.

100 Atava Wrasse

(Des C. Abbott. Litho Format)

1984 (11 Jan). *Fishes (1st series). T* **100** *and similar horiz designs. Multicoloured.* W w **14** *(sideways*)*. P 14½.

246	1 c. Type **100**	20	30
247	4 c. Black-eared Wrasse	30	35
248	6 c. Long-finned Parrotfish	30	35
249	9 c. Yellow-edged Lyretail	30	35
250	10 c. Black-eared Angelfish	30	40
	w. Wmk Crown to right of CA	55·00	
251	15 c. Emery's Damselfish	30	40
252	20 c. Smith's Butterflyfish	40	50
253	35 c. Crosshatched Triggerfish	50	60
254	50 c. Yellow Damselfish	50	75
255	70 c. Pitcairn Angelfish	70	95
256	$1 Easter Island Soldierfish	90	1·25
257	$1.20, Long-finned Anthias	1·75	2·00
	w. Wmk Crown to right of CA	5·50	
258	$2 White Trevally	2·25	2·50
246/58	*Set of* 13	8·00	9·50

*The normal sideways watermark shows Crown to left of CA, *as seen from the back of the stamp.*

For 90 c. and $3 values see Nos. 312/13.

101 "Southern Cross"

(Des J. Cooter. Litho Walsall)

1984 (14 May). *Night Sky. T* **101** *and similar horiz designs.* W w **14** *(sideways)*. P 14.

259	15 c. deep violet-blue, pale rose-lilac and gold	20	20
260	20 c. deep violet-blue, bright yell-grn & gold	30	30
261	70 c. deep violet-blue, yellow-ochre and gold	75	75
262	$1 deep violet-blue, pale blue and gold	1·00	1·00
259/62	*Set of* 4	2·00	2·00

Constellations:—20 c. "Southern Fish"; 70 c. "Lesser Dog"; $1 "The Virgin".

102 Aluminium Longboat

103 "H.M.S. *Portland* standing off Bounty Bay" (J. Linton Palmer)

(Des C. Abbott. Litho Enschedé)

1984 (21 Sept). *"Ausipex" International Stamp Exhibition, Melbourne. Sheet* 134 × 86 *mm containing T* **102** *and similar horiz design. Multicoloured.* W w **14** *(sideways)*. P 13½ × 14.

MS263	50 c. Type **102**; $2 Traditional-style wooden longboat	1·50	2·00

(Des Jennifer Toombs. Litho Questa)

1985 (16 Jan). *19th-Century Paintings (1st series). T* **103** *and similar horiz designs. Multicoloured.* W w **14** *(sideways)*. P 13½ × 14 ($2) *or* 14 *(others)*.

264	6 c. Type **103**	30	20
265	9 c. "Christian's Look Out" (J. Linton Palmer)	30	20
266	35 c. "The Golden Age" (J. Linton Palmer)	65	50
267	$2 "A View of the Village, 1825" (William Smyth) (48×31 *mm*)	1·75	1·60
264/7	*Set of* 4	2·75	2·25

The original printing of No. 267 was incorrectly dated "1835". The mistake was, however, spotted before issue and a replacement printing, correctly dated "1825", was provided. Those stamps dated "1835" were never issued for postal purposes, although examples exist which may have been supplied by various philatelic agents in error.

See also Nos. 308/11.

104 The Queen Mother with the Queen and Princess Margaret, 1980

105 *Act* 6 (container ship)

(Des A. Theobald ($2), C. Abbott (others). Litho Questa)

1985 (7 June). *Life and Times of Queen Elizabeth the Queen Mother. T* **104** *and similar vert designs. Multicoloured.* W w **16**. P 14½ × 14.

268	6 c. Receiving the Freedom of Dundee, 1964	10	20
	w. Wmk inverted	2·00	
269	35 c. Type **104**	30	55
	w. Wmk inverted	4·00	
270	70 c. The Queen Mother in 1983	50	80
271	$1.20, With Prince Henry at his christening (from photo by Lord Snowdon)	70	1·00
	w. Wmk inverted	10·00	
268/71	*Set of* 4	1·40	2·25
MS272	91×73 mm. $2 In coach at Ascot Races. Wmk sideways*	1·50	2·00
	w. Wmk Crown to right of CA	14·00	

*The normal sideways watermark shows Crown to left of CA, *as seen from the back of the stamp.*

(Des E. Nisbet. Litho Format)

1985 (28 Aug). *Ships (1st series). T* **105** *and similar multicoloured designs.* W w **14** *(sideways*)*. P 14 *(Nos. 273/4) or* 14×13½ *(others)*.

273	50 c. Type **105**	90	1·50
	w. Wmk Crown to right of CA	18·00	
274	50 c. *Columbus Louisiana* (container ship)	90	1·50
	w. Wmk Crown to right of CA	27·00	
275	50 c. *Essi Gina* (tanker) (48×35 *mm*)	90	1·50
276	50 c. *Stolt Spirit* (tanker) (48×35 *mm*)	90	1·50
273/6	*Set of* 4	3·25	5·50

*The normal sideways watermark shows Crown to left of CA, *as seen from the back of the stamp.*

See also Nos. 296/9.

106 "Madonna and Child" (Raphael)

107 Green Turtle

(Des Jennifer Toombs. Litho Walsall)

1985 (26 Nov). *Christmas. T* **106** *and similar vert designs showing "Madonna and Child" paintings. Multicoloured.* W w **16**. P 14 × 13½.

277	6 c. Type **106**	40	30
278	9 c. Krause (after Raphael)	40	30
279	35 c. Andreas Mayer	75	50
280	$2 Unknown Austrian master	2·50	3·00
277/80	*Set of* 4	3·50	3·50

(Des J. Thatcher. Litho Questa)

1986 (12 Feb). *Turtles. T* **107** *and similar horiz designs. Multicoloured.* W w **16** *(sideways)*. P 14½.

281	9 c. Type **107**	85	75
282	20 c. Green Turtle and Pitcairn Island	1·40	1·25
283	70 c. Hawksbill Turtle	2·75	3·00
284	$1.20, Hawksbill Turtle and Pitcairn Island	3·25	3·75
281/4	*Set of* 4	7·50	8·00

(Des A. Theobald. Litho Questa)

1986 (21 Apr). *60th Birthday of Queen Elizabeth II. Vert designs as T* **230a** *of Jamaica. Multicoloured.* W w **16**. P 14½×14.

285	6 c. Princess Elizabeth at Royal Lodge, Windsor, 1946	15	15
286	9 c. Wedding of Princess Anne, 1973	15	15
287	20 c. At Order of St. Michael and St. George service, St. Paul's Cathedral, 1961	25	30
288	$1.20, At Electrical Engineering Concert, Royal Festival Hall, 1971	65	1·25
289	$2 At Crown Agents Head Office, London, 1983	1·00	1·75
285/9	*Set of* 5	2·00	3·25

(Des D. Miller. Litho Questa)

1986 (23 July). *Royal Wedding. Square designs as T* **231a** *of Jamaica. Multicoloured.* W w **16**. P 14.

290	20 c. Prince Andrew and Miss Sarah Ferguson	35	50
291	$1.20, Prince Andrew aboard *Bluenose II* off Halifax, Canada, 1985	1·40	2·00

MACHINE LABEL. A 70 c. label inscribed "PITCAIRN IS. STAMPEX 86" was available between 4 and 10 August 1986 at this Adelaide stamp exhibition.

108 John I. Tay (pioneer missionary) and First Church **109** Pitcairn Island Home

(Des A. Theobald. Litho Walsall)

1986 (18 Oct). *Centenary of Seventh-Day Adventist Church on Pitcairn. T* **108** *and similar vert designs. Multicoloured. W* w **16**. *P* 14.

292 6 c. Type **108** 40 40
293 20 c. *Pitcairn* (missionary schooner) and second church (1907) .. .. 1·00 1·00
294 35 c. Baptism at Down Isaac and third church (1945) .. .. .. 1·50 1·50
295 $2 Islanders singing farewell hymn and present church (1954) .. .. 3·25 3·75
292/5 .. .. *Set of* 4 5·50 6·00

(Des E. Nisbet. Litho Format)

1987 (20 Jan). *Ships* (*2nd series*). *Multicoloured designs as T* **105**. *W* w **16** (*sideways on Nos.* 298/9). *P* 14 (*Nos.* 296/7) *or* 14×13½ (*others*).

296 50 c. *Samoan Reefer* (freighter) .. .. 1·25 1·90
297 50 c. *Brussel* (container ship) .. .. 1·25 1·90
298 50 c. *Australian Exporter* (container ship) (48×35 *mm*) .. .. 1·25 1·90
299 50 c. *Taupo* (cargo liner) (48×35 *mm*) .. 1·25 1·90
296/9 .. .. *Set of* 4 4·50 7·00

(Des E. Roberts and D. Robertson. Litho Format)

1987 (21 Apr). *Pitcairn Island Homes. T* **109** *and similar horiz designs showing different houses. W* w **14** (*sideways*). *P* 13½×14.

300 **109** 70 c. black, brt reddish violet & brt violet 60 60
301 – 70 c. black, pale orange-yell & brn-ochre 60 60
302 – 70 c. black, dull blue and ultramarine .. 60 60
303 – 70 c. black, blue-green & deep blue-green 60 60
300/3 .. .. *Set of* 4 2·25 2·25

(Des Jennifer Toombs. Litho Format)

1987 (10 Aug). *Trees of Pitcairn Islands* (*2nd series*). *Horiz designs as T* **99**. *Multicoloured. W* w **16** (*sideways**). *P* 14½.

304 40 c. Leaves and flowers from *Erythrina variegata* .. .. 80 1·10
a. Pair. Nos. 304/5 .. .. .. 1·60 2·10
aw. Wmk Crown to right of CA .. ..
305 40 c. *Erythrina variegata* tree .. .. 80 1·10
306 $1.80, Leaves from *Aleurites moluccana* and nut torch .. .. .. 2·25 2·75
a. Pair. Nos. 306/7 .. .. .. 4·50 5·50
aw. Wmk Crown to right of CA .. .. 80·00
307 $1.80, *Aleurites moluccana* tree .. 2·25 2·75
304/7 .. .. *Set of* 4 5·50 7·00

*The normal sideways watermark shows Crown to left of CA, *as seen from the back of the stamp.*

The two designs of each value were printed together, *se-tenant*, in horizontal and vertical pairs throughout the sheet.

(Des Jennifer Toombs. Litho Questa)

1987 (7 Dec). *19th-Century Paintings* (*2nd series*). *Horiz designs as T* **103** *showing paintings by Lt. Conway Shipley in* 1848. *Multicoloured. W* w **16** (*sideways*). *P* 13½×14 ($1.80) *or* 14 (*others*).

308 20 c. "House and Tomb of John Adams" .. 45 50
309 40 c. "Bounty Bay" 70 70
310 90 c. "School House and Chapel" .. .. 1·25 1·50
311 $1.80, "Pitcairn Island" (48×31 *mm*) .. 2·00 2·50
308/11 .. .. *Set of* 4 4·00 4·75

(Des C. Abbott. Litho Format)

1988 (14 Jan). *Fishes* (*2nd series*). *Horiz designs as T* **100**. *Multicoloured. W* w **16** (*sideways**). *P* 14½.

312 90 c. As No. 249 .. .. .. 2·25 2·50
w. Wmk Crown to right of CA .. .. 15·00
313 $3 Wakanoura Moray .. .. .. 4·25 4·75
w. Wmk Crown to right of CA .. .. 15·00

*The normal sideways watermark shows Crown to left of CA, *as seen from the back of the stamp.*

110 *Bounty* (replica) **111** H.M.S. *Swallow* (survey ship), 1767

(Des M. Bradbery. Litho Questa)

1988 (9 May). *Bicentenary of Australian Settlement. Sheet* 112 × 76 *mm. W* w **16**. *P* 14 × 13½.

MS314 **110** $3 multicoloured .. .. .. 2·75 2·50
w. Wmk inverted .. .. .. 25·00

(Des E. Nisbet. Litho B.D.T.)

1988 (14 Aug). *Ships. T* **111** *and similar horiz designs. Multicoloured. W* w **14** (*sideways*). "1988" *imprint date. P* 13½.

315 5 c. Type **111** 40 40
316 10 c. H.M.S. *Pandora* (frigate), 1791 .. 40 40
317 15 c. H.M.S. *Briton* and H.M.S. *Tagus* (frigates), 1814 .. .. .. 55 55
318 20 c. H.M.S. *Blossom* (survey ship), 1825 .. 60 60
319 30 c. *Lucy Anne* (barque), 1831 .. .. 70 70
320 35 c. *Charles Doggett* (whaling brig), 1831 70 70
321 40 c. H.M.S. *Fly* (sloop), 1838 .. .. 75 75
322 60 c. *Camden* (missionary brig), 1840 .. 1·00 1·00
323 90 c. H.M.S. *Virago* (paddle-sloop), 1853 .. 1·25 1·25
324 $1.20, *Rakaia* (screw-steamer), 1867 .. 1·50 1·50
325 $1.80, H.M.S. *Sappho* (screw-sloop), 1882 1·75 2·00
326 $5 H.M.S. *Champion* (corvette), 1893 .. 4·50 5·00
315/26 .. .. *Set of* 12 12·50 13·00

For 20 c. and 90 c. values as above, but watermarked w **16** (sideways), see Nos. 369 and 374.

112 Raising the Union Jack, 1838 **113** Angel

(Des Jennifer Toombs. Litho Walsall)

1988 (30 Nov). *150th Anniv of Pitcairn Island Constitution. T* **112** *and similar vert designs, each showing different extract from original Constitution. Multicoloured. W* w **14**. *P* 14.

327 20 c. Type **112** 15 20
328 40 c. Signing Constitution on board H.M.S. *Fly*, 1838 .. .. 30 35
329 $1.05, Voters at modern polling station .. 75 80
330 $1.80, Modern classroom .. .. 1·25 1·40
327/30 .. .. *Set of* 4 2·25 2·50

(Des M. Grimsdale. Litho Questa)

1988 (30 Nov). *Christmas. T* **113** *and similar vert designs. Multicoloured. W* w **16**. *P* 14 × 13½.

331 90 c. Type **113** 65 70
a. Horiz strip of 4. Nos. 331/4 .. .. 2·40
332 90 c. Holy Family 65 70
333 90 c. Two Polynesian Wise Men 65 70
334 90 c. Polynesian Wise Man and shepherd .. 65 70
331/4 .. .. *Set of* 4 2·40 2·50

Nos. 331/4 were printed together, *se-tenant*, in horizontal strips of four throughout the sheet.

114 Loading Stores, Deptford **115** R.N.Z.A.F. Lockheed P-3 Orion making Mail Drop, 1985

(Des C. Abbott. Litho Questa)

1989 (22 Feb). *Bicentenary of Pitcairn Island Settlement* (*1st issue*). *T* **114** *and similar horiz designs. Multicoloured. W* w **14** (*sideways*). *P* 14.

335 20 c. Type **114** 60 60
a. Sheetlet. Nos. 335/40 .. .. .. 3·25
336 20 c. H.M.S. *Bounty* leaving Spithead .. 60 60
337 20 c. H.M.S. *Bounty* at Cape Horn 60 60
338 20 c. Anchored in Adventure Bay, Tasmania 60 60
339 20 c. Crew collecting breadfruit 60 60
340 20 c. Breadfruit in cabin 60 60
335/40 .. .. *Set of* 6 3·25 3·25

Nos. 335/40 were printed together, *se-tenant* in sheetlets of six, as two horizontal rows of three separated by a central gutter.

See also Nos. 341/7, 356/61 and 389/94.

(Des C. Abbott. Litho Questa (Nos. 341/6), B.D.T. (No. **MS**347))

1989 (28 Apr). *Bicentenary of Pitcairn Island Settlement* (*2nd issue*). *Horiz designs as T* **114**. *Multicoloured. W* w **14** (*sideways*). *P* 14.

341 90 c. H.M.S. *Bounty* leaving Tahiti .. 1·75 2·00
a. Sheetlet. Nos. 341/6 .. .. .. 9·50
342 90 c. Bligh awoken by mutineers .. .. 1·75 2·00
343 90 c. Bligh before Fletcher Christian .. 1·75 2·00
344 90 c. Provisioning Bounty's launch .. 1·75 2·00
345 90 c. "Mutineers casting Bligh adrift" (Robert Dodd) .. .. .. 1·75 2·00
346 90 c. Mutineers discarding breadfruit plants 1·75 2·00
341/6 .. .. *Set of* 6 9·50 11·00
MS347 110 × 85 mm. 90 c. No. 345; 90 c. Isle of Man 1989 35p. Mutiny stamp; 90 c. Norfolk Island 39 c. Mutiny stamp. W w **16** (sideways) 3·50 4·00

Nos. 341/6 were printed in the same sheet format as Nos. 335/40

(Des A. Theobald. Litho Questa)

1989 (25 July). *Aircraft. T* **115** *and similar horiz designs. Multicoloured. W* w **16** (*sideways*). *P* 14×14½.

348 20 c. Type **115** 70 35
349 80 c. Beech 80 Queen Air on photo-mission, 1983 .. .. 1·60 95
350 $1.05, Boeing-Vertol CH-47 Chinook helicopter landing diesel fuel from U.S.S. *Breton*, 1969 .. .. 1·75 1·25
351 $1.30, R.N.Z.A.F. Lockheed C-130 Hercules dropping bulldozer, 1983 1·75 1·40
348/51 .. .. *Set of* 4 5·25 3·50

116 Ducie Island

(Des A. Theobald. Litho Walsall)

1989 (23 Oct). *Islands of Pitcairn Group. T* **116** *and similar horiz designs. Multicoloured. W* w **14** (*sideways*). *P* 14.

352 15 c. Type **116** 30 25
353 90 c. Henderson Island .. .. .. 1·40 90
354 $1.05, Oeno Island .. .. .. 1·50 1·25
355 $1.30, Pitcairn Island .. .. .. 1·50 1·25
352/5 .. .. *Set of* 4 4·25 3·25

(Des C. Abbott. Litho Questa)

1990 (15 Jan). *Bicentenary of Pitcairn Island Settlement* (*3rd issue*). *Horiz designs as T* **114**. *Multicoloured. W* w **16** (*sideways*). *P* 14.

356 40 c. Mutineers sighting Pitcairn Island .. 80 50
a. Sheetlet. Nos. 356/61 .. .. .. 4·25
357 40 c. Ship's boat approaching landing .. 80 50
358 40 c. Exploring island 80 50
359 40 c. Ferrying goods ashore 80 50
360 40 c. Burning of H.M.S. *Bounty* 80 50
361 40 c. Pitcairn Island village 80 50
356/61 .. .. *Set of* 6 4·25 2·75

Nos. 356/61 were printed in the same sheet format as Nos. 335/40.

117 Ennerdale, Cumbria, and Peter Heywood

(Des D. Ashby. Litho Questa)

1990 (3 May). *"Stamp World London 90" International Stamp Exhibition, London. T* **117** *and similar horiz designs showing English landmarks and Bounty crew members. Multicoloured. W* w **14** (*sideways*). *P* 14.

362 80 c. Type **117** 75 80
363 90 c. St. Augustine's Tower, Hackney, and John Adams 85 90
364 $1.05, Citadel Gateway, Plymouth, and William Bligh .. .. .. 1·00 1·25
365 $1.30, Moorland Close, Cockermouth, and Fletcher Christian .. .. .. 1·25 1·40
362/5 .. .. *Set of* 4 3·50 4·00

(Des E. Nisbet. Litho B.D.T.)

1990 (3 May). *As Nos.* 318 *and* 323, *but W* w **16** (*sideways*). *"1990" imprint date. P* 13½.

369 20 c. H.M.S. *Blossom* (survey ship), 1825 .. 1·00 1·40
a. Booklet pane. No. 369×4 with margins all round .. .. 4·00
374 90 c. H.M.S. *Virago* (paddle-sloop), 1853 .. 1·00 1·40
a. Booklet pane. No. 374×4 with margins all round .. .. 4·00

Nos. 369 and 374 only exist from $4.40 stamp booklets.

(Des D. Miller. Litho Questa)

1990 (4 Aug). *90th Birthday of Queen Elizabeth the Queen Mother. Vert designs as T* **107** (40 c.) *or* **108** ($3) *of Kenya. Multicoloured. W* w **16**. *P* 14×15 (40 c.) *or* 14½ ($3).

378 40 c. multicoloured 50 50
379 $3 black and dull scarlet .. .. 2·75 3·25

Designs:—40 c. Queen Elizabeth, 1937; $3 King George VI and Queen Elizabeth on way to Silver Wedding Service, 1948.

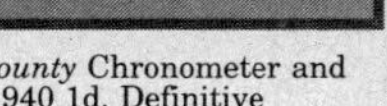

118 *Bounty* Chronometer and 1940 1d. Definitive **119** Stephen's Lory ("Redbreast")

(Des D. Miller. Litho Walsall)

1990 (15 Oct). *50th Anniv of Pitcairn Islands Stamps. T* **118** *and similar horiz designs. Multicoloured.* W w **14** (*sideways*). *P* 13½×14.

380 20 c. Type **118** 60 50
381 80 c. *Bounty* Bible and 1958 4d. definitive 1·25 1·25
382 90 c. *Bounty* Bell and 1969 30 c. definitive 1·40 1·40
383 $1.05, Mutiny on the *Bounty* and 1977 $1 definitive .. .. 1·60 1·75
384 $1.30, Penny Black and 1988 15 c. ship definitive .. .. 1·75 2·00
380/4 .. .. *Set of* 5 6·00 6·25

(Des N. Harvey from paintings by Byatt. Litho Questa)

1990 (6 Dec). *"Birdpex '90" Stamp Exhibition, Christchurch, New Zealand. T* **119** *and similar vert designs. Multicoloured.* W w **14**. *P* 14.

385 20 c. Type **119** 45 40
386 90 c. Henderson Island Fruit Dove ("Wood Pigeon") .. .. 1·25 1·40
387 $1.30, Pitcairn Warbler ("Sparrow") .. 1·60 2·00
388 $1.80, Henderson Island Crake ("Chicken Bird") .. .. 1·75 2·25
385/8 .. .. *Set of* 4 4·50 5·50

Nos. 385/8 carry the "Birdpex '90" logo and inscription in the gutter between the two panes.

(Des N. Shewring. Litho Leigh-Mardon Ltd, Melbourne)

1991 (24 Mar). *Bicentenary of Pitcairn Islands Settlement (4th issue). Celebrations. Horiz designs as T* **114**. *Multicoloured.* W w **16**. *P* 14½.

389 80 c. Re-enacting landing of mutineers .. 1·60 2·00
a. Sheetlet. Nos. 389/94 .. .. .. 8·50
390 80 c. Commemorative plaque .. .. 1·60 2·00
391 80 c. Memorial church service .. .. 1·60 2·00
392 80 c. Cricket match .. .. .. 1·60 2·00
393 80 c. Burning model of *Bounty* .. .. 1·60 2·00
394 80 c. Firework display .. .. .. 1·60 2·00
389/94 .. .. *Set of* 6 8·50 11·00

Nos. 389/94 were printed in the same sheet format as Nos. 335/40.

120 *Europa*

121 Bulldozer

(Des E. Nisbet. Litho Leigh-Mardon Ltd, Melbourne)

1991 (17 June). *Cruise Liners. T* **120** *and similar horiz designs. Multicoloured.* W w **16**. *P* 14½

395 15 c. Type **120** 75 40
396 80 c. *Royal Viking Star* .. .. .. 1·75 1·50
397 $1.30, *World Discoverer* .. .. .. 2·25 2·25
398 $1.80, *Sagafjord* .. .. 2·75 3·00
395/8 .. .. *Set of* 4 6·75 6·50

(Des D. Miller. Litho Questa)

1991 (12 July). *65th Birthday of Queen Elizabeth II and 70th Birthday of Prince Philip. Vert designs as T* **58** *of Kiribati. Multicoloured.* W w **16** (*sideways*). *P* 14½×14.

399 20 c. Prince Philip 40 30
a. Horiz pair. Nos. 399/400 separated by label .. .. 2·00 1·50
400 $1.30, Queen in robes of Order of St. Michael and St. George .. .. 1·60 1·25

Nos. 399/400 were printed in a similar sheet format to Nos. 366/7 of Kiribati.

(Des O. Bell. Litho Questa)

1991 (25 Sept). *Island Transport. T* **121** *and similar diamond-shaped designs. Multicoloured.* W w **14**. *P* 14.

401 20 c. Type **121** 40 30
402 80 c. Two-wheeled motorcycle .. .. 1·25 1·00
403 $1.30, Tractor .. .. 1·25 1·40
404 $1.80, Three-wheeled motorcycle .. 2·00 2·25
401/4 .. .. *Set of* 4 4·50 4·50

122 The Annunciation

123 Insular Shark

(Des Jennifer Toombs. Litho Questa)

1991 (18 Nov). *Christmas. T* **122** *and similar vert designs. Multicoloured.* W w **14**. *P* 14.

405 20 c. Type **122** 30 30
406 80 c. Shepherds and lamb 90 90
407 $1.30, Holy Family .. .. .. 1·25 1·25
408 $1.80, Three Wise Men .. .. .. 1·75 1·75
405/8 .. .. *Set of* 4 3·75 3·75

(Des D. Miller. Litho Questa ($1.80), Leigh-Mardon Ltd, Melbourne (others))

1992 (6 Feb). *40th Anniv of Queen Elizabeth II's Accession. Horiz designs as T* **113** *of Kenya. Multicoloured.* W w **14** (*sideways*) ($1.80) or W w **16** (*sideways*) (*others*). *P* 14.

409 20 c. Bounty Bay 25 25
410 60 c. Sunset over Pitcairn 70 70
411 90 c. Pitcairn coastline 90 90
412 $1 Three portraits of Queen Elizabeth .. 95 95
413 $1.80, Queen Elizabeth II .. .. .. 1·60 1·60
409/13 .. .. *Set of* 5 4·00 4·00

(Des Jane Thatcher. Litho Leigh-Mardon Ltd, Melbourne)

1992 (30 June). *Sharks. T* **123** *and similar horiz designs.* W w **14** (*sideways*). *P* 15×14½.

414 20 c. Type **123** 60 40
415 $1 Sand Tiger .. .. 1·60 1·40
416 $1.50, Black-finned Reef Shark .. .. 1·90 1·90
417 $1.80, Grey Reef Shark .. .. .. 2·00 2·00
414/17 .. .. *Set of* 4 5·50 5·00

124 *Montastrea* sp. and *Acropora* spp. (corals)

(Des I. Loe. Litho Enschedé)

1992 (11 Sept). *The Sir Peter Scott Memorial Expedition to Henderson Island. T* **124** *and similar horiz designs.* W w **14** (*sideways*). *P* 14×14½.

418 20 c. Type **124** 60 50
419 $1 Henderson Sandalwood .. .. .. 1·60 1·40
420 $1.50, Murphy's Petrel .. .. .. 2·40 2·25
421 $1.80, Henderson Hawkmoth .. .. 2·50 2·75
418/21 .. .. *Set of* 4 6·25 6·25

125 Bligh's Birthplace at St. Tudy, Cornwall

(Des Jennifer Toombs. Litho Leigh-Mardon Ltd, Melbourne)

1992 (7 Dec). *175th Death Anniv of William Bligh. T* **125** *and similar horiz design. Multicoloured.* W w **14**. *P* 14½.

422 20 c. Type **125** 40 40
423 $1 Bligh on *Bounty* .. .. .. 1·40 1·40
424 $1.50, Voyage in *Bounty's* launch .. 1·90 2·25
425 $1.80, "William Bligh" (R. Combe) and epitaph .. .. 2·00 2·25
422/5 .. .. *Set of* 4 5·00 5·50

126 H.M.S. *Chichester* (frigate)

127 Queen Elizabeth II in Coronation Robes

(Des A. Theobald. Litho Questa)

1993 (10 Mar). *Modern Royal Navy Vessels. T* **126** *and similar horiz designs. Multicoloured.* W w **16** (*sideways*). *P* 14.

426 15 c. Type **126** 50 40
427 20 c. H.M.S. *Jaguar* (frigate) 50 40
428 $1.80, H.M.S. *Andrew* (submarine) .. 2·50 2·50
429 $3 H.M.S. *Warrior* (aircraft carrier) and Westland Dragonfly helicopter .. .. 4·50 4·75
426/9 .. .. *Set of* 4 7·25 7·25

(Des D. Miller from photograph by Cecil Beaton. Litho Cartor)

1993 (17 June). *40th Anniv of Coronation.* W w **14**. *P* 13.

430 **127** $5 multicoloured .. .. .. 6·00 6·50

ALTERED CATALOGUE NUMBERS

Any Catalogue numbers altered from the last edition are shown as a list in the introductory pages.

128 Pawala Valley Ridge

(Des E. Nisbet. Litho Questa)

1993 (8 Sept). *Island Views. T* **128** *and similar horiz designs. Multicoloured.* W w **14** (*sideways*). *P* 13½×14.

431 10 c. Type **128** 20 20
432 90 c. St. Pauls 90 90
433 $1.20, Matt's Rocks from Water Valley 1·25 1·50
434 $1.50, Ridge Rope to St. Paul's Pool .. 1·50 1·75
435 $1.80, Ship Landing Point .. .. 1·75 2·25
431/5 .. .. *Set of* 5 5·00 6·00

129 Indo-Pacific Tree Gecko

130 Friday October Christian

(Des G. Drummond. Litho Walsall)

1993 (14 Dec). *Lizards. T* **129** *and similar horiz designs. Multicoloured.* W w **14** (*sideways*). *P* 13×13½.

436 20 c. Type **129** 60 40
437 45 c. Stump-toed Gecko 80 90
a. Horiz pair. Nos. 437/8 .. .. 1·60 1·75
438 45 c. Mourning Gecko 80 90
439 $1 Moth Skink .. .. 1·50 1·25
440 $1.50, Snake-eyed Skink .. .. .. 2·00 2·25
a. Horiz pair. Nos. 440/1 .. .. 4·00 4·50
441 $1.50, White-bellied Skink .. .. 2·00 2·25
436/41 .. .. *Set of* 6 7·00 7·00

Nos. 437/8 and 440/1 were each printed together, *se-tenant*, in horizontal pairs throughout the sheet.

1994 (18 Feb). *"Hong Kong '94" International Stamp Exhibition. As Nos. 437/8 and 440/1, but* W w **16** (*sideways*), *optd as T* **272** *of Jamaica.*

442 45 c. Stump-toed Gecko 80 90
a. Horiz pair. Nos. 442/3 .. .. 1·60 1·75
443 45 c. Mourning Gecko 80 90
444 $1.50, Snake-eyed Skink .. .. .. 2·25 2·75
a. Horiz pair. Nos. 444/5 .. .. 4·50 5·50
445 $1.50, White-bellied Skink .. .. 2·25 2·75
442/5 .. .. *Set of* 4 5·50 6·50

(Des Jennifer Toombs. Litho Questa)

1994 (7 Mar). *Early Pitcairners. T* **130** *and similar vert designs. Multicoloured.* W w **14**. *P* 14.

446 5 c. Type **130** 20 30
447 20 c. Moses Young 50 40
448 $1.80, James Russell McCoy .. .. 2·25 2·75
449 $3 Rosalind Amelia Young .. .. 3·75 5·00
446/9 .. .. *Set of* 4 6·00 7·50

131 Landing Stores from Wreck of *Wildwave*, Oeno Island, 1858

132 Fire Coral

(Des C. Abbott. Litho Walsall)

1994 (22 June). *Shipwrecks. T* **131** *and similar horiz designs. Multicoloured.* W w **14** (*sideways*). *P* 14×14½.

450 20 c. Type **131** 55 45
451 90 c. Longboat trying to reach *Cornwallis*, Pitcairn Island, 1875 .. .. .. 1·60 1·50
452 $1.80, *Acadia* aground, Ducie Island, 1881 2·50 3·00
453 $3 Rescuing survivors from *Oregon*, Oeno Island, 1883 .. .. 3·75 4·25
450/3 .. .. *Set of* 4 7·50 8·25

(Des G. Drummond. Litho Walsall)

1994 (15 Sept). *Corals. T* **132** *and similar multicoloured designs.* W w **14** (*sideways on* 90 c). *P* 14.

454 20 c. Type **132** 45 40
455 90 c. Cauliflower Coral and Arc-eyed Hawkfish (*horiz*) .. .. .. 1·50 1·50
456 $1 Lobe Coral and High-finned Rudderfish 1·50 1·60
454/6 .. .. *Set of* 3 3·00 3·25
MS457 100×70 mm. $3 Coral garden and Mailed Butterflyfish (*horiz*). Wmk sideways .. 3·50 4·00

133 Angel and *Ipomoea acuminata*

(Des Jennifer Toombs. Litho Walsall)

1994 (24 Nov). *Christmas. Flowers. T* **133** *and similar multicoloured designs. W w* **14** *(sideways on horiz designs). P* 14×14½ *(horiz) or* 14½×14 *(vert).*

458 20 c. Type **133** 35 25
459 90 c. Shepherds and *Hibiscus rosa-sinensis* (*vert*) .. .. 1·25 1·40
460 $1 Star and *Plumeria rubra* .. .. .. 1·25 1·40
461 $3 Holy Family and *Alpinia speciosa* (*vert*) 3·00 3·25
458/61 .. .. *Set of* 4 5·25 5·75

134 White Tern ("Fairy Tern") on Egg

(Des D. Miller. Litho Enschedé)

1995 (8 Mar). *Birds. T* **134** *and similar multicoloured designs. W w* **14** *(sideways on horiz designs). P* 13½×14 *(horiz) or* 14×13½ *(vert).*

462 5 c. Type **134** 10 10
463 10 c. Red-tailed Tropic Bird chick (*vert*) .. 10 10
464 15 c. Henderson Island Crake with chick .. 15 20
465 20 c. Red-footed Booby feeding chick (*vert*) 15 20
466 45 c. Blue-grey Noddy 30 35
467 50 c. Pitcairn Warbler ("Henderson Reed Warbler") in nest 35 40
468 90 c. Common Noddy 65 70
469 $1 Blue-faced Booby ("Masked Booby") and chick (*vert*) 75 80
470 $1.80, Henderson Island Fruit Dove .. 1·25 1·40
471 $2 Murphy's Petrel .. .. 1·50 1·60
472 $3 Christmas Island Shearwater .. 2·25 2·40
473 $5 Red-tailed Tropic Bird juvenile .. 3·75 4·00
462/73 .. .. *Set of* 12 11·00 12·00

135 Islanders in Longboats

136 Queen Elizabeth the Queen Mother

(Des G. Vasarhelyi. Litho B.D.T.)

1995 (26 June). *Oeno Island Holiday. T* **135** *and similar horiz designs. Multicoloured. W w* **14** *(sideways). P* 14×15.

474 20 c. Type **135** 25 35
475 90 c. Playing volleyball on beach .. .. 1·00 1·10
476 $1.80, Preparing picnic .. .. .. 1·90 2·25
477 $3 Singsong .. .. 3·25 3·75
474/7 .. .. *Set of* 4 5·75 6·75

(Des Jennifer Toombs. Litho Questa)

1995 (4 Aug). *95th Birthday of Queen Elizabeth the Queen Mother. Sheet* 75×90 *mm. W w* **16**. *P* 14½×14.

MS478 **136** $5 multicoloured .. .. .. 5·00 5·00

137 Guglielmo Marconi and Early Wireless, 1901

(Des N. Shewring. Litho Cartor)

1995 (5 Sept). *Centenary of First Radio Transmission. T* **137** *and similar horiz designs. Multicoloured. W w* **14** *(sideways). P* 13.

479 20 c. Type **137** 25 35
480 $1 Pitcairn radio transmitter, c. 1938 .. 1·10 1·25
481 $1.50, Satellite Earth Station equipment, 1994 .. .. 1·75 2·25
482 $3 Communications satellite in orbit, 1992 3·25 3·75
479/82 .. .. *Set of* 4 5·75 7·00

(Des A. Theobald. Litho Walsall)

1995 (24 Oct). *50th Anniv of United Nations. Horiz designs as T* **284** *of Jamaica. Multicoloured. W w* **16** *(sideways). P* 14.

483 20 c. United Nations float, Lord Mayor's Show 30 30
484 $1 R.F.A. *Brambleleaf* (tanker) .. .. 1·40 1·25
485 $1.50, U.N. ambulance .. .. .. 2·00 2·25
486 $3 R.A.F. Lockheed L-1011 TriStar .. 3·50 3·75
483/6 .. .. *Set of* 4 6·50 6·75

138 Early Morning at the Jetty **139** Chinese Junk

(Des L. Harraway. Litho Enschedé)

1996 (30 Jan). *Supply Ship Day. T* **138** *and similar horiz designs. Multicoloured. W w* **14** *(sideways). P* 14×15.

487 20 c. Type **138** 25 30
488 40 c. Longboat meeting *America Star* (supply ship) 45 55
489 90 c. Loading supplies into longboats .. 1·00 1·10
490 $1 Landing supplies on jetty .. .. 1·10 1·25
491 $1.50, Sorting supplies at the Co-op .. 1·75 2·25
492 $1.80, Tractor towing supplies .. .. 1·90 2·25
487/92 .. .. *Set of* 6 5·75 7·00

(Des D. Miller. Litho Cartor)

1996 (21 Apr). *70th Birthday of Queen Elizabeth II. Vert designs as T* **55** *of New Zealand (Tokelau), each incorporating a different photograph of the Queen. Multicoloured. W w* **14**. *P* 13½.

493 20 c. Bounty Bay 30 30
494 90 c. Jetty and landing point, Bounty Bay 1·10 1·10
495 $1.80, Matt's Rocks .. .. 2·00 2·25
496 $3 St. Pauls .. .. 3·50 4·00
493/6 .. .. *Set of* 4 6·25 7·00

(Des C. Abbott. Litho Questa)

1996 (17 May). *"CHINA '96" 9th Asian International Stamp Exhibition, Peking. T* **139** *and similar vert designs. Multicoloured. W w* **14**. *P* 14.

497 $1.80, Type **139** .. .. 1·90 2·25
498 $1.80, H.M.S. *Bounty* .. .. .. 1·90 2·25
MS499 80×79 mm. 90 c. China 1984 8 f. Year of the Rat stamp; 90 c. Polynesian rat eating banana. Wmk sideways .. .. .. 2·00 2·00

140 Island Profile and Radio Call Signs

(Des Jennifer Toombs. Litho Walsall)

1996 (4 Sept). *Amateur Radio Operations from Pitcairn Islands. T* **140** *and similar horiz designs. Multicoloured. W w* **16** *(sideways). P* 13½×14.

500 20 c. Type **140** 30 30
501 $1.50, Radio operator calling for medical assistance .. .. 1·75 1·75
a. Horiz pair. Nos. 501/2 .. .. .. 3·50 3·50
502 $1.50, Doctors giving medical advice by radio .. .. 1·75 1·75
503 $2.50, Andrew Young (first radio operator), 1938 .. .. 2·50 2·50
500/3 .. .. *Set of* 4 5·75 5·75

Nos. 501/2 were printed together, *se-tenant*, in horizontal pairs throughout the sheet.

141 Henderson Island Reed Warbler

142 Coat of Arms

(Des N. Arlott ($2), A. Robinson (others). Litho Walsall)

1996 (20 Nov). *Endangered Species. Local Birds. T* **141** *and similar multicoloured designs. W w* **14** *(sideways on $2). P* 13½×14 *($2) or* 14×13½ *(others).*

504 5 c. Type **141** 20 20
505 10 c. Stephen's Lory 20 20
506 20 c. Henderson Island Crake 35 35
507 90 c. Henderson Island Fruit Dove .. 1·10 1·10
508 $2 White Tern (*horiz*) .. .. .. 2·00 2·25
509 $2 Blue-faced Booby (inscr "Masked Booby") (*horiz*) .. .. 2·00 2·25
504/9 .. .. *Set of* 6 5·25 5·50

Nos. 504/9 were available from philatelic counters in Australia from 1 October 1996

(Des N. Shewring. Litho Questa)

1997 (12 Feb). *"HONG KONG '97" International Stamp Exhibition. Chinese New Year ("Year of the Ox"). Sheet* 82×87 *mm. W w* **14** *(sideways). P* 14½.

MS510 **142** $5 multicoloured .. .. .. 4·50 4·75

143 *David Barker* (supply ship)

(Des G. Vasarhelyi. Litho Questa)

1997 (26 May). *50th Anniv of South Pacific Commission. Sheet* 115×56 *mm, containing T* **143** *and similar horiz design. Multicoloured. W w* **14** *(sideways). P* 13½×14.

MS511 $2.50, Type **143**; $2.50, *McLachlan* (fishing boat) .. .. 4·75 4·75

144 Health Centre

(Des G. Vasarhelyi. Litho Questa)

1997 (12 Sept). *Island Health Care. T* **144** *and similar horiz designs. Multicoloured. W w* **14** *(sideways). P* 13½×14.

512 20 c. Type **144** 30 25
513 $1 Nurse treating patient .. .. .. 1·00 1·00
514 $1.70, Dentist treating woman .. .. 1·75 1·90
515 $3 Evacuating patient by ship .. .. 3·00 3·25
512/15 .. .. *Set of* 4 5·50 5·75

(Des D. Miller. Litho Cartor)

1997 (20 Nov). *Golden Wedding of Queen Elizabeth and Prince Philip. Multicoloured designs as T* **87** *of Kiribati. W w* **14**. *P* 13.

516 20 c. Prince Philip driving carriage .. 30 30
a. Horiz pair. Nos. 516/17 .. .. 60 60
517 20 c. Queen Elizabeth, 1994 .. .. 30 30
518 $1 Prince Philip at Royal Windsor Horse Show, 1996 .. .. 1·00 1·00
a. Horiz pair. Nos. 518/19 .. .. 2·00 2·00
519 $1 Queen Elizabeth with horse .. .. 1·00 1·00
520 $1.70, Queen Elizabeth and Prince Philip at the Derby, 1991 .. .. .. 1·50 1·50
a. Horiz pair. Nos. 520/1 .. .. 3·00 3·00
521 $1.70, Prince Charles hunting, 1995 .. 1·50 1·50
516/21 .. .. *Set of* 6 5·00 5·00

Nos. 516/17, 518/19 and 520/1 were each printed together, *se-tenant*, in horizontal pairs with the backgrounds forming composite designs.

145 Island and Star

(Des Jennifer Toombs. Litho Cartor)

1997 (1 Dec). *Christmas. T* **145** *and similar horiz designs. Multicoloured. W w* **14** *(sideways). P* 13½.

522 20 c. Type **145** 35 25
523 80 c. Hand ringing bell .. .. .. 1·00 80
524 $1.20, Presents in baskets .. .. 1·40 1·50
525 $3 Families outside church .. .. 2·75 3·00
522/5 .. .. *Set of* 4 5·00 5·00

COVER PRICES

Cover factors are quoted at the beginning of each country for most issues to 1945. An explanation of the system can be found on page x. The factors quoted do not, however, apply to philatelic covers.

146 Christian's Cave

(Des L. Harraway. Litho Walsall)

1997 (9 Dec). *Christian's Cave. T* **146** *and similar multicoloured designs showing different views. W* w **16** *(sideways on 5 c., 20 c.). P* 13½×14 *(horiz) or* 14×13½ *(vert).*

526	5 c. Type **146**	10	10
527	20 c. View from the beach	15	20
528	35 c. Cave entrance (*vert*)	25	30
529	$5 Pathway through forest (*vert*) ..	3·75	4·00
526/9	.. .. *Set of* 4	4·00	4·50

STAMP BOOKLETS

1940 (15 Oct). *Black on deep green cover. Stapled.*
SB1 4s. 8d. booklet containing one each ½d., 1d., 1½d., 2d., 3d., 6d., 1s. and 2s. 6d. (Nos. 1/5, 6, 7/8) £2750

Genuine examples of No. SB1 are interleaved with ordinary kitchen wax paper, which frequently tones the stamps, and are secured with staples 17 mm long.

The status of other booklets using different size staples or paper fasteners is uncertain although it is believed that some empty booklet covers were available on the island.

An unofficial booklet was released in 1986 containing Nos. 281/2, each in block of four, with "HELP PRESERVE PITCAIRN" slogan and showing the Flightless Chicken Bird and contents on the cover.

1990 (3 May). *Black on white cover. Stapled.*
SB2 $4.40, booklet containing 20 c. and 90 c., each in pane of 4 (Nos. 369a, 374a) .. .. .. 8·00

No. SB2 also exists overprinted on the cover with "New Zealand 1990" International Stamp Exhibition, Auckland, logo.

An unofficial version of No. SB2 was released in 1990 overprinted for "Birdpex '90" Stamp Exhibition, Christchurch.

1990 (3 May). *"Stamp World London 90" International Stamp Exhibition. As No.* SB2, *but with exhibition logo.*
SB3 $4.40, booklet containing 20 c. and 90 c. each in pane of 4 (Nos. 369a, 374a) .. .. .. 8·00

Prince Edward Island *see* Canada

Qatar

An independent Arab Shaikhdom, with a British postal administration until 23 May 1963.

There was no postal service from Qatar until 18 May 1950. Prior to this date the few foreign residents made their own arrangements for their mail to be carried to Bahrain for onward transmission through the postal services.

The first organised post from the capital, Doha, was an extension of the work in the state by the British Political Officer. From 18 May 1950 British residents were able to send mail via his office. The first three sendings had the Bahrain or British Postal Agencies in Eastern Arabia stamps cancelled by a circular office stamp, but later batches, up to the introduction of the first Doha postmark in July 1950, had the stamps cancelled on arrival at Bahrain.

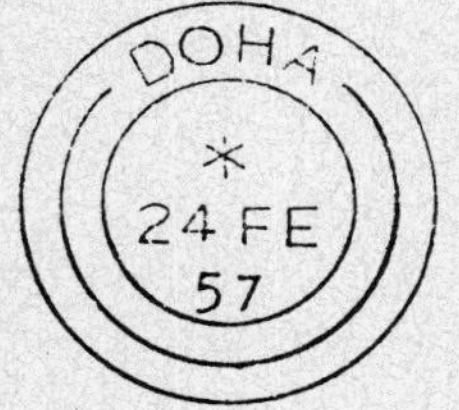

July 1950 Cancellation

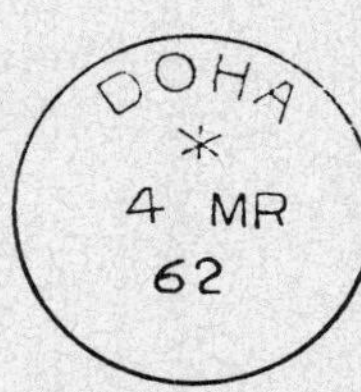

1956 Cancellation

The Post Office became a separate entity in August 1950 when its services were made available to the general public. After initially using the Bahrain surcharges on Great Britain the supply of stamps for the Qatar office was switched to the British Postal Agencies in Eastern Arabia surcharges.

The circular cancellation, dating from July 1950, continued to be used until replaced by a slightly smaller version in early 1956.

A further post office was opened on 1 February 1956 at the Umm Said oil terminal, using its own cancellation.

Both offices were issued with standard oval Registered handstamps, Doha in 1950 and Umm Said in 1956.

1956 Umm Said Cancellation

(Currency. 100 naye paise = 1 rupee)

All stamps to 1960 surcharged on Queen Elizabeth II issues of Great Britain

QATAR NP 1 NP (1)

QATAR 3 NP NP (2)

QATAR 75 NP (3)

1957 (1 Apr)–**59**. (*a*) *Nos.* 540/2, 543*b*/8, 551 *and* 555/6 (*St. Edwards's Crown wmk*), *surch as T* **1** *to* **3**.

1	**1**	1 n.p. on 5d. brown	10	10
2	**2**	3 n.p. on ½d. orange-red	15	15
3		6 n.p. on 1d. ultramarine	15	15
4		9 n.p. on 1½d. green	15	10
5		12 n.p. on 2d. light red-brown	20	40
6	**1**	15 n.p. on 2½d. carmine-red (I)	15	10
7	**2**	20 n.p. on 3d. deep lilac (B.)	15	10
8	**1**	25 n.p. on 4d. ultramarine	40	50
9		40 n.p. on 6d. reddish purple	15	10
		a. Deep claret (21.7.59)	30	10
10		50 n.p. on 9d. bronze-green	40	15
11	**3**	75 n.p. on 1s. 3d. green	50	60
12		1 r. on 1s. 6d. grey-blue	6·00	10
1/12		.. .. *Set of* 12	7·50	2·00

QATAR 2 RUPEES

I

QATAR 2 RUPEES

II

(4)

QATAR 5 RUPEES

I

QATAR 5 RUPEES

II

(5)

QATAR 10 RUPEES

I

QATAR 10 RUPEES

II

(6)

Type I (**4/6**). Type-set overprints. Bold thick letters with sharp corners and straight edges. Bars close together and usually slightly longer than in Type II.

Type II (**4/6**). Plate-printed overprints by Harrison. Thinner letters, rounded corners and rough edges. Bars wider apart.

(*b*) *Nos.* 536/8 (*St. Edward's Crown wmk*) *surcharged with T* **4/6**

			I (1.4.57)		II (18.9.57)	
13	2 r. on 2s. 6d. black-brown ..	..	3·50	2·00	9·00	6·00
14	5 r. on 5s. rose-red ..	..	4·50	2·75	9·00	16·00
15	10 r. on 10s. ultramarine	..	5·50	9·00	45·00	£120
13/15	.. ..	*Set of* 3	12·00	12·50	55·00	£130

QATAR 15 NP

(7)

1957 (1 Aug). *World Scout Jubilee Jamboree. Nos.* 557/9 *surch in two lines as T* **7** (15 *n.p.*) *or in three lines* (*others*).

16	15 n.p. on 2½d. carmine-red	25	35
17	25 n.p. on 4d. ultramarine	25	35
18	75 n.p. on 1s. 3d. green	30	35
16/18	.. .. *Set of* 3	70	95

1960 (26 Apr–28 Sept). *Nos.* 570/5 *and* 579 (*Mult Crown wmk*) *surcharged as T* **1** *or* **2.**

20	**2**	3 n.p. on ½d. orange-red (28.9)	70	1·75
21		6 n.p. on 1d. ultramarine (21.6)	1·25	2·75
22		9 n.p. on 1½d. green (28.9)	75	1·50
23		12 n.p. on 2d. light red-brown (28.9) ..	3·75	6·50
24	**1**	15 n.p. on 2½d. carmine-red (II)	35	10
25	**2**	20 n.p. on 3d. deep lilac (B.) (28.9) ..	35	10
26	**1**	40 n.p. on 6d. deep claret (21.6)	60	30
20/6		.. .. *Set of* 7	7·00	11·50

8 Shaikh Ahmad bin Ali al Thani

9 Peregrine Falcon

10 Dhow

11 Oil Derrick

12 Mosque

(Des O. C. Meronti (T **8**), M. Goaman (T **9**), M. Farrar Bell (T **10**), J. Constable and O. C. Meronti (T **11/12**). Photo Harrison, (T **8/10**). Recess D.L.R. (T **11/12**))

1961 (2 Sept). *P* 14½ (5 *n.p. to* 75 *n.p.*) *or* 13 (1 *r. to* 10 *r.*).

27	**8**	5 n.p. carmine	10	10
28		15 n.p. black	10	10
29		20 n.p. reddish purple	10	10
30		30 n.p. deep green	10	10
31	**9**	40 n.p. red	85	10
32		50 n.p. sepia	1·25	10
33	**10**	75 n.p. ultramarine	60	1·50
34	**11**	1 r. scarlet	70	10
35		2 r. ultramarine	2·00	40
36	**12**	5 r. bronze-green	13·00	1·50
37		10 r. black	35·00	3·50
27/37		.. .. *Set of* 11	48·00	6·50

The Qatar Post Department took over the postal services on 23 May 1963. Later stamp issues will be found listed in Part 19 (*Middle East*) of this catalogue.

Queensland *see* Australia

Rhodesia

Stamps of BECHUANALAND (see BOTSWANA) were used in Matabeleland on the runner post between Gubulawayo and Mafeking (Bechuanaland) from 9 August 1888 until 5 May 1894. Such stamps were cancelled "GUBULAWAYO" or by the barred oval "678" obliteration.

Between 27 June 1890 and 13 May 1892 external mail from Mashonaland sent via Bechuanaland was franked with that territory's stamps. A similar arrangement, using the stamps of MOZAMBIQUE existed for the route via Beira inaugurated on 29 August 1891. In both instances the stamps were cancelled by the post offices receiving the mail from Mashonaland. From 14 May until 31 July 1892 letters via Bechuanaland were franked with a combination of B.S.A Company and Bechuanaland issues.

Rhodesia joined the South African Postal Union on 1 August 1892 when its stamps became valid for international mail. Combination frankings with Mozambique stamps continued to be required until April 1894.

For the use of British Central Africa overprints in North-eastern Rhodesia from 1893 to 1899 see MALAWI (NYASALAND).

PRICES FOR STAMPS ON COVER TO 1945

Nos. 1/7	*from* × 5
Nos. 8/13	—
Nos. 14/17	*from* × 2
Nos. 18/24	*from* × 10
Nos. 25/6	—
Nos. 27/8	*from* × 7
Nos. 29/35	*from* × 10
Nos. 36/7	—
Nos. 41/6	*from* × 6
Nos. 47/50	—
Nos. 51/3	*from* × 2
Nos. 58/64	*from* × 3
Nos. 66/72	*from* × 8
Nos. 73/4	—
Nos. 75/87	*from* × 6
Nos. 88/93*a*	—
Nos. 94/9	*from* × 3
Nos. 100/10	*from* × 5
Nos. 111/13*e*	—
Nos. 114/18	*from* × 7
Nos. 119/60*a*	*from* × 8
Nos. 160*b*/6*b*	—
Nos. 167/78	*from* × 5
Nos. 179/81*a*	—
Nos. 182/5*a*	*from* × 4
Nos. 186/208	*from* × 6
Nos. 209/41	*from* × 5
Nos. 242/54*a*	—
Nos. 255/77	*from* × 5
Nos. 278/9*c*	—
Nos. 280/1	*from* × 10
Nos. 282/310	*from* × 5
Nos. 311/22	—

A. ISSUES FOR THE BRITISH SOUTH AFRICA COMPANY TERRITORY

1

2

½d. (3)

(Recess B.W.)

1892 (2 Jan)*–**93**. *Thin wove paper. P* 14, 14½.

1	**1**	1d. black	9·00	2·00
2		6d. ultramarine	48·00	20·00
3		6d. deep blue (1893)	22·00	3·00
4		1s. grey-brown	32·00	7·50
5		2s. vermilion	40·00	25·00
6		2s. 6d. grey-purple	27·00	28·00
7		2s. 6d. lilac (1893)	38·00	30·00
8		5s. orange-yellow	55·00	50·00
9		10s. deep green	65·00	95·00
10	**2**	£1 deep blue	£170	£130
11		£2 rose-red**	£400	£150
12		£5 sage-green	£1500	£450
13		£10 brown	£2750	£700
1/10		.. .. *Set of* 10	£350	£350

Great caution is needed in buying the high values in either used or unused condition, many stamps offered being revenue stamps cleaned and re-gummed or with forged postmarks.

*Printing of stamps in Types **1**, **2** and **4** commenced in 1890, although none were used for postal purposes before 2 January 1892 when the route to the East Coast was inaugurated.

**For later printings of the £2 see No. 74.

The following sheet watermarks are known on Nos. 1/26: (1) William Collins, Sons & Co's paper watermarked with the firm's monogram, and "PURE LINEN WOVE BANK" in double-lined capitals (1890 and 1891 ptgs). (2) As (1) with "EXTRA STRONG" and "139" added (1892 ptgs). (3) Paper by Wiggins, Teape & Co, watermarked "W T & Co" in script letters in double-lined wavy border (1893 ptgs). (4) The same firm's paper, watermarked "1011" in double-lined figures (1894 ptgs except ½d.). (5) "WIGGINS TEAPE & CO LONDON" in double-lined block capitals (1894 ptg of No. 18). Many values can also be found on a slightly thicker paper without wmk, but single specimens are not easily distinguishable.

1892 (2 Jan). *Nos. 2 and 4 surch as T* 3.
14 1 ½d. on 6d. ultramarine .. .. .. 80·00 £190
15 2d. on 6d. ultramarine .. .. .. 75·00 £275
16 4d. on 6d. ultramarine .. .. .. 95·00 £350
17 8d. on 1s. grey-brown £100 £375

Caution is needed in buying these surcharges as both forged surcharges and forged postmarks exist.

4

5 (ends of scrolls behind legs of springboks)

(T 4. Centre recess; value B.W.)

1892 (2 Jan)–**94**. *Thin wove paper* (*wmks as note after No.* 13). *P* 14, 14½.
18 4 ½d. dull blue and vermilion .. .. 2·50 1·75
19 ½d. deep blue and vermilion (1893) .. 2·75 3·50
20 2d. deep dull green and vermilion .. 14·00 1·75
21 3d. grey-black and green (8.92) .. .. 8·50 2·50
22 4d. chestnut and black .. .. 14·00 2·00
23 8d. rose-lake and ultramarine .. .. 10·00 7·00
24 8d. red and ultramarine (1892) .. .. 10·00 7·00
25 3s. brown and green (1894) .. .. £120 70·00
26 4s. grey-black and vermilion (1893) .. 30·00 45·00
18/26 .. .. *Set of* 7 £170 £120

(Recess P.B. from the Bradbury, Wilkinson plates)

1895. *Thick soft wove paper. P* 12½.
27 4 2d. green and red .. .. .. 20·00 7·00
28 4d. yellow-brown and black .. .. 22·00 10·00
a. Imperf (pair) £1800

(Centre recess; value typo P.B.)

1896–97. *Wove paper. P* 14.

(*a*) *Die I. Plates* 1 *and* 2.

Small dot to the right of the tail of the right-hand supporter in the coat of arms. Body of lion only partly shaded.
29 5 1d. scarlet and emerald .. .. 10·00 3·75
a. Carmine-red and emerald .. ..
30 2d. brown and mauve .. .. 16·00 1·50
31 3d. chocolate and ultramarine .. .. 3·00 1·00
32 4d. ultramarine and mauve .. .. 40·00
a. Imperf between (pair) .. ..
b. Blue and mauve .. .. 17·00 12·00
33 6d. mauve and pink .. .. 70·00 12·00
34 8d. green and mauve/*buff* .. .. 4·50 60
a. Imperf between (pair) ..
b. Imperf (pair) £1800
35 1s. green and blue .. .. 15·00 2·25
36 3s. green and mauve/*blue* .. .. 55·00 30·00
a. Imperf (pair) £4500
37 4s. orange-red and blue/*green* .. .. 42·00 2·00
29/37 .. .. *Set of* 9 £200 60·00

(*b*) *Die II. Plates* 3 *and* 4

No dot. Body of lion heavily shaded all over.
41 5 ½d. slate and violet .. .. 1·75 2·50
42 1d. scarlet and emerald .. .. 2·50 2·50
43 2d. brown and mauve .. .. 6·00 3·75
44 4d. ultramarine and mauve .. .. 60·00 11·00
a. Blue and mauve .. .. 7·50 50
46 6d. mauve and rose .. .. 6·00 50
47 2s. indigo and green/*buff* .. .. 20·00 7·00
48 2s. 6d. brown and purple/*yellow* .. 65·00 40·00
49 5s. chestnut and emerald .. .. 38·00 9·00
50 10s. slate and vermilion/*rose* .. .. 85·00 60·00
41/50 .. .. *Set of* 9 £200 £110

One Penny
(6)

THREE
PENCE.
(7)

(Surchd by *Bulawayo Chronicle*)

1896 (April). *Matabele Rebellion provisionals. Surch with T* 6 *and* 7.
51 6 1d. on 3d. (No. 21) £375 £375
a. "P" in "Penny" inverted £18000
b. "y" in "Penny" inverted .. ..
c. Surch double .. ..
52 1d. on 4s. (No. 26) £250 £225
a. "P" in "Penny" inverted £16000
b. "y" in "Penny" inverted £16000
c. Single bar through original value £900 £1000
53 7 3d. on 5s. (No. 8) £160 £200
a. "R" in "THREE" inverted £17000
b. "T" in "THREE" inverted £20000

Nos. 51 and 52 occur in two settings, one with 9¾ mm between value and upper bar, the other with 11 mm between value and upper bar.

BRITISH
SOUTH AFRICA
COMPANY.
(8)

9 (Ends of scrolls between legs of springboks)

1896 (22 May–Aug). *Cape of Good Hope stamps optd by Argus Printing Co, Cape Town, with T* 8. *Wmk Anchor* (3d. *wmk Crown CA*). *P* 14.
58 6 ½d. grey-black (No. 48*a*) .. .. 8·00 13·00
59 17 1d. rose-red (No. 58) .. .. 9·50 14·00
60 6 2d. deep bistre (No. 50*a*) .. .. 10·00 8·00
61 3d. pale claret (No. 40) .. .. 45·00 65·00
62 4d. blue (No. 51) .. .. 12·00 12·00
a. "COMPANY," omitted £8000
63 4 6d. deep purple (No. 52*a*) .. .. 48·00 60·00
64 6 1s. yellow-ochre (No. 65) (Aug) .. £110 £130
58/64 .. .. *Set of* 7 £225 £275

No. 62 also exists with "COMPANY" partially omitted. Examples with the word completely omitted, as No. 62a, occur on positions on 5 and 6 of the setting from four panes.

(Eng J. A. C. Harrison (vignette), Bain or Rapkin (£1) (frames). Recess Waterlow)

1897. *P* 13½ *to* 16.
66 9 ½d. grey-black and purple .. .. 1·60 3·50
67 1d. scarlet and emerald .. .. 3·00 3·75
68 2d. brown and mauve .. .. 4·25 80
69 3d. brown-red and slate-blue .. .. 2·50 30
a. Imperf between (vert pair) £1900
70 4d. ultramarine and claret .. .. 6·50 1·25
a. Imperf between (horiz pair) £6000 £6000
71 6d. dull purple and pink .. .. 6·50 3·50
72 8d. green and mauve/*buff* .. .. 11·00 40
a. Imperf between (vert pair) .. .. — £2000
73 £1 black and red-brown/*green* £350 £225

(Recess Waterlow, from the Bradbury plate)

1897 (Jan). *P* 15.
74 2 £2 rosy red £1700 £400

10

11

12

(Recess Waterlow)

1898–1908. *P* 13½ *to* 15½.
75 10 ½d. dull bluish green .. .. 2·00 40
a. Yellow-green (1904) .. .. 1·50 40
aa. Imperf vert (horiz pair) .. £650
ab. Imperf (pair) £700
76 ½d. deep green (*shades*) (1908) .. 23·00 80
77 1d. rose (*shades*) .. .. 2·00 30
a. Imperf (pair) £600 £600
b. Imperf between (vert pair) .. £500
78 1d. red (*shades*) (1905) .. .. 3·00 30
a. Imperf vert (horiz pair) £350 £375
ab. Imperf horiz (vert pair) £600
b. Imperf (pair) £500 £500
c. Imperf between (horiz pair) .. † £375
79 2d. brown .. .. 1·50 15
80 2½d. dull blue (*shades*) .. .. 3·75 60
a. Imperf vert (horiz pair) £800 £850
b. Grey-blue (*shades*) (1903) .. 10·00 80
81 3d. claret .. .. 3·75 65
a. Imperf between (vert pair) .. £700
82 4d. olive .. .. 4·25 20
a. Imperf between (vert pair) .. £700
83 6d. reddish purple .. .. 8·00 1·75
a. Reddish mauve (1902) .. .. 12·00 5·00
84 11 1s. bistre .. .. 9·50 1·50
a. Imperf between (vert pair) .. £2500
ab. Imperf between (horiz pair) .. £2750
b. Deep olive-bistre (1907) .. £275
bc. Imperf (pair) £2500
bd. Imperf between (horiz pair) .. £3250
c. Bistre-brown (1908) .. .. 50·00 12·00
d. Brownish yellow (1908) .. .. 14·00 4·75
85 2s. 6d. bluish grey (11.06) .. .. 38·00 65
a. Imperf between (vert pair) .. £1000 £500
b. Imperf (vert pair) .. .. — £5000
86 3s. deep violet (1902) .. .. 11·00 85
a. Deep bluish violet (1908) .. 55·00 9·50
87 5s. brown-orange .. .. 28·00 8·50
88 7s. 6d. black (11.01) .. .. 55·00 14·00
89 10s. grey-green .. .. 17·00 1·00
90 12 £1 greyish red-purple (*p* 15½) (7.01) £170 65·00
a. Perf 14. *Blackish purple* (1902) .. £275 60·00
91 £2 brown (5.08) .. .. 70·00 6·50
92 £5 deep blue (7.01) £3000 £2250
93 £10 lilac (7.01) £3250 £2250
93*a* £20 yellow-bistre (1901?) £13000
75/90 .. .. .. *Set of* 14 £300 80·00
80/1, 85/6, 88/93 Perf "Specimen" .. £900

A £100 cherry-red, perf 13½, was ordered in June 1901, a number of mint, together with several examples showing fiscal cancellations being known.

NEW INFORMATION

The editor is always interested to correspond with people who have new information that will improve or correct the Catalogue.

13 Victoria Falls

RHODESIA.
(14)

(Recess Waterlow)

1905 (13 July). *Visit of British Association and Opening of Victoria Falls Bridge. P* 13½ *to* 15.
94 13 1d. red .. .. .. 2·75 4·00
95 2½d. deep blue .. .. .. 7·50 4·75
96 5d. claret (Optd S. £150) .. .. 20·00 48·00
97 1s. blue-green .. .. .. 20·00 30·00
a. Imperf (pair) £14000
b. Imperf between (horiz pair) .. £18000
c. Imperf between (vert pair) .. £18000
d. Imperf vert (horiz pair) £15000
98 2s. 6d. black £100 £150
99 5s. violet .. .. .. 85·00 40·00
94/9 .. .. .. *Set of* 6 £200 £250
94/9 Perf (5d.) or Optd (others) "Specimen" *Set of* 6 £350

1909 (15 Apr)–**12**. *Optd as T* 14. *P* 13½ *to* 15.
100 10 ½d. green *to* deep green .. .. 1·50 50
a. No stop .. .. .. 45·00 28·00
b. Yellow-green (1911) .. .. 35·00 27·00
101 1d. carmine-rose .. .. 1·50 40
a. No stop .. .. .. 60·00 25·00
b. Imperf between (horiz pair) .. £375
c. Deep carmine-rose .. .. 1·50 30
cd. Imperf between (horiz pair) .. £375
102 2d. brown .. .. .. 1·60 3·25
a. No stop .. .. .. 80·00 55·00
103 2½d. pale dull blue .. .. 1·00 50
a. No stop .. .. .. 32·00 22·00
104 3d. claret .. .. .. 1·60 30
a. No stop .. .. .. 95·00 55·00
b. Opt inverted .. .. † 15·00
105 4d. olive .. .. .. 2·75 60
a. No stop .. .. .. 60·00 55·00
b. Opt inverted .. .. † 15·00
106 6d. reddish purple .. .. 5·00 2·50
a. No stop .. ..
b. Reddish mauve .. ..
c. Dull purple .. .. 14·00 3·50
ca. No stop .. .. .. 80·00 45·00
107 11 1s. bistre .. .. .. 18·00
a. No stop £150
b. Bistre-brown .. ..
ba. No stop .. .. ..
c. Deep brownish bistre .. .. 8·50 2·00
ca. No stop .. .. .. 80·00 35·00
108 2s. 6d. bluish grey .. .. 16·00 6·50
a. No stop .. .. .. 80·00 55·00
b. Opt inverted .. .. † 20·00
109 3s. deep violet .. .. 15·00 6·50
110 5s. orange .. .. .. 25·00 21·00
a. No stop .. .. .. 85·00 65·00
111 7s. 6d. black .. .. .. 65·00 11·00
112 10s. dull green .. .. .. 28·00 9·00
a. No stop £225 £180
113 12 £1 grey-purple .. .. .. £100 65·00
a. Vert pair, lower stamp without opt £22000
b. Opt in violet £325 £180
113*c* £2 brown £3500 £275
113*d* £2 rosy brown (*bluish paper*) (*p* 14½×15) (1912) .. £3250 £275
113*e* £5 deep blue (*bluish paper*) .. £5500 £2750
100/13 .. .. .. *Set of* 14 £225 £110
100/13 Perf "Specimen" .. *Set of* 14 £325

In some values the no stop variety occurs on every stamp in a vertical row of a sheet, in other values only once in a sheet. Other varieties, such as no serif to the right of apex of "A", no serif to top of "E", etc., exist in some values.

No. 113a comes from a sheet with the overprint omitted from the bottom row.

RHODESIA.
5d
(15)

RHODESIA.
TWO SHILLINGS.
(16)

1909 (April)–**11**. *Surch as T* 15 *and* 16 (2s.), *in black*.
114 10 5d. on 6d. reddish purple .. .. 6·50 9·50
a. Surcharge in violet .. .. 90·00
b. Reddish mauve .. ..
c. Dull purple .. .. 13·00 9·50
116 11 7½d. on 2s. 6d. bluish grey .. .. 3·50 2·50
a. Surcharge in violet .. .. 17·00 7·50
ab. Surch double .. .. † £6500
117 10d. on 3s. deep violet .. .. 13·00 15·00
a. Surcharge in violet .. .. 4·00 3·50
118 2s. on 5s. orange .. .. 12·00 7·00
114/18 .. .. .. *Set of* 4 £180

In the 7½d. and 10d. surcharges the bars are spaced as in T 16.

17

18

(Recess Waterlow)

1910 (11 Nov)–**13.** *(a) P* 14.

119 **17** ½d. yellow-green .. 7·50 1·00
a. Imperf between (horiz pair) .. £18000
120 ½d. bluish green .. 15·00 1·50
a. Imperf (pair) .. £8500 £4000
121 ½d. olive-green .. 24·00 1·75
122 ½d. dull green .. 60·00 50·00
123 1d. bright carmine .. 11·00 90
a. Imperf between (vert pair) .. £15000 £10000
124 1d. carmine-lake .. 32·00 1·00
125 1d. rose-red .. 14·00 90
126 2d. black and grey .. 35·00 7·00
127 2d. black-purple and slate-grey .. £160
128 2d. black and slate-grey .. 40·00 4·75
129 2d. black and slate .. 48·00 5·50
130 2d. black and grey-black .. 55·00 9·00
131 2½d. ultramarine .. 17·00 5·00
131*a* 2½d. bright ultramarine .. 15·00 5·00
132 2½d. dull blue .. 20·00 5·50
133 2½d. chalky blue .. 15·00 9·00
134 3d. purple and ochre .. 22·00 24·00
135 3d. purple and yellow-ochre .. 26·00 10·00
136 3d. magenta and yellow-ochre .. 95·00 10·00
137 3d. violet and ochre .. 80·00 75·00
138 4d. greenish black and orange .. 75·00 75·00
139 4d. brown-purple and orange .. 55·00 45·00
140 4d. black and orange .. 26·00 10·00
141 5d. purple-brown and olive-green .. 20·00 35·00
141*a* 5d. purple-brown and olive-yellow .. 20·00 45·00
ab. Error. Purple-brown and ochre .. £550 £150
143 5d. lake-brown and olive .. £225 60·00
143*a* 5d. lake-brown and green .. £18000 £1500
144 6d. red-brown and mauve .. 24·00 24·00
145 6d. brown and purple .. 24·00 9·50
145*a* 6d. bright chestnut and mauve .. £750 60·00
146 8d. black and purple .. £3750
147 8d. dull purple and purple .. £110 70·00
148 8d. greenish black and purple .. £110 65·00
149 10d. scarlet and reddish mauve .. 27·00 48·00
150 10d. carmine and deep purple .. £600 60·00
151 1s. grey-black and deep blue-green 27·00 15·00
151*a* 1s. black and deep blue-green .. 95·00 23·00
152 1s. black and pale blue-green .. 32·00 9·50
152*a* 1s. purple-black and blue-green .. £200 38·00
153 2s. black and ultramarine .. 60·00 50·00
154 2s. black and dull blue .. £900 55·00
154*a* 2s. purple-black and ultramarine .. £2750 £225
155 2s. 6d. black and lake .. £300 £275
155*a* 2s. 6d. black and crimson .. £300 £275
156 2s. 6d. sepia and deep crimson .. £375 £325
156*a* 2s. 6d. bistre-brown and crimson .. £950 £500
157 2s. 6d. black and rose-carmine .. £275 £275
158 3s. green and violet *(shades)* .. £140 £140
158*a* 3s. bright green and magenta .. £1000 £550
159 5s. vermilion and deep green .. £225 £250
160 5s. scarlet and pale yellow-green .. £275 £180
160*a* 5s. crimson and yellow-green .. £225 £180
160*b* 7s. 6d. carmine and pale blue .. £600 £425
161 7s. 6d. carmine and light blue .. £650 £650
162 7s. 6d. carmine and bright blue .. £1600 £800
163 10s. deep myrtle and orange .. £550 £250
164 10s. blue-green and orange .. £375 £300
165 £1 carmine-red and bluish black .. £950 £400
166 £1 rose-scarlet and bluish black .. £1000 £350
166*a* £1 crimson and slate-black .. £1100 £750
b. Error. Scarlet and reddish mauve £8500

(b) P 15

167 **17** ½d. blue-green .. £250 13·00
168 ½d. yellow-green .. £300 11·00
169 ½d. apple-green .. £550 27·00
170 1d. carmine .. £250 8·00
170*a* 1d. carmine-lake .. £400 13·00
170*b* 1d. rose-carmine .. £275 10·00
171 2d. black and grey-black .. £650 27·00
171*a* 2d. black and grey .. £650 27·00
171*b* 2d. black and slate .. £700 27·00
172 2½d. ultramarine *(shades)* .. 70·00 35·00
173 3d. purple and yellow-ochre .. £3750 50·00
173*a* 3d. claret and pale yellow-ochre .. £1800 50·00
174 4d. black and orange *(shades)* .. 38·00 60·00
175 5d. lake-brown and olive .. £750 75·00
176 6d. brown and mauve .. £800 60·00
177 1s. black and blue-green *(shades)* .. £850 55·00
178 2s. black and dull blue .. £1700 £325
179 £1 red and black .. £13000 £3000

(c) P 14×15 *(½d., 3d., 1s.) or* 15×14 *(1d., 4d.)*

179*a* **17** ½d. yellow-green .. † £2500
179*b* 1d. carmine .. † £4000
180 3d. purple and ochre .. £4000 £200
181 4d. black and orange .. £425
181*a* 1s. black and blue-green .. £18000 £2500

(d) P 13½

182 **17** ½d. yellow-green .. £250 40·00
182*a* ½d. green .. £300 40·00
183 1d. bright carmine .. £1700 48·00
184 2½d. ultramarine *(shades)* .. 35·00 55·00
185 8d. black and purple *(shades)* .. 60·00 £200
185*a* 8d. grey-purple and dull purple .. £375 £375
119/185 Optd "Specimen" perf 14 except 2½d. and 8d. perf 13½ .. *Set of* 18 £3000

Plate varieties in T **17** are:—½d., double dot below "D" in right-hand value tablet (R. 3/9) *(from £500 un. £350 used)*; 2d. to £1 excluding 2½d., straight stroke in Queen's right ear known as the "gash in ear" variety (R. 1/2) *(from 3 to 5 times normal)*.

Stamps from the above and the next issue are known compound perf with 14 or 15 on one side only or on adjoining sides but we no longer list them.

Examples of some values are known with a forged registered Bulawayo postmark dated "JA 10 11".

(Recess Waterlow)

1913 (1 Sept)–**22.** *No wmk.* (i) *From single working plates.*

(a) P 14.

186 **18** ½d. blue-green .. 4·75 75
187 ½d. deep green .. 4·00 75
a. Imperf horiz (vert pair) .. £600
188 ½d. yellow-green .. 7·50 75
188*b* ½d. dull green .. 5·00 75
ba. Imperf vert (horiz pair) .. £650 £650
189 **18** ½d. bright green .. 11·00 75
a. Imperf between (vert pair) .. £1000
190 1d. rose-carmine .. 4·00 75
a. Imperf between (horiz pair) .. £600 £500
191 1d. carmine-red *(shades)* .. 8·00 75
a. Imperf between (pair) .. £900
192 1d. brown-red .. 2·75 75
193 1d. red .. 4·00 75
a. Imperf between (horiz pair) .. £600
194 1d. scarlet .. 12·00 1·00
a. Imperf between (horiz pair) .. £750
195 1d. rose-red .. 6·50 75
a. Imperf between (horiz pair) .. £475
b. Imperf between (vert pair) .. £1500
196 1d. rosine .. £500 19·00
197 1½d. brown-ochre (1919) .. 2·50 60
a. Imperf between (horiz pair) .. £500 £500
198 1½d. bistre-brown (1917) .. 2·25 60
a. Imperf between (horiz pair) .. £550 £550
199 1½d. drab-brown (1917) .. 2·75 60
a. Imperf between (horiz pair) .. £500
b. Imperf between (vert pair) .. £1400
200 2½d. deep blue .. 3·25 17·00
201 2½d. bright blue .. 3·25 17·00

(b) P 15

202 **18** ½d. blue-green .. 8·50 9·50
203 ½d. green .. 13·00 7·50
204 1d. rose-red .. £550 22·00
a. Imperf between (horiz pair) .. £9000
205 1d. brown-red .. 2·25 3·75
206 1½d. bistre-brown (1919) .. 22·00 7·00
a. Imperf between (horiz pair) .. £10000
206*b* 1½d. brown-ochre (1917) .. 30·00 9·50
207 2½d. deep blue .. 18·00 29·00
208 2½d. bright blue .. 16·00 28·00

(c) P 14 × 15

208*a* **18** ½d. green .. £4000 £150

(d) P 15×14

208*b* **18** ½d. green .. £4000 £250
208*c* 1½d. drab-brown

(e) P 13½

208*d* **18** 1d. red *(shades)* .. — £425

Die I Die II Die III

The remaining values were printed from double, i.e. head and duty, plates. There are at least four different head plates made from three different dies, which may be distinguished as follows:—

Die I. The King's left ear is neither shaded nor outlined; no outline to top of cap. Shank of anchor in cap badge is complete.

Die II. The ear is shaded all over, but has no outline. The top of the cap has a faint outline. Anchor as Die I.

Die III. The ear is shaded and outlined; a heavy continuous outline round the cap. Shank of anchor is broken just below the lowest line which crosses it.

(ii) *Printed from double plates. Head Die* I. *(a) P* 14.

209 **18** 2d. black and grey .. 8·00 5·00
210 3d. black and yellow .. 70·00 5·00
211 4d. black and orange-red .. 5·00 20·00
212 5d. black and green .. 3·50 7·50
213 6d. black and mauve .. £170 23·00
213*a* 8d. violet and green .. £4250
214 2s. black and brown .. 80·00 70·00

(b) P 15

215 **18** 3d. black and yellow .. 4·00 11·00
216 4d. black and orange-red .. £120 11·00
217 6d. black and mauve .. 3·75 4·00
217*a* 8d. violet and green .. £14000 £14000
218 2s. black and brown .. 10·00 23·00

(iii) *Head Die* II. *(a) P* 14

219 **18** 2d. black and grey .. 12·00 1·50
220 2d. black and brownish grey .. 29·00 3·50
221 3d. black and deep yellow .. 24·00 3·50
222 3d. black and yellow .. 55·00 3·50
223 3d. black and buff .. 6·50 3·50
224 4d. black and orange-red .. 17·00 4·50
225 4d. black and deep orange-red .. 8·00 4·50
226 5d. black and grey-green .. 13·00 24·00
227 5d. black and bright green .. 11·00 24·00
228 6d. black and mauve .. 23·00 1·75
229 6d. black and purple .. 50·00 3·25
230 8d. violet and green .. 9·50 40·00
231 10d. blue and carmine-red .. 14·00 27·00
232 1s. black and greenish blue .. 28·00 27·00
233 1s. black and turquoise-blue .. 6·50 7·00
234 2s. black and brown .. 65·00 7·00
235 2s. black and yellow-brown .. £225 22·00
236 2s. 6d. indigo and grey-brown .. 42·00 21·00
236*a* 2s. 6d. pale blue and brown .. £200 35·00
236*b* 3s. brown and blue .. 65·00 85·00
237 3s. chestnut and bright blue .. 65·00 90·00
238 5s. blue and yellow-green .. £100 55·00
239 5s. blue and blue-green .. 42·00 48·00
240 7s. 6d. blackish purple and slate-black £225 £225
241 10s. crimson and yellow-green .. £160 £200
242 £1 black and purple .. £350 £450
243 £1 black and violet .. £350 £500

(b) P 15

244 **18** 2d. black and grey .. 3·75 3·75
245 4d. black and deep orange-vermilion .. £1100 £250
246 8d. violet and green .. £170 £140
247 10d. blue and red .. 4·50 22·00
248 1s. black and greenish blue .. 32·00 6·50
249 2s. 6d. indigo and grey-brown .. 30·00 65·00
250 3s. chocolate and blue .. £600 £250
251 **18** 5s. blue and yellow-green .. £100 £110
251*a* 5s. blue and blue-green .. £1500
252 7s. 6d. blackish purple and slate-black 90·00 £140
253 10s. red and green .. £150 £250
254 £1 black and purple .. £1200 £1200
254*a* £1 black and deep purple .. £2750 £2500
186/254*a* Optd "Specimen" (various Dies and Perfs) .. *Set of* 19 £2000

(iv) *Head Die* III. *Toned paper, yellowish gum. (a) P* 14

255 **18** 2d. black and brownish grey .. 7·50 3·75
256 2d. black and grey-black .. 5·00 2·00
a. Imperf between (horiz pair) .. £4000
b. Imperf between (horiz strip of 3) £7000
c. Imperf vert (horiz pair) .. £3500 £3500
257 2d. black and grey .. 5·50 2·50
258 2d. black and sepia .. 25·00 4·50
259 3d. black and yellow .. 4·50 1·40
260 3d. black and ochre .. 4·50 1·40
261 4d. black and orange-red .. 9·00 4·00
262 4d. black and dull red .. 8·00 4·50
263 5d. black and pale green .. 6·00 20·00
a. Imperf between (horiz strip of 3) £11000
264 5d. black and green .. 6·00 20·00
265 6d. black and reddish mauve .. 3·75 3·00
a. Imperf between (horiz pair) .. £9000
266 6d. black and dull mauve .. 3·75 3·00
267 8d. mauve and dull blue-green .. 18·00 50·00
268 8d. mauve and greenish blue .. 17·00 48·00
a. Imperf vert (horiz pair) .. £8500
269 10d. indigo and carmine .. 12·00 40·00
270 10d. blue and red .. 11·00 40·00
271 1s. black and greenish blue .. 7·00 4·00
272 1s. black and pale blue-green .. 5·50 3·75
272*a* 1s. black and light blue .. 9·50 8·50
272*b* 1s. black and green .. 55·00 22·00
273 2s. black and brown .. 12·00 15·00
aa. Imperf between (vert pair) .. † £18000
273*a* 2s. black and yellow-brown .. £1700 95·00
274 2s. 6d. dp ultramarine & grey-brn 28·00 40·00
274*a* 2s. 6d. pale blue and pale bistre-brown *(shades)* .. 70·00 45·00
274*b* 3s. chestnut and light blue .. £160 90·00
275 5s. deep blue and blue-green *(shades)* 60·00 50·00
276 5s. blue & pale yell-grn *(shades)* 80·00 50·00
276*a* 7s. 6d. maroon and slate-black .. £750 £1100
277 10s. carmine-lake and yellow-green .. £300 £170
278 £1 black and bright purple .. £375 £500
279 £1 black and deep purple .. £400 £500
279*a* £1 black and violet-indigo .. £475 £550
279*b* £1 black and deep violet .. £450 £550

(b) P 15

279*c* **18** 2d. black and brownish grey .. £5500 £500

Half Penny (19) Half-Penny. (20)

1917 (15 Aug). *No.* 190 *surch at the Northern Rhodesian Administrative Press, Livingstone, with T* **19**, *in violet or violet-black.*

280 **18** ½d. on 1d. rose-carmine *(shades)* .. 2·50 6·00
a. Surch inverted .. £1400 £1400
b. Letters "n n" spaced wider .. 11·00 24·00
c. Letters "n y" spaced wider .. 7·50 18·00

The setting was in two rows of 10 repeated three times in the sheet.

The two colours of the surcharge occur on the same sheet.

1917 (22 Sept). *No.* 190 *surch as T* **20** *(new setting with hyphen, and full stop after "Penny"), in deep violet.*

281 **18** ½d. on 1d. rose-carmine *(shades)* .. 1·75 4·75

1922–24. *New printings on white paper with clear white gum.*

(i) *Single working plates. (a) P* 14

282 **18** ½d. dull green (1922) .. 5·50 2·75
a. Imperf between (vert pair) .. £1700 £1200
283 ½d. deep blue-green (1922) .. 5·50 3·00
284 1d. bright rose (1922) .. 5·50 3·75
285 1d. bright rose-scarlet (1923) .. 5·50 3·50
a. Imperf between (horiz pair) .. £1400
286 1d. aniline red (8.24) .. 20·00 4·25
287 1½d. brown-ochre (1923) .. 6·50 4·00
a. Imperf between (vert pair) .. £1800 £1200

(b) P 15

288 **18** ½d. dull green (1923) .. 40·00
289 1d. bright rose-scarlet (1923) .. 45·00
290 1½d. brown-ochre (1923) .. 48·00

(ii) *Double plates. Head Die* III. *(a) P* 14

291 **18** 2d. black and grey-purple (1922) .. 2·50 1·50
292 2d. black and slate-purple (1923) .. 3·75 2·50
293 3d. black and yellow (1922) .. 10·00 16·00
294 4d. black & orange-vermilion (1922–3) 8·50 18·00
295 6d. jet-black and lilac (1922–3) .. 4·75 3·75
296 8d. mauve and pale blue-green (1922) 30·00 70·00
297 8d. violet and grey-green (1923) .. 30·00 70·00
298 10d. bright ultramarine and red (1922) 10·00 45·00
299 10d. brt ultramarine & carm-red (1923) 14·00 45·00
300 1s. black and dull blue (1922–3) .. 4·25 5·00
a. Imperf between (horiz pair) .. £7500
b. Imperf between (vert pair) .. £9000
301 2s. black and brown (1922–3) .. 19·00 28·00
302 2s. 6d. ultramarine and sepia (1922) .. 38·00 70·00
303 2s. 6d. violet-blue & grey-brown (1923) 45·00 65·00
304 3s. red-brown & turquoise-bl (1922) .. 70·00 85·00
305 3s. red-brown and grey-blue (1923) .. 90·00 £110
306 5s. brt ultramarine and emerald (1922) 85·00 95·00
307 5s. deep blue and bright green (1923) 85·00 95·00
308 7s. 6d. brown-purple and slate (1922) £170 £225
309 10s. crimson and brt yellow-green (1922) £160 £190
310 10s. carmine and yellow-green (1923) .. £160 £225
311 £1 black and deep magenta (1922) .. £500 £650
311*a* £1 black and magenta (1923) .. £450 £650

(*b*) *P* 15 (1923)

312 18 2d. black and slate-purple 38·00
313 4d. black and orange-vermilion 40·00
314 6d. jet-black and lilac 50·00
315 8d. violet and grey-green 50·00
316 10d. bright ultramarine & carmine-red 55·00
317 1s. black and dull blue 60·00
318 2s. black and brown 90·00
319 2s. 6d. violet-blue and grey-brown £100
320 3s. red-brown and grey-blue £130
321 5s. deep blue and bright green £170
322 £1 black and magenta £650

The 1922 printing shows the mesh of the paper very clearly through the gum. In the 1923 printing the gum is very smooth and the mesh of the paper is not so clearly seen. Where date is given as "(1922–23)" two printings were made, which do not differ sufficiently in colour to be listed separately.

Nos. 288/90 and 312/22 were never sent out to Rhodesia, but only issued in London. Any used copies could, therefore, only have been obtained by favour.

Southern Rhodesia, that part of the Company's territory south of the River Zambesi, became a self-governing colony on 1 October 1923. British South Africa Company rule continued in Northern Rhodesia until the administration was transferred to the Colonial Office on 1 April 1924.

The current stamps of Rhodesia, the Admiral series first issued in 1913, continued to be used in Southern Rhodesia until 1 April 1924 (invalidated 1 May 1924) and in Northern Rhodesia until 1 April 1925 (invalidated 30 September 1925).

For issues of NORTHERN and SOUTHERN RHODESIA see ZAMBIA and ZIMBABWE. Between 1954 and 1964 they were merged in the Central African Federation (see RHODESIA and NYASALAND). In 1964 there were again separate issues for Northern and Southern Rhodesia, but after the former became independent as Zambia, Southern Rhodesia was renamed Rhodesia in October 1964. For issues inscribed "RHODESIA" between 1965 and 1978 see ZIMBABWE.

Rhodesia & Nyasaland

Stamps for the Central African Federation of Northern and Southern Rhodesia and Nyasaland Protectorate.

1

2

3 Queen Elizabeth II

(Recess Waterlow)

1954 (1 July)–**56**. *P* 13½×14 (*T* **1**), 13½×13 (*T* **2**) *or* 14½×13½ (*T* **3**).

1 1 ½d. red-orange 15 10
a. Coil stamp. Perf 12½×14 (6.2.56) 30 1·50
2 1d. ultramarine 15 10
a. Coil stamp. Perf 12½×14. *Deep blue* (9.55) 1·50 12·00
ab. Ultramarine (1.10.55) 2·50 11·00
3 2d. bright green 15 10
3*a* 2½d. ochre (15.2.56) 3·00 10
4 3d. carmine-red 20 10
5 4d. red-brown 60 15
6 4½d. blue-green 15 30
7 6d. bright reddish purple 1·75 10
a. Bright purple (5.5.56) 2·75 10
8 9d. violet 65 70
9 1s. grey-black 1·50 10
10 2 1s. 3d. red-orange and ultramarine 2·50 10
11 2s. deep blue and yellow-brown 7·00 1·00
12 2s. 6d. black and rose-red 5·50 1·00
13 5s. violet and olive-green 15·00 3·00
14 3 10s. dull blue-green and orange 17·00 7·00
15 £1 olive-green and lake 27·00 24·00
1/15 *Set of* 16 70·00 32·00

Nos. 1a and 2a printed on rotary machines by subsidiary company, Imprimerie Belge de Securité, in Belgium.

4 De Havilland D.H.106 Comet 1 over Victoria Falls

5 Livingstone and Victoria Falls

(Des J. E. Hughes (3d.), V. E. Horne (1s.). Recess Waterlow)

1955 (15 June). *Centenary of Discovery of Victoria Falls. P* 13½ (*3d.*) *or* 13 (*1s.*).

16 4 3d. ultramarine & dp turquoise-grn 55 30
17 5 1s. purple and deep blue 55 60

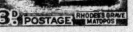

6 Tea Picking

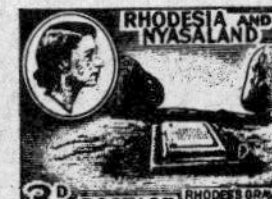

10 Rhodes's Grave

11 Lake Bangweulu

12*a* Rhodesian Railway Trains

19 Federal Coat of Arms

(Des M. Kinsella (9d.). Recess Waterlow (½d., 1d., 2d., 1s.) until 1962, then D.L.R., D.L.R. (2½d., 4d., 6d., 9d., 2s., 2s. 6d.) and B.W. (others))

1959 (12 Aug)–**62**. *T* **6**, **10/11**, **12*a***, **19** *and similar designs. P* 13½×14 (*½d., 1d., 2d.*), 14½ (*2½d., 4d., 6d., 9d., 2s., 2s. 6d.*), 14×13½ (*3d.*), 13½×13 (*1s.*), 14 (*1s. 3d.*) *or* 11 (*others*).

18 ½d. black and light emerald 60 30
a. Coil stamp. Perf 12½×14 2·75 5·50
19 1d. carmine-red and black 15 10
a. Coil stamp. Perf 12½×14 2·75 6·50
ab. Carmine-red and grey-black 3·75 7·50
ac. Carmine-red (centre) omitted £325
20 2d. violet and yellow-brown 1·00 40
21 2½d. purple and grey-blue 40 40
22 3d. black and blue 15 10
a. Black (centre) omitted £9500
b. Printed on the gummed side £250
23 4d. maroon and olive 1·25 10
24 6d. ultramarine and deep myrtle-green 60 10
24*a* 9d. orge-brown & reddish violet (15.5.62) 8·00 2·50
25 1s. light green and ultramarine 80 10
26 1s. 3d. emerald and deep chocolate 3·00 10
27 2s. grey-green and carmine 3·25 60
28 2s. 6d. light blue and yellow-brown 4·25 30
29 5s. deep chocolate and yellow-green 7·00 2·25
30 10s. olive-brown and rose-red 25·00 13·00
31 £1 black and deep violet 45·00 35·00
18/31 *Set of* 15 90·00 48·00

Designs: *Vert* (*as T* **6**)—1d. V.H.F. mast; 2d. Copper mining; 2½d. Fairbridge Memorial. (*As T* **11**)—6d. Eastern Cataract, Victoria Falls. *Horiz* (*as T* **12*a***)—1s. Tobacco; 1s. 3d. Lake Nyasa; 2s. Chirundu Bridge; 2s. 6d. Salisbury Airport. (*As T* **19**)—5s. Rhodes Statue; 10s. Mlanje.

Only three examples from two different sheets, all unused, are believed to exist of No. 22a although further stamps from the same sheets can be found with the centre partially omitted.

20 Kariba Gorge, 1955

(Photo Harrison (3d., 6d.), D.L.R. (others))

1960 (17 May). *Opening of Kariba Hydro-Electric Scheme. T* **20** *and similar horiz designs. P* 14½ × 14 (*3d., 6d.*) *or* 14 (*others*).

32 3d. blackish green and red-orange 60 10
a. Red-orange omitted £2750
33 6d. brown and yellow-brown 70 20
34 1s. slate-blue and green 2·50 2·25
35 1s. 3d. light blue and orange-brown 2·50 1·50
a. Blue and deep orange-brown 6·00 5·00
36 2s. 6d. deep slate-purple and orange-red 3·50 7·00
37 5s. reddish violet and turquoise-blue 8·00 11·00
32/7 *Set of* 6 16·00 20·00

Designs:—6d. 330 kV power lines; 1s. Barrage wall; 1s. 3d. Barrage and lake; 2s. 6d. Interior of power station; 5s. Barrage wall and Queen Mother (top left).

26 Miner Drilling

(Des V. Whiteley. Photo Harrison)

1961 (8 May). *Seventh Commonwealth Mining and Metallurgical Congress. T* **26** *and similar horiz design. P* 15 × 14.

38 6d. olive-green and orange-brown 50 15
39 1s. 3d. black and light blue 50 60

Design:—1s. 3d. Surface installations, Nchanga Mine.

Imperforate examples of the 6d. are believed to be printer's waste.

MINIMUM PRICE

The minimum price quote is 10p which represents a handling charge rather than a basis for valuing common stamps. For further notes about prices see introductory pages.

28 De Havilland D.H.66 Hercules *City of Basra* on Rhodesian Airstrip

31 Tobacco Plant

1962 (6 Feb). *30th Anniv of First London-Rhodesia Airmail Service. T* **28** *and similar horiz designs. P* 14½ × 14.

40 6d. bronze-green and vermilion 35 25
41 1s. 3d. light blue, black and yellow 1·50 50
42 2s. 6d. rose-red and deep violet 6·50 4·25
40/2 *Set of* 3 7·50 4·50

Designs:—1s. 3d. Short S.23 flying boat *Canopus* taking off from Zambesi; 2s. 6d. Hawker Siddeley Comet 4 at Salisbury airport.

(Des V. Whiteley. Photo Harrison)

1963 (18 Feb). *World Tobacco Congress, Salisbury. T* **31** *and similar vert designs. P* 14 × 14½.

43 3d. green and olive-brown 30 10
44 6d. green, brown and blue 40 35
45 1s. 3d. chestnut and indigo 60 45
46 2s. 6d. yellow and brown 1·00 2·75
43/6 *Set of* 4 2·00 3·25

Designs:—6d. Tobacco field; 1s. 3d. Auction floor; 2s. 6d. Cured tobacco.

35 Red Cross Emblem

(Photo Harrison)

1963 (6 Aug). *Red Cross Centenary. P* 14½ × 14.

47 35 3d. red 85 10

36 African "Round Table" Emblem

(Des V. Whiteley. Photo Harrison)

1963 (11 Sept). *World Council of Young Men's Service Clubs, Salisbury. P* 14½ × 14.

48 36 6d. black, gold and yellow-green 50 1·25
49 1s. 3d. black, gold, yell-grn & lilac 50 1·00

STAMP BOOKLETS

1955 (1 Jan). *Black on yellow cover. Stitched.*

SB1 5s. booklet containing twelve ½d. and eighteen 1d. and 2d. (Nos. 1/3) in blocks of 6 40·00

1963 (4 Apr). *Black on yellow cover. Stitched.*

SB2 1s. booklet containing 3d. (No. 22) in block of 4 1·50

POSTAGE DUE STAMPS

After Federation in 1954 existing stocks of postage due stamps from Northern Rhodesia, Nyasaland and Southern Rhodesia continued to be used and were sometimes distributed throughout the federation.

Increased postal rates in July 1956 and in 1959 led to the exhaustion of certain values, in particular the 1d., and various offices then used Rhodesia and Nyasaland postage issues for postage due purposes. There were isolated instances of such stamps being cancelled "POSTAGE DUE" from December 1956 onwards.

Some of these handstamps may have been applied at Bulawayo while others, in violet or black, originate from the Salisbury Delivery Room at Kingsway Post Office. Only the 1d. and 2d. (Nos. 2/3) are known with such handstamps. After mint examples began to appear the Postmaster General suppressed the use of the handstamps in August 1959.

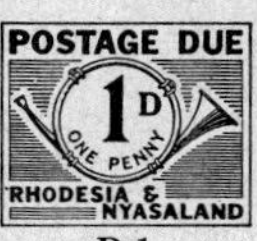

D 1

(Typo Federal Printing and Stationery Dept, Salisbury)

1961 (19 Apr). *P* 12½.

D1 D 1 1d. vermilion 2·25 4·25
a. Imperf between (horiz pair) £350 £400
D2 2d. deep violet-blue 2·25 3·00
D3 4d. green 2·25 8·00
D4 6d. purple 4·50 7·50
a. Imperf between (horiz pair) £950
D1/4 *Set of* 4 10·00 20·00

The 2d. has a stop below the "D".

The stamps of the Federation were withdrawn on 19 February 1964 when all three constituent territories had resumed issuing their own stamps.

Sabah
see Malaysia

St. Helena

CROWN COLONY

PRICES FOR STAMPS ON COVER TO 1945

Nos. 1/5	*from* × 12
Nos. 6/30	*from* × 10
Nos. 34/45	*from* × 15
Nos. 46/52	*from* × 6
Nos. 53/67	*from* × 5
No. 71	—
Nos. 72/86	*from* × 5
Nos. 87/8	*from* × 12
Nos. 89/95	*from* × 5
No. 96	—
Nos. 97/110	*from* × 5
Nos. 111/13	—
Nos. 114/40	*from* × 4

1

ONE PENNY
(2)

FOUR PENCE
(3)

(Recess P.B.)

Wmk Large Star, W w **1**

1856 (1 Jan). *Imperf.*
1 1 6d. blue .. £500 £180

1861 (April(?)). (*a*) *Clean-cut perf* 14 *to* 16
2 1 6d. blue .. £1600 £275
(*b*) *Rough perf* 14 *to* 16
2*a* 1 6d. blue .. £400 £130

NOTE: The issues which follow consist of 6d. stamps, T **1**, printed in various colours and (except in the case of the 6d. values) surcharged with a new value, as T **2** to **10**, *e.g.* stamps described as "1d." are, in fact, 1d. on 6d stamps, and so on.
The numbers in the Type column below refer to the *types of the lettering* of the surcharged value.

(Printed by D.L.R. from P.B. plate)

Two Types of Bar on 1d. value:
A. Bar 16–17 mm long.
B. Bar 18½–19 mm long.

1863 (July). *Wmk Crown CC. Surch as T* **2/3** *with thin bar approximately the same length as the words. Imperf.*
3 2 1d. lake (Type A) .. £110 £160
a. Surch double .. £4250 £2500
b. Surch omitted .. £12000
4 1d. lake (Type B) .. £120 £170
a. Vert pair. Nos. 3/4 .. £6500
5 3 4d. carmine (*bar* 15½–16½ *mm*) .. £500 £250
a. Surch double .. £9500 £8000

ONE PENNY (4 (A)) ONE PENNY (4 (B)) ONE PENNY (4 (C))

TWO PENCE (5) THREE PENCE (6) FOUR PENCE (7)

ONE SHILLING (8) FIVE SHILLINGS (9)

Three Types of Bar:
A. Thin bar (16½ to 17 mm) nearly the same length as the words.
B. Thick bar (14 to 14½ mm) much shorter than the words, except on the 2d. (Nos. 9, 22, 28) where it is nearly the same length.
C. Long bar (17 to 18 mm) same length as the words.

1864–80. *Wmk Crown CC. 6d. as T* **1**, *without surcharge.*
(*a*) *P* 12½ (1864–73)
6 4 1d. lake (Type A) (1864) .. 30·00 24·00
a. Surch double .. £5500
7 1d. lake (Type B) (1868) .. £130 50·00
a. Surch double
b. Imperf .. £2000
8 1d. lake (Type C) (1871) .. 70·00 17·00
a. Surch in blue-black .. £1000 £550
9 5 2d. yellow (Type B) (1868) .. £150 60·00
a. Imperf .. £8500
10 2d. yellow (Type C) (1873) .. 75·00 38·00
a. Surch in blue-black .. £4000 £2250
b. Surch double, one albino
11 6 3d. deep dull purple (Type B) (1868) .. 75·00 50·00
a. Surch double .. — £6000
b. Imperf .. £750
c. *Light purple* .. £2750 £750
12 3d. deep dull purple (Type A) (1873) .. 75·00 50·00
13 7 4d. carmine (Type A) (1864) .. £120 45·00
a. Surch double .. † £5500
14 4d. carmine (Type B) (*words* 18 *mm long*) (1868) .. 85·00 48·00
a. Surch double .. † £4500
b. Surch double (18 + 19 *mm widths*) £15000 £9000
c. Imperf .. £8500
15 4d. carmine-rose (Type B) (*words* 19 *mm long*) (1868) .. £200 £120
a. Surch omitted .. † —
16 – 6d. dull blue (1871) .. £550 £100
a. Ultramarine (1873) .. £325 80·00
17 8 1s. deep yellow-green (Type A) (1864) £180 26·00
a. Surch double .. † £18000
18 1s. deep yellow-green (Type B) (1868) £425 £130
a. Surch double .. £12000
b. Imperf .. £12000
c. Surch omitted* .. £12000
19 1s. deep green (Type C) (1871) .. £300 16·00
a. Surch in blue-black
20 9 5s. orange (Type B) (1868) .. 38·00 60·00
a. Yellow .. £400 £350
(*b*) *P* 14 × 12½ (1876)
21 4 1d. lake (Type B) .. 60·00 15·00
22 5 2d. yellow (Type B) .. 80·00 50·00
23 3d. purple (Type B) .. £180 70·00
24 4d. carmine (Type B) (*words* 16½ *mm long*) .. 85·00 60·00
25 – 6d. milky blue .. £275 42·00
26 8 1s. deep green (Type C) .. £375 20·00
(*c*) *P* 14 (1880)
27 4 1d. lake (Type B) .. 75·00 16·00
28 5 2d. yellow (Type B) .. 85·00 20·00
29 – 6d. milky blue .. £325 48·00
30 8 1s. yellow-green (Type B) .. 20·00 12·00

The only known copy of No. 15a is in the Royal Collection, although a second badly damaged example may exist.
*No. 18c is from a sheet of the 1s. with surcharge misplaced, the fifth row of 12 stamps being thus doubly surcharged and the tenth row without surcharge.

$2\frac{1}{2}$d
(10)

11

12

1884–94. *Wmk Crown CA. T* **1** *surch. Bars similar to Type* B *above* (*except* 2½*d.*, *T* **10**, *and the* 1*s.*, *in which the bar is nearly the same length as the words*). *The* 6*d. as before without surcharge. P* 14.
34 – ½d. emerald (*words* 17 *mm*) (1884) .. 6·50 8·50
a. "N" and "Y" spaced .. £750
b. Surch double .. £1000 £1100
ba. Ditto. "N" and "Y" spaced .. £10000
35 – ½d. green (*words* 17 *mm*) (1885) .. 4·00 8·50
a. "N" and "Y" spaced .. £350 £450
36 – ½d. green (*words* 14½ *mm*) (1893) .. 90 1·25
37 4 1d. red (1887) .. 2·75 2·00
38 1d. pale red (1890) .. 3·50 2·00
39 5 2d. yellow (1894) .. 1·25 3·50
40 10 2½d. ultramarine (1893) .. 2·00 5·00
a. Surch double .. £14000
b. Stamp doubly printed .. £6500
41 6 3d. deep mauve (1887) .. 2·25 2·75
a. Surch double .. — £9000
42 3d. deep reddish lilac (1887) .. 4·50 7·00
a. Surch double .. £8500 £6000
43 7 4d. pale brn (*words* 16½ *mm*) (1890) 12·00 20·00
a. Additional thin bar in surch (R. 7/4) .. £450
43*b* 4d. sepia (*words* 17 *mm*) (1894) .. 17·00 8·00
44 – 6d. grey (1887) .. 10·00 3·50
45 8 1s. yellow-green (1894) .. 30·00 19·00
a. Surch double .. £4250
40/1, 43, 44 Optd "Specimen" *Set of* 4 £180

Examples of the above are sometimes found showing no watermark; these are from the bottom row of the sheet, which had escaped the watermark, the paper being intended for stamps of a different size to Type 1.
Some are found without bar and others with bar at top of stamp, due to careless overprinting.
Nos. 34a and 35a occur on R. 18/12 and show a minimum space between the letters of 0.8 mm. Normal examples are spaced 0.5 mm, but some stamps show intermediate measurements due to loose type. On No. 34ba only one impression of the surcharge shows "N" and "Y" spaced.
Of the 2½d. with double surcharge only six copies exist, and of the 2½d. double printed, one row of 12 stamps existed on one sheet only.

CANCELLATIONS. Nos. 40/5 and No. 20 were sold as remainders in 1904 cancelled with a violet diamond-shaped grill with four interior bars extending over two stamps. These cannot be considered as *used* stamps, and they are consequently not priced in the list.
This violet obliteration is easily removed and many of these remainders have been cleaned and offered as unused; some are repostmarked with a date and name in thin type rather larger than the original, a usual date being "Ap.4.01."

(Typo D.L.R.)

1890–97. *Wmk Crown CA. Plate I for the* 1½*d. Plate II for the other values* (*for differences see Seychelles*). *P* 14.
46 11 ½d. green (1897) .. 2·75 4·50
47 1d. carmine (1896) .. 8·50 1·00
48 1½d. red-brown and green (1890) .. 4·50 7·00
49 11 2d. orange-yellow (1896) .. 5·00 9·50
50 2½d. ultramarine (1896) .. 6·50 10·00
51 5d. mauve (1896) .. 11·00 27·00
52 10d. brown (1896) .. 16·00 48·00
46/52 .. *Set of* 7 48·00 95·00
46/52 Optd "Specimen" .. *Set of* 7 £275

The note below No. 45a *re* violet diamond-shaped grill cancellation also applies to Nos. 48/52.

1902. *Wmk Crown CA. P* 14.
53 12 ½d. green (Mar) .. 1·50 90
54 1d. carmine (24 Feb) .. 4·75 70
53/4 Optd "Specimen" .. *Set of* 2 70·00

13 Government House

14 The Wharf

(Typo D.L.R.)

1903 (May). *Wmk Crown CC. P* 14.
55 13 ½d. brown and grey-green .. 2·00 2·75
w. Wmk inverted .. 85·00
56 14 1d. black and carmine .. 1·50 35
57 13 2d. black and sage-green .. 6·00 1·25
58 14 8d. black and brown .. 18·00 32·00
59 13 1s. brown and brown-orange .. 18·00 40·00
60 14 2s. black and violet .. 48·00 85·00
55/60 .. *Set of* 6 85·00 £150
55/60 Optd "Specimen" .. *Set of* 6 £200

A printing of the 1d. value in Type **14** in red only on Mult Crown CA paper was made in 1911, but not sold to the public. Examples are known overprinted "SPECIMEN" (*Price* £300).

15

(Typo D.L.R.)

1908 (May)–**11.** *P* 14. (*a*) *Wmk Mult Crown CA. Ordinary paper* (2½*d.*) *or chalk-surfaced paper* (4*d.*, 6*d.*).
64 15 2½d. blue .. 1·25 1·40
66 4d. black and red/*yellow* .. 4·50 12·00
a. Ordinary paper (1911) .. 1·25 8·50
67 6d. dull and deep purple .. 9·00 20·00
a. Ordinary paper (1911) .. 3·00 12·00
(*b*) *Wmk Crown CA. Chalk-surfaced paper.*
71 15 10s. green and red/*green* .. £170 £250
64/71 .. *Set of* 4 £170 £250
64/71 Optd "Specimen" .. *Set of* 4 £225

16

17

(Typo D.L.R.)

1912–16. *Wmk Mult Crown CA. P* 14.
72 16 ½d. black and green .. 1·50 8·00
73 17 1d. black and carmine-red .. 2·50 1·75
a. Black and scarlet (1916) .. 20·00 27·00
74 1½d. black and dull orange (1913) .. 2·75 5·50
75 16 2d. black and greyish slate .. 2·50 1·75
76 17 2½d. black and bright blue .. 2·50 5·50
77 16 3d. black and purple/*yellow* (1913) .. 2·25 5·00
78 17 8d. black and dull purple .. 5·50 50·00
79 16 1s. black/*green* .. 8·00 27·00
80 17 2s. black and blue/*blue* .. 32·00 75·00
81 3s. black and violet (1913) .. 48·00 £120
72/81 .. *Set of* 10 95·00 £275
72/81 Optd "Specimen" .. *Set of* 10 £250

No. 73*a* is on thicker paper than 73.

18

19

TACE
Split "A"

(Typo D.L.R.)

1912. *Wmk Mult Crown CA. Chalk-surfaced paper. P* 14.
83 18 4d. black and red/*yellow* .. 7·50 19·00
84 6d. dull and deep purple .. 2·50 5·00
83/4 Optd "Specimen" .. *Set of* 2 60·00

1913. *Wmk Mult Crown CA. P 14.*
85 **19** 4d. black and red/*yellow* .. .. .. 6·50 2·75
a. Split "A" £150
86 6d. dull and deep purple .. .. .. 11·00 20·00
a. Split "A" £250
85/6 Optd "Specimen" .. .. *Set of* 2 70·00

WAR TAX ONE PENNY
(20)

WAR TAX 1d.
(21)

1916 (Sept). *As No. 73a, on thin paper, surch with T* **20**.
87 **17** 1d. + 1d. black and scarlet (Optd S. £50) 85 2·75
a. Surch double .. .. † £6000

1919. *No. 73 on thicker paper, surch with T* **21**.
88 **17** 1d. + 1d. black and carmine-red (*shades*)
(Optd S. £50) .. .. .. 40 3·00

1922 (Jan). *Printed in one colour. Wmk Mult Script CA. P 14.*
89 **17** 1d. green .. .. .. 1·00 23·00
w. Wmk inverted £100
90 1½d. rose-scarlet .. .. .. 6·50 26·00
91 **16** 3d. bright blue .. .. .. 16·00 45·00
y. Wmk inverted and reversed .. £110
89/91 .. .. .. *Set of* 3 21·00 85·00
89/91 Optd "Specimen" .. .. *Set of* 3 75·00

22 Badge of St. Helena

PLATE FLAWS ON THE 1922–37 ISSUE. Many constant plate varieties exist on both the vignette and duty plates of this issue.
The three major varieties are illustrated and listed below with prices for mint examples. Fine used stamps showing these flaws are worth a considerable premium over the mint prices quoted.

a. Broken mainmast. Occurs on R.2/1 of all sheets from the second printing onwards. It does not appear on Nos. 93/6 and 112/13 as these stamps only exist from the initial printing invoiced in May 1922.

b. Torn flag. Occurs on R.4/6 of all sheets from printings up to and including that invoiced in December 1922. The flaw was retouched for the printing invoiced in December 1926 and so does not occur on Nos. 99e, 103 and 107/10.

c. Cleft rock. Occurs on R.5/1 of all sheets from the second printing onwards. It does not appear on Nos. 93/6 and 112/13 as these stamps only exist from the initial printing invoiced in May 1922.

(Des T. Bruce. Typo D.L.R.)

1922 (June)–**37.** *P 14 (a) Wmk Mult Crown CA. Chalk-surfaced paper.*
92 **22** 4d. grey and black/*yellow* (2.23) .. 8·00 6·00
a. Broken mainmast £110
b. Torn flag £110
c. Cleft rock .. .. 95·00
93 1s. 6d. grey and green/*blue-green* .. 22·00 50·00
b. Torn flag £350
94 2s. 6d. grey and red/*yellow* .. 25·00 50·00
b. Torn flag £400
95 5s. grey and green/*yellow* .. 38·00 75·00
b. Torn flag £475
96 £1 grey and purple/*red* .. £400 £450
b. Torn flag £1500
92/6 Optd "Specimen" .. .. *Set of* 5 £500
The paper of No. 93 is bluish on the surface with a full green back.

(*b*) *Wmk Mult Script CA. Ordinary paper (1s. 6d., 2s. 6d., 5s.) or chalk-surfaced paper (others)*
97 **22** ½d. grey and black (2.23) .. 1·25 1·75
a. Broken mainmast .. 38·00
b. Torn flag .. 95·00
c. Cleft rock .. 32·00
w. Wmk inverted .. £150
98 1d. grey and green .. 1·75 1·40
a. Broken mainmast .. 42·00
b. Torn flag .. 80·00
c. Cleft rock .. 38·00
99 1½d. rose-red (2.23) .. 2·75 12·00
a. Broken mainmast .. 85·00
b. Torn flag .. 85·00
c. Cleft rock .. 80·00
d. Carmine-rose .. 24·00 24·00
da. Broken mainmast .. £200
db. Torn flag .. £200
dc. Cleft rock .. £200
e. Deep carmine-red (1937) .. 80·00 £100
ea. Broken mainmast .. £550
ec. Cleft rock .. £550
100 2d. grey and slate (2.23) .. 2·50 2·00
a. Broken mainmast .. 70·00
b. Torn flag .. £110
c. Cleft rock .. 60·00
101 3d. bright blue (2.23) .. 2·00 4·00
a. Broken mainmast .. 70·00
b. Torn flag .. 80·00
c. Cleft rock .. 60·00
x. Wmk reversed .. £250
103 5d. green and carmine/*green* (1927) .. 3·00 5·50
a. Broken mainmast .. £120
c. Cleft rock .. £110
104 6d. grey and bright purple .. 3·50 8·00
a. Broken mainmast .. £140
b. Torn flag .. £130
c. Cleft rock .. £120
105 8d. grey and bright violet (2.23) .. 3·25 6·50
a. Broken mainmast .. £130
b. Torn flag .. £130
c. Cleft rock .. £110
106 1s. grey and brown .. 6·00 9·00
a. Broken mainmast .. £180
b. Torn flag .. £160
c. Cleft rock .. £150
107 1s. 6d. grey and green/*green* (1927) .. 14·00 45·00
a. Broken mainmast .. £225
c. Cleft rock .. £200
108 2s. purple and blue/*blue* (1927) .. 15·00 35·00
a. Broken mainmast .. £225
c. Cleft rock .. £200
109 2s. 6d. grey and red/*yellow* (1927) .. 13·00 50·00
a. Broken mainmast .. £200
c. Cleft rock .. £200
110 5s. grey and green/*yellow* (1927) .. 38·00 75·00
a. Broken mainmast .. £375
c. Cleft rock .. £350
111 7s. 6d. grey and yellow-orange .. 75·00 £120
a. Broken mainmast .. £1800
b. Torn flag .. £550
c. Cleft rock .. £1800
112 10s. grey and olive-green .. £110 £160
b. Torn flag .. £850
113 15s. grey and purple/*blue* .. £800 £1400
b. Torn flag .. £2750
97/112 .. .. *Set of* 15 £250 £350
97/113 Optd "Specimen" .. *Set of* 16 £1000
Examples of all values are known showing a forged St. Helena postmark dated "DE 18 27".

23 Lot and Lot's Wife

24 The "Plantation"

30 St. Helena

32 Badge of St. Helena

(Recess B.W.)

1934 (23 April). *Centenary of British Colonisation. T* **23/4**, **30**, **32** *and similar horiz designs. Wmk Mult Script CA. P 12.*
114 ½d. black and purple .. 75 80
115 1d. black and green .. 65 85
116 1½d. black and scarlet .. 2·50 3·25
117 2d. black and orange .. 1·75 1·25
118 3d. black and blue .. 1·40 4·50
119 6d. black and light blue .. 3·25 3·00
120 1s. black and chocolate .. 6·00 18·00
121 2s. 6d. black and lake .. 35·00 48·00
122 5s. black and chocolate .. 75·00 85·00
123 10s. black and purple .. £200 £250
114/123 .. .. *Set of* 10 £275 £350
114/23 Perf "Specimen" .. *Set of* 10 £350
Design:—1½d. Map of St. Helena; 2d. Quay at Jamestown; 3d. James Valley; 6d. Jamestown; 1s. Munden's Promontory; 5s. High Knoll.
Examples of all values are known showing a forged St. Helena postmark dated "MY 12 34".

1935 (6 May). *Silver Jubilee. As Nos. 114/17 of Jamaica, but ptd by D.L.R. P* 13½×14.
124 1½d. deep blue and carmine .. 75 4·00
f. Diagonal line by turret .. 50·00
125 2d. ultramarine and grey .. 1·25 90
f. Diagonal line by turret .. 70·00
g. Dot to left of chapel .. 85·00
126 6d. green and indigo .. 6·50 2·75
a. Frame printed double, one albino .. £1500
f. Diagonal line by turret .. £130
h. Dot by flagstaff .. £170
127 1s. slate and purple .. 8·50 11·00
h. Dot by flagstaff .. £200
i. Dash by turret .. £200
124/7 .. .. *Set of* 4 15·00 17·00
124/7 Perf "Specimen" .. *Set of* 4 95·00
For illustrations of plate varieties see Omnibus section following Zimbabwe.

1937 (19 May). *Coronation. As Nos. 118/20 of Jamaica.*
128 1d. green .. 40 30
129 2d. orange .. 55 30
130 3d. bright blue .. 80 30
128/30 .. .. *Set of* 3 1·60 80
128/30 Perf "Specimen" .. *Set of* 3 55·00

33 Badge of St. Helena

(Recess Waterlow)

1938 (12 May)–**44.** *Wmk Mult Script CA. P* 12½.
131 **33** ½d. violet .. 10 40
132 1d. green .. 20·00 3·50
132*a* 1d. yellow-orange (8.7.40) .. 20 30
133 1½d. scarlet .. 20 40
134 2d. red-orange .. 20 15
135 3d. ultramarine .. 90·00 22·00
135*a* 3d. grey (8.7.40) .. 30 30
135*b* 4d. ultramarine (8.7.40) .. 2·00 30
136 6d. light blue .. 2·00 30
136*a* 8d. sage-green (8.7.40) .. 3·25 90
b. Olive-green (24.5.44) .. 4·50 4·00
137 1s. sepia .. 90 30
138 2s. 6d. maroon .. 17·00 3·50
139 5s. chocolate .. 18·00 7·50
140 10s. purple .. 18·00 16·00
131/140 .. .. *Set of* 14 £150 50·00
131/40 Perf "Specimen" .. *Set of* 14 £300
See also Nos. 149/51.

1946 (21 Oct). *Victory. As Nos. 141/2 of Jamaica.*
141 2d. red-orange .. 10 10
142 4d. blue .. 10 10
141/2 Perf "Specimen" .. *Set of* 2 60·00

1948 (20 Oct). *Royal Silver Wedding. As Nos. 143/4 of Jamaica.*
143 3d. black .. 30 20
144 10s. violet-blue .. 22·00 27·00

1949 (10 Oct). *75th Anniv of U.P.U. As Nos. 145/8 of Jamaica.*
145 3d. carmine .. 75 30
146 4d. deep blue .. 2·75 90
147 6d. olive .. 90 90
148 1s. blue-black .. 90 1·10
145/8 .. .. *Set of* 4 4·75 3·00

1949 (1 Nov). *Wmk Mult Script CA. P* 12½.
149 **33** 1d. black and green .. 60 80
150 1½d. black and carmine .. 60 80
151 2d. black and scarlet .. 60 80
149/51 .. .. *Set of* 3 1·60 2·25

1953 (2 June). *Coronation. As No. 153 of Jamaica.*
152 3d. black and deep reddish violet .. 1·00 65

34 Badge of St. Helena

35 Heart-shaped Waterfall

(Recess D.L.R.)

1953 (4 Aug)–**59.** *Horiz designs as T* **34**, *and T* **35**. *Wmk Mult Script CA. P 14.*
153 ½d. black and bright green .. 30 30
154 1d. black and deep green .. 15 20
155 1½d. black and reddish purple .. 1·50 70
a. Black & deep reddish purple (14.1.59) 8·00 4·25

No.	Type	Description	Unused	Used
156		2d. black and claret	50	30
157		2½d. black and red	40	30
158		3d. black and brown	3·25	30
159		4d. black and deep blue	40	40
160		6d. black and deep lilac	40	30
161		7d. black and grey-black	65	1·25
162		1s. black and carmine	40	40
163		2s. 6d. black and violet	12·00	7·00
164		5s. black and deep brown	17·00	11·00
165		10s. black and yellow-orange	40·00	22·00
153/65		.. .. *Set of* 13	70·00	40·00

Designs:—1d. Flax plantation; 2d. Lace-making; 2½d. Drying flax; 3d. St. Helena Sand Plover; 4d. Flagstaff and The Barn; 6d. Donkeys carrying flax; 7d. Island map; 1s. The Castle; 2s. 6d. Cutting flax; 5s. Jamestown; 10s. Longwood House.

45 Stamp of 1856

(Recess D.L.R.)

1956 (3 Jan). *St. Helena Stamp Centenary. Wmk Mult Script CA. P* 11½.

No.	Type	Description	Unused	Used
166	**45**	3d. Prussian blue and carmine ..	10	10
167		4d. Prussian blue and reddish brown ..	10	20
168		6d. Prussian blue & dp reddish purple	15	25
166/8		.. .. *Set of* 3	30	50

46 Arms of East India Company

(Recess Waterlow)

1959 (5 May). *Tercentenary of Settlement. T* **46** *and similar horiz designs. W* w **12**. *P* 12½ × 13.

No.	Type	Description	Unused	Used
169		3d. black and scarlet	10	10
170		6d. light emerald and slate-blue	40	65
171		1s. black and orange	40	65
169/71		.. .. .. *Set of* 3	75	1·25

Designs:—6d. East Indiaman *London* off James Bay; 1s. Commemoration Stone.

ST. HELENA
Tristan Relief
9d +

(49)

1961 (12 Oct). *Tristan Relief Fund. Nos.* 46 *and* 49/51 *of Tristan da Cunha surch as T* **49** *by Govt Printer, Jamestown.*

No.	Type	Description	Unused	Used
172		2½ c. + 3d. black and brown-red ..	—	£400
173		5 c. + 6d. black and blue	—	£400
174		7½ c. + 9d. black and rose-carmine ..	—	£475
175		10 c. + 1s. black and light brown ..	—	£550
172/5		.. .. *Set of* 4	£4000	£1600

The above stamps were withdrawn from sale on 19 October, 434 complete sets having been sold.

50 St. Helena Butterflyfish

51 Yellow Canary

53 Queen Elizabeth II

63 Queen Elizabeth II with Prince Andrew (after Cecil Beaton)

(Des V. Whiteley. Photo Harrison)

1961 (12 Dec)–**65**. *T* **50/1, 53, 63** *and similar designs. W* w **12**. *P* 11½ × 12 (*horiz*), 12 × 11½ (*vert*) *or* 14½ × 14 (£1).

No.	Type	Description	Unused	Used
176		1d. brt blue, dull violet, yellow & carmine	10	10
		a. Chalk-surfaced paper (4.5.65) ..	3·25	30
177		1½d. yellow, green, black and light drab ..	30	10
178		2d. scarlet and grey	15	10
179		3d. light blue, black, pink and deep blue	70	20
		a. Chalk-surfaced paper (30.11.65) ..	1·50	50
180		4½d. yellow-green, green, brown and grey	60	40
181		6d. red, sepia and light yellow-olive ..	5·00	45
		a. Chalk-surfaced paper (30.11.65) ..	6·50	50
182		7d. red-brown, black and violet	35	50
183		10d. brown-purple and light blue	35	40
184		1s. greenish yellow, bluish green & brown	55	50
185		1s. 6d. grey, black and slate-blue ..	13·00	3·75
186		2s. 6d. red, pale yellow and turquoise (*chalk-surfaced paper*)	2·50	2·00
187		5s. yellow, brown and green	14·00	3·75
188		10s. orange-red, black and blue	17·00	10·00
189		£1 chocolate and light blue	17·00	17·00
		a. Chalk-surfaced paper (30.11.65) ..	35·00	42·00
176/89 (*cheapest*)		.. .. *Set of* 14	65·00	35·00

Designs: *Horiz* (*as T* **50**)—2d. Brittle Starfish; 7d. Trumpetfish; 10d. Feather Starfish; 2s. 6d. Orange Starfish; 10s. Deep-water Bullseye. *Vert* (*as T* **51**)—4½d. Red-wood Flower; 6d. Madagascar Red Fody; 1s. Gum-wood Flower; 1s. 6d. White Tern; 5s. Night-blooming Cereus.

1963 (4 June). *Freedom from Hunger. As No.* 80 *of Lesotho.*

No.	Type	Description	Unused	Used
190		1s. 6d. ultramarine	1·50	40

1963 (2 Sept). *Red Cross Centenary. As Nos.* 203/4 *of Jamaica.*

No.	Type	Description	Unused	Used
191		3d. red and black	75	25
192		1s. 6d. red and blue	3·00	1·25

FIRST LOCAL POST
4th JANUARY 1965

(64)

65 Badge of St. Helena

1965 (4 Jan). *First Local Post. Nos.* 176, 179, 181 *and* 185 *optd with T* **64**.

No.	Type	Description	Unused	Used
193		1d. bright blue, dull violet, yellow & carmine	10	10
194		3d. light blue, black, pink and deep blue	10	10
195		6d. red, sepia and light yellow-olive ..	40	10
196		1s. 6d. grey, black and slate-blue ..	60	15
193/6		.. .. *Set of* 4	1·00	30

1965 (17 May). *I.T.U. Centenary. As Nos.* 98/9 *of Lesotho.*

No.	Type	Description	Unused	Used
197		3d. blue and grey-brown	35	15
198		6d. bright purple and bluish green ..	55	15

1965 (15 Oct). *International Co-operation Year. As Nos.* 100/1 *of Lesotho.*

No.	Type	Description	Unused	Used
199		1d. reddish purple and turquoise-green ..	20	15
200		6d. deep bluish green and lavender ..	70	15
		w. Wmk inverted		

1966 (24 Jan). *Churchill Commemoration. As Nos.* 102/5 *of Lesotho.*

No.	Type	Description	Unused	Used
201		1d. new blue	15	10
202		3d. deep green	35	10
203		6d. brown	50	15
204		1s. 6d. bluish violet	70	40
201/4		.. .. *Set of* 4	1·50	65

1966 (1 July). *World Cup Football Championships. As Nos.* 57/8 *of Pitcairn Islands.*

No.	Type	Description	Unused	Used
205		3d. violet, yellow-green, lake & yellow-brn ..	50	15
206		6d. chocolate, blue-green, lake & yellow-brn	75	15

1966 (20 Sept). *Inauguration of W.H.O. Headquarters, Geneva. As Nos.* 185/6 *of Montserrat.*

No.	Type	Description	Unused	Used
207		3d. black, yellow-green and light blue ..	75	15
208		1s. 6d. black, light purple and yellow-brown	2·75	55

1966 (1 Dec). 20*th Anniversary of U.N.E.S.C.O. As Nos.* 342/4 *of Mauritius.*

No.	Type	Description	Unused	Used
209		3d. slate-violet, red, yellow and orange ..	1·00	20
210		6d. orange-yellow, violet and deep olive ..	1·75	30
211		1s. 6d. black, bright purple and orange ..	2·50	1·25
209/11		.. .. *Set of* 3	4·75	1·60

(Des W. H. Brown. Photo Harrison)

1967 (5 May). *New Constitution. W* w **12** (*sideways*). *P* 14½ × 14.

No.	Type	Description	Unused	Used
212	**65**	1s. multicoloured	10	10
213		2s. 6d. multicoloured	20	20
		a. Red (ribbon, etc.) omitted	£475	

66 Fire of London

(Des M. Goaman. Recess D.L.R.)

1967 (4 Sept). 300*th Anniv of Arrival of Settlers after Great Fire of London. T* **66** *and similar horiz designs. W* w **12**. *P* 13.

No.	Type	Description	Unused	Used
214		1d. carmine-red and black	15	10
		a. Carmine and black	80	60
215		3d. ultramarine and black	20	10
216		6d. slate-violet and black	20	10
217		1s 6d. olive-green and black	20	10
214/17		.. .. *Set of* 4	65	30

Designs:—3d. East Indiaman *Charles*; 6d. Settlers landing at Jamestown; 1s. 6d. Settlers clearing scrub.

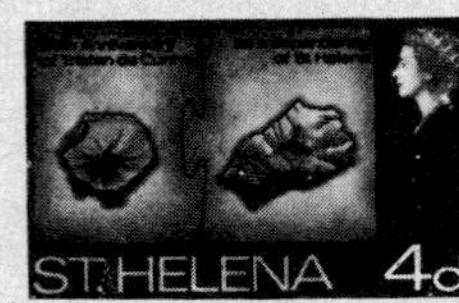

70 Interlocking Maps of Tristan and St. Helena

(Des Jennifer Toombs. Photo Harrison)

1968 (4 June). 30*th Anniv of Tristan da Cunha as a Dependency of St. Helena. T* **70** *and similar horiz design. W* w **12**. *P* 14 × 14½.

No.	Type	Description	Unused	Used
218	**70**	4d. purple and chocolate	10	10
219	–	8d. olive and brown	10	20
220	**70**	1s. 9d. ultramarine and chocolate ..	10	30
221	–	2s. 3d. greenish blue and brown ..	15	30
218/21		.. .. *Set of* 4	35	75

Design:—8d., 2s. 3d. Interlocking maps of St. Helena and Tristan.

72 Queen Elizabeth and Sir Hudson Lowe

(Des M. Farrar Bell. Litho D.L.R.)

1968 (4 Sept). 150*th Anniv of the Abolition of Slavery in St. Helena. T* **72** *and similar horiz design. Multicoloured. W* w **12** (*sideways*). *P* 13 × 12½.

No.	Type	Description	Unused	Used
222		3d. Type **72**	10	10
223		9d. Type **72**	10	15
224		1s. 6d. Queen Elizabeth and Sir George Bingham	15	20
225		2s. 6d. As 1s. 6d.	25	25
222/5		.. .. *Set of* 4	55	55

74 Blue Gum Eucalyptus and Road Construction

(Des Sylvia Goaman. Litho P.B.)

1968 (4 Nov). *Horiz designs as T* **74**. *Multicoloured. W* w **12** (*sideways**). *P* 13½.

No.	Type	Description	Unused	Used
226		½d. Type **74**	10	10
227		1d. Cabbage-tree and electricity development	10	10
		w. Wmk Crown to right of CA ..	3·25	
228		1½d. St. Helena Redwood and dental unit	15	10
229		2d. Scrubweed and pest control ..	15	10
230		3d. Tree-fern and flats in Jamestown ..	30	10
231		4d. Blue gum Eucalyptus, pasture and livestock improvement	20	10
232		6d. Cabbage-tree and schools broadcasting	50	10
233		8d. St. Helena Redwood and country cottages	30	10
234		10d. Scrubweed and new school buildings	30	10
235		1s. Tree-fern and reafforestation ..	30	10
236		1s. 6d. Blue gum Eucalyptus and heavy lift crane	70	1·50
237		2s. 6d. Cabbage-tree and Lady Field Children's Home	80	2·25
238		5s. St. Helena Redwood and agricultural training	90	3·25
239		10s. Scrubweed and New General Hospital	2·50	3·25
240		£1 Tree-fern and lifeboat *John Dutton*	11·00	15·00
226/40		.. .. *Set of* 15	16·00	22·00

*The normal sideways watermark shows Crown to left of CA, *as seen from the back of the stamp.*

See also No. 274 for distinct shade of £1 value.

89 Brig *Perseverance*

93 W.O. and Drummer of the 53rd Foot, 1815

(Des J.W. Litho P.B.)

1969 (19 Apr). *Mail Communications. T* **89** *and similar horiz designs. Multicoloured. W w* **12** *(sideways). P* 13½.
241 4d. Type **89** 20 20
242 8d. *Phoebe* (screw steamer) 30 35
243 1s. 9d. *Llandovery Castle* (liner) 40 50
244 2s. 3d. *Good Hope Castle* (cargo liner) .. 45 60
241/4 .. .. *Set of* 4 1·25 1·50
No. 242 is inscribed "DANE" in error.

(Des R. North. Litho Format)

1969 (3 Sept). *Military Uniforms. T* **93** *and similar vert designs. Multicoloured. W w* **12**. *P* 14.
245 6d. Type **93** 25 15
w. Wmk inverted .. .. 50·00
246 8d. Officer and Surgeon, 20th Foot, 1816 .. 35 15
247 1s. 8d. Drum Major, 66th Foot, 1816, and Royal Artillery Officer, 1820 .. .. 40 25
248 2s. 6d. Private, 91st Foot, and 2nd Corporal, Royal Sappers and Miners, 1832 .. 45 30
245/8 .. .. *Set of* 4 1·25 75

97 Dickens, Mr. Pickwick and Job Trotter (*Pickwick Papers*)

(Des Jennifer Toombs. Litho P.B.)

1970 (9 June). *Death Centenary of Charles Dickens. T* **97** *and similar horiz designs each incorporating a portrait of Dickens. Multicoloured. Chalk-surfaced paper. W w* **12** *(sideways*). P* 13½×13.
249 4d. Type **97** 50 10
a. Shiny unsurfaced paper .. .. 30 1·40
b. Yellow omitted £275
w. Wmk Crown to right of CA .. .. 18·00
250 8d. Mr. Bumble and Oliver (*Oliver Twist*) 60 10
a. Shiny unsurfaced paper .. .. 30 1·60
251 1s. 6d. Sairey Gamp and Mark Tapley (*Martin Chuzzlewit*) 75 15
a. Shiny unsurfaced paper .. .. 40 2·25
252 2s. 6d. Jo and Mr. Turveydrop (*Bleak House*) 90 30
a. Shiny unsurfaced paper .. .. 50 2·50
249/52 .. .. *Set of* 4 2·50 60
249a/52a .. .. *Set of* 4 1·40 7·00
*The normal sideways watermark shows Crown to left of CA, *as seen from the back of the stamp.*
Supplies sent to St. Helena were on paper with a dull surface which reacts to the chalky test and with PVA gum. Crown Agents supplies were from a later printing on shiny paper which does not respond to the chalky test and with gum arabic.

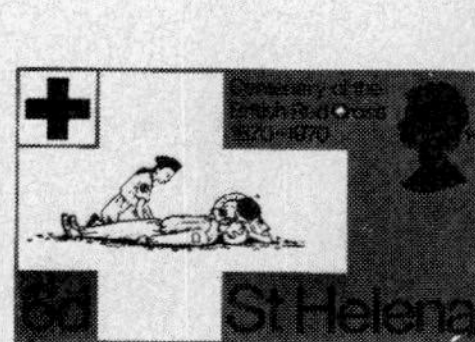

98 "Kiss of Life" **99** Officer's Shako Plate (20th Foot)

(Des Jennifer Toombs. Litho J.W.)

1970 (15 Sept). *Centenary of British Red Cross. T* **98** *and similar horiz designs. W w* **12** *(sideways). P* 14.
253 6d. bistre, vermilion and black 15 10
254 9d. turquoise-green, vermilion and black .. 20 10
255 1s. 9d. pale grey, vermilion and black .. 30 10
256 2s. 3d. pale lavender, vermilion and black .. 30 20
253/6 .. .. *Set of* 4 85 45
Designs:—9d. Nurse with girl in wheelchair; 1s. 9d. Nurse bandaging child's knee; 2s. 3d. Red Cross emblem.

(Des J.W. Litho Questa)

1970 (2 Nov). *Military Equipment (1st issue). T* **99** *and similar vert designs. Multicoloured. W w* **12**. *P* 12.
257 4d. Type **99** 50 20
258 9d. Officer's Breast-plate (66th Foot) .. 60 30
259 1s. 3d. Officer's Full Dress Shako (91st Foot) 70 40
260 2s. 11d. Ensign's Shako (53rd Foot).. .. 90 60
257/60 .. .. *Set of* 4 2·40 1·40
See also Nos. 281/4, 285/8 and 291/4.

100 Electricity Development **101** St. Helena holding the "True Cross"

(Litho P.B.)

1971 (15 Feb). *Decimal Currency. Designs as Nos. 227/40, but with values inscr in decimal currency as in T* **100**. *W w* **12** *(sideways*). P* 13½.
261 ½p. multicoloured 10 10
262 1p. multicoloured (as 1½d.) 10 10
w. Wmk Crown to right of CA .. 50
263 1½p. multicoloured (as 2d.) 10 10
264 2p. multicoloured (as 3d.) .. .. 1·75 90
265 2½p. multicoloured (as 4d.) 10 10
266 3½p. multicoloured (as 6d.) 30 10
267 4½p. multicoloured (as 8d.) 10 10
268 5p. multicoloured (as 10d.) 10 10
269 7½p. multicoloured (as 1s.) 40 35
270 10p. multicoloured (as 1s. 6d.) 30 35
271 12½p. multicoloured (as 2s. 6d.) 30 50
272 25p. multicoloured (as 5s.) .. .. 60 1·25
273 50p. multicoloured (as 10s.) .. .. 1·25 2·00
274 £1 multicoloured† .. .. .. 24·00 18·00
261/74 .. .. .. *Set of* 14 26·00 22·00
*The normal sideways watermark shows Crown to left of CA *as seen from the back of the stamp.*
†Although the design of No. 274 in no way differs from that of No. 240, it was reprinted specially for decimalisation, and differs considerably in shade from No. 240, as do others from their counterparts in the 1968 set.
The main differences in No. 274 are in the mountain which is blue rather than pinkish blue and in the sea which is light blue instead of greenish blue.
See also No. 309.

(Des R. Granger Barrett. Litho Questa)

1971 (5 Apr). *Easter. W w* **12**. *P* 14 × 14½.
275 **101** 2p. multicoloured 10 10
276 5p. multicoloured 15 15
277 7½p. multicoloured 25 20
278 12½p. multicoloured 30 25
275/8 .. .. *Set of* 4 70 60

102 Napoleon (after painting by J.-L. David) and Tomb on St. Helena

(Des J.W. Litho Questa)

1971 (5 May). *150th Death Anniv of Napoleon, T* **102** *and similar vert design. Multicoloured. W w* **12**. *P* 13½.
279 2p. Type **102** 40 40
280 34p. "Napoleon at St. Helena" (H. Delaroche) 85 85

(Des J.W. Litho Questa)

1971 (10 Nov). *Military Equipment (2nd issue). Multicoloured designs as T* **99**. *W w* **12**. *P* 14.
281 1½p. Artillery Private's hanger 55 30
282 4p. Baker rifle and socket bayonet .. 80 60
283 6p. Infantry Officer's sword 80 80
284 22½p. Baker rifle and sword bayonet.. .. 1·25 1·25
281/4 .. .. *Set of* 4 3·00 2·75

(Des and litho J.W.)

1972 (19 June). *Military Equipment (3rd issue). Multicoloured designs as T* **99**. *W w* **12**. *P* 14.
285 2p. multicoloured 40 20
286 5p. reddish lilac, new blue and black .. 50 40
287 7½p. multicoloured 60 50
288 12½p. pale olive-sepia, brown and black .. 70 60
285/8 .. .. *Set of* 4 2·00 1·50
Designs:—2p. Royal Sappers and Miners breast-plate, post 1823; 5p. Infantry sergeant's spontoon, *circa* 1830; 7½p. Royal Artillery officer's breast-plate, *circa* 1830; 12½p. English military pistol, *circa* 1800.

103 St. Helena Sand Plover and White Tern

(Des (from photograph by D. Groves) and photo Harrison)

1972 (20 Nov). *Royal Silver Wedding. Multicoloured; background colour given. W w* **12**. *P* 14 × 14½.
289 **103** 2p. slate-green 25 40
w. Wmk inverted .. .. .. 20·00
290 16p. lake-brown 50 85
w. Wmk inverted .. .. .. 45·00

(Des J.W. Litho Questa)

1973 (20 Sept). *Military Equipment (4th issue). Multicoloured designs as T* **99**. *W w* **12** *(sideways). P* 14.
291 2p. Other Rank's shako, 53rd Foot, 1815 .. 65 55
292 5p. Band and Drums sword, 1830.. .. 80 1·00
293 7½p. Royal Sappers and Miners Officer's hat, 1830 .. .. 1·00 1·25
294 12½p. General's sword, 1831 .. .. 1·50 1·50
291/4 .. .. *Set of* 4 3·50 4·00

1973 (14 Nov). *Royal Wedding. As Nos. 322/3 of Montserrat.*
295 2p. violet-blue 15 10
296 18p. light emerald 25 20

104 *Westminster* and *Claudine* beached, 1849

(Des J.W. Litho Questa)

1973 (17 Dec). *Tercentenary of East India Company Charter. T* **104** *and similar horiz designs. Multicoloured. W w* **12**. *P* 14.
297 1½p. Type **104** 40 45
298 4p. *True Briton*, 1790 .. .. .. 50 70
299 6p. *General Goddard* in action, 1795 .. 50 70
300 22½p. *Kent* burning in the Bay of Biscay, 1825 1·10 2·25
297/300 .. .. *Set of* 4 2·25 3·75

105 U.P.U. Emblem and Ships

(Des J.W. Litho Questa)

1974 (15 Oct). *Centenary of Universal Postal Union. T* **105** *and similar horiz design. Multicoloured. W w* **12** *(sideways on* **MS**303). *P* 14.
301 5p. Type **105** 20 25
302 25p. U.P.U. emblem and letters 40 55
MS303 89 × 84 mm. Nos. 301/2 .. .. .. 75 1·50

106 Churchill in Sailor Suit, and Blenheim Palace **107** Capt. Cook and H.M.S. *Resolution*

(Des Jennifer Toombs. Litho Questa)

1974 (30 Nov). *Birth Centenary of Sir Winston Churchill. T* **106** *and similar horiz design. W w* **14** *(sideways). P* 14.
304 5p. multicoloured 20 20
305 25p. black, flesh and reddish purple .. 40 60
MS306 108×93 mm. Nos. 304/5. W w **12** (sideways*) .. .. 75 2·00
w. Wmk Crown to right of CA £300
Design:—25p. Churchill and River Thames
*The normal sideways watermark shows Crown to left of CA, *as seen from the back of the stamp.*

(Des J. Cooter. Litho Questa)

1975 (14 July). *Bicentenary of Capt. Cook's Return to St. Helena. T* **107** *and similar horiz design. Multicoloured. W w* **14** *(sideways on 25p.). P* 13½.
307 5p. Type **107** 40 40
308 25p. Capt. Cook and Jamestown .. .. 70 1·00

(Litho Questa)

1975 (13 Aug). *As No. 264 but whiter paper. P* 14.
309 2p. multicoloured .. .. 90 5·00

108 *Mellissia begonifolia* (tree) **109** £1 Note

(Des Jennifer Toombs. Litho J.W.)

1975 (20 Oct). *Centenary of Publication of "St. Helena" by J. C. Melliss. T* **108** *and similar multicoloured designs. W w* **14** *(sideways on 12 and 25p.). P* 13.
310 2p. Type **108** 20 30
311 5p. *Melissius adumbratus* (beetle) .. 25 45
312 12p. St. Helena Sand Plover (*horiz*) .. 60 1·00
313 25p. Melliss's Scorpionfish (*horiz*) .. 75 1·40
310/13 .. .. *Set of* 4 1·60 2·75

(Des V. Whiteley Studio. Litho J.W.)

1976 (15 Mar). *First Issue of Currency Notes. T* **109** *and similar horiz design. Multicoloured. W* w **12** (*sideways**). *P* 13½.

314 8p. Type **109** 30 30
w. Wmk Crown to left of CA 1·10
315 33p. £5 Note 60 80

*The normal sideways watermark shows Crown to right of CA, *as seen from the back of the stamp.*

110 1d. Stamp of 1863

(Des C. Abbott. Litho J.W.)

1976 (4 May). *Festival of Stamps, London. T* **110** *and similar designs. W* w **14** (*sideways on 5 and 25p.*). *P* 13½.

316 5p. light red-brown, black and light flesh 15 15
317 8p. black, green and pale dull green 20 30
318 25p. multicoloured 35 45
316/18 *Set of 3* 65 80

Designs: *Vert*—8p. 1d. stamp of 1922. *Horiz*—25p. Mail carrier *Good Hope Castle.*

For miniature sheet containing No. 318 see Ascension No. **MS**218.

111 "High Knoll, 1806" (Capt. Barnett)

(Des C. Abbott. Litho Questa)

1976 (14 Sept)–**82.** *Aquatints and Lithographs of St. Helena. T* **111** *and similar horiz designs. Multicoloured. W* w **14** (*sideways**). *P* 13½ (£1, £2) *or* 14 (*others*).

A. *On white paper. Without imprint date.*

319A 1p. Type **111** 40 70
a. Cream paper (13.6.80) 40 70
aw. Wmk Crown to right of CA 48·00
320A 3p. "The Friar Rock, 1815" (G. Bellasis) 40 70
a. Cream paper (13.6.80) 40 70
321A 5p. "The Column Lot, 1815" (G. Bellasis) 30 70
322A 6p. "Sandy Bay Valley, 1809" (H. Salt) (23.11.76) 30 70
323A 8p. "Scene from Castle Terrace, 1815" (G. Bellasis) 40 70
324A 9p. "The Briars, 1815" (23.11.76) 40 70
w. Wmk Crown to right of CA 4·25
325A 10p. "Plantation House, 1821" (J. Wathen) 50 60
326A 15p. "Longwood House, 1821" (J. Wathen) (23.11.76) 45 55
327A 18p. "St. Paul's Church" (V. Brooks) 45 1·00
328A 26p. "St. James's Valley, 1815" (Capt. Hastings) 45 75
329A 40p. "St. Matthew's Church, 1860" (V. Brooks) 70 1·50
330A £1 "St. Helena, 1815" (G. Bellasis) (47×34 *mm*) 1·50 3·75
a. Gold omitted £750
331A £2 "Sugar Loaf Hill, 1821" (J. Wathen) (47×34 *mm*) (23.11.76) 3·50 6·00
319A/31A *Set of 13* 8·75 17·00

B. *On cream paper with imprint date* ("1982") (10.5.82)

319B 1p. Type **111** 30 60
325B 10p. "Plantation House, 1821" (J. Wathen) 50 1·50
331B £2 "Sugar Loaf Hill, 1821" (J. Wathen) (47×34 *mm*) 3·75 5·00
319B/31B *Set of 3* 4·00 6·50

*The normal sideways watermark shows Crown to left of CA, *as seen from the back of the stamp.* No. 319Aaw occurs in stamp booklets.

112 Duke of Edinburgh paying Homage

(Des M. Shamir. Litho J.W.)

1977 (7 Feb). *Silver Jubilee. T* **112** *and similar horiz designs. Multicoloured.* W w **14** (*sideways*). *P* 13.

332 8p. Royal visit, 1947 10 25
333 15p. Queen's sceptre with dove 20 35
334 26p. Type **112** 30 40
332/4 *Set of 3* 55 90

NEW INFORMATION

The editor is always interested to correspond with people who have new information that will improve or correct the Catalogue.

113 Halley's Comet (from Bayeux Tapestry)

114 Sea Lion

(Des C. Abbott. Litho Questa)

1977 (23 Aug). *Tercentenary of Halley's Visit. T* **113** *and similar horiz designs. Multicoloured. W* w **14** (*sideways*). *P* 14.

335 5p. Type **113** 35 20
336 8p. Late 17th-century sextant 50 20
337 27p. Halley and Halley's Mount, St. Helena 1·00 60
335/7 *Set of 3* 1·75 90

(Des Jennifer Toombs. Litho Questa)

1978 (2 June). *25th Anniv of Coronation. T* **114** *and similar vert designs. P* 15.

338 25p. agate, cerise and silver 30 50
a. Sheetlet. Nos. 338/40 × 2 1·50
339 25p. multicoloured 30 50
340 25p. agate, cerise and silver 30 50
338/40 *Set of 3* 80 1·40

Designs:—No. 338, Black Dragon of Ulster; No. 339, Queen Elizabeth II; No. 340, Type **114**.

Nos. 338/40 were printed together in small sheets of 6, containing two *se-tenant* strips of 3, with horizontal gutter margin between.

115 Period Engraving of St. Helena

(Des J.W. Litho Questa)

1978 (14 Aug). *Wreck of the "Witte Leeuw". T* **115** *and similar horiz designs. Multicoloured. W* w **14** (*sideways*). *P* 14½.

341 3p. Type **115** 15 15
342 5p. Chinese porcelain 15 20
343 8p. Bronze cannon 20 30
344 9p. Chinese porcelain (*different*) 20 35
345 15p. Pewter mug and ceramic flasks 30 55
346 20p. Dutch East Indiaman 40 70
341/6 *Set of 6* 1·25 2·00

116 H.M.S. *Discovery*

117 Sir Rowland Hill

(Des and litho (25p. also embossed) Walsall)

1979 (19 Feb). *Bicentenary of Captain Cook's Voyages,* 1768–79. *T* **116** *and similar vert designs. Multicoloured. P* 11.

347 3p. Type **116** 20 15
348 8p. Cook's portable observatory 20 25
349 12p. *Pharnaceum acidum* (based on sketch by Joseph Banks) 25 35
350 25p. Flaxman/Wedgwood medallion of Captain Cook 35 90
347/50 *Set of 4* 90 1·50

(Des J.W. Litho Questa)

1979 (10 Dec). *Death Centenary of Sir Rowland Hill. T* **117** *and similar designs.* W w **14** (*sideways* on 8 to 32p*). *P* 14.

351 5p. multicoloured 10 15
w. Wmk inverted 75·00
352 8p. multicoloured 15 20
353 20p. multicoloured 30 40
w. Wmk Crown to right of CA 16·00
354 32p. black, magenta and deep mauve 40 55
w. Wmk Crown to right of CA 18·00
351/4 *Set of 4* 80 1·10

Designs: *Horiz*—8p, 1965 1d. 1st Local Post stamp; 20p. 1863 1d. on 6d. stamps; 32p. 1902 1d. stamp.

*The normal sideways watermark shows Crown to left of CA, *as seen from the back of the stamp.*

118 R. F. Seal's Chart of 1823 showing the Elevation of the Coastline

(Des G. Vasarhelyi. Litho Questa)

1979 (10 Dec). *150th Anniv of the Inclined Plane. T* **118** *and similar designs. W* w **14** (*sideways on 5 and 8p.*). *P* 14.

355 5p. black, brownish grey and stone 15 15
356 8p. black, brownish grey and stone 15 20
357 50p. multicoloured 60 75
355/7 *Set of 3* 80 1·00

Designs: *Horiz*—8p. The Inclined Plane in 1829. *Vert*—50p. The Inclined Plane in 1979.

119 Napoleon's Tomb, 1848

120 East Indiaman

(Des J.W. Litho Questa)

1980 (23 Feb). *Centenary of Empress Eugenie's Visit. T* **119** *and similar horiz designs. W* w **14** (*sideways*). *P* 14.

358 5p. gold, reddish brown and pale red-brown 10 20
359 8p. gold, reddish brown and pale bistre 15 25
360 62p. gold, reddish brown & pale orange-brn 65 80
358/60 *Set of 3* 80 1·10
MS361 180 × 110 mm. Nos. 358/60 80 1·10

Designs:—8p. Landing at St. Helena; 62p. At the tomb of Napoleon.

(Des C. Abbott. Litho Format)

1980 (6 May). *"London 1980" International Stamp Exhibition. T* **120** *and similar vert designs. Multicoloured. W* w **14**. *P* 14½.

362 5p. Type **120** 10 15
363 8p. *Dolphin* postal stone 10 15
364 47p. Postal stone outside Castle entrance, Jamestown 50 60
362/4 *Set of 3* 60 80
MS365 111 × 120 mm. Nos. 362/4 60 80

121 Queen Elizabeth the Queen Mother in 1974

(Des and litho Harrison)

1980 (18 Aug*). *80th Birthday of Queen Elizabeth the Queen Mother.* W w **14** (*sideways*). *P* 14.

366 **121** 24p. multicoloured 35 50

*This is the local date of issue; the Crown Agents released the stamp on 4 August.

122 The Briars, 1815

(Des C. Abbott. Litho Questa)

1980 (17 Nov). *75th Anniv of Wellington's Visit. T* **122** *and similar multicoloured design. W* w **14** (*sideways* on 9p.*). *P* 14.

367 9p. Type **122** 15 15
w. Wmk Crown to right of CA 6·00
368 30p. "Wellington" (Goya) (*vert*) 45 45

*The normal sideways watermark shows Crown to left of CA, *as seen from the back of the stamp.*

Nos. 367/8 were each printed in small sheets of 10 stamps.

123 Redwood

124 Detail from Reinel Portolan Chart, *circa* 1530

(Des Daphne Padden. Litho Enschede)

1981 (5 Jan). *Endemic Plants. T* **123** *and similar horiz designs. Multicoloured. W w* **14** (*sideways**). *P* 13½.
369 5p. Type **123** 15 15
w. Wmk Crown to left of CA .. .. 3·50
370 8p. Old Father Live Forever 15 20
371 15p. Gumwood 20 25
372 27p. Black Cabbage 35 45
369/72 .. .. *Set of* 4 75 95
*The normal sideways watermark shows Crown to right of CA on the 5p. and 8p., but Crown to left of CA on the 15p. and 27p, *all as seen from the back of the stamp.*

(Des Harrison. Litho Walsall)

1981 (22 May). *Early Maps. T* **124** *and similar horiz designs. W w* **14** (*sideways*). *P* 14 × 14½.
373 5p. multicoloured 15 15
374 8p. black, brown-lake and grey 15 20
375 20p. multicoloured 30 35
376 30p. multicoloured 35 50
373/6 .. .. *Set of* 4 85 1·10
MS377 114 × 83 mm. 24p. black and grey .. 40 65
Designs:—8p. John Thornton's Map of St. Helena, *circa* 1700; 20p. Map of St. Helena, 1815; 30p. Map of St. Helena, 1817; miniature sheet, Part of Gastaldi's map of Africa, 16th-century.

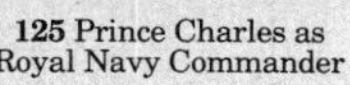

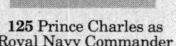

125 Prince Charles as Royal Navy Commander

126 Atlantic Trumpet Triton (*Charonia variegata*)

(Des J.W. Litho Questa)

1981 (22 July). *Royal Wedding. T* **125** *and similar vert designs. Multicoloured. W w* **14**. *P* 14.
378 14p. Wedding bouquet from St. Helena .. 15 20
379 29p. Type **125** 25 30
w. Wmk inverted .. .. .. 4·00
380 32p. Prince Charles and Lady Diana Spencer 30 35
378/80 .. .. *Set of* 3 60 75

(Des J.W. Litho Walsall)

1981 (10 Sept). *Sea Shells. T* **126** *and similar vert designs. Multicoloured. W w* **14**. *P* 14.
381 7p. Type **126** 30 20
382 10p. St. Helena Cowrie (*Cypraea spurca sanctaehelenae*) 35 25
383 25p. Common Purple Janthina (*Janthina janthina*) 60 60
384 53p. Rude Pen Shell (*Pinna rudis*) .. 1·00 1·25
381/4 .. .. *Set of* 4 2·00 2·10

127 Traffic Duty

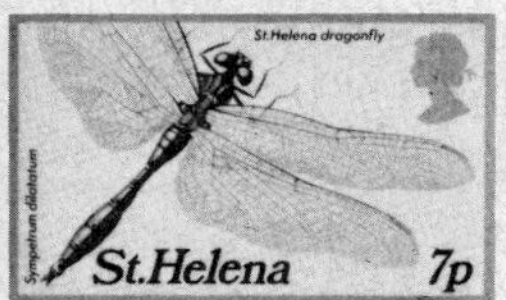

128 *Sympetrum dilatatum* (dragonfly)

(Des BG Studio. Litho Questa)

1981 (5 Nov). *25th Anniv of Duke of Edinburgh Award Scheme. T* **127** *and similar vert designs. Multicoloured. W w* **14**. *P* 14.
385 7p. Type **127** 10 10
386 11p. Signposting 15 15
387 25p. Animal care 30 30
388 50p. Duke of Edinburgh, in Guards' uniform, on horse-back 60 60
385/8 .. .. *Set of* 4 1·00 1·00

(Des C. Abbott. Litho Questa)

1982 (4 Jan). *Insects (1st series). T* **128** *and similar horiz designs. Multicoloured. W w* **14** (*sideways on* 7, 10 *and* 25p., *inverted on* 32p.). *P* 14½.
389 7p. Type **128** 20 20
390 10p. *Aplothorax burchelli* (beetle) .. 25 25
391 25p. *Ampulex compressa* (wasp) 45 45
392 32p. *Labidura herculeana* (earwig) .. 55 55
389/92 .. .. *Set of* 4 1·25 1·25
The 32p. is larger, 45×27 mm.
See also Nos. 411/14.

MINIMUM PRICE

The minimum price quote is 10p which represents a handling charge rather than a basis for valuing common stamps. For further notes about prices see introductory pages.

129 Charles Darwin

130 Prince and Princess of Wales at Balmoral, Autumn 1981

(Des L. Curtis. Litho Questa)

1982 (19 Apr). *150th Anniv of Charles Darwin's Voyage. T* **129** *and similar horiz designs. Multicoloured. W w* **14** (*sideways*). *P* 14.
393 7p. Type **129** 25 25
394 14p. Flagstaff Hill and Darwin's hammer .. 35 50
395 25p. Ring-necked Pheasant and Chukar Partridge 60 85
396 29p. H.M.S. *Beagle* off St. Helena .. 75 1·00
393/6 .. .. *Set of* 4 1·75 2·40

(Des C. Abbott. Litho Format)

1982 (1 July). *21st Birthday of Princess of Wales. T* **130** *and similar vert designs. Multicoloured. W w* **14**. *P* 13½ × 14 (7, 55p.) *or* 13½ (*others*).
397 7p. St. Helena coat of arms 15 20
398 11p. Type **130** 20 20
399 29p. Bride on Palace Balcony 55 65
a. Perf 13½ × 14 .. .. .. 15·00 17·00
b. Imperf (pair) £550
400 55p. Formal portrait .. .. .. 1·10 1·10
397/400 .. .. *Set of* 4 1·75 1·90

1st PARTICIPATION
COMMONWEALTH GAMES 1982

(**131**)

132 Lord Baden-Powell

1982 (25 Oct). *Commonwealth Games, Brisbane. Nos.* 326A *and* 328A *optd with T* **131**.
401 15p. "Longwood House, 1821" (J. Wathen) 25 25
402 26p. "St. James's Valley, 1815" (Capt. Hastings) 45 45

(Des L. McCombie. Litho Walsall)

1982 (29 Nov). *75th Anniv of Boy Scout Movement. T* **132** *and similar designs. W w* **14** (*inverted on* 3p., 29p.; *sideways on* 11p., 59p.). *P* 14.
403 3p. lake-brown, grey and orange-yellow .. 15 15
404 11p. lake-brown, grey & bright yellow-green 30 25
405 29p. lake-brown, grey and reddish orange .. 55 60
406 59p. lake-brown, grey & bright yellow-green 90 1·25
403/6 .. .. *Set of* 4 1·75 2·00
Designs: *Horiz*—11p. Boy Scout (drawing by Lord Baden-Powell); 59p. Camping at Thompsons Wood. *Vert*—29p. Canon Walcott.

133 King and Queen Rocks

134 *Trametes versicolor* ("*Coriolus versicolor*")

(Des C. Abbott. Litho B.D.T.)

1983 (14 Jan). *Views of St. Helena by Roland Svensson. T* **133** *and similar multicoloured designs. W w* **14** (*sideways on* 29p., 59p.). *P* 14.
407 7p. Type **133** 20 20
408 11p. Turk's Cap 25 25
409 29p. Coastline from Jamestown (*horiz*) .. 50 65
410 59p. Mundens Point (*horiz*) .. .. 1·00 1·40
407/10 .. .. *Set of* 4 1·75 2·25

(Des C. Abbott. Litho Questa)

1983 (22 Apr). *Insects (2nd series). Horiz designs as T* **128**. *Multicoloured. W w* **14** (*sideways*). *P* 14½.
411 11p. *Acherontia atropos* (hawk moth) .. 25 30
412 15p. *Helenasaldula aberrans* (shore-bug) .. 30 35
413 29p. *Anchastus compositarum* (click beetle) 40 55
414 59p. *Lamprochrus cossonoides* (weevil) .. 75 1·25
411/14 .. .. *Set of* 4 1·50 2·25

(Des Garden Studio. Litho Format)

1983 (16 June). *Fungi. T* **134** *and similar multicoloured designs. W w* **14** (*sideways on* 29p.). *P* 14.
415 11p. Type **134** 25 25
416 15p. *Pluteus brunneisucus* 35 40
417 29p. *Polyporus induratus* (*horiz*) .. 55 75
418 59p. *Coprinus angulatus* .. .. 80 1·60
415/18 .. .. *Set of* 4 1·75 2·75

135 Java Sparrow

136 Birth of St. Helena

(Des J.W. Litho Questa)

1983 (12 Sept). *Birds. T* **135** *and similar vert designs. Multicoloured. W w* **14**. *P* 14.
419 7p. Type **135** 30 20
420 15p. Madagascar Red Fody 45 35
421 33p. Common Waxbill 80 70
422 59p. Yellow Canary .. .. .. 1·50 1·40
419/22 .. .. *Set of* 4 2·75 2·50

(Des Jennifer Toombs. Litho Questa)

1983 (17 Oct). *Christmas. Life of St. Helena* (1*st series*). *T* **136** *and similar vert design. Multicoloured. W w* **14**. *P* 14 × 13½.
423 10p. Type **136** 20 35
a. Sheetlet Nos. 423/4, each ×5 .. .. 2·00
424 15p. St. Helena being taken to convent .. 20 35
Nos. 423/4 were printed together in small sheets of 10, containing horizontal strips of 5 for each value separated by a horizontal gutter margin.
See also Nos. 450/3 and 468/71.

137 1934 ½d. Stamp

138 Prince Andrew and H.M.S. *Invincible* (aircraft carrier)

(Des C. Abbott. Litho Questa)

1984 (3 Jan). *150th Anniv of St. Helena as a British Colony. T* **137** *and similar square designs showing values of the* 1934 *Centenary of British Colonisation issue or Colony Arms. Multicoloured. W w* **14** (*sideways*). *P* 13½.
425 1p. Type **137** 10 20
426 3p. 1934 1d. stamp 10 20
427 6p. 1934 1½d. stamp 10 30
428 7p. 1934 2d. stamp 15 30
429 11p. 1934 3d. stamp 20 40
430 15p. 1934 6d. stamp 25 45
431 29p. 1934 1s. stamp 50 95
432 33p. 1934 5s. stamp .. .. .. 55 1·25
433 59p. 1934 10s. stamp .. .. .. 1·10 2·00
434 £1 1934 2s. 6d. stamp .. .. .. 2·75 3·25
435 £2 St. Helena Coat of Arms .. .. 3·50 5·00
425/35 .. .. *Set of* 11 7·50 13·00

(Des D. Bowen. Litho Format)

1984 (4 Apr). *Visit of Prince Andrew. T* **138** *and similar horiz design. Multicoloured. W w* **14** (*sideways**). *P* 14.
436 11p. Type **138** 25 25
w. Wmk Crown to right of CA .. .. 65·00
437 60p. Prince Andrew and H.M.S. *Herald* (survey ship) .. .. 75 1·40
*The normal sideways watermark shows Crown to left of CA, *as seen from the back of the stamp.*

139 *St. Helena* (schooner)

140 Twopenny Coin and Donkey

(Des A. Theobald. Litho Questa)

1984 (14 May). *250th Anniv of "Lloyd's List" (newspaper). T* **139** *and similar vert designs. Multicoloured. W w* **14**. *P* 14½ × 14.
438 10p. Type **139** 20 20
439 18p. Solomons Facade (local agent) .. 35 35
440 25p. Lloyd's Coffee House, London .. 50 55
441 50p. *Papanui* (freighter) .. .. 1·00 1·00
438/41 .. .. *Set of* 4 1·90 1·90

(Des G. Drummond. Litho Format)

1984 (23 July). *New Coinage. T* **140** *and similar horiz designs. Multicoloured. W* w **14** (*sideways*). *P* 14.

442 10p. Type **140** .. 30 35
443 15p. Five pence coin and St. Helena Sand Plover .. 35 45
444 29p. Penny coin and Yellow-finned Tuna 55 75
445 50p. Ten pence coin and Arum Lily .. 90 1·25
442/5 .. *Set of* 4 1·90 2·50

141 Mrs. Rebecca Fuller (former Corps Secretary)

142 Queen Elizabeth the Queen Mother aged Two

(Des L. Curtis. Litho Walsall)

1984 (12 Oct). *Centenary of Salvation Army on St. Helena. T* **141** *and similar multicoloured designs. W* w **14** (*sideways on* 11p., 25p.). *P* 14.

446 7p. Type **141** .. 35 45
447 11p. Meals-on-wheels service (*horiz*) .. 45 65
448 25p. Salvation Army Citadel, Jamestown (*horiz*) .. 70 1·25
449 60p. Salvation Army band at Jamestown Clock Tower .. 1·25 2·50
446/9 .. *Set of* 4 2·50 4·25

(Des Jennifer Toombs. Litho Questa)

1984 (9 Nov). *Christmas. Life of St. Helena* (2*nd series*). *Vert designs as T* **136**. *Multicoloured. W* w **14**. *P* 14.

450 6p. St. Helena visits prisoners .. 20 20
451 10p. Betrothal of St. Helena .. 30 30
452 15p. Marriage of St. Helena to Constantius .. 40 40
453 33p. Birth of Constantine .. 70 70
450/3 .. *Set of* 4 1·40 1·40

(Des A. Theobald (70p.), C. Abbott (others). Litho Questa)

1985 (7 June). *Life and Times of Queen Elizabeth the Queen Mother. T* **142** *and similar vert designs. Multicoloured. W* w **16**. *P* 14½×14.

454 11p. Type **142** .. 20 25
455 15p. At Ascot with the Queen .. 20 35
w. Wmk inverted .. 40·00
456 29p. Attending Gala Ballet at Covent Garden .. 40 65
457 55p. With Prince Henry at his christening 60 1·00
454/7 .. *Set of* 4 1·25 2·00
MS458 91×73 mm. 70p. The Queen Mother with Ford "V8 Pilot". Wmk sideways .. 1·40 1·60

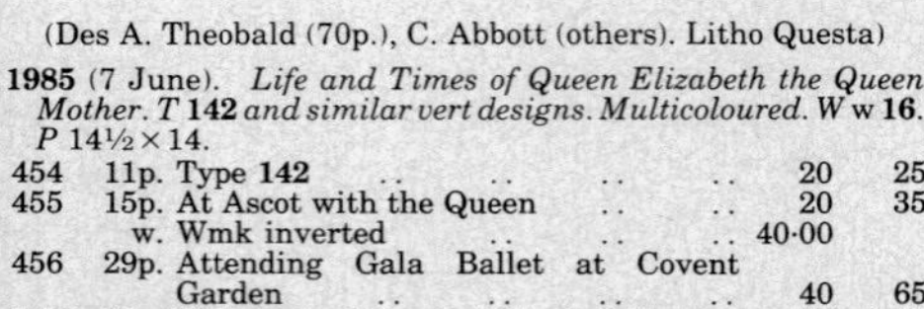

143 Axillary Cardinalfish

144 John J. Audubon

(Des L. Curtis. Litho Walsall)

1985 (12 July). *Marine Life. T* **143** *and similar horiz designs. Multicoloured. W* w **14** (*sideways**). *P* 13×13½.

459 7p. Type **143** .. 25 25
460 11p. Chub Mackerel .. 30 30
461 15p. Skipjack Tuna .. 40 40
462 33p. Yellow-finned Tuna .. 75 75
463 50p. Stump .. 1·25 1·25
w. Wmk Crown to right of CA .. 28·00
459/63 .. *Set of* 5 2·75 2·75

*The normal sideways watermark shows Crown to left of CA, *as seen from the back of the stamp.*

(Des Josephine Martin (11p.). Litho Format)

1985 (2 Sept). *Birth Bicentenary of John J. Audubon* (*ornithologist*). *T* **144** *and similar designs. W* w **14** (*inverted on* 11p., *sideways on others*). *P* 14.

464 11p. black and blackish brown .. 45 25
465 15p. multicoloured .. 55 35
466 25p. multicoloured .. 75 55
467 60p. multicoloured .. 1·40 1·40
464/7 .. *Set of* 4 2·75 2·25

Designs: *Horiz* (from original Audubon paintings)—15p. Moorhen ("Common Gallinule"); 25p. White-tailed Tropic Bird; 60p. Common Noddy.

(Des Jennifer Toombs. Litho Questa)

1985 (14 Oct). *Christmas. Life of St. Helena* (3*rd series*). *Vert designs as T* **136**. *Multicoloured. W* w **14**. *P* 14×13½.

468 7p. St. Helena journeys to the Holy Land .. 25 25
469 10p. Zambres slays the bull .. 30 30
470 15p. The bull restored to life: conversion of St. Helena .. 40 40
471 60p. Resurrection of the corpse: the true Cross identified .. 1·00 1·50
468/71 .. *Set of* 4 1·75 2·25

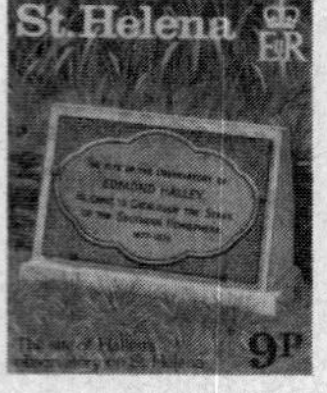

145 Church Provident Society for Women Banner

146 Plaque at Site of Halley's Observatory on St. Helena

(Des A. Theobald. Litho J.W.)

1986 (7 Jan). *Friendly Societies' Banners. T* **145** *and similar horiz designs. Multicoloured. W* w **16** (*sideways**). *P* 13×13½.

472 10p. Type **145** .. 20 25
473 11p. Working Men's Christian Association 20 25
474 25p. Church Benefit Society for Children 40 55
475 29p. Mechanics and Friendly Benefit Society .. 45 65
476 33p. Ancient Order of Foresters .. 50 70
w. Wmk Crown to left of CA .. 10·00
472/6 .. *Set of* 5 1·60 2·10

*The normal sideways watermark shows Crown to right of CA, *as seen from the back of the stamp.*

(Des A. Theobald. Litho Questa)

1986 (21 Apr). *60th Birthday of Queen Elizabeth II. Vert designs as T* **230***a of Jamaica. Multicoloured. W* w **16**. *P* 14½×14.

477 10p. Princess Elizabeth making 21st birthday broadcast, South Africa, 1947 15 20
478 15p. Silver Jubilee photograph, 1977 .. 25 30
479 20p. Princess Elizabeth on board H.M.S. *Vanguard*, 1947 .. 30 35
480 50p. In the U.S.A., 1976 .. 65 75
481 65p. At Crown Agents Head Office, London, 1983 .. 80 90
477/81 .. *Set of* 5 1·90 2·25

(Des L. Curtis. Litho Walsall)

1986 (15 May). *Appearance of Halley's Comet. T* **146** *and similar vert designs. Multicoloured. W* w **14**. *P* 14½×14.

482 9p. Type **146** .. 25 30
483 12p. Edmond Halley .. 30 35
484 20p. Halley's planisphere of the southern stars .. 45 55
485 65p. *Unity* on passage to St. Helena, 1676 .. 1·40 1·60
482/5 .. *Set of* 4 2·10 2·50

(Des D. Miller. Litho Questa)

1986 (23 July). *Royal Wedding. Square designs as T* **231***a of Jamaica. Multicoloured. W* w **16**. *P* 14.

486 10p. Prince Andrew and Miss Sarah Ferguson .. 20 25
w. Wmk inverted .. 20·00
487 40p. Prince Andrew with Governor J. Massingham on St. Helena .. 80 85
w. Wmk inverted .. 20·00

147 James Ross and H.M.S. *Erebus*

(Des C. Abbott. Litho Questa)

1986 (22 Sept). *Explorers. T* **147** *and similar horiz designs. W* w **16** (*sideways*). *P* 14½.

488 1p. deep brown and pink .. 30 90
489 3p. royal blue and grey-blue .. 30 90
490 5p. bronze-green and deep yellow-green .. 30 1·00
491 9p. purple-brown and claret .. 40 1·00
492 10p. deep brown and light brown .. 40 1·00
493 12p. myrtle-green and light green .. 50 1·00
494 15p. red-brown and brown-rose .. 60 1·00
495 20p. deep dull blue and light blue .. 70 1·25
496 25p. sepia and salmon-pink .. 70 1·25
497 40p. bottle-green and dull blue-green 1·00 1·75
498 60p. reddish brown and pale orange-brown .. 1·25 2·00
499 £1 deep turquoise-blue and turquoise-blue 2·00 3·00
500 £2 deep lilac and reddish lilac .. 4·00 5·00
488/500 .. *Set of* 13 11·00 19·00

Designs:—3p. Robert FitzRoy and H.M.S. *Beagle*; 5p. Adam Johann von Krusenstern and *Nadezhda*; 9p. William Bligh and H.M.S. *Resolution*; 10p. Otto von Kotzebue and *Rurik*; 12p. Philip Carteret and H.M.S. *Swallow*; 15p. Thomas Cavendish and *Desire*; 20p. Louis-Antoine de Bougainville and *La Boudeuse*; 25p. Fyedor Petrovich Lütke and *Senyavin*; 40p. Louis Isidore Duperrey and *La Coquille*; 60p. John Byron and H.M.S. *Dolphin*; £1 James Cook and H.M.S. *Endeavour*; £2 Jules Dumont d'Urville and *L'Astrolabe*.

148 Prince Edward and H.M.S. *Repulse* (battle cruiser), 1925

149 St. Helena Tea Plant

(Des E. Nisbet. Litho Questa)

1987 (16 Feb). *Royal Visits to St. Helena. T* **148** *and similar horiz designs. Multicoloured. W* w **16** (*sideways*). *P* 14.

501 9p. Type **148** .. 70 70
502 13p. King George VI and H.M.S. *Vanguard* (battleship), 1947 .. 95 1·00
503 38p. Prince Philip and Royal Yacht *Britannia*, 1957 .. 2·00 2·75
504 45p. Prince Andrew and H.M.S. *Herald* (survey ship), 1984 .. 2·25 3·00
501/4 .. *Set of* 4 5·50 6·75

(Des Annette Robinson. Litho Questa)

1987 (3 Aug). *Rare Plants* (1*st series*). *T* **149** *and similar vert designs. Multicoloured. W* w **16**. *P* 14½×14.

505 9p. Type **149** .. 65 55
506 13p. Baby's Toes .. 80 75
507 38p. Salad Plant .. 1·50 1·75
508 45p. Scrubwood .. 1·75 2·25
505/8 .. *Set of* 4 4·25 4·75

See also Nos. 531/4.

150 Lesser Rorqual

151 *Defence* and Dampier's Signature, 1691

(Des A. Riley. Litho Questa)

1987 (24 Oct). *Marine Mammals. T* **150** *and similar horiz designs. Multicoloured. W* w **16** (*sideways*). *P* 14.

509 9p. Type **150** .. 90 75
510 13p. Risso's Dolphin .. 95 95
511 45p. Sperm Whale .. 2·25 2·50
512 60p. Euphrosyne Dolphin .. 2·50 3·00
509/12 .. *Set of* 4 6·00 6·50
MS513 102×72 mm. 75p. Humpback Whale (48×31 *mm*). P 13½×14 .. 4·50 3·50

1987 (9 Dec). *Royal Ruby Wedding. Nos. 477/81 optd with T* **45***a of Kiribati in silver.*

514 10p. Princess Elizabeth making 21st birthday broadcast, South Africa, 1947 .. 15 30
515 15p. Silver Jubilee photograph, 1977 .. 20 35
a. Opt omitted (vert pair with normal) £200
516 20p. Princess Elizabeth on board H.M.S. *Vanguard*, 1947 .. 35 45
517 50p. In the U.S.A., 1976 .. 60 1·00
518 65p. At Crown Agents Head Office, London, 1983 .. 70 1·40
514/18 .. *Set of* 5 1·75 3·25

No. 515a occurred on the top row of several sheets.

(Des A. Theobald. Litho Walsall)

1988 (1 Mar). *Bicentenary of Australian Settlement. T* **151** *and similar horiz designs showing ships and signatures. Multicoloured. W* w **16** (*sideways*). *P* 14×14½.

519 9p. Type **151** .. 1·50 90
520 13p. H.M.S. *Resolution* (Cook), 1775 .. 2·00 1·75
521 45p. H.M.S. *Providence* (Bligh), 1792 .. 3·25 3·50
522 60p. H.M.S. *Beagle* (Darwin), 1836 .. 4·25 5·00
519/22 .. *Set of* 4 10·00 10·00

152 "The Holy Virgin with the Child"

153 Ebony

(Des N. Harvey. Litho Questa)

1988 (11 Oct). *Christmas. T* **152** *and similar vert designs showing religious paintings. Multicoloured. W* w **14**. *P* 14.

523 5p. Type **152** .. 10 20
524 20p. "Madonna" .. 40 50
525 38p. "The Holy Family with St. John" .. 75 1·25
526 60p. "The Holy Virgin with the Child" .. 1·25 2·00
523/6 .. *Set of* 4 2·25 3·50

(Des D. Miller (8p.), E. Nisbet and D. Miller (others). Litho Questa)

1988 (1 Nov). *300th Anniv of Lloyd's of London. Designs as T* **167a** *of Malawi.* W w **16** (*sideways on* 20, 45*p.*). *P* 14.
527 9p. agate and brown 25 30
528 20p. multicoloured 80 60
529 45p. multicoloured .. .. 1·40 1·40
530 60p. multicoloured .. .. 1·60 1·60
527/30 .. .. *Set of* 4 3·50 3·50

Designs: *Vert*—9p. Lloyd's Underwriting Room, 1886; 60p. *Spangereid* (full-rigged ship) on fire, St. Helena, 1920. *Horiz*—20p. *Edinburgh Castle* (liner); 45p. *Bosun Bird* (freighter).

(Des L. Ninnes. Litho Questa)

1989 (6 Jan). *Rare Plants (2nd series). T* **153** *and similar vert designs. Multicoloured.* W w **16**. *P* 14.
531 9p. Type **153** 40 40
532 20p. St. Helena Lobelia 70 70
533 45p. Large Bellflower .. .. 1·40 1·75
534 60p. She Cabbage Tree .. .. 1·60 2·25
531/4 .. .. *Set of* 4 3·75 4·50

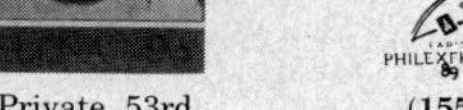

154 Private, 53rd Foot (**155**)

(Des C. Collins. Litho Format)

1989 (5 June). *Military Uniforms of* 1815. *T* **154** *and similar vert designs. Multicoloured.* W w **16**. *P* 14.
535 9p. Type **154** 55 70
a. Horiz strip of 5. Nos. 535/9 .. 4·50
536 13p. Officer, 53rd Foot 65 80
537 20p. Royal Marine 75 90
538 45p. Officer, 66th Foot .. .. 1·40 1·60
539 60p. Private, 66th Foot .. .. 1·60 1·75
535/9 .. .. *Set of* 5 4·50 5·25

Nos. 535/9 were printed together, *se-tenant*, in horizontal strips of five throughout the sheet.

1989 (7 July). *"Philexfrance 89" International Stamp Exhibition, Paris. Nos.* 535/9 *optd with T* **155**.
540 9p. Type **154** 55 70
a. Horiz strip of 5. Nos. 540/4 .. 4·50
541 13p. Officer, 53rd Foot 65 80
542 20p. Royal Marine 75 90
543 45p. Officer, 66th Foot .. .. 1·40 1·60
544 60p. Private, 66th Foot .. .. 1·60 1·75
540/4 .. .. *Set of* 5 4·50 5·25

156 Agricultural Studies **157** "The Madonna with the Pear" (Dürer)

(Des A. Edmonston. Litho Questa)

1989 (24 Aug). *New Prince Andrew Central School. T* **156** *and similar horiz designs. Multicoloured.* W w **16** (*sideways*). *P* 14×14½.
545 13p. Type **156** 45 45
546 20p. Geography lesson 75 75
547 25p. Walkway and classroom block .. 85 85
548 60p. Aerial view of School .. .. .. 2·00 2·50
545/8 .. .. *Set of* 4 3·50 4·00

(Des D. Miller. Litho Questa)

1989 (23 Oct). *Christmas. Religious Paintings. T* **157** *and similar vert designs. Multicoloured.* W w **14**. *P* 14.
549 10p. Type **157** 50 40
550 20p. "The Holy Family under the Appletree" (Rubens) 75 75
551 45p. "The Virgin in the Meadow" (Raphael) 1·75 2·00
552 60p. "The Holy Family with St. John" (Raphael) .. .. 2·25 2·50
549/52 .. .. *Set of* 4 4·75 5·00

COVER PRICES

Cover factors are quoted at the beginning of each country for most issues to 1945. An explanation of the system can be found on page x. The factors quoted do not, however, apply to philatelic covers.

158 Chevrolet "6" 30 cwt Lorry, 1930 **159** Sheep

(Des E. Nesbit. Litho Questa)

1989 (1 Dec). *Early Vehicles. T* **158** *and similar horiz designs. Multicoloured.* W w **16** (*sideways*). *P* 14½.
553 9p. Type **158** 75 60
554 20p. Austin "Seven", 1929 .. .. .. 1·00 90
555 45p. Morris "Cowley" 11.9 h.p., 1929 .. 1·75 2·00
556 60p. Sunbeam 25 h.p., 1932 .. .. .. 2·25 2·50
553/6 .. .. *Set of* 4 5·25 5·50
MS557 93×74 mm. £1 Ford "Model A Fordor" .. 4·25 4·75

(Des Doreen McGuiness. Litho Questa)

1990 (1 Feb). *Farm Animals. T* **159** *and similar vert designs. Multicoloured.* W w **16**. *P* 14.
558 9p. Type **159** 40 50
559 13p. Pigs 45 60
560 45p. Cow and calf .. .. 1·25 1·75
561 60p. Geese .. .. 1·60 2·00
558/61 .. .. *Set of* 4 3·25 4·25

160 1840 Twopence Blue **161** Satellite Dish

(Des D. Miller. Litho Walsall)

1990 (3 May). *"Stamp World London 90" International Stamp Exhibition, London. T* **160** *and similar horiz designs.* W w **14** (*sideways*). *P* 14.
562 13p. black and cobalt 50 50
563 20p. multicoloured 75 85
564 38p. multicoloured .. .. 1·25 1·60
565 45p. multicoloured .. .. 1·60 2·00
562/5 .. .. *Set of* 4 3·75 4·50

Designs:—20p. 1840 Penny Black and 19th-century St. Helena postmark; 38p. Delivering mail to sub-post office; 45p. Mail van and Post Office, Jamestown.

(Des N. Shewring. Litho B.D.T.)

1990 (28 July). *Modern Telecommunications Links. T* **161** *and similar vert designs. Multicoloured.* W w **14**. *P* 13½.
566 20p. Type **161** 60 85
a. Block of 4. Nos. 566/9 .. .. 2·25
567 20p. Digital telephone exchange 60 85
568 20p. Public card phone 60 85
569 20p. Facsimile machine 60 85
566/9 .. .. *Set of* 4 2·25 3·00

Nos. 566/9 were printed together, *se-tenant*, in blocks of 4 throughout the sheet of 16.

(Des D. Miller. Litho Questa)

1990 (4 Aug). *90th Birthday of Queen Elizabeth the Queen Mother. Vert designs as T* **107** (25*p.*) *or* **108** (£1) *of Kenya.* W w **16**. *P* 14×15 (25*p.*) *or* 14½ (£1).
570 25p. multicoloured 75 75
571 £1 black and purple-brown .. .. .. 2·50 3·25

Designs:—25p. Lady Elizabeth Bowes-Lyon, April 1923; £1 Queen Elizabeth visiting communal kitchen, 1940.

162 *Dane* (mail ship), 1857 **163** Baptist Chapel, Sandy Bay

(Des L. Curtis. Litho Walsall)

1990 (13 Sept). *Maiden Voyage of St. Helena II. T* **162** *and similar horiz designs. Multicoloured.* W w **14** (*sideways*). *P* 14×14½.
572 13p. Type **162** 80 70
573 20p. *St. Helena I* offloading at St. Helena 1·10 1·10
574 38p. Launch of *St. Helena II* .. .. 1·75 2·00
575 45p. The Duke of York launching *St. Helena II* .. .. 2·25 2·50
572/5 .. .. *Set of* 4 5·50 5·75
MS576 100×100 mm. £1 *St. Helena II* and outline map of St. Helena .. .. .. 5·50 6·00

No. **MS**576 also contains two imperforate designs of similar stamps from Ascension and Tristan da Cunha without face values.

(Des G. Vasarhelyi. Litho Questa)

1990 (18 Oct). *Christmas. Local Churches. T* **163** *and similar horiz designs. Multicoloured.* W w **14** (*sideways*). *P* 14.
577 10p. Type **163** 30 30
578 13p. St. Martin in the Hills Church .. 35 35
579 20p. St. Helena and the Cross Church .. 55 65
580 38p. St. James Church .. .. .. 1·00 1·60
581 45p. St. Paul's Cathedral .. .. .. 1·25 1·90
577/81 .. .. *Set of* 5 3·25 4·25

164 "Funeral Cortège, Jamestown Wharf" (detail, V. Adam) **165** Officer, Leicestershire Regiment

(Des N. Harvey. Litho Questa)

1990 (15 Dec). *150th Anniv of Removal of Napoleon's Body. T* **164** *and similar horiz designs.* W w **14** (*sideways*). *P* 13½×14.
582 13p. black, sepia and blue-green 60 60
583 20p. black, sepia and ultramarine .. 90 95
584 38p. black, sepia and deep magenta .. 1·75 2·00
585 45p. multicoloured .. .. 2·00 2·25
582/5 .. .. *Set of* 4 4·75 5·25

Designs:—20p. "Coffin being conveyed to the *Belle Poule*" (detail, V. Adam); 38p. "Transfer of the Coffin to the *Normandie*, Cherbourg" (detail, V. Adam); 45p. "Napoleon's Tomb, St. Helena" (T. Sutherland).

(Des C. Collins. Litho Questa)

1991 (2 May). *Military Uniforms of* 1897. *T* **165** *and similar vert designs. Multicoloured.* W w **14**. *P* 14.
586 13p. Type **165** 80 80
587 15p. Officer, York & Lancaster Regiment .. 85 85
588 20p. Colour-sergeant, Leicestershire Regt 1·25 1·25
589 38p. Bandsman, York & Lancaster Regt .. 2·00 2·50
590 45p. Lance-corporal, York & Lancaster Regt 2·50 3·00
586/90 .. .. *Set of* 5 6·75 7·50

(Des D. Miller. Litho Questa)

1991 (1 July). *65th Birthday of Queen Elizabeth II and 70th Birthday of Prince Philip. Vert designs as T* **58** *of Kiribati. Multicoloured.* W w **16** (*sideways*). *P* 14½×14.
591 25p. Queen Elizabeth II .. .. .. 80 1·25
a. Horiz pair. Nos. 591/2 separated by label .. .. 1·60 2·50
592 25p. Prince Philip in naval uniform .. 80 1·25

Nos. 591/2 were printed in similar sheet format to Nos. 366/7 of Kiribati.

166 "Madonna and Child" (T. Vecellio) **167** Matchless (346cc) Motorcycle, 1947

(Des G. Vasarhelyi. Litho Walsall)

1991 (2 Nov). *Christmas. Religious Paintings. T* **166** *and similar vert designs. Multicoloured.* W w **14**. *P* 14.
593 10p. Type **166** 60 55
594 13p. "The Holy Family" (A. Mengs) .. 70 65
595 20p. "Madonna and Child" (W. Dyce) .. 1·00 1·00
596 38p. "The Two Trinities" (B. Murillo) .. 1·75 2·00
597 45p. "The Virgin and Child" (G. Bellini) .. 2·00 2·75
593/7 .. .. *Set of* 5 5·50 6·25

(Des N. Shewring. Litho Questa)

1991 (16 Nov). *"Phila Nippon '91" International Stamp Exhibition, Tokyo. Motorcycles. T* **167** *and similar horiz designs.* W w **16** (*sideways*). *P* 14×14½.
598 13p. Type **167** 75 60
599 20p. Triumph "Tiger 100" (500cc), 1950 .. 1·00 1·00
600 38p. Honda "CD" (175cc), 1967 .. .. 1·75 2·00
601 45p. Yamaha "DTE 400", 1976 .. .. 2·00 2·50
598/601 .. .. *Set of* 4 5·00 5·50
MS602 72×49 mm. 65p. Suzuki "RM" (250cc), 1984 .. .. 5·00 5·50

168 *Eye of the Wind* (cadet brig) and Compass Rose

(Des. R. Watton. Litho Walsall)

1992 (24 Jan). *500th Anniv of Discovery of America by Columbus and Re-enactment Voyages. T* **168** *and similar horiz designs. Multicoloured. W w* **14** *(sideways). P* 13½×14.

603 15p. Type **168** 90 80
604 25p. *Soren Larsen* (cadet brigantine) and map of Re-enactment Voyages 1·60 1·60
605 35p. *Santa Maria, Nina* and *Pinta* 2·25 2·50
606 50p. Columbus and *Santa Maria* 2·50 2·75
603/6 *Set of* 4 6·50 7·00

(Des D. Miller. Litho Questa (50p.), Walsall (others))

1992 (6 Feb). *40th Anniv of Queen Elizabeth II's Accession. Horiz designs as T* **113** *of Kenya. Multicoloured. W w* **14** *(sideways). P* 14.

607 11p. Prince Andrew Central School 40 40
608 15p. Plantation House 55 55
609 25p. Jamestown 85 95
610 35p. Three portraits of Queen Elizabeth 1·10 1·50
611 50p. Queen Elizabeth II 1·40 1·90
607/11 *Set of* 5 3·75 4·75

169 H.M.S. *Ledbury* (minesweeper)

170 Shepherds and Angel Gabriel

(Des N. Shewring. Litho Questa)

1992 (12 June). *10th Anniv of Liberation of Falkland Islands. Ships. T* **169** *and similar square designs. Multicoloured. W w* **14** *(sideways). P* 14.

612 13p. Type **169** 70 70
613 20p. H.M.S. *Brecon* (minesweeper) 90 90
614 38p. *St. Helena I* (mail ship) off South Georgia 1·40 1·75
615 45p. Launch collecting first mail drop, 1982 1·90 2·25
612/15 *Set of* 4 4·50 5·00
MS616 116×116 mm. 13p.+3p. Type **169**; 20p.+4p. As No. 613; 38p.+8p. As No. 614; 45p.+9p. As No. 615 4·00 4·00
The premium on No. **MS**616 were for the S.S.A.F.A.

(Des G. Vasarhelyi. Litho Questa)

1992 (12 Oct). *Christmas. Children's Nativity Plays. T* **170** *and similar horiz designs. W w* **16** *(sideways). P* 13½×14.

617 13p. Type **170** 70 60
618 15p. Shepherds and Three Kings 80 70
619 20p. Mary and Joseph 1·00 1·00
620 45p. Nativity scene 2·25 2·75
617/20 *Set of* 4 4·25 4·50

171 Disc Jockey, Radio St. Helena (25th anniv)

172 Moses in the Bulrush

(Des D. Miller. Litho Questa)

1992 (4 Dec). *Local Anniversaries. T* **171** *and similar horiz designs. Multicoloured. W w* **14** *(sideways). P* 14×14½.

621 13p. Type **171** 60 50
622 20p. Scout parade (75th anniv of Scouting on St. Helena) 1·00 90
623 38p. H.M.S. *Providence* (sloop) and breadfruit (bicent of Capt. Bligh's visit) 1·75 2·00
624 45p. Governor Brooke and Plantation House (bicent) 1·75 2·25
621/4 *Set of* 4 4·50 5·00

(Des M. Martineau. Litho Questa)

1993 (19 Mar). *Flowers (1st series). T* **172** *and similar vert designs. Multicoloured. W w* **16**. *P* 14½.

625 9p. Type **172** 50 50
626 13p. Periwinkle 60 60
627 20p. Everlasting Flower 80 80
628 38p. Cigar Plant 1·60 1·75
629 45p. *Lobelia erinus* 1·90 2·25
625/9 *Set of* 5 4·75 5·50
See also Nos. 676/80.

173 Adult St. Helena Sand Plover and Eggs

174 Yellow Canary ("Swainson's Canary")

(Des N. Arlott. Litho B.D.T.)

1993 (16 Aug). *Endangered Species. St. Helena Sand Plover ("Wirebird"). T* **173** *and similar horiz designs. Multicoloured. W w* **14** *(sideways). P* 13½.

630 3p. Type **173** 35 30
631 5p. Male attending brooding female 35 30
632 12p. Adult with downy young 60 60
633 25p. Two birds in immature plumage 1·00 1·00
634 40p. Adult in flight 1·25 1·60
635 60p. Young bird on rocks 1·75 2·25
630/5 *Set of* 6 4·75 5·50
Nos. 634/5 are without the W.W.F. emblem.

(Des A. Robinson. Litho Questa)

1993 (26 Aug). *Birds. T* **174** *and similar multicoloured designs. W w* **14** *(sideways on 25p., 35p., £1, £2). P* 14½×14 *(vert) or* 14×14½ *(horiz).*

636 1p. Type **174** 10 10
637 3p. Rock Partridge 10 10
638 11p. Rock Dove 20 25
639 12p. Common Waxbill 25 30
640 15p. Common Mynah 30 35
641 18p. Java Sparrow 35 40
642 25p. Red-billed Tropic Bird *(horiz)* 50 55
643 35p. Madeiran Storm Petrel *(horiz)* 70 75
644 75p. Madagascar Red Fody 1·50 1·60
645 £1 White Tern ("Common Fairy Tern") *(horiz)* 2·00 2·10
646 £2 Giant Petrel *(horiz)* 4·00 4·25
647 £5 St. Helena Sand Plover ("Wirebird") 10·00 10·50
636/47 *Set of* 12 18·00 19·00
For miniature sheets containing the 75p or the design of the £5 reissued as a 75p. see Nos. **MS**740 and **MS**745.

175 Football and Teddy Bear

176 Arum Lily

(Des O. Ball and R. Moss. Litho Questa)

1993 (1 Oct). *Christmas. Toys. T* **175** *and similar horiz designs. Multicoloured. W w* **14** *(sideways). P* 14.

648 12p. Type **175** 55 45
649 15p. Yacht and doll 60 50
650 18p. Palette and rocking horse 65 55
651 25p. Model airplane and kite 90 90
652 60p. Guitar and roller skates 1·75 2·25
648/52 *Set of* 5 4·00 4·25

(Litho Questa)

1994 (6 Jan). *Flowers and Children's Art. T* **176** *and similar vert designs. Multicoloured. W w* **16**. *P* 14.

653 12p. Type **176** 40 65
a. Horiz pair. Nos. 653/4 80 1·25
654 12p. "Arum Lily" (Delphia Mittens) 40 65
655 25p. Ebony 75 1·00
a. Horiz pair. Nos. 655/6 1·50 2·00
656 25p. "Ebony" (Jason Rogers) 75 1·00
657 35p. Shell Ginger 95 1·10
a. Horiz pair. Nos. 657/8 1·90 2·10
658 35p. "Shell Ginger" (Jeremy Moyce) 95 1·10
653/8 *Set of* 6 3·75 4·75
The two designs for each value, one showing an actual photograph (face value in yellow) and the other a child's painting (face value in black), were printed together, *se-tenant*, in horizontal pairs throughout the sheets.

177 Abyssinian Guinea Pig

178 Springer's Blenny

(Des Sharon Beeden. Litho Questa)

1994 (18 Feb). *"Hong Kong '94" International Stamp Exhibition. Pets. T* **177** *and similar horiz designs. Multicoloured. W w* **14** *(sideways). P* 14×14½.

659 12p. Type **177** 45 45
660 25p. Common tabby cat 1·00 1·00
661 53p. Plain white and black rabbits 1·75 2·25
662 60p. Golden Labrador 1·90 2·40
659/62 *Set of* 4 4·50 5·50

(Des R. Watton. Litho Walsall)

1994 (6 June). *Fishes. T* **178** *and similar horiz designs. Multicoloured. W w* **16** *(sideways). P* 14×14½.

663 12p. Type **178** 55 55
664 25p. St. Helena Damselfish 1·00 1·00
665 53p. Melliss's Scorpionfish 1·75 2·00
666 60p. St. Helena Wrasse 2·25 2·50
663/6 *Set of* 4 5·00 5·50

179 *Lampides boeticus*

(Des I. Loe. Litho Walsall)

1994 (9 Aug). *Butterflies. T* **179** *and similar horiz designs. Multicoloured. W w* **14** *(sideways). P* 14.

667 12p. Type **179** 60 55
668 25p. *Cynthia cardui* 1·00 1·00
669 53p. *Hypolimnas bolina* 1·75 2·00
670 60p. *Danaus chrysippus* 2·25 2·50
667/70 *Set of* 4 5·00 5·50

180 "Silent Night!"

(Des Jennifer Toombs. Litho Questa)

1994 (6 Oct). *Christmas. Carols. T* **180** *and similar horiz designs. Multicoloured. W w* **16** *(sideways). P* 14½.

671 12p. Type **180** 55 45
672 15p. "While Shepherds watched their Flocks by Night" 60 50
673 25p. "Away in a Manger" 1·00 90
674 38p. "We Three Kings" 1·50 2·00
675 60p. "Angels from the Realms of Glory" 2·25 2·50
671/5 *Set of* 5 5·50 5·75

(Des M. Martineau, adapted D. Miller. Litho Walsall)

1994 (15 Dec). *Flowers (2nd series). Vert designs as T* **172**. *Multicoloured. W w* **16**. *P* 14½×14.

676 12p. Honeysuckle 35 35
677 15p. Gobblegheer 40 40
678 25p. African Lily 70 80
679 38p. Prince of Wales Feathers 1·00 1·50
680 60p. St. Johns Lily 1·75 2·25
676/80 *Set of* 5 3·75 4·75

181 Fire Engine

182 Site Clearance

(Des B. Dove. Litho Walsall)

1995 (2 Feb). *Emergency Services. T* **181** *and similar horiz designs. Multicoloured. W w* **16** *(sideways). P* 14.

681 12p. Type **181** 60 50
682 25p. Lifeboat 85 75
683 53p. Police car 2·00 2·25
684 60p. Ambulance 2·25 2·50
681/4 *Set of* 4 5·25 5·50

(Des N. Shewring. Litho Walsall)

1995 (6 Apr). *Construction of Harpers Valley Earth Dam. T* **182** *and similar horiz designs. Multicoloured. W w* **16** *(sideways). P* 14×14½.

685 25p. Type **182** 80 1·00
a. Horiz strip of 5. Nos. 685/9 3·50
686 25p. Earthworks in progress 80 1·00
687 25p. Laying outlet pipes 80 1·00
688 25p. Revetment block protection 80 1·00
689 25p. Completed dam 80 1·00
685/9 *Set of* 5 3·50 4·50
Nos. 685/9 were printed together, *se-tenant*, in horizontal strips of 5 throughout the sheet, forming a composite design.

(Des R. Watton. Litho Questa)

1995 (8 May). *50th Anniv of End of Second World War. Multicoloured designs as T* **75** *of Kiribati.* W w **14**. P 14.

690 5p. *Lady Denison Pender* (cable ship) .. 40 40
 a. Horiz pair. Nos. 690/1 .. .. 80 80
691 5p. H.M.S. *Dragon* (cruiser) 40 40
692 12p. R.F.A. *Darkdale* (tanker) 65 65
 a. Horiz pair. Nos. 692/3 .. .. 1·25 1·25
693 12p. H.M.S. *Hermes* (aircraft carrier, launched 1919) 65 65
694 25p. Men of St. Helena Rifles .. .. 1·00 1·00
 a. Horiz pair. Nos. 694/5 .. .. 2·00 2·00
695 25p. Governor Major W. J. Bain Gray taking salute .. .. 1·00 1·00
696 53p. 6-inch coastal gun, Ladder Hill .. 1·75 1·75
 a. Horiz pair. Nos. 696/7 .. .. 3·50 3·50
697 53p. Flags signalling "VICTORY" .. 1·75 1·75
690/7 .. .. *Set of* 8 6·75 6·75
MS698 75×85 mm. £1 Reverse of 1939–45 War Medal (*vert*) .. .. 2·50 2·75

The two designs for each value were printed together, *se-tenant*, as horizontal pairs, forming composite designs, in sheets of 8 with decorated margins.

183 Blushing Snail

184 *Epidendrum ibaguense*

(Des I. Loe. Litho B.D.T.)

1995 (29 Aug). *Endemic Invertebrates. T* **183** *and similar horiz designs. Multicoloured.* W w **14** (*sideways*). P 14.

699 12p. Type **183** 55 55
700 25p. Golden Sail Spider .. .. .. 1·00 1·00
701 53p. Spiky Yellow Woodlouse .. .. 1·75 2·00
702 60p. St. Helena Shore Crab .. .. 2·00 2·50
699/702 .. .. *Set of* 4 4·75 5·50
MS703 85×83 mm. £1 Giant Earwig .. .. 3·00 4·00

(Des N. Shewring. Litho Questa)

1995 (1 Sept). *"Singapore '95" International Stamp Exhibition. Orchids. Sheet, 122×74 mm, containing T* **184** *and similar vert design. Multicoloured.* W w **16** (*sideways*). P 14½×14.

MS704 50p. Type **184**; 50p. "Vanda Miss Joaquim" .. .. 2·75 3·50

185 "Santa Claus outside Market" (Jason Alex Rogers)

186 *Walmer Castle*, 1915

(Des B. Dare. Litho Walsall)

1995 (17 Oct). *Christmas. Children's Paintings. T* **185** *and similar horiz designs. Multicoloured.* W w **14** (*sideways*). P 14½.

705 12p. Type **185** 35 35
706 15p. "Santa Claus and band" (Ché David Yon) 45 45
707 25p. "Santa Claus outside Community Centre" (Leon Williams) 70 75
708 38p. "Santa Claus in decorated street" (Stacey McDaniel) .. .. 1·00 1·25
709 60p. "Make a better World" (Kissha Karla Kacy Thomas) .. .. .. 1·75 2·25
705/9 .. .. *Set of* 5 3·75 4·50

(Des J. Batchelor. Litho Walsall)

1996 (8 Jan). *Union Castle Mail Ships (1st series). T* **186** *and similar horiz designs. Multicoloured.* W w **16** (*sideways*). P 14.

710 12p. Type **186** 45 35
711 25p. *Llangibby Castle*, 1934 .. .. 75 65
712 53p. *Stirling Castle*, 1940 .. .. 1·40 1·75
713 60p. *Pendennis Castle*, 1965 .. .. 1·60 2·00
710/13 .. .. *Set of* 4 3·75 4·25

See also Nos. 757/60.

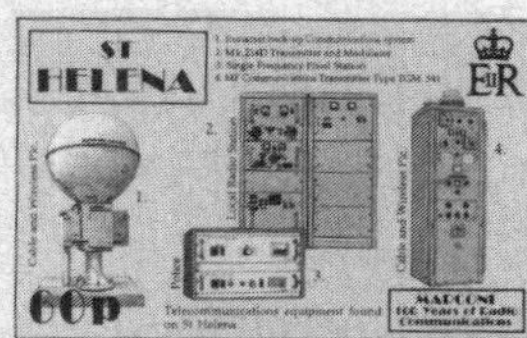

187 Early Telecommunications Equipment

(Des N. Shewring. Litho Walsall)

1996 (28 Mar). *Centenary of Radio. T* **187** *and similar horiz design. Multicoloured.* W w **14** (*sideways*). P 13½×14.

714 60p. Type **187** .. .. 1·50 1·75
715 £1 Guglielmo Marconi and *Elettra* (yacht) 2·25 2·75

(Des D. Miller. Litho Walsall)

1996 (22 Apr). *70th Birthday of Queen Elizabeth II. Vert designs as T* **55** *of New Zealand (Tokelau), each incorporating a different photograph of the Queen. Multicoloured.* W w **16**. P 14½.

716 15p. Jamestown 40 40
717 25p. Prince Andrew School 65 65
718 53p. Castle entrance .. .. .. 1·25 1·75
719 60p. Plantation House .. .. .. 1·50 2·00
716/19 .. .. *Set of* 4 3·50 4·25
MS720 64×66 mm. £1.50, Queen Elizabeth II 3·25 4·00

188 Helicopter Mail to H.M.S. *Protector* (ice patrol ship), 1964

189 "Mr. Porteous's House"

(Des A. Theobald. Litho B.D.T.)

1996 (8 June). *"CAPEX '96" International Stamp Exhibition, Toronto. Mail Transport. T* **188** *and similar horiz designs. Multicoloured.* W w **16** (*sideways*). P 14.

721 12p. Type **188** 50 45
722 25p. Postman on motor scooter, 1965 .. 75 65
723 53p. Loading mail plane, Wideawake Airfield, Ascension Island .. .. 1·40 1·75
724 60p. *St. Helena II* (mail ship) unloading at St. Helena .. .. 1·50 2·00
721/4 .. .. *Set of* 4 3·75 4·25
MS725 98×73 mm. £1 L.M.S. No. 5624 *St. Helena* locomotive (43×27 *mm*). P 13½ .. 2·40 2·75

(Adapted (from contemporary paintings) D. Miller. Litho Walsall)

1996 (12 Aug). *Napoleonic Sites. T* **189** *and similar horiz designs. Multicoloured.* W w **14** (*sideways*). P 14×14½.

726 12p. Type **189** 35 35
727 25p. "The Briars' Pavilion" 65 65
728 53p. "Longwood House" .. .. .. 1·40 1·75
729 60p. "Napoleon's Tomb" .. .. .. 1·50 2·00
726/9 .. .. *Set of* 4 3·50 4·25

190 Frangipani and Sandy Bay from Diana's Peak

191 Black Cabbage Tree

(Des N. Shewring. Litho Questa)

1996 (1 Oct). *Christmas. Flowers and Views. T* **190** *and similar vert designs. Multicoloured.* W w **14**. P 14½×14.

730 12p. Type **190** 40 40
731 15p. Bougainvillaea and Upper Jamestown from Sampson's Battery 50 50
732 25p. Jacaranda and Jacob's Ladder .. 75 75
733 £1 Pink Periwinkle and Lot's Wife Ponds 2·75 3·25
730/3 .. .. *Set of* 4 4·00 4·50

(Des N. Shewring. Litho Questa)

1997 (17 Jan). *Endemic Plants from Diana's Peak National Park. T* **191** *and similar vert designs. Multicoloured.* W w **14** (*sideways*). P 14½×14.

734 25p. Type **191** 70 80
 a. Sheetlet. Nos. 734/9 .. .. 3·75
735 25p. Whitewood 70 80
736 25p. Tree Fern 70 80
737 25p. Dwarf Jellico 70 80
738 25p. Lobelia 70 80
739 25p. Dogwood 70 80
734/9 .. .. *Set of* 6 3·75 4·25

Nos. 734/9 were printed together, *se-tenant*, in sheetlets of 6 with the backgrounds forming a composite design.

(Des D. Miller. Litho Questa)

1997 (3 Feb). *"HONG KONG '97" International Stamp Exhibition. Sheet 130×90 mm, containing design as No. 644.* W w **14** (*sideways*). P 14½×14.

MS740 75p. Madagascar Red Fody .. .. 1·75 2·00

192 Joao da Nova's Lookout sighting St. Helena, 1502

(Des R. Watton. Litho Questa)

1997 (29 May). *500th Anniv of the Discovery of St. Helena (1st issue). T* **192** *and similar vert designs. Multicoloured.* W w **14**. P 14×13½.

741 20p. Type **192** 60 50
742 25p. Don Fernando Lopez (first inhabitant) and cockerel, 1515 .. .. .. 70 60
743 30p. Thomas Cavendish and *Desire*, 1588 80 80
744 80p. *Royal Merchant*, 1591 .. .. 2·10 2·25
741/4 .. .. *Set of* 4 3·75 3·75

(Des D. Miller. Litho Walsall)

1997 (20 June). *Return of Hong Kong to China. Sheet 130×90 mm, containing design as No. 647, but changed face value and imprint date.* W w **14** (*sideways*). P 14½×14.

MS745 75p. St. Helena Sand Plover ("Wirebird") 1·75 2·00

(Des N. Shewring (No. **MS**752), D. Miller (others). Litho Questa (No. **MS**752), B.D.T. (others))

1997 (10 July). *Golden Wedding of Queen Elizabeth and Prince Philip. Multicoloured designs as T* **87** *of Kiribati.* W w **16**. P 13½.

746 10p. Royal Family's Visit, 1947 .. .. 25 25
 a. Horiz pair. Nos. 746/7 .. .. 50 50
747 10p. Wedding photograph of Princess Elizabeth and Prince Philip 25 25
748 15p. Princess Elizabeth and Prince Philip, 1947 .. .. 40 40
 a. Horiz pair. Nos. 748/9 .. .. 80 80
749 15p. Presenting bouquets, Royal Visit, 1947 40 40
750 50p. Prince Philip on Royal Visit, 1957 .. 1·25 1·40
 a. Horiz pair. Nos. 750/1 .. .. 2·50 2·75
751 50p. Wedding party on balcony, 1947 .. 1·25 1·40
746/51 .. .. *Set of* 6 3·50 3·50
MS752 111×70 mm. £1.50, Queen Elizabeth and Prince Philip in landau (*horiz*). W w **14** (sideways). P 14×14½ .. .. .. 3·50 3·75

Nos. 746/7, 748/9 and 750/1 were each printed together, *se-tenant*, in horizontal pairs throughout the sheets.

193 Flower Arrangement

(Des Jennifer Toombs. Litho Walsall)

1997 (29 Sept). *Christmas. 25th Anniv of the Duke of Edinburgh's Award in St. Helena. T* **193** *and similar horiz designs. Multicoloured.* W w **16** (*sideways*). P 13½×14.

753 15p. Type **193** 40 35
754 20p. Calligraphy 50 45
755 40p. Camping .. .. 1·00 1·00
756 75p. Table laid for Christmas dinner .. 2·00 2·25
753/6 .. .. *Set of* 4 3·50 3·50

(Des J. Batchelor. Litho Questa)

1998 (2 Jan). *Union Castle Mail Ships (2nd series). Horiz designs as T* **186**. *Multicoloured.* W w **16** (*sideways*). P 14.

757 20p. *Avondale Castle*, 1900 .. .. 50 45
758 25p. *Dunnottar Castle*, 1936 .. .. 60 55
759 30p. *Llandovery Castle*, 1943 .. .. 75 75
760 80p. *Good Hope Castle*, 1977 .. .. 2·00 2·25
757/60 .. .. *Set of* 4 3·50 3·50

(Des D. Miller. Litho Questa)

1998 (4 Apr). *Diana, Princess of Wales Commemoration. Sheet 145×70 mm containing vert designs as T* **91** *of Kiribati.* W w **14** (*sideways*). P 14½×14.

MS761 30p. Wearing green and white hat, 1983; 30p. Wearing white jacket; 30p. Wearing green jacket, 1996; 30p. In evening dress, 1991 (*sold at* £1.20 + 20p. *charity premium*) .. .. 2·75 3·00

STAMP BOOKLETS

1962 (2 Mar). *Black on green cover. Stitched.*
SB1 4s. 6d. booklet containing 1d., 1½d., 2d., 3d. and 6d. (Nos. 176/9, 181), each in block of 4 .. 50·00

1969. *Black on grey-green cover. Stapled.*
SB2 5s. 4d. booklet containing 1d., 2d., 3d., 4d. and 6d. (Nos. 227, 229/32), each in block of 4 .. 28·00

1971 (24 June). *Black on green cover. Stapled.*
SB3 44p. booklet containing ½p., 1p., 1½p., 2p., 2½p. and 3½p. (Nos. 261/6), each in block of 4 .. 15·00

1981 (June). *Black printed cover showing St. Helena Arms. Stapled.*
SB4 £1 booklet containing 1p., 3p., 5p., 6p. and 10p. (Nos. 319/22A, 325A), each in block of 4 .. 11·00

1984 (1 June). *Black on blue cover showing St. Helena Arms. Stapled.*
SB5 £1.04, booklet containing 1p., 3p., 7p. and 15p. (Nos. 425/6, 428, 430), each in block of 4 .. 5·50

1991 (17 June). *65th Birthday of Queen Elizabeth II and 70th Birthday of Prince Philip. Black on blue cover,* 116×106 *mm, showing St. Helena Arms. Stapled.*
SB6 £1 booklet containing 25p. (Nos. 591/2) in block of 4 stamps and 2 labels .. .. .. 2·50

POSTAGE DUE STAMPS

D 1 Outline Map of St. Helena

(Des L. Curtis. Litho Questa)

1986 (9 June). *W* w **16**. *P* 14½×14.

D1	D 1	1p. deep brown and cinnamon	10	10
D2		2p. deep brown and bright orange ..	10	10
D3		5p. deep brown and orange-vermilion ..	10	15
D4		7p. black and bright reddish violet ..	10	10
D5		10p. black and violet-blue	20	25
D6		25p. black and pale emerald	50	55
D1/6		.. .. *Set of* 6	95	1·10

St. Kitts-Nevis

ST. CHRISTOPHER

From 1760 the postal service for St. Christopher was organised by the Deputy Postmaster General on Antigua. It was not until May 1779 that the first postmaster was appointed to the island and the use of postmarks on outgoing mail commenced.

Stamps of Great Britain were used between May 1858 and the end of March 1860 when control of the postal services passed to the local authorities. In the years which followed, prior to the introduction of St. Christopher stamps in April 1870, a circular "PAID" handstamp was used on overseas mail.

BASSETERRE

Stamps of GREAT BRITAIN *cancelled* "A 12" *as Type* Z 1 *of Jamaica.*

1858 *to* **1860.**
Z1 1d. rose-red (1857), *perf* 14 .. .. £500
Z2 2d. blue (1858) (Plate No. 7) £900
Z3 4d. rose (1857) £300
Z4 6d. lilac (1856) £180
Z5 1s. green (1856) £1100

PRICES FOR STAMPS ON COVER

Nos. 1/9	*from* × 25
Nos. 11/21	*from* × 30
Nos. 22/6	*from* × 25
No. 27	—
No. 28	*from* × 30
Nos. R1/6	—

1

FOUR PENCE
(2)

Halfpenny
(3)

1870 (1 Apr)–**79.** *Wmk Crown CC. (a) P* 12½.
1 1 1d. dull rose .. .. 60·00 40·00
a. Wmk sideways £250 £180
2 1d. magenta (*shades*) (1871) .. .. 45·00 26·00
a. Wmk sideways .. .. .. † £400
4 6d. yellow-green .. .. 90·00 17·00
5 6d. green (1871) .. .. 90·00 7·50

(*b*) *P* 14
6 1 1d. magenta (*shades*) (1875) .. .. 60·00 7·00
a. Bisected diag or vert (½d.) (on cover) (3.82) .. .. † £1300
7 2½d. red-brown (11.79) £170 £225
8 4d. blue (11.79) .. .. £150 15·00
a. Wmk sideways £600 £100
9 6d. green (1876) .. .. 55·00 5·00
a. Imperf between (pair) .. .. ..
b. Wmk sideways .. .. .. £375 90·00

The magenta used for the 1d. was a fugitive colour which reacts to both light and water.

No. 6a was authorised for use between March and June 1882 to make up the 2½d. letter rate and for ½d. book post.

1882 (June)–**90.** *Wmk Crown CA. P* 14.
11 1 ½d. dull green .. .. 60 1·25
a. Wmk sideways £250
12 1d. dull magenta .. .. .. £475 60·00
a. Bisected diagonally (½d.) (on cover)
13 1d. carmine-rose (2.84) .. .. .. 1·00 1·60
a. Bisected (½d.) (on cover)
14 2½d. pale red-brown .. .. .. £170 55·00
15 2½d. deep red-brown .. .. .. £180 60·00
16 2½d. ultramarine (2.84) .. .. .. 1·50 1·50
17 4d. blue .. .. £400 20·00
18 4d. grey (10.84) .. .. 1·25 80
19 6d. olive-brown ((3.90) .. .. .. 80·00 £300
20 1s. mauve (6.86) .. .. 90·00 65·00
21 1s. bright mauve (1890) .. .. .. 80·00 £130
19/20 Optd "Specimen" .. .. *Set of* 2 £120

1884 (Dec). *No.* 9 *surch with T* 2 *by* The Advertiser Press.
22 1 4d. on 6d. green .. .. 55·00 48·00
a. Full stop after "PENCE" .. .. 55·00 48·00
b. Surch double .. .. —£1700

No. 22a occurred on alternate stamps.

1885 (March). *No.* 13 *bisected and each half diagonally surch with T* 3.
23 1 ½d. on half of 1d. carmine-rose .. .. 24·00 38·00
a. Unsevered pair £100 £110
ab. Ditto, one surch inverted £350 £250
b. Surch inverted £200 £100
c. Surch double .. ..

ONE PENNY.
(4)

4d.
(5)

1886 (June). *No.* 9 *surch with T* 4 *or* 5 *each showing a manuscript line through the original value.*
24 1 1d. on 6d. green .. .. .. 16·00 28·00
a. Surch inverted £5000
b. Surch double .. .. .. — £1300
25 4d. on 6d. green.. .. .. .. 48·00 90·00
a. No stop after "d" £180 £250
b. Surch double £1600 £1700

No. 24b is only known penmarked with dates between 21 July and 3 August 1886, or with violet handstamp.

1887 (May). *No.* 11 *surch with T* 4 *showing a manuscript line through the original value.*
26 1 1d. on ½d. dull green .. .. .. 28·00 38·00

ONE PENNY.
(7)

1888 (May). *No.* 16 *surch.*

(*a*) *With T* 4. *Original value unobliterated*
27 1 1d. on 2½d. ultramarine £10000 £8500

(*b*) *With T* 7 *showing a manuscript line through the original value*
28 1 1d. on 2½d. ultramarine .. .. 45·00 48·00
a. Surch inverted £8000 £5500

The 1d. of Antigua was used provisionally in St. Christopher between February and March 1890 during a shortage of 1d. stamps. Such use can be distinguished by the postmark, which is "A 12" in place of "A02" (*price from £120 used*).

REVENUE STAMPS USED FOR POSTAGE

Saint Christopher
(R 1)

SAINT KITTS NEVIS REVENUE
(R 2)

1883. *Nos.* F6 *and* F8 *of Nevis optd with Type* R 1, *in violet. Wmk Crown CA. P* 14.
R1 1d. lilac-mauve £225
R2 6d. green .. .. 65·00 £110

1885. *Optd with Type* R 2. *Wmk Crown CA. P* 14.
R3 1 1d. rose .. .. 1·50 8·50
R4 3d. mauve .. .. 12·00 60·00
R5 6d. orange-brown .. .. .. 6·50 45·00
R6 1s. olive .. .. 1·50 35·00

Other fiscal stamps with overprints as above also exist, but none of these was ever available for postal purposes.

The stamps for St. Christopher was superseded by the general issue for Leeward Islands on 31 October 1890.

Stamps for St. Kitts, issued from 1980 onwards will be found listed after those for the combined colony.

NEVIS

Little is known concerning the early postal affairs of Nevis, but it is recorded that the British G.P.O. was to establish a branch office on the island under an Act of Parliament, passed in 1710, although arrangements may not have been finalised for a number of years afterwards. Nevis appears as "a new office" in the P.O. Accounts of 1787.

Stamps of Great Britain were used on the island from May 1858 until the colonial authorities assumed control of the postal service on 1 May 1860. Between this date and the introduction of Nevis stamps in 1861 No. CC1 was again used on overseas mail.

CHARLESTOWN

CROWNED-CIRCLE HANDSTAMPS

CC 1

CC1 CC 1 NEVIS (R.) (9.1852) .. *Price on cover* £3250

No. CC1, but struck in black, was later used on several occasions up to 1886 where there were shortages of adhesive stamps.

Stamps of GREAT BRITAIN *cancelled* "A 09" *as Type* Z 1 *of Jamaica.*

1858 *to* **1860.**
Z1 1d. rose-red (1857), *perf* 14 .. .. £375
Z2 2d. blue (1858) (Plate Nos. 7, 8) .. ..
Z3 4d. rose (1857) £300
Z4 6d. lilac (1856) £275
Z5 1s. green (1856) .. ..

PRICES FOR STAMPS ON COVER

Nos. 5/22	*from* × 20
Nos. 23/4	*from* × 10
Nos. 25/34	*from* × 20
Nos. 35/6	*from* × 10
Nos. F1/8	*from* × 30

1

2

3

4

The designs on the stamps refer to a medicinal spring on the island

(Recess Nissen & Parker, London)

1861. *Greyish paper. P* 13.
5 1 1d. dull lake .. .. 55·00 35·00
a. On blued paper £200 £100
6 2 4d. rose .. .. 80·00 55·00
a. On blued paper £650 £150
7 3 6d. grey-lilac .. .. 75·00 40·00
a. On blued paper £500 £190
8 4 1s. green .. .. £160 50·00
a. On blued paper £750 £170

1866–76. *White paper. P* 15.
9 1 1d. pale red .. .. 32·00 28·00
10 1d. deep red .. .. 32·00 28·00
11 2 4d. orange .. .. 95·00 19·00
12 4d. deep orange .. .. .. 95·00 19·00
13 4 1s. blue-green .. .. £170 26·00
14 1s. yellow-green (1876) £800 £100
a. Vertically laid paper £11000 £3500
b. No. 9 on sheet with crossed lines on hill £3500 £500
c. Ditto. On laid paper .. .. .. † £8500

Examples of the 4d. exist showing part of a papermakers watermark reading "A. COWAN & SONS EXTRA SUPERFINE".

(Lithographed by transfer from the engraved plates Nissen and Parker, London)

1876–78. *P* 15.
15 1 1d. pale rose-red .. .. 16·00 13·00
a. Imperf (pair) £375
16 1d. deep rose-red .. .. 26·00 19·00
17 1d. vermilion-red (1878) .. .. .. 22·00 19·00
a. Bisected (½d.) (on cover) .. .. † £1400
18 2 4d. orange-yellow .. .. .. £140 27·00
a. Imperf between (vert pair) £3250
19 3 6d. grey (1878) £190 £170
20 4 1s. pale green (1878) .. .. .. 60·00 85·00
a. Imperf.. .. ..
b. Imperf between (horiz strip of three) £4250
c. No. 9 on sheet with crossed lines on hill £225
21 1s. deep green .. .. 65·00 £100
c. No. 9 on sheet with crossed lines on hill

No. 21c occurs on a small part of the deep green printing only.

RETOUCHES. 1d. Lithograph.
i. No. 1 on sheet. Top of hill over kneeling figure redrawn by five thick lines and eight small slanting lines £140 £150
ii. No. 1 on sheet. Another retouch. Three series of short vertical strokes behind the kneeling figure.. .. £140 £150
iii. No. 3 on sheet. Right upper corner star and border below star retouched £140 £150
iv. No. 9 on sheet. Retouch in same position as on No. 3 but differing in detail £160 £170
v. No. 12 on sheet. Dress of standing figure retouched by a number of horizontal and vertical lines £140 £150

1878. *Litho. P* 11½.
22 1 1d. vermilion-red .. .. .. 38·00 48·00
a. Bisected (½d.) (on cover) .. .. † £1400
b. Imperf (pair).. .. .. .. £250
c. Imperf between (horiz pair) .. ..

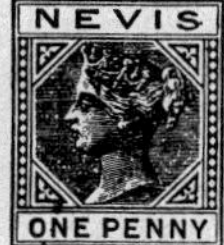
5 (Die I)

NEVIS. ½d.
(6)

(Typo D.L.R.)

1879–80. *Wmk Crown CC. P* 14.
23 5 1d. lilac-mauve (1880) .. .. .. 48·00 26·00
a. Bisected (½d.) (on cover) .. .. † £850
24 2½d. red-brown .. .. 90·00 80·00

1882–90. *Wmk Crown CA. P* 14.
25 5 ½d. dull green (11.83) .. .. .. 2·75 8·00
a. Top left triangle detached .. 75·00
26 1d. lilac-mauve .. .. 80·00 23·00
a. Bisected (½d.) on cover (1883) .. † £700
27 1d. dull rose (11.83) .. .. .. 19·00 11·00
a. Carmine (1884) .. .. .. 4·50 4·00
ab. Top left triangle detached .. £120
28 2½d. red-brown .. .. £100 45·00
29 2½d. ultramarine (11.83) .. .. .. 13·00 8·50
30 4d. blue .. .. £275 45·00
31 4d. grey (1884) .. .. .. 5·50 2·50
32 6d. green (11.83) £350 £350
33 6d. chestnut (10.88) .. .. .. 17·00 48·00
a. Top left triangle detached .. £275
34 1s. pale violet (3.90) .. .. .. 85·00 £160
a. Top left triangle detached .. £650
33/4 Optd "Specimen" .. .. *Set of* 2 £110
For illustration of the "top left triangle detached" variety, which occurs on Plate 2 R. 3/3 of the right pane, see below Montserrat No. 5.

1883. *No.* 26 *bisected vertically and surch with T* 6, *reading upwards or downwards.*
35 ½d. on half 1d. lilac-mauve (V.) .. .. £700 29·00
a. Surch double .. .. — £300
b. Surch on half "REVENUE" stamp No F6 .. .. — £500
36 ½d. on half 1d. lilac-mauve .. .. £850 27·00
a. Surch double .. .. .. — £300
b. Unsevered pair £2500 £375
c. Surch on half "REVENUE" stamp No F6 .. .. — £500

FISCALS USED FOR POSTAGE

Revenue (F 1) REVENUE (F 2)

1882. (*a*) *Stamps of* 1876–78 *optd with Type* F 1.
F1 1 1d. bright red .. .. 40·00
F2 2 1d. rose .. .. 40·00 15·00
F3 4d. orange .. .. 75·00
F4 3 6d. grey £120
F5 4 1s. green £140
a. No. 9 on sheet with crossed lines on hill

(*b*) *Nos.* 26, 30 *and* 32 *optd with Type* F 2
F6 5 1d. lilac-mauve .. .. .. 40·00 40·00
a. Bisected (½d.) (on cover) .. ..
F7 4d. blue .. .. 21·00 48·00
F8 6d. green .. .. 14·00 50·00
Nos. F1/5 were produced from fresh transfers. Similar "REVENUE" handstamps, both with and without stop, were also applied to postage issues.

The stamps of Nevis were superseded by the general issue for Leeward Islands on 31 October 1890. Stamps for Nevis were again issued in 1980 and will be found listed after those for the combined colony.

ST. KITTS-NEVIS

CROWN COLONY

Stamps for the combined colony were introduced in 1903, and were used concurrently with the general issues of Leeward Islands until the latter were withdrawn on 1 July 1956.

PRICES FOR STAMPS ON COVER TO 1945

Nos. 1/9	*from* × 3
No. 10	—
Nos. 11/20	*from* × 3
No. 21	—
Nos. 22/3	*from* × 15
Nos. 24/34	*from* × 3
Nos. 35/6	—
Nos. 37/47	*from* × 2
Nos. 47*a*/*b*	—
Nos. 48/57	*from* × 2
Nos. 58/60	—
Nos. 61/4	*from* × 2
Nos. 65/7	*from* × 5
Nos. 68/77	*from* × 2

1 Christopher Columbus

2 Medicinal Spring

(Typo D.L.R.)

1903. *Wmk Crown CA. P* 14.
1 1 ½d. dull purple and deep green .. 1·50 70
2 2 1d. grey-black and carmine .. 3·25 20
3 1 2d. dull purple and brown .. 2·25 9·50
4 2½d. grey-black and blue .. 15·00 3·75
5 2 3d. deep green and orange .. 7·50 22·00
6 1 6d. grey-black and bright purple .. 3·25 26·00
7 1s. grey-green and orange .. 6·00 11·00
8 2 2s. deep green and grey-black .. 12·00 18·00
9 1 2s. 6d. grey-black and violet .. 18·00 38·00
10 2 5s. dull purple and sage-green .. 48·00 55·00
1/10 .. .. .. *Set of* 10 £110 £170
1/10 Optd "Specimen" .. *Set of* 10 £130

1905–18. *Wmk Mult Crown CA. Chalk-surfaced paper* (1*d.* (*No.* 13), 5*s.*) *or ordinary paper* (*others*). *P* 14.
11 1 ½d. dull purple and deep green .. .. 4·50 5·50
12 ½d. grey-green (1907) 55 35
a. Dull blue-green (1916) .. .. 30 1·25
13 2 1d. grey-black and carmine (1906) .. 1·00 25
14 2 1d. carmine (1907) .. .. .. 1·60 15
a. Scarlet (1916) 35 20
15 1 2d. dull purple and brown .. .. 4·75 4·75
a. Chalk-surfaced paper (1906) .. 4·00 5·00
16 2½d. grey-black and blue (1907) .. 14·00 3·25
17 2½d. bright blue (1907) .. .. 1·75 40
18 2 3d. deep green and orange .. .. 3·50 5·50
a. Chalk-surfaced paper (1906) .. 2·00 2·50
19 1 6d. grey-black and deep violet .. 17·00 32·00
a. Chalk-surfaced paper. *Grey-black and deep purple* (1908) .. .. .. 11·00 23·00
ab. Grey-black and bright purple (1916) 4·50 23·00
20 1s. grey-green and orange (1909) .. 13·00 24·00
a. Chalk-surfaced paper .. .. 2·75 25·00
21 2 5s. dull purple and sage-green (11.18) 30·00 70·00
11/21 .. .. .. *Set of* 11 55·00 £120
12, 14, 17 Optd "Specimen" .. *Set of* 3 60·00

WAR TAX (3) WAR STAMP (3*a*)

1916 (Oct). *Optd with T* 3. *Wmk Mult Crown CA. P* 14.
22 1 ½d. dull blue-green (No. 12*a*) (Optd S. £40) 40 40
a. Deep green 40 40
x. Wmk reversed .. .. .. 35·00
No. 22*a* was a special printing produced for this overprint.

1918 (Aug). *Optd with T* 3*a*. *Wmk Mult Crown CA. P* 14.
23 1 1½d. orange (Optd S. £45) 30 40
a. Short opt (right pane R. 10/1) .. 15·00
No. 23 was a special printing produced for this overprint.
No. 23a shows the overprint 2 mm high instead of 2½ mm.

4

5

(Typo D.L.R.)

1920–22. *Wmk Mult Crown CA* (*sideways*). *Ordinary paper* (½*d. to* 2½*d.*) *or chalk-surfaced paper* (*others*). *P* 14.
24 4 ½d. blue-green .. .. 3·75 4·75
25 5 1d. carmine .. .. 2·25 4·50
26 4 1½d. orange-yellow .. .. .. 1·25 1·50
x. Wmk sideways reversed .. .. 50·00
27 5 2d. slate-grey .. .. 3·00 3·25
28 4 2½d. ultramarine .. .. .. 1·50 7·50
a. "A" of "CA" missing from wmk .. £200
29 5 3d. purple/*yellow* .. .. .. 1·50 9·50
30 4 6d. dull purple and bright mauve .. 3·25 9·50
31 5 1s. grey and black/*green* .. .. 3·25 3·50
32 4 2s. dull purple and blue/*blue* .. 12·00 17·00
x. Wmk sideways reversed £120
33 5 2s. 6d. grey and red/*blue* .. .. 5·00 26·00
x. Wmk sideways reversed .. ..
34 4 5s. green and red/*pale yellow* .. 5·00 35·00
x. Wmk sideways reversed .. .. 75·00
35 5 10s. green and red/*green* .. .. 12·00 48·00
36 4 £1 purple and black/*red* (1922) .. £225 £300
24/36 .. .. .. *Set of* 13 £250 £400
24/36 Optd "Specimen" .. *Set of* 13 £275

1921–9. *Wmk Mult Script CA* (*sideways**). *Chalk-surfaced paper* (2½*d.* (*No.* 44), 3*d.* (*No.* 45*a*) *and* 6*d. to* 5*s.*) *or ordinary paper* (*others*). *P* 14.
37 4 ½d. blue-green .. .. 1·75 1·50
a. Yellow-green (1922) .. .. 1·25 80
38 5 1d. rose-carmine 50 15
39 1d. deep violet (1922) .. .. 3·50 55
a. Pale violet (1929) .. .. 5·50 1·50
40 4 1½d. red (1925) .. .. .. 2·50 2·50
40*a* 1½d. red-brown (1929) 65 30
41 5 2d. slate-grey (1922) 40 60
42 4 2½d. pale bright blue (1922) .. .. 3·00 2·25
43 2½d. brown (1922) .. .. .. 1·75 7·50
44 2½d. ultramarine (1927) .. .. 1·50 3·50
45 5 3d. dull ultramarine (1922) .. .. 70 3·25
45*a* 3d. purple/*yellow* (1927) .. .. 60 3·25
46 4 6d. dull and bright purple (1924) .. 3·75 5·50
aw. Wmk Crown to right of CA .. 2·75 4·50
46*b* 5 1s. black/*green* (1929) .. .. 3·75 6·00
47 4 2s. purple and blue/*blue* (1922) .. 8·00 18·00
47*a* 5 2s. 6d. black and red/*blue* (1927) .. 13·00 25·00
47*b* 4 5s. green and red/*yellow* (1929) .. 38·00 50·00
37/47*b* .. .. .. *Set of* 16 70·00 £110
37/47*b* Optd/Perf "Specimen" .. *Set of* 16 £325
*The normal watermark shows Crown to left of CA, *as seen from the back of the stamp.*
In the Specimen set listed above No. 38 is overprinted. A later printing exists perforated "Specimen" (*Price* £70).

6 Old Road Bay and Mount Misery

(Typo D.L.R.)

1923. *Tercentenary of Colony. Chalk-surfaced paper. P* 14.

(*a*) *Wmk Mult Script CA* (*sideways*)
48 6 ½d. black and green .. .. .. 2·00 6·50
49 1d. black and bright violet .. .. 3·00 1·50
50 1½d. black and scarlet .. .. .. 4·50 10·00
51 6 2d. black and slate-grey .. .. 2·75 1·50
52 2½d. black and brown .. .. 4·50 27·00
53 3d. black and ultramarine .. .. 3·75 14·00
54 6d. black and bright purple .. .. 8·50 28·00
55 1s. black and sage-green .. .. 13·00 28·00
56 2s. black and blue/*blue* .. .. 35·00 48·00
57 2s. 6d. black and red/*blue* .. .. 45·00 70·00
58 10s. black and red/*emerald* £250 £375

(*b*) *Wmk Mult Crown CA* (*sideways*)
59 6 5s. black and red/*pale yellow* .. 65·00 £160
60 £1 black and purple/*red* £700 £1300
48/60 .. .. .. *Set of* 13 £1000 £1800
48/60 Optd "Specimen" .. *Set of* 13 £650
Examples of all values are known showing a forged St. Kitts postmark dated "8 DE 23."

1935 (6 May). *Silver Jubilee. As Nos.* 114/17 *of Jamaica, but ptd by Waterlow. P* 11×12.
61 1d. deep blue and scarlet .. .. .. 1·00 70
k. Kite and vertical log .. .. 40·00
l. Kite and horizontal log .. .. 70·00
62 1½d. ultramarine and grey 75 75
k. Kite and vertical log .. .. 40·00
63 2½d. brown and deep blue .. .. 1·00 80
64 1s. slate and purple .. .. 5·50 14·00
k. Kite and vertical log £130
l. Kite and horizontal log £140
61/4 .. .. .. *Set of* 4 7·50 14·50
61/4 Perf "Specimen" .. *Set of* 4 75·00
For illustrations of plate varieties see Omnibus section following Zimbabwe.

1937 (12 May). *Coronation. As Nos.* 118/20 *of Jamaica.*
65 1d. scarlet 30 20
66 1½d. buff 40 10
67 2½d. bright blue 60 45
65/7 .. .. .. *Set of* 3 1·10 65
65/7 Perf "Specimen" .. *Set of* 3 50·00
Nos. 61/7 are inscribed "ST. CHRISTOPHER AND NEVIS".

7 King George VI

8 King George VI and Medicinal Spring

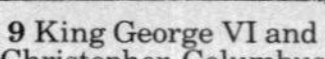

9 King George VI and Christopher Columbus

10 King George VI and Anguilla Island

Break in value tablet (R. 12/5) (1947 ptg only)

Break in oval (R. 12/1) (1938 ptg only)

Break in value tablet frame (R.3/2)

Break in value tablet frame (R.12/3) (ptgs between 1941 and 1945 only)

Break in frame above ornament (R. 2/4) (ptgs between 1941 and 1950)

Break in oval at foot (R. 12/5) (ptgs between 1941 and 1945 only). Sometimes touched-in by hand painting)

Break in oval at left (R. 7/1) (ptgs between 1941 and 1945 only)

(Typo; centre litho (T **10**). D.L.R.)

1938 (15 Aug)–**50**. *Wmk Mult Script CA (sideways on T* **8** *and* **9**). *Chalk-surfaced paper* (10s., £1). *P* 14 (*T* **7** *and* **10**) *or* 13×12 (*T* **8/9**).

68 **7** ½d. green .. .. 3·00 20
a. *Blue-green* (5.4.43) 10 10
69 1d. scarlet .. .. 4·00 70
a. *Carmine* (5.43) 50 40
b. *Carmine-pink* (4.47) .. .. 60·00 16·00
c. *Rose-red* (7.47) 80 80
70 1½d. orange 20 30
71 **8** 2d. scarlet and grey .. .. .. 17·00 2·50
a. Chalk-surfaced paper. *Carmine and deep grey* (5.41*) .. .. .. 50·00 9·50
b. Perf 14. *Scarlet & pale grey* (6.43*) 70 1·25
ba. *Scarlet and deep grey* (6.42*) .. 20·00 5·00
c. Perf 14. Chalk-surfaced paper. *Scarlet and pale grey* (2.50*) .. 1·50 2·00
72 **7** 2½d. ultramarine .. .. .. 3·50 30
a. *Bright ultramarine* (5.4.43) .. 30 30
73 **8** 3d. dull reddish purple and scarlet .. 14·00 3·25
a. Chalk-surfaced paper. *Brown-purple and carmine-red* (1940) .. 18·00 3·75
b. Perf 14. Chalk-surfaced paper. *Dull reddish purple & carm-red* (6.43*) 26·00 3·75
c. Perf 14. Ordinary paper. *Reddish lilac and scarlet* (8.46*) .. 2·00 12·00
d. Perf 14. Ordinary paper. *Purple and bright scarlet* (1.46*) .. .. 4·75 4·75
da. Break in value tablet .. .. 55·00
e. Perf 14. Chalk-surfaced paper. *Deep purple and scarlet* (12.47*) .. 70·00 18·00
f. Perf 14. Ordinary paper. *Rose-lilac and bright scarlet* (1.49*) .. 5·50 6·00
g. Perf 14. Chalk-surfaced paper. *Deep reddish purple & brt scarlet* (8.50*) 3·25 3·75
74 **9** 6d. green and bright purple .. 6·50 1·75
a. Break in oval .. .. .. 70·00
b. Perf 14. Chalk-surfaced paper. *Green and deep claret* (6.43*) .. 50·00 11·00
c. Perf 14. Ordinary paper. *Green and purple* (10.44*) .. .. .. 4·75 1·50
d. Perf 14. Chalk-surfaced paper. *Green and purple* (11.48*) .. .. 3·50 3·00
75 **8** 1s. black and green .. .. .. 12·00 1·25
a. Break in value tablet frame .. 95·00
b. Perf 14 (8.43*) .. .. .. 3·75 85
ba. Break in value tablet frame .. 55·00
c. Perf 14. Chalk-surfaced paper (7.50*) .. .. 2·50 2·50
ca. Break in value tablet frame .. 42·00
76 2s. 6d. black and scarlet .. .. 30·00 9·00
a. Perf 14. Chalk-surfaced paper (12.43*) .. .. 13·00 5·50
ab. Ordinary paper (5.45*) .. .. 12·00 3·75
77 **9** 5s. grey-green and scarlet .. .. 65·00 17·00
a. Perf 14. Chalk-surfaced paper (12.43*) .. .. £130 25·00
ab. Break in value tablet frame .. £300
ac. Break in frame above ornament .. £300
ad. Break in oval at foot £300
ae. Break in oval at left £300
b. Perf 14. Ordinary paper. *Bluish green and scarlet* (9.46*) .. .. 24·00 10·00
ba. Break in value tablet frame .. £130
bb. Break in frame above ornament .. £140
bc. Break in oval at foot £120
bd. Break in oval at left £130
c. Perf 14. Chalk-surfaced paper. *Green & scarlet-vermilion* (10.50*) 27·00 22·00
cb. Break in frame above ornament .. £140
77*d* **10** 10s. black and ultramarine (1.9.48) .. 10·00 19·00
77*e* £1 black and brown (1.9.48) .. .. 10·00 23·00
68/77*e* .. .. *Set of* 12 60·00 55·00
68/77 Perf "Specimen" .. .. *Set of* 10 £180

*Earliest postmark date. Many printings were supplied to St. Kitts–Nevis considerably earlier.

1946 (1 Nov). *Victory. As Nos.* 141/2 *of Jamaica.*

78 1½d. red-orange 10 10
79 3d. carmine 10 10
78/9 Perf "Specimen" .. .. *Set of* 2 60·00

1949 (3 Jan). *Royal Silver Wedding. As Nos.* 143/4 *of Jamaica.*

80 2½d. ultramarine 10 10
81 5s. carmine .. .. 6·00 2·50

1949 (10 Oct). *75th Anniv of U.P.U. As Nos.* 145/8 *of Jamaica.*

82 2½d. ultramarine 35 20
83 3d. carmine-red .. .. 1·00 60
84 6d. magenta 40 30
85 1s. blue-green 40 30
82/5 .. .. *Set of* 4 1·90 1·25

ANGUILLA

TERCENTENARY
1650-1950
(11)

ANGUILLA

TERCENTENARY
1650—1950
(12)

1950 (10 Nov). *Tercentenary of British Settlement in Anguilla. Nos.* 69*c*, 70 *and* 72*a* (*perf* 14) *optd as T* **11** *and new ptgs of T* **8/9** *on chalk-surfaced paper perf* 13×12½ *optd as T* **12**.

86 **7** 1d. rose-red 10 10
87 1½d. orange 10 10
a. Error. Crown missing, W **9***a* .. £1300
b. Error. St. Edward's Crown, W **9***b* .. £800
88 2½d. bright ultramarine 10 10
89 **8** 3d. dull purple and scarlet 10 20
90 **9** 6d. green and bright purple 10 10
91 **8** 1s. black and green (R.) 10 10
a. Break in value tablet frame .. 8·50
86/91 .. .. *Set of* 6 40 50

Nos. 87*a/b* occur on a row in the watermark, in which the crowns and letters "CA" alternate.

(New Currency. 100 cents = 1 West Indian, later East Caribbean, dollar)

1951 (16 Feb). *Inauguration of B.W.I. University College. As Nos.* 149/50 *of Jamaica.*

92 3c. black and yellow-orange 30 15
93 12c. turquoise-green and magenta 30 60

ST. CHRISTOPHER, NEVIS AND ANGUILLA

LEGISLATIVE COUNCIL

13 Bath House and Spa, Nevis

14 Map of the Islands

(Recess Waterlow)

1952 (14 June). *Vert designs as T* **14** (3, 12 *c.*) *or horiz as* **13** (*others*). *Wmk Mult Script CA. P* 12½.

94 1 c. deep green and ochre 15 90
95 2 c. green 40 90
96 3 c. carmine-red and violet 30 80
97 4 c. scarlet 20 20
98 5 c. bright blue and grey 20 10
99 6 c. ultramarine 20 15
100 12 c. deep blue and reddish brown 20 10
101 24 c. black and carmine-red 20 10
102 48 c. olive and chocolate .. .. .. 1·50 1·50
103 60 c. ochre and deep green .. .. .. 1·50 1·75
104 $1.20, deep green and ultramarine .. .. 5·00 2·25
105 $4.80, green and carmine .. .. .. 12·00 18·00
94/105 .. .. *Set of* 12 19·00 23·00

Designs:—2 c. Warner Park; 4 c. Brimstone Hill; 5 c. Nevis from the sea, North; 6 c. Pinney's Beach, Nevis; 12 c. Sir Thomas Warner's Tomb; 24 c. Old Road Bay; 48 c. Sea Island cotton, Nevis; 60 c. The Treasury; $1.20, Salt pond, Anguilla; $4.80, Sugar factory.

1953 (2 June). *Coronation. As No.* 153 *of Jamaica.*

106 2 c. black and bright green 30 15

25 Sombrero Lighthouse

26 Map of Anguilla and Dependencies

(Recess Waterlow (until 1961), then D.L.R.)

1954 (1 Mar)–**63**. *Designs previously used for King George VI issue, but with portrait of Queen Elizabeth II as in T* **25/6** *or new values and designs* (½ *c.*, 8 *c.*, $2.40). *Wmk Mult Script CA. P* 12½.

106*a* ½ c. deep olive (3.7.56) 30 10
107 1 c. deep green and ochre 20 10
a. Deep green and orange-ochre (13.2.62) 1·25 2·25
b. Imperf vert (horiz strip of three) .. † £2500
108 2 c. green 45 10
a. Yellow-green (31.7.63) .. .. 4·50 6·00
109 3 c. carmine-red and violet 65 10
a. Carmine and deep violet (31.7.63) .. 4·50 6·50
110 4 c. scarlet 15 10
111 5 c. bright blue and grey 15 10
112 6 c. ultramarine 50 10
a. Blue (19.2.63) .. .. .. 1·25 30
112*b* 8 c. grey-black (1.2.57) .. .. .. 4·50 10
113 12 c. deep blue and red-brown 15 10
114 24 c. black and carmine-red (1.12.54) .. 15 10
115 48 c. olive-bistre and chocolate (1.12.54) .. 60 50
116 60 c. ochre and deep green (1.12.54) .. 5·50 1·75
117 $1.20, dp green & ultramarine (1.12.54) 18·00 1·75
a. Deep green and violet-blue (19.2.63) .. 27·00 6·50
117*b* $2.40, black and red-orange (1.2.57) .. 10·00 11·00
118 $4.80, green and carmine (1.12.54) .. 13·00 11·00
106*a*/18 .. .. *Set of* 15 48·00 24·00

Design: *Horiz*—½ c., $1.20 Salt Pond; 1 c. Bath House and Spa; 2 c. Warner Park; 4 c. Brimstone Hill; 5 c. Nevis from the sea, North; 6 c. Pinney's Beach; 24 c. Old Road Bay; 48 c. Sea Island cotton; 60 c. The Treasury; $4.80, Sugar factory. *Vert*—3 c. Map of the islands; 12 c. Sir Thomas Warner's Tomb.

Stamps of St. Christopher, Nevis and Anguilla were in concurrent use with the stamps inscribed "LEEWARD ISLANDS" until 1 July 1956, when the general Leeward Islands stamps were withdrawn.

27 Alexander Hamilton and View of Nevis

(Des Eva Wilkin. Recess Waterlow)

1957 (11 Jan). *Birth Bicentenary of Alexander Hamilton. Wmk Mult Script CA. P* 12½.

119 **27** 24 c. green and deep blue 30 15

1958 (22 Apr). *Inauguration of British Caribbean Federation. As Nos.* 175/7 *of Jamaica.*

120 3 c. deep green 60 15
121 6 c. blue .. .. 1·00 1·75
122 12 c. scarlet .. .. 1·50 30
120/2 .. .. *Set of* 3 2·75 2·00

MINISTERIAL GOVERNMENT

28 One Penny Stamp of 1861

(Recess Waterlow)

1961 (15 July). *Nevis Stamp Centenary. T* **28** *and similar horiz designs. W* w **12**. *P* 14.

123 2 c. red-brown and green 15 20
124 8 c. red-brown and deep blue 20 10
125 12 c. black and carmine-red 30 15
126 24 c. deep bluish green and red-orange .. 35 15
123/6 .. .. *Set of* 4 90 50

Designs:—8 c. Fourpence stamp of 1861; 12 c. Sixpence stamp of 1861; 24 c. One shilling stamp of 1861.

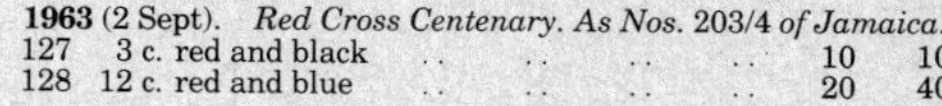

1963 (2 Sept). *Red Cross Centenary. As Nos.* 203/4 *of Jamaica.*

127 3 c. red and black 10 10
128 12 c. red and blue 20 40

32 New Lighthouse, Sombrero

33 Loading Sugar Cane, St. Kitts

(Des V. Whiteley. Photo Harrison)

1963 (20 Nov)–**69**. *Vert designs as T* **32** (2, 3, 15, 25, 60 *c.*, $1, $5) *or horiz as T* **33** (*others*) *in sepia and light blue* (½ *c.*), *greenish yellow and blue* ($1) *or multicoloured* (*others*). *W* w **12** (*upright*). *P* 14.

129 ½ c. Type **32** 10 10
w. Wmk inverted .. .. ..
130 1 c. Type **33** 10 10
131 2 c. Pall Mall Square, Basseterre 10 10
a. White fountain and church £110
w. Wmk inverted .. .. ..
132 3 c. Gateway, Brimstone Hill Fort, St. Kitts 10 10
w. Wmk inverted .. .. ..
133 4 c. Nelson's Spring, Nevis 10 10
w. Wmk inverted .. .. ..
134 5 c. Grammar School, St. Kitts .. .. 1·50 10
135 6 c. Crater, Mt Misery, St. Kitts 10 10
w. Wmk inverted (19.12.69) 30 30
136 10 c. Hibiscus 15 10
137 15 c. Sea Island cotton, Nevis 45 10
w. Wmk inverted .. .. ..
138 20 c. Boat building, Anguilla 20 10
139 25 c. White-crowned Pigeon (turquoise-blue background) 90 10
a. Turquoise-green background (13.4.65) 4·00 1·25
w. Wmk inverted .. .. .. — 65·00
140 50 c. St. George's Church Tower, Basseterre 40 25
141 60 c. Alexander Hamilton .. .. .. 1·00 30
142 $1 Map of St. Kitts-Nevis .. .. 2·50 40
143 $2.50, Map of Anguilla .. .. .. 2·50 2·50
144 $5 Arms of St. Christopher, Nevis and Anguilla .. .. 4·00 3·50
129/44 .. .. *Set of* 16 12·50 7·00

The 1, 4, 5, 6, 10 and 20 c. values exist with PVA gum as well as gum arabic.

See also Nos. 166/71.

OMNIBUS ISSUES

Details, together with prices for complete sets, of the various Omnibus issues from the 1935 Silver Jubilee series to date are included in a special section following Zimbabwe at the end of Volume 2.

ARTS FESTIVAL ST KITTS 1964

(48)

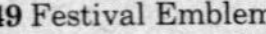
49 Festival Emblem

1964 (14 Sept). *Arts Festival. Nos. 132 and 139 optd as T* **48**.
145 3 c. Gateway, Brimstone Hill Fort, St. Kitts .. 10 15
a. Opt double £190
146 25 c. White-crowned Pigeon 20 15
a. "FESTIVAI" (R. 1/10) .. .. 65·00
w. Wmk inverted .. .. .. — 8·00

1965 (17 May). *I.T.U. Centenary. As Nos. 98/9 of Lesotho.*
147 2 c. bistre-yellow and rose-carmine 10 10
148 50 c. turquoise-blue and yellow-olive 40 50

1965 (15 Oct). *International Co-operation Year. As Nos. 100/1 of Lesotho.*
149 2 c. reddish purple and turquoise-green .. 10 20
150 25 c. deep bluish green and lavender 20 10

1966 (24 Jan). *Churchill Commemoration. As Nos. 102/5 of Lesotho.*
151 ½ c. new blue 10 15
a. Value omitted £160
b. Value at left instead of right .. .. 55·00
152 3 c. deep green 15 10
153 15 c. brown 30 20
154 25 c. bluish violet 35 20
151/4 .. .. *Set of* 4 75 55

1966 (4 Feb). *Royal Visit. As Nos. 183/4 of Montserrat.*
155 3 c. black and ultramarine 20 15
156 25 c. black and magenta 40 15

1966 (1 July). *World Cup Football Championships. As Nos. 57/8 of Pitcairn Islands.*
157 6 c. violet, yellow-green, lake & yellow-brn .. 40 20
158 25 c. chocolate, blue-green, lake & yell-brn .. 60 10

(Photo Harrison)

1966 (15 Aug). *Arts Festival. P* 14 × 14½.
159 **49** 3 c. black, buff, emerald-green and gold 10 10
160 25 c. black, buff, emerald-green and silver 20 10

1966 (20 Sept). *Inauguration of W.H.O. Headquarters, Geneva. As Nos. 185/6 of Montserrat.*
161 3 c. black, yellow-green, and light blue .. 10 10
162 40 c. black, light purple, and yellow-brown .. 20 20

1966 (1 Dec). *20th Anniv of U.N.E.S.C.O. As Nos. 342/4 of Mauritius.*
163 3 c. slate-violet, red, yellow and orange .. 10 10
164 6 c. orange-yellow, violet and deep olive .. 10 10
165 40 c. black, bright purple and orange .. 30 35
163/5 .. .. *Set of* 3 40 45

ASSOCIATED STATEHOOD

1967–69. *As Nos. 129, 131/2, 137, 139 and 142 but wmk sideways.*
166 **20** ½ c. sepia and light blue (9.1.69) .. 20 1·90
167 – 2 c. multicoloured (27.6.67) .. .. 1·75 10
168 – 3 c. multicoloured (16.7.68) 20 10
169 – 15 c. multicoloured (16.7.68) 70 30
170 – 25 c. multicoloured (16.7.68) .. .. 2·50 20
171 – $1 greenish yellow and blue (16.7.68) .. 5·00 4·00
a. Greenish yellow & ultramarine-blue (19.12.69) .. .. 11·00 6·00
166/71 .. .. *Set of* 6 9·25 6·00

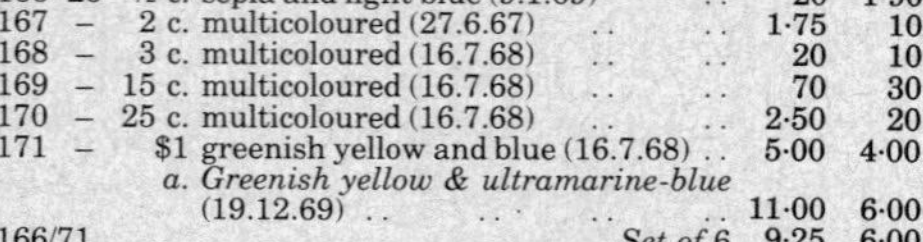

The 2 c. and $1 values exist with PVA gum as well as gum arabic.
Nos. 172/81 vacant.

50 Government Headquarters, Basseterre

53 John Wesley and Cross

(Des V. Whiteley. Photo Harrison)

1967 (1 July). *Statehood. T* **50** *and similar horiz designs. Multicoloured. W* w **12**. *P* 14½ × 14.
182 3 c. Type **50** 10 10
183 10 c. National flag 10 10
w. Wmk inverted .. .. 16·00
184 25 c. Coat of arms 15 15
182/4 .. .. *Set of* 3 30 30

(Litho D.L.R.)

1967 (1 Dec). *West Indies Methodist Conference. T* **53** *and similar vert designs. P* 13 × 13½.
185 3 c. black, cerise and reddish violet 10 10
186 25 c. black, light greenish blue and blue .. 15 10
187 40 c. black, yellow and orange 15 15
185/7 .. .. *Set of* 3 30 30
Designs:—25 c. Charles Wesley and Cross; 40 c. Thomas Coke and Cross.

56 Handley Page H.P.R.7 Dart Herald Aircraft over *Jamaica Producer* (freighter)

57 Dr. Martin Luther King

(Des and litho D.L.R.)

1968 (30 July). *Caribbean Free Trade Area. W* w **12** (*sideways*). *P* 13.
188 **56** 25 c. multicoloured 30 10
189 50 c. multicoloured 30 20

(Des G. Vasarhelyi. Litho Enschedé)

1968 (30 Sept). *Martin Luther King Commemoration. W* w **12**. *P* 12 × 12½.
190 **57** 50 c. multicoloured 10 10

58 "Mystic Nativity" (Botticelli)

60 Tarpon Snook

(Des and photo Harrison)

1968 (27 Nov). *Christmas. Paintings. T* **58** *and similar vert design. Multicoloured. W* w **12** (*sideways*). *P* 14½ × 14.
191 12 c. Type **58** 10 10
192 25 c. "The Adoration of the Magi" (Rubens) .. 10 10
193 40 c. Type **58** 15 10
194 50 c. As 25 c. 15 10
191/4 .. .. *Set of* 4 40 30

(Des G. Drummond. Photo Harrison)

1969 (25 Feb). *Fishes. T* **60** *and similar horiz designs. W* w **12**. *P* 14 × 14½.
195 6 c. multicoloured 10 10
196 12 c. black, turquoise-green & greenish blue 15 10
197 40 c. multicoloured 25 10
198 50 c. multicoloured 30 15
195/8 .. .. *Set of* 4 70 30
Designs:—12 c. Needlefish; 40 c. Horse-eyed Jack; 50 c. Black-finned Snapper.

64 The Warner Badge and Islands

67 "The Adoration of the Kings" (Mostaert)

(Des V. Whiteley. Litho Format)

1969 (1 Sept). *Sir Thomas Warner Commemoration. T* **64** *and similar horiz designs. Multicoloured. W* w **12** (*sideways*). *P* 13½ × 14.
199 20 c. Type **64** 10 10
200 25 c. Sir Thomas Warner's tomb 10 10
201 40 c. Charles I's commission 15 15
199/201 .. .. *Set of* 3 30 30

(Des Enschedé. Litho B.W.)

1969 (17 Nov). *Christmas. Paintings. T* **67** *and similar vert design. Multicoloured. W* w **12** (*sideways*). *P* 13½.
202 10 c. Type **67** 10 10
203 25 c. Type **67** 10 10
204 40 c. "The Adoration of the Kings" (Geertgen) 10 10
205 50 c. As 40 c. 10 10
202/5 .. .. *Set of* 4 30 30

73 Portuguese Caravels (16th-cent)

(Des and litho J.W.)

1970 (2 Feb)–**74.** *Designs as T* **73** *in black, pale orange and emerald* (½ *c.*) *or multicoloured* (*others*). *W* w **12** (*upright on vert designs, sideways* on horiz designs*). *P* 14.
206 ½ c. Pirates and treasure at Frigate Bay (*vert*) 10 10
w. Wmk inverted (15.3.71) 20 20
207 1 c. English two-decker warship, 1650 (*vert*) 30 10
208 2 c. Naval flags of colonising nations (*vert*) 15 10
209 3 c. Rapier hilt (17th-century) (*vert*) .. 15 10
210 4 c. Type **73** 20 10
w. Wmk Crown to right of CA (24.7.74) 40 15
211 5 c. Sir Henry Morgan and fireships, 1669 30 10
w. Wmk Crown to right of CA (24.7.74) 40 30
212 6 c. L'Ollonois and pirate carrack (16th century) 30 10
w. Wmk Crown to right of CA (24.7.74) 40 20
213 10 c. 17th-century smugglers' ship .. 30 10
w. Wmk Crown to right of CA (24.7.74) 40 15
214 15 c. "Pieces-of-eight" (*vert*) (I) .. .. 2·00 40
214*a* 15 c. "Pieces-of-eight" (*vert*) (II) (8.9.70) .. 50 10
215 20 c. Cannon (17th-century) 35 10
w. Wmk Crown to right of CA (24.7.74) 50 20
216 25 c. Humphrey Cole's Astrolabe, 1574 (*vert*) 40 10
217 50 c. Flintlock pistol (17th-century) .. 85 80
w. Wmk Crown to right of CA (24.7.74) 1·25 80
218 60 c. Dutch flute (17th-century) (*vert*) .. 2·25 70
219 $1 Captain Bartholomew Roberts and his crew's death warrant (*vert*) .. .. 2·50 75
220 $2.50, Railing piece (16th-century) .. 2·00 3·25
w. Wmk Crown to right of CA (24.7.74) 2·50 3·25
221 $5 Drake, Hawkins and sea battle .. 2·50 4·50
w. Wmk Crown to right of CA (24.7.74) 4·00 5·00
206/21 .. .. *Set of* 17 13·50 9·50
Nos. 214/*a*. Type I, coin inscribed "HISPANIANUM"; Type II corrected to "HISPANIARUM". No. 214*a* also differs considerably in shade from No. 214.
*The normal sideways watermark shows Crown to left of CA, *as seen from the back of the stamp.*
See also Nos. 269/80 and 322/31.

85 Graveyard Scene (*Great Expectations*)

(Des Jennifer Toombs. Litho B.W.)

1970 (1 May). *Death Centenary of Charles Dickens. T* **85** *and similar designs. W* w **12** (*sideways on horiz designs*). *P* 13.
222 4 c. bistre-brown, gold and deep blue-green .. 10 10
223 20 c. bistre-brown, gold and reddish purple .. 10 10
224 25 c. bistre-brown, gold and olive-green .. 10 10
225 40 c. bistre-brown, gold and ultramarine .. 15 25
222/5 .. .. *Set of* 4 40 40
Designs: *Horiz*—20 c. Miss Havisham and Pip (*Great Expectations*). *Vert*—25 c. Dickens's Birthplace; 40 c. Charles Dickens.

86 Local Steel Band

(Des V. Whiteley. Litho Enschedé)

1970 (1 Aug). *Festival of Arts. T* **86** *and similar horiz designs. Multicoloured. W* w **12** (*sideways*). *P* 13½.
226 20 c. Type **86** 10 10
227 25 c. Local String Band 10 10
228 40 c. Scene from *A Midsummer Night's Dream* 15 15
226/8 .. .. *Set of* 3 30 30

87 1d. Stamp of 1870 and Post Office, 1970

88 "Adoration of the Shepherds" (detail) (Frans van Floris)

(Des J. Cooter. Litho J.W.)

1970 (14 Sept). *Stamp Centenary. T* **87** *and similar horiz designs.* W w **12** (*sideways*). *P* 14½.
229 ½ c. green and rose 10 10
230 20 c. deep blue, green and rose 10 10
231 25 c. brown-purple, green and rose 10 10
232 50 c. scarlet, green and black 30 45
229/32 . . . . . . *Set of* 4 50 50
Designs:—20 c., 25 c. 1d. and 6d. Stamps of 1870; 50 c. 6d. Stamp of 1870 and early postmark.

(Des Enschedé. Litho Format)

1970 (16 Nov). *Christmas. T* **88** *and similar vert design. Multicoloured.* W w **12**. *P* 14.
233 3 c. Type **88** 10 10
234 20 c. "The Holy Family" (Van Dyck) 10 10
235 25 c. As 20 c. 10 10
236 40 c. Type **88** 15 40
233/6 . . . . . . *Set of* 4 30 60

89 Monkey Fiddle

(Des Sylvia Goaman. Litho Format)

1971 (1 Mar). *Flowers. T* **89** *and similar horiz designs. Multicoloured.* W w **12** (*sideways**). *P* 14½.
237 ½ c. Type **89** 10 10
w. Wmk Crown to right of CA 75
238 20 c. Tropical Mountain Violet 15 10
239 30 c. Trailing Morning Glory 15 15
240 50 c. Fringed Epidendrum 30 80
237/40 . . . . . . *Set of* 4 55 95
*The normal sideways watermark shows Crown to left of CA, *as seen from the back of the stamp.*

90 Royal Poinciana

(Des Enschedé. Litho J.W.)

1971 (1 June). *Phillipe de Poincy Commemoration. T* **90** *and similar multicoloured designs.* W w **12** (*sideways on* 20 *and* 30 *c.*). *P* 13½.
241 20 c. Type **90** 10 10
242 30 c. Château de Poincy 10 10
243 50 c. De Poincy's badge (*vert*) 20 15
241/3 . . . . . . *Set of* 3 35 30

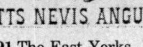

91 The East Yorks **92** "Crucifixion" (Massys)

(Des V. Whiteley. Litho Walsall)

1971 (1 Sept). *Siege of Brimstone Hill, 1782. T* **91** *and similar horiz designs. Multicoloured.* W w **12** (*sideways**). *P* 14½.
244 ½ c. Type **91** 10 10
w. Wmk Crown to right of CA 75
245 20 c. Royal Artillery 35 10
246 30 c. French infantry 45 10
247 50 c. The Royal Scots 60 20
244/7 . . . . . . *Set of* 4 1·25 35
*The normal sideways watermark shows Crown to left of CA, *as seen from the back of the stamp.*

(Des J. Cooter. Litho J.W.)

1972 (1 Apr). *Easter.* W w **12**. *P* 14 × 13½.
248 **92** 4 c. multicoloured 10 10
249 20 c. multicoloured 10 10
250 30 c. multicoloured 10 10
251 40 c. multicoloured 10 10
248/51 . . . . . . *Set of* 4 30 30

COVER PRICES

Cover factors are quoted at the beginning of each country for most issues to 1945. An explanation of the system can be found on page x. The factors quoted do not, however, apply to philatelic covers.

93 "Virgin and Child" (Borgognone) **94** Brown Pelicans

(Des J. Cooter. Litho J.W.)

1972 (2 Oct). *Christmas. T* **93** *and similar multicoloured designs.* W w **12** (*sideways on vert designs*). *P* 14.
252 3 c. Type **93** 10 10
253 20 c. "Adoration of the Kings" (J. Bassano) (*horiz*) 15 10
254 25 c. "Adoration of the Shepherds" (Domenichino) 15 10
255 40 c. "Virgin and Child" (Fiorenzo di Lorenzo) 20 10
252/5 . . . . . . *Set of* 4 45 30

(Des (from photograph by D. Groves) and photo Harrison)

1972 (20 Nov). *Royal Silver Wedding. Multicoloured; background colour given.* W w **12**. *P* 14 × 14½.
256 **94** 20 c. carmine 15 15
w. Wmk inverted . . . . — 35·00
257 25 c. bright blue 15 15

95 Landing on St. Christopher, 1623 **96** "The Last Supper" (Titian)

(Des J.W. Litho Questa)

1973 (28 Jan). *350th Anniv of Sir Thomas Warner's landing on St. Christopher. T* **95** *and similar horiz designs. Multicoloured.* W w **12**. *P* 13½.
258 4 c. Type **95** 15 10
259 25 c. Growing tobacco 15 10
w. Wmk inverted . . . . 1·00
260 40 c. Building fort at Old Road 20 10
261 $2.50, *Concepcion* . . . . . . 80 1·10
258/61 . . . . . . *Set of* 4 1·10 1·25

(Des J. Cooter. Litho Walsall)

1973 (16 Apr). *Easter. T* **96** *and similar multicoloured designs showing paintings of "The Last Supper" by the artists listed.* W w **12** (*sideways on* $2.50). *P* 13½ × 14 ($2.50) *or* 14 × 13½ (*others*).
262 4 c. Type **96** 10 10
263 25 c. Ascr to Roberti 10 10
264 $2.50, Juan de Juanes (*horiz*) 70 60
262/4 . . . . . . *Set of* 3 75 60

VISIT OF
H. R. H. THE PRINCE OF WALES 1973
(**97**)

1973 (31 May). *Royal Visit. Nos. 258/61 optd with T* **97** *by Questa.*
265 4 c. Type **95** 10 15
266 25 c. Growing tobacco 10 15
267 40 c. Building fort at Old Road 15 15
268 $2.50 *Concepcion* 45 50
265/8 . . . . . . *Set of* 4 65 85

(Des J.W. Litho Harrison ($10), J.W. (others))

1973 (12 Sept)–**74**. *As Nos.* 206, 208/9, 211/13, 214*a*/17, 219 *and new horiz design* ($10), *but* W w **12** (*sideways on vert designs, upright on horiz designs*).
269 ½ c. Pirates and treasure at Frigate Bay . . 10 80
270 2 c. Naval flags of colonizing nations . . 20 80
271 3 c. Rapier hilt 20 80
272 5 c. Sir Henry Morgan and fireships, 1669 . . 35 80
273 6 c. L'Ollonois and pirate carrack (16th-century) 35 80
274 10 c. 17th-century smugglers' ship . . 40 80
275 15 c. "Piece-of-eight" (II) 65 85
276 20 c. Cannon (17th-century) . . . . 75 1·10
277 25 c. Humphrey Cole's Astrolabe, 1574 . . 80 1·75
278 50 c. Flintlock pistol (17th-century) . . 1·10 1·50
279 $1 Captain Bartholomew Roberts and his crew's death warrant . . . . 2·75 3·50
280 $10 "The Apprehension of Blackbeard" (Edward Teach) (16.11.74) . . . . 20·00 13·00
269/80 . . . . . . *Set of* 12 25·00 23·00
Nos. 281/4 vacant.

99 Harbour Scene and 2d. Stamp of 1903

(Des V. Whiteley Studio. Litho Enschedé)

1973 (1 Oct). *70th Anniv of First St. Kitts-Nevis Stamps. T* **99** *and similar horiz designs. Multicoloured.* W w **12** (*sideways*). *P* 13 × 13½.
285 4 c. Type **99** 10 10
286 25 c. Sugar-mill and 1d. stamp of 1903 . . 15 10
287 40 c. Unloading boat and ½d. stamp of 1903 35 10
288 $2.50, Rock-carvings and 3d. stamp of 1903 2·00 1·00
285/8 . . . . . . *Set of* 4 2·25 1·10
MS289 144 × 95 mm. Nos. 285/8 . . . . 2·25 4·50

1973 (14 Nov). *Royal Wedding. As Nos.* 322/3 *of Montserrat.*
290 25 c. light emerald 15 10
291 40 c. brown-ochre 15 10

100 "Madonna and Child" (Murillo) **101** "Christ carrying the Cross" (S. del Piombo)

(Des J. Cooter. Litho Format)

1973 (1 Dec). *Christmas. T* **100** *and similar multicoloured designs showing "The Holy Family" by the artists listed.* W w **12** (*sideways on* $1). *P* 13½.
292 4 c. Type **100** 10 10
293 40 c. Mengs 15 10
294 60 c. Sassoferrato 20 15
295 $1 Filippino Lippi (*horiz*) 25 30
292/5 . . . . . . *Set of* 4 55 50

(Des J. Cooter. Litho D.L.R.)

1974 (8 Apr). *Easter. T* **101** *and similar multicoloured designs.* W w **12** (*sideways on* $2.50). *P* 13½.
296 4 c. Type **101** 10 10
297 25 c. "The Crucifixion" (Goya) 15 10
298 40 c. "The Trinity" (Ribera) 15 10
299 $2.50, "The Deposition" (Fra Bartolomeo) (*horiz*) . . . . . . 1·00 75
296/9 . . . . . . *Set of* 4 1·25 75

102 University Centre, St. Kitts **103** Hands reaching for Globe

(Des G. Drummond. Litho Questa)

1974 (1 June). *25th Anniv of University of West Indies. T* **102** *and similar horiz design. Multicoloured.* W w **12** (*sideways**). *P* 13½.
300 10 c. Type **102** 10 10
301 $1 As Type **102** but showing different buildings 20 25
MS302 99×95 mm. Nos. 300/1 . . . . 35 65
w. Wmk Crown to right of CA . . . . 27·00
*The normal sideways watermark shows Crown to left of CA, *as seen from the back of the stamp.*

(Des Jennifer Toombs. Litho Questa)

1974 (5 Aug). *Family Planning. T* **103** *and similar designs.* W w **12** (*sideways on* 25 *c. and* $2.50). *P* 14.
303 4 c. orange-brown, new blue and black . . 10 10
304 25 c. multicoloured 10 10
305 40 c. multicoloured 10 10
306 $2.50, multicoloured 35 55
303/6 . . . . . . *Set of* 4 50 65
Designs: *Horiz*—25 c. Instruction by nurse; $2.50, Emblem and globe on scales. *Vert*—40 c. Family group.

104 Churchill as Army Lieutenant

105 Aeroplane and Map

(Des PAD Studio. Litho Questa)

1974 (30 Nov). *Birth Centenary of Sir Winston Churchill. T* **104** *and similar vert designs. Multicoloured. W* w **12**. *P* 13½.

307	4 c. Type **104**	10	10
308	25 c. Churchill as Prime Minister	15	10
309	40 c. Churchill as Knight of the Garter ..	15	10
310	60 c. Churchill's statue, London	25	15
307/10	.. .. *Set of* 4	50	30
MS311	99 × 148 mm. Nos. 307/10	75	1·25

(Des J.W. Litho Questa)

1974 (16 Dec). *Opening of Golden Rock Airport, St. Kitts. Sheets* 98 × 148 *mm. W* w **12**. *P* 13½.

MS312	**105**	40 c.multicoloured	20	40
MS313		45 c.multicoloured	20	40

106 "The Last Supper" (Doré)

107 E.C.C.A. H.Q. Buildings, Basseterre

(Des PAD Studio. Litho Questa)

1975 (24 Mar). *Easter. T* **106** *and similar vert designs showing paintings by Doré. Multicoloured. W* w **12**. *P* 14½.

314	4 c. Type **106**	10	10
315	25 c. "Christ Mocked"	10	10
316	40 c. "Jesus falling beneath the Cross" ..	10	10
317	$1 "The Erection of the Cross" ..	25	30
314/17	.. .. *Set of* 4	40	40

(Des J. Cooter. Litho Enschedé)

1975 (2 June*). *Opening of East Caribbean Currency Authority's Headquarters. T* **107** *and similar horiz designs. W* w **14** (*sideways*). *P* 13 × 13½.

318	12 c. multicoloured	10	10
319	25 c. multicoloured	10	10
320	40 c. light vermilion, silver and grey-black ..	15	10
321	45 c. multicoloured	15	15
	a. Silver omitted†	85·00	
318/21	.. .. *Set of* 4	30	30

Designs:—25 c. Specimen one-dollar banknote; 40 c. Half-dollar of 1801 and current 4-dollar coin; 45 c. Coins of 1801 and 1960.

*This is the local date of issue; the Crown Agents released the stamps on 28 April.

†This affects the dull silver coin on the left which on No. 321a appears in tones of the black plate.

1975–77. *As Nos.* 207, 209/13, 214*a*/15 *and* 218/19 *but W* w **14** (*sideways* on* 4, 5, 6, 10, 20 *and* 60 *c.*).
A. *White, ordinary paper.*
B. *Cream, chalk-surfaced paper.*

		A		B	
322	1 c. English two-decker warship, 1650	†		30	30
323	3 c. Rapier hilt (17th-century)	20	10	2·25	3·00
324	4 c. Type **73**	20	10	2·25	3·00
325	5 c. Sir Henry Morgan and fireships, 1669	30	50	9·50	9·50
326	6 c. L'Ollonois and pirate carrack (16th century) ..	1·25	10	1·00	2·25
	w. Wmk Crown to right of CA	†		3·25	3·25
327	10 c. 17th-century smugglers' ship	45	15	1·25	2·50
328	15 c. "Pieces-of-eight" (II) ..	55	15	10·00	9·50
329	20 c. Cannon (17th-century) ..	2·75	5·00	2·00	7·50
330	60 c. Dutch flute (17th- cent)	9·00	2·00	†	
331	$1 Captain Bartholomew Roberts and his crew's death warrant	†		9·00	3·00
323A/30A	.. .. *Set of* 8	13·00	7·25		
322B/31B	.. .. *Set of* 9			35·00	35·00

*The normal sideways watermark shows Crown to left of CA on No. 326B and to right of CA on the others, *as seen from the back of the stamp.*

Dates of issue:—11.6.75, Nos. 325A/6A, 329A; 11.6.76, Nos. 323A/4A, 327A/8A, 330A; 17.5.77, Nos. 322B/4B, 326B/7B, 329B; 16.8.77, Nos. 325B, 326Bw, 328B, 331B.

Nos. 332/7 vacant.

108 Evangeline Booth (Salvation Army General)

109 Golfer

(Des Jennifer Toombs. Litho Questa)

1975 (15 Sept). *International Women's Year. T* **108** *and similar vert designs. Multicoloured. W* w **12**. *P* 14.

338	4 c. Type **108**	30	10
339	25 c. Sylvia Pankhurst	35	10
340	40 c. Marie Curie	1·75	80
341	$2.50, Lady Annie Allen (teacher and guider)	1·50	4·00
338/41	.. .. *Set of* 4	3·50	4·50

(Des Sue Lawes. Litho Questa)

1975 (1 Nov). *Opening of Frigate Bay Golf Course. W* w **14** (*sideways*). *P* 13½.

342	**109**	4 c. black and rose-red	60	10
343		25 c. black and greenish yellow	85	10
344		40 c. black and light emerald	1·25	10
345		$1 black and new blue..	1·75	1·50
342/5		.. .. *Set of* 4	4·00	1·60

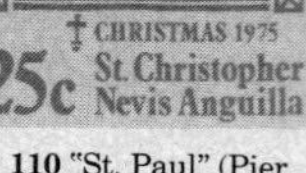

110 "St. Paul" (Pier Francesco Sacchi)

111 "Crucifixion" (detail)

(Des J.W. Litho Questa)

1975 (1 Dec). *Christmas. T* **110** *and similar vert designs showing details from paintings in the National Gallery, London. Multicoloured. W* w **14**. *P* 13½.

346	25 c. Type **110**	25	10
347	40 c. "St James" (Bonifazio di Pitati)	40	10
348	45 c. "St. John the Baptist" (Mola)	40	10
349	$1 "St. Mary" (Raphael)	1·25	90
346/9	.. .. *Set of* 4	2·10	1·00

(Des J. Cooter. Litho Questa)

1976 (14 Apr). *Easter. Stained-glass Windows. T* **111** *and similar vert designs. Multicoloured. W* w **14**. *P* 14 × 13½ (4 *c.*) *or* 14 (*others*).

350	4 c. Type **111**	10	20
	a. Strip of 3. Nos. 350/2	20	
351	4 c. } "Crucifixion"	10	20
352	4 c. }	10	20
353	25 c. "Last Supper"	35	10
354	40 c. "Last Supper" (*different*).. ..	40	10
355	$1 "Baptism of Christ"	70	70
350/5	.. .. *Set of* 6	1·50	1·25

Nos. 350/2 were printed horizontally *se-tenant*, together forming a composite design, No. 350 being the left-hand stamp.

Nos. 353/5 are smaller, 27 × 35 mm.

1976 (8 July). *West Indian Victory in World Cricket Cup. As Nos.* 419/20 *of Jamaica.*

356	12 c. Map of the Caribbean	60	20
357	40 c. Prudential Cup	1·40	50
MS358	95 × 80 mm. Nos. 356/7	3·25	3·75

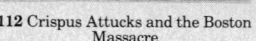

112 Crispus Attucks and the Boston Massacre

113 "The Nativity" (Sforza Book of Hours)

(Des J.W. Litho Questa)

1976 (26 July). *Bicentenary of American Revolution. T* **112** *and similar horiz designs. Multicoloured. W* w **14** (*sideways*). *P* 13½.

359	20 c. Type **112**	20	10
360	40 c. Alexander Hamilton and Battle of Yorktown	35	10
361	45 c. Jefferson and Declaration of Independence	35	10
362	$1 Washington and the Crossing of the Delaware	70	80
359/62	.. .. *Set of* 4	1·40	95

(Des Jennifer Toombs. Litho Questa)

1976 (1 Nov). *Christmas. T* **113** *and similar vert designs. Multicoloured. W* w **14**. *P* 14.

363	20 c. Type **113**	10	10
364	40 c. "Virgin and Child with St. John" (Pintoricchio)	15	10
365	45 c. "Our Lady of Good Children" (Ford Maddox-Brown)	15	10
366	$1 "Little Hands Outstretched to Bless" (Margaret Tarrant)	35	50
363/6	.. .. *Set of* 4	65	60

114 Royal Visit, 1966

115 "Christ on the Cross" (Niccolo di Liberatore)

(Des J.W. Litho Questa)

1977 (7 Feb). *Silver Jubilee. T* **114** *and similar vert designs. Multicoloured. W* w **14**. *P* 13½.

367	50 c. Type **114**	10	10
368	55 c. The Sceptre	10	10
369	$1.50, Bishops paying homage	25	50
367/9	.. .. *Set of* 3	35	60

(Des G. Hutchins. Litho Questa)

1977 (14 Apr*). *Easter. T* **115** *and similar designs showing paintings from the National Gallery, London. Multicoloured. W* w **14** (*sideways on* 50 *c.*). *P* 14.

370	25 c. Type **115**	10	10
371	30 c. "The Resurrection" (imitator of Mantegna)	10	10
372	50 c. "The Resurrection" (Ugolino da Siena) (*horiz*)	15	10
373	$1 "Christ Rising from the Tomb" (Gaudenzio Ferrari)	25	30
370/3	.. .. *Set of* 4	55	45

*This is the local release date; the Crown Agents released the stamps ten days earlier.

116 Estridge Mission

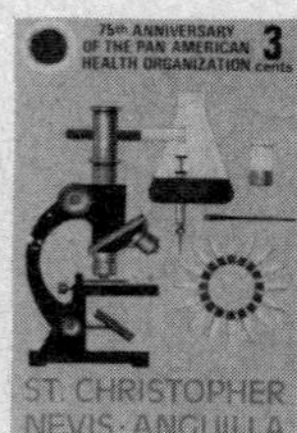

117 Laboratory Instruments

(Des Jennifer Toombs. Litho Cartor)

1977 (27 June). *Bicentenary of Moravian Mission. T* **116** *and similar horiz designs. W* w **14** (*sideways**). *P* 12½.

374	4 c. black, greenish blue and new blue ..	10	10
	w. Wmk Crown to left of CA ..	30	
375	20 c. black, brt mauve & brt reddish violet	10	10
	w. Wmk Crown to left of CA ..	40	
376	40 c. black, yellow and yellow-orange ..	15	15
	w. Wmk Crown to left of CA	60	
374/6	.. .. *Set of* 3	30	30

Designs:—20 c. Mission symbol; 40 c. Basseterre Mission.

*The normal sideways watermark shows Crown to right of CA, *as seen from the back of the stamp.*

(Des G. Hutchins. Litho Questa)

1977 (11 Oct). *75th Anniv of Pan-American Health Organization. T* **117** *and similar vert designs. W* w **14**. *P* 14.

377	3 c. multicoloured	15	10
378	12 c. multicoloured	25	10
379	20 c. multicoloured	35	10
380	$1 red-brown, bright orange and black ..	90	70
377/80	.. .. *Set of* 4	1·50	85

Designs:—12 c. Fat cells, blood cells and nerve cells; 20 c. "Community participation in health"; $1 Inoculation.

118 "Nativity" (West Window)

119 Savanna Monkey with Vervet

(Des Jennifer Toombs. Litho Rosenbaum Bros, Vienna)

1977 (15 Nov). *Christmas. Vert designs as T* **118** *showing stained-glass windows from Chartres Cathedral. Multicoloured. W* w **14** (*inverted*). *P* 13½.

381 4 c. Type **118** 10 10
w. Wmk upright 30
382 6 c. "Three Magi" (West window) .. 10 10
383 40 c. "La Belle Verriere" 35 10
w. Wmk upright 55
384 $1 "Virgin and Child" (Rose window) .. 75 45
w. Wmk upright .. .. .. 2·50
381/4 .. .. *Set of* 4 1·10 55

(Des BG Studio. Litho Questa)

1978 (15 Apr). *The Savanna ("Green") Monkey. T* **119** *and similar vert design. W* w **14**. *P* 14½.

385 **119** 4 c. yellow-brown, rosine and black .. 10 10
386 – 5 c. multicoloured 10 10
387 **119** 55 c. yellow-brown, apple-green & black 30 10
388 – $1.50, multicoloured 75 60
385/8 .. .. .. *Set of* 4 1·10 65
Design:—5 c., $1.50 Savanna Monkeys on branch.

120 Falcon of Edward III

121 Tomatoes

(Des C. Abbott. Litho Questa)

1978 (2 June). *25th Anniv of Coronation. T* **120** *and similar vert designs. P* 15.

389 $1 olive-brown and vermilion 15 20
a. Sheetlet. Nos. 389/91 × 2 75
390 $1 multicoloured 15 20
391 $1 olive-brown and vermilion 15 20
389/91 .. .. .. *Set of* 3 40 55
Designs:—No. 389, Type **120**; No. 390, Queen Elizabeth II; No. 391, Brown Pelican.

(Des BG Studio. Litho D.L.R.)

1978 (8 Sept). *Horiz designs as T* **121**. *Multicoloured. W* w **14** (*sideways**). *P* 14½×14.

392 1 c. Type **121** 10 15
393 2 c. Defence Force band 10 15
394 5 c. Radio and T.V. station 10 10
395 10 c. Technical college 10 10
396 12 c. T.V. assembly plant 10 20
w. Wmk Crown to left of CA .. .. 3·50
397 15 c. Sugar cane harvesting 15 10
398 25 c. Crafthouse (craft centre) 15 10
399 30 c. *Europa* (liner) 60 55
400 40 c. Lobster and sea crab 30 10
401 45 c. Royal St. Kitts Hotel and golf course 2·75 65
w. Wmk Crown to left of CA .. .. 10·00
402 50 c. Pinney's Beach, Nevis 30 10
403 55 c. New runway at Golden Rock .. 30 10
404 $1 Cotton picking 35 30
405 $5 Brewery .. .. 75 1·25
406 $10 Pineapples and peanuts .. .. 1·50 2·50
w. Wmk Crown to left of CA .. .. 60·00
392/406 .. .. .. *Set of* 15 6·50 5·50
*The normal sideways watermark shows Crown to right of CA, *as seen from the back of the stamp.*

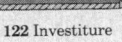

122 Investiture

123 Wise Man with Gift of Gold

(Des L. Curtis. Litho Rosenbaum Bros, Vienna)

1978 (9 Oct). *50th Anniv of Boy Scout Movement on St. Kitts and Nevis. T* **122** *and similar vert designs. Multicoloured. W* w **14**. *P* 13½.

407 5 c. Type **122** 10 10
408 10 c. Map reading 10 10
409 25 c. Pitching tent 20 15
410 40 c. Cooking 35 25
w. Wmk inverted .. .. 14·00
411 50 c. First aid 40 35
w. Wmk inverted .. .. 14·00
412 55 c. Rev. W.A. Beckett (founder of scouting in St. Kitts) 45 45
w. Wmk inverted .. .. 12·00
407/12 .. .. *Set of* 6 1·40 1·10

(Des Jennifer Toombs. Litho Walsall)

1978 (1 Dec). *Christmas. T* **123** *and similar vert designs. Multicoloured. W* w **14**. *P* 13½.

413 5 c. Type **123** 10 10
414 15 c. Wise Man with gift of Frankincense .. 10 10
415 30 c. Wise Man with gift of Myrrh 10 10
416 $2.25, Wise Men paying homage to the infant Jesus 35 50
413/16 .. .. *Set of* 4 50 55

124 *Canna coccinea*

125 St. Christopher 1870–76 1d. Stamp and Sir Rowland Hill

(Des Daphne Padden. Litho Questa)

1979 (19 Mar). *Flowers (1st series). T* **124** *and similar vert designs. Multicoloured. W* w **14**. *P* 14.

417 5 c. Type **124** 10 10
418 30 c. *Heliconia bihai* 30 20
419 55 c. *Ruellia tuberosa* 50 30
420 $1.50, *Gesneria ventricosa* .. .. .. 1·10 1·60
417/20 .. .. *Set of* 4 1·75 2·00
See also Nos. 430/3.

(Des J.W. Litho Walsall)

1979 (2 July). *Death Centenary of Sir Rowland Hill. T* **125** *and similar horiz designs showing stamps and portrait. Multicoloured. W* w **14** (*sideways*). *P* 14½ × 14.

421 5 c. Type **125** 10 10
422 15 c. 1970 Stamp Centenary 50 c. commemorative 10 10
423 50 c. Great Britain 1841 2d. 30 35
424 $2.50, St. Kitts-Nevis 1923 300th Anniversary of Colony £1 commemorative .. 70 1·10
421/4 .. .. *Set of* 4 1·00 1·40

126 "The Woodman's Daughter"

127 Nevis Lagoon

(Des BG Studio. Litho Format)

1979 (12 Nov). *Christmas and International Year of the Child. Paintings by Sir John Millais. T* **126** *and similar vert designs. Multicoloured. W* w **14**. *P* 13½.

425 5 c. Type **126** 10 10
426 25 c. "Cherry Ripe" 25 25
427 30 c. "The Rescue" 25 25
428 55 c. "Bubbles" 30 30
425/8 .. .. *Set of* 4 75 80
MS429 100 × 68 mm. $1 "Christ in the House of His Parents" 70 55

(Des J. Cooter. Litho Questa)

1980 (4 Feb). *Flowers (2nd series). Vert designs as T* **124**. *Multicoloured. W* w **14** (*inverted*). *P* 14.

430 4 c. *Clerodendrum aculeatum* 30 10
431 55 c. *Inga laurina* 40 20
432 $1.50, *Epidendrum difforme* .. .. 1·00 1·25
433 $2 *Salvia serotina* .. .. 1·10 1·75
430/3 .. .. *Set of* 4 2·50 3·00

(Des and litho Secura, Singapore)

1980 (6 May). *"London 1980" International Stamp Exhibition. T* **127** *and similar multicoloured designs. W* w **14** (*sideways** *on 5 and 55 c., inverted on 30 c.*). *P* 13.

434 5 c. Type **127** 10 10
w. Wmk Crown to right of CA .. .. 1·25
435 30 c. Fig Tree Church (*vert*) 20 10
436 55 c. Nisbet Plantation 45 25
w. Wmk Crown to right of CA .. .. 3·25
437 $3 "Nelson" (Fuger) (*vert*) .. .. 1·00 1·60
w. Wmk inverted .. .. .. 4·25
434/7 .. .. *Set of* 4 1·60 1·75
MS438 107×77 mm. 75 c. Detail of "Nelson Falling" (D. Dighton). P 13½×13 .. .. 85 70
a. Wmk sideways .. .. .. 40·00
*The normal sideways watermark shows Crown to left of CA, *as seen from the back of the stamp.*

OFFICIAL STAMPS

OFFICIAL

(O 1)

1980 (3 Mar). *Nos.* 396, 398 *and* 400/6 *optd with Type* O **1**.

O1 12 c. T.V. assembly plant .. .. 80 1·00
w. Wmk Crown to left of CA .. .. 11·00
O2 25 c. Crafthouse (craft centre) 15 20
O3 40 c. Lobster and sea crab 40 50
O4 45 c. Royal St. Kitts Hotel and golf course 1·50 45
w. Wmk Crown to left of CA .. 14·00
O5 50 c. Pinney's Beach, Nevis 30 40
O6 55 c. New runway at Golden Rock .. 30 40
O7 $1 Cotton picking .. .. .. 70 2·25
O8 $5 Brewery .. .. 80 2·50
O9 $10 Pineapples and peanuts .. .. 1·50 3·50
O1/9 .. .. *Set of* 9 5·75 10·00

From 23 June 1980 St. Kitts and Nevis had separate postal authorities, each with their own issues.

ST. KITTS

St. Kitts

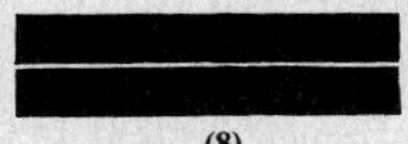

(8)

1980 (23 June). *As Nos.* 394/406 *of St. Christopher, Nevis and Anguilla optd with T* **8**. A. *W* w **14** (*sideways**). B. *No wmk.*

		A		B	
29	5 c. Radio and T.V. station ..	10	15	10	10
30	10 c. Technical college ..	10	15	10	10
	w. Wmk Crown to left of CA	45·00	—	†	
31	12 c. T.V. assembly plant ..	60	80	†	
32	15 c. Sugar cane harvesting ..	10	15	10	10
33	25 c. Crafthouse (craft centre) ..	10	15	10	10
34	30 c. *Europa* (liner)	15	15	10	10
35	40 c. Lobster and sea crab ..	20	20	10	15
36	45 c. Royal St. Kitts Hotel and golf course	50	15	†	
37	50 c. Pinney's Beach, Nevis ..	15	15	†	
38	55 c. New runway at Golden Rock	15	15	15	15
39	$1 Cotton picking	15	25	25	25
40	$5 Brewery	45	1·00	60	1·50
41	$10 Pineapples and peanuts ..	55	1·75	1·00	2·50
29A/41A	.. .. *Set of* 13	2·75	4·75		
29B/41B	.. .. *Set of* 10			2·25	4·50

*The normal sideways watermark shows Crown to right of CA, *as seen from the back of the stamp.*

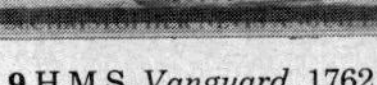

9 H.M.S. *Vanguard*, 1762

10 Queen Elizabeth the Queen Mother at Royal Variety Performance, 1978

(Litho Secura, Singapore)

1980 (8 Aug). *Ships. T* **9** *and similar horiz designs. Multicoloured. W* w **14** (*sideways**). *P* 13×13½.

42 4 c. Type **9** 10 10
a. Opt omitted .. .. 28·00
c. No stop after "ST" 75
w. Wmk Crown to right of CA 10
43 10 c. H.M.S. *Boreas*, 1787 .. .. .. 10 10
a. Opt omitted .. .. 55·00
c. No stop after "ST" 75
w. Wmk Crown to right of CA 10
44 30 c. H.M.S. *Druid*, 1827 .. .. .. 15 10
a. Opt omitted .. .. 55·00
c. No stop after "ST" .. .. .. 1·00
w. Wmk Crown to right of CA 25
45 55 c. H.M.S. *Winchester*, 1831 .. .. 20 15
a. Opt inverted .. .. 75·00
b. Opt omitted .. .. 60·00
c. No stop after "ST" .. .. .. 1·25
w. Wmk Crown to right of CA 50

46 $1.50, Harrison Line *Philosopher*, 1857 .. 40 30
a. Opt omitted .. .. 60·00
c. No stop after "ST" .. .. 1·50
w. Wmk Crown to right of CA 80
47 $2 Harrison Line *Contractor*, 1930 .. 50 40
a. Opt double .. .. 60·00
b. Opt omitted £100
c. No stop after "ST" .. .. 1·50
w. Wmk Crown to right of CA .. .. 1·00
42/7 .. .. *Set of* 6 1·25 90

Nos. 42/7 are overprinted "ST. KITTS" and have the previous combined inscription obliterated.

*The normal sideways watermark shows Crown to left of CA, *as seen from the back of the stamp.*

The "no stop" variety occurs on R. 3/4 of the lower pane.

(Des and litho Format)

1980 (4 Sept). *80th Birthday of Queen Elizabeth the Queen Mother.* W w **14**. *P* 13½.
48 **10** $2 multicoloured 25 60

No. 48 was printed in sheets containing two *se-tenant* stamp-size labels.

11 The Three Wise Men

(Des Walsall. Litho Questa)

1980 (10 Nov). *Christmas. T* **11** *and similar horiz designs. Multicoloured.* W w **14** (*sideways*). *P* 14½ × 14.
49 5 c. Type **11** 10 10
50 15 c. The Shepherds 10 10
51 30 c. Bethlehem 10 10
52 $4 Nativity scene 50 60
49/52 .. .. *Set of* 4 55 65

12 Purple-throated Carib

13 Bananaquit

(Des Jennifer Toombs. Litho Questa)

1981 (5 Feb)–**82**. *Birds. Vert designs as T* **12** (*1 to 10 c.*) *or horiz as T* **13** (*15 c. to $10*). *Multicoloured.* W w **14** (*sideways on 1 to 10 c.*). *P* 13½ × 14 (*1 to 10 c.*) *or* 14 (*15 c. to $10*).
A. *Without imprint date*
B. *With imprint date at foot of design*

		A		B	
53	1 c. Magnificent Frigate Bird ..	15	20	45	35
54	4 c. Wied's Crested Flycatcher	25	20	45	30
55	5 c. Type **12**	25	20	55	30
56	6 c. Burrowing Owl ..	35	30	65	40
57	8 c. Caribbean Martin	30	30	70	30
58	10 c. Yellow-crowned Night Heron	25	20	70	30
59	15 c. Type **13**	25	20	75	30
60	20 c. Scaly-breasted Thrasher ..	30	20	80	30
61	25 c. Grey Kingbird ..	30	20	80	30
62	30 c. Green-throated Carib ..	30	20	80	35
63	40 c. Turnstone	35	30	90	40
64	45 c. Black-faced Grassquit ..	35	30	1·00	45
65	50 c. Cattle Egret ..	40	30	1·10	50
66	55 c. Brown Pelican ..	40	30	1·25	50
67	$1 Lesser Antillean Bullfinch	60	60	2·00	80
68	$2.50, Zenaida Dove	1·25	2·25	3·25	3·00
69	$5 American Kestrel	2·25	3·50	5·00	5·50
70	$10 Antillean Crested Hummingbird	4·50	6·00	8·00	9·00
53/70	.. .. *Set of* 18	11·50	14·00	26·00	21·00

Dates of issue: Without imprint—5.2.81, 5 c. and 10 c. to $10; 30.5.81, 1, 4, 6, 8 c. With imprint—8.6.82, 1 c. to $10.

Imprint dates: "1982", Nos. 53B/70B; "1983", Nos. 59B/64B, 67B/8B.

14 Battalion Company Sergeant, 3rd Regt of Foot ("The Buffs"), *circa* 1801

15 Miriam Pickard (first Guide Commissioner)

(Des G. Vasarhelyi. Litho Format)

1981 (5 Mar). *Military Uniforms* (*1st series*). *T* **14** *and similar vert designs. Multicoloured.* W w **14**. *P* 14½.
71 5 c. Type **14** 10 10
72 30 c. Battalion Company Officer, 45th Regt of Foot, 1796–97 .. .. 15 10
73 55 c. Battalion Company Officer, 9th Regt of Foot, 1790 .. .. 15 10
74 $2.50, Grenadier, 38th Regt of Foot, 1751 .. 45 35
71/4 .. .. *Set of* 4 70 45

See also Nos. 110/13 and 220/6.

(Des D. Shults. Litho Questa)

1981 (23 June–14 Dec). *Royal Wedding. Horiz designs as T* **26/27** *of Kiribati. Multicoloured.* (*a*) W w **14**. *P* 14.
75 55 c. *Saudadoes* 10 10
aw. Wmk inverted .. .. 18·00
b. Sheetlet. No. 75×6 and No. 76 .. 1·10
bw. Wmk inverted £130
76 55 c. Prince Charles and Lady Diana Spencer 40 40
aw. Wmk inverted .. .. 65·00
77 $2.50, *Royal George* 25 30
aw. Wmk inverted .. .. 18·00
b. Sheetlet No. 77×6 and No. 78 .. 2·00
bw. Wmk inverted £130
78 $2.50, As No. 76 .. .. 70 70
aw. Wmk inverted .. .. 65·00
79 $4 *Britannia* 35 50
a. Sheetlet. No. 79×6 and No. 80 .. 2·50
80 $4 As No. 76 .. .. 75 1·00
75/80 .. .. *Set of* 6 2·25 2·75
MS81 120×109 mm. $5 As No. 76. Wmk sideways. P 12 (14 Dec) .. .. 1·00 1·00

(*b*) *Booklet stamps. No wmk. P* 12 (19 Nov)
82 55 c. As No. 76 .. .. 15 30
a. Booklet pane. No. 82×4 with margins all round 55
83 $2.50, As No. 78 .. .. 65 1·25
a. Booklet pane. No. 83×2 with margins all round .. .. 1·25

Nos. 75/80 were printed in sheetlets of seven stamps of the same face value, each containing six of the "Royal Yacht" design and one of the larger design showing Prince Charles and Lady Diana.

Nos. 82/3 come from $9.40 stamp booklets.

(Des Jennifer Toombs. Litho Walsall)

1981 (21 Sept). *50th Anniv of St. Kitts Girl Guide Movement. T* **15** *and similar vert designs. Multicoloured.* W w **14**. *P* 14.
84 5 c. Type **15** 10 10
85 30 c. Lady Baden-Powell's visit, 1964 .. 15 10
86 55 c. Visit of Princess Alice, 1960 .. .. 25 10
87 $2 Thinking-Day parade, 1980's 45 35
84/7 .. .. *Set of* 4 80 45

16 Stained-glass Windows

17 Admiral Samuel Hood

(Des Jennifer Toombs. Litho Format)

1981 (30 Nov). *Christmas. T* **16** *and similar vert designs showing stained-glass windows.* W w **14**. *P* 13 × 14.
88 5 c. multicoloured 10 10
89 30 c. multicoloured 10 10
90 55 c. multicoloured 15 10
w. Wmk inverted .. .. 18·00
91 $3 multicoloured 50 50
88/91 .. .. *Set of* 4 75 60

(Des D. Shults. Litho Format)

1982 (15 Mar). *Bicentenary of Brimstone Hill Siege. T* **17** *and similar horiz designs.* W w **14** (*sideways*). *P* 14.
92 15 c. multicoloured 10 10
93 55 c. multicoloured 20 10
MS94 96 × 71 mm. $5 black, red-orange & yell-brn 1·10 1·10

Designs:—55 c. Marquis De Bouillé; $5 Battle scene.

18 Alexandra, Princess of Wales, 1863

ROYAL BABY

(19)

(Des D. Shults and J. Cooter. Litho Format)

1982 (22 June). *21st Birthday of Princess of Wales. T* **18** *and similar vert designs. Multicoloured.* W w **14**. *P* 13½ × 14.
95 15 c. Type **18** 10 10
w. Wmk inverted .. .. 11·00
96 55 c. Coat of arms of Alexandra of Denmark 15 15
97 $6 Diana, Princess of Wales 55 80
w. Wmk inverted .. .. 8·00
95/7 .. .. *Set of* 3 70 85

1982 (12 July). *Birth of Prince William of Wales. Nos. 95/7 optd with T* **19**
98 15 c. Type **18** 10 10
a. Opt inverted .. .. 9·00
w. Wmk inverted .. .. 25·00
99 55 c. Coat of arms of Alexandra of Denmark 15 15
100 $6 Diana, Princess of Wales 55 80
w. Wmk inverted .. .. 11·00
98/100 .. .. *Set of* 3 70 85

20 Naturalist Badge

21 Santa with Christmas Tree and Gifts

(Des Philatelists (1980) Ltd. Litho Questa)

1982 (18 Aug). *75th Anniv of Boy Scout Movement. T* **20** *and similar vert designs. Multicoloured.* W w **14**. *P* 14 × 13½.
101 5 c. Type **20** 10 10
102 55 c. Rescuer badge 30 15
103 $2 First Aid badge 80 80
101/3 .. .. *Set of* 3 1·10 90

(Des Marcel Frazer (5 c.), Sinclair Herbert (55 c.), Marijka Grey ($1.10), Gary Bowrin ($3). Litho Format)

1982 (20 Oct). *Christmas. Children's Paintings. T* **21** *and similar horiz designs. Multicoloured.* W w **14** (*sideways*). *P* 14 × 13½.
104 5 c. Type **21** 10 10
105 55 c. The Inn 15 10
106 $1.10, Three Kings 20 15
107 $3 Annunciation 40 40
104/7 .. .. *Set of* 4 65 60

22 Cruise Ship *Stella Oceanis* at Basseterre

23 Sir William Smith (founder)

(Des G. Drummond. Litho Format)

1983 (14 Mar). *Commonwealth Day. T* **22** *and similar horiz design. Multicoloured.* W w **14** (*sideways*). *P* 14.
108 55 c. Type **22** 15 10
109 $2 *Queen Elizabeth 2* at Basseterre .. 35 40

(Des G. Vasarhelyi. Litho Format)

1983 (25 May). *Military Uniforms* (*2nd series*). *Vert designs as T* **14**. *Multicoloured.* W w **14**. *P* 14½.
110 15 c. Light Company Private, 15th Regt of Foot, *circa* 1814 .. .. 20 10
111 30 c. Battalion Company Officer, 15th Regt of Foot, *circa* 1780 .. .. 30 15
112 55 c. Light Company Officer, 5th Regt of Foot, *circa* 1822 .. .. 40 20
113 $2.50, Battalion Company Officer, 11th Regt of Foot, *circa* 1804 .. .. 1·10 1·60
110/13 .. .. *Set of* 4 1·75 1·75

(Des J. Cooter. Litho Format)

1983 (27 July). *Centenary of the Boys' Brigade. T* **23** *and similar vert designs. Multicoloured.* W w **14**. *P* 13½.
114 10 c. Type **23** 25 10
115 45 c. B.B. members on steps of Sandy Point Methodist Church 40 20
116 50 c. Brigade drummers 45 25
117 $3 Boys' Brigade badge .. .. .. 1·00 2·75
114/17 .. .. *Set of* 4 1·90 3·00

(24) (24*a*) **25** Montgolfier Balloon, 1783

1983 (19 Sept). *Nos.* 55, 59/63 *and* 66/70 *optd as T* **24** (*horiz* 20 *mm long on Nos.* 119/28)
A. No imprint date
B. With imprint date

		A		B	
118	5 c. Type **12**	15	10	15	10
	a. Opt inverted	†		32·00	—
	b. Pair one without opt . .	†		80·00	—
	c. Opt with T **24*a*** (local opt)	7·00	9·00	1·50	2·00
	ca. Opt inverted (reading upwards)	30·00	—	7·00	—
119	15 c. Type **13**	1·00	1·00	30	10
	a. Opt double	†		7·00	—
120	20 c. Scaly-breasted Thrasher	†		35	10
121	25 c. Grey Kingbird	†		40	10
	a. Opt inverted	†		12·00	—
122	30 c. Green-throated Carib . .	20·00	20·00	45	15
123	40 c. Turnstone	†		50	20
124	55 c. Brown Pelican	50	50	55	30
	a. Opt inverted	†		8·50	—
125	$1 Lesser Antillean Bullfinch	7·50	7·50	1·00	50
126	$2.50, Zenaida Dove . .	2·00	2·00	1·75	1·75
127	$5 American Kestrel . .	2·75	2·75	2·75	3·00
128	$10 Antillean Crested Hummingbird	6·00	6·00	5·00	5·50
118A/28A	. . . . *Set of* 8	35·00	35·00		
118B/28B	. . . . *Set of* 11			12·00	10·50

Imprint dates: "1982", Nos. 118B/19B, 121B/2B, 127B; "1983", Nos. 119B/28B.

(Des A. Theobald. Litho Format)

1983 (28 Sept). *Bicentenary of Manned Flight. T* **25** *and similar multicoloured designs. W* w **15** (*sideways on Nos.* 130/3). *P* 14.

129	10 c. Type **25**	10	10
130	45 c. Sikorsky *Russky Vityaz* biplane (*horiz*)	15	10
131	50 c. Lockheed L-1011 TriStar 500 *Flamingo* (*horiz*)	15	15
132	$2.50, Bell XS-1 (*horiz*)	50	90
129/32	. . . . . . *Set of* 4	75	1·10
MS133	108×145 mm. Nos. 129/32	75	1·25

26 Star over West Indian Town **27** Parrot in Tree

(Des Jennifer Toombs. Litho Format)

1983 (7 Nov). *Christmas. T* **26** *and similar horiz designs. Multicoloured. W* w **15** (*sideways**). *P* 14.

134	15 c. Type **26**	10	10
135	30 c. Shepherds watching Star	10	10
	w. Wmk POST OFFICE reading upwards	20·00	
136	55 c. Mary and Joseph	10	10
137	$2.50, The Nativity	30	40
134/7	. . . . . . *Set of* 4	45	55
MS138	130×130 mm. Nos. 134/7. Wmk upright	50	1·10
	w. Wmk inverted	75·00	

*The normal sideways watermark shows "POST OFFICE" reading downwards.

(Des Court House Studio. Litho Format)

1984 (30 Jan). *Batik Designs* (1*st series*). T **27** *and similar vert designs. W* w **15**. *P* 14 × 13½.

139	45 c. multicoloured	10	10
140	50 c. multicoloured	10	10
	w. Wmk inverted	20·00	
141	$1.50, new blue, bistre-yellow & brt mag	35	60
142	$3 multicoloured	55	1·50
	w. Wmk inverted	27·00	
139/42	. . . . . . *Set of* 4	1·00	2·00

Designs:—50 c. Man under coconut tree; $1.50, Women with fruit; $3 Butterflies.
See also Nos. 169/72.

COVER PRICES

Cover factors are quoted at the beginning of each country for most issues to 1945. An explanation of the system can be found on page x. The factors quoted do not, however, apply to philatelic covers.

28 Cushion Star

(Des G. Drummond. Litho J.W.)

1984 (4 July). *Marine Wildlife. T* **28** *and similar multicoloured designs. W* w **15** (*sideways* on* 5 *c. to* 75 *c.*). *P* 14.

143	5 c. Type **28**	30	30
	w. Wmk POST OFFICE reading downwards		
144	10 c. Rough File shell (*Lima scabra*) . .	35	30
	w. Wmk POST OFFICE reading downwards		
145	15 c. Red-lined Cleaning Shrimp	35	15
146	20 c. Bristleworm	35	15
147	25 c. Flamingo Tongue (*Cyphoma gibbosus*)	40	15
148	30 c. Christmas Tree Worm	40	20
149	40 c. Pink-tipped Anemone	55	25
150	50 c. Smallmouth Grunt	55	30
151	60 c. Glass-eyed Snapper	1·25	75
152	75 c. Reef Squirrelfish	90	70
153	$1 Sea Fans and Flamefish (*vert*) . .	1·00	60
154	$2.50, Reef Butterflyfish (*vert*)	2·25	3·50
155	$5 Black-barred Soldierfish (*vert*) . .	5·50	14·00
	w. Wmk inverted	15·00	
156	$10 Cocoa Damselfish (*vert*)	9·00	14·00
	w. Wmk inverted	15·00	
143/56	. . . . *Set of* 14	21·00	27·00

*The normal sideways watermark shows "POST OFFICE" reading upwards.
For 10 c., 60 c., $5 and $10 with watermark w **16** and imprint dates see Nos. 194/206.

29 Agriculture

(Des G. Vasarhelyi. Litho Questa)

1984 (15 Aug). 25*th Anniv of 4-H Organisation. T* **29** *and similar horiz designs. Multicoloured. W* w **15** (*sideways*). *P*. 14.

157	30 c. Type **29**	30	10
158	55 c. Animal husbandry	40	15
159	$1.10, The 4-H Pledge	70	60
160	$3 On parade	1·25	1·25
157/60	. . . . . . *Set of* 4	2·40	1·90

IMPERFORATES. Issues between Nos. 161 and 184 exist imperforate. Such items are not listed as there is no evidence that they fulfil the criteria outlined on page xi of this catalogue.

30 Construction of Royal St. Kitts Hotel

(Des K. Tatem (15 c.), Tessa Wattley (30 c.), Myrna Elcock and L. Freeman ($1.10), A. Williams ($3), adapted Jennifer Toombs. Litho Format)

1984 (18 Sept). *First Anniv of Independence of St. Kitts-Nevis. T* **30** *and similar multicoloured designs. W* w **15** (*sideways on* 15, 30 *c.*). *P* 14.

161	15 c. Type **30**	15	10
162	30 c. Independence celebrations	20	15
163	$1.10, National Anthem and aerial view (*vert*)	40	60
164	$3 "Dawn of a New Day" (*vert*)	1·00	1·40
161/4	. . . . . . *Set of* 4	1·60	2·00

31 Opening Presents

(Des Jennifer Toombs. Litho Questa)

1984 (1 Nov). *Christmas. T* **31** *and similar horiz designs. Multicoloured. W* w **15** (*sideways*). *P* 14.

165	15 c. Type **31**	15	10
166	60 c. Singing carols	45	35
167	$1 Nativity play	75	60
168	$2 Leaving church on Christmas Day . .	1·40	1·10
165/8	. . . . . . *Set of* 4	2·50	1·90

(Des Court House Studio. Litho Format)

1985 (6 Feb). *Batik Designs* (2*nd series*). *Horiz designs as T* **27**. *W* w **15** (*sideways*). *P* 13½ × 14.

169	15 c. black, bright green and light green . .	15	10
170	40 c. black, bright greenish blue and bright new blue	30	15
171	60 c. black, orange-vermilion and vermilion . .	45	25
172	$3 black, lake-brown and orange-brown . .	1·75	2·25
169/72	. . . . . . *Set of* 4	2·40	2·50

Designs:—15 c. Country bus; 40 c. Donkey cart; 60 c. Rum shop and man on bicycle; $3 *Polynesia* (cruise schooner).

32 Container Ship *Tropic Jade* **33** James Derrick Cardin (leading Freemason)

(Des J. Cooter. Litho Format)

1985 (27 Mar). *Ships. T* **32** *and similar horiz designs. Multicoloured. W* w **15** (*sideways*). *P* 13½×14.

173	40 c. Type **32**	1·00	30
174	$1.20, *Atlantic Clipper* (schooner) . .	2·00	1·50
175	$2 *Mandalay* (schooner)	2·25	2·50
176	$2 *Cunard Countess* (liner)	2·25	2·50
173/6	. . . . . . *Set of* 4	6·75	6·25

(Des G. Vasarhelyi. Litho Format)

1985 (9 Nov). 150*th Anniv of Mount Olive S.C. Masonic Lodge. T* **33** *and similar multicoloured designs. W* w **15** (*sideways on* 15, 75 *c., and* $3). *P* 15.

177	15 c. Type **33**	40	20
178	75 c. Banner of Mount Olive Lodge	75	1·10
179	$1.20, Masonic symbols (*horiz*)	1·25	2·50
180	$3 Lodge Charter (1835)	1·75	4·00
177/80	. . . . . . *Set of* 4	3·75	7·00

34 Map of St. Kitts **35** Queen Elizabeth and Prince Philip on St. Kitts

(Des. J. Cooter. Litho Format)

1985 (27 Nov). *Christmas.* 400*th Anniv of Sir Francis Drake's Visit. T* **34** *and similar vert designs. Multicoloured. P* 15.

181	10 c. Type **34**	15	15
182	40 c. *Golden Hind*	40	35
183	60 c. Sir Francis Drake	40	50
184	$3 Drake's heraldic shield	75	2·25
181/4	. . . . . . *Set of* 4	1·50	3·00

(Des D. Miller. Litho B.D.T.)

1986 (9 July). 60*th Birthday of Queen Elizabeth II. T* **35** *and similar vert designs. Multicoloured. P* 13½.

185	10 c. Type **35**	15	10
186	20 c. Queen Elizabeth on St. Kitts	25	15
187	40 c. At Trooping the Colour	50	30
188	$3 In Sweden	2·00	3·00
185/8	. . . . . . *Set of* 4	2·50	3·00

(Des D. Miller. Litho Walsall)

1986 (23 July). *Royal Wedding. Square designs as T* **231*a*** *of Jamaica. Multicoloured. W* w **16**. *P* 14½×14.

189	15 c. Prince Andrew and Miss Sarah Ferguson	15	10
190	$2.50, Prince Andrew	1·25	2·00

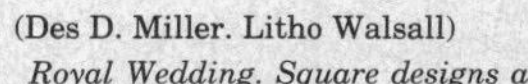

36 Family on Smallholding (37)

(Des K. Tatem (15 c.), A. Williams ($1.20), adapted G. Vasarhelyi. Litho Questa)

1986 (18 Sept). *Agriculture Exhibition. T* **36** *and similar horiz design. Multicoloured. W* w **16** (*sideways*). *P* 13½×14.

191	15 c. Type **36**	20	10
192	$1.20, Hands holding people, computers and crops	1·25	1·60

(Litho Questa)

1986 (5 Nov)–88. *As Nos.* 144, 151 *and* 155/6 *but W* w **16** (*sideways on* 10, 60 *c.*). *With imprint date. P* 14.

194	10 c. Rough File Shell	1·25	85
201	60 c. Glass-eyed Snapper (17.8.88)	2·50	1·60
205	$5 Black-barred Soldierfish (*vert*) (17.8.88)	7·50	10·00
206	$10 Cocoa Damselfish (*vert*) (17.8.88)	11·00	15·00
194/206	*Set of* 4	20·00	25·00

Imprint dates: "1986", No. 194; "1988", Nos. 194, 201, 205/6.

1986 (12 Nov). 40*th Anniv of United Nations Week. Nos.* 185/8 *optd with T* **37** *in gold.*

207	10 c. Type **35**	20	15
208	20 c. Queen Elizabeth on St. Kitts	30	20
209	40 c. At Trooping the Colour	40	30
210	$3 In Sweden	1·75	3·25
	a. Opt triple	75·00	
207/10	*Set of* 4	2·40	3·50

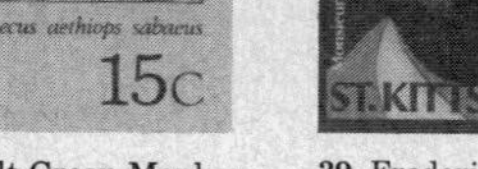

38 Adult Green Monkey with Young

39 Frederic Bartholdi (sculptor)

(Des Doreen McGuinness. Litho Walsall)

1986 (1 Dec). *Green Monkeys on St. Kitts. T* **38** *and similar vert designs. Multicoloured. W* w **16**. *P* 14×13½.

211	15 c. Type **38**	1·50	30
212	20 c. Adult on ground	1·75	30
213	60 c. Young monkey in tree	4·00	1·75
214	$1 Adult grooming young monkey	5·00	4·00
211/14	*Set of* 4	11·00	5·75

(Des D. Miller. Litho Format)

1986 (17 Dec). *Centenary of Statue of Liberty. T* **39** *and similar multicoloured designs. W* w **16** (*sideways on* 60 *c.*, $1.50). *P* 14.

215	40 c. Type **39**	40	30
216	60 c. Torch (1876) and head (1878) on exhibition (*horiz*)	65	60
217	$1.50, *Isere* (French warship) carrying Statue (*horiz*)	1·25	1·75
218	$3 Statue of Liberty, Paris, 1884	2·00	2·75
215/18	*Set of* 4	3·75	4·75
MS219	70×85 mm. $3.50, Head of Statue of Liberty	2·25	3·25

40 Officer, 9th Regt (East Norfolk), 1792

41 Sugar Cane Warehouse

(Des C. Collins. Litho Format)

1987 (25 Feb). *Military Uniforms* (3*rd series*). *T* **40** *and similar vert designs. Multicoloured. W* w **16**. *P* 14½.

220	15 c. Type **40**	40	30
221	15 c. Officer, Regt de Neustrie, 1779	40	30
222	40 c. Sergeant, 3rd Regt ("The Buffs"), 1801	65	45
223	40 c. Officer, French Artillery, 1812	65	45
224	$2 Light Company Private, 5th Regt, 1778	1·75	3·00
225	$2 Grenadier of the Line, 1796	1·75	3·00
220/5	*Set of* 6	5·00	6·75
MS226	121×145 mm. Nos. 220/5	6·75	8·00

The two designs for each value were printed in sheets of 50 containing two panes 5×5 with the British uniform depicted on the left-hand pane and the French on the right.

(Des G. Vasarhelyi. Litho Format)

1987 (15 Apr). *Sugar Cane Industry. T* **41** *and similar vert designs. Multicoloured (colour of panel behind* "ST. KITTS" *given). W* w **16**. *P* 14.

227	15 c. greenish yellow (Type **41**)	20	30
	a. Horiz strip of 5. Nos. 227/31	90	
228	15 c. cinnamon	20	30
229	15 c. lilac	20	30
230	15 c. azure	20	30
231	15 c. pale greenish blue	20	30
232	75 c. bright green	60	85
	a. Horiz strip of 5. Nos. 232/6	2·75	
233	75 c. lilac	60	85
234	75 c. dull green	60	85
235	75 c. orange-yellow	60	85
236	75 c. greenish blue	60	85
227/36	*Set of* 10	3·50	5·25

Designs:—Nos. 227/31, Sugar cane factory; Nos. 232/6, Loading sugar train.

Nos. 227/31 and 232/6 were each printed together, *se-tenant*, in horizontal strips of five throughout the sheets, each strip forming a composite design.

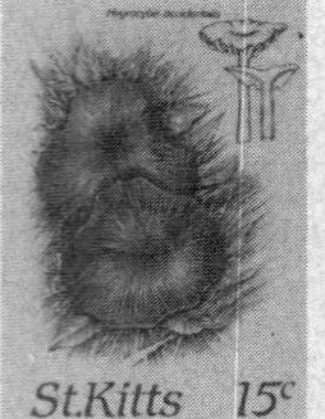

42 B.W.I.A. L-1011 TriStar 500

43 *Hygrocybe occidentalis*

(Des T. Hadler. Litho Format)

1987 (24 June). *Aircraft visiting St. Kitts. T* **42** *and similar horiz designs. Multicoloured. W* w **14** (*sideways*). *P* 14.

237	40 c. Type **42**	75	30
238	60 c. L.I.A.T. Hawker Siddeley Super 748	95	60
239	$1.20, W.I.A. De Havilland D.H.C.6 Twin Otter 300	1·50	2·25
240	$3 American Eagle Aerospatiale/Aeritalia ATR 42	2·75	4·00
237/40	*Set of* 4	5·50	6·50

(Des I. Loe. Litho Questa)

1987 (26 Aug). *Fungi. T* **43** *and similar vert designs. Multicoloured. W* w **16**. *P* 14.

241	15 c. Type **43**	80	20
242	40 c. *Marasmius haematocephalus*	1·25	40
243	$1.20, *Psilocybe cubensis*	2·75	2·75
	w. Wmk inverted	12·00	
244	$2 *Hygrocybe acutoconica*	3·50	3·50
245	$3 *Boletellus cubensis*	4·00	4·50
241/5	*Set of* 5	11·00	10·00

44 Carnival Clown

45 Ixora

(Des Rose Cameron-Smith. Litho Format)

1987 (28 Oct). *Christmas. T* **44** *and similar square designs showing different clowns. Multicoloured. W* w **16** (*sideways*). *P* 14½.

246	15 c. multicoloured	25	15
247	40 c. multicoloured	55	30
248	$1 multicoloured	1·25	1·25
249	$3 multicoloured	2·50	3·50
246/9	*Set of* 4	4·00	4·75

See also Nos. 266/9.

(Des Josephine Martin. Litho Questa)

1988 (20 Jan). *Flowers. T* **45** *and similar vert designs. Multicoloured. W* w **16**. *P* 14½×14.

250	15 c. Type **45**	30	15
251	40 c. Shrimp Plant	55	30
252	$1 Poinsettia	1·00	1·25
253	$3 Honolulu Rose	2·50	3·50
250/3	*Set of* 4	4·00	4·75

46 Fort Thomas Hotel

47 Ball, Wicket and Leeward Islands Cricket Association Emblem

(Des L. Curtis. Litho Walsall)

1988 (20 Apr). *Tourism* (1*st series*). *Hotels. T* **46** *and similar horiz designs. Multicoloured. W* w **14** (*sideways*). *P* 14 × 14½.

254	60 c. Type **46**	60	60
255	60 c. Fairview Inn	60	60
256	60 c. Frigate Bay Beach Hotel	60	60
257	60 c. Ocean Terrace Inn	60	60
258	$3 The Golden Lemon	2·00	2·50
259	$3 Royal St. Kitts Casino and Jack Tar Village	2·00	2·50
260	$3 Rawlins Plantation Hotel and Restaurant	2·00	2·50
254/60	*Set of* 7	7·50	9·00

See also Nos. 270/5.

(Des Joan Thompson. Litho Walsall)

1988 (13 July). 75*th Anniv of Leeward Islands Cricket Tournament. T* **47** *and similar vert design. Multicoloured. W* w **14**. *P* 13 × 13½.

261	40 c. Type **47**	1·50	30
262	$3 Cricket match at Warner Park	3·75	4·50

48 Flag of St. Kitts-Nevis

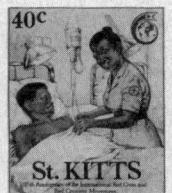

49 Red Cross Nurse with Hospital Patient

(Des L. Curtis. Litho Questa)

1988 (19 Sept). 5*th Anniv of Independence. T* **48** *and similar vert designs. Multicoloured. W* w **16**. *P* 14½ × 14.

263	15 c. Type **48**	25	10
264	60 c. Arms of St. Kitts	75	60
MS265	61 × 53 mm. $5 Princess Margaret presenting Constitutional Instrument to Prime Minister Kennedy Simmonds, 1983. W w **14**	3·00	3·50

(Des Rose Cameron-Smith. Litho Format)

1988 (2 Nov). *Christmas. Square designs as T* **44** *showing carnival masqueraders. W* w **14** (*sideways*). *P* 14½.

266	15 c. multicoloured	10	10
267	40 c. multicoloured	20	25
268	80 c. multicoloured	40	45
269	$3 multicoloured	1·25	2·00
266/9	*Set of* 4	1·75	2·50

(Des L. Curtis. Litho Format)

1989 (25 Jan). *Tourism* (2*nd series*). *Colonial Architecture. Horiz designs as T* **46**. *Multicoloured. W* w **16** (*sideways*). *P* 14.

270	20 c. Georgian house	20	15
271	20 c. Colonial-style house	20	15
272	$1 Romney Manor	70	80
273	$1 Lavington Great House	70	80
274	$2 Government House	1·00	1·60
275	$2 Treasury Building	1·00	1·60
270/5	*Set of* 6	3·50	4·50

For a redrawn version of No. 275 in a miniature sheet, see No. **MS**400.

(Des C. Collins. Litho Format)

1989 (8 May). 125*th Anniv of International Red Cross. T* **49** *and similar vert designs. W* w **16**. *P* 14×14½.

276	40 c. multicoloured	30	30
277	$1 multicoloured	65	75
278	$3 orange-vermilion and black	1·75	2·50
276/8	*Set of* 3	2·40	3·25

Designs:—$1 Loading patient into ambulance; $3 125th anniversary logo.

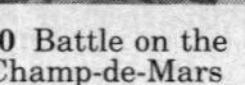

50 Battle on the Champ-de-Mars

51 Outline Map of St. Kitts

(Des D. Miller. Litho B.D.T.)

1989 (7 July). "*Philexfrance* 89" *International Stamp Exhibition, Paris. Sheet* 115×99 *mm. W* w **16**. *P* 14.

MS279	**50** $5 multicoloured	3·25	3·75

(Des A. Theobald ($5), D. Miller (others). Litho Questa)

1989 (20 July). 20*th Anniv of First Manned Landing on Moon. Multicoloured designs as T* **51a** *of Kiribati. W* w **16** (*sideways on* 20 *c.*, $1). *P* 14×13½ (10 *c.*, $2) *or* 14 (*others*).

280	10 c. Lunar rover on Moon	10	10
281	20 c. Crew of "Apollo 13" (30×30 *mm*)	10	10
282	$1 "Apollo 13" emblem (30×30 *mm*)	45	60
283	$2 "Apollo 13" splashdown, South Pacific	95	1·25
280/3	*Set of* 4	1·40	1·75
MS284	100×83 mm. $5 Aldrin leaving "Apollo 11" lunar module. Wmk inverted. P 14×13½	3·50	4·00

(Des D. Miller. Litho B.D.T.)

1989 (25 Oct). *W* w **16**. *P* 15×14.

285	**51** 10 c. deep mauve and black	10	10
286	15 c. bright carmine and black	15	10
287	20 c. yellow-orange and black	15	10
288	40 c. yellow and black	25	20
289	60 c. bright blue and black	40	30
290	$1 yellow-green and black	70	80
285/90	*Set of* 6	1·50	1·25

52 *Santa Mariagallante* passing St. Kitts, 1493

(Des L. Curtis. Litho Questa)

1989 (8 Nov). *500th Anniv of Discovery of America* (1992) *by Columbus* (*1st issue*). *T* **52** *and similar horiz designs. Multicoloured.* W w **16** (*sideways*). *P* 14.

291 15 c. Type **52** 85 20
292 80 c. Arms of Columbus and map of fourth voyage, 1502-04 .. .. .. 2·00 1·50
293 $1 Navigation instruments, *c.* 1500 .. 2·25 1·60
294 $5 Columbus and map of second voyage, 1493-96 .. .. 6·00 8·00
291/4 .. .. *Set of* 4 10·00 10·00

See also Nos. 359/60.

53 Poinciana Tree **54** *Junonia evarete*

(Des G. Vasarhelyi. Litho Walsall)

1989 (17 Nov). *"World Stamp Expo '89" International Stamp Exhibition, Washington. T* **53** *and similar horiz designs. Multicoloured.* W w **14** (*sideways*). *P* 14.

295 15 c. Type **53** 30 10
296 40 c. Fort George Citadel, Brimstone Hill .. 65 30
297 $1 Private, Light Company, 5th Foot, 1778 .. .. 1·40 1·25
298 $3 St. George's Anglican Church .. 3·00 4·50
295/8 .. .. *Set of* 4 4·75 5·50

(Des I. Loe. Litho B.D.T.)

1990 (6 June). *Butterflies. T* **54** *and similar horiz designs. Multicoloured.* W w **14** (*sideways*). *P* 13½×14.

299 15 c. Type **54** 60 20
300 40 c. *Anartia jatrophae* 90 30
301 60 c. *Heliconius charitonia* .. .. .. 1·10 70
302 $3 *Biblis hyperia* .. .. .. 3·00 4·00
299/302 .. .. *Set of* 4 5·00 4·75

(55) **56** Brimstone Hill

1990 (6 June). *"EXPO 90" International Garden and Greenery Exhibition, Osaka. Nos.* 299/302 *optd with T* **55**.

303 15 c. Type **54** 60 20
304 40 c. *Anartia jatrophae* 90 30
305 60 c. *Heliconius charitonia* .. .. .. 1·10 70
306 $3 *Biblis hyperia* .. .. .. 3·00 4·00
303/6 .. .. *Set of* 4 5·00 4·75

(Des D. Miller. Litho Questa)

1990 (30 June). *300th Anniv of English Bombardment of Brimstone Hill. T* **56** *and similar horiz designs. Multicoloured.* W w **16** (*sideways*). *P* 14.

307 15 c. Type **56** 20 10
308 40 c. Restored Brimstone Hill fortifications 35 30
309 60 c. 17th-century English marine and Fort Charles under attack .. .. .. 50 1·00
 a. Horiz pair. Nos. 309/10 .. .. 2·75 3·75
310 $3 English sailors firing cannon .. .. 2·25 2·75
307/10 .. .. *Set of* 4 3·00 3·75

Nos. 307/9 were printed in complete sheets, each containing one value. No. 309 also exists *se-tenant*, as a horizontal pair, with No. 310. Each pair shows a composite design across the two stamps with no margin at the left of the 60 c. or at the right of the $3.

57 Supermarine Spitfire Mk Vb *St. Kitts Nevis I*, 71 Squadron

(Des A. Theobald. Litho B.D.T.)

1990 (15 Sept). *50th Anniv of Battle of Britain. Sheet* 103×76 *mm. containing T* **57** *and similar horiz design. Multicoloured.* W w **16** (*sideways*). *P* 14.

MS311 $3 Type **57**; $3 Supermarine Spitfire Mk Vb *St. Kitts Nevis II*, 345 Squadron .. .. 8·50 8·50

58 *Romney* (freighter)

(Des S. Williams. Litho B.D.T.)

1990 (10 Oct). *Ships. T* **58** *and similar horiz designs. Multicoloured.* W w **14** (*sideways*). *P* 14.

312 10 c. Type **58** 10 10
313 15 c. *Baralt* (freighter) 10 10
314 20 c. *Wear* (mail steamer) 10 10
315 25 c. *Sunmount* (freighter) 10 10
316 40 c. *Inanda* (cargo liner) 20 25
317 50 c. *Alcoa Partner* (freighter) 25 30
318 60 c. *Dominica* (freighter) 25 30
319 80 c. *C.G.M Provence* (container ship) .. 35 40
320 $1 *Director* (freighter) 45 50
321 $1.20, Barque 55 60
322 $2 *Chignecto* (packet steamer) 90 95
323 $3 *Berbice* (mail steamer) .. .. .. 1·40 1·50
324 $5 *Vamos* (freighter) .. .. .. 2·25 2·40
325 $10 *Federal Maple* (freighter) .. .. 4·50 4·75
312/25 .. .. *Set of* 14 11·50 12·00

For 10 c. watermarked w **16** (sideways) see No. 413.
For miniature sheet containing the $3 see No. **MS**472.

59 Single Fork Game

(Des G. Vasarhelyi. Litho Questa)

1990 (14 Nov). *Christmas. Traditional Games. T* **59** *and similar horiz designs. Multicoloured.* W w **16** (*sideways*). *P* 14.

326 10 c. Type **59** 15 10
327 15 c. Boulder breaking 15 10
328 40 c. Double fork 30 30
329 $3 The run up .. .. 1·75 2·25
326/9 .. .. *Set of* 4 2·10 2·50

60 White Periwinkle **61** Census Logo

(Des Annette Robinson. Litho Cartor)

1991 (8 May). *Flowers. T* **60** *and similar multicoloured designs.* W w **14** (*sideways on* 10, 40 *c.*). *P* 14×13½ (10, 40 *c.*) *or* 13½×14 (*others*).

330 10 c. Type **60** 35 15
331 40 c. Pink Oleander 65 30
332 60 c. Pink Periwinkle (*vert*) 95 70
333 $2 White Oleander (*vert*) .. .. 2·00 2·75
330/3 .. .. *Set of* 4 3·50 3·50

(Des G. Vasarhelyi, Litho B.D.T)

1991 (13 May). *National Census.* W w **16**. *P* 14.

334 **61** 15 c. multicoloured 25 15
335 $2.40, multicoloured .. .. .. 2·00 2·50

The $2.40 differs from Type **61** by showing "ST. KITTS" in a curved panel.

(Des D. Miller. Litho Questa)

1991 (17 June). *65th Birthday of Queen Elizabeth II and 70th Birthday of Prince Philip. Vert designs as T* **58** *of Kiribati.* W w **16** (*sideways*). *P* 14½×14.

336 $1.20, Prince Philip .. .. .. 75 1·00
 a. Horiz pair. Nos. 336/7 separated by label .. .. 1·75 2·10
337 $1.80, Queen holding bouquet of flowers 1·00 1·10

Nos. 336/7 were printed together in a similar sheet format to Nos. 366/7 of Kiribati.

62 Nassau Grouper

(Des G. Drummond. Litho Questa)

1991 (28 Aug). *Fishes. T* **62** *and similar horiz designs. Multicoloured.* W w **14** (*sideways*). *P* 14.

338 10 c. Type **62** 45 15
339 60 c. Hogfish .. .. 1·00 50
340 $1 Red Hind .. .. 1·75 1·50
341 $3 Porkfish .. .. 3·25 4·00
338/41 .. .. *Set of* 4 5·75 5·50

63 School of Continuing Studies, St. Kitts, and Chancellor Sir Shridath Ramphal

(Des G. Vasarhelyi. Litho Questa)

1991 (28 Sept). *40th Anniv of University of West Indies. T* **63** *and similar horiz designs. Multicoloured.* W w **16** (*sideways*). *P* 14.

342 15 c. Type **63** 30 15
343 50 c. Administration Building, Barbados .. 60 40
344 $1 Engineering Building, Trinidad and Tobago .. .. 1·10 1·00
345 $3 Mona Campus, Jamaica, and Sir Shridath Ramphal .. .. .. 2·75 3·75
342/5 .. .. *Set of* 4 4·25 4·75

64 Whipping The Bull

(Des Marijka Grey and G. Vasarhelyi. Litho Walsall)

1991 (6 Nov). *Christmas. "The Bull" (Carnival play). T* **64** *and similar horiz designs. Multicoloured.* W w **14** (*sideways*). *P* 14.

346 10 c. Type **64** 30 10
347 15 c. Death of The Bull 30 10
348 60 c. Cast of characters and musicians .. 75 60
349 $3 The Bull in procession .. .. 2·50 3·25
346/9 .. .. *Set of* 4 3·50 3·50

(Des D. Miller. Litho Questa ($3), Leigh-Mardon Ltd, Melbourne (others))

1992 (6 Feb). *40th Anniv of Queen Elizabeth II's Accession. Horiz designs as T* **113** *of Kenya. Multicoloured.* W w **14** (*sideways*) ($3) *or* w **16** (*sideways*) (*others*). *P* 14.

350 10 c. St. Kitts coastline 20 10
351 40 c. Warner Park Pavilion 35 25
352 60 c. Brimstone Hill 50 40
353 $1 Three portraits of Queen Elizabeth .. 75 85
354 $3 Queen Elizabeth II .. .. .. 1·90 2·50
350/4 .. .. *Set of* 5 3·25 3·75

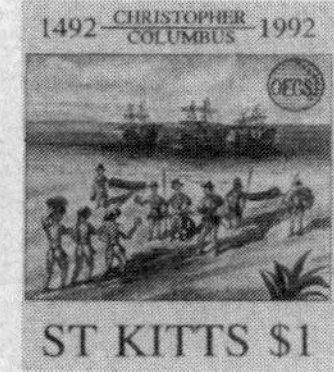

65 Map of St. Kitts–Nevis **66** Columbus meeting Amerindians

(Des L. Curtis. Litho Enschedé)

1992 (8 May). *50th Anniv of St. Kitts-Nevis Red Cross Society. T* **65** *and similar horiz designs. Multicoloured.* W w **14** (*sideways*). *P* 13½×14.

355 10 c. Type **65** 50 20
356 20 c. St. Kitts–Nevis flag 65 25
357 50 c. Red Cross House, St. Kitts 85 70
358 $2.40, Henri Dunant .. .. .. 2·50 3·25
355/8 .. .. *Set of* 4 4·00 4·00

(Adapted G. Vasarhelyi. Litho Cartor)

1992 (6 July). *Organization of East Caribbean States. 500th Anniv of Discovery of America by Columbus* (*2nd issue*). *T* **66** *and similar vert design. Multicoloured.* W w 14. *P* 13.

359 $1 Type **66** .. .. 1·25 1·00
360 $2 Ships approaching island .. .. 2·00 2·50

NEW INFORMATION

The editor is always interested to correspond with people who have new information that will improve or correct the Catalogue.

67 Fountain, Independence Square

68 Joseph and Mary travelling to Bethlehem

(Des D. Miller. Litho Enschedé)

1992 (19 Aug). *Local Monuments. T* **67** *and similar vert designs. Multicoloured.* W w **14**. *P* 12½×13.

361 25 c. Type **67** 25 20
362 50 c. Berkeley Memorial drinking fountain 35 35
363 80 c. Sir Thomas Warner's tomb 55 65
364 $2 War memorial . . . . 1·10 1·75
361/4 . . . . *Set of* 4 2·00 2·75

(Des L. Curtis. Litho Questa)

1992 (28 Oct). *Christmas. T* **68** *and similar vert designs. Multicoloured.* W w **16**. *P* 14½.

365 20 c. Type **68** 30 20
366 25 c. Shepherds and star 30 20
367 80 c. Wise Men with gifts 65 55
368 $3 Mary, Joseph and Holy Child . . 1·75 3·00
365/8 . . . . *Set of* 4 2·75 3·50

(Des A. Theobald. Litho Questa)

1993 (1 Apr). *75th Anniv of Royal Air Force. Aircraft. Horiz designs as T* **166** *of Montserrat. Multicoloured.* W w **14** (*sideways*). *P* 14.

369 25 c. Short Singapore III 45 15
370 50 c. Bristol Type 152 Beaufort Mk II . . 65 30
371 80 c. Westland Whirlwind Series 3 H.A.R.10 helicopter . . . . 1·25 1·00
372 $1.60, English Electric Canberra T.11 . . 1·75 3·00
369/72 . . . . *Set of* 4 3·50 4·00
MS373 110×78 mm. $2 Handley Page 0/400; $2 Fairey Long Range monoplane; $2 Vickers Wellesley; $2 Sepecat Jaguar G.R.1 . . . . 7·00 8·00

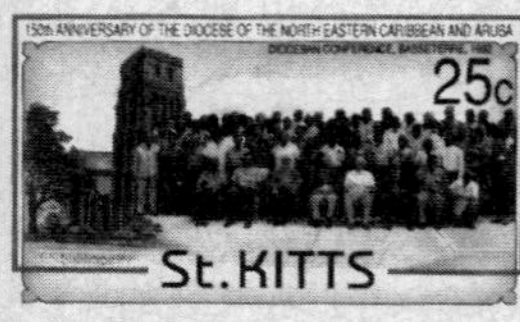

69 Members of Diocesan Conference, Basseterre, 1992

70 1953 Coronation 2 c. Stamp and Ampulla

(Des G. Vasarhelyi. Litho Walsall)

1993 (21 May). *150th Anniv of Anglican Diocese of North-eastern Caribbean and Aruba. T* **69** *and similar multicoloured designs.* W w **16** (*sideways on* 25 c., 80 c.). *P* 13½×14 (*horiz*) *or* 14×13½ (*vert*).

374 25 c. Type **69** 15 10
375 50 c. Cathedral of St. John the Divine (*vert*) 40 35
376 80 c. Coat of arms and motto 70 85
377 $2 The Right Revd. Daniel Davis (first bishop) (*vert*) . . . . 1·50 2·50
374/7 . . . . *Set of* 4 2·50 3·50

(Des D. Miller. Litho Walsall)

1993 (2 June). *40th Anniv of Coronation. T* **70** *and similar vert designs. Multicoloured.* W w **16**. *P* 14½×14.

378 10 c. Type **70** 30 15
379 25 c. 1977 Silver Jubilee $1.50 stamp and anointing spoon 45 15
380 80 c. 1977 Silver Jubilee 55 c. stamp and tassels . . . . 90 1·00
381 $2 1978 25th Anniv of Coronation stamps and sceptre . . . . 1·75 3·25
378/81 . . . . *Set of* 4 3·00 4·00

71 Flags of Girls Brigade and St. Kitts-Nevis

(Des G. Vasarhelyi. Litho Walsall)

1993 (1 July). *Centenary of Girls Brigade. T* **71** *and similar horiz design. Multicoloured.* W w **16** (*sideways*). *P* 13½×14.

382 80 c. Type **71** . . . . 1·00 85
383 $3 Girls Brigade badge and coat of arms 2·75 3·50

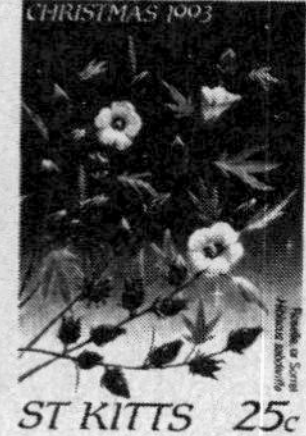

72 Aspects of St. Kitts on Flag

73 *Hibiscus sabdariffa*

(Des Ruth Vaughan (20 c.), S. Richards (80 c.), P. Maynard ($3), adapted D. Miller. Litho B.D.T.)

1993 (10 Sept). *10th Anniv of Independence. T* **72** *and similar horiz designs. Multicoloured.* W w **14** (*sideways*). *P* 14.

384 20 c. Type **72** 20 10
385 80 c. Coat of arms and Independence anniversary logo 80 80
386 $3 Coat of arms and map . . . . 2·50 3·25
384/6 . . . . *Set of* 3 3·25 3·75

(Des Jennifer Toombs. Litho Cartor)

1993 (16 Nov). *Christmas. Flowers. T* **73** *and similar vert designs. Multicoloured.* W w **14**. *P* 13½×14.

387 25 c. Type **73** 15 10
388 50 c. *Euphorbia pulcherrima* 45 45
389 $1.60, *Euphorbia leucocephala* . . . . 1·50 2·25
387/9 . . . . *Set of* 3 1·90 2·50

74 Mesosaurus

75 Sir Shridath Ramphal

(Des N. Shewring. Litho B.D.T.)

1994 (18 Feb). *Prehistoric Aquatic Reptiles. T* **74** *and similar vert designs. Multicoloured.* W w **16**. *P* 14.

390 $1.20, Type **74** . . . . 1·10 1·25
a. Horiz strip of 5. Nos. 390/4 . . . . 5·00
391 $1.20, Placodus . . . . 1·10 1·25
392 $1.20, Liopleurodon . . . . 1·10 1·25
393 $1.20, Hydrotherosaurus . . . . 1·10 1·25
394 $1.20, Caretta . . . . 1·10 1·25
390/4 . . . . *Set of* 5 5·00 5·50

Nos. 390/4 were printed together, *se-tenant*, in horizontal strips of 5 throughout the sheet with the background forming a composite design.

1994 (18 Feb). *"Hong Kong '94" International Stamp Exhibition. Nos. 390/4 optd as T* **272** *of Jamaica.*

395 $1.20, Type **74** . . . . 1·10 1·25
a. Horiz strip of 5. Nos. 395/9 . . . . 5·00
396 $1.20, Placodus . . . . 1·10 1·25
397 $1.20, Liopleurodon . . . . 1·10 1·25
398 $1.20, Hydrotherosaurus . . . . 1·10 1·25
399 $1.20, Caretta . . . . 1·10 1·25
395/9 . . . . *Set of* 5 5·00 5·50

(Des L. Curtis and G. Vasarhelyi. Litho B.D.T.)

1994 (21 Mar). *Centenary of Treasury Building. Sheet* 73×58 *mm. containing horiz design as No. 275, but with redrawn frame and inscriptions.* W w **14** (*sideways*). *P* 13½.

MS400 $10 multicoloured . . . . 7·50 8·50

(Des D. Miller. Litho Questa)

1994 (13 July). *First Recipients of Order of the Caribbean Community. T* **75** *and similar vert designs. Multicoloured.* W w **14**. *P* 14½×14.

401 10 c. Type **75** 10 15
a. Horiz strip of 5. Nos. 401, 402×2, 403/4 45
402 10 c. Star of Order 10 15
403 10 c. Derek Walcott 10 15
404 10 c. William Demas 10 15
405 $1 Type **75** . . . . 90 1·00
a. Horiz strip of 5. Nos. 405, 406×2, 407/8 4·00
406 $1 As No. 402 . . . . 90 1·00
407 $1 As No. 403 . . . . 90 1·00
408 $1 As No. 404 . . . . 90 1·00
401/8 . . . . *Set of* 8 3·75 4·25

Nos. 401/4 and 405/8 were printed together, *se-tenant*, in horizontal strips of 5 throughout the sheets with examples of Nos. 402 or 406 in the second and fourth positions in each strip.

76 Family singing Carols

(Des Jennifer Toombs. Litho B.D.T.)

1994 (31 Oct). *Christmas. International Year of the Family. T* **76** *and similar horiz designs. Multicoloured.* W w **14** (*sideways*). *P* 13½.

409 25 c. Type **76** 15 10
410 25 c. Family unwrapping Christmas presents 15 10
411 80 c. Preparing for Christmas carnival . . 60 60
412 $2.50, Nativity . . . . 1·90 2·75
409/12 . . . . *Set of* 4 2·50 3·25

1995 (13 Jan). *As No.* 312, *but* W w **16** (*sideways*). *P* 14.

413 10 c. Type **58** 10 10

77 Green Turtle swimming

(Des A. Robinson. Litho B.D.T.)

1995 (27 Feb). *Endangered Species. Green Turtle. T* **77** *and similar horiz designs. Multicoloured.* W w **14** (*sideways*). *P* 14.

427 10 c. Type **77** 30 40
a. Strip of 4. Nos. 427/30 . . . . 1·25
428 40 c. Turtle crawling up beach 35 50
429 50 c. Burying eggs 35 50
430 $1 Young heading for sea 45 60
427/30 . . . . *Set of* 4 1·25 1·75

In addition to separate sheets of 50 Nos. 427/30 were also available in small sheets of 16 containing four strips, *se-tenant* both vertically and horizontally.

78 St. Christopher 1d. Stamps of 1870

79 Telecommunication Links between Islands

(Des D. Miller. Litho Cartor)

1995 (10 Apr). *125th Anniv of St. Kitts Postage Stamps. T* **78** *and similar horiz designs, each including the St. Christopher 1870 1d.* W w **14** (*sideways*). *P* 13½.

431 25 c. Type **78** 15 15
432 80 c. St. Kitts–Nevis 1935 Silver Jubilee 1d. 45 50
433 $2.50, St. Kitts–Nevis 1946 Victory 1½d. 1·75 2·25
434 $3 St. Christopher Nevis Anguilla 1953 Coronation 2 c. . . . . 2·00 2·50
431/4 . . . . *Set of* 4 4·00 4·75

(Des R. Watton. Litho Cartor (Nos. 435/8) or Questa (Nos. **MS**439))

1995 (8 May). *50th Anniv of End of Second World War. Multicoloured designs as T* **75** *of Kiribati.* W w **14** (*sideways*). *P* 13½.

435 20 c. Caribbean Regiment patrol, North Africa 15 15
436 50 c. Grumman TBF Avengers (bombers) 35 35
437 $2 Supermarine Spitfire Mk Vb (fighter) 1·25 1·50
438 $8 U.S. Navy destroyer escort . . . . 5·00 6·00
435/8 . . . . *Set of* 4 6·00 7·25
MS439 75×85 mm. $3 Reverse of 1939–45 War Medal (*vert*). Wmk upright. P 14 . . . . 1·75 2·00

(Des D. Miller. Litho Enschedé)

1995 (27 Sept). *10th Anniv of SKANTEL (telecommunications company). T* **79** *and similar vert designs. Multicoloured.* W w **14**. *P* 13×14½.

440 10 c. Type **79** 20 10
441 25 c. Payphone and computer link . . 25 15
442 $2 Telecommunications tower and dish aerial . . . . 2·00 2·25
443 $3 Silhouette of dish aerial at sunset . . 2·25 2·50
440/3 . . . . *Set of* 4 4·25 4·50

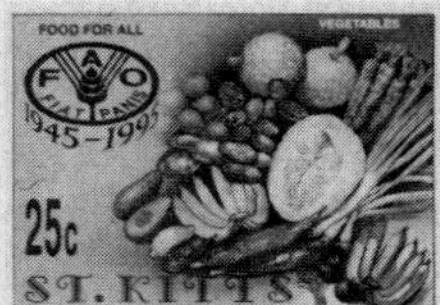

80 Water Treatment Works

81 F.A.O. Emblem and Vegetables

(Des D. Miller. Litho Cartor)

1995 (24 Oct). *50th Anniv of United Nations. T* **80** *and similar horiz designs. Multicoloured. W w* **14** *(sideways). P* 13½×13.

444	40 c. Type **80**	30	25
445	50 c. Beach	35	30
446	$1.60, Dust cart	1·10	1·40
447	$2.50, Forest	1·90	2·50
444/7	*Set of* 4	3·25	4·00

(Des G. Vasarhelyi. Litho Cartor)

1995 (13 Nov). *50th Anniv of Food and Agriculture Organization. T* **81** *and similar horiz designs. Multicoloured. W w* **14** *(sideways). P* 13½.

448	25 c. Type **81**	20	10
449	50 c. Glazed carrots and West Indian peas with rice	35	30
450	80 c. Tania and Cassava plants	50	60
451	$1.50, Waterfall, Green Hill Mountain	90	1·40
448/51	*Set of* 4	1·75	2·25

82 Flame Helmet

83 L.M.S. No. 45614 *Leeward Islands* Steam Locomotive in Green Livery

(Des G. Drummond. Litho Cartor)

1996 (10 Jan). *Sea Shells. T* **82** *and similar vert designs. Multicoloured. W w* **14**. *P* 13.

452	$1.50, Type **82**	95	1·00
	a. Horiz strip of 5. Nos. 452/6	4·25	
453	$1.50, Triton's Trumpet	95	1·00
454	$1.50, King Helmet	95	1·00
455	$1.50, True Tulip	95	1·00
456	$1.50, Queen Conch	95	1·00
452/6	*Set of* 5	4·25	4·50

Nos. 452/6 were printed together, *se-tenant*, in horizontal strips of 5 throughout the sheet.

(Des A. Theobald. Litho Enschedé)

1996 (1 May). *"CAPEX '96" International Stamp Exhibition, Toronto. T* **83** *and similar horiz design. Multicoloured. W w* **14** *(sideways). P* 13½×14.

457	10 c. Type **83**	40	30
MS458	110×80 mm. $10 L.M.S. No. 5614 *Leeward Islands* steam locomotive in red livery (48×31½ *mm*). P 14×14½	5·75	6·00

84 Athlete and National Flag

85 Volunteer Rifleman, 1896

(Des R. Watton. Litho Walsall)

1996 (30 June). *Centennial Olympic Games, Atlanta. T* **84** *and similar vert designs. Multicoloured. W w* **16**. *P* 14.

459	10 c. Type **84**	15	15
460	25 c. High jumper and U.S.A. flag	20	20
461	80 c. Athlete and Olympic flag	50	55
462	$3 Poster for 1896 Olympic Games, Athens	1·75	2·25
459/62	*Set of* 4	2·40	2·75
MS463	70×64 mm. $6 Olympic torch	3·25	3·50

(Des W. Cribbs. Litho Cot Printery Ltd, Barbados)

1996 (1 Nov). *Centenary of Defence Force. T* **85** *and similar vert designs. Multicoloured. W w* **14**. *P* 14.

464	10 c. Type **85**	15	15
465	50 c. Mounted infantryman, 1911	35	35
466	$2 Drummer, 1940–60	1·25	1·60
467	$2.50, Ceremonial uniform, 1996	1·40	1·75
464/7	*Set of* 4	2·75	3·50

86 "Holy Virgin and Child" (A. Colin)

87 Princess Parrotfish

(Des D. Miller. Litho Questa)

1996 (29 Nov). *Christmas. Religious Paintings. T* **86** *and similar vert designs. Multicoloured. W w* **14**. *P* 14½.

468	15 c. Type **86**	15	10
469	25 c. "Holy Family" (after Rubens)	20	10
470	50 c. "Madonna with the Goldfinch" (Krause after Raphael)	40	30
471	80 c. "Madonna on Throne with Angels" (17th-cent Spanish)	60	60
468/71	*Set of* 4	1·25	1·00

(Des D. Miller. Litho Questa)

1997 (3 Feb). *"HONG KONG '97" International Stamp Exhibition. Sheet* 130×90 *mm, containing No.* 323. *W w* **14** *(sideways). P* 14.

MS472	$3 *Berbice* (mail steamer)	1·60	2·00

(Des G. Vasarhelyi. Litho Cartor)

1997 (24 Apr). *Fishes. T* **87** *and similar horiz designs. Multicoloured. P* 13½.

473	$1 Type **87**	60	60
	a. Sheetlet. Nos. 473/84	6·50	
474	$1 Yellow-bellied Hamlet	60	60
475	$1 Coney	60	60
476	$1 Fin-spot Wrasse	60	60
477	$1 Doctor Fish	60	60
478	$1 Squirrelfish	60	60
479	$1 Queen Angelfish	60	60
480	$1 Spanish Hogfish	60	60
481	$1 Red Hind	60	60
482	$1 Red Grouper	60	60
483	$1 Yellow-tailed Snapper	60	60
484	$1 Mutton Hamlet	60	60
473/84	*Set of* 12	6·50	6·50

Nos. 473/84 were printed together, *se-tenant*, in sheetlets of 12.

(Des N. Shewring (No. **MS**491), D. Miller (others). Litho Questa (No. **MS**491), B.D.T. (others))

1997 (10 July). *Golden Wedding of Queen Elizabeth and Prince Philip. Multicoloured designs as T* **87** *of Kiribati. W w* **14**. *P* 13½.

485	10 c. Queen Elizabeth in evening dress	15	15
	a. Horiz pair. Nos. 485/6	30	30
486	10 c. Prince Philip and Duke of Kent at Trooping the Colour	15	15
487	25 c. Queen Elizabeth in phaeton at Trooping the Colour	25	25
	a. Horiz pair. Nos. 487/8	50	50
488	25 c. Prince Philip in naval uniform	25	25
489	$3 Queen Elizabeth and Prince Philip	1·50	1·75
	a. Horiz pair. Nos. 489/90	3·00	3·50
490	$3 Peter Phillips on horseback	1·50	1·75
485/90	*Set of* 6	3·50	3·75
MS491	110×70 mm. $6 Queen Elizabeth and Prince Philip in landau (*horiz*). Wmk sideways. P 14×14½	3·00	3·25

Nos. 485/6, 487/8 and 489/90 were each printed together, *se-tenant*, in horizontal pairs throughout the sheets with the backgrounds forming composite designs.

88 C. A. Paul Southwell (first Chief Minister)

89 Wesley Methodist Church

(Des G. Vasarhelyi. Litho Cartor)

1997 (16 Sept). *National Heroes Day. T* **88** *and similar multicoloured designs. W w* **14** *(sideways on* $3). *P* 13½.

492	25 c. Type **88**	15	15
493	25 c. Sir Joseph France (trade union leader)	15	15
494	25 c. Robert Bradshaw (first Prime Minister)	15	15
495	$3 Sir Joseph France, Robert Bradshaw and C. A. Paul Southwell (*horiz*)	1·75	2·00
492/5	*Set of* 4	2·00	2·25

(Des D. Miller. Litho Walsall)

1997 (31 Oct). *Christmas. Churches. T* **89** *and similar multicoloured designs. W w* **16** *(sideways on horiz designs). P* 13½×14 *(horiz) or* 14×13½ *(vert).*

496	10 c. Type **89**	10	10
497	10 c. Zion Moravian Church	10	10
498	$1.50, St. George's Anglican Church (*vert*)	1·00	1·00
499	$15 Co-Cathedral of the Immaculate Conception (*vert*)	8·50	9·00
496/9	*Set of* 4	8·75	9·00

90 Common Long-tail Skipper

(Des I. Loe. Litho Cot Printery Ltd, Barbados)

1997 (29 Dec). *Butterflies. T* **90** *and similar horiz designs. Multicoloured. W w* **14** *(sideways). P* 14×14½.

500	10 c. Type **90**	10	10
501	15 c. White Peacock	10	10
502	25 c. Caribbean Buckeye	10	15
503	30 c. The Red Rim	15	20
504	40 c. Cassius Blue	20	25
505	50 c. The Flambeau	25	30
506	60 c. Lucas's Blue	25	30
507	90 c. Cloudless Sulphur	40	45
508	$1 The Monarch	45	50
509	$1.20, Fiery Skipper	55	60
510	$1.60, The Zebra	75	80
511	$3 Southern Dagger Tail	1·40	1·50
512	$5 Polydamus Swallowtail	2·25	2·40
513	$10 Tropical Chequered Skipper	4·50	4·75
500/13	*Set of* 14	11·50	12·00

STAMP BOOKLET

1981 (19 Nov). *Royal Wedding. Multicoloured cover, 105×65 mm, showing* The Saudadoes. *Stitched.*

SB1	$9.40, booklet containing eight 55 c. in panes of 4 (No. 82a) and $2.50 in pane of 2 (No. 83a) ..	2·10

OFFICIAL STAMPS

1980 (23 June). *Nos.* 32/41 *additionally optd with Type* O **1** *of St. Christopher, Nevis and Anguilla. A.* W w **14** (*sideways*). B. *No wmk.*

		A		B	
O 1	15 c. Sugar cane harvesting ..	10	10	†	
O 2	25 c. Crafthouse (craft centre) ..	10	10	25	15
O 3	30 c. *Europa* (liner)	10	10	50	30
O 4	40 c. Lobster and sea crab ..	10	15	9·00	16·00
O 5	45 c. Royal St. Kitts Hotel and golf course	15	15	†	
O 6	50 c. Pinney's Beach, Nevis ..	15	15	†	
O 7	55 c. New runway at Golden Rock	15	15	60	60
	a. Opt inverted	27·00	—	†	
O 8	$1 Cotton picking	25	25	1·00	1·00
O 9	$5 Brewery	80	1·50	3·00	4·50
O10	$10 Pineapples and peanuts ..	1·00	2·50	3·50	6·50
	a. Opt inverted	£100	—	†	
O1/10	.. .. .. *Set of* 10	2·50	4·50		
O2/10	.. .. .. *Set of* 7			16·00	26·00

OFFICIAL

(O 1)

1981 (5 Feb). *Nos.* 59A/70A *optd with Type* O 1.

O11	15 c. Type **13**	20	10
O12	20 c. Scaly-breasted Thrasher	20	10
O13	25 c. Grey Kingbird	25	10
O14	30 c. Green-throated Carib	25	10
O15	40 c. Turnstone	35	15
O16	45 c. Black-faced Grassquit	40	20
O17	50 c. Cattle Egret	40	20
O18	55 c. Brown Pelican	50	25
O19	$1 Lesser Antillean Bullfinch	75	45
O20	$2.50, Zenaida Dove	1·60	1·00
O21	$5 American Kestrel	2·75	2·00
O22	$10 Antillean Crested Hummingbird ..	5·00	4·25
O11/22	.. .. *Set of* 12	11·50	8·00

1983 (2 Feb). *Nos.* 75/80 *optd with Type* O **1** (55 *c.*) *or surch also* (*others*).

O23	45 c. on $2.50, *Royal George* (New Blue) ..	15	15
	a. Sheetlet. No. O23×6 and No. O24 ..	1·00	
	b. Surch double	16·00	
	c. Albino surch	7·00	
	f. Deep ultramarine surch	50	
	fd. Surch inverted	4·00	
	fe. Surch inverted (horiz pair)	15·00	
	g. Black opt		
O24	45 c. on $2.50, Prince Charles and Lady Diana Spencer (New Blue)	25	25
	b. Surch double	60·00	
	c. Albino surch	25·00	
	f. Deep ultramarine surch	75	
	fd. Surch inverted	20·00	
	g. Black opt		
O25	55 c. *Saudadoes* (New Blue)	15	15
	a. Sheetlet. No. O25×6 and No. O26 ..	1·10	
	b. Opt double	18·00	
	c. Albino opt	7·00	
	d. Opt inverted	6·00	
	e. Opt inverted (horiz pair)	18·00	
	f. Block of 3 containing No. O25×2 without opt and No. O26 with two opts		
	g. Deep ultramarine opt	60	
	gd. Opt inverted	6·00	
	ge. Opt inverted (horiz pair)	19·00	
O26	55 c. Prince Charles and Lady Diana Spencer (New Blue)	30	30
	b. Opt double	60·00	
	c. Albino opt	27·00	
	d. Opt inverted	23·00	
	f. Deep ultramarine opt	90	
	fd. Opt inverted	23·00	
O27	$1.10 on $4 *Britannia* (Blk.)	30	40
	a. Sheetlet. No. O27×6 and No. O28 ..	2·25	
	b. Surch double	15·00	
	f. Deep ultramarine surch	2·75	
	fd. Surch inverted		
	fe. Surch inverted (horiz pair)		
O28	$1.10 on $4 Prince Charles and Lady Diana Spencer (Blk.)	60	70
	b. Surch double	45·00	
	f. Deep ultramarine surch	25·00	
	fd. Surch inverted		
O23/8	.. .. *Set of* 6	1·60	1·75

Nos. O23fe, O25e, O25ge and O27fe show the surcharge or overprint intended for the large design, inverted and struck across a horizontal pair of the smaller. Nos. O24fd, O26d, O26fd and O28fd each show two inverted surcharges or overprints intended for a horizontal pair of the smaller design.

1984 (4 July). *Nos.* 145/56 *optd with Type* O **1**.

O29	15 c. Red-lined Cleaning Shrimp	70	80
O30	20 c. Bristleworm	80	1·00
O31	25 c. Flamingo Tongue (*Cyphoma gibbosus*)	80	1·00
O32	30 c. Christmas Tree Worm	90	1·25
O33	40 c. Pink-tipped Anemone	1·00	1·25
O34	50 c. Small-mouthed Grunt	1·00	1·25
O35	60 c. Glass-eyed Snapper	1·25	1·50
O36	75 c. Reef Squirrelfish	1·50	2·25
O37	$1 Sea Fans and Flamefish (*vert*) ..	2·00	2·25
O38	$2.50, Reef Butterflyfish (*vert*)	3·75	5·50
O39	$5 Black-barred Soldierfish (*vert*) ..	5·50	5·50
O40	$10 Cocoa Damselfish (*vert*)	8·50	8·50
O29/40	.. .. *Set of* 12	25·00	29·00

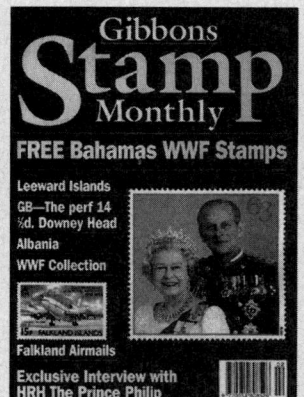

NEVIS

(7)

8 Nevis Lighter

1980 (23 June). *Nos.* 394/406 *of St. Christopher, Nevis and Anguilla optd with T* **7**.

37	5 c. Radio and T.V. station	10	10
38	10 c. Technical college	10	10
	w. Wmk Crown to left of CA	45·00	
39	12 c. T.V. assembly plant	20	30
40	15 c. Sugar cane harvesting	10	10
41	25 c. Crafthouse (craft centre)	10	10
	a. No wmk	1·25	2·50
42	30 c. *Europa* (liner)	20	15
43	40 c. Lobster and sea crab	30	40
44	45 c. Royal St. Kitts Hotel and golf course	70	70
45	50 c. Pinney's Beach, Nevis	20	30
46	55 c. New runway at Golden Rock	15	15
47	$1 Picking cotton	15	30
	a. No wmk	3·25	8·00
48	$5 Brewery	30	50
49	$10 Pineapples and peanuts	40	65
37/49	*Set of* 13	2·50	3·25

1980 (4 Sept). *80th Birthday of Queen Elizabeth the Queen Mother. As T* **10** *of St. Kitts, but inscr* "NEVIS".

50	$2 multicoloured	20	30

No. 50 was printed in sheets including two *se-tenant* stamp-size labels.

(Des Jennifer Toombs. Litho Questa)

1980 (8 Oct). *Boats. T* **8** *and similar multicoloured designs. W* w **14** (*sideways on* 5, 30 *and* 55 *c.*). *P* 14.

51	5 c. Type **8**	10	10
52	30 c. Local fishing boat	10	10
53	55 c. *Caona* (catamaran)	15	10
54	$3 *Polynesia* (cruise schooner) (39×53 *mm*)	30	40
	a. Perf 12 (booklets)	30	60
	ab. Booklet pane of 3	80	
	aw. Wmk inverted	30	
	awb. Booklet pane of 3	80	
51/4	*Set of* 4	55	60

No. 54a comes from $12.30 stamp booklets containing No. 53 × 6 and one pane as No. 54ab. In this pane each stamp is surrounded by white margins, the pane being divided in three by vertical roulettes.

9 Virgin and Child

(Des Jennifer Toombs. Litho Format)

1980 (20 Nov). *Christmas. T* **9** *and similar vert designs. Multicoloured. W* w **14**. *P* 14.

55	5 c. Type **9**	10	10
56	30 c. Angel	10	10
57	$2.50, The Three Wise Men	20	30
55/7	*Set of* 3	20	35

Nos. 55/7 were each printed in sheets of 8 stamps and 1 label.

10 Charlestown Pier

11 New River Mill

(Des Jennifer Toombs. Litho Questa)

1981 (5 Feb)–**82**. *Horiz designs as T* **10** (5, 10 *c.*) *or T* **11** (15 *c. to* $10). *Multicoloured. W* w **14**. *P* 14 × 13½ (5, 10 *c.*) *or* 14 (*others*).
A. *No imprint date*
B. *With imprint date at foot of design* (9.6.82.)

		A		B	
58	5 c. Type **10**	10	10	†	
	w. Wmk inverted	†		30	30
59	10 c. Court House and Library	10	10	†	
	w. Wmk inverted	†		30	30
60	15 c. Type **11**	10	10	10	10
61	20 c. Nelson Museum	10	10	10	10
62	25 c. St. James' Parish Church	15	15	15	15
63	30 c. Nevis Lane	15	15	15	15
64	40 c. Zetland Plantation	20	20	20	20
65	45 c. Nisbet Plantation	20	25	20	25
66	50 c. Pinney's Beach	25	25	25	25
67	55 c. Eva Wilkin's Studio	25	30	25	30
68	$1 Nevis at dawn	40	45	40	45
69	$2.50, Ruins of Fort Charles	55	80	65	80
70	$5 Old Bath House	70	1·00	80	1·00
71	$10 Beach at Nisbet's	90	2·00	1·25	2·00
58/71	*Set of* 14	3·50	5·00	4·00	5·00

Imprint dates: "1982", Nos. 58B/71B; "1983", Nos. 61B/7B, 69B.

(Des D. Shults. Litho Questa)

1981 (23 June–14 Dec). *Royal Wedding. Horiz designs as T* **26/27** *of Kiribati. Multicoloured.* (*a*) *W* w **14**. *P* 14.

72	55 c. *Royal Caroline*	15	15
	a. Sheetlet. No. 72 × 6 and No. 73	1·10	
73	55 c. Prince Charles and Lady Diana Spencer	40	40
74	$2 *Royal Sovereign*	30	30
	aw. Wmk inverted	8·00	
	b. Sheetlet. No. 74×6 and No. 75	2·40	
	bw. Wmk inverted	70·00	
75	$2 As No. 73	80	1·25
	aw. Wmk inverted	35·00	
76	$5 *Britannia*	45	80
	aw. Wmk inverted	4·00	
	b. Sheetlet. No. 76×6 and No. 77	3·25	
	bw. Wmk inverted	35·00	
77	$5 As No. 73	1·00	2·00
	aw. Wmk inverted	17·00	
72/7	*Set of* 6	2·75	4·50
MS78	120×109 mm. $4.50, As No. 73, Wmk sideways. P 12 (14 Dec)	1·10	1·25

(*b*) *Booklet stamps. No wmk. P* 12 (19 Nov)

79	55 c. As No. 72	15	30
	a. Booklet pane. No. 79×4 with margins all round	55	
80	$2 As No. 75	60	1·25
	a. Booklet pane. No. 80×2 with margins all round	1·10	

Nos. 72/7 were printed in sheetlets of seven stamps of the same face value, each containing six of the "Royal Yacht" design and one of the larger design showing Prince Charles and Lady Diana.

Nos. 79/80 come from $8.40 stamp booklets.

12 *Heliconius charithonia*

13 Caroline of Brunswick, Princess of Wales, 1793

(Des Jennifer Toombs. Litho Questa)

1982 (16 Feb). *Butterflies* (1*st series*). *T* **12** *and similar horiz designs. Multicoloured. W* w **14** (*sideways*). *P* 14.

81	5 c. Type **12**	10	10
82	30 c. *Siproeta stelenes*	15	10
83	55 c. *Marpesia petreus*	20	15
84	$2 *Phoebis agarithe*	60	70
81/4	*Set of* 4	90	90

See also Nos. 105/8.

(Des D. Shults and J. Cooter. Litho Format)

1982 (22 June). *21st Birthday of Princess of Wales. T* **13** *and similar vert designs. Multicoloured. W* w **14**. *P* 13½ × 14.

85	30 c. Type **13**	10	10
86	55 c. Coat of arms of Caroline of Brunswick	15	15
87	$5 Diana, Princess of Wales	60	1·00
85/7	*Set of* 3	75	1·10

1982 (12 July). *Birth of Prince William of Wales. Nos.* 85/7 *optd with T* **19** *of St. Kitts.*

88	30 c. Type **13**	10	10
89	55 c. Coat of arms of Caroline of Brunswick	15	15
	a. Opt triple	25·00	
90	$5 Diana, Princess of Wales	60	1·00
88/90	*Set of* 3	75	1·10

14 Cyclist

(Des Philatelists (1980) Ltd. Litho Questa)

1982 (18 Aug). *75th Anniv of Boy Scout Movement. T* **14** *and similar horiz designs. Multicoloured. W* w **14** (*sideways*). *P* 13½ × 14.

91	5 c. Type **14**	20	10
92	30 c. Athlete	25	10
93	$2.50, Camp cook	50	65
91/3	*Set of* 3	85	70

15 Santa Claus

16 Tube Sponge

(Des Eugene Seabrookes (15 c.), Kharenzabeth Glasgow (30 c.), Davia Grant ($1.50), Leonard Huggins ($2.50); adapted Jennifer Toombs. Litho Format)

1982 (20 Oct). *Christmas. Children's Paintings. T* **15** *and similar multicoloured designs. W* w **14** (*sideways on* $1.50 *and* $2.50). *P* 13½ × 14 (15 *c.*, 30 *c.*) *or* 14 × 13½ (*others*).

94	15 c. Type **15**	10	10
95	30 c. Carollers	10	10
96	$1.50, Decorated house and local band (*horiz*)	15	25
97	$2.50, Adoration of the Shepherds (*horiz*)	25	40
94/7	*Set of* 4	45	65

(Des G. Drummond. Litho Format)

1983 (12 Jan). *Corals* (1*st series*). *T* **16** *and similar vert designs. Multicoloured. W* w **14**. *P* 14.

98	15 c. Type **16**	10	10
99	30 c. Stinging coral	15	10
100	55 c. Flower coral	15	10
101	$3 Sea Rod and Red Fire Sponge	50	80
98/101	*Set of* 4	75	90
MS102	82 × 115 mm. Nos. 98/101	1·40	2·50

See also Nos. 423/6.

17 H.M.S. *Boreas* off Nevis

(Des G. Drummond. Litho Format)

1983 (14 Mar). *Commonwealth Day. T* **17** *and similar horiz design. Multicoloured. W* w **14** (*sideways*). *P* 14.

103	55 c. Type **17**	15	10
104	$2 Capt. Horatio Nelson and H.M.S. *Boreas* at anchor	45	60

(Des Jennifer Toombs. Litho Format)

1983 (8 June). *Butterflies* (2*nd series*). *Multicoloured designs as T* **12**. *W* w **14** (*sideways* on* 30 *c. and* $2). *P* 14.

105	30 c. *Pyrgus oileus*	15	10
	w. Wmk Crown to right of CA	16·00	
106	55 c. *Junonia evarete* (*vert*)	20	10
107	$1.10, *Urbanus proteus* (*vert*)	30	40
108	$2 *Hypolimnas misippus*	40	75
	w. Wmk Crown to right of CA	17·00	
105/8	*Set of* 4	95	1·25

*The normal sideways watermark shows Crown to left of CA, *as seen from the back of the stamp.*

INDEPENDENCE
1983

(18)

INDEPENDENCE
1983

(18*a*)

19 Montgolfier Balloon, 1783

1983 (19 Sept). *Nos.* 58 *and* 60/71 *optd as T* **18** (20 *mm long on Nos.* 110/21).
A. *No imprint date*
B. *With imprint date.*

		A		B	
109	5 c. Type **10**	†		10	10
	a. Vert pair, lower stamp without opt.	†		65·00	—
	b. Optd with T **18***a* (local opt)	13·00	11·00	2·00	2·00
	ba. Opt T **18***a* inverted	†		32·00	—
110	15 c. Type **11**	35·00	35·00	10	10
111	20 c. Nelson Museum	5·00	5·00	10	10
112	25 c. St. James' Parish Church	5·00	5·00	10	15
113	30 c. Nevis Lane	90	90	15	15
	a. Opt inverted	†		11·00	—
114	40 c. Zetland Plantation	75	75	15	20
115	45 c. Nisbet Plantation	†		20	25
116	50 c. Pinney's Beach	†		20	25
117	55 c. Eva Wilkin's Studio	75	75	25	30
	a. Opt double	†		12·00	—
118	$1 Nevis at dawn	75	75	40	45
119	$2.50, Ruins of Fort Charles	1·10	1·10	50	70
120	$5 Old Bath House	1·90	2·25	60	85
121	$10 Beach at Nisbet's	3·50	4·25	90	1·25
	a. Opt inverted	60·00	—	†	
109bA/121A	*Set of* 11	60·00	60·00		
109B/121B	*Set of* 13			3·25	4·25

Imprint dates: "1982", Nos. 109B/10B; "1983", Nos. 110B/21B.

(Des A. Theobald. Litho Format)

1983 (28 Sept). *Bicentenary of Manned Flight. T* **19** *and similar multicoloured designs. W* w **15** (*sideways* on* 45 *c. to* $2.50). *P* 14.

122	10 c. Type **19**	10	10
123	45 c. Sikorsky S-38 flying boat (*horiz*)	15	10
124	50 c. Beech 50 Twin Bonanza (*horiz*)	15	10
125	$2.50, Hawker Siddeley Sea Harrier (*horiz*)	30	60
122/5	*Set of* 4	55	70
MS126	118×145 mm. Nos. 122/5. Wmk sideways	75	1·00
	w. Wmk POST OFFICE reading downwards	55·00	

*The normal sideways watermark shows "POST OFFICE" reading downwards on Nos. 122/5 and upwards on No. **MS**126.

20 Mary praying over Holy Child

(Des Jennifer Toombs. Litho Format)

1983 (7 Nov). *Christmas. T* **20** *and similar horiz designs. Multicoloured. W* w **15** *(sideways). P* 14.

127	5 c. Type **20**	10	10
128	30 c. Shepherds with flock	10	10
129	55 c. Three Angels	10	10
130	$3 Boy with two girls	30	60
127/30	*Set of* 4	45	70
MS131	135 × 149 mm. Nos. 127/30	85	1·75

IMPERFORATES AND MISSING COLOURS. Various issues between Nos. 134 and 410 exist either imperforate or with colours omitted. Such items are not listed as there is no evidence that they fulfil the criteria outlined on page xi of this catalogue.

21 *County of Oxford* (1945) **22** Boer War

(Des J. W. Litho Format)

1983 (10 Nov). *Leaders of the World. Railway Locomotives* (1*st series*). *T* **21** *and similar horiz designs, the first in each pair showing technical drawings and the second the locomotive at work. P* 12½.

132	55 c. multicoloured	15	20
	a. Vert pair. Nos. 132/3	30	40
133	55 c. multicoloured	15	20
134	$1 bright crimson, new blue and black	15	20
	a. Vert pair. Nos. 134/5	30	40
135	$1 multicoloured	15	20
136	$1 magenta, new blue and black	15	20
	a. Vert pair. Nos. 136/7	30	40
137	$1 multicoloured	15	20
138	$1 bright crimson, black and greenish yellow	15	20
	a. Vert pair. Nos. 138/9	30	40
139	$1 multicoloured	15	20
140	$1 multicoloured	15	20
	a. Vert pair. Nos. 140/1	30	40
141	$1 multicoloured	15	20
142	$1 greenish yellow, black and new blue	15	20
	a. Vert pair. Nos. 142/3	30	40
143	$1 multicoloured	15	20
144	$1 greenish yellow, black & brt magenta	15	20
	a. Vert pair. Nos. 144/5	30	40
145	$1 multicoloured	15	20
146	$1 multicoloured	15	20
	a. Vert pair. Nos. 146/7	30	40
147	$1 multicoloured	15	20
132/47	*Set of* 16	2·25	3·00

Designs:—Nos. 132/3, *County of Oxford*, Great Britain (1945), 134/5, *Evening Star*, Great Britain (1960); 136/7, Stanier "Class 5", Great Britain (1934); 138/9, *Pendennis Castle*, Great Britain (1924); 140/1, *Winston Churchill*, Great Britain (1946); 142/3, *Mallard*, Great Britain (1935); 144/5, *Britannia*, Great Britain (1951); 146/7, *King George V*, Great Britain (1927).

Nos. 132/3, 134/5, 136/7, 138/9, 140/1, 142/3, 144/5 and 146/7 were printed together, *se-tenant* in vertical pairs throughout the sheets.

See also Nos. 219/26, 277/84, 297/308, 352/9 and 427/42.

(Des Court House Studio. Litho Format)

1984 (11 Apr). *Leaders of the World. British Monarchs* (1*st series*). *T* **22** *and similar vert designs. Multicoloured. P* 12½.

148	5 c. Type **22**	10	10
	a. Horiz pair. Nos. 148/9	10	10
149	5 c. Queen Victoria	10	10
150	50 c. Queen Victoria at Osborne House	10	30
	a. Horiz pair. Nos. 150/1	20	60
151	50 c. Osborne House	10	30
152	60 c. Battle of Dettingen	10	30
	a. Horiz pair. Nos. 152/3	20	60
153	60 c. George II	10	30
154	75 c. George II at the Bank of England	15	30
	a. Horiz pair. Nos. 154/5	30	60
155	75 c. Bank of England	15	30
156	$1 Coat of Arms of George II	15	30
	a. Horiz pair. Nos. 156/7	30	60
157	$1 George II (*different*)	15	30
158	$3 Coat of Arms of Queen Victoria	30	50
	a. Horiz pair. Nos. 158/9	60	1·00
159	$3 Queen Victoria (*different*)	30	50
148/59	*Set of* 12	1·40	3·00

Nos. 148/9, 150/1, 152/3, 154/5, 156/7 and 158/9 were printed together, *se-tenant* in horizontal pairs throughout the sheet.

See also Nos. 231/6.

ALTERED CATALOGUE NUMBERS

Any Catalogue numbers altered from the last edition are shown as a list in the introductory pages.

23 Golden Rock Inn

(Des Jennifer Toombs. Litho J.W.)

1984 (16 May). *Tourism.* (1*st series*). *T* **23** *and similar horiz designs. Multicoloured. W* w **15** (*sideways*). *P* 14.

160	55 c. Type **23**	25	20
161	55 c. Rest Haven Inn	25	20
162	55 c. Cliffdwellers Hotel	25	20
163	55 c. Pinney's Beach Hotel	25	20
160/3	*Set of* 4	90	70

See also Nos. 245/8.

24 Early Seal of Colony

(Des G. Drummond. Litho Format)

1984 (8 June). *W* w **15** (*sideways*). *P* 14.

164	**24**	$15 dull scarlet	2·25	4·00

25 Cadillac

(Des J. W. Litho Format)

1984 (25 July). *Leaders of the World. Automobiles* (1*st series*). *T* **25** *and similar horiz designs, the first in each pair showing technical drawings and the second paintings. P* 12½.

165	1 c. greenish yellow, black and magenta	10	10
	a. Vert pair. Nos. 165/6	10	10
166	1 c. multicoloured	10	10
167	5 c. new blue, magenta and black	10	10
	a. Vert pair. Nos. 167/8	10	10
168	5 c. multicoloured	10	10
169	15 c. multicoloured	10	15
	a. Vert pair. Nos. 169/70	20	30
170	15 c. multicoloured	10	15
171	35 c. magenta, greenish yellow and black	10	25
	a. Vert pair. Nos. 171/2	20	50
172	35 c. multicoloured	10	25
173	45 c. new blue, magenta and black	10	25
	a. Vert pair. Nos. 173/4	20	50
174	45 c. multicoloured	10	25
175	55 c. multicoloured	10	25
	a. Vert pair. Nos. 175/6	20	50
176	55 c. multicoloured	10	25
177	$2.50, magenta, black and greenish yellow	25	60
	a. Vert pair. Nos. 177/8	50	1·10
178	$2.50, multicoloured	25	60
179	$3 new blue, greenish yellow and black	25	70
	a. Vert pair. Nos. 179/80	50	1·40
180	$3 multicoloured	25	70
165/80	*Set of* 16	1·75	4·00

Designs:—Nos. 165/6, Cadillac "V16 Fleetwood Convertible" (1932); 167/8, Packard "Twin Six Touring Car" (1916); 169/70, Daimler, "2 Cylinder" (1886); 171/2, Porsche "911 S Targa" (1970); 173/4, Benz "Three Wheeler" (1885); 175/6, M.G. "TC" (1947); 177/8, Cobra "Roadster 289" (1966), 179/80, Aston Martin "DB6 Hardtop" (1966).

Nos. 165/6, 167/8, 169/70, 171/2, 173/4, 175/6, 177/8 and 179/80 were printed together, *se-tenant* in vertical pairs throughout the sheet.

See also Nos. 203/10, 249/64, 326/37, 360/71 and 411/22.

26 Carpentry **27** Yellow Bell

(Des Jennifer Toombs. Litho Questa)

1984 (1 Aug). 10*th Anniv of Culturama Celebrations. T* **26** *and similar horiz designs. Multicoloured. W* w **15** (*sideways**). *P* 14.

181	30 c. Type **26**	10	10
182	55 c. Grass mat and basket-making	10	10
	w. Wmk POST OFFICE reading upwards	3·50	
183	$1 Pottery-firing	15	25
184	$3 Culturama Queen and dancers	40	55
181/4	*Set of* 4	65	85

*The normal sideways watermark shows "POST OFFICE" reading downwards.

(Des Jennifer Toombs. Litho Format)

1984 (8 Aug)–**86**. *Flowers. T* **27** *and similar vert designs. Multicoloured. W* w **15**. *P* 14. A. *Without imprint date*. B. *With imprint date* ("1986") *at foot of design* (23.7.86).

		A		B	
185	5 c. Type **27**	10	10	†	
186	10 c. Plumbago	10	10	†	
187	15 c. Flamboyant	10	10	†	
188	20 c. Eyelash Orchid	60	15	40	30
189	30 c. Bougainvillea	10	15	†	
190	40 c. Hibiscus *sp.*	70	25	30	30
191	50 c. Night-blooming Cereus	15	20	†	
192	55 c. Yellow Mahoe	20	25	†	
193	60 c. Spider-lily	20	25	†	
194	75 c. Scarlet Cordia	25	30	†	
195	$1 Shell-ginger	35	40	†	
196	$3 Blue Petrea	70	1·10	†	
197	$5 Coral Hibiscus	1·00	2·00	†	
198	$10 Passion Flower	1·50	3·50	†	
185/98	*Set of* 14	5·25	7·75	†	

28 Cotton-picking and Map **29** C.P. Mead

(Des A. Grant (15 c.), Tracy Watkins (55 c.), C. Manners ($1.10), D. Grant ($3), adapted Court House Advertising. Litho Format)

1984 (18 Sept). *First Anniv of Independence of St. Kitts-Nevis. T* **28** *and similar horiz designs. Multicoloured. W* w **15** (*sideways*). *P* 14.

199	15 c. Type **28**	10	10
200	55 c. Alexander Hamilton's birthplace	10	10
201	$1.10, Local agricultural produce	20	40
202	$3 Nevis Peak and Pinneys Beach	50	1·00
199/202	*Set of* 4	75	1·40

(Des J. W. Litho Format)

1984 (23 Oct). *Leaders of the World. Automobiles* (2*nd series*). *Horiz designs as T* **25**, *the first in each pair showing technical drawings and the second paintings. P* 12½.

203	5 c. black, pale new blue and yellow-brown	10	10
	a. Vert pair. Nos. 203/4	10	10
204	5 c. multicoloured	10	10
205	30 c. black, pale turquoise-green & lake-brn	15	15
	a. Vert pair. Nos. 205/6	30	30
206	30 c. multicoloured	15	15
207	50 c. black, pale drab and red-brown	15	15
	a. Vert pair. Nos. 207/8	30	30
208	50 c. multicoloured	15	15
209	$3 black, grey-brown and dull green	30	45
	a. Vert pair. Nos. 209/10	60	90
210	$3 multicoloured	30	45
203/10	*Set of* 8	1·10	1·40

Designs:—Nos. 203/4, Lagonda "Speed Model" touring car (1929); 205/6, Jaguar "E-Type" 4.2 litre (1967); 207/8, Volkswagen "Beetle" (1947); 209/10, Pierce Arrow "V12" (1932).

Nos. 203/10 were issued in a similar sheet format to Nos. 165/80.

(Des Court House Studio. Litho Format)

1984 (23 Oct). *Leaders of the World. Cricketers* (1*st series*). *T* **29** *and similar vert designs, the first in each pair showing a head portrait and the second the cricketer in action. P* 12½.

211	5 c. multicoloured	10	10
	a. Horiz pair. Nos. 211/12	15	15
212	5 c. multicoloured	10	10
213	25 c. multicoloured	30	30
	a. Horiz pair. Nos. 213/14	60	60
214	25 c. multicoloured	30	30
215	55 c. multicoloured	40	40
	a. Horiz pair. Nos. 215/16	80	80
216	55 c. multicoloured	40	40
217	$2.50, multicoloured	1·00	1·25
	a. Horiz pair. Nos. 217/18	2·00	2·50
218	$2.50, multicoloured	1·00	1·25
211/18	*Set of* 8	3·00	3·50

Designs:—Nos. 211/12, C. P. Mead; 213/14, J. B. Statham; 215/16, Sir Learie Constantine; 217/18, Sir Leonard Hutton.

Nos. 211/12, 213/14, 215/16 and 217/18 were printed together, *se-tenant*, in horizontal pairs throughout the sheets.

See also Nos. 237/44.

(Des J. W. Litho Format)

1984 (29 Oct). *Leaders of the World. Railway Locomotives* (2*nd series*). *Horiz designs as T* **21** *the first in each pair showing technical drawings and the second the locomotive at work. P* 12½.

219	5 c. multicoloured	10	10
	a. Vert pair. Nos. 219/20	10	10
220	5 c. multicoloured	10	10
221	10 c. multicoloured	10	10
	a. Vert pair. Nos. 221/2	15	15
222	10 c. multicoloured	10	10
223	60 c. multicoloured	25	25
	a. Vert pair. Nos. 223/4	50	50
224	60 c. multicoloured	25	25
225	$2.50, multicoloured	70	70
	a. Vert pair. Nos. 225/6	1·40	1·40
226	$2.50, multicoloured	70	70
219/26	*Set of* 8	1·75	1·75

Designs:—Nos. 219/20, Class "EF81", Japan (1968); 221/2, Class "5500", France (1927); 223/4, Class "240P", France (1940); 225/6, Shinkansen train, Japan (1964).

Nos. 219/26 were issued in a similar sheet format to Nos. 132/47.

30 Fifer and Drummer from Honeybees Band

(Des Jennifer Toombs. Litho Questa)

1984 (2 Nov). *Christmas. Local Music. T* **30** *and similar horiz designs. Multicoloured. W w* **15** *(sideways). P* 14.

227 15 c. Type **30** .. 15 10
228 40 c. Guitar and "barhow" players from Canary Birds Band .. 25 10
229 60 c. Shell All Stars steel band .. 30 10
230 $3 Organ and choir, St. John's Church, Fig Tree .. 1·25 1·00
227/30 .. *Set of* 4 1·75 1·10

(Des Court House Studio. Litho Format)

1984 (20 Nov). *Leaders of the World. British Monarchs* (2nd *series*). *Vert designs as T* **22**. *Multicoloured. P* 12½.

231 5 c. King John and Magna Carta .. 10 10
a. Horiz pair. Nos. 231/2 .. 10 10
232 5 c. Barons and King John .. 10 10
233 55 c. King John .. 10 15
a. Horiz pair. Nos. 233/4 .. 20 30
234 55 c. Newark Castle .. 10 15
235 $2 Coat of arms .. 25 40
a. Horiz pair. Nos. 235/6 .. 50 80
236 $2 King John (*different*) .. 25 40
231/6 .. *Set of* 6 65 1·00

Nos. 231/6 were issued in a similar sheet format to Nos. 148/59.

(Des Court House Studio. Litho Format)

1984 (20 Nov). *Leaders of the World. Cricketers* (2nd *series*). *Vert designs as T* **29**, *the first in each pair listed showing a head portrait and the second the cricketer in action. P* 12½.

237 5 c. multicoloured .. 10 10
a. Horiz pair. Nos. 237/8 .. 15 15
238 5 c. multicoloured .. 10 10
239 15 c. multicoloured .. 15 15
a. Horiz pair. Nos. 239/40 .. 30 30
240 15 c. multicoloured .. 15 15
241 55 c. multicoloured .. 20 20
a. Horiz pair. Nos. 241/2 .. 40 40
242 55 c. multicoloured .. 20 20
243 $2,50, multicoloured .. 50 60
a. Horiz pair. Nos. 243/4 .. 1·00 1·10
244 $2.50, multicoloured .. 50 60
237/44 .. *Set of* 8 1·60 1·75

Designs:—Nos. 237/8, J. D. Love; 239/40, S. J. Dennis; 241/2, B. W. Luckhurst; 243/4, B. L. D'Oliveira.

Nos. 237/44 were issued in a similar sheet format to Nos. 211/18.

(Des Jennifer Toombs. Litho Format)

1985 (12 Feb). *Tourism* (2nd *series*). *Horiz designs as T* **23**. *Multicoloured. W w* **15** *(sideways). P* 14.

245 $1.20, Croney's Old Manor Hotel .. 15 25
246 $1.20, Montpelier Plantation Inn .. 15 25
247 $1.20, Nisbet's Plantation Inn .. 15 25
248 $1.20, Zetland Plantation Inn .. 15 25
245/8 .. *Set of* 4 55 90

(Des G. Turner (10 c.), J.W. (others). Litho Format)

1985 (20 Feb). *Leaders of the World. Automobiles* (3rd *series*). *Horiz designs as T* **25**, *the first in each pair showing technical drawings and the second paintings. P* 12½.

249 1 c. black, light green and pale green .. 10 10
a. Vert pair. Nos. 249/50 .. 10 10
250 1 c. multicoloured .. 10 10
251 5 c. black, cobalt and pale violet-blue .. 10 10
a. Vert pair. Nos. 251/2 .. 10 10
252 5 c. multicoloured .. 10 10
253 10 c. black, grey-olive and pale green .. 10 10
a. Vert pair. Nos. 253/4 .. 10 10
254 10 c. multicoloured .. 10 10
255 50 c. black, sage-green and pale cinnamon .. 10 10
a. Vert pair. Nos. 255/6 .. 10 20
256 50 c. multicoloured .. 10 10
257 60 c. black, dull yellowish green and pale blue .. 10 10
a. Vert pair. Nos. 257/8 .. 10 20
258 60 c. multicoloured .. 10 10
259 75 c. black, dull vermilion and pale orange .. 10 10
a. Vert pair. Nos. 259/60 .. 15 20
260 75 c. multicoloured .. 10 10
261 $2.50, black, light green and azure .. 20 30
a. Vert pair. Nos. 261/2 .. 40 60
262 $2.50, multicoloured .. 20 30
263 $3 black, bright yellow-green and pale green .. 20 30
a. Vert pair. Nos. 263/4 .. 40 60
264 $3 multicoloured .. 20 30
249/64 .. *Set of* 16 1·00 1·75

Designs:—Nos. 249/50, Delahaye "Type 35 Cabriolet" (1935); 251/2, Ferrari "Testa Rossa" (1958); 253/4, Voisin "Aerodyne" (1934); 255/6, Buick "Riviera" (1963); 257/8, Cooper "Climax" (1960); 259/60, Ford "999" (1904); 261/2, MG "M-Type Midget" (1930); 263/4, Rolls-Royce "Corniche" (1971).

Nos. 249/64 were issued in a similar sheet format to Nos. 165/80.

OMNIBUS ISSUES

Details, together with prices for complete sets, of the various Omnibus issues from the 1935 Silver Jubilee series to date are included in a special section following Zimbabwe at the end of Volume 2.

31 Broad-winged Hawk

32 Eastern Bluebird

(Des Jennifer Toombs. Litho Format)

1985 (19 Mar). *Local Hawks and Herons. T* **31** *and similar horiz designs. Multicoloured. W w* **15** *(sideways). P* 14.

265 20 c. Type **31** .. 1·00 20
266 40 c. Red-tailed Hawk .. 1·25 30
267 60 c. Little Blue Heron .. 1·25 40
268 $3 Great Blue Heron (white phase) .. 2·50 1·90
265/8 .. *Set of* 4 5·50 2·50

No. 268 was re-issued on 24 May 1990 overprinted "40th Anniversary C.S.S." to mark the fortieth anniversary of Charlestown Secondary School. This overprint was only available on First Day Covers.

(Des R. Vigurs. Litho Format)

1985 (25 Mar). *Leaders of the World. Birth Bicentenary of John J. Audubon (ornithologist)* (1st *issue*). *T* **32** *and similar vert designs. Multicoloured. P* 12½.

269 5 c. Type **32** .. 10 10
a. Horiz pair. Nos. 269/70 .. 20 20
270 5 c. Common Cardinal .. 10 10
271 55 c. Belted Kingfisher .. 20 55
a. Horiz pair. Nos. 271/2 .. 40 1·10
272 55 c. Mangrove Cuckoo .. 20 55
273 60 c. Yellow Warbler .. 20 55
a. Horiz pair. Nos. 273/4 .. 40 1·10
274 60 c. Cerulean Warbler .. 20 55
275 $2 Burrowing Owl .. 60 1·25
a. Horiz pair. Nos. 275/6 .. 1·10 2·50
276 $2 Long-eared Owl .. 60 1·25
269/76 .. *Set of* 8 2·00 4·50

Nos. 269/70, 271/2, 273/4 and 275/6 were printed together, *se-tenant*, in horizontal pairs throughout the sheets.

See also Nos. 285/92.

(Des J.W. Litho Format)

1985 (26 Apr). *Leaders of the World. Railway Locomotives* (3rd *series*). *Horiz designs as T* **21**, *the first in each pair showing technical drawings and the second the locomotive at work. P* 12½.

277 1 c. multicoloured .. 10 10
a. Vert pair. Nos. 277/8 .. 10 10
278 1 c. multicoloured .. 10 10
279 60 c. multicoloured .. 20 20
a. Vert pair. Nos. 279/80 .. 40 40
280 60 c. multicoloured .. 20 20
281 90 c. multicoloured .. 25 25
a. Vert pair. Nos. 281/2 .. 50 50
282 90 c. multicoloured .. 25 25
283 $2 multicoloured .. 40 60
a. Vert pair. Nos. 283/4 .. 80 1·10
284 $2 multicoloured .. 40 60
277/84 .. *Set of* 8 1·50 1·75

Designs:—Nos. 277/8, Class "Wee Bogie", Great Britain (1882); 279/80, *Comet*, Great Britain (1851); 281/2, Class "8H", Great Britain (1908); 283/4, Class "A" No. 23, Great Britain (1866).

Nos. 277/84 were issued in a similar sheet format to Nos. 132/47.

(Des R. Vigurs. Litho Format)

1985 (3 June). *Leaders of the World. Birth Bicentenary of John J. Audubon (ornithologist)* (2nd *issue*). *Vert designs as T* **32** *showing original paintings. Multicoloured. P* 12½.

285 1 c. Painted Bunting .. 10 10
a. Horiz pair. Nos. 285/6 .. 10 10
286 1 c. Golden-crowned Kinglet .. 10 10
287 40 c. Common Flicker .. 25 40
a. Horiz pair. Nos. 287/8 .. 50 80
288 40 c. Western Tanager .. 25 40
289 60 c. Varied Thrush ("Sage Thrasher") .. 25 45
a. Horiz pair. Nos. 289/90 .. 50 90
290 60 c. Evening Grosbeak .. 25 45
291 $2.50, Blackburnian Warbler .. 50 80
a. Horiz pair. Nos. 291/2 .. 1·00 1·60
292 $2.50, Northern Oriole .. 50 80
285/92 .. *Set of* 8 1·75 3·00

Nos. 285/92 were issued in a similar sheet format to Nos. 269/76.

Nos. 285/92 exist with yellow omitted from stock dispersed by the liquidator of Format International Security Printers Ltd.

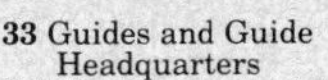

33 Guides and Guide Headquarters

34 The Queen Mother at Garter Ceremony

(Des G. Vasarhelyi. Litho Format)

1985 (17 June). *75th Anniv of Girl Guide Movement. T* **33** *and similar multicoloured designs. W w* **15** *(inverted on* 60 c., *sideways on* 15 c.). *P* 14.

293 15 c. Type **33** .. 10 10
294 60 c. Girl Guide uniforms of 1910 and 1985 (*vert*) .. 15 25
295 $1 Lord and Lady Baden-Powell (*vert*) .. 20 40
296 $3 Princess Margaret in Guide uniform (*vert*) .. 50 1·25
293/6 .. *Set of* 4 75 1·75

(Des T. Hadler (75 c., $1, $2.50), J.W. (others). Litho Format)

1985 (26 July). *Leaders of the World. Railway Locomotives* (4*th series*). *Horiz designs as T* **21**, *the first in each pair showing technical drawings and the second the locomotive at work. P* 12½.

297 5 c. multicoloured .. 10 10
a. Vert pair. Nos. 297/8 .. 10 10
298 5 c. multicoloured .. 10 10
299 30 c. multicoloured .. 10 15
a. Vert pair. Nos. 299/300 .. 15 30
300 30 c. multicoloured .. 10 15
301 60 c. multicoloured .. 15 20
a. Vert pair. Nos. 301/2 .. 30 40
302 60 c. multicoloured .. 15 20
303 75 c. multicoloured .. 15 25
a. Vert pair. Nos. 303/4 .. 30 50
304 75 c. multicoloured .. 15 25
305 $1 multicoloured .. 15 25
a. Vert pair. Nos. 305/6 .. 30 50
306 $1 multicoloured .. 15 25
307 $2.50, multicoloured .. 25 60
a. Vert pair. Nos. 307/8 .. 50 1·10
308 $2.50, multicoloured .. 25 60
297/308 .. *Set of* 12 1·40 2·50

Designs:—Nos. 297/8, *Snowdon Ranger*, Great Britain (1878); 299/300, Large Belpaire passenger locomotive, Great Britain (1904); 301/2, Great Western Railway "County" Class, Great Britain (1904); 303/4, *Nord L'Outrance*, France (1877); 305/6, Q.R. "Class PB-15", Australia (1899); 307/8, D.R.G. "Class 64", Germany (1928).

Nos. 297/308 were issued in a similar sheet format to Nos. 132/47.

(Des Court House Studio. Litho Format)

1985 (31 July). *Leaders of the World. Life and Times of Queen Elizabeth the Queen Mother. Various vertical portraits as T* **34**. *P* 12½.

309 45 c. multicoloured .. 10 15
a. Horiz pair. Nos. 309/10 .. 20 30
310 45 c. multicoloured .. 10 15
311 75 c. multicoloured .. 10 20
a. Horiz pair. Nos. 311/12 .. 20 40
312 75 c. multicoloured .. 10 20
313 $1.20, multicoloured .. 15 35
a. Horiz pair. Nos. 313/14 .. 30 70
314 $1.20, multicoloured .. 15 35
315 $1.50, multicoloured .. 15 40
a. Horiz pair. Nos. 315/16 .. 30 80
316 $1.50, multicoloured .. 15 40
309/16 .. *Set of* 8 90 2·00
MS317 85 × 114 mm. $2 multicoloured; $2 multicoloured .. 50 1·40

The two designs of each value were issued, *se-tenant*, in horizontal pairs within the sheets.

Each *se-tenant* pair shows a floral pattern across the bottom of the portraits which stops short of the left-hand edge on the left-hand stamp and of the right-hand edge on the right-hand stamp.

Nos. 309/16 exist in unissued miniature sheets, one for each value, from stock dispersed by the liquidator of Format International Security Printers Ltd.

Designs as Nos. 309/10 and 315/16, but with face values of $3.50 × 2 and $6 × 2, also exist in additional miniature sheets from a restricted printing issued 27 December 1985.

35 Isambard Kingdom Brunel

36 St. Pauls Anglican Church, Charlestown

(Des Tudor Art Agency. Litho Format)

1985 (31 Aug). *150th Anniv of the Great Western Railway. T* **35** *and similar vert designs showing railway engineers and their achievements. Multicoloured. P* 12½.

318 25 c. Type **35** .. 15 35
a. Horiz pair. Nos. 318/19 .. 30 70
319 25 c. Royal Albert Bridge, 1859 .. 15 35
320 50 c. William Dean .. 20 45
a. Horiz pair. Nos. 320/1 .. 40 90
321 50 c. Locomotive *Lord of the Isles*, 1895 .. 20 45
322 $1 Locomotive *Lode Star*, 1907 .. 25 65
a. Horiz pair. Nos. 322/3 .. 50 1·25
323 $1 G. J. Churchward .. 25 65
324 $2.50, Locomotive *Pendennis Castle*, 1924 .. 35 80
a. Horiz pair. Nos. 324/5 .. 70 1·60
325 $2.50, C. B. Collett .. 35 80
318/25 .. *Set of* 8 1·75 4·00

Nos. 318/19, 320/1, 322/3 and 324/5 were printed together, *se-tenant*, in horizontal pairs throughout the sheets, each pair forming a composite design.

(Des J.W. Litho Format)

1985 (4 Oct). *Leaders of the World. Automobiles (4th series). Horiz designs as T* **25**, *the first in each pair showing technical drawings and the second paintings. P* 12½.

326 10 c. black, azure and brown-red 10 10
a. Vert pair. Nos. 326/7 .. .. .. 10 15
327 10 c. multicoloured 10 10
328 35 c. black, pale turquoise-grn & greenish bl 10 25
a. Vert pair. Nos. 328/9 .. .. .. 15 50
329 35 c. multicoloured 10 25
330 75 c. black, bright green & lt purple-brown 10 40
a. Vert pair. Nos. 330/1 .. .. .. 20 80
331 75 c. multicoloured 10 40
332 $1.15, black, pale cinnamon & olive-green 15 45
a. Vert pair. Nos. 332/3 .. .. .. 30 90
333 $1.15, multicoloured 15 45
334 $1.50, black, pale blue and carmine .. 20 50
a. Vert pair. Nos. 334/5 .. .. .. 40 1·00
335 $1.50, multicoloured 20 50
336 $2 black, rose-lilac and reddish violet .. 25 60
a. Vert pair. Nos. 336/7 .. .. .. 1·10 50
337 $2 multicoloured 25 60
326/37 .. .. *Set of* 12 1·50 4·00

Designs:—Nos. 326/7, Sunbeam "Coupe de l'Auto" (1912); 328/9, Cisitalia "Pininfarina Coupe" (1948); 330/1, Porsche "928 S" (1980); 332/3, MG "K3 Magnette" (1933); 334/5, Lincoln "Zephyr" (1937); 336/7, Pontiac 2 Door (1926).

Nos. 326/37 were issued in a similar sheet format to Nos. 165/80.

1985 (23 Oct). *Royal Visit. Nos.* 76/7, 83, 86, 92/3, 98/9 *and* 309/10 *optd as T* **114** *of Montserrat or surch also.*

338 **16** 15 c. multicoloured .. .. .. 75 1·25
339 – 30 c. multicoloured (No. 92) .. .. 1·75 1·75
340 – 30 c. multicoloured (No. 99) .. .. 75 1·25
341 – 40 c. on 55 c. multicoloured (No. 86) .. 1·75 2·00
342 **34** 45 c. multicoloured .. .. .. 1·50 2·50
a. Horiz pair. Nos. 342/3 .. .. 3·00 5·00
343 – 45 c. multicoloured (No. 310) .. .. 1·50 2·50
344 – 55 c. multicoloured (No. 83) .. .. 1·25 1·25
345 – $1.50 on $5 multicoloured (No. 76) .. 2·00 2·50
aw. Wmk inverted .. ..
b. Sheetlet. No. 345×6 and No. 346 .. 18·00
bw. Wmk inverted .. ..
c. Error. Surch $1.60 .. .. 1·75 2·25
ca. Sheetlet. No. 345c×6 and No. 346c 15·00
346 – $1.50 on $5 multicoloured (No. 77) .. 9·00 11·00
aw. Wmk inverted .. ..
c. Error. Surch $1.60 .. .. 7·50 9·50
347 – $2.50, multicoloured (No. 93) .. .. 2·25 3·00
338/47 .. .. .. *Set of* 10 20·00 26·00

Nos. 345c/ca and 346c had the surcharge intended for similar St. Vincent sheetlets applied by mistake.

(Des G. Drummond. Litho Format)

1985 (5 Nov). *Christmas. Churches of Nevis (1st series). T* **36** *and similar horiz designs. Multicoloured. W w* **15**. *P* 15.

348 10 c. Type **36** 15 10
349 40 c. St. Theresa Catholic Church, Charlestown 35 30
350 60 c. Methodist Church, Gingerland .. 50 50
351 $3 St. Thomas Anglican Church, Lowland 1·75 2·75
348/51 .. .. .. *Set of* 4 2·50 3·25

See also Nos. 462/5.

(Des T. Hadler. Litho Format)

1986 (30 Jan). *Leaders of the World. Railway Locomotives (5th series). Horiz designs as T* **21**, *the first in each pair showing technical drawings and the second the locomotive at work. P* 12½.

352 30 c. multicoloured 15 25
a. Vert pair. Nos. 352/3 .. .. .. 30 50
353 30 c. multicoloured 15 25
354 75 c. multicoloured 25 50
a. Vert pair. Nos. 354/5 .. .. .. 50 1·00
355 75 c. multicoloured 25 50
356 $1.50, multicoloured 40 70
a. Vert pair. Nos. 356/7 .. .. .. 80 1·40
357 $1.50, multicoloured 40 70
358 $2 multicoloured 50 80
a. Vert pair. Nos. 358/9 .. .. .. 1·00 1·60
359 $2 multicoloured 50 80
352/9 .. .. *Set of* 8 2·40 4·00

Designs:—Nos. 342/3, *Stourbridge Lion*, U.S.A. (1829); 354/5, "EP-2 Bi-Polar", U.S.A. (1919); 356/7, U.P. "BO×4" gas turbine, U.S.A. (1953); 358/9, N.Y., N.H. and H.R. "FL9", U.S.A (1955).

Nos. 352/9 were issued in a similar sheet format to Nos. 132/47.

(Des G. Turner (60 c.), J.W. (others). Litho Format)

1986 (30 Jan). *Leaders of the World. Automobiles (5th series). Horiz designs as T* **25**, *the first in each pair showing technical drawings and the second paintings. P* 12½.

360 10 c. black, pale cinnamon and yellow-olive.. 10 10
a. Vert pair. Nos. 360/1 .. .. .. 10 20
361 10 c. multicoloured 10 10
362 60 c. black, salmon and bright scarlet .. 15 25
a. Vert pair. Nos. 362/3 .. .. .. 30 50
363 60 c. multicoloured 15 25
364 75 c. black, pale cinnamon and cinnamon .. 15 25
a. Vert pair. Nos. 364/5 .. .. .. 30 50
365 75 c. multicoloured 15 25
366 $1 black, lavender-grey and violet-grey .. 15 30
a. Vert pair. Nos. 366/7 .. .. .. 30 60
367 $1 multicoloured 15 30
368 $1.50, black, pale olive-yellow & olive-grn 20 35
a. Vert pair. Nos. 368/9 .. .. .. 40 70
369 $1.50, multicoloured 20 35
370 $3 black, azure and cobalt.. .. .. 30 65
a. Vert pair. Nos. 370/1 .. .. .. 60 1·25
371 $3 multicoloured 30 65
360/71 .. .. .. *Set of* 12 1·75 3·25

Designs:—No. 360/1, Adler "Trumpf" (1936); 362/3, Maserati "Tipo 250F" (1957); 364/5, Oldsmobile "Limited" (1910); 366/7, Jaguar "C-Type" (1951); 368/9, ERA "1.5L B Type" (1937); 370/1 Chevrolet "Corvette" (1953).

Nos. 360/71 were issued in a similar sheet format to Nos. 165/80.

37 Supermarine Spitfire Prototype, 1936

(Des J. Batchelor. Litho Format)

1986 (5 Mar). *50th Anniv of the Spitfire (fighter aircraft). T* **37** *and similar horiz designs. Multicoloured. P* 12½.

372 $1 Type **37** 20 50
373 $2.50, Supermarine Spitfire Mk 1A in Battle of Britain, 1940 .. .. 30 1·00
374 $3 Supermarine Spitfire Mk XII over convoy, 1944 .. .. .. 40 1·25
375 $4 Supermarine Spitfire Mk XXIV, 1948 50 1·40
372/5 .. .. .. *Set of* 4 1·25 3·75
MS376 114×86 mm. $6 Supermarine Seafire Mk III on escort carrier H.M.S. *Hunter* .. .. 1·10 3·75

38 Head of Amerindian **39** Brazilian Player

(Litho Format)

1986 (11 Apr). *500th Anniv of Discovery of America* (1992) *(1st issue). T* **38** *and similar vert designs. Multicoloured. P* 12½.

377 75 c. Type **38** 55 55
a. Horiz pair. Nos. 377/8 .. .. .. 1·10 1·10
378 75 c. Exchanging gifts for food from Amerindians 55 55
379 $1.75, Columbus's coat of arms .. .. 1·40 1·75
a. Horiz pair. Nos. 379/80.. .. .. 2·75 3·50
380 $1.75, Breadfruit plant .. .. .. 1·40 1·75
381 $2.50, Columbus's fleet .. .. .. 1·75 2·00
a. Horiz pair. Nos. 381/2 .. .. .. 3·50 4·00
382 $2.50, Christopher Columbus .. .. 1·75 2·00
377/82 .. .. .. *Set of* 6 6·50 7·75
MS383 95×84 mm. $6 Christopher Columbus (*different*) .. .. 6·50 8·50

The two designs of each value were printed together, *se-tenant*, in horizontal pairs throughout the sheets. Each pair forms a composite design showing charts of Columbus's route in the background.

Miniature sheets, each containing $2×2 stamps in the above designs, also exist from a restricted printing and from stock dispersed by the liquidator of Format International Security Printers Ltd.

See also Nos. 546/54, 592/600, 678/84 and 685/6.

(Des Court House Studio. Litho Format)

1986 (21 Apr). *60th Birthday of Queen Elizabeth II. Multicoloured designs as T* **117a** *of Montserrat. P* 12½.

384 5 c. Queen Elizabeth in 1976 .. .. 10 10
385 75 c. Queen Elizabeth in 1953 .. .. 15 25
386 $2 In Australia 20 60
387 $8 In Canberra, 1982 (*vert*) .. .. 75 2·00
384/7 .. .. .. *Set of* 4 1·00 2·50
MS388 85×115 mm. $10 Queen Elizabeth II .. 4·00 6·50

The 5 c., 75 c. and $2 values exist with PVA gum as well as gum arabic.

No. 387 also exists watermarked w **15** (inverted), but no examples have been reported used from Nevis.

Nos. 384/7 exist in separate miniature sheets from unissued stock dispersed by the liquidator of Format International Security Printers Ltd.

(Des Court House Studio. Litho Format)

1986 (16 May). *World Cup Football Championship, Mexico. T* **39** *and similar multicoloured designs. P* 12½ (75 c., $1, $1.75, $6) *or* 15 (*others*).

389 1 c. Official World Cup mascot (*horiz*) .. 10 10
390 2 c. Type **39** 10 10
391 5 c. Danish player 10 10
392 10 c. Brazilian player (*different*) 10 10
393 20 c. Denmark *v* Spain 20 20
394 30 c. Paraguay *v* Chile 30 30
395 60 c. Italy *v* West Germany 45 55
396 75 c. Danish team (56×36 *mm*) 50 65
397 $1 Paraguayan team (56×36 *mm*) .. 55 70
398 $1.75, Brazilian team (56×36 *mm*) .. 75 1·25
399 $3 Italy *v* England .. .. .. 1·10 1·90
400 $6 Italian team (56×36 *mm*) .. .. 1·75 3·00
389/400 .. .. .. *Set of* 12 5·00 8·00
MS401 Five sheets, each 85×115 mm. (a) $1.50. As No. 398. (b) $2 As No. 393. (c) $2 As No. 400. (d) $2.50, As No. 395. (e) $4 As No. 394 .. .. .. *Set of* 5 *sheets* 10·00 13·00

40 Clothing Machinist **41** Gorgonia

(Des G. Vasarhelyi. Litho Questa)

1986 (18 July). *Local Industries. T* **40** *and similar horiz designs. Multicoloured. W w* **15**. *P* 14.

402 15 c. Type **40** 20 15
403 40 c. Carpentry/joinery workshop 45 30
404 $1.20, Agricultural produce market .. 1·25 1·50
405 $3 Fishing boats landing catch .. .. 2·50 3·00
402/5 .. .. *Set of* 4 4·00 4·50

(Des Court House Studio. Litho Format)

1986 (23 July–15 Oct). *Royal Wedding (1st issue). Multicoloured designs as T* **118a** *of Montserrat. P* 12½.

406 60 c. Prince Andrew in midshipman's uniform 15 25
a. Pair. Nos. 406/7.. .. .. .. 30 50
407 60 c. Miss Sarah Ferguson 15 25
408 $2 Prince Andrew on safari in Africa (*horiz*) 40 60
a. Pair. Nos. 408/9.. .. .. .. 80 1·10
409 $2 Prince Andrew at the races (*horiz*) .. 40 60
406/9 .. .. *Set of* 4 1·00 1·40
MS410 115×85 mm. $10 Duke and Duchess of York on Palace balcony after wedding (*horiz*) (15.10.86) .. .. 3·00 5·00

Nos. 406/7 and 408/9 were each printed together, *se-tenant*, in horizontal and vertical pairs throughout the sheets.

Nos. 406/9 imperforate come from souvenir stamp booklets.

Nos. 408/9 exist in *tête-bêche* pairs from unissued stock dispersed by the liquidator of Format International Security Printers Ltd.

See also Nos. 454/7.

(Litho Format)

1986 (15 Aug). *Automobiles (6th series). Horiz designs as T* **25**, *the first in each pair showing technical drawings and the second paintings. P* 12½.

411 15 c. multicoloured 10 10
a. Vert pair. Nos. 411/12 .. .. .. 20 20
412 15 c. multicoloured 10 10
413 45 c. black, light blue and grey-blue .. 20 25
a. Vert pair. Nos. 413/14 .. .. .. 40 50
414 45 c. multicoloured 20 25
415 60 c. multicoloured 20 30
a. Vert pair. Nos. 415/16 .. .. .. 40 60
416 60 c. multicoloured 20 30
417 $1 black, yellow-green and dull green .. 25 40
a. Vert pair. Nos. 417/18 .. .. .. 50 80
418 $1 multicoloured 25 40
419 $1.75, black, pale reddish lilac & deep lilac 30 50
a. Vert pair. Nos. 419/20 .. .. .. 60 1·00
420 $1.75, multicoloured 30 50
421 $3 multicoloured 50 90
a. Vert pair. Nos. 421/2 .. .. .. 1·00 1·75
422 $3 multicoloured 50 90
411/22 .. .. *Set of* 12 2·75 4·25

Designs:—Nos. 411/12, Riley "Brooklands Nine" (1930); 413/14, Alfa Romeo "GTA" (1966); 415/16, Pierce Arrow "Type 66" (1913); 417/18, Willys-Knight "66 A" (1928); 419/20, Studebaker "Starliner" (1953); 421/2, Cunningham "V-8" (1919).

Nos. 411/22 were issued in a similar sheet format to Nos. 165/80.

(Des G. Drummond. Litho Format)

1986 (8 Sept). *Corals (2nd series). T* **41** *and similar vert designs. Multicoloured. W w* **15** (*sideways*). *P* 15.

423 15 c. Type **41** 25 15
424 60 c. Fire Coral 55 55
425 $2 Elkhorn Coral .. .. 90 2·00
426 $3 Vase Sponge and Feather Star .. .. 1·10 2·50
423/6 .. .. *Set of* 4 2·50 4·75

(Des Court House Studio. Litho Format)

1986 (1 Oct). *Railway Locomotives (6th series). Horiz designs as T* **21**, *the first in each pair showing technical drawings and the second the locomotive at work. P* 12½.

427 15 c. multicoloured 10 10
a. Vert pair. Nos. 427/8 .. .. .. 10 20
428 15 c. multicoloured 10 10
429 45 c. multicoloured 15 25
a. Vert pair. Nos. 429/30 .. .. .. 30 50
430 45 c. multicoloured 15 25
431 60 c. multicoloured 20 30
a. Vert pair. Nos. 431/2 .. .. .. 40 60
432 60 c. multicoloured 20 30
433 75 c. multicoloured 20 40
a. Vert pair. Nos. 433/4 .. .. .. 40 80
434 75 c. multicoloured 20 40
435 $1 multicoloured 25 50
a. Vert pair. Nos. 435/6 .. .. .. 50 1·00
436 $1 multicoloured 25 50
437 $1.50, multicoloured 30 60
a. Vert pair. Nos. 437/8 .. .. .. 60 1·10
438 $1.50, multicoloured 30 60
439 $2 multicoloured 40 65
a. Vert pair. Nos. 439/40 .. .. .. 80 1·25
440 $2 multicoloured 40 65

441 $3 multicoloured 55 80
 a. Vert pair. Nos. 441/2 .. .. 1·10 1·60
442 $3 multicoloured 55 80
427/42 .. .. *Set of* 16 3·75 6·25

Designs:—Nos. 427/8, Connor Single Class, Great Britain (1859); 429/30, Class "P2" *Cock o' the North*, Great Britain (1934); 431/2, Class "7000", Japan (1926); 433/4, Palatinate Railway Class "P3", Germany (1897); 435/6, *Dorchester*, Canada (1836); 437/8, "Centennial" Class diesel, U.S.A. (1969); 439/40, *Lafayette*, U.S.A. (1837); 441/2, Class "C-16", U.S.A. (1882).

Nos. 427/42 were issued in a similar sheet format to Nos. 132/47.

(Des Court House Studio. Litho Format)

1986 (28 Oct). *Centenary of Statue of Liberty. Multicoloured designs as T* **121***a of Montserrat. P* 13½×14 ($1, $2) *or* 14×13½ (*others*).

443 15 c. Statue of Liberty and World Trade Centre, Manhattan 20 15
444 25 c. Sailing ship passing Statue 30 20
445 40 c. Statue in scaffolding 30 25
446 60 c. Statue (side view) and scaffolding .. 30 30
447 75 c. Statue and regatta 40 40
448 $1 Tall Ships parade passing Statue (*horiz*) 40 45
449 $1.50, Head and arm of Statue above scaffolding 40 60
450 $2 Ships with souvenir flags (*horiz*) .. 55 80
451 $2.50, Statue and New York waterfront .. 60 90
452 $3 Restoring Statue .. .. .. 80 1·25
443/52 .. .. *Set of* 10 3·75 4·75
MS453 Four sheets, each 85×115 mm. (a) $3.50, Statue at dusk. (b) $4 Head of Statue. (c) $4.50, Statue and lightning. (d) $5 Head and torch at sunset .. .. *Set of* 4 *sheets* 5·00 11·00

1986 (17 Nov). *Royal Wedding* (2*nd issue*). *Nos.* 406/9 *optd as T* **121** *of Montserrat in silver.*

454 60 c. Prince Andrew in midshipman's uniform 15 40
 a. Pair. Nos. 454/5.. .. .. .. 30 80
455 60 c. Miss Sarah Ferguson 15 40
456 $2 Prince Andrew on safari in Africa (*horiz*) 40 1·00
 a. Pair. Nos. 456/7.. .. .. .. 80 2·00
457 $2 Prince Andrew at the races (*horiz*) .. 40 1·00
454/7 .. .. *Set of* 4 1·00 2·50

42 Dinghy sailing

(Des G. Vasarhelyi. Litho Questa)

1986 (21 Nov). *Sports. T* **42** *and similar horiz designs. Multicoloured. P* 14.

458 10 c. Type **42** 10 10
459 25 c. Netball 30 15
460 $2 Cricket .. .. 2·00 2·25
461 $3 Basketball .. .. 2·25 2·50
458/61 .. .. *Set of* 4 4·25 4·50

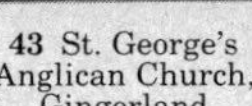

43 St. George's Anglican Church, Gingerland

44 Constitution Document, Quill and Inkwell

(Des J. Cooter. Litho Questa)

1986 (8 Dec). *Christmas. Churches of Nevis* (2*nd series*). *T* **43** *and similar horiz designs. Multicoloured. P* 14.

462 10 c. Type **43** 15 10
463 40 c. Trinity Methodist Church, Fountain .. 30 25
464 $1 Charlestown Methodist Church .. 60 65
465 $5 Wesleyan Holiness Church, Brown Hill .. .. 2·75 3·75
462/5 .. .. *Set of* 4 3·50 4·25

(Des Maxine Marsh. Litho Questa)

1987 (11 Jan). *Bicentenary of U.S. Constitution and* 230*th Birth Anniv of Alexander Hamilton* (*U.S. statesman*). *T* **44** *and similar vert designs. Multicoloured. P* 14.

466 15 c. Type **44** 10 10
467 40 c. Alexander Hamilton and Hamilton House 20 25
468 60 c. Alexander Hamilton 25 35
469 $2 Washington and his Cabinet .. .. 90 1·25
466/9 .. .. *Set of* 4 1·25 1·75
MS470 70×82 mm. $5 Model ship *Hamilton* on float, 1788 .. .. 6·50 7·50

America's Cup
1987 Winners
'Stars & Stripes'

(45)

1987 (20 Feb). *Victory of* Stars and Stripes *in America's Cup Yachting Championship. No.* 54 *optd with T* **45**.

471 $3 Windjammer's S.V. *Polynesia* .. .. 1·10 1·60

46 Fig Tree Church

(Des Maxine Marsh. Litho Questa)

1987 (11 Mar). *Bicentenary of Marriage of Horatio Nelson and Frances Nisbet. T* **46** *and similar horiz designs. Multicoloured. W w* **15**. *P* 14.

472 15 c. Type **46** 15 10
473 60 c. Frances Nisbet 40 30
474 $1 H.M.S. *Boreas* (frigate) .. .. 1·25 1·00
475 $3 Captain Horatio Nelson .. .. 2·50 3·25
472/5 .. .. *Set of* 4 3·75 4·25
MS476 102×82 mm. $3 As No. 473; $3 No. 475 5·00 6·50

47 Queen Angelfish

(Des C. Abbott. Litho Format)

1987 (6 July). *Coral Reef Fishes. T* **47** *and similar triangular designs. Multicoloured. P* 14½.

477 60 c. Type **47** 35 60
 a. Vert pair. Nos. 477/8 .. .. .. 70 1·10
478 60 c. Blue Angelfish 35 60
479 $1 Stoplight Parrotfish (male) 40 80
 a. Vert pair. Nos. 479/80 .. .. .. 80 1·60
480 $1 Stoplight Parrotfish (female) 40 80
481 $1.50, Red Hind 50 90
 a. Vert pair. Nos. 481/2 .. .. .. 1·00 1·75
482 $1.50, Rock Hind 50 90
483 $2.50, Coney (bicoloured phase) .. .. 70 1·50
 a. Vert pair. Nos. 483/4 .. .. .. 1·40 3·00
484 $2.50, Coney (red-brown phase) .. .. 70 1·50
477/84 .. .. *Set of* 8 3·50 6·75

Nos. 477/8, 479/80, 481/2 and 483/4 were each printed together, *se-tenant*, in pairs throughout the sheets. The second design for each value is in the form of an inverted triangle.

Nos. 477/84 exist imperforate from stock dispersed by the liquidator of Format International Security Printers Ltd.

48 *Panaeolus antillarum*

49 Rag Doll

(Des J. Cooter. Litho Format)

1987 (16 Oct). *Fungi* (1*st series*). *T* **48** *and similar vert designs. Multicoloured. W w* **16**. *P* 14.

485 15 c. Type **48** 85 30
486 50 c. *Pycnoporus sanguineus* .. .. .. 1·50 80
487 $2 *Gymnopilus chrysopellus* .. .. 3·00 3·25
488 $3 *Cantharellus cinnabarinus* .. .. 3·25 4·25
485/8 .. .. *Set of* 4 7·75 7·75

See also Nos. 646/54.

(Des J.W. Litho Walsall)

1987 (4 Dec). *Christmas. Toys. T* **49** *and similar horiz designs. Multicoloured. W w* **16** (*sideways*). *P* 14½.

489 10 c. Type **49** 10 10
490 40 c. Coconut boat 20 25
491 $1.20, Sandbox cart 55 60
492 $5 Two-wheeled cart .. .. 2·25 3·75
489/92 .. .. *Set of* 4 2·75 4·25

NEW INFORMATION

The editor is always interested to correspond with people who have new information that will improve or correct the Catalogue.

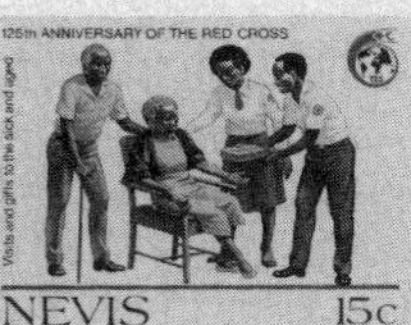

50 Hawk-wing Conch

51 Visiting Pensioners at Christmas

(Des Josephine Martin. Litho Questa)

1988 (15 Feb). *Seashells and Pearls. T* **50** *and similar vert designs. Multicoloured. W w* **16**. *P* 14½×14.

493 15 c. Type **50** 20 15
494 40 c. Rooster-tail Conch 30 20
495 60 c. Emperor Helmet 50 40
496 $2 Queen or Pink Conch .. .. .. 1·60 2·00
497 $3 King Helmet .. .. 1·75 2·25
493/7 .. .. *Set of* 5 4·00 4·50

(Des L. Curtis. Litho Walsall)

1988 (20 June). 125*th Anniv of International Red Cross. T* **51** *and similar horiz designs. Multicoloured. W w* **16** (*sideways*). *P* 14 × 14½.

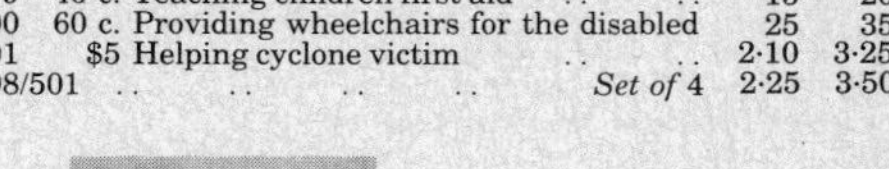

498 15 c. Type **51** 10 10
499 40 c. Teaching children first aid 15 20
500 60 c. Providing wheelchairs for the disabled 25 35
501 $5 Helping cyclone victim .. .. .. 2·10 3·25
498/501 .. .. *Set of* 4 2·25 3·50

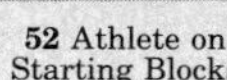

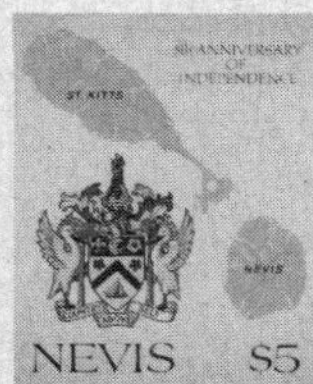

52 Athlete on Starting Blocks

53 Outline Map and Arms of St. Kitts–Nevis

(Des G. Vasarhelyi. Litho Format)

1988 (26 Aug). *Olympic Games, Seoul. T* **52** *and similar vert designs. Multicoloured. W w* **16**. *P* 14.

502 10 c. Type **52** 10 35
 a. Horiz strip of 4. Nos. 502/5 .. .. 2·40
503 $1.20, At start 50 85
504 $2 During race .. .. 85 1·25
505 $3 At finish .. .. 1·25 1·50
502/5 .. .. *Set of* 4 2·40 3·50
MS506 137 × 80 mm. As Nos. 502/5, but each size 24 × 36 mm. Wmk sideways .. .. 2·75 3·75

Nos. 502/5 were printed together, *se-tenant*, in horizontal strips of 4 throughout the sheet, each strip forming a composite design showing an athlete from start to finish of race.

(Des L. Curtis. Litho Questa)

1988 (19 Sept). 5*th Anniv of Independence. W w* **14**. *P* 14½ × 14.

507 **53** $5 multicoloured .. .. 2·10 2·75

(Des D. Miller (15 c., $2.50), E. Nisbet and D. Miller (60 c., $3). Litho Questa)

1988 (31 Oct). 300*th Anniversary of Lloyd's of London. Multicoloured designs as T* **167***a of Malawi. W w* **16** (*sideways on* 60 c., $2.50). *P* 14.

508 15 c. House of Commons passing Lloyd's Bill, 1871 .. .. 20 10
509 60 c. *Cunard Countess* (liner) (*horiz*) .. 1·10 65
510 $2.50, Space shuttle deploying satellite (*horiz*) .. .. 2·25 3·00
511 $3 *Viking Princess* (cargo liner) on fire, 1966 .. .. 2·25 3·00
508/11 .. .. *Set of* 4 5·25 6·00

54 Poinsettia

55 British Fleet off St. Kitts

(Des I. Loe. Litho Questa)

1988 (7 Nov). *Christmas. Flowers. T* **54** *and similar vert designs. Multicoloured. W w* **16**. *P* 14½ × 14.

512 15 c. Type **54** 10 10
513 40 c. Tiger Claws 15 20
514 60 c. Sorrel Flower 25 30
515 $1 Christmas Candle 40 60
516 $5 Snow Bush .. .. 2·10 3·25
512/16 .. .. *Set of* 5 2·75 4·00

(Des Jane Hartley. Litho Format)

1989 (17 Apr). *"Philexfrance 89" International Stamp Exhibition, Paris. Battle of Frigate Bay, 1782. T* **55** *and similar vert designs. Multicoloured.* W w **16**. P 13½×14 ($3) *or* 14 (*others*).

517	50 c. Type **55**	75	1·00
	a. Horiz strip of 3. Nos. 517/19	2·75	
518	$1.20, Battle off Nevis	1·00	1·40
519	$2 British and French fleets exchanging broadsides	1·25	1·60
520	$3 French map of Nevis, 1764	1·60	2·00
517/20	*Set of* 4	4·25	5·50

Nos. 517/19 were printed together, *se-tenant*, in horizontal strips of 3 throughout the sheet, each strip forming a composite design.

56 Cicada

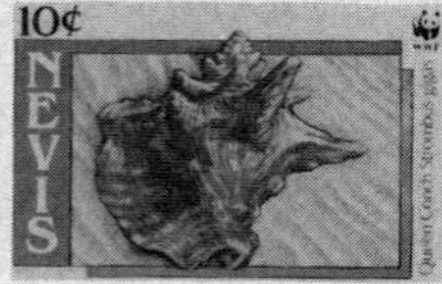

57 Queen or Pink Conch feeding

(Des I. Loe. Litho Questa)

1989 (15 May). *"Sounds of the Night". T* **56** *and similar vert designs. Multicoloured.* W w **16**. P 14.

521	10 c. Type **56**	20	15
522	40 c. Grasshopper	40	35
523	60 c. Cricket	55	50
524	$5 Tree frog	3·75	5·50
521/4	*Set of* 4	4·50	6·00
MS525	135×81 mm. Nos. 521/4	5·50	7·00

(Des A. Theobald ($6), D. Miller (others). Litho Questa)

1989 (20 July). *20th Anniv of First Manned Landing on Moon. Multicoloured designs as T* **51a** *of Kiribati.* W w **16** (*sideways on* 40 c., $2). P 14×13½ (15 c., $3) *or* 14 (*others*).

526	15 c. Vehicle Assembly Building, Kennedy Space Centre	15	10
527	40 c. Crew of "Apollo 12" (30×30 *mm*)	20	20
528	$2 "Apollo 12" emblem (30×30 *mm*)	1·00	1·60
529	$3 "Apollo 12" astronaut on Moon	1·40	1·90
	w. Wmk inverted	30·00	
526/9	*Set of* 4	2·50	3·50
MS530	100×83 mm. $6 Aldrin undertaking lunar seismic experiment. P 14×13½	2·50	3·50

(Des Deborah Dudley Max. Litho Questa)

1990 (31 Jan). *Queen or Pink Conch. T* **57** *and similar horiz designs. Multicoloured.* P 14.

531	10 c. Type **57**	40	15
532	40 c. Queen or Pink Conch from front	70	30
533	60 c. Side view of shell	90	70
534	$1 Back and flare	1·25	1·50
531/4	*Set of* 4	3·00	2·40
MS535	72×103 mm. $5 Underwater habitat	3·50	4·25

58 Wyon Medal Portrait

59

(Des M. Pollard. Litho B.D.T.)

1990 (3 May). *150th Anniv of the Penny Black. T* **58** *and similar vert designs.* P 14×15.

536	15 c. black and brown	15	10
537	40 c. black and deep blue-green	30	25
538	60 c. black	45	55
539	$4 black and ultramarine	2·50	3·25
536/9	*Set of* 4	3·00	3·75
MS540	114×84 mm. $5 blk, brn-lake & pale buff	3·75	4·50

Designs:—40 c. Engine-turned background; 60 c. Heath's engraving of portrait; $4 Essay with inscriptions; $5 Penny Black.

No. **MS**540 also commemorates "Stamp World London 90" International Stamp Exhibition.

(Des S. Pollard. Litho B.D.T.)

1990 (3 May). *500th Anniv of Regular European Postal Services. T* **59** *and similar square designs with different corner emblems.* P 13½.

541	15 c. brown	20	15
542	40 c. deep dull green	35	25
543	60 c. bright reddish violet	55	65
544	$4 ultramarine	2·75	3·50
541/4	*Set of* 4	3·50	4·00
MS545	110×82 mm. $5 brown-lake, pale buff and pale grey	3·75	4·50

Nos. 541/5 commemorate the Thurn and Taxis postal service and the designs are loosely based on those of the initial 1852–58 series.

60 Sand Fiddler Crab

(Des Mary Walters. Litho Questa)

1990 (25 June). *500th Anniv of Discovery of America by Columbus (1992) (2nd issue). New World Natural History – Crabs. T* **60** *and similar horiz designs. Multicoloured.* P 14.

546	5 c. Type **60**	10	10
547	15 c. Great Land Crab	15	15
548	20 c. Blue Crab	15	15
549	40 c. Stone Crab	30	30
550	60 c. Mountain Crab	45	45
551	$2 Sargassum Crab	1·40	1·60
552	$3 Yellow Box Crab	1·75	2·00
553	$4 Spiny Spider Crab	2·25	2·50
546/53	*Set of* 8	6·00	6·50
MS554	Two sheets, each 101×70 mm. (a) $5 Sally Lightfoot. (b) $5 Wharf Crab *Set of* 2 *sheets*	7·00	8·50

(Des Young Phillips Studio. Litho Questa)

1990 (5 July). *90th Birthday of Queen Elizabeth the Queen Mother. Vert designs as T* **198a** *of Lesotho showing portraits, 1930–39.* P 14.

555	$2 brownish black, magenta and pale buff	1·40	1·60
	a. Strip of 3. Nos. 555/7	3·75	
556	$2 brownish black, magenta and pale buff	1·40	1·60
557	$2 brownish black, magenta and pale buff	1·40	1·60
555/7	*Set of* 3	3·75	4·25
MS558	90×75 mm. $6 chestnut, magenta & blk	3·50	4·25

Designs:—No. 555, Duchess of York with corgi; No. 556, Queen Elizabeth in Coronation robes, 1937; No. 557, Duchess of York in garden; No. **MS**558, Queen Elizabeth in Coronation robes, 1937 (*different*).

Nos. 555/7 were printed together, horizontally and vertically *se-tenant*, in sheetlets of 9 (3×3).

61 MaKanaky, Cameroons

62 *Cattleya deckeri*

(Des Young Phillips Studio. Litho Questa)

1990 (1 Oct). *World Cup Football Championship, Italy. Star Players. T* **61** *and similar vert designs. Multicoloured.* P 14.

559	10 c. Type **61**	20	10
560	25 c. Chovanec, Czechoslovakia	30	15
561	$2.50, Robson, England	2·00	2·50
562	$5 Voller, West Germany	3·50	4·00
559/62	*Set of* 4	5·50	6·00
MS563	Two sheets, each 90×75 mm. (a) $5 Maradona, Argentina (b) $5 Gordillo, Spain *Set of* 2 *sheets*	6·25	7·50

(Des Mary Walters. Litho B.D.T.)

1990 (19 Nov). *Christmas. Native Orchids. T* **62** *and similar vert designs. Multicoloured.* P 14.

564	10 c. Type **62**	30	20
565	15 c. *Epidendrum ciliare*	30	20
566	20 c. *Epidendrum fragrans*	40	20
567	40 c. *Epidendrum ibaguense*	55	25
568	60 c. *Epidendrum latifolium*	75	50
569	$1.20, *Maxillaria conferta*	1·10	1·25
570	$2 *Epidendrum strobiliferum*	1·50	2·00
571	$3 *Brassavola cucullata*	1·75	2·50
564/71	*Set of* 8	6·00	6·25
MS572	102×71 mm. $5 *Rodriguezia lanceolata*	6·50	7·00

(Des T. Agans. Litho Questa)

1991 (14 Jan). *350th Death Anniv of Rubens. Multicoloured designs as T* **250** *of Maldive Islands, showing details from "The Feast of Achelous".* P 13½×14.

573	10 c. Two jugs (*vert*)	15	15
574	40 c. Woman at table (*vert*)	30	30
575	60 c. Two servants with fruit (*vert*)	45	45
576	$4 Achelous (*vert*)	2·25	2·75
573/6	*Set of* 4	2·75	3·25
MS577	101×71 mm. $5 "The Feast of Achelous". P 14×13½	2·75	3·50

63 *Agraulis vanillae*

(Des L. Nelson. Litho Questa)

1991 (1 Mar)–**92**. *Butterflies. T* **63** *and similar horiz designs. Multicoloured.* P 14. *A. Without imprint date. B. With imprint date* (1.3.92).

		A		B	
578	5 c. Type **63**	25	30	10	10
579	10 c. *Historis odius*	25	15	10	10
580	15 c. *Marpesia corinna*	30	15	10	10
581	20 c. *Anartia amathea*	40	20	10	10
582	25 c. *Junonia evarete*	40	20	10	10
583	40 c. *Heliconius charithonia*	50	30	20	25
584	50 c. *Marpesia petreus*	50	40	25	30
585	60 c. *Dione juno*	55	40	†	
586	75 c. *Heliconius doris*	65	65	35	40
586c	80 c. As 60 c.	†		35	40
587	$1 *Hypolimnas misippus*	70	70	45	50
588	$3 *Danaus plexippus*	1·75	2·00	1·40	1·50
589	$5 *Heliconius sara*	2·50	3·25	2·25	2·40
590	$10 *Tithorea harmonia*	4·75	6·00	4·50	4·75
591	$20 *Dryas julia*	9·50	11·00	9·25	9·50
578/91	*Set of* 14	21·00	23·00	19·00	20·00

Nos. 579A/B are inscribed "Historis osius", Nos. 581A/B "Anatria amathea", Nos. 583A/B "Heliconius charitonius", Nos. 587A/B "Hypolimanas misippus" and Nos. 591A/B "Dryas iulia" all in error.

Imprint dates: "1992", Nos. 578B/84B, 586B/91B; "1994", Nos. 578B/9B, 582B, 584B, 586cB.

64 "Viking Mars Lander", 1976

(Des T. Agans. Litho Questa)

1991 (23 Apr). *500th Anniv of Discovery of America by Columbus (1992) (3rd issue). History of Exploration. T* **64** *and similar multicoloured designs.* P 14.

592	15 c. Type **64**	20	15
593	40 c. "Apollo 11", 1969	30	25
594	60 c. "Skylab", 1973	45	45
595	75 c. "Salyut 6", 1977	55	55
596	$1 "Voyager 1", 1977	65	65
597	$2 "Venera 7", 1970	1·25	1·40
598	$4 "Gemini 4", 1965	2·50	2·75
599	$5 "Luna 3", 1959	2·75	3·00
592/9	*Set of* 8	7·75	8·50
MS600	Two sheets each 105×76 mm. (a) $6 Bow of *Santa Maria* (*vert*). (b) $6 Christopher Columbus (*vert*) *Set of* 2 *sheets*	8·00	9·00

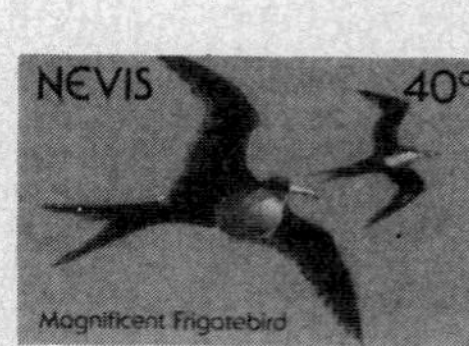

65 Magnificent Frigate Bird

66 *Marasmius haemtocephalus*

(Des Jennifer Toombs. Litho Questa)

1991 (28 May). *Island Birds. T* **65** *and similar horiz designs. Multicoloured.* P 14.

601	40 c. Type **65**	45	45
	a. Sheetlet. Nos. 601/20	8·00	
602	40 c. Roseate Tern	45	45
603	40 c. Red-tailed Hawk	45	45
604	40 c. Zenaida Dove	45	45
605	40 c. Bananaquit	45	45
606	40 c. American Kestrel	45	45
607	40 c. Grey Kingbird	45	45
608	40 c. Prothonotary Warbler	45	45
609	40 c. Blue-hooded Euphonia	45	45
610	40 c. Antillean Crested Hummingbird	45	45
611	40 c. White-tailed Tropic Bird	45	45
612	40 c. Yellow-bellied Sapsucker	45	45
613	40 c. Green-throated Carib	45	45
614	40 c. Purple-throated Carib	45	45
615	40 c. Red-billed Whistling Duck ("Black-bellied Tree-duck")	45	45
616	40 c. Ringed Kingfisher	45	45
617	40 c. Burrowing Owl	45	45
618	40 c. Turnstone	45	45
619	40 c. Great Blue Heron	45	45
620	40 c. Yellow-crowned Night-heron	45	45
601/20	*Set of* 20	8·00	8·00
MS621	76×59 mm. $6 Great Egret	7·50	8·50

Nos. 601/20 were printed together, *se-tenant*, in sheetlets of 20, forming a composite design.

(Des D. Miller. Litho Walsall)

1991 (5 July). *65th Birthday of Queen Elizabeth II. Horiz designs as T* **210** *of Lesotho. Multicoloured.* P 14.

622	15 c. Queen Elizabeth at polo match with Prince Charles	30	20
623	40 c. Queen and Prince Philip on Buckingham Palace balcony	45	35
624	$2 In carriage at Ascot, 1986	1·40	1·75
625	$4 Queen Elizabeth II at Windsor polo match, 1989	2·75	3·75
622/5	*Set of* 4	4·50	5·50
MS626	68×90 mm. $5 Queen Elizabeth and Prince Philip	4·00	5·00

(Des D. Miller. Litho Walsall)

1991 (5 July). *10th Wedding Anniv of Prince and Princess of Wales. Horiz designs as T* **210** *of Lesotho. Multicoloured. P* 14.

627 10 c. Prince Charles and Princess Diana .. 20 20
628 50 c. Prince of Wales and family .. 50 30
629 $1 Prince William and Prince Harry .. 85 90
630 $5 Prince and Princess of Wales .. 3·00 3·50
627/30 .. .. *Set of* 4 4·00 4·50
MS631 68×90 mm. $5 Prince and Princess of Wales in Hungary, and young princes at Christmas .. .. 4·25 5·00

(Litho Questa)

1991 (12 Aug). *"Phila Nippon '91" International Stamp Exhibition, Tokyo. Japanese Railway Locomotives. Multicoloured designs as T* **257** *of Maldive Islands. P* 14.

632 10 c. Class "C62" steam locomotive .. 25 25
633 15 c. Class "C56" steam locomotive (*horiz*) 25 25
634 40 c. Class "C-55" streamlined steam locomotive (*horiz*) 40 40
635 60 c. Class "1400" steam locomotive (*horiz*) 65 65
636 $1 Class "485 Bonnet" diesel rail car .. 85 85
637 $2 Class "C61" steam locomotive .. 1·75 1·75
638 $3 Class "485" express train (*horiz*) .. 2·25 2·25
639 $4 Class "7000" electric train (*horiz*) .. 2·75 2·75
632/9 .. .. *Set of* 8 8·00 8·00
MS640 Two sheets, each, 108×72 mm. (a) $5 Class "D51" steam locomotive (*horiz*). (b) $5 Hikari Bullet Train (*horiz*) .. *Set of* 2 *sheets* 8·00 8·50

(Litho B.D.T.)

1991 (20 Dec). *Christmas. Drawings by Albrecht Dürer. Vert designs as T* **211** *of Lesotho. P* 13.

641 10 c. black and apple-green 10 10
642 40 c. black and yellow-orange 20 25
643 60 c. black and new blue 25 30
644 $3 black and bright mauve .. .. 1·40 2·40
641/4 .. .. *Set of* 4 1·90 2·75
MS645 Two sheets, each 96×124 mm. (a) $6 black. (b) $6 black .. .. *Set of* 2 *sheets* 5·50 6·25

Designs:—10 c. "Mary being Crowned by an Angel"; 40 c. "Mary with the Pear"; 60 c. "Mary in a Halo"; $3 "Mary with Crown of Stars and Sceptre"; $6 (No. **MS**645a) "The Holy Family" (detail); $6 (No. **MS**645b) "Mary at the Yard Gate" (detail).

(Des D. Miller. Litho B.D.T.)

1991 (20 Dec). *Fungi (2nd series). T* **66** *and similar multicoloured designs. P* 14.

646 15 c. Type **66** 10 10
647 40 c. *Psilocybe cubensis* 20 25
648 60 c. *Hygrocybe acutoconica* 25 30
649 75 c. *Hygrocybe occidentalis* 35 40
650 $1 *Boletellus cubensis* 45 50
651 $2 *Gymnopilus chrysopellus* 90 95
652 $4 *Cantharellus cinnabarinus* .. .. 1·90 2·00
653 $5 *Chlorophyllum molybdites* .. .. 2·25 2·40
646/53 .. .. *Set of* 8 6·25 6·75
MS654 Two sheets, each 70×58 mm. (a) $6 *Psilocybe cubensis, Hygrocybe acutoconica* and *Boletellus cubensis* (*horiz*). (b) $6 *Hygrocybe occidentalis, Marasmius haematocephalus* and *Gymnopilus chrysopellus* (*horiz*) *Set of* 2 *sheets* 5·50 5·75

(Des D. Miller. Litho Questa)

1992 (26 Feb). *40th Anniv of Queen Elizabeth II's Accession. Horiz designs as T* **214** *of Lesotho. Multicoloured. P* 14.

655 10 c. Charlestown from the sea 20 10
656 40 c. Charlestown square 30 25
657 $1 Mountain scenery 60 50
658 $5 Early cottage .. .. .. 2·50 3·00
655/8 .. .. *Set of* 4 3·25 3·50
MS659 Two sheets, each 74×97 mm. (a) $6 Queen or Pink Conch on beach. (b) $6 Nevis sunset .. .. *Set of* 2 *sheets* 6·00 6·50

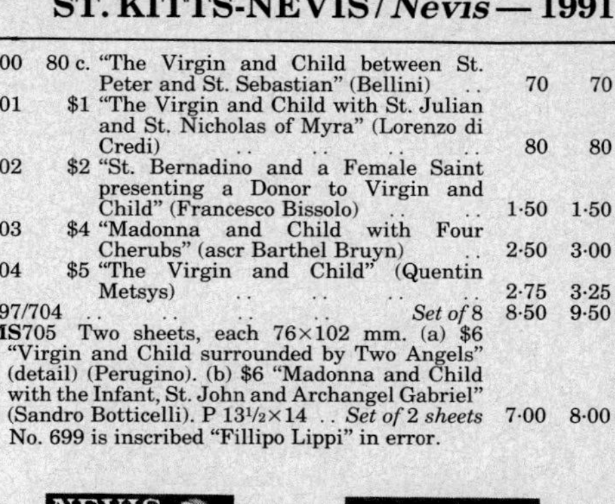

67 Monique Knol (cycling), Netherlands

68 "Landscape" (Mariano Fortuny i Marsal)

(Des R. Sauber. Litho B.D.T.)

1992 (7 May). *Olympic Games, Barcelona. Gold Medal Winners of 1988. T* **67** *and similar vert designs. Multicoloured. P* 14.

660 20 c. Type **67** 30 30
661 25 c. Roger Kingdom (hurdles), U.S.A. .. 30 30
662 50 c. Yugoslavia (men's waterpolo) .. 50 50
663 80 c. Anja Fichtel (foil), West Germany .. 70 70
664 $1 Said Aouita, (mid-distance running), Morocco 80 80
665 $1.50, Yuri Sedykh (hammer throw), U.S.S.R. .. .. 1·10 1·10
666 $3 Shushunova (women's gymnastics), U.S.S.R. .. .. 2·00 2·50
667 $5 Valimir Artemov (men's gymnastics), U.S.S.R. .. .. 2·50 3·00
660/7 .. .. *Set of* 8 7·25 8·25
MS668 Two sheets, each 103×73 mm. (a) $6 Niam Suleymanoglu (weightlifting), Turkey. (b) $6 Florence Griffith-Joyner (women's 100 metres), U.S.A. .. .. *Set of* 2 *sheets* 5·50 6·25

No. 660 is inscribed "FRANCE" in error.

(Litho B.D.T.)

1992 (1 June). *"Granada '92" International Stamp Exhibition, Spain. Spanish Paintings. T* **68** *and similar multicoloured designs. P* 13×13½ (*vert*) *or* 13½×13 (*horiz*).

669 20 c. Type **68** 10 10
670 25 c. "Dona Juana la Loca" (Francisco Pradilla Ortiz) (*horiz*) 10 10
671 50 c. "Idyll" (Fortuny i Marsal) 25 30
672 80 c. "Old Man Naked in the Sun" (Fortuny i Marsal) 35 40
673 $1 "The Painter's Children in the Japanese Salon" (detail) (Fortuny i Marsal) 45 50
674 $2 "The Painter's Children in the Japanese Salon" (different detail) (Fortuny i Marsal) 90 95
675 $3 "Still Life: Sea Bream and Oranges" (Luis Eugenio Meléndez) (*horiz*) .. 1·40 1·50
676 $5 "Still Life: Box of Sweets, Pastry and Other Objects" (Meléndez) .. .. 2·25 2·40
669/76 .. .. *Set of* 8 5·75 6·25
MS677 Two sheets, each 121×95 mm. (a) $6 "Bullfight" (Fortuny i Marsal) (111×86 *mm*). (b) $6 "Moroccans" (Fortuny i Marsal) (111×86 *mm*). Imperf .. .. .. *Set of* 2 *sheets* 5·50 5·75

69 Early Compass and Ship

70 Minnie Mouse

(Des L. Fried. Litho Questa)

1992 (6 July). *500th Anniv of Discovery of America by Columbus (4th issue) and "World Columbian Stamp Expo '92", Chicago. T* **69** *and similar multicoloured designs. P* 14.

678 20 c. Type **69** 25 25
679 50 c. Manatee and fleet 50 50
680 80 c. Green Turtle and *Santa Maria* .. 70 80
681 $1.50, *Santa Maria* and arms .. .. 1·25 1·75
682 $3 Queen Isabella of Spain and commission .. .. 2·25 2·75
683 $5 Pineapple and colonists .. .. 3·00 3·50
678/83 .. .. *Set of* 6 7·25 8·50
MS684 Two sheets, each 101×70 mm. (a) $6 British Storm Petrel and town (*horiz*). (b) $6 Peppers and Carib canoe (*horiz*) *Set of* 2 *sheets* 8·50 10·00

(Des F. Paul ($1), J. Esquino ($2). Litho Questa)

1992 (24 Aug). *500th Anniv of Discovery of America by Columbus (5th issue). Organization of East Caribbean States. Vert designs as Nos. 911/12 of Montserrat. Multicoloured. P* 14½.

685 $1 Columbus meeting Amerindians .. 45 50
686 $2 Ships approaching island 90 95

(Des Kerri Schiff. Litho Questa)

1992 (28 Oct). *Postage Stamp Mega Event, New York. Sheet 100×70 mm containing multicoloured design as T* **219** *of Lesotho. P* 14.

MS687 $6 Empire State Building .. .. 3·00 3·50

(Des Walt Disney Co. Litho Questa)

1992 (9 Nov). *Mickey's Portrait Gallery. T* **70** *and similar multicoloured designs. P* 13½×14.

688 10 c. Type **70** 20 20
689 15 c. Mickey Mouse 20 20
690 40 c. Donald Duck 30 25
691 80 c. Mickey Mouse, 1930 .. .. .. 50 50
692 $1 Daisy Duck 65 65
693 $2 Pluto .. .. 1·25 1·25
694 $4 Goofy .. .. 2·25 2·50
695 $5 Goofy, 1932 .. .. 2·25 2·50
688/95 .. .. *Set of* 8 7·00 7·25
MS696 Two sheets. (a) 102×128 mm. $6 Mickey in armchair (*horiz*). (b) 128×102 mm. $6 Mickey and Minnie in airplane (*horiz*). P 13½ *Set of* 2 *sheets* 7·50 8·00

(Litho Questa)

1992 (16 Nov.). *Christmas. Religious Paintings. Vert designs as T* **218** *of Lesotho. Multicoloured. P* 13½.

697 20 c. "The Virgin and Child between Two Saints" (Giovanni Bellini) 30 15
698 40 c. "The Virgin and Child surrounded by Four Angels" (Master of the Castello Nativity) 45 25
699 50 c. "Virgin and Child surrounded by Angels with St. Frediano and St. Augustine" (detail) (Filippo Lippi) .. 50 30
700 80 c. "The Virgin and Child between St. Peter and St. Sebastian" (Bellini) .. 70 70
701 $1 "The Virgin and Child with St. Julian and St. Nicholas of Myra" (Lorenzo di Credi) 80 80
702 $2 "St. Bernadino and a Female Saint presenting a Donor to Virgin and Child" (Francesco Bissolo) .. .. 1·50 1·50
703 $4 "Madonna and Child with Four Cherubs" (ascr Barthel Bruyn) .. 2·50 3·00
704 $5 "The Virgin and Child" (Quentin Metsys) .. .. 2·75 3·25
697/704 .. .. *Set of* 8 8·50 9·50
MS705 Two sheets, each 76×102 mm. (a) $6 "Virgin and Child surrounded by Two Angels" (detail) (Perugino). (b) $6 "Madonna and Child with the Infant, St. John and Archangel Gabriel" (Sandro Botticelli). P 13½×14 .. *Set of* 2 *sheets* 7·00 8·00

No. 699 is inscribed "Fillipo Lippi" in error.

71 Care Bear and Butterfly

72 Japanese Launch Vehicle H-11

(Des T.C.F.C. Inc. Litho Questa)

1993 (14 Jan). *Ecology. T* **71** *and similar vert design showing Care Bear cartoon characters. Multicoloured. P* 14.

706 80 c. Type **71** 60 60
MS707 71×101 mm. $2 Care Bear on beach .. 1·25 1·50

(Litho Walsall)

1993 (14 Jan). *Bicentenary of the Louvre, Paris. Vert designs as T* **221** *of Lesotho. Multicoloured. P* 12.

708 $1 "The Card Cheat" (left detail) (La Tour) 45 50
a. Sheetlet. Nos. 708/15 .. .. 3·50
709 $1 "The Card Cheat" (centre detail) (La Tour) 45 50
710 $1 "The Card Cheat" (right detail) (La Tour) 45 50
711 $1 "St. Joseph, the Carpenter" (La Tour) 45 50
712 $1 "St. Thomas" (La Tour) 45 50
713 $1 "Adoration of the Shepherds" (left detail) (La Tour) 45 50
714 $1 "Adoration of the Shepherds" (right detail) (La Tour) 45 50
715 $1 "Mary Magdalene with a Candle" (La Tour) 45 50
708/15 .. .. *Set of* 8 3·50 4·00
MS716 70×100 mm. $6 "Archangel Raphael leaving the Family of Tobius" (Rembrandt) (52×85 *mm*). P 14½ .. .. 2·75 3·00

Nos. 708/15 were printed together, *se-tenant*, in sheetlets of 8 stamps and one centre label.

(Des A. Nahigian. Litho Questa)

1993 (14 Jan). *15th Death Anniv of Elvis Presley (singer). Vert designs as Nos. 1772/4 of Maldive Islands. Multicoloured. P* 14.

717 $1 Elvis Presley 45 50
a. Strip of 3. Nos. 717/19 .. .. 1·25
718 $1 Elvis with guitar 45 50
719 $1 Elvis with microphone 45 50
717/19 .. .. *Set of* 3 1·25 1·50

Nos. 717/19 were printed together, horizontally and vertically *se-tenant*, in sheetlets of 9 (3×3).

(Des W. Wright and L. Fried (Nos. 720, 731, **MS**734a), W. Wright and W. Hanson (Nos. 721, 732, **MS**734b), J. Genzo (Nos. 728, **MS**734e), W. Wright (others). Litho B.D.T.)

1993 (14 Jan). *Anniversaries and Events. T* **72** *and similar multicoloured designs. P* 14.

720 15 c. Type **72** 30 20
721 50 c. Airship LZ-129 *Hindenburg* on fire, 1937 (*horiz*) 50 50
722 75 c. Konrad Adenauer and Charles de Gaulle (*horiz*) 65 65
723 80 c. Red Cross emblem and map of Nevis (*horiz*) 70 70
724 80 c. *Resolute*, 1920 .. .. 70 70
725 80 c. Nelson Museum and map of Nevis (*horiz*) 70 70
726 80 c. St. Thomas's Church (*horiz*) 70 70
727 $1 Blue Whale (*horiz*) .. .. .. 1·00 80
728 $3 Mozart .. .. 1·40 1·50
729 $3 Graph and U.N. emblems (*horiz*) .. 1·60 1·60
730 $3 Lions Club emblem .. .. .. 1·60 1·60
731 $5 Soviet "Energia" launch vehicle SL-17 3·00 3·50
732 $5 Lebaudy-Juillot airship No. 1 *La Jaune*, 1903 (*horiz*) .. .. .. 3·00 3·50
733 $5 Adenauer and Pres. Kennedy (*horiz*) 3·00 3·50
720/33 .. .. *Set of* 14 16·00 17·00
MS734 Five sheets. (a) 104×71 mm. $6 Astronaut. (b) 104×71 mm. $6 Zeppelin LZ-5, 1909 (*horiz*). (c) 100×70 mm. $6 Konrad Adenauer (*horiz*). (d) 75×103 mm. $6 *America 3*, 1992 (*horiz*). (e) 98×66 mm. $6 Masked reveller from *Don Giovanni* (*horiz*) .. *Set of* 5 *sheets* 15·00 17·00

Anniversaries and Events:—Nos. 720, 731, **MS**734a, International Space Year; Nos. 721, 732, **MS**734b, 75th death anniv of Count Ferdinand von Zeppelin (airship pioneer); Nos. 722, 733, **MS**734c, 25th death anniv of Konrad Adenauer (German statesman); No. 723, 50th anniv of St. Kitts-Nevis Red Cross; Nos. 724, **MS**734d, Americas Cup Yachting Championship; No. 725, Opening of Nelson Museum; No. 726,

150th anniv of Anglican Diocese of North-eastern Caribbean and Aruba; No. 727, Earth Summit '92, Rio; Nos. 728, **MS**734e, Death bicent of Mozart; No. 729, International Conference on Nutrition, Rome; No. 730, 75th anniv of International Association of Lions Clubs.

73 *Plumeria rubra* **74** Antillean Blue (male)

(Des Mary Walters, Litho Questa)

1993 (26 Mar). *West Indian Flowers. T* **73** *and similar vert designs. Multicoloured. P* 14.
735 10 c. Type **73** 30 20
736 25 c. *Bougainvillea* 40 20
737 50 c. *Allamanda cathartica* 55 40
738 80 c. *Anthurium andraeanum* 75 70
739 $1 *Ixora coccinea* 85 75
740 $2 *Hibiscus rosa-sinensis* 1·50 1·50
741 $4 *Justicia brandegeeana* 2·75 3·25
742 $5 *Antigonon leptopus* 2·75 3·25
735/42 *Set of* 8 9·00 9·25
MS743 Two sheets, each 100×70 mm. (a) $6 *Lantana camara*. (b) $6 *Petrea volubilis* *Set of* 2 *sheets* 7·50 8·50

(Des T. Muse. Litho Questa)

1993 (17 May). *Butterflies. T* **74** *and similar horiz designs. Multicoloured. P* 14.
744 10 c. Type **74** 40 30
745 25 c. Cuban Crescentspot (female) 55 30
746 50 c. Ruddy Daggerwing 70 50
747 80 c. Little Yellow (male) 85 75
748 $1 Atala 1·00 80
749 $1.50, Orange-barred Giant Sulphur 1·40 1·40
750 $4 Tropic Queen (male) 2·75 3·25
751 $5 Malachite 2·75 3·25
744/51 *Set of* 8 9·50 9·50
MS752 Two sheets, each 76×105 mm. (a) $6 Polydamus Swallowtail (male). (b) $6 West Indian Buckeye *Set of* 2 *sheets* 7·50 8·50

(Des Kerri Schiff. Litho Questa)

1993 (2 June). *40th Anniv of Coronation. Vert designs as T* **224** *of Lesotho. P* 13½×14.
753 10 c. multicoloured 10 10
a. Sheetlet. Nos. 753/6×2 6·50
754 80 c. deep chocolate and black 35 40
755 $2 multicoloured 90 95
756 $4 multicoloured 1·90 2·00
753/6 *Set of* 4 3·25 3·25
MS757 71×101 mm. $6 multicoloured. P 14 2·75 3·00
Designs: (38×47 *mm*)—10 c. Queen Elizabeth II at Coronation (photograph by Cecil Beaton); 80 c. Queen wearing Imperial State Crown; $2 Crowning of Queen Elizabeth II; $4 Queen and Prince Charles at polo match. (28½×42½ *mm*)—$6 "Queen Elizabeth II, 1977" (detail) (Susan Crawford).
Nos. 753/6 were printed together in sheetlets of 8 containing two *se-tenant* blocks of 4.

75 Flag and National Anthem **76** "Annunciation of Mary" (Dürer)

(Des Jennifer Toombs. Litho B.D.T.)

1993 (19 Sept). *10th Anniv of Independence of St. Kitts-Nevis. T* **75** *and similar vert design. Multicoloured. P* 13½.
758 25 c. Type **75** 30 10
759 80 c. Brown Pelican and map of St. Kitts-Nevis 70 60

(Des Rosemary DeFiglio. Litho Cartor)

1993 (9 Nov). *World Cup Football Championship* 1994, *U.S.A. Multicoloured designs as T* **278** *of Maldive Islands. P* 14×13½.
760 10 c. Imre Garaba (Hungary) and Michel Platini (France) (*horiz*) 20 15
761 25 c. Diego Maradona (Argentina) and Giuseppe Bergomi (Italy) (*horiz*) 30 15
762 50 c. Luis Fernandez (France) and Vasily Rats (Russia) (*horiz*) 50 40
763 80 c. Victor Munez (Spain) (*horiz*) 70 55
764 $1 Preben Elkjaer (Denmark) and Andoni Goicoechea (Spain) (*horiz*) 80 65
765 $2 Elzo Coelho (Brazil) and Jean Tigana (France) (*horiz*) 1·40 1·40
766 $3 Pedro Troglio (Argentina) and Sergei Alejnikov (Russia) (*horiz*) 1·75 2·00
767 $5 Jan Karas (Poland) and Antonio Luiz Costa (Brazil) (*horiz*) 2·50 3·00
760/7 *Set of* 8 7·25 7·50
MS768 Two sheets. (a) 100×70 mm. $5 Belloumi (Algeria) (*horiz*). (b) 70×100 mm. $5 Trevor Steven (England). P 13 *Set of* 2 *sheets* 7·00 7·50

(Litho Cartor)

1993 (30 Nov). *Christmas. Religious Paintings. T* **76** *and similar designs. Black, pale lemon and red* (*Nos.* 769/73, 776, **MS**777a) *or multicoloured* (*others*). *P* 13.
769 20 c. Type **76** 25 10
770 40 c. "The Nativity" (drawing) (Dürer) 40 25
771 50 c. "Holy Family on a Grassy Bank" (Dürer) 50 30
772 80 c. "The Presentation of Christ in the Temple" (Dürer) 70 50
773 $1 "Virgin in Glory on the Crescent" (Dürer) 80 60
774 $1.60, "The Nativity" (painting) (Dürer) 1·25 1·25
775 $3 "Madonna and Child" (Dürer) 1·75 2·00
776 $5 "The Presentation of Christ in the Temple" (detail) (Dürer) 2·50 3·00
769/76 *Set of* 8 7·25 7·25
MS777 Two sheets, each 105×130 mm. (a) $6 "Mary, Child and the Long-tailed Monkey" (detail) (Dürer). (b) $6 "The Rest on the Flight into Egypt" (detail) (Jean-Honore Fragonard) (*horiz*) *Set of* 2 *sheets* 7·50 8·00

77 Mickey Mouse playing Basketball

(Litho Questa)

1994 (15 Feb). *Sports and Pastimes. T* **77** *and similar multicoloured designs showing Walt Disney cartoon characters. P* 14×13½ (*horiz*) *or* 13½×14 (*vert*).
778 10 c. Type **77** 20 15
779 25 c. Minnie Mouse sunbathing (*vert*) 25 15
780 50 c. Mickey playing volleyball 45 35
781 80 c. Minnie dancing (*vert*) 60 50
782 $1 Mickey playing football 75 60
783 $1.50, Minnie hula hooping (*vert*) 1·25 1·25
784 $4 Minnie skipping (*vert*) 2·50 2·75
785 $5 Mickey wrestling Big Pete 2·50 2·75
778/85 *Set of* 8 7·75 7·75
MS786 Two sheets. (a) 127×102 mm. $6 Mickey, Donald Duck and Goofy in tug of war (black, bright rosine and blue-green). (b) 102×127 mm. $6 Mickey using Test your Strength machine *Set of* 2 *sheets* 8·00 8·00

(Litho Questa)

1994 (18 Feb). *"Hong Kong '94" International Stamp Exhibition. No.* **MS**752 *optd with* "HONG KONG '94" *logo on sheet margins.*
MS787 Two sheets, each 76×105 mm. (a) $6 Polydamas Swallowtail (male). (b) $6 West Indian Buckeye *Set of* 2 *sheets* 7·50 8·00

(Litho Questa)

1994 (6 Apr). *Hummel Figurines. Vert designs as T* **256** *of Maldive Islands. Multicoloured. P* 14.
788 5 c. Girl with umbrella 10 20
789 25 c. Boy holding beer mug and parsnips 25 10
790 50 c. Girl sitting in tree 45 35
791 80 c. Boy in hat and scarf 60 50
792 $1 Boy with umbrella 75 60
793 $1.60, Girl with bird 1·25 1·25
794 $2 Boy on sledge 1·50 1·50
795 $5 Boy sitting in apple tree 2·50 3·00
788/95 *Set of* 8 6·50 6·75
MS796 Two sheets, each 94×125 mm. (a) Nos. 788 and 792/4. (b) Nos. 789/91 and 795 *Set of* 2 *sheets* 6·50 7·00

79 Beekeeper collecting Wild Nest

(Des R. Vigurs. Litho Questa)

1994 (13 June). *Beekeeping. T* **79** *and similar horiz designs. Multicoloured. P* 14.
797 50 c. Type **79** 35 30
798 80 c. Beekeeping club 55 40
799 $1.60, Extracting honey from frames 1·10 1·10
800 $3 Keepers placing queen in hive 2·00 2·25
797/800 *Set of* 4 3·50 3·50
MS801 100×70 mm. $6 Queen and workers in hive and mechanical honey extractor 3·50 4·00

80 Blue Point Himalayan **81** Black Coral

(Des R. Sauber. Litho Questa)

1994 (20 July). *Persian Cats. T* **80** *and similar horiz designs. Multicoloured. P* 14.
802 80 c. Type **80** 35 40
a. Sheetlet. Nos. 802/9 2·75
803 80 c. Black and White Persian 35 40
804 80 c. Cream Persian 35 40
805 80 c. Red Persian 35 40
806 80 c. Persian 35 40
807 80 c. Persian Black Smoke 35 40
808 80 c. Chocolate Smoke Persian 35 40
809 80 c. Black Persian 35 40
802/9 *Set of* 8 2·75 3·00
MS810 Two sheets, each 100×70 mm. (a) $6 Silver Tabby Persian. (b) $6 Brown Tabby Persian *Set of* 2 *sheets* 5·50 5·75
Nos. 802/9 were printed together, *se-tenant*, in sheetlets of 8.

(Des P. Chinelli. Litho Questa)

1994 (25 July). *Endangered Species. Black Coral. T* **81** *and similar vert designs showing forms of coral. P* 14.
811 25 c. multicoloured 30 30
a. Horiz strip of 4. Nos. 811/14 1·40
812 40 c. multicoloured 40 40
813 50 c. multicoloured 40 40
814 80 c. multicoloured 50 50
811/14 *Set of* 4 1·40 1·40
Nos. 811/14 were printed in small sheets of 12 containing three horizontal *se-tenant* strips of 4 with each horizontal row starting with a different value.

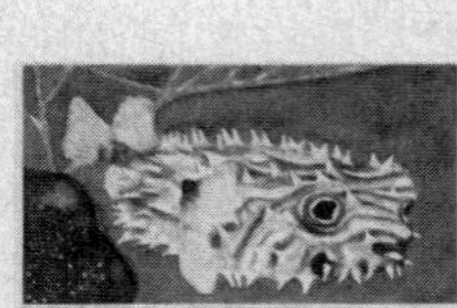

82 Striped Burrfish **83** Symbol 1. Turtles and Cloud

(Des P. Chinelli. Litho Questa)

1994 (25 July). *Fishes. T* **82** *and similar multicoloured designs. P* 14.
815 10 c. Type **82** 20 20
816 50 c. Flame-backed Angelfish 35 35
a. Sheetlet. Nos. 816/23 2·50
817 50 c. Reef Bass 35 35
818 50 c. Long-finned Damselfish ("Honey Gregory") 35 35
819 50 c. Saddle Squirrelfish 35 35
820 50 c. Cobalt Chromis 35 35
821 50 c. Genie's Neon Goby 35 35
822 50 c. Slender-tailed Cardinalfish 35 35
823 50 c. Royal Gramma 35 35
824 $1 Blue-striped Grunt 60 60
825 $1.60, Blue Angelfish 1·00 1·25
826 $3 Cocoa Damselfish 1·50 1·75
815/26 *Set of* 12 5·50 6·00
MS827 Two sheets, each 100×70 mm. (a) $6 Blue Marlin. (b) $6 Sailfish (*vert*) *Set of* 2 *sheets* 7·50 8·00
Nos. 816/23 were printed together, *se-tenant*, in sheetlets of 8 with the backgrounds forming a composite design.
No. 824 is inscribed "BLUESRIPED GRUNT" in error.
Nos. 816a was re-issued on 16 August 1994 showing the "Philakorea '94" International Stamp Exhibition logo on each corner of the sheetlet margins. The stamps show no listable differences.

(Litho Questa)

1994 (16 Aug). *"Philakorea '94" International Stamp Exhibition, Seoul. T* **83** *and similar vert designs showing longevity symbols. Multicoloured. P* 13½×14.
828 50 c. Type **83** 25 30
a. Sheetlet. Nos. 828/35 2·00
829 50 c. Symbol 2. Cranes and bamboo 25 30
830 50 c. Symbol 3. Deer and bamboo 25 30
831 50 c. Symbol 4. Turtles and Sun 25 30
832 50 c. Symbol 5. Cranes under tree 25 30
833 50 c. Symbol 6. Deer and tree 25 30
834 50 c. Symbol 7. Turtles and rock 25 30
835 50 c. Symbol 8. Cranes above tree 25 30
828/35 *Set of* 8 2·00 2·40
Nos. 828/35 were printed together, *se-tenant*, in sheetlets of 8.

84 Twin-roofed House with Veranda

(Des R. Vigurs. Litho Questa)

1994 (22 Aug). *Island Architecture. T* **84** *and similar horiz designs. Multicoloured. P* 14.

836 25 c. Type **84** 20 10
837 50 c. Two-storey house with outside staircase 40 30
838 $1 Government Treasury 70 60
839 $5 Two-storey house with red roof .. 2·75 3·25
836/9 .. .. *Set of* 4 3·50 3·75
MS840 102×72 mm. $6 Raised bungalow with veranda .. .. 3·50 4·00

85 William Demas

86 "The Virgin Mary as Queen of Heaven" (detail) (Jan Provost)

(Litho Questa)

1994 (1 Sept). *First Recipients of Order of Caribbean Community. T* **85** *and similar horiz designs. Multicoloured. P* 14.

841 25 c. Type **85** 20 10
842 50 c. Sir Shridath Ramphal 40 35
843 $1 Derek Walcott 70 60
841/3 .. .. *Set of* 3 1·10 95

(Litho Questa)

1994 (1 Dec). *Christmas. Religious Paintings. T* **86** *and similar vert designs. Multicoloured. P* 14.

844 20 c. Type **86** 20 10
845 40 c. "The Virgin Mary as Queen of Heaven" (different detail) (Provost) 35 25
846 50 c. "The Virgin Mary as Queen of Heaven" (different detail) (Provost) 40 30
847 80 c. "Adoration of the Magi" (detail) (Circle of Van der Goes) 60 40
848 $1 "Adoration of the Magi" (different detail) (Circle of Van der Goes) .. 70 50
849 $1.60, "Adoration of the Magi" (different detail) (Circle of Van der Goes) .. 1·25 1·25
850 $3 "Adoration of the Magi" (different detail) (Circle of Van der Goes) .. 2·00 2·25
851 $5 "The Virgin Mary as Queen of Heaven" (different detail) (Provost) .. .. 3·00 3·50
844/51 .. .. *Set of* 8 7·75 7·75
MS852 Two sheets, each 96×117 mm. (a) $5 "The Virgin Mary as Queen of Heaven" (different detail) (Provost). (b) $6 "Adoration of the Magi" (different detail) (Circle of Van der Goes) .. .. *Set of* 2 *sheets* 7·50 8·00

87 Mickey and Minnie Mouse

(Des Alvin White Studio. Litho Questa)

1995 (14 Feb). *Disney Sweethearts* (1*st series*). *T* **87** *and similar multicoloured designs showing Walt Disney cartoon characters. P* 14×13½.

853 10 c. Type **87** 15 10
854 25 c. Donald and Daisy Duck 30 10
855 50 c. Pluto and Fifi 40 30
856 80 c. Clarabelle Cow and Horace Horsecollar 55 50
857 $1 Pluto and Figaro 75 65
858 $1.50, Polly and Peter Penguin .. .. 1·00 1·25
859 $4 Prunella Pullet and Hick Rooster .. 2·25 2·40
860 $5 Jenny Wren and Cock Robin .. 2·25 2·40
853/60 .. .. *Set of* 8 6·00 6·50
MS861 Two sheets, each 133×107 mm. (a) $6 Daisy Duck (*vert*). (b) $6 Minnie Mouse (*vert*). P 13½×14 .. .. .. *Set of* 2 *sheets* 7·00 7·50

See also Nos. 998/1007.

88 Rufous-breasted Hermit

89 Pointer

(Des Mary Walters (Nos. 862/73), Marilyn Abramowitz (others). Litho Questa).

1995 (30 Mar). *Birds. T* **88** *and similar vert designs. Multicoloured. P* 14.

862 50 c. Type **88** 25 30
a. Sheetlet. Nos. 862/73 .. .. .. 3·00
863 50 c. Purple-throated Carib 25 30
864 50 c. Green Mango 25 30
865 50 c. Bahama Woodstar 25 30
866 50 c. Hispaniolan Emerald 25 30
867 50 c. Antillean Crested Hummingbird .. 25 30
868 50 c. Green-throated Carib 25 30
869 50 c. Antillean Mango 25 30
870 50 c. Vervain Hummingbird 25 30
871 50 c. Jamaican Mango 25 30
872 50 c. Cuban Emerald 25 30
873 50 c. Blue-headed Hummingbird 25 30
874 50 c. Hooded Merganser 25 30
875 80 c. Green-backed Heron 35 40
876 $2 Double-crested Cormorant 90 95
877 $3 Ruddy Duck .. .. 1·40 1·50
862/77 .. .. *Set of* 16 5·75 6·75
MS878 Two sheets, each 100×70 mm. (a) $6 Black Skimmer. (b) $6 Snowy Plover *Set of* 2 *sheets* 5·50 5·75

Nos. 862/73 were printed together, *se-tenant*, in sheetlets of 12.

No. 870 is inscribed "VERVIAN" in error.

(Des D. Miller. Litho B.D.T.)

1995 (23 May). *Dogs. T* **89** *and similar horiz designs. Multicoloured. P* 14.

879 25 c. Type **89** 10 10
880 50 c. Old Danish Pointer 25 30
881 80 c. Irish Setter 35 40
a. Sheetlet. Nos. 881/9 .. .. .. 3·25
882 80 c. Weimaraner 35 40
883 80 c. Gordon Setter 35 40
884 80 c. Brittany Spaniel 35 40
885 80 c. American Cocker Spaniel 35 40
886 80 c. English Cocker Spaniel 35 40
887 80 c. Labrador Retriever 35 40
888 80 c. Golden Retriever 35 40
889 80 c. Flat-coated Retriever 35 40
890 $1 German Short-haired Pointer .. 45 50
891 $2 English Setter 90 95
879/91 .. .. *Set of* 13 4·75 5·50
MS892 Two sheets, each 72×58 mm. (a) $6 German Shepherds. (b) $6 Bloodhounds *Set of* 2 *sheets* 5·50 5·75

Nos. 881/9 were printed together, *se-tenant*, in sheetlets of 9. "POINTER" is omitted from the inscription on No. 890. No. **MS**892a is incorrectly inscribed "SHEPHARD".

90 *Schulumbergera truncata*

91 Scouts backpacking

(Des Mary Walters. Litho Questa)

1995 (20 June). *Cacti. T* **90** *and similar vert designs. Multicoloured. P* 14.

893 40 c. Type **90** 20 25
894 50 c. *Echinocereus pectinatus* 25 30
895 80 c. *Mammillaria zeilmanniana alba* .. 35 40
896 $1.60, *Lobivia hertriehiana* 75 80
897 $2 *Hammatocactus setispinus* 90 95
898 $3 *Astrophytum myriostigma* .. .. 1·40 1·50
893/8 .. .. *Set of* 6 3·75 4·00
MS899 Two sheets, each 106×76 mm. (a) $6 *Opuntia robusta*. (b) $6 *Rhipsalidopsis gaertneri* *Set of* 2 *sheets* 5·50 5·75

(Des B. Hargreaves. Litho Questa)

1995 (20 July). *18th World Scout Jamboree, Netherlands. T* **91** *and similar multicoloured designs. P* 14.

900 $1 Type **91** 45 50
a. Horiz strip. Nos. 900/2 .. .. .. 3·25
901 $2 Scouts building aerial rope way .. 90 95
902 $4 Scout map reading .. .. .. 1·90 2·00
900/2 .. .. *Set of* 3 3·25 3·50
MS903 101×71 mm. $6 Scout in canoe (*vert*) .. 2·75 3·00

Nos. 900/2 were printed together in sheets of 9 containing three *se-tenant* horizontal strips of 3, each forming a composite design.

(Des J. Iskowitz. Litho Questa)

1995 (20 July). *50th Anniv of End of Second World War in Europe. Multicoloured designs as T* **317** *of Maldive Islands. P* 14.

904 $1.25. Clark Gable and aircraft 55 60
a. Sheetlet. Nos. 904/11 .. .. .. 4·25
905 $1.25, Audie Murphy and machine-gunner 55 60
906 $1.25, Glenn Miller playing trombone .. 55 60
907 $1.25, Joe Louis and infantry 55 60
908 $1.25, Jimmy Doolittle and U.S.S. *Hornet* (aircraft carrier) 55 60
909 $1.25, John Hersey and jungle patrol .. 55 60
910 $1.25, John F. Kennedy in patrol boat .. 55 60
911 $1.25, James Stewart and bombers .. 55 60
904/11 .. .. *Set of* 8 4·25 4·75
MS912 101×71 mm. $6 Jimmy Doolittle (*vert*) 2·75 3·00

Nos. 904/11 were printed together, *se-tenant*, in sheetlets of 8 with the stamps arranged in two horizontal strips of 4 separated by a gutter showing ticker-tape parade and U.S. sailor kissing nurse in New York.

92 Oriental and African People

93 Rotary Emblem on Nevis Flag

(Des J. Iskowitz. Litho Questa)

1995 (20 July). *50th Anniv of United Nations. T* **92** *and similar vert designs, each pale lilac and black or multicoloured* (*No.* **MS**916). *P* 14.

913 $1.25, Type **92** 55 60
a. Horiz strip of 3. Nos. 913/15 .. .. 2·50
914 $1.60, Asian people 75 80
915 $3 American and European people .. 1·40 1·50
913/15 .. .. *Set of* 3 2·50 2·75
MS916 105×75 mm. $6 Pres. Nelson Mandela of South Africa .. .. 2·75 3·00

Nos. 913/15 were printed together in sheets of 9 containing three *se-tenant* horizontal strips of 3, each forming a composite design.

(Des J. Iskowitz. Litho Questa)

1995 (20 July). *50th Anniv of Food and Agriculture Organization. Vert designs as T* **92**. *Multicoloured. P* 14.

917 40 c. Woman wearing yellow headdress .. 20 25
a. Horiz strip of 3. Nos. 917/19 .. .. 2·50
918 $2 Babies and emblem 90 95
919 $3 Woman wearing blue headdress .. 1·40 1·50
917/19 .. .. *Set of* 3 2·50 2·75
MS920 105×80 mm. $6 Man carrying hoe .. 2·75 3·00

Nos. 917/19 were printed together in sheets of 9 containing three *se-tenant* horizontal strips of 3, each forming a composite design.

No. **MS**920 is inscribed "1945–1955" in error.

(Des G. Bibby. Litho Questa)

1995 (20 July). *90th Anniv of Rotary International. T* **93** *and similar horiz design. Multicoloured. P* 14.

921 $5 Type **93** .. .. 2·25 2·40
MS922 95×66 mm. $6 Rotary emblem and beach 2·75 3·00

(Litho Questa)

1995 (20 July). *95th Birthday of Queen Elizabeth the Queen Mother. Vert designs as T* **321** *of Maldive Islands. P* 13½×14.

923 $1.50, orange-brown, pale brown and black 70 75
a. Sheetlet. Nos. 923/6×2 .. .. .. 5·50
924 $1.50, multicoloured 70 75
925 $1.50, multicoloured 70 75
926 $1.50, multicoloured 70 75
923/6 .. .. *Set of* 4 2·75 3·00
MS927 102×127 mm. $6 multicoloured .. 2·75 3·00

Designs:—No. 923, Queen Elizabeth the Queen Mother (pastel drawing); No. 924, Wearing pink hat; No. 925, At desk (oil painting); No. 926, Wearing blue hat; No. **MS**927, Wearing tiara.

Nos. 923/6 were printed together in sheetlets of 8, containing two *se-tenant* horizontal strips of 4.

(Des J. Batchelor. Litho Questa)

1995 (20 July). *50th Anniv of End of Second World War in the Pacific. United States Aircraft. Horiz designs as T* **317** *of Maldive Islands. Multicoloured. P* 14.

928 $2 Grumman F4F Wildcat 90 95
a. Sheetlet. Nos. 928/33 .. .. .. 5·25
929 $2 Chance Vought F4U-1A Corsair .. 90 95
930 $2 Vought SB2U Vindicator 90 95
931 $2 Grumman F6F Hellcat 90 95
932 $2 Douglas SDB Dauntless 90 95
933 $2 Grumman TBF-1 Avenger 90 95
928/33 .. .. *Set of* 6 5·25 5·50
MS934 108×76 mm. $6 Chance Vought F4U-1A Corsair on carrier flight deck .. .. .. 2·75 3·00

Nos. 928/33 were printed together, *se-tenant*, in sheetlets of 6 with the stamps arranged in two horizontal strips of 3 separated by a gutter showing U.S.S. *Saratoga* (aircraft carrier).

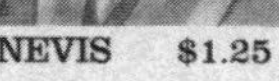

94 Emil von Behring (1901 Medicine)

95 American Eagle Presidents' Club Logo

(Des R. Sauber. Litho Questa)

1995 (20 July). *Centenary of Nobel Trust Fund. Past Prize Winners. T* **94** *and similar vert designs. Multicoloured. P* 14.

935 $1.25, Type **94** 55 60
  a. Sheetlet. Nos. 935/43 .. .. .. 4·75
936 $1.25, Wilhelm Röntgen (1901 Physics) .. 55 60
937 $1.25, Paul Heyse (1910 Literature) .. 55 60
938 $1.25, Le Duc Tho (1973 Peace) 55 60
939 $1.25, Yasunari Kawabata (1968 Literature) 55 60
940 $1.25, Tsung-dao Lee (1957 Physics) .. 55 60
941 $1.25, Werner Heisenberg (1932 Physics) .. 55 60
942 $1.25, Johannes Stark (1919 Physics) .. 55 60
943 $1.25, Wilhelm Wien (1911 Physics) .. 55 60
935/43 .. .. *Set of* 9 4·75 5·25
MS944 101×71 mm. $6 Kenzaburo Oe (1994 Literature) .. .. 2·75 3·00

Nos. 935/43 were printed together, *se-tenant*, in sheetlets of 9.

(Des Y. Lee. Litho Questa)

1995 (28 Aug). *10th Anniv of American Eagle Air Services to the Caribbean. Sheet, 70×100 mm, containing T* **95** *and similar horiz design. Multicoloured. P* 14.

MS945 80 c. Type **95**; $3 Aircraft over Nevis beach .. .. 1·75 1·90

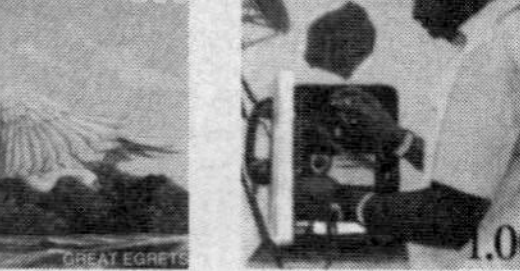

96 Great Egrets

97 SKANTEL Engineer

(Des Grace De Vito. Litho Questa)

1995 (1 Sept). *Marine Life. T* **96** *and similar multicoloured designs. P* 14.

946 50 c. Type **96** 25 30
  a. Sheetlet. Nos. 946/61 .. .. 4·00
947 50 c. 17th-century galleon 25 30
948 50 c. Galleon and Marlin 25 30
949 50 c. Herring Gulls 25 30
950 50 c. Nassau Groupers 25 30
951 50 c. Spotted Eagleray 25 30
952 50 c. Leopard Shark and Hammerhead .. 25 30
953 50 c. Hourglass Dolphins 25 30
954 50 c. Spanish Hogfish 25 30
955 50 c. Jellyfish and Seahorses 25 30
956 50 c. Angelfish and buried treasure .. 25 30
957 50 c. Hawksbill Turtle 25 30
958 50 c. Common Octopus 25 30
959 50 c. Moray Eel 25 30
960 50 c. Queen Angelfish and Butterflyfish .. 25 30
961 50 c. Ghost Crab and Sea Star 25 30
946/61 .. .. .. *Set of* 16 4·00 4·75
MS962 Two sheets. (a) 106×76 mm. $5 Nassau Grouper. (b) 76×106 mm. $5 Queen Angelfish (*vert*) .. .. *Set of* 2 *sheets* 4·50 4·75

Nos. 946/61 were printed together, *se-tenant*, in sheetlets of 16, forming a composite design.

No. **MS**962 also commemorates the "Singapore '95" International Stamp Exhibition.

(Des M. Friedman. Litho Questa)

1995 (23 Oct). *10th Anniv of SKANTEL (telecommunications company). T* **97** *and similar multicoloured designs. P* 14.

963 $1 Type **97** 45 50
964 $1.50, SKANTEL sign outside Nevis office 70 75
MS965 76×106 mm. $5 St. Kitts SKANTEL office (*horiz*) .. .. 2·25 2·40

PRICES OF SETS

Set prices are given for many issues, generally those containing three stamps or more. Definitive sets include one of each value or major colour change, but do not cover different perforations, die types or minor shades. Where a choice is possible the set prices are based on the cheapest versions of the stamps included in the listings.

98 "Rucellai Madonna and Child" (detail) (Duccio)

99 View of Nevis Four Seasons Resort

(Litho Questa)

1995 (1 Dec). *Christmas. Religious Paintings by Duccio di Buoninsegna. T* **98** *and similar vert designs. Multicoloured. P* 13½×14.

966 20 c. Type **98** 10 10
967 50 c. "Angel from the Rucellai Madonna" (detail) 25 30
968 80 c. "Madonna and Child" (*different*) .. 35 40
969 $1 "Angel from the Annunciation" (detail) 45 50
970 $1.60, "Madonna and Child" (*different*) .. 75 80
971 $3 "Angel from the Rucellai Madonna" (*different*) .. .. 1·40 1·50
966/71 .. .. *Set of* 6 3·25 3·50
MS972 Two sheets, each 102×127 mm. (a) $5 "Nativity with the Prophets Isaiah and Ezekiel" (detail). (b) $6 "The Crevole Madonna" (detail) *Set of* 2 *sheets* 5·00 5·25

(Des M. Friedman. Litho Questa)

1996 (14 Feb). *5th Anniv of Four Seasons Resort, Nevis. T* **99** *and similar horiz designs. Multicoloured. P* 14.

973 25 c. Type **99** 10 15
974 50 c. Catamarans, Pinney's Beach .. 25 30
975 80 c. Robert Trent Jones II Golf Course .. 35 40
976 $2 Prime Minister Simeon Daniel laying foundation stone 90 95
973/6 .. .. *Set of* 4 1·60 1·75
MS977 76×106 mm. $6 Sunset over resort .. 2·75 3·00

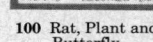

100 Rat, Plant and Butterfly

101 Ancient Greek Boxers

(Des Y. Lee. Litho Questa)

1996 (28 Feb). *Chinese New Year ("Year of the Rat"). T* **100** *and similar vert designs. Multicoloured. P* 14.

978 $1 Type **100** 45 50
  a. Block of 4. Nos. 978/81 .. .. 1·75
979 $1 Rat with prickly plant 45 50
980 $1 Rat and bee 45 50
981 $1 Rat and dragonfly 45 50
978/81 .. .. .. *Set of* 4 1·75 2·00
MS982 74×104 mm. Nos. 978/81 .. .. 1·90 2·00
MS983 74×104 mm. $3 Rat eating .. .. 1·40 1·50

Nos. 978/81 were printed together, *se-tenant*, in blocks of 4 throughout sheets of 16.

(Des B. Durand. Litho B.D.T.)

1996 (28 May). *Olympic Games, Atlanta. Previous Medal Winners. T* **101** *and similar multicoloured designs. P* 14.

984 25 c. Type **101** 10 10
985 50 c. Mark Spitz (U.S.A.) (Gold – swimming, 1972) 25 30
986 80 c. Siegbert Horn (East Germany) (Gold – single kayak slalom, 1972) 35 40
987 $1 Jim Thorpe on medal (U.S.A.), 1912 (*vert*) 45 50
  a. Sheetlet. Nos. 987/95 .. .. 4·00
988 $1 Glenn Morris on medal (U.S.A.), 1936 (*vert*) 45 50
989 $1 Bob Mathias on medal (U.S.A.), 1948 and 1952 (*vert*) 45 50
990 $1 Rafer Johnson on medal (U.S.A.), 1960 (*vert*) 45 50
991 $1 Bill Toomey (U.S.A.), 1968 (*vert*) .. 45 50
992 $1 Nikolay Avilov (Russia), 1972 (*vert*) .. 45 50
993 $1 Bruce Jenner (U.S.A.), 1976 (*vert*) .. 45 50
994 $1 Daley Thompson (Great Britain), 1980 and 1984 (*vert*) 45 50
995 $1 Christian Schenk (East Germany), 1988 (*vert*) 45 50
996 $3 Olympic Stadium and Siegestor Arch, Munich (*vert*) .. .. .. 1·40 1·50
984/96 .. .. *Set of* 13 6·00 6·50
MS997 Two sheets, each 105×75 mm. (a) $5 Willi Holdorf (West Germany) (Gold – decathlon, 1964) (*vert*). (b) $5 Hans-Joachim Walde (West Germany) (Silver – decathlon, 1968) (*vert*) *Set of* 2 *sheets* 4·50 4·75

Nos. 987/95 were printed together, *se-tenant*, in sheetlets of 9 and depict decathlon gold medal winners.

(Des Alvin White Studios. Litho Questa)

1996 (17 June). *Disney Sweethearts (2nd series). Horiz designs as T* **87** *showing Walt Disney cartoon characters. Multicoloured. P* 14×13½.

998 $2 Pocahontas and John Smith 90 95
  a. Sheetlet. Nos. 998/1006 .. .. 8·00
999 $2 Mowgli and the Girl 90 95
1000 $2 Belle and the Beast 90 95
1001 $2 Cinderella and Prince Charming .. 90 95
1002 $2 Pinocchio and the Dutch Girl .. 90 95
1003 $2 Grace Martin and Henry Coy .. 90 95
1004 $2 Snow White and the Prince 90 95
1005 $2 Aladdin and Jasmine 90 95
1006 $2 Pecos Bill and Slue Foot Sue 90 95
998/1006 .. .. *Set of* 9 8·00 8·50
MS1007 Two sheets, each 110×130 mm. (a) $6 Sleeping Beauty and Prince Phillip (*vert*). P 13½×14. (b) $6 Ariel and Eric. P 14×13½. *Set of* 2 *sheets* 5·50 5·75

Nos. 998/1006 were printed together, *se-tenant*, in sheetlets of 9.

102 Qian Qing Gong, Peking

(Des Y. Lee. Litho Questa)

1996 (1 July). *"CHINA '96" 9th Asian International Stamp Exhibition, Peking. Peking Pagodas. T* **102** *and similar multicoloured designs. P* 14.

1008 $1 Type **102** 45 50
  a. Sheetlet. Nos. 1008/16 .. .. 4·00
1009 $1 Temple of Heaven 45 50
1010 $1 Zhongnanhai 45 50
1011 $1 Da Zing Hall, Shehyang Palace .. 45 50
1012 $1 Temple of the Sleeping Buddha .. 45 50
1013 $1 Huang Qiong Yu, Altar of Heaven .. 45 50
1014 $1 The Grand Bell Temple 45 50
1015 $1 Imperial Palace 45 50
1016 $1 Pu Tuo Temple 45 50
1008/16 .. .. .. *Set of* 9 4·00 4·50
MS1017 104×74 mm. $6 Summer Palace of Emperor Wan Yan-liang (*vert*) .. .. 2·75 3·00

Nos. 1008/16 were printed together, *se-tenant*, in sheetlets of 9.

(Litho Questa)

1996 (1 July). *70th Birthday of Queen Elizabeth II. Vert designs as T* **334** *of Maldive Islands. Multicoloured. P* 13½×14.

1018 $2 As Type **334** of Maldive Islands .. 90 95
  a. Strip of 3. Nos. 1018/20 .. .. 2·75
1019 $2 Wearing evening dress 90 95
1020 $2 In purple hat and coat 90 95
1018/20 .. .. .. *Set of* 3 2·75 3·00
MS1021 125×103 mm. $6 Taking the salute at Trooping the Colour .. .. .. 2·75 3·00

Nos. 1018/20 were printed together, *se-tenant*, in horizontal and vertical strips of 3 throughout sheets of 9.

103 Children reading Book

(Des R. Sauber. Litho Questa)

1996 (1 July). *50th Anniv of U.N.I.C.E.F. T* **103** *and similar multicoloured designs. P* 14.

1022 25 c. Type **103** 10 10
1023 50 c. Doctor and child 25 30
1024 $4 Children .. .. 1·90 2·00
1022/4 .. .. .. *Set of* 3 2·25 2·40
MS1025 75×105 mm. $6 Young girl (*vert*) .. 2·75 3·00

104 Cave Paintings, Tassili n'Ajjer, Algeria

(Des M. Friedman. Litho Questa)

1996 (1 July). *50th Anniv of U.N.E.S.C.O. T* **104** *and similar multicoloured designs. P* 13½×14 ($2) *or* 14×13½ (*others*).

1026 25 c. Type **104** 10 10
1027 $2 Temple, Tikai National Park, Guatemala (*vert*) 90 95
1028 $3 Temple of Hera, Samos, Greece .. 1·40 1·50
1026/8 .. .. .. *Set of* 3 2·40 2·50
MS1029 106×76 mm. $6 Pueblo, Taos, U.S.A 2·75 3·00

105 American Academy of Ophthalmology Logo

106 *Rothmannia longiflora*

(Des M. Friedman. Litho Questa)

1996 (1 July). *Centenary of American Academy of Ophthalmology. P* 14.
1030 **105** $5 multicoloured . . . . . . 2·25 2·40

(Des T. Wood. Litho Questa)

1996 (24 Sept). *Flowers. T* **106** *and similar vert designs. Multicoloured. P* 14.
1031 25 c. Type **106** 10 10
1032 50 c. *Gloriosa simplex* 25 30
1033 $1 *Monodora myristica* 45 50
a. Sheetlet. Nos. 1033/41 . . . . 4·00
1034 $1 Giraffe 45 50
1035 $1 *Adansonia digitata* 45 50
1036 $1 *Ansellia gigantea* 45 50
1037 $1 *Geissorhiza rochensis* 45 50
1038 $1 *Arctotis venusta* 45 50
1039 $1 *Gladiotus cardinalis* 45 50
1040 $1 *Eucomis bicolor* 45 50
1041 $1 *Protea obtusifolia* 45 50
1042 $2 *Catharanthus roseus* 90 95
1043 $3 *Plumbago auriculata* . . . . 1·40 1·50
1031/43 . . . . *Set of* 13 6·75 7·25
MS1044 75×105 mm. $5 *Strelitzia reginae* . . 2·25 2·40
Nos. 1033/41 were printed together, *se-tenant*, in sheetlets of 9.

107 Western Meadowlark on Decoration

108 Ox (from "Five Oxen" by Han Huang)

(Des R. Rundo. Litho B.D.T.)

1996 (2 Dec). *Christmas. Birds. T* **107** *and similar multicoloured designs. P* 14.
1045 25 c. Type **107** 10 10
1046 50 c. American Goldfinch with decorations (*horiz*) 25 30
1047 80 c. Santa Claus, sleigh and reindeer (*horiz*) 35 40
1048 $1 Western Meadowlark on stocking . . 45 50
1049 $1.60, Mockingbird with snowman decoration 75 80
1050 $5 Yellow-rumped Caieque and bauble 2·25 2·40
1045/50 . . . . *Set of* 6 4·25 4·50
MS1051 Two sheets. (a) 106×76 mm. $6 Macaw (*horiz*). (b) 76×106 mm. $6 Vermilion Flycatcher (*horiz*) . . . . *Set of 2 sheets* 5·50 5·75

(Des Y. Lee. Litho Questa)

1997 (16 Jan). *Chinese New Year ("Year of the Ox"). T* **108** *and similar oxen from the painting by Han Huang. Sheet* 230×93 *mm. P* 14×15.
MS1052 50 c., 80 c., $1.60, $2 multicoloured . . 2·25 2·40
The fifth ox appears on a small central label

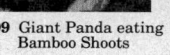

109 Giant Panda eating Bamboo Shoots

110 Elquemedo Willett

(Des L. Fried. Litho Questa)

1997 (12 Feb). *"HONG KONG '97" International Stamp Exhibition. Giant Pandas. T* **109** *and similar vert designs. Multicoloured. P* 14.
1053 $1.60, Type **109** 75 80
a. Sheetlet. Nos. 1053/8 . . . . 4·50
1054 $1.60, Head of Panda 75 80
1055 $1.60, Panda with new-born cub . . 75 80
1056 $1.60, Panda hanging from branch . . 75 80
1057 $1.60, Panda asleep on tree . . 75 80
1058 $1.60, Panda climbing trunk . . 75 80
1053/8 . . . . *Set of* 6 4·50 4·75
MS1059 73×103 mm. $5 Panda with cub . . 2·25 2·40
Nos. 1053/8 were printed together, *se-tenant*, in sheetlets of 6, with enlarged right-hand margin.

(Des M. Friedman. Litho B.D.T.)

1997 (1 May). *Nevis Cricketers. T* **110** *and similar multicoloured designs. P* 14.
1060 25 c. Type **110** 10 15
1061 80 c. Stuart Williams 35 40
1062 $2 Keith Arthurton 90 95
1060/2 . . . . *Set of* 3 1·40 1·50
MS1063 Two sheets, each 106×76 mm. (a) $5 Willett, Arthurton and Williams as part of the 1990 Nevis team (*horiz*); (b) $5 Williams and Arthurton as part of the 1994 West Indies team *Set of 2 sheets* 4·50 4·75

111 Crimson-speckled Moth

(Des Rinah Lyamph. Litho B.D.T.)

1997 (12 May). *Butterflies and Moths. T* **111** *and similar horiz designs. Multicoloured. P* 14.
1064 10 c. Type **111** 10 10
1065 25 c. Purple Emperor 10 15
1066 50 c. Regent Skipper 25 30
1067 80 c. Provence Burnet Moth 35 40
1068 $1 Common Wall Butterfly 45 50
1069 $1 Red-lined Geometrid 45 50
a. Sheetlet. Nos. 1069/77 . . . . 4·00
1070 $1 Boisduval's Autumnal Moth . . 45 50
1071 $1 Blue Pansy 45 50
1072 $1 Common Clubtail 45 50
1073 $1 Tufted Jungle King 45 50
1074 $1 Lesser Marbled Fritillary . . 45 50
1075 $1 Peacock Royal 45 50
1076 $1 Emperor Gum Moth 45 50
1077 $1 Orange Swallow-tailed Moth . . 45 50
1078 $4 Cruiser Butterfly . . . . 1·90 2·00
1064/78 . . . . *Set of* 15 7·25 8·00
MS1079 Two sheets. (a) 103×73 mm. $5 Great Purple ("*Saskiai charondal*"). (b) 73×103 mm. $5 Jersey Tiger Moth . . . . *Set of 2 sheets* 4·50 4·75
Nos. 1069/77 were printed together, *se-tenant*, in sheetlets of 9.
No. 1073 is inscribed "TUFTED JUNGLE QUEEN" in error

112 Boy with Two Pigeons ("Two Pigeons")

(Des R. Rundo. Litho Questa)

1997 (29 May). *300th Anniv of Mother Goose Nursery Rhymes. Sheet* 72×102 *mm. P* 14.
MS1080 **112** $5 multicoloured . . . . 2·25 2·40

113 Paul Harris and Literacy Class

(Des J. Iskowitz. Litho Questa)

1997 (29 May). *50th Death Anniv of Paul Harris (founder of Rotary International). T* **113** *and similar horiz design. Multicoloured. P* 14.
1081 $2 Type **113** 90 95
MS1082 78×108 mm. $5 Football coaching session, Chile . . . . 2·25 2·40

(Litho Questa)

1997 (29 May). *Golden Wedding of Queen Elizabeth and Prince Philip. Horiz designs as T* **350** *of Maldive Islands. Multicoloured. P* 14.
1083 $1 Queen Elizabeth II 45 50
a. Sheetlet. Nos. 1083/8 . . . . 2·75
1084 $1 Royal coat of arms 45 50
1085 $1 Queen Elizabeth wearing red hat and coat with Prince Philip 45 50
1086 $1 Queen Elizabeth in blue coat and Prince Philip 45 50
1087 $1 Caernarvon Castle 45 50
1088 $1 Prince Philip in R.A.F. uniform . . 45 50
1083/8 . . . . *Set of* 6 2·75 3·00
MS1089 100×70 mm. $5 Queen Elizabeth at Coronation . . . . 2·25 2·40
Nos. 1083/8 were printed together, *se-tenant*, in sheetlets of 6.

(Des J. Iskowitz. Litho Questa)

1997 (29 May). *"Pacific '97" International Stamp Exhibition, San Francisco. Death Centenary of Heinrich von Stephan. Horiz designs as T* **351** *of Maldive Islands. P* 14.
1090 $1.60, turquoise-green 75 80
a. Sheetlet. Nos. 1090/2 . . . . 2·25
1091 $1.60, chestnut 75 80
1092 $1.60, deep blue 75 80
1090/2 . . . . *Set of* 3 2·25 2·40
MS1093 82×118 mm. $5 sepia . . 2·25 2·40
Designs:—No. 1090, Russian reindeer post, 1859; No. 1091, Von Stephan and Mercury; No. 1092, *City of Cairo* (paddle-steamer), Mississippi, 1800's; No. **MS**1093, Von Stephan and Bavarian postal messenger, 1640.
Nos. 1090/2 were printed together, *se-tenant*, in sheets of 3 with enlarged right-hand margin.

1997 (29 May). *Birth Centenary of Hiroshige (Japanese painter). "One Hundred Famous Views of Edo". Vert designs as T* **352** *of Maldive Islands. Multicoloured. P* $13^1/_2$×14.
1094 $1.60, "Scattered Pines, Tone River" . . 75 80
a. Sheetlet. Nos. 1094/9 . . . . 4·50
1095 $1.60, "Mouth of Nakagawa River" . . 75 80
1096 $1.60, "Niijuku Ferry" 75 80
1097 $1.60, "Horie and Nekozane" . . 75 80
1098 $1.60, "Konodai and the Tone River" . . 75 80
1099 $1.60, "Maple Trees, Tekona Shrine and Bridge, Mama" 75 80
1094/9 . . . . *Set of* 6 4·50 4·75
MS1100 Two sheets, each 102×127 mm. (a) $6 "Mitsumata Wakarenofuchi". (b) $6 "Moto-Hachiman Shrine, Sunamura" . . *Set of 2 sheets* 5·50 5·75
Nos. 1094/9 were printed together, *se-tenant*, in sheetlets of 6.

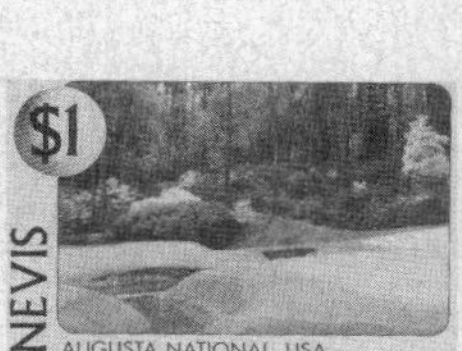

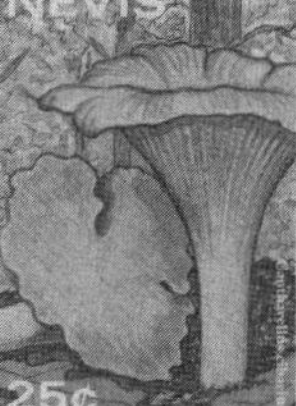

114 Augusta National Course, U.S.A.

115 *Cantharellus cibarius*

(Des M. Friedman. Litho B.D.T.)

1997 (15 July). *Golf Courses of the World. T* **114** *and similar horiz designs. Multicoloured. P* 14.
1101 $1 Type **114** 45 50
a. Sheetlet. Nos. 1101/9 . . . . 4·00
1102 $1 Cabo del Sol, Mexico 45 50
1103 $1 Cypress Point, U.S.A. 45 50
1104 $1 Lost City, South Africa 45 50
1105 $1 Moscow Country Club, Russia . . 45 50
1106 $1 New South Wales, Australia . . 45 50
1107 $1 Royal Montreal, Canada 45 50
1108 $1 St. Andrews, Scotland 45 50
1109 $1 Four Seasons Resort, Nevis . . 45 50
1101/9 . . . . *Set of* 9 4·00 4·50
Nos. 1101/9 were printed together, *se-tenant*, in sheetlets of 9.

(Des D. Miller. Litho Enschedé)

1997 (12 Aug). *Fungi. T* **115** *and similar vert designs. Multicoloured. P* 13.
1110 25 c. Type **115** 10 10
1111 50 c. *Stropharia aeruginosa* 25 30
1112 80 c. *Suillus hiteus* 35 40
a. Sheetlet. Nos. 1112/17 . . . . 2·10
1113 80 c. *Amanita muscaria* 35 40
1114 80 c. *Lactarius rufus* 35 40
1115 80 c. *Amanita rubescens* 35 40
1116 80 c. *Armillaria mellea* 35 40
1117 80 c. *Russula sardonia* 35 40
1118 $1 *Boletus edulis* 45 50
a. Sheetlet. Nos. 1118/23 . . . . 2·75
1119 $1 *Pholiota lenta* 45 50
1120 $1 *Cortinarius bolaris* 45 50
1121 $1 *Coprinus picaceus* 45 50
1122 $1 *Amanita phalloides* 45 50
1123 $1 *Cystolepiota aspera* 45 50
1124 $3 *Lactarius turpis* . . . . 1·40 1·50
1125 $4 *Entoloma clypeatum* . . . . 1·90 2·00
1110/25 . . . . *Set of* 16 8·75 9·25
MS1126 Two sheets, each 98×68 mm. (a) $5 *Galerina mutabilis*. (b) $5 *Gymnopilus junonius* *Set of 2 sheets* 4·50 4·75
Nos. 1112/17 and 1118/23 were each printed together, *se-tenant*, in sheetlets of 6 with the backgrounds forming composite designs.

116 Diana, Princess of Wales

117 Victoria Govt Railways Pacific Type Locomotive

(Des Y. Lee. Litho)

1997 (19 Sept). *Diana, Princess of Wales Commemoration. T* **116** *and similar vert portraits. Multicoloured. P* 14.

1127 $1 Type **116** 65 70
a. Sheetlet. Nos. 1127/35 .. .. 5·25
1128 $1 Wearing white blouse 65 70
1129 $1 In wedding dress, 1981 .. .. 65 70
1130 $1 Wearing turquoise blouse 65 70
1131 $1 Wearing tiara 65 70
1132 $1 Wearing blue blouse 65 70
1133 $1 Wearing pearl necklace 65 70
1134 $1 Wearing diamond drop earrings .. 65 70
1135 $1 Wearing sapphire necklace and earrings 65 70
1127/35 .. .. *Set of* 9 5·25 5·75

Nos. 1127/35 were printed together, *se-tenant*, in sheetlets of 9 with an illustrated right-hand margin.

(Des D. Miller. Litho Questa)

1997 (29 Sept). *Trains of the World. T* **117** *and similar horiz designs. Multicoloured. P* 14.

1136 10 c. Type **117** 10 10
1137 50 c. Japanese Imperial Govt Railways express locomotive 25 30
1138 80 c. L.M.S. Rail turbine-driven locomotive 35 40
1139 $1 Swiss Federal Railways electric locomotive 45 50
1140 $1.50, Sudan Govt Railways "Mikado" freight locomotive 70 75
a. Sheetlet. Nos. 1140/5 .. .. 4·25
1141 $1.50, Egyptian State Railways *Mohammed Ali el Kebir* 70 75
1142 $1.50, Southern Railways *Leatherhead* 70 75
1143 $1.50, Irish Great Southern Railways Drumm Battery train 70 75
1144 $1.50, German State Railways Pacific locomotive 70 75
1145 $1.50, Chinese Canton–Hankow Railways locomotive 70 75
1146 $2 L.M.S. Compound locomotive .. 90 95
1147 $3 Irish Great Northern Railway *Kestrel* 1·40 1·50
1136/47 .. .. *Set of* 12 7·75 8·25
MS1148 Two sheets, each 71×48 mm. (a) $5 L.M.S. High Pressure locomotive. (b) $5 G.W.R. *King George V* .. .. .. *Set of* 2 *sheets* 4·50 4·75

Nos. 1140/5 were printed together, *se-tenant*, in sheetlets of 6.

118 "Selection of Angels" (detail) (Dürer)

119 Tiger (semi-circular character at top left)

(Litho Questa)

1997 (26 Nov). *Christmas. Paintings. T* **118** *and similar multicoloured designs. P* 14.

1149 20 c. Type **118** 10 10
1150 25 c. "Selection of Angels" (different detail) (Dürer) 10 15
1151 50 c. "Andromeda and Perseus" (Rubens) 25 30
1152 80 c. "Harmony" (detail) (Raphael) .. 35 40
1153 $1.60, "Harmony" (different detail) (Raphael) 75 80
1154 $5 "Holy Trinity" (Raphael) .. 2·25 2·40
1149/54 .. .. *Set of* 6 3·75 4·25
MS1155 Two sheets, each 114×104 mm. (a) $5 "Study Muse" (Raphael) (*horiz*). (b) $5 "Ezekiel's Vision" (Raphael) (*horiz*) .. *Set of* 2 *sheets* 4·50 4·75

(Des K. Wang. Litho B.D.T.)

1998 (19 Jan). *Chinese New Year ("Year of the Tiger"). T* **119** *and similar multicoloured designs showing symbolic tigers. P* 14.

1156 80 c. Type **119** 35 40
a. Sheetlet. Nos. 1156/9 .. .. 1·40
1157 80 c. Oblong character at bottom right .. 35 40
1158 80 c. Circular character at top left .. 35 40
1159 80 c. Square character at bottom right .. 35 40
1156/9 .. .. *Set of* 4 1·40 1·60
MS1160 67×97 mm. $2 Tiger (*vert*) 90 95

Nos. 1156/9 were printed together, *se-tenant*, in sheetlets of 4.

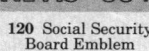

120 Social Security Board Emblem

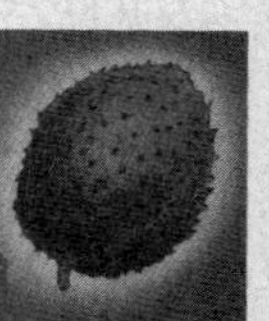

121 Soursop

(Des M. Friedman. Litho Cartor)

1998 (2 Feb). *20th Anniv of Social Security Board. T* **120** *and similar multicoloured designs. P* 13.

1161 30 c. Type **120** 15 20
1162 $1.20, Opening of Social Security Building, Charlestown (*horiz*) .. 55 60
MS1163 100×70 mm. $6 Social Security staff (59×39 *mm*). P 13½×13 .. .. .. 2·75 3·00

(Des Zina Saunders. Litho Questa)

1998 (9 Mar). *Fruits. T* **121** *and similar vert designs. Multicoloured. P* 14.

1164 5 c. Type **121** 10 10
1165 10 c. Carambola 10 10
1166 25 c. Guava 10 15
1167 30 c. Papaya 15 20
1168 50 c. Mango 25 30
1169 60 c. Golden Apple 25 30
1170 80 c. Pineapple 35 40
1171 90 c. Watermelon 40 45
1172 $1 Bananas 45 50
1173 $1.80, Orange 80 85
1174 $3 Honeydew .. .. 1·40 1·50
1175 $5 Cantelope .. .. 2·25 2·40
1176 $10 Pomegranate .. .. .. 4·50 4·75
1164/76 .. .. *Set of* 13 11·00 12·00

STAMP BOOKLETS

1980 (8 Oct). *Boats. Multicoloured cover,* 175×95 *mm. Stitched.*

SB1 $12.30, booklet containing 55 c. (No. 53) in block of 6 and $3 in pane of 3 (No. 54ab) .. 1·60

1981 (19 Nov). *Royal Wedding. Multicoloured cover,* 105×65 *mm, showing* The Royal Charlotte. *Stitched.*

SB2 $8.40, booklet containing eight 55 c. in panes of 4 (No. 79a) and $2 in pane of 2 (No. 80a) .. 2·00

1986 (23 July). *Royal Wedding. Gold* (*No.* SB3) *or silver* (*No.* SB4) *on orange-red covers,* 152×80 *mm. Stapled.*

SB3 $7.20, booklet (Westminster Abbey) containing twelve 60 c. (Nos. 406/7) in blocks of 4 .. 3·00
SB4 $10.40, booklet (State Coach) containing 60 c. and $2 (Nos. 406/9, but imperforate) in blocks of 4 3·50

OFFICIAL STAMPS

1980 (4 July*). *Nos.* 40/9 *additionally optd with Type* O 1 *of St. Christopher, Nevis and Anguilla.*

O 1 15 c. Sugar cane harvesting 10 10
O 2 25 c. Crafthouse (craft centre) 10 10
a. "OFFICIAL" opt double .. .. 35·00
b. "OFFICIAL" opt omitted (in horiz pair with normal) .. .. 75·00
c. Optd on No. 41a .. .. .. 4·25 7·00
O 3 30 c. *Europa* (liner) 10 10
O 4 40 c. Lobster and sea crab 15 15
O 5 45 c. Royal St. Kitts Hotel and golf course .. 20 20
a. Opt inverted .. .. .. 13·00
O 6 50 c. Pinney's Beach, Nevis 15 20
a. Opt inverted .. .. .. 65·00
O 7 55 c. New runway at Golden Rock .. 15 20
a. Opt double .. .. .. 12·00
O 8 $1 Picking cotton 15 25
O 9 $5 Brewery 45 55
a. Opt inverted .. .. .. 70·00
O10 $10 Pineapples and peanuts 70 90
O1/10 .. .. *Set of* 10 2·00 2·50

*Earliest known date of use.

1981 (Mar). *Nos.* 60A/71A *optd with Type* O 1 *of St. Kitts.*

O11 15 c. New River Mill 10 10
O12 20 c. Nelson Museum 10 10
O13 25 c. St. James' Parish Church 10 15
O14 30 c. Nevis Lane 15 15
O15 40 c. Zetland Plantation 15 20
O16 45 c. Nisbet Plantation 20 25
O17 50 c. Pinney's Beach 20 25
O18 55 c. Eva Wilkin's Studio 25 30
O19 $1 Nevis at dawn 30 35
O20 $2.50, Ruins of Fort Charles 50 65
O21 $5 Old Bath House 70 80
O22 $10 Beach at Nisbet's .. .. 1·25 1·40
O11/22 .. .. *Set of* 12 3·50 4·25

1983 (2 Feb). *Nos.* 72/7 *optd with Type* O 1 *of St. Kitts* (55 *c.*) *or surch also* (*others*).

O23 45 c. on $2 *Royal Sovereign* (New Blue) .. 10 15
aw. Wmk inverted .. .. .. 10·00
b. Sheetlet. No. O23×6 and No. O24 .. 70
bw. Wmk inverted .. .. .. 80·00
c. Surch inverted .. .. .. 8·00
d. Surch inverted (horiz pair) .. .. 30·00
e. Albino surch .. .. .. 6·50
ea. Albino surch inverted .. ..
f. Horiz pair, one without surch ..
g. Deep ultramarine surch 40 50
gc. Surch inverted .. .. .. 5·00
gd. Surch inverted (horiz pair) .. .. 14·00
h. Black surch .. .. .. 55·00
O24 45 c. on $2 Prince Charles and Lady Diana Spencer (New Blue) 20 25
aw. Wmk inverted .. .. .. 35·00
c. Surch inverted .. .. .. 20·00
e. Albino surch .. .. .. 15·00
g. Deep ultramarine surch 40 50
gc. Surch inverted .. .. .. 14·00
h. Black surch £150
O25 55 c. *Royal Caroline* (New Blue) 10 15
b. Sheetlet. No. O25×6 and No. O26 .. 75
e. Albino opt .. .. .. 7·00
ea. Albino opt inverted .. .. 10·00
eb. Albino opt inverted (horiz pair) .. 12·00
g. Deep ultramarine opt 75
gc. Opt inverted .. .. .. 5·00
gd. Opt inverted (horiz pair) .. .. 18·00
ge. Opt double .. .. .. 14·00
h. Black opt .. .. .. 55·00
O26 55 c. Prince Charles and Lady Diana Spencer (New Blue) 25 25
e. Albino opt .. .. .. 15·00
ea. Albino opt inverted .. .. 20·00
g. Deep ultramarine opt .. .. 1·00
gc. Opt inverted .. .. .. 18·00
gd. Opt double .. .. .. 27·00
h. Black opt £150
O27 $1.10 on $5 *Britannia* (Blk.) 20 25
aw. Wmk inverted .. .. .. 10·00
b. Sheetlet. No. O27×6 and No. O28 .. 1·60
bw. Wmk inverted .. .. .. 80·00
e. Albino surch .. .. .. 7·50
g. Deep ultramarine surch .. .. 6·00
gc. Surch inverted .. .. .. 6·50
gd. Surch inverted (horiz pair) .. .. 32·00

O28	$1.10 on $5 Prince Charles and Lady Diana Spencer (Blk.)	55	60
	aw. Wmk inverted	35·00	
	e. Albino surch	22·00	
	g. Deep ultramarine surch	35·00	
	gc. Surch inverted	38·00	
O23/8	.. .. *Set of* 6	1·25	1·40

Nos. O23d, O23gd, O25eb, O25gd and O27gd show the surcharge or overprint intended for the large design inverted and struck across a horizontal pair of the smaller. Nos. O24c, O24gc, O26ea, O26gc and O28gc each show two inverted surcharges intended for a horizontal pair of the smaller design.

1985 (2 Jan). *Nos.* 187/98 *optd with Type* O 1 *of St. Kitts.*

O29	15 c. Flamboyant	15	15
O30	20 c. Eyelash Orchid	30	20
O31	30 c. Bougainvillea	30	30
O32	40 c. Hibiscus sp.	30	30
O33	50 c. Night-blooming Cereus	35	35
O34	55 c. Yellow Mahoe	35	35
O35	60 c. Spider-lily	40	40
O36	75 c. Scarlet Cordia	45	45
O37	$1 Shell-ginger	60	60
O38	$3 Blue Petrea	1·25	1·75
O39	$5 Coral Hibiscus	2·00	2·25
O40	$10 Passion Flower	3·00	3·00
O29/40	.. .. *Set of* 12	8·50	9·00

1993 (1 Mar). *Nos.* 578B/91B *optd with Type* O 1 *of St. Kitts.*

O41	5 c. Type **63**	10	10
O42	10 c. *Historis odius*	10	10
O43	15 c. *Marpesia corinna*	10	10
O44	20 c. *Anartia amathea*	10	10
O45	25 c. *Junonia evarete*	10	10
O46	40 c. *Heliconius charithonia*	20	25
O47	50 c. *Marpesia petreus*	25	30
O48	75 c. *Heliconius doris*	35	40
O49	80 c. *Dione juno*	35	40
O50	$1 *Hypolimnas misippus*	45	50
O51	$3 *Danaus plexippus*	1·40	1·50
O52	$5 *Heliconius sara*	2·25	2·40
O53	$10 *Tithorea harmonia*	4·50	4·75
O54	$20 *Dryas julia*	9·25	9·50
O41/54	.. .. *Set of* 14	19·00	20·00

Imprint date: "1992", Nos. O41/54.

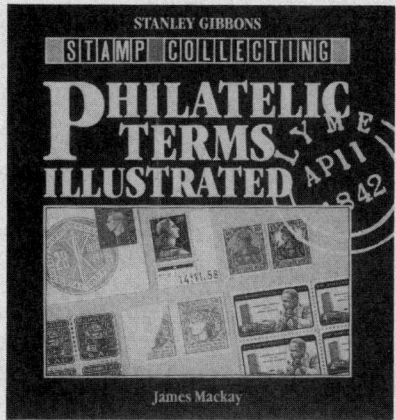

St. Lucia

Although a branch office of the British G.P.O. was not opened at Castries, the island capital, until 1844 some form of postal arrangements for overseas mails existed from at least 1841 when the issue of a Ship Letter handstamp is recorded.

The stamps of Great Britain were used on the island from May 1858 until the end of April 1860 when the local authorities assumed responsibility for the postal service. No. CC1 was again used on overseas mail between 1 May and the introduction of St. Lucia stamps in December 1860.

CASTRIES

CROWN-CIRCLE HANDSTAMPS

CC1

CC1 CC1 ST. LUCIA (R.) (1.5.1844) *Price on cover* £750

No. CC1 was utilised, struck in black, during a shortage of 1d. stamps in late April and early May 1904. *Price on cover* £325.

Stamps of GREAT BRITAIN *cancelled* "A 11" *as Type* Z 1 *of Jamaica.*

1858 *to* **1860**

Z1 1d. rose-red (1857), *perf* 14 . . £900
Z2 2d. blue (1855)
Z3 4d. rose (1857) . . £325
Z4 6d. lilac (1856) . . £200
Z5 1s. green (1856) . . £900

PRICES FOR STAMPS ON COVER TO 1945

Nos. 1/3	*from* × 60
Nos. 5/8	*from* × 30
Nos. 9/10	†
Nos. 11/24	*from* × 15
Nos. 25/30	*from* × 10
Nos. 31/6	*from* × 6
Nos. 39/42	*from* × 10
Nos. 43/50	*from* × 15
Nos. 51/2	—
Nos. 53/62	*from* × 6
No. 63	*from* × 15
Nos. 64/75	*from* × 4
Nos. 76/7	—
Nos. 78/88	*from* × 3
No. 89	*from* × 4
No. 90	*from* × 20
Nos. 91/112	*from* × 3
Nos. 113/24	*from* × 2
Nos. 125/7	*from* × 10
Nos. 128/41	*from* × 2
Nos. D1/6	*from* × 10
Nos. F1/28	—

CROWN COLONY

1

Half
penny

(2)

(Recess P.B.)

1860 (18 Dec). *Wmk Small Star, W* w **2**. *P* 14 *to* 16.

1 **1** (1d.) rose-red . . 80·00 60·00
a. Imperf vert (horiz pair)
b. Double impression . . £1800
2 (4d.) blue . . £200 £150
a. Deep blue
b. Imperf vert (horiz pair)
3 (6d.) green . . £250 £200
a. Imperf vert (horiz pair)
b. Deep green . . £300 £225

(Recess D.L.R.)

1863. *Wmk Crown CC. P* 12½.

5 **1** (1d.) lake . . 55·00 80·00
b. Brownish lake . . 75·00 75·00
7 (4d.) indigo . . 85·00 85·00
8 (6d.) emerald-green . . £150 £150

Prepared for use, but not issued. Surch as T **2**

9 **1** ½d. on (6d.) emerald-green . . 50·00
10 6d. on (4d.) indigo . . £900

All three values exist imperforate from proof sheets.

1864 (19 Nov)–**76.** *Wmk Crown CC.* (*a*) *P* 12½.

11 **1** (1d.) black . . 16·00 12·00
a. Intense black . . 15·00 11·00
12 (4d.) yellow . . £120 30·00
b. Lemon-yellow . . £1500
c. Chrome-yellow . . £130 30·00
d. Olive-yellow . . £250 70·00
13 **1** (6d.) violet . . 80·00 28·00
a. Mauve . . £130 28·00
b. Deep lilac . . 90·00 32·00
14 (1s.) brown-orange . . £275 25·00
b. Orange . . £200 25·00
c. Pale orange . . £150 25·00
ca. Imperf between (horiz pair)

(*b*) *P* 14

15 **1** (1d.) black (6.76) . . 18·00 15·00
a. Imperf between (horiz pair)
16 (4d.) yellow (6.76) . . 65·00 18·00
a. Olive-yellow . . £190 80·00
17 (6d.) mauve (6.76) . . 65·00 30·00
a. Pale lilac . . 65·00 18·00
b. Violet . . £170 60·00
18 (1s.) orange (10.76) . . £200 22·00
a. Deep orange . . £130 16·00

All four values exist imperforate from proof sheets.

HALFPENNY

(3)

2½ PENCE

(4)

5

1881 (Sept). *Surch with T* **3** *or* **4**. *Wmk Crown CC. P* 14

23 **1** ½d. green . . 55·00 75·00
24 2½d. brown-red . . 24·00 19·00

The 1d. black is known surcharged "1d." in violet ink by hand, but there is no evidence that this was done officially.

1882–84. *Surch as T* **3**. *Wmk Crown CA.* (*a*) *P* 14

25 **1** ½d. green (1882) . . 14·00 23·00
26 1d. black (C.) . . 19·00 8·50
a. Bisected (on cover) . . † —
27 4d. yellow . . £170 17·00
28 6d. violet . . 23·00 26·00
29 1s. orange . . £250 £160

(*b*) *P* 12

30 **1** 4d. yellow . . £250 28·00

Deep blue stamps, wmk Crown CA, perf 14 or 12, are fiscals from which the overprint "THREE PENCE—REVENUE", or "REVENUE", has been fraudulently removed.

(Typo D.L.R.)

1883 (6 July)–**86.** *Wmk Crown CA. Die* I. *P* 14.

31 **5** ½d. dull green . . 5·00 3·25
32 1d. carmine-rose . . 28·00 7·50
33 2½d. blue . . 25·00 1·50
a. Top left triangle detached . . £275 65·00
34 4d. brown (1885) . . 23·00 70
a. Top left triangle detached . . £275 55·00
35 6d. lilac (1886) . . £250 £200
36 1s. orange-brown (1885) . . £350 £140

The 4d. and 6d. exist imperforate from proof sheets.

For illustration of "top left triangle detached" variety on this and the following issue see above No. 6 of Montserrat.

1886–87. *Wmk Crown CA. Die* I. *P* 14.

39 **5** 1d. dull mauve . . 3·25 5·50
a. Top left triangle detached . . 70·00
40 3d. dull mauve and green . . 80·00 14·00
41 6d. dull mauve and blue (1887) . . 3·50 7·50
a. Top left triangle detached . . 80·00
42 1s. dull mauve and red (1887) . . 85·00 17·00
a. Top left triangle detached . . £400
39/42 . . *Set of* 4 £150 40·00
39/42 Optd "Specimen" . . *Set of* 4 £170

The 1d. exists imperforate from proof sheets.

1891–98. *Wmk Crown CA. Die* II. *P* 14.

43 **5** ½d. dull green . . 1·25 60
44 1d. dull mauve . . 1·50 20
45 2d. ultramarine and orange (1898) . . 1·00 1·00
46 2½d. ultramarine . . 2·25 60
47 3d. dull mauve and green . . 3·25 5·50
48 4d. brown . . 1·75 2·25
49 6d. dull mauve and blue . . 17·00 17·00
50 1s. dull mauve and red . . 3·25 5·00
51 5s. dull mauve and orange . . 35·00 £110
52 10s. dull mauve and black . . 75·00 £110
43/52 . . *Set of* 10 £120 £225
45, 51, 52 Optd "Specimen" . . *Set of* 3 £120

For description and illustration of differences between Die I and Die II see Introduction.

ONE
HALF
PENNY

(6)

½d

(7)

ONE
PENNY

(8)

N — Normal "N"

N — Thick "N"

Three types of T **8**

I. All letters "N" normal.
II. Thick diagonal stroke in first "N".
III. Thick diagonal stroke in second "N".

1891–92. (*a*) *Stamps of Die* I *surch.*

53 **6** ½d. on 3d. dull mauve and green . . 90·00 65·00
a. Small "A" in "HALF" . . £200 £140
b. Small "O" in "ONE" . . £200 £140
c. Top left triangle detached . . £425
54 **7** ½d. on half 6d. dull mauve and blue . . 14·00 3·25
a. No fraction bar . . £180 £120
b. Surch sideways . . £700
c. Surch double . . £500 £500
d. "2" in fraction omitted . . £400 £450
e. Thick "1" with sloping serif . . £180 £110
f. Surch triple . . £800
g. Figure "1" used as fraction bar . . £400 £225
55 **8** 1d. on 4d. brown (I) (12.91) . . 3·00 3·00
a. Surch double . . £180
b. Surch inverted . . £700 £600
c. Type II . . 22·00 20·00
ca. Surch double . . £325
cb. Surch inverted . . — £700
d. Type III . . 22·00 20·00
e. Top left triangle detached . . 95·00 95·00

(*b*) *Stamp of Die* II *surch*

56 **6** ½d. on 3d. dull mauve and green . . 45·00 18·00
a. Surch double . . £700 £600
b. Surch inverted . . £1700 £600
c. Surch both sides . . — £650
d. Small "O" in "ONE" . . £140 90·00
e. Small "A" in "HALF" . . £140 90·00
f. "ONE" misplaced ("O" over "H") . . £140 90·00

9

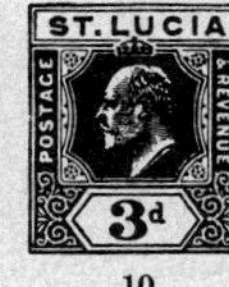

10

(Typo D.L.R.)

1902–3. *Wmk Crown CA. P* 14.

58 **9** ½d. dull purple and green . . 2·00 1·25
59 1d. dull purple and carmine . . 4·00 45
60 2½d. dull purple and ultramarine . . 13·00 5·50
61 **10** 3d. dull purple and yellow . . 4·00 8·50
62 1s. green and black . . 10·00 19·00
58/62 . . *Set of* 5 30·00 30·00
58/62 Optd "Specimen" . . *Set of* 5 £100

11 The Pitons

(Recess D.L.R.)

1902 (15 Dec). 400*th Anniv of Discovery by Columbus. Wmk Crown CC, sideways. P* 14

63 **11** 2d. green and brown . . 7·50 1·75
63 Optd "Specimen" . . 60·00

This stamp was formerly thought to have been issued on 16 December but it has been seen on a postcard clearly postmarked 15 December.

1904–10. *Wmk Mult Crown CA. Chalk-surfaced paper* (*Nos.* 71, 73/5 *and* 77) *or ordinary paper* (*others*). *P* 14.

64 **9** ½d. dull purple and green . . 3·00 20
a. Chalk-surfaced paper . . 2·00 95
65 ½d. green (1907) . . 1·75 80
66 1d. dull purple and carmine . . 4·00 80
a. Chalk-surfaced paper . . 2·00 80
67 1d. carmine (1907) . . 3·00 30
68 2½d. dull purple and ultramarine . . 7·50 1·25
a. Chalk-surfaced paper . . 5·50 3·75
69 2½d. blue (1907) . . 3·75 1·50
70 **10** 3d. dull purple and yellow . . 3·75 3·00
71 3d. purple/*yellow* (1909) . . 2·00 10·00
72 6d. dull purple and violet (1905) . . 10·00 12·00
a. Chalk-surfaced paper . . 15·00 16·00
ab. Dull purple and bright purple (1907) 5·50 18·00
73 6d. dull purple (1910) . . 24·00 42·00
74 1s. green and black (1905) . . 24·00 16·00
75 1s. black/*green* (1909) . . 4·00 7·00
76 5s. green and carmine (1905) . . 50·00 £120
77 5s. green and red/*yellow* (1907) . . 50·00 60·00
64/77 . . *Set of* 14 £160 £250
65, 67, 69, 71/2, 72*ab* and 75/7 Optd "Specimen" . . *Set of* 9 £180

Examples of Nos. 71/7 are known with a forged Castries postmark dated "JA 21 09".

12

13

14

15 16

(Typo D.L.R.)

1912–21. *Die* I. *Wmk Mult Crown CA. Chalk-surfaced paper* (3*d. to* 5*s.*). *P* 14.

78 **12** ½d. deep green . . 70 40
a. Yellow-green (1916) . . 65 30
79 1d. carmine-red . . 1·90 10
a. Scarlet (1916) . . 3·00 10
b. Rose-red . . 5·50 50
80 **13** 2d. grey . . 1·50 4·00
a. Slate-grey (1916) . . 13·00 11·00
81 **12** 2½d. ultramarine . . 3·25 2·75
a. Bright blue . . 1·75 2·75
b. Deep bright blue (1916) . . 9·50 9·50

82 15 3d. purple/*yellow* .. .. .. 1·25 2·00
b. Die II. *On pale yellow* (1921) .. 6·50 24·00
bw. Wmk inverted .. .. ..
83 14 4d. black and red/*yellow* .. .. 90 1·75
a. White back (Optd S. £25) .. .. 70 1·50
84 15 6d. dull and bright purple .. .. 2·00 7·50
a. Grey-purple and purple (1918) .. 16·00 16·00
85 1s. black/*green* .. .. .. 2·50 4·50
a. On blue-green (*olive back*) (1918) .. 4·50 6·00
86 1s. orange-brown (1920) .. .. 8·00 42·00
87 16 2s. 6d. black and red/*blue* .. .. 20·00 27·00
88 15 5s. green and red/*yellow* .. .. 20·00 75·00
78/88 .. .. *Set of* 11 55·00 £150
78/88 Optd "Specimen" .. .. *Set of* 11 £180

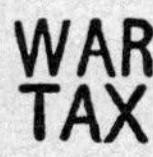

(17)

WAR TAX
(18)

1916 (June). *No. 79a optd locally with T* **17**.
89 12 1d. scarlet .. .. 7·00 7·00
a. Opt double £350 £375
b. Carmine-red .. .. 45·00 28·00

For the overprinting with Type **17** the top margin of the sheet was folded beneath the top row of stamps so that marginal examples from this row show an inverted albino impression of the overprint in the top margin.

1916 (Sept). *No. 79a optd in London with T* **18**.
90 12 1d. scarlet (Optd S. £40) 30 30

1921–30. *Die II. Wmk Mult Script CA. Chalk-surfaced paper (3d. (No. 100) to 5s.). P 14.*
91 12 ½d. green 30 30
92 1d. rose-carmine .. .. .. 6·50 12·00
93 1d. deep brown (1922) 70 15
94 14 1½d. dull carmine (1922) .. .. 50 2·00
95 13 2d. slate-grey 30 15
96 12 2½d. bright blue .. .. .. 3·00 2·75
97 2½d. orange (1925) .. .. 10·00 48·00
98 2½d. dull blue (1926) .. .. 3·00 2·50
99 15 3d. bright blue (1922) .. .. 4·25 14·00
a. Dull blue (1924) .. .. 1·50 11·00
100 3d. purple/*pale yellow* (1926) .. 70 10·00
a. Deep purple/pale yellow (1930) .. 8·50 12·00
101 14 4d. black and red/*yellow* (1924) .. 1·00 2·50
102 15 6d. grey-purple and purple .. .. 1·75 4·75
103 1s. orange-brown .. .. 1·75 3·25
104 16 2s. 6d. black and red/*blue* (1924) .. 17·00 26·00
105 15 5s. green and red/*pale yellow* (1923) 38·00 75·00
91/105 .. .. .. *Set of* 15 75·00 £180
91/105 Optd "Specimen" .. .. *Set of* 15 £225

1935 (6 May). *Silver Jubilee. As Nos. 114/17 of Jamaica, but ptd by D.L.R. P* 13½×14.
109 ½d. black and green 15 25
f. Diagonal line by turret .. .. 18·00
110 2d. ultramarine and grey 45 25
f. Diagonal line by turret .. .. 30·00
111 2½d. brown and deep blue 90 65
f. Diagonal line by turret .. .. 42·00
g. Dot to left of chapel .. .. 65·00
112 1s. slate and purple .. .. 3·75 6·50
h. Dot by flagstaff £150
109/12 .. .. .. *Set of* 4 4·75 7·00
109/12 Perf "Specimen" .. *Set of* 4 75·00

For illustrations of plate varieties see Omnibus section following Zimbabwe.

19 Port Castries

20 Columbus Square, Castries

21 Ventine Falls

25 The Badge of the Colony

(Recess D.L.R.)

1936 (1 Mar-Apr). *T* **19/21**, **25** *and similar designs. Wmk Mult Script CA. P* 14 *or* 13 × 12 (1*s. and* 10*s.*).
113 19 ½d. black and bright green 30 45
a. Perf 13 × 12 (8.4.36) .. .. 1·25 6·00
114 20 1d. black and brown 40 10
a. Perf 13 × 12 (8.4.36) .. .. 2·00 2·50
115 21 1½d. black and scarlet 55 30
a. Perf 12 × 13 .. .. 5·00 1·75
116 19 2d. black and grey 40 15
117 20 2½d. black and blue 40 15
118 21 3d. black and dull green .. .. 1·25 70
119 19 4d. black and red-brown .. .. 30 1·00
120 20 6d. black and orange .. .. 85 1·00
121 – 1s. black and light blue .. .. 1·25 2·00
122 – 2s. 6d. black and ultramarine .. 7·50 14·00
123 – 5s. black and violet .. .. 8·00 20·00
124 25 10s. black and carmine .. .. 42·00 65·00
113/124 .. .. .. *Set of* 12 55·00 95·00
113/24 Perf "Specimen" .. *Set of* 12 £180

Designs: *Vert* (*as T* **21**)—2s. 6d. Inniskilling monument. *Horiz* (*as T* **19**)—1s. Fort Rodney, Pigeon Island; 5s. Government House.

Examples of most values are known with a forged Castries postmark dated "1 MR 36".

1937 (12 May). *Coronation. As Nos. 118/20 of Jamaica, but ptd by B.W. P* 11×11½.
125 1d. violet 30 30
126 1½d. carmine 55 20
127 2½d. blue 55 40
125/7 .. .. .. *Set of* 3 1·25 80
125/7 Perf "Specimen" .. .. *Set of* 3 55·00

26 King George VI

27 Columbus Square

28 Government House

31 Device of St. Lucia

(Des E. Crafer (T **26**), H. Fleury (5s.). Recess Waterlow (½d. to 3½d., 8d., 3s., 5s., £1), D.L.R. (6d., 1s.) and B.W. (2s., 10s.))

1938 (22 Sept)–**48**. *T* **26/8**, **31** *and similar designs. Wmk Mult Script CA (sideways on 2s.).*
128 26 ½d. green (*p* 14½ × 14) 75 10
a. Perf 12½ (1943) 10 10
129 1d. violet (*p* 14½ × 14) 90 75
a. Perf 12½ (1938) 10 15
129*b* 1d. scarlet (*p* 12½) (1947) 10 10
c. Perf 14½ × 14 (1948) 10 10
130 1½d. scarlet (*p* 14½ × 14) .. .. 1·25 40
a. Perf 12½ (1943) 15 45
131 2d. grey (*p* 14½ × 14) 70 90
a. Perf 12½ (1943) 10 10
132 2½d. ultramarine (*p* 14½ × 14) .. 1·25 15
a. Perf 12½ (1943) 10 10
132*b* 2½d. violet (*p* 12½) (1947) 30 10
133 3d. orange (*p* 14½ × 14) 15 10
a. Perf 12½ (1943) 10 10
133*b* 3½d. ultramarine (*p* 12½) (1947) .. 30 15
134 27 6d. claret (*p* 13½) .. .. 2·25 50
a. Carmine-lake (*p* 13½) (1945) .. 1·75 35
b. Perf 12. *Claret* (1948) .. .. 1·00 45
134*c* 26 8d. brown (*p* 12½) (1946) .. 2·50 30
135 28 1s. brown (*p* 13½) 55 30
a. Perf 12 (1948) 40 20
136 – 2s. blue and purple (*p* 12) .. 3·50 1·25
136*a* 26 3s. bright purple (*p* 12½) (1946) .. 8·00 2·25
137 – 5s. black and mauve (*p* 12½) .. 14·00 6·00
138 31 10s. black/*yellow* (*p* 12) .. .. 4·50 9·00
141 26 £1 sepia (*p* 12½) (1946) .. .. 11·00 8·00
128a/141 .. .. .. *Set of* 17 40·00 26·00
128/41 Perf "Specimen" .. *Set of* 17 £300

Designs: *Horiz* (*as T* **28**)—2s. The Pitons; 5s. *Lady Hawkins* loading bananas.

1946 (8 Oct). *Victory. As Nos. 141/2 of Jamaica.*
142 1d. lilac 10 10
143 3½d. blue 10 10
142/3 Perf "Specimen" .. .. *Set of* 2 50·00

1948 (26 Nov). *Royal Silver Wedding. As Nos. 143/4 of Jamaica.*
144 1d. scarlet 15 10
145 £1 purple-brown .. .. .. 13·00 35·00

(New Currency. 100 cents = 1 West Indian, later Eastern Caribbean dollar)

32 King George VI

33 Device of St. Lucia

(Recess Waterlow (**32**), B.W. (**33**))

1949 (1 Oct)–**50**. *Value in cents or dollars. Wmk Mult Script CA. P* 12½ (1 *c. to* 16 *c.*), 11 × 11½ (*others*).
146 32 1 c. green 10 10
a. Perf 14 (1949) .. .. .. 1·25 40
147 2 c. magenta 10 10
a. Perf 14½ × 14 (1949) .. .. 1·50 1·00
148 3 c. scarlet 10 60
149 4 c. grey 10 10
a. Perf 14½ × 14 .. .. .. † £5000
150 5 c. violet 10 10
151 6 c. orange 15 60
152 7 c. ultramarine .. .. .. 1·00 1·25
153 12 c. claret .. .. 3·00 80
a. Perf 14½ × 14 (1950) £425 £300
154 16 c. brown .. .. 1·50 20
155 33 24 c. light blue 30 10
156 48 c. olive-green .. .. .. 1·50 85
157 $1.20, purple .. .. .. 2·25 5·50
158 $2.40, blue-green .. .. .. 3·00 17·00
159 $4.80, rose-carmine .. .. .. 6·00 18·00
146/159 .. .. .. *Set of* 14 17·00 40·00

Most examples of Nos. 146a and 147a were produced as coils, but a few sheets in these perforations were distributed and blocks of four are scarce.

1949 (10 Oct). *75th Anniv of U.P.U. As Nos. 145/8 of Jamaica.*
160 5 c. violet 20 20
161 6 c. orange .. .. 1·10 75
162 12 c. magenta 30 20
163 24 c. blue-green 65 20
160/3 .. .. *Set of* 4 2·00 1·25

1951 (16 Feb). *Inauguration of B.W.I. University College. As Nos. 149/50 of Jamaica.*
164 3 c. black and scarlet 45 40
165 12 c. black and deep carmine 45 40

34 Phoenix rising from Burning Buildings

NEW 1951 CONSTITUTION
(35)

(Flames typo, rest recess B.W.)

1951 (19 June). *Reconstruction of Castries. Wmk Mult Script CA. P* 13½ × 13.
166 34 12 c. red and blue 15 60

1951 (25 Sept). *New Constitution. Nos. 147, 149/50 and 153 optd with T* **35** *by Waterlow. P* 12½.
167 32 2 c. magenta 15 40
168 4 c. grey 15 40
169 5 c. violet 15 30
170 12 c. claret 15 50
167/70 .. .. .. *Set of* 4 55 1·40

1953 (2 June). *Coronation. As No. 153 of Jamaica.*
171 3 c. black and scarlet 50 10

36 Queen Elizabeth II

37 Device of St. Lucia

(Recess Waterlow (T **36**), until 1960, then D.L.R. B.W. (T **37**))

1953 (28 Oct)–**63**. *Wmk Mult Script CA. P* 14½×14 (*T* **36**) *or* 11×11½ (*T* **37**)
172 36 1 c. green (1.4.54) 10 10
173 2 c. magenta 10 10
174 3 c. red (2.9.54) 10 10
175 4 c. slate (7.1.54) 10 10
176 5 c. violet (1.4.54) 10 10
a. Slate-violet (19.2.63) .. .. 7·00 1·50
177 6 c. orange (2.9.54) 15 10
a. Brown-orange (26.9.61) .. .. 5·50 30
178 8 c. lake (2.9.54) 20 10
179 10 c. ultramarine (2.9.54) 10 10
a. Blue (14.8.62) 30 10
180 15 c. red-brown (2.9.54) 30 10
a. Brown (30.10.57) 30 10
181 37 25 c. deep turquoise-blue (2.9.54) .. 30 10
182 50 c. deep olive-green (2.9.54) .. 4·50 50
183 $1 bluish green (2.9.54) .. .. 4·00 1·40
184 $2.50, carmine (2.9.54) .. .. 5·00 4·25
172/84 .. .. .. *Set of* 13 13·00 6·00

1958 (22 Apr). *Inauguration of British Caribbean Federation. As Nos. 175/7 of Jamaica:*
185 3 c. deep green 40 20
186 6 c. blue .. .. 65 1·50
187 12 c. scarlet 90 75
185/7 .. .. *Set of* 3 1·75 2·25

MINISTERIAL GOVERNMENT

38 Columbus's *Santa Maria* off the Pitons

39 Stamp of 1860

(Recess Waterlow)

1960 (1 Jan). *New Constitution for the Windward and Leeward Islands. W w* **12**. *P* 13.
188 38 8 c. carmine-red 40 35
189 10 c. red-orange 40 35
190 25 c. deep blue 60 40
188/90 .. .. *Set of* 3 1·25 1·00

(Eng H. Bard. Recess Waterlow)

1960 (18 Dec). *Stamp Centenary. W* w **12**. *P* 13½.
191 **39** 5 c. rose-red and ultramarine 15 10
192 16 c. deep blue and yellow-green.. .. 40 60
193 25 c. green and carmine-red 40 20
191/3 .. .. *Set of* 3 85 80

1963 (4 June). *Freedom from Hunger. As No.* 80 *of Lesotho*.
194 25 c. bluish green 30 10

1963 (2 Sept). *Red Cross Centenary. As Nos.* 203/4 *of Jamaica*.
195 4 c. red and black 15 30
196 25 c. red and blue .. .. 50 1·10

40 Queen Elizabeth II **41**
(after A. C. Davidson-Houston)

42 Fishing Boats **43** Castries Harbour

44 Vigie Beach **45** Queen Elizabeth II

(Des V. Whiteley. Photo Harrison)

1964 (1 Mar)–**69**. *Designs as T* **40/5**, *W* w **12**. *P* 14½ (*T* **40**), *others* 14½×14 (*vert*) *or* 14×14½ (*horiz*).
197 **40** 1 c. crimson 10 10
w. Wmk inverted 75
198 2 c. bluish violet 30 30
w. Wmk inverted .. .. — 5·00
199 4 c. turquoise-green 35 30
a. Deep turquoise (5.8.69) .. .. 1·50 1·25
w. Wmk inverted .. .. — 5·00
200 5 c. Prussian blue 30 10
w. Wmk inverted .. ..
201 6 c. yellow-brown 45 40
202 **41** 8 c. multicoloured 10 10
203 10 c. multicoloured 50 10
204 **42** 12 c. multicoloured 30 50
205 – 15 c. multicoloured 20 10
206 – 25 c. multicoloured 20 10
207 **43** 35 c. blue and buff .. .. 2·00 10
208 – 50 c. multicoloured .. .. 1·50 10
209 **44** $1 multicoloured .. .. 1·25 65
210 **45** $2.50, multicoloured .. .. 2·00 1·50
197/210 .. .. *Set of* 14 8·50 3·25
Designs: *Horiz as T* 42/3—15 c. Pigeon Island; 25 c. Reduit Beach; 50 c. The Pitons.
See also No. 249.

1964 (23 Apr). *400th Birth Anniv of William Shakespeare. As No.* 156 *of Montserrat*.
211 10 c. blue-green 10 10

1965 (17 May). *I.T.U. Centenary. As Nos.* 98/9 *of Lesotho*.
212 2 c. mauve and magenta 10 10
213 50 c. lilac and light olive-green 70 55

1965 (25 Oct). *International Co-operation Year. As Nos.* 100/1 *of Lesotho*.
214 1 c. reddish purple and turquoise-green .. 10 10
215 25 c. deep bluish green and lavender 20 20

1966 (24 Jan). *Churchill Commemoration. As Nos.* 102/5 *of Lesotho*.
216 4 c. new blue 10 10
217 6 c. deep green 15 30
218 25 c. brown 20 15
219 35 c. bluish violet 30 20
216/19 .. .. *Set of* 4 65 65

1966 (4 Feb). *Royal Visit. As Nos.* 183/4 *of Montserrat*.
220 4 c. black and ultramarine 20 20
221 25 c. black and magenta 60 60

1966 (1 July). *World Cup Football Championship, England. As Nos.* 57/8 *of Pitcairn Islands*.
222 4 c. violet, yellow-green, lake & yellow-brn .. 20 10
223 25 c. chocolate, blue-green, lake & yellow-brn 55 30

1966 (20 Sept). *Inauguration of W.H.O. Headquarters, Geneva. As Nos.* 185/6 *of Montserrat*.
224 4 c. black, yellow-green and light blue .. 10 10
225 25 c. black, light purple and yellow-brown .. 25 20

1966 (1 Dec). *20th Anniv of U.N.E.S.C.O. As Nos.* 342/4 *of Mauritius*.
226 4 c. slate-violet, red, yellow and orange .. 10 10
227 12 c. orange-yellow, violet and deep olive .. 20 30
228 25 c. black, bright purple and orange.. .. 35 35
226/8 .. .. *Set of* 3 60 65

ASSOCIATED STATEHOOD

STATEHOOD
1st MARCH 1967
(49)

STATEHOOD
1st MARCH 1967
(50)

51 Map of St. Lucia

(Optd by Art Printery, Castries from dies supplied by Harrison. Photo Harrison (No. 240))

1967 (7 Mar). *Statehood*. (a) *Postage. Nos.* 198 *and* 200/9 *optd with T* **49** (2, 5, 6 *c.*) *or T* **50** (*others*) *in red*.
229 2 c. bluish violet 20 15
a. Horiz pair, one without opt .. ..
230 5 c. Prussian blue 10 10
a. Opt inverted .. .. 45·00
231 6 c. yellow-brown 10 10
232 8 c. multicoloured 20 10
a. Opt double £1500
233 10 c. multicoloured 25 10
234 12 c. multicoloured 20 10
235 15 c. multicoloured 25 30
236 25 c. multicoloured 30 30
237 35 c. blue and buff 50 35
238 50 c. multicoloured 50 55
239 $1 multicoloured 50 55
229/39 .. .. *Set of* 11 2·75 2·25
(b) *Air. P* 14½ × 14.
240 **51** 15 c. new blue 10 10

Overprinted 1 c. and $2.50 stamps were prepared for issue but were not put on sale over the post office counter. Later, however, they were accepted for franking (*Price for set of* 2 *£3.75 mint, £9 used*).

The $2.50 also exists with overprint in black, instead of red, and the 25 c. U.N.E.S.C.O. value is also known with a similar overprint in blue or black.

52 "Madonna and Child with the Infant Baptist" (Raphael) **53** Batsman and Sir Frederick Clarke (Governor)

(Des and photo Harrison)

1967 (16 Oct). *Christmas. W* w **12** (*sideways*). *P* 14½.
241 **52** 4 c. multicoloured 10 10
242 25 c. multicoloured 30 10

(Des V. Whiteley. Photo Harrison)

1968 (8 Mar). *M.C.C.'s West Indies Tour. W* w **12** (*sideways*). *P* 14½ × 14.
243 **53** 10 c. multicoloured 20 30
244 35 c. multicoloured 45 55

54 "The Crucified Christ with the Virgin Mary, Saints and Angels" (Raphael) **55** "Noli me tangere" (detail by Titian)

(Des and photo Harrison)

1968 (25 Mar). *Easter. W* w **12** (*sideways*). *P* 14 × 14½.
245 **54** 10 c. multicoloured 10 10
246 **55** 15 c. multicoloured 10 10
247 **54** 25 c. multicoloured 15 10
248 **55** 35 c. multicoloured 15 10
a. Yellow (sunset) omitted £140
245/8 .. .. *Set of* 4 40 30

1968 (14 May)*. *As No.* 205 *but W* w **12** (*sideways*).
249 15 c. multicoloured 30 30
*This is the London release date. Stamps from this printing were available some months earlier on St. Lucia.

56 Dr. Martin Luther King **57** "Virgin and Child in Glory" (Murillo)

(Des V. Whiteley. Litho D.L.R.)

1968 (4 July). *Martin Luther King Commemoration. W* w **12**. *P* 13½ × 14.
250 **56** 25 c. blue, black and flesh 15 15
251 35 c. violet-black, black and flesh .. 15 15

(Des and photo Harrison)

1968 (17 Oct). *Christmas. Paintings. T* **57** *and similar vert design. Multicoloured. W* w **12** (*sideways*). *P* 14½ × 14.
252 5 c. Type **57** 10 10
253 10 c. "Madonna with Child" (Murillo) .. 10 10
254 25 c. Type **57** 15 10
255 35 c. As 10 c. 15 10
252/5 .. .. *Set of* 4 40 30

59 Purple-throated Carib

(Des V. Whiteley. Litho Format)

1969 (10 Jan). *Birds. T* **59** *and similar horiz design. Multicoloured. W* w **12** (*sideways*). *P* 14.
256 10 c. Type **59** 55 35
257 15 c. St. Lucia Amazon 70 40
258 25 c. Type **59** 90 45
259 35 c. As 15 c. .. .. 1·25 50
256/9 .. .. *Set of* 4 3·00 1·50

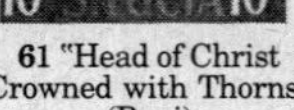

61 "Head of Christ Crowned with Thorns" (Reni) **62** "Resurrection of Christ" (Sodoma)

(Des and photo Harrison)

1969 (20 Mar). *Easter. W* w **12** (*sideways*). *P* 14½ × 14.
260 **61** 10 c. multicoloured 10 10
261 **62** 15 c. multicoloured 10 10
262 **61** 25 c. multicoloured 15 15
263 **62** 35 c. multicoloured 15 15
260/3 .. .. *Set of* 4 40 40

63 Map showing "CARIFTA" Countries

(Des J. Cooter. Photo Harrison)

1969 (29 May). *First Anniv of CARIFTA* (*Caribbean Free Trade Area*). *T* **63** *and similar horiz designs. Multicoloured. W* w **12**. *P* 14.
264 5 c. Type **63** 10 10
265 10 c. Type **63** 10 10
266 25 c. Handclasp and names of CARIFTA countries 15 15
267 35 c. As 25 c. 15 15
264/7 .. .. *Set of* 4 40 40

65 Emperor Napoleon and Empress Josephine

66 "Virgin and Child" (P. Delaroche)

(Des and litho Enschedé)

1969 (22 Sept). *Birth Bicentenary of Napoleon Bonaparte. P* 14 × 13.

No.	Type	Description	Unused	Used
268	**65**	15 c. multicoloured	10	10
269		25 c. multicoloured	10	10
270		35 c. multicoloured	10	10
271		50 c. multicoloured	15	55
268/71		*Set of* 4	30	75

(Des J. W. Photo Harrison)

1969 (27 Oct). *Christmas. Paintings. T* **66** *and similar vert design. Multicoloured. W* w **12** *(sideways). P* 14½ × 14.

No.	Description	Unused	Used
272	5 c. Type **66**	10	10
273	10 c. "Holy Family" (Rubens)	10	10
274	25 c. Type **66**	20	10
275	35 c. As 10 c.	20	10
272/5	*Set of* 4	50	30

68 House of Assembly

69 "The Sealing of the Tomb" (Hogarth)

(Des J. Cooter ($10), Sylvia and M. Goaman (others). Litho Questa ($10), Format (others))

1970 (2 Feb)–**73**. *T* **68** *and similar designs. Multicoloured. W* w **12** *(sideways* on* 1 *c. to* 35 *c. and* $10). *P* 14.

No.	Description	Unused	Used
276	1 c. Type **68**	10	10
277	2 c. Roman Catholic Cathedral	15	10
278	4 c. The Boulevard, Castries	90	10
	w. Wmk Crown to right of CA	4·50	
279	5 c. Castries Harbour	1·00	10
280	6 c. Sulphur springs	15	10
281	10 c. Vigie Airport	45	10
282	12 c. Reduit Beach	20	10
283	15 c. Pigeon Island	30	10
284	25 c. The Pitons and yacht	80	10
	w. Wmk Crown to right of CA	9·00	
285	30 c. Marigot Bay	40	10
	w. Wmk Crown to right of CA	8·00	
286	50 c. Diamond Waterfall (*vert*)	70	80
287	$1 Flag of St. Lucia (*vert*)	60	70
288	$2.50, St. Lucia Coat of Arms (*vert*)	80	1·75
289	$5 Queen Elizabeth II (*vert*)	2·00	4·00
289*a*	$10 Map of St. Lucia (*vert*) (3.12.73)	6·00	9·00
276/89*a*	*Set of* 15	13·00	15·00

*The normal sideways watermark shows Crown to left of CA, *as seen from the back of the stamp.*

See also Nos. 367/8 and 395/8.

(Des V. Whiteley. Litho Enschedé)

1970 (7 Mar). *Easter. Triptych by Hogarth. T* **69** *and similar multicoloured designs. W* w **12** *(sideways). Roul.* 9 × *P* 12½.

No.	Description	Unused	Used
290	25 c. Type **69**	15	20
	a. Strip of 3. Nos. 290/2	55	
291	35 c. "The Three Marys at the Tomb"	15	20
292	$1 "The Ascension" (39 × 55 *mm*)	30	40
290/2	*Set of* 3	55	70

Nos. 290/2 were issued in sheets of 30 (6 × 5) containing the Hogarth Triptych spread over all three values of the set. This necessitated a peculiar arrangement with the $1 value (which depicts the centre portion of the triptych) 10 mm higher than the other values in the *se-tenant* strip.

72 Charles Dickens and Dickensian Characters

(Des V. Whiteley. Litho B.W.)

1970 (8 June). *Death Centenary of Charles Dickens. W* w **12** *(sideways). P* 14.

No.	Type	Description	Unused	Used
293	**72**	1 c. multicoloured	10	10
294		25 c. multicoloured	20	10
295		35 c. multicoloured	25	10
296		50 c. multicoloured	35	80
293/6		*Set of* 4	70	90

73 Nurse and Emblem

(Des R. Granger Barrett. Litho J.W.)

1970 (18 Aug). *Centenary of British Red Cross. T* **73** *and similar horiz designs. Multicoloured. W* w **12** *(sideways*). P* 14.

No.	Description	Unused	Used
297	10 c. Type **73**	15	10
298	15 c. Flags of Great Britain, Red Cross and St. Lucia	25	20
299	25 c. Type **73**	35	35
300	35 c. As 15 c.	40	35
	w. Wmk Crown to right of CA	14·00	
297/300	*Set of* 4	1·00	85

*The normal sideways watermark shows Crown to left of CA, *as seen from the back of the stamp.*

74 "Madonna with the Lilies" (Luca della Robbia)

75 "Christ on the Cross" (Rubens)

(Des P. B. Litho and embossed Walsall)

1970 (16 Nov). *Christmas. P* 11.

No.	Type	Description	Unused	Used
301	**74**	5 c. multicoloured	10	10
302		10 c. multicoloured	15	10
303		35 c. multicoloured	30	10
304		40 c. multicoloured	30	30
301/4		*Set of* 4	75	50

(Des and litho Enschedé)

1971 (29 Mar). *Easter. T* **75** *and similar vert design. Multicoloured. W* w **12**. *P* 13½ × 13.

No.	Description	Unused	Used
305	10 c. Type **75**	10	10
	w. Wmk inverted	30	
306	15 c. "Descent from the Cross" (Rubens)	15	10
	w. Wmk inverted	30	
307	35 c. Type **75**	30	10
308	40 c. As 15 c.	30	40
	w. Wmk inverted	80	
305/8	*Set of* 4	75	60

76 Moule à Chique Lighthouse

(Des J. W. Litho Questa)

1971 (1 May). *Opening of Beane Field Airport. T* **76** *and similar horiz design. Multicoloured. W* w **12** *(sideways). P* 14½ × 14.

No.	Description	Unused	Used
309	5 c. Type **76**	30	15
310	25 c. Boeing 727-200 aircraft landing at Beane Field	45	15

77 Morne Fortune

78 Morne Fortune, Modern View

(Des V. Whiteley. Litho Questa)

1971 (10 Aug). *Old and New Views of St. Lucia. T* **77/8** *and similar horiz designs. Multicoloured. W* w **12** *(sideways*). P* 13½×13.

No.	Description	Unused	Used
311	5 c. Type **77**	10	15
	a. Pair. Nos. 311/12	15	30
312	5 c. Type **78**	10	15
313	10 c. Old view of Castries city	10	15
	a. Pair. Nos. 313/14	15	30
314	10 c. Modern view of Castries city	10	15
315	25 c. Old view of Pigeon Island	20	30
	a. Pair. Nos. 315/16	40	60
316	25 c. Modern view of Pigeon Island	20	30
317	50 c. Old view from Government House	40	65
	a. Pair. Nos. 317/18	80	1·25
	w. Wmk Crown to right of CA	75	
	wa. Pair. Nos. 317w/18w	1·50	
318	50 c. Modern view of Government House	40	65
	w. Wmk Crown to right of CA	75	
311/18	*Set of* 8	1·25	2·25

*The normal sideways watermark shows Crown to left of CA, *as seen from the back of the stamp.*

Each value of this issue was printed horizontally and vertically *se-tenant* in two designs showing respectively old and new views of St. Lucia.

The old views are taken from paintings by J. H. Caddy.

79 "Virgin and Child with Two Angels" (Verrocchio)

80 "St. Lucia" (Dolci School) and Coat of Arms

(Des J. Cooter. Litho J.W.)

1971 (15 Oct). *Christmas. T* **79** *and similar vert designs. Multicoloured. W* w **12**. *P* 14.

No.	Description	Unused	Used
319	5 c. Type **79**	10	10
320	10 c. "Virgin and Child, St. John the Baptist and an Angel" (Morando)	10	10
321	35 c. "Madonna and Child" (Battista)	15	10
322	40 c. Type **79**	20	25
319/22	*Set of* 4	40	40

(Des and litho Harrison)

1971 (13 Dec). *National Day. W* w **12**. *P* 14×14½.

No.	Type	Description	Unused	Used
323	**80**	5 c. multicoloured	10	10
324		10 c. multicoloured	15	10
325		25 c. multicoloured	25	10
		w. Wmk inverted	16·00	
326		50 c. multicoloured	45	40
323/6		*Set of* 4	85	50

81 "The Dead Christ Mourned" (Carracci)

(Des G. Drummond. Litho Questa)

1972 (15 Feb). *Easter. T* **81** *and similar horiz design. Multicoloured. W* w **12**. *P* 14.

No.	Description	Unused	Used
327	10 c. Type **81**	10	10
328	25 c. "Angels weeping over the dead Christ" (Guercino)	20	10
329	35 c. Type **81**	30	10
330	50 c. As 25 c.	40	40
327/30	*Set of* 4	85	45

82 Science Block and Teachers' College

(Des P. Powell. Litho Questa)

1972 (18 Apr). *Morne Educational Complex. T* **82** *and similar horiz designs. Multicoloured. W* w **12**. *P* 14.

No.	Description	Unused	Used
331	5 c. Type **82**	10	10
	w. Wmk inverted	1·40	
332	15 c. University Centre	10	10
333	25 c. Secondary School	10	10
334	35 c. Technical College	15	10
331/4	*Set of* 4	30	30

83 Steamship Stamp and Map

(Des J. Cooter. Litho Questa)

1972 (22 June). *Centenary of First Postal Service by St. Lucia Steam Conveyance Co Ltd. T* **83** *and similar horiz designs. W* w **12**. *P* 14.

No.	Description	Unused	Used
335	5 c. multicoloured	15	10
	w. Wmk inverted		
336	10 c. ultramarine, mauve and black	20	10
337	35 c. lt rose-carmine, pale greenish bl & blk	60	10
338	50 c. multicoloured	1·00	1·00
335/8	*Set of* 4	1·75	1·00

Designs:—10 c. Steamship stamp and Castries Harbour; 35 c. Steamship stamp and Soufrière; 50 c. Steamship stamps.

84 "The Holy Family" (Sebastiano Ricci)

(Des J. Cooter. Litho J.W.)

1972 (18 Oct). *Christmas. W w* **12** *(sideways). P* 14½.
339 **84** 5 c. multicoloured 10 10
340 10 c. multicoloured 10 10
341 35 c. multicoloured 20 10
342 40 c. multicoloured 25 15
339/42 . . . . *Set of* 4 50 30

85 Arms and St. Lucia Amazon 86 Week-day Headdress

(Des (from photograph by D. Groves) and photo Harrison)

1972 (20 Nov). *Royal Silver Wedding. Multicoloured; background colour given. W w* **12.** *P* 14 × 14½.
343 **85** 15 c. carmine 20 20
w. Wmk inverted . . . . . . 18·00
344 35 c. yellow-olive 20 20
w. Wmk inverted . . . . . . 26·00

(Des Sylvia Goaman. Litho A. & M.)

1973 (1 Feb). *Local Headdresses. T* **86** *and similar vert designs. Multicoloured. W w* **12.** *P* 13.
345 5 c. Type **86** 10 10
346 10 c. Formal style 10 10
347 25 c. Unmarried girl's style 15 10
348 50 c. Ceremonial style 25 50
345/8 . . . . *Set of* 4 45 60

87 Coat of Arms 88 H.M.S. *St. Lucia*, 1803

(Des and litho Harrison)

1973–76. *Coil Stamps. P* 14½ × 14.
A. W w **12** *upright* (19.4.73). B. W w **12** *sideways* (1976).

			A		B	
349 **87**	5 c. olive-green		10	50	75	1·60
350	10 c. new blue		15	50	75	1·60
351	25 c. lake-brown		15	50	13·00	—
349/51		*Set of* 3	35	1·40		

For 10 c. value watermarked w **16** see No. 953.

(Des R. Granger Barrett. Litho Questa)

1973 (24 May). *Historic Ships. T* **88** *and similar horiz designs. Multicoloured. W w* **12.** *P* 13½ × 14.
352 15 c. Type **88** 20 10
353 35 c. H.M.S. *Prince of Wales*, 1765 . . . . 25 10
354 50 c. *Oliph Blossom*, 1605 . . . . . . 40 20
355 $1 H.M.S. *Rose*, 1757 . . . . . . 55 65
352/5 . . . . *Set of* 4 1·25 90
MS356 122 × 74 mm. Nos. 352/5 . . . . . . 1·25 2·75

89 Plantation and Flower 90 "The Virgin with Child" (Maratta)

(Des PAD Studio. Litho Walsall)

1973 (26 July). *Banana Industry. T* **89** *and similar horiz designs. Multicoloured. W w* **12.** *P* 14.
357 5 c. Type **89** 10 10
358 15 c. Aerial spraying 15 10
359 35 c. Boxing plant 20 10
w. Wmk inverted . . . . . . 4·00
360 50 c. Loading a boat 50 40
357/60 . . . . *Set of* 4 85 45

(Des J. Cooter. Litho Walsall)

1973 (17 Oct). *Christmas. T* **90** *and similar vert designs. Multicoloured. W w* **12** *(sideways*). P* 13½.
361 5 c. Type **90** 10 10
362 15 c. "Madonna in the Meadow" (Raphael) 10 10
363 35 c. "The Holy Family" (Bronzino) . . 20 10
364 50 c. "Madonna of the Pear" (Dürer) . . 30 35
w. Wmk Crown to right of CA . . . . 2·00
361/4 . . . . *Set of* 4 60 40

*The normal sideways watermark shows Crown to left of CA, *as seen from the back of the stamp.*

1973 (14 Nov). *Royal Wedding. As Nos.* 322/3 *of Montserrat.*
365 40 c. grey-green 10 10
366 50 c. rosy lilac 10 10

1974 (15 Mar). *As Nos.* 277/8 *but wmk upright.*
367 2 c. Roman Catholic Cathedral 60 70
368 4 c. The Boulevard, Castries 80 90

91 "The Betrayal" 92 3-Escalins Coins, 1798

(Des J. Cooter. Litho D.L.R.)

1974 (1 Apr). *Easter. T* **91** *and similar horiz designs showing paintings by Ugolino da Siena. Multicoloured. W w* **12** *(sideways on Nos.* 369/72, *upright on* **MS**373). *P* 13.
369 5 c. Type **91** 10 10
370 35 c. "The Way to Calvary" 15 10
371 80 c. "The Deposition" 15 15
372 $1 "The Resurrection" 20 25
369/72 . . . . *Set of* 4 50 40
MS373 180 × 140 mm. Nos. 369/72 . . . . 1·00 2·00

(Des J. Cooter. Litho Format)

1974 (20 May). *Coins of Old St. Lucie. T* **92** *and similar vert designs. Multicoloured. W w* **12** *(sideways). P* 14 × 13½.
374 15 c. Type **92** 15 10
375 35 c. 6-escalins coins, 1798 . . . . . . 20 10
376 40 c. 2-livres 5-sols coins, 1813 . . . . 20 10
377 $1 6-livres 15-sols coins, 1813 . . . . 55 65
374/7 . . . . *Set of* 4 1·00 75
MS378 151 × 115 mm. Nos. 374/7 . . . . 1·25 2·75

93 Baron de Laborie 94 "Virgin and Child" (Andrea del Verrocchio)

(Des J. W. Litho Questa)

1974 (29 Aug). *Past Governors of St. Lucia. T* **93** *and similar vert designs. Multicoloured. W w* **12** *(sideways*). P* 14.
379 5 c. Type **93** 10 10
380 35 c. Sir John Moore 10 10
381 80 c. Sir Dudley Hill 15 10
w. Wmk Crown to right of CA . . . . 35·00
382 $1 Sir Frederick Clarke 25 35
379/82 . . . . *Set of* 4 50 50
MS383 153×117 mm. Nos. 379/82. Wmk upright 50 2·00
w. Wmk inverted . . . . . . 50·00

*The normal sideways watermark shows Crown to left of CA, *as seen from the back of the stamp.*

(Des PAD Studio. Litho D.L.R.)

1974 (18 Nov). *Christmas. T* **94** *and similar vert designs. Multicoloured. W w* **12.** *P* 13 × 13½.
384 5 c. Type **94** 10 10
385 35 c. "Virgin and Child" (Andrea della Robbia) 10 10
386 80 c. "Madonna and Child" (Luca della Robbia) 15 15
387 $1 "Virgin and Child" (Rossellino) . . 20 25
384/7 . . . . *Set of* 4 40 40
MS388 92 × 140 mm. Nos. 384/7 . . . . 90 2·00

95 Churchill and Montgomery 96 "Christ on the Cross" (School of Van der Weyden)

(Des PAD Studio. Litho Format)

1974 (30 Nov). *Birth Centenary of Sir Winston Churchill. T* **95** *and similar horiz design. Multicoloured. W w* **12** *(sideways). P* 14.
389 5 c. Type **95** 10 10
390 $1 Churchill and Truman 30 35

(Des J. Cooter. Litho Questa)

1975 (27 Mar). *Easter. T* **96** *and similar vert designs. Multicoloured. W w* **12.** *P* 13½.
391 5 c. Type **96** 10 10
392 35 c. "Noli me tangere" (Romano) 10 10
393 80 c. "Calvary" (Gallego) 20 20
394 $1 "Noli me tangere" (Correggio) 30 35
391/4 . . . . *Set of* 4 55 60

1975 (28 July). *As Nos.* 278 *etc. but W w* **14** *(sideways).*
395 4 c. The Boulevard, Castries . . . . . . 1·10 2·00
396 5 c. Castries Harbour . . . . 1·10 1·10
397 10 c. Vigie Airport . . . . 1·40 1·40
398 15 c. Pigeon Island . . . . 2·25 2·00
395/8 . . . . *Set of* 4 5·25 6·00

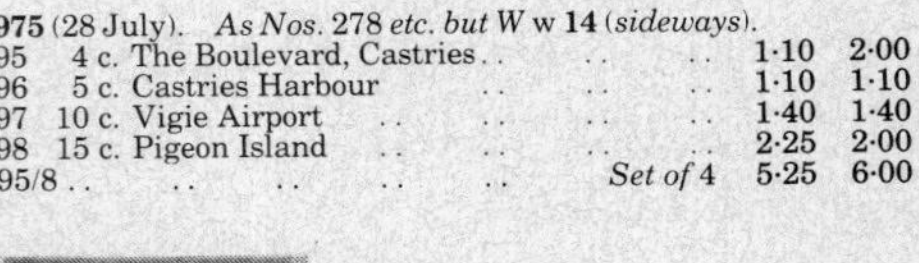

97 "Nativity" (French Book of Hours) 98 American Schooner *Hanna*

(Des J. Cooter. Litho Questa)

1975 (12 Dec). *Christmas. T* **97** *and similar vert designs. Multicoloured. W w* **12.** *P* 14½.
399 5 c. Type **97** 10 10
400 10 c. "King" (stained glass window) 10 15
a. Horiz strip of 3. Nos. 400/2 30
401 10 c. "Virgin and Child" (stained glass window) 10 15
402 10 c. "King and Cattle" (stained glass window) 10 15
403 40 c. "Nativity" (Hastings Book of Hours) 30 20
404 $1 "Virgin and Child with Saints" (Borgognone) 70 60
399/404 . . . . *Set of* 6 1·25 1·25
MS405 105×109 mm. Nos. 399 and 403/4 . . 75 1·00

Nos. 400/2 were printed horizontally *se-tenant* within the sheet to form a composite design of the Epiphany.

(Des J. W. Litho Format)

1976 (26 Jan). *Bicentenary of American Revolution. T* **98** *and similar horiz designs showing ships. Multicoloured. P* 14½.
406 ½ c. Type **98** 10 10
407 1 c. *Prince of Orange* (British sailing packet) 10 10
408 2 c. H.M.S. *Edward* (sloop) 10 10
409 5 c. *Millern* (British merchantman) 30 10
410 15 c. *Surprise* (American lugger) 60 10
411 35 c. H.M.S. *Serapis* (frigate) . . . . 1·10 20
412 50 c. *Randolph* (American frigate) . . . . 1·25 1·00
413 $1 *Alliance* (American frigate) . . . . 2·25 2·50
406/13 . . . . *Set of* 8 5·00 3·50
MS414 142×116 mm. Nos. 410/13. P 13 . . 3·00 4·50

99 Laughing Gull 100 H.M.S. *Ceres*

(Des J.W. Litho Questa)

1976 (17 May)–**79.** *Birds. T* **99** *and similar vert designs. Multicoloured. Ordinary paper. W w* **12** *(1 c.) or w* **14** *(others). P* 14.
415 1 c. Type **99** 30 90
416 2 c. Little Blue Heron 30 90
417 4 c. Belted Kingfisher 35 90
418 5 c. St. Lucia Amazon . . . . 1·75 90
419 6 c. St. Lucia Oriole . . . . 1·25 90
420 8 c. Brown Trembler . . . . 1·50 1·50
421 10 c. American Kestrel . . . . 1·25 35
422 12 c. Red-billed Tropic Bird . . . . . . 2·00 2·50
423 15 c. Moorhen . . . . 1·25 15
424 25 c. Common Noddy . . . . 1·75 1·50
a. Chalk-surfaced paper (7.79) . . . . 1·00 30
425 35 c. Sooty Tern . . . . 3·25 1·25
a. Chalk-surfaced paper (1979) . . . . 3·25 3·25
426 50 c. Osprey . . . . 6·00 3·50
427 $1 White-breasted Trembler . . . . . . 4·00 3·50
428 $2.50, St. Lucia Black Finch . . . . . . 7·00 6·00
429 $5 Red-necked Pigeon . . . . 7·00 4·50
430 $10 Caribbean Elaenia . . . . 7·00 8·00
a. Chalk-surfaced paper (7.79) . . . . 4·00 7·50
415/30a . . . . *Set of* 16 38·00 32·00

1976 (19 July). *West Indian Victory in World Cricket Cup. As Nos. 419/20 of Jamaica.*

431 50 c. Caribbean map .. .. 1·00 1·00
432 $1 Prudential Cup .. .. 1·50 2·50
MS433 92 × 79 mm. Nos. 431/2 .. .. .. 3·25 4·50

(Des J. Cooter. Litho Walsall)

1976 (4 Sept). *Royal Navy Crests. T* **100** *and similar vert designs. Multicoloured.* W w **14** (*inverted*). *P* 14.

434 10 c. Type **100** 35 10
435 20 c. H.M.S. *Pelican* 60 10
436 40 c. H.M.S. *Ganges* 85 10
437 $2 H.M.S. *Ariadne* .. .. 2·00 2·00
434/7 .. .. *Set of* 4 3·50 2·00

101 "Madonna and Child" (Murillo)

102 Queen Elizabeth II

(Des J. Cooter. Litho Questa)

1976 (15 Nov). *Christmas. T* **101** *and similar vert designs. Multicoloured.* W w **14**. *P* 13½.

438 10 c. Type **101** 10 10
439 20 c. "Madonna and Child with Angels" (Costa) 10 10
440 50 c. "Madonna and Child Enthroned" (Isenbrandt) 15 10
441 $2 "Madonna and Child with St. John" (Murillo) 50 65
438/41 .. .. .. *Set of* 4 70 75
MS442 105 × 93 mm. $2.50, As Type **101** .. 1·00 1·25

(Des Daphne Padden. Litho Questa)

1977 (7 Feb). *Silver Jubilee.* W w **14** (*sideways**). *P* 14.

443 **102** 10 c. multicoloured 10 10
444 20 c. multicoloured 10 10
w. Wmk Crown to right of CA .. £110
445 40 c. multicoloured 10 15
446 $2 multicoloured 40 90
443/6 .. .. .. *Set of* 4 50 1·00
MS447 128×95 mm. **102** $2.50, multicoloured 45 1·00

*The normal sideways watermark shows Crown to left of CA, *as seen from the back of the stamp.*

Nos. 443/6 were each issued in sheets of five stamps and one label.

103 Scouts from Tapion School

104 "Nativity" (Giotto)

(Des J. W. Litho Format)

1977 (17 Oct). *Caribbean Boy Scout Jamboree. T* **103** *and similar vert designs. Multicoloured. P* 14½.

448 ½ c. Type **103** 10 10
449 1 c. Sea scouts 10 10
450 2 c. Scout from Micoud 10 10
451 10 c. Two scouts from Tapion School .. 15 10
452 20 c. Venture scouts 15 10
453 50 c. Scout from Gros Islet 30 45
454 $1 Sea scouts in motor boat .. .. 50 1·00
448/54 .. .. .. *Set of* 7 1·00 1·60
MS455 75 × 85 mm. $2.50, As $1 .. .. 1·10 3·00

(Des J. W. Litho Questa)

1977 (31 Oct). *Christmas. T* **104** *and similar vert designs. Multicoloured. P* 14.

456 ½ c. Type **104** 10 10
457 1 c. "Perugia triptych" (Fra Angelico) .. 10 10
458 2 c. "Virgin and Child" (El Greco) 10 10
459 20 c. "Madonna of the Rosary" (Caravaggio) .. 15 10
460 50 c. "Adoration of the Magi" (Velazquez) .. 20 10
461 $1 "Madonna of Carmel" (Tiepolo) 30 35
462 $2.50, "Adoration of the Magi" (Tiepolo) .. 45 80
456/62 .. .. .. *Set of* 7 1·00 1·25

105 "Susan Lunden"

106 Yeoman of the Guard and Life Guard

(Des C. Abbott. Litho Harrison)

1977 (28 Nov). *400th Birth Anniv of Rubens. T* **105** *and similar vert designs. Multicoloured.* W w **14** (*sideways*). *P* 14 × 15.

463 10 c. Type **105** 10 10
464 35 c. "The Rape of the Sabine Women" (detail) 15 10
465 50 c. "Ludovicus Nonnius" 30 10
466 $2.50, "Minerva protects Pax from Mars" (detail) 85 80
463/6 .. .. .. *Set of* 4 1·25 90
MS467 145 × 120 mm. Nos. 463/6 .. .. 1·25 2·25

(Des J. W. Litho Questa)

1978 (2 June). *25th Anniv of Coronation. T* **106** *and similar horiz designs. Multicoloured. P* 14.

468 15 c. Type **106** 10 10
469 20 c. Groom and postillion 10 10
470 50 c. Footman and coachman 10 10
471 $3 State trumpeter and herald 35 80
468/71 .. .. .. *Set of* 4 50 90
MS472 114 × 88 mm. $5 Master of the Horse and Gentleman-at-Arms 60 90

Nos. 468/71 also exist perf 12 (*Price for set of* 4 60p. *mint or used*) from additional sheetlets of 3 stamps and one label. Stamps perforated 14 are from normal sheets of 50.

107 Queen Angelfish

(Des G. Vasarhelyi. Litho Format)

1978 (19 June). *Fishes. T* **107** *and similar horiz designs. Multicoloured. P* 15.

473 10 c. Type **107** 15 10
474 20 c. Four-eyed Butterflyfish 30 10
475 50 c. French Angelfish 60 30
476 $2 Yellow-tailed Damselfish .. .. 1·10 1·75
473/6 .. .. .. *Set of* 4 1·90 2·00
MS477 155×89 mm. $2.50, Rock Beauty .. 1·75 1·90

Nos. 473/6 exist imperforate from stock dispersed by the liquidator of Format International Security Printers Ltd.

108 French Grenadier and Map of the Battle

109 The Annunciation

(Des J. W. Litho Questa)

1978 (29 Nov). *Bicentenary of Battle of Cul-de-Sac. T* **108** *and similar horiz designs. Multicoloured. P* 14

478 10 c. Type **108** 25 10
479 30 c. British Grenadier officer and map of St. Lucia (Bellin), 1762 .. .. .. 45 10
480 50 c. Coastline from Gros Islet to Cul-de-Sac and British fleet opposing French landings 65 15
481 $2.50, General James Grant, 1798, and Light Infantrymen of 46th Regiment .. .. 1·75 1·25
478/81 .. .. .. *Set of* 4 2·75 1·40

(Des Jennifer Toombs. Litho Questa)

1978 (4 Dec). *Christmas. T* **109** *and similar horiz design. Multicoloured.* W w **14**. *P* 14.

482 30 c. Type **109** 10 10
483 50 c. Type **109** 15 10
484 55 c. The Nativity 15 10
485 80 c. As 55 c. 20 20
482/5 .. .. .. *Set of* 4 55 40

INDEPENDENT

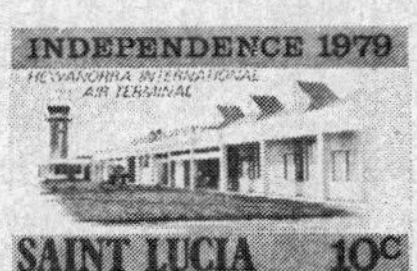

110 Hewanorra International Air Terminal

(Des J. W. Litho Questa)

1979 (22 Feb). *Independence. T* **110** *and similar horiz designs. Multicoloured.* W w **14** (*sideways*). *P* 14.

486 10 c. Type **110** 10 10
487 30 c. New coat of arms 10 10
488 50 c. Government House and Sir Allen Lewis (first Governor-General) 15 10
489 $2 French, St. Lucia and Union flags on map of St. Lucia 30 45
486/9 .. .. .. *Set of* 4 50 55
MS490 127 × 80 mm. Nos. 486/9 .. .. 50 1·00

111 Popes Paul VI and John Paul I

(Des J.W. Litho Harrison)

1979 (28 May). *Pope Paul VI Commemoration. T* **111** *and similar horiz designs. Multicoloured.* W w **14** (*sideways*). *P* 14½ × 14.

491 10 c. Type **111** 10 10
492 30 c. President Sadat of Egypt with Pope Paul 20 10
493 50 c. Pope Paul with Secretary-General U Thant 35 20
494 55 c. Pope Paul and Prime Minister Golda Meir of Israel 40 25
495 $2 Martin Luther King received in audience by Pope Paul .. .. .. 1·00 80
491/5 .. .. .. *Set of* 5 1·75 1·25

112 Dairy Farming

(Des G. Drummond. Litho Format)

1979 (2 July). *Agriculture Diversification. T* **112** *and similar horiz designs. Multicoloured.* W w **14** (*sideways*). *P* 14.

496 10 c. Type **112** 10 10
497 35 c. Fruit and vegetables 10 10
498 50 c. Water conservation 10 10
499 $3 Copra industry 35 70
496/9 .. .. .. *Set of* 4 50 85

113 Lindbergh and Sikorsky S-38A Flying Boat

114 "A Prince of Saxony" (Cranach the Elder)

(Des L. Curtis. Litho Walsall)

1979 (2 Oct). *50th Anniv of Lindbergh's Inaugural Airmail Flight via St. Lucia. T* **113** *and similar horiz designs.* W w **14** (*sideways*). *P* 14.

500 10 c. black, Indian red and pale orange .. 25 10
501 30 c. multicoloured 30 10
502 50 c. multicoloured 30 10
503 $2 multicoloured 50 40
500/3 .. .. .. *Set of* 4 1·25 50

Designs:—30 c. Sikorsky S-38A flying boat and route map; 50 c. Arrival at La Toc, September, 1929; $2 Letters on first flight.

(Litho Questa)

1979 (6 Dec). *International Year of the Child. Paintings. T* **114** *and similar vert designs. Multicoloured. P.* 14.

504 10 c. Type **114** 10 10
505 50 c. "The Infanta Margarita" (Velazquez) .. 15 10
506 $2 "Girl playing Badminton" (Chardin) .. 40 40
507 $2.50, "Mary and Francis Wilcox" (Stock) .. 45 45
504/7 .. .. .. *Set of* 4 95 80
MS508 113 × 94 mm. $5 "Two Children" (Picasso) 1·10 1·25

115 Notice of Introduction of Penny Post

116 "Madonna and Child" (Bernardino Fungai)

(Des J.W. Litho Questa)

1979 (10 Dec). *Death Centenary of Sir Rowland Hill. T* **115** *and similar vert designs. Multicoloured. P* 14.

509 10 c. Type **115** 10 10
510 50 c. Original stamp sketch 15 10
511 $2 1860 1d. stamp 35 50
512 $2.50, Penny Black stamp 45 60
509/12 .. .. .. *Set of* 4 85 1·10
MS513 111 × 85 mm. $5 Sir Rowland Hill .. 70 90

Nos. 509/12 also exist perf 12 (*Price for set of* 4 85p. *mint or used*) from additional sheetlets of 5 stamps and one label. Stamps perforated 14 are from normal sheets of 40.

(Des R. Vigurs. Litho Walsall)

1980 (14 Jan). *Christmas* (1979) *and International Year of the Child. T* **116** *and similar vert designs showing "Madonna and Child" paintings by various artists. Multicoloured.* W w **14**. *P* 14.

514	10 c. Type **116**	10	10
	w. Wmk inverted	18·00	
515	50 c. Carlo Dolci	25	10
516	$2 Titian	70	40
517	$2.50, Giovanni Bellini	75	50
514/17	*Set of* 4	1·60	95
MS518	94×120 mm. Nos. 514/17	1·60	1·60

117 St. Lucia Steam Conveyance Company Cover, 1873

118 Mickey Mouse astride Rocket

(Des G. Drummond. Litho Questa)

1980 (6 May). *"London 1980" International Stamp Exhibition. T* **117** *and similar horiz designs. Multicoloured.* W w **14** (*sideways*). *P* 14.

519	10 c. Type **117**	10	10
520	30 c. S.S. *Assistance* 1d. postmark of 1879	10	10
521	50 c. Postage due handstamp of 1929	15	10
522	$2 Crowned-circle paid stamp of 1844	40	55
519/22	*Set of* 4	60	65
MS523	85 × 76 mm. Nos. 519/22	65	90

(Litho Format)

1980 (29 May). *10th Anniv of Moon Landing* (1979). *Walt Disney Cartoon Characters. T* **118** *and similar multicoloured designs showing characters in space scenes. P* 11.

524	½ c. Type **118**	10	10
525	1 c. Donald Duck being towed by rocket (*horiz*)	10	10
526	2 c. Minnie Mouse on Moon	10	10
527	3 c. Goofy hitching lift to Mars	10	10
528	4 c. Goofy and moondog (*horiz*)	10	10
529	5 c. Pluto burying bone on Moon (*horiz*)	10	10
530	10 c. Donald Duck and love-sick martian (*horiz*)	10	10
531	$2 Donald Duck paddling spaceship (*horiz*)	1·75	1·00
532	$2.50, Mickey Mouse driving moonbuggy (*horiz*)	2·00	1·10
524/32	*Set of* 9	3·75	2·00
MS533	102 × 127 mm. $5 Goofy leaping from space-ship on to Moon. P 13½	3·25	2·75

119 Queen Elizabeth the Queen Mother

(Litho Questa)

1980 (4 Aug). *80th Birthday of Queen Elizabeth the Queen Mother. P* 14.

534	**119** 10 c. multicoloured	15	10
535	$2.50, multicoloured	35	1·00
MS536	85 × 65 mm. **119** $3 multicoloured	60	1·50

120 Hawker Siddeley H.S.748

(Des A. Theobald. Litho Harrison)

1980 (11 Aug). *Transport. Horiz designs as T* **120**. *Multicoloured.* W w **14** (*sideways on* 5 c. *to* $1). *P* 14½ × 14.

537	5 c. Type **120**	30	30
538	10 c. Douglas DC-10-30 airliner	65	20
539	15 c. Local bus	35	30
540	20 c. Refrigerated freighter	35	30
541	25 c. Britten Norman Islander aircraft	65	20
542	30 c. *Charles* (pilot boat)	40	40
543	50 c. Boeing 727-200 airliner	1·00	60
544	75 c. *Cunard Countess* (liner)	65	1·00
545	$1 Lockheed L-1011 TriStar 500 airliner	85	1·10
546	$2 Cargo liner	1·25	2·00
547	$5 Boeing 707-420 airliner	4·50	6·00
548	$10 *Queen Elizabeth 2* (liner)	5·00	8·00
537/48	*Set of* 12	14·00	18·00

For stamps with watermark W w **15** see Nos. 690/8.

121 Shot-putting

122 Coastal Landscape within Cogwheel

(Des M. Diamond. Litho Questa)

1980 (22 Sept). *Olympic Games, Moscow. T* **121** *and similar horiz designs. Multicoloured. P* 14.

549	10 c. Type **121**	10	10
550	50 c. Swimming	20	10
551	$2 Gymnastics	70	50
552	$2.50, Weightlifting	80	60
549/52	*Set of* 4	1·60	1·10
MS553	108×83 mm. $5 Athletes with Olympic Torch	1·25	1·40

(Des BG Studio. Litho Questa)

1980 (30 Sept). *75th Anniv of Rotary International. T* **122** *and similar vert designs showing different coastal landscapes within cogwheels. P* 14.

554	10 c. multicoloured	10	10
555	50 c. multicoloured	15	10
556	$2 greenish black, carmine & greenish yell	40	40
557	$2.50, multicoloured	50	55
554/7	*Set of* 4	1·00	1·00
MS558	103 × 106 mm. $5 multicoloured	1·25	1·75

123 Sir Arthur Lewis

(Des J. W. Litho Questa)

1980 (23 Oct). *Nobel Prize Winners. T* **123** *and similar vert designs. Multicoloured. P* 14.

559	10 c. Type **123**	10	10
560	50 c. Martin Luther King Jnr.	20	15
561	$2 Ralph Bunche	50	60
562	$2.50, Albert Schweitzer	70	80
559/62	*Set of* 4	1·25	1·40
MS563	115 × 91 mm. $5 Albert Einstein	1·75	2·00

1980
HURRICANE

$1.50 RELIEF

(124)

1980 (3 Nov). *Hurricane Relief. Nos.* 539/40 *and* 543 *surch with T* **124**.

564	$1.50 on 15 c. Local bus	30	40
565	$1.50 on 20 c. Refrigerated freighter	30	40
566	$1.50 on 50 c. Boeing 727-200 airliner	30	40
564/6	*Set of* 3	80	1·10

125 "The Nativity" (Giovanni Battista)

126 Brazilian Agouti

(Des J. Cooter. Litho Questa)

1980 (1 Dec). *Christmas. Paintings. T* **125** *and similar vert designs. Multicoloured.* W w **14**. *P* 14 × 13½.

567	10 c. Type **125**	10	10
	w. Wmk inverted	15·00	
568	30 c. "Adoration of the Kings" (Pieter the Elder)	10	10
569	$2 "Adoration of the Shepherds" (ascribed to Murillo)	40	60
567/9	*Set of* 3	50	60
MS570	102×88 mm. $1×3, Angel with people of St. Lucia (*composite design*) (*each* 30×75 *mm*). P 14½×14	80	90

(Des G. Drummond. Litho Questa)

1981 (19 Jan). *Wildlife. T* **126** *and similar vert designs. Multicoloured. P* 14.

571	10 c. Type **126**	15	10
572	50 c. St. Lucia Amazon	1·00	10
573	$2 Purple-throated Carib	1·50	80
574	$2.50, Fiddler Crab	1·25	1·00
571/4	*Set of* 4	3·50	1·75
MS575	103×87 mm. $5 *Danaus plexippus* (butterfly)	2·40	2·50

127 Prince Charles at Balmoral

128 Lady Diana Spencer

(Des J. W. Litho Questa)

1981 (23 June). *Royal Wedding. T* **127** *and similar vert designs. Multicoloured. P* 14.

576	25 c. Prince Charles and Lady Diana Spencer	10	10
577	50 c. Clarence House	10	10
578	$4 Type **127**	40	55
576/8	*Set of* 3	50	60
MS579	96 × 82 mm. $5 Glass Coach and coachman	50	50

Nos. 576/8 also exist perforated 12 (*price for set of* 3 50p *mint or used*) from additional sheetlets of five stamps and one label. These stamps have changed background colours.

(Manufactured by Walsall)

1981 (23 June). *Royal Wedding. Booklet stamps. T* **128** *and similar vert designs. Multicoloured. Roul* 5 × *imperf* Self-adhesive.*

580	50 c. Type **128**	15	30
	a. Booklet pane. Nos. 580/1 each × 3	1·25	
581	$2 Prince Charles	30	60
582	$5 Prince Charles and Lady Diana Spencer	1·25	1·75
	a. Booklet pane of 1	1·25	
580/2	*Set of* 3	1·50	2·40

*The 50 c. and $2 values were each separated by various combinations of rotary knife (giving a straight edge) and roulette. The $5 value exists only with straight edges.

129 "The Cock"

130 "Industry"

(Des J.W. Litho Questa)

1981 (20 July). *Birth Centenary of Picasso. T* **129** *and similar vert designs. Multicoloured. P* 13½ × 14.

583	30 c. Type **129**	25	10
584	50 c. "Man with an Ice-Cream"	35	10
585	55 c. "Woman dressing her Hair"	35	10
586	$3 "Seated Woman"	95	85
583/6	*Set of* 4	1·75	1·00
MS587	128 × 102 mm. $5 "Night Fishing at Antibes"	2·50	2·50

(Des Walsall. Litho Format)

1981 (28 Sept). *25th Anniv of Duke of Edinburgh Award Scheme. T* **130** *and similar vert designs. Multicoloured.* W w **14**. *P* 14½.

588	10 c. Type **130**	10	10
589	35 c. "Community service"	15	10
590	50 c. "Physical recreation"	15	10
591	$2.50, Duke of Edinburgh speaking at Caribbean Conference, 1975	45	70
588/91	*Set of* 4	70	75

131 Louis Braille

132 "Portrait of Fanny Travis Cochran" (Cecilia Beaux)

(Des J.W. Litho Questa)

1981 (10 Nov). *International Year for Disabled Persons. Famous Disabled People. T* **131** *and similar horiz designs. Multicoloured. P* 14.

592 10 c. Type **131** 10 10
593 50 c. Sarah Bernhardt 20 10
594 $2 Joseph Pulitzer 60 70
595 $2.50, Henri de Toulouse-Lautrec 65 85
592/5 .. .. *Set of* 4 1·40 1·60
MS596 115 × 90 mm. $5 Franklin Delano Roosevelt .. .. 1·00 1·25

(Des BG Studio. Litho Questa)

1981 (1 Dec). *Decade for Women. Paintings. T* **132** *and similar vert designs. Multicoloured. P* 14.

597 10 c. Type **132** 10 10
598 50 c. "Women with Dove" (Marie Laurencin) 20 10
599 $2 "Portrait of a Young Pupil of David" (Aimee Duvivier) 60 70
600 $2.50, "Self-portrait" (Rosalba Carriera) .. 65 85
597/600 .. .. *Set of* 4 1·40 1·60
MS601 104 × 78 mm. $5 "Self-portrait" (Elizabeth Vigee-le-Brun) .. .. 1·00 1·25

133 "The Adoration of the Magi" (Sfoza)

134 1860 1d. Stamp

(Des BG Studio. Litho Format)

1981 (15 Dec). *Christmas Paintings. T* **133** *and similar vert designs. Multicoloured. W w* **14**. *P* 14.

602 10 c. Type **133** 10 10
603 30 c. "The Adoration of the Kings" (Orcanga) 20 10
604 $1.50, "The Adoration of the Kings" (Gerard) 45 50
605 $2.50, "The Adoration of the Kings" (Foppa) 75 85
602/5 .. .. *Set of* 4 1·25 1·25

(Des J.W. Litho Questa)

1981 (29 Dec). *First Anniv of U.P.U. Membership. T* **134** *and similar horiz designs. Multicoloured. P* 14.

606 10 c. Type **134** 20 10
607 30 c. 1969 First anniversary of Caribbean Free Trade Area 25 c. commemorative .. 40 10
608 50 c. 1979 Independence $2 commemorative 45 50
609 $2 U.P.U. emblem with U.P.U. and St. Lucia flags .. .. 95 2·25
606/9 .. .. *Set of* 4 1·75 2·50
MS610 128 × 109 mm. $5 U.P.U. Headquarters, Berne, and G.P.O. Building, Castries .. .. 1·25 1·50

135 Scene from Football Match

(Des Clover Mill. Litho Format)

1982 (15 Feb). *World Cup Football Championship, Spain. T* **135** *and similar horiz designs showing scenes from different matches. P* 15.

611 10 c. multicoloured 20 10
612 50 c. multicoloured 70 15
613 $2 multicoloured .. .. 1·50 90
614 $2.50, multicoloured .. .. 1·75 1·00
611/14 .. .. *Set of* 4 3·75 1·90
MS615 104 × 84 mm. $5 multicoloured .. .. 2·50 2·25

136 Pigeon Island National Park

137 Map-reading

(Des J. Cooter. Litho Format)

1982 (13 Apr). *Bicentenary of Battle of the Saints. T* **136** *and similar horiz designs. Multicoloured. W w* **14**. *P* 14.

616 10 c. Type **136** 25 15
617 35 c. Battle scene 80 15
618 50 c. Rodney (English admiral) and De Grasse (French admiral) .. .. 1·10 65
619 $2.50, Map of the Saints, Martinique and St. Lucia .. .. 3·25 4·50
616/19 .. .. *Set of* 4 5·00 5·00
MS620 125 × 75 mm. Nos. 616/19 .. .. 5·50 7·00

(Litho Questa)

1982 (4 Aug). *75th Anniv of Boy Scout Movement. T* **137** *and similar vert designs. Multicoloured. W w* **14**. *P* 14.

621 10 c. Type **137** 10 10
622 50 c. First Aid practice 30 15
623 $1.50, Camping 75 80
624 $2.50, Campfire singsong .. .. 1·25 1·50
621/4 .. .. *Set of* 4 2·25 2·25

138 Leeds Castle

139 "Adoration of the Kings" (detail, Jan Brueghel)

(Des PAD Studio. Litho Questa)

1982 (1 Sept). *21st Birthday of Princess of Wales. T* **138** *and similar vert designs. Multicoloured. P* 14½ × 14.

625 50 c. Type **138** 30 20
626 $2 Princess Diana boarding aircraft .. .. 1·25 75
627 $4 Wedding .. .. 1·75 1·40
625/7 .. .. *Set of* 3 3·00 2·10
MS628 102 × 75 mm. $5 Princess of Wales .. 3·00 2·00

(Des PAD Studio. Litho Harrison)

1982 (10 Nov). *Christmas. T* **139** *and similar vert designs depicting details from paintings. Multicoloured. W w* **14**. *P* 14.

629 10 c. Type **139** 10 10
630 30 c. "Nativity" (Lorenzo Costa) 15 10
631 50 c. "Virgin and Child" (Fra Filippo Lippi) .. 25 15
632 80 c. "Adoration of the Shepherds" (Nicolas Poussin) 40 55
629/32 .. .. *Set of* 4 75 75

140 The Pitons

141 Crown Agents Headquarters, Millbank, London

(Des D. Bowen. Litho Questa)

1983 (14 Mar). *Commonwealth Day. T* **140** *and similar horiz designs. Multicoloured. W w* **14** *(sideways). P* 14.

633 10 c. Type **140** 10 10
634 30 c. Tourist beach 15 10
635 50 c. Banana harvesting 20 15
636 $2 Flag of St. Lucia .. .. 60 1·00
633/6 .. .. *Set of* 4 85 1·10

(Des L. Curtis. Litho Questa)

1983 (1 Apr). *150th Anniv of Crown Agents. T* **141** *and similar vert designs. Multicoloured. W w* **14**. *P* 14.

637 10 c. Type **141** 10 10
638 15 c. Road construction 10 10
639 50 c. Road network map 20 25
640 $2 First St. Lucia stamp .. .. 60 1·25
637/40 .. .. *Set of* 4 80 1·50

IMPERFORATES AND MISSING COLOURS. Various issues between Nos. 641 and 947 exist either imperforate or with colours omitted. Such items are not listed as there is no evidence that they fulfil the criteria outlined on page xi of this catalogue.

142 Communications at Sea

(Des J.W. Litho Format)

1983 (12 July). *World Communications Year. T* **142** *and similar horiz designs. Multicoloured. P* 14½.

641 10 c. Type **142** 15 10
642 50 c. Communications in the air 40 15
643 $1.50, T.V. transmission via satellite .. 90 75
644 $2.50, Computer communications .. .. 1·40 1·25
641/4 .. .. *Set of* 4 2·50 2·00
MS645 107 × 88 mm. $5 Weather satellite .. 2·00 2·75

143 Long-jawed Squirrelfish

(Des G. Drummond. Litho Format)

1983 (23 Aug). *Coral Reef Fishes. T* **143** *and similar horiz designs. Multicoloured. P* 14½.

646 10 c. Type **143** 10 10
647 50 c. Banded Butterflyfish 20 15
648 $1.50, Black-barred Soldierfish 60 85
649 $2.50 Yellow-tailed Snapper .. .. .. 80 1·40
646/9 .. .. *Set of* 4 1·50 2·25
MS650 122×97 mm. $5 Red Hind .. .. 2·50 3·25

144 *Duke of Sutherland* (1930)

145 "The Niccolini-Cowper Madonna"

(Des J.W. Litho Format)

1983 (14 Oct). *Leaders of the World. Railway Locomotives (1st series). T* **144** *and similar horiz designs, the first in each pair showing technical drawings and the second the locomotive at work. P* 12½.

651 35 c. multicoloured 15 20
a. Vert pair. Nos. 651/2 .. .. 30 40
652 35 c. multicoloured 15 20
653 35 c. multicoloured 15 20
a. Vert pair. Nos. 653/4 .. .. 30 40
654 35 c. multicoloured 15 20
655 50 c. multicoloured 20 30
a. Vert pair. Nos. 655/6 .. .. 40 60
656 50 c. multicoloured 20 30
657 50 c. multicoloured 20 30
a. Vert pair. Nos. 657/8 .. .. 40 60
658 50 c. multicoloured 20 30
659 $1 multicoloured 30 50
a. Vert pair. Nos. 659/60 .. .. 60 1·00
660 $1 multicoloured 30 50
661 $1 multicoloured 30 50
a. Vert pair. Nos. 661/2 .. .. 60 1·00
662 $1 multicoloured 30 50
663 $2 multicoloured 40 70
a. Vert pair. Nos. 663/4 .. .. 80 1·40
664 $2 multicoloured 40 70
665 $2 multicoloured 40 70
a. Vert pair. Nos. 665/6 .. .. 80 1·40
666 $2 multicoloured 40 70
651/66 .. .. *Set of* 16 3·50 6·50

Designs:—Nos. 651/2, *Duke of Sutherland*, Great Britain (1930); 653/4, *City of Glasgow*, Great Britain (1940); 655/6, *Lord Nelson*, Great Britain (1926); 657/8, *Leeds United*, Great Britain (1928); 659/60, *Bodmin*, Great Britain (1945); 661/2, *Eton*, Great Britain (1930); 663/4, *Flying Scotsman*, Great Britain (1923); 665/6, *Rocket*, Great Britain (1829).

Nos. 651/2, 653/4, 655/6, 657/8, 659/60, 661/2, 663/4 and 665/6 were printed together, *se-tenant*, in vertical pairs throughout the sheets.

See also Nos. 715/26, 761/76, 824/31 and 858/73.

(Litho Format)

1983 (21 Nov). *Christmas. 500th Birth Anniv of Raphael. T* **145** *and similar vert designs showing details of Raphael paintings. Multicoloured. W w* **14**. *P* 14.

667 10 c. Type **145** 10 10
668 30 c. "The Holy Family with a Palm Tree" .. 20 10
669 50 c. "The Sistine Madonna" 25 30
670 $5 "The Alba Madonna" .. .. 1·50 3·25
667/70 .. .. *Set of* 4 1·75 3·25

146 George III

147 Clarke & Co's Drug Store

(Des Court House Studio. Litho Format)

1984 (13 Mar). *Leaders of the World. British Monarchs. T* **146** *and similar vert designs. Multicoloured. P* 12½.

671 5 c. Battle of Waterloo 10 10
a. Horiz pair. Nos. 671/2 .. .. 10 10
672 5 c. Type **146** 10 10
673 10 c. George III at Kew 10 10
a. Horiz pair. Nos. 673/4 .. .. 10 15
674 10 c. Kew Palace 10 10
675 35 c. Coat of Arms of Elizabeth I 10 20
a. Horiz pair. Nos. 675/6 .. .. 10 40
676 35 c. Elizabeth I 10 20
677 60 c. Coat of Arms of George III 15 30
a. Horiz pair. Nos. 677/8 .. .. 30 60
678 60 c. George III (*different*) 15 30
679 $1 Elizabeth I at Hatfield 15 35
a. Horiz pair. Nos. 679/80 .. .. 30 70

680 $1 Hatfield Palace 15 35
681 $2.50, Spanish Armada 30 60
a. Horiz pair. Nos. 681/2 60 1·10
682 $2.50, Elizabeth I (*different*) 30 60
671/82 *Set of* 12 1·25 2·75

Nos. 671/2, 673/4, 675/6, 677/8, 679/80 and 681/2 were printed together in *se-tenant* horizontal pairs throughout the sheets.

Unissued 30, 50 c., $1, $2.50 and $5 values, showing Alfred the Great or Richard I, exist from stock dispersed by the liquidator of Format International Security Printers Ltd.

(Des J. Cooter. Litho Questa)

1984 (6 Apr). *Historic Buildings. T* **147** *and similar multi-coloured designs.* W w **15** (*sideways on* 45 *c. to* $2.50). *P* 14 × 13½ (10 *c.*) *or* 13½ × 14 (*others*).
683 10 c. Type **147** 10 10
684 45 c. Colonial architecture (*horiz*) 30 25
685 65 c. Colonial "chattel" house (*horiz*) 45 35
686 $2.50, Treasury after 1906 earthquake (*horiz*) 1·75 1·60
683/6 *Set of* 4 2·40 2·00

1984 (15 May). *As Nos.* 540/42, 545/6 *and* 548, *but W w* **15** (*sideways on* 20 *c. to* $1). *P* 14½ × 14.
690 20 c. Refrigerated freighter 1·50 30
691 25 c. Britten Norman Islander aircraft 2·00 35
692 30 c. *Charles* (pilot boat) 1·75 45
695 $1 Lockheed L-1011 Tristar 500 airliner 4·25 90
696 $2 Cargo liner 5·00 2·75
698 $10 *Queen Elizabeth 2* (liner) 10·00 13·00
690/8 *Set of* 6 22·00 16·00

148 Logwood

(Des J. Cooter. Litho Format)

1984 (12 June). *Forestry Resources. T* **148** *and similar multi-coloured designs. W w* **15** (*inverted on* 65 *c., sideways on others*). *P* 14 × 13½ (65 *c.*) *or* 13½ × 14 (*others*).
699 10 c. Type **148** 10 10
700 45 c. Calabash 30 30
701 65 c. Gommier (*vert*) 35 55
702 $2.50, Raintree 60 2·75
699/702 *Set of* 4 1·10 3·25

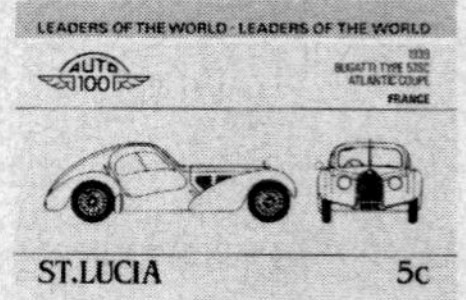

149 Bugatti Type "57SC Atlantic Coupe"

(Des J.W. Litho Format)

1984 (25 June). *Leaders of the World. Automobiles* (1*st series*). *T* **149** *and similar horiz designs, the first in each pair showing technical drawings and the second paintings. P* 12½.
703 5 c. black, reddish lavender and lemon 10 10
a. Vert pair. Nos. 703/4 10 10
704 5 c. multicoloured 10 10
705 10 c. black, azure and rose-carmine 10 10
a. Vert pair. Nos. 705/6 10 10
706 10 c. multicoloured 10 10
707 $1 black, pale green and orange-brown 15 25
a. Vert pair. Nos. 707/8 30 50
708 $1 multicoloured 15 25
709 $2.50, black, pale flesh and slate-blue 30 40
a. Vert pair. Nos. 709/10 60 80
710 $2.50, multicoloured 30 40
703/10 *Set of* 8 80 1·25

Designs:—Nos. 703/4, Bugatti Type "57SC Atlantic Coupe"; 705/6, Chevrolet "Bel Air Convertible"; 707/8, Alfa Romeo "1750 GS (Zagato)"; 709/10, Duesenberg "S J Roadster".

Nos. 703/4, 705/6, 707/8 and 709/10 were printed together, *se-tenant*, in vertical pairs throughout the sheets.

See also Nos. 745/60, 789/96 and 902/13.

150 Pygmy Gecko **151** Men's Volleyball

(Des Jennifer Toombs. Litho Format)

1984 (8 Aug). *Endangered Wildlife. T* **150** *and similar horiz designs. Multicoloured. W w* **15** (*sideways*). *P* 14.
711 10 c. Type **150** 30 10
712 45 c. Maria Island Ground Lizard 70 50
713 65 c. Green Iguana 75 85
714 $2.50, Couresse Snake 1·60 3·50
711/14 *Set of* 4 3·00 4·50

(Des J.W. Litho Format)

1984 (21 Sept). *Leaders of the World. Railway Locomotives* (2*nd series*). *Horiz designs as T* **144**, *the first in each pair showing technical drawings and the second the locomotive at work. P* 12½.
715 1 c. multicoloured 10 10
a. Vert pair. Nos. 715/16 10 10
716 1 c. multicoloured 10 10
717 15 c. multicoloured 10 15
a. Vert pair. Nos. 717/18 15 30
718 15 c. multicoloured 10 15
719 50 c. multicoloured 15 20
a. Vert pair. Nos. 719/20 30 40
720 50 c. multicoloured 15 20
721 75 c. multicoloured 15 25
a. Vert pair. Nos. 721/2 30 50
722 75 c. multicoloured 15 25
723 $1 multicoloured 20 30
a. Vert pair. Nos. 723/4 40 60
724 $1 multicoloured 20 30
725 $2 multicoloured 25 50
a. Vert pair. Nos. 725/6 50 1·00
726 $2 multicoloured 25 50
715/26 *Set of* 12 1·50 2·50

Designs:—Nos. 715/16, *Taw*, Great Britain (1897); 717/18, "Crocodile 1.C.C.1." type, Switzerland (1920); 719/20, *The Countess*, Great Britain (1903); 721/2, Class "GE6/6 C.C.", Switzerland (1921); 723/4, Class "P8", Germany (1906); 725/6, *Der Adler*, Germany (1835).

Nos. 715/26 were issued in a similar sheet format to Nos. 651/66.

Nos. 715/26 exist imperforate from stock dispersed by the liquidator of Format International Security Printers Ltd.

(Des Court House Studio. Litho Format)

1984 (21 Sept). *Leaders of the World. Olympic Games, Los Angeles. T* **151** *and similar vert designs. Multicoloured. P* 12½.
727 5 c. Type **151** 10 10
a. Horiz pair. Nos. 727/8 10 10
728 5 c. Women's volleyball 10 10
729 10 c. Women's hurdles 10 10
a. Horiz pair. Nos. 729/30 10 10
730 10 c. Men's hurdles 10 10
731 65 c. Show jumping 15 20
a. Horiz pair. Nos. 731/2 30 40
732 65 c. Dressage 15 20
733 $2.50, Women's gymnastics 40 50
a. Horiz pair. Nos. 733/4 80 1·00
734 $2.50, Men's gymnastics 40 50
727/34 *Set of* 8 1·10 1·40

Nos. 727/8, 729/30, 731/2, 733/4 were printed together, *se-tenant*, in horizontal pairs throughout the sheets.

Examples of No. 537 exist overprinted "RUMBRIDGE PACK R.F.C./1984 TOUR". This was a private souvenir, connected with a tour to St. Lucia by an English rugby club in October 1984. It was not sold by the St. Lucia Post Office or Philatelic Bureau.

152 Glass of Wine and Flowers **153** Slaves preparing Manioc

(Des G. Vasarhelyi. Litho Format)

1984 (31 Oct). *Christmas. T* **152** *and similar vert designs. Multi-coloured. W w* **15**. *P* 14.
735 10 c. Type **152** 10 10
736 35 c. Priest and decorated altar 10 10
737 65 c. Nativity scene 15 25
738 $3 Holy Family 50 1·50
w. Wmk inverted 5·00
735/8 *Set of* 4 60 1·75
MS739 147×77 mm. Nos. 735/8 2·00 4·50

(Des J. Cooter. Litho Format)

1984 (12 Dec). *150th Anniv of Abolition of Slavery. T* **153** *and similar vert designs. Each black and yellow-ochre. W w* **15**. *P* 14 × 13½.
740 10 c. Type **153** 10 10
741 35 c. Sifting and cooking cassava flour 10 10
742 55 c. Cooking pot, and preparing tobacco 10 20
743 $5 Stripping tobacco leaves for twist tobacco 55 1·50
740/3 *Set of* 4 65 1·60
MS744 154 × 110 mm. As Nos. 740/3, but without dates and side inscription and with the face values in different positions 1·50 4·50

(Des Artists International (65 c.), J.W. (others). Litho Format)

1984 (19 Dec). *Leaders of the World. Automobiles* (2*nd series*). *Horiz designs as T* **149**, *the first in each pair showing technical drawings and the second paintings. P* 12½.
745 10 c. black, pale green and lake-brown 10 10
a. Vert pair. Nos. 745/6 10 15
746 10 c. multicoloured 10 10
747 30 c. black, azure and bright yellow-green 15 15
a. Vert pair. Nos. 747/8 30 30
748 30 c. multicoloured 15 15
749 55 c. black, greenish yellow and orange-brown 20 30
a. Vert pair. Nos. 749/50 40 60
750 55 c. multicoloured 20 30
751 65 c. black, grey and brown-lilac 20 35
a. Vert pair. Nos. 751/2 40 70
752 65 c. multicoloured 20 35
753 75 c. black, pale cinnamon, & orange-verm 20 35
a. Vert pair. Nos. 753/4 40 70
754 75 c. multicoloured 20 35
755 $1 black, pale cinnamon and dull violet-blue 20 40
a. Vert pair. Nos. 755/6 40 80
756 $1 multicoloured 20 40
757 $2 black, pale green and orange-red 25 50
a. Vert pair. Nos. 757/8 50 1·00
758 $2 multicoloured 25 50
759 $3 black, pale cinnamon & orange-verm 30 60
a. Vert pair. Nos. 759/60 60 1·10
760 $3 multicoloured 30 60
745/60 *Set of* 16 2·75 4·75

Designs:—Nos. 745/6, Panhard and Levassor; 747/8, N.S.U. "RO-80" Saloon; 749/50, Abarth "Bialbero"; 751/2, TVR "Vixen 2500M"; 753/4, Ford "Mustang" Convertible; 755/6, Ford "Model T"; 757/8, Aston Martin" DB3S"; 759/60, Chrysler "Imperial CG Dual Cowl" Phaeton.

Nos. 745/60 were issued in a similar sheet format to Nos. 703/10.

(Des T. Hadler (5, 15, 35 c.), J.W. (others). Litho Format)

1985 (4 Feb). *Leaders of the World. Railway Locomotives* (3*rd series*). *Horiz designs as T* **144**, *the first in each pair showing technical drawings and the second the locomotive at work. P* 12½.
761 5 c. multicoloured 10 10
a. Vert pair. Nos. 761/2 10 10
762 5 c. multicoloured 10 10
763 15 c. multicoloured 10 15
a. Vert pair. Nos. 763/4 20 30
764 15 c. multicoloured 10 15
765 35 c. multicoloured 15 15
a. Vert pair. Nos. 765/6 30 30
766 35 c. multicoloured 15 15
767 60 c. multicoloured 15 15
a. Vert pair. Nos. 767/8 30 30
768 60 c. multicoloured 15 15
769 75 c. multicoloured 15 20
a. Vert pair. Nos. 769/70 20 40
770 75 c. multicoloured 15 20
771 $1 multicoloured 15 20
a. Vert pair. Nos. 771/2 30 40
772 $1 multicoloured 15 20
773 $2 multicoloured 25 40
a. Vert pair. Nos. 773/4 50 80
774 $2 multicoloured 25 40
775 $2.50, multicoloured 30 55
a. Vert pair. Nos. 775/6 60 1·10
776 $2.50, multicoloured 30 55
761/76 *Set of* 16 2·25 3·25

Designs:—Nos. 761/2, Class "C53", Japan (1928); 763/4, Class "Heavy L", India (1885); 765/6, Class "B18¼", Australia (1926); 767/8, *Owain Glyndwr*, Great Britain (1923); 769/70, *Lion*, Great Britain (1838); 771/2, Coal type locomotive, Great Britain (1873); 773/4, No. 2238, Class "Q6", Great Britain (1921); 775/6, Class "H", Great Britain (1920).

Nos. 761/76 were issued in a similar sheet format to Nos. 651/66.

154 Girl Guide Badge in Shield and Crest of St. Lucia **155** *Clossiana selene*

(Des Court House Studio. Litho Questa)

1985 (21 Feb). *75th Anniv of Girl Guide Movement and 60th Anniv of Guiding in St. Lucia. W w* **15**. *P* 14.
777 **154** 10 c. multicoloured 30 10
778 35 c. multicoloured 1·00 15
779 65 c. multicoloured 1·50 65
780 $3 multicoloured 3·75 4·50
777/80 *Set of* 4 6·00 4·75

(Des Jennifer Toombs. Litho Format)

1985 (28 Feb). *Leaders of the World. Butterflies. T* **155** *and similar vert designs. Multicoloured. P* 12½.
781 15 c. Type **155** 10 10
a. Horiz pair. Nos. 781/2 15 15
782 15 c. *Inachis io* 10 10
783 40 c. *Philaethria dido* (s sp *wernecke*i) 10 15
a. Horiz pair. Nos. 783/4 20 30
784 40 c. *Callicore sorana* 10 15
785 60 c. *Kallima inachus* 15 15
a. Horiz pair. Nos. 785/6 30 30
786 60 c. *Hypanartia paullus* 15 15
787 $2.25, *Morpho helena* 25 50
a. Horiz pair. Nos. 787/8 50 1·00
788 $2.25, *Ornithoptera meridionalis* 25 50
781/8 *Set of* 8 1·00 1·60

Nos. 781/2, 783/4, 785/6 and 787/8 were printed together, *se-tenant*, in horizontal pairs throughout the sheets.

(Des J.W. Litho Format)

1985 (29 Mar). *Leaders of the World. Automobiles* (3*rd series*). *Horiz designs as T* **149**, *the first in each pair showing technical drawings and the second paintings. P* 12½.
789 15 c. black, cobalt and Indian red 10 10
a. Vert pair. Nos. 789/90 15 20
790 15 c. multicoloured 10 10
791 50 c. black, pale orange and deep rose-red 15 20
a. Vert pair. Nos. 791/2 30 40
792 50 c. multicoloured 15 20
793 $1 black, pale green and reddish orange 15 20
a. Vert pair. Nos. 793/4 30 40
794 $1 multicoloured 15 20
795 $1.50, black, pale green & pale red-brown 20 35
a. Vert pair. Nos. 795/6 40 70
796 $1.50, multicoloured 20 35
789/96 *Set of* 8 1·00 1·50

Designs:—Nos. 789/90, Hudson "Eight" (1940); 791/2, KdF (1937); 793/4, Kissel "Goldbug" (1925); 795/6, Ferrari "246 GTS" (1973).

Nos. 789/96 were issued in a similar sheet format to Nos. 703/10.

156 Grenadier, 70th Regiment, *c* 1775 **157** Messerschmitt Bf 109E

(Des J. Cooter. Litho Format)

1985 (7 May). *Military Uniforms. T* **156** *and similar vert designs. Multicoloured. W w* **15** *(sideways). With imprint date. P* 15.

797 5 c. Type **156**.. .. 25 40
798 10 c. Officer, Grenadier Company, 14th Regiment, 1780 .. 25 15
799 20 c. Officer, Battalion Company, 46th Regiment, 1781 .. 40 30
800 25 c. Officer, Royal Artillery, *c.* 1782 .. 40 15
801 30 c. Officer, Royal Engineers, 1782 .. 60 30
802 35 c. Officer, Battalion Company, 54th Regiment, 1782 .. 50 20
803 45 c. Private, Grenadier Company, 14th Regiment, 1782 .. 80 40
804 50 c. Gunner, Royal Artillery, 1796.. 80 40
805 65 c. Private, Battalion Company, 85th Regiment, *c.* 1796 .. 70 55
806 75 c. Private, Battalion Company, 76th Regiment, 1796 .. 75 70
807 90 c. Private, Battalion Company, 81st Regiment, *c.* 1796 .. 85 70
808 $1 Sergeant, 74th (Highland) Regiment, 1796 .. 90 70
809 $2.50, Private, Light Company, 93rd Regiment, 1803 .. 3·50 6·00
810 $5 Private, Battalion Company, 1st West India Regiment, 1803 .. 6·50 11·00
811 $15 Officer, Royal Artillery, 1850 .. 11·00 17·00
797/811 .. *Set of* 15 25·00 35·00

Imprint dates: "1984", Nos. 797/811; "1986", Nos. 799/800.

Examples of the 5, 10, 15, 45, 50 c. and $20 with "1986" imprint date, and in some cases imperforate, come from stock dispersed by the liquidator of Format International Security Printers Ltd.

For 5, 10, 30, 45, 50 c., $2.50, $5, and additional values, all without watermark see Nos. 928/46.

For 5, 10, 20, 25 c. and additional values, all watermarked w **16** (sideways) see Nos. 993/1003.

(Des J.W. Litho Format)

1985 (30 May). *Leaders of the World. Military Aircraft. T* **157** *and similar horiz designs, the first in each pair showing paintings and the second technical drawings. P* 12½.

812 5 c. multicoloured .. 10 10
a. Vert pair. Nos. 812/13 .. 10 10
813 5 c. black, pale new blue and pale yellow .. 10 10
814 55 c. multicoloured .. 20 35
a. Vert pair. Nos. 814/15 .. 40 70
815 55 c. black, pale new blue and pale yellow .. 20 35
816 60 c. multicoloured .. 20 35
a. Vert pair. Nos. 816/17 .. 40 70
817 60 c. black, pale new blue and pale yellow .. 20 35
818 $2 multicoloured .. 35 65
a. Vert pair. Nos. 818/19 .. 70 1·25
819 $2 black, pale new blue and pale yellow .. 35 65
812/19 .. *Set of* 8 1·40 2·50

Designs:—Nos. 812/13, Messerschmitt Bf 109E; 814/15, Avro Type 683 Lancaster Mk 1; 816/17, North American P-51D Mustang; 818/19, Supermarine Spitfire Mk II.

Nos. 812/13, 814/15, 816/17 and 818/19 were printed together, *se-tenant*, in vertical pairs throughout the sheets.

158 Magnificent Frigate Birds, Frigate Island Bird Sanctuary **159** Queen Elizabeth the Queen Mother

(Des G. Drummond. Litho Format)

1985 (20 June). *Nature Reserves. T* **158** *and similar horiz designs. Multicoloured. W w* **15**. *P* 15.

820 10 c. Type **158**.. .. 35 20
821 35 c. Mangrove Cuckoo, Scorpion Island, Savannes Bay .. 65 45
822 65 c. Lesser Yellowlegs, Maria Island Reserve .. 75 85
823 $3 Audubon's Shearwaters, Lapins Island Reserve .. 1·00 5·00
820/3 .. *Set of* 4 2·50 6·00

(Des Tudor Art Agency ($2.50), J.W. (others). Litho Format)

1985 (26 June). *Leaders of the World. Railway Locomotives (4th series). Horiz designs as T* **144**, *the first in each pair showing technical drawings and second the locomotive at work. P* 12½.

824 10 c. multicoloured .. 10 10
a. Vert pair. Nos. 824/5 .. 20 20
825 10 c. multicoloured .. 10 10
826 30 c. multicoloured .. 15 15
a. Vert pair. Nos. 826/7 .. 30 30
827 30 c. multicoloured .. 15 15
828 75 c. multicoloured .. 20 20
a. Vert pair. Nos. 828/9 .. 40 40
829 75 c. multicoloured .. 20 20
830 $2.50, multicoloured .. 40 55
a. Vert pair. Nos. 830/1 .. 80 1·10
831 $2.50, multicoloured .. 40 55
824/31 .. *Set of* 8 1·50 1·75

Designs:—Nos. 824/5, No. 28 tank locomotive, Great Britain (1897); 826/7, No. 1621 Class "M", Great Britain (1893); 828/9, Class "Dunalastair", Great Britain (1896); 830/1, No. 2290 "Big Bertha" type, Great Britain (1919).

Nos. 824/31 were issued in a similar sheet format to Nos. 651/66.

(Des Court House Studio. Litho Format)

1985 (16 Aug). *Leaders of the World. Life and Times of Queen Elizabeth the Queen Mother. Various vertical portraits as T* **159**. *P* 12.

832 40 c. multicoloured .. 10 20
a. Horiz pair. Nos. 832/3 .. 10 40
833 40 c. multicoloured .. 10 20
834 75 c. multicoloured .. 10 25
a. Horiz pair. Nos. 834/5 .. 15 50
835 75 c. multicoloured .. 10 25
836 $1.10, multicoloured .. 15 35
a. Horiz pair. Nos. 836/7 .. 30 70
837 $1.10, multicoloured .. 15 35
838 $1.75, multicoloured .. 20 55
a. Horiz pair. Nos. 838/9 .. 35 1·10
839 $1.75, multicoloured .. 20 55
832/9 .. *Set of* 8 70 2·50
MS840 84×114 mm. $2 mult; $2 mult .. 60 1·40

The two designs of each value were issued, *se-tenant*, in horizontal pairs within the sheets.

Each *se-tenant* pair shows a floral pattern across the bottom of the portraits which stops short of the left-hand edge on the left-hand stamp and of the right-hand edge on the right-hand stamp.

Nos. 832/9, together with two unissued 25 c. designs, exist in miniature sheets, one for each value, from stock dispersed by the liquidator of Format International Security Printers Ltd.

Designs as Nos. 832/3 and 836/7, but with face values of $3 × 2 and $6 × 2, also exist in additional miniature sheets from a restricted printing issued 31 December 1985.

160 "Youth playing Banjo" (Wayne Whitfield) **161** "Papa Jab"

(Litho Format)

1985 (5 Sept). *International Youth Year. Paintings by Young St. Lucians. T* **160** *and similar designs. W w* **15** *(sideways). P* 15.

841 10 c. black, new blue and bright magenta .. 10 10
842 45 c. multicoloured .. 30 25
843 75 c. multicoloured .. 50 45
844 $3.50, multicoloured .. 2·00 2·50
841/4 .. *Set of* 4 2·50 3·00
MS845 123×86 mm. $5 multicoloured .. 1·25 3·50

Designs: *Vert (as T* **160***)*—45 c. "Motorcyclist" (Mark Maragh); 75 c. "Boy and Girl at Pitons" (Bartholomew Eugene); $3.50, "Abstract" (Lyndon Samuel). *Horiz (80 × 55 mm)*—$5 Young people and St. Lucia landscapes.

1985 (26 Oct). *Royal Visit. Nos.* 649, 685/6, 702, 713, 778 *and* 836/7 *optd as T* **114** *of Montserrat.*

846 **154** 35 c. multicoloured .. 4·00 2·75
847 – 65 c. multicoloured (No. 685) .. 1·00 2·50
848 – 65 c. multicoloured (No. 713) .. 3·75 3·50
849 – $1.10, multicoloured (No. 836) .. 4·75 6·50
a. Horiz pair. Nos. 849/50 .. 9·50 13·00
850 – $1.10, multicoloured (No. 837) .. 4·75 6·50
851 – $2.50, multicoloured (No. 649) .. 5·00 6·50
852 – $2.50, multicoloured (No. 686) .. 1·00 2·50
853 – $2.50, multicoloured (No. 702) .. 1·00 2·50
846/53 .. *Set of* 8 23·00 30·00

(Litho Format)

1985 (24 Dec). *Christmas. Masqueraders. T* **161** *and similar vert designs. Multicoloured. P* 15.

854 10 c. Type **161**.. .. 15 10
855 45 c. "Paille Bananne" .. 25 25
856 65 c. "Cheval Bois" .. 30 75
854/6 .. *Set of* 3 60 1·00
MS857 70×83 mm. $4 "Madonna and Child" (Dunstan St. Omer) .. 90 1·90

(Des T. Hadler. Litho Format)

1986 (27 Jan). *Leaders of the World. Railway Locomotives (5th series). Horiz designs as T* **144**, *the first in each pair showing technical drawings and the second the locomotive at work. P* 12½.

858 5 c. multicoloured .. 10 15
a. Vert pair. Nos. 858/9 .. 10 30
859 5 c. multicoloured .. 10 15
860 15 c. multicoloured .. 15 15
a. Vert pair. Nos. 860/1 .. 30 30
861 15 c. multicoloured .. 15 15
862 30 c. multicoloured .. 20 30
a. Vert pair. Nos. 862/3 .. 40 60
863 30 c. multicoloured .. 20 30
864 60 c. multicoloured .. 25 40
a. Vert pair. Nos. 864/5 .. 50 80
865 60 c. multicoloured .. 25 40
866 75 c. multicoloured .. 30 50
a. Vert pair. Nos. 866/7 .. 60 1·00
867 75 c. multicoloured .. 30 50
868 $1 multicoloured .. 35 60
a. Vert pair. Nos. 868/9 .. 70 1·10
869 $1 multicoloured .. 35 60
870 $2.25, multicoloured .. 45 80
a. Vert pair. Nos. 870/1 .. 90 1·60
871 $2.25, multicoloured .. 45 80
872 $3 multicoloured .. 45 80
a. Vert pair. Nos. 872/3 .. 90 1·60
873 $3 multicoloured .. 45 80
858/73 .. *Set of* 16 4·00 6·50

Designs:—Nos. 858/9, Rack loco *Tip Top*, U.S.A (1983); 860/1, *Stephenson*, Great Britain (1975); 862/3, No. 737 Class "D", Great Britain (1901); 864/5, No. 13 Class "2-CO-2", Great Britain (1922); 866/7, *Electra*, Great Britain (1954); 868/9, *City of Newcastle*, Great Britain (1922); 870/1, Von Kruckenburg propeller-driven rail car, Germany (1930); 872/3, No. 860, Japan (1893).

Nos. 858/73 were issued in a similar sheet format to Nos. 651/66.

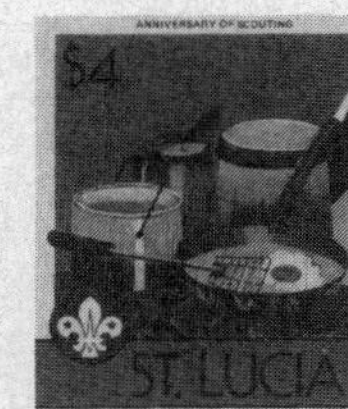

162 Campfire Cooking Utensils

(Des Court House Studio. Litho Format)

1986 (3 Mar). *75th Annivs of Girl Guide Movement and Boy Scouts of America. Two sheets, each* 85×113 *mm, containing vert designs as T* **162**. *Multicoloured. P* 12½.

MS874 $4 Type **162**: $4 Scout salute .. 1·75 3·25
MS875 $6 Wickerwork: $6 Lady Baden-Powell .. 2·75 4·25

The two stamps in each sheet were printed together, *se-tenant*, in horizontal pairs, each forming a composite design.

Nos. **MS**874/5 exist with plain or decorative margins.

Overprints on these miniature sheets commemorating "Capex '87" International Stamp Exhibition, Toronto, were not authorised by the St. Lucia administration.

(Des Court House Studio. Litho Format)

1986 (21 Apr). *60th Birthday of Queen Elizabeth II (1st issue). Multicoloured designs as T* **117***a of Montserrat. P* 12½.

876 5 c. Queen Elizabeth II .. 10 10
877 $1 Princess Elizabeth .. 15 30
878 $3.50, Queen Elizabeth II (*different*) .. 40 90
879 $6 In Canberra, 1982 (*vert*).. .. 55 1·40
876/9 .. *Set of* 4 1·00 2·40
MS880 85×115 mm. $8 Queen Elizabeth II (*different*) .. 4·00 6·00

Nos. 876/9 exist in separate miniature sheets from stock dispersed by the liquidator of Format International Security Printers Ltd.

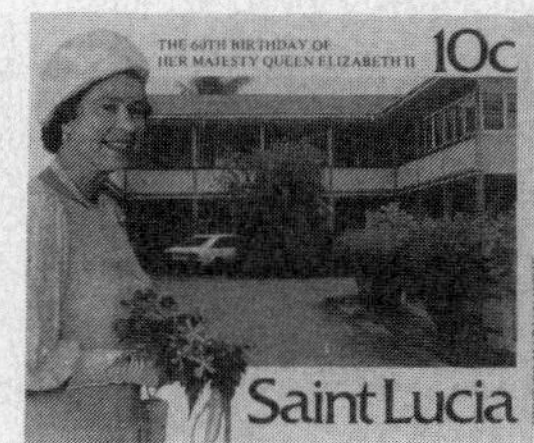

163 Queen Elizabeth and Marian Home

(Des Court House Studio. Litho Questa)

1986 (14 June). *60th Birthday of Queen Elizabeth II (2nd issue). T* **163** *and similar horiz designs. Multicoloured. W w* **15** *(sideways). P* 14×15.

881 10 c. Type **163**.. .. 25 15
882 45 c. Queen addressing rally, Mindoo Phillip Park, 1985 .. 55 35
883 50 c. Queen opening Leon Hess Comprehensive School, 1985 .. 65 50
884 $5 Queen Elizabeth and Government House, Castries .. 2·50 4·00
881/4 .. *Set of* 4 3·50 4·50
MS885 121×85 mm. $7 Queen Elizabeth and Royal Yacht *Britannia*, Castries.. .. 4·25 7·00

164 Pope John Paul II kissing Ground, Castries Airport

(Des Court House Studio. Litho Questa)

1986 (7 July). *Visit of Pope John Paul II. T* **164** *and similar multicoloured designs.* W w **15** (*sideways on* 55, 60 *c.*). *P* 14½ × 14 (80 *c.*) *or* 14 × 14½ (*others*).
886 55 c. Type **164** 70 70
887 60 c. Pope and St. Joseph's Convent . . 70 80
888 80 c. Pope and Castries Catholic Cathedral (*vert*) . . 1·10 1·60
886/8 . . *Set of* 3 2·25 2·75
MS889 85 × 123 mm. $6 Pope John Paul II (*vert*). P 14½ × 14 . . 5·00 6·50

(Litho Format)

1986 (12 Aug). *Royal Wedding (1st issue). Multicoloured designs as T* **118a** *of Montserrat. P* 12½.
890 80 c. Miss Sarah Ferguson . . 40 65
a. Pair. Nos. 890/1 . . 80 1·25
891 80 c. Prince Andrew . . 40 65
892 $2 Prince Andrew and Miss Sarah Ferguson (*horiz*) . . 1·00 1·60
a. Pair. Nos. 892/3 . . 2·00 3·00
893 $2 Prince Andrew with Mrs Nancy Reagan (*horiz*) . . 1·00 1·60
890/3 . . *Set of* 4 2·50 4·00
Nos. 890/1 and 892/3 were each printed together, *se-tenant*, in horizontal and vertical pairs throughout the sheets.
Nos. 890/3 imperforate come from souvenir stamp booklets.
See also Nos. 897/901.

165 Peace Corps Teacher with Students

166 Prince Andrew in Carriage

(Des J. Cooter. Litho Questa)

1986 (25 Sept). *25th Anniv of United States Peace Corps. T* **165** *and similar multicoloured designs.* W w **15** (*sideways on* $2). *P* 14.
894 80 c. Type **165** . . 35 40
895 $2 President John Kennedy (*vert*) . . 1·10 1·60
896 $3.50, Peace Corps emblem between arms of St. Lucia and U.S.A. . . 1·60 2·50
894/6 . . *Set of* 3 2·75 4·00

(Des Court House Studio. Litho Format)

1986 (15 Oct). *Royal Wedding (2nd issue). T* **166** *and similar vert designs. Multicoloured. P* 15.
897 50 c. Type **166** . . 40 30
898 80 c. Miss Sarah Ferguson in coach . . 50 50
899 $1 Duke and Duchess of York at altar . . 55 60
900 $3 Duke and Duchess of York in carriage . . 1·00 2·00
897/900 . . *Set of* 4 2·25 3·00
MS901 115 × 85 mm. $7 Duke and Duchess of York on Palace balcony after wedding (*horiz*) . . 3·50 5·00
Examples of an unissued $10 miniature sheet exist from stock dispersed by the liquidator of Format International Security Printers Ltd.

(Des Court House Studio. Litho Format)

1986 (23 Oct). *Automobiles (4th series). Horiz designs as T* **149**, *the first in each pair showing technical drawings and the second paintings. P* 12½.
902 20 c. multicoloured . . 15 15
a. Vert pair. Nos. 902/3 . . 30 30
903 20 c. multicoloured . . 15 15
904 50 c. multicoloured . . 20 20
a. Vert pair. Nos. 904/5 . . 40 40
905 50 c. multicoloured . . 20 20
906 60 c. multicoloured . . 20 20
a. Vert pair. Nos. 906/7 . . 40 40
907 60 c. multicoloured . . 20 20
908 $1 multicoloured . . 20 20
a. Vert pair. Nos. 908/9 . . 40 40
909 $1 multicoloured . . 20 20
910 $1.50, multicoloured . . 20 20
a. Vert pair. Nos. 910/11 . . 40 40
911 $1.50, multicoloured . . 20 20
912 $3 multicoloured . . 30 45
a. Vert pair. Nos. 912/13 . . 60 90
913 $3 multicoloured . . 30 45
902/13 . . *Set of* 12 2·40 2·50
Designs:—Nos. 902/3, AMC "AMX" (1969); 904/5, Russo-Baltique (1912); 906/7, Lincoln "K.B." (1932); 908/9, Rolls Royce "Phantom II Continental" (1933); 910/11, Buick "Century" (1939); 912/13, Chrysler "300 C" (1957).
Nos. 902/13 were issued in a similar sheet format to Nos. 703/10.

167 Chak-Chak Band

(Des Jennifer Toombs. Litho Format)

1986 (7 Nov). *Tourism (1st series). T* **167** *and similar horiz designs. Multicoloured.* W w **15**. *P* 15.
914 15 c. Type **167** . . 10 10
915 45 c. Folk dancing . . 15 15
916 80 c. Steel band . . 30 50
917 $5 Limbo dancing . . 75 2·25
914/17 . . *Set of* 4 1·10 2·75
MS918 157 × 109 mm. $10 Fire-eating. Wmk sideways . . 3·50 7·00
See also Nos. 988/92.

168 St. Ann Catholic Church, Mon Repos

169 Outline Map of St. Lucia

(Litho Format)

1986 (3 Dec). *Christmas. T* **168** *and similar multicoloured designs. P* 15.
919 10 c. Type **168** . . 10 10
920 40 c. St. Joseph the Worker Catholic Church, Gros Islet . . 20 15
921 80 c. Holy Trinity Anglican Church, Castries 30 50
922 $4 Our Lady of the Assumption Catholic Church, Soufriere (*vert*) . . 75 2·25
919/22 . . *Set of* 4 1·25 2·75
MS923 120 × 101 mm. $7 St. Lucy Catholic Church, Micoud . . 2·25 5·00

(Des L. Curtis. Litho Walsall)

1987 (24 Feb)–**89**. W w **14** (*sideways*). *P* 14. A. *No imprint at foot.* B. *With imprint date.*

			A		B	
924 **169**	5 c. black and cinnamon . .		15	15	20	20
925	10 c. black and pale emerald		15	15	20	20
926	45 c. black & bright orange		45	45	†	
927	50 c. black and violet-blue		45	45	50	50
927*c*	$1 black and bright rose		65	65	†	
924/7*c* . .	*Set of* 5		1·75	1·75	†	

Dates of issue:—24.2.87, Nos. 924A/7A; 9.88, Nos. 924B/5B; 17.3.89, Nos. 927B, 927cA.
Imprint dates: "1988", Nos. 924B/5B; "1989", No. 927B.
For 5 c. and 10 c. watermarked w **16** (sideways) see Nos. 1018/19.

(Des J. Cooter. Litho Format)

1987 (16 Mar). *As Nos.* 797/8, 801, 803/4, 809/10 *and new values* (15, 60, 80 *c. and* $20), *all without wmk.* "1986" *imprint date. P* 15.
928 5 c. Type **156** . . 20 20
929 10 c. Officer, Grenadier Company, 14th Regiment, 1780 . . 25 25
930 15 c. Private, Battalion Company, 2nd West India Regiment, 1803 . . 35 35
933 30 c. Officer, Royal Engineers, 1782 . . 45 45
935 45 c. Private, Grenadier Company, 14th Regiment, 1782 . . 50 50
936 50 c. Gunner, Royal Artillery, 1796 . . 60 60
937 60 c. Officer, Battalion Company, 5th Regiment, 1778 . . 70 70
940 80 c. Officer, Battalion Company, 27th Regiment, *c.* 1780 . . 90 90
943 $2.50, Private, Light Company, 93rd Regiment, 1803 . . 3·00 4·00
944 $5 Private, Battalion Company, 1st West India Regiment, 1803 . . 3·75 8·00
946 $20 Private, Grenadier Company, 46th Regiment, 1778 . . 17·00 23·00
928/46 . . *Set of* 11 25·00 35·00
Imprint dates: "1986", Nos. 928/46; "1987", No. 944.
For various values watermarked w **16** (sideways) see Nos. 993/1003.

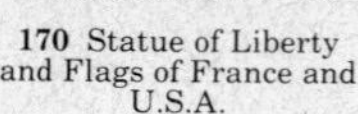

170 Statue of Liberty and Flags of France and U.S.A.

171 First Cadastral Survey Map and Surveying Instruments, 1775

(Des A. Theobald. Litho Format)

1987 (29 Apr). *Centenary of Statue of Liberty* (1986). *T* **170** *and similar vert designs. Multicoloured.* W w **16**. *P* 14½.
947 15 c. Type **170** . . 15 10
948 80 c. Statue and *Mauretania I* (liner) . . 75 65
949 $1 Statue and Concorde . . 1·75 1·00
950 $5 Statue and flying boat at sunset . . 2·25 4·25
947/50 . . *Set of* 4 4·50 5·50
MS951 107 × 88 mm. $6 Statue and Manhattan at night. Wmk sideways . . 3·00 4·25
Unissued $3.50, $4 and $5 miniature sheets exist from stock dispersed by the liquidator of Format International Security Printers Ltd.

1987 (July). *Coil stamp. As No.* 350, *but* W w **16**. *P* 14½ × 14.
953 **87** 10 c. turquoise-green . . 40 40

(Des N. Shewring. Litho Walsall)

1987 (31 Aug). *New Cadastral Survey of St. Lucia. T* **171** *and similar vert designs. Multicoloured.* W w **16**. *P* 14.
955 15 c. Type **171** . . 60 15
956 60 c. Map and surveying instruments, 1814 1·25 85
957 $1 Map and surveying instruments, 1888 1·50 1·50
958 $2.50, Cadastral survey map and surveying instruments, 1987 . . 2·75 3·50
955/8 . . *Set of* 4 5·50 5·50

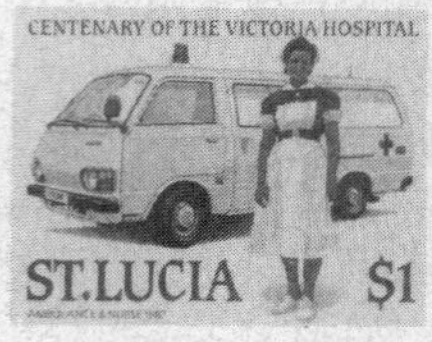

172 Ambulance and Nurse, 1987

173 "The Holy Family"

(Des C. Abbott. Litho Questa)

1987 (4 Nov). *Centenary of Victoria Hospital, Castries. T* **172** *and similar horiz designs. Multicoloured.* W w **16** (*sideways*). *P* 14 × 14½.
959 **172** $1 multicoloured . . 1·75 2·00
a. Pair. Nos. 959/60 . . 3·50 4·00
960 – $1 indigo . . 1·75 2·00
961 – $2 multicoloured . . 2·25 2·50
a. Pair. Nos. 961/2 . . 4·50 5·00
962 – $2 indigo . . 2·25 2·50
959/62 . . *Set of* 4 7·25 8·00
MS963 86 × 68 mm. $4.50, multicoloured . . 6·50 8·00
Designs:—No. 960, Nurse and carrying hammock, 1913; No. 961, $2 Victoria Hospital, 1987; No. 962, Victoria Hospital, 1887; No. **MS**963, Hospital gates, 1987.
Nos. 959/60 and 961/2 were each printed together, *se-tenant*, in horizontal and vertical pairs throughout the sheets.

(Des D. Miller. Litho Format)

1987 (30 Nov). *Christmas. T* **173** *and similar square designs showing paintings. Multicoloured.* W w **16** (*sideways*). *P* 14½.
964 15 c. Type **173** . . 30 10
965 50 c. "Adoration of the Shepherds" . . 60 30
966 60 c. "Adoration of the Magi" . . 60 80
967 90 c. "Madonna and Child" . . 85 2·00
964/7 . . *Set of* 4 2·10 2·75
MS968 82 × 67 mm. $6 Type **173** . . 3·00 5·00

174 St Lucia Amazon perched on Branch

175 Carib Clay Zemi

(Des W. Oliver. Litho Walsall)

1987 (18 Dec). *St. Lucia Amazon. T* **174** *and similar vert designs. Multicoloured.* W w **16**. *P* 14.
969 15 c. Type **174** . . 1·50 40
970 35 c. Pair in flight . . 2·50 55
971 50 c. Perched on branch (rear view) . . 3·50 2·25
972 $1 Emerging from tree . . 4·75 5·00
969/72 . . *Set of* 4 11·00 7·50

(Des C. Collins. Litho Walsall)

1988 (24 Feb). *Amerindian Artifacts. T* **175** *and similar vert designs. Multicoloured.* W w **16**. *P* 14½ × 14.
973 25 c. Type **175** . . 15 10
974 30 c. Troumassee cylinder . . 20 15
975 80 c. Three pointer stone . . 45 45
976 $3.50, Dauphine petroglyph . . 1·75 3·25
973/6 . . *Set of* 4 2·25 3·50

176 East Caribbean Currency

177 Rural Telephone Exchange

(Des D. Miller (10 c.), S. Conlin (others). Litho B.D.T.)

1988 (29 Apr). *50th Anniv of St. Lucia Co-operative Bank. T* **176** *and similar horiz designs. Multicoloured.* W w **14** (*sideways*). *P* 15 × 14.
977 10 c. Type **176** . . 20 10
978 45 c. Castries branch . . 55 35
979 60 c. As 45 c. . . 75 95
980 80 c. Vieux Fort branch . . 1·25 1·60
977/80 . . *Set of* 4 2·50 2·75

(Des A. Theobald. Litho Walsall)

1988 (10 June). *50th Anniv of Cable and Wireless (West Indies) Ltd. T* **177** *and similar horiz designs. Multicoloured. W w* **16** *(sideways). P* 14.

981	15 c. Type **177**	10	10
982	25 c. Early and modern telephones	15	15
983	80 c. St. Lucia Teleport dish aerial	40	45
984	$2.50, Map showing Eastern Caribbean Microwave System	1·00	1·60
981/4	*Set of* 4	1·40	2·10

178 Stained Glass Window

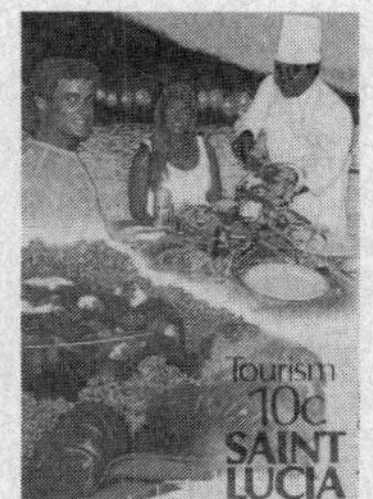

179 Garnished Lobsters

(Des O. Bell. Litho Format)

1988 (15 Aug). *Centenary of Methodist Church in St. Lucia. T* **178** *and similar diamond-shaped designs. Multicoloured. W w* **16** *(sideways). P* 14½.

985	15 c. Type **178**	10	10
986	80 c. Church interior	40	45
987	$3.50, Methodist Church, Castries	1·50	2·25
985/7	*Set of* 3	1·75	2·50

(Des D. Miller. Litho Harrison)

1988 (15 Sept). *Tourism (2nd series). T* **179** *and similar vert designs showing local delicacies. Multicoloured. W w* **16**. *P* 14 × 13½.

988	10 c. Type **179**	55	65
	a. Horiz strip of 4. Nos. 988/91	4·00	
989	30 c. Cocktail and tourists at buffet	65	75
990	80 c. Fresh fruits and roasted breadfruit	1·10	1·25
991	$2.50, Barbecued Red Snappers (fish)	2·25	2·50
988/91	*Set of* 4	4·00	4·50
MS992	88 × 104 mm. $5.50, Fruit stall, Castries market. P 14½ × 14	2·25	3·00

Nos. 988/91 were printed together, *se-tenant*, in horizontal strips of four throughout the sheet, forming a composite design of tourists at beach barbecue.

(Des J. Cooter. Litho Format)

1988 (Sept)–**89**. *As Nos.* 797/800, 930, 937, 940 *and* 946, *but W w* **16** *(sideways). With imprint date. P* 15.

993	5 c. Type **156** (6.89)	60	70
994	10 c. Officer, Grenadier Company, 14th Regiment, 1780 (6.89)	75	50
995	15 c. Private, Battalion Company, 2nd West India Regiment, 1803	90	65
996	20 c. Officer, Battalion Company, 46th Regiment, 1781 (6.89)	1·00	85
997	25 c. Officer, Royal Artillery, *c.* 1782	1·00	85
999	60 c. Officer, Battalion Company, 5th Regiment, 1778	1·75	1·75
1000	80 c. Officer, Battalion Company, 27th Regiment, *c.* 1780	2·00	2·00
1003	$20 Private, Grenadier Company, 46th Regiment, 1778 (6.89)	21·00	28·00
993/1003	*Set of* 8	26·00	32·00

Imprint dates: "1988", Nos. 995, 997, 999/1000; "1989", Nos. 993/7, 1003.

(Des D. Miller (10 c.), L. Curtis and D. Miller (60 c.), E. Nisbet and D. Miller (80 c.), S. Noon and D. Miller ($2.50). Litho Questa)

1988 (17 Oct). *300th Anniv of Lloyd's of London. Designs as T* **167***a of Malawi. W w* **14** *(sideways on* 60, 80 *c.). P* 14.

1004	10 c. black, grey-lilac and brown	45	15
1005	60 c. multicoloured	1·25	75
1006	80 c. multicoloured	1·60	1·25
1007	$2.50, multicoloured	3·00	4·50
1004/7	*Set of* 4	5·75	6·00

Designs: *Vert*—10 c. San Francisco earthquake, 1906; $2.50, Castries fire, 1948. *Horiz*—60 c. Castries Harbour; 80 c. *Lady Nelson* (hospital ship) 1942.

180 Snow on the Mountain

181 Princess Alexandra presenting Constitution

(Des R. Gorringe. Litho Format)

1988 (22 Nov). *Christmas. Flowers. T* **180** *and similar vert designs. Multicoloured. W w* **16**. *P* 14.

1008	15 c. Type **180**	30	10
1009	45 c. Christmas Candle	55	50
1010	60 c. Balisier	70	90
	w. Wmk inverted	2·00	
1011	80 c. Poinsettia	1·00	1·60
	w. Wmk inverted	2·00	
1008/11	*Set of* 4	2·25	2·75
MS1012	79×75 mm. $5.50, Christmas flower arrangement. Wmk sideways	2·50	3·25

(Des S. Noon. Litho Walsall)

1989 (22 Feb). *10th Anniv of Independence. T* **181** *and similar vert designs. Multicoloured. W w* 14. *P* 13½ × 13.

1013	15 c. Type **181**	30	10
1014	80 c. Geothermal well	80	60
1015	$1 Sir Arthur Lewis Community College	70	60
1016	$2.50, Pointe Seraphine shopping centre	1·10	2·00
1013/16	*Set of* 4	2·50	3·00
MS1017	47 × 62 mm. $5 Man with national flag. W w **16**.	2·25	3·00

1989 (12 Apr). *As Nos.* 924B/5B, *but W w* **16** *(sideways). With* "1989" *imprint date. P* 14.

1018	**169**	5 c. black and cinnamon	80	80
1019		10 c. black and pale emerald	80	80

182 *Gerronema citrinum*

183 Local Revolutionary Declaration, 1789 and View of St. Lucia

(Des Josephine Martin. Litho Questa)

1989 (31 May). *Fungi. T* **182** *and similar vert designs. Multicoloured. W w* **16**. *P* 14½×14.

1022	15 c. Type **182**	80	20
1023	25 c. *Lepiota spiculata*	1·00	20
1024	50 c. *Calocybe cyanocephala*	1·75	1·10
1025	$5 *Russula puiggarii*	6·50	8·50
1022/5	*Set of* 4	9·00	9·00

(Litho Questa)

1989 (14 July). *Bicentenary of the French Revolution. T* **183** *and similar multicoloured designs each including the "Philexfrance" International Stamp Exhibition logo. W w* **14** *(sideways on* 60 *c.,* $3.50*). P* 14.

1026	10 c. Type **183**	25	15
1027	60 c. Hoisting Revolutionary flag, Morne Fortune, 1791 (*horiz*)	1·50	80
1028	$1 Declaration of Rights of Man and view of St. Lucia	1·75	1·50
1029	$3.50, Arrival of Capt. La Crosse, Gros Islet, 1792 (*horiz*)	5·50	7·00
1026/9	*Set of* 4	8·00	8·50

184 Red Cross Headquarters, St. Lucia

185 Christmas Lantern

(Des A. Theobald. Litho Questa)

1989 (10 Oct). *125th Anniv of International Red Cross. T* **184** *and similar horiz designs. Multicoloured. W w* **16** *(sideways). P* 14×14½.

1030	50 c. Type **184**	1·25	1·25
1031	80 c. Red Cross seminar, Castries, 1987	1·75	2·00
1032	$1 Red Cross ambulance	2·00	2·25
1030/2	*Set of* 3	4·50	5·00

(Des Jennifer Toombs. Litho Questa)

1989 (17 Nov). *Christmas. T* **185** *and similar horiz designs showing decorative "building" lanterns. W w* **16** *(sideways). P* 14×14½.

1033	10 c. multicoloured	20	10
1034	50 c. multicoloured	55	40
1035	90 c. multicoloured	85	1·00
1036	$1 multicoloured	1·00	1·25
1033/6	*Set of* 4	2·40	2·50

MINIMUM PRICE

The minimum price quote is 10p which represents a handling charge rather than a basis for valuing common stamps. For further notes about prices see introductory pages.

186 Gwi Gwi

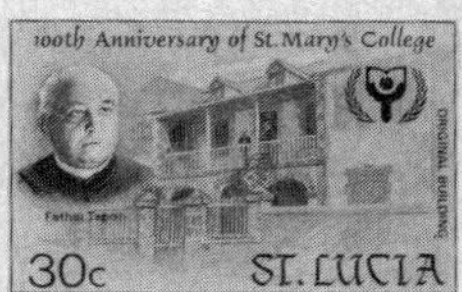

187 Father Tapon and Original College Building

(Des R. Gorringe. Litho B.D.T.)

1990 (21 Feb–25 June). *Endangered Trees. T* **186** *and similar vert designs. Multicoloured. W w* **16**. "1990" *imprint date. P* 14.

1037	10 c. Chinna (12 Apr)	30	30
1038	15 c. Latanier (12 Apr)	40	40
1039	20 c. Type **186**	30	30
1040	25 c. L'Encens	40	40
1041	50 c. Bois Lélé	60	60
1042	80 c. Bois D'Amande (12 Apr)	50	40
1043	95 c. Mahot Piman Grand Bois (25 June)	60	50
1044	$1 Balata (25 June)	60	50
1045	$1.50, Pencil Cedar (12 Apr)	1·00	1·00
1046	$2.50, Bois Cendre (25 June)	1·40	1·50
1047	$5 Lowye Cannelle (25 June)	2·50	3·00
1048	$25 Chalantier Grand Bois	11·50	14·00
1037/48	*Set of* 12	18·00	21·00

For these designs, but watermark w **14**, see Nos. 1081/5.

(Des G. Vasarhelyi. Litho Questa)

1990 (6 June). *International Literacy Year. Centenary of St. Mary's College, Castries. T* **187** *and similar horiz designs. Multicoloured. W w* **14** *(sideways). P* 14.

1049	30 c. Type **187**	15	15
1050	45 c. Brother M. C. Collins and St. Mary's College	25	25
1051	75 c. Literacy class	45	55
1052	$2 Children approaching "door to knowledge"	1·50	2·00
1049/52	*Set of* 4	2·10	2·75

(Des D. Miller. Litho Questa)

1990 (3 Aug). *90th Birthday of Queen Elizabeth the Queen Mother. Vert designs as T* **107** *(*50 *c.) or* **108** *(*$5*) of Kenya. W w* **16**. *P* 14×15 *(*50 *c.) or* 14½ *(*$5*).*

1053	50 c. multicoloured	35	35
1054	$5 brownish black and deep violet-blue	2·75	3·50

Designs:—50 c. Crowning of Queen Consort, 1937; $5 Queen Elizabeth arriving at New Theatre, London, 1949.

(**188**)

189 "Adoration of the Magi" (Rubens)

1990 (13 Aug). *"EXPO 90" International Garden and Greenery Exhibition, Osaka. No.* 1047 *optd with T* **188**.

1055	$5 Lowye Cannelle	2·75	3·50

(Des D. Miller. Litho Questa)

1990 (3 Dec). *Christmas. Religious Paintings. T* **189** *and similar vert designs. Multicoloured. W w* **16**. *P* 14.

1056	10 c. Type **189**	25	10
1057	30 c. "Adoration of the Shepherds" (Murillo)	60	15
1058	80 c. "Adoration of the Magi" (Rubens) (*different*)	1·50	75
1059	$5 "Adoration of the Shepherds" (Philippe de Champaigne)	4·50	5·50
1056/9	*Set of* 4	6·25	6·00

190 *Vistafjord* (liner)

191 *Battus polydamas*

(Des E. Nisbet. Litho Walsall)

1991 (27 Mar). *Cruise Ships. T* **190** *and similar horiz designs. Multicoloured. W w* **14** *(sideways). P* 14½.

1060 50 c. Type **190** .. .. 1·00 30
1061 80 c. *Windstar* (schooner) .. .. .. 1·50 1·10
1062 $1 *Unicorn* (brig) .. .. 1·75 1·50
1063 $2.50, Game-fishing launch .. .. .. 4·00 5·50
1060/3 .. .. *Set of* 4 7·50 7·50
MS1064 82×65 mm. $5 Ships in Castries Harbour .. .. 5·50 6·00

(Des I. Loe. Litho Walsall)

1991 (15 Aug). *Butterflies. T* **191** *and similar vert designs. Multicoloured. W w* **16**. *P* 14.

1065 60 c. Type **191** .. .. 1·50 65
1066 80 c. *Strymon simaethis* .. .. .. 1·75 1·10
1067 $1 *Mestra cana* .. .. 2·25 1·25
1068 $2.50, *Allosmaitia piplea* .. .. .. 4·50 5·50
1065/8 .. .. *Set of* 4 9·00 7·75

192 Mural, Jacmel Church

193 Yacht and Map

(Des D. Miller. Litho Questa)

1991 (20 Nov). *Christmas. Paintings by Duncan St. Omer. T* **192** *and similar multicoloured designs. W w* **16** *(sideways on* 10, 80 c.). *P* 14½.

1069 10 c. Type **192** 20 10
1070 15 c. "Red Madonna" (*vert*) 30 10
1071 80 c. Mural, Monchy Church .. .. .. 1·25 70
1072 $5 "Blue Madonna" (*vert*) .. .. .. 4·00 5·50
1069/72 .. .. *Set of* 4 5·25 5·75

(Des P. Devarreaux. Litho Questa)

1991 (10 Dec). *Atlantic Rally for Cruising Yachts. T* **193** *and similar horiz design. Multicoloured. W w* **16** *(sideways). P* 14.

1073 60 c. Type **193** .. .. 1·25 1·25
1074 80 c. Yachts off St. Lucia .. .. .. 1·50 1·50

(Adapted G. Vasarhelyi. Litho Cartor)

1992 (6 July). *Organization of East Caribbean States. 500th Anniv of Discovery of America by Columbus. Vert designs as T* **66** *of St. Kitts. Multicoloured. W w* **14**. *P* 13.

1075 $1 Columbus meeting Amerindians .. 1·75 1·75
1076 $2 Ships approaching island .. .. 2·50 2·75

194 Amerindian Village

195 "Virgin and Child" (Delaroche)

(Des D. Miller. Litho Cartor)

1992 (7 Aug). *Discovery of St. Lucia. T* **194** *and similar horiz designs. Multicoloured. W w* **14** *(sideways). P* 13½.

1077 15 c. Type **194** 35 20
1078 40 c. Ships of Juan de la Cosa and islands, 1499 .. .. 1·25 50
1079 50 c. Columbus sailing between Martinique and St. Lucia, 1502 .. .. .. 1·40 70
1080 $5 Legendary shipwreck of Gimie .. 5·50 7·00
1077/80 .. .. *Set of* 4 7·75 7·75

1992 (Aug)–**95**. *As Nos.* 1037/41, *but W w* **14**. *With imprint date. P* 14.

1081 10 c. Chinna (11.12.92) 10 10
1082 15 c. Latanier (11.12.92) 15 15
1083 20 c. Type **186** (4.95) 50 50
1084 25 c. L'Encens (5.94) 20 20
1085 50 c. Bois Lélé 30 30
1081/5 .. .. *Set of* 5 1·10 1·10

Imprint dates: "1992", Nos. 1081/2, 1085; "1993", Nos. 1081, 1085; "1994", Nos. 1081/2, 1084/5; "1995", No. 1083.

(Des D. Miller. Litho Walsall)

1992 (9 Nov). *Christmas. Religious Paintings. T* **195** *and similar vert designs. Multicoloured. W w* **14**. *P* 14½.

1092 10 c. Type **195** 30 10
1093 15 c. "The Holy Family" (Rubens) 30 10
1094 60 c. "Virgin and Child" (Luini) .. .. 1·50 1·40
1095 80 c. "Virgin and Child" (Sassoferrato) .. 1·75 1·75
1092/5 .. .. *Set of* 4 3·50 3·00

OMNIBUS ISSUES

Details, together with prices for complete sets, of the various Omnibus issues from the 1935 Silver Jubilee series to date are included in a special section following Zimbabwe at the end of Volume 2.

196 "Death" and Gravestone

197 "Gros Piton from Delcer, Choiseul" (Dunstan St. Omer)

(Adapted D. Miller. Litho Cartor)

1993 (1 Feb). *Anti-drugs Campaign. W w* **14**. *P* 13½.

1096 **196** $5 multicoloured .. .. .. 5·00 6·00

(Des G. Vasarhelyi. Litho Cartor)

1993 (1 Nov). *Carib Art. T* **197** *and similar horiz designs. Multicoloured. W w* **14** *(sideways). P* 13.

1097 20 c. Type **197** 20 10
1098 75 c. "Reduit Bay" (Derek Walcott) 75 75
1099 $5 "Woman and Child at River" (Nancy Cole Auguste) .. .. 4·25 5·75
1097/9 .. .. *Set of* 3 4·75 6·00

198 "The Madonna of the Rosary" (Murillo)

199 The Pitons

(Des D. Miller. Litho B.D.T.)

1993 (6 Dec). *Christmas. Religious Paintings. T* **198** *and similar horiz designs. Multicoloured. W w* **14** *(sideways). P* 14.

1100 15 c. Type **198** 15 10
1101 60 c. "The Madonna and Child" (Van Dyck) 55 55
1102 95 c. "The Annunciation" (Champaigne) .. 80 1·25
1100/2 .. .. *Set of* 2 1·40 1·60

(Des G. Vasarhelyi. Litho Cartor)

1994 (25 July). *Bicentenary of the Abolition of Slavery in St. Lucia. W w* **14**. *P* 13½.

1103 **199** 20 c. multicoloured 50 45
MS1104 115×75 mm. **199** $5 multicoloured .. 4·00 5·00

200 *Euphorbia pulcherrima*

201 18th-century Map of St. Lucia

(Adapted D. Miller from local designs. Litho Enschedé)

1994 (9 Dec). *Christmas. Flowers. T* **200** *and similar vert designs. Multicoloured. W w* **14**. *P* 12½×13.

1105 20 c. Type **200** 15 10
1106 75 c. *Heliconia rostrata* 55 50
1107 95 c. *Alpinia purpurata* 75 75
1108 $5.50, *Anthurium andreanum* .. .. 3·75 5·00
1105/8 .. .. *Set of* 4 4·75 5·75

See also Nos. 1122/5 and 1156/9.

(Litho Cartor)

1995 (28 Apr). *Bicentenary of Battle of Rabot. T* **201** *and similar horiz designs. Multicoloured. W w* **14** *(sideways). P* 13½.

1109 20 c. Type **201** 15 15
1110 75 c. Insurgent slaves 55 55
1111 95 c. 9th Foot (Royal Norfolk Regiment) attacking .. .. 80 1·10
1109/11 .. .. *Set of* 3 1·40 1·60
MS1112 150×100 mm. $5.50, Plan of battle. P 13 3·25 3·75

(Des R. Watton. Litho Cartor (Nos. 1113/16) or Questa (No. **MS**1117))

1995 (8 May). *50th Anniv of End of Second World War. Multicoloured designs as T* **75** *of Kiribati. W w* **14** *(sideways). P* 13½.

1113 20 c. St. Lucian members of the A.T.S. .. 30 15
1114 75 c. German U-boat off St. Lucia .. 80 65
1115 95 c. Bren gun-carriers of the Caribbean Regiment, North Africa .. .. 1·00 1·00
1116 $1.10, Supermarine Spitfire Mk V *St. Lucia* .. .. 1·25 1·50
1113/16 .. .. *Set of* 4 3·00 3·00
MS1117 75×85 mm. $5.50, Reverse of 1939–45 War Medal (*vert*). Wmk upright. P 14 .. 3·25 3·50

(Des A. Theobald. Litho B.D.T.)

1995 (24 Oct). *50th Anniv of United Nations. Horiz designs as T* **284** *of Jamaica. Multicoloured. W w* **14** *(sideways). P* 14.

1118 10 c. Sud Aviation SE 330 Puma helicopter, Cambodia, 1991–93 .. .. .. 15 10
1119 65 c. Renault lorry, Bosnia, 1995 .. .. 50 50
1120 $1.35, Transall C-160 aircraft, Cambodia, 1991–93 .. .. 95 1·25
1121 $5 Douglas DC-3 aircraft, Korea, 1950–54 .. .. 3·75 4·50
1118/21 .. .. *Set of* 4 4·75 5·75

(Adapted D. Miller. Litho Cartor)

1995 (20 Nov). *Christmas. Flowers. Vert designs as T* **200**, *each including Madonna and Child. Multicoloured. W w* **14**. *P* 13×13½.

1122 15 c. *Eranthemum nervosum* 15 10
1123 70 c. Bougainvillea 45 45
1124 $1.10, *Allamanda cathartica* 70 80
1125 $3 *Rosa sinensis* .. .. 1·75 2·50
1122/5 .. .. *Set of* 4 2·75 3·50

202 Calypso King

203 Dry River Bed

(Des G. Vasarhelyi. Litho B.D.T.)

1996 (19 Feb). *Carnival. T* **202** *and similar vert designs. Multicoloured. W w* **16**. *P* 14.

1126 20 c. Type **202** 25 10
1127 65 c. Carnival dancers 65 55
1128 95 c. King of the Band float 85 85
1129 $3 Carnival Queen .. .. 2·25 3·00
1126/9 .. .. *Set of* 4 3·50 4·00

(Des A. St. Omer and G. Vasarhelyi (20, 55 c.), G. Vasarhelyi ($5). Litho Cot Printery Ltd, Barbados)

1996 (5 Mar). *Inauguration of New Irrigation Project. T* **203** *and similar vert designs. Multicoloured. W w* **14**. *P* 14.

1130 20 c. Type **203** 10 10
1131 65 c. People bathing in stream 40 45
1132 $5 New dam .. .. 3·00 3·50
1130/2 .. .. *Set of* 3 3·25 3·50

204 Produce Market

(Des D. Miller. Litho Cot Printery Ltd, Barbados)

1996 (11 May). *Tourism. T* **204** *and similar horiz designs. Multicoloured. W w* **14** *(sideways). P* 14.

1133 65 c. Type **204** 45 45
1134 75 c. Horse-riding on beach 55 55
1135 95 c. Bride and groom 70 70
1136 $5 Jazz band .. .. 2·75 3·50
1133/6 .. .. *Set of* 4 4·00 4·75

205 Athlete of 1896

(Des S. Noon (15 c.), R. Watton (75 c.). Litho Cot Printery Ltd, Barbados)

1996 (19 July). *Centenary of Modern Olympic Games. T* **205** *and similar horiz designs. Multicoloured. W w* **14** *(sideways). P* 14.

1137 15 c. Type **205** 20 20
a. Horiz pair. Nos. 1137/8 .. .. .. 40 40
1138 15 c. Athlete of 1996 .. .. 20 20
1139 75 c. Catamaran and yacht 65 65
a. Horiz pair. Nos. 1139/40 .. .. 1·25 1·25
1140 75 c. Sailing dinghies 65 65
1137/40 .. .. *Set of* 4 1·50 1·50

Nos. 1137/8 and 1139/40 were each printed together, *se-tenant*, in horizontal pairs forming composite designs, throughout the sheets.

206 Spanish Royal Standard, 1502, and Caravel

(Des J. Batchelor. Litho B.D.T.)

1996 (16 Sept)–**97**. *Flags and Ships. T* **206** *and similar horiz designs. Multicoloured. W* w **16** (*sideways*). *P* 14×15.

1141	10 c. Type **206**	10	10
1142	15 c. Skull and crossbones, 1550, and pirate carrack	10	10
1143	20 c. Dutch royal standard, 1650, and galleon	10	10
1144	25 c. Union Jack, 1739, and ship of the line	10	15
1145	40 c. French royal standard, 1750, and ship of the line	20	25
1146	50 c. Martinique and St. Lucia flag, 1766, and French brig (18.11.96)	25	30
1147	55 c. White Ensign, 1782, and frigate squadron (18.11.96)	25	30
1148	65 c. Red Ensign, 1782, and frigates in action (18.11.96)	30	35
1149	75 c. Blue Ensign, 1782, and brig (18.11.96)	35	40
1150	95 c. The Tricolour, 1792, and French frigate (18.11.96)	45	50
1151	$1 Union Jack, 1801, and West Indies Grand Fleet (8.1.97)	45	50
1152	$2.50, Confederate States of America flag, 1861, and cruiser (8.1.97)	1·10	1·25
1153	$5 Canadian flag, 1915–19, and "V & W" class destroyer (8.1.97)	2·25	2·40
1154	$10 United States flag, 1942–48, and "Fletcher" class destroyer (8.1.97)	4·50	4·75
1155	$25 Flag of St. Lucia and cruise liner (8.1.97)	11·50	12·00
1141/55	*Set of* 15	21·00	23·00

(Des Jennifer Toombs. Litho Questa)

1996 (27 Nov). *Christmas. Flowers. Vert designs as T* **200**, *each including Madonna and Child. Multicoloured. W* w **16**. *P* 14.

1156	20 c. *Cordia sebestena*	15	10
1157	75 c. *Cryptosegia grandiflora*	50	50
1158	95 c. *Hibiscus elatus*	65	65
1159	$5 *Caularthron bicornutum*	3·25	3·75
1156/9	*Set of* 4	4·00	4·50

(Des N. Shewring (No. **MS**1166), D. Miller (others). Litho Questa (No. **MS**1166), Cot Printery Ltd, Barbados (others))

1997 (10 July). *Golden Wedding of Queen Elizabeth and Prince Philip. Multicoloured designs as T* **87** *of Kiribati. W* w **14**. *P* 14½×14.

1160	75 c. Queen Elizabeth at Warwick, 1996	45	45
	a. Horiz pair. Nos. 1160/1	90	90
1161	75 c. Prince Philip with carriage horses	45	45
1162	95 c. Prince Philip	55	55
	a. Horiz pair. Nos. 1162/3	1·10	1·10
1163	95 c. Queen in phaeton at Trooping the Colour	55	55
1164	$1 Queen Elizabeth and Prince Philip at Sandringham, 1982	65	65
	a. Horiz pair. Nos. 1164/5	1·25	1·25
1165	$1 Princess Anne show jumping	65	65
1160/5	*Set of* 6	3·00	3·00
MS1166	110×70 mm. $5 Queen Elizabeth and Prince Philip in landau (*horiz*). Wmk sideways. P 14×14½	2·75	3·00

Nos. 1160/1, 1162/3 and 1164/5 were each printed together, *se-tenant*, in horizontal pairs throughout the sheets with the backgrounds forming composite designs.

207 *St. George* capsized, 1935

(Des E. Nisbet. Litho B.D.T.)

1997 (14 July). *Marine Disasters. T* **207** *and similar horiz designs. Multicoloured. W* w **16** (*sideways*). *P* 14×15.

1167	20 c. Type **207**	20	10
1168	55 c. Wreck of *Belle of Bath* (freighter)	35	30
1169	$1 *Ethelgonda* (freighter) aground on rocks, 1897	65	65
1170	$2.50, Hurricane, 1817	1·50	1·75
1167/70	*Set of* 4	2·40	2·50

208 Attack on Praslin

(Des R. Watton. Litho Questa)

1997 (15 Aug). *Bicentenary of the Brigands' War. T* **208** *and similar horiz designs. Multicoloured. W* w **14** (*sideways*). *P* 13½×14.

1171	20 c. Type **208**	20	10
1172	55 c. British troops at Battle of Dennery	35	30
1173	70 c. Discussing peace agreement	50	50
1174	$3 Members of 1st West India Regiment	1·75	1·90
1171/4	*Set of* 4	2·50	2·50

209 "Roseau Church" (detail, Dunstan St. Omer)

(Des D. Miller. Litho B.D.T.)

1997 (1 Dec). *Christmas. Paintings by Dunstan St. Omer. T* **209** *and similar horiz designs. Multicoloured. W* w **16** (*sideways*). *P* 14×15.

1175	20 c. Type **209**	20	10
1176	60 c. Altar piece, Regional Seminary, Trinidad	45	35
1177	95 c. "Our Lady of the Presentation", Trinidad	60	60
1178	$5 "The Four Days of Creation"	2·75	3·00
1175/8	*Set of* 4	3·50	3·50

STAMP BOOKLETS

1981 (23 June). *Royal Wedding. Multicoloured cover, 165×90 mm. Stitched.*

SB1 $12.50, booklet containing *se-tenant* pane of 6 and pane of 1 (Nos. 580a, 582a) .. .. 2·25

1986 (12 Aug). *Royal Wedding. Gold (No. SB2) or silver (No. SB3) on deep carmine-red covers, 152×80 mm. Stapled.*

SB2 $9.60, booklet (Westminster Abbey) containing twelve 80 c. (Nos. 890/1) in blocks of 4 .. 4·75
SB3 $11.20, booklet (State Coach) containing 80 c. and $2 (Nos. 890/3, but imperf) in blocks of 4 .. 5·50

POSTAGE DUE STAMPS

D 1

No. No.

Normal Wide fount

(Type-set Government Printing Office)

1930. *Each stamp individually handstamped with different number. No wmk. No gum. Rough perf 12. (a) Horizontally laid paper.*

D1 D 1 1d. black/*blue* .. .. 3·50 13·00
a. Wide, wrong fount "No." .. 11·00 32·00
b. Missing stop after "ST" .. .. 55·00 95·00
c. Missing stop after "LUCIA" .. 55·00 95·00
d. Handstamped number double .. £250
e. Two different numbers on same stamp £325

(b) Wove paper

D2 D 1 2d. black/*yellow* .. .. .. 10·00 38·00
a. Wide, wrong fount "No." .. 26·00 90·00
b. Imperf between (vert pair) .. £4000
c. Missing stop after "ST" £120 £225
d. Incorrect number with correction above £425
e. Two different numbers on same stamp £475

It is believed that there were three settings of the 1d. and two of the 2d., the same type being used for both values.

For the initial setting of the 1d. the wide "No." variety occurs on the last four stamps in the bottom row of the sheet of 60 (6 × 10). In later settings first the second and then later the first stamps in the same row were changed to show the variety. Nos. D1b and D2c occur on R.5/3 and No. D1c on R.9/2.

Some sheets from the initial printing of the 1d. show a paper-maker's watermark, "KINGSCLERE" in double-lined capitals above a crown, across a number of stamps.

The sheets had all outer edges, except that at the left, imperforate. It would appear that they were bound into books from which they could be detached, using the perforations at the left-hand edge.

The handstamped numbers were applied at the Post Office, using numbering machines. Each value had its own sequence of numbers and it is possible to recognise, by minor differences in fount, the use of two such machines. This is especially noticeable on examples of Nos. D1d and D2d where the corrections are often applied using a second machine. No. D2d shows the incorrect number partly erased and a correction struck across it.

D 2

D 3

D 4 St. Lucia Coat of Arms

(Typo D.L.R.)

1933–47. *Wmk Mult Script CA. P 14.*

D3 D 2 1d. black .. .. 4·25 5·00
D4 2d. black .. .. 15·00 7·50
D5 4d. black (28.6.47) .. .. .. 4·50 28·00
D6 8d. black (28.6.47) .. .. .. 4·50 38·00
D3/6 .. .. *Set of* 4 25·00 70·00
D3/6 Perf "Specimen" .. .. *Set of* 4 £130

1949 (1 Oct)–**52.** *Value in cents. Wmk Mult Script CA. Typo. P 14.*

D 7 D 3 2 c. black .. .. 1·75 22·00
a. Chalk-surfaced paper (27.11.52) 10 6·50
ab. Error. Crown missing, W **9a** 85·00
ac. Error. St. Edward's Crown, W **9b** 30·00
D 8 4 c. black .. .. 3·50 15·00
a. Chalk-surfaced paper (27.11.52) .. 30 8·00
ab. Error. Crown missing, W **9a** .. £110
ac. Error. St. Edward's Crown, W **9b** 42·00
D 9 8 c. black .. .. 3·25 19·00
a. Chalk-surfaced paper (27.11.52) .. 2·25 25·00
ac. Error. St. Edward's Crown, W **9b** £190
D10 16 c. black .. .. 12·00 55·00
a. Chalk-surfaced paper (27.11.52) .. 3·25 40·00
ac. Error. St. Edward's Crown, W **9b** £275
D7/10 .. .. *Set of* 4 19·00 £100
D7a/10a .. .. *Set of* 4 5·25 70·00

1965 (9 Mar). *As Nos.* D7/8, *but wmk* w **12**. *Ordinary paper. P* 14.

D11 D 3 2 c. black .. .. 35 8·00
D12 4 c. black .. .. 45 8·00

Nos D9a, D10a and D11/12 exist with a similar overprint to Type **49** in red (*Price for set of* 4 *£150 mint*).

(Des L. Curtis. Litho Format)

1981 (4 Aug). W w **14**. *P* 14.

D13 D 4 5 c. brown-purple 10 45
D14 15 c. emerald 15 50
D15 25 c. red-orange 15 50
D16 $1 deep ultramarine .. .. .. 30 1·25
D13/16 .. .. *Set of* 4 60 2·40

(Des L. Curtis. Litho Questa)

1991 (14 Feb). W w **16**. *P* 15×14.

D17 D 4 5 c. deep carmine 10 10
D18 15 c. emerald 10 10
D19 25 c. red-orange 10 10
D20 $1 ultramarine 45 50
D17/20 .. .. *Set of* 4 75 80

OFFICIAL STAMPS

OFFICIAL OFFICIAL

(O 1) (O 2)

1983 (13 Oct). *Nos.* 537/48 *optd with Type* O **1**.

O 1 5 c. Type **120** 15 10
O 2 10 c. Douglas DC-10-30 airliner 25 10
O 3 15 c. Local bus 30 15
O 4 20 c. Refrigerated freighter 40 20
O 5 25 c. Britten Norman Islander aircraft .. 50 20
O 6 30 c. *Charles* (pilot boat) 55 25
O 7 50 c. Boeing 727-200 airliner 70 35
O 8 75 c. *Cunard Countess* (liner) 85 50
O 9 $1 Lockheed L-1011 TriStar 500 airliner 1·25 75
O10 $2 Cargo liner .. .. 1·75 1·75
O11 $5 Boeing 707-420 airliner .. .. 3·50 3·50
O12 $10 *Queen Elizabeth 2* (liner) .. .. 6·50 7·50
O1/12 .. .. *Set of* 12 15·00 14·00

1985 (7 May). *Nos.* 797/811 *optd with Type* O **2**.

O13 5 c. Type **156** 40 50
O14 10 c. Officer, Grenadier Company, 14th Regiment, 1780.. .. .. .. 40 50
O15 20 c. Officer, Battalion Company, 46th Regiment, 1781 .. .. 40 50
O16 25 c. Officer, Royal Artillery, *c* 1782 .. 40 50
O17 30 c. Officer, Royal Engineers, 1782 .. 50 60
O18 35 c. Officer, Battalion Company, 54th Regiment, 1782 .. .. 50 60
O19 45 c. Private, Grenadier Company, 14th Regiment, 1782.. .. .. .. 60 75
O20 50 c. Gunner, Royal Artillery, 1796 .. 60 75
O21 65 c. Private, Battalion Company, 85th Regiment, *c* 1796 .. .. .. 80 1·00
O22 75 c. Private, Battalion Company, 76th Regiment, 1796.. .. .. .. 90 1·50
O23 90 c. Private, Battalion Company, 81st Regiment, *c* 1796 .. .. .. 1·00 1·50
O24 $1 Sergeant, 74th (Highland) Regiment, 1796 .. .. 1·10 1·50
O25 $2.50, Private, Light Company, 93rd Regiment, 1803 .. .. 2·50 3·50
O26 $5 Private, Battalion Company, 1st West India Regiment, 1803 .. .. .. 4·00 3·50
O27 $15 Officer, Royal Artillery, 1850.. .. 9·00 10·00
O13/27 .. .. *Set of* 15 21·00 24·00

OFFICIAL

(O 3)

1990 (21 Feb–25 June). *Nos.* 1037/48 *optd with Type* O **3**.

O28 10 c. Chinna (12 Apr) 10 10
O29 15 c. Latanier (12 Apr) 10 10
O30 20 c. Type **186** 10 10
O31 25 c. L'Encens 10 10
O32 50 c. Bois Lélé 25 30
O33 80 c. Bois D'Amande (12 Apr) 35 40
O34 95 c. Mahot Piman Grand Bois (25 June) 45 50
O35 $1 Balata (25 June) 45 50
O36 $1.50, Pencil Cedar (12 Apr) 70 75
O37 $2.50, Bois Cendre (25 June) .. .. 1·10 1·25
O38 $5 Lowye Cannelle (25 June) .. .. 2·25 2·40
O39 $25 Chalantier Grand Bois .. .. 11·50 12·00
O28/39 .. .. *Set of* 12 17·00 18·00

POSTAL FISCAL STAMPS

Nos. F1/28 were authorised for postal use from 14 April 1885.

CANCELLATIONS. Many used examples of the Postal Fiscal stamps have had previous pen cancellations removed before being used postally.

SHILLING STAMP One Penny Stamp HALFPENNY Stamp

(F 1) (F 2) (F 3)

1881. *Wmk Crown CC. P* 14. *(a) Surch as Type* F **1**.

F1 1 ONE PENNY STAMP, black (C.) .. 42·00 48·00
a. Surch inverted £700 £700
b. Surch double £650 £700
F2 FOUR PENNY STAMP, yellow.. .. 70·00 70·00
a. Bisected (2d.) (on cover) .. ..
F3 SIX PENCE STAMP, mauve £130 £130
F4 SHILLING STAMP, orange .. .. 65·00 65·00
a. "SHILEING" £650
b. "SHILDING" £650 £600

(b) Surch as Type F **2**

F 7 1 One Penny Stamp, black (R.) .. .. 42·00 48·00
a. Surch double £700
F 8 Four Pence Stamp, yellow .. .. 70·00 65·00
F 9 Six Pence Stamp, mauve .. .. 70·00 65·00
F10 Shilling Stamp, orange .. .. 75·00 85·00

(c) Surch as Type F **3**

F11 1 Halfpenny Stamp, green.. .. .. 48·00 55·00
a. "Stamp" double £450 £450
F12 One Shilling Stamp, orange (*wmk Crown CA*) .. .. 75·00 70·00
a. "Stamp" double £450 £500

A fiscally used example of No. F1b is known showing one red and one black surcharge.

FOUR PENCE REVENUE Revenue REVENUE

(F 4) (F 5) (F 6)

1882. *Wmk Crown CA. Surch as Type* F **4**. *(a) P* 14.

F13 1 1d. black (C.) .. .. 27·00 22·00
F14 2d. pale blue .. .. 18·00 9·50
F15 3d. deep blue (C.) .. .. .. 60·00 45·00
F16 4d. yellow .. .. 22·00 4·00
F17 6d. mauve .. .. 38·00 25·00

(b) P 12

F18 1 1d. black (C.) .. .. 27·00 23·00
F19 3d. deep blue (C.) .. .. .. 40·00 20·00
F20 1s. orange .. .. 45·00 13·00

For imperforate examples of the 1d., 2d. and 1d. of 1884 see note below No.36

1883. *Nos.* 25, 26, 30 *and* 32 *optd locally as Type* F **5**.

(a) Word 11 mm long

F21 1d. black (C.) .. .. 27·00 40·00
a. Opt inverted .. ..
b. Opt double £275 £350

(b) Word 13 mm

F22 1d. black (C.) .. .. — 65·00

(c) Word 15½ *mm*

F23 ½d. green .. .. — 55·00
a. "Revenue" double .. .. .. — £250
F24 1d. black (C.) .. .. 25·00 10·00
a. "Revenue" double £140
b. "Revenue" triple £275
c. "Revenue" double, one inverted .. £250 £300
F25 1d. rose (No. 32) .. .. .. — 60·00
F26 4d. yellow .. .. — 65·00

1884–85. *Optd with Type* F **6**. *Wmk Crown CA. P* 14.

F27 5 1d. slate (C.) .. .. 18·00 12·00
F28 1d. dull mauve (Die I) (1885) .. .. 18·00 7·50

St. Vincent

Although postal markings for St. Vincent are recorded as early as 1793 it was not until 1852 that the British G.P.O. opened a branch office at Kingstown, the island's capital.

The stamps of Great Britain were used between May 1858 and the end of April 1860. From 1 May in that year the local authorities assumed responsibility for the postal services and fell back on the use of No. CC1 until the introduction of St. Vincent stamps in 1861.

KINGSTOWN

CROWNED-CIRCLE HANDSTAMPS

CC 1

CC1 CC 1 ST. VINCENT (R.) (30.1.1852) *Price on cover* £800

Stamps of GREAT BRITAIN *cancelled* "A 10" *as Type* Z 1 *of Jamaica.*

1858 *to* **1860**.
Z1 1d. rose-red (1857), *perf* 14 .. £550
Z2 2d. blue (1855) ..
Z3 4d. rose (1857) .. £350
Z4 6d. lilac (1856) .. £250
Z5 1s. green (1856) .. £1000

PRICES FOR STAMPS ON COVER TO 1945

Nos. 1/7	*from* × 15
No. 8	—
No. 9	*from* × 15
No. 10	—
Nos. 11/19	*from* × 10
Nos. 20/1	*from* × 6
Nos. 22/5	*from* × 10
Nos. 26/8	—
Nos. 29/31	*from* × 12
No. 32	—
Nos. 33/4	*from* × 10
No. 35	—
Nos. 36/8	*from* × 8
Nos. 39/41	*from* × 15
Nos. 42/5	*from* × 8
No. 46	*from* × 15
Nos. 47/54	*from* × 4
Nos. 55/8	*from* × 8
No. 59	*from* × 10
No. 60	*from* × 6
Nos. 61/3	*from* × 8
Nos. 67/75	*from* × 3
Nos. 76/84	*from* × 2
Nos. 85/92	*from* × 3
No. 93	—
Nos. 94/8	*from* × 3
Nos. 99/107	*from* × 2
Nos. 108/19	*from* × 3
No. 120	—
No. 121	*from* × 3
No. 122	*from* × 5
No. 123	—
No. 124	*from* × 5
Nos. 126/9	*from* × 10
Nos. 131/45	*from* × 3
Nos. 146/8	*from* × 6
Nos. 149/59	*from* × 2

CROWN COLONY

1

d.
1

(2)

3

(T 1, 3 and 7 recess P.B.)

1861 (8 May). *No wmk. Rough to intermediate perf* 14 *to* 16.
1 1 1d. rose-red .. 40·00 14·00
a. Imperf vert (horiz pair) .. £300
b. Imperf (pair) .. £250
2 6d. deep yellow-green .. £6500 £200

The perforations on the 1d. are usually rough, but individual examples can be found on which some, or all, of the holes have the appearance of intermediate perforations. All examples of the 6d. show intermediate perforations.

1862 (Sept). *No wmk. Rough perf* 14 *to* 16.
4 1 6d. deep green .. 55·00 18·00
a. Imperf between (horiz pair) .. £2500
b. Imperf (pair) .. £550

1863–68. *No wmk.* (*a*) *P* 11 *to* 12½.
5 1 1d. rose-red (3.63) .. 32·00 15·00
6 4d. deep blue (*shades*) (1866) .. £275 £110
a. Imperf between (horiz pair) ..
7 6d. deep green (7.68) .. £200 60·00
8 1s. slate-grey (8.66) .. £1800 £900

(*b*) *P* 14 *to* 16
9 1 1s. slate-grey (*shades*) .. £300 £130

(*c*) *P* 11 *to* 12½ × 14 *to* 16
10 1 1d. rose-red .. £3000 £1100
11 1s. slate-grey (*shades*) .. £225 £120

1869. *Colours changed. No wmk. P* 11 *to* 12½.
12 1 4d. yellow .. £350 £150
13 1s. indigo .. £325 90·00
14 1s. brown .. £450 £160

1871 (Apr). *Wmk Small Star, W* w **2**. *Rough perf* 14 *to* 16.
15 1 1d. black .. 45·00 10·00
a. Imperf between (vert pair) .. £5500
16 6d. deep green .. £250 70·00
a. Wmk sideways ..

1872. *Colour changed. W* w **2**. *P* 11 *to* 12½.
17 1 1s. deep rose-red .. £750 £140

1872–75. *W* w **2**. (*a*) *Perf about* 15.
18 1 1d. black (*shades*) (1872) .. 40·00 7·50
19 6d. dull blue-green (*shades*) (1873) .. £750 35·00
a. Wmk sideways ..
ab. Wmk sideways. *Dp blue-green* (1875) £600 38·00

(*b*) *P* 11 *to* 12½×15
20 1 1s. lilac-rose (1873) .. £5000 £350

1875. *Colour changed. W* w **2**. *P* 11 *to* 12½.
21 1 1s. claret .. £600 £250

1876–78. *W* w **2**. (*a*) *P* 11 *to* 12½×15.
22 1 1d. black (*shades*) (1876) .. 60·00 8·50
a. Imperf between (horiz pair) .. † £4750
23 6d. pale green (*wmk sideways*) (1877) £500 48·00
24 1s. vermilion (2.77) .. £750 85·00
a. Imperf vert (horiz pair) ..

(*b*) *P* 11 *to* 12½
25 1 4d. deep blue (7.77) .. £450 90·00

(*c*) *Perf about* 15
26 1 6d. pale green (*wmk sideways*) (3.77) .. £1500 £450
a. Wmk upright. *Lt yellow-green* (1878) £650 25·00
27 1s. vermilion (1878?) .. † £9500
a. Imperf .. † £6500

1880 (May). *No.* 19*a divided vertically by a line of perforation gauging* 12, *and surch locally with T* **2** *in red.*
28 1 1d. on half 6d. deep blue-green .. £425 £325
a. Unsevered pair .. £1500 £1100

1880 (June). *W* w **2**. *P* 11 *to* 12½.
29 1 1d. olive-green .. £110 3·50
30 6d. bright green .. £325 60·00
31 1s. bright vermilion .. £650 50·00
a. Imperf between (horiz pair) .. £7000
32 3 5s. rose-red .. £1000 £1200
a. Imperf .. £3750

d
1
2

(4)

ONE PENNY

(5)

4d

(6)

1881. *Nos.* 30/31 *surch locally. No.* 33 *is divided vertically like No.* 28.
33 4 ½d. on half 6d. bright green (R.) (1.9) .. £160 £160
a. Unsevered pair .. £400 £400
b. Fraction bar omitted (pair with and without bar) .. £3500 £4000
34 5 1d. on 6d. bright green (30.11) .. £400 £275
35 6 4d. on 1s. bright vermilion (28.11) .. £1300 £700

No. 33 exists showing the "1" of "½" with a straight serif. Some examples come from a constant variety on R. 6/20, but others are the result of faulty type.

It is believed that Type 4 was applied as a setting of 36 (6×6) surcharges repeated three times on each sheet across rows 1 to 9. The missing fraction bar occurs on R. 6/3 of the setting.

The tenth vertical row of stamps appears to have been surcharged from a separate setting of 12 (2×6) on which the constant "straight serif" flaw occurs on the bottom right half-stamp.

Three unused single copies of No. 33 are known with the surcharge omitted.

It is believed that Nos. 34 and 35 were surcharged in settings of 30 (10×3).

No. 34 was only on sale between the 30 November and 3 December when supplies of No. 37 became available.

7

2½ PENCE

(8)

1d
~~2½ PENCE~~

(9)

1881 (Dec). *W* w **2**. *P* 11 *to* 12½.
36 7 ½d. orange (*shades*) .. 7·00 2·75
37 1 1d. drab (*shades*) .. £500 7·50
38 4d. bright blue .. £1200 £110
a. Imperf between (horiz pair) ..

(Recess D.L.R. from Perkins, Bacon plates)

1882 (Nov)–**83.** *No.* 40 *is surch with T* **8**. *Wmk Crown CA. P* 14.
39 1 1d. drab .. 38·00 1·60
40 2½d. on 1d. lake (1883) .. 10·00 40
41 4d. ultramarine .. £375 29·00
a. Dull ultramarine .. £950 £350

1883–84. *Wmk Crown CA. P* 12.
42 7 ½d. green (1884) .. 75·00 25·00
43 1 4d. ultramarine-blue .. £375 19·00
a. Grey-blue .. £1000 £300
44 6d. bright green .. £150 £300
45 1s. orange-vermilion .. £110 55·00

The ½d. orange, 1d. rose-red, 1d. milky blue (without surcharge) and 5s. carmine-lake which were formerly listed are now considered to be colour trials. They are, however, of great interest. (*Prices un.* ½d. £900, 1d. red £900, 1d. blue £1200, 5s. £1500.)

1885 (Mar). *No.* 40 *further surch locally as in T* **9**.
46 1 1d. on 2½d. on 1d. lake .. 19·00 16·00

Stamps with three cancelling bars instead of two are considered to be proofs.

1885–93. *No.* 49 *is surch with T* **8**. *Wmk Crown CA. P* 14.
47 7 ½d. green .. 1·00 50
a. Deep green .. 2·50 50
48 1 1d. rose-red .. 2·75 90
a. Rose (1886) .. 4·50 1·50
b. Red (1887) .. 1·60 75
c. Carmine-red (1889) .. 24·00 3·50
49 2½d. on 1d. milky blue (1889) .. 23·00 4·75
50 4d. red-brown .. £850 22·00
51 4d. purple-brown (1886) .. 45·00 75
a. Chocolate (1887) .. 45·00 1·25
52 6d. violet (1888) .. £120 £140
53 3 5s. lake (1888) .. 27·00 50·00
a. Printed both sides .. £3750
b. Brown-lake (1893) .. 30·00 50·00
49, 51, 52 Optd "Specimen" .. *Set of* 3 £180

2½d.

(10)

5
PENCE

(11)

1890 (Aug). *No.* 51*a surch locally with T* **10**.
54 1 2½d. on 4d. chocolate .. 65·00 90·00
a. No fraction bar (R. 1/7, 2/4) .. £300 £350

1890–93. *No.* 55 *is surch with T* **8**. *Colours changed. Wmk Crown CA. P* 14.
55 1 2½d. on 1d. grey-blue (1890) .. 17·00 55
a. Blue (1893) .. 1·25 35
56 4d. yellow (1893) (Optd S. £30) .. 1·60 6·00
57 6d. dull purple (1891) .. 2·25 8·00
58 1s. orange (1891) .. 5·50 11·00
a. Red-orange (1892) .. 11·00 17·00

1892 (Nov). *No.* 51*a surch locally with T* **11**, *in purple.*
59 1 5d. on 4d. chocolate (Optd S. £30) .. 15·00 25·00

Some letters are known double due to loose type, the best known being the first "E", but they are not constant.

FIVE PENCE

(12)

13

14

1893–94. *Surch with T* **12**. *Wmk Crown CA. P* 14.
60 1 5d. on 6d. carmine-lake (Optd S. £45) .. 20·00 30·00
a. Deep lake (1893) .. 1·00 1·75
b. Lake (1894) .. 1·75 4·25
c. Surch double .. £4000 £2500

(Recess D.L.R.)

1897 (13 July). *New values. Wmk Crown CA. P* 14.
61 1 2½d. blue .. 2·75 1·75
62 5d. sepia .. 5·50 18·00
61/2 Optd "Specimen" *Set of* 2 60·00

1897 (6 Oct). *Surch as T* **12**. *Wmk Crown CA. P* 14.
63 1 3d. on 1d. mauve (Optd S. £40) .. 6·00 17·00
a. Red-mauve .. 10·00 27·00

(Typo D.L.R.)

1899 (1 Jan). *Wmk Crown CA. P 14.*
67 13 ½d. dull mauve and green 2·50 1·50
68 1d. dull mauve and carmine 4·00 80
69 2½d. dull mauve and blue 4·00 2·00
70 3d. dull mauve and olive 4·00 9·50
71 4d. dull mauve and orange 4·00 14·00
72 5d. dull mauve and black 7·00 13·00
73 6d. dull mauve and brown 13·00 28·00
74 14 1s. green and carmine 13·00 48·00
75 5s. green and blue 75·00 £130
67/75 *Set of* 9 £110 £225
67/75 Optd "Specimen" *Set of* 9 £170

15

16

(Typo D.L.R.)

1902. *Wmk Crown CA. P 14.*
76 15 ½d. dull purple and green 2·00 60
77 1d. dull purple and carmine 2·75 30
78 16 2d. dull purple and black 2·00 2·25
79 15 2½d. dull purple and blue 4·00 3·25
80 3d. dull purple and olive 3·25 2·50
81 6d. dull purple and brown 11·00 30·00
82 16 1s. green and carmine 18·00 50·00
83 15 2s. green and violet 25·00 55·00
84 16 5s. green and blue 65·00 £110
76/84 *Set of* 9 £120 £225
76/84 Optd "Specimen" *Set of* 9 £120

1904–11. *Wmk Mult Crown CA. Ordinary paper* (½d., 1d., 1s.) *or chalk-surfaced paper* (*others*). *P 14.*
85 15 ½d. dull purple and green (1905) 5·00 1·75
a. Chalk-surfaced paper 1·25 80
86 1d. dull purple and carmine 16·00 75
a. Chalk-surfaced paper 16·00 90
88 2½d. dull purple and blue (1906) 13·00 32·00
89 6d. dull purple and brown (1905) 13·00 32·00
90 16 1s. green and carmine (1906) 16·00 42·00
a. Chalk-surfaced paper 10·00 42·00
91 15 2s. purple and bright blue/*blue* (3.09?) 22·00 42·00
92 16 5s. green and red/*yellow* (3.09?) 17·00 48·00
93 £1 purple and black/*red* (22.7.11) £250 £300
85/93 *Set of* 8 £300 £425
91/3 Optd "Specimen" *Set of* 3 £180

Examples of most values are known showing a forged Kingstown postmark, code letter "O", dated "JA 7 10". This has also been seen on some values of the 1899 and 1902 issues.

17

18

(Recess D.L.R.)

1907–08. *Wmk Mult Crown CA. P 14.*
94 17 ½d. green (2.7.07) 2·00 1·75
95 1d. carmine (26.4.07) 3·00 15
96 2d. orange (5.08) 1·00 6·50
97 2½d. blue (8.07) 24·00 8·50
98 3d. violet (1.6.07) 6·00 15·00
94/8 *Set of* 5 32·00 29·00
94/8 Optd "Specimen" *Set of* 5 £100

1909. *No dot below "d". Wmk Mult Crown CA. P 14.*
99 18 1d. carmine (3.09) 1·25 30
100 6d. dull purple (16.1.09) 5·50 30·00
101 1s. black/*green* (16.1.09) 3·75 8·50
99/101 *Set of* 3 9·50 35·00
99/101 Optd "Specimen" *Set of* 3 65·00

1909 (Nov)–**11.** *T* **18**, *redrawn* (*dot below "d", as in T* **17**). *Wmk Mult Crown CA. P 14.*
102 ½d. green (31.10.10) 1·50 40
103 1d. carmine 1·50 15
104 2d. grey (3.8.11) 4·00 8·50
105 2½d. ultramarine (25.7.10) 8·00 3·25
106 3d. purple/*yellow* 2·50 4·75
107 6d. dull purple 6·00 5·00
102/7 *Set of* 6 21·00 20·00
102 and 104/6 Optd "Specimen" *Set of* 4 85·00

19

ONE

PENNY.

(20)

(Recess D.L.R.)

1913 (1 Jan)–**17.** *Wmk Mult Crown CA. P 14.*
108 19 ½d. green 45 20
109 1d. red 60 25
a. Rose-red 1·00 65
b. Scarlet (1.17) 13·00 4·50
w. Wmk inverted
y. Wmk inverted and reversed 75·00
110 2d. grey 7·00 25·00
a. Slate 2·50 25·00
111 2½d. ultramarine 35 50
112 3d. purple/*yellow* 80 5·00
a. On lemon 2·75 12·00
ax. Wmk reversed
b. On pale yellow 2·50 9·00
113 19 4d. red/*yellow* 80 2·00
114 5d. olive-green (7.11.13) 2·25 13·00
x. Wmk reversed
115 6d. claret 2·00 4·50
116 1s. black/*green* 1·50 3·50
117 1s. bistre (1.5.14) 3·75 17·00
118 18 2s. blue and purple 4·75 23·00
119 5s. carmine and myrtle 13·00 48·00
x. Wmk reversed £150
120 £1 mauve and black 75·00 £150
108/20 *Set of* 13 95·00 £250
108/20 Optd "Specimen" *Set of* 13 £250

Nos. 118/20 are from new centre and frame dies, the motto "PAX ET JUSTITIA" being slightly over 7 mm long, as against just over 8 mm in Nos. 99 to 107. Nos. 139/41 are also from the new dies.

1915. *No. 116 surch with T* **20**.
121 19 1d. on 1s. black/*green* (R.) 7·50 23·00
a. "ONE" omitted £850 £750
b. "ONE" double £650
c. "PENNY" and bar double £650 £650

The spacing between the two words varies from 7¾ mm to 10 mm.

WAR STAMP.
(21)

WAR STAMP.
(22)

WAR STAMP
(24)

1916 (June). *No. 109 optd locally with T* **21**. *(a) First and second settings; words 2 to 2½ mm apart.*
122 19 1d. red 3·25 5·00
a. Opt double £140 £140
b. Comma for stop 8·00 12·00
w. Wmk inverted

In the first printing every second stamp has the comma for stop. The second printing of this setting has full stops only. These two printings can therefore only be distinguished in blocks or pairs.

(b) Third setting; words only 1½ mm apart
123 19 1d. red 75·00
a. Opt double £1100

Stamps of the first setting are offered as this rare one. Care must be taken to see that the distance between the lines is not over 1½ mm.

(c) Fourth setting; optd with T **22**. *Words 3½ mm apart*
124 19 1d. carmine-red 3·00 9·00
a. Opt double £200
w. Wmk inverted
y. Wmk inverted and reversed

1916 (Aug)–**18.** *T* **19**, *from new printings, optd with T* **24**.
126 1d. carmine-red (Optd S. £60) 30 80
w. Wmk inverted
x. Wmk reversed
127 1d. pale rose-red 80 80
w. Wmk inverted 60·00
x. Wmk reversed
128 1d. deep rose-red 50 80
129 1d. pale scarlet (1918) 30 80

1921–32. *Wmk Mult Script CA. P 14.*
131 19 ½d. green (3.21) 1·75 30
132 1d. carmine (6.21) 1·00 70
a. Red 1·75 15
132*b* 1½d. brown (1.12.32) 1·75 15
133 2d. grey (3.22) 1·75 40
133*a* 2½d. bright blue (12.25) 1·00 40
134 3d. bright blue (3.22) 90 6·00
135 3d. purple/*yellow* (1.12.26) 75 1·50
135*a* 4d. red/*yellow* (9.30) 1·75 6·00
136 5d. sage-green (8.3.24) 80 6·00
137 6d. claret (1.11.27) 90 3·50
138 1s. bistre-brown (9.21) 5·50 18·00
a. Ochre (1927) 2·00 14·00
139 18 2s. blue and purple (8.3.24) 6·50 13·00
140 5s. carmine and myrtle (8.3.24) 16·00 32·00
141 £1 mauve and black (9.28) 75·00 £120
131/41 *Set of* 14 95·00 £180
131/41 Optd/Perf "Specimen" *Set of* 14 £250

1935 (6 May). *Silver Jubilee. As Nos. 114/17 of Jamaica, but ptd by Waterlow. P* 11×12.
142 1d. deep blue and scarlet 40 1·25
143 1½d. ultramarine and grey 1·00 2·50
144 2½d. brown and deep blue 1·90 2·75
145 1s. slate and purple 2·00 3·50
l. Kite and horizontal log £190
142/5 *Set of* 4 4·75 9·00
142/5 Perf "Specimen" *Set of* 4 75·00

For illustration of plate variety see Omnibus section following Zimbabwe.

1937 (12 May). *Coronation. As Nos. 118/20 of Jamaica, but ptd by B.W. P* 11×11½.
146 1d. violet 35 40
147 1½d. carmine 40 30
148 2½d. blue 45 1·25
146/8 *Set of* 3 1·10 1·75
146/8 Perf "Specimen" *Set of* 3 50·00

25

26 Young's Island and Fort Duvernette

27 Kingstown and Fort Charlotte

28 Bathing Beach at Villa

29 Victoria Park, Kingstown

NEW CONSTITUTION 1951
(29*a*)

(Recess B.W.)

1938 (11 Mar)–**47.** *Wmk Mult Script CA. P 12.*
149 25 ½d. blue and green 10 10
150 26 1d. blue and lake-brown 10 10
151 27 1½d. green and scarlet 20 10
152 25 2d. green and black 40 35
153 28 2½d. blue-black and blue-green 20 40
153*a* 29 2½d. green and purple-brown (1947) 20 20
154 25 3d. orange and purple 20 10
154*a* 28 3½d. blue-black and blue-green (1947) 40 1·25
155 25 6d. black and lake 1·00 40
156 29 1s. purple and green 1·00 60
157 25 2s. blue and purple 6·00 75
157*a* 2s. 6d. red-brown and blue (1947) 1·00 3·50
158 5s. scarlet and deep green 10·00 2·50
158*a* 10s. violet and brown (1947) 3·75 8·00
aw. Wmk inverted — £1300
159 £1 purple and black 16·00 15·00
149/59 *Set of* 15 35·00 28·00
149/59 Perf "Specimen" *Set of* 15 £250

1946 (15 Oct). *Victory. As Nos. 141/2 of Jamaica.*
160 1½d. carmine 10 10
161 3½d. blue 10 10
160/1 Perf "Specimen" *Set of* 2 50·00

1948 (30 Nov). *Royal Silver Wedding. As Nos. 143/4 of Jamaica.*
162 1½d. scarlet 10 10
163 £1 bright purple 15·00 17·00

No. 163 was originally printed in black, but the supply of these was stolen in transit. A few archive examples exist, some perforated "Specimen".

(New Currency. 100 cents = 1 West Indian, later East Caribbean dollar)

1949 (26 Mar)–**52.** *Value in cents and dollars. Wmk Mult Script CA. P 12.*
164 25 1 c. blue and green 20 65
164*a* 1 c. green and black (10.6.52) 30 1·50
165 26 2 c. blue and lake-brown 15 30
166 27 3 c. green and scarlet 40 40
166*a* 25 3 c. orange and purple (10.6.52) 30 1·50
167 4 c. green and black 35 20
167*a* 4 c. blue and green (10.6.52) 30 15
168 29 5 c. green and purple-brown 15 10
169 25 6 c. orange and purple 40 40
169*a* 27 6 c. green and scarlet (10.6.52) 30 1·25
170 28 7 c. blue-black and blue-green 3·50 45
170*a* 10 c. blue-black and blue-green (10.6.52) 50 20
171 25 12 c. black and lake 35 15
172 29 24 c. purple and green 35 45
173 25 48 c. blue and purple 1·50 1·50
174 60 c. red-brown and blue 1·75 2·00
175 $1.20, scarlet and deep green 4·25 4·00
176 $2.40, violet and brown 6·00 9·00
177 $4.80, purple and black 11·00 18·00
164/77 *Set of* 19 28·00 35·00

1949 (10 Oct). *75th Anniv of U.P.U. As Nos. 145/8 of Jamaica.*
178 5 c. blue 25 15
179 6 c. purple 55 90
180 12 c. magenta 30 80
181 24 c. blue-green 50 25
178/81 *Set of* 4 1·40 1·90

1951 (16 Feb). *Inauguration of B.W.I. University College. As Nos. 149/50 of Jamaica.*
182 3 c. deep green and scarlet 30 30
183 12 c. black and purple 30 30

1951 (21 Sept). *New Constitution. Optd with T* **29***a by B.W.*
184 27 3 c. green and scarlet 15 40
185 25 4 c. green and black 15 30
186 29 5 c. green and purple-brown 15 30
187 25 12 c. black and lake 40 30
184/7 *Set of* 4 75 1·10

1953 (2 June). *Coronation. As No. 153 of Jamaica.*
188 4 c. black and green 30 20

30

31

(Recess Waterlow (until 1961), then D.L.R.)

1955 (16 Sept)–**63**. *Wmk Mult Script CA. P* 13½×14 (*T* **30**) *or* 14 (*T* **31**).

189	**30**	1 c. orange	10	10
		a. Deep orange (11.12.62)	3·75	4·25
190		2 c. ultramarine	10	10
		a. Blue (26.9.61)	90	40
191		3 c. slate	30	10
192		4 c. brown	20	10
193		5 c. scarlet	40	10
194		10 c. reddish violet	20	10
		a. Deep lilac (12.2.58)	40	10
195		15 c. deep blue	65	30
196		20 c. green	60	10
197		25 c. black-brown	50	10
198	**31**	50 c. red-brown	4·50	1·75
		a. Chocolate (11.6.58)	5·00	1·25
199		$1 myrtle-green	8·00	1·00
		a. Deep myrtle-green (11.6.58)	14·00	4·00
		b. Deep yellowish green (15.1.63)	22·00	10·00
200		$2.50, deep blue	14·00	7·00
		a. Indigo-blue (30.7.62)	32·00	14·00
189/200		*Set of* 12	26·00	8·50

See also Nos. 207/20 and **MS**633.

1958 (22 Apr). *Inauguration of British Caribbean Federation. As Nos.* 175/7 *of Jamaica.*

201	3 c. deep green	30	20
202	6 c. blue	40	1·00
203	12 c. scarlet	70	45
201/3	*Set of* 3	1·25	1·50

MINISTERIAL GOVERNMENT

1963 (4 June). *Freedom from Hunger. As No.* 80 *of Lesotho.*

204	8 c. reddish violet	60	50

1963 (2 Sept). *Red Cross Centenary. As Nos.* 203/4 *of Jamaica.*

205	4 c. red and black	15	20
206	8 c. red and blue	35	50

(Recess D.L.R.)

1964–65. *As* 1955 *but wmk* w **12**. (*a*) *P* 12½ (14 Jan–Feb 1964).

207	**30**	10 c. deep lilac	40	45
208		15 c. deep blue	70	50
209		20 c. green (24.2.64*)	4·00	75
210		25 c. black-brown	80	50
211	**31**	50 c. chocolate	7·00	9·50
207/11		*Set of* 5	11·50	10·50
		(*b*) *P* 13×14 (*T* **30**) *or* 14 (*T* **31**)		
212	**30**	1 c. orange (15.12.64)	15	10
213		2 c. blue (15.12.64)	15	10
214		3 c. slate (15.12.64)	50	10
215		5 c. scarlet (15.12.64)	15	10
216		10 c. deep lilac (15.12.64)	15	10
217		15 c. deep blue (9.11.64)	80	30
218		20 c. green (1964)	45	10
		w. Wmk inverted		
219		25 c. black-brown (20.10.64)	1·25	25
220	**31**	50 c. chocolate (18.1.65)	4·75	8·00
212/20		*Set of* 9	7·50	8·00

*This is the earliest known date recorded in St. Vincent although it may have been put on sale on 14.1.64.

32 Scout Badge and Proficiency Badges

33 Tropical Fruits

(Des V. Whiteley. Litho Harrison)

1964 (23 Nov). *50th Anniv of St. Vincent Boy Scouts Association.* W w **12**. *P* 14½.

221	**32**	1 c. yellow-green and chocolate	10	10
222		4 c. blue and brown-purple	10	10
223		20 c. yellow and black-violet	30	10
224		50 c. red and bronze-green	45	50
221/4		*Set of* 4	80	60

(Des V. Whiteley. Photo Harrison)

1965 (23 Mar). *Botanic Gardens Bicentenary. T* **33** *and similar multicoloured designs.* W w **12**. *P* 14½ × 13½ (*horiz*) *or* 13½ × 14½ (*vert*).

225	1 c. Type **33**	10	10
226	4 c. Breadfruit and H.M.S. *Providence* (sloop), 1793	10	10
227	25 c. Doric Temple and pond (*vert*)	15	10
228	40 c. Talipot Palm and Doric Temple (*vert*)	30	80
225/8	*Set of* 4	50	90

1965 (17 May). *I.T.U. Centenary. As Nos.* 98/9 *of Lesotho.*

229	4 c. light blue and light olive-green	20	10
230	48 c. ochre-yellow and orange	55	45

37 Boat-building, Bequia (inscr "BEOUIA")

(Des M. Goaman. Photo Harrison)

1965 (16 Aug)–**67**. *T* **37** *and similar multicoloured designs.* W w **12**. *P* 14½ × 13½ (*horiz designs*) *or* 13½ × 14½ (*vert*).

231	1 c. Type **37** ("BEOUIA")	10	85
231*a*	1 c. Type **37** ("BEQUIA") (27.6.67)	65	30
232	2 c. Friendship Beach, Bequia	10	10
233	3 c. Terminal Building, Arnos Vale Airport	30	10
	w. Wmk inverted	6·00	
234	4 c. Woman with bananas (*vert*)	1·00	30
	w. Wmk inverted		
235	5 c. Crater Lake	15	10
236	6 c. Carib Stone (*vert*)	15	40
237	8 c. Arrowroot (*vert*)	30	10
238	10 c. Owia Salt Pond	30	10
239	12 c. Deep water wharf	70	10
240	20 c. Sea Island cotton (*vert*)	30	10
	w. Wmk inverted	—	30·00
241	25 c. Map of St. Vincent and islands (*vert*)	35	10
	w. Wmk inverted	22·00	
242	50 c. Breadfruit (*vert*)	50	30
243	$1 Baleine Falls (*vert*)	4·00	30
244	$2.50, St. Vincent Amazon (*vert*)	18·00	4·50
245	$5 Arms of St. Vincent (*vert*)	5·00	7·50
231/45	*Set of* 16	27·00	13·00

The 1 c. (No. 231*a*), 2 c., 3 c., 5 c. and 10 c. exist with PVA gum as well as gum arabic.

See also No. 261.

1966 (24 June). *Churchill Commemoration. As Nos.* 102/5 *of Lesotho.*

246	1 c. new blue	10	10
247	4 c. deep green	20	10
248	20 c. brown	35	30
249	40 c. bluish violet	55	1·00
246/9	*Set of* 4	1·00	1·25

1966 (4 Feb). *Royal Visit. As Nos.* 183/4 *of Montserrat.*

250	4 c. black and ultramarine	1·00	20
251	25 c. black and magenta	2·50	80

1966 (20 Sept). *Inauguration of W.H.O. Headquarters, Geneva. As Nos.* 185/6 *of Montserrat.*

252	4 c. black, yellow-green and light blue	30	10
253	25 c. black, light purple and yellow-brown	70	80

1966 (1 Dec). *20th Anniv of U.N.E.S.C.O. As Nos.* 342/4 *of Mauritius.*

254	4 c. slate-violet, red, yellow and orange	30	10
255	8 c. orange-yellow, violet and deep olive	55	10
256	25 c. black, bright purple and orange	1·25	60
254/6	*Set of* 3	1·90	70

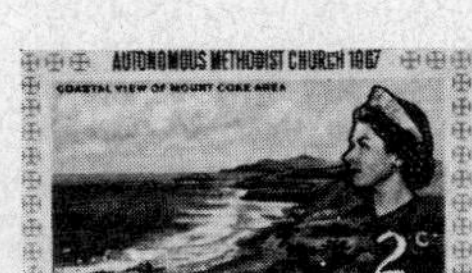

38 Coastal View of Mount Coke Area

(Des and photo Harrison)

1967 (1 Dec). *Autonomous Methodist Church. T* **38** *and similar horiz designs. Multicoloured.* W w **12**. *P* 14 × 14½.

257	2 c. Type **38**	10	10
258	8 c. Kingstown Methodist Church	10	10
259	25 c. First Licence to perform marriages	25	10
260	35 c. Conference Arms	25	10
257/60	*Set of* 4	55	30

1968 (20 Feb). *As No.* 234, *but* W w **12** *sideways.*

261	4 c. Woman with bananas	30	30

The above exists with PVA gum as well as gum arabic.

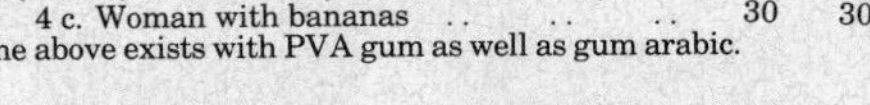

39 Meteorological Institute

(Des G. Vasarhelyi. Photo Harrison)

1968 (28 May). *World Meteorological Day.* W w **12**. *P* 14 × 14½.

262	**39**	4 c. multicoloured	10	10
263		25 c. multicoloured	10	10
264		35 c. multicoloured	15	10
262/4		*Set of* 3	30	20

40 Dr. Martin Luther King and Cotton Pickers

(Des V. Whiteley. Litho D.L.R.)

1968 (28 Aug). *Martin Luther King Commemoration.* W w **12** (*sideways*). *P* 13.

265	**40**	5 c. multicoloured	10	10
266		25 c. multicoloured	10	10
267		35 c. multicoloured	10	10
265/7		*Set of* 3	20	20

41 Speaker addressing Demonstrators

42 Scales of Justice and Human Rights Emblem'

(Des V. Whiteley. Photo Enschedé)

1968 (1 Nov). *Human Rights Year. P* 13 × 14 (3 c.) *or* 14 × 13 (35 c.).

268	**41**	3 c. multicoloured	10	10
269	**42**	35 c. royal blue and turquoise-blue	20	10

43 Male Masquerader

44 Steel Bandsman

(Des V. Whiteley. Litho Format)

1969 (17 Feb). *St. Vincent Carnival. T* **43/4** *and similar designs. P* 14.

270	1 c. multicoloured	10	10
271	5 c. red and deep chocolate	10	10
272	8 c. multicoloured	10	10
273	25 c. multicoloured	15	20
270/3	*Set of* 4	30	40

Designs: *Horiz*—8 c. Carnival Revellers. *Vert*—25 c. Queen of Bands.

METHODIST
CONFERENCE
MAY
1969
(**47**)

1969 (14 May). *Methodist Conference. Nos.* 257/8, 241 *and* 260 *optd with T* **47**.

274	2 c. multicoloured	10	15
275	8 c. multicoloured	20	40
276	25 c. multicoloured	25	40
277	35 c. multicoloured	1·25	3·00
274/7	*Set of* 4	1·50	3·50

48 "Strength in Unity"

49 Map of "CARIFTA" Countries

(Des J. Cooter. Litho D.L.R.)

1969 (1 July). *First Anniv of CARIFTA* (*Caribbean Free Trade Area*). W w **12** (*sideways on T* **48**). *P* 13.

278	**48**	2 c. black, pale buff and red	10	10
279	**49**	5 c. multicoloured	10	10
280	**48**	8 c. black, pale buff and pale green	10	10
281	**49**	25 c. multicoloured	35	15
278/81		*Set of* 4	50	30

ASSOCIATED STATEHOOD

50 Flag of St. Vincent

(Des V. Whiteley, based on local designs. Photo Harrison)

1969 (27 Oct). *Statehood. T* **50** *and similar horiz designs.* W w **12**. *P* 14 × 14½.

282	4 c. multicoloured	10	10
283	10 c. multicoloured	10	10
284	50 c. grey, black and orange	35	20
282/4	*Set of* 3	50	30

Designs:—10 c. Battle scene with insets of Petroglyph and Carib chief Chatoyer; 50 c. Carib House with maces and scales.

51 Green Heron

(Des J.W. Photo Harrison)

1970 (12 Jan)–**71**. *T* **51** *and similar multicoloured designs. Chalk-surfaced paper. W* w **12** (*sideways* on* 1, 2, 3, 6, 8, 20, 25 *c.*, $1, $2.50 *and upright on others*). *P* 14.

285	½ c. House Wren (*vert*)	10	85
286	1 c. Type **51**	35	2·25
	a. Glazed, ordinary paper (9.8.71)	30	1·50
	aw. Wmk Crown to right of CA	1·25	1·75
287	2 c. Lesser Antillean Bullfinches	15	40
	w. Wmk Crown to right of CA	13·00	
288	3 c. St. Vincent Amazons	15	30
289	4 c. Rufous-throated Solitaire (*vert*)	20	30
290	5 c. Red-necked Pigeon (*vert*)	3·75	30
	a. Glazed, ordinary paper (9.8.71)	1·50	30
291	6 c. Bananaquits	30	30
292	8 c. Purple-throated Carib	40	20
	w. Wmk Crown to right of CA	28·00	
293	10 c. Mangrove Cuckoo (*vert*)	30	10
294	12 c. Common Black Hawk (*vert*)	40	10
295	20 c. Bare-eyed Thrush	60	15
296	25 c. Hooded Tanager	70	20
297	50 c. Blue Hooded Euphonia	2·00	75
	w. Wmk inverted	40·00	
298	$1 Barn Owl (*vert*)	7·50	4·00
299	$2.50, Yellow-bellied Elaenia (*vert*)	7·00	4·75
300	$5 Ruddy Quail Dove	12·00	6·50
285/300	*Set of* 16	30·00	18·00

*The normal sideways watermark shows Crown to left of CA, *as seen from the back of the stamp.*

See also Nos. 361/8 and 396/8.

52 De Havilland D.H.C.6 Twin Otter 100

(Des R. Granger Barrett. Litho Enschedé)

1970 (13 Mar). *20th Anniv of Regular Air Services. T* **52** *and similar horiz designs. Multicoloured. W* w **12** (*sideways*). *P* 14 × 13.

301	5 c. Type **52**	10	10
302	8 c. Grumman G.21 Goose	15	10
303	10 c. Hawker Siddeley H.S.748	20	10
304	25 c. Douglas DC-3	65	30
301/4	*Set of* 4	1·00	40

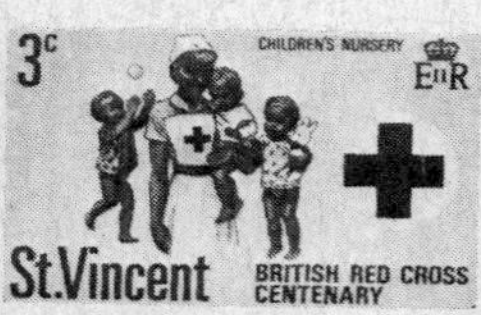

53 "Children's Nursery"

54 "Angel and the Two Marys at the Tomb" (stained-glass window)

(Des R. Granger Barrett. Photo Harrison)

1970 (1 June). *Centenary of British Red Cross. T* **53** *and similar horiz designs. Multicoloured. W* w **12**. *P* 14.

305	3 c. Type **53**	10	10
306	5 c. "First Aid"	15	10
	w. Wmk inverted	45·00	
307	12 c. "Voluntary Aid Detachment"	35	50
	w. Wmk inverted	2·25	
308	25 c. "Blood Transfusion"	55	50
305/8	*Set of* 4	1·00	1·00

(Des L. Curtis. Litho J.W.)

1970 (7 Sept). *150th Anniv of St. George's Cathedral, Kingstown. T* **54** *and similar multicoloured designs. W* w **12** (*sideways* on horiz designs*). *P* 14.

309	½ c. Type **54**	10	10
310	5 c. St. George's Cathedral (*horiz*)	10	10
	w. Wmk Crown to right of CA		
311	25 c. Tower, St. George's Cathedral	10	10
312	35 c. Interior, St. George's Cathedral (*horiz*)	15	10
313	50 c. Type **54**	20	30
309/13	*Set of* 5	45	35

*The normal sideways watermark shows Crown to left of CA, *as seen from the back of the stamp.*

55 "The Adoration of the Shepherds" (Le Nain)

(Des J. Cooter. Litho Questa)

1970 (23 Nov). *Christmas. T* **55** *and similar vert design. Multicoloured. W* w **12** (*sideways* on* 25 *c.*, 50 *c.*). *P* 14.

314	8 c. "The Virgin and Child" (Bellini)	10	10
315	25 c. Type **55**	10	10
	w. Wmk Crown to right of CA	90	
316	35 c. As 8 c.	10	10
317	50 c. Type **55**	15	20
	w. Wmk Crown to right of CA	1·50	
314/17	*Set of* 4	35	30

*The normal sideways watermark shows Crown to left of CA, *as seen from the back of the stamp.*

56 New Post Office and 6d. Stamp of 1861

(Des J. Cooter. Litho Questa)

1971 (29 Mar). *110th Anniv of First St. Vincent Stamps. T* **56** *and similar horiz design. Multicoloured. W* w **12** (*sideways*). *P* 14.

318	2 c. Type **56**	10	10
319	4 c. 1d. Stamp of 1861 and New Post Office	10	10
320	25 c. Type **56**	10	10
321	$1 As 4 c.	35	45
318/21	*Set of* 4	45	50

57 Trust Seal and Wildlife

58 "Madonna appearing to St. Anthony" (Tiepolo)

(Des G. Drummond. Litho J.W.)

1971 (4 Aug). *St. Vincent's National Trust. T* **57** *and similar horiz design. Multicoloured. W* w **12** (*sideways*). *P* 13½ × 14.

322	12 c. Type **57**	40	15
323	30 c. Old Cannon, Fort Charlotte	35	20
324	40 c. Type **57**	55	35
325	45 c. As 30 c.	40	70
322/5	*Set of* 4	1·50	1·25

(Des J. Cooter. Litho Questa)

1971 (6 Oct). *Christmas. T* **58** *and similar horiz design. Multicoloured. W* w **12** (*sideways* on* 10 *c. and* $1). *P* 14½×14 (10 *c.*, $1) *or* 14×14½ (5 *c.*, 25 *c.*).

326	5 c. Type **58**	10	10
327	10 c. "The Holy Family on the Flight into Egypt" (detail, Pietro da Cortona)	10	10
	w. Wmk Crown to right of CA	1·50	
328	25 c. Type **58**	10	10
329	$1 As 10 c.	40	35
	w. Wmk Crown to right of CA	2·25	2·50
326/9	*Set of* 4	50	40

*The normal sideways watermark shows Crown to left of CA, *as seen from the back of the stamp.*

59 Careening

60 Private, Grenadier Company, 32nd Foot (1764)

(Des J. Cooter. Litho J.W.)

1971 (25 Nov). *The Grenadines of St. Vincent. T* **59** *and similar vert designs. Multicoloured. W* w **12**. *P* 13½.

330	1 c. Type **59**	10	10
331	5 c. Seine fishermen	10	10
332	6 c. Map of the Grenadines	10	10
333	15 c. Type **59**	15	10
334	20 c. As 5 c.	20	10
335	50 c. As 6 c.	50	80
330/5	*Set of* 6	80	1·00
MS336	177 × 140 mm. Nos. 330/5	7·50	11·00

(Des and litho J.W.)

1972 (14 Feb). *Military Uniforms. T* **60** *and similar vert designs. Multicoloured. W* w **12**. *P* 14 × 13½.

337	12 c. Type **60**	90	15
338	30 c. Officer, Battalion Company, 31st Foot (1772)	1·25	65
339	50 c. Private, Grenadier Company, 6th Foot (1772)	2·00	1·25
337/9	*Set of* 3	3·75	1·90

61 Breadnut Fruit

62 Candlestick Cassia

(Des P. Powell. Litho Questa)

1972 (16 May). *Fruit. T* **61** *and similar vert designs. Multicoloured. W* w **12** (*sideways*). *P* 13½.

340	3 c. Type **61**	10	10
341	5 c. Pawpaw	10	10
342	12 c. Plumrose or Roseapple	20	30
343	25 c. Mango	60	70
340/3	*Set of* 4	80	1·00

(Des Sylvia Goaman. Litho B.W.)

1972 (31 July). *Flowers. T* **62** *and similar vert designs. Multicoloured. P* 13 ($1) *or* 13½ × 14 (*others*).

344	1 c. Type **62**	10	10
345	30 c. Lobster Claw	20	10
346	40 c. White Trumpet	25	15
347	$1 Soufriere tree	70	1·25
344/7	*Set of* 4	1·10	1·40

63 Sir Charles Brisbane and Coat of Arms

(Des Jennifer Toombs. Litho J.W.)

1972 (29 Sept). *Birth Bicentenary of Sir Charles Brisbane. T* **63** *and similar horiz designs. W* w **12** (*sideways*). *P* 13½.

348	20 c. yellow-ochre, gold and red-brown	15	10
349	30 c. light yellow, light mauve and black	40	10
350	$1 multicoloured	1·40	70
348/50	*Set of* 3	1·75	75
MS351	171 × 111 mm. Nos. 348/50 (*sold at* $2)	4·50	6·50

Designs:—30 c. H.M.S. *Arethusa*, 1807; $1 H.M.S. *Blake*, 1808.

64 Arrowroot and Breadfruit

(Des (from photograph by D. Groves) and photo Harrison)

1972 (20 Nov). *Royal Silver Wedding. Multicoloured; background colour given. W* w **12**. *P* 14 × 14½.

352	**64**	30 c. red-brown	10	10
353		$1 myrtle-green	20	20
		w. Wmk inverted	£250	

65 Sighting St. Vincent

66 "The Last Supper" (French Stained-glass Window)

(Des J. Cooter. Litho Enschedé)

1973 (31 Jan). *475th Anniv of Columbus's Third Voyage to the West Indies. T* **65** *and similar triangular designs. Multicoloured. W* w **12**. *P* 13½.

354	5 c. Type **65**	25	30
355	12 c. Caribs watching Columbus's fleet	45	30
356	30 c. Christopher Columbus	1·00	90
357	50 c. *Santa Maria*	1·50	2·25
354/7	*Set of* 4	3·00	3·25

(Des J. Cooter. Litho Questa)

1973 (19 Apr). *Easter. T* **66** *and similar vert designs. Multicoloured. W* w **12** *(sideways). P* 14 × 13½.

358 **66** 15 c. multicoloured 10 10
a. Horiz strip of 3. Nos. 358/60 .. 45
359 – 60 c. multicoloured 20 20
360 – $1 multicoloured 20 20
358/60 .. .. *Set of* 3 45 45

Nos. 358, 360 and 359 were printed, in that order, horizontally *se-tenant* throughout a sheet of 45 stamps, and form a composite design of "The Last Supper".

1973 (13 June–23 Nov). *As Nos. 285 etc., but W* w **12** *upright on 2, 3, 6, 20 c. and sideways* on others. Glazed paper.*

361 2 c. Lesser Antillean Bullfinches (23.11) .. 30 45
362 3 c. St. Vincent Amazons (23.11) 30 45
363 4 c. Rufous-throated Solitaire (*vert*) (23.11) 30 30
364 5 c. Red-necked Pigeon (*vert*) 50 20
w. Wmk Crown to left of CA (23.11) .. 90 80
365 6 c. Bananaquits (23.11) 40 60
366 10 c. Mangrove Cuckoo (*vert*) (23.11) .. 55 15
367 12 c. Common Black Hawk (*vert*) (23.11) .. 85 75
368 20 c. Bare-eyed Thrush (23.11) .. .. 1·25 40
361/8 .. .. .. *Set of* 8 4·00 3·00

*The normal sideways watermark shows Crown to right of CA on No. 364 and to left of CA on the others, *as seen from the back of the stamp.*

For the 1 c. value with watermark upright see Grenadines of St. Vincent No. 3a.

67 William Wilberforce and Poster **68** P.P.F. Symbol

(Des Jennifer Toombs. Litho D.L.R.)

1973 (11 July). *140th Death Anniv of William Wilberforce. T* **67** *and similar horiz designs. Multicoloured. W* w **12.** *P* 14 × 13½.

369 30 c. Type **67** 15 10
w. Wmk inverted .. .. .. 40·00
370 40 c. Slaves cutting cane 20 15
371 50 c. Wilberforce and medallion 20 15
369/71 .. .. *Set of* 3 50 35

(Des PAD Studio. Litho Walsall)

1973 (3 Oct). *21st Anniv of International Planned Parenthood Federation. T* **68** *and similar vert design. Multicoloured. W* w **12** *(sideways). P* 14.

372 12 c. Type **68** 10 10
373 40 c. "IPPF" and symbol 20 20

1973 (14 Nov). *Royal Wedding. As Nos. 322/3 of Montserrat.*

374 50 c. deep blue 15 10
375 70 c. grey-green 15 10

69 Administrative Block, Mona

(Des PAD Studio. Litho Questa)

1973 (13 Dec). *25th Anniv of West Indies University. T* **69** *and similar multicoloured designs. W* w **12** *(sideways on* $1). *P* 14.

376 5 c. Type **69** 10 10
377 10 c. University Centre, Kingstown 10 10
378 30 c. Aerial view, Mona University 15 10
379 $1 University coat of arms (*vert*) 35 60
376/9 .. .. *Set of* 4 50 65

30c

(70) **71** "The Descent from the Cross" (Sansovino)

1973 (15 Dec). *Nos. 297, 292 and 298 surch in half sheets with T* **70**, *by the Govt Printer, St. Vincent.*

380 30 c. on 50 c. multicoloured .. .. 2·00 1·00
a. Surch double .. .. .. 22·00
b. Surch double (on front) and single inverted (on reverse) .. .. 65·00
c. Surch double, one inverted .. .. 50·00
d. Surch inverted .. .. ..
381 40 c. on 8 c. multicoloured .. .. 2·00 1·00
a. Surch double .. .. .. 28·00
b. Surch inverted £130
382 $10 on $1 multicoloured .. .. 10·00 7·50
a. Surch double .. .. .. 95·00
b. Surch inverted £110
c. Surch double, one inverted £110
380/2 .. .. *Set of* 3 12·50 8·50

SPECIMEN STAMPS. From No. 383 onwards the stamps of St. Vincent exist overprinted "SPECIMEN", these being produced for publicity purposes.

(Des PAD Studio. Litho Enschedé)

1974 (10 Apr). *Easter. T* **71** *and similar vert designs showing sculptures. Multicoloured. W* w **12** *(sideways). P* 14 × 13½.

383 5 c. Type **71** 10 10
384 30 c. "The Deposition" (English, 14th-century) 10 10
385 40 c. "Pieta" (Fernandez) 10 10
386 $1 "The Resurrection" (French, 16th-century) 20 25
383/6 .. .. *Set of* 4 30 30

72 *Istra*

(Des J.W. Litho Questa)

1974 (28 June). *Cruise Ships. T* **72** *and similar horiz designs. Multicoloured. W* w **12** *(sideways*). P* 14.

387 15 c. Type **72** 20 10
w. Wmk Crown to right of CA .. .. 27·00
388 20 c. *Oceanic* 25 10
389 30 c. *Aleksandr Pushkin* 25 10
390 $1 *Europa* 50 30
387/90 .. .. *Set of* 4 1·10 40
MS391 134×83 mm. Nos. 387/90 .. .. 1·00 2·75

*The normal sideways watermark shows Crown to left of CA, *as seen from the back of the stamp.*

73 U.P.U. Emblem

(Des J.W. Litho Questa)

1974 (25 July). *Centenary of Universal Postal Union. T* **73** *and similar horiz designs. Multicoloured. W* w **12.** *P* 14.

392 5 c. Type **73** 10 10
w. Wmk inverted .. .. .. 27·00
393 12 c. Globe within posthorn 10 10
394 60 c. Map of St. Vincent and hand-cancelling 20 10
395 90 c. Map of the World 25 30
392/5 .. .. *Set of* 4 50 40

74 Royal Tern **75** Scout Badge and Emblems

(Des J.W. Litho Questa)

1974 (29 Aug). *T* **74** *and similar vert designs. Multicoloured. Glazed paper. W* w **12** *(sideways on 40 c. and* $10). *P* 14.

396 30 c. Type **74** .. .. 2·00 90
397 40 c. Brown Pelican .. .. .. 2·00 90
398 $10 Magnificent Frigate Bird .. .. 18·00 11·00
396/8 .. .. *Set of* 3 20·00 11·50

(Des Sylvia Goaman. Litho Enschedé)

1974 (9 Oct). *Diamond Jubilee of Scout Movement in St. Vincent. W* w **12.** *P* 13 × 13½.

399 **75** 10 c. multicoloured 10 10
400 25 c. multicoloured 20 10
401 45 c. multicoloured 30 25
402 $1 multicoloured 55 80
399/402 .. .. *Set of* 4 1·00 1·10

76 Sir Winston Churchill **77** The Shepherds

(Des C. Abbott. Litho Questa)

1974 (28 Nov). *Birth Centenary of Sir Winston Churchill. T* **76** *and similar vert designs. Multicoloured. W* w **12.** *P* 14.

403 25 c. Type **76** 15 10
404 35 c. Churchill in military uniform 15 10
405 45 c. Churchill in naval uniform 20 10
406 $1 Churchill in air-force uniform 30 70
403/6 .. .. *Set of* 4 70 80

(Des Jennifer Toombs. Litho Enschedé)

1974 (5 Dec). *Christmas. T* **77** *and similar vert designs. W* w **12.** *P* 12 × 12½.

407 **77** 3 c. violet-blue and black 10 10
a. Horiz strip of 4. Nos. 407/10 .. 20
408 – 3 c. violet-blue and black 10 10
409 – 3 c. violet-blue and black 10 10
410 – 3 c. violet-blue and black 10 10
411 **77** 8 c. apple-green and black 10 10
412 – 35 c. rose and deep maroon 15 10
413 – 45 c. olive-bistre and brown-black .. 15 10
414 – $1 lavender and slate-black 30 50
407/14 .. .. *Set of* 8 75 85

Designs:—Nos. 408, 412 Mary and crib; Nos. 409, 413 Joseph, ox and ass; Nos. 410, 414 The Magi.

Nos. 407/10 were issued horizontally *se-tenant* within the sheet, together forming a composite design of the Nativity.

78 Faces

(Des G. Drummond. Litho D.L.R.)

1975 (7–27 Feb). *Kingstown Carnival. T* **78** *and similar horiz designs. Multicoloured. W* w **12.** *P* 14 × 13½.

415 1 c. Type **78** 10 10
a. Booklet pane. No. 415 × 2 plus printed label (27.2) 35
b. Booklet pane. Nos. 415, 417 and 419 (27.2) 40
416 15 c. Pineapple women 15 15
a. Booklet pane. Nos. 416, 418 and 420 (27.2) 50
417 25 c. King of the Bands 15 15
418 35 c. Carnival dancers 15 15
419 45 c. Queen of the Bands 15 20
420 $1.25, "African Splendour" 25 55
415/20 .. .. *Set of* 6 75 1·10
MS421 146 × 128 mm. Nos. 415/20 .. .. 1·00 3·00

79 French Angelfish

Two types of $2.50:

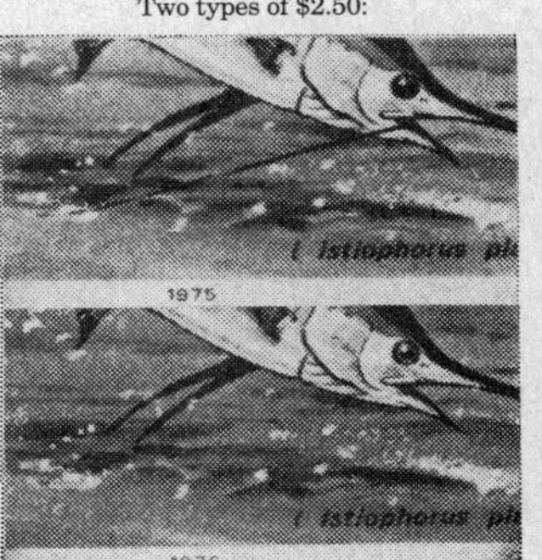

Type I. Fishing-line attached to fish's mouth. Imprint "1975".
Type II. Fishing-line omitted. Imprint "1976".

(Des G. Drummond. Litho Questa)

1975 (10 Apr)–**76.** *Marine Life. T* **79** *and similar horiz designs. Multicoloured. W* w **14** *(sideways*). With imprint date. P* 14½.

422 1 c. Type **79** 15 80
w. Wmk Crown to right of CA .. .. 17·00
423 2 c. Spot-finned Butterflyfish 15 95
424 3 c. Yellow Jack 15 55
425 4 c. Spanish Mackerel 20 10
426 5 c. French Grunt 20 45
w. Wmk Crown to right of CA .. .. 23·00
427 6 c. Spotted Goatfish 20 90
428 8 c. Ballyhoo .. .. 20 1·50
429 10 c. Sperm Whale 30 10
430 12 c. Humpback Whale .. .. .. 40 1·60
431 15 c. Scribbled Cowfish .. .. .. 1·25 1·60
w. Wmk Crown to right of CA .. .. 11·00
432 15 c. Skipjack Tuna (14.10.76) .. .. 3·50 80
433 20 c. Queen Angelfish 40 10
434 25 c. Princess Parrotfish 45 20
435 35 c. Red Hind .. .. 65 1·50
436 45 c. Atlantic Flyingfish 80 90
437 50 c. Porkfish .. .. 65 1·50
438 70 c. Yellow-finned Tuna (14.10.76) .. 6·00 70
439 90 c. Pompano (14.10.76) .. .. .. 6·00 70
440 $1 Queen Triggerfish 90 20
441 $2.50, Sailfish (I) .. .. .. 3·50 6·50
a. Type II (12.7.76) .. .. .. 2·25 1·50
442 $5 Dolphin (fish) .. .. .. 3·75 2·50
443 $10 Blue Marlin .. .. .. 3·75 8·50
422/43 .. .. *Set of* 22 29·00 25·00

*The normal sideways watermark shows Crown to left of CA, *as seen from the back of the stamp.*

Imprint dates: "1975", Nos. 422/31, 433/7, 440/1, 442/3; "1976", Nos. 425, 429, 432/3, 438/40, 441a; "1977", Nos. 422/4, 426/8, 430, 432, 437, 443; "1978", No. 429.

80 Cutting Bananas

(Des G. Drummond. Litho Questa)

1975 (26 June). *Banana Industry. T* **80** *and similar horiz designs. Multicoloured. W* w **12** (*sideways*). *P* 13½.

447	25 c. Type **80**	15	10
448	35 c. Packaging Station, La Croix	15	10
449	45 c. Cleaning and boxing	20	15
450	70 c. Shipping bananas aboard *Geestide* (freighter)	40	30
447/50	.. .. *Set of* 4	80	50

81 Snorkel Diving

(Des G. Drummond. Litho Questa)

1975 (31 July). *Tourism. T* **81** *and similar horiz designs. Multicoloured. W* w **14** (*sideways*). *P* 13½.

451	15 c. Type **81**	40	15
452	20 c. Aquaduct Golf Course	1·25	75
453	35 c. Steel Band at Mariner's Inn	45	15
454	45 c. Sunbathing at Young Island ..	45	25
455	$1.25, Yachting marina	1·40	2·50
451/5	.. .. *Set of* 5	3·50	3·50

82 George Washington, John Adams, Thomas Jefferson and James Madison

(Des G. Drummond. Litho Questa)

1975 (11 Sept). *Bicentenary of American Revolution. T* **82** *and similar horiz designs. P* 14.

456	½ c. black and lavender	10	10
457	1 c. black and light emerald	10	10
458	1½ c. black and light magenta	10	10
459	5 c. black and bright yellow-green	10	10
460	10 c. black and light violet-blue	10	10
461	25 c. black and dull orange-yellow	10	10
462	35 c. black and light greenish blue	15	15
463	45 c. black and bright rose	15	15
464	$1 black and light orange	30	40
465	$2 black and light yellow-olive	40	75
456/65	.. .. .. *Set of* 10	1·10	1·50
MS466	179 × 156 mm. Nos. 456/65	1·50	1·75

Presidents:—1 c. Monroe, Quincy Adams, Jackson, van Buren; 1½ c. W. Harrison, Tyler, Polk, Taylor; 5 c. Fillmore, Pierce, Buchanan, Lincoln; 10 c. Andrew Johnson, Grant, Hayes, Garfield; 25 c. Arthur, Cleveland, B. Harrison, McKinley; 35 c. Theodore Roosevelt, Taft, Wilson, Harding; 45 c. Coolidge, Hoover, Franklin Roosevelt, Truman; $1 Eisenhower, Kennedy, Lyndon Johnson, Nixon; $2 Pres. Ford and White House.

Nos. 456/65 were each issued in sheets of ten stamps and two *se-tenant* labels.

83/4 "Shepherds"

(Des Jennifer Toombs. Litho Harrison)

1975 (4 Dec). *Christmas. T* **83/4** *and similar triangular designs. P* 13½×14. A. *W* w **12** (*upright or inverted*). B. *W* w **12** (*sideways to left or right*).

467	3 c. black and magenta ..	10	10	10	10
	a. Block of 4. Nos. 467/70 ..	30	30	30	30
468	3 c. black and magenta ..	10	10	10	10
469	3 c. black and magenta ..	10	10	10	10
470	3 c. black and magenta ..	10	10	10	10
471	8 c. black & lt greenish blue ..	10	10	10	10
	a. Pair. Nos. 471/2	15	15	15	15
472	8 c. black & lt greenish blue ..	10	10	10	10
473	35 c. black and yellow	15	20	15	20
	a. Pair. Nos. 473/4	30	40	30	40
474	35 c. black and yellow	15	20	15	20
475	45 c. black and yellow-green ..	20	30	20	30
	a. Pair. Nos. 475/6	40	60	40	60
476	45 c. black and yellow-green ..	20	30	20	30
477	$1 black and bright lilac ..	40	80	40	80
	a. Pair. Nos. 477/8 ..	80	1·60	80	1·60
478	$1 black and bright lilac ..	40	80	40	80
467/78	.. .. *Set of* 12	1·75	2·75	1·75	2·75

Designs:—No. 467, "Star of Bethlehem"; 468, "Holy Trinity"; 469, As T **83**; 470, "Three Kings"; 471/2, As 467; 473/4, As 468; 475/6, T **83/4**; 477/8 As 470. The two designs of each denomination (Nos. 471/8) differ in that the longest side is at the foot or at the top as shown in T **83/4**.

Each denomination was printed in sheets of 16, the designs being *se-tenant* and so arranged that the watermark comes upright, inverted, sideways right and sideways left (*same price for either watermark position*).

85 Carnival Dancers

(Des G. Drummond. Litho Questa)

1976 (19 Feb). *Kingstown Carnival. T* **85** *and similar horiz designs. Multicoloured. W* w **14** (*sideways**). *P* 13½.

479	1 c. Type **85**	10	10
	a. Booklet pane. Nos. 479 and 480 plus printed label	20	
	w. Wmk Crown to right of CA	60	
480	2 c. Humpty-Dumpty people	10	10
	a. Booklet pane. Nos. 480/2	30	
	w. Wmk Crown to right of CA	90	
481	5 c. Smiling faces	10	10
	w. Wmk Crown to right of CA	90	
482	35 c. Dragon worshippers	15	10
	a. Booklet pane. Nos. 482/4	60	
	w. Wmk Crown to right of CA	2·00	
483	45 c. Carnival tableaux	20	15
	w. Wmk Crown to right of CA	1·00	
484	$1.25, Bumble-Bee dancers	30	45
	w. Wmk Crown to right of CA	1·50	
479/84	.. .. *Set of* 6	70	80

*The normal sideways watermark shows Crown to left of CA, *as seen from the back of the stamp.*

70¢

(86)

87 Blue-headed Hummingbird and Yellow Hibiscus

1976 (8 Apr). *Nos. 424 and 437 surch as T* **86**. *"1975" imprint date.*

485	70 c. on 3 c. Horse-eyed Jack	55	1·00
	a. Surch inverted	25·00	
486	90 c. on 50 c. Porkfish	55	1·25
	a. Surch inverted	25·00	

(Des G. Drummond. Litho Walsall)

1976 (20 May). *Hummingbirds and Hibiscuses. T* **87** *and similar vert designs. Multicoloured. W* w **14** (*inverted*). *P* 13½.

487	5 c. Type **87**	35	10
488	10 c. Antillean Crested Hummingbird and Pink Hibiscus	60	15
489	35 c. Purple-throated Carib and White Hibiscus	1·40	55
	a. No wmk	27·00	
490	45 c. Blue-headed Hummingbird and Red Hibiscus	1·50	65
	w. Wmk upright	1·00	90
491	$1.25 Green-throated Carib and Peach Hibiscus	9·50	5·50
487/91	.. .. *Set of* 5	12·00	6·25

1976 (16 Sept). *West Indian Victory in World Cricket Cup. As Nos. 419/20 of Jamaica.*

492	15 c. Map of the Caribbean	75	25
493	45 c. Prudential Cup	1·25	1·00

88 St Mary's Church, Kingstown

(Des G. Drummond. Litho Questa)

1976 (18 Nov). *Christmas. T* **88** *and similar horiz designs. Multicoloured. W* w **14** (*sideways*). *P* 14.

494	35 c. Type **88**	15	10
495	45 c. Anglican Church, Georgetown	15	10
496	50 c. Methodist Church, Georgetown	20	10
497	$1.25, St. George's Cathedral, Kingstown ..	40	60
494/7	.. .. *Set of* 4	80	70

89 Barrancoid Pot-stand

(Des G. Vasarhelyi. Litho J.W.)

1976 (16 Dec). *National Trust. T* **89** *and similar horiz designs. Multicoloured. W* w **14** (*sideways*). *P* 13½.

498	5 c. Type **89**	10	10
499	45 c. National Museum	15	10
500	70 c. Carib sculpture	20	20
501	$1 Ciboney petroglyph	30	50
498/501	.. .. *Set of* 4	60	75

90 William I, William II, Henry I and Stephen

(Des G. Vasarhelyi. Litho J.W.)

1977 (7 Feb). *Silver Jubilee. T* **90** *and similar horiz designs. Multicoloured. P* 13½. (*a*) *W* w **14** (*sideways**). *From sheets.*

502	½ c. Type **90**	10	10
503	1 c. Henry II, Richard I, John, Henry III	10	10
504	1½ c. Edward I, Edward II, Edward III, Richard II	10	10
	w. Wmk Crown to left of CA	24·00	
505	2 c. Henry IV, Henry V, Henry VI, Edward IV	10	10
506	5 c. Edward V, Richard III, Henry VII, Henry VIII	10	10
507	10 c. Edward VI, Lady Jane Grey, Mary I, Elizabeth I	10	10
	w. Wmk Crown to left of CA	55·00	
508	25 c. James I, Charles I, Charles II, James II	10	10
509	35 c. William III, Mary II, Anne, George I	10	10
510	45 c. George II, George III, George IV ..	10	10
	w. Wmk Crown to right of CA	40	35
511	75 c. William IV, Victoria, Edward VII ..	15	25
	w. Wmk Crown to left of CA	60	60
512	$1 George V, Edward VIII, George VI ..	20	40
	w. Wmk Crown to left of CA	75	75
513	$2 Elizabeth II leaving Westminster Abbey	30	60
	w. Wmk Crown to left of CA	15·00	
502/13	.. .. *Set of* 12	1·00	1·60
MS514	170×146 mm. Nos. 502/13. P 14½×14	1·00	2·00

(*b*) *No wmk. From booklets*

515	½ c. Type **90**	50	1·50
	a. Booklet pane. Nos. 515/18 *se-tenant* ..	1·75	
516	1 c. As No. 503	50	1·50
517	1½ c. As No. 504	50	1·50
518	2 c. As No. 505	50	1·50
519	5 c. As No. 506	50	1·50
	a. Booklet pane. Nos. 519/22 *se-tenant* ..	1·75	
520	10 c. As No. 507	50	1·50
521	25 c. As No. 508	50	1·50
522	35 c. As No. 509	50	1·50
523	45 c. As No. 510	50	1·50
	a. Booklet pane. Nos. 523/6 *se-tenant* ..	1·75	
524	75 c. As No. 511	50	1·50
525	$1 As No. 512	50	1·50
526	$2 As No. 513	50	1·50
515/26	.. .. *Set of* 12	5·00	15·00

*The normal sideways watermark shows Crown to left of CA on the 45 c., and to the right of CA on others, *as seen from the back of the stamp.*

Nos. 502/13 were each issued in sheets of ten stamps and two *se-tenant* labels.

91 Grant of Arms

(Des G. Drummond. Litho Questa)

1977 (12 May). *Centenary of Windward Is Diocese. T* **91** *and similar horiz designs. Multicoloured. W* w **14** (*sideways*). *P* 13½.

527	15 c. Type **91**	10	10
528	35 c. Bishop Berkeley and mitres	10	10
529	45 c. Map and arms of diocese	10	10
530	$1.25, St. George's Cathedral and Bishop Woodroffe	30	55
527/30	.. .. *Set of* 4	45	60

CARNIVAL 1977

JUNE 25TH-JULY 5TH

(92)

1977 (2 June). *Kingstown Carnival. Nos. 426, 429, 432/3 and 440 optd with T* **92**.

531	5 c. French Grunt	10	10
	a. Red opt	35·00	
	b. Hyphen omitted	1·40	
	w. Wmk Crown to right of CA	28·00	

532 10 c. Sperm Whale (R.) 10 10
a. Opt double (R. and Blk.) 50·00
b. Hyphen omitted 1·60
533 15 c. Skipjack Tuna (R.) 10 10
a. Black opt 35·00
b. Hyphen omitted 2·00
534 20 c. Queen Angelfish (R.) 10 10
a. Opt inverted 17·00
b. Black opt 40·00
c. Hyphen omitted 2·25
535 $1 Queen Triggerfish 40 70
a. Red opt 50·00
b. Hyphen omitted 3·50
531/5 *Set of* 5 70 95

The variety showing the hyphen omitted from the second line of the overprint occurred on R. 4/4 of the lower pane.

Imprint dates: "1975", Nos. 531/2, 534/5; "1976", Nos. 532/5; "1977", Nos. 531, 533.

93 Guide and Emblem

CARIBBEAN
VISIT 1977

(94)

(Des PAD Studio. Litho J.W.)

1977 (1 Sept). *50th Anniv of St. Vincent Girl Guides. T* **93** *and similar vert designs. The $2 value is additionally optd. "1930–1977". Multicoloured. W w* **14.** *P* 13½.

536 5 c. Type **93** 10 10
537 15 c. Early uniform, ranger, guide and brownie 15 10
w. Wmk inverted 10·00
538 20 c. Early uniform and guide 15 10
539 $2 Lady Baden-Powell 50 90
a. Optd dates omitted 15·00
b. Optd dates double 50·00
536/9 *Set of* 4 75 1·00

1977 (27 Oct). *Royal Visit. No.* 513 *optd with T* **94**.

540 $2 Queen Elizabeth leaving Westminster Abbey 30 30
a. Opt inverted 35·00
w. Wmk Crown to left of CA 22·00

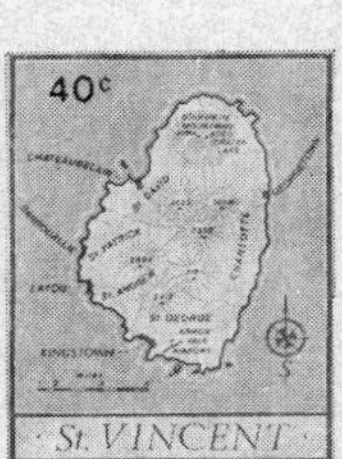

95 Map of St. Vincent **96** Opening Verse and Scene

(Des G. Drummond. Litho Questa)

1977–78. *Provisionals. W w* **12.** *P* 14½ × 14.

541 **95** 20 c. blk, dull violet-bl & pale bl (31.1.78) 15 15
542 40 c. black, dull orange & flesh (30.11.77) 25 20
a. Black (value) omitted 17·00
543 40 c. black, magenta and salmon (31.1.78) 20 15
541/3 *Set of* 3 55 45

Nos. 541/3 were printed in 1974, without value, for provisional use; they were locally surcharged before going on sale.

(Des Jennifer Toombs. Litho Enschedé)

1977 (1 Dec). *Christmas. Scenes and Verses from the carol "While Shepherds Watched their Flocks by Night". T* **96** *and similar vert designs. Multicoloured. W w* **14.** *P* 13 × 11.

544 5 c. Type **96** 10 10
545 10 c. Angel consoling shepherds 10 10
546 15 c. View of Bethlehem 10 10
547 25 c. Nativity scene 10 10
548 50 c. Throng of Angels 10 10
549 $1.25, Praising God 30 65
544/9 *Set of* 6 50 85
MS550 150 × 170 mm. Nos. 544/9. P 13½ 90 1·75

97 *Cynthia cardui* and *Bougainvillea glabra var. alba*

(Des Daphne Padden. Litho Walsall)

1978 (6 Apr). *Butterflies and Bougainvilleas. T* **97** *and similar horiz designs. Multicoloured. W w* **14** *(sideways). P* 14.

551 5 c. Type **97** 15 10
552 25 c. *Dione juno* and "Golden Glow" 20 10
553 40 c. *Anartia amathea* and "Mrs McLean" 30 10
554 50 c. *Hypolimnas misippus* and "Cyphen" 35 10
555 $1.25, *Pseudolycaena marsyas* and "Thomasii" 70 70
551/5 *Set of* 5 1·60 90

(Des G. Drummond. Litho J.W.)

1978 (2 June). *25th Anniv of Coronation. Horiz designs as Nos.* 422/5 *of Montserrat. Multicoloured. W w* **14** *(sideways). P* 13.

556 40 c. Westminster Abbey 10 10
557 50 c. Gloucester Cathedral 10 10
558 $1.25, Durham Cathedral 15 15
559 $2.50, Exeter Cathedral 15 25
556/9 *Set of* 4 30 45
MS560 130 × 102 mm. Nos. 556/9. P 13½ × 14 40 85

Nos. 556/9 were each printed in sheets of ten stamps and two *se-tenant* labels.

98 Rotary International Emblem and Motto **99** "Co-operation in Education Leads to Mutual Understanding and Respect"

(Des G. Hutchins. Litho Questa)

1978 (13 July). *International Service Clubs. T* **98** *and similar horiz designs showing club emblems and mottoes. Multicoloured. W w* **14** *(sideways). P* 14½.

561 40 c. Type **98** 15 10
562 50 c. Lions International 15 10
563 $1 Jaycees 35 50
561/3 *Set of* 3 60 55

(Des G. Hutchins. Litho Questa)

1978 (7 Sept). *10th Anniv of Project School to School (St. Vincent-Canada school twinning project). T* **99** *and similar multicoloured design showing flags and blackboard. W w* **14** *(sideways on $2). P* 14.

564 40 c. Type **99** 10 10
565 $2 "Co-operation in Education Leads to the Elimination of Racial Intolerance" (*horiz*) 40 50

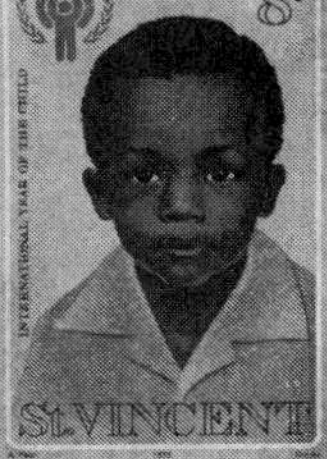

100 Arnos Vale Airport **101** Young Child

(Des G. Drummond. Litho Questa)

1978 (19 Oct). *75th Anniv of Powered Flight. T* **100** *and similar horiz designs. Multicoloured. W w* **14** *(sideways). P* 14½ × 14.

566 10 c. Type **100** 10 10
567 40 c. Wilbur Wright landing Wright Flyer I 15 10
568 50 c. Orville Wright in Wright Flyer III 15 10
569 $1.25, Orville Wright and Wright Flyer I airborne 45 35
566/9 *Set of* 4 70 45

(Des A. Paish. Litho Questa)

1979 (14 Feb). *International Year of the Child. T* **101** *and similar vert designs showing portraits of young children. W w* **14.** *P* 14 × 13½.

570 8 c. black, gold and pale yellow-green 10 10
571 20 c. black, gold and pale rose-lilac 10 10
572 50 c. black, gold and pale violet-blue 15 10
573 $2 black, gold and flesh 50 50
570/3 *Set of* 4 75 55

10c+5c

SOUFRIERE
RELIEF
FUND 1979

(102)

103 Sir Rowland Hill

(Des G. Drummond. Litho Questa)

1979 (17 Apr). *Soufrière Eruption Relief Fund. Designs as T* **95** *but surchd as T* **102** *by Reliance Printery, Kingstown. W w* **12.** *P* 14½ × 14.

574 10 c. + 5 c. violet-blue and pale rose-lilac 10 15
575 50 c. + 25 c. yellow-brown and buff 20 20
576 $1 + 50 c. reddish brown and brownish grey 25 30
577 $2 + $1 deep green and apple-green 40 50
574/7 *Set of* 4 75 1·00

(Des J.W. Litho Harrison)

1979 (31 May). *Death Centenary of Sir Rowland Hill. T* **103** *and similar horiz designs. Multicoloured. W w* **14** *(sideways*). P* 14.

578 40 c. Type **103** 15 10
579 50 c. Penny Black and Twopenny Blue stamps 15 15
580 $3 1861 1d. and 6d. stamps 40 1·10
578/80 *Set of* 3 60 1·25
MS581 170×123 mm. Nos. 578/80, 594/5 and 599 (see footnote after No. 601) 1·40 2·50
w. Wmk Crown to right of CA 35·00

*The normal sideways watermark shows Crown to left of CA, *as seen from the back of the stamp.*

Nos. 578/80 were each printed in sheets including two *se-tenant* stamp-size labels.

104 First and Latest Buccament Postmarks and Map of St. Vincent

ST VINCENT AND
THE GRENADINES
AIR SERVICE 1979

(105)

(Des J.W. Litho Harrison)

1979 (31 May–1 Sept). *St. Vincent Post Offices. Horiz designs as T* **104** *showing first and latest postmarks and map of St. Vincent. Multicoloured. W w* **14** *(sideways*). With imprint date. P* 14.

582 1 c. Type **104** 10 10
583 2 c. Sion Hill 10 10
584 3 c. Cumberland 10 10
585 4 c. Questelles 10 10
586 5 c. Layou 10 10
w. Wmk Crown to right of CA 32·00
587 6 c. New Ground 10 10
588 8 c. Mesopotamia 10 10
589 10 c. Troumaca 10 10
590 12 c. Arnos Vale 15 10
591 15 c. Stubbs 15 10
592 20 c. Orange Hill 15 10
593 25 c. Calliaqua 15 10
594 40 c. Edinboro 25 20
595 40 c. Colonarie 30 25
596 80 c. Biabou 40 35
597 $1 Chateaubelair 50 50
598 $2 Head P.O., Kingstown 60 80
599 $3 Barrouallie 75 1·25
600 $5 Georgetown 1·25 2·00
601 $10 Kingstown 2·25 4·00
582/601 *Set of* 20 6·50 9·00

*The normal sideways watermark shows Crown to left of CA, *as seen from the back of the stamp.*

Dates of issue:—40, 50 c., $3 (from No. **MS**581 and booklets only) 31.5.79; others, and 40, 50 c., $3 from sheets, 1.9.79.

Imprint dates: "1979", Nos. 582/601; "1981", No. 597; "1982", Nos. 586, 589, 593.

See also Nos. **MS**581 and **MS**637.

1979 (6 Aug). *Opening of St. Vincent and the Grenadines Air Service. No.* 566 *optd with T* **105,** *in red, by Reliance Printery, Kingstown.*

602 10 c. Type **100** 10 10
w. Wmk Crown to right of CA 35·00 10·00

*The normal sideways watermark shows Crown to left of CA, *as seen from the back of the stamp.*

INDEPENDENT

106 National Flag and *Ixora coccinea* (flower)

(Des J.W. Litho Enschedé)

1979 (27 Oct). *Independence. T* **106** *and similar horiz designs. Multicoloured. W w* **14** *(sideways*). P* 12½×12.

603 20 c. Type **106** 15 10
604 50 c. House of Assembly and *Ixora stricta* (flower) 20 10
w. Wmk Crown to right of CA 5·00
605 80 c. Prime Minister R. Milton Cato and *Ixora williamsii* (flower) 25 20
603/5 *Set of* 3 55 30

*The normal sideways watermark shows Crown to left of CA, *as seen from the back of the stamp.*

INDEPENDENCE 1979

(107)

1979 (27 Oct). *Independence. Nos.* 422, 425/30, 432, 434, 437/40, 441a *and* 443 *optd with T* **107**, *by Letchworth Press, Barbados.*

606 1 c. Type **79** 10 10
607 4 c. Spanish Mackerel 10 10
608 5 c. French Grunt 10 10
609 6 c. Spotted Goatfish 10 10
610 8 c. Ballyhoo 10 10
611 10 c. Sperm Whale 15 15
612 12 c. Humpback Whale 15 15
613 15 c. Skipjack Tuna 15 15
614 25 c. Princess Parrotfish 20 20
615 50 c. Porkfish 35 35
616 70 c. Yellow-finned Tuna 45 45
617 90 c. Pompano 60 50
618 $1 Queen Triggerfish 60 50
619 $2.50, Sailfish (II) .. .. .. 1·25 1·00
a. Opt inverted £100
b. Optd on Type I (No. 441) .. .. 9·00 9·00
620 $10 Blue Marlin .. .. 2·75 4·25
606/20 .. .. *Set of* 15 6·00 7·00

Imprint dates: "1975", Nos. 606/10, 612, 614/15, 619b, 620; "1976", Nos. 607, 616/19; "1977", Nos. 606, 608/10, 612/13, 615, 620; "1978", No. 611; "1979", Nos. 607/8, 610, 614, 618, 620.

108 Virgin and Child

109 *Polistes cinctus* (wasp) and Oleander

(Des Jennifer Toombs. Litho Questa)

1979 (1 Nov). *Christmas. Scenes and Verses from the carol "Silent Night". T* **108** *and similar horiz designs. Multicoloured. W w* **14** *(sideways). P* 13½.

621 10 c. Type **108** 10 10
622 20 c. Jesus in manger 10 10
623 25 c. Shepherds 10 10
624 40 c. Angel 10 10
625 50 c. Angels with infant Jesus 10 10
626 $2 Nativity scene 40 45
621/6 .. .. *Set of* 6 55 60
MS627 151 × 170 mm. Nos. 621/6 .. .. 70 1·25

(Des J.W. Litho Walsall)

1979 (13 Dec). *Flowers and Insects. T* **109** *and similar vert designs showing insects and different varieties of Oleander flower. Multicoloured. W w* **14**. *P* 14.

628 5 c. Type **109** 10 10
629 10 c. *Pyrophorus noctiluca* (click beetle) .. 10 10
630 25 c. *Stagmomantis limbata* (mantid) .. 10 10
631 50 c. *Psiloptera lampetis* (beetle) .. 10 10
632 $2 *Diaprepies abbreviatus* (weevil) .. 30 30
628/32 .. .. *Set of* 5 50 40

(Des and litho D.L.R.)

1980 (28 Feb). *Centenary of St. Vincent "Arms" Stamps. Sheet* 116×72 *mm containing designs as T* **31**. *W w* **14** *(sideways**). *P* 14×13½.

MS633 116×72 mm. 50 c. reddish brown; $1 deep grey-green; $2.50 deep blue 50 75
w. Wmk Crown to left of CA .. .. 11·00

*The normal sideways watermark shows Crown to right of CA, *as seen from the back of the stamp.*

110 Queen Elizabeth II

(Des J.W. Litho Harrison)

1980 (24 Apr). *"London 1980" International Stamp Exhibition. T* **110** *and similar horiz designs. Multicoloured. W w* **14** *(sideways). P* 14.

634 80 c. Type **110** 15 20
635 $1 Great Britain 1954 3d. and St. Vincent 1954 5 c. definitive stamps 20 30
636 $2 Unadopted postage stamp design of 1971 35 60
634/6 .. .. *Set of* 3 60 1·00
MS637 165 × 115 mm. Nos. 596/8 and 634/6 .. 75 1·50

Nos. 634/6 were each printed in sheets containing 2 *se-tenant* stamp-size labels.

MINIMUM PRICE

The minimum price quote is 10p which represents a handling charge rather than a basis for valuing common stamps. For further notes about prices see introductory pages.

111 Steel Band

112 Football

(Des G. Drummond. Litho Questa)

1980 (12 June). *Kingstown Carnival. T* **111** *and similar horiz design. Multicoloured. W w* **14** *(sideways). P* 13½ × 14.

638 20 c. Type **111** 15 30
a. Pair. Nos. 638/9 .. .. .. 30 60
639 20 c. Steel band (*different*) 15 30

Nos. 638/9 were printed together, *se-tenant*, in horizontal and vertical pairs throughout the sheet.

(Des Polygraphic. Litho Rosenbaum Bros, Vienna)

1980 (7 Aug). *"Sport for All". T* **112** *and similar vert designs. Multicoloured. W w* **14** *(inverted). P* 13½.

640 10 c. Type **112** 10 10
w. Wmk upright .. .. .. 20·00
641 60 c. Cycling 30 15
642 80 c. Basketball 40 40
643 $2.50, Boxing .. .. 40 1·25
640/3 .. .. *Set of* 4 1·10 1·60

HURRICANE
RELIEF
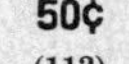
50¢

(113)

114 Brazilian Agouti

1980 (7 Aug). *Hurricane Relief. As Nos.* 640/3, *but W w* **14** *(upright), surch with T* **113**.

644 10 c. + 50 c. Type **112** 15 15
645 60 c. + 50 c. Cycling 20 25
646 80 c. + 50 c. Basketball 35 40
w. Wmk inverted .. .. .. 20·00
647 $2.50 + 50 c. Boxing 40 85
w. Wmk inverted .. .. .. 20·00
644/7 .. .. *Set of* 4 1·00 1·50

(Des L. Curtis. Litho Questa)

1980 (2 Oct). *Wildlife. T* **114** *and similar horiz designs. Multicoloured. W w* **14** *(sideways). P* 14 × 14½.

648 25 c. Type **114**.. .. .. .. 10 10
649 50 c. Giant Toad 15 10
650 $2 Small Indian Mongoose 40 55
648/50 .. .. *Set of* 3 60 60

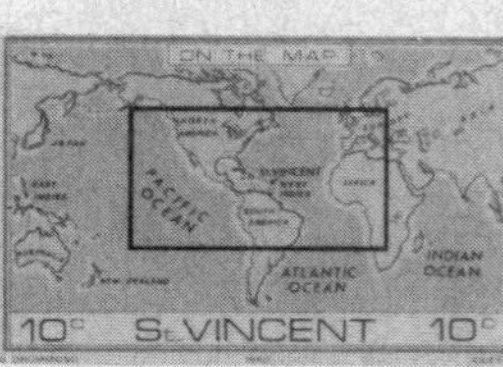

115 Map of World showing St. Vincent

116 *Ville de Paris* (French ship of the line), 1782

(Des G. Drummond. Litho Questa)

1980 (4 Dec). *St. Vincent "On the Map". T* **115** *and similar designs depicting maps showing St. Vincent. Multicoloured. W w* **14** *(sideways). P* 13½ × 14.

651 10 c. Type **115** 10 10
652 50 c. Western hemisphere 15 10
653 $1 Central America 30 15
654 $2 St. Vincent 50 30
651/4 .. .. *Set of* 4 90 50
MS655 143 × 95 mm. No. 654. P 12 .. .. 50 75

(Des J.W. Litho Rosenbaum Bros, Vienna)

1981 (19 Feb). *Sailing Ships. T* **116** *and similar vert designs. Multicoloured. W w* **14**. *P* 13½.

656 50 c. Type **116** 55 20
657 60 c. H.M.S. *Ramillies* (ship of the line), 1782 .. .. 60 40
658 $1.50, H.M.S. *Providence* (sloop), 1793 1·25 1·75
659 $2 *Dee* (paddle-steamer packet) .. .. 1·50 2·00
656/9 .. .. *Set of* 4 3·50 4·00

117 Arrowroot Cultivation

(Des G. Drummond. Litho Format)

1981 (21 May). *Agriculture. T* **117** *and similar horiz designs. Multicoloured. W w* **14** *(sideways). P* 14.

660 25 c. Type **117** 10 15
a. Pair. Nos. 660/1 .. .. .. 20 30
661 25 c. Arrowroot processing 10 15
662 50 c. Banana cultivation 15 25
a. Pair. Nos. 662/3 .. .. .. 30 50
663 50 c. Banana export packaging station .. 15 25
664 60 c. Coconut plantation 15 30
a. Pair. Nos. 664/5 .. .. .. 30 60
665 60 c. Copra drying frames 15 30
666 $1 Cocoa cultivation 30 45
a. Pair. Nos. 666/7 .. .. .. 60 90
667 $1 Cocoa beans and sun drying frames .. 30 45
660/7 .. .. *Set of* 8 1·25 2·00

The two designs of each value were printed together, *se-tenant*, in horizontal and vertical pairs throughout the sheet.

(Des D. Shults. Litho Questa)

1981 (17 July–26 Nov). *Royal Wedding. Horiz designs as T* **26/7** *of Kiribati. Multicoloured. (a) W w* **15**. *P* 14.

668 60 c. *Isabella* 15 15
b. Sheetlet. No. 668×6 and No. 669 .. 1·10
669 60 c. Prince Charles and Lady Diana Spencer 30 30
670 $2.50, *Alberta* (tender) 30 30
aw. Wmk inverted .. .. .. 13·00
b. Sheetlet. No. 670×6 and No. 671 .. 2·50
bw. Wmk inverted £100
671 $2.50, As No. 669 .. .. .. 70 70
aw. Wmk inverted .. .. .. 40·00
672 $4 *Britannia* 35 40
aw. Wmk inverted .. .. .. 13·00
b. Sheetlet. No. 672×6 and No. 673 .. 2·75
bw. Wmk inverted £100
673 $4 As No. 669 .. .. 1·00 1·25
aw. Wmk inverted .. .. .. 40·00
668/73 .. .. *Set of* 6 2·50 2·75
MS674 120×109 mm. $5 As No. 669. Wmk sideways. P 12 (26 Nov) 75 75

(*b*) *Booklet stamps. No wmk. P* 12 (26 Nov)

675 60 c. As No. 668 .. .. 15 25
a. Booklet pane. No. 675×4 with margins all round 50
676 $2.50, As No. 671 .. .. .. 65 1·25
a. Booklet pane. No. 676×2 with margins all round .. .. 1·25

Nos. 668/73 were printed in sheetlets of seven stamps of the same face value, each containing six of the "Royal Yacht" design and one of the larger design showing Prince Charles and Lady Diana.

Nos. 675/6 come from $9.80 stamp booklets.

118 Kingstown General Post Office 119

(Des G. Drummond. Litho Questa)

1981 (1 Sept). *U.P.U. Membership. W w* **14** *(sideways). P* 14.

677 **118** $2 multicoloured 40 90
a. Horiz pair. Nos. 677/8 .. .. 80 1·75
678 **119** $2 multicoloured 40 90

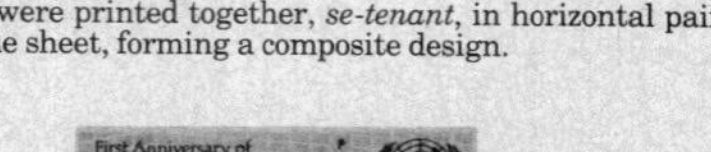

Nos. 677/8 were printed together, *se-tenant*, in horizontal pairs throughout the sheet, forming a composite design.

120 St. Vincent Flag with Flags of other U.N. Member Nations

(Des L. Curtis. Litho Format)

1981 (11 Sept). *First Anniv of U.N. Membership. T* **120** *and similar horiz design. Multicoloured. W w* **14** *(sideways). P* 13½ × 14.

679 $1.50, Type **120** 35 25
680 $2.50, Prime Minister Robert Milton Cato .. 55 50

Nos. 679/80 are inscribed "ST. VINCENT and the GRENADINES" and were each printed in small sheets of 6 including one *se-tenant* stamp-size label.

121 Silhouettes of Figures at Old Testament Reading, and Bible Extract

(Des Jennifer Toombs. Litho Security Printers (M), Malaysia)

1981 (19 Nov). *Christmas. T* **121** *and similar horiz designs showing silhouettes of figures. Multicoloured. W w* **14** *(sideways**). *P* 12.

681 50 c. Type **121** 15 10
682 60 c. Madonna, and angel 15 10
w. Wmk Crown to left of CA 80

683 $1 Madonna, and Bible extract 25 25
w. Wmk Crown to left of CA .. .. 1·40
684 $2 Joseph and Mary travelling to Bethlehem 50 50
w. Wmk Crown to left of CA .. .. 2·25
681/4 .. .. *Set of* 4 95 85
MS685 129×127 mm. Nos. 681/4. P 13½ .. 95 1·40
w. Wmk Crown to right of CA .. .. 4·50

*The normal sideways watermark shows Crown to left of CA, *as seen from the back of the stamp*, on the 50 c. and the miniature sheet but to right on the other values.

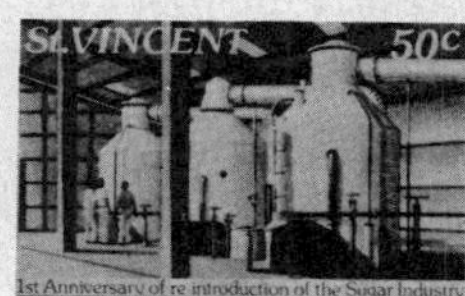

122 Sugar Boilers

(Des L. Curtis. Litho Format)

1982 (5 Apr). *First Anniv of Re-introduction of Sugar Industry. T* **122** *and similar horiz designs. Multicoloured.* W w **14** (*sideways*). *P* 14.
686 50 c. Type **122** 25 15
687 60 c. Sugar drying plant 25 20
688 $1.50, Sugar mill machinery 55 75
689 $2 Crane loading sugar cane .. .. .. 75 1·00
686/9 .. .. *Set of* 4 1·60 1·90

123 Butterfly Float

124 Augusta of Saxe-Gotha, Princess of Wales, 1736

(Des G. Vasarhelyi. Photo Heraclio Fournier)

1982 (10 June). *Carnival* 1982. *T* **123** *and similar multicoloured designs. P* 13½.
690 50 c. Type **123** 20 15
691 60 c. Angel dancer (*vert*) 20 15
692 $1.50, Winged dancer (*vert*) 50 80
693 $2 Eagle float .. .. 70 1·50
690/3 .. .. *Set of* 4 1·50 2·40

(Des D. Shults and J. Cooter. Litho Format)

1982 (1 July). *21st Birthday of Princess of Wales. T* **124** *and similar vert designs. Multicoloured.* W w **15**. *P* 13½×14.
694 50 c. Type **124** 15 20
w. Wmk inverted 50
695 60 c. Coat of arms of Augusta of Saxe-Gotha 15 25
w. Wmk inverted 75
696 $6 Diana, Princess of Wales .. .. .. 70 1·25
w. Wmk inverted .. .. 3·50
694/6 .. .. *Set of* 3 90 1·50

125 Scout Emblem

126 De Havilland D.H.60G Gipsy Moth

(Des L. Curtis. Litho Questa)

1982 (15 July). *75th Anniv of Boy Scout Movement. T* **125** *and similar vert design. Multicoloured.* W w **14**. *P* 14.
697 $1.50, Type **125** .. .. 70 1·00
698 $2.50, 75th anniv emblem .. .. 90 1·50

1982 (19 July). *Birth of Prince William of Wales. Nos.* 694/6 *optd with T* **19** *of St. Kitts.*
699 50 c. Type **124** 15 20
700 60 c. Coat of arms of Augusta of Saxe-Gotha 15 25
a. Opt inverted .. .. 30·00
w. Wmk inverted .. .. 7·00
701 $6 Diana, Princess of Wales .. .. .. 70 1·50
a. Opt double .. .. 11·00
w. Wmk inverted .. .. 9·00
699/701 .. .. *Set of* 3 90 1·75

(Des A. Theobald. Litho Questa)

1982 (29 July). *50th Anniv of Airmail Service. T* **126** *and similar horiz designs. Multicoloured.* W w **14** (*sideways*). *P* 14.
702 50 c. Type **126** 55 30
703 60 c. Grumman G.21 Goose, 1952 .. .. 65 40
704 $1.50, Hawker Siddeley H.S.748, 1968 .. 1·25 1·50
705 $2 Britten Norman "long nose" Trislander, 1982 .. .. 1·40 2·00
702/5 .. .. *Set of* 4 3·50 3·75

127 *Geestport* (freighter)

(Des G. Drummond. Litho Format)

1982 (27 Dec). *Ships. T* **127** *and similar horiz designs. Multicoloured.* W w **14** (*sideways*). *P* 14.
706 45 c. Type **127** 40 25
707 60 c. *Stella Oceanis* (liner) 50 40
708 $1.50, *Victoria* (liner) .. .. 95 1·50
709 $2 *Queen Elizabeth 2* (liner) .. .. .. 1·25 2·00
706/9 .. .. *Set of* 4 2·75 3·75

128 *Pseudocorynactis caribbeorum*

(Des McCombie-De Bay. Litho Security Printers (M), Malaysia)

1983 (10 Feb). *Marine Life. T* **128** *and similar multicoloured designs.* W w **14** (*sideways** *on* 60 *c.*, $1.50, $2). *P* 12.
710 50 c. Type **128** 65 25
711 60 c. *Actinoporus elegans* (*vert*) 75 40
712 $1.50, *Arachnanthus nocturnus* (*vert*) .. 1·40 1·75
w. Wmk Crown to left of CA .. .. .. 5·50
713 $2 Reid's Seahorse (*vert*) .. .. .. 1·60 2·00
710/13 .. .. *Set of* 4 4·00 4·00

*The normal sideways watermark shows Crown to right of CA, *as seen fron the back of the stamp.*

129 Satellite View of St. Vincent

45¢ ▬

(**130**)

(Des R. Vigurs. Litho Questa)

1983 (14 Mar). *Commonwealth Day. T* **129** *and similar horiz designs. Multicoloured.* W w **14** (*sideways*). *P* 14.
714 45 c. Type **129** 15 20
715 60 c. Flag of St. Vincent 20 25
716 $1.50, Prime Minister R. Milton Cato .. 30 65
717 $2 Harvesting bananas 45 90
714/17 .. .. *Set of* 4 1·00 1·75

Nos. 714/17 are inscribed "St. Vincent & The Grenadines".

1983 (26 Apr). *No.* 681 *surch with T* **130** *by Reliance Printery, Kingstown.*
718 45 c. on 50 c. Type **121** 40 30

131 Symbolic Handshake

132 Sir William Smith (founder)

(Des J.W. Litho Security Printers (M), Malaysia)

1983 (6 July). *10th Anniv of Treaty of Chaguaramas. T* **131** *and similar vert designs. Multicoloured.* W w **14** (*sideways*). *P* 11½ × 12.
719 45 c. Type **131** 25 20
w. Wmk Crown to left of CA .. .. .. 3·00
720 60 c. Commerce emblem 30 30
w. Wmk Crown to left of CA .. .. .. 3·00
721 $1.50 Caribbean map .. .. 60 1·00
722 $2 Flags of member countries and map of St. Vincent .. .. 85 1·25
719/22 .. .. *Set of* 4 1·75 2·50

*The normal sideways watermark shows Crown to right of CA, *as seen from the back of the stamp.*

(Des L. Curtis. Litho Security Printers (M), Malaysia)

1983 (6 Oct). *Centenary of Boys' Brigade. T* **132** *and similar vert designs. Multicoloured.* W w **14**. *P* 12 × 11½.
723 45 c. Type **132** 25 25
724 60 c. On parade 30 35
725 $1.50, Craftwork .. .. 70 1·10
726 $2 Community service .. .. 95 1·60
723/6 .. .. *Set of* 4 2·00 3·00

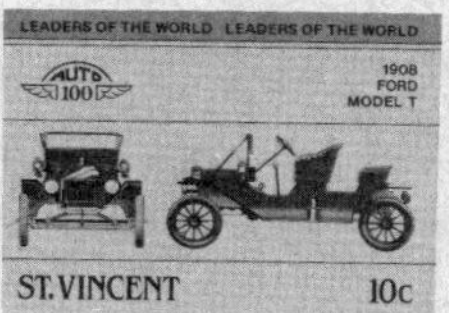

133 Ford "Model T" (1908)

(Des J.W. Litho Format)

1983 (25 Oct). *Leaders of the World. Automobiles (1st series). T* **133** *and similar horiz designs, the first in each pair showing technical drawings and the second paintings. P* 12½.
727 10 c. multicoloured 10 10
a. Vert pair. Nos. 727/8 .. .. .. 10 10
728 10 c. multicoloured 10 10
729 60 c. multicoloured 15 15
a. Vert pair. Nos. 729/30 .. .. .. 30 30
730 60 c. multicoloured 15 15
731 $1.50, multicoloured 15 20
a. Vert pair. Nos. 731/2 .. .. .. 30 40
732 $1.50, multicoloured 15 20
733 $1.50, multicoloured 15 20
a. Vert pair. Nos. 733/4 .. .. .. 30 40
734 $1.50, multicoloured 15 20
735 $2 multicoloured 20 30
a. Vert pair. Nos. 735/6 .. .. .. 40 60
736 $2 multicoloured 20 30
737 $2 multicoloured 20 30
a. Vert pair. Nos. 737/8 .. .. .. 40 60
738 $2 multicoloured 20 30
727/38 .. .. *Set of* 12 1·60 2·25

Designs:—Nos. 727/8, Ford "Model T" (1908); 729/30, Supercharged Cord "812" (1937); 731/2, Citroen "Open Tourer" (1937); 733/4, Mercedes Benz "300SL Gull-Wing" (1954); 735/6, Rolls-Royce "Phantom I" (1925); 737/8, Ferrari "Boxer 512BB" (1976).

Nos. 727/8, 729/30, 731/2, 733/4, 735/6 and 737/8 were printed together, *se-tenant*, in vertical pairs throughout the sheets.

See also Nos. 820/9, 862/7, 884/92 and 959/70.

134 Appearance of the Nativity Star

(Des Jennifer Toombs. Litho Security Printers (M), Malaysia)

1983 (15 Nov). *Christmas. T* **134** *and similar horiz designs showing the Shepherds.* W w **14**. *P* 12.
739 10 c. Type **134** 10 10
740 50 c. Message of the Angel 20 10
741 $1.50, The Heavenly Host 50 65
742 $2.40, Worshipping Jesus .. .. .. 75 1·00
739/42 .. .. *Set of* 4 1·40 1·60
MS743 130×130 mm. Nos. 739/42. Wmk sideways .. .. 1·25 1·75

135 *King Henry VIII*

(Des J.W. Litho Format)

1983 (8 Dec). *Leaders of the World. Railway Locomotives (1st series). T* **135** *and similar horiz designs, the first in each pair showing technical drawings and the second the locomotive at work. P* 12½.
744 10 c. multicoloured 10 10
a. Vert pair. Nos. 744/5 .. .. .. 10 10
745 10 c. multicoloured 10 10
746 10 c. multicoloured 10 10
a. Vert pair. Nos. 746/7 .. .. .. 10 10
747 10 c. multicoloured 10 10
748 25 c. multicoloured 10 10
a. Vert pair. Nos. 748/9 .. .. .. 15 20
749 25 c. multicoloured 10 10
750 50 c. multicoloured 15 20
a. Vert pair. Nos. 750/1 .. .. .. 30 40
751 50 c. multicoloured 15 20
752 60 c. multicoloured 15 20
a. Vert pair Nos. 752/3 .. .. .. 30 40
753 60 c. multicoloured 15 20
754 75 c. multicoloured 15 25
a. Vert pair. Nos. 754/5 .. .. .. 30 50
755 75 c. multicoloured 15 25

756	$2.50, multicoloured	30	55
	a. Vert pair. Nos. 756/7	60	1·10
757	$2.50, multicoloured	30	55
758	$3 multicoloured	35	70
	a. Vert pair. Nos. 758/9	70	1·40
759	$3 multicoloured	35	70
744/59	*Set of* 16	2·25	3·75

Designs:—Nos. 744/5, *King Henry VIII*, Great Britain (1927); 746/7, *Royal Scots Greys*, Great Britain (1961); 748/9, *Hagley Hall*, Great Britain (1928); 750/1, *Sir Lancelot*, Great Britain (1926); 752/3 Class "B12", Great Britain (1912); 754/5, Deeley "Compound" type, Great Britain (1902); 756/7, *Cheshire*, Great Britain (1927); 758/9, Bullied "Austerity" Class Q1, Great Britain (1942).

Nos. 744/59 were issued in a similar sheet format to Nos. 727/38.

See also Nos. 792/807, 834/41, 872/83, 893/904 and 1001/8.

136 Fort Duvernette

(Des Walsall. Litho Questa)

1984 (13 Feb). *Fort Duvernette. T* **136** *and similar horiz designs. Multicoloured. W w* **15** *(sideways). P* 14 × 14½.

760	35 c. Type **136**	20	30
761	45 c. Soldiers on fortifications	25	30
762	$1 Cannon facing bay	40	60
763	$3 Map of St. Vincent and mortar	1·25	1·75
760/3	*Set of* 4	1·90	2·75

137 White Frangipani

(Des J. Cooter. Litho Harrison)

1984 (2 Apr). *Flowering Trees and Shrubs. T* **137** *and similar horiz designs. Multicoloured. W w* **14** *(sideways*). P* 13½×14.

764	5 c. Type **137**	20	10
765	10 c. Genip	25	10
766	15 c. Immortelle	30	10
767	20 c. Pink Poui	40	10
768	25 c. Buttercup	50	10
769	35 c. Sandbox	65	20
770	45 c. Locust	80	25
771	60 c. Colville's Glory	1·00	60
772	75 c. Lignum Vitae	1·00	75
773	$1 Golden Shower	1·00	1·00
	w. Wmk Crown to right of CA	20·00	
774	$5 Angelin	4·00	9·00
775	$10 Roucou	5·50	15·00
764/75	*Set of* 12	14·00	24·00

*The normal sideways watermark shows Crown to left of CA, *as seen from the back of the stamp.*

138 Trench Warfare, First World War

139 Musical Fantasy Costume

(Des Court House Studio. Litho Format)

1984 (25 Apr). *Leaders of the World. British Monarchs. T* **138** *and similar vert designs. Multicoloured. P* 12½.

776	1 c. Type **138**	10	10
	a. Horiz pair. Nos. 776/7	10	10
777	1 c. George V and trenches	10	10
778	5 c. Battle of Bannockburn	10	10
	a. Horiz pair. Nos. 778/9	10	10
779	5 c. Edward II and battle	10	10
780	60 c. George V	20	20
	a. Horiz pair. Nos. 780/1	40	40
781	60 c. York Cottage, Sandringham	20	20
782	75 c. Edward II	20	20
	a. Horiz pair. Nos. 782/3	40	40
783	75 c. Berkeley Castle	20	20
784	$1 Coat of arms of Edward II	20	25
	a. Horiz pair. Nos. 784/5	40	50
785	$1 Edward II (*different*)	20	25
786	$4 Coat of arms of George V	50	60
	a. Horiz pair. Nos. 786/7	1·00	1·10
787	$4 George V and Battle of Jutland	50	60
776/87	*Set of* 12	2·00	2·25

Nos. 776/7, 778/9, 780/1, 782/3, 784/5 and 786/7 were printed together, *se-tenant*, in horizontal pairs throughout the sheets, each pair forming a composite design.

(Des G. Vasarhelyi. Litho Questa)

1984 (25 June). *Carnival 1984. T* **139** *and similar horiz designs showing Carnival costumes. Multicoloured. W w* **15** *(sideways). P* 14.

788	35 c. Type **139**	15	15
789	45 c. African princess	20	20
790	$1 Market woman	40	40
791	$3 Carib hieroglyph	1·25	1·75
788/91	*Set of* 4	1·75	2·25

IMPERFORATES AND MISSING COLOURS. Various issues between Nos. 792 and 1132 exist either imperforate or with colours omitted. Such items are not listed as there is no evidence that they fulfil the criteria outlined on page xi of this catalogue.

(Des J.W. Litho Format)

1984 (27 July). *Leaders of the World. Railway Locomotives (2nd series). Horiz designs as T* **135**, *the first in each pair showing technical drawings and the second the locomotive at work. P* 12½.

792	1 c. multicoloured	10	10
	a. Vert pair. Nos. 792/3	10	10
793	1 c. multicoloured	10	10
794	2 c. multicoloured	10	10
	a. Vert pair. Nos. 794/5	10	10
795	2 c. multicoloured	10	10
796	3 c. multicoloured	10	10
	a. Vert pair. Nos. 796/7	10	10
797	3 c. multicoloured	10	10
798	50 c. multicoloured	20	30
	a. Vert pair. Nos. 798/9	40	60
799	50 c. multicoloured	20	30
800	75 c. multicoloured	25	35
	a. Vert pair. Nos. 800/1	50	70
801	75 c. multicoloured	25	35
802	$1 multicoloured	30	40
	a. Vert pair. Nos. 802/3	60	80
803	$1 multicoloured	30	40
804	$2 multicoloured	40	55
	a. Vert pair. Nos. 804/5	80	1·10
805	$2 multicoloured	40	55
806	$3 multicoloured	50	65
	a. Vert pair. Nos. 806/7	1·00	1·25
807	$3 multicoloured	50	65
792/807	*Set of* 16	3·00	4·25

Designs:—Nos. 792/3, Liberation Class, France (1945); 794/5, *Dreadnought*, Great Britain (1967); 796/7, No. 242A1, France (1946); 798/9, Class "Dean Goods", Great Britain (1883); 800/1, Hetton Colliery No. 1, Great Britain (1822); 802/3, *Penydarren*, Great Britain (1804); 804/5, *Novelty*, Great Britain (1829); 806/7, Class "44", Germany (1925).

Nos. 792/807 were issued in a similar sheet format to Nos. 727/38.

140 Slaves tilling Field

141 Weightlifting

(Des G. Vasarhelyi. Litho Questa)

1984 (1 Aug). *150th Anniv of Emancipation of Slaves on St. Vincent. T* **140** *and similar horiz designs. Multicoloured. W w* **15** *(sideways). P* 14.

808	35 c. Type **140**	20	20
809	45 c. Sugar-cane harvesting	25	25
810	$1 Cutting sugar-cane	45	60
811	$3 William Wilberforce and African slave caravan	1·25	2·50
808/11	*Set of* 4	2·00	3·25

(Des Court House Studio. Litho Format)

1984 (30 Aug). *Leaders of the World. Olympic Games, Los Angeles. T* **141** *and similar vert designs. Multicoloured. P* 12½.

812	1 c. Judo	10	10
	a. Horiz pair. Nos. 812/13	10	10
813	1 c. Type 141	10	10
814	3 c. Pursuit cycling	10	10
	a. Horiz pair. Nos. 814/15	10	10
815	3 c. Cycle road-racing	10	10
816	60 c. Women's backstroke swimming	15	15
	a. Horiz pair. Nos. 816/17	30	30
817	60 c. Men's butterfly swimming	15	15
818	$3 Sprint start	40	55
	a. Horiz pair. Nos. 818/19	80	1·10
819	$3 Finish of long distance race	40	55
812/19	*Set of* 8	1·10	1·40

Nos. 812/13, 814/15, 816/17 and 818/19 were printed together, *se-tenant*, in horizontal pairs throughout the sheets.

(Des J.W. Litho Format)

1984 (22 Oct). *Leaders of the World. Automobiles (2nd series). Horiz designs as T* **133**, *the first in each pair showing technical drawings and the second paintings. P* 12½.

820	5 c. black, drab and bright green	10	10
	a. Vert pair. Nos. 820/1	10	10
821	5 c. multicoloured	10	10
822	20 c. black, pink and pale new blue	10	15
	a. Vert pair. Nos. 822/3	20	30
823	20 c. multicoloured	10	15
824	55 c. black, pale green and lake-brown	20	25
	a. Vert pair. Nos. 824/5	40	50
825	55 c. multicoloured	20	25
826	$1.50, black, pale turq-grn & turq-grn	25	35
	a. Vert pair. Nos. 826/7	50	70
827	$1.50, multicoloured	25	35
828	$2.50, black, turquoise-green and lilac	30	40
	a. Vert pair. Nos. 828/9	60	80
829	$2.50, multicoloured	30	40
820/9	*Set of* 10	1·50	2·10

Designs:—Nos. 820/1, Austin-Healey "Sprite" (1958); 822/3, Maserati "Ghibli Coupé" (1971); 824/5, Pontiac "GTO" (1964); 826/7, Jaguar "D-Type" (1957); 828/9, Ferrari "365 GTB4 Daytona" (1970).

Nos. 820/9 were issued in a similar sheet format to Nos. 727/38.

142 Grenadier, 70th Regt of Foot, 1773

143 N. S. Taylor

(Des J. Cooter. Litho Questa)

1984 (12 Nov). *Military Uniforms. T* **142** *and similar vert designs. Multicoloured. W w* **15**. *P* 14.

830	45 c. Type **142**	40	30
831	60 c. Grenadier, 6th Regt of Foot, 1775	50	35
832	$1.50, Grenadier, 3rd Regt of Foot, 1768	1·00	1·10
833	$2 Battalion Company officer, 14th Regt of Foot, 1780	1·25	1·60
830/3	*Set of* 4	2·75	3·00

(Des J.W. Litho Format)

1984 (21 Nov). *Leaders of the World. Railway Locomotives (3rd series). Horiz designs as T* **135**, *the first in each pair showing technical drawings and the second the locomotive at work. Multicoloured. P* 12½.

834	5 c. multicoloured	10	10
	a. Vert pair. Nos. 834/5	10	15
835	5 c. multicoloured	10	10
836	40 c. multicoloured	15	20
	a. Vert pair. Nos. 836/7	30	40
837	40 c. multicoloured	15	20
838	75 c. multicoloured	15	25
	a. Vert pair. Nos. 838/9	30	50
839	75 c. multicoloured	15	25
840	$2.50, multicoloured	50	80
	a. Vert pair. Nos. 840/1	1·00	1·60
841	$2.50, multicoloured	50	80
834/41	*Set of* 8	1·40	2·40

Designs:—Nos. 834/5 Class "20", Rhodesia (1954); 836/7, *Southern Maid*, Great Britain (1928); 838/9, *Prince of Wales*, Great Britain (1911); 840/1, Class "05", Germany (1935).

Nos. 834/41 were issued in a similar sheet format to Nos. 727/38.

(Des Court House Studio. Litho Format)

1985 (7 Jan). *Leaders of the World. Cricketers. T* **143** *and similar vert designs, the first in each pair showing a head portrait and the second the cricketer in action. P* 12½.

842	5 c. multicoloured	10	10
	a. Horiz pair. Nos. 842/3	10	10
843	5 c. multicoloured	10	10
844	35 c. multicoloured	35	20
	a. Horiz pair. Nos. 844/5	70	40
845	35 c. multicoloured	35	20
846	50 c. multicoloured	45	30
	a. Horiz pair. Nos. 846/7	90	60
847	50 c. multicoloured	45	30
848	$3 multicoloured	1·00	1·25
	a. Horiz pair. Nos. 848/9	2·00	2·50
849	$3 multicoloured	1·00	1·25
842/9	*Set of* 8	3·25	3·25

Designs:—Nos. 842/3, N. S. Taylor; 844/5. T. W. Graveney; 846/7, R. G. D. Willis; 848/9, S. D. Fletcher.

Nos. 842/3, 844/5, 846/7, and 848/9 were printed together, *se-tenant*, in vertical pairs throughout the sheets.

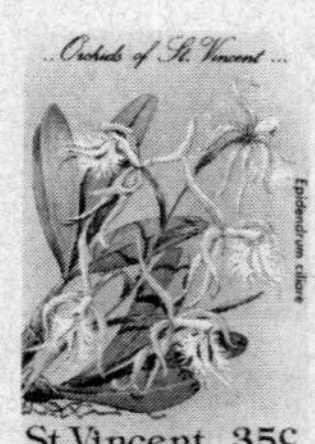

144 Eye Lash Orchid

145 Brown Pelican

(Des G. Drummond. Litho Format)

1985 (31 Jan). *Orchids. T* **144** *and similar vert designs. Multicoloured. W w* **15**. *P* 14.

850	35 c. Type **144**	20	30
851	45 c. *Ionopsis utricularioides*	20	30
852	$1 *Epidendrum secundum*	30	65
853	$3 *Oncidium altissimum*	40	2·00
850/3	*Set of* 4	1·00	3·00

(Des R. Vigurs. Litho Format)

1985 (7 Feb). *Leaders of the World. Birth Bicentenary of John J. Audubon (ornithologist). T* **145** *and similar vert designs. Multicoloured. P* 12½.

854	15 c. Type **145**	15	10
	a. Horiz pair. Nos. 854/5	30	20
855	15 c. Green Heron	15	10
856	40 c. Pileated Woodpecker	15	20
	a. Horiz pair. Nos. 856/7	30	40
857	40 c. Common Flicker	15	20
858	60 c. Painted Bunting	15	30
	a. Horiz pair. Nos. 858/9	30	60
859	60 c. White-winged Crossbill	15	30
860	$2.25, Red-shouldered Hawk	45	90
	a. Horiz pair. Nos. 860/1	90	1·75
861	$2.25, Common Caracara	45	90
854/61	*Set of* 8	1·60	2·75

Nos. 854/5, 856/7, 858/9 and 860/1 were printed together, *se-tenant*, in horizontal pairs throughout the sheets.

(Des Artists International. Litho Format)

1985 (11 Mar). *Leaders of the World. Automobiles* (3rd *series*). *Horiz designs as T* **133**, *the first in each pair showing technical drawings and the second paintings. P* 12½.

862 1 c. black, pale lemon and blue-green .. 10 10
a. Vert pair. Nos. 862/3 .. .. 10 10
863 1 c. multicoloured 10 10
864 55 c. black, pale new blue and violet-grey .. 15 25
a. Vert pair. Nos. 864/5 .. .. 30 50
865 55 c. multicoloured 15 25
866 $2 black, pale lemon & dull reddish purple 40 70
a. Vert pair. Nos. 866/7 .. .. 80 1·40
867 $2 multicoloured 40 70
862/7 .. .. *Set of* 6 1·00 1·60

Designs:—Nos. 862/3, Lancia "Aprilia" (1937); 864/5, Pontiac "Firebird Trans Am" (1973); 866/7, Cunningham "C-5R" (1953).

Nos. 862/7 were issued in a similar sheet format to Nos. 727/38.

146 Pepper **147** Bamboo Flute

(Des G. Drummond. Litho Format)

1985 (22 Apr). *Herbs and Spices. T* **146** *and similar vert designs. Multicoloured. W* w **15**. *P* 14.

868 25 c. Type **146**.. .. .. 10 10
869 35 c. Sweet Marjoram 10 15
870 $1 Nutmeg 20 50
871 $3 Ginger .. .. 55 2·25
868/71 .. .. *Set of* 4 75 2·75

The scientific name on the 35 c. is incorrectly spelt "Marjorana hortensis".

(Des. T. Hadler ($2.50), J.W. (others). Litho Format)

1985 (26 Apr). *Leaders of the World. Railway Locomotives* (4*th series*). *Horiz designs as T* **135**, *the first in each pair showing technical drawings and the second the locomotive at work. P* 12½.

872 1 c. multicoloured 10 10
a. Vert pair. Nos. 872/3 .. .. 10 10
873 1 c. multicoloured 10 10
874 10 c. multicoloured 10 10
a. Vert pair. Nos. 874/5 .. .. 10 15
875 10 c. multicoloured 10 10
876 40 c. multicoloured 15 30
a. Vert pair. Nos. 876/7 .. .. 30 60
877 40 c. multicoloured 15 30
878 60 c. multicoloured 15 30
a. Vert pair. Nos. 878/9 .. .. 30 60
879 60 c. multicoloured 15 30
880 $1 multicoloured 25 40
a. Vert pair. Nos. 880/1 .. .. 50 80
881 $1 multicoloured 25 40
882 $2.50, multicoloured 40 60
a. Vert pair. Nos. 882/3 .. .. 80 1·10
883 $2.50, multicoloured 40 60
872/83 .. .. *Set of* 12 1·75 3·00

Designs:—Nos. 872/3, *Glen Douglas*, Great Britain (1913); 874/5, *Fenchurch*, Great Britain (1872); 876/7, No. 1 "Stirling Single", Great Britain (1870); 878/9, No. 158A, Great Britain (1866); 880/1, No. 103 Class "Jones Goods", Great Britain (1893); 882/3, *The Great Bear*, Great Britain (1908).

Nos. 872/83 were issued in a similar sheet format to Nos. 727/38.

(Des J.W. (25 c.), G. Turner ($1), Artists International (others). Litho Format)

1985 (7 June). *Leaders of the World. Automobiles* (4*th series*). *Horiz designs as T* **133**, *the first in each pair showing technical drawings and the second paintings. P* 12½.

884 25 c. black, greenish grey and brown-red .. 10 10
a. Vert pair. Nos. 884/5 .. .. 15 20
885 25 c. multicoloured 10 10
886 60 c. black, pale flesh and red-orange .. 15 20
a. Vert pair. Nos. 886/7 .. .. 30 40
887 60 c. multicoloured 15 20
888 $1 black, azure and dull lavender 15 25
a. Vert pair. Nos. 888/9 .. .. 30 50
889 $1 multicoloured 15 25
890 $1.50, black, pale blue and scarlet .. 20 30
a. Vert pair. Nos. 890/1 .. .. 40 60
891 $1.50, multicoloured 20 30
884/91 .. .. *Set of* 8 1·00 1·50
MS892 180×121 mm. $4×2 As Nos. 890/1; $5×2 As Nos. 888/9. P 14 .. .. .. 1·75 4·50

Designs:—Nos. 884/5, Essex "Coach" (1922); 886/7, Nash "Rambler" (1950); 888/9, Ferrari "Tipo 156" (1961); 890/1, Eagle-Weslake "Type 58" (1967).

Nos. 884/91 were issued in a similar sheet format to Nos. 727/38.

(Des J.W. (5 c., 30 c., $1), T. Hadler (others). Litho Format)

1985 (27 June). *Leaders of the World. Railway Locomotives* (5*th series*). *Horiz designs as T* **135**, *the first in each pair showing technical drawings and the second the locomotive at work. P* 12½.

893 5 c. multicoloured 10 10
a. Vert pair. Nos. 893/4 .. .. 10 10
894 5 c. multicoloured 10 10
895 30 c. multicoloured 15 20
a. Vert pair. Nos. 895/6 .. .. 30 40
896 30 c. multicoloured 15 20
897 60 c. multicoloured 20 30
a. Vert pair. Nos. 897/8 .. .. 40 60
898 60 c. multicoloured 20 30
899 75 c. multicoloured 20 30
a. Vert pair. Nos. 899/900 .. .. .. 40 60
900 75 c. multicoloured 20 30
901 $1 multicoloured 25 40
a. Vert pair. Nos. 901/2 .. .. 50 80
902 $1 multicoloured 25 40
903 $2.50, multicoloured 30 60
a. Vert pair. Nos. 903/4 .. .. 60 1·10
904 $2.50, multicoloured 30 60
893/904 .. .. *Set of* 12 2·00 3·25

Designs:—Nos. 893/4, Tank locomotive *Loch*, Great Britain (1874); 895/6, Class "47XX", Great Britain (1919); 897/8, Class "121", France (1876); 899/900, Class "24", Germany (1927); 901/2 Tank locomotive No. 1008, Great Britain (1889); 903/4, Class "PS-4", U.S.A. (1926).

Nos. 893/904 were issued in a similar sheet format to Nos. 727/38.

(Des Jennifer Toombs. Litho Format)

1985 (10 July). *Traditional Musical Instruments. T* **147** *and similar multicoloured designs. W* w **15** (*sideways on* $1, $2). *P* 15.

905 25 c. Type **147**.. .. .. 10 15
906 35 c. Quatro (four-stringed guitar) 10 25
907 $1 Ba-ha (bamboo pipe) (*vert*) 25 55
908 $2 Goat-skin drum (*vert*) .. .. .. 35 1·10
905/8 .. .. *Set of* 4 70 1·90
MS909 141×100 mm. Nos. 905/8 .. .. 2·00 4·50

148 Queen Elizabeth the Queen Mother **149** Elvis Presley

(Des Court House Studio. Litho Format)

1985 (9 Aug). *Leaders of the World. Life and Times of Queen Elizabeth the Queen Mother. Various vertical portraits as T* **148**. *P* 12½.

910 35 c. multicoloured 10 20
a. Horiz pair. Nos. 910/11.. .. .. .. 10 40
911 35 c. multicoloured 10 20
912 85 c. multicoloured 10 25
a. Horiz pair. Nos. 912/13.. .. .. .. 15 50
913 85 c. multicoloured 10 25
914 $1.20, multicoloured 15 30
a. Horiz pair. Nos. 914/15.. .. .. .. 25 60
915 $1.20, multicoloured 15 30
916 $1.60, multicoloured 15 35
a. Horiz pair. Nos. 916/17.. .. .. .. 25 70
917 $1.60, multicoloured 15 35
910/17 .. .. *Set of* 8 60 2·00
MS918 85×114 mm. $2.10, multicoloured; $2.10, multicoloured .. .. 50 1·50

The two designs of each value were issued, *se-tenant*, in horizontal pairs within the sheets.

Each *se-tenant* pair shows a floral pattern across the bottom of the portraits which stops short of the left-hand edge on the left-hand stamp and of the right-hand edge on the right-hand stamp.

Designs as Nos. 910/11 and 912/13, but with face values of $6×2 and $3.50×2, also exist in additional miniature sheets from a restricted printing issued 19 December 1985.

(Des Court House Studio. Litho Format)

1985 (16 Aug). *Leaders of the World. Elvis Presley* (*entertainer*). *Various vertical portraits as T* **149**. *Multicoloured, background colours given. P* 12½.

919 10 c. multicoloured (T **149**) 40 15
a. Horiz pair. Nos. 919/20.. .. .. .. 80 30
920 10 c. multicoloured (bright blue) 40 15
921 60 c. multicoloured (brown) 50 35
a. Horiz pair. Nos. 921/2 .. .. .. 1·00 70
922 60 c. multicoloured (pale grey) 50 35
923 $1 multicoloured (brown) 65 55
a. Horiz pair. Nos. 923/4 .. .. .. 1·25 1·10
924 $1 multicoloured (bright blue) 65 55
925 $5 multicoloured (azure) .. .. .. 90 1·75
a. Horiz pair. Nos. 925/6 .. .. .. 1·75 3·50
926 $5 multicoloured (bright blue) .. .. 90 1·75
919/26 .. .. *Set of* 8 4·25 5·00
MS927 Four sheets each 145 × 107 mm. (a) 30 c. As Nos. 919/20 each × 2; (b) 50 c. As Nos. 921/2 each × 2; (c) $1.50 As Nos. 923/4 each × 2; (d) $4.50 As Nos. 925/6 each × 2 *Set of* 4 *sheets* 20·00 20·00

The two designs of each value were printed together, *se-tenant*, in horizontal pairs throughout the sheets.

Two similar designs, each with a face value of $4, were prepared, but not issued.

St. Vincent Philatelic Services Ltd. report that unauthorised reprints of Nos. 919/27 exist, poorly printed on whiter paper.

150 Silos and Conveyor Belt **151** Michael Jackson

(Des G. Vasarhelyi. Litho Format)

1985 (17 Oct). *St. Vincent Flour Milling Industry. T* **150** *and similar horiz designs. Multicoloured. W* w **15**. *P* 15.

928 20 c. Type **150**.. .. .. 10 15
929 30 c. Roller mills 10 20
930 75 c. Administration building 20 35
931 $3 Bran finishers .. .. 50 1·40
928/31 .. .. *Set of* 4 70 1·90

1985 (27 Oct). *Royal Visit. Nos.* 672/3, 697/8, 711, 724 *and* 912/13 *optd as T* **114** *of Montserrat or surch also*.

932 – 60 c. multicoloured (No. 711) .. .. 1·50 2·00
933 – 60 c. multicoloured (No. 724) .. .. 1·75 2·25
934 – 85 c. multicoloured (No. 912) .. .. 2·50 4·00
a. Horiz pair. Nos. 934/5 .. .. 5·00 8·00
935 – 85 c. multicoloured (No. 913) .. .. 2·50 4·00
936 **125** $1.50, multicoloured .. .. .. 1·75 2·75
937 – $1.60 on $4 multicoloured (No. 672) .. 1·00 2·25
a. Sheetlet. No. 937×6 and No. 938 .. 14·50
ab. Sheetlet. No. 937×6 and No. 938a .. 13·50
938 – $1.60 on $4 multicoloured (No. 673) (surch $1.60 only) .. .. .. 10·00 14·00
a. Additionally optd "CARIBBEAN ROYAL VISIT—1985" .. .. 8·00
939 – $2.50, multicoloured (No. 698) .. .. 2·00 3·50
932/9 .. .. *Set of* 8 21·00 30·00

No. 938 shows a new face value only. "CARIBBEAN ROYAL VISIT—1985" being omitted from the surcharge. No. 938a is the corrected version issued subsequently.

(Des Court House Studio. Litho Format)

1985 (2 Dec). *Leaders of the World. Michael Jackson* (*entertainer*). *Various vertical portraits as T* **151**. *Multicoloured. P* 12½.

940 60 c. multicoloured 25 30
a. Horiz pair. Nos. 940/1 .. .. .. 50 60
941 60 c. multicoloured 25 30
942 $1 multicoloured 30 45
a. Horiz pair. Nos. 942/3 .. .. .. 60 90
943 $1 multicoloured 30 45
944 $2 multicoloured 45 80
a. Horiz pair. Nos. 944/5 .. .. .. 90 1·60
945 $2 multicoloured 45 80
946 $5 multicoloured .. .. 70 1·75
a. Horiz pair. Nos. 946/7 .. .. .. 1·40 3·50
947 $5 multicoloured .. .. 70 1·75
940/7 .. .. *Set of* 8 3·00 6·00
MS948 Four sheets, each 144×109 mm. (a) 45 c. As Nos. 940/1 each × 2; (b) 90 c. As Nos. 942/3 each × 2; (c) $1.50 As Nos. 944/5 each × 2; (d) $4 As Nos. 946/7 each × 2. *Set of* 4 *sheets* 4·00 7·50

The two designs for each value were printed together, *se-tenant*, in horizontal pairs throughout the sheets. The left-hand design shows the face value at top left (as on Type **151**) and the right-hand design at top right.

St. Vincent Philatelic Services Ltd. report that unauthorised reprints of Nos. 940/7 exist, poorly printed on whiter paper.

152 "The Serenaders" (Kim de Freitas) **153** *Santa Maria*

(Litho Format)

1985 (9 Dec). *Christmas. Children's Paintings. T* **152** *and similar vert designs. Multicoloured. W* w **15**. *P* 13½ × 14.

949 25 c. Type **152**.. .. .. 10 15
950 75 c. "Poinsettia" (Jackie Douglas) 20 40
951 $2.50, "Jesus our Master" (Bernadette Payne) .. .. 55 2·00
949/51 .. .. *Set of* 3 75 2·25

(Litho Format)

1986 (23 Jan). 500*th Anniv of Discovery of America* (1992) *by Columbus* (1*st issue*). *T* **153** *and similar vert designs. Multicoloured. P* 12½.

952 60 c. Type **153** 30 40
a. Horiz pair. Nos. 952/3 .. .. .. 60 80
953 60 c. Christopher Columbus 30 40
954 $1.50, Columbus at Spanish Court .. .. 55 1·00
a. Horiz pair. Nos. 954/5 .. .. .. 1·10 2·00
955 $1.50, King Ferdinand and Queen Isabella of Spain .. .. 55 1·00
956 $2.75, *Santa Maria* and fruits .. .. 90 2·00
a. Horiz pair. Nos. 956/7 .. .. .. 1·75 4·00
957 $2.75, Maize and fruits .. .. .. 90 2·00
952/7 .. .. *Set of* 6 3·00 6·00
MS958 95×85 mm. $6 Christopher Columbus (*different*) .. .. 2·25 4·50

The two designs of each value were printed together, *se-tenant*, in horizontal pairs within the sheets.

See also Nos. 1125/31, 1305/24, 1639/57, 1677/85, 1895/1901 and 1981/2.

(Des Artists International. Litho Format)

1986 (27 Jan). *Leaders of the World. Automobiles* (5*th series*). *Horiz designs as T* **133**, *the first in each pair showing technical drawings and the second paintings. P* 12½.

959 30 c. black, cobalt and dull orange 10 15
a. Vert pair. Nos. 959/60 .. .. .. 20 30
960 30 c. multicoloured 10 15
961 45 c. black, lavender-grey and blue 10 15
a. Vert pair. Nos. 961/2 .. .. .. 20 30
962 45 c. multicoloured 10 15
963 60 c. black, bright blue and vermilion .. 15 15
a. Vert pair. Nos. 963/4 .. .. 30 30

964 60 c. multicoloured 15 15
965 90 c. black, greenish yellow and bright blue 20 20
a. Vert pair. Nos. 965/6 .. .. 40 40
966 90 c. multicoloured 20 20
967 $1.50, black, pale rose-lilac & brt magenta 25 35
a. Vert pair. Nos. 967/8 .. .. 50 70
968 $1.50, multicoloured 25 35
969 $2.50, black, blue and bright blue .. 25 40
a. Vert pair. Nos. 969/70 .. .. 50 80
970 $2.50, multicoloured 25 40
959/70 .. .. *Set of* 12 1·90 2·50

Designs:—Nos. 959/60, Cadillac "Type 53" (1916); 961/2, Triumph "Dolomite" (1939); 963/4, Panther "J-72" (1972); 965/6, Ferrari "275 GTB/4" (1967); 967/8, Packard "Caribbean" (1953); 969/70, Bugatti "Type 41 Royale" (1931).

Nos. 959/70 were issued in a similar sheet format to Nos. 727/38.

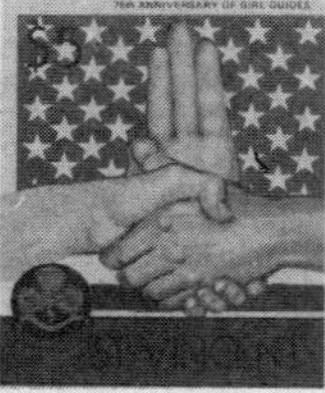

154 Guide Salute and Handclasp **155** Halley's Comet

(Des Court House Studio. Litho Format)

1986 (25 Feb). *75th Annivs of Girl Guide Movement and Boy Scouts of America. Two sheets, each* 85 × 113 *mm, containing vert designs as T* **154**. *Multicoloured. P* 12½.

MS971 $5 Type **154**: $5 Palette and paintbrushes 2·00 5·00
MS972 $6 Cross-tied logs: $6 Lord Baden-Powell 2·00 6·00

The two stamps in each sheet were printed together, *se-tenant*, in horizontal pairs, each forming a composite design.

Nos. **MS**971/2 exist with plain or decorative margins.

Overprints on these miniature sheets commemorating "Capex '87" International Stamp Exhibition, Toronto, were not authorised by the St. Vincent administration.

(Des G. Vasarhelyi. Litho Format)

1986 (14 Apr). *Appearance of Halley's Comet. T* **155** *and similar horiz designs. Multicoloured. W* w **15**. *P* 15.

973 45 c. Type **155**.. .. .. 25 20
974 60 c. Edmond Halley 25 30
975 75 c. Newton's telescope and astronomers .. 30 55
976 $3 Amateur astronomer on St. Vincent .. 60 2·25
973/6 .. .. *Set of* 4 1·25 3·00
MS977 155 × 104 mm. Nos. 973/6 .. .. 2·50 4·50

(Des Court House Studio. Litho Format)

1986 (21 Apr). *60th Birthday of Queen Elizabeth II (1st issue). Multicoloured designs as T* **117a** *of Montserrat. P* 12½.

978 10 c. Queen Elizabeth II 10 10
979 90 c. Princess Elizabeth 20 30
980 $2.50, Queen gathering bouquets from crowd 35 75
981 $8 In Canberra, 1982 (*vert*) .. .. 1·00 2·25
978/81 .. .. .. *Set of* 4 1·40 3·00
MS982 85×115 mm. $10 Queen Elizabeth II (*different*) .. .. 3·00 6·00

See also Nos. 996/1000

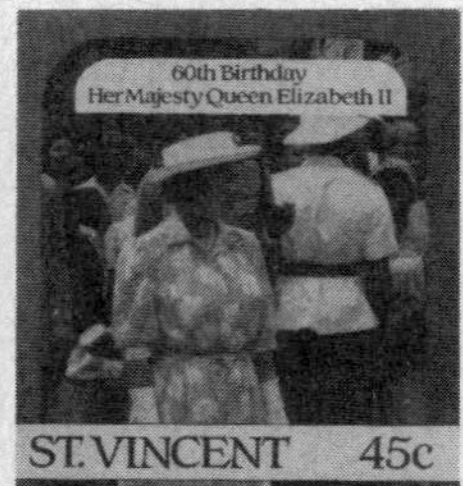

156 Mexican Player **157** Queen Elizabeth at Victoria Park, Kingstown

(Des Court House Studio. Litho Format)

1986 (7 May–3 July). *World Cup Football Championship, Mexico. T* **156** *and similar multicoloured designs. P* 12½ (75 c., $2, $4, $5) *or* 15 (*others*).

983 1 c. Football and world map (*horiz*) .. 10 10
984 2 c. Type **156**.. .. .. 10 10
985 5 c. Mexican player (*different*) 10 10
986 5 c. Hungary v Scotland 10 10
987 10 c. Spain v Scotland 10 10
988 30 c. England v U.S.S.R. (*horiz*) 20 20
989 45 c. Spain v France 30 30
990 75 c. Mexican team (56 × 36 *mm*) 45 45
991 $1 England v Italy.. .. .. .. 75 65
992 $2 Scottish team (56 × 36 *mm*) .. .. 1·10 1·50
993 $4 Spanish team (56 × 36 *mm*) .. .. 2·10 2·75
994 $5 English team (56 × 36 *mm*) .. .. 2·25 3·25
983/94 .. .. .. *Set of* 12 6·50 8·50
MS995 Six sheets, each 84×114 mm. (a) $1.50, As Type **156**. P 15 (3 July); (b) $1.50, As No. 993. P 12½; (c) $2.25, As No. 992. P 12½; (d) $2.50, As No. 990. P 12½; (e) $3 As No. 989. P 15 (3 July); (f) $5.50, As No. 994. P 12½ *Set of* 6 *sheets* 7·00 10·00

(Des Court House Studio. Litho Questa)

1986 (14 June). *60th Birthday of Queen Elizabeth II (2nd issue). T* **157** *and similar vert designs showing scenes from* 1985 *Royal Visit. Multicoloured. W* w **15**. *P* 15 × 14.

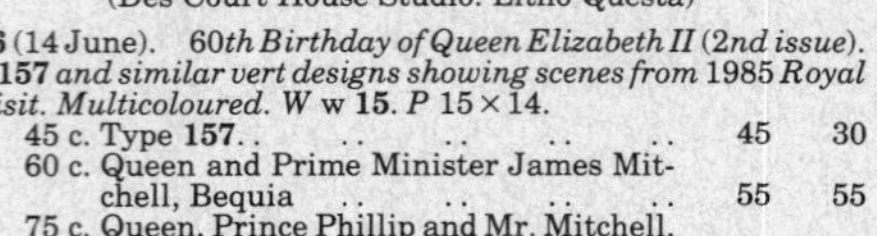

996 45 c. Type **157**.. .. .. 45 30
997 60 c. Queen and Prime Minister James Mitchell, Bequia 55 55
998 75 c. Queen, Prince Phillip and Mr. Mitchell, Port Elizabeth, Bequia 65 65
999 $2.50, Queen, Prince Phillip and Mr. Mitchell watching Independence Day parade, Victoria Park .. .. .. 1·40 2·50
996/9 .. .. *Set of* 4 2·75 3·50
MS1000 121 × 85 mm. $3 Queen at Victoria Park 2·75 3·75

(Des T. Hadler. Litho Format)

1986 (15 July). *Leaders of the World. Railway Locomotives (6th series). Horiz designs as T* **135**. *Multicoloured. P* 12½.

1001 30 c. multicoloured 10 10
a. Vert pair. Nos. 1001/2 .. .. .. 20 20
1002 30 c. multicoloured 10 10
1003 50 c. multicoloured 20 20
a. Vert pair. Nos. 1003/4 .. .. .. 40 40
1004 50 c. multicoloured 20 20
1005 $1 multicoloured 25 30
a. Vert pair. Nos. 1005/6 .. .. .. 50 60
1006 $1 multicoloured 25 30
1007 $3 multicoloured 50 70
a. Vert pair. Nos. 1007/8 .. .. .. 1·00 1·40
1008 $3 multicoloured 50 70
1001/8 .. .. *Set of* 8 1·75 2·25

Designs:—Nos. 1001/2, Class "ED41 BZZB" rack and adhesion locomotive, Japan (1926); 1003/4, Locomotive *The Judge*, Chicago Railroad Exposition, U.S.A. (1883); 1005/6, Class "E60C" electric locomotive, U.S.A. (1973); 1007/8, Class "SD40-2" diesel locomotive, U.S.A. (1972).

Nos. 1001/8 were issued in a similar sheet format to Nos. 727/38.

Nos. 1007/8 exist with the green omitted from stock dispersed by the liquidator of Format International Security Printers Ltd.

(Des Court House Studio. Litho Format)

1986 (18 July–15 Oct). *Royal Wedding (1st issue). Multicoloured designs as T* **118a** *of Montserrat. P* 12½.

1009 60 c. Profile of Prince Andrew 20 25
a. Pair. Nos. 1009/10 .. .. .. 40 50
1010 60 c. Miss Sarah Ferguson 20 25
1011 $2 Prince Andrew with Mrs. Nancy Reagan (*horiz*).. .. .. .. 45 75
a. Pair. Nos. 1011/12 .. .. .. 90 1·50
1012 $2 Prince Andrew in naval uniform (*horiz*) 45 75
1009/12 .. .. .. *Set of* 4 1·10 1·75
MS1013 115 × 85 mm. $10 Duke and Duchess of York in carriage after wedding (*horiz*) (15.10) .. 3·00 4·50

Nos. 1009/10 and 1011/12 were printed together, *se-tenant*, in horizontal and vertical pairs throughout the sheets.

Nos. 1009/12 imperforate come from souvenir stamp booklets.

158 *Acrocomia aculeata* **159** Cadet Force Emblem and Cadets of 1936 and 1986

(Des J. Cooter. Litho Questa)

1986 (30 Sept). *Timber Resources of St. Vincent. T* **158** *and similar vert designs. Multicoloured. W* w **15** (*sideways*). *P* 14.

1014 10 c. Type **158** 40 20
1015 60 c. *Pithecellobium saman*.. .. .. 1·25 80
1016 75 c. White Cedar .. .. 1·60 95
1017 $3 *Andira inermis* .. .. .. 3·50 4·50
1014/17 .. .. .. *Set of* 4 6·00 5·75

(Des G. Vasarhelyi. Litho Questa)

1986 (30 Sept). *50th Anniv of St. Vincent Cadet Force* (45 c., $2) *and 75th Anniv of St. Vincent Girls' High School* (*others*). *T* **159** *and similar multicoloured designs. W* w **15** (*sideways on* 45 *c.*). *P* 14.

1018 45 c. Type **159** 40 30
1019 60 c. Grimble Building, Girls' High School (*horiz*) 45 40
1020 $1.50, High School pupils (*horiz*) .. 1·25 1·75
1021 $2 Cadets on parade (*horiz*) .. .. 1·75 2·25
1018/21 .. .. .. *Set of* 4 3·50 4·25

1986 (15 Oct). *Royal Wedding (2nd issue). Nos.* 1009/12 *optd as T* **121** *of Montserrat in silver.*

1022 60 c. Profile of Prince Andrew 40 65
a. Pair. Nos. 1022/3 .. .. .. 80 1·25
1023 60 c. Miss Sarah Ferguson 40 65
1024 $2 Prince Andrew with Mrs. Nancy Reagan (*horiz*).. .. .. .. 1·25 2·00
a. Pair. Nos. 1024/5 .. .. .. 2·50 4·00
1025 $2 Prince Andrew in naval uniform (*horiz*) .. .. 1·25 2·00
1022/5 .. .. .. *Set of* 4 3·00 4·75

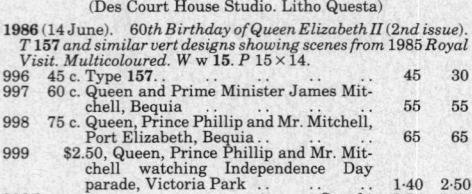

160 King Arthur

(Des G. Vasarhelyi. Litho Format)

1986 (3 Nov). *The Legend of King Arthur. T* **160** *and similar horiz designs. Multicoloured. P* 14 × 13½.

1026 30 c. Type **160** 40 40
1027 45 c. Merlin taking baby Arthur 50 50
1028 60 c. Arthur pulling sword from stone .. 60 60
1029 75 c. Camelot 70 70
1030 $1 Arthur receiving Excalibur from the Lady of the Lake 80 80
1031 $1.50, Knights at the Round Table .. 1·00 1·25
1032 $2 The Holy Grail .. .. .. 1·25 1·50
1033 $5 Sir Lancelot jousting .. .. 2·00 2·75
1026/33 .. .. .. *Set of* 8 6·50 7·75

Nos. 1026/9 cancelled-to-order exist imperforate from stock dispersed by the liquidator of Format International Security Printers Ltd.

161 Statue of Liberty Floodlit **162** Fishing for Tri Tri

(Des Court House Studio. Litho Format)

1986 (26 Nov). *Centenary of Statue of Liberty. T* **161** *and similar vert designs showing aspects of the Statue. P* 14 × 13½.

1034 15 c. multicoloured 10 10
1035 25 c. multicoloured 15 15
1036 40 c. multicoloured 20 25
1037 55 c. multicoloured 25 30
1038 75 c. multicoloured 35 45
1039 90 c. multicoloured 45 60
1040 $1.75, multicoloured .. .. .. 75 1·10
1041 $2 multicoloured .. .. 80 1·25
1042 $2.50, multicoloured .. .. .. 85 1·60
1043 $3 multicoloured .. .. 1·00 1·75
1034/43 .. .. .. *Set of* 10 4·50 6·75
MS1044 Three sheets, each 85 × 115 mm. $3.50; $4; $5 .. .. .. *Set of* 3 *sheets* 4·50 8·50

(Des T. Hadler. Litho Format)

1986 (10 Dec). *Freshwater Fishing. T* **162** *and similar horiz designs. Multicoloured. P* 15.

1045 75 c. Type **162** 25 40
a. Pair. Nos. 1045/6 .. .. .. 50 80
1046 75 c. Plumier's Goby ("Tri Tri") 25 40
1047 $1.50, Crayfishing 35 80
a. Pair. Nos. 1047/8 .. .. .. 70 1·60
1048 $1.50, Crayfish 35 80
1045/8 .. .. .. *Set of* 4 1·10 2·10

Nos. 1045/6 and 1047/8 were each printed together, *se-tenant*, in horizontal and vertical pairs throughout the sheets.

WORLD POPULATION
5 BILLION
11TH JULY 1987

163 Baby on Scales (**164**)

(Des C. Abbott. Litho Format)

1987 (10 June). *Child Health Campaign. T* **163** *and similar vert designs. Multicoloured. P* 14.

1049 10 c. Type **163** 10 10
1050 50 c. Oral rehydration therapy 45 55
1051 75 c. Breast feeding 60 90
1052 $1 Nurse giving injection .. .. 85 1·25
1049/52 .. .. .. *Set of* 4 1·75 2·50

1987 (10 June). *World Population Control. Nos.* 1049/52 *optd with T* **164**.

1053 10 c. Type **163** 10 10
1054 50 c. Oral rehydration therapy 50 55
1055 75 c. Breast feeding 65 90
1056 $1 Nurse giving injection .. .. 90 1·25
1053/6 .. .. .. *Set of* 4 1·90 2·50

165 Hanna Mandlikova

166 Miss Prima Donna, Queen of the Bands, 1986

(Litho Format)

1987 (22 June). *International Lawn Tennis Players. T* **165** *and similar vert designs. Multicoloured. P* 12½.

1057 40 c. Type **165** 25 25
1058 60 c. Yannick Noah 25 35
1059 80 c. Ivan Lendl 25 40
1060 $1 Chris Evert 25 40
1061 $1.25, Steffi Graf 25 50
1062 $1.50, John McEnroe 25 55
1063 $1.75, Martina Navratilova with Wimbledon trophy 30 65
1064 $2 Boris Becker with Wimbledon trophy 30 75
1057/64 .. .. *Set of* 8 1·90 3·50
MS1065 115×85 mm. $2.25 As No. 1063; $2.25 As No. 1064 .. .. 1·40 3·50

Designs as Nos. 1063/4, but each with a face value of $10, also exist embossed on gold foil from a restricted printing.

(Des Young Phillips. Litho Format)

1987 (29 June). *10th Anniv of Carnival. T* **166** *and similar vert designs. Multicoloured. P* 12½.

1066 20 c. Type **166** 10 15
1067 45 c. Donna Young, Miss Carnival, 1985 .. 15 15
1068 55 c. Miss St. Vincent and the Grenadines, 1986 .. .. 15 15
1069 $3.70, "Spirit of Hope" costume, 1986 .. 50 1·40
1066/9 .. .. *Set of* 4 75 1·75

The 45 c. value is inscribed "Miss Carival" in error.

(167)

168 Queen Victoria, 1841

1987 (26 Aug). *10th Death Anniv of Elvis Presley (entertainer). Nos. 919/27 optd with T* **167** *in silver.*

1070 10 c. multicoloured (T **149**) 10 10
a. Horiz pair. Nos. 1070/1 .. .. .. 20 20
1071 10 c. multicoloured (bright blue) 10 10
1072 60 c. multicoloured (brown) 25 30
a. Horiz pair. Nos. 1072/3 .. .. .. 50 60
1073 60 c. multicoloured (pale grey) 25 30
1074 $1 multicoloured (brown) 30 45
a. Horiz pair. Nos. 1074/5 .. .. .. 60 90
1075 $1 multicoloured (bright blue) 30 45
1076 $5 multicoloured (azure) .. .. .. 1·40 2·25
a. Horiz pair. Nos. 1076/7 .. .. 2·75 4·50
1077 $5 multicoloured (bright blue) .. .. 1·40 2·25
1070/7 .. .. *Set of* 8 3·50 5·50
MS1078 Four sheets, each 145 × 107 mm. (a) 30 c. As Nos. 1070/1 each × 2; (b) 50 c. As Nos. 1072/3 each × 2; (c) $1.50, As Nos. 1074/5 each × 2; (d) $4.50, As Nos. 1076/7 each × 2 .. .. 7·50 10·00

(Des Young Phillips. Litho Format)

1987 (15 Oct). *Royal Ruby Wedding and 150th Anniv of Queen Victoria's Accession. T* **168** *and similar vert designs. Multicoloured. P* 12½.

1079 15 c. Type **168** 10 10
1080 75 c. Queen Elizabeth and Prince Andrew, 1960 .. .. 25 35
1081 $1 Coronation, 1953 .. .. 30 40
1082 $2.50, Duke of Edinburgh, 1948 .. .. 90 1·40
1083 $5 Queen Elizabeth II, *c.* 1980 .. .. 1·40 1·90
1079/83 .. .. *Set of* 5 2·50 3·75
MS1084 85×115 mm. $6 Princess Elizabeth with Prince Charles at his Christening, 1948 .. 2·50 4·50

ALTERED CATALOGUE NUMBERS

Any Catalogue numbers altered from the last edition are shown as a list in the introductory pages.

169 Karl Benz and Benz Three-wheeler (1886)

(Litho Format)

1987 (4 Dec). *Century of Motoring. T* **169** *and similar horiz designs. Multicoloured. P* 12½.

1085 $1 Type **169** 40 60
1086 $2 Enzo Ferrari and Ferrari "Dino 206SP" (1966) .. .. 50 1·10
1087 $4 Charles Rolls and Sir Henry Royce and Rolls-Royce "Silver Ghost" (1907) .. 65 1·50
1088 $5 Henry Ford and Ford "Model T" (1908) .. 65 1·75
1085/8 .. .. *Set of* 4 2·00 4·50
MS1089 Four sheets, each 144×75 mm. (a) $3 As Type **169**. (b) $5 As No. 1086. (c) $6 As No. 1087. (d) $8 As No. 1088 .. *Set of* 4 *sheets* 9·50 18·00

Nos. 1085/8 with the gold omitted and Nos. 1088 and **MS**1089d with Henry Ford facing right all exist from stock dispersed by the liquidator of Format International Security Printers Ltd.

170 Everton Football Team

(Litho Format)

1987 (4 Dec). *English Football Teams. T* **170** *and similar horiz designs. Multicoloured. P* 12½.

1090 $2 Type **170** .. .. 1·25 1·25
1091 $2 Manchester United .. .. .. 1·25 1·25
1092 $2 Tottenham Hotspur .. .. .. 1·25 1·25
1093 $2 Arsenal .. .. 1·25 1·25
1094 $2 Liverpool .. .. 1·25 1·25
1095 $2 Derby County .. .. 1·25 1·25
1096 $2 Portsmouth .. .. 1·25 1·25
1097 $2 Leeds United .. .. 1·25 1·25
1090/7 .. .. *Set of* 8 9·00 9·00

171 Five Cent Coins

172 Charles Dickens

(Des Questa ($20), Young Phillips Studio (others))

1987 (11 Dec)–**91**. *East Caribbean Currency. T* **171** *and similar multicoloured designs.* (a) *Litho Format. P* 15

1098 5 c. Type **171** 10 10
1099 6 c. Two cent coins 10 10
1100 10 c. Ten cent coins 10 10
1101 12 c. Two and ten cent coins 10 10
1102 15 c. Five cent coins 15 10
1103 20 c. Ten cent coins 20 10
1104 25 c. Twenty-five cent coins 20 15
1105 30 c. Five and twenty-five cent coins .. 20 15
1106 35 c. Twenty-five and ten cent coins .. 25 20
1107 45 c. Twenty-five and two ten cent coins 40 30
1108 50 c. Fifty cent coins 40 30
1109 65 c. Fifty, ten and five cent coins .. 50 45
1110 75 c. Fifty and twenty-five cent coins .. 60 50
1111 $1 One dollar note (*horiz*) 75 65
1112 $2 Two one dollar notes (*horiz*) .. 1·25 1·75
1113 $3 Three one dollar notes (*horiz*) .. 1·50 2·25
1114 $5 Five dollar note (*horiz*) .. .. 3·25 4·50
1115 $10 Ten dollar note (*horiz*) .. .. 4·50 7·00
1098/1115 .. .. .. *Set of* 18 13·00 17·00

(*b*) *Litho Questa. P* 14 (1989–91)

1115*a* 5 c. Type **171** 10 10
1115*c* 10 c. Ten cent coins 10 10
1115*e* 15 c. Five cent coins 15 15
1115*f* 20 c. Ten cent coins 15 15
1115*g* 25 c. Twenty-five cent coins 15 15
1115*j* 45 c. Twenty-five and two ten cent coins 30 25
1115*k* 50 c. Fifty cent coins 40 35
1115*l* 65 c. Fifty, ten and five cent coins .. 50 50
1115*m* 75 c. Fifty and twenty-five cent coins .. 55 55
1115*n* $1 One dollar note (*horiz*) 65 65
1115*o* $2 Two one dollar notes (*horiz*) .. 1·25 1·50
1115*q* $5 Five dollar note (*horiz*) .. .. 2·50 3·00
1115*s* $20 Twenty-dollar note (*horiz*) (7.11.89) 9·25 11·00
1115*a*/*s* .. .. *Set of* 13 14·50 16·00

No. 1100 overprinted "SPECIMEN" and with the blue omitted exists from stock dispersed by the liquidator of Format International Security Printers Ltd.

(Des Jennifer Toombs. Litho Format)

1987 (17 Dec). *Christmas. 175th Birth Anniv of Charles Dickens. T* **172** *and similar vert designs. Multicoloured. P* 14 × 14½.

1116 6 c. Type **172** 10 15
a. Horiz pair. Nos. 1116/17 .. .. 15 30
1117 6 c. "Mr. Fezziwig's Ball" 10 15
1118 25 c. Type **172** 15 20
a. Horiz pair. Nos. 1118/19 .. .. 30 40
1119 25 c. "Scrooge's Third Visitor" 15 20
1120 50 c. Type **172** 25 45
a. Horiz pair. Nos. 1120/1 .. .. 50 90
1121 50 c. "The Cratchits' Christmas" 25 45
1122 75 c. Type **172** 35 65
a. Horiz pair. Nos. 1122/3 .. .. 70 1·25
1123 75 c. "A Christmas Carol" 35 65
1116/23 .. .. *Set of* 8 1·50 2·50
MS1124 141 × 101 mm. $5 Teacher reading to class .. .. 1·75 4·00

Nos. 1116/17, 1118/19, 1120/1 and 1122/3 were printed together, *se-tenant*, in horizontal pairs throughout the sheets, each pair forming a composite design showing an open book. The first design in each pair shows Type **172** and the second a scene from *A Christmas Carol*.

173 *Santa Maria*

174 Brown Pelican

(Des M. Pollard. Litho Format)

1988 (11 Jan). *500th Anniv of Discovery of America (1992) by Columbus (2nd issue). T* **173** *and similar square designs. Multicoloured. P* 14.

1125 15 c. Type **173** 15 15
1126 75 c. *Nina* and *Pinta* 30 50
1127 $1 Compass and hourglass 30 60
1128 $1.50, Claiming the New World for Spain 40 80
1129 $3 Arawak village .. .. .. 60 1·25
1130 $4 Blue and Yellow Macaw, Cuban Tody, pineapple and maize .. .. 70 1·75
1125/30 .. .. *Set of* 6 2·25 4·50
MS1131 114×86 mm. $5 Columbus, Arms and *Santa Maria*. P 13½×14 .. .. .. 2·25 4·75

Further unissued $2 and $5 miniature sheets exist from stock dispersed by the liquidator of Format International Security Printers Ltd.

(Des Maxine Marsh. Litho Format)

1988 (15 Feb). *P* 14.

1132 **174** 45 c. multicoloured 30 30

For similar 55 c. value see No. 1304.

175 Windsurfing

(Litho Format)

1988 (26 Feb). *Tourism. T* **175** *and similar multicoloured designs. P* 15.

1133 10 c. Type **175** 10 10
1134 45 c. Scuba diving 20 25
1135 65 c. Aerial view of Young Island (*horiz*) 30 50
1136 $5 Cruising yacht (*horiz*) .. .. 2·10 3·00
1133/6 .. .. *Set of* 4 2·40 3·50
MS1136*a* 115×85 mm. $10 Two windsurfers off St. Vincent (60×40 *mm*). P 12½ .. .. 1·75 4·50

176 *Nuestra Senora del Rosario* (Spanish galleon) and Spanish Knight's Cross

(Litho Format)

1988 (29 July). *400th Anniv of Spanish Armada. T* **176** *and similar horiz designs. Multicoloured. P* 12½.

1137 15 c. Type **176** 15 10
1138 75 c. *Ark Royal* (galleon) and English Armada medal 30 35

1139 $1.50, English fleet and Drake's dial .. 50 65
1140 $2 Dismasted Spanish galleon and 16th-century shot 55 75
1141 $3.50, Attack of English fireships at Calais and 16th-century grenade .. 70 1·40
1142 $5 *Revenge* (English galleon) and Drake's Drum .. .. 90 1·75
1137/42 .. .. *Set of* 6 2·75 4·50
MS1143 123×92 mm. $8 Sighting the Armada 2·00 4·50

177 D. K. Lillee

178 Athletics

(Litho Format)

1988 (29 July). *Cricketers of* 1988 *International Season. T* **177** *and similar square designs. Multicoloured. P* 14.
1144 15 c. Type **177** 30 30
1145 50 c. G. A. Gooch 50 50
1146 75 c. R. N. Kapil Dev 70 70
1147 $1 S. M. Gavaskar 85 85
1148 $1.50, M. W. Gatting .. .. .. 1·25 1·50
1149 $2.50, Imran Khan .. .. .. 1·50 2·00
1150 $3 I. T. Botham .. .. 1·50 2·25
1151 $4 I. V. A. Richards .. .. .. 1·75 2·50
1144/51 .. .. *Set of* 8 7·50 9·50
MS1152 130 × 80 mm. $2 As $4; $3.50, As $3 2·75 4·50

Examples of No. **MS**1152 imperforate or part perforate exist from stock dispersed by the liquidator of Format International Security Printers Ltd.

(Des S. Angela. Litho Questa)

1988 (7 Dec). *Olympic Games, Seoul. T* **178** *and similar multicoloured designs. P* 14.
1153 10 c. Type **178** 10 10
1154 50 c. Long jumping (*vert*) 20 25
1155 $1 Triple jumping 40 50
1156 $5 Boxing (*vert*) .. .. 2·10 2·75
1153/6 .. .. *Set of* 4 2·50 3·25
MS1157 85 × 63 mm. $10 Olympic flame .. 4·25 5·50

A different set of six values and a miniature sheet for this event was not issued, but exists from stock dispersed by the liquidator of Format International Security Printers Ltd.

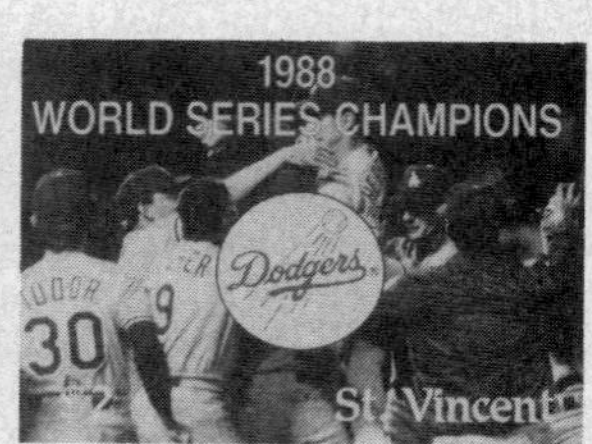

179 Babe Ruth 180 Los Angeles Dodgers (National League Champions)

(Litho Questa)

1988 (7 Dec). *Famous Baseball Players* (1*st series*). *P* 14.
1158 **179** $2 multicoloured .. .. .. 1·40 1·40

No. 1158 also exists embossed on gold foil from a restricted printing.

See also Nos. 1264/75, 1407, 1408/88, 2152/4, 2155/6, 2426 and 3004/12.

(Des W. Storozuk. Litho Questa)

1988 (7 Dec). 1988 *Baseball World Series. Sheet* 115×85 *mm containing T* **180** *and similar horiz design. Multicoloured. P* 14×13½.
MS1159 $2 Type **180**; $2 Team logos of Dodgers and Oakland Athletics .. .. 2·00 2·25

(Des Walt Disney Co. Litho Questa)

1988 (23 Dec). *Christmas. "Mickey's Christmas Train". Multicoloured designs as T* **171a** *of Lesotho. P* 14×13½.
1160 1 c. Minnie Mouse in parcels van (*horiz*) 10 10
1161 2 c. Mordie and Ferdie on low-loader wagon (*horiz*) 10 10
1162 3 c. Chip n'Dale in wagon with Christmas trees (*horiz*) 10 10
1163 4 c. Donald Duck's nephews riding with reindeer (*horiz*) 10 10
1164 5 c. Donald and Daisy Duck in restaurant car (*horiz*) 10 10
1165 10 c. Grandma Duck, Uncle Scrooge McDuck, Goofy and Clarabelle carol singing in carriage (*horiz*) .. 10 10
1166 $5 Mickey Mouse driving locomotive (*horiz*) .. .. 3·25 3·50
1167 $6 Father Christmas in guard's van (*horiz*) .. .. 4·00 4·50
1160/7 .. .. *Set of* 8 6·75 7·50
MS1168 Two sheets, each 127 × 102 mm, (a) $5 Mickey Mouse and nephews at railway station. (b) $5 Mickey and Minnie Mouse on carousel. P 13½×14 .. .. .. *Set of* 2 *sheets* 7·00 8·00

181 Mickey Mouse as Snake Charmer

(Des Walt Disney Co. Litho Questa)

1989 (8 Feb). *"India-89" International Stamp Exhibition, New Delhi. T* **181** *and similar multicoloured designs showing Walt Disney cartoon characters in India. P* 14×13½.
1169 1 c. Type **181** 10 10
1170 2 c. Goofy with Chowsingha Antelope .. 10 10
1171 3 c. Mickey and Minnie Mouse with Common Peafowl 10 10
1172 5 c. Goofy with Briolette Diamond and Mickey Mouse pushing mine truck .. 10 10
1173 10 c. Clarabelle with Orloff Diamond .. 10 10
1174 25 c. Mickey Mouse as tourist and Regent Diamond, Louvre, Paris 20 15
1175 $4 Minnie and Mickey Mouse with Kohinoor Diamond .. .. .. 3·50 3·50
1176 $5 Mickey Mouse and Goofy with Indian Rhinoceros .. .. 3·50 3·50
1169/76 .. .. *Set of* 8 6·75 6·75
MS1177 Two sheets, each 127 × 102 mm. (a) $6 Mickey Mouse riding Indian elephant. P 14×13½. (b) $6 Mickey Mouse as postman delivering Hope Diamond to Smithsonian Museum, U.S.A. (*vert*). P 13½×14. *Set of* 2 *sheets* 8·00 10·00

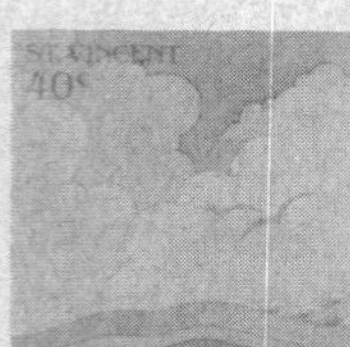

182 Harry James 183 Birds in Flight

(Des A. Nahigian. Litho Questa)

1989 (3 Apr). *Jazz Musicians. T* **182** *and similar horiz designs. Multicoloured. P* 14.
1178 10 c. Type **182** 20 15
1179 15 c. Sidney Bechet 30 15
1180 25 c. Benny Goodman 40 20
1181 35 c. Django Reinhardt 45 20
1182 50 c. Lester Young 60 35
1183 90 c. Gene Krupa 85 85
1184 $3 Louis Armstrong .. .. .. 2·00 2·50
1185 $4 Duke Ellington .. .. 2·50 2·75
1178/85 .. .. *Set of* 8 6·50 6·50
MS1186 Two sheets, each 107×92 mm. (a) $5 Charlie Parker. (b) $5 Billie Holliday *Set of* 2 *sheets* 7·50 8·00

(Des N. Waldman. Litho B.D.T.)

1989 (10 Apr). *Wildlife Conservation. Noah's Ark. T* **183** *and similar square designs. Multicoloured. P* 14.
1187 40 c. Type **183** 30 30
a. Sheetlet. Nos. 1187/211 .. .. 6·50
1188 40 c. Rainbow (left side) 30 30
1189 40 c. Noah's Ark on mountain 30 30
1190 40 c. Rainbow (right side) 30 30
1191 40 c. Birds in flight (*different*) 30 30
1192 40 c. Cow elephant 30 30
1193 40 c. Bull elephant 30 30
1194 40 c. Top of eucalyptus tree 30 30
1195 40 c. Kangaroos 30 30
1196 40 c. Hummingbird 30 30
1197 40 c. Lions 30 30
1198 40 c. White-tailed Deer 30 30
1199 40 c. Koala in fork of tree 30 30
1200 40 c. Koala on branch 30 30
1201 40 c. Hummingbird approaching flower .. 30 30
1202 40 c. Keel-billed Toucan and flower .. 30 30
1203 40 c. Keel-billed Toucan facing right .. 30 30
1204 40 c. Camels 30 30
1205 40 c. Giraffes 30 30
1206 40 c. Mountain Sheep 30 30
1207 40 c. Ladybirds on leaf 30 30
1208 40 c. Swallowtail butterfly 30 30
1209 40 c. Swallowtail butterfly behind leaves 30 30
1210 40 c. Pythons 30 30
1211 40 c. Dragonflies 30 30
1187/211 .. .. *Set of* 25 6·50 6·50

Nos. 1187/211 were printed together, *se-tenant*, in a sheetlet of 25, forming a composite design showing Noah's Ark and animals released after the Flood.

(Litho Questa)

1989 (17 Apr). *Easter. 500th Birth Anniv of Titian (artist). Vert designs as T* **186a** *of Lesotho. Multicoloured. P* 13½×14.
1212 5 c. "Baptism of Christ" (detail) 10 10
1213 30 c. "Temptation of Christ" 25 15
1214 45 c. "Ecce Homo" 40 25
1215 65 c. "Noli Me Tangere" (fragment) .. 55 55
1216 75 c. "Christ carrying the Cross" (detail) .. 60 65
1217 $1 "Christ crowned with Thorns" (detail) 70 75
1218 $4 "Lamentation over Christ" (detail) .. 2·75 3·25
1219 $5 "The Entombment" (detail) .. .. 3·25 3·75
1212/19 .. .. *Set of* 8 7·75 8·50
MS1220 (a) 98×111 mm. $6 "Pietà "(detail). (b) 114×95 mm. $6 "The Deposition" (detail) *Set of* 2 *sheets* 7·00 8·00

184 *Ile de France*

185 Space Shuttle deploying West German Satellite, 1983

(Des W. Wright. Litho Questa)

1989 (21 Apr). *Ocean Liners. T* **184** *and similar horiz designs. Multicoloured. P* 14.
1221 10 c. Type **184** 40 20
1222 40 c. *Liberté* 75 30
1223 50 c. *Mauretania I* (launched 1906) .. 80 40
1224 75 c. *France* .. .. 1·25 1·00
1225 $1 *Aquitania* .. .. 1·50 1·10
1226 $2 *United States* .. .. 2·25 2·50
1227 $3 *Olympic* .. .. 3·00 3·25
1228 $4 *Queen Elizabeth* .. .. .. 3·00 3·50
1221/8 .. .. *Set of* 8 11·50 11·00
MS1229 Two sheets, each 141×108 mm. (a) $6 *Queen Mary* (85×28 *mm*). (b) $6 *Queen Elizabeth 2* (85×28 *mm*) .. .. .. *Set of* 2 *sheets* 9·00 11·00

(Des M. Dorfman. Litho Questa)

1989 (26 Apr). *International Co-operation in Space. T* **185** *and similar vert designs. Multicoloured. P* 14.
1230 40 c. Type **185** 50 20
1231 60 c. Vladimir Remek (Czech cosmonaut) and "Soyuz 28", 1978 .. .. 70 50
1232 $1 Projected "Hermes" space plane and "Columbus" Space Station 90 90
1233 $4 Ulf Merbold (West German astronaut), 1983, and proposed European Spacelab .. .. 2·75 3·50
1230/3 .. .. *Set of* 4 4·25 4·50
MS1234 93×67 mm. $5 Meeting in space of "Apollo/Soyuz" mission crews, 1975 .. 2·75 3·50

186 "Mercury 9" Capsule and Astronaut Cooper

187 Head of St. Vincent Amazon

(Des M. Dorfman. Litho Questa)

1989 (26 Apr). *25th Anniv of Launching of "Telstar II" Communications Satellite* (1988). *T* **186** *and similar vert designs, each showing satellite and T.V. screen. Multicoloured. P* 14.
1235 15 c. Type **186** 20 15
1236 35 c. Martin Luther King addressing crowd, 1963 .. .. 30 20
1237 50 c. Speedskater. Winter Olympic Games, Innsbruck, 1964 .. .. .. 45 45
1238 $3 Pope John XXIII blessing crowd .. 1·75 2·50
1235/8 .. .. *Set of* 4 2·40 3·00
MS1239 107×77 mm. $5 Launch of "Telstar II", 1963 .. .. 2·75 3·50

(Des L. McQueen. Litho Questa)

1989 (3 May). *Wildlife Conservation. St. Vincent Amazon ("St. Vincent Parrot"). T* **187** *and similar multicoloured designs. P* 14.
1240 10 c. Type **187** 55 30
1241 20 c. St. Vincent Amazon in flight .. 90 45
1242 40 c. Feeding (*vert*) .. .. .. 1·75 65
1243 70 c. At entrance to nest (*vert*) .. .. 2·25 3·00
1240/3 .. .. *Set of* 4 5·00 4·00

188 Blue-hooded Euphonia ("Mistletoe Bird")

(Des Tracy Pedersen. Litho Questa)

1989 (3 May). *Birds of St. Vincent. T* **188** *and similar multicoloured designs. P* 14.
1244 25 c. Type **188** 45 20
1245 75 c. Common Black Hawk ("Crab Hawk") 1·00 65
1246 $2 Mangrove Cuckoo ("Coucou") .. 1·75 1·90

1247 $3 Hooded Tanager ("Prince Bird") .. 2·00 2·25
1244/7 .. .. *Set of* 4 4·75 4·50
MS1248 Two sheets. (a) 75×105 mm. $5 Rufous-throated Solitaire ("Soufriere Bird") (*vert*). (b) 105×75 mm. $5 Purple-throated Carib ("Doctor Bird") .. .. *Set of* 2 *sheets* 5·50 7·00

(Litho Questa)

1989 (6 July). *Japanese Art. Multicoloured designs as T* **187a** *of Lesotho. P* 14×13½.
1249 10 c. "Autumn Flowers in Front of the Full Moon" (Hiroshige) 10 10
1250 40 c. "Hibiscus" (Hiroshige) 25 25
1251 50 c. "Iris" (Hiroshige) 30 30
1252 75 c. "Morning Glories" (Hiroshige) 50 50
1253 $1 "Dancing Swallows" (Hiroshige) 65 65
1254 $2 "Sparrow and Bamboo" (Hiroshige) .. 1·50 1·50
1255 $3 "Yellow Bird and Cotton Rose" (Hiroshige) .. .. 2·00 2·00
1256 $4 "Judos Chrysanthemums in a Deep Ravine in China" (Hiroshige) .. 2·25 2·25
1249/56 .. .. *Set of* 8 6·75 6·75
MS1257 Two sheets, each 102×76 mm. (a) $6 "Rural Cottages in Spring" (Sotatsu). P 14×13½. (b) $6 "The Six Immortal Poets portrayed as Cats" (Kuniyoshi) (*vert*). P 13½×14
Set of 2 *sheets* 7·00 8·50
Nos. 1249/56 were each printed in sheetlets of 10 containing two horizontal strips of 5 stamps separated by printed labels commemorating Emperor Hirohito.

189 Schooner

190 Johnny Bench

(Des J. Batchelor. Litho Questa)

1989 (7 July). *"Philexfrance 89" International Stamp Exhibition, Paris, and Bicentenary of French Revolution. T* **189** *and similar multicoloured designs, showing 18th-century French naval vessels. P* 13½×14.
1258 30 c. Type **189** 50 20
1259 55 c. Corvette 70 50
1260 75 c. Frigate 95 85
1261 $1 Ship of the line .. .. .. 1·25 1·10
1262 $3 *Ville de Paris* (ship of the line) .. 3·00 4·50
1258/62 .. .. *Set of* 5 5·75 6·50
MS1263 76×108 mm. $6 Map of St. Vincent in 18th century (*vert*). P 14×13½ .. .. 3·50 4·50

(Des Rosemary De Figlio and W. Storozuk. Litho Questa)

1989 (23 July). *Famous Baseball Players (2nd series). T* **190** *and similar vert designs. Multicoloured. P* 14.
1264 $2 Type **190** .. .. 1·10 1·00
1265 $2 Red Schoendienst .. .. .. 1·10 1·00
1266 $2 Carl Yastrzemski .. .. .. 1·10 1·00
1267 $2 Ty Cobb .. .. 1·10 1·00
1268 $2 Willie Mays .. .. 1·10 1·00
1269 $2 Stan Musial .. .. 1·10 1·00
1270 $2 Ernie Banks .. .. 1·10 1·00
1271 $2 Lou Gehrig .. .. 1·10 1·00
1272 $2 Jackie Robinson .. .. .. 1·10 1·00
1273 $2 Bob Feller .. .. 1·10 1·00
1274 $2 Ted Williams .. .. .. 1·10 1·00
1275 $2 Al Kaline .. .. 1·10 1·00
1264/75 .. .. *Set of* 12 12·00 11·00
Nos. 1264/75 also exist embossed on gold foil from a restricted printing.

191 Dante Bichette, 1989
192 Chris Sabo

(Des Rosemary De Figlio. Litho Questa)

1989 (23 July). *Major League Baseball Rookies. T* **191** *and similar vert designs. Multicoloured. P* 13½×14.
1276 60 c. Type **191** 50 50
a. Sheetlet. Nos. 1276/84 .. .. 4·00
1277 60 c. Carl Yastrzemski, 1961 .. .. 50 50
1278 60 c. Randy Johnson, 1989 .. .. 50 50
1279 60 c. Jerome Walton, 1989 .. .. 50 50
1280 60 c. Ramon Martinez, 1989 .. .. 50 50
1281 60 c. Ken Hill, 1989 .. .. .. 50 50
1282 60 c. Tom McCarthy, 1989 .. .. 50 50
1283 60 c. Gaylord Perry, 1963 .. .. 50 50
1284 60 c. John Smoltz, 1989 .. .. 50 50
1285 60 c. Bob Milacki, 1989 .. .. 50 50
a. Sheetlet. Nos. 1285/93 .. .. 4·00
1286 60 c. Babe Ruth, 1915 .. .. .. 50 50
1287 60 c. Jim Abbott, 1989 .. .. .. 50 50
1288 60 c. Gary Sheffield, 1989 .. .. 50 50
1289 60 c. Gregg Jeffries, 1989 .. .. 50 50
1290 60 c. Kevin Brown, 1989 .. .. .. 50 50
1291 60 c. Cris Carpenter, 1989 .. .. 50 50
1292 60 c. Johnny Bench, 1968 .. .. 50 50
1293 60 c. Ken Griffey Jr, 1989 .. .. 50 50
1276/93 .. .. *Set of* 18 8·00 8·00
Nos. 1276/84 and 1285/93 were each printed together, *se-tenant*, in sheetlets of 9.

(Des Rosemary De Figlio. Litho Questa)

1989 (23 July). *Major League Baseball Award Winners. T* **192** *and similar vert designs. Multicoloured. P* 13½×14.
1294 60 c. Type **192** 50 50
a. Sheetlet. Nos. 1294/302 .. .. 4·00
1295 60 c. Walt Weiss 50 50
1296 60 c. Willie Mays 50 50
1297 60 c. Kirk Gibson 50 50
1298 60 c. Ted Williams 50 50
1299 60 c. Jose Canseco 50 50
1300 60 c. Gaylord Perry 50 50
1301 60 c. Orel Hershiser 50 50
1302 60 c. Frank Viola 50 50
1294/1302 .. .. .. *Set of* 9 4·00 4·00
Nos. 1294/302 were printed together, *se-tenant*, in a sheetlet of 9.

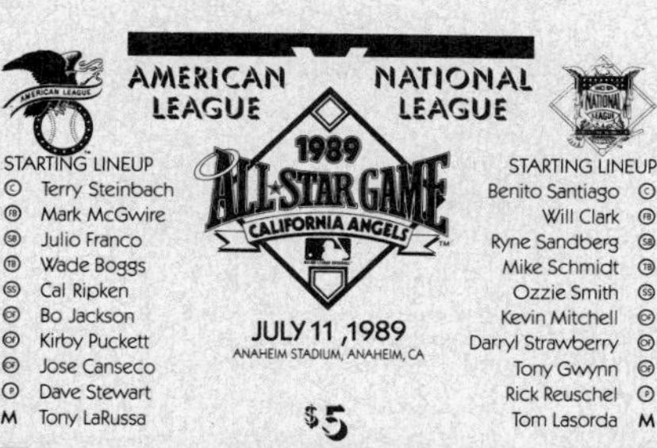

193 All-Star Game Line-up
(*Illustration reduced. Actual size* 115 × 80 *mm*)

(Des Rosemary De Figlio. Litho Questa)

1989 (23 July). *American League v National League All-Star Game, 1989. Sheet* 115×81 *mm. Imperf.*
MS1303 **193** $5 multicoloured .. .. .. 2·40 2·75

194 St. Vincent Amazon

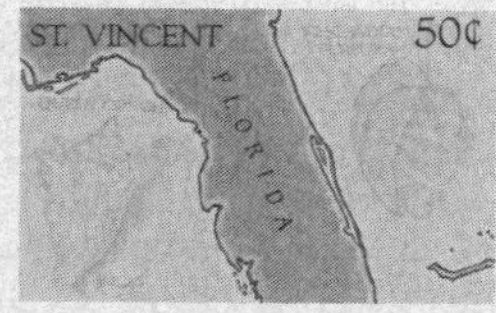

195 Queen or Pink Conch and Wide-mouthed Purpura Shells

(Des Maxine North. Litho Questa)

1989 (31 July). *P* 15×14.
1304 **194** 55 c. multicoloured 45 35

(Des I. MacLaury. Litho B.D.T.)

1989 (31 Aug). *500th Anniv of Discovery of America by Columbus* (1992) (*3rd issue*). *T* **195** *and similar horiz designs. P* 14.
1305 50 c. multicoloured 35 35
a. Sheetlet. Nos. 1305/24 .. .. 6·00
1306 50 c. multicoloured 35 35
1307 50 c. dull ultramarine, black & brt new blue 35 35
1308 50 c. dull ultramarine, black & brt new blue 35 35
1309 50 c. multicoloured 35 35
1310 50 c. multicoloured 35 35
1311 50 c. multicoloured 35 35
1312 50 c. black and bright new blue 35 35
1313 50 c. multicoloured 35 35
1314 50 c. multicoloured 35 35
1315 50 c. multicoloured 35 35
1316 50 c. multicoloured 35 35
1317 50 c. multicoloured 35 35
1318 50 c. multicoloured 35 35
1319 50 c. multicoloured 35 35
1320 50 c. multicoloured 35 35
1321 50 c. multicoloured 35 35
1322 50 c. multicoloured 35 35
1323 50 c. multicoloured 35 35
1324 50 c. multicoloured 35 35
1305/24 .. .. *Set of* 20 6·00 6·00
Designs:—No. 1305, Type **195**; 1306, Caribbean reef fishes; 1307, Sperm Whale; 1308, Fleet of Columbus; 1309, Sharksucker (fish); 1310, Columbus planting flag; 1311, Navigational instruments; 1312, Sea monster; 1313, Kemp's Ridley Turtle; 1314, Magnificent Frigate Bird; 1315, Caribbean Manatee; 1316, Caribbean Monk Seal; 1317, Mayan chief, dugout canoe and caravel; 1318, Blue-footed Boobies; 1319, Venezuelan pile village; 1320, Atlantic Wing Oyster and Lion's-paw Scallop; 1321, Great Hammerhead and Short-finned Mako; 1322, Brown Pelican and Hyacinth Macaw; 1323, Venezuelan bowmen; 1324, Capuchin and Squirrel Monkeys.
Nos. 1305/24 were printed together, *se-tenant*, in a sheetlet of 20 (4×5), forming a composite design of a Caribbean map showing the voyages of Columbus.

196 Command Module *Columbia* returning to Earth

(Des W. Wright. Litho Questa)

1989 (11 Sept). *20th Anniv of First Manned Landing on Moon. T* **196** *and similar multicoloured designs. P* 14.
1325 35 c. Type **196** 30 25
1326 75 c. Lunar module *Eagle* landing .. 60 55
1327 $1 "Apollo 11" launch 70 65
1328 $2 Buzz Aldrin on Moon .. .. 1·10 1·25
a. Horiz strip of 4. Nos. 1328/31 .. 4·00
1329 $2 Lunar module *Eagle* .. .. 1·10 1·25
1330 $2 Earthrise from the Moon .. .. 1·10 1·25
1331 $2 Neil Armstrong .. .. .. 1·10 1·25
1332 $3 *Eagle* and *Columbia* in Moon Orbit .. 1·50 1·75
1325/32 .. .. *Set of* 8 6·75 7·50
MS1333 Two sheets, each 108×79 mm. (a) $3 Command Module *Columbia*, $3 Lunar Module *Eagle*. (b) $6 Neil Armstrong stepping on to Moon (*vert*) .. .. .. *Set of* 2 *sheets* 7·00 8·50
Nos. 1328/31 were printed together, *se-tenant*, in horizontal strips of four throughout the sheet.

197 Jay Howell and Alejandro Pena

1989 (23 Sept). *Centenary of the Los Angeles Dodgers (1st issue). Baseball Players. T* **197** *and similar horiz designs. Multicoloured. Litho. P* 12½.
1334 60 c. Type **197** 45 45
a. Sheetlet. Nos. 1334/41 .. .. 3·50
1335 60 c. Mike Davis and Kirk Gibson .. 45 45
1336 60 c. Fernando Valenzuela and John Shelby 45 45
1337 60 c. Jeff Hamilton and Franklin Stubbs 45 45
1338 60 c. Aerial view of Dodger stadium .. 45 45
1339 60 c. Ray Searage and John Tudor .. 45 45
1340 60 c. Mike Sharperson and Mickey Hatcher 45 45
1341 60 c. Coaching staff 45 45
1342 60 c. John Wetteland and Ramon Martinez 45 45
1343 60 c. Tim Belcher and Tim Crews .. 45 45
a. Sheetlet. Nos. 1343/51 .. .. 3·50
1344 60 c. Orel Hershiser and Mike Morgan .. 45 45
1345 60 c. Mike Scioscia and Rick Dempsey .. 45 45
1346 60 c. Dave Anderson and Alfredo Griffin 45 45
1347 60 c. Dodgers emblem 45 45
1348 60 c. Kal Daniels and Mike Marshall .. 45 45
1349 60 c. Eddie Murray and Willie Randolph 45 45
1350 60 c. Tom Lasorda and Jose Gonzalez .. 45 45
1351 60 c. Lenny Harris, Chris Gwynn and Billy Bean 45 45
1334/51 .. .. *Set of* 18 7·00 7·00
Nos. 1334/42 and 1343/51 were each printed together, *se-tenant*, in sheetlets of 9.
For similar stamps, but rouletted 7, see Nos. 1541/58.

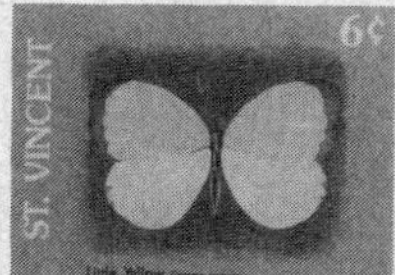

198 *Eurema venusta*

199 Young Footballers

(Des D. Bruckner. Litho Questa)

1989 (16 Oct). *Butterflies. T* **198** *and similar multicoloured designs. P* 14×14½.
1352 6 c. Type **198** 25 15
1353 10 c. *Historis odius* 30 15
1354 15 c. *Cynthia virginiensis* 40 15
1355 75 c. *Leptotes cassius* 80 65
1356 $1 *Battus polydamas* 90 75
1357 $2 *Astraptes talus* .. .. .. 2·00 2·25
1358 $3 *Danaus gilippus* .. .. .. 2·50 2·75
1359 $5 *Myscelia antholia* .. .. .. 3·50 4·00
1352/9 .. .. *Set of* 8 9·50 9·75
MS1360 Two sheets, each 76×103 mm. (a) $6 *Danaus plexippus* (*vert*). (b) $6 *Eurema daira* (*vert*). P 14½×14 .. *Set of* 2 *sheets* 8·00 9·00

(Des R. Vigurs. Litho B.D.T.)

1989 (16 Oct). *World Cup Football Championship, Italy (1st issue)* (1990). *T* **199** *and similar horiz designs. Multicoloured. P* 14.
1361 10 c. Type **199** 35 15
1362 55 c. Youth football teams 70 30
1363 $1 St. Vincent team in training .. 1·25 90
1364 $5 National team with trophies .. 3·00 4·00
1361/4 .. .. *Set of* 4 4·75 4·75
MS1365 Two sheets, each 103×73 mm. (a) $6 Youth team. (b) $6 National team *Set of* 2 *sheets* 9·00 10·00
See also Nos. 1559/63.

200 St. Vincent Amazon

+10c
CALIF. EARTHQUAKE
RELIEF

(**201**)

(Des Tracy Pedersen. Litho Questa)

1989 (1 Nov). *Wildlife. T* **200** *and similar multicoloured designs. P* 14.
1366 65 c. Type **200** .. 75 65
1367 75 c. Whistling Warbler .. 90 75
1368 $5 Black Snake .. 4·00 5·00
1366/8 .. *Set of* 3 5·00 5·75
MS1369 97×70 mm. $6 Volcano Plant (*vert*) .. 3·50 4·75

1989 (17 Nov). *California Earthquake Relief Fund. Nos.* 1276/1302 *surch as T* **201**.
1370 60 c. + 10 c. Type **191** .. 40 40
a. Sheetlet. Nos. 1370/8 .. 3·25
1371 60 c. + 10 c. Carl Yastrzemski .. 40 40
1372 60 c. + 10 c. Randy Johnson .. 40 40
1373 60 c. + 10 c. Jerome Walton .. 40 40
1374 60 c. + 10 c. Ramon Martinez .. 40 40
1375 60 c. + 10 c. Ken Hill .. 40 40
1376 60 c. + 10 c. Tom McCarthy .. 40 40
1377 60 c. + 10 c. Gaylord Perry .. 40 40
1378 60 c. + 10 c. John Smoltz .. 40 40
1379 60 c. + 10 c. Bob Milacki .. 40 40
a. Sheetlet. Nos. 1379/87 .. 3·25
1380 60 c. + 10 c. Babe Ruth .. 40 40
1381 60 c. + 10 c. Jim Abbott .. 40 40
1382 60 c. + 10 c. Gary Sheffield .. 40 40
1383 60 c. + 10 c. Gregg Jeffries .. 40 40
1384 60 c. + 10 c. Kevin Brown .. 40 40
1385 60 c. + 10 c. Cris Carpenter .. 40 40
1386 60 c. + 10 c. Johnny Bench .. 40 40
1387 60 c. + 10 c. Ken Griffey Jr .. 40 40
1388 60 c. + 10 c. Type **192** .. 40 40
a. Sheetlet. Nos. 1388/96 .. 3·25
1389 60 c. + 10 c. Walt Weiss .. 40 40
1390 60 c. + 10 c. Willie Mays .. 40 40
1391 60 c. + 10 c. Kirk Gibson .. 40 40
1392 60 c. + 10 c. Ted Williams .. 40 40
1393 60 c. + 10 c. Jose Canseco .. 40 40
1394 60 c. + 10 c. Gaylord Perry .. 40 40
1395 60 c. + 10 c. Orel Hershiser .. 40 40
1396 60 c. + 10 c. Frank Viola .. 40 40
1370/96 .. *Set of* 27 9·50 9·50

(Des Walt Disney Co. Litho Questa)

1989 (17 Nov). *"World Stamp Expo '89" International Stamp Exhibition, Washington (1st issue). Multicoloured designs as T* **234** *of Maldive Islands showing Walt Disney cartoon characters and U.S. monuments. P* 13½×14.
1397 1 c. Mickey and Minnie Mouse by Seagull Monument, Utah (*vert*) .. 10 10
1398 2 c. Mickey Mouse and Goofy at Lincoln Memorial (*vert*) .. 10 10
1399 3 c. Mickey and Minnie Mouse at Crazy Horse Memorial, South Dakota (*vert*) 10 10
1400 4 c. Mickey Mouse saluting "Uncle Sam" Wilson statue, New York (*vert*) .. 10 10
1401 5 c. Goofy and Mickey Mouse at Benjamin Franklin Memorial, Philadelphia (*vert*) .. 10 10
1402 10 c. Goofy and Mickey Mouse at George Washington statue, New York (*vert*) 10 10
1403 $3 Mickey Mouse at John F. Kennedy's birthplace, Massachusetts (*vert*) .. 3·50 4·00
1404 $6 Mickey and Minnie Mouse at Mount Vernon, Virginia (*vert*) .. 5·50 6·00
1397/1404 .. *Set of* 8 8·00 9·00
MS1405 Two sheets, each 127×100 mm. (a) $5 Mickey and Minnie Mouse over Mount Rushmore, South Dakota. (b) $5 Mickey Mouse and Donald Duck at Stone Mountain, Georgia. P 14×13½ .. *Set of* 2 *sheets* 9·00 10·00

(Des Design Element. Litho Questa)

1989 (17 Nov). *"World Stamp Expo '89" International Stamp Exhibition, Washington (2nd issue). Sheet 61×78 mm containing multicoloured designs as T* **193***a of Lesotho. P* 14.
MS1406 $5 Washington Monument (*vert*) 2·10 2·50

202 Nolan Ryan

(Des W. Storozuk. Litho)

1989 (30 Nov). *Famous Baseball Players (3rd series). P* 12½.
1407 **202** $2 multicoloured .. 85 1·00
a. Sheetlet of 9 .. 7·75

No. 1407 was printed in sheetlets of 9, with each stamp showing a different commemorative inscription.

203 Early Wynn

204 Arms and 1979 Independence 50 c. Stamp

(Des Susan Gansbourg. Litho)

1989 (30 Nov). *Famous Baseball Players (4th series). T* **203** *and similar horiz designs. P* 12½.
1408/88 30 c. × 81 multicoloured .. *Set of* 81 16·00 18·00

Nos. 1408/88 were issued as nine sheetlets, each of 9 different designs. No. 1456 (Mike Greenwell) was also available in sheetlets containing nine examples of the one design.

(Des and litho Questa)

1989 (20 Dec). *10th Anniv of Independence. P* 14.
1489 **204** 65 c. multicoloured .. 50 50
MS1490 57×77 mm. **204** $10 multicoloured .. 5·00 5·75

(Litho Questa)

1989 (20 Dec). *Christmas. Paintings by Botticelli and Da Vinci. Vert designs as T* **193***b of Lesotho. Multicoloured. P* 14.
1491 10 c. Holy Family (detail, "The Adoration of the Magi") (Botticelli) .. 15 10
1492 25 c. Crowd (detail, "The Adoration of the Magi") (Botticelli) .. 25 15
1493 30 c. "The Madonna of the Magnificat" (detail) (Botticelli) .. 25 15
1494 40 c. "The Virgin and Child with St. Anne and St. John the Baptist" (detail) (Da Vinci) .. 30 20
1495 55 c. Angel (detail,"The Annunciation") (Da Vinci) .. 40 30
1496 75 c. Virgin Mary (detail, "The Annunciation") (Da Vinci) .. 50 50
1497 $5 "Madonna of the Carnation" (detail) (Da Vinci) .. 3·00 3·50
1498 $6 "The Annunciation" (detail) (Botticelli) .. 3·50 4·00
1491/8 .. *Set of* 8 7·50 8·00
MS1499 Two sheets, each 70×94 mm. (a) $5 "The Virgin of the Rocks" (detail) (Da Vinci). (b) $5 Holy Family (detail, "The Adoration of the Magi") (Botticelli) .. *Set of* 2 *sheets* 5·50 6·50

205 Boy Scout, 1989

206 Man and Blind Girl

(Des A. Fagbohun. Litho Questa)

1989 (20 Dec). *75th Anniv of Boy Scout and 60th Anniv of Girl Guide Movements in St. Vincent. T* **205** *and similar multicoloured designs, each showing portrait of Lord or Lady Baden-Powell. P* 14.
1500 35 c. Type **205** .. 55 35
1501 35 c. Guide, ranger and brownie .. 55 35
1502 55 c. Boy scout in original uniform .. 75 35
1503 55 c. Mrs. Jackson (founder of St. Vincent Girl Guides) .. 75 35
1504 $2 Scouts' 75th Anniv logo .. 2·00 2·75
1505 $2 Mrs. Russell (Girl Guide leader, 1989) 2·00 2·75
1500/5 .. *Set of* 6 6·00 6·25
MS1506 Two sheets, each 105×75 mm. (a) $5 Scout in canoe. (b) $5 Scout and Guide with flagpoles (*horiz*) .. *Set of* 2 *sheets* 8·00 9·00

(Des W. Hanson Studio. Litho Questa)

1990 (5 Mar). *25th Anniv of Lions Club of St. Vincent* (1989). *T* **206** *and similar multicoloured designs. P* 14.
1507 10 c. Type **206** .. 40 20
1508 65 c. Handing out school books (*horiz*) .. 70 50
1509 75 c. Teacher explaining diabetes (*horiz*) 80 60
1510 $2 Blood sugar testing machine (*horiz*) 1·75 2·00
1511 $4 Distributing book on drugs (*horiz*) .. 2·75 3·50
1507/11 .. *Set of* 5 5·75 6·00

(Des W. Wright. Litho Questa)

1990 (2 Apr). *50th Anniv of Second World War. Horiz designs as T* **242** *of Maldive Islands. Multicoloured. P* 14.
1512 5 c. Scuttling of *Admiral Graf Spee* (German pocket battleship), 1939 .. 10 10
1513 10 c. General De Gaulle and French resistance, 1940 .. 15 15
1514 15 c. British tank, North Africa, 1940 .. 20 20
1515 25 c. U.S.S. *Reuben James* (destroyer) in periscope sight, 1941 .. 30 30
1516 30 c. General MacArthur and map of S.W. Pacific, 1942 .. 35 35
1517 40 c. American parachute drop on Corregidor, 1945 .. 40 40
1518 55 c. H.M.S. *King George V* (battleship) engaging *Bismarck* (German battleship), 1941 .. 55 55
1519 75 c. American battleships entering Tokyo Bay, 1945 .. 70 70
1520 $5 Hoisting the Soviet flag on the Reichstag, Berlin, 1945 .. 3·25 3·25
1521 $6 American aircraft carriers, Battle of Philippines Sea, 1944 .. 3·75 3·75
1512/21 .. *Set of* 10 8·75 8·75
MS1522 100×70 mm. $6 Japanese Mitsubishi A6M Zero-Sen fighter, Battle of Java Sea, 1942 3·75 4·25

207 Two Pence Blue

Sixth No-Hitter
11 June 90
Oakland Athletics

(**208**)

(Des M. Pollard. Litho B.D.T)

1990 (3 May). *150th Anniv of the Penny Black. T* **207** *and similar vert designs. P* 14×15.
1523 $2 black, blue-green and bright magenta 1·25 1·50
1524 $4 black and bright magenta .. 2·50 3·25
MS1525 130×99 mm. $6 black, scarlet & yellow 4·00 4·75
Designs:—$4, $6 Penny Black.

(Des Walt Disney Co. Litho Questa)

1990 (3 May). *"Stamp World London 90" International Stamp Exhibition. British Uniforms. Multicoloured designs as T* **239***a of Maldive Islands showing Walt Disney cartoon characters. P* 13½×14.
1526 5 c. Scrooge McDuck as 18th-century admiral (*vert*) .. 20 15
1527 10 c. Huey as Light Infantry bugler, 1854 (*vert*) .. 25 15
1528 15 c. Minnie Mouse as Irish Guards drummer, 1900 (*vert*) .. 35 20
1529 25 c. Goofy as Seaforth Highlanders lance-corporal, 1944 (*vert*) .. 45 30
1530 $1 Mickey Mouse as 58th Regiment ensign, 1879 (*vert*) .. 1·25 1·00
1531 $2 Donald Duck as Royal Engineers officer, 1813 (*vert*) .. 1·90 2·00
1532 $4 Mickey Mouse as Duke of Edinburgh's Royal Regiment drum major (*vert*) .. 3·00 3·50
1533 $5 Goofy as Cameronians sergeant piper, 1918 (*vert*) .. 3·00 3·50
1526/33 .. *Set of* 8 9·25 9·75
MS1534 Two sheets, each 120×100 mm. (a) $6 Goofy as officer in King's Lifeguard of Foot, 1643. P 13½×14. (b) $6 Mickey Mouse as Grenadier Guards drummer (*vert*). P 14×13½ *Set of* 2 *sheets* 7·00 8·00

1990 (23 June). *Nolan Ryan–Sixth No-hitter. No.* 1407 *optd with T* **208**.
1535 **202** $2 multicoloured .. 95 1·00
a. Sheetlet of 9 .. 7·75

(Des Young Phillips Studio. Litho Questa)

1990 (5 July). *90th Birthday of Queen Elizabeth the Queen Mother. Vert designs as T* **198***a of Lesotho showing portraits,* 1950–59. *P* 14.
1536 $2 black, bright sage-green and magenta 1·25 1·50
a. Strip of 3. Nos. 1536/8 .. 3·25
1537 $2 black, bright sage-green and magenta 1·25 1·50
1538 $2 black, bright sage-green and magenta 1·25 1·50
1536/8 .. *Set of* 3 3·25 4·00
MS1539 90×75 mm. $6 multicoloured .. 3·25 4·00
Designs:—No. 1536, Queen Elizabeth signing visitors' book; Nos. 1537, **MS**1539, Queen Elizabeth in evening dress; No. 1538, Queen Elizabeth the Queen Mother in Coronation robes, 1953.

Nos. 1536/8 were printed together, horizontally and vertically *se-tenant*, in sheetlets of 9 (3×3).

300th Win
Milwaukee Brewers
July 31, 1990

(**209**)

210 Maradona, Argentina

1990 (3 Aug). *Nolan Ryan–300th Win. No.* 1407 *optd with T* **209**.
1540 **202** $2 multicoloured .. 95 1·00
a. Sheetlet of 9 .. 7·75

1990 (21 Sept). *Centenary of Los Angeles Dodgers (2nd issue). Baseball Players. Multicoloured designs as T* **197**. *Litho. Rouletted* 7.
1541 60 c. Mickey Hatcher and Jay Howell .. 45 45
a. Sheetlet. Nos. 1541/9 .. 3·50
1542 60 c. Juan Samuel and Mike Scioscia .. 45 45

1543 60 c. Lenny Harris and Mike Hartley .. 45 45
1544 60 c. Ramon Martinez and Mike Morgan 45 45
1545 60 c. Aerial view of Dodger stadium .. 45 45
1546 60 c. Stan Javier and Don Aase .. 45 45
1547 60 c. Ray Searage and Mike Sharperson .. 45 45
1548 60 c. Tim Belcher and Pat Perry 45 45
1549 60 c. Dave Walsh, Jose Vizcaino, Jim Neidlinger, Jose Offerman and Carlos Hernandez 45 45
1550 60 c. Hubie Brooks and Orel Hershiser .. 45 45
a. Sheetlet. Nos. 1550/8 .. .. 3·50
1551 60 c. Tom Lasorda and Tim Crews .. 45 45
1552 60 c. Fernando Valenzuela and Eddie Murray 45 45
1553 60 c. Kal Daniels and Jose Gonzalez .. 45 45
1554 60 c. Dodgers emblem 45 45
1555 60 c. Chris Gwynn and Jeff Hamilton .. 45 45
1556 60 c. Kirk Gibson and Rick Dempsey .. 45 45
1557 60 c. Jim Gott and Alfredo Griffin .. 45 45
1558 60 c. Ron Perranoski, Bill Russell, Joe Ferguson, Joe Amalfitano, Mark Cresse, Ben Hines and Manny Mota 45 45
1541/58 .. .. *Set of* 18 7·00 7·00

Nos. 1541/9 and 1550/8 were each printed together, *se-tenant*, in sheetlets of nine.

(Des Young Phillips Studio. Litho Questa)

1990 (24 Sept). *World Cup Football Championship, Italy* (2nd *issue*). *T* **210** *and similar vert designs. Multicoloured. P* 14.

1559 10 c. Type **210** 25 15
1560 75 c. Valderrama, Colombia 65 65
1561 $1 Francescoli, Uruguay 85 85
1562 $5 Beulemans, Belgium .. .. 3·50 4·25
1559/62 .. .. *Set of* 4 4·75 5·25
MS1563 Two sheets, each 101×85 mm. (a) $6 Klinsmann, West Germany. (b) $6 Careca, Brazil .. .. *Set of* 2 *sheets* 7·50 8·50

(211)

JOE DELOACH U.S.A. STEVE LEWIS U.S.A. PAUL ERANG KENYA

(212)

1990 (18 Oct). 95*th Anniv of Rotary International. Nos.* 1230/8 *optd with T* **211**.

1564 10 c. Type **186** 30 20
1565 40 c. *Liberté* 50 40
1566 50 c. *Mauretania I* (launched 1906) .. 55 45
1567 75 c. *France* 80 60
1568 $1 *Aquitania* 90 80
1569 $2 *United States* .. .. .. 1·60 1·60
1570 $3 *Olympic* .. .. 2·00 2·25
1571 $4 *Queen Elizabeth* .. .. .. 2·25 2·50
1564/71 .. .. *Set of* 8 8·00 8·00
MS1572 Two sheets, each 141×108 mm. (a) $6 *Queen Mary* (85×28 *mm*). (b) $6 *Queen Elizabeth* 2 (85×28 *mm*) .. .. .. *Set of* 2 *sheets* 8·00 9·00

1990 (18 Oct). *Olympic Medal Winners, Seoul. Nos.* 1153/7 *optd as T* **212**.

1573 10 c. Type **178** 20 20
1574 50 c. Long jumping (optd "CARL LEWIS U.S.A.") 60 60
a. Opt inverted .. .. .. † —
1575 $1 Triple jumping (optd "HRISTO MARKOV BULGARIA") 90 90
1576 $5 Boxing (optd "HENRY MASKE E. GERMANY") .. .. .. 3·25 3·75
a. Opt inverted .. .. .. † —
1573/6 .. .. *Set of* 4 4·50 5·00
MS1577 85×63 mm. $10 Olympic flame* 7·50 8·00

*No. **MS**1577 is overprinted "FINAL MEDAL STANDINGS" and medal totals for either South Korea and Spain or U.S.S.R. and U.S.A. on the margin (*same price for either opt*).

213 *Dendrophylax funalis* and *Dimerandra emarginata*

214 "Miraculous Draught of Fishes" (detail, Rubens)

(Litho B.D.T.)

1990 (23 Nov). *"EXPO 90" International Garden and Greenery Exposition, Osaka. Orchids. T* **213** *and similar vert designs. Multicoloured. P* 14.

1578 10 c. Type **213** 35 20
1579 15 c. *Epidendrum elongatum* 40 25
1580 45 c. *Comparettia falcata* 60 30
1581 60 c. *Brassia maculata* 75 60
1582 $1 *Encyclia cochleata* and *Encyclia cordigera* 90 80
1583 $2 *Cyrtopodium punctatum* .. .. 1·50 1·75
1584 $4 *Cattleya labiata* .. .. .. 2·50 2·50
1585 $5 *Bletia purpurea* .. .. .. 2·75 3·25
1578/85 .. .. *Set of* 8 8·75 9·00
MS1586 Two sheets, each 108×78 mm. (a) $6 *Vanilla planifolia Jackson*. (b) $6 *Ionopsis utricularioides* .. .. .. *Set of* 2 *sheets* 7·50 8·50

(Litho Questa)

1990 (3 Dec). *Christmas.* 350*th Death Anniv of Rubens. T* **214** *and similar vert designs. Multicoloured. P* 13½×14.

1587 10 c. Type **214** 25 20
1588 45 c. "Crowning of Holy Katherine" (detail) 45 25
1589 50 c. "St. Ives of Treguier" (detail) .. 50 30
1590 65 c. "Allegory of Eternity" (detail) .. 65 45
1591 $1 "St. Bavo receives Monastic Habit of Ghent" (detail) 90 80
1592 $2 "Crowning of Holy Katherine" (different detail) .. .. .. 1·50 1·50
1593 $4 "St. Bavo receives Monastic Habit of Ghent" (different detail) .. .. 2·75 3·25
1594 $5 "Communion of St. Francis" (detail) 3·00 3·25
1587/94 .. .. *Set of* 8 9·00 9·00
MS1595 Four sheets. (a) 70×100 mm. $6 "Allegory of Eternity" (different detail). P 13½×14. (b) 70×100 mm. $6 As 50 c. P 13½×14. (c) 100×70 mm. $6 As Type **214** (*horiz*). P 14×13½. (d) 100×70 mm. $6 "St. Bavo receives Monastic Habit of Ghent" (different detail) (*horiz*). P 14×13½ .. *Set of* 4 *sheets* 12·50 13·00

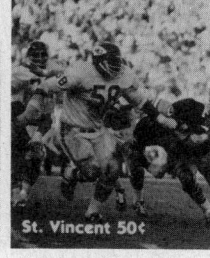

215 Geoffrey Chaucer

St. Vincent 50¢

216 American Football Game

(Des N. Waldman. Litho Cartor)

1990 (12 Dec). *International Literacy Year* (1*st issue*). *Chaucer's* Canterbury Tales. *T* **215** *and similar square designs. Multicoloured. P* 13½.

1596 40 c. Type **215** 35 35
a. Sheetlet. Nos. 1596/1619 .. .. 7·50
1597 40 c. "When April with his showers..." .. 35 35
1598 40 c. "When Zephyr also has..." .. 35 35
1599 40 c. "And many little birds..." .. 35 35
1600 40 c. "And palmers to go seeking out..." .. 35 35
1601 40 c. Quill in ink well and open book .. 35 35
1602 40 c. Green bird in tree 35 35
1603 40 c. Brown bird in tree and franklin's head 35 35
1604 40 c. Purple bird in tree and banner .. 35 35
1605 40 c. Canterbury 35 35
1606 40 c. Knight's head 35 35
1607 40 c. Black bird in tree and squire's head 35 35
1608 40 c. Friar 35 35
1609 40 c. Franklin 35 35
1610 40 c. Prioress and monk holding banner .. 35 35
1611 40 c. Summoner, Oxford clerk and parson 35 35
1612 40 c. Serjeant-at-Law and knight on horseback 35 35
1613 40 c. Squire 35 35
1614 40 c. "In fellowship..." 35 35
1615 40 c. Cockerel and horse's legs 35 35
1616 40 c. Hens 35 35
1617 40 c. Hen and rabbit 35 35
1618 40 c. Horses' legs and butterfly 35 35
1619 40 c. "And briefly, when the sun..." .. 35 35
1596/1619 .. .. .. *Set of* 24 7·50 7·50

Nos. 1596/1619 were printed together, *se-tenant*, as a sheetlet of 24, forming a composite design.

See also Nos. 1777/1802.

(Litho Cartor)

1990 (17 Dec). *Death Centenary of Van Gogh* (*painter*). *Vert designs as T* **255** *of Maldive Islands. Multicoloured. P* 13.

1620 1 c. Self-portrait, 1889 .. .. .. 30 30
a. Vert strip of 4. Nos. 1620/3 .. .. 1·10
1621 5 c. Self-portrait, 1886 .. .. .. 30 30
1622 10 c. Self-portrait with hat and pipe, 1888 30 30
1623 15 c. Self-portrait at easel, 1888 .. .. 30 30
1624 20 c. Self-portrait, 1887 .. .. .. 75 75
a. Vert strip of 4. Nos. 1624/7 .. .. 6·75
1625 45 c. Self-portrait, 1889 (*different*) .. 90 90
1626 $5 Self-portrait with pipe, 1889 .. 2·75 3·00
1627 $6 Self-portrait wearing straw hat, 1887 3·00 3·25
1620/7 .. .. *Set of* 8 7·00 7·50

Nos. 1620/3 and 1624/7 were each printed in sheets of 16 (4×4) with the four values vertically *se-tenant*.

(Litho Questa)

1990 (30 Dec). *Hummel Figurines. Vert designs as T* **256** *of Maldive Islands. Multicoloured. P* 14.

1628 10 c. "The Photographer" 15 15
1629 15 c. "Ladder and Rope" 15 15
1630 40 c. "Druggist" 30 30
1631 60 c. "Hello" 45 45
1632 $1 "Boots" 80 80
1633 $2 "The Artist" .. .. 1·40 1·40
1634 $4 "Waiter" .. .. 2·50 2·50
1635 $5 "The Postman" .. .. .. 2·75 2·75
1628/35 .. .. *Set of* 8 7·50 7·50
MS1636 Two sheets, each 94×121 mm. (a) Nos. 1628, 1631/2 and 1635. (b) Nos. 1629/30 and 1633/4 .. .. .. *Set of* 2 *sheets* 7·50 8·50

1991 (15 Jan). 25*th Anniv of Super Bowl American Football Championship* (1*st issue*). *T* **216** *and similar vert designs. Multicoloured. Litho. P* 13½×14.

MS1637 Twenty-five sheets, each 127×101 mm, containing 50 c. × 2 as horiz pairs forming composite designs of game scenes or 50 c. × 3 (final sheet) showing Vince Lombardi Trophy and helmets of participating teams *Set of* 25 *sheets* 15·00

217 Programme Cover of XXV Super Bowl (*Illustration reduced. Actual size* 105×95 *mm*)

1991 (15 Jan). 25*th Anniv of Super Bowl American Football Championships* (2*nd issue*). *T* **217** *and similar multicoloured designs, each showing a different programme cover illustration. Litho. Imperf.*

MS1638 Twenty-five sheets, 125×99 mm or 99×125 mm, each with a face value of $2 *Set of* 25 *sheets* 26·00

218 U.S.A. 1893 1 c. Columbus Stamp

1991 (18 Mar). 500*th Anniv of Discovery of America* (1992) *by Columbus* (4*th issue*). *T* **218** *and similar horiz designs showing U.S.A* 1893 *Columbian Exposition, Chicago, stamps* (*Nos.* 1639/54) *or ships* (*others*). *Multicoloured. Litho. P* 13½×14.

1639 1 c. Type **218** 10 10
a. Sheetlet. Nos. 1639/46 and 1655 .. 5·00
1640 2 c. U.S.A. Columbus 2 c. 10 10
1641 3 c. U.S.A. Columbus 3 c. 10 10
1642 4 c. U.S.A. Columbus 4 c. 10 10
1643 5 c. U.S.A. Columbus 5 c. 10 10
1644 6 c. U.S.A. Columbus 6 c. 10 10
1645 8 c. U.S.A. Columbus 8 c. 10 10
1646 10 c. U.S.A. Columbus 10 c. 10 10
1647 15 c. U.S.A. Columbus 15 c. 10 10
a. Sheetlet. Nos. 1647/54 and 1656 .. 11·50
1648 30 c. U.S.A. Columbus 30 c. 15 20
1649 50 c. U.S.A. Columbus 50 c. 25 30
1650 $1 U.S.A. Columbus $1 .. .. 50 55
1651 $2 U.S.A. Columbus $2 .. .. 95 1·00
1652 $3 U.S.A. Columbus $3 .. .. 1·40 1·50
1653 $4 U.S.A. Columbus $4 .. .. 2·00 2·10
1654 $5 U.S.A. Columbus $5 .. .. 2·40 2·50
1655 $10 *Santa Maria*, Scarlet Macaw and tropical flower .. .. .. 5·00 5·25
1656 $10 Logo, *Santa Maria* and Amerindian hut .. .. 5·00 5·25
1639/56 .. .. *Set of* 18 16·00 17·00
MS1657 Two sheets, each 98×72 mm. (a) $6 Sailors on ship's fo'c'sle. (b) $6 Ship's figurehead *Set of* 2 *sheets* 8·00 9·00

Nos. 1639/46 and 1655 and Nos. 1647/54 and 1656 were each printed together, *se-tenant*, in sheetlets of 9.

219 Pebbles and Hoppy boxing

(Des Hanna-Barbera Productions. Litho Questa)

1991 (25 Mar). *Sports. T* **219** *and similar horiz designs showing characters from the Flintstones cartoons. Multicoloured. P* 14×13½.

1658 10 c. Type **219** 20 10
1659 15 c. Fred Flintstone and Dino playing football 30 15
1660 45 c. Fred losing rowing race to Barney Rubble 50 30
1661 55 c. Betty Rubble, Wilma Flintstone and Pebbles in dressage competition .. 70 50
1662 $1 Fred playing basketball .. .. 1·00 1·00
1663 $2 Bamm Bamm wrestling Barney with Fred as referee .. .. .. 1·50 1·50
1664 $4 Fred and Barney playing tennis .. 2·75 2·75
1665 $5 Fred, Barney and Dino cycling .. 2·75 2·75
1658/65 .. .. *Set of* 8 8·75 8·75
MS1666 Two sheets, each 117×95 mm. (a) $6 Fred at the plate in baseball game. (b) $6 Fred running to homeplate .. *Set of* 2 *sheets* 7·50 8·00

220 Board Meeting

(Des Hanna-Barbera Productions. Litho Questa)

1991 (25 March). *The Jetsons (cartoon film). T* **220** *and similar multicoloured designs. P* 14×13½ (60 c., $1, $2) *or* 13½×14 (*others*).
1667 5 c. Type **220** 15 10
1668 20 c. Jetsons with Dog 30 15
1669 45 c. Judy and Apollo Blue 50 25
1670 50 c. Cosmo Spacely and George Jetson .. 50 35
1671 60 c. George and Elroy catching cogs (*horiz*) 70 50
1672 $1 Judy, Apollo, Elroy and Teddy in cavern (*horiz*) .. .. .. 1·00 1·00
1673 $2 Drill destroying the cavern (*horiz*) .. 1·50 1·50
1674 $4 Jetsons celebrating with the Grungees 2·75 2·75
1675 $5 The Jetsons returning home .. 2·75 2·75
1667/75 .. .. *Set of* 9 9·00 8·50
MS1676 Two sheets, each 114×76 mm. (a) $6 The Jetsons in spacecraft (*horiz*). (b) $6 The Jetsons in control room (*horiz*). P 14×13½ *Set of* 2 *sheets* 7·00 8·00

(Des T. Agans. Litho Questa)

1991 (13 May). *500th Anniv of Discovery of America by Columbus,* (1992) (*5th issue*). *History of Exploration. Multicoloured designs as T* **64** *of St. Kitts-Nevis (Nevis). P* 14.
1677 5 c. "Sänger 2" (projected space shuttle) .. 15 15
1678 10 c. "Magellan" satellite, 1990 .. .. 15 15
1679 25 c. "Buran" space shuttle 25 25
1680 75 c. Projected "Freedom" space station .. 65 65
1681 $1 Projected Mars mission space craft .. 80 80
1682 $2 "Hubble" telescope, 1990 .. .. 1·60 1·60
1683 $4 Projected Mars mission "sailship" .. 2·50 2·50
1684 $5 Projected "Craf" satellite .. .. 2·50 2·50
1677/84 .. .. *Set of* 8 7·75 7·75
MS1685 Two sheets, each 105×71 mm. (a) $6 Bow of caravel (*vert*). (b) $6 Caravel under full sail .. .. *Set of* 2 *sheets* 7·00 8·00

(Des D. Miller. Litho Walsall)

1991 (5 July). *65th Birthday of Queen Elizabeth II. Horiz designs as T* **210** *of Lesotho. Multicoloured. P* 14.
1686 5 c. Queen and Prince Philip during visit to Spain, 1988 .. .. .. 15 15
1687 60 c. Queen and Prince Philip in landau .. 60 45
1688 $2 Queen at Caen Hill Waterway, 1990 1·75 1·75
1689 $4 Queen at Badminton, 1983 .. .. 3·00 3·25
1686/9 .. .. *Set of* 4 5·00 5·00
MS1690 68×91 mm. $5 Queen Elizabeth II in 1988 and Prince Philip in 1989 .. .. 3·25 3·75

(Des D. Miller. Litho Walsall)

1991 (5 July). *10th Wedding Anniv of the Prince and Princess of Wales. Horiz designs as T* **210** *of Lesotho. Multicoloured. P* 14.
1691 20 c. Prince and Princess in hard hats, 1987 30 20
1692 25 c. Portraits of Prince and Princess and sons 30 20
1693 $1 Prince Henry and Prince William, both in 1988 .. .. .. 90 90
1694 $5 Princess Diana in France and Prince Charles in 1987 .. .. 4·25 4·25
1691/4 .. .. *Set of* 4 5·25 5·00
MS1695 68×90 mm. $5 Princes Henry and William in Majorca, and Princess Diana presenting polo trophy to Prince Charles .. 3·75 3·75

221 Class "D 51" Steam Locomotive

(Des K. Gromell. Litho Cartor)

1991 (12 Aug). *"Phila Nippon '91" International Stamp Exhibition, Tokyo. Japanese Trains. T* **221** *and similar multicoloured designs. P* 13½.
1696 75 c. Type **221** 50 50
a. Sheetlet. Nos. 1696/1704 .. .. 4·00
1697 75 c. Class "9600" steam locomotive .. 50 50
1698 75 c. Goods wagons and chrysanthemum emblem 50 50
1699 75 c. Passenger coach 50 50
1700 75 c. Decorated class "C 57" steam locomotive 50 50
1701 75 c. Oil tanker wagon 50 50
1702 75 c. Class "C 53" steam locomotive .. 50 50
1703 75 c. First Japanese steam locomotive .. 50 50
1704 75 c. Class "C 11" steam locomotive .. 50 50
1705 $1 Class "181" electric train 60 60
a. Sheetlet. Nos. 1705/13 .. .. 4·75
1706 $1 Class "EH-10" electric locomotive .. 60 60
1707 $1 Passenger coaches and Special Express symbol 60 60
1708 $1 Sendai City class "1" tram 60 60
1709 $1 Class "485" electric train 60 60
1710 $1 Sendai City street cleaning tram .. 60 60
1711 $1 Hakari "Bullet" train 60 60
1712 $1 Class "ED-11" electric locomotive .. 60 60
1713 $1 Class "EF-66" electric locomotive .. 60 60
1696/1713 .. .. .. *Set of* 18 8·75 8·75
MS1714 Four sheets, each 108×77 mm. (a) $6 Class "C 55" steam locomotive (*vert*). P 13×13½. (b) $6 Series "400" electric train. P 13½×13. (c) $6 Class "C 62" steam locomotive (*vert*). P 13×13½. (d) $6 Super Hitachi electric train. P 13×13½. .. .. *Set of* 4 *sheets* 15·00 16·00
Nos. 1696/1704 and 1705/13 were each printed together, *se-tenant*, in sheetlets of 9.

222 Marcello Mastroianni (actor)

(Des J. Iskowitz. Litho Cartor)

1991 (22 Aug). *Italian Entertainers. T* **222** *and similar multicoloured designs. P* 13.
1715 $1 Type **222** 70 70
a. Sheetlet. Nos. 1715/23 .. .. 5·75
1716 $1 Sophia Loren (actress) 70 70
1717 $1 Mario Lanza (singer) 70 70
1718 $1 Federico Fellini (director) 70 70
1719 $1 Arturo Toscanini (conductor) .. 70 70
1720 $1 Anna Magnani (actress) 70 70
1721 $1 Giancarlo Giannini (actor) 70 70
1722 $1 Gina Lollobrigida (actress) 70 70
1723 $1 Enrico Caruso (operatic tenor) .. 70 70
1715/23 .. .. *Set of* 9 5·75 5·75
MS1724 117×80 mm. $6 Luciano Pavarotti (operatic tenor) (*horiz*) .. .. .. 5·50 6·00
Nos. 1715/23 were printed together, *se-tenant*, in sheetlets of 9.

223 Madonna

(Des J. Iskowitz. Litho Cartor)

1991 (22 Aug). *Madonna (American singer). T* **223** *and similar vert portraits. Multicoloured. P* 13.
1725 $1 Type **223** 80 80
a. Sheetlet. Nos. 1725/33 .. .. 6·50
1726 $1 In strapless dress 80 80
1727 $1 Wearing necklaces, looking right .. 80 80
1728 $1 In green dress 80 80
1729 $1 Wearing necklaces, looking to front .. 80 80
1730 $1 With wrist bangles 80 80
1731 $1 With hand to face 80 80
1732 $1 In purple dress 80 80
1733 $1 With microphone 80 80
1725/33 .. .. *Set of* 9 6·50 6·50
MS1734 79×118 mm. $6 Madonna (25×40 *mm*). P 12×13 .. .. 6·50 7·00
Nos. 1725/33 were printed together, *se-tenant*, in sheetlets of 9.

224 John Lennon

(Des J. Iskowitz. Litho Cartor)

1991 (22 Aug). *John Lennon (British musician). T* **224** *and similar vert portraits. Multicoloured. P* 13.
1735 $1 + 2 c. Type **224** 80 80
a. Sheetlet. Nos. 1735/43 .. .. 6·50
1736 $1 + 2 c. With Beatle hair cut 80 80
1737 $1 + 2 c. In cap 80 80
1738 $1 + 2 c. In red polka-dot shirt 80 80
1739 $1 + 2 c. In green polo-neck jumper and jacket 80 80
1740 $1 + 2 c. In glasses and magenta jacket .. 80 80
1741 $1 + 2 c. With long hair and glasses .. 80 80
1742 $1 + 2 c. In black jumper 80 80
1743 $1 + 2 c. In polo-neck jumper 80 80
1735/43 .. .. *Set of* 9 6·50 6·50
Nos. 1735/43 were printed together, *se-tenant*, in sheetlets of 9.

225 Free French Resistance Fighters, 1944

226 Myrvyn Bennion

(Des L. Fried (Nos. 1746, 1749/51, **MS**1761a), W. Hanson (Nos. 1747, 1753, 1760, **MS**1761d), J. Iskowitz (Nos. 1752, 1759, **MS**1761b), W. Wright (Nos. 1754/8). Litho Questa)

1991 (18 Nov). *Anniversaries and Events. T* **225** *and similar multicoloured designs. P* 14.
1744 10 c. Type **225** 15 15
1745 45 c. De Gaulle with Churchill, 1944 .. 40 40
1746 50 c. Protestor with banner 45 45
1747 65 c. Tales around the camp fire (*vert*) .. 50 50
1748 75 c. Liberation of Paris, 1944 .. .. 60 60
1749 75 c. Building Berlin Wall 60 60
1750 90 c. German flag and protestors' shadows 70 70
1751 $1 Presidents Bush and Gorbachev shaking hands 80 80
1752 $1 *Marriage of Figaro* 80 80
1753 $1.50, British trenches and Mafeking Siege 3d. stamp .. .. .. 1·00 1·00
1754 $1.50, Modern Trans-Siberian steam locomotive .. .. 1·00 1·00
1755 $1.50, Map of Switzerland and woman in traditional costume .. .. 1·00 1·00
1756 $1.65, Lilienthal's signature and *Flugzeug Nr. 13 Doppledecker* .. 1·50 1·50
1757 $2 Street fighting, Kiev .. .. 2·00 2·00
1758 $2 Gottfried Leibniz (mathematician) .. 2·00 2·00
1759 $3 *The Clemency of Titus* .. .. 2·00 2·00
1760 $3.50, Angelfish and scout diver .. 2·25 2·25
1744/60 .. .. *Set of* 17 16·00 16·00
MS1761 Four sheets. (a) 101×72 mm. $4 Arms of Berlin. (b) 77×116 mm. $4 Mozart and signature (*vert*). (c) 77×116 mm. $5 President De Gaulle (*vert*). (d) 117×89 mm. $5 Scout badge and Jamboree emblem .. *Set of* 4 *sheets* 13·00 15·00
Anniversaries and Events:—Nos. 1744/5, 1748, **MS**1761c, Birth centenary of Charles de Gaulle (French statesman); Nos. 1746, 1749/51, **MS**1761a, Bicentenary of Brandenburg Gate, Berlin; Nos. 1747, 1753, 1760, **MS**1761d, 50th death anniv of Lord Baden-Powell and World Scout Jamboree, Korea; Nos. 1752, 1759, **MS**1761b, Death bicentenary of Mozart; No. 1754 Centenary of Trans-Siberian Railway; No. 1755, 700th anniv of Swiss Confederation; No. 1756, Centenary of Otto Lilienthal's gliding experiments; No. 1757, 50th anniv of capture of Kiev; No. 1758, 750th anniv of Hanover.

(Des D. Ben-Ami. Litho Questa)

1991 (18 Nov). *50th Anniv of Japanese Attack on Pearl Harbor. T* **226** *and similar horiz designs showing recipients of Congressional Medal of Honor. Multicoloured. P* 14½×15.
1762 $1 Type **226** 70 70
a. Sheetlet. Nos. 1762/76 .. .. 9·50
1763 $1 George Cannon 70 70
1764 $1 John Finn 70 70
1765 $1 Francis Flaherty 70 70
1766 $1 Samuel Fuqua 70 70
1767 $1 Edwin Hill 70 70
1768 $1 Herbert Jones 70 70
1769 $1 Isaac Kidd 70 70
1770 $1 Jackson Pharris 70 70
1771 $1 Thomas Reeves 70 70
1772 $1 Donald Ross 70 70
1773 $1 Robert Scott 70 70
1774 $1 Franklin van Valkenburgh 70 70
1775 $1 James Ward 70 70
1776 $1 Cassin Young 70 70
1762/76 .. .. *Set of* 15 9·50 9·50
Nos. 1762/76 were printed together, *se-tenant*, in sheetlets of 15.

(Des Walt Disney Co. Litho Questa)

1991 (18 Nov). *International Literacy Year (1990) (2nd issue). Multicoloured designs as T* **246** *of Maldive Islands, but horiz, showing scenes from Disney cartoon films. P* 14×13½.

(*a*) The Prince and the Pauper
1777 5 c. Mickey Mouse, Goofy and Pluto as pauper pals 15 15
1778 10 c. Mickey as the bored prince 15 15
1779 15 c. Donald Duck as the valet 20 20
1780 25 c. Mickey as the prince and the pauper 25 25
1781 60 c. Exchanging clothes 55 55
1782 75 c. Prince and pauper with suit of armour 65 65
1783 80 c. Throwing food from the battlements 70 70
1784 $1 Pete as Captain of the Guard .. 85 85
1785 $2 Mickey and Donald in the dungeon 1·50 1·50
1786 $3 Mickey and Donald at dungeon window .. .. 1·75 1·75

1787 $4 Goofy rescuing Mickey and Donald 2·50 2·50
1788 $5 Crowning the real prince .. .. 2·50 2·50
1777/88 .. .. *Set of* 12 10·50 10·50
MS1789 Four sheets, each 127×101 mm. (a) $6 Crowning the wrong prince. (b) $6 Pete holding Mickey. (c) $6 The pauper on the throne. (d) $6 Mickey telling troops to seize the guard *Set of* 4 *sheets* 14·00 15·00

(*b*) The Rescuers Down Under
1790 5 c. Miss Bianca 15 15
1791 10 c. Bernard 15 15
1792 15 c. Matre d'Francoise 20 20
1793 25 c. Wilbur the Albatross 25 25
1794 60 c. Jake the Kangaroo mouse 55 55
1795 75 c. Bernard, Bianca and Jake in the outback 65 65
1796 80 c. Bianca and Bernard to the rescue .. 70 70
1797 $1 Marahute the Eagle 85 85
1798 $2 Cody and Marahute with eggs .. 1·50 1·50
1799 $3 McLeach and his pet, Joanna the Goanna .. .. 1·75 1·75
1800 $4 Frank the Frill-necked Lizard .. 2·50 2·50
1801 $5 Red Kangaroo, Krebbs Koala and Polly Platypus .. .. .. 2·50 2·75
1790/1801 .. .. *Set of* 12 10·50 10·50
MS1802 Four sheets, each 127×102 mm. (a) $6 The Rescuers. (b) $6 Ethiopian and Japanese mice delegates. (c) $6 Wilbur carrying Bianca and Bernard. (d) $6 Wilbur in pain *Set of* 4 *sheets* 14·00 15·00

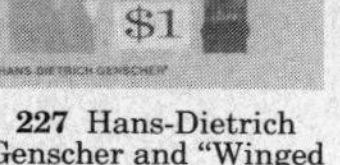

227 Hans-Dietrich Genscher and "Winged Victory" Statue

228 Walt Disney Characters decorating Christmas Tree, 1982

(Des J. Puvilland. Litho Questa)

1991 (25 Nov). *European History. T* **227** *and similar vert designs. Multicoloured. P* 14½×14.
1803 $1 Type **227** .. .. 1·00 1·00
a. Sheetlet. Nos. 1803/10 .. .. 7·00
1804 $1 Destruction of Berlin Wall .. .. 1·00 1·00
1805 $1 Churchill, De Gaulle and Appeal to the French, 1940 .. .. 1·00 1·00
1806 $1 Eisenhower, De Gaulle and D-Day, 1944 .. .. 1·00 1·00
1807 $1 Brandenburg Gate, Berlin (bicent) .. 1·00 1·00
1808 $1 Chancellor Helmut Kohl and meeting of Berlin Mayors, 1989 .. .. .. 1·00 1·00
1809 $1 De Gaulle with Chancellor Adenauer 1·00 1·00
1810 $1 Pres. Kennedy's visit to Europe, 1961, Washington and Lafayette .. .. 1·00 1·00
1803/10 .. .. *Set of* 8 7·00 7·00
MS1811 106×88 mm. $6 Casablanca Conference, 1942, and demolition of Berlin Wall (24½×39 *mm*). P 14 .. .. .. 4·00 5·00
Nos. 1803/10 were printed together, *se-tenant*, in sheetlets of 8.

(Des J. Puvilland. Litho Questa)

1991 (25 Nov). *Famous Golfers. Vert designs as T* **227**. *Multicoloured. P* 14½×14.
1812 $1 Gary Player .. .. 1·10 1·10
a. Sheetlet. Nos. 1812/19 .. .. 8·00
1813 $1 Nick Faldo .. .. 1·10 1·10
1814 $1 Severiano Ballesteros .. .. .. 1·10 1·10
1815 $1 Ben Hogan .. .. 1·10 1·10
1816 $1 Jack Nicklaus .. .. 1·10 1·10
1817 $1 Greg Norman .. .. 1·10 1·10
1818 $1 José-Maria Olazabal .. .. .. 1·10 1·10
1819 $1 Bobby Jones .. .. 1·10 1·10
1812/19 .. .. *Set of* 8 8·00 8·00
Nos. 1812/19 were printed together, *se-tenant*, in sheetlets of 8.

(Des. J. Puvilland. Litho Questa)

1991 (25 Nov). *Famous Entertainers. Vert designs as T* **227**. *Multicoloured. P* 14½.
1820 $2 Michael Jackson .. .. 1·75 1·75
a. Sheetlet. Nos. 1820/7 .. .. .. 12·00
1821 $2 Madonna .. .. 1·75 1·75
1822 $2 Elvis Presley .. .. 1·75 1·75
1823 $2 David Bowie .. .. 1·75 1·75
1824 $2 Prince .. .. 1·75 1·75
1825 $2 Frank Sinatra .. .. 1·75 1·75
1826 $2 George Michael .. .. 1·75 1·75
1827 $2 Mick Jagger .. .. 1·75 1·75
1820/7 .. .. *Set of* 8 12·00 12·00
MS1828 Two sheets, each 110×82 mm. (a) $6 Madonna (29×43 *mm*). (b) $6 Elvis Presley (29×43 *mm*). P 14 .. .. *Set of* 2 *sheets* 8·50 9·00
Nos. 1820/7 were printed together, *se-tenant*, in sheetlets of 8.

(Des J. Puvilland. Litho Questa)

1991 (25 Nov). *Famous Chess Masters. Vert designs as T* **227**. *Multicoloured. P* 14½.
1829 $1 Francoise Philidor 90 90
a. Sheetlet. Nos. 1829/36 .. .. 6·50
1830 $1 Karl Anderssen 90 90
1831 $1 Wilhelm Steinitz 90 90
1832 $1 Alexandrovich Alekhine 90 90
1833 $1 Boris Spassky 90 90
1834 $1 Robert Fischer 90 90
1835 $1 Anatoly Karpov 90 90
1836 $1 Garry Kasparov 90 90
1829/36 .. .. *Set of* 8 6·50 6·50
Nos. 1829/36 were printed together, *se-tenant*, in sheetlets of 8.

(Des J. Puvilland. Litho Questa)

1991 (25 Nov). *Nobel Prizewinners. Vert designs as T* **227**. *Multicoloured. P* 14½.
1837 $1 Albert Einstein (mathematical physicist) 70 70
a. Sheetlet. Nos. 1837/44 .. .. 5·00
1838 $1 Wilhelm Rontgen (physicist) 70 70
1839 $1 William Shockley (chemist) 70 70
1840 $1 Charles Townes (physicist) 70 70
1841 $1 Lev Landau (physicist) 70 70
1842 $1 Guglielmo Marconi (applied physicist) 70 70
1843 $1 Willard Libby (chemist) 70 70
1844 $1 Ernest Lawrence (nuclear physicist) .. 70 70
1837/44 .. .. *Set of* 8 5·00 5·00
Nos. 1837/44 were printed together, *se-tenant*, in sheetlets of 8.

(Des Walt Disney Co. Litho Questa)

1991 (23 Dec). *Christmas. Walt Disney Christmas Cards. T* **228** *and similar vert designs. Multicoloured. P* 13½×14.
1845 10 c. Type **228** 15 15
1846 45 c. Mickey and Moose, 1980 .. .. 40 30
1847 55 c. Mickey, Pluto and Donald carrying bauble, 1970 .. .. 50 40
1848 75 c. Duckling and egg shell, 1943 .. 70 70
1849 $1.50, Walt Disney characters decorating globe, 1941 .. .. 1·25 1·25
1850 $2 The Lady and the Tramp by Christmas tree, 1986 .. .. 1·50 1·50
1851 $4 Walt Disney characters carol singing, 1977 .. .. 2·75 2·75
1852 $5 Mickey in fairy-tale castle, 1965 .. 2·75 3·00
1845/52 .. .. *Set of* 8 9·00 9·00
MS1853 Two sheets. (a) 102×128 mm. $6 Characters in balloon basket, 1966. (b) 128×102 mm. $6 Characters in national costumes, 1966 *Set of* 2 *sheets* 9·00 9·50

229 Kings Hill

(Litho Questa)

1992 (17 Feb). *Preserving the Environment. T* **229** *and similar horiz designs. Multicoloured. P* 14.
1854 10 c. Type **229** 20 20
1855 55 c. Planting sapling 50 45
1856 75 c. Doric Temple, Botanic Gardens .. 60 55
1857 $2 18th-century map of Kings Hill .. 1·40 1·75
1854/7 .. .. *Set of* 4 2·40 2·75

(Des D. Miller. Litho Questa)

1992 (2 Mar). *40th Anniv of Queen Elizabeth II's Accession. Horiz designs as T* **214** *of Lesotho. Multicoloured. P* 14.
1858 10 c. Kingstown from the cliffs 15 15
1859 20 c. Deep water wharf, Kingstown .. 25 15
1860 $1 Residential suburb, Kingstown .. 60 60
1861 $5 Kingstown from the interior .. 2·50 3·00
1858/61 .. .. *Set of* 4 3·25 3·50
MS1862 Two sheets, each 75×92 mm. (a) $6 Deep water wharf (*different*). (b) $6 Beach *Set of* 2 *sheets* 7·00 7·25
Two different $5 designs and two $10 miniature sheets, all embossed on gold foil, also exist from a limited printing.

230 Women's Luge

(Litho Questa)

1992 (21 Apr). *Winter Olympic Games, Albertville (1st issue). T* **230** *and similar multicoloured designs. P* 14.
1863 10 c. Type **230** 15 15
1864 15 c. Women's figure skating (*vert*) .. 20 20
1865 25 c. Two-man bobsleigh 25 25
1866 30 c. Mogul skiing (*vert*) 30 30
1867 45 c. Nordic combination 40 40
1868 55 c. Ski jump 55 55
1869 75 c. Men's giant slalom 65 65
1870 $1.50, Women's slalom (*vert*) .. .. 1·10 1·10
1871 $5 Ice hockey .. .. 3·25 3·50
1872 $8 Biathlon (*vert*) .. .. .. 4·25 4·50
1863/72 .. .. *Set of* 10 10·00 10·50
MS1873 Two sheets, each 100×70 mm. (a) $6 Women's speed skating (*vert*). (b) $6 Men's downhill skiing (*vert*) .. .. *Set of* 2 *sheets* 8·50 9·00
See also Nos. 1966/80.

231 Women's Synchronized Swimming

(Litho Questa)

1992 (21 Apr). *Olympic Games, Barcelona. T* **231** *and similar multicoloured designs. P* 14.
1874 10 c. Type **231** 10 10
1875 15 c. Men's high jump (*vert*) 10 10
1876 25 c. Men's small-bore rifle shooting .. 10 10
1877 30 c. Men's 200 metres (*vert*) 15 20
1878 45 c. Men's judo (*vert*) 20 25
1879 55 c. Men's 200 metres freestyle swimming 25 30
1880 75 c. Men's javelin (*vert*) 35 40
1881 $1.50, Men's 4000 metre pursuit cycling (*vert*) .. .. 1·50 1·50
1882 $5 Boxing (*vert*) .. .. 2·50 3·00
1883 $8 Women's basketball (*vert*) .. .. 7·00 7·50
1874/83 .. .. *Set of* 10 11·00 12·00
MS1884 Two sheets, each 100×70 mm. (a) $15 Sailboarding (*vert*). (b) $15 Men's singles tennis (*vert*) .. .. *Set of* 2 *sheets* 17·00 17·00

(Des Walt Disney Co. Litho Questa)

1992 (28 Apr). *International Stamp Exhibitions. Multicoloured designs as T* **215** *of Lesotho showing Walt Disney cartoon characters.*

(*a*) *"Granada '92" Spain. The Three Pigs in Spanish Uniforms. P* 13½×14
1885 15 c. The Wolf as General of Spanish Moors 15 10
1886 40 c. Pig as Captain of Infantry 30 25
1887 $2 Pig as Halberdier .. .. .. 1·00 1·10
1888 $4 Pig as Nobleman .. .. .. 1·90 2·25
1885/8 .. .. *Set of* 4 3·00 3·25
MS1889 128×102 mm. $6 Nobleman at castle window .. .. 2·75 3·50

(*b*) *"World Columbian Stamp Expo '92". Chicago Landmarks. P* 14×13½
1890 10 c. Mickey Mouse and Goofy looking at Picasso sculpture (*horiz*) 15 15
1891 50 c. Mickey and Donald Duck admiring Robie House (*horiz*) 35 35
1892 $1 Calder sculpture in Sears Tower (*horiz*) 55 60
1893 $5 Goofy in Buckingham Memorial Fountain (*horiz*) .. .. .. 2·25 2·40
1890/3 .. .. *Set of* 4 3·00 3·25
MS1894 128×102 mm. $6 Mickey painting Minnie. P 13½×14 .. .. .. 2·75 3·50

232 *Nina*

(Des W. Wright. Litho Questa)

1992 (22 May). *500th Anniv of Discovery of America by Columbus (6th issue). "World Columbian Stamp Expo '92", Chicago. T* **232** *and similar multicoloured designs. P* 14.
1895 5 c. Type **232** 25 25
1896 10 c. *Pinta* 25 25
1897 45 c. *Santa Maria* 50 50
1898 55 c. Fleet leaving Palos, 1492 .. .. 55 55
1899 $4 Christopher Columbus (*vert*) .. 3·00 3·25
1900 $5 Arms of Columbus (*vert*) .. .. 3·00 3·25
1895/1900 .. .. *Set of* 6 6·75 7·25
MS1901 Two sheets, each 115×86 mm. (a) $6 *Santa Maria* sighting land (42½×57 *mm*). (b) $6 Route of voyage (42½×57 *mm*) .. *Set of* 2 *sheets* 8·50 9·50

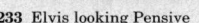

233 Elvis looking Pensive

234 Bonnie Blair

(Des J. Iskowitz. Litho Questa)

1992 (25 May). *15th Death Anniv of Elvis Presley (1st issue). T* **233** *and similar vert designs. Multicoloured. P* 13½×14.
1902 $1 Type **233** 75 75
a. Sheetlet. Nos. 1902/10 .. .. 6·00
1903 $1 Wearing black and yellow striped shirt 75 75
1904 $1 Singing into microphone 75 75
1905 $1 Wearing wide-brimmed hat 75 75
1906 $1 With microphone in right hand .. 75 75
1907 $1 In Army uniform 75 75
1908 $1 Wearing pink shirt 75 75

1909 $1 In yellow shirt 75 75
1910 $1 In jacket and bow tie 75 75
1902/10 .. .. *Set of* 9 6·00 6·00
MS1911 76×107 mm. $6 In blue shirt ($28^1/_2$×$42^1/_2$ *mm*). P 14 .. .. .. 5·50 5·50
Nos. 1902/10 were printed together, *se-tenant*, in sheetlets of 9.
See also Nos. 2029/37, 2038/46 and 2047/9.

(Des and litho Stamp Venturers, Virginia)

1992 (25 May). *Bonnie Blair's Victories in* 500 *Metres Speed Skating at Calgary and Albertville Olympic Games. T* **234** *and similar multicoloured designs. P* $13^1/_2$.
1912 $3 Type **234** .. .. 1·90 2·00
MS1913 185×127 mm. $2 Turning corner (*horiz*); $2 With skates in arms (43×51 *mm*); $2 On straight (*horiz*) .. .. 4·50 4·75

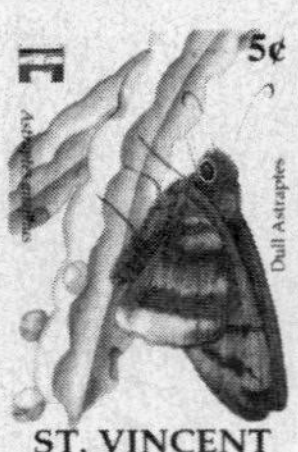

235 *Astraptes anaphus*

236 *Collybia subpruinosa*

(Des Wendy Smith-Griswold. Litho Questa)

1992 (15 June). *"Genova '92" International Thematic Stamp Exhibition* (*1st issue*). *Butterflies. T* **235** *and similar multicoloured designs. P* 14.
1914 5 c. Type **235** 20 20
1915 10 c. *Anartia jatrophae* (*horiz*) 20 20
1916 35 c. *Danaus eresimus* 40 40
1917 45 c. *Battus polydamus* 45 45
1918 55 c. *Junonia evarete* (*horiz*) 50 50
1919 65 c. *Urbanus proteus* 60 60
1920 75 c. *Pyrgus oileus* (*horiz*) 65 65
1921 $1 *Biblis hyperia* 75 75
1922 $2 *Eurema daira* .. .. .. 1·25 1·25
1923 $3 *Leptotes cassius* (*horiz*) .. .. 1·75 1·75
1924 $4 *Ephyriades brunnea* (*horiz*) .. .. 2·25 2·25
1925 $5 *Victorina stelenes* .. .. .. 2·50 2·50
1914/25 .. .. *Set of* 12 10·50 10·50
MS1926 Three sheets, each 98×72 mm. (a) $6 *Phoebis sennae*. (b) $6 *Heliconius charitonius* (*horiz*). (c) $6 *Dryas julia* (*horiz*) *Set of* 3 *sheets* 12·00 13·00
See also Nos. 1940/52.

(Des R. Sauber. Litho Questa)

1992 (2 July). *Fungi. T* **236** *and similar vert designs. Multicoloured. P* 14.
1927 10 c. Type **236** 20 15
1928 15 c. *Gerronema citrinum* 25 15
1929 20 c. *Amanita antillana* 30 20
1930 45 c. *Dermoloma atrobrunneum* 45 35
1931 50 c. *Inopilus maculosus* 50 40
1932 65 c. *Pulveroboletus brachyspermus* .. 65 55
1933 75 c. *Mycena violacella* 70 60
1934 $1 *Xerocomus brasiliensis* 70 70
1935 $2 *Amanita ingrata* .. .. .. 1·40 1·60
1936 $3 *Leptonia caeruleocapitata* .. .. 1·75 2·00
1937 $4 *Limacella myochroa* .. .. .. 2·25 2·50
1938 $5 *Inopilus magnificus* .. .. .. 2·50 2·50
1927/38 .. .. *Set of* 12 10·50 10·50
MS1939 Three sheets, each 101×68 mm. (a) $6 *Limacella guttata*. (b) $6 *Amanita agglutinata*. (c) $6 *Trogia buccinalis* .. .. *Set of* 3 *sheets* 11·00 12·00
No. 1936 is inscribed "*Leptonia caeruleocaptata*" in error.

237 Rufous-breasted Hermit

238 Coral Vine

(Des Mary Walters. Litho Questa)

1992 (2 July). *"Genova '92" International Thematic Stamp Exhibition* (*2nd issue*). *Hummingbirds. T* **237** *and similar vert designs. Multicoloured. P* 14.
1940 5 c. Type **237** 15 15
1941 15 c. Hispaniolan Emerald 20 20
1942 45 c. Green-throated Carib 35 35
1943 55 c. Jamaican Mango 45 45
1944 65 c. Vervain Hummingbird 60 60
1945 75 c. Purple-throated Carib 70 70
1946 90 c. Green Mango 75 75
1947 $1 Bee Hummingbird 80 80
1948 $2 Cuban Emerald .. .. .. 1·50 1·50
1949 $3 Puerto Rican Emerald .. .. .. 1·90 1·90
1950 $4 Antillean Mango .. .. .. 2·40 2·40
1951 $5 Streamertail .. .. .. 2·75 2·75
1940/51 .. .. *Set of* 12 11·00 11·00
MS1952 Three sheets, each 98×67 mm. (a) $6 Bahama Woodstar. (b) $6 Antillean Crested Hummingbird. (c) $6 Blue-headed Hummingbird *Set of* 3 *sheets* 12·00 13·00

(Des Dot Barlowe. Litho B.D.T.)

1992 (22 July). *Medicinal Plants. T* **238** *and similar vert designs. Multicoloured. P* 14.
1953 75 c. Type **238** 60 60
a. Sheetlet. Nos. 1953/64 .. .. .. 6·50
1954 75 c. Cocoplum 60 60
1955 75 c. Angel's Trumpet 60 60
1956 75 c. Lime 60 60
1957 75 c. White Ginger 60 60
1958 75 c. Pussley 60 60
1959 75 c. Sea Grape 60 60
1960 75 c. Indian Mulberry 60 60
1961 75 c. Plantain 60 60
1962 75 c. Lignum Vitae 60 60
1963 75 c. Periwinkle 60 60
1964 75 c. Guava 60 60
1953/64 .. .. *Set of* 12 6·50 6·50
MS1965 Three sheets, each 98×69 mm. (a) $6 Wild Sage. (b) $6 Clove Tree. (c) $6 Aloe *Set of* 3 *sheets* 10·50 11·00
Nos. 1953/64 were printed together, *se-tenant*, in sheetlets of 12.

239 Kristi Yamaguchi (U.S.A.) (figure skating)

(Des J. Puvilland. Litho Questa)

1992 (10 Aug). *Winter Olympic Games, Albertville* (*2nd issue*). *Gold Medal Winners. T* **239** *and similar vert designs. Multicoloured. P* 14.
1966 $1 Type **239** 80 80
a. Sheetlet. Nos. 1966/72 .. .. .. 5·00
1967 $1 Pernilla Wiberg (Sweden) (giant slalom skiing) 80 80
1968 $1 Lyubov Yegorova (C.I.S.) (10 kms cross-country skiing) 80 80
1969 $1 Josef Polig (Italy) (combined alpine skiing) 80 80
1970 $1 Fin Christian-Jagge (Norway) (slalom skiing) 80 80
1971 $1 Kerrin Lee-Gartner (Canada) (downhill skiing) 80 80
1972 $1 Steffania Belmondo (Italy) (30 kms cross-country skiing) 80 80
1973 $1 Alberto Tomba (Italy) (giant slalom skiing) 80 80
a. Sheetlet. Nos. 1973/9 .. .. .. 5·00
1974 $1 Fabrice Guy (France) (nordic combined skiing) 80 80
1975 $1 Patrick Ortlieb (Austria) (downhill skiing) 80 80
1976 $1 Vegard Ulvang (Norway) (nordic cross-country skiing) 80 80
1977 $1 Edgar Grospiron (France) (freestyle mogul skiing) 80 80
1978 $1 Andre Aamodt (Norway) (super giant slalom skiing) 80 80
1979 $1 Viktor Petrenko (C.I.S.) (figure skating) 80 80
1966/79 .. .. *Set of* 14 10·00 10·00
MS1980 Two sheets. (a) 108×78 mm. $6 Kristi Yamaguchi (U.S.A.) (figure skating) (*different*). (b) 111×81 mm. $6 Alberto Tomba (Italy) (giant slalom skiing) (*different*) .. *Set of* 2 *sheets* 8·50 9·50
Nos. 1966/72 and 1973/9 were each printed together, *se-tenant*, in sheetlets of 7 stamps and 1 stamp-size label.
No. 1968 is inscribed "LYUBOV EGOROVA" in error.

(Des F. Paul ($1), J. Esquino ($2). Litho Questa)

1992 (24 Aug). 500*th Anniv of Discovery of America by Columbus* (*7th issue*). *Organization of East Caribbean States. Vert designs as Nos.* 911/12 *of Montserrat. Multicoloured. P* $14^1/_2$.
1981 $1 Columbus meeting Amerindians 75 75
1982 $2 Ships approaching island .. .. 1·25 1·50

240 *Pinocchio*

(Des Euro-Disney, Paris. Litho Cartor)

1992 (11 Sept). *Opening of Euro-Disney Resort, Paris. T* **240** *and similar multicoloured designs. P* 13.
1983 $1 Type **240** .. .. 1·00 1·00
a. Sheetlet. Nos. 1983/8 .. .. .. 5·50
1984 $1 *Alice in Wonderland* .. .. .. 1·00 1·00
1985 $1 *Bambi* .. .. 1·00 1·00
1986 $1 *Cinderella* .. .. 1·00 1·00
1987 $1 *Snow White and the Seven Dwarfs* .. 1·00 1·00
1988 $1 *Peter Pan* .. .. 1·00 1·00
1983/8 .. .. *Set of* 6 5·50 5·50
MS1989 187×101 mm. $5 Mickey Mouse (56×76 *mm*). P $12^1/_2$ .. .. 4·50 4·75
Nos. 1983/8 were printed together, *se-tenant*, in sheetlets of 6.

(Des Kerri Schiff. Litho Questa)

1992 (28 Oct). *Postage Stamp Mega Event, New York. Multicoloured design as T* **219** *of Lesotho. Sheet* 100×70 *mm. P* 14.
MS1990 $6 Jacob K. Javits Convention Centre (*horiz*) .. .. 4·00 4·25
No. **MS**1990 is inscribed "Jaritts" in error.

241 Spanish Galleon and Paddle-steamer

(Litho Questa)

1992 (28 Oct). *First use of Adhesive Stamps on Trans-Atlantic Mail,* 1840, *Commemoration. Sheet* 100×70 *mm. P* 14.
MS1991 **241** $6 multicoloured .. .. .. 4·50 5·00

(Litho Questa)

1992 (16 Nov). *Christmas. Religious Paintings. Vert designs as T* **218** *of Lesotho. Multicoloured. P* $13^1/_2$×14.
1992 10 c. "Hospitality refused to the Virgin Mary and Joseph" (detail) (Metsys) 20 20
1993 40 c. "The Nativity" (detail) (Dürer) .. 40 30
1994 45 c. "The Nativity" (Geertgen Tot Sint Jans) 40 30
1995 50 c. "The Nativity" (Jacopo Tintoretto) .. 50 35
1996 55 c. "The Nativity" (detail) (Follower of Calcar) 50 35
1997 65 c. "The Nativity" (Workshop of Fra Angelico) 60 50
1998 75 c. "The Nativity" (Master of the Louvre Nativity) 65 50
1999 $1 "The Nativity" (detail) (Lippi) .. 80 75
2000 $2 "The Nativity" (Petrus Christus) .. 1·50 1·50
2001 $3 "The Nativity" (detail) (Edward Burne-Jones) .. .. .. 2·00 2·25
2002 $4 "The Nativity" (detail) (Giotto) .. 2·50 2·75
2003 $5 "Birth of Christ" (detail) (Domenico Ghirlandaio) .. .. .. 2·75 3·00
1992/2003 .. .. .. *Set of* 12 11·50 11·50
MS2004 Three sheets, each 72×99 mm. (a) $6 "Birth of Christ" (detail) (Gerard Horenbout). (b) $6 "The Nativity" (detail) (Botticelli). (c) $6 "The Nativity" (detail) (Jean Fouquet) *Set of* 3 *sheets* 12·00 13·00

242 Gaston

(Des Rosemary DeFiglio and Walt Disney Co. Litho Questa)

1992 (15 Dec). *Walt Disney's* Beauty and the Beast (*cartoon film*). *T* **242** *and similar multicoloured designs. P* 14×$13^1/_2$ (*horiz*) *or* $13^1/_2$×14 (*vert*).
2005 2 c. Type **242** 15 15
2006 3 c. Belle and her father, Maurice .. 15 15
2007 5 c. Lumiere, Mrs. Potts and Cogsworth 20 20
2008 10 c. Philippe 20 20
2009 15 c. Beast and Lumiere 20 20
2010 20 c. Lumiere and Feather Duster 20 20
2011 60 c. Belle and Gaston 40 40
a. Sheetlet. Nos. 2011/19 .. .. .. 3·25
2012 60 c. Maurice 40 40
2013 60 c. The Beast 40 40
2014 60 c. Mrs. Potts 40 40
2015 60 c. Belle and enchanted vase 40 40
2016 60 c. Belle discovers enchanted rose .. 40 40
2017 60 c. Belle with wounded Beast 40 40
2018 60 c. Belle 40 40
2019 60 c. Household objects alarmed 40 40
2020 60 c. Belle and Chip (*vert*) 40 40
a. Sheetlet. Nos. 2020/7 .. .. .. 3·25
2021 60 c. Lumiere (*vert*) 40 40
2022 60 c. Cogsworth (*vert*) 40 40
2023 60 c. Armoire (*vert*) 40 40
2024 60 c. Belle and Beast (*vert*) 40 40
2025 60 c. Feather Duster (*vert*) 40 40
2026 60 c. Footstool (*vert*) 40 40
2027 60 c. Belle sitting on stone (*vert*) .. 40 40
2005/27 .. .. *Set of* 23 7·50 7·50
MS2028 Five sheets. (a) 127×103 mm. $6 Lumiere (*vert*). (b) 127×103 mm. $6 Belle reading book (*vert*). (c) 127×103 mm. $6 The Beast (*vert*). (d) 127×103 mm. $6 Belle dancing (*vert*). (e) 103×127 mm. $6 Lumiere, Chip and Mrs. Potts .. .. .. *Set of* 5 *sheets* 17·00 18·00
Nos. 2011/19 and 2020/7 were each printed together, *se-tenant* in sheetlets of 9 (Nos. 2011/19) or 8 (Nos. 2020/7).

15th Anniversary (243)

15th Anniversary Elvis Presley's Death August 16, 1977 (244)

1992 (15 Dec). *15th Death Anniv of Elvis Presley (2nd issue). Nos.* 1902/10 *optd with T* **243**.

2029	$1 Type **233**	80	80
	a. Sheetlet. Nos. 2029/37	6·50	
2030	$1 Wearing black and yellow striped shirt	80	80
2031	$1 Singing into microphone	80	80
2032	$1 Wearing wide-brimmed hat	80	80
2033	$1 With microphone in right hand	80	80
2034	$1 In Army uniform	80	80
2035	$1 Wearing pink shirt	80	80
2036	$1 In yellow shirt	80	80
2037	$1 In jacket and bow tie	80	80
2029/37	*Set of* 9	6·50	6·50

1992 (15 Dec). *15th Death Anniv of Elvis Presley (3rd issue). Nos.* 1820/7 *and* **MS**1828b *optd as T* **244**.

2038	$2 Michael Jackson	1·50	1·50
	a. Sheetlet. Nos. 2038/45	11·00	
2039	$2 Madonna	1·50	1·50
2040	$2 Elvis Presley	1·50	1·50
2041	$2 David Bowie	1·50	1·50
2042	$2 Prince	1·50	1·50
2043	$2 Frank Sinatra	1·50	1·50
2044	$2 George Michael	1·50	1·50
2045	$2 Mick Jagger	1·50	1·50
2038/45	*Set of* 8	11·00	11·00
MS2046	110×82 mm. $6 Elvis Presley (29×43 *mm*)	6·50	6·50

No. **MS**2046 is overprinted on the sheet margin.

(Des A. Nahigian. Litho Walsall)

1992 (15 Dec). *15th Death Anniv of Elvis Presley (4th issue). Vert designs as Nos.* 1768/70 *of Maldive Islands. Multicoloured. P* 14.

2047	$1 Elvis Presley	1·50	1·50
	a. Strip of 3. Nos. 2047/9	4·00	
2048	$1 Elvis with guitar	1·50	1·50
2049	$1 Elvis with microphone	1·50	1·50
2047/9	*Set of* 3	4·00	4·00

Nos. 2047/9 were printed together, horizontally and vertically *se-tenant*, in sheetlets of 9 (3×3).

245 Fifer Pig building House of Straw

(Des Rosemary DeFiglio and Walt Disney Co. Litho Questa)

1992 (15 Dec). *Walt Disney Cartoon Films. T* **245** *and similar multicoloured designs. P* $14\times13^1/_2$ *(horiz) or* $13^1/_2\times14$ *(vert).*

2050/2138	60 c. × 89 multicoloured *Set of* 89	27·00	30·00
MS2139	Twenty sheets, each 128×103 mm or 103×128 mm. $6×20 multicoloured *Set of* 20 *sheets*	60·00	70·00

Nos. 2050/2138 were printed as ten *se-tenant* sheetlets, each of nine different designs except for that for *Darkwing Duck* which contains eight vertical designs (Nos. 2131/8). The other nine sheetlets depict scenes from *The Three Little Pigs, Thru the Mirror, Clock Cleaners, Orphans Benefit, The Art of Skiing, Symphony Hour, How to Play Football, The Small One* and *Chip N'Dale Rescue Rangers.*

No. **MS**2139 contains two sheets for each film, one sheet for *The Three Little Pigs* being in a vertical format. The stamp designs for *The Three Little Pigs* (horizontal sheet), *How to Play Football* (one), *Chip N'Dale Rescue Rangers* (both) and *Darkwing Duck* (both) are vertical.

For Nos. 2050/8 and **MS**2139a/b (*The Three Little Pigs*) with different face values see Nos. 2852/61.

246 Scottie Pippen

247 Tom Seaver

(Des J. Genzo. Litho Questa)

1992 (15 Dec). *Olympic Gold Medal Winners, Barcelona. T* **246** *and similar horiz designs showing members of U.S.A. basketball team. Multicoloured. P* 14.

2140	$2 Type **246**	90	95
	a. Sheetlet. Nos. 2140/5	5·25	
2141	$2 Earvin "Magic" Johnson	90	95
2142	$2 Larry Bird	90	95
2143	$2 Christian Laettner	90	95
2144	$2 Karl Malone	90	95
2145	$2 David Robinson	90	95
2146	$2 Michael Jordan	90	95
	a. Sheetlet. Nos. 2146/51	5·25	
2147	$2 Charles Barkley	90	95
2148	$2 John Stockton	90	95
2149	$2 Chris Mullin	90	95
2150	$2 Clyde Drexler	90	95
2151	$2 Patrick Ewing	90	95
2140/51	*Set of* 12	10·50	11·00

Nos. 2140/5 and 2146/51 were each printed together, *se-tenant*, in sheetlets of 6.

(Des W. Storozuk. Litho Questa)

1992 (21 Dec). *Famous Baseball Players (5th issue). T* **247** *and similar vert designs. Multicoloured. P* 14.

2152	$2 Type **247**	1·40	1·40
2153	$2 Roberto Clemente	1·40	1·40
2154	$2 Hank Aaron	1·40	1·40
2152/4	*Set of* 3	3·50	3·50

248 Don Mattingly

249 Earth and U.N. Emblem

(Des J. Iskowitz. Litho Questa)

1992 (21 Dec). *Famous Baseball Players (6th issue). T* **248** *and similar vert design. Multicoloured. P* 14.

2155	$5 Type **248**	3·00	3·50
2156	$5 Howard Johnson	3·00	3·50

(Des W. Wright and L. Fried (Nos. 2157, 2167), W. Wright and W. Hanson (Nos. 2158, 2170, **MS**2171a), W. Wright (others). Litho Questa)

1992 (22 Dec). *Anniversaries and Events. T* **249** *and similar multicoloured designs. P* 14.

2157	10 c. Type **249**	30	20
2158	45 c. Airship LZ-11 *Viktoria Luise* over Kiel Regatta, 1912 (*vert*)	50	25
2159	75 c. Adenauer and German flag	60	50
2160	75 c. Trophy and Bill Koch (skipper) of *America III*, 1992	60	50
2161	$1 Konrad Adenauer	60	50
2162	$1 Snow Leopard and emblem	60	50
2163	$1.50, Caribbean Manatee	90	90
2164	$2 Humpback Whale	1·50	1·50
2165	$3 Adenauer and Pres. Kennedy, 1962	1·60	1·60
2166	$3 Doctor checking patient's eye	1·60	1·60
2167	$4 *Discovery* space shuttle (*vert*)	2·25	2·25
2168	$4 Adenauer and Pope John XXIII, 1960	2·25	2·25
2169	$5 Schumacher and racing car	3·00	3·00
2170	$6 Zeppelin LZ-1 over Lake Constance, 1900	3·50	3·75
2157/70	*Set of* 14	18·00	18·00
MS2171	Five sheets. (a) 70×100 mm. $6 Cabin of airship LZ-127 *Graf Zeppelin.* (b) 70×100 mm. $6 Douglas DC-6 airplane from Berlin Airlift. (c) 100×70 mm. $6 Konrad Adenauer making speech. (d) 70×100 mm. $6 Woolly Spider Monkey. (e) 119×89 mm. $6 Schumacher winning race *Set of* 5 *sheets*	18·00	19·00

Anniversaries and Events:—Nos. 2157, 2167, International Space Year; Nos. 2158, 2170, **MS**2171a, 75th death anniv of Count Ferdinand von Zeppelin; Nos. 2159, 2161, 2165, 2168, **MS**2171b/c, 25th death anniv of Konrad Adenauer (German statesman); No. 2160, Americas Cup Yachting Championship; Nos. 2162/4, **MS**2171d, Earth Summit '92, Rio; No. 2166, 75th anniv of International Association of Lions Clubs; No. 2169, **MS**2171e, Michael Schumacher's Victory in 1992 Belgium Grand Prix.

(Des T.C.F.C. Inc. Litho Questa)

1992 (28 Dec). *Ecology. Multicoloured designs as T* **71** *of St. Kitts-Nevis (Nevis). P* 14.

2172	75 c. Care Bear and American White Pelican	55	45
MS2173	101×72 mm. $2 Care Bear in hot air balloon (*horiz*)	1·10	1·25

250 Farmer, Fisherman and Emblem

(Litho Questa)

1993 (4 Feb). *International Conference on Nutrition, Rome. P* 14.

2174	**250** 65 c. multicoloured	70	70

ALTERED CATALOGUE NUMBERS

Any Catalogue numbers altered from the last edition are shown as a list in the introductory pages.

251 Coastal Village

(Litho Questa)

1993 (4 Feb). *"Uniting the Windward Islands". T* **251** *and similar horiz designs. Multicoloured. P* 14.

2175	10 c. Type **251**	30	20
2176	40 c. Children from different islands	70	60
2177	45 c. Children and palm tree	70	60
2175/7	*Set of* 3	1·50	1·25

252 Fisherman holding Catch

253 Brown Pelican

(Litho Questa)

1993 (4 Feb). *Fishing. T* **252** *and similar horiz designs. Multicoloured. P* 14.

2178	5 c. Type **252**	15	15
2179	10 c. Fish market	15	15
2180	50 c. Fishermen landing catch	60	60
2181	$5 Fishing with nets	3·00	3·50
2178/81	*Set of* 4	3·50	4·00

(Des J. Genzo. Litho Questa)

1993 (1 Apr). *Migratory Birds. T* **253** *and similar multicoloured designs. P* 14.

2182	10 c. Type **253**	30	20
2183	25 c. Red-necked Grebe (*horiz*)	35	20
2184	45 c. Belted Kingfisher (*horiz*)	45	30
2185	55 c. Yellow-bellied Sapsucker	50	30
2186	$1 Great Blue Heron	75	60
2187	$2 Common Black Hawk ("Crab Hawk") (*horiz*)	1·40	1·40
2188	$4 Yellow Warbler	2·25	2·50
2189	$5 Northern Oriole (*horiz*)	2·25	2·50
2182/9	*Set of* 8	7·50	7·25
MS2190	Two sheets, each 100×70 mm. (a) $6 Blue-winged Teal (*horiz*). (b) $6 White Ibis (*horiz*) *Set of* 2 *sheets*	7·50	8·00

254 Sergeant Major

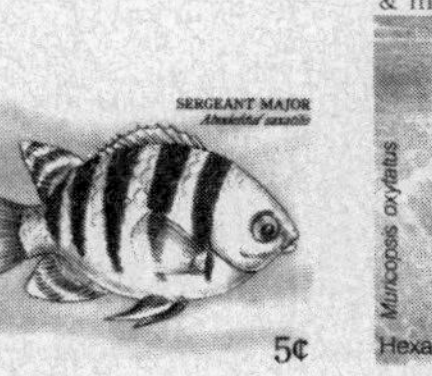

255 Hexagonal Muricop (*Muricopsis oxytatus*)

(Des W. Storozuk. Litho Questa)

1993 (13 Apr). *Fishes. T* **254** *and similar multicoloured designs. P* 14.

2191	5 c. Type **254**	30	20
2192	10 c. Rainbow Parrotfish	35	20
2193	55 c. Hogfish	45	30
2194	75 c. Porkfish	50	40
2195	$1 Spot-finned Butterflyfish	75	60
2196	$2 Buffalo Trunkfish	1·40	1·40
2197	$4 Queen Triggerfish	2·25	2·50
2198	$5 Queen Angelfish	2·25	2·50
2191/8	*Set of* 8	7·50	7·25
MS2199	Two sheets, each 100×70 mm. (a) $6 Bigeye (*vert*). (b) $6 Small-mouthed Grunt (*vert*) *Set of* 2 *sheets*	7·00	7·50

(Litho Walsall)

1993 (19 Apr). *Bicentenary of the Louvre, Paris. Paintings by various artists. Designs as T* **221** *of Lesotho. P* 12.

2200/39	$1×40 multicoloured *Set of* 40	18·00	19·00
MS2240	Three sheets, either 70×100 mm or 100×70 mm. $6×3 multicoloured. P $14^1/_2$ *Set of* 3 *sheets*	8·25	8·50

Nos. 2200/39 were printed as *se-tenant* sheetlets, each of eight different designs and one centre label. The five sheetlets show paintings by Géricault, Ingres, Le Sueur and Poussin, Poussin, and Boucher, Brueghel, Dumont, Gainsborough, Goya and Van Eyck.

The three sheets of No. **MS**2240 depict paintings by Chassériau (52×85 *mm*), Delacroix and Ingres (both 85×52 *mm*).

(Litho B.D.T.)

1993 (24 May). *Shells. T* **255** *and similar multicoloured designs. P* 14.
2241 10 c. Type **255** 10 10
2242 15 c. Caribbean Vase (*Vasum muricatum*) 10 10
2243 30 c. Measled Cowrie (*Cypraea zebra*) .. 15 20
2244 45 c. Dyson's Keyhole Limpet (*Diodora dysoni*) 20 25
2245 50 c. Atlantic Hairy Triton (*Cymatium pileare martinianum*) 25 30
2246 65 c. Orange-banded Marginella (*Marginella avena*) 30 35
2247 75 c. Bleeding Tooth (*Nerita peloronta*) .. 35 40
2248 $1 Queen or Pink Conch (*Strombus gigas*) 45 50
2249 $2 Hawk-wing Conch (*Strombus raninus*) 90 95
2250 $3 Music Volute (*Voluta musica*) .. 1·40 1·50
2251 $4 Alphabet Cone (*Conus spurius*) .. 1·90 2·00
2252 $5 Antillean or Incomparable Cone (*Conus cedonulli*) .. .. .. 2·25 2·40
2241/52 .. .. *Set of* 12 8·25 9·00
MS2253 Three sheets, each 103×76 mm. (a) $6 Wide-mouthed Purpura (*Purpura patula*) (*horiz*). (b) $6 Netted Olive (*Oliva reticularis*) (*horiz*). (c) $6 Flame Auger (*Terebra taurina*) (*horiz*) .. .. *Set of* 3 *sheets* 11·00 12·00

256 Ishihara holding Tennis Racket

257 *Erynnyis ello*

1993 (24 May). *7th Death Anniv of Yujiro Ihishara (Japanese actor). T* **256** *and similar designs. Litho. P* 13½×14.
2254 55 c. black, light grey and dull ultramarine 60 60
a. Sheetlet. Nos. 2254/62 .. .. .. 4·75
2255 55 c. black, light grey and dull ultramarine 60 60
2256 55 c. black, light grey and dull ultramarine 60 60
2257 55 c. multicoloured 60 60
2258 55 c. multicoloured 60 60
2259 $1 multicoloured 60 60
2260 $1 multicoloured 60 60
2261 $1 multicoloured 60 60
2262 $1 multicoloured 60 60
2254/62 .. .. *Set of* 9 4·75 4·75
MS2263 Four sheets, each 180×140 mm. (a) 55 c., $1, $2 × 2 multicoloured. P 14½×14. (b) 55 c. black, light grey and gold; $1 multicoloured; $2 black, light grey and gold; $2 multicoloured. P 13½×14. (c) 55 c., $2, $4, multicoloured. P 14×14½. (d) 55 c., $4 × 2 multicoloured. P 14×14½ .. *Set of* 4 *sheets* 17·00 19·00

Designs: *Vert* (*as T* **256**)—No. 2255, Ishihara holding camera; No. 2256, In striped shirt; No. 2257, Holding drink and cigarette; No. 2258, On board yacht; No. 2259, In naval uniform; No. 2260, In jacket and tie; No. 2261, Wearing sunglasses; No. 2262, Wearing pink shirt; No. **MS**2263b, 55 c. As No. 2255, $1 In formal suit, $2 In white jacket, $2 With guitar. (28×37 *mm*) —No. **MS**2263a, 55 c. As No. 2259, $1 Laughing, $2 In striped shirt, $2 As No. 2258. *Horiz* (56×37 *mm*)—No. **MS**2263c, 55 c. In yellow shirt with actress, $2 In checked jacket with actress, $4 In bar with actress; No. **MS**2263d, 55 c. With cigarette, $4 As No. 2262, $4 As 2261.

Nos. 2254/62 were printed together, *se-tenant*, in sheetlets of 9.

(Des Kerri Schiff. Litho Questa)

1993 (7 June). *40th Anniv of Coronation. Vert designs as T* **224** *of Lesotho. P* 13½×14.
2264 45 c. multicoloured 20 25
a. Sheetlet. Nos. 2264/7×2 .. .. 6·50
2265 65 c. multicoloured 30 35
2266 $2 blackish olive and black 90 95
2267 $4 multicoloured .. .. 1·90 2·00
2264/7 .. .. *Set of* 4 3·25 3·50
MS2268 70×100 mm. $6 multicoloured. P 14 2·75 3·00

Designs:—45 c. Queen Elizabeth II at Coronation (photograph by Cecil Beaton); 65 c. Queen Elizabeth opening Parliament; $2 Queen Elizabeth during Coronation; $4 Queen Elizabeth with corgi. (28½×42½ *mm*)—$6 "Queen Elizabeth as a Young Girl" (detail)

Nos. 2264/7 were printed together in sheetlets of 8, containing two *se-tenant* blocks of 4.

(Litho Questa)

1993 (14 June). *Moths. T* **257** *and similar vert designs. Multicoloured. P* 14.
2269 10 c. Type **257** 15 10
2270 50 c. *Aellopos tantalus* 35 30
2271 65 c. *Erynnyis alope* 40 35
2272 75 c. *Manduca rustica* 45 40
2273 $1 *Xylophanes pluto* 55 50
2274 $2 *Hyles lineata* .. .. 1·25 1·25
2275 $4 *Pseudosphinx tetrio* .. .. .. 2·25 2·50
2276 $5 *Protambulyx strigilis* .. .. .. 2·25 2·50
2269/76 .. .. *Set of* 8 6·75 7·00
MS2277 Two sheets, each 100×70 mm. (a) $6 *Utetheisa ornatrix*. (b) $6 *Xylophanes tersa* *Set of* 2 *sheets* 7·00 7·50

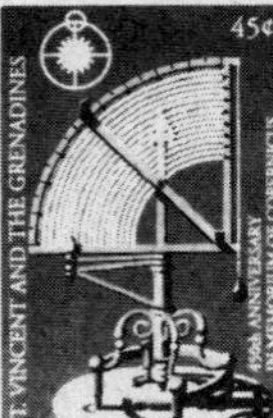

258 Early Astronomical Quadrant

259 Supermarine Spitfire

(Des Kerri Schiff (Nos. 2280, 2284, 2292, 2294, **MS**2297c, e). Litho Questa)

1993 (30 June). *Anniversaries and Events. T* **258** *and similar designs. Venetian red and black* (*Nos.* 2281, 2293, **MS**2297d) *or multicoloured* (*others*). *P* 14.
2278 45 c. Type **258** 20 25
2279 45 c. "Massacre in Korea" (Picasso) (*horiz*) 20 25
2280 45 c. Marc Girardelli (Luxembourg) (giant slalom) (*horiz*) 20 25
2281 45 c. Willy Brandt and Pres. Nixon, 1971 (*horiz*) 20 25
2282 45 c. Count Johannes and Countess Gloria of Thurn and Taxis 30 25
2283 65 c. Count and Countess of Thurn and Taxis with children (*horiz*) 50 35
2284 65 c. Masako Owada and engagement photographs (*horiz*) 50 40
2285 $1 "Family of Saltimbanques" (Picasso) (*horiz*) 45 50
2286 $1 Princess Stephanie of Monaco .. 60 60
2287 $1 "Deux Tetes" (left detail) (S. Witkiewicz) 60 60
a. Horiz pair. Nos. 2287 and 2289 .. 2·10 2·10
2288 $2 Countess Gloria of Thurn & Taxis .. 1·25 1·25
2289 $3 "Deux Tetes" (right detail) (S. Witkiewicz) .. .. 1·50 1·50
2290 $4 Launch of American space shuttle 1·90 2·00
2291 $4 "La Joie de Vivre" (Picasso) (*horiz*) 1·90 2·00
2292 $5 Paul Accola (Switzerland) (downhill skiing) (*horiz*) .. .. 2·50 2·50
2293 $5 Willy Brandt and Robert F. Kennedy, 1967 (*horiz*) .. .. 2·50 2·50
2294 $5 Prince Naruhito in traditional dress and engagement photographs (*horiz*) 2·50 2·50
2295 $5 Pres. Clinton with school children (*horiz*) .. .. 2·50 2·50
2296 $6 Bogusz Church, Gozlin (*horiz*) .. 3·00 3·00
2278/96 .. .. *Set of* 19 22·00 22·00
MS2297 Seven sheets. (a) 110×76 mm. $5 Copernicus. (b) 110×76 mm. $6 "Woman eating a Melon and Boy writing" (detail) (Picasso). (c) 110×76 mm. $6 Thommy Moe (U.S.A.) (downhill skiing). (d) 110×76 mm. $6 Willy Brandt at signing of Common Declaration, 1973 (*horiz*). (e) 110×76 mm. $6 Masako Owada. (f) 76×110 mm. $6 "Dancing" (detail) (Wladyslaw Roguski). (g) 76×110 mm. $6 Pres. Clinton wearing stetson *Set of* 7 *sheets* 24·00 25·00

Anniversaries and Events:—Nos. 2278, 2290, **MS**2297a, 450th death anniv of Copernicus (astronomer); Nos. 2279, 2285, 2291, **MS**2297b, 20th death anniv of Picasso (artist); Nos. 2280, 2292, **MS**2297c, Winter Olympic Games '94, Lillehammer; Nos. 2281, 2293, **MS**2297d, 80th birth anniv of Willy Brandt (German politician); Nos. 2282/3, 2288, 500th anniv of Thurn and Taxis postal service (1990); Nos. 2284, 2294, **MS**2297e, Marriage of Crown Prince Naruhito of Japan; No. 2286, Marriage of Princess Stephanie of Monaco; Nos. 2287, 2289, 2296, **MS**2297f, "Polska '93" International Stamp Exhibition, Poznań; Nos. 2295, **MS**2297g, Inauguration of U.S. President William Clinton.

Nos. 2287 and 2289 were printed together, *se-tenant*, in horizontal pairs throughout the sheet.

(Litho Questa)

1993 (30 June). *Aviation Anniversaries. T* **259** *and similar multicoloured designs. P* 14.
2298 50 c. Type **259** 25 30
2299 $1 Eckener, and airship LZ-127 *Graf Zeppelin* over Egypt, 1931 .. 65 50
2300 $1 Blanchard and Pres. Washington with balloon, 1793 .. .. 65 50
2301 $2 De Havilland D.H.98 Mosquito Mk VI 90 95
2302 $2 Eckener and airship LZ-127 *Graf Zeppelin* over New York, 1928 .. 90 95
2303 $3 Eckener and airship LZ-127 *Graf Zeppelin* over Tokyo, 1929 .. 1·75 1·75
2304 $4 Blanchard's balloon ascending from Walnut St Prison, Philadelphia .. 2·25 2·50
2298/304 .. .. *Set of* 7 6·50 6·50
MS2305 Three sheets, each 100×70 mm. (a) $6 Hawker Hurricane Mk I. (b) $6 Dr. Hugo Eckener (*vert*). (c) $6 Blanchard's balloon (*vert*) *Set of* 3 *sheets* 10·50 11·00

Anniversaries:—Nos. 2298, 2301, **MS**2305a, 75th anniv of Royal Air Force; Nos. 2299, 2302/3, **MS**2305b, 125th birth anniv of Hugo Eckener (airship commander); Nos. 2300, 2304, **MS**2305c, Bicent of first airmail flight.

No. 2303 is inscribed "Toyko" in error.

PRICES OF SETS

Set prices are given for many issues, generally those containing three stamps or more. Definitive sets include one of each value or major colour change, but do not cover different perforations, die types or minor shades. Where a choice is possible the set prices are based on the cheapest versions of the stamps included in the listings.

260 First Ford Car, Model "T" and "V8"

261 Pope John Paul II and Denver Skyline

(Litho Questa)

1993 (29 July). *Centenaries of Henry Ford's First Petrol Engine* (*Nos.* 2306, 2309, **MS**2310a) *and Karl Benz's First Four-wheeled Car* (*others*). *T* **260** *and similar vert designs. Multicoloured. P* 14.
2306 $1 Type **260** 45 50
2307 $2 Benz racing car, 1908, "Stuttgart" and "540K" 90 95
2308 $3 Benz car, 1894, "Tourenwagen" and "Blitzen Benz" .. .. 1·40 1·50
2309 $4 Ford "Runabout", 1903, Model "T" Tourer and saloon, 1935 .. .. 1·90 2·00
2306/9 .. .. *Set of* 4 4·50 4·75
MS2310 Two sheets, each 100×70 mm. (a) $6 Henry Ford. (b) $6 Karl Benz .. *Set of* 2 *sheets* 5·50 5·75

(Des and litho Questa)

1993 (13 Aug). *Papal Visit to Denver, Colorado, U.S.A. T* **261** *and similar horiz design. Multicoloured. P* 14.
2311 $1 Type **261** 65 60
MS2312 100×70 mm. $6 Pope and clock tower 3·50 3·75

No. 2311 was issued in small sheets of 9 with commemorative inscriptions on the margins.

262 Corvette of 1953

(Des J. Gordon. Litho Questa)

1993 (13 Aug). *40th Anniv of Corvette Range of Cars. T* **262** *and similar horiz designs. Multicoloured. P* 14×13½.
2313 $1 Type **262** 65 65
a. Sheetlet. Nos. 2313/24 .. .. 6·75
2314 $1 1993 model 65 65
2315 $1 1958 model 65 65
2316 $1 1960 model 65 65
2317 $1 "40" and symbolic chequered flag emblem 65 65
2318 $1 1961 model 65 65
2319 $1 1963 model 65 65
2320 $1 1968 model 65 65
2321 $1 1973 model 65 65
2322 $1 1975 model 65 65
2323 $1 1982 model 65 65
2324 $1 1984 model 65 65
2313/24 .. .. *Set of* 12 6·75 6·75

Nos. 2313/24 were printed together, *se-tenant*, in sheetlets of 12.

263 Gedung Shrine, 1920

(Des Kerri Schiff. Litho Questa)

1993 (16 Aug). *Asian International Stamp Exhibitions. T* **263** *and similar multicoloured designs.*

(*a*) *"Indopex '93", Surabaya, Indonesia. P* 14×13½
2325/54 5, 10, 20, 45, 55, 75 c., $1×2, $1.50×18, $2, $4, $5×2 .. .. *Set of* 30 21·00 22·00
MS2355 Three sheets. (a) 105×135 mm. $6 Relief of Sudamala epic, Mt Lawu. P 14×13½. (b) 105×135 mm. $6 Plaque from Banyumas, Java. P 14×13½. (c) 135×105 mm. $6 Panel from Ramayana reliefs (*vert*). P 13½×14 *Set of* 3 *sheets* 8·25 8·50

Nos. 2325/32 and 2351/4 show Indonesian scenes. Nos. 2333/50 were printed in three *se-tenant* sheetlets of 6 showing masks (Nos. 2333/8) or paintings (Nos. 2339/50).

(*b*) *"Taipei '93", Taiwan. P* 14×13½
2356/85 5, 10, 20, 45, 55, 75 c., $1×2, $1.50×18, $2, $4, $5×2 .. .. *Set of* 30 21·00 22·00

MS2386 Three sheets, each 135×105 mm. (a) $6 Two Stone Guardians, Longmen Caves, Henan. P 14×13½. (b) $6 Stone Guardian, Longmen Caves, Henan (*vert*). P 13½×14. (c) $6 Giant Buddha, Yungang Caves (*vert*). P 13½×14 *Set of 3 sheets* 8·25 8·50

Nos. 2356/63 and 2382/5 show Chinese scenes. Nos. 2364/81 were printed in three *se-tenant* sheetlets of 6 showing kites (Nos. 2364/9) or paintings (Nos. 2370/81).

The "St" of "St. Vincent" is omitted from the bottom left stamp, inscribed "Nezha Stirs Up the Sea", on all examples of one of the sheetlets of six.

(c) *"Bangkok '93", Thailand. P 13½×14 (5, 55 c., $2, $4) or 14×13½ (others)*

2387/416 5, 10, 20, 45, 55, 75 c., $1×2, $1.50×18, $2, $4, $5×2 .. .. *Set of* 30 21·00 22·00

MS2417 Three sheets, each 105×135 mm. (a) $6 Masked dancer. P 14×13½. (b) $6 Standing Buddha, Hua Hin (*vert*). P 13½×14. (c) $6 Carved roof boss, Dusit Mahaprasad (*vert*). P 13½×14 .. .. *Set of 3 sheets* 8·25 8·50

Nos. 2387/94 and 2413/16 show Thai scenes with the 5, 55 c., $2 and $4 being vertical. Nos. 2395/412 were printed in three *se-tenant* sheetlets of 6 showing murals from Buddhaisawan Chapel (Nos. 2395/400), paintings (Nos. 2401/6) or sculptures (Nos. 2407/12).

264 Players from St. Vincent and Mexico

(Litho Questa)

1993 (2 Sept). *Qualifying Rounds for World Cup Football Championship, U.S.A. T* **264** *and similar horiz designs showing different matches. Multicoloured. P* 14.

2418 5 c. Type **264** 10 10
2419 10 c. Honduras 10 10
2420 65 c. Costa Rica 45 35
2421 $5 St. Vincent goalkeeper .. .. .. 3·00 3·50
2418/21 .. .. *Set of* 4 3·25 3·50

265 Fish Delivery Van

(Litho Questa)

1993 (2 Sept). *Japanese Aid for Fishing Industry. T* **265** *and similar multicoloured designs. P* 14.

2422 10 c. Type **265** 15 10
2423 50 c. Fish aggregation device (*vert*) 35 30
2424 75 c. Game fishing launch 50 50
2425 $5 Fish market .. .. 3·00 3·50
2422/5 .. .. *Set of* 4 3·50 4·00

(Des W. Storozuk. Litho Questa)

1993 (4 Oct). *Famous Baseball Players (7th issue). Multicoloured design as T* **247**. *P* 14.

2426 $2 Reggie Jackson .. .. 1·10 1·10

(Litho Questa)

1993 (18 Nov). *Christmas. Religious Paintings. Designs as T* **76** *of Nevis (St. Kitts-Nevis). Black, pale lemon and red (Nos. 2427/9, 2434,* **MS**2435a) *or multicoloured (others). P* 13½×14.

2427 10 c. "Adoration of the Magi" (detail) (Dürer) 15 10
2428 35 c. "Adoration of the Magi" (different detail) (Dürer) 30 20
2429 40 c. "Adoration of the Magi" (different detail) (Dürer) 35 25
2430 50 c. "Holy Family with Saint Francis" (detail) (Rubens) 45 30
2431 55 c. "Adoration of the Shepherds" (detail) (Rubens) 45 30
2432 65 c. "Adoration of the Shepherds" (different detail) (Rubens) 55 40
2433 $1 "Holy Family" (Rubens) 75 60
2434 $5 "Adoration of the Magi" (different detail) (Dürer) .. .. 2·25 2·75
2427/34 .. .. *Set of* 8 4·75 4·50

MS2435 Two sheets, each 103×127 mm. (a) $6 "Adoration of the Magi" (different detail) (Dürer) (*horiz*). P 14×13½. (b) $6 "Holy Family with Sts. Elizabeth and John" (detail) (Rubens). P 13½×14 .. .. .. *Set of 2 sheets* 7·00 7·50

267 Barbra Streisand

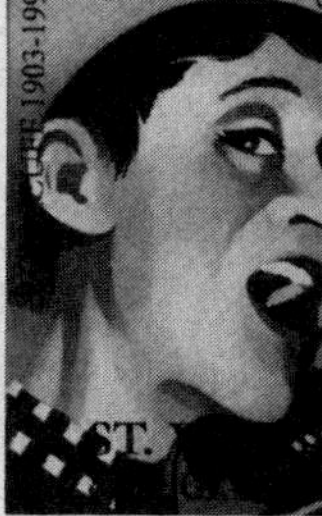

268 Roy Acuff

(Litho Questa)

1993 (31 Dec). *Barbra Streisand's Grand Garden Concert. P* 14.

2436 **267** $2 multicoloured .. .. 1·10 1·10

(Des K. Tanner. Litho Questa)

1994 (17 Jan). *Legends of Country Music. T* **268** *and similar vert designs. Multicoloured. P* 14.

2437 $1 Type **268** 45 50
a. Sheetlet. Nos. 2437/48 .. .. 5·25
2438 $1 Patsy Cline in pink shirt 45 50
2439 $1 Jim Reeves in dinner jacket 45 50
2440 $1 Hank Williams in brown jacket 45 50
2441 $1 Hank Williams in purple jacket 45 50
2442 $1 Roy Acuff with microphone 45 50
2443 $1 Patsy Cline wearing white scarf 45 50
2444 $1 Jim Reeves with microphone 45 50
2445 $1 Jim Reeves in orange jacket 45 50
2446 $1 Patsy Cline with microphone 45 50
2447 $1 Hank Williams in grey jacket 45 50
2448 $1 Roy Acuff in grey jacket 45 50
2437/48 .. .. *Set of* 12 5·25 6·00

Nos. 2437/48 were printed together, *se-tenant*, in sheetlets of 12.

269 Mobile Library

270 Woman planting Breadfruit

(Litho Cartor)

1994 (24 Jan). *Centenary of Library Service. T* **269** *and similar horiz designs. Multicoloured. P* 14×13½.

2449 5 c. Type **269** 10 10
2450 10 c. Old Public Library building 10 10
2451 $1 Family reading 45 50
2452 $1 Line of books joining youth and old man 45 50
2449/52 .. .. *Set of* 4 1·10 1·25

(Litho Cartor)

1994 (24 Jan). *Bicentenary of Introduction of Breadfruit. T* **270** *and similar vert designs. Multicoloured. P* 13½×14.

2453 10 c. Type **270** 15 10
2454 45 c. Captain Bligh with breadfruit plant 30 25
2455 65 c. Slice of breadfruit 40 40
2456 $5 Breadfruit growing on branch .. 3·00 3·50
2453/6 .. .. *Set of* 4 3·50 3·75

271 Family Picnic

(Litho Cartor)

1994 (14 Feb). *International Year of the Family (1st issue). T* **271** *and similar multicoloured designs. P* 13½×14 *($1) or* 14×13½ *(others).*

2457 10 c. Type **271** 15 10
2458 50 c. Family in church 30 30
2459 65 c. Working in the garden 40 35
2460 75 c. Jogging 45 45
2461 $1 Family group (*vert*) 55 60
2462 $2 On the beach .. .. 1·25 1·40
2457/62 .. .. *Set of* 6 2·75 2·75

See also No. 2836.

(Des W. Hanson. Litho Questa)

1994 (18 Feb). *"Hong Kong '94" International Stamp Exhibition (1st issue). Horiz designs as T* **293** *of Maldive Islands. Multicoloured. P* 14.

2463 40 c. Hong Kong 1992 $2.30 Olympic Games stamp and "Hong Kong Harbour in 19th Century" (left detail) 20 25
a. Horiz pair. Nos. 2463/4 .. .. 40 50
2464 40 c. St. Vincent 1991 $3.50 Scouts Jamboree stamp and "Hong Kong Harbour in 19th Century" (right detail) 20 25

Nos. 2463/4 were printed together, *se-tenant*, in horizontal pairs throughout the sheet with the centre part of each pair forming the complete painting.

(Des Kerri Schiff. Litho Questa)

1994 (18 Feb). *"Hong Kong '94" International Stamp Exhibition (2nd issue). Multicoloured designs as T* **294** *of Maldive Islands. P* 14.

2465/94 40 c. × 12, 45 c. × 12, 50 c. × 6 *Set of* 30 6·00 7·75

Nos. 2465/94 were printed as five *se-tenant* sheetlets, each of six different designs, depicting Ching porcelain (40 c.), dragon boat races (40 c.), seed-stitch purses (45 c.), junks (45 c.) and Qing ceramic figures (vert designs) (50 c.).

272 Bird on a Flowering Spray Plate, Qianlong

273 Blue Flasher

(Litho Questa)

1994 (18 Feb). *"Hong Kong '94" International Stamp Exhibition (3rd issue). T* **272** *and similar vert designs. Multicoloured. P* 13½×14.

2495 50 c. Type **272** 25 30
a. Sheetlet. Nos. 2495/500 .. .. 1·50
2496 50 c. Large decorated dish, Kangxi .. 25 30
2497 50 c. Cocks on rocky ground plate, Yongzheng 25 30
2498 50 c. Green decorated dish, Yuan .. 25 30
2499 50 c. Porcelain pug dog 25 30
2500 50 c. Dish decorated with Dutch ship, Qianlong 25 30
2495/500 .. .. *Set of* 6 1·50 1·75

MS2501 Two sheets, each 126×95 mm. (a) $2 Dr. Sun Yat-sen. (b) $2 Chiang Kai-shek *Set of 2 sheets* 1·90 2·00

Nos. 2495/500 were printed together, *se-tenant*, in sheetlets of 6.

No. 2497 is incorrectly inscribed "Cocks on a Rocky Groung".

(Des M. Malamud. Litho Questa)

1994 (18 Feb). *Butterflies. T* **273** *and similar horiz designs. Multicoloured. P* 14½.

2502 50 c. Type **273** 25 30
a. Sheetlet. Nos. 2502/17 .. .. 4·00
2503 50 c. Tiger Swallowtail 25 30
2504 50 c. Lustrous Copper 25 30
2505 50 c. Tailed Copper 25 30
2506 50 c. Blue Copper 25 30
2507 50 c. Ruddy Copper 25 30
2508 50 c. Viceroy 25 30
2509 50 c. California Sister 25 30
2510 50 c. Mourning Cloak 25 30
2511 50 c. Red Passion-flower 25 30
2512 50 c. Small Flambeau 25 30
2513 50 c. Blue Wave 25 30
2514 50 c. Chiricahua Metalmark 25 30
2515 50 c. Monarch 25 30
2516 50 c. Anise Swallowtail 25 30
2517 50 c. Buckeye 25 30
2502/17 .. .. *Set of* 16 4·00 4·75

Nos. 2502/17 were printed together, *se-tenant*, in sheetlets of 16.

274 Antonio Cabrini

275 *Epidendrum ibaguense*

(Des Kerri Schiff. Litho Questa)

1994 (22 Mar). *Juventus Football Club (Italy) Commemoration. T* **274** *and similar multicoloured designs showing past and present players. P* 14.

2518 $1 Type **274** 60 60
2519 $1 Michel Platini and Roberto Baggio .. 60 60
2520 $1 Roberto Bettega 60 60
2521 $1 Gaetano Scirea 60 60
2522 $1 Jurgen Kohler 60 60
2523 $1 Marco Tardelli 60 60
2524 $1 Paolo Rossi 60 60
2525 $1 Giuseppe Furino 60 60
2526 $1 Dino Zoff 60 60

2527 $1 Franco Causio 60 60
2528 $1 Claudio Gentile 60 60
2518/28 .. .. *Set of* 11 6·00 6·00
MS2529 100×70 mm. $6 U.E.F.A. Cup, Cup Winners Cup and European Cup trophies (all won by Juventus) (*horiz*) .. .. .. 3·50 3·75

(Des R. Brickman. Litho Questa)

1994 (6 Apr). *Orchids. T* **275** *and similar vert designs. Multicoloured. P* 14.
2530 10 c. Type **275** 30 20
2531 25 c. *Ionopsis utricularioides* 40 30
2532 50 c. *Brassavola cucullata* 50 50
2533 65 c. *Enclyclia cochleata* 60 60
2534 $1 *Liparis nervosa* 75 75
2535 $2 *Vanilla phaeantha* .. .. .. 1·40 1·40
2536 $4 *Elleanthus cephalotus* .. .. 2·50 2·50
2537 $5 *Isochilus linearis* .. .. .. 2·50 2·50
2530/7 .. .. *Set of* 8 8·00 8·00
MS2538 Two sheets, each 100×70 mm. (a) $6 *Rodriguezia lanceolata*. (b) $6 *Eulophia alta* *Set of* 2 *sheets* 7·00 7·50

276 Dimorphodon

(Des Yemi. Litho B.D.T.)

1994 (20 Apr). *Prehistoric Animals* (1*st series*). *T* **276** *and similar horiz designs. Multicoloured. P* 14.
2539 75 c. Type **276** 50 50
a. Sheetlet. Nos. 2539/46 .. .. 3·50
2540 75 c. Camarasaurus 50 50
2541 75 c. Spinosaurus 50 50
2542 75 c. Allosaurus 50 50
2543 75 c. Rhamphorhynchus 50 50
2544 75 c. Pteranodon and body of Allosaurus 50 50
2545 75 c. Eudimorphodon 50 50
2546 75 c. Ornithomimus 50 50
2547 75 c. Protoavis 50 50
a. Sheetlet. Nos. 2547/54 .. .. 3·50
2548 75 c. Pteranodon 50 50
2549 75 c. Quetzalcoatlus 50 50
2550 75 c. Lesothosaurus 50 50
2551 75 c. Heterodontosaurus 50 50
2552 75 c. Archaeopteryx 50 50
2553 75 c. Cearadactylus 50 50
2554 75 c. Anchisaurus 50 50
2539/54 .. .. *Set of* 16 7·00 7·00
Nos. 2539/46 and 2547/54 were each printed together, *se-tenant*, in sheetlets of 8 forming composite designs.

277 Triceratops

(Litho and thermography Cartor)

1994 (20 Apr). *"Hong Kong '94" International Stamp Exhibition (4th issue). Prehistoric Animals. Sheet* 206×121 *mm, containing T* **277** *and similar multicoloured designs. P* 13.
MS2555 $1.50, Type **277**; $1.50, Tyrannosaurus rex (*vert*); $1.50, Diplodocus; $1.50, Stegosaurus (*vert*) .. .. 2·75 3·00

278 Albertosaurus

(Des W. Wright. Litho B.D.T.)

1994 (20 Apr). *Prehistoric Animals (2nd series). T* **278** *and similar multicoloured designs. P* 14.
2556/603 75 c. × 48 .. .. .. *Set of* 48 20·00 22·00
MS2604 Four sheets, each 115×86 mm. (a) $6 Tyrannosaurus rex. (b) $6 Triceratops. (c) $6 Pteranodon and Diplodocus carnegii. (d) $6 Styracosaurus (*vert*) .. .. *Set of* 4 *sheets* 14·00 15·00
Nos. 2556/603 were printed together, *se-tenant*, as four sheetlets of 12 with Nos. 2556/79 being horizontal and Nos. 2580/603 vertical. The species depicted are Albertosaurus, Chasmosaurus, Brachiosaurus, Coelophysis, Deinonychus, Anatosaurus, Iguanodon, Baryonyx, Steneosaurus, Nanotyrannus, Camptosaurus, Camarasaurus, Hesperonis, Mesosaurus, Plesiosaurus Dolichorhynchops, Squalicorax, Tylosaurus, Plesiosoar, Stenopterygius Ichthyosaurus, Steneosaurus, Eurhinosaurus Longirostris, Cryptocleidus Oxoniensis, Caturus, Protostega, Dimorphodon, Pterodactylus, Rhamphorhynchus, Pteranodon, Gallimimus, Stegosaurus, Acanthopholis, Trachodon, Thecodonts, Ankylosaurus, Compsognathus, Protoceratops, Quetzalcoatlus, Diplodocus, Spinosaurus, Apatosaurus, Ornitholestes, Lesothosaurus, Trachodon, Protoavis, Oviraptor, Coelophysis, Ornitholestes and Archaeopteryx.

279 Mickey Mouse as Pilot

(Litho Questa)

1994 (5 May). *65th Anniv of Mickey Mouse* (1993). *T* **279** *and similar multicoloured designs showing Walt Disney cartoon characters. P* 13½×14.
2605 5 c. Type **279** 20 20
2606 10 c. Mickey in Foreign Legion 20 20
2607 15 c. Mickey as frontiersman 30 30
2608 20 c. Mickey, Goofy and Donald Duck .. 30 30
2609 35 c. Horace Horsecollar and Clarabelle Cow 40 40
2610 50 c. Minnie Mouse, Frankie and Figuro 50 50
2611 75 c. Donald and Pluto 60 60
2612 80 c. Mickey holding balloons 65 65
2613 85 c. Daisy Duck and Minnie 65 65
2614 95 c. Minnie 70 70
2615 $1 Mickey in red trousers 70 70
2616 $1.50, Mickey raising hat .. .. 1·10 1·10
2617 $2 Mickey with hands in pockets .. 1·40 1·40
2618 $3 Mickey and Minnie .. .. .. 2·25 2·25
2619 $4 Mickey with birthday cake .. .. 2·50 2·50
2620 $5 Mickey as Uncle Sam .. .. 2·50 2·50
2605/20 .. .. *Set of* 16 13·50 13·50
MS2621 Four sheets. (a) 102×127 mm. $6 Pluto looking at portrait of Mickey. P 13½×14. (b) 127×102 mm. $6 Mickey and camera (*horiz*). P 14×13½. (c) 127×102 mm. $6 Minnie disco dancing (*horiz*). P 14×13½. (d) 127×102 mm. $6 Donald with Mickey's baby photo (*horiz*). P 14×13½ .. .. .. *Set of* 4 *sheets* 15·00 15·00

280 Argentine Team

(Litho Questa)

1994 (12 May). *World Cup Football Championship, U.S.A. T* **280** *and similar horiz designs showing competing teams. Multicoloured. P* 13½.
2622 50 c. Type **280** 30 30
2623 50 c. Belgium 30 30
2624 50 c. Bolivia 30 30
2625 50 c. Brazil 30 30
2626 50 c. Bulgaria 30 30
2627 50 c. Cameroun 30 30
2628 50 c. Colombia 30 30
2629 50 c. Germany 30 30
2630 50 c. Greece 30 30
2631 50 c. Netherlands 30 30
2632 50 c. Republic of Ireland 30 30
2633 50 c. Italy 30 30
2634 50 c. Mexico 30 30
2635 50 c. Morocco 30 30
2636 50 c. Nigeria 30 30
2637 50 c. Norway 30 30
2638 50 c. Rumania 30 30
2639 50 c. Russia 30 30
2640 50 c. Saudi Arabia 30 30
2641 50 c. South Korea 30 30
2642 50 c. Spain 30 30
2643 50 c. Sweden 30 30
2644 50 c. Switzerland 30 30
2645 50 c. U.S.A. 30 30
2622/45 .. .. *Set of* 24 7·00 7·00
Nos. 2622/45 were each printed, *se-tenant*, in sheetlets of 8 stamps and one centre label.

281 Marilyn Monroe

(Litho Questa)

1994 (16 May). *Marilyn Monroe (American film star) Commemoration. T* **281** *and similar vert designs showing different portraits. Multicoloured. P* 13½×14.
2646 $1 Type **281** 45 50
a. Sheetlet. Nos. 2646/54 .. .. 4·00
2647 $1 Asleep 45 50
2648 $1 With long hair style and pendulum earrings 45 50
2649 $1 Wearing striped sweater 45 50
2650 $1 With gloved hand to face 45 50
2651 $1 With bare hand to face 45 50
2652 $1 In black and white dress 45 50
2653 $1 In sequined evening dress 45 50
2654 $1 With short hair and no earrings .. 45 50
2646/54 .. .. *Set of* 9 4·00 4·50
Nos. 2646/54 were printed together, *se-tenant*, in sheetlets of 9.

282 Capt. Jean-Luc Picard

(Litho Questa)

1994 (27 June). *Star Trek – The Next Generation (T.V. series). T* **282** *and similar multicoloured designs. P* 13½.
2655 $2 Type **282** 90 95
a. Sheetlet. Nos. 2656/63 .. .. 8·00
2656 $2 Commander William Riker 90 95
2657 $2 Lt-Commander Data 90 95
2658 $2 Lt. Worf 90 95
2659 $2 Crew members 90 95
2660 $2 Dr. Beverley Crusher 90 95
2661 $2 Lt. Worf and female crew member .. 90 95
2662 $2 Q wearing hat 90 95
2663 $2 Counsellor Deanna Troi 90 95
2655/63 .. .. *Set of* 9 8·00 8·50
MS2664 83×101 mm. $10 As No. 2659 (59×40 *mm*). P 14×14½ .. .. 4·50 4·75
Nos. 2655/63 were printed together, *se-tenant*, in sheetlets of 9 with No. 2659 also issued as separate sheetlets of 9.
A $50 value embossed on gold foil also exists from a limited printing.

283 Shigetatsu Matsunaga (Yokohama Marinos)

284 Jef United Team

(Litho Questa)

1994 (1 July). *Japanese Professional Football League. Multicoloured. P 14.*

(a) Vert designs as T **283** *showing individual players and league emblem*

2665/76 55 c. × 8, $1.50 × 4 .. .. *Set of* 12 6·00 6·00

Designs:—55 c. Masami Ihara (Yokohama Marinos); Shunzoh Ohno (Kashima Antlers); Luiz Carlos Pereira (Verdy Kawasaki); Tetsuji Hashiratani (Verdy Kawasaki); Carlos Alberto Souza dos Santos (Kashima Antlers); Yasuto Honda (Kashima Antlers); Kazuyoshi Miura (Verdy Kawasaki); $1.50, League emblem; Takumi Horiike (Shimizu S-Pulse); Rui Ramos (Verdy Kawasaki); Ramon Angel Diaz (Yokohama Marinos).

Nos. 2665/76 were printed together, *se-tenant*, in sheetlets of 12.

(b) Horiz designs as T **284** *showing teams*

2677/88 55 c. × 8, $1.50 × 4 .. .. *Set of* 12 6·00 6·00

Designs:—55 c. Verdy Yomiuri; Yokohama Marinos; A. S. Flügels; Bellmare; Shimizu S-Pulse; Jubilo Iwata; Panasonic Gamba Osaka; $1.50, Kashima Antlers; Red Diamonds; Nagoya Grampus Eight; Sanfrecce Hiroshima.

Nos. 2677/88 were printed together, *se-tenant*, in sheetlets of 12.

(c) Horiz designs as T **284** *showing players and teams arranged as individual sheetlets of 6 containing two horizontal strips of 3 either side of a central team photograph*

2689/94 55 c. × 3, $1.50 × 2, $3 A. S. Flügels 3·50 3·75
2695/700 55 c. × 3, $1.50 × 2, $3 Bellmare .. 3·50 3·75
2701/6 55 c. × 3, $1.50 × 2, $3 Panasonic Gamba Osaka .. .. 3·50 3·75
2707/12 55 c. × 3, $1.50 × 2, $3 Jef United .. 3·50 3·75
2713/18 55 c. × 3, $1.50 × 2, $3 Jubilo Iwata .. 3·50 3·75
2719/24 55 c. × 3, $1.50 × 2, $3 Kashima Antlers 3·50 3·75
2725/30 55 c. × 3, $1.50 × 2, $3 Nagoya Grampus Eight .. .. 3·50 3·75
2731/6 55 c. × 3, $1.50 × 2, $3 Sanfrecce Hiroshima .. .. 3·50 3·75
2737/42 55 c. × 3, $1.50 × 2, $3 Shimizu S-Pulse 3·50 3·75
2743/8 55 c. × 3, $1.50 × 2, $3 Red Diamonds 3·50 3·75
2749/54 55 c. × 3, $1.50 × 2, $3 Verdy Kawasaki 3·50 3·75
2755/60 55 c. × 3, $1.50 × 2, $3 Yokohama Marinos .. .. 3·50 3·75
2689/760 .. .. .. *Set of* 12 *sheetlets* 42·00 45·00

(Des W. Hanson. Litho Questa)

1994 (12 July). *25th Anniv of First Moon Landing. Horiz designs as T* **302** *of Maldive Islands. Multicoloured. P 14.*

2761 $1 Fred Whipple and Halley's Comet .. 45 50
a. Sheetlet. Nos. 2761/9 .. .. .. 4·00
2762 $1 Robert Gilruth and "Gemini 12" .. 45 50
2763 $1 George Mueller and space walk from "Gemini IV" 45 50
2764 $1 Charles Berry and Johnsville Centrifuge 45 50
2765 $1 Christopher Kraft and "Apollo 4" .. 45 50
2766 $1 James van Allen and "Explorer I" .. 45 50
2767 $1 Robert Goddard and Goddard-liquid fuel rocket 45 50
2768 $1 James Webb and "Spirit of 76" flight 45 50
2769 $1 Rocco Patrone and "Apollo 8" .. 45 50
2770 $1 Walter Dornberger and German rocket 45 50
a. Sheetlet. Nos. 2770/8 .. .. .. 4·00
2771 $1 Alexander Lippisch and Messerschmitt ME 163B Komet (airplane) 45 50
2772 $1 Kurt Debus and "A4b" rocket .. 45 50
2773 $1 Hermann Oberth and projected spaceship 45 50
2774 $1 Hanna Reitsch and "Reichenberg" flying bomb 45 50
2775 $1 Ernst Stuhlinger and "Explorer I" .. 45 50
2776 $1 Werner von Braun and rocket-powered Heinkel He 112 .. .. 45 50
2777 $1 Arthur Rudolph and rocket motor .. 45 50
2778 $1 Willy Ley and rocket airplane .. 45 50
2761/78 .. .. *Set of* 18 8·00 9·00
MS2779 Two sheets, each 131×109 mm. (a) $6 Eberhardt Rees and German rocket (50×37 *mm*). (b) $6 Hogler Toftoy (50×37 *mm*). P 14×13½ .. .. 5·50 5·75

Nos. 2761/9 and 2770/8 were each printed together, *se-tenant*, in sheetlets of 9.

(Des J. Batchelor. Litho Questa)

1994 (19 July). *50th Anniv of D-Day. Horiz designs as T* **304** *of Maldive Islands. Multicoloured. P 14.*

2780 40 c. Supply convoy 20 25
2781 $5 Unloading beached supply ship .. 2·25 2·40
MS2782 106×76 mm. $6 Liberty ship .. .. 2·75 3·00

285 Yorkshire Terrier Bitch

286 Mark Ramprakash (England) and Wisden Trophy

(Des D. Miller. Litho Questa)

1994 (21 July). *Chinese New Year ("Year of the Dog"). T* **285** *and similar vert designs. Multicoloured. P 14.*

2783 10 c. Type **285** 10 10
2784 25 c. Yorkshire Terrier dog 10 10
2785 50 c. Golden Retriever 25 30
2786 50 c. Pomeranian 25 30
a. Sheetlet. Nos. 2786/97 .. .. 3·00
2787 50 c. English Springer Spaniel 25 30
2788 50 c. Bearded Collie 25 30
2789 50 c. Irish Wolfhound 25 30
2790 50 c. Pekingese 25 30
2791 50 c. Irish Setter 25 30
2792 50 c. Old English Sheepdog 25 30
2793 50 c. Basset Hound 25 30
2794 50 c. Cavalier King Charles Spaniel .. 25 30
2795 50 c. Kleiner Münsterlander 25 30
2796 50 c. Shetland Sheepdog 25 30
2797 50 c. Dachshund 25 30
2798 65 c. Bernese Mountain Dog 30 35
2799 $1 Vorstehhund 45 50
2800 $2 Tibetan Terrier 90 95
2801 $4 West Highland Terrier .. .. 1·90 2·00
2802 $5 Shih Tzu .. .. 2·25 2·40
2783/802 .. .. *Set of* 20 9·25 10·00
MS2803 Two sheets, each 100×100 mm. (a) $6 Afghan Hound with puppy. (b) $6 German Shepherd .. .. .. *Set of* 2 *sheets* 5·50 5·75

Nos. 2786/97 were printed together, *se-tenant*, in sheetlets of 12.

(Des Kerri Schiff. Litho Questa)

1994 (25 July). *Centenary of International Olympic Committee. Gold Medal Winners. Multicoloured designs as T* **303** *of Maldive Islands. P 14.*

2804 45 c. Peter Frennel (Germany) (20 km walk), 1972 .. .. 20 25
2805 50 c. Kijung Son (Japan) (marathon), 1936 25 30
2806 75 c. Jesse Owens (U.S.A.) (100 and 200 metres), 1936 .. .. 35 40
2807 $1 Greg Louganis (U.S.A.) (diving), 1984 and 1988 .. .. 45 50
2804/7 .. .. *Set of* 4 1·25 1·40
MS2808 106×76 mm. $6 Katja Seizinger (Germany) (women's downhill skiing), 1994 (*horiz*) .. .. 2·75 3·00

(Des A. Melville-Brown. Litho Questa)

1994 (25 July). *Centenary of First English Cricket Tour to the West Indies (1995). T* **286** *and similar multicoloured designs. P 14.*

2809 10 c. Type **286** 30 20
2810 30 c. Phil Simmonds (West Indies) and Wisden Trophy 40 20
2811 $2 Garfield Sobers (West Indies) (*vert*) 1·40 1·50
2809/11 .. .. *Set of* 3 1·90 1·75
MS2812 76×96 mm. $3 First English touring team, 1895 (black and grey-brown) .. .. 1·75 1·90

(Des Kerri Schiff. Litho Questa (Nos. 2813/14, 2831/5) or B.D.T. (Nos. 2815/30))

1994 (25 July). *"Philakorea '94" International Stamp Exhibition, Seoul. Multicoloured designs as T* **305** *of Maldive Islands. P 13½ (Nos. 2815/30) or 14 (others).*

2813 10 c. Oryon Waterfall (*vert*) 10 10
2814 45 c. Indoor sports stadium, Pyongyang .. 20 25
2815 50 c. Illuminated character with house at bottom right 25 30
a. Sheetlet. Nos. 2815/22 .. .. 2·00
2816 50 c. Illuminated character with red dots in centre 25 30
2817 50 c. Illuminated character with animal at right 25 30
2818 50 c. Illuminated character with flowers at bottom right 25 30
2819 50 c. Illuminated character with dragon at left 25 30
2820 50 c. Illuminated character with house at top 25 30
2821 50 c. Illuminated character with dragon at top 25 30
2822 50 c. Illuminated character with sun at top 25 30
2823 50 c. Fish and character 25 30
a. Sheetlet. Nos. 2823/30 .. .. 2·00
2824 50 c. Two pheasants and character .. 25 30
2825 50 c. Plant and cabinet 25 30
2826 50 c. Vases and cabinet 25 30
2827 50 c. Books on decorated cabinet .. 25 30
2828 50 c. Pheasant, decorated cabinet and vase 25 30
2829 50 c. Pheasant and lamp on table .. 25 30
2830 50 c. Cabinet, vase and table 25 30
2831 65 c. Pombong, Chonhwadae (*vert*) .. 30 35
2832 75 c. Uisangdae, Naksansa (*vert*) .. 35 40
2833 $1 Buddha of the Sokkuram Grotto, Kyangju 45 50
2834 $2 Moksogwon 90 95
2813/34 .. .. *Set of* 22 6·25 7·25
MS2835 Two sheets. (a) 70×100 mm. $4 Chongdong Mirukbul (*vert*). (b) 100×70 mm. $4 Tiger hunting scene (embroidery) *Set of* 2 *sheets* 3·75 4·00

Nos. 2815/22 and 2823/30, each 24×47 mm, were printed together, *se-tenant*, in sheetlets of 8.

Nos. 2825/6 and 2830 are inscr "Bookshlef" in error.

287 St. Vincent Family

288 Sir Shridath Ramphal and Map of Guyana

(Litho Questa)

1994 (1 Sept). *International Year of the Family (2nd issue). P 14.*

2836 **287** 75 c. multicoloured 35 40

(Litho Questa)

1994 (1 Sept). *First Recipients of Order of the Caribbean Community. T* **288** *and similar multicoloured designs. P 14.*

2837 $1 Type **288** 70 50
2838 $2 Derek Walcott and map of St. Lucia .. 1·25 1·25
2839 $5 William Demas and map of Trinidad (*horiz*) .. .. 3·00 3·25
2837/9 .. .. *Set of* 3 4·50 4·50

No. 2838 is inscribed "Wilcott" in error.

289 Twin-engined Airliner, Bequia Airport

(Litho Questa)

1994 (1 Dec). *50th Anniv of International Civil Aviation Organization. T* **289** *and similar horiz designs. Multicoloured. P 14.*

2840 10 c. Type **289** 10 10
2841 65 c. Union Island Airport 30 35
2842 75 c. L.I.A.T. 8-100 at E. T. Joshua Airport 35 40
2843 $1 Aircraft and logo 45 50
2844 $1 Britten Norman Islander at J. F. Mitchell Airport, Bequia 45 50
2840/4 .. .. *Set of* 5 1·60 1·75

290 "The Annunciation" **291** Mealy Amazon Parrot

(Litho Questa)

1994 (15 Dec). *Christmas. Religious Paintings from Jean de Berry's* Book of Hours. *T* **290** *and similar vert designs. Multicoloured. P 13½×14.*

2845 10 c. Type **290** 15 10
2846 45 c. "The Visitation" 35 25
2847 50 c. "The Nativity" 40 30
2848 65 c. "The Purification of the Virgin" (detail) 50 35
2849 75 c. "Presentation of Jesus in the Temple" 60 40
2850 $5 "Flight into Egypt" .. .. .. 3·00 3·25
2845/50 .. .. *Set of* 6 4·50 4·25
MS2851 110×126 mm. $6 "Adoration of the Magi" (detail) .. .. 3·50 3·75

No. 2847 is inscribed "The Annunciation" in error.

1995 (24 Jan). *Chinese New Year ("Year of the Pig") (1st issue). Designs as Nos. 2050/8 and* **MS**2139*a/b, but with different face values and with Year of the Pig logo. P 14×13½.*

2852 30 c. Type **245** 15 20
a. Sheetlet. Nos. 2852/60 .. .. 1·25
2853 30 c. Fiddler Pig building house of sticks 15 20
2854 30 c. Practical Pig building house of bricks 15 20
2855 30 c. The Big Bad Wolf 15 20
2856 30 c. Wolf scaring Fiddler and Fifer Pig .. 15 20
2857 30 c. Wolf blowing down straw house .. 15 20
2858 30 c. Wolf in sheep costume 15 20
2859 30 c. Wolf blowing down stick house .. 15 20
2860 30 c. Wolf attempting to blow down brick house 15 20
2852/60 .. .. *Set of* 9 1·25 1·75
MS2861 Two sheets. (a) 103×128 mm. $3 Original sketch of Practical Pig building house of brick. P 14×13½. (b) 128×103 mm. $3 Practical Pig playing piano (*vert*). P 13½×14 *Set of* 2 *sheets* 2·75 3·00

Nos. 2852/60 were printed together, *se-tenant*, in sheetlets of 9.

See also Nos. 2900/3.

(Des D. Burkhart. Litho Questa)

1995 (25 Apr). *Parrots. T* **291** *and similar multicoloured designs. P 14.*

2862 $1 Type **291** 45 50
a. Sheetlet. Nos. 2862/70 .. .. 4·00
2863 $1 Nanday Conure 45 50
2864 $1 Black-headed Caique 45 50
2865 $1 Scarlet Macaw 45 50
2866 $1 Red-masked Conure 45 50
2867 $1 Blue-headed Parrot 45 50
2868 $1 Hyacinth Macaw 45 50
2869 $1 Sun Conure 45 50
2870 $1 Blue and Yellow Macaw 45 50
2862/70 .. .. *Set of* 9 4·00 4·50
MS2871 104×76 mm. $5 White-eared Conure (*vert*) .. .. 2·25 2·40

Nos. 2862/70 were printed together, *se-tenant*, in sheetlets of 9, the backgrounds forming a composite design.

292 Snowshoe

(Des D. Burkhart. Litho Questa)

1995 (25 Apr). *Cats. T* **292** *and similar multicoloured designs. P* 14.

2872 $1 Type **292** 45 50
a. Sheetlet. Nos. 2872/80 .. .. 4·00
2873 $1 Abyssinian 45 50
2874 $1 Ocicat 45 50
2875 $1 Tiffany 45 50
2876 $1 Russian Blue 45 50
2877 $1 Siamese 45 50
2878 $1 Bi-colour 45 50
2879 $1 Malayan 45 50
2880 $1 Manx 45 50
2872/80 .. .. *Set of* 9 4·00 4·50
MS2881 104×76 mm. $6 Birman (*vert*) .. 2·75 3·00

Nos. 2872/80 were printed together, *se-tenant*, in sheetlets of 9, the background forming a composite design.

293 Blue-faced Booby ("Masked Booby")

(Des D. Burkhart. Litho Questa)

1995 (2 May). *Birds. T* **293** *and similar multicoloured designs. P* 14.

2882 75 c. Type **293** 35 40
a. Vert strip of 4. Nos. 2882/5 .. 1·40
2883 75 c. Pair of Blue-faced Boobies 35 40
2884 75 c. Blue-faced Booby preening 35 40
2885 75 c. Blue-faced Booby stretching .. 35 40
2886 75 c. Great Egrets 35 40
a. Sheetlet. Nos. 2886/97 .. .. 4·25
2887 75 c. Roseate Spoonbills 35 40
2888 75 c. Ring-billed Gull 35 40
2889 75 c. Ruddy Quail Dove 35 40
2890 75 c. Royal Terns 35 40
2891 75 c. Killdeers 35 40
2892 75 c. Osprey 35 40
2893 75 c. Magnificent Frigate Bird 35 40
2894 75 c. Blue-faced Boobies ("Masked Booby") 35 40
2895 75 c. Green Heron 35 40
2896 75 c. Double-crested Cormorants .. 35 40
2897 75 c. Brown Pelican 35 40
2882/97 .. .. *Set of* 16 5·50 6·25
MS2898 Two sheets, each 100×69 mm. (a) $5 Greater Flamingo (*vert*). (b) $6 Purple Gallinule (*vert*) .. .. *Set of* 2 *sheets* 5·00 5·25

Nos. 2882/5, which show the W.W.F emblem, were printed together, *se-tenant*, in sheets of 12 (3×4) each vertical row containing one of each design.

Nos. 2886/97 were printed together, *se-tenant*, in sheetlets of 12, the background forming a composite design.

294 Churchill, Roosevelt and Stalin at Yalta Conference

295 Pig

(Des J. Gordon. Litho Questa)

1995 (8 May). 50*th Anniv of V.E. Day. P* 13½.

2899 **294** $1 multicoloured 45 50

No. 2899 was printed in sheets of 9.

A $50 value in the same design, but embossed on gold foil, exists from a limited printing.

(Des Y. Lee. Litho Questa)

1995 (8 May). *Chinese New Year ("Year of the Pig") (2nd issue). T* **295** *and similar multicoloured designs showing central panel in colours indicated. P* 14.

2900 75 c. Type **295** (myrtle-green) 35 40
a. Horiz strip of 3. Nos. 2900/2 .. .. 1·00
2901 75 c. Pig (orange-brown) 35 40
2902 75 c. Pig (rosine) 35 40
2900/2 .. .. *Set of* 3 1·00 1·25
MS2903 71×101 mm. $2 Two pigs (*horiz*) 90 95

Nos. 2900/2 were printed together, *se-tenant*, in horizontal strips of 3 throughout the sheet of 9.

296 National Flag and Globe

297 Globe and Peace Dove

(Litho Questa)

1995 (8 May). 18*th World Scout Jamboree, Netherlands. T* **296** *and similar vert designs. Multicoloured. P* 14.

2904 $1 Type **296** 45 50
2905 $4 Lord Baden-Powell .. .. .. 1·90 2·00
2906 $5 Handshake .. .. 2·25 2·40
2904/6 .. .. *Set of* 3 4·50 4·75
MS2907 Two sheets, each 81×112 mm. (a) $6 Scout greeting. (b) $6 Scout salute *Set of* 2 *sheets* 5·50 5·75

(Des W. Wright. Litho Questa)

1995 (8 May). 50*th Anniv of End of Second World War in Europe. Horiz designs as T* **317** *of Maldive Islands. Multicoloured. P* 14.

2908 $2 Tank of U.S. First Army 90 95
a. Sheetlet. Nos. 2908/15 .. .. 7·00
2909 $2 V2 rocket 90 95
2910 $2 Consolidated B-24 Liberator bombers 90 95
2911 $2 French troops advancing to Strasbourg 90 95
2912 $2 Gloster G.41 Meteor fighter 90 95
2913 $2 Berlin on fire 90 95
2914 $2 Soviet tanks in Berlin 90 95
2915 $2 *Chicago Daily Tribune* headline .. 90 95
2908/15 .. .. *Set of* 8 7·00 7·50
MS2916 107×77 mm. $6 Sortie markings on aircraft (57×42½ *mm*) .. .. .. 2·75 3·00

Nos. 2908/15 were printed together, *se-tenant*, in sheetlets of 8 with the stamps arranged in two horizontal strips of 4 separated by a gutter showing Auschwitz Concentration Camp.

No. 2909 is inscribed "Y2" in error.

(Des R. Martin. Litho Questa)

1995 (8 May). 50*th Anniv of United Nations. T* **297** *and similar vert designs. Multicoloured. P* 14.

2917 $2 Type **297** 90 95
a. Horiz strip of 3. Nos. 2917/19 .. 2·50
2918 $2 Liberty 90 95
2919 $2 U.N. Building, New York, and peace dove 90 95
2917/19 .. .. *Set of* 3 2·50 2·75
MS2920 71×107 mm. $6 Asian child .. 2·75 3·00

Nos. 2917/19 were printed together in sheets of 9 containing three *se-tenant* horizontal strips of 3 forming a composite design.

No. **MS**2920 is inscribed "1945–1955" in error.

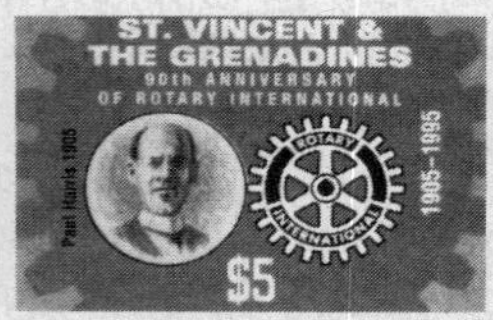

298 Women preparing Food **299** Paul Harris (founder) and Logo

(Des R. Martin. Litho Questa)

1995 (8 May). 50*th Anniv of Food and Agriculture Organization. T* **298** *and similar vert designs. Multicoloured. P* 14.

2921 $2 Type **298** 90 95
a. Horiz strip of 3. Nos. 2921/3 .. 2·50
2922 $2 Woman mixing food 90 95
2923 $2 Harvesting grain 90 95
2921/3 .. .. *Set of* 3 2·50 2·75
MS2924 76×106 mm. $6 Baby and logo .. 2·75 3·00

Nos. 2921/3 were printed together in sheets of 9 containing three *se-tenant* horizontal strips of 3 forming a composite design.

No. **MS**2924 is inscribed "1945–1955" in error.

(Litho Questa)

1995 (8 May). 90*th Anniv of Rotary International. T* **299** *and similar horiz design. Multicoloured. P* 14.

2925 $5 Type **299** .. .. 2·25 2·40
MS2926 113×79 mm. $6 National flag and logo 2·75 3·00

(Litho Questa)

1995 (8 May). 95*th Birthday of Queen Elizabeth the Queen Mother. Vert designs as T* **321** *of Maldive Islands. P* 13½×14.

2927 $1.50, orange-brown, pale brown and black 70 75
a. Sheetlet. Nos. 2927/30×2 .. 5·50
2928 $1.50, multicoloured 70 75
2929 $1.50, multicoloured 70 75
2930 $1.50, multicoloured 70 75
2927/30 .. .. *Set of* 4 2·75 3·00
MS2931 102×127 mm. $6 multicoloured .. 2·75 3·00

Designs:—No. 2927, Queen Elizabeth the Queen Mother (pastel drawing); No. 2928, Wearing blue hat; No. 2929, At desk (oil painting); No. 2930, Wearing mauve dress; No. **MS**2931, Wearing yellow dress.

Nos. 2927/30 were printed together in sheetlets of 8, containing two *se-tenant* horizontal strips of 4.

(Des J. Batchelor. Litho Questa)

1995 (8 May). 50*th Anniv of End of Second World War in the Pacific. Horiz designs as T* **317** *of Maldive Islands. Multicoloured. P* 14.

2932 $2 Douglas Devastator torpedo bomber .. 90 95
a. Sheetlet. Nos. 2932/7 .. .. 5·25
2933 $2 Doolittle's North American B-25 Mitchell *Ruptured Duck* 90 95
2934 $2 Curtiss SB2C Helldiver bomber .. 90 95
2935 $2 U.S.S. *Yorktown* (aircraft carrier) .. 90 95
2936 $2 U.S.S. *Wasp* (aircraft carrier) .. 90 95
2937 $2 U.S.S. *Lexington* (aircraft carrier) sinking 90 95
2932/7 .. .. *Set of* 6 5·25 5·50
MS2938 107×77 mm. $6 American aircraft carriers .. .. 2·75 3·00

Nos. 2932/7 were printed together, *se-tenant*, in sheetlets of 6 with the stamps arranged in two horizontal strips of 3 separated by a gutter showing U.S.S. *Hornet* (aircraft carrier) launching B-25's.

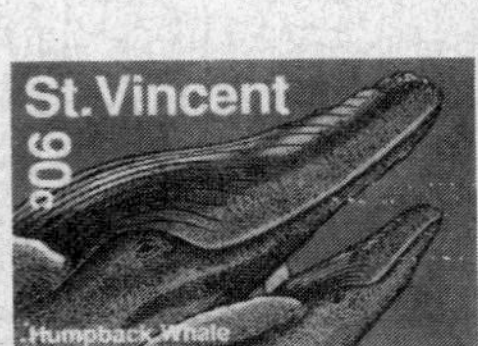

300 Head of Humpback Whales **301** Symbolic Disabled Athlete

(Des D. Miller. Litho B.D.T.)

1995 (23 May). *Marine Life. T* **300** *and similar multicoloured designs. P* 14.

2939 90 c. Type **300** 40 45
a. Sheetlet. Nos. 2939/47 .. .. 3·50
2940 90 c. Green Turtles 40 45
2941 90 c. Bottlenose Dolphin 40 45
2942 90 c. Monk Seals 40 45
2943 90 c. Krill 40 45
2944 90 c. Blue Sharks 40 45
2945 90 c. Porkfish 40 45
2946 90 c. Reef Butterflyfish 40 45
2947 90 c. Shipwreck 40 45
2948 $1 Beaugregory (fish) (*horiz*) 45 50
a. Sheetlet. Nos. 2948/51 .. .. 1·75
2949 $1 Grey Angelfish (*horiz*) 45 50
2950 $1 Yellow-tailed Damselfish (*horiz*) .. 45 50
2951 $1 Four-eyed Butterflyfish (*horiz*) .. 45 50
2939/51 .. .. *Set of* 13 5·25 6·00
MS2952 Two sheets, each 100×70 mm. (a) $6 Sea Anemones. (b) $6 *Physalia physalis* (jelly fish) .. .. .. *Set of* 2 *sheets* 5·50 5·75

Nos. 2939/47 were printed together, *se-tenant*, in sheetlets of 9 forming a composite design. Nos. 2948/51 were printed together, *se-tenant*, in sheetlets of 4.

(Des J. Gordon. Litho Questa)

1995 (6 July). *Paralympic Games '95, Connecticut. P* 13½×14.

2953 **301** $1 chrome-yellow, royal blue and black 45 50

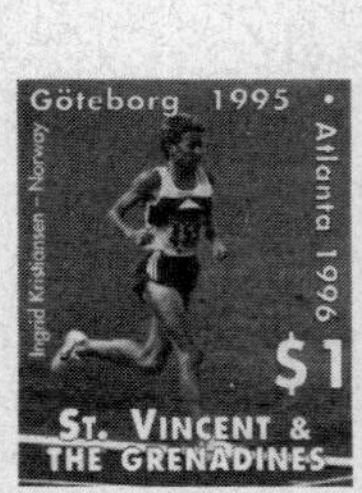

302 Ingrid Kristiansen

303 Nolan Ryan in Blue Jersey

(Des K. Sandven. Litho Questa)

1995 (31 July). *World Athletic Championships, Gothenburg. Norwegian Athletes. T* **302** *similar multicoloured designs. P* 14×14½ (*No.* 2959) *or* 14½×14 (*others*).

2954 $1 Type **302** 45 50
a. Sheetlet. Nos. 2954/9 .. .. 2·50
2955 $1 Trine Hattestad 45 50
2956 $1 Grete Waitz 45 50
2957 $1 Vebjörn Rodal 45 50
2958 $1 Geir Moen 45 50
2959 $1 Steinar Hoen (*horiz*) 45 50
2954/9 .. .. *Set of* 6 2·50 3·00

Nos. 2954/9 were printed together, *se-tenant*, in sheetlets of 6.

(Des J. Gordon. Litho Questa)

1995 (1 Aug). *Retirement of Nolan Ryan (baseball player)* (1993). *T* **303** *and similar vert designs. Multicoloured. P* 13½.
2960 $1 Type **303** 45 50
a. Sheetlet. Nos. 2960/8 4·00
2961 $1 With glove 45 50
2962 $1 In white jersey 45 50
2963 $1 Making pitch from left 45 50
2964 $1 Texas Rangers "All Star Game" emblem 45 50
a. Sheetlet. Nos. 2964×4 and 2973×5 4·00
2965 $1 Making pitch from right 45 50
2966 $1 Bleeding from blow to mouth 45 50
2967 $1 Preparing to pitch 45 50
2968 $1 Waving cap 45 50
2969 $1 Wearing "NY" cap 45 50
a. Sheetlet. Nos. 2969/77 4·00
2970 $1 Wearing stetson with dog 45 50
2971 $1 Wearing "T" cap 45 50
2972 $1 Throwing American football 45 50
2973 $1 Nolan Ryan Foundation emblem 45 50
2974 $1 With son 45 50
2975 $1 Laughing 45 50
2976 $1 With family 45 50
2977 $1 Wearing "H" cap 45 50
2960/77 *Set of* 18 8·00 9·00
MS2978 146×101 mm. $6 After final game for Texas Rangers 2·75 3·00

Nos. 2960/68, 2964 and 2973, and 2969/77 were printed together, *se-tenant*, in sheetlets of 9.

A $30 value embossed on gold foil also exists from a limited printing.

304 Breast and Bowl of Baby Food

(Des Y. Lee. Litho Questa)

1995 (4 Aug). *"Baby Friendly" Campaign. T* **304** *and similar multicoloured designs. P* 14.
2979 15 c. Type **304** 10 10
2980 20 c. Hands squeezing milk into bowl (*vert*) 10 10
2981 90 c. Breast feeding (*vert*) 40 45
2982 $5 Breast feeding emblem (*vert*) 2·25 2·40
2979/82 *Set of* 4 2·75 3·00

305 Aerial View of Leeward Coastal Road

306 "The God of Fire" (woodcut) (Shunichi Kadowaki)

(Des Y. Lee. Litho Questa)

1995 (8 Aug). *25th Anniv of Caribbean Development Bank. T* **305** *and similar multicoloured designs. P* 14.
2983 10 c. Type **305** 10 10
2984 15 c. Feeder roads project 10 10
2985 25 c. *Anthurium andraeanum* (flower) 10 10
2986 50 c. Coconut Palm tree (*vert*) 25 30
2987 65 c. Fairhall Housing Scheme 30 35
2983/7 *Set of* 5 85 95

(Litho Questa)

1995 (8 Aug). *Japanese Art. P* 14.
2988 **306** $1.40, multicoloured 65 70

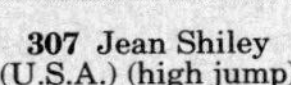

307 Jean Shiley (U.S.A.) (high jump)

308 Frank Thomas

(Des J. Iskowitz. Litho Questa)

1995 (24 Aug). *Olympic Games, Atlanta* (1996) (*1st issue*). *T* **307** *and similar vert designs. Multicoloured. P* 14.
2989 $1 Type **307** 45 50
a. Sheetlet. Nos. 2989/96 3·50
2990 $1 Ruth Fuchs (Germany) (javelin) 45 50
2991 $1 Alessandro Andrei (Italy) (shot put) 45 50
2992 $1 Dorando Pietri (Italy) (marathon) 45 50
2993 $1 Heide Rosendahl (Germany) (long jump) 45 50
2994 $1 Mitsuoki Watanabe (Japan) (gymnastics) 45 50
2995 $1 Yasuhiro Yamashita (Japan) (judo) 45 50
2996 $1 Dick Fosbury (U.S.A.) (high jump) 45 50
2997 $2 Long jumper and dove 90 95
a. Sheetlet. Nos. 2997/3002 5·25
2998 $2 Hurdler and deer 90 95
2999 $2 Sprinter and cheetah 90 95
3000 $2 Marathon runner and tiger 90 95
3001 $2 Gymnast and dove 90 95
3002 $2 Rower and duck 90 95
2989/3002 *Set of* 14 9·00 9·50
MS3003 Two sheets (a) 70×100 mm. $5 Magic Johnson (U.S.A.) (basketball). (b) 106×76 mm. $5 Swimmers hand (*horiz*) *Set of* 2 *sheets* 4·50 4·75

Nos. 2989/96 and 2997/3002 were each printed together, *se-tenant*, in sheetlets of 8 (Nos. 2989/96) or 6 (Nos. 2997/3002).

See also Nos. 3357/400.

(Des J. Gordon. Litho Questa)

1995 (6 Sept). *Famous Baseball Players* (*8th series*). *T* **308** *and similar vert designs. Multicoloured. P* 13½×14.
3004 $1 Type **308** 45 50
a. Sheetlet. Nos. 3004/12 4·00
3005 $1 Cal Ripken Jnr wearing "8" jersey and helmet 45 50
3006 $1 Ken Griffey Jnr wearing "S" cap 45 50
3007 $1 Ken Griffey Jnr wearing turquoise-blue jersey 45 50
3008 $1 Frank Thomas in "Sox" cap with bat on shoulder 45 50
3009 $1 Cal Ripken Jnr with ball and glove 45 50
3010 $1 Cal Ripkin Jnr wearing Orioles cap 45 50
3011 $1 Ken Griffey Jnr wearing "Seattle" jersey and helmet 45 50
3012 $1 Frank Thomas wearing "Chicago 35" jersey 45 50
3004/12 *Set of* 9 4·00 4·50

Nos. 3004/12 were printed together, *se-tenant*, in sheetlets of 9.

A $30 value embossed on gold foil also exists from a limited printing.

309 John Lennon

(Des R. Martin (Nos. 3013/21, **MS**3064a), S. Stevens (Nos. 3022/30, **MS**3064b), M. Leboff (Nos. 3031/6), J. Iskowitz (Nos. 3037/45), M. Chatrik (Nos. 3046/63, **MS**3064c/d). Litho Questa)

1995 (18 Sept). *Centenary of Cinema. Entertainers. T* **309** *and similar vert designs. Multicoloured. P* 13½×14.
3013/21 $1 × 9, John Lennon (as T **309**)
a. Sheetlet. Nos. 3013/21 4·25
3022/30 $1 × 9, Elvis Presley
a. Sheetlet. Nos. 3022/30 4·25
3031/6 $1 × 6, Elvis Presley
a. Sheetlet. Nos. 3031/6 2·75
3037/45 $1 × 9, Marilyn Monroe (with stairway in centre of sheetlet)
a. Sheetlet. Nos. 3037/45 4·25
3046/54 $1 × 9, Marilyn Monroe (with superimposed full length portrait)
a. Sheetlet. Nos. 3046/54 4·25
3055/63 $1 × 9, Marilyn Monroe (design with hand raised in centre of top row)
a. Sheetlet. Nos. 3055/63 4·25
3013/63 *Set of* 51 24·00 25·00
MS3064 Four sheets. (a) 110×80 mm. $6 John Lennon. (b) 80×110 mm. $6 Elvis Presley. (c) 80×110 mm. $6 Marilyn Monroe wearing red jacket. (d) 70×100 mm. $6 Marilyn Monroe in black slip *Set of* 4 *sheets* 11·00 11·50

Nos. 3013/21, 3022/30, 3031/6, 3037/45, 3046/54 and 3055/63 were each printed together, *se-tenant*, in sheetlets of 6 (Nos. 3031/6) or 9 (others).

$20 (Elvis Presley) and £30 (Marilyn Monroe) values embossed on gold foil also exist from limited printings.

310 Heinrich Boll (1972 Literature)

(Des R. Sauber. Litho Questa)

1995 (2 Oct). *Centenary of Nobel Prize Trust Fund. T* **310** *and similar horiz designs. Multicoloured. P* 14.
3065/3112 $1×46 *Set of* 48 22·00 24·00
MS3113 Four sheets, each 74×104 mm. (a) $6 Adolf Windaus (1928 Chemistry). (b) $6 Hideki Yukawa (1949 Physics). (c) $6 Bertha von Suttner (1905 Peace). (d) $6 Karl Landsteiner (1930 Medicine) *Set of* 4 *sheets* 11·00 11·50

Designs:—No. 3065, Type **310**; No. 3066, Walther Bothe (1954 Physics); No. 3067, Richard Kuhn (1938 Chemistry); No. 3068, Hermann Hesse (1946 Literature); No. 3069, Knut Hamsun (1920 Literature); No. 3070, Konrad Lorenz (1973 Medicine); No. 3071, Thomas Mann (1929 Literature); No. 3072, Fridtjof Nansen (1922 Peace); Nos. 3073, Fritz Pregl (1923 Chemistry); No. 3074, Christian Lange (1921 Peace); No. 3075, Otto Loewi (1936 Medicine); No. 3076, Erwin Schrodinger (1933 Physics); No. 3077, Giosue Carducci (1906 Literature); No. 3078, Wladyslaw Reymont (1924 Literature); No. 3079, Ivan Bunin (1933 Literature); No. 3080, Pavel Cherenkov (1958 Physics); No. 3081, Ivan Pavlov (1904 Medicine); No. 3082, Pyotr Kapitza (1978 Physics); No. 3083, Lev Landau (1962 Physics); No. 3084, Daniel Bovet (1957 Medicine); No. 3085, Henryk Sienkiewicz (1905 Literature); No. 3086, Aleksandr Prokhorov (1964 Physics); No. 3087, Julius von Jauregg (1927 Medicine); No. 3088, Grazia Deledda (1926 Literature); No. 3089, Bjornstjerne Bjornson (1903 Literature); No. 3090, Frank Kellogg (1929 Peace); No. 3091, Gustav Hertz (1925 Physics); No. 3092, Har Khorana (1968 Medicine); No. 3093, Kenichi Fukui (1981 Chemistry); No. 3094, Henry Kissinger (1973 Peace); No. 3095, Martin Luther King Jr. (1964 Peace); No. 3096, Odd Hassel (1969 Chemistry); No. 3097, Polykarp Kusch (1955 Physics); No. 3098, Ragnar Frisch (1969 Economics); No. 3099, Willis Lamb Jr. (1955 Physics); No. 3100, Sigrid Undset (1928 Literature); No. 3101, Robert Barany (1914 Medicine); No. 3102, Ernest Walton (1951 Physics); No. 3103, Alfred Fried (1911 Peace); No. 3104, James Franck (1925 Physics); No. 3105, Werner Forssmann (1956 Medicine); No. 3106, Yasunari Kawabata (1968 Literature); No. 3107, Wolfgang Pauli (1945 Physics); No. 3108, Jean-Paul Sartre (1964 Literature); No. 3109, Aleksandr Solzhenitsyn (1970 Literature); No. 3110, Hermann Staudinger (1953 Chemistry); No. 3111, Igor Tamm (1958 Physics); No. 3112, Samuel Beckett (1969 Literature).

Nos. 3065/76, 3077/88, 3089/100 and 3101/12 were each printed together, *se-tenant*, in sheetlets of 12.

311 "ET4-03" High-speed Electric Train, Germany

312 Grey Wolf

(Des W. Wright. Litho Questa)

1995 (3 Oct). *History of Transport. T* **311** *and similar horiz designs showing modern passenger trains (Nos. 3114/19) or classic cars (Nos. 3120/5). Multicoloured. P* 14.
3114 $1.50, Type **311** 70 75
a. Sheetlet. Nos. 3114/19 4·00
3115 $1.50, "TGV" train, France 70 75
3116 $1.50, Class "87" electric locomotive, Great Britain 70 75
3117 $1.50, Class "Beijing" electric locomotive, China 70 75
3118 $1.50, AMTRAK turbo train, U.S.A. 70 75
3119 $1.50, Class "RC4" electric locomtive, Sweden 70 75
3120 $1.50, Duesenberg Model "J", 1931 70 75
a. Sheetlet. Nos. 3120/5 4·00
3121 $1.50, Sleeve-valve Minerva, 1913 70 75
3122 $1.50, Delage "D.8. SS", 1933 70 75
3123 $1.50, Bugatti "Royale Coupe' De Ville", 1931–32 70 75
3124 $1.50, Rolls Royce "Phantom I Landau-ette", 1926 70 75
3125 $1.50, Mercedes Benz "S236/120/180PS", 1927 70 75
3114/25 *Set of* 12 8·25 9·00
MS3126 Two sheets, each 105×75 mm. (a) $5 Hispano-Suiza Type "H6B" sports car, 1924 (85×28½ *mm*). (b) $6 "Eurostar" train, Great Britain and France (85×28½ *mm*) *Set of* 2 *sheets* 5·00 5·25

Nos. 3114/19 and 3120/5 were printed together, *se-tenant*, in sheetlets of 6.

Nos. 3120/5 also include the "Singapore '95" International Stamp Exhibition logo.

(Des M. Friedman. Litho Questa)

1995 (1 Dec). *Centenary of Sierra Club (environmental protection society)* (1992). *T* **312** *and similar multicoloured designs. P* 14.
3127 $1 Type **312** 45 50
a. Sheetlet. Nos. 3127/35 4·00
3128 $1 Grey Wolf cub 45 50
3129 $1 Head of Grey Wolf 45 50
3130 $1 Hawaiian Goose 45 50
3131 $1 Pair of Hawaiian Geese 45 50
3132 $1 Head of Jaguar 45 50
3133 $1 Liontail Macaque 45 50
3134 $1 Sand Cat kitten 45 50
3135 $1 Three Sand Cat kittens 45 50
3136 $1 Orang-Utan in tree (*horiz*) 45 50
a. Sheetlet. Nos. 3136/44 4·00
3137 $1 Orang-Utan on ground (*horiz*) 45 50
3138 $1 Young Orang-Utan (*horiz*) 45 50
3139 $1 Jaguar lying down (*horiz*) 45 50
3140 $1 Head of Jaguar (*horiz*) 45 50
3141 $1 Pair of Sand Cats (*horiz*) 45 50
3142 $1 Hawaiian Goose (*horiz*) 45 50
3143 $1 Three Liontail Macaque (*horiz*) 45 50
3144 $1 Head of Liontail Macaque (*horiz*) 45 50
3127/44 *Set of* 18 8·00 9·00

Nos. 3127/35 and 3136/44 were printed together, *se-tenant*, in sheetlets of 9.

Nos. 3136/8 are inscribed "Orangutang" in error.

313 River Nile, Egypt

(Des R. Sauber. Litho Questa)

1995 (1 Dec). *Natural Landmarks. T* **313** *and similar horiz designs. Multicoloured. P* 14.

3145 $1.10, Type **313** 50 55
a. Sheetlet. Nos. 3145/52 .. .. 4·00
3146 $1.10, River Yangtze, China 50 55
3147 $1.10, Niagara Falls, U.S.A.–Canada border 50 55
3148 $1.10, Victoria Falls, Zambia–Zimbabwe border 50 55
3149 $1.10, Grand Canyon, U.S.A. 50 55
3150 $1.10, Sahara Desert, Algeria 50 55
3151 $1.10, Mt Kilimanjaro, Tanzania .. 50 55
3152 $1.10, River Amazon, Brazil 50 55
3145/52 .. .. *Set of* 8 4·00 4·25
MS3153 106×76 mm. $6 Haleakala Crater, Hawaii .. .. 2·75 3·00

Nos. 3145/52 were printed together, *se-tenant*, in sheetlets of 8.

314 Lionel Santa Car

(Des Rosemary DeFiglio. Litho Questa)

1995 (7 Dec). *Christmas. Antique Disney Toys. T* **314** *and similar horiz designs. Multicoloured. P* 14×13½.

3154 1 c. Type **314** 10 10
3155 2 c. Mickey Mouse "choo-choo" 10 10
3156 3 c. Minnie Mouse pram 10 10
3157 5 c. Mickey Mouse acrobats pull-toy .. 10 10
3158 10 c. Mickey and Pluto clockwork cart .. 10 10
3159 25 c. Mickey Mouse motorcycle 20 10
3160 $3 Lionel Mickey Mouse handcar .. 2·00 2·00
3161 $5 Casey Jr. Disneyland train .. .. 3·50 3·50
3154/61 .. .. *Set of* 8 5·50 5·50
MS3162 Two sheets. (a) 127×100 mm. $6 Lionel streamlined locomotive and Mickey Mouse wagon. (b) 100×127 mm. $6 "Silver Link" locomotive and Mickey the Stoker tender *Set of* 2 *sheets* 5·50 5·75

315 Symbolic Rat

316 Spock giving Vulcan Salute

(Des Y. Lee. Litho Questa)

1996 (2 Jan). *Chinese New Year ("Year of the Rat"). T* **315** *and similar vert designs showing different rats. P* 14½.

3163 **315** 75 c. black, mauve and yellow-olive .. 35 40
a. Horiz strip of 3. Nos. 3163/5 .. 1·00
3164 – 75 c. black, orange-red and yellow-olive 35 40
3165 – 75 c. black, claret & dp turquoise-green 35 40
3163/5 .. .. *Set of* 3 1·00 1·25
MS3166 100×50 mm. $1 Type **315**; $1 As No. 3164; $1 As No. 3165 .. .. .. 1·40 1·50
MS3167 71×102 mm. $2 black, orge-red & yell-ol 90 95

Nos. 3163/5 were printed together, *se-tenant*, as horizontal strips of 3 in sheets of 9.

(Des J. Gordon. Litho Questa)

1996 (4 Jan). *30th Anniv of* Star Trek *Television Series. T* **316** *and similar vert designs. Multicoloured. P* 13½×14.

3168 $1 Type **316** 45 50
a. Sheetlet. Nos. 3168/76 .. .. 4·00
3169 $1 Capt. Kirk and Spock dressed as gangsters 45 50
3170 $1 Kirk in front of computer 45 50
3171 $1 Kirk with Tribbles 45 50
3172 $1 Kirk, Spock and Lt. Uhura in front of Time Portal 45 50
3173 $1 Uhura and Lt. Sulu 45 50
3174 $1 Romulan commander and crew .. 45 50
3175 $1 City and planet 45 50
3176 $1 Khan 45 50
3177 $1 Spock with phaser 45 50
a. Sheetlet. Nos. 3177/85 .. .. 4·00
3178 $1 Capt. Kirk 45 50
3179 $1 Lt. Uhura 45 50
3180 $1 Lt. Sulu 45 50
3181 $1 Starship U.S.S. *Enterprise* 45 50
3182 $1 Dr. McCoy 45 50
3183 $1 Chief Engineer Scott 45 50
3184 $1 Kirk, Spock and McCoy 45 50
3185 $1 Chekov 45 50
3168/85 .. .. *Set of* 18 8·00 9·00
MS3186 152×107 mm. $6 Spock and Uhura .. 2·75 3·00

Nos. 3168/76 and 3177/85 were printed together, *se-tenant*, in sheetlets of 9.

A $30 value embossed on gold foil also exists from a limited printing.

317 Goofy the Stamp Dealer

(Des Alvin White Studio. Litho Questa)

1996 (8 Jan). *Occupations (1st series). T* **317** *and similar multicoloured designs showing Walt Disney cartoon characters at work. P* 14×13½ (*horiz*) *or* 13½×14 (*vert*).

3187/95 10 c. × 9 (Type **317**; Supermarket assistant; Car salesman; Florist; Fast food assistant; Street vendor; Gift shop assistant; Hobby shop assistant; Baker)
a. Sheetlet. Nos. 3187/95 40
3196/204 50 c. × 9 (Delivery man; Truck driver; Aircraft flight crew; Train crew; Bus driver; Tour guide; Cycle messenger; Tram conductor; Air traffic controller)
a. Sheetlet. Nos. 3196/204 .. 2·10
3205/13 75 c. × 9 (Postal inspector; Traffic policeman; Private detectives; Highway Patrolman; Justice of the Peace; Security guard; Judge and lawyer; Sheriff; Court stenographer)
a. Sheetlet. Nos. 3205/13 .. .. 3·00
3214/22 90 c. × 9 (Basketball player; Referee; Athletic coach; Ice skater; Golfer and caddy; Sports commentator; Tennis players; Football coach; Racing car driver)
a. Sheetlet. Nos. 3214/22 .. .. 3·75
3223/31 95 c. × 9 (Paleontologist; Archaeologist; Inventor; Astronaut; Chemist; Engineer; Computer expert; Astronomer; Zoologist)
a. Sheetlet. Nos. 3223/31 .. .. 4·00
3232/9 $1.10 × 8 (Classroom teacher; Nursery school teacher; Music teacher; Electronic teacher; School psychologist; School principal; Professor; Graduate (all *vert*))
a. Sheetlet. Nos. 3232/9 .. .. 4·00
3240/8 $1.20 ×9 (Ship builders; Fisherman; Pearl diver; Underwater photographer; Bait and tackle shop owner; Swim suit models; Marine life painter; Life guard; Lighthouse keeper)
a. Sheetlet. Nos. 3240/8 .. .. 5·00
3187/3248 .. .. .. *Set of* 62 22·00 24·00
MS3249 Seven sheets, each 127×102 mm. (a) $6 Ice cream seller. (b) $6 Tug boat captain (*vert*). (c) $6 Members of Jury (*vert*). (d) $6 Cheerleaders (*vert*). (e) $6 Oceanographer. (f) $6 Librarian (*vert*). (g) $6 Deep sea diver (*vert*) *Set of* 7 *sheets* 19·00 20·00

Nos. 3187/95, 3196/3204, 3205/13, 3214/22, 3223/31, 3232/9, and 3240/8 were each printed together, *se-tenant*, in sheetlets of 8 (Nos. 3232/9) or 9 (others).

See also Nos. 3510/56.

(Litho Questa)

1996 (1 Feb). *125th Anniv of Metropolitan Museum of Art, New York. Multicoloured designs as T* **331** *of Maldive Islands. P* 13½×14.

3250/7 75 c. × 8 ("Moses striking Rock" (Abraham Bloemaert); "The Last Communion" (Botticelli); "The Musicians" (Caravaggio); "Francesco Sassetti and Son" (Ghirlandaio); "Pepito Costa y Bunells" (Goya); "Saint Andrew" (Martini); "The Nativity" (The Dutch School); "Christ Blessing" (Solario))
a. Sheetlet. Nos. 3250/7 plus centre label .. .. 2·75
3258/66 90 c. × 9 ("Madame Cézanne", "Still Life with Apples and Pears"; "Man in a Straw Hat"; "Still Life with a Ginger Jar"; "Madame Cézanne in a Red Dress"; "Still Life with Crockery"; "Dominique Aubert"; "Still Life with Flowers"; "The Card Players" (all by Cézanne))
a. Sheetlet. Nos. 3258/66 .. .. 3·75
3267/75 $1 × 9 ("Bullfight" (Goya); "Portrait of a Man" (Hals); "Mother and Son" (Sully); "Portrait of a Young Man" (Memling); "Matilde Stoughton de Jaudenes" (Stuart); "Josef de Jaudenes y Nebot" (Stuart); "Mont Sainte-Victoire" (Cézanne); "Gardanne" (Cézanne); "Empress Eugenie" (Winterhalter)
a. Sheetlet. Nos. 3267/75 .. .. 4·25
3276/84 $1.10 × 9 ("The Dissolute Household" (Steen); "Gerard de Lairesse" (Rembrandt); "Juan de Pareja" (Velázquez); "Curiosity" (Ter Borch); "The Companions of Rinaldo" (Poussin); "Don Gaspar de Guzman" (Velázquez); "Merry Company on a Terrace" (Steen); "Pilate washing Hands" (Rembrandt); "Portrait of a Man" (Van Dyck))
a. Sheetlet. Nos. 3276/84 .. .. 4·50
3250/84 .. .. *Set of* 35 15·00 16·00
MS3285 Four sheets, each 95×70 mm. (a) $6 "Hagar in the Wilderness" (Corot) (81×53 *mm*). P 14. (b) $6 "Two Young Peasant Women" (Pissarro) (81×53 *mm*). P 14. (c) $6 "Young Ladies from the Village" (Courbet) (81×53 *mm*). P 14. (d) $6 "Allegory of the Planets and Continents" (Tiepolo) (81×53 *mm*). P 14 *Set of* 4 *sheets* 11·00 11·50

Nos. 3250/7, 3258/66, 3267/75 and 3276/84 were each printed together, *se-tenant*, in sheetlets of 8 stamps and one centre label (Nos. 3250/7) or 9 (others).

318 Alien Band

319 Yoda

(Des J. Gordon. Litho Walsall (Nos. 3292/5))

1996 (19 Mar). Star Wars (*film trilogy*). (*a*) *T* **318** *and similar horiz designs. Multicoloured. P* 14.

3286 35 c. Type **318** 40 40
a. Sheetlet. Nos. 3286/91 .. .. 2·25
3287 35 c. Darth Vader in battle 40 40
3288 35 c. Fighter ship 40 40
3289 35 c. Space craft orbiting planet 40 40
3290 35 c. Space craft and shuttle 40 40
3291 35 c. Luke Skywalker on space bike .. 40 40

(*b*) *Self-adhesive. T* **319** *and similar multicoloured designs. P* 7

3292 $1 Darth Vader 70 70
a. Strip of 3. Nos. 3292/4 .. .. 1·90 1·90
3293 $1 Type **319** 70 70
3294 $1 Storm Trooper 70 70
3286/94 .. .. .. *Set of* 9 4·00 4·00
MS3295 148×71 mm. $2×3 Designs as Nos. 3292/4 but triangular, 65×36½ mm. P 9 .. 2·75 3·00

Nos. 3286/91 were printed together, *se-tenant*, in sheetlets of 6.

Nos. 3292/4 were printed in horizontal and vertical strips of 3 throughout the sheet of 9, with each stamp being separate on the backing paper with die-cut perforations.

Three $2 values embossed on gold foil also exist from a limited printing.

320 *Anteos menippe*

321 Michael Jordan (basketball player)

(Des T. Woods. Litho Questa)

1996 (15 Apr). *Butterflies. T* **320** *and similar vert designs. Multicoloured. P* 14.

3296 70 c. Type **320** 30 35
3297 90 c. *Papilio lycophron* 40 45
a. Sheetlet. Nos. 3297/3305 .. .. 3·50
3298 90 c. *Prepona buckleyana* 40 45
3299 90 c. *Parides agavus* 40 45
3300 90 c. *Papilio cacicus* 40 45
3301 90 c. *Euryades duponchelli* 40 45
3302 90 c. *Diaethria dymena* 40 45
3303 90 c. *Orimba jansoni* 40 45
3304 90 c. *Polystichtis siaka* 40 45
3305 90 c. *Papilio machaonides* 40 45

3306 $1 *Eunica alcmena* 45 50
3307 $1.10, *Doxocopa lavinia* 50 55
3308 $2 *Tithorea tarricina* 90 95
3296/3308 .. .. .. *Set of* 13 5·75 6·50
MS3309 Two sheets, each 75×104 mm (a) $5 *Adelpha albia*. (b) $6 *Themone pais* *Set of* 2 *sheets* 5·00 5·25

Nos. 3297/3305 were printed together, *se-tenant*, in sheetlets of 9, the backgrounds forming a composite design.

(Des J. Gordon. Litho Questa)

1996 (17 Apr). *Sports Legends.* (a) *Vert designs as T* **321**. *P* 14.
3310 $2 Type **321** 90 95
a. Sheetlet. Nos. 3310×16 and 3312 .. 17·00
3311 $2 Joe Montana (American footballer) 90 95
a. Sheetlet. Nos. 3311×16 and 3313 .. 18·00

(*b*) *Size* 69×103 *mm. Imperf*
3312 $6 Michael Jordan .. .. .. 2·75 3·00
3313 $10 Joe Montana .. .. .. 4·50 4·75
3310/13 .. .. .. *Set of* 4 9·00 9·50

Nos. 3310 with 3312 and 3311 with 3313 were each printed in sheetlets of 16 of the $2 with an example of the larger imperforate stamp included in the enlarged right-hand margin.

322 The Monkey King

(Des Y. Lee. Litho Walsall)

1996 (10 May). *"CHINA '96" 9th Asian International Stamp Exhibition* (1*st issue*). *Chinese Animated Films* – Uproar in Heaven (*Nos.* 3314/18) *and* Nezha conquers the Dragon King (*Nos.* 3315/19). *T* **322** *and similar multicoloured designs. P* 12.
3314 15 c. Type **322** 10 10
a. Sheetlet. Nos. 3314/23×2 .. 1·40
3315 15 c. Monkey King flying towards illuminated pole 10 10
3316 15 c. Monkey King and flying horses .. 10 10
3317 15 c. Monkey King picking fruit .. 10 10
3318 15 c. Monkey King drinking from flask .. 10 10
3319 15 c. Nezha waking up 10 10
3320 15 c. Nezha swimming with fish .. 10 10
3321 15 c. Nezha on back of sea serpent .. 10 10
3322 15 c. Nezha with sword 10 10
3323 15 c. Nezha in battle 10 10
3314/23 .. .. .. *Set of* 10 70 75
MS3324 Two sheets, each 85×105 mm. (a) 75 c. Monkey King (*vert*). (b) 75 c. Nezha (*vert*) *Set of* 2 *sheets* 70 75

Nos. 3314/23 were printed together, *se-tenant*, in sheetlets of 20 containing two of each design.

323 Chongqing Dazu Buddha

(Des Y. Lee. Litho Walsall)

1996 (10 May). *"CHINA '96" 9th Asian International Stamp Exhibition* (2*nd issue*). *Sheet* 115×80 *mm. P* 12.
MS3325 **323** $2 multicoloured 90 95

(Litho Questa)

1996 (12 June). *70th Birthday of Queen Elizabeth II. Multicoloured designs as T* **334** *of Maldive Islands showing different photographs. P* $13^1/_2$×14.
3326 $2 As Type **334** of Maldive Islands .. 90 95
a. Strip of 3. Nos. 3326/8 .. .. 2·75
3327 $2 Wearing Garter robes .. 90 95
3328 $2 Wearing pink hat and coat .. 90 95
3326/8 .. .. .. *Set of* 3 2·75 2·90
MS3329 125×103 mm. $6 On Buckingham Palace balcony (*horiz*). P 14×$13^1/_2$ .. 2·75 2·90

Nos. 3326/8 were printed together, *se-tenant*, in horizontal and vertical strips of 3 throughout sheets of 9.

324 West Indian Boy

(Litho Questa)

1996 (11 July). *50th Anniv of U.N.I.C.E.F. T* **324** *and similar horiz designs. Multicoloured. P* 14.
3330 $1 Type **324** 45 50
3331 $1.10, European girls 50 55
3332 $2 South-east Asian girl 90 95
3330/2 .. .. .. *Set of* 3 1·90 2·00
MS3333 104×74 mm. $5 Arab boy .. .. 2·25 2·40

325 Menorah and The Knesset

(Des Rachel Deitch. Litho Questa)

1996 (11 July). *3000th Anniv of Jerusalem. T* **325** *and similar horiz designs. Multicoloured. P* 14.
3334 $1 Type **325** 45 50
3335 $1.10, The Monteflore Windmill .. 50 55
3336 $2 Shrine of the Book 90 95
3334/6 .. .. .. *Set of* 3 1·90 2·00
MS3337 104×74 mm. $5 Old City, Jerusalem 2·25 2·40

The captions on Nos. 3334 and 3336 were transposed in error.

326 Walter Winchell

327 Bananaquit

(Des J. Iskowitz. Litho Questa)

1996 (11 July). *Centenary of Radio. Entertainers. T* **326** *and similar vert designs. Multicoloured. P* $13^1/_2$×14.
3338 90 c. Type **326** 40 45
3339 $1 Fred Allen 45 50
3340 $1.10, Hedda Hopper 50 55
3341 $2 Eve Arden 90 95
3338/41 .. .. .. *Set of* 4 2·25 2·50
MS3342 72×102 mm. $6 Major Bowes .. 2·75 3·00

(Des Jennifer Toombs. Litho B.D.T.)

1996 (11 July). *Birds. T* **327** *and similar multicoloured designs. P* 14.
3343 60 c. Type **327** 25 30
3344 $1 Rufous-throated Solitaire .. 45 50
3345 $1 Purple Martin (*horiz*) 45 50
a. Sheetlet. Nos. 3345/53 .. .. 4·00
3346 $1 Broad-winged Hawk (*horiz*) .. 45 50
3347 $1 White-tailed Tropic Bird (*horiz*) .. 45 50
3348 $1 Black-winged Stilt (*horiz*) .. 45 50
3349 $1 Bridled Tern (*horiz*) 45 50
3350 $1 Blue-hooded Euphonia (*horiz*) .. 45 50
3351 $1 Turnstone (*horiz*) 45 50
3352 $1 Green-throated Carib (*horiz*) .. 45 50
3353 $1 Yellow-crowned Night Heron (*horiz*) 45 50
3354 $1.10, Hooded Tanager 50 55
3355 $2 Purple-throated Carib 90 95
3343/55 .. .. .. *Set of* 13 6·00 6·75
MS3356 Two sheets, each 89×92 mm. (a) $5 Red-billed Whistling Duck. (b) $6 St. Vincent Amazon .. .. .. *Set of* 2 *sheets* 5·00 5·25

Nos. 3345/53 were printed together, *se-tenant*, in sheetlets of 9 with the backgrounds forming a composite design.

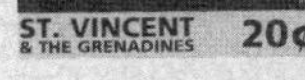

328 Maurice King (St. Vincent) (weightlifting), Pan American Games, 1959

329 Notre Dame Cathedral, Paris

(Des M. Friedman and S. Stines. Litho Questa)

1996 (19 July). *Olympic Games, Atlanta. T* **328** *and similar multicoloured designs. P* 14.
3357 20 c. Type **328** 10 10
3358 70 c. Eswort Coombs (St. Vincent) (400m sprint), World University Student Games) 30 35
3359 90 c. Pamenos Ballantyne (St. Vincent) (O.E.C.S. road-running) and Benedict Ballantyne (St. Vincent) (Guiness Half-marathon, 1994) 40 45
3360 90 c. Ancient Greek runners, Olympia (*horiz*) 40 45
3361 $1 London landmarks (*horiz*) .. 45 50
3362 $1 Women's archery (Korea), 1988, 1992 45 50
a. Sheetlet. Nos. 3362/70 .. .. 4·00
3363 $1 Gymnastics (Japan), 1960–76 .. 45 50
3364 $1 Basketball (U.S.A.), 1936, 1948–68, 1976, 1984 and 1992 .. .. 45 50
3365 $1 Soccer (Spain), 1992 .. .. 45 50
3366 $1 Water polo (Hungary), 1956 .. 45 50
3367 $1 Baseball (Cuba), 1992 .. .. 45 50
3368 $1 Kayak (Germany), 1980 .. .. 45 50
3369 $1 Fencing (France), 1980 .. .. 45 50
3370 $1 Cycling (Germany), 1908, 1964, 1972–76 and 1992 .. .. 45 50
3371 $1 Vitaly Shcherbo (Russia) (gymastics), 1992 .. .. .. 45 50
a. Sheetlet. Nos. 3371/9 .. .. 4·00
3372 $1 Fu Mingxia (China) (diving), 1992 .. 45 50
3373 $1 Wilma Rudolph (U.S.A.) (track and field), 1960 .. .. .. 45 50
3374 $1 Rafer Johnson (U.S.A.) (decathlon), 1960 .. .. .. 45 50
3375 $1 Teofilo Stevenson (Cuba) (boxing), 1972–80 .. .. .. 45 50
3376 $1 Babe Didrikson (U.S.A.) (track and field), 1932 .. .. .. 45 50
3377 $1 Kyoko Iwasaki (Japan) (swimming), 1992 .. .. .. 45 50
3378 $1 Yoo Namkyu (Korea) (table tennis), 1988 .. .. .. 45 50
3379 $1 Michael Gross (Germany) (swimming), 1984–88 .. .. 45 50
3380 $1 Yasuhiro Yamashita (Japan) (judo), 1984 (*horiz*) 45 50
a. Sheetlet. Nos. 3380/8 .. .. 4·00
3381 $1 Peter Rono (Kenya) (1500m race), 1988 (*horiz*) 45 50
3382 $1 Aleksandr Kourlovitch (Russia) (weight-lifting), 1988 (*horiz*) .. 45 50
3383 $1 Juha Tiainen (Finland) (hammer throw), 1984 (*horiz*) 45 50
3384 $1 Sergei Bubka (Russia) (pole vault), 1988 (*horiz*) 45 50
3385 $1 Q.F. Newall (Great Britain) (archery), 1908 (*horiz*) 45 50
3386 $1 Nadia Comaneci (Rumania) (gymnastics), 1976 (*horiz*) 45 50
3387 $1 Carl Lewis (U.S.A.) (long jump), 1988 (*horiz*) 45 50
3388 $1 Bob Mathias (U.S.A.) (decathlon), 1948 (*horiz*) 45 50
3389 $1 Chuhei Nambu (Japan) (triple jump), 1932 (*horiz*) 45 50
a. Sheetlet. Nos. 3389/97 .. .. 4·00
3390 $1 Duncan McNaughton (Canada) (high jump), 1932 (*horiz*) 45 50
3391 $1 Jack Kelly (U.S.A.) (single sculls), 1920 (*horiz*) 45 50
3392 $1 Jackie Joyner-Kersee (U.S.A.) (heptathlon), 1988 (*horiz*) .. 45 50
3393 $1 Tyrell Biggs (U.S.A.) (super heavy-weight boxing), 1984 (*horiz*) .. 45 50
3394 $1 Larisa Latynina (Russia) (gymnastics), 1964 (*horiz*) 45 50
3395 $1 Bob Garrett (U.S.A.) (discus), 1896 (*horiz*) 45 50
3396 $1 Paavo Nurmi (Finland) (5000 m), 1924 (*horiz*) 45 50
3397 $1 Eric Lemming (Sweden) (javelin), 1908 (*horiz*) 45 50
3398 $1.10, Rodney Jack (St. Vincent) (1995 Caribbean Nations Football Cup) .. 50 55
3399 $1.10, Dorando Pietri (Italy) (marathon), 1908 .. .. .. 50 55
3400 $2 Yachting (*horiz*) 90 95
3357/400 .. .. .. *Set of* 44 20·00 22·00
MS3401 Four sheets. (a) 74×104 mm. $5 Olympic flag (*horiz*). (b) 74×104 mm. $5 Carl Lewis (U.S.A.) (relay). (c) 104×74 mm. $5 Hannes Kolehmainen (Finland) (marathon), 1920 (*horiz*). (d) 104×74 mm. $5 Alexander Ditiatin (Russia) (gymnastics), 1980 (*horiz*) *Set of* 4 *sheets* 9·25 9·50

Nos. 3362/70, 3371/9, 3380/8 and 3389/97, which show Olympic gold medal winners, were each printed, *se-tenant*, in sheetlets of 9.

No. 3371 is inscribed "GYMNASTIECS" in error.

(Des Alvin White Studios. Litho Questa)

1996 (25 July). The Hunchback of Notre Dame. *T* **329** *and similar multicoloured designs showing scenes from the Disney cartoon film. Multicoloured. P* $13^1/_2$×14 (*vert*) *or* 14×$13^1/_2$ (*horiz*).
3402/7 10 c. × 6 (Type **329**; People watching puppet show; Judge Frollo on black horse; Quasimodo and his parents captured; Gargoyles; Quasimodo)
a. Sheetlet. Nos. 3402/7 25
3408/16 30 c. × 9 (Captain Phoebus meets Esmeralda; Captain Phoebus and Judge Frollo; Esmeralda dancing; Esmeralda and candidates for King of Fools; Quasimodo wearing crown; Quasimodo pelted; Quasimodo carrying Esmeralda; Phoebus on black horse; Quasimodo, Esmeralda and a wounded Phoebus (*all horiz*))
a. Sheetlet. Nos. 3408/16 .. .. 1·25

3417/25 $1 × 9 (Quasimodo chained to bell tower; Three gargoyles and Quasimodo; Quasimodo pulling down pillars; Quasimodo rescuing Esmeralda; Phoebus leading citizens; Quasimodo throwing wood; Quasimodo weeping over Esmeralda; Quasimodo and Frollo fighting; Quasimodo and Esmeralda on ledge (*all horiz*))
 a. Sheetlet. Nos. 3417/25 . . . . 4·00
3426/33 $1 × 8 (Quasimodo; Phoebus; Laverne and Hugo; Clopin; Frollo; Esmeralda; Victor; Djali)
 a. Sheetlet. Nos. 3426/33 . . . . 3·50
3402/33 . . . . *Set of* 31 9·00 9·50
MS3434 Five sheets. (a) 124×102 mm. $6 Quasimodo, Phoebus and Esmeralda (*horiz*). (b) 124×102 mm. $6 Esmeralda. (c) 124×102 mm. $6 Quasimodo cheering. (d) 104×126 mm. $6 Esmeralda and Quasimodo (*horiz*). (e) 104×126 mm. $6 Esmeralda and Phoebus (*horiz*) *Set of* 5 *sheets* 16·50 17·00

Nos. 33402/7, 3408/16, 3417/25 and 3426/33 were each printed together, *se-tenant*, in sheetlets of 6 (Nos. 3402/7), 8 (Nos. 3426/33) or 9 (Nos. 3408/16).

No. 3416 is inscribed "wonded phoebus" in error.

330 French Angelfish **331** *Beloperone guttata*

(Des D. Burkhardt. Litho Questa)

1996 (10 Aug). *Fishes. T* **330** *and similar horiz designs. Multicoloured. P* 14.

3435 70 c. Type **330** 30 35
3436 90 c. Red-spotted Hawkfish 40 45
3437 $1 Barred Hamlet 45 50
 a. Sheetlet. Nos. 3437/45 . . . . 4·00
3438 $1 Flamefish 45 50
3439 $1 Caribbean Long-nosed Butterflyfish 45 50
3440 $1 Royal Gramma ("Fairy Basslet") . . 45 50
3441 $1 Red-tailed Parrotfish 45 50
3442 $1 Black-barred Soldierfish 45 50
3443 $1 Three-spotted Damselfish 45 50
3444 $1 Candy Basslet 45 50
3445 $1 Spot-finned Hogfish 45 50
3446 $1 Jackknife Fish 45 50
 a. Sheetlet. Nos. 3446/54 . . . . 4·00
3447 $1 Surgeon Fish 45 50
3448 $1 Muttonfish 45 50
3449 $1 Seahorse 45 50
3450 $1 Comber Fish 45 50
3451 $1 Angel Shark 45 50
3452 $1 Moray Eel 45 50
3453 $1 Bicolour Parrotfish 45 50
3454 $1 *Tritonium nodiferum* (sea snail) . . 45 50
3455 $1.10, Balloonfish ("Spiny Puffer") . . 50 55
3456 $2 Grey Triggerfish 90 95
3435/56 . . . . *Set of* 21 10·00 11·00
MS3457 Two sheets, each 106×76 mm. (a) $5 Queen Triggerfish. (b) $6 Blue Marlin *Set of* 2 *sheets* 5·00 5·25

Nos. 3437/45 and 3446/54 were each printed together, *se-tenant*, in sheetlets of 9 with the backgrounds of Nos. 3446/54 forming a composite design.

No. 3445 is inscribed "HOFGFISH" in error.

(Des Jennifer Toombs. Litho B.D.T.)

1996 (15 Aug). *Flowers. T* **331** *and similar horiz designs. Multicoloured. P* 13½×14.

3458 70 c. Type **331** 30 35
3459 90 c. *Datura candida* 40 45
 a. Sheetlet. Nos. 3459/67 . . . . 3·50
3460 90 c. *Amherstia nobilis* 40 45
3461 90 c. *Ipomoea acuminata* 40 45
3462 90 c. *Bougainvillea glabra* 40 45
3463 90 c. *Cassia alata* 40 45
3464 90 c. *Cordia sebestena* 40 45
3465 90 c. *Opuntia dilenii* 40 45
3466 90 c. *Cryptostegia grandiflora* 40 45
3467 90 c. *Rodriguezia lanceolata* 40 45
3468 $1 *Epidendrum elongatum* 45 50
3469 $1.10, *Petrea volubilis* 50 55
3470 $2 *Oncidium altissimum* 90 95
3458/70 . . . . *Set of* 13 6·00 6·50
MS3471 Two sheets, each 78×64 mm. (a) $5 *Hibiscus rosa-sinensis*. (b) $5 *Acalypha hispida*

Nos. 3459/67 were printed together, *se-tenant*, in sheetlets of 9 with the backgrounds forming a composite design.

332 *Doric*, 1923 **333** Elvis Presley

1996 (5 Sept). *Passenger Ships. T* **332** *and similar horiz designs. Multicoloured. Litho. P* 14.

3472 $1.10, Type **332** 50 55
 a. Sheetlet. Nos. 3472/7 . . . . 3·00
3473 $1.10, *Nerissa*, 1926 . . . . 50 55
3474 $1.10, *Howick Hall*, 1910 . . . . 50 55
3475 $1.10, *Jervis Bay*, 1922 . . . . 50 55
3476 $1.10, *Vauban*, 1912 . . . . 50 55
3477 $1.10, *Orinoco*, 1928 . . . . 50 55
3478 $1.10, *Lady Rodney*, 1929 . . . . 50 55
 a. Sheetlet. Nos. 3478/83 . . . . 3·00
3479 $1.10, *Empress of Russia*, 1913 . . . . 50 55
3480 $1.10, *Providence*, 1914 . . . . 50 55
3481 $1.10, *Reina Victori-Eugenia*, 1913 . . 50 55
3482 $1.10, *Balmoral Castle*, 1910 . . . . 50 55
3483 $1.10, *Tivives*, 1911 . . . . 50 55
3472/83 . . . . *Set of* 12 6·00 6·50
MS3484 Two sheets, each 106×76 mm. (a) $6 *Aquitania*, 1914. (b) $6 *Imperator*, 1913 *Set of* 2 *sheets* 5·50 5·75

Nos. 3472/7 and 3478/83 were each printed together, *se-tenant*, in sheetlets of 6.

(Des Y. Lee. Litho Questa)

1996 (8 Sept). *Elvis Presley (singer) Commemoration. T* **333** *and similar vert designs showing different portraits. Multicoloured. P* 13½×14.

3485 $2 Type **333** 90 95
 a. Sheetlet. Nos. 3485/90 . . . . 5·50
3486 $2 Wearing checked shirt with guitar . . 90 95
3487 $2 Playing piano 90 95
3488 $2 Wearing black jacket and playing guitar 90 95
3489 $2 Wearing white shirt and black tie . . 90 95
3490 $2 Singing into studio microphone . . 90 95
3485/90 . . . . *Set of* 6 5·50 5·75

Nos. 3485/90 were printed together, *se-tenant*, in sheetlets of 6 with an enlarged illustrated margin.

334 Sandy Koufax (baseball player) **335** Richard Petty's 1990 Pontiac

(Des J. Gordon. Litho Questa)

1996 (26 Sept). *Sports Legends. Sandy Koufax. T* **334** *and similar vert designs. Multicoloured. P* 14 *or imperf* (*No.* 3494).

3491 $2 Type **334** 90 95
 a. Sheetlet. Nos. 3491×6, 3492/3 each × 5 and 3494 . . . . 2·75
3492 $2 Pitching ball 90 95
3493 $2 Preparing to pitch with arm raised . . 90 95
3494 $6 Sandy Koufax (69×103 *mm*) . . 2·75 3·00
3491/4 . . . . *Set of* 4 5·00 5·75

Nos. 3491/4 were printed in sheetlets containing 16 $2 stamps and one example of the imperforate $6 included in the enlarged right-hand margin.

A $30 value embossed on gold foil also exists from a limited printing.

(Des W. Wright. Litho Questa)

1996 (26 Sept). *Richard Petty (stock car driver) Commemoration. T* **335** *and similar horiz designs. Multicoloured. P* 14.

3495 $2 Type **335** 90 95
 a. Sheetlet. Nos. 3495/8 . . . . 3·50
3496 $2 Richard Petty 90 95
3497 $2 1972 Plymouth 90 95
3498 $2 1974 Dodge 90 95
3495/8 . . . . *Set of* 4 3·50 3·75
MS3499 Two sheets. (a) 104×74 mm. $5 1970 Plymouth "Superbird" (84×28 *mm*). (b) 64×48 mm. $6 1996 25th Anniversary STP Pontiac *Set of* 2 *sheets* 5·00 5·25

Nos. 3495/8 were printed together, *se-tenant*, in sheetlets of 4 with an enlarged illustrated margin.

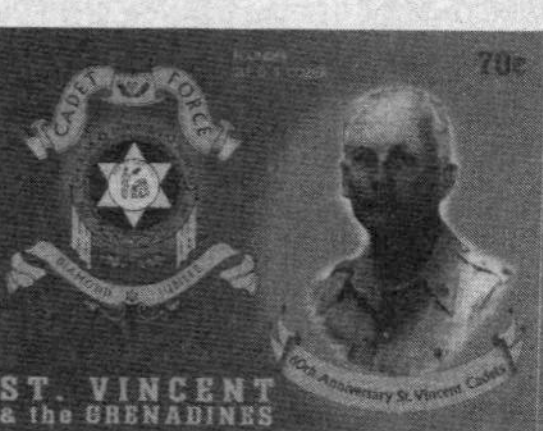

336 D. S. Cozier (founder) and Cadet Force Emblem

(Litho Questa)

1996 (23 Oct). *60th Anniv of St. Vincent Army Cadet Force. T* **336** *and similar horiz design. Multicoloured. P* 14×13½.

3500 70 c. Type **336** 30 35
3501 90 c. Emblem and first cadets with Cozier 40 45

337 "Virgin and Child" (detail, Memling) **338** Sylvester Stallone in *Rocky IV*

(Litho Questa)

1996 (14 Nov). *Christmas. Religious Paintings. T* **337** *and similar vert designs. Multicoloured. P* 13½×14.

3502 70 c. Type **337** 30 35
3503 90 c. "St. Anthony" (detail, Memling) . . 40 45
3504 $1 "Madonna and Child" (detail, D. Bouts) 45 50
3505 $1.10, "Virgin and Child" (detail, Lorenzo Lotto) 50 55
3506 $2 "St. Roch" (detail, Lotto) 90 95
3507 $5 "St. Sebastian" (detail, Lotto) . . 2·25 2·40
3502/7 . . . . *Set of* 6 4·75 5·25
MS3508 Two sheets, each 106×76 mm. (a) $5 "Virgin and Child with St. Roch and St. Sebastian" (Lotto). (b) $5 "Virgin and Child with St. Anthony and Donor" (Memling) *Set of* 2 *sheets* 4·50 4·75

(Des Shannon. Litho Questa)

1996 (21 Nov). *20th Anniv of* Rocky (*film*). *Sheet* 143×182 *mm. P* 14×13½.

MS3509 **338** $2×3 multicoloured . . . . 2·75 3·00

No. **MS**3509 was printed with an enlarged illustrated left-hand margin.

(Des Alvin White Studios. Litho Questa)

1996 (3 Dec). *Occupations (2nd series). Multicoloured designs as Nos.* 3196/3248, *but all with face value of* 10 c. *P* 14×13½ (*horiz*) *or* 13½×14 (*vert*).

3510/17 10 c. × 8 As Nos. 3196/9 and 3201/4
 a. Sheetlet. Nos. 3510/17 and central label 35
3518/25 10 c. × 8 As Nos. 3205/8 and 3210/13
 a. Sheetlet. Nos. 3518/25 and central label 35
3526/33 10 c. × 8 As Nos. 3214/17 and 3519/22
 a. Sheetlet. Nos. 3526/33 and central label 35
3534/41 10 c. × 8 As Nos. 3523/6 and 3528/31
 a. Sheetlet. Nos. 3534/41 and central label 35
3542/8 10 c. × 7 As Nos. 3232/4 and 3236/9 (all vert)
 a. Sheetlet. Nos. 3542/8 and top right-hand corner label 30
3549/56 10 c. × 8 As Nos. 3240/3 and 3245/8
 a. Sheetlet. Nos. 3549/56 and central label 35
3510/56 . . . . *Set of* 47 2·00 2·25

Nos. 3510/17, 3518/25, 3526/33, 3534/41, 3542/8 and 3549/56 were printed together, *se-tenant*, in sheetlets of 7 (Nos. 3542/8) or 8 (others). In each case one stamp shown on the original sheetlet has been replaced with a stamp-sized label as indicated.

339 Symbolic Ox **340** Lieut. Tuvok

(Des Y. Lee. Litho Questa)

1997 (2 Jan). *Chinese New Year ("Year of the Ox"). T* **339** *and similar vert designs showing different oxen. P* 14½×15.

3557 $1 black, salmon and brown-rose . . 45 50
 a. Horiz strip of 3. Nos. 3557/9 . . . . 1·40
3558 $1 black, emerald and lilac 45 50
3559 $1 black, bright rose and rose-carmine . . 45 50
3557/9 . . . . *Set of* 3 1·40 1·50
MS3560 97×48 mm. Nos. 3557/9 . . . . 90 95
MS3561 71×101 mm. $2 black, dull orange and orange-yellow 90 95

Nos. 3557/9 were printed together, *se-tenant*, as horizontal strips of 3 in sheets of 9.

1997 (23 Jan). Star Trek Voyager (*television series*). *T* **340** *and similar vert designs. Multicoloured. Litho. P* 13½×14.
3562 $2 Type **340** 90 95
a. Sheetlet. Nos. 3562/70 8·00
3563 $2 Kes 90 95
3564 $2 Tom Paris 90 95
3565 $2 The Doctor 90 95
3566 $2 Captain Katherine Janeway 90 95
3567 $2 B'Elanna Torres 90 95
3568 $2 Neelix 90 95
3569 $2 Harry Kim 90 95
3570 $2 First Officer Chakotay 90 95
3562/70 *Set of* 9 8·00 8·50
MS3571 88×120 mm. $6 Crew of the *Star Trek Voyager* (28×45 *mm*) 2·75 3·00
Nos. 3562/70 were printed together, *se-tenant*, in sheetlets of 9.
A $30 value embossed on gold foil also exists from a limited printing.

341 Mickey Mantle
342 Hong Kong Waterfront

(Des J. Gordon. Litho Questa)

1997 (10 Feb). *Sports Legends. Mickey Mantle (baseball player). T* **341** *and similar vert design. Multicoloured. P* 14 (*No.* 3572) *or imperf* (*No.* 3573).
3572 $2 Type **341** 90 95
a. Sheetlet. Nos. 3572×16 and 3573 17·00
3573 $6 Mickey Mantle (67×100 *mm*) 2·75 3·00
Nos. 3572/3 were printed together, *se-tenant*, in sheetlets containing 16 $2 stamps and one example of the imperforate $6 included in the enlarged illustrated right-hand margin.

(Des S. Nicodemus (No. **MS**3584). Litho B.D.T.)

1997 (12 Feb). *"Hong Kong '97" International Stamp Exhibition. T* **342** *and similar horiz designs showing the Hong Kong waterfront by day (Nos.* 3574/8) *or night (Nos.* 3579/83). *Multicoloured. P* 14.
3574 90 c. Type **342** 40 45
a. Sheetlet. Nos. 3574/83 4·00
3575 90 c. Two ferries in foreground 40 45
3576 90 c. Construction site on waterfront 40 45
3577 90 c. One launch 40 45
3578 90 c. Hong Kong Bank and yellow building in centre 40 45
3579 90 c. Large building with spire on right 40 45
3580 90 c. Electronic billboards including HITACHI 40 45
3581 90 c. Mansions on hillside at right 40 45
3582 90 c. Toshiba and NEC billboards in centre 40 45
3583 90 c. Hong Kong bank building under Union Jack 40 45
3574/83 *Set of* 10 4·00 4·50
MS3584 Three sheets, each 127×85 mm. (a) $2 Boy and girl at Full Moon Festival; $2 Couple on bridge; $2 Two girls with lanterns. (b) $2 Incense candles; $2 Buddhist monk at Polin Monastery; $2 Orchids. (c) $2 Wanchai Market; $2 Chinese couple in street; $2 Man choosing fruit. (*all designs* 34×25 *mm*). P 13½ *Set of* 3 *sheets* 8·25 8·50
Nos. 3574/83 were printed together, *se-tenant* in two horizontal strips of five forming two composite designs.
A $30 value embossed on gold foil also exists from a limited printing.

(Des M. Freedman and Dena Rubin. Litho Questa)

1997 (24 Mar). *50th Anniv of U.N.E.S.C.O. Multicoloured designs as T* **348** *of Maldive Islands. P* 13½×14 (*vert*) *or* 14×13½ (*horiz*).
3585 70 c. Lord Howe Island, Australia 30 35
3586 90 c. Uluru-kata Tjuta National Park, Australia 40 45
3587 $1 Cave paintings, Kakadu National Park, Australia 40 45
3588 $1.10, Te Wahipounamu National Park, New Zealand 50 55
3589 $1.10, Castle, Himeji-jo, Japan 50 55
a. Sheetlet. Nos. 3589/96 and central label 4·00
3590 $1.10, Temple, lake and gardens, Kyoto, Japan 50 55
3591 $1.10, Walkway, Kyoto, Japan 50 55
3592 $1.10, Buddha, Temple of Ninna-ji, Japan 50 55
3593 $1.10, View from castle, Himeji-jo, Japan 50 55
3594 $1.10, Forest, Shirakami-sanchi, Japan 50 55
3595 $1.10, Forest and mountains, Yakushima, Japan 50 55
3596 $1.10, Forest, Yakushima, Japan 50 55
3597 $1.10, City of San Gimignano, Italy 50 55
a. Sheetlet. Nos. 3597/3604 and central label 4·00
3598 $1.10, Cathedral of Santa Maria Asunta, Pisa, Italy 50 55
3599 $1.10, Cathedral of Santa Maria Fiore, Florence, Italy 50 55
3600 $1.10, Archaeological site, Valley of the Boyne, Ireland 50 55
3601 $1.10, Church of St Savin-sur-Gartempe, France 50 55
3602 $1.10, Regency mansion, Bath, England 50 55
3603 $1.10, Rooftop view of Bath, England 50 55
3604 $1.10, Street in Bath, England 50 55
3605 $1.10, Monastery of Rossanou, Meteora, Greece 50 55
a. Sheetlet. Nos. 3605/12 and central label 4·00
3606 $1.10, Ceiling painting, Mount Athos, Greece 50 55
3607 $1.10, Monastery Osios Varlaam, Meteora, Greece 50 55
3608 $1.10, Ruins, Athens, Greece 50 55
3609 $1.10, Carvings, Acropolis Museum, Athens, Greece 50 55
3610 $1.10, Painted cloisters, Mount Athos, Greece 50 55
3611 $1.10, Lake, Mount Athos, Greece 50 55
3612 $1.10, Painting above door, Mount Athos, Greece 50 55
3613 $1.50, Palace, Wudang Mountains, China (*horiz*) 70 75
a. Sheetlet. Nos. 3613/17 and label 3·50
3614 $1.50, Caves, Mogao, China (*horiz*) 70 75
3615 $1.50, House, Taklamakan Desert, China (*horiz*) 70 75
3616 $1.50, Section going through forest, Great Wall, China (*horiz*) 70 75
3617 $1.50, Section going through desert, Great Wall, China (*horiz*) 70 75
3618 $1.50, House and church, Quedlinburg, Germany (*horiz*) 70 75
a. Sheetlet. Nos. 3618/22 and label 3·50
3619 $1.50, Decorated house fronts, Quedlinburg (*horiz*) 70 75
3620 $1.50, Decorative house windows, Quedlinburg, Germany (*horiz*) 70 75
3621 $1.50, House front, Quedlinburg, Germany (*horiz*) 70 75
3622 $1.50, Church spires, Quedlinburg (*horiz*) 70 75
3623 $1.50, Valley of the Ingenios, Cuba (*horiz*) 70 75
a. Sheetlet. Nos. 3623/7 and label 3·50
3624 $1.50, City of Zacatecas, Mexico (*horiz*) 70 75
3625 $1.50, Lima, Peru (*horiz*) 70 75
3626 $1.50, Monastic ruins, Paraguay (*horiz*) 70 75
3627 $1.50, Mayan ruins, Copan, Honduras (*horiz*) 70 75
3628 $2 Tongariro National Park, New Zealand (*horiz*) 90 95
3629 $5 Tongariro National Park, New Zealand 2·25 2·40
3585/629 *Set of* 45 27·00 30·00
MS3630 Seven sheets, each 127×102 mm. (a) $5 Great Wall, China (*horiz*). (b) $5 Venice, Italy (*horiz*). (c) $5 Dunbuang Oasis, China (*horiz*). (d) $5 Wall, Quedlinburg, Germany (*horiz*). (e) $5 Meteora Monastery, Greece (*horiz*). (f) $5 Himeji-jo, Japan (*horiz*). (g) $5 Dome of the Rock, Jerusalem (*horiz*) *Set of* 7 *sheets* 16·00 17·00
Nos. 3589/96, 3597/604 and 3605/12 were each printed together, *se-tenant*, in sheetlets of 8 stamps with a central label and Nos. 3613/17, 3618/22 and 3623/7 in sheetlets of 5 stamps with a top left-hand corner label.

343 Microwave Radio Relay Tower, Dorsetshire Hill
344 Smooth-billed Ani

(Des M. Freedman. Litho Questa)

1997 (3 Apr). *125th Anniv of Telecommunications in St. Vincent. T* **343** *and similar multicoloured designs (except* 70 c.). *P* 14½.
3631 5 c. Type **343** 10 10
3632 10 c. Cable and Wireless headquarters, Kingstown 10 10
3633 20 c. Microwave relay tower (*vert*) 10 10
3634 35 c. Cable and Wireless complex, Arnos Vale 15 20
3635 50 c. Cable and Wireless tower, Mount St. Andrew 25 30
3636 70 c. Early cable ship (black & bluish violet) 30 35
3637 90 c. Eastern telecommunications network map, 1872 40 45
3638 $1.10, World telegraph map, 1876 50 55
3631/8 *Set of* 8 1·75 2·00

(Litho Questa)

1997 (7 Apr). *Birds of the World. T* **344** *and similar vert designs. Multicoloured. P* 14.
3639 60 c. Type **344** 25 30
3640 70 c. Belted Kingfisher 30 35
3641 90 c. Blackburnian Warbler 40 45
3642 $1 Blue Grosbeak 45 50
a. Sheetlet. Nos. 3642/7 2·75
3643 $1 Bananaquit 45 50
3644 $1 Cedar Waxwing 45 50
3645 $1 Ovenbird 45 50
3646 $1 Hooded Warbler 45 50
3647 $1 Flicker 45 50
3648 $1.10, Blue Tit 50 55
3649 $2 Chaffinch 90 95
3650 $2 Song Thrush 90 95
a. Sheetlet. Nos. 3650/5 5·50
3651 $2 Robin 90 95
3652 $2 Blackbird 90 95
3653 $2 Great Spotted Woodpecker 90 95
3654 $2 Wren 90 95
3655 $2 Kingfisher 90 95
3656 $5 Ruddy Turnstone 2·25 2·40
3639/56 *Set of* 18 13·00 14·00
MS3657 Two sheets, each 101×75 mm. (a) $5 St. Vincent Parrot. (b) $5 Tawny Owl *Set of* 2 *sheets* 4·50 4·75
Nos. 3642/7 and 3650/5 were each printed together, *se-tenant*, in sheetlets of 6 with the backgrounds forming composite designs.

345 Mandarin Duck
346 Frank Robinson

(Des R. Rundo. Litho Questa)

1997 (7 Apr). *Sea Birds. T* **345** *and similar multicoloured designs. P* 15×14½ (*horiz*) *or* 14½×15 (*vert*).
3658 70 c. Type **345** 30 35
3659 90 c. Green Heron 45 50
3660 $1 Ringed Teal drake 45 50
3661 $1.10 Blue-footed Booby and chick 50 55
3662 $1.10, Crested Auklet (*vert*) 50 55
a. Sheetlet. Nos. 3662/7 3·00
3663 $1.10, Whiskered Auklet (*vert*) 50 55
3664 $1.10, Pigeon Guillemot (*vert*) 50 55
3665 $1.10, Adelie Penguins (*vert*) 50 55
3666 $1.10, Rockhopper Penguin (*vert*) 50 55
3667 $1.10, Emperor Penguin and chick (*vert*) 50 55
3668 $2 Australian Jacana (*vert*) 90 95
3669 $5 Reddish Egret (*vert*) 2·25 2·40
3658/69 *Set of* 12 7·75 8·50
MS3670 Two sheets, each 101×75 mm. (a) $5 Flamingos. (b) $5 Snowy Egrets *Set of* 2 *sheets* 4·50 4·75
Nos. 3662/7 were printed together, *se-tenant*, in sheetlets of 6 with the backgrounds forming a composite design.

1997 (15 Apr). *Baseball Legends. T* **346** *and similar vert designs.* (a) *P* 14×15 (*Nos.* 3671/86) *or imperf* (*No.* 3687).
3671 $1 Type **345** 45 50
a. Sheetlet. Nos. 3671/87 10·00
3672 $1 Satchel Paige 45 50
3673 $1 Billy Williams 45 50
3674 $1 Reggie Jackson 45 50
3675 $1 Roberto Clemente 45 50
3676 $1 Ernie Banks 45 50
3677 $1 Hank Aaron 45 50
3678 $1 Roy Campanella 45 50
3679 $1 Willie McCovey 45 50
3680 $1 Monte Irvin 45 50
3681 $1 Willie Stargell 45 50
3682 $1 Rod Carew 45 50
3683 $1 Ferguson Jenkins 45 50
3684 $1 Bob Gibson 45 50
3685 $1 Lou Brock 45 50
3686 $1 Joe Morgan 45 50
3687 $6 Jackie Robinson (67×101 *mm*) 2·75 3·00
3671/87 *Set of* 17 10·00 11·00

(*b*) *Self-adhesive. P* 7
MS3688 133×67 mm. $1×3 Jackie Robinson (32×46 *mm*) 1·40 1·50
Nos. 3671/87 were printed together, *se-tenant*, in sheetlets containing 16 $2 stamps and one example of the imperforate $6 included in the enlarged illustrated right-hand margin.

(Des R. Rundo. Litho Questa)

1997 (3 June). *300th Anniv of Mother Goose Nursery Rhymes. Sheet, 102×72 mm containing horiz design as T* **112** *of St. Kitts–Nevis (Nevis). Multicoloured. P* 14.
MS3689 $5 Girl sewing ("Curly-Locks") 2·25 2·40

347 Child's Face and U.N.E.S.C.O. Emblem
348 Couple with Dog

(Litho Questa)

1997 (3 June). *10th Anniv of Chernobyl Nuclear Disaster. T* **347** *and similar vert design. Multicoloured. P* 13½×14.
3690 $2 Type **347** 90 95
3691 $2 As Type **347** but inscribed "CHABAD'S CHILDREN OF CHERNOBYL" at foot 90 95

(Des J. Iskowitz. Litho Questa)

1997 (3 June). *50th Death Anniv of Paul Harris (founder of Rotary International). Horiz designs as T* **113** *of St. Kitts–Nevis (Nevis). Multicoloured. P* 14.
3692 $2 Paul Harris and Thai children receiving blankets 90 95
MS3693 78×108 mm. $5 Luis Vincente Giay (International President) with President Carter of the United States .. .. 2·25 2·40

(Litho Questa)

1997 (3 June). *Golden Wedding of Queen Elizabeth and Prince Philip. Horiz designs as T* **350** *of Maldive Islands. Multicoloured. P* 14.
3694 $1.10, Queen Elizabeth II 50 55
a. Sheetlet. Nos. 3694/9 .. .. .. 3·00
3695 $1.10, Royal coat of arms 50 55
3696 $1.10, Queen Elizabeth and Prince Philip 50 55
3697 $1.10, Queen Elizabeth and Prince Philip on royal visit 50 55
3698 $1.10, Buckingham Palace 50 55
3699 $1.10, Prince Philip in naval uniform .. 50 55
3694/9 .. .. *Set of* 6 3·00 3·25
MS3700 100×70 mm. $5 Queen Elizabeth on Coronation day .. .. 2·25 2·40
Nos. 3694/9 were printed together, *se-tenant*, in sheetlets of 6.

(Des J. Iskowitz. Litho Questa)

1997 (3 June). *"Pacific '97" International Stamp Exhibition, San Francisco. Death Centenary of Heinrich von Stephan (founder of the U.P.U). Horiz designs as T* **351** *of Maldive Islands. P* 14.
3701 $2 violet and black 90 95
a. Sheetlet. Nos. 3701/3 .. .. .. 2·75
3702 $2 chestnut and black 90 95
3703 $2 dull blue and black 90 95
3701/3 .. .. *Set of* 3 2·75 3·00
MS3704 82×118 mm. $5 sepia .. .. 2·25 2·40
Designs:—No. 3701, Bicycle postman, India, 1800's; No. 3702, Von Stephan and Mercury; No. 3703, Ox-drawn postal cart, Indochina; No. **MS**3704, Von Stephan and post rider, Indochina
Nos. 3701/3 were printed together, *se-tenant*, in sheetlets of 3 with enlarged right-hand margin.

1996 (3 June). *Birth Bicentenary of Hiroshige (Japanese painter). "One Hundred Famous Views of Edo". Vert designs as T* **352** *of Maldive Islands. Multicoloured. Litho. P* 13½×14.
3705 $1.50, "Furukawa River, Hiroo" 70 75
a. Sheetlet. Nos. 3705/10 .. .. 4·25
3706 $1.50, "Chiyogaike Pond, Meguro" .. 70 75
3707 $1.50, "New Fuji, Meguro" 70 75
3708 $1.50, "Moon-viewing Point" 70 75
3709 $1.50, "Ushimachi, Takanawa" 70 75
3710 $1.50, "Original Fuji, Meguro" 70 75
3705/10 .. .. *Set of* 6 4·25 4·50
MS3711 Two sheets, each 102×127 mm. (a) $5 "Gotenyama, Shinagawa". (b) $5 "Shinagawa Susaki" .. .. *Set of 2 sheets* 4·50 4·75
Nos. 3705/10 were printed together, *se-tenant*, in sheetlets of 6.

(Des R. Sauber. Litho Questa)

1997 (3 June). *175th Anniv of Brothers Grimm's Third Collection of Fairy Tales. T* **348** *and similar vert designs showing* "Old Sultan" *(Nos. 3712/14) and* "The Cobbler and the Elves" *(Nos. 3715/17). Multicoloured. P* 13½×14.
3712 $2 Type **348** 90 95
a. Sheetlet. Nos. 3712/14 .. .. 2·75
3713 $2 Sheepdog on hillside 90 95
3714 $2 Wolf and sheepdog 90 95
3715 $2 The cobbler 90 95
a. Sheetlet. Nos. 3715/17 .. .. 2·75
3716 $2 The elves 90 95
3717 $2 Cobbler with elf 90 95
3712/17 .. .. *Set of* 6 5·50 5·75
MS3718 Two sheets. (a) 124×96 mm. $5 Couple and baby with Old Sultan. (b) 96×124 mm. $5 Elf .. .. *Set of 2 sheets* 4·50 4·75
Nos. 3712/14 and 3715/17 were each printed together, *se-tenant*, in sheetlets of 3 with illustrated margins.

349 Deng Xiaoping

350 Alphonso Theodore Roberts

1997 (3 June). *Deng Xiaoping (Chinese statesman) Commemoration. T* **349** *and similar designs. Litho. P* 14.
3719 $2 agate 90 95
a. Sheetlet. Nos. 3719/22 .. .. 3·50
3720 $2 agate 90 95
3721 $2 agate 90 95
3722 $2 agate 90 95
3723 $2 blue and slate-blue 90 95
a. Sheetlet. Nos. 3723/6 .. .. 3·50
3724 $2 blue and slate-blue 90 95
3725 $2 blue and slate-blue 90 95
3726 $2 blue and slate-blue 90 95
3727 $2 black 90 95
a. Sheetlet. Nos. 3727/30 .. .. 3·50
3728 $2 black 90 95
3729 $2 black 90 95
3730 $2 black 90 95
3719/30 .. .. *Set of* 12 10·50 11·50
MS3731 76×106 mm. $5 multicoloured .. 2·25 2·40
Designs: *Vert*—No. 3719, Type **349**; No. 3720, Looking left; No. 3721, In military uniform; No. 3722, Full face; No. 3723, Looking right; No. 3724, Smiling; No. 3725, With head tilted to right; No. 3726, Looking down; No. 3727, Looking right; No. 3728, Looking left; No. 3729, Full face; No. 3730, Facing left and smiling. *Horiz*—No. **MS**3731 Deng Xiaoping and Zhuo Lin.
Nos. 3719/22, 3723/6 and 3727/30 were each printed together, *se-tenant*, in sheetlets of 4 with enlarged illustrated right-hand margins.

(Litho Questa)

1997 (20 June). *Inaugural Cricket Test Match at Arnos Vale. T* **350** *and similar multicoloured design. P* 13½×14 *(90 c.) or* 14×13½ *($5).*
3732 90 c. Type **350** 40 45
3733 $5 Arnos Vale cricket ground *(horiz)* .. 2·25 2·40

351 "Cinemax" Mardi Gras Band

352 Hand above Globe of Flowers

(Litho B.D.T.)

1997 (24 July). *20th Anniv of Vincy Mas Carnival. T* **351** *and similar multicoloured designs. P* 15×14 *(horiz) or* 14×15 *(vert).*
3734 10 c. Type **351** 10 10
3735 20 c. Queen of the Bands "Jacintha Ballantyne" 10 10
3736 50 c. Queen of the Bands "Out of the Frying Pan and into the Fire" *(vert)* .. 25 30
3737 70 c. King of the Bands "Conquistodore" 30 35
3738 90 c. Starlift Steel Orchestra 45 50
3739 $2 Frankie McIntosh (musical arranger) *(vert)* 90 95
3734/9 .. .. *Set of* 6 2·00 2·25

(Litho Questa)

1997 (28 Aug). *World Cup Football Championship, France (1998). Designs as T* **246** *of Lesotho. P* 14×13½ *(horiz) or* 13½×14 *(vert).*
3740 70 c. multicoloured 30 35
3741 90 c. agate 40 45
3742 $1 multicoloured 45 50
3743/50 $1 × 8 (grey-black; multicoloured; grey-black; grey-black; grey-black; grey-black; multicoloured; grey-black)
a. Sheetlet. Nos. 3743/50 and central label .. .. 3·75
3751/8 $1 × 8 (each multicoloured)
a. Sheetlet. Nos. 3751/8 and central label .. .. 3·75
3759/66 $1 × 8 (multicoloured; grey-black; multicoloured; grey-black; grey-black; multicoloured; grey-black; multicoloured)
a. Sheetlet. Nos. 3759/66 and central label .. .. 3·75
3767/74 $1 × 8 (slate-blue; multicoloured; slate-blue; multicoloured; multicoloured; slate-blue; multicoloured; slate-blue)
a. Sheetlet. Nos. 3767/74 and central label .. .. 3·75
3775 $1.10, sepia 50 55
3776 $2 multicoloured 90 95
3777 $10 grey-black .. .. .. 4·50 4·75
3740/77 .. .. *Set of* 38 22·00 23·00
MS3778 Four sheets, each 102×127 mm. (a) $5 multicoloured. (b) $5 multicoloured. (c) $5 grey-black. (d) $5 grey-black .. *Set of 4 sheets* 9·25 9·50
Designs: *Horiz*—No. 3740, Beckenbauer, West Germany; No. 3741; Moore, England; No. 3742, Lato, Poland; No. 3759 Argentine and West German players, 1986; Nos. 3760 and 3769, English and West German players, 1966; No. 3761 Goal mouth melee, 1986; No. 3762, Italian and West German players, 1982; Nos. 3763 and 3770, English player heading ball, 1966; No. 3764, Argentine player with ball, 1978; No. 3765, Argentine player chasing ball, 1978; No. 3766, Dutch player with ball; No. 3767, Wembley Stadium, England 1966; No. 3768, West German player with ball; No. 3771, English player in air heading ball; No. 3772, German player tackling English player; No. 3773, Celebrating English team; No. 3774, Celebrating German player; No. 3775, Pele, Brazil; No. 3776, Maier, West Germany; No. 3777, Eusebio, Portugal; No. **MS**3778d, Paulao, Angola. *Vert*—No. 3743 Argentine player kicking ball; No. 3744, Argentine player holding trophy; No. 3745, Goal mouth melee: No. 3746, Dutch player; No. 3747, Celebrating Argentine player; No. 3748, Argentine tackling Dutch player; No. 3749, Argentine and two Dutch players; No. 3750, Players attempting to head ball; No. 3751, Bergkamp, Netherlands; No. 3752, Seaman, England; No. 3753, Schmeichel, Denmark; No. 3754, Ince, England; No. 3755, Futre, Portugal; No. 3756, Ravanelli, Italy; No. 3757, Keane, Republic of Ireland; No. 3758, Gascoigne, England; No. **MS**3778a, Salvatori Schillaci, Italy; No. **MS**3778b, Ally McCoist, Scotland; No. **MS**3778c, Mario Kempes, Argentina.
Nos. 3743/50, 3751/8, 3759/66 and 3767/74 were each printed together, *se-tenant*, in sheetlets of 8 stamps and 1 central label.

(Des M. Friedman. Litho B.D.T.)

1997 (16 Sept). *10th Anniv of the Signing of the Montreal Protocol on Substances that Deplete the Ozone Layer. P* 14.
3779 **352** 90 c. multicoloured 40 45

353 *Rhyncholaelia digbyana*

354 Snow Leopard

(Des W. Wright. Litho Questa)

1997 (18 Sept). *Orchids of the World. T* **353** *and similar multicoloured designs. P* 14.
3780 90 c. Type **353** 40 45
3781 $1 *Laeliocattleya* "Chitchat Tangerine" .. 45 50
3782 $1 *Eulophia speciosa* 45 50
a. Sheetlet. Nos. 3782/90 .. .. 4·00
3783 $1 *Aerangis rhodosticta* 45 50
3784 $1 *Angraecum infundibularea* 45 50
3785 $1 *Calanthe sylvatica* 45 50
3786 $1 *Phalaenopsis mariae* 45 50
3787 $1 *Paphiopedilum insigne* 45 50
3788 $1 *Dendrobium nobile* 45 50
3789 $1 *Aerangis kotschyana* 45 50
3790 $1 *Cyrtorchis chailluana* 45 50
3791 $1.10, *Doritis pulcherrima* 50 55
3792 $2 *Phalaenopsis* "Barbara Moler" .. 90 95
3780/92 .. .. *Set of* 13 6·25 7·00
MS3793 Two sheets, each 106×81 mm. (a) $5 *Sanguine broughtonia (50×37 mm).* P 14×13½. (b) $5 *Brassavola nodosa* "Lady of the Night" *(50×37 mm).* P 14×13½ .. *Set of 2 sheets* 4·50 4·75
Nos. 3782/90 were printed together, *se-tenant*, in sheetlets of 9.

(Litho Questa)

1997 (18 Sept). *Sierra Club Conservation. T* **354** *and similar multicoloured designs. P* 14.
3794/802 20 c. × 9 (Type **354**; Polar Bear; Plants, Isle Royale National Park; Waterway, Isle Royale National Park; Denali National Park at night; Denali National Park; Plants, Joshua Tree National Park; Mountains, Joshua Tree National Park; Rock, Joshua Tree National Park)
a. Sheetlet. Nos. 3794/802 80
3803/11 40 c. × 9 (Mountain Gorilla showing teeth; Mountain Gorilla; Young Mountain Gorilla; Snow Leopard; Young Snow Leopard; Polar Bear; Polar Bear cub; Denali National Park; Isle Royale National Park *(all vert)*)
a. Sheetlet. Nos. 3803/11 .. .. 1·75
3812/20 50 c. × 9 (Sifaka with young; Sifaka on branch; Head of Sifaka; Peregrine Falcon; Peregrine Falcon with stretched wings; Galapagos Tortoise; Waterfall, African rainforest; Tree, African rainforest; China's Yellow Mountains *(all vert)*)
a. Sheetlet. Nos. 3812/20 .. .. 2·25
3821/9 60 c. × 9 (Head of Red Panda; Red Panda on branch; Red Panda on ground; Peregrine Falcon with chicks; Head of Galapagos Tortoise; Galapagos Tortoise on grass; African rainforest; Tops of trees, China's Yellow Mountains; Gorge, China's Yellow Mountains)
a. Sheetlet. Nos. 3821/9 .. .. 2·50
3830/8 70 c. × 9 (Mountain Lion; Siberian Tiger; Head of Siberian Tiger; Red Wolf; Black Bear; Lake, Wolong National Reserve; Belize rainforest; Base of tree, Belize rainforest; Mountains, Wolong National Reserve)
a. Sheetlet. Nos. 3830/8 .. .. 2·75
3839/47 90 c. × 9 (Siberian Tiger; Head of Mountain Lion; Mountain Lion cubs; Black Bear on branch; Head of Black Bear; Red Wolf; Head of Red Wolf; Belize rainforest; Wolong National Reserve *(all vert)*)
a. Sheetlet. Nos. 3839/47 .. .. 3·50
3848/56 $1 × 9 (Indri hanging from tree; Indri face on; Indri holding onto tree; Gopher Tortoise inside shell; Gopher Tortoise on ground; Black-footed Ferret facing forward; Head of Black-footed Ferret; Haleakala National Park; Grand Teton National Park *(all vert)*)
a. Sheetlet. Nos. 3848/56 .. .. 4·00

3857/65 $1.10 × 9 (Black-footed Ferret; Gopher Tortoise; River, Grand Teton National Park; Hillside, Grand Teton National Park; River, Haleakala National Park; Plants, Haleakala National Park; Misty view of Madagascar rainforest; Trees, Madagascar rainforest; Cleared forest, Madagascar rain-forest)
a. Sheetlet. Nos. 3857/65 .. .. .. 4·50
3794/865 .. .. *Set of* 72 22·00 23·00
MS3866 Three sheets, each 110×80 mm. $5 Lake, Olympic National Park. (b) $5 Hillside, Olympic National Park (*vert*). (c) $5 Snow-covered Mountains, Olympic National Park (*vert*) .. .. *Set of 3 sheets* 7·00 7·25

Nos. 3794/802, 3803/11, 3812/20, 3821/9, 3830/8, 3839/47, 3848/56 and 3857/65 were each printed together, *se-tenant*, in sheetlets of 9.

355 Raised Stern of *Titanic*

356 "Morrison Hotel" Album Cover, February 1970

(Litho Questa)

1997 (5 Nov). *85th Anniv of the Sinking of the* Titanic (*liner*). *T* **355** *and similar vert designs. Multicoloured. P* 14.

3867 $1 Type **355** 45 50
a. Sheetlet. Nos. 3867/71 .. .. 2·25
3868 $1 Lifeboat rowing away 45 50
3869 $1 One funnel and lifeboat being lowered into water 45 50
3870 $1 Two funnels 45 50
3871 $1 One funnel in water and lifeboat rowing away 45 50
3867/71 .. .. *Set of* 5 2·25 2·50

Nos. 3867/71 were printed together, *se-tenant*, in sheetlets of 5 forming a composite design.

(Litho Questa)

1997 (5 Nov). *30th Anniv of The Doors* (*rock group*) *and Rock and Roll Hall of Fame, Cleveland. T* **356** *and similar square designs. Multicoloured. P* 14.

3872 90 c. Type **356** 40 45
a. Sheetlet. No. 3872×8 .. .. 3·25
3873 95 c. "Waiting for the Sun" album cover, April 1968 .. .. 45 50
a. Sheetlet. No. 3874×8 .. .. 3·50
3874 $1 Rock and Roll Hall of Fame and Museum, Cleveland, Ohio 45 50
a. Sheetlet. No. 3874×8 .. .. 3·50
3875 $1 "L.A. Women" album cover, April 1971 .. .. 45 50
a. Sheetlet. No. 3875×8 .. .. 3·50
3876 $1.10, "The Soft Parade" album cover, July 1969 .. .. 50 55
a. Sheetlet. No. 3876×8 .. .. 4·00
3877 $1.20, "Strange Days" album cover, October 1967 .. .. .. 55 60
a. Sheetlet. No. 3877×8 .. .. 4·50
3878 $1.50, Rock and Roll Hall of Fame guitar logo 70 75
a. Sheetlet. No. 3878×8 .. .. 5·50
3879 $1.50, "The Doors" album cover, January 1967 .. .. 70 75
a. Sheetlet. No. 3879×8 .. .. 5·50
3872/9 .. .. *Set of* 8 4·25 4·50

Nos. 3872/9 were each printed, *se-tenant*, in sheetlets of 8 containing two vertical strips of four separated by a larger representation of the design.

357 Joe "King" Oliver

358 Constantin Brancusi

(Des Andrea Mistretta. Litho Questa)

1997 (5 Nov). *New Orleans School of Jazz Commemoration. T* **357** *and similar horiz designs. Multicoloured. P* 14×13½.

3880 $1 Type **357** 45 50
a. Sheetlet. Nos. 3880/5 .. .. 2·75
3881 $1 Louis Armstrong 45 50
3882 $1 Sidney Bechet 45 50
3883 $1 Nick Larocca 45 50
3884 $1 Louis Prima 45 50
3885 $1 "Buddy" Charles Bolden 45 50
3880/5 .. .. *Set of* 6 2·75 3·00

Nos. 3880/5 were printed together, *se-tenant*, in sheetlets of 6.

(Des Zina Saunders (portraits), R. Sauber (others). Litho Questa)

1997 (5 Nov). *Famous Sculptors and Opera Singers. T* **358** *and similar multicoloured designs. P* 14.

3886 $1.10, Type **358** 50 55
a. Sheetlet. Nos. 3886/93 .. .. 4·00
3887 $1.10, "The New Born" (Brancusi) (56×42 *mm*) 50 55
3888 $1.10, "Four Elements" (Calder) (56×42 *mm*) 50 55
3889 $1.10, Alexander Calder 50 55
3890 $1.10, Isamu Noguchi 50 55
3891 $1.10, "Dodge Fountain" (Noguchi) (56×42 *mm*) 50 55
3892 $1.10, "The Shuttlecock" (Oldenburg) (56×42 *mm*) 50 55
3893 $1.10, Claes Oldenburg 50 55
3894 $1.10, Lily Pons 50 55
a. Sheetlet. Nos. 3894/3901 .. .. 4·00
3895 $1.10, Lily Pons in Donizetti's *Lucia di Lammermoor* (56×42 *mm*) 50 55
3896 $1.10, Maria Callas in Bellini's *I Puritani* (56×42 *mm*) 50 55
3897 $1.10, Maria Callas 50 55
3898 $1.10, Beverly Sills 50 55
3899 $1.10, Beverly Sills in Donizetti's *La Fille du Regiment* (56×42 *mm*) 50 55
3900 $1.10, Jessye Norman in Schoenberg's *Erwartung* (56×42 *mm*) 50 55
3901 $1.10, Jessye Norman 50 55
3902 $1.10, Enrico Caruso 50 55
a. Sheetlet. Nos. 3902/9 .. .. 4·00
3903 $1.10, Enrico Caruso in Verdi's *Rigoletto* (56×42 *mm*) 50 55
3904 $1.10, Mario Lanza in *The Seven Hills of Rome* (56×42 *mm*) 50 55
3905 $1.10, Mario Lanza 50 55
3906 $1.10, Luciano Pavarotti 50 55
3907 $1.10, Luciano Pavarotti in Donizetti's *L'Elisir d'Amore* (56×42 *mm*) .. 50 55
3908 $1.10, Placido Domingo in Puccini's *Tosca* (56×42 *mm*) 50 55
3909 $1.10, Placido Domingo 50 55
3886/909 .. .. *Set of* 24 12·00 13·00

Nos. 3886/93, 3894/3901 and 3902/9 were each printed together, *se-tenant*, in sheetlets of 8 with illustrated margins.

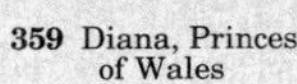

359 Diana, Princess of Wales

360 "The Sisitine Madonna" (detail, Raphael)

(Des J. Iskowitz. Litho Questa)

1997 (20 Nov). *Diana, Princess of Wales Commemoration. T* **359** *and similar vert designs. Multicoloured. P* 14.

3910 $2 Type **359** 90 95
a. Sheetlet. Nos. 3910/13 .. .. 3·50
3911 $2 Wearing pearl-drop earrings 90 95
3912 $2 Wearing black jacket 90 95
3913 $2 Wearing blue jacket and pearl earrings 90 95
3914 $2 Wearing tiara 90 95
a. Sheetlet. Nos. 3914/17 .. .. 3·50
3915 $2 In black evening dress 90 95
3916 $2 Wearing blue jacket 90 95
3917 $2 Wearing beige blouse 90 95
3910/17 .. .. *Set of* 8 7·00 7·25
MS3918 Two sheets, each 100×70 mm. (a) $6 Wearing light blue jacket. (b) $6 Wearing white blouse .. .. .. *Set of 2 sheets* 5·50 5·75

Nos. 3910/13 and 3914/17 were each printed together, *se-tenant*, in sheetlets of 4 with illustrated margins.

(Litho B.D.T.)

1997 (26 Nov). *Christmas. Paintings and Sculptures. T* **360** *and similar multicoloured designs. P* 14.

3919 60 c. Type **360** 25 30
3920 70 c. "Angel" (Edward Burne-Jones) .. 30 35
3921 90 c. "Cupid" (sculpture, Etienne-Maurice Flaconet) 40 45
3922 $1 "Saint Michael" (sculpture, Hubert Gerhard) 45 50
3923 $1.10, "Apollo and the Hoare" (Giambattista Tiepolo) 50 55
3924 $2 "Madonna in a Garland of Flowers" (detail, Rubens and Bruegel the Elder) 90 95
3919/24 .. .. *Set of* 6 2·75 3·00
MS3925 Two sheets, each 106×95 mm. (a) $5 "Madonna in a Garland of Flowers" (different detail, Rubens and Bruegel the Elder). (b) $5 "The Sacrifice of Isaac" (Giambattista Tiepolo) (detail) (*horiz*) .. .. .. *Set of 2 sheets* 4·50 4·75

NEW INFORMATION

The editor is always interested to correspond with people who have new information that will improve or correct the Catalogue.

361 Symbolic Tiger

362 Children and School Savings Bank

(Des Y. Lee. Litho Questa)

1998 (5 Jan). *Chinese New Year* ("*Year of the Tiger*"). *T* **361** *and similar vert designs showing different tigers. P* 14½.

3926 **361** $1 black, olive-grey and grey-brown 45 50
a. Sheetlet. Nos. 3926/8 .. .. 1·25
3927 – $1 black, silver and ochre 45 50
3928 – $1 black, lilac and brown-rose .. 45 50
3926/8 .. .. *Set of* 3 1·25 1·50
MS3929 71×101 mm. $2 black, brown-lilac and dull orange 90 95

Nos. 3926/8 were printed together, *se-tenant*, as a sheetlet containing a horizontal strip of 3.

(Litho B.D.T.)

1998 (5 Jan). *Economic Development. T* **362** *and similar multicoloured designs. P* 13½.

3930 20 c. Type **362** 10 10
3931 90 c. Agricultural workers and Credit Union Office (*vert*) 40 45
3932 $1.10, Freighter at quay 50 55
3930/2 .. .. *Set of* 3 1·00 1·10

363 Ice Hockey

(Litho Questa)

1998 (2 Feb). *Winter Olympic Games, Nagano. T* **363** *and similar multicoloured designs. P* 14.

3933 70 c. Type **363** 30 35
3934 $1.10, Bob-sleigh 50 55
3935 $1.10, Bjorn Daehlie (Norway) (Gold medal, Nordic skiing, 1994) 50 55
a. Sheetlet. Nos. 3935/42 .. .. 4·00
3936 $1.10, Gillis Grafstrom (Sweden) (Gold medal, figure skating, 1924, 1928) .. 50 55
3937 $1.10, Sonja Henie (Norway) (Gold medal, figure skating, 1928, 1932) .. 50 55
3938 $1.10, Ingemar Stenmark (Sweden) (Gold medal, slalom and giant slalom, 1980) 50 55
3939 $1.10, Christan Jagge (Norway) (Gold medal, slalom, 1992) 50 55
3940 $1.10, Tomas Gustafson (Sweden) (Gold medal, 5000m speed skating, 1992) 50 55
3941 $1.10, Johann Olav Koss (Norway) (Gold medal, 1500m speed skating, 1992, 1994) 50 55
3942 $1.10, Thomas Wassberg (Sweden) (Gold medal, 50km cross country skiing, 1984) 50 55
3943 $1.50, Downhill (red suit) (*vert*) .. 70 75
a. Sheetlet. Nos. 3943/8 .. .. 4·25
3944 $1.50, Two-man bobsleigh (*vert*) .. 70 75
3945 $1.50, Ski jump (red suit) (*vert*) .. 70 75
3946 $1.50, Downhill (red and white suit) (*vert*) 70 75
3947 $1.50, Luge (*vert*) 70 75
3948 $1.50, Biathlon (*vert*) 70 75
3949 $1.50, Downhill (yellow and red suit) (*vert*) 70 75
a. Sheetlet. Nos. 3949/54 .. .. 4·25
3950 $1.50, Figure skating (*vert*) 70 75
3951 $1.50, Ski jump (green suit) (*vert*) .. 70 75
3952 $1.50, Speed skating (*vert*) 70 75
3953 $1.50, Four-man bobsleigh (*vert*) .. 70 75
3954 $1.50, Cross-country skiing (*vert*) .. 70 75
3955 $2 Pairs figure skating 90 95
3956 $2 Ski jump (*vert*) 90 95
3933/56 .. .. *Set of* 24 15·00 16·00
MS3957 Two sheets. (a) 110×80 mm. $5 Ice Hockey. (b) 80×100 mm. $5 Downhill (*vert*) *Set of 2 sheets* 2·25 2·40

Nos. 3935/42, 3943/8 and 3949/54 were each printed together, *se-tenant*, in sheetlets of 8 (Nos. 3935/42) or 6 with the backgrounds forming composite designs (Nos. 3943/8 and 3949/54).

STAMP BOOKLETS

1974 (5 Sept). *Blue and green printed covers. Size 98×58 mm (No. SB1), or 150×48 mm (No. SB2). Stapled. Back cover in six different designs*:
(a) Kingstown Harbour
(b) Indian Bay
(c) St. Mary's R.C. Church, Kingstown
(d) St. George's Cathedral, Kingstown
(e) View of the interior
(f) Sunset over Young Island

SB1 60 c. booklet (*any cover*) containing 1 c., 2 c., 3 c., 4 c. and 5 c. (Nos. 286a, 361/4) in blocks of 4 1·25
Set of 6 different cover designs 7·00
SB2 75 c. booklet (*any cover*) containing 1 c., 2 c., 3 c., 4 c. and 5 c. (Nos. 286a, 361/4) in strips of 5 1·25
Set of 6 different cover designs 7·00

1975 (27 Feb). *Kingstown "Carnival'75". Multicoloured cover. Stapled.*
SB3 $2.50, booklet containing two panes of two 1 c. plus label (No. 415a) and two different *se-tenant* panes of 3 (Nos. 415b, 416a) .. 1·25

1976 (19 Feb). *Kingstown "Carnival'76". Multicoloured cover. Stapled.*
SB4 $2.50, booklet containing two *se-tenant* panes of 2 stamps and 1 label (No. 479a) and two different *se-tenant* panes of 3 (Nos. 480a, 482a) .. 1·25

1977 (7 Feb). *Silver Jubilee. Black and red printed cover, 105×71 mm. Stapled.*
SB5 $5 booklet containing three different *se-tenant* panes of 4 (Nos. 515a, 519a, 523a) .. .. 5·00

1978 (20 July). *25th Anniv of Coronation. Multicoloured cover as No.* SB3 *of Montserrat. Stapled.*
SB6 $9.30, booklet containing 40 c., 50 c., $1.25 and $2.50 (Nos. 556/9) in pairs .. .. .. 1·10

1979 (31 May). *Death Centenary of Sir Rowland Hill. Silver, black and blue printed cover, 108×32 mm. Stapled.*
SB7 $7.80, booklet containing two 40 c. (Nos. 578, 594), two 50 c. (Nos. 579, 595) and two $3 (Nos. 580, 599), each in *se-tenant* pairs taken from No. **MS**581 .. .. 1·25

1979 (1 Sept). *Brown and cream (No.* SB8*) or deep blue and pale blue (No.* SB9*) covers, 100×60 mm. Stapled.*
SB8 $3 booklet containing 5 c., 20 c. and 50 c. (Nos. 586, 592, 595) in blocks of 4 .. .. .. 1·75
SB9 $5 booklet containing 10 c., 25 c., 40 c. and 50 c. (Nos. 589, 593/5) in blocks of 4 .. .. 2·50

1980 (24 Apr). *"London 1980" International Stamp Exhibition. Black printed cover, 108×60 mm, showing exhibition emblem and St. Vincent arms. Stapled.*
SB10 $15.20, booklet containing 80 c., $1 and $2 (Nos. 634/6) in blocks of 4 .. .. .. 2·50

1981 (26 Nov). *Royal Wedding. Multicoloured cover, 105×65 mm, showing* The Isabella. *Stitched.*
SB11 $9.80, booklet containing eight 60 c. in panes of 4 (No. 675a) and two $2.50 in pane of 2 (No. 676a) .. .. 2·25

1986 (18 July). *Royal Wedding. Gold (No.* SB12*) or silver (No.* SB13*) on ultramarine covers, 152×80 mm. Stapled.*
SB12 $7.20, booklet (Westminster Abbey) containing twelve 60 c. (Nos. 1009/10) in blocks of 4 2·50
SB13 $10.40, booklet (State Coach) containing 60 c. and $2 (Nos. 1009/12, but imperf) in blocks of 4 .. .. 3·50

OFFICIAL STAMPS

OFFICIAL

(O 1)

1982 (11 Oct). *Nos.* 668/73 *optd with Type* O 1.

O1	60 c. *Isabella*	15	20
	a. Sheetlet. No. O1 × 6 and No. O2	1·25	
	b. Opt double		
	c. Albino opt	8·00	
O2	60 c. Prince Charles and Lady Diana Spencer	50	50
	b. Opt double		
	c. Albino opt	23·00	
O3	$2.50, *Alberta* (tender)	20	30
	a. Sheetlet. No. O3 × 6 and No. O4	1·75	
	b. Opt inverted	22·00	
	c. Opt inverted (horiz pair).. ..	70·00	
	d. Albino opt	15·00	
O4	$2.50, Prince Charles and Lady Diana Spencer	70	70
	b. Opt inverted	70·00	
	c. Albino opt	45·00	
O5	$4 *Britannia*	30	40
	a. Sheetlet. No. O5 × 6 and No. O6	2·50	
	b. Opt double		
	c. Albino opt	11·00	
	d. Opt inverted		
	e. Opt inverted (horiz pair)..		
O6	$4 Prince Charles and Lady Diana Spencer	1·00	1·00
	b. Opt double		
	c. Albino opt	45·00	
	d. Opt inverted		
O1/6	.. .. *Set of* 6	2·50	2·75

Nos. O3c and O5e show the long overprint, intended for Nos. O4 or O6, inverted and struck across a horizontal pair of Nos. O3 or O5. Nos. O4b and O6d show two examples of Type O 1 inverted on the same stamp.

POSTAL FISCAL STAMPS

The following were primarily intended for the payment of passport fees, but were also valid for postal purposes and are frequently found used on parcels.

$5

STAMP DUTY

(F 1)

F 2 St. Vincent Coat of Arms

1980 (Feb). *Stamps as T* **95**, *without value, surch as Type* F **1**. *W w* **12**. *P* 14½ × 14.

F1	$5 deep lavender and azure..	2·00	2·00
F2	$10 light green and apple green	3·50	4·50
F3	$20 reddish purple and pale rose-lilac ..	5·50	10·00
F1/3	.. .. *Set of* 3	10·00	15·00

(Des Harrison. Recess D.L.R.)

1980 (19 May). *W w* **14**. *P* 14 × 13.

F4	F **2** $5 chalky blue	1·75	2·25
F5	$10 deep green	3·00	3·75
F6	$20 brown-red	5·00	8·50
F4/6	.. .. *Set of* 3	8·75	13·00

1984 (22 May). *As No.* F6, *but W w* **15**. *P* 12.

F9	F **2** $20 brown-red	6·00	8·00

A 10 c. in a design similar to Type F **2**, but inscribed "REVENUE", was issued in April 1988. Examples can be found used on commercial mail, but such use was unauthorised.

GRENADINES OF ST. VINCENT

A group of islands south of St. Vincent which includes Bequia, Mustique, Canouan and Union.

For stamps inscribed "The Grenadines of St. VINCENT" issued by St. Vincent in 1971, see under St. Vincent Nos. 330/6.

Stamps of the Grenadines of St. Vincent exist overprinted "SPECIMEN", these being produced for publicity purposes.

1973 (14 Nov). *Royal Wedding. As Nos.* 322/3 *of Montserrat.*

1	25 c. light green	10	10
2	$1 ochre	15	15

GRENADINES OF

(1)

2 Map of Bequia

1974 (24 Apr). *Stamps of St. Vincent. T* **51** *etc. optd in litho with T* 1 *by Harrison & Sons. Glazed paper. W w* **12** *(sideways on* 4, 5, 10, 12, 50 *c. and* $5).

3	1 c. Green Heron	10	10
	a. Opt omitted	50·00	
	b. Albino opt	45·00	
4	2 c. Lesser Antillean Bullfinches	15	15
	w. Wmk inverted	3·25	
5	3 c. St. Vincent Amazons	75	75
6	4 c. Rufous-throated Solitaire	15	10
7	5 c. Red-necked Pigeon	15	10
8	6 c. Bananaquits	15	10
9	8 c. Purple-throated Carib	15	10
10	10 c. Mangrove Cuckoo	15	10
11	12 c. Common Black Hawk	20	15
	a. Opt double	£130	
12	20 c. Bare-eyed Thrush	35	20
13	25 c. Hooded Tanager	40	20
14	50 c. Blue-hooded Euphonia	70	40
	a. Albino opt	80·00	
15	$1 Barn Owl	1·50	75
16	$2.50, Yellow-bellied Elaenia	1·50	1·00
17	$5 Ruddy Quail Dove	1·75	1·75
3/17	*Set of* 15	7·00	5·00

(Des G. Drummond. Litho Enschedé)

1974 (9 May). *Maps (1st series). T* **2** *and similar vert designs. W w* **12** *(sideways*). P* 13×12½.

18	5 c. black, light dull green & deep dull green	10	10
	w. Wmk Crown to right of CA	5·00	
19	15 c. multicoloured	10	10
20	20 c. multicoloured	10	10
21	30 c. black, light rose-lilac and lake	10	10
22	40 c. black, lavender and deep ultramarine	10	10
23	$1 black, cobalt and bright ultramarine	20	20
18/23	*Set of* 6	45	35

Maps:—15 c. The Grenadines and Prune Island (inset); 20 c. Mayreau Island and Tobago Cays; 30 c. Mustique Island; 40 c. Union Island; $1 Canouan Island.

*The normal sideways watermark shows Crown to left of CA, *as seen from the back of the stamp.*

Nos. 18/23 were each issued in sheets of ten stamps and two *se-tenant* labels.

See also Nos. 85/8.

GRENADINES OF

(3)

4 Boat-building

1974 (7 June). *Nos.* 361/2 *of St. Vincent optd in typo with T* **3** *by Govt Printer, St. Vincent. Glazed paper. W w* **12**.

24	2 c. Lesser Antillean Bullfinches	25	30
25	3 c. St. Vincent Amazons	25	30
	a. Opt double	38·00	
	b. Albino opt	8·00	
	c. Chalky paper. Wmk sideways (No. 288)	9·00	18·00

1974 (25 July). *Centenary of Universal Postal Union. As Nos.* 392/5 *of St. Vincent but colours and face-values changed and inscr* "Grenadines of St. Vincent".

26	2 c. U.P.U. emblem	10	10
	a. Red (U.P.U. emblem) omitted	£650	
	w. Wmk inverted	26·00	
27	15 c. Globe within posthorn	10	10
28	40 c. Map of St. Vincent and hand-cancelling	10	10
29	$1 Map of the World	25	15
26/9	*Set of* 4	40	30

No. 26a was caused by a paper fold.

(Des G. Drummond. Litho Questa)

1974. *Bequia Island (1st series). T* **4** *and similar horiz designs. Multicoloured. P* 14 (a) *W w* **12** *(sideways*)* (26.9.74).

30	5 c. Type **4**	35	1·50
	w. Wmk Crown to right of CA	£100	
31	30 c. Careening at Port Elizabeth	10	10
32	35 c. Admiralty Bay	10	10
33	$1 Fishing boat race	15	25
	(b) *W w* **14** *(sideways)* (12.74)		
34	5 c. Type **4**	10	15
30/4	*Set of* 5	65	1·75

*The normal sideways watermark shows Crown to left of CA, *as seen from the back of the stamp.*

No. 34 differs in shade from No. 30, notably in the shirt of the man at right, which is red on No. 34 instead of purple.

Nos. 30/4 were each issued in sheets of ten stamps and two *se-tenant* labels.

See also Nos. 185/8.

5 Music Volute (*Voluta musica*)

(Des R. Granger Barrett. Litho Questa)

1974 (27 Nov)–**77**. *Shells and Molluscs. Horiz designs as T* **5**. *Multicoloured. W w* **14** *(sideways*). P* 14.

A. *No imprint.* B. *Imprint at foot*

		A		B	
35	1 c. American Thorny Oyster (*Spondylas americanus*)	10	10	†	
	w. Wmk Crown to right of CA	7·00	—	†	
36	2 c. Zigzag Scallop (*Pecten ziczac*)	10	10	†	
37	3 c. Reticulated Cowrie-helmet (*Cypraecassis testiculus*)	10	10	†	
38	4 c. Type **5**	10	10	10	10
39	5 c. Amber Pen Shell (*Pinna carnea*)	10	10	10	10
40	6 c. Angular Triton (*Cymatium femorale*)	10	10	10	10
41	8 c. Flame Helmet (*Cassis flammea*)	10	10	10	10
42	10 c. Caribbean Olive (*Oliva caribaeensis*)	10	10	10	10
	a. Corrected imprint	†		70	10
43	12 c. American or Common Sun-dial (*Architectonica nobilis*)	10	10	†	
44	15 c. Glory of the Atlantic Cone (*Conus granulatus*)	25	20	80	15
45	20 c. Flame Auger (*Terebra taurina*)	30	35	30	20
	a. Corrected imprint	†		1·25	15
46	25 c. King Venus (*Chione paphia*)	50	20	80	15
47	35 c. Long-spined Star Shell (*Astraea phoebia*)	35	30	35	25
	a. Corrected imprint	†		1·25	25
48	45 c. Speckled Tellin (*Tellina listeri*)	35	30	†	
49	50 c. Rooster-tail Conch (*Strombus gallus*)	40	25	45	30
50	$1 Green Star Shell (*Astraea tuber*)	60	75	60	60
51	$2.50, Antillean or Incomparable Cone (*Conus cedonulli*)	80	90	3·50	80
52	$5 Rough File Shell (*Lima scabra*)	1·25	1·50	4·50	1·75
52*a*	$10 Measled Cowrie (*Cypraea zebra*)	5·50	2·00	†	
35A/52aA	*Set of* 19	9·50	6·50		
38B/52B	*Set of* 13			10·00	4·00

*The normal sideways watermark shows Crown to left of CA, *as seen from the back of the stamp.*

Dates of issue: 27.11.74, Nos. 35A/52A; 12.7.76, Nos. 52*a*A, 38B/42B, 45B, 47B and 49B/50B; 2.6.77, Nos. 42aB, 44B, 45aB, 46B, 47aB, 51B, 52B.

Imprint dates: "1976", Nos. 38B/42B, 45B, 47B, 49B/50B; "1977", Nos. 42aB, 44B, 45aB, 46B, 47aB, 51B/2B.

On Nos. 42aB, 44B, 45aB, 46B, 47aB, 51B and 52B the designer's name is correctly spelt as "R. Granger Barrett". Previously the last name had been spelt "Barratt".

1974 (28 Nov). *Birth Centenary of Sir Winston Churchill. As Nos.* 403/6 *of St. Vincent but colours and face-values changed and inscr* "GRENADINES OF ST. VINCENT".

53	5 c. Type **75**	10	10
54	40 c. As 35 c.	10	10
55	50 c. As 45 c.	10	10
56	$1 As $1	20	20
53/6	*Set of* 4	35	40

6 Cotton House, Mustique

(Des G. Drummond. Litho Questa)

1975 (27 Feb). *Mustique Island. T* **6** *and similar horiz designs. Multicoloured. W w* **14** *(sideways). P* 14.

57	5 c. Type **6**	10	10
58	35 c. "Blue Waters", Endeavour Bay	10	10
59	45 c. Endeavour Bay	10	10
60	$1 "Les Jolies Eaux", Gelliceaux Bay	25	20
57/60	*Set of* 4	40	30

Nos. 57/60 were each issued in sheets of ten stamps and two *se-tenant* labels.

7 *Danaus plexippus*

(Des G. Drummond. Litho Questa)

1975 (15 May). *Butterflies. T* **7** *and similar horiz designs. Multicoloured. W w* **14** *(sideways). P* 14.

61	3 c. Type **7**	20	10
62	5 c. *Agraulis vanillae*	25	10
63	35 c. *Battus polydamas*	80	10
64	45 c. *Evenus dindymus* and *Junonia evarete*	1·00	10
65	$1 *Anartia jatrophae*	1·75	45
61/5	*Set of* 5	3·50	75

8 Resort Pavilion

(Des G. Drummond. Litho Harrison)

1975 (24 July). *Petit St. Vincent. T* **8** *and similar horiz designs. Multicoloured. W w* **14** *(sideways*). P* 14.

66	5 c. Type **8**	10	10
67	35 c. The Harbour	10	10
68	45 c. The Jetty	15	15
	w. Wmk Crown to right of CA	27·00	
69	$1 Sailing in coral lagoon	50	65
	w. Wmk Crown to right of CA	27·00	
66/9	*Set of* 4	70	85

*The normal sideways watermark shows Crown to left of CA, *as seen from the back of the stamp.*

Nos. 66/9 were each issued in sheets of ten stamps and two *se-tenant* labels.

9 Ecumenical Church, Mustique

(Des G. Drummond. Litho Questa)

1975 (20 Nov). *Christmas. T* **9** *and similar horiz designs. Multicoloured. W w* **12** *(sideways). P* 14.

70	5 c. Type **9**	10	10
71	25 c. Catholic Church, Union Island	10	10
72	50 c. Catholic Church, Bequia	10	10
73	$1 Anglican Church, Bequia	25	15
70/3	*Set of* 4	40	30

10 Sunset Scene

(Des G. Drummond. Litho J.W.)

1976 (26 Feb). *Union Island (1st series). T* **10** *and similar horiz designs. W w* **12** *(sideways*) (5 c.) or W w* **14** *(sideways) (others). P* 13½.

74	5 c. Type **10**	10	10
	w. Wmk Crown to left of CA	20·00	
75	35 c. Customs and Post Office, Clifton	10	10
76	45 c. Anglican Church, Ashton	10	10
77	$1 Mail schooner, Clifton Harbour	25	20
74/7	*Set of* 4	45	30

*The normal sideways watermark on the 5 c. shows Crown to right of CA, *as seen from the back of the stamp.*

Nos. 74/7 were each issued in sheets of ten stamps and two *se-tenant* labels.

See also Nos. 242/5.

11 Staghorn Coral

(Des G. Drummond. Litho Questa)

1976 (13 May). *Corals. T* **11** *and similar horiz designs. Multicoloured. W w* **14** *(sideways). P* 14.

78	5 c. Type **11**	10	10
79	35 c. Elkhorn coral	25	10
80	45 c. Pillar coral	30	10
81	$1 Brain coral	80	20
78/81	*Set of* 4	1·25	30

12 25 c. Bicentennial Coin

(Des J. Cooter. Litho Questa)

1976 (15 July). *Bicentenary of American Revolution. T* **12** *and similar horiz designs. W w* **14** *(sideways). P* 13½.

82	25 c. silver, black and light violet-blue	10	10
83	50 c. silver, black and light rose-red	20	10
84	$1 silver, black and mauve	25	20
82/4	*Set of* 3	50	30

Designs:—50 c. Half-dollar coin; $1 One dollar coin.

Nos. 82/4 were each issued in sheets of ten stamps and two *se-tenant* labels.

(Des G. Drummond. Litho Questa)

1976 (23 Sept). *Maps (2nd series). Vert designs as T* **2**, *showing various islands as detailed below. W w* **14**. *P* 13½.

A. Bequia D. Mustique F. Prune
B. Canouan E. Petit St. Vincent G. Union
C. Mayreau

To indicate individual islands, use the above letters as a suffix to the following catalogue numbers.

85	5 c. black, myrtle-green and pale emerald	10	10
	a. Booklet pane. Nos. 85/6 and 88 plus printed label	45	
	b. Booklet pane. Nos. 85 × 2 and 86 plus printed label	30	
86	10 c. black, ultramarine and greenish blue	10	10
	a. Booklet pane. Nos. 86 × 2 and 87 plus printed label	40	
87	35 c. black, red-brown and bright rose	20	20
	a. Booklet pane. Nos. 87 × 2 and 88 plus printed label	65	
88	45 c. black, scarlet and yellow-orange	25	25
85/8	*Set of* 4 *(one island)*	60	60
85/8	*Set of* 28 *(seven islands)*	4·00	4·00

Nos. 85/8 were only issued in $2.50 stamp booklets.

13 Station Hill School and Post Office

(Des G. Drummond. Litho Questa)

1976 (2 Dec). *Mayreau Island. T* **13** *and similar horiz designs. Multicoloured. W w* **14** *(sideways). P* 14.

89	5 c. Type **13**	10	10
90	35 c. Church at Old Wall	10	10
91	45 c. La Sourciere Anchorage	10	10
92	$1 Saline Bay	25	15
89/92	*Set of* 4	40	30

Nos. 89/92 were each issued in sheets of ten stamps and two *se-tenant* labels.

14 Coronation Crown Coin

(Des G. Vasarhelyi. Litho Questa)

1977 (3 Mar). *Silver Jubilee. T* **14** *and similar horiz designs. Multicoloured. W w* **14** *(sideways). P* 14.

93	25 c. Type **14**	15	10
94	50 c. Silver Wedding Crown	20	10
95	$1 Silver Jubilee Crown	20	15
93/5	*Set of* 3	50	30

Nos. 93/5 were each issued in sheets of ten stamps and two *se-tenant* labels.

15 Fiddler Crab

(Des BG Studio. Litho Questa)

1977 (19 May). *Crustaceans. T* **15** *and similar horiz designs. Multicoloured. W w* **14** *(sideways*). P* 14.

96	5 c. Type **15**	10	10
	w. Wmk Crown to right of CA	7·00	
97	35 c. Ghost crab	20	10
	w. Wmk Crown to right of CA	22·00	
98	50 c. Blue crab	25	10
	w. Wmk Crown to right of CA	4·50	
99	$1.25, Spiny lobster	55	40
	w. Wmk Crown to right of CA	22·00	
96/9	*Set of* 4	95	55

*The normal sideways watermark shows Crown to left of CA, *as seen from the back of the stamp.*

16 Snorkel Diving

(Des G. Drummond. Litho Questa)

1977 (25 Aug). *Prune Island. T* **16** *and similar horiz designs. Multicoloured. W w* **14** *(sideways*). P* 14½.

100	5 c. Type **16**	10	10
101	35 c. Palm Island Resort	10	10
102	45 c. Casuarina Beach	10	15
103	$1 Palm Island Beach Club	30	70
	w. Wmk Crown to right of CA	20·00	
100/3	*Set of* 4	50	85

*The normal sideways watermark shows Crown to left of CA, *as seen from the back of the stamp.*

Nos. 100/3 were each issued in sheets of ten stamps and two *se-tenant* labels.

17 Mustique Island

(Des G. Drummond. Litho Questa)

1977 (31 Oct). *Royal Visit. Previously unissued stamps without face values, locally surch with new inscription. W w* **12**. *P* 14½ × 14.

104	**17**	40 c. turquoise-green and blue-green (Blk. (value) and R.)	15	10
105		$2 yellow-ochre and yellow-brown (R. (value) and B.)	40	25

18 The Clinic, Charlestown

(Des G. Drummond. Litho Harrison)

1977 (8 Dec). *Canouan Island (1st series).* T **18** *and similar horiz designs. Multicoloured. W w* **14**. *P* 14½.

106	5 c. Type **18**	10	10
107	35 c. Town jetty, Charlestown	10	10
108	45 c. Mail schooner arriving at Charlestown	10	10
109	$1 Grand Bay	30	65
106/9	*Set of* 4	50	80

Nos. 106/9 were each issued in sheets of ten stamps and two *se-tenant* labels.

See also Nos. 307/10.

19 Tropical Mockingbird

(Des J.W. Litho Enschedé)

1978 (11 May). *Birds and their Eggs. Horiz designs as T* **19**. *Multicoloured. W w* **14** *(sideways*). With imprint date. P* 12½×12.

110	1 c. Type **19**	10	30
111	2 c. Mangrove Cuckoo	15	30
112	3 c. Osprey	20	30
	w. Wmk Crown to right of CA	12·00	
113	4 c. Smooth-billed Ani	20	30
114	5 c. House Wren	20	40
	w. Wmk Crown to right of CA	11·00	
115	6 c. Bananaquit	20	40
116	8 c. Carib Grackle	20	45
	w. Wmk Crown to right of CA		
117	10 c. Yellow-bellied Elaenia	20	45
	w. Wmk Crown to right of CA	17·00	
118	12 c. Collared Plover	30	60
119	15 c. Cattle Egret	30	45
120	20 c. Red-footed Booby	30	45
	w. Wmk Crown to right of CA	8·50	
121	25 c. Red-billed Tropic Bird	30	45
122	40 c. Royal Tern	45	60
	w. Wmk Crown to right of CA	15·00	
123	50 c. Grenada Flycatcher	45	60
124	80 c. Purple Gallinule	70	70
125	$1 Broad-winged Hawk	75	90
	w. Wmk Crown to right of CA	15·00	
126	$2 Scaly-breasted Ground Dove	90	1·60
127	$3 Laughing Gull	1·25	1·75
128	$5 Common Noddy	2·25	2·00
129	$10 Grey Kingbird	5·00	3·00
110/29	*Set of* 20	13·00	14·00

*The normal sideways watermark shows Crown to left of CA, *as seen from the back of the stamp.*

Imprint dates: "1978", Nos. 110/29; "1979", Nos. 116, 120, 124/6; "1980", Nos. 114/15, 117, 119, 121.

See also Nos. **MS**155 and **MS**170.

(Des G. Drummond. Litho J.W.)

1978 (2 June). *25th Anniv of Coronation. Horiz designs as Nos.* 422/5 *of Montserrat. Multicoloured.* W w **14** *(sideways). P* 13.

130	5 c. Worcester Cathedral	10	10
131	40 c. Coventry Cathedral	10	10
132	$1 Winchester Cathedral	15	10
133	$3 Chester Cathedral	25	35
130/3	*Set of* 4	45	50
MS134	130 × 102 mm. Nos. 130/3. P 13½ × 14	45	80
	a. Top horiz pair imperf three sides	£350	

Nos. 130/3 were each issued in sheets of ten stamps and two *se-tenant* labels.

No. **MS**134a shows the 5 c. and 40 c. stamps in the sheet perforated along the top, but imperforate on the other three sides.

20 Green Turtle

21 Three Kings following Star

(Des R. Granger Barrett. Litho Walsall)

1978 (20 July). *Turtles. T* **20** *and similar horiz designs. Multicoloured. W w* **14** *(sideways). P* 14.

135	5 c. Type **20**	10	10
136	40 c. Hawksbill turtle	15	10
137	50 c. Leatherback turtle	15	10
138	$1.25, Loggerhead turtle	40	40
135/8	*Set of* 4	65	60

(Des Jennifer Toombs. Litho Questa)

1978 (2 Nov). *Christmas. Scenes and Verses from the Carol "We Three Kings of Orient Are". T* **21** *and similar vert designs. Multicoloured. W w* **14**. *P* 14 × 13½.

139	5 c. Type **21**	10	10
140	10 c. King with gift of Gold	10	10
141	25 c. King with gift of Frankincense	10	10
142	50 c. King with gift of Myrrh	10	10
143	$2 Three Kings paying homage to infant Jesus	30	20
139/43	*Set of* 5	45	30
MS144	154 × 175 mm. Nos. 139/43	70	1·25

PRICES OF SETS

Set prices are given for many issues, generally those containing three stamps or more. Definitive sets include one of each value or major colour change, but do not cover different perforations, die types or minor shades. Where a choice is possible the set prices are based on the cheapest versions of the stamps included in the listings.

22 Sailing Yachts **23** False Killer Whale

(Des G. Drummond. Litho Questa)

1979 (25 Jan). *National Regatta. T* **22** *and similar vert designs showing sailing yachts.* W w **14**. *P* 14.

145 5 c. multicoloured .. 10 10
146 40 c. multicoloured .. 20 10
147 50 c. multicoloured .. 25 10
148 $2 multicoloured .. 75 60
145/8 .. *Set of* 4 1·10 75

(Des L. Curtis. Litho Questa)

1979 (8 Mar). *Wildlife. Horiz designs as T* **114** *of St. Vincent. Multicoloured.* W w **14** (*sideways*). *P* 14 × 14½.

149 20 c. Green Iguana .. 10 10
150 40 c. Common Opossum ("Manicou") .. 15 10
151 $2 Red-legged Tortoise .. 60 65
149/51 .. *Set of* 3 75 75

Nos. 149/51 were each printed in four panes of 12 throughout the sheet, each pane including two *se-tenant* labels.

(Des J.W. Litho. Enschedé)

1979 (21 May). *Death Centenary of Sir Rowland Hill. Horiz designs as T* **103** *of St. Vincent. Multicoloured.* W w **14** (*sideways**). *P* 12½×12.

152 80 c. Sir Rowland Hill .. 15 15
153 $1 Great Britain 1d. and 4d. stamps of 1858 with "A10" (Kingstown, St. Vincent) postmark .. 15 25
154 $2 St. Vincent ½d. and 1d. stamps of 1894 with Bequia postmark .. 25 40
152/4 .. *Set of* 3 50 70
MS155 165×115 mm. Nos. 124/6 ("1979" imprint date) and 152/4 .. 1·40 2·50
w. Wmk Crown to right of CA .. 30·00

*The normal sideways watermark shows Crown to left of CA, *as seen from the back of the stamp.*

Nos. 152/4 were printed in sheets including two *se-tenant* stamp-size labels.

1979 (24 Oct). *International Year of the Child. As Nos.* 570/3 *of St. Vincent.*

156 6 c. black, silver and pale blue .. 10 10
157 40 c. black, silver and salmon .. 10 10
158 $1 black, silver and buff .. 20 10
159 $3 black, silver and lilac .. 45 30
156/9 .. *Set of* 4 65 45

(Des J.W. Litho Enschedé)

1979 (27 Oct). *Independence. Horiz designs as T* **106** *of St. Vincent. Multicoloured.* W w **14** (*sideways**). *P* 12½×12.

160 5 c. National flag and *Ixora salicifolia* (flower) .. 10 10
w. Wmk Crown to right of CA .. 8·00
161 40 c. House of Assembly and *Ixora odorata* (flower) .. 10 10
162 $1 Prime Minister R. Milton Cato and *Ixora javanica* (flower) .. 20 20
160/2 .. *Set of* 3 30 30

*The normal sideways watermark shows Crown to left of CA, *as seen from the back of the stamp.*

(Des R. Granger Barrett. Litho Walsall)

1980 (31 Jan). *Whales and Dolphins. T* **23** *and similar horiz designs. Multicoloured.* W w **14** (*sideways**). *P* 14.

163 10 c. Type **23** .. 60 10
w. Wmk Crown to right of CA .. 2·25
164 50 c. Spinner Dolphin .. 60 35
w. Wmk Crown to right of CA .. 20·00
165 90 c. Bottle-nosed Dolphin .. 70 80
w. Wmk Crown to right of CA .. 2·50
166 $2 Short-finned Pilot Whale ("Blackfish") 2·00 1·50
163/6 .. *Set of* 4 3·50 2·50

*The normal sideways watermark shows Crown to left of CA, *as seen from the back of the stamp.*

(Des J.W. Litho Enschedé)

1980 (24 Apr). *"London 1980" International Stamp Exhibition. Horiz designs as T* **110** *of St. Vincent. Multicoloured.* W w **14** (*sideways*). *P* 12½ × 12.

167 40 c. Queen Elizabeth II .. 10 10
168 50 c. St Vincent 1965 2 c. definitive .. 15 10
169 $3 1973 Royal Wedding commemoratives 40 1·00
167/9 .. *Set of* 3 60 1·10
MS170 165×115 mm. Nos. 122/3, 127 ("1980" imprint date) and 167/9 .. 2·00 2·50

Nos. 167/9 were printed in sheets including two *se-tenant* stamp-size labels.

(Des Polygraphic. Litho Rosenbaum Bros, Vienna)

1980 (7 Aug). *"Sport for All". Vert designs as T* **112** *of St. Vincent. Multicoloured.* W w **14**. *P* 13½.

171 25 c. Running .. 10 10
172 50 c. Sailing .. 10 10
w. Wmk inverted .. 8·00
173 $1 Long jumping .. 20 20
174 $2 Swimming .. 30 30
171/4 .. *Set of* 4 60 60

1980 (7 Aug). *Hurricane Relief. Nos.* 171/4 *surch with T* **113** *of St. Vincent.*

175 25 c.+50 c. Running .. 10 25
176 50 c.+50 c. Sailing .. 15 30
177 $1+50 c. Long jumping .. 20 40
178 $2+50 c. Swimming .. 30 55
175/8 .. *Set of* 4 65 1·40

24 Scene and Verse from the Carol "De Borning Day" **25** Post Office, Port Elizabeth

(Des Jennifer Toombs. Litho Questa)

1980 (13 Nov). *Christmas. T* **24** *and similar vert designs showing scenes and verses from the carol "De Borning Day".* W w **14**. *P* 14 × 13½.

179 5 c. multicoloured .. 10 10
180 50 c. multicoloured .. 10 10
181 60 c. multicoloured .. 10 10
182 $1 multicoloured .. 15 15
183 $2 multicoloured .. 25 25
179/83 .. *Set of* 5 50 50
MS184 159 × 178 mm. Nos. 179/83 .. 50 1·40

(Des G. Drummond. Litho Questa)

1981 (19 Feb). *Bequia Island (2nd series). T* **25** *and similar horiz designs. Multicoloured.* W w **14** (*sideways*). *P* 14½ × 14.

185 50 c. Type **25** .. 15 15
186 60 c. Moonhole .. 15 20
187 $1.50, Fishing boats, Admiralty Bay .. 30 40
188 $2 *Friendship Rose* (yacht) at jetty .. 40 55
185/8 .. *Set of* 4 90 1·10

The $2 value was originally printed with the country name in black and the face value in white. A quantity of these were stolen in transit before issue and the remainder were not placed on sale, the stamp being reprinted with the inscriptions in red.

Nos. 185/8 were each printed in sheets including two *se-tenant* stamp-size labels.

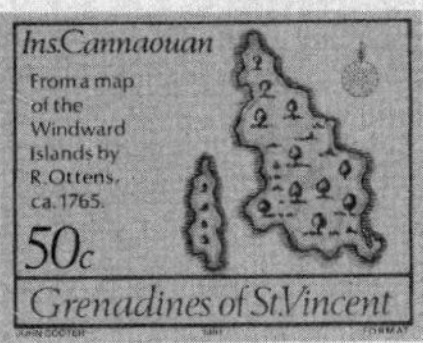

26 Ins. Cannaouan (map of Windward Islands by R. Ottens, *circa* 1765) **27** Bar Jack

(Des J. Cooter. Litho Format)

1981 (2 Apr). *Details from Early Maps. T* **26** *and similar horiz designs. Multicoloured.* W w **14** (*sideways*). *P* 13½.

189 50 c. Type **26** .. 30 30
a. Pair. Nos. 189/90 .. 60 60
190 50 c. Cannouan Is. (chart by J. Parsons, 1861) 30 30
191 60 c. Ins. Moustiques (map of Windward Islands by R. Ottens, *circa* 1765) .. 30 35
a. Pair. Nos. 191/2 .. 60 70
192 60 c. Mustique Is. (chart by J. Parsons, 1861) 30 35
193 $2 Ins. Bequia (map of Windward Islands by R. Ottens, *circa* 1765) .. 50 75
a. Pair. Nos. 193/4 .. 1·00 1·50
194 $2 Bequia Is. (map surveyed in 1763 by T. Jefferys) .. 50 75
189/94 .. *Set of* 6 2·00 2·50

The two designs of each value were printed together, *se-tenant*, in horizontal and vertical pairs throughout the sheet.

(Des D. Shults. Litho Questa)

1981 (17 July–26 Nov). *Royal Wedding. Horiz designs as T* **26/27** *of Kiribati. Multicoloured.* (a) W w **15**. *P* 14.

195 50 c. *Mary* .. 10 15
b. Sheetlet. No. 195×6 and No. 196 .. 85
196 50 c. Prince Charles and Lady Diana Spencer .. 35 40
197 $3 *Alexandra* .. 20 30
aw. Wmk inverted .. 11·00
b. Sheetlet. No. 197×6 and No. 198 .. 1·75
bw. Wmk inverted .. 90·00
198 $3 As No. 196 .. 80 90
aw. Wmk inverted .. 40·00
199 $3.50, *Britannia* .. 25 35
aw. Wmk inverted .. 11·00
b. Sheetlet. No. 199×6 and No. 200 .. 2·10
bw. Wmk inverted .. 90·00
200 $3.50, As No. 196 .. 85 90
aw. Wmk inverted .. 40·00
195/200 .. *Set of* 6 2·25 2·75
MS201 120×109 mm. $5 As No. 196. Wmk sideways. P 12 (26 Nov) .. 75 75

(*b*) *Booklet stamps. No wmk. P* 12 (26 Nov)

202 50 c. As No. 195 .. 15 30
a. Booklet pane. No. 202×4 with margins all round .. 55
203 $3 As No. 198 .. 80 1·25
a. Booklet pane. No. 203×2 with margins all round .. 1·60

Nos. 195/200 were printed in sheetlets of seven stamps of the same face value, each containing six of the "Royal Yacht" design and one of the larger design showing Prince Charles and Lady Diana.

Nos. 202/3 come from $10 stamp booklets.

(Des N. Weaver. Litho Questa)

1981 (9 Oct). *Game Fish. T* **27** *and similar horiz designs. Multicoloured.* W w **14** (*sideways*). *P* 14.

204 10 c. Type **27** .. 15 10
205 50 c. Tarpon .. 30 10
206 60 c. Cobia .. 35 10
207 $2 Blue Marlin .. 1·00 70
204/7 .. *Set of* 4 1·60 85

28 H.M.S. *Experiment* (frigate) **29** Prickly Pear Fruit

(Des J. Cooter. Litho Security Printers (M), Malaysia)

1982 (28 Jan). *Ships. Horiz designs as T* **28**. *Multicoloured.* W w **14**. *P* 13½ × 13.

208 1 c. Type **28** .. 10 10
209 3 c. *Lady Nelson* (cargo liner) .. 15 10
210 5 c. *Daisy* (brig) .. 20 10
211 6 c. Carib canoe .. 20 10
212 10 c. *Hairoun Star* (freighter) .. 30 10
213 15 c. *Jupiter* (liner) .. 40 10
214 20 c. *Christina* (steam yacht) .. 40 10
215 25 c. *Orinoco* (mail paddle-steamer) .. 55 15
216 30 c. H.M.S. *Lively* (frigate) .. 55 15
217 50 c. *Alabama* (Confederate warship) .. 70 25
218 60 c. *Denmark* (freighter) .. 80 30
w. Wmk inverted .. 4·00
219 75 c. *Santa Maria* .. 1·10 50
220 $1 *Baffin* (research vessel) .. 1·10 55
221 $2 *Queen Elizabeth 2* (liner) .. 2·00 1·25
222 $3 R.Y. *Britannia* .. 2·25 1·75
w. Wmk inverted
223 $5 *Geeststar* (freighter) .. 2·40 2·50
224 $10 *Grenadines Star* (ferry) .. 4·50 5·00
208/24 .. *Set of* 17 16·00 11·50

(Des G. Drummond. Litho Harrison)

1982 (5 Apr). *Prickly Pear Cactus. T* **29** *and similar vert designs. Multicoloured.* W w **14**. *P* 14.

225 10 c. Type **29** .. 15 15
226 50 c. Prickly Pear flower buds .. 35 35
227 $1 Flower of Prickly Pear Cactus .. 60 60
228 $2 Prickly Pear Cactus .. 1·25 1·25
225/8 .. *Set of* 4 2·10 2·10

30 Anne Neville, Princess of Wales, 1470 **31** Old and New Uniforms

(Des D. Shults and J. Cooter. Litho Format)

1982 (1 July). *21st Birthday of Princess of Wales. T* **30** *and similar vert designs. Multicoloured.* W w **15**. *P* 13½ × 14.

229 50 c. Type **30** .. 10 15
w. Wmk inverted .. 9·00
230 60 c. Coat of arms of Anne Neville .. 10 15
231 $6 Diana, Princess of Wales .. 60 80
w. Wmk inverted .. 11·00
229/31 .. *Set of* 3 70 1·00

(Des L. Curtis. Litho W.S. Cowell Ltd)

1982 (15 July). *75th Anniv of Boy Scout Movement. T* **31** *and similar vert design. Multicoloured. W w* **14** *(inverted). P* 14½.

232 $1.50, Type **31** 60 75
233 $2.50, Lord Baden-Powell .. .. 90 1·00

ROYAL BABY

BEQUIA

(32)

33 Silhouette Figures of Mary and Joseph

1982 (19 July). *Birth of Prince William of Wales. Nos.* 229/31 *optd with various island names as T* **32**.

A. Bequia B. Canouan C. Mayreau
D. Mustique E. Union Island

To indicate individual islands, use the above letters as a suffix to the following catalogue numbers.

234 50 c. Type **30** 10 15
a. Opt A (Bequia) double .. .. .. 30·00
b. Opt C (Mayreau) inverted .. .. 22·00
c. Opt D (Mustique) inverted .. .. 22·00
wA. Wmk inverted .. .. 8·00
wB. Wmk inverted .. .. 8·00
wC. Wmk inverted .. .. 8·00
wD. Wmk inverted .. .. 8·00
wE. Wmk inverted .. .. 8·00
235 60 c. Coat of arms of Anne Neville .. 10 15
a. Opt D (Mustique) inverted .. .. 30·00
b. Opt E (Union Island) inverted .. 45·00
c. Opt E (Union Island) double £110
236 $6 Diana, Princess of Wales 60 80
wA. Wmk inverted .. .. 10·00
wB. Wmk inverted .. .. 12·00
wC. Wmk inverted .. .. 14·00
wD. Wmk inverted .. .. 14·00
wE. Wmk inverted .. .. 12·00
234/6 .. .. *Set of* 3 70 1·00

(Des Jennifer Toombs. Litho Security Printers (M), Malaysia)

1982 (18 Nov). *Christmas. T* **33** *and similar horiz designs showing silhouettes of figures. Multicoloured. W w* **14**. *P* 13½.

237 10 c. Type **33** 10 10
238 $1.50, Animals in stable 45 45
239 $2.50, Mary and Joseph with baby Jesus .. 60 60
237/9 .. .. *Set of* 3 1·00 1·00
MS240 168 × 99 mm. Nos. 237/9 .. .. .. 1·00 2·00

45¢

(34)

35 Power Station, Clifton

1983 (26 Apr). *No.* 123 *surch with T* **34** *by Reliance Printery, Kingstown.*

241 45 c. on 50 c. Grenada Flycatcher 30 30

(Des G. Drummond. Litho Security Printers (M), Malaysia)

1983 (12 May). *Union Island (2nd series). T* **35** *and similar horiz designs. Multicoloured. W w* **14**. *P* 13½.

242 50 c. Type **35** 20 15
243 60 c. Sunrise, Clifton harbour 20 15
w. Wmk inverted .. .. .. 27·00
244 $1.50, Junior Secondary School, Ashton 50 40
245 $2 Frigate Rock and Conch Shell Beach 65 55
w. Wmk inverted .. .. .. 27·00
242/5 .. .. *Set of* 4 1·40 1·10

Nos. 242/5 were each printed in sheets including two *se-tenant* stamp-size labels.

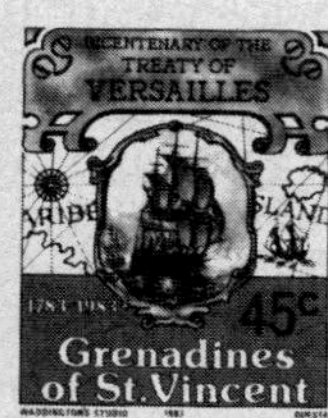

36 British Man-of-war

37 Montgolfier Balloon, 1783

(Des J.W. Litho Questa)

1983 (4 Aug). *Bicentenary of Treaty of Versailles. T* **36** *and similar vert designs. Multicoloured. W w* **14**. *P* 14½.

246 45 c. Type **36** 25 15
247 60 c. American man-of-war 25 15
248 $1.50, Soldiers carrying U.S. flags .. 65 45
249 $2 British troops in battle 75 55
246/9 .. .. *Set of* 4 1·75 1·10

(Des A. Theobald. Litho Format)

1983 (15 Sept). *Bicentenary of Manned Flight. T* **37** *and similar multicoloured designs. W w* **14** *(sideways on Nos.* 251/53). *P* 14.

250 45 c. Type **37** 10 15
251 60 c. Ayres Turbo Thrush Commander (*horiz*) 15 15
252 $1.50, Lebaudy-Juillot airship No. 1 *La Jaune* (*horiz*) 35 45
253 $2 Space shuttle *Columbia* (*horiz*) .. 40 55
250/3 .. .. *Set of* 4 90 1·10
MS254 110×145 mm. Nos. 250/3. Wmk sideways 90 1·50

38 Coat of Arms of Henry VIII

39 Quarter Dollar and Half Dollar, 1797

(Des Court House Studio. Litho Format)

1983 (25 Oct). *Leaders of the World. British Monarchs. T* **38** *and similar vert designs. Multicoloured. P* 12½.

255 60 c. Type **38** 20 25
a. Horiz pair. Nos. 255/6 .. .. 40 50
256 60 c. Henry VIII 20 25
257 60 c. Coat of Arms of James I 20 25
a. Horiz pair. Nos. 257/8 .. .. 40 50
258 60 c. James I 20 25
259 75 c. Henry VIII 20 25
a. Horiz pair. Nos. 259/60 .. .. 40 50
260 75 c. Hampton Court 20 25
261 75 c. James I 20 25
a. Horiz pair. Nos. 261/2 .. .. 40 50
262 75 c. Edinburgh Castle 20 25
263 $2.50, The *Mary Rose* 25 35
a. Horiz pair. Nos. 263/4 .. .. 50 70
264 $2.50, Henry VIII and Portsmouth harbour 25 35
265 $2.50, Gunpowder Plot 25 35
a. Horiz pair. Nos. 265/6 .. .. 50 70
266 $2.50, James I and the Gunpowder Plot 25 35
255/66 .. .. *Set of* 12 2·40 3·00

Nos. 255/6, 257/8, 259/60, 261/2, 263/4 and 265/6 were printed together, *se-tenant*, in horizontal pairs throughout the sheets.

(Des J. Cooter. Litho Walsall)

1983 (1 Dec). *Old Coinage. T* **39** *and similar vert designs. Multicoloured. W w* **14**. *P* 14.

267 20 c. Type **39** 10 10
268 45 c. Nine Bitts, 1811–14 .. .. .. 15 15
269 75 c. Twelve Bitts and Six Bitts, 1811–14 .. 25 25
270 $3 Sixty-six Shillings, 1798 .. .. .. 80 80
267/70 .. .. *Set of* 4 1·10 1·10

40 Class "D 13"

(Des J.W. Litho Format)

1984 (15 Mar). *Leaders of the World. Railway Locomotives (1st series). T* **40** *and similar horiz designs, the first in each pair showing technical drawings and the second the locomotive at work. P* 12½.

271 5 c. multicoloured 10 10
a. Vert pair. Nos. 271/2 .. .. 10 10
272 5 c. multicoloured 10 10
273 10 c. multicoloured 10 10
a. Vert pair. Nos. 273/4 .. .. 10 15
274 10 c. multicoloured 10 10
275 15 c. multicoloured 15 15
a. Vert pair. Nos. 275/6 .. .. 30 30
276 15 c. multicoloured 15 15
277 35 c. multicoloured 20 20
a. Vert pair. Nos. 277/8 .. .. 40 40
278 35 c. multicoloured 20 20
279 45 c. multicoloured 20 20
a. Vert pair. Nos. 279/80 .. .. 40 40
280 45 c. multicoloured 20 20
281 60 c. multicoloured 20 20
a. Vert pair. Nos. 281/2 .. .. 40 40
282 60 c. multicoloured 20 20
283 $1 multicoloured 20 25
a. Vert pair. Nos. 283/4 .. .. 40 50
284 $1 multicoloured 20 25
285 $2.50, multicoloured 25 35
a. Vert pair. Nos. 285/6 .. .. 50 70
286 $2.50, multicoloured 25 35
271/86 .. .. *Set of* 16 2·25 2·50

Designs:—Nos. 271/2, Class "D 13", U.S.A. (1892); 273/4, High Speed Train "125", Great Britain (1980); 275/6, Class "T 9", Great Britain (1899); 277/8, *Claud Hamilton*, Great Britain (1900); 279/80, Class "J", U.S.A. (1941); 281/2, Class "D 16", U.S.A. (1895); 283/4, *Lode Star*, Great Britain (1907); 285/6, *Blue Peter*, Great Britain (1948).

Nos. 271/2, 273/4, 275/6, 277/8, 279/80, 281/2, 283/4 and 285/6 were printed together, *se-tenant* in vertical pairs throughout the sheet.

See also Nos. 311/26, 351/9, 390/7, 412/19, 443/58, 504/19 and 520/35.

41 Spotted Eagle Ray

(Des G. Drummond. Litho Format)

1984 (26 Apr). *Reef Fishes. T* **41** *and similar horiz designs. Multicoloured. W w* **15** *(sideways*). P* 14.

287 45 c. Type **41** 15 20
w. Wmk POST OFFICE reading upwards 6·00
288 60 c. Queen Triggerfish 15 35
289 $1.50, White-spotted Filefish .. .. 25 1·00
290 $2 Schoolmaster .. .. 35 1·25
287/90 .. .. *Set of* 4 80 2·50

*The normal sideways watermark shows "POST OFFICE" reading downwards.

42 R. A. Woolmer

43 Junior Secondary School

(Des Court House Studio. Litho Format)

1984 (16 Aug). *Leaders of the World. Cricketers (1st series). T* **42** *and similar vert designs, the first in each pair showing a portrait and the second the cricketer in action. P* 12½.

291 1 c. multicoloured 10 10
a. Horiz pair. Nos. 291/2 .. .. 10 10
292 1 c. multicoloured 10 10
293 3 c. multicoloured 10 10
a. Horiz pair. Nos. 293/4 .. .. 10 10
294 3 c. multicoloured 10 10
295 5 c. multicoloured 10 10
a. Horiz pair. Nos. 295/6 .. .. 10 10
296 5 c. multicoloured 10 10
297 30 c. multicoloured 20 20
a. Horiz pair. Nos. 297/8 .. .. 40 40
298 30 c. multicoloured 20 20
299 60 c. multicoloured 30 30
a. Horiz pair. Nos. 299/300 .. .. 60 60
300 60 c. multicoloured 30 30
301 $1 multicoloured 40 40
a. Horiz pair. Nos. 301/2 .. .. 80 80
302 $1 multicoloured 40 40
303 $2 multicoloured 45 70
a. Horiz pair. Nos. 303/4 .. .. 90 1·40
304 $2 multicoloured 45 70
305 $3 multicoloured 55 80
a. Horiz pair. Nos. 305/6 .. .. 1·10 1·60
306 $3 multicoloured 55 80
291/306 .. .. *Set of* 16 3·50 4·50

Designs:—Nos. 293/4, K. S. Ranjitsinhji; 295/6, W. R. Hammond; 297/8, D. L. Underwood; 299/300, W. G. Grace; 301/2, E. A. E. Baptiste; 303/4, A. P. E. Knott; 305/6, L. E. G. Ames.

See also Nos. 331/8 and 364/9.

(Des G. Drummond. Litho Questa)

1984 (3 Sept). *Canouan Island (2nd series). T* **43** *and similar horiz designs. Multicoloured. W w* **15** *(sideways). P* 14.

307 35 c. Type **43** 20 20
308 45 c. Police Station 25 25
309 $1 Post Office 50 50
310 $3 Anglican Church .. .. 1·25 1·50
307/10 .. .. *Set of* 4 2·00 2·25

IMPERFORATES AND MISSING COLOURS. Various issues between Nos. 311 and 572 exist either imperforate or with colours omitted. Such items are not listed as there is no evidence that they fulfil the criteria outlined on page xi of this catalogue.

(Des J.W. Litho Format)

1984 (9 Oct). *Leaders of the World. Railway Locomotives (2nd series). Horiz designs as T* **40**, *the first in each pair showing technical drawings and the second the locomotive at work. P* 12½.

311 1 c. multicoloured 10 10
a. Vert pair. Nos. 311/12 .. .. 10 10
312 1 c. multicoloured 10 10
313 5 c. multicoloured 10 10
a. Vert pair. Nos. 313/14 .. .. 10 10
314 5 c. multicoloured 10 10
315 20 c. multicoloured 15 15
a. Vert pair. Nos. 315/16 .. .. 30 30
316 20 c. multicoloured 15 15
317 35 c. multicoloured 15 15
a. Vert pair. Nos. 317/18 .. .. 30 30
318 35 c. multicoloured 15 15
319 60 c. multicoloured 20 20
a. Vert pair. Nos. 319/20 .. .. 40 40
320 60 c. multicoloured 20 20
321 $1 multicoloured 20 25
a. Vert pair. Nos. 321/2 .. .. 40 50
322 $1 multicoloured 20 25
323 $1.50, multicoloured 25 30
a. Vert pair. Nos. 323/4 .. .. 50 60
324 $1.50, multicoloured 25 30

325 $3 multicoloured 35 55
a. Vert pair. Nos. 325/6 .. .. 70 1·10
326 $3 multicoloured 35 55
311/26 .. .. *Set of* 16 2·40 3·00

Designs:—Nos. 311/12, Class "C62", Japan (1948); 313/14, Class "V", Great Britain (1903); 315/16, *Catch-Me-Who-Can*, Great Britain (1808), 317/18, Class "E10", Japan (1948); 319/20, *J. B. Earle*, Great Britain (1904); 321/2, *Lyn*, Great Britain (1898); 323/4, *Talyllyn*, Great Britain (1865); 325/6, *Cardean*, Great Britain (1906).

Nos. 311/26 were issued in a similar sheet format to Nos. 271/86.

44 Lady of the Night

45 Facel "Vega HK500"

(Des Jennifer Toombs. Litho Questa)

1984 (15 Oct). *Night-blooming Flowers. T* **44** *and similar vert designs. Multicoloured. W* w **15**. *P* 14.

327 35 c. Type **44** 35 30
328 45 c. Four o'clock 45 35
329 75 c. Mother-in-Law's Tongue 60 60
330 $3 Queen of the Night .. .. .. 2·00 2·75
327/30 .. .. *Set of* 4 3·00 3·50

(Des Court House Studio. Litho Format)

1984 (28 Nov). *Leaders of the World. Cricketers* (2nd series). *Vert designs as T* **42**, *the first in each pair listed showing a head portrait and the second the cricketer in action. P* 12½.

331 5 c. multicoloured 10 10
a. Horiz pair. Nos. 331/2 .. .. .. 10 10
332 5 c. multicoloured 10 10
333 30 c. multicoloured 25 20
a. Horiz pair. Nos. 333/4 .. .. .. 50 40
334 30 c. multicoloured 25 20
335 $1 multicoloured 35 40
a. Horiz pair. Nos. 335/6 .. .. .. 70 80
336 $1 multicoloured 35 40
337 $2.50, multicoloured 65 80
a. Horiz pair. Nos. 337/8 .. .. .. 1·25 1·60
338 $2.50, multicoloured 65 80
331/8 .. .. *Set of* 8 2·25 2·50

Designs:—Nos. 331/2, S. F. Barnes; 333/4, R. Peel; 335/6, H. Larwood; 337/8, Sir John Hobbs.

Nos. 331/8 were issued in a similar sheet format to Nos. 291/306.

(Des J.W. Litho Format)

1984 (28 Nov). *Leaders of the World. Automobiles* (1st series). *T* **45** *and similar horiz designs, the first in each pair showing technical drawings and the second paintings. P* 12½.

339 5 c. black, azure and dull yellow-green .. 10 10
a. Vert pair. Nos. 339/40 .. .. .. 10 10
340 5 c. multicoloured 10 10
341 25 c. black, pale lilac and pink 10 10
a. Vert pair. Nos. 341/2 .. .. .. 20 20
342 25 c. multicoloured 10 10
343 50 c. black, pale blue and pale orange .. 15 15
a. Vert pair. Nos. 343/4 .. .. .. 30 30
344 50 c. multicoloured 15 15
345 $3 black, stone and brown lake 30 45
a. Vert pair. Nos. 345/6 .. .. .. 60 90
346 $3 multicoloured 30 45
339/46 .. .. *Set of* 8 1·00 1·25

Designs:—Nos. 339/40, Facel "Vega HK500"; 341/2, B.M.W. "328"; 343/4, Frazer-Nash "TT Replica 1.5L"; 345/6, Buick "Roadmaster Riviera".

Nos. 339/40, 341/2, 343/4 and 345/6 were printed together, *se-tenant*, in vertical pairs throughout the sheets.

See also Nos. 378/85 and 431/42.

46 The Three Wise Men and Star

(Des Jennifer Toombs. Litho Format)

1984 (3 Dec). *Christmas. T* **46** *and similar horiz designs. Multicoloured. W* w **15** (*sideways*). *P* 14½.

347 20 c. Type **46** 10 10
348 45 c. Journeying to Bethlehem 15 25
349 $3 Presenting gifts .. .. 70 1·40
347/9 .. .. *Set of* 3 75 1·60
MS350 177 × 107 mm. Nos. 347/9. Wmk inverted 90 2·00

(Des J.W. Litho Format)

1985 (31 Jan). *Leaders of the World. Railway Locomotives* (3rd series). *Horiz designs as T* **40**, *the first in each pair showing technical drawings and the second the locomotive at work. P* 12½.

351 1 c. multicoloured 10 10
a. Vert pair. Nos. 351/2 .. .. .. 10 10
352 1 c. multicoloured 10 10
353 15 c. multicoloured 10 10
a. Vert pair Nos. 353/4 .. .. .. 15 15
354 15 c. multicoloured 10 10
355 75 c. multicoloured 20 25
a. Vert pair. Nos. 355/6 .. .. .. 40 50
356 75 c. multicoloured 20 25
357 $3 multicoloured 50 70
a. Vert pair. Nos. 357/8 .. .. .. 1·00 1·40
358 $3 multicoloured 50 70
351/8 .. .. *Set of* 8 1·40 1·90
MS359 142 × 122 mm. Nos. 355/8. *W* w **15**. .. 3·00 6·50

Designs:—Nos. 351/2, P.L.M. "Grosse C", France (1898); 353/4, Class "C12", Japan (1932); 355/6, Class "D50", Japan (1923); 357/8, *Fire Fly*, Great Britain (1840).

Nos. 351/8 were issued in a similar sheet format to Nos. 271/86.

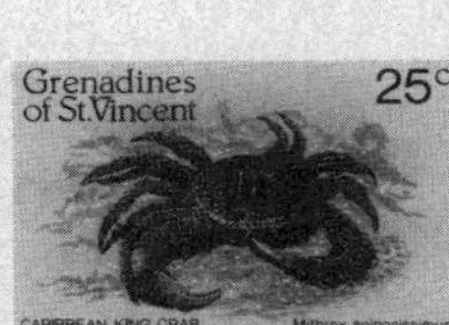

47 Caribbean King Crab

48 *Cypripedium calceolus*

(Des G. Drummond. Litho Format)

1985 (11 Feb). *Shell Fish. T* **47** *and similar horiz designs. Multicoloured. W* w **15** (*sideways*). *P* 14.

360 25 c. Type **47** 20 15
361 60 c. Queen or Pink Conch (*Strombus gigas*) 30 35
362 $1 White Sea Urchin 35 55
363 $3 West Indian Top Shell or Wilk (*Cittarium pica*) .. .. 75 1·75
360/3 .. .. *Set of* 4 1·40 2·50

(Des Court House Studio. Litho Format)

1985 (22 Feb). *Leaders of the World. Cricketers* (3rd series). *Vert designs as T* **42** (55 c., 60 c.), *the first in each pair showing a head portrait and the second the cricketer in action, or horiz designs showing teams* ($2). *P* 12½.

364 55 c. multicoloured 25 35
a. Horiz pair. Nos. 364/5 .. .. .. 50 70
365 55 c. multicoloured 25 35
366 60 c. multicoloured 25 40
a. Horiz pair. Nos. 366/7 .. .. .. 50 80
367 60 c. multicoloured 25 40
368 $2 multicoloured 60 85
369 $2 multicoloured 60 85
364/9 .. .. *Set of* 6 2·00 2·75

Designs: *Vert* (*as T* **42**)—Nos. 364/5, M. D. Moxon; 366/7, L. Potter. *Horiz* (59 × 42 *mm*)—No. 368, Kent team; 369, Yorkshire team.

Nos. 364/5 and 366/7 were issued in a similar sheet format to Nos. 291/306.

(Des Jennifer Toombs. Litho Format)

1985 (13 Mar). *Leaders of the World. Flowers. T* **48** *and similar vert designs. Multicoloured. P* 12½.

370 5 c. Type **48** 10 10
a. Horiz pair. Nos. 370/1 .. .. .. 10 10
371 5 c. *Gentiana asclepiadea* 10 10
372 55 c. *Clianthus formosus* 15 20
a. Horiz pair. Nos. 372/3 .. .. .. 30 40
373 55 c. *Clemisia coriacea* 15 20
374 60 c. *Erythronium americanum* 15 20
a. Horiz pair. Nos. 374/5 .. .. .. 30 40
375 60 c. *Laelia anceps* 15 20
376 $2 *Leucadendron discolor* 35 50
a. Horiz pair. Nos. 376/7 .. .. .. 70 1·00
377 $2 *Meconopsis horridula* 35 50
370/7 .. .. *Set of* 8 1·10 1·60

Nos. 370/1, 372/3, 374/5 and 376/7 were printed together, *se-tenant*, in horizontal pairs throughout the sheets.

(Des J.W. (5 c.), G. Turner (others). Litho Format)

1985 (9 Apr). *Leaders of the World. Automobiles* (2nd series). *Horiz designs as T* **45**, *the first in each pair showing technical drawings and the second paintings. P* 12½.

378 5 c. black, pale lemon and turquoise-blue .. 10 10
a. Vert pair. Nos. 378/9 .. .. .. 10 10
379 5 c. multicoloured 10 10
380 60 c. black, pale yellow and pale orange .. 15 15
a. Vert pair. Nos. 380/1 .. .. .. 30 30
381 60 c. multicoloured 15 15
382 $1 black, pale green and azure 15 20
a. Vert pair. Nos. 382/3 .. .. .. 30 40
383 $1 multicoloured 15 20
384 $1.50, black, pale cobalt and light green .. 15 25
a. Vert pair. Nos. 384/5 .. .. .. 30 50
385 $1.50, multicoloured 15 25
378/85 .. .. *Set of* 8 80 1·10

Designs:—Nos. 378/9, Winton (1903); 380/1, Invicta 4½ litre (1931); 382/3, Daimler "SP250 Dart" (1959); 384/5, Brabham "Repco BT19" (1966).

Nos. 378/85 were issued in a similar sheet format to Nos. 339/46.

49 Windsurfing

(Des G. Vasarhelyi. Litho Format)

1985 (9 May). *Tourism. Watersports. T* **49** *and similar horiz designs. Multicoloured. W* w **15** (*sideways*). *P* 14.

386 35 c. Type **49** 15 15
387 45 c. Water-skiing 15 15
388 75 c. Scuba-diving 15 25
389 $3 Deep-sea game fishing .. .. .. 35 1·40
386/9 .. .. *Set of* 4 70 1·75

(Des J.W. (50 c.), T. Hadler (others). Litho Format)

1985 (17 May). *Leaders of the World. Railway Locomotives* (4th series). *Horiz designs as T* **40**, *the first in each pair showing technical drawings and the second the locomotive at work. P* 12½.

390 10 c. multicoloured 10 10
a. Vert pair. Nos. 390/1 .. .. .. 10 10
391 10 c. multicoloured 10 10
392 40 c. multicoloured 20 20
a. Vert pair. Nos. 392/3 .. .. .. 40 40
393 40 c. multicoloured 20 20
394 50 c. multicoloured 20 20
a. Vert pair. Nos. 394/5 .. .. .. 40 40
395 50 c. multicoloured 20 20
396 $2.50, multicoloured 70 80
a. Vert pair. Nos. 396/7 .. .. .. 1·40 1·60
397 $2.50, multicoloured 70 80
390/7 .. .. *Set of* 8 2·00 2·25

Designs:—Nos. 390/1, Class "581" 12-car train, Japan (1968); 392/3, Class "231-132BT", Algeria (1936); 394/5, *Slieve Gullion*, Great Britain (1913); 396/7, Class "Beattie" well tank, Great Britain (1874).

Nos. 390/7 were issued in a similar sheet format to Nos. 271/86.

50 Passion Fruits and Blossom

51 Queen Elizabeth the Queen Mother

(Des G. Drummond. Litho Format)

1985 (24 June). *Fruits and Blossoms. T* **50** *and similar horiz designs. Multicoloured. W* w **15**. *P* 15.

398 30 c. Type **50** 15 20
399 75 c. Guava 35 40
400 $1 Sapodilla 45 55
401 $2 Mango .. .. 75 1·10
398/401 .. .. *Set of* 4 1·50 2·00
MS402 145×120 mm. Nos. 398/401. Wmk sideways. P 14½×15 .. .. 2·00 2·25

(Des Court House Studio. Litho Format)

1985 (31 July). *Leaders of the World. Life and Times of Queen Elizabeth the Queen Mother. Various vertical portraits as T* **51**. *P* 12½.

403 40 c. multicoloured 10 20
a. Horiz pair. Nos. 403/4 .. .. .. 10 40
404 40 c. multicoloured 10 20
405 75 c. multicoloured 10 20
a. Horiz pair. Nos. 405/6 .. .. .. 15 40
406 75 c. multicoloured 10 20
407 $1.10, multicoloured 15 20
a. Horiz pair. Nos. 407/8 .. .. .. 25 40
408 $1.10, multicoloured 15 20
409 $1.75, multicoloured 15 30
a. Horiz pair. Nos. 409/10 .. .. .. 25 60
410 $1.75, multicoloured 15 30
403/10 .. .. *Set of* 8 65 1·60
MS411 85 × 114 mm. $2 multicoloured; $2 multicoloured .. .. 50 1·50

The two designs of each value were issued, *se-tenant*, in horizontal pairs within the sheets.

Each *se-tenant* pair shows a floral pattern across the bottom of the portraits which stops short of the left-hand edge on the left-hand stamp and of the right-hand edge on the right-hand stamp.

Designs as Nos. 403/4 and 407/8, but with face values of $4 × 2 and $5 × 2, also exist in additional miniature sheets from a restricted printing issued 19 December 1985.

(Des J.W. (35 c.), T. Hadler (others). Litho Format)

1985 (16 Sept). *Leaders of the World. Railway Locomotives* (5th series). *Horiz designs as T* **40**, *the first in each pair showing technical drawings and the second the locomotive at work. P* 12½.

412 35 c. multicoloured 15 20
a. Vert pair. Nos. 412/13 .. .. .. 30 40
413 35 c. multicoloured 15 20
414 70 c. multicoloured 20 30
a. Vert pair. Nos. 414/15 .. .. .. 40 60
415 70 c. multicoloured 20 30
416 $1.20, multicoloured 30 40
a. Vert pair. Nos. 416/17 .. .. .. 60 80
417 $1.20, multicoloured 30 40
418 $2 multicoloured 40 65
a. Vert pair. Nos. 418/19 .. .. .. 80 1·25
419 $2 multicoloured 40 65
412/19 .. .. *Set of* 8 1·90 2·75

Designs:—Nos. 412/13, *Coronation*, Great Britain (1937); 414/15, Class "E18", Germany (1935); 416/17, "Hayes" type, U.S.A. (1854), 418/19, Class "2120", Japan (1890).

Nos. 412/19 were issued in a similar sheet format to Nos. 271/86.

1985 (27 Oct). *Royal Visit. Nos.* 199/200, 222, 287, 398 *and* 407/8 *optd as T* **114** *of Montserrat or surch also.*
420 **50** 30 c. multicoloured .. .. 80 1·25
421 **41** 45 c. multicoloured .. .. 1·00 1·75
422 – $1.10, multicoloured (No. 407) .. 1·75 3·75
a. Horiz pair. Nos. 422/3 .. .. 3·50 7·50
423 – $1.10, multicoloured (No. 408) .. 1·75 3·75
424 – $1.50 on $3.50, mult (No. 199) 2·00 2·25
a. Sheetlet. No. 424 × 6 and No. 425 .. 19·00
425 – $1.50 on $3.50, mult (No. 200) 13·00 15·00
426 – $3 multicoloured (No. 222) .. .. 2·25 3·00
420/6 .. .. *Set of* 7 20·00 28·00

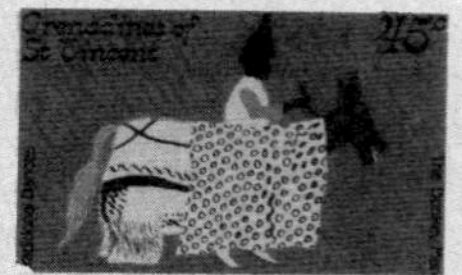

52 Donkey Man

(Des Jennifer Toombs. Litho Format)

1985 (16 Dec). *Traditional Dances. T* **52** *and similar multicoloured designs. P* 15.
427 45 c. Type **52** 15 30
428 75 c. Cake Dance (*vert*) 20 40
429 $1 Bois-Bois Man (*vert*) 25 55
430 $2 Maypole Dance .. .. 45 1·10
427/30 .. .. *Set of* 4 95 2·10

(Des Artists International (15 c.), J.W. ($3), G. Turner (others). Litho Format)

1986 (20 Feb). *Leaders of the World. Automobiles* (3rd series). *Horiz designs as T* **45**, *the first in each pair showing technical drawings and the second paintings. P* 12½.
431 15 c. black, pale rose-lilac and dull mauve .. 10 10
a. Vert pair. Nos. 431/2 .. .. .. 15 20
432 15 c. multicoloured 10 10
433 45 c. black, pale yellow and light brown .. 15 20
a. Vert pair. Nos. 433/4 .. .. .. 30 40
434 45 c. multicoloured 15 20
435 60 c. black, pale green and turquoise-blue .. 15 25
a. Vert pair. Nos. 435/6 .. .. .. 30 50
436 60 c. multicoloured 15 25
437 $1 black, pale cinnamon and sage-green .. 15 25
a. Vert pair. Nos. 437/8 .. .. .. 30 50
438 $1 multicoloured 15 25
439 $1.75, black, pale yellow and pale orange .. 20 35
a. Vert pair. Nos. 439/40 .. .. .. 40 70
440 $1.75, multicoloured 20 35
441 $3 multicoloured 30 45
a. Vert pair. Nos. 441/2 .. .. .. 60 90
442 $3 multicoloured 30 45
431/42 .. .. *Set of* 12 1·90 3·00

Designs:—Nos. 431/2, Mercedes-Benz 4.5 litre (1914); 433/4, Rolls Royce "Silver Wraith" (1954); 435/6, Lamborghini "Countach" (1974); 437/8, Marmon "V-16" (1932): 439/40, Lotus-Ford "49 B" (1968); 441/2, Delage 1.5 litre (1927).

Nos. 431/42 were issued in a similar sheet format to Nos. 339/46.

(Des T. Hadler (15 c., $3), J.W. (others). Litho Format)

1986 (14 Mar). *Leaders of the World. Railway Locomotives* (6th series). *Horiz designs as T* **40**, *the first in each pair showing technical drawings and the second the locomotive at work. P* 12½.
443 15 c. multicoloured 15 10
a. Vert pair. Nos. 443/4 .. .. .. 30 20
444 15 c. multicoloured 15 10
445 45 c. multicoloured 25 20
a. Vert pair. Nos. 445/6 .. .. .. 50 40
446 45 c. multicoloured 25 20
447 60 c. multicoloured 30 30
a. Vert pair. Nos. 447/8 .. .. .. 60 60
448 60 c. multicoloured 30 30
449 75 c. multicoloured 30 35
a. Vert pair. Nos. 449/50 .. .. .. 60 70
450 75 c. multicoloured 30 35
451 $1 multicoloured 30 40
a. Vert pair. Nos. 451/2 .. .. .. 60 80
452 $1 multicoloured 30 40
453 $1.50, multicoloured 30 50
a. Vert pair. Nos. 453/4 .. .. .. 60 1·00
454 $1.50, multicoloured 30 50
455 $2 multicoloured 35 65
a. Vert pair. Nos. 455/6 .. .. .. 70 1·25
456 $2 multicoloured 35 65
457 $3 multicoloured 40 80
a. Vert pair. Nos. 457/8 .. .. .. 80 1·40
458 $3 multicoloured 40 80
443/58 .. .. *Set of* 16 4·25 5·50

Designs:—Nos. 443/4, Class "T15", Germany (1897); 445/6, Class "13", Great Britain (1900); 447/8, *Halesworth*, Great Britain (1879); 449/50, Class "Problem", Great Britain (1859); 451/2, Class "Western" diesel, Great Britain (1961); 453/4, Drummond's "Bug", Great Britain (1899); 455/6, Class "Clan", Great Britain (1951); 457/8, Class "1800", Japan (1884).

Nos. 443/58 were issued in a similar sheet format to Nos. 271/86.

(Des Court House Studio. Litho Format)

1986 (21 Apr). 60*th Birthday of Queen Elizabeth II. Multicoloured designs as T* **117a** *of Montserrat. P* 12½.
459 5 c. Queen Elizabeth II 15 15
460 $1 At Princess Anne's christening, 1950 .. 30 35
461 $4 Princess Elizabeth 60 90
462 $6 In Canberra, 1982 (*vert*) .. .. .. 75 1·50
459/62 .. .. *Set of* 4 1·60 2·50
MS463 85 × 115 mm. $8 Queen Elizabeth II (*different*) .. .. 2·00 4·25

53 Handmade Dolls

(Des G. Drummond. Litho Format)

1986 (22 Apr). *Handicrafts. T* **53** *and similar horiz designs. Multicoloured. W w* **15**. *P* 15.
464 10 c. Type **53** 10 10
465 60 c. Basketwork 20 35
466 $1 Scrimshaw work 30 50
467 $3 Model sailing dinghy .. .. 80 1·90
464/7 .. .. *Set of* 4 1·25 2·50

54 Uruguayan Team

(Des Court House Studio. Litho Format)

1986 (7 May). *World Cup Football Championship, Mexico. T* **54** *and similar multicoloured designs. P* 12½ (1 c., 10 c., $4, $5) *or* 15 (*others*).
468 1 c. Type **54** 10 10
469 10 c. Polish team 10 10
470 45 c. Bulgarian player (28 × 42 *mm*) 25 30
471 75 c. Iraqi player (28 × 42 *mm*) 35 40
472 $1.50, South Korean player (28 × 42 *mm*) .. 75 90
473 $2 Northern Irish player (28 × 42 *mm*) .. 1·00 1·40
474 $4 Portuguese team .. .. 1·50 1·75
475 $5 Canadian team .. .. 1·60 1·75
468/75 .. .. *Set of* 8 5·00 6·00
MS476 Two sheets, 85 × 114 mm. (a) $1 As No. 474: (b) $3 Type **54**. P 12½ *Set of* 2 *sheets* 1·50 2·50

55 *Marasmius pallescens*

56 *Brachymesia furcata*

(Des G. Drummond. Litho Questa)

1986 (23 May). *Fungi. T* **55** *and similar vert designs. Multicoloured. W w* **15** (*sideways*). *P* 14.
477 45 c. Type **55** .. .. 2·00 75
478 60 c. *Leucocoprinus fragilissimus* .. .. 2·25 1·10
479 75 c. *Hygrocybe occidentalis* .. .. .. 2·75 1·60
480 $3 *Xerocomus hypoxanthus* .. .. .. 7·50 7·00
477/80 .. .. *Set of* 4 13·00 9·50

(Des Court House Studio. Litho Format)

1986 (18 July–15 Oct). *Royal Wedding* (1st *issue*). *Multicoloured designs as T* **118a** *of Montserrat. P* 12½.
481 60 c. Miss Sarah Ferguson and Princess Diana applauding 15 25
a. Pair. Nos. 481/2 .. .. 30 50
482 60 c. Prince Andrew at shooting match .. 15 25
483 $2 Prince Andrew and Miss Sarah Ferguson (*horiz*) 50 80
a. Pair. Nos. 483/4 .. .. 1·00 1·60
484 $2 Prince Charles, Prince Andrew, Princess Anne and Princess Margaret on balcony (*horiz*) 50 80
481/4 .. .. *Set of* 4 1·10 1·90
MS485 115 × 85 mm. $8 Duke and Duchess of York in carriage after wedding (*horiz*) (15.10.86) 2·75 3·75

Nos. 481/2 and 483/4 were printed together, *se-tenant*, in horizontal and vertical pairs throughout the sheets.

Nos. 481/4 imperforate come from souvenir stamp booklets.

1986 (15 Oct). *Royal Wedding* (2nd *issue*). *Nos.* 481/4 *optd as T* **121** *of Montserrat in silver.*
486 60 c. Miss Sarah Ferguson and Princess Diana applauding 30 50
a. Pair. Nos. 486/7 .. .. 60 1·00
487 60 c. Prince Andrew at shooting match .. 30 50
488 $2 Prince Andrew and Miss Sarah Ferguson (*horiz*) .. .. 1·00 1·25
a. Pair. Nos. 488/9 .. .. 2·00 2·50
489 $2 Prince Charles, Prince Andrew, Princess Anne and Princess Margaret on balcony (*horiz*) .. .. 1·00 1·25
486/9 .. .. *Set of* 4 2·40 3·25

(Des M. Hillier. Litho Format)

1986 (19 Nov). *Dragonflies. T* **56** *and similar multicoloured designs. P* 15.
490 45 c. Type **56** 15 20
491 60 c. *Lepthemis vesiculosa* 20 40
492 75 c. *Perithemis domitta* 20 45
493 $2.50, *Tramea abdominalis* (*vert*) .. .. 40 1·40
490/3 .. .. *Set of* 4 85 2·25

(Des Court House Studio. Litho Format)

1986 (26 Nov). *Centenary of Statue of Liberty. Vert views of Statue as T* **121a** *of Montserrat in separate miniature sheets. Multicoloured. P* 14 × 13½.
MS494 Nine sheets, each 85 × 115 mm. $1.50; $1.75; $2; $2.50; $3; $3.50; $5; $6; $8 *Set of* 9 *sheets* 8·50 16·00

57 American Kestrel

58 Santa playing Steel Band Drums

(Des Toni Lance. Litho Questa)

1986 (26 Nov). *Birds of Prey. T* **57** *and similar vert designs. Multicoloured. P* 14.
495 10 c. Type **57** 50 30
496 45 c. Common Black Hawk .. .. .. 1·40 50
497 60 c. Peregrine Falcon .. .. 1·50 1·10
498 $4 Osprey .. .. 4·25 6·00
495/8 .. .. *Set of* 4 7·00 7·00

(Des Court House Studio. Litho Questa)

1986 (26 Nov). *Christmas. T* **58** *and similar vert designs. Multicoloured. P* 14.
499 45 c. Type **58** 30 30
500 60 c. Santa windsurfing 35 35
501 $1.25, Santa skiing 60 85
502 $2 Santa limbo dancing .. .. 1·10 1·60
499/502 .. .. *Set of* 4 2·10 2·75
MS503 166 × 128 mm. Nos. 499/502 .. .. 7·00 8·00

(Litho Format)

1987 (5 May). *Railway Locomotives* (7th *series*). *Horiz designs, as T* **40**, *the first in each pair showing technical drawings and the second the locomotive at work. Multicoloured. P* 12½.
504 10 c. multicoloured 15 10
a. Vert pair. Nos. 504/5 .. .. .. 30 10
505 10 c. multicoloured 15 10
506 40 c. multicoloured 25 25
a. Vert pair. Nos. 506/7 .. .. .. 50 50
507 40 c. multicoloured 25 25
508 50 c. multicoloured 30 30
a. Vert pair. Nos. 508/9 .. .. .. 60 60
509 50 c. multicoloured 30 30
510 60 c. multicoloured 35 30
a. Vert pair. Nos. 510/11 .. .. .. 70 60
511 60 c. multicoloured 35 30
512 75 c. multicoloured 40 40
a. Vert pair. Nos. 512/13 .. .. .. 80 80
513 75 c. multicoloured 40 40
514 $1 multicoloured 40 50
a. Vert pair. Nos. 514/15 .. .. .. 80 1·00
515 $1 multicoloured 40 50
516 $1.25, multicoloured 40 60
a. Vert pair. Nos. 516/17 .. .. .. 80 1·25
517 $1.25, multicoloured 40 60
518 $1.50, multicoloured 55 75
a. Vert pair. Nos. 518/19 .. .. .. 1·10 1·50
519 $1.50, multicoloured 55 75
504/19 .. .. *Set of* 16 5·00 5·75

Designs:—Nos. 504/5, Class "1001", No. 1275, Great Britain (1874); 506/7, Class "4P Garratt", Great Britain (1927); 508/9, *Papyrus*, Great Britain (1929); 510/11, Class "V1", Great Britain (1930); 512/13, Class "40" diesel, No. D200, Great Britain (1958); 514/15, Class "42 Warship" diesel, Great Britain (1958); 516/17, Class "P-69", U.S.A. (1902); 518/19, Class "60-3 Shay", No. 15, U.S.A. (1913).

Nos. 504/19 were issued in a similar sheet format to Nos. 271/86.

(Litho Format)

1987 (26 Aug). *Railway Locomotives* (8th *series*). *Horiz designs as T* **40**, *the first in each pair showing technical drawings and the second the locomotive at work. P* 12½.
520 10 c. multicoloured 15 15
a. Vert pair. Nos. 520/1 .. .. .. 30 30
521 10 c. multicoloured 15 15
522 40 c. multicoloured 25 30
a. Vert pair. Nos. 522/3 .. .. .. 50 60
523 40 c. multicoloured 25 30
524 50 c. multicoloured 30 35
a. Vert pair. Nos. 524/5 .. .. .. 60 70
525 50 c. multicoloured 30 35
526 60 c. multicoloured 35 40
a. Vert pair. Nos. 526/7 .. .. .. 70 80
527 60 c. multicoloured 35 40
528 75 c. multicoloured 35 45
a. Vert pair. Nos. 528/9 .. .. .. 70 90
529 75 c. multicoloured 35 45
530 $1 multicoloured 40 45
a. Vert pair. Nos. 530/1 .. .. .. 80 90

531 $1 multicoloured 40 45
532 $1.50, multicoloured 55 55
a. Vert pair. Nos. 532/3 .. .. 1·10 1·10
533 $1.50, multicoloured 55 55
534 $2 multicoloured 65 70
a. Vert pair. Nos. 534/5 .. .. 1·25 1·40
535 $2 multicoloured 65 70
520/35 .. .. *Set of* 16 5·25 6·00

Designs:—Nos. 520/1, Class "142", East Germany (1977); 522/3, Class "120", West Germany (1979); 524/5, Class "X", Australia (1954); 526/7, Class "59", Great Britain (1986); 528/9, New York Elevated Railroad *Spuyten Duyvel*, U.S.A. (1875); 530/1, Camden & Amboy Railroad *Stevens* (later *John Bull*), U.S.A. (1831); 532/3, "Royal Hudson" Class "H1-d", No. 2850, Canada (1938), 534/5, "Pioneer Zephyr" 3-car set, U.S.A. (1934).

Nos. 520/35 were issued in a similar sheet format to Nos. 271/86.

59 Queen Elizabeth with Prince Andrew

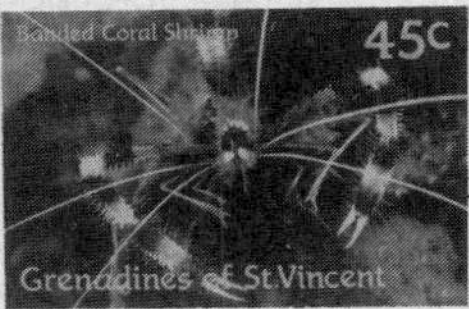

60 Banded Coral Shrimp

(Des Young Phillips. Litho Format)

1987 (15 Oct). *Royal Ruby Wedding and 150th Anniv of Queen Victoria's Accession. T* **59** *and similar vert designs. P* 12½.
536 15 c. multicoloured 20 15
537 45 c. deep chocolate, black & greenish yellow 25 20
538 $1.50, multicoloured 30 50
539 $3 multicoloured 45 80
540 $4 multicoloured .. .. 50 1·10
536/40 .. .. *Set of* 5 1·50 2·50
MS541 85 × 115 mm. $6 multicoloured .. .. 1·25 2·50

Designs:—45 c. Queen Victoria and Prince Albert, *c* 1855; $1.50, Queen and Prince Philip after Trooping the Colour, 1977; $3 Queen and Duke of Edinburgh, 1953; $4 Queen in her study, *c* 1980; $6 Princess Elizabeth, 1947.

(Litho Format)

1987 (17 Dec). *Marine Life. T* **60** *and similar horiz designs. Multicoloured. P* 15.
542 45 c. Type **60** 40 35
543 50 c. Arrow Crab and Flamingo Tongue .. 45 50
544 65 c. Cardinalfish 55 90
545 $5 Spotted Moray .. .. 2·00 3·75
542/5 .. .. *Set of* 4 3·00 5·00
MS546 85×115 mm. $5 Porcupinefish ("Puffer Fish") .. .. 2·25 4·50

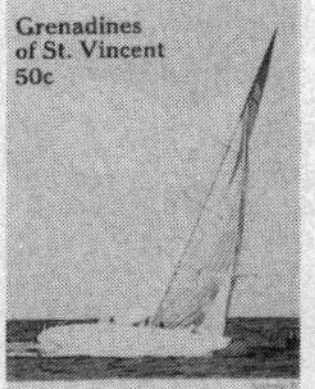

61 *Australia IV*

62 Seine-fishing Boats racing

(Litho Format)

1988 (31 Mar). *Ocean Racing Yachts. T* **61** *and similar vert designs. Multicoloured. P* 12½.
547 50 c. Type **61** 35 35
548 65 c. *Crusader II* 40 50
549 75 c. *New Zealand II* 45 60
550 $2 *Italia* .. .. 70 1·25
551 $4 *White Crusader* .. .. 80 2·00
552 $5 *Stars and Stripes* .. .. 85 2·25
547/52 .. .. *Set of* 6 3·25 6·25
MS553 100×140 mm. $1 *Champosa V* .. 85 1·50

(Litho Format)

1988 (31 Mar). *Bequia Regatta. T* **62** *and similar horiz designs. Multicoloured. P* 15.
554 5 c. Type **62** 10 15
555 50 c. *Friendship Rose* (cruising yacht) .. 15 30
556 75 c. Fishing boats racing 20 45
557 $3.50, Yachts racing .. .. 75 2·25
554/7 .. .. *Set of* 4 1·00 2·75
MS558 115×85 mm. $8 Port Elizabeth, Bequia (60×40 *mm*). P 12½ .. .. 3·00 5·00

COVER PRICES

Cover factors are quoted at the beginning of each country for most issues to 1945. An explanation of the system can be found on page x. The factors quoted do not, however, apply to philatelic covers.

63 Britten Norman Islander making Night Approach

(Litho Format)

1988 (26 May). *Mustique Airways. T* **63** *and similar multicoloured designs. P* 14 × 13½.
559 15 c. Type **63** 10 15
560 65 c. Beech 58 Baron aircraft in flight .. 15 35
561 75 c. Britten Norman Islander over forest 15 35
562 $5 Beech 58 Baron on airstrip .. .. 1·00 2·25
559/62 .. .. *Set of* 4 1·25 2·75
MS563 115×85 mm. $10 Baleine Falls (36×56 *mm*). P 12½ .. .. 3·00 5·50

64 *Sv. Pyotr* in Arctic (Bering)

65 Asif Iqbal Razvi

(Litho Format)

1988 (29 July). *Explorers. T* **64** *and similar square designs. Multicoloured. P* 14 × 13½.
564 15 c. Type **64** 35 20
565 75 c. Bering's ships in pack ice 40 30
566 $1 Livingstone's steam launch *Ma-Robert* on Zambesi 40 40
567 $2 Meeting of Livingstone and H. M. Stanley at Ujiji 50 75
568 $3 Speke and Burton at Tabori 50 90
569 $3.50, Speke and Burton in canoe on Lake Victoria .. .. 50 1·10
570 $4 Sighting the New World, 1492 .. 60 1·25
571 $4.50, Columbus trading with Indians .. 60 1·40
563/71 .. .. *Set of* 8 3·50 5·50
MS572 Two sheets, each 115 × 85 mm. (a) $5 Sextant and coastal scene. (b) $5 *Santa Maria* at anchor. P 13½ × 14 .. .. *Set of* 2 *sheets* 2·25 5·00

An unissued $6 miniature sheet, showing the *Santa Maria*, exists from stock dispersed by the liquidator of Format International Security Printers Ltd.

(Litho Format)

1988 (29 July). *Cricketers of* 1988 *International Season. T* **65** *and similar multicoloured designs. P* 15.
573 20 c. Type **65** 30 30
574 45 c. R. J. Hadlee 50 50
575 75 c. M. D. Crowe 70 80
576 $1.25, C. H. Lloyd .. .. 1·00 1·25
577 $1.50, A. R. Boarder .. .. 1·25 1·50
578 $2 M. D. Marshall .. .. 1·50 2·00
579 $2.50, G. A. Hick .. .. 1·50 2·25
580 $3.50, C. G. Greenidge (*horiz*) .. .. 1·60 2·75
573/80 .. .. *Set of* 8 7·50 10·00
MS581 115 × 85 mm. $3 As $2 .. .. .. 4·00 5·00

66 Pam Shriver

(Litho Format)

1988 (29 July). *International Tennis Players. T* **66** *and similar multicoloured designs. P* 12½.
582 15 c. Type **66** 30 20
583 50 c. Kevin Curran (*vert*) 30 30
584 75 c. Wendy Turnbull (*vert*) 40 35
585 $1 Evonne Cawley (*vert*) 50 50
586 $1.50, Ilie Nastase 60 65
587 $2 Billie Jean King (*vert*) 65 75
588 $3 Bjorn Borg (*vert*) .. .. .. 75 1·25
589 $3.50, Virginia Wade with Wimbledon trophy (*vert*) .. .. 80 1·50
582/9 .. .. *Set of* 8 3·75 5·00
MS590 115 × 85 mm. $2.25, Stefan Edberg with Wimbledon cup; $2.25, Steffi Graf with Wimbledon trophy .. .. 1·50 3·25

No. 584 is inscribed "WENDY TURNBALL" in error.

Examples of an unissued set of six values and a miniature sheet for the 1988 Olympic Games at Seoul exist from stock dispersed by the liquidator of Format International Security Printers Ltd.

67 Mickey and Minnie Mouse visiting Fatehpur Sikri

(Des Walt Disney Co. Litho Questa)

1989 (8 Feb). *"India-89" International Stamp Exhibition, New Delhi. T* **67** *and similar multicoloured designs showing Walt Disney cartoon characters in India. P* 14×13½.
591 1 c. Type **67** 10 10
592 2 c. Mickey and Minnie Mouse aboard "Palace on Wheels" train 10 10
593 3 c. Mickey and Minnie Mouse passing Old Fort, Delhi 10 10
594 5 c. Mickey and Minnie Mouse on camel, Pinjore Gardens, Haryana 10 10
595 10 c. Mickey and Minnie Mouse at Taj Mahal, Agra 10 10
596 25 c. Mickey and Minnie Mouse in Chandni Chowk, Old Delhi 15 10
597 $4 Goofy on elephant with Mickey and Minnie Mouse at Agra Fort, Jaipur .. 2·50 3·00
598 $5 Goofy, Mickey and Minnie Mouse at Gandhi Memorial, Cape Comorin .. 2·75 3·25
591/8 .. .. *Set of* 8 5·00 6·00
MS599 Two sheets, each 127 × 102 mm. (a) $6 Mickey and Minnie Mouse in vegetable cart, Jaipur. P 14 × 13½. (b) $6 Mickey and Minnie Mouse leaving carriage, Qutab Minar, New Delhi (*vert*). P 13½ × 14 .. *Set of* 2 *sheets* 8·00 9·00

(Litho Questa)

1989 (6 July). *Japanese Art. Horiz designs as T* **187a** *of Lesotho. Multicoloured. P* 14×13½.
600 5 c. "The View at Yotsuya" (Hokusai) .. 15 15
601 30 c. "Landscape at Ochanomizu" (Hokuju) 30 30
602 45 c. "Itabashi" (Eisen) 40 40
603 65 c. "Early Summer Rain" (Kunisada) .. 55 55
604 75 c. "High Noon at Kasumigaseki" (Kuniyoshi) 60 60
605 $1 "The Yoshiwara Embankment by Moonlight" (Kuniyoshi) 75 75
606 $4 "The Bridge of Boats at Sano" (Hokusai) .. .. 2·50 2·75
607 $5 "Lingering Snow on Mount Hira" (Kunitora) .. .. 2·75 3·00
600/7 .. .. *Set of* 8 7·00 7·50
MS608 Two sheets, each 103×76 mm. (a) $6 "Colossus of Rhodes" (Kunitora). (b) $6 "Shinobazu Pond" (Kokan) .. *Set of* 2 *sheets* 6·00 7·00

Nos. 600/7 were each printed in sheetlets of 10 containing two horizontal strips of 5 stamps separated by printed labels commemorating Emperor Hirohito.

68 Player with Ball and Mt Vesuvius

69 Arawak smoking Tobacco

(Des J. Genzo. Litho B.D.T.)

1989 (10 July). *World Cup Football Championship, Italy* (1st issue). *T* **68** *and similar vert designs each showing players and Italian landmarks. Multicoloured. P* 14.
609 $1.50, Type **68** .. .. 1·10 1·25
a. Sheetlet. Nos. 609/16 .. .. .. 8·00
610 $1.50, Fallen player, opponent kicking ball and Coliseum .. .. 1·10 1·25
611 $1.50, Player blocking ball and Venice .. 1·10 1·25
612 $1.50, Player tackling and Forum, Rome 1·10 1·25
613 $1.50, Two players competing for ball and Leaning Tower, Pisa .. .. .. 1·10 1·25
614 $1.50, Goalkeeper and Florence .. .. 1·10 1·25
615 $1.50, Two players competing for ball and St. Peter's, Vatican .. .. .. 1·10 1·25
616 $1.50, Player kicking ball and Pantheon 1·10 1·25
609/16 .. .. *Set of* 8 8·00 9·00

Nos. 609/16 were printed together, *se-tenant*, in a sheetlet of 8.

See also Nos. 680/4.

(Des D. Miller. Litho B.D.T.)

1989 (2 Oct). *500th Anniv of Discovery of America* (1992) *by Columbus* (1st *issue*). *Pre-Columbian Arawak Society. T* **69** *and similar vert designs. Multicoloured. P* 14.
617 25 c. Type **69** 25 25
618 75 c. Arawak rolling cigar 50 55
619 $1 Applying body paint 65 70
620 $1.50, Making fire .. .. 90 1·25
a. Horiz strip of 4. Nos. 620/3 .. .. 3·25
621 $1.50, Cassava production .. .. .. 90 1·25

622 $1.50, Woman baking bread .. .. 90 1·25
623 $1.50, Using stone implement .. .. 90 1·25
624 $4 Arawak priest .. .. .. 2·25 2·50
617/24 .. .. *Set of* 8 6·50 8·00
MS625 Two sheets, each 70×84 mm. (a) $6 Arawak chief. (b) $6 Men returning from fishing expedition .. .. .. *Set of* 2 *sheets* 8·00 9·00

Nos. 620/4 were printed together, *se-tenant*, in horizontal strips of 4 throughout the sheet of 20, each strip forming a composite design.

See also Nos. 818/24 and 864/5.

70 Command Module Columbia

71 *Marpesia petreus*

(Des W. Wright. Litho B.D.T.)

1989 (2 Oct). *20th Anniv of First Manned Landing on Moon. T* **70** *and similar multicoloured designs. P* 14.

626 5 c. Type **70** 15 15
627 40 c. Astronaut Neil Armstrong saluting U.S. flag 70 70
628 55 c. *Columbia* above lunar surface .. 80 80
629 65 c. Lunar module *Eagle* leaving Moon .. 80 80
630 70 c. *Eagle* on Moon 80 80
631 $1 *Columbia* re-entering Earth's atmosphere .. .. 1·00 1·00
632 $3 "Apollo 11" emblem .. .. .. 2·25 2·25
633 $5 Armstrong and Aldrin on Moon .. 3·00 3·00
626/33 .. .. *Set of* 8 8·50 8·50
MS634 Two sheets, each 110×82 mm. (a) $6 Launch of "Apollo 11" (*vert*). (b) $6 "Apollo 11" splashdown .. .. .. *Set of* 2 *sheets* 7·00 8·00

(Des D. Bruckner. Litho Questa)

1989 (16 Oct). *Butterflies. T* **71** *and similar horiz designs. Multicoloured. P* 14½.

635 5 c. Type **71** 20 20
636 30 c. *Papilio androgeus* 60 50
637 45 c. *Strymon maesites* 75 50
638 65 c. *Junonia coenia* .. .. .. 1·00 1·00
639 75 c. *Eurema gratiosa* .. .. .. 1·25 1·25
640 $1 *Hypolimnas misippus* .. .. .. 1·50 1·50
641 $4 *Urbanus proteus* .. .. .. 3·50 3·75
642 $5 *Junonia evarete* .. .. .. 3·75 4·00
635/42 .. .. *Set of* 8 11·50 11·50
MS643 Two sheets. (a) 76×104 mm. $6 *Phoebis agarithe*. (b) 104×76 mm. $6 *Dryas julia* *Set of* 2 *sheets* 11·00 12·00

72 *Solanum urens*

73 Goofy and Mickey Mouse in Rolls-Royce "Silver Ghost", 1907

(Des Mary Walters. Litho Questa)

1989 (1 Nov). *Flowers from St. Vincent Botanical Gardens. T* **72** *and similar vert designs. Multicoloured. P* 14.

644 80 c. Type **72** 80 80
645 $1.25, *Passiflora andersonii* .. .. 1·10 1·10
646 $1.65, *Miconia andersonii* .. .. 1·40 1·40
647 $1.85, *Pitcairnia sulphurea* .. .. 1·60 1·60
644/7 .. .. *Set of* 4 4·50 4·50

(Des Walt Disney Co. Litho Questa)

1989 (20 Dec). *Christmas. T* **73** *and similar horiz designs showing Walt Disney cartoon characters and cars. Multicoloured. P* 14×13½.

648 5 c. Type **73** 20 15
649 10 c. Daisy Duck driving first Stanley Steamer, 1897 .. .. .. 20 15
650 15 c. Horace Horsecollar and Clarabelle Cow in Darracq "Genevieve", 1904 .. 25 20
651 45 c. Donald Duck driving Detroit electric coupe, 1914 .. .. .. 50 35
652 55 c. Mickey and Minnie Mouse in first Ford, 1896 .. .. 55 40
653 $2 Mickey Mouse driving Reo "Runabout", 1904 .. .. 2·00 2·00
654 $3 Goofy driving Winton mail truck, 1899 2·75 2·75
655 $5 Mickey and Minnie Mouse in Duryea car, 1893 .. .. .. 3·50 4·00
648/55 .. .. *Set of* 8 9·00 9·00
MS656 Two sheets, each 127×102 mm. (a) $6 Mickey and Minnie Mouse in Pope-Hartford, 1912. (b) $6 Mickey and Minnie Mouse in Buick "Model 10", 1908. P 13½×14 .. *Set of* 2 *sheets* 9·50 11·00

(Des W. Wright. Litho Questa)

1990 (2 Apr). *50th Anniv of Second World War. Horiz designs as T* **242** *of Maldive Islands. Multicoloured. P* 14.

657 10 c. Destroyers in action, First Battle of Narvik, 1940 .. .. .. 25 25
658 15 c. Allied tank at Anzio, 1944 .. .. 35 35
659 20 c. U.S. carrier under attack, Battle of Midway, 1942 .. .. .. 40 40
660 45 c. U.S. North American B-25 Mitchell bombers over Gustav Line, 1944 .. 70 70
661 55 c. Map showing Allied zones of Berlin, 1945 .. .. 75 75
662 65 c. German U-boat pursuing convoy, Battle of the Atlantic, 1943 .. 80 80
663 90 c. Allied tank, North Africa, 1943 .. 1·00 1·00
664 $3 U.S. forces landing on Guam, 1944 .. 2·50 2·50
665 $5 Crossing the Rhine, 1945 .. .. 3·50 3·50
666 $6 Japanese battleships under attack, Leyte Gulf, 1944 .. .. 4·00 4·00
657/66 .. .. *Set of* 10 13·00 13·00
MS667 100×70 mm. $6 Avro Type 683 Lancaster Mk III on "Dambusters" raid, 1943 5·00 5·50

(Des Walt Disney Co. Litho Questa)

1990 (3 May). *"Stamp World London 90" International Stamp Exhibition (1st issue). Mickey's Shakespeare Company. Multicoloured designs as T* **239***a of Maldive Islands showing Walt Disney cartoon characters. P* 14×13½.

668 20 c. Goofy as Mark Anthony (*Julius Caesar*) 30 20
669 30 c. Clarabelle Cow as the Nurse (*Romeo and Juliet*) 35 25
670 45 c. Pete as Falstaff (*Henry IV*) 50 40
671 50 c. Minnie Mouse as Portia (*The Merchant of Venice*) 55 40
672 $1 Donald Duck as Hamlet (*Hamlet*) .. 1·00 85
673 $2 Daisy Duck as Ophelia (*Hamlet*) .. 1·75 2·00
674 $4 Donald and Daisy Duck as Benedick and Beatrice (*Much Ado About Nothing*) .. .. 3·00 3·25
675 $5 Minnie Mouse and Donald Duck as Katherine and Petruchio (*The Taming of the Shrew*) .. .. .. 3·00 3·25
668/75 .. .. *Set of* 8 9·50 9·50
MS676 Two sheets, each 127×101 mm. (a) $6 Clarabelle as Titania (*A Midsummer Night's Dream*) (*vert*). (b) $6 Mickey Mouse as Romeo (*Romeo and Juliet*) (*vert*). P 13½×14 *Set of* 2 *sheets* 9·00 9·50

74 Exhibition Emblem

75 Scaly-breasted Ground Dove

(Des M. Pollard. Litho B.D.T.)

1990 (3 May). *"Stamp World London 90" International Stamp Exhibition (2nd issue). 150th Anniv of Penny Black. T* **74** *and similar vert designs. P* 14×15.

677 $1 black, brown-rose and magenta .. 1·25 1·25
678 $5 black, grey-lilac and ultramarine .. 3·50 4·00
MS679 130×100 mm. $6 black and pale blue .. 4·25 5·00

Designs:—$5 Negative image of Penny Black; $6 Penny Black.

(Des Young Phillips Studio. Litho Questa)

1990 (24 Sept). *World Cup Football Championship, Italy (2nd issue). Multicoloured designs as T* **210** *of St. Vincent, but horiz. P* 14.

680 25 c. McCleish, Scotland 55 40
681 50 c. Rasul, Egypt 80 70
682 $2 Lindenberger, Austria .. .. .. 2·25 2·25
683 $4 Murray, U.S.A. .. .. .. 3·50 3·75
680/3 .. .. *Set of* 4 6·25 6·25
MS684 Two sheets, each 102×77 mm. (a) $6 Robson, England. (b) $6 Gullit, Netherlands *Set of* 2 *sheets* 10·00 10·00

(Des Dorothy Novick. Litho B.D.T.)

1990 (23 Nov). *"EXPO 90" International Garden and Greenery Exposition, Osaka. Orchids. Vert designs as T* **213** *of St. Vincent. Multicoloured. P* 14.

685 5 c. *Paphiopedilum* 30 30
686 25 c. *Dendrobium phalaenopsis* and *Cymbidium hybrid* 60 60
687 30 c. *Miltonia candida hybrid* 70 70
688 50 c. *Epidendrum ibaguense* and *Cymbidium* Elliot Rogers .. .. .. 1·00 1·00
689 $1 *Rossioglossum grande* .. .. 1·50 1·50
690 $2 *Phalaenopsis* Elisa Chang Lou and *Masdevallia coccinea* .. .. 1·75 1·75
691 $4 *Cypripedium acaule* and *Cypripedium calceolus* .. .. .. 2·75 2·75
692 $5 *Orchis spectabilis* .. .. 3·00 3·00
685/92 .. .. *Set of* 8 10·50 10·50
MS693 Two sheets, each 108×78 mm. (a) $6 *Dendrobium anosmum*. (b) $6 *Epidendrum ibaguense* and *Phalaenopsis* .. *Set of* 2 *sheets* 11·00 11·00

(Des W. Wright. Litho B.D.T.)

1990 (26 Nov). *Birds of the Caribbean. T* **75** *and similar horiz designs. Multicoloured. P* 14.

694 5 c. Type **75** 20 20
695 25 c. Purple Martin 40 40
696 45 c. Painted Bunting 70 70
697 55 c. Blue-hooded Euphonia 80 80
698 75 c. Blue-grey Tanager .. .. .. 1·00 1·00
699 $1 Red-eyed Vireo .. .. .. 1·25 1·25
700 $2 Palm Chat .. .. 2·00 2·00
701 $3 Northern Jacana .. .. .. 2·50 2·50
702 $4 Green-throated Carib .. .. 2·75 2·75
703 $5 St. Vincent Amazon .. .. .. 3·00 3·00
694/703 .. .. .. *Set of* 10 13·00 13·00
MS704 Two sheets, each 117×87 mm. (a) $3 Magnificent Frigate Bird; $3 Bananaquit. (b) $6 Red-legged Honeycreeper .. *Set of* 2 *sheets* 7·00 8·00

(Des Young Phillips Studio. Litho B.D.T.)

1991 (14 Feb). *90th Birthday of Queen Elizabeth the Queen Mother. Vert designs as T* **198***a of Lesotho. P* 14.

705 $2 multicoloured .. .. .. 1·25 1·25
a. Sheetlet. Nos. 705/13 .. .. .. 10·00
706 $2 multicoloured .. .. .. 1·25 1·25
707 $2 multicoloured .. .. .. 1·25 1·25
708 $2 multicoloured .. .. .. 1·25 1·25
709 $2 multicoloured .. .. .. 1·25 1·25
710 $2 multicoloured .. .. .. 1·25 1·25
711 $2 multicoloured .. .. .. 1·25 1·25
712 $2 multicoloured .. .. .. 1·25 1·25
713 $2 multicoloured .. .. .. 1·25 1·25
714 $2 multicoloured .. .. .. 1·25 1·25
a. Sheetlet. Nos. 714/22 .. .. .. 10·00
715 $2 multicoloured .. .. .. 1·25 1·25
716 $2 multicoloured .. .. .. 1·25 1·25
717 $2 black and rose-lilac .. .. 1·25 1·25
718 $2 black and rose-lilac .. .. 1·25 1·25
719 $2 black, pale yellow-olive and rose-lilac 1·25 1·25
720 $2 multicoloured .. .. .. 1·25 1·25
721 $2 black and rose-lilac .. .. 1·25 1·25
722 $2 multicoloured .. .. .. 1·25 1·25
723 $2 multicoloured .. .. .. 1·25 1·25
a. Sheetlet. Nos. 723/31 .. .. .. 10·00
724 $2 multicoloured .. .. .. 1·25 1·25
725 $2 multicoloured .. .. .. 1·25 1·25
726 $2 multicoloured .. .. .. 1·25 1·25
727 $2 multicoloured .. .. .. 1·25 1·25
728 $2 multicoloured .. .. .. 1·25 1·25
729 $2 multicoloured .. .. .. 1·25 1·25
730 $2 multicoloured .. .. .. 1·25 1·25
731 $2 multicoloured .. .. .. 1·25 1·25
705/31 .. .. .. *Set of* 27 27·00 27·00
MS732 Nine sheets containing details of designs indicated. (a) 120×115 mm. $5 As No. 705. (b) 115×120 mm. $5 As No. 710. (c) 115×120 mm. $5 As No. 712. (d) 115×120 mm. $5 As No. 715. (e) 120×115 mm. $5 As No. 719. (f) 120×115 mm. $5 As No. 720. (g) 120×115 mm. $5 As No. 724. (h) 120×115 mm. $5 As No. 726. (i) 120×115 mm. $5 As No. 730 .. *Set of* 9 *sheets* 24·00 26·00

Designs:—No. 705, Lady Elizabeth Bowes-Lyon with brother; No. 706, Young Lady Elizabeth in long dress; No. 707, Young Lady Elizabeth wearing a hat; No. 708, Lady Elizabeth leaning on wall; No. 709, Lady Elizabeth on pony; No. 710, Studio Portrait; No. 711, Lady Elizabeth in evening dress; No. 712, Duchess of York in fur-lined cloak; No. 713, Duchess of York holding rose; No. 714, Coronation, 1937; No. 715, King and Queen with Princess Elizabeth at Royal Lodge, Windsor; No. 716, Queen Elizabeth in blue hat; No. 717, King George VI and Queen Elizabeth; No. 718, Queen Elizabeth with Princess Elizabeth; No. 719, Queen Elizabeth watching sporting fixture; No. 720, Queen Elizabeth in white evening dress; No. 721, Princess Anne's christening, 1950; No. 722, Queen Mother with yellow bouquet; No. 723, Queen Mother and policewoman; No. 724, Queen Mother at ceremonial function; No. 725, Queen Mother in pink coat; No. 726, Queen Mother in academic robes; No. 727, Queen Mother in carriage with Princess Margaret; No. 728, Queen Mother in blue coat and hat; No. 729, Queen Mother with bouquet; No. 730, Queen Mother outside Clarence House on her birthday; No. 731, Queen Mother in turquoise coat and hat.

Nos. 705/13, 714/22 and 723/31 were printed, *se-tenant*, in sheetlets of nine.

(Litho Walsall)

1991 (11 June). *Death Centenary of Vincent van Gogh (artist) (1990). Multicoloured designs as T* **255** *of Maldive Islands. P* 13½.

733 5 c. "View of Arles with Irises" (*horiz*) .. 20 20
734 10 c. "Saintes-Maries" 20 20
735 15 c. "Old Woman of Arles" 25 25
736 20 c. "Orchard in Blossom, bordered by Cypresses" (*horiz*) 30 30
737 25 c. "Three White Cottages in Saintes-Maries" (*horiz*) 30 30
738 35 c. "Boats at Saintes-Maries" (*horiz*) .. 40 40
739 40 c. "Interior of a Restaurant in Arles" (*horiz*) 45 45
740 45 c. "Peasant Women" 50 50
741 55 c. "Self-portrait" 60 60
742 60 c. "Pork Butcher's Shop from a Window" 70 70
743 75 c. "The Night Cafe in Arles" (*horiz*) .. 80 80
744 $1 "2nd Lieut. Millet of the Zouaves" (*horiz*) 95 95
745 $2 "The Café Terrace, Place du Forum, Arles at Night" .. .. .. 1·50 1·50
746 $3 "The Zouave" .. .. 2·00 2·00
747 $4 "The Two Lovers" (detail) .. .. 2·75 2·75
748 $5 "Still Life" (*horiz*) .. .. .. 3·00 3·00
733/48 .. .. *Set of* 16 13·50 13·50
MS749 Four sheets, each 112×76 mm. (a) $5 "Street in Saintes-Maries" (*horiz*). (b) $5 "Lane near Arles" (*horiz*). (c) $6 "Harvest at La Crau, with Montmajour in the Background" (*horiz*). (d) $6 "The Sower". Imperf. .. .. *Set of* 4 *sheets* 13·00 14·00

(Des D. Miller. Litho Walsall)

1991 (5 July). *65th Birthday of Queen Elizabeth II. Horiz designs as T* **210** *of Lesotho. Multicoloured. P* 14.

750 15 c. Inspecting the Yeomen of the Guard .. 25 20
751 40 c. Queen Elizabeth II with the Queen Mother at the Derby, 1988 .. .. 40 30
752 $2 The Queen and Prince Philip leaving Euston, 1986 .. .. 1·75 2·00
753 $4 The Queen at the Commonwealth Institute, 1987 .. .. .. 2·50 3·00
750/3 .. .. *Set of* 4 4·50 5·00
MS754 68×90 mm. $5 Queen Elizabeth and Prince Philip with Prince Andrew in naval uniform .. .. 3·25 3·75

(Des D. Miller. Litho Walsall)

1991 (5 July). *10th Wedding Anniv of Prince and Princess of Wales. Horiz designs as T* **210** *of Lesotho. Multicoloured. P* 14.

755 10 c. Prince and Princess at polo match, 1987 .. .. 25 20
756 50 c. Separate family portraits 55 40
757 $1 Prince William and Prince Henry at Kensington Palace, 1991 .. .. 90 90
758 $5 Portraits of Prince Charles and Princess Diana .. .. .. 3·25 3·75
755/8 .. .. *Set of* 4 4·50 4·75
MS759 68×90 mm. $5 Separate portraits of Prince and Princess and sons .. .. .. 3·75 4·00

76 First Japanese Steam Locomotive and Map

(Des K. Gromell. Litho Cartor)

1991 (12 Aug). *"Phila Nippon '91" International Stamp Exhibition, Tokyo. Japanese Railway Locomotives. T* **76** *and similar designs, each in black, scarlet-vermilion and dull blue-green. P* 14×13½.

760 10 c. Type **76** 40 40
761 25 c. First imported American steam locomotive 55 55
762 35 c. Class "8620" steam locomotive .. 70 70
763 50 c. Class "C53" steam locomotive .. 90 90
764 $1 Class "DD-51" diesel locomotive .. 1·50 1·50
765 $2 Class "KTR001 Tango Explorer" electric rail car (inscr "RF22327") 2·00 2·00
766 $4 Class "EF55" electric locomotive .. 2·75 2·75
767 $5 Class "EF58" electric locomotive .. 3·00 3·00
760/7 .. .. *Set of* 8 10·50 10·50
MS768 Four sheets, each 114×73 mm showing frontal views. (a) $6 Class "9600" steam locomotive (*vert*). (b) $6 Class "C57" steam locomotive (*vert*). (c) $6 Class "C62" steam locomotive (*vert*). (d) $6 Class "4100" steam locomotive (*vert*) .. .. *Set of* 4 *sheets* 14·00 15·00

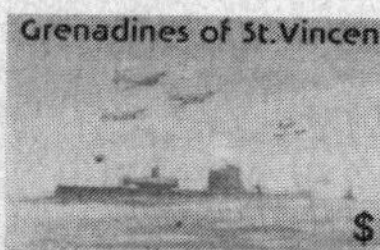

77 President Gorbachev and Brandenburg Gate

78 Japanese Aircraft and Submarines leaving Truk

(Des L. Fried (Nos. 769, 771/2, **MS**783a/b), J. Iskowitz (Nos. 773, 781, **MS**783e/f), W. Hanson (Nos. 777, 782, **MS**783h/i), W. Wright (Nos. 774/6, 778/80, **MS**783g, j/k). Litho Questa)

1991 (18 Nov). *Anniversaries and Events. T* **77** *and similar designs. Rose-lilac, yellow-green and black (No.* **MS**781k) *or multicoloured (others). P* 14.

769 45 c. Type **77** 40 40
770 60 c. General De Gaulle in Djibouti, 1959 55 55
771 65 c. "DIE MAUER MUSS WEG!" slogan 65 65
772 80 c. East German border guard escaping to West 80 80
773 $1 *Abduction from the Seraglio* .. .. 1·25 1·25
774 $1.50, Lilienthal and glider .. .. 1·60 1·60
775 $1.75, Trans-Siberian logo .. .. 1·60 1·60
776 $1.75, Trans-Siberian steam locomotive (*vert*) .. .. 1·60 1·60
777 $2 Czechoslovakia 1918 20 h. stamp and scout delivering mail .. .. 1·90 1·90
778 $2 Zurich couple maypole dancing .. 1·90 1·90
779 $2 Man and woman in Vaud traditional costumes .. .. 1·90 1·90
780 $2 Georg Laves (architect) and Hoftheater 1·90 1·90
781 $3 Dresden, 1749 .. .. .. 2·00 2·00
782 $4 Scouts and cog train on Snowdon (*vert*) 2·50 2·50
769/82 .. .. *Set of* 14 18·00 18·00
MS783 Eleven sheets. (a) 100×71 mm. $5 Arms of Berlin. (b) 100×71 mm. $5 Berlin police badge. (c) 77×112 mm. $5 De Gaulle in civilian dress. (d) 69×101 mm. $5 General Charles de Gaulle (*vert*). (e) 75×101 mm. $5 Portrait of Mozart (*vert*). (f) 75×101 mm. $5 Bust of Mozart (*vert*). (g) 115×85 mm. $5 Trans-Siberian express leaving Moscow at night (43×56 *mm*). (h) 118×89 mm. $5 Jamboree emblem (buff background) (*vert*). (i) 118×89 mm. $5 Jamboree emblem (bluish violet background) (*vert*). (j) 101×72 mm. $5 Arms of Appenzell and Thurgau. (k) 101×72 mm. $5 Old Hanover *Set of* 11 *sheets* 27·00 28·00

Anniversaries and Events:—Nos. 769, 771/2, **MS**783a/b, Bicentenary of Brandenburg Gate; Nos. 770, **MS**783c/d, Birth centenary of Charles de Gaulle (French statesman); Nos. 773, 781, **MS**783e/f, Death bicentenary of Mozart; No. 774 Centenary of Otto Lilienthal's gliding experiments; Nos. 775/6, **MS**783g, Centenary of Trans-Siberian Railway; Nos. 777, 782, **MS**783h/i, 50th death anniv of Lord Baden-Powell and World Scout Jamboree, Korea; Nos. 778/9, **MS**783j, 700th anniv of Swiss Confederation; Nos. 780, **MS**783k, 750th anniv of Hanover.

(Des J. Batchelor. Litho Questa)

1991 (18 Nov). *50th Anniv of Japanese Attack on Pearl Harbor. T* **78** *and similar horiz designs. Multicoloured. P* 14½×15.

784 $1 Type **78** .. .. 1·10 1·10
a. Sheetlet. Nos. 784/93 .. .. .. 10·00
785 $1 *Akagi* (Japanese aircraft carrier) .. 1·10 1·10
786 $1 Nakajima B5N2 "Kate" aircraft .. 1·10 1·10
787 $1 Nakajima B5N2 "Kate" bombers attacking Battleship Row .. .. 1·10 1·10
788 $1 Burning aircraft, Ford Island airfield .. 1·10 1·10
789 $1 Doris Miller winning Navy Cross .. 1·10 1·10
790 $1 U.S.S. *West Virginia* and *Tennessee* (battleships) ablaze .. .. 1·10 1·10
791 $1 U.S.S. *Arizona* (battleship) sinking .. 1·10 1·10
792 $1 U.S.S. *New Orleans* (cruiser) .. .. 1·10 1·10
793 $1 President Roosevelt declaring war .. 1·10 1·10
784/93 .. .. *Set of* 10 10·00 10·00

Nos. 784/93 were printed together, *se-tenant*, in sheetlets of 10 with the stamps arranged in two horizontal rows of 5 separated by a map of Pearl Harbor.

(Des Walt Disney Co. Litho Questa)

1991 (23 Dec). *Christmas. Walt Disney Company Christmas Cards. Multicoloured designs as T* **228** *of St. Vincent. P* 14×13½.

794 10 c. Pluto pulling Mickey Mouse in sledge, 1974 (*horiz*) 25 20
795 55 c. Mickey, Pluto and Donald Duck watching toy band, 1961 (*horiz*) .. 70 60
796 65 c. "The Same Old Wish", 1942 (*horiz*) .. 75 75
797 75 c. Mickey, Peter Pan, Donald Duck and Nephews with Merlin the magician, 1963 (*horiz*) 85 85
798 $1.50, Mickey, Donald and leprechauns, 1958 (*horiz*) .. .. 1·50 1·75
799 $2 Mickey and friends with book *Old Yeller*, 1957 (*horiz*) .. .. .. 1·75 2·00
800 $4 Mickey controlling Pinocchio, 1953 (*horiz*) .. .. 3·00 3·25
801 $5 Cinderella and Prince dancing, 1987 (*horiz*) .. .. 3·00 3·25
794/801 .. .. *Set of* 8 10·50 11·50
MS802 Two sheets, each 128×102 mm. (a) $6 Santa Claus and American bomber, 1942. (b) $6 Snow White, 1957. P 13½×14 .. *Set of* 2 *sheets* 10·50 11·50

(Des D. Miller. Litho Questa)

1992 (2 Mar). *40th Anniv of Queen Elizabeth II's Accession. Horiz designs as T* **214** *of Lesotho. Multicoloured. P* 14.

803 15 c. View across bay 20 15
804 45 c. Schooner at anchor, Mayreau .. 45 25
805 $2 Hotel on hillside .. .. .. 1·25 1·50
806 $4 Tourist craft at anchor .. .. 2·50 3·00
803/6 .. .. *Set of* 4 4·00 4·50
MS807 Two sheets, each 74×97 mm. (a) $6 Beach and palms. (b) $6 Aerial view of hotel by beach .. .. .. *Set of* 2 *sheets* 5·50 6·25

(Des Walt Disney Co. Litho Questa)

1992 (28 Apr). *International Stamp Exhibitions. Multicoloured designs as T* **215** *of Lesotho, showing Walt Disney cartoon characters. P* 14×13½.

(*a*) *"Granada '92", Spain. Spanish Explorers*

808 15 c. Big Pete as Hernando Cortes in Mexico (*horiz*) 20 15
809 40 c. Mickey Mouse as Hernando de Soto at Mississippi River (*horiz*) 40 30
810 $2 Goofy as Vasco Nunez de Balboa sights Pacific (*horiz*) .. .. .. 1·50 1·50
811 $4 Donald Duck as Francisco Coronado on Rio Grande (*horiz*) .. .. .. 2·50 2·75
808/11 .. .. *Set of* 4 4·25 4·25
MS812 127×102 mm. $6 Mickey as Ponce de Leon. P 13½×14 .. .. .. 3·50 4·00

(*b*) *"World Columbian Stamp Expo '92", Chicago, Local Personalities*

813 10 c. Mickey Mouse and Pluto outside Walt Disney's birthplace (*horiz*) 20 20
814 50 c. Donald Duck and nephews in George Pullman's railway sleeping car (*horiz*) 55 55
815 $1 Daisy Duck as Jane Addams (social reformer) and Hull House (*horiz*) .. 85 85
816 $5 Mickey as Carl Sandburg (novelist, poet and historian) (*horiz*) .. .. 3·00 3·00
813/16 .. .. *Set of* 4 4·25 4·25
MS817 127×102 mm. $6 Daisy as Mrs O'Leary with her cow (source of Chicago fire of 1871). P 13½×14 .. .. 3·50 4·00

79 King Ferdinand and Queen Isabella of Spain

(Des W. Wright. Litho Questa)

1992 (22 May). *500th Anniv of Discovery of America by Columbus (2nd issue). T* **79** *and similar multicoloured designs. P* 14.

818 10 c. Type **79** 25 25
819 45 c. *Santa Maria* and *Nina* in Acul Bay, Haiti 50 50
820 55 c. *Santa Maria* (*vert*) 55 55
821 $2 Ships of Columbus (*vert*) .. .. 1·40 1·40
822 $4 Wreck of *Santa Maria* .. .. 2·50 2·50
823 $5 *Pinta* and *Nina* .. .. .. 2·75 2·75
818/23 .. .. *Set of* 6 7·25 7·25
MS824 Two sheets, each 114×85 mm. (a) $6 Columbus landing on San Salvador. (b) $6 *Santa Maria* in storm .. .. .. *Set of* 2 *sheets* 7·00 8·00

(Des J. Barberis. Litho Questa)

1992 (15 June). *"Genova '92" International Thematic Stamp Exhibition (1st issue). Butterflies. Multicoloured designs as T* **235** *of St. Vincent. P* 14.

825 15 c. *Paulogramma* sp (*horiz*) 50 50
826 20 c. *Heliconius cydno* (*horiz*) 50 50
827 30 c. *Eutresis hypereia* (*horiz*) 60 60
828 45 c. *Eurytides columbus* 70 70
829 55 c. *Papilio ascolius* (*horiz*) 80 80
830 75 c. *Anaea pasibula* (*horiz*) 90 90
831 80 c. *Heliconius doris* (*horiz*) 90 90
832 $1 *Perisama pitheas* (*horiz*) 95 95
833 $2 *Batesia hypochlora* (*horiz*) .. .. 1·50 1·50
834 $3 *Heliconius erato* (*horiz*) .. .. 1·90 1·90
835 $4 *Elzunia cassandrina* (*horiz*) .. .. 2·25 2·25
836 $5 *Sais ivcidice* (*horiz*) .. .. .. 2·40 2·40
825/36 .. .. *Set of* 12 12·50 12·50
MS837 Three sheets, each 109×79 mm. (a) $6 *Oleria tigilla* (*horiz*). (b) $6 *Dismorphia orise* (*horiz*). (c) $6 *Podotricha telesiphe* (*horiz*) *Set of* 3 *sheets* 11·00 12·00

See also Nos. 851/63.

(Des R. Sauber. Litho Questa)

1992 (2 July). *Fungi. Vert designs as T* **236** *of St. Vincent. Multicoloured. P* 14.

838 10 c. *Entoloma bakeri* 30 30
839 15 c. *Hydropus paraensis* 35 35
840 20 c. *Leucopaxillus gracillimus* 40 40
841 45 c. *Hygrotrama dennisianum* 50 50
842 50 c. *Leucoagaricus hortensis* 60 60
843 65 c. *Pyrrhoglossum pyrrhum* 70 70
844 75 c. *Amanita craeoderma* 80 80
845 $1 *Lentinus bertieri* .. .. .. 1·00 1·00
846 $2 *Dennisiomyces griseus* .. .. 1·60 1·60
847 $3 *Xerulina asprata* .. .. .. 2·00 2·00
848 $4 *Hygrocybe acutoconica* .. .. 2·75 2·75
849 $5 *Lepiota spiculata* .. .. .. 3·00 3·00
838/49 .. .. *Set of* 12 12·50 12·50
MS850 Three sheets, each 101×68 mm. (a) $6 *Pluteus crysophlebius*. (b) $6 *Amanita lilloi*. (c) $6 *Lepiota volvatua* .. .. *Set of* 3 *sheets* 12·00 13·00

(Des Susan Carlson. Litho Questa)

1992 (2 July). *"Genova '92" International Thematic Stamp Exhibition (2nd issue). Hummingbirds. Multicoloured designs as T* **237** *of St. Vincent. P* 14.

851 5 c. Antillean Crested Hummingbird (female) (*horiz*) 30 30
852 10 c. Blue-tailed Emerald (female) 30 30
853 35 c. Antillean Mango (male) (*horiz*) .. 45 45
854 45 c. Antillean Mango (female) (*horiz*) .. 45 45
855 55 c. Green-throated Carib (*horiz*) 55 55
856 65 c. Green Violetear (male) 70 70
857 75 c. Blue-tailed Emerald (male) (*horiz*) .. 80 80
858 $1 Purple-throated Carib .. .. 1·00 1·00
859 $2 Copper-rumped Hummingbird (*horiz*) 2·00 2·00
860 $3 Rufous-breasted Hermit .. .. 2·75 2·75
861 $4 Antillean Crested Hummingbird (male) 3·50 3·50
862 $5 Green-breasted Mango (male) .. 3·75 3·75
851/62 .. .. *Set of* 12 15·00 15·00
MS863 Three sheets, each 105×74 mm. (a) $6 Blue-tailed Emerald. (b) $6 Antillean Mango. (c) $6 Antillean Crested Hummingbird *Set of* 3 *sheets* 13·00 14·00

(Des F. Paul ($1), J. Esquino ($2). Litho Questa)

1992 (24 Aug). *500th Anniv of Discovery of America by Columbus (3rd issue). Organization of East Caribbean States. Vert designs as Nos. 911/12 of Montserrat. Multicoloured. P* 14½.

864 $1 Columbus meeting Amerindians .. 60 70
865 $2 Ships approaching island .. .. 1·25 1·75

(Litho Questa)

1992 (14 Sept). *Olympic Games, Albertville and Barcelona. Multicoloured designs as T* **216** *of Lesotho. P* 14.

866 10 c. Men's volleyball 25 25
867 15 c. Men's gymnastics (*horiz*) 35 35
868 25 c. Men's cross-country skiing 45 45
869 30 c. Men's 110 metres hurdles (*horiz*) .. 50 50
870 45 c. Men's 120 metre ski-jump (*horiz*) .. 60 60
871 55 c. Women's 4×100 metre relay .. 65 65
872 75 c. Men's triple jump 80 80
873 80 c. Men's mogul skiing 80 80
874 $1 Men's 110 metre butterfly swimming (*horiz*) 95 95
875 $2 "Tornado" Class yachting (*horiz*) .. 1·60 1·60
876 $3 Men's decathlon (*horiz*) .. .. 1·90 1·90
877 $5 Show jumping (*horiz*) .. .. 2·75 2·75
866/77 .. .. *Set of* 12 10·50 10·50
MS878 Three sheets, each 101×70 mm. (a) $6 Ice hockey (*horiz*). (b) $6 Men's single luge (*horiz*). (c) $6 Football .. .. .. *Set of* 3 *sheets* 14·00 14·00

(Litho Questa)

1992 (16 Nov). *Christmas. Religious Paintings. Vert designs as T* **218** *of Lesotho. Multicoloured. P* 13½×14.

879 10 c. "Our Lady with St. Roch and St. Anthony of Padua" (Giorgione) .. 30 30
880 40 c. "Anthony of Padua" (Master of the Embroidered Leaf) 55 55
881 45 c. "Madonna and Child" (detail) (Orazio Gentileschi) 60 60
882 50 c. "Madonna and Child with St. Anne" (detail) (Da Vinci) 65 65
883 55 c. "The Holy Family" (Crespi) 70 70
884 65 c. "Madonna and Child" (Del Sarto) .. 80 80
885 75 c. "Madonna and Child with Sts. Lawrence and Julian" (Gentile da Fabriano) 90 90
886 $1 "Virgin and Child" (detail) (School of Parma) .. .. 1·10 1·10
887 $2 "Madonna with the Iris" (detail) (style of Dürer) .. .. 1·75 1·75

888 $3 "Virgin and Child with St. Jerome and St. Dominic" (Lippi) .. .. .. 2·25 2·25
889 $4 "Rapolano Madonna" (Ambrogio Lorenzetti) .. .. 2·75 2·75
890 $5 "The Virgin and Child with Angels in a Garden with a Rose Hedge" (Stefano da Verona) .. .. 2·75 2·75
879/90 .. .. *Set of* 12 13·50 13·50
MS891 Three sheets, each 73×98 mm. (a) $6 "Madonna and Child with Grapes" (detail) (Cranach the Elder). (b) $6 "Virgin and Child with St. John the Baptist" (detail) (Botticelli). (c) $6 "Madonna and Child with St. Anne" (different detail) (Da Vinci) .. .. *Set of 3 sheets* 14·00 14·00

80 *Nina* in Baracoa Harbour

(Des W. Wright (Nos. 892/3, 896, 902, **MS**906a/c), W. Wright and L. Fried (Nos. 900, **MS**906f), J. Genzo (Nos. 904, **MS**906g). Litho Questa)

1992 (15 Dec). *Anniversaries and Events.* T **80** *and similar multicoloured designs. P* 14.

892 10 c. Type **80** 40 40
893 75 c. Zeppelin LZ-3 .. .. .. 1·25 1·25
894 75 c. Blind man with guide dog (*vert*) .. 1·25 1·25
895 75 c. Training guide dog .. .. .. 1·25 1·25
896 $1 Ships of Columbus 90 90
897 $1 Adenauer, state arms and German flag 1·25 1·25
898 $1 *America III* and *Il Moro* (yachts) with trophy .. .. 1·25 1·25
899 $1 Hands breaking bread and emblem (*vert*) .. .. 1·25 1·25
900 $2 "Voyager 2" and planet .. .. 2·00 2·00
901 $3 Adenauer and children watching Berlin Airlift .. .. .. 2·00 2·00
902 $4 Airship LZ-37 in flames .. .. 2·75 2·75
903 $4 Adenauer and ruins in Cologne .. 2·75 2·75
904 $4 Mozart with his wife Constanze (*vert*) 2·75 2·75
905 $5 Adenauer and modern office blocks 2·75 2·75
892/905 .. .. *Set of* 14 21·00 21·00
MS906 Seven sheets. (a) 100×70 mm. $6 Columbus sighting land. (b) 100×70 mm. $6 Count von Zeppelin facing left. (c) 110×70 mm. $6 Count von Zeppelin facing right. (d) 100×70 mm. $6 Konrad Adenauer (*vert*). (e) 100×70 mm. $6 Konrad Adenauer. (f) 100×70 mm. $6 "Mars Observer" spacecraft. (g) 100×70 mm. $6 Costume for "Don Giovanni" by Cassandre *Set of 7 sheets* 26·00 28·00

Anniversaries and Events:—Nos. 892, 896, **MS**906a, 500th anniv of discovery of America by Columbus; Nos. 893, 902, **MS**906b/c, 75th death anniv of Count Ferdinand von Zeppelin (airship pioneer); Nos. 894/5, 75th anniv of International Association of Lions Clubs; Nos. 897, 901, 903, 905, **MS**906d/e, 25th death anniv of Konrad Adenauer (German statesman); No. 898, Americas Cup yachting championship; No. 899, International Conference on Nutrition, Rome; Nos. 900, **MS**906f, International Space Year; Nos. 904, **MS**906g, Death bicentenary of Mozart.

81 Olivia and Flaversham

(Des Walt Disney Co. Litho Questa)

1992 (15 Dec). *Walt Disney Cartoon Films.* T **81** *and similar designs. P* 14×13½ (*horiz*) *or* 13½×14 (*vert*).

907/50 60 c.×44 multicoloured .. *Set of* 44 16·00 18·00
MS951 Ten sheets, each 127×103 mm. $6×10 multicoloured. P 14×13½ (*horiz*) or 13½×14 (*vert*) .. .. *Set of* 10 *sheets* 35·00 38·00

Nos. 907/50 were printed as five *se-tenant* sheetlets, each of nine different designs except for that for *Darkwing Duck* which contains eight vertical designs (Nos. 943/50). The other four sheetlets depict scenes from *The Great Mouse Detective, Oliver and Company, The Legend of Sleepy Hollow* and *Ducktales the Movie*.

No. **MS**951 contains two sheets for each film. On one sheet in the pairs for *The Legend of Sleepy Hollow, Ducktales the Movie* and *Darkwing Duck* the stamp design is vertical.

(Des A. Nahigian. Litho Walsall)

1992 (15 Dec). *15th Death Anniv of Elvis Presley (singer). Vert designs as Nos.* 1768/70 *of Maldive Islands. Multicoloured. P* 14.

952 $1 Elvis Presley .. .. 1·50 1·50
a. Strip of 3. Nos. 952/4 .. .. .. 4·00
953 $1 Elvis with guitar .. .. .. 1·50 1·50
954 $1 Elvis with microphone .. .. 1·50 1·50
952/4 .. .. *Set of* 3 4·00 4·00

Nos. 952/4 were printed together, horizontally and vertically *se-tenant*, in sheetlets of 9 (3×3).

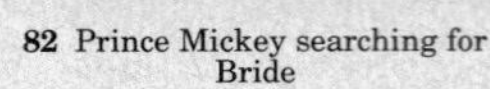

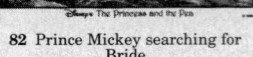

82 Prince Mickey searching for Bride

83 Oleander

(Des Walt Disney Co. Litho Questa)

1992 (15 Dec). *Tales of Uncle Scrooge (fairy stories).* T **82** *and similar designs showing Walt Disney cartoon characters. P* 14×13½.

955/1008 60 c.×54 multicoloured .. *Set of* 54 18·00 20·00
MS1009 Twelve sheets, each 128×102 mm or 102×128 mm. $6×12 multicoloured. P 14×13½ (*horiz*) or 13½×14 (*vert*) .. *Set of* 12 *sheets* 40·00 45·00

Nos. 955/1008 (issued as six sheetlets, each of nine different designs) depict scenes from "The Princess and the Pea", "Little Red Riding Hood", "Goldilocks and the Three Bears", "The Pied Piper of Hamelin", "Hop O'-My-Thumb" and "Puss in Boots".

No. **MS**1009 contains two sheets for each story, all being horizontal with the exception of the second sheet for "Puss in Boots". Of the stamp designs in these miniature sheets the two for "Little Red Riding Hood" and one of each for "Goldilocks and the Three Bears", "The Pied Piper of Hamelin" and "Puss in Boots" are vertical.

(Litho China Security Ptg Ltd, Hong Kong)

1994 (20 May). *Medicinal Plants.* T **83** *and similar vert designs. Multicoloured. P* 13½×13.

1010 5 c. Type **83** 10 10
1011 10 c. Beach Morning Glory 10 10
1012 30 c. Calabash 15 20
1013 45 c. Portia Tree 20 25
1014 55 c. Cashew 25 30
1015 75 c. Prickly Pear 35 40
1016 $1 Shell Ginger 45 50
1017 $1.50, Avocado Pear 70 75
1018 $2 Mango 90 95
1019 $3 Blood Flower .. .. .. 1·40 1·50
1020 $4 Sugar Apple .. .. .. 1·90 2·00
1021 $5 Barbados Lily .. .. .. 2·25 2·40
1010/21 .. .. *Set of* 12 8·75 9·25

STAMP BOOKLETS

1976 (26 Sept). *Tourism. Multicoloured covers,* 152×75 *mm, showing maps of seven different islands. Stapled.*

SB1 $2.50, booklet containing four different *se-tenant* panes of 3 stamps and 1 label (Nos. 85a/b, 86a, 87a) .. .. 1·75
Set of 7 booklets showing different islands 12·00

1978 (20 July). *25th Anniv of Coronation. Multicoloured cover as No.* SB3 *of Montserrat. Stapled.*

SB2 $8.90, booklet containing 5 c., 40 c., $1 and $3 (Nos. 130/3) in pairs .. .. 1·25

1979 (31 May). *Death Centenary of Sir Rowland Hill. Black, gold and red printed cover,* 108×32 *mm. Stapled.*

SB3 $7.60, booklet containing two 80 c. (Nos. 124, 152), two $1 (Nos. 125, 153) and two $2 (Nos. 126, 154), each value as a *se-tenant* pair taken from No. **MS**155 .. .. 1·50

1980 (24 Apr). *"London 1980" International Stamp Exhibition. Black printed cover,* 110×60 *mm. Stapled.*

SB4 $15.60, booklet containing 40 c., 50 c. and $3 (Nos. 167/9), each in block of 4 .. .. 2·25

1981 (26 Nov). *Royal Wedding. Multicoloured cover,* 105×65 *mm, showing* The Mary. *Stitched.*

SB5 $10 booklet containing eight 50 c. in panes of 4 (No. 202a) and two $3 in pane of 2 (No. 203a) 2·40

1986 (18 July). *Royal Wedding. Gold* (*No.* SB6) *or silver* (*No.* SB7) *on emerald covers,* 152×80 *mm. Stapled.*

SB6 $7.20, booklet (Westminster Abbey) containing twelve 60 c. (Nos. 481/2) in blocks of 4 .. 2·50
SB7 $10.40, booklet (State Coach) containing 60 c. and $2 (Nos. 481/4, but imperforate) in blocks of 4 3·50

OFFICIAL STAMPS

1982 (11 Oct). *Nos.* 195/200 *optd with Type* O 1 *of St. Vincent.*

O1 50 c. *Mary* 10 15
a. Sheetlet. No. O1 × 6 and No. O2 .. 75
b. Opt double .. ..
c. Albino opt .. .. 3·00
d. Horiz pair, one without opt ..
O2 50 c. Prince Charles and Lady Diana Spencer 30 35
b. Opt double .. ..
c. Albino opt .. .. 7·50
O3 $3 *Alexandra* 25 30
a. Sheetlet. No. O3 × 6 and No. O4 .. 1·90
b. Opt double .. .. 32·00
c. Albino opt .. .. 5·00
O4 $3 Prince Charles and Lady Diana Spencer 65 70
b. Opt double £130
c. Albino opt .. .. 18·00
O5 $3.50, *Britannia* 30 35
a. Sheetlet. No. O5 × 6 and No. O6 .. 2·40
c. Albino opt .. .. 6·00
O6 $3.50, Prince Charles and Lady Diana Spencer 80 90
c. Albino opt .. .. 20·00
O1/6 .. .. *Set of* 6 2·10 2·50

Appendix

The following issues for individual islands in the Grenadines group fall outside the criteria for full listing as detailed on page xi of the General Catalogue Information in this edition.

BEQUIA

1984

Leaders of the World. Railway Locomotives (*1st series*). *Two designs for each value, the first showing technical drawings and the second the locomotive at work.* 1, 5, 10, 25, 35, 45 c., $1.50, $2, *each* × 2

Grenadines of St. Vincent 1982 Ships definitives (Nos. 208/24) optd "BEQUIA". 1, 3, 5, 6, 10, 15, 20, 25, 30, 50, 60, 75 c., $1, $2, $3, $5, $10

Leaders of the World. Automobiles (*1st series*). *Two designs for each value, the first showing technical drawings and the second the car in action.* 5, 40 c., $1, $1.50, *each* × 2

Leaders of the World. Olympic Games, Los Angeles. 1, 10, 60 c., $3, *each* × 2

Leaders of the World. Railway Locomotives (*2nd series*). *Two designs for each value, the first showing technical drawings and the second the locomotive at work.* 1, 5, 10, 35, 75 c., $1, $2.50, $3, *each* × 2

Leaders of the World. Automobiles (*2nd series*). *Two designs for each value, the first showing technical drawings and the second the car in action.* 5, 10, 20, 25, 75 c., $1, $2.50, $3, *each* × 2

1985

Leaders of the World. Railway Locomotives (*3rd series*). *Two designs for each value, the first showing technical drawings and the second the locomotive at work.* 25, 55, 60 c., $2, *each* × 2

Leaders of the World. Dogs. 25, 35, 55 c., $2, *each* × 2

Leaders of the World, Warships of the Second World War. Two designs for each value, the first showing technical drawings and the second the ship at sea. 15, 50 c., $1, $1.50, *each* × 2

Leaders of the World. Flowers. 10, 20, 70 c., $2.50, *each* × 2

Leaders of the World. Automobiles (*3rd series*). *Two designs for each value, the first showing technical drawings and the second the car in action.* 5, 25, 50 c., $1, $1.25, $2, *each* × 2

Leaders of the World. Railway Locomotives (*4th series*). *Two designs for each value, the first showing technical drawings and the second the locomotive at work.* 25, 55, 60, 75 c., $1, $2.50, *each* × 2

Leaders of the World. Life and Times of Queen Elizabeth the Queen Mother. Two designs for each value, showing different portraits. 20, 65 c., $1.35, $1.80, *each* × 2
Leaders of the World. Automobiles (4th series). Two designs for each value, the first showing technical drawings and the second the car in action. 20, 45 c., $1.50, $2, *each* × 2

1986

Leaders of the World. Automobiles (5th series). Two designs for each value, the first showing technical drawings and the second the car in action. 25, 50, 65, 75 c., $1, $3, *each* × 2
60th Birthday of Queen Elizabeth II. 5, 75 c., $2, $8
World Cup Football Championship, Mexico. 1, 2, 5, 10, 45, 60, 75 c., $1.50, $1.50, $2, $3.50, $6
Royal Wedding (1st issue). 60 c., $2, *each* × 2
Railway Engineers and Locomotives. $1, $2.50, $3, $4
Royal Wedding (2nd issue). Previous issue optd "Congratulations T.R.H. The Duke & Duchess of York". 60 c., $2, *each* × 2.
Automobiles (6th series). Two designs for each value, the first showing technical drawings and the second the car in action. 20, 60, 75, 90 c., $1, $3, *each* × 2

1987

Automobiles (7th series). Two designs for each value, the first showing technical drawings and the second the car in action. 5, 20, 35, 60, 75, 80 c., $1.25, $1.75, *each* × 2
Royal Ruby Wedding. 15, 75 c., $1, $2.50, $5
Railway Locomotives (5th series). Two designs for each value, the first showing technical drawings and the second the locomotive at work. 15, 25, 40, 50, 60, 75 c., $1, $2, *each* × 2

1988

Explorers. 15, 50 c., $1.75, $2, $2.50, $3, $3.50, $4
International Lawn Tennis Players. 15, 45, 80 c., $1.25, $1.75, $2, $2.50, $3

1989

"Philexfrance 89" International Stamp Exhibition, Paris. Walt Disney Cartoon Characters. 1, 2, 3, 4, 5, 10 c., $5, $6

1991

Centenary of Otto Lilienthal's Gliding Experiments. $5
50th Anniv of Japanese Attack on Pearl Harbor. 50 c., $1
Death Bicent of Mozart 10, 75 c., $4
50th Death Anniv of Lord Baden-Powell and World Scout Jamboree, Korea. 50 c, $1, $2, $3

1997

Diana, Princess of Wales Commemoration. $1

CANOUAN

1997

Diana, Princess of Wales Commemoration. $1

MUSTIQUE

1997

Diana, Princess of Wales Commemoration. $1

UNION ISLAND

1984

Leaders of the World. British Monarchs. Two designs for each value, forming a composite picture. 1, 5, 10, 20, 60 c., $3, *each* × 2
Leaders of the World. Railway Locomotives (1st series). Two designs for each value, the first showing technical drawings and the second the locomotive at work. 5, 60 c., $1, $2
Grenadines of St. Vincent 1982 Ships definitives (Nos. 208/24) optd "UNION ISLAND". 1, 3, 5, 6, 10, 15, 20, 25, 30, 50, 60, 75 c., $1, $2, $3, $5, $10
Leaders of the World. Cricketers. Two designs for each value, the first showing a portrait and the second the cricketer in action. 1, 10, 15, 55, 60, 75 c., $1.50, $3, *each* × 2
Leaders of the World. Railway Locomotives (2nd series). Two designs for each value, the first showing technical drawings and the second the locomotive at work. 5, 10, 20, 25, 75 c., $1, $2.50, $3, *each* × 2

1985

Leaders of the World. Automobiles (1st series). Two designs for each value, the first showing technical drawings and the second the car in action. 1, 50, 75 c., $2.50, *each* × 2
Leaders of the World. Birth Bicent of John J. Audubon (ornithologist). Birds. 15, 50 c., $1, $1.50, *each* × 2
Leaders of the World. Railway Locomotives (3rd series). Two designs for each value, the first showing technical drawings and the second the locomotive at work. 5, 50, 60 c., $2, *each* × 2
Leaders of the World. Butterflies. 15, 25, 75 c., $2, *each* × 2
Leaders of the World. Automobiles (2nd series). Two designs for each value, the first showing technical drawings and the second the car in action. 5, 60 c., $1, $1.50, *each* × 2
Leaders of the World. Automobiles (3rd series). Two designs for each value, the first showing technical drawings and the second the car in action. 10, 55, 60, 75, 90 c., $1, $1.50, $2, *each* × 2
Leaders of the World. Life and Times of Queen Elizabeth the Queen Mother. Two designs for each value, showing different portraits. 55, 70 c., $1.05, $1.70, *each* × 2

1986

Leaders of the World. Railway Locomotives (4th series). Two designs for each value, the first showing technical drawings and the second the locomotive at work. 15, 30, 45, 60, 75 c., $1.50, $2.50, $3, *each* × 2
60th Birthday of Queen Elizabeth II. 10, 60 c., $2, $8
World Cup Football Championship, Mexico. 1, 10, 30, 75 c., $1, $2.50, $3, $6
Royal Wedding (1st issue). 60 c., $2, *each* × 2
Automobiles (4th series). Two designs for each value, the first showing technical drawings and the second the car in action. 10, 60, 75 c., $1, $1.50, $3, *each* × 2
Royal Wedding (2nd issue). Previous issue optd as Bequia. 60 c., $2, *each* × 2
Railway Locomotives (5th series). Two designs for each value, the first showing technical drawings and the second the locomotive at work. 15, 45, 60, 75 c., $1, $1.50, $2, $3, *each* × 2

1987

Railway Locomotives (6th series). Two designs for each value, the first showing technical drawings and the second the locomotive at work. 15, 25, 40, 50, 60, 75 c., $1, $2, *each* × 2
Royal Ruby Wedding. 15, 45 c., $1.50, $3, $4
Railway Locomotives (7th series). Two designs for each value, the first showing technical drawings and the second the locomotive at work. 15, 20, 30, 45, 50, 75 c., $1, $1.50, *each* × 2

1989

"Philexfrance 89" International Stamp Exhibition, Paris. Walt Disney Cartoon Characters. 1, 2, 3, 4, 5, 10 c., $5, $6

1997

Diana, Princess of Wales Commemoration. $1

Samoa

PRICES FOR STAMPS ON COVER TO 1945	
Nos. 1/20 are very rare used on cover.	
Nos. 21/40	*from* × 20
Nos. 41/8	*from* × 100
Nos. 49/56	*from* × 4
Nos. 57/64	*from* × 12
Nos. 65/8	*from* × 2
Nos. 69/97	*from* × 20
Nos. 101/9	*from* × 3
Nos. 110/14	—
Nos. 115/21	*from* × 3
Nos. 122/32	—
Nos. 134/64	*from* × 3
Nos. 165/76	—
Nos. 177/214	*from* × 2

INDEPENDENT KINGDOM OF SAMOA

The first postal service in Samoa was organised by C. L. Griffiths, who had earlier run the *Fiji Times* Express post in Suva. In both instances the principal purpose of the service was the distribution of newspapers of which Griffiths was the proprietor. The first issue of the *Samoa Times* (later the *Samoa Times and South Sea Gazette*) appeared on 6 October 1877 and the newspaper continued in weekly publication until 27 August 1881.

Mail from the Samoa Express post to addresses overseas was routed via New South Wales, New Zealand or U.S.A. and received additional franking with stamps of the receiving country on landing.

Cancellations, inscribed "APIA SAMOA", did not arrive until March 1878 so that examples of Nos. 1/9 used before that date were cancelled in manuscript.

1

A
2nd State (Nos. 4/9)

B
3rd State (Nos. 10/19)

(Des H. H. Glover. Litho S. T. Leigh & Co, Sydney, N.S.W.)

1877 (1 Oct)–**80.**

A. 1*st state: white line above* "X" *in* "EXPRESS" *not broken.* *P* 12½

1	**1**	1d. ultramarine	£250	£120
2		3d. deep scarlet	£275	£110
3		6d. bright violet	£275	£110
		a. Pale lilac	£300	£110

B. 2*nd state: white line above* "X" *broken by a spot of colour, and dot between top of* "M" *and* "O" *of* "SAMOA". *P* 12½ (1878–79)

4	**1**	1d. ultramarine	90·00	95·00
5		3d. bright scarlet	£275	£130
6		6d. bright violet	£170	90·00
7		1s. dull yellow	£150	90·00
		a. Line above "X" not broken	£180	£120
		b. Perf 12 (1879)	80·00	95·00
		c. Orange-yellow	95·00	£100
8		2s. red-brown	£275	£200
		a. Chocolate	£300	£350
9		5s. green	£800	£1000

C. 3*rd state: line above* "X" *repaired, dot merged with upper right serif of* "M" (1879). (*a*) *P* 12½

10	**1**	1d. ultramarine	90·00	90·00
11		3d. vermilion	£120	£120
12		6d. lilac	£120	85·00
13		2s. brown	£250	£250
		a. Chocolate	£250	£250
14		5s. green	£500	£500
		a. Line above "X" not repaired (R.2/3)	£650	

(*b*) *P* 12

15	**1**	1d. blue	24·00	40·00
		a. Deep blue	32·00	70·00
		b. Ultramarine	28·00	40·00
16		3d. vermilion	48·00	70·00
		a. Carmine-vermilion	48·00	80·00
17		6d. bright violet	40·00	48·00
		a. Deep violet	40·00	80·00
18		2s. deep brown	£150	£250
19		5s. yellow-green	£400	£600
		a. Deep green	£375	£550
		b. Line above "X" not repaired (R.2/3)	£500	

D. 4*th state: spot of colour under middle stroke of* "M". *P* 12 (1880)

20	**1**	9d. orange-brown	60·00	£120

Originals exist imperf, but are not known used in this state.

On sheets of the 1d., 1st state, at least eight stamps have a stop after "PENNY". In the 2nd state, three stamps have the stop, and in the 3rd state, only one.

In the 1st state, all the stamps, 1d., 3d. and 6d., were in sheets of 20 (5 × 4) and also the 1d. in the 3rd state.

All values in the 2nd state, all values except the 1d. in the 3rd state and No. 20 were in sheets of 10 (5 × 2).

As all sheets of all printings of the originals were imperf at the outer edges, the only stamps which can have perforations on all four sides are Nos. 1 to 3*a*, 10 and 15 to 15*b*, all other originals being imperf on one or two sides.

The perf 12 stamps, which gauge 11.8, are generally very rough but later the machine was repaired and the 1d., 3d. and 6d. are known with clean-cut perforations.

Remainders of the 1d., unissued 2d. rose, 6d. (in sheets of 21 (7 × 3), 3d., 9d., 1s. (in sheets of 12 (4 × 3)) and of the 2s. and 5s. (sheet format unknown) were found in the Samoan post office when the service closed down in 1881. The remainders are rare in complete sheets, but of very little value as singles, compared with the originals.

Reprints of all values, in sheets of 40 (8 × 5), were made after the originals had been withdrawn from sale. These are practically worthless.

The majority of both reprints and remainders are in the 4th state as the 9d. with the spot of colour under the middle stroke of the "M", but a few stamps (both remainders and reprints) do not show this, while on some it is very faint.

There are three known types of forgery, one of which is rather dangerous, the others being crude.

The last mail despatch organised by the proprietors of the Samoa Express took place on 31 August 1881, although one cover is recorded postmarked 24 September 1881.

After the withdrawal of the Samoa Express service it would appear that the Apia municipality appointed a postmaster to continue the overseas post. Covers are known franked with U.S.A. or New Zealand stamps in Samoa, or routed via Fiji.

In December 1886 the municipal postmaster, John Davis, was appointed Postmaster of the Kingdom of Samoa by King Malietoa. Overseas mail sent via New Zealand was subsequently accepted without the addition of New Zealand stamps, although letters to the U.S.A. continued to require such franking until August 1891.

2 Palm Trees

3 King Malietoa Laupepa

4*a* 6 mm

4*b* 7 mm

4*c* 4 mm

Description of Watermarks

(These are the same as W **12***a/c* of New Zealand)

W **4***a*. 6 mm between "N Z" and star; broad irregular star; comparatively wide "N"; "N Z" 11½ mm wide.

W **4***b*. 7 mm between "N Z" and star; narrower star; narrow "N"; "N Z" 10 mm wide.

W **4***c*. 4 mm between "N Z" and star; narrow star; wide "N"; "N Z" 11 mm wide.

(Des A. E. Cousins (T **3**). Dies eng W. R. Bock and A. E. Cousins (T **2**) or A. E. Cousins (T **3**). Typo Govt Ptg Office, Wellington)

1886–1900. (i) *W* **4***a*. (*a*) *P* 12½ (Oct–Nov 1886).

21	**2**	½d. purple-brown	17·00	42·00
22		1d. yellow-green	6·50	12·00
23		2d. dull orange	18·00	8·50
24		4d. blue	32·00	8·50
25		1s. rose-carmine	65·00	8·00
		a. Bisected (2½d.) (on cover)* ..	†	£325
26		2s. 6d. reddish lilac	55·00	65·00

(*b*) *P* 12 × 11½ (July–Nov 1887)

27	**2**	½d. purple-brown	80·00	80·00
28		1d. yellow-green	£100	23·00
29		2d. yellow	90·00	£140
30		4d. blue	£250	£200
31		6d. brown-lake	22·00	9·50
32		1s. rose-carmine	—	£190
33		2s. 6d. reddish lilac	£350	

(ii) *W* **4***c*. *P* 12 × 11½ (May 1890)

34	**2**	½d. purple-brown	70·00	24·00
35		1d. green	50·00	30·00
36		2d. brown-orange	75·00	38·00
37		4d. blue	£130	5·00
38		6d. brown-lake	£275	11·00
39		1s. rose-carmine	£325	13·00
40		2s. 6d. reddish lilac	£375	8·50

(iii) *W* **4***b*. (*a*) *P* 12 × 11½ (1890–92)

41	**2**	½d. pale purple-brown	3·25	3·25
		a. Blackish purple	3·25	3·25
42		1d. myrtle-green (5.90)	18·00	1·40
		a. Green	18·00	1·40
		b. Yellow-green	18·00	1·40
43		2d. dull orange (5.90)	24·00	1·75
44	**3**	2½d. rose (11.92)	75·00	3·50
		a. Pale rose	75·00	3·50
45	**2**	4d. blue	£225	16·00
46		6d. brown-lake	£110	8·00
47		1s. rose-carmine	£225	4·50
48		2s. 6d. slate-lilac	—	7·00

(*b*) *P* 12½ (Mar 1891–92)

49	**2**	½d. purple-brown		
50		1d. green		
51		2d. orange-yellow	—	£160
52	**3**	2½d. rose (1.92)	20·00	4·50
53	**2**	4d. blue	—	£450
54		6d. brown-purple	£2250	£850
55		1s. rose-carmine	—	£450
56		2s. 6d. slate-lilac		

(*c*) *P* 11 (May 1895–1900)

57	**2**	½d. purple-brown	1·50	1·75
		a. Deep purple-brown	1·00	1·75
		b. Blackish purple (1900)	1·25	35·00
58		1d. green	3·75	1·75
		a. Bluish green (1897)	3·75	1·75
		b. Deep green (1900)	1·60	22·00
59		2d. pale yellow	38·00	38·00
		a. Orange (1896)	38·00	38·00
		b. Bright yellow (1.97)	8·50	4·50
		c. Pale ochre (10.97)	4·50	1·25
		d. Dull orange (1900)	6·50	
60	**3**	2½d. rose	1·60	4·50
		a. Deep rose-carmine (1900) ..	1·25	42·00
61	**2**	4d. blue	7·00	2·00
		a. Deep blue (1900)	85	50·00
62		6d. brown-lake	6·50	3·00
		a. Brown-purple (1900)	1·75	60·00
63		1s. rose	7·00	3·75
		a. Dull rose-carmine/toned (5.98) ..	2·25	35·00
		b. Carmine (1900)	1·25	
64		2s. 6d. purple	55·00	10·00
		a. Reddish lilac (wmk inverted) (1897)	9·00	7·50
		b. Deep purple/toned (wmk reversed) (5.98)	4·75	9·50
		ba. Imperf between (vert pair)	£350	
		c. Slate-violet	£120	

*Following a fire on 1 April 1895 which destroyed stocks of all stamps except the 1s. value perf 12½, this was bisected diagonally and used as a 2½d. stamp for overseas letters between 24 April and May 1895, and was cancelled in blue. Fresh supplies of the 2½d. did not arrive until July 1895, although other values were available from 23 May.

Examples of the 1s. rose perforated 11, No. 63, were subsequently bisected and supplied cancelled-to-order by the post office to collectors, often with backdated cancellations. Most of these examples were bisected vertically and all were cancelled in black (*Price* £7).

The dates given relate to the earliest dates of printing in the various watermarks and perforations and not to issue dates.

The perf 11 issues (including those later surcharged or overprinted), are very unevenly perforated owing to the large size of the pins. Evenly perforated copies are extremely hard to find.

For the 2½d. black, see Nos. 81/2 and for the ½d. green and 1d. red-brown, see Nos. 88/9.

FIVE PENCE (5)

FIVE PENCE (6)

5d (7)

1893 (Nov–Dec). *Handstamped singly, at Apia.*

(*a*) *In two operations*

65	**5**	5d. on 4d. blue (37)	48·00	42·00
		a. Bars omitted	£500	£400
66		5d. on 4d. blue (45)	60·00	£100
67	**6**	5d. on 4d. blue (37)	85·00	£110
68		5d. on 4d. blue (45)	90·00	

(*b*) *In three operations* (Dec)

69	**7**	5d. on 4d. blue (37) (R.)	20·00	28·00
		a. Stop after "d"	£250	60·00
		b. Bars omitted		
70		5d. on 4d. blue (45) (R.)	24·00	50·00

In Types **5** and **6** the bars obliterating the original value vary in length from 13½ to 16½ mm and can occur with either the thick bar over the thin one or vice versa.

Double handstamps exist but we do not list them.
No. 69a came from a separate handstamp which applied the "5d." at one operation. Where the "d" was applied separately its position in relation to the "5" naturally varies.

8

Surcharged
1½d.
(9)

R
3d.
(10)

The "R" in Type **10** indicates use for registration fee.

(Des and die eng A. E. Cousins. Typo New Zealand Govt Ptg Office)

1894–1900. *W* **4b** *(sideways). (a) P* 11½ × 12.
71 **8** 5d. dull vermilion (3.94) .. .. .. 26·00 2·75
a. Dull red .. .. .. 26·00 3·75
(b) P 11
72 **8** 5d. dull red (1895) .. .. .. 15·00 6·50
a. Deep red (1900) .. .. .. 1·75 14·00

1895–1900. *W* **4b.**
(i) *Handstamped with T* **9** *or* **10.** *(a) P* 12 × 11½ (26.1.95)
73 **2** 1½d. on 2d. dull orange (B.) .. .. 9·50 5·50
74 3d. on 2d. dull orange .. .. .. 32·00 8·50
(b) P 11 (6.95)
75 **2** 1½d. on 2d. orange (B.) .. .. .. 2·25 5·00
a. Pair, one without handstamp ..
b. On 2d. yellow .. .. .. 75·00 60·00
76 3d. on 2d. orange .. .. .. 6·50 8·50
a. On 2d. yellow .. .. .. 75·00 60·00
(ii) *Surch printed*. P* 11
77 **2** 1½d. on 2d. orange-yellow (B.) £100
(iii) *Handstamped as T* **9** *or* **10.**† *P* 11 (1896)
78 **2** 1½d. on 2d. orange-yellow (B.) .. .. 2·50 22·00
79 3d. on 2d. orange-yellow .. .. 3·25 45·00
a. Imperf between (vert pair) .. £400
b. Pair, one without handstamp
(iv) *Surch typo as T* **10.** *P* 11 (Feb 1900)
80 **2** 3d. on 2d. deep red-orange (G.) .. .. 1·50 £130

*It is believed that this was type-set from which clichés were made and set up in a forme and then printed on a hand press. This would account for the clear indentation on the back of the stamp and the variation in the position on the stamps which probably resulted from the clichés becoming loose in the forme.
†In No. 78 the "2" has a serif and the handstamp is in pale greenish blue instead of deep blue. In No. 79 the "R" is slightly narrower. In both instances the stamp is in a different shade.
A special printing in a distinctly different colour was made for No. 80 and the surcharge is in green.
Most of the handstamps exist double.

1896 (Aug). *Printed in the wrong colour. W* **4b.** *(a) P* 10 × 11.
81 **3** 2½d. black .. .. 1·00 3·00
(b) P 11
82 **3** 2½d. black .. .. 60·00 65·00
a. Mixed perfs 10 and 11 .. .. £350

Surcharged
2½d.
(11)

PROVISIONAL
GOVT.
(12)

1898–99. *W* **4b.** *P* 11. *(a) Handstamped as T* **11** (10.98).
83 **2** 2½d. on 1s. dull rose-carmine/*toned* .. 35·00 42·00
(b) Surch as T **11** (1899)
84 **2** 2½d. on 1d. bluish green (R.) .. .. 75 2·25
a. Surch inverted .. .. .. — £350
85 2½d. on 1s. dull rose-carmine/*toned* (R.) 5·50 11·00
a. Surch double £350
86 2½d. on 1s. dull rose-carmine/*toned* (Blk.) 5·50 11·00
a. Surch double £450
87 2½d. on 2s. 6d. deep purple/*toned* .. 6·00 13·00

The typographed surcharge was applied in a setting of nine, giving seven types differing in the angle and length of the fractional line, the type of stop, etc.

1899. *Colours changed. W* **4b.** *P* 11.
88 **2** ½d. dull blue-green .. .. .. 1·10 1·75
a. Deep green .. .. .. 1·10 1·75
89 1d. deep red-brown .. .. .. 1·10 1·75

1899–1900. *Provisional Government. New printings optd with T* **12** *(longer words and shorter letters on 5d.). W* **4b.** *P* 11.
90 **2** ½d. dull blue-green (R.) .. .. .. 75 2·25
a. Yellowish green (1900) .. .. 85 3·25
91 1d. chestnut (B.) .. .. .. 1·75 4·50
92 2d. dull orange (R.) .. .. .. 1·50 4·75
a. Orange-yellow (1900) .. .. 1·25 4·75
93 4d. deep dull blue (R.) .. .. .. 70 5·50
94 **8** 5d. dull vermilion (B.) .. .. .. 1·75 6·00
a. Red (1900) .. .. .. 1·75 6·00
95 **2** 6d. brown-lake (B.) .. .. .. 1·25 5·50
96 1s. rose-carmine (B.) .. .. .. 1·50 17·00
97 2s. 6d. reddish purple (R.) .. .. 4·75 18·00
90/7 .. .. *Set of* 8 12·50 55·00

The Samoan group of islands was partitioned on 1 March 1900: Western Samoa (Upolu, Savaii, Apolima and Manono) to Germany and Eastern Samoa (Tutuila, the Manu'a Is and Rose Is) to the United States. German issues of 1900–14 will be found listed in Part 7 (*Germany*) of this catalogue, there were no U.S. issues.
The Samoan Kingdom post office run by John Davis was suspended in March 1900.

WESTERN SAMOA

NEW ZEALAND OCCUPATION

The German Islands of Samoa surrendered to the New Zealand Expeditionary Force on 30 August 1914 and were administered by New Zealand until 1962.

G.R.I.
1 d.
(13)

G.R.I.
1 Shillings.
(14)

SETTINGS. Nos. 101/9 were surcharged by a vertical setting of ten, repeated ten times across the sheet. Nos. 110/14 were from a horizontal setting of four repeated five times in the sheet.
Nos. 101b, 102a and 104a occurred on position 6. The error was corrected during the printing of No. 102.
Nos. 101c, 102c, 104d and 105b are from position 10.
Nos. 101d, 102e and 104b are from position 1.
No. 108b is from position 9.

(Surch by *Samoanische Zeitung*, Apia)

1914 (3 Sept). *German Colonial issue (ship) (no wmk) inscr "SAMOA" surch as T* **13** *or* **14** *(mark values).*
101 ½d. on 3 pf. brown .. .. .. 24·00 9·00
a. Surch double £650 £500
b. No fraction bar .. .. .. 55·00 30·00
c. Comma after "I" £600 £400
d. "1" to left of "2" in "½" .. .. 55·00 30·00
102 ½d. on 5 pf. green .. .. .. 48·00 10·00
a. No fraction bar .. .. .. £120 55·00
c. Comma after "I" £350 £170
d. Surch double £650 £500
e. "1" to left of "2" in "½" .. .. £100 40·00
103 1d. on 10 pf. carmine .. .. .. 95·00 40·00
a. Surch double £650 £500
104 2½d. on 20 pf. ultramarine .. .. 32·00 10·00
a. No fraction bar .. .. .. 75·00 38·00
b. "1" to left of "2" in "½" .. .. 75·00 38·00
c. Surch inverted £800 £750
d. Comma after "I" £450 £325
e. Surch double £650 £550
105 3d. on 25 pf. black and red/*yellow* .. 55·00 40·00
a. Surch double £750 £600
b. Comma after "I" £4750 £1000
106 4d. on 30 pf. black and orange/*buff* .. £110 60·00
107 5d. on 40 pf. black and carmine.. .. £110 70·00
108 6d. on 50 pf. black and purple/*buff* .. 60·00 35·00
a. Surch double £850 £800
b. Inverted "9" for "6" £170 £100
109 9d. on 80 pf. black and carmine/*rose* .. £200 £100
110 "1 shillings" on 1 m. carmine £3000 £3500
111 "1 shilling" on 1 m. carmine £9500 £7000
112 2s. on 2 m. blue £3000 £2750
113 3s. on 3 m. violet-black £1400 £1200
a. Surch double £8000 £9000
114 5s. on 5 m. carmine and black £1100 £1000
a. Surch double £11000 £11000

No. 108b is distinguishable from 108, as the "d" and the "9" are not in a line, and the upper loop of the "9" turns downwards to the left.

UNAUTHORISED SURCHARGES. Examples of the 2d. on 20 pf., 3d. on 30 pf., 3d. on 40 pf., 4d. on 40 pf., 6d. on 80 pf., 2s. on 3 m. and 2s. on Marshall Islands 2 m., together with a number of errors not listed above, were produced by the printer on stamps supplied by local collectors. These were not authorised by the New Zealand Military Administration.

SAMOA.
(15)

1914 (29 Sept)–**15.** *Stamps of New Zealand. T* **50, 51, 52** *and* **27,** *optd as T* **15,** *but opt only 14 mm long on all except* 2½*d. Wmk "N Z" and Star, W* **43** *of New Zealand.*
115 ½d. yellow-green (R.) (*p* 14×15) 45 30
116 1d. carmine (B.) (*p* 14×15) 45 10
117 2d. mauve (R.) (*p* 14×14½) (10.14) .. 75 95
118 2½d. deep blue (R.) (*p* 14) (10.14) .. 1·50 1·75
w. Wmk inverted .. .. ..
119 6d. carmine (B.) (*p* 14×14½) (10.14) .. 1·50 1·75
a. Perf 14×13½ .. .. .. 17·00 20·00
b. Vert pair. Nos. 119/a (1915) .. 45·00 70·00
120 6d. pale carmine (B.) (*p* 14×14½) (10.14) 10·00 10·00
121 1s. vermilion (B.) (*p* 14×14½) (10.14) .. 4·00 12·00
115/21 .. .. *Set of* 6 7·75 15·00

1914–24. *Postal Fiscal stamps as Type* F **4** *of New Zealand optd with T* **15.** *W* **43** *of New Zealand (sideways). Chalk-surfaced "De La Rue" paper.*
(a) P 14 (Nov 1914–17)
122 2s. blue (R.) (9.17) .. .. .. 80·00 £100
123 2s. 6d. grey-brown (B.) (9.17) .. .. 5·50 8·50
124 5s. yellow-green (R.) .. .. .. 12·00 11·00
125 10s. maroon (B.) .. .. .. 21·00 28·00
126 £1 rose-carmine (B.) .. .. .. 60·00 45·00
(b) P 14½×14, *comb* (1917–24)
127 2s. deep blue (R.) (3.18) .. .. 4·75 5·50
128 2s. 6d. grey-brown (B.) (10.24) .. £200 £140
129 3s. purple (R.) (6.23) .. .. .. 14·00 38·00
130 5s. yellow-green (R.) (9.17) .. .. 15·00 15·00
131 10s. maroon (B.) (11.17) .. .. 48·00 42·00
132 £1 rose-carmine (B.) (3.18) .. .. 60·00 70·00

We no longer list the £2 value as it is doubtful if this was used for postal purposes.
See also Nos. 165/6*e*.

1916–19. *King George V stamps of New Zealand optd as T* **15,** *but 14 mm long. (a) Typo. P* 14×15.
134 **61** ½d. yellow-green (R.) 40 70
135 1½d. slate (R.) (1917) 40 25
136 1½d. orange-brown (R.) (1919) 30 40
137 2d. yellow (R.) (14.2.18) 90 20
138 3d. chocolate (B.) (1919) .. .. .. 1·00 14·00
(b) Recess. P 14×13½
139 **60** 2½d. blue (R.) 45 35
a. Perf 14×14½ 75 60
b. Vert pair. Nos. 139/a .. .. 15·00 23·00
140 3d. chocolate (B.) (1917) .. .. .. 45 1·00
a. Perf 14×14½ 35 90
b. Vert pair. Nos. 140/a .. .. 15·00 26·00
141 6d. carmine (B.) (5.5.17) .. .. .. 1·50 3·25
a. Perf 14×14½ .. .. .. 1·25 90
b. Vert pair. Nos. 141/a .. .. 17·00 30·00
142 1s. vermilion (B.) .. .. .. 1·50 1·50
a. Perf 14×14½ .. .. .. 3·75 9·00
b. Vert pair. Nos. 142/a .. .. 22·00 42·00
134/42 .. .. *Set of* 9 6·00 17·00

LEAGUE OF NATIONS MANDATE

Administered by New Zealand.

1920 (July). *Victory. Nos.* 453/8 *of New Zealand optd as T* **15,** *but 14 mm long.*
143 ½d. green (R.) .. .. 2·50 4·50
144 1d. carmine (B.) .. .. 2·00 3·75
145 1½d. brown-orange (R.) .. .. .. 1·50 6·00
146 3d. chocolate (B.) .. .. 7·00 8·50
147 6d. violet (R.) .. .. 4·00 6·50
148 1s. orange-red (B.) .. .. 13·00 11·00
143/8 .. .. *Set of* 6 27·00 35·00

16 Native Hut

SILVER JUBILEE
OF
KING GEORGE V
1910 - 1935.
(17)

(Eng B.W. Recess-printed at Wellington, N.Z.)

1921 (23 Dec). *W* **43** *of New Zealand. (a) P* 14×14½.
149 **16** ½d. green .. .. 1·10 5·00
150 1d. lake .. .. 2·00 20
151 1½d. chestnut .. .. 70 8·00
152 2d. yellow .. .. 2·25 2·00
149/52 .. .. *Set of* 4 5·50 13·50
(b) P 14 × 13½
153 **16** ½d. green .. .. 3·00 1·75
154 1d. lake .. .. 3·25 20
155 1½d. chestnut .. .. 7·50 7·50
156 2d. yellow .. .. 8·50 40
157 2½d. grey-blue .. .. 1·50 5·50
158 3d. sepia .. .. 1·50 3·50
159 4d. violet .. .. 1·50 3·00
160 5d. light blue .. .. 1·50 5·50
161 6d. bright carmine .. .. .. 1·50 4·50
162 8d. red-brown .. .. 1·50 9·00
163 9d. olive-green .. .. 1·75 18·00
164 1s. vermilion .. .. 1·50 18·00
153/64 .. .. *Set of* 12 30·00 70·00

1925–28. *Postal Fiscal stamps as Type* F **4** *of New Zealand optd with T* **15.** *W* **43** *of New Zealand (sideways). P* 14½×14.
(a) Thick, opaque, white chalk-surfaced "Cowan" paper
165 2s. blue (R.) (12.25) £120 £140
166 2s. 6d. deep grey-brown (B.) (10.28) .. 65·00 85·00
166*a* 3s. mauve (R.) (9.25) .. .. .. 50·00 60·00
166*b* 5s. yellow-green (R.) (11.26) .. .. 14·00 30·00
ba. Opt at top of stamp £1100
166*c* 10s. brown-red (B.) (12.25) .. .. £100 75·00
166*d* £1 rose-pink (B.) (11.26) .. .. 55·00 70·00
165/6*d* .. .. *Set of* 6 £350 £400
(b) Thin, hard, chalk-surfaced "Wiggins Teape" paper
166*e* £1 rose-pink (B.) (1928) .. .. — £850

1926–27. *T* **72** *of New Zealand, optd with T* **15,** *in red.*
(a) "Jones" paper
167 2s. deep blue (11.26) .. .. .. 4·50 14·00
168 3s. mauve (10.26) .. .. 10·00 35·00
w. Wmk inverted .. .. .. 10·00 35·00
(b) "Cowan" paper
169 2s. light blue (10.11.27) .. .. .. 5·50 40·00
170 3s. pale mauve (10.11.27) .. .. .. 45·00 85·00

1932 (Aug). *Postal Fiscal stamps as Type* F **6** *of New Zealand optd with T* **15.** *W* **43** *of New Zealand. Thick, opaque, white chalk-surfaced "Cowan" paper. P* 14.
171 2s. 6d. deep brown (B.) .. .. .. 15·00 35·00
172 5s. green (R.) .. .. 24·00 38·00
173 10s. carmine-lake (B.) .. .. .. 45·00 90·00
174 £1 pink (B.) .. .. 60·00 £120
175 £2 bright purple (R.) £650
176 £5 indigo-blue (R.) £1600

The £2 and £5 values were primarily for fiscal use.

1935 (7 May). *Silver Jubilee. Optd with T* **17.** *P* 14 × 13½.
177 **16** 1d. lake 30 30
a. Perf 14 × 14½ .. .. .. 85·00 £150
178 2½d. grey-blue 60 65
179 6d. bright carmine .. .. .. 2·75 2·50
177/9 .. .. *Set of* 3 3·25 3·00

18 Samoan Girl

19 Apia

21 Chief and Wife

25 Lake Lanuto'o

(Recess D.L.R.)

1935 (7 Aug). *T* **18/19, 21, 25** *and similar designs. W* **43** *of New Zealand ("N Z" and Star). P* 14×13½ (½d., 2½d., 2s., 3s.), 14 (2d.) *or* 13½×14 (*others*).

No.	Description		
180	½d. green	10	35
181	1d. black and carmine	10	10
182	2d. black and orange	3·50	2·50
	aw. Wmk inverted		
	b. Perf 13½×14	4·00	4·25
183	2½d. black and blue	10	10
184	4d. slate and sepia	60	15
185	6d. bright magenta	40	10
186	1s. violet and brown	30	10
187	2s. green and purple-brown	80	50
188	3s. blue and brown-orange	1·50	3·50
180/8	*Set of* 9	6·50	6·00

Designs: *Horiz*—2d. River scene; 4d. Canoe and house; 6d. R. L. Stevenson's home "Vailima"; 1s. Stevenson's Tomb. *Vert* (*as T* **25**)—3s. Falefa Falls.

See also Nos. 200/3.

WESTERN
SAMOA.
(27)

1935–42. *Postal Fiscal stamps as Type* F **6** *of New Zealand optd with T* **27**. *W* **43** *of New Zealand. P* 14.

(*a*) *Thick, opaque chalk-surfaced "Cowan" paper* (7.8.35)

No.	Description		
189	2s. 6d. deep brown (B.)	4·75	14·00
190	5s. green (B.)	10·00	18·00
191	10s. carmine-lake (B.)	45·00	60·00
192	£1 pink (B.)	60·00	95·00
193	£2 bright purple (R.)	£140	£300
194	£5 indigo-blue (R.)	£250	£550

(*b*) *Thin, hard chalk-surfaced "Wiggins, Teape" paper* (1941–42)

No.	Description		
194*a*	5s. green (B.) (6.42)	80·00	90·00
194*b*	10s. pale carmine-lake (B.) (6.41)	£130	£130
194*c*	£2 bright purple (R.) (2.42)	£500	£700
194*d*	£5 indigo-blue (R.) (2.42)	£850	£1000

The £2 and £5 values were primarily for fiscal use.

See also Nos. 207/14.

28 Coastal Scene

31 Robert Louis Stevenson

(Des J. Berry (1d. and 1½d.). L. C. Mitchell (2½d. and 7d.). Recess B.W.)

1939 (29 Aug). *25th Anniv of New Zealand Control. T* **28, 31** *and similar horiz designs. W* **98** *of New Zealand. P* 13½ × 14 *or* 14 × 13½ (7*d*.).

No.	Description		
195	1d. olive-green and scarlet	30	10
196	1½d. light blue and red-brown	45	30
197	2½d. red-brown and blue	90	65
198	7d. violet and slate-green	6·50	2·50
195/8	*Set of* 4	7·50	3·25

Designs:—1½d. Map of Western Samoa; 2½d. Samoan dancing party.

32 Samoan Chief

33 Apia Post Office

(Recess B.W.)

1940 (2 Sept). *W* **98** *of New Zealand* (*Mult "N Z" and Star*). *P* 14 × 13½.

No.	Type	Description		
199	32	3d. on 1½d. brown	10	10

T **32** was not issued without surcharge.

(T **33**. Des L. C. Mitchell. Recess B.W.)

1944–49. *As Nos.* 180, 182/3 *and T* **33**. *W* **98** *of New Zealand* (*Mult "N Z" and Star*) (*sideways on* 2½*d*.). *P* 14 *or* 13½ × 14 (5*d*.).

No.	Description		
200	½d. green	30	13·00
202	2d. black and orange	2·50	5·50
203	2½d. black and blue (1948)	4·25	21·00
205	5d. sepia and blue (8.6.49)	1·00	50
200/5	*Set of* 4	7·25	35·00

1945–53. *Postal Fiscal stamps as Type* F **6** *of New Zealand optd with T* **27**. *W* **98** *of New Zealand. Thin hard, chalk-surfaced "Wiggins Teape" paper. P* 14.

No.	Description		
207	2s. 6d. deep brown (B.) (6.45)	4·00	10·00
	w. Wmk inverted	5·00	8·00
208	5s. green (B.) (5.45)	9·00	9·50
	w. Wmk inverted	10·00	11·00
209	10s. carmine-lake (B.) (4.46)	17·00	17·00
	w. Wmk inverted	23·00	25·00
210	£1 pink (B.) (6.48)	90·00	£160
	w. Wmk inverted		
211	30s. brown (8.48)	£150	£300
	w. Wmk inverted	£225	£350
212	£2 bright purple (R.) (11.47)	£150	£275
	w. Wmk inverted	£180	£275
213	£3 green (8.48)	£180	£375
	w. Wmk inverted	£250	£425
214	£5 indigo-blue (R.) (1946)	£300	£450
	w. Wmk inverted (5.53)	£325	£450
207/10	*Set of* 4	£100	£160

The £2 to £5 values were mainly used for fiscal purposes.

See also Nos. 232/5.

WESTERN
SAMOA
(34)

1946 (4 June). *Peace Issue. Nos.* 668, 670 *and* 674/5 *of New Zealand optd with T* **34** (*reading up and down at sides on* 2*d*.).

No.	Description		
215	1d. green	10	10
	w. Wmk inverted	£130	
216	2d. purple (B.)	10	10
217	6d. chocolate and vermilion	20	10
218	8d. black and carmine (B.)	20	10
215/18	*Set of* 4	50	30

UNITED NATIONS TRUST TERRITORY

Administered by New Zealand.

35 Making Siapo Cloth

42 Thatching a Native Hut

43 Preparing Copra

44 Samoan Chieftainess

(Recess B.W.)

1952 (10 Mar). *T* **35, 42/4** *and similar designs. W* **98** *of New Zealand* (*sideways on* 1*s. and* 3*s*.). *P* 13 (½*d*., 2*d*., 5*d. and* 1*s*.) *or* 13½ (*others*).

No.	Description		
219	½d. claret and orange-brown	10	1·25
220	1d. olive-green and green	10	15
221	2d. carmine-red	10	10
222	3d. pale ultramarine and indigo	40	10
223	5d. brown and deep green	4·00	70
224	6d. pale ultramarine and rose-magenta	75	10
225	8d. carmine	30	30
226	1s. sepia and blue	15	10
227	2s. yellow-brown	1·40	60
228	3s. chocolate and brown-olive	3·00	2·75
219/28	*Set of* 10	9·00	5·50

Designs: *Horiz* (*as T* **43**)—1d. Native houses and flags; 3d. Malifa Falls (wrongly inscribed "Aleisa Falls"); 6d. Bonito fishing canoe; 8d. Cacao harvesting. *Vert* (*as T* **35**)—2d. Seal of Samoa; 5d. Tooth-billed Pigeon.

1953 (25 May). *Coronation. Designs as Nos.* 715 *and* 717 *of New Zealand, but inscr* "WESTERN SAMOA".

No.	Description		
229	2d. brown	1·00	15
230	6d. slate-grey	1·00	35

WESTERN
SAMOA
(45)

1955 (14 Nov). *Postal Fiscal stamps as Type* F **6** *of New Zealand optd with T* **45**. *W* **98**. *Chalk-surfaced "Wiggins, Teape" paper. P* 14.

No.	Description		
232	5s. green (B.)	11·00	20·00
233	10s. carmine-lake (B.)	11·00	27·00
234	£1 pink (B.)	18·00	38·00
235	£2 bright purple (R.)	80·00	£150
232/5	*Set of* 4	£110	£200

The £2 value was mainly used for fiscal purposes.

46 Native Houses and Flags

47 Seal of Samoa

(Recess B.W.)

1958 (21 Mar). *Inauguration of Samoan Parliament. T* **46/7** *and similar horiz design. W* **98** *of New Zealand* (*sideways*). *P* 13½ × 13 (6*d*.) *or* 13½ (*others*).

No.	Description		
236	4d. cerise	15	10
237	6d. deep reddish violet	15	15
238	1s. deep ultramarine	90	25
236/8	*Set of* 3	1·10	40

Design:—1s. Map of Samoa, and the Mace.

INDEPENDENT

Samoa became independent on 1 January 1962.

49 Samoan Fine Mat

50 Samoa College

(Litho B.W.)

1962 (2 July). *Independence. T* **49/50** *and similar designs. W* **98** *of New Zealand* (*sideways on horiz stamps*). *P* 13½.

No.	Description		
239	1d. brown and rose-carmine	10	10
240	2d. brown, green, yellow and red	10	10
241	3d. brown, blue-green and blue	10	10
242	4d. magenta, yellow, blue and black	15	10
243	6d. yellow and blue	60	10
244	8d. bluish green, yellow-green and blue	60	10
245	1s. brown and bluish green	20	10
246	1s. 3d. yellow-green and blue	1·25	35
247	2s. 6d. red and ultramarine	2·50	1·75
248	5s. ultramarine, yellow, red and drab	3·50	3·00
239/48	*Set of* 10	8·00	5·00

Designs: *Horiz*—3d. Public library; 4d. Fono House; 6d. Map of Samoa; 8d. Airport; 1s. 3d. "Vailima"; 2s. 6d. Samoan flag; 5s. Samoan seal. *Vert*—1s. Samoan orator.

See Nos. 257/62.

59 Seal and Joint Heads of State

60 Signing the Treaty

(Des L. C. Mitchell. Photo Harrison)

1963 (1 Oct). *First Anniv of Independence. W* **98** *of New Zealand. P* 14.

No.	Type	Description		
249	59	1d. deep sepia and green	10	10
250		4d. deep sepia and blue	10	10
251		8d. deep sepia and rose-pink	10	10
252		2s. deep sepia and orange	20	15
249/52		*Set of* 4	35	30

(Des L. C. Mitchell. Photo Enschedé)

1964 (1 Sept). *2nd Anniv of New Zealand–Samoa Treaty of Friendship. P* 13½.

No.	Type	Description		
253	60	1d. multicoloured	10	10
254		8d. multicoloured	10	10
255		2s. multicoloured	20	10
256		3s. multicoloured	20	30
253/6		*Set of* 4	40	45

61 Kava Bowl

1965 (4 Oct)–**66?** *As Nos.* 239, 241/5, *but W* **61** (*sideways on horiz designs*).

257	1d. brown and rose-carmine	20	60
258	3d. brown, blue-green and blue (1966?)	27·00	3·75
259	4d. magenta, yellow, blue and black	25	60
260	6d. yellow and blue	75	50
261	8d. bluish green, yellow-green and blue	30	10
262	1s. brown and bluish green	25	60
257/62	*Set of* 6	27·00	5·50

62 Red-tailed Tropic Bird **63** Flyingfish

(Des L. C. Mitchell. Photo Harrison)

1965 (29 Dec). *Air. W* **61** (*sideways*). *P* 14½.

263	**62**	8d. black, red-orange and blue	50	10
264	**63**	2s. black and blue	75	20

64 Aerial View of Deep Sea Wharf

(Des Tecon Co (U.S.A.). Photo Enschedé)

1966 (3 Mar). *Opening of First Deep Sea Wharf, Apia. T* **64** *and similar horiz design. Multicoloured. W* **61** (*sideways*). *P* 13½.

265	1d. Type **64**	10	10
266	8d. Aerial view of wharf and bay	15	10
267	2s. As 8d.	25	20
268	3s. Type **64**	30	30
265/8	*Set of* 4	70	55

66 W.H.O. Building

(Des M. Goaman. Photo D.L.R.)

1966 (4 July). *Inauguration of W.H.O. Headquarters. Geneva. T* **66** *and similar horiz design. W* **61** (*sideways**). *P* 14.

269	3d. yellow-ochre, blue and light slate-lilac	35	10
270	4d. blue, yellow, green & light orange-brown	40	15
271	6d. reddish lilac, emerald and yellow-olive	45	20
	w. Wmk legs to left	1·75	
272	1s. blue, yellow, green and turquoise-green	80	25
269/72	*Set of* 4	1·75	60

Designs:—3d., 6d. Type **66**; 4d., 1s. W.H.O. Building on flag.

*The normal sideways watermark has the legs of the bowl pointing to the right, *as seen from the back of the stamp.*

HURRICANE RELIEF
6d

(68)

1966 (1 Sept). *Hurricane Relief Fund. No.* 261 *surch with T* **68** *by Bradbury, Wilkinson.*

273	8d. + 6d. bluish green, yellow-green and blue	10	10

69 Hon. Tuatagaloa L. S. (Minister of Justice)

(Des and photo Harrison)

1967 (16 Jan). *Fifth Anniv of Independence. T* **69** *and similar horiz designs. W* **61** (*sideways*). *P* 14½ × 14.

274	3d. sepia and bluish violet	10	10
275	8d. sepia and light new blue	10	10
276	2s. sepia and olive	10	10
277	3s. sepia and magenta	15	15
274/7	*Set of* 4	30	30

Designs:—8d. Hon. F. C. F. Nelson (minister of Works, Marine and Civil Aviation); 2s. Hon. To'omata T. L. (minister of Lands); Hon. Fa'alava'au G. (minister of Post Office, Radio and Broadcasting).

73 Samoan Fales (houses), 1890

(Des V. Whiteley. Photo Harrison)

1967 (16 May). *Centenary of Mulinu'u as Seat of Government. T* **73** *and similar horiz design. Multicoloured. W* **61**. *P* 14½ × 14.

278	8d. Type **73**	15	10
279	1s. Fono (Parliament) House, 1967	15	10

(New Currency. 100 sene or cents=1 tala or dollar)

75 Carunculated Honeyeater

76 Black-breasted Honeyeater

(Des V. Whiteley. Litho Format ($2, $4). Photo Harrison (others))

1967 (10 July)–**69**. *Decimal currency. Multicoloured designs as T* **75** (1 *s. to* $1) *or* **76** ($2, $4). *W* **61** (*sideways*). *P* 13½ ($2, $4) *or* 14 × 14½ (*others*).

280	1 s. Type **75**	10	10
281	2 s. Pacific Pigeon	10	10
282	3 s. Samoan Starling	10	10
283	5 s. White-vented Flycatcher	15	10
284	7 s. Red-headed Parrot Finch	15	10
285	10 s. Purple Swamphen	20	10
286	20 s. Barn Owl	2·25	40
287	25 s. Tooth-billed Pigeon	1·00	15
288	50 s. Island Thrush	1·00	30
289	$1 Samoan Fantail	1·50	1·75
289*a*	$2 Type **76** (14.7.69)	4·50	7·00
289*b*	$4 Savaii White Eye (6.10.69)	42·00	45·00
280/9*b*	*Set of* 12	48·00	48·00

85 Nurse and Child

(Des G. Vasarhelyi. Photo D.L.R.)

1967 (1 Dec). *South Pacific Health Service. T* **85** *and similar horiz designs. Multicoloured. P* 14.

290	3 s. Type **85**	15	10
291	7 s. Leprosarium	20	10
292	20 s. Mobile X-ray Unit	35	25
293	25 s. Apia Hospital	40	30
290/3	*Set of* 4	1·00	60

PRICES OF SETS

Set prices are given for many issues, generally those containing three stamps or more. Definitive sets include one of each value or major colour change, but do not cover different perforations, die types or minor shades. Where a choice is possible the set prices are based on the cheapest versions of the stamps included in the listings.

89 Thomas Trood **93** Cocoa

(Des M. Farrar-Bell. Litho B.W.)

1968 (15 Jan). *6th Anniv of Independence. T* **89** *and similar horiz designs. Multicoloured. P* 13½.

294	2 s. Type **89**	10	10
295	7 s. Dr. Wilhelm Solf	10	10
296	20 s. J. C. Williams	10	10
297	25 s. Fritz Marquardt	15	10
294/7	*Set of* 4	30	30

(Des Jennifer Toombs. Photo Enschedé)

1968 (15 Feb). *Agricultural Development. T* **93** *and similar vert designs. W* **61**. *P* 13 × 12½.

298	3 s. deep red-brown, yellow-green and black	10	10
299	5 s. myrtle-green, greenish yellow & lt brn	10	10
300	10 s. scarlet, blackish brown and olive-yellow	10	10
301	20 s. yellow-bistre, yellow and blackish olive	15	15
298/301	*Set of* 4	30	30

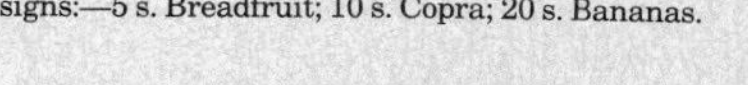

Designs:—5 s. Breadfruit; 10 s. Copra; 20 s. Bananas.

97 Women weaving Mats

(Des G. Vasarhelyi. Photo Harrison)

1968 (22 Apr). *21st Anniv of the South Pacific Commission. T* **97** *and similar horiz designs. Multicoloured. W* **61**. *P* 14½ × 14.

302	7 s. Type **97**	10	10
303	20 s. Palm trees and bay	15	10
304	25 s. Sheltered cove	15	15
302/4	*Set of* 3	30	30

1928-1968
KINGSFORD-SMITH
TRANSPACIFIC FLIGHT
20
SENE =

(100)

1968 (13 June). *40th Anniv of Kingsford Smith's Trans-Pacific Flight. No.* 285 *surch with T* **100**.

305	20 s. on 10 s. Purple Swamphen	10	10

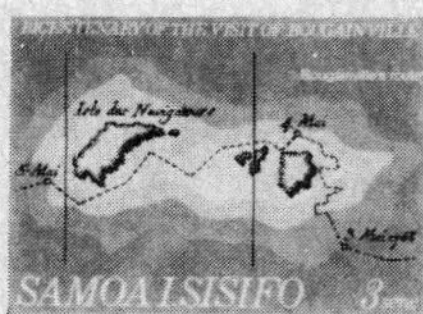

101 Bougainville's Route

(Des Jennifer Toombs. Litho B.W.)

1968 (17 June). *Bicentenary of Bougainville's Visit to Samoa. T* **101** *and similar horiz designs. W* **61** (*sideways*). *P* 14.

306	3 s. new blue and black	10	10
307	7 s. light ochre and black	15	10
308	20 s. multicoloured	45	20
309	25 s. multicoloured	60	30
306/9	*Set of* 4	1·10	55

Designs:—7 s. Louis de Bougainville; 20 s. Bougainvillea flower; 25 s. Ships *La Boudeuse* and *L'Etoile*.

105 Globe and Human Rights Emblem **106** Dr. Martin Luther King

(Des G. Vasarhelyi. Photo Harrison)

1968 (26 Aug). *Human Rights Year.* W **61**. P 14.

310	**105**	7 s. greenish blue, brown and gold	10	10
311		20 s. orange, green and gold	10	15
312		25 s. violet, green and gold	15	15
310/12		*Set of* 3	30	30

(Des and litho D.L.R.)

1968 (23 Sept). *Martin Luther King Commemoration.* W **61**. P 14½ × 14.

313	**106**	7 s. black and olive-green	15	10
314		20 s. black and bright purple	15	10

107 Polynesian Version of Madonna and Child **108** Frangipani—*Plumeria acuminata*

(Des and litho D.L.R.)

1968 (14 Oct). *Christmas.* W **61**. P 14.

315	**107**	1 s. multicoloured	10	10
316		3 s. multicoloured	10	10
317		20 s. multicoloured	10	10
318		30 s. multicoloured	15	15
315/18		*Set of* 4	30	30

(Des J.W. Litho Format)

1969 (20 Jan). *Seventh Anniv of Independence. T* **108** *and similar multicoloured designs.* P 14½.

319	2 s. Type **108**	10	10
320	7 s. Hibiscus (*vert*)	15	10
321	20 s. Red-Ginger (*vert*)	40	10
322	30 s. "Moso'oi"	60	80
319/22	*Set of* 4	1·10	1·00

109 R. L. Stevenson and *Treasure Island* **110** Weightlifting

(Des Jennifer Toombs. Litho D.L.R.)

1969 (21 Apr). *75th Death Anniv of Robert Louis Stevenson. Horiz designs, each showing portrait as in T* **109**. *Multicoloured.* W **61** (*sideways*). P 14.

323	3 s. Type **109**	15	10
324	7 s. *Kidnapped*	20	10
325	20 s. *Dr. Jekyll and Mr. Hyde*	35	50
326	22 s. *Weir of Hermiston*	40	50
323/6	*Set of* 4	1·00	1·00

(Des J. Mason. Photo Note Ptg Branch, Reserve Bank of Australia)

1969 (21 July). *Third South Pacific Games, Port Moresby. T* **110** *and similar vert designs.* P 13½.

327	3 s. black and sage-green	10	10
328	20 s. black and light blue	10	10
329	22 s. black and dull orange	15	15
327/9	*Set of* 3	30	30

Designs:—20 s. Yachting; 22 s. Boxing.

113 U.S. Astronaut on the Moon and the Splashdown near Samoan Islands

(Des J. Mason. Photo Note Ptg Branch, Reserve Bank of Australia)

1969 (24 July). *First Man on the Moon.* P 13½.

330	**113**	7 s. multicoloured	15	15
331		20 s. multicoloured	15	15

114 "Virgin with Child" (Murillo)

(Des and photo Heraclio Fournier)

1969 (13 Oct). *Christmas. T* **114** *and similar vert designs. Multicoloured.* P 14.

332	1 s. Type **114**	10	10
333	3 s. "The Holy Family" (El Greco)	10	10
334	20 s. "The Nativity" (El Greco)	35	10
335	30 s. "The Adoration of the Magi" (detail, Velazquez)	40	15
332/5	*Set of* 4	70	30
MS336	116 × 126 mm. Nos. 332/5	75	1·25

115 Seventh Day Adventists' Sanatorium, Apia

(Des V. Whiteley. Litho Format)

1970 (19 Jan). *Eighth Anniv of Independence. T* **115** *and similar designs.* W **61** (*sideways on* 2, 7 *and* 22 *s.*). P 14.

337	2 s. yellow-brown, pale slate and black	10	10
338	7 s. violet, buff and black	10	10
339	20 s. rose, lilac and black	15	10
340	22 s. olive-green, cinnamon and black	15	15
337/40	*Set of* 4	30	30

Designs: *Horiz*—7 s. Rev. Father Violette and Roman Catholic Cathedral, Apia; 22 s. John Williams, 1797–1839, and London Missionary Society Church, Sapapali'l. *Vert*—20 s. Mormon Church of Latter Day Saints, Tuasivi-on-Safotulafai.

119 Wreck of *Adler* (German steam gunboat)

(Des J.W. Litho Questa)

1970 (27 Apr). *Great Apia Hurricane of* 1889. *T* **119** *and similar horiz designs. Multicoloured.* W **61** (*sideways*). P 13½.

341	5 s. Type **119**	30	10
342	7 s. U.S.S. *Nipsic* (steam sloop)	30	10
343	10 s. H.M.S. *Calliope* (screw corvette)	40	25
344	20 s. Apia after the hurricane	1·10	75
341/4	*Set of* 4	1·90	1·10

120 Sir Gordon Taylor's Short S.25 Sandringham 7 Flying Boat *Frigate Bird III*

(Des R. Honisett. Photo Note Ptg Branch, Reserve Bank of Australia)

1970 (27 July). *Air. Aircraft. T* **120** *and similar horiz designs. Multicoloured.* P 13½ × 13.

345	3 s. Type **120**	45	10
346	7 s. Polynesian Airlines Douglas DC-3	70	10
347	20 s. Pan-American Sikorsky S-42A flying boat *Samoan Clipper*	2·00	60
348	30 s. Air Samoa Britten Norman Islander	2·25	1·75
	a. Pale purple omitted	£250	
345/8	*Set of* 4	4·75	2·25

ALTERED CATALOGUE NUMBERS

Any Catalogue numbers altered from the last edition are shown as a list in the introductory pages.

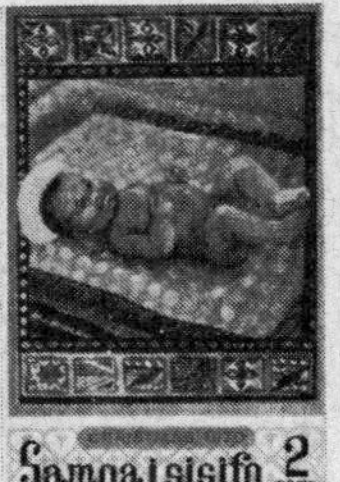

121 Kendal's Chronometer and Cook's Sextant **122** "Peace for the World" (F. B. Eccles)

(Des J. Berry, adapted J. Cooter. Litho Questa)

1970 (14 Sept). *Cook's Exploration of the Pacific. T* **121** *and similar designs.* W **61** (*sideways on* 30 *s.*). P 14.

349	1 s. carmine, silver and black	15	15
350	2 s. multicoloured	30	15
351	20 s. black, bright blue and gold	75	25
352	30 s. multicoloured	1·50	80
349/52	*Set of* 4	2·50	1·25

Designs: *Vert*—2 s. Cook's statue, Whitby; 20 s. Cook's head. *Horiz* (83 × 25 *mm*)—30 s. Cook, H.M.S. *Endeavour* and island.

(Des from paintings. Photo Heraclio Fournier)

1970 (26 Oct). *Christmas. T* **122** *and similar vert designs. Multicoloured.* P 13.

353	2 s. Type **122**	10	10
354	3 s. "The Holy Family" (W. E. Jahnke)	10	10
355	20 s. "Mother and Child" (F. B. Eccles)	15	10
356	30 s. "Prince of Peace" (Meleane Fe'ao)	20	15
353/6	*Set of* 4	35	30
MS357	111 × 158 mm. Nos. 353/6	60	1·25

123 Pope Paul VI **124** Native and Tree

(Des J. Cooter. Litho Format)

1970 (20 Nov). *Visit of Pope Paul to Samoa.* W **61**. P 14×14½.

358	**123**	8 s. black and grey-blue	15	15
359		20 s. black and plum	35	15

(Des G. Drummond from sketches by the American Timber Co. Litho Questa)

1971 (1 Feb). *Timber Industry. T* **124** *and similar multicoloured designs.* P 13½.

360	3 s. Type **124**	10	10
361	8 s. Bulldozer in clearing (*horiz*)	15	10
362	20 s. Log in sawmill (*horiz*)	30	10
363	22 s. Floating logs and harbour	30	15
360/3	*Set of* 4	70	30

125 Fautasi (large canoe) in Apia Harbour and first stamps of Samoa and U.S.A.

(*Half-sized illustration. Actual size* 84 × 26 *mm*)

(Des E. Roberts. Photo Courvoisier)

1971 (12 Mar). *"Interpex" Stamp Exhibition, New York. Sheet* 138 × 80 *mm.* P 11½.

MS364	**125**	70 s. multicoloured	85	1·40

126 Siva Dance **127** "Queen Salamasina"

(Des and litho J.W.)

1971 (9 Aug). *Tourism. T* **126** *and similar horiz designs. Multicoloured.* W **61** *(sideways). P* 14.

365	5 s. Type **126**	40	10
366	7 s. Samoan cricket	1·00	60
367	8 s. Hideaway Hotel	1·00	35
368	10 s. Aggie Grey and her hotel	1·00	60
365/8	*Set of* 4	3·00	1·40

(Des Jennifer Toombs. Litho J.W.)

1971 (20 Sept). *Myths and Legends of Old Samoa (1st series). T* **127** *and similar vert designs from carvings by S. Ortquist. Multicoloured.* W **61** *(sideways). P* 14 × 13½.

369	3 s. Type **127**	10	10
370	8 s. "Lu and his Sacred Hens"	15	10
371	10 s. "God Tagaloa fishes Samoa from the sea"	20	10
372	22 s. "Mount Vaea and the Pool of Tears"	35	40
369/72	*Set of* 4	70	50

See also Nos. 426/9.

128 "The Virgin and Child" (Bellini)

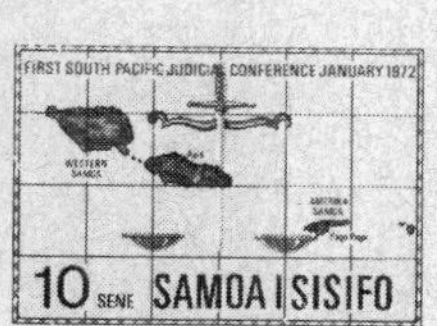

129 Map and Scales of Justice

(Des J. Cooter. Litho J.W.)

1971 (4 Oct). *Christmas. T* **128** *and similar design.* W **61**. *P* 14 × 13½.

373	**128**	2 s. multicoloured	10	10
374		3 s. multicoloured	10	10
375	–	20 s. multicoloured	30	10
376	–	30 s. multicoloured	40	20
373/6		*Set of* 4	75	35

Design: *Vert*—20 s., 30 s. "The Virgin and Child with St. Anne and John the Baptist" (Leonardo da Vinci).

(Des E. Roberts. Photo Courvoisier)

1972 (10 Jan). *First South Pacific Judicial Conference. P* 11½ × 11.

377	**129**	10 s. multicoloured	15	15

Issued on matt, almost invisible gum.

130 Asau Wharf, Savaii

131 Flags of Member Countries

(Des V. Whiteley. Litho A. & M.)

1972 (10 Jan). *Tenth Anniv of Independence. T* **130** *and similar horiz designs. Multicoloured.* W **61** *(sideways). P* 13.

378	1 s. Type **130**	10	10
379	8 s. Parliament Building	10	10
380	10 s. Mothers' Centre	10	10
381	22 s. "Vailima" Residence and rulers	20	25
378/81	*Set of* 4	40	30

(Des V. Whiteley. Litho Questa)

1972 (17 Mar). *25th Anniv of South Pacific Commission. T* **131** *and similar multicoloured designs.* W **61** *(sideways on 8 s. and 10 s.). P* 14 × 13½ *(3 and 7 s.) or* 13½ × 14 *(others).*

382	3 s. Type **131**	10	15
383	7 s. Flag and Afoafouvale Misimoa (Secretary-General)	10	15
384	8 s. H.Q. building, Nouméa *(horiz)*	15	15
385	10 s. Flags and area map *(horiz)*	15	15
382/5	*Set of* 4	40	55

132 Expedition Ships

133 Bull Conch (*Strombus taurus*)

(Des J. Berry; adapted J. Cooter. Litho Questa)

1972 (14 June). *250th Anniv of sighting of Western Samoa by Jacob Roggeveen. T* **132** *and similar horiz designs. Multicoloured.* W **61** *(sideways, except 2 s.). P* 14½.

386	2 s. Type **132**	15	10
387	8 s. Ships in storm	45	10
388	10 s. Ships passing island	50	10
389	30 s. Route of Voyage (85 × 25 *mm*)	1·75	1·50
386/9	*Set of* 4	2·50	1·60

(Des Format ($5) or J.W. (others). Litho Format ($5), Questa (others))

1972 (18 Oct)–**76**. *T* **133** *and similar multicoloured designs.* W **61** *(sideways, on 1 s. to 50 s.). White, ordinary paper. P* 13½ *($1 to $5) or* 14½ *(others).*

390	1 s. Type **133**	30	30
	a. Cream, chalk-surfaced paper (30.11.76)	1·75	2·00
391	2 s. *Oryctes rhinoceros* (beetle)	30	30
	a. Cream, chalk-surfaced paper (30.11.76)	1·75	2·00
392	3 s. Skipjack Tuna	30	65
393	4 s. Painted Crab	30	30
	a. Cream, chalk-surfaced paper (30.11.76)	1·75	2·00
394	5 c. Melon Butterflyfish	35	30
	a. Cream, chalk-surfaced paper (30.11.76)	1·75	2·00
395	7 s. *Danaus hamata* (butterfly)	2·00	70
396	10 s. Trumpet Triton (*Charonia tritonis*)	2·50	70
397	20 s. *Chrysochroa abdominalis* (beetle)	1·25	30
398	50 s. Spiny Lobster	2·00	2·75
399	$1 *Gnathothlibus erotus* (moth) (29×45 *mm*)	8·00	4·50
399*a*	$2 Green Turtle (29×45 *mm*) (18.6.73)	5·50	3·50
399*b*	$4 Black Marlin (29×45 *mm*) (27.3.74)	3·00	7·00
399*c*	$5 Green Tree Lizard (29×45 *mm*) (30.6.75)	3·00	8·50
390/9*c*	*Set of* 13	26·00	27·00

134 "The Ascension"

135 Erecting a Tent

(Des PAD Studio. Litho Harrison)

1972 (1 Nov). *Christmas. Stained-glass Windows in Apia. T* **134** *and similar vert designs. Multicoloured.* W **61**. *P* 14 × 14½.

400	1 s. Type **134**	10	10
401	4 s. "The Blessed Virgin and Infant Christ"	10	10
402	10 s. "St. Andrew blessing Samoan canoe"	10	10
403	30 s. "The Good Shepherd"	40	30
400/3	*Set of* 4	50	40
MS404	70 × 159 mm. Nos. 400/3	90	1·25

(Des G. Drummond. Litho Format)

1973 (29 Jan). *Boy Scout Movement. T* **135** *and similar horiz designs. Multicoloured.* W **61** *(sideways). P* 14.

405	2 s. Saluting the flag	10	10
406	3 s. First-aid	10	10
407	8 s. Type **135**	25	10
408	20 s. Samoan action-song	90	85
405/8	*Set of* 4	1·10	95

136 Hawker Siddeley H.S.748

(Des E. Roberts. Photo Courvoisier)

1973 (9 Mar). *Air. T* **136** *and similar horiz designs showing aircraft at Faleolo Airport. Multicoloured. P* 11½.

409	8 s. Type **136**	55	15
410	10 s. Hawker Siddeley H.S.748 in flight	65	15
411	12 s. Hawker Siddeley H.S.748 on runway	75	35
412	22 s. B.A.C. One Eleven	1·10	60
409/12	*Set of* 4	2·75	1·10

Issued on matt, almost invisible gum.

PRICES OF SETS

Set prices are given for many issues, generally those containing three stamps or more. Definitive sets include one of each value or major colour change, but do not cover different perforations, die types or minor shades. Where a choice is possible the set prices are based on the cheapest versions of the stamps included in the listings.

137 Apia General Hospital

138 Mother and Child, and Map

(Des C. Abbott. Litho Questa)

1973 (20 Aug). *25th Anniv of W.H.O. T* **137** *and similar vert designs. Multicoloured.* W **61**. *P* 14.

413	2 s. Type **137**	10	10
414	8 s. Baby clinic	20	10
415	20 s. Filariasis research	45	20
416	22 s. Family welfare	45	30
413/16	*Set of* 4	1·10	55

(Des W. E. Jahnke (3 s.), Fiasili Keil (4 s.), E. Cooter (others); adapted Jennifer Toombs. Litho J.W.)

1973 (15 Oct). *Christmas. T* **138** *and similar vert designs. Multicoloured.* W **61**. *P* 14.

417	3 s. Type **138**	10	10
418	4 s. Mother and child, and village	10	10
419	10 s. Mother and child, and beach	10	10
420	30 s. Samoan stable	55	50
417/20	*Set of* 4	65	55
MS421	144×103 mm. Nos. 417/20	65	75
	w. Wmk inverted	30·00	

139 Boxing

(Des G. Drummond. Litho Questa)

1974 (24 Jan). *Commonwealth Games, Christchurch. T* **139** *and similar horiz designs. Multicoloured.* W **61** *(sideways). P* 14.

422	8 s. Type **139**	10	10
423	10 s. Weightlifting	10	10
424	20 s. Bowls	20	10
425	30 s. Athletics stadium	35	45
422/5	*Set of* 4	70	60

(Des Jennifer Toombs. Litho Questa)

1974 (13 Aug). *Myths and Legends of Old Samoa (2nd series). Vert designs as T* **127** *from carvings by S. Ortquist. Multicoloured.* W **61**. *P* 14 × 13½.

426	2 s. Tigilau and sacred dove	10	10
427	8 s. Pili, his sons and fishing net	10	10
428	20 s. Sina and the origin of the coconut	30	10
429	30 s. The warrior, Nafanua	45	55
426/9	*Set of* 4	80	65

140 Mail-van at Faleolo Airport

(Des E. Roberts. Photo Heraclio Fournier)

1974 (4 Sept). *Centenary of Universal Postal Union. T* **140** *and similar horiz designs. Multicoloured. P* 13 × 12½ *(50 s.) or* 13 *(others).*

430	8 s. Type **140**	35	10
431	20 s. *Mariposa* (cargo liner) at Apia Wharf	50	15
432	22 s. Early Post Office, Apia, and letter	50	25
433	50 s. William Willis and *Age Unlimited* (raft) (87×29 *mm*)	95	1·25
430/3	*Set of* 4	2·10	1·60
MS434	140×82 mm. No. 433	90	1·75

141 "Holy Family" (Sebastiano)

(Des PAD Studio. Litho Enschedé)

1974 (25 Nov). *Christmas. T* **141** *and similar horiz designs. Multicoloured.* W **61** *(sideways). P* 13×13½.

435	3 s. Type **141**	10	10
436	4 s. "Virgin and Child with Saints" (Lotto)	10	10
437	10 s. "Madonna and Child with St. John" (Titian)	20	10
438	30 s. "Adoration of the Shepherds" (Rubens)	55	45
435/8	*Set of* 4	75	50
MS439	128 × 87 mm. Nos. 435/8	80	1·40

142 Winged Passion Flower

(Des J.W. Litho Questa)

1975 (15 Jan). *Tropical Flowers. T* **142** *and similar multicoloured designs.* **W 61** *(sideways on 8 and 30 s.). P* 14.

440	8 s. Type **142**	15	10
441	20 s. Gardenia *(vert)*	30	25
442	22 s. *Barringtonia samoensis (vert)*	30	30
443	30 s. Malay apple	35	75
440/3	*Set of* 4	1·00	1·25

143 *Joyita* (inter-island coaster) loading at Apia

144 "Pate" Drum

(Des E. Roberts. Photo Heraclio Fournier)

1975 (14 Mar). *"Interpex 1975" Stamp Exhibition, New York, and "Joyita Mystery". T* **143** *and similar horiz designs. Multicoloured. P* 13½.

444	1 s. Type **143**	10	10
445	8 s. *Joyita* sails for Tokelau Islands	15	10
446	20 s. Taking to rafts	20	25
447	22 s. *Joyita* abandoned	25	30
448	50 s. Discovery of *Joyita* north of Fiji	70	1·75
444/8	*Set of* 5	1·25	1·75
MS449	150 × 100 mm. Nos. 444/8. Imperf	1·50	3·50

(Des Iosua To'afa; adapted L. Curtis. Litho Harrison)

1975 (30 Sept). *Musical Instruments. T* **144** *and similar vert designs. Multicoloured.* **W 61** *(sideways). P* 14.

450	8 s. Type **144**	10	10
451	20 s. "Lali" drum	20	10
452	22 s. "Logo" drum	20	10
453	30 s. "Pu" shell horn	35	30
450/3	*Set of* 4	75	50

145 "Mother and Child" (Meleane Fe'ao)

146 "The Boston Massacre, 1770" (Paul Revere)

(Des local artists; adapted G. Vasarhelyi. Litho Walsall)

1975 (25 Nov). *Christmas. T* **145** *and similar vert designs. Multicoloured.* **W 61** *(inverted). P* 14.

454	3 s. Type **145**	10	10
455	4 s. "The Saviour" (Polataia Tuigamala)	10	10
456	10 s. "A Star is Born" (Iosua To'afa)	10	10
457	30 s. "Madonna and Child" (Ernesto Coter)	30	45
454/7	*Set of* 4	45	50
MS458	101 × 134 mm. Nos. 454/7	60	1·25

(Des J. Cooter. Litho Walsall)

1976 (20 Jan). *Bicentenary of American Revolution. T* **146** *and similar horiz designs. Multicoloured.* **W 61** *(sideways*). P* 13½.

459	7 s. Type **146**	20	15
	w. Wmk legs to left	2·00	
460	8 s. "The Declaration of Independence" (Trumbull)	20	15
	w. Wmk legs to left	3·00	
461	20 s. "The Ship that Sank in Victory, 1779" (Ferris)	60	20
462	22 s. "Pitt addressing the Commons, 1782" (R. A. Hickel)	60	20
463	50 s. "The Battle of Princeton" (Mercer)	1·25	1·50
459/63	*Set of* 5	2·50	2·00
MS464	160×125 mm. Nos. 459/63	6·50	8·00
	w. Wmk legs to left	35·00	

*The normal sideways watermark has the legs of the bowl pointing to the right, *as seen from the back of the stamp.*

147 Mullet Fishing

(Des V. Whiteley Studio. Litho Harrison)

1976 (27 Apr). *Fishing. T* **147** *and similar horiz designs. Multicoloured.* **W 61.** *P* 14.

465	10 s. Type **147**	10	10
466	12 s. Fish traps	15	10
467	22 s. Samoan fishermen	30	10
468	50 s. Net fishing	85	70
465/8	*Set of* 4	1·25	90

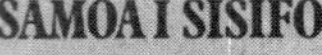

148 Paul Revere's Ride

(Des J. Berry. Photo Heraclio Fournier)

1976 (29 May). *"Interphil" Stamp Exhibition. Sheet* 120 × 80 *mm. P* 13.

MS469	**148** $1 gold, black and emerald	1·50	1·50

149 Boxing

150 Mary and Joseph going to Bethlehem

(Des C. Abbott. Litho Questa)

1976 (21 June). *Olympic Games, Montreal. T* **149** *and similar horiz designs. Multicoloured.* **W 61** *(sideways*). P* 14.

470	10 s. Type **149**	10	10
471	12 s. Wrestling	10	10
	w. Wmk legs to left	35·00	
472	22 s. Javelin	15	10
473	50 s. Weightlifting	45	50
470/3	*Set of* 4	70	60

*The normal sideways watermark has the legs of the bowl pointing to the right, *as seen from back of the stamp.*

(Des C. Abbott. Litho Questa)

1976 (18 Oct). *Christmas. T* **150** *and similar vert designs. Multicoloured.* **W 61.** *P* 13½.

474	3 s. Type **150**	10	10
475	5 s. The Shepherds	10	10
476	22 s. The Holy Family	15	10
477	50 s. The Magi	55	65
474/7	*Set of* 4	70	75
MS478	124×115 mm. Nos. 474/7	80	1·75

151 Queen Elizabeth and View of Apia

(Des BG Studio. Litho Questa)

1977 (11 Feb). *Silver Jubilee and Royal Visit. T* **151** *and similar horiz designs. Multicoloured.* **W 61** *(sideways*). P* 13½.

479	12 s. Type **151**	10	10
	w. Wmk legs to left	7·00	
480	26 s. Presentation of Spurs of Chivalry	15	20
481	32 s. Queen and Royal Yacht *Britannia*	20	25
	w. Wmk legs to left	30·00	
482	50 s. Queen leaving Abbey	20	60
479/82	*Set of* 4	60	1·00

*The normal sideways watermark has the legs of the bowl pointing to the right, *as seen from the back of the stamp.*

MINIMUM PRICE

The minimum price quote is 10p which represents a handling charge rather than a basis for valuing common stamps. For further notes about prices see introductory pages.

152 Map of Flight Route

(Des C. Abbott. Litho Walsall)

1977 (20 May). *50th Anniv of Lindbergh's Translantic Flight. Horiz designs showing the* Spirit of St. Louis. *Multicoloured.* **W 61** *(sideways*). P* 14.

483	22 s. Type **152**	25	10
484	24 s. In flight	35	15
485	26 s. Landing	35	15
	w. Wmk legs to left	3·00	
486	50 s. Col. Lindbergh	80	75
483/6	*Set of* 4	1·60	1·00
MS487	194×93 mm. Nos. 483/6	2·40	2·75
	w. Wmk legs to left	40·00	

*The normal sideways watermark has the legs of the bowl pointing to the right, *as seen from the back of the stamp.*

153 3d. Express Stamp and First Mail Notice

(Des J. Cooter. Litho Questa)

1977 (29 Aug). *Stamp Centenary. T* **153** *and similar horiz designs.* **W 61** *(sideways). P* 13½.

488	12 s. lemon, red and sepia	20	10
489	13 s. multicoloured	20	15
490	26 s. multicoloured	45	30
491	50 s. multicoloured	80	1·50
488/91	*Set of* 4	1·50	1·75

Designs:—13 s. Early cover and 6d. Express; 26 s. Apia Post Office and 1d. Express; 50 s. Schooner *Energy,* 1877, and 6d. Express.

154 Apia Automatic Telephone Exchange

155 "Samoan Nativity" (P. Feata)

(Des J.W. Litho Questa)

1977 (28 Oct*). *Telecommunications Project. T* **154** *and similar horiz designs. Multicoloured.* **W 61** *(sideways). P* 14.

492	12 s. Type **154**	15	10
493	13 s. Mulinuu Radio Terminal	15	10
494	26 s. Old and new telephones	30	20
495	50 s. "Global communication"	50	70
492/5	*Set of* 4	1·00	1·00

*The above were originally scheduled for release on 11 July and were put on sale by the Crown Agents in England on that date.

(Designs adapted by J.W. Litho Questa)

1977 (31 Oct). *Christmas. T* **155** *and similar vert designs. Multicoloured.* **W 61.** *P* 14.

496	4 s. Type **155**	10	10
497	6 s. "The Offering" (E. Saofaiga)	10	10
498	26 s. "Madonna and Child" (F. Tupou)	20	10
499	50 s. "Emmanuel" (M. Sapa'u)	35	40
496/9	*Set of* 4	55	50
MS500	117×159 mm. Nos. 496/9	55	85

156 Polynesian Airlines Boeing 737

(Des E. Roberts. Litho Heraclio Fournier)

1978 (21 Mar). *Aviation Progress. T* **156** *and similar horiz designs. Multicoloured. P* 14.

501	12 s. Type **156**	20	10
502	24 s. Wright brothers Flyer I	40	20
503	26 s. Kingsford Smith's Fokker F.VIIa/3m *Southern Cross*	40	20
504	50 s. Concorde	1·10	85
501/4	*Set of* 4	1·90	1·25
MS505	150×120 mm. Nos. 501/4	2·25	2·75

157 Hatchery, Aleipata   **158** Pacific Pigeon

(Des J.W. Litho Questa)

1978 (14 Apr). *Hawksbill Turtle Conservation Project. T* **157** *and similar horiz design. Multicoloured. W* **61** *(sideways). P* 14½ × 14.
506 24 s. Type **157** 1·00 30
507 $1 Turtle 3·75 1·60

(Des Jennifer Toombs. Litho Questa)

1978 (21 Apr). *25th Anniv of Coronation. T* **158** *and similar vert designs. P* 15.
508 26 s. black, brown and deep magenta 20 30
a. Sheetlet. Nos. 508/10 × 2 1·00
509 26 s. multicoloured 20 30
510 26 s. black, brown and deep magenta 20 30
508/10 *Set of* 3 50 80
Designs:—No. 508, King's Lion; No. 509, Queen Elizabeth II; No. 510, Type **158**.
Nos. 508/10 were printed together in small sheets of 6, containing two *se-tenant* strips of 3, with horizontal gutter margin between.

159 Flags of Western Samoa and Canada with Canadian National Tower   **160** Captain Cook

(Des BG Studio. Litho Walsall)

1978 (9 June). *"Capex '78" International Stamp Exhibition, Toronto. Sheet* 119 × 79 *mm. W* **61**. *P* 14½.
MS511 **159** $1 blue, red and black 1·00 1·40

(Des J. Berry. Litho Harrison)

1978 (28 Aug). *250th Birth Anniv of Captain Cook. T* **160** *and similar vert designs. Multicoloured. W* **61**. *P* 14½ × 14.
512 12 s. Type **160** 30 15
513 24 s. Cook's cottage, Gt Ayton, Yorkshire 50 35
514 26 s. Old drawbridge over the river Esk, Whitby 55 35
515 50 s. H.M.S. *Resolution* 1·00 1·50
512/15 *Set of* 4 2·10 2·10

SAMOA I SISIFO
Christmas 1978 4 sene

161 Thick-edged Cowrie (*Cypraea caurica*)   **162** "Madonna on the Crescent"

(Photo Courvoisier)

1978 (15 Sept)–**80**. *Shells. Horiz designs as T* **161**. *Multicoloured. P* 12½.
516 1 s. Type **161** 15 10
517 2 s. Controversial Isabelle Cowrie (*Cypraea isabella controversa*) 15 10
518 3 s. Money Cowrie (*Cypraea moneta*) 25 10
519 4 s. Eroded Cowrie (*Cypraea erosa*) 30 10
520 6 s. Honey Cowrie (*Cypraea helvola*) 30 10
521 7 s. Asellus or Banded Cowrie (*Cypraea asellus*) 35 10
522 10 s. Globular or Globe Cowrie (*Cypraea globulus*) 40 10
523 11 s. Mole Cowrie (*Cypraea talpa*) 40 10
524 12 s. Children's Cowrie (*Cypraea childreni*) 40 10
525 13 s. Flag Cone (*Conus vexillum vexillum*) (20.11.78) 40 10
526 14 s. Soldier Cone (*Conus miles*) (20.11.78) 40 10
527 24 s. Textile or Cloth of Gold Cone (*Conus textile*) (20.11.78) 40 10
528 26 s. Lettered Cone (*Conus litteratus*) (20.11.78) 45 10
529 50 s. Tesselate or Tiled Cone (*Conus tessulatus*) (20.11.78) 50 15
530 $1 Black Marble Cone (*Conus marmoreus nigrescens*) (20.11.78) 80 60
530*a* $2 Marlin-spike Auger (*Terebra maculata*) (18.7.79) 85 70
530*b* $3 Scorpion Conch (*Lambis scorpius*) (18.7.79) 1·00 1·25
530*c* $5 Common or Major Harp (*Harpa major*) (26.8.80) 1·75 2·25
516/30*c* *Set of* 18 8·25 4·75
Nos. 530*a/c* are larger, size 36×26 mm.
Issued on matt, almost invisible gum.

(Des C. Abbott. Litho Questa)

1978 (6 Nov). *Christmas. Woodcuts by Dürer. T* **162** *and similar vert designs. W* **61**. *P* 14.
531 4 s. black and yellow-brown 10 10
w. Wmk inverted £200
532 6 s. black and turquoise-blue 10 10
533 26 s. black and bright blue 15 10
534 50 s. black and bright violet 35 50
531/4 *Set of* 4 50 55
MS535 103×154 mm. Nos. 531/4 70 1·00
Designs:—6 s. Nativity"; 26 s. "Adoration of the Magi"; 50 s. "Annunciation".

163 Boy with Coconuts   **164** *Charles W. Morgan*

(Des G. Drummond. Litho Questa)

1979 (10 Apr). *International Year of the Child. T* **163** *and similar horiz designs. Multicoloured. W* **61** *(sideways). P* 14.
536 12 s. Type **163** 15 10
537 24 s. White Sunday 20 15
538 26 s. Children at pump 20 15
539 50 s. Young girl with ukulele 60 80
536/9 *Set of* 4 1·00 1·10

(Des J. Cooter. Litho Format)

1979 (29 May). *Sailing Ships (1st series). Whaling Ships. T* **164** *and similar horiz designs. Multicoloured. W* **61** *(sideways). P* 13½.
540 12 s. Type **164** 40 10
541 14 s. *Lagoda* 40 10
542 24 s. *James T. Arnold* 60 20
543 50 s. *Splendid* 80 85
540/3 *Set of* 4 2·00 1·10
See also Nos. 561/4 and 584/7.

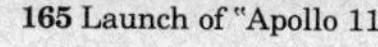

12
SENE
SAMOA I SISIFO

165 Launch of "Apollo 11"   **166** Sir Rowland Hill (statue) and Penny Black

(Des J.W. Litho Questa)

1979 (20 June). *10th Anniv of Moon Landing. T* **165** *and similar designs in chocolate and dull vermilion* (12 *s.*) *or multicoloured (others). W* **61** *(sideways on* 14, 26 *s. and* $1). *P* 14½ × 14 (12, 24, 50 *s.*) *or* 14 × 14½ *(others)*.
544 12 s. Type **165** 20 10
545 14 s. Lunar module and astronaut on Moon (*horiz*) 25 10
546 24 s. View of Earth from Moon 30 15
547 26 s. Astronaut on Moon (*horiz*) 30 15
548 50 s. Lunar and Command modules in Space 45 55
549 $1 Command module after splash-down (*horiz*) 1·00 1·50
544/9 *Set of* 6 2·25 2·25
MS550 90 × 130 mm. No. 549 1·00 1·75
No. **MS**550 is inscribed "Spashdown" in error.

(Des and litho J.W.)

1979 (27 Aug). *Death Centenary of Sir Rowland Hill. T* **166** *and similar vert designs. Multicoloured. W* **61**. *P* 14.
551 12 s. Type **166** 15 10
552 24 s. Two-penny Blue with "Maltese Cross" postmark 15 15
553 26 s. Sir Rowland Hill and Penny Black 15 15
554 $1 Two-penny Blue and Sir Rowland Hill (statue) 45 75
551/4 *Set of* 4 80 1·00
MS555 128×95 mm. Nos. 551/4 80 1·60
w. Wmk inverted 35·00

167 Anglican Church, Apia

(Des A. Peake. Photo Courvoisier)

1979 (22 Oct). *Christmas. Churches. T* **167** *and similar horiz designs. P* 11½.
556 4 s. black and pale blue 10 10
557 6 s. black and bright yellow-green 10 10
558 26 s. black and yellow-ochre 15 10
559 50 s. black and reddish lilac 30 30
556/9 *Set of* 4 45 35
MS560 150 × 124 mm. Nos. 556/9 75 1·25
Designs:—6 s. Congregational Christian, Leulumoega; 26 s. Methodist, Piula; 50 s. Protestant, Apia.
Issued on matt, almost invisible gum.

(Des J. Cooter. Litho Format)

1980 (22 Jan). *Sailing Ships (2nd series). Whaling Ships. Horiz designs as T* **164**. *Multicoloured. W* **61** *(sideways) P* 13½.
561 12 s. *William Hamilton* 35 10
562 14 s. *California* 35 15
563 24 s. *Liverpool II* 40 25
564 50 s. *Two Brothers* 60 1·10
561/4 *Set of* 4 1·50 1·40

168 "Equipment for a Hospital"

(Des M. Goaman (12, 50 s.), E. Roberts (others). Photo Heraclio Fournier)

1980 (26 Mar). *Anniversaries. T* **168** *and similar horiz designs. Multicoloured. P* 13½ × 14.
565 12 s. Type **168** 45 10
566 13 s. John Williams, dove with olive twig and commemorative inscription 45 20
567 14 s. Dr. Wilhelm Solf (instigator), flag and commemorative inscription 50 15
568 24 s. Cairn Monument 65 25
569 26 s. Williams Memorial, Savai'i 70 25
570 50 s. Paul P. Harris (founder) 1·25 2·00
565/70 *Set of* 6 3·50 2·75
Commemorations:—12, 50 s. 75th anniversary of Rotary International; 13, 26 s. 150th anniversary of John Williams' (missionary) arrival in Samoa; 14, 24 s. 80th anniversary of raising of German flag.

169 Samoan Village Scene

(Des J.W. Litho Walsall)

1980 (6 May). *"London 1980" International Stamp Exhibition. Sheet* 140 × 81 *mm. W* **61** *(sideways). P* 14.
MS571 **169** $1 multicoloured 60 90

170 Queen Elizabeth the Queen Mother in 1970

(Des Harrison. Litho Questa)

1980 (4 Aug). *80th Birthday of Queen Elizabeth the Queen Mother. P* 14.
572 **170** 50 s. multicoloured 30 30

171 1964 2nd Anniversary of New Zealand–Samoa Treaty of Friendship 2 s. Commemorative and "Zeapex '80" Emblem

(Des E. Roberts. Photo Heraclio Fournier)

1980 (23 Aug). *"Zeapex '80" International Stamp Exhibition, Auckland. Sheet* 130 × 80 *mm. P* 14.
MS573 **171** $1 multicoloured 60 90

172 Afiamalu Satellite Earth Station

(Des and photo Courvoisier)

1980 (20 Sept). *Afiamalu Satellite Earth Station. T* **172** *and similar horiz designs. Multicoloured. P* 11½.

574 12 s. Type **172** 15 10
575 14 s. Satellite station (*different*) 20 10
576 24 s. Satellite station and map of Savai'i and Upolu 30 15
577 50 s. Satellite and globe 60 60
574/7 .. .. *Set of* 4 1·10 85

173 Afiamalu Satellite Earth Station 24 s. Commemorative Stamp and "Sydpex 80" Emblem

(Des E. Roberts. Litho Sprintpak, Mayne Nickless Ltd, Australia)

1980 (29 Sept). *"Sydpex 80" International Stamp Exhibition, Sydney. Sheet* 130 × 80 *mm. Imperf.*

MS578 **173** $2 multicoloured .. .. .. 1·00 1·00

174 "The Saviour" (J. Poynton)

175 President Franklin D. Roosevelt and Hyde Park (family home)

(Des G. Vasarhelyi. Litho Format)

1980 (28 Oct). *Christmas. Paintings. T* **174** *and similar vert designs. Multicoloured. W* **61**. *P* 13½.

579 8 s. Type **174** 10 10
580 14 s. "Madonna and Child" (Lealofi F. Siaopo) 10 10
581 27 s. "Nativity" (Pasila Feata) 15 10
582 50 s. "Yuletide" (R. P. Aiono) 25 40
579/82 .. .. *Set of* 4 55 55
MS583 90×105 mm. Nos. 579/82 .. .. 1·00 1·50
w. Wmk inverted .. .. 15·00

(Des J. Cooter. Litho Format)

1981 (26 Jan). *Sailing Ships* (3*rd series*). *Horiz designs as T* **164**. *Multicoloured. P* 13½.

584 12 s. *Ocean* (whaling ship) 30 10
585 18 s. *Horatio* (whaling ship) 40 15
586 27 s. H.M.S. *Calliope* (screw corvette) .. 55 25
587 32 s. H.M.S. *Calypso* (screw corvette) .. 60 50
584/7 .. .. .. *Set of* 4 1·60 90

(Des J.W. Litho Format)

1981 (29 Apr). *International Year for Disabled Persons. President Franklin D. Roosevelt Commemoration. T* **175** *and similar horiz designs. Multicoloured. P* 14.

588 12 s. Type **175** 15 10
589 18 s. Roosevelt's inauguration, 4 March 1933 15 10
590 27 s. Franklin and Eleanor Roosevelt .. 20 15
591 32 s. Roosevelt's Lend-lease Bill (Atlantic convoy, 1941) 25 20
592 38 s. Roosevelt the philatelist 25 25
593 $1 Campobello House (summer home) .. 50 90
588/93 .. .. .. *Set of* 6 1·40 1·50

176 Hotel Tusitala

177 Wedding Bouquet from Samoa

(Des and litho Walsall)

1981 (29 June). *Tourism. T* **176** *and similar horiz designs. Multicoloured. W* **61** (*sideways*). *P* 14½ × 14.

594 12 s. Type **176** 15 10
595 18 s. Apia Harbour 25 15
596 27 s. Aggie Grey's Hotel 25 20
597 32 s. Preparation for Ceremonial Kava .. 30 30
598 54 s. Piula water pool 55 55
594/8 .. .. *Set of* 5 1·40 1·10

(Des J.W. Litho Walsall)

1981 (22 July). *Royal Wedding. T* **177** *and similar vert designs. Multicoloured. W* **61**. *P* 14.

599 18 s. Type **177** 15 10
600 32 s. Prince Charles as Colonel-in-Chief, Gordon Highlanders 20 10
601 $1 Prince Charles and Lady Diana Spencer 30 50
599/601 .. .. *Set of* 3 60 60

178 Tattooing Instruments

179 Black Marlin

(Des E. Roberts. Litho Cambec Press, Melbourne)

1981 (29 Sept). *Tattooing. T* **178** *and similar horiz designs. Multicoloured. P* 13½.

602 12 s. Type **178** 15 20
a. Horiz strip of 4. Nos. 602/5 .. .. 1·00
603 18 s. First stage of tattooing 20 25
604 27 s. Progressive stage 25 30
605 $1 Completed tattoo 50 70
602/5 .. .. *Set of* 4 1·00 1·25

Nos. 602/5 were printed together, *se-tenant*, in horizontal strips of 4 throughout the sheet.

(Des E. Roberts. Litho Cambec Press, Melbourne)

1981 (9 Oct). *"Philatokyo '81" International Stamp Exhibition, Tokyo. Sheet* 130 × 80 *mm. P* 14 × 13½.

MS606 **179** $2 multicoloured .. .. .. 1·00 1·00

180 *Thespesia populnea*

181 George Washington's Pistol

(Des and litho J.W.)

1981 (30 Nov). *Christmas. Flowers. T* **180** *and similar vert designs. Multicoloured. W* **61**. *P* 13½.

607 11 s. Type **180** 15 10
w. Wmk inverted .. .. .. 3·50
608 15 s. Copper Leaf 20 15
609 23 s. *Allamanda cathartica* 30 25
610 $1 Mango .. .. 75 1·00
607/10 .. .. .. *Set of* 4 1·25 1·40
MS611 86×120 mm. Nos. 607/10 .. .. 1·40 2·25

(Des J.W. Litho Format)

1982 (26 Feb). *250th Birth Anniv of George Washington. T* **181** *and similar horiz designs, each in black, ochre and stone. P* 13½.

612 23 s. Type **181** 25 30
613 25 s. Mount Vernon (Washington's house) .. 25 30
614 34 s. George Washington 30 40
612/14 .. .. .. *Set of* 3 70 90
MS615 104 × 103 mm. $1 Washington taking Oath of Office as President .. .. .. 70 1·00

182 *Forum Samoa* (container ship)

(Des E. Roberts. Litho Cambec Press, Melbourne)

1982 (24 May). *20th Anniv of Independence. T* **182** *and similar horiz designs. Multicoloured. P* 13½ × 14.

616 18 s. Type **182** 30 20
617 23 s. "Air services" 40 30
618 25 s. N.P.F. (National Provident Fund) Building, Apia 40 30
619 $1 "Telecommunications" .. .. .. 1·10 1·00
616/19 .. .. .. *Set of* 4 2·00 1·60

MINIMUM PRICE

The minimum price quote is 10p which represents a handling charge rather than a basis for valuing common stamps. For further notes about prices see introductory pages.

183 Scouts map-reading and "75"

184 Boxing

(Des J.W. Litho Walsall)

1982 (20 July). *75th Anniv of Boy Scout Movement. T* **183** *and similar horiz designs. Multicoloured. W* **61** (*sideways*). *P* 14½.

620 5 s. Type **183** 10 10
621 38 s. Scout salute and "75" 40 40
622 44 s. Scout crossing river by rope, and "75" .. 50 50
623 $1 "Tower" of Scouts and "75" .. .. 1·00 1·00
620/23 .. .. .. *Set of* 4 1·75 1·75
MS624 93 × 81 mm. $1 As No. 623 but with portrait of Lord Baden-Powell replacing emblem (47 × 35 *mm*). P 11 .. .. 1·00 1·10

(Des Garden Studio. Litho Walsall)

1982 (20 Sept). *Commonwealth Games, Brisbane. T* **184** *and similar vert designs. Multicoloured. W w* **14**. *P* 14½.

625 23 s. Type **184** 20 20
626 25 s. Hurdling 20 20
627 34 s. Weightlifting 25 30
628 $1 Bowling .. .. 75 1·50
625/8 .. .. .. *Set of* 4 1·25 2·00

185 "Mary and Joseph" (Emma Dunlop)

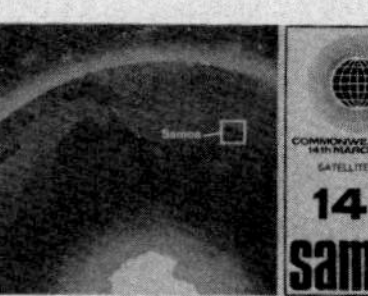

186 Satellite View of Australasia

(Des J.W. Litho Questa)

1982 (15 Nov). *Christmas. Children's Pictures. T* **185** *and similar horiz designs. Multicoloured. W* **61** (*sideways*). *P* 14 × 14½.

629 11 s. Type **185** 15 10
630 15 s. "Mary, Joseph and baby Jesus" (Marie Tofaeono) 15 15
631 38 s. "Madonna and Child" (Ralph Laban and Fetalaiga Fareni) 40 30
632 $1 "Mother and Child" (Panapa Pouesi) .. 90 2·00
629/32 .. .. .. *Set of* 4 1·40 2·25
MS633 130 × 119 mm. Nos. 629/32 .. .. 1·60 2·75

(Des Walsall. Litho Enschedé)

1983 (23 Feb). *Commonwealth Day. T* **186** *and similar horiz designs. Multicoloured. W w* **14** (*sideways*). *P* 13 × 13½.

634 14 s. Type **186** 10 10
635 29 s. Flag of Samoa 15 20
636 43 s. Harvesting copra 25 25
637 $1 Head of State Malietoa Tanumafili II .. 50 80
634/7 .. .. .. *Set of* 4 90 1·25

187 Douglas DC-1

(Des J.W. Litho Questa)

1983 (7 June). *Bicentenary of Manned Flight and 50th Anniv of Douglas Commercial Aircraft. Sheet,* 215 × 113 *mm, containing horiz designs as T* **187**. *Multicoloured. W w* **14** (*sideways*). *P* 14.

MS638 32 s. × 10, each design showing a different Douglas aircraft from the DC-1 to the DC-10 3·25 3·25

188 Pole-vaulting

189 Lime

(Des McCombie Skinner Studio. Litho Format)

1983 (31 Aug). *South Pacific Games. T* **188** *and similar vert designs. Multicoloured.* W w **14.** *P* 14 × 14½.
639 8 s. Type **188** . . 35 10
640 15 s. Netball . . 45 20
641 25 s. Tennis . . 70 50
642 32 s. Weight-lifting . . 70 70
643 35 s. Boxing . . 75 85
644 46 s. Football . . 90 1·10
645 48 s. Golf . . 1·00 1·40
646 56 s. Rugby . . 1·10 1·60
639/46 . . *Set of* 8 5·50 5·75

(Des E. Roberts. Litho Enschedé)

1983 (28 Sept)–**84.** *Fruit. T* **189** *and similar vert designs. Multicoloured.* W w **14** (*inverted on* 1 *s.*). *P* 13½ ($2 *to* $5) *or* 14 × 13½ (*others*).
647 1 s. Type **189** . . 10 60
648 2 s. Star fruit . . 10 70
649 3 s. Mangosteen . . 10 70
650 4 s. Lychee . . 10 70
651 7 s. Passion fruit . . 15 70
652 8 s. Mango . . 15 70
653 11 s. Pawpaw . . 20 70
654 13 s. Pineapple . . 20 70
655 14 s. Breadfruit . . 20 70
656 15 s. Banana . . 30 70
657 21 s. Cashew Nut (30.11.83) . . 1·75 1·25
658 25 s. Guava (30.11.83) . . 1·75 70
659 32 s. Water Melon (30.11.83) . . 1·75 1·25
660 48 s. Sasalapa (30.11.83) . . 2·00 2·00
661 56 s. Avocado (30.11.83) . . 2·00 2·00
662 $1 Coconut (30.11.83) . . 2·00 2·00
663 $2 Vi Apple (11.4.84) . . 1·75 3·00
664 $4 Grapefruit (11.4.84) . . 2·50 4·50
665 $5 Orange (11.4.84) . . 3·00 4·75
647/65 . . *Set of* 19 18·00 25·00
Nos. 663/5 are larger, size 25 × 35½ mm.

190 On Parade **191** Togitogiga Falls, Upolu

(Des Brian Melton Studio. Litho Format)

1983 (10 Oct). *Centenary of Boys' Brigade. Sheet* 120 × 83 *mm.* W w **14.** *P* 14.
MS668 **190** $1 multicoloured . . 2·50 2·00

(Litho Format)

1984 (15 Feb). *Scenic Views. T* **191** *and similar horiz designs. Multicoloured.* W w **14** (*sideways*). *P* 14.
669 25 s. Type **191** . . 40 15
670 32 s. Lano Beach, Savai'i . . 50 60
671 48 s. Mulinu'u Point, Upolu . . 70 1·10
672 56 s. Nu'utele Island . . 70 1·75
669/72 . . *Set of* 4 2·10 3·25

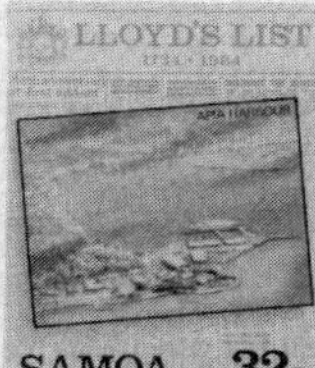

19 th U.P.U. CONGRESS
HAMBURG 1984

192 Apia Harbour **(193)**

(Des Jennifer Toombs. Litho Questa)

1984 (24 May). *250th Anniv of "Lloyd's List" (newspaper). T* **192** *and similar vert designs. Multicoloured.* W w **14.** *P* 14 × 14½.
673 32 s. Type **192** . . 25 20
674 48 s. Apia hurricane, 1889 . . 40 45
675 60 s. *Forum Samoa* (container ship) . . 45 50
676 $1 *Matua* (inter-island freighter) . . 75 80
673/6 . . *Set of* 4 1·75 1·75

1984 (7 June). *Universal Postal Union Congress, Hamburg. No.* 662 *optd with T* **193.**
677 $1 Coconut . . 1·40 80

194 Olympic Stadium

(Des Garden Studio. Litho Format)

1984 (26 June). *Olympic Games, Los Angeles. T* **194** *and similar horiz designs. Multicoloured.* W w **14** (*sideways*). *P* 14½.
678 25 s. Type **194** . . 20 20
679 32 s. Weightlifting . . 20 25
680 48 s. Boxing . . 30 45
681 $1 Running . . 60 80
678/81 . . *Set of* 4 1·10 1·50
MS682 170 × 120 mm. Nos. 678/81 . . 1·40 1·60

195 Government Aircraft Factory N24A Nomad

(Des E. Roberts. Litho Walsall)

1984 (21 Sept). *"Ausipex" International Stamp Exhibition, Melbourne. Sheet* 131 × 80 mm. W w **14** (*sideways*). *P* 14.
MS683 **195** $2.50, multicoloured . . 4·00 5·00

196 "Faith"

(Litho Walsall)

1984 (7 Nov). *Christmas. "The Three Virtues" (Raphael). T* **196** *and similar horiz designs. Multicoloured.* W w **14** (*sideways*). *P* 14.
684 25 s. Type **196** . . 30 15
685 35 s. "Hope" . . 40 40
686 $1 "Charity" . . 1·60 2·50
684/6 . . *Set of* 3 2·10 2·75
MS687 63 × 76 mm. Nos. 684/6 . . 2·50 3·50

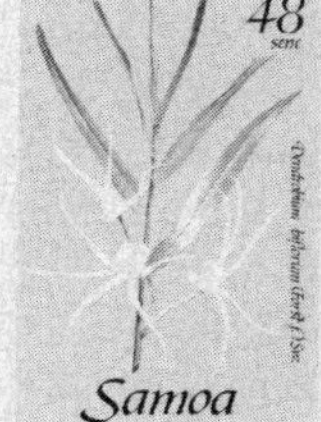

197 *Dendrobium biflorum* **198** Ford "Model A", 1903

(Des Jennifer Toombs. Litho Format)

1985 (23 Jan). *Orchids* (1*st series*). *T* **197** *and similar vert designs. Multicoloured. P* 14.
688 48 s. Type **197** . . 55 35
689 56 s. *Dendrobium vaupelianum Kraenzl* . . 65 45
690 67 s. *Glomera montana* . . 80 60
691 $1 *Spathoglottis plicata* . . 1·10 1·10
688/91 . . *Set of* 4 2·75 2·25
See also Nos. 818/21.

(Des A. Theobald. Litho Walsall)

1985 (26 Mar). *Veteran and Vintage Cars. T* **198** *and similar horiz designs. Multicoloured. P* 14.
692 48 s. Type **198** . . 1·00 50
693 56 s. Chevrolet "Tourer", 1912 . . 1·10 75
694 67 s. Morris "Oxford", 1913 . . 1·25 1·25
695 $1 Austin "Seven", 1923 . . 1·75 2·50
692/5 . . *Set of* 4 4·50 4·50

199 *Dictyophora indusiata* **200** The Queen Mother at Liverpool Street Station

(Des Doreen McGuinness. Litho Walsall)

1985 (17 Apr). *Fungi. T* **199** *and similar vert designs. Multicoloured. P* 14½.
696 48 s. Type **199** . . 1·10 55
697 56 s. *Ganoderma tornatum* . . 1·25 85
698 67 s. *Mycena chlorophos* . . 1·60 1·75
699 $1 *Mycobonia flava* . . 2·25 3·25
696/9 . . *Set of* 4 5·50 5·75

(Des A. Theobald ($2), C. Abbott (others). Litho Questa)

1985 (7 June). *Life and Times of Queen Elizabeth the Queen Mother. T* **200** *and similar vert designs. Multicoloured.* W w **16.** *P* 14½ × 14.
700 32 s. At Glamis Castle, aged 9 . . 30 25
701 48 s. At Prince Henry's Christening with other members of the Royal family . . 40 35
702 56 s. Type **200** . . 45 45
703 $1 With Prince Henry at his christening (from photo by Lord Snowdon) . . 75 1·25
700/3 . . *Set of* 4 1·75 2·10
MS704 91 × 73 mm. $2 Arriving at Tattenham Corner Station with the Queen. Wmk sideways . . 2·25 1·75

201 Map of Pacific and Exhibition Logo **202** I.Y.Y. Emblem and Map (Alaska—Arabian Gulf)

(Des D. Hartley. Litho Enschedé)

1985 (26 Aug). *"Expo '85" World Fair, Japan. Sheet* 70 × 45 *mm. P* 14.
MS705 **201** $2 multicoloured . . 1·50 2·00

(Des Garden Studio. Litho B.D.T.)

1985 (18 Sept) *International Youth Year. T* **202** *and similar vert designs, showing background map and emblem (Nos.* 706 *and* 710) *or raised arms (others). Multicoloured. P* 14.
706 60 s. Type **202** . . 40 45
a. Horiz strip of 5. Nos. 706/10 . . 1·75
707 60 s. Raised arms (Pakistan–Mexico) . . 40 45
708 60 s. Raised arms (Central America–China) . . 40 45
709 60 s. Raised arms (Japan–Greenland) . . 40 45
710 60 s. As Type **202** (Iceland–Siberia) . . 40 45
706/10 . . *Set of* 5 1·75 2·00
Nos. 706/10 were printed together, *se-tenant,* in horizontal strips of 5, throughout the sheet, the background forming a composite design of three continuous world maps.

203 "System" **204** *Hypolimnas bolina*

(Des L. Curtis. Litho Format)

1985 (5 Nov). *Christmas. T* **203** *and similar vert designs showing illustrations by Millicent Sowerby for R. L. Stevenson's "A Child's Garden of Verses". Multicoloured. P* 14 × 14½.
711 32 s. Type **203** . . 20 25
712 48 s. "Time to Rise" . . 30 35
713 56 s. "Auntie's Skirts" . . 35 40
714 $1 "Good Children" . . 65 1·00
711/14 . . *Set of* 4 1·40 1·75
MS715 87 × 109 mm. Nos. 711/14 . . 1·75 3·00

(Des Annette Robinson. Litho Walsall)

1986 (13 Feb). *Butterflies. T* **204** *and similar vert designs. Multicoloured.* W w **16.** *P* 14½ × 14.
716 25 s. Type **204** . . 35 30
717 32 s. *Belenois java* . . 40 30
718 48 s. *Deudorix epijarbas* . . 60 45
719 56 s. *Badamia exclamationis* . . 65 85
720 60 s. *Danaus hamata* . . 65 85
721 $1 *Catochrysops taitensis* . . 1·00 1·75
716/21 . . *Set of* 6 3·25 4·00

205 Halley's Comet over Apia **206** U.S.S. *Vincennes* (frigate)

(Des N. Shewring. Litho Walsall)

1986 (24 Mar). *Appearance of Halley's Comet. T* **205** *and similar horiz designs. Multicoloured. W w* **16** *(sideways). P* 14 × 14½.

722 32 s. Type **205** 30 20
723 48 s. Edmond Halley 45 35
724 60 s. Comet passing Earth 50 40
725 $2 Preparing *Giotto* spacecraft .. .. 1·25 1·50
722/5 .. .. *Set of* 4 2·25 2·25

(Des A. Theobald. Litho Questa)

1986 (21 Apr). *60th Birthday of Queen Elizabeth II. Vert designs as T* **230a** *of Jamaica. Multicoloured. W w* **16**. *P* 14½×14.

726 32 s. Engagement photograph, 1947 .. 15 20
727 48 s. Queen with Liberty Bell, U.S.A., 1976 .. 20 35
728 56 s. At Apia, 1977 .. .. 25 40
729 67 s. At Badminton Horse Trials, 1978 .. 30 45
730 $2 At Crown Agents Head Office, London, 1983 .. .. 80 1·25
726/30 .. .. *Set of* 5 1·50 2·40

(Des E. Nisbet. Litho Questa)

1986 (22 May). *"Ameripex '86" International Stamp Exhibition, Chicago. T* **206** *and similar horiz designs. Multicoloured. P* 14 × 14½.

731 48 s. Type **206** 30 35
732 56 s. Sikorsky S-42A flying boat 35 40
733 60 s. U.S.S. *Swan* (patrol boat) 35 40
734 $2 "Apollo 10" descending .. .. 1·10 1·50
731/4 .. .. *Set of* 4 1·90 2·40

207 Vailima

(Des E. Roberts. Litho Cambec Press, Melbourne)

1986 (4 Aug). *"Stampex '86" Stamp Exhibition, Adelaide. Sheet* 158 × 97 *mm. P* 13½.

MS735 **207** $3 multicoloured .. .. .. 3·50 3·50

208 High-finned Grouper

(Des P. Rymers. Litho Walsall)

1986 (13 Aug). *Fishes. T* **208** *and similar horiz designs. Multicoloured. P* 14.

736 32 s. Type **208** 50 30
737 48 s. Scarlet-finned Squirrelfish 80 40
738 60 s. Yellow-edged Lyretail ("Lunartail Grouper") 90 80
739 67 s. Yellow-striped Snapper .. .. 95 1·25
740 $1 Big-scaled Soldierfish .. .. 1·25 1·75
736/40 .. .. *Set of* 5 4·00 4·00

209 Samoan Prime Ministers, American Presidents and Parliament House

210 *Hibiscus rosa-sinensis* and Map of Samoa

(Des N. Shewring. Litho Format)

1986 (1 Dec). *Christmas. 25th Anniv of United States Peace Corps. T* **209** *and similar horiz design. Multicoloured. P* 14½.

741 45 s. Type **209** 25 30
742 60 s. French and American Presidents, Samoan Prime Minister and Statue of Liberty 35 40
MS743 131 × 72 mm. Nos. 741/2 .. .. .. 3·50 4·50

No. **MS**743 also commemorates the Centenary of the Statue of Liberty.

(Des local artist, adapted G. Vasarhelyi. Litho Format)

1987 (16 Feb). *25th Anniv of Independence. T* **210** *and similar multicoloured designs. P* 14½ × 14 ($2) *or* 14 × 14½ *(others)*.

744 15 s. Type **210** 25 10
745 45 s. Parliament Building, Apia 40 30
746 60 s. Longboat race at Independence celebration 45 40
747 70 s. Peace dove and laurel wreath .. 50 50
748 $2 Head of State Malietoa Tanumafili II and national flag *(horiz)* .. .. 1·25 1·75
744/8 .. .. *Set of* 5 2·50 2·75

211 Gulper (*Eurypharynx*)

(Des J. Walker. Litho Format)

1987 (31 Mar). *Deep Ocean Fishes. T* **211** *and similar horiz designs. Multicoloured. P* 14.

749 45 s. Type **211** 45 30
750 60 s. Hatchetfish 60 60
751 70 s. Bearded Angelfish 70 95
752 $2 Swallower (*Saccopharynx*) .. .. 1·40 2·75
749/52 .. .. *Set of* 4 2·75 4·25

212 Workmen trimming Logs and building Fale (traditional house)

(Des Jennifer Toombs. Litho Questa)

1987 (13 June). *"Capex 87" International Stamp Exhibition, Toronto. Sheet* 122 × 66 *mm. P* 14½.

MS753 **212** $3 multicoloured .. .. .. 1·60 1·75

213 Lefaga Beach, Upolu

214 Abel Tasman

(Des D. Miller. Litho Questa)

1987 (29 July). *Coastal Scenery. T* **213** *and similar horiz designs. Multicoloured. P* 14.

754 45 s. Type **213** 70 30
755 60 s. Vaisala Beach, Savaii 90 40
756 70 s. Solosolo Beach, Upolu 95 60
757 $2 Neiafu Beach, Savaii .. .. .. 1·75 2·00
754/7 .. .. *Set of* 4 3·75 3·00

(Des M. Bradbery. Litho Questa)

1987 (30 Sept). *Bicentenary of Australian Settlement* (1988) *(1st issue). Explorers of the Pacific. T* **214** *and similar horiz designs. Multicoloured. P* 14 × 14½.

758 40 s. Type **214** 50 25
759 45 s. Capt. James Cook 65 30
760 80 s. Comte Louis-Antoine de Bougainville 80 65
761 $2 Comte Jean de la Perouse .. .. 1·40 1·60
758/61 .. .. *Set of* 4 3·00 2·50
MS762 90 × 73 mm. No. 761 .. .. .. 1·40 1·50

See also Nos. 768/72.

(215)

216 Christmas Tree

1987 (16 Oct). *"Hafnia" International Stamp Exhibition, Copenhagen. No.* **MS**762 *optd with T* **215** *in red.*

MS763 90 × 73 mm. $2 Comte Jean de la Perouse .. .. 1·75 1·75

(Des Josephine Martin. Litho Questa)

1987 (30 Nov). *Christmas. T* **216** *and similar square designs. Multicoloured. P* 14.

764 40 s. Type **216** 30 25
765 45 s. Family going to church 40 30
766 50 s. Bamboo fire-gun 45 30
767 80 s. Inter-island transport .. .. .. 1·10 70
764/7 .. .. *Set of* 4 2·00 1·40

OMNIBUS ISSUES

Details, together with prices for complete sets, of the various Omnibus issues from the 1935 Silver Jubilee series to date are included in a special section following Zimbabwe at the end of Volume 2.

217 Samoa Coat of Arms and Australia Post Logo

218 Airport Terminal and Douglas DC-9 Airliner taking off

(Des A. Theobald. Litho Questa)

1988 (27 Jan). *Bicentenary of Australian Settlement (2nd issue). Postal Services. T* **217** *and similar vert designs. Multicoloured. P* 14½ × 14.

768 45 s. Type **217** 75 75
a. Horiz strip of 5. Nos. 768/72 .. .. 3·25
769 45 s. Samoan mail van and Boeing 727 airplane 75 75
770 45 s. Loading Boeing 727 mail plane .. 75 75
771 45 s. Australian mail van and Boeing 727 75 75
772 45 s. "Congratulations Australia" message on airmail letter 75 75
768/72 .. .. *Set of* 5 3·25 3·25

Nos. 768/72 were printed together, *se-tenant*, in horizontal strips of 5 throughout the sheet, Nos. 769/71 forming a composite design.

(Des E. Nisbet. Litho Walsall)

1988 (24 Mar). *Opening of Faleolo Airport. T* **218** *and similar horiz designs. Multicoloured. P* 13 × 13½.

773 40 s. Type **218** 55 25
774 45 s. Boeing 727 .. .. 60 30
775 60 s. De Havilland D.H.C.6 Twin Otter .. 75 60
776 70 s. Boeing 737 .. .. 85 85
777 80 s. Boeing 727 and control tower .. 90 1·00
778 $1 Douglas DC-9 over "fale" (house) .. 1·00 1·25
773/8 .. .. *Set of* 6 4·25 3·75

219 "Expo '88" Pacific Islands Village

220 Mormon Temple, Apia

(Des C. Abbott. Litho Walsall)

1988 (30 Apr). *"Expo '88" World Fair, Brisbane. T* **219** *and similar horiz designs. Multicoloured. P* 14 × 14½.

779 45 s. Type **219** 30 30
780 70 s. Expo Complex and monorail .. .. 1·00 1·00
781 $2 Map of Australia showing Brisbane .. 1·75 2·00
779/81 .. .. *Set of* 3 2·75 3·00

(Des Jennifer Toombs. Litho CPE Australia Ltd, Melbourne)

1988 (9 June). *Centenary of Arrival of the Latter-Day Saints in Samoa. Sheet* 86 × 77 *mm. P* 13½.

MS782 **220** $3 multicoloured .. .. .. 1·50 1·60

221 Athletics

222 Spotted Triller

(Des D. Miller. Litho Format)

1988 (10 Aug). *Olympic Games, Seoul. T* **221** *and similar vert designs. Multicoloured. P* 14.

783 15 s. Type **221** 10 10
784 60 s. Weightlifting 30 35
785 80 s. Boxing 40 45
786 $2 Olympic stadium .. .. 1·10 1·25
783/6 .. .. *Set of* 4 1·75 1·90
MS787 85 × 100 mm. Nos. 783/6 .. .. 1·90 2·10

(Des D. Johnston. Litho CPE Australia Ltd, Melbourne (Nos. 788/97), Questa (Nos. 798/803))

1988 (17 Aug)–**89**. *Birds. Multicoloured.*

(a) Vert designs as T **222**. *P* 13½

788 10 s. Type **222** 50 30
789 15 s. Samoan Wood Rail 60 35
790 20 s. Flat-billed Kingfisher 75 45
791 25 s. Samoan Fantail 75 45
792 35 s. Scarlet Robin 80 55
793 40 s. Black-breasted Honeyeater ("Mao") .. 80 55
794 50 s. Cardinal Honeyeater 90 40
795 65 s. Yellow-fronted Whistler .. .. .. 1·25 50
796 75 s. Many-coloured Fruit Dove .. .. 1·40 60
797 85 s. White-throated Pigeon .. .. .. 1·50 70

(b) Horiz designs, each 45 × 28 mm. P 13½ × 14.

798 75 s. Silver Gull (28.2.89) .. .. .. 1·25 80
799 85 s. Great Frigate Bird (28.2.89) .. .. 1·40 90
800 90 s. Eastern Reef Heron (28.2.89) .. .. 1·50 1·25
801 $3 Short-tailed Albatross (28.2.89) .. 1·25 1·40
802 $10 White Tern (31.7.89) .. .. .. 4·50 4·75
803 $20 Shy Albatross (31.7.89) .. .. 8·75 9·00
788/803 .. .. *Set of* 16 25·00 21·00

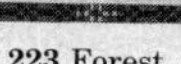

223 Forest

224 Congregational Church of Jesus, Apia

(Des G. Vasarhelyi. Litho Questa)

1988 (25 Oct). *National Conservation Campaign. T* **223** *and similar multicoloured designs. P 14 × 13½ (15, 40, 45 s.) or 13½ × 14 (others).*

807 15 s. Type **223** 40 15
808 40 s. Samoan handicrafts 50 30
809 45 s. Forest wildlife 75 35
810 50 s. Careful use of water (*horiz*) 75 40
811 60 s. Fishing (*horiz*) .. .. .. 1·00 60
812 $1 Coconut plantation (*horiz*) .. .. 1·10 1·00
807/12 .. .. *Set of* 6 4·00 2·50

(Des N. Shewring. Litho Format)

1988 (14 Nov). *Christmas. Samoan Churches. T* **224** *and similar vert designs. Multicoloured. P 14.*

813 15 s. Type **224** 15 10
814 40 s. Roman Catholic Church, Leauva'a .. 35 25
815 45 s. Congregational Christian Church, Moataa 40 30
816 $2 Baha'i Temple, Vailima .. .. 1·50 1·75
813/16 .. .. *Set of* 4 2·25 2·25
MS817 143 × 64 mm. Nos. 813/16 .. .. 2·40 2·50

225 *Phaius flavus*

226 *Eber* (German gunboat)

(Des H. Bevan. Litho Questa)

1989 (31 Jan). *Orchids (2nd series). T* **225** *and similar vert designs. Multicoloured. P 14 × 13½.*

818 15 s. Type **225** 15 10
819 45 s. *Calanthe triplicata* 35 30
820 60 s. *Luisia teretifolia* 40 35
821 $3 *Dendrobium mohlianum* .. .. 1·75 2·00
818/21 .. .. *Set of* 4 2·40 2·50

(Des E. Nisbet. Litho Walsall)

1989 (16 Mar). *Centenary of Great Apia Hurricane. T* **226** *and similar horiz designs. Multicoloured. P 14.*

822 50 s. Type **226** 75 55
a. Horiz strip of 4. Nos. 822/5 .. .. 3·50
823 65 s. *Olga* (German corvette) 85 65
824 85 s. H.M.S. *Calliope* (screw corvette) .. 1·00 75
825 $2 U.S.S. *Vandalia* (corvette) .. .. 1·50 1·40
822/5 .. .. *Set of* 4 3·50 3·00

Nos. 822/5 were printed together, *se-tenant*, in horizontal strips of 4 throughout the sheet.

See also No. **MS**839.

227 Samoan Red Cross Youth Group on Parade

228 Virgin Mary and Joseph

(Des L. Curtis. Litho Questa)

1989 (15 May). *125th Anniv of International Red Cross. T* **227** *and similar vert designs. Multicoloured. P 14½×14.*

826 50 s. Type **227** 30 30
827 65 s. Blood donors 40 45
828 75 s. Practising first aid 45 55
829 $3 Red Cross volunteers carrying patient 1·60 2·25
826/9 .. .. *Set of* 4 2·50 3·25

(Des A. Theobald ($3), D. Miller (others). Litho Questa)

1989 (20 July). *20th Anniv of First Manned Landing on Moon. Multicoloured designs as T* **126** *of Ascension. W w* **16** *(sideways on 50, 65 c.). P 14×13½ (18 s., $2) or 14 (others).*

830 18 s. Saturn rocket on mobile launcher .. 30 15
831 50 s. Crew of "Apollo 14" (30×30 *mm*) .. 50 35
832 65 s. "Apollo 14" emblem (30×30 *mm*) .. 65 45
833 $2 Tracks of lunar transporter .. .. 1·50 1·75
830/3 .. .. *Set of* 4 2·75 2·40
MS834 100×83 mm. $3 Aldrin with U.S. flag on Moon. P 14×13½ .. .. 2·25 3·00

(Des T. Chance. Litho Cartor)

1989 (1 Nov). *Christmas. T* **228** *and similar horiz designs. Multicoloured. P 13½.*

835 18 s. Type **228** 30 10
836 50 s. Shepherds 65 30
837 55 s. Donkey and ox 70 35
838 $2 Three Wise Men .. .. .. 2·25 3·25
835/8 .. .. *Set of* 4 3·50 3·50

(Litho Walsall)

1989 (17 Nov). *"World Stamp Expo '89" International Stamp Exhibition, Washington. Sheet 91×105 mm containing designs as Nos. 824/5. Multicoloured. W* **61**. *Imperf.*

MS839 85 s. H.M.S. *Calliope*; $2 U.S.S. *Vandalia* 3·75 4·25

229 Pao Pao Outrigger

(Des R. Roberts. Litho Note Ptg Branch, Reserve Bank of Australia)

1990 (31 Jan). *Local Transport. T* **229** *and similar horiz designs. Multicoloured. P 14×15.*

840 18 s. Type **229** 30 20
841 55 s. Fautasi (large canoe) 75 65
842 60 s. Polynesian Airlines De Havilland D.H.C.6 Twin Otter aircraft .. .. 1·25 90
843 $3 *Lady Samoa* (ferry) .. .. .. 3·50 4·00
840/3 .. .. *Set of* 4 5·25 5·25

230 Bismarck and Brandenburg Gate, Berlin

(Des G. Vasarhelyi. Litho Cartor)

1990 (19 Apr). *Treaty of Berlin, 1889, and Opening of Berlin Wall, 1989. T* **230** *and similar horiz designs. Multicoloured. P 14×13½.*

844 75 s. Type **230** .. .. 1·50 1·75
a. Horiz pair. Nos. 844/5 .. .. 4·25 4·75
845 $3 *Adler* (German steam gunboat) .. 2·75 3·00

Nos. 844/5 were printed together, *se-tenant*, in horizontal pairs throughout the sheet, each pair forming a composite design showing Berliners on the Wall near the Brandenburg Gate.

231 Penny Black and Alexandra Palace, London

(Des G. Vasarhelyi. Litho Cartor)

1990 (3 May). *"Stamp World London 90" International Stamp Exhibition. P 14×13½.*

846 **231** $3 multicoloured .. .. .. 2·25 2·75

232 Visitors' Bureau

(Des D. Miller. Litho B.D.T.)

1990 (30 July). *Tourism. T* **232** *and similar horiz designs. Multicoloured. P 14.*

847 18 s. Type **232** 30 10
848 50 s. Village resort 55 30
849 65 s. Aggie's Hotel 70 60
850 $3 Swimming pool, Tusitala Hotel .. 2·50 3·50
847/50 .. .. *Set of* 4 3·50 4·00

233 1964 2nd Anniv of Treaty of Friendship 3 s. Commemorative and "NZ 1990" Logo

(Des N. Eustis. Litho Leigh-Mardon Ltd, Melbourne)

1990 (24 Aug). *"New Zealand 1990" International Stamp Exhibition, Auckland. Sheet 130×85 mm. P 13.*

MS851 **233** $3 multicoloured .. .. .. 2·75 3·50

234 "Virgin and Child" (Bellini)

235 William Draper III (administrator) and 40th Anniv Logo

(Des G. Vasarhelyi. Litho Security Printers (M), Malaysia)

1990 (31 Oct). *Christmas. Paintings. T* **234** *and similar vert designs. Multicoloured. P 12½.*

852 18 s. Type **234** 30 10
853 50 s. "Virgin and Child with St. Peter and St. Paul" (Bouts) 70 30
854 55 s. "School of Love" (Correggio) 75 35
855 $3 "Virgin and Child" (Cima) .. .. 3·25 4·25
852/5 .. .. *Set of* 4 4·50 4·50

The 55 s. value should have shown "The Madonna of the Basket" by the same artist and is so inscribed.

(Des D. Miller. Litho Cartor)

1990 (26 Nov). *40th Anniv of U.N. Development Programme. P 13½.*

856 **235** $3 multicoloured .. .. .. 2·50 3·25

236 Black-capped Lory

237 Peter Fatialofa (Samoan captain)

(Des R. Roberts. Litho B.D.T.)

1991 (8 Apr). *Parrots. T* **236** *and similar vert designs. Multicoloured. P 13½.*

857 18 s. Type **236** 50 30
858 50 s. Eclectus Parrot 80 55
859 65 s. Scarlet Macaw .. .. .. 1·00 70
860 $3 Palm Cockatoo .. .. .. 2·50 3·50
857/60 .. .. *Set of* 4 4·25 4·50

(Des D. Miller. Litho Questa)

1991 (17 June). *65th Birthday of Queen Elizabeth II and 70th Birthday of Prince Philip. Vert designs as T* **58** *of Kiribati. Multicoloured. W w* **16** *(sideways). P 14½×14.*

861 75 s. Prince Philip in the countryside .. 90 1·25
a. Horiz pair. Nos. 861/2 separated by label .. .. 2·40 3·00
862 $2 Queen wearing yellow lei .. .. 1·50 1·75

Nos. 861/2 were printed together in a similar sheet format to Nos. 366/7 of Kiribati.

(Des G. Vasarhelyi. Litho Questa)

1991 (21 Oct). *World Cup Rugby Championships. Sheet* 121×75 *mm. P* $14^{1}/_{2}$×14.
MS863 **237** $5 multicoloured . . . . . . 6·50 7·00

238 "O Come All Ye Faithful"

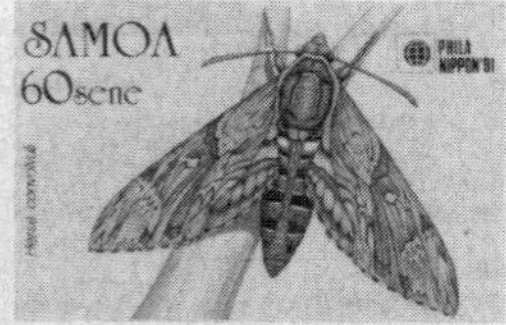

239 *Herse convolvuli*

(Des Jennifer Toombs. Litho Questa)

1991 (31 Oct). *Christmas. Carols* (1*st series*). *T* **238** *and similar horiz designs. Multicoloured. P* 14×$14^{1}/_{2}$.
864 20 s. Type **238** 40 10
865 60 s. "Joy to the World" 75 40
866 75 s. "Hark the Herald Angels sing" . . 95 70
867 $4 "We wish you a Merry Christmas" . . 3·75 4·75
864/7 . . . . . . *Set of* 4 5·25 5·50
See also Nos. 886/9 and 907/11.

(Des I. Loe. Litho Questa)

1991 (16 Nov). *"Phila Nippon '91" International Stamp Exhibition, Tokyo. Samoan Hawkmoths. T* **239** *and similar horiz designs. P* $13^{1}/_{2}$×14.
868 60 s. Type **239** 85 70
869 75 s. *Gnathothlibus erotus* 95 80
870 85 s. *Deilephila celerio* . . . . 1·10 1·00
871 $3 *Cephonodes armatus* . . . . 3·50 4·00
868/71 . . . . . . *Set of* 4 5·75 6·00

240 Head of State inspecting Guard of Honour

241 Samoa Express 1d. Stamp, 1877

(Des G. Vasarhelyi and D. Miller. Litho Walsall)

1992 (8 Jan). *30th Anniv of Independence. T* **240** *and similar horiz designs. Multicoloured. P* 14.
872 50 s. Type **240** 70 30
873 65 s. Siva ceremony 75 50
874 $1 Commemorative float . . . . 1·25 1·25
875 $3 Raising Samoan flag . . . . 3·00 3·75
872/5 . . . . . . *Set of* 4 5·25 5·25

(Des D. Miller. Litho Questa ($3), Leigh-Mardon Ltd, Melbourne (others))

1992 (6 Feb). *40th Anniv of Queen Elizabeth II's Accession. Horiz designs as T* **113** *of Kenya. Multicoloured. W w* **14** (*sideways*) ($3) *or w* **16** (*sideways*) (*others*). *P* 14.
876 20 s. Queen and Prince Philip with umbrellas 30 10
877 60 s. Queen and Prince Philip on Royal Yacht . . . . . . 1·00 70
878 75 s. Queen in multicoloured hat . . 75 75
879 85 s. Three portraits of Queen Elizabeth . . 85 85
880 $3 Queen Elizabeth II . . . . . . 2·25 3·00
876/80 . . . . . . *Set of* 5 4·75 4·75

(Des L. Curtis. Litho Questa)

1992 (17 Apr). *500th Anniv of Discovery of America by Columbus. Sheet* 91×70 *mm. P* $14^{1}/_{2}$×14.
MS881 **241** $4 multicoloured . . . . . . 3·00 3·75

242 Weightlifting

243 Narrow-banded Batfish

(Des D. Miller. Litho Questa)

1992 (28 July). *Olympic Games, Barcelona. T* **242** *and similar vert designs. Multicoloured. P* 14.
882 60 s. Type **242** 80 70
883 75 s. Boxing 90 80
884 85 s. Running . . . . . . 1·00 1·00
885 $3 Montjuic Olympic Stadium, Barcelona 3·00 4·00
882/5 . . . . . . *Set of* 4 5·25 6·00

(Des Jennifer Toombs. Litho Walsall)

1992 (28 Oct). *Christmas. Carols* (2*nd series*). *Horiz designs as T* **238.** *Multicoloured. P* 14×$14^{1}/_{2}$.
886 50 s. "God rest you Merry Gentle-men" . . 55 30
887 60 s. "While Shepherds watched their Flocks by Night" 65 55
888 75 s. "Away in a Manger, no Crib for a Bed" 75 70
889 $4 "O little Town of Bethlehem" . . 3·25 4·50
886/9 . . . . . . *Set of* 4 4·75 5·50

(Des G. Drummond. Litho Walsall)

1993 (17 Mar). *Fishes. T* **243** *and similar horiz designs. Multicoloured. P* 14.
890 60 s. Type **243** 70 60
891 75 s. Clown Surgeonfish 85 85
892 $1 Black-tailed Snapper . . . . 1·25 1·50
893 $3 Long-nosed Emperor . . . . 2·75 3·75
890/3 . . . . . . *Set of* 4 5·00 6·00

244 Samoan Players performing Traditional War Dance

(Des G. Vasarhelyi. Litho Questa)

1993 (12 May). *Rugby World Cup Seven-a-Side Championship, Edinburgh. T* **244** *and similar multicoloured designs. P* $13^{1}/_{2}$×14.
894 60 s. Type **244** 75 65
895 75 s. Two players (*vert*) 85 75
896 85 s. Player running with ball and badge (*vert*) 95 95
897 $3 Edinburgh Castle . . . . 3·50 4·25
894/7 . . . . . . *Set of* 4 5·50 6·00

245 Flying Foxes hanging from Branch

246 Exhibition Emblem

(Des Jennifer Toombs. Litho Questa)

1993 (10 June). *Endangered Species. Flying Foxes. T* **245** *and similar horiz designs. Multicoloured. P* 14×$14^{1}/_{2}$.
898 20 s. Type **245** 60 30
899 50 s. Flying Fox with young . . . . 1·00 70
900 60 s. Flying Foxes hunting for food . . 1·25 90
901 75 s. Flying Fox feeding from plant . . 1·50 1·40
898/901 . . . . . . *Set of* 4 4·00 3·00

(Des and litho Walsall)

1993 (16 Aug). *"Taipei '93" Asian International Stamp Exhibition, Taiwan. Sheet* 137×64 *mm. P* 14.
MS902 **246** $5 lemon, light greenish blue & black 5·50 6·50

247 Globe, Letter and Flowers

(Des G. Vasarhelyi. Litho Walsall)

1993 (8 Oct). *World Post Day. T* **247** *and similar horiz designs. Multicoloured. P* 14.
903 60 s. Type **247** 55 45
904 75 s. Post Office counter 70 80
905 85 s. Hands exchanging letter 80 90
906 $4 Globe, national flags and letter . . 3·50 5·00
903/6 . . . . . . *Set of* 4 5·00 6·50

(Des Jennifer Toombs. Litho Walsall)

1993 (1 Nov). *Christmas. Carols* (3*rd series*). *Horiz designs as T* **238.** *Multicoloured. P* 14×$14^{1}/_{2}$.
907 20 s. "Silent Night" 25 10
908 60 s. "As with Gladness Men of Old" . . 65 45
909 75 s. "Mary had a Baby - yes, Lord!" . . 80 55
910 $1.50, "Once in Royal David's City" . . 1·40 1·75
911 $3 "Angels from the Realms of Glory" . . 3·50 4·50
907/11 . . . . . . *Set of* 5 6·00 6·50

248 *Alveopora allingi*

(Des I. Loe. Litho B.D.T.)

1994 (18 Feb). *Corals. T* **248** *and simlar horiz designs. Multicoloured. P* 14.
912 20 s. Type **248** 30 10
913 60 s. *Acropora polystoma* 65 45
914 90 s. *Acropora listeri* 90 90
915 $4 *Acropora grandis* . . . . 2·75 3·75
912/15 . . . . . . *Set of* 4 4·25 4·75

1994 (18 Feb). *"Hong Kong '94" International Stamp Exhibition. Nos.* 912/15 *optd as T* **272** *of Jamaica.*
916 20 s. Type **248** 30 10
917 60 s. *Acropora polystoma* 65 45
918 90 s. *Acropora listeri* 90 90
919 $4 *Acropora grandis* . . . . 2·75 3·75
916/19 . . . . . . *Set of* 4 4·25 4·75

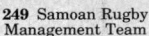

249 Samoan Rugby Management Team

250 *Anaphaeis java* and *Acraea andromacha* (butterflies)

(Des G. Vasarhelyi. Litho Walsall)

1994 (11 Apr). *Samoan National Rugby Team. T* **249** *and similar horiz designs. Multicoloured. P* 14.
920 70 s. Type **249** 70 60
921 90 s. Test match against Wales . . 80 80
922 95 s. Test match against New Zealand . . 80 80
923 $4 Apia Park Stadium . . . . 3·50 5·00
920/3 . . . . . . *Set of* 4 5·25 6·50

(Des R. Watton. Litho Cartor)

1994 (16 Aug). *"Philakorea '94" International Stamp Exhibition, Seoul. Sheet* 99×82 *mm. P* 13×$13^{1}/_{2}$.
MS924 **250** $5 multicoloured . . . . . . 3·75 4·50

251 Solo Singer and Choir

252 *Equator* (schooner)

(Des Patricia Altman. Litho Southern Colour Print, Dunedin, New Zealand)

1994 (22 Sept). *Teuila Tourism Festival. T* **251** *and similar horiz designs. Multicoloured. P* $13^{1}/_{2}$.
925 70 s. Type **251** 65 45
926 90 s. Fire dancer 75 65
927 95 s. Festival float 75 65
928 $4 Band outside hotel . . . . 3·75 4·50
925/8 . . . . . . *Set of* 4 5·50 5·50

(Des C. Abbott. Litho Walsall)

1994 (21 Nov). *Death Centenary of Robert Louis Stevenson* (*author*). *T* **252** *and similar multicoloured designs. P* 14.
929 70 s. Type **252** 60 50
930 90 s. Robert Louis Stevenson 70 80
931 $1.20, Stevenson's tomb, Mt Vaea . . 95 1·25
932 $4 Vailima House (*horiz*) . . . . 3·25 4·00
929/32 . . . . . . *Set of* 4 5·00 6·00

PRICES OF SETS

Set prices are given for many issues, generally those containing three stamps or more. Definitive sets include one of each value or major colour change, but do not cover different perforations, die types or minor shades. Where a choice is possible the set prices are based on the cheapest versions of the stamps included in the listings.

253 Santa Claus on House   **254** Lotofaga Beach, Aleipata

(Des D. Miller. Litho Questa)

1994 (30 Nov). *Christmas. Children's Paintings. T* **253** *and similar vert designs. Multicoloured. P* 14.

933 70 s. Type **253** 60 50
934 95 s. Star over house and palm trees .. 70 70
935 $1.20, Family outing .. .. .. 95 1·10
936 $4 "Merry Christmas" .. .. .. 3·25 4·00
933/6 .. .. *Set of* 4 5·00 5·75

(Des D. Miller. Litho Enschedé)

1995 (29 Mar). *Scenic Views. T* **254** *and similar horiz designs. Multicoloured. P* $14^1/_2\times13^1/_2$.

937 5 s. Type **254** 10 10
938 10 s. Nuutele Island 10 10
939 30 s. Satuiatua, Savaii 10 15
940 50 s. Sinalele, Aleipata 20 25
941 60 s. Paradise Beach, Lefaga 25 30
942 70 s. Houses at Piula Cave 30 35
943 80 s. Taga blowholes 35 40
944 90 s. View from East Coast road 40 45
945 95 s. Outrigger canoes, Leulumoega .. 45 50
946 $1 Parliament Building 45 50
937/46 .. .. *Set of* 10 2·50 3·00

255 Under-12s' Rugby Players   **256** Leatherback Turtle

(Des G. Vasarhelyi. Litho Enshedé)

1995 (25 May). *World Cup Rugby Championship, South Africa. T* **255** *and similar horiz designs. Multicoloured. P* $14^1/_2\times13$.

957 70 s. Type **255** 55 55
958 90 s. Secondary school players 70 70
959 $1 Samoan and New Zealand test match 75 75
960 $4 Ellis Park Stadium, Johannesburg .. 2·75 3·50
957/60 .. .. *Set of* 4 4·25 5·00

(Des R. Watton. Litho Cartor (Nos. 961/4) or Questa (Nos. **MS**965))

1995 (31 May). *50th Anniv of End of Second World War. Multicoloured designs as T* **75** *of Kiribati. P* $13^1/_2$.

961 70 s. Vought Sikorsky OS2U Kingfisher (seaplane) 65 55
962 90 s. Chance Vought F4U Corsair (fighter) 80 70
963 95 s. U.S. transport and landing craft 85 75
964 $3 U.S. marines landing on Samoa .. 3·00 3·50
961/4 .. .. *Set of* 4 4·75 5·00
MS965 75×85 mm. $4 Reverse of 1939–45 War Medal (*vert*). P 14 .. .. 2·40 2·75

(Des D. Miller. Litho Cartor)

1995 (24 Aug). *Year of the Sea Turtle. T* **256** *and similar vert designs. Multicoloured. P* $13\times13^1/_2$.

966 70 s. Type **256** 55 55
967 90 s. Loggerhead Turtle 70 70
968 $1 Green Turtle 75 75
969 $4 Pacific Ridley Turtle .. .. .. 2·75 3·50
966/9 .. .. *Set of* 4 4·25 5·00

257 *Phaius tankervilleae*   **258** Madonna and Child

(Des Jennifer Toombs. Litho B.D.T.)

1995 (1 Sept). *"Singapore '95" International Stamp Exhibition. Orchids. Sheet* 76×100 *mm. P* $13^1/_2$.

MS970 **257** $5 multicoloured .. .. 3·25 3·75

For further miniature sheet using this design as a $2.50 value see No. **MS**1006.

(Des A. Theobald. Litho Walsall)

1995 (24 Oct). *50th Anniv of United Nations. Horiz designs as T* **284** *of Jamaica. Multicoloured. P* 14.

971 70 s. Hospital lorry, Bosnia, 1995 .. .. 70 55
972 90 s. Bell Sioux helicopter and ambulance, Korea, 1952 .. .. 90 70
973 $1 Bell 212 helicopter, Bosnia, 1995 .. 1·00 75
974 $4 R.N.Z.A.F. Hawker Siddeley Andover, Somalia, 1995 .. .. 3·00 3·50
971/4 .. .. *Set of* 4 5·00 5·00

(Des D. Miller. Litho Walsall)

1995 (15 Nov). *Christmas. T* **258** *and similar vert designs. Multicoloured. P* $14^1/_2\times14$.

975 25 s. Type **258** 20 10
976 70 s. Wise Man wearing green turban .. 60 50
977 90 s. Wise Man with Child in manger .. 75 65
978 $5 Wise Man wearing red turban .. 3·50 4·00
975/8 .. .. *Set of* 4 4·75 4·75

259 Hands cupped under Waterfall and Bird   **260** Moon Hare preparing Elixir of Life

(Des G. Vasarhelyi. Litho Walsall)

1996 (26 Jan). *Environment. Water Resources. T* **259** *and similar vert designs. Multicoloured. P* 14.

979 70 s. Type **259** 50 50
980 90 s. Young girl and "WATER FOR LIFE" slogan 65 65
981 $2 Village and waterfall .. .. .. 1·40 1·75
982 $4 Irrigation system .. .. .. 2·75 3·50
979/82 .. .. *Set of* 4 4·75 5·75

(Des D. Miller. Litho Walsall)

1996 (22 Apr). *70th Birthday of Queen Elizabeth II. Vert designs as T* **55** *of New Zealand (Tokelau), each incorporating a different photograph of the Queen. Multicoloured. P* $14^1/_2$.

983 70 s. Main Street, Apia 50 40
984 90 s. Beach scene, Neiafu 65 50
985 $1 Vailima House (Head of State's residence) 75 60
986 $3 Parliament Building .. .. .. 2·00 3·00
983/6 .. .. *Set of* 4 3·50 4·00
MS987 64×66 mm. $5 Queen Elizabeth II .. 3·00 3·50

(Des N. Shewring. Litho B.D.T.)

1996 (18 May). *Moon Festival. Sheet* 103×83 *mm. P* 14.

MS988 **260** $2.50, multicoloured .. .. .. 1·60 1·75

No. **MS**988 also includes the "CHINA '96" International Stamp Exhibition logo on the sheet margin.

261 Meeting Venue   **262** Boxing

(Des N. Shewring. Litho Enschedé)

1996 (19 June). *63rd Session of the EU-ACP Council of Ministers. Sheet* 135×71 *mm. P* $13^1/_2$.

MS989 **261** $5 multicoloured .. .. .. 3·00 3·50

(Des D. Miller. Litho Enschedé)

1996 (15 July). *Centenary of Modern Olympic Games. T* **262** *and similar vert designs. Multicoloured. P* $13^1/_2$.

990 70 s. Type **262** 60 40
991 90 s. Running 70 55
992 $1 Weightlifting 80 60
993 $4 Throwing the javelin .. .. .. 2·75 3·50
990/3 .. .. *Set of* 4 4·25 4·50

ALTERED CATALOGUE NUMBERS

Any Catalogue numbers altered from the last edition are shown as a list in the introductory pages.

263 Festival Logo   **264** Young Children

(Des D. Miller. Litho Questa)

1996 (13 Sept). *7th Pacific Festival of Arts, Apia. T* **263** *and similar vert designs. Multicoloured. P* 14.

994 60 s. Type **263** 40 35
995 70 s. Decorated pottery 50 40
996 80 s. Textile pattern 55 55
997 90 s. Traditional dancing 60 60
998 $1 Carved poles 70 70
999 $4 Man wearing traditional headdress and necklace .. .. 2·00 2·25
994/9 .. .. *Set of* 6 4·25 4·25

(Des G. Vasarhelyi. Litho Questa)

1996 (24 Oct). *50th Anniv of U.N.I.C.E.F. T* **264** *and similar horiz designs. Multicoloured. P* 14.

1000 70 s. Type **264** 45 40
1001 90 s. Children in hospital 60 60
1002 $1 Child receiving injection 70 70
1003 $4 Mothers and children .. .. 2·00 2·25
1000/3 .. .. *Set of* 4 3·25 3·50

265 Many-coloured Fruit Dove

(Des N. Arlott. Litho Questa)

1997 (3 Feb). *"HONG KONG '97" International Stamp Exhibition. Sheet* 130×90 *mm. P* 14.

MS1004 **265** $3 multicoloured .. .. .. 1·75 2·00

266 First U.S.A. and Samoa Postage Stamps

(Des G. Vasarhelyi. Litho Questa)

1997 (29 May). *"Pacific '97" International Stamp Exhibition, San Francisco. Sheet* 96×70 *mm. P* $14^1/_2\times15$.

MS1005 **266** $5 multicoloured .. .. .. 2·75 3·00

(Des Jennifer Toombs. Litho Walsall)

1997 (20 June). *Return of Hong Kong to China. Sheet* 130×90 *mm, containing design as T* **257**, *but with new value and imprint date. W w* **14**. *P* $14^1/_2\times14$.

MS1006 **257** $2.50, multicoloured .. .. 1·50 1·60

(Des N. Shewring (No. **MS**1013), D. Miller (others). Litho Questa (No. **MS**1013), Cartor (others))

1997 (10 July). *Golden Wedding of Queen Elizabeth and Prince Philip. Multicoloured designs as T* **87** *of Kiribati. W w* **14**. *P* 13.

1007 70 s. Queen Elizabeth 45 45
a. Horiz pair. Nos. 1007/8 .. .. 90 90
1008 70 s. Prince Philip carriage-driving at Royal Windsor Horse Show, 1996 .. 45 45
1009 90 s. Queen Elizabeth and horse 65 65
a. Horiz pair. Nos. 1009/10 .. .. 1·25 1·25
1010 90 s. Prince Philip laughing 65 65
1011 $1 Prince Philip and Prince Edward with Zara Phillips on horseback, 1993 .. 65 65
a. Horiz pair. Nos. 1011/12 .. .. 1·25 1·25
1012 $1 Queen Elizabeth and Prince William 65 65
1007/12 .. .. *Set of* 6 3·00 3·00
MS1013 111×70 mm. $5 Queen Elizabeth and Prince Philip in landau (*horiz*). No wmk. P $14\times14^1/_2$ .. .. 3·00 3·25

Nos. 1007/8, 1009/10 and 1011/12 were each printed together, *se-tenant*, in horizontal pairs throughout the sheets with the backgrounds forming composite designs.

267 Dolphin on Surface

(Des D. Miller. Litho Questa)

1997 (17 Sept). *26th Anniv of Greenpeace (environmental organisation). T* **267** *and similar horiz designs. Multicoloured. P* 13½×14.

1014	50 s. Type **267**	30	25
1015	60 s. Two dolphins swimming underwater	40	30
1016	70 s. Heads of two dolphins underwater . .	45	40
1017	$1 Dolphin "laughing"	55	60
1014/17	. . . . *Set of* 4	1·50	1·40
MS1018	113×91 mm. $1.25×4 As Nos. 1014/17	2·50	2·75

268 Christmas Bells **269** Mangrove Fruit

(Des D. Miller. Litho Questa)

1997 (19 Nov). *Christmas. T* **268** *and similar horiz designs. Multicoloured. P* 14.

1019	70 s. Type **268**	45	35
1020	80 s. Christmas bauble	50	40
1021	$2 Candle	1·40	1·50
1022	$3 Christmas star	1·60	1·75
1019/22	. . . . *Set of* 4	3·50	3·50

(Des Doreen McGuiness. Litho Cartor)

1998 (26 Feb). *Mangroves. T* **269** *and similar vert designs. Multicoloured. P* 13½.

1023	70 s. Type **269**	30	35
1024	80 s. Mangrove seedlings	35	40
1025	$2 Mangrove roots	90	95
1026	$4 Mangrove tree on seashore	1·75	1·90
1023/6	. . . . *Set of* 4	3·25	3·50

(Des D. Miller. Litho Questa)

1998 (31 Mar–17 Apr). *Diana, Princess of Wales Commemoration. Vert designs as T* **91** *of Kiribati. Multicoloured. P* 14½×14.

1027	50 s. Wearing red jacket, 1990 (17 Apr) . .	20	25
MS1028	145×70 mm. $1.40, As 50 s.; $1.40 Wearing tweed jacket, 1981; $1.40, Wearing red dress, 1988; $1.40, Carrying bouquets, 1993 (*sold at $5.60 + 75 s. charity premium*) . .	2·75	3·00

270 Westland Wallace

(Des A. Theobald. Litho Cartor)

1998 (1 Apr). *80th Anniv of the Royal Air Force. T* **270** *and similar horiz designs. Multicoloured. P* 13½.

1029	70 s. Type **270**	30	35
1030	80 s. Hawker Fury Mk I	35	40
1031	$2 Vickers Varsity	90	95
1032	$5 BAC Jet Provost	2·25	2·40
1029/32	. . . . *Set of* 4	3·75	4·00
MS1033	110×77 mm. $2 Norman Thompson N.T.2b; $2 Nieuport 27 Scout; $2 Miles Magister; $2 Bristol Bomber	3·50	3·75

STAMP BOOKLETS

1958. *Blue on yellow (No.* SB1) *and blue (No.* SB3) *or black on pink (No.* SB2). *Stapled.*

SB1	2s. 7d. booklet containing ½d. and 2d. (Nos. 219, 221), each in block of 6, 1d. and 3d. (Nos. 220, 222), each in block of 4	
SB2	6s. booklet containing 1d., 3d., 6d. and 8d. (Nos. 220, 222, 224/5), each in block of 4	
SB3	9s. 9d. booklet containing ½d., 2d., 5d. and 1s. (Nos. 219, 221, 223, 226), each in block of 6	
	Set of 3	£275

1960 (Apr). *Contents as Nos.* SB1/3, *but arms and inscription in black, and colour of covers changed. Stapled.*

SB4	2s. 7d. Green cover	
	a. Buff cover	
SB5	6s. Grey cover	
	a. Blue cover	
SB6	9s. 9d. Yellow cover	
	a. White cover	
	Set of 3 (*Nos.* SB4, SB5, SB6)	£130
	Set of 3 (*Nos.* SB4a, SB5a, SB6a)	£130

1962 (Sept). *Black on buff (No.* SB7) *or green (No.* SB8) *covers. Inscr* "POSTAGE STAMP BOOKLET NO. 1" (11*s.* 9*d.*) *or* "NO. 2" (6*s.* 9*d.*). *Stapled.*

SB7	6s. 9d. booklet containing one each of 1d., 2d., 3d., 4d., 6d., 8d., 1s., 1s. 3d. and 2s. 6d. (Nos. 239/47) (loose in cellophane bag)	48·00
SB8	11s. 9d. booklet containing one each of 1d., 2d., 3d., 4d., 6d., 8d., 1s., 1s. 3d., 2s. 6d. and 5s. (Nos. 239/48) (loose in cellophane bag)	48·00

1962 (Sept)–**64.** *Black on pink (No.* SB9) *or blue (No.* SB10) *covers. Inscr* "POSTAGE STAMP BOOKLET NO. 3" (12*s.*) *or* "NO. 4" (6*s.*). *Stapled.*

SB9	6s. booklet containing 1d., 3d., 6d. and 8d. (Nos. 239, 241, 243/4), each in block of 4	42·00
SB10	12s. booklet containing 1d., 2d., 3d., 4d., 6d., 8d. and 1s. (Nos. 239/45), each in block of 4 . .	42·00

1964 (Sept)–**67.** *As Nos.* SB9/10 *but containing stamps with mixed wmks (W* **98** *of New Zealand or W* **61** *of Samoa). Stapled.*

SB11	6s. As No. SB9 . . . . *From*	42·00
SB12	12s. As No. SB10 . . . . . . *From*	48·00

1965 (Feb)–**67.** *As Nos.* SB7/8, *but containing stamps with mixed wmks (W* **98** *of New Zealand or W* **61** *of Samoa). Stapled.*

SB13	6s. 9d. As No. SB7 . . . . . . *From*	42·00
SB14	11s. 9d. As No. SB8 . . . . . . *From*	50·00

The composition of Nos. SB11/14 can vary as to the watermark and as it is possible to substitute stamps of one watermark for those of another, both in the cellophane bags and the blocks, we do not attempt to list them in greater detail. Prices will vary according to the contents.

Sarawak *see* Malaysia

Seychelles

Seychelles was administered as a dependency of Mauritius from 1810 until 1903, although separate stamp issues were provided from April 1890 onwards.

The first post office was opened, at Victoria on Mahé, on 11 December 1861 and the stamps of Mauritius were used there until 1890. No further post offices were opened until 1901.

Z 1

Stamps of MAURITIUS *cancelled with Type* Z **1**.

1848–59

Z1	2d. blue (intermediate impression) (No. 14)	£8500

1859–61.

Z2	6d. blue (No. 32)	£750
Z3	6d. dull purple-slate (No. 33)	£1400
Z4	1s. vermilion (No. 34)	£1200

1860–63. (*Nos.* 45/53).

Z 5	1d. purple-brown	£130
Z 6	2d. blue	£170
Z 7	4d. rose	£130
Z 8	6d. green	£500
Z 9	6d. slate	£400
Z10	9d. dull purple	80·00
Z11	1s. buff	£225
Z12	1s. green	£425

1862.

Z13	6d. slate (No. 54)	£800

1863–72. (*Nos.* 56/72).

Z14	1d. purple-brown	90·00
Z14*a*	1d. brown	75·00
Z15	1d. bistre	80·00
Z16	2d. pale blue	85·00
Z17	2d. bright blue	85·00
Z18	3d. deep red	£120
Z19	3d. dull red	75·00
Z20	4d. rose	45·00
Z21	6d. dull violet	£180
Z22	6d. yellow-green	90·00
Z23	6d. blue-green	60·00
Z24	9d. yellow-green	£850
Z25	10d. maroon	£250
Z26	1s. yellow	85·00
Z27	1s. blue	£225
Z28	1s. orange	85·00
Z29	5s. rosy mauve	£600
Z30	5s. bright mauve	£600

1876. (*Nos.* 76/7).

Z31	½d. on 9d. dull purple	£200
Z32	½d. on 10d. maroon	£200

1877. (*Nos.* 79/82).

Z33	½d. on 10d. rose	£375
Z34	1d. on 4d. rose-carmine	
Z35	1s. on 5s. rosy mauve	
Z36	1s. on 5s. bright mauve	

1878. (*Nos.* 83/91).

Z37	2 c. dull rose (lower label blank)	65·00
Z38	4 c. on 1d. bistre	£275
Z39	8 c. on 2d. blue	38·00
Z40	13 c. on 3d. orange-red	90·00
Z41	17 c. on 4d. rose	38·00
Z42	25 c. on 6d. slate-blue	80·00
Z43	38 c. on 9d. pale violet	£350
Z44	50 c. on 1s. green	90·00
Z45	2 r. 50 on 5s. bright mauve	£350

1879–80. (*Nos.* 92/100).

Z46	2 c. Venetian red	£100
Z47	4 c. orange	£110
Z48	8 c. blue	38·00
Z49	13 c. slate	£800
Z50	17 c. rose	80·00
Z51	25 c. olive-yellow	£150
Z52	38 c. bright purple	£1100
Z53	50 c. green	£700
Z54	2 r. 50, brown-purple	£650

1883–90.

Z55	2 c. Venetian red (No. 102)	75·00
Z56	2 c. green (No. 103)	£130
Z57	4 c. orange (No. 104)	65·00
Z58	4 c. carmine (No. 105)	75·00
Z59	16 c. chestnut (No. 109)	48·00
Z60	25 c. olive-yellow (No. 110)	95·00
Z61	50 c. orange (No. 111)	£800

1883.

Z62	16 c. on 17 c. rose (No. 112)	£120

1883.

Z63	16 c. on 17 c. rose (No. 115)	38·00

1885.

Z64	2 c. on 38 c. bright purple (No. 116)	

1887.

Z65	2 c. on 13 c. slate (No. 117)	

POSTAL FISCAL

1889.

ZR1	4 c. lilac (No. R2)	£400

Mauritius stamps are occasionally found cancelled with the "SEYCHELLES" cds. Examples are known dated between 25 and 29 February 1884 when it seems that Type Z 1 may have been mislaid (*Price from* £225).

We no longer list the G.B. 1862 6d. lilac with this obliteration as there is no evidence that the stamps of Great Britain were sold by the Victoria post office.

PRICES FOR STAMPS ON COVER TO 1945

Nos. 1/8	*from* × 20
Nos. 9/24	*from* × 30
No. 25	*from* × 10
No. 26	*from* × 20
No. 27	*from* × 10
Nos. 28/32	*from* × 20
No. 33	*from* × 5
No. 34	*from* × 30
Nos. 35/6	—
Nos. 37/40	*from* × 40
Nos. 41/2	*from* × 25
Nos. 43/5	*from* × 10
Nos. 46/50	*from* × 30
Nos. 51/4	*from* × 10
Nos. 55/6	—
Nos. 57/9	*from* × 10
Nos. 60/7	*from* × 20
Nos. 68/70	—
Nos. 71/81	*from* × 10
Nos. 82/131	*from* × 5
Nos. 132/4	*from* × 10
Nos. 135/49	*from* × 3

(Currency: 100 cents = 1 Mauritius, later Seychelles rupee)

DEPENDENCY OF MAURITIUS

PRINTERS. Nos. 1 to 123 were typographed by De La Rue & Co.

1

Die I

Die II

In Die I there are lines of shading in the middle compartment of the diadem which are absent from Die II.

1890 (5 April)**–92.** *Wmk Crown CA. P* 14. (i) *Die* I.

1	1	2 c. green and carmine	1·75	9·00
2		4 c. carmine and green	18·00	11·00
3		8 c. brown-purple and blue	4·50	3·50
4		10 c. ultramarine and brown	4·75	12·00
5		13 c. grey and black	5·00	11·00
6		16 c. chestnut and blue	3·00	3·50
7		48 c. ochre and green	18·00	16·00
8		96 c. mauve and carmine	48·00	48·00
1/8		*Set of* 8	90·00	£100
1/8 Optd "Specimen"		*Set of* 8	£180	

(ii) *Die* II (1892)

9	1	2 c. green and rosine	1·50	90
10		4 c. carmine and green	1·50	1·00
11		8 c. brown-purple and ultramarine	4·25	1·75
12		10 c. bright ultramarine and brown	5·50	3·25
13		13 c. grey and black	2·00	1·75
14		16 c. chestnut and ultramarine	35·00	8·50
9/14		*Set of* 6	45·00	15·00

3 cents

(2)

18 CENTS

(3)

4

1893 (1 Jan). *Surch locally as T* **2**.

15	3 c. on 4 c. (No. 10)	1·10	1·50
	a. Surch inverted	£300	£375
	b. Surch double	£475	
	c. Surch omitted (in pair with normal)	£4750	
16	12 c. on 16 c. (No. 6)	1·50	3·75
	a. Surch inverted	£450	
	b. Surch double	—	£4500
17	12 c. on 16 c. (No. 14)	6·00	1·75
	a. Surch double	£3750	£3750
	b. Surch omitted (in pair with normal)		
18	15 c. on 16 c. (No. 6)	8·00	13·00
	a. Surch inverted	£300	£350
	b. Surch double	£1100	£1100
19	15 c. on 16 c. (No. 14)	7·50	2·50
	a. Surch inverted	£850	£900
	b. Surch double	£650	£700
	c. Surch triple	£3250	
20	45 c. on 48 c. (No. 7)	15·00	4·75
21	90 c. on 96 c. (No. 8)	35·00	28·00
15/21	*Set of* 7	65·00	50·00

Nos. 15, 16, 18, 19 and 20 exist with "cents" omitted and with "cents" above value due to misplacement of the surcharge.

Most examples of the inverted surcharge error No. 16a were officially defaced with a red vertical ink line (*Price* £200, *unused*). Similarly examples of No. 19a exist defaced with a horizontal ink line (*Price* £400, *unused*).

1893 (Nov). *New values. Die* II. *Wmk Crown CA. P* 14.

22	1	3 c. dull purple and orange	1·00	30
23		12 c. sepia and green	1·50	50
24		15 c. sage-green and lilac	4·25	2·00
25		45 c. brown and carmine	23·00	32·00
22/5		*Set of* 4	27·00	32·00
22/5 Optd "Specimen"		*Set of* 4	90·00	

1896 (1 Aug). *No.* 25 *surch as T* **3**.

26	1	18 c. on 45 c. brown and carmine	7·00	2·75
		a. Surch double	£1300	£1300
		b. Surch triple	£1600	
27		36 c. on 45 c. brown and carmine	8·00	45·00
		a. Surch double	£1400	
26/7 Optd "Specimen"		*Set of* 2	70·00	

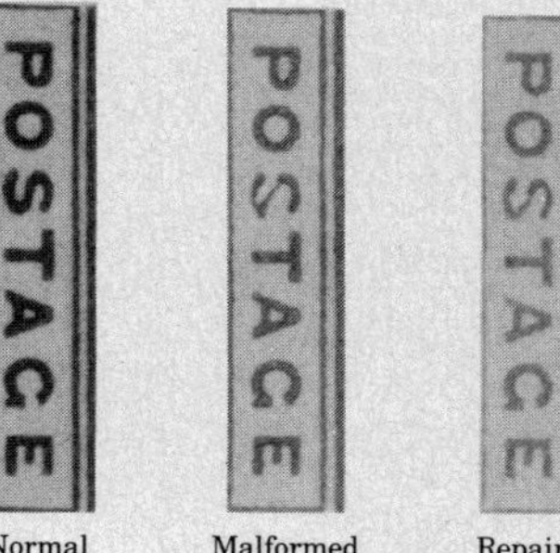

Normal — Malformed "S" — Repaired "S"

The malformed "S" occurs on R. 7/3 of the left pane from Key Plate 2. It is believed that the repair to it took place in mid-1898. Both states may occur on other stamps in Types 1 and 4. Stamps subsequently printed from Key Plate 3 showed the "S" normal.

1897–1900. *Colours changed and new values. Die* II. *Wmk Crown CA. P* 14.

28	1	2 c. orange-brown and green (1900)	1·50	60
		a. Repaired "S"	£110	
29		6 c. carmine (1900)	2·75	40
		a. Repaired "S"	£170	
30		15 c. ultramarine (1900)	3·00	3·00
		a. Repaired "S"	£170	
31		18 c. ultramarine	2·75	90
32		36 c. brown and carmine	17·00	4·00
33	4	75 c. yellow and violet (1900)	48·00	70·00
		a. Repaired "S"	£300	
34		1 r. bright mauve and deep red	9·50	3·50
35		1 r. 50, grey and carmine (1900)	55·00	85·00
		a. Repaired "S"	£300	
36		2 r. 25, bright mauve and green (1900)	80·00	85·00
		a. Repaired "S"	£375	
28/36		*Set of* 9	£200	£225
28/36 Optd "Specimen"		*Set of* 9	£200	

3 cents

(5)

6 cents

(5a)

1901 (21 June–Oct). *Surch locally with T* **5** *or* **5a**.

37	3 c. on 10 c. bright ultramarine and brown (No. 12) (10.01)	50	60
	a. Surch double	£600	
	b. Surch triple		
	c. Malformed "S"	£100	
38	3 c. on 16 c. chestnut and ultramarine (No. 14) (8.01)	1·25	2·50
	a. Surch inverted	£600	£600
	b. Surch double	£500	
	c. "3 cents" omitted	£500	£550
	d. Malformed "S"	£120	
39	3 c. on 36 c. brown and carmine (No. 32)	40	50
	a. Surch double	£700	£800
	b. "3 cents" omitted	£650	£700
40	6 c. on 8 c. brn-pur & ultram (No. 11) (8.01)	50	2·00
	a. Surch inverted	£650	£750
37/40	*Set of* 4	2·40	5·00
37/40 H/S "Specimen"	*Set of* 4	£100	

1902 (June). *Surch locally as T* 5.

No.	Type	Description	Unused	Used
41	1	2 c. on 4 c. carmine and green (No. 10)	1·60	2·75
42	4	30 c. on 75 c. yellow and violet (No. 33)	1·25	4·00
		a. Narrow "0" in "30" (R. 3/6, 5/2-4)	10·00	42·00
		b. Repaired "S"	£160	
43		30 c. on 1 r. bright mauve & dp red (No. 34)	4·50	22·00
		a. Narrow "0" in "30" (R. 3/6, 5/2-4)	22·00	80·00
		b. Surch double	£1300	
44		45 c. on 1 r. bright mauve & dp red (No. 34)	3·50	22·00
45		45 c. on 2 r. 25, brt mauve & grn (No. 36)	32·00	60·00
		a. Narrow "5" in "45" (R. 4/1)	£140	£250
		b. Repaired "S"	£275	
41/5		*Set of* 5	38·00	£100
41/5 H/S "Specimen"		*Set of* 5	£120	

6 7

3 cents

(8)

Dented frame (R. 1/6 of left pane)

1903 (26 May). *Wmk Crown CA. P* 14.

No.	Type	Description	Unused	Used
46	6	2 c. chestnut and green	1·75	1·00
		a. Dented frame	50·00	
47		3 c. dull green	1·00	1·25
		a. Dented frame	45·00	
48		6 c. carmine	2·00	65
		a. Dented frame	60·00	
49		12 c. olive-sepia and dull green	2·25	1·75
		a. Dented frame	65·00	
50		15 c. ultramarine	4·00	1·50
		a. Dented frame	95·00	
51		18 c. sage-green and carmine	3·50	6·00
		a. Dented frame	90·00	
52		30 c. violet and dull green	5·50	9·50
		a. Dented frame	£100	
53		45 c. brown and carmine	7·00	11·00
		a. Dented frame	£160	
		w. Wmk inverted	£180	
54	7	75 c. yellow and violet	9·50	25·00
		a. Dented frame	£160	
55		1 r. 50, black and carmine	40·00	70·00
		a. Dented frame	£275	
56		2 r. 25, purple and green	27·00	85·00
		a. Dented frame	£225	
46/56		*Set of* 11	90·00	£190
46/56 Optd "Specimen"		*Set of* 11	£190	

1903. *Surch locally with T* 8.

No.	Type	Description	Unused	Used
57	6	3 c. on 15 c. ultramarine (3.7)	75	2·50
		a. Dented frame	85·00	
58		3 c. on 18 c. sage-green and carmine (2.9)	2·00	27·00
		a. Dented frame	£130	
59		3 c. on 45 c. brown and carmine (21.7)	1·75	2·00
		a. Dented frame	£110	
57/9		*Set of* 3	4·00	28·00
57/9 H/S "Specimen"		*Set of* 3	80·00	

CROWN COLONY

The Seychelles became a Separate Crown Colony by Letters Patent dated 31 August 1903.

1906. *Wmk Mult Crown CA. P* 14.

No.	Type	Description	Unused	Used
60	6	2 c. chestnut and green	1·00	3·50
		a. Dented frame	45·00	
61		3 c. dull green	1·00	75
		a. Dented frame	48·00	
62		6 c. carmine	1·25	50
		a. Dented frame	55·00	
63		12 c. olive-sepia and dull green	3·00	2·25
		a. Dented frame	85·00	
64		15 c. ultramarine	2·75	2·00
		a. Dented frame	75·00	
65		18 c. sage-green and carmine	3·00	6·00
		a. Dented frame	80·00	
66		30 c. violet and dull green	6·00	7·50
		a. Dented frame	£140	
67		45 c. brown and carmine	3·00	6·00
		a. Dented frame	£120	
68	7	75 c. yellow and violet	8·50	55·00
		a. Dented frame	£170	
69		1 r. 50, black and carmine	50·00	55·00
		a. Dented frame	£300	
70		2 r. 25, purple and green	32·00	55·00
		a. Dented frame	£250	
60/70		*Set of* 11	£100	£170

9

10

1912 (Apr)–13. *Wmk Mult Crown CA. P* 14.

No.	Type	Description	Unused	Used
71	9	2 c. chestnut and green	40	3·25
		a. Split "A"	32·00	
72		3 c. green	70	40
		a. Split "A"	45·00	
73	9	6 c. aniline carmine (6.13)	9·00	4·50
		a. *Carmine-red*	2·75	45
		b. Split "A"	80·00	45·00
74		12 c. olive-sepia and dull green (1.13)	1·00	3·50
		a. Split "A"	55·00	
75		15 c. ultramarine	2·00	40
		a. Split "A"	75·00	45·00
76		18 c. sage-green and carmine (1.13)	1·75	3·50
		a. Split "A"	75·00	
77		30 c. violet and green (1.13)	5·00	1·25
		a. Split "A"	£110	75·00
78		45 c. brown and carmine (1.13)	2·50	28·00
		a. Split "A"	85·00	
79	10	75 c. yellow and violet (1.13)	2·50	5·50
		a. Split "A"	90·00	
80		1 r. 50, black and carmine (1.13)	5·50	85
		a. Split "A"	£160	75·00
81		2 r. 25, dp magenta & grn (*shades*) (1.13)	38·00	2·50
		a. Split "A"	£300	£110
71/81		*Set of* 11	55·00	45·00
71/81 Optd "Specimen"		*Set of* 11	£200	

For illustration of "Split A" flaw see above St. Helena No. 83.

11

12

13

1917–22. *Die I. Wmk Mult Crown CA. Chalk-surfaced paper* (18 *c. to* 5 *r.*). *P* 14.

No.	Type	Description	Unused	Used
82	11	2 c. chestnut and green	30	2·00
83		3 c. green	1·50	80
84	12	5 c. deep brown (1920)	1·50	5·00
85	11	6 c. carmine	1·00	90
		a. Rose (1919)	4·50	2·00
86		12 c. grey (1919)	50	1·00
87		15 c. ultramarine	75	1·25
88		18 c. purple/*yellow* (1919)	2·75	20·00
		a. On orange-buff (1920)	14·00	50·00
		b. On buff (1920)		
		c. Die II. *On pale yellow* (1922)	75	15·00
89	13	25 c. black and red/*buff* (1920)	1·50	25·00
		a. On orange buff (1920)	40·00	70·00
		b. Die II. *On pale yellow* (1922)	1·50	8·00
90	11	30 c. dull purple and olive (1918)	1·50	7·00
91		45 c. dull purple and orange (1919)	3·00	28·00
92	13	50 c. dull purple and black (1920)	4·00	19·00
93		75 c. black/*blue-green* (*olive back*) (1918)	1·40	12·00
		a. Die II. *On emerald back* (1922)	1·40	17·00
94		1 r. dull purple and red (1920)	8·00	38·00
95		1 r. 50, reddish purple & blue/*blue* (1918)	9·00	48·00
		a. Die II. *Blue-pur & blue/blue* (1922)	10·00	28·00
96		2 r. 25, yellow-green and violet (1918)	42·00	£120
97		5 r. green and blue (1920)	60·00	£190
82/97		*Set of* 16	£120	£425
82/97 Optd "Specimen"		*Set of* 16	£300	

1921–32. *Die II. Wmk Mult Script CA. Chalk-surfaced paper* (18 *c. and* 25 *c. to* 5 *r.*). *P* 14.

No.	Type	Description	Unused	Used
98	11	2 c. chestnut and green	15	15
99		3 c. green	90	15
100		3 c. black (1922)	80	30
101		4 c. green (1922)	80	1·75
102		4 c. sage-green and carmine (1928)	4·50	13·00
103	12	5 c. deep brown	75	4·50
104	11	6 c. carmine	2·25	7·50
		w. Wmk inverted	85·00	
105		6 c. deep mauve (1922)	50	10
106	13	9 c. red (1927)	2·25	3·50
107	11	12 c. grey	1·75	20
		a. Die I (1932)	7·00	65
108		12 c. carmine-red (1922)	45	20
110		15 c. bright blue	2·00	50·00
111		15 c. yellow (1922)	60	2·50
112		18 c. purple/*pale yellow* (1925)	2·25	9·50
113	13	20 c. bright blue (1922)	1·25	35
		a. Dull blue (1924)	6·00	55
114		25 c. black and red/*pale yellow* (1925)	2·50	8·50
115	11	30 c. dull purple and olive	1·00	12·00
116		45 c. dull purple and orange (1926)	1·00	5·00
117	13	50 c. dull purple and black	2·00	2·25
118		75 c. black/*emerald* (1924)	8·00	19·00
119		1 r. dull purple and red	12·00	18·00
		a. Die I (1932)	12·00	35·00
121		1 r. 50, purple and blue/*blue* (1924)	12·00	19·00
122		2 r. 25, yellow-green and violet	9·00	13·00
123		5 r. yellow-green and blue	48·00	£120
98/123		*Set of* 24	£100	£275
98/123 Optd "Specimen"		*Set of* 24	£400	

The 3 c. green and 12 c. grey (Die II) were reissued in 1927. "Specimens" of these also exist.

1935 (6 May). *Silver Jubilee. As Nos.* 114/17 *of Jamaica. P* 11×12.

No.	Description	Unused	Used
128	6 c. ultramarine and grey-black	70	1·25
	a. Extra flagstaff	£190	£225
	b. Short extra flagstaff	£150	
	c. Lightning conductor	£190	
	d. Flagstaff on right-hand turret	£200	
	e. Double flagstaff	£200	
129	12 c. green and indigo	2·00	70
	a. Extra flagstaff	£2750	£2500
	b. Short extra flagstaff	£225	£150
	c. Lightning conductor	£1000	
	d. Flagstaff on right-hand turret	£275	
	e. Double flagstaff	£275	
130	20 c. brown and deep blue	2·00	70
	a. Extra flagstaff	£225	£250
	b. Short extra flagstaff	£160	
	c. Lightning conductor	£225	
	d. Flagstaff on right-hand turret	£225	
	e. Double flagstaff	£225	
131	1 r. slate and purple	4·00	9·00
	a. Extra flagstaff	£150	£180
	b. Short extra flagstaff	£200	
	c. Lightning conductor	£130	
	d. Flagstaff on right-hand turret	£275	
128/31	*Set of* 4	8·00	10·50
128/31 Perf "Specimen"	*Set of* 4	85·00	

For illustrations of plate varieties see Omnibus section following Zimbabwe.

1937 (12 May). *Coronation. As Nos.* 118/20 *of Jamaica, but ptd by B.W. P* $11\times11\frac{1}{2}$.

No.	Description	Unused	Used
132	6 c. sage-green	35	15
133	12 c. orange	50	30
134	20 c. blue	70	65
132/4	*Set of* 3	1·40	1·00
132/4 Perf "Specimen"	*Set of* 3	55·00	

14 Coco-de-mer Palm

15 Giant Tortoise

16 Fishing Pirogue

(Photo Harrison)

1938 (1 Jan)–49. *Wmk Mult Script CA. Chalk-surfaced paper. P* $14\frac{1}{2}\times13\frac{1}{2}$ (*vert*) *or* $13\frac{1}{2}\times14\frac{1}{2}$ (*horiz*).

No.	Type	Description	Unused	Used
135	14	2 c. purple-brown (10.2.38)	85	40
		a. Ordinary paper (18.11.42)	20	75
136	15	3 c. green	6·50	1·25
136*a*		3 c. orange (8.8.41)	1·25	50
		ab. Ordinary paper (18.11.42)	55	1·25
137	16	6 c. orange	6·50	2·50
137*a*		6 c. greyish green (8.8.41)	3·00	70
		aw. Wmk inverted	£400	
		b. Ordinary paper. *Green* (18.11.42)	55	1·00
		c. Green (5.4.49)	2·00	75
138	14	9 c. scarlet (10.2.38)	10·00	2·00
138*a*		9 c. grey-blue (8.8.41)	3·50	40
		ab. Ordinary paper (18.11.42)	5·00	90
		ac. Ordinary paper. *Dull bl* (19.11.45)	4·00	1·50
		ad. Dull blue (5.4.49)	8·50	5·00
		aw. Wmk inverted		
139	15	12 c. reddish violet	38·00	1·25
139*a*		15 c. brown-carmine (8.8.41)	4·50	30
		ab. Ordinary paper. *Brn-red* (18.11.42)	3·75	1·50
139*c*	14	18 c. carmine-lake (8.8.41)	4·00	60
		ca. Ordinary paper (18.11.42)	3·25	1·50
		cb. Rose-carmine (5.4.49)	8·50	8·00
140	16	20 c. blue	42·00	5·00
140*a*		20 c. brown-ochre (8.8.41)	3·75	45
		ab. Ordinary paper (18.11.42)	2·50	1·25
141	14	25 c. brown-ochre	60·00	14·00
142	15	30 c. carmine (10.2.38)	60·00	9·00
142*a*		30 c. blue (8.8.41)	3·50	50
		ab. Ordinary paper (18.11.42)	1·75	2·50
143	16	45 c. chocolate (10.2.38)	8·50	1·25
		a. Ordinary paper. *Pur-brn* (18.11.42)	1·75	1·75
		b. Purple-brown (5.4.49)	9·50	9·00
144	14	50 c. deep reddish violet (10.2.38)	3·75	60
		a. Ordinary paper (18.11.42)	1·00	2·00
144*b*		50 c. bright lilac (13.6.49)	60	1·50
145	15	75 c. slate-blue (10.2.38)	85·00	38·00
145*a*		75 c. deep slate-lilac (8.8.41)	5·00	1·25
		ab. Ordinary paper (18.11.42)	1·25	2·00
146	16	1 r. yellow-green (10.2.38)	£100	48·00
146*a*		1 r. grey-black (8.8.41)	6·00	85
		ab. Ordinary paper (18.11.42)	1·25	2·25
147	14	1 r. 50, ultramarine (10.2.38)	11·00	1·50
		a. Ordinary paper (18.11.42)	4·50	4·00
		aw. Wmk inverted	£1200	
148	15	2 r. 25, olive (10.2.38)	16·00	4·00
		a. Ordinary paper (18.11.42)	10·00	10·00
149	16	5 r. red (10.2.38)	7·00	3·25
		a. Ordinary paper (18.11.42)	12·00	13·00
135/49		*Set of* 25	£400	£120
135/49 (*excl No.* 144*b*) Perf "Specimen"		*Set of* 24	£375	

Lamp on mast flaw (R. 1/5)

1946 (23 Sept). *Victory. As Nos.* 141/2 *of Jamaica.*

No.	Description	Unused	Used
150	9 c. light blue	10	10
151	30 c. deep blue	10	10
	a. Lamp on mast flaw	15·00	
150/1 Perf "Specimen"	*Set of* 2	50·00	

Line by crown (R. 1/3)

1948 (5 Nov). *Royal Silver Wedding. As Nos.* 143/4 *of Jamaica.*
152 9 c. ultramarine 15 25
a. Line by crown 15·00
153 5 r. carmine 11·00 21·00

1949 (10 Oct). *75th Anniv of U.P.U. As Nos.* 145/8 *of Jamaica, but inscribed* "SEYCHELLES" *in recess.*
154 18 c. bright reddish purple 30 15
155 50 c. purple 1·25 50
156 1 r. grey 40 15
157 2 r. 25, olive 50 60
154/7 *Set of* 4 2·25 1·25

17 Sailfish

18 Map of Indian Ocean

(Photo Harrison)

1952 (3 Mar). *Various designs as T* **14/16** *but with new portrait and crown as in T* **17/18**. *Chalk-surfaced paper. Wmk Mult Script CA. P* 14½ × 13½ *(vert) or* 13½ × 14½ *(horiz).*
158 **17** 2 c. lilac 50 70
a. Error. Crown missing, W **9a** £350
b. Error. St. Edward's Crown, W **9b** £110
159 **15** 3 c. orange 50 30
a. Error. Crown missing, W **9a** £300
b. Error. St. Edward's Crown, W **9b** £110
160 **14** 9 c. chalky blue 50 1·25
a. Error. Crown missing, W **9a** £475
b. Error. St. Edward's Crown, W **9b** £180
161 **16** 15 c. deep yellow-green 40 75
a. Error. Crown missing, W **9a** £400
b. Error. St. Edward's Crown, W **9b** £180
162 **18** 18 c. carmine-lake 65 20
a. Error. Crown missing, W **9a** £475
b. Error. St. Edward's Crown, W **9b** £225
163 **16** 20 c. orange-yellow 90 60
a. Error. Crown missing, W **9a** £550
b. Error. St. Edward's Crown, W **9b** £300
164 **15** 25 c. vermilion 70 70
a. Error. Crown missing, W **9a** £600
b. Error. St. Edward's Crown, W **9b** £275
165 **17** 40 c. ultramarine 70 90
a. Error. Crown missing, W **9a** £600
b. Error. St. Edward's Crown, W **9b** £325
166 **16** 45 c. purple-brown 70 30
a. Error. Crown missing, W **9a** £700
b. Error. St. Edward's Crown, W **9b** £350
167 **14** 50 c. reddish violet 1·25 60
a. Error. Crown missing, W **9a** £750
b. Error. St. Edward's Crown, W **9b** £375
168 **18** 1 r. grey-black 2·50 1·75
b. Error. St. Edward's Crown, W **9b** £650
169 **14** 1 r. 50, blue 5·00 9·00
b. Error. St. Edward's Crown, W **9b** £850
170 **15** 2 r. 25, brown-olive 6·50 9·50
b. Error. St. Edward's Crown, W **9b** £700
171 **18** 5 r. red 6·50 12·00
b. Error. St. Edward's Crown, W **9b** £600
172 **17** 10 r. green 14·00 23·00
158/72 *Set of* 15 38·00 55·00
See *Introduction* re the watermark errors.

1953 (2 June). *Coronation. As No.* 153 *of Jamaica.*
173 9 c. black and deep bright blue 50 50

19 Sailfish

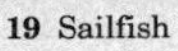

20 Seychelles Flying Fox

(Photo Harrison)

1954 (1 Feb)–**61**. *Designs previously used for King George VI issue, but with portrait of Queen Elizabeth II, as in T* **19** *and T* **20**. *Chalk-surfaced paper. Wmk Mult Script CA. P* 14½ × 13½ *(vert) or* 13½ × 14½ *(horiz).*
174 **19** 2 c. lilac 10 10
175 – 3 c. orange 10 10
175*a* **20** 5 c. violet (25.10.57) 30 30
176 – 9 c. chalky blue 10 10
176*a* – 10 c. chalky blue (15.9.56) 40 60
ab. Blue (11.7.61) 6·50 3·50
177 – 15 c. deep yellow-green 20 15
178 – 18 c. crimson 10 10
179 – 20 c. orange-yellow 30 20
180 – 25 c. vermilion 60 85
180*a* – 35 c. crimson (15.9.56) 2·75 90
181 **19** 40 c. ultramarine 30 25
182 – 45 c. purple-brown 20 15
183 – 50 c. reddish violet 30 20
183*a* – 70 c. purple-brown (15.9.56) 4·00 1·25
184 – 1 r. grey-black 50 40
185 – 1 r. 50, blue 3·50 3·75
186 – 2 r. 25, brown-olive 3·50 7·00
187 – 5 r. red 18·00 8·00
188 **19** 10 r. green 28·00 18·00
174/88 *Set of* 19 55·00 38·00
Designs: *Horiz*—15 c., 20 c., 45 c., 70 c. Fishing pirogue; 18 c., 35 c., 1 r., 5 r. Map of Indian Ocean. *Vert*—3 c., 25 c., 2 r. 25, Giant Tortoise; 9 c., 50 c., 1 r. 50, Coco de Mer Palm.

21 "La Pierre de Possession"

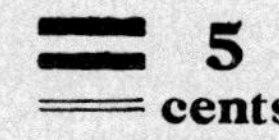

(22)

(Photo Harrison)

1956 (15 Nov). *Bicentenary of "La Pierre de Possession". Wmk Mult Script CA. P* 14½ × 13½.
189 **21** 40 c. ultramarine 15 10
190 1 r. black 15 10

191 191a 191 191b 191 191c

1957 (16 Sept). *No.* 182 *surch with T* **22**.
191 5 c. on 45 c. purple-brown 15 10
a. Italic "e" 3·75
b. Italic "s" 3·75
c. Italic "c" 3·75
d. Thick bars omitted £650
e. Surch double £325
There were two settings of this surcharge. The first setting contained No. 191a on R. 3/1, No. 191b on R. 5/3, No. 191c on R. 6/1 and 9/2, and No. 191d on R. 5/2. Nos. 191a and 191d did not occur on the second setting which shows No. 191b on R. 1/4, and No. 191c on R. 5/1 and R. 10/4.

23 Mauritius 6d. Stamp with Seychelles "B 64" Cancellation

(Recess: cancellation typo B.W.)

1961 (11 Dec). *Centenary of First Seychelles Post Office. W w* **12**. *P* 11½.
193 **23** 10 c. blue, black and purple 25 10
194 35 c. blue, black and myrtle-green 50 10
195 2 r. 25, blue, black and orange-brown 1·00 45
193/5 *Set of* 3 1·60 50

24 Black Parrot

29 Anse Royale Bay

40 Colony's Badge

(Des V. Whiteley. Photo Harrison)

1962 (21 Feb)–**68**. *T* **24**, **29**, **40** *and similar designs. W w* **12** *(upright). P* 13½ × 14½ *(horiz designs and 10 r.) or* 14½ × 13½ *(others).*
196 5 c. multicoloured 1·50 10
197 10 c. multicoloured 1·50 10
198 15 c. multicoloured 30 10
199 20 c. multicoloured 30 10
200 25 c. multicoloured 30 10
200*a* 30 c. multicoloured (15.7.68) 4·00 3·00
201 35 c. multicoloured 1·75 2·00
202 40 c. multicoloured 20 75
203 45 c. multicoloured (1.8.66) 3·50 3·75
204 50 c. multicoloured 40 25
205 70 c. ultramarine and light blue 6·00 3·00
206 75 c. multicoloured (1.8.66) 2·25 3·50
207 1 r. multicoloured 30 10
208 1 r. 50, multicoloured 5·50 6·00
209 2 r. 25, multicoloured 5·50 4·00
210 3 r. 50, multicoloured 2·25 5·50
211 5 r. multicoloured 3·50 2·50
212 10 r. multicoloured 12·00 4·50
196/212 *Set of* 18 42·00 35·00
Designs: *Vert (as T* **24**)—10 c. Vanilla vine; 15 c. Fisherman; 20 c. Denis Island lighthouse; 25 c. Clock Tower, Victoria; 50 c. Cascade Church; 70 c. Sailfish; 75 c. Coco-de-Mer palm. *Horiz (as T* **29**)—30 c., 35 c. Anse Royale Bay; 40 c. Government House; 45 c. Fishing pirogue; 1 r. Cinnamon; 1 r. 50, Copra; 2 r. 25, Map; 3 r. 50, Land settlement; 5 r. Regina Mundi Convent.
The 1 r. exists with PVA gum as well as gum arabic, but the 30 c. exists with PVA gum only.
See also Nos. 233/7.
For stamps of the above issue overprinted "B.I.O.T." see under British Indian Ocean Territory.

1963 (4 June). *Freedom from Hunger. As No.* 80 *of Lesotho.*
213 70 c. reddish violet 60 25

1963 (16 Sept). *Red Cross Centenary. As Nos.* 203/4 *of Jamaica.*
214 10 c. red and black 25 10
215 75 c. red and blue 75 40

(41) **42** Seychelles Flying Fox

1965 (15 Apr). *Nos.* 201 *and* 205 *surch as T* **41**.
216 45 c. on 35 c. multicoloured 10 15
217 75 c. on 70 c. ultramarine and light blue 20 15

1965 (1 June). *I.T.U. Centenary. As Nos.* 98/9 *of Lesotho.*
218 5 c. orange and ultramarine 10 10
219 1 r. 50, mauve and apple-green 50 25

1965 (25 Oct). *International Co-operation Year. As Nos.* 100/1 *of Lesotho.*
220 5 c. reddish purple and turquoise-green 10 10
221 40 c. deep bluish green and lavender 20 20

1966 (24 Jan). *Churchill Commemoration. As Nos.* 102/5 *of Lesotho.*
222 5 c. new blue 15 10
223 15 c. deep green 35 10
224 75 c. brown 60 10
225 1 r. 50, bluish violet 90 60
222/5 *Set of* 4 1·75 80

1966 (1 July). *World Cup Football Championships. As Nos.* 57/8 *of Pitcairn Islands.*
226 15 c. violet, yellow-green, lake & yellow-brn 15 10
227 1 r. chocolate, blue-green, lake & yellow-brn 25 20

1966 (20 Sept). *Inauguration of W.H.O. Headquarters, Geneva. As Nos.* 185/6 *of Montserrat.*
228 20 c. black, yellow-green and light blue 15 10
229 50 c. black, light purple and yellow-brown 25 20

1966 (1 Dec). *20th Anniv of U.N.E.S.C.O. As Nos.* 342/4 *of Mauritius.*
230 15 c. slate-violet, red, yellow and orange 20 10
231 1 r. orange-yellow, violet and deep olive 35 10
232 5 r. black, bright purple and orange 80 1·00
230/2 *Set of* 3 1·25 1·00

1967–69. *As Nos.* 196/7, 204 *and new values as T* **42** *but wmk w* **12** *(sideways).*
233 5 c. multicoloured (7.2.67) 35 1·50
234 10 c. multicoloured (4.6.68) 30 15
235 50 c. multicoloured (13.5.69) 1·75 3·50
236 60 c. red, blue and blackish brown (15.7.68) 1·75 45
237 85 c. ultramarine and light blue (as No. 205) (15.7.68) 90 40
233/7 *Set of* 5 4·50 5·50
The 10 c. exists with PVA gum as well as gum arabic, but the 50 c. to 85 c. exist with PVA gum only.

UNIVERSAL
ADULT
SUFFRAGE
1967

(43)

44 Money Cowrie, Mole Cowrie and Tiger Cowrie

1967 (18 Sept). *Universal Adult Suffrage. As Nos.* 198 *and* 206, *but W w* **12** *(sideways), and Nos.* 203 *and* 210 *(wmk upright), optd with T* **43**.
238 15 c. multicoloured 10 10
a. Opt double
239 45 c. multicoloured 10 10
240 75 c. multicoloured 10 10
241 3 r. 50, multicoloured 20 15
238/41 *Set of* 4 30 30

(Des V. Whiteley. Photo Harrison)

1967 (4 Dec). *International Tourist Year. T* **44** *and similar horiz designs. Multicoloured.* W w **12**. *P* 14 × 13.

242	15 c. Type **44**	20	10
243	40 c. Beech Cone, Textile or Cloth of Gold Cone and Virgin Cone	25	10
244	1 r. Arthritic Spider Conch	35	10
245	2 r. 25, Subulate Auger and Trumpet Triton Shells	60	65
242/5	*Set of* 4	1·25	75

= 30

(48)

49 Farmer with Wife and Children at Sunset

1968 (16 Apr). *Nos.* 202/3 *and as No.* 206 *surch as T* **48** (30 *c.*) *or with* "CENTS" *added, and three bars (others).* W w **12** *(sideways on No.* 248).

246	30 c. on 40 c. multicoloured	10	10
247	60 c. on 45 c. multicoloured	15	10
248	85 c. on 75 c. multicoloured	20	15
246/8	*Set of* 3	40	30

(Des Mary Hayward. Litho Harrison)

1968 (2 Sept). *Human Rights Year.* W w **12**. *P* 14½ × 13½.

249	**49** 20 c. multicoloured	10	10
250	50 c. multicoloured	10	10
251	85 c. multicoloured	10	10
252	2 r. 25, multicoloured	20	55
249/52	*Set of* 4	30	70

50 Expedition landing at Anse Possession

54 Apollo Launch

(Des Mary Hayward. Litho and die-stamped Harrison)

1968 (30 Dec). *Bicentenary of First Landing on Praslin. T* **50** *and similar multicoloured designs.* W w **12** *(sideways on* 50 *c.,* 85 *c.). P* 14.

253	20 c. Type **50**	30	10
254	50 c. French warships at anchor (*vert*)	35	15
255	85 c. Coco-de-Mer and Black Parrot (*vert*)	70	20
256	2 r. 25, French warships under sail	70	1·25
253/6	*Set of* 4	1·75	1·50

(Des V. Whiteley. Litho Format)

1969 (9 Sept). *First Man on the Moon. T* **54** *and similar horiz designs. Multicoloured.* W w **12** *(sideways on horiz designs). P* 13½.

257	5 c. Type **54**	10	20
258	20 c. Module leaving Mother-ship for Moon	15	10
259	50 c. Astronauts and Space Module on Moon	20	15
260	85 c. Tracking station	25	15
261	2 r. 25, Moon craters with Earth on the "Horizon"	45	1·25
257/61	*Set of* 5	1·00	1·60

59 Picault's Landing, 1742

60 Badge of Seychelles

(Des Mary Hayward. Litho Enschedé)

1969 (3 Nov)–**75**. *Horiz designs as T* **59/60**. *Multicoloured.* W w **12** *(sideways*). Slightly toned paper. P* 13×12½.

262	5 c. Type **59**	10	10
	w. Wmk Crown to right of CA	1·25	
263	10 c. U.S. satellite-tracking station	10	10
	a. Whiter paper (8.3.73)	70	60
264	15 c. *Königsberg I* (German cruiser) at Aldabra, 1914†	2·25	2·00
	a. Whiter paper (8.3.73)	5·50	4·25
265	20 c. Fleet re-fuelling off St. Anne, 1939–45	55	10
	a. Whiter paper (13.6.74)	1·25	1·75
266	25 c. Exiled Ashanti King Prempeh	20	10
	a. Whiter paper (8.3.73)	65	1·75
267	30 c. Laying Stone of Possession, 1756	1·00	3·25
268	40 c. As 30 c. (11.12.72)	1·50	1·25
	a. Whiter paper (13.6.74)	1·60	1·60
269	50 c. Pirates and treasure	30	15
	a. Whiter paper (13.6.74)	1·50	1·75
270	60 c. Corsairs attacking merchantman	1·00	1·50
271	65 c. As 60 c. (11.12.72)	4·00	5·00
	aw. Wmk Crown to left of CA	4·00	
	b. Whiter paper (13.8.75)	6·50	9·00
272	85 c. Impression of proposed airport	1·75	1·75
273	95 c. As 85 c. (11.12.72)	5·00	4·25
	a. Whiter paper (13.6.74)	4·50	3·25
274	1 r. French Governor capitulating to British naval officer, 1794	35	15
	a. Whiter paper (8.3.73)	1·00	1·00
275	1 r. 50, H.M.S. *Sybille* (frigate) and *Chiffone* (French frigate) in battle, 1801	1·75	2·00
	a. Whiter paper (8.3.73)	3·50	8·00
276	3 r. 50, Visit of the Duke of Edinburgh, 1956	1·50	2·00
	a. Whiter paper (13.8.75)	2·50	13·00
277	5 r. Chevalier Queau de Quincy	1·50	2·50
278	10 r. Indian Ocean chart, 1574	3·25	5·50
279	15 r. Type **60**	4·00	10·00
262/79	*Set of* 18	26·00	35·00
263a/76a	*Set of* 11	25·00	38·00

*The normal sideways watermark shows Crown to right of CA on the 40, 65 and 95 c. and to left of CA on the others, *as seen from the back of the stamp.*

†The design is incorrect in that it shows *Königsberg II* and the wrong date ("1915").

The stamps on the whiter paper are highly glazed, producing shade variations and are easily distinguishable from the original printings on toned paper.

74 White Terns, French Warship and Island

(Des A. Smith; adapted V. Whiteley. Litho D.L.R.)

1970 (27 Apr). *Bicentenary of First Settlement, St. Anne Island. T* **74** *and similar horiz designs. Multicoloured.* W w **12** *(sideways). P* 14.

280	20 c. Type **74**	60	10
281	50 c. Spot-finned Flyingfish, ship and island	40	10
282	85 c. Compass and chart	40	10
283	3 r. 50, Anchor on sea-bed	60	65
280/3	*Set of* 4	1·75	75

78 Girl and Optician's Chart

20c
SEYCHELLES

79 Pitcher Plant

(Des A. Smith. Litho Questa)

1970 (4 Aug). *Centenary of British Red Cross. T* **78** *and similar multicoloured designs.* W w **12** *(sideways on horiz designs). P* 14.

284	20 c. Type **78**	40	10
285	50 c. Baby, scales and milk bottles	40	10
286	85 c. Woman with child and umbrella (*vert*)	40	10
287	3 r. 50, Red Cross local H.Q. building	1·50	2·00
284/7	*Set of* 4	2·40	2·00

(Des G. Drummond. Litho J.W.)

1970 (29 Dec). *Flowers. T* **79** *and similar vert designs. Multicoloured.* W w **12**. *P* 14.

288	20 c. Type **79**	45	15
289	50 c. Wild Vanilla	55	15
290	85 c. Tropic-Bird Orchid	1·40	30
291	3 r. 50, Vare Hibiscus	2·50	1·50
288/91	*Set of* 4	4·50	1·90
MS292	81 × 133 mm. Nos. 288/91. Wmk inverted	5·50	13·00

80 Seychelles "On the Map"

81 Piper PA-31 Navajo

(Des and litho J.W.)

1971 (18 May). *"Putting Seychelles on the Map". Sheet* 152 × 101 *mm.* W w **12** *(sideways). P* 13½.

MS293	**80** 5 r. multicoloured	2·25	8·50

(Des and litho J.W.)

1971 (28 June). *Airport Completion. T* **81** *and similar multi-coloured designs showing aircraft.* W w **12** *(sideways on horiz designs). P* 14 × 14½ (5, 20 *and* 60 *c.) or* 14½ *(others).*

294	5 c. Type **81**	20	10
295	20 c. Westland Wessex HAS-1 helicopter	45	10
296	50 c. Consolidated PBY-5A Catalina amphibian (*horiz*)	60	10
297	60 c. Grumman SA-16 Albatross	65	10
298	85 c. Short S.26 "G" Class flying boat *Golden Hind* (*horiz*)	85	10
299	3 r. 50, Supermarine Walrus Mk 1 amphibian (*horiz*)	4·50	3·00
294/9	*Set of* 6	6·50	3·25

40c

82 Santa Claus delivering Gifts (Jean-Claude Waye Hive)

(83)

(Des Jennifer Toombs. Litho A. & M.)

1971 (12 Oct). *Christmas. Drawings by local children. T* **82** *and similar horiz designs. Multicoloured.* W w **12** *(sideways*). P* 13½.

300	10 c. Type **82**	10	10
	w. Wmk Crown to left of CA	35	
301	15 c. Santa Claus seated on turtle (Edison Thérésine)	10	10
	w. Wmk Crown to left of CA	40	
302	3 r. 50, Santa Claus landing on island (Isabelle Tirant)	40	70
300/2	*Set of* 3	50	70

*The normal sideways watermark shows Crown to right of CA, *as seen from the back of the stamp.*

1971 (21 Dec). *Nos.* 267, 270 *and* 272 *surch in grey as T* **83**.

303	40 c. on 30 c. Laying Stone of Possession, 1756	30	55
304	65 c. on 60 c. Corsairs attacking merchantman	40	75
305	95 c. on 85 c. Impression of proposed airport	45	1·00
303/5	*Set of* 3	1·00	2·10

ROYAL VISIT 1972

(84)

85 Seychelles Brush Warbler

1972 (20 Mar). *Royal Visit. Nos.* 265 *and* 277 *optd with T* **84**.

306	20 c. Fleet re-fuelling off St. Anne, 1939–45	15	20
307	5 r. Chevalier Queau de Quincy (Gold)	1·50	2·50

(Des R. Gillmor. Litho Questa)

1972 (24 July). *Rare Seychelles Birds. T* **85** *and similar vert designs. Multicoloured.* W w **12** *(sideways*). P* 13½.

308	5 c. Type **85**	55	40
309	20 c. Bare-legged Scops Owl	1·75	50
310	50 c. Seychelles Blue Pigeon	1·75	65
	w. Wmk Crown to right of CA	17·00	
311	65 c. Seychelles Magpie Robin	2·25	75
312	95 c. Seychelles Paradise Flycatcher	2·50	2·50
313	3 r. 50, Seychelles Kestrel	7·00	9·50
308/13	*Set of* 6	14·00	13·00
MS314	144×162 mm. Nos. 308/13	20·00	27·00
	w. Wmk Crown to right of CA	£150	

*The normal sideways watermark shows Crown to left of CA, *as seen from the back of the stamp.*

86 Fireworks Display

95c
SEYCHELLES

87 Giant Tortoise and Sailfish

(Des V. Whiteley. Litho Questa)

1972 (18 Sept). *"Festival '72". T* **86** *and similar multicoloured designs. W* w **12** (*sideways* on* 10 *and* 25 *c.*). *P* 14.
315 10 c. Type **86** 10 10
w. Wmk Crown to right of CA .. .. 8·00
316 15 c. Pirogue race (*horiz*) 10 10
317 25 c. Floats and costumes 10 10
318 5 r. Water skiing (*horiz*) 60 80
315/18 .. .. *Set of* 4 65 80
*The normal sideways watermark shows Crown to left of CA, *as seen from the back of the stamp.*

(Des (from photograph by D. Groves) and photo Harrison)

1972 (20 Nov). *Royal Silver Wedding. Multicoloured; background colour given. W* w **12**. *P* 14 × 14½.
319 **87** 95 c. turquoise-blue 15 10
320 1 r. 50, red-brown 15 10
w. Wmk inverted .. .. .. 2·75

1973 (14 Nov). *Royal Wedding. As Nos.* 322/3 *of Montserrat.*
321 95 c. ochre 10 10
322 1 r. 50, dull deep blue 10 10

88 Seychelles Squirrelfish

(Des G. Drummond. Litho Questa)

1974 (5 Mar). *Fishes. T* **88** *and similar horiz designs. Multicoloured. W* w **12**. *P* 14½ × 14.
323 20 c. Type **88** 25 10
324 50 c. Harlequin Filefish 35 15
325 95 c. Pennant Coralfish ("Papillon") .. 40 30
326 1 r. 50, Oriental Sweetlips ("Peau d'ane canal") .. .. .. 85 1·25
323/6 .. .. *Set of* 4 1·60 1·60

89 Globe and Letter

(Des Sylvia Goaman. Litho Enschedé)

1974 (9 Oct). *Centenary of Universal Postal Union. T* **89** *and similar horiz designs. Multicoloured. W* w **12** (*sideways**). *P* 12½×12.
327 20 c. Type **89** 10 10
w. Wmk Crown to right of CA .. .. 22·00
328 50 c. Globe and radio beacon 20 10
329 95 c. Globe and postmark 35 40
330 1 r. 50, Emblems within "UPU" 50 70
327/30 .. .. *Set of* 4 1·00 1·10
*The normal sideways watermark shows Crown to left of CA, *as seen from the back of the stamp.*

VISIT OF
Q.E. II

90 Sir Winston Churchill (**91**)

(Des G. Vasarhelyi. Litho Questa)

1974 (30 Nov). *Birth Centenary of Sir Winston Churchill. T* **90** *and similar horiz design. Multicoloured. W* w **12**. *P* 14.
331 95 c. Type **90** 20 15
332 1 r. 50, Profile portrait 35 40
MS333 81×109 mm. Nos. 331/2 .. .. 60 1·75
w. Wmk inverted £100

1975 (8 Feb). *Visit of R.M.S. "Queen Elizabeth II". Nos.* 265a, 269a, 273a *and* 275a *optd with T* **91**.
334 20 c. Fleet re-fuelling off St. Anne, 1939–45 15 15
335 50 c. Pirates and treasure 20 20
336 95 c. Impression of proposed airport (Sil) .. 25 35
337 1 r. 50, H.M.S. *Sybille* (frigate) and *Chiffone* (French frigate) in battle, 1801 .. .. 35 60
334/7 .. .. *Set of* 4 85 1·10

PRICES OF SETS

Set prices are given for many issues, generally those containing three stamps or more. Definitive sets include one of each value or major colour change, but do not cover different perforations, die types or minor shades. Where a choice is possible the set prices are based on the cheapest versions of the stamps included in the listings.

INTERNAL
SELF-GOVERNMENT
OCTOBER
1975

(**92**)

93 Queen Elizabeth I

1975 (1 Oct). *Internal Self-Government. Nos.* 265a, 271b, 274a, *and* 276a *optd with T* **92** *in gold, by Enschedé.*
338 20 c. Fleet re-fuelling off St. Anne, 1939–45 .. 15 15
339 65 c. Corsairs attacking merchantman .. 25 30
340 1 r. French Governor capitulating to British naval officer, 1794 .. .. .. 30 35
341 3 r. 50, Visit of Duke of Edinburgh, 1956 .. 75 1·50
338/41 .. .. *Set of* 4 1·25 2·00

(Des C. Abbott. Litho Walsall)

1975 (15 Dec). *International Women's Year. T* **93** *and similar vert designs. Multicoloured. W* w **14** (*inverted*). *P* 13½.
342 10 c. Type **93** 10 10
343 15 c. Gladys Aylward 10 10
344 20 c. Elizabeth Fry 10 10
345 25 c. Emmeline Pankhurst 10 10
346 65 c. Florence Nightingale 25 20
347 1 r. Amy Johnson 40 35
348 1 r. 50, Joan of Arc 50 60
349 3 r. 50, Eleanor Roosevelt .. .. 1·50 2·50
342/9 .. .. *Set of* 8 2·50 3·50

94 Map of Praslin and Postmark

95 First Landing, 1609 (inset portrait of Premier James Mancham)

(Des J.W. Litho Questa)

1976 (30 Mar). *Rural Posts. T* **94** *and similar vert designs showing maps and postmarks. Multicoloured. W* w **14**. *P* 14.
350 20 c. Type **94** 20 10
351 65 c. La Digue 30 20
352 1 r. Mahé with Victoria postmark .. 35 25
353 1 r. 50, Mahé with Anse Royale postmark .. 55 90
350/3 .. .. *Set of* 4 1·25 1·25
MS354 166 × 127 mm. Nos. 350/3 .. .. 2·00 3·00

INDEPENDENT

(Des G. Drummond. Litho J.W.)

1976 (29 June). *Independence. T* **95** *and similar vert designs. Multicoloured. W* w **12** (*sideways*). *P* 13½.
355 20 c. Type **95** 15 10
356 25 c. The Possession Stone 15 10
357 40 c. First settlers, 1770 .. .. 20 15
358 75 c. Chevalier Queau de Quincy 25 20
359 1 r. Sir Bickham Sweet-Escott 25 20
360 1 r. 25, Legislative Building 40 50
361 1 r. 50, Seychelles badge 45 60
362 3 r. 50, Seychelles flag .. .. 90 1·60
355/62 .. .. *Set of* 8 2·50 3·00

96 Flags of Seychelles and U.S.A.

(Des and litho J.W.)

1976 (12 July). *Seychelles Independence and American Independence Bicentenary. T* **96** *and similar horiz design. Multicoloured. W* w **12** (*sideways*). *P* 13½.
363 1 r. Type **96** 25 15
364 10 r. Statehouses of Seychelles and Philadelphia .. .. 1·50 2·25

97 Swimming

98 Seychelles Paradise Flycatcher

(Des J.W. Litho Questa)

1976 (26 July). *Olympic Games, Montreal. T* **97** *and similar horiz designs. W* w **14** (*sideways*). *P* 14.
365 20 c. ultramarine, cobalt and sepia 10 10
366 65 c. bottle-green, apple-green and grey-black 35 10
367 1 r. chestnut, blue-green and grey-black .. 35 10
368 3 r. 50, crimson, rose and grey-black .. 50 2·00
365/8 .. .. *Set of* 4 1·10 2·00
Designs:—65 c. Hockey; 1 r. Basketball; 3 r. 50, Football.

(Des Mrs. R. Fennessy. Litho Questa)

1976–77. *Fourth Pan-African Ornithological Congress, Seychelles. T* **98** *and similar multicoloured designs. W* w **14** (*sideways on Nos.* 370/1). *P* 14. *A. Ordinary paper* (8.11.76). *B. Chalky paper* (7.3.77).

		A		B	
369	20 c. Type **98**	40	20	40	20
370	1 r. 25, Seychelles Sunbird (*horiz*)	1·10	80	1·10	80
371	1 r. 50, Seychelles Brown White Eye (*horiz*)	1·50	1·00	1·50	1·00
372	5 r. Black Parrot	2·50	3·50	2·50	3·50
369/72	*Set of* 4	5·00	5·00	5·00	5·00
MS373	161 × 109 mm. Nos. 369/72	6·50	8·50	†	
	a. 5 r. value in miniature sheet imperf	£850			

Independence
1976

(**99**)

100 Inauguration of George Washington

1976 (22 Nov). *Independence. Nos.* 265a, 269, 271b, 273a, 274a, 276a *and* 277/9 *optd with T* **99** (*No.* 271 *additionally surch*). *W* w **12** (*sideways**).
374 20 c. Fleet re-fuelling off St. Anne, 1939–45 70 1·50
375 50 c. Pirates and treasure .. .. .. 60 1·75
376 95 c. Impression of proposed airport .. 1·25 1·75
a. Opt inverted .. .. .. 85·00
w. Wmk Crown to right of CA .. 4·00
377 1 r. French Governor capitulating to British naval officer, 1794 .. .. 55 1·75
378 3 r. 50, Visit of Duke of Edinburgh, 1956 2·75 3·50
a. Opt inverted .. .. .. 75·00
b. On No. 276 .. .. .. 3·50 3·50
ba. Opt inverted £100
379 5 r. Chevalier Queau de Quincy .. .. 3·00 5·00
380 10 r. Indian Ocean chart, 1574 .. .. 5·50 10·00
381 15 r. Type **60** .. .. .. 7·50 10·00
382 25 r. on 65 c. Corsairs attacking merchantman .. .. 10·00 16·00
374/82 .. .. *Set of* 9 28·00 45·00
*The normal sideways watermark shows Crown to left of CA, *as seen from the back of the stamp.*

(Des Jennifer Toombs. Litho Questa)

1976 (21 Dec). *Bicentenary of American Revolution. T* **100** *and similar horiz designs. P* 14 × 13½.
383 1 c. crimson and light rose 10 10
384 2 c. violet and light lilac 10 10
385 3 c. bright blue and azure 10 10
386 4 c. chestnut and light yellow 10 10
387 5 c. emerald and light yellow-green 10 10
388 1 r. 50, sepia and cinnamon 60 35
389 3 r. 50, dp turquoise-blue & pale blue-green .. 80 80
390 5 r. chestnut and light yellow .. .. 1·00 1·00
391 10 r. chalky blue and azure .. .. 1·75 2·00
383/91 .. .. *Set of* 9 4·00 4·00
MS392 141 × 141 mm. 25 r. plum and magenta 3·50 6·50
Designs:—2 c. Jefferson and Louisiana Purchase; 3 c. William Seward and Alaska Purchase; 4 c. Pony Express, 1860; 5 c. Lincoln's Emancipation Proclamation; 1 r. 50 Transcontinental Railroad, 1869; 3 r. 50 Wright Brothers flight, 1903; 5 r. Henry Ford's assembly-line, 1913; 10 r. J. F. Kennedy and 1969 Moon-landing; 25 r. Signing Independence Declaration, 1776.

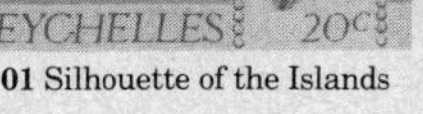

101 Silhouette of the Islands

102 Cruiser *Aurora* and Flag

(Des G. Hutchins (Nos. 395/8), J.W. (others). Litho Questa)

1977 (5 Sept). *Silver Jubilee. T* **101** *and similar multicoloured designs.* W w **14** (*sideways* on 20 and 40 c., 5 and 10 r.*). *P* 14.

393 20 c. Type **101** 10 10
w. Wmk Crown to right of CA .. .. 95·00
394 40 c. Silhouette (*different*) 10 10
395 50 c. The Orb (*vert*) 10 10
396 1 r. St. Edward's Crown (*vert*) 10 10
397 1 r. 25, Ampulla and Spoon (*vert*) .. 10 15
398 1 r. 50, Sceptre with Cross (*vert*) .. 10 15
399 5 r. Silhouette (*different*) 25 30
400 10 r. Silhouette (*different*) 45 60
393/400 .. .. *Set of* 8 1·00 1·25
MS401 133×135 mm. 20 c., 50 c., 1 r., 10 r. all wmk sideways .. .. 55 1·40
w. Wmk Crown to right of CA £150

*The normal sideways watermark shows Crown to left of CA, *as seen from the back of the stamp.*

(Litho State Printing Works, Moscow)

1977 (7 Nov). *60th Anniv of Russian October Revolution. P* 12 × 12½.

402 **102** 1 r. 50, multicoloured 55 30
MS403 101 × 129 mm. No. 402 .. .. .. 80 1·10

103 Coral Scene

(Des G. Drummond. Litho Walsall (40 c., 1 r., 1 r. 25, 1 r. 50), J.W. or Questa (25 c. (No. 408B)), J.W. (others))

1977–84. *Multicoloured designs as T* **103**. *Rupee values show* "Re" *or* "Rs". W w **14** (*sideways on* 10, 20, 50 *and* 75 *c.*). *P* 14½ × 14 (*40 c., 1 r., 1 r. 25, 1 r. 50*), 13 (*5, 10, 15, 20 r.*) *or* 14 (*others*).

A. *No imprint.* B. *Imprint date at foot*

No.	Value	Description	A		B	
404	5 c.	Reef Fish	30	80	†	
405	10 c.	Hawksbill Turtle	40	10	10	10
406	15 c.	Coco-de-Mer	30	90	15	15
407	20 c.	Wild Vanilla Orchid	1·50	20	1·75	1·25
408	25 c.	*Hypolimnas misippus* (butterfly)	1·50	45	1·75	1·75
409	40 c.	Type **103**	30	10	15	10
410	50 c.	Giant Tortoise	20	10	30	10
411	75 c.	Crayfish	20	10	30	30
412	1 r.	Madagascar Red Fody	1·25	10	6·00	40
		w. Wmk inverted	†		8·50	—
413	1 r.	25, White Tern	1·25	20	†	
414	1 r.	50, Seychelles Flying Fox	1·50	20	2·00	50
415	3 r.	50, Green Gecko	75	2·25	†	
416	5 r.	Octopus	2·00	40	†	
417	10 r.	Tiger Cowrie (*Cypraea tigris*)	2·25	2·50	†	
418	15 r.	Pitcher Plant	2·25	2·50	†	
419	20 r.	Coat of arms	2·50	2·50	†	
404A/19A		*Set of* 16	16·00	12·00		
405B/14B		*Set of* 9			11·00	4·25

Dates of issue: Without imprint 10.11.77, 40 c., 1 r. to 1 r. 50; 6.2.78, 10, 20, 50, 75 c., 5 r., 20 r.; 10.4.78, others. With imprint 14.3.80, 10, 15, 25, 40, 50, 75, 1 r., 1 r. 50; 5.84, 20 c.

The 40 c., 1 r., 1 r. 25 and 1 r. 50 values are horizontal designs, 31 × 27 mm; the 5, 10, 15 and 20 r. are vertical, 28 × 36 mm; the others are horizontal, 29 × 25 mm.

Imprint dates: "1979", Nos. 405B/6B, 408B/14B; "1981", No. 409B; "1982", Nos. 405B/9B; "1988", No. 408B (Questa).

For rupee values showing face value as "R" see Nos. 487/94.

For 10 c. and 50 c. with watermark w **14** (upright) and printed by Questa see Nos. 718 and 722. A printing of the 25 c. by Questa on the same date has the same perforation and watermark as J.W. printings of No. 408B.

For 50 c. and 3 r. (inscr "Rs") with watermark w **16** and printed by Questa see Nos. 732/8.

104 St. Roch Roman Catholic Church, Bel Ombre

(Des G. Drummond. Litho Walsall)

1977 (5 Dec). *Christmas. T* **104** *and similar horiz designs. Multicoloured.* W w **14** (*sideways*). *P* 13½ × 14.

420 20 c. Type **104** 10 10
421 1 r. Anglican cathedral, Victoria 10 10
422 1 r. 50, Roman Catholic cathedral, Victoria 15 10
423 5 r. St. Mark's Anglican church, Praslin .. 30 45
420/3 .. .. *Set of* 4 50 55

105 Liberation Day ringed on Calendar

106 Stamp Portraits of Edward VII, George V and George VI

(Des local artists; adapted L. Curtis. Litho Questa)

1978 (5 June). *Liberation Day. T* **105** *and similar vert designs. Multicoloured.* W w **14**. *P* 14 × 13½.

424 40 c. Type **105** 10 10
425 1 r. 25, Hands holding bayonet, torch and flag 15 10
426 1 r. 50, Fisherman and farmer 15 15
427 5 r. Soldiers and rejoicing people 35 40
424/7 .. .. *Set of* 4 60 60

(Des G. Drummond. Litho Questa)

1978 (21 Aug). *25th Anniv of Coronation. T* **106** *and similar vert designs. Multicoloured.* W w **14**. *P* 14.

428 40 c. Type **106** 10 10
429 1 r. 50, Victoria and Elizabeth II 10 10
430 3 r. Queen Victoria Monument 20 25
431 5 r. Queen's Building, Victoria 30 35
428/31 .. .. *Set of* 4 60 65
MS432 87 × 129 mm. Nos. 428/31 .. .. 60 85

107 Gardenia

(Des G. Hutchins. Litho Questa)

1978 (16 Oct). *Wildlife. T* **107** *and similar horiz designs. Multicoloured.* W w **14** (*sideways*). *P* 13½ × 14.

433 40 c. Type **107** 15 10
434 1 r. 25, Seychelles Magpie Robin .. .. 1·00 25
435 1 r. 50, Seychelles Paradise Flycatcher .. 1·00 35
436 5 r. Green Turtle .. .. 1·00 85
433/6 .. .. *Set of* 4 2·75 1·40

108 Possession Stone

109 Seychelles Fody

(Des G. Hutchins. Litho Questa)

1978 (15 Dec). *Bicentenary of Victoria. T* **108** *and similar horiz designs. Multicoloured.* W w **14** (*sideways*). *P* 13½ × 14.

437 20 c. Type **108** 10 10
438 1 r. 25, Plan of 1782 "L'Etablissement" .. 15 15
439 1 r. 50, Clock Tower 15 15
440 5 r. Bust of Pierre Poivre 40 50
437/40 .. .. *Set of* 4 65 75

(Des G. Drummond. Litho Questa)

1979 (27 Feb). *Birds* (*1st series*). *T* **109** *and similar vert designs. Multicoloured.* W w **14**. *P* 14.

441 2 r. Type **109** 55 50
a. Horiz strip of 5. Nos. 441/5 .. .. 2·50
442 2 r. Green Heron 55 50
443 2 r. Thick-billed Bulbul 55 50
444 2 r. Seychelles Cave Swiftlet.. .. .. 55 50
445 2 r. Grey-headed Lovebird 55 50
441/5 .. .. *Set of* 5 2·50 2·25

Nos. 441/5 were printed together, *se-tenant*, in horizontal strips of 5 throughout the sheet.

See also Nos. 463/7, 500/4 and 523/7.

110 Patrice Lumumba

111 1978 5 r. Liberation Day Commemorative and Sir Rowland Hill

(Des G. Vasarhelyi. Litho Questa)

1979 (5 June). *African Liberation Heroes. T* **110** *and similar vert designs.* W w **14**. *P* 14 × 14½.

446 40 c. black, deep violet and lilac 10 10
447 2 r. black, blue and pale blue 20 25
448 2 r. 25, black, reddish brown & orange-brn .. 20 30
449 5 r. black, bronze-green and dull green .. 45 80
446/9 .. .. *Set of* 4 80 1·25

Designs:—2 r. Kwame Nkrumah; 2 r. 25, Dr. Eduardo Mondlane; 5 r. Hamilcar Cabral.

(Des J.W. Litho Questa)

1979 (27 Aug). *Death Centenary of Sir Rowland Hill. T* **111** *and similar vert designs showing stamps and Sir Rowland Hill. Multicoloured.* W w **14**. *P* 14.

450 40 c. Type **111** 10 10
451 2 r. 25, 1972 50 c. Rare Birds commemorative 35 40
452 3 r. 1962 50 c. definitive 45 55
450/2 .. .. *Set of* 3 75 95
MS453 112 × 88 mm. 5 r. 1892 4 c. definitive. Wmk inverted 40 55

112 Child with Book

113 The Herald Angel

(Des BG Studio. Litho Questa)

1979 (26 Oct). *International Year of the Child. T* **112** *and similar multicoloured designs.* W w **14** (*sideways on 40 c. and 2 r. 25*). *P* 14½.

454 40 c. Type **112** 10 10
455 2 r. 25, Children of different races 15 30
456 3 r. Young child with ball (*vert*) 20 45
457 5 r. Girl with glove-puppet (*vert*) 35 65
454/7 .. .. *Set of* 4 70 1·25

Nos. 454/7 were each printed in sheets including two *se-tenant* stamp-size labels.

(Des J. Cooter. Litho Walsall)

1979 (3 Dec). *Christmas. T* **113** *and similar multicoloured designs.* W w **14** (*sideways on 3 r.*). *P* 14½ × 14 (*3 r.*) *or* 14 × 14½ (*others*).

458 20 c. Type **113** 10 10
459 2 r. 25, The Virgin and Child 30 40
460 3 r. The Three Kings (*horiz*) 40 55
458/60 .. .. *Set of* 3 65 90
MS461 87 × 75 mm. 5 r. The Flight into Egypt (*horiz*) (wmk sideways). P 14½ × 14 .. 50 70

R.1.10

(**114**)

115 Seychelles Kestrel

1979 (7 Dec). *As Nos.* 415 *but with* "1979" *imprint date, surch with T* **114**.

462 1 r. 10 on 3 r. 50, Green Gecko 30 30

(Des G. Drummond. Litho Questa)

1980 (29 Feb). *Birds* (*2nd series*). *Seychelles Kestrel. T* **115** *and similar vert designs. Multicoloured.* W w **14** (*inverted*). *P* 14.

463 2 r. Type **115** 70 50
a. Horiz strip of 5. Nos. 463/7 .. .. 3·25
aw. Wmk upright .. .. 55·00
464 2 r. Pair of Seychelles Kestrels 70 50
465 2 r. Seychelles Kestrel with eggs 70 50
466 2 r. Seychelles Kestrel on nest with chick .. 70 50
467 2 r. Seychelles Kestrel chicks in nest .. 70 50
463/7 .. .. *Set of* 5 3·25 2·25

Nos. 463/7 were printed together, *se-tenant*, in horizontal strips of 5 throughout the sheet.

116 10 Rupees Banknote **117** Sprinting

(Des B. Grout. Litho Questa)

1980 (18 Apr). *"London 1980" International Stamp Exhibition. New Currency. T* **116** *and similar multicoloured designs showing banknotes. W* w **14** *(sideways on 40 c. and 1 r. 50). P* 14.

468 40 c. Type **116** 10 10
469 1 r. 50, 25 rupees 25 15
470 2 r. 25, 50 rupees (*vert*) 35 25
471 5 r. 100 rupees (*vert*) 65 75
468/71 .. .. *Set of* 4 1·25 1·10
MS472 119 × 102 mm. Nos. 468/71 (wmk sideways) 1·25 1·40

(Des J.W. Litho Questa)

1980 (13 June). *Olympic Games, Moscow. T* **117** *and similar vert designs. Multicoloured. W* w **14**. *P* 14 × 14½.

473 40 c. Type **117** 10 10
474 2 r. 25, Weightlifting 20 20
475 3 r. Boxing 30 30
476 5 r. Yachting 60 40
473/6 .. .. *Set of* 4 1·10 80
MS477 90 × 121 mm. Nos. 473/6 .. .. .. 1·40 2·25

118 Boeing 747-200 **119** Female Palm

(Des A. Theobald. Litho Questa)

1980 (22 Aug). *International Tourism Conference, Manila. T* **118** *and similar horiz designs. Multicoloured. W* w **14** *(sideways). P* 14.

478 40 c. Type **118** 10 10
479 2 r. 25, Bus 25 30
480 3 r. Cruise liner 35 40
481 5 r. *La Belle Coralline* (tourist launch) .. 55 65
478/81 .. .. *Set of* 4 1·10 1·25

(Des L. Curtis. Litho Harrison)

1980 (14 Nov). *Coco-de-Mer (palms). T* **119** *and similar vert designs. Multicoloured. W* w **14**. *P* 14.

482 40 c. Type **119** 10 10
483 2 r. 25, Male Palm 25 20
484 3 r. Artefacts 40 35
485 5 r. Fisherman's gourd 55 55
482/5 .. .. *Set of* 4 1·10 1·00
MS486 82×140 mm. Nos. 482/5 .. .. .. 1·60 1·60
w. Wmk inverted £150

1981 (9 Jan)–**91**. *As Nos.* 412/14, 415 *(but new value), and* 416/19 *all with face values redrawn to show* "R" *instead of* "Re" *or* "Rs" *and imprint date at foot. Chalk-surfaced paper.*

487 1 r. Madagascar Red Fody .. .. .. 1·00 40
a. Ordinary paper (11.86) 50 50
488 1 r. 10, Green Gecko 40 50
489 1 r. 25, White Tern .. .. 2·50 1·00
490 1 r. 50, Seychelles Flying Fox 45 60
a. Ordinary paper (11.91) .. .. .. 1·75 2·00
491 5 r. Octopus .. .. 1·25 1·40
492 10 r. Tiger Cowrie (*Cypraea tigris*) .. .. 2·75 3·25
493 15 r. Pitcher Plant .. .. 3·75 4·50
494 20 r. Coat of arms .. .. 5·00 6·00
487/94 .. .. *Set of* 8 15·00 16·00

Imprint dates: "1980", Nos. 487/94; "1981", No. 490; "1982", Nos. 487, 490; "1985", No. 491; "1986", No. 487a; "1988", No. 487; "1990", No. 487a; "1991", Nos. 487a, 490a.

For 1 r. 25, 3 r. and 5 r. watermarked w **16** see Nos. 735/8.

120 Vasco da Gama's *Sao Gabriel*, 1497 **121** Male White Tern

(Des J.W. Litho Format)

1981 (27 Feb). *Ships. T* **120** *and similar horiz designs. Multicoloured. W* w **14** *(sideways). P* 14½ × 14.

495 40 c. Type **120** 15 10
496 2 r. 25, Mascarenhas' caravel, 1505 .. .. 50 55
497 3 r. 50, Darwin's H.M.S. *Beagle*, 1831 .. 70 1·00
498 5 r. *Queen Elizabeth 2* (liner), 1968 .. 85 1·40
495/8 .. .. *Set of* 4 2·00 2·75
MS499 141 × 91 mm. Nos. 495/98 .. .. .. 2·00 3·50

(Des G. Drummond. Litho Questa)

1981 (10 Apr). *Birds (3rd series). White Tern. T* **121** *and similar vert designs. Multicoloured. W* w **14**. *P* 14.

500 2 r. Type **121** 90 65
a. Horiz strip of 5. Nos. 500/4 .. .. 4·00
501 2 r. Pair of White Terns 90 65
502 2 r. Female White Tern 90 65
503 2 r. Female White Tern on nest, and egg .. 90 65
504 2 r. White Tern and chick 90 65
500/4 .. .. *Set of* 5 4·00 3·00

Nos. 500/4 were printed together, *se-tenant*, in horizontal strips of 5 throughout the sheet.

(Des D. Shults. Litho Questa)

1981 (23 June–16 Nov). *Royal Wedding. Horiz designs as T* **26**/**27** *of Kiribati. Multicoloured. (a) W* w **15**. *P* 14.

505 1 r. 50, *Victoria and Albert I* 20 25
a. Sheetlet. No. 505×6 and No. 506 .. 1·60
506 1 r. 50, Prince Charles and Lady Diana Spencer 50 75
507 5 r. *Cleveland* 60 60
a. Sheetlet. No. 507×6 and No. 508 .. 4·50
508 5 r. As No. 506 .. .. 1·50 2·50
509 10 r. *Britannia* .. .. 1·00 1·50
aw. Wmk inverted .. .. 14·00
b. Sheetlet. No. 509×6 and No. 510 .. 7·50
bw. Wmk inverted £110
510 10 r. As No. 506 .. .. 2·25 2·75
aw. Wmk inverted .. .. 48·00
505/10 .. .. *Set of* 6 5·50 7·50
MS511 120×109 mm. 7 r. 50, As No. 506. Wmk sideways. P 12 (16 Nov) .. .. .. 1·00 1·00

(*b*) *Booklet stamps. No wmk. P* 12 (16 Nov)

512 1 r. 50, As No. 505 .. .. 20 50
a. Booklet pane. No. 512×4 with margins all round 80
513 5 r. As No. 508 .. .. 80 1·75
a. Booklet pane. No. 513×2 with margins all round .. .. 1·60

Nos. 505/10 were printed in sheetlets of seven stamps of the same face value, each containing six of the "Royal Yacht" design and one of the larger design showing Prince Charles and Lady Diana.

Nos. 512/13 come from 22 r. stamp booklets.

122 Britten Norman Islander **123** Seychelles Flying Foxes in Flight

(Litho Harrison)

1981 (27 July). *10th Anniv of Opening of Seychelles International Airport. Aircraft. T* **122** *and similar horiz designs. Multicoloured. W* w **14** *(sideways*). P* 14½.

514 40 c. Type **122** 15 10
515 2 r. 25, Britten Norman "long nose" Trislander 55 45
w. Wmk Crown to right of CA .. .. 11·00
516 3 r. 50, Vickers Super VC-10 airliner .. 80 70
517 5 r. Boeing 747-100 airliner .. .. 1·00 1·00
514/17 .. .. *Set of* 4 2·25 2·00

**The normal sideways watermark shows Crown to left of CA, as seen from the back of the stamp.*

(Litho Format)

1981 (9 Oct). *Seychelles Flying Fox (Roussette). T* **123** *and similar vert designs. Multicoloured. W* w **14**. *P* 14.

518 40 c. Type **123** 10 10
519 2 r. 25, Flying Fox eating 30 45
520 3 r. Flying Fox climbing across tree branch 45 70
521 5 r. Flying Fox hanging from tree branch .. 55 1·00
518/21 .. .. *Set of* 4 1·25 2·00
MS522 95×130 mm. Nos. 518/21 .. .. .. 1·75 3·75

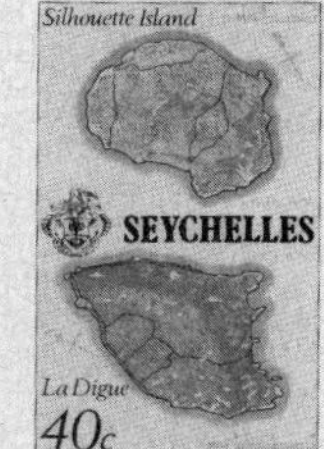

124 Chinese Little Bittern (male) **125** Silhouette Island and La Digue

(Des G. Drummond. Litho Questa)

1982 (4 Feb). *Birds (4th series). Chinese Little Bittern. T* **124** *and similar vert designs. Multicoloured. W* w **14**. *P* 14.

523 3 r. Type **124** .. .. 2·00 1·00
a. Horiz strip of 5. Nos. 523/7 .. .. 9·00
524 3 r. Chinese Little Bittern (female) .. .. 2·00 1·00
525 3 r. Hen on nest .. .. 2·00 1·00
526 3 r. Nest and eggs .. .. 2·00 1·00
527 3 r. Hen with chicks .. .. 2·00 1·00
523/7 .. .. *Set of* 5 9·00 4·50

Nos. 523/7 were printed together, *se-tenant*, in horizontal strips of 5 throughout the sheet.

(Des J. Cooter. Litho Format)

1982 (22 Apr). *Modern Maps. T* **125** *and similar vert designs. Multicoloured. W* w **14**. *P* 14½.

528 40 c. Type **125** 15 10
529 1 r. 50, Denis and Bird Islands 30 25
530 2 r. 75, Praslin 55 65
531 7 r. Mahé .. .. 1·00 2·00
528/31 .. .. *Set of* 4 1·75 2·75
MS532 92 × 128 mm. Nos. 528/31 .. .. 3·25 5·00

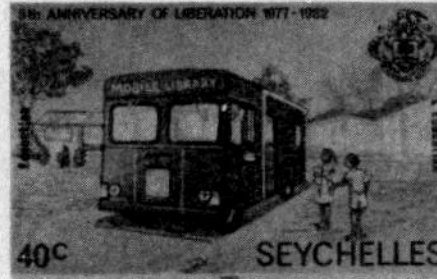

126 "Education"

(Des PAD Studio. Litho Harrison)

1982 (5 June). *5th Anniv of Liberation. T* **126** *and similar horiz designs. Multicoloured. W* w **14** *(sideways). P* 14.

533 40 c. Type **126** 10 10
534 1 r. 75, "Health" 25 25
535 2 r. 75, "Agriculture" 35 45
536 7 r. "Construction" .. .. 1·10 1·40
533/6 .. .. *Set of* 4 1·50 2·00
MS537 128 × 120 mm. Nos. 533/6. P 14½ .. 4·00 6·50

127 Tourist Board Emblem **128** Tata Bus

(Des and litho Harrison)

1982 (1 Sept). *Tourism. T* **127** *and similar horiz designs. Multicoloured. W* w **14** *(sideways). P* 14.

538 1 r. 75, Type **127** 25 35
539 1 r. 75, Northolme Hotel 25 35
540 1 r. 75, Reef Hotel 25 35
541 1 r. 75, Barbarous Beach Hotel 25 35
542 1 r. 75, Coral Strand Hotel 25 35
543 1 r. 75, Beau Vallon Bay Hotel 25 35
544 1 r. 75, Fisherman's Cove Hotel 25 35
545 1 r. 75, Mahé Beach Hotel 25 35
538/45 .. .. *Set of* 8 1·75 2·50

(Des C. Abbott. Litho Harrison)

1982 (18 Nov). *Land Transport. T* **128** *and similar horiz designs. Multicoloured. W* w **14** *(sideways). P* 14.

546 20 c. Type **128** 10 10
547 1 r. 75, Mini-moke 25 25
548 2 r. 75, Ox-cart 40 55
549 7 r. Truck .. .. 1·10 1·75
546/9 .. .. *Set of* 4 1·60 2·40

129 Radio Seychelles Control Room

(Des A. Theobald. Litho Questa)

1983 (25 Feb). *World Communications Year. T* **129** *and similar horiz designs. Multicoloured. W* w **14** *(sideways). P* 14.

550 40 c. Type **129** 10 10
551 2 r. 75, Satellite Earth Station 35 50
552 3 r. 50, Radio Seychelles Television control room 60 75
553 5 r. Postal services sorting office .. .. 80 1·25
550/3 .. .. *Set of* 4 1·60 2·25

130 Agricultural Experimental Station

(Des L. Curtis. Litho Questa)

1983 (14 Mar). *Commonwealth Day. T* **130** *and similar horiz designs. Multicoloured.* W w **14** (*sideways*). *P* 14.

554 40 c. Type **130** 10 10
555 2 r. 75, Food processing plant 35 40
556 3 r. 50, Unloading fish catch 50 60
557 7 r. Seychelles flag 75 1·40
554/7 *Set of* 4 1·50 2·25

131 Denis Island Lighthouse

(Des Harrison. Litho Format)

1983 (14 July). *Famous Landmarks. T* **131** *and similar horiz designs. Multicoloured.* W w **14** (*sideways*). *P* 14 × 13½.

558 40 c. Type **131** 10 10
559 2 r. 75, Victoria Hospital 30 45
560 3 r. 50, Supreme Court 35 65
561 7 r. State House 55 1·40
558/61 *Set of* 4 1·10 2·25
MS562 110 × 98 mm. Nos. 558/61 2·75 6·50

132 *Royal Vauxhall* Balloon, 1836

(Des A. Theobald. Litho Harrison)

1983 (15 Sept). *Bicentenary of Manned Flight. T* **132** *and similar horiz designs. Multicoloured.* W w **14** (*sideways*). *P* 14.

563 40 c. Type **132** 15 10
564 1 r. 75, De Havilland D.H.50J 50 30
565 2 r. 75, Grumman SA-16 Albatross flying boat 75 55
566 7 r. Swearingen Merlin IIIA 1·60 1·75
563/6 *Set of* 4 2·75 2·25

133 Douglas DC-10-30 Aircraft

134 Swamp Plant and Moorhen

(Des Park Advertising. Litho Walsall)

1983 (26 Oct). *1st International Flight of Air Seychelles.* W w **14** (*sideways*). *P* 14.

567 **133** 2 r. multicoloured 1·75 1·75

(Des L. Curtis. Litho Questa)

1983 (17 Nov). *Centenary of Visit to Seychelles by Marianne North (botanic artist). T* **134** *and similar vert designs. Multicoloured.* W w **14**. *P* 14.

568 40 c. Type **134** 15 10
569 1 r. 75, *Wormia flagellaria* 50 30
570 2 r. 75, Asiatic Pancratium 65 60
571 7 r. Pitcher Plant 1·25 1·60
568/71 *Set of* 4 2·25 2·25
MS572 90 × 121 mm. Nos. 568/71 3·50 6·50

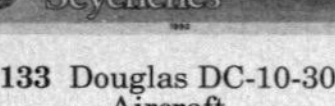

(135)

1983 (28 Dec). *Nos. 505/10 surch as T* **135**.

573 50 c. on 1 r. 50, *Victoria and Albert I* 15 15
a. Sheetlet. No. 573 × 6 and No. 574 1·10
b. Albino surch 32·00
c. Surch double, one albino 35·00
d. Surch double, one inverted 55·00
e. Surch double, one in 2 r. 25 value 45·00
574 50 c. on 1 r. 50, Prince Charles and Lady Diana Spencer 40 70
b. Albino surch 75·00
c. Surch double, one albino 85·00
d. Surch double, one inverted £130
e. Surch double, one in 2 r. 25 value £110
575 2 r. 25 on 5 r. *Cleveland* 45 50
a. Sheetlet. No. 575 × 6 and No. 576 3·25
576 2 r. 25 on 5 r. As No. 574 1·00 1·90
577 3 r. 75 on 10 r. *Britannia* 75 80
a. Sheetlet. No. 577 × 6 and No. 578 5·50
b. Albino surch 30·00
c. Surch double 75·00
578 3 r. 75 on 10 r. As No. 574 1·40 2·50
b. Albino surch 65·00
c. Surch double £225
573/8 *Set of* 6 3·75 6·00

136 Coconut Vessel

137 Victoria Port

(Des Jennifer Toombs. Litho Format)

1984 (29 Feb). *Traditional Handicrafts. T* **136** *and similar horiz designs. Multicoloured.* W w **14** (*sideways*). *P* 14.

579 50 c. Type **136** 15 10
580 2 r. Scarf and doll 50 70
581 3 r. Coconut-fibre roses 60 1·00
582 10 r. Carved fishing boat and doll 1·50 3·50
579/82 *Set of* 4 2·50 4·75

(Des C. Collins. Litho Questa)

1984 (21 May). *250th Anniv of "Lloyd's List" (newspaper). T* **137** *and similar vert designs. Multicoloured.* W w **14**. *P* 14½×14.

583 50 c. Type **137** 25 10
584 2 r. Cargo liner 65 55
585 3 r. *Sun Viking* (liner) 90 80
586 10 r. Loss of R.F.A. *Ennerdale II* (tanker) 2·40 2·75
583/6 *Set of* 4 3·75 3·75

138 Old S.P.U.P. Office

(Des D. Miller. Litho B.D.T.)

1984 (2 June). *20th Anniv of Seychelles People's United Party. T* **138** *and similar multicoloured designs.* W w **14** (*sideways on 50 c., 3 r.*). *P* 14.

587 50 c. Type **138** 15 10
588 2 r. Liberation statue (*vert*) 40 50
589 3 r. New S.P.U.P. office 50 80
590 10 r. President René (*vert*) 1·50 3·25
587/90 *Set of* 4 2·25 4·25

139 1949 U.P.U. 2 r. 25 Stamp

(Des M. Joyce. Litho Harrison)

1984 (18 June). *Universal Postal Union Congress, Hamburg. Sheet* 70 × 85 *mm.* W w **14** (*sideways*). *P* 14½.

MS591 **139** 5 r. yellow-olive, flesh and black 1·40 2·25

140 Long Jumping

(Des L. Curtis. Litho Questa)

1984 (28 July). *Olympic Games, Los Angeles. T* **140** *and similar horiz designs. Multicoloured.* W w **14** (*sideways*). *P* 14.

592 50 c. Type **140** 10 10
593 2 r. Boxing 40 45
594 3 r. Swimming 60 75
595 10 r. Weightlifting 1·75 2·50
592/5 *Set of* 4 2·50 3·50
MS596 100 × 100 mm. Nos. 592/5 2·50 4·25

141 Sub-aqua Diving

(Des A. Theobald. Litho Questa)

1984 (24 Sept). *Water Sports. T* **141** *and similar horiz designs. Multicoloured.* W w **14** (*sideways*). *P* 14.

597 50 c. Type **141** 20 10
598 2 r. Paraskiing 80 45
599 3 r. Sailing 1·00 75
600 10 r. Water-skiing 2·40 2·50
597/600 *Set of* 4 4·00 3·50

142 Humpback Whale

143 Two Bare-legged Scops Owls in Tree

(Des A. Jardine. Litho Questa)

1984 (19 Nov). *Whale Conservation. T* **142** *and similar horiz designs. Multicoloured.* W w **14** (*sideways*). *P* 14.

601 50 c. Type **142** 1·50 20
602 2 r. Sperm Whale 2·75 1·75
603 3 r. Black Right Whale 3·00 2·50
604 10 r. Blue Whale 6·00 8·00
601/4 *Set of* 4 12·00 11·00

(Des I. Lewington. Litho Walsall)

1985 (11 Mar). *Birth Bicentenary of John J. Audubon (ornithologist). Bare-legged Scops Owl. T* **143** *and similar vert designs. Multicoloured.* W w **14**. *P* 14.

605 50 c. Type **143** 1·50 40
606 2 r. Owl on branch 2·25 2·00
w. Wmk inverted † —
607 3 r. Owl in flight 2·50 2·25
608 10 r. Owl on ground 4·75 8·00
605/8 *Set of* 4 10·00 11·50

144 Giant Tortoises

145 The Queen Mother with Princess Anne and Prince Andrew, 1970

(Des D. Miller. Litho Format)

1985 (15 Mar). *"Expo '85" World Fair, Japan. T* **144** *and similar vert designs. Multicoloured.* W w **14**. *P* 14.

609 50 c. Type **144** 60 10
610 2 r. White Terns 1·50 1·50
611 3 r. Windsurfing 1·50 2·00
612 5 r. Coco-de-Mer 1·60 2·75
609/12 *Set of* 4 4·75 5·75
MS613 130 × 80 mm. Nos. 609/12 4·75 6·50

For these designs without "Expo '85" inscription see No. **MS**650.

(Des A. Theobald (10 r.), C. Abbott (others). Litho Questa)

1985 (7 June). *Life and Times of Queen Elizabeth the Queen Mother. T* **145** *and similar vert designs. Multicoloured.* W w **16**. *P* 14½ × 14.

614 50 c. The Queen Mother in 1930 10 10
615 2 r. Type **145** 35 50
616 3 r. On her 75th Birthday 50 70
617 5 r. With Prince Henry at his christening (from photo by Lord Snowdon) 80 1·25
614/17 *Set of* 4 1·60 2·40
MS618 91×73 mm. 10 r. Arriving at Blenheim Palace by Westland Wessex helicopter. Wmk sideways 2·25 2·25

MINIMUM PRICE

The minimum price quote is 10p which represents a handling charge rather than a basis for valuing common stamps. For further notes about prices see introductory pages.

146 Boxing **147** Agriculture Students

(Des O. Bell. Litho Questa)

1985 (24 Aug). *2nd Indian Ocean Islands Games. T* **146** *and similar horiz designs. Multicoloured. W w* **14** *(sideways). P* 14.

619 50 c. Type **146** . . 15 10
620 2 r. Football . . 55 50
621 3 r. Swimming . . 75 75
622 10 r. Windsurfing . . 2·40 2·75
619/22 . . *Set of* 4 3·50 3·50

1985 (1 Nov). *Acquisition of 1st Air Seychelles "Airbus". As No. 735, but additionally inscribed* "AIR SEYCHELLES FIRST AIRBUS". "1985" *imprint date.*

623 1 r. 25, White Tern . . 1·75 1·75

(Des Joan Thompson. Litho Questa)

1985 (28 Nov). *International Youth Year. T* **147** *and similar vert designs. Multicoloured. W w* **16**. *P* 14.

624 50 c. Type **147** . . 10 10
625 2 r. Construction students building wall . . 55 50
626 3 r. Carpentry students . . 70 70
627 10 r. Science students . . 2·25 2·75
624/7 . . *Set of* 4 3·25 3·50

148 Ford "Model T" (1919) **149** Five Foot Transit Instrument

(Des J.W. Litho Questa)

1985 (18 Dec). *Vintage Cars. T* **148** *and similar horiz designs. Multicoloured. W w* **16** *(sideways). P* 14.

628 50 c. Type **148** . . 40 10
629 2 r. Austin "Seven" (1922) . . 1·25 1·00
630 3 r. Morris "Oxford" (1924) . . 1·40 1·25
631 10 r. Humber "Coupé" (1929) . . 2·75 4·00
628/31 . . *Set of* 4 5·25 5·75

(Des Harrison. Litho Format)

1986 (28 Feb). *Appearance of Halley's Comet. T* **149** *and similar vert designs. Multicoloured. W w* **16**. *P* 14.

632 50 c. Type **149** . . 30 10
633 2 r. Eight foot quadrant . . 1·00 50
634 3 r. Comet's orbit . . 1·25 75
635 10 r. Edmond Halley . . 2·25 2·40
632/5 . . *Set of* 4 4·25 3·50

150 Ballerina **151** Ferry to La Digue

(Des C. Abbott. Litho Format)

1986 (4 Apr). *Visit of Ballet du Louvre Company. "Giselle". T* **150** *and similar vert designs. Multicoloured. W w* **16**. *P* 13½.

636 2 r. Type **150** . . 50 60
637 3 r. Male dancer . . 60 90
MS638 80 × 90 mm. 10 r. Pas de deux . . 1·40 2·40

(Des A. Theobald. Litho Questa)

1986 (21 Apr). *60th Birthday of Queen Elizabeth II. Vert designs as T* **230a** *of Jamaica. Multicoloured. W w* **16**. *P* 14½×14.

639 50 c. Wedding photograph, 1947 . . 10 10
640 1 r. 25, At State Opening of Parliament, 1982 . . 25 35
641 2 r. Queen accepting bouquet, Seychelles, 1972 . . 30 50
642 3 r. On board Royal Yacht *Britannia*, Qatar, 1979 . . 40 75
643 5 r. At Crown Agents Head Office, London, 1983 . . 60 1·25
639/43 . . *Set of* 5 1·40 2·75

(Des G. Drummond. Litho Questa)

1986 (22 May). *"Ameripex '86" International Stamp Exhibition, Chicago. Inter-island Communications. T* **151** *and similar multicoloured designs. W w* **16** *(sideways on 50 c., 7r.). P* 14.

644 50 c. Type **151** . . 60 10
645 2 r. Telephone kiosk (*vert*) . . 1·25 60
646 3 r. Post Office counter, Victoria (*vert*) . . 1·40 85
647 7 r. Air Seychelles Britten Norman "short nose" Trislander aircraft . . 4·00 2·00
644/7 . . *Set of* 4 6·50 3·25

152 Crests of Seychelles and Knights of Malta

LAZOURNEN ENTERNASYONAL KREOL

(**153**)

(Des Jennifer Toombs. Litho Format)

1986 (7 June). *Seychelles Knights of Malta Day. W w* **16** *(sideways). P* 14.

648 **152** 5 r. multicoloured . . 1·10 1·40
MS649 101 × 81 mm. No. 648 . . 2·25 3·25

1986 (12 July). *Seychelles Philatelic Exhibition, Tokyo. Miniature sheet, 130 × 80 mm, containing stamps as Nos. 609/12, but without "Expo '85" inscription and emblem. W w* **16**. *P* 14.

MS650 As Nos. 609/12 . . 2·50 3·00

(Des D. Miller. Litho Questa)

1986 (23 July). *Royal Wedding. Vert designs as T* **231a** *of Jamaica. Multicoloured. W w* **16**. *P* 14.

651 2 r. Prince Andrew and Miss Sarah Ferguson . . 35 50
652 10 r. Prince Andrew boarding Wessex helicopter, 1983 . . 1·25 2·40

1986 (28 Oct). *International Creole Day. No. 487a optd with T* **153**. "1986" *imprint date.*

653 1 r. Madagascar Red Fody . . 1·50 1·00

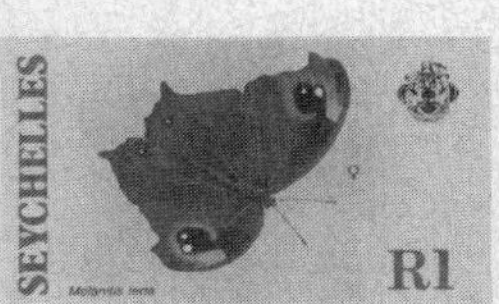

154 Pope John Paul at Seychelles Airport **155** *Melanitis leda*

(Des L. Curtis. Litho Questa)

1986 (1 Dec). *Visit of Pope John Paul II. T* **154** *and similar vert designs, each showing Pope and Seychelles scene. Multicoloured. W w* **16**. *P* 14½ × 14.

654 50 c. Type **154** . . 60 10
655 2 r. Catholic Cathedral, Victoria . . 1·75 90
656 3 r. Baie Lazare Parish Church . . 2·25 1·60
657 10 r. Aerial view of People's Stadium . . 3·75 5·00
654/7 . . *Set of* 4 7·50 6·75
MS658 95 × 106 mm. Nos. 654/7. Wmk inverted . . 10·00 12·00

(Des R. Lewington. Litho Questa)

1987 (18 Feb). *Butterflies. T* **155** *and similar horiz designs. Multicoloured. W w* **16** *(sideways). P* 14½.

659 1 r. Type **155** . . 1·00 30
660 2 r. *Phalanta philiberti* . . 1·60 85
661 3 r. *Danaus chrysippus* . . 1·90 1·60
662 10 r. *Euploea mitra* . . 5·00 6·00
659/62 . . *Set of* 4 8·50 8·00

156 Royal Oak Scallop (*Cryptopecten pallium*) **157** Statue of Liberation

(Des Josephine Martin. Litho Walsall)

1987 (7 May). *Seashells. T* **156** *and similar vert designs. Multicoloured. W w* 14. *P* 14½ × 14.

663 1 r. Type **156** . . 1·25 30
664 2 r. Golden Thorny Oyster (*Spondylus versicolor*) . . 2·00 85
665 3 r. Ventral or Single Harp (*Harpa ventricosa*) and Ornate Pitar Venus (*Lioconcha ornata*) . . 2·25 1·60
666 10 r. Silver Conch (*Strombus lentiginosus*) 5·50 6·00
663/6 . . *Set of* 4 10·00 8·00

(Des Harrison. Litho Format)

1987 (5 June). *10th Anniv of Liberation. T* **157** *and similar multicoloured designs. W w* **16** *(sideways on* 2 *r.,* 3 *r.). P* 14.

667 1 r. Type **157** . . 20 25
668 2 r. Seychelles Hospital (*horiz*) . . 35 50
669 3 r. Orphanage Village (*horiz*) . . 55 75
670 10 r. Proposed Sail-fish Monument . . 1·40 2·50
667/70 . . *Set of* 4 2·25 3·50

158 Seychelles Savings Bank, Praslin

(Des A. Theobald. Litho Format)

1987 (25 June). *Centenary of Banking in Seychelles. T* **158** *and similar horiz designs. W w* **16** *(sideways). P* 14.

671 1 r. bronze-green and sage-green . . 20 25
672 2 r. bistre-brown and salmon . . 35 50
673 10 r. royal blue and cobalt . . 1·40 2·50
671/3 . . *Set of* 3 1·75 3·00

Designs:—2 r. Development Bank; 10 r. Central Bank.

1987 (9 Dec). *Royal Ruby Wedding. Nos. 639/43 optd with T* **45a** *of Kiribati in silver.*

674 50 c. Wedding photograph, 1947 . . 15 15
a. Opt inverted . . 75·00
675 1 r. 25, At State Opening of Parliament, 1982 . . 25 40
676 2 r. Queen accepting bouquet, Seychelles, 1972 . . 30 60
677 3 r. On board Royal Yacht *Britannia*, Qatar, 1979 . . 40 85
678 5 r. At Crown Agents Head Office, London, 1983 . . 60 1·40
674/8 . . *Set of* 5 1·50 3·00

159 Tuna-canning Factory

(Des O. Bell. Litho B.D.T.)

1987 (11 Dec). *Seychelles Fishing Industry. T* **159** *and similar diamond-shaped designs. Multicoloured. W w* **16**. *P* 14.

679 50 c. Type **159** . . 15 15
680 2 r. Trawler . . 45 50
681 3 r. Weighing catch . . 70 75
682 10 r. Unloading net . . 2·25 2·40
w. Wmk inverted . . 28·00
679/82 . . *Set of* 4 3·25 3·50

160 Water Sports **161** Young Turtles making for Sea

(Des Jennifer Toombs. Litho Questa)

1988 (9 Feb). *Tourism. T* **160** *and similar horiz designs, each showing beach hotel. Multicoloured. W w* **16** *(sideways). P* 14½.

683 1 r. Type **160** . . 40 25
684 2 r. Speedboat and yachts . . 75 65
685 3 r. Yacht at anchor . . 1·10 1·25
686 10 r. Hotel at night . . 3·00 4·50
683/6 . . *Set of* 4 4·75 6·00

(Des Doreen McGuinness. Litho Questa)

1988 (22 Apr). *The Green Turtle. T* **161** *and similar vert designs. Multicoloured. W w* **14**. *P* 14½ × 14.

687 2 r. Type **161** . . 1·50 2·00
a. Vert pair. Nos. 687/8 . . 3·00 4·00
688 2 r. Young turtles hatching . . 1·50 2·00
689 3 r. Female turtle leaving sea . . 1·75 2·25
a. Vert pair. Nos. 689/90 . . 3·50 4·50
690 3 r. Female laying eggs . . 1·75 2·25
687/90 . . *Set of* 4 6·00 7·75

Nos. 687/8 and 689/90 were each printed together, *se-tenant*, in vertical pairs throughout the sheets, each pair forming a composite design.

162 Shot Put

163 Police Motorcyclists

(Des O. Bell. Litho Walsall)

1988 (29 July). *Olympic Games, Seoul. T* **162** *and similar vert designs. Multicoloured.* W w **16**. *P* 14½.

691 1 r. Type **162** 30 25
692 2 r. Type **162** 55 60
a. Horiz strip of 5. Nos. 692/6 .. .. 2·50
693 2 r. High jump 55 60
694 2 r. Gold medal winner on podium .. 55 60
695 2 r. Athletics 55 60
696 2 r. Javelin 55 60
697 3 r. As No. 694 .. .. 60 65
698 4 r. As No. 695 .. .. 80 85
699 5 r. As No. 696 .. .. 1·00 1·10
691/9 .. .. *Set of* 9 4·75 5·25
MS700 121×52 mm. 10 r. Tennis. W w **14** (sideways*) .. .. 4·00 5·00
w. Wmk Crown to right of CA .. .. 50·00

*The normal sideways watermark shows Crown to left of CA, *as seen from the back of the stamp.*

Nos. 691, 693 and 697/9 were each printed in sheets of 50 of one design. No. 693 also exists from sheets containing Nos. 692/6 printed together, *se-tenant,* in horizontal strips of five.

(Des D. Miller (1 r.), L. Curtis and D. Miller (2 r.), E. Nisbet and D. Miller (3 r.), S. Noon and D. Miller (10 r.). Litho Questa)

1988 (30 Sept). *300th Anniv of Lloyd's of London. Multicoloured designs as T* **167a** *of Malawi.* W w **16** (*sideways on* 2, 3 *r.*). *P* 14.

701 1 r. Leadenhall Street, 1928 .. .. .. 60 25
702 2 r. *Cinq Juin* (travelling post office) (*horiz*) 1·25 65
703 3 r. *Queen Elizabeth 2* (liner) (*horiz*) .. 1·75 1·10
704 10 r. Loss of LZ-129 *Hindenburg* (airship), 1937 .. .. 4·50 4·00
701/4 .. .. *Set of* 4 7·25 5·50

(Des A. Theobald. Litho Questa)

1988 (25 Nov). *1st Anniv of Defence Forces Day. T* **163** *and similar horiz designs. Multicoloured.* W w **14** (*sideways*). *P* 14.

705 1 r. Type **163** .. .. 1·50 40
706 2 r. Hindustan Aircraft Chetak helicopter 2·75 2·25
707 3 r. *Andromanche* (patrol boat) .. .. 2·75 2·75
708 10 r. BRDM armoured car .. .. .. 6·50 8·50
705/8 .. .. *Set of* 4 12·00 12·50

164 Father Christmas with Basket of Presents

165 *Dendrobium sp.*

(Des S. Hoareau (50 c.), R. Leste (2 r.), F. Anacoura (3 r.), A. McGaw (10 r.), adapted N. Harvey. Litho B.D.T.)

1988 (1 Dec). *Christmas. T* **164** *and similar vert designs. Multicoloured.* W w **14**. *P* 13½.

709 50 c. Type **164** 15 10
710 2 r. Bird and gourd filled with presents .. 70 70
711 3 r. Father Christmas basket weaving .. 90 90
712 10 r. Christmas bauble and palm tree .. 2·50 3·00
709/12 .. .. *Set of* 4 3·75 4·25

(Des Annette Robinson. Litho Questa)

1988 (21 Dec). *Orchids (1st series). T* **165** *and similar multicoloured designs.* W w **16** (*sideways on* 2, 10 *r.*). *P* 14.

713 1 r. Type **165** 45 25
714 2 r. *Arachnis hybrid* (*horiz*) 75 65
715 3 r. *Vanda caerulea* 95 95
716 10 r. *Dendrobium phalaenopsis* (*horiz*) .. 2·75 4·25
713/16 .. .. *Set of* 4 4·50 5·50

See also Nos. 767/70 and 795/8.

(Litho Questa)

1988 (30 Dec). *As Nos.* 405B *and* 410B, *but* W w **14** (*upright*). *"1988" imprint date. P* 14.

718 10 c. Hawksbill Turtle 75 75
722 50 c. Giant Tortoise .. .. 1·25 1·25

A Questa new printing of the 25 c. was issued on the same date. It has the same watermark and perforation as No. 408B.

166 India 1976 25 p. Nehru Stamp

167 Pres. Rene addressing Rally at Old Party Office

(Des O. Bell. Litho B.D.T.)

1989 (30 Mar). *Birth Centenary of Jawaharlal Nehru (Indian statesman). T* **166** *and similar horiz design, each showing flags of Seychelles and India. Multicoloured.* W w **16** (*sideways*). *P* 13½.

724 2 r. Type **166** 75 50
725 10 r. Jawaharlal Nehru .. .. 2·75 3·50

(Litho Walsall (1 r. 25), Questa (others))

1989 (May)–**91**. *As Nos.* 410, 415 (*but new value*), 489 *and* 491, *but* W w **16**. *Chalk-surfaced paper* (1 *r.* 25). *Imprint date at foot. P* 14½×14 (1 *r.* 25), 14×14½ (5 *r.*) *or* 14 (*others*).

732 50 c. Giant Tortoise (11.91) .. .. .. 1·25 1·25
735 1 r. 25, White Tern .. .. 2·00 2·50
736 3 r. Green Gecko (as No. 415) (11.91) .. 2·25 2·75
738 5 r. Octopus (1.91) .. .. 3·25 4·00
732/8 .. .. *Set of* 4 8·00 9·50

Imprint dates: "1989", No. 735; "1990", No. 738; "1991", Nos. 732, 736.

(Des D. Miller. Litho Walsall)

1989 (5 June). *25th Anniv of Seychelles People's United Party. T* **167** *and similar vert designs. Multicoloured.* W w **16**. *P* 14.

742 1 r. Type **167** 20 25
743 2 r. Women with Party flags and Maison du Peuple 40 45
744 3 r. President Rene making speech and Torch of Freedom 60 65
745 10 r. President Rene, Party flag and Torch of Freedom .. .. 2·00 2·50
742/5 .. .. *Set of* 4 2·75 3·50

(Des A. Theobald (10 r.), D. Miller (others). Litho Questa)

1989 (20 July). *20th Anniv of First Manned Landing on Moon. Multicoloured designs as T* **51a** *of Kiribati.* W w **16** (*sideways on* 2, 3 *r.*). *P* 14×13½ (1, 5 *r.*) *or* 14 (*others*).

746 1 r. Lift off of "Saturn 5" rocket 35 25
747 2 r. Crew of "Apollo 15" (30×30 *mm*) .. 65 65
748 3 r. "Apollo 15" emblem (30×30 *mm*) .. 80 90
749 5 r. James Irwin saluting U.S. flag on Moon 1·50 1·75
746/9 .. .. *Set of* 4 3·00 3·25
MS750 100×83 mm. 10 r. Aldrin alighting from "Apollo 11" on Moon. P 14×13½ .. .. 5·00 6·50

168 British Red Cross Ambulance, Franco-Prussian War, 1870

169 Black Parrot and Map of Praslin

(Des A. Theobald. Litho Questa)

1989 (12 Sept). *125th Anniv of International Red Cross. T* **168** *and similar horiz designs.* W w **16** (*sideways*). *P* 14½.

751 1 r. black and orange-vermilion .. .. 1·25 35
752 2 r. black, light green and orange-vermilion 1·75 1·50
753 3 r. black and orange-vermilion .. .. 2·25 2·25
754 10 r. black and orange-vermilion .. .. 6·50 8·00
751/4 .. .. *Set of* 4 10·50 11·00

Designs:—2 r. *Liberty* (hospital ship), 1914–18; 3 r. Sunbeam "Standard" army ambulance, 1914–18; 10 r. "White Train", South Africa, 1899–1902.

(Des I. Loe. Litho Questa)

1989 (16 Oct). *Island Birds. T* **169** *and similar vert designs. Multicoloured.* W w **16**. *P* 14½×14.

755 50 c. Type **169** .. .. 1·00 35
756 2 r. Sooty Tern and Ile aux Vaches .. 2·00 1·75
757 3 r. Seychelles Magpie Robin and Frégate 2·25 2·25
758 5 r. Roseate Tern and Aride .. .. 2·75 4·25
755/8 .. .. *Set of* 4 7·25 7·75
MS759 83×109 mm. Nos. 755/8 .. .. .. 8·00 9·00

MINIMUM PRICE

The minimum price quote is 10p which represents a handling charge rather than a basis for valuing common stamps. For further notes about prices see introductory pages.

170 Flags of Seychelles and France

(Adapted D. Miller from local artwork. Litho B.D.T.)

1989 (17 Nov). *Bicentenary of French Revolution and "World Stamp Expo '89", International Stamp Exhibition, Washington. T* **170** *and similar horiz designs.* W w **16** (*sideways*). *P* 14.

760 2 r. multicoloured .. .. 1·75 1·50
761 5 r. black, new blue and scarlet .. .. 3·00 3·75
MS762 78×100 mm. 10 r. multicoloured .. 4·50 6·00

Designs:—5 r. Storming the Bastille, Paris, 1789; 10 r. Reading Revolutionary proclamation, Seychelles, 1791.

171 Beau Vallon School

172 *Disperis tripetaloides*

(Des L. Curtis. Litho B.D.T.)

1989 (29 Dec). *25th Anniv of African Development Bank. T* **171** *and similar multicoloured designs.* W w **16** (*sideways on* 1, 2 *r.*). *P* 14.

763 1 r. Type **171** 45 25
764 2 r. Seychelles Fishing Authority Headquarters 80 80
765 3 r. *Variola* (fishing boat) (*vert*) .. .. 2·00 2·00
766 10 r. *Deneb* (fishing boat) (*vert*) .. .. 5·50 7·00
763/6 .. .. *Set of* 4 8·00 9·00

(Des N. Shewring. Litho Questa)

1990 (26 Jan). *Orchids (2nd series). T* **172** *and similar vert designs. Multicoloured.* W w **16**. *P* 14.

767 1 r. Type **172** .. .. 1·25 30
768 2 r. *Vanilla phalaenopsis* .. .. .. 1·75 1·50
769 3 r. *Angraecum eburneum* subsp *superbum* 2·00 2·00
770 10 r. *Polystachya concreta* .. .. .. 5·00 6·50
767/70 .. .. *Set of* 4 9·00 9·25

See also Nos. 795/8.

173 Seychelles 1903 2 c. and Great Britain 1880 1½d. Stamps

174 Fumiyo Sako

(Des D. Miller. Litho Security Printers (M), Malaysia)

1990 (3 May). *"Stamp World London 90" International Stamp Exhibition. T* **173** *and similar horiz designs, each showing stamps. Multicoloured.* W w **14** (*sideways*). *P* 12½.

771 1 r. Type **173** 75 25
772 2 r. Seychelles 1917 25 c. and G.B. 1873 1s. 1·25 1·25
773 3 r. Seychelles 1917 2 c. and G.B. 1874 6d. 1·75 2·25
774 5 r. Seychelles 1890 2 c. and G.B. 1841 1d. red-brown .. .. 2·50 3·50
771/4 .. .. *Set of* 4 5·75 6·50
MS775 88×60 mm. 10 r. Seychelles 1961 Post Office Centenary 2 r. 25 and G.B. 1840 Penny Black. Wmk upright .. .. 5·00 6·50

(Des D. Miller. Litho B.D.T.)

1990 (8 June). *"EXPO 90" International Garden and Greenery Exhibition, Osaka. T* **174** *and similar vert designs. Multicoloured.* W w **14**. *P* 14.

776 2 r. Type **174** .. .. 1·00 1·00
777 3 r. Male and female Coco-de-Mer palms 1·25 1·25
778 5 r. Pitcher Plant and Aldabra Lily .. 1·75 2·25
779 7 r. Arms of Seychelles and Gardenia .. 2·50 3·00
776/9 .. .. *Set of* 4 6·00 6·75
MS780 130×85 mm. Nos. 776/9. Wmk inverted 6·50 8·00

175 Air Seychelles Boeing 767-200ER over Island

176 Adult Class

(Des D. Miller. Litho Questa)

1990 (27 July). *Air Seychelles "Boeing 767-200ER" World Record-breaking Flight* (1989). *W w* **16**. *P* 14×14½.
781 **175** 3 r. multicoloured .. .. .. 2·00 2·00
No. 781 was printed in sheetlets of 10, containing two horizontal strips of 5, separated by a central gutter showing a map of the flight route from Grand Rapids, U.S.A. to the Seychelles.

(Des D. Miller. Litho Questa)

1990 (4 Aug). *90th Birthday of Queen Elizabeth the Queen Mother. Vert designs as T* **107** (2 *r.*) *or* **108** *of Kenya. W w* **16**. *P* 14×15 (2 *r.*) *or* 14½ (10 *r.*).
782 2 r. multicoloured .. .. .. 1·00 75
783 10 r. brownish black and violet .. .. 3·00 3·75
Designs:—2 r. Queen Elizabeth in Coronation robes, 1937; 10 r. Queen Elizabeth visiting Lord Roberts Workshops, 1947.

(Des G. Vasarhelyi. Litho Questa)

1990 (8 Sept). *International Literacy Year. T* **176** *and similar vert designs. Multicoloured. W w* **14**. *P* 14.
784 1 r. Type **176** 60 25
785 2 r. Reading a letter .. .. .. 1·25 1·25
786 3 r. Following written instructions .. 1·75 1·75
787 10 r. Typewriter, calculator and crossword 4·00 6·00
784/7 .. .. *Set of* 4 7·00 8·25

177 Sega Dancers

178 Beach

(Des Jennifer Toombs. Litho Cartor)

1990 (27 Oct). *Kreol Festival. Sega Dancing. T* **177** *and similar vert designs. Multicoloured. W w* **14**. *P* 13½×14.
788 2 r. Type **177** .. .. 1·10 1·40
a. Horiz strip of 5. Nos. 788/92 .. .. 5·00
789 2 r. Dancing couple (girl in yellow dress) 1·10 1·40
790 2 r. Female Sega dancer .. .. 1·10 1·40
791 2 r. Dancing couple (girl in floral pattern skirt) .. .. 1·10 1·40
792 2 r. Dancing couple (girl in red patterned skirt) .. .. 1·10 1·40
788/92 .. .. *Set of* 5 5·00 6·00
Nos. 788/92 were printed together, *se-tenant*, in horizontal strips of 5 throughout the sheet.

(Des D. Miller. Litho Questa)

1990 (10 Dec). *First Indian Ocean Regional Seminar on Petroleum Exploration. T* **178** *and similar horiz design. Multicoloured. W w* **16** (*sideways*). *P* 14½.
793 3 r. Type **178** .. .. 1·50 1·25
794 10 r. Geological map .. .. .. 4·50 5·50

(Des N. Shewring. Litho Questa)

1991 (1 Feb). *Orchids* (*3rd series*). *Vert designs as T* **172**. *Multicoloured. W w* **16**. *P* 14.
795 1 r. *Bulbophyllum intertextum* .. .. 1·00 35
796 2 r. *Agrostophyllum occidentale* .. .. 1·75 1·50
797 3 r. *Vanilla planifolia* .. .. .. 2·00 2·00
798 10 r. *Malaxis seychellarum* .. .. .. 5·25 6·00
795/8 .. .. *Set of* 4 9·00 9·00

(Des D. Miller. Litho Questa)

1991 (17 June). *65th Birthday of Queen Elizabeth II and 70th Birthday of Prince Philip. Vert designs as T* **58** *of Kiribati. Multicoloured. W w* **16** (*sideways*). *P* 14½×14.
799 4 r. Queen in evening dress .. .. 1·60 2·00
a. Horiz pair. Nos. 799/800 separated by label .. .. 3·00 4·00
800 4 r. Prince Philip in academic robes .. 1·60 2·00
Nos. 799/800 were printed in a similar sheet format to Nos. 366/7 of Kiribati.

179 *Precis rhadama*

180 "The Holy Virgin, Joseph, The Holy Child and St. John" (S. Vouillemont after Raphael)

(Des I. Loe. Litho Walsall)

1991 (15 Nov). *"Phila Nippon '91" International Stamp Exhibition, Tokyo. Butterflies. T* **179** *and similar horiz designs. W w* **14** (*sideways*). *P* 14×14½.
801 1 r. 50, Type **179** .. .. 1·50 65
802 3 r. *Lampides boeticus* .. .. .. 2·00 2·00
803 3 r. 50, *Zizeeria knysna* .. .. .. 2·25 2·25
804 10 r. *Phalanta phalantha* .. .. .. 6·00 7·00
801/4 .. .. *Set of* 4 10·50 10·50
MS805 78×81 mm. 10 r. *Eagris sabadius* .. 5·00 5·50

(Des D. Miller. Litho B.D.T.)

1991 (2 Dec). *Christmas. Woodcuts. T* **180** *and similar vert designs. W w* **16**. *P* 13½×14.
806 50 c. black, brown-ochre and bright crimson 50 15
807 1 r. black, brown-ochre and myrtle-green 80 25
808 2 r. black, brown-ochre and blue .. .. 1·60 1·10
809 7 r. black, brown-ochre & deep violet-blue 4·00 5·50
806/9 .. .. *Set of* 4 6·25 6·25
Designs:—1 r. "The Holy Virgin, the Child and Angel" (A. Blooting after Van Dyck); 2 r. "The Holy Family, St. John and St. Anna" (L. Vorsterman after Rubens); 7 r. "The Holy Family, Angel and St. Cathrin" (C. Bloemaert).

(Des D. Miller. Litho Questa (5 r.), Walsall (others))

1992 (6 Feb). *40th Anniv of Queen Elizabeth II's Accession. Horiz designs as T* **113** *of Kenya. Multicoloured. W w* **14** (*sideways*). *P* 14.
810 1 r. Seychelles coastline 55 25
811 1 r. 50, Clock Tower, Victoria 70 40
812 3 r. Victoria harbour .. .. .. 1·40 1·50
813 3 r. 50, Three portraits of Queen Elizabeth 1·50 1·75
814 5 r. Queen Elizabeth II .. .. .. 1·60 2·50
810/14 .. .. *Set of* 5 5·25 5·75

181 Seychelles Brush Warbler

(Des I. Loe. Litho B.D.T.)

1993 (1 Mar). *Flora and Fauna. T* **181** *and similar multicoloured designs. W w* **14** (*sideways on horiz designs*). *With imprint date. P* 13½.
815 10 c. Type **181** 10 10
816 25 c. Bronze Gecko (*vert*) 10 10
817 50 c. Seychelles Tree Frog 10 15
818 1 r. Seychelles Splendid Palm (*vert*) .. 25 30
819 1 r. 50, Seychelles Skink (*vert*) 35 40
820 2 r. Giant Tenebrionid Beetle 50 55
821 3 r. Seychelles Sunbird 70 75
822 3 r. 50, Seychelles Killifish 85 90
823 4 r. Seychelles Magpie Robin .. .. 95 1·00
824 5 r. Seychelles Vanilla (plant) (*vert*) .. 1·25 1·40
825 10 r. Tiger Chameleon .. .. .. 2·40 2·50
826 15 r. Coco-de-mer (*vert*) .. .. .. 3·50 3·75
827 25 r. Seychelles Paradise Flycatcher (*vert*) 6·00 6·25
828 50 r. Giant Tortoise .. .. .. 12·00 12·50
815/28 .. .. *Set of* 14 29·00 30·00
Imprint dates: "1993", Nos. 815/28; "1994", Nos. 818, 824/5, 827/8; "1996", Nos. 815/17, 820, 826.

182 Archbishop George Carey and Anglican Cathedral, Victoria

183 Athletics

(Des G. Vasarhelyi. Litho Cartor)

1993 (8 June). *First Visit of an Archbishop of Canterbury to Seychelles. T* **182** *and similar horiz design. Multicoloured. W w* **14** (*sideways*). *P* 13½.
834 3 r. Type **182** .. .. 1·75 1·25
835 10 r. Archbishop Carey with Air France Boeing 747-400 and Air Seychelles Boeing 737-200 airliners .. .. 3·75 5·00

(Des S. Noon. Litho Walsall)

1993 (21 Aug). *4th Indian Ocean Island Games. T* **183** *and similar vert designs. Multicoloured. W w* **14**. *P* 14½×14.
836 1 r. 50, Type **183** 55 55
837 3 r. Football .. .. 1·00 1·00
838 3 r. 50, Cycling .. .. 1·75 1·75
839 10 r. Yachting .. .. 3·25 4·50
836/9 .. .. *Set of* 4 6·00 7·00

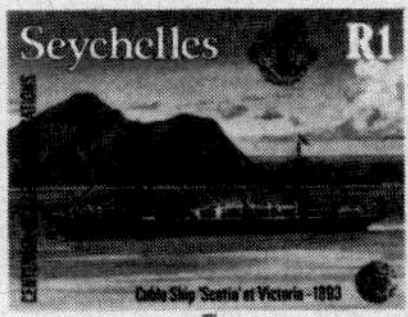

184 *Scotia* (cable ship) off Victoria, 1893

(Des C. Abbott. Litho Cartor)

1993 (12 Nov). *Centenary of Telecommunications. T* **184** *and similar horiz designs. Multicoloured. W w* **14** (*sideways*). *P* 13.
840 1 r. Type **184** .. .. 1·00 50
841 3 r. Eastern Telegraph Co office, Victoria, 1904 .. .. 1·75 1·75
842 4 r. HF Transmitting Station, 1971 .. 1·90 1·90
843 10 r. New Telecoms House, Victoria, 1993 4·00 5·00
840/3 .. .. *Set of* 4 7·75 8·25

R1

(**185**)

1994 (18 Feb). *"Hong Kong '94" International Stamp Exhibition. Nos. 62, 64 and 66/7 of Zil Elwannyen Sesel surch as T* **185**.
844 1 r. on 2 r. 10, Souimanga Sunbird .. 40 30
845 1 r. 50, on 2 r. 75, Sacred Ibis 55 60
846 3 r. 50, on 7 r. Seychelles Kestrel (*vert*) .. 1·40 1·60
847 10 r. on 15 r. Comoro Blue Pigeon (*vert*) .. 3·00 3·75
844/7 .. .. *Set of* 4 4·75 5·75

186 *Eurema floricola*

187 Lady Elizabeth Bowes-Lyon

(Des I. Loe. Litho Walsall)

1994 (16 Aug). *Butterflies. T* **186** *and similar horiz designs. Multicoloured. W w* **16** (*sideways*). *P* 14×14½.
848 1 r. 50, Type **186** .. .. 1·25 60
849 3 r. *Coeliades forestan* .. .. .. 2·00 2·00
850 3 r. 50, *Borbo borbonica* .. .. .. 2·25 2·25
851 10 r. *Zizula hylax* .. .. 4·50 5·50
848/51 .. .. *Set of* 4 9·00 9·25

(Des Jennifer Toombs. Litho B.D.T.)

1995 (26 Sept). *95th Birthday of Queen Elizabeth the Queen Mother. T* **187** *and similar vert designs. Multicoloured. W w* **14**. *P* 14.
852 1 r. 50, Type **187** 50 40
853 3 r. Duchess of York on wedding day, 1923 1·00 1·00
854 3 r. 50, Queen Elizabeth .. .. .. 1·10 1·25
855 10 r. Queen Elizabeth the Queen Mother .. 3·25 4·50
852/5 .. .. *Set of* 4 5·25 6·50

188 Female Seychelles Paradise Flycatcher feeding Chick

189 Swimming

(Des N. Shewring. Litho B.D.T.)

1996 (12 July). *Endangered Species. Seychelles Paradise Flycatcher. T* **188** *and similar vert designs. Multicoloured.* W w **16**. *P* 14.

856	1 r. Type **188**	45	45
	a. Strip of 4. Nos. 856/9	1·60	
857	1 r. Male bird in flight	45	45
858	1 r. Female bird on branch	45	45
859	1 r. Male bird on branch	45	45
856/9	*Set of* 4	1·60	1·60
MS860	60×53 mm. 10 r. Pair on branch	4·00	4·25

In addition to normal sheets of each value Nos. 856/9 were also available in sheets of 16 with the stamps horizontally and vertically *se-tenant.*

(Des R. Watton. Litho Walsall)

1996 (15 July). *Centenary of Modern Olympic Games. T* **189** *and similar vert designs. Multicoloured.* W w **16**. *P* 14.

861	50 c. Type **189**	40	20
862	1 r. 50, Running	60	45
863	3 r. Sailing	1·25	1·25
864	5 r. Boxing	1·90	2·25
861/4	*Set of* 4	3·75	3·75

190 Archbishop Makarios at Table

191 Comoro Blue Pigeon

(Litho Walsall)

1996 (19 Aug). *40th Anniv of Exile of Archbishop Makarios of Cyprus to Seychelles. T* **190** *and similar vert design. Multicoloured.* W w **14**. *P* 14.

865	3 r. Type **190**	1·00	1·00
866	10 r. Archbishop Makarios in priest's robes	3·00	3·50

(Des N. Arlott. Litho Questa)

1996 (11 Nov). *Birds. T* **191** *and similar vert designs. Multicoloured.* W w **14**. *P* $14^{1}/_{2}$.

867	3 r. Type **191**	1·25	1·25
	a. Horiz pair. Nos. 867/8	2·50	2·50
868	3 r. Seychelles Blue Pigeon	1·25	1·25
869	3 r. Souimanga Sunbird	1·25	1·25
	a. Horiz pair. Nos. 869/70	2·50	2·50
870	3 r. Seychelles Sunbird	1·25	1·25
871	3 r. Red-headed Fody	1·25	1·25
	a. Horiz pair. Nos. 871/2	2·50	2·50
872	3 r. Seychelles Fody	1·25	1·25
873	3 r. Madagascar White Eye	1·25	1·25
	a. Horiz pair. Nos. 873/4	2·50	2·50
874	3 r. Seychelles White Eye	1·25	1·25
867/74	*Set of* 8	9·00	9·00

Nos. 867/8, 869/70, 871/2 and 873/4 were each printed together, *se-tenant,* in horizontal pairs throughout the sheets with the background of each pair forming a composite design showing a regional map.

R1.50 —

(**192**)

1997 (12 Feb). *"HONG KONG '97" International Stamp Exhibition. No. 226 of Zil Elwannyen Sesel surch with T* **192**.

875	1 r. 50 on 2 r. Western Reef Heron ("Dimorphic Little Egret")	60	60

(Des N. Shewring (No. **MS**882), D. Miller (others). Litho Questa (No. **MS**882), Cartor (others))

1997 (20 Nov). *Golden Wedding of Queen Elizabeth and Prince Philip. Multicoloured designs as T* **87** *of Kiribati.* W w **14**. *P* 13.

876	1 r. Queen Elizabeth wearing red and white suit	35	35
	a. Horiz pair. Nos. 876/7	70	70
877	1 r. Prince Philip driving carriage	35	35
878	1 r. 50, Prince Philip	45	45
	a. Horiz pair. Nos. 878/9	90	90
879	1 r. 50, Queen Elizabeth with horse	45	45
880	3 r. Prince Charles and Princess Anne on horseback	90	90
	a. Horiz pair. Nos. 880/1	1·75	1·75
881	3 r. Prince Philip and Queen Elizabeth	90	90
876/81	*Set of* 6	3·00	3·00
MS882	110×70 mm. 10 r. Queen Elizabeth and Prince Philip in landau (*horiz*). Wmk sideways. P $14^{1}/_{2}$	3·00	3·25

Nos. 876/7, 878/9 and 880/1 were each printed together, *se-tenant,* in horizontal pairs throughout the sheets with the backgrounds forming composite designs.

(Des D. Miller. Litho Questa)

1998 (31 Mar). *Diana, Princess of Wales Commemoration. Sheet, 145×70 mm, containing vert designs as T* **91** *of Kiribati. Multicoloured.* W w **14** (*sideways*). *P* $14^{1}/_{2}$×14.

MS883	3 r. Wearing red jacket, 1992; 3 r. Wearing floral dress, 1981; 3 r. Wearing blue and black jacket, 1993; 3 r. Wearing white dress, Nepal 1993 (*sold at* 12 r. + 2 r. *charity premium*)	3·25	3·50

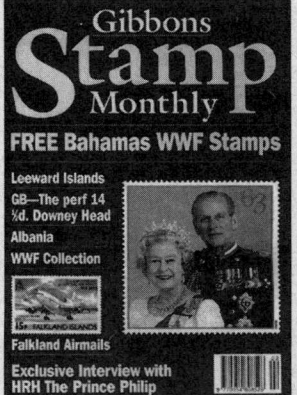

STAMP BOOKLETS

1979 (25 Apr). *Deep green on green (No. SB1), deep blue on blue (No. SB2) or black printed (No. SB3) covers, 120×75 mm, showing Seychelles arms. Stapled.*
SB1 5 r. booklet containing four 20 c. and 25 c. and eight 40 c. (Nos. 407/9) in blocks of 4 .. 8·00
SB2 10 r. booklet containing four 50 c., 75 c. and 1 r. 25 (Nos. 410/11, 413) in pairs .. .. .. 8·00
SB3 20 r. booklet containing four 1 r. 50 and 3 r. 50 (Nos. 402, 415) in pairs .. .. .. 11·00

1979 (26 Oct). *Red (No. SB4) or blue (No. SB5) printed covers, 118×78 mm, showing Seychelles arms. Stamps attached by selvedge.*
SB4 15 r. booklet containing 10 c., 15 c., 1 r. 50 and 2 r. (Nos. 405/6, 414, 447), each in block of 4 .. 8·00
SB5 20 r. booklet containing four 25 c., 1 r. 25 and 2 r. (Nos. 408, 413, 441/2 or 444/5) in blocks of 4, and two 3 r. (No. 452) in pair .. .. 12·00

1980 (29 Feb). *75th Anniv of Rotary International (No. SB6) and Centenary of Visit of General Gordon (No. SB7). Orange (No. SB6) or black (No. SB7) printed covers, 120×79 mm. Stamps attached by selvedge.*
SB6 15 r. booklet containing four 15 c., 1 r. and 1 r. 10 on 3 r. 50, and two 3 r. (Nos. 406, 412, 460, 462) in pairs .. .. .. 9·00
SB7 20 r. booklet containing 75 c., 2 r. and 2 r. 25 (Nos. 411, 441/2 or 444/5, 459), each in block of 4 9·00

1980 (28 Nov). *Black on orange (No. SB8) or black printed (No. SB9) covers, 123×80 mm, showing Clock Tower, Central Victoria. Stamps attached by selvedge.*
SB8 15 r. booklet containing four 40 c., 1 r. and 1 r. 25 (Nos. 409B, 412B, 413) in blocks of 4 and four 1 r. 10 on 3 r. 50 (No. 462) in pairs .. 15·00
SB9 20 r. booklet containing 1 r. 25, 1 r. 50 and 2 r. 25 (Nos. 413, 414B, 474), each in block of 4 .. 11·00

1981 (27 Feb). *Ships. Multicoloured cover, 160×93 mm. Stapled.*
SB10 35 r. 15, booklet containing 40 c. (No. 495) in block of 10, 5 r. (No. 498) in strip of 4 and No. **MS**499 .. .. 8·50

1981 (16 Nov). *Royal Wedding. Multicoloured cover, 105×65 mm, showing* The Victoria and Albert I. *Stitched.*
SB11 22 r. booklet containing eight 1 r. 50 in panes of four (No. 512a) and 5 r. in pane of two (No. 513a) .. .. 2·75

POSTAGE DUE STAMPS

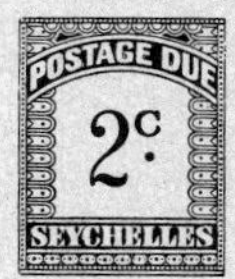

D 1

(Frame recess, value typo B.W.)

1951 (1 Mar). *Wmk Mult Script CA. P* 11½.
D1 D 1 2 c. scarlet and carmine .. .. 80 1·50
D2 3 c. scarlet and green .. .. .. 1·25 1·50
D3 6 c. scarlet and bistre .. .. .. 1·25 1·25
D4 9 c. scarlet and orange .. .. .. 1·50 1·25
D5 15 c. scarlet and violet .. .. .. 1·75 10·00
D6 18 c. scarlet and blue .. .. .. 1·75 10·00
D7 20 c. scarlet and brown .. .. .. 1·75 10·00
D8 30 c. scarlet and claret .. .. .. 1·75 7·50
D1/8 .. .. *Set of* 8 10·50 38·00

1964 (7 July)–**65**. *As* 1951 *but W w* **12**.
D 9 D 1 2 c. scarlet and carmine .. .. 2·25 11·00
D10 3 c. scarlet and green (14.9.65) .. 1·25 13·00

(Litho Walsall)

1980 (29 Feb). *Design as Type* D 1 *but redrawn, size* 18 × 22 *mm. W w* **14** (*sideways*). *P* 14.
D11 5 c. rosine and magenta 15 70
D12 10 c. rosine and deep blue-green 15 70
D13 15 c. rosine and bistre 20 70
D14 20 c. rosine and orange-brown 20 70
D15 25 c. rosine and bright violet 20 70
D16 75 c. rosine and maroon 30 70
D17 80 c. rosine and deep grey-blue 30 70
D18 1 r. rosine and deep reddish purple 30 70
D11/18 .. .. *Set of* 8 1·60 5·00

PRICES OF SETS

Set prices are given for many issues, generally those containing three stamps or more. Definitive sets include one of each value or major colour change, but do not cover different perforations, die types or minor shades. Where a choice is possible the set prices are based on the cheapest versions of the stamps included in the listings.

ZIL ELWANNYEN SESEL

(SEYCHELLES OUTER ISLANDS)

For use from Aldabra, Coetivy, Farquhar and the Amirante Islands, served by the M.V. *Cinq-Juin* travelling post office.

I Inscr "ZIL ELOIGNE SESEL"

1 Reef Fish

2 *Cinq Juin*

1980 (20 June)–**81**. *Designs as Nos.* 404/11 (*with imprint*) *and* 487/94 *of Seychelles but inscr.* "ZIL ELOIGNE SESEL" *as in T* **1**. *W w* **14** (*sideways on* 10, 20, 50, 75 *c.*). *P* 14½ × 14 (40 *c.*, 1 *r.*, 1 *r.* 25, 1*r.* 50), 13½ (5, 10, 15, 20 *r.*) *or* 14 (*others*).
1 5 c. Type **1** 15 40
2 10 c. Hawksbill Turtle 15 20
3 15 c. Coco-de-Mer 15 20
4 20 c. Wild Vanilla 20 20
5 25 c. *Hypolimnas misippus* (butterfly) .. 60 30
6 40 c. Coral scene 30 40
7 50 c. Giant Tortoise 30 30
8 75 c. Crayfish 35 30
9 1 r. Madagascar Red Fody 75 50
10 1 r. 10, Green Gecko 40 40
11 1 r. 25, White Tern 90 45
12 1 r. 50, Seychelles Flying Fox 45 35
w. Wmk inverted .. .. .. 1·50
13 5 r. Octopus .. .. .. 70 1·00
a. Perf 13 (1981) .. .. .. 65 1·50
14 10 r. Tiger Cowrie (*Cypraea tigris*) .. 1·00 1·50
a. Perf 13 (1981) .. .. .. 80 2·50
15 15 r. Pitcher Plant .. .. .. 1·25 2·50
a. Perf 13 (1981) .. .. .. 1·10 2·50
16 20 r. Seychelles coat of arms .. .. 1·40 3·25
a. Perf 13 (1981) .. .. .. 1·40 3·75
1/16 .. .. *Set of* 16 7·50 11·00
Imprint dates: "1980", Nos. 1/16; "1981", Nos. 1/12, 13a/16a.

(Des L. Curtis. Litho Walsall)

1980 (24 Oct). *Establishment of Travelling Post Office. T* **2** *and similar horiz designs. Multicoloured. W w* **14** (*sideways*). *P* 14.
17 1 r. 50, Type **2** 20 15
18 2 r. 10, Hand-stamping covers 25 20
19 5 r. Map of Zil Eloigne Sesel 40 40
17/19 .. .. *Set of* 3 75 65
Nos. 17/19 were printed in sheets including two *se-tenant* stamp-size labels.
The original version of No. 19 incorrectly showed the Agalega Islands as Seychelles territory. A corrected version was prepared prior to issue and stamps in the first type were intended for destruction. Mint examples and some used on first day covers are known, originating from supplies sent to some philatelic bureau standing order customers in error. Such stamps are not listed as they were not available from Seychelles post offices or valid for postage.

3 Yellow-finned Tuna

(Des G. Drummond. Litho Rosenbaum Bros, Vienna)

1980 (28 Nov). *Marine Life. T* **3** *and similar horiz designs. Multicoloured. W w* **14**. *P* 14.
20 1 r. 50, Type **3** 20 15
w. Wmk inverted .. .. .. 22·00
21 2 r. 10, Blue Marlin 35 20
w. Wmk inverted .. .. .. 27·00
22 5 r. Sperm Whale 70 50
w. Wmk inverted .. .. .. 22·00
20/2 .. .. *Set of* 3 1·10 75
Nos. 20/2 were printed in sheets including two *se-tenant* stamp-size labels.

(Des D. Shults. Litho Questa)

1981 (23 June–16 Nov). *Royal Wedding. Horiz designs as T* **26/27** *of Kiribati. Multicoloured. (a) W w* **15**. *P* 14.
23 40 c. *Royal Escape* 10 10
aw. Wmk inverted .. .. .. 15·00
b. Sheetlet. No. 23×6 and No. 24 .. 90
bw. Wmk inverted £110
24 40 c. Prince Charles and Lady Diana Spencer 40 55
aw. Wmk inverted .. .. .. 48·00
25 5 r. *Victoria and Albert II* 40 40
a. Sheetlet. No. 25×6 and No. 26 .. 3·50
26 5 r. As No. 24 .. .. .. 1·40 1·75
27 10 r. *Britannia* 85 85
a. Sheetlet. No. 27×6 and No. 28 .. 6·25
28 10 r. As No. 24 .. .. .. 2·00 3·25
23/8 .. .. *Set of* 6 4·50 6·25
MS29 120×109 mm. 7 r. 50, As No. 24. Wmk sideways. P 12 (16 Nov) .. .. 1·40 1·75

(*b*) *Booklet stamps. No wmk. P* 12 (16 Nov)
30 40 c. As No. 23 .. .. .. 35 75
a. Booklet pane. No. 30×4 with margins all round .. .. 1·25
31 5 r. As No. 26 .. .. .. 1·00 1·75
a. Booklet pane. No. 31×2 with margins all round .. .. 2·00
Nos. 23/8 were printed in sheetlets of seven stamps of the same face value, each containing six of the "Royal Yacht" design and one of the larger design showing Prince Charles and Lady Diana.
Nos. 30/1 come from 13 r. 20 stamp booklets.

4 Wright's Skink

(Des and litho Walsall)

1981 (11 Dec). *Wildlife* (1*st series*). *T* **4** *and similar horiz designs. Multicoloured. W w* **14** (*sideways*). *P* 14.
32 1 r. 40, Type **4** 15 15
33 2 r. 25, Tree Frog 20 20
34 5 r. Robber Crab 40 40
32/4 .. .. *Set of* 3 65 65
See also Nos. 45/7.

5 *Cinq Juin* ("Communications")

(Des L. Curtis. Litho Harrison)

1982 (11 Mar). *Island Development. Ships. T* **5** *and similar horiz designs. W w* **14**. *P* 14 × 14½.
35 1 r. 75, black and orange 50 20
w. Wmk inverted .. .. .. 24·00
36 2 r. 10, black and turquoise-blue .. 60 30
w. Wmk inverted .. .. .. 3·00
37 5 r. black and bright scarlet 70 50
35/7 .. .. *Set of* 3 1·60 90
Designs:—2 r. 10, *Junon* ("fisheries protection"); 5 r. *Diamond M. Dragon* (drilling ship).

II Inscr "ZIL ELWAGNE SESEL"

6 *Paulette*

(Des L. Curtis. Litho Harrison)

1982 (22 July). *Local Mail Vessels. T* **6** *and similar horiz designs. Multicoloured. W w* **14** (*sideways*). *P* 14.
38 40 c. Type **6** 25 25
39 1 r. 75, *Janette* 50 60
40 2 r. 75, *Lady Esme* 60 75
41 3 r. 50, *Cinq Juin* 70 85
38/41 .. .. *Set of* 4 1·90 2·25

7 Birds flying over Island

8 Red Land Crab

(Des Harrison. Litho Format)

1982 (19 Nov). *Aldabra, World Heritage Site. T* **7** *and similar horiz designs. Multicoloured. W w* **14** (*sideways*). *P* 14.
42 40 c. Type **7** 30 15
43 2 r. 75, Map of the atoll 60 35
44 7 r. Giant Tortoises 80 75
42/4 .. .. *Set of* 3 1·50 1·10

(Des G. Drummond. Litho Questa)

1983 (25 Feb). *Wildlife* (2*nd series*). *T* **8** *and similar horiz designs. Multicoloured. W w* **14** (*sideways*). *P* 14 × 14½.
45 1 r. 75, Type **8** 25 25
46 2 r. 75, Black Terrapin 35 35
47 7 r. Madagascar Green Gecko 80 80
45/7 .. .. *Set of* 3 1·25 1·25

9 Map of Poivre Island and Île du Sud

10 Aldabra Warbler

(Des J. Cooter. Litho Format)

1983 (27 Apr). *Island Maps. T* **9** *and similar vert designs. Multicoloured.* W w **14**. *P* 14.

48 40 c. Type **9** 15 15
49 1 r. 50, Île des Roches 30 25
50 2 r. 75, Astove Island.. .. .. .. 50 40
51 7 r. Coëtivy Island .. .. 80 1·10
48/51 .. .. *Set of* 4 1·60 1·75
MS52 93 × 129 mm. Nos. 48/51 .. .. 1·75 3·00

(Des G. Drummond. Litho Harrison)

1983 (13 July). *Birds. T* **10** *and similar multicoloured designs.* W w **14** (*sideways on* 5 c. *to* 2 r. 75). "1983" *imprint date. P* 14½.

53 5 c. Type **10** 40 40
54 10 c. Zebra Dove ("Barred Ground Dove") .. 90 40
55 15 c. Madagascar Nightjar 30 10
56 20 c. Madagascar Cisticola ("Malagasy Grass Warbler") 30 10
57 25 c. Madagascar White Eye 45 30
58 40 c. Mascarene Fody 30 10
59 50 c. White-throated Rail .. .. .. 1·00 30
60 75 c. Black Bulbul 40 25
61 2 r. Western Reef Heron ("Dimorphic Little Egret") .. .. 2·00 85
62 2 r. 10, Souimanga Sunbird 50 55
63 2 r. 50, Madagascar Turtle Dove 60 65
64 2 r. 75, Sacred Ibis 70 75
65 3 r. 50, Black Coucal (*vert*) 90 95
66 7 r. Seychelles Kestrel (*vert*) .. .. 1·75 1·90
67 15 r. Comoro Blue Pigeon (*vert*) .. .. 4·00 4·25
68 20 r. Greater Flamingo (*vert*) .. .. 5·25 5·50
53/68 .. .. *Set of* 16 18·00 14·00

For 5 c., 10 c., 25 c., 50 c. and 2 r. values in these designs, but inscribed "Zil Elwannyen Sesel", see Nos. 100/7, 165/73 and 226.

11 Windsurfing

(Des G. Wilby. Litho Questa)

1983 (27 Sept). *Tourism. T* **11** *and similar horiz designs. Multicoloured.* W w **14** (*sideways*). *P* 14.

69 50 c. Type **11** 10 10
70 2 r. Hotel 25 25
71 3 r. View of beach 35 35
72 10 r. Islands at sunset .. .. .. 1·40 1·75
69/72 .. .. *Set of* 4 1·75 2·10

1983 (16–28 Dec). *Nos.* 23/8 *surch as T* **135** *of Seychelles.*

73 30 c. on 40 c. *Royal Escape* 25 25
a. Sheetlet. No. 73 × 6 and No. 74 .. 1·75
b. Surch double .. .. 50·00
c. Error. Surch 50 c. (as Seychelles No. 573) 60·00
74 30 c. on 40 c. Prince Charles and Lady Diana Spencer 50 60
b. Surch double £130
c. Error. Surch 50 c. (as Seychelles No. 574) £140
75 2 r. on 5 r. *Victoria and Albert II* (28.12.83) .. 70 70
a. Sheetlet. No. 75 × 6 and No. 76 .. 5·00
b. Albino surch .. .. 40·00
c. Surch double .. .. 75·00
76 2 r. on 5 r. As No. 74 (28.12.83) .. .. 1·25 1·75
b. Albino surch .. .. 65·00
c. Surch double £200
77 3 r. on 10 r. *Britannia* (28.12.83) 85 85
a. Sheetlet. No. 77 × 6 and No. 78 .. 6·00
78 3 r. on 10 r. As No. 74 (28.12.83) .. .. 1·60 2·50
73/8 .. .. *Set of* 6 4·75 6·00

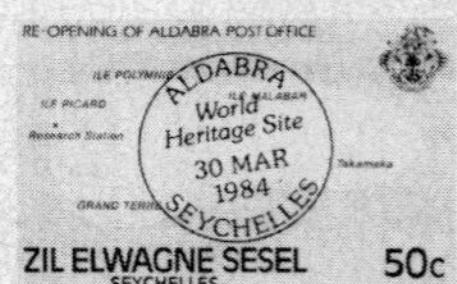

12 Map of Aldabra and Commemorative Postmark

(Des L. Curtis. Litho Questa)

1984 (30 Mar). *Re-opening of Aldabra Post Office. T* **12** *and similar horiz designs. Multicoloured.* W w **14** (*sideways*). *P* 14.

79 50 c. Type **12** 15 25
80 2 r. 75, White-throated Rail 60 95
81 3 r. Giant Tortoise .. .. 60 1·10
82 10 r. Red-footed Booby .. .. .. 2·25 3·25
79/82 .. .. *Set of* 4 3·25 5·00

13 Fishing from Launch

(Des L. Curtis. Litho Walsall)

1984 (31 May). *Game Fishing. T* **13** *and similar multicoloured designs.* W w **14** (*sideways on* 50 c., 10 *r.*). *P* 14.

83 50 c. Type **13** 15 20
84 2 r. Hooked fish (*vert*) 45 65
85 3 r. Weighing catch (*vert*) 60 85
86 10 r. Fishing from boat (*different*) .. .. 2·00 2·75
83/6 .. .. *Set of* 4 2·75 4·00

14 Giant Hermit Crab

15 Constellation of "Orion"

(Des G. Drummond. Litho Format)

1984 (24 Aug). *Crabs. T* **14** *and similar horiz designs. Multicoloured.* W w **14** (*sideways*). *P* 14½.

87 50 c. Type **14** 25 40
88 2 r. Fiddler Crabs .. .. 65 1·10
89 3 r. Sand Crab .. .. 80 1·50
90 10 r. Spotted Pebble Crab .. .. .. 2·50 4·25
87/90 .. .. *Set of* 4 3·75 6·50

(Des A. Theobald. Litho Format)

1984 (16 Oct). *The Night Sky. T* **15** *and similar vert designs. Multicoloured.* W w **14**. *P* 14.

91 50 c. Type **15** 25 15
92 2 r. "Cygnus" 60 55
93 3 r. "Virgo" 80 80
94 10 r. "Scorpio" .. .. 2·00 2·25
91/4 .. .. *Set of* 4 3·25 3·25

III Inscr "ZIL ELWANNYEN SESEL"

16 *Lenzites elegans*

17 The Queen Mother attending Royal Opera House, Covent Garden

(Des G. Drummond. Litho Walsall)

1985 (31 Jan). *Fungi. T* **16** *and similar vert designs. Multicoloured.* W w **14**. *P* 14.

95 50 c. Type **16** 85 85
96 2 r. *Xylaria telfairei* .. .. .. 2·00 2·00
97 3 r. *Lentinus sajor-caju* .. .. .. 2·00 2·00
98 10 r. *Hexagonia tenuis* .. .. .. 3·50 3·50
95/8 .. .. *Set of* 4 7·50 7·50

(Litho Harrison)

1985 (May)–**87**. *As Nos.* 54, 57, 59 *and* 61 *but inscr* "Zil Elwannyen Sesel". W w **14** (*sideways*). *P* 14½.

100 10 c. Zebra Dove ("Barred Ground Dove") 1·25 1·50
103 25 c. Madagascar White Eye .. .. 1·00 1·00
105 50 c. White-throated Rail (1.7.87) .. 1·75 1·25
107 2 r. Western Reef Heron ("Dimorphic Little Egret") .. .. 4·25 4·50
100/7 .. .. *Set of* 4 7·50 7·50

Imprint dates: "1985", Nos. 100, 103, 107; "1987", Nos. 100, 105.

For 10 c., 50 c. and 2 r. values watermarked w **16** (sideways) see Nos. 165/73 and 226.

(Des A. Theobald (10 r.), C. Abbott (others). Litho Questa)

1985 (7 June). *Life and Times of Queen Elizabeth the Queen Mother. T* **17** *and similar vert designs. Multicoloured.* W w **16**. *P* 14½ × 14.

115 1 r. The Queen Mother, 1936 (from photo by Dorothy Wilding) 20 25
w. Wmk inverted .. .. .. 5·00
116 2 r. With Princess Anne at Ascot, 1974 .. 35 50
w. Wmk inverted 65
117 3 r. Type **17** 45 70
w. Wmk inverted .. .. .. 14·00
118 5 r. With Prince Henry at his christening (from photo by Lord Snowdon) .. 60 1·25
115/18 .. .. *Set of* 4 1·40 2·40
MS119 91×73 mm. 10 r. In a launch, Venice, 1985. Wmk sideways .. .. .. 1·50 2·75

18 Giant Tortoise

(Des. G. Vasarhelyi. Litho J.W.)

1985 (27 Sept). *Giant Tortoises of Aldabra* (1*st series*). *T* **18** *and similar horiz designs. Multicoloured.* W w **16** (*sideways*). *P* 14.

120 50 c. Type **18** .. .. 2·25 60
121 75 c. Giant Tortoises at stream .. .. 2·50 80
122 1 r. Giant Tortoises on grassland .. .. 2·75 90
123 2 r. Giant Tortoise (side view) .. .. 3·50 1·25
120/3 .. .. *Set of* 4 10·00 3·25
MS124 70 × 60 mm. 10 r. Two Giant Tortoises. P 13 × 13½ .. .. 9·50 9·00

For stamps as Nos. 120/3, but without circular inscription around W.W.F. emblem, see Nos. 153/6.

19 Phoenician Trading Ship (600 B.C.)

20 *Acropora palifera* and *Tubastraea coccinea*

(Des N. Shewring. Litho Format)

1985 (25 Oct). *Famous Visitors. T* **19** *and similar horiz designs. Multicoloured.* W w **14** (*sideways*). *P* 14.

125 50 c. Type **19** 80 80
126 2 r. Sir Hugh Scott and H.M.S. *Sealark*, 1908 .. .. 1·75 2·00
127 10 r. Vasco da Gama and *Sao Gabriel*, 1502 3·50 4·50
125/7 .. .. *Set of* 3 5·50 6·50

(Des A. Theobald. Litho Questa)

1986 (21 Apr). *60th Birthday of Queen Elizabeth II. Vert designs as T* **230***a of Jamaica. Multicoloured.* W w **16**. *P* 14½×14.

128 75 c. Princess Elizabeth at Chester, 1951 .. 15 25
129 1 r. Queen and Duke of Edinburgh at Falklands Service, St. Paul's Cathedral, 1985 .. .. 15 25
130 1 r. 50, At Order of St. Michael and St. George service, St. Paul's Cathedral, 1968 .. .. 25 40
131 3 r. 75, In Mexico, 1975 .. .. .. 40 90
132 5 r. At Crown Agents Head Office, London, 1983 .. .. 45 1·25
128/32 .. .. *Set of* 5 1·25 2·75

(Des D. Miller. Litho Questa)

1986 (23 July). *Royal Wedding. Square designs as T* **231***a of Jamaica. Multicoloured.* W w **16**. *P* 14.

133 3 r. Prince Andrew and Miss Sarah Ferguson on Buckingham Palace balcony 45 75
134 7 r. Prince Andrew in naval uniform .. .. 65 1·75

(Des I. Loe. Litho Harrison)

1986 (17 Sept). *Coral Formations. T* **20** *and similar vert designs. Multicoloured.* W w **16**. *P* 14.

135 2 r. Type **20** .. .. 1·50 1·50
a. Horiz strip of 5. Nos. 135/9 .. .. 6·75
136 2 r. *Echinopora lamellosa* and *Favia pallida* 1·50 1·50
137 2 r. *Sarcophyton sp.* and *Porites lutea* .. 1·50 1·50
138 2 r. *Goniopora sp.* and *Goniastrea retiformis* 1·50 1·50
139 2 r. *Tubipora musica* and *Fungia fungites* .. 1·50 1·50
135/9 .. .. *Set of* 5 6·75 6·75

Nos. 135/9 were printed together, *se-tenant*, in horizontal strips of 5 throughout the sheet, forming a composite design.

21 *Hibiscus tiliaceus*

22 Teardrop Butterflyfish and Lined Butterflyfish

(Des Annette Robinson. Litho Walsall)

1986 (12 Nov). *Flora. T* **21** *and similar vert designs. Multicoloured.* W w **16**. *P* 14.

140 50 c. Type **21** 35 30
141 2 r. *Crinum angustum* .. .. .. 1·60 1·25
142 3 r. *Phaius tetragonus* .. .. .. 2·25 1·75
143 10 r. *Rothmannia annae* .. .. .. 3·75 3·75
140/3 .. .. *Set of* 4 7·00 6·25

(Des G. Drummond. Litho Questa)

1987 (26 Mar). *Coral Reef Fishes. T* **22** *and similar vert designs. Multicoloured.* W w **16**. *P* 14.

144 2 r. Type **22** .. .. 1·10 1·10
a. Horiz strip of 5. Nos. 144/8 .. .. 5·00
145 2 r. Knifejaw .. .. 1·10 1·10
146 2 r. Narrow-banded Batfish .. .. .. 1·10 1·10
147 2 r. Ringed Sergeant .. .. 1·10 1·10
148 2 r. Lined Butterflyfish and Meyer's Butterflyfish .. .. 1·10 1·10
144/8 .. .. *Set of* 5 5·00 5·00

Nos. 144/8 were printed together, *se-tenant*, in horizontal strips of 5 throughout the sheet, forming a composite design.

23 Coconut

24 "Vallee de Mai" (Christine Harter)

(Des R. Gorringe. Litho Walsall)

1987 (26 Aug). *Trees. T* **23** *and similar vert designs. Multicoloured.* W w **16**. *P* 14½.

149 1 r. Type **23** 80 80
150 2 r. Mangrove .. .. 1·40 1·60
151 3 r. Pandanus Palm .. .. 2·00 2·25
152 5 r. Indian Almond .. .. 3·00 3·25
149/52 .. .. *Set of* 4 6·50 7·00

(Des G. Vasarhelyi. Litho Questa)

1987 (9 Sept). *Giant Tortoises of Aldabra (2nd series). Designs as Nos.* 120/3, *but without circular inscr around W.W.F. emblem. Multicoloured.* W w **16** (*sideways*). *P* 14.

153 50 c. As Type **18** .. .. 1·75 1·75
154 75 c. Giant Tortoises at stream .. .. 2·50 2·50
155 1 r. Giant Tortoises on grassland .. .. 3·50 3·50
156 2 r. Giant Tortoise (side view) .. .. 4·50 4·50
153/6 .. .. *Set of* 4 11·00 11·00

1987 (9 Dec). *Royal Ruby Wedding. Nos.* 128/32 *optd with T* **45a** *of Kiribati in silver.*

157 75 c. Princess Elizabeth at Chester, 1951 .. 20 20
158 1 r. Queen and Duke of Edinburgh at Falklands Service, St. Paul's Cathedral, 1985 .. .. 25 25
159 1 r. 50, At Order of St. Michael and St. George service, St. Paul's Cathedral, 1968 .. .. 35 40
160 3 r. 75, In Mexico, 1975 .. .. .. 60 90
161 5 r. At Crown Agents Head Office, London, 1983 .. .. 80 1·25
157/61 .. .. *Set of* 5 2·00 2·75

(Des D. Miller. Litho Questa)

1987 (16 Dec). *Tourism. T* **24** *and similar vert designs. Multicoloured.* W w **16**. *P* 14.

162 3 r. Type **24** .. .. 2·00 1·60
a. Horiz strip of 3. Nos. 162/4 .. .. 5·50
163 3 r. Ferns .. .. 2·00 1·60
164 3 r. Bamboo .. .. 2·00 1·60
162/4 .. .. *Set of* 3 5·50 4·25

Nos. 162/4 were printed together, *se-tenant*, in horizontal strips of 3 throughout the sheet, forming the complete picture.

(Litho Harrison)

1988 (July–24 Nov). *As No.* 53, *but inscr "Zil Elwannyen Sesel", and Nos.* 100, 105 *and* 107, *all* W w **16** (*sideways*). *"1988" imprint date. P* 14½.

165 5 c. Type **10** (24.11) .. .. 1·00 1·00
166 10 c. Zebra Dove ("Barred Ground Dove") (24.11) .. .. 1·00 1·00
171 50 c. White-throated Rail (24.11) .. .. 1·50 1·50
173 2 r. Western Reef Heron ("Dimorphic Little Egret") .. .. 4·25 4·75
165/73 .. .. *Set of* 4 7·00 7·50

For 2 r. printed by Walsall and perforated 14×14½ see No. 226.

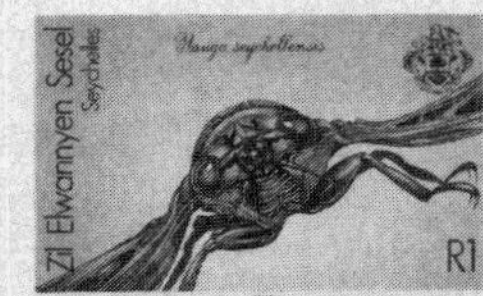

25 *Yanga seychellensis* (beetle)

(Des I. Loe. Litho Walsall)

1988 (28 July). *Insects. T* **25** *and similar horiz designs. Multicoloured.* W w 14 (*sideways*). *P* 14.

180 1 r. Type **25** .. .. 1·00 80
181 2 r. *Belenois aldabrensis* (butterfly) .. 1·75 1·40
182 3 r. *Polyspilota seychelliana* (mantid) .. 2·00 2·00
183 5 r. *Polposipus herculeanus* (beetle) .. 2·50 2·75
180/3 .. .. *Set of* 4 6·50 6·25

26 Olympic Rings

(Des Joan Thompson. Litho Format)

1988 (31 Aug). *Olympic Games, Seoul. Sheet* 99 × 73 *mm.* W w **16** (*sideways*). *P* 14.

MS184 **26** 10 r. multicoloured .. .. .. 2·40 2·40

(Des D. Miller (1 r.), E. Nisbet and D. Miller (2 r.), O. Bell and D. Miller (3 r.), A. Theobald and D. Miller (5 r.). Litho Walsall)

1988 (28 Oct). *300th Anniv of Lloyd's of London. Multicoloured designs as T* **167a** *of Malawi.* W w **14** (*sideways on* 2, 3 *r.*). *P* 14.

185 1 r. Modern Lloyd's Building, London .. 70 55
186 2 r. *Retriever* (cable ship) (*horiz*) .. .. 1·00 90
187 3 r. *Chantel* (fishing boat) (*horiz*) .. .. 1·75 1·40
188 5 r. Wreck of *Torrey Canyon* (tanker), Cornwall, 1967 .. .. 2·25 1·75
185/8 .. .. *Set of* 4 5·25 4·25

27 "Father Christmas landing with Presents" (Jean-Claude Boniface)

(Adapted G. Vasarhelyi. Litho Questa)

1988 (18 Nov). *Christmas. Children's Paintings. T* **27** *and similar multicoloured designs.* W w **16** (*sideways on* 1, 5 *r.*). *P* 13½ × 14 (*horiz*) *or* 14 × 13½ (*vert*).

189 1 r. Type **27** 35 35
190 2 r. "Church" (Francois Barra) (*vert*) .. 60 60
191 3 r. "Father Christmas flying on Bird" (Wizy Ernesta) (*vert*) 85 85
192 5 r. "Father Christmas in Sleigh over Island" (Federic Lang) .. .. .. 1·40 1·40
189/92 .. .. *Set of* 4 2·75 2·75

(Des A. Theobald (10 r.), D. Miller (others). Litho Questa)

1989 (20 July). *20th Anniv of First Manned Landing on Moon. Multicoloured designs as T* **51a** *of Kiribati.* W w **16** (*sideways on* 2, 3 *r.*). *P* 14×13½ (1, 5 *r.*) *or* 14 (*others*).

193 1 r. Firing Room, Launch Control Centre .. 70 70
194 2 r. Crews of "Apollo-Soyuz" mission (30×30 *mm*) .. .. 1·10 1·10
195 3 r. "Apollo-Soyuz" emblem (30×30 *mm*) .. 1·40 1·50
196 5 r. "Apollo" and "Soyuz" docking in space 2·00 2·25
193/6 .. .. *Set of* 4 4·75 5·00
MS197 82×100 mm. 10 r. Recovery of "Apollo 11". P 14×13½ .. .. 6·50 7·00

28 Dumb Cane

29 Tec-Tec Broth

(Des Lynn Chadwick. Litho Questa)

1989 (9 Oct). *Poisonous Plants (1st series). T* **28** *and similar horiz designs. Multicoloured.* W w **16** (*sideways*). *P* 14.

198 1 r. Type **28** .. .. 1·25 1·25
199 2 r. Star of Bethlehem .. .. .. 1·75 1·75
200 3 r. Indian Liquorice .. .. .. 2·00 2·00
201 5 r. Black Nightshade .. .. .. 2·75 2·75
198/201 .. .. *Set of* 4 7·00 7·00

See also Nos. 214/17.

(Des O. Bell. Litho B.D.T.)

1989 (18 Dec). *Creole Cooking. T* **29** *and similar vert designs. Multicoloured.* W w **16**. *P* 14.

202 1 r. Type **29** .. .. 1·25 1·25
203 2 r. Pilaff á la Seychelloise .. .. .. 1·75 1·75
204 3 r. Mullet grilled in banana leaves .. 2·00 2·00
205 5 r. Daube .. .. 2·75 2·75
202/5 .. .. *Set of* 4 7·00 7·00
MS206 125×80 mm. Nos. 202/5 .. .. 7·50 8·00

Stamps from No. **MS**206 have the white margin omitted on one or both vertical sides.

30 1980 Marine Life 5 r. Stamp

(Des D. Miller. Litho Security Printers (M), Malaysia)

1990 (3 May). *"Stamp World London 90" International Stamp Exhibition. T* **30** *and similar horiz designs showing stamps. Multicoloured.* W w **14** (*sideways*). *P* 12½.

207 1 r. Type **30** .. .. 1·25 1·25
208 2 r. 1980 5 r. definitive .. .. .. 1·75 1·75
209 3 r. 1983 2 r. 75 definitive .. .. .. 2·00 2·00
210 5 r. 1981 Wildlife 5 r. .. .. .. 2·75 2·75
207/10 .. .. *Set of* 4 7·00 7·00
MS211 124×84 mm. Nos. 207/10. Wmk upright 7·50 8·00

(Des D. Miller. Litho Questa)

1990 (4 Aug). *90th Birthday of Queen Elizabeth the Queen Mother. Vert designs as T* **107** (2 *r.*) *or* **108** (10 *r.*) *of Kenya.* W w **16**. *P* 14×15 (2 *r.*) *or* 14½ (10 *r.*).

212 2 r. multicoloured .. .. 1·50 1·50
213 10 r. black and orange-brown .. .. 3·25 4·00

Designs:—2 r. Duchess of York with baby Princess Elizabeth, 1926; 10 r. King George VI and Queen Elizabeth visiting bombed district, London, 1940.

(Des Lynn Chadwick. Litho Security Printers (M), Malaysia)

1990 (5 Nov). *Poisonous Plants (2nd series). Horiz designs as T* **28**. *Multicoloured.* W w **14** (*sideways*). *P* 12½.

214 1 r. Ordeal Plant .. .. 1·25 1·25
215 2 r. Thorn Apple .. .. 1·75 1·75
216 3 r. Strychnine Tree .. .. .. 2·00 2·00
217 5 r. Bwa Zasmen .. .. 2·75 2·75
214/17 .. .. *Set of* 4 7·00 7·00

(Litho Walsall)

1991 (Jan). *As No.* 173, *but different printer.* W w **16** (*sideways*). *"1990" imprint date. P* 14×14½.

226 2 r. Western Reef Heron ("Dimorphic Little Egret") .. .. 2·50 2·50

(Des D. Miller. Litho Questa)

1991 (17 June). *65th Birthday of Queen Elizabeth II and 70th Birthday of Prince Philip. Vert designs as T* **58** *of Kiribati. Multicoloured.* W w **16** (*sideways*). *P* 14½×14.

234 4 r. Queen Elizabeth II .. .. .. 1·60 1·75
a. Horiz pair. Nos. 234/5 separated by label .. .. 3·00 3·50
235 4 r. Prince Philip .. .. 1·60 1·75

Nos. 234/5 were printed in a similar sheet format to Nos. 366/7 of Kiribati.

31 *St. Abbs* (full-rigged ship), 1860

32 *Lomatopyllum aldabrense* (plant)

(Des J. Batchelor. Litho Walsall)

1991 (28 Oct). *Shipwrecks. T* **31** *and similar horiz designs. Multicoloured.* W w **14** (*sideways*). *P* 14.

236 1 r. 50, Type **31** .. .. 1·50 1·50
237 3 r. *Norden* (barque), 1862 .. .. .. 2·00 2·00
238 3 r. 50, *Clan Mackay* (freighter), 1894 .. 2·25 2·25
239 10 r. *Glenlyon* (freighter), 1905 .. .. 5·50 6·00
236/9 .. .. *Set of* 4 10·00 10·50

(Des D. Miller. Litho Questa (5 r.), Walsall (others))

1992 (6 Feb). *40th Anniv of Queen Elizabeth II's Accession. Horiz designs as T* **113** *of Kenya. Multicoloured.* W w **14** (*sideways*). *P* 14.

240 1 r. Beach 60 60
241 1 r. 50, Aerial view of Desroches 85 85
242 3 r. Tree-covered coastline .. .. .. 1·25 1·50
243 3 r. 50, Three portraits of Queen Elizabeth II 1·40 1·60
244 5 r. Queen Elizabeth II .. .. .. 1·60 2·00
240/4 .. .. *Set of* 5 5·00 6·00

(Des D. Miller. Litho Questa)

1992 (19 Nov). *10th Anniv of Aldabra as a World Heritage Site. T* **32** *and similar vert designs. Multicoloured.* W w **14**. *P* 14½×14.

245 1 r. 50, Type **32** .. .. 1·25 1·25
246 3 r. White-throated Rail .. .. .. 2·25 2·25
247 3 r. 50, Robber Crab .. .. .. 2·25 2·25
248 10 r. Aldabra Drongo .. .. .. 6·50 7·50
245/8 .. .. *Set of* 4 11·00 12·00

STAMP BOOKLETS

1980 (28 Nov). *Black on yellow cover, 126×80 mm, showing map of Zil Elwannyen Sesel. Stamps attached by selvedge.*
SB1 25 r. booklet containing 40 c., 1 r. and 1 r. 10 (Nos. 6, 9/10), each in block of 4, and three 5 r. (No. 13) in pair and single .. .. .. 14·00

1981 (16 Nov). *Royal Wedding. Multicoloured cover, 105×65 mm, showing the* Royal Escape. *Stitched.*
SB2 13 r. 20, booklet containing eight 40 c. in panes of 4 (No. 30a) and two 5 r. in pane of 2 (No. 31a) 4·00

Sierra Leone

PRICES FOR STAMPS ON COVER TO 1945

Nos. 1/15	*from* × 10
Nos. 16/26	*from* × 15
Nos. 27/34	*from* × 20
Nos. 35/7	*from* × 10
No. 38	—
No. 39	*from* × 15
Nos. 41/52	*from* × 8
No. 53	—
No. 54	*from* × 40
Nos. 55/63	*from* × 5
Nos. 64/71	—
Nos. 73/84	*from* × 4
No. 85	—
Nos. 86/97	*from* × 4
No. 98	—
Nos. 99/110	*from* × 4
No. 111	—
Nos. 112/26	*from* × 2
Nos. 127/30	—
Nos. 131/45	*from* × 2
Nos. 146/8	—
Nos. 155/66	*from* × 2
No. 167	—
Nos. 168/78	*from* × 2
Nos. 179/80	—
Nos. 181/4	*from* × 6
Nos. 185/7	*from* × 5
Nos. 188/200	*from* × 2

CROWN COLONY AND PROTECTORATE

The first settlement in Sierra Leone intended as a home for repatriated Africans, and subsequently those released by the Royal Navy from slave ships, was established in 1787. The Sierra Leone Company was created by Act of Parliment in 1791, but its charter was surrendered in 1808 and the coastal settlements then became a Crown Colony. The inland region was proclaimed a British protectorate on 21 August 1896.

A post office was established in 1843 but, until the inclusion of Freetown in the British Post Office packet system in 1850, overseas mail was carried at irregular intervals by passing merchant or naval vessels.

The stamps of GREAT BRITAIN were not sold at Sierra Leone post offices, although examples from ships of the West African Squadron do exist with local cancellations.

PRINTERS. All issues of Sierra Leone until 1932 were typographed by De La Rue & Co. Ltd, London.

1

2

HALF PENNY

(3)

Dot after "SIX" and break in octagonal frame (R. 19/11)

1859 (21 Sept)–**74.** *No wmk. P* 14.
1 1 6d. dull purple .. .. £200 50·00
2 6d. grey-lilac (1865) .. .. £225 40·00
a. Dot after "SIX" .. .. — £250
3 6d. reddish violet (*p* 12½) (1872) .. .. £350 60·00
a. Dot after "SIX" .. .. — £350
4 6d. reddish lilac (1874) .. .. .. 38·00 27·00
a. Dot after "SIX" £200 £140

Imperforate proofs exist.

The paper used for the 6d. value often shows varying degrees of blueing, caused by a chemical reaction.

The 6d. plate contained 240 stamps arranged in panes of 20 (4×5) with the sheets containing 12 such panes in four horizontal rows of three.

1872–73. *Wmk Crown CC. P* 12½. (*a*) *Wmk sideways* (April 1872).
7 2 1d. rose-red .. .. 65·00 27·00
8 3d. buff .. .. £110 35·00
9 4d. blue .. .. £150 38·00
10 1s. green .. .. £300 50·00

(*b*) *Wmk upright* (Sept 1873)
11 2 1d. rose-red .. .. 75·00 30·00
12 2d. magenta .. .. £110 48·00
13 3d. saffron-yellow .. .. .. £500 85·00
14 4d. blue .. .. £250 50·00
15 1s. green .. .. £400 90·00

1876. *Wmk Crown CC. P* 14.
16 2 ½d. brown .. .. 2·00 6·00
17 1d. rose-red .. .. 45·00 10·00
18 1½d. lilac (Nov) .. .. 45·00 6·00
19 2d. magenta .. .. 50·00 3·75
20 3d. buff .. .. 48·00 4·00
21 4d. blue .. .. £110 6·50
22 1s. green .. .. 55·00 6·50
16/22 .. .. *Set of* 7 £300 38·00

1883 (June–26 Sept). *Wmk Crown CA. P* 14.
23 2 ½d. brown .. .. 18·00 48·00
24 1d. rose-red (26.9.83) .. .. .. £200 35·00
25 2d. magenta .. .. 45·00 7·50
26 4d. blue .. .. £850 28·00

1884 SIERRA 5s. LEONE SURCHARGE. From 2 June 1884 the administration decided that, as a temporary measure, revenue and fiscal duties were to be paid with ordinary postage stamps. At that time there was no postage value higher than 1s., so a local surcharge, reading "SIERRA 5s. LEONE", was applied to No. 22 (*Price* £200 *unused*). Until withdrawal on 1 March 1885 this surcharge was valid for both fiscal and postal purposes, although no genuine postal cover or piece has yet been found. One mint example is known with overprint inverted (*Price* £600).

Remainders of the surcharge were cancelled by a horizontal red brush stroke (*Price* £30 *with upright surcharge*, £150 *with inverted surcharge*).

1884 (July)–**91.** *Wmk Crown CA. P* 14.
27 2 ½d. dull green 40 70
28 1d. carmine .. .. 2·00 70
a. Rose-carmine (1885?) .. .. 28·00 8·50
29 1½d. pale violet (1889) .. .. .. 2·25 5·50
30 2d. grey .. .. 25·00 2·25
31 2½d. ultramarine (1891) .. .. .. 7·00 85
32 3d. yellow (1889) .. .. 2·00 7·00
33 4d. brown .. .. 1·50 1·00
34 1s. red-brown (1888) .. .. .. 15·00 10·00
27/34 .. .. *Set of* 8 50·00 25·00
27/8, 30/1, 33/4 (*perf* 14) Optd "Specimen" *Set of* 6 £475
27/8, 30, 33 (*perf* 12) Optd "Specimen" .. *Set of* 4 £650

1885–96. *Wmk Crown CC. P* 14.
35 1 6d. dull violet (1885) .. .. .. 55·00 22·00
a. Bisected (3d.) (on cover) .. .. † £2500
b. Dot after "SIX" .. .. .. — £100
36 6d. brown-purple (1890) (Optd S. £60) .. 13·00 14·00
a. Dot after "SIX" .. .. .. 70·00 70·00
37 6d. purple-lake (1896) .. .. .. 2·00 6·50
a. Dot after "SIX" .. .. .. 30·00 50·00

Proofs of the 6d. brown-purple exist from 1889 on Crown CA watermark and perforated 12 (*Price* £1500, *unused*).

1893 (18 Jan). *Surch with T* **3.** (*a*) *On No.* 18. *Wmk Crown CC.*
38 2 ½d. on 1½d. lilac £425 £500
a. "PFNNY" (R. 3/1) £1900 £2500

(*b*) *On No.* 29. *Wmk Crown CA*
39 2 ½d. on 1½d. pale violet .. .. .. 2·75 3·00
a. Surch inverted £100 £100
b. "PFNNY" (R. 3/1) .. .. .. 70·00 70·00
ba. Ditto. Surch inverted £1800

On Nos. 38/9 the surcharge and the cancelling bars were applied separately so that No. 39a exists with the bars either normal or inverted with the rest of the surcharge.

Forged surcharges exist with "HALF PENNY" shown on one line.

The 6d. fiscal, inscribed "STAMP DUTY" as Type **6**, surcharged "ONE-PENNY" is known used for postage between June and August 1894, but no official sanction for such usage has been found.

4

5

1896–97. *Wmk Crown CA. P* 14.
41 4 ½d. dull mauve and green (1897) .. 1·00 2·00
42 1d. dull mauve and carmine .. .. 1·00 1·25
43 1½d. dull mauve and black (1897) .. 3·00 12·00
44 2d. dull mauve and orange .. .. 2·25 5·00
45 2½d. dull mauve and ultramarine .. 1·40 1·00
46 5 3d. dull mauve and slate .. .. 7·00 7·00
47 4d. dull mauve and carmine (1897) .. 8·50 13·00
48 5d. dull mauve and black (1897) .. 9·00 11·00
49 6d. dull mauve (1897) .. .. .. 7·00 16·00
50 1s. green and black .. .. .. 6·00 16·00
51 2s. green and ultramarine .. .. 24·00 35·00
52 5s. green and carmine .. .. .. 50·00 £120
53 £1 purple/*red* £140 £350
41/53 .. .. *Set of* 13 £225 £500
41/53 Optd "Specimen" .. .. *Set of* 13 £200

Examples of most values are known showing forged oval registered postmarks dated "16 JUL 11" or "4 SP 11".

6

POSTAGE AND REVENUE

(7)

2½d. (8) 2½d. (9) 2½d. (10)

2½d. (11) 2½d. (12) 2½d. (13)

POSTAGE AND REVENUE (14)   **REVENUE** Italic "N" (R. 3/4 of the setting)

1897 (1 Mar). *Fiscal stamps as T* **6**. *Wmk CA over Crown, w* **7**. *P 14. (a) Optd with T* **7**.

54		1d. dull purple and green	1·75	2·00
		a. Opt double	£1400	£1400

(b) Optd with T **7** *and surch T* **8, 10, 11** *(with square stop) or* **12** *with six thin bars across the original face value.*

55	8	2½d. on 3d. dull purple and green	11·00	13·00
		a. Surch double	£15000	
		b. Surch double (Types **8** + **10**)	£12000	
		c. Surch double (Types **8** + **11**)	£20000	
56	10	2½d. on 3d. dull purple and green	50·00	65·00
57	11	2½d. on 3d. dull purple and green	£140	£170
58	12	2½d. on 3d. dull purple and green	£300	£375
59	8	2½d. on 6d. dull purple and green	8·50	13·00
60	10	2½d. on 6d. dull purple and green	40·00	50·00
61	11	2½d. on 6d. dull purple and green	£100	£110
62	12	2½d. on 6d. dull purple and green	£225	£250

Nos. 55/8 and 59/62 were surcharged from a setting of 30 (10×3) which contained twenty-two examples of Type **8** (including three with square stops), five of Type **10**, two of Type **11** and one of Type **12**.

Two examples are known of No. 55a, five of No. 55b (of which two are in the Royal Collection) and two of No. 55c (one in the Royal Collection). A unique example of a double surcharge on No. 55 showing Types **8** + **12** is also in the Royal Collection.

(c) Optd with T **14** *and surch T* **8, 9, 10, 11** *(with round stop) or* **13** *with five thin bars across the original face value*

63	8	2½d. on 1s. dull lilac	80·00	60·00
64	9	2½d. on 1s. dull lilac	£1200	£1200
65	10	2½d. on 1s. dull lilac	£700	£700
66	11	2½d. on 1s. dull lilac	£400	£400
		a. Italic "N"	£1000	£1000
66*b*	13	2½d. on 1s. dull lilac	£1200	£1200
67	8	2½d. on 2s. dull lilac	£1500	£1600
68	9	2½d. on 2s. dull lilac	£32000	£35000
69	10	2½d. on 2s. dull lilac	£14000	
70	11	2½d. on 2s. dull lilac	£7500	£8500
		a. Italic "N"	£15000	£15000
71	13	2½d. on 2s. dull lilac	£32000	£35000

The setting of 30 (10×3) used for both Nos. 63/6*b* and 67/71 contained twenty-two examples of Type **8** (including one with square stop), one of Type **9**, two of Type **10**, four of Type **11** (including one with italic "N") and one of Type **13**.

Most examples of Nos. 63/6*b* are water-stained. Stamps in this condition are worth about 30% of the price quoted.

15

16

1903. *Wmk Crown CA. P 14.*

73	15	½d. dull purple and green	3·00	3·75
74		1d. dull purple and rosine	1·75	60
75		1½d. dull purple and black	1·25	7·00
76		2d. dull purple and brown-orange	3·75	14·00
77		2½d. dull purple and ultramarine	4·50	7·00
78	16	3d. dull purple and grey	8·00	11·00
79		4d. dull purple and rosine	7·00	12·00
80		5d. dull purple and black	8·00	26·00
81		6d. dull purple	11·00	13·00
82		1s. green and black	13·00	38·00
83		2s. green and ultramarine	40·00	48·00
84		5s. green and carmine	60·00	90·00
85		£1 purple/*red*	£200	£225
73/85		*Set of* 13	£300	£400
73/85 Optd "Specimen"		*Set of* 13	£180	

1904–5. *Wmk Mult Crown CA. Ordinary paper* (1d.) *or chalk-surfaced paper* (*others*). *P 14.*

86	15	½d. dull purple and green (1905)	5·00	3·75
87		1d. dull purple and rosine	80	70
		a. Chalk-surfaced paper (1905)	3·00	1·25
88		1½d. dull purple and black (1905)	2·75	11·00
89		2d. dull purple and brown-orange (1905)	4·25	3·75
90		2½d. dull purple and ultramarine (1905)	4·50	2·00
91	16	3d. dull purple and grey (1905)	26·00	3·25
		w. Wmk inverted	45·00	
92		4d. dull purple and rosine (1905)	5·50	6·00
		w. Wmk inverted	75·00	
93		5d. dull purple and black (1905)	12·00	22·00
94		6d. dull purple (1905)	4·00	3·25
95		1s. green and black (1905)	7·50	9·00
96		2s. green and ultramarine (1905)	15·00	25·00
97		5s. green and carmine (1905)	28·00	48·00
98		£1 purple/*red* (1905)	£200	£225
86/98		*Set of* 13	£275	£325

1907–12. *Wmk Mult Crown CA. Ordinary paper* (½d. *to* 2½d.) *or chalk-surfaced paper* (*others*). *P 14.*

99	15	½d. green	35	30
100		1d. carmine	9·50	60
		a. Red	4·00	50
101		1½d. orange (1910)	60	2·00
102		2d. greyish slate (1909)	80	1·50
103		2½d. blue	2·25	2·00
104	16	3d. purple/*yellow* (1909)	7·50	2·75
		a. Ordinary paper (1912)	7·50	8·50
105		4d. black and red/*yellow* (1908)	2·25	1·10
106		5d. purple and olive-green (1908)	5·50	5·00
107		6d. dull and bright purple (1908)	5·50	6·50
108		1s. black/*green* (1908)	5·50	5·00
109		2s. purple and bright blue/*blue* (1908)	15·00	17·00
110		5s. green and red/*yellow* (1908)	32·00	48·00
111		£1 purple and black/*red* (1911)	£180	£180
99/111		*Set of* 13	£225	£225
99/111 Optd "Specimen"		*Set of* 13	£300	

Most values from the 1903, 1904–05 and 1907–12 issues are known with forged postmarks. These include oval registered examples dated "16 JUL 11" or "4 SP 11".

USED HIGH VALUES. The £2 and £5 values of the King George V series were intended for fiscal use only. Before the introduction of the airmail service at the end of 1926 there was no postal rate for which they could be used. Under the airmail rates used between 1926 and 1932 it is just possible that a very heavy letter may have required a £2 value. Postmarks on the £5 and on the £2 before December 1926 can only have been applied "by favour" or, in the case of the cds type, are on stamps removed from telegraph forms. Used prices quoted for Nos. 129/30 and 147/8 are for "by favour" cancellations.

17

18

19

20

1912–21. *Die I. Wmk Mult Crown CA. Chalk-surfaced paper* (3d. *and* 6d. *to* £5). *P 14.*

112	17	½d. blue-green	2·25	1·75
		a. Yellow-green	2·00	1·75
		b. Deep green (1919)	4·25	2·25
113		1d. carmine-red	1·25	10
		a. Scarlet (1916)	2·50	90
		b. Rose-red (1918)	3·50	70
114		1½d. orange (1913)	1·50	1·50
		a. Orange-yellow (1919)	3·75	95
115		2d. greyish slate (1913)	1·00	10
		w. Wmk inverted	30·00	30·00
116		2½d. deep blue (1913)	9·50	2·50
		a. Ultramarine (1917)	1·00	65
116*b*	20	3d. purple/*yellow*	3·00	2·75
		ba. On pale yellow	3·25	3·25
117	18	4d. black and red/*yellow* (1913)	2·50	7·00
		a. On lemon (1915)	4·00	6·00
		b. Die II. *On pale yellow* (1921)	4·25	4·25
118		5d. purple and olive-green (1913)	1·00	4·25
119		6d. dull and bright purple (1913)	3·25	4·00
120	19	7d. purple and orange (1913)	2·25	7·00
121		9d. purple and black (1913)	5·00	9·00
122	18	10d. purple and red (1913)	3·00	16·00
124	20	1s. black/*green*	4·25	4·50
		a. On blue-green, green back	4·50	3·00
		w. Wmk inverted	45·00	45·00
125		2s. blue and purple/*blue*	11·00	4·50
126		5s. red and green/*yellow*	12·00	22·00
127		10s. red and green/*green*	55·00	£100
		a. Carmine and blue-green/green	75·00	£120
		b. Carmine and yellow-green/green	75·00	£120
128		£1 black and purple/*red*	£130	£170
129		£2 blue and dull purple (S. £100)	£475	£650
130		£5 orange and green (S. £225)	£1200	£1500
112/28		*Set of* 17	£200	£325
112/28 Optd "Specimen"		*Set of* 17	£275	

1921–27. *Die II. Wmk Mult Script CA. Chalk-surfaced paper* (6d. *to* £5). *P 14.*

131	17	½d. dull green	1·00	15
		a. Bright green	3·00	90
132		1d. bright violet (Die I) (1924)	1·25	1·50
		a. Die II (1925)	2·50	10
133		1½d. scarlet (1925)	80	60
134		2d. grey (1922)	70	10
135		2½d. ultramarine	65	4·00
136	18	3d. bright blue (1922)	60	40
137		4d. black and red/*pale yellow* (1925)	1·75	2·75
138		5d. purple and olive-green	60	60
139		6d. grey-purple and bright purple	1·25	2·00
		y. Wmk inverted and reversed		
140	19	7d. purple and orange (1927)	2·25	16·00
141		9d. purple and black (1922)	2·50	12·00
142	18	10d. purple and red (1925)	2·25	19·00
143	20	1s. black/*emerald* (1925)	4·75	6·00
144		2s. blue and dull purple/*blue*	8·50	10·00
		w. Wmk inverted	85·00	90·00
145		5s. red and green/*yellow* (1927)	8·50	40·00
146		10s. red and green/*green* (1927)	70·00	£140
147		£2 bl & dull pur (1923) (Optd S. £100)	£425	£650
148		£5 orange & brn (1923) (Optd S. £225)	£1100	£1500
131/46		*Set of* 16	95·00	£225
131/46 Optd "Specimen"		*Set of* 16	£250	

21 Rice Field

22 Palms and Cola Tree

(Eng J.A.C. Harrison (T **21**))

1932 (1 Mar). *Wmk Mult Script CA. (a) Recess Waterlow. P* 12½.

155	21	½d. green	15	20
156		1d. violet	20	10
157		1½d. carmine	30	1·25
		a. Imperf between (horiz pair)		
158		2d. brown	30	10
159		3d. blue	60	1·50
160	21	4d. orange	60	4·00
161		5d. bronze-green	75	1·60
162		6d. light blue	50	1·60
163		1s. lake	1·25	3·75

(b) Recess B.W. P 12.

164	22	2s. chocolate	4·00	4·25
165		5s. deep blue	11·00	16·00
166		10s. green	55·00	£110
167		£1 purple	85·00	£170
155/67		*Set of* 13	£140	£275
155/67 Perf "Specimen"		*Set of* 13	£180	

23 Arms of Sierra Leone

24 Old Slave Market, Freetown

27 African Elephant

28 King George V

(Des Father F. Welsh. Recess B.W.)

1933 (2 Oct). *Centenary of Abolition of Slavery and of Death of William Wilberforce. T* **23/4, 27/8** *and similar designs. Wmk Mult Script CA (sideways on horiz designs). P* 12.

168		½d. green	45	1·25
169		1d. black and brown	40	10
170		1½d. chestnut	4·25	4·50
171		2d. purple	2·75	20
172		3d. blue	2·75	1·75
173		4d. brown	6·50	10·00
174		5d. green and chestnut	7·00	16·00
175		6d. black and brown-orange	7·00	8·00
176		1s. violet	4·75	17·00
177		2s. brown and light blue	22·00	38·00
178		5s. black and purple	£140	£160
179		10s. black and sage-green	£160	£225
180		£1 violet and orange	£300	£375
168/180		*Set of* 13	£600	£750
168/80 Perf "Specimen"		*Set of* 13	£500	

Designs: *Vert*—1d. "Freedom"; 1½d. Map of Sierra Leone; 4d. Government sanatorium. *Horiz*—3d. Native fruit seller; 5d. Bullom canoe; 6d. Punting near Banana; 1s. Government buildings; 2s. Bunce Island; £1 Freetown harbour.

1935 (6 May). *Silver Jubilee. As Nos. 114/17 of Jamaica. P* 11×12.

181		1d. ultramarine and grey-black	80	1·25
		a. Extra flagstaff	42·00	
		b. Short extra flagstaff	85·00	
		c. Lightning conductor	30·00	
182		3d. brown and deep blue	1·00	7·50
		a. Extra flagstaff	60·00	
		b. Short extra flagstaff	£170	
		c. Lightning conductor	60·00	
183		5d. green and indigo	1·40	7·50
		a. Extra flagstaff	90·00	
		b. Short extra flagstaff	£200	
		c. Lightning conductor	90·00	
184		1s. slate and purple	5·50	3·50
		a. Extra flagstaff	£225	
		b. Short extra flagstaff	£190	
		c. Lightning conductor	£190	
181/4		*Set of* 4	8·00	18·00
181/4 Perf "Specimen"		*Set of* 4	80·00	

For illustrations of plate varieties see Omnibus section following Zimbabwe.

1937 (12 May). *Coronation. As Nos. 118/20 of Jamaica, but ptd by B.W.*

185		1d. orange	70	50
186		2d. purple	90	50
187		3d. blue	2·00	3·25
185/7		*Set of* 3	3·25	3·75
185/7 Perf "Specimen"		*Set of* 3	55·00	

30 Freetown from the Harbour

31 Rice Harvesting

(Recess Waterlow)

1938 (1 May)–**44.** *Wmk Mult Script CA (sideways). P* 12½.

No.	Type	Description	Unused	Used
188	30	½d. black and blue-green	15	30
189		1d. black and lake	40	40
		a. Imperf between (vert pair)	†	—
190	31	1½d. scarlet	20·00	60
190*a*		1½d. mauve (1.2.41)	30	60
191		2d. mauve	40·00	1·75
191*a*		2d. scarlet (1.2.41)	30	80
192	30	3d. black and ultramarine	40	40
193		4d. black and red-brown (20.6.38)	80	1·75
194	31	5d. olive-green (20.6.38)	5·00	3·50
195		6d. grey (20.6.38)	75	40
196	30	1s. black and olive-green (20.6.38)	1·50	50
196*a*	31	1s. 3d. yellow-orange (1.7.44)	40	40
197	30	2s. black and sepia (20.6.38)	4·50	1·75
198	31	5s. red-brown (20.6.38)	10·00	5·00
199		10s. emerald-green (20.6.38)	16·00	7·50
200	30	£1 deep blue (20.6.38)	17·00	18·00
188/200		*Set of* 16	£100	38·00
188/200 Perf "Specimen"		*Set of* 16	£250	

1946 (1 Oct). *Victory. As Nos.* 141/2 *of Jamaica.*

No.	Description	Unused	Used
201	1½d. lilac	15	10
202	3d. ultramarine	15	10
201/2 Perf "Specimen"	*Set of* 2	55·00	

1948 (1 Dec). *Royal Silver Wedding. As Nos.* 143/4 *of Jamaica.*

No.	Description	Unused	Used
203	1½d. bright purple	15	15
204	£1 indigo	16·00	16·00

1949 (10 Oct). *75th Anniv of U.P.U. As Nos.* 145/8 *of Jamaica.*

No.	Description	Unused	Used
205	1½d. purple	20	30
206	3d. deep blue	90	2·00
207	6d. grey	35	2·25
208	1s. olive	35	1·00
205/8	*Set of* 4	1·60	5·00

1953 (2 June). *Coronation. As No.* 153 *of Jamaica, but ptd by B.W.*

No.	Description	Unused	Used
209	1½d. black and purple	30	30

32 Cape Lighthouse

33 Cotton Tree, Freetown

(Recess Waterlow)

1956 (2 Jan)–**61.** *Designs as T* **32/3.** *Wmk Mult Script CA. P* 13½ × 13 (*horiz*) *or* 14 (*vert*).

No.	Description	Unused	Used
210	½d. black and deep lilac	90	1·75
211	1d. black and olive	90	30
212	1½d. black and ultramarine	1·60	3·00
213	2d. black and brown	70	10
214	3d. black and bright blue	1·25	10
	a. Perf 13 × 13½	1·75	8·50
215	4d. black and slate-blue	2·50	95
216	6d. black and violet	1·00	30
217	1s. black and scarlet	1·25	20
218	1s. 3d. black and sepia	9·50	10
219	2s. 6d. black and chestnut	12·00	5·50
220	5s. black and deep green	2·25	1·75
221	10s. black and bright reddish purple	3·50	2·50
	a. Black and purple (19.4.61)	10·00	25·00
222	£1 black and orange	11·00	16·00
210/22	*Set of* 13	42·00	29·00

Designs: *Horiz*—1d. Queen Elizabeth II Quay; 1½d. Piassava workers; 4d. Iron ore production, Marampa; 6d. Whale Bay, York Village; 1s. 3d. Bristol 170 Freighter Mk 31 airplane and map; 10s. Law Courts, Freetown; £1, Government House. *Vert*—3d. Rice harvesting; 1s. Bullom canoe; 2s. 6d. Orugu Railway Bridge; 5s. Kuranko Chief.

Nos. 210/11 and 214 exist in coils, constructed from normal sheets.

INDEPENDENT

45 Palm Fruit Gathering

46 Licensed Diamond Miner

52

(Des K. Penny (½d., 1s.), Messrs Thoma, Turrell and Larkins (1d., 3d., 6d., 2s. 6d.), W. G. Rumley (1½d., 5s.), J. H. Vandi (2d., 10s.), R. A. Sweet (4d., 1s 3d.), J. White (£1). Recess B.W.)

1961 (27 Apr). *Independence. T* **45/6** *and similar designs. W* **52.** *P* 13½.

No.	Description	Unused	Used
223	½d. chocolate and deep bluish green	20	10
224	1d. orange-brown and myrtle-green	1·25	10
225	1½d. black and emerald	20	10
226	2d. black and ultramarine	20	10
227	3d. orange-brown and blue	20	10
228	4d. turquoise-blue and scarlet	20	10
229	6d. black and purple	20	10
230	1s. chocolate and yellow-orange	20	10
231	1s. 3d. turquoise-blue and violet	20	10
232	2s. 6d. deep green and black	2·75	20
233	5s. black and red	1·00	1·25
234	10s. black and green	1·00	1·25
235	£1 carmine-red and yellow	8·00	5·00
223/235	*Set of* 13	14·00	7·50

Designs: *Vert*—1½d., 5s. Bundu mask; 2d., 10s. Bishop Crowther and Old Fourah Bay College; 1s. Palm fruit gathering; £1, Forces Bugler. *Horiz*—3d., 6d. Sir Milton Margai; 4d., 1s. 3d. Lumley Beach, Freetown; 2s. 6d. Licensed diamond miner.

53 Royal Charter, 1799

55 Old House of Representatives, Freetown, 1924

(Des C. P. Rang (3d., 4d.), F. H. Burgess (1s. 3d.). Recess B.W.)

1961 (25 Nov). *Royal Visit. T* **53, 55** *and similar designs. W* **52.** *P* 13½.

No.	Description	Unused	Used
236	3d. black and rose-red	15	10
237	4d. black and violet	15	90
238	6d. black and yellow-orange	20	10
239	1s. 3d. black and blue	2·50	90
236/9	*Set of* 4	2·75	1·75

Designs: *Vert*—4d. King's Yard Gate, Freetown, 1817. *Horiz*—1s. 3d. Royal Yacht *Britannia* at Freetown.

57 Campaign Emblem

(Recess B.W.)

1962 (7 Apr). *Malaria Eradication. W* **52.** *P* 11 × 11½.

No.	Type	Description	Unused	Used
240	57	3d. carmine-red	10	10
241		1s. 3d. deep green	20	10

58 Fireball Lily

59 Jina-gbo

(Des M. Goaman. Photo Harrison)

1963 (1 Jan). *Flowers. Vert designs as T* **58** (½d., 1½d., 3d., 4d., 1s., 2s. 6d., 5s., 10s.) *or horiz as T* **59** (*others*). *Multicoloured. W* **52** (*sideways on vert designs*). *P* 14.

No.	Description	Unused	Used
242	½d. Type **58**	10	10
243	1d. Type **59**	10	10
244	1½d. Stereospermum	20	10
245	2d. Black-eyed Susan	20	10
246	3d. Beniseed	20	10
247	4d. Blushing Hibiscus	20	10
248	6d. Climbing Lily	30	10
249	1s. Beautiful Crinum	40	10
250	1s. 3d. Blue Bells	1·50	20
251	2s. 6d. Broken Hearts	1·25	30
252	5s. Ra-ponthi	1·25	80
253	10s. Blue Plumbago	2·50	1·50
254	£1 African Tulip Tree	8·00	7·00
242/254	*Set of* 13	14·50	9·00

71 Threshing Machine and Corn Bins

(Des V. Whiteley. Recess B.W.)

1963 (21 Mar). *Freedom from Hunger. T* **71** *and similar horiz design. W* **52.** *P* 11½ × 11.

No.	Description	Unused	Used
255	3d. black and yellow-ochre	15	10
256	1s. 3d. sepia and emerald-green	35	10

Design:—1s. 3d. Girl with onion crop.

2nd Year of Independence 19 Progress 63 Development

3d.

(73)

2nd Year Independence Progress Development 1963

10d.

(74)

(Optd by Govt Printer, Freetown)

1963 (27 Apr). *Second Anniv of Independence. Surch or optd as T* **73/4.** (*a*) *Postage.*

No.	Description	Unused	Used
257	3d. on ½d. black & deep lilac (No. 210) (R.)	40	10
	a. Small "c" in "INDEPENDENCE"	3·50	5·00
258	4d. on 1½d. black & ultram (No. 212) (Br.)	15	10
259	6d. on ½d. black & deep lilac (No. 210) (O.)	30	10
	a. Small "c" in "INDEPENDENCE"	4·00	5·50
260	10d. on 3d. black & bright blue (No. 214) (R.)	50	10
261	1s. 6d. on 3d. black & brt bl (No. 214) (V.)	30	20
262	3s. 6d. on 3d. black & brt bl (No. 214) (Ult.)	40	20
	(*b*) *Air. Additionally optd* "AIR MAIL"		
263	7d. on 1½d. black & ultram (No. 212) (C.)	20	10
264	1s. 3d. on 1½d. blk & ultram (No. 212) (R.)	20	10
265	2s. 6d. black and chestnut (No. 219) (V.)	70	20
266	3s. on 3d. black & bright blue (No. 214) (B.)	40	20
267	6s. on 3d. black & bright blue (No. 214) (R.)	1·00	20
268	11s. on 10s. black and bright reddish purple (No. 221) (C.)	1·40	85
269	11s. on £1 black and orange (No. 222) (C.)	£500	£180
257/268	*Set of* 12	5·00	2·25

75 Centenary Emblem

(Des M. Goaman. Recess B.W.)

1963 (1 Nov). *Centenary of Red Cross. T* **75** *and similar vert designs. W* **52.** *P* 11 × 11½.

No.	Description	Unused	Used
270	3d. red and violet	30	10
271	6d. red and black	45	15
272	1s. 3d. red and deep bluish green	65	20
270/2	*Set of* 3	1·25	40

Designs:—6d. Red Cross emblem; 1s. 3d. Centenary emblem.

1853–1859–1963 Oldest Postal Service Newest G.P.O. in West Africa

1s.

(78)

1853–1859–1963 Oldest Postage Stamp Newest G.P.O. in West Africa AIRMAIL

(79)

1963 (4 Nov). *Postal Commemorations. Optd or surch by Govt Printer, Freetown.* (*a*) *Postage. As T* **78.**

No.	Description	Unused	Used
273	3d. black and bright blue (No. 214)	10	10
	a. "1895" for "1859" (R. 3/3)	2·50	
	b. "1853/1859/1963" (R. 2/3)	2·50	
	ba. As No. 273b, but showing "S vice" also (R. 2/3)		
274	4d. on 1½d. black & ultram (No. 212) (C.)	10	10
	a. "1895" for "1859" (R. 1/2)	3·50	
	b. "1853*1859*1963" (R. 3/2)	2·75	
	c. "1853 1859*1963" (R. 11/4)	3·75	
	d. No stop after "O", but stop after "Africa" (R. 10/1)	2·75	
275	9d. on 1½d. black & ultram (No. 212) (V.)	10	10
	a. "1853*1859*1963" (R. 3/2, 11/4)	2·40	
	b. No stop after "O" (R. 6/5)		
	c. No stop after "O", but stop after "Africa" (R. 10/1)	2·75	

No.	Type	Description	Unused	Used
276		1s. on 1s. 3d. turq-blue & vio (No. 231) (C.)	10	10
		a. "1853*1859*1963" (R. 3/4, 10/2)	3·00	
277		1s. 6d. on ½d. black and deep lilac (No. 210) (Mag.)	15	10
		a. "1853*1859*1963" (R. 11/1)	4·50	
		b. "1853 1859*1963" (R. 4/5)	6·50	
278		2s. on 3d. black & brt blue (No. 214) (Br.)	15	10
		a. "1895" for "1859" (R. 4/10)	8·00	
		b. "1853/1859/1963" (R. 2/3)	6·00	
		(b) Air. As T **79**		
279		7d. on 3d. black & rose-red (No. 236) (Br.)	20	50
		a. "1895" for "1859" (R.3/6, 4/4)	3·25	
		b. "1853·1859·1963" (R.2/3, 4/10)	2·50	
		c. No stop after "O" (R.1/2)	3·50	
280		1s. 3d. black and blue (No. 239) (C.)	2·00	1·00
		a. "1895" for "1859" (R.7/3)	20·00	
		b. "1853*1859*1963" (R.3/2, 10/4)	7·00	
		c. No stop after "O" (R.8/3)	8·00	
281		2s. 6d. on 4d. turq-blue & scarlet (No. 228)	1·25	20
		a. "1895" for "1859" (R.7/3)	48·00	
		b. "1853*1859*1963" (R.3/2, 10/4)	6·00	
		c. No stop after "O" (R.8/3)	9·00	
282		3s. on 3d. black and rose-red (No. 236) (V.)	2·25	1·75
		a. "1895" for "1859" (R.3/3)	£250	
		b. "1853·1859·1963" (R.2/3, 4/10)	10·00	
		c. No stop after "O" (R.1/2)	13·00	
283		6s. on 6d. blk & yell-orge (No. 238) (Ult.)	1·00	70
		a. "1895" for "1859" (R.1/1)	48·00	
		b. "1853*1859*1963" (R.3/2, 10/4)	7·00	
		c. No stop after "O" (R.8/3)	11·00	
284		£1 black and orange (No. 222) (R.)	16·00	14·00
		a. "1895" for "1859" (R.11/4)	£225	
		b. "1853*1859*1963" (R.4/5, 11/1)	38·00	
273/84		*Set of* 12	21·00	16·00

The events commemorated are: 1853, "First Post Office"; 1859, "First Postage Stamps"; and 1963 "Newest G.P.O." in West Africa. Nos. 273, 278 have the overprint in five lines; Nos. 279, 282 in six lines (incl "AIRMAIL").

Some of the overprint varieties were corrected during printing.

80 Lion Emblem and Map

81 Globe and Map

Extended "A" in "SIERRA" (R. 3/3, later corrected on the 4d. value)

(Recess and litho Walsall Lithographic Co. Ltd)

1964 (10 Feb). *World's Fair, New York. Imperf. Self-adhesive.*

No.	Type	Description	Unused	Used
		(a) Postage.		
285	**80**	1d. multicoloured	10	10
286		3d. multicoloured	10	10
		a. Lion omitted		
287		4d. multicoloured	10	10
		b. Extended "A"	2·00	
288		6d. multicoloured	10	10
		b. Extended "A"	2·00	
289		1s. multicoloured	10	10
		a. "POSTAGE 1/-" omitted	35·00	
		b. Extended "A"	2·00	
290		2s. multicoloured	20	10
		b. Extended "A"	2·50	
291		5s. multicoloured	40	25
		a. "POSTAGE 5/-" omitted	35·00	
		b. Extended "A"	3·50	
		(b) Air.		
292	**81**	7d. multicoloured	10	10
293		9d. multicoloured	10	10
		a. "AIR MAIL 9d." omitted		
294		1s. 3d. multicoloured	15	10
		a. "AIR MAIL 1/3" omitted	35·00	
295		2s. 6d. multicoloured	20	10
296		3s. 6d. multicoloured	20	10
		a. "AIR MAIL 3/6" omitted		
297		6s. multicoloured	40	30
		a. "AIR MAIL 6/-" omitted	40·00	
298		11s. multicoloured	55	80
		a. "AIR MAIL 11/-" omitted	42·00	
285/98		*Set of* 14	2·00	1·90

Nos. 285/98 were issued in sheets of 30 (6 × 5) on green (postage) or yellow (airmail) backing paper with the emblems of Samuel Jones & Co. Ltd, self-adhesive paper-makers, on the back.

WARNING. These and later self-adhesive stamps should be kept on their backing paper except commercially used, which should be retained on cover or piece.

82 Inscription and Map

83 Pres. Kennedy and Map

(Recess and litho Walsall)

1964 (11 May). *President Kennedy Memorial Issue. Imperf. Self-adhesive. (a) Postage. Green backing paper.*

No.	Type	Description	Unused	Used
299	**82**	1d. multicoloured	10	10
300		3d. multicoloured	10	10
301		4d. multicoloured	10	10
302		6d. multicoloured	10	10
		b. Extended "A"	2·00	
303		1s. multicoloured	10	10
		b. Extended "A"	2·00	
304		2s. multicoloured	15	15
		b. Extended "A"	2·00	
305		5s. multicoloured	35	25
		b. Extended "A"	3·00	
		(b) Air. Yellow backing paper		
306	**83**	7d. multicoloured	10	10
307		9d. multicoloured	10	10
308		1s. 3d. multicoloured	15	10
309		2s. 6d. multicoloured	25	20
310		3s. 6d. multicoloured	25	20
311		6s. multicoloured	45	45
312		11s. multicoloured	70	80
299/312		*Set of* 14	2·25	2·00

(New Currency. 100 cents = 1 leone)

3c (84) AIRMAIL 7c (85) Le 1·00 (86)

1964–66. *Decimal currency. Various stamps surch locally.*

No.	Type	Description	Unused	Used
		(i) *First issue* (4.8.64). *(a) Postage. Surch as T* **84**		
313	–	1 c. on 6d. multicoloured (No. 248) (R.)	10	10
314	**53**	2 c. on 3d. black and rose-red	10	10
315	–	3 c. on 3d. multicoloured (No. 246)	10	10
		a. Surch inverted	£140	
316	**45**	5 c. on ½d. chocolate & dp bluish grn (B.)	10	10
317	**71**	8 c. on 3d. black & yellow-ochre (R.)	10	10
318	–	10 c. on 1s. 3d. mult (No. 250) (R.)	10	10
319	–	15 c. on 1s. multicoloured (No. 249)	15	10
320	**55**	25 c. on 6d. black & yellow-orange (V.)	30	25
321	–	50 c. on 2s. 6d. dp grn & blk (No. 232) (O.)	1·50	65
		(b) Air. As T **85** *or* **86** *(Nos. 326/7)*		
322	–	7 c. on 1s. 3d. sepia and emerald-green (No. 256) (B.)	10	10
		a. Surch omitted (in horiz pair with normal)		
		b. Surch double	60·00	
323	–	20 c. on 4d. turq-blue & scarlet (No. 228)	25	15
324	–	30 c. on 10s. black & green (No. 234) (R.)	40	30
325	–	40 c. on 5s. black and red (No. 233) (B.)	50	40
326	**83**	1 l. on 1s. 3d. multicoloured (R.)	75	90
327		2 l. on 11s. multicoloured	1·25	1·60
313/27		*Set of* 15	4·75	4·00

1c (87) TWO LEONES Le 2·00 (88)

No.	Type	Description	Unused	Used
		(ii) *Second issue* (20.1.65). *Surch as T* **87** *or* **88** *(Nos. 332/3)*		
		(a) Postage		
328	–	1 c. on 3d. orge-brown & blue (No. 227)	10	10
329	**82**	2 c. on 1d. multicoloured	10	10
330		4 c. on 3d. multicoloured	10	10
		a. Error. 4 c. on 1d.	£140	
		b. Stamp omitted (in pair with normal)		
331	–	5 c. on 2d. multicoloured (No. 245)	10	10
332	–	1 l. on 5s. multicoloured (No. 252) (Gold)	1·25	1·25
333	–	2 l. on £1 carm-red & yell (No. 235) (B.)	2·25	2·25
		a. Surch double (B. + Blk.)	—	65·00
		(b) Air		
334	**83**	7 c. on 7d. multicoloured (R.)	10	10
335		60 c. on 9d. multicoloured	50	45
328/35		*Set of* 8	3·75	3·75

On No. 330b the stamp became detached before the surcharge was applied so that "4c" appears on the backing paper.

NEW INFORMATION

The editor is always interested to correspond with people who have new information that will improve or correct the Catalogue.

1c Normal — 1c Small "c" (R. 3/3)

No.	Type	Description	Unused	Used
		(iii) *Third issue* (4.65). *Surch in figures (various sizes).*		
		(a) Postage		
336	–	1 c. on 1½d. black & emer (No. 225) (R.)	10	10
		a. Small "c"	4·00	
337	**82**	2 c. on 3d. multicoloured	10	10
338	**80**	2 c. on 4d. multicoloured	10	10
		b. Extended "A"	2·00	
339	**59**	3 c. on 1d. multicoloured	10	10
340	–	3 c. on 2d. black & ultram (No. 226) (R.)	10	10
341	–	5 c. on 1s. 3d. turq-bl & vio (No. 231) (R.)	10	10
		a. Surch inverted		
342	**82**	15 c. on 6d. multicoloured	80	50
		b. Extended "A"	7·00	
343		15 c. on 1s. multicoloured (R.)	1·25	90
		b. Extended "A"	10·00	
344	–	20 c. on 6d. black & purple (No. 229) (R.)	30	15
345	–	25 c. on 6d. multicoloured (No. 248) (R.)	35	20
346	–	50 c. on 3d. orge-brown & bl (No. 227) (R.)	80	55
347	**80**	60 c. on 5s. multicoloured (V.)	3·25	1·75
		b. Extended "A"	25·00	
348	**82**	1 l. on 4d. multicoloured (R.)	3·75	3·25
349	–	2 l. on £1 carm-red & yell (No. 235) (B.)	7·00	4·50
		(b) Air		
350	**81**	7 c. on 9d. multicoloured	15	10
336/50		*Set of* 15	16·00	11·00

2c (89) TWO Leones (90)

No.	Type	Description	Unused	Used
		(iv) *Fourth issue* (9.11.65). *Surch as T* **89**. *(a) Postage*		
351	**80**	1 c. on 6d. multicoloured (V.)	2·25	7·00
		b. Extended "A"	20·00	
352		1 c. on 2s. multicoloured (V.)	2·25	7·00
		b. Extended "A"	20·00	
353	**82**	1 c. on 2s. multicoloured (V.)	2·25	7·00
		b. Extended "A"	20·00	
354		1 c. on 5s. multicoloured (V.)	2·25	7·00
		b. Extended "A"	20·00	
		(b) Air		
355	**81**	2 c. on 1s. 3d. multicoloured	2·25	7·00
356	**83**	2 c. on 1s. 3d. multicoloured	2·25	7·00
357		2 c. on 3s. 6d. multicoloured	2·25	7·00
358	**81**	3 c. on 7d. multicoloured	2·25	7·00
359	**83**	3 c. on 9d. multicoloured	2·25	7·00
360	**81**	5 c. on 2s. 6d. multicoloured	2·25	7·00
361	**83**	5 c. on 2s. 6d. multicoloured	2·25	7·00
362	**81**	5 c. on 3s. 6d. multicoloured	2·25	7·00
363		5 c. on 6s. multicoloured	2·25	7·00
364	**83**	5 c. on 6s. multicoloured	2·25	7·00
351/64		*Set of* 14	28·00	90·00
		(v) *Fifth issue* (28.1.66). *Air. No. 374 further surch with T* **90**		
365	–	2 l. on 30 c. on 6d. multicoloured	1·50	1·50

(**91** Margai and Churchill)

1965 (19 May). *Sir Milton Margai and Sir Winston Churchill Commemoration. Nos. 242/3, 245/50 and 252/4 surch as T* **91** *on horiz designs or with individual portraits on vert designs as indicated.*

No.	Type	Description	Unused	Used
		(a) Postage		
366		2 c. on 1d. Type **59**	10	10
		a. Horiz pair, one with "2 c" omitted		
		b. Surch omitted (in horiz pair with normal)		
367		3 c. on 3d. Beniseed (Margai)	10	10
		a. Portrait and "3 c" double	£150	
		b. Portrait and "3 c" double, one inverted	£150	
		c. "3 c" omitted	£400	
368		10 c. on 1s. Beautiful Crinum (Churchill)	20	10
		a. "10 c" omitted	£275	
369		20 c. on 1s. 3d. Blue Bells	40	10
		a. Portraits and "20 c" double, one inverted	£150	
		b. "20 c" omitted	£400	
370		50 c. on 4d. Blushing Hibiscus (Margai)	90	35
		a. Portrait inverted	£150	
		ab. Portrait inverted and "50 c" omitted	£150	
371		75 c. on 5s. Ra-ponthi (Churchill)	2·25	90
		a. Surch value inverted		
		(b) Air. Additionally optd "AIRMAIL"		
372		7 c. on 2d. Black-eyed Susan	20	10
		a. "AIRMAIL" and "7 c." omitted	£150	
		b. "AIRMAIL" and "7 c" double, one inverted	£150	
373		15 c. on ½d. Type **58** (Margai)	35	10
		a. "AIRMAIL" and "15 c" double, one inverted	£150	
		b. Portrait double, one inverted	£150	
374		30 c. on 6d. Climbing Lily (O. and W.)	1·25	25
		a. "AIRMAIL" and "30 c" double, one inverted	£150	
		b. "AIRMAIL" and "30 c" omitted	£150	

375 1 l. on £1 African Tulip Tree .. .. 4·00 1·00
a. "AIRMAIL" and "1 l" double, one inverted .. £150
b. "AIRMAIL" and "1 l" omitted .. £400
376 2 l. on 10s. Blue Plumbago (Churchill) .. 11·00 5·00
a. Surch value omitted .. £150
366/76 .. *Set of* 11 18·00 7·00

On Nos. 366/76 the portraits and commemorative inscription were applied in a separate operation from the surcharge and, on Nos. 372/6, the word "AIRMAIL".

92 Cola Plant and Nut

93 Arms of Sierra Leone

94 Inscription and Necklace

(Des M. Meers. Manufactured by Walsall Lithographic Co, Ltd)

1965 (Nov). *Imperf. Self-adhesive.*

A. *Embossed on silver foil, backed with paper bearing advertisements. Emerald, olive-yellow and carmine; denominations in colours given. Postage.*

377 **92** 1 c. emerald .. 25 10
378 2 c. carmine .. 25 10
379 3 c. olive-yellow .. 25 10
380 4 c. silver/*emerald* .. 30 10
381 5 c. silver/*carmine* .. 30 10

B. *Typo and embossed on cream paper backed with advertisements*

(*a*) *Postage*

382 **93** 20 c. multicoloured .. 1·75 50
383 50 c. multicoloured .. 3·50 3·50

(*b*) *Air*

384 **93** 40 c. multicoloured .. 3·25 3·50

C. *Die-stamped and litho, with advertisements on white paper backing (see footnote). Air.*

385 **94** 7 c. multicoloured .. 70 15
a. Bright green and gold (inscr and face value) omitted .. 95·00
386 15 c. multicoloured .. 1·00 70
377/86 .. *Set of* 10 10·50 8·00

The above stamps were issued in single form with attached tabs to remove the backing paper, with the exception of No. 385 which was in sheets of 25 bearing a single large advertisement on the back.

No. 385a shows the die-stamping omitted.

For other stamps in Type **92** see Nos. 421/31 and 435/42*a*. For 10 c. stamps in Type **93** see Nos. 433/*b*.

2c
FIVE YEARS
INDEPENDENCE
1961-1966
(95)

15c
AIRMAIL
FIVE YEARS
INDEPENDENCE
1961-1966
(96)

1966 (27 Apr). *Fifth Anniv of Independence. Various stamps surch.*

(*a*) *Postage. As T* **95**

387 1 c. on 6d. multicoloured (No. 248) .. 10 10
388 2 c. on 4d. multicoloured (No. 247) .. 10 10
389 3 c. on 1½d. black & ultram (No. 212) (B.) .. 10 10
390 8 c. on 1s. multicoloured (No. 249) (B.) .. 15 10
391 10 c. on 2s. 6d. multicoloured (No. 251) (B.) .. 15 10
392 20 c. on 2d. black and brown (No. 213) (B.) .. 20 10

(*b*) *Air. As T* **96**

393 7 c. on 3d. red and violet (No. 270) .. 10 10
394 15 c. on 1s. multicoloured (No. 249) .. 20 10
395 25 c. on 2s. 6d. multicoloured (No. 251) .. 65 60
396 50 c. on 1½d. multicoloured (No. 244) .. 1·00 80
397 1 l. on 4d. multicoloured (No. 247) .. 1·60 1·60
387/397 .. *Set of* 11 3·75 3·00

The inscription on No. 387 is in larger type.

97 Lion's Head

98 Map of Sierra Leone

(Des and embossed Walsall)

1966 (12 Nov). *First Sierra Leone Gold Coinage Commemoration. Circular designs, embossed on gold foil, backed with paper bearing advertisements. Imperf.* (*a*) *Postage.*

(i) *¼ golde coin. Diameter 1½ in.*

398 **97** 2 c. magenta and yellow-orange .. 10 10
399 **98** 3 c. emerald and bright purple .. 10 10

(ii) *½ golde coin. Diameter 2⅛ in.*

400 **97** 5 c. vermilion and ultramarine .. 10 10
401 **98** 8 c. turquoise-blue and black .. 15 15

(iii) *1 golde coin. Diameter 3¼ in.*

402 **97** 25 c. violet and emerald .. 35 35
403 **98** 1 l. orange and cerise .. 2·50 2·75

(*b*) *Air.* (i) *¼ golde coin. Diameter 1½ in.*

404 **98** 7 c. red-orange and cerise .. 10 10
405 **97** 10 c. cerise and greenish blue .. 15 15

(ii) *½ golde coin. Diameter 2⅛ in.*

406 **98** 15 c. orange and cerise .. 25 25
407 **97** 30 c. bright purple and black .. 40 45

(iii) *1 golde coin. Diameter 3¼ in.*

408 **98** 50 c. bright green and purple .. 75 75
409 **97** 2 l. black and emerald .. 3·75 4·00
398/409 .. *Set of* 12 7·50 8·00

12½
(99)

17½
(100)

=17½
(101)

1967 (2 Dec). *Decimal Currency Provisionals. Surch as T* **99** (*Nos.* 410/13), *T* **100** (*Nos.* 415/17) *or T* **101** (*others*). (*a*) *Postage.*

410 – 6½ c. on 75 c. on 5s. mult (No. 371) (R.) 15 15
411 – 7½ c. on 75 c. on 5s. mult (No. 371) (S.) 15 15
412 – 9½ c. on 50 c. on 4d. mult (No. 370) (G.) 20 20
413 – 12½ c. on 20 c. on 1s. 3d. multicoloured (No. 369) (V.) .. 25 25
414 **93** 17½ c. on 50 c. multicoloured .. 1·40 1·40
415 **82** 17½ c. on 1 l. on 4d. mult (No. 348) (B.) 1·40 1·40
416 18½ c. on 1 l. on 4d. mult (No. 348) .. 1·40 1·40
417 **80** 18½ c. on 60 c. on 5s. mult (No. 347) .. 4·00 4·50
b. Extended "A" .. 40·00
418 **93** 25 c. on 50 c. multicoloured .. 60 70

(*b*) *Air*

419 **93** 11½ c. on 40 c. multicoloured .. 20 20
420 25 c. on 40 c. multicoloured .. 60 70
410/20 .. *Set of* 11 9·25 10·00

102 Eagle

(Manufactured by Walsall)

1967 (2 Dec)–**69.** *Decimal Currency. Imperf. Self-adhesive.*

(*a*) *Postage. As T* **92**, *but embossed on white paper, backed with paper bearing advertisements. Background colours given first, and value tablet colours in brackets*

421 **92** ½ c. carmine-red (carmine/*white*) .. 10 10
422 1 c. carmine (carmine/*white*) .. 15 10
423 1½ c. orange-yellow (green/*white*) .. 20 15
424 2 c. carmine-red (green/*white*) .. 35 10
425 2½ c. apple-green (yellow/*white*) .. 50 40
426 3 c. carmine-red (white/*carmine*) .. 30 10
427 3½ c. reddish purple (white/*green*) .. 50 40
428 4 c. carmine-red (white/*green*) .. 50 15
429 4½ c. dull green (green/*white*) .. 50 40
430 5 c. carmine (yellow/*white*) .. 50 15
431 5½ c. brown-red (green/*white*) .. 50 50

(*b*) *Air. T* **102** *embossed on black paper, backed with paper bearing advertisements; or,* (*No.* 433), *as T* **93**, *typo and embossed on cream paper, also with advertisements*

432 **102** 9½ c. red and gold/*black* .. 60 60
432*a* 9½ c. blue and gold/*black* (10.9.69) .. 5·00 5·00
433 **93** 10 c. multicoloured (red frame) .. 65 65
a. Face value omitted ..
433*b* 10 c. mult (black frame) (10.9.69) .. 5·50 5·50
434 **102** 15 c. green and gold/*black* .. 85 85
434*a* 15 c. red and gold/*black* (10.9.69) .. 6·00 6·00
421/34*a* .. *Set of* 17 20·00 19·00

The ½, 1½, 2, 2½, 3, 3½ and 5 c. also exist without advertisements.

The footnote below Nos. 377/86 also applies here.

Although only released for collectors on 2 December, the 5 c. was known to be in use locally in February and the 3 c. in March. The 1 c. and 2 c. were also released locally some months earlier.

See also Nos. 538/44.

1968. *No advertisements on back, and colours in value tablet reversed. Background colours given first, and value tablet colours in brackets.*

435 **92** ½ c. carmine-red (white/*green*) .. 10 10
436 1 c. carmine (white/*carmine*) .. 15 10
437 2 c. carmine (white/*green*) .. 4·25 4·50
438 2½ c. apple-green (white/*yellow*) .. 4·75 5·00
439 3 c. carmine-red (carmine/*white*) .. 1·75 65

On Nos. 435 and 438, the figure "½" is larger than in Nos. 421 and 425.

It is believed that the ½ c. was released in February, the 2½ c. in April and the others in March.

The 1 c. also exists with advertisements on the backing paper.

The footnote below Nos. 377/86 also applies here.

1968–69. *No advertisements on back, colours changed and new value* (7 c.). *Background colours given first, and value tablet colours in brackets.* (*a*) *Postage.*

440 **92** 2 c. pink (white/*brown-lake*) .. 1·75 1·50
441 2½ c. deep bluish green (white/*orange*) .. 1·75 1·50
442 3½ c. olive-yellow (blue/*white*) .. 2·25 1·60

(*b*) *Air*

442*a* **92** 7 c. yellow (carmine/*white*) (10.9.69) .. 6·50 3·50
435/42*a* .. *Set of* 9 21·00 17·00

On Nos. 441/2 the fraction "½" is larger than in Nos. 425 and 427.

It is believed that the 3½ c. was released in March 1968 and the 2 and 2½ c. in May 1968.

The 2 c. also exists with advertisements on the backing paper.

The footnote below Nos. 377/86 also applies here.

103 Outline Map of Africa

(Litho Walsall)

1968 (25 Sept). *Human Rights Year. Each value comes in six types, showing different territories in yellow, as below. Imperf. Self-adhesive.*

A. Portuguese Guinea.
B. South Africa.
C. Mozambique.
D. Rhodesia.
E. South West Africa.
F. Angola.

To indicate yellow territory use above letters as suffix to the following catalogue numbers.

(*a*) *Postage*

Each Territory

443 **103** ½ c. multicoloured .. 10 10
444 2 c. multicoloured .. 10 10
445 2½ c. multicoloured .. 10 10
446 3½ c. multicoloured .. 10 10
447 10 c. multicoloured .. 15 15

448 **103** 11½ c. multicoloured 20 20
449 15 c. multicoloured 25 25

(b) Air

450 **103** 7½ c. multicoloured 15 15
451 9½ c. multicoloured 20 20
452 14½ c. multicoloured 25 25
453 18½ c. multicoloured 30 30
454 25 c. multicoloured 40 40
455 1 l. multicoloured .. .. 4·00 5·50
456 2 l. multicoloured .. .. 10·00 12·00
443/56 Each territory .. .. *Set of* 14 14·00 18·00
443/56 Six territories .. .. *Set of* 84 75·00 £100

Nos. 443/56 were issued in sheets of 30 (6 × 5) on backing paper depicting diamonds or the coat of arms on the reverse. The six types occur once in each horizontal row.

(104)

1968 (30 Nov). *Mexico Olympics Participation.*

(a) Postage. No. 383 surch or optd (No. 461) as T **104**

457 **93** 6½ c. on 50 c. multicoloured 20 15
458 17½ c. on 50 c. multicoloured 25 20
459 22½ c. on 50 c. multicoloured 40 35
a. Surch double £170
460 28½ c. on 50 c. multicoloured 50 60
461 50 c. multicoloured 80 90

(b) Air. No. 384 surch or optd (No. 466) as T **104** *in red*

462 **93** 6½ c. on 40 c. multicoloured 20 15
a. Surch double £190
463 17½ c. on 40 c. multicoloured 25 20
464 22½ c. on 40 c. multicoloured 40 35
465 28½ c. on 40 c. multicoloured 50 60
466 40 c. multicoloured 80 90
457/66 .. .. *Set of* 10 3·75 3·75

105 1859 6d.

111 1965 15 c. Self-adhesive

(Litho Walsall)

1969 (1 Mar). *Fifth Anniv of World's First Self-adhesive Postage Stamps. Reproductions of earlier issues. Multicoloured. Imperf. Self-adhesive.*

(a) Postage. Vert designs.

467 1 c. Type **105** 10 10
468 2 c. 1965 2 c. self-adhesive 10 10
469 3½ c. 1961 Independence £1 .. .. 10 10
470 5 c. 1965 20 c. self-adhesive 10 10
471 12½ c. 1948 Royal Silver Wedding £1 .. 30 15
472 1 l. 1923 £2 .. .. 4·25 2·75

(b) Air. Horiz designs

473 7½ c. Type **111** 20 10
474 9½ c. 1967 9½ c. self-adhesive 20 10
475 20 c. 1964 1s. 3d. self-adhesive 40 25
476 30 c. 1964 President Kennedy Memorial 6s. commemorative self-adhesive .. 55 35
477 50 c. 1933 Centenary of Abolition of Slavery £1 commemorative .. .. 2·00 1·00
478 2 l. 1963 2nd Anniversary of Independence 11s. commemorative .. .. 16·00 13·00
467/478 .. .. *Set of* 12 22·00 16·00

Nos. 467 and 473 were issued with tabs as note under Nos. 377/86 and No. 474 exists with tabs and also in the normal version on backing paper.

All values are on white backing paper with advertisements printed on the reverse.

117 Ore Carrier, Globe and Flags of Sierra Leone and Japan

118 Ore Carrier, Map of Europe and Africa and Flags of Sierra Leone and Netherlands

The 3½ c., 9½ c., 2 l. and 10 c., 50 c., 1 l. are as T **118** but show respectively the flags of Great Britain and West Germany instead of the Netherlands.

(Litho Walsall)

1969 (10 July). *Pepel Port Improvements. Imperf. Self-adhesive, backed with paper bearing advertisements. (a) Postage.*

479 **117** 1 c. multicoloured 10 10
480 **118** 2 c. multicoloured 10 10
481 – 3½ c. multicoloured 10 10
482 – 10 c. multicoloured 10 10
483 **118** 18½ c. multicoloured 20 25
484 – 50 c. multicoloured 80 85

(b) Air

485 **117** 7½ c. multicoloured 10 10
486 – 9½ c. multicoloured 15 10
487 **117** 15 c. multicoloured 20 25
488 **118** 25 c. multicoloured 30 35
489 – 1 l. multicoloured .. .. 1·75 1·75
490 – 2 l. multicoloured .. .. 2·50 4·00
479/90 .. .. *Set of* 12 5·50 7·00

119 African Development Bank Emblem

120 Boy Scouts Emblem in "Diamond"

(Litho and embossed Walsall)

1969 (10 Sept). *Fifth Anniv of African Development Bank. Self-adhesive, backed with paper bearing advertisements. Imperf.*

(a) Postage

491 **119** 3½ c. deep green, gold and blue .. 25 40

(b) Air

492 **119** 9½ c. bluish violet, gold and apple-green 35 70

(Litho Walsall)

1969 (6 Dec). *Boy Scouts Diamond Jubilee. T* **120** *and similar design. Imperf. Self-adhesive, backed with paper bearing advertisements.*

(a) Postage

493 **120** 1 c. multicoloured 10 10
494 2 c. multicoloured 10 10
495 3½ c. multicoloured 15 10
496 4½ c. multicoloured 15 15
497 5 c. multicoloured 15 15
498 75 c. multicoloured .. .. 8·00 4·00

(b) Air

499 – 7½ c. multicoloured 35 30
500 – 9½ c. multicoloured 45 35
501 – 15 c. multicoloured 70 50
502 – 22 c. multicoloured .. .. 1·25 70
503 – 55 c. multicoloured .. .. 6·50 3·00
504 – 3 l. multicoloured .. .. 60·00 42·00
493/504 .. .. *Set of* 12 70·00 45·00

Design: *Octagonal Shape* (65×51 *mm*)—Nos. 499/504 Scout saluting, Baden-Powell and badge.

MINIMUM PRICE

The minimum price quote is 10p which represents a handling charge rather than a basis for valuing common stamps. For further notes about prices see introductory pages.

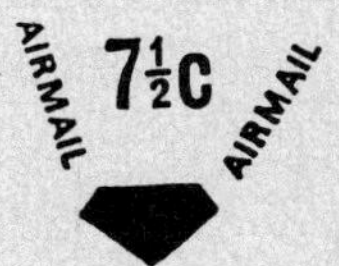

(121)

1970 (28 Mar). *Air. No. 443 surch as T* **121**.

Each Territory

505 **103** 7½ c. on ½ c. multicoloured (G.) .. 20 10
506 9½ c. on ½ c. multicoloured (P.) .. 20 10
507 15 c. on ½ c. multicoloured (B.) .. 40 25
508 28 c. on ½ c. multicoloured (G.) .. 70 55
509 40 c. on ½ c. multicoloured (B.) .. 1·25 1·40
510 2 l. on ½ c. multicoloured (Sil.) .. 6·00 10·00
505/10 Each Territory .. .. *Set of* 6 8·00 11·00
505/10 Six Territories .. .. *Set of* 36 45·00 60·00

122 Expo Symbol and Maps of Sierra Leone and Japan

(Litho Walsall)

1970 (22 June). *World Fair, Osaka. T* **122** *and similar design. Imperf. Self-adhesive, backed with paper bearing advertisements.*

(a) Postage

511 **122** 2 c. multicoloured 10 10
512 3½ c. multicoloured 10 10
513 10 c. multicoloured 15 10
514 12½ c. multicoloured 15 10
515 20 c. multicoloured 20 10
516 45 c. multicoloured 45 45

(b) Air

517 – 7½ c. multicoloured 10 10
518 – 9½ c. multicoloured 15 10
519 – 15 c. multicoloured 20 10
520 – 25 c. multicoloured 40 20
521 – 50 c. multicoloured 55 50
522 – 3 l. multicoloured .. .. 3·00 5·50
511/22 .. .. *Set of* 12 4·50 6·50

Design: *Chrysanthemum shape* (43 × 42 *mm*)—Nos. 517/22 Maps of Sierra Leone and Japan.

123 Diamond

124 Palm Nut

(Litho and embossed Walsall)

1970 (3 Oct). *Imperf. Self-adhesive, backed with paper bearing advertisements.*

523 **123** 1 c. multicoloured 10 10
524 1½ c. multicoloured 10 10
525 2 c. multicoloured 10 10
526 2½ c. multicoloured 10 10
527 3 c. multicoloured 15 10
528 3½ c. multicoloured 15 10
529 4 c. multicoloured 15 10
530 5 c. multicoloured 20 10
531 **124** 6 c. multicoloured 25 10
532 7 c. multicoloured 30 15
533 8½ c. multicoloured 40 15
534 9 c. multicoloured 40 15
535 10 c. multicoloured 45 15
536 11½ c. multicoloured 55 20
537 18½ c. multicoloured 85 45

1970 (3 Oct). *Air. As T* **102**, *but embossed on white paper. Backed with paper bearing advertisements.*

538 **102** 7½ c. gold and red 35 10
539 9½ c. rose and bright green 40 10
540 15 c. pink and greenish blue 70 20
541 25 c. gold and purple .. .. .. 1·25 50
542 50 c. bright green and orange .. .. 2·50 1·75
543 1 l. royal blue and silver .. .. 6·00 8·00
544 2 l. ultramarine and gold .. .. 11·00 17·00
523/44 .. .. *Set of* 22 23·00 26·00

126 "Jewellery Box" and Sewa Diadem

(Litho and embossed Walsall)

1970 (30 Dec). *Diamond Industry. T* **126** *and similar design. Imperf (backing paper roul 20). Self-adhesive, backed with paper bearing advertisements. (a) Postage.*

545	**126**	2 c. multicoloured	30	10
546		3½ c. multicoloured	30	10
547		10 c. multicoloured	55	15
548		12½ c. multicoloured	75	25
549		40 c. multicoloured	1·75	1·00
550		1 l. multicoloured	10·00	8·50
		(b) Air		
551	–	7½ c. multicoloured	50	10
552	–	9½ c. multicoloured	60	10
553	–	15 c. multicoloured	95	30
554	–	25 c. multicoloured	1·40	60
555	–	75 c. multicoloured	5·50	4·50
556	–	2 l. multicoloured	24·00	20·00
545/556		.. .. *Set of* 12	42·00	32·00

Design: *Horiz* (63 × 61 *mm*)—Nos. 551/6, Diamond and curtain.

10c
AIRMAIL

127 "Traffic Changeover" (128)

(Manufactured by Walsall)

1971 (1 Mar). *Changeover to Driving on the Right of the Road. Imperf (backing paper roul 20). Self-adhesive, backed with paper bearing advertisements. (a) Postage.*

557	**127**	3½ c. yellow-orange, ultram & blk	1·50	1·00
		(b) Air		
558	**127**	9½ c. ultramarine, yell-orge & blk	2·00	2·50

1971 (1 Mar). *Air. Surch as T* **128**, *in red (No. 559), blue (Nos. 560 and 562) or black (others).*

559	10 c. on 2d. black and ultramarine (No. 226) ..	40	20
560	20 c. on 1s. chocolate & yell-orge (No. 230) ..	70	45
561	50 c. on 1d. multicoloured (No. 243)	1·25	1·25
562	70 c. on 30 c. multicoloured (No. 476)	2·00	3·50
563	1 l. on 30 c. multicoloured (No. 476)	3·00	4·50
559/63	.. .. *Set of* 5	6·50	9·00

REPUBLIC

129 Flag and Lion's Head

130 Pres. Siaka Stevens

(Manufactured by Walsall)

1971 (27 Apr). *Tenth Anniv of Independence. T* **129** *and similar design. Imperf. Self-adhesive, backed with paper bearing advertisements. (a) Postage.*

564	**129**	2 c. multicoloured	10	10
565		3½ c. multicoloured	10	10
566		10 c. multicoloured	15	10
567		12½ c. multicoloured	20	10
568		40 c. multicoloured	70	40
569		1 l. multicoloured	1·50	2·50
		(b) Air		
570	–	7½ c. multicoloured	15	10
571	–	9½ c. multicoloured	15	10
572	–	15 c. multicoloured	25	10
573	–	25 c. multicoloured	35	35
574	–	75 c. multicoloured	1·25	1·50
575	–	2 l. multicoloured	4·00	6·50
564/75		.. .. *Set of* 12	8·00	10·50

Design: *"Map" shaped as T* **129**—Nos. 570/5, Bugles and lion's head.

(Litho D.L.R.)

1972 (5 Dec)–**78.** *Multicoloured; colour of background given. P* 13.
A. *Glazed ordinary paper.*
B. *Chalk-surfaced paper* (1975–78).

			A		B	
576	**130**	1 c. light rose-lilac ..	10	10	40	40
577		2 c. lavender (*shades*) ..	10	10	30	30
578		4 c. cobalt	10	10	65	40
579		5 c. light cinnamon ..	10	10	65	30
580		7 c. light rose	15	10	90	30
581		10 c. olive-bistre	15	10	90	30
582		15 c. pale yellow-green ..	25	15	1·50	75
583		18 c. yellow-ochre	25	15	1·50	1·00
584		20 c. pale greenish blue ..	30	15	1·50	1·25
585		25 c. orange-ochre	35	15	1·50	1·25
586		50 c. light turquoise-green	1·00	55	4·00	3·25
587		1 l. bright reddish mauve (*shades*)	1·50	1·00	4·50	3·75
588		2 l. orange-salmon ..	2·75	3·50	11·00	17·00
589		5 l. light stone	6·50	8·50	18·00	32·00
576/89		.. .. .. *Set of* 14	12·00	13·00	42·00	55·00

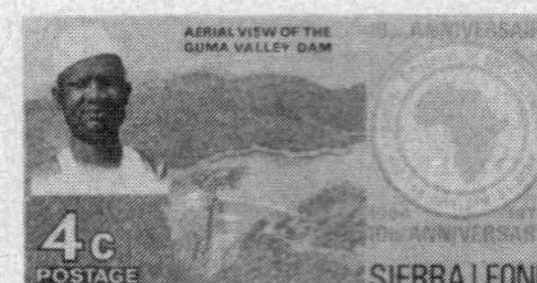

131 Guma Valley Dam and Bank Emblem

(Litho D.L.R.)

1975 (14 Jan). *Tenth Anniv of African Development Bank* (1974). *P* 13½ × 13. *(a) Postage.*

590	**131**	4 c. multicoloured	45·00	28·00
		(b) Air		
591	**131**	15 c. multicoloured	1·00	80

132 Opening Ceremony

(Litho D.L.R.)

1975 (25 Aug). *Opening of New Congo Bridge and President Stevens' 70th Birthday. P* 12½ × 13. *(a) Postage.*

592	**132**	5 c. multicoloured	3·00	1·50
		(b) Air		
593	**132**	20 c. multicoloured	50	25

133 Presidents Tolbert and Stevens, and Handclasp

(Litho D.L.R.)

1975 (3 Oct). *1st Anniv of Mano River Union. P* 12½ × 13. *(a) Postage.*

594	**133**	4 c. multicoloured	30	40
		(b) Air		
595	**133**	15 c. multicoloured	20	20

134 "Quaid-i-Azam" (Mohammed Ali Jinnah)

135 Queen Elizabeth II

(Litho Pakistan Security Printing Corporation)

1977 (28 Jan). *Birth Centenary of Mohammed Ali Jinnah (Quaid-i-Azam). P* 13.

596	**134**	30 c. multicoloured	75	30

(Des A. Larkins. Litho De La Rue, Colombia)

1977 (28 Nov). *Silver Jubilee. P* 12½ × 12.

597	**135**	5 c. multicoloured	10	10
598		1 l. multicoloured	65	80

136 College Buildings

137 St. Edward's Crown and Sceptres

(Des A. Larkins. Litho De La Rue, Colombia)

1977 (19 Dec). *150th Anniv of Fourah Bay College. T* **136** *and similar vert design. Multicoloured. P* 12 × 12½ (5 *c.*) *or* 12½ × 12 (20 *c.*).

599	5 c. Type **136**	10	10
600	20 c. The old college	35	30

(Des L. Curtis. Litho Harrison)

1978 (14 Sept). *25th Anniv of Coronation. T* **137** *and similar vert designs. Multicoloured. P* 14½ × 14.

601	5 c. Type **137**	10	10
602	50 c. Queen Elizabeth II in Coronation Coach	20	40
603	1 l. Queen Elizabeth II and Prince Philip ..	35	60
601/3	.. .. *Set of* 3	50	1·00

138 *Myrina silenus*

139 Young Child's Face

(Des J. Cooter. Litho Questa)

1979 (9 Apr). *Butterflies (1st series). T* **138** *and similar horiz designs. Multicoloured. P* 14½ × 14.

604	5 c. Type **138**	10	10
605	15 c. *Papilio nireus*	25	15
606	25 c. *Catacroptera cloanthe*	40	15
607	1 l. *Druryia antimachus*	1·50	1·50
604/7	.. .. *Set of* 4	2·00	1·60

See also Nos. 646/9.

(Des BG Studio. Litho Walsall)

1979 (13 Aug). *International Year of the Child and 30th Anniv of S.O.S. International (child distress organisation). T* **139** *and similar vert designs. Multicoloured. W w* **14**. *P* 14 × 13½.

608	5 c. Type **139**	10	10
609	27 c. Young child with baby	20	25
610	1 l. Mother with young child	50	1·10
608/10	.. .. *Set of* 3	65	1·25
MS611	114 × 84 mm. No. 610. Wmk sideways ..	75	1·75

140 Presidents Stevens (Sierra Leone) and Tolbert (Liberia), Dove with Letter and Bridge

(Des L. Curtis. Litho Questa)

1979 (3 Oct). *5th Anniv of Mano River Union and 1st Anniv of Postal Union. W w* **14** *(sideways). P* 13½ × 14.

612	**140**	5 c. sepia, orange and greenish yellow ..	10	10
613		22 c. sepia, orge-yell & brt reddish violet	10	15
614		27 c. sepia, light blue and orange ..	10	15
615		35 c. sepia, blue-green and orange-red ..	15	20
616		1 l. sepia, brt reddish violet & lt blue ..	50	1·00
612/16		.. .. *Set of* 5	75	1·40
MS617		144 × 73 mm. No. 616	55	1·00

141 Great Britain 1848 10d. Stamp

142 Knysna Turaco

(Des J.W. Litho Walsall)

1979 (19 Dec). *Death Centenary of Sir Rowland Hill. T* **141** *and similar vert designs showing stamps. W w* **14**. *P* 14 × 14½.
618 10 c. black, orange-brown and new blue .. 15 10
w. Wmk inverted .. .. 1·50
619 15 c. black, brown-ochre and greenish blue 20 15
w. Wmk inverted .. .. 1·25
620 50 c. black, carmine and greenish yellow .. 40 70
w. Wmk inverted .. .. 1·00
618/20 .. .. *Set of* 3 65 85
MS621 90×99 mm. 1 l. black, carm-red & flesh 60 80
Designs:—15 c. 1872 4d.; 50 c. 1961 £1 Independence commemorative; 1 l. 1912 £1.

(Des J.W. Format)

1980 (29 Jan)–**82**. *Birds. Multicoloured designs as T* **142**. *W w* **14** *(sideways*) on* 1, 2, 3, 5, 7 *c.,* 1, 2 *and* 5 *l.). P* 14.

A. *No imprint.* B. *Imprint date at foot*

		A		B	
622	1 c. Type **142**	40	1·00	30	1·25
	w. Wmk Crown to right of CA	35·00	—		†
623	2 c. Olive-bellied Sunbird ..	40	1·00	40	1·25
624	3 c. Western Black-headed Oriole	70	1·00	40	1·25
	w. Wmk Crown to right of CA	10·00	—		†
625	5 c. Spur-winged Goose ..	70	40	40	65
626	7 c. Didric Cuckoo	60	40	11·50	4·50
627	10 c. Grey Parrot *(vert)* ..	70	70	40	70
628	15 c. Blue Quail *(vert)* ..	1·25	1·75	50	1·75
629	20 c. African Wood Owl *(vert)*	1·40	2·00	50	2·00
630	30 c. Great Blue Turaco *(vert)*	1·40	2·00	50	2·25
	w. Wmk inverted	2·00	—		†
631	40 c. Blue-breasted Kingfisher *(vert)*	1·40	2·50	60	2·25
632	50 c. Black Crake *(vert)* ..	1·40	2·25	60	2·25
633	1 l. Hartlaub's Duck ..	1·40	2·50	60	3·50
634	2 l. Black Bee Eater ..	2·50	4·00	1·25	6·50
635	5 l. Barrow's Bustard ..	5·50	9·00	2·00	11·00
622/35	.. .. *Set of* 14	17·00	27·00	18·00	38·00

*The normal sideways watermark shows Crown to left of CA, *as seen from the back of the stamp.*
Dates of issue: No Imprint—29.1.80. With Imprint—21.12.81 5, 10, 15, 30, 40, 50 c., 1 l., 2 l., 5 l.; 15.3.82 1, 2, 3, 20 c.; 11.10.82 7 c.
Imprint dates: "1981", Nos. 622B/5B, 627B/35B; "1982", Nos. 622B/35B.
Nos. 622A/35A exist imperforate from stock dispersed by the liquidator of Format International Security Printers Ltd.
For similar stamps, but without watermark, see Nos. 760/73.

143 Paul P. Harris (founder), President Stevens of Sierra Leone and Rotary Emblem

(Des BG Studio. Litho Walsall)

1980 (23 Feb). *75th Anniv of Rotary International. W w* **14** *(sideways). P* 13½.
636 **143** 5 c. multicoloured 10 10
637 27 c. multicoloured 10 10
638 50 c. multicoloured 20 25
639 1 l. multicoloured 40 55
636/9 .. .. *Set of* 4 65 85

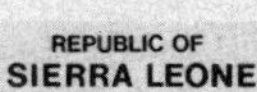

144 *Maria,* 1884

145 Organisation for African Unity Emblem

(Des L. Dunn. Litho Walsall)

1980 (6 May). *"London 1980" International Stamp Exhibition. Mail Ships. T* **144** *and similar horiz designs. Multicoloured. W w* **14** *(sideways). P* 14.
640 6 c. Type **144** 30 10
641 31 c. *Tarquah,* 1902 .. .. 40 35
642 50 c. *Aureol,* 1951 .. .. 50 70
643 1 l. *Africa Palm,* 1974 .. .. .. 60 1·60
640/3 .. .. *Set of* 4 1·60 2·50

(Des L. Curtis. Litho Questa)

1980 (1 July). *African Summit Conference, Freetown. W w* **14**. *P* 14 × 14½.
644 **145** 20 c. black, light blue and bright purple 10 10
645 1 l. black, bright purple and light blue 45 45

NEW INFORMATION

The editor is always interested to correspond with people who have new information that will improve or correct the Catalogue.

146 *Graphium policenes*

147 Arrival at Freetown Airport

(Des I. Loe. Litho Questa)

1980 (6 Oct). *Butterflies (2nd series). T* **146** *and similar vert designs. Multicoloured. W w* **14**. *P* 13½.
646 5 c. Type **146** 10 10
647 27 c. *Charaxes varanes* 30 15
648 35 c. *Charaxes brutus* 35 25
649 1 l. *Euphaedra zaddachi* .. .. .. 1·10 1·40
646/9 .. .. *Set of* 4 1·75 1·75

(Des L. Curtis. Litho Format)

1980 (5 Dec). *Tourism. T* **147** *and similar vert designs. Multicoloured. W w* **14**. *P* 13½.
650 6 c. Type **147**.. .. .. 10 10
651 26 c. Welcome to tourists 15 20
652 31 c. Freetown cotton tree 15 25
653 40 c. Beinkongo Falls 25 30
654 50 c. Sports facilities 30 40
655 1 l. African Elephant .. .. .. 1·25 95
650/5 .. .. *Set of* 6 2·00 2·00

148 Servals

149 Soldiers (Defence)

(Des P. Oxenham. Litho Questa)

1981 (28 Feb). *Wild Cats. T* **148** *and similar horiz designs. Multicoloured. W w* **14** *(sideways). P* 13½ × 14.
656 6 c. Type **148** 20 10
a. Horiz pair. Nos. 656/7 .. .. .. 40 20
657 6 c. Serval cubs 20 10
658 31 c. African Golden Cats 50 30
a. Horiz pair. Nos. 658/9 .. .. .. 1·00 60
659 31 c. African Golden Cat cubs.. .. .. 50 30
660 50 c. Leopards 70 45
a. Horiz pair. Nos. 660/1 .. .. .. 1·40 90
661 50 c. Leopard cubs 70 45
662 1 l. Lions .. .. 1·00 80
a. Horiz pair. Nos. 662/3 .. .. .. 2·00 1·60
663 1 l. Lion cubs.. .. .. 1·00 80
656/63 .. .. *Set of* 8 4·25 2·75
The two designs of each value were printed together, *se-tenant,* in horizontal pairs throughout the sheet, forming composite designs.

(Des G. Hutchins. Litho Walsall)

1981 (18 Apr). *20th Anniv of Independence and 10th Anniv of Republic. National Services. T* **149** *and similar multicoloured designs. W w* **14** *(sideways on* 31 *c. and* 1 *l.). P* 14½.
664 6 c. Type **149** 40 10
665 31 c. Nurses administering first aid, and ambulance (Health) *(horiz)* .. .. 1·25 20
666 40 c. Controlling traffic (Police Force) .. 2·25 60
667 1 l. Patrol boat (Coastguard) *(horiz)* .. 2·75 1·75
664/7 .. .. *Set of* 4 6·00 2·40

150 Wedding Bouquet from Sierra Leone

151 Sandringham

(Des J.W. Litho Harrison)

1981 (22 July). *Royal Wedding (1st issue). T* **150** *and similar vert designs. Multicoloured. W w* **14**. *P* 14.
668 31 c. Type **150** 15 20
669 45 c. Prince Charles as helicopter pilot .. 15 30
670 1 l. Prince Charles and Lady Diana Spencer .. .. 35 1·10
w. Wmk inverted .. .. 35·00
668/70 .. .. *Set of* 3 60 1·40

(Des J.W. Litho Format)

1981 (9 Sept–30 Nov). *Royal Wedding (2nd issue). T* **151** *and similar vert designs. Multicoloured. (a) Sheet stamps. P* 12.
671 35 c. Type **151** 15 25
672 60 c. Prince Charles in outdoor clothes .. 20 40
673 1 l. 50, Prince Charles and Lady Diana Spencer 40 90
671/3 .. .. *Set of* 3 65 1·40
MS674 96 × 83 mm. 3 l. Royal Landau. P 14 .. 65 65

(b) Booklet stamps. P 14 (30 Nov)
675 70 c. Type **151** 75 90
a. Booklet pane. Nos. 675/6 × 2 plus two printed labels .. .. 2·75
676 1 l. 30, As 60 c. 75 90
677 2 l. As 1 l. 50 .. .. 1·50 2·00
a. Booklet pane of 1 .. .. 1·50
675/7 .. .. *Set of* 3 2·75 3·50
Nos. 671/3 were each printed in small sheets of 6 including one *se-tenant* stamp-size label.

152 "Physical Recreation"

153 Pineapples

(Des BG Studio. Litho Questa)

1981 (30 Sept). *25th Anniv of Duke of Edinburgh Award Scheme and President's Award Scheme Publicity. T* **152** *and similar vert designs. Multicoloured. W w* **14**. *P* 14.
678 6 c. Type **152** 10 10
679 31 c. "Community service" 15 10
680 1 l. Duke of Edinburgh 30 40
681 1 l. President Siaka Stevens.. .. .. 30 40
678/81 .. .. *Set of* 4 70 85

(Des BG Studio. Litho Questa)

1981 (16 Oct). *World Food Day (1st issue). T* **153** *and similar vert designs. Multicoloured. W w* **14**. *P* 14.
682 6 c. Type **153** 10 10
683 31 c. Groundnuts 15 10
684 50 c. Cassava fruits 20 15
685 1 l. Rice plants 50 50
682/5 .. .. *Set of* 4 75 70

154 Groundnuts

(Litho Format)

1981 (2 Nov). *World Food Day (2nd issue). Agricultural Industry. T* **154** *and similar horiz designs. Multicoloured. P* 14½.
686 6 c. Type **154** 10 10
687 31 c. Cassava 25 10
688 50 c. Rice 40 25
689 1 l. Pineapples 65 70
686/9 .. .. *Set of* 4 1·25 1·00
Examples of Nos. 686/9 *se-tenant* come from unissued sheetlets dispersed by the liquidator of Format International Security Printers Ltd.

155 Scouts with Cattle

(156)

(Des M. Diamond. Litho Questa)

1982 (23 Aug). *75th Anniv of Boy Scout Movement. T* **155** *and similar horiz designs. Multicoloured. P* 14.
690 20 c. Type **155** 25 10
691 50 c. Scouts picking flowers 50 40
692 1 l. Lord Baden-Powell .. .. .. 90 1·00
693 2 l. Scouts fishing .. .. 1·90 2·00
690/3 .. .. *Set of* 4 3·25 3·00
MS694 101 × 70 mm. 3 l. Scouts raising flag .. 2·75 3·25

1982 (30 Aug)–**85**. *Nos. 668/74 surch as T* **156**.
695 50 c. on 31 c. Type **150** 40 40
696 50 c. on 35 c. Type **151** 40 40
697 50 c. on 45 c. Prince Charles as helicopter pilot 40 40
698 50 c. on 60 c. Prince Charles in outdoor clothes 40 40
699 90 c. on 1 l. Prince Charles and Lady Diana Spencer 75 75
699*a* 1 l. 30 on 60 c. Prince Charles in outdoor clothes (1985) .. .. .. 1·75 2·00
699*b* 2 l. on 35 c. Type **151** (1985) .. .. 2·75 3·00
ba. Surch double .. .. 20·00
700 2 l. on 1 l. 50, Prince Charles and Lady Diana Spencer .. .. 1·50 1·75
700*a* 8 l. on 1 l. 50, Prince Charles and Lady Diana Spencer (1985) .. .. .. 8·75 9·50
695/700*a* .. .. *Set of* 9 15·00 17·00
MS701 95 × 83 mm. 3 l. 50 on 3 l. Royal Landau .. 1·00 1·00
Nos. 699*a*/*b* and 700*a* also exist surcharged in blue from a limited printing *(Price for set of 3 £50 mint).*

157 Heading

158 Prince and Princess of Wales

(Des PAD Studio. Litho Questa)

1982 (7 Sept). *World Cup Football Championship, Spain. T* **157** *and similar vert designs. Multicoloured. P* 14.

No.	Description		
702	20 c. Type **157**	45	15
703	30 c. Dribbling	70	20
704	1 l. Tackling	2·25	2·25
705	2 l. Goalkeeping	3·50	3·75
702/5	*Set of* 4	6·25	5·75
MS706	92 × 75 mm. 3 l. Shooting	4·75	3·00

Nos. 702/5 were each printed in small sheets of 6 including one, *se-tenant*, stamp-sized label.

(Des PAD Studio. Litho Questa)

1982 (15 Sept). *21st Birthday of Princess of Wales. T* **158** *and similar vert designs. Multicoloured. P* 14½ × 14.

No.	Description		
707	31 c. Caernarvon Castle	20	15
708	50 c. Type **158**	40	15
709	2 l. Princess of Wales	1·75	75
707/9	*Set of* 3	2·10	95
MS710	103 × 75 mm. 3 l. Princess of Wales (*different*)	1·40	1·00

Nos. 707/9 also exist in sheetlets of 5 stamps and 1 label.

1982 (15 Oct). *Birth of Prince William of Wales. Nos.* 707/10 *optd with T* **212a** *of Jamaica.*

No.	Description		
711	31 c. Caernarvon Castle	15	15
712	50 c. Type **158**	30	15
713	2 l. Princess of Wales	1·00	75
711/13	*Set of* 3	1·25	95
MS714	103 × 75 mm. 3 l. Princess of Wales (*different*)	1·25	1·00

Nos. 711/13 also exist in sheetlets of 5 stamps and 1 label.

159 Washington with Troops

160 Temptation of Christ

(Des C. Mill. Litho Questa)

1982 (30 Oct). *250th Birth Anniv of George Washington. T* **159** *and similar multicoloured designs. P* 14.

No.	Description		
715	6 c. Type **159**	10	10
716	31 c. Portrait of Washington (*vert*)	20	20
717	50 c. Washington with horse	35	35
718	1 l. Washington standing on battlefield (*vert*)	65	80
715/18	*Set of* 4	1·10	1·25
MS719	103 × 71 mm. 2 l. Washington at home	75	1·25

(Des N. Waldman Studio. Litho Questa)

1982 (18 Nov). *Christmas. Stained-glass Windows. T* **160** *and similar vert designs. Multicoloured. P* 13½ × 14.

No.	Description		
720	6 c. Type **160**	10	10
721	31 c. Baptism of Christ	15	20
722	50 c. Annunciation	20	40
723	1 l. Nativity	55	90
720/3	*Set of* 4	85	1·40
MS724	74 × 104 mm. 2 l. Mary and Joseph	70	1·10

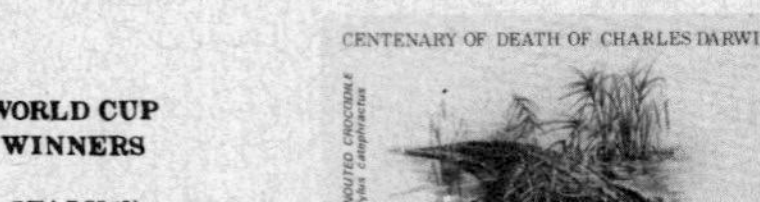

WORLD CUP
WINNERS
ITALY (3)
vs.
W. GERMANY (1)

(**161**)

162 Long Snouted Crocodile

1982 (2 Dec). *World Cup Football Championship Winners. Nos.* 702/6 *optd with T* **161**.

No.	Description		
725	20 c. Type **157**	15	20
726	30 c. Dribbling	20	30
727	1 l. Tackling	55	55
728	2 l. Goalkeeping	1·00	1·75
725/8	*Set of* 4	1·75	2·75
MS729	91 × 75 mm. 3 l. Shooting	1·00	2·00

(Des G. Drummond. Litho Questa)

1982 (10 Dec). *Death Centenary of Charles Darwin. T* **162** *and similar horiz designs. Multicoloured. P* 14.

No.	Description		
730	6 c. Type **162**	60	20
731	31 c. Rainbow Lizard	1·50	75
732	50 c. River Turtle	2·00	2·00
733	1 l. Chameleon	3·25	4·50
730/3	*Set of* 4	6·50	6·75
MS734	90 × 70 mm. 2 l. Royal Python (*vert*)	2·25	3·00

163 Diogenes

(Des Design Images. Litho Questa)

1983 (28 Jan). *500th Birth Anniv of Raphael. Details from painting "The School of Athens". T* **163** *and similar multi-coloured designs. P* 13½.

No.	Description		
735	6 c. Type **163**	15	10
736	31 c. Euclid, Ptolemy, Zoroaster, Raphael and Sodoma	30	30
737	50 c. Euclid and his pupils	45	45
738	2 l. Pythagoras, Francesco Maria della Rovere and Heraclitus	1·40	1·40
735/8	*Set of* 4	2·00	2·00
MS739	101 × 126 mm. 3 l. Plato and Aristotle (*vert*)	1·50	2·00

164 Agricultural Training

165 Map of Africa and Flag of Sierra Leone

(Litho Questa)

1983 (14 Mar). *Commonwealth Day. T* **164** *and similar horiz designs. Multicoloured. P* 14.

No.	Description		
740	6 c. Type **164**	10	10
741	10 c. Tourism development	10	10
742	50 c. Broadcasting training	45	45
743	1 l. Airport services	1·50	1·25
740/3	*Set of* 4	1·75	1·60

(Des M. Diamond. Litho J.W.)

1983 (29 Apr). *25th Anniv of Economic Commission for Africa. P* 13.

No.		Description		
744	**165**	1 l. multicoloured	80	1·10

166 Chimpanzees in Tree

(Des J. Iskowitz. Litho Questa)

1983 (19 May). *Endangered Species. T* **166** *and similar multi-coloured designs. P* 14.

No.	Description		
745	6 c. Type **166**	1·50	20
746	10 c. Three Chimpanzees (*vert*)	1·75	30
747	31 c. Chimpanzees swinging in tree (*vert*)	3·25	90
748	60 c. Group of Chimpanzees	5·50	7·50
745/8	*Set of* 4	11·00	8·00
MS749	115 × 80 mm. 3 l. African Elephant	2·50	2·25

167 Traditional Communications

168 Montgolfier Balloon, Paris, 1783

(Des R. Sauber. Litho Questa)

1983 (14 July). *World Communications Year. T* **167** *and similar horiz designs. Multicoloured. P* 14.

No.	Description		
750	6 c. Type **167**	10	10
751	10 c. Mail via Mano River	15	10
752	20 c. Satellite ground station	15	10
753	1 l. British packet, *circa* 1805	90	65
750/3	*Set of* 4	1·10	80
MS754	115 × 85 mm. 2 l. Telecommunications	80	1·25

(Des Artists International. Litho Questa)

1983 (31 Aug). *Bicentenary of Manned Flight. T* **168** *and similar multicoloured designs. P* 14.

No.	Description		
755	6 c. Type **168**	25	10
756	20 c. Wolfert's *Deutschland* airship, Berlin, 1879 (*horiz*)	55	20
757	50 c. Amundsen's airship N.1 *Norge*, North Pole, 1926 (*horiz*)	1·50	1·50
758	1 l. *Cap Sierra* sport balloon, Freetown, 1983	1·50	2·00
755/8	*Set of* 4	3·50	3·50
MS759	115×85 mm. 2 l. Airship of 21st century	1·00	1·75

1983 (Oct). *Birds. As Nos.* 622B/35B *but without wmk.* "1983" *imprint date.*

No.	Description		
760	1 c. Type **142**	90	1·75
761	2 c. Olive-bellied Sunbird	90	1·75
763	5 c. Spur-winged Goose	1·10	70
765	10 c. Grey Parrot (*vert*)	1·10	70
766	15 c. Blue Quail (*vert*)	1·50	1·50
767	20 c. African Wood Owl (*vert*)	2·50	2·00
768	30 c. Great Blue Turaco (*vert*)	1·75	2·25
769	40 c. Blue-breasted Kingfisher (*vert*)	2·75	3·25
770	50 c. Black Crake (*vert*)	2·75	3·25
772	2 l. Black Bee Eater	5·00	11·00
773	5 l. Barrow's Bustard	10·00	17·00
760/73	*Set of* 11	27·00	40·00

Nos. 760/73 exist imperforate from stock dispersed by the liquidator of Format International Security Printers Ltd.

Examples of the 1, 2, 3 c. and 2 l. with 1981 imprint date come from the liquidator's stock.

169 Mickey Mouse

(Litho Format)

1983 (18 Nov). *Space Ark Fantasy. T* **169** *and similar horiz designs featuring Disney cartoon characters. Multicoloured. P* 13½.

No.	Description		
774	1 c. Type **169**	10	10
775	1 c. Huey, Dewey and Louie	10	10
776	3 c. Goofy in spaceship	10	10
777	3 c. Donald Duck	10	10
778	10 c. Ludwig von Drake	10	10
779	10 c. Goofy	10	10
780	2 l. Mickey Mouse and Giraffe in spaceship	1·25	1·60
781	3 l. Donald Duck floating in space	1·75	2·00
774/81	*Set of* 8	3·00	3·50
MS782	140 × 116 mm. 5 l. Mickey Mouse leaving spaceship	3·00	3·50

170 Graduates from Union Training Programme

(Des G. Vasarhelyi. Litho Format)

1984 (8 Feb). *10th Anniv of the Mano River Union. T* **170** *and similar horiz designs. Multicoloured. P* 15.

No.	Description		
783	6 c. Type **170**	10	10
784	25 c. Intra-Union trade	10	10
785	31 c. Member Presidents on map	10	10
786	41 c. Signing ceremony marking Guinea's accession	15	15
783/6	*Set of* 4	30	30
MS787	75 × 113 mm. No. 786	35	90

No. 783 exists imperforate from stock dispersed by the liquidator of Format International Security Printers Ltd.

171 Gymnastics

172 "Apollo 11" Lift-off

(Des J. Iskowitz. Litho Questa)

1984 (27 Mar). *Olympic Games, Los Angeles. T* **171** *and similar horiz designs. Multicoloured. P* 14.

788 90 c. Type **171** 30 40
789 1 l. Hurdling 30 40
790 3 l. Javelin-throwing .. .. 75 1·25
788/90 .. .. *Set of* 3 1·25 1·90
MS791 104 × 71 mm. 7 l. Boxing .. .. 1·10 2·00

(Des J. Iskowitz. Litho Questa)

1984 (14 May). *15th Anniv of First Moonwalk. T* **172** *and similar multicoloured designs. P* 14.

792 50 c. Type **172** 20 20
793 75 c. Lunar module 30 30
794 1 l. 25, First Moonwalk 45 45
795 2 l. 50, Lunar exploration 85 85
792/5 .. .. *Set of* 4 1·60 1·60
MS796 99 × 69 mm. 5 l. Family watching Moonwalk on television (*horiz*) .. .. 1·60 2·25

173 Concorde

(Des Susan David. Litho Walsall)

1984 (19 June). *Universal Postal Union Congress, Hamburg. T* **173** *and similar horiz design. Multicoloured. P* 14.

797 4 l. Type **173** .. .. 2·75 1·75
MS798 100 × 70 mm. 4 l. Heinrich von Stephan (founder of U.P.U.) .. .. 2·00 2·75

174 Citroen "Traction Avante"

25c

(**175**)

(Des Susan David. Litho Format)

1984 (16 July). *United Nations Decade for African Transport. T* **174** *and similar horiz designs. Multicoloured. P* 14½ × 15.

799 12 c. Type **174** 30 10
800 60 c. Locomobile 50 35
801 90 c. A.C. "Ace" 65 45
802 1 l. Vauxhall "Prince Henry" 65 45
803 1 l. 50, Delahaye "135" 80 70
804 2 l. Mazda "1105" 90 90
799/804 .. .. *Set of* 6 3·50 2·50
MS805 107 × 75 mm. 6 l. Volkswagen "Beetle". P 15 .. .. 3·75 4·50

1984 (3 Aug). *Surch as T* **175**. (a) *On Nos.* 625, 627 *and* 634. A. *No imprint.* B. *Imprint date at foot.*

		A		B	
806	25 c. on 10 c. Grey Parrot (*vert*)	4·75	4·75	4·75	4·75
807	40 c. on 10 c. Grey Parrot (*vert*)	4·75	4·75	4·75	4·75
808	50 c. on 2 l. Black Bee Eater	4·75	4·75	4·75	4·75
809	70 c. on 5 c. Spur-winged Goose	4·75	4·75	4·75	4·75
810	10 l. on 5 c. Spur-winged Goose	11·00	11·00	11·00	11·00
806/10	*Set of* 5	27·00	27·00	27·00	27·00

(b) *On Nos.* 763, 765 *and* 772

811 25 c. on 10 c. Grey Parrot (*vert*) 75 85
812 40 c. on 10 c. Grey Parrot (*vert*) 50 70
813 50 c. on 2 l. Black Bee Eater 50 70
814 70 c. on 5 c. Spur-winged Goose 50 70
815 10 l. on 5 c. Spur-winged Goose .. .. 3·00 3·50
811/15 .. .. *Set of* 5 4·75 5·75

Imprint dates: "1981", Nos. 806B/10B; "1982", Nos. 806B/10B; "1983", Nos. 811/15.

AUSIPEX 84

(**176**)

177 Portuguese Caravel

1984 (22 Aug). *"Ausipex" International Stamp Exhibition, Melbourne. Optd with T* **176**. (a) *On Nos.* 632 *and* 635. A. *No imprint.* B. *Imprint date at foot.*

		A		B	
816	50 c. Black Crake	5·00	5·00	5·00	5·00
817	5 l. Barrow's Bustard	15·00	15·00	15·00	15·00

(b) *On Nos.* 770 *and* 773

818 50 c. Black Crake .. .. 1·00 75
819 5 l. Barrow's Bustard .. .. 2·75 2·00

Imprint dates: "1981", Nos. 816B/17B; "1982", Nos. 816B/17B; "1983", Nos. 818/19.

(Des G. Drummond. Litho Questa)

1984 (5 Sept)–**85**. *History of Shipping. T* **177** *and similar horiz designs. Multicoloured.* A. *P* 14. *Without imprint date below design.* B. *P* 12. *With imprint date ("1985") below design (2 c. to 10 l.) or without imprint date (15, 25 l.).*

		A		B	
820	2 c. Type **177**	65	1·25	55	1·25
821	5 c. *Merlin* of Bristol	75	85	55	70
822	10 c. *Golden Hind*	1·00	85	75	70
823	15 c. *Mordaunt*	1·25	90	†	
824	20 c. *Atlantic* (transport)	1·25	1·00	80	60
825	25 c. H.M.S. *Lapwing*	1·25	1·00	80	60
826	30 c. *Traveller* (brig)	1·50	1·00	80	60
827	40 c. *Amistad* (schooner)	1·50	1·00	90	60
828	50 c. H.M.S. *Teazer*	1·50	1·00	1·00	60
829	70 c. *Scotia* (cable ship)	1·75	1·75	1·75	1·75
830	1 l. H.M.S. *Alecto*	2·00	1·75	1·75	1·75
831	2 l. H.M.S. *Blonde*	8·00	6·00	2·00	2·50
832	5 l. H.M.S. *Fox*	11·00	10·00	2·75	4·00
833	10 l. *Accra* (liner)	14·00	16·00	3·25	5·00
833*c*	15 l. H.M.S. *Favourite*	2·50	3·00	—	—
833*d*	25 l. H.M.S. *Euryalus*	2·75	3·50	—	—
820A/33dA	*Set of* 16	48·00	45·00		
820B/33B	*Set of* 13			16·00	19·00

Dates of issue:—Without imprint 5.9.84, 2 c., to 1 l.; 9.10.84, 2 l., 5 l.; 7.11.84, 10 l; 15.11.85, 15 l., 25 l. With imprint 7.85, 2 c. to 10 l.

178 Mail Runner approaching Mano River Depot, *c* 1843

179 "Madonna and Child" (Pisanello)

(Des Susan David. Litho Walsall)

1984 (9 Oct). *125th Anniv of First Postage Stamps. T* **178** *and similar horiz designs. Multicoloured. P* 14.

834 50 c. Type **178** 35 15
835 2 l. Isaac Fitzjohn, First Postmaster, receiving letters, 1855 .. .. 1·25 85
836 3 l. 1859 packet franked with four 6d. stamps 1·75 1·50
834/6 .. .. *Set of* 3 3·00 2·25
MS837 100 × 70 mm. 5 l. Sierra Leone 1859 6d. purple and Great Britain 1840 Penny Black stamps .. .. 1·50 1·60

(Litho Walsall)

1984 (15 Nov). *Christmas. Madonna and Child paintings by artists named. T* **179** *and similar vert designs. Multicoloured. P* 14.

838 20 c. Type **179** 10 10
839 1 l. Memling 40 40
840 2 l. Raphael 75 90
841 3 l. Van der Werff .. .. 1·10 1·40
838/41 .. .. *Set of* 4 2·00 2·50
MS842 100 × 69 mm. 6 l. Picasso .. .. 2·75 2·75

180 Donald Duck in the "The Wise Little Hen"

(Litho Questa)

1984 (26 Nov). *50th Birthday of Donald Duck. Walt Disney Cartoon Characters. T* **180** *and similar horiz designs. Multicoloured. P* 12 (2 *l.*) *or* 14 × 13½ (*others*).

843 1 c. Type **180** 10 10
844 2 c. Mickey Mouse and Donald Duck in "Boat Builders" 10 10
845 3 c. Panchito, Donald Duck and Jose Carioca in "The Three Caballeros" .. 10 10
846 4 c. Donald Duck meeting Pythagoras in "Mathmagic Land" 10 10
847 5 c. Donald Duck and nephew in "The Mickey Mouse Club" 10 10
848 10 c. Mickey Mouse, Goofy and Donald Duck in "Donald on Parade" 10 10
849 1 l. Donald Duck riding donkey in "Don Donald" .. .. 1·00 1·00
850 2 l. Donald Duck in "Donald Gets Drafted" 2·00 2·00
851 4 l. Donald Duck meeting children in Tokyo Disneyland .. .. 3·25 3·25
843/51 .. .. *Set of* 9 6·00 6·00
MS852 126 × 102 mm. 5 l. Style sheet for Donald Duck .. .. 3·75 2·50

No. 850 was printed in sheetlets of 8.

181 Fischer's Whydah

(Des Susan David. Litho Walsall)

1985 (31 Jan). *Birth Bicentenary of John J. Audubon (ornithologist). Songbirds of Sierra Leone. T* **181** *and similar horiz designs. Multicoloured. P* 14.

853 40 c. Type **181** .. .. 1·75 55
854 90 c. Spotted Flycatcher .. .. 3·00 1·75
855 1 l. 30, Garden Warbler .. .. 3·25 3·50
856 3 l. Speke's Weaver .. .. 5·50 7·50
853/6 .. .. *Set of* 4 12·00 12·00
MS857 100 × 70 mm. 5 l. Great Grey Shrike .. 2·75 3·00

182 Fishing

(Des M. Zacharow. Litho Walsall)

1985 (14 Feb). *International Youth Year. T* **182** *and similar horiz designs. Multicoloured. P* 14.

858 1 l. 15, Type **182** 45 55
859 1 l. 50, Sawing timber 60 75
860 2 l. 15, Rice farming 75 95
858/60 .. .. *Set of* 3 1·60 2·00
MS861 100 × 70 mm. 5 l. Polishing diamonds .. 1·75 1·50

183 Eddie Rickenbacker and Spad "XIII", 1918

(Des K. Gromol. Litho Walsall)

1985 (28 Feb). *40th Anniv of International Civil Aviation Organization. T* **183** *and similar horiz designs. Multicoloured. P* 14.

862 70 c. Type **183** .. .. 1·50 75
863 1 l. 25, Samuel P. Langley and *Aerodrome A*, 1903 .. .. 2·00 1·75
864 1 l. 30, Orville and Wilbur Wright with Wright Flyer I, 1903 .. .. 2·00 1·75
865 2 l. Charles Lindbergh and Ryan NYP Special *Spirit of St. Louis*, 1927 .. 2·25 2·75
862/5 .. .. *Set of* 4 7·00 6·25
MS866 100×69 mm. 5 l. Sierra Leone Airlines Boeing 707-384C .. .. 2·00 1·75

184 "Temptation of Christ" (Botticelli)

185 The Queen Mother at St. Paul's Cathedral

(Des C. Walters. Litho Questa)

1985 (29 Apr). *Easter. Religious Paintings. T* **184** *and similar multicoloured designs. P* 14.

867 45 c. Type **184** 30 15
868 70 c. "Christ at the Column" (Velasquez) .. 55 35
869 1 l. 55, "Pietà" (Botticelli) (*vert*) 90 75
870 10 l. "Christ on the Cross" (Velasquez) (*vert*) 4·75 5·00
867/70 .. .. *Set of* 4 6·00 5·75
MS871 106 × 76 mm. 12 l. "Man of Sorrows" (Botticelli) .. .. 4·00 4·00

(Des J.W. Litho Questa)

1985 (8 July). *Life and Times of Queen Elizabeth the Queen Mother. T* **185** *and similar multicoloured designs. P* 14.

872 1 l. Type **185** 20 25
873 1 l. 70, With her racehorse, "Double Star", at Sandown (*horiz*) 30 40
874 10 l. At Covent Garden, 1971 .. .. .. 1·75 2·50
872/4 .. .. *Set of* 3 2·00 2·75
MS875 56 × 85 mm. 12 l. With Princess Anne at Ascot .. .. 1·75 2·25

75th ANNIVERSARY
OF GIRL GUIDES

70c

(**186**)

1985 (25 July). *75th Anniv of Girl Guide Movement. Nos.* 690/4 *surch as T* **186**.
876 70 c. on 20 c. Type **155** 30 30
877 1 l. 30 on 50 c. Scouts picking flowers .. 55 55
878 5 l. on 1 l. Lord Baden-Powell .. .. 1·60 1·60
879 7 l. on 2 l. Scouts fishing .. .. .. 2·25 2·25
876/9 .. .. *Set of* 4 4·25 4·25
MS880 101 × 70 mm. 15 l. on 3 l. Scouts raising flag .. .. 3·75 4·00

MA YANHONJG
CHINA
GOLD MEDAL
Le2

(**187**)

1985 (25 July). *Olympic Gold Medal Winners, Los Angeles. Nos.* 788/91 *surch as T* **187**.
881 2 l. on 90 c. Type **171** (surch T **187**) 50 55
882 4 l. on 1 l. Hurdling (surch "E. MOSES U.S.A. GOLD MEDAL") .. .. .. 1·00 1·25
883 8 l. on 3 l. Javelin-throwing (surch "A. HAERKOENEN FINLAND GOLD MEDAL") .. .. 2·00 2·10
881/3 .. .. *Set of* 3 3·25 3·50
MS884 104 × 71 mm. 15 l. on 7 l. Boxing (surch "M. TAYLOR U.S.A. GOLD MEDAL") .. .. 3·25 3·75

70c

188 Chater-Lea (1905) at Hill Station House (**189**)

(Des A. DiLorenzo. Litho Questa)

1985 (15 Aug). *Centenary of the Motor Cycle and Decade for African Transport. T* **188** *and similar horiz designs. Multicoloured. P* 14.
885 1 l. 40, Type **188** .. .. 1·00 1·00
886 2 l. Honda "XR 350 R" at Queen Elizabeth II Quay, Freetown .. .. 1·40 1·40
887 4 l. Kawasaki "Vulcan" at Bo Clock Tower .. 2·50 2·50
888 5 l. Harley-Davidson "Electra-Glide" in Makeni village .. .. 2·75 2·75
885/8 .. .. *Set of* 4 7·00 7·00
MS889 104 × 71 mm. 12 l. Millet (1893) .. .. 4·25 4·25

(Des Susan David. Litho Questa)

1985 (3 Sept). *300th Birth Anniv of Johann Sebastian Bach (composer). Vert designs as T* **204***a of Maldive Islands. P* 14.
890 70 c. multicoloured 75 25
891 3 l. multicoloured .. .. 1·75 80
892 4 l. multicoloured .. .. 1·90 1·10
893 5 l. multicoloured .. .. 2·25 1·40
890/3 .. .. *Set of* 4 6·00 3·25
MS894 103 × 77 mm. 12 l. black .. .. .. 4·50 3·50
Designs:—70 c. Viola pomposa; 3 l. Spinet; 4 l. Lute; 5 l. Oboe; 12 l. "Johann Sebastian Bach" (Toby E. Rosenthal).

1985 (30 Sept). *Surch as T* **189**. (*a*) *On Nos.* 707/10
895 70 c. on 31 c. Caernarvon Castle 30 30
896 4 l. on 50 c. Type **158** .. .. .. 2·00 2·50
897 5 l. on 2 l. Princess of Wales .. .. 2·50 3·00
MS898 103 × 75 mm. 15 l. on 3 l. Princess of Wales (*different*) .. .. 6·50 6·00

(*b*) *On Nos.* 711/14
899 1 l. 30 on 31 c. Caernarvon Castle .. .. 1·25 1·25
900 5 l. on 50 c. Type **158** .. .. .. 3·00 3·50
901 7 l. on 2 l. Princess of Wales .. .. 4·00 4·50
895/7, 899/901 .. .. .. *Set of* 6 11·50 13·50
MS902 103×75 mm. 15 l. on 3 l. Princess of Wales (*different*) .. .. 6·50 6·00

190 "Madonna and Child" (Crivelli) **191** Player kicking Ball

(Litho Questa)

1985 (18 Oct). *Christmas. "Madonna and Child" Paintings by artists named. T* **190** *and similar vert designs. Multicoloured. P* 14.
903 70 c. Type **190** 25 10
904 3 l. Bouts 80 40
905 4 l. Da Messina 95 55
906 5 l. Lochner .. .. 1·10 65
903/6 .. .. *Set of* 4 2·75 1·50
MS907 113 × 85 mm. 12 l. Miniature from Book of Kells .. .. 1·50 1·60

(Des Walt Disney Productions. Litho Questa)

1985 (30 Oct). *150th Birth Anniv of Mark Twain (author). Vert designs as T* **160***a of Lesotho showing Walt Disney cartoon characters illustrating Mark Twain quotations. Multicoloured. P* 13½×14.
908 1 l. 50, Snow White and Bashful 40 30
909 3 l. Three Little Pigs 60 80
910 4 l. Donald Duck and nephew 70 95
911 5 l. Pinocchio and Figaro the cat .. .. 85 1·25
908/11 .. .. *Set of* 4 2·25 3·00
MS912 126 × 101 mm. 15 l. Winnie the Pooh .. 3·25 2·50

(Des Walt Disney Productions. Litho Questa)

1985 (3 Oct). *Birth Bicentenaries of Grimm Brothers (folklorists). Designs as T* **160***b of Lesotho, but horiz, showing Walt Disney cartoon characters from "Rumpelstiltskin". Multicoloured. P* 14×13½.
913 70 c. The Miller (Donald Duck) and his daughter (Daisy Duck) meet the King (Uncle Scrooge) 20 25
914 1 l. 30, The King puts the Miller's daughter to work 35 40
915 2 l. Rumpelstiltskin demands payment .. 50 55
916 10 l. The King with gold spun from straw .. 2·75 3·50
913/16 .. .. *Set of* 4 3·50 4·25
MS917 126 × 100 mm. 15 l. The King and Queen with baby .. .. 4·75 4·50

(Litho Format)

1985 (28 Nov). *40th Anniv of United Nations Organization. Multicoloured designs as T* **159** *of Lesotho showing United Nations (New York) stamps. P* 14½.
918 2 l. John Kennedy and 1954 Human Rights 8 c. 70 70
919 4 l. Albert Einstein (scientist) and 1958 Atomic Energy 3 c. .. .. .. 1·40 1·60
920 7 l. Maimonides (physician) and 1956 W.H.O. 8 c. .. .. 3·75 4·25
918/20 .. .. *Set of* 3 5·25 6·00
MS921 110 × 85 mm. 12 l. Martin Luther King (civil rights leader) (*vert*) .. .. .. 1·25 1·75

(Des M. Lemel. Litho Questa)

1986 (3 Mar). *World Cup Football Championship, Mexico. T* **191** *and similar vert designs. Multicoloured. P* 14.
922 70 c. Type **191** 35 10
923 3 l. Player controlling ball 80 50
924 4 l. Player chasing ball 95 70
925 5 l. Player kicking ball (*different*) .. .. 1·40 80
922/5 .. .. *Set of* 4 3·25 1·90
MS926 105 × 74 mm. 12 l. Player kicking ball (*different*) .. .. 1·50 1·75

191*a* Times Square, 1905 **192** Chicago-Milwaukee "Hiawatha Express'

(Des J. Iskowitz. Litho Questa)

1986 (11 Mar). *Centenary of Statue of Liberty (1st issue). T* **191***a and similar multicoloured designs. P* 14.
927 40 c. Type **191***a* 10 10
928 70 c. Times Square, 1986 .. .. .. 15 10
929 1 l. "Tally Ho" coach, *c* 1880 (*horiz*) 25 15
930 10 l. Express bus, 1986 (*horiz*) .. .. 1·75 1·90
927/30 .. .. *Set of* 4 2·00 2·00
MS931 105×75 mm. 12 l. Statue of Liberty .. 2·25 2·25
See also Nos. 1001/9.

(Des W. Hanson. Litho Questa)

1986 (1 Apr). *Appearance of Halley's Comet (1st issue). Horiz designs as T* **162***a of Lesotho. Multicoloured. P* 14.
932 15 c. Johannes Kepler (astronomer) and Paris Observatory 30 10
933 50 c. N.A.S.A. Space Shuttle landing, 1985 .. 40 10
934 70 c. Halley's Comet (from Bayeux Tapestry) 40 15
935 10 l. Comet of 530 A.D. and Merlin predicting coming of King Arthur .. .. 1·75 1·60
932/5 .. .. *Set of* 4 2·50 1·75
MS936 101 × 70 mm. 12 l. Halley's Comet .. 1·50 1·60
See also Nos. 988/92.

(Des and litho Questa)

1986 (23 Apr). *60th Birthday of Queen Elizabeth II. Vert designs as T* **163***a of Lesotho. P* 14.
937 10 c. black and yellow 10 10
938 1 l. 70, multicoloured 45 35
939 10 l. multicoloured .. .. .. 1·75 2·00
937/9 .. .. *Set of* 3 2·00 2·25
MS940 120 × 85 mm. 12 l. black and grey-brown 1·50 1·60
Designs:—10 c. Princess Elizabeth inspecting guard of honour, Cranwell, 1951; 1 l. 70, In Garter robes; 10 l. At Braemar Games, 1970; 12 l. Princess Elizabeth, Windsor Castle, 1943.

(Des P. Rhymer. Litho Questa)

1986 (22 May). *"Ameripex" International Stamp Exhibition, Chicago. American Trains. T* **192** *and similar horiz designs. Multicoloured. P* 14.
941 50 c. Type **192** 70 40
942 2 l. Rock Island Line "The Rocket" .. 1·40 1·50
943 4 l. Rio Grande "Prospector" .. .. 2·25 2·75
944 7 l. Southern Pacific "Daylight Express" .. 2·75 4·25
941/4 .. .. *Set of* 4 6·50 8·00
MS945 105 × 85 mm. 12 l. Pennsylvania "Broadway" .. .. 2·50 2·25

(Litho Questa)

1986 (1 July). *Royal Wedding. Vert designs as T* **170***a of Lesotho. Multicoloured. P* 14.
946 10 c. Prince Andrew and Miss Sarah Ferguson 10 10
947 1 l. 70, Prince Andrew at clay pigeon shoot 30 35
948 10 l. Prince Andrew in naval uniform .. 1·40 1·75
946/8 .. .. *Set of* 3 1·60 2·00
MS949 88 × 88 mm. 12 l. Prince Andrew and Miss Sarah Ferguson (*different*) .. .. 2·25 1·60

193 *Monodora myristica* **194** Handshake and Flags of Sierra Leone and U.S.A.

(Des G. Drummond. Litho Format)

1986 (25 Aug). *Flowers of Sierra Leone. T* **193** *and similar vert designs. Multicoloured. P* 15.
950 70 c. Type **193** 15 10
951 1 l. 50, *Gloriosa simplex* 20 15
952 4 l. *Mussaenda erythrophylla* 35 25
953 6 l. *Crinum ornatum* 50 40
954 8 l. *Bauhinia purpurea* 60 60
955 10 l. *Bombax costatum* 70 70
956 20 l. *Hibiscus rosasinensis* .. .. 1·25 1·50
957 30 l. *Cassia fistula* .. .. .. 1·75 2·00
950/7 .. .. *Set of* 8 5·00 5·00
MS958 Two sheets, each 101 × 92 mm. (a) 40 l. *Clitoria ternatea*. (b) 40 l. *Plumbago auriculata* *Set of 2 sheets* 5·00 5·00

(Litho Questa)

1986 (26 Aug). *25th Anniv of United States Peace Corps. P* 14.
959 **194** 10 l. multicoloured 70 70

Le30

70¢

195 Transporting Goods by Canoe (**196**) (**197**)

(Des T. O'Toole. Litho Questa)

1986 (1 Sept). *International Peace Year. T* **195** *and similar horiz designs. Multicoloured. P* 14.
960 1 l. Type **195** 25 15
961 2 l. Teacher and class 35 25
962 5 l. Rural post office 70 50
963 10 l. Fishermen in longboat .. .. 1·50 1·25
960/3 .. .. *Set of* 4 2·50 1·90

1986 (15 Sept). *Various stamps surch.*
(*a*) *As T* **196** *on Nos.* 820A, 826/7A *and* 829A
964 30 l. on 2 c. Type **177** .. .. .. 2·00 2·50
965 40 l. on 30 c. *Traveller* (brig) .. .. 2·50 3·00
966 45 l. on 40 c. *Amistad* (schooner) .. 2·75 3·25
967 50 l. on 70 c. *Scotia* (cable ship) .. 3·00 3·25
(*b*) *As T* **197** *on Nos.* 937 *and* 939/40 (*in silver on Nos.* 968/9)
968 70 c. on 10 c. black and yellow 20 10
969 45 l. on 10 l. multicoloured .. .. 2·75 2·50
MS970 120 × 85 mm. 50 l. on 12 l. black and grey-brown .. .. 2·50 3·00
(*c*) *As T* **197** *on Nos.* 946 *and* 948/9, *in silver*
971 70 c. on 10 c. Prince Andrew and Miss Sarah Ferguson 10 10
972 45 l. on 10 l. Prince Andrew in naval uniform 2·40 2·50
964/9, 971/2 .. .. .. *Set of* 8 14·00 15·00
MS973 88×88 mm. 50 l. on 12 l. Prince Andrew and Miss Sarah Ferguson (*different*) .. .. 2·50 3·00

1986 (15 Sept). *World Cup Football Championship Winners, Mexico. Nos.* 922/6 *optd with T* **213***a of Maldive Islands or surch also, all in gold.*
974 70 c. Type **191** 30 10
975 3 l. Player controlling ball 55 30
976 4 l. Player chasing ball 60 40
977 40 l. on 5 l. Player kicking ball (*different*) .. 5·50 4·50
974/7 .. .. *Set of* 4 6·25 4·75
MS978 105 × 74 mm. 40 l. on 12 l. Player kicking ball (*different*) .. .. 2·50 2·50

198 Mickey and Minnie Mouse as Jack and Jill

(Des Walt Disney Co. Litho Format)

1986 (22 Sept). *"Stockholmia '86" International Stamp Exhibition, Sweden. T* **198** *and similar horiz designs showing Walt Disney cartoon characters in scenes from nursery rhymes. Multicoloured. P* 11.

979	70 c. Type **198**	10	10
980	1 l. Donald Duck as Wee Willie Winkie ..	15	15
981	2 l. Minnie Mouse as Little Miss Muffet ..	20	20
982	4 l. Goofy as Old King Cole	40	40
983	5 l. Clarabelle as Mary Quite Contrary ..	50	50
984	10 l. Daisy Duck as Little Bo Peep ..	90	1·00
985	25 l. Daisy Duck and Minnie Mouse in "Polly put the Kettle on"	2·00	2·75
986	35 l. Goofy, Mickey Mouse and Donald Duck as the Three Men in a Tub	2·50	3·25
979/86	.. .. *Set of* 8	6·00	7·50
MS987	Two sheets, each 127×102 mm. P 14×13½. (a) 40 l. Aunt Matilda as the Old Woman in the Shoe. (b) 40 l. Goofy as Simple Simon .. .. .. *Set of 2 sheets*	6·00	6·50

1986 (15 Oct). *Appearance of Halley's Comet (2nd issue). Nos.* 932/6 *optd as T* **213***b of Maldive Islands (in silver on* 50 *l.) or surch also.*

988	50 c. N.A.S.A. Space Shuttle landing, 1985 ..	15	10
989	70 c. Halley's Comet (from Bayeux Tapestry)	15	10
990	1 l. 50 on 15 c. Johannes Kepler (astronomer) and Paris Observatory	15	10
991	45 l. on 10 l. Comet of 530 A.D. and Merlin predicting coming of King Arthur ..	4·00	3·75
988/91	.. .. *Set of* 4	4·00	3·75
MS992	101×70 mm. 50 l. on 12 l. Halley's Comet	3·25	3·75

199 "Virgin and Child with St. Dorothy"

200 Nomoli (soapstone figure)

(Litho Questa)

1986 (17 Nov). *Christmas. Paintings by Titian. T* **199** *and similar multicoloured designs. P* 14.

993	70 c. Type **199**	10	10
994	1 l. 50, "The Gypsy Madonna" (*vert*) ..	15	10
995	20 l. "The Holy Family"	2·25	2·50
996	30 l. "Virgin and Child in an Evening Landscape" (*vert*)	2·75	3·25
993/6	.. .. *Set of* 4	4·75	5·50
MS997	76×102 mm. 40 l. "Madonna with the Pesaro Family" (*vert*)	6·00	7·00

(Des A. DiLorenzo. Litho Format)

1987 (2 Jan). *Bicentenary of Sierra Leone. T* **200** *and similar vert designs. Multicoloured. P* 15.

998	2 l. Type **200**	10	15
999	5 l. King's Yard Gate, Royal Hospital, 1817 ..	20	40
MS1000	100×70 mm. 60 l. Early 19th-century British warship at Freetown	2·75	3·75

201 Removing Top of Statue's Torch

202 Emblem, Mother with Child and Syringe

(Litho Questa)

1987 (2 Jan). *Centenary of Statue of Liberty* (1986) (*2nd issue*). *T* **201** *and similar multicoloured designs. P* 14.

1001	70 c. Type **201**	10	10
1002	1 l. 50, View of Statue's torch and New York Harbour (*horiz*)	10	10
1003	2 l. Crane lifting torch	10	10
1004	3 l. Workman steadying torch	10	15
1005	4 l. Statue's crown (*horiz*)	15	20
1006	5 l. Statue of Liberty (side view) and fireworks	20	25
1007	10 l. Statue of Liberty and fireworks ..	40	45
1008	25 l. Bedloe Island, Statue and fireworks (*horiz*)	1·00	1·40
1009	30 l. Statue's face	1·25	1·75
1001/9	.. .. *Set of* 9	3·00	4·00

(Litho Questa)

1987 (18 Mar). *40th Anniv of U.N.I.C.E.F. P* 14.

1010	**202** 10 l. multicoloured	40	55

ALTERED CATALOGUE NUMBERS

Any Catalogue numbers altered from the last edition are shown as a list in the introductory pages.

203 *U.S.A.*, 1987

204 Mickey Mouse as Mountie and Parliament Building, Ottawa

(Des S. Heinmann. Litho Questa)

1987 (15 June). *America's Cup Yachting Championship. T* **203** *and similar multicoloured designs. P* 14.

1011	1 l. Type **203**	10	10
1012	1 l. 50, *New Zealand II*, 1987 (*horiz*) ..	10	10
1013	2 l. 50, *French Kiss*, 1987	10	10
1014	10 l. *Stars and Stripes*, 1987 (*horiz*) ..	65	45
1015	15 l. *Australia II*, 1983	90	75
1016	25 l. *Freedom*, 1980	1·60	1·40
1017	30 l. *Kookaburra*, 1987 (*horiz*)	1·75	1·60
1011/17	.. .. *Set of* 7	4·50	4·00
MS1018	100×70 mm. 50 l. *Constellation*, 1964	2·00	2·50

(Des Walt Disney Co. Litho Format)

1987 (15 June). *"Capex '87" International Stamp Exhibition, Toronto. T* **204** *and similar horiz designs showing Walt Disney cartoon characters in Canada. Multicoloured. P* 11.

1019	2 l. Type **204**	20	20
1020	5 l. Goofy dressed as Mountie and totem poles	35	35
1021	10 l. Goofy windsurfing and Donald Duck fishing off Perce Rock	60	45
1022	20 l. Goofy with mountain goat in Rocky Mountains	1·00	1·25
1023	25 l. Donald Duck and Mickey Mouse in Old Quebec	1·25	1·40
1024	45 l. Goofy emerging from igloo and *Aurora Borealis*	1·75	2·50
1025	50 l. Goofy as gold prospector and post office, Yukon	2·00	3·00
1026	75 l. Dumbo flying over Niagara Falls ..	3·25	4·50
1019/26	.. .. *Set of* 8	9·25	12·00
MS1027	Two sheets, each 127×101 mm. (a) 100 l. Mickey Mouse driving chuckwagon in Calgary Stampede. (b) 100 l. Mickey Mouse and Goofy as Vikings in Newfoundland. P 14×13½ *Set of 2 sheets*	8·00	12·00

205 *Salamis temora*

206 Cycling

(Des S. Heinmann. Litho Questa)

1987 (4 Aug)–**89.** *Butterflies. T* **205** *and similar vert designs. Multicoloured.* "Sierra Leone" *in black.* A. *Without imprint date. P* 14. B. *Without imprint date. P* 12.

		A		B	
1028	10 c. Type **205**	1·25	40	75	40
1029	20 c. *Stugeta marmorea* ("Iolaus marmorea") ..	1·25	40	1·00	40
1030	40 c. *Graphium ridleyanus*	1·25	40	1·00	40
1031	1 l. *Papilio bromius* ..	1·25	40	1·00	40
1032	2 l. *Iterus zalmoxis* ("Papilio zalmoxis")	1·25	60	1·25	60
1033	3 l. *Cymothoe sangaris* ..	1·50	60	1·25	60
1034	5 l. *Graphium tynderaeus*	1·50	40	1·25	30
1035	10 l. *Graphium policenes* ..	2·50	70	1·25	30
1036	20 l. *Tanuetheira timon* ("Iolaus timon") ..	4·50	2·50	1·50	60
1037	25 l. *Danaus limniace* ..	4·75	2·75	1·50	30
1038	30 l. *Papilio hesperus* ..	4·75	3·50	1·75	65
1039	45 l. *Charaxes smaragdalis*	8·00	4·50	1·75	30
1040	60 l. *Charaxes lucretius* ..	2·00	4·25	2·00	2·25
1041	75 l. *Antanartia delius* ..	2·50	4·25	2·25	2·75
1042	100 l. *Abisara talantus* ..	3·25	6·00	5·50	6·50
1028/42	.. .. *Set of* 15	38·00	28·00	23·00	15·00

C. *With "1989" imprint date. P* 14
D. *With "1989" imprint date. P* 12½×11½

		C		D	
1028	10 c. Type **205**	40	40	70	—
1029	20 c. *Stugeta marmorea* ("Iolaus marmorea") ..	40	40	70	—
1030	40 c. *Graphium ridleyanus*	40	40	70	—
1031	1 l. *Papilio bromius* ..	60	60	1·00	—
1032	2 l. *Iterus zalmoxis* ("Papilio zalmoxis")	75	75	1·50	—
1033	3 l. *Cymothoe sangaris* ..	90	90	1·50	—
1033*e*	3 l. As 40 c.	2·00	2·00	†	
1034*e*	9 l. As 3 l. (No. 1033) ..	2·75	2·75	—	—
1035*e*	12 l. Type **205**	3·00	3·00	—	—
1035*f*	16 l. As 20 c.	3·00	3·00	—	—

E. *With "1989" imprint date. P* 12

		E	
1033*e*	3 l. As 40 c.	—	—

Nos. 1028D/35*f*D show a larger perforation hole on every sixth perforation, both vertically and horizontally.

Dates of issue:—4.8.87, Nos. 1028A/42A; 6.88, Nos. 1028B/37B; 8.88, Nos. 1038B/9B; 10,88, Nos. 1040B/1B; 3.89, No. 1042B; 1989, Nos. 1028C/35*f*C, 1028D/35*f*D, 1033*e*E.

For similar stamps, but with "Sierra Leone" in blue, see Nos. 1658/72.

(Des BG Studio. Litho Questa)

1987 (10 Aug). *Olympic Games, Seoul* (1988) (*1st issue*). *T* **206** *and similar vert designs. Multicoloured. P* 14.

1043	5 l. Type **206**	20	25
1044	10 l. Three Day Eventing	40	50
1045	45 l. Athletics	1·75	2·00
1046	50 l. Tennis	2·00	2·40
1043/6	.. .. *Set of* 4	4·00	4·75
MS1047	73×84 mm. 100 l. Olympic gold medal ..	4·00	4·50

See also Nos. 1137/41.

206*a* "The Quarrel" (Chagall)

206*b* "Apollo 8" Spacecraft (first manned Moon orbit), 1968

(Litho Questa)

1987 (17 Aug). *Birth Centenary of Marc Chagall (artist). T* **206***a and similar multicoloured designs. P* 13½×14.

1048	3 l. Type **206***a*	15	15
1049	5 l. "Rebecca giving Abraham's Servant a Drink"	20	25
1050	10 l. "The Village"	40	45
1051	20 l. "Ida at the Window"	60	65
1052	25 l. "Promenade"	1·00	1·10
1053	45 l. "Peasants"	2·00	2·25
1054	50 l. "Turquoise Plate" (ceramic) ..	2·25	2·25
1055	75 l. "Cemetery Gate"	3·25	3·75
1048/55	.. .. *Set of* 8	9·00	9·75
MS1056	Two sheets, each 110 × 95 mm. (a) 100 l. "Wedding Feast" (stage design) (104 × 78 *mm*). (b) 100 l. "The Falling Angel" (104 × 78 *mm*). Imperf .. .. .. *Set of 2 sheets*	9·00	10·00

(Des W. Wright. Litho Format)

1987 (28 Aug). *Milestones of Transportation. T* **206***b and similar multicoloured designs. P* 15.

1057	3 l. Type **206***b*	15	15
1058	5 l. Blanchard's balloon (first U.S. balloon flight), 1793 (*horiz*)	20	20
1059	10 l. Amelia Earhart's Lockheed Vega 5B (first solo transatlantic flight by woman), 1932 (*horiz*)	40	40
1060	15 l. Vicker's FB-27 Vimy (first non-stop transatlantic flight), 1919 (*horiz*) ..	60	70
1061	20 l. British "Mk 1" tank (first combat tank), 1916 (*horiz*)	80	90
1062	25 l. Vought-Sikorsky VS-300 (first U.S. helicopter flight), 1939 (*horiz*) ..	90	1·00
1063	30 l. Wright brothers' Flyer I (first powered flight), 1903 (*horiz*)	1·10	1·25
1064	35 l. Bleriot XI (first cross Channel flight), 1909 (*horiz*)	1·25	1·40
1065	40 l. Paraplane (first flexible-wing ultralight), 1983	1·50	1·75
1066	50 l. Daimler's first motorcycle, 1885 ..	1·75	2·00
1057/66	.. .. *Set of* 10	7·75	8·75
MS1067	114×83 mm. 100 l. "Rhinegold Express" (first electric railway) (*horiz*)	3·75	5·50

207 Evonne Goolagong

(Des W. Storozuk. Litho Questa)

1987 (4 Sept). *Wimbledon Tennis Champions. T* **207** *and similar horiz designs. Multicoloured. P* 14.

1068	2 l. Type **207**	35	35
1069	5 l. Martina Navratilova	55	55
1070	10 l. Jimmy Connors	85	85
1071	15 l. Bjorn Borg	1·25	1·25
1072	30 l. Boris Becker	2·25	2·25
1073	40 l. John McEnroe	2·50	2·50
1074	50 l. Chris Evert Lloyd	2·75	2·75
1075	75 l. Virginia Wade	3·50	3·50
1068/75	.. .. *Set of* 8	12·50	12·50
MS1076	Two sheets, each 105×75 mm. (a) 100 l. Boris Becker (*different*). (b) 100 l. Steffi Graf *Set of 2 sheets*	13·00	13·00

208 Ducats, *Santa Maria* and Issac Abravanel (financier)

209 Cotton Tree

(Litho Questa)

1987 (11 Sept). *500th Anniv of Discovery of America by Columbus* (1992). *T* **208** *and similar horiz designs. Multicoloured. P* 14.

1077 5 l. Type **208** 70 20
1078 10 l. Astrolabe, *Pinta* and Abraham Zacuto (astronomer) 80 35
1079 45 l. Maravedis (coins), *Nina* and Luis de Santangel (financier) .. .. 2·50 3·00
1080 50 l. Carib and Spaniard with tobacco plant and Luis de Torres (translator) .. 2·75 3·25
1077/80 .. .. *Set of* 4 6·00 6·00
MS1081 101 × 70 mm. 100 l. Christopher Columbus and map .. .. 3·00 3·50

(Des Mary Walters. Litho Questa)

1987 (15 Sept). *Flora and Fauna. T* **209** *and similar horiz designs. Multicoloured. P* 14.

1082 3 l. Type **209** 15 15
1083 5 l. Dwarf Crocodile 35 25
1084 10 l. Kudu 40 35
1085 20 l. Yellowbells 65 65
1086 25 l. Hippopotamus and calf .. .. .. 1·75 1·25
1087 45 l. Comet Orchid .. .. 3·25 2·50
1088 50 l. Baobab Tree .. .. 2·25 2·50
1089 75 l. Elephant and calf .. .. 4·25 5·00
1082/9 .. .. *Set of* 8 11·50 11·50
MS1090 Two sheets, each 100 × 70 mm. (a) 100 l. Bananas, Coconut Palm, Papayas and Pineapple. (b) 100 l. Leopard .. *Set of* 2 *sheets* 5·75 7·00

210 Scouts at Ayers Rock

210a White House

(Des R. Vigurs. Litho Format)

1987 (5 Oct). *World Scout Jamboree, Australia. T* **210** *and similar horiz designs. Multicoloured. P* 15.

1091 5 l. Type **210** 30 20
1092 15 l. Scouts sailing yacht 65 65
1093 40 l. Scouts and Sydney skyline .. .. 1·50 2·50
1094 50 l. Scout, Sydney Harbour Bridge and Opera House .. .. 2·00 2·75
1091/4 .. .. *Set of* 4 4·00 5·50
MS1095 114 × 78 mm. 100 l. Flags of Sierra Leone, Australia and Boy Scouts .. .. 3·00 3·50

Stamps in the design of the 50 l., but with a face value of 1 l. 50, exist from stock dispersed by the liquidator of Format International Security Printers Ltd.

(Des and litho Questa)

1987 (9 Nov). *Bicentenary of U.S. Constitution. T* **210a** *and similar multicoloured designs. P* 14.

1096 5 l. Type **210a** 15 20
1097 10 l. George Washington (Virginia delegate) (*vert*) 30 35
1098 30 l. Patrick Henry (statesman) (*vert*) .. 90 95
1099 65 l. State Seal, New Hampshire .. .. 1·90 2·40
1096/9 .. .. *Set of* 4 3·00 3·50
MS1100 105 × 75 mm. 100 l. John Jay (jurist) (*vert*) .. .. 3·00 3·50

210b Mickey and Minnie Mouse on Space Mountain

(Des Walt Disney Company. Litho Questa)

1987 (9 Dec). *60th Anniv of Mickey Mouse* (*Walt Disney cartoon character*). *T* **210b** *and similar horiz designs showing cartoon characters at Tokyo Disneyland. Multicoloured. P* 14×13½.

1101 20 c. Type **210b** 10 10
1102 40 c. Mickey Mouse at Country Bear Jamboree 10 10
1103 80 c. Mickey Mouse as bandleader and Minnie Mouse, Goofy and Pluto as musicians 10 10
1104 1 l. Goofy, Mickey Mouse and children in canoe and Mark Twain's river boat .. 10 10
1105 2 l. Mickey Mouse, Goofy and Chip n'Dale on Western River Railroad 10 10
1106 3 l. Goofy and Mickey Mouse as Pirates of the Caribbean 15 15
1107 10 l. Mickey Mouse, Goofy and children aboard Big Thunder Mountain train .. 55 55
1108 20 l. Mickey Mouse, Morty and Ferdie in boat and Goofy on flying carpet .. 1·25 1·50
1109 30 l. Mickey and Minnie Mouse in kimonos at Disneyland entrance .. .. 1·75 2·00
1101/9 .. .. *Set of* 9 3·50 4·00
MS1110 127 × 102 mm. 65 l. Mickey and Minnie Mouse in kimonos at Cinderella's Castle .. 4·25 4·00

211 "The Annunciation" (detail) (Titian)

211a Wedding of Princess Elizabeth and Duke of Edinburgh, 1947

(Litho Questa)

1987 (21 Dec). *Christmas. Religious Paintings by Titian. T* **211** *and similar multicoloured designs. P* 14.

1111 2 l. Type **211** 20 10
1112 10 l. "Madonna and Child with Saints" .. 60 35
1113 20 l. "Madonna and Child with Saints Ulfus and Brigid" .. .. 1·10 1·25
1114 35 l. "The Madonna of the Cherries" .. 1·90 2·75
1111/14 .. .. *Set of* 4 3·50 4·00
MS1115 70 × 100 mm. 65 l. "The Pesaro Altarpiece" (*vert*) .. .. 3·50 4·00

(Des and litho Questa)

1988 (15 Feb). *Royal Ruby Wedding. T* **211a** *and similar vert designs. P* 14.

1116 2 l. deep brown, black and grey 10 10
1117 3 l. multicoloured 10 10
1118 10 l. deep brown, black and orange 30 35
1119 50 l. multicoloured .. .. 2·00 2·50
1116/19 .. .. *Set of* 4 2·25 2·75
MS1120 76 × 100 mm. 65 l. multicoloured .. 2·25 2·50

Designs:—3 l. Prince Charles' christening photograph, 1949; 10 l. Queen Elizabeth II with Prince Charles and Princess Anne, *c.* 1951; 50 l. Queen Elizabeth, *c.* 1960; 65 l. Wedding photograph, 1947.

212 *Russula cyanoxantha*

213 Golden Pheasant Panchax

(Des L. Nelson. Litho Questa)

1988 (29 Feb). *Fungi. T* **212** *and similar vert designs. Multicoloured. P* 14.

1121 3 l. Type **212** 45 30
1122 10 l. *Lycoperdon perlatum* .. .. .. 1·10 70
1123 20 l. *Lactarius deliciosus* .. .. .. 1·90 2·00
1124 30 l. *Boletus edulis* .. .. 2·25 2·75
1121/4 .. .. *Set of* 4 5·25 5·25
MS1125 100 × 70 mm. 65 l. *Amanita muscaria* 4·00 4·50

(Des Mary Walters. Litho Format)

1988 (13 Apr). *Fishes of Sierra Leone. T* **213** *and similar horiz designs. Multicoloured. P* 15.

1126 3 l. Type **213** 10 15
1127 10 l. Banded Panchax 20 30
1128 20 l. Jewel Cichlid 40 75
1129 35 l. Freshwater Butterflyfish .. .. .. 75 1·40
1126/9 .. .. *Set of* 4 1·25 2·40
MS1130 99×69 mm. 65 l. Long-finned Tetra .. 2·25 3·00

 OLYMPHILEX' 88

(**213a**)

1988 (19 Apr). *Stamp Exhibitions. Nos.* 1016, 1072 *and* 1079 *optd as T* **213a** *with various emblems.*

1131 25 l. *Freedom*, 1980 (optd "INDEPENDENCE 40, Israel") .. .. 1·10 1·40
1132 30 l. Boris Becker (optd Type **213a**) .. 1·25 1·75
1133 45 l. Maravedis (coins), *Nina* and Luis de Santangel (financier) (optd "PRAGA 88", Prague) .. .. 1·75 2·25
1131/3 .. .. *Set of* 3 3·75 4·75

214 Hands holding Coffee Beans and Woman with Cocoa

215 Basketball

(Des L. Lamm. Litho Questa)

1988 (3 May). *International Fund for Agricultural Development. T* **214** *and similar horiz designs. Multicoloured. P* 14.

1134 3 l. Type **214** 20 20
1135 15 l. Tropical fruits and man climbing palm tree 70 80
1136 25 l. Sheaf of rice and harvesters .. .. 1·25 1·50
1134/6 .. .. *Set of* 3 1·90 2·25

(Des L. Fried. Litho Questa)

1988 (15 June). *Olympic Games, Seoul (2nd issue). T* **215** *and similar vert designs. Multicoloured. P* 14.

1137 3 l. Type **215** 10 10
1138 10 l. Judo 30 35
1139 15 l. Gymnastics 45 55
1140 40 l. Synchronized swimming .. .. .. 1·25 1·75
1137/40 .. .. *Set of* 4 2·00 2·50
MS1141 73 × 101 mm. 65 l. Sierra Leone athlete 1·90 2·50

216 Swallow-tailed Bee Eater

217 *Aureol* (liner)

(Des L. Nelson. Litho Questa)

1988 (25 June). *Birds. T* **216** *and similar vert designs. Multicoloured. P* 14.

1142 3 l. Type **216** 65 65
1143 5 l. Double-toothed Barbet 80 80
1144 8 l. African Golden Oriole .. .. .. 1·00 1·00
1145 10 l. Red Bishop .. .. 1·00 1·00
1146 12 l. Red-billed Shrike .. .. 1·00 1·00
1147 20 l. European Bee Eater .. .. 1·25 1·25
1148 35 l. Common Gonolek ("Barbary Shrike") 1·90 1·90
1149 40 l. Western Black-headed Oriole .. .. 2·00 2·00
1142/9 .. .. *Set of* 8 8·75 8·75
MS1150 Two sheets, each 111 × 82 mm. (a) 65 l. Purple Heron. (b) 65 l. Saddle-bill Stork *Set of* 2 *sheets* 3·75 4·50

(Des D. Miller. Litho Questa)

1988 (1 July). *Ships. T* **217** *and similar horiz designs. Multicoloured. P* 14.

1151 3 l. Type **217** 50 30
1152 10 l. *Dunkwa* (freighter) .. .. 1·25 80
1153 15 l. *Melampus* (container ship) .. .. 1·75 1·60
1154 30 l. *Dumbaia* (freighter) .. .. 2·50 3·00
1151/4 .. .. *Set of* 4 5·50 5·00
MS1155 95 × 95 mm. 65 l. Loading container ship, Freetown .. .. 2·25 2·50

(Litho Questa)

1988 (22 Aug). *500th Birth Anniv of Titian (artist). Vert designs as T* **186a** *of Lesotho showing paintings. Multicoloured. P* 13½×14.

1156 1 l. "The Concert" (detail) 10 10
1157 2 l. "Philip II of Spain" 15 15
1158 3 l. "Saint Sebastian" (detail) 20 20
1159 5 l. "Martyrdom of St. Peter Martyr" .. 30 30
1160 15 l. "St. Jerome" 75 85
1161 20 l. "St. Mark enthroned with Saints" .. 90 1·10
1162 25 l. "Portrait of a Young Man" .. .. 1·10 1·40
1163 30 l. "St. Jerome in Penitence" .. .. 1·25 1·50
1156/63 .. .. *Set of* 8 4·25 5·00
MS1164 Two sheets, each 110 × 95 mm. (a) 50 l. "Self Portrait". (b) 50 l. "Orpheus and Eurydice" *Set of* 2 *sheets* 4·00 4·50

218 Sikorsky S-58 Helicopter lowering "Mercury" Capsule to Flight Deck

219 Famine Relief Convoy crossing Desert

(Des W. Hanson. Litho B.D.T.)

1988 (26 Sept). *25th Death Anniv of John F. Kennedy (American statesman). U.S. Space Achievements. T* **218** *and similar horiz designs. Multicoloured. P* 14.

1165 3 l. Type **218** 45 15
1166 5 l. *Liberty Bell* 7 capsule descending (*vert*) 45 20
1167 15 l. Launch of first manned American capsule (*vert*) 70 70
1168 40 l. *Freedom* 7 orbiting Earth .. .. 1·50 2·00
1165/8 .. .. *Set of* 4 2·75 2·75
MS1169 98 × 69 mm. 65 l. President Kennedy and quotation .. .. 1·90 2·25

(Des J. Genzo. Litho B.D.T.)

1988 (1 Nov). *125th Anniv of International Red Cross. T* **219** *and similar multicoloured designs. P* 14.
1170 3 l. Type **219** 40 40
1171 10 l. Rifle and map of Battle of Solferino, 1859 .. .. 1·50 90
1172 20 l. World War II hospital ship in Pacific 2·00 2·00
1173 40 l. Red Cross tent and World War I German biplanes .. .. 3·00 3·25
1170/3 .. .. *Set of* 4 6·25 6·00
MS1174 100 × 70 mm. 65 l. Henri Dunant (founder), Alfred Nobel and Peace Prize scroll (*horiz*) .. .. 2·40 3·00

(Des Walt Disney Company. Litho Questa)

1988 (1 Dec). *Christmas. "Mickey's Christmas Dance". Vert designs as T* **171a** *of Lesotho showing Walt Disney cartoon characters. Multicoloured. P* 13½×14.
1175 10 l. Donald Duck's nephews playing as band 70 80
a. Sheetlet. Nos. 1175/82 .. .. 5·00
1176 10 l. Clarabelle 70 80
1177 10 l. Goofy 70 80
1178 10 l. Scrooge McDuck and Grandma Duck 70 80
1179 10 l. Donald Duck 70 80
1180 10 l. Daisy Duck 70 80
1181 10 l. Minnie Mouse 70 80
1182 10 l. Mickey Mouse 70 80
1175/82 .. .. *Set of* 8 5·00 5·50
MS1183 Two sheets, each 127 × 102 mm. (a) 70 l. Mickey Mouse dancing the Charleston. (b) 70 l. Mickey Mouse jiving .. .. *Set of 2 sheets* 6·50 6·50
Nos. 1175/82 were printed together, *se-tenant* as a composite design, in sheetlets of eight.

220 "Adoration of the Magi" (detail)

GRAND SLAM WINNER
(221)

(Litho Questa)

1988 (15 Dec). *Christmas. Religious Paintings by Rubens. T* **220** *and similar vert designs. Multicoloured. P* 13½ × 14.
1184 3 l. Type **220** 15 15
1185 3 l. 60, "Adoration of the Shepherds" (detail) 15 15
1186 5 l. "Adoration of the Magi" (detail) .. 25 25
1187 10 l. "Adoration of the Shepherds" (different detail) 40 40
1188 20 l. "Virgin and Child surrounded by Flowers" 75 75
1189 40 l. "St. Gregory the Great and Other Saints" (detail) .. .. .. 1·60 1·75
1190 60 l. "Adoration of the Magi" (detail) .. 2·25 2·75
1191 80 l. "Madonna and Child with Saints" (detail) .. .. 2·75 3·25
1184/91 .. .. *Set of* 8 7·50 8·50
MS1192 Two sheets, each 76 × 113 mm. (a) 100 l. "Virgin and Child enthroned with Saints". (b) 100 l. "St. Gregory the Great and Other Saints" *Set of 2 sheets* 7·00 9·00

1989 (16 Jan). *Steffi Graf's "Grand Slam" Tennis Victories. No.* **MS**1076b *optd* "GOLD MEDALIST" (*No.* **MS**1193e) *or with T* **221** (*others*), *each with different inscription on sheet margin, all in gold.*
MS1193 105×75 mm. 100 l. Steffi Graf. (a) Optd "AUSTRALIAN OPEN JANUARY 11–24, 1988 GRAF v EVERET". (b) Optd "FRENCH OPEN MAY 23–JUNE 5, 1988 GRAF v ZVEREVA". (c) Optd "WIMBLEDON JUNE 20–JULY 4, 1988 GRAF v NAVRATILOVA". (d) Optd "U.S. OPEN AUGUST 29–SEPTEMBER 11, 1988 GRAF v SABATINI". (e) Optd "SEOUL OLYMPICS 1988 GRAF v SABATINI" *Set of 5 sheets* 16·00 15·00
Each marginal overprint includes score of match involved. No. **MS**1193a is overprinted "EVERET" in error for "EVERT".

222 Brazil v. Sweden, 1958

223 Decathlon (Gold, C. Schenk, East Germany)

(Des J. McDaniel. Litho B.D.T.)

1989 (28 Apr). *World Cup Football Championship, Italy* (1*st issue*). *T* **222** *and similar vert designs, each showing action from previous World Cup finals. Multicoloured. P* 14.
1194 3 l. Type **222** 40 30
1195 6 l. West Germany v. Hungary, 1954 .. 50 40
1196 8 l. England v. West Germany, 1966 .. 60 45
1197 10 l. Argentina v. Netherlands, 1978 .. 70 50
1198 12 l. Brazil v. Czechoslovakia, 1962 .. 75 75
1199 20 l. West Germany v. Netherlands, 1974 1·00 1·00
1200 30 l. Italy v. West Germany, 1982 .. 1·40 1·60
1201 40 l. Brazil v. Italy, 1970 .. .. 1·75 1·90
1194/201 .. .. *Set of* 8 6·25 6·25
MS1202 Two sheets, each 73×104 mm. (a) 100 l. Argentina v. West Germany, 1986. (b) 100 l. Uruguay v. Brazil, 1950 .. *Set of 2 sheets* 6·75 6·75
See also Nos. 1455/74.

(Des L. Fried. Litho B.D.T.)

1989 (28 Apr). *Olympic Medal Winners, Seoul* (1988). *T* **223** *and similar horiz designs. Multicoloured. P* 14.
1203 3 l. Type **223** 50 30
1204 6 l. Men's heavyweight judo (Gold, H. Saito, Japan) 60 40
1205 10 l. Women's cycle road race (Silver, J. Niehaus, West Germany) 80 50
1206 15 l. Men's single sculls (Gold, T. Lange, East Germany) .. .. .. 1·00 80
1207 20 l. Men's 50 metres freestyle swimming (Gold, M. Biondi, U.S.A.) .. .. 1·10 1·00
1208 30 l. Men's 100 metres (Gold, C. Lewis, U.S.A.) .. .. 1·50 1·50
1209 40 l. Dressage (Gold, West Germany) .. 1·60 1·75
1210 50 l. Greco-Roman wrestling (57 kg) (Gold, A. Sike, Hungary) .. .. .. 1·75 1·90
1203/10 .. .. *Set of* 8 8·00 7·50
MS1211 Two sheets, each 70×100 mm. (a) 100 l. Olympic gold medal. (b) 100 l. Olympic torch and rings .. .. *Set of 2 sheets* 6·75 6·75

224 Map of Union States, Mail Lorry and Post Office

(Des J. Genzo. Litho B.D.T.)

1989 (19 May). *15th Anniv of Mano River Union. T* **224** *and similar horiz designs. Multicoloured. P* 14.
1212 1 l. Type **224** 10 10
1213 3 l. Map of West Africa and Presidents Momoh, Conte and Doe 20 20
1214 10 l. Construction of Freetown–Monrovia Highway 60 60
1212/14 .. .. *Set of* 3 80 80
MS1215 96×68 mm. 15 l. Presidents signing anniversary meeting communique .. .. 1·00 1·00

225 *Richard III*

SIERRA LEONE Le3

226 Centenary Logo

(Des G. Vasarhelyi. Litho B.D.T.)

1989 (30 May). *425th Birth Anniv of Shakespeare. T* **225** *and similar horiz designs. Multicoloured. P* 13.
1216 15 l. Type **225** 60 60
a. Sheetlet. Nos. 1216/23 .. .. 4·25
1217 15 l. *Othello* (Iago) 60 60
1218 15 l. *Two Gentlemen of Verona* 60 60
1219 15 l. *Macbeth* (Lady Macbeth) 60 60
1220 15 l. *Hamlet* 60 60
1221 15 l. *The Taming of the Shrew* 60 60
1222 15 l. *The Merry Wives of Windsor* 60 60
1223 15 l. *Henry IV* (Sir John Falstaff) 60 60
1224 15 l. *Macbeth* (The Witches) 60 60
a. Sheetlet. Nos. 1224/31 .. .. 4·25
1225 15 l. *Romeo and Juliet* 60 60
1226 15 l. *Merchant of Venice* 60 60
1227 15 l. *As You Like It* 60 60
1228 15 l. *The Taming of the Shrew* (banquet scene) 60 60
1229 15 l. *King Lear* 60 60
1230 15 l. *Othello* (Othello and Desdemona) .. 60 60
1231 15 l. *Henry IV* (Justice Shallow) 60 60
1216/31 .. .. *Set of* 16 8·50 8·50
MS1232 Two sheets, each 117×82 mm. (a) 100 l. Shakespeare and arms (49×36 *mm*). (b) 100 l. Shakespeare (49×36 *mm*) .. *Set of 2 sheets* 8·00 8·00
Nos. 1216/23 and 1224/31 were each printed together, *se-tenant*, in sheetlets of eight stamps and one central stamp-size label.

(Litho Questa)

1989 (8 June). *Centenary of Ahmadiyya Muslim Society. P* 14.
1233 **226** 3 l. brownish black and new blue .. 30 30

(Litho Questa)

1989 (3 July). *Japanese Art* (1*st series*). *Paintings by Seiho. Multicoloured designs as T* **187a** *of Lesotho. P* 14×13½ (3, 10, 12, 40 *l.*) *or* 13½×14 (*others*).
1234 3 l. "Lapping Waves" 20 20
1235 6 l. "Hazy Moon" (*vert*) 30 30
1236 8 l. "Passing Spring" (*vert*) 30 30
1237 10 l. "Mackerels" 30 30
1238 12 l. "Calico Cat" 30 30
1239 30 l. "The First Time to be a Model" (*vert*) 60 70
1240 40 l. "Kingly Lion" 80 90
1241 75 l. "After a Shower" (*vert*) .. .. 1·40 1·75
1234/41 .. .. *Set of* 8 3·75 4·25
MS1242 Two sheets, each 102×77 mm. (a) 150 l. "Dozing in the midst of all the Chirping" (detail) (*vert*). P 13½×14. (b) 150 l. "Domesticated Monkeys and Rabbits" (detail). P 14×13½ *Set of 2 sheets* 6·50 7·00
Nos. 1234/41 were each printed in sheetlets of 10 containing two horizontal or vertical strips of 5 stamps separated by printed labels commemorating Emperor Hirohito.
See also Nos. 1321/51.

227 Robespierre and Bastille

(Des Design Element. Litho B.D.T.)

1989 (13 July). *"Philexfrance 89" International Stamp Exhibition, Paris, and Bicentenary of French Revolution. T* **227** *and similar multicoloured designs. P* 14.
1243 6 l. Type **227** 45 35
1244 20 l. Danton and Louvre 90 80
1245 45 l. Queen Marie Antoinette and Notre Dame .. .. 1·40 1·25
1246 80 l. Louis XVI and Palace of Versailles .. 2·00 2·75
1243/6 .. .. *Set of* 4 4·25 4·75
MS1247 77×107 mm. 150 l. Celebrating crowd, Paris (*vert*) .. .. 3·25 4·00

228 "Sputnik" Satellite in Orbit, 1957

SIERRA LEONE Le3

229 *Bulbophyllum barbigerum*

(Des G. Vasarhelyi. Litho B.D.T.)

1989 (20 July). *History of Space Exploration. T* **228** *and similar horiz designs. P* 14.
1248/301 10 l.×27, 15 l.×27 multicoloured *Set of* 54 22·00 23·00
MS1302 Three sheets, each 112×90 mm. 100 l. ×3 multicoloured .. .. *Set of 3 sheets* 12·00 13·00
Nos. 1248/301 were issued as six sheetlets, each of nine different designs.

(Des W. Hanson Studio. Litho B.D.T.)

1989 (8 Sept). *Orchids of Sierra Leone. T* **229** *and similar vert designs. Multicoloured. P* 14.
1303 3 l. Type **229** 55 40
1304 6 l. *Bulbophyllum falcatum* 85 60
1305 12 l. *Habenaria macrara* .. .. .. 1·25 90
1306 20 l. *Eurychone rothchildiana* .. .. 1·60 1·40
1307 50 l. *Calyptrochilum christyanum* .. 2·25 2·25
1308 60 l. *Bulbophyllum distans* .. .. 2·50 2·75
1309 70 l. *Eulophia guineensis* .. .. .. 2·50 2·75
1310 80 l. *Diaphananthe pellucida* .. .. 2·75 3·25
1303/10 .. .. *Set of* 8 13·00 13·00
MS1311 Two sheets, each 112×80 mm. (a) 100 l. *Cyrtorchis arcuata* and Pagoda, Kew Gardens. (b) 100 l. *Eulophia cucullata* .. *Set of 2 sheets* 14·00 14·00

230 *Salamis temora*

(Des Mary Walters. Litho B.D.T.)

1989 (11 Sept). *Butterflies. T* **230** *and similar multicoloured designs. P* 14.
1312 6 l. Type **230** 75 75
1313 12 l. *Pseudacraea lucretia* .. .. .. 1·10 1·10
1314 18 l. *Charaxes boueti* (*vert*) .. .. 1·40 1·40
1315 30 l. *Graphium antheus* (*vert*) .. .. 2·00 2·00
1316 40 l. *Colotis protomedia* .. .. .. 2·25 2·25
1317 60 l. *Asterope pechueli* (*vert*) .. .. 2·75 2·75
1318 72 l. *Coenyra aurantiaca* .. .. .. 3·00 3·00
1319 80 l. *Precis octavia* (*vert*) .. .. 3·00 3·00
1312/19 .. .. *Set of* 8 14·50 14·50
MS1320 Two sheets, each 100×70 mm. (a) 100 l. *Charaxes cithaeron* (*vert*). (b) 100 l. *Euphaedra themis* .. .. *Set of 2 sheets* 14·00 14·00

(Litho Questa)

1989 (13 Nov). *Japanese Art (2nd series). Paintings by Hiroshige of "The Fifty-three Stations on the Tokaido Road". Horiz designs as T* **187***a of Lesotho. Multicoloured. P* 14×13½.

1321 25 l. "Ferry-boat to Kawasaki" 70 70
1322 25 l. "The Hilly Town of Hodogaya" .. 70 70
1323 25 l. "Lute Players at Fujisawa" 70 70
1324 25 l. "Mild Rainstorm at Oiso" 70 70
1325 25 l. "Lake Ashi and Mountains of Hakone" 70 70
1326 25 l. "Twilight at Numazu" 70 70
1327 25 l. "Mount Fuji from Hara" 70 70
1328 25 l. "Samurai Children riding through Yoshiwara" 70 70
1329 25 l. "Mountain Pass at Yui" 70 70
1330 25 l. "Harbour at Ejiri" 70 70
1331 25 l. "Halt at Fujieda" 70 70
1332 25 l. "Misty Kanaya on the Oi River" .. 70 70
1333 25 l. "The Bridge to Kakegawa" 70 70
1334 25 l. "Teahouse at Fukuroi" 70 70
1335 25 l. "The Ford at Mistuke" 70 70
1336 25 l. "Coolies warming themselves at Hamamatsu" 70 70
1337 25 l. "Imakiri Ford at Maisaka" 70 70
1338 25 l. "Pacific Ocean from Shirasuka" .. 70 70
1339 25 l. "Futakawa Street-singers" 70 70
1340 25 l. "Repairing Yoshida Castle" 70 70
1341 25 l. "The Inn at Akasaka" 70 70
1342 25 l. "The Bridge to Okazaki" 70 70
1343 25 l. "Samurai's Wife entering Narumi" .. 70 70
1344 25 l. "Harbour at Kuwana" 70 70
1345 25 l. "Autumn in Ishiyakushi" 70 70
1346 25 l. "Snowfall at Kameyama" 70 70
1347 25 l. "The Frontier-station of Seki" .. 70 70
1348 25 l. "Teahouse at Sakanoshita" 70 70
1349 25 l. "Kansai Houses at Minakushi" .. 70 70
1350 25 l. "Kusatsu Station" 70 70
1321/50 .. .. *Set of* 30 19·00 19·00

MS1351 Two sheets, each 102×75 mm. (a) 120 l. "Nihom Bridge, Edo". (b) 120 l. "Sanjo Bridge, Kyoto" .. .. *Set of 2 sheets* 6·50 7·00

The English captions of the two miniature sheets of No. **MS**1351 are transposed. The sheet showing the Nihom Bridge, Edo, has a group of fishmongers in the left foreground.

(Des Design Element. Litho Questa)

1989 (17 Nov). *"World Stamp Expo '89" International Stamp Exhibition, Washington (1st issue). Landmarks of Washington. Sheet 78×61 mm containing horiz design as T* **193***a of Lesotho. Multicoloured. P* 14.

MS1352 100 l. Jefferson Memorial .. .. 1·00 1·50

231 Formosan Sika Deer

(Des J. Genzo. Litho B.D.T.)

1989 (29 Nov). *"World Stamp Expo '89" International Stamp Exhibition, Washington (2nd issue). Endangered Fauna. T* **231** *and similar multicoloured designs. P* 14.

1353 6 l. Humpback Whale 50 40
1354 9 l. Type **231** 40 40
1355 16 l. Spanish Lynx 65 60
1356 20 l. Goitred Gazelle 60 60
1357 30 l. Japanese Sea Lion 65 65
1358 50 l. Long-eared Owl .. .. .. 1·50 1·25
1359 70 l. Lady Amherst's ("Chinese Copper") Pheasant .. .. 1·50 1·50
1360 100 l. Siberian Tiger .. .. .. 2·25 2·50
1353/60 .. .. *Set of* 8 7·25 7·25

MS1361 Two sheets, each 103×75 mm. (a) 150 l. Mauritius Kestrel (*vert*). (b) 150 l. Japanese Crested Ibis (*vert*) .. .. *Set of 2 sheets* 7·00 7·00

(Des Walt Disney Co. Litho Questa)

1989 (18 Dec). *Christmas. Horiz designs as T* **73** *of St. Vincent Grenadines showing Walt Disney cartoon characters with cars. Multicoloured. P* 14×13½.

1362 3 l. Mickey Mouse and Goofy in Rolls-Royce "Phantom II Roadstar", 1934 55 30
1363 6 l. Mickey and Minnie Mouse in Mercedes-Benz "500K", 1935 .. 70 40
1364 10 l. Mickey and Minnie Mouse with Jaguar "SS-100", 1938 .. .. 80 45
1365 12 l. Mickey Mouse and Goofy with U.S. army jeep, 1941 .. .. .. 90 55
1366 20 l. Mickey and Minnie Mouse with Buick Roadmaster Sedan "Model 91", 1937 1·25 90
1367 30 l. Mickey Mouse driving 1948 Tucker 1·50 1·25
1368 40 l. Mickey and Minnie Mouse in Alfa Romeo, 1933 .. .. .. 1·60 1·40
1369 50 l. Mickey and Minnie Mouse with 1937 Cord .. .. 1·75 1·60
1362/9 .. .. *Set of* 8 8·25 6·00

MS1370 Two sheets, each 127×101 mm. (a) 100 l. Mickey in Fiat Topolino, 1938. (b) 100 l. Mickey Mouse with gifts and Pontiac "Model 401", 1931 .. .. .. *Set of 2 sheets* 5·00 5·50

(Litho Questa)

1989 (22 Dec). *Christmas. Paintings by Rembrandt. Vert designs as T* **193***b of Lesotho. Multicoloured. P* 14.

1371 3 l. "The Adoration of the Magi" .. 40 30
1372 6 l. "The Holy Family with a Cat" .. 50 40
1373 10 l. "The Holy Family with Angels" .. 60 45
1374 15 l. "Simeon in the Temple" 75 55
1375 30 l. "The Circumcision" .. .. 1·25 1·10
1376 90 l. "The Holy Family" .. .. 2·25 2·50
1377 100 l. "The Visitation" .. .. .. 2·25 2·50
1378 120 l. "The Flight into Egypt" .. .. 2·50 2·75
1371/8 .. .. *Set of* 8 9·50 9·50

MS1379 Two sheets, each 70×95 mm. (a) 150 l. "The Adoration of the Shepherds" (detail). (b) 150 l. "The Presentation of Jesus in the Temple" (detail) .. .. *Set of 2 sheets* 4·00 4·50

232 Johann Kepler (astronomer)

(Des G. Vasarhelyi. Litho Questa)

1990 (15 Jan). *Exploration of Mars. T* **232** *and similar horiz designs showing astronomers, spacecraft and Martian landscapes. P* 14.

1380/1415 175 l. × 36 multicoloured .. *Set of* 36 60·00 70·00

MS1416 Two sheets, each 105×85 mm. (a) 150 l. The "Face" on Mars. (b) 150 l. Section of space station .. .. *Set of 2 sheets* 7·50 8·00

Nos. 1380/1415 were issued as four sheetlets each of nine different designs.

232*a* Dolittle's North American B-25 Mitchell *Ruptured Duck*, 1942

(Des J. Batchelor. Litho Questa)

1990 (5 Feb). *50th Anniv of Second World War. American Aircraft. T* **232***a and similar horiz designs. Multicoloured. P* 14.

1417 1 l. Type **232***a* 10 10
1418 2 l. Consolidated B-24 Liberator .. 15 10
1419 3 l. Douglas A20J Boston attacking Japanese convoy, Bismark Sea, 1943 15 10
1420 9 l. Lockheed P-38 Lightning 35 25
1421 12 l. Martin B-26 Marauder 45 30
1422 16 l. Two Boeing B-17F Flying Fortress bombers 60 50
1423 50 l. North American B-25D Mitchell bomber .. .. 1·50 1·50
1424 80 l. Boeing B-29 Superfortress .. 2·00 2·25
1425 90 l. Boeing B-17G Flying Fortress bomber .. .. 2·00 2·25
1426 100 l. Boeing B-29 Superfortress *Enola Gay* .. .. 2·25 2·50
1417/26 .. .. *Set of* 10 8·50 8·75

MS1427 Two sheets, each 106×77 mm. (a) 150 l. North American B-25 Mitchell *Ruptured Duck* taking off from U.S.S. *Hornet*, 1942. (b) 150 l. Boeing B-17G Flying Fortress of 447th Bomber Group .. .. *Set of 2 sheets* 6·00 6·50

233 Mickey Mouse at Bauxite Mine

234 Olivier as Antony in *Antony and Cleopatra*, 1951

(Des Walt Disney Co. Litho Questa)

1990 (23 Apr). *Sierra Leone Sites and Scenes. T* **233** *and similar multicoloured designs, each showing Walt Disney cartoon characters. P* 14×13½.

1428 3 l. Type **233** 15 15
1429 6 l. Scrooge McDuck panning for gold .. 15 15
1430 10 l. Minnie Mouse at Lungi Airport .. 20 20
1431 12 l. Mickey Mouse at Old Fourah Bay College 25 20
1432 16 l. Mickey Mouse mining bauxite .. 35 25
1433 20 l. Huey, Dewey and Louie harvesting rice 40 30
1434 30 l. Mickey and Minnie Mouse admire the Freetown Cotton Tree .. 50 40
1435 100 l. Mickey Mouse flying over Rutile Mine .. .. 1·75 1·90
1436 200 l. Mickey Mouse fishing at Goderich .. 2·50 3·00
1437 225 l. Mickey and Minnie Mouse at Bintumani Hotel .. .. 2·50 3·00
1428/37 .. .. *Set of* 10 8·00 8·50

MS1438 Two sheets, each 130×100 mm. (a) 250 l. Dwarfs with diamonds. P 14×13½. (b) 250 l. Mickey and Minnie Mouse at King Jimmy Market (*vert*). P 13½×14 .. *Set of 2 sheets* 6·00 6·50

(Des J. Iskowitz. Litho Questa)

1990 (27 Apr). *Sir Laurence Olivier (actor) Commemoration. T* **234** *and similar vert designs. Multicoloured. P* 14.

1439 3 l. Type **234** 30 20
1440 9 l. As King Henry V in *Henry V*, 1943 40 30
1441 16 l. As Oedipus in *Oedipus*, 1945 .. 55 35
1442 20 l. As Heathcliffe in *Wuthering Heights*, 1939 .. .. 60 40
1443 30 l. As Szell in *Marathon Man*, 1976 .. 70 55
1444 70 l. As Othello in *Othello*, 1964 .. 1·25 1·40
1445 175 l. As Michael in *Beau Geste*, 1929 .. 2·25 2·50
1446 200 l. As King Richard III in *Richard III*, 1956 .. .. 2·50 2·75
1439/46 .. .. *Set of* 8 7·75 7·75

MS1447 Two sheets, each 98×68 mm. (a) 250 l. As Hamlet in *Hamlet*, 1947. (b) 250 l. As Sir Hugh Dowding in *The Battle of Britain*, 1969 *Set of 2 sheets* 6·50 6·50

235 Penny Black **236** Cameroons World Cup Team

(Des M. Pollard. Litho Questa)

1990 (3 May). *150th Anniv of the Penny Black. P* 14×13½.

1448 **235** 50 l. deep ultramarine .. .. 1·50 1·50
1449 100 l. purple-brown .. .. 2·25 2·25

MS1450 145×106 mm. **235** 250 l. black .. 3·50 4·00

(Des Young Phillips Studio. Litho Questa)

1990 (11 May). *World Cup Football Championship, Italy (2nd issue). Finalists. T* **236** *and similar horiz designs. Multicoloured. P* 14×13½.

1451/74 15 l. × 8 (Type **236**, Colombia, Costa Rica, Egypt, Rumania, South Korea, U.A.E., Yugoslavia), 30 l. × 8 (Austria, Belgium, Czechoslovakia, Netherlands, Scotland, Sweden, Uruguay, U.S.S.R.), 45 l. × 8 (Argentina, Brazil, England, Ireland, Italy, Spain, U.S.A., West Germany) .. .. .. *Set of* 24 14·00 15·00

No. 1452 is inscribed "COLUMBIA" in error.

Each design of Nos. 1451/74 was issued in separate sheetlets of 8 stamps with a central label showing the World Cup and Championship logo.

237 Great Crested Grebe

(Des Mary Walters. Litho Questa)

1990 (4 June). *Birds. T* **237** *and similar horiz designs. Multicoloured. P* 14.

1475 3 l. Type **237** 20 20
1476 6 l. Green Wood Hoopoe 25 25
1477 10 l. African Jacana 30 30
1478 12 l. Avocet 35 35
1479 20 l. Peters's Finfoot 40 40
1480 80 l. Glossy Ibis .. .. 1·25 1·50
1481 150 l. Hammerkop .. .. .. 1·75 2·00
1482 200 l. Black-throated Honeyguide .. 2·00 2·50
1475/82 .. .. *Set of* 8 6·00 6·75

MS1483 Two sheets, each 100×70 mm. (a) 250 l. African Palm Swift. (b) 250 l. Painted Snipe *Set of 2 sheets* 7·00 7·50

(Des Walt Disney Co. Litho Questa)

1990 (6 June). *"Stamp World London 90" International Stamp Exhibition. British Costumes. Multicoloured designs as T* **239***a of Maldive Islands showing Walt Disney cartoon characters. P* 13½×14.

1484 3 l. Mickey Mouse as a Yeoman Warder (*vert*) 15 15
1485 6 l. Scrooge McDuck as a lamplighter (*vert*) 15 15
1486 12 l. Goofy as a medieval knight (*vert*) .. 20 20
1487 15 l. Clarabelle as Anne Boleyn (*vert*) .. 20 20
1488 75 l. Minnie Mouse as Queen Elizabeth I (*vert*) .. .. 1·75 1·75
1489 100 l. Donald Duck as a chimney sweep (*vert*) .. .. 2·00 2·00
1490 125 l. Pete as King Henry VIII (*vert*) .. 2·25 2·25
1491 150 l. Clarabelle, Minnie Mouse and Daisy Duck as May dancers (*vert*) .. 2·25 2·25
1484/91 .. .. *Set of* 8 8·00 8·00

MS1492 Two sheets, each 127×102 mm. (a) 250 l. Donald Duck as a lawyer (*vert*). P 13½×14. (b) 250 l. Minnie Mouse as Queen Boadicea. P 14×13½. .. .. *Set of 2 sheets* 6·50 7·00

(Des Young Phillips Studio. Litho Questa)

1990 (5 July). *90th Birthday of Queen Elizabeth the Queen Mother. Vert designs as T* **198a** *of Lesotho showing portraits. 1980–89. Multicoloured. P* 14.

1493 75 l. Queen Mother on Remembrance Sunday .. .. 85 1·00
a. Strip of 3. Nos. 1493/5 .. .. 2·25
1494 75 l. Queen Mother in yellow hat .. .. 85 1·00
1495 75 l. Waving to crowds on 85th birthday .. 85 1·00
1493/5 .. .. *Set of* 3 2·25 2·75
MS1496 90×75 mm. 250 l. As No. 1495 .. 2·25 2·50

Nos. 1493/5 were printed together, horizontally and vertically *se-tenant*, in sheetlets of 9 (3×3).

Nos. 1493/6 exist imperforate from a limited printing.

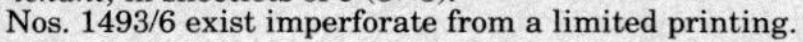

238 Golden Cat

239 Rabbit

(Des S. Barlowe. Litho Questa)

1990 (24 Sept). *Wildlife. T* **238** *and similar multicoloured designs. P* 14.

1497 25 l. Type **238** 45 45
a. Sheetlet. Nos. 1497/1514 .. .. 7·00
1498 25 l. White-backed Night Heron 45 45
1499 25 l. Bateleur 45 45
1500 25 l. Marabou Stork 45 45
1501 25 l. White-faced Whistling Duck .. 45 45
1502 25 l. Aardvark 45 45
1503 25 l. Royal Antelope 45 45
1504 25 l. Pygmy Hippopotamus 45 45
1505 25 l. Leopard 45 45
1506 25 l. Sacred Ibis 45 45
1507 25 l. Mona Monkey 45 45
1508 25 l. African Darter 45 45
1509 25 l. Chimpanzee 45 45
1510 25 l. African Elephant 45 45
1511 25 l. Potto 45 45
1512 25 l. African Manatee 45 45
1513 25 l. African Fish Eagle 45 45
1514 25 l. African Spoonbill 45 45
1497/1514 .. .. .. *Set of* 18 7·00 7·00
MS1515 106×76 mm. 150 l. Crowned Eagle (*vert*) .. .. 4·50 5·00

Nos. 1497/1514 were printed together, *se-tenant*, in sheetlets of 18 with the background forming a map of Sierra Leone.

Nos. 1497/1515 exist imperforate from a limited printing.

(Litho Questa)

1990 (22 Oct). *Fairground Carousel Animals. T* **239** *and similar vert designs. Multicoloured. P* 14.

1516 5 l. Type **239** 15 15
1517 10 l. Horse with panther saddle 20 20
1518 20 l. Ostrich 30 30
1519 30 l. Zebra 40 40
1520 50 l. Horse 55 55
1521 80 l. Sea monster 80 80
1522 100 l. Giraffe .. .. 1·00 1·00
1523 150 l. Armoured horse .. .. .. 1·40 1·40
1524 200 l. Camel .. .. 1·75 1·75
1516/24 .. .. *Set of* 9 6·00 6·00
MS1525 Two sheets (a) 98×68 mm. 300 l. Masked horse. (b) 68×98 mm. 300 l. Baden-Powell as Centaur .. .. *Set of* 2 *sheets* 7·00 8·00

Nos. 1516/25 exist imperforate from a limited printing.

(Des B. Grout. Litho B.D.T.)

1990 (12 Nov). *Olympic Games, Barcelona* (1992). *Multicoloured designs as T* **202** *of Lesotho. P* 14.

1526 5 l. Start of Men's 100 metres 20 15
1527 10 l. Men's 4×400 metres relay 25 20
1528 20 l. Men's 100 metres in progress .. 40 30
1529 30 l. Weightlifting 50 40
1530 40 l. Freestyle wrestling 55 45
1531 80 l. Water polo 80 90
1532 150 l. Women's gymnastics .. .. 1·40 1·50
1533 200 l. Cycling .. .. 2·25 2·25
1526/33 .. .. *Set of* 8 5·75 5·50
MS1534 Two sheets, each 103×75 mm. (a) 400 l. Boxing (*horiz*). (b) 400 l. Olympic flag (*horiz*) *Set of* 2 *sheets* 7·00 8·00

Nos. 1526/34 exist imperforate from a limited printing.

240 Morty assembling Bicycle by Christmas Tree

241 "Holy Family with St. Elizabeth" (Mantegna)

(Des Walt Disney Co. Litho B.D.T.)

1990 (17 Dec). *Christmas. "The Night before Christmas". T* **240** *and similar designs showing Walt Disney cartoon characters in scenes from Clement Moore's poem. P* 13.

1535/58 50 l. × 8, 75 l. × 8, 100 l. × 8 *Set of* 24 15·00 17·00
MS1559 Six sheets, each 129×107 mm. 400 l. × 6 multicoloured .. .. *Set of* 6 *sheets* 15·00 17·00

Nos. 1535/58 were issued as three sheetlets of eight, each containing stamps of the same face value *se-tenant*.

Of the stamps in No. **MS**1559 four horizontal and two vertical.

(Litho Cartor)

1990 (17 Dec). *Christmas. Paintings. T* **241** *and similar vert designs. Multicoloured. P* 13.

1560 10 l. "Holy Family resting" (Rembrandt) 25 15
1561 20 l. Type **241** 35 20
1562 30 l. "Virgin and Child with an Angel" (Correggio) 45 30
1563 50 l. "Annunciation" (Bernardo Strozzi) 70 45
1564 100 l. "Madonna and Child appearing to St. Anthony" (Lippi) .. .. .. 1·25 80
1565 175 l. "Virgin and Child" (Giovanni Boltraffio) .. .. 1·90 2·00
1566 200 l. "Esterhazy Madonna" (Raphael) .. 2·00 2·25
1567 300 l. "Coronation of Mary" (Andrea Orcagna) .. .. 2·50 2·75
1560/7 .. .. *Set of* 8 8·50 8·00
MS1568 Two sheets, each 75×114 mm. (a) 400 l. "Adoration of the Shepherds" (Bronzino). (b) 400 l. "Adoration of the Shepherds" (Gerard David) .. .. *Set of* 2 *sheets* 8·00 8·50

(Litho Questa)

1990 (24 Dec). *350th Death Anniv of Rubens* (1*st issue*). *Multicoloured designs as T* **250** *of Maldive Islands, but vert. P* 13½×14.

1569 5 l. "Helena Fourment as Hagar in the Wilderness" (detail) 10 10
1570 10 l. "Isabella Brant" 15 15
1571 20 l. "Countess of Arundel and her Party" (detail) 20 20
1572 60 l. "Countess of Arundel and her Party" (different detail) 50 50
1573 80 l. "Nicolaas Rockox" 70 70
1574 100 l. "Adriana Perez" 80 80
1575 150 l. "George Villiers, Duke of Buckingham" (detail) .. .. .. 1·40 1·75
1576 300 l. "Countess of Buckingham" .. 2·25 2·50
1569/76 .. .. *Set of* 8 5·50 6·00
MS1577 Two sheets, each 71×100 mm. (a) 350 l. "Giovanni Carlo Dorio" (detail). (b) 350 l. "Veronica Spinola Dorio" (detail) *Set of* 2 *sheets* 6·50 7·00

See also Nos. 1595/603.

242 *Chlorophyllum molybdites*

243 "The Flight of St. Barbara" (detail) (Rubens)

(Des Mary Walters. Litho Questa)

1990 (31 Dec). *Fungi. T* **242** *and similar vert designs. Multicoloured. P* 14.

1578 3 l. Type **242** 30 15
1579 5 l. *Lepista nuda* 30 15
1580 10 l. *Clitocybe nebularis* 40 20
1581 15 l. *Cyathus striatus* 50 30
1582 20 l. *Bolbitius vitellinus* 55 35
1583 25 l. *Leucoagaricus naucinus* 55 40
1584 30 l. *Suillus luteus* 60 45
1585 40 l. *Podaxis pistillaris* 70 55
1586 50 l. *Oudemansiella radicata* 80 60
1587 60 l. *Phallus indusiatus* 90 70
1588 80 l. *Macrolepiota rhacodes* .. .. 1·00 1·10
1589 100 l. *Mycena pura* .. .. .. 1·25 1·25
1590 150 l. *Volvariella volvacea* .. .. 1·60 1·75
1591 175 l. *Omphalotus olearius* .. .. 1·90 2·25
1592 200 l. *Sphaerobolus stellatus* .. .. 2·00 2·50
1593 250 l. *Schizophyllum commune* .. .. 2·25 2·75
1578/93 .. .. *Set of* 16 14·00 14·00
MS1594 Four sheets, each 101×70 mm. (a) 350 l. *Hypholoma fasciculare*. (b) 350 l. *Psilocybe coprophila*. (c) 350 l. *Agaricus campestris*. (d) 350 l. *Suillus granulatus* .. *Set of* 4 *sheets* 15·00 15·00

(Litho Questa)

1991 (8 Apr). *Easter. 350th Death Anniv of Rubens* (1990) (2*nd issue*). *T* **243** *and similar vert designs. Multicoloured. P* 13½×14.

1595 10 l. Type **243** 20 15
1596 20 l. "The Last Judgement" (detail) .. 30 20
1597 30 l. "St. Gregory of Nazianzus" .. 40 30
1598 50 l. "Doubting Thomas" 55 45
1599 80 l. "The Way to Calvary" (detail) .. 1·00 1·00
1600 100 l. "St. Gregory with Sts. Domitilla, Maurus and Papianus" .. .. 1·10 1·10
1601 175 l. "Sts. Gregory, Maurus and Papianus" .. .. 1·75 2·00
1602 300 l. "Christ and the Penitent Sinners" 2·75 4·00
1595/1602 .. .. *Set of* 8 7·25 8·25
MS1603 Two sheets, each 70×101 mm. (a) 400 l. "The Last Judgement" (different detail). (b) 400 l. "The Way to Calvary" (different detail) *Set of* 2 *sheets* 7·00 7·50

244 Class "1400" Steam Locomotive

(Des K. Gromell. Litho Questa)

1991 (13 May). *"Phila Nippon '91" International Stamp Exhibition, Tokyo. Japanese Trains. T* **244** *and similar horiz designs. Each multicoloured* (*Nos.* 1604/11) *or black and rosine* (*No.* **MS**1612). *P* 14.

1604 10 l. Type **244** 25 20
1605 20 l. Class "C 55" streamline steam locomotive 35 25
1606 30 l. Class "ED 17" electric locomotive .. 50 40
1607 60 l. Class "EF 13" double-ended electric locomotive 80 75
1608 100 l. Baldwin Class "Mikado" steam locomotive .. .. 1·10 1·10
1609 150 l. Class "C 62" steam locomotive .. 1·40 1·75
1610 200 l. Class "KiHa 81" diesel train .. 1·75 2·00
1611 300 l. Class "8550" steam locomotive .. 2·25 2·50
1604/11 .. .. *Set of* 8 7·50 8·00
MS1612 Four sheets, each 106×76 mm. (a) 400 l. Class "9600" steam locomotive. (b) 400 l. Class "D 51" steam locomotive. (c) 400 l. Class "7000" electric train. (d) 400 l. Hikari "Bullet" train *Set of* 4 *sheets* 13·00 14·00

245 Turquoise Killifish

(Des W. Hanson Studio. Litho Questa)

1991 (3 June). *Fishes. T* **245** *and similar horiz designs. Multicoloured. P* 14.

1613 10 l. Type **245** 40 20
1614 20 l. Red-chinned Panchax 50 25
1615 30 l. Peters' Killifish 70 40
1616 60 l. Micro-walkeri Killifish .. .. 1·10 80
1617 100 l. Freshwater Butterflyfish .. .. 1·40 1·00
1618 150 l. Green Panchax .. .. .. 1·75 2·00
1619 200 l. Six-banded Lyretail .. .. 2·00 2·25
1620 300 l. Nile Pufferfish .. .. .. 2·25 2·50
1613/20 .. .. *Set of* 8 9·00 8·50
MS1621 Two sheets, each 96×70 mm. (a) 400 l. Spot-finned Squeaker. (b) 400 l. Two-striped Panchax .. .. .. *Set of* 2 *sheets* 6·50 6·50

Nos. 1613/21 exist imperforate from a limited printing.

(Litho Walsall)

1991 (28 June). *Death Centenary of Vincent van Gogh* (*artist*). *Multicoloured designs as T* **255** *of Maldive Islands. P* 13½.

1622 10 c. "The Langlois Bridge at Arles" (*horiz*) 10 10
1623 50 c. "Tree in Garden at Saint-Paul Hospital" 10 10
1624 1 l. "Wild Flowers and Thistles in a Vase" 10 10
1625 2 l. "Still Life: Vase with Oleanders and Books" (*horiz*) 10 10
1626 5 l. "Farmhouses in a Wheatfield near Arles" (*horiz*) 10 10
1627 10 l. "Self-portrait, September 1889" .. 15 15
1628 20 l. "Patience Escalier" 25 20
1629 30 l. "Doctor Félix Rey" 35 30
1630 50 l. "The Iris" 55 45
1631 60 l. "The Shepherdess" 60 50
1632 80 l. "Vincent's House in Arles" (*horiz*) .. 85 70
1633 100 l. "The Road Menders" (*horiz*) .. 95 80
1634 150 l. "The Garden of Saint-Paul Hospital" 1·50 1·50
1635 200 l. "View of the Church, Saint-Paul-de-Mausole" (*horiz*) .. .. .. 1·75 1·75
1636 250 l. "Seascape at Saintes-Maries" (*horiz*) 1·90 2·00
1637 300 l. "Pietà" .. .. 2·25 2·50
1622/37 .. .. *Set of* 16 10·00 10·00
MS1638 Six sheets. (a) 102×76 mm. 400 l. "Haystacks in Provence" (96×70 *mm*). (b) 102×76 mm. 400 l. "The Trinquetaille Bridge" (96×70 *mm*). (c) 102×76 mm. 400 l. "Vineyards with a View of Auvers" (96×70 *mm*). (d) 102×76 mm. 400 l. "The Garden of Saint-Paul Hospital" (96×107 *mm*). (e) 76×102 mm. 400 l. "Church at Auvers-sur-Dise" (70×96 *mm*). (f) 76×102 mm. 400 l. "Two Poplars on a Road through the Hills" (70×96 *mm*). Imperf .. .. *Set of* 6 *sheets* 16·00 16·00

Nos. 1622/38 exist imperforate from a limited printing.

(Des D. Miller. Litho Walsall)

1991 (5 July). *65th Birthday of Queen Elizabeth II. Horiz designs as T* **210** *of Lesotho. Multicoloured. P* 14.

1639 10 l. The Queen and Prince Charles at polo match 15 10
1640 30 l. The Queen at Windsor, 1989 .. 20 20
1641 200 l. The Queen and Princess Diana in Nigeria, 1989 .. .. .. 1·75 2·00
1642 250 l. The Queen and Prince Philip .. 2·00 2·25
1639/42 .. .. *Set of* 4 3·75 4·00
MS1643 68×90 mm. 400 l. Separate photographs of the Queen and Prince Philip in 1987 and 1988 3·25 3·75

Nos. 1639/43 exist imperforate from a limited printing.

(Des D. Miller. Litho Walsall)

1991 (5 July). *10th Wedding Anniv of Prince and Princess of Wales. Horiz designs as T* **210** *of Lesotho. Multicoloured. P* 14.

1644 20 l. Prince and Princess of Wales in August 1987 .. .. 25 15
1645 80 l. Separate photographs of Prince, Princess and sons 75 85
1646 100 l. Prince Henry in Majorca and Prince William on his first day at school .. 85 95
1647 300 l. Prince Charles at Caister, April 1988, and Princess Diana in Hyde Park, May 1989 .. .. .. 2·25 2·75
1644/7 .. .. *Set of* 4 3·50 4·25
MS1648 68×90 mm. 400 l. Prince, Princess and Prince Henry in Majorca and Prince William going to school .. .. 3·75 4·00

Nos. 1644/8 exist imperforate from a limited printing.

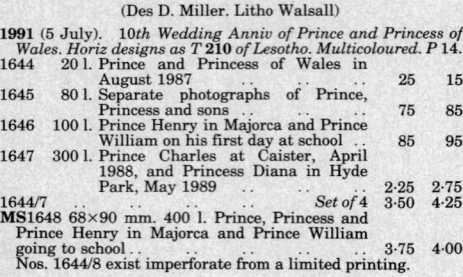

246 *Graphium latreillianus and Ancistrochilus rothschildianus*

(Des I. Maclaury. Litho Cartor)

1991 (5 Aug). *Butterflies and Flowers. T* **246** *and similar horiz designs. Multicoloured. P* 14×13½.

1649 10 l. Type **246** 45 20
1650 30 l. *Euphraedra eleus* and *Clitoria ternatea* 70 45
1651 50 l. *Graphium antheus* and *Gloriosa simplex* 90 60
1652 60 l. *Salamis cacta* and *Stenandriopsis guineensis* .. .. 1·10 80
1653 80 l. *Kallima rumia* and *Cassia fistula* .. 1·40 1·00
1654 100 l. *Hypolimnas salmacis* and *Amorphophallus abyssinicus* .. .. 1·75 1·25
1655 200 l. *Danaus formosa* and *Nephthytis afzelii* .. .. 2·50 2·50
1656 300 l. *Graphium leonidas* and *Clappertonia ficifolia* .. .. .. 3·00 3·25
1649/56 .. .. *Set of* 8 10·50 9·00
MS1657 Four sheets, each 102×74 mm. (a) 400 l. *Charaxes cynthia* and *Plumbago auriculata.* (b) 400 l. *Colias electo* and *Combretum grandiflorum.* (c) 400 l. *Cynandra opis* and *Bombax costatum.* (d) 400 l. *Eurema brigitta* and *Monodora myristica.* P 13×12 .. *Set of 4 sheets* 13·00 13·00

1991 (Oct). *Butterflies. Designs as Nos.* 1028/42, *but* "Sierra Leone" *in blue. Multicoloured. With* "1990" *imprint date at foot.* A. *P* 14. B. *P* 12½×11½.

			A	A	B	B
1658	10 c.	*Danaus limniace* ..	6·50	20	†	
1660	50 c.	*Graphium ridleyanus*	6·50	20	40	—
1661	1 l.	*Papilio bromius* ..	6·50	20	†	
1662	2 l.	*Iterus zalmoxis* ("Papilio zalmoxis")	6·50	20	†	
1663	5 l.	*Graphium tynderaeus*	—	20	†	
1665	10 l.	*Graphium policenes* ..	6·50	20	†	
1666	20 l.	*Tanuetheira timon* ("Iolaus timon") ..	—	30	†	
1667	30 l.	*Cymothoe sangaris* ..	—	40	†	
1668	50 l.	Type **205**	6·50	45	70	—
1669	60 l.	*Charaxes lucretius* ..	6·50	55	†	
1670	80 l.	*Stugeta marmorea* ("Iolaus marmorea") ..	12·00	65	90	—
1671	100 l.	*Abisara talantus* ..	—	65	†	
1672	300 l.	*Papilio hesperus* ..	12·00	1·50	2·50	—

C. *P* 12

1660C 50 c. *Graphium ridleyanus* 40
1668C 50 l. Type **205** 90
1670C 80 l. *Stugeta marmorea* ("Iolaus marmorea") .. .. .. 1·10
1672C 300 l. *Papilio hesperus* .. .. .. 2·50

Nos. 1660B/72B show a larger perforation hole on every sixth perforation, both vertically and horizontally.

247 Audie Murphy in *To Hell and Back*

248 Meissen China Parrot Ornament, Munich Botanic Garden

(Des R. Jung. Litho Questa)

1991 (14 Oct). *Films of Second World War. T* **247** *and similar horiz designs. Multicoloured. P* 14.

1675 2 l. Type **247** 10 10
1676 5 l. Jack Palance in *Attack* 15 15
1677 10 l. Greer Garson and Walter Pidgeon in *Mrs. Miniver* 20 20
1678 20 l. Heavy artillery from *The Guns of Navarone* 30 30
1679 30 l. Charlie Chaplin and Paulette Goddard in *The Great Dictator* .. 40 40
1680 50 l. Steam locomotive from *The Train* 60 60
1681 60 l. Diary and fountain pen from *The Diary of Anne Frank* 70 70
1682 80 l. William Holden in *The Bridge on the River Kwai* 90 90
1683 100 l. Tallulah Bankhead in *Lifeboat* and Alfred Hitchcock (director) .. 1·00 1·00
1684 200 l. John Wayne in *Sands of Iwo Jima* 1·90 1·90
1685 300 l. Van Johnson and Spencer Tracy in *Thirty Seconds over Tokyo* .. 2·75 2·75
1686 350 l. Humphrey Bogart and Ingrid Bergman in *Casablanca* .. .. 3·00 3·00
1675/86 .. .. *Set of* 12 11·00 11·00
MS1687 Three sheets, each 116×76 mm. (a) 450 l. George C. Scott in *Patton.* (b) 450 l. Gregory Peck in *Twelve O'Clock High.* (c) 450 l. Burning American cruiser from *Tora! Tora! Tora!* .. .. *Set of 3 sheets* 11·00 11·00

Nos. 1675/87 exist imperforate from a limited printing.

(Des Dot Barlowe. Litho Questa)

1991 (28 Oct). *Botanical Gardens of the World. T* **248** *and similar multicoloured designs. P* 14.

1688/1735 60 l.×48 .. .. .. *Set of* 48 18·00 19·00
MS1736 Three sheets, each 97×69 mm. (a) 600 l. Munich Botanic Garden. (b) 600 l. Kyoto Botanic Garden. (c) 600 l. Brooklyn Botanic Garden *Set of 3 sheets* 11·00 12·00

Nos. 1688/1735 were issued as *se-tenant* sheetlets, each of 16 (4×4), depicting features and plants from Munich (Nos. 1688/1703), Kyoto (Nos. 1704/19) and Brooklyn (Nos. 1720/35). The single designs in the three minature sheets of No. **MS**1736 are horizontal.

(Litho Walsall)

1991 (9 Dec). *Christmas. Drawings and Paintings by Albrecht Dürer. Vert designs as T* **211** *of Lesotho. P* 12.

1737 6 l. black and bright magenta 15 10
1738 60 l. black and new blue 35 30
1739 80 l. multicoloured 45 40
1740 100 l. multicoloured 65 65
1741 200 l. multicoloured .. .. .. 1·60 1·60
1742 300 l. multicoloured .. .. .. 2·00 2·00
1743 700 l. multicoloured .. .. .. 4·75 5·00
1737/43 .. .. *Set of* 7 9·00 9·00
MS1744 Two sheets, each 102×127 mm. (a) 600 l. multicoloured. (b) 600 l. multicoloured. P 14 .. .. *Set of 2 sheets* 7·50 7·50

Designs:—6 l. "Mary being Crowned by Two Angels"; 60 l. "St. Christopher"; 80 l. "Virgin and Child with St. Anne" (detail); 100 l. "Virgin with the Pear" (detail); 200 l. "Madonna and Child" (detail); 300 l. "The Virgin in Half-Length" (detail); 700 l. "The Madonna with the Siskin" (detail); 600 l. (No. **MS**1744a) "Virgin and Child with St. Anne", 600 l. (No. **MS**1744b) "The Feast of the Rose Garlands" (detail).

Nos. 1737/44 exist imperforate from a limited printing.

249 National Theatre, Prague

(Des J. Iskowitz (Nos. 1745/6, 1750, **MS**1751a), W. Hanson Studio (Nos. 1747/9, **MS**1751b). Litho Questa)

1991 (20 Dec). *Anniversaries and Events. T* **249** *and similar multicoloured designs. P* 14.

1745 50 l. Type **249** 15 15
1746 100 l. St. Peter's Abbey, Salzburg .. 30 30
1747 250 l. Sea Scouts learning sailing .. 85 85
1748 300 l. Sierra Leone scouts emblem and Lord Baden-Powell .. .. 1·00 1·00
1749 400 l. Scouts playing baseball at Mt. Sorak Jamboree .. .. 1·40 1·40
1750 500 l. Scene from *Idomeneo* .. .. 1·75 1·75
1745/50 .. .. *Set of* 6 5·00 5·00
MS1751 Two sheets. (a) 75×105 mm. 600 l. Bust of Mozart (*vert*). (b) 89×117 mm. 750 l. 17th World Scout Jamboree emblem (*vert*) *Set of 2 sheets* 8·00 8·50

Anniversaries and Events:—Nos. 1745/6, 1750, **MS**1751a, Death bicentenary of Mozart; Nos. 1747/9, **MS**1751b, 50th death anniv of Lord Baden-Powell and World Scout Jamboree, Korea.

250 Aichi D3A "Val" Dive Bomber

251 Greater Flamingo

(Des. J. Batchelor. Litho Questa)

1991 (20 Dec). *50th Anniv of Japanese Attack on Pearl Harbor. T* **250** *and similar horiz designs. Multicoloured. P* 14½×15.

1752 75 l. Type **250** 50 50
a. Sheetlet. Nos. 1752/66 .. .. 6·50
1753 75 l. Japanese Aichi D3A "Val" dive bomber and smoke 50 50
1754 75 l. Battleship Row burning 50 50
1755 75 l. Planes and burning dockyard .. 50 50
1756 75 l. Burning installations 50 50
1757 75 l. Two Japanese Aichi D3A "Val" dive bombers 50 50
1758 75 l. Burning ships and hangars .. 50 50
1759 75 l. Airfield under attack 50 50
1760 75 l. American Curtiss P-40C fighter .. 50 50
1761 75 l. Japanese Mitsubishi A6M Zero-Sen fighter-bombers 50 50
1762 75 l. Japanese Mitsubishi A6M Zero-Sen fighter-bombers over suburb .. 50 50
1763 75 l. Japanese Nakajima B5N "Kate" bombers attacking ships 50 50
1764 75 l. Japanese Nakajima B5N "Kate" aircraft on fire 50 50
1765 75 l. Japanese Nakajima B5N "Kate" bombers over jungle 50 50
1766 75 l. Mitsubishi A6M Zero-Sen fighters .. 50 50
1752/66 .. .. *Set of* 15 6·50 6·50

Nos. 1752/66 were printed together, *se-tenant*, in sheetlets of 15 forming a composite design showing an aerial view.

(Des Walt Disney Co. Litho Questa)

1991 (24 Dec). *Christmas. Walt Disney Christmas Cards. Multicoloured designs as T* **228** *of St. Vincent. P* 14×13½.

1767 12 l. Mickey Mouse, Donald Duck and characters from *Peter Pan,* 1952 (*horiz*) 15 10
1768 30 l. Disney characters reading *Alice in Wonderland,* 1950 (*horiz*) .. 20 10
1769 60 l. Sleepy and animals, 1938 (*horiz*) .. 35 20
1770 75 l. Mickey, Minnie, Donald and Pluto posting card, 1936 (*horiz*) .. 35 25
1771 100 l. Disney cartoon characters, 1984 (*horiz*) 45 35
1772 125 l. Mickey and Donald singing carols with Donald's nephews and Pluto reading, 1954 (*horiz*) 70 70
1773 150 l. *101 Dalmatians,* 1960 (*horiz*) .. 80 80
1774 200 l. Mickey and Donald opening presents, 1948 (*horiz*) .. .. 1·00 1·00
1775 300 l. Mickey, Minnie, Morte and Ferde decorating tree, 1983 (*horiz*) .. 1·40 1·50
1776 400 l. Donald decorating tree and nephews watching television, 1956 (*horiz*) .. 1·75 2·00
1777 500 l. Characters from Disney films, 1972 (*horiz*) .. .. 1·90 2·25
1778 600 l. Mickey, Donald, Pluto and friends singing, 1964 (*horiz*) .. .. 2·00 2·50
1767/78 .. .. *Set of* 12 10·00 10·50
MS1779 Three sheets, each 128×102 mm. (a) 900 l. Mad Hatter's tea party, 1950; (b) 900 l. Disneyland, 1955. (c) 900 l. Seven Dwarfs in toboggan, 1959. P 13½×14 .. *Set of 3 sheets* 10·00 11·00

(Des Walt Disney Co. Litho B.D.T.)

1992 (9 Mar). *Mickey's World Tour. Multicoloured designs as T* **270** *of Maldive Islands showing Walt Disney cartoon characters in different countries. P* 13.

1780 6 l. Minnie Mouse as Chiquita with Pluto, Cuba 15 10
1781 10 l. Goofy as Olympic discus champion, Greece 15 10
1782 20 l. Donald and Daisy Duck as flamenco dancers, Spain 15 10
1783 30 l. Goofy and Donald as guardsman, England 20 15
1784 50 l. Mickey and Minnie at Paris fashion show, France 30 20
1785 100 l. Goofy in the Alps, Switzerland .. 50 35
1786 200 l. Daisy and Minnie in grass skirts, Hawaii .. .. 1·00 1·25
1787 350 l. Mickey, Donald and Goofy as ancient Egyptians (*horiz*) .. .. 1·60 1·75
1788 500 l. Daisy and Minnie as cancan dancers, France (*horiz*) .. .. 2·00 2·50
1780/8 .. .. *Set of* 9 5·50 6·00
MS1789 Three sheets, each 83×105 mm. (a) 700 l. Mickey playing bagpipes, Scotland. (b) 700 l. Donald the gondolier, Italy. (c) 700 l. Mickey and Goofy smashing plates, Greece *Set of 3 sheets* 10·00 11·00

(Des D. Miller. Litho Questa)

1992 (9 Mar). *40th Anniv of Queen Elizabeth II's Accession. Horiz designs as T* **214** *of Lesotho. Multicoloured. P* 14.

1790 60 l. State House 35 20
1791 100 l. Beach 55 40
1792 300 l. Parliament Building .. .. 1·60 1·75
1793 400 l. Canoe on beach .. .. .. 1·90 2·00
1790/3 .. .. *Set of* 4 4·00 4·00
MS1794 Two sheets, each 75×97 mm. (a) 700 l. Jungle hillside. (b) 700 l. Freetown *Set of 2 sheets* 8·50 9·00

(Litho B.D.T.)

1992 (25 May). *"Granada '92" International Stamp Exhibition, Spain. Paintings by Francisco Zurbarán. Vert designs as T* **68** *of St. Kitts-Nevis (Nevis). Multicoloured. P* 13.

1795 1 l. "Visit of St. Thomas Aquinas to St. Bonaventure" 10 10
1796 10 l. "St. Gregory" 10 10
1797 30 l. "St. Andrew" 20 20
1798 50 l. "St. Gabriel the Archangel" .. 30 30
1799 60 l. "The Blessed Henry Suso" 30 30
1800 100 l. "St. Lucy" 40 40
1801 300 l. "St. Casilda" 95 95
1802 400 l. "St. Margaret of Antioch" .. 1·40 1·40
1803 500 l. "St. Apollonia" .. .. .. 1·60 1·60
1804 600 l. "St. Bonaventure at Council of Lyons" .. .. 1·75 1·75
1805 700 l. "St. Bonaventure on his Bier" .. 2·00 2·00
1806 800 l. "The Martyrdom of St. James" (detail) .. .. 2·25 2·25
1795/1806 .. .. .. *Set of* 12 10·00 10·00
MS1807 Three sheets. (a) 95×112 mm. 900 l. "The Martyrdom of St. James". (b) 95×112 mm. 900 l. "The Young Virgin". (c) 112×95 mm. 900 l. "St. Hugh in the Refectory". Imperf *Set of 3 sheets* 7·50 8·00

Nos. 1795/1806 exist imperforate from a limited printing.

(Des D. Burkhart, Litho B.D.T.)

1992 (8 June). *Prehistoric Animals. Multicoloured designs as T* **217** *of Lesotho, but vert. P* 14.

1808 50 l. Rhamphorhynchus 45 45
a. Sheetlet. Nos. 1808/27 8·00
1809 50 l. Pteranodon 45 45
1810 50 l. Dimorphodon 45 45
1811 50 l. Pterodactyl 45 45
1812 50 l. Archaeopteryx 45 45
1813 50 l. Iguanodon 45 45
1814 50 l. Hypsilophodon 45 45
1815 50 l. Nothosaurus 45 45
1816 50 l. Brachiosaurus 45 45
1817 50 l. Kentrosaurus 45 45
1818 50 l. Plesiosaurus 45 45
1819 50 l. Trachodon 45 45
1820 50 l. Hesperornis 45 45
1821 50 l. Henodus 45 54
1822 50 l. Steneosaurus 45 45
1823 50 l. Stenopterygius 45 45
1824 50 l. Eurhinosaurus 45 45
1825 50 l. Placodus 45 45
1826 50 l. Mosasaurus 45 45
1827 50 l. Mixosaurus 45 45
1808/27 *Set of* 20 8·00 8·00
MS1828 106×76 mm. No. 1820 90 1·00

Nos. 1808/27 were printed together, *se-tenant*, in sheetlets of 20 forming a composite design.

No. 1811 is inscribed "Pteradactyl" and No. 1826 "Mosasaurs", both in error.

(Des P. Chinelli. Litho B.D.T.)

1992 (20 July). *Birds. T* **251** *and similar vert designs. Multicoloured. P* 14.

1829 30 l. Type **251** 30 30
1830 50 l. African White-crested Hornbill 35 35
1831 100 l. Crested Touraco 55 55
1832 170 l. Yellow-spotted Barbet 95 95
1833 200 l. African Spoonbill 1·10 1·10
1834 250 l. Saddle-bill Stork 1·25 1·25
1835 300 l. Red-faced Lovebird ("Red Headed Lovebird") 1·50 1·50
1836 600 l. Yellow-billed Barbet 3·75 3·75
1829/36 *Set of* 8 8·75 8·75
MS1837 Two sheets, each 72×101 mm. (a) 1000 l. Fire-bellied Woodpecker. (b) 1000 l. Swallow-tailed Bee Eater *Set of* 2 *sheets* 10·00 10·00

(Litho Questa)

1992 (8 Sept). *Olympic Games, Albertville and Barcelona. Multicoloured designs as T* **216** *of Lesotho. P* 14.

1838 10 l. Marathon 15 15
1839 20 l. Men's parallel bars 20 20
1840 30 l. Men's discus 20 20
1841 50 l. Men's 110 metres hurdles (*horiz*) 30 30
1842 60 l. Women's longjump 30 30
1843 100 l. Men's floor exercise (*horiz*) 45 45
1844 200 l. Windsurfing 80 80
1845 250 l. Women's biathlon 1·00 1·00
1846 300 l. Cycle road race 1·50 1·50
1847 400 l. Weightlifting 1·75 1·75
1848 500 l. Men's speed skating 2·25 2·25
1849 600 l. Men's downhill skiing (*horiz*) 3·25 3·25
1838/49 *Set of* 12 11·00 11·00
MS1850 Three sheets, each 102×71 mm. (a) 900 l. Football (*horiz*). (b) 900 l. Men's single luge (*horiz*). (c) 900 l. Pairs ice dancing *Set of* 3 *sheets* 11·00 12·00

Nos. 1838/50 exist imperforate from a limited printing.

252 Minnie Mouse and Chip decorating Christmas Tree

(Des Walt Disney Co. Litho Questa)

1992 (16 Nov). *Christmas. T* **252** *and similar multicoloured designs, each showing Walt Disney cartoon characters. P* $13^1/_2$×14.

1851 10 l. Type **252** 10 10
1852 20 l. Goofy as Father Christmas 15 10
1853 30 l. Daisy Duck and Minnie decorating Christmas Tree 20 10
1854 50 l. Mickey Mouse, and Goofy lighting candle 30 20
1855 80 l. Big Pete as Father Christmas 40 40
1856 100 l. Donald Duck as Father Christmas 40 40
1857 150 l. Morty and Ferdie decorating cake 75 75
1858 200 l. Mickey and bauble 85 85
1859 300 l. Goofy and toy Father Christmas 1·10 1·10
1860 500 l. Chip and Dale with sledge 1·60 1·75
1861 600 l. Donald and Dale with musical instruments 1·75 2·00
1862 800 l. Huey, Dewy and Louie making patterns in snow 2·25 2·75
1851/62 *Set of* 12 9·00 9·50
MS1863 Three sheets, each 128×102 mm. (a) 900 l. Mickey as Father Christmas. P $13^1/_2$×14. (b) 900 l. Chip and Christmas tree fairy (*horiz*). P 14×$13^1/_2$. (c) 900 l. Mickey and Minnie (*horiz*). P 14×$13^1/_2$ *Set of* 3 *sheets* 11·00 12·00

253 Toy Pennsylvania Railroad GG-1 Electric Locomotive No. 6-18306, 1992

254 African Pygmy Goose

(Des W. Hanson. Litho B.D.T.)

1992 (23 Nov). *"Genova '92" International Thematic Stamp Exhibition. Toy Trains. T* **253** *and similar horiz designs showing electric locomotives and rolling stock manufactured by Lionel. Multicoloured. P* 14.

1864 150 l. Type **253** 75 75
a. Sheetlet. Nos. 1864/72 6·75
1865 150 l. Wabash Railroad Hudson locomotive No. 8610, 1985 75 75
1866 150 l. Locomotive No. 1911, 1911 75 75
1867 150 l. Chesapeake & Ohio locomotive No. 6-18627, 1992 75 75
1868 150 l. Gang car No. 50, 1954 75 75
1869 150 l. Rock Island & Peoria locomotive No. 8004, 1980 75 75
1870 150 l. Western Maryland Railroad Shay locomotive No. 6-18023, 1992 75 75
1871 150 l. Boston & Albany Railroad Hudson locomotive No. 784, 1986 75 75
1872 150 l. Locomotive No. 6, 1906 75 75
1873 170 l. Special F-3 diesel locomotive, 1947 75 75
a. Sheetlet. Nos. 1873/81 6·75
1874 170 l. Pennsylvania Railroad switcher locomotive No. 6-18905, 1992 75 75
1875 170 l. No. 1 Trolley, 1913 75 75
1876 170 l. Seaboard Railroad freight diesel locomotive, 1958 75 75
1877 170 l. Pennsylvania S-2 turbine locomotive, 1991 75 75
1878 170 l. Western Pacific diesel locomotive No. 6-18822, 1992 75 75
1879 170 l. Locomotive No. 10, 1929 75 75
1880 170 l. Locomotive No. 400E, 1931 75 75
1881 170 l. Locomotive No. 384E, 1928 75 75
1882 170 l. Pennsylvania Railroad Torpedo locomotive No. 238EW, 1936 75 75
a. Sheetlet. Nos. 1882/90 6·75
1883 170 l. Denver & Rio Grande Western Alco locomotive No. 6-18107, 1992 75 75
1884 170 l. Locomotive No. 408E, 1930 75 75
1885 170 l. Mickey Mouse 60th Birthday boxcar No. 19241, 1991 75 75
1886 170 l. Polished brass locomotive No. 54, 1913 75 75
1887 170 l. Broadway Limited locomotive No. 392E, 1936 75 75
1888 170 l. Great Northern EP-5 locomotive No. 18302, 1988 75 75
1889 170 l. Locomotive No. 6, 1918 75 75
1890 170 l. Locomotive No. 400E, 1933 75 75
1864/90 *Set of* 27 18·00 18·00
MS1891 Three sheets, each 119×90 mm. (a) 1000 l. Joshua Lionel Cowen commemorative locomotive (50×37 *mm*). (b) 1000 l. Trolley No. 300 (50×37 *mm*). (c) 1000 l. Locomotive No. 381E, 1928 (50×37 *mm*). P 13 *Set of* 3 *sheets* 12·00 12·00

Nos. 1864/72, 1873/81 and 1882/90 were each printed together, *se-tenant*, in sheetlets of 9.

Nos. 1874 and 1877 are inscribed "Pennsylvannia" in error.

(Litho Questa)

1992 (1 Dec)–**97**. *Birds. T* **254** *and similar horiz designs. Multicoloured. P* 14×15. *A. Without imprint date. B. With imprint date.*

			A	A	B	B
1892	50 c.	Type **254**	20	20	†	
1893	1 l.	Spotted Eagle Owl	30	20	†	
1894	2 l.	Crested Touraco	30	20	†	
1895	5 l.	Saddle-bill Stork	30	20	†	
1896	10 l.	African Golden Oriole	30	20	†	
1897	20 l.	Malachite Kingfisher	35	20	†	
1898	30 l.	Red-crowned Bishop ("Fire-crowned Bishop")	35	20	†	
1899	40 l.	Fire-bellied Woodpecker	35	20	†	
1900	50 l.	Red-billed Fire Finch	75	75	10	10
1901	80 l.	Blue Flycatcher	35	25	†	
1902	100 l.	Crested Malimbe	1·40	1·40	15	20
1903	150 l.	Vitelline Masked Weaver	1·75	1·75	20	25
1904	170 l.	Great Blue Turaco ("Blue Plantain-eater")	70	60	†	
1905	200 l.	Superb Sunbird	2·00	2·00	30	35
1906	250 l.	Swallow-tailed Bee Eater	90	80	40	45
1907	300 l.	Cabanis's Yellow Bunting	2·50	2·50	45	50
1908	500 l.	Egyptian Plover ("Crocodile Bird")	2·75	2·75	75	80
1909	750 l.	White-faced Scops Owl	1·10	1·25	†	
1910	1000 l.	African Blue Cuckoo Shrike	2·75	2·75	1·50	1·60
1911	2000 l.	White-necked Bald Crow ("Bare-headed Rock Fowl")	3·00	3·25	†	
1912	3000 l.	African Red-tailed Buzzard	12·00	13·00	4·50	4·75
1892A/1912A		*Set of* 21	30·00	30·00		
1900B/12B		*Set of* 9			8·00	8·75

Dates of issue:—Without imprint 1.12.92, 50 c. to 3000 l. With imprint 1994, 50, 100, 150, 200, 300 l.; 1996, 500, 1000, 3000 l.; 1997, 250 l.

Imprint dates: "1994", Nos. 1900B, 1902B/3B, 1905B, 1907B; "1996", Nos. 1902B, 1905B, 1907B/8B, 1910B, 1912B; "1997", Nos. 1902B, 1905B/8B.

(Litho Questa)

1992 (7 Dec). *Christmas. Religious Paintings. Vert designs as T* **218** *of Lesotho. Multicoloured. P* $13^1/_2$×14.

1916 1 l. "Virgin and Child" (Fiorenzo di Lorenzo) 10 10
1917 10 l. "Madonna and Child on a Wall" (School of Bouts) 15 15
1918 20 l. "Virgin and Child with the Flight into Egypt" (Master of Hoogstraeten) 20 20
1919 30 l. "Madonna and Child before Firescreen" (Robert Campin) 25 20
1920 50 l. "Mary in a Rosegarden" (detail) (Hans Memling) 30 25
1921 100 l. "Virgin Mary and Child" (Lucas Cranach the Elder) 55 45
1922 170 l. "Virgin and Child" (Rogier van der Weyden) 1·00 1·00
1923 200 l. "Madonna and Saints" (detail) (Perugino) 1·10 1·10
1924 250 l. "Madonna Enthroned with Sts Catherine and Barbara" (Master of Hoogstraeten) 1·25 1·25
1925 300 l. "The Virgin in a Rose Arbour" (Stefan Lochner) 1·50 1·50
1926 500 l. "Madonna with Child and Angels" (Botticelli) 2·50 2·75
1927 1000 l. "Madonna and Child with young St. John the Baptist (Fra Bartolommeo) 4·50 5·00
1916/27 *Set of* 12 12·00 12·50
MS1928 Three sheets, each 76×102 mm. (a) 900 l. "Virgin and Child" (detail) (Jan Gossaert). (b) 900 l. "Virgin and Child (detail) (Lucas Cranach the Younger). (c) 900 l. "The Virgin with the Green Cushion" (detail) (Andrea Solario) *Set of* 3 *sheets* 10·50 10·50

255 Mickey Mouse and Sousaphone (magazine cover, 1936)

256 Emblems

(Des Walt Disney Co. Litho Questa)

1992 (17 Dec). *Mickey Mouse in Literature. T* **255** *and similar multicoloured designs each showing Walt Disney cartoon characters on magazine or book covers. P* $13^1/_2$×14.

1929 10 l. Type **255** 15 10
1930 20 l. Mickey and Minnie Mouse, 1936 20 10
1931 30 l. Mickey and Donald Duck, 1936 20 10
1932 40 l. Mickey, Minnie and Goofy in car, 1937 20 15
1933 50 l. Mickey as Ringmaster, 1937 20 15
1934 60 l. Mickey as Father Christmas, 1937 25 25
1935 70 l. Donald and Goofy representing 1937 and 1938 25 25
1936 150 l. Mickey and Minnie steering ship, 1935 70 70
1937 170 l. Mickey and Tanglefoot the horse, 1936 75 75
1938 200 l. Mickey tied up 85 85
1939 300 l. Mickey and Goofy in jungle 1·00 1·10
1940 400 l. Mickey and Goofy on submarine 1·40 1·60
1941 500 l. Mickey and Minnie singing and dancing, 1931 1·50 1·75
1929/41 *Set of* 13 7·00 7·00
MS1942 Three sheets. (a) 127×102 mm. 900 l. Mickey reading to Morty and Ferdie, 1933 (*horiz*). P 14×$13^1/_2$. (b) 102×127 mm. 900 l. Mickey with book, 1935 (*horiz*). P 14×$13^1/_2$. (c) 102×127 mm. 900 l. Mickey the hunter, 1948. P $13^1/_2$×14 *Set of* 3 *sheets* 9·50 10·00

(Des W. Wright and L. Fried (Nos. 1952, **MS**1954c). Litho B.D.T.)

1993 (14 Jan). *Anniversaries and Events. T* **256** *and similar multicoloured designs. P* 14.

1943 150 l. Type **256** 70 70
1944 170 l. Cow and cereal with emblems 80 80
1945 170 l. Airship LZ-127 *Graf Zeppelin* 80 80
1946 200 l. Starving child and W.H.O. emblem 95 95
1947 250 l. Summit emblem and cottonwood tree 1·25 1·25
1948 250 l. Lions Club emblem and World map 1·25 1·25
1949 300 l. Emblem and African Elephant 1·40 1·40
1950 300 l. Columbus, King Ferdinand and Queen Isabella 1·40 1·40
1951 500 l. Landing in the New World 2·25 2·25
1952 600 l. American space shuttle 2·40 2·40
1953 700 l. Construction drawings of LZ-127 *Graf Zeppelin* 2·75 2·75
1943/53 *Set of* 11 14·50 14·50
MS1954 Three sheets. (a) 100×70 mm. 900 l. Count Ferdinand von Zeppelin (*vert*). (b) 97×67 mm. 900 l. Christopher Columbus (*vert*). (c) 100×70 mm. 900 l. American astronaut on space walk *Set of* 3 *sheets* 10·50 11·50

Anniversaries and Events:—Nos. 1943/4 International Conference on Nutrition, Rome; Nos. 1945, 1953, **MS**1954a, 75th death anniv of Count Ferdinand von Zeppelin (airship pioneer); No. 1946, United Nations World Health Organization Projects; Nos. 1947, 1949, Earth Summit '92, Rio; No. 1948, 75th anniv of International Association of Lions Clubs; Nos. 1950/1, **MS**1954b 500th anniv of discovery of America by Columbus; Nos. 1952, **MS**1954c, International Space Year.

257 Joe Louis

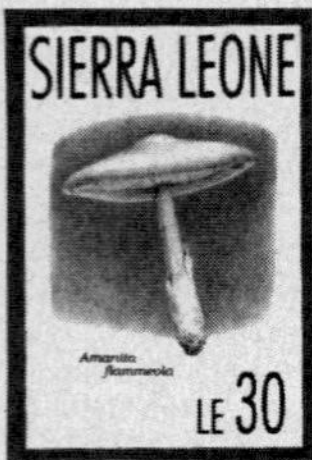

258 *Amanita flammeola*

(Des P. Wolff. Litho Questa)

1993 (8 Feb). *Centenary of Modern Boxing (1st issue) World Champions. T* **257** *and similar vert designs. Multicoloured. P* 13½×14.

1955 200 l. Type **257** 30 35
a. Sheetlet. Nos. 1955/62 .. .. 2·40
1956 200 l. Archie Moore 30 35
1957 200 l. Muhammad Ali 30 35
1958 200 l. George Foreman 30 35
1959 200 l. Joe Frazier 30 35
1960 200 l. Marvin Hagler 30 35
1961 200 l. Sugar Ray Leonard 30 35
1962 200 l. Evander Holyfield 30 35
1955/62 .. .. *Set of* 8 2·40 2·75
MS1963 128×102 mm. 1000 l. Muhammad Ali (*different*) .. .. 1·50 1·60

Nos. 1955/62 were printed together, *se-tenant*, in sheetlets of 8.

(Des P. Wolff. Litho Questa)

1993 (8 Feb). *Centenary of Modern Boxing (2nd issue). Boxing Films. Vert designs as T* **257**. *Multicoloured. P* 13½×14.

1964 200 l. Wallace Beery (*The Champ*) .. 30 35
a. Sheetlet. Nos. 1964/71 .. .. 2·40
1965 200 l. William Holden (*Golden Boy*) .. 30 35
1966 200 l. John Garfield (*Body and Soul*) .. 30 35
1967 200 l. Kirk Douglas (*Champion*) 30 35
1968 200 l. Robert Ryan (*The Set-Up*) .. 30 35
1969 200 l. Anthony Quinn (*Requiem for a Heavyweight*) 30 35
1970 200 l. Elvis Presley (*Kid Galahad*) .. 30 35
1971 200 l. Jeff Bridges (*Fat City*) 30 35
1964/71 .. .. *Set of* 8 2·40 2·75
MS1972 Two sheets, each 128×102 mm. (a) 1000 l. Errol Flynn (*Gentleman Jim*). (b) 1000 l. Sylvester Stallone (*Rocky III*) .. *Set of* 2 *sheets* 3·00 3·25

Nos. 1964/71 were printed together, *se-tenant*, in sheetlets of 8.

(Litho Walsall)

1993 (8 Mar). *Bicentenary of the Louvre, Paris. Multicoloured designs as T* **221** *of Lesotho. P* 12.

1973 70 l. "Young Orphan at a Cemetery" (Delacroix) 10 10
a. Sheetlet. Nos. 1973/80 80
1974 70 l. "Algerian Women in their Apartment" (left detail) (Delacroix) 10 10
1975 70 l. "Algerian Women in their Apartment" (right detail) (Delacroix) 10 10
1976 70 l. "Dante and Virgil" (Delacroix) .. 10 10
1977 70 l. "Self-portrait" (Delacroix) 10 10
1978 70 l. "Massacre of Chios" (left detail) (Delacroix) 10 10
1979 70 l. "Massacre of Chios" (right detail) (Delacroix) 10 10
1980 70 l. "Frédéric Chopin" (Delacroix) .. 10 10
1981 70 l. "Entry of the Crusaders into Constantinople" (left detail) (Delacroix) .. 10 10
a. Sheetlet. Nos. 1981/8 80
1982 70 l. "Entry of the Crusaders into Constantinople" (right detail) (Delacroix) .. 10 10
1983 70 l. "Jewish Wedding, Morocco" (left detail) (Delacroix) 10 10
1984 70 l. "Jewish Wedding, Morocco" (right detail) (Delacroix) 10 10
1985 70 l. "Death of Sardanopoulous" (left detail) (Delacroix) 10 10
1986 70 l. "Death of Sardanopoulous" (right detail) (Delacroix) 10 10
1987 70 l. "Liberty leading the People" (left detail) (Delacroix) 10 10
1988 70 l. "Liberty leading the People" (right detail) (Delacroix) 10 10
1973/88 .. .. *Set of* 16 1·60 1·60
MS1989 100×70 mm. 900 l. "The Sabine Women" (Louis David) (85×53 *mm*). P 14½ .. 1·25 1·40

Nos. 1973/80 and 1981/8 were printed together, *se-tenant*, in sheetlets of 8 stamps and one centre label.

(Des I. MacLaury. Litho Questa)

1993 (5 May). *Mushrooms. T* **258** *and similar vert designs. Multicoloured. P* 14.

1990 30 l. Type **258** 10 10
1991 50 l. *Cantharellus pseudocibarius* .. 10 10
1992 100 l. *Volvariella volvacea* 15 20
1993 200 l. *Termitomyces microcarpus* 30 35
1994 300 l. *Auricularia auricula-judae* 45 50
1995 400 l. *Lentinus tuber-regium* ("*Pleurotus tuberregium*") 60 65
1996 500 l. *Schizophyllum commune* 75 80
1997 600 l. *Termitomyces robustus* 85 90
1990/7 .. .. *Set of* 8 3·25 3·50
MS1998 Two sheets, each 106×76 mm. (a) 1000 l. *Daldinia concentrica*. (b) 1000 l. *Phallus rubicundus* .. .. *Set of* 2 *sheets* 3·00 3·25

Nos. 1990/8 exist imperforate from a limited printing.

259 *Pseudacraea boisduvali*

260 Black Persian

(Des L. Nelson. Litho Questa)

1993 (5 May). *Butterflies. T* **259** *and similar vert designs. Multicoloured. P* 14.

1999 20 l. Type **259** 35 20
2000 30 l. *Salamis temora* 40 25
2001 50 l. *Charaxes jasius* 40 30
2002 100 l. *Amblypodia anita* 50 40
2003 150 l. *Papilio nireus* 60 60
2004 170 l. *Danaus chrysippus* 65 65
2005 200 l. *Meneris tulbaghia* 70 70
2006 250 l. *Precis octavia* 75 75
2007 300 l. *Palla ussheri* 80 80
2008 500 l. *Catacroptera cloanthe* .. .. 1·25 1·25
2009 600 l. *Cynthia cardui* .. .. 1·40 1·40
2010 700 l. *Euphaedra neophron* .. .. .. 1·50 1·50
1999/2010 .. .. *Set of* 12 8·50 8·00
MS2011 Three sheets, each 100×70 mm. (a) 1000 l. *Papilio zalmoxis*. (b) 1000 l. *Hypolimnas salmacis*. (c) 1000 l. *Kallimoides rumia* *Set of* 3 *sheets* 7·00 7·50

Nos. 1999/2011 exist imperforate from a limited printing.

(Des Jennifer Toombs. Litho Questa)

1993 (17 May). *Cats. T* **260** *and similar multicoloured designs. P* 14.

2012 150 l. Type **260** 20 25
a. Sheetlet. Nos. 2012/23 .. .. .. 2·40
2013 150 l. Blue-point Siamese 20 25
2014 150 l. American Wirehair 20 25
2015 150 l. Birman 20 25
2016 150 l. Scottish Fold 20 25
2017 150 l. American Shorthair Red Tabby .. 20 25
2018 150 l. Blue and White Persian Bicolour .. 20 25
2019 150 l. Havana Brown 20 25
2020 150 l. Norwegian Forest Cat 20 25
2021 150 l. Brown Tortie Burmese 20 25
2022 150 l. Angora 20 25
2023 150 l. Exotic Shorthair 20 25
2024 150 l. Somali 20 25
a. Sheetlet. Nos. 2024/35 .. .. .. 2·40
2025 150 l. Egyptian Mau Smoke 20 25
2026 150 l. Chocolate-point Siamese 20 25
2027 150 l. Mi-Ke Japanese Bobtail 20 25
2028 150 l. Chinchilla 20 25
2029 150 l. Red Burmese 20 25
2030 150 l. British Shorthair Brown Tabby .. 20 25
2031 150 l. Blue Persian 20 25
2032 150 l. British Silver Classic Tabby 20 25
2033 150 l. Oriental Ebony 20 25
2034 150 l. Red Persian 20 25
2035 150 l. British Calico Shorthair 20 25
2012/35 .. .. *Set of* 24 4·75 6·00
MS2036 Two sheets, each 108×65 mm. (a) 1000 l. American Shorthair Blue Tabby. (b) 1000 l. Seal-point Colourpoint .. *Set of* 2 *sheets* 3·00 3·25

Nos. 2012/23 and 2024/35 were printed together, *se-tenant*, in sheetlets of 12.

Nos. 2012/36 exist imperforate from a limited printing.

261 Gorilla

(Des T. Wood. Litho Questa)

1993 (17 June). *Wildlife. T* **261** *and similar horiz designs. Multicoloured. P* 14.

2037 30 l. Type **261** 40 30
2038 100 l. Bongo 50 35
2039 150 l. Potto 60 60
2040 170 l. Chimpanzee 80 80
2041 200 l. Dwarf Galago 90 90
2042 300 l. African Linsang .. .. 1·10 1·25
2043 500 l. Banded Duiker .. .. 1·50 1·60
2044 750 l. Diana Monkey .. .. 2·00 2·50
2037/44 .. .. *Set of* 8 7·00 7·50
MS2045 Two sheets, each 106×77 mm. (a) 1200 l. African Elephant. (b) 1200 l. Leopard *Set of* 2 *sheets* 7·00 7·50

Nos. 2037/45 exist imperforate from a limited printing.

262 *Clerodendrum thomsonae*

263 Royal Family

(Litho Questa)

1993 (5 July). *Flowers. T* **262** *and similar horiz designs. Multicoloured. P* 14.

2046 30 l. Type **262** 30 20
2047 40 l. *Passiflora quadrangularis* 35 25
2048 50 l. *Hydrangea macrophylla* 35 25
2049 60 l. *Begonia semperflorens* 40 30
2050 100 l. *Hibiscus rosa-sinensis* 50 40
2051 150 l. *Lagerstroemia indica* 75 75
2052 170 l. *Bougainvillea glabra* 85 85
2053 200 l. *Plumbago capensis* .. .. 1·00 1·00
2054 250 l. *Gerbera jamesonae* .. .. 1·25 1·25
2055 300 l. *Thunbergia alata* .. .. .. 1·40 1·50
2056 500 l. *Gloriosa superba* .. .. .. 1·75 2·00
2057 900 l. *Viola odorata* .. .. 2·75 3·25
2046/57 .. .. *Set of* 12 10·50 11·00
MS2058 Three sheets, each 72×102 mm. (a) 1200 l. *Hibiscus rosa-sinensis* (*different*). (b) 1200 l. *Passiflora quadrangularis* (*different*). (c) 1200 l. *Gloriosa superba* (*different*) *Set of* 3 *sheets* 12·00 13·00

Nos. 2046/58 exist imperforate from a limited printing.

(Litho B.D.T.)

1993 (8 Nov). *Anniversaries and Events. T* **263** *and similar vert designs. Black (No. 2061) or multicoloured (others). P* 14.

2059 100 l. Type **263** 15 20
2060 170 l. "Woman with Hat" (Picasso) .. 25 30
2061 200 l. Coronation procession 30 35
2062 200 l. "Buste de Femme" (Picasso) .. 30 35
2063 250 l. Early telescope 35 40
2064 600 l. Queen Elizabeth II in Coronation robes (from photograph by Cecil Beaton) 85 90
2065 800 l. "Maya with a Doll" (Picasso) .. 1·10 1·25
2066 800 l. Craters on Moon .. .. .. 1·10 1·25
2059/66 .. .. *Set of* 8 4·25 5·00
MS2067 Two sheets. (a) 100×70 mm. 1000 l. "Woman of Algiers" (detail) (Picasso). (b) 73×103 mm. 1500 l. "Queen Elizabeth II" (detail) (Pietro Annigoni) .. .. .. *Set of* 2 *sheets* 3·75 4·00

Anniversaries and Events:—Nos. 2059, 2061, 2064, **MS**2067b, 40th anniv of Coronation; Nos. 2060, 2062, 2065, **MS**2067a, 20th death anniv of Picasso (artist); Nos. 2063, 2066, 450th death anniv of Copernicus (astronomer).

(Litho Questa)

1993 (2 Dec). *Christmas. Religious Paintings. Vert designs as T* **76** *of Nevis (St. Kitts-Nevis). Black, pale lemon and red (Nos. 2071/4,* **MS**2076b*) or multicoloured (others). P* 13½×14.

2068 50 l. "Madonna of the Fish" (detail) (Raphael) 15 10
2069 100 l. "Madonna of the Fish" (different detail) (Raphael) 25 20
2070 150 l. "Madonna and Child enthroned with Five Saints" (detail) (Raphael) .. 45 30
2071 200 l. "The Circumcision" (detail) (Dürer) 55 45
2072 250 l. "The Circumcision" (different detail) (Dürer) 65 55
2073 300 l. "The Circumcision" (different detail) (Dürer) 75 75
2074 500 l. "Holy Family with Saints and Two Angels playing Music" (detail) (Dürer) .. .. 1·40 1·60
2075 800 l. "The Holy Family with the Lamb" (detail) (Raphael) .. .. .. 1·90 2·40
2068/75 .. .. *Set of* 8 5·50 5·75
MS2076 Two sheets. (a) 102×127 mm. 1200 l. "Madonna of the Fish" (different detail) (Raphael). (b) 127×102 mm. 1200 l. "Holy Family with Saints and Two Angels playing Music" (different detail) (Dürer) *Set of* 2 *sheets* 6·00 7·00

265 Donald Duck and Toy Train

(Des Alvin White Studios (Nos. 2079/81, 2083, **MS**2085d), Rosemary DeFiglio (others). Litho Questa)

1993 (13–17 Dec). *Christmas. T* **265** *and similar multicoloured designs showing Walt Disney cartoon characters in Christmas scenes. P* 13½×14.

2077 50 l. Type **265** 25 10
2078 100 l. Disney carol singers 40 20
2079 170 l. Mickey drinking punch (17 Dec) .. 70 70
2080 200 l. Pluto with cream-covered bones (17 Dec) 85 85
2081 250 l. Goofy eating angel cakes (17 Dec) 1·00 1·00
2082 500 l. Donald's nephews decorating Christmas tree .. .. 1·75 2·00
2083 600 l. Donald dropping Christmas cake on foot (17 Dec) .. .. 2·00 2·50
2084 800 l. Uncle Scrooge and Daisy under mistletoe .. .. 2·25 2·50
2077/84 .. .. *Set of* 8 8·25 8·75
MS2085 Four sheets. (a) 127×102 mm. 1200 l. Father Christmas in sleigh. P 13½×14. (b) 102×127 mm. 1200 l. Disney carol singers in wood (*horiz*). P 14×13½. (c) 127×102 mm. 1200 l. Father Christmas (*horiz*). P 14×13½. (d) 127×102 mm. 1200 l. Mickey and Minnie with turkey (*horiz*). P 14×13½ (17 Dec) *Set of* 4 *sheets* 13·00 13·50

(Litho Questa)

1993 (22 Dec). *World Cup Football Championship, U.S.A. (1994) (1st issue). Vert designs as T* **278** *of Maldive Islands. Multicoloured. P* 13½×14.

2086 30 l. José Brown with goalkeeper (Argentina) 25 20
2087 50 l. Gary Lineker (England) 35 25
2088 100 l. Carlos Valderrama (Colombia) .. 45 35
2089 250 l. Tomas Skuhravy (Czechoslovakia) and Hector Marchena (Costa Rica) 1·00 1·00
2090 300 l. Butragueno (Spain) .. .. 1·25 1·25
2091 400 l. Roger Milla (Cameroun) .. .. 1·50 1·75
2092 500 l. Roberto Donadoni (Italy) .. .. 1·75 2·00
2093 700 l. Enzo Scifo (Belgium) .. .. 2·25 2·50
2086/93 .. .. *Set of* 8 8·00 8·50

MS2094 Two sheets. (a) 70×100 mm. 1200 l. Mark Wright (England) and Stephane Demol (Belgium). (b) 100×70 mm. 1200 l. Socrates (Brazil). P 13 .. .. .. *Set of* 2 *sheets* 8·00 8·50

See also Nos. 2130/6.

(Des W. Hanson. Litho Questa)

1994 (18 Feb). *"Hong Kong '94" International Stamp Exhibition (1st issue). Horiz designs as T* **293** *of Maldive Islands. Multicoloured. P* 14.

2095 200 l. Hong Kong 1985 $1.70 Bauhinia stamp and Pagoda, Tiger Baum Garden 30 35
a. Horiz pair. Nos. 2095/6 .. .. 60 70
2096 200 l. Sierra Leone 1989 70 l. Orchid stamp and Aw Par Gardens 30 35

Nos. 2095/6 were printed together, *se-tenant*, in horizontal pairs throughout the sheet.

(Des Kerri Schiff. Litho Questa)

1994 (18 Feb). *"Hong Kong '94" International Stamp Exhibition (2nd issue). Ching Dynasty Carved Lacquerware. Multicoloured designs as T* **294** *of Maldive Islands, but horiz. P* 14.

2097 100 l. Bowl 15 20
a. Sheetlet. Nos. 2097/102 90
2098 100 l. Four-wheeled box 15 20
2099 100 l. Flower container 15 20
2100 100 l. Box with human figure design .. 15 20
2101 100 l. Shishi dog 15 20
2102 100 l. Box with persimmon design .. 15 20
2097/102 .. .. *Set of* 6 90 1·10

Nos. 2097/102 were printed together, *se-tenant*, in sheetlets of 6.

(**266**)

267 Pekingese

1994 (18 Feb). *"Hong Kong '94" International Stamp Exhibition (3rd issue). Nos.* 2013, 2025 *and* **MS**2036 *optd with T* **266**.

2103 150 l. Blue-point Siamese 20 25
a. Sheetlet. Nos. 2012, 2014/23 and 2103 .. .. 2·40
2104 150 l. Egyptian Mau Smoke 20 25
a. Sheetlet. Nos. 2024, 2026/35 and 2104 .. .. 2·40

MS2105 Two sheets, each 108×65 mm. (a) 1000 l. American Shorthair Blue Tabby. (b) 1000 l. Seal-point Colourpoint .. *Set of* 2 *sheets* 3·00 3·25

Nos. 2103a and 2104a only show overprint Type **266** on Nos. 2103 and 2104, and on the sheetlet margins. On No. **MS**2105 Type **266** appears on the margins of the miniature sheets.

(Des R. Sauber. Litho Questa)

1994 (20 June). *Chinese New Year ("Year of the Dog"). T* **267** *and similar horiz designs. Multicoloured. P* 14.

2106 100 l. Type **267** 15 20
a. Sheetlet. Nos. 2106/13 .. .. 4·75
2107 150 l. Dobermann Pinscher 20 25
2108 200 l. Tibetan Terrier 30 35
2109 250 l. Weimaraner 35 40
2110 400 l. Rottweiler 60 65
2111 500 l. Akita 75 80
2112 600 l. Schnauzer 85 90
2113 1000 l. Tibetan Spaniel .. .. .. 1·50 1·60
2106/13 .. .. *Set of* 8 4·50 5·00

MS2114 Two sheets, each 116×88 mm. (a) 1200 l. Wire-haired Pointing Griffon. (b) 1200 l. Shih Tzu .. .. .. *Set of* 2 *sheets* 3·50 3·75

Nos. 2106/13 were printed together, *se-tenant*, in sheetlets of 8.

(Des J. Batchelor. Litho B.D.T.)

1994 (11 July). *50th Anniv of D-Day. Horiz designs as T* **304** *of Maldive Islands. Multicoloured. P* 14.

2115 500 l. British paratroop drop .. .. 1·25 1·25
2116 750 l. U.S. paratrooper jumping from aircraft .. .. 1·75 1·75

MS2117 106×76 mm. 1000 l. U.S. paratrooper preparing to jump from Douglas C-47 Dakota 2·00 2·25

(Des Kerri Schiff. Litho Questa (Nos. 2119/26), B.D.T. (others))

1994 (11 July). *"Philakorea '94" International Stamp Exhibition, Seoul. Multicoloured designs as T* **305** *of Maldive Islands. P* 14 *(Nos.* 2118, 2127/8*) or* 13 *(others).*

2118 100 l. Traditional wedding 40 25
2119 200 l. Tiger and cubs 60 60
a. Sheetlet. Nos. 2119/26 .. .. 4·25
2120 200 l. Munsa-pasal 60 60
2121 200 l. Extinct Korean tiger 60 60
2122 200 l. Tiger and bamboo 60 60
2123 200 l. Tiger, three cubs and magpies .. 60 60
2124 200 l. Tiger, two cubs and magpies .. 60 60
2125 200 l. Mountain spirit 60 60
2126 200 l. Tiger and magpie 60 60
2127 400 l. Royal tombs, Kaesong .. .. 1·00 1·00
2128 600 l. Terraced fields, Chungmu .. .. 1·50 1·75
2118/28 .. .. *Set of* 11 7·00 7·00

MS2129 100×70 mm. 1200 l. Tiger hunt. P 14 2·75 3·00

Nos. 2119/26, each 23×48 mm, were printed together, *se-tenant*, in sheetlets of 8 and show paintings of tigers.

No. **MS**2129 is inscribed "Sierre Leone" in error.

268 Kim Ho (South Korea)

(Litho Questa)

1994 (15 July). *World Cup Football Championship, U.S.A. (2nd issue). T* **268** *and similar horiz designs. Multicoloured. P* 14.

2130 250 l. Type **268** 75 75
a. Sheetlet. Nos. 2130/5 .. .. 4·00
2131 250 l. Cobi Jones (U.S.A.) ("No. 13") .. 75 75
2132 250 l. Claudio Suarez (Mexico) ("No. 2") .. 75 75
2133 250 l. Tomas Brolin (Sweden) ("No. 11") .. 75 75
2134 250 l. Ruud Gullit (Holland) (red shirt without number) 75 75
2135 250 l. Andreas Herzog (Austria) (white shirt without number) 75 75
2130/5 .. .. *Set of* 6 4·00 4·00

MS2136 Two sheets. (a) 70×100 mm. 1500 l. Player and Giant Stadium, New Jersey. (b) 100×70 mm. 1500 l. Sierra Leone national team *Set of* 2 *sheets* 6·00 6·50

Nos. 2130/5 were printed together, *se-tenant*, in sheetlets of 6.

(Des W. Hanson. Litho Questa)

1994 (20 July). *25th Anniv of First Moon Landing. Multicoloured designs as T* **302** *of Maldive Islands. P* 14.

2137 200 l. Buzz Aldrin gathering Moon samples 30 35
a. Sheetlet. Nos. 2137/42 .. .. 1·75
2138 200 l. Lunar Module *Eagle* on Moon's surface 30 35
2139 200 l. Tranquility Base 30 35
2140 200 l. Aldrin with U.S. flag 30 35
2141 200 l. Plaque 30 35
2142 200 l. "Apollo 11" crew with stamps .. 30 35
2143 200 l. Edwin Aldrin 30 35
a. Sheetlet. Nos. 2143/8 .. .. 1·75
2144 200 l. Michael Collins 30 35
2145 200 l. Neil Armstrong 30 35
2146 200 l. "Apollo 11" lift off 30 35
2147 200 l. Aldrin descending to Moon's surface 30 35
2148 200 l. Reflection in Aldrin's face shield .. 30 35
2137/48 .. .. *Set of* 12 3·50 4·00

MS2149 103×73 mm. 1000 l. First lunar footprint (*vert*) .. .. 1·50 1·60

Nos. 2137/42 and 2143/8 were each printed together, *se-tenant*, in sheetlets of 6.

269 White-necked Bald Crow ("White-necked Picathartes") feeding Chicks

270 *Aerangis kotschyana*

(Litho Questa)

1994 (10 Aug). *Birds. T* **269** *and similar multicoloured designs. P* 14.

2150 50 l. Type **269** 50 50
a. Vert strip of 4. Nos. 2150/3 .. 2·40
2151 100 l. Adult White-necked Bald Crow .. 60 60
2152 150 l. Pair of White-necked Bald Crows .. 75 75
2153 200 l. Young White-necked Bald Crow .. 80 80
2154 250 l. Black Kite 85 85
2155 300 l. Superb Sunbird 95 95
2156 500 l. Martial Eagle .. .. .. 1·60 1·75
2157 800 l. Red Bishop .. .. .. 2·00 2·50
2150/7 .. .. *Set of* 8 7·25 8·00

MS2158 Two sheets, each 90×65 mm. (a) 1200 l. Greater Flamingo (*vert*). (b) 1200 l. White-necked Bald Crow (*vert*) .. *Set of* 2 *sheets* 4·75 5·00

Nos. 2150/3, which carry the W.W.F. Panda emblem, were printed together, *se-tenant*, as vertical strips of four in sheetlets of 12.

Nos. 2150/7 exist imperforate from a limited printing.

(Des D. Burkhart. Litho Questa)

1994 (1 Sept). *Orchids. T* **270** *and similar vert designs. Multicoloured. P* 14.

2159 50 l. Type **270** 15 10
2160 100 l. *Brachycorythis kalbreyeri* 25 20
2161 150 l. *Diaphananthe pellucida* 35 30
2162 200 l. *Eulophia guineensis* 45 40
2163 300 l. *Eurychone rothschildiana* 65 65
2164 500 l. *Tridactyle tridactylites* .. .. 1·25 1·25
2165 750 l. *Cyrtorchis arcuata* .. .. 1·75 2·00
2166 900 l. *Ancistrochilus rothschildianus* .. 2·00 2·50
2159/66 .. .. *Set of* 8 6·00 6·50

MS2167 Two sheets, each 117×78 mm. (a) 1500 l. *Plectrelminthus caudatus*. (b) 1500 l. *Polystachaya affinis* .. .. *Set of* 2 *sheets* 6·50 7·00

(Litho Questa)

1994 (19 Dec). *Christmas. Religious Paintings. Vert designs as T* **290** *of St. Vincent. Multicoloured. P* 13½×14.

2168 50 l. "The Birth of the Virgin" (Murillo) 25 10
2169 100 l. "Education of the Virgin" (Murillo) 35 20
2170 150 l. "Annunciation" (detail) (Filippino Lippi) 60 55
2171 200 l. "Marriage of the Virgin" (Bernard van Orley) 75 70
2172 250 l. "The Visitation" (Nicolas Vleughels) 90 90
2173 300 l. "Castelfranco Altarpiece" (detail) (Giorgione) .. .. 1·10 1·10
2174 400 l. "Adoration of the Magi" (workshop of Bartholome Zeitblom) .. .. 1·40 1·60
2175 600 l. "Presentation of Infant Jesus in the Temple" (Master of the Prado) .. 1·75 2·25
2168/75 .. .. *Set of* 8 6·25 6·50

MS2176 Two sheets, each 115×95 mm. (a) 1500 l. "Nativity Altarpiece" (detail) (Lorenzo Monaco). (b) 1500 l. "Allendale Nativity" (detail) (Giorgione) .. .. .. *Set of* 2 *sheets* 6·50 7·00

271 Family working in Field

(Litho Questa)

1994 (20 Dec). *International Year of the Family. T* **271** *and similar horiz design. Multicoloured. P* 14.

2177 300 l. Type **271** 45 50
2178 350 l. Family on beach 50 55

272 Mickey Mouse stroking Cat

(Des Alvin White Studios. Litho Questa)

1995 (23 Jan). *Christmas. T* **272** *and similar multicoloured designs showing Walt Disney cartoon characters. P* 14×13½ *(horiz) or* 13½×14 *(vert).*

2179 50 l. Type **272** 25 10
2180 100 l. Goofy with Christmas tree and axe (*vert*) 30 20
2181 150 l. Donald Duck giving Daisy Duck a plant 55 45
2182 200 l. Donald finding Chipmunk in stocking (*vert*) 70 60
2183 250 l. Minnie Mouse in airplane 85 85
2184 300 l. Goofy in snowball (*vert*) .. .. 1·00 1·00
2185 400 l. Goofy with Chip N' Dale at mail box 1·25 1·40
2186 500 l. Mickey and Donald on sledge (*vert*) 1·50 1·60
2187 600 l. Mickey and Minnie making snow-mouse .. .. 1·75 2·25
2188 800 l. Mickey and Pluto with cake (*vert*) 2·00 2·50
2179/88 .. .. *Set of* 10 9·00 9·75

MS2189 Two sheets. (a) 108×133 mm. 1500 l. Goofy caught up in Christmas lights. (b) 130×108 mm. 1500 l. Mickey asleep in armchair (*vert*) .. .. *Set of* 2 *sheets* 6·50 7·00

273 "Madonna Duck" (after Da Vinci)

274 Ragnar Lundberg (Sweden) (1952 pole vault bronze medal)

(Des Alvin White Studios. Litho Questa)

1995 (23 Jan). *Donald's Gallery of Old Masters. T* **273** *and similar multicoloured designs showing Donald and Daisy Duck in portraits inspired by famous paintings. P* 13½×14.

2190 50 l. Type **273** 10 10
2191 100 l. "Portrait of a Venetian Duck" (after Tintoretto) 15 20
2192 150 l. "Duck with a Glove" (after Frans Hals) 20 25

2193 200 l. "Donald with a Pink" (after Massys) 30 35
2194 250 l. "Pinkie Daisy" (after Lawrence) .. 35 40
2195 300 l. "Donald's Whistling Mother" (after Whistler) 45 50
2196 400 l. "El Quacko" (after El Greco) .. 60 65
2197 500 l. "The Noble Snob" (after Rembrandt) 75 80
2198 600 l. "The Blue Duck" (after Gainsborough) 85 90
2199 800 l. "Modern Quack" (after Picasso) .. 1·10 1·25
2190/9 .. .. *Set of* 10 4·75 5·25
MS2200 Two sheets, each 133×108 mm. (a) 1500 l. "Soup's On" (detail) (after Brueghel). P 13½×14. (b) 1500 l. "Two Duck Dancers" (detail) (after Degas) (*horiz*). P 14×13½ *Set of* 2 *sheets* 5·50 6·00

(Litho Questa)

1995 (6 Feb). *Centenary of International Olympic Committee. Medal Winners. T* **274** *and similar multicoloured designs. P* 14.
2201 75 l. Type **274** 10 10
a. Sheetlet. Nos. 2201/12 .. .. 1·10
2202 75 l. Karin Janz (Germany) (1972 gymnastics silver) 10 10
2203 75 l. Matthias Volz (Germany) (1936 gymnastics bronze) 10 10
2204 75 l. Carl Lewis (U.S.A.) (1988 long jump gold) 10 10
2205 75 l. Sara Simeoni (Italy) (1976 high jump silver) 10 10
2206 75 l. Daley Thompson (Great Britain) (1980 decathlon gold) 10 10
2207 75 l. Japan and Britain (1964 football) .. 10 10
2208 75 l. Gabriella Dorio (Italy) (1984 1500 metres gold) 10 10
2209 75 l. Daniela Hunger (Germany) (1988 swimming gold) 10 10
2210 75 l. Kyoko Iwasaki (Japan) (1992 swimming bronze) 10 10
2211 75 l. Italian team (1960 water polo gold) 10 10
2212 75 l. David Wilkie (Great Britain) (1976 swimming gold) 10 10
2213 200 l. Katja Seizinger (Germany) (1994 alpine skiing gold) 30 35
a. Sheetlet. Nos. 2213/24 .. .. 3·50
2214 200 l. Hot air balloon showing Olympic Rings 30 35
2215 200 l. Elvis Stojko (Canada) (1994 figure skating silver) 30 35
2216 200 l. Jans Weissflog (Germany) (1994 ski jumping gold) 30 35
2217 200 l. Bjorn Daehlie (Norway) (1994 cross-country skiing gold) 30 35
2218 200 l. German team (1994 four-man bobsled gold) 30 35
2219 200 l. Markus Wasmeier (Germany) (1994 alpine skiing gold) 30 35
2220 200 l. Georg Hackl (Germany) (1994 luge gold) 30 35
2221 200 l. Jayne Torvill and Christopher Dean (Great Britain) (1994 ice dancing, bronze) 30 35
2222 200 l. Bonnie Blair (U.S.A.) (1994 speed skating gold) 30 35
2223 200 l. Nancy Kerrigan (U.S.A.) (1994 figure skating silver) 30 35
2224 200 l. Sweden team (1994 ice hockey gold) 30 35
2201/24 .. .. *Set of* 24 4·50 5·25
MS2225 Two sheets, each 100×70 mm. (a) 1000 l. Medal winners (1994 women's figure skating) (*horiz*). (b) 1000 l. Athlete holding Olympic Torch (*horiz*) .. .. *Set of* 2 *sheets* 3·00 3·25
Nos. 2201/12 and 2213/24 were printed together, *se-tenant*, in sheetlets of 12 forming composite designs.

275 Ceratosaurus

(Des D. Burkhart. Litho Questa)

1995 (4 May). *Prehistoric Animals. T* **275** *and similar multicoloured designs. P* 14.
2226 200 l. Type **275** 30 35
a. Sheetlet. Nos. 2226/37 .. .. 3·50
2227 200 l. Brachiosaurus 30 35
2228 200 l. Pteranodon 30 35
2229 200 l. Stegoceras 30 35
2230 200 l. Saurolophus 30 35
2231 200 l. Ornithomumus 30 35
2232 200 l. Compsognathus 30 35
2233 200 l. Deinonychus 30 35
2234 200 l. Ornitholestes 30 35
2235 200 l. Archaeopteryx 30 35
2236 200 l. Heterodontosaurus 30 35
2237 200 l. Lesothosaurus 30 35
2226/37 .. .. *Set of* 12 3·50 4·00
MS2238 130×58 mm. 100 l. Triceratops (*vert*); 250 l. Protoceratops (*vert*); 400 l. Monoclonius (*vert*); 800 l. Styracosaurus (*vert*) .. .. 2·25 2·40
MS2239 Two sheets, each 99×79 mm. (a) 2500 l. Rhamphorynchus (*vert*). (b) 2500 l. Deinonychus (*vert*) .. .. .. *Set of* 2 *sheets* 7·25 7·50
Nos. 2226/37 were printed together, *se-tenant*, in sheetlets of 12 forming a composite design.

276 Pig (on red panel)

(Des Y. Lee. Litho Questa)

1995 (8 May). *Chinese New Year ("Year of the Pig"). T* **276** *and similar multicoloured designs. P* 14.
2240 100 l. Type **276** 15 20
a. Block of 4. Nos. 2240/3 60
ab. Error. Stamp shows face value as "75 c." .. ..
2241 100 l. Pig facing right (on green panel) .. 15 20
2242 100 l. Pig facing left (on green panel) .. 15 20
2243 100 l. Pig facing right (on red panel) .. 15 20
2240/3 .. .. *Set of* 4 60 80
MS2244 77×105 mm. 500 l. Two pigs (*vert*) .. 75 80
Nos. 2240/3 were printed together, *se-tenant*, as blocks of 4 in sheets of 16.
No. 2240ab comes from the initial supplies sent to Freetown and withdrawn on day of issue when the incorrect face values were noticed.

(Litho Questa)

1995 (10 May). *Centenary of Sierra Club (environmental protection society) (1992). Endangered Species. Multicoloured designs as T* **296** *of Maldive Islands. P* 14.
2245 150 l. Black-faced Impalas (*horiz*) .. 20 25
a. Sheetlet. Nos. 2245/53 .. 1·75
2246 150 l. Herd of Black-faced Impalas (*horiz*) 20 25
2247 150 l. Black-faced Impalas drinking (*horiz*) 20 25
2248 150 l. Bonobo with young (*horiz*) .. 20 25
2249 150 l. Black-footed Cat in foliage (*horiz*) 20 25
2250 150 l. Close-up of Black-footed Cat (*horiz*) 20 25
2251 150 l. L'Hoest's Monkey on all fours (*horiz*) 20 25
2252 150 l. L'Hoest's Monkey squatting (*horiz*) 20 25
2253 150 l. Pair of Mandrills (*horiz*) .. 20 25
2254 150 l. L'Hoest's Monkey 20 25
a. Sheetlet. Nos. 2254/62 .. 1·75
2255 150 l. Black-footed Cat 20 25
2256 150 l. Head of Colobus Monkey .. 20 25
2257 150 l. Colobus Monkey in tree fork .. 20 25
2258 150 l. Head of Mandrill 20 25
2259 150 l. Bonobo with young 20 25
2260 150 l. Bonobo asleep on log 20 25
2261 150 l. Mandrill facing right 20 25
2262 150 l. Colobus Monkey on log .. 20 25
2245/62 .. .. *Set of* 18 3·50 4·50
Nos. 2245/53 and 2254/62 were each printed together, *se-tenant*, in sheetlets of 9.

277 Denver and Rio Grande Western Railroad

(Des W. Wright. Litho China Security Ptg Ltd)

1995 (23 May). *Railways of the World. T* **277** *and similar horiz designs. Multicoloured. P* 14.
2263/74 200 l. × 12 (Type **277**; Central of Georgia; Seaboard Air Line; Missouri Pacific Lines; Atchison, Topeka and Santa Fe; Chicago, Milwaukee, St. Paul and Pacific; Texas and Pacific; Minneapolis, St. Paul and Sault Ste. Marie; Western Pacific; Great Northern; Baltimore and Ohio; Chicago, Rock Island and Pacific)
a. Sheetlet. Nos. 2263/74 .. .. 3·50 3·75
2275/86 200 l. × 12 (Southern Pacific; Belgian National; Indian; Southern Australian; Union Pacific; British Railways "Royal Scot" express; German Federal; Japanese National; Pennsylvania; East African; Milwaukee "Hiawatha" express; Paris–Orleans)
a. Sheetlet. Nos. 2275/86 .. .. 3·50 3·75
2287/98 250 l. × 12 (Eurostar Express; E.T.R. "401" Pendoling tilting train, British Rail Intercity "125"; Virgin express; French National TGV; Amtrak "Southwest Chief" express; French National TGV "Atlantique" express; Greek "Peloponnese Express"; Japanese "Shin-Kansen" train; Canadian National train; Australian XPT high-speed train; Chinese "SS1" electric locomotive)
a. Sheetlet. Nos. 2287/98 .. .. 4·25 4·50
2299/310 300 l. × 12 (Canadian National "U1-F" locomotive; Central Pacific Railways No. 119 locomotive; L.N.E.R. No. 4468 *Mallard* locomotive; New York Central "Empire State Express"; Canadian National "4-8-4" locomotive; Australian Class "38" locomotive; Canadian Pacific "4-6-2" express; Southern Railway Class "West Country" locomotive; Norfolk & Western Class "J" locomotive; China Class "RM" locomotive; Soviet Union Class "P-36" locomotive; G.W.R. Class "King" locomotive)
a. Sheetlet. Nos. 2298/310 .. 5·50 5·75
2263/310 .. .. *Set of* 48 17·00 18·00
MS2311 Five sheets, each 107×79 mm containing larger designs, 56½×42½ mm. (a) 1500 l. British Railways No. 45627 *Sierra Leone* locomotive. (b) 1500 l. China Railways Class "OJ" locomotive. (c) 1500 l. Denver and Rio Grande Western Railroad "California Zephyr" express. (d) 1500 l. China Railways "Beijing to Shanghai Express". (e) 1500 l. China Railways first train across Yangtze Bridge, 1968 *Set of* 5 *sheets* 11·50 12·00
Nos. 2263/74, 2275/86, 2287/98 and 2299/310 were each printed together, *se-tenant*, in sheetlets of 12.

278 National Flag and Scout Emblems

1995 (10 July). *18th World Scout Jamboree, Netherlands. T* **278** *and similar horiz designs. Multicoloured. Litho. P* 14.
2312 400 l. Type **278** 60 65
a. Horiz strip of 3. Nos. 2312/14 .. 2·25
2313 500 l. Lord Baden-Powell 75 80
2314 600 l. Scout sign 85 90
2312/14 .. .. *Set of* 3 2·25 2·40
MS2315 80×111 mm. 1500 l. Scout saluting .. 2·25 2·40
Nos. 2312/14 were printed in sheets of 9 containing three *se-tenant* horizontal strips.

(Des W. Wright. Litho)

1995 (10 July). *50th Anniv of End of Second World War in Europe. Horiz designs as T* **317** *of Maldive Islands showing warships. Multicoloured. P* 14.
2316 250 l. U.S.S. *Idaho* (battleship) 35 40
a. Sheetlet. Nos. 2316/23 .. .. 2·75
2317 250 l. H.M.S. *Ark Royal* (aircraft carrier) 35 40
2318 250 l. *Admiral Graf Spee* (German pocket battleship) 35 40
2319 250 l. American destroyer 35 40
2320 250 l. H.M.S. *Nelson* (battleship) .. 35 40
2321 250 l. U.S.S. *PT 109* (motor torpedo boat) 35 40
2322 250 l. U.S.S. *Iowa* (battleship) .. 35 40
2323 250 l. *Bismark* (German battleship) .. 35 40
2316/23 .. .. *Set of* 8 2·75 3·25
MS2324 105×74 mm. 1500 l. H.M.S. *Indomitable* (aircraft carrier) (57×42½ *mm*) .. .. 2·25 2·40
Nos. 2316/23 were printed together, *se-tenant*, in sheetlets of 8 with the stamps arranged in two horizontal strips of 4 separated by a gutter showing German U-boat pursuing Allied convoy.

(Des R. Rundo. Litho)

1995 (10 July). *50th Anniv of the United Nations. Multicoloured designs as T* **319** *of Maldive Islands, but vert. P* 14.
2325 300 l. U.N. emblem above podium .. 45 50
a. Horiz strip of 3. Nos. 2325/7 .. 1·75
2326 400 l. U Thant (Secretary-General, 1961–71) 60 65
2327 500 l. Peace dove and U.N. Building, New York 75 80
2325/7 .. .. *Set of* 3 1·75 1·90
MS2328 105×74 mm. 1500 l. Dag Hammarskjold (Secretary-General, 1953–61) .. .. .. 2·25 2·40
Nos. 2325/7 were printed together in sheets of 9 containing three *se-tenant* horizontal strips of 3 forming a composite design.

(Des R. Rundo. Litho)

1995 (10 July–Sept). *50th Anniv of Food and Agriculture Organization. Multicoloured designs as T* **298** *of St. Vincent. P* 14.
2329 300 l. Fisherman in boat (*horiz*) .. 45 50
a. Horiz strip of 3. Nos. 2329/31 .. 1·75
2330 400 l. Boy carrying wood (*horiz*) .. 60 65
2331 500 l. Woman with fruit (*horiz*) .. 75 80
2329/31 .. .. *Set of* 3 1·75 1·90
MS2332 76×106 mm. 1500 l. Mother and child (without date below emblem on woman's shoulder) (Sept) .. .. .. 2·25 2·40
a. Inscr "1945–55" below emblem on woman's shoulder .. ..
Nos. 2329/31 were printed together in sheets of 9 containing three *se-tenant* horizontal strips.
No. **MS**2332a comes from the initial supplies sent to Freetown and withdrawn on day of issue when the wrong date was noticed.

(Litho Questa)

1995 (10 July). *90th Anniv of Rotary International. Horiz designs as T* **299** *of St. Vincent. Multicoloured. P* 14.
2333 500 l. National flag and Rotary logo .. 75 80
MS2334 105×75 mm. 1000 l. Paul Harris (founder) and logo .. .. 1·50 1·60

(Litho Questa)

1995 (10 July). *95th Birthday of Queen Elizabeth the Queen Mother. Vert designs as T* **321** *of Maldive Islands*. P 13½×14.
2335 400 l. orange-brown, pale brown and black 60 65
a. Sheetlet. Nos. 2335/8×2 2·40
2336 400 l. multicoloured 60 65
2337 400 l. multicoloured 60 65
2338 400 l. multicoloured 60 65
2335/8 *Set of* 4 2·40 2·50
MS2339 102×127 mm. 1500 l. multicoloured 2·25 2·40

Designs:—No. 2335, Queen Elizabeth the Queen Mother (pastel drawing); No. 2336, Holding bouquet of flowers; Nos. 2337, At desk (oil painting); No. 2338, Wearing pink evening dress; No. **MS**2339, Wearing blue hat.

Nos. 2335/8 were printed together in sheetlets of 8, containing two *se-tenant* horizontal strips of 4.

(Des J. Batchelor. Litho Questa)

1995 (10 July). *50th Anniv of End of Second World War in the Pacific. Horiz designs as T* **317** *of Maldive Islands. Multicoloured*. P 14.
2340 300 l. American B-17 bomber 45 50
a. Sheetlet. Nos. 2340/5 2·75
2341 300 l. American B-25 bomber 45 50
2342 300 l. American Consolidated B-24 Liberator bomber 45 50
2343 300 l. U.S.S. *Missouri* (battleship) 45 50
2344 300 l. American Douglas A-20 Boston bomber 45 50
2345 300 l. American battle fleet in Lingayen Gulf 45 50
2340/5 *Set of* 6 2·75 3·00
MS2346 108×76 mm. 1500 l. Nose of B-29 Superfortress 1·50 1·60

Nos. 2340/5 were printed together, *se-tenant*, in sheetlets of 6 with the stamps arranged in two horizontal strips of 3 separated by a gutter showing sinking U.S.S. *Arizona* (battleship).

No. 2340 is inscribed "B-179" in error.

279 Black-spotted Pufferfish

280 Flame Lily

(Des Y. Lee. Litho Questa)

1995 (4 Sept). *"Singapore '95" International Stamp Exhibition (1st issue). Marine Life. T* **279** *and similar multicoloured designs*. P 14.
2347 300 l. Type **279** 45 50
a. Sheetlet. Nos. 2347/55 4·00
2348 300 l. Coral Hind 45 50
2349 300 l. Hawksbill Turtle 45 50
2350 300 l. Hogfish 45 50
2351 300 l. Emperor Angelfish 45 50
2352 300 l. Red-tailed Butterflyfish 45 50
2353 300 l. Lemon Butterflyfish 45 50
2354 300 l. Green-beaked Parrot Fish 45 50
2355 300 l. Spotted Reef Moray 45 50
2356 300 l. Cape Pigeons 45 50
a. Sheetlet. Nos. 2356/64 4·00
2357 300 l. Pelican 45 50
2358 300 l. Puffin 45 50
2359 300 l. Humpback Whale 45 50
2360 300 l. Greater Shearwater 45 50
2361 300 l. Bottlenose Dolphin 45 50
2362 300 l. Gurnards 45 50
2363 300 l. Atlantic Salmon 45 50
2364 300 l. John Dory 45 50
2347/64 *Set of* 18 8·00 9·00
MS2365 Two sheets. (a) 71×101 mm. 1500 l. Ocean Surgeonfish. (b) 101×71 mm. 1500 l. Pennant Coralfish ("Angelfish") (*vert*) *Set of* 2 *sheets* 4·50 4·75

Nos. 2347/55 and 2356/64 were printed together, *se-tenant*, in sheetlets of 9 forming composite designs.

(Des T. Pedersen. Litho Questa)

1995 (5 Sept). *"Singapore '95" International Stamp Exhibition (2nd issue). African Flora and Fauna. T* **280** *and similar vert designs. Multicoloured*. P 14.
2366 300 l. Type **280** 45 50
a. Sheetlet. Nos. 2366/73 3·50
2367 300 l. Grant's Gazelle 45 50
2368 300 l. Dogbane 45 50
2369 300 l. Gold-banded Forester 45 50
2370 300 l. Horned Chameleon 45 50
2371 300 l. Malachite Kingfisher 45 50
2372 300 l. Leaf Beetle 45 50
2373 300 l. Acanthus 45 50
2374 300 l. African Tulip Tree 45 50
a. Sheetlet. Nos. 2374/81 3·50
2375 300 l. Senegal Bush Locust 45 50
2376 300 l. Killfish 45 50
2377 300 l. Bird of Paradise (flower) 45 50
2378 300 l. Mandrill 45 50
2379 300 l. Painted Reed Frog 45 50
2380 300 l. Large Spotted Acraea 45 50
2381 300 l. Carmine Bee Eater 45 50
2366/81 *Set of* 16 7·00 8·00
MS2382 Two sheets, each 103×73 mm. (a) 1500 l. Elephant. (b) 1500 l. Lion *Set of* 2 *sheets* 4·50 4·75

Nos. 2366/73 and 2374/81 were printed together, *se-tenant*, in sheetlets of 8.

281 School Building and Emblem

(Litho Questa)

1995 (27 Sept). *150th Anniv of Sierra Leone Grammar School*. P 14.
2383 **281** 300 l. sepia, deep magenta and black 45 50

(Litho Questa)

1995 (1 Dec). *Christmas. Religious Paintings. Vert designs as T* **98** *of St. Kitts-Nevis (Nevis). Multicoloured*. P 13½×14.
2384 50 l. "Holy Family" (detail) (Beccafumi) 10 15
2385 100 l. "The Rest on the Flight into Egypt" (detail) (Federico Barocci) 15 20
2386 150 l. "The Virgin" (Jacopo Bellini) 20 25
2387 200 l. "The Flight" (Cavaliere d'Arpino) 30 35
2388 600 l. "Adoration of the Magi" (detail) (Francken) 85 90
2389 800 l. "The Annunciation" (Cima de Conegliano) 1·10 1·25
2384/9 *Set of* 6 2·75 3·00
MS2390 Two sheets, each 102×127 mm. (a) 1500 l. "Virgin and Child" (detail) (Cranach). (b) 1500 l. "Madonna and Child" (detail) (Berlinghiero) *Set of* 2 *sheets* 4·50 4·75

282 Mickey Mouse Doll

283 Andrew Huxley (1963 Medicine)

(Des Rosemary DeFiglio. Litho Questa)

1995 (4 Dec). *Christmas. Disney Toys. T* **282** *and similar vert designs. Multicoloured*. P 13½×14.
2391 5 l. Type **282** 10 10
2392 10 l. Donald Duck drum-major doll 10 10
2393 15 l. Donald Duck wind-up toy 10 10
2394 20 l. Donald Duck toothbrush holder 10 10
2395 25 l. Mickey Mouse telephone 10 10
2396 30 l. Mickey Mouse walking toy 10 10
2397 800 l. Toy film projector 1·10 1·25
2398 1000 l. Goofy tricycle toy 1·50 1·60
2391/8 *Set of* 8 2·75 3·00
MS2399 Two sheets, each 133×107 mm. (a) 1500 l. Black Mickey Mouse doll. (b) 1500 l. First Mickey Mouse book *Set of* 2 *sheets* 4·50 4·75

(Des R. Martin (Nos. 2400/8), Shyna Magid (others). Litho Questa)

1995 (29 Dec). *Centenary of Nobel Prize Trust Fund. T* **283** *and similar vert designs. Multicoloured*. P 14.
2400/8 250 l. × 9 (Type **283**; Nelson Mandela (1993 Peace); Gabriela Mistral (1945 Literature); Otto Diels (1950 Chemistry); Hannes Alfven (1970 Physics); Wole Soyinka (1986 Literature); Hans Dehmelt (1989 Physics); Desmond Tutu (1984 Peace); Leo Esaki (1973 Physics))
a. Sheetlet. Nos. 2400/8 3·25 3·50
2409/17 250 l. × 9 (Tobias Asser (1911 Peace); Andrei Sakharov (1975 Peace); Frédéric Passy (1901 Peace); Dag Hammarskjöld (1961 Peace); Aung San Suu Kyi (1991 Peace); Ludwig Quidde (1927 Peace); Elie Wiesel (1986 Peace); Bertha von Suttner (1905 Peace); The Dalai Lama (1989 Peace))
a. Sheetlet. Nos. 2409/17 3·25 3·50
2418/26 250 l. × 9 (Richard Zsigmondy (1925 Chemistry); Robert Huber (1988 Chemistry); Wilhelm Ostwald (1909 Chemistry); Johann Deisenhofer (1988 Chemistry); Heinrich Wieland (1922 Chemistry); Gerhard Herzberg (1971 Chemistry); Hans von Euler-Chelpin (1929 Chemistry); Richard Willsätter (1915 Chemistry); Fritz Haber (1918 Chemustry))
a. Sheetlet. Nos. 2418/26 3·25 3·50
2427/35 250 l. × 9 (Maria Goeppert Mayer (1963 Physics); Iréne Joliot-Curie (1935 Chemistry); Mother Teresa (1979 Peace); Selma Lagerlöf (1909 Literature); Rosalyn Yalow (1977 Medicine); Dorothy Hodgkin (1964 Chemistry); Rita Levi-Montalcini (1986 Medicine); Mairead Corrigan (1976 Peace); Betty Williams (1976 Peace))
a. Sheetlet. Nos. 2427/35 3·25 3·50
2400/35 *Set of* 36 13·00 14·00
MS2436 Three sheets, each 80×110 mm. (a) 1500 l. Albert Einstein (1921 Physics). (b) 1500 l. Wilhelm Röntgen (1901 Physics). (c) 1500 l. Sin-Itiro Tomonaga (1965 Physics) *Set of* 3 *sheets* 6·75 7·00

Nos. 2400/8, 2409/17, 2418/26 and 2427/35 were each printed together, *se-tenant*, in sheetlets of 9.

284 Rat

(Des Y. Lee. Litho Questa)

1996 (2 Jan). *Chinese New Year ("Year of the Rat"). T* **284** *and similar designs with background colour given*. P 14.
2437 **284** 200 l. mult (yellow-brown background) 30 35
a. Block of 4. Nos. 2437/40 1·25
2438 – 200 l. mult (rose-red background) 30 35
2439 – 200 l. mult (orange-verm background) 30 35
2440 – 200 l. mult (turquoise-bl background) 30 35
2437/40 *Set of* 4 1·25 1·40
MS2441 110×84 mm. Nos. 2437/40 1·25 1·40
MS2442 76×106 mm. 500 l. multicoloured (orange-red background) (*vert*) 75 80

Nos. 2437/40 were printed together, *se-tenant*, as blocks of 4 in sheets of 16.

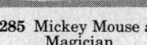

285 Mickey Mouse as Magician

286 Lumiére Brothers (cine camera inventors) and Train

(Litho Questa)

1996 (29 Jan). *Disney Circus Performers. T* **285** *and similar multicoloured designs showing cartoon characters*. P 13½×14.
2443 100 l. Type **285** 15 20
2444 200 l. Clarabelle Cow walking tightrope 30 35
2445 250 l. Donald Duck and nephews as clowns 35 40
2446 300 l. Donald as lion tamer 45 50
2447 800 l. Minnie Mouse riding bareback 1·10 1·25
2448 1000 l. Goofy on trapeze 1·50 1·60
2443/8 *Set of* 6 3·75 4·25
MS2449 Two sheets, each 104×125 mm. (a) 1500 l. Mickey with dinosaur (*horiz*). (b) 1500 l. Pluto balancing ball on nose (*horiz*). P 14×13½ *Set of* 2 *sheets* 4·50 4·75

1996 (26 Feb). *Centenary of Cinema. T* **286** *and similar vert designs. Multicoloured. Litho*. P 13½×14.
2450 250 l. Type **286** 35 40
a. Sheetlet. Nos. 2450/8 3·25
2451 250 l. Georges Méliès (director) 35 40
2452 250 l. Toshiro Méfune (director) 35 40
2453 250 l. David O. Selznick (director) 35 40
2454 250 l. Character from *Metropolis* 35 40
2455 250 l. Akira Kurosawa (director) 35 40
2456 250 l. Charlie Chaplin (actor) 35 40
2457 250 l. Marlène Dietrich (actress) 35 40
2458 250 l. Steven Spielberg (director) 35 40
2459 250 l. Film camera 35 40
a. Sheetlet. Nos. 2459/67 3·25
2460 250 l. Pete (dog) 35 40
2461 250 l. Silver (horse) 35 40
2462 250 l. Rin-Tin-Tin (dog) 35 40
2463 250 l. King Kong (gorilla) 35 40
2464 250 l. Flipper (dolphin) 35 40
2465 250 l. Great White Shark from *Jaws* 35 40
2466 250 l. Elsa (lioness) 35 40
2467 250 l. Whale from *Moby Dick* 35 40
2450/67 *Set of* 18 6·50 7·25
MS2468 Two sheets, each 109×80 mm. (a) 1500 l. Cecil B. De Mille (producer). (b) 1500 l. Lassie (dog) *Set of* 2 *sheets* 4·50 4·75

Nos. 2450/8 and 2459/67 were printed together, *se-tenant*, in sheetlets of 9 forming composite designs.

(Litho Questa)

1996 (29 Apr). *125th Anniv of Metropolitan Museum of Art, New York. Multicoloured designs as T* **331** *of Maldive Islands. P* 13½×14.

2469/76 200 l. × 8 ("Honfleur" (detail) (Jongkind); "A Boat on the Shore" (detail) (Courbet); "Barges at Pontoise" (detail) (Pissarro); "The Dead Christ with Angels" (Manet); "Salisbury Cathedral" (detail) (Constable); "Lady with a Setter Dog" (detail) (Eakins); "Tahitian Women Bathing" (detail) (Gauguin); "Majas on a Balcony" (detail) (Goya))
a. Sheetlet. Nos. 2469/76 plus centre label .. 2·40 2·50
2477/84 200 l. × 8 ("In the Meadow"; "By the Seashore" (detail); "Still Life with Peaches and Grapes" (detail); "Marguerite Bérard"; "Young Girl in Pink and Black Hat"; "Waitress at Duval's Restaurant" (detail); "A Road in Louveciennes" (detail); "Two Young Girls at the Piano" (detail) (all by Renoir))
a. Sheetlet. Nos. 2477/84 plus centre label .. 2·40 2·50
2485/92 200 l. × 8 ("Morning, An Overcast Day, Rouen" (detail) (Pissarro); "The Horse Fair" (detail) (Bonheur); "High Tide: The Bathers" (detail) (Homer); "The Dance Class" (Degas); "The Brioche" (detail) (Manet); "The Grand Canal, Venice" (detail) (Turner); "St. Tecia interceding for plague-stricken Este" (detail) (Tiepolo); "Bridge at Villeneuve" (detail) (Sisley))
a. Sheetlet. Nos. 2485/92 plus centre label .. 2·40 2·50
2493/2500 200 l. × 8 ("Madame Charpentier" (detail) (Renoir); "Head of Christ" (detail) (Rembrandt); "The Standard-bearer" (detail) (Rembrandt); "Girl Asleep" (Vermeer); "Lady with a Lute" (Vermeer); "Portrait of a Woman" (detail) (Rembrandt); "La Grenouillére" (detail) (Monet); "Woman with Chrysanthemums" (detail) (Degas))
a. Sheetlet. Nos. 2493/2500 plus centre label .. 2·40 2·50
2469/2500 .. *Set of* 32 9·50 10·00
MS2501 Four sheets, each 95×70 mm. (a) 1500 l. "The Death of Socrates" (J. L. David) (85×56 *mm*). P 14. (b) 1500 l. "Battle of Constantine and Licinius" (detail) (Rubens) (85×56 *mm*). P 14. (c) 1500 l. "Samson and Delilah" (detail) (Rubens) (85×56 *mm*). P 14. (d) 1500 l. "The Emblem of Christ appearing to Constantine" (detail) (Rubens) (85×56 *mm*). P 14 .. *Set of* 4 *sheets* 9·00 9·25

Nos. 2469/76, 2477/84, 2485/92 and 2493/500 were each printed together, *se-tenant*, in sheetlets of 8 stamps and one centre label.

287 Olympic Stadium, Los Angeles, 1932

288 *Cantharellus cinnabarinus*

(Litho Questa)

1996 (11 June). *Olympic Games, Atlanta. T* **287** *and similar multicoloured designs. P* 14.

2502 100 l. Type **287** .. 15 20
2503 150 l. Archery .. 20 25
2504 300 l. Hockey .. 45 50
a. Sheetlet. Nos. 2504/9 .. 2·75
2505 300 l. Swimming .. 45 50
2506 300 l. Equestrian .. 45 50
2507 300 l. Boxing .. 45 50
2508 300 l. Pommel horse exercises .. 45 50
2509 300 l. 100m running .. 45 50
2510 500 l. Rings exercises .. 75 80
2511 600 l. Pole vault .. 85 90
2502/11 .. *Set of* 10 4·50 5·25
MS2512 104×75 mm. 1500 l. Running (*vert*) .. 2·25 2·40

Nos. 2504/9 were printed together, *se-tenant*, in sheetlets of 6.

(Litho Questa)

1996 (17 June). *Fungi. T* **288** *and similar multicoloured designs. P* 14.

2513 50 l. Type **288** .. 10 10
2514 250 l. *Poronidulus conchifer* and *Aphyllophorales polyporaceae* .. 35 40
a. Sheetlet. Nos. 2514/21 .. 2·75
2515 250 l. *Ceratiomyxa fruticulosa* .. 35 40
2516 250 l. *Cortinarius semisanguineus* and *Cortinariaceae agaricales* .. 35 40
2517 250 l. *Volvamella surrecta* and *Pluteaceae agricales* .. 35 40
2518 250 l. *Lepiota cepaestipes* .. 35 40
2519 250 l. *Amanita rubescans* .. 35 40
2520 250 l. *Phyllotopsis nidulans* and *Tricholomataceas agaricales* .. 35 40
2521 250 l. *Lysyrus gardneri* and *Clathraceae phallales* .. 35 40
2522 250 l. *Lactarius indigo* .. 35 40
a. Sheetlet. Nos. 2522/9 .. 2·75
2523 250 l. *Coprinus quadrifidus* .. 35 40
2524 250 l. *Geopyxis carbonaria* .. 35 40
2525 250 l. *Astraeus hygrometricus* .. 35 40
2526 250 l. *Agaicaceae agaricales* .. 35 40
2527 250 l. *Mycena maculata* .. 35 40
2528 250 l. *Lactarius delciosus* .. 35 40
2529 250 l. *Amanita fulva* .. 35 40
2530 300 l. *Suillus grevillci* .. 35 40
2531 400 l. *Morchella esculenta* .. 60 65
2532 500 l. *Cortinamaceae agaricales* .. 75 80
2513/32 .. *Set of* 20 7·00 8·00
MS2533 Two sheets, each 110×80 mm. (a) 1500 l. *Psathyrella epimyces* (*horiz*). (b) 1500 l. *Rhodotus parmatus* (*horiz*) .. *Set of* 2 *sheets* 4·50 5·00

Nos. 2514/21 and 2522/9 were each printed together, *se-tenant*, in sheetlets of 8.

289 Abyssinian Cat

290 Three Asian Girls reading

1996 (17 June). *Cats. T* **289** *and similar vert designs. Multicoloured. Litho. P* 14.

2534 200 l. Type **289** .. 30 35
a. Sheetlet. Nos. 2534/45 .. 3·50
2535 200 l. British Tabby .. 30 35
2536 200 l. Norwegian Forest Cat .. 30 35
2537 200 l. Maine Coon .. 30 35
2538 200 l. Bengal .. 30 35
2539 200 l. Asian .. 30 35
2540 200 l. American Curl .. 30 35
2541 200 l. Devon Rex .. 30 35
2542 200 l. Tonkinese .. 30 35
2543 200 l. Egyptian Mau .. 30 35
2544 200 l. Burmese .. 30 35
2545 200 l. Siamese .. 30 35
2546 200 l. British Shorthair .. 30 35
a. Sheetlet. Nos. 2546/57 .. 3·50
2547 200 l. Tiffany .. 30 35
2548 200 l. Birman .. 30 35
2549 200 l. Somali .. 30 35
2550 200 l. Malayan .. 30 35
2551 200 l. Japanese Bobtail .. 30 35
2552 200 l. Himalayan .. 30 35
2553 200 l. Tortoiseshell .. 30 35
2554 200 l. Oriental .. 30 35
2555 200 l. Ocicat .. 30 35
2556 200 l. Chartreux .. 30 35
2557 200 l. Ragdoll .. 30 35
2534/57 .. *Set of* 24 7·25 7·50
MS2558 Two sheets, each 110×80 mm. (a) 2000 l. Persian. (b) 2000 l. Burmilla *Set of* 2 *sheets* 6·00 6·25

Nos. 2534/45 and 2546/57 were each printed together, *se-tenant*, in sheetlets of 12.

(Litho Questa)

1996 (15 July). *70th Birthday of Queen Elizabeth II. Vert designs as T* **334** *of Maldive Islands showing different photographs. Multicoloured. P* 13½×14.

2559 600 l. As Type **334** of Maldive Islands .. 85 90
a. Strip of 3. Nos. 2559/61 .. 2·50
2560 600 l. Receiving posy .. 85 90
2561 600 l. Carrying bouquets .. 85 90
2559/61 .. *Set of* 3 2·50 2·75
MS2562 125×103 mm. 1500 l. Waving from balcony .. 2·25 2·50

Nos. 2559/61 were printed together, *se-tenant*, in horizontal and vertical strips of 3 throughout sheets of 9.

(Litho Questa)

1996 (15 July). *50th Anniv of U.N.I.C.E.F. T* **290** *and similar horiz designs. Multicoloured. P* 14.

2563 300 l. Type **290** .. 45 50
2564 400 l. African children reading .. 60 65
2565 500 l. Children in class .. 75 80
2563/5 .. *Set of* 3 1·75 2·00
MS2566 104×74 mm. 1500 l. Children's faces .. 2·25 2·40

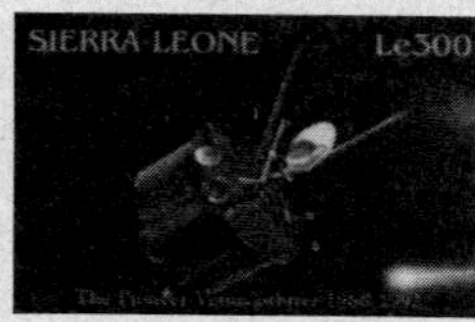

291 "Pioneer" Spacecraft in Venus Orbit, 1986–1992

1996 (15 July). *Space Exploration. T* **291** *and similar horiz designs. Multicoloured. Litho. P* 14.

2567 300 l. Type **291** .. 45 50
a. Sheetlet. Nos. 2567/72 .. 2·50
2568 300 l. Hubble Space Telescope .. 45 50
2569 300 l. "Voyager" Space Probe .. 45 50
2570 300 l. Space Shuttle *Challenger* .. 45 50
2571 300 l. "Pioneer II" Space Probe .. 45 50
2572 300 l. "Viking I" Mars Lander .. 45 50
2567/72 .. *Set of* 6 2·50 3·00
MS2573 104×74 mm. 1500 l. Space Shuttle *Challenger* landing .. 2·25 2·40

Nos. 2567/72 were printed together, *se-tenant*, in sheetlets of 6, the background forming a composite design.

292 Rat

1996 (15 July). *Chinese Lunar Calendar. T* **292** *and similar vert designs. Multicoloured. Litho. P* 13½.

2574 150 l. Type **292** .. 20 25
a. Sheetlet. Nos. 2574/85 .. 2·40
2575 150 l. Ox .. 20 25
2576 150 l. Tiger .. 20 25
2577 150 l. Hare .. 20 25
2578 150 l. Dragon .. 20 25
2579 150 l. Snake .. 20 25
2580 150 l. Horse .. 20 25
2581 150 l. Sheep .. 20 25
2582 150 l. Monkey .. 20 25
2583 150 l. Cockerel .. 20 25
2584 150 l. Dog .. 20 25
2585 150 l. Pig .. 20 25
2574/85 .. *Set of* 12 2·40 3·00

Nos. 2574/85 were printed together, *se-tenant*, in sheetlets of 12.

293 *Charaxes pleione*

294 *Begonia multiflora* "Rambouillet"

(Litho Questa)

1996 (15 Aug). *Butterflies. T* **293** *and similar horiz designs. Multicoloured. P* 14.

2586 150 l. Type **293** .. 20 25
2587 200 l. *Eurema brigitta* .. 30 35
2588 250 l. *Precis orithya* .. 35 40
a. Sheetlet. Nos. 2588/96 .. 3·25
2589 250 l. *Palla ussheri* .. 35 40
2590 250 l. *Junonia orithya* .. 35 40
2591 250 l. *Cymothoe sangaris* .. 35 40
2592 250 l. *Cyrestis camillus* .. 35 40
2593 250 l. *Precis rhadama* .. 35 40
2594 250 l. *Precis cebrene* .. 35 40
2595 250 l. *Hypolimnas misippus* .. 35 40
2596 250 l. *Colotis danae* .. 35 40
2597 300 l. *Charaxes ameliae* .. 45 50
2598 500 l. *Kallimoides rumia* .. 75 80
2586/98 .. *Set of* 13 4·75 5·50
MS2599 Two sheets, each 100×70 mm. (a) 1500 l. *Papilio antimachus*. (b) 1500 l. *Charaxes bohemani* .. *Set of* 2 *sheets* 4·50 4·75

Nos. 2588/96 were printed together, *se-tenant*, in sheetlets of 9.

(Litho Questa)

1996 (19 Aug). *Flowers. T* **294** *and similar vert designs. Multicoloured. P* 14.

2600 150 l. *Tulipa* "Georgette" .. 20 25
2601 200 l. *Helichrysum bracteatum* "Monstrosum" .. 30 35
2602 200 l. Fountain .. 30 35
a. Sheetlet. Nos. 2602/10 .. 2·75
2603 200 l. Type **294** .. 30 35
2604 200 l. *Narcissus* "Trumpet Daffodil" .. 30 35
2605 200 l. *Crocus speciosus* .. 30 35
2606 200 l. *Chrysanthemum frutescens* "Marguerite" .. 30 35
2607 200 l. *Petunia* "Polaris" and *Danaus gilippus* (butterfly) .. 30 35
2608 200 l. *Cosmos pipinnatus* "Sensation" and *Papilio calguanabus* (butterfly) .. 30 35
2609 200 l. *Anemone coronaris* .. 30 35
2610 200 l. *Convolvulus minor* .. 30 35
2611 300 l. *Paphiopedilum* "Claire de Lune" .. 45 50
a. Sheetlet. Nos. 2611/19 .. 4·00

2612 300 l. *Cymbidium* "Peach Bloom" .. 45 50
2613 300 l. Yacht 45 50
2614 300 l. *Miltonia* "Peach Blossom" .. 45 50
2615 300 l. *Parides gundalachianus* (butterfly) 45 50
2616 300 l. *Laeliocattleya* "Grand Gate" .. 45 50
2617 300 l. *Lycaste aromatica* 45 50
2618 300 l. *Brassolaeliocattleya* "Golden Land" 45 50
2619 300 l. *Cymbidium* "Southern Lace" and *Catastica teutila* (butterfly) .. 45 50
2620 400 l. *Viola* "Pansy" 60 65
2621 500 l. *Phalaenopsis* "Pink Beauty" .. 75 80
2600/21 .. .. *Set of* 22 8·50 9·00
MS2622 Two sheets, each 80×110 mm. (a) 1500 l. *Helianthus annuus*. (b) 1500 l. *Cymbidium* "Lucifer" .. .. *Set of* 2 *sheets* 4·50 4·75

Nos. 2602/10 and 2611/19 were each printed together, *se-tenant*, in sheetlets of 9, with the backgrounds forming composite designs.

295 Greek War Galley (4th-century B.C.)

296 "The Sea Dragon's Daughter"

1996 (29 Oct). *History of Ships. T* **295** *and similar horiz designs. Multicoloured. Litho. P* 14.

2623 300 l. Type **295** 45 50
a. Sheetlet. Nos. 2623/31 .. .. 4·00
2624 300 l. Roman war galley (A.D. 50) .. 45 50
2625 300 l. Viking longship (9th-century) .. 45 50
2626 300 l. Flemish carrack (15th-century) .. 45 50
2627 300 l. Merchantman (16th-century) .. 45 50
2628 300 l. Tudor galleon (16th-century) .. 45 50
2629 300 l. Elizabethan galleon (17th-century) 45 50
2630 300 l. Dutch warship (17th-century) .. 45 50
2631 300 l. *Maestrale* (18th-century Maltese galley) 45 50
2632 300 l. *Cutty Sark* (19th-century clipper) .. 45 50
a. Sheetlet. Nos. 2632/40 .. .. 4·00
2633 300 l. *Great Britain*, 1846 (steam/sail liner) 45 50
2634 300 l. H.M.S. *Dreadnought*, 1906 (battle-ship) 45 50
2635 300 l. *Queen Elizabeth*, 1940 (liner) .. 45 50
2636 300 l. Ocean-going yacht, 1962 .. .. 45 50
2637 300 l. *United States*, 1952 (liner) .. 45 50
2638 300 l. Nuclear-powered submarine, 1950s 45 50
2639 300 l. Super tanker, 1960s 45 50
2640 300 l. U.S.S. *Enterprise*, 1961 (aircraft carrier) 45 50
2623/40 .. .. *Set of* 18 8·00 9·00
MS2641 Two sheets, each 96×66 mm. (a) 1500 l. Egyptian ship (1480 B.C.) (56×42 *mm*). (b) 1500 l. *Legend of the Seas*, 1996 (cruise ship) (56×42 *mm*) .. .. .. *Set of* 2 *sheets* 4·50 4·75

Nos. 2623/31 and 2632/40 were each printed together, *se-tenant*, in sheetlets of 9.

No. 2634 is inscribed "Dreadnaught" in error.

(Litho Questa)

1996 (12 Dec). *Christmas. Religious Paintings. Vert designs as T* **337** *of St. Vincent. Multicoloured. P* 13½×14.

2642 200 l. "Madonna of Humility" (Filippo Lippi) 30 35
2643 250 l. "Coronation of the Virgin" (Lippi) .. 35 40
2644 400 l. "The Annunciation" (Lippi) .. 60 65
2645 500 l. "Annunciation" (*different*) (Lippi) .. 75 80
2646 600 l. "Barbadori Altarpiece" (Lippi) .. 85 90
2647 800 l. "Coronation of the Virgin" (*different*) (Lippi) .. .. 1·10 1·25
2642/7 .. .. *Set of* 6 4·00 4·25
MS2648 Two sheets, each 76×106 mm. (a) 2000 l. "Adoration of the Magi" (Rubens). (b) 2000 l. "Holy Family with St. Anne" (Rubens) *Set of* 2 *sheets* 5·75 6·00

No. 2646 is inscribed "Alterpiece" in error.

(Des L. Birmingham. Litho Questa)

1996 (19 Dec). *Legends of the Seas. Forty sheets, each* 105×75 *mm, containing T* **296** *and similar multicoloured designs. P* 14.

MS2649 (a) 1500 l. Type **296**; (b) 1500 l. *Homo aquaticus*; (c) 1500 l. Chinese sea fairy; (d) 1500 l. Sea totem pole; (e) 1500 l. *The Turtle* (fantasy submarine) (*horiz*); (f) 1500 l. Mermaid (*horiz*); (g) 1500 l. "How the Whale Got its Throat" (*horiz*); (h) 1500 l. Killer Whale crest; (i) 1500 l. Odysseus and siren (*horiz*); (j) 1500 l. "The Little Mermaid" (Hans Christian Andersen) (*horiz*); (k) 1500 l. Squamish Indians (*horiz*); (l) 1500 l. Boy on Dolphin; (m) 1500 l. Atlantis airship (*horiz*); (n) 1500 l. Sea Bishop (*horiz*); (o) 1500 l. "Twenty Thousand Leagues Under the Sea" (Jules Verne); (p) 1500 l. "Whale Song" (*horiz*); (q) 1500 l. Arion (*horiz*); (r) 1500 l. Dragonrider of Pern (*horiz*); (s) 1500 l. Kelpie (*horiz*); (t) 1500 l. Natsihlane on Sea Lion (*horiz*); (u) 1500 l. Triton; (v) 1500 l. Lang (dragon) (*horiz*); (w) 1500 l. *The Flying Dutchman* (*horiz*); (x) 1500 l. Lilith; (y) 1500 l. "Queen of the Orkney Islands"; (z) 1500 l. Merman; (za) 1500 l. Sea Centaur; (zb) 1500 l. Albatross (*horiz*); (zc) 1500 l. *The Rime of the Ancient Mariner* (Samuel Coleridge); (zd) 1500 l. Haida Eagle (*horiz*); (ze) 1500 l. Poseidon; (zf) 1500 l. Captain Ahab (*Moby Dick*); (zg) 1500 l. Underwater City; (zh) 1500 l. Jonah and the Whale; (zi) 1500 l. Waskos (*horiz*); (zj) 1500 l. Tom Swift (*horiz*); (zk) 1500 l. Arthropod sea monsters; (zl) 1500 l. Sea Serpent; (zm) 1500 l. Aphrodite (*horiz*); (zn) 1500 l. Ship's figurehead *Set of* 40 *sheets* 85·00 95·00

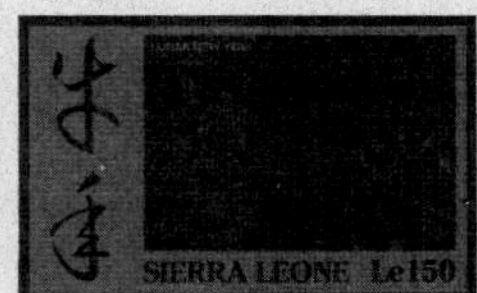

297 Ox

(Des Y. Lee. Litho Questa)

1997 (8 Jan). *Chinese New Year ("Year of the Ox"). T* **297** *and similar multicoloured designs. P* 14.

2650 250 l. Type **297** (on purple panel) .. 35 40
a. Block of 4. Nos. 2650/3 .. .. 1·40
2651 250 l. Ox (on green panel) 35 40
2652 250 l. Ox (on blue panel) 35 40
2653 250 l. Ox (on brown panel) 35 40
2650/3 .. .. *Set of* 4 1·40 1·60
MS2654 106×76 mm. Nos. 2650/3 .. 1·40 1·60
MS2655 106×76 mm. 800 l. Ox (*vert*) .. .. 1·10 1·25

Nos. 2650/3 were printed together, *se-tenant*, as blocks of 4 in sheets of 16.

298 Aladdin and Jasmine

299 Hong Kong Skyline by Day

(Litho Questa)

1997 (27 Jan). *Christmas. Aladdin. T* **298** *and similar multicoloured designs showing Disney cartoon characters. P* 13½×14.

2656 10 l. Type **298** 10 10
2657 15 l. Genie and Santa Claus 10 10
2658 20 l. Aladdin and Jasmine on magic carpet 10 10
2659 25 l. Genie as a Christmas tree .. 10 10
2660 30 l. Genie as Santa Claus and Aladdin 10 10
2661 100 l. Aladdin, Jasmine and Genie on magic carpet 15 20
2662 800 l. Genie writing letter to Santa Claus 1·10 1·25
2663 1000 l. Genie with four heads .. 1·50 1·60
2656/63 .. .. *Set of* 8 3·00 3·25
MS2664 Two sheets, each 127×101 mm. (a) 2000 l. Aladdin under a pile of gold; (b) 2000 l. Aladdin and Jasmine on magic carpet (*horiz*). P 14×13½ .. .. .. *Set of* 2 *sheets* 5·75 6·00

(Des M. Friedman. Litho B.D.T.)

1997 (12 Feb). *"Hong Kong '97" International Stamp Exhibition. Two sheets, each* 125×68 *mm, containing T* **299** *and similar vert designs. Multicoloured. P* 14.

MS2665 (a) 500 l. × 4 forming panorama of central Hong Kong by day. (b) 500 l. × 4 forming panorama of central Hong Kong by night *Set of* 2 *sheets* 3·00 3·25

(Des M. Freedman and Dena Rubin. Litho Questa)

1997 (24 Mar). *50th Anniv of U.N.E.S.C.O. Multicoloured designs as T* **348** *of Maldive Islands. P* 13½×14 (*vert*) *or* 14×13½ (*horiz*).

2666 60 l. Church, Kizhi Pogost, Russia .. 10 10
2667 200 l. Durmitor National Park, Yugoslavia 30 35
2668 250 l. Nessebar, Bulgaria 35 40
2669 300 l. Roros, Norway 45 50
a. Sheetlet. Nos. 2669/76 and central label .. .. 3·50
2670 300 l. Varsovia city gate, Poland .. 45 50
2671 300 l. Nuestra Senora Cathedral, Luxembourg 45 50
2672 300 l. Tower, Vilnius, Lithuania 45 50
2673 300 l. Jelling, Denmark 45 50
2674 300 l. Petajavesi Church, Finland .. 45 50
2675 300 l. Round house, Sweden 45 50
2676 300 l. Berne Cathedral, Switzerland .. 45 50
2677 300 l. Slopes of Mount Kilimanjaro, Tanzania 45 50
a. Sheetlet. Nos. 2677/84 and central label .. .. 3·50
2678 300 l. Tombs, Fasil Ghebbi, Ethiopia .. 45 50
2679 300 l. Mount Ruwenzori National Park, Uganda 45 50
2680 300 l. Nubia Monument, Abu Simbel, Egypt 45 50
2681 300 l. Tsingy of Bemaraha Nature Reserve, Madagascar 45 50
2682 300 l. House, Djenné, Mali 45 50
2683 300 l. Traditional house, Ghana 45 50
2684 300 l. House, Abomey, Benin 45 50
2685 400 l. Gateway, Bukhara, Uzbekistan .. 60 65
2686 500 l. Monastery, Petchersk, Ukraine .. 75 80
2687 500 l. Tower, Himeji-jo, Japan (*horiz*) .. 75 80
a. Sheetlet. Nos. 2687/91 and label .. 3·75
2688 500 l. Gateway, Himeji-jo, Japan (*horiz*) 75 80
2689 500 l. Outer wall and turrets, Himeji-jo, Japan (*horiz*) 75 80
2690 500 l. Village, Himeji-jo, Japan (*horiz*) .. 75 80
2691 500 l. Ornate gables, Himeji-jo, Japan (*horiz*) 75 80
2692 800 l. Mountains, Slovakia .. .. 1·10 1·25
2666/92 .. .. *Set of* 27 14·00 15·00
MS2693 Two sheets, each 127×102 mm. (a) 2000 l. Djudj National Bird Sanctuary, Senegal (*horiz*). (b) 2000 l. The Acropolis, Athens, Greece (*horiz*) .. .. .. *Set of* 2 *sheets* 6·00 6·25

Nos. 2669/76 and 2677/84 were each printed together, *se-tenant* in sheetlets of 8 stamps with a central label and Nos. 2687/91 in sheetlets of 5 stamps with a top left-hand corner label.

No. 2676 is inscribed "BERNA", No. 2677 "KILIMANDJARO" and No. 2686 "MONESTRY", all in error.

(Des R. Rundo. Litho Questa)

1997 (23 June). *300th Anniv of Mother Goose Nursery Rhymes. Two sheets, each* 72×102 *mm, containing horiz designs as T* **112** *of St. Kitts-Nevis (Nevis). Multicoloured. P* 14.

MS2694 (a) 1500 l. "Three Blind Mice". (b) 1500 l. Woman in pink dress ("Myself") .. *Set of* 2 *sheets* 4·25 4·50

(Litho Questa)

1997 (23 June). *10th Anniv of Chernobyl Nuclear Disaster. Vert designs as T* **347** *of St. Vincent. Multicoloured. P* 13½×14.

2695 1000 l. Child's face and U.N.E.S.C.O. emblem .. .. 1·50 1·60
2696 1500 l. As 1000 l., but inscribed "CHABAD'S CHILDREN OF CHERNOBYL" at foot .. .. 2·25 2·40

(Litho Questa)

1997 (23 June). *Golden Wedding of Queen Elizabeth and Prince Philip. Horiz designs as T* **350** *of Maldive Islands. Multicoloured (except Nos. 2699/700). P* 14.

2697 400 l. Queen Elizabeth II 60 65
a. Sheetlet. Nos. 2697/702 .. .. 3·50
2698 400 l. Royal coat of arms 60 65
2699 400 l. Queen Elizabeth with Prince Philip in military uniform (grey-black) .. 60 65
2700 400 l. Queen Elizabeth with Prince Philip in naval mess dress (grey-black) .. 60 65
2701 400 l. St. James's Palace 60 65
2702 400 l. Prince Philip 60 65
2697/702 .. .. *Set of* 6 3·50 4·00
MS2703 100×70 mm. 1500 l. Queen Elizabeth with Prince Philip in naval uniform .. .. 2·25 2·40

Nos. 2697/702 were printed together, *se-tenant*, in sheetlets of 6.

1997 (23 June). *Birth Bicentenary of Hiroshige (Japanese painter). "One Hundred Famous Views of Edo". Vert designs as T* **352** *of Maldive Islands. Multicoloured. Litho. P* 13½×14.

2704 400 l. "Hatsune Riding Grounds, Bakuro-cho" 60 65
a. Sheetlet. Nos. 2704/9 .. .. 3·50
2705 400 l. "Mannen Bridge, Fukagawa" .. 60 65
2706 400 l. "Ryogoku Bridge and the Great Riverbank" 60 65
2707 400 l. "Asakusa River, Great Riverbank, Miyato River" 60 65
2708 400 l. "Silk-goods Lane, Odenma-cho" .. 60 65
2709 400 l. "Mokuboji Temple, Uchigawa Inlet, Gozensaihata" 60 65
2704/9 .. .. *Set of* 6 3·50 4·00
MS2710 Two sheets, each 102×127 mm. (a) 1500 l. "Nihonbashi Bridge and Edobashi Bridge". (b) 1500 l. "Tsukudajima from Eitai Bridge" .. .. .. *Set of* 2 *sheets* 4·25 4·50

Nos. 2704/9 were printed together, *se-tenant*, in sheetlets of 6.

300 Hong Kong Skyline

(Litho Questa)

1997 (23 June). *Return of Hong Kong to China. T* **300** *and similar horiz designs showing modern Hong Kong or Deng Xiaoping (800 l.). P* 14.

2711 400 l. multicoloured 60 65
a. Sheetlet of 3 .. .. .. 1·75
2712 500 l. multicoloured 75 80
a. Sheetlet of 3 .. .. .. 2·25
2713 550 l. multicoloured 80 85
a. Sheetlet of 3 .. .. .. 2·40
2714 600 l. multicoloured 85 90
a. Sheetlet of 3 .. .. .. 2·50
2715 650 l. multicoloured 90 95
a. Sheetlet of 3 .. .. .. 2·75
2716 800 l. multicoloured .. .. .. 1·10 1·25
a. Sheetlet of 3 .. .. .. 3·25
2711/16 .. .. *Set of* 6 5·00 5·50

Nos. 2711/16 were each printed *se-tenant*, in sheetlets of 3 with an illustrated left or right-hand margin.

301 Calgary Stadium, 1988

302 *Vindula erota*

(Litho Questa)

1997 (16 July). *Winter Olympic Games, Nagano, Japan* (1998). *T* **301** *and similar multicoloured designs. P* 14.

2717 250 l. Type **301** .. 35 40
2718 300 l. Freestyle Skiing Aerials, 1994 (*vert*) 45 50
2719 300 l. Peggy Fleming (U.S.A.) (figure skating, 1968) (*vert*) 45 50
a. Sheetlet. Nos. 2719/22 each × 2 3·50
2720 300 l. Japanese competitor (Nordic combined–ski jump, 1992/4) (*vert*) 45 50
2721 300 l. German team (two-man luge, 1968 to 1992) (*vert*) 45 50
2722 300 l. Frank-Peter Roetsch (East Germany) (biathlon, 1988) (*vert*) 45 50
2723 500 l. Ice Hockey (*vert*) 75 80
2724 800 l. Dan Jansen (U.S.A.) (speed skating, 1994) (*vert*) 1·10 1·25
2717/24 *Set of* 8 4·00 5·00
MS2725 Two sheets. (a) 106×76 mm. 1500 l. Jamaican bobsleigh team (*vert*). (b) 76×106 mm. 1500 l. Johann Olav Koss (Norway) (speed skating, 1992/4) (*vert*) .. *Set of* 2 *sheets* 4·25 4·50

Nos. 2719/22 were printed together, *se-tenant*, in sheetlets of 8 containing two of each design.

(Litho Questa)

1997 (23 July). *World Cup Football Championship, France* (1998). *Designs as T* **246** *of Lesotho. P* 13½×14 (*vert*) *or* 14×13½ (*horiz*).

2726 100 l. black 15 20
2727 150 l. black 20 25
2728 200 l. black 30 35
2729 250 l. black 35 40
2730 300 l. multicoloured 45 50
a. Sheetlet. Nos. 2730/7 and two labels 3·50
2731 300 l. multicoloured 45 50
2732 300 l. multicoloured 45 50
2733 300 l. multicoloured 45 50
2734 300 l. multicoloured 45 50
2735 300 l. multicoloured 45 50
2736 300 l. multicoloured 45 50
2737 300 l. multicoloured 45 50
2738 500 l. black 75 80
2739 600 l. black 85 90
2726/39 *Set of* 14 6·00 6·75
MS2740 Two sheets, each 127×102 mm. (a) 1500 l. agate. (b) 1500 l. multicoloured *Set of* 2 *sheets* 4·25 4·50

Designs: *Vert*—No. 2726, Stabile, Uruguay; No. 2727, Schavio, Italy; No. 2728, Kocsis, Hungary; No. 2729, Nejedly, Czechoslovakia; No. 2730, Dwight Yorke, Trinidad and Tobago; No. 2731, Dennis Bergkamp, Netherlands; No. 2732, Steve McManaman, England; No. 2733, Ryan Giggs, Wales; No. 2734, Romario, Brazil; No. 2735, Faustino Asprilla, Colombia; No. 2736, Roy Keane, Republic of Ireland; No. 2737, Peter Schmeichel, Denmark; No. 2738, Leonidas, Brazil; No. 2739, Ademir, Brazil. *Horiz*—No. **MS**2740a, Pele, Brazil; No. **MS**2740b, Lato, Poland.

Nos. 2730/7 were printed together, *se-tenant*, in sheetlets of 8 stamps and 2 labels, one at each end of the bottom row.

(Litho Questa)

1997 (1 Aug). *Butterflies of the World. T* **302** *and similar multicoloured designs. P* 14.

2741 150 l. Type **302** .. 20 25
2742 200 l. *Pereute leucodrosime* 30 35
2743 250 l. *Dynastor napolean* 35 40
2744 300 l. *Thauria aliris* 45 50
2745 500 l. *Lycaena dispar* 75 80
a. Sheetlet. Nos. 2745/50 4·50
2746 500 l. *Graphium sarpedon* 75 80
2747 500 l. *Euploe core* 75 80
2748 500 l. *Papilio cresphontes* 75 80
2749 500 l. *Colotis danae* 75 80
2750 500 l. *Battus philenor* 75 80
2751 600 l. *Papilio aegeus* 85 90
2752 600 l. *Mylothris chloris* 85 90
a. Sheetlet. Nos. 2752/7 5·00
2753 600 l. *Argynnis lathonia* 85 90
2754 600 l. *Elymnias agondas* 85 90
2755 600 l. *Palla ussheri* 85 90
2756 600 l. *Papilio glaucus* 85 90
2757 600 l. *Cercyonis pegala* 85 90
2758 800 l. *Amblypodia anita* 1·10 1·25
2759 1500 l. *Kallimoides rumia* 2·25 2·40
2760 2000 l. *Papilio dardanas* 3·00 3·25
2741/60 *Set of* 20 18·00 19·00
MS2761 Two sheets, each 74×103 mm. (a) 3000 l. *Hebomoia glaucippe* (*horiz*). (b) 3000 l. *Colias eurytheme* (*horiz*) .. *Set of* 2 *sheets* 8·50 8·75

Nos. 2745/50 and 2752/7 were each printed together, *se-tenant*, in sheetlets of 6 with the backgrounds forming composite designs.

303 Lon Chaney in *Phantom of the Opera*, 1925

304 Shetland Sheepdog

(Des Zina Saunders (Nos. 2762/70, **MS**2780b), Michelle Amatrula (Nos. 2771/9, **MS**2780a). Litho B.D.T.)

1997 (15 Aug). *Famous Films. T* **303** *and similar vert designs showing Horror classics* (*Nos. 2762/70*) *or the films of Alfred Hitchcock* (*Nos. 2771/9*). *Multicoloured. P* 14.

2762 300 l. Type **303** 45 50
a. Sheetlet. Nos. 2762/70 4·00
2763 300 l. Boris Karloff in *The Mummy*, 1932 45 50
2764 300 l. Fredric March in *Dr. Jekyll and Mr Hyde*, 1932 45 50
2765 300 l. Lon Chaney Jr. in *The Wolf Man*, 1941 45 50
2766 300 l. Charles Laughton in *Island of Lost Souls*, 1933 45 50
2767 300 l. Lionel Atwill in *Mystery of the Wax Museum*, 1933 45 50
2768 300 l. Bela Lugosi in *Dracula*, 1931 45 50
2769 300 l. Vincent Price in *The Haunted Palace*, 1963 45 50
2770 300 l. Elsa Lanchester in *Bride of Frankenstein*, 1935 45 50
2771 350 l. Ray Milland in *Dial M for Murder*, 1954 50 55
a. Sheetlet. Nos. 2771/9 4·50
2772 350 l. James Stewart and Kim Novak in *Vertigo*, 1958 50 55
2773 350 l. Cary Grant, Ingrid Bergman and Claude Rains in *Notorious*, 1946 50 55
2774 350 l. Farley Granger and John Dall in *Rope*, 1948 50 55
2775 350 l. Cary Grant in *North by Northwest*, 1959 50 55
2776 350 l. James Stewart and Grace Kelly in *Rear Window*, 1954 50 55
2777 350 l. Joan Fontaine and Laurence Olivier in *Rebecca*, 1940 50 55
2778 350 l. Tippi Hedren in *The Birds*, 1963 50 55
2779 350 l. Janet Leigh in *Psycho*, 1960 50 55
2762/79 *Set of* 18 8·50 9·50
MS2780 Two sheets. (a) 72×102 mm. 1500 l. Alfred Hitchcock. (b) 82×82 mm. 3000 l. Boris Karloff in *Son of Frankenstein*, 1939 *Set of* 2 *sheets* 8·50 9·50

Nos. 2762/70 and 2771/9 were each printed together, *se-tenant*, in sheetlets of 9 with the backgrounds forming composite designs.

(Des R. Martin. Litho Questa)

1997 (29 Aug). *Dogs and Cats. T* **304** *and similar multicoloured designs. P* 14.

2781 100 l. Type **304** 15 20
2782 150 l. American Shorthair Tabby cat 20 25
2783 200 l. British Shorthair cat 30 35
2784 250 l. Alaskan Husky 35 40
2785 400 l. Basset Hound 60 65
a. Sheetlet. Nos. 2785/90 3·50
2786 400 l. Irish Setter 60 65
2787 400 l. St. Bernard 60 65
2788 400 l. German Shepherd 60 65
2789 400 l. Dalmatian 60 65
2790 400 l. Cocker Spaniel 60 65
2791 400 l. Chartreux cat 60 65
a. Sheetlet. Nos. 2791/6 3·50
2792 400 l. Abyssinian cat 60 65
2793 400 l. Burmese cat 60 65
2794 400 l. White Angora cat 60 65
2795 400 l. Japanese Bobtail cat 60 65
2796 400 l. Cymric cat 60 65
2797 500 l. Turkish Angora cat 75 80
2798 600 l. Jack Russell Terrier 85 90
2781/98 *Set of* 18 9·50 10·50
MS2799 Two sheets, each 106×75 mm. (a) 1500 l. Boxer (31×63 *mm*). (b) 1500 l. Egyptian Mau cat (63×31 *mm*) .. *Set of* 2 *sheets* 4·25 4·50

Nos. 2785/90 and 2791/6 were each printed together, *se-tenant*, in sheetlets of 6 with enlarged illustrated right-hand margins.

305 *Ansellia africana*

306 Daisy Duck

(Litho Questa)

1997 (1 Sept). *Orchids of the World. T* **305** *and similar vert designs. Multicoloured. P* 14.

2800 150 l. Type **305** 20 25
2801 200 l. *Maxillaria praestans* 30 35
2802 250 l. *Cymbidium mimi* 35 40
2803 300 l. *Dendrobium bigibbum* 45 50
2804 400 l. *Laelia anceps* 60 65
a. Sheetlet. Nos. 2804/9 3·50
2805 400 l. *Paphiopedilum fairrieanum* 60 65
2806 400 l. *Restrepia lansbergii* 60 65
2807 400 l. *Yamadara cattleya* 60 65
2808 400 l. *Cleistes divaricata* 60 65
2809 400 l. *Calypso bulbosa* 60 65
2810 500 l. *Encyclia vitellina* 75 80
2811 800 l. *Epidendrum prismatocarpum* 85 90
2800/11 *Set of* 12 6·50 7·50
MS2812 Two sheets, each 76×106 mm. (a) 1500 l. *Paphiopedilum tonsum*. (b) 1500 l. *Odontoglossum schlieperianum Set of* 2 *sheets* 4·25 4·50

Nos. 2804/9 were printed together, *se-tenant*, in sheetlets of 6.

(Litho Questa)

1997 (1 Oct). *Christmas. Disney Holidays. T* **306** *and similar multicoloured designs. P* 13½×14.

2813 50 l. Type **306** 10 10
a. Sheetlet. Nos. 2813/18 45
2814 50 l. Huey, Dewey and Louie 10 10
2815 50 l. Donald Duck 10 10
2816 50 l. Minnie Mouse 10 10
2817 50 l. Morty and Ferdie 10 10
2818 50 l. Mickey Mouse 10 10
2819 150 l. As No. 2814 20 25
2820 200 l. As No. 2817 30 35
2821 250 l. Type **306** 35 40
2822 300 l. As No. 2816 45 50
2823 400 l. As No. 2818 60 65
2824 500 l. As No. 2815 75 80
2825 600 l. Pluto 85 90
2826 800 l. Goofy 1·10 1·25
2813/26 *Set of* 14 5·00 5·25
MS2827 Two sheets. (a) 114×140 mm. 2000 l. Mickey Mouse in sleigh. P 13½×14. (b) 140×114 mm. 2000 l. Mickey, Donald and Daisy (*horiz*). P 14×13½ .. *Set of* 2 *sheets* 6·00 6·25

Nos. 2813/18 were printed together, *se-tenant*, in sheetlets of 6.

307 Benoist Type XIV

308 "The Annunciation" (Titian)

(Des W. Wright. Litho Questa)

1997 (6 Oct). *Development of the Civil Airliner. T* **307** *and similar horiz designs. Multicoloured. P* 14½×14.

2828 600 l. Type **307** 85 90
a. Sheetlet. Nos. 2828/31 3·50
2829 600 l. Douglas DC-3 85 90
2830 600 l. Junkers JU52/3m sea plane 85 90
2831 600 l. Sikorsky S-42 flying boat 85 90
2832 600 l. Sud Caravelle 6 85 90
a. Sheetlet. Nos. 2832/5 3·50
2833 600 l. Boeing 707 85 90
2834 600 l. De Havilland Comet 85 90
2835 600 l. Airbus Industrie A300 85 90
2828/35 *Set of* 8 7·00 7·25
MS2836 Two sheets, each 121×96 mm. (a) 2000 l. Lockheed L.1649A Starliner (91×34 *mm*). (b) 2000 l. Concorde (91×34 *mm*). P 13½×14 .. *Set of* 2 *sheets* 6·00 6·25

Nos. 2828/31 and 2832/5 were each printed together in sheetlets of 4 containing two vertical pairs separated by a large aircraft illustration.

(Litho B.D.T.)

1997 (24 Dec). *Christmas. Religious Paintings. T* **308** *and similar multicoloured designs. P* 14.

2837 100 l. Type **308** 15 20
2838 150 l. "The Annunciation" (Titian) (*different*) 20 25
2839 200 l. "Madonna of Foligno" (Raphael) 30 35
2840 250 l. "The Annunciation" (Michelino) 35 40
2841 500 l. "The Prophet Isaiah" (Michelangelo) 75 80
2842 600 l. "Three Angels" (Master of the Rhenish Housebook) 85 90
2837/42 *Set of* 6 2·50 3·00
MS2843 Two sheets, each 105×95 mm. (a) 2000 l. "The Fall of the Rebel Angels" (Bruegel the Elder) (*horiz*). (b) 2000 l. Angel and Monk (Anon) (*horiz*) .. *Set of* 2 *sheets* 6·00 6·25

(Litho Questa)

1998 (12 Jan). *Diana, Princess of Wales Commemoration. Vert designs as T* **249** *of Lesotho. Multicoloured* (*except Nos. 2844, 2849, 2854 and 2856*). *P* 14.

2844 400 l. With daffodils (violet and black) 60 65
a Sheetlet. Nos. 2844/9 3·50
2845 400 l. Carrying bouquet 60 65

2846 400 l. With Mother Theresa 60 65
2847 400 l. Wearing green and black jacket .. 60 65
2848 400 l. With shawl over head 60 65
2849 400 l. In evening dress (brt carmine & blk) 60 65
2850 400 l. Wearing choker and earrings .. 60 65
a. Sheetlet. Nos. 2850/5 .. .. 3·50
2851 400 l. With Prince William 60 65
2852 400 l. Wearing grey-blue jacket and hat 60 65
2853 400 l. Wearing white jacket 60 65
2854 400 l. Wearing hat (chestnut and black) 60 65
2855 400 l. Wearing black evening dress .. 60 65
2856 400 l. Laughing (slate-blue and black) .. 60 65
a. Sheetlet. Nos. 2856/61 .. .. 3·50
2857 400 l. Wearing blue and white jacket and hat 60 65
2858 400 l. Wearing green jacket with arms folded 60 65
2859 400 l. Wearing black and white hat .. 60 65
2860 400 l. Wearing open white shirt 60 65
2861 400 l. Getting out of car 60 65
2844/61 .. .. *Set of* 18 10·50 11·50
MS2862 Three sheets. (a) 100×70 mm. 1500 l. Spooning food into bowl. (b) 100×70 mm. 1500 l. Wearing grey-blue hat and jacket. (c) 70×100 mm. 1500 l. Inspecting guard of honour *Set of 3 sheets* 6·50 6·75

Nos. 2844/9, 2850/5 and 2856/61 were each printed together, *se-tenant*, in sheetlets of 6.

309 Tiger

1998 (26 Jan). *Chinese New Year ("Year of the Tiger"). T* **309** *and similar designs with the tiger in the colour given. Litho. P* 14.

2863 **309** 250 l. multicoloured (deep mauve) .. 35 40
a. Sheetlet. Nos. 2863/6 .. .. 1·40
2864 – 250 l. multicoloured (carmine-lake) 35 40
2865 – 250 l. multicoloured (bright purple) 35 40
2866 – 250 l. multicoloured (dull vermilion) 35 40
2863/6 .. .. *Set of* 4 1·40 1·50
MS2867 76×106 mm. 800 l. multicoloured (*vert*) 1·10 1·25

Nos. 2863/6 were printed together, *se-tenant*, in sheetlets of 4.

STAMP BOOKLETS

1929.
SB1 1s. booklet containing twelve 1d. (No. 132a) ..
SB2 2s. booklet containing twelve 2d. (No. 134) ..

1981 (30 Nov). *Royal Wedding. Multicoloured cover,* 164×92 *mm, showing Prince Charles and Lady Diana. Stapled.*
SB3 6 l. booklet containing *se-tenant* pane of 4 stamps and 1 label and pane of 1 2 l. (Nos. 675a, 677a) 4·00

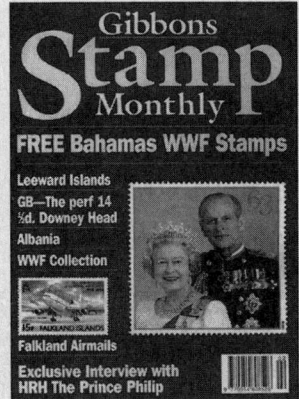

Singapore

A Crown Colony until the end of 1957. From 1 August 1958, an internally self-governing territory designated the State of Singapore. From 16 September 1963, part of the Malaysian Federation until 9 August 1965, when it became an independent republic within the Commonwealth.

Stamps in the Crown Colony Victory design with face values of 8 c. and 15 c. were prepared for Singapore in 1946, but were not issued.

(Currency. 100 cents = 1 Malayan, later Singapore dollar)

CROWN COLONY

(Typo D.L.R.)

1948 (1 Sept)–**52.** *As T* **58** *of Malaysia (Straits Settlements), but inscribed* "SINGAPORE" *at foot. Wmk Mult Script CA. Chalk-surfaced paper. (a) P* 14.

No.	Description	Unused	Used
1	1 c. black	15	30
2	2 c. orange	15	10
3	3 c. green	50	30
4	4 c. brown	20	60
5	6 c. grey	40	30
6	8 c. scarlet (1.10.48)	30	30
7	10 c. purple	20	10
8	15 c. ultramarine (1.10.48)	7·50	10
9	20 c. black and green (1.10.48)	3·50	20
10	25 c. purple and orange (1.10.48)	4·00	15
11	40 c. red and purple (1.10.48)	8·00	5·00
12	50 c. black and blue (1.10.48)	3·25	10
13	$1 blue and purple (1.10.48)	10·00	1·50
14	$2 green and scarlet (25.10.48)	48·00	3·25
15	$5 green and brown (1.10.48)	£120	3·75
1/15	*Set of* 15	£180	14·00
	(b) *P* 17½×18		
16	1 c. black (21.5.52)	50	2·50
17	2 c. orange (31.10.49)	70	80
19	4 c. brown (1.7.49)	70	10
19a	5 c. bright purple (1.9.52)	2·50	90
21	6 c. grey (10.12.52)	90	75
21a	8 c. green (1.9.52)	4·00	3·00
22	10 c. purple (9.2.50)	50	10
22a	12 c. scarlet (1.9.52)	4·00	6·00
23	15 c. ultramarine (9.2.50)	11·00	10
24	20 c. black and green (31.10.49)	3·00	2·25
24a	20 c. bright blue (1.9.52)	4·00	10
25	25 c. purple and orange (9.2.50)	80	10
25a	35 c. scarlet and purple (1.9.52)	4·00	90
26	40 c. red and purple (4.5.51*)	25·00	8·50
27	50 c. black and blue (9.2.50)	7·50	10
28	$1 blue and purple (31.10.49)	13·00	20
	a. Error. St. Edward's Crown, W **9b**	£4250	
29	$2 green and scarlet (24.5.51)	£110	1·75
	a. Error. St. Edward's Crown. W **9b**	£4250	
	w. Wmk inverted		
30	$5 green and brown (19.12.51)	£180	1·75
	w. Wmk inverted		
16/30	*Set of* 18	£325	27·00

* Earliest known postmark date.

Nos. 28a and 29a occur on rows in the watermark in which the crowns and letters "CA" alternate.

Postal forgeries of the 50 c., $1 and $2 exist on unwatermarked paper and perforated 14×14½.

1948 (25 Oct). *Royal Silver Wedding. As Nos.* 143/4 *of Jamaica.*

No.	Description	Unused	Used
31	10 c. violet	75	30
32	$5 brown	£110	29·00

1949 (10 Oct). *75th Anniv of U.P.U. As Nos.* 145/8 *of Jamaica.*

No.	Description	Unused	Used
33	10 c. purple	75	30
34	15 c. deep blue	6·00	2·25
35	25 c. orange	6·00	2·25
36	50 c. blue-black	6·00	3·00
33/6	*Set of* 4	17·00	7·00

1953 (2 June). *Coronation. As No.* 153 *of Jamaica.*

No.	Description	Unused	Used
37	10 c. black and reddish purple	1·75	10

1 Chinese Sampan — **2** Raffles Statue

3 Singapore River — **4** Arms of Singapore

(Des Dr. C. A. Gibson-Hill, except 25 c., 30 c., 50 c. and $5 (from photographs, etc.). Photo Harrison (1 c. to 50 c.). Recess (centre typo on $5) B.W. (others))

1955 (4 Sept)–**59.** *Designs as T* **1/4**. *Wmk Mult Script CA. P* 13½×14½ (1 *c. to* 50 *c.*) *or* 14 (*others*).

No.	Description	Unused	Used
38	1 c. black	10	50
39	2 c. yellow-orange	1·50	1·00
40	4 c. brown	90	15
	w. Wmk inverted	£140	
41	5 c. bright purple	65	15
42	6 c. deep grey-blue	65	40
43	8 c. turquoise-blue	1·25	70
44	10 c. deep lilac	3·00	10
45	12 c. rose-carmine	3·00	2·75
46	20 c. ultramarine	2·25	10
	a. Blue (13.3.58)	3·25	20
47	25 c. orange-red and bluish violet	3·00	70
	a. Orange-red and purple (21.1.59)	11·00	2·00
48	30 c. violet and brown-purple	3·75	10
49	50 c. blue and black	2·25	10
50	$1 blue and deep purple	30·00	20
	a. Deep purple (Queen's head) omitted	£8000	
51	$2 blue-green and scarlet	42·00	1·25
52	$5 yellow, red, brown and slate-black	42·00	4·25
38/52	*Set of* 15	£120	10·50

Designs: *Horiz as T* **1**—2 c. Malay kolek; 4 c. Twa-kow lighter; 5 c. Lombok sloop; 6 c. Trengganu pinas; 8 c. Palari schooner; 10 c. Timber tongkong; 12 c. Hainan junk; 20 c. Cocos-Keeling schooner; 25 c. Douglas DC-4M2 "Argonaut" aircraft; 30 c. Oil tanker; 50 c. *Chusan III* (liner).

Plate 2A and 2B of the 10 c. (12 April 1960) and the blue "3A" and "3B" plates of the 50 c. "3A–2A", "3B–2B" (part of the 24 January 1961 issue and later printings) were printed with a finer screen (250 dots per inch, instead of the normal 200) (*Price* 10 c.. £3·50 *un*, 20*p us*. 50 c. £3·50 *un*, 10*p us*).

No. 50a was caused by a paper fold.

INTERNAL SELF-GOVERNMENT

16 The Singapore Lion — **17** State Flag

(Photo Harrison)

1959 (1 June). *New Constitution. W* w **12**. *P* 11½ × 12.

No.	Type	Description	Unused	Used
53	**16**	4 c. yellow, sepia and rose-red	65	60
54		10 c. yellow, sepia and reddish purple	1·00	30
55		20 c. yellow, sepia and bright blue	2·25	2·75
56		25 c. yellow, sepia and green	2·50	2·00
57		30 c. yellow, sepia and violet	2·50	3·00
58		50 c. yellow, sepia and deep slate	3·25	3·00
53/8		*Set of* 6	11·00	10·50

(Litho Enschedé)

1960 (3 June). *National Day. W* w **12** (*sideways**). *P* 13½.

No.	Type	Description	Unused	Used
59	**17**	4 c. red, yellow and blue	75	90
		w. Wmk Crown to right of CA	60·00	
60		10 c. red, yellow and grey	2·25	30
		w. Wmk Crown to right of CA	60·00	

*The normal sideways watermark shows Crown to left of CA, *as seen from the back of the stamp.*

18 Clasped Hands

(Photo Enschedé)

1961 (3 June). *National Day. W* w **12**. *P* 13½.

No.	Type	Description	Unused	Used
61	**18**	4 c. black, brown and pale yellow	1·00	85
62		10 c. black, deep green and pale yellow	1·25	10

19 *Arachnis "Maggie Oei"* (orchid) — **20** Yellow Seahorse

21 Tiger Barb — **24** *Vanda "Tan Chay Yan"* (orchid)

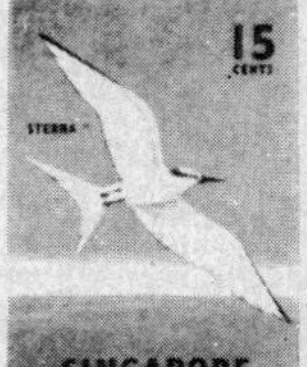

26a Black-naped Tern — **30** White-rumped Shama

(Photo Harrison (orchids, fish and 15 c. bird) D.L.R. (birds, except 15 c.))

1962 (31 Mar)–**66.** *T* **19/21, 24, 26a, 30** *and similar designs. W* w **12**. *P* 12½ (i), 14½×13½ (ii), 13½×14½ (iii), 13½×13 (iv) *or* 13×13½ (v).

No.	Description	Unused	Used
63	1 c. multicoloured (i) (10.3.63)	30	75
64	2 c. brown and green (ii)	30	1·25
65	4 c. black and orange-red (iii)	30	30
	a. Black omitted	£250	
66	5 c. red and black (iii)	20	10
	a. Red omitted	£250	
67	6 c. black and greenish yellow (ii)	55	70
68	8 c. multicoloured (i) (10.3.63)	1·25	3·50
69	10 c. red-orange and black (iii)	40	10
	a. Red-orange omitted	£150	
70	12 c. multicoloured (i) (10.3.63)	1·25	3·50
70a	15 c. multicoloured (i) (9.11.66)	1·75	10
	ab. Orange (eye) omitted	27·00	
	aw. Wmk inverted	7·00	
71	20 c. orange and blue (ii)	40	10
	a. Orange omitted	£275	
72	25 c. black and orange (iii)	75	10
73	30 c. multicoloured (i) (10.3.63)	1·25	10
	a. Yellow (flowers) omitted	55·00	
74	50 c. multicoloured (iv) (10.3.63)	1·25	10
75	$1 multicoloured (iv) (10.3.63)	18·00	60
76	$2 multicoloured (iv) (10.3.63)	14·00	75
77	$5 multicoloured (v) (10.3.63)	27·00	4·00
	w. Wmk inverted	£110	
63/77	*Set of* 16	60·00	14·00

Designs: *Horiz* (*as T* **21**)—5 c. Orange Clownfish; 10 c. Harlequinfish; 25 c. Three-spotted Goramy. (*As T* **30**)—$1 White-breasted Kingfisher. *Vert* (*as T* **20**)—6 c. Archerfish; 20 c. Copper-banded Butterflyfish. (*As T* **24**)—12 c. *Grammatophyllum speciosum* (orchid); 30 c. *Vanda* "Miss Joaquim" (orchid). (*As T* **26a**)—$2 Yellow-bellied Sunbird; $5 White-bellied Sea Eagle.

The 15 c., 30c., $2 and $5 exist with PVA gum as well as gum arabic.

See also Nos. 83/8

34 "The Role of Labour in Nation-Building" — **35** Blocks of Flats, Singapore

(Photo Courvoisier)

1962 (3 June). *National Day. P* 11½ × 12.

No.	Type	Description	Unused	Used
78	**34**	4 c. yellow, rose-carmine and black	70	1·25
79		10 c. yellow, blue and black	90	50

(Photo Harrison)

1963 (3 June). *National Day. W* w **12**. *P* 12½.

No.	Type	Description	Unused	Used
80	**35**	4 c. orange-red, black, blue & turq-blue	40	65
81		10 c. orange-red, blk, yell-olive & turq-bl	85	15
		w. Wmk inverted	35·00	

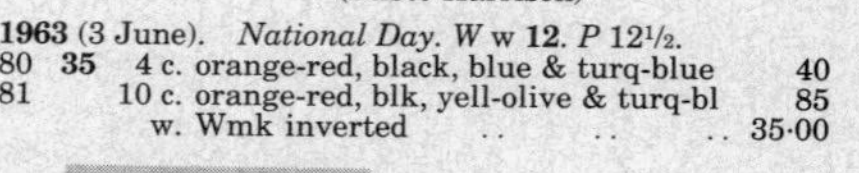

36 Dancers in National Costume — **37** Workers

(Photo Harrison)

1963 (8 Aug). *South East Asia Cultural Festival. W* w **12**. *P* 14 × 14½.

No.	Type	Description	Unused	Used
82	**36**	5 c. multicoloured	40	40

INDEPENDENT REPUBLIC

1966 (1 Mar)–**67.** *As Nos.* 63, 66, 69, 72, 74/5, *but W* w **12** (*sideways**).

No.	Description	Unused	Used
83	1 c. multicoloured (22.6.67)	10	2·00
84	5 c. red and black (30.5.67)	2·25	1·75
85	10 c. red-orange and black (19.5.67†)	1·25	55
86	25 c. black and orange (9.66†)	70	1·50
	w. Wmk Crown to right of CA	2·50	
87	50 c. multicoloured (11.1.66†)	4·50	3·00
	a. Imperf (pair)	£425	
88	$1 multicoloured (18.5.67)	16·00	9·00
83/8	*Set of* 6	22·00	16·00

*The normal sideways watermark show Crown to left of CA, *as seen from the back of the stamp.*

†The 25 and 50 c. values were not released in London until 30.5.67 and 9.6.66. The 25 c. value, however, is known used in September 1966 and the 50 c. on 11.1.66. The 10 c., released in London on 30 May 1967, is known used locally on 19 May.

The 1 c. and 25 c. exist with PVA gum as well as gum arabic.

(Photo D.L.R.)

1966 (9 Aug). *First Anniv of Republic. W* w **12** (30 *c.*) *or no wmk (others). P* 12½ × 13.

89	**37**	15 c. multicoloured	75	30
90		20 c. multicoloured	1·00	1·00
91		30 c. multicoloured	1·25	1·75
89/91		*Set of* 3	2·75	2·75

38 Flag Procession

(Photo D.L.R.)

1967 (9 Aug). *National Day. P* 14 × 14½.

92	**38**	6 c. rosine, brown and slate	50	75
93		15 c. reddish purple, brown and slate	80	10
94		50 c. bright blue, brown and slate	1·50	1·60
92/4		*Set of* 3	2·50	2·25

Nos. 92/4 are respectively inscribed "Build a Vigorous Singapore" in Chinese, Malay and Tamil in addition to the English inscription.

39 Skyscrapers and Afro-Asian Map

40 Symbolical Figure wielding Hammer, and Industrial Outline of Singapore

(Photo D.L.R.)

1967 (7 Oct). *2nd Afro-Asian Housing Congress. P* 14 × 13.

95	**39**	10 c. multicoloured	30	10
		a. Opt omitted	£450	£450
96		25 c. multicoloured	75	1·00
97		50 c. multicoloured	1·40	1·60
95/7		*Set of* 3	2·25	2·40

The above were originally scheduled for release in 1966, and when finally issued were overprinted with the new date and a black oblong obliterating the old date.

(Photo Harrison)

1968 (9 Aug). *National Day. Inscription at top in Chinese* (6 *c.*), *Malay* (15 *c.*) *or Tamil* (50 *c.*). *P* 13½ × 14.

98	**40**	6 c. orange-red, black and gold	35	65
99		15 c. apple-green, black and gold	45	15
100		50 c. greenish blue, black and gold	1·00	1·25
98/100		*Set of* 3	1·60	1·90

41 Half check Pattern

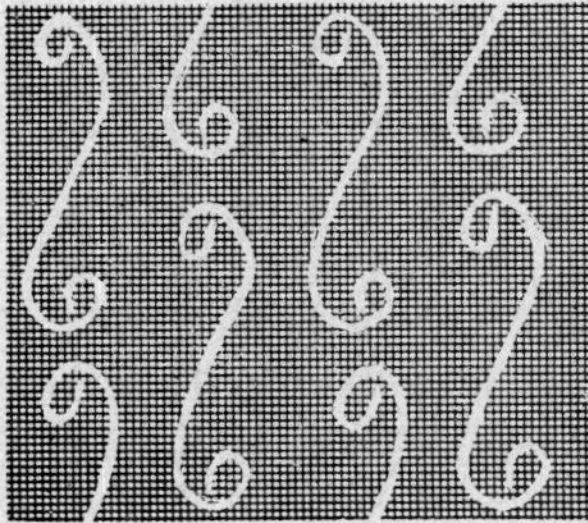

42 Scrolled "S" multiple

43 Mirudhangam

44 Pi Pa

45 Sword Dance

51 Dragon Dance

(Photo D.L.R. (5 c. to $1), Japanese Govt Printing Bureau, Tokyo (others))

1968–73. *T* **43/5, 51** *and similar designs.* 5 *c. to* $1: *Chalk-surfaced paper; W* **41**; *P* 14. *Others: Ordinary paper; W* **42** *upright* (1 *c.*, $5) *or sideways* (4 *c.*, $2, $10); *P* 13½.

101	1 c. multicoloured (10.11.69)	15	2·25
102	4 c. multicoloured (10.11.69)	60	2·75
103	5 c. multicoloured (29.12.68)	60	80
	a. Glazed unsurfaced paper (16.12.70)	8·50	7·00
	b. Chalky paper. Perf 13 (27.6.73)	5·00	7·00
104	6 c. black, lemon and orange (1.12.68)	90	1·50
105	10 c. multicoloured (29.12.68)	20	10
	a. Glazed unsurfaced paper (16.12.70)	11·00	8·00
	b. Chalky paper. Perf 13 (14.7.73*)	5·50	6·50
106	15 c. multicoloured (29.12.68)	60	10
107	20 c. multicoloured (1.12.68)	50	75
	a. Perf 13 (12.9.73)	8·00	11·00
108	25 c. multicoloured (29.12.68)	80	70
	a. Perf 13 (27.6.73)	4·75	9·00
109	30 c. multicoloured (1.12.68)	40	70
	a. Perf 13 (12.9.73)	9·50	13·00
110	50 c. blk, orge-red & lt yell-brown (1.12.68)	50	50
	a. Perf 13 (12.9.73)	11·00	22·00
111	75 c. multicoloured (1.12.68)	2·50	2·00
112	$1 multicoloured (29.12.68)	4·00	80
	a. Perf 13 (12.9.73)	15·00	18·00
113	$2 multicoloured (10.11.69)	3·50	1·00
114	$5 multicoloured (10.11.69)	12·00	2·00
115	$10 multicoloured (6.12.69)	35·00	15·00
101/15	*Set of* 15	55·00	27·00
103b/12a	*Set of* 7	50·00	75·00

Designs: *Vert (as T* **45**)—6 c. Lion dance; 10 c. Bharatha Natyam; 15 c. Tari Payong; 20 c. Kathak Kali; 25 c. Lu Chih Shen and Lin Chung; 50 c. Tari Lilin; 75 c. Tarian Kuda Kepang; $1 Yao Chi. *(As T* **44**)—$2, Rebab; $10 Ta Ku. *Horiz (as T* **43**)—$5 Vina.

*Earliest known date of use.

58 E.C.A.F.E. Emblem

59 "100000" and Slogan as Block of Flats

(Des Eng Siak Loy. Photo Japanese Govt Ptg Bureau, Tokyo)

1969 (15 Apr). *25th Plenary Session of the U.N. Economic Commission for Asia and the Far East. P* 13.

116	**58**	15 c. black, silver and pale blue	40	20
117		30 c. black, silver and red	85	1·25
118		75 c. black, silver and violet-blue	1·40	2·50
116/18		*Set of* 3	2·40	3·50

(Des Tay Siew Chiah. Litho B.W.)

1969 (20 July). *Completion of* "100,000 *Homes for the People*" *Project. P* 13½.

119	**59**	25 c. black and emerald	1·00	50
120		50 c. black and deep blue	1·25	1·25

60 Aircraft over Silhouette of Singapore Docks

61 Sea Shells

(Des Eng Siak Loy and Han Kuan Cheng. Litho B.W.)

1969 (9 Aug). *150th Anniv of Founding of Singapore. T* **60** *and similar vert designs. P* 14 × 14½.

121	15 c. black, vermilion and yellow	2·50	70
122	30 c. black, blue and new blue	2·50	1·75
123	75 c. multicoloured	4·50	2·00
124	$1 black and vermilion	9·50	9·50
125	$5 vermilion and black	35·00	55·00
126	$10 black and bright green	48·00	55·00
121/6	*Set of* 6	90·00	£110
MS127	120 × 120 mm. Nos. 121/6. P 13½	£450	£475

Designs:—30 c. U.N. emblem and outline of Singapore; 75 c. Flags and outline of Malaysian Federation; $1 Uplifted hands holding crescent and stars; $5 Tail of Japanese aircraft and searchlight beams; $10 Bust from statue of Sir Stamford Raffles.

(Des Tay Siew Chiah (15 c.), Eng Siak Loy (others). Litho Rosenbaum Bros, Vienna)

1970 (15 Mar). *World Fair, Osaka. T* **61** *and similar vert designs. Multicoloured. P* 13½.

128	15 c. Type **61**	1·50	15
129	30 c. Veil-tailed Guppys	2·75	90
130	75 c. Greater Flamingo and Helmeted Hornbill	7·50	3·75
131	$1 Orchid	7·50	6·00
128/31	*Set of* 4	17·00	9·75
MS132	94×154 mm. Nos. 128/31	24·00	22·00

62 "Kindergarten"

63 Soldier charging

(Des Choy Weng Yang. Litho B.W.)

1970 (1 July). *Tenth Anniv of People's Association. T* **62** *and similar square designs. P* 13½.

133	15 c. agate and bright orange	85	20
134	50 c. ultramarine and yellow-orange	2·25	2·75
135	75 c. bright purple and black	3·50	4·50
133/5	*Set of* 3	6·00	6·50

Designs:—50 c. "Sport"; 75 c. "Culture".

(Des Choy Weng Yang. Litho Rosenbaum Bros, Vienna)

1970 (9 Aug). *National Day. T* **63** *and similar vert designs. Multicoloured. P* 13½.

136	15 c. Type **63**	1·25	20
137	50 c. Soldier on assault course	3·75	3·50
138	$1 Soldier jumping	5·00	8·50
136/8	*Set of* 3	9·00	11·00

64 Sprinters

(Des Choy Weng Yang. Photo Japanese Govt Ptg Bureau, Tokyo)

1970 (23 Aug). *Festival of Sports. T* **64** *and similar horiz designs. P* 13 × 13½.

139	10 c. magenta, black and ultramarine	2·00	3·00
	a. Horiz strip of 4. Nos. 139/42	9·00	
140	15 c. black, ultramarine and red-orange	2·50	3·25
141	25 c. black, red-orange and bright green	2·75	3·50
142	50 c. black, bright green and magenta	3·00	3·50
139/42	*Set of* 4	9·00	12·00

Designs:—15 c. Swimmers; 25 c. Tennis-players; 50 c. Racing-cars.

Nos. 139/42 were issued together *se-tenant* in horizontal strips of four within the sheet.

65 *Neptune Aquamarine* (freighter)

(Des W. Lee. Litho Rosenbaum Bros, Vienna)

1970 (1 Nov). *Singapore Shipping. T* **65** *and similar horiz designs. P* 12.

143	15 c. multicoloured	2·75	65
144	30 c. yellow-ochre and ultramarine	6·00	5·50
145	75 c. yellow-ochre and vermilion	10·00	8·50
143/5	*Set of* 3	17·00	13·00

Designs:—30 c. Container berth; 75 c. Ship-building.

66 Country Names forming Circle

(Des W. Lee. Litho D.L.R.)

1971 (1 Jan). *Commonwealth Heads of Government Meeting, Singapore. T* **66** *and similar horiz designs. Multicoloured. P* 14 ($1) *or* 15 × 14½ (*others*).

146 15 c. Type **66** . . 90 20
147 30 c. Flags in circle . . 1·75 80
148 75 c. Commonwealth flags . . 3·25 3·75
149 $1 Commonwealth flags linked to Singapore (63 × 61 *mm*) . . 4·25 6·50
146/9 . . *Set of* 4 9·00 10·00

Imperforate examples of Nos. 146/7 overprinted "Specimen" are from printer's sample sheets.

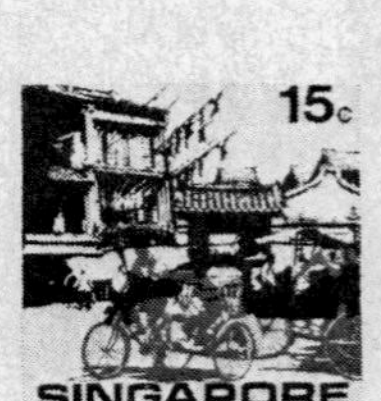

67 Bicycle Rickshaws

68 Chinese New Year

(Des Eng Siak Loy (15, 20 and 30 c.), W. Lee (others). Litho B.W.)

1971 (4 Apr). *Visit A.S.E.A.N. Year* (*A.S.E.A.N. = Association of South East Asian Nations*). *T* **67** *and similar designs. P* 13 × 13½ (50, 75 c.) *or* 11½ (*others*).

150 15 c. black, deep bluish violet and orange . . 80 25
151 20 c. indigo, orange and turquoise-blue . . 1·10 1·00
152 30 c. vermilion and deep maroon . . 1·40 1·75
153 50 c. multicoloured . . 4·75 7·50
154 75 c. multicoloured . . 6·50 9·50
150/4 . . *Set of* 5 13·00 18·00

Designs: *As T* **67**—20 c. Houseboat "village" and sampans; 30 c. Bazaar. *Horiz* (68×18 *mm*)—50 c. Modern harbour skyline; 75 c. Religious buildings.

(Des W. Lee. Litho Rosenbaum Bros, Vienna)

1971 (9 Aug). *Singapore Festivals. T* **68** *and similar vert designs. Multicoloured. P* 14.

155 15 c. Type **68** . . 1·25 15
156 30 c. Hari Raya . . 3·00 2·50
157 50 c. Deepavali . . 4·00 6·50
158 75 c. Christmas . . 5·00 7·50
155/8 . . *Set of* 4 12·00 15·00
MS159 150 × 125 mm. Nos. 155/8 . . 70·00 48·00

69 "Dish" Aerial

(Des W. Lee. Litho B.W.)

1971 (23 Oct). *Opening of Satellite Earth Station. P* 13½.

160 **69** 15 c. multicoloured . . 3·00 1·50
161 – 30 c. multicoloured . . 13·00 11·00
a. Block of 4. Nos. 161/4 . . 50·00
162 – 30 c. multicoloured . . 13·00 11·00
163 – 30 c. multicoloured . . 13·00 11·00
164 – 30 c. multicoloured . . 13·00 11·00
160/4 . . *Set of* 5 50·00 40·00

Designs:—Nos. 161/4 were printed in *se-tenant* blocks of four throughout the sheet, the four stamps forming a composite design similar to T **69**. They can be identified by the colour of the face value which is: yellow (No. 161), green (No. 162), magenta (No. 163) or orange (No. 164).

70 "Singapore River and Fort Canning, 1843–7" (Lieut. E. A. Porcher)

(Des W. Lee. Litho B.W.)

1971 (5 Dec). *Art. T* **70** *and similar horiz designs. Multicoloured. P* 12½ × 13 (50 c. *and* $1) *or* 13 (*others*).

165 10 c. Type **70** . . 2·50 2·50
166 15 c. "The Padang, 1851" (J. T. Thomson) . . 3·50 4·00
167 20 c. "Singapore Waterfront, 1848–9" . . 4·50 4·50
168 35 c. "View from Fort Canning, 1846" (J. T. Thomson) . . 9·00 9·00
169 50 c. "View from Mt Wallich, 1857" (P. Carpenter) (69 × 47 *mm*) . . 13·00 14·00
170 $1 "Singapore Waterfront, 1861" (W. Gray) (69 × 47 *mm*) . . 16·00 19·00
165/70 . . *Set of* 6 45·00 48·00

71 One Dollar of 1969

(Des W. Lee. Litho B.W.)

1972 (4 June). *Coins. T* **71** *and similar horiz designs. P* 13½.

171 15 c. orange, black and deep green . . 1·25 35
172 35 c. black and vermilion . . 2·75 3·00
173 $1 yellow, black and bright blue . . 5·00 8·00
171/3 . . *Set of* 3 8·00 10·00

Designs:—15 c. One-cent coin of George V; $1 One hundred and fifty dollar gold coin of 1969.

72 "Moon Festival" (Seah Kim Joo)

73 Lanterns and Fish

(Des W. Lee. Litho State Bank Note Printing Works, Helsinki)

1972 (9 July). *Contemporary Art. T* **72** *and similar multicoloured designs. P* 12½.

174 15 c. Type **72** . . 80 30
175 35 c. "Complimentary Forces" (Thomas Yeo) (36 × 54 *mm*) . . 2·00 3·00
176 50 c. "Rhythm in Blue" (Yusman Aman) (36 × 54 *mm*) . . 3·00 4·00
177 $1 "Gibbons" (Chen Wen Hsi) . . 5·50 7·00
174/7 . . *Set of* 4 10·00 13·00

(Des Eng Siak Loy. Litho State Bank Note Printing Works, Helsinki)

1972 (9 Aug). *National Day. T* **73** *and similar vert designs symbolising Festivals. Multicoloured. P* 12½.

178 15 c. Type **73** . . 75 20
179 35 c. Altar and candles . . 1·40 2·75
180 50 c. Jug, bowl and gifts . . 2·00 4·00
181 75 c. Candle . . 3·00 5·50
178/81 . . *Set of* 4 6·50 11·00

74 Student Welding

75 *Maria Rickmers* (barque)

(Des Eng Siak Loy. Photo Kultura, Budapest)

1972 (1 Oct). *Youth. T* **74** *and similar horiz designs. P* 12.

182 15 c. multicoloured . . 80 30
183 35 c. multicoloured . . 2·50 3·50
184 $1 red-orange, blue-violet & yellowish grn 4·50 8·00
182/4 . . *Set of* 3 7·00 10·50

Designs:—35 c. Sport; $1 Dancing.

(Des Choy Weng Yang (Nos. 185/7), Eng Siak Loy (**MS**188). Litho Harrison)

1972 (17 Dec). *Shipping. T* **75** *and similar multicoloured designs. P* 14 × 14½.

185 15 c. *Neptune Ruby* (container ship) (42×29 *mm*) . . 2·25 80
186 75 c. Type **75** . . 7·50 7·50
187 $1 Chinese junk . . 8·00 8·50
185/7 . . *Set of* 3 16·00 15·00
MS188 152×84 mm. Nos. 185/7 . . 42·00 42·00

76 P.Q.R. Slogan

77 Jurong Bird Park

(Des W. Lee. Litho B.W.)

1973 (25 Feb). *"Prosperity through Quality and Reliability" Campaign. T* **76** *and similar vert designs. P* 14.

189 **76** 15 c. multicoloured . . 60 15
190 – 35 c. multicoloured . . 2·00 3·25
191 – 75 c. multicoloured . . 2·25 3·75
192 – $1 multicoloured . . 2·25 5·00
189/92 . . *Set of* 4 6·50 11·00

Nos. 190/2 show various P.Q.R. emblems.

(Des Han Kuan Cheng. Litho Harrison)

1973 (29 Apr). *Singapore Landmarks. T* **77** *and similar vert designs. P* 12½.

193 15 c. black and red-orange . . 1·00 15
194 35 c. black and myrtle-green . . 2·50 3·25
195 50 c. black and red-brown . . 3·25 4·25
196 $1 black and purple . . 5·00 6·50
193/6 . . *Set of* 4 10·50 13·00

Designs:—35 c. National Theatre; 50 c. City Hall; $1 Fullerton Building and Singapore River.

78 Aircraft Tail-fins

79 "Culture"

(Des W. Lee. Litho B.W.)

1973 (24 June). *Aviation. T* **78** *and similar horiz designs. Multicoloured. P* 13½ × 13.

197 10 c. Type **78** . . 50 10
198 35 c. Emblem of Singapore Airlines and destinations . . 1·75 2·00
199 75 c. Emblem on tail-fin . . 2·25 2·50
200 $1 Emblems encircling the globe . . 2·75 3·50
197/200 . . *Set of* 4 6·50 7·25

(Des Eng Siak Loy. Litho Harrison)

1973 (9 Aug). *National Day. T* **79** *and similar vert designs. P* 13½.

201 **79** 10 c. orange and black . . 2·00 2·25
a. Block of 4. Nos. 201/4 . . 8·50
202 – 35 c. orange and black . . 2·25 2·75
203 – 50 c. orange and black . . 2·50 3·00
204 – 75 c. orange and black . . 2·75 3·50
201/4 . . *Set of* 4 8·50 10·50

Nos. 201/4 were printed in *se-tenant* blocks of four within the sheet, and form a composite design representing Singapore's culture.

80 Athletics, Judo and Boxing

81 Agave

82 Mangosteen

(Des C. Lim. Photo Heraclio Fournier)

1973 (1 Sept). *Seventh S.E.A.P.* Games. T* **80** *and similar designs. P* 14 (10 *to* 35 *c.*) *or* 13 × 14 (*others*).

205 10 c. gold, silver and indigo . . 55 20
206 15 c. gold and grey-black . . 1·75 1·50
207 25 c. gold, silver and black . . 1·50 1·75
208 35 c. gold, silver and deep blue . . 3·00 3·25
209 50 c. multicoloured . . 2·00 4·00
210 $1 silver, royal blue and yellow-green . . 3·25 7·00
205/10 . . *Set of* 6 11·00 16·00
MS211 130 × 111 mm. Nos. 205/10. P 13 × 14 . . 30·00 32·00

Designs: *As T* **80**—15 c. Cycling, weight-lifting, pistol-shooting and sailing; 25 c. Footballs; 35 c. Table-tennis bat, shuttlecock, tennis ball and hockey stick. *Horiz* (41 × 25 *mm*):—50 c. Swimmers; $1 Stadium.

*S.E.A.P. = South East Asian Peninsula.

(Des W. Lee (1 c. to 75 c.), Eng Siak Loy (others). Photo Heraclio Fournier)

1973. *Various multicoloured designs as T* **81/2**. *With fluorescent security markings.*

(*a*) *Stylized flowers and plants, size as T* **81**. *P* 13 (30.9.73)

212 1 c. Type **81** . . 90 65
213 5 c. *Coleus blumei* . . 10 45
a. Booklet pane. Nos. 213×4, 214×4, 216×2 . . 7·00
214 10 c. *Vinca rosea* . . 15 10
215 15 c. *Helianthus angustifolius* . . 1·00 10
a. Green printed double . . † —
216 20 c. *Licuala grandis* . . 45 60
217 25 c. *Wedelia trilobata* . . 2·50 55
218 35 c. *Chrysanthemum frutescens* . . 90 90
219 50 c. *Costus malorticanus* . . 1·00 55
220 75 c. *Gerbera jamesonii* . . 2·50 90

(*b*) *Fruits, size as T* **82**. *P* 12½ × 13 (1.11.73)

221 $1 Type **82** . . 1·50 40
222 $2 Jackfruit . . 3·25 1·25
223 $5 Coconut . . 6·00 9·00
224 $10 Pineapple . . 12·00 16·00
212/24 . . *Set of* 13 29·00 28·00

Booklet pane No. 213a has the upper and lower edges imperforate and there are margins at left and right.

83 Tiger and Orang-Utans

84 Delta Guppy

(Des Eng Siak Loy. Litho B.W.)

1973 (16 Dec). *Singapore Zoo. T* **83** *and similar vert designs. Multicoloured. P* 13.

225 5 c. Type **83** 85 85
226 10 c. Leopard and Waterbuck .. .. .. 1·00 45
227 35 c. Leopard and Thamin .. .. .. 4·50 5·00
228 75 c. Horse and Lion .. .. 6·00 7·00
225/8 .. .. *Set of* 4 11·00 12·00

(Des Eng Siak Loy. Photo Heraclio Fournier)

1974 (21 Apr). *Tropical Fish. T* **84** *and similar vert designs. Multicoloured. P* 14.

229 5 c. Type **84** 60 50
230 10 c. Half-black Delta Guppy 60 15
231 35 c. Delta Guppy (*different*) .. .. .. 2·50 3·50
232 $1 Black Delta Guppy .. .. 4·50 6·00
229/32 .. .. *Set of* 4 7·50 9·00

85 Scout Badge within "9"

86 U.P.U. Emblem and Multiple "Centenary"

(Des W. Lee. Litho Harrison)

1974 (9 June). *Ninth Asia-Pacific Scout Conference. P* 13½ × 14½.

233 **85** 10 c. multicoloured 40 10
234 75 c. multicoloured .. .. 1·60 2·00

(Des W. Lee. Litho Harrison)

1974 (7 July). *Centenary of Universal Postal Union. T* **86** *and similar vert designs. P* 14 × 13½.

235 10 c. orange-brown, purple-brown and gold .. 20 10
a. Gold (U.P.U. symbol) omitted £275
236 35 c. new blue, deep blue and gold .. .. 55 1·60
237 75 c. multicoloured .. .. 1·25 2·75
235/7 .. .. *Set of* 3 1·75 4·00

Designs:—35 c. U.P.U. emblem and multiple U.N. symbols; 75 c. U.P.U. emblem and multiple peace doves.

87 Family Emblem

88 "Tree and Sun" (Chia Keng San)

(Des Eng Siak Loy. Litho B.W.)

1974 (9 Aug). *World Population Year. T* **87** *and similar horiz designs. Multicoloured. P* 12½ × 13½.

238 10 c. Type **87** 30 10
239 35 c. Male and female symbols .. .. .. 80 1·60
a. Emerald (male symbol) omitted £425
240 75 c. World population map .. .. .. 1·75 3·25
238/40 .. .. *Set of* 3 2·50 4·50

(Des Eng Siak Loy. Photo Heraclio Fournier)

1974 (1 Oct). *Universal Children's Day. T* **88** *and similar vert designs showing children's paintings. Multicoloured. P* 13½.

241 5 c. Type **88** 40 50
242 10 c. "My Daddy and Mummy" (Angeline Ang) 40 20
243 35 c. "A Dump Truck" (Si-Hoe Yeen Joong) 2·50 3·50
244 50 c. "My Aunt" (Raymond Teo) .. .. 2·75 4·25
241/4 .. .. *Set of* 4 5·50 7·75
MS245 138×100 mm. Nos. 241/4. P 13 .. 20·00 22·00

89 Street Scene

(Des Loy Chin. Litho Secura, Singapore)

1975 (26 Jan). *Singapore Views. T* **89** *and similar horiz designs. Multicoloured. P* 14.

246 15 c. Type **89** 80 20
247 20 c. Singapore River .. .. 1·50 1·50
248 $1 "Kelong" (fish-trap) .. .. .. 5·00 7·50
246/8 .. .. *Set of* 3 6·50 8·25

90 Emblem and Lighters' Prows

91 Satellite Earth Station, Sentosa

(Des Choy Weng Yang. Litho Secura, Singapore)

1975 (10 Mar). *Ninth Biennial Conference of International Association of Ports and Harbours, Singapore. T* **90** *and similar horiz designs. Multicoloured. P* 14.

249 5 c. Type **90** 30 15
250 25 c. Freighter and ship's wheel .. .. 1·75 1·50
251 50 c. Oil-tanker and flags .. .. .. 2·25 3·00
252 $1 Container-ship and propellers .. .. 3·50 6·00
249/52 .. .. *Set of* 4 7·00 9·50

(Des Sim Tong Khern. Photo Heraclio Fournier)

1975 (29 June). *"Science and Industry". T* **91** *and similar multicoloured designs. P* 13½.

253 10 c. Type **91** 35 10
254 35 c. Oil refineries (*vert*) .. .. .. 2·50 2·75
255 75 c. "Medical Sciences" .. .. .. 2·75 4·00
253/5 .. .. *Set of* 3 5·00 6·00

92 "Homes and Gardens"

93 South African Crowned Cranes

(Des Tay Siew Chiah. Litho Secura, Singapore)

1975 (9 Aug). *Tenth National Day. T* **92** *and similar square designs. Multicoloured. P* 13½.

256 10 c. Type **92** 20 10
257 35 c. "Shipping and Ship-building" .. .. 1·75 2·00
258 75 c. "Communications and Technology" .. 2·25 3·50
259 $1 "Trade, Commerce and Industry" .. 2·50 4·00
256/9 .. .. *Set of* 4 6·00 8·50

(Des Eng Siak Loy. Litho Harrison)

1975 (5 Oct). *Birds. T* **93** *and similar vert designs. Multicoloured. P* 14½ × 13½.

260 5 c. Type **93** .. .. 1·75 80
261 10 c. Great Indian Hornbill .. .. .. 1·75 30
262 35 c. White-breasted Kingfisher and White-collared Kingfisher .. .. 9·50 9·50
263 $1 Sulphur-crested Cockatoo and Blue and Yellow Macaw .. .. 14·00 16·00
260/3 .. .. *Set of* 4 24·00 24·00

94 "Equality"

95 Yellow Flame

(Des Tay Siew Chiah. Litho Secura, Singapore)

1975 (7 Dec). *International Women's Year. T* **94** *and similar square designs. Multicoloured. P* 13½.

264 10 c. Type **94** 25 10
265 35 c. "Development" .. .. 2·25 3·00
266 75 c. "Peace" .. .. 3·25 6·00
264/6 .. .. *Set of* 3 5·25 8·00
MS267 128 × 100 mm. Nos. 264/6 .. .. 15·00 18·00

(Des Tay Siew Chiah. Litho Secura, Singapore)

1976 (18 Apr). *Wayside Trees. T* **95** *and similar vert designs. Multicoloured. P* 14.

268 10 c. Type **95** 60 10
269 35 c. Cabbage Tree .. .. 2·50 3·50
270 50 c. Rose of India .. .. 2·75 3·50
271 75 c. Variegated Coral Tree .. .. .. 3·25 6·25
268/71 .. .. *Set of* 4 8·00 12·00

96 *Arachnis hookeriana × Vanda* Hilo Blue

97 Festival Symbol and Band

(Des Eng Siak Loy. Litho Secura, Singapore)

1976 (20 June). *Singapore Orchids. T* **96** *and similar vert designs. Multicoloured. P* 14.

272 10 c. Type **96** .. .. 1·50 10
273 35 c. *Arachnis Maggie Oei × Vanda insignis* 4·00 4·00
274 50 c. *Arachnis Maggie Oei × Vandu* Rodman 4·75 4·50
275 75 c. *Arachnis hookeriana × Vanda* Dawn Nishimura .. .. 6·00 8·00
272/5 .. .. *Set of* 4 14·50 15·00

(Des Han Kuan Cheng. Litho Harrison)

1976 (9 Aug). *Tenth Anniv of Singapore Youth Festival. Horiz designs showing festival symbol as T* **97**. *Multicoloured. P* 12½.

276 10 c. Type **97** 20 10
277 35 c. Athletes .. .. 1·25 1·25
278 75 c. Dancers .. .. 1·40 2·00
276/8 .. .. *Set of* 3 2·50 3·00

98 "Queen Elizabeth Walk"

(Des H. Weepaul. Litho Secura, Singapore)

1976 (14 Nov). *Paintings of Old Singapore, circa 1905–10, by A. L. Watson. T* **98** *and similar horiz designs. Multicoloured. With fluorescent security markings. P* 14.

279 10 c. Type **98** 50 20
280 50 c. "The Padang" .. .. 3·75 4·00
281 $1 "Raffles Place" .. .. 4·50 5·50
279/81 .. .. *Set of* 3 8·00 8·75
MS282 164 × 91 mm. Nos. 279/81. P 13½ .. 18·00 22·00

99 Chinese Costume

100 Radar, Missile and Soldiers

(Des Margaret Heng. Litho Harrison)

1976 (19 Dec). *Bridal Costumes. T* **99** *and similar vert designs. Multicoloured. P* 14½.

283 10 c. Type **99** 65 10
284 35 c. Indian costume .. .. 2·25 2·50
285 75 c. Malay costume .. .. 3·75 5·75
283/5 .. .. *Set of* 3 6·00 7·50

(Des Eng Siak Loy. Litho Harrison)

1977 (12 Mar). *Tenth Anniv of National Service. T* **100** *and similar vert designs. Multicoloured. P* 14½.

286 10 c. Type **100** 65 10
287 50 c. Tank and soldiers .. .. 2·50 2·50
288 75 c. Soldiers, wireless operators, pilot and Douglas A-4 Skyhawk aircraft .. .. 3·50 3·50
286/8 .. .. *Set of* 3 6·00 5·50

101 Lyrate Cockle (*Lyrocardium lyratum*)

102 Spotted Hermit Crab

(Des Tay Siew Chiah. Litho Secura, Singapore)

1977. *Multicoloured designs as T* **101/2**. *With fluorescent security markings. P* 13×13½. (*a*) *Shells as T* **101** (9.4.77).

289 1 c. Type **101** .. .. 50 1·25
290 5 c. Folded or Plicate Scallop (*Decatopecten plicus*) 20 10
a. Booklet pane. Nos. 290×4 and 291×8 *se-tenant* .. .. 3·75

291 10 c. Marble Cone (*Conus marmoreus marmoreus*) 20 10
a. Imperf (pair) £400
292 15 c. Scorpion Conch (*Lambis scorpius*) .. 1·00 40
293 20 c. Amplustre or Royal Paper Bubble (*Aplustrum amplustre*) .. 90 10
294 25 c. Spiral Babylon (*Babylonia spirata*) .. 1·25 1·50
295 35 c. Royal Thorny or Spiny Oyster (*Spondylus regius*) .. 1·50 1·50
296 50 c. Maple-leaf Triton or Winged Frog Shell (*Biplex perca*) .. 2·00 10
297 75 c. Troschel's Murex (*Murex troscheli*) .. 3·00 20

(*b*) *Fish and Crustaceans as T* **102** (4.6.77)

298 $1 Type **102** .. 2·25 15
299 $2 Zuge's Stingray .. 2·25 75
300 $5 Cuttlefish .. 4·00 2·25
301 $10 Lionfish .. 7·50 5·50
289/301 .. *Set of* 13 24·00 12·00

Booklet pane No. 290a has the upper and lower edges imperforate and there are margins at left and right.

103 Shipbuilding

104 Keyhole and Banknotes

(Des W. Lee. Litho Secura, Singapore)

1977 (1 May). *Labour Day. T* **103** *and similar horiz designs. Multicoloured. P* 13 × 12½.
302 10 c. Type **103** .. 30 10
303 50 c. Building construction .. 1·25 1·00
304 75 c. Road construction .. 1·75 1·25
302/4 .. *Set of* 3 3·00 2·00

(Des Tay Siew Chiah. Litho Secura, Singapore)

1977 (16 July). *Centenary of Post Office Savings Bank. T* **104** *and similar vert designs. Multicoloured. P* 13.
305 10 c. Type **104** .. 30 10
a. Perf 14
306 35 c. On-line banking service .. 1·25 50
a. Perf 14
307 75 c. GIRO service .. 2·75 1·50
a. Perf 14
305/7 .. *Set of* 3 3·75 1·90

105 Flags of Member Nations

106 "Chingay Procession" (Liang Yik Yin)

(Des Eng Siak Loy. Litho Secura, Singapore)

1977 (8 Aug). *Tenth Anniv of A.S.E.A.N. (Association of South-East Asian Nations). T* **105** *and similar vert designs. Multicoloured. P* 14.
308 10 c. Type **105** .. 30 10
309 35 c. "Agriculture" .. 1·00 50
310 75 c. "Industry" .. 2·00 1·10
308/10 .. *Set of* 3 3·00 1·50

(Des H. Weepaul. Litho Secura, Singapore)

1977 (1 Oct). *Children's Art. T* **106** *and similar horiz designs. Multicoloured. P* 12½.
311 10 c. Type **106** .. 30 10
312 35 c. "At the Bus Stop" (Chong Khing Ann) .. 1·00 50
313 75 c. "Playground" (Yap Li Hwa) .. 2·25 2·75
311/13 .. *Set of* 3 3·25 3·00
MS314 160 × 97 mm. Nos. 311/13 .. 13·00 15·00

107 "Life Sciences"

108 Botanical Gardens and Esplanade, Jurong Bird Park

(Des Tay Siew Chiah. Litho Format)

1977 (10 Dec). *Singapore Science Centre. T* **107** *and similar vert designs. Multicoloured. P* 14½×14.
315 10 c. Type **107** .. 10 10
316 35 c. "Physical sciences" .. 45 30
a. Deep green and brown omitted .. £300
317 75 c. "Science and technology" .. 1·25 1·75
318 $1 Singapore Science Centre .. 1·50 1·75
315/18 .. *Set of* 4 3·00 3·50

(Des C. Kiat. Litho Harrison)

1978 (22 Apr). *Parks and Gardens. T* **108** *and similar multicoloured designs. P* 14½.
319 10 c. Type **108** .. 20 10
320 35 c. Lagoon, East Coast Park (*vert*) .. 80 70
321 75 c. Botanical Gardens (*vert*) .. 1·50 2·00
319/21 .. *Set of* 3 2·25 2·50

109 Red-whiskered Bulbul

111 Map of South East Asia showing Cable Network

110 Thian Hock Keng Temple

(Des Eng Siak Loy. Litho Secura, Singapore)

1978 (1 July). *Singing Birds. T* **109** *and similar vert designs. Multicoloured. P* 13½×14.
322 10 c. Type **109** .. 60 20
323 35 c. Oriental White Eye .. 1·75 1·25
324 50 c. White-rumped Shama .. 2·00 2·00
325 75 c. White-crested Laughing Thrush and Hwamei .. 2·25 3·25
322/5 .. *Set of* 4 6·00 6·00

(Des Eng Siak Loy. Litho Secura, Singapore)

1978 (9 Aug). *National Monuments. T* **110** *and similar horiz designs. Multicoloured. P* 13½.
326 10 c. Type **110** .. 45 55
327 10 c. Hajjah Fatimah Mosque .. 45 55
328 10 c. Armenian Church .. 45 55
329 10 c. Sri Mariamman Temple .. 45 55
326/9 .. *Set of* 4 1·60 2·00
MS330 173 × 86 mm. 35 c. × 4, as Nos. 326/9 .. 4·25 3·75

Stamps from No. **MS**330 are similar in design to Nos. 326/9 but have no borders and the inscriptions are slightly larger.

(Des J. Heng. Litho Secura, Singapore)

1978 (3 Oct). *A.S.E.A.N. (Association of South East Asian Nations) Submarine Cable Network (1st issue). Completion of Philippines–Singapore section. P* 14 (*around design as well as stamp*).
331 **111** 10 c. multicoloured .. 15 10
332 35 c. multicoloured .. 60 55
333 50 c. multicoloured .. 80 85
334 75 c. multicoloured .. 90 1·25
331/4 .. *Set of* 4 2·25 2·50

See also Nos. 385/8 and 458/62.

112 *Neptune Spinel* (bulk carrier)

(Des P. Wee Hui Hong. Litho Secura, Singapore)

1978 (18 Nov). *10th Anniv of Neptune Orient Shipping Lines. T* **112** *and similar horiz designs. Multicoloured. P* 13½×14.
335 10 c. Type **112** .. 70 15
336 35 c. *Neptune Aries* (tanker) .. 1·75 1·00
337 50 c. *Anro Temasek* (container ship) .. 2·00 2·00
338 75 c. *Neptune Pearl* (container ship) .. 2·50 3·00
335/8 .. *Set of* 4 6·25 5·50

113 Concorde

114 10 Kilometre Marker

(Des P. Wee Hui Hong. Litho Secura, Singapore)

1978 (16 Dec). *Aviation. T* **113** *and similar horiz designs. Multicoloured. P* 13½.
339 10 c. Type **113** .. 1·00 30
340 35 c. Boeing 747-200 .. 1·25 1·00
341 50 c. Vickers Vimy .. 1·50 1·75
342 75 c. Wright Brothers' Wright Flyer I .. 1·75 3·00
339/42 .. *Set of* 4 5·00 5·50

(Des W. Lee. Litho Secura, Singapore)

1979 (24 Feb). *Metrication. T* **114** *and similar vert designs. Multicoloured. P* 13½.
343 10 c. Type **114** .. 15 10
344 35 c. Tape measure .. 30 50
345 75 c. Weighing scales .. 60 1·25
343/5 .. *Set of* 3 95 1·75

115 Vanda Hybrid

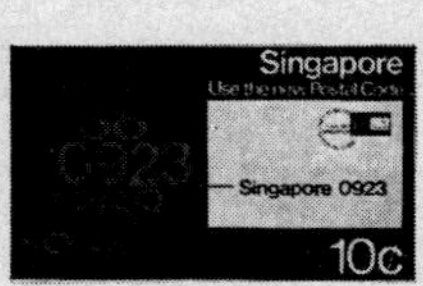

116 Envelope with new Singapore Postcode

(Des P. Wee Hui Hong. Litho Harrison)

1979 (14 Apr). *Orchids. T* **115** *and similar designs showing different varieties of Vanda Hybrid. P* 15×14 (10, 35 c.) *or* 14×15 (*others*).
346 10 c. multicoloured .. 30 10
347 35 c. multicoloured .. 75 75
348 50 c. multicoloured (*vert*) .. 90 1·00
349 75 c. multicoloured (*vert*) .. 1·25 1·40
346/9 .. *Set of* 4 2·75 2·75

(Des P. Wee Hui Hong. Litho Secura, Sinapore)

1979 (1 July). *Postal Code Publicity. P* 13.
350 **116** 10 c. multicoloured .. 10 10
351 – 50 c. multicoloured .. 60 80

The 50 c. design is as Type **116**, but the envelope is addressed to the Philatelic Bureau, General Post Office and has the postcode "Singapore 0104".

117 Early Telephone and Overhead Cables

118 "Lantern Festival" (Eng Chun-Ngan)

(Des Eng Siak Loy. Litho J.W.)

1979 (5 Oct). *Centenary of Telephone Service. T* **117** *and similar horiz designs. P* 13½×13.
352 10 c. yellow-brown and new blue .. 15 10
353 35 c. bright orange, blue and reddish violet .. 30 40
354 50 c. blue, dp turquoise-grn & yellowish grn .. 45 70
355 75 c. yellowish green and bright orange .. 65 1·25
352/5 .. *Set of* 4 1·40 2·25

Designs:—35 c. Telephone dial and world map; 50 c. Modern telephone and city scene; 75 c. Latest computerised telephone and circuit diagram.

(Des Han Kuan Cheng. Litho Secura, Singapore)

1979 (10 Nov). *International Year of the Child. Children's Drawings. T* **118** *and similar horiz designs. Multicoloured. P* 13.
356 10 c. Type **118** .. 10 10
357 35 c. "Singapore Harbour" (Wong Chien Chien) .. 30 40
358 50 c. "Use Your Hands" (Leong Choy Yeen) .. 40 70
359 75 c. "Soccer" (Tan Cheong Hin) .. 60 1·25
356/9 .. *Set of* 4 1·25 2·25
MS360 154 × 98 mm. Nos. 356/9 .. 4·75 4·25

119 View of Gardens

120 Hainan Junk

(Des Eng Siak Loy. Litho Secura, Singapore)

1979 (15 Dec). *120th Anniv of Botanic Gardens. T* **119** *and similar horiz designs showing different views of the gardens. P* 13½.
361 10 c. multicoloured .. 30 10
a. Imperf (pair) .. £500
362 50 c. multicoloured .. 1·00 1·50
363 $1 multicoloured .. 1·50 2·50
361/3 .. *Set of* 3 2·50 3·50

(Des Eng Siak Loy. Litho J.W.)

1980 (5 Apr)–**84**. *Ships. Multicoloured designs as T* **120**. *Ordinary paper* (1 c., 10 c.), *phosphorised paper* ($1 *to* $10) *and ordinary or phosphorised paper* (*others*). *P* 14 (1 *to* 75 c.) *or* 13½ ($1 *to* $10).
364 1 c. Type **120** (26.4.80) .. 50 90
365 5 c. Full-rigged clipper (26.4.80) .. 30 55
366 10 c. Fujian junk (26.4.80) .. 30 10
p. One narrow (4 mm) phosphor band (12.81) .. 45 30
pa. One wide (10 mm) phosphor band (2.84) .. 1·50 2·25
367 15 c. Golekkan (sailing craft) (26.4.80) .. 40 15
368 20 c. Palari (sailing craft) (26.4.80) .. 70 40
369 25 c. East Indiaman (26.4.80) .. 80 50

370 35 c. Galleon (26.4.80) 90 50
371 50 c. Caravel (26.4.80) 60 70
372 75 c. Jiangsu trading junk (26.4.80) .. 1·25 1·50
373 $1 *Kedah* (coaster) (42×25 *mm*) .. 70 55
a. Imperf (pair) £275
374 $2 *Murex* (tanker) (42×25 *mm*) .. 1·25 90
375 $5 *Chusan* (screw steamer) (42×25 *mm*) 3·00 3·00
376 $10 *Braganza* (paddle-steamer) (42×25 *mm*) .. .. 6·00 6·00
364/76 .. .. *Set of* 13 15·00 14·00

121 Straits Settlements 1867 1½ c. Stamp and Map of Singapore, 1843

122 C.P.F. Emblem and "Keys to Retirement Benefits"

(Des P. Wee Hui Hong. Litho Secura, Singapore)

1980 (6 May). *"London 1980" International Stamp Exhibition. T* **121** *and similar vert designs. Multicoloured. P* 13.
377 10 c. Type **121** 20 10
378 35 c. Straits Settlements 1906 $500 stamp and treaty between Johore and British Colony of Singapore 35 25
379 $1 1948 $2 stamp and map of Malaysia .. 70 1·10
380 $2 1969 150th Anniversary of Singapore $10 commemorative and letter to Col. Addenbrooke from Sir Stamford Raffles .. 1·25 2·25
377/80 .. .. *Set of* 4 2·25 3·25
MS381 148 × 104 mm. Nos. 377/80 .. .. 3·00 4·50

(Des P. Wee Hui Hong. Litho Secura, Singapore)

1980 (1 July). *25th Anniv of Central Provident Fund Board. T* **122** *and similar vert designs showing C.P.F. emblem. Multicoloured. P* 13.
382 10 c. Type **122** 10 10
383 50 c. "C.P.F. savings for home ownership" .. 40 40
384 $1 "C.P.F. savings for old-age" .. .. 75 1·25
382/4 .. .. *Set of* 3 1·10 1·60

123 Map of South East Asia showing Cable Network

124 A.S.E.A.N. Trade Fair Emblem

(Des J. Heng. Litho Secura, Singapore)

1980 (8 Aug). *A.S.E.A.N. (Association of South East Asian Nations) Submarine Cable Network (2nd issue). Completion of Indonesia–Singapore Section. P* 14 *(around design as well as stamp).*
385 **123** 10 c. multicoloured 10 10
386 35 c. multicoloured 40 30
387 50 c. multicoloured 50 75
388 75 c. multicoloured .. .. 65 1·25
385/8 .. .. *Set of* 4 1·50 2·25

(Des P. Wee Hui Hong. Litho Secura, Singapore)

1980 (3 Oct). *A.S.E.A.N. (Association of South East Asian Nations) Trade Fair. P* 13.
389 **124** 10 c. multicoloured 10 10
a. Perf 13½×14 .. .. .. 30·00
390 35 c. multicoloured 30 30
a. Perf 13½×14 .. .. .. 10·00
391 75 c. multicoloured .. .. 60 1·00
a. Perf 13½×14 .. .. .. 15·00
389/91 .. .. *Set of* 3 85 1·25

125 Ixora

126 International Currency Symbols

(Des S. Tan and Chua Ban Har. Litho J.W.)

1980 (8 Nov). *National Tree Planting Day. Flowers. T* **125** *and similar horiz designs. Multicoloured. P* 13½ × 13.
392 10 c. Type **125** 10 10
393 35 c. Allamanda 40 45
394 50 c. Sky Vine 50 70
395 75 c. Bougainvillea .. .. 60 1·10
392/5 .. .. *Set of* 4 1·40 2·00

(Des P. Wee Hui Hong. Litho Secura, Singapore)

1981 (24 Jan). *10th Anniv of Monetary Authority of Singapore. P* 14.
396 **126** 10 c. black, vermilion & greenish yellow 10 10
397 35 c. multicoloured 30 30
398 75 c. multicoloured .. .. 55 1·25
396/8 .. .. *Set of* 3 80 1·50

(**127**)

128 Woodwork

1981 (4 Mar). *No. 65 surch with T* **127**.
399 **21** 10 c. on 4 c. black and orange-red .. 30 40

(Des Sng Tong Beng. Litho J.W.)

1981 (11 Apr). *Technical Training. T* **128** *and similar vert designs. Multicoloured. P* 13 × 13½.
400 10 c. Type **128** 10 10
401 35 c. Building construction 25 25
402 50 c. Electronics 40 60
403 75 c. Precision machining .. .. .. 50 1·10
400/3 .. .. *Set of* 4 1·10 1·75

129 Figures representing various Sports

130 "The Rights to Environmental Aids"

(Des Lim Ching San. Litho J.W.)

1981 (25 Aug). *"Sports for All". T* **129** *and similar vert designs showing figures representing various sports. P* 14.
404 10 c. multicoloured 30 10
405 75 c. multicoloured .. .. 2·00 2·25
406 $1 multicoloured .. .. 2·50 3·00
404/6 .. .. *Set of* 3 4·25 4·75

(Des Chua Ban Har. Litho Harrison)

1981 (24 Nov). *International Year for Disabled Persons. T* **130** *and similar vert designs. Multicoloured. One centre phosphor band (10 c.) or phosphorised paper (others). P* 14½.
407 10 c. Type **130** 10 10
408 35 c. "The right to social integration" 40 25
409 50 c. "The right to education" 60 50
410 75 c. "The right to work" 80 90
407/10 .. .. *Set of* 4 1·75 1·60
Nos. 407/10 were printed with phosphor bands or on phosphorised paper similar to that used on contemporary Great Britain issues.

131 Control Tower and Passenger Terminal Building, Changi Airport

132 *Parthenos sylvia*

(Des J. Heng. Litho Secura, Singapore Ltd)

1981 (29 Dec). *Opening of Changi Airport. P* 14 × 13½.
411 **131** 10 c. multicoloured 10 10
412 35 c. multicoloured 35 20
413 50 c. multicoloured 45 60
414 75 c. multicoloured .. .. 60 1·10
415 $1 multicoloured .. .. 70 1·40
411/15 .. .. *Set of* 5 2·00 3·00
MS416 154 × 105 mm. Nos. 411/15 .. .. 2·25 4·00
The five values show different background emblems representing the Parks and Recreation Dept, Public Works Dept, Telecommunications Authority, Port of Singapore and Dept of Civil Aviation.

(Des Eng Siak Loy. Litho J.W.)

1982 (3 Mar). *Butterflies. T* **132** *and similar horiz designs. Multicoloured. One centre phosphor band (10 c.) or phosphorised paper (others). P* 14.
417 10 c. Type **132** 40 15
418 50 c. *Danaus vulgaris* .. .. 1·25 75
419 $1 *Trogonoptera brookiana* .. .. .. 1·75 1·75
417/19 .. .. *Set of* 3 3·00 2·40

133 A.S.E.A.N. Emblem

134 Football and Stylised Player

(Des P. Wee Hui Hong. Litho Secura, Singapore)

1982 (14 June). *15th Anniv of A.S.E.A.N. (Association of South East Asian Nations). One centre phosphor band (10 c.) or phosphorised paper (others). P* 14½×14.
420 **133** 10 c. multicoloured 10 10
421 35 c. multicoloured 30 35
422 – 50 c. multicoloured 40 65
423 – 75 c. multicoloured .. .. 60 1·00
420/3 .. .. *Set of* 4 1·25 1·90
The 50 and 75 c. values are as Type **133**, but are inscribed "15th ASEAN Ministerial Meeting".

(Des P. Wee Hui Hong. Litho Secura, Singapore)

1989 (9 July). *World Cup Football Championship, Spain. T* **134** *and similar vert designs. One centre phosphor band (10 c.) or phosphorised paper (others). P* 12.
424 10 c. black, bright blue and greenish blue .. 20 10
425 75 c. multicoloured .. .. 75 1·50
426 $1 multicoloured .. .. 95 1·50
424/6 .. .. *Set of* 3 1·75 2·75
Designs:—75 c. Football and World Cup, Asian Zone Four emblem; $1 Football and globe.

135 Sultan Shoal Lighthouse, 1896

136 Yard Gantry Cranes

(Des Eng Siak Loy. Litho Secura, Singapore)

1982 (7 Aug). *Lighthouses of Singapore. T* **135** *and similar horiz designs. Multicoloured. One centre phosphor band (10 c.) or phosphorised paper (others). P* 12.
427 10 c. Type **135** 50 15
428 75 c. Horsburgh Lighthouse, 1855 .. .. 1·40 1·75
429 $1 Raffles Lighthouse, 1855 .. .. 1·50 2·00
427/9 .. .. *Set of* 3 3·00 3·50
MS430 148 × 104 mm. Nos. 427/9 .. .. 3·25 4·25
No. **MS**430 was printed on plain paper without phosphor.

(Des Goh Seng Lim. Litho Secura, Singapore)

1982 (15 Sept). *10th Anniv of Container Terminal. T* **136** *and similar horiz designs. Multicoloured. One centre phosphor band (10 c.) or phosphorised paper (others). P* 13½.
431 10 c. Type **136** 10 10
432 35 c. Computer 25 30
433 50 c. Freightlifter 35 50
434 75 c. Straddle carrier 65 70
431/4 .. .. *Set of* 4 1·25 1·40

137 Scouts on Parade

138 Productivity Movement Slogans

(Des Poh Siew Wah. Litho Secura, Singapore)

1982 (15 Oct). *75th Anniv of Boy Scout Movement. T* **137** *and similar vert designs. Multicoloured. One centre phosphor band (10 c.) or phosphorised paper (others). P* 14×13½.
435 10 c. Type **137** 15 10
436 35 c. Scouts hiking 45 25
437 50 c. Scouts building tower 65 35
438 75 c. Scouts canoeing 95 80
435/8 .. .. *Set of* 4 2·00 1·25

(Des M. Gan. Litho Secura, Singapore)

1982 (17 Nov). *Productivity Movement. T* **138** *and similar diamond-shaped designs. One centre phosphor band* (10 c.) *or phosphorised paper* (*others*). *P* 13½.

439 10 c. orange and emerald 10 10
440 35 c. yellow-ochre and deep dull blue 35 40
441 50 c. maroon, bistre-yellow and brownish grey 55 80
442 75 c. maroon and lemon .. .. .. 75 1·10
439/42 .. .. *Set of* 4 1·60 2·25

Designs:—35 c. Family and housing ("Benefits of Productivity"); 50 c. Works meeting ("Quality Control Circles"); 75 c. Aspects of Singapore business ("Everybody's Business").

139 Commonwealth Logo and Country Names **140** Soccer

(Des Eng Siak Loy. Litho Secura, Singapore)

1983 (14 Mar). *Commonwealth Day. One centre phosphor band* (10 c.) *or phosphorised paper* (*others*). *P* 13 × 13½.

443 **139** 10 c. multicoloured 10 10
444 35 c. multicoloured 20 25
445 75 c. multicoloured 45 85
446 $1 multicoloured .. .. .. 65 1·00
443/6 .. .. *Set of* 4 1·25 2·00

(Des Lim Ching San. Litho Secura, Singapore)

1983 (28 May). *12th South-East Asia Games. T* **140** *and similar vert designs. Multicoloured. One centre phosphor band* (10 c.) *or phosphorised paper* (*others*). *P* 13½ × 13.

447 10 c. Type **140** 10 10
448 35 c. Racket games 20 25
449 75 c. Athletics 45 50
450 $1 Swimming 65 70
447/50 .. .. *Set of* 4 1·25 1·40

141 Policeman and Family **142** 1977 ASEAN Stamps and Statue of King Chulalongkorn

(Des Lim Ching San. Litho J.W.)

1983 (24 June). *Neighbourhood Watch Scheme. T* **141** *and similar horiz designs. Multicoloured. One wide centre phosphor band* (10 c.) *or phosphorised paper* (*others*). *P* 14.

451 10 c. Type **141** 15 10
452 35 c. Policeman and children 55 35
453 75 c. Policeman and inhabitants with linked arms .. .. 1·00 1·00
451/3 .. .. *Set of* 3 1·50 1·25

(Des Sylvia Tan and Ko Hui-Huy. Litho J.W.)

1983 (4 Aug). *Bangkok International Stamp Exhibition. T* **142** *and similar vert designs. Multicoloured. One wide centre phosphor band* (10 c.), *phosphorised paper* (35 c., $1) *or ordinary paper* (*miniature sheet*). *P* 14.

454 10 c. Type **142** 15 10
455 35 c. 1980 ASEAN stamps and map of South-East Asia 45 50
456 $1 1982 ASEAN stamps and signatures of Heads of State .. .. .. 1·10 1·60
454/6 .. .. *Set of* 3 1·50 2·00
MS457 147 × 104 mm. Nos. 454/6 .. 2·50 3·50

143 Map of South-East Asia showing Cable Network

(Des J. Heng. Litho Secura, Singapore)

1983 (27 Sept). *A.S.E.A.N.* (*Association of South-East Asian Nations*) *Submarine Cable Network* (*3rd issue*). *Completion of Malaysia-Singapore-Thailand section. One centre phosphor band* (10 c.), *phosphorised paper* (35 c. *to* 75 c.) *or ordinary paper* (*miniature sheet*). *P* 13½ (*around design as well as stamp*).

458 **143** 10 c. multicoloured 15 10
459 35 c. multicoloured 55 75
460 50 c. multicoloured .. .. .. 80 1·25
461 75 c. multicoloured .. .. .. 1·25 1·75
458/61 .. .. *Set of* 4 2·50 3·50
MS462 146 × 100 mm. Nos. 331, 388, 458/61 .. 3·00 3·50

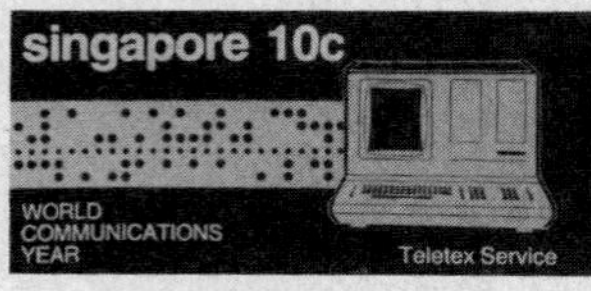

144 Teletex Service

(Des Sylvia Tan and Ko Hui-Huy. Litho Enschedé)

1983 (10 Nov). *World Communications Year. T* **144** *and similar horiz designs. Phosphorised paper. P* 12½ × 13.

463 10 c. greenish yellow, light emerald and black 20 15
464 35 c. greenish yellow, brt rose-red & chocolate 55 65
465 75 c. bright yellow-green, greenish blue and deep violet-blue .. .. 1·00 1·40
466 $1 greenish yell, olive-brn & brownish blk 1·25 2·00
463/6 .. .. *Set of* 4 2·75 3·75

Designs:—35 c. World telephone numbering plan; 75 c. Satellite transmission; $1 Sea communications.

145 Blue-breasted Banded Rail **146** House of Tan Yeok Nee

(Des Poh Siew Wah. Litho Harrison)

1984 (15 Mar). *Coastal Birds. T* **145** *and similar horiz designs. Multicoloured. One wide centre phosphor band* (10 c.) *or phosphorised paper* (*others*). *P* 14½ × 13½.

467 10 c. Type **145** 60 15
468 35 c. Black Bittern .. .. 1·50 1·40
469 50 c. Brahminy Kite .. .. 1·75 1·90
470 75 c. Moorhen .. .. 2·00 2·75
467/70 .. .. *Set of* 4 5·25 5·50

(Des Poh Siew Wah. Litho Secura, Singapore)

1984 (7 June). *National Monuments. T* **146** *and similar vert designs. Multicoloured. One centre phosphor band* (10 c.) *or phosphorised paper* (*others*). *P* 12.

471 10 c. Type **146** 15 10
472 35 c. Thong Chai building 55 60
473 50 c. Telok Ayer market 75 90
474 $1 Nagore Durgha shrine .. .. .. 1·25 2·00
471/4 .. .. *Set of* 4 2·40 3·25

147 1970 $1 National Day Stamp **148** Schoolchildren

(Des P. Hong. Litho Secura, Singapore)

1984 (9 Aug–23 Nov). *"25 Years of Nation Building." T* **147** *and similar vert designs showing various Singapore stamps. Multicoloured. One centre phosphor band* (10 c.) *or phosphorised paper* (*others*). *P* 14 × 14½.

475 10 c. Type **147** 15 10
476 35 c. 1981 $1 "Sports for All" stamp 60 60
477 50 c. 1969 25 c. "100,000 Homes for the People" stamp 75 90
478 75 c. 1976 10 c. Wayside Trees stamp .. .. 90 1·25
479 $1 1981 $1 Opening of Changi Airport stamp 1·00 1·75
480 $2 1981 10 c. Monetary Authority stamp .. 1·90 3·50
475/80 .. .. *Set of* 6 4·75 7·25
MS481 132 × 106 mm. Nos. 475/80. P 12½ (23 Nov) 6·00 7·00

No. **MS**481 is on ordinary paper without a phosphor band on the 10 c. stamp.

(Des Lim Ching San. Litho Secura, Singapore)

1984 (26 Oct). *"Total Defence". T* **148** *and similar vert designs. One centre phosphor band. P* 12.

482 10 c. brown and orange-vermilion 15 20
a. Horiz strip of 5. Nos. 482/6 65
483 10 c. brown, yellow-olive and new blue .. 15 20
484 10 c. brown, bright violet and pale salmon .. 15 20
485 10 c. brown, orange-brown and mauve .. 15 20
486 10 c. brown, yellow and yellow-olive 15 20
482/6 .. .. *Set of* 5 65 90

Designs:—No. 482, Type **148**; 483, People of Singapore; 484, Industrial workers; 485, Civil Defence first aid worker; 486, Anti-aircraft gun crew.

Nos. 482/6 were printed together, *se-tenant*, in horizontal strips of five throughout the sheet.

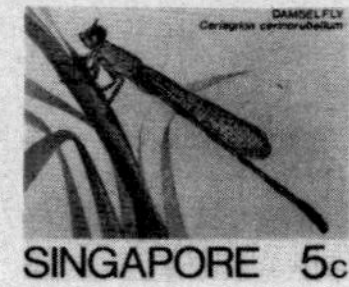

149 Coleman Bridge **150** *Ceriagrion cerinorubellum* (damselfly)

(Des Eng Siak Loy. Recess Harrison)

1985 (15 Mar). *Bridges of Singapore. T* **149** *and similar horiz designs. One phosphor band* (10 c.) *or phosphorised paper* (*others*). *P* 14½ × 14.

487 10 c. black (Type **149**) 15 10
488 35 c. black (Cavenagh Bridge) 30 30
489 75 c. black (Elgin Bridge) 55 55
490 $1 black (Benjamin Sheares Bridge) .. 70 70
487/90 .. .. *Set of* 4 1·50 1·50

(Des Eng Siak Loy. Litho Japanese Govt Ptg Bureau, Tokyo, to 1986, thereafter Leigh-Mardon Ltd, Melbourne (5 c. to 75 c.). Recess and photo Japanese Govt Ptg Bureau, Tokyo ($1 to $10))

1985 (24 Apr)–**89.** *Insects. T* **150** *and similar horiz designs. Multicoloured. One narrow* (5 *mm*) *phosphor band* (10 c.) *or phosphorised paper* (*others*). *P* 13×13½.

491 5 c. Type **150** .. .. 1·00 30
a. Leigh-Mardon ptg (9.12.86) .. .. 1·50 80
492 10 c. *Apis javana* (bee) .. .. .. 1·00 30
a. Leigh-Mardon ptg (on phosphorised paper) (24.10.88) .. .. .. 1·50 55
493 15 c. *Delta arcuata* (wasp) .. .. .. 1·25 50
a. Leigh-Mardon ptg (4.4.87) .. .. 9·00 1·00
494 20 c. *Xylocopa caerulea* (bee) .. .. 1·00 70
a. Leigh-Mardon ptg (15.12.86) .. .. 11·00 1·25
495 25 c. *Donacia javana* (water beetle) .. 1·00 80
a. Leigh-Mardon ptg (22.9.86) .. .. 11·00 1·50
496 35 c. *Heteroneda reticulata* (ladybird) .. 1·25 30
a. Leigh-Mardon ptg (28.5.88) .. .. 12·00 1·50
497 50 c. *Catacanthus nigripes* (bug) .. .. 1·50 55
a. Leigh-Mardon ptg (23.1.89) .. .. 30·00 2·25
498 75 c. *Chremistica pontianaka* (cicada) .. 1·50 1·50
a. Leigh-Mardon ptg (3.7.89) .. .. 38·00 4·00
499 $1 *Homoexipha lycoides* (cricket) (5.6.85) 1·75 60
500 $2 *Traulia azureipennis* (grasshopper) (5.6.85) .. .. 1·50 1·25
501 $5 *Trithemis aurora* (dragonfly) (5.6.85) 2·75 3·50
502 $10 *Scambophyllum sanguinolentum* (grasshopper) (5.6.85) .. .. .. 5·75 7·50
491/502 .. .. *Set of* 12 19·00 16·00
491a/8a .. .. *Set of* 8 £100 11·50

Nos. 499/502 are larger, 35×30 mm.

Although the work of the two printers is very similar as far as shade, paper and perforation are concerned Leigh-Mardon used new printing plates taken from the original colour separations and, in consequence, each value does differ from its predecessor printed by the Japanese Government Printing Bureau:

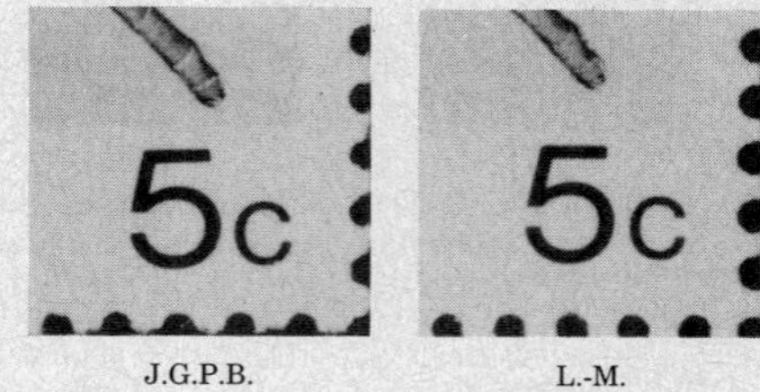

J.G.P.B. L.-M.

5 c. On the J.G.P.B. printing the tail of the insect is ½ mm from the bottom edge of the vignette. On the L.-M. printing the distance is 1 mm.

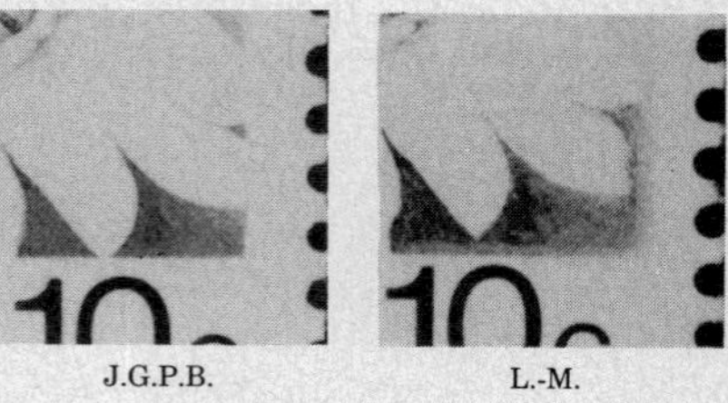

J.G.P.B. L.-M.

10 c. The J.G.P.B. printing shows the petals at bottom right cut by the edge of the design. On the L.-M. printing all three petals are complete.

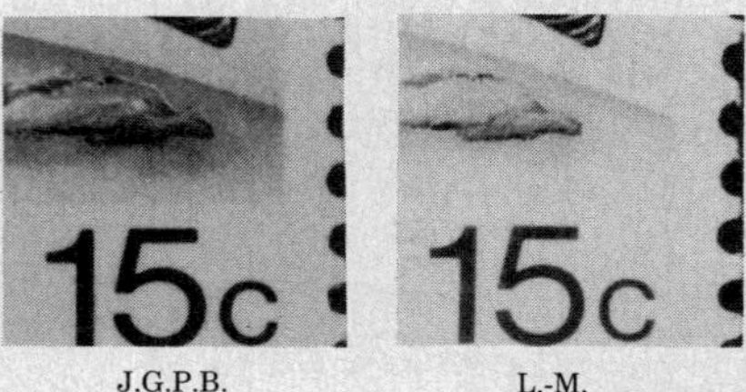

J.G.P.B. L.-M.

15 c. The J.G.P.B. printing shows the rock at bottom right 1½ mm from the right-hand edge. On the L.-M. stamp this distance is 2 mm.

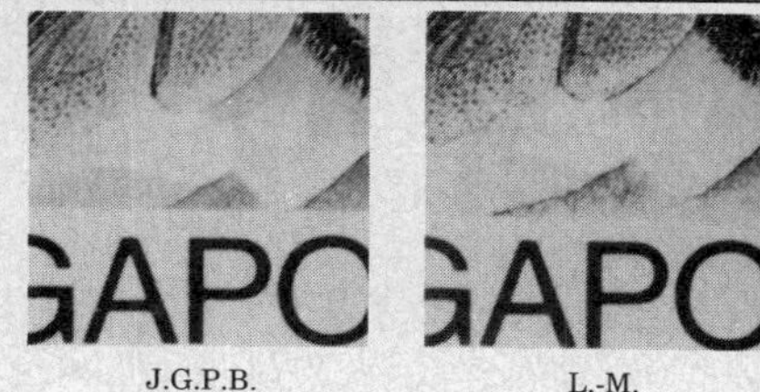

J.G.P.B. L.-M.

20 c. On the J.G.P.B. stamp the pink flowers above "SINGAPORE" touch the edge of the vignette. For the L.-M. printing the right-hand petal is clear of the edge.

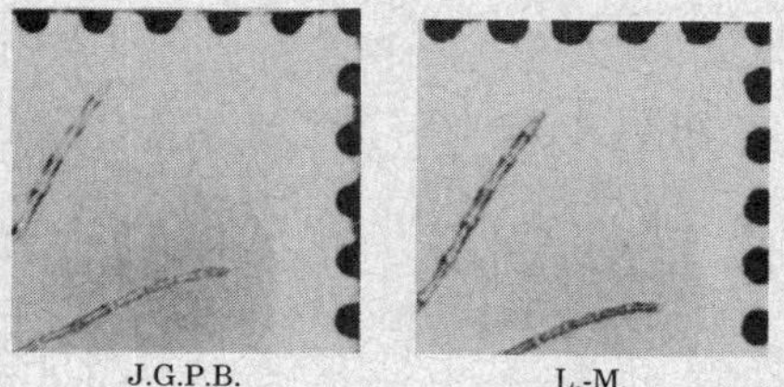

J.G.P.B. L.-M.

25 c. The J.G.P.B. printing shows the uppermost feeler of the water beetle touching the top of the design. On the L.-M. stamp the feeler does not reach the edge of the design.

J.G.P.B. L.-M.

35 c. On the J.G.P.B. printing the vein on the leaf at bottom left stops just short of the corner of the design. The L.-M. stamp shows this vein reaching the left-hand edge of the design above the corner.

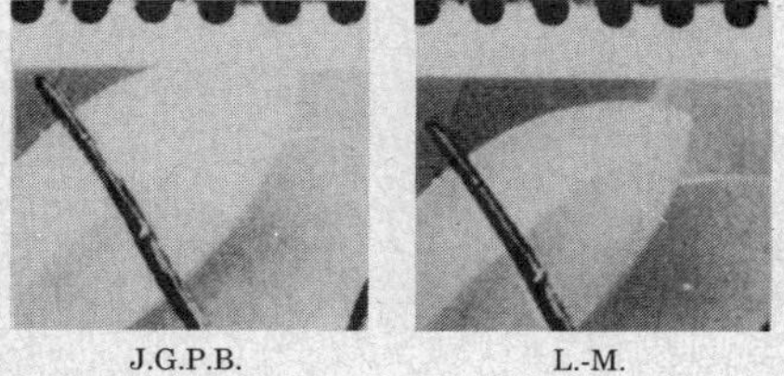

J.G.P.B. L.-M.

50 c. The J.G.P.B. stamp has the uppermost leaf cut by the top edge of the design. On the L.-M. printing the leaf is complete.

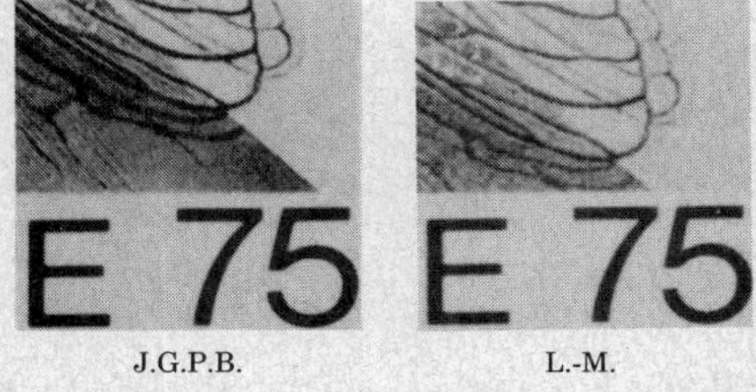

J.G.P.B. L.-M.

75 c. On the J.G.P.B. printing the shadow of the wings is 1½mm above the bottom edge of the vignette. For the L.-M. stamp the shadow touches the bottom edge.

151 Tennis, Canoeing, Judo and Children Playing

(Des M. Chiew. Litho Secura, Singapore)

1985 (1 July). *25th Anniv of the People's Association. T* **151** *and similar horiz designs. Multicoloured. One phosphor band (10 c.) or phosphorised paper (others). P* 13½ × 14.

No.	Description	Unused	Used
503	10 c. Type **151**..	25	10
504	35 c. Lion dance, martial arts and athletes with flags	30	30
505	50 c. Tae-kwon-do, Indian dance and Dragon dance	40	40
506	75 c. Boxing, table tennis, basketball and dancing	75	75
503/6	*Set of* 4	1·50	1·40

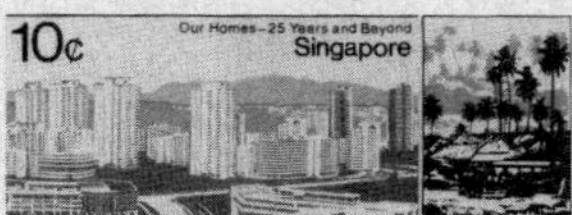

152 Modern Housing Estate and Squatter Settlement

(Des Eng Siak Loy. Litho Secura, Singapore)

1985 (9 Aug). *25th Anniv of Housing and Development Board. Horiz designs as T* **152** *with different aspects of housing shown at left. Multicoloured. One phosphor band (10 c.) or phosphorised paper (others). P* 13½ × 14.

No.	Description	Unused	Used
507	10 c. Type **152**..	15	10
508	35 c. Singapore family (Home-ownership)	30	30
509	50 c. Group of residents (Community development)	40	40
510	75 c. Construction workers (Building technology)	55	55
507/10	*Set of* 4	1·25	1·25
MS511	126 × 105 mm. Nos. 507/10	3·25	3·50

153 Brownies **154** Badges and Emblems of Singapore Youth Organizations

(Des Foo Lye Lin. Litho J.W.)

1985 (6 Nov). *75th Anniv of Girl Guide Movement. T* **153** *and similar vert designs. One phosphor band (10 c.) or phosphorised paper (others). Multicoloured. P* 14.

No.	Description	Unused	Used
512	10 c. Type **153**	15	10
513	35 c. Guides practising first aid	35	30
514	50 c. Senior Branch	45	45
515	75 c. Adult leaders and guides	65	75
512/15	*Set of* 4	1·40	1·40

(Des Eng Siak Loy. Litho Secura, Singapore)

1985 (18 Dec). *International Youth Year. T* **154** *and similar horiz designs. Multicoloured. One phosphor band (10 c.) or phosphorised paper (others). P* 12.

No.	Description	Unused	Used
516	10 c. Type **154**..	10	10
517	75 c. Hand protecting sapling	70	55
518	$1 Stylised figures and dove	90	70
516/18	*Set of* 3	1·50	1·25

155 Guava **156** Laboratory Technician and Salesmen with Bar Graph

(Des Poh Siew Wah. Litho J.W.)

1986 (26 Feb). *Singapore Fruits. T* **155** *and similar vert designs. Multicoloured. One centre phosphor band (10 c.) or phosphorised paper (others). P* 14.

No.	Description	Unused	Used
519	10 c. Type **155**..	30	10
520	35 c. Jambu Air	85	45
521	50 c. Rambutan	1·10	70
522	75 c. Ciku	1·40	1·10
519/22	*Set of* 4	3·25	2·00

(Des W. Lee. Litho Secura, Singapore)

1986 (1 May). *25th Anniv of National Trades Union Congress. T* **156** *and similar vert designs. Multicoloured. One phosphor band. P* 13½.

No.	Description	Unused	Used
523	10 c. Type **156**..	25	40
	a. Horiz strip of 4. Nos. 523/6	90	
524	10 c. Computer operator and welder	25	40
525	10 c. Draughtsmen and surveyors	25	40
526	10 c. Group of workers	25	40
523/6	*Set of* 4	90	1·40
MS527	148 × 100 mm. As Nos. 523/6, but each stamp with a face value of 35 c. Phosphorised paper	2·75	3·25

Nos. 523/6 were printed together, *se-tenant*, in horizontal strips of 4 throughout the sheet, forming a composite design.

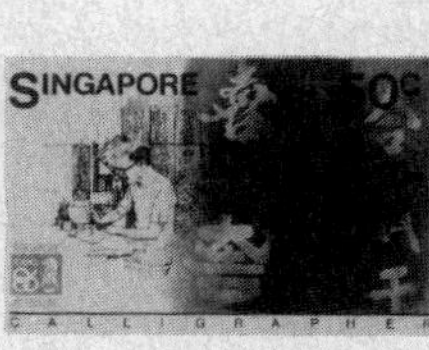

157 Calligraphy **158** Industrial Automation

(Des Chua Ban Har. Litho (50 c. also die-stamped) Leigh-Mardon Ltd, Melbourne)

1986 (2 May). *"Expo '86" World Fair, Vancouver. T* **157** *and similar horiz designs. Multicoloured. "All-over" phosphor. P* 14 × 14½.

No.	Description	Unused	Used
528	50 c. Type **157**..	45	75
	a. Horiz strip of 3. Nos. 528/30	1·60	
529	75 c. Garland maker	60	95
530	$1 Batik printer	75	1·25
528/30	*Set of* 3	1·60	2·75

Nos. 528/30 were printed together, *se-tenant*, in horizontal strips of 3 throughout the sheet.

(Des Eng Siak Loy. Litho J.W.)

1986 (1 Aug). *25th Anniv of Economic Development Board. T* **158** *and similar vert designs. Multicoloured. Phosphorised paper. P* 15 × 14½.

No.	Description	Unused	Used
531	10 c. Type **158**..	10	10
532	35 c. Manufacture of aircraft components	25	30
533	50 c. Electronics industry	30	50
534	75 c. Biotechnology industry	50	90
531/4	*Set of* 4	1·00	1·60

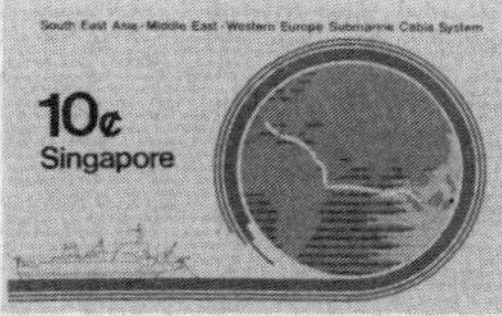

159 Map showing Route of Cable and *Vercors* (cable ship)

(Des J. Heng. Litho Secura, Singapore)

1986 (8 Sept). *SEA–ME–WE Submarine Cable Project. Phosphorised paper. P* 13½.

No.	Description	Unused	Used
535 **159**	10 c. multicoloured	40	10
536	35 c. multicoloured	85	45
537	50 c. multicoloured	1·10	80
538	75 c. multicoloured	1·40	1·40
535/8	*Set of* 4	3·25	2·50

160 Stylized Citizens **161** Peace Doves and People of Different Races

(Des W. Lee. Litho Secura, Singapore)

1986 (15 Oct). *21st Anniv of Citizens' Consultative Committees. T* **160** *and similar vert designs showing citizens. Phosphorised paper. P* 12.

No.	Description	Unused	Used
539	10 c. multicoloured	30	35
	a. Block of 4. Nos. 539/42	1·90	
540	35 c. multicoloured	45	50
541	50 c. multicoloured	55	60
542	75 c. multicoloured	75	80
539/42	*Set of* 4	1·90	2·00

Nos. 539/42 were printed together, *se-tenant*, in blocks of 4 throughout the sheet, each block forming a composite design.

(Des Eng Siak Loy. Litho Secura, Singapore)

1986 (17 Dec). *International Peace Year. T* **161** *and similar horiz designs. Multicoloured. Phosphorised paper. P* 14 × 13½.

No.	Description	Unused	Used
543	10 c. Type **161**..	15	10
544	35 c. Doves and map of ASEAN countries	40	45
545	$1 Doves and globe	95	1·75
543/5	*Set of* 3	1·40	2·00

162 Orchard Road **163** Flags of Member Nations and Logo

(Des Chua Ban Har. Litho Secura, Singapore)

1987 (25 Feb). *Singapore Skyline. T* **162** *and similar horiz designs. Multicoloured. Phosphorised paper. P* 12.

No.	Description	Unused	Used
546	10 c. Type **162**..	15	10
547	50 c. Central Business District	50	65
548	75 c. Marina Centre and Raffles City	75	1·25
546/8	*Set of* 3	1·25	1·75

(Des Chua Ban Har. Litho Secura, Singapore)

1987 (15 June). *20th Anniv of Association of South-east Asian Nations. Phosphorised paper. P* 12.

No.	Description	Unused	Used
549 **163**	10 c. multicoloured	10	10
550	35 c. multicoloured	30	30
551	50 c. multicoloured	45	45
552	75 c. multicoloured	55	55
549/52	*Set of* 4	1·25	1·25

164 Soldier with Rocket Launcher and Tank

165 Singapore River and Dragon Boats

(Des M. Ng Puay Chiew. Litho Questa)

1987 (1 July). *20th Anniv of National Service. T* **164** *and similar vert designs. Multicoloured. Phosphorised paper. P* 15×14.

553 10 c. Type **164** 55 70
 a. Horiz strip of 4. Nos. 553/6 .. .. 2·00
554 10 c. Radar operator and patrol boat .. 55 70
555 10 c. Fighter pilot, General Dynamics F-16 Fighting Falcon and Douglas A-4 Skyhawk aircraft 55 70
556 10 c. Servicemen pledging allegiance .. 55 70
553/6 .. .. *Set of* 4 2·00 2·50
MS557 148×100 mm. 35 c. × 5. As Nos. 553/6 and Singapore lion symbol (scarlet and black) 3·25 3·75

Nos. 553/6 were printed together, *se-tenant*, in horizontal strips of 4 throughout the sheet.

(Des Ng Keng Seng. Litho Secura, Singapore)

1987 (2 Sept). *River Conservation. T* **165** *and similar square designs. Multicoloured. Phosphorised paper. P* 13½.

558 10 c. Type **165**.. .. .. 30 10
559 50 c. Kallang Basin, canoe and fishing punt 80 80
560 $1 Kranji Reservoir, athletes and cyclist .. 2·00 2·00
558/60 .. .. *Set of* 3 2·75 2·50

166 Majapahit Gold Bracelet and Museum

(Des M. Ng Puay Chiew. Litho Secura, Singapore)

1987 (12 Oct). *Centenary of National Museum. T* **166** *and similar horiz designs, each showing different drawings of Museum. Multicoloured. Phosphorised paper. P* 13½×14.

561 10 c. Type **166**.. .. .. 30 10
562 75 c. Ming fluted kendi (water vessel) .. 1·25 1·25
563 $1 Patani hulu pekakak keris (sword) .. 1·40 1·50
561/3 .. .. *Set of* 3 2·75 2·50

167 Omni-theatre

(Des Eng Siak Loy. Litho Leigh-Mardon Ltd, Melbourne)

1987 (10 Dec). *10th Anniv of Singapore Science Centre. T* **167** *and similar horiz designs. Multicoloured. Phosphorised paper. P* 14½.

564 10 c. Type **167** 15 10
565 35 c. Omni-planetarium .. .. .. 1·25 45
566 75 c. Model of body cell .. .. .. 1·50 1·25
567 $1 Physical sciences exhibits .. .. 1·50 1·75
564/7 .. .. *Set of* 4 4·00 3·25

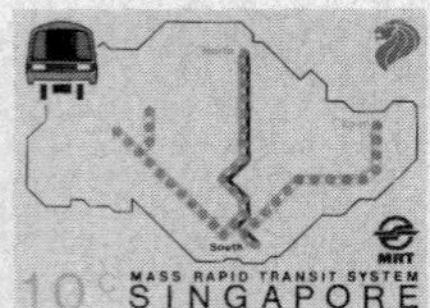

168 Modern Anti-aircraft Gun

169 Route Map

(Des L. Teck Chong. Litho Secura, Singapore)

1988 (22 Feb). *Centenary of Singapore Artillery. T* **168** *and similar horiz designs. Multicoloured. Phosphorised paper. P* 13½×14.

568 10 c. Type **168** 55 15
569 35 c. 25-pounder field gun firing salute .. 1·25 70
570 50 c. Gunner and 12-pounder gun, c. 1920 1·50 1·50
571 $1 Gunner and Maxim gun, 1889 .. 2·25 2·75
568/71 .. .. *Set of* 4 5·00 4·50

(Des Ng Keng Seng. Litho Secura, Singapore)

1988 (12 Mar). *Singapore Mass Rapid Transit System. T* **169** *and similar horiz designs. Multicoloured. Phosphorised paper. P* 13½ × 14.

572 10 c. Type **169** 50 15
573 50 c. Train on elevated section .. .. 1·75 1·50
574 $1 Train in tunnel .. .. .. 2·75 2·75
572/4 .. .. *Set of* 3 4·50 4·00

170 Camera, Film and Outside Broadcast Van

(Des E. Soriano. Litho CPE Australia Ltd, Melbourne)

1988 (4 Apr). *25th Anniv of Television in Singapore. T* **170** *and similar horiz designs. Multicoloured. Phosphorised paper. P* 13½ × 14.

575 10 c. Type **170** 35 10
576 35 c. Camera, studio lights and microphone 60 40
577 75 c. Television set and transmitter .. 90 90
578 $1 Globe on TV screen and dish aerial .. 1·25 1·40
575/8 .. .. *Set of* 4 2·75 2·50

MACHINE LABELS. From 19 April 1988 self-adhesive labels in the above design, with the background printed in orange and grey, were available from machines situated outside a number of Singapore post offices. Face values between 5 c. and $2 could be selected and the location of individual machines is indicated by the code number, from 0001 to 0050, at bottom left.

The designs was changed to three lions' heads in red on 5 June 1989, to the Fullerton Building G.P.O. in brown on 8 September 1990, to Haw Par Villa in red on 2 October 1991, to trishaws in brown on 1 December 1992, to the Singapore skyline in turquoise-green on 5 April 1994 and to orchids in red on 1 April 1995.

Vertical labels inscribed "SINGAPORE POSTAGE" with face values and, in some instances a weight, also exist. These were introduced in January 1983 and come from machines used by P. O. counter clerks to process parcels and registered mail. For a time, 1986–87, these labels were on self-adhesive paper.

171 Water Droplet and Blocks of Flats

172 Greeting Neighbours

(Des Ng Keng Seng. Litho CPE Australia Ltd, Melbourne)

1988 (4 May). *25th Anniv of Public Utilities Board. T* **171** *and similar vert designs, each showing a different skyline. Multicoloured. Phosphorised paper. P* 13½.

579 10 c. Type **171** 20 10
580 50 c. Electric light bulb and city centre .. 1·00 80
581 $1 Gas flame and factories .. .. 1·90 1·90
579/81 .. .. *Set of* 3 2·75 2·50
MS582 116 × 75 mm. Nos. 579/81 .. .. 3·25 3·75

(Des M. Ng Puay Chiew. Litho Leigh-Mardon Ltd, Melbourne)

1988 (6 July). *10th Anniv of National Courtesy Campaign. T* **172** *and similar horiz designs, each showing campaign mascot "Singa". Multicoloured. Phosphorised paper. P* 14½.

583 10 c. Type **172** 15 10
584 30 c. Queueing at checkout 40 30
585 $1 Helping the elderly .. .. .. 1·25 1·00
583/5 .. .. *Set of* 3 1·60 1·25

173 Modern 30 Metre Turntable Fire Appliance

174 Container Ships and Warehouses

(Des Eng Siak Loy. Litho Secura, Singapore)

1988 (1 Nov). *Centenary of Fire Service. T* **173** *and similar horiz design. Multicoloured. Phosphorised paper. P* 13½.

586 10 c. Type **173** 75 25
587 $1 Steam fire engine, *c.* 1890 .. .. 2·75 2·00

(Des Ng Keng Seng. Litho Secura, Singapore)

1989 (3 Apr). *25th Anniv of Singapore Port Authority. T* **174** *and similar vert designs. Multicoloured. Phosphorised paper. P* 14×13½.

588 10 c. Type **174** 30 10
589 30 c. Shipping and oil storage depot .. 65 35
590 75 c. Container ships and Singapore skyline 1·25 1·00
591 $1 Container port at night .. .. 1·40 1·25
588/91 .. .. *Set of* 4 3·25 2·40

175 "Sago Street"

176 North-west Singapore City, 1920

(Litho Questa)

1989 (17 May). *Paintings of Chinatown by Choo Keng Kwang. T* **175** *and similar square designs. Multicoloured. Phosphorised paper. P* 14½.

592 10 c. Type **175** 20 10
593 35 c. "Pagoda Street" 75 40
594 75 c. "Trengganu Street" .. .. .. 1·40 1·00
595 $1 "Temple Street" .. .. .. 1·50 1·25
592/5 .. .. *Set of* 4 3·50 2·50

(Des L. Teck Chong. Litho Harrison)

1989 (26 July). *Maps of Singapore. T* **176** *and similar multicoloured designs. Phosphorised paper. P* 14×14½ (15 c.) *or* 12½×13 (*others*).

596 15 c. Type **176** (top left) 90 90
 a. Block of 4. Nos. 596/9 .. .. .. 3·25
597 15 c. North-east Singapore (top right) .. 90 90
598 15 c. South-west Singapore (bottom left) .. 90 90
599 15 c. South-east Singapore (bottom right) .. 90 90
600 50 c. Singapore Island and Dependencies, 1860s .. .. 1·75 1·75
601 $1 British Settlement of Singapore, 1820s 2·50 2·50
596/601 .. .. *Set of* 6 7·00 7·00

Nos. 596/9 were printed together, *se-tenant*, in blocks of 4 throughout the sheet, each block forming a composite design. Individual stamps can be identified by the position of the lion emblem which is quoted in brackets.

177 Clown Triggerfish

178 "Hari Raya Puasa" (Loke Yoke Yun)

(Des Eng Siak Loy. Litho Harrison)

1989 (6 Sept). *Fishes. T* **177** *and similar horiz designs. Multicoloured. Phosphorised paper. P* 13½.

602 15 c. Type **177** 85 20
603 30 c. Blue-girdled Angelfish .. .. .. 1·50 80
604 75 c. Emperor Angelfish .. .. .. 2·75 2·75
605 $1 Regal Angelfish .. .. .. 3·00 3·50
602/5 .. .. *Set of* 4 7·25 6·50

(Adapted S. Ang Woon Beng. Litho Harrison)

1989 (25 Oct). *Festivals of Singapore. Children's Drawings. T* **178** *and similar vert designs. Multicoloured. Phosphorised paper. P* 14½.

606 15 c. Type **178** 40 10
607 35 c. "Chinese New Year" (Simon Koh) .. 70 55
608 75 c. "Thaipusam" (Henry Setiono) .. 1·40 1·00
609 $1 "Christmas" (Wendy Ang Lin Min) .. 1·75 1·50
606/9 .. .. *Set of* 4 3·75 2·75
MS610 126×75 mm. Nos. 606/9. P 14 .. .. 4·00 3·25

179 North Entrance of Stadium

180 "Singapore River, 1839" (Louis le Breton)

(Des Lim Ching San. Litho Harrison)

1989 (27 Dec). *Opening of Singapore Indoor Stadium. T* **179** *and similar horiz designs. Multicoloured. Phosphorised paper. P* 14.

611 30 c. Type **179** 85 30
612 75 c. Arena .. .. 1·75 1·50
613 $1 East entrance .. .. 2·00 1·75
611/13 .. .. *Set of* 3 4·25 3·25
MS614 104×104 mm. Nos. 611/13 .. .. 4·50 3·50

(Des Choy Weng Yang. Litho Leigh-Mardon Ltd, Melbourne)

1990 (21 Mar). *Lithographs of 19th-century Singapore. T* **180** *and similar horiz designs. Multicoloured. Phosphorised paper. P* 13.

615 15 c. Type **180** 40 10
 a. Booklet pane. No. 615×10 .. .. 6·00
616 30 c. "Chinatown, 1837" (Barthelemy Lauvergne) 80 45
617 75 c. "Singapore Harbour, 1837" (Barthelemy Lauvergne) .. .. 1·50 1·10
618 $1 "View from the French Resident's House, 1824" (Deroy) .. .. .. 1·75 1·40
615/18 .. .. *Set of* 4 4·00 2·75

The upper and lower edges of booklet pane No. 615a are imperforate.

181 1969 150th Anniv of Singapore Stamp Issue

(Des Sylvia Tan. Litho Leigh-Mardon Pty Ltd, Melbourne)

1990 (3 May). *150th Anniv of the Penny Black. T* **181** *and similar horiz designs, each showing a different map in the background. Multicoloured. Phosphorised paper. P* 13½.

619 50 c. Type **181** .. .. 1·00 60
620 75 c. Indian stamps, including bisect, used from Singapore in 1859 .. .. 1·25 1·00
621 $1 Indian stamps used from Singapore in 1854 .. .. 1·90 1·50
622 $2 Penny Black and Two Pence Blue .. 3·00 3·50
619/22 .. .. *Set of* 4 6·50 6·00
MS623 134×90 mm. Nos. 619/22 .. .. 8·00 6·50

No. **MS**623 also commemorates the "Stamp World London 90" international stamp exhibition.

182 Zoological Gardens

183 Chinese Opera Singer and Siong Lim Temple

(Des Ng Keng Seng (5 to 75 c.), Lim Ching San ($1 to $10). Photo (5 to 75 c.) or recess and photo ($1 to $10) Harrison)

1990 (4 July)–**91**. *Tourism. Multicoloured. Phosphorised paper.* (a) *T* **182** *and similar square designs. P* 14½.

624 5 c. Type **182** 30 40
625 15 c. Sentosa Island 30 10
 a. Booklet pane. No. 625×10 .. .. 8·00
626 20 c. Singapore River 30 20
 a. Booklet pane. No. 626×10 (6.3.91) .. 3·50
627 25 c. Dragon Boat Festival 55 25
628 30 c. Raffles Hotel 70 30
629 35 c. Coffee shop bird singing contest .. 1·25 35
630 40 c. Jurong Bird Park .. .. .. 1·50 40
631 50 c. Chinese New Year boat float .. .. 1·25 45
632 75 c. Peranakan Place .. .. .. 1·75 70

(b) *T* **183** *and similar horiz designs. P* 15×14 (9.10.90)

633 $1 Type **183** .. .. 2·50 90
634 $2 Malay dancer and Sultan Mosque .. 3·25 1·75
635 $5 Indian dancer and Sri Mariamman Temple .. .. 6·00 5·50
636 $10 Ballet dancer and Victoria Memorial Hall .. .. 10·00 10·00
624/36 .. .. *Set of* 13 26·00 19·00

The upper and lower edges of booklet panes Nos. 625a and 626a are imperforate.

184 Armed Forces Personnel

185 Stag's Horn Fern

(Des Chua Ban Har. Litho Harrison)

1990 (16 Aug). *25th Anniv of Independence. T* **184** *and similar horiz designs. Multicoloured. Phosphorised paper. P* 14×15.

637 15 c. Type **184** 40 15
 a. Perf 14 .. .. 85 1·00
 ab. Booklet pane. No. 637a×10 .. .. 8·50
638 35 c. Inhabitants of Singapore 90 75
639 75 c. Workers and technological achievements .. .. 1·60 1·75
640 $1 Cultural activities .. .. .. 1·75 2·50
637/40 .. .. *Set of* 4 4·25 4·75

No. 637a only comes from $1.50 stamp booklets in which the pane, No. 637ab, has margins at left and right.

(Des Poh Siew Wah. Litho Questa)

1990 (14 Nov). *Ferns. T* **185** *and similar horiz designs. Multicoloured. Phosphorised paper. P* 14.

641 15 c. Type **185** 25 10
642 35 c. Maiden Hair Fern 60 45
643 75 c. Bird's Nest Fern .. .. .. 1·25 1·00
644 $1 Rabbit's Foot Fern .. .. .. 1·60 1·60
641/4 .. .. *Set of* 4 3·25 2·75

186 Carved Dragon Pillar, Hong San See Temple

187 *Vanda* "Miss Joaquim"

(Des L. Teck Chong. Litho Leigh-Mardon Ltd, Melbourne)

1991 (23 Jan). *National Monuments. T* **186** *and similar multicoloured designs. Phosphorised paper. P* 14½.

645 20 c. Type **186** 30 40
 a. Vert pair. Nos. 645/6 .. .. .. 60 80
646 20 c. Hong San See Temple (40×25 *mm*) .. 30 40
647 50 c. Interior of dome, Abdul Gaffoor Mosque 55 65
 a. Vert pair. Nos. 647/8 .. .. .. 1·10 1·25
648 50 c. Abdul Gaffoor Mosque (40×25 *mm*) .. 55 65
649 75 c. Statue of Vishnu, Sri Perumal Hindu Temple .. .. 80 1·00
 a. Vert pair. Nos. 649/50 .. .. .. 1·60 2·00
650 75 c. Sri Perumal Temple (40×25 *mm*) .. 80 1·00
651 $1 Stained glass window, St Andrew's Cathedral .. .. 90 1·25
 a. Vert pair. Nos. 651/2 .. .. .. 1·75 2·50
652 $1 St Andrew's Cathedral (40×25 *mm*) .. 90 1·25
645/52 .. .. *Set of* 8 4·50 6·00

The two designs for each value were printed together, *se-tenant*, in vertical pairs throughout the sheets.

(Des Chua Ban Har. Litho Leigh-Mardon Ltd, Melbourne)

1991 (24 Apr). *"Singapore '95" International Stamp Exhibition. Orchids* (1st issue). *T* **187** *and similar horiz design. Multicoloured. Phosphorised paper. P* 14.

653 $2 Type **187** .. .. 3·00 3·25
 a. Horiz pair. Nos. 653/4 .. .. .. 6·00 6·50
654 $2 *Dendrobium* "Anocha" .. .. .. 3·00 3·25
MS655 123×80 mm. Nos. 653/4 .. .. 6·50 7·00

Nos. 653/4 were issued together, *se-tenant*, in sheets of 30 (6×5), showing No. 653 in vertical rows 1 and 4, Nos. 654 in vertical rows 3 and 6, and stamp-size labels with exhibition emblem in vertical rows 2 and 5.

See also Nos. 674/6, 725/7, 755/7, 795/7 and **MS**818.

188 Changi Airport Terminal II, 1991, and Boeing 747-400

189 *Arachnopsis* "Eric Holttum"

(Des L. Teck Chong. Recess and litho Harrison)

1991 (1 June). *Singapore Civil Aviation. T* **188** *and similar horiz designs. Multicoloured. Phosphorised paper. P* 13½×14½.

656 20 c. Type **188** 85 20
657 75 c. Changi Airport Terminal I, 1981, and Boeing 747-200 .. .. .. 2·00 1·25
658 $1 Paya Lebar Airport, 1955–1981, and Concorde .. .. 2·25 1·50
659 $2 Kallang Airport, 1937–1955, and Douglas DC-2 .. .. 3·50 4·50
656/9 .. .. *Set of* 4 7·75 6·75

(Des Chua Ban Har. Litho Questa)

1991 (7 Aug). *Orchid Dress Motifs. T* **189** *and similar horiz designs. Multicoloured. Phosphorised paper. P* 14½×14.

660 20 c. Type **189** .. .. 1·00 20
661 30 c. *Cattleya meadii* .. .. .. 1·25 90
662 $1 *Calanthe vestita* .. .. .. 3·00 3·50
660/2 .. .. *Set of* 3 4·75 4·25

190 Long-tailed Tailor Bird

191 Productivity Discussion

(Des M. Ng Puay Chiew. Litho Leigh-Mardon Ltd, Melbourne)

1991 (19 Sept). *Garden Birds. T* **190** *and similar horiz designs. Multicoloured. Phosphorised paper. P* 14.

663 20 c. Type **190** 45 20
 a. Booklet pane. No. 663×10 .. .. 9·00
664 35 c. Scarlet-backed Flowerpecker .. .. 1·50 80
665 75 c. Black-naped Oriole .. .. .. 2·25 2·00
666 $1 Common Iora .. .. .. 2·50 2·75
663/6 .. .. *Set of* 4 6·00 5·25

Booklet pane No. 663a has the upper and lower edges imperforate and there are margins at left and right.

(Des Foo Lye Lin. Litho Questa)

1991 (1 Nov). *10th Anniv of Productivity Movement. T* **191** *and similar vert design. Multicoloured. Phosphorised paper. P* 14×14½.

667 20 c. Type **191** 30 20
668 $1 Construction workers .. .. .. 95 1·40

192 Railway Creeper

193 "Singapore Waterfront" (Georgette Chen Liying)

(Des Eng Siak Loy. Litho Leigh-Mardon Ltd, Melbourne)

1991 (16 Nov). *"Phila Nippon '91" International Stamp Exhibition, Tokyo. Wild Flowers. T* **192** *and similar vert designs. Multicoloured. Phosphorised paper. P* 14½×14.

669 30 c. Type **192** 75 25
670 75 c. Asystasia .. .. 1·25 75
671 $1 Singapore Rhododendron .. .. 1·50 1·25
672 $2 Coat Buttons .. .. 2·50 2·75
669/72 .. .. *Set of* 4 5·50 4·50
MS673 132×90 mm. Nos. 669/72 .. .. 6·00 6·50

(Des Chua Ban Har. Litho Leigh-Mardon Ltd, Melbourne)

1992 (22 Jan). *"Singapore '95" International Stamp Exhibition. Orchids* (2nd issue). *Horiz designs as T* **187**. *Multicoloured. Phosphorised paper. P* 14.

674 $2 *Dendrobium* "Sharifah Fatimah" .. 2·75 3·25
 a. Horiz pair. Nos. 674/5 .. .. .. 5·50 6·50
675 $2 *Phalaenopsis* "Shim Beauty" .. .. 2·75 3·25
MS676 123×80 mm. Nos. 674/5 .. .. 6·00 7·00

Nos. 674/5 were printed in the same sheet format as Nos. 653/4.

(Des Lim Ching San. Litho Secura, Singapore)

1992 (11 Mar). *Local Artists* (1st series). *T* **193** *and similar square designs. Multicoloured. Phosphorised paper. P* 14.

677 20 c. Type **193** 30 20
678 75 c. "Kampung Hut" (Lim Cheng Hoe) .. 75 80
679 $1 "The Bridge" (Poh Siew Wah) .. .. 95 1·10
680 $2 "Singapore River" (Lee Boon Wang) .. 1·90 2·75
677/80 .. .. *Set of* 4 3·50 4·25

See also Nos. 818/21.

194 Football

195 Chinese Family and Samfu Pattern

(Des L. Teck Chong. Litho Leigh-Mardon Ltd, Melbourne)

1992 (24 Apr). *Olympic Games, Barcelona. T* **194** *and similar horiz designs. Multicoloured. Phosphorised paper. P* 14.

681 20 c. Type **194** 25 20
682 35 c. Athletics 35 30
683 50 c. Swimming 55 55
684 75 c. Basketball .. .. 1·25 1·10
685 $1 Tennis .. .. 1·50 1·50
686 $2 Yachting .. .. 2·00 2·25
681/6 .. .. *Set of* 6 5·50 5·50
MS687 132×90 mm. Nos. 681/6 .. .. 7·00 7·50

(Des Chua Ban Har. Litho Leigh-Mardon Ltd, Melbourne)

1992 (22 May). *Singapore Costumes of 1910. T* **195** *and similar vert designs. Multicoloured. Phosphorised paper. P* 14½.

688 20 c. Type **195** 30 20
689 35 c. Malay family and sarong pattern .. 40 45
690 75 c. Indian family and sari pattern .. 90 1·25
691 $2 Straits Chinese family and belt pattern 2·00 2·75
688/91 .. .. *Set of* 4 3·25 4·25

NEW INFORMATION

The editor is always interested to correspond with people who have new information that will improve or correct the Catalogue.

196 Infantryman, Air Force Pilot and Navy Gunner

197 Crafts from A.S.E.A.N. Countries

(Des T. Koh. Litho Leigh-Mardon Ltd, Melbourne)

1992 (1 July). *25th Anniv of National Service. T* **196** *and similar horiz designs. Multicoloured. Phosphorised paper. P* 14½.

692 20 c. Type **196** 60 20
693 35 c. Navy diver, General Dynamics F-16 Fighting Falcon and FH-88 155 mm howitzer 85 65
694 $1 General Dynamics F-16 Fighting Falcon in flight, corvette and AMX-13SM1 tank .. .. 2·50 3·00
692/4 .. .. *Set of* 3 3·50 3·50

(Des Chua Ban Har. Litho Questa)

1992 (8 Aug). *25th Anniv of A.S.E.A.N (Association of South East Asian Nations). T* **197** *and similar horiz designs. Multicoloured. Phosphorised paper. P* 14×14½.

695 20 c. Type **197** 40 20
696 35 c. National dances 90 70
697 $1 National landmarks .. .. 2·00 2·75
695/7 .. .. *Set of* 3 3·00 3·25

198 Mosaic Crab

199 Coins

(Des Chua Ban Har. Litho Leigh-Mardon Ltd, Melbourne)

1992 (21 Aug). *Crabs. T* **198** *and similar horiz designs. Multicoloured. Phosphorised paper. P* 14½.

698 20 c. Type **198** 35 25
a. Booklet pane. No. 698×10 .. .. 4·00
699 50 c. Johnson's Freshwater Crab .. .. 1·00 1·25
700 75 c. Singapore Freshwater Crab .. .. 1·50 1·75
701 $1 Swamp Forest Crab .. .. .. 1·75 2·50
698/701 .. .. *Set of* 4 4·25 5·25

The upper and lower edges of booklet pane No. 698a are imperforate.

(Des Lim Ching San. Litho Leigh-Mardon Ltd, Melbourne)

1992 (2 Oct). *25th Anniv of Singapore Currency. T* **199** *and similar square designs. Multicoloured. Phosphorised paper. P* 14½.

702 20 c. Type **199** .. .. 75 1·00
a. Block of 4. Nos. 702/5 .. .. .. 5·50
703 75 c. Currency note from "orchid" series .. 1·50 2·00
704 $1 Currency note from "ship" series .. 1·75 2·25
705 $2 Currency note from "bird" series .. 2·25 2·50
702/5 .. .. *Set of* 4 5·50 7·00

Nos. 702/5 were printed together, *se-tenant*, as blocks of four throughout the sheet of 20, each block forming a composite design.

200 Sun Bear

201 "Thank You"

(Des Eng Siak Loy. Litho Leigh-Mardon Ltd, Melbourne)

1993 (13 Jan). *South-East Asian Mammals. T* **200** *and similar horiz designs. Multicoloured. Phosphorised paper. P* 14½.

706 20 c. Type **200** 30 20
707 30 c. Orang-utan 45 40
708 75 c. Slow Loris .. .. 1·10 1·10
709 $2 Greater Malay Chevrotain ("Large Mouse Deer") .. .. 2·25 2·75
706/9 .. .. *Set of* 4 3·50 4·00

(Des N. Loh Fook Chee. Litho Printset Cambec Pty Ltd, Australia)

1993 (10 Feb). *Greetings Stamps. T* **201** *and similar square designs. Multicoloured. Phosphorised paper. P* 14½×14.

710 20 c. Type **201** 55 80
a. Booklet pane. Nos. 710/14 × 2 .. 4·50
711 20 c. "Congratulations" 55 80
712 20 c. "Best Wishes" 55 80
713 20 c. "Happy Birthday" 55 80
714 20 c. "Get Well Soon" 55 80
710/14 .. .. *Set of* 5 2·50 3·50

Nos. 710/14 were only available from $2 booklets. The upper and lower edges of booklet pane No. 710a are imperforate and there are margins at both left and right.

202 Shophouses

203 "Cranes" (painting) (Chen Wen Hsi)

(Des Ng Keng Seng ($2), W. Kee (others). Litho Leigh-Mardon Ltd, Melbourne)

1993 (10 Mar). *Conservation of Tanjong Pagar District. T* **202** *and similar horiz designs. Multicoloured. Phosphorised paper. P* 14.

715 20 c. Type **202** 35 20
716 30 c. Jinrikisha Station 75 50
717 $2 View of Tanjong Pagar .. .. .. 3·25 3·25
715/17 .. .. *Set of* 3 4·00 3·50

(Des L. Teck Chong. Photo Courvoisier)

1993 (28 May). *"Indopex '93" International Philatelic Exhibition, Surabaya. Phosphorised granite paper. P* 12.

718 **203** $2 multicoloured .. .. 2·00 2·75

204 Football

205 *Danaus chrysippus*

(Des L. Teck Chong. Litho Questa)

1993 (12 June). *17th South-East Asia Games, Singapore. T* **204** *and similar vert designs. Multicoloured. Phosphorised paper. P* 14.

719 20 c. Type **204** 30 20
720 35 c. Basketball 70 55
721 50 c. Badminton 90 85
722 75 c. Athletics .. .. 1·00 1·25
723 $1 Waterpolo .. .. 1·40 1·75
724 $2 Yachting .. .. 2·25 3·00
719/24 .. .. *Set of* 6 6·00 7·00

(Des Chua Ban Har. Litho Leigh-Mardon Ltd, Melbourne)

1993 (13 Aug). *"Singapore '95" International Stamp Exhibition. Orchids (3rd issue). Multicoloured designs as T* **187**, *but each* 25×35 *mm. Phosphorised paper. P* 14½.

725 $2 *Phalaenopsis amabilis* .. .. .. 3·00 3·25
a. Horiz pair. Nos. 725/6 .. .. .. 6·00 6·50
726 $2 *Vanda sumatrana* .. .. 3·00 3·25
MS727 123×80 mm. Nos. 725/6 .. .. .. 6·50 7·00

Nos. 725/6 were printed in the same sheet format as Nos. 653/4.

No. **MS**727 also commemorates "Taipei '93" Asian International Stamp Exhibition, Taiwan.

(Des Eng Siak Loy. Litho Leigh-Mardon Ltd, Melbourne)

1993 (21 Aug). *Butterflies. T* **205** *and similar horiz designs. Multicoloured. Phosphorised paper. P* 14½.

728 20 c. Type **205** 30 20
a. Booklet pane. No. 728×10 .. .. 4·75
729 50 c. *Cethosia hypsea* 65 60
730 75 c. *Amathusia phidippus* .. .. .. 90 1·10
731 $1 *Papilio demolion* .. .. 1·25 1·60
728/31 .. .. *Set of* 4 2·75 3·25

The upper and lower edges of booklet pane No. 728a are imperforate.

206 Papaya

207 Egrets drinking

(Des Poh Siew Wah. Litho Leigh-Mardon Ltd, Melbourne)

1993 (1 Oct). *"Bangkok '93" International Stamp Exhibition. Local Fruits. T* **206** *and similar vert designs. Multicoloured. Phosphorised paper. P* 14½×14.

732 20 c. Type **206** 40 20
733 35 c. Pomegranate 60 45
734 75 c. Starfruit .. .. 1·25 1·00
735 $2 Durian .. .. 2·25 2·75
732/5 .. .. *Set of* 4 4·00 4·00
MS736 120×89 mm. Nos. 732/5 .. .. .. 4·00 4·50

(Des Eng Siak Loy. Litho Enschedé)

1993 (10 Nov). *Endangered Species. Swinhoe's Egret ("Chinese Egret"). T* **207** *and similar square designs. Multicoloured. Phosphorised paper. P* 13½.

737 20 c. Type **207** 40 60
a. Horiz strip of 4. Nos. 737/40 .. .. 1·75
738 25 c. Egrets eating 45 65
739 30 c. Egrets searching for fish 55 75
740 35 c. Egrets in flight 55 75
737/40 .. .. *Set of* 4 1·75 2·50

Nos. 737/40 were printed together, *se-tenant*, in horizontal strips of 4 throughout the sheet, with the background forming a composite design.

208 Palm Tree

209 Tiger Cowrie

(Des Eng Siak Loy. Photo Avery Dennison, Pasadena)

1993 (24 Nov). *Self-adhesive Automatic Cash Machine Stamps. Phosphorised polyester film. Die-cut.*

741 **208** (20 c.) multicoloured 15 20

No. 741 was issued, in sheets of 15 (5×3), from bank automatic cash machines and philatelic centres. It was only valid for use on mail to local addresses and was initially sold at 20 c. Advertising on the backing paper originally featured Speedpost, but this was subsequently changed to details of "Singapore '95" on 20 January 1995.

(Des Sylvia Tan)

1994 (12 Jan)–**97**. *Reef Life (1st series). T* **209** *and similar horiz designs. Multicoloured. Phosphorised paper. P* 13×13½ (5 *c. to* 75 *c.*) *or* 14* ($1 *to* $10).

(*a*) *Litho* (5 *c. to* 75 *c.*) *or recess and litho* ($1 *to* $10) *Leigh-Mardon Ltd. Melbourne*

742 5 c. Type **209** 30 30
743 20 c. Sea-fan 30 20
a. Booklet pane. No. 743×10 .. .. 3·50
744 25 c. Tunicate 40 25
745 30 c. Clown Anemonefish 40 30
746 35 c. Ruppell's Nudibranch 50 40
747 40 c. Sea-urchin 60 50
748 50 c. Soft coral 70 50
749 75 c. Pin Cushion Star .. .. 1·00 70
750 $1 Knob coral (31×27 *mm*) (23.3.94) .. 1·40 90
751 $2 Mushroom coral (31×27 *mm*) (23.3.94) .. .. 2·25 2·25
752 $5 Bubble coral (31×27 *mm*) (23.3.94) .. 5·00 5·50
753 $10 Octopus coral (31×27 *mm*) (23.3.94) .. 9·00 10·00
742/53 .. .. *Set of* 12 20·00 20·00

(*b*) *Photo Enschedé* (5 *c. to* 50 *c.*) *or litho and embossed Questa* ($1 *to* $10)

753*a* 5 c. Type **209** (27.1.97) .. .. .. 3·50 75
753*b* 25 c. Tunicate (4.4.96) .. .. 9·00 50
753*c* 30 c. Clown Anemonefish (22.3.96) .. .. 2·25 60
753*d* 35 c. Ruppell's Nudibranch (13.1.97) .. .. 2·50 75
753*e* 40 c. Sea-urchin (9.9.96) .. .. .. 2·75 1·00
753*f* 50 c. Soft coral (23.2.96) .. .. .. 3·00 1·00
753*g* $1 Knob coral (31×27 *mm*) (4.11.96) .. 7·00 2·00
753*h* $2 Mushroom coral (31×27 *mm*) (2.12.97) .. .. 10·00 8·00
753*i* $5 Bubble coral (31×27 *mm*) (5.5.97) .. 25·00 9·50
753*j* $10 Octopus coral (31×27 *mm*) (13.1.97) 35·00 14·00
753*a/j* .. .. *Set of* 10 90·00 35·00

The upper and lower edges of booklet pane No. 743a are imperforate and there are margins at left and right.

*Nos. 750/3 and 753*g/j* include a large elliptical hole in both the top and bottom perforations. On the Questa printings this is more elongated than on those produced by Leigh-Mardon.

Nos. 750/3 show a large central lion emblem printed in yellow fluorescence as a security marking. On Nos. 753*g/j* this is replaced by lines of smaller images, also in yellow fluorescence, and by a larger lion emblem in colourless embossing.

On the Leigh-Mardon printings of the $1 to $10 "SINGAPORE" and the face value are shaded. On the Questa printings of these values they are white.

For similar design inscribed "FOR LOCAL ADDRESSES ONLY" see Nos. 784/5c.

(Des Chua Ban Har. Litho Leigh-Mardon Ltd, Melbourne)

1994 (18 Feb). *"Singapore '95" International Stamp Exhibition. Orchids (4th issue). Multicoloured designs as T* **187**, *but each* 25×35 *mm. Phosphorised paper. P* 14½.

755 $2 *Paphiopedilum victoriaregina* .. .. 3·00 3·25
a. Horiz pair. Nos. 755/6 .. .. .. 6·00 6·50
756 $2 *Dendrobium smillieae* .. .. .. 3·00 3·25
MS757 123×80 mm. Nos. 755/6 .. .. .. 6·00 6·50

Nos. 755/6 were printed in the same sheet format as Nos. 653/4.

No. **MS**757 also commemorates "Hong Kong '94" International Stamp Exhibition.

210 Dancers

(Des Elsie Koh. Litho Questa)

1994 (18 May). *Singapore Festival of Arts. T* **210** *and similar horiz designs. Multicoloured. Phosphorised paper. P* 13½×14.

758 20 c. Type **210** 30 20
759 30 c. Actors and puppet 45 45
760 50 c. Musicians 65 85
761 $1 Artists .. .. 1·25 2·00
758/61 .. .. *Set of* 4 2·40 3·25

211 Civilian taking Pledge, National Day Parade and Soldier with Anti-tank Missile

212 Black-crowned Night Heron

(Des D. Kuah. Litho Enschedé)

1994 (1 July). *25th Anniv of Operationally-ready National Servicemen. T* **211** *and similar horiz designs. Multicoloured. Phosphorised paper. P* 13½.

762 20 c. Type **211** 60 20
763 30 c. Serviceman on beach with family and on jungle patrol 70 60
764 35 c. Serviceman relaxing at home and with machine gun 85 70
765 75 c. National Service officer at work and commanding patrol .. .. .. 1·75 2·00
762/5 .. .. *Set of* 4 3·50 3·25

(Des Eng Siak Loy. Litho Leigh-Mardon Ltd, Melbourne)

1994 (16 Aug). *Herons. T* **212** *and similar square designs. Multicoloured. Phosphorised paper. P* 14.

766 20 c. Type **212** 40 50
a. Block of 4. Nos. 766/9 .. .. 2·40
b. Booklet pane. No. 766×10 .. .. 4·00
767 50 c. Green Heron ("Little Heron") .. 60 75
768 75 c. Purple Heron 75 90
769 $1 Grey Heron .. .. 85 1·10
766/9 .. .. *Set of* 4 2·40 3·00

Nos. 766/9 were printed together, *se-tenant*, in blocks of 4 throughout the sheet, each block forming a composite design.

The upper and lower edges of booklet pane No. 766b are imperforate and there are margins at left and right.

213 Traditional and Modern Education

214 Balloons

(Des Lim Ching San. Litho Enschedé)

1994 (31 Aug). *175th Anniv of Modern Singapore. T* **213** *and similar horiz designs. Multicoloured. Phosphorised paper. P* 13½×14.

770 20 c. Type **213** 25 20
771 50 c. Rickshaws and M.R.T. train 55 65
772 75 c. Sampans and modern container port 80 1·10
773 $1 Victorian buildings and modern skyline 1·25 1·75
770/3 .. .. *Set of* 4 2·50 3·25
MS774 135×95 mm. Nos. 770/3 .. .. 3·00 3·75

No. **MS**774 also exists with the "Singpex '94" logo added in gold for sale at this philatelic exhibition.

(Des Chua Ban Har. Litho Printset-Cambec Pty Ltd, Australia)

1994 (14 Sept). *Self-adhesive Greetings Stamps. T* **214** *and similar vert designs. Multicoloured. Phosphorised paper. P* 11½.

775 (20 c.) Type **214** 35 50
a. Booklet pane. Nos. 775/9, each × 2 3·00
776 (20 c.) Fireworks 35 50
777 (20 c.) Gift-wrapped parcel 35 50
778 (20 c.) Bouquet of flowers 35 50
779 (20 c.) Birthday cake 35 50
775/9 .. .. *Set of* 5 1·60 2·25

Nos. 775/9 are inscribed "For Local Addresses Only" and were available from booklets of 10 sold for $2.

215 Logo and Globe

(Des N. Loh Fook Chee. Litho Questa)

1994 (5 Oct). *50th Anniv of International Civil Aviation Organization. T* **215** *and similar horiz designs. Phosphorised paper. P* 14.

780 20 c. Type **215** 20 20
781 35 c. Boeing 747 and Changi Airport control tower 50 45
782 75 c. Projected hypersonic aircraft over airport 75 90
783 $2 Control tower, satellite and Boeing 747 1·90 2·50
780/3 .. .. *Set of* 4 3·00 3·50

(Des Sylvia Tan)

1994 (16 Nov)–**97**. *Reef Life (2nd series). Multicoloured design as T* **209**, *but inscr "FOR LOCAL ADDRESSES ONLY".*

(*a*) *Litho Leigh-Mardon Ltd, Melbourne. Phosphorised paper. P* 13×13½

784 (20 c.) Blue-spotted Stingray 20 25

(*b*) *Litho Leigh-Mardon Ltd, Melbourne. Self-adhesive. Phosphor frame. P* 9.

785 (20 c.) As No. 784 .. .. 20 25
a. Booklet pane. No. 785×10 .. .. 2·00
b. Broad phosphor band (12.4.95) .. 40 40
ba. Booklet pane. No. 785b×10 .. 3·75

(*c*) *Photo Enschedé. Phosphorised paper. P* 13×13½

785*c* (22 c.) As No. 784 (2.12.97) .. .. 3·00 50

Booklet panes Nos. 785a and 785ba are arranged as two blocks of four and a pair with backing card forming the booklet cover.

Nos. 784/5 were initially sold at 20 c., but this was increased to 22 c. on 1 April 1995.

The inscriptions on No. 785*c* are redrawn so that the "SINGAPORE" is 26 mm long instead of 26½ and the others are also smaller. On No. 784 the "y" of "stingray" is to the right of the "A" in "SINGAPORE"; on No. 785*c* it is under the left leg of the "A".

216 Singapore International Convention and Exhibition Centre, Suntec City

217 "Love, LOVE, Love"

(Des M. Ng Puay Chiew. Litho Enschedé)

1995 (11 Jan). *Opening of Singapore International Convention and Exhibition Centre. T* **216** *and similar horiz designs. Multicoloured. Phosphorised paper. P* 13½.

786 (20 c.) Type **216** 20 20
787 75 c. Suntec City skyline 75 75
788 $1 Temasek Boulevard .. .. 95 1·10
789 $2 Fountain Terrace .. .. 1·75 2·40
786/9 .. .. *Set of* 4 3·25 4·00

No. 786 is inscribed "FOR LOCAL ADDRESSES ONLY".

Nos. 786 and 789 also exist in miniature sheets issued at the "Singapore '95" exhibition. A different marginal illustration was used for each of the ten days of the exhibition.

(Des Design Objectives. Litho Printset-Cambec Pty Ltd, Australia)

1995 (8 Feb). *Self-adhesive Greeting Stamps. T* **217** *and similar vert designs. Phosphor frame. P* 11½.

790 **217** (20 c.) multicoloured 30 40
a. Booklet pane. Nos. 790/4, each × 2 .. .. 2·75
791 – (20 c.) vermilion and black 30 40
792 – (20 c.) multicoloured 30 40
793 – (20 c.) multicoloured 30 40
794 – (20 c.) multicoloured 30 40
790/4 .. .. *Set of* 5 1·40 1·75

Designs:—No. 791, "LOVE" forming spiral around heart; No. 792, "LOVE, LOVE"; No. 793, "Love" in four different languages; No. 794, Geometric symbols.

Nos. 709/4 are inscribed "For Local Addresses Only" and were available from booklets of 10 initially sold for $2, but increased to $2.20 from 1 April 1995.

(Des Chua Ban Har. Litho Leigh-Mardon Ltd, Melbourne)

1995 (15 Mar). *"Singapore '95" International Stamp Exhibition. Orchids (5th issue). Horiz designs as T* **187**. *Multicoloured. Phosphorised paper. P* 14.

795 $2 *Vanda* "Marlie Dolera" .. .. 2·00 2·75
a. Horiz pair. Nos. 795/6 .. .. 4·00 5·50
796 $2 *Vanda limbata* .. .. .. 2·00 2·75
MS797 123×80 mm. Nos. 795/6 with sheet margins showing animals from Singapore Zoo 4·00 5·50

Nos. 795/6 were printed in the same sheet format as Nos. 653/4.

No. **MS**797 also exists imperforate from the "Singapore '95" exhibition catalogue.

For further miniature sheet containing these stamps see No. **MS**817.

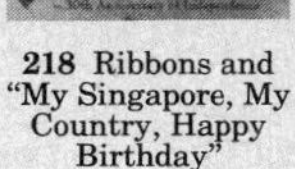

218 Ribbons and "My Singapore, My Country, Happy Birthday"

219 Rejoicing Crowd and 1945 B.M.A. $5 Stamp

(Des L. Teck Chong. Litho Enschedé)

1995 (19 Apr). *30th Anniv of Independence. T* **218** *and similar multicoloured designs. Phosphorised paper. P* 13½.

798 (22 c.) Type **218** 20 20
799 50 c. Chinese inscr and 1985 Housing and Development 50 c. stamp (*horiz*) .. 65 65
800 75 c. National anthem, Civil Aviation 20 c. and inscr in Malay (*horiz*) 90 90
801 $1 National flag, 1986 Economic Development Board $1 and inscr in Tamil .. .. 1·25 1·50
798/801 .. .. *Set of* 4 2·75 3·00
MS802 120×78 mm. Nos. 798/801 .. .. 2·75 3·00

No. 798 is inscribed "For Local Addresses Only".

(Des Chua Ban Har. Litho Enschedé)

1995 (21 June). *50th Anniv of End of Second World War. T* **219** *and similar multicoloured designs. Phosphorised paper. P* 14×13½ (*vert*) *or* 13½×14 (*horiz*).

803 (22 c.) Type **219** 30 20
804 60 c. Lord Mountbatten accepting Japanese surrender at Singapore and 1945 B.M.A. 15 c. stamp 80 70
805 70 c. Emergency food kitchen (*horiz*) .. 80 85
806 $2 Police road block during State of Emergency (*horiz*) .. .. .. 2·50 3·00
803/6 .. .. *Set of* 4 4·00 4·25

No. 803 is inscribed "For Local Addresses Only".

220 Yellow-faced Angelfish

221 Envelope, Stamps and Museum

(Des Sylvia Tan. Litho Enschedé)

1995 (19 July). *Marine Fishes. T* **220** *and similar horiz designs. Multicoloured. Phosphorised paper. P* 13½×14.

807 (22 c.) Type **220** 35 25
808 60 c. Harlequin Sweetlips 80 70
809 70 c. Lionfish 90 90
810 $1 Pennant Coralfish ("Longfin Bannerfish") .. .. 1·25 1·50
807/10 .. .. *Set of* 4 3·00 3·00

No. 807 is inscribed "For Local Addresses Only".

(Des Poh Siew Wah. Litho Japanese Govt Ptg Bureau, Tokyo)

1995 (19 Aug). *Opening of Singapore Philatelic Museum. T* **221** *and similar vert designs, each showing Museum. Multicoloured. Phosphorised paper. P* 13×13½.

811 (22 c.) Type **221** 30 25
812 50 c. Stamps and stamp booklet 70 55
813 60 c. Stamps and philatelic equipment .. 80 80
814 $2 Museum displays .. .. .. 2·25 2·75
811/14 .. .. *Set of* 4 3·75 4·00

No. 811 is inscribed "FOR LOCAL ADDRESSES ONLY".

222 Two, Four and Six Digit Post Codes

(Des L. Huei Hoon. Litho Printset-Cambec Pty Ltd, Australia)

1995 (1 Sept). *Introduction of Six Digit Postal Codes. T* **222** *and similar horiz design. Multicoloured. Phosphorised paper. P* 14×14½.

815 (22 c.) Type **222** 30 25
816 $2 Six empty post code boxes .. .. 2·25 2·50

No. 815 is inscribed "For local addresses only".

(Des Chua Ban Har. Litho Leigh-Mardon Ltd, Melbourne)

1995 (1 Sept). *"Singapore '95" International Stamp Exhibition. Orchids (6th issue). Sheet 123×80 mm, containing Nos. 795/6 with sheet margins showing Sentosa Gardens. Phosphorised paper. P* 14.

MS817 $2×2 multicoloured .. .. .. 4·50 4·75

No. **MS**817 also exists either with the marginal illustration in a single colour or with the stamps imperforate, both showing an additional gold embossed inscription. Such miniature sheets were distributed to individual collectors contributing to exhibition funds.

223 "Tropical Fruits" (Georgette Chen Liying)

(Des Poh Siew Wah. Litho Japanese Govt Ptg Bureau, Tokyo)

1995 (20 Oct). *Local Artists (2nd series). T* **223** *and similar multicoloured designs. Phosphorised paper. P* 13½×13 ($2) *or* 12½ (*others*).

818 (22 c.) Type **223** 30 25
819 30 c. "Bali Beach" (Cheong Soo Pieng) .. 40 30
820 70 c. "Gibbons" (Chen Wen Hsi) 80 80
821 $2 "Shi (Lion)" (Pan Shou) (22½×38½ *mm*) .. .. 2·25 2·75
818/21 .. .. *Set of* 4 3·25 3·75

No. 818 is inscribed "FOR LOCAL ADDRESSES ONLY".

224 Bukit Pasoh, Chinatown

225 Pair of Rats

(Des Poh Siew Wah. Litho Enschedé)

1996 (17 Jan). *Architectural Conservation. T* **224** *and similar horiz designs. Multicoloured. Phosphorised paper. P* 13½×14.

822	(22 c.) Type **224**	30	25
823	35 c. Jalan Sultan, Kampong Glam ..	40	40
824	70 c. Dalhousie Lane, Little India ..	70	80
825	$1 Supreme Court, Civic District ..	95	1·25
822/5	.. .. *Set of* 4	2·10	2·40

No. 822 is inscribed "FOR LOCAL ADDRESSES ONLY".

Two Types of No. 826i

Type I (sheets of 50) – Top left emblem cut by curved "FOR LOCAL ADDRESSES ONLY" label. Bottom right emblem clear of right edge of design.

Type II (*se-tenant* sheetlets of 18) – Top left emblem clear of curved label. Bottom right emblem cut by right edge of design.

(Des N. Loh Fook Chee. Litho, Southern Colour Print, Dunedin)

1996 (9 Feb). *Chinese New Year ("Year of the Rat"). T* **225** *and similar vert design. Multicoloured. Phosphorised paper. P* 12.

826	(22 c.) Type **225** (I)	30	25
	b. Type II	50	50
	ba. Pair. Nos. 826b/7	2·75	3·00
827	$2 Rat holding orange	2·25	2·50

No. 826 is inscribed "FOR LOCAL ADDRESSES ONLY".

In addition to separate sheets of 50, the stamps were also issued in sheetlets of 18 horizontally and vertically *se-tenant*.

For these stamps in miniature sheets see Nos. **MS**832/3 and **MS**838.

226 The Straits of Singapore, 1794 (Thomas Jefferys)

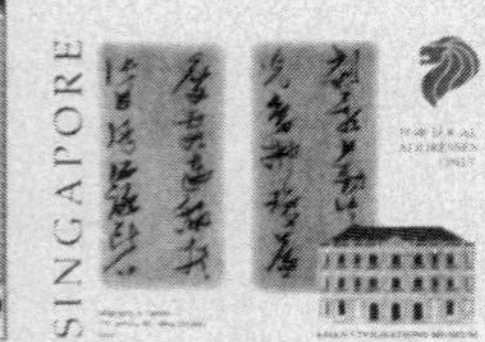

227 17th-century Chinese Calligraphy by Zhang Ruitu and Museum Building

(Des D. Kuah. Litho Southern Colour Print, Dunedin, New Zealand)

1996 (13 Mar). *Old Maps. T* **226** *and similar horiz designs. Multicoloured. Phosphorised paper. P* 12.

828	(22 c.) Type **226**	35	25
829	60 c. Singapore (19th-century)	65	65
830	$1 Singapore by James Duncan, 1835 ..	1·00	1·10
831	$2 Singapore by J. B. Tassin, 1839 ..	2·00	2·50
828/31	.. .. *Set of* 4	3·50	4·00

No. 828 is inscribed "FOR LOCAL ADDRESSES ONLY" and was sold for 22 c.

(Litho Southern Colour Print, Dunedin)

1996 (21 Mar). *"Indonesia 96" International Youth Stamp Exhibition, Bandung. Sheet* 123×80 *mm. Phosphorised paper. P* 12.

MS832	22 c. As Type **225**; $2 No. 827	2·25	2·75

(Litho Southern Colour Print, Dunedin)

1996 (18 May). *"CHINA '96" 9th Asian International Stamp Exhibition, Peking. Sheet* 123×80 *mm. Phosphorised paper. P* 12.

MS833	22 c. As Type **225**; $2 No. 827	2·25	2·75

(Des M. Ng Puay Chiew. Litho Enschedé)

1996 (5 June). *Inauguration of Asian Civilizations Museum. T* **227** *and similar horiz designs, each including museum building. Multicoloured. Phosphorised paper. P* 13½.

834	(22 c.) Type **227**	30	25
835	60 c. Javanese divination manuscript, 1842	60	60
836	70 c. 19th-century temple hanging, South India	70	70
837	$2 17th to 19th-century calligraphic implements, Iran and Turkey ..	2·00	2·50
834/7	.. .. *Set of* 4	3·25	3·50

No. 834 is inscribed "FOR LOCAL ADDRESSES ONLY" and was sold for 22 c.

(Litho Southern Colour Print, Dunedin)

1996 (8 June). *"CAPEX '96" International Stamp Exhibition, Toronto. Sheet* 123×80 *mm. Phosphorised paper. P* 12.

MS838	22 c. As Type **225**; $2 No. 827	2·25	2·75

228 "Children in Library" (Ivan Chang)

229 Wind Surfing and Dinghy Sailing

(Adapted Design Business Ltd. Litho SNP Cambec, Australia)

1996 (10 July). *Self-adhesive Greetings Stamps. "Courtesy". Children's Drawings. T* **228** *and similar horiz designs. Multicoloured. Phosphorised paper. P* 11½.

839	(22 c.) Type **228**	20	25
	a. Booklet pane. No. 839×10 ..	2·50	
	b. Booklet pane. No. 839×5, No. 840×2 and Nos. 841/3	4·25	
840	35 c. "Children crossing Road" (Cheong Kah Yin)	30	35
841	50 c. "Waiting for Bus" (Jeannie Fong) ..	45	50
842	60 c. "In the Rain" (Liew Cai Yun) ..	50	55
843	$1 "On the Train" (Yong Wan Quan) ..	85	90
839/43	.. .. *Set of* 5	2·25	2·50
MS844	200×130 mm. 22 c. As Type **228** and Nos. 840/3. Phosphor frame	2·10	2·25

No. 839 is inscribed "For Local Addresses Only".

Nos. 839/43 were only issued in $2.20 and $3.90 stamp booklets or as No. **MS**844.

(Des N. Loh Fook Chee. Litho Southern Colour Print, Dunedin)

1996 (19 July). *Olympic Games, Atlanta. T* **229** *and similar vert designs. Multicoloured. Phosphorised paper. P* 14½.

845	(22 c.) Type **229**	30	25
846	60 c. Tennis and football	75	65
847	70 c. Pole vaulting and hurdling	80	75
848	$2 Diving and swimming	2·00	2·25
845/8	.. .. *Set of* 4	3·50	3·50
MS849	120×70 mm. 22 c. As Type **229** and Nos. 846/8	4·00	4·50

No. 845 is inscribed "For Local Addresses Only".

230 *Cinnamomum iners*

231 Panmen Gate, Suzhou, China

(Des Poh Siew Wah. Litho Southern Colour Print, Dunedin)

1996 (11 Sept). *Singapore Trees. T* **230** *and similar vert designs. Multicoloured. Phosphorised paper. P* 13½.

850	(22 c.) Type **230**	30	25
851	60 c. *Hibiscus tiliaceus*	70	70
852	70 c. *Parkia speciosa*	80	80
853	$1 *Terminalia catappa*	1·25	1·40
850/3	.. .. *Set of* 4	2·75	2·75

No. 850 is inscribed "FOR LOCAL ADDRESSES ONLY".

(Des Jiang Zhi Nan, adapted Sylvia Tan. Litho Enschedé)

1996 (9 Oct). *Singapore–China Joint Issue. T* **231** *and similar horiz design. Multicoloured. Phosphorised paper. P* 13×13½.

854	(22 c.) Type **231**	30	25
855	60 c. Singapore waterfront	80	85
MS856	120×78 mm. 22 c. As T **231** and No. 855	1·10	1·25

No. 854 is inscribed "FOR LOCAL ADDRESSES ONLY"

No. **MS**856 also exists overprinted "SINGAPORE–CHINA STAMP EXHIBITION 9–13 OCT '96" for sale at this exhibition.

232 Conference Logo

(Des Design Objectives. Litho Harrison)

1996 (20 Nov). *Inaugural Ministerial Conference of World Trade Organization. Phosphorised paper. P* 13½.

857	**232** (22 c.) multicoloured	30	25
858	60 c. multicoloured	70	70
859	$1 multicoloured	1·25	1·40
860	$2 multicoloured	2·25	2·75
857/60	.. .. *Set of* 4	4·00	4·50

No. 857 is inscribed "For local addresses Only".

233 Ox

234 Shuttlecock

(Des N. Loh Fook Chee. Litho Enschedé)

1997 (10 Jan). *Chinese New Year ("Year of the Ox"). T* **233** *and similar horiz design showing stylised ox. Phosphorised paper. P* 13½×14.

861	(22 c.) multicoloured	30	25
	a. Pair. Nos. 861/2	2·50	2·75
862	$2 multicoloured	2·25	2·50

No. 861 is inscribed "FOR LOCAL ADDRESSES ONLY" and was sold for 22 c.

In addition to separate sheets of 50 Nos. 861/2 were also issued in sheetlets of 18 with the stamps horizontally and vertically *se-tenant.*

(Litho Enschedé)

1997 (12 Feb). *"HONG KONG '97" Internatioanl Stamp Exhibition. Chinese New Year ("Year of the Ox"). Sheet* 123×80 *mm. Phosphorised paper. P* 13½×14.

MS863	22 c. As Type **233**; $2 No. 862	2·40	2·50

(Des Chua Ban Har. Litho Southern Colour Print, Dunedin)

1997 (21 Feb). *"SINGPEX '97" International Stamp Exhibition. Traditional Games. T* **234** *and similar vert designs. Multicoloured. Phosphorised paper. P* 14½×15.

864	(22 c.) Type **234**	25	30
865	35 c. Marbles	40	35
866	60 c. Tops	60	60
867	$1 Fivestones	95	1·00
864/7	.. .. *Set of* 4	2·00	2·00
MS868	140×75 mm. 22 c. As Type **234** and Nos. 865/7	2·25	2·40

No. 864 is inscribed "For Local Addresses Only" and was sold for 22 c.

235 Bullock Cart

236 Taxi

(Des Design Business Ltd. Eng C. Slania ($1 to $10))

1997 (19 Mar–23 Apr). *Transportation. Multicoloured. Phosphorised paper. (a) Litho Ashton-Potter Canada. T* **235** *and similar designs. P* 13½.

869	5 c. Type **235**	10	10
870	20 c. Bicycle (*vert*)	15	20
871	(22 c.) Jinrickshaw (*vert*)	15	20
872	30 c. Electric tram	20	25
873	35 c. Trolley bus	25	30
874	40 c. Trishaw (*vert*)	30	35
875	50 c. Vintage car (*vert*)	35	40
876	60 c. Horse-drawn carriage	40	45
877	70 c. Fire engine	50	55
MS878	132×76 mm. 22 c. As No. 871 and Nos. 869/70, 872/7	2·40	2·50

(*b*) *Recess and litho Enschedé. T* **236** *and similar designs. P* 13 (23 Apr)

879	$1 Type **236**	70	75
880	$2 Bus (43×24 *mm*)	1·40	1·50
881	$5 Mass Rapid Transport train ..	3·50	3·75
882	$10 Light Rapid Transport train (43×24 *mm*)	7·00	7·25
869/77, 879/82	.. .. .. *Set of* 11	14·50	15·50
MS883	119×71 mm. Nos. 879/82	12·50	13·00

(*c*) *Litho Ashton-Potter Canada. Self-adhesive. P* 12.

884	(22 c.) As No. 871	15	20
	a. Booklet pane. No. 884×10	1·50	

Nos. 871 and 884 are inscribed "For Local Addresses Only". In addition to booklets containing No. 884a the self-adhesive version was also available in sheets of 20 (2 panes 5×2).

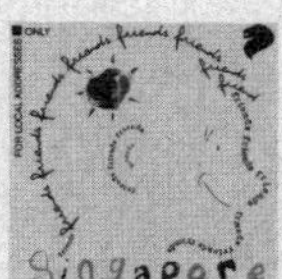

237 Man's Head

238 Family with Car

(Des L. Teck Chong. Litho Enschedé)

1997 (14 May). *Self-adhesive Greeting Stamps. "Friends". T* **237** *and similar vert designs. Multicoloured. Phosphorised paper. P* 15.

885	(22 c.) Type **237**	15	20
	a. Booklet pane. Nos. 885/9, each × 2	1·50	
886	(22 c.) Hands holding umbrella	15	20
887	(22 c.) Two penguins	15	20
888	(22 c.) Two butterflies	15	20
889	(22 c.) Cup and saucer	15	20
890	(22 c.) Large flower	15	20
	a. Booklet pane. Nos. 890/4, each × 2	1·50	
891	(22 c.) Candle	15	20
892	(22 c.) Tree	15	20
893	(22 c.) Jar with stars	15	20
894	(22 c.) Simple telephone	15	20
885/94	*Set of* 10	1·50	2·00

Nos. 885/94 are inscribed "FOR LOCAL ADDRESSES ONLY" and were available from two different booklets of 10, each sold for $2.20.

(Litho Enschedé)

1997 (29 May). *"Pacific '97" International Stamp Exhibition, San Francisco. Sheet 123×80 mm, containing designs as Nos. 861/2. Phosphorised paper. P* 13½×14.

MS895 22 c. As Type **233**; $2 No. 862 .. .. 2·25 2·50

(Des D. Kuah. Litho Southern Colour Print, Dunedin)

1997 (16 July). *Renovation of Housing and Development Board Estates. T* **238** *and similar vert designs. Multicoloured. Phosphorised paper. P* 14.

896	(22 c.) Type **238**	25	30
897	30 c. Family at playground	35	30
898	70 c. Couple walking through garden	70	70
899	$1 Family on balcony	95	1·00
896/9	*Set of* 4	2·00	2·00

No. 896 is inscribed "FOR LOCAL ADDRESSES ONLY" and was sold for 22 c.

239 Globe and Hand Clasp

240 Flower and Tree ("Clean Environment")

(Des M. Chiew. Litho Southern Colour Print, Dunedin)

1997 (8 Aug). *30th Anniv of A.S.E.A.N. (Association of Southeast Asian Nations). T* **239** *and similar semi-circular designs. Multicoloured. Phosphorised paper. P* 15 *(and* 14 *around design).*

900	(22 c.) Type **239**	25	20
901	35 c. Dancers, kite flying and decorated truck	45	40
902	60 c. Dish aerial and map	70	70
903	$1 National landmarks	1·25	1·40
900/3	*Set of* 4	2·40	2·40

No. 900 is inscribed "FOR LOCAL ADDRESSES ONLY" and was sold for 22 c.

(Des Design Objectives. Litho Enschedé)

1997 (13 Sept). *25th Anniv of the Ministry of the Environment. T* **240** *and similar vert designs. Multicoloured. Phosphorised paper. P* 13½.

904	(22 c.) Type **240**	20	20
	a. Booklet pane. No. 904×10 with margins all round	1·50	
905	60 c. Fish and river ("Clean Waters")	55	55
906	70 c. Bird and sky ("Clean Air")	65	65
907	$1 Dustbin and block of flats ("Clean Homes")	90	90
904/7	*Set of* 4	2·10	2·10

No. 904 is inscribed "FOR LOCAL ADDRESSES ONLY" and was sold for 22 c.

NEW INFORMATION

The editor is always interested to correspond with people who have new information that will improve or correct the Catalogue.

241 *Drupa morum*

242 Tiger

(Des R. Saichumdee. Litho Enschedé)

1997 (9 Oct). *Singapore–Thailand Joint Issue. Sea Shells. T* **241** *and similar horiz designs. Multicoloured. Phosphorised paper. P* 13½×14.

908	(22 c.) Type **241**	25	20
909	35 c. *Nerita chamaeleon*	35	30
910	60 c. *Littoraria melanostoma*	55	55
911	$1 *Cryptospira elegans*	90	1·00
908/11	*Set of* 4	1·90	1·90
MS912	125×80 mm. 22 c. As Type **241** and Nos. 909/11	2·00	2·25

No. 908 is inscribed "FOR LOCAL ADDRESSES ONLY" and was sold for 22 c.

1997 (19 Nov). *"Shanghai '97" International Stamp and Coin Exhibition. Sheet 123×80 mm. Phosphorised paper. P* 13½×14.

MS913 22 c. As Type **233**; $2 No. 862 .. .. 1·60 1·75

(Des N. Loh Fook Chee. Litho Enschedé)

1998 (9 Jan). *Chinese New Year ("Year of the Tiger"). T* **242** *and similar horiz design showing stylised tigers. Phosphorised paper. P* 13½×14.

914	(22 c.) multicoloured	15	20
915	$2 multicoloured	1·40	1·50

No. 914 is inscribed "FOR LOCAL ADDRESSES ONLY" and was sold for 22 c.

STAMP BOOKLETS

1969 (1 Nov). *Black on green cover. Stapled.*
SB1 $1.80, booklet containing twelve 15 c. (No. 106) in blocks of 4 .. .. 35·00

1973 (30 Sept). *Grey and black printed cover. Pane attached by selvedge.*
SB2 $1 booklet containing *se-tenant* pane of 10 (No. 213a) .. .. 7·00

1977 (9 Apr). *Blue printed cover. Pane attached by selvedge.*
SB3 $1 booklet containing *se-tenant* pane of 12 (No. 290a) .. .. 3·75

1980 (26 Apr). *Green printed cover. Stamps attached by selvedge.*
SB4 $1 booklet containing 10 c. (No. 366) in block of 10 3·50

B 1 Full-rigged Sailing Ship

1990 (21 Mar). *Lithographs of 19th-century Singapore. Black printed cover as Type* B **1**. *Pane attached by selvedge.*
SB5 $1.50, booklet containing pane of ten 15 c. (No. 615a) .. .. 6·00

B 2 Mouth of Singapore River

1990 (4 July). *Tourism. Deep ultramarine, light greenish blue and light emerald printed cover as Type* B **2**. *Pane attached by selvedge.*
SB6 $1.50, booklet containing pane of ten 15 c. (No. 625a) .. .. 8·00

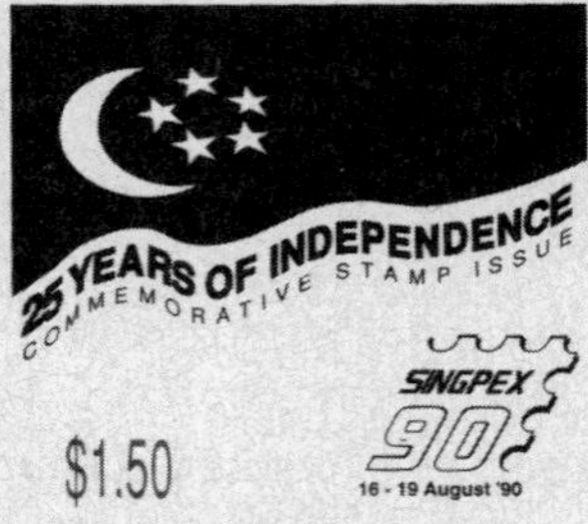

B 3 National Flag and "Singpex 90" National Stamp Exhibition Emblem

1990 (16 Aug). *25th Anniv of Independence. Red. black and grey printed cover as Type* B **3**. *Pane attached by selvedge.*
SB7 $1.50, booklet containing pane of ten 15 c. (No. 637ab) .. .. 8·50

1991 (6 Mar). *Tourism. Deep ultramarine, light greenish blue and light emerald printed cover as Type* B **2**. *Pane attached by selvedge.*
SB8 $2 booklet containing pane of ten 20 c. (No. 626a) 7·00

B 4 "Mobil 1" Oil Can

1991 (15 May). *Tourism. Multicoloured cover as Type* B **4**. *Pane attached by selvedge.*
SB9 $2 booklet containing pane of ten 20 c. (No. 626a) 7·00

B 5 Kingfisher

1991 (19 Sept). *Garden Birds. Multicoloured cover as Type* B **5**. *Pane attached by selvedge.*
SB10 $2 booklet containing pane of ten 20 c. (No. 663a) 9·00

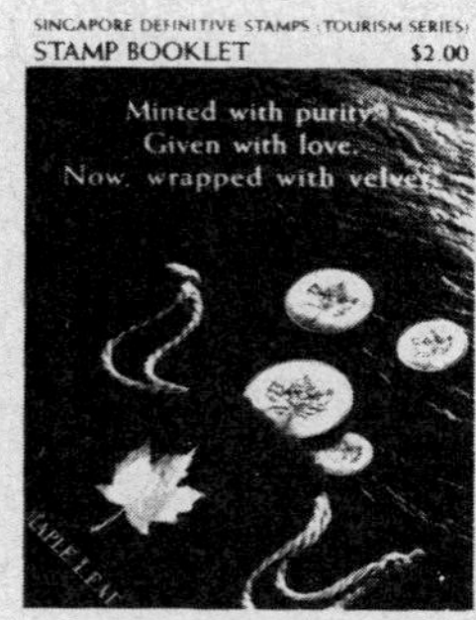

B 6 Maple Leaf Gold Coins

1991 (11 Nov). *Tourism. Multicoloured cover as Type* B **6**. *Pane attached by selvedge.*
SB11 $2 booklet containing pane of ten 20 c. (No. 626a) 7·00

B 7 Swamp Forest Crab

1992 (21 Aug). *Crabs. Multicoloured cover as Type* B **7**. *Pane attached by selvedge.*
SB12 $2 booklet containing pane of ten 20 c. (No. 698a) 4·00

B 8 Aspects of Singapore

1992 (1 Sept). *"Kuala Lumpur '92" International Stamp Exhibition. Multicoloured cover as Type* B **8**. *Pane attached by selvedge.*
SB13 $2 booklet containing pane of ten 20 c. (No. 626a) 3·50

B 9 Children and Party Streamers

1993 (10 Feb). *Greetings Stamps. Multicoloured cover as Type* B **9**. *Pane attached by selvedge.*
SB14 $2 booklet containing pane of ten 20 c. in five different designs (No. 710a) .. .. 4·50

B 10 Butterflies and Flowers

1993 (21 Aug). *Butterflies. Multicoloured cover as Type* B **10**. *Pane attached by selvedge.*
SB15 $2 containing pane of ten 20 c. (No. 728a) .. 4·75

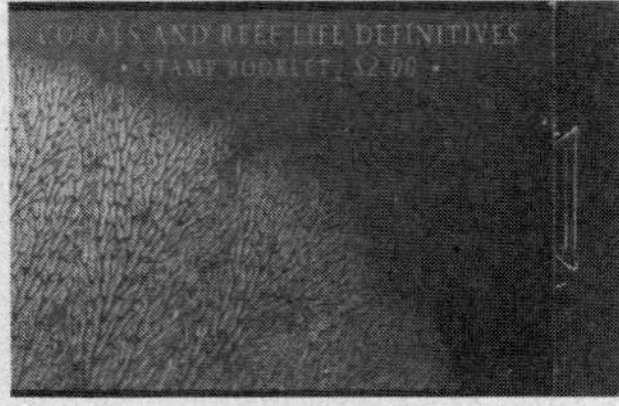

B 11 Sea-fan

1994 (12 Jan–20 May). *Reef Life (1st series). Multicoloured cover as Type* B **11** *with black bands at top and bottom. Pane attached by selvedge.*
SB16 $2 booklet containing pane of ten 20 c. (No. 743a) 3·50
a. Blue bands at top and bottom of cover (31 Mar) .. .. 4·50
ab. Revised cover showing silver inscr in three lines with the second and third lines aligned at right (20 May) .. .. 4·50

B 12 Grey Heron

1994 (16 Aug). *Herons. Multicoloured cover as Type* B **12**. *Pane attached by selvedge.*
SB17 $2 booklet containing pane of ten 20 c. (No. 766b) 4·00

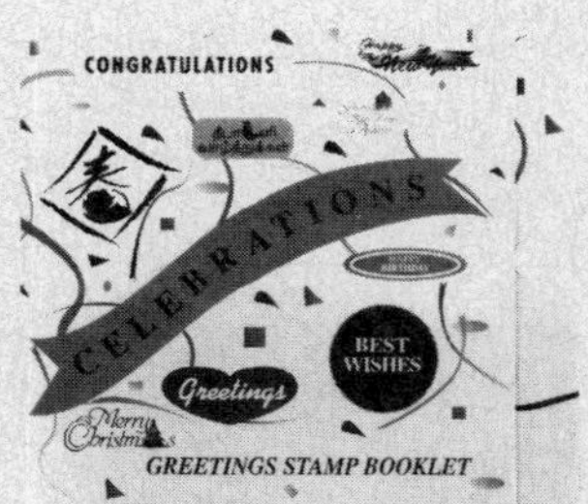

B 13 Greetings Messages

1994 (14 Sept). *Greetings Stamps. Multicoloured cover as Type* B **13**. *Self-adhesive.*
SB18 ($2) booklet containing pane of ten self-adhesive stamps (No. 775a) .. .. 3·00
The booklet cover, which forms the backing card for the stamps also incorporates 10 self-adhesive labels.

1994 (16 Nov). *Reef Life (2nd series). Multicoloured cover as Type* B **11** *showing Blue-spotted Stingray. Self-adhesive.*
SB19 ($2) booklet containing pane of ten self-adhesive stamps (No. 785a) .. .. .. 2·00

爱
GREETINGS STAMP BOOKLET
Stickers can be peeled off for use with stamps

B **14** Symbols of Love

1995 (8 Feb). *Greetings Stamps. Multicoloured cover as Type* B **14**. *Self-adhesive.*
SB20 ($2.20) booklet containing pane of ten self-adhesive stamps (No. 790a) .. .. 2·75
The booklet cover, which forms the backing card for the stamps also incorporates 10 self-adhesive labels.

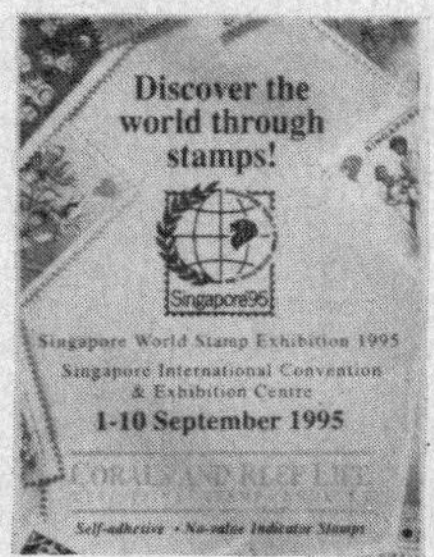

B **15** Exhibition Logo and Stamps (inscr "Discover the World through Stamps")

1995 (12 Apr–5 July). *"Singapore '95" International Stamp Exhibition. Multicoloured covers as Type* B **15**. *Self-adhesive.*
SB21 ($2.20) booklet containing pane of ten self-adhesive stamps (No. 785ba) (Type B **15**) .. 3·75
SB22 ($2.20) booklet containing pane of ten self-adhesive stamps (No. 785ba) (vert design for "POSTECH 1995" Postal Equipment and Machinery Exhibition) (7 June) .. .. 3·75
SB23 ($2.20) booklet containing pane of ten self-adhesive stamps (No. 785ba) (horiz cover showing map and inscr "We've Got The Route to Real Excitement!" (5 July) .. .. 3·75

B **16** Yellow-faced Angelfish

1995 (19 July). *Marine Fishes. Multicoloured cover as Type* B **16**. *Pane attached by selvedge.*
SB24 ($2.20) booklet containing ten 22 c. stamps (No. 807) .. .. 3·25

B **17** "6 DIGIT POSTAL CODE"

1995 (1 Sept). *Introduction of Six Digit Postal Codes. Multicoloured cover as Type* B **17**. *Self-adhesive.*
SB25 ($2.20) booklet containing pane of ten self-adhesive stamps (No. 785ba) .. .. 3·75

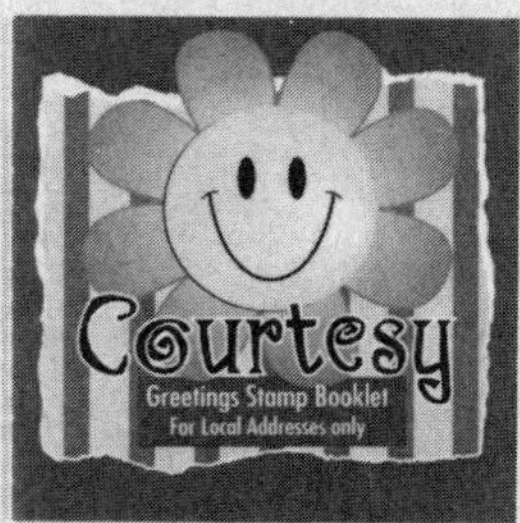

B **18** Smiling Flower

1996 (10 July). *Greetings Stamps. "Courtesy". Children's Drawings. Multicoloured covers as Type* B **18**. *Self-adhesive.*
SB26 ($2.20) booklet containing pane of ten self-adhesive stamps (No. 839a) (Type B **18**) .. 2·50
SB27 $3.90 booklet containing pane of ten self-adhesive stamps (No. 839b) (cover showing smiling flowers) .. .. 4·25
The booklet covers, which forms the backing card for the stamps also incorporate 10 self-adhesive labels.

B **19** *Cinnamomum iners*

1996 (11 Sept). *Singapore Trees. Multicoloured cover as Type* B **19**. *Pane attached by selvedge.*
SB28 ($2.20) booklet containing ten 22 c. stamps (No. 850) .. .. 2·75

B **20** Jinrickshaw

1997 (19 Mar). *Transportation. Multicoloured cover as Type* B **20**. *Self-adhesive.*
SB29 ($2.20) booklet containing pane of ten self-adhesive stamps (No. 884a) .. .. 1·50

B **21** Apple

1997 (14 May). *Greetings stamps. "Friends". Multicoloured covers as Type* B **21**. *Self-adhesive.*
SB30 ($2.20) booklet containing pane of ten self-adhesive stamps (No. 885a) (Type B **21**, "friendship" in vermilion) .. .. .. 1·50
SB31 ($2.20) booklet containing pane of ten self-adhesive stamps (No. 890a) (as Type B **21**, but "friendship" in ultramarine) .. .. 1·50
The booklet covers, which form the backing cards for the stamps each incorporate 10 self-adhesive labels.

B **22** Flowers

1997 (13 Sept). *25th Anniv of the Ministry of the Environment. Multicoloured cover as Type* B **22**. *Pane attached by selvedge.*
SB32 ($2.20) booklet containing pane of ten (22 c.) (No. 904a) .. .. 1·50

POSTAGE DUE STAMPS

The postage due stamps of Malayan Postal Union were in use in Singapore until replaced by the following issues.

D 1

D 2

D 3

(Litho B.W.)

1968 (1 Feb)–**69**. *Toned paper. W* w **12**. *P* 9.

D1	D 1	1 c. green	60	1·50
D2		2 c. red	60	2·00
D3		4 c. yellow-orange	90	4·50
D4		8 c. chocolate	50	90
D5		10 c. magenta	50	90
		a. White paper (16.12.69)	80	4·00
D6		12 c. slate-violet	1·25	1·50
		a. White paper (16.12.69)	5·00	7·50
D7		20 c. new blue	2·00	3·25
		a. White paper (16.12.69)	8·00	11·00
D8		50 c. drab	8·50	5·00
D1/8		*Set of* 8	13·00	18·00

1973. *White paper. W* w **12**. *P* 13 × 13½.

D 9	D 1	10 c. bright magenta (27.4)	75	4·50
D10		50 c. sage-green (24.8)	8·00	12·00

1977–78. *White paper. No wmk. P* 13 × 13½.

D11	D 1	1 c. green	42·00	35·00
D12		4 c. yellow-orange	42·00	55·00
D13		10 c. bright magenta	45·00	32·00
D14		20 c. new blue	50·00	42·00
D15		50 c. sage-green	60·00	48·00
D11/15		*Set of* 5	£225	£190

(Litho Secura, Singapore)

1978 (25 Sept)–**81**. *No wmk. P* 13 × 13½.

D16	D 2	1 c. blue-green	65	3·00
		a. Perf 12 × 11½ (1981)	15	2·00
D17		4 c. pale orange	75	4·00
		a. Perf 12 × 11½ (1981)	20	3·00
D18		10 c. cerise	85	2·25
		a. Perf 12 × 11½ (1981)	50	1·50
D19		20 c. light blue	95	2·50
		a. Perf 12 × 11½ (1981)	65	2·00
D20		50 c. yellow-green	1·60	2·75
		a. Perf 12 × 11½ (1981)	90	2·50
D16/20		*Set of* 5	4·25	13·00
D16a/20a		*Set of* 5	2·25	10·00

(Litho Secura, Singapore)

1989 (12 July)–**97**. *P* 13×13½.

D21	D 3	1 c. bright emerald (7.11.97)		
D22		4 c. orange-brown (7.11.97)		
D23		5 c. bright mauve	20	30
D24		10 c. carmine	20	30
D25		20 c. bright greenish blue	30	50
D26		50 c. yellow-green	60	85
D27		$1 blackish brown (30.4.93)	1·25	1·50

Postage Due stamps were withdrawn on 31 December 1997 and replaced by labels from electronic machines.

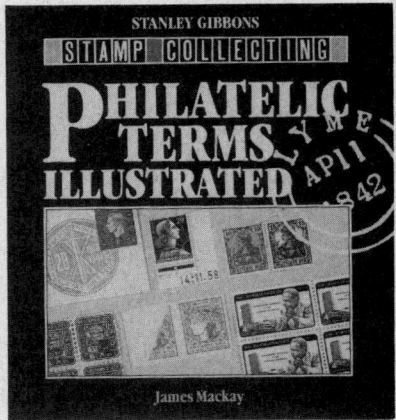

Solomon Islands

(*formerly* British Solomon Islands)

The first British Resident Commissioner, Charles Woodford, was appointed in 1896 and a administrative centre established at Tulagi.

Mail was initially sent unstamped by sealed bag to Sydney where New South Wales stamps were applied and cancelled. Later the Resident Commissioner kept a stock of New South Wales stamps which were still not cancelled until arrival at Sydney. From April 1906 Mr. Woodford used a vertical oblong "BRITISH SOLOMON ISLANDS PAID" handstamp in place of New South Wales stamps which were then added to many of the covers by the postal authorities in Sydney.

PRICES FOR STAMPS ON COVER TO 1945

Nos. 1/7	*from* × 12
Nos. 8/17	*from* × 25
Nos. 18/36	*from* × 6
Nos. 37/8	—
Nos. 39/51	*from* × 6
No. 52	—
Nos. 53/6	*from* × 2
Nos. 57/9	*from* × 6
Nos. 60/72	*from* × 2
Nos. D1/8	*from* × 5

BRITISH PROTECTORATE

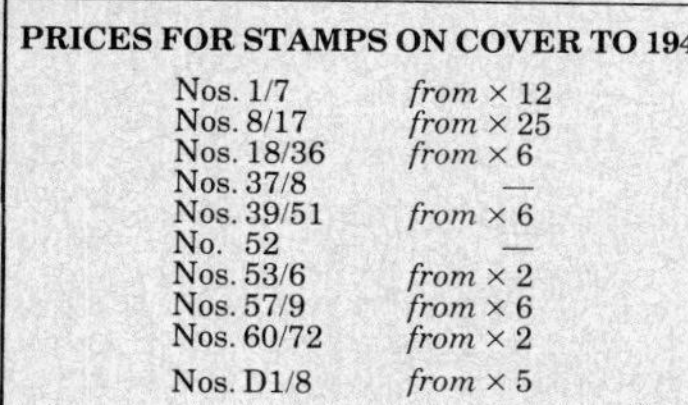

1 2

(Des C. M. Woodford. Litho W. E. Smith & Co, Sydney)

1907 (14 Feb). *No wmk. P* 11.
1 1 ½d. ultramarine .. .. .. 8·50 14·00
2 1d. rose-carmine .. .. .. 22·00 25·00
3 2d. indigo .. .. .. 26·00 30·00
a. Imperf between (horiz pair) .. £11000
4 2½d. orange-yellow .. .. .. 32·00 38·00
a. Imperf between (vert pair) .. £4000
b. Imperf between (horiz pair) .. £5000 £4000
5 5d. emerald-green .. .. .. 50·00 65·00
6 6d. chocolate .. .. .. 55·00 60·00
a. Imperf between (vert pair) .. £3500
7 1s. bright purple .. .. .. 75·00 75·00
1/7 .. .. *Set of* 7 £225 £275

Three types exist of the ½d. and 2½d., and six each of the other values, differing in minor details.

Forgeries of Nos. 1/7 show different perforations and have the boat paddle touching the shore. Genuine stamps show a gap between the paddle and the shore.

(Recess D.L.R.)

1908 (1 Nov)–**11**. *Wmk Mult Crown CA (sideways). P* 14.
8 2 ½d. green .. .. .. 1·50 80
9 1d. red .. .. .. 1·25 50
10 2d. greyish slate .. .. .. 1·25 1·00
11 2½d. ultramarine .. .. .. 3·75 2·00
11*a* 4d. red/*yellow* (6.3.11) .. .. 3·25 11·00
12 5d. olive .. .. .. 8·50 8·00
13 6d. claret .. .. .. 10·00 6·50
14 1s. black/*green* .. .. .. 8·50 9·50
15 2s. purple/*blue* (7.3.10) .. .. 38·00 50·00
16 2s. 6d. red/*blue* (7.3.10) .. .. 48·00 70·00
17 5s. green/*yellow* (7.3.10) .. .. 75·00 £100
8/17 .. .. .. *Set of* 11 £170 £225
8/17 Optd "Specimen" .. .. *Set of* 11 £250

The ½d. and 1d. were issued in 1913 on rather thinner paper and with brownish gum.

3 4

(T 3 and 4. Typo D.L.R.)

1913. *Inscribed* "POSTAGE POSTAGE". *Wmk Mult Crown CA. P* 14.
18 3 ½d. green (1.4) .. .. .. 80 3·50
19 1d. red (1.4) .. .. .. 80 13·00
20 3d. purple/*yellow* (27.2) .. .. 80 4·00
a. On orange-buff .. .. 5·50 24·00
21 11d. dull purple and scarlet (27.2) .. 3·00 12·00
18/21 .. .. .. *Set of* 4 4·75 29·00
18/21 Optd "Specimen" .. *Set of* 4 70·00

1914 (Mar)–**23**. *Inscribed* "POSTAGE REVENUE". *Wmk Mult Crown CA. Chalk-surfaced paper (3d. to £1). P* 14.
22 4 ½d. green .. .. .. 80 10·00
23 ½d. yellow-green (1917) .. .. 3·50 16·00
24 1d. carmine-red .. .. .. 1·50 1·00
25 1d. scarlet (1917) .. .. .. 4·50 6·50
26 2d. grey (7.14) .. .. .. 2·75 9·00
27 2½d. ultramarine (7.14) .. .. 2·00 5·00
28 3d. purple/*pale yellow* (3.23) .. .. 18·00 80·00
29 4d. black and red/*yellow* (7.14) .. 2·00 2·50
30 5d. dull purple and olive-green (7.14) .. 20·00 30·00
31 4 5d. brown-purple and olive-green (7.14) 20·00 30·00
32 6d. dull and bright purple (7.14) .. 6·00 14·00
33 1s. black/*green* (7.14) .. .. 4·50 7·00
a. On blue-green, olive back (1923) .. 7·50 21·00
34 2s. purple and blue/*blue* (7.14) .. 7·00 10·00
35 2s. 6d. black and red/*blue* (7.14) .. 8·50 20·00
36 5s. green and red/*yellow* (7.14) .. 27·00 45·00
a. On orange-buff (1920) .. .. 45·00 70·00
37 10s. green and red/*green* (7.14) .. 75·00 80·00
38 £1 purple and black/*red* (7.14) .. £200 £120
22/38 .. .. .. *Set of* 14 £325 £400
22/38 Optd "Specimen" .. *Set of* 14 £400

Variations in the coloured papers are mostly due to climate and do not indicate separate printings.

1922–31. *Wmk Mult Script CA. Chalk-surfaced paper (4d. and 5d. to 10s.). P* 14.
39 4 ½d. green (10.22) .. .. .. 30 2·50
40 1d. scarlet (4.23) .. .. .. 10·00 9·00
41 1d. dull violet (2.27) .. .. .. 1·00 6·00
42 3 1½d. bright scarlet (7.24) .. .. 2·25 40
43 4 2d. slate-grey (4.23) .. .. .. 2·50 12·00
44 3d. pale ultramarine (11.23) .. .. 70 3·25
45 4d. black and red/*yellow* (7.27) .. 3·50 20·00
45*a* 4½d. red-brown (1931) .. .. 3·00 18·00
46 5d. dull purple and olive-green (12.27) 2·75 23·00
47 6d. dull and bright purple (12.27) .. 3·75 23·00
48 1s. black/*emerald* (12.27) .. .. 2·75 12·00
49 2s. purple and blue/*blue* (2.27) .. 8·00 30·00
50 2s. 6d. black and red/*blue* (12.27) .. 7·50 32·00
51 5s. green and red/*pale yellow* (12.27) .. 24·00 50·00
52 10s. green and red/*emerald* (1.25) .. 90·00 95·00
39/52 .. .. .. *Set of* 15 £140 £300
39/52 Optd/Perf "Specimen" .. *Set of* 15 £300

1935 (6 May). *Silver Jubilee. As Nos.* 114/17 *of Jamaica, but ptd by D.L.R. P* 13½×14.
53 1½d. deep blue and carmine .. .. 1·00 70
f. Diagonal line by turret .. .. 50·00
h. Dot by flagstaff .. .. 80·00
54 3d. brown and deep blue .. .. 3·00 5·50
f. Diagonal line by turret .. .. 90·00
h. Dot by flagstaff £140
55 6d. light blue and olive-green .. .. 7·50 12·00
a. Frame printed double, one albino ..
b. Frame printed triple, two albino .. £1200
h. Dot by flagstaff £200
56 1s. slate and purple .. .. 7·50 9·00
a. Frame printed double, one albino .. £1500
f. Diagonal line by turret £170
h. Dot by flagstaff £225
i. Dash by turret £225
53/6 .. .. .. *Set of* 4 17·00 24·00
53/6 Perf "Specimen" .. .. *Set of* 4 90·00

The second albino impression on No. 55b is sometimes almost co-incidental with the inked impression of the frame.

For illustrations of plate varieties see Omnibus section following Zimbabwe.

1937 (13 May). *Coronation. As Nos.* 118/20 *of Jamaica, but ptd by B.W. P* 11×11½.
57 1d. violet 30 50
58 1½d. carmine 30 60
59 3d. blue 50 50
57/9 .. .. .. *Set of* 3 1·00 1·40
57/9 Perf "Specimen" .. .. *Set of* 3 60·00

5 Spears and Shield

6 Native Constable and Chief

7 Canoe House

8 Roviana Canoe

(Recess D.L.R. (2d., 3d., 2s. and 2s. 6d.), Waterlow (others))

1939 (1 Feb)–**1951**. *T* 5/8 *and similar designs. Wmk Mult Script CA. P* 13½ *(2d., 3d., 2s. and 2s. 6d.) or* 12½ *(others).*
60 ½d. blue and blue-green 15 80
61 1d. brown and deep violet 30 70
62 1½d. blue-green and carmine .. .. 70 1·25
63 2d. orange-brown and black .. .. 80 1·50
a. Perf 12 (7.11.51) .. .. 30 1·50
64 2½d. magenta and sage-green .. .. 1·50 1·00
a. Imperf horiz (vert pair) .. £8000
65 3d. black and ultramarine .. .. 1·00 1·00
a. Perf 12 (29.11.51) .. .. 1·25 2·00
66 4½d. green and chocolate .. .. 5·00 13·00
67 6d. deep violet and reddish purple .. 75 1·00
68 1s. green and black .. .. 1·25 65
69 2s. black and orange .. .. 6·00 4·00
70 2s. 6d. black and violet .. .. 26·00 4·50
71 5s. emerald-green and scarlet .. .. 32·00 9·00
72 10s. sage-green and magenta (27.4.42) .. 6·00 8·50
60/72 .. .. .. *Set of* 13 70·00 42·00
60/72 Perf "Specimen" .. *Set of* 13 £275

Designs: *Horiz (as T* **8**)—1½d. Artificial Island, Malaita; 1s. Breadfruit; 5s. Malaita canoe. *(As T* **7**)—3d. Roviana canoes; 2s. Tinakula volcano; 2s. 6d. Common Scrub Hen. *Vert (as T* **6**)—4½d., 10s. Native house, Reef Islands; 6d. Coconut plantation.

1946 (15 Oct). *Victory. As Nos.* 141/2 *of Jamaica.*
73 1½d. carmine 15 70
74 3d. blue 15 10
73/4 Perf "Specimen" .. .. *Set of* 2 55·00

Pocket handkerchief flaw (R. 1/6)

1949 (14 Mar). *Royal Silver Wedding. As Nos.* 143/4 *of Jamaica.*
75 2d. black 50 40
a. Pocket handkerchief flaw .. .. 19·00
76 10s. magenta .. .. .. 13·00 10·00

1949 (10 Oct). *75th Anniv of U.P.U. As Nos.* 145/8 *of Jamaica.*
77 2d. red-brown .. .. .. 1·00 1·00
78 3d. deep blue .. .. .. 2·25 1·00
79 5d. deep blue-green .. .. .. 1·00 1·40
80 1s. blue-black .. .. .. 1·00 1·00
77/80 .. .. .. *Set of* 4 4·75 4·00

1953 (2 June). *Coronation. As No.* 153 *of Jamaica.*
81 2d. black and grey-black 50 85

17 Ysabel Canoe

18 Roviana Canoe

24 Native Constable and Chief

25 Arms of the Protectorate

(Des Miss I. R. Stinson (½d.), R. Bailey (2½d.), R. A. Sweet (5d., 1s., 1s. 3d.), Capt. J. Brett Hilder (6d., 8d., 9d., 5s.). Recess B.W. (½d., 2½d., 5d., 6d., 8d., 9d., 1s., 1s. 3d., 5s.), D.L.R. (1d., 2d., 2s.), Waterlow (1½d., 3d., 2s. 6d., 10s., £1), until 1962, then D.L.R.)

1956 (1 Mar)–**63**. *T* **17/18**, **24/5** *and similar horiz designs. Wmk Mult Script CA. P* 12 *(1d., 2d., 2s.),* 13 *(1½d., 3d., 2s 6d., 10s., £1) or* 11½ *(others).*
82 ½d. orange and purple 15 50
83 1d. yellow-green and red-brown .. 15 15
84 1½d. slate-green and carmine-red .. 15 60
a. Slate-green and brown-red (31.7.63) 60 40
85 2d. deep brown and dull green .. 30 30
86 2½d. black and blue 50 50
87 3d. blue-green and red 50 15
88 5d. black and blue 30 55
89 6d. black and turquoise-green .. 50 25
90 8d. bright blue and black 25 15
90*a* 9d. emerald and black (28.1.60) .. 3·25 80
91 1s. slate and yellow-brown 50 50
a. Slate and orange-brown (13.6.61) .. 3·50 3·00
91*b* 1s. 3d. black and blue (28.1.60) .. 6·00 1·75
ba. Black and pale ultramarine (11.12.62) 10·00 3·25
92 2s. black and carmine .. .. 13·00 1·50
93 2s. 6d. emerald and bright purple .. 7·50 45
a. Emerald and reddish purple (19.2.63) 11·00 1·75
94 5s. red-brown .. .. .. 14·00 3·25
95 10s. sepia .. .. .. 18·00 4·25
96 £1 black and blue (5.11.58) .. .. 42·00 35·00
82/96 .. .. .. *Set of* 17 90·00 42·00

Designs: *(As T* **17**)—5d., 1s. 3d. Map; 6d. *Miena* (schooner); 1s. Voyage of H.M.S. *Swallow*, 1767; 2s. 6d. Native house, Reef Islands; 5s. Mendaña and *Todos los Santos*. *(As T* **25**)—1d. Roviana canoe; 1½d. Artificial Island, Malaita; 2d. Canoe house; 3d. Malaita Canoe; 8d., 9d. Henderson airfield, Guadalcanal; 2s. Tinakula volcano.

LEGISLATIVE COUNCIL

32 Great Frigate Bird

(Litho Enschedé)

1961 (19 Jan). *New Constitution, 1960. W* w **12** (*sideways**). *P* 13×12½.
97 **32** 2d. black and turquoise-green .. 10 30
w. Wmk Crown to right of CA .. 10 30
98 3d. black and rose-carmine 10 10
w. Wmk Crown to right of CA .. 10 10
99 9d. black and reddish purple 15 30
w. Wmk Crown to right of CA .. 15 30
97/9 .. .. *Set of* 3 30 60
*This issue with watermark sideways exists in almost equal quantities with the watermark showing Crown to left or right of CA.

1963 (4 June). *Freedom from Hunger. As No.* 80 *of Lesotho.*
100 1s. 3d. ultramarine .. .. 1·50 35

1963 (2 Sept). *Red Cross Centenary. As Nos.* 203/4 *of Lesotho.*
101 2d. red and black 50 20
102 9d. red and blue .. .. 1·00 80

1963–64. *As Nos.* 83/5, 87, 89, 90*a and* 91*a*/3, *but wmk* w **12**.
103 1d. yellow-green and red-brown (9.7.64) 25 30
104 1½d. slate-green and red (9.7.64) 25 50
105 2d. deep brown and dull green (9.7.64) 20 20
106 3d. light blue-green and scarlet (16.11.63) 55 15
a. Yellowish green and red (9.7.64) .. 1·25 1·75
107 6d. black and turquoise (7.7.64) 60 40
108 9d. emerald and black (7.7.64) 20 35
109 1s. 3d. black and blue (7.7.64) 60 70
110 2s. black and carmine (9.7.64) .. .. 1·00 5·50
111 2s. 6d. emerald & reddish purple (9.7.64) 14·00 11·00
103/11 .. .. *Set of* 9 16·00 17·00

33 Makira Food Bowl

2 c (48)

(Des M. Farrar-Bell. Litho D.L.R.)

1965 (24 May). *Horiz designs as T* **33**. *W* w **12**. *P* 13 × 12½.
112 ½d. black, deep slate-blue and light blue .. 10 70
113 1d. black, orange and yellow 70 30
114 1½d. black, blue and yellow-green 35 50
115 2d. black, ultramarine and light blue .. 60 60
116 2½d. black, light brown & pale yellow-brown 10 45
117 3d. black, green and light green 10 10
118 6d. black, magenta and yellow-orange .. 35 60
119 9d. brownish blk, dp bluish grn & pale yell 40 15
120 1s. black, chocolate and magenta 90 15
121 1s. 3d. black and rose-red .. .. .. 3·50 2·25
122 2s. black, bright purple and lilac .. .. 7·00 3·00
123 2s. 6d. black, olive-brown and light brown 1·00 70
124 5s. black, ultramarine and violet .. .. 12·00 5·00
125 10s. black, olive-green and yellow .. .. 14·00 4·00
126 £1 black, deep reddish violet and pink .. 12·00 5·00
112/126 .. .. *Set of* 15 45·00 20·00
Designs:—1d. *Dendrobium veratrifolium* (orchid); 1½d. Chiragra Spider Conch; 2d. Blyth's Hornbill; 2½d. Ysabel shield; 3d. Rennellese club; 6d. Moorish Idol; 9d. Lesser Frigate Bird; 1s. *Dendrobium macrophyllum* (orchid); 1s. 3d. *Dendrobium spectabilis* (orchid); 2s. Sanford's Sea Eagle; 2s. 6d. Malaita belt; 5s. *Ornithoptera victoreae* (butterfly); 10s. Ducorp's Cockatoo; £1, Western canoe figurehead.

1965 (28 June). *I.T.U. Centenary. As Nos.* 98/9 *of Lesotho.*
127 2d. orange-red and turquoise-blue 20 10
128 3d. turquoise-blue and olive-brown 20 10

1965 (25 Oct). *International Co-operation Year. As Nos.* 100/1 *of Lesotho.*
129 1d. reddish purple and turquoise-green .. 10 10
130 2s. 6d. deep bluish green and lavender .. 45 15

1966 (24 Jan). *Churchill Commemoration. As Nos.* 102/5 *of Lesotho.*
131 2d. new blue 15 10
132 9d. deep green 25 10
133 1s. 3d. brown 35 10
134 2s. 6d. bluish violet 40 25
131/4 .. .. *Set of* 4 1·00 40

(New Currency. 100 cents = 1 Australian, later Solomon Islands dollar)

8 c. — Normal "8"
8 c. — Inverted "8" (No. 142a) (R. 9/2. Later corrected)

1966–67. *Decimal Currency. Nos.* 112/26 *variously surch as T* **48** *by De La Rue. A. Wmk upright. B. Wmk sideways.*

		A		B	
135	1 c. on ½d.	10	10	10	10
136	2 c. on 1d.	10	10	10	10
137	3 c. on 1½d.	10	10	15	10
138	4 c. on 2d.	15	10	15	10
139	5 c. on 6d.	15	10	15	10
140	6 c. on 2½d.	15	10	10	10
141	7 c. on 3d.	15	10	10	10
142	8 c. on 9d.	25	10	15	10
	a. Inverted "8"	23·00	16·00	†	
	b. Surch omitted (vert pair)	£2500	—	†	
143	10 c. on 1s.	30	10	40	10
144	12 c. on 1s. 3d.	†		65	10
145	13 c. on 1s. 3d.	1·50	15	4·50	1·75
146	14 c. on 3d.	†		40	10
147	20 c. on 2s.	2·00	25	3·25	30
148	25 c. on 2s. 6d.	60	40	2·50	35
149	35 c. on 2d.	†		1·75	25
	a. Surch omitted (horiz pair with normal)	†		£2500	—
	b. Surch value only omitted	†		—	—
150	50 c. on 5s. (R.)	5·50	2·75	10·00	5·50
151	$1 on 10s.	3·00	3·00	6·00	1·25
152	$2 on £1	2·75	6·50	5·00	3·00
135A/52A	.. .. *Set of* 15	15·00	12·00		
135B/52B	.. .. *Set of* 18			30·00	11·50

Dates of issue: 1967—1 March, 12 c., 14 c., 35 c. 1966—14 February. All watermark upright. 1966—All other watermark sideways.

The positions of the bars in the surcharge vary considerably from stamp to stamp within the sheets.

The stamps with sideways watermark are all from new printings and in some instances there are marked shade variations from Nos. 112/26 which were used for making Nos. 135A/152A.

No. 142b comes from the bottom left-hand corner of the sheet and was covered by a paper fold. The bottom stamp in the pair is completely without surcharge and the upper has the surcharge value and one bar missing.

1966 (1 July). *World Cup Football Championships. As Nos.* 57/8 *of Pitcairn Islands.*
153 8 c. violet, yellow-green, lake & yellow-brn .. 15 10
154 35 c. chocolate, blue-green, lake & yellow-brn 30 10

1966 (20 Sept). *Inauguration of W.H.O. Headquarters, Geneva. As Nos.* 185/6 *of Montserrat.*
155 3 c. black, yellow-green and light blue .. 20 10
156 50 c. black, light purple and yellow-brown .. 60 20

1966 (1 Dec). *20th Anniv of U.N.E.S.C.O. As Nos.* 342/4 *of Mauritius.*
157 3 c. slate-violet, red, yellow and orange .. 15 10
158 25 c. orange-yellow, violet and deep olive .. 30 15
159 $1 black, bright purple and orange .. 75 70
157/9 .. .. *Set of* 3 1·10 85

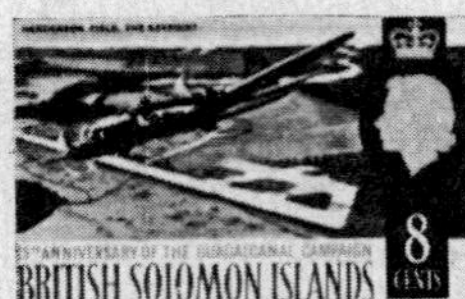

49 Henderson Field

(Des V. Whiteley. Photo Harrison)

1967 (28 Aug). *25th Anniv of Guadalcanal Campaign (Pacific War). T* **49** *and similar horiz design. Multicoloured. W* w **12**. *P* 14 × 14½.
160 8 c. Type **49** 15 10
161 35 c. Red Beach landings 15 10

51 Mendaña's *Todos los Santos* off Point Cruz

(Des V. Whiteley. Photo Harrison)

1968 (7 Feb). *Quatercentenary of the Discovery of Solomon Is. T* **51** *and similar horiz designs. Multicoloured. W* w **12**. *P* 14.
162 3 c. Type **51** 20 10
163 8 c. Arrival of missionaries 20 10
164 35 c. Pacific Campaign, World War II .. 40 10
165 $1 Proclamation of the Protectorate .. 60 1·50
162/5 .. .. *Set of* 4 1·25 1·60

55 Vine Fishing

(Des R. Granger Barrett. Photo Harrison)

1968 (20 May)–**71**. *Horiz designs as T* **55**. *Chalk-surfaced paper. W* w **12**. *P* 14½.
166 1 c. turquoise-blue, black and brown .. 10 10
a. Glazed, ordinary paper (9.8.71) .. 90 90
aw. Wmk inverted .. .. 1·25
167 2 c. apple-green, black and brown .. 10 10
aw. Wmk inverted. Glazed, ordinary paper (9.8.71) 90 90
168 3 c. green, myrtle-green and black .. 10 10
a. Glazed, ordinary paper (9.8.71) .. 90 90
169 4 c. bright purple, black and brown .. 15 10
a. Glazed, ordinary paper (9.8.71) .. 90 90
170 6 c. multicoloured 30 10
171 8 c. multicoloured 25 10
a. Glazed, ordinary paper (9.8.71) .. 1·50 1·60
172 12 c. yellow-ochre, brown-red and black .. 65 40
a. Glazed, ordinary paper (9.8.71) .. 2·25 2·50
aw. Wmk inverted .. .. 4·00
173 14 c. orange-red, chocolate and black .. 2·00 2·00
174 15 c. multicoloured 80 70
a. Glazed, ordinary paper (9.8.71) .. 2·50 3·75
175 20 c. bright blue, red and black .. .. 3·50 2·25
a. Glazed, ordinary paper (9.8.71) .. 4·25 7·00
176 24 c. rose-red, black and yellow .. .. 2·00 2·25
177 35 c. multicoloured .. .. 2·00 50
178 45 c. multicoloured .. .. 1·50 50
179 $1 violet-blue light green and black .. 2·50 2·00
180 $2 multicoloured .. .. 6·00 5·00
w. Wmk inverted .. .. 80·00
166/80 .. .. *Set of* 15 18·00 14·00
166a/75a .. .. *Set of* 8 13·00 17·00
Designs:—2 c. Kite fishing; 3 c. Platform fishing; 4 c. Net fishing; 6 c. Gold Lip shell diving; 8 c. Night fishing; 12 c. Boat building; 14 c. Cocoa; 15 c. Road building; 20 c. Geological survey; 24 c. Hauling timber; 35 c. Copra; 45 c. Harvesting rice; $1, Honiara Port; $2, Internal air service.
The stamps on glazed, ordinary paper exist with PVA gum only. The 1 c. to 12 c. and 20 c. on chalk-surfaced paper exist with PVA gum as well as gum arabic, but the others exist with gum arabic only.

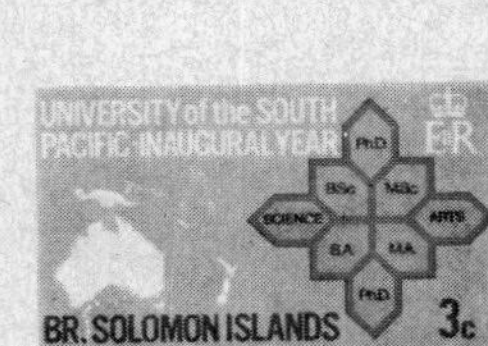

70 Map of Australasia and Diagram

71 Basketball Player

(Des R. Gates. Litho Enschedé)

1969 (10 Feb). *Inaugural Year of the South Pacific University. P* 12½ × 12.
181 **70** 3 c. multicoloured 10 10
182 12 c. multicoloured 10 10
183 35 c. multicoloured 15 10
181/3 .. .. *Set of* 3 30 20

(Des J. Cooter. Photo Harrison)

1969 (13 Aug). *Third South Pacific Games, Port Moresby. T* **71** *and similar vert designs. Multicoloured. W* w **12** (*sideways**). *P* 14½×14.
184 3 c. Type **71** 10 10
w. Wmk Crown to right of CA 65 80
185 8 c. Footballer 10 10
186 14 c. Sprinter 10 10
187 45 c. Rugby player 20 15
184/7 .. .. *Set of* 4 40 30
MS188 126×120 mm. Nos. 184/7 .. .. 3·50 8·00
*The normal sideways watermark shows Crown to left of CA, *as seen from the back of the stamp.*
Stamps from the miniature sheets differ slightly from those in the ordinary sheets, particularly the 14 c. value, which has a shadow below the feet on the runner. The footballer and rugby player on the 8 c. and 45 c. values also have shadows below their feet, but these are more pronounced than on the stamps from the ordinary sheets.

75 South Sea Island with Star of Bethlehem

76 Southern Cross, "PAX" and Frigatebird (stained glass window)

(Des L. Curtis. Photo Harrison)

1969 (21 Nov). *Christmas. W* w **12** (*sideways*). *P* 14½ × 14.
189 **75** 8 c. black, violet and turquoise-green .. 10 10
190 **76** 35 c. multicoloured 20 20

77 "Paid" Stamp, New South Wales 1896–1906 2d. Stamp and 1906–07 Tulagi Postmark

(Des G. Drummond. Litho B.W.)

1970 (15 Apr). *Inauguration of New G.P.O. Honiara. T* **77** *and similar horiz designs. W* w **12** (*sideways*). *P* 13.
191 7 c. light magenta, deep blue and black .. 20 15
192 14 c. sage-green, deep blue and black .. 25 15
193 18 c. multicoloured 25 15
194 23 c. multicoloured 30 20
191/4 .. .. *Set of* 4 90 60
Designs:—14 c. 1906–07 2d. stamp and C. M. Woodford; 18 c. 1910–14 5s. stamp and Tulagi postmark, 1913; 23 c. New G.P.O., Honiara.

81 Coat of Arms

83 British Red Cross H.Q., Honiara

(Des V. Whiteley. Photo Harrison)

1970 (15 June). *New Constitution. T* **81** *and similar design. W* w **12** (*sideways on* 18 *c.*). *P* 14½ × 14 (18 *c.*) *or* 14 × 14½ (35 *c.*).

195	18 c. multicoloured	15	10
196	35 c. pale apple-green, deep blue and ochre ..	30	20

Design: *Horiz*—35 c. Map.

(Des L. Curtis. Litho Questa)

1970 (17 Aug). *Centenary of British Red Cross. T* **83** *and similar horiz design. W* w **12** (*sideways*). *P* 14 × 14½.

197	3 c. multicoloured	10	10
198	35 c. blue, vermilion and black	25	20

Design:—35 c. Wheelchair and map.

86 Reredos (Altar Screen)

(Des L. Curtis. Litho J.W.)

1970 (19 Oct). *Christmas. T* **86** *and similar design. W* w **12** (*sideways on* 45 *c.*). *P* 14 × 13½ (8 *c.*) *or* 13½ × 14 (45 *c.*).

199	8 c. ochre and bluish violet	10	10
200	45 c. chestnut, yellow-orange & blackish brn	25	20

Design: *Vert*—8 c. Carved angel.

87 La Perouse and *La Boussole*

(Des J.W. Litho Questa)

1971 (28 Jan). *Ships and Navigators* (1*st series*). *T* **87** *and similar horiz designs. Multicoloured. W* w **12** (*sideways*). *P* 14.

201	3 c. Type **87**	55	20
202	4 c. Astrolabe and Polynesian Reed Map ..	55	20
203	12 c. Abel Tasman and *Heemskerk*	80	30
204	35 c. Te Puki canoe, Santa Cruz	1·25	50
201/4	.. .. *Set of* 4	2·75	1·10

See also Nos. 215/18, 236/9, 254/7 and 272/5.

88 J. Atkin, Bishop Patteson and S. Taroaniara

(Des J.W. Litho Questa)

1971 (5 April). *Death Centenary of Bishop Patteson. T* **88** *and similar multicoloured designs. W* w **12** (*sideways on* 2 *c.*, 4 *c.*). *P* 14½ × 14 (2 *c.*, 4 *c.*) *or* 14 × 14½ (*others*).

205	2 c. Type **88**	10	10
206	4 c. Last Landing at Nukapu	10	10
207	14 c. Memorial Cross and Nukapu (*vert*) ..	10	10
208	45 c. Knotted Leaf and canoe (*vert*)	20	10
205/8	.. .. *Set of* 4	30	30

89 Torch Emblem and Boxers

90 Melanesian Lectern

(Des C. Debenham. Litho Questa)

1971 (9 Aug). *Fourth South Pacific Games, Tahiti. T* **89** *and similar horiz designs. Multicoloured. W* w **12** (*sideways**). *P* 14.

209	3 c. Type **89**	10	10
210	8 c. Emblem and footballers	10	10
	w. Wmk Crown to right of CA	38·00	
211	12 c. Emblem and runner	10	10
212	35 c. Emblem and skin-diver	15	15
209/12	.. .. *Set of* 4	30	30

*The normal sideways watermark shows Crown to left of CA, *as seen from the back of the stamp.*

(Des C. Abbott. Litho A. & M.)

1971 (15 Nov). *Christmas. T* **90** *and similar vert design. Multicoloured. W* w **12**. *P* 13½.

213	9 c. Type **90**	10	10
	w. Wmk inverted	40	
214	45 c. "United we Stand" (Margarita Bara)	20	20
	w. Wmk inverted	90	

(Des J.W. Litho Questa)

1972 (1 Feb). *Ships and Navigators* (2*nd series*). *Horiz designs as T* **87**. *Multicoloured. W* w **12** (*sideways*). *P* 14.

215	4 c. Bougainville and *La Boudeuse*	30	10
216	9 c. Horizontal planisphere and ivory backstaff	50	10
217	15 c. Philip Carteret and H.M.S. *Swallow* ..	60	15
218	45 c. Malaita canoe	2·75	90
215/18	.. .. *Set of* 4	3·75	1·10

91 *Cupha woodfordi*

(Des R. Granger Barrett. Litho Questa)

1972 (3 July)–**73**. *T* **91** *and similar horiz designs. Multicoloured. Cream paper. W* w **12** (*upright on* $5, *sideways* on others*). *P* 14.

219	1 c. Type **91**	15	30
220	2 c. *Ornithoptera priamus*	25	40
221	3 c. *Vindula sapor*	25	40
222	4 c. *Papilio ulysses*	25	40
223	5 c. Big-eyed Trevally	25	30
	w. Wmk Crown to right of CA	1·75	1·75
224	8 c. Australian Bonito	40	50
225	9 c. Blue Demoiselle	50	55
226	12 c. *Costus speciosus*	1·25	80
227	15 c. Clown Clownfish ("Orange Anenome Fish")	1·25	1·00
	w. Wmk Crown to right of CA	30·00	
228	20 c. *Spathoglottis plicata*	3·00	1·75
229	25 c. *Ephemerantha comata*	3·00	1·50
230	35 c. *Dendrobium cuthbertsonii*	3·00	2·25
231	45 c. *Heliconia salomonica*	2·50	3·00
232	$1 Dotty Triggerfish	3·00	4·50
233	$2 *Ornithoptera alottei*	9·00	15·00
233*a*	$5 Great Frigate Bird (2.7.73)	14·00	15·00
219/33*a*	.. .. *Set of* 16	38·00	42·00

*The normal sideways watermark shows Crown to left of CA, *as seen from the back of the stamp.*

The 1 to 4 c. and $2 are butterflies; the 5 to 9 c., 15 c. and $1 are fishes; the 12 c. and 20 to 45 c. are flowers and the $5 a bird.

92 Greetings and Message Drum

(Des (from photograph by D. Groves) and photo Harrison)

1972 (20 Nov). *Royal Silver Wedding. Multicoloured; background colour given. W* w **12**. *P* 14 × 14½.

234	**92**	8 c. rose-carmine	10	10
		w. Wmk inverted	4·50	
235		45 c. deep yellow-olive	20	20
		w. Wmk inverted	35·00	

(Des J.W. Litho Questa)

1973 (9 Mar). *Ships and Navigators* (3*rd series*). *Horiz designs as T* **87**. *Multicoloured. W* w **12**. *P* 14.

236	4 c. D'Entrecasteaux and *La Recherche* ..	30	15
237	9 c. Ship's hour-glass and chronometer ..	60	15
	w. Wmk inverted	2·00	
238	15 c. Lt. Shortland and H.M.S. *Alexander*	75	20
239	35 c. Tomoko (war canoe)	2·00	1·00
236/9	.. .. *Set of* 4	3·25	1·40

COVER PRICES

Cover factors are quoted at the beginning of each country for most issues to 1945. An explanation of the system can be found on page x. The factors quoted do not, however, apply to philatelic covers.

93 Pan Pipes

(Des and litho J.W.)

1973 (1 Oct). *Musical Instruments. T* **93** *and similar horiz designs. Multicoloured. W* w **12**. *P* 13½.

240	4 c. Type **93**	10	10
241	9 c. Castanets	10	10
242	15 c. Bamboo flute	15	10
243	35 c. Bauro gongs	35	25
244	45 c. Bamboo band	35	30
240/4	.. .. *Set of* 5	90	65

(Des PAD Studio. Litho Questa)

1973 (14 Nov). *Royal Wedding. As Nos.* 322/3 *of Montserrat.*

245	4 c. deep grey-blue	10	10
246	35 c. bright blue	15	10
	w. Wmk Crown to right of CA	65·00	

*The normal sideways watermark shows CA to left of CA, *as seen from the back of the stamp.*

94 "Adoration of the Kings" (Jan Brueghel)

(Des PAD Studio. Litho Questa)

1973 (26 Nov). *Christmas. T* **94** *and similar designs showing "Adoration of the Kings" by the artists listed. Multicoloured. W* w **12** (*sideways on* 22 *c.*). *P* 13½ (45 *c.*) *or* 14 (*others*).

247	8 c. Type **94**	10	10
248	22 c. Pieter Brueghel (*vert*)	30	25
249	45 c. Botticelli (48 × 35 *mm*)	60	50
247/9	.. .. *Set of* 3	90	70

95 Queen Elizabeth II and Map

96 "Postman"

(Des G. Drummond. Litho Questa)

1974 (18 Feb). *Royal Visit. W* w **12**. *P* 13½.

250	**95**	4 c. multicoloured	25	10
		w. Wmk inverted	1·25	
251		9 c. multicoloured	30	10
252		15 c. multicoloured	40	20
253		35 c. multicoloured	60	1·25
		w. Wmk inverted	6·50	
250/3		.. .. *Set of* 4	1·40	1·40

(Des and litho J.W.)

1974 (15 May). *Ships and Navigators* (4*th series*). *Horiz designs as T* **87**. *Multicoloured. W* w **12** (*sideways*). *P* 14.

254	4 c. Commissioner landing from S.S. *Titus* ..	20	10
255	9 c. Radar scanner	20	10
256	15 c. Natives being transported to a "Blackbirder" brig	35	15
257	45 c. Lieut. John F. Kennedy's *P.T.* 109 ..	1·50	90
254/7	.. .. *Set of* 4	2·00	1·10

(Des Jennifer Toombs. Litho Questa)

1974 (29 Aug). *Centenary of Universal Postal Union. T* **96** *and similar designs showing Origami figures. W* w **12** (*sideways on* 9 *and* 45 *c.*). *P* 14.

258	4 c. light yellow-green, deep green and black	10	10
259	9 c. light olive-bistre, lake-brown and black	10	10
260	15 c. mauve, purple and black	15	10
261	45 c. cobalt, dull ultramarine and black ..	35	80
258/61	.. .. *Set of* 4	65	90

Designs: *Horiz*—9 c. Carrier-pigeon; 45 c. Pegasus. *Vert*—15 c. St. Gabriel.

97 "New Constitution" Stamp of 1970

(Des R. Granger Barrett. Litho Questa)

1974 (16 Dec). *New Constitution. T* **97** *and similar horiz design. W* w **14** (*sideways*). *P* 14.

262	**97**	4 c. multicoloured	10	10
263	–	9 c. dull rose-red, black & lt yell-ochre	15	10
264	–	15 c. dull rose-red, blk & lt greenish yell	20	10
265	**97**	35 c. multicoloured	45	50
262/5		*Set of* 4	80	60
MS266		134 × 84 mm. Nos. 262/5	1·75	3·50

Design:—9 c., 15 c. "New Constitution" stamp of 1961 (inscr "1960").

98 Golden Whistler

(Des G. Drummond. Litho Questa)

1975 (7 Apr). *Birds. T* **98** *and similar horiz designs. Multicoloured. W* w **12**. *P* 14.

267	1 c. Type **98**	45	65
268	2 c. Common Kingfisher	50	80
269	3 c. Red-bibbed Fruit Dove	55	85
270	4 c. Little Button Quail	55	85
271	$2 Duchess Lorikeet	9·50	10·50
267/71	*Set of* 5	10·50	12·00

See also Nos. 305/20.

(Des and litho J.W.)

1975 (29 May). *Ships and Navigators* (5*th series*). *Horiz designs as T* **87**. *Multicoloured. W* w **12**. *P* 13½.

272	4 c. *Walande* (coaster)	45	10
273	9 c. *Melanesian* (coaster)	60	10
274	15 c. *Marsina* (container ship)	80	15
275	45 c. *Himalaya* (liner)	1·50	1·50
272/5	*Set of* 4	3·00	1·60

99 800-Metres Race

(Des PAD Studio, Litho Walsall)

1975 (4 Aug). *Fifth South Pacific Games, Guam. T* **99** *and similar horiz designs. Multicoloured. W* w **14** (*sideways**). *P* 13½.

276	4 c. Type **99**	10	10
	w. Wmk Crown to right of CA	4·50	
277	9 c. Long-jump	10	10
278	15 c. Javelin-throwing	15	10
279	45 c. Football	45	45
276/9	*Set of* 4	70	55
MS280	130×95 mm. Nos. 276/9	4·00	4·00

*The normal sideways watermark shows Crown to left of CA, *as seen from the back of the stamp.*

100 Christmas Scene and Candles **(101)**

(Des G. Vasarhelyi. Litho Questa)

1975 (13 Oct). *Christmas. T* **100** *and similar horiz designs. Multicoloured. W* w **12** (*sideways*). *P* 14.

281	15 c. Type **100**	20	10
282	35 c. Shepherds, angels and candles	40	15
283	45 c. The Magi and candles	50	40
281/3	*Set of* 3	1·00	60
MS284	140 × 130 mm. Nos. 281/3	4·00	4·50

1975 (12 Nov). *Nos.* 267/70, 223/32, 271 *and* 233*a with obliterating bar as T* **101** *over* "BRITISH".

285	1 c. Type **98**	60	55
286	2 c. Common Kingfisher	70	55
287	3 c. Red-bibbed Fruit Dove	70	55
288	4 c. Little Button Quail	75	55
289	5 c. Big-eyed Trevally	45	55
290	8 c. Australian Bonito	50	60
291	9 c. Blue Demoiselle	50	60
292	12 c. *Costus speciosus*	1·50	1·00
293	15 c. Clown Clownfish ("Orange Anemone Fish")	1·75	1·25
294	20 c. *Spathoglottis plicata*	2·75	1·50
295	25 c. *Ephemerantha comata*	2·75	1·75
296	35 c. *Dendrobium cuthbertsonii*	3·50	1·75
297	45 c. *Heliconia salomonica*	3·50	3·00
298	$1 Dotty Triggerfish (*cream paper*)	3·00	2·00
	a. White paper	4·75	4·50
299	$2 Duchess Lorikeet	8·00	10·00
300	$5 Great Frigate Bird (*white paper*)	6·00	13·00
	a. Cream paper	23·00	23·00
285/300	*Set of* 16	30·00	35·00

SELF-GOVERNMENT

102 Ceremonial Food-bowl

(Des J. Cooter. Litho Questa)

1976 (12 Jan). *Artefacts* (1*st series*). *T* **102** *and similar multicoloured designs. W* w **12** (*upright on* 35 *c.; sideways on others*). *P* 14.

301	4 c. Type **102**	10	10
302	15 c. Chieftains' money	10	10
303	35 c. Nguzu-nguzu (canoe protector spirit) (*vert*)	25	20
304	45 c. Nguzu-nguzu canoe prow	30	25
301/4	*Set of* 4	65	55

See also Nos. 337/40, 353/6 and 376/9.

103 Golden Whistler

(Des G. Drummond. Litho Questa)

1976 (8 Mar–6 Dec). *Nos.* 267/71 *with new country inscr* (*omitting* "BRITISH") *as T* **103**, *and new values. Multicoloured. W* w **14** (*sideways**). *P* 14.

305	1 c. Type **103**	30	50
306	2 c. Common Kingfisher	50	60
307	3 c. Red-bibbed Fruit Dove	50	50
	w. Wmk Crown to right of CA	14·00	
308	4 c. Little Button Quail	50	50
309	5 c. Willie Wagtail	50	60
310	6 c. Golden Cowrie	60	50
311	10 c. Glory of the Sea Cone	60	60
312	12 c. Rainbow Lory	60	80
313	15 c. Chambered or Pearly Nautilus	65	40
314	20 c. Venus Comb Murex	1·25	45
315	25 c. Commercial Trochus	85	50
316	35 c. Blood-red Volute	1·00	70
317	45 c. Orange Spider Conch	1·00	1·25
318	$1 Trumpet Triton	2·75	3·00
319	$2 Duchess Lorikeet	5·50	4·75
320	$5 Great Frigate Bird (6 Dec)	5·50	6·00
305/20	*Set of* 16	20·00	19·00

*The normal sideways watermark shows Crown to left of CA, *as seen from the back of the stamp.*

104 Coastwatchers, 1942 **105** Alexander Graham Bell

(Des J. Cooter. Litho Walsall)

1976 (24 May). *Bicentenary of American Revolution. T* **104** *and similar horiz designs. Multicoloured. W* w **14** (*sideways**). *P* 14.

321	6 c. Type **104**	25	10
322	20 c. *Amagiri* (Japanese destroyer) ramming U.S.S. *PT109* and Lt. J. F. Kennedy	75	30
	w. Wmk Crown to right of CA	20·00	
323	35 c. Henderson Airfield	1·25	40
324	45 c. Map of Guadalcanal	1·25	70
	w. Wmk Crown to right of CA	12·00	
321/4	*Set of* 4	3·25	1·40
MS325	95×115 mm. Nos. 321/4	5·50	8·00

*The normal sideways watermark shows Crown to left of CA, *as seen from the back of the stamp.*

(Des P. Powell. Litho Harrison)

1976 (26 July). *Telephone Centenary. T* **105** *and similar vert designs. W* w **14** (*sideways**). *P* 14½×14.

326	6 c. multicoloured	10	10
327	20 c. multicoloured	15	10
328	35 c. brown-orange, lt orange & lt vermilion	30	15
	w. Wmk Crown to right of CA	30·00	
329	45 c. multicoloured	40	35
326/9	*Set of* 4	85	55

Designs:—20 c. Radio telephone via satellite; 35 c. Ericson's magneto telephone; 45 c. Stick telephone and first telephone.

*The normal sideways watermark shows Crown to left of CA, *as seen from the back of the stamp.*

106 B.A.C. One Eleven 200/400 **107** The Communion Plate

(Des and litho Walsall)

1976 (13 Sept). *50th Anniv of First Flight to Solomon Islands. T* **106** *and similar horiz designs. Multicoloured. W* w **14** (*sideways*). *P* 14.

330	6 c. Type **106**	35	10
331	20 c. Britten Norman Islander	65	15
332	35 c. Douglas DC-3	90	20
333	45 c. De Havilland D.H.50A seaplane A8-1	95	55
330/3	*Set of* 4	2·50	85

(Des Jennifer Toombs. Litho Questa)

1977 (7 Feb). *Silver Jubilee. T* **107** *and similar vert designs. Multicoloured. W* w **14**. *P* 13½.

334	6 c. Queen's visit, 1974	10	10
	w. Wmk inverted	90·00	
335	35 c. Type **107**	15	20
336	45 c. The Communion	25	45
334/6	*Set of* 3	45	65

108 Carving from New Georgia **109** Spraying Roof and Mosquito

(Des J. Cooter. Litho Questa)

1977 (9 May). *Artefacts* (2*nd series*). *T* **108** *and similar vert designs showing carvings. W* w **14**. *P* 14.

337	6 c. multicoloured	10	10
338	20 c. multicoloured	10	10
339	35 c. slate-black, grey and rose-red	20	15
340	45 c. multicoloured	25	30
337/40	*Set of* 4	55	50

Designs:—20 c. Sea adaro (spirit); 35 c. Shark-headed man; 45 c. Man from Ulawa or Malaita.

(Des G. Vasarhelyi. Litho Questa)

1977 (27 July). *Malaria Eradication. T* **109** *and similar horiz designs. Multicoloured. W* w **14** (*sideways**). *P* 14.

341	6 c. Type **109**	10	10
342	20 c. Taking blood samples	15	10
343	35 c. Microscope and map	20	15
344	45 c. Delivering drugs	30	40
	w. Wmk Crown to right of CA	28·00	
341/4	*Set of* 4	65	60

*The normal sideways watermark shows Crown to left of CA, *as seen from the back of the stamp.*

110 The Shepherds **111** Feather Money

(Des M. and G. Shamir. Litho Questa)

1977 (12 Sept). *Christmas. T* **110** *and similar vert designs. Multicoloured. W* w **14**. *P* 14.

345	6 c. Type **110**	10	10
346	20 c. Mary and Jesus in stable	10	10
347	35 c. The Three Kings	20	15
348	45 c. "The Flight into Egypt"	25	25
345/8	*Set of* 4	50	45

(Des D.L.R. Litho Harrison)

1977 (24 Oct). *Introduction of Solomon Islands Coins and Banknotes. T* **111** *and similar horiz designs. Multicoloured. W* w **14**. *P* 14 × 14½.

349 6 c. Type **111** 10 10
a. Horiz pair. Nos. 349/50 .. .. .. 20 20
350 6 c. New currency coins 10 10
351 45 c. New currency notes 25 25
a. Horiz pair. Nos. 351/2 .. .. .. 50 50
352 45 c. Shell money 25 25
349/52 .. .. *Set of* 4 60 60

The two designs of each value were printed in horizontal *se-tenant* pairs throughout their sheets.

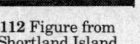

112 Figure from Shortland Island

113 Sandford's Sea Eagle

(Des J. Cooter. Litho Questa)

1978 (11 Jan). *Artefacts (3rd series). T* **112** *and similar vert designs. W* w **14**. *P* 14.

353 6 c. multicoloured 10 10
354 20 c. multicoloured 10 10
355 35 c. deep brown, black and orange 20 15
356 45 c. multicoloured 25 30
353/6 .. .. *Set of* 4 55 50

Designs:—20 c. Ceremonial shield; 35 c. Santa Cruz ritual figure; 45 c. Decorative combs.

(Des Jennifer Toombs. Litho Questa)

1978 (21 Apr). *25th Anniv of Coronation. T* **113** *and similar vert designs. Multicoloured. P* 15.

357 45 c. black, vermilion and silver 15 25
a. Sheetlet. Nos. 357/9 × 2 75
358 45 c. multicoloured 15 25
359 45 c. black, vermilion and silver 15 25
357/9 .. .. *Set of* 3 40 65

Designs:—No. 357, King's Dragon; No. 358, Queen Elizabeth II; No. 359, Type **113**.

Nos. 357/9 were printed together in small sheets of 6, containing two *se-tenant* strips of 3, with horizontal gutter margin between.

INDEPENDENT

114 National Flag

115 John

(Des L. Curtis. Litho Questa)

1978 (7 July). *Independence. T* **114** *and similar vert designs. Multicoloured. W* w **14**. *P* 14.

360 6 c. Type **114** 10 10
361 15 c. Governor-General's flag 20 10
362 35 c. The Cenotaph, Honiara 35 30
363 45 c. National coat of arms 40 50
360/3 .. .. *Set of* 4 95 85

(Des J.W. Litho Questa)

1978 (4 Oct). *450th Death Anniv of Dürer. Details from his Painting "Four Apostles". T* **115** *and similar vert designs. Multicoloured. W* w **14**. *P* 14.

364 6 c. Type **115** 10 10
365 20 c. Peter 15 10
366 35 c. Paul 20 15
367 45 c. Mark 30 30
364/7 .. .. *Set of* 4 60 50

116 Firelighting

117 H.M.S. *Discovery*

(Des K. G. Watkinson; adapted J.W. Litho Questa)

1978 (15 Nov). *50th Anniv of Scouting in Solomon Islands. T* **116** *and similar horiz designs. Multicoloured. W* w **14** *(sideways). P* 14.

368 6 c. Type **116** 15 10
369 20 c. Camping 20 20
370 35 c. Solomon Islands Scouts 40 40
371 45 c. Canoeing 50 70
368/71 .. .. *Set of* 4 1·10 1·25

(Des and litho (45 c. also embossed) Walsall)

1979 (16 Jan). *Bicentenary of Captain Cook's Voyages, 1768–79. T* **117** *and similar vert designs. P* 11.

372 8 c. multicoloured 30 10
373 18 c. multicoloured 30 15
374 35 c. black, yellowish green and silver .. 40 25
375 45 c. multicoloured 40 40
372/5 .. .. *Set of* 4 1·25 80

Designs:—18 c. "Captain Cook" (Nathaniel Dance); 35 c. Sextant; 45 c. Flaxman/Wedgwood medallion of Captain Cook.

118 Fish Net Float

119 Running

(Des J. Cooter. Litho Questa)

1979 (21 Mar). *Artefacts (4th series). T* **118** *and similar designs. W* w **14** *(sideways on 8 and 35 c.). P* 14.

376 8 c. multicoloured 10 10
377 20 c. multicoloured 10 10
378 35 c. black, grey and rose 15 15
379 45 c. black, chestnut and apple-green .. 20 30
376/9 .. .. *Set of* 4 45 50

Designs: *Vert*—20 c. Armband of shell money; 45 c. Forehead ornament. *Horiz*—35 c. Ceremonial food bowl.

(Des L. Curtis. Litho Format)

1979 (4 June). *South Pacific Games, Fiji. T* **109** *and similar horiz designs. Multicoloured. W* w **14** *(sideways). P* 13½.

380 8 c. Type **119** 10 10
381 20 c. Hurdling 10 10
382 35 c. Football 15 15
383 45 c. Swimming 25 35
380/3 .. .. *Set of* 4 55 50

120 1908 6d. Stamp

121 Sea Snake

(Des J.W. Litho Format)

1979 (16 Aug). *Death Centenary of Sir Rowland Hill. T* **120** *and similar vert designs showing stamps. W* w **14**. *P* 14.

384 8 c. carmine and pale rose 10 10
385 20 c. deep mauve and pale mauve 15 30
386 35 c. multicoloured 25 45
384/6 .. .. *Set of* 3 45 75
MS387 121 × 121 mm. 45 c. rosine, deep dull green and pink 45 65

Designs:—20 c. Great Britain 1856 6d.; 35 c. 1978 45 c. Independence commemorative; 45 c. 1922 10s.

(Des L. Curtis. Litho Enschedé)

1979 (18 Sept)–**83**. *Reptiles. Vert designs as T* **121**. *Multicoloured. W* w **14**. *P* 13½×13.

A. *No imprint*. B. *Imprint date at foot*.

No.		Description	A		B	
388	1 c.	Type **121**	10	60	†	
389	3 c.	Red-banded Tree Snake	10	60	†	
390	4 c.	Whip Snake	10	60	†	
391	6 c.	Pacific Boa	10	60	†	
392	8 c.	Skink	10	40	†	
393	10 c.	Gecko (*Lepidodactylus lugubris*)	10	40	†	
394	12 c.	Monitor	50	70	†	
	w.	Wmk inverted	2·50	—	30	80
395	15 c.	Anglehead	30	50	†	
396	20 c.	Giant Toad	30	50	†	
397	25 c.	Marsh Frog	60	70	†	
	w.	Wmk inverted	†		30	90
398	30 c.	Horned Frog	1·50	1·00	1·00	1·75
	w.	Wmk inverted	†		1·25	1·75
399	35 c.	Tree Frog	30	70	†	
399*a*	40 c.	Burrowing Snake ..	†		45	1·75
400	45 c.	Guppy's Snake	30	1·25	†	
400*a*	50 c.	Tree Gecko	†		50	75
401	$1	Large Skink	75	2·75	1·50	90
402	$2	Guppy's Frog	75	2·75	†	
403	$5	Estuarine Crocodile ..	1·50	6·00	4·00	4·00
	aw.	Wmk inverted	†		12·00	—
403*b*	$10	Hawksbill Turtle ..	†		6·50	6·75
388/403		.. .. *Set of* 16	6·25	18·00		
394/403*b*		.. .. *Set of* 8			13·00	16·00

Dates of issue:—18.9.79, Nos. 388A/403A; 25.1.82, Nos. 401B, 403B; 27.8.82, Nos. 394wB, 397wB; 20.9.82, No. 403*b*B; 24.1.83, Nos. 399*a*B, 400*a*B; 31.8.83, No. 398B.

Imprint dates: "1982", Nos. 394wB, 397wB, 401B, 403B, 403*b*B; "1983", Nos. 398B, 399*a*B, 400*a*B.

122 "Madonna and Child" (Morando)

123 H.M.S. *Curacoa* (frigate), 1839

(Des BG Studio. Litho Questa)

1979 (15 Nov). *Christmas. International Year of the Child. T* **122** *and similar vert designs showing "Madonna and Child" paintings by various artists. Multicoloured. W* w **14**. *P* 14 × 14½.

404 4 c. Type **122** 10 10
405 20 c. Luini 15 15
406 35 c. Bellini 20 15
407 50 c. Raphael 30 70
404/7 .. .. *Set of* 4 65 1·00
MS408 92 × 133 mm. Nos. 404/7 .. .. .. 1·25 2·00

(Des L. Curtis. Litho Questa)

1980 (23 Jan). *Ships and Crests (1st series). T* **123** *and similar horiz designs. Multicoloured. W* w **14** *(sideways*). P* 14.

409 8 c. Type **123** 30 10
w. Wmk Crown to right of CA .. .. 15·00
410 20 c. H.M.S. *Herald* (survey ship), 1854 .. 45 30
411 35 c. H.M.S. *Royalist* (screw corvette), 1889 65 60
412 45 c. H.M.S. *Beagle* (survey schooner), 1878 70 1·25
w. Wmk Crown to right of CA .. .. 42·00
409/12 .. .. *Set of* 4 1·75 2·00

*The normal sideways watermark shows Crown to left of CA, *as seen from the back of the stamp*.

See also Nos. 430/3.

124 *Solomon Fisher* (fishery training vessel)

(Des G. Hutchins. Litho Secura, Singapore)

1980 (27 Mar). *Fishing. Ancillary Craft. T* **124** *and similar horiz designs. Multicoloured. W* w **14** *(sideways). P* 13½.

413 8 c. Type **124** 15 10
414 20 c. *Solomon Hunter* (fishery training vessel) 20 20
415 45 c. *Ufi Na Tasi* (refrigerated fish transport) 35 40
416 80 c. Research Vessel .. .. 60 1·50
413/16 .. .. *Set of* 4 1·10 2·00

125 *Comliebank* (cargo-liner) and 1935 Tulagi Registered Letter Postmark

(Des A. Theobald. Litho Questa)

1980 (6 May). *"London 1980" International Stamp Exhibition. Mail-carrying Transport. T* **125** *and similar horiz designs. Multicoloured. W* w **14** *(sideways). P* 14½ × 14.

417 45 c. Type **125** 25 40
a. Sheetlet. Nos. 417/20 90
418 45 c. Douglas C-47 Skytrain (U.S. Army Postal Service, 1943) 25 40
419 45 c. B.A.C. One Eleven airliner and 1979 Honiara postmark 25 40
420 45 c. *Corabank* (container ship) and 1979 Auki postmark 25 40
417/20 .. .. *Set of* 4 90 1·40

Nos. 417/20 were printed together as a sheetlet containing a *se-tenant* block of 4.

MINIMUM PRICE

The minimum price quote is 10p which represents a handling charge rather than a basis for valuing common stamps. For further notes about prices see introductory pages.

126 Queen Elizabeth the Queen Mother

127 Angel with Trumpet

(Des Harrison. Litho Questa)

1980 (4 Aug). *80th Birthday of Queen Elizabeth the Queen Mother. W w* **14** *(sideways). P* 14.
421 **126** 45 c. multicoloured 30 35

(Des C. Abbott. Litho Walsall)

1980 (2 Sept). *Christmas. T* **127** *and similar vert designs. Multicoloured. W w* **14**. *P* 14½ × 14.
422 8 c. Type **127** 10 10
423 20 c. Angel with fiddle 10 10
424 45 c. Angel with trumpet (*different*) 25 25
425 80 c. Angel with lute 40 45
422/5 . . . . *Set of* 4 70 75

128 *Parthenos sylvia*

129 Francisco Antonio Maurelle

(Des J. Cooter. Litho Secura, Singapore)

1980 (12 Nov). *Butterflies (1st series). T* **128** *and similar horiz designs. Multicoloured. W w* **14** *(sideways*). P* 13½.
426 8 c. Type **128** 10 10
w. Wmk Crown to right of CA . . . . 30·00
427 20 c. *Delias schoenbergi* 25 20
w. Wmk Crown to right of CA 80
428 45 c. *Jamides cephion* 40 40
w. Wmk Crown to right of CA . . . . 40·00
429 80 c. *Ornithoptera victoriae* . . . . 1·00 1·40
w. Wmk Crown to right of CA . . . . 7·00
426/9 . . . . *Set of* 4 1·60 1·90
*The normal sideways watermark shows Crown to left of CA, *as seen from the back of the stamp.*
See also Nos. 456/9 and 610/13.

(Des L. Curtis. Litho Questa)

1981 (14 Jan). *Ships and Crests (2nd series). Horiz designs as T* **123**. *Multicoloured. W w* **14** *(sideways*). P* 14.
430 8 c. H.M.S. *Mounts Bay* (frigate), 1959 . . 15 10
w. Wmk Crown to right of CA . . . . 12·00
431 20 c. H.M.S. *Charybdis* (frigate), 1970 . . 25 20
432 45 c. H.M.S. *Hydra* (survey ship), 1972 . . 50 40
433 $1 Royal Yacht *Britannia*, 1974 . . 1·40 1·75
430/3 . . . . *Set of* 4 2·10 2·25
*The normal sideways watermark shows Crown to left of CA, *as seen from the back of the stamp.*

(Des J. Cooter. Litho Questa)

1981 (23 Mar). *Bicentenary of Maurelle's Visit and Production of Bauche's Chart, 1791 (No.* **MS**438). *T* **129** *and similar designs. Wmk CA Diagonal (sideways on 8 c. and $1). P* 13½ × 14 (8 c., $1) *or* 14 × 13½ (*others*).
434 8 c. black, deep brown and greenish yellow . . 15 10
435 10 c. black, vermilion and stone 20 10
436 45 c. multicoloured 60 65
437 $1 multicoloured . . . . 1·00 1·10
434/7 . . . . *Set of* 4 1·75 1·75
MS438 126 × 91 mm. 25 c. × 4, each black, vermilion and stone (wmk sideways). P 14½ . . . . 90 1·10
Designs: *Horiz*—10 c. Bellin's map of 1742 showing route of *La Princesa*; 45 c. *La Princesa*. *Vert*—$1 Spanish compass cards, 1745 and 1757. No. **MS**438, "Chart of a part of the South Sea" (*each stamp* 44 × 28 *mm*).
Stamps in No. **MS**438 were printed to form a composite design.

130 Netball

131 Prince Charles as Colonel-in-Chief, Royal Regiment of Wales

(Des R. Granger Barrett. Litho Security Printers (M), Malaysia)

1981 (7 July). *Mini South Pacific Games. T* **130** *and similar vert designs. Multicoloured. W w* **14**. *P* 12.
439 8 c. Type **130** 10 10
440 10 c. Tennis 15 15
w. Wmk inverted . . . . . .
441 25 c. Running 25 25
442 30 c. Football 25 25
443 45 c. Boxing 40 40
439/43 . . . . *Set of* 5 1·00 1·00
MS444 102×67 mm $1 Stylised athletes (wmk sideways) . . . . 1·00 1·10

(Des and litho J.W.)

1981 (22 July). *Royal Wedding. T* **131** *and similar vert designs. Multicoloured. W w* **14**. *P* 13½ × 13.
445 8 c. Wedding bouquet from Solomon Islands 10 10
446 45 c. Type **131** 15 15
447 $1 Prince Charles and Lady Diana Spencer 45 70
445/7 . . . . *Set of* 3 60 85

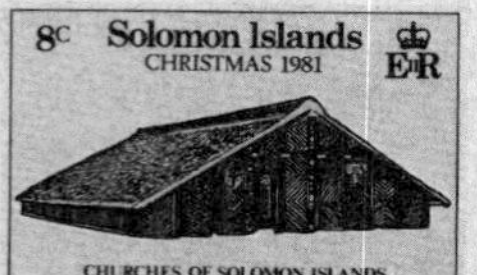

132 "Music"

133 Primitive Church

(Des BG Studio. Litho Questa)

1981 (28 Sept). *25th Anniv of Duke of Edinburgh Award Scheme. T* **132** *and similar vert designs. Multicoloured. W w* **14**. *P* 14.
448 8 c. Type **132** 10 10
449 25 c. "Handicrafts" 10 10
450 45 c. "Canoeing" 15 10
451 $1 Duke of Edinburgh 35 60
448/51 . . . . *Set of* 4 60 75

(Des BG Studio. Litho Format)

1981 (12 Oct). *Christmas. Churches. T* **133** *and similar horiz designs. W w* **14** *(sideways). P* 14.
452 8 c. black, buff and cobalt 10 10
453 10 c. multicoloured 10 10
454 25 c. black, buff and dull green 15 10
455 $2 multicoloured . . . . 70 1·25
452/5 . . . . *Set of* 4 90 1·25
Designs:—10 c. St. Barnabas Anglican Cathedral, Honiara; 25 c. Early church; $2 Holy Cross Cathedral, Honiara.

(Des J. Cooter. Litho Secura, Singapore)

1982 (5 Jan). *Butterflies (2nd series). Horiz designs as T* **128**. *Multicoloured. W w* **14** *(sideways*). P* 13½×13.
456 10 c. *Doleschallia bisaltide* 15 10
w. Wmk Crown to right of CA . . . . 2·75
457 25 c. *Papilio bridgei* 35 25
w. Wmk Crown to right of CA . . . . 9·00
458 35 c. *Taenaris phorcas* 40 30
aw. Wmk Crown to right of CA . . . . 4·00
b. Wmk inverted . . . . 50·00
459 $1 *Graphium sarpedon* . . . . . . 1·50 1·50
456/9 . . . . *Set of* 4 2·25 1·90
*The normal sideways watermark shows Crown to left of CA, *as seen from the back of the stamp.*
No. 458b shows a change of watermark position from sideways to inverted.

50 CENTS SURCHARGE
CYCLONE RELIEF FUND
1982

(**134**)

135 Pair of Sanford's Sea Eagles constructing Nest

5 CENTS SURCHARGE
CYCLONE RELIEF FUND
1982

"0" of "50" omitted from surcharge (R. 4/5)

1982 (3 May). *Cyclone Relief Fund. No. 447 surch with T* **134** *in red.*
460 $1 + 50 c. Prince Charles and Lady Diana Spencer . . . . 1·00 2·50
a. "0" omitted . . . . 10·00

(Des N. Arlott. Litho Walsall)

1982 (15 May). *Sanford's Sea Eagle. T* **135** *and similar vert designs. Multicoloured. W w* **14**. *P* 14.
461 12 c. Type **135** 35 50
a. Horiz strip of 5. Nos. 461/5 . . . . 1·75
462 12 c. Egg and chick 35 50
463 12 c. Hen feeding chicks 35 50
464 12 c. Fledgelings 35 50
465 12 c. Young bird in flight 35 50
466 12 c. Pair of birds and village dwellings . . 35 50
461/6 . . . . *Set of* 6 1·90 2·75
Nos. 461/6 were printed together, *se-tenant*, in various combinations throughout sheets also including one stamp-size label.

136 Wedding Portrait

137 Flags of Solomon Islands and United Kingdom

(Des Jennifer Toombs. Litho Walsall)

1982 (1 July). *21st Birthday of Princess of Wales. T* **136** *and similar vert designs. Multicoloured. W w* **14**. *P* 14½ × 14.
467 12 c. Solomon Islands coat of arms . . 10 10
468 40 c. Lady Diana Spencer at Broadlands, May 1981 . . . . 50 40
469 50 c. Type **136** 70 50
470 $1 Formal portrait . . . . . . 1·50 1·50
467/70 . . . . *Set of* 4 2·50 2·25

(Des Studio 53. Litho Questa)

1982 (11 Oct). *Royal Visit (Nos. 471/2,* **MS**475) *and Commonwealth Games, Brisbane (Nos. 473/4,* **MS**476). *T* **137** *and similar square designs. Multicoloured. W w* **14** *(sideways). P* 14.
471 12 c. Type **137** 15 20
a. Pair. Nos. 471/2 . . . . . . 30 40
472 12 c. Queen and Prince Philip 15 20
473 25 c. Running 30 45
a. Pair. Nos. 473/4 . . . . . . 60 90
474 25 c. Boxing 30 45
471/4 . . . . *Set of* 4 80 1·25
MS475 123 × 123 mm. Nos. 471/2 and $1 Royal Yacht *Britannia* . . . . 1·75 2·50
MS476 123 × 123 mm. Nos. 473/4 and $1 Royal Yacht *Britannia* . . . . 1·75 2·50
Nos. 471/2 and 473/4 were each printed in small sheets of 10, including 2 *se-tenant*, stamp-size, labels, the two stamp designs appearing *se-tenant*, both horizontally and vertically.

138 Boy Scouts

(Des McCombie Skinner. Litho Format)

1982 (4 Nov). *75th Anniv of Boy Scout Movement (Nos. 477, 479, 481, 483) and Centenary of Boys' Brigade (others). T* **138** *and similar horiz designs. Multicoloured. W w* **14** *(sideways). P* 14.
477 12 c. Type **138** 15 15
478 12 c. Boys' Brigade cadets 15 15
479 25 c. Lord Baden-Powell 20 40
480 25 c. Sir William Smith 20 40
481 35 c. Type **138** 20 50
482 35 c. As No. 478 . . . . 20 50
483 50 c. As No. 479 . . . . 30 1·10
484 50 c. As No. 480 . . . . 30 1·10
477/84 . . . . *Set of* 8 1·50 3·75

139 Leatherback Turtle

(Des L. Curtis. Litho Format)

1983 (5 Jan). *Turtles. T* **139** *and similar horiz designs. Multicoloured. W w* **14** *(sideways). P* 14½.
485 18 c. Type **139** 25 25
486 35 c. Loggerhead turtle 45 45
487 45 c. Pacific Ridley turtle 60 60
488 50 c. Green turtle 65 65
485/8 . . . . *Set of* 4 1·75 1·75

140 Black Olive (*Oliva vidula*), General Cone (*Conus generalis*) and Troschel's Murex (*Murex troscheli*)

(Des W. Fenton. Litho Questa)

1983 (14 Mar). *Commonwealth Day. Shells. T* **140** *and similar horiz designs. Multicoloured. W* w **14** (*sideways*). *P* 14.
489 12 c. Type **140** 15 15
490 35 c. Romu, Kurila, Kakadu and money belt 35 40
491 45 c. Shells from "Bride-price" necklaces .. 50 60
492 50 c. Commercial Trochus (*Trochus niloticus*) polished and in its natural state 55 65
489/92 .. .. *Set of* 4 1·40 1·60

141 Montgolfier Balloon

(Des A. Theobald. Litho Format)

1983 (30 June). *Bicentenary of Manned Flight. T* **141** *and similar horiz designs. Multicoloured. W* w **14** (*sideways**). *P* 14.
493 30 c. Type **141** 40 40
494 35 c. R.A.A.F. Lockheed C-130 Hercules .. 45 45
495 40 c. Wright brothers' Type A 55 55
w. Wmk Crown to right of CA .. .. 35·00
496 45 c. Space shuttle *Columbia* 60 60
497 50 c. Beech C55 Baron 65 65
493/7 .. .. *Set of* 5 2·40 2·40
*The normal sideways watermark shows Crown to left of CA, *as seen from the back of the stamp.*

142 Weto Dancers

(Des J.W. Litho Format)

1983 (25 Aug). *Christmas. T* **142** *and similar horiz designs. Multicoloured. W* w **14** (*sideways*). *P* 14.
498 12 c. Type **142** 10 10
499 15 c. Custom wrestling 10 20
500 18 c. Girl dancers 15 20
501 20 c. Devil dancers 15 20
502 25 c. Bamboo band 20 35
503 35 c. Gilbertese dancers 25 45
504 40 c. Pan pipers 25 55
505 45 c. Girl dancers 30 65
506 50 c. Cross surrounded by flowers 30 70
498/506 .. .. *Set of* 9 1·60 3·00
MS507 153 × 112 mm. Nos. 498/506 .. .. 1·60 3·00
Stamps from No. **MS**507 are without the inscription, "Christmas 1983", shown on Nos. 498/506.

143 Earth Satellite Station **144** *Calvatia gardneri*

(Des Jennifer Toombs. Litho Format)

1983 (19 Dec). *World Communications Year. T* **143** *and similar horiz designs. Multicoloured. W* w **14** (*sideways*). *P* 14.
508 12 c. Type **143** 20 15
509 18 c. Ham radio operator 25 20
510 25 c. 1908 2½d. Canoe stamp 35 30
511 $1 1908 6d. Canoe stamp .. .. .. 1·25 2·75
508/11 .. .. *Set of* 4 1·90 3·00
MS512 131 × 103 mm. No. 511 .. .. .. 1·40 2·25

(Des Gillian Tomblin. Litho Enschedé)

1984 (30 Jan). *Fungi. T* **144** *and similar vert designs. Multicoloured. W* w **14**. *P* 13½.
513 6 c. Type **144** 10 10
514 18 c. *Marasmiellus inoderma* 20 25
a. Booklet pane of 6 .. .. .. 4·00
w. Wmk inverted .. .. .. 50·00
515 35 c. *Pycnoporus sanguineus* 35 45
a. Booklet pane of 6 .. .. .. 4·00
w. Wmk inverted .. .. .. 40·00
516 $2 *Filoboletus manipularis* .. .. .. 2·25 3·00
513/16 .. .. *Set of* 4 2·50 3·50
Booklet panes Nos. 514a and 515a were from special sheets providing blocks of 6 (3×2) with vertical margins at both the left and right of each pane.

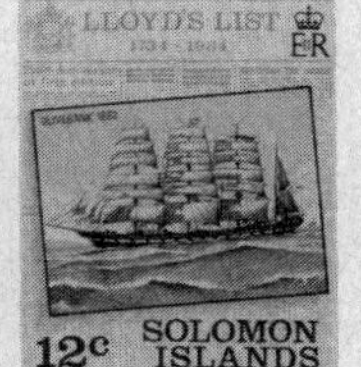

145 Cross surrounded by Flowers **146** *Olivebank* (barque), 1892

(Des J.W. Litho Format)

1984 (16 Apr). *Visit of Pope John Paul II. W* w **14** (*sideways*). *P* 14.
517 **145** 12 c. multicoloured 20 15
518 50 c. multicoloured .. .. .. 65 1·10

(Des Studio 53. Litho Questa)

1984 (21 Apr). *250th Anniv of "Lloyd's List" (newspaper). T* **146** *and similar vert designs. Multicoloured. W* w **14**. *P* 14.
519 12 c. Type **146** 70 15
520 15 c. *Tinhow* (freighter), 1906 .. .. 75 40
521 18 c. *Oriana* (liner) at Point Cruz, Honiara 85 60
522 $1 *Silwyn Range* (container ship), Point Cruz, Honiara .. .. .. 1·40 3·25
519/22 .. .. *Set of* 4 3·25 4·00

(Des Jennifer Toombs. Litho Format)

1984 (18 June). *Universal Postal Union Congress, Hamburg. As No.* **MS**512 *but with changed sheet inscriptions and U.P.U. logo in margin. Multicoloured. W* w **14** (*sideways*). *P* 14.
MS523 $1 1908 6d. Canoe stamp .. .. .. 1·40 1·40

147 Village Drums **148** Solomon Islands Flag and Torch-bearer

(Des McCombie Skinner Studio. Litho Questa)

1984 (2 July). *20th Anniv of Asia-Pacific Broadcasting Union. T* **147** *and similar horiz designs. Multicoloured. W* w **14** (*sideways*). *P* 13½ × 14.
524 12 c. Type **147** 15 15
525 45 c. Radio City, Guadalcanal 60 60
526 60 c. S.I.B.C. studios, Honiara 75 80
527 $1 S.I.B.C. Broadcasting House .. .. 1·25 1·40
524/7 .. .. *Set of* 4 2·50 2·75

(Des McCombie Skinner Studio. Litho Format)

1984 (4 Aug–22 Sept). *Olympic Games, Los Angeles. T* **148** *and similar multicoloured designs. W* w **14** (*sideways on* 25 c. *to* $1). *P* 14 × 13½ (12 c.) *or* 13½ × 14 (*others*).
528 12 c. Type **148** 15 10
529 25 c. Lawson Tama Stadium, Honiara (*horiz*) 30 25
a. Booklet pane Nos. 529/30, each × 2 (22.9.84) .. .. 1·90
530 50 c. Honiara Community Centre (*horiz*) .. 45 50
531 95 c. Alick Wickham inventing crawl stroke, Bronte Baths, New South Wales, 1898 (*horiz*) (22.9.84) .. .. .. 5·00 6·50
a. Booklet pane of 1 .. .. .. 5·00
532 $1 Olympic Stadium, Los Angeles (*horiz*) .. 70 1·10
528/32 .. .. *Set of* 5 6·00 7·50
No. 531 only exists from $3·95 stamp booklets.

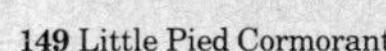

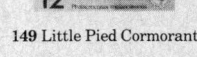

149 Little Pied Cormorant **150** The Queen Mother with Princess Margaret at Badminton Horse Trials

(Des I. Loe. Litho Questa)

1984 (21 Sept). *"Ausipex" International Stamp Exhibition, Melbourne. Birds. T* **149** *and similar vert designs. Multicoloured. W* w **14**. *P* 14½.
533 12 c. Type **149** 40 30
534 18 c. Spotbill Duck 55 30
535 35 c. Rufous Night Heron 80 50
536 $1 Eastern Broad-billed Roller ("Dollar-bird") .. .. 1·60 2·75
533/6 .. .. *Set of* 4 3·00 3·50
MS537 130 × 96 mm. Nos. 533/6 .. .. .. 3·00 3·75

(Des A. Theobald ($1.50), C. Abbott (others). Litho Questa)

1985 (7 June). *Life and Times of Queen Elizabeth the Queen Mother. T* **150** *and similar vert designs. Multicoloured. W* w **16**. *P* 14½ × 14.
538 12 c. With Winston Churchill at Buckingham Palace, VE Day, 1945 .. .. 10 10
539 25 c. Type **150** 20 30
w. Wmk inverted .. .. .. 1·50
540 35 c. At a St. Patrick's Day parade 25 35
541 $1 With Prince Henry at his christening (from photo by Lord Snowdon) .. 75 95
w. Wmk inverted .. .. .. 40·00
538/41 .. .. *Set of* 4 1·10 1·50
MS542 91 × 73 mm. $1.50, In a gondola, Venice, 1985. Wmk sideways .. .. 1·10 1·50

151 Japanese Memorial Shrine, Mount Austen, Guadalcanal

(Des D. Slater. Litho Questa)

1985 (28 June). *"Expo '85" World Fair, Japan. T* **151** *and similar horiz designs. Multicoloured. W* w **14** (*sideways*). *P* 14.
543 12 c. Type **151** 10 10
544 25 c. Digital telephone exchange equipment 25 30
545 45 c. Fishing vessel *Soltai No. 7* 50 55
546 85 c. Coastal village scene .. .. .. 90 1·40
543/6 .. .. *Set of* 4 1·60 2·10

152 Titiana Village **153** Girl Guide Activities

(Des O. Bell. Litho Walsall)

1985 (30 Aug). *Christmas. "Going Home for the Holiday". T* **152** *and similar horiz designs. Multicoloured. W* w **14** (*sideways*). *P* 14½.
547 12 c. Type **152** 10 10
548 25 c. Sigana, Santa Isabel 25 30
549 35 c. Artificial Island and Langa Lagoon .. 30 35
547/9 .. .. *Set of* 3 60 70

(Des D. Slater. Litho Walsall)

1985 (30 Sept). *75th Anniv of Girl Guide Movement* (12, 45 c.) *and International Youth Year* (*others*). *T* **153** *and similar vert designs. Multicoloured. W* w **16**. *P* 14.
550 12 c. Type **153** 60 10
551 15 c. Boys playing and child in wheelchair (Stop Polio) 65 40
552 25 c. Runners and Solomon Island scenes .. 90 70
553 35 c. Runners and Australian scenes ("Run Round Australia") .. .. .. 1·10 80
554 45 c. Guide colour party and badges .. 1·25 90
550/4 .. .. *Set of* 5 4·00 2·50
MS555 100 × 75 mm. Nos. 552/3 .. .. .. 75 85

154 Osprey **155** Water-powered Generator, Iriri

(Des Annette Robinson and C. Abbott. Litho Format)

1985 (25 Nov). *Birth Bicentenary of John J. Audubon (ornithologist). Sheet 121×107 mm containing T* **154** *and similar vert design. W w* **16**. *P* 14.
MS556 45 c. black, gold and deep blue; 50 c. (×2) multicoloured .. .. 3·00 3·50
Design:—45 c. John J. Audubon.

(Des B. Drake. Litho Walsall)

1986 (24 Jan). *Village Hydro-electric Schemes. Sheet 109×135 mm. containing T* **155** *and similar vert design. Multicoloured. W w* **16**. *P* 14.
MS557 30 c. Type **155**; 60 c. Domestic lighting 75 80
w. Wmk inverted .. .. 75·00

156 Building Red Cross Centre, Gizo　**157** U.S. Memorial Obelisks, Henderson Airfield, Guadalcanal

(Des N. Shewring. Litho Walsall)

1986 (27 Mar). *Operation Raleigh (volunteer project). T* **156** *and similar diamond-shaped designs. Multicoloured. W w* **14**. *P* 14½×14.
558 18 c. Type **156** 80 20
559 30 c. Exploring rainforest .. .. 1·50 45
560 60 c. Observing Halley's Comet .. .. .. 2·25 1·40
561 $1 *Sir Walter Raleigh* (support ship) and *Zebu* (brigantine) .. .. 2·75 2·00
558/61 .. .. *Set of* 4 6·50 3·50
Details of watermark and perforation for the stamps are given with the designs oriented so that the royal cypher appears in the top left corner.

(Des A. Theobald. Litho Questa)

1986 (21 Apr). *60th Birthday of Queen Elizabeth II. Vert designs as T* **230a** *of Jamaica. Multicoloured. W w* **16**. *P* 14½×14.
562 5 c. Princess Elizabeth and Duke of Edinburgh at Clydebank Town Hall, 1947 .. 10 10
563 18 c. At St. Paul's Cathedral for Queen Mother's 80th birthday service, 1980 .. 15 20
564 22 c. With children, Solomon Islands, 1982 .. 20 25
565 55 c. At Windsor Castle on her 50th birthday, 1976 .. .. 40 45
566 $2 At Crown Agents Head Office, London, 1983 .. .. 1·40 1·50
562/6 .. .. *Set of* 5 2·00 2·25

(Des D. Miller. Litho Cambec Press, Melbourne)

1986 (22 May). *"Ameripex '86" International Stamp Exhibition, Chicago. International Peace Year. Sheet 100×75 mm containing T* **157** *and similar horiz design. Multicoloured. P* 13½.
MS567 55 c. Type **157**; $1.65 Peace Corps emblem, President Kennedy and Statue of Liberty (25th anniv of Peace Corps) .. .. 1·50 1·60

(Des D. Miller. Litho Questa)

1986 (23 July). *Royal Wedding. Square designs as T* **231a** *of Jamaica. Multicoloured. W w* **16**. *P* 14.
568 55 c. Prince Andrew and Miss Sarah Ferguson 40 55
569 60 c. Prince Andrew at helm of Yacht *Bluenose II* off Nova Scotia, 1985 .. .. 45 70

+50c Cyclone Relief Fund 1986

158 *Freedom* (winner 1980)　(**159**)

(Des J. Dixon. Litho Leigh-Mardon Ltd, Melbourne)

1986 (22 Aug). *America's Cup Yachting Championship (1987) (1st issue). T* **158** *and similar vert designs. P* 14½.
570 18 c. multicoloured 15 25
a. Sheet of 50 .. .. 25·00
571 30 c. multicoloured .. .. 75 1·25
572 $1 multicoloured .. .. 75 1·25
570/2 .. .. *Set of* 3 1·50 2·50
Nos. 570/2 were issued as a sheet of 50, each horizontal strip of 5 being separated by gutter margins. The sheet contains 20 different designs at 18 c., 10 at 30 c. and 20 at $1. Individual stamps depict yachts, charts, the America's Cup or the emblem of the Royal Perth Yacht Club.
See also No. **MS**575.

1986 (23 Sept). *Cyclone Relief Fund. Nos.* 541 *and* **MS**567 *surch as T* **159** *in red.*
573 $1+50 c. Queen Mother with Prince Henry at his christening (from photo by Lord Snowdon) .. .. 75 1·25
MS574 100×75 mm. 55 c.+25 c. Type **157**; $1.65+75 c. Peace Corps emblem, President Kennedy and Statue of Liberty (25th anniv of Peace Corps) .. .. 3·00 3·00
The surcharges on No. **MS**574 are vertical, in smaller type (length 16½ mm) and do not include "1986".

(Des J. Dixon. Litho Leigh-Mardon Ltd, Melbourne)

1987 (4 Feb). *America's Cup Yachting Championship (2nd issue). Sheet 111×75 mm, containing vert design as T* **158**. *Multicoloured. P* 14½.
MS575 $5 *Stars and Stripes* (1987 winner) .. 3·50 4·25
Similar miniature sheets showing the yacht *Kookaburra III* were prepared, but destroyed once the result of the Cup races was known. It is believed that at least one example of this unissued miniature sheet has survived.
No. **MS**575 was also issued printed on gold foil and sold at a premium of $20 over the face value of the stamp.

160 *Dendrophyllia gracilis*　**161** *Cassia fistula*

(Des D. Miller. Litho Format)

1987 (11 Feb). *Corals. T* **160** *and similar horiz designs. Multicoloured. W w* **16** *(sideways). P* 14.
576 18 c. Type **160** 20 15
577 45 c. *Dendronephthya sp* 60 50
578 60 c. *Clavularia sp* .. .. 80 1·25
579 $1.50, *Melithaea squamata* .. .. .. 1·60 3·00
576/9 .. .. *Set of* 4 3·00 4·50

(Des Gill Tomblin. Litho Walsall)

1987 (12 May)–**88**. *Flowers. T* **161** *and similar vert designs. Multicoloured. W w* **16**. *P* 14½×14.
580 1 c. Type **161** 10 20
581 5 c. *Allamanda cathartica* 20 30
582 10 c. *Catharanthus roseus* 30 30
w. Wmk inverted .. ..
583 18 c. *Mimosa pudica* 50 10
584 20 c. *Hibiscus rosa-sinensis* 50 15
585 22 c. *Clerodendrum thomsonae* 50 15
586 25 c. *Bauhinia variegata* 50 20
587 28 c. *Gloriosa rothschildiana* 55 20
588 30 c. *Heliconia solomonensis* 60 20
589 40 c. *Episcia* hybrid 70 20
590 45 c. *Bougainvillea* hybrid 70 25
591 50 c. *Alpinia purpurata* 70 25
592 55 c. *Plumeria rubra* 75 35
w. Wmk inverted .. .. 21·00
593 60 c. *Acacia farnesiana* 85 60
594 $1 *Ipomea purpurea* .. .. 2·00 80
595 $2 *Dianella ensifolia* .. .. .. 3·00 4·00
596 $5 *Passiflora foetida* .. .. .. 4·50 7·50
597 $10 *Hemigraphis* sp (1.3.88) .. .. 7·00 11·00
580/97 .. .. *Set of* 8 22·00 24·00

162 Mangrove Kingfisher on Branch　**163** *Dendrobium conanthum*

(Des Josephine Martin. Litho Format)

1987 (15 July). *Mangrove Kingfisher. T* **162** *and similar vert designs. Multicoloured. W w* **14**. *P* 14.
598 60 c. Type **162** .. .. 2·00 2·50
a. Horiz strip of 4. Nos. 598/601 .. .. 7·00
599 60 c. Kingfisher diving .. .. .. 2·00 2·50
600 60 c. Entering water .. .. 2·00 2·50
601 60 c. Kingfisher with prey .. .. .. 2·00 2·50
598/601 .. .. *Set of* 4 7·00 9·00
Nos. 598/601 were printed together, *se-tenant*, in horizontal strips of 4 throughout the sheet, forming a composite design.

(Des Sue Wickison. Litho Walsall)

1987 (23 Sept). *Christmas. Orchids (1st series). T* **163** *and similar vert designs. Multicoloured. W w* **16**. *P* 13½×13.
602 18 c. Type **163** 85 10
603 30 c. *Spathoglottis plicata* .. .. .. 1·50 20
604 55 c. *Dendrobium gouldii* .. .. .. 1·75 50
605 $1.50, *Dendrobium goldfinchii* .. .. 3·75 3·00
602/5 .. .. *Set of* 4 7·00 3·50
See also Nos. 640/3 and 748/51.

164 Telecommunications Control Room and Satellite　**165** Pupa of *Ornithoptera victoriae*

(Des D. Hartley. Litho CPE Australia Ltd, Melbourne)

1987 (16 Nov). *Asia-Pacific Transport and Communications Decade. T* **164** *and similar horiz designs. Multicoloured. P* 13½.
606 18 c. Type **164** 20 15
607 30 c. De Havilland D.H.C.6 Twin Otter 300 mail plane 45 20
608 60 c. Guadalcanal road improvement project 50 60
609 $2 Beech 80 Queen Air and Henderson Control Tower .. .. 2·00 2·50
606/9 .. .. *Set of* 4 2·75 3·00

(Des R. Lewington. Litho Questa)

1987 (25 Nov). *Butterflies (3rd series).* Ornithoptera victoriae *(Queen Victoria's Birdwing). T* **165** *and similar vert designs. Multicoloured. W w* **16** *(sideways). P* 14½×14.
610 45 c. Type **165** .. .. 2·75 2·75
a. Strip of 4. Nos. 610/13 .. .. .. 10·00
611 45 c. Larva .. .. 2·75 2·75
612 45 c. Female butterfly .. .. 2·75 2·75
613 45 c. Male butterfly .. .. 2·75 2·75
610/13 .. .. *Set of* 4 10·00 10·00
Nos. 610/13 were printed together, *se-tenant*, in horizontal and vertical strips of 4 throughout the sheet of 16.

166 Student and National Agriculture Training Institute　**167** Building Fishing Boat

(Des D. Miller. Litho Format)

1988 (12 Feb). *10th Anniv of International Fund for Agricultural Development. T* **166** *and similar square designs. Multicoloured. W w* **16**. *P* 14½.
614 50 c. Type **166** 40 55
aw. Wmk inverted .. .. 5·00
b. Horiz pair. Nos. 614/15 .. .. .. 80 1·10
bw. Wmk inverted .. .. 10·00
615 50 c. Students working in fields 40 55
aw. Wmk inverted .. .. 5·00
616 $1 Transport by lorry .. .. .. 65 1·00
aw. Wmk inverted .. .. 9·00
b. Horiz pair. Nos. 616/17 .. .. .. 1·25 2·00
bw. Wmk inverted .. .. 18·00
617 $1 Canoe transport .. .. 65 1·00
aw. Wmk inverted .. .. 9·00
614/17 .. .. *Set of* 14 1·90 2·75
Nos. 614/15 and 616/17 were printed together, *se-tenant*, in horizontal pairs throughout the sheets, each pair forming a composite design.

(Des N. Shewring. Litho CPE Australia Ltd, Melbourne)

1988 (28 Apr). *"Expo '88" World Fair, Brisbane. T* **167** *and similar horiz designs. Multicoloured. P* 13½×14.
618 22 c. Type **167** 20 15
619 80 c. War canoe 50 45
620 $1.50, Traditional village 95 85
618/20 .. .. *Set of* 3 1·50 1·25
MS621 130 × 53 mm. Nos. 618/20 .. .. 1·50 1·40
No. **MS**621 also exists, as a restricted issue, surcharged $3.50 for "New Zealand 1990" International Stamp Exhibition, Auckland.

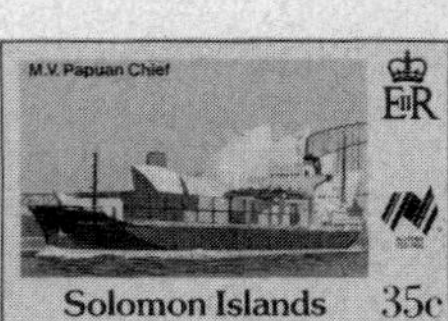

168 *Todos los Santos* in Estrella Bay, 1568　**169** *Papuan Chief* (container ship)

(Des M. Bradbury and J. Sayer. Litho Walsall)

1988 (6 July). *10th Anniv of Independence. T* **168** *and similar horiz designs. Multicoloured. W w* **14** *(sideways*). P* 13×13½.
622 22 c. Type **168** 65 15
w. Wmk Crown to right of CA .. .. 8·00
623 55 c. Raising the Union Jack, 1893 .. .. 90 45
624 80 c. High Court Building .. .. .. 1·25 1·10
625 $1 Dancers at traditional celebration .. 1·40 1·40
622/5 .. .. *Set of* 4 3·75 2·75
*The normal sideways watermark shows Crown to left of CA, *as seen from the back of the stamp.*

(Des E. Nisbet. Litho Walsall)

1988 (30 July). *Bicentenary of Australian Settlement and "Sydpex '88" National Stamp Exhibition, Sydney. T* **169** *and similar horiz designs. Multicoloured. W w* **16** *(sideways). P* 14.

626	35 c. Type **169**	70	25
627	60 c. *Nimos* (container ship)	85	40
628	70 c. *Malaita* (liner)	95	65
629	$1.30, *Makambo* (inter-island freighter)	1·40	1·50
626/9	*Set of* 4	3·50	2·50
MS630	140×76 mm. Nos. 626/9. W w **14** (sideways)	2·00	2·00

170 Archery

171 *Bulbophyllum dennisii*

(Des Joan Thompson. Litho Walsall)

1988 (5 Aug). *Olympic Games, Seoul. T* **170** *and similar multicoloured designs. W w* **16**. *P* 14½.

631	22 c. Type **170**	40	15
632	55 c. Weightlifting	60	40
633	70 c. Athletics	70	55
634	80 c. Boxing	80	60
631/4	*Set of* 4	2·25	1·50
MS635	100 × 80 mm. $2 Olympic Stadium (*horiz*). W w **14** (sideways)	1·25	1·25

(Des D. Miller (22, 65 c.), O. Bell and D. Miller (50 c.), E. Nisbet and D. Miller ($2). Litho Questa)

1988 (31 Oct). *300th Anniv of Lloyd's of London. Designs as T* **167a** *of Malawi. W w* **16** *(sideways on 50, 65 c.). P* 14.

636	22 c. brownish black and brown	30	15
637	50 c. multicoloured	1·10	30
638	65 c. multicoloured	1·25	55
639	$2 multicoloured	2·75	1·75
636/9	*Set of* 4	4·75	2·50

Designs: *Vert*—22 c. King George V and Queen Mary laying foundation stone of Leadenhall Street Building, 1925; $2 *Empress of China* (liner), 1911. *Horiz*—50 c. *Forthbank* (container ship); 65 c. Soltel satellite communications station.

(Des Sue Wickison. Litho Walsall)

1989 (20 Jan). *Orchids (2nd series). T* **171** *and similar vert designs. Multicoloured. W w* **14**. *P* 13½ × 13.

640	22 c. Type **171**	55	15
641	35 c. *Calanthe langei*	70	30
642	55 c. *Bulbophyllum blumei*	90	55
643	$2 *Grammatophyllum speciosum*	2·00	2·00
640/3	*Set of* 4	3·75	2·75

172 Red Cross Workers with Handicapped Children

173 Varicose Nudibranch (*Phyllidia varicosa*)

(Des A. Theobald. Litho Questa)

1989 (16 May). *125th Anniv of International Red Cross. T* **172** *and similar horiz designs. Multicoloured. W w* **16** *(sideways). P* 14½.

644	35 c. Type **172**	35	35
	a. Horiz pair. Nos. 644/5	70	70
645	35 c. Handicapped Children Centre minibus	35	35
646	$1.50, Blood donor	1·25	1·25
	a. Horiz pair. Nos. 646/7	2·50	2·50
647	$1.50, Balance test	1·25	1·25
644/7	*Set of* 4	3·00	3·00

Nos. 644/5 and 646/7 were each printed together, *se-tenant*, in horizontal pairs throughout the sheets, each pair forming a composite design.

(Des Sue Wickison. Litho Questa)

1989 (30 June). *Nudibranchs (Sea Slugs). T* **173** *and similar horiz designs. Multicoloured. W w* **14** *(sideways). P* 14×14½.

648	22 c. Type **173**	60	15
649	70 c. Bullock's Nudibranch (*Chromodoris bullocki*)	1·50	1·25
650	80 c. *Chromodoris leopardus*	1·60	1·40
651	$1.50, *Phidiana indica*	2·50	3·00
648/51	*Set of* 4	5·50	5·25

(Des A. Theobald ($4), D. Miller (others). Litho Questa)

1989 (20 July). *20th Anniv of First Manned Landing on Moon. Multicoloured designs as T* **51a** *of Kiribati. W w* **16** *(sideways on 35, 70 c.). P* 14×13½ (22, 80 c.) *or* 14 (*others*).

652	22 c. "Apollo 16" descending by parachute	45	10
653	35 c. Launch of "Apollo 16" (30×30 *mm*)	70	40
654	70 c. "Apollo 16" emblem (30×30 *mm*)	1·25	1·25
655	80 c. Ultra-violet colour photograph of Earth	1·40	1·40
652/5	*Set of* 4	3·50	2·75
MS656	100×83 mm. $4 Moon's surface seen from Space. Wmk inverted. P 14×13½	3·00	3·00

174 Five Stones Catch

175 Fishermen and Butterfly

(Des D. Miller ($3), R. Stewart (others). Litho B.D.T. ($3) or Walsall (others))

1989 (19 Nov). *"World Stamp Expo '89", International Stamp Exhibition, Washington. Children's Games. T* **174** *and similar multicoloured designs. W w* **16** *(sideways on 67, 73 c.). P* 14.

657	5 c. Type **174**	10	20
658	67 c. Blowing soap bubbles (*horiz*)	1·10	1·25
659	73 c. Coconut shell game (*horiz*)	1·10	1·25
660	$1 Seed wind sound	1·60	1·75
657/60	*Set of* 4	3·50	4·00
MS661	72×72 mm. $3 Softball. *W* w **14**	4·50	4·50

(Des N. Kohia and C. Vendi, adapted G. Vasarhelyi. Litho Questa)

1989 (30 Nov). *Christmas. T* **175** *and similar horiz designs. Multicoloured. W w* **16** *(sideways). P* 14.

662	18 c. Type **175**	40	10
663	25 c. The Nativity	55	20
664	45 c. Hospital ward at Christmas	1·00	30
665	$1.50, Village tug-of-war	2·50	3·50
662/5	*Set of* 4	4·00	3·75

176 Man wearing Headband, Necklace and Sash

177 Spindle Cowrie or Tokio's Volva (*Phenacovolva tokioi*)

(Des Sue Wickison. Litho Questa)

1990 (14 Mar). *Personal Ornaments. T* **176** *and similar vert designs. Multicoloured. W w* **14**. *P* 14.

666	5 c. Type **176**	15	30
667	12 c. Pendant	30	20
668	18 c. Man wearing medallion, nose ring and earrings	30	20
669	$2 Forehead ornament	3·50	4·00
666/9	*Set of* 4	3·75	4·25

First day covers of Nos. 666/9 were postmarked 26 February 1990, which was the originally intended date of issue, but the stamps were not placed on sale until 14 March.

(Des Lynn Chadwick. Litho Questa)

1990 (23 July). *Cowrie Shells. T* **177** *and similar horiz designs. Multicoloured. W w* **14** *(sideways). P* 14.

670	4 c. Type **177**	20	15
671	20 c. All-red Map Cowrie (*Cypraea mappa panerythra*)	55	30
672	35 c. Sieve Cowrie (*Cypraea cribaria*)	75	35
673	50 c. Umbilical Ovula or Little Egg Cowrie (*Calpurnus verrucosus*)	1·00	1·25
674	$1 Valentine or Prince Cowrie (*Cypraea valentia*)	1·75	2·25
670/4	*Set of* 5	3·75	3·75

(Des D. Miller. Litho Questa)

1990 (4 Aug). *90th Birthday of Queen Elizabeth the Queen Mother. Vert designs as T* **107** (25 *c.*) *or* **108** ($5) *of Kenya. P* 14×15 (25 *c.*) *or* 14½ ($5).

675	25 c. multicoloured	75	25
676	$5 black and deep claret	3·50	4·25

Designs:—25 c. Queen Mother, 1987; $5 King George VI and Queen Elizabeth inspecting bomb damage to Buckingham Palace, 1940.

178 Postman with Mail Van

(Des N. Shewring. Litho Questa)

1990 (15 Oct). *150th Anniv of the Penny Black. T* **178** *and similar horiz designs. Multicoloured. W w* **14** *(sideways). P* 14.

677	35 c. Type **178**	70	25
678	45 c. General Post Office	80	40
679	50 c. 1907 ½d. stamp	85	85
680	55 c. Child collecting stamps	90	1·00
681	60 c. Penny Black and Solomon Islands 1913 1d. stamp	95	1·40
677/81	*Set of* 5	3·75	3·50

179 Purple Swamphen

180 *Cylas formicarius* (weevil)

(Des N. Arlott. Litho Questa)

1990 (5 Dec). *"Birdpex '90" Stamp Exhibition, Christchurch, New Zealand. T* **179** *and similar horiz designs showing birds. Multicoloured. W w* **14** *(sideways). P* 14.

682	10 c. Type **179**	45	30
683	25 c. Mackinlay's Cuckoo Dove ("Rufous Brown Pheasant Dove")	65	30
684	30 c. Superb Fruit Dove	75	35
685	45 c. Cardinal Honeyeater	1·00	45
686	$2 Finsch's Pygmy Parrot	2·00	3·00
682/6	*Set of* 5	4·25	4·00

(Des Josephine Martin. Litho B.D.T.)

1991 (16 Jan). *Crop Pests. T* **180** *and similar vert designs. Multicoloured. W w* **14**. *P* 14.

687	7 c. Type **180**	40	15
688	25 c. *Dacus cucurbitae* (fruit-fly)	65	20
689	40 c. *Papuana uninodis* (beetle)	85	40
690	90 c. *Pantorhytes biplagiastus* (weevil)	1·50	1·75
691	$1.50, *Scapanes australis* (beetle)	2·00	2·75
687/91	*Set of* 5	4·75	4·75

(Des D. Miller. Litho Questa)

1991 (17 June). *65th Birthday of Queen Elizabeth II and 70th Birthday of Prince Philip. Vert designs as T* **58** *of Kiribati. Multicoloured. W w* **16** *(sideways). P* 14½×14.

692	90 c. Prince Philip in evening dress	1·00	1·25
	a. Horiz pair. Nos. 692/3 separated by label	2·40	3·00
693	$2 Queen Elizabeth II	1·40	1·75

Nos. 692/3 were printed in a similar sheet format to Nos. 366/7 of Kiribati.

181 Child drinking from Coconut

182 Volleyball

(Des G. Vasarhelyi. Litho Walsall)

1991 (24 June). *Health Campaign. T* **181** *and similar horiz designs. Multicoloured. W w* **14** *(sideways). P* 14.

694	5 c. Type **181**	10	20
695	75 c. Mother feeding child	90	90
696	80 c. Breast feeding	1·00	1·00
697	90 c. Local produce	1·25	1·40
694/7	*Set of* 4	2·75	3·25

A 65 c. value, showing healthy and less healthy foods, was prepared, but not issued.

(Des N. Shewring. Litho Questa)

1991 (8 Aug). *9th South Pacific Games. T* **182** *and similar vert designs. Multicoloured. W w* **16**. *P* 14.

698	25 c. Type **182**	70	20
699	40 c. Judo	85	45
700	65 c. Squash	1·25	1·50
701	90 c. Bowling	1·60	2·25
698/701	*Set of* 4	4·00	4·00
MS702	92×112 mm. $2 Games emblem. Wmk sideways	3·75	4·50

183 Preparing Food for Christmas

184 Yellow-finned Tuna

(Des G. Vasarhelyi. Litho B.D.T.)

1991 (28 Oct). *Christmas. T* **183** *and similar horiz designs. Multicoloured. W w* **14** *(sideways). P* 14.

703	10 c. Type **183**	30	10
704	25 c. Christmas Day church service	60	15
705	65 c. Christmas Day feast	1·50	85
706	$2 Cricket match	3·25	4·00
703/6	*Set of* 4	5·00	4·50
MS707	138×110 mm. Nos. 703/6	5·00	5·50

(Des O. Bell. Litho Leigh-Mardon Ltd, Melbourne)

1991 (16 Nov). *"Phila Nippon '91" International Stamp Exhibition, Tokyo. Tuna Fishing. T* **184** *and similar multicoloured designs.* W w **16** (*sideways*). P 14.

708 5 c. Type **184** 10 20
709 30 c. Pole and line tuna fishing boat . . 60 25
710 80 c. Pole and line fishing . . . . 1·50 1·75
711 $2 Processing "arabushi" (smoked tuna) 2·75 3·50
708/11 . . . . *Set of* 4 4·50 5·00
MS712 101×80 mm. 80 c. Plate of "tori nanban" (25×42 *mm*); 80 c. Bowl of "aka miso" (25×42 *mm*). P 14½ . . . . 1·50 1·75

(Des D. Miller. Litho Questa ($5), Leigh-Mardon Ltd, Melbourne (others))

1992 (6 Feb). *40th Anniv of Queen Elizabeth II's Accession. Horiz designs as T* **113** *of Kenya. Multicoloured.* W w **14** (*sideways*) (20 c., 40 c., $5) *or* w **16** (5 c., 60 c.). P 14.

713 5 c. Aerial view of Honiara . . 15 20
714 20 c. Sunset across lagoon . . 30 15
715 40 c. Honiara harbour . . 60 35
716 60 c. Three portraits of Queen Elizabeth . . 75 80
717 $5 Queen Elizabeth II . . 3·25 3·75
713/17 . . . . *Set of* 5 4·50 4·75

185 Mendana's Fleet in Thousand Ships Bay, 1568

186 Sgt-major Jacob Vouza

(Des J. Batchelor. Litho Leigh-Mardon Ltd, Melbourne)

1992 (24 Apr). *"Granada '92" International Stamp Exhibition, Spain. Mendana's Discovery of Solomon Islands. T* **185** *and similar horiz designs.* W w **14** (*sideways*). P 15×14½.

718 10 c. Type **185** 35 15
719 65 c. Map of voyage 80 60
720 80 c. Alvaro Mendana de Niera . . 1·10 1·25
721 $1 Settlement at Graciosa Bay . . 1·40 1·50
722 $5 Mendana's fleet at sea . . 3·50 4·25
718/22 . . . . *Set of* 5 6·50 7·00

(Des T. Rider, adapted G. Vasarhelyi. Litho Enschedé)

1992 (3 May). *Birth Centenary of Sgt-major Jacob Vouza (war hero). T* **186** *and similar vert designs. Multicoloured.* W w **14**. P 14×13½.

723 25 c. Type **186** 40 25
a. Booklet pane. Nos. 723 and 725, each × 2, with margins all round . . 2·40
724 70 c. Vouza in U.S. Marine corps battle dress 80 90
a. Booklet pane. Nos. 724 and 726, each × 2, with margins all round . . 3·50
725 90 c. Vouza in U.S. Marine corps uniform 90 1·00
726 $2 Statue of Vouza . . 1·25 2·00
723/6 . . . . *Set of* 4 3·00 3·75
MS727 113×76 mm. $4 Sgt-major Vouza in ceremonial uniform . . 4·00 4·50

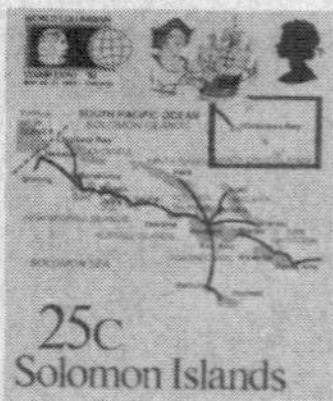

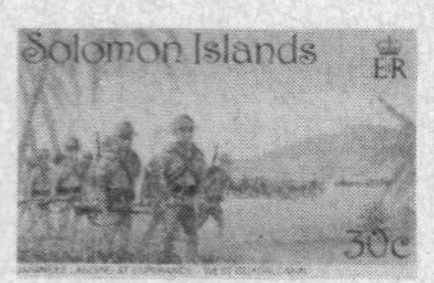

187 Solomon Airlines Domestic Routes

188 Japanese Troops landing at Esperance

(Des D. Miller. Litho Enschedé)

1992 (22 May). *500th Anniv of Discovery of America by Columbus and "World Columbian Stamp Expo '92" Exhibition, Chicago. T* **187** *and similar vert designs. Multicoloured.* W w **14**. P 14×13½.

728 25 c. Type **187** 60 20
729 80 c. Solomon Airlines Boeing 737-400 *Guadalcanal* . . 1·40 1·25
730 $1.50, Solomon Airlines international routes . . 2·00 2·25
731 $5 Columbus and *Santa Maria* . . 4·75 6·00
728/31 . . . . *Set of* 4 8·00 8·75
MS732 120×94 mm. Nos. 728/31 . . 8·00 9·00

(Des J. Batchelor. Litho Questa)

1992 (7 Aug). *50th Anniv of Battle of Guadalcanal. T* **188** *and similar horiz designs. Multicoloured.* P 14.

733 30 c. Type **188** 80 80
a. Sheetlet. Nos. 733/7 . . 3·50
734 30 c. American troops in landing-craft . . 80 80
735 30 c. Australian cruiser . . 80 80
736 30 c. U.S. Navy post office . . 80 80
737 30 c. R.N.Z.A.F. Consolidated PBY-5A Catalina flying boat . . 80 80
738 80 c. U.S. Marine Corps Grumman F4F Wildcat fighters . . 1·00 1·00
a. Sheetlet. Nos. 738/47 . . 9·00
739 80 c. Henderson Field . . 1·00 1·00
740 80 c. U.S.S. *Quincy* (heavy cruiser) . . 1·00 1·00
741 80 c. H.M.A.S. *Canberra* (heavy cruiser) . . 1·00 1·00
742 80 c. U.S. Marine Corps landing craft . . 1·00 1·00
743 80 c. *Ryujo* (Japanese aircraft carrier) . . 1·00 1·00
744 80 c. Japanese Mitsubishi A6M Zero-Sen fighters . . 1·00 1·00
745 80 c. Japanese Mitsubishi G4M "Betty" bombers . . 1·00 1·00
746 80 c. Japanese destroyer . . 1·00 1·00
747 80 c. *Chockai* (Japanese heavy cruiser) . . 1·00 1·00
733/47 . . . . *Set of* 15 12·50 12·50

Nos. 733/7 and 738/47 were each printed together, *se-tenant*, in sheetlets with the 30 c. designs as a horizontal strip of 5 below a label showing Henderson Field and the 80 c. designs in two horizontal strips of 5 separated by a gutter showing night naval action off Savo Island.

It was originally intended that the 30 c. sheetlet should also contain ten stamps, but the top row of five was removed before the sheetlets were issued.

No. 745 is inscribed "BEACHEAD" in error.

189 *Dendrobium* hybrid

190 Stalk-eyed Ghost Crab

(Des Annette Robinson. Litho Leigh-Mardon Ltd, Melbourne)

1992 (14 Dec). *Orchids (3rd series). T* **189** *and similar horiz designs. Multicoloured.* W w **14** (*sideways*). P 14½.

748 15 c. Type **189** 50 20
749 70 c. *Vanda* "Amy Laycock" . . 1·00 90
750 95 c. *Dendrobium mirbelianum* . . 1·25 1·25
751 $2.50, *Dendrobium macrophyllum* . . 2·00 3·00
748/51 . . . . *Set of* 4 4·25 4·75

For stamps in these designs, but with different face values and inscribed "*World Orchid Conference*" or "*Indopex '93*" see Nos. 771/2 and 773/4.

(Des G. Drummond. Litho Cartor)

1993 (15 Jan). *Crabs. T* **190** *and similar horiz designs. Multicoloured.* W w **14** (*sideways*). P 13.

752 5 c. Type **190** 10 10
753 10 c. Red-spotted Crab . . 10 10
754 25 c. Flat Crab . . 10 10
755 30 c. Land Hermit Crab . . 10 10
756 40 c. Grapsid Crab . . 10 10
757 45 c. Red and White Painted Crab . . 10 10
758 55 c. Swift-footed Crab . . 15 20
759 60 c. Spanner Crab . . 15 20
760 70 c. Red Hermit Crab . . 20 25
761 80 c. Red-eyed Crab . . 20 25
762 90 c. Rathbun Red Crab . . 25 30
763 $1 Coconut Crab . . 25 30
764 $1.10, Red-spotted White Crab . . 30 35
765 $4 Ghost Crab . . 1·10 1·25
766 $10 Mangrove Fiddler Crab . . 2·75 3·00
752/66 . . . . *Set of* 15 5·75 6·25

For miniature sheet containing the $4 see No. **MS**874.

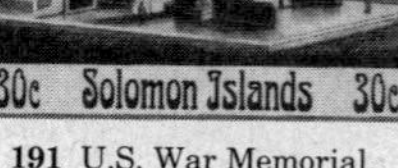

191 U.S. War Memorial, Skyline Ridge

192 U.S.S. *PT 109* being rammed by *Amagiri* (Japanese destoyer)

(Des G. Vasarhelyi. Litho Walsall)

1993 (19 Apr). *50th Anniv of Second World War. T* **191** *and similar horiz designs. Multicoloured.* W w **14** (*sideways*). P 14.

767 30 c. Type **191** 30 20
768 80 c. National flags at half mast . . 75 90
769 95 c. Major-general Alexander Vandegrift and map . . 85 1·00
770 $4 Aerial dogfight, U.S. carrier and Solomon Islands scouts . . 3·50 4·50
767/70 . . . . *Set of* 4 4·75 6·00

(Des Annette Robinson. Litho Leigh-Mardon Ltd, Melbourne)

1993 (24 Apr). *14th World Orchid Conference, Glasgow. Designs as Nos. 748 and 751, but different face values, additionally inscr "World Orchid Conference".* W w **14** (*sideways*). P 14½.

771 20 c. Type **189** 25 25
772 $3 *Dendrobium macrophyllum* . . 1·75 2·25

(Des Annette Robinson. Litho Leigh-Mardon Ltd, Melbourne)

1993 (29 May). *"Indopex '93" International Philatelic Exhibition, Surabaya. Designs as Nos. 749/50, but different face values, additionally inscr "Indopex '93 Exhibition".* W w **14** (*sideways*). P 14½.

773 85 c. *Vanda* "Amy Laycock" . . 90 1·00
774 $1.15, *Dendrobium mirbelianum* . . 1·00 1·25

(Des J. Batchelor and G. Vasarhelyi. Litho Walsall)

1993 (30 July). *50th Anniv of Sinking of U.S.S. PT 109 (motor torpedo-boat commanded by John F. Kennedy). T* **192** *and similar horiz designs. Multicoloured.* W w **14** (*sideways*). P 13×13½.

775 30 c. Type **192** 30 20
776 50 c. Kennedy thanking islander . . 45 45
777 95 c. Message in coconut shell and islanders in canoe . . 75 1·00
778 $1.10, Pres. Kennedy and medal . . 1·00 1·40
775/8 . . . . *Set of* 4 2·25 2·75
MS779 77×43 mm. $5 U.S.S. *PT 109* . . 4·25 5·00

1993 (14 Aug). *"Taipei '93" Asian International Stamp Exhibition, Taiwan. No.* **MS**732 *optd "TAIPEI '93" and emblem on sheet margin.*

MS780 120×94 mm. Nos. 728/31 . . 4·50 5·50

193 Nicobar Pigeon

194 Pair of Dachshunds

(Des A. Robinson. Litho B.D.T.)

1993 (21 Sept). *Endangered Species. Nicobar Pigeon. T* **193** *and similar square designs. Multicoloured.* W w **14** (*sideways*). P 14.

781 30 c. Type **193** 35 20
782 50 c. Pigeon on ground . . 50 35
783 65 c. Pair of Pigeons perched on branches 60 50
784 70 c. Pigeon on branch looking left . . 65 60
785 $1.10, Pigeon on branch looking right . . 1·00 1·10
786 $3 Pigeons in flight . . 2·25 2·75
781/6 . . . . *Set of* 6 4·75 5·00

(Des Doreen McGuiness. Litho Walsall)

1994 (18 Feb). *"Hong Kong '94" International Stamp Exhibition. Chinese New Year ("Year of the Dog"). T* **194** *and similar horiz designs. Multicoloured.* W w **14** (*sideways*). P 14½.

787 30 c. Type **194** 25 20
788 80 c. German Shepherd Dog . . 65 75
789 95 c. Pair of Dobermann Pinschers . . 70 90
790 $1.10, Australian Cattle Dog . . 80 1·25
787/90 . . . . *Set of* 4 2·25 2·75
MS791 70×55 mm. $4 Boxer . . 4·00 4·50

No. **MS**791 surcharged "19–25 Aug. Jakarta '95 Surcharge $2.00" was only available at this philatelic exhibition in Indonesia.

195 Striped Dolphin

(Des N. Shewring. Litho Walsall)

1994 (9 May). *Dolphins. T* **195** *and similar horiz designs. Multicoloured.* W w **16** (*sideways*). P 14.

792 75 c. Type **195** 75 65
793 85 c. Risso's Dolphin . . 80 80
794 $1.15, Common Dolphin . . 1·10 1·25
795 $2.50, Spinner Dolphin . . 2·25 2·50
796 $3 Bottlenose Dolphin . . 2·50 3·00
792/6 . . . . *Set of* 5 6·75 7·50

196 *Vindula sapor*

197 Girl in Brisbane writing letter to Family in Santa Isabel

(Des K. McGee. Litho Enschedé)

1994 (16 Aug). *"Philakorea '94" International Stamp Exhibition, Seoul. Butterflies. T* **196** *and similar horiz designs. Multicoloured.* W w **14** (*sideways*). P 13½×14.

797 70 c. Type **196** 50 55
a. Sheetlet. Nos. 797/805 . . 4·00
798 70 c. *Papilio aegeus* . . 50 55
799 70 c. *Graphium hicetaon* . . 50 55
800 70 c. *Graphium mendana* . . 50 55
801 70 c. Exhibition logo . . 50 55
802 70 c. *Graphium meeki* . . 50 55
803 70 c. *Danaus schenkii* . . 50 55

804 70 c. *Papilio ptolychus* 50 55
805 70 c. *Phaedyma fissizonata vella* 50 55
797/805 .. .. *Set of* 9 4·00 4·50
Nos. 797/805 were printed together, *se-tenant*, in sheetlets of 9.

(Des S. Noon. Litho Cartor)

1994 (18 Aug). *International Year of the Family.* *T* **197** *and similar vert designs. Multicoloured.* *W* w **14**. *P* 13.
806 $1.10, Type **197** 75 85
a. Horiz strip of 5. Nos. 806/10 .. .. 3·25
807 $1.10, Boeing 737-400 leaving Brisbane .. 75 85
808 $1.10, Boeing 737-400 at Henderson Airfield and De Havilland D.H.C.6 Twin Otter leaving for Santa Isabel .. 75 85
809 $1.10, De Havilland D.H.C.6 Twin Otter at Fera Airfield, Santa Isabel 75 85
810 $1.10, Family reunited 75 85
806/10 .. .. *Set of* 5 3·25 3·75
MS811 160×75 mm. Nos. 806/10 .. .. 3·25 3·75
Nos. 806/10 were printed together, *se-tenant*, in horizontal strips of 5 throughout the sheet.

198 Cook Island Volcano, 1967

199 La Perouse with King Louis XVI and Map

(Des N. Shewring. Litho Questa)

1994 (24 Oct). *Volcanoes.* *T* **198** *and similar horiz designs. Multicoloured.* *W* w **14** (*sideways*). *P* 14×14½.
812 30 c. Type **198** 30 15
813 70 c. Kavachi underwater eruption, 1977 .. 50 60
814 80 c. Kavachi volcano forming temporary island, 1978 .. .. .. 60 70
815 90 c. Tinakula volcanic island .. .. 80 1·00
812/15 .. .. *Set of* 4 2·00 2·25
MS816 130×60 mm. $2 Map of Solomon Islands volcanoes; $2 Diagram showing formation of volcanic islands. Wmk upright .. .. 2·50 3·00

(Des R. Watton. Litho Walsall)

1994 (16 Dec). *Loss of the La Perouse Expedition, Santa Cruz Islands, 1788.* *T* **199** *and similar horiz designs. Multicoloured.* *W* w **16** (*sideways*). *P* 14×14½.
817 30 c. Type **199** 30 20
818 80 c. Map of Ile de La Perouse 65 60
819 95 c. *L'Astrolabe* 75 75
820 $1.10, *La Boussole* .. .. .. 90 1·00
821 $3 *L'Astrolabe* foundering on reef .. 2·00 2·75
817/21 .. .. *Set of* 5 4·25 4·75

200 Hermit Crab, Shells and Dancers

(Des B. Dare. Litho Leigh-Mardon Ltd, Melbourne)

1995 (17 Feb). *Visit South Pacific Year.* *T* **200** *and similar horiz designs. Multicoloured.* *W* w **14** (*sideways*). *P* 15×14½.
822 30 c. Type **200** 15 15
823 50 c. *Dendrobium rennellii* (orchid) and *Danaus plexippus* (butterfly) 35 35
824 95 c. Scuba diver and fish 50 75
825 $1.15, Grapsid Crab, canoes, rusty Second World War gun and catamaran 60 90
822/5 .. .. *Set of* 4 1·40 1·90
MS826 98×81 mm. $4 Yellow-bibbed Lory .. 2·75 3·25

201 Emblem and Bananas

202 *Calanthe triplicata*

(Des Sue Wickison. Litho Southern Colour Print, Dunedin, New Zealand)

1995 (5 Apr). *50th Anniv of Food and Agriculture Organization. Fruits.* *T* **201** *and similar horiz designs. Multicoloured.* *W* w **14**. *P* 12.
827 70 c. Type **201** 50 50
828 75 c. Paw paws 50 50
829 95 c. Pomelos 65 75
830 $2 Star fruits .. .. .. 1·40 2·00
827/30 .. .. *Set of* 4 2·75 3·25
MS831 90×75 mm. $3 Mangos .. .. 1·60 2·00

(Des R. Watton. Litho Cartor (Nos. 832/5) or Questa (No. **MS**836))

1995 (8 May). *50th Anniv of End of Second World War. Multicoloured designs as T* **75** *of Kiribati.* *W* w **14** (*sideways*). *P* 13½.
832 95 c. Vice-Admiral Nagumo and *Akagi* (Japanese aircraft carrier) 65 65
833 $1 Rear-Admiral Fletcher and U.S.S. *Yorktown* (aircraft carrier) 65 65
834 $2 Vice-Admiral Ghormley and U.S.S. *Wasp* (aircraft carrier) .. .. 1·25 1·50
835 $3 Vice-Admiral Halsey and U.S.S. *Enterprise* (aircraft carrier) .. .. 1·90 2·25
832/5 .. .. *Set of* 4 4·00 4·50
MS836 75×85 mm. $5 Reverse of 1939–45 War Medal (*vert*). Wmk upright. P 14 .. .. 2·25 2·40

(Des Sue Wickison. Litho Questa)

1995 (1 Sept). *Orchids.* *T* **202** *and similar vert designs. Multicoloured.* *W* w **14**. *P* 14.
837 45 c. Type **202** 45 20
838 75 c. *Dendrobium mohlianum* 65 60
839 85 c. *Flickingeria comata* 75 75
840 $1.15, *Dendrobium spectabile* .. .. 1·10 1·40
837/40 .. .. *Set of* 4 2·75 2·75
MS841 75×90 mm. $4 *Coelogyne asperata* .. 2·25 2·75
No. **MS**841 includes the "Singapore '95" International Stamp Exhibition emblem on the sheet margin.

203 Start of Canoe Race

(Des G. Vasarhelyi. Litho Cartor)

1995 (6 Nov). *Christmas. Local Festivities.* *T* **203** *and similar horiz designs. Multicoloured.* *W* w **14** (*sideways*). *P* 13½.
842 90 c. Type **203** 45 45
843 $1.05, Pan-pipe players and Christmas Tree 45 50
844 $1.25, Picnic on the beach 55 60
845 $1.45, Church service and infant Jesus .. 70 90
842/5 .. .. *Set of* 4 1·90 2·25

204 Marconi demonstrating Radio Transmitter, Salisbury Plain, 1896

205 Palm Lorikeet

(Des N. Shewring. Litho Walsall)

1996 (28 Feb). *Centenary of Radio.* *T* **204** *and similar square designs. Multicoloured.* *W* w **14** (*sideways*). *P* 14½×14.
846 $1.05, Type **204** 45 45
847 $1.20, Ship's radio room, 1900 .. .. 55 60
848 $1.35, Wireless transmitter, Croydon Aerodrome, 1920 .. .. .. 65 80
849 $1.45, Marconi in Japan, 1933 .. .. 70 90
846/9 .. .. *Set of* 4 2·10 2·50

(Des R. Parks. Litho Questa)

1996 (10 Apr). *Birds.* *T* **205** *and similar horiz designs. Multicoloured.* *W* w **14** (*sideways*). *P* 14.
850 75 c. Type **205** 50 35
851 $1.05, Duchess Lorikeet 65 65
852 $1.20, Yellow-bibbed Lory 70 70
853 $1.35, Cardinal Lory 85 90
854 $1.45, Meek's Lorikeet 85 95
850/4 .. .. *Set of* 5 3·25 3·25
MS855 94×69 mm. $3 Rainbow Lory ("Lorikeet") 1·90 2·25

ALTERED CATALOGUE NUMBERS

Any Catalogue numbers altered from the last edition are shown as a list in the introductory pages.

206 Dug-out Canoe on Beach and Canoe with Outboard Motor

207 Tokyo 1964 Poster

(Des R. Watton. Litho Cartor)

1996 (8 June). *"CAPEX '96" International Stamp Exhibition, Toronto. Mail Transport.* *T* **206** *and similar horiz designs.* *W* w **14** (*sideways*). *P* 13.
856 40 c. Type **206** 30 20
857 90 c. Postman with bicycle 50 55
858 $1.20, Post van 65 80
859 $1.45, *Tulagi Express* (cruise launch) .. 90 1·25
856/9 .. .. *Set of* 4 2·10 2·50
MS860 88×73 mm. $4 "Tepuke" (traditional canoe) .. .. 1·90 2·40

(Des D. Miller. Litho Walsall)

1996 (30 June). *Centenary of Modern Olympic Games.* *T* **207** *and similar vert designs showing promotional posters from previous games.* *W* w **16**. *P* 14×13½.
861 90 c. Type **207** 50 40
862 $1.20, Los Angeles, 1932 .. .. 60 70
863 $1.35, Paris, 1924 .. .. .. 65 80
864 $2.50, London, 1908 .. .. .. 1·10 1·50
861/4 .. .. *Set of* 4 2·50 3·00

208 Suiesi and Map of Makira Bay

209 Sandford's Sea Eagle

(Des G. Vasarhelyi. Litho Questa)

1996 (12 Sept). *150th Anniv of First Christian Mission.* *T* **208** *and similar horiz designs. Multicoloured.* *W* w **14** (*sideways*). *P* 13½×14.
865 40 c. Type **208** 30 20
866 65 c. Surimahe and sketches of artefacts by Revd. L. Verguet 45 35
867 $1.35, Bishop Espalle and grave, Isabel .. 60 80
868 $1.45, John Claude Colin and Makira Mission 65 90
865/8 .. .. *Set of* 4 1·75 2·00

(Des N. Arlott. Litho Questa)

1996 (21 Oct). *"Taipei '96" 10th Asian International Stamp Exhibition, Taiwan. Sheet* 100×80 *mm.* *W* w **14** (*inverted*). *P* 14×13½.
MS869 **209** $1.50, multicoloured 75 90

210 Children eating Fruit

(Des Jennifer Toombs. Litho Questa)

1996 (21 Nov). *50th Anniv of U.N.I.C.E.F.* *T* **210** *and similar horiz designs. Multicoloured.* *W* w **14** (*sideways*). *P* 14½.
870 40 c. Type **210** 25 20
871 $1.05, Children in canoes 50 50
872 $1.35, Doctor and child 60 75
873 $2.50, Teacher and child .. .. 1·00 1·40
870/3 .. .. *Set of* 4 2·10 2·50

(Des D. Miller. Litho Questa)

1997 (3 Feb). *"HONG KONG '97" International Stamp Exhibition. Sheet* 130×90 *mm, containing design as No.* 765. *Multicoloured.* *W* w **14** (*sideways*). *P* 14×14½.
MS874 $4 Ghost Crab .. .. 1·50 1·75

1997 (21 Feb). *"Singpex '97" International Stamp Exhibition. No.* 797a *optd* "SINGPEX '97 FEBRUARY 21–23 SINGAPORE" *and logo within "perforation" frame in red across the entire sheetlet.*
875 70 c. Type **196** 30 35
a. Sheetlet. Nos. 875/83 . . . . 2·40
876 70 c. *Papilio aegeus* 30 35
877 70 c. *Graphium hicetaon* 30 35
878 70 c. *Graphium mendana* 30 35
879 70 c. Exhibition logo 30 35
880 70 c. *Graphium meeki* 30 35
881 70 c. *Danaus schenkii* 30 35
882 70 c. *Papilio ptolychus* 30 35
883 70 c. *Phaedyma fissizonata vella* 30 35
875/83 . . . . *Set of* 9 2·40 2·75
Individual stamps show parts of the overprint only.
Nos. 875/83 also exist with the overprint in black from a limited printing.

211 Common Phalanger

212 Whale and Calf

(Des Sue Wickison. Litho Southern Colour Print, Dunedin)

1997 (21 Apr). *Common Phalanger ("Northern Common Cuscus"). T* **211** *and similar horiz designs. Multicoloured. W* w **14** *(sideways). P* 12.
884 15 c. Type **211** 20 10
885 60 c. Common Phalanger eating fruit . . 25 30
886 $2.50, Common Phalanger hanging on branch 75 80
887 $3 Two Common Phalangers 85 95
884/7 . . . . *Set of* 4 1·90 1·90

(Des Mary Butterfield. Litho Questa)

1997 (29 May). *"Pacific '97" International Stamp Exhibition, San Francisco. Sheet* 96×74 *mm, containing T* **212** *and similar multicoloured design. W* w **14**. *P* 15×14½ *(vert) or* 14½×15 *(horiz).*
MS888 $2 Type **212**; $2 Whale breaking surface (*horiz*) . . . . 1·60 1·75

(Des N. Shewring (No. **MS**893), D. Miller (others). Litho Questa (No. **MS**893), Cartor (others))

1997 (10 July). *Golden Wedding of Queen Elizabeth and Prince Philip. Multicoloured designs as T* **87** *of Kiribati. W* w **14**. *P* 13.
889 $3 Prince Philip playing polo . . . . 1·25 1·40
a. Horiz pair. Nos. 889/90 . . . . 2·50 2·75
890 $3 Queen Elizabeth . . . . . . 1·25 1·40
891 $3 Queen Elizabeth leading two horses . . 1·25 1·40
a. Horiz pair. Nos. 891/2 . . . . 2·50 2·75
892 $3 Prince Philip . . . . . . 1·25 1·40
889/92 . . . . *Set of* 4 4·50 5·00
MS893 110×70 mm. $3 Queen Elizabeth and Prince Philip in landau (*horiz*). Wmk sideways. P 14×14½ . . . . 1·25 1·40
Nos. 889/90 and 891/2 were each printed together, *se-tenant*, in horizontal pairs throughout the sheets with the backgrounds forming composite designs.

213 Turtle laying Eggs

(Des Doreen McGuiness. Litho Walsall)

1997 (29 Sept). *50th Anniv of the South Pacific Commission. Common Green Turtle. T* **213** *and similar horiz designs. W* w **16** *(sideways). Multicoloured. P* 14.
894 50 c. Type **213** 30 20
895 90 c. Young turtles heading towards sea . . 50 40
896 $1.50, Four turtles swimming under water 70 80
897 $2 Pair of turtles swimming 85 95
894/7 . . . . *Set of* 4 2·10 2·10

214 Oni Mako Player

215 Golden Whistler

(Des G. Vasarhelyi. Litho Cartor)

1997 (24 Nov). *Christmas. T* **214** *and similar horiz designs. Multicoloured. W* w **14** *(sideways). P* 13½.
898 $1.10, Type **214** 40 35
899 $1.40, Ysabel dancing women 50 40
900 $1.50, Pan pipers from Small Malaita . . 50 45
901 $1.70, Western bamboo band 60 60
898/901 . . . . *Set of* 4 1·75 1·60

(Des G. Vasarhelyi. Litho Questa)

1997 (5 Dec). *"Bangkok '97" China Stamp Exhibition, Thailand. Christmas. Sheet* 135×87 *mm, containing T* **215** *and similar vert design. Multicoloured. W* w **14** *(sideways). P* 14.
MS902 $1.50, Type **215**; $1.50, *Papilio aegeus* and *Graphium meeki* (butterflies) . . . . 1·25 1·40

STAMP BOOKLETS

1959 (1 Apr). *Black on buff (No.* SB1) *or grey (No.* SB2) *covers. Stapled.*
SB1 4s. booklet containing eight 1d., 2d. and 3d. (Nos. 83, 85, 87) in blocks of 4 . . . . . . 35·00
SB2 11s. booklet containing eight 1d. and 8d., and four 3d. and 1s. (Nos. 83, 87, 90/1) in blocks of 4 45·00

1960 (May)–**64**. *Black on green (No.* SB3) *or orange (No.* SB4) *covers. Stapled.*
SB3 5s. booklet containing eight 1d., 1½d., 2d. and 3d. (Nos. 83/5, 87) in blocks of 4 . . . . 55·00
SB4 £1 booklet containing eight 1d., 2d., 3d., 9d. and 1s. 3d. (Nos. 83, 85, 87, 90*a*, 91*a*) in blocks of 4 90·00
a. Contents as No. SB4, but Nos. 103, 85, 106*a*, 108/9 (1964) . . . .

1982 (11 Oct). *Royal Visit and Commonwealth Games, Brisbane. Light green and apple-green cover,* 90×108 *mm, showing two-headed figure. Stamps attached by selvedge.*
SB5 $2.96, booklet containing 12 c. (Nos. 471/2) and 25 c. (Nos. 473/4), each value in block of eight and two labels . . . . 4·50

1984 (30 Jan). *Fungi. Black and greenish yellow cover,* 122×92 *mm. Panes attached by selvedge.*
SB6 $3.18, booklet containing 18 c. and 35 c., each in pane of 6 (Nos. 514a, 515a) . . . . . . 8·00

1984 (22 Sept). *Olympic Games, Los Angeles. Multicoloured cover,* 125×82 *mm, showing Australian, American and Solomon Islands flags. Stitched.*
SB7 $3.95, booklet containing two *se-tenant* panes of 4 and pane of one 95 c. (Nos. 529a, 531a) . . 8·00

1992 (3 May). *Birth Centenary of Sgt-Major Jacob Vouza (war hero). Black on bright green cover, size* 131×92 *mm, showing Guadalcanal. Panes attached by selvedge.*
SB8 $11.70, booklet containing two different *se-tenant* panes of 4 (Nos. 723a, 724a) and No. **MS**727 8·50

POSTAGE DUE STAMPS

D 1

(Typo B.W.)

1940 (1 Sept). *Wmk Mult Script CA. P* 12.
D1 D 1 1d. emerald-green . . . . . . 6·00 6·50
D2 2d. scarlet . . . . 6·50 6·50
D3 3d. brown . . . . 6·50 10·00
D4 4d. blue . . . . 10·00 11·00
D5 5d. grey-green . . . . 11·00 18·00
D6 6d. purple . . . . 11·00 15·00
D7 1s. violet . . . . 15·00 26·00
D8 1s. 6d. turquoise-green . . . . . . 26·00 45·00
D1/8 . . . . *Set of* 8 80·00 £120
D1/8 Perf "Specimen" . . . . *Set of* 8 £150

Somaliland Protectorate

Egyptian post offices were opened in Somaliland during 1876 and the stamps of Egypt were used there until the garrisons were withdrawn in 1884.

Cancellations for these offices have been identified as follows (for illustrations of postmark types see SUDAN).

BARBARA (Berbera). Open 1876 to 1 November 1884. Circular datestamp as Sudan Type I.

ZEILA. Open 1876 to 1 November 1884. Circular datestamp as Sudan Types G and I, sometimes inscr ZEJLA. One example with seal type cancellation as Sudan Type B is also known.

Stamps of India were used at the two post offices from 1 January 1887 until 1903 usually cancelled with circular datestamps or the "B" obliterator used by all offices controlled from Bombay.

The Protectorate Post Office was established on 1 June 1903, when control of British Somaliland was transferred from the British Government to the British Foreign Office.

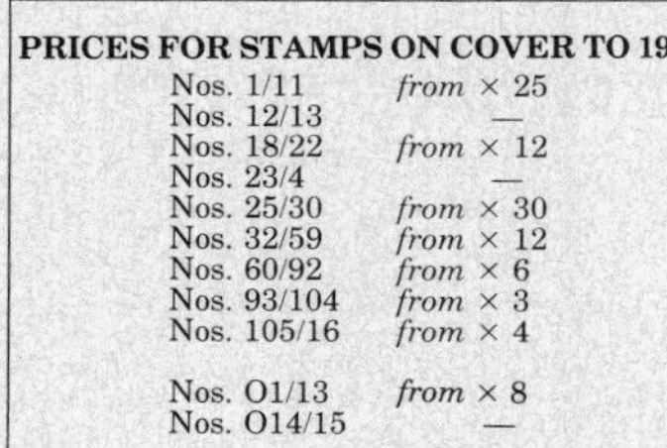

PRICES FOR STAMPS ON COVER TO 1945	
Nos. 1/11	from × 25
Nos. 12/13	—
Nos. 18/22	from × 12
Nos. 23/4	—
Nos. 25/30	from × 30
Nos. 32/59	from × 12
Nos. 60/92	from × 6
Nos. 93/104	from × 3
Nos. 105/16	from × 4
Nos. O1/13	from × 8
Nos. O14/15	—

(Currency. 12 pies = 1 anna; 16 annas = 1 rupee)

BRITISH SOMALILAND

(1)

2

3

SETTINGS OF TYPE 1

In all printings the ½, 1, 2, 2½, 3, 4, 8, 12 a. and 1 r. values were overprinted from a setting of 240 (2 panes 12 × 10, one above the other), covering the entire sheet at one operation.

The 6 a., which was in sheets of 320 (4 panes, each 8 × 10), had a modified setting of 160, applied twice to each sheet.

The high values were overprinted in sheets of 96 (8 panes, each 4 × 3).

The settings for the low value stamps contained two slightly different styles of overprint, identified by the position of "B" of "BRITISH". Type A shows this letter over the "M" of "SOMALILAND" and Type B over the "OM".

For the first printing with the overprint at the top of the design the 240 position setting showed all the stamps in the upper pane and 63 in the lower as Type A, with the remaining 57 as Type B. When the setting was used for the printing with overprint at foot it was amended slightly so that one of the Type A examples in the upper pane became a Type B.

The 6 a. value with overprint at top shows 250 examples of Type A and 70 as Type B in each sheet. This proportion altered in the printing with overprint at foot to 256 as Type A and 64 as Type B.

OVERPRINT VARIETIES

Missing second "I" in "BRITISH"—Occurs on the stamps with overprint at top from R.2/6 of the upper pane and R.5/1 of the lower, although it is believed that the example on the 2½ a. (No. 4a) only occurs from the second position. On the later printing with overprint at foot a similar error can be found on R.7/12 of the upper pane. Some examples of both these errors show traces of the letter remaining, but the prices quoted are for stamps with it completely omitted.

Figure "1" for first "I" in "BRITISH"—Occurs on R.6/4 of the upper pane for all printings of the 240 impression setting. In addition it has been reported from R.7/12 of the Queen Victoria 2½, 12 a. and 1 r. with overprint at foot. Both versions of the 6 a. show the variety on R.6/4 of the upper left and upper right panes.

Curved overprint—Occurs on R.3/4 of the top right-hand pane of the high values.

"SUMALILAND"—Occurs on R.2/9 of the upper pane for all low values with the overprint at foot, except the 6 a. A similar variety occurs on the high values from the same series on R.1/3 of the top left pane.

"SOMAL.LAND"—Occurs on R.7/5 of the lower pane from the 240 impression setting with the overprint at foot. In addition the Edwardian values of this series also have an example on R.6/7. The 6 a. has examples of the flaw on R.6/9 and R.7/5 of both the lower right and left panes. A similar variety occurs on the high values from the same series at R.3/4 of the third pane in the left-hand column.

1903 (1 June). *Nos. 80, 94, 96, 98, 100, 106/9, 114/16 and 118 of India (Queen Victoria) optd with T* **1**, *at top of stamp, in Calcutta. Wmk Elephant Head (6 a.) or Star (others).*

1 ½ a. yellow-green .. 2·50 3·25
a. "BRIT SH" .. £150
2 1 a. carmine .. 2·75 2·75
a. "BRIT SH" .. £170 £250
b. "BR1TISH" .. £120
3 2 a. pale violet .. 1·75 1·00
a. "BRIT SH" .. £275 £350
b. "BR1TISH" .. £225
c. Opt double .. £650
4 2½ a. ultramarine .. 2·00 1·75
a. "BRIT SH" .. £400
b. "BR1TISH" .. £250
5 3 a. brown-orange .. 2·50 2·00
a. "BRIT SH" .. £425
b. "BR1TISH" .. £275
6 4 a. slate-green .. 3·00 2·75
a. "BR1TISH" .. £275
7 6 a. olive-bistre .. 4·50 4·50
a. "BR1TISH" .. £190
8 8 a. dull mauve .. 3·00 5·00
a. "BR1TISH" .. £275
9 12 a. purple/*red* .. 2·50 7·00
a. "BR1TISH" .. £275
10 1 r. green and aniline carmine .. 5·00 10·00
a. "BR1TISH" .. £325
11 2 r. carmine and yellow-brown .. 23·00 40·00
a. Curved opt .. £200
12 3 r. brown and green .. 18·00 45·00
a. Curved opt .. £200
13 5 r. ultramarine and violet .. 26·00 50·00
a. Curved opt .. £250
1/13 .. *Set of* 13 85·00 £160

1903 (1 Sept–2 Nov). *Stamps of India optd with T* **1**, *at bottom of stamp, in Calcutta. (a) On Nos. 80, 100, 106/9 and 118 (Queen Victoria).*

18 2½ a. ultramarine (2.11) .. 1·75 4·75
a. "BR1TISH" .. £150
b. "SUMALILAND" .. £190
c. "SOMAL.LAND" .. £190
19 6 a. olive-bistre (2.11) .. 4·00 4·50
a. "BR1TISH" .. £200
b. "SOMAL.LAND" .. £120
20 12 a. purple/*red* (2.11) .. 3·75 12·00
a. "BR1TISH" .. £180
b. "SUMALILAND" .. £275
c. "SOMAL.LAND" .. £275
21 1 r. green and aniline carmine (2.11) .. 2·25 11·00
a. "BR1TISH" .. £200
b. "SUMALILAND" .. £325
c. "SOMAL.LAND" .. £325
22 2 r. carmine and yellow-brown (2.11) .. 55·00 90·00
a. Curved opt .. £350
b. "SUMALILAND" .. £350
c. "SOMAL.LAND" .. £350
23 3 r. brown and green (2.11) .. 60·00 95·00
a. Opt double, both inverted with one albino .. £550
b. Curved opt .. £375
c. "SUMALILAND" .. £375
d. "SOMAL.LAND" .. £375
24 5 r. ultramarine and violet (2.11) .. 55·00 80·00
a. Curved opt .. £325
b. "SUMALILAND" .. £325
c. "SOMAL.LAND" .. £325

(b) On Nos. 122/4, 127/8 and 133 (King Edward VII)

25 ½ a. green .. 1·75 55
a. "BRIT SH" .. £300
b. "BR1TISH" .. 65·00
c. "SUMALILAND" .. 65·00
d. "SOMAL.LAND" .. 35·00
26 1 a. carmine (8.10) .. 1·00 30
a. "BRIT SH" .. £190
b. "BR1TISH" .. 70·00 70·00
c. "SUMALILAND" .. 70·00
d. "SOMAL.LAND" .. 35·00 35·00
27 2 a. violet (2.11) .. 1·50 2·50
a. "BRIT SH" .. £800
b. "BR1TISH" .. £150
c. "SUMALILAND" .. £150
d. "SOMAL.LAND" .. 60·00
28 3 a. orange-brown (2.11) .. 1·75 2·50
a. "BR1TISH" .. £150
b. "SUMALILAND" .. £150
c. "SOMAL.LAND" .. 65·00
29 4 a. olive (2.11) .. 1·50 4·00
a. "BR1TISH" .. £160
b. "SUMALILAND" .. £160
c. "SOMAL.LAND" .. 70·00
30 8 a. purple (2.11) .. 1·50 2·25
a. "BR1TISH" .. £180
b. "SUMALILAND" .. £180
c. "SOMAL.LAND" .. 90·00
18/30 .. *Set of* 13 £160 £275

(Typo D.L.R.)

1904 (15 Feb–3 Sept). *(a) Wmk Crown CA. P 14.*

32 **2** ½ a. dull green and green .. 60 3·00
33 1 a. grey-black and red (3.9) .. 4·50 2·25
34 2 a. dull and bright purple (3.9) .. 1·50 1·50
35 2½ a. bright blue (3.9) .. 1·75 3·00
36 3 a. chocolate and grey-green (3.9) .. 1·00 2·25
37 4 a. green and black (3.9) .. 1·50 2·75
38 6 a. green and violet (3.9) .. 3·00 13·00
39 8 a. grey-black and pale blue (3.9) .. 3·00 5·50
40 12 a. grey-black and orange-buff (3.9) .. 5·50 11·00

(b) Wmk Crown CC. P 14

41 **3** 1 r. green (3.9) .. 12·00 35·00
42 2 r. dull and bright purple (3.9) .. 35·00 65·00
43 3 r. green and black (3.9) .. 35·00 75·00
44 5 r. grey-black and red (3.9) .. 35·00 75·00
32/44 .. *Set of* 13 £120 £275
32/44 Optd "Specimen" .. *Set of* 13 £180

1905 (July)–**11**. *Wmk Mult Crown CA. Ordinary paper. P 14.*

45 **2** ½ a. dull green and green .. 70 5·50
46 1 a. grey-black and red (10.7.05) .. 8·50 3·00
a. Chalk-surfaced paper (1906) .. 7·00 1·60
47 2 a. dull and bright purple .. 5·50 7·50
a. Chalk-surfaced paper (1909) .. 5·00 9·00
48 2½ a. bright blue .. 3·00 10·00
49 3 a. chocolate and grey-green .. 1·50 12·00
a. Chalk-surfaced paper (1911) .. 7·00 16·00
50 4 a. green and black .. 3·00 12·00
a. Chalk-surfaced paper (1911) .. 8·50 24·00
51 6 a. green and violet .. 2·50 19·00
a. Chalk-surfaced paper (1911) .. 15·00 26·00
52 8 a. grey-black and pale blue .. 4·00 6·50
a. Chalk-surfaced paper. *Black and blue* (27.1.11) .. 40·00 70·00
53 **2** 12 a. grey-black and orange-buff .. 5·50 10·00
a. Chalk-surfaced paper. *Black and orange-brown* (9.11.11) .. 16·00 55·00

1909 (30 Apr–May). *Wmk Mult Crown CA. P 14.*

58 **2** ½ a. bluish green (May) .. 17·00 20·00
59 1 a. red (Optd S. £25) .. 2·50 1·50
45/59 .. *Set of* 11 45·00 95·00

4

5

(Typo D.L.R.)

1912 (Nov)–**19**. *Wmk Mult Crown CA. Chalk-surfaced paper (2 a. and 3 a. to 5 r.). P 14.*

60 **4** ½ a. green (11.13) .. 40 6·50
w. Wmk inverted .. 15·00 60·00
61 1 a. red .. 1·75 50
a. Scarlet (1917) .. 3·00 1·25
62 2 a. dull and bright purple (12.13) .. 3·50 10·00
a. Dull purple and violet-purple (4.19) 16·00 25·00
63 2½ a. bright blue (10.13) .. 90 7·50
64 3 a. chocolate and grey-green (10.13) .. 1·50 4·75
w. Wmk inverted .. 75·00
65 4 a. green and black (12.12) .. 1·00 8·00
66 6 a. green and violet (4.13) .. 1·75 4·50
67 8 a. grey-black and pale blue (10.13) .. 2·25 12·00
68 12 a. grey-black and orange-buff (10.13) 1·75 16·00
69 **5** 1 r. green .. 8·50 12·00
70 2 r. dull purple and purple (4.19) .. 18·00 65·00
71 3 r. green and black (4.19) .. 50·00 £110
72 5 r. black and scarlet (4.19) .. 50·00 £150
60/72 .. *Set of* 13 £130 £350
60/72 Optd "Specimen" .. *Set of* 13 £160

1921. *Wmk Mult Script CA. Chalk-surfaced paper (2 a. and 3 a. to 5 r.). P 14.*

73 **4** ½ a. blue-green .. 2·50 6·50
74 1 a. carmine-red .. 2·75 50
75 2 a. dull and bright purple .. 3·25 1·00
76 2½ a. bright blue .. 1·00 3·50
77 3 a. chocolate and green .. 2·50 7·50
78 4 a. green and black .. 2·50 5·50
79 6 a. green and violet .. 1·50 13·00
80 8 a. grey-black and pale blue .. 2·00 5·00
81 12 a. grey-black and orange-buff .. 7·00 15·00
82 **5** 1 r. dull green .. 6·50 45·00
83 2 r. dull purple and purple .. 20·00 42·00
84 3 r. dull green and black .. 32·00 £100
85 5 r. black and scarlet .. 60·00 £150
73/85 .. *Set of* 13 £130 £350
73/85 Optd "Specimen" .. *Set of* 13 £160

Examples of most values are known showing a forged Berbera postmark dated "21 OC 1932".

1935 (6 May). *Silver Jubilee. As Nos. 114/17 of Jamaica, but ptd by Waterlow. P* 11×12.

86 1 a. deep blue and scarlet .. 2·00 1·75
m. "Bird" by turret .. 60·00
87 2 a. ultramarine and grey .. 2·00 1·50
k. Kite and vertical log .. 45·00
88 3 a. brown and deep blue .. 2·00 8·00
k. Kite and vertical log .. 75·00
l. Kite and horizontal log .. 65·00
89 1 r. slate and purple .. 5·50 8·00
k. Kite and vertical log .. £110
l. Kite and horizontal log .. 95·00
86/9 .. *Set of* 4 10·50 17·00
86/9 Perf "Specimen" .. *Set of* 4 75·00

For illustrations of plate varieties see Omnibus section following Zimbabwe.

1937 (13 May). *Coronation. As Nos. 118/20 of Jamaica.*

90 1 a. scarlet .. 15 10
91 2 a. grey-black .. 55 85
92 3 a. bright blue .. 70 55
90/2 .. *Set of* 3 1·25 1·40
90/2 Perf "Specimen" .. *Set of* 3 55·00

6 Berbera Blackhead Sheep

7 Lesser Kudu

8 Somaliland Protectorate

(Des H. W. Claxton. Recess Waterlow)

1938 (10 May). *Portrait to left. Wmk Mult Script CA. P* 12½.

93 **6** ½ a. green .. 20 3·25
94 1 a. scarlet .. 20 50
95 2 a. maroon .. 30 60
96 3 a. bright blue .. 6·00 7·50
97 **7** 4 a. sepia .. 3·00 4·50
98 6 a. violet .. 4·25 9·00
99 8 a. grey .. 85 9·00
100 12 a. red-orange .. 2·50 9·50

101 **8** 1 r. green .. .. 8·50 32·00
102 2 r. purple .. .. 11·00 32·00
103 3 r. bright blue .. .. 17·00 22·00
104 5 r. black .. .. 17·00 22·00
a. Imperf between (horiz pair) £11000
93/104 .. .. *Set of* 12 65·00 £140
93/104 Perf "Specimen" .. *Set of* 12 £140

Examples of most values are known showing a forged Berbera postmark dated "15 AU 38".

> Following the Italian Occupation, from 19 August 1940 until 16 March 1941, the stamps of ADEN were used at Berbera from 1 July 1941 until 26 April 1942.

9 Berbera Blackhead Sheep

5 Cents (10)

1 Shilling (11)

(Recess Waterlow)

1942 (27 Apr). *As T* **6/8** *but with full-face portrait of King George VI, as in T* **9**. *Wmk Mult Script CA. P* 12½.

105 **9** ½ a. green 20 10
106 1 a. scarlet 20 10
107 2 a. maroon 40 10
108 3 a. bright blue 90 20
109 **7** 4 a. sepia .. .. 1·50 20
110 6 a. violet .. .. 2·25 20
111 8 a. grey 90 20
112 12 a. red-orange .. .. 2·75 20
113 **8** 1 r. green .. .. 1·00 40
114 2 r. purple .. .. 1·00 3·50
115 3 r. bright blue .. .. 1·50 6·50
116 5 r. black .. .. 5·00 4·00
105/16 .. .. .. *Set of* 12 16·00 14·00
105/16 Perf "Specimen" .. *Set of* 12 £140

1946 (15 Oct). *Victory. As Nos.* 141/2 *of Jamaica. P* 13½×14.

117 1 a. carmine 10 10
a. Perf 13½ .. .. 9·50 42·00
118 3 a. blue 10 10
117/18 Perf "Specimen" .. *Set of* 2 48·00

1949 (28 Jan). *Royal Silver Wedding. As Nos.* 143/4 *of Jamaica.*

119 1 a. scarlet 10 10
120 5 r. black .. .. 3·50 3·25

1949 (10 Oct). *75th Anniv of U.P.U. As Nos.* 145/8 *of Jamaica. Surch with face values in annas.*

121 1 a. on 10 c. carmine 30 15
122 3 a. on 30 c. deep blue (R.) 75 40
123 6 a. on 50 c. purple 40 40
124 12 a. on 1s. red-orange 55 40
121/4 .. .. *Set of* 4 1·75 1·25

(New Currency. 100 cents = 1 shilling)

1951 (1 Apr). 1942 *issue surch as T* **10/11**.

125 5 c. on ½ a. green 10 30
126 10 c. on 2 a. maroon 10 20
127 15 c. on 3 a. bright blue 30 30
128 20 c. on 4 a. sepia 50 20
129 30 c. on 6 a. violet 70 20
130 50 c. on 8 a. grey 55 20
131 70 c. on 12 a. red-orange .. .. 1·00 2·75
132 1 s. on 1 r. green 50 20
133 2 s. on 2 r. purple .. .. 2·50 7·00
134 2 s. on 3 r. bright blue .. .. 2·75 2·50
135 5 s. on 5 r. black (R.) .. .. 3·50 4·00
125/35 .. .. .. *Set of* 11 11·00 16·00

1953 (2 June). *Coronation. As No.* 153 *of Jamaica.*

136 15 c. black and green 30 20

12 Camel and Gurgi

13 Askari

(Recess B.W.)

1953 (15 Sept)–**58**. *T* **12/13** *and similar horiz designs. Wmk Mult Script CA. P* 12½.

137 **12** 5 c. slate-black 15 50
138 **13** 10 c. red-orange .. .. 1·75 60
a. Salmon (20.3.58) .. .. .. 6·00 1·75
139 **12** 15 c. blue-green 50 60
140 20 c. scarlet 50 40
141 **13** 30 c. reddish brown .. .. 2·00 40
142 – 35 c. blue .. .. 1·50 1·50
143 – 50 c. brown and rose-carmine .. .. .. 2·00 55
144 – 1 s. light blue 50 30
145 – 1 s. 30, ultramarine and black (1.9.58) 7·00 3·25
146 – 2 s. brown and bluish violet .. .. 18·00 3·50
147 – 5 s. red-brown and emerald .. .. 18·00 6·00
148 – 10 s. brown and reddish violet .. .. 14·00 14·00
137/48 .. .. .. *Set of* 12 60·00 28·00

Designs:—35 c., 2 s. Somali Stock Dove; 50 c., 5 s. Martial Eagle; 1 s. Berbera Blackhead Sheep; 1 s. 30, Sheikh Isaaq's Tomb; 10 s. Taleh Fort.

OPENING OF THE LEGISLATIVE COUNCIL 1957 (19)

LEGISLATIVE COUNCIL UNOFFICIAL MAJORITY, 1960 (20)

1957 (21 May). *Opening of Legislative Council. Nos.* 140 *and* 144 *optd with T* **19**.

149 20 c. scarlet 10 15
150 1 s. light blue 30 15

1960 (5 Apr). *Legislative Council's Unofficial Majority. Nos.* 140 *and* 145 *optd as T* **20**.

151 20 c. scarlet 10 15
152 1 s. 30, ultramarine and black 40 15

OFFICIAL STAMPS

SERVICE

BRITISH SOMALILAND (O 1)

BRITISH SOMALILAND (O 2)

O.H.M.S. (O 3)

SETTING OF TYPE O 1

The 240 impression setting used for the Official stamps differs considerably from that on the contemporary postage issue with overprint at foot, although the "BR1TISH" error can still be found on R.6/4 of the upper pane. The Official setting is recorded as consisting of 217 overprints as Type A and 23 as Type B.

OVERPRINT VARIETIES

Figure "1" for first "I" in "BRITISH". Occurs on R.6/4 of the upper pane as for the postage issue.
"BRITIS H"—Occurs on R.8, stamps 4 and 10 of the lower pane.

1903 (1 June). *Nos.* O45, O48, O49*a and* O50/1 *of India* (*Queen Victoria optd* "O.H.M.S.") *additionally optd with Type* **O 1** *in Calcutta.*

O1 ½ a. yellow-green .. .. 4·75 48·00
a. "BR1TISH" £225
b. "BRITIS H" £110
O2 1 a. carmine .. .. 12·00 8·00
a. "BR1TISH" £250 £250
b. "BRITIS H" £120
O3 2 a. pale violet .. .. 8·00 48·00
a. "BR1TISH" £275
b. "BRITIS H" £140
O4 8 a. dull mauve .. .. 10·00 £375
a. "BR1TISH" £550
b. "BRITIS H" £275
c. Stop omitted after "M" of "O.H.M.S." (lower pane R. 12/10) £1100
O5 1 r. green and carmine .. .. .. 10·00 £550
a. "BR1TISH" £550
b. "BRITIS H" £275
O1/5 .. .. *Set of* 5 40·00 £900

No. O4*c* was caused by an attempt to correct a minor spacing error of the "O.H.M.S." overprint which is known on the equivalent India Official stamp.

SETTING OF TYPE O 2

This 240 impression setting of "BRITISH SOMALILAND" also differs from that used to prepare the postage issue with overprint at foot, although many of the errors from the latter still occur in the same positions for the Official stamps. The setting used for Nos. O6/9*f* contained 180 overprints as Type A and 60 as Type B.

OVERPRINT VARIETIES

Missing second "I" in "BRITISH"—Occurs R.7/12 of upper pane as for the postage issue.
Figure "1" for first "I" in "BRITISH"—Occurs R.6/4 of upper pane as for the postage issue.
"SUMALILAND"—Occurs R.2/9 of the upper pane as for the postage issue.
"SOMAL.LAND"—Occurs R.6/7 of the lower pane as for the postage issue.

SERVICE (O 2*a*)

"SERVICE" in wrong fount (Type O 2*a*)—Occurs R.1/7 of lower pane.

1903. *Prepared for use but not issued. Nos.* 106, 122/4 *and* 133 *of India* (1 *r. Queen Victoria, rest King Edward VII*), *optd with Type* **O 2** *in Calcutta.*

O6 ½ a. green 40
a. "BRIT SH" .. .. 65·00
b. "BR1TISH" .. .. 45·00
c. "SUMALILAND" .. .. 45·00
d. "SOMAL.LAND" .. .. 32·00
e. "SERVICE" as Type O 2*a* .. .. .. 40·00
O7 1 a. carmine 40
a. "BRIT SH" .. .. 65·00
b. "BR1TISH" .. .. 45·00
c. "SUMALILAND" .. .. 45·00
d. "SOMAL.LAND" .. .. 32·00
e. "SERVICE" as Type O 2*a* .. .. .. 40·00
O8 2 a. violet 70
a. "BRIT SH" .. .. 95·00
b. "BR1TISH" .. .. 65·00
c. "SUMALILAND" .. .. 65·00
d. "SERVICE" as Type O 2*a* .. .. .. 45·00
O9 8 a. purple .. .. 4·00
a. "BRIT SH" £1200
b. "BR1TISH" £325
c. "SUMALILAND" £325
d. "SERVICE" as Type O 2*a* £325
O9*f* 1 r. green and aniline carmine .. .. .. 17·00
fa. "BRIT SH" £1200
fb. "BR1TISH" £325
fc. "SUMALILAND" £325
fd. "SOMAL.LAND" £325
fe. "SERVICE" as Type O 2*a* £325
O6/9*f* .. .. *Set of* 5 20·00

Used examples of Nos. O6/9*f* are known, but there is no evidence that such stamps did postal duty.

SETTING OF TYPE O 3

The anna values were overprinted in sheets of 120 (2 panes 6 × 10) from a setting matching the pane size. The full stop after the "M" on the fifth vertical column was either very faint or completely omitted. The prices quoted are for stamps with the stop missing; examples with a partial stop are worth much less.

The 1 r. value was overprinted from a separate setting of 60 which did not show the "missing stop" varieties.

1904 (1 Sept)–**05**. *Stamps of Somaliland Protectorate optd with Type* **O 3**. *P* 14. (*a*) *Wmk Crown CA*.

O10 **2** ½ a. dull green and green .. .. 3·25 48·00
a. No stop after "M" £275
O11 1 a. grey-black and carmine .. .. 3·25 7·00
a. No stop after "M" £200 £275
O12 2 a. dull and bright purple .. .. £130 50·00
a. No stop after "M" £1200 £650
O13 8 a. grey-black and pale blue .. .. 60·00 £130
a. No stop after "M" £450

(*b*) *Wmk Mult Crown CA*

O14 **2** 2 a. dull and bright purple, **O** (7.05?) 75·00 £650
a. No stop after "M" £1200

(*c*) *Wmk Crown CC*

O15 **3** 1 r. green £160 £475
O10/13, O15 .. .. *Set of* 5 £250 £600
O10/13, O15 Optd "Specimen" .. *Set of* 5 £120

All Somaliland Protectorate stamps were withdrawn from sale on 25 June 1960 and until the unification on 1 July, issues of Italian Somalia together with Nos. 353/5 of Somalia Republic were used. Later issues will be found listed in Part 14 (*Africa since Independence N–Z*) of this catalogue.

South Africa

South Africa as a nation, rather than a geographical term, came into being with the creation of the Union of South Africa on 31 May 1910.

The development, both political and philatelic, of the area is very complex and the method adopted by the catalogue is to first list, in alphabetical order, the various colonies and republics which formed this federation, followed by stamps for the Union of South Africa and Republic of South Africa with the issues for the four Bantu "homelands" (granted independence in the 1970s but reincorporated into the Republic of South Africa in 1994) at the end.

The section is divided as follows:

I. CAPE OF GOOD HOPE. British Kaffraria. Mafeking Siege Stamps. Vryburg
II. GRIQUALAND WEST
III. NATAL.
IV. NEW REPUBLIC.
V. ORANGE FREE STATE. Orange River Colony
VI. TRANSVAAL. Pietersburg. Local British Occupation Issues
VII. ZULULAND
VIII. BRITISH ARMY FIELD OFFICES DURING SOUTH AFRICAN WAR
IX. UNION OF SOUTH AFRICA
X. REPUBLIC OF SOUTH AFRICA
XI. BOPHUTHATSWANA
XII. CISKEI
XIII. TRANSKEI
XIV. VENDA

I. CAPE OF GOOD HOPE

PRICES FOR STAMPS ON COVER

Nos. 1/4	*from* × 4
Nos. 5/14	*from* × 3
Nos. 18/21	*from* × 5
No. 22	—
Nos. 23/6	*from* × 5
Nos. 27/31	*from* × 8
Nos. 32/3	*from* × 10
No. 34	*from* × 25
No. 35	*from* × 20
No. 36	*from* × 10
Nos. 37/8	*from* × 25
Nos. 39/45	*from* × 10
Nos. 46/7	*from* × 12
Nos. 48/54	*from* × 10
Nos. 55/6	*from* × 25
No. 57	*from* × 50
Nos. 58/69	*from* × 10
Nos. 70/8	*from* × 6

PRICES. Our prices for early Cape of Good Hope are for stamps in very fine condition. Exceptional copies are worth more, poorer copies considerably less.

1 Hope

2

(Des Charles Bell, Surveyor-General. Eng W. Humphrys. Recess P.B.)

1853 (1 Sept). *W* **2.** *Imperf. (a) Paper deeply blued.*

1 1 1d. pale brick-red £3500 £275
a. Deep brick-red £5000 £300
2 4d. deep blue £2000 £160

Plate proofs of the 4d. in a shade similar to the issued stamp exist on ungummed watermarked paper. The blueing on the reverse of these proofs is uneven giving a blotchy appearance.

(b) Paper slightly blued (blueing not so pronounced at back)

3 1 1d. brick-red £3000 £200
a. Brown-red £3250 £225
4 4d. deep blue £1300 £110
a. Blue £1400 £150

Both values are known with wmk sideways.

1855–8. *W* **2.** *(a) Imperf.*

5 1 1d. brick-red/*cream toned paper* (1857) . . £5000 £900
a. Rose (1858) £450 £200
b. Deep rose-red £600 £225
6 4d. deep blue/*white paper* (1855) . . £500 45·00
a. Blue . . . . £300 45·00
b. Bisected (on cover) . . . . . . † £35000
7 6d. slate-lilac/*blued paper* (18.2.58) . . £4250 £450
b. Pale rose-lilac/white paper £700 £200
c. Deep rose-lilac/white paper £1700 £300
d. Slate-purple/blued paper £3500 £1000
e. Bisected (on cover) . . . . . . † —
8 1s. brt yellow-green/*white paper* (18.2.58) £2500 £180
a. Deep dark green £225 £500

The method adopted for producing the plate of the 4d., 6d. and 1s stamps involved the use of two dies, so that there are two types of each of these values, differing slightly in detail, but produced in equal numbers.

All values of this issue are known with watermark sideways. The 1d. value in dull rose on ungummed watermarked paper with watermark sideways is a plate proof.

The 4d. is known bisected in 1858 and used with two other 4d. values to pay the inland registered fee. The 6d. is known bisected and used with 1d. for 4d. rate.

The paper of No. 5 is similar to that of Nos. 1/4, but is without the blueing. It is much thicker than the white paper used for later printings of the 1d. The evolution of the paper on these Cape of Good Hope stamps is similar to that on the line-engraved issues of Great Britain. Examples of the 6d. slate-lilac apparently on white paper have had the blueing washed out.

The 4d. value is known printed in black on white watermarked paper. Eleven authenticated copies have been recorded, the majority of which show cancellations or, at least, some indication that they have been used.

It was, at one time, believed that these stamps came from a small supply printed in black to mark the death of the Prince Consort, but references to examples can be found in the philatelic press before news of this event reached Cape Town.

It is now thought that these stamps represent proof sheets, possibly pressed into service during a shortage of stamps in 1861.

There is, however, no official confirmation of this theory. (*Price £30000 un, £25000 with obliteration*).

(b) Unofficially rouletted

9 1 1d. brick-red . . . . † £3000
10 4d. blue . . . . † £2250
11 6d. rose-lilac . . . . † £1500
12 1s. bright yellow-green . . . . . . † £3250
a. Deep dark green . . . . . . † £3500

These rouletted stamps are best collected on cover.

3 Hope

(Local provisional (so-called "wood-block") issue. Engraved on steel by C. J. Roberts. Printed from stereotyped plates by Saul Solomon & Co, Cape Town)

1861 (Feb–April). *Laid paper. Imperf.*

13 3 1d. vermilion (27 February) £13000 £2000
a. Carmine (7 March) £22000 £3000
b. Brick-red (10 April) £32000 £4250
c. Error. Pale milky blue . . . . — £28000
ca. Pale bright blue . . . . . . — £30000
14 4d. pale milky blue (23 February) £9000 £1500
aa. Retouch or repair to rt-hand corner — £5500
a. Pale grey-blue (March?) £10000 £1500
b. Pale bright blue (March?) . . £10000 £1900
ba. Retouch or repair to rt-hand corner — £5500
c. Deep bright blue (12 April) . . £85000 £4500
d. Blue £13000 £3000
e. Error. Vermilion £95000 £40000
ea. Carmine . . . . — £95000
f. Sideways *tête-bêche* (pair) . . . . † £65000

Nos. 13/14 were each issued in *tête-bêche* pairs normally joined at edges bearing the same inscription ("POSTAGE" against "POSTAGE", etc). No. 14f, of which only one used example is known, comes from the first printing and shows the right-hand stamp misplaced so that "FOUR PENCE" adjoins "POSTAGE".

Both values were officially reprinted in March, 1883, on wove paper. The 1d. is in deep red, and the 4d. in a deeper blue than that of the deepest shade of the issued stamp.

Specimens of the reprints have done postal duty, but their use thus was not intended. There are no reprints of the errors or of the retouched 4d.

Further reprints were made privately but with official permission, in 1940/41, in colours much deeper than those of any of the original printings, and on thick carton paper.

Examples of the 4d. are known unofficially rouletted.

Early in 1863, Perkins Bacon Ltd handed over the four plates used for printing the triangular Cape of Good Hope stamps to De La Rue & Co, Ltd, who made all the subsequent printings.

(Printed from the P.B. plates by D.L.R.)

1863–4. *Imperf. (a) W* **2.**

18 1 1d. deep carmine-red £110 £225
a. Deep brown-red £350 £250
b. Brownish red £350 £225
19 4d. deep blue . . . . £110 48·00
a. Blue . . . . £130 60·00
b. Slate-blue £2000 £500
c. Steel-blue £2000 £300
20 6d. bright mauve £150 £450
21 1s. bright emerald-green £350 £450
a. Pale emerald-green £1000

(b) Wmk Crown CC (sideways)

22 1 1d. deep carmine-red £15000

No. 22 was a trial printing, and is only known unused.

Our prices for the 4d. blue are for stamps which are blue by comparison with the other listed shades. An exceptionally pale shade is recognised by specialists and is rare.

All values of this issue are known with watermark lying sideways.

With the exception of the 4d., these stamps may be easily distinguished from those printed by Perkins Bacon by their colours, which are quite distinct.

The De La Rue stamps of all values are less clearly printed, the figure of Hope and the lettering of the inscriptions standing out less boldly, while the fine lines of the background appear blurred and broken when examined under a glass. The background as a whole often shows irregularity in the apparent depth of colour, due to wear of the plates.

For note regarding the two dies of the 4d., 6d., and 1s. values, see after No. 8.

All the triangular stamps were demonetised as from 1 October 1900.

4 "Hope" seated, with vine and ram. (With outer frame-line)

Four Pence.

(5)

(Des Charles Bell; die engraved on steel and stamps typo by D.L.R.)

1864–77. *With outer frame-line surrounding the design. Wmk Crown CC. P* 14.

23 4 1d. carmine-red (5.65) . . . . . . 85·00 16·00
a. Rose-red . . . . 80·00 15·00
24 4d. pale blue (8.65) . . . . . . 95·00 2·00
a. Blue . . . . £100 2·00
b. Ultramarine . . . . £250 55·00
c. Deep blue (1872) . . . . . . £140 3·00
25 6d. pale lilac (before 21.3.64) . . . . £100 18·00
a. Deep lilac . . . . £200 6·50
b. Violet (to bright) (1877) . . . . £120 1·50
26 1s. deep green (1.64) . . . . . . £500 16·00
a. Green . . . . £100 2·00
b. Blue-green . . . . £110 3·50

The 1d. rose-red, 6d. lilac, and 1s. blue-green are known imperf, probably from proof sheets.

The 1d. and 4d. stamps of this issue may be found with side and/or top outer frame-lines missing, due to wear of the plates.

See also Nos. 44 and 52/3.

(Surch by Saul Solomon & Co, Cape Town)

1868 (17 Nov). *No. 25a surch with T* **5.**

27 4 4d. on 6d. deep lilac (R.) . . . . . . £170 14·00
a. "Peuce" for "Pence" £1800 £700
b. "Fonr" for "Four" . . . . . . — £700

Specimens may also be found with bars omitted or at the top of the stamp, due to misplacement of the sheet.

The space between the words and bars varies from 12½ to 16 mm, stamps with spacing 15½ and 16 mm being rare. There were two printings, one of 120,000 in November 1868 and another of 1,000,000 in December. Stamps showing widest spacings are probably from the earlier printing.

6 (No outer frame-line)

(Die re-engraved. Typo D.L.R.)

1871–6. *Outer frame-line removed. Wmk Crown CC. P* 14.

28 6 ½d. grey-black (*shades*) (12.75) . . 10·00 4·50
29 1d. carmine-red (*shades*) (2.72) . . 26·00 40
30 4d. dull blue (*shades*) (12.76) . . 90·00 50
b. Ultramarine . . . . . . £200 50·00
31 5s. yellow-orange (25.8.71) . . . . £225 12·00

The ½d., 1d. and 5s. are known imperf, probably from proof sheets.

See also Nos. 36, 39, 40/3, 48/51, 54, 61/2 and 64/8.

ONE PENNY **THREE PENCE**

(7) (8)

(Surch by Saul Solomon & Co, Cape Town)

1874–6. *Nos. 25a and 26a surch with T* **7.**

32 4 1d. on 6d. deep lilac (R.) (1.9.74) . . £375 70·00
a. "E" of "PENNY" omitted . . . . — £850
33 1d. on 1s. green (11.76) . . . . . . 55·00 30·00

These provisionals are found with the bar only, either across the centre of the stamp or at top, with value only; or with value and bar close together, either at top or foot. Such varieties are due to misplacement of sheets during surcharging.

1879 (1 Nov). *No. 30 surch with T* **8.**

34 6 3d. on 4d. blue (R.) . . . . . . 80·00 1·25
a. "PENCB" for "PENCE" £1500 £275
b. "THE.EE" for "THREE" £1800 £350
c. Surch double £7500 £2750
d. Variety b. double

The double surcharge must also have existed showing variety a. but only variety b. is known.

There are numerous minor varieties, including letters broken or out of alignment, due to defective printing and use of poor type.

The spacing between the bar and the words varies from 16½ to 18 mm.

THREEPENCE **3** **3**

(9) (10) (11)

(Surch by D.L.R.)

1880 (Feb). *Special printing of the 4d. in new colour, surch, with T* **9.** *Wmk Crown CC.*

35 6 3d. on 4d. pale dull rose . . . . . . 50·00 1·50

A minor constant variety exists with foot of "P" in "PENCE" broken off, making the letter appear shorter.

1880 (1 July). *Wmk Crown CC. P* 14.

36 6 3d. pale dull rose . . . . £160 18·00

(Surch by Saul Solomon & Co, Cape Town)

1880 (Aug). *No. 36 surch.*

37 10 "3" on 3d. pale dull rose . . . . . . 55·00 75
a. Surch inverted . . . . . . £800 40·00
b. Vert pair. Nos. 37/8 . . . . . . £800 £325
38 11 "3" on 3d. pale dull rose . . . . . . £140 4·50
a. Surch inverted £7000 £900

The "3" (T **10**) is sometimes found broken. Vert pairs are known showing the two types of surcharge *se-tenant*, and vertical strips of three exist, the top stamp having surcharge T **10**, the middle stamp being without surcharge, and the lower stamp having surcharge T **11** (*Price for strip of* 3 *£3750 un.*).

1881 (Jan). *Wmk Crown CC. P* 14.

39 6 3d. pale claret . . . . 95·00 1·75
a. Deep claret . . . . £100 1·50

This was a definite colour change made at the request of the Postmaster-General owing to the similarity between the colours of the 1d. stamp and the 3d. in pale dull rose. Imperf copies are probably from proof sheets.

Proofs of this value were printed in brown, on unwatermarked wove paper and imperf, but the colour was rejected as unsuitable.

1882 (July)–**83.** *Wmk Crown CA. P* 14.

40 6 ½d. black (1.9.82) . . . . 16·00 55
a. Grey-black . . . . 13·00 30
41 1d. rose-red . . . . 35·00 60
a. Deep rose-red . . . . 40·00 60
42 2d. pale bistre (1.9.82) . . . . . . 75·00 30
a. Deep bistre . . . . 80·00 30
43 3d. pale claret . . . . 6·00 90
a. Deep claret . . . . 9·00 75
44 4 6d. mauve (to bright) (8.82) . . . . 70·00 70
45 6 5s. orange (8.83) £750 £200

Imperf pairs of the ½d., 1d. and 2d. are known, probably from proof sheets.

One Half-penny.

(12)

13 "Cabled Anchor"

(Surch by Saul Solomon & Co, Cape Town)

1882 (July). *Nos. 39a and 43a surch with T* **12.**

46 6 ½d. on 3d. deep claret (Wmk CC) . . £1700 £130
a. Hyphen omitted . . . . . . — £3250
47 ½d. on 3d. deep claret (Wmk CA) . . 16·00 2·00
a. "p" in "penny" omitted £2000 £700
b. "y" in "penny" omitted £1000
c. Hyphen omitted £500 £350

Varieties also exist with broken and defective letters, and with the obliterating bar omitted or at the top of the stamp.

1884–90. *W* **13.** *P* 14.

48 6 ½d. black (1.86) . . . . 2·00 10
a. Grey-black . . . . 2·00 10
49 1d. rose-red (12.85) . . . . . . 2·00 10
a. Carmine-red . . . . 2·00 10
50 2d. pale bistre (12.84) . . . . . . 17·00 60
a. Deep bistre . . . . 5·00 10
51 4d. blue (6.90) . . . . 5·50 15
a. Deep blue . . . . 6·00 15

No.	Type	Description	Unused	Used
52	4	6d. reddish purple (12.84)	60·00	1·60
		a. *Purple (shades)*	5·00	15
		b. *Bright mauve*	9·50	40
53		1s. green (12.85)	95·00	4·00
		a. *Blue-green* (1889)	48·00	30
54	6	5s. orange (7.87)	55·00	3·00
48/54		*Set of* 7	£110	3·50

All the above stamps are known in imperf pairs, probably from proof sheets.

For later shade and colour changes, etc., see Nos. 61, etc.

2½d

(14)

15

ONE PENNY.

(16)

(Surch by D.L.R.)

1891 (Mar). *Special printing of the 3d. in new colour, surch with T* **14**.

No.	Type	Description	Unused	Used
55	6	2½d. on 3d. pale magenta	3·00	80
		a. *Deep magenta*	2·50	20
		b. "1" with horiz serif	50·00	32·00

No. 55b occurs on two stamps (Nos. 8 and 49) of the pane of 60.

Two types of "d" are found in the surcharge, one with square end to serif at top, and the other with pointed serif.

1892 (June). *W* **13**. *P* 14.

No.	Type	Description	Unused	Used
56	15	2½d. sage-green	4·00	10
		a. *Olive-green*	6·50	55

See also No. 63.

(Surch by W. A. Richards & Sons, Cape Town)

1893 (Mar). *Nos.* 50/*a surch with T* **16**.

No.	Type	Description	Unused	Used
57	6	1d. on 2d. pale bistre	2·50	30
		a. *Deep bistre*	1·40	30
		b. No stop after "PENNY"	42·00	11·00
		c. Surch double	—	£400

No. 57b occurs on stamp No. 42 of the upper left-hand pane, and on No. 6 of the lower right-hand pane.

Minor varieties exist showing broken letters and letters out of alignment or widely spaced. Also with obliterating bar omitted, due to misplacement of the sheet during surcharging.

17 "Hope" standing. Table Bay in background

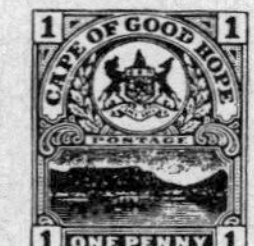

18 Table Mountain and Bay with Arms of the Colony

(Des Mr. Mountford. Typo D.L.R.)

1893 (Oct)–**1902**. *W* **13**. *P* 14.

No.	Type	Description	Unused	Used
58	17	½d. green (9.98)	80	10
59		1d. rose-red	1·25	30
		a. *Carmine*	45	10
60		3d. magenta (3.02)	4·00	60

The 1d. is known in imperf pairs, probably from proof sheets.

1893–98. *New colours, etc. W* **13**. *P* 14.

No.	Type	Description	Unused	Used
61	6	½d. yellow-green (12.96)	1·50	10
		a. *Green*	2·75	20
62		2d. chocolate-brown (3.97)	2·00	10
63	15	2½d. pale ultramarine (3.96)	3·00	15
		a. *Ultramarine*	3·00	10
64	6	3d. bright magenta (9.98)	3·50	40
65		4d. sage-green (3.97)	3·50	80
66		1s. blue-green (12.93)	40·00	2·00
		a. *Deep blue-green*	60·00	7·00
67		1s. yellow-ochre (5.96)	7·00	90
68		5s. brown-orange (6.96)	55·00	3·50
61/8		*Set of* 8	£100	7·00

(Des E. Sturman. Typo D.L.R.)

1900 (Jan). *W* **13**. *P* 14.

No.	Type	Description	Unused	Used
69	18	1d. carmine	1·25	10

19

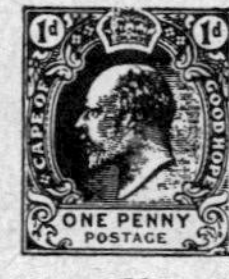

20

21

22 23 24

25 26

27

(Typo D.L.R.)

1902 (Dec)–**04**. *W* **13**. *P* 14.

No.	Type	Description	Unused	Used
70	19	½d. green	1·00	10
71	20	1d. carmine	80	10
		w. Wmk inverted		
		y. Wmk inverted and reversed		
72	21	2d. brown (10.04)	5·00	55
		w. Wmk inverted		
73	22	2½d. ultramarine (3.04)	2·75	6·50
74	23	3d. magenta (4.03)	5·00	30
75	24	4d. olive-green (2.03)	4·50	55
76	25	6d. bright mauve (3.03)	9·00	30
77	26	1s. yellow-ochre	9·50	65
78	27	5s. brown-orange (2.03)	60·00	8·00
70/8		*Set of* 9	85·00	65·00

All values exist in imperf pairs, from proof sheets.

STAMP BOOKLETS

1902. *Black on red cover. Stapled.*

No.	Description	Price
SB1	1s. ½d. booklet containing twelve 1d. (No. 71) in blocks of 6	£2000

1902. *Black on red cover. Stapled.*

No.	Description	Price
SB2	2s. 7d. booklet containing thirty 1d. (No. 71) in blocks of 6	£2000

OFFICIAL STAMPS

The following stamps, punctured with a double triangle device, were used by the Stationery and Printed Forms Branch of the Cape of Good Hope Colonial Secretary's Department between 1904 and 1906. Later South Africa issues may have been similarly treated, but this has not been confirmed.

(O 1)

1904. *Various issues punctured as Type* O **1**. (*a*) *Nos.* 50 *and* 52*a*.

No.	Type	Description	Used
O 1	6	2d. pale bistre	10·00
O 2	4	6d. purple	10·00
		(*b*) *Nos.* 58 *and* 60	
O 3	17	½d. green	12·00
O 4		3d. magenta	10·00
		(*c*) *Nos.* 62 *and* 64/5	
O 5	6	2d. chocolate-brown	10·00
O 6		3d. bright magenta	12·00
O 7		4d. sage-green	12·00
		(*d*) *No.* 69	
O 8	18	1d. carmine	10·00
		(*e*) *Nos.* 70/2 *and* 74/8	
O 9	19	½d. green	12·00
O10	20	1d. carmine	7·00
O11	21	2d. brown	10·00
O12	23	3d. magenta	10·00
O13	24	4d. olive-green	10·00
O14	25	6d. bright mauve	10·00
O15	26	1s. yellow-ochre	12·00
O16	27	5s. brown-orange	30·00

Nos. O1/16 are only known used.

Cape of Good Hope became a province of the Union of South Africa on 31 May 1910.

BRITISH KAFFRARIA

The history of the Cape eastern frontier was punctuated by a series of armed conflicts with the native population, known as the Kaffir Wars. After a particularly violent outbreak in 1846 the Governor, Sir Harry Smith, advanced the line of the Cape frontier to the Keikama and Tyumie Rivers. In the area between the new frontier and the Kei River a buffer state, British Kaffraria, was established on 17 December 1847. This area was not annexed to the Cape, but was administered as a separate Crown dependency by the Governor of Cape Colony in his capacity as High Commissioner for South Africa.

The territory, with its administration based on King William's Town, used the stamps of the Cape of Good Hope from 1853 onwards, the mail being sent via Port Elizabeth or overland from the Cape. Covers from British Kaffraria franked with the triangular issues are rare.

The first postal marking known from British Kaffraria is the 1849 type octagonal numeral No. 47 from Port Beaufort. Oval postmarks of the 1853 type were used at Alice, Aliwal North, Bedford, Fort Beaufort, King William's Town and Queenstown. In 1864 numeral cancellations were issued to all post offices within the Cape system and it is known that the following numbers were initially assigned to post towns in Kaffraria: 4 (King William's Town), 7 (Bedford), 11 (Queenstown), 29 (East London), 32 (Fort Beaufort), 38 (Aliwal North) and 104 (Cathcart).

It is believed that post offices may have also existed at Adelaide, Barkly East, Sterkstoom and Stutterheim, but, to date, no examples of handstamps or cancellations are known from them during the British Kaffraria period.

Following the decimation by famine of the Xhosa tribes in 1857 British Kaffraria was annexed to Cape Colony in 1865. The area eventually formed the basis of the Ciskei independent "homeland".

MINIMUM PRICE

The minimum price quote is 10p which represents a handling charge rather than a basis for valuing common stamps. For further notes about prices see introductory pages.

MAFEKING SIEGE STAMPS

PRICES FOR STAMPS ON COVER

Nos. 1/16	*from* × 12
Nos. 17/18	*from* × 20
Nos. 19/20	*from* × 15
Nos. 21/2	*from* × 10

23 MARCH to 17 MAY 1900

There are numerous forgeries of the Mafeking overprints, many of which were brought home by soldiers returning from the Boer War.

MAFEKING,
3d.
BESIEGED.

(1)

MAFEKING
3d.
BESIEGED.

(2)

(Surcharged by Townsend & Co, Mafeking)

1900 (23 Mar–28 Apr). *Various stamps surch as T* **1** *and* **2**.

No.	Type	Description	Unused	Used
		(*a*) *Cape of Good Hope stamps surch as T* **1** (23 Mar)		
1	6	1d. on ½d. green	£170	48·00
2	17	1d. on ½d. green (24.3)	£225	60·00
3		3d. on 1d. carmine	£170	48·00
4	6	6d. on 3d. magenta (24.3)	£25000	£250
5		1s. on 4d. sage-green (24.3)	£5500	£325

A variety in the setting of each value exists without comma after "MAFEKING".

No.	Type	Description	Unused	Used
		(*b*) *Nos.* 59 *and* 61/3 *of Bechuanaland Protectorate* (*optd on Great Britain*) *surch as T* **1**		
6		1d. on ½d. vermilion (28.3)	£170	48·00
		a. Surch inverted	†	£4000
		b. Vert pair, surch *tête-bêche*	†	£19000
7		3d. on 1d. lilac (4.4)	£850	75·00
		a. Surch double	†	£14000
8		6d. on 2d. green and carmine (6.4)	£1400	65·00
9		6d. on 3d. purple/*yellow* (30.3)	£4000	£250
		a. Surch inverted	†	£18000
		b. Surch double		
		(*c*) *Nos.* 12 *and* 35 *of British Bechuanaland* (*optd on Great Britain*) *surch as T* **1**		
10		6d. on 3d. lilac and black (27.3)	£350	60·00
11		1s. on 4d. green and purple-brown (29.3)	£1200	65·00
		a. Surch double (both Type **1**)	†	£15000
		ab. Surch double (Type **1** and Type **2**)	£6000	£4000
		b. Surch treble	†	£15000
		c. Surch double, one inverted	†	£15000
		(*d*) *Nos.* 61/2 *and* 65 *of Bechuanaland Protectorate* (*optd on Great Britain*) *surch as T* **2**		
12		3d. on 1d. lilac (1 Apr)	£900	60·00
		a. Surch double	†	£6500
13		6d. on 2d. green and carmine (25 Apr)	£1100	60·00
14		1s. on 6d. purple/*rose-red* (12 Apr)	£3750	85·00
		(*e*) *Nos.* 36/7 *of British Bechuanaland* (*optd on Great Britain*) *surch as T* **2**		
15		1s. on 6d. purple/*rose-red* (28 Apr)	£13000	£600
16		2s. on 1s. green (13 Apr)	£7000	£325

On the stamps overprinted "BECHUANALAND PROTECTORATE" and "BRITISH BECHUANALAND" the local surcharge is so adjusted as not to overlap the original overprint.

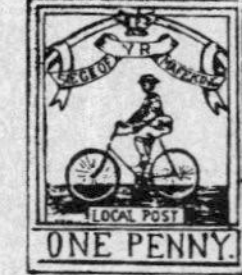

3 Cadet Sergt.-major Goodyear

4 General Baden-Powell

(Des Dr. W. A. Hayes (T **3**), Capt. H. Greener (T **4**))

1900 (7–11 Apr). *Produced photographically by Dr. D. Taylor. Horiz laid paper with sheet wmk* "OCEANA FINE". *P* 12.

No.	Type	Description	Unused	Used
		(*a*) 18½ *mm wide.* (*b*) 21 *mm wide*		
17	3	1d. pale blue/*blue*	£800	£275
18		1d. deep blue/*blue*	£800	£275
19	4	3d. pale blue/*blue* (*a*)	£1200	£400
		a. Reversed design	£45000	£35000
20		3d. deep blue/*blue* (*a*)	£1200	£350
		a. Imperf between (horiz pair)	†	£48000
		b. Double print	†	£16000
21		3d. pale blue/*blue* (*b*) (11.4)	£6500	£750
22		3d. deep blue/*blue* (*b*) (11.4)	£7000	£950

These stamps vary a great deal in colour from deep blue to pale grey.

No. 18 imperforate and without gum is believed to be a proof (*Price for unused pair* £15000).

No. 19a comes from a sheet of 12 printed in reverse of which nine, three mint and six used, are known to have survived.

VRYBURG

PRICES FOR STAMPS ON COVER

Nos. 1/4	*from* × 5
Nos. 11/12	*from* × 2

BOER OCCUPATION

Vryburg was occupied by Boer forces on 15 October 1899. Unoverprinted stamps of Transvaal were used initially. Nos. 1/4 were only available from 24 to 29 November. The Boers evacuated the town on 7 May 1900.

½ PENCE

Z.A.R.

(1)

1899 (24 Nov). *Cape stamps surch as T* **1**. *With* 12 *mm between the lines on No.* 3 *and* 10 *mm on all other values.*

1 **6** ½ PENCE green .. .. £200 80·00
a. Italic "Z" £1700 £700
b. 12 mm between lines of surch .. £1700 £700
2 **17** 1 PENCE rose £225 £100
a. Italic "Z" £1900 £800
b. 12 mm between lines of surch .. £1900 £800
c. "I" for "1" £1200 £500
3 **4** 2 PENCE on 6d. mauve £2250 £500
a. Italic "Z" £10000 £4250
4 **15** 2½ PENCE on 2½d. blue £2000 £425
a. Italic "Z" £10000 £4250
b. 12 mm between lines of surch .. £10000 £4250

The "2 PENCE" on 6d. shows the surcharge 12 mm high. It is possible that this was the first value surcharged as the remaining three show the height reduced to 10 mm with the exception of one position in the second vertical row of the setting. The italic "Z" occurs in one position in the sixth vertical row. It is believed that the setting was of 60 (6×10).

BRITISH REOCCUPATION

(2)

1900 (16 May). *Provisionals issued by the Military Authorities. Stamps of Transvaal handstamped with T* **2**.

11 **30** ½d. green .. .. — £1700
11*a* 1d. rose-red (No. 206)
12 1d. rose-red and green (No. 217) .. £7500 £3000
13 2d. brown and green .. ..
14 2½d. dull blue and green .. ..

No. 11 is known used with double handstamp and Nos. 11/12 with the overprint reading downwards

II. GRIQUALAND WEST

Griqualand West was situated to the North of Cape Colony, bounded on the north by what became British Bechuanaland and on the east by the Orange Free State.

The area was settled in the early nineteenth century by the Griqua tribal group, although many members of the tribe, including the paramount chief, migrated to Griqualand East (between Basutoland and the east coast of South Africa) in 1861–63. There was little European involvement in Griqualand West before 1866, but in that year the diamond fields along the Vaal River were discovered. Sovereignty was subsequently claimed by the Griqua Chief, the Orange Free State and the South African Republic (Transvaal). In 1871 the British authorities arbitrated in favour of the Griqua Chief who promptly ceded his territory to Great Britain. Griqualand West became a separate Crown Colony in January 1873.

During the initial stages of the prospecting boom mail was passed via the Orange Free State, but a post office connected to the Cape Colony postal system was opened at Klip Drift (subsequently Barkly) in late 1870. Further offices at De Beer's New Rush (subsequently Kimberley), Douglas and Du Toit's Pan (subsequently Beaconsfield) were open by September 1873.

Cape of Good Hope stamps to the 5s. value were in use from October 1871, but those originating in Griqualand West can only be identified after the introduction of Barred Oval Diamond Numeral cancellations in 1873. Numbers known to have been issued in the territory are:

1 De Beers N.R. (New Rush) (subsequently Kimberley)
3 Junction R. & M. (Riet and Modder Rivers)
4 Barkly
6 or 9 Du Toit's Pan (subsequently Beaconsfield)
8 Langford (transferred to Douglas)
10 Thornhill

PRICES FOR STAMPS ON COVER

The stamps of Griqualand West are worth from ×10 the price quoted for used stamps, when on cover from the territory.

FORGED OVERPRINTS. Many stamps show forged overprints. Great care should be taken when purchasing the scarcer items.

Stamps of the Cape of Good Hope, Crown CC, perf 14, overprinted.

1874 (Sept). *No. 24a of Cape of Good Hope surch* "1d." *in red manuscript by the Kimberley postmaster.*

1 1d. on 4d. blue £750 £1300

G. W.

(1)

1877 (Mar). *Nos.* 29/30 *of Cape of Good Hope optd with T* **1**.

2 1d. carmine-red .. .. £425 75·00
a. Opt double .. .. † £1600
3 4d. dull blue (R.) .. .. £325 65·00

G (1*a*) G (2) G (3) G (4) G (5) G (6)

G (7) G (8) G (9) G (10) G (11)

G (12) *G* (13) *G* (14)

1877 (Mar)–**78**. *Nos.* 24*a*, 25*a*, 26*a and* 28/31 *Cape of Good Hope optd with capital* "G".

(*a*) *First printing. Optd with T* **1***a*/**6** *and* **8** *in black* (1*d.*) *or red* (*others*)

4 ½d. grey-black
a. Opt Type 1*a* .. .. 16·00 20·00
b. Opt Type 2 .. .. 38·00 45·00
c. Opt Type 3 .. .. 22·00 26·00
d. Opt Type 4 .. .. 38·00 45·00
e. Opt Type 5 .. .. 42·00 50·00
f. Opt Type 6 .. .. 20·00 24·00
g. Opt Type 8 .. .. £325 £350
5 1d. carmine-red
a. Opt Type 1*a* .. .. 17·00 12·00
b. Opt Type 2 .. .. 40·00 28·00
c. Opt Type 3 .. .. 22·00 18·00
d. Opt Type 4 .. .. 40·00 28·00
e. Opt Type 5 .. .. 45·00 32·00
f. Opt Type 6 .. .. 17·00 12·00
g. Opt Type 8 .. .. *
6 4d. blue (with frame-line) (No. 24*a*)
a. Opt Type 1*a* .. .. £150 26·00
b. Opt Type 2 .. .. £375 75·00
c. Opt Type 3 .. .. £275 38·00
d. Opt Type 4 .. .. £375 75·00
e. Opt Type 5 .. .. £425 85·00
f. Opt Type 6 .. .. £200 35·00
g. Opt Type 8 .. .. — £450
7 4d. dull blue (without frame-line) (No. 30)
a. Opt Type 1*a* .. .. £110 18·00
b. Opt Type 2 .. .. £275 48·00
c. Opt Type 3 .. .. £180 24·00
d. Opt Type 4 .. .. £275 48·00
e. Opt Type 5 .. .. £325 60·00
f. Opt Type 6 .. .. £170 23·00
g. Opt Type 8 .. .. £1200 £325
8 6d. deep lilac
a. Opt Type 1*a* .. .. 85·00 20·00
b. Opt Type 2 .. .. £180 50·00
c. Opt Type 3 .. .. £120 27·00
d. Opt Type 4 .. .. £180 50·00
e. Opt Type 5 .. .. £225 65·00
f. Opt Type 6 .. .. £110 26·00
g. Opt Type 8 .. .. — £400
9 1s. green
a. Opt Type 1*a* .. .. £100 17·00
ab. Opt inverted .. .. — £350
b. Opt Type 2 .. .. £225 38·00
ba. Opt inverted .. ..
c. Opt Type 3 .. .. £160 22·00
d. Opt Type 4 .. .. £225 38·00
da. Opt inverted .. ..
e. Opt Type 5 .. .. £275 45·00
f. Opt Type 6 .. .. £150 20·00
fa. Opt inverted .. ..
g. Opt Type 8 .. .. — £400
10 5s. yellow-orange
a. Opt Type 1*a* .. .. £400 19·00
b. Opt Type 2 .. .. — 42·00
c. Opt Type 3 .. .. £550 23·00
d. Opt Type 4 .. .. — 42·00
e. Opt Type 5 .. .. £950 50·00
f. Opt Type 6 .. .. £500 22·00
g. Opt Type 8 .. .. £1900

*The 1d. with overprint Type 8 from this setting can only be distinguished from that of the second printing when *se-tenant* with overprint Type **3**.

Nos. 4/10 were overprinted by a setting of 120 covering two panes of 60 (6×10). This setting contained 41 examples of Type **1***a*, 10 of Type **2**, 23 of Type **3**, 10 of Type **4**, 8 of Type **5**, 27 of Type **6** and 1 of Type **8**. Sub-types of Types **1***a* and **2** exist. The single example of Type **8** occurs on R. 7/4 of the right-hand pane.

It is believed that there may have been an additional setting used for the 5s. which was in considerable demand to cover the postage and registration on diamond consignments. It is also possible that single panes of this value and of the 1s. were overprinted using the right-hand half of the normal 120 setting.

(*b*) *Second printing. Optd with T* **6**/**14** *in black* (1878)

11 1d. carmine-red
a. Opt Type 6 .. .. *
b. Opt Type 7 .. .. 19·00 13·00
c. Opt Type 8 .. .. 38·00 24·00
d. Opt Type 9 .. .. 20·00 14·00
e. Opt Type 10 .. .. 55·00 50·00
f. Opt Type 11 .. .. 42·00 32·00
g. Opt Type 12 .. .. 50·00 45·00
h. Opt Type 13 .. .. 85·00 75·00
i. Opt Type 14 .. .. £300 £250
12 4d. dull blue (without frame-line) (No. 30)
a. Opt Type 6 .. .. £225 42·00
b. Opt Type 7 .. .. 90·00 18·00
c. Opt Type 8 .. .. £200 40·00
d. Opt Type 9 .. .. £100 19·00
e. Opt Type 10 .. .. £275 60·00
f. Opt Type 11 .. .. £225 48·00
g. Opt Type 12 .. .. £250 55·00
h. Opt Type 13 .. .. £425 £120
i. Opt Type 14 .. .. — £375
13 6d. deep lilac
a. Opt Type 6 .. .. £350 75·00
b. Opt Type 7 .. .. £170 40·00
ba. Opt double .. ..
c. Opt Type 8 .. .. £325 70·00
d. Opt Type 9 .. .. £190 45·00
da. Opt double .. .. — £550
e. Opt Type 10 .. .. £400 £110
ea. Opt double .. .. † £700
f. Opt Type 11 .. .. £350 80·00
g. Opt Type 12 .. .. £350 £100
h. Opt Type 13 .. .. £550 £180
i. Opt Type 14 .. .. £1400 £475

*The 1d. with overprint Type **6** from this setting can only be distinguished from that of the first printing when *se-tenant* with Types **11**, **12** or **13**.

Nos. 11/13 were overprinted by another double-pane setting of 120 in which only Types **6** and **8** were repeated from that used for the first printing. The second printing setting contained 12 examples of Type **6**, 30 of Type **7**, 13 of Type **8**, 27 of Type **9**, 9 of Type **10**, 11 of Type **11**, 11 of Type **12**, 6 of Type **13** and 1 of Type **14**. Sub-types of Types **7** and **12** exist.

G (15) *G* (16) G (17)

1878 (June). *Nos.* 24*a*, 25*a and* 28/30 *of Cape of Good Hope optd with small capital* "G", *T* **15**/**16**.

14 **15** ½d. grey-black (R.) .. .. .. 5·50 7·00
a. Opt inverted .. .. 7·00 7·00
b. Opt double .. .. 32·00 42·00
c. Opt double, both inverted .. .. 60·00 80·00
d. Black opt .. .. £140 75·00
da. Opt inverted £140
db. Opt double, one inverted in red .. £275
dc. Opt double, one inverted (Type **16**) in red .. .. 80·00
15 **16** ½d. grey-black (R.) .. .. .. 7·00 7·00
a. Opt inverted .. .. 7·00 8·50
b. Opt double .. .. 55·00 55·00
c. Opt double, both inverted .. ..
d. Black opt .. .. 32·00 32·00
da. Opt inverted .. .. 32·00 32·00
db. Opt double, one inverted (Type **15**) in red £110
16 **15** 1d. carmine-red .. .. 6·50 4·50
a. Opt inverted .. .. 6·50 6·50
b. Opt double .. .. £130 32·00
c. Opt double, both inverted .. .. £130 48·00
d. Opt double, both inverted with one in red .. .. 26·00 28·00
e. Opt double, both inverted with one (Type **16**) in red .. .. ..
17 **16** 1d. carmine-red .. .. 6·50 6·50
a. Opt inverted .. .. 60·00 22·00
b. Opt double .. .. — 65·00
c. Opt double, both inverted .. .. — 80·00
d. Opt double, both inverted with one in red .. .. 60·00 60·00
18 **15** 4d. blue (with frame-line) (No. 24*a*) .. — £100
19 **16** 4d. blue (with frame-line) (No. 24a) .. — £100
20 **15** 4d. dull blue (without frame-line) (No. 30) 90·00 20·00
a. Opt inverted .. .. £150 60·00
b. Opt double .. .. — £140
c. Opt double, both inverted .. .. — £190
d. Red opt .. .. £225 75·00
da. Opt inverted .. .. £700 55·00
21 **16** 4d. dull blue (without frame-line) (No. 30) £110 8·50
a. Opt inverted .. .. £160 22·00
b. Opt double .. .. — £150
c. Opt double, both inverted .. .. — £190
d. Red opt .. .. — 60·00
da. Opt inverted .. .. £225 60·00
22 **15** 6d. deep lilac .. .. 90·00 19·00
23 **16** 6d. deep lilac .. .. — 19·00

Nos. 14/23 were also overprinted using a double-pane setting of 120. Based on evidence from surviving ½d. and 1d. sheets all overprints in the left-hand pane were roman, Type **15**, and all those in the right-hand pane italic, Type **16**, except for R. 1/6, 4/5, 6/6, 7/6, 8/6, 9/6 and 10/6 which were Type **15**. There is considerable evidence to suggest that after the ½d. value had been overprinted the setting was amended to show a Type **15**, instead of a Type **16**, on R. 10/5 of the right-hand pane. Two strikes of the setting were required to overprint the sheets of 240 and it would appear that on many sheets the bottom two panes had the overprints inverted.

1879. *Nos.* 25*b*, 26*b and* 28/31 *of Cape of Good Hope optd with small capital* "G", *T* **17**.

24 ½d. grey-black .. .. 10·00 5·50
a. Opt double £325 £225
25 1d. carmine-red .. .. 10·00 3·50
a. Opt inverted .. .. — 75·00
b. Opt double .. .. — £120
c. Opt treble .. .. — £170
26 4d. dull blue .. .. 20·00 3·50
a. Opt double .. .. — 95·00
27 6d. violet .. .. 95·00 6·00
a. Opt inverted .. .. — 24·00
b. Opt double £450 £140
28 1s. green .. .. 80·00 3·50
a. Opt double .. .. £250 80·00
29 5s. yellow-orange .. .. £300 6·00
a. Opt double .. .. £350 60·00
b. Opt treble .. .. — £250

Nos. 24/9 were also overprinted using a setting of 120 which contained a number of minor type varieties.

Griqualand West was merged with Cape Colony in October 1880. The remaining stock of the overprinted stamps was returned from Kimberley to Cape Town and redistributed among various post offices in Cape Colony where they were used as ordinary Cape stamps.

NEW INFORMATION

The editor is always interested to correspond with people who have new information that will improve or correct the Catalogue.

III. NATAL

PRICES FOR STAMPS ON COVER

Nos. 1/7	*from* × 2
Nos. 9/25	*from* × 3
Nos. 26/56	*from* × 4
Nos. 57/8	—
Nos. 59/73	*from* × 5
Nos. 76/84	*from* × 4
Nos. 85/93	*from* × 3
Nos. 96/103	*from* × 6
Nos. 104/5	*from* × 5
Nos. 106/25	*from* × 6
Nos. 127/42	*from* × 4
Nos. 143/5*a*	—
Nos. 146/57	*from* × 4
No. 162	—
Nos. 165/71	*from* × 3
No. F1	—
Nos. O1/6	*from* × 10

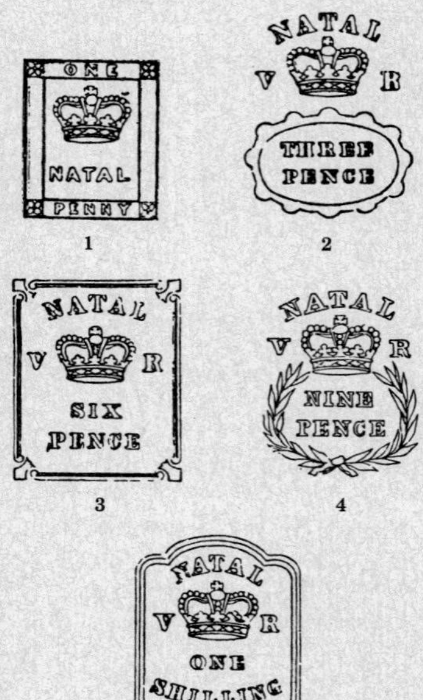
1 2 3 4 5

(Embossed in plain relief on coloured wove paper)

1857 (26 May)–**61**. *Imperf.*
1 1 1d. rose (1858) — £1700
2 1d. buff (1861) — £1000
3 1d. blue (8.59) — £1100
4 2 3d. rose — £400
a. *Tête-bêche* (pair) — £30000
5 3 6d. green — £1100
6 4 9d. blue — £7000
7 5 1s. buff — £5500

All the above have been reprinted more than once, and the early reprints of some values cannot always be distinguished with certainty from originals.

Stamps on surface-coloured paper, perforated 12½, are fiscals.

NOTE. The value of the above stamps depends on their dimensions, and the clearness of the embossing, but our prices are for fine used.

6

7

(Eng C. H. Jeens. Recess P.B.)

1859–60. *No wmk. P* 14.
9 6 1d. rose-red (1860) £120 70·00
10 3d. blue £130 42·00
a. Imperf between (vert pair) † £5000

No. 10a is only known from a cover of 1867 franked with two such pairs.

1861. *No wmk. Intermediate perf* 14 *to* 16.
11 6 3d. blue £200 65·00

1861–62. *No wmk. Rough perf* 14 *to* 16.
12 6 3d. blue 95·00 32·00
a. Imperf between (pair) £2500
b. Imperf (pair) — £2000
13 6d. grey (1862) £150 50·00

1862. *Wmk Small Star. Rough perf* 14 *to* 16.
15 6 1d. rose-red £110 60·00

The 1d. without watermark and the 3d. watermark Small Star, both imperforate, are proofs.

(Recess D.L.R.)

1863. *Thick paper. No wmk. P* 13.
18 6 1d. lake 85·00 27·00
19 1d. carmine-red 85·00 24·00

1863–65. *Wmk Crown CC. P* 12½.
20 6 1d. brown-red £120 35·00
21 1d. rose 85·00 30·00
22 1d. bright-red 85·00 28·00
23 6d. lilac 55·00 16·00
24 6d. violet 38·00 25·00

(Typo D.L.R.)

1867 (April). *Wmk Crown CC. P* 14.
25 7 1s. green £130 27·00

POSTAGE (7*a*)   Postage. (7*b*)   Postage. (7*c*)

Postage. (7*d*)   POSTAGE. (7*e*)

1869 (23 Aug). *Optd horiz in Natal. No wmk* (3*d.*), *wmk Crown CC* (*others*). *P* 14 *or* 14–16 (3*d.*), 12½ (1*d.*, 6*d*) *or* 14 (1*s.*).

(*a*) *With T* 7*a* (*tall capitals without stop*)
26 6 1d. rose £325 70·00
27 1d. bright red £275 60·00
28 3d. blue (No. 10) £1300 £500
28*a* 3d. blue (No. 11) £450 £200
28*b* 3d. blue (No. 12) £400 80·00
29 6d. lilac — 60·00
30 6d. violet £375 70·00
31 7 1s. green £5000 £1000

(*b*) *With T* 7*b* (12¾ *mm long*)
32 6 1d. rose £300 65·00
33 1d. bright red £250 55·00
a. Opt double † £1000
34 3d. blue (No. 10) — £225
34*a* 3d. blue (No. 11) £400 £170
34*b* 3d. blue (No. 12) £375 70·00
35 6d. lilac £400 55·00
36 6d. violet £325 65·00
37 7 1s. green £4000 £750

(*c*) *With T* 7*c* (13¾ *mm long*)
38 6 1d. rose £500 £190
39 1d. bright red £650 £170
40 3d. blue (No. 10)
40*a* 3d. blue (No. 11) — £650
40*b* 3d. blue (No. 12) £950 £275
41 6d. lilac £1000 £130
42 6d. violet £900 £130
43 7 1s. green — £1600

(*d*) *With T* 7*d* (14½ *to* 15½ *mm long*)
44 6 1d. rose £450 £160
45 1d. bright red £450 £140
46 3d. blue (No. 10)
46*a* 3d. blue (No. 11) — £275
46*b* 3d. blue (No. 12) — £200
47 6d. lilac — 85·00
48 6d. violet £850 85·00
49 7 1s. green £7500 £1400

(*e*) *With T* 7*e* (*small capitals with stop*)
50 6 1d. rose 80·00 29·00
51 1d. bright red £140 27·00
52 3d. blue (No. 10) £225 60·00
53 3d. blue (No. 11) £130 40·00
54 3d. blue (No. 12) £160 35·00
a. Opt double † £850
54*b* 6d. lilac £160 55·00
55 6d. violet £120 45·00
56 7 1s. green £180 60·00

It is believed that there were two settings of these overprints. The first setting, probably of 240, contained 60 examples of Type 7*a*, 72 of Type 7*b*, 20 of Type 7*c*, 28 of Type 7*d* and 60 of Type 7*e*. The second, probably of 60 (6×10), contained Type 7*e* only.

(8)

1870. *No.* 25 *optd with T* 8 *by De La Rue.*
57 7 1s. green (C.) — £3250
58 1s. green (Blk.) — £1200
a. Opt double — £2000
59 1s. green (G.) 60·00 10·00

For 1s. orange, see No. 108.

POSTAGE POSTAGE (9)   POSTAGE POSTAGE (10)   POSTAGE (11)

1870–73. *Optd with T* 9 *by De La Rue. Wmk Crown CC. P* 12½.
60 6 1d. bright red 65·00 13·00
61 3d. bright blue (R.) (1872) 70·00 13·00
62 6d. mauve (1873) £140 25·00

1873 (July). *Fiscal stamp optd locally with T* 10. *Wmk Crown CC. P* 14.
63 7 1s. purple-brown £130 18·00

1874 (July). *No* 21 *optd locally with T* 11.
65 6 1d. rose £180 60·00
a. Opt double

12

13

14

15

16

(Typo D.L.R.)

1874 (Jan)–**99.** *Wmk Crown CC* (*sideways on* 5*s.*). *P* 14.
66 12 1d. dull rose 21·00 2·00
67 1d. bright rose 21·00 2·00
68 13 3d. blue 85·00 14·00
a. Perf 14×12½ £1500 £850
69 14 4d. brown (1878) 90·00 11·00
a. Perf 12½ £325 65·00
70 15 6d. bright reddish violet 35·00 6·00
71 16 5s. maroon (1882) £150 32·00
a. Perf 15½×15 (1874) £190 75·00
72 5s. rose 65·00 28·00
73 5s. carmine (H/S S. £160) 60·00 26·00
a. Wmk upright (1899)

POSTAGE (17)   POSTAGE (18)   ½ HALF (19)

1875–76. *Wmk Crown CC. P* 14 (1*s.*) *or* 12½ (*others*). (*a*) *Optd locally with T* 17.
76 6 1d. rose 95·00 42·00
a. Opt double £750 £425
77 1d. bright red 90·00 55·00

(*b*) *Optd locally with T* 18 (14½ *mm long, without stop*)
81 6 1d. rose (1876) 80·00 50·00
a. Opt inverted £900 £400
82 1d. yellow (1876) 70·00 65·00
a. Opt double, one albino £200
83 6d. violet (1876) 50·00 5·50
a. Opt double — £550
b. Opt inverted £650 £150
84 7 1s. green (1876) 80·00 4·50
a. Opt double — £325

TYPE 19. There are several varieties of this surcharge, of which T 19 is an example. They may be divided as follows:

(*a*) "½" 4½ mm high, "2" has straight foot.
(*b*) As last but "½" is 4 mm high.
(*c*) As last but "2" has curled foot.
(*d*) "½" 3½ mm. high, "2" has straight foot.
(*e*) As last but "2" has curled foot.
(*f*) As last but "2" smaller.

As the "½" and "HALF" were overprinted separately, they vary in relative position, and are frequently overlapping.

1877 (13 Feb). *No.* 66 *surch locally as T* 19.
85 12 ½d. on 1d. rose (*a*) 22·00 65·00
a. "½" double
86 ½d. on 1d. rose (*b*) £100
87 ½d. on 1d. rose (*c*) 90·00
88 ½d. on 1d. rose (*d*) 50·00 85·00
89 ½d. on 1d. rose (*e*) 50·00
90 ½d. on 1d. rose (*f*) 60·00

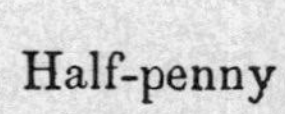

(21)

23

ONE HALF-PENNY. (24)

1877 (7 Oct)–**79.** *T* 6 (*wmk Crown CC. P* 12½) *surch locally as T* 21.
91 ½d. on 1d. yellow 8·00 11·00
a. Surch inverted £250 £180
b. Surch double £250 £180
c. Surch omitted (lower stamp, vertical pair) £1500 £1100
d. "POSTAGE" omitted (in pair with normal) £1500
e. "S" of "POSTAGE" omitted (R. 8/3) £225 £190
f. "T" of "POSTAGE" omitted £225 £250
92 1d. on 6d. violet (10.10.77) 48·00 8·50
a. "S" of "POSTAGE" omitted (R. 8/3) £325 £150

93 1d. on 6d. rose (12.2.79) .. .. .. 90·00 32·00
a. Surch inverted £500 £300
b. Surch double .. .. — £250
c. Surch double, one inverted £250 £200
d. Surch four times £375 £200
e. "S" of "POSTAGE" omitted (R. 8/3) .. £400 £300

No. 93c. is known with one surcharge showing variety "S" of "POSTAGE" omitted.

Other minor varieties exist in these surcharges.

(Typo D.L.R.)

1880 (13 Oct). *Wmk Crown CC. P* 14.
96 **23** ½d. blue-green .. .. 9·00 13·00
a. Imperf between (vert pair) .. ..

1882 (20 Apr)–**89**. *Wmk Crown CA. P* 14.
97 **23** ½d. blue-green (23.4.84) .. .. 85·00 16·00
a. Dull green (10.4.85) 75 30
99 **12** 1d. rose (*shades*) (1.84) .. .. 1·50 10
a. Carmine .. .. 2·00 20
100 **13** 3d. blue (23.4.84) .. .. .. 90·00 17·00
101 3d. grey (11.89) .. .. .. 2·50 95
102 **14** 4d. brown .. .. 3·00 65
103 **15** 6d. mauve .. .. 3·25 80
97*a*/103 .. .. .. *Set of* 6 95·00 18·00
97*a*, 99*a*, 101/3 H/S "Specimen" .. *Set of* 5 £250

1885 (26 Jan). *No. 99 surch locally with T* **24**.
104 **12** ½d. on 1d. rose .. .. .. 16·00 11·00
a. No hyphen after "HALF" .. .. 60·00 42·00

TWO PENCE

TWO PENCE

TWOPENCE HALFPENNY

(25) 26 (27)

1886 (7 Jan). *No. 101 surch with T* **25** *by D.L.R.*
105 **13** 2d. on 3d. grey .. .. .. 18·00 5·50

(Typo D.L.R.)

1887 (Sept)–**89**. *Wmk Crown CA. P* 14.
106 **26** 2d. olive-green Die I* (Optd S. £70) .. 25·00 1·10
107 2d. olive-green Die II (1889) (H/S S. £60) 2·25 1·10

*The differences between Dies I and II are shown in the Introduction.

1888 (16 Mar). *As No. 25, but colour changed and wmk Crown CA, optd with T* **8** *by D.L.R.*
108 **7** 1s. orange (C.) (H/S S. £90) .. .. 3·50 85
a. Opt double .. .. —£1500

1891 (22 Apr). *Surch locally with T* **27**.
109 **14** 2½d. on 4d. brown (H/S S. £50) .. 11·00 8·50
a. "TWOPENGE" .. .. .. 55·00
b. "HALFPENN" £225 £180
c. Surch double £250 £180
d. Surch inverted £350 £275

POSTAGE.

Half-Penny

POSTAGE.

28 (29) Varieties of long-tailed letters

(Typo D.L.R.)

1891 (June). *Wmk Crown CA. P* 14.
113 **28** 2½d. bright blue (H/S S. £60) .. 3·50 50

1895 (12 Mar). *No. 24 surch locally with T* **29** *in carmine.*
114 ½d. on 6d. violet (H/S S. £50) .. 1·25 2·75
a. "Ealf-Penny" .. .. .. 20·00 24·00
b. "Half-Pennv" and long "P" .. .. 17·00 24·00
ba. "Half Pennv" and long "T" and "A" 17·00 24·00
c. No stop after "POSTAGE" and long "P", "T" and "A" .. .. .. 17·00 24·00
d. Long "P" .. .. 2·25 3·75
e. Long "T" .. .. 2·25 3·75
f. Long "A" .. .. 3·25 4·50
g. Long "P" and "T" .. .. .. 2·25 3·75
h. Long "P" and "A" .. .. .. 2·25 3·75
i. Long "T" and "A" .. .. .. 3·00 4·25
k. Long "P", "T" and "A" .. .. 3·00 4·25
ka. Long "P", "T" and "A" with comma after "POSTAGE" .. .. 6·50 9·00
l. Surch double £250
la. Surch double, one vertical £250
m. "POSTAGE" omitted £1000

The surcharge was applied as a setting of 60 (12×5) which contained seventeen normals, one each of Nos. 114a, 114b, 114ba, 114c, six of No. 114d, six of 114e, three of 114f, six of 114g, seven of 114h, five of No. 114i, four of No. 114k and two of No. 114ka.

HALF

(30) 31 32

1895 (18 Mar). *No. 99 surch locally with T* **30**.
125 HALF on 1d. rose (*shades*) (H/S S. £50) .. 80 75
a. Surch double £325 £325
b. "H" with longer left limb .. .. 20·00
c. Pair, one without surcharge .. ..

No. 125b occurs on the second, fourth, sixth etc., stamps of the first vertical row of the righthand pane. It was very soon corrected.

In some printings what appears to be a broken "E" (with the top limb removed) was used instead of "L" in "HALF" on the last stamp in the sheet (*Price* £30)

(Typo D.L.R.)

1902–03. *Inscr* "POSTAGE REVENUE". *Wmk Crown CA. P* 14.
127 **31** ½d. blue-green 65 15
128 1d. carmine .. .. .. 2·50 15
129 1½d. green and black .. .. 1·25 1·50
130 2d. red and olive-green .. .. 1·00 25
131 2½d. bright blue .. .. .. 1·00 3·00
132 3d. purple and grey .. .. 1·00 70
133 4d. carmine and cinnamon .. .. 2·75 10·00
134 5d. black and orange .. .. 1·25 2·75
w. Wmk inverted .. .. .. — 60·00
135 6d. green and brown-purple .. .. 1·25 1·40
136 1s. carmine and pale blue .. .. 2·75 1·40
137 2s. green and bright violet .. .. 48·00 9·00
138 2s. 6d. purple .. .. .. 35·00 12·00
139 4s. deep rose and maize .. .. 60·00 70·00
a. Imperf between (horiz pair) ..
127/39 .. .. .. *Set of* 13 £140 £100
127/39 Optd "Specimen" .. .. *Set of* 13 £160

No. 139a is also imperforate between stamp and left-hand margin.

(Typo D.L.R.)

1902–3. *Wmk Crown CC. P* 14.
140 **32** 5s. dull blue and rose .. .. 20·00 8·50
141 10s. deep rose and chocolate .. 55·00 26·00
142 £1 black and bright blue .. .. £130 45·00
143 £1 10s. green and violet (Optd S. £65) £250 75·00
144 £5 mauve and black (Optd S. £100) .. £1800 £450
145 £10 green and orange (Optd S. £200) .. £6000 £2500
145*a* £20 red and green (Optd S. £325) .. £12000 £5500
140/2 Optd "Specimen" .. .. *Set of* 3 £100

USED HIGH VALUES. Collectors are warned against fiscally used high value Natal stamps with penmarks cleaned off and forged postmarks added.

1904–8. *Wmk Mult Crown CA. Chalk-surfaced paper* (£1 10s.). *P* 14.
146 **31** ½d. blue-green .. .. .. 3·00 15
147 1d. rose-carmine .. .. .. 3·00 15
a. Booklet pane of 6, one stamp optd "NOT FOR USE" £250
148 1d. deep carmine .. .. .. 5·50 20
149 2d. red and olive-green .. .. 4·75 3·25
152 4d. carmine and cinnamon .. .. 2·75 1·00
153 5d. black and orange (1908) .. .. 3·00 3·50
155 1s. carmine and pale blue .. .. 60·00 6·50
156 2s. dull green and bright violet .. 50·00 29·00
157 2s. 6d. purple .. .. .. 40·00 30·00
162 **32** £1 10s. brown-orange and deep purple (1908) (Optd S. £170) £1000 £1800
146/57 .. .. *Set of* 9 £150 65·00

1908–9. *Inscr* "POSTAGE POSTAGE". *Wmk Mult Crown CA. P* 14.
165 **31** 6d. dull and bright purple .. .. 4·50 2·00
166 1s. black/*green* .. .. .. 6·00 2·00
167 2s. purple and bright blue/*blue* .. 15·00 3·00
168 2s. 6d. black and red/*blue* .. .. 25·00 3·00
169 **32** 5s. green and red/*yellow* .. .. 18·00 20·00
170 10s. green and red/*green* .. .. 50·00 55·00
171 £1 purple and black/*red* £225 £190
165/71 .. .. .. *Set of* 7 £300 £250
165/71 Optd "Specimen" .. .. *Set of* 7 £180

STAMP BOOKLETS

1904. *Black on red cover. Stapled.*
SB1 2s. 6d. booklet containing thirty 1d. (No. 147) in blocks of 6 .. .. £1800

The first stamp of the first block in No. SB1 was cancelled "NOT FOR USE", the additional penny being used to defray the cost of production.

1905. *Black on red cover. Stapled.*
SB2 2s. 7d. booklet containing thirty 1d. (No. 147) in blocks of 6 .. ..

FISCALS USED FOR POSTAGE

1869. *Embossed on coloured wove, surfaced paper. P* 12½.
F1 **1** 1d. yellow .. .. 50·00 80·00

Examples of 1d. yellow and 6d. rose values as Type **6**, 1s. purple-brown as Type **7** and various values between 5s. and £10 in the design illustrated above are believed to exist postally used, but, as such use was not authorised, they are not now listed.

OFFICIAL STAMPS

OFFICIAL

(O 1)

1904. *T* **31**, *wmk Mult Crown CA, optd with Type* O 1. *P* 14.
O1 ½d. blue-green .. .. 3·00 35
O2 1d. carmine .. .. 2·00 60
O3 2d. red and olive-green .. .. .. 16·00 9·00
O4 3d. purple and grey .. .. .. 8·50 4·00
O5 6d. green and brown-purple .. .. 28·00 35·00
O6 1s. carmine and pale blue .. .. 90·00 £150
O1/6 .. .. *Set of* 6 £130 £180

The use of stamps overprinted as above was discontinued after 30 May 1907. Stamps perforated with the letters "N.G.R." were for use on Government Railways.

Natal became a province of the Union of South Africa on 31 May 1910.

IV. NEW REPUBLIC

During the unrest following the death of Cetshwayo, the Zulu king, in 1884, a group of Boers from the Transvaal offered their support to his son, Dinizulu. The price for this support was the cession of a sizeable portion of Zulu territory to an independent Boer republic. The New Republic, centred on Vryheid, was proclaimed on 16 August 1884 with the remaining Zulu territory becoming a protectorate of the new administration. The first reference to an organised postal service occurs in December 1884.

Alarmed by these developments the British authorities annexed the southernmost part of the land grant, around St. Lucia Bay, to prevent access to the Indian Ocean. The remainder of the New Republic was, however, recognised as independent on 22 October 1886. Zululand was annexed by the British on 22 May 1887.

Difficulties beset the New Republic, however, and its Volksraad voted for union with the South African Republic (Transvaal). The two republics united on 21 July 1888. In 1903 the territory of the former New Republic was transferred to Natal.

Mail from Vryheid in 1884–85 was franked with issues of Transvaal (for dispatches made via Utrecht) or Natal (for those sent via Dundee from August 1885 onwards). Issues of the New Republic were never accepted as internationally valid by these administrations so that all external mail continued to show Transvaal or Natal stamps used in combination with those of the republic.

PRICES FOR STAMPS ON COVER

No. 1	—
Nos. 2/5	*from* × 50
Nos. 6/25	—
Nos. 26/9	*from* × 50
Nos. 30/47	—
Nos. 48/50	*from* × 50
No. 51	—
Nos. 52/3	*from* × 50
Nos. 72/5	*from* × 50
Nos. 76/7*b*	—
Nos. 78/80	*from* × 50
Nos. 81/95	—

1

Printed with a rubber handstamp on paper bought in Europe and sent out ready gummed and perforated.

1886 (7 Jan)–**87.** *Various dates indicating date of printing. P* 11½.

A. *Without Arms.* (i) *Yellow paper*
1 **1** 1d. black (9.1.86) .. .. .. † £2750
2 1d. violet (9.1.86) .. .. .. 10·00 12·00
a. "1d." omitted (in pair with normal) (24.4.86) £1500
3 2d. violet (9.1.86) .. .. .. 10·00 15·00
a. "d" omitted (13.10.86) .. ..
4 3d. violet (13.1.86) .. .. .. 23·00
a. "d" omitted (13.10.86) .. ..
b. *Tête-bêche* (pair) (13.10.86) .. ..
5 4d. violet (30.8.86) .. .. .. 35·00
6 6d. violet (20.2.86) .. .. .. 30·00
a. "6d." omitted (in pair with normal) (2.7.86) .. ..
7 9d. violet (13.1.86) .. .. .. 30·00
8 1s. violet (30.8.86) .. .. .. 65·00
a. "1s." omitted (in pair with normal) (6.9.86) .. ..
9 1/s. violet (13.10.86) £500
10 1/6 violet (30.8.86) .. .. .. 65·00
11 1s. 6d. violet (13.1.86) £400
a. *Tête-bêche* (pair) (6.9.86) .. ..
b. "d" omitted (13.10.86) .. .. 85·00
12 2s. violet (30.8.86) .. .. .. 38·00
a. *Tête-bêche* (pair) (6.9.86) £475
13 2/6 violet (13.1.86) £150
14 2s. 6d. violet (1.86) .. .. .. 95·00
15 4/s. violet (17.1.87) £400
16 5s. violet (1.86) .. .. .. 28·00 30·00
a. "s" omitted (in pair with normal) (7.3.86) £2000
17 5/6 violet (20.2.86) .. .. .. 35·00
18 5s. 6d. violet (13.1.86) £160

No.	Type	Description	Un.	Us.
19	1	7/6 violet (13.1.86)	£170	
20		7s. 6d. violet (24.5.86)	95·00	
21		10s. violet (13.1.86)	95·00	
		a. *Tête-bêche* (pair) (2.7.86)		
22		10s. 6d. violet (1.86)	£170	
		a. "d" omitted (1.86)	48·00	
23		13s. violet (24.11.86)	£400	
24		£1 violet (13.1.86)	£120	
		a. *Tête-bêche* (pair) (13.10.86)		
25		30s. violet (13.1.86)	95·00	
		a. *Tête-bêche* (pair) (24.11.86)	£500	
		(ii) *Blue granite paper*		
26	1	1d. violet (20.1.86)	13·00	14·00
		a. "d" omitted (24.11.86)	£375	
		b. "1" omitted (in pair with normal) (24.11.86)		
27		2d. violet (24.1.86)	13·00	14·00
		a. "d" omitted (24.4.86)	£750	
		b. "2d." omitted (in pair with normal) (24.4.86)		
28		3d. violet (13.10.86)	16·00	18·00
		a. *Tête-bêche* (pair) (13.10.86)	£275	
29		4d. violet (24.5.86)	13·00	16·00
30		6d. violet (24.5.86)	25·00	21·00
		a. "6" omitted (in pair with normal) (24.5.86)	£1500	
31		9d. violet (6.9.86)	24·00	
32		1s. violet (1.86)	28·00	30·00
		a. *Tête-bêche* (pair) (21.5.86)	£300	
		b. "1s." omitted (in pair with normal) (29.4.86)	£1500	
33		1s. 6d. violet (2.7.86)	35·00	
		a. *Tête-bêche* (pair) (6.9.86)	£475	
34		1/6 violet (6.9.86)	£150	
35		2s. violet (21.5.86)	£120	
		a. "2s." omitted (in pair with normal) (24.5.86)	£1500	
36		2s. 6d. violet (19.8.86)	£140	
37		2/6 violet (19.8.86)	£180	
38		4/s. violet (17.1.87)	£200	
39		5/6 violet (13.1.86)	£200	
		a. "/" omitted (13.1.87)		
40		5s. 6d. violet (13.1.86)	£170	
41		7/6 violet (13.1.86)	£200	
41*a*		7s. 6d. violet (13.1.86)		
42		10s. violet (1.86)	£200	£200
		a. *Tête-bêche* (pair) (2.7.86)	£400	
		b. "s" omitted (13.1.86)		
43		10s. 6d. violet (1.86)	£200	
		a. *Tête-bêche* (pair) (13.1.86)		
		b. "d" omitted (1.86)	£450	
44		12s. violet (13.1.86)	£300	
45		13s. violet (17.1.87)	£400	
46		£1 violet (13.1.86)	£250	
47		30s. violet (13.1.86)	£250	

B. *With embossed Arms of New Republic.* (i) *Yellow paper*

No.	Type	Description	Un.	Us.
48	1	1d. violet (20.1.86)	13·00	15·00
		a. Arms inverted (20.1.86)	25·00	25·00
		b. Arms *tête-bêche* (pair) (14.4.86)	£100	£120
49		2d. violet (30.8.86)	13·00	15·00
		a. Arms inverted (24.11.86)	23·00	28·00
50		4d. violet (2.12.86)	18·00	22·00
		a. Arms inverted (12.86)	95·00	60·00
		b. Arms *tête-bêche* (pair) (12.86)	£250	
51		6d. violet (2.12.86)	45·00	
		(ii) *Blue granite paper*		
52	1	1d. violet (20.1.86)	14·00	16·00
		a. Arms inverted (10.2.86)	35·00	40·00
		b. Arms *tête-bêche* (pair) (3.11.86)		
53		2d. violet (24.5.86)	14·00	16·00
		a. Arms inverted (30.8.86)	48·00	
		b. Arms *tête-bêche* (pair) (2.12.86)	£500	£500

Stamps as Type 1 were produced as and when stocks were required, each printing including in its design the date on which it was prepared. The dates quoted above for Nos. 1/53 are those on which the various stamps first appeared. Details of the various printing dates are given below. From these dates it can be seen that some values share common printing dates, and, it is believed, that the different values were produced *se-tenant* within the same sheet, at least in some instances. A reported proof sheet in the Pretoria Postal Museum, on yellow paper and embossed, contains 4 examples of the 6d. value and 3 each of the 3d., 4d., 9d., 1s., 1/6, 2/-, 2/6, 3s., 4s., 5s., 5/6, 7/6, 10/-, 10/6, £1 and 30/-.

The significance, if any, of the two coloured papers and the use of the embossing machine have never been satisfactorily explained. Both the different papers and the embossing machine were introduced in January 1886, and occur throughout the period that the stamps with dates were used.

PRINTINGS

Date	*Paper*	*Face value*	*Cat. No.*	*Un.*	*Us.*
Jan 86	*Yellow*	5s.	16	28·00	30·00
		10s. 6d.	22	£170	
		10s. 6d.	22a	80·00	
	Blue	1s.	32		
		10s.	42	£200	£200
		10s. 6d.	43	£200	
		10s. 6d.	43b	£450	
7 Jan 86	*Yellow*	10s. 6d.	22	£160	
	Blue	10s.	42		
		10s. 6d.	43	£450	
9 Jan 86	*Yellow*	1d.	1	†	£2500
		1d.	2	10·00	12·00
		2d.	3	10·00	15·00
13 Jan 86	*Yellow*	1d.	2	35·00	
		2d.	3	14·00	15·00
		3d.	4	40·00	
		9d	7	£200	
		1s. 6d.	11	£400	
		2/6	13	£160	
		2s. 6d.	14	95·00	
		5s. 6d.	18		
		7/6	19	£170	
		10s.	21		
		£1	24	£130	
		30s.	25	95·00	
	Blue	5/6	39	£200	
		5s. 6d.	40	£170	
		7/6	41	£200	
		7s. 6d.	41*a*		
		10s.	42	£400	
		10s.	42b		
		10s. 6d.	43	£200	
		10s. 6d.	43a		
		12s.	44	£300	
		£1	46	£250	
		30s.	47	£250	
20 Jan 86	*Yellow*	1d.	2		
	Blue	1d.	26	£250	
	Yellow, embossed	1d.	48	32·00	
		1d.	48a	48·00	
	Blue, embossed	1d.	52	95·00	
Jan 20 86	*Blue*	1d.	26	23·00	
	Blue, embossed	1d.	52	£100	
24 Jan 86	*Blue*	1d.	26	18·00	
		2d.	27	30·00	
10 Feb 86	*Yellow*	1d.	2		
	Yellow, embossed	1d.	48		
		1d.	48a	48·00	
	Blue, embossed	1d.	52	£130	
		1d.	52a	35·00	
20 Feb 86	*Yellow*	6d.	6		
		1s. 6d.	11		
		2s. 6d.	14	£130	
		5/6	17	£120	
		5s. 6d.	18		
7 Mar 86	*Yellow*	1d.	2	£110	
		2/6	13		
		2s. 6d.	14	95·00	
		5s.	16	£200	85·00
		5s.	16a		
		5/6	17	35·00	
		5s. 6d.	18	£160	
	Blue	2d.	27	95·00	
		1s.	32		
17 Mar 86	*Yellow*	1d.	2	95·00	
	Yellow, embossed	1d.	48	48·00	
	Blue, embossed	1d.	52	95·00	
		1d.	52a	80·00	
26 Mar 86	*Blue, embossed*	1d.	52a	£130	
14 Apr 86	*Yellow*	1d.	2		
	Yellow, embossed	1d.	48	23·00	
		1d.	48a	£120	
		1d.	48b	£100	£120
	Blue, embossed	1d.	52	45·00	
		1d.	52a		
24 Apr 86	*Yellow*	1d.	2	£100	
		1d.	2a	£1500	
		5s.	16		
	Blue	2d.	27	28·00	
		2d.	27a	£750	
		2d.	27b		
29 Apr 86	*Blue*	1s.	32	£110	
		1s.	32b		
21 May 86	*Yellow*	6d.	6	£130	
	Blue	1d.	26	85·00	
		1s.	32	28·00	30·00
		1s.	32a	£300	
		1s.	32b	£1500	
		2s.	35	£275	
23 May 86	*Blue, embossed*	1d.	52a	95·00	
24 May 86	*Yellow*	1d.	2	95·00	
		2d.	3	£120	
		5s.	16	70·00	
		7/6	19	£170	
		7s. 6d.	20	95·00	
	Blue	1d.	26	13·00	14·00
		2d.	27	—	£300
		4d.	29	85·00	
		6d.	30	£120	
		6d.	30a		
		1s.	32	£200	
		1s.	32b		
		2s.	35	£120	
		2s.	35a	£1500	
	Blue, embossed	2d.	53		
26 May 86	*Yellow*	1d.	2		
	Blue	1d.	26	£110	
	Yellow, embossed	1d.	48	£250	
		1d.	48a	95·00	
	Blue, embossed	1d.	52	£130	
		1d.	52a	48·00	50·00
28 May 86	*Yellow, embossed*	1d.	48	32·00	
30 Jun 86	*Yellow*	1d.	2		
	Blue	1d.	26		
Jun 30 86	*Blue*	1d.	26	15·00	16·00
	Yellow, embossed	1d.	48	14·00	16·00
		1d.	48a	25·00	28·00
		1d.	48b	£200	£225
	Blue, embossed	1d.	52	45·00	40·00
2 Jul 86	*Yellow*	6d.	6	£200	
		6d.	6a		
		9d	7	95·00	95·00
		10s.	21		
		10s.	21a		
	Blue	1s. 6d.	33	35·00	
		10s.	42	£200	
		10s.	42a	£400	
		10s. 6d.	43		
		10s. 6d.	43b		
3 Jul 86	*Blue*	10s.	42		
Jul 7 86	*Yellow*	1d.	2		
	Blue	1d.	26		
	Yellow, embossed	1d.	48	25·00	
		1d.	48a	95·00	95·00
	Blue, embossed	1d.	52	14·00	16·00
		1d.	52a	55·00	40·00
4 Aug 86	*Yellow*	1d.	2		
	Yellow, embossed	1d.	48	55·00	
	Blue, embossed	1d.	52	35·00	
		1d.	52a		
19 Aug 86	*Yellow*	2/6	13		
		2s. 6d.	14	£140	
	Blue	2s. 6d.	36	£140	
		2/6	37	£180	
30 Aug 86	*Yellow*	1d.	2	10·00	12·00
		2d.	3	11·00	
		3d.	4	23·00	
		4d.	5	48·00	
		6d.	6	32·00	
		9d.	7	48·00	
		1s.	8	65·00	
		1/6	10	65·00	
		2s.	12	95·00	
		2/6	13	£150	
	Blue	2d.	27	13·00	14·00
	Yellow, embossed	2d.	49		
	Blue, embossed	2d.	53	42·00	
		2d.	53a	£110	
6 Sep 86	*Yellow*	1d.	2	12·00	
		2d.	3	8·50	9·00
		3d.	4	38·00	
		4d.	5	40·00	
		6d.	6	30·00	
		9d.	7	30·00	
		1s.	8	95·00	
		1s.	8a		
		1/6	10	70·00	
		1s. 6d.	11	£400	
		1s. 6d.	11a		
		2s.	12	£100	
		2s.	12a	£475	
		2/6	13	£150	
		2s. 6d.	14		
		5s.	16	£140	
		7s. 6d.	20	£200	
		10s.	21	95·00	
		£1	24	£120	
	Blue	6d.	30	20·00	21·00
		9d.	31	£110	
		1s.	32	65·00	
		1s. 6d.	33	£140	
		1s. 6d.	33a	£475	
		1/6	34		
		2s. 6d.	36		
		2/6	37	£400	
		10s. 6d.	43		
13 Sep 86	*Yellow*	1d.	2		
	Yellow, embossed	1d.	48	48·00	
		1d.	48a	48·00	
	Blue, embossed	1d.	52	85·00	
6 Oct 86	*Yellow*	1d.	2		
	Blue	1d.	26	85·00	
	Yellow, embossed	1d.	48	23·00	18·00
		1d.	48a		
	Blue, embossed	1d.	52	45·00	18·00
		1d.	52a	85·00	
13 Oct 86	*Yellow*	1d.	2	12·00	12·00
		2d.	3	10·00	11·00
		2d.	3a		
		3d.	4	23·00	25·00
		3d.	4a		
		3d.	4b		
		4d.	5	35·00	
		6d.	6	30·00	32·00
		9d.	7	35·00	
		1s.	8	70·00	
		1/s	9	£500	
		1/6	10	£150	
		1s. 6d.	11b	85·00	
		2s.	12	38·00	
		2/6	13	£160	
		5s.	16	42·00	
		10s.	21	95·00	£100
		10s. 6d.	22a	48·00	
		£1	24	£120	
		£1	24a		
	Blue	2d.	27	13·00	14·00
		3d.	28	16·00	18·00
		3d.	28a	£275	
		4d.	29	28·00	28·00
		1s.	32	28·00	
		1/6	34	£150	
		2s.	35	£120	
3 Nov 86	*Yellow*	1d.	2	28·00	
	Blue	1d.	26		
	Yellow, embossed	1d.	48	13·00	15·00
		1d.	48a	25·00	28·00
		1d.	48b	£100	£120
	Blue, embossed	1d.	52	14·00	
		1d.	52a	35·00	40·00
		1d.	52b		
13 Nov 86	*Yellow*	1d.	2	35·00	
24 Nov 86	*Yellow*	1d.	2	14·00	
		2d.	3	10·00	11·00
		3d.	4	30·00	32·00
		1/6	10		
		10s.	21	£200	
		13s.	23	£400	
		30s.	25	95·00	
		30s.	25a	£500	
	Blue	1d.	26	38·00	17·00
		1d.	26a	£375	
		1d.	26b		
		2d.	27	18·00	
		2d.	27a		
		4d.	29	13·00	16·00
		6d.	30	20·00	21·00
		9d.	31	24·00	
		1s.	32	45·00	48·00
		1/6	34	£160	
		2s.	35	£140	
	Yellow, embossed	2d.	49	£160	
		2d.	49a		
26 Nov 86	*Yellow*	1/6	10	£140	
2 Dec 86	*Yellow*	1d.	2		
		2d.	3		
	Blue	2d.	27		
	Yellow, embossed	1d.	48	13·00	15·00
		1d.	48a	£160	
		2d.	49	13·00	15·00
		2d.	49a	23·00	28·00
		4d.	50	80·00	
		6d.	51	45·00	
	Blue, embossed	1d.	52	28·00	
		1d.	52a	£160	
		2d.	53	14·00	16·00
		2d.	53a	48·00	
		2d.	53b	£500	£500
3 Dec 86	*Yellow, embossed*	6d.	51		
Dec 86	*Yellow*	6d.	6		
	Blue	4d.	29		
	Yellow, embossed	4d.	50	18·00	22·00
		4d.	50a	95·00	60·00
		4d.	50b	£250	
		6d.	51	42·00	
4 Jan 87	*Yellow*	1d.	2	35·00	

Date	Paper	Face value	Cat. No.	Un.	Us.
		2d.	3	32·00	
		13s.	23	£400	
	Blue	1d.	26	13·00	14·00
		2d.	27	16·00	14·00
	Blue, embossed	2d.	53	42·00	
13 Jan 87	*Blue*	5/6	39	£400	
		5/6	39a		
		7/6	41	£400	
17 Jan 87	*Yellow*	1d.	2	38·00	
		2d.	3	30·00	
		3d.	4	45·00	
		4/s.	15	£200	
	Blue	1d.	26	75·00	
		4/s.	38	£200	
		13s.	45	£400	
		30s.	47	£250	
20 Jan 87	*Blue*	2d.	27	32·00	
	Yellow, embossed	2d.	49	50·00	
		2d.	49a	£140	
	Blue, embossed	2d.	53	42·00	
		2d.	53a	95·00	
Jan 20 87	*Yellow, embossed*	1d.	48a	£400	

1887 (Jan–Mar). *As T* **1**, *but without date. With embossed Arms.*

(*a*) *Blue granite paper*

72 1d. violet .. .. 14·00 14·00
a. Imperf between (pair)
b. Stamps *tête-bêche* (pair) .. £325
c. Arms *tête-bêche* (pair)
d. Arms inverted .. 23·00 23·00
e. Arms omitted .. £110 £110
f. Arms sideways
73 2d. violet .. 8·50 8·50
a. Stamps *tête-bêche* (pair) .. £275
b. Arms inverted .. 23·00 23·00
c. Arms omitted .. £110 95·00
d. Arms *tête-bêche* (pair)
74 3d. violet .. 13·00 13·00
a. Stamps *tête-bêche* (pair) .. £375
b. Arms *tête-bêche* (pair)
c. Arms inverted .. 48·00 48·00
75 4d. violet .. 13·00 13·00
a. Stamps *tête-bêche* (pair) .. £325
b. Arms *tête-bêche* (pair) .. £275
c. Arms inverted .. 85·00
76 6d. violet .. 13·00 13·00
a. Arms inverted .. 85·00
77 1/6 violet .. 14·00 14·00
a. Arms inverted .. 80·00
77*b* 2/6 violet .. † £750

(*b*) *Yellow paper* (March 1887)

78 2d. violet (*arms omitted*) .. 13·00
79 3d. violet .. 13·00 13·00
a. Imperf between (pair)
b. Stamps *tête-bêche* (pair) .. £325 £350
c. Arms *tête-bêche* (pair) .. £200
d. Arms inverted .. 23·00 23·00
da. Double impression
80 4d. violet .. 13·00 13·00
a. Arms inverted .. 14·00 14·00
81 6d. violet .. 8·00 8·00
a. Arms *tête-bêche* (pair) .. £350
b. Arms inverted .. 42·00 42·00
c. Arms omitted .. 80·00
ca. Double impression
82 9d. violet .. 8·50 8·50
a. Arms inverted .. £200
b. Arms *tête-bêche* (pair) .. £350
83 1s. violet .. 8·50 8·50
a. Arms inverted .. 70·00
84 1/6 violet .. 17·00 14·0
85 2s. violet .. 18·00 16·00
a. Arms inverted .. 55·00 50·00
b. Arms omitted .. 70·00
86 2/6 violet .. 23·00 23·00
a. Arms inverted .. 28·00 28·00
87 3s. violet .. 42·00 42·00
a. Arms inverted .. 45·00 45·00
b. Stamps *tête-bêche* (pair) .. £450
88 4s. violet .. 11·00 11·00
a. Arms omitted .. £180
88*b* 4/s violet
ba. Arms omitted .. £130
89 5s. violet .. 13·00 13·00
a. Imperf between (pair)
b. Arms inverted .. — 80·00
90 5/6 violet .. 12·00 12·00
91 7/6 violet .. 14·00 17·00
a. Arms *tête-bêche* (pair)
a. Arms inverted .. 45·00
92 10s. violet .. 12·00 12·00
a. Imperf between (pair)
b. Arms *tête-bêche* (pair) .. £120
c. Arms inverted .. 23·00
d. Arms omitted .. £110 45·00
93 10/6 violet .. 16·00 16·00
a. Imperf between (pair)
b. Arms inverted
94 £1 violet .. 45·00 45·00
a. Stamps *tête-bêche* (pair) .. £300 £350
b. Arms inverted .. 55·00
95 30s. violet .. £110

New Republic united with the South African Republic (Transvaal) on 21 July 1888. In 1903 the territory of the former New Republic was transferred to Natal.

ALTERED CATALOGUE NUMBERS

Any Catalogue numbers altered from the last edition are shown as a list in the introductory pages.

V. ORANGE FREE STATE

PRICES FOR STAMPS ON COVER

Nos. 1/9	*from* × 15
Nos. 10/13	*from* × 12
Nos. 18/19	*from* × 15
No. 20	—
Nos. 21/42	*from* × 12
Nos. 48/51	*from* × 25
Nos. 52/138	*from* × 10
Nos. 139/51	*from* × 7
Nos. F1/17	—
Nos. PF1/3	—
No. M1	—

1

(Typo D.L.R.)

1868 (1 Jan)–**94**. *P* 14.

1 1 1d. pale brown .. 6·00 85
2 1d. red-brown .. 6·00 35
3 1d. deep brown .. 8·00 40
4 6d. pale rose (1868) .. 35·00 6·00
5 6d. rose (1871) .. 9·00 5·00
6 6d. rose-carmine (1891) .. 15·00 12·00
7 6d. bright carmine (1894) .. 8·50 2·00
8 1s. orange-buff .. 65·00 5·00
9 1s. orange-yellow .. 21·00 1·50
a. Double print .. — £2500

4 4 4 4

(**2**) (*a*) (*b*) (*c*) (*d*)

1877. *No.* 5 *surcharged T* **2** (*a*) *to* (*d*).

10 1 4d. on 6d. rose (*a*) .. £225 55·00
a. Surch inverted .. — £550
b. Surch double (*a* + *c*)
c. Surch double, one inverted (*a* + *c* inverted) .. — £1300
d. Surch double, one inverted (*a* inverted + *c*)
11 4d. on 6d. rose (*b*) .. £1200 £160
a. Surch inverted .. — £1100
b. Surch double (*b* + *d*)
12 4d. on 6d. rose (*c*) .. £110 25·00
a. Surch inverted .. — £325
b. Surch double
13 4d. on 6d. rose (*d*) .. £150 35·00
a. Surch inverted .. £1100 £375

1878 (July). *P* 14.

18 1 4d. pale blue .. 14·00 2·50
19 4d. ultramarine .. 4·00 2·50
20 5s. green .. 8·50 10·00

1d. 1d. 1d. 1d. 1d. 1d.

(**3**) (*a*) (*b*) (*c*) (*d*) (*e*) (*f*)

Type 3: (*a*) Small "1" and "d." (*b*) Sloping serif. (*c*) Same size as (*b*), but "1" with straighter horizontal serif. (*d*) Taller "1" with horizontal serif and antique "d". (*e*) Same size as (*d*) but with sloping serif and thin line at foot. (*f*) as (*d*) but with Roman "d".

1881 (19 May). *No.* 20 *surch T* **3** (*a*) *to* (*f*) *with heavy black bar cancelling the old value.*

21 1 1d. on 5s. green (*a*) .. 70·00 12·00
22 1d. on 5s. green (*b*) .. 40·00 12·00
a. Surch inverted .. — £650
b. Surch double .. — £650
23 1d. on 5s. green (*c*) .. £140 60·00
a. Surch inverted .. — £950
b. Surch double .. — £1000
24 1d. on 5s. green (*d*) .. 60·00 12·00
a. Surch inverted .. £950 £650
b. Surch double .. — £650
25 1d. on 5s. green (*e*) .. £375 £200
a. Surch inverted .. — £1700
b. Surch double .. — £1600
26 1d. on 5s. green (*f*) .. 60·00 12·00
a. Surch inverted .. — £600
b. Surch double .. — £650

No. 21 was the first printing in one type only. Nos. 22 to 25 constitute the second printing about a year later, and are all found on the same sheet; and No. 26 the third printing of which about half have the stop raised.

Owing to defective printing examples of Nos. 22 and 24/5 may be found with the obliterating bar at the top of the stamps or, from the top row, without the bar.

½d

(**4**)

1882 (Aug). *No.* 20 *surch with T* **4** *and with a thin black line cancelling old value.*

36 1 ½d. on 5s. green .. 8·00 3·75
a. Surch double .. £350 £300
b. Surch inverted .. — £700

3d 3d 3d 3d 3d

(**5**) (*a*) (*b*) (*c*) (*d*) (*e*)

1882. *No.* 19 *surch with T* **5** (*a*) *to* (*e*) *with thin black line cancelling value.*

38 1 3d. on 4d. ultramarine (*a*) .. 65·00 23·00
a. Surch double .. — £700
39 3d. on 4d. ultramarine (*b*) .. 65·00 18·00
a. Surch double .. — £700
40 3d. on 4d. ultramarine (*c*) .. 26·00 16·00
a. Surch double .. — £700
41 3d. on 4d. ultramarine (*d*) .. 65·00 19·00
a. Surch double .. — £700
42 3d. on 4d. ultramarine (*e*) .. £150 60·00
a. Surch double .. — £1300

Examples of Nos. 39 and 41/2 exist without the cancelling bar due to the misplacement of the surcharge.

1883–84. *P* 14.

48 1 ½d. chestnut .. 1·00 50
49 2d. pale mauve .. 6·50 40
50 2d. bright mauve .. 6·50 30
51 3d. ultramarine .. 2·00 2·00

For 1d. purple, see No. 68.

2d 2d 2d

(**6**) (*a*) (*b*) (*c*)

1888 (Sept–Oct). *No.* 51 *surch with T* **6**(*a*), (*b*) *or* (*c*).

(*a*) *Wide* "2". (*b*) *Narrow* "2"

52 1 2d. on 3d. ultramarine (*a*) (Sept) .. 38·00 9·00
a. Surch inverted .. — £700
53 2d. on 3d. ultramarine (*b*) .. 20·00 2·00
a. Surch inverted .. — £300
b. "2" with curved foot (*c*) .. — £500

1d 1d 1d

(**7**) (*a*) (*b*) (*c*)

1890 (Dec)–**91.** *Nos.* 51 *and* 19 *surch with T* **7** (*a*) *to* (*c*).

54 1 1d. on 3d. ultramarine (*a*) .. 2·25 60
a. Surch double .. 75·00 70·00
c. "1" and "d" wide apart .. £140 £110
55 1d. on 3d. ultramarine (*b*) .. 12·00 2·50
a. Surch double .. £200 £225
57 1d. on 4d. ultramarine (*a*) .. 18·00 3·50
a. Surch double .. £120 £110
b. Surch double (*a* + *b*) .. £250
c. Surch triple
58 1d. on 4d. ultramarine (*b*) .. 75·00 50·00
a. Surch double .. £325 £275
59 1d. on 4d. ultramarine (*c*) .. £1200 £475
a. Surch double

The settings of the 1d. on 3d. and on 4d. are not identical. The variety (*c*) does not exist on the 3d.

2½d.

(**8**)

1892 (Oct). *No* 51 *surch with T* **8**.

67 1 2½d. on 3d. ultramarine .. 6·50 70
a. No stop after "d" .. 65·00

1894 (Sept). *Colour changed. P* 14.

68 1 1d. purple .. 1·75 30

½d ½d ½d

(**9**) (*a*) (*b*) (*c*)

½d ½d ½d ½d

(*d*) (*e*) (*f*) (*g*)

Types (*a*) and (*e*) differ from types (*b*) and (*f*) respectively, in the serifs of the "1", but owing to faulty overprinting this distinction is not always clearly to be seen.

1896 (Sept). *No.* 51 *surch with T* **9** (*a*) *to* (*g*).

69 1 ½d. on 3d. ultramarine (*a*) .. 2·75 8·00
70 ½d. on 3d. ultramarine (*b*) .. 5·50 5·50
71 ½d. on 3d. ultramarine (*c*) .. 5·00 2·50
72 ½d. on 3d. ultramarine (*d*) .. 5·00 2·25
73 ½d. on 3d. ultramarine (*e*) .. 5·00 2·25
74 ½d. on 3d. ultramarine (*f*) .. 6·00 8·00
75 ½d. on 3d. ultramarine (*g*) .. 3·25 2·50
a. Surch double .. 13·00 10·00
b. Surch triple .. 60·00 60·00

The double and triple surcharges are often different types, but are always type (*g*), or in combination with type (*g*).

Double surcharges in the same type, but without the "d" and bar, also exist, probably from a trial sheet prepared by the printer. Both mint and used examples are known.

Halve
Penny.

(**10**)

2½

(**11**)

1896. *No.* 51 *surch with T* **10**.
77 1 ½d. on 3d. ultramarine 35 50

(i) *Errors in setting*
78 1 ½d. on 3d. (no stop) 9·50 22·00
79 ½d. on 3d. ("Peuny") 9·50 22·00

(ii) *Surch inverted*
81 1 ½d. on 3d. 55·00
81*a* ½d. on 3d. (no stop)
81*b* ½d. on 3d. ("Peuny") £1500

(iii) *Surch double, one inverted*
81*c* 1 ½d. on 3d. (Nos. 77 and 81) £180 £200
81*d* ½d. on 3d. (Nos. 77 and 81*a*) £750 £750
81*e* ½d. on 3d. (Nos. 77 and 81*b*) £850 £850
81*f* ½d. on 3d. (Nos. 81 and 78)
82 ½d. on 3d. (Nos. 81 and 79) — £850

Examples from the top horizontal row can be found without the bar due to the surcharge being misplaced.

Nos. 69 to 75 also exist surcharged as last but they are considered not to have been issued with authority (*Prices from* £30 *each, unused*).

1897 (1 Jan). *No.* 51 *surch with T* **11.** (*a*) *As in illustration.* (*b*) *With Roman* "1" *and antique* "2" *in fraction.*
83 1 2½d. on 3d. ultramarine (*a*) 2·75 80
83*a* 2½d. on 3d. ultramarine (*b*) £140 90·00

1897. *P* 14.
84 1 ½d. yellow (March) 1·75 35
85 ½d. orange 1·75 35
87 1s. brown (Aug) 13·00 1·50

The 6d. blue was prepared for use in the Orange Free State, but had not been brought into use when the stamps were seized in Bloemfontein. A few have been seen without the "V.R.I." overprint, but they were not authorized or available for postage (*Price* £55).

BRITISH OCCUPATION

V. R. I. — V. R. I. — V. R. I.

4d — ½d — ½d

31 (Level stops) — (**32**) (Raised stops) (**33**)
Thin "V" — Thick "V"

V. R. I.

Inserted "R"

(Surch by Curling & Co, Bloemfontein)

1900. *T* **1** *surch as T* **31/33** (*2½d. on 3d. optd* "V.R.I." *only*).

(*a*) *First printings surch as T* **31** *with stops level* (March)
101 ½d. on ½d. orange 1·75 1·75
a. No stop after "V" 17·00 18·00
b. No stop after "I" £160 £160
c. "½" omitted £170 £170
d. "I" omitted
e. "V.R.I." omitted £160
f. Value omitted £100
g. Small "½" 50·00 50·00
h. Surch double £140
102 1d. on 1d. purple 1·50 80
a. Error. Brown £600 £400
b. No stop after "V" 10·00 10·00
c. No stop after "R" £150 £160
d. No stop after "I"
e. "1" omitted £170 £180
f. "I" omitted £300 £300
g. "I" and stop after "R" omitted £300 £300
h. "V.R.I." omitted £140
i. "d" omitted £300
j. Value omitted 80·00
k. Inverted stop after "R" £200
l. Wider space between "1" and "d" £100 £100
m. "V" and "R" close £150
n. Pair, one without surch £400
o. "V" omitted £750
103 2d. on 2d. bright mauve 80 80
a. No stop after "V" 10·00 14·00
b. No stop after "R" £250
c. No stop after "I" £250
d. "V.R.I." omitted £300
e. Value omitted
104 2½d. on 3d. ultramarine (*a*) 8·00 5·50
a. No stop after "V" 70·00 70·00
105 2½d. on 3d. ultramarine (*b*) £180 £180
106 3d. on 3d. ultramarine 1·75 95
a. No stop after "V" 14·00 14·00
b. Pair, one without surch £400
c. "V.R.I." omitted
d. Value omitted
107 4d. on 4d. ultramarine 4·50 8·00
a. No stop after "V" 50·00 55·00
108 6d. on 6d. bright carmine 35·00 35·00
a. No stop after "V" £250 £275
b. "6" omitted £300 £300
109 6d. on 6d. blue 3·75 2·75
a. No stop after "V" 30·00 32·00
b. "6" omitted 60·00 65·00
c. "V.R.I." omitted
110 1s. on 1s. brown 5·00 2·75
a. Error. Orange-yellow £2750 £2250
b. No stop after "V" 30·00 30·00
c. "1" omitted £100 £100
d. "1" omitted and spaced stop after "s" £120 £130
e. "V.R.I." omitted £150 £150
f. Value omitted £150 £150
g. Raised stop after "s" 10·00 10·00
h. Wider space between "1" and "s" £150 £150
111 5s. on 5s. green 17·00 35·00
a. No stop after "V" £200 £225
b. "5" omitted £900 £900
c. Inverted stop after "R" £650 £650
d. Wider space between "5" and "s" £120 £120
e. Value omitted

All values are found with a rectangular, instead of an oval, stop after "R". Misplaced surcharges (upwards or sideways) occur.

(*b*) *Subsequent printings.* (i) *Surch as T* **32**
112 ½d. on ½d. orange 30 20
a. Raised and level stops mixed 1·75 2·00
b. Pair, one with level stops 9·50 13·00
c. No stop after "V" 2·50 2·75
d. No stop after "I" 26·00 27·00
e. "V" omitted £550
f. Small "½" 14·00 16·00
g. As a, and small "½" 14·00 16·00
i. Space between "V" and "R"
j. Value omitted
113 1d. on 1d. purple 30 20
a. Raised and level stops mixed 1·40 1·90
b. Pair, one with level stops 19·00 20·00
c. No stop after "V" 3·25 5·50
d. No stop after "R" 15·00 16·00
e. No stop after "I" 15·00 16·00
f. No stops after "V" and "I" £275
g. Surch inverted £300
h. Surch double 95·00 85·00
i. Pair, one without surch £200
j. Short figure "1" £100 £100
k. Space between "V" and "R" 60·00 65·00
l. Space between "R" and "I" £100
m. Space between "1" and "d" £180
n. Inserted "R" £300
o. Inserted "V" £700
114 2d. on 2d. bright mauve 50 30
a. Raised and level stops mixed 4·50 4·50
b. Pair, one with level stops 7·50 8·00
c. Surch inverted £300 £300
d. "I" raised
e. Pair, one without surch
f. No stop after "V" £1000
115 2½d. on 3d. ultramarine (*a*) £200 £180
a. Raised and level stops mixed
116 2½d. on 3d. ultramarine (*b*) £1200
117 3d. on 3d. ultramarine 30 30
a. Raised and level stops mixed 6·50 6·50
b. Pair, one with level stops 17·00 18·00
c. No stop after "V" £140 £140
d. No stop after "R" £350 £450
e. "I" omitted £400
f. Surch double £400
g. Surch double, one diagonal £350
h. Ditto, diagonal surch with mixed stops £6500
n. Inserted "R"
o. Space between "3" and "d"
118 4d. on 4d. ultramarine 1·25 2·25
a. Raised and level stops mixed 7·50 10·00
b. Pair, one with level stops 18·00 25·00
119 6d. on 6d. bright carmine 35·00 48·00
a. Raised and level stops mixed £140 £140
b. Pair, one with level stops £200 £250
120 6d. on 6d. blue 70 40
a. Raised and level stops mixed 7·50 7·50
b. Pair, one with level stops 19·00 20·00
c. No stop after "V" £500
d. No stop after "R"
e. Value omitted
121 1s. on 1s. brown 1·75 45
a. Error. Orange-yellow £1300 £1300
b. Raised and level stops mixed 14·00 16·00
c. Pair, one with level stops 27·00 30·00
f. "s" omitted
g. "V.R.I." omitted
122 5s. on 5s. green (H/S S. £50) 6·50 8·50
a. Raised and level stops mixed £300 £300
b. Pair, one with level stops £900
c. Short top to "5" 60·00 70·00

(ii) *Surch as T* **33**
123 ½d. on ½d. orange 2·00 90
124 1d. on 1d. purple 2·00 35
a. Inverted "1" for "I" 17·00 18·00
b. No stops after "R" and "I" 85·00 65·00
c. No stop after "R" 38·00 42·00
d. Surch double £300 £300
n. Inserted "R" £400 £400
125 2d. on 2d. bright mauve 4·00 5·50
a. Inverted "1" for "I" 24·00 27·00
126 2½d. on 3d. ultramarine (*a*) £600 £700
127 2½d. on 3d. ultramarine (*b*)
128 3d. on 3d. ultramarine 4·50 6·50
a. Inverted "1" for "I" 65·00 70·00
b. Surch double £450
ba. Surch double, one diagonal £400
129 6d. on 6d. bright carmine £425
130 6d. on 6d. blue 7·50 15·00
131 1s. on 1s. brown 12·00 7·50
132 5s. on 5s. green (H/S S. £150) 38·00 48·00

Stamps with thick "V" occur in certain positions in *later* settings of the type with stops above the line (T **32**). *Earlier* settings with stops above the line have all stamps with thin "V".

Some confusion has previously been caused by the listing of certain varieties as though they occurred on stamps with thick "V", in fact they occur on stamps showing the normal thin "V", included in the settings which also contained the thick "V".

As small blocks of unsurcharged Free State stamps could be handed in for surcharging, varieties thus occur which are not found in the complete settings.

The inserted "R" variety occurs on positions 6 (T **32**) and 12 (T **33**) of the forme. The "R." of the original surcharge failed to print and the "R", but not the full stop, was added by the use of a handstamp. Traces of the original letter are often visible. The broken "V" flaw, also shown in the illustration, does not appear on No. 124n.

ORANGE RIVER COLONY

CROWN COLONY

ORANGE RIVER COLONY. — 4d — E. R. I. 6d

(**34**) — (**35**) — (**36**)

1900 (10 Aug)–**02.** *Nos.* 58*a*, 61*a and* 67 *of Cape of Good Hope* (*wmk Cabled Anchor. P* 14) *optd with T* **34** *by W. A. Richards and Sons, Cape Town.*
133 ½d. green (13.10.00) 20 10
a. No stop 7·00 14·00
b. Opt double £550 £600
134 1d. carmine (May 1902) 30 10
a. No stop 12·00 20·00
135 2½d. ultramarine 30 35
a. No stop 55·00 65·00
133/5 *Set of* 3 70 45

In the ½d. and 2½d., the "no stop" after "COLONY" variety was the first stamp in the left lower pane. In the 1d. it is the twelfth stamp in the right lower pane on which the stop was present at the beginning of the printing but became damaged and soon failed to print.

1902 (14 Feb). *Surch with T* **35** *by "Bloemfontein Express".*
136 4d. on 6d. on 6d. blue (No. 120) (R.) 70 75
a. No stop after "R" 32·00 38·00
b. No stop after "I"
c. Surch on No. 130 (Thick "V") 1·75 5·00
ca. Inverted "1" for "I" 5·50 13·00

1902 (Aug). *Surch with T* **36**.
137 1 6d. on 6d. blue 2·00 6·00
a. Surch double, one inverted
b. Wide space between "6" and "d" (R.4/2) 60·00 85·00

One Shilling ✻

(**37**) — **38** King Edward VII, Springbok and Gnu

1902 (Sept). *Surch with T* **37**.
138 1 1s. on 5s. green (O.) 6·00 7·50
a. Thick "V" 14·00 26·00
b. Short top to "5" 70·00 75·00
c. Surch double

(Typo D.L.R.)

1903 (3 Feb)–**04.** *Wmk Crown CA. P* 14.
139 **38** ½d. yellow-green (6.7.03) 6·50 1·25
140 1d. scarlet 2·75 10
w. Wmk inverted — 75·00
141 2d. brown (6.7.03) 3·75 70
142 2½d. bright blue (6.7.03) 1·40 50
143 3d. mauve (6.7.03) 5·50 90
144 4d. scarlet and sage-green (6.7.03) 24·00 2·00
a. "IOSTAGE" for "POSTAGE" £800 £450
145 6d. scarlet and mauve (6.7.03) 6·50 80
146 1s. scarlet and bistre (6.7.03) 25·00 1·75
147 5s. blue and brown (31.10.04) 75·00 22·00
139/47 *Set of* 9 £140 27·00
139/47 Optd "Specimen" *Set of* 9 £150

No. 144a occurs on R.10/2 of the upper left pane.

Several of the above values are found with the overprint "C.S.A.R.", in black, for use by the Central South African Railways.

1905 (Nov)–**09.** *Wmk Mult Crown CA. P* 14.
148 **38** ½d. yellow-green (28.7.07) 8·00 30
149 1d. scarlet 6·00 20
150 4d. scarlet and sage-green (8.11.07) 4·50 1·75
a. "IOSTAGE" for "POSTAGE" £180 £150
151 1s. scarlet and bistre (2.09) 35·00 12·00
148/51 *Set of* 4 48·00 13·00

POSTCARD STAMPS

From 1889 onwards the Orange Free State Post Office sold postcards franked with adhesives as Type 1, some subsequently surcharged, over which the State Arms had been overprinted.

There are five known dies of the Arms overprint which can be identified as follows:

(a) Shield without flags. Three cows (two lying down, one standing) at left. Point of shield complete.
(b) Shield with flags. Four cows (two lying down, two standing) at left (*illustrated*).
(c) Shield with flags. Three cows (one lying down, two standing) at left.
(d) Shield without flags. Three cows (one lying down, two standing) at left.
(e) Shield without flags. Three cows (two lying down, one standing) at left. Point of shield broken.

There are also other differences between the dies.

PRICES. Those in the left-hand column are for unused examples on complete postcard; those on the right for used examples off card. Examples used on postcard are worth more.

1889 (Feb). *No.* 2 (*placed sideways on card*) *optd Shield Type* (a).
P1 1 1d. red-brown 70·00 32·00
a. Optd Shield Type (b) 24·00 5·50

1891 (Aug). *No.* 48 *optd Shield Type* (b).
P2 1 ½d. chestnut 3·50 1·25
a. Optd Shield Type (c) 8·00 3·50
b. Optd Shield Type (d) 4·00 1·75
c. Optd Shield Type (e) 9·50 4·00

1892 (June). *No. 54 optd Shield Type* (b).
P3 1 1d. on 3d. ultramarine .. .. .. 70·00 38·00
a. Optd Shield Type (c) .. .. .. 11·00 2·50

1½d. 1½d. 1½d.

(P 1) (P 2) (P 3)

1892 (Sept)–**95**. *Nos. 50/1 optd Shield Type* (b) *or* (d) (*No.* P6) *and surch with Types* P 1/3.
P4 1 1½d. on 2d. bright mauve (Type P 1) (11.92) 6·00 3·00
P5 1½d. on 2d. bright mauve (Type P 2) (9.93) 3·50 1·25
a. Surch inverted
P6 1½d. on 2d. brt mauve (Type P 3) (R.) (6.95) 9·00 3·50
P7 1½d. on 3d. ultramarine (Type P 1) .. 5·50 1·75

No. P5a shows the stamp affixed to the card upside down with the surcharge correctly positioned in relation to the card.

½d.

(P 4)

1895 (Aug). *No. 48 optd Shield Type* (e) *and surch with Type* P 4.
P8 1 ½d. on ½d. chestnut .. .. 9·00 2·25

1½d. 1½d.

(P 5) (P 6)

1895 (Dec)–**97**. *No. 50 optd Shield Type* (e) *and surch with Types* P 5/6.
P 9 1 1½d. on 2d. bright mauve (Type P 5) .. 4·50 2·25
P10 1½d. on 2d. brt mauve (Type P 6) (12.97) 5·00 2·75
P11 1½d. on 2d. bright mauve (as Type P 6, but without stop) (12.97) .. .. 5·00 2·75

1897 (Mar). *No. 85 optd Shield Type* (d).
P12 1 ½d. orange .. .. .. 9·00 1·25
a. Optd Shield Type (e) .. .. 10·00 2·25

V.R.I.

(P 7)

1900. *Nos.* P10/11 *optd as T* **31/2** *or with Type* P 7.
P13 1 1½d. on 2d. bright mauve (No. P10) (T **31**) 20·00 4·50
P14 1½d. on 2d. bright mauve (No. P11) (T **31**) 20·00 4·50
P15 1½d. on 2d. bright mauve (No. P10) (T **32**) 20·00 4·50
P16 1½d. on 2d. bright mauve (No. P11) (T **32**) 20·00 4·50
P17 1½d. on 2d. brt mve (No. P10) (Type P **7**) 30·00 8·50
P18 1½d. on 2d. brt mve (No. P11) (Type P **7**) 30·00 8·50

POLICE FRANK STAMPS

The following frank stamps were issued to members of the Orange Free State Mounted Police ("Rijdende Dienst Macht") for use on official correspondence.

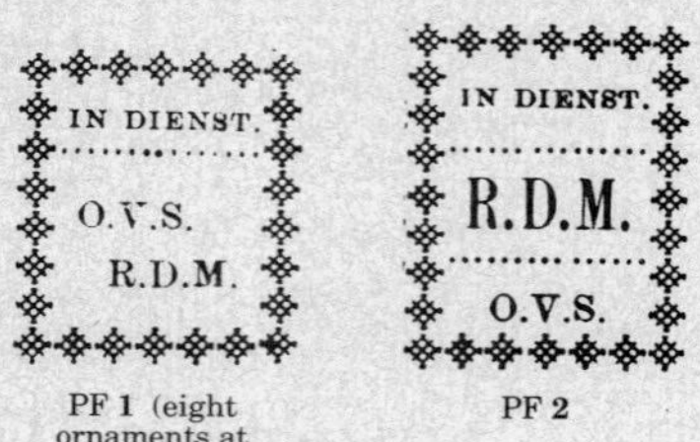

PF 1 (eight ornaments at left and right) PF 2

1896. *P* 12.
PF1 PF 1 (–) Black £190

No. PF1 was printed in horizontal strips of 5 surrounded by wide margins.

1898. *As Type* PF **1**, *but with nine ornaments at left and right.* *P* 12.
PF2 (–) Black £130 £160

No. PF2 was printed in blocks of 4 (2×2) surrounded by wide margins.

1899. *P* 12.
PF3 PF 2 (–) Black/*yellow* £120 £120

No. PF3 was printed in sheets of 24 (6×4) with the edges of the sheet imperforate. It is believed that they were produced from a setting of 8 (2×4) repeated three times.

Examples of No. PF3 are known postmarked as late as 28 April 1900. The O.F.S. Mounted Police were disbanded by the British authorities at the end of the following month.

MILITARY FRANK STAMP

M 1

(Typeset Curling & Co, Bloemfontein)

1899 (15 Oct). *P* 12.
M1 M 1 (–) Black/*bistre-yellow* .. .. 12·00 45·00

Supplies of No. M1 were issued to members of the Orange Free State army on active service during the Second Boer War. To pass free through the O.F.S. fieldpost system letters had to be franked with No. M1 or initialled by the appropriate unit commander. The franks were in use between October 1899 and February 1900.

No. M1 was printed in sheets of 20 (5×4) using a setting of five different types in a horizontal row. The colour in the paper runs in water.

Typeset forgeries can be identified by the appearance of 17 pearls, instead of the 16 of the originals, in the top and bottom frames. Forgeries produced by lithography omit the stops after "BRIEF" and "FRANKO".

FISCAL STAMPS USED FOR POSTAGE

The following were issued in 1878 (Nos. F1 and F3 in 1882) and were authorised for postal use between 1882 and 1886.

F 1 F 2

(Typo D.L.R.)

1882–86. *P* 14.
F 1 F 1 6d. pearl-grey .. .. .. 5·50 9·50
F 2 6d. purple-brown .. .. .. 20·00 15·00
F 3 F 2 1s. purple-brown .. .. .. 6·50 13·00
F 4 1s. pearl-grey .. .. .. 32·00 40·00
F 5 1s. 6d. blue .. .. .. 12·00 9·00
F 6 2s. magenta .. .. .. 12·00 9·00
F 7 3s. chestnut .. .. .. 15·00 40·00
F 8 4s. grey .. ..
F 9 5s. rose .. .. .. 17·00 17·00
F10 6s. green .. .. .. — 42·00
F11 7s. violet .. .. ..
F12 10s. orange .. .. .. 35·00 26·00
F13 £1 purple .. .. .. 45·00 28·00
F14 £2 red-brown .. .. .. 50·00
F14*a* £4 carmine .. .. ..
F15 £5 green .. .. .. 75·00 35·00

A fiscally used example of No. F2 exists showing "ZES PENCE" double, one inverted.

The 8s. yellow was prepared but we have no evidence of its use postally without surcharge Type F 3.

ZES PENCE.

(F 3)

1886. *Surch with Type* F **3**.
F16 F 2 6d. on 4s. grey .. .. ..
F17 6d. on 8s. yellow £150

Postage stamps overprinted for use as Telegraph stamps and used postally are omitted as it is impossible to say with certainty which stamps were genuinely used for postal purposes.

Orange Free State became a province of the Union of South Africa on 31 May 1910.

VI. TRANSVAAL

(*formerly* South African Republic)

PRICES FOR STAMPS ON COVER

Nos. 1/6 are rare used on cover.

Nos. 7/80	*from* × 20
Nos. 86/155	*from* × 3
Nos. 156/62	*from* × 6
Nos. 163/9	*from* × 5
Nos. 170/225	*from* × 10
Nos. 226/34	*from* × 20
Nos. 235/7	—
Nos. 238/43	*from* × 12
Nos. 244/55	*from* × 4
Nos. 256/7	*from* × 6
Nos. 258/9	—
Nos. 260/76	*from* × 20
Nos. F1/5	*from* × 5
Nos. D1/7	*from* × 20

The issues for Pietersburg, Lydenburg, Rustenburg, Schweizer Renecke and Wolmaransstad are very rare when on cover.

1 (Eagle with spread wings)

2

3

(Typo Adolph Otto, Gustrow, Mecklenburg-Schwerin)

1870 (1 May). *Thin paper, clear and distinct impressions.*

(*a*) *Imperf*
1 1 1d. brown-lake £350
a. Orange-red £350 £350
2 6d. bright ultramarine £130 £130
a. Pale ultramarine £150 £160
3 1s. deep green £550 £550
a. *Tête-bêche* (pair) .. ..

(*b*) *Fine roulette*, 15½ *to* 16
4 1 1d. brown-lake .. .. .. 85·00
a. Brick-red .. .. .. 65·00
b. Orange-red .. .. .. 65·00
c. Vermilion .. .. .. 65·00
5 6d. bright ultramarine .. .. 60·00 60·00
a. Pale ultramarine .. .. 70·00
6 1s. deep green £130 £130
a. Yellow-green .. .. .. £100 95·00
b. Emerald-green .. .. .. 80·00 80·00

Examples of Nos. 1/6 may have been sold to dealers at some stage between their arrival in Transvaal during August 1869 and the sale of stamps to the public for postal purposes on 1 May 1870.

PLATES. The German printings of the 1d., 6d. and 1s. in Type **1** were from two pairs of plates, each pair printing sheets of 80 in two panes of five horizontal rows of eight.

One pair of plates, used for Nos. 4*a*, 4*c*, 5*a* and 6/*a*, produced stamps spaced 1¼ to 1½ mm apart with the rouletting close to the design on all four sides. The 1d. from these "narrow" plates shows a gap in the outer frame line at the bottom right-hand corner. The second pair, used for Nos. 1/3, 4, 4*b*, 5/*a* and 6*b*, had 2½ to 3½ mm between the stamps. These "wide" plates were sent to the Transvaal in 1869 and were used there to produce either single or double pane printings until 1883.

The 6d. and 1s. "wide" plates each had an inverted *cliché*. When printed these occurred on right-hand pane R. 4/1 of the 6d. and right-hand pane R.1/1 of the 1s. These were never corrected and resulted in *tête-bêche* pairs of these values as late as 1883.

REPRINTS AND IMITATIONS. A number of unauthorised printings were made of these stamps by the German printer. Many of these can be identified by differences in the central arms, unusual colours or, in the case of the 1d., by an extra frame around the numeral tablets at top.

Genuine stamps always show the "D" of "EENDRAGT" higher than the remainder of the word, have no break in the border above "DR" and depict the flagstaff at bottom right, behind "MAGT", stopping short of the central shield. They also show the eagle's eye as a clear white circle. On the forgeries the eye is often blurred.

The most difficult of the reprints to detect is the 1s. yellow-green which was once regarded as genuine, but was subsequently identified, by J. N. Luff in *The Philatelic Record* 1911–12, as coming from an unauthorised plate of four. Stamps from this plate show either a white dot between "EEN" and "SHILLING" or a white flaw below the wagon pole.

(Typo M. J. Viljoen, Pretoria)

1870 (1 May–4 July).

I. *Thin gummed paper from Germany. Impressions coarse and defective.* (*a*) *Imperf*
8 1 1d. dull rose-red .. .. .. 70·00
a. Reddish pink .. .. .. 60·00
b. Carmine-red .. .. .. 55·00 65·00
9 6d. dull ultramarine .. .. £250 60·00
a. *Tête-bêche* (pair) .. ..

(*b*) *Fine roulette*, 15½ *to* 16
10 1 1d. carmine-red £700 £250
11 6d. dull ultramarine .. .. £180 90·00
a. Imperf between (vert pair) .. £550

(*c*) *Wide roulette*, 6½
12 1 1d. carmine-red .. .. .. — £850

II. *Thick, hard paper with thin yellow smooth gum* (*No.* 15) *or yellow streaky gum* (*others*). (*a*) *Imperf*
13 1 1d. pale rose-red .. .. .. 60·00
a. Carmine-red .. .. .. 60·00 70·00
14 1s. yellow-green .. .. .. 85·00 75·00
a. *Tête-bêche* (pair) £14000
b. Bisected (6d.) (on cover) .. † £1200

(*b*) *Fine roulette*, 15½ *to* 16
15 1 1d. carmine-red (24 May) .. 80·00
16 6d. ultramarine (10 May) .. 80·00 80·00
a. *Tête-bêche* (pair) .. £22000 £17000
17 1s. yellow-green £550 £550

III. *Medium paper, blotchy heavy printing and whitish gum. Fine roulette* 15½ *to* 16 (4 *July*)
18 1 1d. rose-red .. .. .. 60·00 75·00
a. Carmine-red .. .. .. 38·00 45·00
b. Crimson. From over-inked plate £130
19 6d. ultramarine .. .. .. 75·00 65·00
a. *Tête-bêche* (pair) .. ..
b. Deep ultram. From over-inked plate £400 £150
20 1s. deep green .. .. .. £100 65·00
a. From over-inked plate .. £450 £150

The rouletting machine producing the wide 6½ gauge was not introduced until 1875.

Nos. 18*b*, 19*b* and 20a were printed from badly over-inked plates giving heavy blobby impressions.

(Typo J. P. Borrius, Potchefstroom)

1870 (Sept)–**71**. *Stout paper, but with colour often showing through, whitish gum.* (*a*) *Imperf*
21 1 1d. black £120 £100

(*b*) *Fine roulette*, 15½ *to* 16
22 1 1d. black .. .. .. 15·00 25·00
a. Grey-black .. .. .. 15·00 25·00
23 6d. blackish blue (7.71) .. £120 60·00
a. Dull blue .. .. .. 90·00 75·00

(Typo Adolph Otto, Gustrow, Mecklenburg-Schwerin)

1871 (July). *Thin paper, clear and distinct impressions. Fine roulette,* 15½ *to* 16.

No.	Type	Description	Unused	Used
24	2	3d. pale reddish lilac	80·00	90·00
		a. Deep lilac	85·00	95·00
		b. Vert laid paper		

No. 24 and later printings in the Transvaal were produced from a pair of plates in the same format as the 1869 issue. All genuine stamps have a small dot on the left leg of the eagle.

Imperforate examples in the issued shade, without the dot on eagle's leg, had been previously supplied by the printer, probably as essays, but were not issued for postal purposes. They exist *tête-bêche (price for un pair* £3250).

Imperforate and rouletted stamps in other colours are reprints.

(Typo J. P. Borrius, Potchefstroom)

1872–74. *Fine roulette,* 15½ *to* 16. *(a) Thin transparent paper*

No.	Type	Description	Unused	Used
25	1	1d. black	£170	£550
26		1d. bright carmine	£140	50·00
27		6d. ultramarine	£100	40·00
28		1s. green	£120	50·00
		(b) Thinnish opaque paper, clear printing (Dec 1872)		
29	1	1d. reddish pink	55·00	38·00
		a. Carmine-red	55·00	38·00
30	2	3d. grey-lilac	85·00	45·00
31	1	6d. ultramarine	55·00	27·00
		a. Pale ultramarine	65·00	29·00
32		1s. yellow-green	70·00	38·00
		a. Green	70·00	38·00
		aa. Bisected (6d.) (on cover)	†	£1400
		(c) Thickish wove paper (1873–74)		
33	1	1d. dull rose	£400	70·00
		a. Brownish rose	£475	£110
		b. Printed on both sides		
34		6d. milky blue	£140	45·00
		a. Deep dull blue	85·00	40·00
		aa. Imperf (pair)	£600	
		ab. Imperf between (horiz pair)	£650	
		ac. Wide roulette 6½		
		(d) Very thick dense paper (1873–74)		
35		1d. dull rose	£500	£120
		a. Brownish rose	£375	95·00
36		6d. dull ultramarine	£170	65·00
		a. Bright ultramarine	£180	60·00
37		1s. yellow-green	£750	£550

(Typo P. Davis & Son, Pietermaritzburg)

1874 (Sept). *P* 12½. *(a) Thin transparent paper.*

No.	Type	Description	Unused	Used
38	1	1d. pale brick-red	80·00	35·00
		a. Brownish red	75·00	35·00
39		6d. deep blue	£120	50·00
		(b) Thicker opaque paper		
40	1	1d. pale red	£130	65·00
41		6d. blue	£100	45·00
		a. Imperf between (pair)		
		b. Deep blue	£100	45·00

(Typo Adolph Otto, Gustrow, Mecklenburg-Schwerin)

1874 (Oct). *Thin smooth paper, clearly printed. Fine roulette* 15½ *to* 16.

No.	Type	Description	Unused	Used
42	3	6d. bright ultramarine	60·00	22·00
		a. Bisected (3d.) (on cover)		

Stamps in other shades of blue, brown or red, often on other types of paper, are reprints.

(Typo J. F. Celliers on behalf of Stamp Commission, Pretoria)

1875 (29 Apr)–**77.**

I. *Very thin, soft opaque (semi-pelure) paper. (a) Imperf*

No.	Type	Description	Unused	Used
43	1	1d. orange-red	£120	45·00
		a. Pin-perf		
44	2	3d. lilac	80·00	40·00
45	1	6d. blue	75·00	38·00
		a. Milky blue	£120	40·00
		aa. *Tête-bêche* (pair)	£9500	
		ab. Pin-perf	—	£250
		(b) Fine roulette, 15½ *to* 16		
46	1	1d. orange-red	£400	£130
47	2	3d. lilac	£425	£140
48	1	6d. blue	£400	£130
		(c) Wide roulette, 6½		
49	1	1d. orange-red	—	£150
50	2	3d. lilac	£550	£225
51	1	6d. blue	—	£120
		a. Bright blue	—	£120
		b. Milky blue	—	£120

II. *Very thin, hard transparent (pelure) paper* (1875–76) *(a) Imperf*

No.	Type	Description	Unused	Used
52	1	1d. brownish red	48·00	27·00
		a. Orange-red	38·00	22·00
		b. Dull red	42·00	42·00
		ba. Pin-perf	£425	£250
53	2	3d. lilac	45·00	38·00
		a. Pin-perf	—	£225
		b. Deep lilac	55·00	38·00
54	1	6d. pale blue	45·00	45·00
		a. Blue	45·00	38·00
		ab. *Tête-bêche* (pair)		
		ac. Pin-perf	—	£200
		b. Deep blue	50·00	42·00
		(b) Fine roulette 15½ *to* 16		
55	1	1d. orange-red	£250	£120
		a. Brown-red	£250	£120
56	2	3d. lilac	£325	£110
57	1	6d. blue	£150	95·00
		a. Deep blue	£150	£110
		(c) Wide roulette, 6½		
58	1	1d. orange-red	£700	£160
		a. Bright red	—	£140
59	2	3d. lilac	—	£190
60	1	6d. deep blue	£700	90·00

III. *Stout hard-surfaced paper with smooth, nearly white, gum* (1876). *(a) Imperf*

No.	Type	Description	Unused	Used
61	1	1d. bright red	20·00	14·00
62	2	3d. lilac	£300	£100
63	1	6d. bright blue	90·00	20·00
		a. *Tête-bêche* (pair)		
		b. Pale blue	90·00	22·00
		c. Deep blue (deep brown gum)	55·00	18·00
		ca. *Tête-bêche* (pair)	—	£14000
		(b) Fine roulette, 15½ *to* 16		
64	1	1d. bright red	£400	£150
65	2	3d. lilac	£275	
66	1	6d. bright blue	—	£110
		a. Deep blue (deep brown gum)	—	£250
		(c) Wide roulette, 6½		
67	1	1d. bright red	£450	£140
68		6d. pale blue	—	£200
		a. Deep blue (deep brown gum)	£500	£250

IV. *Coarse, soft white paper* (1876–77). *(a) Imperf*

No.	Type	Description	Unused	Used
69	1	1d. brick-red	£100	50·00
70		6d. deep blue	£160	50·00
		a. Milky blue	£275	90·00
71		1s. yellow-green	£275	£100
		a. Bisected (6d.) (on cover)	†	£1200
		(b) Fine roulette, 15½ *to* 16		
72	1	1d. brick-red	—	£250
73		6d. deep blue	—	£130
74		1s. yellow-green	£550	£275
		(c) Wide roulette, 6½		
75	1	1d. brick-red	—	£300
76		6d. deep blue	—	£750
77		1s. yellow-green	—	£800
		(d) Fine × wide roulette		
78	1	1d. brick-red	£550	£250

V. *Hard, thick, coarse yellowish paper* (1876–77)

No.	Type	Description	Unused	Used
79	1	1d. brick-red *(imperf)*	—	£200
80		1d. brick-red *(wide roulette)*	—	£300

The pin-perforated stamps have various gauges and were probably produced privately or by one or more post offices other than Pretoria.

On Nos. 63c/ca, 66*a* and 68*a* the brown gum used was so intense that it caused staining of the paper which is still visible on used examples.

See also Nos. 171/4.

FIRST BRITISH OCCUPATION

By 1876 conditions in the Transvaal had deteriorated and the country was faced by economic collapse, native wars and internal dissension. In early 1877 Sir Theophilus Shepstone, appointed Special Commissioner to the South African Republic by the British Government, arrived in Pretoria and on 12 April annexed the Transvaal with the acquiesence of at least part of the European population.

V. R. TRANSVAAL. (4)

V. R. TRANSVAAL. (5)

T **4** is the normal overprint, but Setting I No. 11 (R. 2/3) has a wider-spaced overprint as T **5**.

1877 (Apr). *Optd with T* **4** *in red. (a) Imperf.*

No.	Type	Description	Unused	Used
86	2	3d. lilac *(semi-pelure)* (No. 44)	£1100	£250
		a. Opt Type **5**		
87		3d. lilac *(pelure)* (No. 53)	£1100	£160
		a. Opt Type **5**	—	£1400
		b. Opt on back	£3000	£3000
		c. Opt double, in red and in black	£4750	
88	1	6d. milky blue (No. 70)	£1300	£160
		a. Opt inverted	—	£4250
		b. Opt double	£3500	£750
		c. Opt Type **5**	£4250	
		d. Deep blue	—	£225
89		1s. yellow-green (No. 71)	£475	£160
		a. Bisected (6d.) (on cover)	†	£1300
		b. Opt inverted	—	£3250
		c. Opt Type **5**	£3000	£750
		d. *Tête-bêche* (pair)		
		(b) Fine roulette, 15½ *to* 16		
90	2	3d. lilac *(pelure)* (No. 56)	—	£1100
91	1	6d. deep blue (No. 73)	—	£1100
92		1s. yellow-green (No. 74)	£1100	£500
		a. Opt Type **5**		
		(c) Wide roulette, 6½		
93	2	3d. lilac *(pelure)* (No. 59)	—	£1100
		a. Opt Type **5**		
94	1	6d. deep blue (No. 76)	—	£1100
		a. Opt Type **5**		
95		1s. yellow-green (No. 77)	£2750	£1000
		a. Opt inverted	—	£3500

Nos. 88a, 89b and 95a occurred on the inverted *cliché* of the basic stamps.

1877 (June). *Optd with T* **4** *in black.*

I. *Very thin, hard transparent (pelure) paper*

No.	Type	Description	Unused	Used
96	1	1d. orange-red *(imperf)* (No. 52*a*)	£170	95·00
97		1d. orange-red *(fine roulette)* (No. 55)	—	£1000

II. *Stout hard-surfaced paper with smooth, nearly white, gum*

No.	Type	Description	Unused	Used
98	1	1d. bright red *(imperf)* (No. 61)	20·00	20·00
		a. Opt inverted	£475	£400
		b. Opt Type **5**	£550	£600
99		1d. bright red *(fine roulette)* (No. 64)	£140	45·00
		a. Opt inverted		
		b. Opt double	—	£750
		c. Imperf between (horiz pair)	£650	
100		1d. bright red *(wide roulette)* (No. 67)	£475	£140
100*a*		1d. bright red *(fine×wide roulette)* (No. 78)		

III. *New ptgs on coarse, soft white paper. (a) Imperf*

No.	Type	Description	Unused	Used
101	1	1d. brick-red (5.77)	20·00	20·00
		a. Opt double	—	£900
		b. Opt Type **5**	£600	
102	2	3d. lilac	70·00	35·00
		a. Opt inverted		
		b. Deep lilac	£140	80·00
103	1	6d. dull blue	85·00	30·00
		a. Opt double	£2750	
		b. Opt inverted	£1200	£150
		d. Opt Type **5**	—	£750
		da. Opt Type **5** inverted		
		e. Blue (bright to deep)	£150	27·00
		ea. Bright blue, opt inverted	—	£475
		f. Pin-perf	—	£450
104		1s. yellow-green	85·00	40·00
		a. Opt inverted	£900	£180
		b. *Tête-bêche* (pair)	£15000	£15000
		c. Opt Type **5**	£2750	£900
		d. Bisected (6d.) (on cover)	†	£1000
		(b) Fine roulette, 15½ *to* 16		
105	1	1d. brick-red	65·00	65·00
		a. Imperf horiz (vert strip of 3)		
		b. Imperf between (horiz pair)	†	£600
106	2	3d. lilac	£140	55·00
107	1	6d. dull blue	£160	45·00
		a. Opt inverted	—	£550
		b. Opt Type **5**	£3500	
108		1s. yellow-green	£160	80·00
		a. Opt inverted	£800	£375
		b. Opt Type **5**	—	£2500
		(c) Wide roulette, 6½		
109	1	1d. brick-red	£550	£140
		a. Opt Type **5**	—	£650
110	2	3d. lilac	—	£550
111	1	6d. dull blue	—	£1100
		a. Opt inverted	—	£3000
112		1s. yellow-green	£350	£120
		a. Opt inverted	£1100	£475

1877 (31 Aug). *Optd with T* **4** *in black.*

No.	Type	Description	Unused	Used
113	1	6d. blue/*rose (imperf)*	70·00	45·00
		a. Bisected (3d.) (on cover)		
		b. Opt inverted	85·00	45·00
		c. *Tête-bêche* (pair)		
		d. Opt omitted	£2750	£2000
114		6d. blue/*rose (fine roulette)*	£150	60·00
		a. Opt inverted	£425	60·00
		b. *Tête-bêche* (pair)		
		c. Opt omitted		
		d. Bisected (3d.) (on cover)		
115		6d. blue/*rose (wide roulette)*		
		a. Opt inverted		
		b. Opt omitted		

Nos. 113/15 were overprinted from a setting of 40 which was applied upright to one pane in each sheet and inverted on the other.

V. R. Transvaal (6)

V. R. Transvaal (7)

1877 (28 Sept)–**79.** *Optd with T* **6** *in black. (a) Imperf*

No.	Type	Description	Unused	Used
116	1	1d. red/*blue*	45·00	24·00
		a. "Transvral" (Right pane R. 2/3)	£4000	£2000
		b. Opt double	£3000	
		c. Opt inverted	£600	£300
		d. Opt omitted		
117		1d. red/*orange* (6.12.77)	15·00	16·00
		a. Pin-perf		
		b. Printed both sides		
		c. Opt double	£2500	
		d. Optd with Type **7** (15.4.78)	45·00	38·00
118	2	3d. mauve/*buff* (24.10.77)	38·00	24·00
		a. Opt inverted	—	£550
		b. Pin-perf		
		c. Bisected (1½d.) (on cover)	†	—
		d. Optd with Type **7** (15.4.78)	50·00	32·00
		da. Pin-perf	£550	£550
119		3d. mauve/*green* (18.4.79)	£140	40·00
		a. Pin-perf		
		b. Opt inverted	—	£1500
		c. Opt double		
		d. Printed both sides	†	—
		e. Optd with Type **7**	95·00	32·00
		ea. Opt inverted	—	£1500
		eb. Printed both sides		
		f. Opt omitted	—	£2750
120	1	6d. blue/*green* (27.11.77)	75·00	32·00
		a. Deep blue/green	90·00	35·00
		b. Broken "Y" for "V" in "V.R." (Left pane R. 3/7)	—	£550
		c. Small "v" in "Transvaal" (Left pane R. 5/2)	—	£550
		d. "V..R." (Right pane R. 3/4)	—	£550
		e. *Tête-bêche* (pair)	—	£14000
		f. Opt inverted	—	£700
		g. Pin-perf		
		h. Bisected (3d.) (on cover)	†	—
121		6d. blue/*blue* (20.3.78)	48·00	22·00
		a. *Tête-bêche* (pair)		
		b. Opt inverted	—	£700
		c. Opt omitted	—	£1600
		d. Opt double	—	£2500
		e. Pin-perf		
		f. Bisected (3d.) (on cover)	†	£600
		g. Optd with Type **7**	95·00	27·00
		ga. *Tête-bêche* (pair)	£11000	
		gb. Opt inverted	—	£400
		gc. Bisected (3d.) (on cover)	†	—

(b) Fine roulette, 15½ to 16

122 1 1d. red/*blue* .. .. .. 70·00 32·00
a. "Transvral" (Right pane R. 2/3) .. .. — £2250
123 1d. red/*orange* (6.12.77) .. .. .. 28·00 22·00
a. Imperf between (pair) £500
b. Optd with Type **7** (15.4.78) £130 £110
124 2 3d. mauve/*buff* (24.10.77) .. .. 85·00 22·00
a. Imperf horiz (vert pair) £600
b. Opt inverted .. .. .. — £2500
c. Optd with Type **7** (15.4.78) .. .. £130 95·00
ca. Imperf between (pair) .. ..
125 3d. mauve/*green* (18.4.79) £550 £150
a. Optd with Type **7** £500 £150
126 1 6d. blue/*green* (27.11.77) .. .. 70·00 22·00
a. "V..R" (Right pane R. 3/4) .. .. — £1000
b. *Tête-bêche* (pair) .. .. ..
c. Opt inverted .. .. .. — £500
d. Opt omitted .. .. .. — £3000
e. Bisected (3d.) (on cover) .. .. † £550
127 6d. blue/*blue* (20.3.78) .. .. £180 48·00
a. Opt inverted .. .. .. — £900
b. Opt omitted .. .. .. — £2500
c. Imperf between (pair) .. ..
d. Bisected (3d.) (on cover) .. .. † £600
e. Optd with Type **7** £300 £100
ea. Opt inverted .. .. .. — £800

(c) Wide roulette, 6¼

128 1 1d. red/*orange* (15.4.78) £250 £100
a. Optd with Type **7** .. .. — £250
129 2 3d. mauve/*buff* (24.10.77) .. .. — £100
a. Optd with Type **7** (15.4.78) .. .. — £300
130 3d. mauve/*green* (18.4.79) £375 £275
a. Optd with Type **7** .. .. .. — £300
131 1 6d. blue/*green* (27.11.77) .. .. — £850
132 6d. blue/*blue* (20.3.78) .. .. — £250
a. Opt inverted .. .. ..
b. Optd with Type **7** .. .. .. — £300
ba. Opt inverted .. .. ..

Nos. 116/32 were overprinted from various settings covering sheets of 80 or panes of 40 (8×5). Initially these settings contained Type **6** only, but from March 1878 settings also contained examples of Type **7**. Details of these mixed settings are as follows:
1d. red/*orange* (sheets of 80): all Type **6** except for 16 Type **7**.
3d. mauve/*buff* (panes of 40): 16 Type **7**.
3d. mauve/*green* (panes of 40): uncertain, some panes at least contained 27 Type **7**.
6d. blue/*blue* (sheets of 80): either 24 or 27 Type **7**.

9

(Recess B.W.)

1878 (26 Aug)–**80**. *P* 14, 14½.

133 9 ½d. vermilion (1880) .. .. .. 16·00 55·00
134 1d. pale red-brown .. .. .. 7·50 3·00
a. Brown-red .. .. .. 7·00 2·50
135 3d. dull rose .. .. .. 9·00 3·25
a. Claret .. .. .. 13·00 4·75
136 4d. sage-green .. .. .. 13·00 4·25
137 6d. olive-black .. .. .. 6·50 3·25
a. Black-brown .. .. .. 8·00 2·75
138 1s. green .. .. .. 95·00 32·00
139 2s. blue .. .. .. £140 65·00

The above prices are for specimens perforated on all four sides. Stamps from margins of sheets, with perforations absent on one or two sides, can be supplied for about 30% less.

1 Penny (10) 1 Penny (11) 1 Penny (12)

1 Penny (13) 1 Penny (14)

1 PENNY (15) *1 Penny* (16)

1879 (22 Apr). *No. 137a surch with T* **10** *to* **16**.

A. *In black*. B. *In red*.

		A		B	
140 10	1d. on 6d.	65·00	40·00	£180	£120
141 11	1d. on 6d.	£160	75·00	£450	£250
142 12	1d. on 6d.	£160	75·00	£450	£250
143 13	1d. on 6d.	70·00	45·00	£200	£140
144 14	1d. on 6d.	£425	£130	—	£1500
145 15	1d. on 6d.	35·00	22·00	£110	60·00
146 16	1d. on 6d.	£150	70·00	£400	£225

Nos. 140/6 were surcharged from a setting of 60 containing eleven examples of Type **10**, four of Type **11**, four of Type **12**, nine of Type **13**, two of Type **14** (although there may have been only one in the first two ptgs), twenty-five of Type **15** and five of Type **16**.
The red surcharges may have been produced first.

V. R. V. R.

Transvaal Transvaal

(16*a*) Small "T" (R. 2/8, 3/8, 4/8, 5/8 on right pane of 1d. and left pane of 3d.)

1879 (Aug–Sept). *Optd with T* **16a** *in black*. *(a) Imperf*.

147 1 1d. red/*yellow* .. .. .. 38·00 32·00
a. Small "T" £225 £150
b. Red/orange .. .. .. 32·00 25·00
ba. Small "T" £160 £150
148 2 3d. mauve/*green* (Sept) .. .. 35·00 20·00
a. Small "T" .. .. .. £160 85·00
149 3d. mauve/*blue* (Sept) .. .. 40·00 25·00
a. Small "T" .. .. .. £170 85·00

(b) Fine roulette 15½ to 16

150 1 1d. red/*yellow* £350 £200
a. Small "T" £800 £550
b. Red/orange £750 £375
ba. Small "T" .. .. ..
151 2 3d. mauve/*green* £700 £225
a. Small "T" .. .. ..
152 3d. mauve/*blue* .. .. .. — £160
a. Small "T" .. .. .. — £600

(c) Wide roulette 6½

153 1 1d. red/*yellow* £600 £600
a. Small "T" .. .. ..
b. Red/orange .. .. ..
154 2 3d. mauve/*green* .. .. ..
a. Small "T" .. .. ..
155 3d. mauve/*blue* .. .. ..

(d) Pin-perf about 17

156 1 1d. red/*yellow* .. .. .. — £450
a. Small "T" .. .. ..
157 2 3d. mauve/*blue* .. .. .. — £600

SECOND REPUBLIC

Following the first Boer War the independence of the South African Republic was recognised by the Convention of Pretoria from 8 August 1881.
Nos. 156/62 remained valid and some values were available for postage until 1885.

EEN PENNY

(17)

1882 (11 Aug). *No. 136 surch with T* **17**.

170 9 1d. on 4d. sage-green .. .. .. 7·00 3·75
a. Surch inverted £300 £200

Used examples of a similar, but larger, surcharge (width 20 mm) are known. These were previously considered to be forgeries, but it is now believed that some, at least, may represent a trial printing of the "EEN PENNY" surcharge.

(Typo J. F. Celliers)

1883 (20 Feb). *Re-issue of T* **1** *and* **2**. *P* 12.

171 1 1d. grey (*to* black) (Apr) .. .. 3·75 1·25
a. Imperf vert (horiz pair) £250
172 2 3d. grey-black (*to* black)/*rose* .. .. 18·00 3·75
a. Bisected (1d.) (on cover) .. .. † £500
173 3d. pale red (Mar) .. .. .. 6·50 1·75
a. Bisected (1d.) (on cover) .. .. † £500
b. Chestnut .. .. .. 22·00 3·50
ba. Imperf between (horiz pair) .. .. † —
c. Vermilion .. .. .. 22·00 4·50
174 1 1s. green (*to* deep) (July) .. .. 35·00 2·75
a. Bisected (6d.) (on cover) .. .. † £375
b. *Tête-bêche* (pair) £650 £120

Reprints are known of Nos. 172, 173, 173*b* and 173*c*. The paper of the first is *bright rose* in place of *dull rose*, and the impression is brownish black in place of grey-black to deep black. The reprints on white paper have the paper thinner than the originals, and the gum yellowish instead of white. The colour is a dull deep orange-red.

18

PERFORATIONS. Stamps perforated 11½×12 come from the first vertical row of sheets of the initial printing otherwise perforated 12½×12.

REPRINTS. Reprints of the general issues 1885–93, 1894–95, 1895–96 and 1896–97 exist in large quantities produced using the original plates from 1911 onwards. They cannot readily be distinguished from genuine originals except by comparison with used stamps, but the following general characteristics may be noted. The reprints are all perf 12½, large holes; the paper is whiter and thinner than that usually employed for the originals and their colours lack the lustre of those of the genuine stamps.
Forged surcharges have been made on these reprints.

(Des J. Vurtheim. Typo Enschedé)

1885 (13 Mar)–**1893**. *P* 12½.

175 18 ½d. grey (30.3.85) 30 10
a. Perf 13½ .. .. .. 4·75 90
b. Perf 12½×12 .. .. .. 1·75 10
ba. Perf 11½×12 .. .. .. 20·00 6·00
176 18 1d. carmine 30 10
a. Perf 12½×12 .. .. .. 70 10
aa. Perf 11½×12 .. .. .. 12·00 2·75
b. Rose 30 10
ba. Perf 12½×12 .. .. .. 65 10
177 2d. brown-purple (*p* 12½×12) (9.85) .. 1·40 1·40
178 2d. olive-bistre (14.4.87) 40 10
a. Perf 12½×12 .. .. .. 3·50 10
179 2½d. mauve (*to* bright) (8.93) .. .. 1·25 40
180 3d. mauve (*to* bright) .. .. .. 1·50 70
a. Perf 12½×12 .. .. .. 6·00 75
aa. Perf 11½×12 .. .. .. 27·00 17·00
181 4d. bronze-green .. .. .. 2·25 50
a. Perf 13½ .. .. .. 6·00 85
b. Perf 12½×12 .. .. .. 13·00 65
ba. Perf 11½×12 .. .. .. £160 60·00
182 6d. pale dull blue .. .. .. 3·50 2·00
a. Perf 13½ .. .. .. 4·50 70
b. Perf 12½×12 .. .. .. 5·50 20
ba. Perf 11½×12 .. .. ..
183 1s. yellow-green .. .. .. 2·50 35
a. Perf 13½ .. .. .. 20·00 5·50
b. Perf 12½×12 .. .. .. 7·50 45
184 2s. 6d. orange-buff (*to* buff) (2.12.85) .. 3·50 1·60
a. Perf 12½×12 .. .. .. 13·00 3·50
185 5s. slate (2.12.85) .. .. .. 5·00 2·75
a. Perf 12½×12 .. .. .. 25·00 4·00
186 10s. fawn (2.12.85) .. .. .. 26·00 5·50
187 £5 dp grn (3.92)* (Optd "Monster" £150) £3250 £180

Singles of the 6d. pale dull blue imperforate have been reported used in 1893.
*Most examples of No. 187 on the market are either forgeries or reprints.

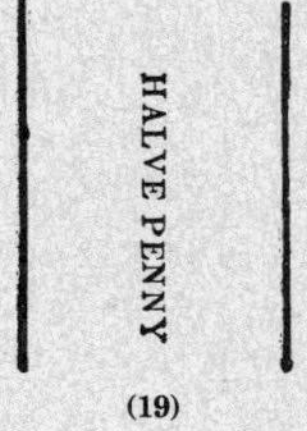

(19)

1885 (22 May–Aug). *Surch with T* **19**. A. *Reading down*. B. *Reading up*.

		A		B	
188 2	½d. on 3d. (No. 173) ..	3·50	7·00	3·50	7·00
189 1	½d. on 1s. (No. 174) (Aug)	12·00	30·00	12·00	30·00
	a. *Tête-bêche* (pair) ..	†		£600	£300

Nos. 188/9 were surcharged by a setting of 40. After the left pane had been surcharged reading down the sheets were turned so that the right pane had the surcharges reading up.

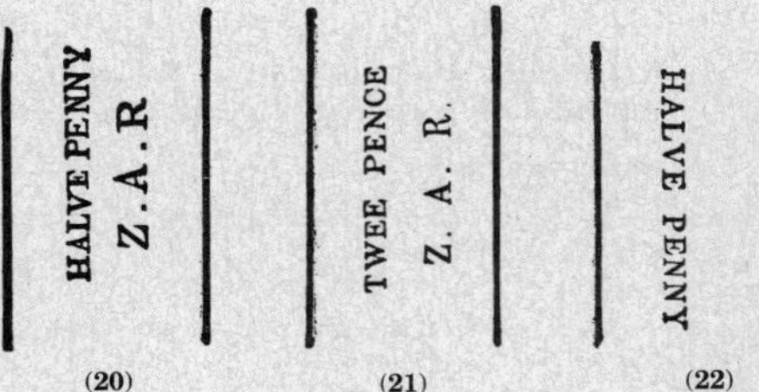

(20) (21) (22)

1885 (1 Sept). *No. 137a surch with T* **20/1** *in red*.

190 9 ½d. on 6d. black-brown .. .. 30·00 50·00
191 2d. on 6d. black-brown .. .. 3·00 4·50

1885 (28 Sept). *No. 180a surch with T* **22**.

192 18 ½d. on 3d. mauve .. .. .. 2·25 2·25
a. "PRNNY" (R. 6/6) .. .. 30·00 45·00
b. 2nd "N" inverted (R. 3/8) .. .. 70·00 85·00
c. Perf 11½×12 .. .. .. 8·50 8·00

2d 2d

(23) (24)

1887 (15 Jan). *No. 180a surch with T* **23/4**.

193 18 2d. on 3d. mauve (Type **23**) .. .. 4·50 4·50
a. Surch double .. .. .. — £225
b. Perf 11½×12 .. .. .. 19·00 10·00
194 2d. on 3d. mauve (Type **24**) .. .. 75 1·60
a. Surch double .. .. .. — £160
b. Perf 11½×12 .. .. .. 4·50 6·00

Nos. 193/4 were surcharged from the same setting of 60 (10 × 6) which showed Type **24** on the top five horizontal rows and Type **23** on the sixth horizontal row.

Halve Penny

(25)

1 Penny

(26)

2½ Pence

(27)

2½ Pence

(28)

Two types of surcharge:
A. Vertical distance between bars 12½ mm.
B. Distance 13½ mm.

1893. *T* **18** *surch. P* 12½. (*a*) *In red.*

195 **25** ½d. on 2d. olive-bistre (A) (27 May) .. 70 70
a. Surch inverted .. 1·75 1·50
b. Surch Type B .. 1·50 1·50
ba. Surch inverted .. 4·75 7·50

(*b*) *In black*

196 **25** ½d. on 2d. olive-bistre (A) (2 July) .. 75 60
a. Surch inverted .. 4·00 4·50
b. Extra surch on back inverted .. £150
c. Surch Type B .. 1·10 1·10
ca. Surch inverted .. 17·00 14·00
cb. Extra surch on back inverted .. £250
197 **26** 1d. on 6d. blue (A) (26 Jan) .. 45 30
a. Surch double .. 50·00 40·00
b. Surch inverted .. 1·40 1·60
c. Surch Type B .. 70 55
ca. Surch inverted .. 4·50 3·25
cb. Surch double .. — 70·00
d. Pair with and without surch .. £200
198 **27** 2½d. on 1s. green (A) (2 Jan) .. 80 1·60
a. "2/1/2" for "2½" (R. 1/10) .. 27·00 35·00
b. Surch inverted .. 6·50 7·50
ba. Surch inverted and "2/1/2" for "2½" £325 £275
c. Extra surch on back inverted .. £400 £400
d. Surch double, one inverted .. £600
e. Surch Type B .. 1·50 2·25
ea. Surch inverted .. 7·50 14·00
199 **28** 2½d. on 1s. green (A) (24 June) .. 2·50 2·75
a. Surch double .. 45·00 40·00
b. Surch inverted .. 7·00 7·00
c. Surch Type B .. 6·50 7·00
ca. Surch double .. 70·00 80·00
cb. Surch inverted .. 16·00 16·00

Surcharge Types **25/8** all show a similar setting of the horizontal bars at top and bottom. On horizontal rows 1 to 4 and 6 the bars are 12½ mm apart and on row 5 the distance is 13½ mm.

29 (Wagon with shafts)

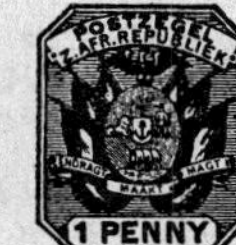

30 (Wagon with pole)

1894 (July). *P* 12½.

200 **29** ½d. grey .. 40 10
201 1d. carmine .. 40 10
202 2d. olive-bistre .. 40 10
203 6d. pale dull blue .. 1·00 40
204 1s. yellow-green .. 6·00 8·00

For note *re* reprints, see below T **18**.

1895 (16 Mar)–**96**. *P* 12½.

205 **30** ½d. pearl-grey (1895) .. 30 10
a. Lilac-grey .. 30 10
206 1d. rose-red .. 30 10
207 2d. olive-bistre (1895) .. 30 10
208 3d. mauve (1895) .. 55 10
209 4d. olive-black (1895) .. 1·25 60
210 6d. pale dull blue (1895) .. 1·25 40
211 1s. yellow-green (18.3.95) .. 1·75 75
212 5s. slate (1896) .. 10·00 17·00
212*a* 10s. pale chestnut (1896) .. 10·00 3·50
205/8, 211 Optd "Monster" .. *Set of* 5 £150

For note *re* reprints, see below T **18**.

Halve Penny

(31)

1d.

(**32**—Round dot)

1d.

(**32*a***—Square dot)

1895 (July–August). *Nos.* 211 *and* 179 *surch with T* **31/2**.

213 **30** ½d. on 1s. green (R.) .. 30 10
a. Surch spaced .. 85 75
b. "Pennij" for "Penny" (R. 6/6) .. 42·00 50·00
c. Surch inverted .. 3·50 4·50
d. Surch double .. 60·00 85·00
214 **18** 1d. on 2½d. bright mauve (G.) .. 30 10
a. Surch inverted .. 17·00 14·00
b. Surch double .. 60·00 60·00
c. Surch on back only .. 70·00
d. Surch Type **32*a*** .. 1·25 1·25
da. Surch inverted .. 60·00
e. Surch treble .. £500

The normal space between "Penny" and the bars is 3 mm. On No. 213a, which comes from the fifth horizontal row of the setting, this is increased to 4 mm. Copies may be found in which one or both of the bars have failed to print.

Type **32*a*** with square stop occurred on R. 3/3-4, 3/6-8, 4/4-5, 4/7-8, 4/10, 6/3, 6/7-8 and 6/10 of the setting of 60.

33

34

1895 (July). *Fiscal stamp optd* "POSTZEGEL". *P* 11½.

215 **33** 6d. bright rose (G.) .. 50 1·40
a. Imperf between (pair) ..

(Litho The Press Printing and Publishing Works, Pretoria)

1895 (6 Sept). *Introduction of Penny Postage. P* 11.

215*b* **34** 1d. red (pale *to* deep) .. 1·25 1·40
ba. Imperf between (pair) .. 60·00 65·00
bb. Imperf vert (horiz pair) ..
bc. Imperf (pair) ..

1896–97. *P* 12½.

216 **30** ½d. green (1896) .. 20 10
217 1d. rose-red and green (1896) .. 20 10
218 2d. brown and green (2.97) .. 20 10
219 2½d. dull blue and green (6.96) .. 30 10
220 3d. purple and green (3.97) .. 70 70
221 4d. sage-green and green (3.97) .. 70 70
222 6d. lilac and green (11.96) .. 40 70
223 1s. ochre and green (3.96) .. 50 15
224 2s. 6d. dull violet and green (6.96) .. 1·25 1·25

For note *re* reprints, see below T **18**.

SECOND BRITISH OCCUPATION

The Second Boer War began on 11 October 1899 and was concluded by the Peace of Vereeniging on 31 May 1902. Pretoria was occupied by the British on 5 June 1900 and a civilian postal service began operating thirteen days later.

FORGERIES. The forgeries of the "V.R.I." and "E.R.I." overprints most often met with can be recognised by the fact that the type used is perfect and the three stops are always in alignment with the bottom of the letters. In the genuine overprints, which were made from old type, it is impossible to find all three letters perfect and all three stops perfect and in exact alignment with the bottom of the letters.

V. R. I.

(35)

E. R. I.

(36)

E. R. I. Half Penny

(37)

1900 (18 June). *Optd with T* **35**.

226 **30** ½d. green .. 15 15
a. No stop after "V" .. 10·00
b. No stop after "R" .. 8·00
c. No stop after "I" .. 6·50
d. Opt inverted .. 8·00
e. Opt double ..
f. "V.I.R." (R.4/4) .. £500
227 1d. rose-red and green .. 15 15
a. No stop after "V" .. 10·00
b. No stop after "R" .. 8·00
c. No stop after "I" .. 5·00
d. Opt inverted .. 8·00
e. Opt double .. 60·00
f. No stops after "R" and "I" .. 65·00 65·00
g. Opt omitted (in pair with normal) £250
228 2d. brown and green .. 1·60 60
a. No stop after "V" .. 23·00
c. No stop after "I" .. 27·00
d. Opt inverted .. 13·00
e. Opt double ..
f. "V.I.R." (R.4/4) .. £500
229 2½d. dull blue and green .. 60 70
a. No stop after "V" .. 17·00
b. No stop after "R" .. 40·00
c. No stop after "I" .. 13·00
d. Opt inverted .. 8·00
230 3d. purple and green .. 60 65
a. No stop after "V" .. 20·00
b. No stop after "R" .. 40·00
c. No stop after "I" .. 26·00
d. Opt inverted .. 60·00
231 4d. sage-green and green .. 1·25 30
a. No stop after "V" .. 35·00
b. No stop after "R" .. 45·00
c. No stop after "I" .. 30·00
d. Opt inverted .. 20·00
f. "V.I.R." (R.4/4) .. £500
232 6d. lilac and green .. 1·25 60
a. No stop after "V" .. 15·00
b. No stop after "R" .. 20·00
c. No stop after "I" .. 20·00
d. Opt inverted .. 20·00
233 1s. ochre and green .. 1·25 1·40
a. No stop after "V" .. 15·00
b. No stop after "R" .. 15·00
c. No stop after "I" .. 27·00
d. Opt inverted .. 26·00
e. Opt double .. 60·00
234 **30** 2s. 6d. dull violet and green .. 2·00 4·00
a. No stop after "V" .. 27·00
b. No stop after "R" .. 60·00
235 5s. slate .. 4·00 6·00
a. No stop after "V" .. 85·00
236 10s. pale chestnut .. 6·00 8·00
a. No stop after "V" .. 70·00
c. No stop after "I" .. 70·00
237 **18** £5 deep green* .. £1800 £750
a. No stop after "V" ..
234/7 Optd "Specimen" .. *Set of* 4 £200

*Many examples of No. 237 on the market are forgeries and the stamps should only be purchased if accompanied by a recent expert committee certificate.

The error "V.I.R." occurred on R.4/4 in the first batch of stamps to be overprinted—a few sheets of the ½d., 2d. and 4d. The error was then corrected and stamps showing it are very rare.

A number of different settings were used to apply the overprint to Nos. 226/37. The missing stop varieties listed above developed during overprinting and occur on different positions in the various settings.

1901 (Jan)–**02**. *Optd with T* **36**.

238 **30** ½d. green .. 30 30
239 1d. rose-red and green (20.3.01) .. 30 10
a. "E" of opt omitted .. 65·00
240 3d. purple and green (6.02) .. 1·75 2·00
241 4d. sage-green and green (6.02) .. 1·75 2·00
242 2s. 6d. dull violet and green (10.02) .. 5·50 8·00

1901 (July). *Surch with T* **37**.

243 **30** ½d. on 2d. brown and green .. 40 40
a. No stop after "E" (R.4/6) .. 45·00

38 (POSTAGE REVENUE)

39 (POSTAGE POSTAGE)

(Typo D.L.R.)

1902 (1 Apr)–**03**. *Wmk Crown CA. P* 14.

244 **38** ½d. black and bluish green .. 1·25 20
w. Wmk inverted .. 70·00 50·00
245 1d. black and carmine .. 1·25 15
w. Wmk inverted .. 50·00 40·00
246 2d. black and purple .. 2·00 40
247 2½d. black and blue .. 3·00 1·25
w. Wmk inverted .. 30·00 15·00
248 3d. black and sage-green (1903) .. 4·00 40
249 4d. black and brown (1903) .. 4·00 60
250 6d. black and orange-brown .. 2·00 60
251 1s. black and sage-green .. 9·00 4·75
252 2s. black and brown .. 23·00 27·00
253 **39** 2s. 6d. magenta and black .. 12·00 7·50
254 5s. black and purple/*yellow* .. 18·00 18·00
255 10s. black and purple/*red* .. 40·00 22·00
244/55 .. *Set of* 12 £110 75·00
244/55 Optd "Specimen" .. *Set of* 12 £130

The colour of the "black" centres varies from brownish grey or grey to black.

1903. *Wmk Crown CA. P* 14.

256 **39** 1s. grey-black and red-brown .. 7·00 1·60
257 2s. grey-black and yellow .. 11·00 8·00
258 £1 green and violet .. £140 90·00
259 £5 orange-brown and violet .. £1200 £450
256/9 Optd "Specimen" .. *Set of* 4 £180

1904–09. *Wmk Mult Crown CA. Ordinary paper. P* 14.

260 **38** ½d. black and bluish green .. 4·00 1·75
w. Wmk inverted .. 70·00 50·00
y. Wmk inverted and reversed .. 60·00 20·00
261 1d. black and carmine .. 2·75 15
262 2d. black and purple (*chalk-surfaced paper*) (1906) .. 5·00 45
263 2½d. black and blue (1905) .. 6·00 3·50
a. Chalk-surfaced paper .. 6·00 1·10
264 3d. black & sage-green (*chalk-surfaced paper*) (1906) .. 3·25 30
265 4d. black and brown (*chalk-surfaced paper*) (1906) .. 3·00 40
w. Wmk inverted .. — 50·00
266 6d. black and orange (1905) .. 4·00 40
a. Chalk-surfaced paper. *Black and brown-orange* (1906) .. 2·00 40
w. Wmk inverted .. — 60·00
267 **39** 1s. black and red-brown (1905) .. 3·75 40
268 2s. black and yellow (1906) .. 14·00 4·00
269 2s. 6d. magenta and black (1909) .. 24·00 2·75
270 5s. black and purple/*yellow* .. 12·00 1·50
271 10s. black and purple/*red* (1907) .. 27·00 2·50
272 £1 green and violet (1908) .. £130 20·00
a. Chalk-surfaced paper .. £140 15·00
260/72 .. *Set of* 13 £200 27·00

There is considerable variation in the "black" centres as in the previous issue.

OMNIBUS ISSUES

Details, together with prices for complete sets, of the various Omnibus issues from the 1935 Silver Jubilee series to date are included in a special section following Zimbabwe at the end of Volume 2.

1905–09. *Wmk Mult Crown CA. P* 14.

273	**38**	½d. yellow-green	1·50	10
		a. Deep green (1908)	2·00	20
		w. Wmk inverted	£100	60·00
274		1d. scarlet	1·00	10
		aw. Wmk inverted		
		b. Wmk Cabled Anchor, T **13** of Cape of Good Hope	†	£325
275		2d. purple (1909)	3·25	30
276		2½d. bright blue (1909)	9·00	2·50
273/6		*Set of* 4	13·00	2·50
273/6 Optd "Specimen"		*Set of* 4	50·00	

A 2d. grey, T **38**, was prepared for use but not issued. It exists overprinted "Specimen", *price* £120.

The monocoloured ½d. and 1d. are printed from new combined plates. These show a slight alteration in that the frame does not touch the crown.

Many of the King's Head stamps are found overprinted or perforated "C.S.A.R.", for use by the Central South African Railways.

STAMP BOOKLETS

1905 (July). *Black on red cover. Stapled.*
SB1 2s. 7d. booklet containing thirty 1d. (No. 261) in blocks of 6 .. £2000

1905. *Black on red cover. Stapled.*
SB2 2s. 7d. booklet containing thirty 1d. (No. 274) in blocks of 6 .. £2000

1909. *Black on red cover. Stapled.*
SB3 2s. 6d. booklet containing ten ½d. (No. 273) in block of 6 and block of 4, and twenty-four 1d. (No. 274) in blocks of 6 .. £2500

Stocks of No. SB3 were supplied containing twelve examples of the ½d., it being intended that the postal clerks would remove two stamps before the booklets were sold. In some instances this did not occur.

POSTAL FISCAL STAMPS

1900–02. *Fiscal stamps as in T* **33**, *but optd with T* **35**. *P* 11½.

F1	1d. pale blue	—	45·00
F2	6d. dull carmine	—	60·00
F3	1s. olive-bistre	—	75·00
F4	1s. 6d. brown	—	90·00
F5	2s. 6d. dull purple	—	£100

Nos. F1/5, previously listed as Nos. 1/5 of Volksrust, are fiscal issues which are known postally used from various Transvaal post offices between June 1900 and June 1902.

Other fiscal stamps are found apparently postally used, but these were used on telegrams not on postal matter.

POSTAGE DUE STAMPS

D 1

(Typo D.L.R.)

1907. *Wmk Mult Crown CA. P* 14.

D1	D 1	½d. black and blue-green	2·75	1·25
D2		1d. black and scarlet	3·50	85
D3		2d. brown-orange	3·50	1·25
D4		3d. black and blue	6·50	4·00
D5		5d. black and violet	2·00	12·00
D6		6d. black and red-brown	4·25	12·00
D7		1s. scarlet and black	8·00	7·00
D1/7		*Set of* 7	27·00	35·00

Transvaal became a province of the Union of South Africa on 31 May 1910.

PIETERSBURG

After the fall of Pretoria to the British in June 1900 the Transvaal government withdrew to the north of the country. Those post offices in areas not occupied by the British continued to function, but by early the following year supplies of stamps were exhausted. The following stamps were then authorised by the State Secretary and remained in use in some towns to early May 1901. Pietersburg itself was taken by British forces on 9 April.

PRICES. Genuinely used examples are very rare. Stamps cancelled by favour exist and are worth the same as the unused prices quoted.

The issued stamps are initialled by the Controller J. T. de V. Smit. All values exist without his signature and these are believed to come from remainders abandoned when the Boers evacuated Pietersburg.

P 1 P 2

P 3

TYPES P 1/3. Each value was printed in sheets of 24 (6×4) of which the first two horizontal rows were as Type P **1**, the third row as Type P **2** and the fourth as Type P **3**. The stamps were issued to post offices in blocks of 12.

(Type-set *De Zoutpansberg Wachter* Press, Pietersburg)

1901 (20 Mar (1*d.*)–3 Apr (*others*)). A. *Imperf.*

(*a*) *Controller's initials in black*

1	P 1	½d. black/*green*	15·00
		e. Controller's initials omitted	95·00
2	P 2	½d. black/*green*	45·00
		d. Controller's initials omitted	95·00
3	P 3	½d. black/*green*	45·00
		d. Controller's initials omitted	95·00
4	P 1	1d. black/*red*	3·50
5	P 2	1d. black/*red*	5·50
6	P 3	1d. black/*red*	7·00
7	P 1	2d. black/*orange*	6·00
8	P 2	2d. black/*orange*	14·00
9	P 3	2d. black/*orange*	22·00
10	P 1	4d. black/*blue*	5·50
11	P 2	4d. black/*blue*	9·50
12	P 3	4d. black/*blue*	32·00
13	P 1	6d. black/*green*	9·50
14	P 2	6d. black/*green*	15·00
15	P 3	6d. black/*green*	40·00
16	P 1	1s. black/*yellow*	8·00
17	P 2	1s. black/*yellow*	14·00
18	P 3	1s. black/*yellow*	25·00

(*b*) *Controller's initials in red*

19	P 1	½d. black/*green*	15·00
20	P 2	½d. black/*green*	35·00
21	P 3	½d. black/*green*	40·00

B. *P* 11½. (*a*) *Controller's initials in red*

22	P 1	½d. black/*green*	5·50
		c. Imperf vert (horiz pair)	95·00
23	P 2	½d. black/*green*	17·00
		c. Imperf vert (horiz pair)	£120
24	P 3	½d. black/*green*	12·00
		b. Imperf vert (horiz pair)	£120

(*b*) *Controller's initials in black*

25	P 1	1d. black/*red*	2·00
		m. Imperf vert (horiz pair)	55·00
		n. Imperf between (vert pair: No. 25 + No. 26)	
		o. Imperf horiz (vert pair)	
26	P 2	1d. black/*red*	2·75
		f. Imperf vert (horiz pair)	80·00
		g. Imperf horiz (vert pair: No. 26 + No. 27)	
27	P 3	1d. black/*red*	4·00
		f. Imperf vert (horiz pair)	80·00
28	P 1	2d. black/*orange*	5·50
29	P 2	2d. black/*orange*	8·00
30	P 3	2d. black/*orange*	14·00

For the ½d. the First printing had initials in either black or red, those of the Second printing had them in black and all of the Third were in red.

CONSTANT VARIETIES

Rows 1 *and* 2 *are as Type* P **1**, *Row* 3 *as Type* P **2** *and Row* 4 *as Type* P **3**.

½d. value
First printing—Imperf

R.1/1 & 4	Top left "½" inverted, no stop after right "AFR"	(No. 19c)	70·00
R.1/2	Top right "½" inverted	(No. 19d)	90·00
R.1/3	"⅓" at lower right	(No. 19e)	90·00
R.1/5	"POSTZFGEL"	(No. 19f)	90·00
R.1/6	Left spray inverted, "AFB" at right	(No. 19g)	90·00
R.2/1	"REB" at left, left side of inner frame 3 mm too high	(No. 19h)	90·00
R.2/2	"BEP" at left	(No. 19i)	90·00
R.2/3	"POSTZEOEL"	(No. 19j)	90·00
R.2/4	"AER" at right, left side of inner frame 2 mm too high	(No. 19k)	90·00
R.2/5	No stop after date	(No. 19l)	90·00
R.2/6	No stop after "PENNY"	(No. 19m)	
R.3/1	"⅓" at top left, "PE" of "PENNY" spaced	(No. 20c)	90·00
R.3/2	Right spray inverted	(No. 20d)	90·00
R.3/3	Top left "½" inverted	(No. 20e)	90·00
R.3/4	No stop after "2" at left	(No. 20f)	
R.3/5	Centre figures "½" level	(No. 20g)	
R.3/6	"POSTZEGFL", no stop after right "AFR"	(No. 20h)	
R.4/3	"⅓" at top right	(No. 21b)	90·00
R.4/4	Lower left "½" inverted	(No. 21c)	90·00
R.4/5	"¼" at top left	(No. 21d)	90·00
R.4/6	Left spray inverted, "901" for "1901"	(No. 21e)	

This printing was produced first and was then adapted for the higher values.

Second printing

R.1/2	No stop after left "AFR"	*Imperf*	(No. 1a)	60·00
R.1/3	"⅓" at top left, no bar over lower right "½"	*Imperf*	(No. 1b)	60·00
R.1/6	No stop after date	*Imperf*	(No. 1c)	60·00
R.2/5	"BEP" at left, no stop after date	*Imperf*	(No. 1d)	60·00
R.3/3	"AFB" at left	*Imperf*	(No. 2a)	60·00
		Perf	(No. 23a)	
R.3/4	"POSTZEGEI"	*Imperf*	(No. 2b)	60·00
		Perf	(No. 23b)	
R.3/6	No bar over lower right "½"	*Imperf*	(No. 2c)	60·00
R.4/1	No stop after right "AFR"	*Imperf*	(No. 3a)	60·00
R.4/4	No stop after left "Z", no bar under top right "½"	*Imperf*	(No. 3b)	60·00
		Perf	(No. 23c)	
R.4/5	"POSTZECEL AER" at left	*Imperf*	(No. 3c)	60·00

Third printing

R.1/4	No stop after right "AFR"	*Imperf*	(No. 19a)	70·00
		Perf	(No. 22a)	40·00
R.2/1	Left side of inner frame too high	*Imperf*	(No. 19b)	70·00
		Perf	(No. 22b)	40·00
R.3/5	Centre figures "½" level	*Imperf*	(No. 20a)	70·00
		Perf	(No. 23d)	40·00
R.3/6	No stop after right "AFR"	*Imperf*	(No. 20b)	70·00
		Perf	(No. 23e)	40·00
R.4/6	Hyphen between right "AFR" and "REP"	*Imperf*	(No. 21a)	70·00
		Perf	(No. 24a)	40·00

1d. value
First printing

R.1/2	Inverted "1" at lower left, first "1" of date dropped	*Imperf*	(No. 4a)	35·00
		Perf	(No. 25a)	22·00
R.1/3	No bar under top left "1"	*Imperf*	(No. 4b)	35·00
		Perf	(No. 25b)	22·00
R.1/4	No bar over lower right "1"	*Imperf*	(No. 4c)	35·00
		Perf	(No. 25c)	22·00
R.1/5	"POSTZFGEL"	*Imperf*	(No. 4d)	35·00
		Perf	(No. 25d)	22·00
R.1/6	"AFB" at right	*Imperf*	(No. 4e)	35·00
		Perf	(No. 25e)	22·00
R.2/1	"REB" at left	*Imperf*	(No. 4f)	35·00
		Perf	(No. 25f)	22·00
R.2/2	"BEP" at left	*Imperf*	(No. 4g)	35·00
		Perf	(No. 25g)	22·00
R.2/3	"POSTZEOEL"	*Imperf*	(No. 4h)	35·00
		Perf	(No. 25h)	22·00
R.2/4	"AER" at right	*Imperf*	(No. 4i)	35·00
		Perf	(No. 25i)	22·00
R.2/5	No stop after date	*Imperf*	(No. 4j)	35·00
		Perf	(No. 25j)	22·00
R.2/6	No stop after "PENNY"	*Imperf*	(No. 4k)	35·00
		Perf	(No. 25k)	22·00
R.3/2	Right spray inverted	*Imperf*	(No. 5a)	35·00
		Perf	(No. 26a)	22·00
R.3/3	No bar over lower left "1"	*Imperf*	(No. 5b)	35·00
		Perf	(No. 26b)	22·00
R.3/4	No stop after left "Z"	*Imperf*	(No. 5c)	35·00
		Perf	(No. 26c)	22·00
R.3/6	"POSTZEGFL", no stop after right "AFR"	*Imperf*	(No. 5d)	35·00
		Perf	(No. 26d)	22·00
R.4/1	No stop after right "AFR"	*Imperf*	(No. 6a)	35·00
		Perf	(No. 27a)	22·00
R.4/2 & 6	Left spray inverted	*Imperf*	(No. 6b)	22·00
		Perf	(No. 27b)	13·00
R.4/3	"POSTZEGEI"	*Imperf*	(No. 6c)	35·00
		Perf	(No. 27c)	22·00
R.4/4	No bar under top right "1"	*Imperf*	(No. 6d)	35·00
		Perf	(No. 27d)	22·00

Second printing

R.1/2	First "1" in date dropped	*Imperf*	(No. 4l)	35·00
		Perf	(No. 25l)	22·00
R.3/6	No stop after right "AFR"	*Imperf*	(No. 5e)	35·00
		Perf	(No. 26e)	22·00
R.4/5	Dropped "P" in "PENNY"	*Imperf*	(No. 6e)	35·00
		Perf	(No. 27e)	22·00

It has been suggested that there may have been a third printing.

2d. value
First printing—Imperf

R.1/1	"1" at lower right	(No. 7a)	45·00
R.1/2	No stop after left "AFR" (*on small part of printing*)	(No. 7b)	90·00
R.1/3	No bar over lower right "2" (*on small part of printing*)	(No. 7c)	90·00
R.1/3	"PENNY" for "PENCE"	(No. 7d)	45·00
R.1/5	"POSTZFGEL"	(No. 7e)	45·00
R.1/6	"AFB" at right	(No. 7f)	45·00
R.2/1	"REB" at left	(No. 7g)	45·00
R.2/2	"AFB" at left	(No. 7h)	45·00
R.2/3	"POSTZEOEL"	(No. 7i)	45·00
R.2/4	"AER" at right	(No. 7j)	45·00
R.2/5	No stop after date	(No. 7k)	45·00
R.2/6	No stop after date, vertical line after "POSTZEGEL"	(No. 7l)	45·00
R.3/2	Right spray inverted	(No. 8a)	45·00
R.3/3	No bar over lower left "2"	(No. 8b)	45·00
R.3/4	Centre "2" inverted, no stop after left "Z"	(No. 8c)	45·00
R.3/6	"POSTZEGFL", no stop after right "AFR"	(No. 8d)	45·00
R.4/1	Centre "2" wider, no stop after right "AFR" (*occurs on second printing also*)	(No. 9a)	38·00
R.4/2	Centre "2" wider, left spray inverted	(No. 9b)	45·00
R.4/3	"POSTZEGEI"	(No. 9c)	45·00
R.4/4	No bar under top right "2"	(No. 9d)	45·00
R.4/5	"1" at lower left, "P" in "PENCE" dropped	(No. 9e)	45·00
R.4/6	Left spray inverted	(No. 9f)	45·00

Second printing

R.1/2	First "1" in date dropped	*Imperf*	(No. 7m)	45·00
		Perf	(No. 28a)	30·00
R.2/1	No stop after left "REP"	*Imperf*	(No. 7n)	45·00
		Perf	(No. 28b)	30·00
R.3/4	No stop after left "Z"	*Imperf*	(No. 8e)	45·00

COVER PRICES

Cover factors are quoted at the beginning of each country for most issues to 1945. An explanation of the system can be found on page x. The factors quoted do not, however, apply to philatelic covers.

R.3/6	No stop after right "AFR"	*Imperf*	(No. 8f)	45·00
		Perf	(No. 29a)	30·00
R.4/1	Centre 2 wider, no stop after right "AFR" (*occurs on first printing also*)	*Imperf*	(No. 9a)	38·00
		Perf	(No. 30a)	30·00
R.4/2	Centre "2" wider	*Imperf*	(No. 9g)	45·00
		Perf	(No. 30b)	30·00
R.4/5	"P" in "PENCE" dropped	*Imperf*	(No. 9h)	45·00
		Perf	(No. 30c)	30·00

It has been suggested that there was a third printing of this value.

4d. value

First printing

R.1/2	No stop after left "AFR'	(No. 10a)	45·00
R.1/3	No bar over lower right "4"	(No. 10b)	45·00
R.1/3	"PENNY" for "PENCE" (*on small part of printing*)	(No. 10c)	90·00
R.1/5	"POSTZFGEL"	(No. 10d)	45·00
R.1/6	"AFB" at right	(No. 10e)	45·00
R.2/1	"REB" at left	(No. 10f)	45·00
R.2/2	"AFB" at left	(No. 10g)	45·00
R.2/3	"POSTZEOEL"	(No. 10h)	45·00
R.2/4	"AER" at right	(No. 10i)	45·00
R.2/5	No stop after date	(No. 10j)	45·00
R.3/2	Right spray inverted	(No. 11a)	45·00
R.3/3	No bar over lower left "4" (*on small part of printing*)	(No. 11b)	90·00
R.3/4	No stop after left "Z"	(No. 11c)	45·00
R.3/6	"POSTZEGFL"	(No. 11d)	45·00
R.4/1	Centre "4" wider, no stop after right "AFR"	(No. 12a)	45·00
R.4/2	Centre "4" wider, left spray inverted	(No. 12b)	45·00
R.4/3	"POSTZEGEI"	(No. 12c)	45·00
R.4/4	No bar under top right "4"	(No. 12d)	45·00
R.4/5	"AER" at left, "P" in "PENCE" dropped	(No. 12e)	45·00
R.4/6	Left spray inverted	(No. 12f)	45·00

Second printing

R.2/1	Left inner frame too high	(No. 10k)	45·00
R.4/1–2	Centre "4" wider	(No. 12g)	35·00
R.4/5	"P" in "PENCE" dropped	(No. 12h)	45·00

6d. value

First printing

R.1/2	No stop after left "AFR"	(No. 13a)	55·00
R.1/3	No bar over lower right "6"	(No. 13b)	55·00
R.1/3	"PENNY" for "PENCE" (*on small part of printing*)	(No. 13c)	£100
R.1/5	"POSTZFGEL"	(No. 13d)	55·00
R.1/6	"AFB" at right	(No. 13e)	55·00
R.2/1	"REB" at left	(No. 13f)	55·00
R.2/2	"AFB" at left	(No. 13g)	55·00
R.2/3	"POSTZEOEL"	(No. 13h)	55·00
R.2/4	"AER" at right	(No. 13i)	55·00
R.2/5	No stop after date	(No. 13j)	55·00
R.3/2	Right spray inverted	(No. 14a)	55·00
R.3/4	Centre "6" inverted, no stop after left "Z" (*on small part of printing*)	(No. 14b)	£100
R.3/4	No stop after left "Z"	(No. 14c)	55·00
R.3/6	"POSTZEGFL"	(No. 14d)	55·00
R.4/1	Centre "6" wider, no stop after right "AFR"	(No. 15a)	55·00
R.4/2	Centre "6" wider, left spray inverted	(No. 15b)	55·00
R.4/3	"POSTZEGEI"	(No. 15c)	55·00
R.4/4	No bar under top right "6"	(No. 15d)	55·00
R.4/5	"AER" at left, "P" in "PENCE" dropped	(No. 15e)	55·00
R.4/6	Left spray inverted	(No. 15f)	55·00

Second printing

R.2/1	Left inner frame too high, no stop after left "REP"	(No. 13k)	55·00
R.4/1–2	Centre "6" wider	(No. 15g)	40·00
R.4/5	"P" in "PENCE" dropped	(No. 15h)	55·00

1s. value

R.1/2	No stop after left "AFR"	(No. 16a)	40·00
R.1/3	No bar over lower right "1"	(No. 16b)	40·00
R.2/5	No stop after date	(No. 16c)	40·00
R.3/3	Centre "1" inverted (*on small part of printing*)	(No. 17a)	
R.3/4	"POSTZEGEI", no stop after left "Z"	(No. 17b)	40·00
R.4/1	No stop after right "AFR"	(No. 18a)	40·00
R.4/4	No bar under top right "1"	(No. 18b)	40·00
R.4/5	"AER" at left	(No. 18c)	40·00

LOCAL BRITISH OCCUPATION ISSUES DURING THE SOUTH AFRICAN WAR 1900–2

Stamps of the Transvaal Republic, unless otherwise stated, variously overprinted or surcharged.

LYDENBURG

Lydenburg fell to the British on 6 September 1900.

V.R.I.
3d.

(L 1)

1900 (Sept). *Nos. 215b and 217 surch as Type* L **1**, *others optd "V.R.I" only.*

1	30	½d. green	£110	£110
2		1d. rose-red and green	£100	90·00
2a	34	1d. on 1d. red		
3	30	2d. brown and green	£750	£550
4		2½d. blue and green	£1800	£750
5		3d. on 1d. rose-red and green	85·00	75·00
6		3d. purple and green		
7		4d. sage-green and green	£2500	£600
8		6d. lilac and green	£1800	£500
9		1s. ochre and green	£3250	£2000

The above were cancelled by British Army postal service postmarks. These overprints with Transvaal cancellations are believed to be forgeries.

RUSTENBURG

The British forces in Rustenburg, west of Pretoria, were besieged by the Boers during June 1900. When relieved on the 22 June 1900 no "V.R.I" stamps were available so a local handstamp was applied.

V.R.

(R 1)

1900 (23 June). *Handstamped with Type* R **1** *in violet.*

1	30	½d. green	£130	85·00
2		1d. rose-red and green	95·00	65·00
3		2d. brown and green	£275	95·00
4		2½d. blue and green	£160	85·00
5		3d. purple and green	£200	£100
6		6d. lilac and green	£1000	£300
7		1s. ochre and green	£1400	£700
8		2s. 6d. dull violet and green	£8000	£3750
		a. Handstamp in black		† £7000

Nos. 2 and 5 exist with the handstamp inverted.

SCHWEIZER RENECKE

BESIEGED

(SR 1)

1900 (Sept). *Handstamped with Type* SR **1** *in black, reading vert up or down.* (a) *On stamps of Transvaal.*

1	30	½d. green	†	£225
2		1d. rose-red and green	†	£225
3		2d. brown and green	†	£300
4		6d. lilac and green	†	£800

(b) *On stamps of Cape of Good Hope*

5	17	½d. green	†	£400
6		1d. carmine	†	£400

Schweizer Renecke, near the Bechuanaland border, was under siege from 1 August 1900 to 9 January 1901. The British commander authorised the above stamps shortly after 19 August. All stamps were cancelled with the dated circular town postmark ("Schweizer Renecke, Z.A.R."), usually after having been stuck on paper before use. Unused, without the postmark, do not exist.

No. 4 exists with double handstamp.

WOLMARANSSTAD

A British column occupied this town in the south-west of the Transvaal for two weeks in June 1900.

Cancelled V-R-I. (L 3) — Cancelled V-R-I. (L 4)

1900 (June). *Optd with Type* L **3**.

1	30	½d. green (B.)	£225	£350
		a. Opt inverted	£700	
		b. Opt in black		
2		1d. rose-red and green (B.)	£150	£250
		a. Opt in green	£1800	
3		2d. brown and green (B.)	£1600	£1600
		a. Opt in black	£3000	
4		2½d. blue and green (R.)	£1600	
		a. Opt in blue	£2750	£2750
		b. Opt in black		
5		3d. purple and green (B.)	£2750	£3000
6		4d. sage-green and green (B.)	£3500	£4000
7		6d. lilac and green (B.)	£3500	£4000
8		1s. ochre and green (B.)	—	£7000

The two lines of the overprint were handstamped separately. The ½d. exists with two impressions of the "Cancelled" handstamp, the 2½d. with two impressions of "V-R-I", one in red and one in blue and the 3d. with "Cancelled" in green and "V.R.I." in blue.

1900 (July). *Optd with Type* L **4**.

9	34	1d. red (B.)	£150	£275

The 1d. in Type **30** is also known with this overprint.

VII. ZULULAND

Zululand remained an independent kingdom until annexed by Great Britain on 19 May 1887 when it was declared a Crown Colony.

The first European postal service was operated by a Natal postal agency at Eshowe opened in 1876 which cancelled Natal stamps with a "No. 56 P.O. Natal" postmark. The agency closed during the Zulu War of 1879 and did not re-open until 1885 when a Eshowe postmark was provided. "ZULULAND" was added to the cancellation in 1887 and stamps of Natal continued to be used until replaced by the overprinted series on 1 May 1888.

PRICES FOR STAMPS ON COVER

Nos. 1/2	*from* × 100
Nos. 3/10	*from* × 20
No. 11	—
Nos. 12/16	*from* × 20
Nos. 20/3	*from* × 30
No. 24	*from* × 20
Nos. 25/6	*from* × 12
Nos. 27/9	—
No. F1	*from* × 100

ZULULAND (1) — ZULULAND. (2)

1888 (1 May)–**93**. (a) *Nos. 173, 180, 197, 200/2, 205a, 207a/8, 209 and 211 of Great Britain (Queen Victoria) optd with T* **1**.

1	½d. vermilion (11.88)	2·25	2·50
2	1d. deep purple	24·00	3·75
3	2d. grey-green and carmine	11·00	22·00
4	2½d. purple/*blue* (9.91)	17·00	20·00
5	3d. purple/*yellow*	24·00	22·00
6	4d. green and deep brown	40·00	55·00
7	5d. dull purple and blue (3.93)	90·00	£120
8	6d. purple/*rose-red*	11·00	17·00
9	9d. dull purple and blue (4.92)	85·00	85·00
10	1s. dull green (4.92)	£110	£120
11	5s. rose (4.92)	£500	£600
1/11	*Set of* 11	£800	£950
1 and 3/11 H/S "Specimen"	*Set of* 10	£600	

(b) *No. 97a of Natal optd with T* **2**.

12	½d. dull green (with stop) (7.88)	55·00	70·00
	a. Opt double	£1000	£1100
	b. Opt inverted	£1100	
	d. Opt omitted (vert pair with normal)	£5500	
13	½d. dull green (without stop)	22·00	35·00
	a. Opt double	£1100	£1200

1893 (29 Nov*). *T* **15** *of Natal (Wmk Crown CA. P 14) optd with T* **1**.

16	6d. dull purple	55·00	55·00

*Earliest known date of use.

3

4

(Typo D.L.R.)

1894 (18 Apr)–**96**. *Wmk Crown CA. P* 14.

20	3	½d. dull mauve and green	2·00	4·25
21		1d. dull mauve and carmine	5·00	1·25
22		2½d. dull mauve and ultramarine	14·00	8·00
23		3d. dull mauve and olive-brown	8·00	3·00
24	4	6d. dull mauve and black	20·00	20·00
25		1s. green	35·00	38·00
26		2s. 6d. green and black (2.96)	75·00	85·00
27		4s. green and carmine	£110	£150
28		£1 purple/*red*	£450	£475
29		£5 purple and black/*red* (Optd S. £400)	£4250	£1500
20/8		*Set of* 9	£600	£650
20/8 Optd "Specimen"		*Set of* 9	£350	

Dangerous forgeries exist of the £1 and £5.

FISCAL STAMP USED FOR POSTAGE

1891 (5 May*). *Fiscal stamp of Natal (Wmk Crown CA. P 14) optd with T* **1**.

F1	1d. dull mauve (Optd S. £60)	3·00	3·00
	a. Top left triangle detached	£100	£100

*Earliest known date of postal use. A proclamation published in the *Natal Government Gazette* on 27 June 1891 authorised the use of this stamp for postal purposes, but it is clear from the wording that such use had already commenced.

Other values, 1s. to £20 as No. F1 exist apparently with postmarks, but, as these were never authorised for postal use, they are no longer listed.

Zululand was annexed to Natal on 31 December 1897 and its stamps were withdrawn from sale on 30 June 1898.

VIII. BRITISH ARMY FIELD OFFICES DURING SOUTH AFRICAN WAR, 1899–1902

Z 1

Z 2

Stamps of GREAT BRITAIN *used by British Army Field Offices in South Africa cancelled as Types* Z 1, Z 2 *or similar postmarks.*

1881. *Stamp of Queen Victoria.*

Z1	1d. lilac (16 *dots*)	5·00

1883–84. *Stamp of Queen Victoria.*

Z2	5s. rose	£200

1887–92. *Stamps of Queen Victoria.*

Z 3	½d. vermilion	6·00
Z 4	1½d. dull purple and green	20·00
Z 5	2d. grey-green and carmine	12·00
Z 6	2½d. purple/*blue*	6·00
Z 7	3d. purple/*yellow*	12·00
Z 8	4d. green and brown	16·00
Z 9	4½d. green and carmine	45·00
Z10	5d. dull purple and blue (Die II)	14·00
Z11	6d. purple/*rose-red*	10·00
Z12	9d. dull purple and blue	45·00
Z13	10d. dull purple and carmine	45·00
Z14	1s. dull green	70·00
Z15	£1 green	£750

1900. *Stamps of Queen Victoria.*

Z16	½d. blue-green	6·00
Z17	1s. green and carmine	£110

1902. *Stamps of King Edward VII.*

Z18	½d. blue-green	7·00
Z19	1d. scarlet	5·00
Z20	1½d. purple and green	
Z21	2d. yellowish green and carmine-red	
Z22	2½d. ultramarine	10·00
Z23	3d. purple/*orange-yellow*	
Z24	4d. green and grey-brown	
Z25	5d. dull purple and ultramarine	
Z26	6d. pale dull purple	15·00
Z27	9d. dull purple and ultramarine	
Z28	10d. dull purple and carmine	
Z29	1s. dull green and carmine	

ARMY OFFICIAL STAMPS

1896–1901. *Stamps of Queen Victoria optd* "ARMY OFFICIAL".

ZO1	½d. vermilion	£100
ZO2	½d. blue-green	£100
ZO3	1d. lilac (*16 dots*)	85·00
ZO4	6d. purple/*rose-red*	

IX. UNION OF SOUTH AFRICA

The province continued to use their existing issues until the introduction of Nos. 3/17. From 19 August 1910 the issues of any province were valid for use throughout the Union until they were demonetised on 31 December 1937.

PRICES FOR STAMPS ON COVER TO 1945	
Nos. 1/15	*from* × 4
Nos. 16/17	—
Nos. 18/21	*from* × 6
Nos. 26/32	*from* × 2
No. 33	*from* × 4
Nos. 34/110	*from* × 1
Nos. D1/7	*from* × 4
Nos. D8/33	*from* × 6
Nos. O1/33	*from* × 4

1

(Des H. S. Wilkinson. Recess D.L.R.)

1910 (4 Nov). *Opening of Union Parliament. Inscribed bilingually. Wmk Multiple Rosettes. P* 14.

1	1	2½d. deep blue (H/S S. £325)	3·00	3·00
2		2½d. blue	1·75	1·40

The deep blue shade is generally accompanied by a blueing of the paper.

The price quoted for the "Specimen" handstamp is for the small italic type with capital and lower case letters.

2

3

4 Springbok's Head

(Typo D.L.R.)

1913 (1 Sept)–**24.** *Inscribed bilingually. W* 4. (*a*) *P* 14.

3	2	½d. green	1·00	20
		a. Stamp doubly printed	£11000	
		b. Blue-green	1·75	20
		c. Yellow-green	2·25	30
		d. Printed on the gummed side	£500	
		w. Wmk inverted	2·00	35
4	2	1d. rose-red (*shades*)	85	10
		a. Carmine-red	1·75	10
		b. Scarlet (*shades*)	1·50	15
		c. Printed on the gummed side		
		w. Wmk inverted	2·50	40
5		1½d. chestnut (*shades*) (23.8.20)	45	10
		a. *Tête-bêche* (pair)	1·75	18·00
		b. Printed on the gummed side	£500	
		w. Wmk inverted	45	10
6	3	2d. dull purple	1·25	10
		a. Deep purple	2·50	10
		b. Printed on the gummed side	£500	
		w. Wmk inverted	3·25	1·25
7		2½d. bright blue	3·25	1·25
		a. Deep blue	5·00	3·00
		w. Wmk inverted	60·00	60·00
8		3d. black and orange-red	8·00	30
		a. Black and dull orange-red	9·00	70
		w. Wmk inverted	16·00	6·50
9		3d. ultramarine (*shades*) (4.10.22)	3·50	1·75
		w. Wmk inverted	8·50	4·75
10		4d. orange-yellow and olive-green	8·00	45
		a. Orange-yellow and sage-green	5·50	45
		w. Wmk inverted	8·00	50
11		6d. black and violet	5·50	50
		a. Black and bright violet	7·50	50
		aw Wmk inverted	16·00	8·50
12		1s. orange	15·00	80
		a. Orange-yellow	25·00	1·00
		w. Wmk inverted	18·00	1·25
13		1s. 3d. violet (*shades*) (1.9.20)	12·00	7·00
		w. Wmk inverted		
14		2s. 6d. purple and green	55·00	1·00
15		5s. purple and blue	£110	7·50
		a. Reddish purple and light blue	£110	8·00
		w. Wmk inverted	—	£1500
16		10s. deep blue and olive-green	£180	5·50
		w. Wmk inverted	£3500	£2000
17		£1 green and red (7.16)	£600	£350
		a. Pale olive-green and red (1924)	£800	£1200
3/17		*Set of* 15	£900	£350
3/8, 10/17		Optd or H/S "Specimen" *Set of* 14	£1300	

(*b*) *Coil stamps. P* 14×*imperf*

18	2	½d. green	4·75	1·00
		w. Wmk inverted	—	£250
19		1d. rose-red (13.2.14)	7·00	3·75
		a. Scarlet	9·00	6·50
		w. Wmk inverted	£450	£250
20		1½d. chestnut (15.11.20)	8·50	13·00
		w. Wmk inverted	†	—
21	3	2d. dull purple (7.10.21)	8·50	4·25
18/21		*Set of* 4	26·00	20·00

The 6d. exists with "Z" of "ZUID" wholly or partly missing due to wear of plate (*Price wholly missing, £80 un, £38 us*).

5 De Havilland D.H.9 Biplane

(Eng A. J. Cooper. Litho *Cape Times* Ltd)

1925 (26 Feb). *Air. Inscr bilingually. P* 12.

26	5	1d. carmine	4·50	9·00
27		3d. ultramarine	8·50	9·50
28		6d. magenta	12·00	14·00
29		9d. green	23·00	48·00
26/9		*Set of* 4	42·00	70·00

Beware of forgeries of all values perforated 11, 11½ or 13.

INSCRIPTIONS. From 1926 until 1951 (also Nos. 167 and 262/5), most issues were inscribed in English and Afrikaans alternately throughout the sheets.

PRICES for Nos. 30/135 are for unused horizontal pairs, used horizontal pairs and used singles (either inscription), *unless otherwise indicated*. Vertical pairs are worth between 30% and 50% of the prices quoted for horizontal pairs.

6 Springbok

7 *Dromedaris* (Van Riebeeck's ship)

8 Orange Tree

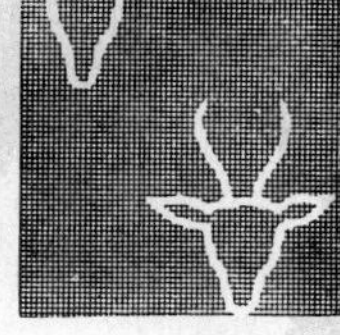

9

(Typo Waterlow until 1927, thereafter Govt Printer, Pretoria)

1926 (2 Jan)–**27.** *W* 9. *P* 14½×14.

			Un pair	*Used pair*	*Used single*
30	6	½d. black and green	2·50	3·00	10
		a. Missing "1" in "½"	£2000		
		b. Centre omitted (in pair with normal)	£1200		
		cw. Wmk inverted	3·50	3·00	
		d. Perf 13½×14 (1927)	50·00	50·00	4·00
		da. *Tête-bêche* (pair)	£850		
		dw. Wmk inverted	50·00	50·00	
31	7	1d. black and carmine	2·00	45	10
		a. Imperf (vert pair)*	£750		
		b. Imperf 3 sides (vert pair)*	£750	£800	
		cw. Wmk inverted	4·00	90	
		d. Perf 13½×14 (1927)	60·00	50·00	4·00
		da. *Tête-bêche* (pair)	£950		
		dw. Wmk inverted	60·00	50·00	
32	8	6d. green and orange (1.5.26)	35·00	35·00	1·50
		w. Wmk inverted	55·00	65·00	
30/2		*Set of* 3	35·00	35·00	1·50

No. 30a exists in Afrikaans only. Nos. 30d and 31d were only issued in booklets.

*Both Nos. 31a and 31b occur in blocks of four with the other vertical pair imperforate at left.

For ½d. with pale grey centre, see No. 126.

For rotogravure printing see Nos. 42, etc.

10 "Hope"

(Recess B.W.)

1926 (2 Jan). *T* 10. *Inscribed in English* (E) *or Afrikaans* (A). *W* 9 (*upright or inverted in equal quantities*).

		Single stamps E		A	
33	4d. grey-blue (*shades*)	1·25	75	1·25	75

In this value the English and Afrikaans inscriptions are on separate sheets.

This stamp is known with private perforations or roulettes.

11 Union Buildings, Pretoria

12 Groot Schuur

12*a* A Native Kraal

13 Black and Blue Wildebeest

14 Ox-wagon inspanned

15 Ox-wagon outspanned

16 Cape Town and Table Bay

(Recess B.W.)

1927 (1 Mar)–**30.** *W* 9. *P* 14.

			Un pair	*Used pair*	*Used single*
34	11	2d. grey and maroon	12·00	18·00	60
		aw. Wmk inverted	£300	£350	
		b. Perf 14×13½ (2.30)	15·00	19·00	70
35	12	3d. black and red	20·00	27·00	60
		a. Perf 14×13½ (1930)	38·00	40·00	80
35*b*	12*a*	4d. brown (23.3.28)	30·00	48·00	1·00
		bw. Wmk inverted	£450	£400	
		c. Perf 14×13½ (1930)	40·00	55·00	1·25
36	13	1s. brown and deep blue	35·00	48·00	1·00
		a. Perf 14×13½ (1930)	48·00	50·00	1·25
37	14	2s. 6d. green and brown	£110	£300	16·00
		a. Perf 14×13½ (1930)	£250	£375	22·00

38	15	5s. black and green	£225	£500	35·00
		a. Perf 14×13½ (1930) ..	£350	£600	40·00
39	16	10s. bright blue and brown ..	£150	£130	10·00
		a. Centre inverted (*single stamp*)	£9000		
		b. Perf 14×13½ (1930) ..	£160	£140	11·00
34/9		.. .. *Set of* 7	£500	£950	55·00
34/9 H/S "Specimen"		.. *Set of* 7	£850		

17 De Havilland D.H.60 Cirrus Moth

(Typo Govt Ptg Wks, Pretoria)

1929 (16 Aug). *Air. Inscribed bilingually. No wmk. P* 14 × 13½.

			Un single	Us single
40	17	4d. green	5·50	2·50
41		1s. orange	15·00	12·00

PRINTER. All the following issues, except *where stated otherwise*, are printed by rotogravure (the design having either plain lines or a dotted screen) by the Government Printer, Pretoria.

I II

The two types of the 1d. differ in the spacing of the horizontal lines in the side panels:—Type I close; Type II wide. The Afrikaans had the spacing of the words POSSEEL-INKOMSTE close in Type I and more widely spaced in Type II.

Window flaw (R. 20/4 on all ptgs before 1937)

Spear flaw (R. 9/2)

Twisted horn (Cyl 7020 R.1/5)

1930–45. *T* 6 *to* 8 *and* 11 *to* 14 *redrawn,* "SUIDAFRIKA" *(in one word) on Afrikaans stamps. W* 9. *P* 15 × 14 *(½d., 1d., and 6d.) or* 14.

			Un pair	Used pair	Used single
42		½d. black and green (5.30)	2·00	2·00	10
		a. Two English or two Afrikaans stamps *se-tenant* (vert strip of 4)	40·00		
		b. *Tête-bêche*	£850		
		w. Wmk inverted	1·50	1·25	10
43		1d. black and carmine (I) (4.30) ..	3·00	1·75	10
		a. *Tête-bêche*	£1000		
		b. Frame omitted (*single stamp*) ..	£450		
		cw. Wmk inverted	3·00	1·25	10
43*d*		1d. black and carmine (II) (8.32) ..	28·00	2·25	10
		dw. Wmk inverted	28·00	2·25	10
44		2d. slate-grey and lilac (4.31) ..	16·00	7·00	20
		a. *Tête-bêche*	£3000		
		b. Frame omitted (*single stamp*) ..	£1400		
		cw. Wmk inverted	15·00	6·00	20
44*d*		2d. blue and violet (3.38)	£225	60·00	2·50
45		3d. black and red (11.31)	50·00	65·00	2·00
		aw. Wmk inverted	48·00	60·00	1·25
		b. Window flaw	£120		
45*c*		3d. blue (10.33)	15·00	6·50	20
		cw. Wmk inverted	8·50	4·75	10
		d. Window flaw	35·00		
		e. Centre omitted			
46		4d. brown (19.11.32)	£200	£140	11·00
		aw. Wmk inverted	42·00	35·00	40
		b. Spear flaw	£130		
46*c*		4d. brown (*shades*) (*again redrawn*) (1936)	3·25	3·00	10
		cw. Wmk inverted	9·50	5·00	10
47		6d. green and orange (*wmk inverted*) (13.5.31)	17·00	2·00	10
		w. Wmk upright (8.32)	25·00	3·00	10
48		1s. brown and deep blue (14.9.32)	75·00	35·00	40
		aw. Wmk inverted	48·00	23·00	25
		b. Twisted horn flaw	£130		
49		2s. 6d. grn & brn (*shades*) (24.12.32)	95·00	£100	3·25
		aw. Wmk inverted	95·00	£100	3·25
49*b*		2s. 6d. blue and brown (1945) ..	20·00	9·00	20
42/9*b*		.. .. .. *Set of* 13	£425	£275	8·75

For similar designs with "SUID-AFRIKA" hyphenated, see Nos. 54 etc. and Nos. 114 etc.

Nos. 42/3, 43*d*/4 exist in coils.

No. 42a comes from the coil printing on the cylinder for which two horizontal rows were incorrectly etched so that two Afrikaans-inscribed stamps were followed by two English. This variety is normally without a coil join, although some examples do occur showing a repair join.

The 1d. (Type I) exists without watermark from a trial printing (*Price* £25 *un*).

Although it appears to be printed in one colour No. 45*c* was produced from vignette and frame cylinders in the same way as the bicoloured version. The clouds in the background, which are present on No. 45e, were printed from the frame cylinder.

Nos. 45b, 45d, 46b and 48b all occur on printings with either upright or inverted watermark. The price quoted is for the cheapest version in each instance.

The Rotogravure printings may be distinguished from the preceding Typographed and Recess printed issues by the following tests:—

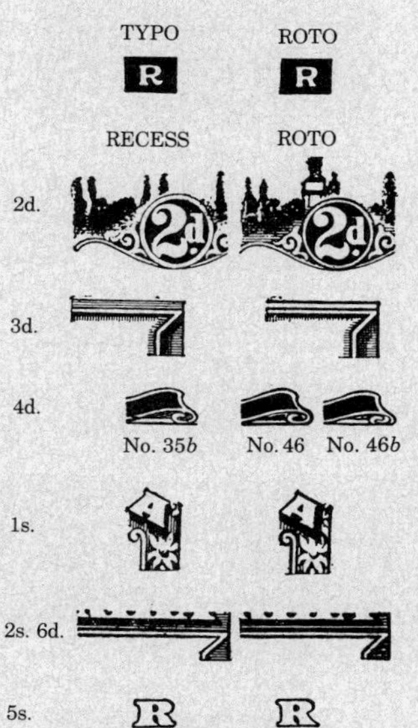

ROTOGRAVURE:

½d., 1d. and 6d. Leg of "R" in "AFR" ends squarely on the bottom line.

2d. The newly built War Memorial appears to the left of the value.

3d. Two fine lines have been removed from the top part of the frame.

4d. No. 46. The scroll is in solid colour.
No. 46*b*. The scroll is white with a crooked line running through it. (No. 35*b*. The scroll is shaded by the diagonal lines.)

1s. The shading of the last "A" partly covers the flower beneath.

2s. 6d. The top line of the centre frame is thick and leaves only one white line between it and the name.

5s. (Nos. 64/*a*). The leg of the "R" is straight.

Rotogravure impressions are generally coarser.

18 Church of the Vow

19 "The Great Trek" (C. Michell)

20 A Voortrekker

21 Voortrekker Woman

Blurred "SOUTH AFRICA" and red "comet" flaw (Cyls 6917/6922 R. 2/7)

(Des J. Prentice (½d., 2d., 3d.)

1933 (3 May)–**36.** *Voortrekker Memorial Fund. W* 9 *(sideways). P* 14.

50	18	½d. + ½d. black and green (16.1.36)	3·75	4·00	50
51	19	1d. + ½d. grey-black and pink ..	3·25	1·50	25
		a. Blurred "SOUTH AFRICA" and red "comet" flaw	40·00		
52	20	2d. + 1d. grey-green and purple ..	4·00	4·00	55
53	21	3d. + 1½d. grey-green and blue ..	7·00	5·00	70
50/3		.. .. .. *Set of* 4	16·00	13·00	1·75

22 Gold Mine

22*a* Groot Schuur

Dies of 6d.

I

II

III

23 Groot Constantia

"Falling ladder" flaw (R. 5/10)

1933–48. "SUID-AFRIKA" *(hyphenated) on Afrikaans stamps. W* 9. *P* 15×14 *(½d., 1d. and 6d.) or* 14 *(others).*

54	6	½d. grey and green (*wmk inverted*) (9.35)	3·25	1·25	10
		aw. Wmk upright (1936)	7·00	1·40	10
		b. Coil stamp. Perf 13½×14 (1935)	28·00	50·00	1·00
		bw. Wmk upright	28·00	50·00	1·00
		c. Booklet pane of 6 (with adverts on margins) (*wmk upright*)	20·00		

56 **7** 1d. grey & car (*shades*) (19.4.34) 50 65 10
a. Imperf (pair) £140
b. Frame omitted (*single stamp*) £250
cw. Wmk inverted 40 65 10
d. Coil stamp. Perf 13½×14 (1935) .. .. .. 32·00 55·00 1·40
dw. Wmk inverted .. .. 32·00 55·00 1·40
e. Booklet pane of 6 (with adverts on margins) (1935) 9·00
f. Booklet pane of 6 (with blank margins) (1937) .. 12·00
h. Booklet pane of 6 (with postal slogans on margins) (1948) .. .. .. 4·00
i. Grey & brt rose-carm (7.48) 55 50 10
57 **22** 1½d. green & brt gold (12.11.36) 2·00 1·50 10
a. Shading omitted from mine dump (in pair with normal) £150
bw. Wmk inverted .. .. 1·50 1·50 10
c. Blue-grn & dull gold (8.40) 6·50 2·75 10
58 **11** 2d. blue and violet (11.38) .. 60·00 30·00 1·00
58*a* 2d. grey and dull purple (5.41) 38·00 55·00 1·25
59 **22*a*** 3d. ultramarine (2.40) .. 5·50 1·50 10
61 **8** 6d. green & vermilion (I) (10.37) 80·00 20·00 70
a. "Falling ladder" flaw .. £180
61*b* 6d. green & vermilion (II) (6.38) 28·00 1·00 10
61*c* 6d. grn & red-orge (III) (11.46) 13·00 75 10
62 **13** 1s. brown & chalky blue (2.39) 40·00 7·50 10
a. Frame omitted (*single stamp*) £1700
64 **15** 5s. black and green (10.33) .. 50·00 45·00 1·75
aw. Wmk inverted .. .. £100 80·00 3·00
b. Black and blue-green (9.44) 35·00 14·00 35
64*b* **23** 10s. blue and sepia (8.39) .. 65·00 14·00 70
ba. Blue & blackish brn (8.39) 42·00 4·00 30
54/9, 61*c*/64*ba* .. .. *Set of* 10 £200 £100 3·00

The ½d. and 1d. coil stamps may be found in blocks emanating from the residue of the large rolls which were cut into sheets and distributed to Post Offices.

Nos. 54 and 56 also exist in coils.

1d. Is printed from Type II. Frames of different sizes exist due to reductions made from time to time for the purpose of providing more space for the perforations.

3d. In No. 59 the frame is unscreened and composed of solid lines. Centre is diagonally screened. Scrolls above "3d." are clear lined, light in the middle and dark at sides.

6d. Die I. Green background lines faint. "SUID-AFRIKA" 16¼ mm long.

Die II. Green background lines heavy. "SUID-AFRIKA" 17 mm long. "S" near end of tablet. Scroll open.

Die III. Scroll closed up and design smaller (18 × 22 mm).

Single specimens of the 1933–48 issue inscribed in English may be distinguished from those of 1930–45 as follows:—

½d. and 1d. Centres in grey instead of varying intensities of black.

2d. The letters of "SOUTH AFRICA" are narrower and thinner.

3d. The trees are taller and the sky is without lines.

6d. The frame is vermilion.

1s. The frame is chalky blue.

For similar designs, but printed in screened rotogravure, see Nos. 114 to 122a.

BOOKLET PANES. Booklets issued in 1935 contained ½d. and 1d. stamps in panes with advertisements in the top and bottom margins and no margin at right (Nos. 54b and 56d). These were replaced in 1937 by editions showing blank margins on all four sides (Nos. 56e and 75ba). Following a period when the booklet panes were without margins, a further 3s. booklet was issued in 1948 which had four margins on the panes and postal slogans at top and bottom (Nos. 56h, 87b and 114a).

24

JIPEX
1936
(24*a*)

"Cleft skull" flaw (R. 14/2)

(Des J. Booysen)

1935 (1 May). *Silver Jubilee. Inscr bilingually.* *W* **9**. *P* 15×14.
65 **24** ½d. black and blue-green .. 2·25 12·00 10
a. "Cleft skull" flaw .. .. 6·00
66 1d. black and carmine .. .. 2·25 4·00 10
a. "Cleft skull" flaw .. .. 6·00
67 3d. blue .. .. 17·00 50·00 2·25
a. "Cleft skull" flaw .. .. 42·00
68 6d. green and orange .. .. 30·00 65·00 3·25
a. "Cleft skull" flaw .. .. 75·00
65/8 .. .. .. *Set of* 4 45·00 £120 5·00

In stamps with English at top the ½d., 3d. and 6d. have "SILWER JUBILEUM" to left of portrait, and "POSTAGE REVENUE" or "POSTAGE" (3d. and 6d.) in left value tablet. In the 1d., "SILVER JUBILEE" is to the left of portrait. In alternate stamps the positions of English and Afrikaans inscriptions are reversed.

1936 (2 Nov). *Johannesburg International Philatelic Exhibition. Optd with T* **24*a***.

			Un sheet	Us sheet
MS69	**6**	½d. grey and green (No. 54) ..	4·50	10·00
MS70	**7**	1d. grey and carmine (No. 56)	3·50	7·00

Issued each in miniature sheet of six stamps with marginal advertisements.

25

25*a*

"Mouse" flaw (R. 4/1)

(Des J. Prentice)

1937 (12 May). *Coronation.* *W* **9** (*sideways**). *P* 14.
71 **25** ½d. grey-black and blue-green .. 25 70 10
w. Wmk horns to left 25 70 10
72 1d. grey-black and carmine .. 35 50 10
w. Wmk horns to left 35 50 10
73 1½d. orange and greenish blue .. 50 50 10
a. "Mouse" flaw .. .. 5·00
w. Wmk horns to left 50 50 10
74 3d. ultramarine .. .. .. 3·00 2·25 10
w. Wmk horns to left .. .. 3·00 2·25 10
75 1s. red-brown and turquoise-blue 4·50 4·25 15
a. Hyphen on Afrikaans stamp omitted (R. 2/13) .. .. 45·00
w. Wmk horns to left .. .. 4·50 4·25 15
71/5 .. .. *Set of* 5 7·75 7·50 40

*The normal sideways watermark shows the horns of the Springbok pointing to the right, *as seen from the back of the stamp.*

No. 75a shows the hyphen completely omitted and the top of the "K" damaged. A less distinct flaw, on which part of the hyphen is still visible and with no damage to the "K", occurs on R. 4/17.

"Tick" flaw on ear and spot on nose (multipositive flaw (occurring in 1947) (R. 3/4, or 3/1 on some ptgs of No. 114)

1937–40. *W* **9**. *P* 15×14.
75*b* **25*a*** ½d. grey and green .. .. 7·50 90 10
ba. Booklet pane of 6 (with blank margins) (1937) .. .. 42·00
bd. Grey and blue-green (1940) 5·50 90 10
be. "Tick" flaw and spot on nose 50·00

The lines of shading in T **25*a*** are all horizontal and thicker than in T **6**. In Nos. 75*b* and 75*bd* the design is composed of solid lines. For stamps with designs composed of dotted lines, see No. 114. Later printings of No. 75*bd* have a smaller design.

26 Voortrekker Ploughing

27 Wagon crossing Drakensberg

28 Signing of Dingaan–Retief Treaty

29 Voortrekker Monument

(Des W. Coetzer and J. Prentice)

1938 (14 Dec). *Voortrekker Centenary Memorial Fund.* *W* **9**. *P* 14 (*Nos. 76/7*) *or* 15 × 14 (*others*).
76 **26** ½d. + ½d. blue and green .. 10·00 4·00 30
77 **27** 1d. + 1d. blue and carmine .. 11·00 5·00 40
78 **28** 1½d. + 1½d. chocolate & blue-grn 15·00 9·50 80
79 **29** 3d. + 3d. bright blue .. .. 17·00 11·00 1·00
76/9 .. .. .. *Set of* 4 48·00 27·00 2·25

30 Wagon Wheel

31 Voortrekker Family

Three bolts in wheel rim (R. 15/5)

(Des W. Coetzer and J. Prentice)

1938 (14 Dec). *Voortrekker Commemoration.* *W* **9**. *P* 15×14.
80 **30** 1d. blue and carmine .. .. 4·00 4·25 30
a. Three bolts in wheel rim .. 25·00
81 **31** 1½d. greenish blue and brown .. 6·00 4·25 30

32 Old Vicarage, Paarl, now a museum

33 Symbol of the Reformation

34 Huguenot Dwelling, Drakenstein Mountain Valley

(Des J. Prentice)

1939 (17 July). *250th Anniv of Huguenot Landing in South Africa and Huguenot Commemoration Fund.* *W* **9**. *P* 14 (*Nos. 82/3*) *or* 15 × 14 (*No. 84*).
82 **32** ½d. + ½d. brown and green .. 4·75 5·00 30
83 **33** 1d. + 1d. green and carmine .. 11·00 5·50 30
84 **34** 1½d. + 1½d. blue-green and purple 26·00 12·00 1·00
82/4 .. .. .. *Set of* 3 38·00 20·00 1·40

34*a* Gold Mine

1941 (Aug)–**48.** *W* **9** (*sideways*). *P* 14 × 15.
87 **34*a*** 1½d. blue-grn and yellow-buff (*shades*) 65 30 10
a. Yellow-buff (centre) omitted £1500
b. Booklet pane of 6 (with postal slogans on margins) (1948) .. .. .. 3·50

COVER PRICES

Cover factors are quoted at the beginning of each country for most issues to 1945. An explanation of the system can be found on page x. The factors quoted do not, however, apply to philatelic covers.

35 Infantry

36 Nurse and Ambulance

37 Airman

38 Sailor, Destroyer and Lifebelts

39 Women's Auxiliary Services

40 Artillery

41 Electric Welding

42 Tank Corps

42a Signaller

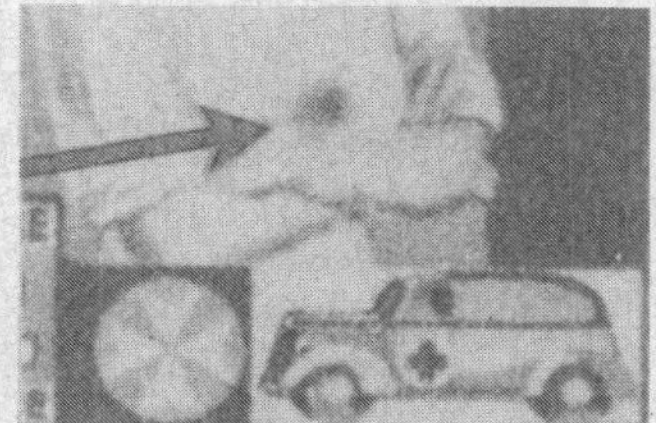

"Stain" on uniform (R. 14/11)

"Cigarette" flaw (R. 18/2)

1941–46. *War Effort. W* **9** (*sideways on 2d., 4d., 6d.*). *P* 14 (*2d., 4d., 6d.*) *or* 15 × 14 (*others*). (*a*) *Inscr alternately.*

88	**35**	½d. green (19.11.41)	1·50	1·50	10
		a. Blue-green (7.42)	3·00	2·00	10
89	**36**	1d. carmine (3.10.41)	2·00	1·25	10
		a. "Stain" on uniform flaw ..	20·00		
90	**37**	1½d. myrtle-green (12.1.42) ..	1·50	1·00	10
91	**39**	3d. blue (1.8.41)	20·00	22·00	50
		a. "Cigarette" flaw	70·00		
92	**40**	4d. orange-brown (20.8.41) ..	18·00	12·00	15
		a. Red-brown (6.42)	32·00	28·00	1·25
93	**41**	6d. red-orange (3.9.41) ..	12·00	8·50	15
94	**42a**	1s. 3d. olive-brown (2.1.43) ..	12·00	6·00	20
		a. Blackish brown (5.46) ..	4·00	6·00	20

(*b*) *Inscr bilingually*

			Un single	*Us single*
95	**38**	2d. violet (15.9.41)	90	30
96	**42**	1s. brown (27.10.41)	3·25	50
88/96		.. .. .. *Set of* 7 *pairs and* 2 *singles*	55·00	48·00

ALTERED CATALOGUE NUMBERS

Any Catalogue numbers altered from the last edition are shown as a list in the introductory pages.

43 Infantry

44 Nurse

45 Airman

46 Sailor

47 Women's Auxiliary Services

48 Electric Welding

49 Heavy Gun in Concrete Turret

50 Tank Corps

Unit (*pair*)

Unit (*triplet*)

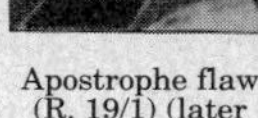

Apostrophe flaw (R. 19/1) (later corrected)

"Bursting Shell" (R. 11/20)

1942–44. *War Effort. Reduced sizes. In pairs perf* 14 (P) *or strips of three, perf* 15×14 (T), *subdivided by roulette* 6½. *W* **9** (*sideways* on 3d., 4d. and 1s.*). (*a*) *Inscr alternately.*

			Un unit	*Us unit*	*Us single*
97	**43**	½d. blue-green (T) (10.42) ..	70	1·25	10
		a. Green (3.43)	2·75	1·75	10
		b. Greenish blue (7.44) ..	2·00	1·25	10
		c. Roulette omitted	£500		
98	**44**	1d. carmine-red (T) (5.1.43) ..	1·50	1·00	10
		a. Bright carmine (3.44) ..	1·00	60	10
		b. Both roulettes omitted ..	£425		
		ba. Left-hand roulette omitted	£550		
99	**45**	1½d. red-brown (P) (9.42) ..	65	1·25	10
		a. Roulette 13 (8.42)	1·50	3·50	15
		b. Roulette omitted	£225	£250	
100	**46**	2d. violet (P) (2.43)	90	1·25	10
		a. Reddish violet (6.43) ..	1·50	50	10
		b. Roulette omitted	£400		
101	**47**	3d. blue (T) (10.42)	7·00	14·00	10
		c. Apostrophe flaw	50·00		
102	**48**	6d. red-orange (P) (10.42) ..	2·00	1·40	10
		(*b*) *Inscr bilingually*			
103	**49**	4d. slate-green (T) (10.42) ..	18·00	4·50	10
104	**50**	1s. brown (P) (11.42)	15·00	2·00	10
		a. "Bursting shell"	60·00		
97/104		.. .. .. *Set of* 8	40·00	23·00	65

*The sideways watermark shows springbok heads to left on the 3d. and 1s., and to right on the 4d., *all as seen from the back of the stamp.*

52

53

1943. *Coil stamps. Redrawn. In single colours with plain background. W* **9**. *P* 15 × 14.

			Un pair	*Used pair*	*Used single*
105	**52**	½d. blue-green (18.2.43) ..	75	3·25	20
106	**53**	1d. carmine (9.43)	2·00	3·00	15

Quoted prices are for *vertical* pairs.

54 Union Buildings, Pretoria

1945–46. *Redrawn. W* **9**. *P* 14.

107	**54**	2d. slate and violet (3.45) ..	10·00	2·50	10
		a. Slate & brt vio (*shades*) (10.46)	2·50	7·00	15

In Nos. 107 and 107*a* the Union Buildings are shown at a different angle from Nos. 58 and 58*a*. Only the centre is screened i.e., composed of very small square dots of colour arranged in straight diagonal lines. For whole design screened and colours changed, see No. 116. No. 107*a* also shows "2" of "2d." clear of white circle at top.

55 "Victory"

56 "Peace"

57 "Hope"

1945 (3 Dec). *Victory. W* **9**. *P* 14.

108	**55**	1d. brown and carmine.. ..	20	80	10
109	**56**	2d. slate-blue and violet ..	20	85	10
110	**57**	3d. deep blue and blue	20	1·25	10
108/10		.. .. .. *Set of* 3	55	2·75	25

58 King George VI

59 King George VI and Queen Elizabeth

60 Queen Elizabeth II as Princess, and Princess Margaret

"Bird" on "2" (Cyl 6912 R. 10/6)

(Des J. Prentice)

1947 (17 Feb). *Royal Visit. W* **9**. *P* 15 × 14.

111	**58**	1d. black and carmine	10	10	10
112	**59**	2d. violet	15	30	10
		a. "Bird" on "2" flaw	2·50		
113	**60**	3d. blue	15	30	10
111/13		.. .. .. *Set of* 3	35	60	20

"Flying saucer" flaw (Cyl 17 R. 17/2)

5s.

1947–54. "SUID-AFRIKA" *hyphenated on Afrikaans stamps. Printed from new cylinders with design in screened rotogravure. W* **9**. *P* 15×14 (½*d.*, 1*d. and* 6*d.*) *or* 14 (*others*).

114 **25a** ½d. grey and green (frame only screened) (1947) .. 80 1·50 10
a. Booklet pane of 6 (with postal slogans on margins) (1948) .. .. .. 3·00
b. "Tick" flaw and spot on nose .. .. .. 30·00
c. Entire design screened (2.49) .. .. .. 80 1·50 10
ca. Booklet pane of 6 (with margin at right) (1951) .. 3·50
115 **7** 1d. grey and carmine (1.9.50) 70 85 10
a. Booklet pane of 6 (with margin at right) (1951) .. 4·00
116 **54** 2d. slate-blue & purple (3.50) 80 4·25 10
117 **22a** 3d. dull blue (4.49) .. .. 2·00 4·00 10
117a 3d. blue (3.51) .. .. 2·25 3·25 10
ab. "Flying saucer" flaw .. 17·00
b. Deep blue (1954) .. 60·00 50·00 3·00
118 **12a** 4d. brown (22.8.52) .. .. 1·00 6·00 10
119 **8** 6d. grn & red-orge (III) (1.50) 1·75 40 10
a. Grn & brn-orge (III) (1951) 1·50 40 10
120 **13** 1s. brown & chalky blue (1.50) 10·00 4·50 10
a. Blackish brown & ultram (4.52) .. .. 18·00 7·50 15
121 **14** 2s. 6d. green and brown (8.49) 10·00 24·00 70
122 **15** 5s. blk & pale bl-grn (I) (9.49) 45·00 45·00 90
122a 5s. blk & dp yell-grn (II) (1.54) 70·00 70·00 2·00
114/22 .. .. .. *Set of* 9 65·00 80·00 1·50

In screened rotogravure the design is composed of very small squares of colour arranged in straight diagonal lines.

½d. Size 17¾ × 21¾ mm. Early printings have only the frame screened.

1d. Size 18 × 22 mm. For smaller, redrawn design, see No. 135.

2d. For earlier issue with centre only screened, and in different colours, see Nos. 107/*a*.

3d. No. 117. Whole stamp screened with irregular grain. Scrolls above "3d." solid and toneless. Printed from two cylinders.

No. 117*a*/*b*. Whole stamp diagonally screened. Printed from one cylinder. Clouds more pronounced.

4d. Two groups of white leaves below name tablet and a clear white line down left and right sides of stamp.

61 Gold Mine

62 King George VI and Queen Elizabeth

1948 (1 Apr). *W* **9** (*sideways*). *In pair, perf* 14, *sub-divided by roulette* 6½.

			Un unit of 4	Us unit	Used single
124	**61**	1½d. blue-green and yellow-buff	1·75	3·00	10

(Des J. Booysen and J. Prentice)

1948 (26 Apr). *Silver Wedding. W* **9**. *P* 14.

			Un pair	Used pair	Used single
125	**62**	3d. blue and silver	50	50	10

(Typo Government Printer, Pretoria)

1948 (July). *W* **9**. *P* 14½ × 14.

126 **6** ½d. pale grey and blue-green .. 85 8·00 65

This was an economy printing made from the old plates of the 1926 issue for the purpose of using up a stock of cut paper. For the original printing in black and green, see No. 30.

63 *Wanderer* (emigrant ship) entering Durban

Extended rigging on mainmast (R. 14/2)

(Des J. Prentice)

1949 (2 May). *Centenary of Arrival of British Settlers in Natal. W* **9**. *P* 15 × 14.

127 **63** 1½d. claret 30 30 10
a. Extended rigging .. .. 5·00

64 Hermes

65 Wagons approaching Bingham's Berg

Serif on "C" (R. 1/1)

"Lake" in East Africa (R. 2/19)

(Des J. Booysen and J. Prentice)

1949 (1 Oct). *75th Anniv of Universal Postal Union. As T* **64** *inscr* "UNIVERSAL POSTAL UNION" *and* "WERELDPOSUNIE" *alternately. W* **9** (*sideways*). *P* 14 × 15.

128 **64** ½d. blue-green 60 85 10
129 1½d. brown-red 60 85 10
130 3d. bright blue .. .. .. 1·00 1·40 10
a. Serif on "C" .. .. 16·00
b. "Lake" in East Africa .. 16·00
128/30 .. .. .. *Set of* 3 2·00 2·75 25

(Des W. Coetzer and J. Prentice)

1949 (1 Dec). *Inauguration of Voortrekker Monument, Pretoria. T* **65** *and similar horiz designs. W* **9**. *P* 15 × 14.

		Un single	Us single
131	1d. magenta	10	10
132	1½d. blue-green	10	10
133	3d. blue	10	10
131/3	.. .. .. *Set of* 3	20	20

Designs:—1½d. Voortrekker Monument, Pretoria; 3d. Bible, candle and Voortrekkers.

68 Union Buildings, Pretoria

1950 (Apr)–**51**. *W* **9** (*sideways*). *P* 14×15.

			Un pair	Used pair	Used single
134	**68**	2d. blue and violet	30	50	10
		a. Booklet panes of 6 (with margin at right) (1951)	4·00		

1951 (22 Feb). *As No.* 115, *but redrawn with the horizon clearly defined. Size reduced to* 17¼ × 21¼ *mm.*

135 **7** 1d. grey and carmine .. .. 75 1·00 10

PRICES. All later issues except Nos. 167 and 262/5 are inscribed bilingually and prices are for single copies, unused and used.

69 Seal and Monogram

70 "Maria de la Quellerie" (D. Craey)

(Des Miss R. Reeves and J. Prentice (1d., 4½d.), Mrs T. Campbell and J. Prentice (others))

1952 (14 Mar). *Tercentenary of Landing of Van Riebeeck. T* **69/70** *and similar designs. W* **9** (*sideways on* 1*d. and* 4½*d.*). *P* 14 × 15 (1*d. and* 4½*d.*) *or* 14 × 15 (*others*).

136 ½d. brown-purple and olive-grey .. 10 10
137 1d. deep blue-green 10 10
138 2d. deep violet 50 10
139 4½d. blue 10 10
140 1s. brown 40 10
136/40 .. .. .. *Set of* 5 90 30

Designs: *Horiz*—2d. Arrival of Van Riebeeck's ships; 1s. "Landing at the Cape" (C. Davidson Bell). *Vert*—4½d. "Jan van Riebeeck" (D. Craey).

SATISE (**74**) SADIPU (**75**)

76 Queen Elizabeth II

1952 (26 Mar). *South African Tercentenary International Stamp Exhibition, Cape Town. No.* 137 *optd with T* **74** *and No.* 138 *with T* **75**.

141 1d. deep blue-green .. .. .. 15 1·60
142 2d. deep violet 30 90

(Des H. Kumst)

1953 (3 June). *Coronation. W* **9** (*sideways*). *P* 14×15.

143 **76** 2d. deep violet-blue 30 10
a. Ultramarine 30 10

77 1d. "Cape Triangular" Stamp

(Des H. Kumst)

1953 (1 Sept). *Centenary of First Cape of Good Hope Stamp. T* **77** *and similar horiz design. W* **9**. *P* 15 × 14.

144 1d. sepia and vermilion 10 10
145 4d. deep blue and light blue 20 20

Design:—4d. Four pence "Cape Triangular" stamp.

79 Merino Ram

80 Springbok

81 Aloes

(Des A. Hendriksz and J. Prentice (4½d.))

1953 (1 Oct). *W* **9**. *P* 14.

146 **79** 4½d. slate-purple and yellow 20 10
147 **80** 1s. 3d. chocolate .. .. .. 1·50 10
148 **81** 1s. 6d. vermilion and deep blue-green 80 40
146/8 .. .. .. *Set of* 3 2·25 45

82 Arms of Orange Free State and Scroll

(Des H. Kumst)

1954 (23 Feb). *Centenary of Orange Free State. W* **9**. *P* 15 × 14.

149 **82** 2d. sepia and pale vermilion 10 10
150 4½d. purple and slate 20 50

83 Warthog

92 Springbok

93 Gemsbok

(Des H. Kumst)

1954 (14 Oct). *T* **83, 92/3** *and similar designs. W* **9** *(sideways on large vert designs). P* 15 × 14 *(½d. to 2d.), 14 (others).*

151	½d. deep blue-green . .	. .	10	10
152	1d. brown-lake	. .	10	10
153	1½d. sepia	. .	10	10
154	2d. plum	. .	10	10
155	3d. chocolate and turquoise-blue	. .	15	10
156	4d. indigo and emerald	. .	40	10
157	4½d. blue-black and grey-blue	. .	60	1·50
158	6d. sepia and orange	. .	50	10
159	1s. deep brown and pale chocolate . .	. .	80	10
160	1s. 3d. brown and bluish green	. .	1·50	10
161	1s. 6d. brown and rose	. .	1·75	60
162	2s. 6d. brown-black and apple-green	. .	3·50	20
163	5s. black-brown and yellow-orange	. .	10·00	1·40
164	10s. black and cobalt . .	. .	17·00	4·50
151/64		*Set of* 14	32·00	7·50

Designs: *Vert (as T* **83**)—1d. Black Wildebeest; 1½d. Leopard; 2d. Mountain Zebra. *(As T* **93**)—3d. White Rhinoceros; 4d. African Elephant; 4½d. Hippopotamus; 1s. Greater Kudu; 2s. 6d. Nyala; 5s. Giraffe; 10s. Sable Antelope. *Horiz (as T* **92**)—6d. Lion.

No. 152 exists in coils.

See also Nos. 170/7 and 185/97.

97 President Kruger

98 President M. Pretorius

(Des H. Kumst)

1955 (21 Oct). *Centenary of Pretoria. W* **9** *(sideways). P* 14 × 15.

165	**97**	3d. slate-green . .	10	10
166	**98**	6d. maroon	10	20

99 A. Pretorius, Church of the Vow and Flag

100 Settlers' Block-wagon and House

(Des H. Kumst)

1955 (1 Dec). *Voortrekker Covenant Celebrations, Pietermaritzburg. W* **9**. *P* 14.

			Un pair	Us pair	Us single
167	**99**	2d. blue and magenta . .	45	3·25	10

(Des H. Kumst)

1958 (1 July). *Centenary of Arrival of German Settlers in South Africa. W* **9**. *P* 14.

168	**100**	2d. chocolate and pale purple . .	10	10

101 Arms of the Academy

(Des H. Kumst)

1959 (1 May). *50th Anniv of the South African Academy of Science and Art, Pretoria. W* **9**. *P* 15 × 14.

169	**101**	3d. deep blue and turquoise-blue	10	10
		a. Deep blue printing omitted	£1600	

102 Union Coat of Arms

1 S — I　　1 S — II

1959–60. *As Nos.* 151/2, 155/6, 158/9 *and* 162/3, *but W* **102** *(sideways on Nos.* 172/3 *and* 175/7).

170	½d. deep greenish blue (12.60)	15	4·50
171	1d. brown-lake (I) (11.59) . .	10	10
	a. Redrawn. Type II (10.60)	20	10
172	3d. chocolate and turquoise-blue (9.59)	15	10
173	4d. indigo and emerald (1.60)	50	20
174	6d. sepia and orange (2.60) . .	70	80
175	1s. deep brown and pale chocolate (11.59)	6·00	40
176	2s. 6d. brown-black & apple-green (12.59)	2·75	4·00
177	5s. black-brown & yellow-orange (10.60)	6·00	28·00
170/7	*Set of* 8	14·50	35·00

Nos. 171/a. In Type II "1d. Posgeld Postage" is more to the left in relation to "South Africa", with "1" almost central over "S" instead of to right as in Type I.

No. 171 exists in coils.

103 Globe and Antarctic Scene

(Des H. Kumst)

1959 (16 Nov). *South African National Antarctic Expedition. W* **102**. *P* 14 × 15.

178	**103**	3d. blue-green and orange	20	10

104 Union Flag

106 "Wheel of Progress"

(Des V. Ivanoff and H. Kumst (1s.), H. Kumst (others))

1960 (2 May). *50th Anniv of Union of South Africa. T* **104, 106** *and similar designs. W* **102** *(sideways on 4d. and 6d.). P* 14 × 15 *(4d., 6d.) or* 15 × 14 *(others).*

179	4d. orange-red and blue	30	10
180	6d. red, brown and light green	30	10
181	1s. deep blue and light yellow	30	10
182	1s. 6d. black and light blue . .	1·10	2·00
179/82	*Set of* 4	1·75	2·00

Designs: *Vert*—6d. Union Arms. *Horiz*—1s. 6d. Union Festival emblem.

See also No. 190, 192/3.

108 Locomotives of 1860 and 1960

(Des V. Ivanoff)

1960 (2 May). *Centenary of South African Railways. W* **102**. *P* 15 × 14.

183	**108**	1s. 3d. deep blue	2·00	30

109 Prime Ministers Botha, Smuts, Hertzog, Malan, Strijdom and Verwoerd

1960 (31 May). *Union Day. W* **102**. *P* 15×14.

184	**109**	3d. brown and pale brown	10	10
		a. Pale brown omitted*	£2250	

*This is due to a rectangular piece of paper adhering to the background cylinder, resulting in R.2/1 missing the colour completely and six adjoining stamps having it partially omitted. The item in block of eight is probably unique.

(New Currency. 100 cents=1 rand)

1961 (14 Feb). *As previous issues but with values in cents and rand. W* **102** *(sideways on* 3½ *c.,* 7½ *c.,* 20 *c.,* 50 *c.,* 1 *r.). P* 15 × 14 *(½ c., to* 2½ *c.,* 10 *c.),* 14 × 15 *(*3½ *c.,* 7½ *c.) or* 14 *(others).*

185	½ c. deep bluish green (as 151)	10	10
186	1 c. brown-lake (as 152)	10	10
187	1½ c. sepia (as 153) . .	10	10
188	2 c. plum (as 154) . .	10	10
189	2½ c. brown (as 184) . .	20	10
190	3½ c. orange-red and blue (as 179)	15	1·25
191	5 c. sepia and orange (as 158)	20	10
192	7½ c. red, brown and light green (as 180)	20	1·50
193	10 c. deep blue and light yellow (as 181)	30	30
194	12½ c. brown and bluish green (as 160)	1·00	1·75
195	20 c. brown and rose (as 161)	2·25	3·25
196	50 c. black-brown & orange-yellow (as 163)	6·00	10·00
197	1 r. black and cobalt (as 164)	18·00	26·00
185/97	*Set of* 13	25·00	40·00

X. REPUBLIC OF SOUTH AFRICA

OUTSIDE THE COMMONWEALTH

111 Kafferboom Flower

112 Afrikander Bull

110 African Pygmy Kingfisher

113 Pouring Gold

114 Groot Constantia

115 Burchell's Gonolek

116 Baobab Tree

117 Maize

118 Cape Town Castle Entrance

119 Protea

120 Secretary Bird

121 Cape Town Harbour

122 Strelitzia

Two types of ½ c.:

I　　II

Type I from sheets. Spurs of branch indistinct.

Type II from coils. Spurs strengthened.

Three types of 1 c.:

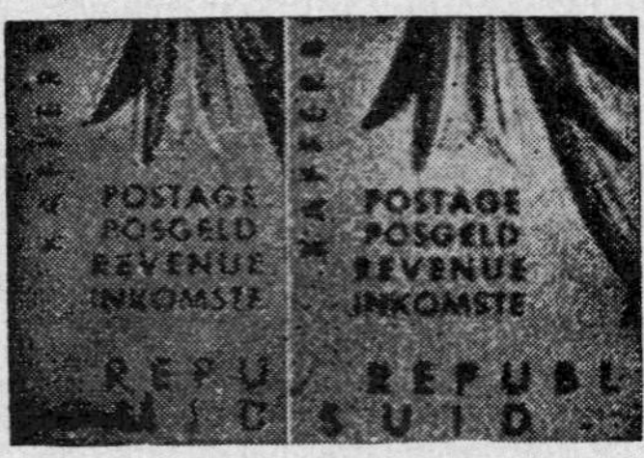

I II

III

Type I. Lowest point of flower between "OS" of "POSTAGE". Right-hand petal over "E".
Type II. Flower has moved fractionally to the right so that lowest point is over "S" of "POSTAGE". Right-hand petal over "E".
Type III. Lowest point directly over "O". Right-hand petal over "G".

Two types of 2½ c.

In Type I the lines of the building are quite faint. In Type II all lines of the building have been strengthened by re-engraving.

(Des Mrs. T. Campbell (½ c., 3 c., 1 r.); Miss N. Desmond (1 c.); De La Rue (2½ c., 5 c., 12½ c.); H. L. Prager (50 c.); Govt. Ptg Dept artist (others))

1961 (31 May)–**63**. *Unsurfaced paper.* W **102** (*sideways* on* ½ c., 1½ c., 2½ c., 5 c. *to* 20 c.). *P* 14×15 (½ c., 1½ c.), 15×14 (1 c.), *or* 14 (*others*).

198 **110** ½ c. bright blue, carmine & brown (I) .. 10 10
a. Perf 14 (3.63) 10 15
b. Type II (coils) (18.5.63) .. 70 90
199 **111** 1 c. red and olive-grey (I) 10 10
a. Type II (1.62) 10 10
b. Type III (coils) (5.63) .. .. 1·00 1·50
200 **112** 1½ c. brown-lake and light purple .. 10 10
201 **113** 2 c. ultramarine and yellow .. 90 10
202 **114** 2½ c. violet and green (I) 15 10
aw. Wmk top of arms to right .. 30 10
b. Type II. *Dp violet & green* (9.61) 20 10
203 **115** 3 c. red and deep blue 80 10
204 **116** 5 c. yellow and greenish blue .. 30 10
205 **117** 7½ c. yellow-brown and light green 60 10
206 **118** 10 c. sepia and green 75 10
207 **119** 12½ c. red, yellow and black-green .. 2·00 30
a. Yellow omitted £600
b. Red omitted £650
208 **120** 20 c. turquoise-blue, carm & brn-orge 3·50 30
209 **121** 50 c. black and bright blue .. .. 30·00 2·00
210 **122** 1 r. orange, olive-green & light blue 20·00 2·00
198/210 .. .. *Set of* 13 50·00 4·00

*The normal sideways watermark shows the top of the arms to left, *as seen from the back of the stamp.*

1961–74 *Definitives*

Key to designs, perfs, watermarks, papers and phosphors

Value	*Type*	*Perf*	*W* **102.** *Ordinary*	*No wmk. Ordinary*	*W* **127.** *Chalky*
½ c.	**110** (I)	14×15	198	—	—
	(I)	14	198a	—	—
	(II)	14×15	198b	—	—
1 c.	**111** (I)	15×14	199	211	—
	(II)		199a	211a	227
	(III)		199b	—	—
1½ c.	**112**	14×15	200	—	228
2 c.	**113**	14	201	212	229
2½ c.	**114** (I)	14	202	—	—
	(II)		202a	213/*a*	230/*a*
3 c.	**115**	14	203	214	—
5 c.	**116**	14	204	215	231
7½ c.	**117**	14	205	216	232
10 c.	**118**	14	206	217/*b*	233/*a*
12½ c.	**119**	14	207	—	—
20 c.	**120**	14	208	218	234/*a*
50 c.	**121**	14	209	219	235
1 r.	**122**	14	210	—	236

Redrawn Designs

		W **127** *Upright or Tête-bêche. Plain or phosphorised*	*W* **127** *Tête-bêche. Phos frame*	*No wmk. Phosphorised Glossy*	*No wmk. Phosphorised Chalky*
½ c. **130***a*	14	238	—	—	—
	14×15	238*b*	—	—	—
	14	238*c*/*d*	—	—	—
1 c. **131**	15×14	239	—	—	—
	13½×14	239a	—	—	—
1½ c. **132**	14×15	240/*b*	284	—	—
	14×13½	240c	—	—	—
2 c. **133**	14	241/*a*	285/*a*	315a	—
	12½	—	—	315	315b
2½ c. **134**	14	242/*a*	286/*a*	—	—
3 c. **135**	14	243/*a*	287	—	—
	12½	—	—	316	316a
4 c. **134**	14	243*b*	288	—	—
5 c. **136**	14	244/*a*	289	318a	—
	12½	—	—	318	318b
6 c. **137**	14	—	290	—	—
	12½	—	—	—	319
7½ c. **137**	14	245	291	—	—
9 c. **139**	14	245*a*	292	—	—
	12½	—	—	320/*a*	—
10 c. **138**	14	246/a	293	321a	—
	12½	—	—	321	321b
12½ c. **139**	14	247/*a*	294	—	—
15 c. **140**	14	248	295	—	—
20 c. **141**	14	249/*a*	296/*a*	—	—
	12½	—	—	323	323a
50 c. **142**	14	250	—	—	—
	12½	—	—	324	324a
1 r. **143**	14	251	—	—	—
	12½	—	—	325	—

New Designs

		W **127** *Tête-bêche. Plain or phos-phorised*	*W* **127** *Tête-bêche. Phos-frame*	*No wmk. Phosphorised Glossy*	*No wmk. Phosphorised Chalky*
½ c. **168**	14 × 13½	276	282	—	—
	14 × 14½	276a	—	313	—
	14 × 15	—	282a	—	—
1 c. **169**	13½ × 14	277	283	—	—
	14	—	—	314	—
4 c. **182**	14	310/*a*	—	—	—
	12½	—	—	317/*b*	317c
15 c. **182***a*	14	311	—	—	—
	12½	—	—	—	322

1961 (Aug)–**63.** *As Nos.* 199, 201/6 *and* 208/9 *but without wmk.*

211 **111** 1 c. red and olive-grey (I) 20 30
a. Type II (9.62) 45 40
212 **113** 2 c. ultramarine and yellow (8.63) 7·00 40
213 **114** 2½ c. deep violet and green (II) .. 30 10
a. Violet and green (12.61) .. 30 10
214 **115** 3 c. red and deep blue (10.61) .. 45 10
215 **116** 5 c. yellow & greenish blue (12.61) 50 10
216 **117** 7½ c. yellow-brown & lt green (3.62) 80 30
217 **118** 10 c. sepia and green (11.61) .. 1·00 40
a. Sepia and emerald .. .. 40·00 17·00
b. Sepia-brown & lt green (7.63) 2·25 45
218 **120** 20 c. turq-bl, carm & brn-orge (4.63) 14·00 4·25
219 **121** 50 c. black and bright blue (8.62) .. 14·00 4·25
211/19 .. .. *Set of* 9 35·00 8·75

123 Blériot XI Monoplane and Boeing 707 Airliner over Table Mountain

124 Folk-dancers

1961 (1 Dec). *50th Anniv of First South African Aerial Post.* W **102** (*sideways*). *P* 14 × 15.

220 **123** 3 c. blue and red 40 10

(Des K. Esterhuysen)

1962 (1 Mar). *50th Anniv of Volkspele (folk-dancing) in South Africa.* W **102** (*sideways*). *P* 14 × 15.

221 **124** 2½ c. orange-red and brown 15 10

125 *The Chapman* (emigrant ship)

1962 (20 Aug). *Unveiling of Precinct Stone, British Settlers Monument, Grahamstown.* W **102.** *P* 15 × 14.

222 **125** 2½ c. turquoise-green and purple .. 40 10
223 12½ c. blue and deep chocolate .. 3·00 1·75

126 Red Disa (orchid), Castle Rock and Gardens

(Des M. F. Stern)

1963 (14 Mar). *50th Anniv of Kirstenbosch Botanic Gardens, Cape Town. P* 13½ × 14.

224 **126** 2½ c. multicoloured 20 10
a. Red (orchid, etc) omitted .. £1500

127 (normal version)

128 Centenary Emblem and Nurse

129 Centenary Emblem and Globe

1963 (30 Aug). *Centenary of Red Cross. Chalk-surfaced paper. Wmk* **127** (*sideways on* 2½ c.). *P* 14 × 13½ (2½ c.) *or* 15 × 14 (12½ c.).

225 **128** 2½ c. red, black and reddish purple .. 20 10
w. Wmk reversed .. .. 3·00 1·40
226 **129** 12½ c. red and indigo .. .. 3·25 1·00
a. Red cross omitted £1300

1963–67. *As* 1961–3 *but chalk-surfaced paper and W* **127** (*sideways on* 1½ c., 2½ c., 5 c., 7½ c., 10 c., 20 c.). *P* 15 × 14 (1 c.), 14 × 15 (1½ c.), *or* 14 (*others*).

227 **111** 1 c. red and olive-grey (II) (9.63) .. 10 10
w. Wmk reversed 65 65
228 **112** 1½ c. brown-lake & light purple (1.67) 1·75 1·75
229 **113** 2 c. ultramarine and yellow (11.64) 15 20
230 **114** 2½ c. violet and green (I) (10.63) .. 10 10
a. Brt reddish vio & emer (II) (3.66) 35 20
aw. Wmk inverted .. .. 2·50 90
231 **116** 5 c. yellow and greenish blue (9.66) 1·25 30
232 **117** 7½ c. yellow-brown & brt grn (23.2.66) 7·50 4·75
233 **118** 10 c. sepia-brown & lt emerald (9.64) 40 10
a. Sepia-brown and green (1.67) .. 45 10
234 **120** 20 c. turq-blue, carm & brn-orge (7.64) 1·50 70
a. Dp turq-bl, carm & flesh (20.7.65) 1·75 70
235 **121** 50 c. black and ultramarine (4.66) .. 30·00 8·50
236 **122** 1 r. orange, lt green & pale bl (7.64) 55·00 38·00
227/36 .. .. *Set of* 10 90·00 48·00

In the 2½ c. (No. 230*a*), 5 c., 7½ c., 10 c. (Jan 1967 printing only) and 50 c. the watermark is indistinct but they can easily be distinguished from the stamps without watermark by their shades and the chalk-surfaced paper which is appreciably thicker and whiter.

130 Assembly Building, Umtata

1963 (11 Dec). *First Meeting of Transkei Legislative Assembly. Chalk-surfaced paper.* W **127.** *P* 15 × 14.

237 **130** 2½ c. sepia and light green 10 10
a. Light green omitted £1300

130*a* African Pygmy Kingfisher

131 Kafferboom Flower

132 Afrikander Bull

133 Pouring Gold

134 Groot Constantia

135 Burchell's Gonolek

136 Baobab Tree

137 Maize

138 Cape Town Castle Entrance

139 Protea

140 Industry

141 Secretary Bird

142 Cape Town Harbour

143 Strelitzia

(15 c. des C. E. F. Skotnes)

Redrawn types.

½ c. "½C" larger and "REPUBLIEK VAN REPUBLIC OF" smaller.

3 c. and 12½ c. Inscriptions and figures of value larger.

Others. "SOUTH AFRICA" and "SUID-AFRIKA" larger and bolder. The differences vary in each design but are easy to see by comparing the position of the letters of the country name with "REPUBLIC OF" and "REPUBLIEK VAN".

1964–72. *As* 1961–63 *but designs redrawn and new values* (4 *c.,* 9 *c. and* 15 *c.*). *Chalk-surfaced paper. W* **127** (*sideways* on* ½, 1½, 2½, 4, 5, 7½, 9, 10, 15 *and* 20 *c.*). *P* 14×15 (1½ *c.*), 15×14 (1 *c.*) *or* 14 (*others*).

No.	Type		Un	Us
238	**130***a*	½ c. brt blue, carm & brn (21.5.64)	10	10
		a. Imperf (pair)	£275	
		b. Perf 14×15. *Brt blue, carmine and yellow-brown* (6.7.67) ..	20	20
		c. Perf 14. *Bright blue, lake and yellow-brown* (3.68)	30	30
		d. Perf 14. *Bright blue, carmine-lake and yellow-brown* (9.68)	30	10
239	**131**	1 c. red and olive-grey (9.3.67) ..	10	10
		a. Perf 13½×14 (7.68)	30	10
240	**132**	1½ c. dull red-brn & lt pur (21.9.67)	15	10
		a. Purple-brown & lt pur (1968)	15	10
		b. Brt red-brown & lt pur (5.68)	15	10
		c. Perf 14×13½. *Red-brown and light purple* (14.8.69) ..	55	55
241	**133**	2 c. ultramarine & yellow (8.1.68)	20	10
		a. Blue and yellow (10.71) ..	30	10
242	**134**	2½ c. violet and green (19.4.67) ..	20	10
		a. Reddish violet and green (8.67)	20	10
		w. Wmk top of RSA to right ..	£180	65·00
243	**135**	3 c. red and deep blue (11.64) ..	30	10
		a. Brown-red and deep blue (3.72)	35	30
243*b*	**134**	4 c. violet and green (10.71) ..	75	30
244	**136**	5 c. yellow & greenish bl (14.2.68)	40	10
		a. Lemon & dp greenish bl (10.71)	8·00	90
245	**137**	7½ c. yellow-brn & brt grn (26.7.67)	60	10
245*a*	**139**	9 c. red, yellow & slate-green (2.72)	9·00	3·50
246	**138**	10 c. sepia and green (10.6.68) ..	1·75	10
		a. Brown and pale green (7.68)	4·25	3·25
247	**139**	12½ c. red, yellow & blk-green (3.64)	1·75	40
		a. Red, pale yell & bl-grn (2.2.66)	2·75	40
248	**140**	15 c. black, light olive-yellow and red-orange (1.3.67)	1·75	25
249	**141**	20 c. turquoise-blue, carmine and brown-orange (2.68)	4·50	15
		a. Turquoise-blue, carmine and orange-buff (12.71)	5·00	1·00
250	**142**	50 c. black and bright blue (17.6.68)	4·00	40
251	**143**	1 r. orange, lt green & lt bl (6.65)	4·00	1·00
		w. Wmk inverted		
238/51		.. .. *Set of* 16	25·00	5·25

*The normal sideways watermark shows the top of RSA to left *as seen from the back of the stamp.*

WATERMARK. Two forms of the watermark Type **127** exist in the above issue: the normal Type **127** (sometimes indistinct), and a very faint *tête-bêche* watermark, i.e. alternately facing up and down, which was introduced in mid-1967. As it is extremely difficult to distinguish these on single stamps we do not list it.

The ½ (both perfs), 1, 2, 2½, 3, 15 c. and 1 r. are known in both forms, the 1½, 4, 5, 7½, 9, 10, 20 and 50 c. only in the *tête-bêche* form, and the 12½ c. Type **127** only.

GUM. The 2, 3, 5, 20, 50 c. and 1 r. exist with PVA gum as well as gum arabic.

PHOSPHORISED PAPER. From October 1971 onwards phosphor bands (see Nos. 282/96) gave way to phosphorised paper which cannot be distinguished from non-phosphor stamps without the aid of a lamp. For this reason we do not distinguish these printings in the above issue, but some are slightly different shades which are listed in the *Elizabethan Catalogue* and all have PVA gum.

The 4 c. and 9 c. are on phosphorised paper only and differ from Nos. 288 and 292 by the lack of phosphor bands.

145 "Springbok" Badge of Rugby Board

147 Calvin

1964 (8 May). *75th Anniv of South African Rugby Board. Chalk-surfaced paper. T* **145** *and similar horiz design. W* **127** (*sideways on* 2½ *c.*). *P* 14 × 15 (2½ *c.*) *or* 15 × 14 (12½ *c.*).

No.		Un	Us
252	2½ c. yellow-brown and deep green.. ..	15	10
253	12½ c. black and light yellow-green	4·50	4·25

Design:—12½ c. Rugby footballer.

1964 (10 July). *400th Death Anniv of Calvin (Protestant reformer). Chalk-surfaced paper. W* **127** (*sideways*). *P* 14 × 13½.

No.	Type		Un	Us
254	**147**	2½ c. cerise, violet and brown	10	10

148 Nurse's Lamp **149** Nurse holding Lamp

I. Screened base to lamp II. Clear base to lamp

1964 (12 Oct). *50th Anniv of South African Nursing Association. Chalk-surfaced paper. W* **127** (*sideways on* 2½ *c.*). *P* 14 × 15 (2½ *c.*) *or* 15 × 14 (12½ *c.*).

No.	Type		Un	Us
255	**148**	2½ c. ultramarine and dull gold (Type I)	10	10
256		2½ c. brt blue & yellow-gold (Type II) ..	30	10
		a. Ultramarine and dull gold	15	10
257	**149**	12½ c. bright blue and gold	3·25	2·25
		a. Gold omitted	£1200	
255/7		.. .. *Set of* 3	3·25	2·25

150 I.T.U. Emblem and Satellites

1965 (17 May). *I.T.U. Centenary. T* **150** *and similar horiz design. Chalk-surfaced paper. W* **127**. *P* 15 × 14.

No.		Un	Us
258	2½ c. orange and blue	25	10
259	12½ c. brown-purple and green	3·00	1·75

Design:—12½ c. I.T.U. emblem and symbols.

152 Pulpit in Groote Kerk, Cape Town **153** Church Emblem

1965 (21 Oct). *Tercentenary of Nederduites Gereformeerde Kerk (Dutch Reformed Church) in South Africa. Chalk-surfaced paper. W* **127** (*sideways on* 2½ *c., inverted on* 12½ *c.*). *P* 14 × 15 (2½ *c.*) *or* 15 × 14 (12½ *c.*).

No.	Type		Un	Us
260	**152**	2½ c. brown and light yellow	15	10
261	**153**	12½ c. black, light orange and blue ..	1·75	1·25

154 Diamond **155** Bird in flight

(Des C. E. F. Skotnes)

1966 (31 May). *Fifth Anniv of Republic. T* **154/5** *and similar designs. Chalk-surfaced paper. W* **127** (*sideways on* 1 *c.,* 3 *c.*). *P* 14 × 13½ (1 *c.*), 13½ × 14 (2½ *c.*), 14 × 15 (3 *c.*) *or* 15 × 14 (7½ *c.*).

No.		*Un pair*	*Us pair*	*Us single*
262	1 c. black, bluish green & olive-yell	45	45	10
263	2½ c. blue, deep blue & yellow-green	1·25	1·25	10
264	3 c. red, greenish yellow & red-brn	4·75	4·75	10
265	7½ c. blue, ultramarine and yellow	5·50	6·00	20
262/5	.. .. *Set of* 4	11·00	11·00	40

Designs: *Vert*—3 c. Maize plants. *Horiz*—7½ c. Mountain landscape.

Nos. 262/5 exist on Swiss-made paper with *tête-bêche* watermark from a special printing made for use in presentation albums for delegates to the U.P.U. Congress in Tokyo in 1969, as supplies of the original Harrison paper were by then exhausted (*Set of* 4 *pairs price* £140 *mint*).

158 Verwoerd and Union Buildings, Pretoria

(Des from portrait by Dr. Henkel)

1966 (6 Dec). *Verwoerd Commemoration. T* **158** *and similar designs. Chalk-surfaced paper. W* **127** (*sideways on* 3 *c.*). *P* 14 × 15 (3 *c.*) *or* 15 × 14 (*others*).

No.		Un	Us
266	2½ c. blackish brown and turquoise ..	10	10
267	3 c. blackish brown and yellow-green ..	10	10
	a. Blackish brown (portrait) omitted	£2750	
268	12½ c. blackish brown and greenish blue	70	60
266/8	.. .. *Set of* 3	80	60

Designs: *Vert*—3 c. "Dr. H.F. Verwoerd" (I. Henkel). *Horiz*—12½ c. Verwoerd and map of South Africa.

161 "Martin Luther" (Cranach the Elder) **162** Wittenberg Church Door

1967 (31 Oct). *450th Anniv of Reformation. W* **127** ((*sideways*), *normal on* 2½ *c., tête-bêche on* 12½ *c.*). *P* 14 × 15.

No.	Type		Un	Us
269	**161**	2½ c. black and rose-red	10	10
270	**162**	12½ c. black and yellow-orange	1·75	2·50

163 "Profile of Pres. Fouché" (I. Henkel) **164** Portrait of Pres. Fouché

1968 (10 Apr). *Inauguration of President Fouché. W* **127** (*sideways*). *P* 14 × 15.

No.	Type		Un	Us
271	**163**	2½ c. chocolate and pale chocolate ..	10	10
272	**164**	12½ c. deep blue and light blue ..	80	1·25

No. 272 also exists with the watermark *tête-bêche* (*Price un* £1; *used* £1.50).

165 Hertzog in 1902

1968 (21 Sept). *Inauguration of General Hertzog Monument, Bloemfontein. T* **165** *and similar designs. W* **127** (*tête-bêche on* 2½ *c., inverted on* 3 *c., sideways on* 12½ *c.*). *P* 14 × 13½ (12½ *c.*) *or* 13½ × 14 (*others*).

No.		Un	Us
273	2½ c. black, brown and olive-yellow ..	10	10
274	3 c. black, red-brown, red-orange and yellow	15	10
275	12½ c. black, red and yellow-orange	2·00	1·50
273/5	.. .. *Set of* 3	2·00	1·50

Designs: *Horiz*—3 c. Hertzog in 1924. *Vert*—12½ c. Hertzog Monument.

168 African Pygmy Kingfisher **169** Kafferboom Flower

1969. *W* **127** *(tête-bêche, sideways on* ½ *c.). P* 14 × 13½ *(*½ *c.) or* 13½ × 14 *(*1 *c.).*

276	**168**	½ c. new bl, carm-red & yell-ochre (1.69)	10	30
		a. Coil. Perf 14 × 14½ (5.69)	2·25	2·50
277	**169**	1 c. rose-red and olive-brown (1.69)	10	10

See also Nos. 282/3 and 313/14.

170 Springbok and Olympic Torch **171** Professor Barnard and Groote Schuur Hospital

1969 (15 Mar). *South African Games, Bloemfontein. W* **127** *(tête-bêche, sideways). P* 14 × 13½.

278	**170**	2½ c. black, blue-black, red & sage-grn	15	10
279		12½ c. black, blue-blk, red & cinnamon	1·00	1·75

1969 (7 July). *World's First Heart Transplant and 47th South African Medical Association Congress. T* **171** *and similar horiz design. W* **127** *(tête-bêche). P* 13½ × 14 *(*2½ *c.) or* 15 × 14 *(*12½ *c.).*

280	2½ c. plum and rose-red	15	10
281	12½ c. carmine-red and royal blue	2·00	2·25

Design:—12½ c. Hands holding heart.

1969–72. *As* 1964–72 *issue, Nos.* 276/7, *and new value* (6 *c.*), *but with phosphor bands printed horizontally and vertically between the stamp designs, over the perforations, producing a frame effect. W* **127** *arranged tête-bêche (upright on* 1, 2 *and* 3 *c., sideways on others). P* 14×13½ *(*½, 1½ *c.),* 13½×14 *(*1 *c.), or* 14 *(others).*

282	**168**	½ c. new blue, carmine-red and yellow-ochre (1.70)	15	70
		a. Coil. Perf 14×15 (2.71)	3·25	3·75
		w. Wmk reversed	65	55
283	**169**	1 c. rose-red & olive-brown (12.69)	15	10
		w. Wmk reversed	55	35
284	**132**	1½ c. red-brown & light purple (12.69)	20	10
285	**133**	2 c. ultramarine and yellow (11.69)	30	10
		a. *Dp ultramarine & yellow* (8.70)	90	50
286	**134**	2½ c. violet and green (1.70)	25	10
		a. *Purple and green* (24.7.70)	1·00	10
		w. Wmk reversed	18·00	15·00
287	**135**	3 c. red and deep blue (30.9.69)	70	10
288	**134**	4 c. violet and green (1.3.71)	40	40
289	**136**	5 c. yellow & greenish bl (17.11.69)	85	10
290	**137**	6 c. yellow-brown & brt grn (3.5.71)	1·00	30
291		7½ c. yellow-brn & brt grn (17.11.69)	4·00	30
292	**139**	9 c. red, yellow & black-grn (17.5.71)	1·50	30
293	**138**	10 c. brown and pale green (1.70)	2·00	10
294	**139**	12½ c. red, yell & black-grn (2.5.70)	5·50	2·75
295	**140**	15 c. blk, lt ol-yellow & red-orge (1.70)	2·25	1·75
296	**141**	20 c. turquoise-blue, carmine and brown-orange (18.2.70)	11·00	1·75
		a. *Turquoise-blue, carmine and orange-buff* (9.72)	11·00	70
282/96		*Set of* 15	27·00	7·00

No. 286 exists on normal RSA wmk as well as RSA *tête-bêche* wmk.

The 1, 2, 2½, 3, 10, 15 and 20 c. exist with PVA gum as well as gum arabic, but the 4, 6 and 9 c. exist with PVA gum only.

For stamps without wmk, see Nos. 313, etc.

173 Mail Coach **174** Transvaal Stamp of 1869

1969 (6 Oct). *Centenary of First Stamps of South African Republic (Transvaal). Phosphor bands on all four sides (*2½ *c.). W* **127** *(tête-bêche, sideways on* 12½ *c.). P* 13½ × 14 *(*2½ *c.) or* 14 × 13½ *(*12½ *c.).*

297	**173**	2½ c. yellow, indigo and yellow-brown	15	10
298	**174**	12½ c. emerald, gold and yellow-brown	3·25	3·25

PHOSPHOR FRAME. Nos. 299/306 have phosphor applied on all four sides as a frame.

175 "Water 70" Emblem **177** "The Sower"

1970 (14 Feb). *Water 70 Campaign. T* **175** *and similar design. W* **127** *(tête-bêche (sideways on* 2½ *c.)). P* 14 × 13½ *(*2½ *c.) or* 13½ × 14 *(*3 *c.).*

299	2½ c. green, bright blue and chocolate	30	10
300	3 c. Prussian blue, royal blue and buff	30	20

Design: *Horiz*—3 c. Symbolic waves.

1970 (24 Aug). 150*th Anniv of Bible Society of South Africa. T* **177** *and similar horiz design (gold die-stamped on* 12½ *c.). W* **127** *(tête-bêche, sideways on* 2½ *c.). P* 14 × 13½ *(*2½ *c.) or* 13½ × 14 *(*12½ *c.).*

301	2½ c. multicoloured	15	10
302	12½ c. gold, black and blue	2·00	2·75

Design:—12½ c. "Biblia" and open book.

178 J. G. Strijdom and Strijdom Tower **179** Map and Antarctic Landscape

1971 (22 May). *"Interstex" Stamp Exhibition, Cape Town. P* 14 × 13½.
A. *W* **127** *(sideways tête-bêche).* B. *W* **102** *(sideways).*

			A		B	
303	**178**	5 c. light greenish blue, black and pale yellow	20	10	1·75	5·00

1971 (22 May). *Tenth Anniv of Antarctic Treaty. W* **127** *(tête-bêche). P* 13½ × 14.

304	**179**	12½ c. blue-black, greenish bl & orge-red	2·50	5·00

180 "Landing of British Settlers, 1820" (T. Baines)

1971 (31 May). *Tenth Anniv of the Republic of South Africa. T* **180** *and similar design. W* **127** *(tête-bêche sideways on* 4 *c.). P* 13½ × 14 *(*2 *c.) or* 14 × 13½ *(*4 *c.).*

305	2 c. pale flesh and brown-red	15	20
	w. Wmk reversed	60	60
306	4 c. green and black	15	10
	w. Wmk reversed	1·40	85

Design: *Vert*—4 c. Presidents Steyn and Kruger and Treaty of Vereeniging Monument.

No. 306 exists with PVA gum as well as gum arabic.

PHOSPHORISED PAPER. All issues from here are on phosphorised paper *unless otherwise stated.*

181 View of Dam

(Des C. Bridgeford (4 c.), C. Lindsay (others))

1972 (4 Mar). *Opening of Hendrik Verwoerd Dam. T* **181** *and similar horiz designs. Multicoloured. W* **127** *(tête-bêche). P* 13½ × 14.

307	4 c. Type **181**	20	10
308	5 c. Aerial view of Dam	25	10
309	10 c. Dam and surrounding country (58 × 21 *mm*)	1·50	2·50
307/9	*Set of* 3	1·75	2·50

182 Sheep **182a** Lamb

(Des K. Esterhuysen (4 c.), H. Botha (15 c.))

1972 (15 May–Oct). *W* **127** *(tête-bêche). P* 14.

310	**182**	4 c. olive-brn, yell, pale bl & slate-bl	30	10
		a. *Grey-olive, yellow, bright blue and slate-blue* (10.72)	30	10
311	**182a**	15 c. pale stone, deep blue and dull blue	3·25	20

Other shades exist of the 4 c.

See also Nos. 317 and 322.

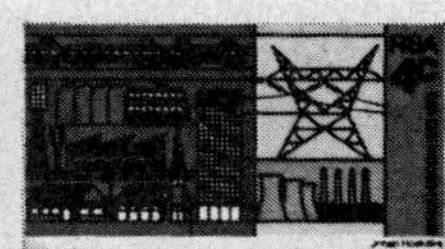

183 Black and Siamese Cats **184** Transport and Industry

1972 (19 Sept). *Centenary of Societies for the Prevention of Cruelty to Animals. W* **127** *(sideways tête-bêche). P* 14 × 13½.

312	**183**	5 c. multicoloured	1·75	10

1972–74. *As Nos.* 310/11 *and* 282 *etc. but no wmk. P* 14 × 14½ *(*½ *c.),* 14 *(*1 *c.) or* 12½ *(others). Phosphorised, glossy paper.*

313	**168**	½ c. bright blue, scarlet and yellow-ochre (coil) (6.73)	15·00	16·00
314	**169**	1 c. rose-red and olive-brown (1.74)	40	10
315	**133**	2 c. blue and orange-yellow (11.72)	15	10
		a. Perf 14. *Deep ultramarine and orange-yellow* (coil) (7.73)	11·00	13·00
		b. Chalky paper (17.7.74)	40	70
316	**135**	3 c. scarlet and deep blue (8.5.73)	50	15
		a. Chalky paper (18.2.74)	1·25	1·25
317	**182**	4 c. grey-blue, yellow, blue and bluish slate* (1.10.73)	30	30
		a. *Olive-sepia, yellow, azure and slate-blue* (18.2.74)	60	30
		b. *Lavender-brown, pale yellow, blue and bluish slate** (26.7.74)	30	20
		c. Chalky paper* (22.8.74)	60	45
318	**136**	5 c. orge-yell & greenish bl (4.10.73)	2·00	80
		a. Perf 14. *Yellow and light greenish blue* (coil) (7.73)	12·00	14·00
		b. Chalky paper (5.74)	2·25	1·25
319	**137**	6 c. yellow-brown and bright green (*chalky paper*) (22.7.74)	2·50	3·25
320	**139**	9 c. red, yellow-green & grn-blk (6.73)	1·75	2·00
		a. *Red, deep yellowish green and green-black* (4.74)	2·75	1·50
321	**138**	10 c. reddish brown & brt grn (8.5.73)	85	50
		a. Perf 14 (coil) (6.73)	14·00	16·00
		b. Chalky paper (17.7.74)	1·50	70
322	**182a**	15 c. pale stone, deep blue and dull blue (*chalky paper*) (4.9.74)	5·00	6·00
323	**141**	20 c. turquoise-blue, rose-carmine and orange-buff (8.5.73)	3·25	55
		a. Chalky paper (5.74)	5·00	70
324	**142**	50 c. black and bright blue (6.73)	4·50	1·50
		a. Chalky paper (22.7.74)	9·50	7·00
325	**143**	1 r. orange, lt green & lt blue (8.10.73)	12·00	2·50
		a. Orange omitted	£1200	
313/25		*Set of* 13	42·00	30·00

*On these stamps the colours are known to vary within the sheet.

No. 314 also differs in that the central design has been moved down about 1 mm.

Nos. 317/c also differ from No. 310 by measuring 26¼ × 21 mm instead of 27¼ × 21¾ mm.

No. 325a exists on the bottom row of one sheet.

(Des J. Hoekstra (4 c.), M. Barnett (others))

1973 (1 Feb). 50*th Anniv of ESCOM (Electricity Supply Commission). T* **184** *and similar vert designs. Multicoloured. P* 12 × 12½ *(*4 *c.) or* 12½ *(others).*

326	4 c. Type **184**	20	10
327	5 c. Pylon (21 × 28 *mm*)	30	10
328	15 c. Cooling Towers (21 × 28 *mm*)	3·00	3·50
326/8	*Set of* 3	3·25	3·50

185 University Coat of arms **187** C. J. Langenhoven

186 Rescuing Sailors

(Des P. de Wet (15 c.), H. Meiring (others))

1973 (2 Apr). *Centenary of University of South Africa. T* **185** *and similar designs. W* **127** *(tête-bêche) (*5 *c.) or no wmk (others). P* 12 × 12½ *(*5 *c.) or* 12½ *(others).*

329	4 c. multicoloured	20	10
330	5 c. multicoloured	30	15
331	15 c. black and gold	3·00	3·50
329/31	*Set of* 3	3·25	3·50

Designs: *Horiz* (37 × 21 *mm*)—5 c. University Complex, Pretoria. *Vert (As T* **185**)—15 c. Old University Building, Cape Town.

WATERMARK. All issues from this date are on unwatermarked paper, *unless otherwise stated.*

(Des M. Barnett)

1973 (2 June). *Bicentenary of Rescue by Wolraad Woltemade.* T **186** *and similar horiz designs. P* 11½ × 12½.

332 4 c. lt red-brown, lt yellow-green and black .. 25 10
333 5 c. yellow-olive, light yellow-green & black 40 10
334 15 c. red-brown, light yellow-green and black 7·00 7·00
332/4 .. .. *Set of* 3 7·00 7·00

Designs:—5 c. *De Jonge Thomas* foundering; 15 c. *De Jonge Thomas* breaking up and sailors drowning.

(Des J. Mostert)

1973 (1 Aug). *Birth Centenary of C. J. Langenhoven (politician and composer of national anthem).* T **187** *and similar designs. P* 12½ (4 *and* 5 c.) *or* 11½ × 12½ (15 c.).

335 **187** 4 c. multicoloured 25 10
336 – 5 c. multicoloured 35 10
337 – 15 c. multicoloured .. .. 5·00 6·00
335/7 .. .. *Set of* 3 5·00 6·00

Nos. 336/7 are as T **187** but with motifs rearranged. The 5 c. is vert, 21 × 38 mm, and the 15 c. is horiz, 38 × 21 mm.

188 Communications Map

(Des C. Webb)

1973 (1 Oct). *World Communications Day. P* 12½.

(*a*) *No wmk. Glossy paper*

338 **188** 15 c. multicoloured .. .. 80 1·40

(*b*) *W* **127** (*tête-bêche*). *Chalky paper*

339 **188** 15 c. multicoloured .. .. 1·50 5·00

189 Restored Buildings

190 Burgerspond (obverse and reverse)

(Des W. Jordaan)

1974 (14 Mar). *Restoration of Tulbagh.* T **189** *and similar multi-coloured design. P* 12½.

340 4 c. Type **189** 15 10
341 5 c. Restored Church Street (58 × 21 *mm*) .. 40 60

(Des P. de Wet. Litho)

1974 (6 Apr). *Centenary of the Burgerspond (coin). P* 12½ × 12.

342 **190** 9 c. brown, orange-red & pale yell-olive 60 95

191 Dr. Malan

192 Congress Emblem

(Des I. Henkel)

1974 (22 May). *Birth Centenary of Dr. D. F. Malan (Prime Minister). P* 12½ × 12.

343 **191** 4 c. blue and light blue 15 10

(Des Ingrid Paul)

1974 (13 June). *15th World Sugar Congress, Durban. P* 12 × 12½.

344 **192** 15 c. deep ultramarine and silver .. 1·00 1·50

193 "50" and Radio Waves

(Des Ingrid Paul)

1974 (13 July). *50th Anniv of Broadcasting in South Africa. P* 12 × 12½.

345 **193** 4 c. red and black 10 10

194 Monument Building

(Des G. Cunningham)

1974 (13 July). *Inauguration of British Settlers' Monument, Grahamstown. P* 12 × 12½.

346 **194** 5 c. red and black 10 10

195 Stamps of the South African Provinces

(Des K. Esterhuysen)

1974 (9 Oct). *Centenary of Universal Postal Union. P* 12½.

347 **195** 15 c. multicoloured 90 80

196 Iris

197 Bokmakierie Shrikes

(Des E. de Jong. Recess and photo)

1974 (20 Nov)–**76**. *Multicoloured. Glossy paper* (2, 3, 4, 6, 7, 30 *c. and* 1 *r.*) *or chalk-surfaced paper* (*others*). *P* 12½ (1 *to* 25 *c.*) *or* 12×12½ (*others*).

(*a*) *Vert designs as* T **196** *showing flowers, or horiz designs showing birds or fish*

348 1 c. Type **196** 10 10
349 2 c. Wild Heath 15 10
a. Chalk-surfaced paper (2.75) 10 10
350 3 c. Geranium 30 10
a. Chalk-surfaced paper (*deep claret back-ground*) (6.75) 10 10
ab. Imperf (pair) £140
ac. Brown-purple background (6.76) .. 10 10
351 4 c. Arum Lily 30 10
a. Chalk-surfaced paper (2.75) 10 10
ab. Imperf (pair) £140
352 5 c. Cape Gannet 20 10
353 6 c. Galjoen (fish) 25 10
354 7 c. Bontrok Seabream 25 10
355 9 c. Dusky Batfish 30 10
356 10 c. Moorish Idol 30 10
357 14 c. Roman Seabream 30 10
358 15 c. Greater Double-collared Sunbird .. 30 10
359 20 c. Yellow-billed Hornbill 45 10
360 25 c. Barberton Daisy 45 10

(*b*) *Horiz designs as* T **197**

361 30 c. Type **197** .. .. 8·00 70
362 50 c. Stanley Cranes .. .. 2·50 35
363 1 r. Bateleurs .. .. 8·50 3·00
348/63 .. .. *Set of* 16 20·00 4·25

A used block of 4 and a single on cover of No. 351 have been seen with the yellow omitted.

1974 (20 Nov)–**76**. *Coil stamps. As Nos.* 348/9, 352 *and* 356 *but photo, colours changed. Glossy paper. P* 12½.

370 1 c. reddish violet and pink 75 50
a. Perf 14. Chalk-surfaced paper (12.75) .. 55 50
371 2 c. bronze-green and yellow-ochre 80 50
a. Chalk-surfaced paper (7.75) .. .. 1·10 50
b. Perf 14. Chalk-surfaced paper (11.76?) .. 1·40 40
372 5 c. black and light slate-blue .. .. 2·25 80
373 10 c. deep violet-blue and light blue .. .. 5·50 7·00
a. Perf 14. Chalk-surfaced paper (4.76) .. 4·25 4·75
370/3 .. .. *Set of* 4 7·00 6·00

198 Voortrekker Monument and Encampment

(Des J. Hoekstra)

1974 (6 Dec). *25th Anniv of Voortrekker Monument, Pretoria. P* 12½.

374 **198** 4 c. multicoloured 20 30

199 SASOL Complex

200 President Diederichs

(Des C. Webb)

1975 (26 Feb). *25th Anniv of SASOL (South African Coal, Oil and Gas Corporation Ltd). P* 11½ × 12½.

375 **199** 15 c. multicoloured .. .. 1·00 1·75

(Des J. L. Booysen. Recess (4 c.) or photo (15 c.))

1975 (19 Apr). *Inauguration of the State President. P* 12½ × 11½.

376 **200** 4 c. agate and gold 10 10
377 15 c. royal blue and gold .. .. .. 50 1·25

201 Jan Smuts

202 "Dutch East Indiaman, Table Bay"

(Des J. Hoekstra. Recess and photo)

1975 (24 May). *Jan Smuts Commemoration. P* 12½ × 11½.

378 **201** 4 c. black and olive-black 10 10

(Des J. Hoekstra. Photo (Nos. 379/82) or litho (**MS**383))

1975 (18 June). *Death Centenary of Thomas Baines (painter).* T **202** *and similar horiz designs. Multicoloured. P* 11½ × 12½.

379 5 c. Type **202** 15 10
380 9 c. "Cradock, 1848" 30 20
381 15 c. "Thirsty Flat, 1848" 50 50
382 30 c. "Pretoria, 1874" .. .. 80 1·75
379/82 .. .. *Set of* 4 1·60 2·25
MS383 120 × 95 mm. Nos. 379/82 .. .. .. 1·60 4·25

203 Gideon Malherbe's House, Paarl

(Des P. de Wet. Recess and photo)

1975 (14 Aug). *Centenary of Genootskap van Regte Afrikaners (Afrikaner Language Movement). P* 12½.

384 **203** 4 c. multicoloured 10 10

204 "Automatic Sorting"

205 Title Page of *Die Afrikaanse Patriot*

(Des J. Sampson)

1975 (11 Sept). *Postal Mechanisation. P* 12½ × 11½.

385 **204** 4 c. multicoloured 10 10

(Des K. Esterhuysen. Recess and photo (4 c.). Des P. de Wet. Litho (5 c.))

1975 (10 Oct). *Inauguration of the Language Monument, Paarl.* T **205** *and similar vert design. P* 12½ × 11½.

386 4 c. black, pale stone and bright orange .. 10 10
387 5 c. multicoloured 10 10

Design:—5 c. "Afrikaanse Taalmonument".

206 Table Mountain

(Des P. Bosman and J. Hoekstra. Litho)

1975 (13 Nov). *Tourism. T* **206** *and similar horiz designs. Multicoloured. P* 12½.
388 15 c. Type **206** .. .. 4·50 5·00
a. Block of 4. Nos. 388/91 .. .. 16·00
ab. Yellow-orange and pale lemon ("RSA 15 c") omitted £1400 £800
389 15 c. Johannesburg .. .. .. 4·50 5·00
390 15 c. Cape Vineyards .. .. .. 4·50 5·00
391 15 c. Lions in Kruger National Park .. 4·50 5·00
388/91 .. .. *Set of* 4 16·00 18·00

Nos. 388/91 were printed together, *se-tenant*, in blocks of 4 throughout the sheet.

Nos. 388/91 were printed in six colours. At least two sheets, one of which was subsequently used to prepare official first day covers at Pretoria, had the final two colours, yellow-orange and pale lemon, omitted.

207 Globe and Satellites

(Des J. Hoekstra. Litho)

1975 (3 Dec). *Satellite Communication. P* 12½.
392 **207** 15 c. multicoloured 30 30

208 Bowls

(209)

(Des J. Maskew. Litho)

1976. *Sporting Commemorations. T* **208** *and similar vert designs. P* 12½ × 11½.
393 15 c. black and light sage-green (18.2) .. 30 70
394 15 c. black and bright yellow-green (15.3) .. 75 1·40
395 15 c. black and pale yellow-olive (16.8) .. 40 60
396 15 c. black and apple-green (2.12) 60 55
393/6 .. .. *Set of* 4 1·90 3·00
MS397 161 × 109 mm. Nos. 393/6 (2.12) .. 2·00 4·00

Designs:—No. 393, Type **208** (World Bowls Championships, Johannesburg); No. 394, Batsman (Centenary of Organised Cricket in South Africa); No. 395, Polo player; No. 396, Gary Player (golfer).

1976 (6 Apr). *South Africa's Victory in World Bowls Championships. No. 393 optd with T* **209** *in gold.*
398 **208** 15 c. black and light sage-green 30 80

210 "Picnic under a Baobab Tree"

(Des J. Hoekstra. Photo (4 c.) or litho (others and **MS**403))

1976 (20 Apr). *Birth Centenary of Erich Mayer (painter). T* **210** *and similar horiz designs. Multicoloured. P* 11½ × 12½.
399 4 c. Type **210** 15 10
a. Imperf (pair) £950
400 10 c. "Foot of the Blaauwberg" 35 25
401 15 c. "Harbeespoort Dam" .. .. 60 1·25
402 20 c. "Street scene, Doornfontein" .. .. 80 1·50
399/402 .. .. .. *Set of* 4 1·75 2·75
MS403 121 × 95 mm. Nos. 399/402 .. .. 2·00 4·00

211 Cheetah

212 "Emily Hobhouse" (H. Naude)

(Des P. Bosman. Photo (3 c.) or litho (others))

1976 (5 June). *World Environmental Day. T* **211** *and similar horiz designs. Multicoloured. P* 11½ × 12½.
404 3 c. Type **211** 15 10
405 10 c. Black Rhinoceros 70 40
406 15 c. Blesbok .. .. 85 1·25
407 20 c. Mountain Zebra .. .. .. 1·25 2·00
404/7 .. .. *Set of* 4 2·75 3·25

(Des J. Hoekstra)

1976 (8 June). *50th Death Anniv of Emily Hobhouse (welfare worker). P* 12½ × 11½.
408 **212** 4 c. multicoloured 10 10

213 Steam Packet, 1876

214 Family with Globe

(Des K. Esterhuysen. Litho)

1976 (5 Oct). *Ocean Mail Service Centenary. P* 11½ × 12½.
409 **213** 10 c. multicoloured 60 85
a. Imperf (horiz pair) £900

(Des I. Ross)

1976 (6 Nov). *Family Planning and Child Welfare. P* 12½ × 11½.
410 **214** 4 c. chestnut and light salmon 10 10

215 Glasses of Wine

216 Dr. Jacob du Toit

First "die" of Afrikaans inscription at left omitted (R. 1/3 on every third sheet)

(Des H. Botha. Litho)

1977 (14 Feb). *International Wine Symposium, Cape Town. P* 12½ × 11½.
411 **215** 15 c. multicoloured 40 85
a. "die" omitted .. .. .. 15·00 19·00

(Des J. Hoekstra)

1977 (21 Feb). *Birth Centenary of J. D. du Toit (theologian and poet). P* 12½ × 11½.
412 **216** 4 c. multicoloured 10 10

217 Palace of Justice

218 *Protea repens*

(Des H. Meiring)

1977 (18 May). *Centenary of Transvaal Supreme Court. P* 11½ × 12½.
413 **217** 4 c. red-brown 10 10

(Des D. Findlay. Photo (1, 2, 3 c. (No. 416), 4, 5, 8, 10 to 20 c. (Nos. 425/a) and coil stamps) or litho (others))

1977 (27 May)–**82.** *Vert designs as T* **218** *showing Proteas or other Succulents. Multicoloured. (a) Sheet stamps. P* 12½.
414 1 c. Type **218** 10 10
415 2 c. *P punctata* 15 30
416 3 c. *P neriifolia (photo) (p* 12½) 10 10
416*a* 3 c. *P neriifolia (litho) (p* 14 × 13½) (1.10.79) 10 30
417 4 c. *P longifolia* 10 10
a. Imperf (pair) £100
418 5 c. *P cynaroides* 10 10
a. Perf 14 × 13½ (4.3.81) 10 10
b. Imperf (pair) £200
419 6 c. *P canaliculata* 35 60
a. Black (face value and inscr at foot) omitted .. .. 90·00
b. Perf 14 × 13½ (25.10.79*) 30 60
420 7 c. *P lorea* 25 60
a. Emerald ("RSA") omitted £110
b. Perf 14 × 13½ (19.9.80) 20 60
421 8 c. *P mundii* 20 30
a. Perf 14 × 13½ (10.7.81) 15 10
422 9 c. *P roupelliae* 20 60
a. Perf 14 × 13½ (22.12.78) .. .. 3·75 2·50
423 10 c. *P aristata* 30 10
a. Perf 14 × 13½ (12.1.82) 20 30
424 15 c. *P eximia* 25 10
425 20 c. *P magnifica (photo)* 30 10
a. Perf 14 × 13½ (16.2.78) 60 90
425*b* 20 c. *P magnifica (litho) (p* 14 × 13½) (24.5.82) 1·00 80
426 25 c. *P grandiceps* 60 50
a. Emerald ("RSA" and leaves) omitted £160
b. Black (face value and inscr) omitted £160
c. Perf 14×13½ (3.6.80) 40 50
427 30 c. *P amplexicaulis* 45 10
a. Perf 14×13½ (19.10.80) 40 40
428 50 c. *Leucospermum cordifolium* 65 15
a. Perf 14×13½ (9.10.80) 45 15
429 1 r. *Paranomus reflexus* .. .. .. 1·00 95
a. Perf 14×13½ (30.7.80) 80 75
430 2 r. *Orothamnus zeyheri* .. .. .. 2·25 2·50
a. Perf 14×13½ (22.5.81) .. .. 1·50 1·00

(*b*) *Coil stamps. Imperf × perf* 14
431 1 c. *Leucadendron argenteum* 35 60
432 2 c. *Mimetes cucullatus* 35 60
433 5 c. *Serruria florida* 35 60
434 10 c. *Leucadendron sessile* 35 70
414/34 .. .. *Set of* 21 6·25 6·75

*Sheets dated 15 August 1979.

There were two emerald plates used for the 7 c.; one for the design and background and a second, common with other values in the issue, used to apply "RSA". No. 420a shows this second emerald plate omitted.

Later printings of the coil stamps come with every fifth stamp numbered on the back.

219 Gymnast

220 Metrication Symbol on Globe

(Des D. Cowie. Litho)

1977 (15 Aug). *Eighth Congress of International Association of Physical Education and Sports for Girls and Women. P* 12½ × 11½.
435 **219** 15 c. black, salmon-red and yellow .. 30 30

(Des L. Wilsenach. Litho)

1977 (15 Sept). *Metrication. P* 12 × 12½.
436 **220** 15 c. multicoloured 30 30

221 Atomic Diagram

(Des R. Sargent. Litho)

1977 (8 Oct). *Uranium Development. P* 12 × 12½.
437 **221** 15 c. multicoloured 30 30

222 National Flag

(Des J. Hoekstra)

1977 (11 Nov). *50th Anniv of National Flag. P* 12 × 12½.
438 **222** 5 c. multicoloured 10 10

223 Walvis Bay, 1878

(Des A. H. Barrett. Litho)

1978 (10 Mar). *Centenary of Annexation of Walvis Bay. P* 12½.
439 **223** 15 c. multicoloured 60 60

COVER PRICES

Cover factors are quoted at the beginning of each country for most issues to 1945. An explanation of the system can be found on page x. The factors quoted do not, however, apply to philatelic covers.

224 Dr. Andrew Murray

225 Steel Rail

(Des J. Hoekstra. Litho)

1978 (9 May). 150*th Birth Anniv of Dr. Andrew Murray (church statesman). P* 12½ × 12.
440 **224** 4 c. multicoloured 10 10

(Des H. Botha. Litho)

1978 (5 June). 50*th Anniv of I.S.C.O.R. (South African Iron and Steel Industrial Corporation). P* 12½.
441 **225** 15 c. multicoloured 30 30

226 Richards Bay

(Des A. H. Barrett. Litho)

1978 (31 July). *Harbours. T* **226** *and similar horiz design. Multicoloured. P* 12½.
442 15 c. Type **226** .. .. 50 1·00
a. Pair. Nos. 442/3 .. .. 1·00 2·00
443 15 c. Saldanhabaai .. .. 50 1·00
Nos. 442/3 were printed together, *se-tenant*, in horizontal and vertical pairs throughout the sheet.

227 "Shepherd's Lonely Dwelling, Riversdale"

228 Pres. B. J. Vorster

(Des G. Mynhardt. Litho)

1978 (21 Aug). 125*th Birth Anniv of J. E. A. Volschenk (painter). T* **227** *and similar horiz designs. Multicoloured. P* 12½.
444 10 c. Type **227** 20 20
445 15 c. "Clouds and Sunshine, Laneberg Range, Riversdale" 50 35
446 20 c. "At the Foot of the Mountain" .. .. 70 1·00
447 25 c. "Evening on the Veldt" .. .. .. 80 1·75
444/7 .. .. *Set of* 4 2·00 3·00
MS448 124 × 90 mm. Nos. 444/7 .. .. .. 2·00 4·00

(Des A. H. Barrett. Litho)

1978 (10 Oct). *Inauguration of President Vorster. P* 14 × 13½.
449 **228** 4 c. brown-purple and gold 60 20
a. Perf 12½ × 12 .. .. .. 10 10
450 15 c. dull violet and gold 25 60

229 Golden Gate

(Des A. H. Barrett. Litho)

1978 (13 Nov). *Tourism. T* **229** *and similar horiz designs. Multicoloured. P* 12½.
451 10 c. Type **229** 20 15
452 15 c. Blyde River Canyon 40 50
453 20 c. Amphitheatre, Drakensberg .. .. 65 1·25
454 25 c. Cango Caves .. .. 85 1·75
451/4 .. .. *Set of* 4 1·90 3·25

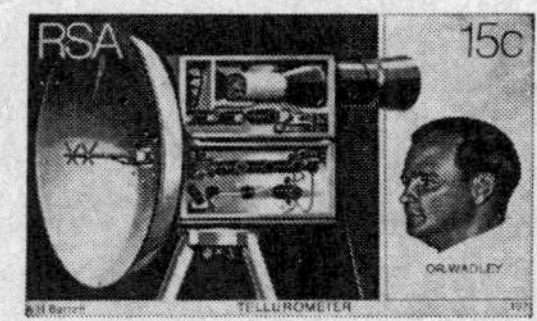

230 Dr. Wadley (inventor) and Tellurometer

(Des A. H. Barrett. Litho)

1979 (12 Feb). 25*th Anniv of Tellurometer (radio distance measurer). P* 12½.
455 **230** 15 c. multicoloured 20 20

231 1929 4d. Airmail Stamp

(Des G. Mynhardt. Litho)

1979 (30 Mar). 50*th Anniv of Stamp Production in South Africa. P* 14.
456 **231** 15 c. green, cream and slate 30 20

232 "Save Fuel"

(Des A. H. Barrett)

1979 (2 Apr). *Fuel Conservation. P* 12 × 12½.
457 **232** 4 c. black and vermilion 25 50
a. Pair. Nos. 457/8 .. .. 50 1·00
458 – 4 c. black and vermilion 25 50
No. 458 is as T **232** but has face value and country initials in bottom left-hand corner, and Afrikaans inscription above English.
Nos. 457/8 were printed together, *se-tenant*, in horizontal and vertical pairs throughout the sheet.

233 Isandlwana

234 "Health Care"

(Des A. H. Barrett. Litho)

1979 (25 May). *Centenary of Zulu War. T* **233** *and similar horiz designs in black and rose-red, showing drawings. P* 14.
459 4 c. Type **233** 15 10
460 15 c. Ulundi 45 45
461 20 c. Rorke's Drift 60 75
459/61 .. .. *Set of* 3 1·10 1·10
MS462 125 × 90 mm. Nos. 459/61. P 12½ .. 2·25 3·50

(Des J. Hoekstra. Litho)

1979 (19 June). *Health Year. P* 12½ × 12.
463 **234** 4 c. multicoloured 10 10
a. Perf 14 × 13½ 30 30

235 Children looking at Candle

(Des G. Mynhardt. Litho)

1979 (13 Sept). 50*th Anniv of Christmas Stamp Fund. P* 14.
464 **235** 4 c. multicoloured 10 10
a. Gold (inscr) omitted .. .. ..

236 University of Cape Town

237 "Gary Player"

(Des G. Mynhardt. Litho)

1979 (1 Oct). 50*th Anniv of University of Cape Town. P* 13½ × 14.
465 **236** 4 c. multicoloured 20 30
a. Perf 12 × 12½ 15 15

(Des H. de Klerk. Litho)

1979 (4 Oct). *"Rosafari 1979" World Rose Convention, Pretoria. T* **237** *and similar vert designs. Multicoloured. P* 14 × 13½.
466 4 c. Type **237** 15 10
467 15 c. "Prof. Chris Barnard" 40 40
468 20 c. "Southern Sun" 50 60
469 25 c. "Soaring Wings" 55 70
466/9 .. .. *Set of* 4 1·40 1·60
MS470 100 × 125 mm. Nos. 466/9 .. .. 1·40 2·50

238 University of Stellenbosch

239 F.A.K. Emblem

(Des A. H. Barrett. Litho)

1979 (8 Nov). 300*th Anniv of Stellenbosch (oldest town in South Africa). T* **238** *and similar horiz design. Multicoloured. P* 14.
471 4 c. Type **238** 10 10
472 15 c. Rhenish Church on the Braak 20 40

(Des J. Hoekstra)

1979 (18 Dec). 50*th Anniv of F.A.K. (Federation of Afrikaans Cultural Societies). P* 12½ × 12.
473 **239** 4 c. multicoloured 10 15

240 "Still-life with Sweet Peas"

241 "Cullinan II"

(Des G. Mynhardt. Litho)

1980 (6 May). *Paintings by Pieter Wenning. T* **240** *and similar multicoloured design. P* 14 × 13½.
474 5 c. Type **240** 10 10
475 25 c. "House in the Suburbs, Cape Town" (44½ × 37 *mm*) 40 60
MS476 94 × 121 mm. Nos. 474/5 .. .. .. 1·25 1·60

(Des A. H. Barrett. Litho)

1980 (12 May). *World Diamond Congresses, Johannesburg. T* **241** *and similar vert design. Multicoloured. P* 14.
477 15 c. Type **241** 60 60
478 20 c. "Cullinan I (Great Star of Africa)" .. 65 65

242 C. L. Leipoldt

243 University of Pretoria

(Des J. Hoekstra. Litho)

1980 (3 Sept). *Birth Centenary of C. L. Leipoldt (poet). P* 14 × 13½.
479 **242** 5 c. multicoloured 10 10

(Des P. de Wet. Litho)

1980 (9 Oct). 50*th Anniv of University of Pretoria. P* 14 × 13½.
480 **243** 5 c. multicoloured 10 10

244 "Marine with Shipping" (Willem van de Velde)

(Des G. Mynhardt. Litho)

1980 (3 Nov). *Paintings from South African National Gallery, Cape Town. T* **244** *and similar multicoloured designs. P* 14.
481 5 c. Type **244** 15 10
482 10 c. "Firetail and his Trainer" (George Stubbs) 20 20
483 15 c. "Lavinia" (Thomas Gainsborough) (*vert*) 25 45
484 20 c. "Classical Landscape" (Pieter Post) .. 30 65
481/4 .. .. *Set of* 4 80 1·25
MS485 126 × 90 mm. Nos. 481/4 .. .. .. 1·00 1·75

245 Joubert, Kruger and M. Pretorius (Triumvirate Government)

246 Boers advancing up Amajuba Mountain

(Des A. H. Barrett. Litho)

1980 (15 Dec). *Centenary of Paardekraal Monument (cairn commemorating formation of Boer Triumvirate Government). T* **245** *and similar multicoloured design. P* 14 × 13½ (5 *c.*) *or* 13½ × 14 (10 *c.*).

486 5 c. Type **245** 10 10
487 10 c. Paardekraal Monument (*vert*) 20 40

(Des Diana Arbuthnot. Litho)

1981 (27 Feb). *Centenary of Battle of Amajuba. T* **246** *and similar multicoloured design. P* 13½ × 14 (5 *c.*) *or* 14 × 13½ (15 *c.*).

488 5 c. Type **246** 20 10
489 15 c. British troops defending hill (*horiz*) . . 40 65

247 Ballet *Raka*

(Des H. Botha. Litho)

1981 (23 May). *Opening of State Theatre, Pretoria. T* **247** *and similar horiz design. Multicoloured. P* 14.

490 20 c. Type **247** 25 30
491 25 c. Opera *Aida* 40 35
MS492 110 × 90 mm. Nos. 490/1 . . . . . . 65 70

248 Former Presidents C. R. Swart, J. J. Fouché, N. Diederichs and B. J. Vorster

(Des A. H. Barrett. Litho)

1981 (30 May). *20th Anniv of Republic. T* **248** *and similar design. P* 14.

493 5 c. black, grey-olive and bistre 15 10
494 15 c. multicoloured 30 30
Design: (28 × 22 *mm*)—15 c. President Marais Viljoen.

249 Girl with Hearing Aid

250 Microscope

251 *Calanthe natalensis*

(Des Mare Mouton. Litho)

1981 (12 June). *Centenary of Institutes for Deaf and Blind, Worcester. T* **249** *and similar vert design. Multicoloured. P* 13½ × 14.

495 5 c. Type **249** 10 10
496 15 c. Boy reading braille 20 25

(Des N. Hanna. Litho)

1981 (10 July). *50th Anniv of National Cancer Association. P* 13½ × 14.

497 **250** 5 c. multicoloured 10 10

(Des Jeanette Stead. Litho)

1981 (11 Sept). *Tenth World Orchid Conference, Durban. T* **251** *and similar vert designs. Multicoloured. P* 14.

498 5 c. Type **251** 15 10
499 15 c. *Eulophia speciosa* 30 35
500 20 c. *Disperis fanniniae* 40 65
501 25 c. *Disa uniflora* 50 90
498/501 . . . . *Set of* 4 1·25 1·75
MS502 120 × 91 mm. Nos. 498/501 . . . . 2·25 2·00

252 Voortrekkers in Uniform

253 Lord Baden-Powell

254 Dr. Robert Koch

(Des J. Hoekstra. Litho)

1981 (30 Sept). *50th Anniv of Voortrekker Movement (Afrikaans cultural youth organization). P* 14.

503 **252** 5 c. multicoloured 10 10

(Des J. Meyer. Litho)

1982 (22 Feb). *75th Anniv of Boy Scout Movement. P* 13½ × 14.

504 **253** 15 c. multicoloured 15 15

(Des J. Meyer. Litho)

1982 (24 Mar). *Centenary of Discovery of Tubercle Bacillus by Dr. Robert Koch. P* 13½ × 14.

505 **254** 20 c. multicoloured 15 30

255 *Maria van Riejbeck* (submarine)

256 Old Provost, Grahamstown

(Des A. H. Barrett. Litho)

1982 (2 Apr). *25th Anniv of Simonstown as South African Navy Base. T* **255** *and similar horiz designs. Multicoloured. P* 14.

506 8 c. Type **255** 10 10
507 15 c. Missile patrol vessel 15 30
508 20 c. Minesweeper 25 50
509 25 c. Harbour patrol boats 30 70
506/9 . . . . *Set of* 4 70 1·40
MS510 125 × 90 mm. Nos. 506/9 . . . . . . 2·00 2·00

(Des A. H. Barrett. Recess (Nos. 511, 512*b*, 513, 514, 515*a*, 516*a*, 521, 522*a*, 524, 525, 526 and 527), photo (Nos. 528/31) or litho (others))

1982 (15 July)–**87.** *South African Architecture. Designs as T* **256.** (*a*) *Sheet stamps. P* 14.

511 1 c. reddish brown (*recess*) 15 20
511*a* 1 c. reddish brown (*litho*) (2.4.84) . . 30 30
ab. Imperf (horiz pair) . . . . . . 35·00
512 2 c. yellow-olive (*litho*) 20 30
512*a* 2 c. deep green (*litho*) (9.5.83) 90 30
512*b* 2 c. bottle green (*recess*) (28.11.83) . . 10 20
512*c* 2 c. bottle green (*litho*) (21.11.85) . . 70 30
513 3 c. violet (*recess*) 30 30
513*a* 3 c. violet (*litho*) (28.11.85) . . . . 1·75 50
514 4 c. brown-olive (*recess*) 20 15
514*a* 4 c. brown-olive (*litho*) (25.3.85) . . 70 30
515 5 c. carmine (*litho*) 40 30
515*a* 5 c. brown-purple (*recess*) (11.11.83) . . 10 10
ab. Imperf (pair) £100
516 6 c. deep blue-green (*litho*) 45 40
516*a* 6 c. blackish green (*recess*) (9.8.84) . . 80 30
517 7 c. dull yellowish green (*litho*) 30 40
518 8 c. greenish blue (*litho*) 30 30
518*a* 8 c. indigo (*litho*) (3.1.83) 40 10
519 9 c. deep mauve (*litho*) 40 20
520 10 c. Venetian red (*litho*) 40 30
520*a* 10 c. purple-brown (*litho*) (26.1.83) . . 35 10
520*b* 11 c. cerise (*litho*) (2.4.84) 40 15
520*c* 12 c. deep violet-blue (*litho*) (1.4.85) . . 70 10
520*d* 14 c. lake-brown (*litho*) (1.4.86) . . . . 1·00 10
521 15 c. deep violet-blue (*recess*) 30 15
521*a* 16 c. rosine (*litho*) (1.4.87) . . . . 1·00 50
522 20 c. vermilion (*litho*) 65 30
522*a* 20 c. brownish black (*recess*) (15.6.83) . . 80 10
522*b* 20 c. brownish black (*litho*) (14.11.85) . . 1·50 15
523 25 c. bistre (*litho*) 50 30
523*a* 25 c. ochre (*litho*) (3.6.87) . . . . 1·75 55
524 30 c. agate (*recess*) 65 30
524*a* 30 c. reddish brown (*litho*) (12.3.86) . . 95 30
525 50 c. deep turquoise-blue (*recess*) 80 30
a. Deep slate-blue (18.3.83) . . . . 1·75 65
525*b* 50 c. turquoise-blue (*litho*) (13.10.86) . . 2·25 30
526 1 r. deep violet (*recess*) . . . . . . 1·00 15
526*a* 1 r. deep violet (*litho*) (17.12.86) . . 1·50 40
527 2 r. deep carmine (*recess*) . . . . . . 1·60 40
527*a* 2 r. deep carmine (*litho*) (5.12.85) . . 1·25 50
511/27 . . . . *Set of* 21 (*one of each value*) 9·50 4·00

Designs: (28 × 20 *mm*)—2 c. Tuynhuys, Cape Town; 3 c. Appèlhof, Bloemfontein; 4 c. Raadsaal, Pretoria; 5 c. Cape Town Castle; 6 c. Goewermentsgebou, Bloemfontein; 7 c. Drostdy, Graaff-Reinet; 8 c. Leeuwenhof, Cape Town; 9 c. Libertas, Pretoria; 10 c. City Hall, Pietermaritzburg; 11 c. City Hall, Kimberley; 12 c. City Hall, Port Elizabeth; 14 c. City Hall, Johannesburg; 15 c. Matjesfontein; 16 c. City Hall, Durban; 20 c. Post Office, Durban; 25 c. Melrose House, Pretoria. (45 × 28 *mm*)—30 c. Old Legislative Assembly Building, Pietermaritzburg; 50 c. Raadsaal, Bloemfontein; 1 r. Houses of Parliament, Cape Town; 2 r. Uniegebou, Pretoria.

For certain printings of Nos. 511/27*a* the design width of each stamp was reduced by a millimetre. Of the original set of 17 all showed "wide" designs with the exception of the 1 r. Changes in design size occurred in subsequent printings so that Nos. 512*c*, 513, 521 and 524 can be found in both wide and narrow versions. Of the remainder Nos. 511*a*, 512*b*, 513*a*, 514*a*, 515*a*, 516*a*, 520*b*/*d*, 521*a*, 522*a*/*b*, 524*a*, 525*a*/*b*, 526 and 527*a* exist as "narrow" designs only.

(*b*) *Coil stamps. P* 14 × *imperf*

528 1 c. brown 30 60
529 2 c. yellow-green 30 65
530 5 c. lake-brown 30 65
531 10 c. light brown 30 70
528/31 . . . . *Set of* 4 1·10 2·40

Designs: (28 × 20 *mm*)—1 c. Drostdy, Swellendam; 2 c. City Hall, East London; 5 c. Head Post Office, Johannesburg; 10 c. Morgenster, Somerset West.

257 Bradysaurus

258 Gough Island Base

(Des Sheila Nowers. Litho)

1982 (1 Dec). *Karoo Fossils. T* **257** *and similar horiz designs. Multicoloured. P* 14.

532 8 c. Type **257** 40 10
533 15 c. Lystrosaurus 55 75
534 20 c. Euparkeria 70 85
535 25 c. Thrinaxodon . . . . 80 1·10
532/5 . . . . *Set of* 4 2·25 2·50
MS536 107 × 95 mm. Nos. 532/5 . . . . 2·50 3·00

(Des D. Thorpe. Litho)

1983 (19 Jan). *Weather Stations. T* **258** *and similar horiz designs. Multicoloured. P* 13½ × 14.

537 8 c. Type **258** 20 10
538 20 c. Marion Island base 45 45
539 25 c. Taking meteorological readings 45 50
540 40 c. Launching weather balloon, Sanae . . 70 90
537/40 . . . . *Set of* 4 1·60 1·75

259 Class "S2" Light Shunting Locomotive

260 Rugby

(Des H. Botha. Litho)

1983 (27 Apr). *Steam Railway Locomotives. T* **259** *and similar horiz designs. Multicoloured. P* 14.

541 10 c. Type **259** 35 10
542 20 c. Class "16E" express locomotive . . 70 75
543 25 c. Class "6H" locomotive . . . . . . 80 1·00
544 40 c. Class "15F" main-line locomotive . . 1·25 1·75
541/4 . . . . *Set of* 4 2·75 3·25

(Des Sheila Nowers. Litho)

1983 (20 July). *Sport in South Africa. T* **260** *and similar multicoloured designs. P* 14.

545 10 c. Type **260** 15 10
546 20 c. Soccer (*horiz*) 35 40
547 25 c. Yachting 45 50
548 40 c. Horse-racing (*horiz*) 75 95
545/8 . . . . *Set of* 4 1·50 1·75

261 Plettenberg Bay

262 Thomas Pringle

(Des A. H. Barrett. Litho)

1983 (12 Oct). *Tourism. Beaches. T* **261** *and similar horiz designs. Multicoloured. P* 14.

549 10 c. Type **261** 10 10
550 20 c. Durban 25 30
551 25 c. West coast 30 35
552 40 c. Clifton 50 65
549/52 . . . . *Set of* 4 1·10 1·25
MS553 128 × 90 mm. Nos. 549/52 . . . . 1·75 2·50

(Des J. van Ellinckhuijzen. Litho)

1984 (24 Feb). *South African English Authors. T* **262** *and similar vert designs. P* 14.

No.	Description		
554	10 c. olive-brown, yellow-brown and grey	10	10
555	20 c. olive-brown, deep bluish green and grey	25	40
556	25 c. olive-brown, deep brown-rose and grey	30	50
557	40 c. olive-brown, olive-ochre and grey	50	85
554/7	*Set of* 4	1·10	1·75

Designs:—20 c. Pauline Smith; 25 c. Olive Schreiner; 40 c. Sir Percy Fitzpatrick.

263 Manganese

(Des H. Botha. Litho)

1984 (8 June). *Strategic Minerals. T* **263** *and similar horiz designs. Multicoloured. P* 14.

No.	Description		
558	11 c. Type **263**	40	10
559	20 c. Chromium	75	75
560	25 c. Vanadium	90	1·00
561	30 c. Titanium	1·00	1·25
558/61	*Set of* 4	2·75	2·75

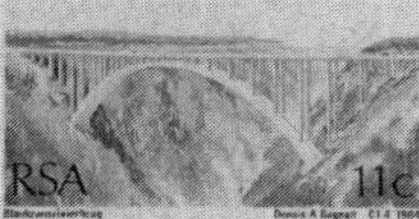

264 Bloukrans River Bridge

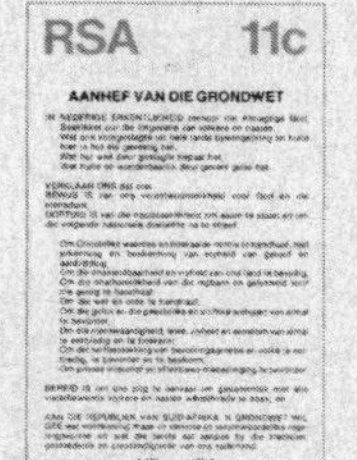

265 Preamble to the Constitution in Afrikaans

(Des D. Bagnall. Litho)

1984 (24 Aug). *South African Bridges. T* **264** *and similar horiz designs. Multicoloured. P* 14.

No.	Description		
562	11 c. Type **264**	40	10
563	25 c. Durban four level interchange	80	75
564	30 c. Mfolozi rail bridge	85	95
565	45 c. Gouritz River bridge	1·10	1·75
562/5	*Set of* 4	2·75	3·25

(Des G. Mynhardt. Litho)

1984 (3 Sept). *New Constitution. T* **265** *and similar vert designs. P* 14.

No.	Description		
566	11 c. stone, black and bistre	90	1·25
	a. Horiz pair. Nos. 566/7	1·75	2·50
567	11 c. stone, black and bistre	90	1·25
568	25 c. stone, deep claret and bistre	60	65
569	30 c. multicoloured	60	65
566/9	*Set of* 4	2·75	3·50

Designs:—No. 566, Preamble to the Constitution in English; 568, Last two lines of National Anthem; 569, South African coat of arms.

Nos. 566/7 were printed together, *se-tenant*, in horizontal pairs.

266 Pres. P. W. Botha

267 Pro Patria Medal

1984 (2 Nov). *Inauguration of President Botha. Litho. P* 14.

No.	Description		
570 **266**	11 c. multicoloured	30	10
571	25 c. multicoloured	55	40

(Des B. Jackson. Litho)

1984 (9 Nov). *Military Decorations. T* **267** *and similar vert designs. Multicoloured. P* 14.

No.	Description		
572	11 c. Type **267**	25	10
573	25 c. De Wet Decoration	40	45
574	30 c. John Chard Decoration	45	65
575	45 c. Honoris Crux (Diamond) Decoration	55	1·10
572/5	*Set of* 4	1·50	2·10
MS576	71 × 116 mm. Nos. 572/5	1·50	3·00

268 "Reflections" (Frans Oerder)

269 Cape Parliament Building

1985 (22 Feb). *Paintings by Frans Oerder. T* **268** *and similar horiz designs. Multicoloured. Litho. P* 14.

No.	Description		
577	11 c. Type **268**	30	15
578	25 c. "Ladies in a Garden"	45	35
579	30 c. "Still-life with Lobster"	50	45
580	50 c. "Still-life with Marigolds"	80	70
577/80	*Set of* 4	1·90	1·50
MS581	129 × 74 mm. Nos. 577/80	2·00	3·00

(Des A. H. Barrett. Litho)

1985 (15 May). *Centenary of Cape Parliament Building. T* **269** *and similar horiz designs. Multicoloured. P* 14.

No.	Description		
582	12 c. Type **269**	30	10
583	25 c. Speaker's Chair	55	55
584	30 c. "National Convention 1908–9" (Edward Roworth)	70	80
585	50 c. Republic Parliamentary emblem	1·10	1·50
	a. Black (inscr and outline) omitted	£275	
582/5	*Set of* 4	2·40	2·75

270 Freesia

271 Sugar Bowl

(Des Sheila Nowers. Litho)

1985 (23 Aug). *Floral Emigrants. T* **270** *and similar vert designs. Multicoloured. P* 14.

No.	Description		
586	12 c. Type **270**	35	10
587	25 c. Nerine	65	65
588	30 c. Ixia	75	80
589	50 c. Gladiolus	1·10	1·50
586/9	*Set of* 4	2·50	2·75

(Des H. Botha. Litho)

1985 (5 Nov). *Cape Silverware. T* **271** *and similar multicoloured designs. P* 14.

No.	Description		
590	12 c. Type **271**	35	10
591	25 c. Teapot	70	60
592	30 c. Loving cup (*vert*)	70	80
593	50 c. Coffee pot (*vert*)	1·00	2·00
590/3	*Set of* 4	2·50	3·00

272 Blood Donor Session

273 National Flag

(Des Sheila Nowers. Litho)

1986 (20 Feb). *Blood Donor Campaign. T* **272** *and similar horiz designs. Multicoloured. P* 14.

No.	Description		
594	12 c. Type **272**	45	10
595	20 c. Baby receiving blood transfusion	75	80
596	25 c. Operation in progress	80	95
597	30 c. Ambulanceman and accident victim	95	1·60
594/7	*Set of* 4	2·75	3·00

(Des J. Hoekstra. Litho)

1986 (30 May). *25th Anniv of Republic of South Africa. T* **273** *and similar horiz design. Multicoloured. P* 14.

No.	Description		
598	14 c. Type **273**	75	1·00
	a. Horiz pair. Nos. 598/9	1·50	2·00
599	14 c. As Type **273**, but inscr "UNITY IS STRENGTH"	75	1·00

Nos. 598/9 were printed together, *se-tenant*, in horizontal pairs throughout the sheet.

274 Drostdyhof, Graaff-Reinet

(Des A. H. Barrett. Litho)

1986 (14 Aug). *Restoration of Historic Buildings. T* **274** *and similar horiz designs. Multicoloured. P* 14.

No.	Description		
600	14 c. Type **274**	30	10
601	20 c. Pilgrim's Rest mining village	55	70
602	25 c. Strapp's Store, Bethlehem	60	90
603	30 c. Palmdene, Pietermaritzburg	75	1·40
600/3	*Set of* 4	2·00	2·75

NEW INFORMATION

The editor is always interested to correspond with people who have new information that will improve or correct the Catalogue.

MACHINE LABELS. From 14 August 1986 gummed labels in the above design, ranging in value from 1 c. to 99 r. 99, were available from an experimental machine at Sunnyside Post Office in Pretoria. The machine was moved to the "Johannesburg 100" exhibition from 6 to 11 October 1986 and was then reinstalled at Sunnyside on 17 October 1986. Further machines were introduced subsequently and each can be identified by a code number, between P.001 and P.034, at right.

Commemorative labels were subsequently available at "PAARL 300" (1987), "PIETERMARITZBURG 150" (1988), "WANDERERS 101" (1989), "STAMPS 150" (1990), "CAPE TOWN 1991", "PRETORIA 92", eTHEKWINI (Durban 1993) and "BENONI '94" stamp exhibitions. All machines were withdrawn on 30 November 1994.

PHILATELIC FOUNDATION MINIATURE SHEETS. These miniature sheets were issued by the Philatelic Foundation of Southern Africa and not the postal administration. They could be purchased by post or from a limited number of philatelic offices at a premium in aid of various national and international stamp exhibitions.

275 Von Brandis Square, Johannesburg, *c* 1900

(Des J. van Niekerk. Litho)

1986 (25 Sept). *Centenary of Johannesburg. T* **275** *and similar horiz designs. Multicoloured. P* 14.

No.	Description		
604	14 c. Type **275**	35	15
605	20 c. Gold mine (26 × 20 *mm*)	1·00	1·25
606	25 c. Johannesburg skyline, 1986	1·00	1·40
607	30 c. Gold bars (26 × 20 *mm*)	1·50	2·25
604/7	*Set of* 4	3·50	4·50

The 30 c. value exists as a Philatelic Foundation miniature sheet.

276 Gordon's Rock, Paarlberg

277 *Cicindela regalis*

(Des A. H. Barrett. Litho)

1986 (20 Nov). *Rock Formations. T* **276** *and similar vert designs. Multicoloured. P* 14.

No.	Description		
608	14 c. Type **276**	60	10
609	20 c. The Column, Drakensberg	85	90
610	25 c. Maltese Cross, Sederberge	95	1·25
611	30 c. Bourke's Luck Potholes, Blyde River Gorge	1·25	1·60
608/11	*Set of* 4	3·25	3·25

(Des E. Holm. Litho)

1987 (6 Mar). *South African Beetles. T* **277** *and similar vert designs. Multicoloured. P* 14.

No.	Description		
612	14 c. Type **277**	50	10
613	20 c. *Trichostetha fascicularis*	70	75
614	25 c. *Julodis viridipes*	85	1·00
615	30 c. *Ceroplesis militaris*	1·10	1·75
612/15	*Set of* 4	2·75	3·25

278 Eland, Sebaaieni Cave

(Des H. Botha. Litho)

1987 (4 June). *Rock Paintings. T* **278** *and similar horiz designs. Multicoloured. P* 14.

No.	Description		
616	16 c. Type **278**	50	10
617	20 c. Leaping lion, Clocolan	75	75
618	25 c. Black Wildebeest, uMhlwazini Valley	90	1·00
619	30 c. Bushman dance, Floukraal	1·10	1·75
616/19	*Set of* 4	3·00	3·25

279 Oude Pastorie, Paarl

(Des A. H. Barrett. Litho)

1987 (3 Sept). *300th Anniv of Paarl. T* **279** *and similar horiz designs. Multicoloured. P* 14.

620	16 c. Type **279**	30	10
621	20 c. Grapevines	50	70
622	25 c. Wagon-building	55	85
623	30 c. KWV Cathedral Wine Cellar	75	1·50
620/3	*Set of* 4	1·90	2·75

The 30 c. value exists as a Philatelic Foundation miniature sheet.

(280)

281 "Belshazzar's Feast" (Rembrandt)

1987 (16 Nov). *Natal Flood Relief Fund* (1*st issue*). *No.* 521*a surch as T* **280** *in Afrikaans or English.*

624	16 c. + 10 c. rosine (surch T **280**)	45	70
	a. Pair. Nos. 624/5	90	1·40
625	16 c. + 10 c. rosine (surch "NATAL FLOOD DISASTER")	45	70

Nos. 624/5 were surcharged together, *se-tenant*, in horizontal and vertical pairs throughout the sheet.

See also Nos. 629/30 and 635/6.

(Des Sheila Nowers. Litho)

1987 (19 Nov). *The Bible Society of South Africa. T* **281** *and similar multicoloured designs. P* 14.

626	16 c. "The Bible" in 75 languages (54 × 34 *mm*)	40	10
627	30 c. Type **281**	70	85
628	50 c. "St. Matthew and the Angel" (Rembrandt) (*vert*)	90	1·25
626/8	*Set of* 3	1·75	2·00

A 40 c. value, showing the inscription "The Word of God" in various languages, was prepared, but due to religious objections was recalled before issue. Isolated examples are known to have been sold to the public and some used have also been reported (*Price £550 mint, £650 used*).

1987 (1 Dec). *Natal Flood Relief Fund* (2*nd issue*). *No.* 626 *surch as T* **280**, *but larger* (*Afrikaans version 32 mm wide*).

629	16 c. + 10 c. multicoloured (surch "NATAL FLOOD DISASTER")	45	70
	a. Pair. Nos. 629/30	90	1·40
630	16 c. + 10 c. multicoloured (surch as T **280**)	45	70

Nos. 629/30 were surcharged together, *se-tenant*, in horizontal and vertical pairs throughout the sheet.

These stamps are known postmarked at Mooirivier on 25 November 1987.

282 Bartolomeu Dias and Cape of Good Hope

283 Huguenot Monument, Franschhoek

(Des Sheila Nowers. Litho)

1988 (3 Feb). *500th Anniv of Discovery of Cape of Good Hope by Bartolomeu Dias. T* **282** *and similar horiz designs. Multicoloured. P* 14.

631	16 c. Type **282**	55	10
632	30 c. Kwaaihoek Monument	80	85
633	40 c. Caravels	90	1·25
634	50 c. Martellus map, c. 1489	1·25	1·75
631/4	*Set of* 4	3·25	3·50

The 50 c. value exists as a Philatelic Foundation miniature sheet.

1988 (1 Mar). *Natal Flood Relief Fund* (3*rd issue*). *No.* 631 *surch as T* **280**, *but larger* (*Afrikaans version 19 mm wide*).

635	16 c. + 10 c. multicoloured (surch as T **280**)	45	70
	a. Pair. Nos. 635/6	90	1·40
636	16 c. + 10 c. multicoloured (surch "NATAL FLOOD DISASTER")	45	70

Nos. 635/6 were surcharged together, *se-tenant*, in horizontal and vertical pairs throughout the sheet.

(Des H. Botha. Litho)

1988 (13 Apr). *300th Anniv of Arrival of First French Huguenots at the Cape. T* **283** *and similar vert designs. Multicoloured. P* 14.

637	16 c. Type **283**	30	10
638	30 c. Map of France showing Huguenot areas	70	80
639	40 c. Title page of French/Dutch New Testament of 1672	80	1·25
640	50 c. St. Bartholomew's Day Massacre, Paris, 1572	1·00	1·50
637/40	*Set of* 4	2·50	3·25

National Flood Disaster +10c

(284)

285 Pelican Point Lighthouse, Walvis Bay

1988 (13 Apr). *National Flood Relief Fund. Nos.* 637/40 *surch as T* **284** *in English* (E) *or in Afrikaans* ("*Nasionale Vloedramp*") (A).

641	16 c. + 10 c. multicoloured (E)	40	65
	a. Pair. Nos. 641/2	80	1·25
642	16 c. + 10 c. multicoloured (A)	40	65
643	30 c. + 10 c. multicoloured (A)	55	75
	a. Pair. Nos. 643/4	1·10	1·50
644	30 c. + 10 c. multicoloured (E)	55	75
645	40 c. + 10 c. multicoloured (A)	70	90
	a. Pair. Nos. 645/6	1·40	1·75
646	40 c. + 10 c. multicoloured (E)	70	90
647	50 c. + 10 c. multicoloured (E)	90	1·25
	a. Pair. Nos. 647/8	1·75	2·50
648	50 c. + 10 c. multicoloured (A)	90	1·25
641/8	*Set of* 8	4·50	6·25

The two versions of each surcharge were printed together, *se-tenant*, both horizontally and vertically, throughout the sheets.

(Des Sheila Nowers. Litho)

1988 (9 June). *Lighthouses. T* **285** *and similar horiz designs. Multicoloured. P* 14.

649	16 c. Type **285**	50	10
650	30 c. Green Point, Cape Town	70	70
651	40 c. Cape Agulhas	90	1·10
652	50 c. Umhlanga Rocks, Durban	1·25	1·60
649/52	*Set of* 4	3·00	3·25
MS653	132 × 112 mm. Nos. 649/52	3·50	3·25

286 *Huernia zebrina*

287 Map of Great Trek Routes

(Des H. Botha)

1988 (1 Sept)–**93**. *Succulents. T* **286** *and similar horiz designs. Multicoloured.*

(*a*) *Sheet stamps. Litho. P* 14

654	1 c. Type **286**	10	10
	a. Coil strip. Nos. 654/7 and 662 (11.5.93)	50	
655	2 c. *Euphorbia symmetrica*	10	10
656	5 c. *Lithops dorotheae*	10	10
657	7 c. *Gibbaeum nebrownii*	15	10
658	10 c. *Didymaotus lapidiformis*	15	10
659	16 c. *Vanheerdea divergens*	30	10
659*a*	18 c. *Faucaria tigrina* (1.4.89)	50	10
660	20 c. *Conophytum mundum*	30	10
660*a*	21 c. *Gasteria armstrongii* (2.4.90)	40	10
661	25 c. *Cheiridopsis peculiaris*	40	10
	a. Imperf (pair)	£180	
662	30 c. *Tavaresia barklyi*	40	20
663	35 c. *Dinteranthus witmotianus*	40	20
664	40 c. *Frithia pulchra*	45	25
665	50 c. *Lapidaria margaretae*	50	25
666	90 c. *Dioscorea elephantipes*	75	45
667	1 r. *Trichocaulon cactiforme*	75	50
668	2 r. *Crassula columnaris*	1·25	90
668*a*	5 r. *Anacampseros albissima* (1.3.90)	3·00	2·40
654/68*a*	*Set of* 18	9·00	5·25

(*b*) *Coil stamps. Photo. P* 14 × *imperf.*

669	1 c. *Adromischus marianiae*	1·00	1·50
670	2 c. *Titanopsis calcarea*	50	50
671	5 c. *Dactylopsis digitata*	50	50
672	10 c. *Pleiospilos bolusii*	55	55
669/72	*Set of* 4	2·25	2·75

Multi-value coil strip No. 654*a* was produced by the South African Post Office for use by a large direct mail marketing firm. Strips were also available from the Philatelic Service.

For similar design, but without face value and inscribed "Standardised mail" in English and Afrikaans, see No. 778.

(Des J. van Niekerk (16 c.). Litho)

1988 (21 Nov). *150th Anniv of Great Trek. T* **287** *and similar multicoloured designs. P* 14.

673	16 c. Type **287**	60	10
674	30 c. "Exodus" (tapestry by W. Coetzer) (56 × 20 *mm*)	90	90
675	40 c. "Crossing the Drakensberg" (tapestry by W. Coetzer) (77 × 20 *mm*)	1·10	1·10
676	50 c. "After the Service, Church of the Vow" (J. H. Pierneef) (*horiz*)	1·40	1·75
673/6	*Set of* 4	3·50	3·50

288 Coelacanth

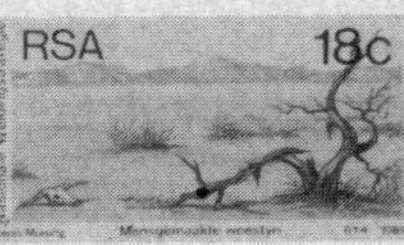

289 Man-made Desert

(Des A. McBride. Litho)

1989 (9 Feb). *50th Anniv of Discovery of Coelacanth. T* **288** *and similar horiz designs. Multicoloured. P* 14.

677	16 c. Type **288**	65	15
678	30 c. Prof. J. L. B. Smith and Dr. M. Courtenay-Latimer examining Coelacanth	1·00	1·25
679	40 c. J. L. B. Smith Institute of Ichthyology, Grahamstown	1·25	1·50
680	50 c. Coelacanth and *GEO* midget submarine	1·50	2·00
677/80	*Set of* 4	4·00	4·50

The 50 c. value exists as a Philatelic Foundation miniature sheet and also as a corporate miniature sheet, containing two examples, sponsored by Two Oceans Environmental Trust. See note above No. 822.

(Des D. Murphy. Litho)

1989 (3 May). *National Grazing Strategy. T* **289** *and similar horiz designs. Multicoloured. P* 14.

681	18 c. Type **289**	40	15
682	30 c. Formation of erosion gully	65	75
683	40 c. Concrete barrage in gully	70	1·00
684	50 c. Reclaimed veldt	80	1·40
681/4	*Set of* 4	2·25	3·00

290 South Africa *v* France Match, 1980

291 "Composition in Blue"

(Des B. Jackson. Litho)

1989 (22 June). *Centenary of South African Rugby Board. T* **290** *and similar horiz designs. Multicoloured. P* 14.

685	18 c. Type **290**	45	15
686	30 c. South Africa *v* Australia, 1963	75	85
687	40 c. South Africa *v* New Zealand, 1937	90	1·25
688	50 c. South Africa *v* British Isles, 1896	1·00	1·40
685/8	*Set of* 4	2·75	3·25

1989 (3 Aug). *Paintings by Jacob Hendrik Pierneef. T* **291** *and similar horiz designs. Multicoloured. Litho. P* 14.

689	18 c. Type **291**	30	15
690	30 c. "Zanzibar"	50	60
691	40 c. "The Bushveld"	65	90
692	50 c. "Cape Homestead"	75	1·10
689/92	*Set of* 4	2·00	2·50
MS693	114 × 86 mm. Nos. 689/92	2·00	2·50

292 Pres. F. W. de Klerk

293 Gas-drilling Rig, Mossel Bay

1989 (20 Sept). *Inauguration of President F. W. de Klerk. T* **292** *and similar vert design. Multicoloured. Litho. P* 14.

694	18 c. Type **292**	40	15
695	45 c. F. W. de Klerk (*different*)	70	1·10

(Des H. Botha. Litho)

1989 (19 Oct). *Energy Sources. T* **293** *and similar horiz designs. Multicoloured. P* 14 × 14½.

696	18 c. Type **293**	40	10
697	30 c. Coal to oil conversion plant	70	70
698	40 c. Nuclear power station	80	85
699	50 c. Thermal electric power station	90	1·25
696/9	*Set of* 4	2·50	2·50

294 Electric Goods Train and Map of Railway Routes

295 Great Britain 1840 Penny Black

(Des A. H. Barrett. Litho)

1990 (15 Feb). *Co-operation in Southern Africa. T* **294** *and similar horiz designs. Multicoloured. P* 14½×14.

700 18 c. Cahora Bassa Hydro-electric Scheme, Mozambique, and map of transmission lines (68×26 *mm*) 50 25
701 30 c. Type **294** 70 70
702 40 c. Projected dam on upper Orange River, Lesotho and map of Highlands Water Project (68×26 *mm*) 85 90
703 50 c. Cow, syringe, and outline map of Africa 95 1·10
700/3 .. .. *Set of* 4 2·75 2·75
MS704 136×78 mm. Nos. 700/3 .. .. 2·75 2·75

1990 (12 May). *National Stamp Day. T* **295** *and similar vert designs showing stamps. Multicoloured. Litho. P* 14.

705 21 c. Type **295** 40 50
a. Horiz strip of 5. Nos. 705/9 .. .. 1·75
706 21 c. Cape of Good Hope 1853 4d. triangular pair 40 50
707 21 c. Natal 1857 1s. 40 50
708 21 c. Orange Free State 1868 1s. 40 50
709 21 c. Transvaal 1869 1s. 40 50
705/9 .. .. *Set of* 5 1·75 2·25

Nos. 705/9 were printed together, *se-tenant*, in horizontal strips of 5 throughout the sheet.

296 Knysna Turaco

297 Karoo Landscape near Britstown

(Des C. Finch-Davies. Litho)

1990 (2 Aug). *Birds. T* **296** *and similar vert designs. Multicoloured. P* 14.

710 21 c. Type **296** 50 20
711 35 c. Red-capped Robin Chat 70 80
712 40 c. Rufous-naped Bush Lark 70 90
713 50 c. Bokmakierie Shrike .. .. .. 90 1·40
710/13 .. .. *Set of* 4 2·50 3·00

The 50 c. value exists as a Philatelic Foundation miniature sheet.

1990 (1 Nov). *Tourism. T* **297** *and similar horiz designs. Multicoloured. Litho. P* 14.

714 50 c. Type **297** .. .. 85 1·10
a. Block of 4. Nos. 714/17 .. .. 3·00
715 50 c. Camps Bay, Cape of Good Hope .. 85 1·10
716 50 c. Giraffes in Kruger National Park .. 85 1·10
717 50 c. Boschendal Vineyard, Drakenstein Mts 85 1·10
714/17 .. .. *Set of* 4 3·00 4·00

Nos. 714/17 were printed together, *se-tenant*, in blocks of 4 throughout the sheet.

298 Woltemade Cross for Bravery

299 Boer Horses

(Des J. Hoekstra. Litho)

1990 (6 Dec). *National Orders. T* **298** *and similar vert designs. Multicoloured. P* 14.

718 21 c. Type **298** 25 30
a. Horiz strip of 5. Nos. 718/22 .. .. 1·10
719 21 c. Order of the Southern Cross 25 30
720 21 c. Order of the Star of South Africa .. 25 30
721 21 c. Order for Meritorious Service .. 25 30
722 21 c. Order of Good Hope 25 30
718/22 .. .. *Set of* 5 1·10 1·40
MS723 143×70 mm. Nos. 718/22 .. .. 1·10 1·40

Nos. 718/22 were printed together, *se-tenant*, in horizontal strips of 5 throughout the sheet.

(Des A. Ainslie. Litho)

1991 (12 Feb). *Animal Breeding in South Africa. T* **299** *and similar horiz designs. Multicoloured. P* 14.

724 21 c. Type **299** 45 50
a. Horiz strip of 5. Nos. 724/8 .. .. 2·00
725 21 c. Bonsmara bull 45 50
726 21 c. Dorper sheep 45 50
727 21 c. Ridgeback dogs 45 50
728 21 c. Putterie racing pigeons 45 50
724/8 .. .. *Set of* 5 2·00 2·25

Nos. 724/8 were printed together, *se-tenant*, in horizontal strips of five throughout the sheet.

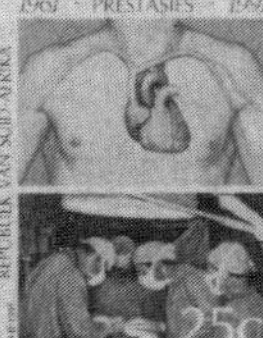

300 Diagram of Human Heart and Transplant Operation

301 State Registration of Nurses Act, 1891

(Des A. H. Barrett. Litho)

1991 (30 May). *30th Anniv of Republic. Scientific and Technological Achievements. T* **300** *and similar multicoloured designs. P* 14.

729 25 c. Type **300** 20 10
730 40 c. Matimba Power Station (*horiz*) .. 35 35
731 50 c. Dolos design breakwater (*horiz*) .. 45 45
732 60 c. Western Deep Levels gold mine .. 60 60
729/32 .. .. *Set of* 4 1·40 1·40

The 60 c. value exists as a Philatelic Foundation miniature sheet.

(Des T. Marais. Litho)

1991 (15 Aug). *Centenary of State Registration for Nurses and Midwives. P* 14.

733 **301** 60 c. multicoloured 60 60

302 South Africa Post Office Ltd Emblem

303 Sir Arnold Theiler (veterinarian)

(Des Liza van der Wal. Litho)

1991 (1 Oct). *Establishment of Post Office Ltd and Telekom Ltd. T* **302** *and similar horiz design. Multicoloured. P* 14×14½.

734 27 c. Type **302** 25 25
a. Vert pair. Nos. 734/5 .. .. 50 50
735 27 c. Telekom SA Ltd emblem 25 25

Nos. 734/5 were printed together, *se-tenant*, in vertical pairs throughout the sheet.

(Des A. H. Barrett. Litho)

1991 (9 Oct). *South African Scientists. T* **303** *and similar horiz designs. Multicoloured. P* 14.

736 27 c. Type **303** 30 15
737 45 c. Sir Basil Schonland (physicist) .. 60 60
738 65 c. Dr. Robert Broom (palaeontologist) .. 80 90
739 85 c. Dr. Alex du Toit (geologist) .. .. 1·00 1·50
736/9 .. .. *Set of* 4 2·40 2·75

304 *Agulhas* (Antarctic research ship)

305 Soil Conservation

(Des Liza van der Wal (27 c.), T. Marais (65 c.). Litho)

1991 (5 Dec). *30th Anniv of Antarctic Treaty. T* **304** *and similar horiz design. Multicoloured. P* 14.

740 27 c. Type **304** 50 10
741 65 c. Chart showing South African National Antarctic Expedition base .. .. 1·25 80

(Des J. van Niekerk. Litho)

1992 (6 Feb). *Environmental Conservation. T* **305** *and similar horiz designs. Multicoloured. P* 14×14½.

742 27 c. Type **305** 30 10
743 65 c. Water pollution 75 55
744 85 c. Air pollution 95 75
742/4 .. .. *Set of* 3 1·75 1·25

The 65 c. value exists as a Philatelic Foundation miniature sheet.

306 Dutch Fleet approaching Table Bay

307 Queen Anne Settee, *c* 1750

(Des J. van Niekerk. Litho)

1992 (9 May). *National Stamp Day. Cape of Good Hope Postal Stones. T* **306** *and similar horiz designs. Multicoloured. P* 14.

745 35 c. Type **306** 45 35
a. Horiz strip of 5. Nos. 745/9 .. .. 2·00
746 35 c. Landing for water and provisions .. 45 35
747 35 c. Discovering a postal stone 45 35
748 35 c. Leaving letters under a stone .. 45 35
749 35 c. Reading letters 45 35
745/9 .. .. *Set of* 5 2·00 1·60

Nos. 745/9 were printed together, *se-tenant*, in horizontal strips of 5 throughout the sheet

1992 (9 July). *Antique Cape Furniture. T* **307** *and similar multicoloured designs. Litho. P* 14.

750 35 c. Type **307** 35 35
a. Sheetlet. Nos. 750/9 .. .. 3·25
751 35 c. Stinkwood settee, *c* 1800 .. .. 35 35
752 35 c. Canopy bed, *c* 1800 (*vert*) 35 35
753 35 c. 19th-century rocking cradle 35 35
754 35 c. Waterbutt, *c* 1800 (*vert*) 35 35
755 35 c. Flemish style cabinet, *c* 1700 (*vert*) .. 35 35
756 35 c. Armoire, *c* 1780 (*vert*) 35 35
757 35 c. Late 17th-century church chair (*vert*) 35 35
758 35 c. Tub chair, *c* 1770 (*vert*) 35 35
759 35 c. Bible desk, *c* 1750 (*vert*) 35 35
750/9 .. .. *Set of* 10 3·25 3·25

Nos. 750/9 were printed together, *se-tenant*, as a sheetlet of 10.

308 Grand Prix Motor Racing

309 "Women's Monument" (Van Wouw)

(Des Liza van der Wal (35 c. (No. 761)), C. Prinsloo (55 c.), B. Jackson (70, 90 c., 1 r. 05). Litho)

1992 (24 July). *Sports. T* **308** *and similar horiz designs. Multicoloured. P* 14×14½.

760 35 c. Type **308** 25 25
761 35 c. Football 25 25
762 55 c. Total Paris–Cape Motor Rally .. 35 35
763 70 c. Athletics 50 50
764 90 c. Rugby 65 65
765 1 r. 05, Cricket .. .. 1·00 1·00
760/5 .. .. *Set of* 6 2·75 2·75
MS766 167×69 mm. Nos. 760/5 .. .. 3·25 3·00

1992 (8 Oct). *130th Birth Anniv of Anton van Wouw (sculptor). T* **309** *and similar vert designs. Multicoloured. Litho. P* 14.

767 35 c. Type **309** 30 20
768 70 c. "Sekupu Player" 60 60
769 90 c. "The Hunter" 80 80
770 1 r. 05, "Postman Lehman" .. .. 85 1·00
767/70 .. .. *Set of* 4 2·25 2·40
MS771 96×149 mm. Nos. 767/70 .. .. 2·25 2·40

310 Walvis Bay Harbour

311 Bristol "Boxkite", 1907

1993 (28 Jan). *South African Harbours. T* **310** *and similar horiz designs. Multicoloured. Litho. P* 14.

772 35 c. Type **310** 30 20
773 55 c. East London 40 35
774 70 c. Port Elizabeth 60 50
775 90 c. Cape Town 80 75
776 1 r. 05, Durban 85 95
772/6 .. .. *Set of* 5 2·75 2·50
MS777 147×112 mm. Nos. 772/6 .. .. 2·75 2·50

(Des H. Botha. Litho)

1993 (1 Apr). *Succulents. Design as T* **286**, *but inscr "Standardised mail" in English and Afrikaans. P* 14.

778 (–) *Stapelia grandiflora* 40 25

No. 778 was sold at 45 c.

(Des D. Stahmer. Litho)

1993 (7 May). *Aviation in South Africa. T* **311** *and similar horiz designs. Multicoloured. P* 14.

779 45 c. Type **311** 55 30
a. Sheetlet. Nos. 779/803 .. .. 12·00
780 45 c. Voisin "Boxkite", 1909 .. .. 55 30
781 45 c. Bleriot XI, 1911 .. .. .. 55 30
782 45 c. Paterson No. 2 biplane, 1913 .. 55 30
783 45 c. Henri Farman H.F.27, 1915 .. .. 55 30
784 45 c. Royal Aircraft Factory B.E.2E., 1918 55 30
785 45 c. Vickers Vimy *Silver Queen II*, 1920 .. 55 30
786 45 c. Royal Aircraft Factory S.E.5A., 1921 55 30
787 45 c. Avro 504k, 1921 .. .. .. 55 30
788 45 c. Armstrong Whitworth A.W.15 Atalanta, 1930 .. .. 55 30
789 45 c. De Havilland D.H.66 Hercules, 1931 55 30
790 45 c. Westland Wapiti, 1931 .. .. 55 30
791 45 c. Junkers F-13, 1932 .. .. .. 55 30

792 45 c. Handley Page H.P.42, 1933 .. .. 55 30
793 45 c. Junkers Ju 52/3m, 1934 .. .. 55 30
794 45 c. Junkers Ju 86, 1936 .. .. .. 55 30
795 45 c. Hawker Hartbees, 1936 .. .. 55 30
796 45 c. Short S.23 Empire "C" Class flying boat *Canopus*, 1937 .. .. .. 55 30
797 45 c. Miles Master II and Airspeed A.S.10 Oxford, 1940 .. .. .. 55 30
798 45 c. North American AT-6 Harvard Mk IIa, 1942 .. .. 55 30
799 45 c. Short S.25 Sunderland flying boat, 1945 .. .. 55 30
800 45 c. Avro Type 685 York, 1946 .. .. 55 30
801 45 c. Douglas DC-7B, 1955 .. .. 55 30
802 45 c. Sikorsky S-55c helicopter, 1956 .. 55 30
803 45 c. Boeing 707-344, 1959 .. .. 55 30
779/803 .. .. *Set of* 25 12·00 6·50

Nos. 779/803 were printed together, *se-tenant*, in sheetlets of 25 (5×5).

Nos. 779 and 803 exist as a Philatelic Foundation miniature sheet.

312 Table Mountain Ghost Frog

313 Dragoons carrying Mail between Cape Town and False Bay, 1803

Two types of species inscr:
I. Species name in Latin.
II. Species name in English.

Two types of "Standardised mail" stamp (No. 821):
III. Small rhinoceros. Inscr "DICEROS BICORNIS".
IV. Redrawn with larger rhinoceros. Inscr "BLACK RHINOCEROS".

(Des D. Murphy. Litho)

1993 (3 Sept)–**97**. *Endangered Fauna. T* **312** *and similar horiz designs. Multicoloured. P* 14. (a) *Face values as T* **312**

804 1 c. Type **312** (I) 10 10
a. Coil strip. Nos. 804, 805×2 and 808×2 (15.4.94) 50
b. Coil. Imperf × p 14 (1.9.95) 10 10
ba. Coil strip. Nos. 804b, 805b×2, 806b and 810b (50 c. stamp at right) .. 55
bb. Coil strip. As No. 804ba, but 50 c. stamp in centre (1.12.95) 55
c. Type II (coil. Imperf × p 14) (1.8.96) 10 10
ca. Coil strip. Nos. 804c, 805c×2, 807c and 811c 20
805 2 c. Smith's Dwarf Chameleon (I) .. 10 10
b. Coil. Imperf × p 14 (1.9.95) .. 10 10
c. Type II (coil. Imperf × p 14) (1.8.96) 10 10
806 5 c. Giant Girdle-tailed Lizard (I) .. 10 10
a. Coil strip. Nos. 806/7, each × 2, and 808 (24.8.94) 50
b. Coil. Imperf × p 14 (2.95) 10 10
ba. Coil strip. Nos. 806b×2, 807b×2 and 808b 50
807 10 c. Geometric Tortoise (I) 10 10
b. Coil. Imperf × p 14 (2.95) 20 20
c. Type II (coil. Imperf × p 14) (1.8.96) 10 10
808 20 c. Southern African Hedgehog (I) .. 10 10
b. Coil. Imperf × p 14 (2.95) 20 20
c. Type II (25.6.97) 10 10
809 40 c. Riverine Rabbit (I) 20 10
c. Type II (27.3.97) 10 10
810 50 c. Samango Monkey (I) 25 20
b. Coil. Imperf × p 14 (1.9.95) .. 30 20
c. Type II (1.7.97) 10 10
811 55 c. Aardwolf (I) 25 20
c. Type II (coil. Imperf × p 14) (1.8.96) 15 20
812 60 c. Cape Hunting Dog (I) 15 20
813 70 c. Roan Antelope (I) 30 25
c. Type II (19.5.97) 20 25
814 75 c. African Striped Weasel (I) 20 25
815 80 c. Kori Bustard (I) 20 25
815*a* 85 c. Lemon-breasted Seedeater (I) (2.10.95) 20 25
816 90 c. Jackass Penguin (I) 45 30
a. Booklet pane. No. 816×10 with outer edges of pane imperf (1.12.95) .. 2·40
c. Type II (18.6.97) 25 30
817 1 r. Wattled Crane (I) 45 30
c. Type II (6.8.96) 25 30
818 2 r. Blue Swallow (I) 70 55
c. Type II (23.7.97) 50 55
819 5 r. Martial Eagle (I) .. .. .. 1·75 1·40
c. Type II (18.6.97) .. .. .. 1·25 1·40
820 10 r. Bateleur (I) .. .. .. 2·50 2·75
804/20 .. .. *Set of* 18 6·75 7·50

(b) *Inscr* "Standardised mail" *in English and Afrikaans* (No. 821) *or* "Airmail postcard rate" (*others*)

821 (45 c.) Black Rhinoceros (III) 30 25
a. Booklet pane. No. 821×10 with outer edges of pane imperf (14.2.95) .. 2·50
b. Type IV (9.4.96) 30 25
ba. Booklet pane No. 821b×10 with outer edges of pane imperf .. .. 2·50
821*c* (1 r.) White Rhinoceros (II) (8.5.96) .. 35 30
ca. Horiz strip of 5. Nos. 821*c*/*g* .. 1·50
cb. Pane. Nos. 821*c*/*g* plus 3 advertising and 2 airmail labels with margins all round .. .. 1·50
cc. Booklet pane. Nos. 821*c*/*g* plus 5 airmail labels with outer edges of pane imperf .. .. 1·50
821*d* (1 r.) Buffalo (II) (8.5.96) 35 30
821*e* (1 r.) Lion (II) (8.5.96) 35 30
821*f* (1 r.) Leopard (II) (8.5.96) 35 30
821*g* (1 r.) African Elephant (II) (8.5.96) .. 35 30
821*c*/*g* .. .. *Set of* 6 1·75 1·60

Multi-value coil strips Nos. 804a, 804ba/bb, 804ca, 806a and 806ba were produced by the South African Post Office for use by Reader's Digest. Strips were also available from the Philatelic Service and philatelic counters.

Nos. 804ba/bb and 804ca each include a label showing the Reader's Digest emblem at left. In each instance the righthand stamp (50 c. on No. 804ba, 5 c. on No. 804bb and 55 c. on No. 804ca) is imperforate on three sides.

No. 804ba originally had a black label, but was re-issued with a red label on 1 December 1995. No. 804bb had a blue label and No. 804ca a green one, but this was re-issued with an orange label on 11 November 1996.

No. 806ba occurs with both the left and righthand stamps (5 c. and 20 c.), or just the righthand stamp, imperforate on three sides.

No. 821 was initially sold at 45 c. and No. 821b was only issued in stamp booklets, initially sold at 6 r. The "Standardised mail" rate was increased to 50 c. in August 1994, 60 c. in April 1996, 70 c. in August 1996 and to 1 r. on 7 April 1997.

Nos. 821*c*/*g*, which were each initially sold at 1 r., were printed together, *se-tenant*, in sheets of 10 containing two horizontal strips of 5.

No. 821b exists as a corporate miniature sheet sponsored by MILSET and commemorating the "ESI '97" Exhibition at Pretoria.

No. 821*e* exists as a corporate miniature sheet sponsored by Coach House.

For stamps with elliptical perforations see Nos. 913/18.

CORPORATE MINIATURE SHEETS. Such miniature sheets were introduced in 1996 and were produced for firms or other corporate bodies to use for advertising and publicity purposes. Each sponsor has to agree to purchase a minimun of 10,000 sheets with further supplies being placed on sale, at face value, by the South Africa Philatelic Bureau, philatelic counters and overseas agents.

(Des J. van Niekerk. Litho)

1993 (8 Oct). *National Stamp Day. Early 19th-century Postal Services. T* **313** *and similar horiz designs. Multicoloured. P* 14.

822 45 c. Type **313** 30 25
823 65 c. Ox wagon carrying Stellenbosch to Cape Town mail, 1803 .. .. 45 50
824 85 c. Khoi-Khoin mail runners from Stellenbosch, 1803 .. .. .. 65 70
825 1 r. 05, Mounted postmen, 1804 .. .. 80 90
822/5 .. .. *Set of* 4 2·00 2·10

314 Flowers from Namaqualand

1993 (12 Nov). *Tourism. T* **314** *and similar horiz designs. Multicoloured. Litho. P* 14.

826 85 c. Type **314** (Afrikaans inscr) 65 55
a. Horiz strip of 5. Nos. 826/30 .. 3·00
827 85 c. North Beach, Durban (English inscr) 65 55
828 85 c. Lion (German inscr) 65 55
829 85 c. Apple Express excursion train (Dutch inscr) 65 55
830 85 c. Gemsbok (antelope) (French inscr) .. 65 55
826/30 .. .. *Set of* 5 3·00 2·40

Nos. 826/30 were printed together, *se-tenant*, in horizontal strips of 5 throughout the sheet.

315 Grapes and Packing Bench

(Des B. Jackson. Litho)

1994 (28 Jan). *Export Fruits. T* **315** *and similar horiz designs. Multicoloured. P* 14½×14.

831 85 c. Type **315** 50 50
832 90 c. Apple and picker 50 50
833 1 r. 05, Plum and fork-lift truck 60 60
834 1 r. 25, Orange and tractor with trailer .. 70 70
835 1 r. 40, Avocado and loading freighter .. 80 80
831/5 .. .. *Set of* 5 2·75 2·75

The 85 c. value exists as a Philatelic Foundation miniature sheet.

316 "Children of Different Races" (Nicole Davies)

317 Pres. Mandela

1994 (8 Apr). *Peace Campaign. Children's Paintings. T* **316** *and similar horiz designs. Multicoloured. Litho. P* 14½×14.

836 45 c. Type **316** 25 20
837 70 c. "Dove and Tree" (Robynne Lawrie) .. 40 40
838 95 c. "Children and Dove" (Batami Nothmann) 55 55
839 1 r. 15, "Multi-racial Crowd" (Karen Uys) 75 80
836/9 .. .. *Set of* 4 1·75 1·75

No. 839 exists as a corporate miniature sheet sponsored by I.G.P.C. and commemorating Chernobyl's Children charities.

(Des Liza van der Wal (70 c., 95c.). Litho)

1994 (10 May). *Inauguration of President Nelson Mandela. T* **317** *and similar multicoloured designs. P* 14×14½ (45 c.) *or* 14½×14 (*others*).

840 45 c. Type **317** 35 20
841 70 c. South African national anthems .. 55 50
842 95 c. New national flag 75 75
843 1 r. 15, Union Buildings, Pretoria .. 95 1·10
840/3 .. .. *Set of* 4 2·40 2·25

318 Tug *McEwen* towing *Winchester Castle* (liner), 1935

(Des Sheila Nowers. Litho)

1994 (13 May). *Tugboats. T* **318** *and similar horiz designs. Multicoloured. P* 14½×14.

844 45 c. Type **318** 30 20
845 70 c. *Sir William Hoy* with *Karanja* (liner), 1970 .. .. 50 40
846 95 c. *Sir Charles Elliott* and wreck of *Dunedin Star* (liner), 1942 .. .. 65 55
847 1 r. 15, *Eland* and freighter at wharf, 1955 85 75
848 1 r. 35, *Pioneer* (paddle tug) and sailing ships, 1870 .. .. 95 90
844/8 .. .. *Set of* 5 2·75 2·50
MS849 163×84 mm. Nos. 844/8 .. .. 2·75 2·50

COMMONWEALTH MEMBER
1 JUNE 1994

319 "Mother hands out Work" (Emile du Toit)

1994 (1 July). *International Year of the Family. Children's Paintings. T* **319** *and similar horiz designs. Multicoloured. Litho. P* 14.

850 45 c. Type **319** 30 30
a. Vert strip of 5. Nos. 850/4 .. 1·25
851 45 c. "My Friends and I at Play" (Patrick Mackenzie) 30 30
852 45 c. "Family Life" (Michelle du Pisani) .. 30 30
853 45 c. "Sunday in Church" (Elizabeth Nel) .. 30 30
854 45 c. "I visit my Brother in Hospital" (Zwelinzema Sam) 30 30
850/4 .. .. *Set of* 5 1·25 1·25

Nos. 850/4 were printed together, *se-tenant*, in vertical strips of 5 throughout the sheet.

320 Hands holding Invoice and Bulk Mail Envelope

(Des J. van Niekerk. Litho)

1994 (30 Sept). *National Stamp Day. T* **320** *and similar horiz designs. Multicoloured. P* 14.

855 50 c. Type **320** 30 25
856 70 c. Certified mail 40 40
857 95 c. Registered mail 50 55
858 1 r. 15, Express Delivery mail 60 65
855/8 .. .. *Set of* 4 1·60 1·75

321 *Erica tenuifolia*

(Des J. van Niekerk. Litho)

1994 (18 Nov). *Heathers. T* **321** *and similar vert designs. Multicoloured. P* 14.
859 95 c. Type **321** 45 45
a. Horiz strip of 5. Nos. 859/63 .. .. 2·00
860 95 c. *Erica urna-viridis* 45 45
861 95 c. *Erica decora* 45 45
862 95 c. *Erica aristata* 45 45
863 95 c. *Erica dichrus* 45 45
859/63 .. .. *Set of* 5 2·00 2·00
Nos. 859/63 were printed together, *se-tenant*, in horizontal strips of 5 throughout the sheet.

322 Warthogs (Eastern Transvaal) and Map

(Des A. Ainslie. Litho)

1995 (18 Jan–30 June). *Tourism. T* **322** *and similar horiz designs, each including map. Multicoloured. P* 14½×14. (*a*) *Face values as T* **322**
864 50 c. Type **322** 30 25
865 50 c. Lost City Resort (North-West Province) (15 Feb) 30 25
(*b*) *Inscr* "Standardised mail" *in English and Afrikaans*
866 (60 c.) White Rhinoceros and calf (Kwazulu/ Natal) (28 April) 30 25
867 (60 c.) Cape Town waterfront (Western Cape) (12 May) 30 25
868 (60 c.) Baobab tree (Northern Transvaal) (30 June) 30 25
a. Vert strip of 5. Nos. 868/72 .. 1·40
869 (60 c.) Highland Route (Free State) (30 June) 30 25
870 (60 c.) Augrabies Falls (Northern Cape) (30 June) 30 25
871 (60 c.) Herd of elephants, Addo National Park (Eastern Cape) (30 June) .. 30 25
872 (60 c.) Union Buildings, Pretoria (Gauteng) (30 June) 30 25
864/72 .. .. *Set of* 9 2·25 2·00
Nos. 868/72 were printed together, *se-tenant*, in sheets of 10 containing two vertical *se-tenant* strips of 5.
No. 864 exists as a Philatelic Foundation miniature sheet.
No. 868 exists imperforate on three sides with a *se-tenant* stamp-size label as a corporate product sponsored by Coach House. The same value subsequently appeared as a corporate miniature sheet.

323 De Havilland D.H.9 Biplane and Cheetah D Jet Fighter

(Des Anne de Goede (50 c.), A. H. Barrett (95 c.). Litho)

1995 (1 Feb). *Aviation Anniversaries. T* **323** *and similar horiz design. Multicoloured. P* 14.
873 50 c. Type **323** (75th anniv of South African Air Force) 45 30
874 95 c. Vickers Vimy *Silver Queen II* (75th anniv of first Trans-African flight) .. 60 60

324 Player running with Ball and Silhouettes

325 Rural Water Purification System

1995 (25 May). *World Cup Rugby Championship, South Africa. T* **324** *and similar multicoloured designs. Litho. P* 14.
875 (60 c.) Type **324** 20 25
a. Perf 14×imperf (booklets) 20 25
ab. Booklet pane. Nos. 875a/6a, each × 5 2·00
876 (60 c.) Player running with ball and silhouettes (*vert*) 20 25
a. Imperf × perf 14 (booklets) .. 20 25
ab. Booklet pane. No. 876a×10 .. 2·00
877 1 r. 15, Player taking ball from scrum (68×26½ *mm*) 40 45
875/7 .. .. *Set of* 3 80 95
MS878 109×61 mm. No. 876 .. .. .. 45 50
Nos. 875/6 are inscribed "STANDARD POSTAGE" in English and Afrikaans.

(Des J. van Niekerk. Litho)

1995 (15 June). *50th Anniv of C.S.I.R. (technological research organization). P* 14.
879 **325** (60 c.) multicoloured 30 30
No. 879 in inscribed "Standardised mail" in English and Afrikaans.

326 Player with Ball

327 Dr. John Gilchrist, South African Pilchards and *Africana* (oceanographic research ship)

1995 (28 June). *South Africa's Victory in Rugby World Cup. T* **326** *and similar multicoloured design. Litho. P* 14.
880 (60 c.) Type **326** 30 30
881 (60 c.) South African player holding trophy aloft (*vert*) 30 30
Nos. 880/1 are inscribed "STANDARD POSTAGE" in English and Afrikaans.

(Des D. Thorpe. Litho)

1995 (25 Aug). *Centenary of Marine Science in South Africa. P* 14.
882 **327** (60 c.) multicoloured 30 30
No. 882 is inscribed "Standard Postage" in English and Afrikaans.

328 Singapore Lion

329 People building Flag Wall

(Des A. Ainslie. Litho)

1995 (1 Sept). *"Singapore '95" International Stamp Exhibition. Sheet* 71×55 *mm. P* 14.
MS883 **328** (60 c.) multicoloured 45 50
No. **MS**883 is inscribed "STANDARD POSTAGE" in English and Afrikaans.
A second printing of No. **MS**883 included the date, "DEC 1995", on the sheet margin at bottom left.

1995 (16 Sept–1 Dec). *Masakhane Campaign. Litho. P* 14.
884 **329** (60 c.) multicoloured (34×24 *mm*) .. 20 20
a. Booklet pane. No. 884×10 .. 2·00
884*b* (60 c.) mult (26×20 *mm*) (1 Dec) .. 20 20
ba. Booklet pane. No. 884*b*×10 .. 2·00
Nos. 884 and 884*b* are inscribed "STANDARD POSTAGE" in English and Afrikaans.
No. 884*b* was only issued in 6 r. stamp booklets.
Nos. 884a and 884ba show the three outer edges of the panes imperforate.

330 Papal Arms

331 Gandhi wearing Suit

1995 (16 Sept). *Visit of Pope John Paul II. Litho. P* 14.
885 **330** (60 c.) multicoloured 30 30
No. 885 is inscribed "STANDARD POSTAGE" in English and Afrikaans.

(Des A. Ainslie. Litho)

1995 (2 Oct). *India–South Africa Co-operation. 125th Birth Anniv of Mahatma Gandhi* (1994). *T* **331** *and similar vert design. P* 14.
886 (60 c.) deep violet 40 25
887 1 r. 40, bistre-brown 60 85
MS888 71×71 mm. No. 887 .. .. .. 70 85
Design:—1 r. 40, Gandhi wearing dhoti.
No. 886 is inscribed "STANDARD POSTAGE" in English and Afrikaans.
Stamps in similar designs were issued by India.
No. 886 exists as a corporate miniature sheet sponsored by Pradip Jain and commemorating the 50th anniversary of the Congress Alliance for a Democratic South Africa.

332 Traditional African Postman

333 "50" and U.N. Emblem

(Des C. Emslie. Litho)

1995 (9 Oct). *World Post Day. P* 14.
889 **332** (60 c.) multicoloured 30 30
No. 889 is inscribed "STANDARD POSTAGE" in English and Afrikaans.
No. 889 exists as a corporate miniature sheet sponsored by the South African Stamp Colour Catalogue.

(Des C. Emslie. Litho)

1995 (19 Oct). *"Total Stampex '95" and "Ilsapex '98" Stamp Exhibitions. Sheet,* 70×66 *mm, containing T* **332** *and "ILSAPEX '98" logo. Imperf.*
MS890 5 r. multicoloured .. .. .. 2·00 2·25

(Des C. Emslie (No. 891), A. Ainslie and F. Frescura (No. **MS**892). Litho)

1995 (24 Oct). *50th Annivs of United Nations and U.N.E.S.C.O. T* **333** *and similar multicoloured design. P* 14.
891 (60 c.) Type **333** 30 30
MS892 101×78 mm. (60 c.) Traditional village (30×47 *mm*) 30 30
Nos. 891/2 are inscribed "STANDARD POSTAGE" in English and Afrikaans.

334 *Afrivoluta pringlei*

335 Map of Africa and Player

336 South African Player, Map and Trophy

(Des L. Kriedemann. Litho)

1995 (24 Nov). *Sea Shells. T* **334** *and similar vert designs. Multicoloured. P* 14½×14.
893 (60 c.) Type **334** 35 35
a. Horiz strip of 5. Nos. 893/7 .. .. 1·60
894 (60 c.) *Lyria africana* 35 35
895 (60 c.) *Marginella mosaica* 35 35
896 (60 c.) *Conus pictus* 35 35
897 (60 c.) *Gypreaea fultoni* 35 35
893/7 .. .. *Set of* 5 1·60 1·60
Nos. 893/7 were printed together, *se-tenant*, as horizontal strips of 5 in sheets of 10, each stamp being inscribed "STANDARD POSTAGE" in English and Afrikaans.
No. 893 is inscribed "priglei" in error.

(Des M. de Jong (Nos. 898/902), Z. Mashinini (No. **MS**903). Litho)

1996 (10 Jan). *African Nations Football Championship, South Africa. T* **335** *and similar vert designs showing map and players. P* 14½×14.
898 **335** (60 c.) multicoloured ("RSA" in deep ultramarine) 35 35
a. Horiz strip of 5. Nos. 898/902 .. 1·60
899 – (60 c.) multicoloured ("RSA" in brown-ochre) 35 35
900 – (60 c.) multicoloured ("RSA" in brt scar) 35 35
901 – (60 c.) multicoloured ("RSA" in ol-grey) 35 35
902 – (60 c.) multicoloured ("RSA" in dp emer) 35 35
898/902 .. .. *Set of* 5 1·60 1·60
MS903 75×55 mm. (60 c.) mult (young player) 35 35
Nos. 898/902 were printed together, *se-tenant*, as horizontal strips of 5 in sheets of 10.
Nos. 898/903 are inscribed "STANDARD POSTAGE" in English and Afrikaans.

(Des M. de Jong. Litho)

1996 (8 Feb). *South Africa's Victory in African Nations Football Championship. P* 14.
904 **336** (60 c.) multicoloured 30 20
a. Football missing above date at bottom right (R. 1/2) .. .. 1·50

No. 904 is inscribed "STANDARD POSTAGE" in English and Afrikaans.

It is understood that No. 904a occurs on every tenth sheet.

337 Historical Buildings, Bloemfontein

338 Rat

(Des J. van Beukering. Litho)

1996 (28 Mar). *150th Anniv of City of Bloemfontein. P* 14.
905 **337** (60 c.) multicoloured 30 20

No. 905 is inscribed "Standard Postage" in English and Afrikaans.

(Des D. Murphy. Litho)

1996 (18 May). *"CHINA '96" 9th Asian International Stamp Exhibition, Peking. Sheet* 109×85 *mm. P* 14.
MS906 **338** 60 c. multicoloured 45 50

339 "Man in a Donkey Cart" (Gerard Sekoto)

1996 (1 June). *Gerard Sekoto (artist) Commemoration. T* **339** *and similar multicoloured designs. Litho. P* 14.
907 1 r. Type **339** 30 30
908 2 r. "Song of the Pick" 80 80
MS909 108×70 mm. 2 r. "Yellow Houses, Sophiatown" (detail) (*vert*) .. .. .. 1·00 1·10

340 Parliament Building, Cape Town

341 Children playing

(Des A. Ainslie. Litho)

1996 (8 June). *"CAPEX '96" International Stamp Exhibition, Toronto. Sheet* 72×49 *mm. P* 14.
MS910 **340** 2 r. multicoloured .. .. .. 1·00 1·10

1996 (8 June). *Youth Day. Litho. P* 14.
911 **341** (60 c.) multicoloured 30 20

No. 911 is inscribed "STANDARD POSTAGE" in English and Afrikaans.

342 Marathon Runners

(Des M. de Jong. Litho)

1996 (8 June). *75th Anniv of Comrades Marathon. P* 14.
912 **342** (60 c.) multicoloured 30 20

No. 912 is inscribed "Standard postage" in English and Afrikaans.

(Des D. Murphy. Litho)

1996 (1 July)–**97**. *Endangered Fauna. As Nos.* 808c, 810c, 812 *(but with English inscr),* 817c, 821b *and new value (20 r.) but P* 14½ *(20 r.) or* 14 *(others), each with two elliptical holes on horizontal sides. (a) Face values as T* **312**
913 20 c. Southern African Hedgehog (II) (28.5.97) 10 10
914 50 c. Samango Monkey (II) (1.7.97) .. 15 20
915 60 c. Cape Hunting Dog (II) (12.5.97) .. 15 20
916 1 r. Wattled Crane (II) (11.6.97) .. 25 30
917 20 r. Fish Eagle (II) (34×24 *mm*) (20.3.97) 5·00 5·25

(*b*) *Inscr.* "Standardised mail" *in English and Afrikaans*
918 (60 c.) Black Rhinoceros (IV) 15 20
913/18 .. .. *Set of* 6 5·75 6·00

The "Standardised mail" rate was increased to 70 c. in August 1996 and to 1 r. on 7 April 1997. The printing of No. 918 issued on 1 July 1996 was shared between the Government Printer and Cape & Transvaal Printers.

343 Cycling

344 Constitutional Assembly Logo

(Des M. de Jong. Litho)

1996 (5 July). *Olympic Games, Atlanta. T* **343** *and similar vert designs. Multicoloured. P* 14.
919 (70 c.) Type **343** 30 30
a. Horiz strip of 5. Nos. 919/23 .. 1·25
920 (70 c.) Swimming 30 30
921 (70 c.) Boxing 30 30
922 (70 c.) Running 30 30
923 (70 c.) Pole vaulting 30 30
924 1 r. 40, South African Olympic emblem 55 55
919/24 .. .. *Set of* 6 1·90 1·90

Nos. 919/23, which are inscribed "STANDARD POSTAGE" in English and Afrikaans, were printed together in sheets of 10 containing two *se-tenant* horizontal strips of 5.

(Des M. de Jong. Litho)

1996 (1 Aug). *New Democratic Constitution. P* 14.
925 **344** (70 c.) myrtle-green, orange-red & blk 30 30
a. Horiz strip of 5. Nos. 925/9 .. 1·25
926 (70 c.) brt turquoise-blue, dp vio, & blk 30 30
927 (70 c.) dp violet, orange-yellow & black 30 30
928 (70 c.) ultramarine, scarlet and black 30 30
929 (70 c.) scarlet, orange-yellow and black 30 30
925/9 .. .. *Set of* 5 1·25 1·25

Nos. 925/9 are inscribed "Standard Postage" in English and Afrikaans and were printed together, *se-tenant*, in horizontal strips of 5 throughout the sheet.

345 *Sea Pioneer* (bulk carrier)

346 "Xhosa Woman" (G. Pemba)

(Des E. Wale (No. 927), P. Bilas (others). Litho)

1996 (5 Aug). *50th Anniv of South African Merchant Marine. T* **345** *and similar horiz designs. Multicoloured. P* 14.
930 (70 c.) Type **345** 40 40
a. Horiz pair. Nos. 930/1 .. .. 80 80
931 (70 c.) *Winterberg* (container ship) .. 40 40
932 1 r. 40, *Langkloof* (freighter) 80 80
a. Horiz pair. Nos. 932/3 .. .. 1·60 1·60
933 1 r. 40, *Vaal* (liner) 80 80
930/3 .. .. *Set of* 4 2·25 2·25
MS934 102×63 mm. 2 r. *Constantia* (freighter) and tug (71×30 *mm*) (inscr "SOUTH AFRICAN MERCHANT MARINE 1946–1996" on top margin) 95 95

Nos. 930/1 are inscribed "Standard Postage" in English and Afrikaans.

Nos. 930/1 and 932/3 were printed together, *se-tenant*, in horizontal pairs throughout the sheets.

No. 931 exists as a corporate miniature sheet sponsored by Safmarine. No. **MS**934 also comes with the top margin inscription replaced by "Safmarine" and logo.

1996 (9 Aug). *National Women's Day. Litho. P* 14.
935 **346** 70 c. multicoloured 30 25

347 Postman delivering Letters

348 Candles and Holly

(Des J. van Niekerk. Litho)

1996 (9 Oct). *World Post Day. P* 14.
936 **347** 70 c. multicoloured 25 25

(Des A. Ainslie. Litho)

1996 (9 Oct). *Christmas. P* 14.
937 **348** 70 c. multicoloured 25 25
a. Booklet pane. No. 937×10 .. 2·25

No. 937a has the three outer edges of the pane imperforate.

No. 937 exists as a corporate miniature sheet sponsored by SANTA and sold at 2 r. for charitable purposes.

349 "Liner *Oranje* at Cape Town" (E. Wale)

1996 (9 Oct). *"Bloemfontein 150" National Stamp Show. Sheet* 86×56 *mm. Litho. P* 14.
MS938 **349** 2 r. multicoloured .. .. .. 1·00 1·00

350 Max Theiler (Medicine, 1951)

351 Early Motor Car

1996 (4 Nov). *South African Nobel Laureates. T* **350** *and similar vert designs. Litho. P* 14.
939 (70 c). dull violet and maroon 30 30
a. Sheetlet. Nos. 939/48 .. .. 2·75
940 (70 c.) dp bluish green, maroon & dull violet 30 30
941 (70 c.) maroon and dull violet 30 30
942 (70 c.) dp bluish green, maroon & dull violet 30 30
943 (70 c.) dull violet and maroon 30 30
944 (70 c.) dull violet and maroon 30 30
945 (70 c.) dp bluish green, maroon & dull violet 30 30
946 (70 c.) maroon and dull violet 30 30
947 (70 c.) dp bluish green, maroon & dull violet 30 30
948 (70 c.) dull violet and maroon 30 30
939/48 .. .. *Set of* 10 2·75 2·75

Designs—No. 939, Type **350**; No. 940, Albert Luthuli (Peace, 1961); No. 941, Alfred Nobel; No. 942, Allan Cormack (Medicine, 1979); No. 943, Aaron Klug (Chemistry, 1982); No. 944, Desmond Tutu (Peace, 1984); No. 945, Nadine Gordimer (Literature, 1991); No. 946, Nobel Prizes symbol; No. 947, Nelson Mandela (Peace, 1993); No. 948, F. W. de Klerk (Peace, 1993).

Nos. 939/48, which are inscribed "Standard Postage" in English and Afrikaans, were printed together, *se-tenant*, in sheets of 10.

No. 941 exists as a corporate miniature sheet sponsored by AECI and celebrating the centenary of Modderfontein Industrial Complex.

(Des D. Bagnall. Litho)

1997 (4 Jan). *Centenary of Motoring in South Africa. P* 14.
949 **351** (70 c.) multicoloured 30 25

No. 949 is inscribed "STANDARD POSTAGE" in English and Afrikaans.

No. 949 exists as a corporate minature sheet sponsored by Total.

352 Lion

(Des A. Ainslie. Litho)

1997 (12 Feb). *"Hong Kong '97" International Stamp Exhibition. Sheet* 82×68 *mm. P* 14 *(with two elliptical holes on each vertical side).*
MS950 **352** 3 r. ultramarine, gold and rosine .. 1·10 1·10

STAMP BOOKLETS

1913. *Black on red cover. With* "UNION OF SOUTH AFRICA" *at top and* "UNIE VAN ZUID AFRIKA" *at foot. Stapled.*
SB1 2s. 6d. booklet containing twelve ½d. and twenty-four 1d. (Nos. 3/4) in blocks of 6 .. .. £3500

1913–20. *Black on red cover with* "UNION OF SOUTH AFRICA" *and* "UNIE VAN ZUID AFRIKA" *both at top. Stapled.*
SB2 2s. 6d. booklet containing twelve ½d. and twenty-four 1d. (Nos. 3/4) in blocks of 6 .. .. £3250
a. Black on pink cover (1920) £3000

1921. *Black on salmon-pink cover with* "UNION OF SOUTH AFRICA" *and* "UNIE VAN ZUID AFRIKA" *either side of arms and telegraph rates beneath. Stapled.*
SB3 3s. booklet containing twelve ½d., 1d. and 1½d. (Nos. 3/5) in blocks of 6 .. .. .. £500

1922. *Black on salmon-pink cover as No.* SB3 *surch. Stapled.*
SB4 3s. 6d. on 3s. booklet containing twelve ½d., 1d. and 2d. (Nos. 3/4, 6) in blocks of 6 .. .. £425

1926. *Black on salmon-pink cover as No.* SB3. *Stitched.*
SB5 2s. 6d. booklet containing twelve ½d. and twenty-four 1d. (Nos. 30/1) £375

1927. *Black on salmon-pink cover as No.* SB3, *but inscr* "Union of South Africa" *and* "Unie van Suidafrika". *Stitched.*
SB6 2s. 6d. booklet containing twelve ½d. and twenty-four 1d. (Nos. 30d, 31d) £3250

1930. *Black on pink cover as No.* SB6, *but with advertisement at foot instead of telegraph rates. Stitched.*
SB7 2s. 6d. booklet containing twelve ½d. and twenty-four 1d. (Nos. 42/3) in blocks of 6 .. .. £250

1931. *Black on pink cover. Smaller inscr and advertisement on front cover. Stitched.*
SB8 3s. booklet containing twelve 1d. (No. 43) in blocks of 6 and twelve 2d. (No. 44) in blocks of 4 .. £300

1935. *Black on lemon cover. Advertisement on front cover. Stitched.*
SB9 2s. 6d. booklet containing two panes of six ½d. (No. 54c) and four panes of six 1d. (No. 56e), all with adverts on margins £100

1937. *Black on lemon cover. Advertisement on front cover. Stitched.*
SB10 2s. 6d. booklet containing two panes of six ½d. (No. 75ba) and four panes of six 1d. (No. 56f), all with blank margins £200

1937. *Machine vended booklets. Red cover. Stitched.*
SB11 6d. booklet containing four ½d. and 1d. (Nos. 75*b*, 56) in pairs .. .. 7·00

1938. *Machine vended booklets. Blue cover. Stitched.*
SB12 3d. booklet containing ½d. and 1d. (Nos. 75*b*, 56), each in pair .. .. 28·00

1938. *Black on buff cover. Union arms at top left with advertisement at foot. Stitched.*
SB13 2s. 6d. booklet containing twelve ½d. and twenty-four 1d. (Nos. 75*b*, 56) in blocks of 6 £300

1939. *Black on buff cover. Union arms centred at top with advertisement at foot. Stitched.*
SB14 2s. 6d. booklet containing twelve ½d. and twenty-four 1d. (Nos. 75*b*, 56) in blocks of 6 £150

1939–40. *Green on buff cover. Union arms centred at top with large advertisement at bottom left. Stitched.*
SB15 2s. 6d. booklet containing twelve ½d. and twenty-four 1d. (Nos. 75*b*, 56) in blocks of 6 £2500
a. Blue on buff cover (1940) .. .. 70·00

1941. *Blue on buff cover as No.* SB15. *Stitched.*
SB17 2s. 6d. booklet containing twelve ½d. and 1d. (Nos. 75*b*, 56) in blocks of 6 and 1½d. (No. 57) in block of 4 .. .. £110

1948. *Black on buff cover. With advertisement. Stitched.*
SB18 3s. booklet containing two panes of six ½d., 1d. and 1½d. (Nos. 114a, 56h, 87b), all with postal slogans on margins, and pane of air mail labels .. .. 22·00

1951. *Black on buff cover. Stitched.*
SB19 3s. 6d. booklet containing two panes of six ½d., 1d. and 2d. (Nos. 114ca, 115a, 134a), each with margins at right .. .. .. 15·00

COVER PRICES

Cover factors are quoted at the beginning of each country for most issues to 1945. An explanation of the system can be found on page x. The factors quoted do not, however, apply to philatelic covers.

B 1 City Hall, Durban

1988 (1 Mar–13 Apr). *Flood Relief Fund. Multicoloured covers as Type* B 1. *Stamps attached by selvedge.*
SB20 2 r. 60, booklet (cover Type B 1) containing 16 c. + 10 c. (Nos. 624/5) in block of 10 .. .. 5·50
SB21 2 r. 60, booklet (cover, 139×85 mm, showing Bible) containing 16 c. + 10 c. (Nos. 629/30) in block of 10 .. .. 5·50
SB22 2 r. 60, booklet (cover showing Bartolomeu Dias) containing 16 c. + 10 c. (Nos. 635/6) in block of 10 .. .. 5·50
SB23 2 r. 60, booklet (cover, 125×90 mm, showing Huguenot Monument, Franschhoek) containing ten 16 c. + 10 c. (Nos. 641/2) in block of 10 (13 Apr) .. .. 5·50

B 2 Stamp No. 787

1993 (7 May). *Aviation in South Africa. Multicoloured cover as Type* B 2. *Stamps attached by selvedge.*
SB24 4 r. 50, booklet containing 45 c. (Nos. 779/803) in block of 10 .. .. 4·50

Five versions of No. SB24 exist showing different combinations of Nos. 779/803, *se-tenant* in panes of 10 (2×5). The Philatelic Bureau sold the booklets in sets of ten, each pane being numbered at foot.

1993 (3 Sept). *Endangered Fauna. Multicoloured cover as Type* B 2 *but showing No.* 821. *Stamps attached by selvedge.*
SB25 4 r. 50, booklet containing "Standardised mail" stamp (No. 821) in block of 10 .. .. 3·00

B 3 Lioness and Cubs Drinking
(Illustration further reduced. Actual size 142×64 mm)

1993 (12 Nov). *Tourism. Multicoloured covers as Type* B 3. *Stamps attached by selvedge. Five different cover designs*:
(a) Type B 3
(b) Luxury hotel
(c) Table Mountain
(d) Blue Train
(e) Field of flowers
SB26 8 r. 50, booklet containing 85 c. (Nos. 826/30) in block of 10 (*any cover*) .. .. .. 7·00
Set of 5 *different cover designs* 32·00

B 4

1995 (14 Feb)–**96.** *Endangered Fauna. Ultramarine and bright scarlet cover as Type* B 4. *Stamps attached by selvedge with outer edges of pane imperf.*
SB27 (4 r. 50) booklet containing pane of 10 "Standardised mail" stamps (No. 821a) 2·50
a. Containing booklet pane No. 821ba (9.4.96) 2·50

No. SB27 as initially sold at 4 r. 50 which was increased to 5 r. on 30 September 1994, to 6 r. on 1 April 1995 and to 7 r. in August 1996.

1995 (Mar). *Tourism. Booklet No.* SB26 *with additional label inscr* "FOR OVERSEAS POSTCARDS ONLY USE 1 × 85 c + 1 × 5 c = 90 c."
SB28 9 r. booklet containing 85 c. (Nos. 826/30 in block of 10 plus 5 c. (No. 806) in strip of 10) (*any cover*) .. ..
a. With 5 c. (No. 656) in block of 10 (5×2) ..
b. With 5 c. (No. 806) in block of 10 (5×2) ..

1995 (Apr). *Tourism. Booklet No.* SB24 *with additional label inscr* "FOR OVERSEAS POSTCARDS" ONLY USE 2 × 45 c Stamps = 90 c".
SB29 4 r. 50, booklet containing 45 c. (Nos. 799/803) in block of 10 .. ..

B 5 Player running with Ball

1995 (25 May). *World Cup Rugby Championship, South Africa. Multicoloured cover as Type* B 5. *Stamps attached by selvedge.*
SB30 (6 r.) booklet containing pane of 10 "STANDARDISED POSTAGE" stamps (No. 875ab) .. .. 3·00
SB31 (6 r.) booklet containing pane of 10 "STANDARDISED POSTAGE" stamps (No. 876ab) .. .. 3·00

1995 (16 Sept–1 Dec). *Masakhane Campaign. Bright scarlet and bright ultramarine covers as Type* B 4. *Stamps attached by selvedge.*
SB32 (6 r.) booklet containing pane of ten "STANDARD POSTAGE" stamps (No. 884a) .. .. 2·00
SB33 (6 r.) booklet containing pane of ten "STANDARD POSTAGE" stamps (No. 884ba) (1 Dec) .. 2·00

B 6 Jackass Penguin

1995 (1 Dec). *Endangered Fauna. Multicoloured cover as Type* B 6. *Stamps attached by selvedge.*
SB34 9 r. booklet containing pane of ten 90 c. (No. 816a) .. .. 2·40

B 7 Lion

1996 (8 May–Dec). *Tourism. Multicoloured cover as Type* B 7. *Stamps attached by selvedge.*
SB35 (5 r.) booklet containing pane of 5 "Airmail postcard rate" stamps and five labels (No. 821cc) .. .. 1·50
a. As No. SB35, but with additional tab and hole at right (Dec) .. .. .. 1·25

B 8 Drummer and Decorations

1996 (9 Oct). *Christmas. Multicoloured cover as Type* B 8. *Stamps attached by selvedge.*
SB36 7 r. booklet containing pane of ten 70 c. (No. 937a) .. .. 2·25

1996 (Nov). *Tourism. Multicoloured cover as Type* B 7, *but larger with inscr at right. Stamps affixed by selvedge.*
SB37 (5 r.) booklet containing pane of 5 "Airmail postcard rate" stamps, 3 advertising and 2 airmail labels (No. 821cb) .. .. 1·50

POSTAGE DUE STAMPS

D 1

UNION OF SOUTH AFRICA (A) UNION OF SOUTH AFRICA (B)

(Typo D.L.R.)

1914–22. *Inscribed bilingually. Lettering as* A. *W* **4.** *P* 14.

			Un single	Used single
D1	D 1	½d. black and green (19.3.15)	1·50	3·75
D2		1d. black and scarlet (19.3.15)	1·75	10
		a. Black ptd double	£1400	
		w. Wmk inverted	75·00	
D3		2d. black and reddish violet (12.12.14)	5·50	30
		a. Black and bright violet (1922)	5·50	40
		w. Wmk inverted	£110	
D4		3d. black and bright blue (2.2.15)	2·25	40
		w. Wmk inverted	25·00	
D5		5d. black and sepia (19.3.15)	4·00	18·00
D6		6d. black and slate (19.3.15)	7·00	22·00
D7		1s. red and black (19.3.15)	60·00	£140
D1/7		*Set of* 7	70·00	£160

There are interesting minor varieties in some of the above values, e.g. ½d. to 3d., thick downstroke to "d"; 1d., short serif to "1"; raised "d"; 2d., forward point of "2" blunted; 3d., raised "d"; very thick "d".

(Litho Govt Printer, Pretoria)

1922. *Lettering as* A. *No wmk. Rouletted.*

D 8	D 1	½d. black and bright green (6.6.22)	1·00	10·00
D 9		1d. black and rose-red (3.10.22)	80	1·00
D10		1½d. black and yellow-brown (3.6.22)	1·25	1·75
D8/10		*Set of* 3	2·75	11·50

(Litho Govt Printer, Pretoria)

1922–26. *Type* D 1 *redrawn. Lettering as* B. *P* 14.

D11	½d. black and green (1.8.22)	50	1·75
D12	1d. black and rose (16.5.23)	65	15
D13	1½d. black and yellow-brown (12.1.24)	80	1·25
D14	2d. black and pale violet (16.5.23)	70	70
	a. Imperf (pair)	£225	£300
	b. Black and deep violet	8·50	3·25
D15	3d. black and blue (3.7.26)	6·50	15·00
D16	6d. black and slate (9.23)	10·00	6·00
D11/16	*Set of* 6	17·00	22·00

The locally printed stamps, perf 14, differ both in border design and in figures of value from the rouletted stamps. All values except the 3d. and 6d. are known with closed "G" in "POSTAGE" usually referred to as the "POSTADE" variety. This was corrected in later printings.

D 2

D 3

D 4

Blunt "2" (R. 3/6, 8/6)

(Typo Pretoria)

1927–28. *Inscribed bilingually. No wmk. P* 13½×14.

D17	D 2	½d. black and green	60	3·00
		a. Blunt "2"	7·50	
D18		1d. black and carmine	1·00	30
D19		2d. black and mauve	1·25	30
		a. Black and purple	10·00	80
D20		3d. black and blue	6·00	18·00
D21		6d. black and slate	17·00	6·00
D17/21		*Set of* 5	23·00	25·00

1932–42. *Type* D 2 *redrawn. W* **9.** *P* 15×14.

(a) Frame roto, value typo

D22	½d. black and blue-green (1934)	2·25	1·75
	w. Wmk inverted	1·75	1·60
D23	2d. black and deep purple (10.4.33)	6·00	1·75
	w. Wmk inverted	7·00	1·75

(b) Whole stamp roto

D25	1d. black and carmine (*wmk inverted*) (3.34)	1·75	10
D26	2d. black and deep purple (1940)	18·00	10
	a. Thick (double) "2d." (R. 5/6, R. 18/2)	£180	20·00
	w. Wmk inverted	18·00	10
D27	3d. black and Prussian blue (3.8.32)	22·00	14·00
D28	3d. deep blue and blue (*wmk inverted*) (1935)	6·00	30
	a. Indigo and milky blue (*wmk inverted*) (1942)	55·00	2·75
	w. Wmk upright	30·00	
D29	6d. green and brown-ochre (*wmk inverted*) (7.6.33)	23·00	8·50
	a. Green and bright orange (*wmk inverted*) (1938)	10·00	4·00
D22/9a	*Set of* 7	60·00	19·00

In No. D26 the value, when magnified, has the meshed appearance of a photogravure screen, whereas in No. D23 the black of the value is solid.

1943–44. *Inscr bilingually. Roto. W* **9.** *In units of three, perf* 15 × 14 *subdivided by roulette* 6½.

			Un unit	Us unit	Us single
D30	D 3	½d. blue-green (1944)	10·00	32·00	30
D31		1d. carmine	9·50	4·75	10
D32		2d. dull violet	6·50	11·00	15
		a. Bright violet	16·00	40·00	65
D33		3d. indigo (1943)	48·00	70·00	1·25
D30/3		*Set of* 4	65·00	£110	1·90

Split "D" (R. 7/5 on every fourth sheet)

1948–49. *New figure of value and capital* "D". *Whole stamp roto. W* **9.** *P* 15 × 14.

D34	D 4	½d. black and blue-green	6·00	9·00
D35		1d. black and carmine	9·00	4·50
D36		2d. black and violet (1949)	10·00	4·50
		a. Thick (double) "2D." (R. 15/5–6, R. 16/5–6)	50·00	24·00
D37		3d. deep blue and blue	15·00	15·00
		a. Split "D"	£140	
D38		6d. green and bright orange (1949)	25·00	8·00
D34/8		*Set of* 5	60·00	38·00

1950–58. *As Type* D 4, *but* "SUID-AFRIKA" *hyphenated. Whole stamp roto. W* **9.** *P* 15 × 14.

D39	1d. black and carmine (5.50)	70	30
D40	2d. black and violet (4.51)	50	20
	a. Thick (double) "2D." (R. 15/5–6, R. 16/5–6)	8·00	6·00
	b. Black and reddish violet (12.52)	70	20
	ba. Thick (double) "2D."	8·00	6·00
	bb. Black (value) omitted	£1600	
D41	3d. deep blue and blue (5.50)	4·50	2·00
	a. Split "D"	80·00	
D42	4d. deep myrtle-green and emerald (2.58)	12·00	13·00
D43	6d. green and bright orange (3.50)	7·00	9·00
D44	1s. black-brown and purple-brown (2.58)	12·00	13·00
D39/44	*Set of* 6	32·00	35·00

No. D40bb occurs in horizontal pair with a normal.

D 5

D 6 Afrikaans at top

D 7 English at top

1961 (14 Feb). *Values in cents as Type* D **5.** *Whole stamp roto. W* **102.** *P* 15 × 14.

D45	1 c. black and carmine	20	3·25
D46	2 c. black and violet	35	3·25
D47	4 c. deep myrtle-green and emerald	80	7·50
D48	5 c. deep blue and blue	1·75	7·50
D49	6 c. green and orange-red	8·50	8·50
D50	10 c. sepia and brown-lake	9·00	10·00
D45/50	*Set of* 6	19·00	35·00

1961 (31 May)–**69.** *Roto. W* **102.** *P* 15 × 14.

D51	D 6	1 c. black and carmine	40	60
D52	D 7	1 c. black and carmine (6.62)	40	3·75
D53		2 c. black and deep reddish violet	40	55
D54	D 6	4 c. dp myrtle-green & light emerald	3·25	2·25
D54*a*	D 7	4 c. dp myrtle-grn & lt emerald (6.69)	14·00	18·00
D55		5 c. deep blue and grey-blue	2·75	4·00
D56		5 c. black and grey-blue (6.62)	1·75	7·50
D57	D 6	6 c. deep green and red-orange	8·00	5·50
D58	D 7	10 c. sepia and purple-brown	3·50	1·75
D51/8		*Set of* 9	30·00	40·00

1967 (Dec)–**71.** *Roto. W* **127** (*tête-bêche*). *P* 15 × 14.

D59	D 6	1 c. black and carmine	20	55
D60	D 7	1 c. black and carmine	20	30
D61	D 6	2 c. black and deep reddish violet	30	95
D62	D 7	2 c. black and deep reddish violet	30	95
D62*b*		4 c. dp myrtle-green & emerald (6.69)*	26·00	26·00
D62*c*	D 6	4 c. dp myrtle-green & emerald (6.69)*	£200	£200
D63		4 c. black and pale green (4.71)	25·00	25·00
D64	D 7	4 c. black and pale green (4.71)	25·00	25·00
D65	D 6	5 c. black and deep blue	50	50
D66	D 7	5 c. black and deep blue	50	50
D67	D 6	6 c. green and orange-red (1968)	4·50	8·50
D68	D 7	6 c. green and orange-red (1968)	4·50	8·50
D69	D 6	10 c. black and purple-brown	1·00	2·75
		a. Black and brown-lake (12.69)	1·00	2·75
D70	D 7	10 c. black and purple-brown	1·00	2·75
		a. Black and brown-lake (12.69)	1·00	2·75
D59/70a except D62b/c		*Set of* 12	55·00	65·00

Nos. D59/70 were printed in two panes, one with inscriptions as Type D **6** and the other as Type D **7**.

*Nos. D54a, D62b/c and further supplies of D54 were part of a printing released in June 1969. Most sheets were printed on paper with the Arms watermark, but some were printed on RSA paper with the watermark upright and faint. Of these many were spoilt, but a few sheets were issued in Types D **7** and D **6**, the latter being very scarce.

1971 *Roto. W* **127** (*tête-bêche*). *P* 14.

D71	D 6	2 c. black and deep reddish violet	22·00	7·00
D72	D 7	2 c. black and deep reddish violet	22·00	7·00
D74		4 c. deep myrtle-green & light emerald	45·00	40·00
D71/4		*Set of* 3	80·00	48·00

Nos. D71/4 were also printed in double panes as Nos. D59/70. Although the 4 c. as Type D **6** must have been printed it has not been possible to confirm that any were actually issued.

D 8

1972 (22 Mar). *English at right* (1, 4 *and* 8 *c.*) *or at left* (*others*). *W* **127** (*sideways tête-bêche*). *Chalk-surfaced paper* (4 *c. to* 10 *c.*). *P* 14×13½.

D75	D 8	1 c. deep yellowish green	50	2·00
D76		2 c. bright orange	70	2·75
D77		4 c. plum	1·75	3·25
D78		6 c. chrome-yellow	1·75	4·50
D79		8 c. ultramarine	2·00	5·00
D80		10 c. bright scarlet	6·00	7·00
D75/80		*Set of* 6	11·50	22·00

The 6 c. also exists on phosphorised paper.

The use of Postage Due stamps ceased in 1975.

OFFICIAL STAMPS

OFFICIAL. OFFISIEEL. (O 1)

OFFISIEEL OFFICIAL (O 2)

(Approximate measurements of the space between the two lines of overprint are quoted in millimetres, either in the set headings or after individual listings)

1926 (1 Dec). *Optd with Type* O **1** (*reading upwards with stops and* 12½ *mm between lines of opt*).

(a) On 1913 *issue* (*No.* 6)

O1	3	2d. purple	18·00	1·75

(b) On 1926 *issue* (*Nos.* 30/2)

			Un pair	Us pair	Us single
O2	6	½d. black and green	4·75	13·00	1·50
O3	7	1d. black and carmine	2·50	4·50	50
O4	8	6d. green and orange	£550	75·00	10·00
		w. Wmk inverted	£900	£350	

The overprint occurs on both the London and Pretoria printings of Nos. 30/2. For the lower two values the overprinted London printings are scarcer than the Pretoria, but for the 6d. the ratio is reversed.

1928–30. *Nos.* 32 *and* 34 *optd as Type* O **1** (*reading upwards without stops*).

O5	11	2d. grey & maroon (*p* 14) (17½ *mm*)	5·00	18·00	2·00
		a. Lines of opt 19 mm apart (1929)	4·00	12·00	1·50
		ab. On No. 34a (*p* 14×13½) (1930)	25·00	35·00	5·00
O6	8	6d. green and orange (11½–12 *mm*)	18·00	27·00	2·75

1929–31. *Optd with Type* O **2.** *(a) On* 1926 (*Typo*) *issue* (*Nos.* 30/2) (13½–15 *mm between lines of opt*).

O7	6	½d. black and green	2·00	2·50	35
		a. Stop after "OFFISIEEL" on English inscr stamp (1930)	32·00	32·00	3·25
		b. Ditto, but on Afrikaans inscr stamp (1930)	40·00	40·00	3·25
O8	7	1d. black and carmine	3·00	4·00	45
O9	8	6d. green and orange	9·50	32·00	3·25
		a. Stop after "OFFISIEEL" on English inscr stamp (1930)	65·00	£110	10·00
		b. Ditto, but on Afrikaans inscr stamp (1930)	75·00	£120	12·00

(b) On 1927 (*Recess*) *issue* (*Nos.* 36a/7) (17½–19 *mm between lines of opt*)

O10	13	1s. brown and deep blue (1931)	32·00	90·00	9·50
		a. Stop after "OFFICIAL" on Afrikaans inscr stamp (R. 10/1, 10/7)	£100	£225	
		b. Lines of opt 22 mm apart	£250		
O11	14	2s. 6d. green and brown (1931)	60·00	£150	19·00
		a. Stop after "OFFICIAL" on Afrikaans inscr stamp (R. 10/1)	£275	£475	
O7/11		*Set of* 5	95·00	£250	29·00

The "stop" varieties for the ½d., and 6d. occur on R. 5/3, 5/11, 8/12, 15/3, 15/11, 18/12 with English inscriptions and R. 9/10, 9/12, 19/10, 19/12 with Afrikaans on the 1930 overprinting only.

As only the lefthand panes of the 2s. 6d. were overprinted in 1931 the stop variety only occurs once. A further overprinting in 1932 was on both panes, but did not include No. O11a.

1930–47. *Nos.* 42/4 *and* 47/9 ("SUIDAFRIKA" *in one word*) *optd with Type* O **2.**

O12	6	½d. black and green (9½–12½ *mm*) (1931)	2·25	3·75	40
		a. Stop after "OFFISIEEL" on English inscr stamp	38·00	45·00	4·00
		b. Ditto, but on Afrikaans inscr stamp	32·00	40·00	3·50
		w. Wmk inverted (1934)	5·00	6·00	60

O13 **7** 1d. black & carm (I) (12½ *mm*) 4·50 4·50 55
a. Stop after "OFFISIEEL" on English inscr stamp .. 40·00 48·00 4·00
b. Ditto, but on Afrikaans inscr stamp .. .. .. 35·00 40·00 3·50
cw. Wmk inverted (1931) .. 4·50 4·50 55
d. On Type II (No. 43*d*) (12½–13½ *mm*) (1933) .. .. 10·00 9·00 90
da. Opt double £275 £300
O14 **11** 2d. slate-grey and lilac (20½–22½ *mm*) (1931) .. .. 6·00 11·00 1·50
w. Wmk inverted (1934) .. 50·00 85·00 8·00
O15 2d. blue and violet (20½–22½ *mm*) (1938) .. .. £100 £100 9·00
O16 **8** 6d. green & orange (12½–13½ *mm*) (*wmk inverted*) (1931) 7·00 8·50 85
a. Stop after "OFFISIEEL" on English inscr stamp .. 65·00 70·00 6·50
b. Ditto, but on Afrikaans inscr stamp .. .. .. 55·00 60·00 5·50
c. "OFFISIEEL" reading upwards (R. 17/12, 18/12, 19/12, 20/12) (1933) .. £400
w. Wmk upright (1935) .. 50·00 75·00 7·00
O17 **13** 1s. brown and deep blue (19 *mm*) (*wmk inverted*) (1932) 45·00 80·00 8·50
a. Lines of opt 21 mm apart (*wmk inverted*) (1933) .. 48·00 70·00 7·50
ab. Twisted horn flaw .. ..
aw. Wmk upright (1936) .. 60·00 £100 10·00
O18 **14** 2s. 6d. green and brown (17½–18½ *mm*) (1933) .. .. 75·00 £130 15·00
a. Lines of opt 21 mm apart (1934) .. .. .. 48·00 75·00 8·50
aw. Wmk inverted (1937) .. £200
O19 2s. 6d. blue and brown (19½–20 *mm*) (11.47) .. .. 30·00 70·00 6·50
a. Diaeresis over second "E" of "OFFISIEEL" on Afrikaans inscr stamp (R. 6/2) .. £700 £800
b. Ditto, but on English inscr stamp (R. 6/3) £700 £800

The stop varieties for the ½d., 1d. and 6d. occur on R. 9/10, 9/12, 19/10, 19/12 with English inscriptions and R. 5/3, 5/11, 8/12, 15/3, 15/11, 18/12 with Afrikaans on the 1930 and 1931 overprintings only.

OFFICIAL OFFISIEEL
(O 3)

OFFISIEEL OFFICIAL
(O 4)

1935–49. *Nos.* 54, 56/8, 61/2 *and* 64*a*/*b* ("SUID-AFRIKA" *hyphenated*) *optd.*

(*a*) *With Type* O **2** (*reading downwards with* "OFFICIAL" *at right*)

O20 **6** ½d. grey and green (12½ *mm*) (*wmk inverted*) (1936) .. 3·50 18·00 1·75
w. Wmk upright (1937) .. 3·50 18·00 1·25
O21 **7** 1d. grey and carmine (11½–13 *mm*) (*wmk inverted*) .. 2·50 2·50 35
aw. Wmk upright (1937) .. 1·50 1·75 20
b. Grey & bright rose-carmine (No. 56*i*) (1949) .. .. 2·25 3·00 30
O22 **22** 1½d. green and bright gold (20 *mm*) (*wmk inverted*) (1937) 25·00 19·00 1·75
aw. Wmk upright (1939) ..
b. Blue-green and dull gold (No. 57*c*) (1941) .. .. 40·00 11·00 1·10
O23 **11** 2d. blue & violet (20 *mm*) (1939) £100 22·00 2·25
O24 **8** 6d. green and vermilion (I) (11½–13 *mm*) (1937) .. 80·00 42·00 3·75
a. "Falling ladder" flaw .. £275
b. Die II (No. 61*b*) (1938) .. 10·00 11·00 1·25
c. Die III. *Green & red-orange* (No. 61*c*) (11.47) .. .. 4·00 8·50 85
O25 **13** 1s. brown and chalky blue (20 *mm*) (1939) .. .. 70·00 28·00 2·25
a. Diaeresis over second "E" of "OFFISIEEL" on both English and Afrikaans inscr stamps (1941) £1200 £850
b. Ditto, but on English inscr stamp only (11.47) £1100 £750
O26 **15** 5s. black and blue-green (20 *mm*) (6.48) .. .. .. 50·00 £120 13·00
O27 **23** 10s. blue and blackish brown (No. 64*ba*) (20 *mm*) (6.48) .. 85·00 £180 23·00

(*b*) *With Type* O **3** (*reading downwards with* "OFFICIAL" *at left and* 18–19 *mm between lines of opt*)

O28 **15** 5s. black and blue-green (1940) 80·00 £100 12·00
O29 **23** 10s. blue and sepia (1940) .. £325 £325 38·00

(*c*) *With Type* O **4** (*reading upwards with* "OFFICIAL" *at right and* 18½ *mm between lines of opt*

O30 **11** 2d. grey and dull purple (No. 58*a*) (1941) .. .. 6·50 22·00 2·25

No. O25*a* first appeared in the 1941 overprinting where the variety occurs on stamps 5 and 6 of an unidentified row. The variety reappears in the November 1947 overprinting where the stamps involved are R. 6/1 and 2. No. 25*b* occurs on R. 6/3 of the same overprinting.

Horizontal rows of 6 of the 1s. exist with "OFFICIAL" twice on the first stamp and "OFFISIEEL" twice on the last stamp. Such rows are believed to come from two half sheets which were overprinted in 1947, but not placed into normal stock.

MINIMUM PRICE

The minimum price quote is 10p which represents a handling charge rather than a basis for valuing common stamps. For further notes about prices see introductory pages.

OFFICIAL OFFISIEEL
(O 5)

OFFICIAL OFFISIEEL
(O 6)

1937–44. *No.* 75*b* (*redrawn design*) *optd.* (*a*) *With Type* O **2** (*reading downwards with* "OFFICIAL" *at right and* 11–12½ *mm between lines of opt*)

O31 **25*a*** ½d. grey and green .. .. 9·50 11·00 1·25
a. Grey and blue-green (No. 75*bd*) (1944) .. .. 1·25 6·00 60

(*b*) *With Type* O **5** (*reading up and down with* "OFFICIAL" *at left and diaeresis over the second* "E" *of* "OFFISIEEL". 10 *mm between lines of opt*)

O32 **25*a*** ½d. grey and blue-green (No. 75*bd*) (1944) .. .. 15·00 20·00 2·00

1944–50. *Nos.* 87 *and* 134 *optd.* (*a*) *With Type* O **2** (*reading downwards with* "OFFICIAL" *at right*)

O33 **34*a*** 1½d. blue-green and yellow-buff (14½ *mm*) .. .. 2·50 8·50 80
a. With diaeresis over second "E" of "OFFISIEEL" .. £300 £180
b. Lines of opt 16½ mm apart (6.48) .. .. .. 2·25 6·50 50

(*b*) *With Type* O **6** (*reading upwards with* "OFFICIAL" *at left and* 16 *mm between lines of opt*)

O34 **34*a*** 1½d. bl-green & yell-buff (1949) 28·00 42·00 4·00
O35 **68** 2d. blue and violet (1950) .. £1400 £1800 £170

Two different formes were used to overprint Type **34*a*** between 1944 and 1946. The first, applied to the left halves of sheets only, had a diaeresis over the second "E" of "OFFISIEEL" on all positions of the setting, except for R. 1/2, 2/2 and 3/2. The second form, from which the majority of the stamps came, was applied twice to overprint complete sheets, had no diaeresis.

1947 (Nov)**–49.** *No.* 107 *optd with Type* O **2** (*reading downwards with* "OFFICIAL" *at right and* 20 *mm between lines of opt*).

O36 **54** 2d. slate and violet .. .. 2·25 17·00 1·75
a. With diaeresis over second "E" of "OFFISIEEL" (R. 1/5-6, 11/5-6) £300 £450
b. Slate-purple and bright violet (No. 107*a*) (1949) .. .. 5·50 14·00 1·60

1949–50. *Nos.* 114 *and* 120 *optd with Type* O **2** (*reading downwards with* "OFFICIAL" *at right*).

O37 **25*a*** ½d. grey and green (11 *mm*) .. 1·25 7·00 70
O38 **13** 1s. brown and chalky blue (17½–18½ *mm*) (1950) .. 9·00 27·00 2·50

OFFISIEEL OFFICIAL
(O 7)

1950 (June)**–54.** *Optd as Type* O **7** *using stereo blocks measuring either* 10 (½*d.*, 1*d.*, 6*d.*), 14½ (1½*d.*, 2*d.*) *or* 19 *mm* (*others*) *between the lines of opt.*

O39 **25*a*** ½d. grey and green (No. 114*c*) (6.51) .. .. .. 70 1·50 15
O41 **7** 1d. grey & bright rose-carmine (No. 56*i*) .. .. .. 1·00 5·00 50
O42 1d. grey & car (No. 115) (3.51) 1·00 2·25 20
O43 1d. grey & car (No. 135) (6.52) 90 2·00 20
O44 **34*a*** 1½d. blue-green and yellow-buff (No. 87) (3.51) .. .. 1·40 3·50 30
O45 **68** 2d. blue and violet (No. 134) 1·00 2·00 20
a. Opt inverted £1200
O46 **8** 6d. green & red-orge (No. 119) 1·00 3·50 35
a. Green and brown-orange (No. 119*a*) (6.51) .. .. 1·50 3·50 35
O47 **13** 1s. brn & chalky bl (No. 120) 5·50 18·00 2·00
a. Blackish brown and ultram (No. 120*a*) (1.54) .. .. £150 £160 18·00
O48 **14** 2s. 6d. green & brn (No. 121) 8·50 35·00 3·50
O49 **15** 5s. black and blue-green (No. 64*a*) (3.51) .. .. .. £170 90·00 9·00
O50 5s. black and pale blue-green (I) (No. 122) (2.53) .. 50·00 75·00 6·50
a. Black & deep yellow-green (II) (No. 122*a*) (1.54) .. 70·00 85·00 9·00
O51 **23** 10s. blue and blackish brown (No. 64*ba*) .. .. .. 70·00 £170 22·00

The use of official stamps ceased in January 1955.

XI. BOPHUTHATSWANA

The Tswana Territory Authority was established by South Africa in 1968, and was granted internal self-government in 1972 under the Bantu Homelands Constitution Act. Bophuthatswana became fully independent on 6 December 1977. This independence did not receive international political recognition, but the stamps were accepted as valid on international mail.

PRINTERS. All the following stamps were printed in lithography by the South African Government Printer, Pretoria.

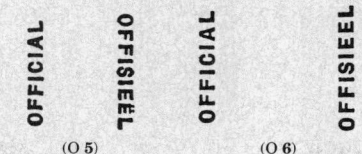

1 Hands releasing Dove

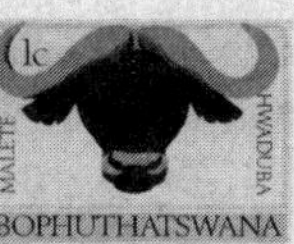

2 African Buffalo (totem of Malete and Hwaduba tribes)

(Des A. H. Barrett)

1977 (6 Dec). *Independence. T* **1** *and similar horiz designs. Multicoloured. P* 12½.

1 4 c. Type **1** 50 45
2 10 c. Leopard (national emblem) .. .. 1·00 70
3 15 c. Coat of arms .. .. 1·75 1·00
4 20 c. National flag .. .. 2·00 1·40
1/4 .. .. *Set of* 4 4·75 3·25

(Des A. H. Barrett)

1977 (6 Dec)**–82.** *Tribal Totems. T* **2** *and similar horiz designs. Multicoloured. P* 12½.

5 1 c. Type **2** 30 15
a. Perf 14 (15.4.81) 20 15
6 2 c. Bush Pig (Kolobeng) 30 15
a. Perf 14 (21.6.82) 20 15
7 3 c. Chacma Baboon (Hurutshe and Tlharo) 30 15
a. Perf 14 (18.8.82) 20 15
8 4 c. Leopard (national emblem) .. .. 3·00 1·25
a. Perf 14 (6.7.79) 20 10
9 5 c. Crocodile (Kwena and Fokeng) .. 1·00 50
a. Perf 14 (25.1.80) 20 10
10 6 c. Savanna Monkey (Kgatla) 20 10
11 7 c. Lion (Taung) .. .. 1·40 60
a. Perf 14 (18.12.79) 30 15
12 8 c. Spotted Hyena (Phiring) 35 15
a. Perf 14 (2.2.82) 20 15
13 9 c. Cape Porcupine (Rokologadi) .. 25 15
14 10 c. Aardvark (Tlokwa) 25 10
a. Perf 14 (21.6.82) 25 10
15 15 c. Tilapia (fish) (Tlhaping) 30 15
16 20 c. Hunting Dog (Tlhalerwa) 25 20
17 25 c. Common Duiker (Mfatlha) 40 30
18 30 c. African Elephant (Tlhako, Tloung and Pô) 60 35
19 50 c. Python (Nogeng) 70 40
20 1 r. Hippopotamus (Kubung) .. .. 1·40 1·00
21 2 r. Greater Kudu (Rolong) .. .. 1·75 2·25
5/21 .. .. *Set of* 17 (*cheapest*) 6·00 5·00

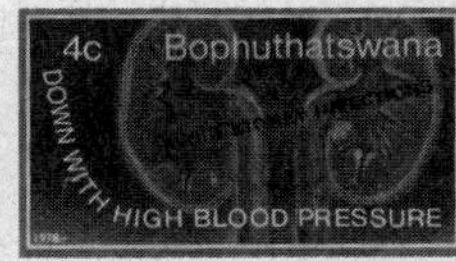

3 Infected Kidney

(Des A. H. Barrett)

1978 (4 Apr). *World Hypertension Month. T* **3** *and similar horiz designs. Multicoloured. P* 12×12½.

22 4 c. Type **3** 50 25
23 10 c. Heart and spoon of salt 70 70
24 15 c. Spoon reflecting skull, knife and fork 1·25 1·25
22/4 .. .. *Set of* 3 2·25 2·00

4 Skull behind Wheel of Car

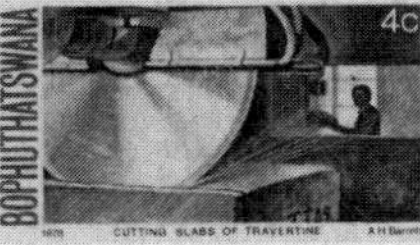

5 Cutting Slabs of Travertine

1978 (12 July). *Road Safety. T* **4** *and similar horiz designs. Multicoloured. P* 12×12½.

25 4 c. Type **4** 70 40
26 10 c. Child knocked off tricycle .. .. 1·10 80
27 15 c. Pedestrian stepping in front of car .. 1·25 1·10
28 20 c. Cyclist ignoring stop sign .. .. 1·75 1·75
25/8 .. .. *Set of* 4 4·25 3·50

(Des A. H. Barrett)

1978 (3 Oct). *Semi-precious Stones. T* **5** *and similar horiz designs. Multicoloured. P* 12×12½.

29 4 c. Type **5** 65 25
30 10 c. Polishing travertine .. .. .. 1·25 85
31 15 c. Sorting semi-precious stones .. 1·50 1·25
32 20 c. Factory at Taung .. .. .. 2·25 1·60
29/32 .. .. *Set of* 4 5·00 3·50

6 Wright Flyer I

(Des A. H. Barrett)

1978 (1 Dec). *75th Anniv of First Powered Flight by Wright Brothers. T* **6** *and similar horiz design. P* 12½.

33 10 c. black, deep grey-blue and brown-red 1·25 1·00
34 15 c. black, deep grey-blue and brown-red 1·75 1·50
Design:—15 c. Orville and Wilbur Wright.

7 Pres. Lucas M. Mangope

8 Drying Germinated Wheat Sorghum

(Des A. H. Barrett)

1978 (6 Dec). *First Anniv of Independence. T* **7** *and similar vert design. Multicoloured. P* 12½.

35 4 c. Type **7** . . 15 15
36 15 c. Full face portrait of President . . 55 55

(Des A. H. Barrett)

1979 (28 Feb). *Sorghum Beer-making. T* **8** *and similar horiz designs. Multicoloured. P* 13½×14.

37 4 c. Type **8** . . 35 20
38 15 c. Cooking the ground grain . . 95 75
39 20 c. Sieving the liquid . . 1·10 85
40 25 c. Drinking the beer . . 1·50 1·25
37/40 . . *Set of 4* 3·50 2·75

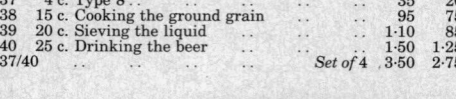

9 Kallie Knoetze (South Africa)

10 Emblem and Drawing by Hendrick Sebapo of Local Fable

1979 (2 June). *Knoetze–Tate Boxing Match. T* **9** *and similar horiz design. Multicoloured. P* 13½×14.

41 15 c. Type **9** . . 75 75
a. Pair. Nos. 41/2 . . 1·50 1·50
42 15 c. John Tate (U.S.A.) . . 75 75
Nos. 41/2 were printed together, *se-tenant*, in pairs throughout the sheet.

1979 (7 June). *International Year of the Child. Children's Drawings of Local Fables. T* **10** *and similar horiz designs. Multicoloured. P* 14.

43 4 c. Type **10** . . 25 20
44 15 c. Family with animals (Daisy Morapedi) 35 35
45 20 c. Man's head and landscape (Peter Tladi) 45 45
46 25 c. Old man, boy and donkey (Hendrick Sebapo) . . 60 60
43/6 . . *Set of 4* 1·50 1·40

11 Miner and Molten Platinum

12 Cattle

(Des B. Sargent)

1979 (15 Aug). *Platinum Industry. T* **11** *and similar horiz designs. P* 13½×14.

47 4 c. multicoloured . . 25 10
48 15 c. multicoloured . . 35 30
49 20 c. multicoloured . . 45 45
50 25 c. black, grey and deep grey . . 60 65
47/50 . . *Set of 4* 1·50 1·40
Designs:—15 c. Platinum granules and industrial use; 20 c. Telecommunications satellite; 25 c. Jewellery.

(Des A. H. Barrett)

1979 (25 Oct). *Agriculture. T* **12** *and similar horiz designs. Multicoloured. P* 13½×14.

51 5 c. Type **12** . . 20 20
52 15 c. Picking cotton . . 25 25
53 20 c. Scientist examining maize 30 30
54 25 c. Catch of fish . . 35 35
51/4 . . *Set of 4* 1·00 1·00

13 Cigarettes forming Cross

14 *Landolphia capensis*

15 Pied Babbler

(Des A. H. Barrett)

1980 (5 Mar). *Anti-smoking Campaign. P* 14×13½.

55 **13** 5 c. multicoloured . . 40 20

(Des. D. Findlay)

1980 (4 June). *Edible Wild Fruits. T* **14** *and similar vert designs. Multicoloured. P* 14×13½.

56 5 c. Type **14** . . 15 15
57 10 c. *Vangueria infausta* . . 30 30
58 15 c. *Bequaertiodendron magalismontanum* 40 40
59 20 c. *Sclerocarya caffra* . . 55 55
56/9 . . *Set of 4* 1·25 1·25

(Des D. Findlay)

1980 (10 Sept). *Birds. T* **15** *and similar vert designs. Multicoloured. P* 14×13½.

60 5 c. Type **15** . . 30 20
61 10 c. Carmine Bee Eater . . 40 35
62 15 c. Shaft-tailed Whydah . . 60 60
63 20 c. Meyer's Parrot . . 70 65
60/3 . . *Set of 4* 1·75 1·60

16 Sun City Hotel

17 Deaf Child

(Des P. Roos and G. Mynhardt)

1980 (5 Dec). *Tourism. Sun City. T* **16** *and similar horiz designs. Multicoloured. P* 13½×14.

64 5 c. Type **16** . . 10 15
65 10 c. Gary Player Country Club . . 40 30
66 15 c. Casino . . 45 50
67 20 c. Extravaganza . . 50 70
64/7 . . *Set of 4* 1·25 1·50

(Des H. Botha)

1981 (30 Jan). *International Year of Disabled Persons. T* **17** *and similar vert designs. Multicoloured. P* 14×13½.

68 5 c. Type **17** . . 15 10
69 15 c. Blind child . . 30 20
70 20 c. Archer in wheelchair . . 45 35
71 25 c. Tuberculosis X-ray . . 60 60
68/71 . . *Set of 4* 1·40 1·10

18 "Behold the Lamb of God..."

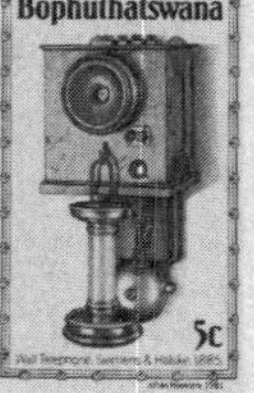

19 Siemens and Halske Wall Telephone, 1885

(Des J. Meyer)

1981 (1 Apr). *Easter. T* **18** *and similar horiz designs. Multicoloured. P* 13½×14.

72 5 c. Type **18** . . 10 10
73 15 c. Bread ("I am the bread of life") 25 25
74 20 c. Shepherd ("I am the good shepherd...") 35 35
75 25 c. Wheatfield ("Unless a grain of wheat falls into the earth and dies...") 45 45
72/5 . . *Set of 4* 1·00 1·00

(Des J. Hoekstra)

1981 (31 July). *History of the Telephone* (1*st series*). *T* **19** *and similar vert designs. Multicoloured. P* 14×13½.

76 5 c. Type **19** . . 10 10
77 15 c. Ericsson telephone, 1895 . . 25 25
78 20 c. Hasler telephone, 1900 . . 35 35
79 25 c. Mix and Genest wall telephone, 1904 45 45
76/9 . . *Set of 4* 1·00 1·00
See also Nos. 92/5, 108/11 and 146/9.

20 *Themeda triandra*

21 Boy Scout

22 Jesus arriving at Bethany (John 12:1)

(Des D. Findlay)

1981 (25 Nov). *Indigenous Grasses* (1*st series*). *T* **20** *and similar vert designs. Multicoloured. P* 14×13½.

80 5 c. Type **20** . . 10 10
81 15 c. *Rhynchelytrum repens* . . 25 25
82 20 c. *Eragrostis capensis* . . 30 30
83 25 c. *Monocymbium ceresiiforme* . . 40 40
80/3 . . *Set of 4* 95 95
See also Nos. 116/19.

(Des Sheila Nowers)

1982 (29 Jan). *75th Anniv of Boy Scout Movement. T* **21** *and similar vert designs. Multicoloured. P* 14×13½.

84 5 c. Type **21** . . 15 10
85 15 c. Mafeking siege stamps . . 35 35
86 20 c. Original cadet . . 40 40
87 25 c. Lord Baden-Powell . . 45 45
84/7 . . *Set of 4* 1·25 1·10

(Des J. Meyer)

1982 (1 Apr). *Easter. Palm Sunday. T* **22** *and similar vert designs. Multicoloured. P* 14×13½.

88 15 c. Type **22** . . 25 25
89 20 c. Jesus sending disciples for donkey (Matthew 21:1,2) . . 30 30
90 25 c. Disciples taking donkey (Mark 11:5,6) 40 40
91 30 c. Disciples with donkey and foal (Matthew 21:7) . . 45 45
88/91 . . *Set of 4* 1·25 1·25

23 Ericsson Telephone, 1878

24 Old Parliament Building

(Des J. Hoekstra)

1982 (3 Sept). *History of the Telephone* (2*nd series*). *T* **23** *and similar vert designs. Multicoloured. P* 14.

92 8 c. Type **23** . . 15 10
93 15 c. Ericsson telephone, 1885 . . 20 20
94 20 c. Ericsson telephone, 1893 . . 20 20
95 25 c. Siemens and Halske telephone, 1898 . . 30 30
92/5 . . *Set of 4* 75 70

(Des A. H. Barrett)

1982 (12 Dec). *Fifth Anniv of Independence. T* **24** *and similar horiz designs. Multicoloured. P* 13½×14.

96 8 c. Type **24** . . 10 10
97 15 c. New government offices . . 20 20
98 20 c. University, Mmabatho . . 25 25
99 25 c. Civic Centre, Mmabatho . . 30 30
96/9 . . *Set of 4* 75 75

25 White Rhinoceros

(Des P. Bosman)

1983 (5 Jan). *Pilanesberg Nature Reserve. T* **25** *and similar horiz designs. Multicoloured. P* 13½×14.

100 8 c. Type **25** . . 30 10
101 20 c. Common Zebras . . 40 30
102 25 c. Sable Antelope . . 40 35
103 40 c. Hartebeest . . 60 60
100/3 . . *Set of 4* 1·50 1·10

26 Disciples bringing Donkeys to Jesus (Matthew 21:7)

27 Kori Bustard

(Des Sheila Nowers)

1983 (30 Mar). *Easter. Palm Sunday. T* **26** *and similar horiz designs. Multicoloured. P* 14×13½.
104 8 c. Type **26** 10 10
105 20 c. Jesus stroking colt (Mark 11:7) .. 30 30
106 25 c. Jesus enters Jerusalem on donkey (Matthew 21:8) 35 35
107 40 c. Crowd welcoming Jesus (Mark 11:9) 60 60
104/7 .. .. *Set of* 4 1·25 1·25

(Des I. Ellithorne)

1983 (22 June). *History of the Telephone (3rd series). Vert designs as T* **19**. *Multicoloured. P* 14×13½.
108 10 c. A.T.M. table telephone, *c.* 1920 .. 15 10
109 20 c. A/S Elektrisk wall telephone, *c.* 1900 30 30
110 25 c. Ericsson wall telephone, *c.* 1900 .. 35 35
111 40 c. Ericsson wall telephone, *c.* 1900 (*different*) 60 60
108/11 .. .. *Set of* 4 1·25 1·25

(Des D. Finlay)

1983 (14 Sept). *Birds of the Veld. T* **27** *and similar vert designs. Multicoloured. P* 14.
112 10 c. Type **27** 30 20
113 20 c. Little Black Bustard ("Black Korhaan") 45 45
114 25 c. Crested Bustard ("Red-crested Korhaan") 55 55
115 40 c. Barrow's Bustard ("Stanley Bustard") 70 80
112/15 .. .. *Set of* 4 1·75 1·75

(Des D. Findlay)

1984 (20 Jan). *Indigenous Grasses (2nd series). Vert designs as T* **20**. *Multicoloured. P* 14½×14.
116 10 c. *Panicum maximum* 15 10
117 20 c. *Hyparrhenia dregeana* 25 20
118 25 c. *Cenchrus ciliaris* 35 35
119 40 c. *Urochloa brachyura* 60 70
116/19 .. .. *Set of* 4 1·25 1·25

28 Money-lenders in the Temple (Mark 11:11)

29 Car Upholstery, Ga-Rankuwa

(Des J. van Niekerk)

1984 (23 Mar). *Easter. T* **28** *and similar horiz designs. Multicoloured. P* 14½×14.
120 10 c. Type **28** 15 10
121 20 c. Jesus driving the money-lenders from the Temple (Mark 11:15) 25 20
122 25 c. Jesus and fig tree (Matthew 21:19) .. 35 35
123 40 c. The withering of the fig tree (Matthew 21:19) 60 70
120/3 .. .. *Set of* 4 1·25 1·25

(Des A. H. Barrett)

1984 (2 Apr)–**94**. *Industries. T* **29** *and similar horiz designs. Multicoloured. Chalk-surfaced paper (except Nos.* 134/5). *P* 14.
124 1 c. Textile mill (25.10.85) 10 10
a. Ordinary paper (18.7.94) 30 30
125 2 c. Sewing sacks, Selosesha (25.10.85) .. 10 10
a. Ordinary paper (5.6.92) 30 30
126 3 c. Ceramic tiles, Babelegi (25.10.85) .. 10 10
127 4 c. Sheepskin car seat covers (25.10.85) .. 10 10
a. Ordinary paper (3.7.92) 30 30
128 5 c. Crossbow manufacture (25.10.85) .. 15 10
a. Ordinary paper (16.11.92) 30 30
129 6 c. Automobile parts, Babelegi (25.10.85) 15 10
a. Ordinary paper (26.6.92) 30 30
130 7 c. Hosiery, Babelegi (25.10.85) .. 15 10
a. Ordinary paper (26.6.92) 30 30
131 8 c. Specialised bicycle factory, Babelegi (25.10.85) 30 10
132 9 c. Lawn mower assembly line (25.10.85) 30 15
133 10 c. Dress factory, Thaba 'Nchu (25.10.85) 20 10
134 11 c. Molten platinum (*ordinary paper*) .. 60 20
135 12 c. Type **29** (1.4.85) (*ordinary paper*) .. 40 15
a. Chalk-surfaced paper (5.12.85) .. 40 15
136 14 c. Maize mill, Mafeking (1.4.86) .. 50 15
137 15 c. Plastic bags, Babelegi (25.10.85) .. 25 15
a. Ordinary paper (3.7.92) 75 45
137*b* 16 c. Brick factory, Mmabatho (1.4.87) .. 60 15
137*c* 18 c. Cutlery manufacturing, Mogwase (3.7.89) 60 15
138 20 c. Men's clothing, Babelegi (25.10.85) 25 15
a. Ordinary paper (26.6.92) .. 1·00 50
138*b* 21 c. Welding bus chassis (3.8.90) .. 50 50
ba. Strip of five. Nos. 138*b/f* .. 2·25
138*c* 21 c. Fitting engine to bus chassis (3.8.90) 50 50
138*d* 21 c. Bus body construction (3.8.90) .. 50 50
138*e* 21 c. Spraying and finishing bus (3.8.90) 50 50
138*f* 21 c. Finished buses (3.8.90) 50 50
139 25 c. Chromium plating pram parts (25.10.85) 30 20
a. Ordinary paper (24.1.92) 60 30
140 30 c. Spray painting metal beds (25.10.85) 40 25
a. Ordinary paper (1.2.89) 75 50
141 50 c. Milk processing plant (25.10.85) .. 65 40
a. Ordinary paper (1.2.89) 85 75
142 1 r. Modern printing works (25.10.85) .. 1·25 75
143 2 r. Industrial complex, Babelegi (25.10.85) .. .. 3·00 2·75
124/43 .. .. *Set of* 27 11·50 8·00
Nos. 138*b/f* were printed together, *se-tenant*, in strips of five throughout the sheet.

(Des I. Ellithorne)

1984 (20 July). *History of the Telephone (4th series). Vert designs as T* **19**. *Multicoloured. P* 14.
146 11 c. Schuchhardt table telephone, 1905 .. 15 10
147 20 c. Siemens wall telephone, 1925 .. 25 20
148 25 c. Ericsson table telephone, 1900 .. 30 30
149 30 c. Oki table telephone, 1930 .. .. 40 50
146/9 .. .. *Set of* 4 1·00 1·00

30 Yellow-throated Plated Lizard

31 Giving Oral Vaccine against Polio

(Des Sheila Nowers)

1984 (25 Sept). *Lizards. T* **30** *and similar horiz designs. Multicoloured. P* 14×14½.
150 11 c. Type **30** 20 10
151 25 c. Transvaal Girdled Lizard 40 30
152 30 c. Ocellated Sand Lizard 45 40
153 45 c. Bibron's Thick-toed Gecko 65 60
150/3 .. .. *Set of* 4 1·50 1·25

(Des D. Thorpe)

1985 (25 Jan). *Health. T* **31** *and similar vert designs. Multicoloured. P* 14.
154 11 c. Type **31** 30 10
155 25 c. Vaccinating against measles 40 30
156 30 c. Examining child for diphtheria .. 45 40
157 50 c. Examining child for whooping cough 60 65
154/7 .. .. *Set of* 4 1·60 1·25

32 Chief Montshiwa of Barolong booRatshidi

33 The Sick flock to Jesus in the Temple (Matthew 21:14)

(Des A. H. Barrett)

1985 (11 Mar). *Centenary of Mafeking. T* **32** *and similar vert design. P* 14½×14.
158 11 c. black, grey and orange 20 10
159 25 c. black, grey and dull violet-blue .. 40 30
Design:—25 c. Sir Charles Warren.

(Des J. van Niekerk)

1985 (2 Apr). *Easter. T* **33** *and similar horiz designs. Multicoloured. P* 14.
160 12 c. Type **33** 20 10
161 25 c. Jesus cures the sick (Matthew 21:14) 30 20
162 30 c. Children praising Jesus (Matthew 21:15) 35 30
163 50 c. Community leaders discussing Jesus's acceptance of praise (Matthew 21:15,16) 50 60
160/3 .. .. *Set of* 4 1·25 1·10

34 *Faurea saligna* and Planting Sapling

35 Jesus at the House of Mary and Martha, Bethany (John 12:2)

(Des B. Jackson)

1985 (4 July). *Tree Conservation. T* **34** *and similar vert designs. Multicoloured. P* 14.
164 12 c. Type **34** 20 10
165 25 c. *Boscia albitrunca* and Kudu 25 20
166 30 c. *Erythrina lysistemon* and Mariqua Sunbird 35 30
167 50 c. *Bequaertiondendron magalismontanum* and bee 55 50
164/7 .. .. *Set of* 4 1·25 1·00

COVER PRICES

Cover factors are quoted at the beginning of each country for most issues to 1945. An explanation of the system can be found on page x. The factors quoted do not, however, apply to philatelic covers.

(Des J. van Niekerk)

1986 (6 Mar). *Easter. T* **35** *and similar horiz designs. Multicoloured. P* 14½×14.
168 12 c. Type **35** 25 10
169 20 c. Mary anointing Jesus's feet (John 12:3) 30 20
170 25 c. Mary drying Jesus's feet with her hair (John 12:3) 35 25
171 30 c. Disciple condemns Mary for anointing Jesus's head with oil (Matthew 26:7) 45 50
168/71 .. .. *Set of* 4 1·25 95

PHILATELIC FOUNDATION MINIATURE SHEETS. These miniature sheets were issued by the Philatelic Foundation of Southern Africa and not by the postal administration. They could be purchased by post or from a limited number of philatelic offices at a premium in aid of various national and international stamp exhibitions.

36 "Wesleyan Mission Station and Residence of Moroka, Chief of the Barolong, 1834" (C. D. Bell)

37 Farmer using Tractor (agricultural development)

1986 (15 May). *Paintings of Thaba 'Nchu. T* **36** *and similar horiz designs. Multicoloured. P* 14×14½.
172 14 c. Type **36** 20 15
173 20 c. "James Archbell's Congregation, 1834" (Charles Davidson Bell) 30 25
174 25 c. "Mission Station at Thaba 'Nchu, 1850" (Thomas Baines) 40 40
172/4 .. .. *Set of* 3 80 70
The 25 c. value exists as a Philatelic Foundation miniature sheet.

(Des Sheila Nowers)

1986 (6 Aug). *Temisano Development Project. T* **37** *and similar horiz designs. Multicoloured. P* 14.
175 14 c. Type **37** 20 10
176 20 c. Children at school (community development) 30 20
177 25 c. Repairing engine (training) 35 30
178 30 c. Grain elevator (secondary industries) 50 50
175/8 .. .. *Set of* 4 1·25 1·00

38 Stewardesses and Cessna Citation II of B.O.P. Airways

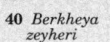

39 Netball

(Des R. Smith)

1986 (16 Oct). *B.O.P. Airways. T* **38** *and similar horiz designs. Multicoloured. P* 14.
179 14 c. Type **38** 25 10
180 20 c. Passengers disembarking from Boeing 707 .. .. 40 20
181 25 c. Mmabatho International Airport .. 50 35
182 30 c. B.O.P. Airways Cessna Citation II .. 60 50
179/82 .. .. *Set of* 4 1·60 1·10

(Des B. Jackson)

1987 (22 Jan). *Sports. T* **39** *and similar vert designs. Multicoloured. P* 14×14½.
183 14 c. Type **39** 20 15
184 20 c. Tennis 30 30
185 25 c. Football 30 30
186 30 c. Athletics 45 50
183/6 .. .. *Set of* 4 1·10 1·10

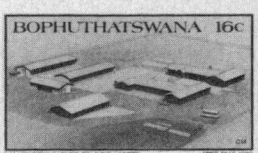

40 *Berkheya zeyheri*

41 E. M. Mokgoko Farmer Training Centre

(Des Jeanette Stead)

1987 (23 Apr). *Wild Flowers. T* **40** *and similar vert designs. Multicoloured. P* 14×14½.
187 16 c. Type **40** 25 15
188 20 c. *Plumbago auriculata* 35 35
189 25 c. *Pterodiscus speciosus* 35 35
190 30 c. *Gazania krebsiana* 40 50
187/90 .. .. *Set of* 4 1·25 1·25
The 25 c. value exists as a Philatelic Foundation miniature sheet.

(Des E. Dias)

1987 (6 Aug). *Tertiary Education. T* **41** *and similar horiz designs. Multicoloured. P* 14½×14.

191	16 c. Type **41**		20	15
192	20 c. Main lecture block, University of Bophuthatswana		30	35
193	25 c. Manpower Centre		30	35
194	30 c. Hotel Training School		30	50
191/4		*Set of* 4	1·00	1·25

42 Posts

43 Jesus entering Jerusalem on Donkey (John 12:12–14)

(Des J. van Niekerk)

1987 (4 Dec). *Tenth Anniv of Independence. Communications. T* **42** *and similar horiz designs. Multicoloured. P* 14½×14.

195	16 c. Type **42**		25	15
196	30 c. Telephone		35	35
197	40 c. Radio		35	35
198	50 c. Television		40	50
195/8		*Set of* 4	1·25	1·25

(Des J. van Niekerk)

1988 (31 Mar). *Easter. T* **43** *and similar horiz designs. Multicoloured. P* 14½×14.

199	16 c. Type **43**		25	15
200	30 c. Judas negotiating with chief priests (Mark 14:10–11)		35	35
201	40 c. Jesus washing the disciples' feet (John 13:5)		35	35
202	50 c. Jesus handing bread to Judas (John 13:26)		40	50
199/202		*Set of* 4	1·25	1·25

44 Environment Education

45 Sunflowers

(Des A. H. Barrett)

1988 (23 June). *National Parks Board. T* **44** *and similar horiz designs. Multicoloured. P* 14½×14.

203	16 c. Type **44**		25	15
204	30 c. Rhinoceros (Conservation)		40	40
205	40 c. Catering workers		40	40
206	50 c. Cheetahs (Tourism)		55	65
203/6		*Set of* 4	1·40	1·40

The 50 c. value exists as a Philatelic Foundation miniature sheet.

(Des A. H. Barrett)

1988 (15 Sept). *Crops. T* **45** *and similar horiz designs. Multicoloured. P* 14½×14.

207	16 c. Type **45**		25	15
208	30 c. Peanuts		35	35
209	40 c. Cotton		45	45
210	50 c. Cabbages		60	60
207/10		*Set of* 4	1·50	1·40

46 Ngotwane Dam

47 The Last Supper (Matthew 26:26)

(Des Estelle Marais)

1988 (17 Nov). *Dams. T* **46** *and similar horiz designs. Multicoloured. P* 14½×14.

211	16 c. Type **46**		30	20
212	30 c. Groothoek dam		50	50
213	40 c. Sehujwane dam		50	50
214	50 c. Molatedi dam		70	70
211/14		*Set of* 4	1·75	1·75

(Des J. van Niekerk)

1989 (9 Mar). *Easter. T* **47** *and similar horiz designs. Multicoloured. P* 14½×14.

215	16 c. Type **47**		35	20
216	30 c. Jesus praying in Garden of Gethsemane (Matthew 26.39)		50	50
217	40 c. Judas kissing Jesus (Mark 14:45)		60	60
218	50 c. Peter severing ear of High Priest's slave (John 18:10)		75	90
215/18		*Set of* 4	2·00	2·00

48 Cock (Thembi Atong)

49 Black-shouldered Kite

1989 (11 May). *Children's Art. T* **48** *and similar horiz designs depicting winning entries in National Children's Day Art Competition. Multicoloured. P* 14½×14.

219	18 c. Type **48**		30	20
220	30 c. Traditional thatched hut (Muhammad Mahri)		40	40
221	40 c. Airplane, telephone wires and houses (Tshepo Mashokwi)		45	45
222	50 c. City scene (Miles Brown)		50	60
219/22		*Set of* 4	1·50	1·50

1989 (1 Sept). *Birds of Prey. T* **49** *and similar vert designs showing paintings by Claude Finch-Davies. Multicoloured. P* 14×14½.

223	18 c. Type **49**		70	30
224	30 c. Pale Chanting Goshawk		90	75
225	40 c. Lesser Kestrel		1·25	1·10
226	50 c. Short-toed Eagle		1·60	1·50
223/6		*Set of* 4	4·00	3·25

The 50 c. value exists as a Philatelic Foundation miniature sheet.

50 Bilobial House

51 Early Learning Schemes

(Des A. George)

1989 (28 Nov). *Traditional Houses. T* **50** *and similar horiz designs. Multicoloured. P* 14½×14.

227	18 c. Type **50**		25	20
228	30 c. House with courtyards at front and side		35	35
229	40 c. House with conical roof		35	35
230	50 c. House with rounded roof		40	50
227/30		*Set of* 4	1·25	1·25

(Des D. McLean)

1990 (11 Jan). *Community Services. T* **51** *and similar horiz designs. Multicoloured. P* 14.

231	18 c. Type **51**		25	20
232	30 c. Clinics		35	35
233	40 c. Libraries		35	35
234	50 c. Hospitals		40	45
231/4		*Set of* 4	1·25	1·25

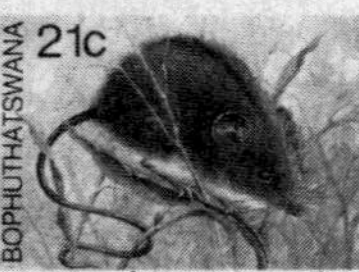

52 Lesser Climbing Mouse

53 Variegated Sandgrouse

(Des A. Ainslie)

1990 (11 Apr). *Small Mammals. T* **52** *and similar horiz designs. Multicoloured. P* 14.

235	21 c. Type **52**		30	20
236	30 c. Zorilla		40	40
237	40 c. Transvaal Elephant Shrew		60	60
238	50 c. Large-toothed Rock Hyrax		80	85
235/8		*Set of* 4	1·90	1·90

The 50 c. value exists as a Philatelic Foundation miniature sheet.

1990 (12 July). *Sandgrouse. T* **53** *and similar horiz designs showing paintings by Claude Finch-Davies. Multicoloured. P* 14×14½.

239	21 c. Type **53**		70	30
240	35 c. Double-banded Sandgrouse		85	75
241	40 c. Namaqua Sandgrouse		1·00	90
242	50 c. Yellow-throated Sandgrouse		1·25	1·40
239/42		*Set of* 4	3·50	3·00

54 Basketry

55 Sud Aviation SE 3130 Alouette II Helicopter

(Des Sheila Nowers)

1990 (4 Oct). *Traditional Crafts. T* **54** *and similar vert designs. Multicoloured. P* 14½.

243	21 c. Type **54**		35	20
244	35 c. Tanning		50	50
245	40 c. Beer making		55	55
246	50 c. Pottery		60	70
243/6		*Set of* 4	1·75	1·75

1990 (12 Dec). *Bophuthatswana Air Force. T* **55** *and similar horiz designs. Multicoloured. P* 14½×14.

247	21 c. Type **55**		70	70
	a. Horiz strip of 5. Nos. 247/51		3·25	
248	21 c. MBB-Kawasaki Bk-117 helicopter		70	70
249	21 c. Pilatus PC-7 Turbo Trainer		70	70
250	21 c. Pilatus PC-6 Turbo Porter		70	70
251	21 c. CASA C-212 Aviocar		70	70
247/51		*Set of* 5	3·25	3·25

Nos. 247/51 were printed together, *se-tenant*, in horizontal strips of 5 throughout the sheet.

56 Wild Custard Apple

57 Arrest of Jesus (Mark 14:46)

(Des Gillian Condy)

1991 (24 Jan). *Edible Wild Fruit. T* **56** *and similar vert designs. Multicoloured. P* 14×14½.

252	21 c. Type **56**		35	25
253	35 c. Spine-leaved Monkey Orange		50	50
254	40 c. Sycamore Fig		55	55
255	50 c. Kei Apple		60	70
252/5		*Set of* 4	1·75	1·75

(Des J. van Niekerk)

1991 (21 Mar). *Easter. T* **57** *and similar horiz designs. Multicoloured. P* 14½×14.

256	21 c. Type **57**		35	25
257	35 c. First trial by the Sanhedrin (Mark 14:53)		50	50
258	40 c. Assault and derision of Jesus after sentence (Mark 14:65)		55	55
259	50 c. Servant girl recognizing Peter (Mark 14:67)		60	70
256/9		*Set of* 4	1·75	1·75

58 Class "7A" Locomotive

59 Caneiro Chart, 1502

(Des C. Becker)

1991 (4 July). *Steam Locomotives. T* **58** *and similar horiz designs. Multicoloured. P* 14.

260	25 c. Class "6A" locomotive with water trucks and caboose (71×25 *mm*)		55	55
261	40 c. Type **58**		75	75
262	50 c. Two class "6Z" locomotives pulling Cecil Rhode's funeral train (71×25 *mm*)		85	95
263	60 c. Class "8" locomotive at Mafeking station, 1904		1·10	1·25
260/3		*Set of* 4	3·00	3·25

The 60 c. value exists as a Philatelic Foundation miniature sheet.

See also Nos. 293/6.

(Des C. Becker (25, 40 c.), T. Marais (others))

1991 (12 Sept). *Old Maps (1st series). T* **59** *and similar vert designs. Multicoloured. P* 14×14½.

264	25 c. Type **59**		60	40
265	40 c. Cantino Chart, 1502		85	85
266	50 c. Giovanni Contarini's map, 1506		90	1·00
267	60 c. Martin Waldseemüller's map, 1507		1·10	1·25
264/7		*Set of* 4	3·00	3·25

See also Nos. 268/71 and 297/300.

60 Fracanzano Map, 1508

61 Delivery of Jesus to Pilate (Mark 15:1)

(Des Liza van der Wal)

1992 (9 Jan). *Old Maps (2nd series). T* **60** *and similar horiz designs. Multicoloured. P* 14½×14.

268 27 c. Type **60** 60 40
269 45 c. Martin Waldseemüller's map (from edition of Ptolemy), 1513 .. .. 85 85
270 65 c. Section of Waldseemüller's woodcut *Carta Marina Navigatora Portugallan Navigationes*, 1516 .. .. .. 90 1·00
271 85 c. Map from Laurent Fries's *Geographia*, 1522 .. .. 1·10 1·25
268/71 .. .. *Set of* 4 3·00 3·25

(Des J. van Niekerk)

1992 (1 Apr). *Easter. T* **61** *and similar horiz designs. Multicoloured. P* 14½×14.

272 27 c. Type **61** 25 20
273 45 c. Scourging of Jesus (Mark 15:15) .. 40 40
274 65 c. Placing crown of thorns on Jesus's head (Mark 15:17–18) 50 60
275 85 c. Soldiers mocking Jesus (Mark 15:19) 60 70
272/5 .. .. *Set of* 4 1·60 1·75

62 Sweet Thorn

63 View of Palace across Lake

(Des Gillian Condy)

1992 (18 June). *Acacia Trees. T* **62** *and similar horiz designs. Multicoloured. P* 14½×14.

276 35 c. Type **62** 30 25
277 70 c. Camel Thorn 50 50
278 90 c. Umbrella Thorn 60 70
279 1 r. 05, Black Thorn 70 85
276/9 .. .. *Set of* 4 1·90 2·10

The 70 c. value exists as a Philatelic Foundation miniature sheet.

1992 (19 Nov). *The Lost City Complex, Sun City. T* **63** *and similar horiz designs. Multicoloured. P* 14×14½.

280 35 c. Type **63** 35 40
   a. Horiz strip of 5. Nos. 280/4 .. .. 1·50
281 35 c. Palace façade 35 40
282 35 c. Palace porte cochère 35 40
283 35 c. Palace lobby 35 40
284 35 c. Tusk Bar, Palace 35 40
280/4 .. .. *Set of* 5 1·50 1·75

Nos. 280/4 were printed together, *se-tenant*, in horizontal strips of 5 throughout the sheet.

64 Light Sussex

65 Pilate offering to release Barabbas (Luke 23:25)

(Des M. Ginn)

1993 (12 Feb). *Chickens. T* **64** *and similar horiz designs. Multicoloured. P* 14½×14.

285 35 c. Type **64** 30 25
286 70 c. Rhode Island Red 50 50
287 90 c. Brown Leghorn 60 70
288 1 r. 05, White Leghorn 70 85
285/8 .. .. *Set of* 4 1·90 2·10

The 70 c. value exists as a Philatelic Foundation miniature sheet.

(Des J. van Niekerk)

1993 (5 Mar). *Easter. T* **65** *and similar horiz designs. Multicoloured. P* 14½×14.

289 35 c. Type **65** 45 25
290 70 c. Jesus falling under cross (John 19:17) 75 75
291 90 c. Simon of Cyrene carrying cross (Mark 15:21) .. .. 90 1·00
292 1 r. 05, Jesus being nailed to cross (Mark 15:23) .. .. 1·10 1·25
289/92 .. .. *Set of* 4 2·75 3·00

66 Mafeking Locomotive Shed, 1933

(Des C. Becker)

1993 (18 June). *Steam Locomotives (2nd series). T* **66** *and similar multicoloured designs. P* 14.

293 45 c. Type **66** 55 55
294 65 c. Saddle-tank locomotive No. 5 (34×25 *mm*) 65 65
295 85 c. Class "16B" locomotive pulling "White Train" during Prince George's visit, 1934 .. .. 85 85
296 1 r. 05, Class "19D" locomotive (34×25 *mm*) 1·10 1·25
293/6 .. .. *Set of* 4 2·75 3·00
MS297 127×113 mm. Nos. 293/6 .. .. 2·75 3·25

67 Sebastian Münster's Map (from edition of Ptolemy), 1540

68 Crucifixion (Luke 23:33)

(Des C. Prinsloo)

1993 (20 Aug). *Old Maps (3rd series). T* **67** *and similar horiz designs. Multicoloured. P* 14½×14.

298 45 c. Type **67** 50 40
299 65 c. Jacopo Gastaldi's map, 1564 .. .. 65 65
300 85 c. Map from Mercator's *Atlas*, 1595 .. 75 75
301 1 r. 05, Map from Ortelius's *Theatrum Orbis Terrarum*, 1570 .. .. 90 1·00
298/301 .. .. *Set of* 4 2·50 2·50

(Des J. van Niekerk)

1994 (25 Mar). *Easter. T* **68** *and similar horiz designs. Multicoloured. P* 14½×14.

302 35 c. Type **68** 45 45
303 65 c. Soldiers and Jews mocking Jesus (Luke 23:35–36) 75 75
304 85 c. Soldier offering Jesus vinegar (Luke 23:36) 85 85
305 1 r. 05, Jesus on cross and charge notice (Luke 23:38) .. .. 1·25 1·25
302/5 .. .. *Set of* 4 3·00 3·00

Bophuthatswana was reincorporated into the Republic of South Africa on 27 April 1994. Its postal service continued to operate, using South African stamps, until 1 April 1996 when it was integrated with that of the Republic.

XII. CISKEI

The Ciskei Territorial Authority was established in 1961 and autonomous government was granted in 1972 under the Bantu Homelands Constitution Act. Ciskei became fully independent on 4 December 1981. This independence did not receive international political recognition, but the stamps were accepted as valid on international mail.

PRINTERS. All the following stamps were printed in lithography by the South African Government Printer, Pretoria.

1 Dr. Lennox Sebe, Chief Minister

2 Knysna Turaco

(Des A. H. Barrett)

1981 (4 Dec). *Independence. T* **1** *and similar vert designs. Multicoloured. P* 14.

1 5 c. Type **1** 10 10
2 15 c. Coat of arms 20 15
3 20 c. Flag 30 30
4 25 c. Mace 35 25
1/4 .. .. *Set of* 4 85 70

(Des D. Findlay)

1981 (4 Dec)–**90**. *Birds. T* **2** *and similar vert designs. Multicoloured. P* 14.

5 1 c. Type **2** 20 15
6 2 c. Cape Wagtail 20 15
7 3 c. White-browed Coucal 30 15
8 4 c. Yellow-tufted Malachite Sunbird .. 20 15
9 5 c. Stanley Crane 20 15
10 6 c. African Red-winged Starling .. 20 15
11 7 c. Giant Kingfisher 20 15
12 8 c. Hadada Ibis 30 15
13 9 c. Black Cuckoo 30 15
14 10 c. Black-collared Barbet 30 15
14*a* 11 c. African Black-headed Oriole (2.4.84) 55 30
14*b* 12 c. Malachite Kingfisher (1.4.85) .. 70 30
14*c* 14 c. Hoopoe (1.4.86) .. .. .. 1·00 30
15 15 c. African Fish Eagle 30 30
15*a* 16 c. Cape Puff-back Flycatcher (1.4.87) .. 65 30
15*b* 18 c. Long-tailed Whydah (3.7.89) .. 1·00 30
16 20 c. Cape Longclaw 40 30
16*a* 21 c. Lemon Dove (3.7.90) .. .. 1·50 60
17 25 c. Cape Dikkop 30 30
18 30 c. African Green Pigeon 40 40
19 50 c. Cape Parrot 60 60
20 1 r. Narina Trogon .. .. .. 1·25 1·25
21 2 r. Cape Eagle Owl .. .. .. 2·50 2·50
5/21 .. .. *Set of* 23 12·00 8·25

3 Cecilia Makiwane (first Xhosa nurse)

4 Boom Sprayer

(Des A. H. Barrett)

1982 (30 Apr). *Nursing. T* **3** *and similar multicoloured designs. P* 14×13½ *(vert) or* 13½×14 *(horiz).*

22 8 c. Type **3** 15 10
23 15 c. Operating theatre 30 30
24 20 c. Matron lighting nurse's lamp *(horiz)* .. 40 40
25 25 c. Nurses and patient *(horiz)* 50 50
22/5 .. .. *Set of* 4 1·25 1·10

(Des A. H. Barrett)

1982 (20 Aug). *Pineapple Industry. T* **4** *and similar horiz designs. Multicoloured. P* 13½×14.

26 8 c. Type **4** 15 10
27 15 c. Harvesting 25 30
28 20 c. Despatch to cannery 30 40
29 30 c. Packing for local market 40 50
26/9 .. .. *Set of* 4 1·00 1·10

5 Brown Hare

6 Assegai

1982 (29 Oct). *Small Mammals. T* **5** *and similar horiz designs. Multicoloured. P* 13½×14.

30 8 c. Type **5** 15 15
31 15 c. Cape Fox 30 25
32 20 c. Cape Ground Squirrel 40 30
33 25 c. Caracal 50 35
30/3 .. .. *Set of* 4 1·25 95

(Des D. Findlay)

1983 (2 Feb). *Trees (1st series). T* **6** *and similar vert designs. Multicoloured. P* 14×13½.

34 8 c. Cabbage Tree 15 10
35 20 c. Type **6** 30 30
36 25 c. Cape Chestnut 35 35
37 40 c. Outeniqua Yellowwood 50 55
34/7 .. .. *Set of* 4 1·10 1·10

See also Nos. 52/5.

7 Dusky Shark

8 Lovedale

(Des Sheila Nowers)

1983 (13 Apr). *Sharks. T* **7** *and similar horiz designs. Multicoloured. P* 14.

38 8 c. Type **7** 15 15
39 20 c. Sand Tiger ("Ragged-tooth Shark") .. 40 40
40 25 c. Tiger Shark (57×21 *mm*) 45 45
41 30 c. Scalloped Hammerhead (57×21 *mm*) .. 50 50
42 40 c. Great White Shark (57×21 *mm*) .. 70 70
38/42 .. .. *Set of* 5 2·00 2·00

(Des A. H. Barrett)

1983 (6 July). *Educational Institutions. T* **8** *and similar horiz designs. P* 14.

43 10 c. stone, light brown and black 10 10
44 20 c. pale stone, olive-sepia and black .. 20 20
45 25 c. pale cinnamon, Venetian red and black 25 25
46 40 c. cinnamon, pinkish brown and black .. 40 45
43/6 .. .. *Set of* 4 80 85

Designs:—20 c. Fort Hare; 25 c. Healdtown; 40 c. Lennox Sebe.

9 White Drill Uniform

10 Sandprawn

(Des A. May)

1983 (28 Sept). *British Military Uniforms* (*1st series*). *6th* (*Warwickshire*) *Regiment of Foot, 1821–27. T* **9** *and similar vert designs. Multicoloured. P* 14.

47 20 c. Type **9** 40 40
a. Horiz strip of 5. Nos. 47/51 . . . . 1·75
48 20 c. Light Company privates 40 40
49 20 c. Grenadier Company sergeants . . 40 40
50 20 c. Officers in undress blue frock-coats . . 40 40
51 20 c. Officer and field officer in parade order 40 40
47/51 . . . . *Set of* 5 1·75 1·75

Nos. 47/51 were printed together, *se-tenant*, in horizontal strips of 5 throughout the sheet.

See also Nos. 64/8 and 95/8.

(Des D. Findlay)

1984 (6 Jan). *Trees* (*2nd series*). *Vert designs as T* **6**. *Multicoloured. P* 14.

52 10 c. *Rhus chirindensis* 20 15
53 20 c. *Phoenix reclinata* 35 35
54 25 c. *Ptaeroxylon obliquum* 40 40
55 40 c. *Apodytes dimidiata* 55 55
52/5 . . . . *Set of* 4 1·40 1·25

(Des D. Thorpe)

1984 (12 Apr). *Fish-bait. T* **10** *and similar horiz designs. Multicoloured. P* 14×14½.

56 11 c. Type **10** 20 15
57 20 c. Coral Worm 30 30
58 25 c. Bloodworm 35 35
59 30 c. Red-bait 40 40
56/9 . . . . *Set of* 4 1·10 1·10

11 Banded Sand Martin

(Des Sheila Nowers)

1984 (17 Aug). *Migratory Birds. T* **11** *and similar horiz designs. Multicoloured. P* 14½×14.

60 11 c. Type **11** 25 20
61 25 c. House Martin 50 50
62 30 c. Greater Striped Swallow 60 60
63 45 c. Barn Swallow ("European Swallow") . . 80 85
60/3 . . . . *Set of* 4 1·90 1·90

(Des A. May)

1984 (26 Oct). *British Military Uniforms* (*2nd series*). *Cape Mounted Rifles. Vert designs as T* **9**. *Multicoloured. P* 14.

64 25 c. (1) Trooper in field and sergeant in undress uniforms, 1830 . . . . 45 45
a. Horiz strip of 5. Nos. 64/8 . . . . 2·00
65 25 c. (2) Trooper and sergeant in full dress, 1835 . . . . 45 45
66 25 c. (3) Officers in undress, 1830 . . . . 45 45
67 25 c. (4) Officers in full dress, 1827–34 . . 45 45
68 25 c. (5) Officers in full dress, 1834 . . . . 45 45
64/8 . . . . *Set of* 5 2·00 2·00

Nos. 64/8 were printed together, *se-tenant*, in horizontal strips of 5 throughout the sheet. Each stamp is inscribed at the foot with a number from "D1.5" to "D5.5". The first number is given in brackets in the listing to aid identification.

12 White Steenbras

13 Brownies holding Handmade Doll

(Des D. Thorpe)

1985 (7 Mar). *Coastal Angling. T* **12** *and similar horiz designs. Multicoloured. P* 14.

69 11 c. Type **12** 30 20
70 25 c. Bronze Seabream 50 50
71 30 c. Kob 60 60
72 50 c. Spotted Grunt 85 85
69/72 . . . . *Set of* 4 2·00 1·90

(Des Sheila Nowers)

1985 (3 May). *International Youth Year. 75th Anniv of Girl Guide Movement. T* **13** *and similar horiz designs. Multicoloured. P* 14½×14.

73 12 c. Type **13** 15 10
74 25 c. Rangers planting trees 25 25
75 30 c. Guides with flag 30 30
76 50 c. Guides building fire 60 65
73/6 . . . . *Set of* 4 1·10 1·10

14 Furniture making

15 *Antelope*

(Des B. Jackson)

1985 (8 Aug). *Small Businesses. T* **14** *and similar horiz designs. Multicoloured. P* 14.

77 12 c. Type **14** 15 10
78 25 c. Dressmaking 30 30
79 30 c. Welding 30 30
80 50 c. Basketry 60 65
77/80 . . . . *Set of* 4 1·25 1·25

(Des R. Reynolds)

1985 (15 Nov). *Sail Troopships. T* **15** *and similar horiz designs. Multicoloured. P* 14.

81 12 c. Type **15** 20 15
82 25 c. *Pilot* 45 45
83 30 c. *Salisbury* 45 45
84 50 c. *Olive Branch* 80 85
81/4 . . . . *Set of* 4 1·75 1·75

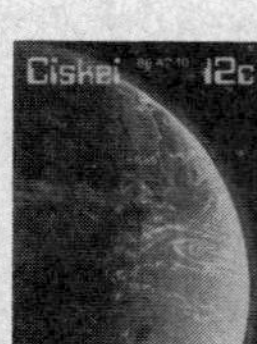

16 Earth showing Africa

17 Fifer in Winter Dress

(Des J. van Ellinckhuijzen)

1986 (20 Mar). *Appearance of Halley's Comet. T* **16** *and similar vert designs. Multicoloured. P* 14.

85 12 c. (1) Earth showing South America . . 1·10 90
a. Sheetlet. Nos. 85/94 . . . . . . 10·00
86 12 c. (2) Type **16** . . . . . . 1·10 90
87 12 c. (3) Stars and Moon . . . . . . 1·10 90
88 12 c. (4) Moon and Milky Way . . . . 1·10 90
89 12 c. (5) Milky Way and stars . . . . 1·10 90
90 12 c. (6) Earth showing Australia . . . . 1·10 90
91 12 c. (7) Earth and meteor . . . . . . 1·10 90
92 12 c. (8) Meteor, Moon and comet tail . . 1·10 90
93 12 c. (9) Comet head and Moon . . . . 1·10 90
94 12 c. (10) Sun . . . . 1·10 90
85/94 . . . . *Set of* 10 10·00 8·00

Nos. 85/94 were printed together, *se-tenant*, in sheetlets of 10 forming a composite design of the southern skies in April. Each stamp is inscribed with a number from "A1-10" to "A10-10". The first number is given in bracket in the listing to aid identification.

PHILATELIC FOUNDATION MINIATURE SHEETS. These miniature sheets were issued by the Philatelic Foundation of Southern Africa and not by the postal administration. They could be purchased by post or from a limited number of philatelic offices at a premium in aid of various national and international stamp exhibitions.

(Des A. May)

1986 (12 June). *British Military Uniforms* (*3rd series*). *98th Regiment of Foot. T* **17** *and similar vert designs. Multicoloured. P* 14.

95 14 c. Type **17** 20 15
96 20 c. Private in summer dress 30 30
97 25 c. Grenadier in full summer dress . . 35 35
98 30 c. Sergeant-major in full winter dress . . 50 50
95/8 . . . . *Set of* 4 1·25 1·10

The 30 c. value exists as a Philatelic Foundation miniature sheet.

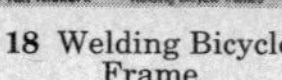

18 Welding Bicycle Frame

19 President Dr. Lennox Sebe

(Des J. van Niekerk)

1986 (18 Sept). *Bicycle Factory, Dimbaza. T* **18** *and similar horiz designs. Multicoloured. P* 14½×14.

99 14 c. Type **18** 20 15
100 20 c. Spray-painting frame 30 30
101 25 c. Installing wheel-spokes 35 35
102 30 c. Final assembly 50 50
99/102 . . . . *Set of* 4 1·25 1·10

(Des J. van Niekerk)

1986 (4 Dec). *Fifth Anniv of Independence. T* **19** *and similar horiz designs. Multicoloured. P* 14×14½.

103 14 c. Type **19** 15 15
104 20 c. National Shrine, Ntaba kaNdoda . . 20 30
105 25 c. Legislative Assembly, Bisho 25 35
106 30 c. Automatic telephone exchange, Bisho 35 50
103/6 . . . . *Set of* 4 85 1·10

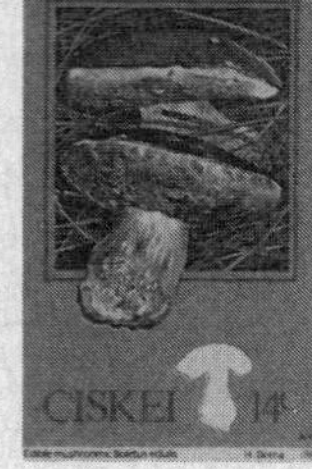

20 *Boletus edulis*

21 Nkone Cow and Calf

(Des H. Botha)

1987 (19 Mar). *Edible Mushrooms. T* **20** *and similar vert designs. Multicoloured. P* 14×14½.

107 14 c. Type **20** 25 15
108 20 c. *Macrolepiota zeyheri* 40 40
109 25 c. *Termitomyces* spp 50 50
110 30 c. *Russula capensis* 60 60
107/10 . . . . *Set of* 4 1·60 1·50

The 20 c. value exists as a Philatelic Foundation miniature sheet.

(Des D. Murphy)

1987 (18 June). *Nkone Cattle. T* **21** *and similar horiz designs. Multicoloured. P* 14½×14.

111 16 c. Type **21** 20 15
112 20 c. Nkone cow 25 30
113 25 c. Nkone bull 30 35
114 30 c. Herd of Nkone 40 55
111/14 . . . . *Set of* 4 1·00 1·25

22 Wire Windmill

23 Seven Birds

(Des A. H. Barrett)

1987 (17 Sept). *Homemade Toys. T* **22** *and similar multicoloured designs. P* 14×14½ (*vert*) *or* 14½×14 (*horiz*).

115 16 c. Type **22** 20 15
116 20 c. Rag doll 25 30
117 25 c. Clay horse (*horiz*) 30 35
118 30 c. Wire car (*horiz*) 40 55
115/18 . . . . *Set of* 4 1·00 1·25

(Des J. van Niekerk)

1987 (6 Nov). *Folklore* (*1st series*). *Sikulume. T* **23** *and similar horiz designs. Multicoloured. P* 14½×14.

119 16 c. Type **23** 20 15
120 20 c. Cannibals chasing Sikulume 25 30
121 25 c. Sikulume attacking the inabulele . . 30 35
122 30 c. Chief Mangangezulu chasing Sikulume and his bride 40 55
119/22 . . . . *Set of* 4 1·00 1·25

See also Nos. 127/36, 153/6 and 161/4.

24 Bush Lily (*Clivia nobilis*)

25 Numbakatali crying and Second Wife feeding Crows

(Des A. Batten)

1988 (17 Mar). *Protected Flowers. T* **24** *and similar vert designs. Multicoloured. P* 14×14½.

123 16 c. Type **24** 20 15
124 30 c. Harebell (*Dierama pulcherrimum*) . . 35 35

125	40 c. Butterfly Iris (*Moraea reticulata*)	40	40
126	50 c. Vlei Lily (*Crinum campanulatum*)	60	65
123/6	*Set of* 4	1·40	1·40

The 50 c. value exists as a Philatelic Foundation miniature sheet.

(Des J. van Niekerk)

1988 (27 May). *Folklore (2nd series). Mbulukazi. T* **25** *and similar horiz designs. Multicoloured. P* 14×14½.

127	16 c. Type **25**	30	35
	a. Sheetlet. Nos. 127/36	2·75	
128	16 c. Numbakatali telling doves of her childlessness	30	35
129	16 c. Numbakatali finding children in earthenware jars	30	35
130	16 c. Broad Breast sees Mbulukazi and brother at river	30	35
131	16 c. Broad Breast asking to marry Mbulukazi	30	35
132	16 c. Broad Breast and his two wives, Mbulukazi and her half-sister Mahlunguluza	30	35
133	16 c. Mahlunguluza pushing Mbulukazi from precipice to her death	30	35
134	16 c. Mbulukazi's ox tearing down Mahlunguluza's hut	30	35
135	16 c. Ox licking Mbulukazi back to life	30	35
136	16 c. Mahlunguluza being sent back to her father in disgrace	30	35
127/36	*Set of* 10	2·75	3·25

Nos. 127/36 were printed together, *se-tenant*, in sheetlets of 10.

26 Oranges and Grafted Rootstocks in Nursery   **27** *Amanita phalloides*

(Des B. Jackson)

1988 (29 Sept). *Citrus Farming. T* **26** *and similar horiz designs. Multicoloured. P* 14×14½.

137	16 c. Type **26**	20	15
138	30 c. Lemons and inarching rootstock onto mature tree	40	40
139	40 c. Tangerines and fruit being hand-picked	50	50
140	50 c. Oranges and fruit being graded	60	65
137/40	*Set of* 4	1·50	1·50

(Des H. Botha)

1988 (1 Dec). *Poisonous Fungi. T* **27** *and similar vert designs. Multicoloured. P* 14×14½.

141	16 c. Type **27**	60	30
142	30 c. *Chlorophyllum molybdites*	95	75
143	40 c. *Amanita muscaria*	1·25	1·10
144	50 c. *Amanita pantherina*	1·40	1·25
141/4	*Set of* 4	3·75	3·00

28 Kat River Dam   **29** Taking Eggs from Rainbow Trout

(Des Sheila Nowers)

1989 (2 Mar). *Dams. T* **28** *and similar horiz designs. Multicoloured. P* 14½×14.

145	16 c. Type **28**	35	25
146	30 c. Cata Dam	55	50
147	40 c. Binfield Park Dam	65	65
148	50 c. Sandile Dam	70	80
145/8	*Set of* 4	2·00	2·00

(Des B. Kent)

1989 (8 June). *Trout Hatcheries. T* **29** *and similar horiz designs. Multicoloured. P* 14½×14.

149	18 c. Type **29**	25	15
150	30 c. Fertilized eyed trout ova and alevins	45	45
151	40 c. Five-week-old fingerlings	55	55
152	50 c. Adult male	60	65
149/52	*Set of* 4	1·75	1·60

The 50 c. value exists as a Philatelic Foundation miniature sheet.

30 Lion and Little Jackal killing Eland   **31** Cape Horse-cart

(Des J. van Niekerk)

1989 (21 Sept). *Folklore (3rd series). Little Jackal and the Lion. T* **30** *and similar horiz designs. Multicoloured. P* 14½×14.

153	18 c. Type **30**	20	15
154	30 c. Little Jackal's children carrying meat to clifftop home	35	35
155	40 c. Little Jackal pretending to be trapped	40	40
156	50 c. Lion falling down cliff face	45	50
153/6	*Set of* 4	1·25	1·25

(Des J. Huntly)

1989 (7 Dec). *Animal-drawn Transport. T* **31** *and similar horiz designs. Multicoloured. P* 14×14½.

157	18 c. Type **31**	20	15
158	30 c. Jubilee spider	35	35
159	40 c. Ballantine half-tent ox-drawn wagon	40	40
160	50 c. Voortrekker wagon	45	50
157/60	*Set of* 4	1·25	1·25

32 Mpunzikazi offering Food to Five Heads   **33** Handweaving on Loom

(Des J. van Niekerk)

1990 (15 Mar). *Folklore (4th series). The Story of Makanda Mahlanu (Five Heads). T* **32** *and similar horiz designs. Multicoloured. P* 14½×14.

161	18 c. Type **32**	20	15
162	30 c. Five Heads killing Mpunzikazi with his tail	35	35
163	40 c. Mpunzanyana offering food to Five Heads	40	40
164	50 c. Five Heads transformed into a man	45	50
161/4	*Set of* 4	1·25	1·25

(Des I. Ellithorne)

1990 (14 June). *Handmade Carpets. T* **33** *and similar vert designs. Multicoloured. P* 14×14½.

165	21 c. Type **33**	30	20
166	35 c. Spinning	50	50
167	40 c. Dyeing yarn	60	60
168	50 c. Knotting carpet	60	70
165/8	*Set of* 4	1·75	1·75

The 50 c. value exists as a Philatelic Foundation miniature sheet.

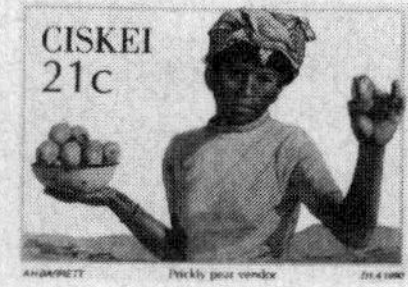

34 Wooden Beam Plough, 1855   **35** Prickly Pear Vendor

(Des J. Huntly)

1990 (6 Sept). *Ploughs. T* **34** *and similar horiz designs. Multicoloured. P* 14½×14.

169	21 c. Type **34**	25	20
170	35 c. Triple disc plough, 1895	40	40
171	40 c. Reversible disc plough, 1895	50	50
172	50 c. "Het Volk" double furrow plough, 1910	60	65
169/72	*Set of* 4	1·60	1·60

(Des A. H. Barrett)

1990 (29 Nov). *Prickly Pear. T* **35** *and similar horiz designs. Multicoloured. P* 14½×14.

173	21 c. Type **35**	30	20
174	35 c. Prickly pear bushes	50	50
175	40 c. Whole and opened fruits	60	60
176	50 c. Bushes in bloom	70	80
173/6	*Set of* 4	1·90	1·90

36 African Marsh Owl   **37** São Bras (now Mossel Bay) on Map, 1500

(Des D. Finlay)

1991 (7 Feb). *Owls. T* **36** *and similar vert designs. Multicoloured. P* 14×14½.

177	21 c. Type **36**	65	40
178	35 c. African Scops Owl	80	80
179	40 c. Barn Owl	90	1·00
180	50 c. African Wood Owl	1·25	1·40
177/80	*Set of* 4	3·25	3·25

The 50 c. value exists as a Philatelic Foundation miniature sheet.

(Des J. van Niekerk)

1991 (11 May). *Stamp Day. D'Ataide's Letter of* 1501. *T* **37** *and similar horiz designs. Multicoloured. P* 14×14½.

181	25 c. Type **37**	50	50
	a. Horiz strip of 5. Nos. 181/5	2·25	
182	25 c. Bartolomeo Dias's ship foundering off Cabo Tormentoso (now Cape of Good Hope) during voyage to India, 1500	50	50
183	25 c. Captain Pedro d'Ataide landing at São Bras, 1501	50	50
184	25 c. D'Ataide leaving letter relating death of Dias on tree	50	50
185	25 c. Captain João da Nova finding letter, 1501	50	50
181/5	*Set of* 5	2·25	2·25

Nos. 181/5 were printed together, *se-tenant*, in horizontal strips of 5 throughout the sheet.

The inscriptions at the foot of Nos. 181 and 182 are transposed.

38 Comet Nucleus   **39** Fort Armstrong and Xhosa Warrior

(Des J. van Ellinckhuijzen)

1991 (1 Aug). *The Solar System. T* **38** *and similar horiz designs. Multicoloured. P* 14.

186	1 c. Type **38**	20	15
187	2 c. Trojan asteroids	20	15
188	5 c. Meteoroids	20	15
189	7 c. Pluto	30	15
190	10 c. Neptune	30	15
191	20 c. Uranus	50	20
192	25 c. Saturn	60	20
193	30 c. Jupiter	65	30
194	35 c. Planetoids in asteroid belt	65	40
195	40 c. Mars	80	50
196	50 c. The Moon	90	70
197	60 c. Earth	1·00	80
198	1 r. Venus	1·50	1·25
199	2 r. Mercury	2·50	2·25
200	5 r. The Sun	4·50	4·50
186/200	*Set of* 15	13·00	10·50
MS201	197×93 mm. Nos. 186/200	13·50	13·50

(Des D. Bagnall)

1991 (7 Nov). *19th-century Frontier Forts. T* **39** *and similar horiz designs. Multicoloured. P* 14×14½.

202	27 c. Type **39**	40	30
203	45 c. Keiskamma Hoek Post and Sir George Grey (governor of Cape Colony, 1854–58)	55	55
204	65 c. Fort Hare and Xhosa Chief Sandile	70	70
205	85 c. Peddie Cavalry Barracks and cavalryman	1·10	1·25
202/5	*Set of* 4	2·50	2·50

40 Cumulonimbus   **41** "Intelsat VI" Communications Satellite

(Des J. Meyer)

1992 (19 Mar). *Cloud Formations. T* **40** *and similar vert designs. Multicoloured. P* 14.

206	27 c. Type **40**	40	25
207	45 c. Altocumulus	65	65
208	65 c. Cirrus	80	80
209	85 c. Cumulus	1·00	1·10
206/9	*Set of* 4	2·50	2·50

(Des J. van Ellinckhuijzen)

1992 (4 June). *International Space Year. Satellites over Southern Africa. T* **41** *and similar horiz designs. Multicoloured. P* 14.

210	35 c. Type **41**	40	25
211	70 c. "G P S Navstar" (navigation)	80	80
212	90 c. "Meteosat" (meteorology)	1·10	1·10
213	1 r. 05, "Landsat VI" (Earth resources survey)	1·25	1·40
210/13	*Set of* 4	3·25	3·25

The 70 c. value exists as a Philatelic Foundation miniature sheet.

42 Universal Disc-harrow, 1914

43 Mpekweni Sun Marine Resort

(Des J. Huntly)

1992 (20 Aug). *Agricultural Tools. T* **42** *and similar horiz designs. Multicoloured. P* 14.

214	35 c. Type **42**	40	25
215	70 c. Clod crusher and pulveriser, 1914	80	70
216	90 c. Self-dump hay rake, 1910	1·10	95
217	1 r. 05, McCormick hay tedder, 1900	1·10	1·10
214/17	*Set of* 4	3·00	2·75

1992 (5 Nov). *Hotels. T* **43** *and similar horiz designs. Multicoloured. P* 14.

218	35 c. Type **43**	40	25
219	70 c. Katberg Protea Hotel	80	80
220	90 c. Fish River Sun Hotel	1·10	1·10
221	1 r. 05, Amatola Sun Hotel, Amatole Mountains	1·10	1·25
218/21	*Set of* 4	3·00	3·00

44 Vasco da Gama, *São Gabriel* and Voyage round Cape of Good Hope, 1497

45 Canary

(Des J. van Niekerk)

1993 (19 May). *Navigators. T* **44** *and similar horiz designs. Multicoloured. P* 14.

222	45 c. Type **44**	55	30
223	65 c. James Cook, H.M.S. *Endeavour* and first voyage, 1768–71	90	75
224	85 c. Ferdinand Magellan, *Vitoria* and circumnavigation, 1519	1·10	90
225	90 c. Sir Francis Drake, *Golden Hind* and circumnavigation, 1577–80	1·10	95
226	1 r. 05, Abel Tasman, *Heemskerk* and discovery of Tasmania, 1642	1·25	1·25
222/6	*Set of* 5	4·50	3·75

The ship on No. 222 is wrongly inscribed "San Gabriel", that on No. 224 "Victoria" and that on No. 226 "Heemskerck".

(Des J. Steyn (65 c.), M. Goetz (85 c.))

1993 (16 July). *Cage Birds. T* **45** *and similar vert designs. Multicoloured. P* 14.

227	45 c. Type **45**	45	30
228	65 c. Budgerigar	70	60
229	85 c. Peach-faced Lovebirds	90	80
230	90 c. Cockatiel	95	85
231	1 r. 05, Gouldian Finch	1·00	1·10
227/31	*Set of* 5	3·50	3·25

The 85 c. value exists as a Philatelic Foundation miniature sheet.

46 Goshen Church (Moravian Mission), Whittlesea

47 Jointed Cactus

(Des C. Meijer)

1993 (17 Sept). *Churches and Missions. T* **46** *and similar horiz designs. P* $14^1/_2$×14.

232	45 c. stone, black and scarlet	35	20
233	65 c. azure, black and scarlet	60	60
234	85 c. cinnamon, black and scarlet	80	80
235	1 r. 05, pale olive-yellow, black and scarlet	90	1·00
232/5	*Set of* 4	2·40	2·40

Designs:—65 c. Kamastone Mission Church; 85 c. Richie Thompson Memorial Church (Hertzog Mission), nr. Seymour; 1 r. 05, Bryce Ross Memorial Church (Pirie Mission), nr. Dimbaza.

(Des Auriol Batten)

1993 (5 Nov). *Invader Plants. T* **47** *and similar vert designs. Multicoloured. P* 14.

236	45 c. Type **47**	40	30
237	65 c. Thorn Apple	70	60
238	85 c. Coffee Weed	90	80
239	1 r. 05, Poisonous Wild Tobacco	1·00	1·00
236/9	*Set of* 4	2·75	2·40
MS240	98×125 mm. Nos. 236/9	2·75	2·75

48 *Losna* (steamer) (near Fish River), 1921

49 "Herman Steyn"

(Des Sheila Nowers)

1994 (18 Feb). *Shipwrecks. T* **48** *and similar horiz designs. Multicoloured. P* 14.

241	45 c. Type **48**	50	30
242	65 c. *Catherine* (barque) (Waterloo Bay), 1846	80	60
243	85 c. *Bennebroek* (East Indiaman) (near Mtana River), 1713	1·00	90
244	1 r. 05, *São João Baptista* (galleon) (between Fish and Kei Rivers), 1622	1·25	1·25
241/4	*Set of* 4	3·25	2·75

1994 (15 Apr). *Hybrid Roses. T* **49** *and similar horiz designs. Multicoloured. P* 14.

245	45 c. Type **49**	35	30
246	70 c. "Esther Geldenhuys"	60	60
247	95 c. "Margaret Wasserfall"	80	80
248	1 r. 15, "Professor Fred Ziady"	1·00	1·00
245/8	*Set of* 4	2·50	2·40
MS249	149×114 mm. Nos. 245/8	2·50	2·50

Ciskei was reincorporated into the Republic of South Africa on 27 April 1994. Its postal service continued to operate, using South African stamps, until 1 April 1996 when it was integrated with that of the Republic.

XIII. TRANSKEI

The Natives Land Act of 1913 laid down that Transkei should be reserved entirely for Black ownership and occupation. In 1963 Transkei was granted internal self-government by the South African Parliament and subsequently the Republic of Transkei was established, on 26 October 1976, as the first of the independent "black homelands".

This independence did not receive international political recognition, but the stamps were accepted as valid on international mail.

PRINTERS. All the following stamps were printed in lithography by the South African Government Printer, Pretoria.

1 Lubisi Dam

2 K. D. Matanzima

(Des A. H. Barrett)

1976 (26 Oct)–**83**. *Transkei Scenes and Occupations. T* **1** *and similar horiz designs. Multicoloured. P* 12×$12^1/_2$.

1	1 c. Type **1**	10	10
	a. Perf 14 (28.3.83)	30	20
2	2 c. Soil cultivation	10	10
	a. Perf 14 (5.7.82)	15	10
3	3 c. Threshing sorghum	10	10
	a. Perf 14 (6.7.82)	15	10
4	4 c. Transkei matron	2·25	15
	a. Perf 14 (15.11.79)	15	10
5	5 c. Grinding maize	2·25	15
	a. Perf 14 (8.4.80)	15	10
6	6 c. Cutting *Phormium tenax*	15	10
	a. Perf 14 (8.7.82)	15	10
7	7 c. Herd-boy	40	10
8	8 c. Felling timber	20	10
	a. Perf 14 (20.1.82)	35	15
9	9 c. Agricultural schooling	15	15
	a. Perf 14 (13.7.82)	25	25
10	10 c. Tea picking	30	15
	a. Perf 14 (11.8.80)	20	15
11	15 c. Carrying wood	40	25
	a. Perf 14 (16.10.81)	30	15
12	20 c. Weaving industry	40	20
	a. Perf 14 (15.10.80)	35	15
13	25 c. Cattle	45	25
	a. Perf 14 (26.10.81)	60	50
14	30 c. Sledge transportation	85	50
	a. Perf 14 (13.8.80)	75	45
15	50 c. Coat of arms and map	65	50
	a. Perf 14 (13.11.81)	80	60
16	1 r. Administration building, Umtata	1·00	1·25
17	2 r. The Bunga (Parliamentary building), Umtata	1·75	2·25
1/17	*Set of* 17 (*cheapest*)	5·75	5·25

1976 (26 Oct). *Independence. T* **2** *and similar vert designs. Multicoloured. P* $12^1/_2$.

18	4 c. Type **2**	25	20
19	10 c. Flag and mace	45	45
20	15 c. K. D. Matanzima, Paramount Chief (*different*)	85	85
21	20 c. Coat of arms	95	1·00
18/21	*Set of* 4	2·25	2·25

3 Beech 100 King Air of Transkei Airways

4 *Artemisia afra*

(Des A. H. Barrett)

1977 (11 Feb). *Transkei Airways' Inaugural Flight. T* **3** *and similar horiz design. Multicoloured. P* 12×$12^1/_2$.

22	4 c. Type **3**	30	25
23	15 c. Beech 100 King Air of Transkei Airways landing at Matanzima airport and on ground	1·25	1·50

(Des D. Findlay)

1977 (16 May). *Medicinal Plants (1st series). T* **4** *and similar vert designs. Multicoloured. P* $12^1/_2$×12.

24	4 c. Type **4**	15	10
25	10 c. *Bulbine natalensis*	85	75
26	15 c. *Melianthus major*	1·00	95
27	20 c. *Cotyledon orbiculata*	1·75	1·75
24/7	*Set of* 4	3·50	3·25

See also Nos. 88/91.

5 Disc Jockey

6 Blind Basket Weaver

(Des A. H. Barrett)

1977 (26 Oct). *First Anniv of Transkei Radio. T* **5** *and similar horiz design. Multicoloured. P* 12×$12^1/_2$.

28	4 c. Type **5**	15	10
29	15 c. Announcer	60	60

(Des A. H. Barrett)

1977 (18 Nov). *Help for the Blind. T* **6** *and similar vert designs. P* $12^1/_2$×12.

30	4 c. black, grey-lilac and gold	15	10
31	15 c. black, drab and gold	35	35
32	20 c. black, pinkish brown and gold	75	80
30/2	*Set of* 3	1·10	1·10

Designs:—15 c. Hands reading braille; 20 c. Blind woman spinning.

7 Men's Carved Pipes

(Des A. H. Barrett)

1978 (1 Mar). *Carved Pipes. T* **7** *and similar horiz designs. Multicoloured. P* 12×$12^1/_2$.

33	4 c. Type **7**	10	10
34	10 c. Two men's pipes	20	20
35	15 c. Multi-bowled men's pipes	60	80
36	20 c. Woman's pipe and witch-doctor's pipe	75	90
33/6	*Set of* 4	1·50	1·75

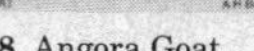
8 Angora Goat

9 *Carissa bispinosa*

(Des A. H. Barrett)

1978 (9 June). *Weaving Industry. T* **8** *and similar horiz designs. Multicoloured. P* 12×$12^1/_2$.

37	4 c. Type **8**	15	10
38	10 c. Spinning mohair	25	25
39	15 c. Dyeing mohair	50	50
40	20 c. Weaving mohair rug	70	75
37/40	*Set of* 4	1·40	1·40

(Des D. Findlay)

1978 (25 Sept). *Edible Wild Fruits. T* **9** *and similar vert designs. Multicoloured. P* 12½×12.

41 4 c. Type **9** 15 10
42 10 c. *Dovyalis caffra* 30 25
43 15 c. *Harpephyllum caffrum* 55 55
44 20 c. *Syzygium cordatum* 60 70
41/4 .. .. *Set of* 4 1·40 1·40

10 Calipers

11 Chi Cha Youth

(Des A. H. Barrett)

1978 (30 Nov). *Care of Cripples. T* **10** *and similar vert designs. P* 12½×12.

45 4 c. black, pale brown and gold 15 10
46 10 c. black, grey and gold 40 40
47 15 c. black, olive-yellow and gold 50 55
45/7 .. .. *Set of* 3 95 95

Designs:—10 c. Child in wheelchair; 15 c. Nurse examining child's leg.

1979 (3 Jan). *Abakwetha (coming-of-age ceremony of Xhosa males). T* **11** *and similar horiz designs. Multicoloured. P* 12½.

48 4 c. Type **11** 15 10
49 10 c. Youths in three-month seclusion .. 30 25
50 15 c. Umtshilo dance 55 55
51 20 c. Burning of seclusion hut at end of final ceremony 60 70
48/51 .. .. *Set of* 4 1·40 1·40

12 President K. D. Matanzima

13 Windpump

14 Magwa Falls

1979 (20 Feb). *Inauguration of Second State President. P* 14×13½.

52 **12** 4 c. brown-red and gold 15 10
53 15 c. deep olive and gold 50 45

(Des K. De Beer)

1979 (13 Mar). *Water Resources. T* **13** *and similar multicoloured designs. P* 14.

54 4 c. Type **13** 15 10
55 10 c. Woman ladling water into jar 30 25
56 15 c. Indwe River Dam (*horiz*) 55 55
57 20 c. Ncora Dam (*horiz*) 60 70
54/7 .. .. *Set of* 4 1·40 1·40

(Des A. H. Barrett)

1979 (4 Sept). *Waterfalls. T* **14** *and similar multicoloured designs. P* 14×13½ (*vert*) *or* 13½×14 (*horiz*).

58 4 c. Type **14** 15 10
59 10 c. Bawa Falls 30 25
60 15 c. Waterfall Bluff (*horiz*) 55 55
61 20 c. Tsitsa Falls (*horiz*) 60 70
58/61 .. .. *Set of* 4 1·40 1·40

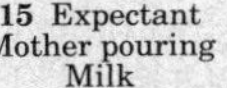

15 Expectant Mother pouring Milk

16 Black Gnat (dry fly)

(Des A. H. Barrett)

1979 (3 Dec). *Child Health. T* **15** *and similar vert designs. Multicoloured. P* 14×13½.

62 5 c. Type **15** 15 10
63 15 c. Mother breast-feeding baby 45 45
64 20 c. Immunising child 60 65
62/4 .. .. *Set of* 3 1·10 1·10

(Des A. H. Barrett)

1980 (15 Jan). *Fishing Flies* (1*st series*). *T* **16** *and similar horiz designs. Multicoloured. P* 14.

65 5 c. Type **16** 35 35
a. Strip of 5. Nos. 65/9 .. .. .. 1·60
66 5 c. Zug Bug (nymph) 35 35
67 5 c. March Brown (wet fly) 35 35
68 5 c. Durham Ranger (salmon fly) 35 35
69 5 c. Colonel Bates (streamer) 35 35
65/9 .. .. *Set of* 5 1·60 1·60

Nos. 65/9 were printed together, *se-tenant*, in strips of 5, both horizontally and vertically, within the sheet.

See also Nos. 83/7, 99/103, 116/20 and 133/7.

17 Rotary Emblem

18 *Encephalartos altensteinii*

19 Red-chested Cuckoo

(Des G. Mynhardt and H. De Klerk)

1980 (22 Feb). *75th Anniv of Rotary International. P* 14×13½.

70 **17** 15 c. bright blue and gold 35 30

(Des D. Findlay)

1980 (30 Apr). *Cycads. T* **18** *and similar vert designs. Multicoloured. P* 14×13½.

71 5 c. Type **18** 15 10
72 10 c. *Encephalartos princeps* 25 25
73 15 c. *Encephalartos villosus* 40 40
74 20 c. *Encephalartos friderici-guilielmi* .. 50 55
71/4 .. .. *Set of* 4 1·10 1·10

(Des D. Findlay)

1980 (30 July). *Birds. T* **19** *and similar vert designs. Multicoloured. P* 14×13½.

75 5 c. Type **19** 20 10
76 10 c. Cape Puff-back Flycatcher 45 25
77 15 c. South African Crowned Crane 65 60
78 20 c. Spectacled Weaver 70 70
75/8 .. .. *Set of* 4 1·75 1·50

20 Hole in the Wall

(Des A. H. Barrett)

1980 (29 Oct). *Tourism. T* **20** *and similar horiz designs. Multicoloured. P* 14.

79 5 c. Type **20** 15 10
80 10 c. Port St. Johns 25 25
81 15 c. The Citadel (rock) 40 40
82 20 c. The Archway (rock) 50 55
79/82 .. .. *Set of* 4 1·10 1·10

(Des A. H. Barrett)

1981 (15 Jan). *Fishing Flies* (2*nd series*). *Horiz designs as T* **16**. *Multicoloured. P* 14.

83 10 c. Kent's Lightning (streamer) 25 25
a. Strip of 5. Nos. 83/7 .. .. .. 1·10
84 10 c. Wickham's Fancy (dry fly) 25 25
85 10 c. Jock Scott (wet fly) 25 25
86 10 c. Green Highlander (salmon fly) 25 25
87 10 c. Tan Nymph 25 25
83/7 .. .. *Set of* 5 1·10 1·10

Nos. 83/7 were printed together, *se-tenant*, in strips of 5, both horizontally and vertically, within the sheet.

(Des D. Findlay)

1981 (15 Apr). *Medicinal Plants* (2*nd series*). *Vert designs as T* **4**. *Multicoloured. P* 14×13½.

88 5 c. *Leonotis leonurus* 15 10
89 15 c. *Euphorbia bupleurifolia* 35 35
90 20 c. *Pelargonium reniforme* 45 45
91 25 c. *Hibiscus trionum* 50 55
88/91 .. .. *Set of* 4 1·25 1·25

21 Eyamakhwenkwe

(Des A. H. Barrett)

1981 (28 Aug). *Xhosa Women's Headdresses. T* **21** *and similar horiz designs. Multicoloured. P* 14.

92 5 c. Type **21** 10 10
93 15 c. Eyabafana 30 35
94 20 c. Umfazana 35 45
95 25 c. Ixhegokazi 40 55
92/5 .. .. *Set of* 4 1·00 1·25
MS96 126×91 mm. Nos. 92/5 .. .. .. 1·00 1·25

22 State House, Umtata

(Des P. Semra'd)

1981 (26 Oct). *Fifth Anniv of Independence. T* **22** *and similar horiz design. P* 14.

97 5 c. black, lake-brown and emerald 15 10
98 15 c. black, lake-brown and emerald 45 30

Design:—15 c. University of Transkei.

(Des A. H. Barrett)

1982 (6 Jan). *Fishing Flies* (3*rd series*). *Horiz designs as T* **16**. *Multicoloured. P* 14.

99 10 c. Blue Charm 25 25
a. Strip of 5. Nos. 99/103 .. .. .. 1·10
100 10 c. Royal Coachman 25 25
101 10 c. Light Spruce 25 25
102 10 c. Montana Nymph 25 25
103 10 c. Butcher 25 25
99/103 .. .. *Set of* 5 1·10 1·10

Nos. 99/103 were printed together, *se-tenant*, in strips of 5, both horizontally and vertically, within the sheet.

23 Cub Scout

24 Hippocrates

(Des H. Botha)

1982 (14 May). *75th Anniv of Boy Scout Movement. T* **23** *and similar vert designs. Multicoloured. P* 14.

104 8 c. Type **23** 15 10
105 10 c. Scout planting tree 15 10
106 20 c. Scout on raft 35 30
107 25 c. Scout with dog 35 30
104/7 .. .. *Set of* 4 90 70

(Des J. Meyer)

1982 (5 Oct). *Celebrities of Medicine* (1*st series*). *T* **24** *and similar vert designs. Multicoloured. P* 14.

108 15 c. Type **24** 25 20
109 20 c. Antonie van Leeuwenhoek 35 30
110 25 c. William Harvey 45 40
111 30 c. Joseph Lister 50 45
108/11 .. .. *Set of* 4 1·40 1·25

See also Nos. 125/8, 160/3, 176/9, 249/52, 273/6, 281/4 and 305/8.

25 City Hall

26 Hotel Complex, Mzamba

(Des A. H. Barrett)

1982 (10 Nov). *Centenary of Umtata. T* **25** *and similar horiz designs. Multicoloured. P* 13½×14.

112 8 c. Type **25** 10 10
113 15 c. The Bunga 15 15
114 20 c. Botha Sigcau Building 20 20
115 25 c. Palace of Justice and K. D. Matanzima Building 25 30
112/15 .. .. *Set of* 4 65 65

(Des A. H. Barrett)

1983 (2 Mar). *Fishing Flies* (4*th series*). *Horiz designs as T* **16**. *Multicoloured. P* 14.

116 20 c. Alexandra 25 25
a. Strip of 5. Nos. 116/20 .. .. .. 1·10
117 20 c. Kent's Marbled Sedge 25 25
118 20 c. White Marabou 25 25
119 20 c. Mayfly Nymph 25 25
120 20 c. Silver Wilkinson 25 25
116/20 .. .. *Set of* 5 1·10 1·10

Nos. 116/20 were printed together, *se-tenant*, in strips of 5, both horizontally and vertically, within the sheet.

(Des A. H. Barrett)

1983 (25 May). *Wildcoast Holiday Complex, Mzamba. T* **26** *and similar horiz designs. Multicoloured. P* 14.

121 10 c. Type **26** 15 15
122 20 c. Beach scene 25 25
123 25 c. Casino 35 35
124 40 c. Carousel 50 50
121/4 .. .. *Set of* 4 1·10 1·10

(Des J. Meyer)

1983 (17 Aug). *Celebrities of Medicine* (2nd *series*). *Vert designs as T* **24**. *Multicoloured. P* 14.

125 10 c. Edward Jenner 15 15
126 20 c. Gregor Mendel 30 30
127 25 c. Louis Pasteur 35 35
128 40 c. Florence Nightingale 55 55
125/8 .. .. *Set of* 4 1·25 1·25

27 Lady Frere Post Office

(Des A. H. Barrett)

1983 (9 Nov). *Transkei Post Offices* (1st *series*). *T* **27** *and similar horiz designs. Multicoloured. P* 14.

129 10 c. Type **27** 15 15
130 20 c. Idutywa 25 30
131 25 c. Lusikisiki 30 35
132 40 c. Cala 40 55
129/32 .. .. *Set of* 4 1·00 1·25

See also Nos. 156/9.

(Des A. H. Barrett)

1984 (10 Feb). *Fishing Flies* (5th *series*). *Horiz designs as T* **16**. *Multicoloured. P* 14.

133 20 c. Silver Grey 45 45
a. Strip of 5. Nos. 133/7 .. .. .. 2·00
134 20 c. Ginger Quill 45 45
135 20 c. Hardy's Favourite 45 45
136 20 c. March Brown 45 45
137 20 c. Kent's Spectrum Mohawk 45 45
133/7 .. .. *Set of* 5 2·00 2·00

Nos. 133/7 were printed together, *se-tenant*, in strips of 5, both horizontally and vertically, within the sheet.

28 Amagqira

29 Soil Erosion by Overgrazing

(Des A. H. Barrett)

1984 (2 Apr)–**91**. *Xhosa Culture. T* **28** *and similar horiz designs. Multicoloured. Ordinary paper. P* 14.

138 1 c. Type **28** (6.7.84) 20 10
a. Chalk-surfaced paper (7.1.91) 30 10
139 2 c. Horsemen (6.7.84) 20 10
140 3 c. Mat making (6.7.84) 20 10
141 4 c. Xhosa dancers (6.7.84) 20 10
142 5 c. Shopping with donkeys (6.7.84) .. 20 10
143 6 c. Young musicians (6.7.84) 30 15
144 7 c. Fingo brides (6.7.84) 30 20
145 8 c. Tasting the beer (6.7.84) 30 20
146 9 c. Thinning the maize (6.7.84) 30 30
147 10 c. Dancing demonstration (6.7.84) .. 30 15
148 11 c. Water from the river 30 15
148*a* 12 c. Preparing a meal (1.4.85) 30 15
148*b* 14 c. Weeding mealies (*chalk-surfaced paper*) (1.4.86) 30 20
149 15 c. National sport: stick fighting (6.7.84) 20 20
149*a* 16 c. Morning pasture (*chalk-surfaced paper*) (1.4.87) 30 20
150 20 c. Abakhwetha dance (6.7.84) 30 25
150*a* 21 c. Building of initiation hut (*chalk-surfaced paper*) (3.7.90) 75 20
151 25 c. Tribesman singing (6.7.84) 30 25
152 30 c. Jovial matrons (6.7.84) 70 35
153 50 c. Pipe making (6.7.84) 70 60
154 1 r. Intonjane (6.7.84) .. .. 80 1·10
155 2 r. Abakhwetha (6.7.84) .. .. .. 1·50 2·00
138/55 .. .. *Set of* 22 8·00 6·50

(Des A. H. Barrett)

1984 (11 May). *Transkei Post Offices* (2nd *series*). *Horiz designs as T* **27**. *Multicoloured. P* 14.

156 11 c. Umzimkulu 15 15
157 20 c. Mount Fletcher 25 25
158 25 c. Qumbu 25 25
159 30 c. Umtata 45 50
156/9 .. .. *Set of* 4 1·00 1·00

(Des J. Meyer)

1984 (12 Oct). *Celebrities of Medicine* (3rd *series*). *Vert designs as T* **24**. *Multicoloured. P* 14.

160 11 c. Nicholas of Cusa 20 15
161 25 c. William Morton 30 25
162 30 c. Wilhelm Röntgen 40 40
163 45 c. Karl Landsteiner 60 60
160/3 .. .. *Set of* 4 1·40 1·25

(Des A. H. Barrett)

1985 (7 Feb). *Soil Conservation. T* **29** *and similar horiz designs showing restoration of eroded landscape. Multicoloured. P* $14^1/_2 \times 14$.

164 11 c. Type **29** 20 15
165 25 c. Removal of stock and construction of walls as sediment collectors 30 25
166 30 c. Regeneration of vegetation 40 40
167 50 c. Cattle grazing in lush landscape .. 60 60
164/7 .. .. *Set of* 4 1·40 1·25

30 Tsitsa Bridge

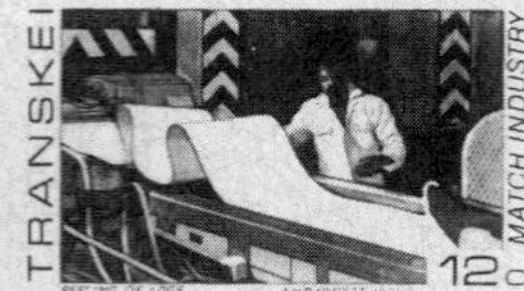

31 Veneer-peeling Machine

(Des D. Bagnall)

1985 (18 Apr). *Bridges. T* **30** *and similar horiz designs. Multicoloured. P* 14.

168 12 c. Type **30** 20 15
169 25 c. White Kei Bridge 25 25
170 30 c. Mitchell Bridge 35 35
171 50 c. Umzimvubu Bridge 55 60
168/71 .. .. *Set of* 4 1·25 1·25

(Des A. H. Barrett)

1985 (25 July). *Match Industry, Butterworth. T* **31** *and similar horiz designs. Multicoloured. P* $14^1/_2 \times 14$.

172 12 c. Type **31** 20 15
173 25 c. Cutting wood to match-size 25 25
174 30 c. Dipping splints in chemical to form match heads 35 35
175 50 c. Boxing matches 60 65
172/5 .. .. *Set of* 4 1·25 1·25

(Des J. Meyer)

1985 (20 Sept). *Celebrities of Medicine* (4th *series*). *Vert designs as T* **24**. *Multicoloured. P* 14.

176 12 c. Andreas Vesalius 20 15
177 25 c. Marcello Malpighi 40 40
178 30 c. Francois Magendie 45 45
179 50 c. William Stewart Halsted 65 70
176/9 .. .. *Set of* 4 1·50 1·50

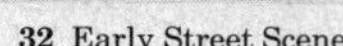

32 Early Street Scene

33 *Aloe ferox*

(Des A. H. Barrett)

1986 (6 Feb). *Historic Port St. Johns. T* **32** *and similar horiz designs. Multicoloured. P* $14^1/_2 \times 14$.

180 12 c. Type **32** 20 15
181 20 c. *Umzimvubu* (coaster) anchored at old jetty 35 35
182 25 c. Wagons off-loading maize at jetty .. 40 40
183 30 c. View of town at end of 19th century 45 45
180/3 .. .. *Set of* 4 1·25 1·25
MS184 130×94 mm. Nos. 180/3 .. .. 1·25 1·25

PHILATELIC FOUNDATION MINIATURE SHEETS. These miniature sheets were issued by the Philatelic Foundation of Southern Africa and not the postal administration. They could be purchased by post or from a limited number of philatelic offices at a premium in aid of various national and international stamp exhibitions.

(Des D. Findlay)

1986 (1 May). *Aloes. T* **33** *and similar vert designs. Multicoloured. P* $14^1/_2 \times 14$.

185 14 c. Type **33** 20 15
186 20 c. *Aloe arborescens* 30 30
187 25 c. *Aloe maculata* 35 35
188 30 c. *Aloe ecklonis* 45 45
185/8 .. .. *Set of* 4 1·10 1·10

The 30 c. value exists as a Philatelic Foundation miniature sheet.

34 First Falls Station, Umtata River

35 Prime Minister George Matanzima

(Des R. Smith)

1986 (24 July). *Hydro-electric Power Stations. T* **34** *and similar horiz designs. Multicoloured. P* $14^1/_2 \times 14$.

189 14 c. Type **34** 20 15
190 20 c. Second Falls, Umtata River 25 25
191 25 c. Ncora, Qumanco River 40 40
192 30 c. Collywobbles, Mbashe River 50 50
189/92 .. .. *Set of* 4 1·25 1·10

(Des J. van Niekerk)

1986 (26 Oct). *Tenth Anniv of Independence. T* **35** *and similar horiz designs. Multicoloured. P* $14^1/_2 \times 14$.

193 14 c. Type **35** 15 15
194 20 c. Technical College, Umtata 25 30
195 25 c. University of Transkei, Umtata .. 30 40
196 30 c. Palace of Justice, Umtata 40 50
193/6 .. .. *Set of* 4 1·00 1·10

36 Piper PA-23 Apache 235 *Ulundi* flying through Clouds

37 Pondo Girl

(Des H. Botha)

1987 (5 Feb). *Tenth Anniv of Transkei Airways Corporation. T* **36** *and similar horiz designs. Multicoloured. P* $14^1/_2 \times 14$.

197 14 c. Type **36** 20 15
198 20 c. Tail fin of *Ulundi* 30 30
199 25 c. Beech 100 King Air 40 40
200 30 c. Control tower, K. D. Matanzima Airport 55 60
197/200 .. .. *Set of* 4 1·25 1·25

(Des A. H. Barrett)

1987 (22 May). *Transkei Beadwork. T* **37** *and similar vert designs. Multicoloured. P* $14 \times 14^1/_2$.

201 16 c. Type **37** 20 15
202 20 c. Bomvana woman 30 30
203 25 c. Xessibe woman 40 40
204 30 c. Xhosa man 55 60
201/4 .. .. *Set of* 4 1·25 1·25

The 25 c. value exists as a Philatelic Foundation miniature sheet.

38 *Latrodectus indistinctus*

39 Common Black Pigs

(Des Liza van der Wal (16, 30 c.), T. Marais (others))

1987 (27 Aug). *Spiders. T* **38** *and similar vert designs. Multicoloured. P* $14 \times 14^1/_2$.

205 16 c. Type **38** 20 15
206 20 c. *Nephila pilipes* 30 30
207 25 c. *Lycosidae sp* 40 40
208 30 c. *Argiope nigrovittata* 50 55
205/8 .. .. *Set of* 4 1·25 1·25

(Des B. Jackson)

1987 (22 Oct). *Domestic Animals. T* **39** *and similar horiz designs. Multicoloured. P* $14 \times 14^1/_2$.

209 16 c. Type **39** 20 15
210 30 c. Goats 30 30
211 40 c. Merino sheep 45 45
212 50 c. Cattle 55 55
209/12 .. .. *Set of* 4 1·40 1·25

40 *Plocamium corallorhiza*

41 Spinning

(Des D. Thorpe)

1988 (18 Feb). *Seaweed. T* **40** *and similar vert designs. Multicoloured. P* 14×14½.
213 16 c. Type **40** 20 15
214 30 c. *Gelidium amanzii* 30 30
215 40 c. *Ecklonia biruncinata* 40 40
216 50 c. *Halimeda cuneata* 50 55
213/16 .. .. *Set of* 4 1·25 1·25

(Des B. Jackson)

1988 (5 May). *Blanket Factory, Butterworth. T* **41** *and similar horiz designs. Multicoloured. P* 14½×14.
217 16 c. Type **41** 20 15
218 30 c. Warping 30 30
219 40 c. Weaving 40 40
220 50 c. Raising the nap 50 55
217/20 .. .. *Set of* 4 1·25 1·25

42 Map showing Wreck Site **43** Small-spotted Cat

(Des Sheila Nowers)

1988 (4 Aug). *206th Anniv of Shipwreck of* Grosvenor *(East Indiaman). T* **42** *and similar horiz designs. Multicoloured. P* 14½×14.
221 16 c. Type **42** 40 20
222 30 c. "The Wreck of the *Grosvenor*" (R. Smirke) 50 50
223 40 c. Dirk hilt, divider and coins from wreck 55 55
224 50 c. "African Hospitality" (G. Morland) .. 60 70
221/4 .. .. *Set of* 4 1·90 1·75
The 50 c. value exists as a Philatelic Foundation miniature sheet.

(Des D. Murphy)

1988 (20 Oct). *Endangered Animals. T* **43** *and similar horiz designs. Multicoloured. P* 14½×14.
225 16 c. Type **43** 30 20
226 30 c. Blue Duiker 50 50
227 40 c. Oribi 65 65
228 50 c. Hunting Dog 80 90
225/8 .. .. *Set of* 4 2·00 2·00

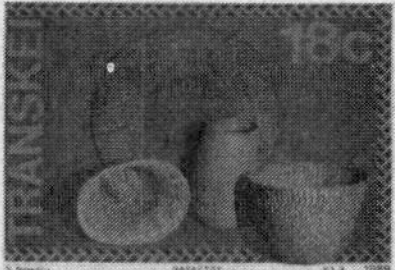

44 Class "14 CRB" Steam Locomotives **45** Mat, Baskets and Jar

(Des D. Hall-Green)

1989 (19 Jan). *Trains. T* **44** *and similar multicoloured designs. P* 14×14½ *(horiz) or* 14½×14 *(vert).*
229 16 c. Type **44** 20 15
230 30 c. Class "14 CRB" locomotive and passenger train at Toleni Halt .. 40 40
231 40 c. Steam train on Great Kei River Bridge (*vert*) 60 60
232 50 c. Steam train in Kei Valley (*vert*) .. 65 65
229/32 .. .. *Set of* 4 1·75 1·60
The 50 c. value exists as a Philatelic Foundation miniature sheet.

(Des Sheila Nowers)

1989 (20 Apr). *Basketry. T* **45** *and similar horiz designs. Multicoloured. P* 14½×14.
233 18 c. Type **45** 20 15
234 30 c. Basket and jar 30 30
235 40 c. Jars and bag 40 40
236 50 c. Dish and jars 55 60
233/6 .. .. *Set of* 4 1·25 1·25

46 Chub Mackerel **47** Broom Cluster Fig

(Des D. Thorpe)

1989 (20 July). *Seafood. T* **46** *and similar horiz designs. Multicoloured. P* 14½×14.
237 18 c. Type **46** 30 15
238 30 c. Squid 45 45
239 40 c. Perna or Brown Mussels 55 55
240 50 c. Rock Lobster 70 85
237/40 .. .. *Set of* 4 1·75 1·75

(Des B. Jackson)

1989 (5 Oct). *Trees. T* **47** *and similar horiz designs. Multicoloured. P* 14×14½.
241 18 c. Type **47** 30 15
242 30 c. Natal Fig 45 45
243 40 c. Broad-leaved Coral 55 55
244 50 c. Cabbage Tree 70 85
241/4 .. .. *Set of* 4 1·75 1·75

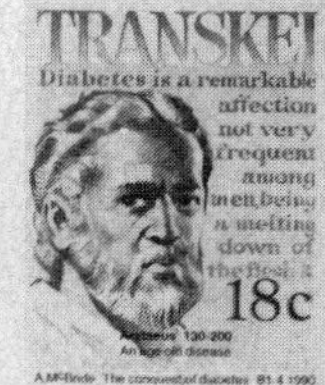

48 *Ginkgo koningensis* **49** Aretaeus (discoverer of diabetes)

(Des L. Kriedemann)

1990 (18 Jan). *Plant Fossils. T* **48** *and similar horiz designs. Multicoloured. P* 14.
245 18 c. Type **48** 45 25
246 30 c. *Pseudoctenis spatulata* 70 70
247 40 c. *Rissikia media* 80 85
248 50 c. *Taeniopteris anavolans* .. .. 90 1·10
245/8 .. .. *Set of* 4 2·50 2·50

(Des A. McBride)

1990 (29 Mar). *Celebrities of Medicine (5th series). Diabetes Research. T* **49** *and similar vert designs. Multicoloured. P* 14×14½.
249 18 c. Type **49** 40 20
250 30 c. Claude Bernard (discovered sugar formation by liver) 60 60
251 40 c. Oscar Minkowski (discovered pancreas removal caused diabetes) 70 80
252 50 c. Frederick Banting (discoverer of insulin) .. .. 90 1·00
249/52 .. .. *Set of* 4 2·40 2·40

50 Diviner dancing to Drum **51** Soldier Lily

(Des A. H. Barrett)

1990 (28 June). *Diviners. T* **50** *and similar vert designs. Multicoloured. P* 14×14½.
253 21 c. Type **50** 40 20
254 35 c. Lecturing Imichetywa (novitiates) .. 60 60
255 40 c. Neophyte initiation 70 80
256 50 c. Diviner's induction ceremony .. 90 1·00
253/6 .. .. *Set of* 4 2·40 2·40
The 50 c. value exists as a Philatelic Foundation miniature sheet.

(Des A. Batten)

1990 (20 Sept). *Flowers. T* **51** *and similar vert designs. Multicoloured. P* 14.
257 21 c. Type **51** 30 20
258 35 c. *Disa crassicornis* 50 50
259 40 c. Christmas Bells 60 60
260 50 c. Port St. John's Creeper 80 90
257/60 .. .. *Set of* 4 2·00 2·00

52 Pink Ink Plant **53** Common Dolphin

(Des A. Batten)

1991 (10 Jan). *Parasitic Plants. T* **52** *and similar vert designs. Multicoloured. P* 14×14½.
261 21 c. Type **52** 40 20
262 35 c. White Harveya 60 60
263 40 c. *Alectra sessiliflora* 70 80
264 50 c. *Hydnora africana* .. .. .. 90 1·00
261/4 .. .. *Set of* 4 2·40 2·40

(Des D. Thorpe)

1991 (4 Apr). *Dolphins. T* **53** *and similar horiz designs. Multicoloured. P* 14½×14.
265 25 c. Type **53** 45 25
266 40 c. Bottle-nosed Dolphin 70 70
267 50 c. Humpbacked Dolphin .. .. .. 90 1·00
268 60 c. Risso's Dolphin .. .. 1·00 1·10
265/8 .. .. *Set of* 4 2·75 2·75

54 South African Crowned Crane **55** Emil von Behring and Shibasaburo Kitasako (diphtheria)

(Des A. Ainslie)

1991 (20 June). *Endangered Birds. T* **54** *and similar vert designs. Multicoloured. P* 14×14½.
269 25 c. Type **54** 55 30
270 40 c. Cape Vulture 80 70
271 50 c. Wattled Crane .. .. 1·00 90
272 60 c. Egyptian Vulture .. .. 1·25 1·25
269/72 .. .. *Set of* 4 3·25 2·75
The 60 c. value exists as a Philatelic Foundation miniature sheet.

(Des J. van Niekerk)

1991 (26 Sept). *Celebrities of Medicine (6th series). Vaccine Development. T* **55** *and similar horiz designs. Multicoloured. P* 14×14½.
273 25 c. Type **55** 45 25
274 40 c. Camille Guérin and Albert Calmette (tuberculosis) 80 80
275 50 c. Jonas Salk (poliomyelitis) .. .. 1·00 1·10
276 60 c. John Enders (measles) .. .. .. 1·10 1·25
273/6 .. .. *Set of* 4 3·00 3·00

56 *Eulophia speciosa* **57** Thomas Weller (researcher into infectious viruses)

(Des A. Batten)

1992 (20 Feb). *Orchids. T* **56** *and similar vert designs. Multicoloured. P* 14.
277 27 c. Type **56** 25 15
278 45 c. *Satyrium sphaerocarpum* 40 40
279 65 c. *Disa scullyi* 60 65
280 85 c. *Disa tysonii* 80 85
277/80 .. .. *Set of* 4 1·90 1·90

(Des J. van Niekerk)

1992 (1 Apr). *Celebrities of Medicine (7th series). T* **57** *and similar horiz designs. Multicoloured. P* 14.
281 27 c. Type **57** 45 25
282 45 c. Ignaz Semmelweis 70 70
283 65 c. Sir James Simpson .. .. 90 1·00
284 85 c. René Laënnec .. .. 1·10 1·40
281/4 .. .. *Set of* 4 2·75 3·00

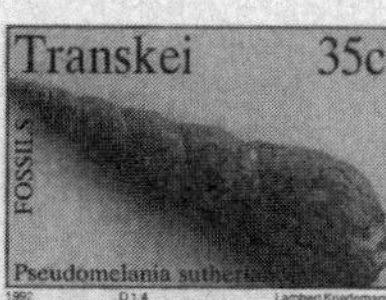

58 Red-billed Pintail **59** *Pseudomelania sutherlandi* (gastropod)

1992 (16 July). *Waterfowl. T* **58** *and similar horiz designs. Multicoloured. P* 14.
285 35 c. Type **58** 50 50
a. Pair. Nos. 285/6 .. .. 1·00 1·00
286 35 c. Hottentot Teal 50 50
287 70 c. Maccoa Duck 80 80
a. Pair. Nos. 287/8 .. .. 1·60 1·60
288 70 c. White-backed Duck 80 80
289 90 c. African Black Duck .. .. .. 1·00 1·00
a. Pair. Nos. 289/90 .. .. 2·00 2·00
290 90 c. Egyptian Goose .. .. 1·00 1·00
291 1 r. 05, Cape Shoveler .. .. .. 1·25 1·25
a. Pair. Nos. 291/2 .. .. 2·25 2·25
292 1 r. 05, Cape Teal .. .. 1·25 1·25
285/92 .. .. *Set of* 8 6·25 6·25
The two designs of each value were printed together, *se-tenant*, in pairs within the sheets.
No. 287 exists as a Philatelic Foundation miniature sheet.

(Des L. Kriedemann)

1992 (17 Sept). *Marine Fossils. T* **59** *and similar horiz designs. Multicoloured. P* 14.

293	35 c. Type **59**	65	35
294	70 c. *Gaudryceras denseplicatum* (ammonite)	95	95
295	90 c. *Neithea quinquecostata* (bivalve)	1·25	1·40
296	1 r. 05, *Pugilina acuticarinatus* (gastropod)	1·40	1·50
293/6	*Set of* 4	3·75	3·75

60 Papillon

61 Fabrosaurus

(Des D. Murphy)

1993 (12 Feb). *Dogs. T* **60** *and similar horiz designs. Multicoloured. P* 14.

297	35 c. Type **60**	50	30
298	70 c. Pekinese	80	80
299	90 c. Chihuahua	1·00	1·10
300	1 r. 05, Dachshund	1·25	1·40
297/300	*Set of* 4	3·25	3·25

The 70 c. value exists as a Philatelic Foundation miniature sheet.

(Des L. Kriedemann)

1993 (18 June). *Prehistoric Animals. T* **61** *and similar horiz designs. Multicoloured. P* 14.

301	45 c. Type **61**	65	35
302	65 c. Diictodon	95	95
303	85 c. Chasmatosaurus	1·40	1·50
304	1 r. 05, Rubidgea	1·50	1·60
301/4	*Set of* 4	4·00	4·00

62 Sir Alexander Fleming and Howard Florey

63 Laughing Doves

(Des J. van Niekerk)

1993 (20 Aug). *Celebrities of Medicine (8th series). T* **62** *and similar horiz designs. Multicoloured. P* 14.

305	45 c. Type **62**	60	35
306	65 c. Alexis Carrel	95	95
307	85 c. James Lind	1·25	1·40
308	1 r. 05, Santiago Ramón y Cajal	1·40	1·50
305/8	*Set of* 4	3·75	3·75

(Des Julia Birkhead)

1993 (15 Oct). *Doves. T* **63** *and similar horiz designs. Multicoloured. P* 14.

309	45 c. Type **63**	50	30
310	65 c. Tambourine Doves	80	80
311	85 c. Emerald-spotted Wood Doves	1·00	1·10
312	1 r. 05, Namaqua Doves	1·25	1·40
309/12	*Set of* 4	3·25	3·25
MS313	92×83 mm. Nos. 309/12	3·25	3·25

64 *Clan Lindsay* (steamer) on rocks, Mazeppa Bay, 1898

(Des J. van Niekerk)

1994 (18 Mar). *Shipwrecks. T* **64** *and similar horiz designs. Multicoloured. P* 14.

314	45 c. Type **64**	65	45
315	65 c. *Horizon* (freighter) on rocks near River Mngazi, 1967	1·00	1·00
316	85 c. *Oceanos* (pleasure cruiser) sinking near Coffee Bay, 1991	1·25	1·40
317	1 r. 05, *Forresbank* (freighter) on fire near River Mtakatye, 1958	1·40	1·60
314/17	*Set of* 4	3·75	4·00

The 85 c. value exists as a Philatelic Foundation miniature sheet.

Transkei was reincorporated into the Republic of South Africa on 27 April 1994. Its postal service continued to operate, using South African stamps, until 1 April 1996 when it was integrated with that of the Republic.

XIV. VENDA

The Venda Territory Authority was established in 1969 and was granted internal self-government on 1 February 1973 under the Bantu Homelands Constitution Act. Venda became fully independent on 13 September 1979. This independence did not receive international political recognition, but the stamps were accepted as valid on international mail.

PRINTERS. All the following stamps were printed in lithography by the South African Government Printer, Pretoria.

1 Flag and Mace

2 *Tecomaria capensis*

(Des A. H. Barrett)

1979 (13 Sept). *Independence. T* **1** *and similar horiz designs. Multicoloured. P* 14.

1	4 c. Type **1**	25	25
2	15 c. Government Buildings, Thohoyandou	60	80
3	20 c. Chief Minister P. R. Mphephu	85	1·10
4	25 c. Coat of arms	1·25	1·50
1/4	*Set of* 4	2·75	3·25

(Des D. Findlay)

1979 (13 Sept)–**85.** *Flowers. T* **2** *and similar vert designs. Multicoloured. P* 14 (11, 12 *c.*) *or* 12½ (*others*).

5	1 c. Type **2**	10	10
	a. Perf 14 (30.4.82)	10	10
6	2 c. *Catophractes alexandri*	30	15
	a. Perf 14 (6.5.81)	20	15
7	3 c. *Tricliceras longipedunculatum*	30	10
	a. Perf 14 (18.8.82)	30	15
8	4 c. *Dissotis princeps*	30	10
9	5 c. *Gerbera jamesonii*	1·75	35
	a. Perf 14 (15.1.80)	30	10
10	6 c. *Hibiscus mastersianus*	15	10
11	7 c. *Nymphaea caerulea*	20	10
12	8 c. *Crinum lugardiae*	45	25
	a. Perf 14 (27.1.82)	30	15
13	9 c. *Xerophyta retinervis*	20	15
14	10 c. *Hypoxis angustifolia*	40	25
	a. Perf 14 (4.3.83)	40	15
14*b*	11 c. *Combretum microphyllum* (2.4.84)	30	15
14*c*	12 c. *Clivia caulescens* (1.4.85)	30	15
15	15 c. *Pycnostachys urticifolia*	30	15
16	20 c. *Zantedeschia jucunda*	55	15
17	25 c. *Leonotis mollis*	2·00	1·00
	a. Perf 14 (22.1.80)	50	40
18	30 c. *Littonia modesta*	40	25
19	50 c. *Protea caffra*	40	30
	a. Perf 14 (17.2.84)	1·40	1·25
20	1 r. *Adenium multiflorum*	1·00	65
21	2 r. *Strelitzia caudata*	1·75	2·00
5/21	*Set of* 19 (*cheapest*)	7·00	4·75

3 Man drinking Beer

4 Tea Plants in Nursery

(Des A. H. Barrett)

1980 (13 Feb). *Wood Carvings. T* **3** *and similar multicoloured designs. P* 14.

22	5 c. Type **3**	15	15
23	10 c. Frying mealies in gourd	30	30
24	15 c. King Nebuchadnezzar (*horiz*)	50	50
25	20 c. Python squeezing woman to death (*horiz*)	60	70
22/5	*Set of* 4	1·40	1·50

(Des A. H. Barrett)

1980 (14 May). *Tea Cultivation. T* **4** *and similar horiz designs. Multicoloured. P* 14.

26	5 c. Type **4**	15	10
27	10 c. Tea pluckers	30	30
28	15 c. Withering in the factory	40	40
29	20 c. Cut, twist, curl unit	50	55
26/9	*Set of* 4	1·25	1·25

ALTERED CATALOGUE NUMBERS

Any Catalogue numbers altered from the last edition are shown as a list in the introductory pages.

5 Young Banana Plants

6 *Precis tugela*

(Des A. H. Barrett)

1980 (13 Aug). *Banana Cultivation. T* **5** *and similar horiz designs. Multicoloured. P* 14.

30	5 c. Type **5**	15	10
31	10 c. Cutting "hands"	30	30
32	15 c. Sorting and dividing into clusters	40	40
33	20 c. Packing	50	55
30/3	*Set of* 4	1·25	1·25

(Des D. Findlay)

1980 (13 Nov). *Butterflies. T* **6** *and similar vert designs. Multicoloured. P* 14.

34	5 c. Type **6**	20	15
35	10 c. *Charaxes bohemani*	40	40
36	15 c. *Catacroptera cloanthe*	55	55
37	20 c. *Papilio dardanus*	65	70
34/7	*Set of* 4	1·60	1·60

7 Collared Sunbird

8 Nwanedi Dam

(Des J. Hoekstra)

1981 (16 Feb). *Sunbirds. T* **7** *and similar vert designs. Multicoloured. P* 14.

38	5 c. Type **7**	20	15
39	15 c. Mariqua Sunbird	55	55
40	20 c. Southern White-bellied Sunbird	60	60
41	25 c. Scarlet-chested Sunbird	75	80
38/41	*Set of* 4	1·90	1·90

(Des A. H. Barrett)

1981 (6 May). *Lakes and Waterfalls. T* **8** *and similar horiz designs. Multicoloured. P* 14.

42	5 c. Type **8**	15	10
43	15 c. Mahovhohovho Falls	35	35
44	20 c. Phiphidi Falls	45	45
45	25 c. Lake Fundudzi	50	55
42/5	*Set of* 4	1·25	1·25

9 *Cynorkis kassnerana*

10 Mbila

(Des Jeannette Stead)

1981 (11 Sept). *Orchids. T* **9** *and similar vert designs. Multicoloured. P* 14.

46	5 c. Type **9**	15	10
47	15 c. *Eulophia fridericii*	35	35
48	20 c. *Bonatea densiflora*	45	45
49	25 c. *Mystacidium brayboniae*	50	55
46/9	*Set of* 4	1·25	1·25
MS50	96×120 mm. Nos. 46/9	1·25	1·40

(Des J. Hoekstra)

1981 (13 Nov). *Musical Instruments. T* **10** *and similar horiz designs. P* 14.

51	5 c. yellow-orange and black	10	10
52	15 c. red-orange and black	30	35
53	20 c. orange-brown and black	40	45
54	25 c. brown-ochre and black	40	55
51/4	*Set of* 4	1·00	1·25

Designs:—15 c. Phalaphala; 20 c. Tshizambi; 25 c. Ngoma.

11 Gathering Sisal

(Des B. Ashton)

1982 (26 Feb). *Sisal Cultivation. T* **11** *and similar horiz designs. Multicoloured. P* 13½×14.

55 5 c. Type **11** 15 10
56 10 c. Drying 25 30
57 20 c. Grading 35 45
58 25 c. Baling 40 55
55/8 .. .. *Set of* 4 1·00 1·25

12 Bison Petrograph, Altamira, Spain

(Des H. Botha)

1982 (15 June). *History of Writing* (1st *series*). *T* **12** *and similar horiz designs. Multicoloured. P* 14.

59 8 c. Type **12** 15 10
60 15 c. Petroglyph, Eastern California .. 30 30
61 20 c. Pictograph script (Sumerian tablet) .. 40 40
62 25 c. Bushman burial stone, Humansdorp .. 45 45
59/62 .. .. *Set of* 4 1·10 1·10

No. 59 is inscribed "AHAMIRA" in error.
See also Nos. 75/8, 87/90, 107/10, 139/42, 171/4 and 203/6.

13 *Euphorbia ingens* **14** *Rana angolensis*

(Des D. Findlay)

1982 (17 Sept). *Indigenous Trees* (1st *series*). *T* **13** *and similar horiz designs. Multicoloured. P* 14.

63 8 c. Type **13** 15 10
64 15 c. *Pterocarpus angolensis* 30 30
65 20 c. *Ficus ingens* 40 40
66 25 c. *Adansonia digitata* 50 55
63/6 .. .. *Set of* 4 1·25 1·25

See also Nos. 79/82, 95/8 and 227/30.

(Des A. H. Barrett)

1982 (26 Nov). *Frogs. T* **14** *and similar horiz designs. Multicoloured. P* 14.

67 8 c. Type **14** 15 10
68 15 c. *Chiromantis xerampelina* 30 30
69 20 c. *Leptopelis* sp 40 40
70 25 c. *Ptychadena anchietae* 50 55
67/70 .. .. *Set of* 4 1·25 1·25

15 European Bee Eater

(Des Sheila Nowers)

1983 (16 Feb). *Migratory Birds* (1st *series*). *T* **15** *and similar horiz designs. Multicoloured. P* 14.

71 8 c. Type **15** 25 15
72 20 c. Tawny Eagle ("Steppe Eagle") .. 65 65
73 25 c. Violet Starling ("Plum-coloured Starling") .. 75 75
74 40 c. Abdim's Stork ("White-bellied Stork") 1·40 1·50
71/4 .. .. *Set of* 4 2·75 2·75

See also Nos. 91/4.

(Des H. Botha)

1983 (11 May). *History of Writing* (2nd *series*). *Multicoloured designs as T* **12**, *but vert. Multicoloured. P* 14.

75 10 c. Indus Valley script 15 10
76 20 c. Sumerian cuneiform 25 25
77 25 c. Egyptian hieroglyphics 30 30
78 40 c. Chinese handscroll 65 70
75/8 .. .. *Set of* 4 1·25 1·25

(Des D. Findlay)

1983 (3 Aug). *Indigenous Trees* (2nd *series*). *Horiz designs as T* **13**. *Multicoloured. P* 14.

79 10 c. *Gardenia spatulifolia* 15 10
80 20 c. *Hyphaene natalensis* 30 30
81 25 c. *Albizia adianthifolia* 40 40
82 40 c. *Sesamothamnus lugardii* 55 60
79/82 .. .. *Set of* 4 1·25 1·25

16 Avocado **17** African Paradise Flycatcher

(Des B. Jackson)

1983 (26 Oct). *Subtropical Fruit. T* **16** *and similar horiz designs. Multicoloured. P* 14.

83 10 c. Type **16** 15 10
84 20 c. Mango 30 30
85 25 c. Papaya 40 40
86 40 c. Litchi 55 60
83/6 .. .. *Set of* 4 1·25 1·25

(Des H. Botha)

1984 (17 Feb). *History of Writing* (3rd *series*). *Horiz designs as T* **12**. *Multicoloured. P* 14×14½.

87 10 c. Evolution of cuneiform sign 15 10
88 20 c. Evolution of Chinese character .. 30 30
89 25 c. Development of Cretan hieroglyphics 40 40
90 40 c. Development of Egyptian hieroglyphics 55 60
87/90 .. .. *Set of* 4 1·25 1·25

(Des Sheila Nowers)

1984 (26 Apr). *Migratory Birds* (2nd *series*). *T* **17** *and similar vert designs. Multicoloured. P* 14½×14.

91 11 c. White Stork 30 20
92 20 c. Type **17** 50 50
93 25 c. Black Kite ("Yellow-billed Kite") .. 60 60
94 30 c. Wood Sandpiper 70 85
91/4 .. .. *Set of* 4 1·90 1·90

(Des D. Findlay)

1984 (21 June). *Indigenous Trees* (3rd *series*). *Horiz designs as T* **13**. *Multicoloured. P* 14.

95 11 c. *Afzelia quanzensis* 15 10
96 20 c. *Peltophorum africanum* 30 30
97 25 c. *Gyrocarpus americanus* 40 40
98 30 c. *Acacia sieberana* 50 55
95/8 .. .. *Set of* 4 1·25 1·25

18 Dzata Ruins, Nzhelele Valley **19** White-browed Robin Chat

(Des B. Jackson)

1984 (13 Sept). *Fifth Anniv of Independence. T* **18** *and similar horiz designs. Multicoloured. P* 14.

99 11 c. Type **18** 15 10
100 25 c. Traditional hut 25 30
101 30 c. Sub-economical house 30 35
102 45 c. Modern home 45 65
99/102 .. .. *Set of* 4 1·00 1·25

(Des Sheila Nowers)

1985 (10 Jan). *Songbirds. T* **19** *and similar vert designs. Multicoloured. P* 14½×14.

103 11 c. Type **19** (inscr "Heuglin's Robin") .. 35 20
104 25 c. Black-collared Barbet 50 45
105 30 c. African Black-headed Oriole 65 55
106 50 c. Kurrichane Thrush .. .. .. 1·00 1·00
103/6 .. .. *Set of* 4 2·25 2·00

(Des H. Botha)

1985 (21 Mar). *History of Writing* (4th *series*). *Horiz designs as T* **12**. *Multicoloured. P* 14.

107 11 c. Southern Arabic characters 15 10
108 25 c. Phoenician characters 30 30
109 30 c. Aramaic characters 40 40
110 50 c. Canaanite characters 75 75
107/10 .. .. *Set of* 4 1·40 1·40

20 Transvaal Red Milkwood **21** *Pellaea dura*

(Des Sheila Nowers)

1985 (21 June). *Food from the Veld* (1st *series*). *T* **20** *and similar vert designs. Multicoloured. P* 14.

111 12 c. Type **20** 15 10
112 25 c. Buffalo Thorn 30 30
113 30 c. Wild Water Melon 35 35
114 50 c. Brown Ivory 55 60
111/14 .. .. *Set of* 4 1·25 1·25

See also Nos. 163/6.

(Des D. Findlay)

1985 (5 Sept). *Ferns. T* **21** *and similar vert designs. Multicoloured. P* 14.

115 12 c. Type **21** 15 10
116 25 c. *Actiniopteris radiata* 30 30
117 30 c. *Adiantum hispidulum* 40 40
118 50 c. *Polypodium polypodioides* 65 70
115/18 .. .. *Set of* 4 1·40 1·40

22 Three-lined Grass Snake **23** Etruscan Dish

1986 (16 Jan)–**93**. *Reptiles. T* **22** *and similar horiz designs. Multicoloured. Chalk-surfaced paper. P* 14.

119 1 c. Type **22** 10 10
a. Ordinary paper (29.5.89) 30 30
120 2 c. Mole Snake 10 10
a. Ordinary paper (29.5.89) 40 40
121 3 c. Ornate Scrub Lizard 10 10
122 4 c. Puff Adder 10 10
123 5 c. Three-lined Skink 10 10
a. Ordinary paper (12.7.93) 40 40
124 6 c. Egyptian Cobra 15 10
125 7 c. Blue-tailed Kopje Skink 15 10
126 8 c. Spotted Bush Snake 20 20
a. Ordinary paper (12.7.93) 40 40
127 9 c. Yellow-throated Plated Lizard .. 20 20
128 10 c. Northern Lined Shovelsnout .. 20 20
a. Ordinary paper (20.7.93) 40 40
129 14 c. Transvaal Flat Lizard (1.4.86) .. 90 20
130 15 c. Soutpansberg Lizard 30 20
a. Ordinary paper (13.9.89) 40 40
131 16 c. Iguana Water Leguan (1.4.87) .. 60 20
132 18 c. Black Mamba (*ordinary paper*) (3.7.89) 75 20
133 20 c. Transvaal Flat Gecko 30 20
a. Ordinary paper (17.9.90) 65 55
133*b* 21 c. Flap-necked Chameleon (*ordinary paper*) (3.8.90) 75 20
134 25 c. Longtailed Garter Snake 40 30
135 30 c. Tigroid Thick-toed Gecko 45 35
a. Ordinary paper (4.9.92) 75 75
136 50 c. Cape File Snake 70 50
137 1 r. Soutpansberg Girdled Lizard .. 1·25 1·00
a. Ordinary paper (9.7.90) .. .. 2·25 2·25
138 2 r. African Python .. .. .. 2·00 2·25
a. Ordinary paper (27.1.89) .. .. 3·75 3·75
119/38 .. .. *Set of* 21 8·50 6·00

(Des H. Botha)

1986 (10 Apr). *History of Writing* (5th *series*). *T* **23** *and similar vert designs. Multicoloured. P* 14×14½.

139 14 c. Type **23** 15 10
140 20 c. Greek inscription, AD 70 .. .. 30 30
141 25 c. Roman inscription 40 40
142 30 c. Cyrillic inscription (Byzantine mosaic) 55 60
139/42 .. .. *Set of* 4 1·25 1·25

24 Planting Pine Seedlings

(Des B. Jackson)

1986 (26 June). *Forestry. T* **24** *and similar horiz designs. Multicoloured. P* 14.

143 14 c. Type **24** 20 15
144 20 c. Mule hauling logs 30 30
145 25 c. Off-loading logs at sawmill 40 40
146 30 c. Using timber in construction .. 55 60
143/6 .. .. *Set of* 4 1·25 1·25

PHILATELIC FOUNDATION MINIATURE SHEETS. These miniature sheets were issued by the Philatelic Foundation of Southern Africa and not the postal administration. They could be purchased by post or from a limited number of philatelic offices at a premium in aid of various national and international stamp exhibitions.

25 Maxwell, 1910 **26** Comb Duck

(Des A. H. Barrett)

1986 (4 Sept). *FIVA International Veteran Car Rally. T* **25** *and similar horiz designs. Multicoloured. P* 14½×14.

147 14 c. Type **25** .. 20 15
148 20 c. Bentley 4½ l., 1929 .. 30 30
149 25 c. Plymouth Coupé, 1933 .. 40 40
150 30 c. Mercedes Benz 220, 1958 .. 55 60
147/50 .. *Set of* 4 1·25 1·25

The 30 c. value exists as a Philatelic Foundation miniature sheet.

(Des A. H. Barrett)

1987 (8 Jan). *Waterfowl. T* **26** *and similar multicoloured designs. P* 14×14½ (*vert*) *or* 14½×14 (*horiz*).

151 14 c. Type **26** .. 60 35
152 20 c. White-faced Whistling Duck .. 70 60
153 25 c. Spur-winged Goose (*horiz*) .. 90 80
154 30 c. Egyptian Goose (*horiz*) .. 1·10 1·10
151/4 .. *Set of* 4 3·00 2·50

The 25 c. value exists as a Philatelic Foundation miniature sheet.

27 "Iron Master" **28** Tigerfish

(Des L. Kriedemann)

1987 (9 Apr). *Wood Sculptures by Meshack Matamela Raphalalani. T* **27** *and similar vert designs. Multicoloured. P* 14½×14.

155 16 c. Type **27** .. 15 15
156 20 c. "Distant Drums" .. 25 25
157 25 c. "Sunrise" .. 30 30
158 30 c. "Obedience" .. 40 40
155/8 .. *Set of* 4 1·00 1·00

(Des D. Thorpe)

1987 (2 July). *Freshwater Fishes. T* **28** *and similar horiz designs. Multicoloured. P* 14×14½.

159 16 c. Type **28** .. 25 20
160 20 c. Barred Minnow .. 35 35
161 25 c. Mozambique Mouthbrooder .. 45 45
162 30 c. Sharp-toothed Catfish .. 55 60
159/62 .. *Set of* 4 1·40 1·40

29 Cross-berry **30** Picking Berries

(Des Sheila Nowers)

1987 (2 Oct). *Food from the Veld* (*2nd series*). *T* **29** *and similar vert designs. Multicoloured. P* 14×14½.

163 16 c. Type **29** .. 20 15
164 30 c. Wild Date Palm .. 30 30
165 40 c. Tree Fuchsia .. 40 40
166 50 c. Wild Cucumber .. 50 55
163/6 .. *Set of* 4 1·25 1·25

(Des B. Jackson)

1988 (21 Jan). *Coffee Industry. T* **30** *and similar horiz designs. Multicoloured. P* 14½×14.

167 16 c. Type **30** .. 20 20
168 30 c. Weighing bags of berries .. 30 30
169 40 c. Drying beans in sun .. 35 35
170 50 c. Roasting graded beans .. 45 45
167/70 .. *Set of* 4 1·10 1·10

31 "Universal Love" in Chinese **32** College

(Des H. Botha)

1988 (28 Apr). *History of Writing* (*6th series*). *T* **31** *and similar horiz designs. P* 14½×14.

171 16 c. stone, black and bright scarlet .. 25 20
172 30 c. stone, black and bright scarlet .. 35 35
173 40 c. stone, black and deep rose-red .. 45 45
174 50 c. black and gold .. 55 60
171/4 .. *Set of* 4 1·40 1·40

Designs:—30 c. "Picture of a lion on a stone" in Devanagari (Indian script); 40 c. "Information" in Russian; 50 c. "Peace be upon you" in Thuluth (Arabic script).

(Des L. Kriedemann)

1988 (18 Aug). *Fifth Anniv of Shayandima Nurses' Training College. T* **32** *and similar horiz designs. Multicoloured. P* 14½×14.

175 16 c. Type **32** .. 25 20
176 30 c. Students using microscope .. 40 40
177 40 c. Anatomy class .. 50 50
178 50 c. Clinical training .. 55 60
175/8 .. *Set of* 4 1·50 1·50

33 "Fetching Water" **34** Ndongwana (clay bowls)

1988 (6 Oct). *Watercolours by Kenneth Thabo. T* **33** *and similar horiz designs. Multicoloured. P* 14½×14.

179 16 c. Type **33** .. 25 20
180 30 c. "Grinding Maize" .. 40 40
181 40 c. "Offering Food" .. 50 50
182 50 c. "Kindling the Fire" .. 55 60
179/82 .. *Set of* 4 1·50 1·50

The 50 c. value exists as a Philatelic Foundation miniature sheet.

(Des L. Kriedemann)

1989 (5 Jan). *Traditional Kitchenware. T* **34** *and similar horiz designs. Multicoloured. P* 14½×14.

183 16 c. Type **34** .. 20 20
184 30 c. Ndilo (wooden porridge bowls) .. 30 30
185 40 c. Mufaro (basket with lid) .. 40 40
186 50 c. Muthatha (dish woven from ilala palm) 45 45
183/6 .. *Set of* 4 1·25 1·25

35 Domba **36** Southern Ground Hornbill

(Des K. Thabo)

1989 (5 Apr). *Traditional Dances. T* **35** *and similar horiz designs. Multicoloured. P* 14½×14.

187 18 c. Type **35** .. 20 20
188 30 c. Tshinzerere .. 30 30
189 40 c. Malende .. 40 40
190 50 c. Malombo .. 45 45
187/90 .. *Set of* 4 1·25 1·25

(Des M. Enslin)

1989 (27 June). *Endangered Birds. T* **36** *and similar vert designs. Multicoloured. P* 14½×14.

191 18 c. Type **36** .. 60 30
192 30 c. Lappet-faced Vulture .. 90 70
193 40 c. Bateleur .. 1·10 90
194 50 c. Martial Eagle .. 1·40 1·25
191/4 .. *Set of* 4 3·50 2·75

The 50 c. value exists as a Philatelic Foundation miniature sheet.

37 Pres. Gota F. N. Ravele **38** Lion

(Des A. H. Barrett)

1989 (13 Sept). *Tenth Anniv of Independence. T* **37** *and similar horiz designs. Multicoloured. P* 14½×14.

195 18 c. Type **37** .. 20 20
196 30 c. Presidential offices .. 30 30
197 40 c. President's residence .. 40 40
198 50 c. Thohoyandou Sports Stadium .. 45 45
195/8 .. *Set of* 4 1·25 1·25

(Des D. Murphy)

1990 (1 Mar). *Nwanedi National Park. T* **38** *and similar vert designs. Multicoloured. P* 14×14½.

199 18 c. Type **38** .. 30 25
200 30 c. Common Zebra .. 55 55
201 40 c. Cheetah .. 65 65
202 50 c. White Rhinoceros .. 75 80
199/202 .. *Set of* 4 2·00 2·00

The 50 c. value exists as a Philatelic Foundation miniature sheet.

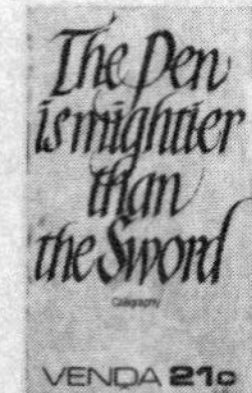

39 Calligraphy **40** *Aloe globuligemma*

(Des H. Botha)

1990 (23 May). *History of Writing* (*7th series*). *T* **39** *and similar vert designs. P* 14½×14.

203 21 c. black and grey .. 20 15
204 30 c. black and reddish brown .. 30 30
205 40 c. black and yellowish green .. 40 40
206 50 c. blue, new blue and black .. 50 60
203/6 .. *Set of* 4 1·25 1·25

Designs:—30 c. Part of score for Beethoven's *Moonlight Sonata*; 40 c. Characters from personal computer; 50 c. Television picture of message transmitted into outer space from Arecibo 1000 radio telescope.

(Des G. Marx)

1990 (23 Aug). *Aloes. T* **40** *and similar vert designs. Multicoloured. P* 14½×14.

207 21 c. Type **40** .. 30 25
208 35 c. *Aloe aculeata* .. 50 50
209 40 c. *Aloe lutescens* .. 60 60
210 50 c. *Aloe angelica* .. 70 75
207/10 .. *Set of* 4 1·90 1·90

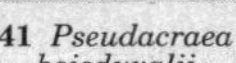

41 *Pseudacraea boisduvalii* **42** Cape Puff-back Flycatchers

(Des E. Forbes)

1990 (15 Nov). *Butterflies. T* **41** *and similar vert designs. Multicoloured. P* 14×14½.

211 21 c. Type **41** .. 50 40
212 35 c. *Papilio nireus* .. 80 70
213 40 c. *Charaxes jasius* .. 90 90
214 50 c. *Aeropetes tulbaghia* .. 1·10 1·10
211/14 .. *Set of* 4 3·00 2·75

1991 (7 Mar). *Birds. T* **42** *and similar horiz designs showing paintings by Claude Finch-Davies. Multicoloured. P* 14½×14.

215 21 c. Type **42** .. 50 40
216 35 c. Red-capped Robin Chat .. 75 75
217 40 c. Collared Sunbirds .. 85 85
218 50 c. Yellow-streaked Greenbul .. 1·10 1·25
215/18 .. *Set of* 4 2·75 2·75

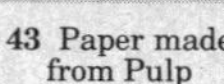

43 Paper made from Pulp **44** Venda Sun Hotel Complex, Thohoyandou

(Des H. Botha)

1991 (6 June). *Inventions* (*1st series*). *T* **43** *and similar vert designs. Multicoloured. P* 14½×14.

219 25 c. Type **43** .. 45 35
220 40 c. Magnetic compass .. 80 70
221 50 c. Abacus .. 90 85
222 60 c. Gunpowder .. 1·25 1·00
219/22 .. *Set of* 4 3·00 2·50

The 60 c. value exists as a Philatelic Foundation miniature sheet.

See also Nos. 239/42 and 259/62.

1991 (29 Aug). *Tourism. T* **44** *and similar horiz designs. Multicoloured. P* 14½×14.

223	25 c. Type **44**	45	30
224	40 c. Mphephu Resort	70	70
225	50 c. Sagole Spa	80	80
226	60 c. Luphephe-Nwanedi Resort	90	1·10
223/6	*Set of* 4	2·50	2·50

(Des D. Findlay)

1991 (21 Nov). *Indigenous Trees (4th series). Horiz designs as T* **13**. *Multicoloured. P* 14½×14.

227	27 c. Fever Tree	45	30
228	45 c. Transvaal Beech	80	70
229	65 c. Transvaal Wild Banana	95	90
230	85 c. Sausage Tree	1·25	1·40
227/30	*Set of* 4	3·00	3·00

45 Setting the Web

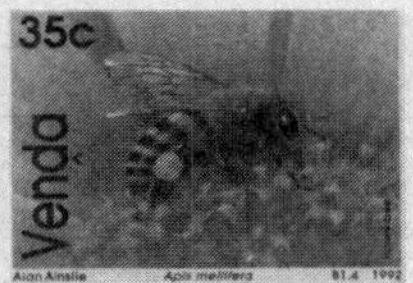

46 *Apis mellifera*

1992 (5 Mar). *Clothing Factory. T* **45** *and similar horiz designs. Multicoloured. P* 14.

231	27 c. Type **45**	35	25
232	45 c. Knitting	50	50
233	65 c. Making up garment	70	80
234	85 c. Inspection of finished product	85	1·10
231/4	*Set of* 4	2·25	2·40

(Des A. Ainslie)

1992 (21 May). *Bees. T* **46** *and similar horiz designs. Multicoloured. P* 14.

235	35 c. Type **46**	55	40
236	70 c. *Anthidium cordiforme*	95	90
237	90 c. *Megachile frontalis*	1·25	1·25
238	1 r. 05, *Xylocopa caffra*	1·40	1·40
235/8	*Set of* 4	3·75	3·50

The 70 c. value exists as a Philatelic Foundation miniature sheet.

47 Egyptian Plough

48 Nile Crocodile

(Des H. Botha)

1992 (13 Aug). *Inventions (2nd series). T* **47** *and similar horiz designs. Multicoloured. P* 14.

239	35 c. Type **47**	55	40
240	70 c. Early wheel, Mesopotamia	95	90
241	90 c. Making bricks, Egypt	1·25	1·25
242	1 r. 05, Early Egyptian sailing ship	1·40	1·40
239/42	*Set of* 4	3·75	3·50

(Des A. Ainslie)

1992 (15 Oct). *Crocodile Farming. T* **48** *and similar horiz designs. Multicoloured. P* 14½×14.

243	35 c. Type **48**	55	40
244	70 c. Egg laying	95	90
245	90 c. Eggs hatching	1·40	1·40
246	1 r. 05, Mother carrying young	1·50	1·60
243/6	*Set of* 4	4·00	3·75

49 Burmese

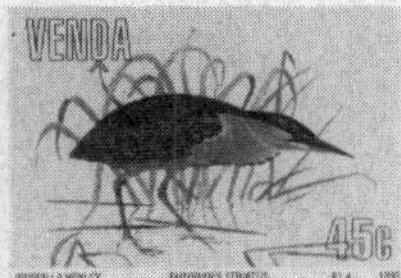

50 Green Heron

(Des Sheila Nowers)

1993 (19 May). *Domestic Cats. T* **49** *and similar horiz designs. Multicoloured. P* 14.

247	45 c. Type **49**	65	45
248	65 c. Tabby	90	90
249	85 c. Siamese	1·25	1·25
250	1 r. 05, Persian	1·40	1·40
247/50	*Set of* 4	3·75	3·75

The 65 c. value exists as a Philatelic Foundation miniature sheet.

(Des Priscilla Henley)

1993 (16 July). *Herons. T* **50** *and similar horiz designs. Multicoloured. P* 14.

251	45 c. Type **50**	70	50
252	65 c. Black-crowned Night Heron	95	95
253	85 c. Purple Heron	1·25	1·25
254	1 r. 05, Black-headed Heron	1·50	1·75
251/4	*Set of* 4	4·00	4·00
MS255	86×132 mm. Nos. 251/4	4·00	4·25

51 Punching out Sole Lining

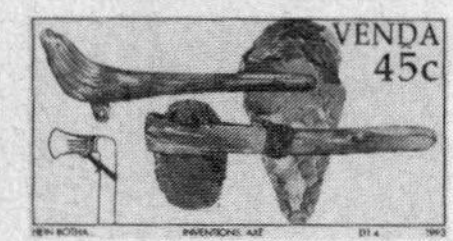

52 Axes

1993 (17 Sept). *Shoe Factory. T* **51** *and similar horiz designs. Multicoloured. P* 14×14½.

256	45 c. Type **51**	30	25
257	65 c. Shaping heel	55	60
258	85 c. Joining the upper to inner sole	75	85
259	1 r. 05, Forming sole	90	1·10
256/9	*Set of* 4	2·25	2·50

(Des H. Botha)

1993 (5 Nov). *Inventions (3rd series). T* **52** *and similar horiz designs. Multicoloured. P* 14.

260	45 c. Type **52**	40	35
261	65 c. Armour	75	65
262	85 c. Arches	95	85
263	1 r. 05, Pont du Gard aqueduct	1·10	1·25
260/3	*Set of* 4	2·75	2·75

53 Cocker Spaniel

54 Savanna Monkey

(Des D. Murphy)

1994 (14 Jan). *Dogs. T* **53** *and similar horiz designs. Multicoloured. P* 14.

264	45 c. Type **53**	55	40
265	65 c. Maltese	85	85
266	85 c. Scottish Terrier	1·10	1·10
267	1 r. 05, Miniature Schnauzer	1·40	1·60
264/7	*Set of* 4	3·50	3·50

The 85 c. value exists as a Philatelic Foundation miniature sheet.

(Des A. Ainslie)

1994 (4 Mar). *Monkeys. T* **54** *and similar horiz designs. Multicoloured. P* 14½×14.

268	45 c. Type **54**	55	45
269	65 c. Lesser Bushbaby	80	80
270	85 c. Diademed Monkey	1·10	1·10
271	1 r. 05, Thick-tailed Bushbaby	1·40	1·60
268/71	*Set of* 4	3·50	3·50
MS272	119×70 mm. Nos. 268/71	3·50	3·50

55 Red-shouldered Glossy Starlings

(Des Julia Birkhead)

1994 (29 Apr). *Starlings. T* **55** *and similar horiz designs. Multicoloured. P* 14.

273	45 c. Type **55**	60	55
274	70 c. Violet Starlings	90	90
275	95 c. African Red-winged Starlings	1·10	1·10
276	1 r. 15, Wattled Starlings	1·25	1·40
273/6	*Set of* 4	3·50	3·50

Venda was reincorporated into the Republic of South Africa on 27 April 1994. Its postal service continued to operate, using South African stamps, until 1 April 1996 when it was integrated with that of the Republic.

South Arabian Federation

ADEN

The first post office in Aden opened during January 1839, situated in what became known as the Crater district. No stamps were initially available, but, after the office was placed under the Bombay Postal Circle, stocks of the 1854 ½ a. and 1 a. stamps were placed on sale in Aden from 10 October 1854. Supplies of the 2 a. and 4 a. values did not arrive until December. Most Indian issues from the 1854 lithographs up to 1935 Silver Jubilee set can be found with Aden postmarks.

During January 1858 a further office, Aden Steamer Point, was opened in the harbour area and much of the business was transferred to it by 1869. The original Aden post office, in Crater, was renamed Aden Cantonment, later to be changed again to Aden Camp.

The first cancellation used with the Indian stamps was a plain diamond of dots. This type was also used elsewhere so that attribution to Aden is only possible when on cover. Aden was assigned "124" in the Indian postal number system and this formed the main feature of marks from 1858, either on its own or as part of a duplex.

1858 "124" Cancellation

1870 Aden Duplex

1872 Aden Steamer Point Duplex

Both post offices used this number until 1871 when Aden Cantonment was assigned "125", only to have this swiftly amended to "124A" in the same year.

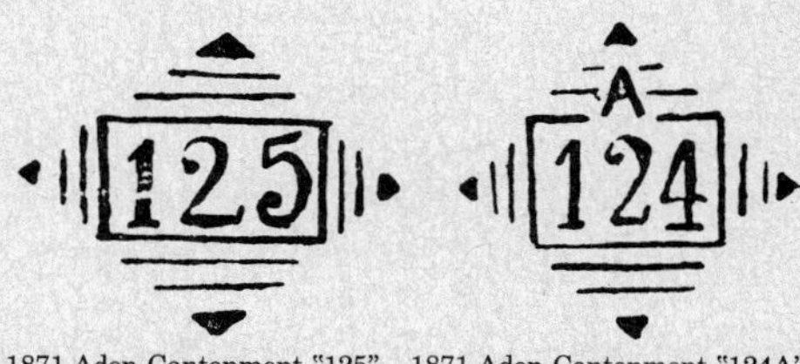

1871 Aden Cantonment "125" Cancellation

1871 Aden Cantonment "124A" Cancellation

Cancellations inscribed "Aden Steamer Point" disappear after 1874 and this office was then known simply as Aden. Following this change the office was given number "B-22" under the revised Indian P.O. scheme and this number appears as a major part of the cancellations from 1875 to 1886, either on its own or as part of a duplex, Aden Camp, the alternative name for the Cantonment office, became "B-22/1".

1875 Aden Duplex

Squared-circle types for Aden and Aden Cantonment were introduced in 1884 and 1888 to be in turn replaced by standard Indian double and single circle from 1895 onwards.

A number of other post offices were opened between 1891 and 1937:

- Dthali (*opened* 1903, *initially using* "EXPERIMENTAL P.O. B-84" *postmark; closed* 1907)
- Kamaran (*opened c* 1915, *but no civilian postmarks known before* 1925)
- Khormaksar (*opened* 1892; *closed* 1915; *reopened* 1925)
- Maalla (*opened* 1923; *closed* 1931)
- Nobat-Dakim (*opened* 1904, *initially using* "EXPERIMENTAL P.O. B-84" *postmark; closed* 1905)
- Perim (*opened* 1915; *closed* 1936)
- Sheikh Othman (*opened* 1891; *closed* 1915; *reopened* 1922; *closed* 1937)

PRICES FOR STAMPS ON COVER TO 1945

Nos. 1/15	*from* × 6
Nos. 16/27	*from* × 3

(Currency. 12 pies = 1 anna; 16 annas = 1 rupee)

1 Dhow

3 Aidrus Mosque, Crater

(Recess D.L.R.)

1937 (1 Apr). *Wmk Mult Script CA sideways. P* 13 × 12.
1 1 ½ a. yellow-green . . 3·50 1·40
2 9 p. deep green . . 3·50 1·60
3 1 a. sepia . . 3·50 70
4 2 a. scarlet . . 3·50 2·00
5 2½ a. bright blue . . 3·25 80
6 3 a. carmine . . 9·00 6·50
7 3½ a. grey-blue . . 6·50 2·00
8 8 a. pale purple . . 19·00 5·50
9 1 r. brown . . 28·00 6·00
10 2 r. yellow . . 48·00 16·00
11 5 r. deep purple . . 90·00 65·00
12 10 r. olive-green . . £200 £250
1/12 . . *Set of* 12 £375 £325
1/12 Perf "Specimen" . . *Set of* 12 £300

1937 (12 May). *Coronation. As Nos.* 118/20 *of Jamaica. P* 14.
13 1 a. sepia . . 75 80
14 2½ a. light blue . . 1·00 1·40
15 3½ a. grey-blue . . 1·25 2·50
13/15 . . *Set of* 3 2·75 4·25
13/15 Perf "Specimen" . . *Set of* 3 70·00

(Recess Waterlow)

1939 (19 Jan)–**48**. *Horiz designs as T* **3**. *Wmk Mult Script CA. P* 12½.
16 ½ a. yellowish green . . 50 60
a. Bluish green (9.48) . . 2·00 3·50
17 ¾ a. red-brown . . 1·25 1·25
18 1 a. pale blue . . 20 25
19 1½ a. scarlet . . 55 60
20 2 a. sepia . . 20 25
21 2½ a. deep ultramarine . . 40 30
22 3 a. sepia and carmine . . 60 25
23 8 a. red-orange . . 55 40
23*a* 14 a. sepia and light blue (15.1.45) . . 2·25 1·00
24 1 r. emerald-green . . 2·25 1·50
25 2 r. deep blue and magenta . . 4·75 1·75
26 5 r. red-brown and olive-green . . 11·00 7·00
27 10 r. sepia and violet . . 29·00 11·00
16/27 . . *Set of* 13 48·00 23·00
16/27 Perf "Specimen" . . *Set of* 13 £180
Designs:—½ a., 2 a., Type **3**; ¾ a., 5 r. Adenese Camel Corps; 1 a., 2 r. The Harbour; 1½ a., 1 r. Adenese Dhow; 2½ a., 8 a. Mukalla; 3 a., 14 a., 10 r. "Capture of Aden, 1839" (Capt. Rundle).

1946 (15 Oct). *Victory. As Nos.* 141/2 *of Jamaica.*
28 1½ a. carmine . . 15 70
29 2½ a. blue . . 15 30
w. Wmk inverted . . £350
28/9 Perf "Specimen" . . *Set of* 2 50·00

1949 (7 Jan). *Royal Silver Wedding. As Nos.* 143/4 *of Jamaica.*
30 1½ a. scarlet (*p* 14×15) . . 40 80
31 10 r. mauve (*p* 11½×11) . . 27·00 29·00

1949 (10 Oct). *75th Anniv of U.P.U. As Nos.* 145/8 *of Jamaica, surch with new values by Waterlow.*
32 2½ a. on 20 c. ultramarine . . 75 1·50
33 3 a. on 30 c. carmine-red . . 1·75 1·50
34 8 a. on 50 c. orange . . 1·60 1·50
35 1 r. on 1 s. blue . . 2·10 2·75
32/5 . . *Set of* 4 5·75 6·50

(New Currency. 100 cents = 1 shilling)

5
CENTS

(12)

1951 (1 Oct). *Nos.* 18 *and* 20/7 *surch with new values, in cents or shillings, as T* **12**, *or in one line between bars* (30 *c.*) *by Waterlow.*
36 5 c. on 1 a. pale blue . . 15 40
37 10 c. on 2 a. sepia . . 15 45
38 15 c. on 2½ a. deep ultramarine . . 20 1·00
a. Surch double . . £600
39 20 c. on 3 a. sepia and carmine . . 25 40
40 30 c. on 8 a. red-orange (R.) . . 25 65
41 50 c. on 8 a. red-orange . . 25 35
42 70 c. on 14 a. sepia and light blue . . 1·75 1·25
43 1 s. on 1 r. emerald-green . . 35 30
44 2 s. on 2 r. deep blue and magenta . . 6·50 2·50
a. Surch albino . . £350
45 5 s. on 5 r. red-brown and olive-green . . 16·00 8·00
46 10 s. on 10 r. sepia and violet . . 23·00 10·00
36/46 . . *Set of* 11 42·00 23·00

1953 (2 June). *Coronation. As No.* 153 *of Jamaica.*
47 15 c. black and green . . 70 1·25

14 Minaret

25 "Aden in 1572" (F. Hogenberg)

Recess Waterlow, D.L.R. from 5 Dec 1961)

1953 (15 June)–**63**. *T* **14** *and similar designs, and T* **25**. *Wmk Mult Script CA. P* 13½×13 (*No.* 72), 12×13½ (*Nos.* 57, 64, 66, 68) *or* 12 (*others*).
48 5 c. yellowish green . . 20 10
49 5 c. bluish green (1.6.55) . . 40 2·25
a. Perf 12 × 13½ (12.4.56) . . 10 40
50 10 c. orange . . 40 10
51 10 c. vermilion (1.2.55) . . 10 30
52 15 c. blue-green . . 1·25 60
53 15 c. greenish grey (26.4.59) . . 3·00 3·75
a. Deep greenish grey (16.1.62) . . 7·00 9·00
b. Greenish slate (13.11.62) . . 8·00 10·00
54 25 c. carmine-red . . 85 45
55 25 c. deep rose-red (15.3.56) . . 2·00 80
a. Rose-red (13.3.62) . . 7·00 2·75
56 35 c. deep ultramarine . . 2·50 2·00
57 35 c. deep blue (15.10.58) . . 4·50 2·50
a. Violet-blue (17.2.59) . . 7·00 2·50
58 50 c. dull blue . . 20 10
59 50 c. deep blue (1.7.55) . . 75 1·25
a. Perf 12×13½ (12.4.56) . . 75 20
aw. Wmk inverted
60 70 c. brown-grey . . 20 10
61 70 c. black (20.9.54) . . 85 35
a. Perf 12×13½ (12.4.56) . . 90 20
62 1 s. sepia and reddish violet . . 30 10
63 1 s. black and violet (1.7.55) . . 1·50 10
64 1 s. 25, blue and black (16.7.56) . . 2·25 60
a. Dull blue and black (16.1.62) . . 8·00 60
65 2 s. sepia and rose-carmine . . 1·25 50
66 2 s. black and carmine-red (1.3.56) . . 7·50 50
aw. Wmk inverted
b. Black and carmine-rose (22.1.63) . . 17·00 8·50
67 5 s. sepia and dull blue . . 1·25 50
68 5 s. black and deep dull blue (11.4.56) . . 5·00 70
a. Black and blue (11.12.62) . . 22·00 9·00
69 10 s. sepia and olive . . 1·75 8·00
70 10 s. black and bronze-green (20.9.54) . . 13·00 1·25
71 20 s. chocolate and reddish lilac . . 6·50 10·00
72 20 s. black and deep lilac (7.1.57) . . 40·00 14·00
a. Deep black and deep lilac (14.5.58) . . 48·00 18·00
48/72 . . *Set of* 25 80·00 42·00
Designs: (*as Type* **14**). *Horiz*—10 c. Camel transport; 15 c. Crater; 25 c. Mosque; 1 s. Dhow building. *Vert*—35 c. Dhow; 50 c. Map; 70 c. Salt works; 1 s. 25 Colony's badge; 2 s. Aden Protectorate levy; 5 s. Crater Pass; 10 s. Tribesman.
On No. 70 the tribesman's skirt is shaded with cross-hatching instead of with mainly diagonal lines as in No. 69.

1954 (27 Apr). *Royal Visit. As No.* 62 *but inscr* "ROYAL VISIT 1954" *at top.*
73 1 s. sepia and reddish violet . . 30 40

تعديل
الدستور
١٩٥٩

(26)

REVISED
CONSTITUTION
1959

(27)

1959 (26 Jan). *Revised Constitution. No.* 53 *optd with T* **26**, *and No.* 64 *optd with T* **27**, *in red, by Waterlow.*
74 15 c. slate-green . . 30 1·75
75 1 s. 25, blue and black . . 1·50 1·00

1963 (4 June). *Freedom from Hunger. As No.* 80 *of Lesotho.*
76 1 s. 25, bluish green . . 1·75 1·60

1964 (5 Feb)–**65**. *As Nos.* 48, *etc. but wmk* w **12**. *P* 12 (10 *c.*, 15 *c.*, 25 *c.*, 1 *s.*) *or* 12 × 13½ (*others*).
77 5 c. green (16.2.65) . . 40 3·00
78 10 c. bright orange . . 20 75
79 15 c. greenish grey . . 30 3·50
w. Wmk inverted . . 75·00
80 25 c. carmine-red . . 30 40
81 35 c. indigo-violet . . 2·75 2·75
82 50 c. indigo-blue . . 20 30
a. Pale indigo-blue (16.2.65) . . 30 30
aw. Wmk inverted
83 70 c. black . . 30 1·40
a. Brownish grey (16.2.65) . . 30 1·00
84 1 s. black and violet (10.3.64) . . 11·00 2·25
85 1 s. 25, ultramarine and black (10.3.64) . . 11·00 2·25
86 2 s. black and carmine-rose (16.2.65) . . 2·75 24·00
77/86 . . *Set of* 10 26·00 35·00

The stamps of Aden were withdrawn on 31 March 1965 and superseded by those of the South Arabian Federation.

ADEN PROTECTORATE STATES

KATHIRI STATE OF SEIYUN

The stamps of ADEN were used in Kathiri State of Seiyun from 22 May 1937 until 1942. A further office was opened at Tarim on 11 December 1940.

PRICES FOR STAMPS ON COVER TO 1945
Nos. 1/11 *from* × 10

1 Sultan of Seiyun

2 Seiyun

(Recess D.L.R.)

1942 (July–Oct). *Designs as T* **1/2**. *Wmk Mult Script CA. T* **1**, *perf* 14; *others, perf* 12 × 13 (*vert*) *or* 13 × 12 (*horiz*).
1 ½ a. blue-green . . 15 35
2 ¾ a. brown . . 15 45
3 1 a. blue . . 20 35
4 1½ a. carmine . . 30 40
5 2 a. sepia . . 30 60
6 2½ a. blue . . 65 1·00
7 3 a. sepia and carmine . . 1·00 1·40
8 8 a. red . . 50 50
9 1 r. green . . 1·50 75
10 2 r. blue and purple . . 7·00 9·00
11 5 r. brown and green . . 17·00 12·00
1/11 . . *Set of* 11 26·00 24·00
1/11 Perf "Specimen" . . *Set of* 11 £140
Designs:—½ to 1 a. Type **1**. *Vert as T* **2**—2 a. Tarim; 2½ a. Mosque, Seiyun; 1 r. South Gate, Tarim; 5 r. Mosque entrance, Tarim. *Horiz as T* **2**—3 a. Fortress, Tarim; 8 a. Mosque, Seiyun; 2 r. A Kathiri house.

VICTORY
ISSUE
8TH JUNE 1946

(10)

1946 (15 Oct). *Victory. No.* 4 *optd with T* **10**, *and No.* 6 *optd similarly but in four lines, by De La Rue.*
12 1½ a. carmine . . 10 30
13 2½ a. blue (R.) . . 10 10
a. Opt inverted . . £375
12/13 Perf "Specimen" . . *Set of* 2 55·00
No. 13 is known with overprint double but the second impression is almost coincident with the first.

1949 (17 Jan). *Royal Silver Wedding. As Nos.* 143/4 *of Jamaica.*
14 1½ a. scarlet . . 30 2·00
15 5 r. green . . 12·00 9·00

1949 (10 Oct). *75th Anniv of U.P.U. As Nos.* 145/8 *of Jamaica, surch with new values by Waterlow.*
16 2½ a. on 20 c. ultramarine . . 25 50
17 3 a. on 30 c. carmine-red . . 1·00 65
18 8 a. on 50 c. orange . . 40 75
19 1 r. on 1 s. blue . . 60 90
16/19 . . *Set of* 4 2·00 2·50

5 CTS (11)

50 CENTS (12)

5/- (13)

1951 (1 Oct). *Currency changed. Nos.* 3 *and* 5/11 *surch as T* **11** (5 *c.*), **12** (10 *c.* ("CTS"), 15 *c.* ("CTS"), 20 *c. and* 50 *c.*) *or* **13** (1*s. to* 5*s.*), *by Waterlow.*
20 5 c. on 1 a. blue (R.) . . 15 20
21 10 c. on 2 a. sepia . . 30 20
22 15 c. on 2½ a. blue . . 15 20
23 20 c. on 3 a. sepia and carmine . . 15 50
24 50 c. on 8 a. red . . 15 20
25 1 s. on 1 r. green . . 20 50
26 2 s. on 2 r. blue and purple . . 2·25 14·00
27 5 s. on 5 r. brown and green . . 13·50 29·00
20/27 . . *Set of* 8 15·00 40·00

1953 (2 June). *Coronation. As No.* 153 *of Jamaica.*
28 15 c. black and deep green . . 30 1·40

14 Sultan Hussein

15 Tarim

(Des Freya Stark and H. Ingram. Recess D.L.R.)

1954 (15 Jan). *As Nos.* 1/11 (*but with portrait of Sultan Hussein as in T* **14/15**). *Wmk Mult Script CA. T* **14**, *perf* 12½; *others, perf* 12 × 13 (*vert*) *or* 13 × 12 (*horiz*).
29 5 c. sepia . . 10 10
30 10 c. deep blue . . 15 10
31 15 c. deep bluish green . . 15 10
32 25 c. carmine-red . . 15 10
33 35 c. deep blue . . 15 10
34 50 c. deep brown and carmine-red . . 15 10
35 1 s. brown-orange . . 15 10
36 2 s. deep yellow-green . . 4·00 2·00
37 5 s. deep blue and violet . . 6·00 3·00
38 10 s. yellow-brown and violet . . 6·00 6·50
29/38 . . *Set of* 10 15·00 11·00

16 Qarn Adh Dhabi

17 Seiyun

(Recess D.L.R.)

1964 (1 July). *Designs as T* **16/17**. *W w* **12**. *P* 12 × 13 (70 *c.*) *or* 13 × 12 (*others*).
39 70 c. black . . 1·75 65
40 1 s. 25 c. blue-green . . 1·75 5·50
41 1 s. 50 c. deep reddish violet . . 1·75 5·50
39/41 . . *Set of* 3 4·75 10·50
Design: *Horiz as T* **17**—1 s. 50 c. Gheil Omer.

(New Currency. 1000 fils = 1 dinar)

SOUTH ARABIA 5 FILS — **19**
SOUTH ARABIA 500 FILS — **(20)**
SOUTH ARABIA 50 FILS — **(21)**

1966 (1 Apr). *New Currency. Nos. 29/41 surch as T* **19/21**.

No.	Description	Unused	Used
42	5 f. on 5 c. (**19**)	15	10
	a. Surch quadruple, one inverted	55·00	
43	5 f. on 10 c. (**19**) (R.)	15	30
44	10 f. on 15 c. (**21**) (R.)	15	30
	a. Surch inverted	85·00	
45	15 f. on 25 c. (**20**)	20	30
	w. Wmk inverted	42·00	
46	20 f. on 35 c. (**20**) (R.)	15	30
47	25 f. on 50 c. (**21**) (R.)	15	40
48	35 f. on 70 c. (**20**) (R.)	20	1·25
49	50 f. on 1 s. (**21**)	20	15
50	65 f. on 1 s. 25 (**21**)	20	15
51	75 f. on 1 s. 50 (**21**)	20	30
52	100 f. on 2 s. (**20**) (R.)	35·00	42·00
53	250 f. on 5 s. (**21**) (R.)	1·40	3·75
54	500 f. on 10 s. (**20**)	1·75	3·75
42/54	*Set of* 13	35·00	45·00

SOUTH ARABIA 5 FILS — **(22)**
SOUTH ARABIA 50 FILS — **(23)**
SOUTH ARABIA 15 FILS — **(24)**

1966. *Nos. 29/41 surch with T* **22/4**.

No.	Description	Unused	Used
55	5 f. on 5 c. (**22**) (B.)	70	30
	a. Surch inverted	60·00	
56	5 f. on 10 c. (**22**) (R.)	1·00	30
57	10 f. on 15 c. (**23**) (Y.)	1·00	30
	a. Surch inverted	50·00	
58	15 f. on 25 c. (**24**) (B.)	1·00	30
	a. Surch inverted	60·00	
59	20 f. on 35 c. (**24**) (Y.)	1·00	30
60	25 f. on 50 c. (**23**) (B.)	1·00	30
61	35 f. on 70 c. (**24**) (Br.)	1·00	40
62	50 f. on 1 s. (**23**) (G.)	1·00	60
	a. Stop after "FILS"	16·00	
63	65 f. on 1 s. 25 (**23**) (Y.)	1·00	1·00
64	75 f. on 1 s. 50 (**23**) (G.)	1·00	1·75
	a. Surch inverted	60·00	
65	100 f. on 2 s. (**24**) (Y.)	2·75	1·75
	a. Surch inverted	50·00	
66	250 f. on 5 s. (**23**) (Y.)	2·75	3·50
	a. Surch inverted	50·00	
67	500 f. on 10 s. (**24**) (G.)	2·75	7·00
55/67	*Set of* 13	16·00	16·00

HELSINKI 1952 — **(25)**
INTERNATIONAL COOPERATION THROUGH OLYMPICS — **(26)**

1966. *History of Olympic Games. Nos. 57, 59, 61/7 Optd as T* **25/6** *in red.*

No.	Description	Unused	Used
68	10 f. on 15 c. deep bluish green (**25** ("LOS ANGELES 1932"))	25	25
	a. Optd as T **25** inverted		
69	20 f. on 35 c. deep blue (**25** ("BERLIN 1936"))	35	35
70	35 f. on 70 c. black (**26**)	35	35
	a. Opt T **26** inverted	10·00	
71	50 f. on 1 s. brown-orange (**25** ("LONDON 1948"))	40	40
	a. Stop after "FILS"	10·00	
72	65 f. on 1 s. 25, blue-green (**25**)	55	80
73	75 f. on 1 s. 50, deep reddish violet (**25** ("MELBOURNE 1956"))	70	1·25
74	100 f. on 2 s. deep yellow-green (**25** ("ROME 1960"))	80	1·40
75	250 f. on 5 s. deep blue and violet (**25** ("TOKYO 1964"))	1·40	2·75
	a. Surch inverted	60·00	
76	500 f. on 10 s. yellow-brown and violet (**25** ("MEXICO CITY 1968"))	1·75	3·75
68/76	*Set of* 9	6·00	10·00

CHAMPION: ENGLAND — **(27)**
FOOTBALL 1966 — **(28)**

1966 (19 Sept). *World Cup Football Championships. Nos. 57, 59, 61/2, 65/7 optd with T* **27/8**.

No.	Description	Unused	Used
77	10 f. on 15 c. deep bluish green (**27**)	70	30
78	20 f. on 35 c. deep blue (**28**)	90	40
79	35 f. on 70 c. black (**28**)	1·25	40
80	50 f. on 1 s. brown-orange (**27**)	1·40	40
	a. Stop after "FILS"	17·00	
81	100 f. on 2 s. deep yellow-green (**28**)	3·75	1·75
82	250 f. on 5 s. deep blue and violet (**27**)	7·50	4·50
83	500 f. on 10 s. yellow-brown and violet (**28**)	9·50	7·00
77/83	*Set of* 7	22·00	13·50

29 "Telstar"

(Photo State Ptg Wks, Vienna)

1966 (25 Oct). *I.T.U. Centenary* (1965). *T* **29** *and similar vert designs. P* 13½.

No.	Description	Unused	Used
84	5 f. blackish green, black and reddish violet	1·25	25
85	10 f. maroon, black and bright green	1·40	30
86	15 f. Prussian blue, black and orange	1·75	40
87	25 f. blackish green, black and orange-red	2·50	50
88	35 f. maroon, black and deep olive-yellow	2·75	70
89	50 f. Prussian blue, black and orange-brown	3·25	1·10
90	65 f. blackish green, black and orange-yellow	3·75	1·25
84/90	*Set of* 7	15·00	4·00

Designs:—10, 35 f. "Relay"; 15, 50 f. "Ranger"; others, Type **29**.

32 Churchill at Easel

(Photo State Ptg Wks, Vienna)

1966 (Dec). *Sir Winston Churchill's Paintings. T* **32** *and similar designs in black and gold* (5 *f.*) *or multicoloured* (*others*). *P* 13½.

No.	Description	Unused	Used
91	5 f. Type **32**	1·50	15
92	10 f. "Antibes"	1·75	15
93	15 f. "Flowers" (*vert*)	1·75	20
94	20 f. "Tapestries"	1·75	35
95	25 f. "Village, Lake Lugano"	1·75	35
96	35 f. "Church, Lake Como" (*vert*)	2·00	40
97	50 f. "Flowers at Chartwell" (*vert*)	2·25	65
98	65 f. Type **32**	2·75	90
91/8	*Set of* 8	14·00	2·75

WORLD PEACE PANDIT NEHRU — **(39)**

40 "Master Crewe as Henry VIII" (Sir Joshua Reynolds)

1967. *"World Peace". Nos. 57, 59, 61/7 optd as T* **39** *in various sizes of type.*

No.	Description	Unused	Used
99	10 f. on 15 c. deep bluish green (Type **39**) (R.)	1·25	85
100	20 f. on 35 c. deep blue ("WINSTON CHURCHILL") (R.)	4·50	2·25
101	35 f. on 70 c. black ("DAG HAMMARSKJOLD") (B.)	50	80
102	50 f. on 1 s. brown-orange ("JOHN F. KENNEDY") (R.)	60	90
	a. Stop after "FILS"	15·00	
103	65 f. on 1 s. 25, blue-green ("LUDWIG ERHARD") (Pk.)	70	1·10
104	75 f. on 1 s. 50 dp reddish violet ("LYNDON JOHNSON") (B.)	80	1·25
105	100 f. on 2 s. deep yellow-green ("ELEANOR ROOSEVELT") (B.)	1·00	1·75
106	250 f. on 5 s. dp blue and violet ("WINSTON CHURCHILL") (R.)	13·00	9·50
107	500 f. on 10 s. yellow-brown & violet ("JOHN F. KENNEDY") (R.)	5·00	10·00
99/107	*Set of* 9	24·00	25·00

(Photo State Ptg Wks, Vienna)

1967. *Paintings. T* **40** *and similar multicoloured designs. P* 13½.

No.	Description	Unused	Used
108	5 f. Type **40**	30	25
109	10 f. "The Dancer" (Degas)	35	30
110	15 f. "The Fifer" (Manet)	40	35
111	20 f. "Stag at Sharkey's" (boxing match, G. Bellows)	45	40
112	25 f. "Don Manuel Osorio" (Goya)	50	45
113	35 f. "St. Martin distributing his Cloak" (A. van Dyck)	70	65
114	50 f. "The Blue Boy" (Gainsborough)	85	75
115	65 f. "The White Horse" (Gauguin)	1·10	1·00
116	75 f. "Mona Lisa" (Da Vinci) (45×62 *mm*)	1·40	1·25
108/16	*Set of* 9	5·50	4·75

SCOTT CARPENTER — **(49)**

50 Churchill Crown

1967. *American Astronauts. Nos. 57, 59, 61/2 and 65/6 optd as T* **49** *in various sizes of type, in red.*

No.	Description	Unused	Used
117	10 f. on 15 c. deep bluish green ("ALAN SHEPARD, JR.")	55	1·00
118	20 f. on 35 c. dp blue ("VIRGIL GRISSOM")	70	1·25
119	35 f. on 70 c. black ("JOHN GLENN, JR.")	95	1·50
120	50 f. on 1 s. brown-orange (Type **49**)	95	1·50
	a. Stop after "FILS"	16·00	
121	100 f. on 2 s. deep yellow-green ("WALTER SCHIRRA, JR.")	2·25	3·50
122	250 f. on 5 s. deep blue & violet ("GORDON COOPER, JR.")	3·50	6·50
	a. Opt (as T **49**) double	£100	
117/122	*Set of* 6	8·00	13·50

1967 (Mar). *Churchill Commemoration. Photo. P* 13½.

No.	Description	Unused	Used
123 **50**	75 f. multicoloured	9·00	6·50

Appendix

The following stamps have either been issued in excess of postal needs, or have not been made available to the public in reasonable quantities at face value. Miniature sheets, imperforate stamps etc., are excluded from this section.

1967

Hunting. 20 *f.*
Olympic Games, Grenoble. Postage 10, 25, 35, 50, 75 *f. Air* 100, 200 *f.*
Scout Jamboree, Idaho. Air 150 *f.*
Paintings by Renoir. Postage 10, 35, 50, 65, 75 *f. Air* 100, 200, 250 *f.*
Paintings by Toulouse-Lautrec. Postage 10, 35, 50, 65, 75 *f. Air* 100, 200, 250 *f.*

The National Liberation Front is said to have taken control of Kathiri State of Seiyun on 1 October 1967.

QU'AITI STATE IN HADHRAMAUT

The stamps of ADEN were used in Qu'aiti State in Hadhramaut from 22 April 1937 until 1942. The main post office was at Mukalla. Other offices existed at Du'an (*opened* 1940), Gheil Ba Wazir (*opened* 1942), Haura (*opened* 1940), Shibam (*opened* 1940) and Shihr (*opened* 1939).

PRICES FOR STAMPS ON COVER TO 1945
Nos. 1/11 *from* × 6

I. ISSUES INSCR "SHIHR AND MUKALLA"

1 Sultan of Shihr and Mukalla

2 Mukalla Harbour

VICTORY ISSUE 8TH JUNE 1946 — **(10)**

(Recess D.L.R.)

1942 (July)–**46**. *Wmk Mult Script CA. Designs as T* **1** (½ *to* 1 *a.*) *or T* **2** (*others*). *P* 14 (½ *to* 1 *a.*), 12 × 13 (1½, 2, 3 *a. and* 1 *r.*) *or* 13 × 12 (*others*).

No.	Description	Unused	Used
1	½ a. blue-green	50	40
	a. Olive-green (12.46)	24·00	35·00
2	¾ a. brown	50	30
3	1 a. blue	60	60
4	1½ a. carmine	70	40
5	2 a. sepia	80	60
6	2½ a. blue	40	30
7	3 a. sepia and carmine	80	40
8	8 a. red	50	40
9	1 r. green	1·75	1·50
	a. "A" of "CA" missing from wmk	†	—
10	2 r. blue and purple	10·00	8·00
11	5 r. brown and green	14·00	10·00
1/11	*Set of* 11	27·00	21·00
1/11 Perf "Specimen"	*Set of* 11	£140	

Designs: *Vert*—2 a. Gateway of Shihr; 3 a. Outpost of Mukalla; 1 r. Du'an. *Horiz*—2½ a. Shibam; 8 a. 'Einat; 2 r. Mosque in Hureidha; 5 r. Meshhed.

1946 (15 Oct). *Victory. No. 4 optd. with T* **10** *and No. 6 optd similarly, but in three lines, by De La Rue.*
12 1½ a. carmine 10 30
13 2½ a. blue (R.) 10 10
12/13 Perf "Specimen" .. .. *Set of* 2 55·00

1949 (17 Jan). *Royal Silver Wedding. As Nos.* 143/4 *of Jamaica.*
14 1½ a. scarlet .. .. 50 2·00
15 5 r. green .. .. 13·00 9·00

1949 (10 Oct). *75th Anniv of U.P.U. As Nos.* 145/8 *of Jamaica, surch with new values by Waterlow.*
16 2½ a. on 20 c. ultramarine 20 20
17 3 a. on 30 c. carmine-red .. .. 1·10 50
18 8 a. on 50 c. orange 55 60
19 1 r. on 1s. blue 60 50
a. Surch omitted £1100
16/19 .. .. *Set of* 4 2·25 1·60

1951 (1 Oct). *Currency changed. Surch with new values in cents or shillings as T* **11** (5 *c.*), **12** (10 *c.* ("CTS"), 15 *c.*, 20 *c. and* 50 *c.*) *or* **13** (1 *s. to* 5 *s.*) *of Seiyun, by Waterlow.*
20 5 c. on 1 a. blue (R.) 15 15
21 10 c. on 2 a. sepia 15 15
22 15 c. on 2½ a. blue 15 15
23 20 c. on 3 a. sepia and carmine 30 20
a. Surch double, one albino.. .. .. £170
24 50 c. on 8 a. red 20 40
25 1 s. on 1 r. green 45 25
26 2 s. on 2 r. blue and purple .. .. .. 5·00 8·00
27 5 s. on 5 r. brown and green .. .. .. 8·00 13·00
20/27 .. .. *Set of* 8 13·00 20·00

1953 (2 June). *Coronation. As No.* 153 *of Jamaica.*
28 15 c. black and deep blue 75 55

II. ISSUES INSCR "HADHRAMAUT"

11 Metal Work

22 Metal Work

(Des Mme M. de Sturler Raemaekers. Recess D.L.R.)

1955 (1 Sept)–**63**. *T* **11** *and similar designs. Wmk Mult Script CA. P* 11½ × 13–13½ (*vert*) *or* 14 (*horiz*).
29 5 c. greenish blue 30 10
30 10 c. grey-black 40 10
31 15 c. deep green 30 10
a. Bronze-green (9.3.63) 30 30
32 25 c. carmine-red 40 10
33 35 c. blue 50 10
34 50 c. orange-red 40 10
a. Red-orange (9.3.63) 40 30
35 90 c. sepia 50 15
36 1 s. black and deep lilac 50 10
37 1 s. 25, black and red-orange 55 55
38 2 s. black and indigo .. .. .. 4·00 60
39 5 s. black and bluish green .. .. 5·00 1·50
40 10 s. black and lake .. .. .. 5·50 5·50
29/40 .. .. *Set of* 12 17·00 8·00

Designs: *Vert*—10 c. Mat-making; 15 c. Weaving; 25 c. Pottery; 35 c. Building; 50 c. Date cultivation; 90 c. Agriculture. *Horiz*—1 s. Fisheries; 1 s. 25, 10 s. Lime-burning; 2 s. Dhow building; 5 s. Agriculture.

1963 (20 Oct). *As Nos.* 29/40 *but with inset portrait of Sultan Awadh bin Saleh el-Qu'aiti as in T* **22** *and wmk* w **12**.
41 5 c. greenish blue 10 20
42 10 c. grey-black 10 30
43 15 c. bronze-green 10 30
44 25 c. carmine-red 10 20
45 35 c. blue 10 50
46 50 c. red-orange 10 30
47 70 c. deep brown (as 90 c.) 15 30
48 1 s. black and deep lilac 20 20
49 1 s. 25, black and red-orange .. .. 45 2·25
50 2 s. black and indigo-blue .. .. .. 3·25 1·00
51 5 s. black and bluish green .. .. .. 12·00 17·00
52 10 s. black and lake .. .. 15·00 17·00
41/52 .. .. *Set of* 12 28·00 35·00

(New Currency. 1000 fils = 1 dinar)

1966 (1 Apr). *New currency. Nos.* 41/52 *surch as T* **20/21** *of Kathiri State of Seiyun.*
53 5 f. on 5 c. greenish blue (**20**) (R.) 10 40
54 5 f. on 10 c. grey-black (**20**) (R.) 10 40
55 10 f. on 15 c. bronze-green (**20**) (R.) 10 30
56 15 f. on 25 c. carmine-red (**20**) 10 40
57 20 f. on 35 c. blue (**20**) (R.) 10 90
58 25 f. on 50 c. red-orange (**20**).. .. .. 10 40
59 35 f. on 70 c. deep brown (**20**) (R.) 10 40
60 50 f. on 1 s. black and deep lilac (**21**) (R.) .. 10 30
61 65 f. on 1 s. 25, black and red-orange (**21**) (R.) 40 30
62 100 f. on 2 s. black and indigo-blue (**21**) (R.) .. 70 75
63 250 f. on 5 s. black and bluish green (**21**) (R.).. 1·00 1·50
64 500 f. on 10 s. black and lake (**21**) (R.) .. 18·00 3·00
53/64 .. .. *Set of* 12 19·00 8·00

1874–1965
WINSTON CHURCHILL
(**23**)

1917-1963
JOHN F. KENNEDY
(**24**)

1966. *Churchill Commemoration. Nos.* 54/6 *optd with T* **23**.
65 5 f. on 10 c. grey-black (R.) .. .. .. 5·50 7·50
66 10 f. on 15 c. bronze-green (R.) .. .. 6·50 8·50
a. Opt T **23** inverted .. .. .. 75·00
67 15 f. on 25 c. carmine-red (B.).. .. .. 8·50 11·00
65/7 .. .. *Set of* 3 18·00 24·00

1966. *President Kennedy Commemoration. Nos.* 57/9 *optd with T* **24**.
68 20 f. on 35 c. blue (R.) .. .. 2·00 6·00
69 25 f. on 50 c. red-orange (B.) .. .. .. 2·50 6·50
70 35 f. on 70 c. deep brown (B.) .. .. .. 3·50 7·50
68/70 .. .. *Set of* 3 7·25 18·00

25 World Cup Emblem

(Photo State Ptg Wks. Vienna)

1966. *World Cup Football Championship, England. T* **25** *and similar diamond-shaped designs. P* 13½.
71 5 f. maroon and yellow-orange .. .. 1·75 25
72 10 f. slate-violet and light green .. .. 2·00 25
73 15 f. maroon and yellow-orange .. .. 2·25 30
74 20 f. slate-violet and light green .. .. 2·50 40
75 25 f. blackish green and orange-red .. .. 2·75 55
76 35 f. blue and yellow .. .. 3·25 80
77 50 f. blackish green and orange-red .. .. 3·75 1·10
78 65 f. blue and yellow .. .. 4·50 1·40
71/78 .. .. *Set of* 8 20·00 4·50

Designs:—10, 35 f. Wembley Stadium; 15, 50 f. Footballers; 20 f. Jules Rimet Cup and football; 25, 65 f. Type **25**.

29 Mexican Hat and Blanket

(Photo State Ptg Wks, Vienna)

1966 (25 Oct). *Pre-Olympic Games, Mexico* (1968). *P* 13½.
79 **29** 75 f. sepia and light yellow-green .. 1·25 75

30 Telecommunications Satellite

(Photo State Ptg Wks, Vienna)

1966 (Dec). *International Co-operation Year* (1965). *T* **30** *and similar horiz designs. P* 13½.
80 5 f. maroon, bright purple and emerald .. 2·25 35
81 10 f. violet, orange, blue-green and new blue 2·50 35
82 15 f. maroon, new blue and red .. .. 2·75 40
83 20 f. Prussian blue, purple and red .. 3·00 45
84 25 f. violet, olive-yellow, red and emerald .. 3·00 50
85 35 f. maroon, rose-red and new blue .. 3·50 80
a. New blue (face values) omitted .. £150
86 50 f. maroon, green and red .. .. 4·50 1·25
87 65 f. chocolate, bluish violet and red .. 5·00 1·75
80/87 .. .. *Set of* 8 23·00 5·25

Designs:—10 f. Olympic runner (inscribed "ROME 1960"); 15 f. Fishes; 25 f. Olympic runner (inscribed "TOKIO 1964"); 50 f. Tobacco plant; others, Type **30**.

NEW INFORMATION

The editor is always interested to correspond with people who have new information that will improve or correct the Catalogue.

Appendix

The following stamps have either been issued in excess of postal needs, or have not been made available to the public in reasonable quantities at face value. Miniature sheets, imperforate stamps etc. are excluded from this section.

1967

Stampex Stamp Exhibition, London. Postage 5, 10, 15, 20, 25 *f. Air* 50, 65 *f.*
Amphilex International Stamp Exhibition, Amsterdam. Air 75 *f.*
Olympic Games, Mexico (1968), 75 *f.*
Paintings. Postage 5, 10, 15, 20, 25 *f. Air* 50, 65 *f.*
Scout Jamboree, Idaho. Air 35 *f.*
Space Research. Postage 10, 25, 35, 50, 75 *f. Air* 100, 250 *f.*

The National Liberation Front is said to have taken control of Qu'aiti State in Hadhramaut on 17 September 1967.

MAHRA SULTANATE OF QISHN AND SOCOTRA

(Currency. 1000 fils = 1 dinar)

1 Mahra Flag

(Des and litho Harrison)

1967 (12 Mar). *Flag in green, black and vermilion; inscriptions in black; background colours given. P* 14 × 14½.
1 **1** 5 f. mauve .. .. 1·50 30
2 10 f. buff.. .. .. 1·50 30
3 15 f. sage-green .. .. 1·50 30
4 20 f. red-orange .. .. 1·50 30
5 25 f. yellow-brown .. .. 1·50 30
6 35 f. turquoise-green .. .. .. 1·50 30
7 50 f. new blue .. .. 1·50 30
8 65 f. blackish brown .. .. .. 1·50 30
9 100 f. violet .. .. 1·50 30
10 250 f. rose-red .. .. 1·50 35
11 500 f. grey-green .. .. 1·50 50
1/11 .. .. *Set of* 11 15·00 3·25

Appendix

The following stamps have either been issued in excess of postal needs, or have not been made available to the public in reasonable quantities at face value. Miniature sheets, imperforate stamps etc., are excluded from this section.

1967

Scout Jamboree, Idaho. 15, 75, 100, 150 *f.*
President Kennedy Commemoration. Postage 10, 15, 25, 50, 75, 100, 150 *f. Air* 250, 500 *f.*
Olympic Games, Mexico (1968). *Postage* 10, 25, 50 *f. Air* 250, 500 *f.*

The National Liberation Front is said to have taken control of Mahra Sultanate of Qishn and Socotra on 1 October 1967.

SOUTH ARABIAN FEDERATION

Comprising Aden and most of the territories of the former Western Aden Protectorate plus one from the Eastern Aden Protectorate.

(Currency. 100 cents=1 shilling)

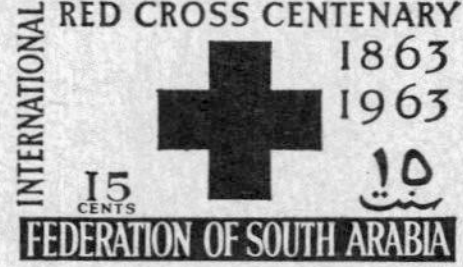

1 Red Cross Emblem

1963 (25 Nov). *Red Cross Centenary. W* w **12.** *P* 13½.
1 **1** 15 c. red and black 40 30
2 1 s. 25, red and blue 85 95

(New Currency. 1000 fils=1 dinar)

2 Federal Crest

3 Federal Flag

(Des V. Whiteley. Photo Harrison)

1965 (1 Apr). *P* 14½ × 14 (*T* **2**) *or* 14½ (*T* **3**).
3 **2** 5 f. blue 20 10
4 10 f. violet-blue 20 10
5 15 f. turquoise-green 20 10
6 20 f. green 20 10
7 25 f. yellow-brown 20 10
8 30 f. yellow-bistre 20 10
9 35 f. chestnut 20 10
10 50 f. red 20 10
11 65 f. yellow-green 30 30
12 75 f. crimson 30 10

13 3 100 f. multicoloured 30 10
14 250 f. multicoloured .. .. 3·00 30
15 500 f. multicoloured .. .. 6·50 50
16 1 d. multicoloured .. .. 13·00 7·00
3/16 .. .. *Set of* 14 22·00 7·50

4 I.C.Y. Emblem

(Des V. Whiteley. Litho Harrison)

1965 (24 Oct). *International Co-operation Year.* W w **12.** P 14½.
17 4 5 f. reddish purple and turquoise-green 20 10
18 65 f. deep bluish green and lavender .. 70 20

5 Sir Winston Churchill and St. Paul's Cathedral in Wartime

(Des Jennifer Toombs. Photo Harrison)

1966 (24 Jan). *Churchill Commemoration. No wmk.* P 14.
19 5 5 f. black, cerise, gold and new blue .. 10 10
20 10 f. black, cerise, gold and deep green 30 10
21 65 f. black, cerise, gold and brown .. 80 20
22 125 f. black, cerise, gold and bluish violet 1·25 1·75
19/22 .. .. *Set of* 4 2·25 1·90

6 Footballer's Legs, Ball and Jules Rimet Cup

(Des V. Whiteley. Litho Harrison)

1966 (1 July). *World Cup Football Championship, England. No wmk.* P 14.
23 6 10 f. violet, yellow-green, lake & yell-brn 50 10
24 50 f. chocolate, blue-grn, lake & yell-brn 1·50 20

7 W.H.O. Building

(Des M. Goaman. Litho Harrison)

1966 (20 Sept). *Inauguration of W.H.O. Headquarters, Geneva. No wmk.* P 14.
25 7 10 f. black, yellow-green and light blue 50 10
26 75 f. black, light purple and yellow-brown 1·25 45

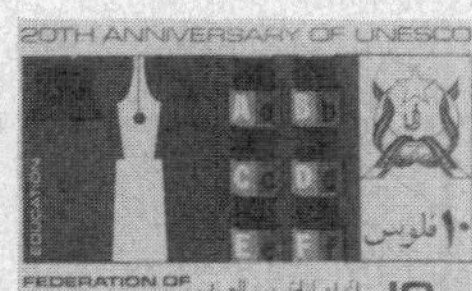

8 "Education"

9 "Science"

10 "Culture"

(Des Jennifer Toombs. Litho Harrison)

1966 (15 Dec). *20th Anniv of U.N.E.S.C.O. No wmk.* P 14.
27 8 10 f. slate-violet, red, yellow and orange 30 20
28 9 65 f. orange-yellow, vio & dp olive .. 1·25 1·40
29 10 125 f. black, bright purple and orange .. 3·25 4·75
27/9 .. .. *Set of* 3 4·25 5·75

The South Arabian Federation became fully independent on 30 November 1967. Later issues for this area will be found listed in Part 19 (*Middle East*) of this catalogue under Yemen People's Democratic Republic.

South Australia *see* Australia

Southern Cameroons *see* Cameroon

Southern Nigeria *see* Nigeria

Southern Rhodesia *see* Zimbabwe

South Georgia and the South Sandwich Islands

As South Georgia was a dependency of the Falkland Islands between 1963 and 1980 stamps so inscribed are listed under FALKLAND ISLANDS DEPENDENCIES.

Under the new constitution, effective 3 October 1985, South Georgia and South Sandwich Islands ceased to be dependencies of the Falkland Islands.

(Des A. Theobald. Litho Questa)

1986 (21 Apr). *60th Birthday of Queen Elizabeth II. Vert designs as T* **230a** *of Jamaica. Multicoloured.* W w **16.** P 14½×14.
153 10p. Four generations of Royal Family at Prince Charles' christening, 1948 .. 35 35
154 24p. With Prince Charles and Lady Diana Spencer, Buckingham Palace, 1981 .. 60 65
155 29p. In robes of Order of the British Empire, St. Paul's Cathedral, London .. 60 70
156 45p. At banquet, Canada, 1976 .. .. 80 95
157 58p. At Crown Agents Head Office, London, 1983 .. .. 1·00 1·25
153/7 .. .. *Set of* 5 3·00 3·50

25a Prince Andrew and Miss Sarah Ferguson at Ascot

26 Southern Black-backed Gull

(Des D. Miller. Litho Questa)

1986 (10 Nov). *Royal Wedding.* T **25a** *and similar vert designs. Multicoloured.* W w **16.** P 14½×14.
158 17p. Type **25a** .. .. 75 1·10
159 22p. Wedding photograph .. .. 85 1·25
160 29p. Prince Andrew with Westland WG-13 Lynx helicopter on board H.M.S. *Brazen* .. .. 1·50 1·50
158/60 .. .. *Set of* 3 2·75 3·50

(Des T. Chater. Litho Walsall)

1987 (24 Apr). *Birds.* T **26** *and similar multicoloured designs.* W w **16** (*sideways on horiz designs*). P 14½.
161 1p. Type **26** 40 60
162 2p. Blue-eyed Cormorant 50 60
163 3p. Snowy Sheathbill (*vert*) 60 70
w. Wmk inverted .. .. .. 35·00
164 4p. Great Skua (*vert*) 50 70
165 5p. Pintado Petrel ("Cape Pigeon") .. 50 70
166 6p. Georgian Diving Petrel 50 70
167 7p. South Georgia Pipit (*vert*) 60 85
168 8p. Georgian Teal ("South Georgian Pintail") (*vert*) 60 85
169 9p. Fairy Prion .. .. 60 1·10
170 10p. Chinstrap Penguin .. .. .. 80 1·10
171 20p. Macaroni Penguin (*vert*) .. .. 90 1·40
172 25p. Light-mantled Sooty Albatross (*vert*) 90 1·50
w. Wmk inverted £225
173 50p. Giant Petrel (*vert*) .. .. 1·50 2·25
174 £1 Wandering Albatross .. .. 2·25 3·50
175 £3 King Penguin (*vert*) .. .. 6·00 7·50
161/75 .. .. *Set of* 15 15·00 22·00

26a I.G.Y. Logo

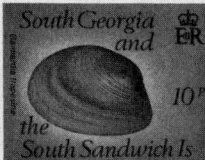

27 *Gaimardia trapesina*

(Des L. Curtis. Litho Questa)

1987 (5 Dec). *30th Anniv of International Geophysical Year.* T **26a** *and similar vert designs.* W w **16.** P 14½×14.
176 24p. black and pale turquoise-blue 70 55
177 29p. multicoloured 75 60
178 58p. multicoloured .. .. 1·40 1·25
176/8 .. .. *Set of* 3 2·50 2·10
Designs:—29p. Grytviken; 58p. Glaciologist using hand-drill to take core sample.

(Des I. Strange. Litho Questa)

1988 (26 Feb). *Sea Shells.* T **27** *and similar horiz designs. Multicoloured.* W w **16** (*sideways**). P 14×14½.
179 10p. Type **27** 45 30
w. Wmk Crown to right of CA ..
180 24p. *Margarella tropidophoroides* .. 70 60
181 29p. *Trophon geversianus* 75 65
182 58p. *Chlanidota densesculpta* .. .. 1·25 1·25
w. Wmk Crown to right of CA .. † —
179/82 .. .. *Set of* 4 2·75 2·50
*The normal sideways watermark shows Crown to left of CA, *as seen from the back of the stamp.*

(Des E. Nisbet and D. Miller (24p.), D. Miller (others). Litho Questa)

1988 (17 Sept). *300th Anniv of Lloyd's of London. Designs as* T **167a** *of Malawi.* W w **16** (*sideways on* 24, 29*p.*). P 14.
183 10p. brownish black and brown 40 40
184 24p. multicoloured 75 75
185 29p. brownish black and emerald 80 80
186 58p. brownish black and carmine-red .. 1·40 1·40
183/6 .. .. *Set of* 4 3·00 3·00
Designs: *Vert*—10p. Queen Mother at opening of new Lloyd's building, 1957; 58p. *Horatio* (tanker) on fire, 1916. *Horiz*—24p. *Lindblad Explorer* (cruise liner); 29p. Whaling station, Leith Harbour.

28 Glacier Headwall

29 Retracing Shackleton's Trek

(Des I. Loe. Litho Questa)

1989 (31 July). *Glacier Formations.* T **28** *and similar horiz designs. Multicoloured.* W w **16** (*sideways*). P 14.
187 10p. Type **28** 40 35
188 24p. Accumulation area 80 70
189 29p. Ablation area 90 80
190 58p. Calving front .. .. 1·60 1·40
187/90 .. .. *Set of* 4 3·25 3·00

(Des O. Bell. Litho Questa)

1989 (28 Nov). *25th Anniv of Combined Services Expedition to South Georgia.* T **29** *and similar horiz designs. Multicoloured.* W w **16** (*sideways*). P 14×14½.
191 10p. Type **29** 40 35
192 24p. Surveying at Royal Bay 90 70

193 29p. H.M.S. *Protector* (ice patrol ship) .. 1·00 80
194 58p. Raising Union Jack on Mount Paget .. 1·60 1·40
191/4 .. .. *Set of* 4 3·50 3·00

(Des D. Miller. Litho Questa)

1990 (15 Sept). *90th Birthday of Queen Elizabeth the Queen Mother. Vert designs as T* **107** *(26p.) or* **108** *(£1) of Kenya. W* w **16**. *P* 14×15 (26p.) *or* 14½ (£1).
195 26p. multicoloured .. .. .. 1·00 1·25
196 £1 black and dull ultramarine .. .. 2·75 3·25
Designs:—26p. Queen Mother; £1 King George VI and Queen Elizabeth with A.R.P. wardens, 1940.

30 *Brutus*, Prince Olav Harbour

31 Contest between two Bull Elephant Seals

(Des D. Miller. Litho Questa)

1990 (22 Dec). *Wrecks and Hulks. T* **30** *and similar vert designs. Multicoloured. W* w **16**. *P* 14×14½.
197 12p. Type **30** 55 40
198 26p. *Bayard*, Ocean Harbour .. .. 1·00 80
199 31p. *Karrakatta*, Husvik .. .. .. 1·10 95
200 62p. *Louise*, Grytviken .. .. .. 1·90 1·75
197/200 .. .. *Set of* 4 4·00 3·50

(Des D. Miller. Litho Questa)

1991 (2 July). *65th Birthday of Queen Elizabeth II and 70th Birthday of Prince Philip. Vert designs as T* **58** *of Kiribati. Multicoloured. W* w **16** *(sideways). P* 14½×14.
201 31p. Queen Elizabeth II .. .. .. 1·00 1·40
a. Horiz pair. Nos. 201/2 separated by label .. .. 2·00 2·75
202 31p. Prince Philip in Grenadier Guards uniform .. .. 1·00 1·40
Nos. 201/2 were printed in a similar sheet format to Nos. 366/7 of Kiribati

(Des D. Miller. Litho Questa)

1991 (2 Nov). *Elephant Seals. T* **31** *and similar horiz designs. Multicoloured. W* w **14** *(sideways). P* 14.
203 12p. Type **31** 50 50
204 26p. Adult Elephant Seal .. .. .. 1·00 1·00
205 29p. Seal throwing sand .. .. .. 1·10 1·10
206 31p. Head of Elephant Seal .. .. 1·10 1·10
207 34p. Seals on beach .. .. .. 1·25 1·25
208 62p. Cow seal with pup .. .. .. 2·00 2·00
203/8 .. .. *Set of* 6 6·25 6·25

(Des D. Miller. Litho Questa (68p.), Walsall (others))

1992 (6 Feb). *40th Anniv of Queen Elizabeth II's Accession. Horiz designs as T* **113** *of Kenya. Multicoloured. W* w **14** *(sideways). P* 14.
209 7p. Ice-covered mountains 30 30
210 14p. Zavodovski Island 45 55
211 29p. Gulbrandsen Lake 80 95
212 34p. Three portraits of Queen Elizabeth .. 90 1·10
213 68p. Queen Elizabeth II .. .. .. 1·40 1·50
209/13 .. .. *Set of* 5 3·50 4·00

32 Adult Teal and Young Bird

(Des G. Drummond. Litho Questa)

1992 (12 Mar). *Endangered Species. Georgian Teal ("South Georgia Teal"). T* **32** *and similar horiz designs. Multicoloured. W* w **16** *(sideways). P* 14.
214 2p. Type **32** 30 20
215 6p. Adult with eggs 40 30
216 12p. Teals swimming 60 50
217 20p. Adult and two chicks 90 90
214/17 .. .. *Set of* 4 2·00 1·75

(Des N. Shewring. Litho Questa)

1992 (20 June). *10th Anniv of Liberation. Square designs as T* **169** *of St. Helena. Multicoloured. W* w **16** *(sideways). P* 14.
218 14p. + 6p. King Edward Point 70 70
219 29p. + 11p. *Queen Elizabeth 2* (liner) in Cumberland Bay .. .. .. 1·25 1·25
220 34p. + 16p. Royal Marines hoisting Union Jack on South Sandwich Islands .. 1·60 1·60
221 68p. + 32p. H.M.S. *Endurance* (ice patrol ship) and Westland AS.1 Wasp helicopter .. .. 3·00 3·00
218/21 .. .. *Set of* 4 6·00 6·00
MS222 116×116 mm. Nos. 218/21 .. .. 6·00 6·00
The premiums on Nos. 218/22 were for the S.S.A.F.A.

33 Disused Whale Factory, Grytviken

34 Pair of Swimming Penguins

(Des D. Miller. Litho B.D.T.)

1993 (29 June). *Opening of South Georgia Whaling Museum. T* **33** *and similar horiz designs. Multicoloured. W* w **14** *(sideways). P* 13½.
223 15p. Type **33** 55 55
224 31p. Whaler's lighter and whale bones .. 1·00 1·00
225 36p. Aerial view of King Edward Cove .. 1·25 1·25
226 72p. Museum building .. .. .. 2·25 2·50
223/6 .. .. *Set of* 4 4·50 4·75

(Des N. Arlott. Litho Questa)

1993 (10 Dec). *Macaroni Penguin. T* **34** *and similar horiz designs. Multicoloured. W* w **14** *(sideways). P* 14½.
227 16p. Type **34** 60 45
228 34p. Group of penguins .. .. .. 1·25 1·00
229 39p. Two juvenile penguins .. .. 1·40 1·25
230 78p. Two adult penguins .. .. .. 2·25 2·25
227/30 .. .. *Set of* 4 5·00 4·50

35 Hourglass Dolphin

(Des R. Watton. Litho B.D.T.)

1994 (24 Jan). *Whales and Dolphins. T* **35** *and similar horiz designs. Multicoloured. W* w **14** *(sideways). P* 14.
231 1p. Type **35** 10 10
232 2p. Southern Right Whale Dolphin .. 10 10
233 5p. Long-finned Pilot Whale 10 10
234 8p. Southern Bottlenose Whale 15 20
235 9p. Killer Whale 20 25
236 10p. Minke Whale 20 25
237 20p. Sei Whale 40 45
238 25p. Humpback Whale 50 55
239 50p. Southern Right Whale .. .. 1·00 1·10
240 £1 Sperm Whale .. .. .. 2·00 2·10
241 £3 Fin Whale .. .. 6·00 6·25
242 £5 Blue Whale .. .. 10·00 10·50
231/42 .. .. *Set of* 12 20·00 21·00

1994 (18 Feb). *"Hong Kong '94" International Stamp Exhibition. Nos. 227/30 optd as T* **272** *of Jamaica.*
243 16p. Type **34** 60 60
244 34p. Group of penguins .. .. .. 1·25 1·25
245 39p. Two juvenile penguins .. .. 1·40 1·40
246 78p. Two adult penguins .. .. .. 2·25 2·25
243/6 .. .. *Set of* 4 5·00 5·00

36 Bull Elephant Seals

(Des D. Miller. Litho Questa)

1994 (28 Sept). *"Life in the Freezer". T* **36** *and similar multicoloured designs showing scenes from the B.B.C. Natural History Unit series. W* w **16** *(sideways on 17, 40p.). P* 14½.
247 17p. Type **36** 50 50
248 35p. Young Fur Seal *(vert)* 90 90
249 40p. Pair of Grey-headed Albatrosses .. 1·40 1·40
250 65p. King Penguins in courtship display *(vert)* .. .. 2·25 2·50
247/50 .. .. *Set of* 4 4·50 4·75

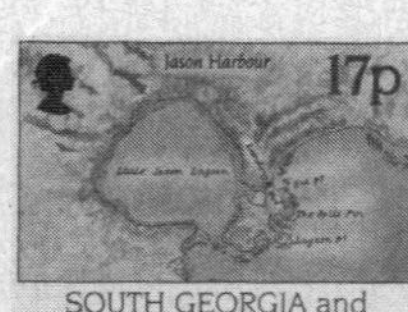

37 Map of Jason Harbour

38 *Damien II* (research schooner)

(Des R. Watton. Litho Walsall)

1994 (1 Dec). *Centenary of C.A. Larsen's First Voyage to South Georgia. T* **37** *and similar horiz designs. Multicoloured. W* w **16** *(sideways*). P* 14×14½.
251 17p. Type **37** 60 60
w. Wmk Crown to right of CA .. .. 42·00
252 35p. *Castor* (whaling ship), 1886 .. .. 1·10 1·10
253 40p. *Hertha* (whaling ship), 1884 .. .. 1·25 1·25
254 65p. *Jason* (whaling ship), 1881 .. .. 2·25 2·50
251/4 .. .. *Set of* 4 4·75 5·00
*The normal sideways watermark shows Crown to left of CA, *as seen from the back of the stamp.*

(Des R. Watton. Litho Questa)

1995 (8 May). *50th Anniv of End of Second World War. Multicoloured designs as T* **75** *of Kiribati. W* w **16** *(sideways). P* 14.
255 50p. H.M.S. *Queen of Bermuda* (armed merchant cruiser), Leith Harbour, 1941 .. .. 1·50 1·75
a. Horiz pair. Nos. 255/6 .. .. 3·00 3·50
256 50p. Norwegian Defence Force 4-inch coastal gun, Hansen Point .. .. 1·50 1·75
MS257 75×85 mm. £1 Reverse of 1939–45 War Medal *(vert)*. W w **14** .. .. .. 2·25 2·50
Nos. 255/6 were printed together, *se-tenant*, in horizontal pairs throughout the sheet, each pair forming composite design.

(Des N. Shewring. Litho Walsall)

1995 (16 Nov). *Sailing Ships. T* **38** *and similar vert designs. Multicoloured. W* w **16**. *P* 14½.
258 35p. Type **38** .. .. 1·25 1·50
259 40p. *Curlew* (cutter) .. .. .. 1·40 1·60
260 76p. *Mischief* (yacht) .. .. .. 2·25 2·50
258/60 .. .. *Set of* 3 4·50 5·00

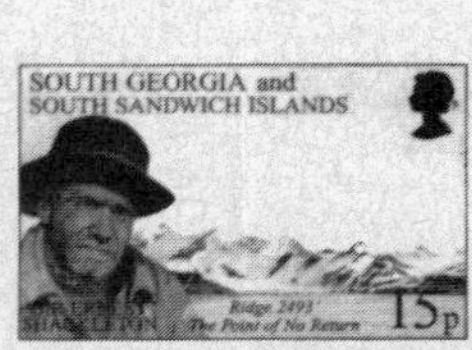

39 Sir Ernest Shackleton and Ridge 2493

40 Chinstrap Penguin swimming

(Des M. Skidmore. Litho Walsall)

1996 (20 May). *80th Anniv of Sir Ernest Shackleton's Trek across South Georgia. T* **39** *and similar horiz designs. Multicoloured. W* w **16** *(sideways). P* 14.
261 15p. Type **39** 65 65
262 20p. Frank Worsley and King Haakon Bay 70 70
263 30p. Map of route 85 85
264 65p. Tom Crean and manager's villa, Stromness whaling station .. .. 1·40 1·40
261/4 .. .. *Set of* 4 3·25 3·25

(Des T. Chater. Litho Questa)

1996 (8 Nov). *Chinstrap Penguins. T* **40** *and similar vert designs. Multicoloured. W* w **14**. *P* 14½×14.
265 17p. Type **40** 55 55
266 35p. Mutual display 90 90
267 40p. Adult feeding chicks .. .. .. 1·10 1·10
268 76p. Feeding on krill .. .. .. 1·90 1·90
265/8 .. .. *Set of* 4 4·00 4·00

(Litho Walsall)

1997 (20 June). *Return of Hong Kong to China. Sheet* 130×90 *mm, containing design as No. 268, but with imprint date. W* w **14** *(sideways). P* 14½×14.
MS269 76p. Feeding on krill .. .. .. 1·75 2·00

(Des N. Shewring (No. **MS**276), D. Miller (others). Litho Questa)

1997 (10 July). *Golden Wedding of Queen Elizabeth and Prince Philip. Multicoloured designs as T* **87** *of Kiribati. W* w **16**. *P* 14½.
270 15p. Queen Elizabeth wearing red hat, 1996 40 40
a. Horiz pair. Nos. 270/1 .. .. .. 80 80
271 15p. Prince Philip in carriage-driving at Royal Windsor Horse Show 40 40
272 17p. Queen Elizabeth with show jumping team, 1993 .. .. 45 45
a. Horiz pair. Nos. 272/3 .. .. .. 90 90
273 17p. Prince Philip smiling 45 45
274 40p. Princess Anne on horseback and Queen Elizabeth .. .. 1·25 1·25
a. Horiz pair. Nos. 274/5 .. .. .. 2·50 2·50
275 40p. Zara Phillips horse riding and Prince Philip .. .. 1·25 1·25
270/5 .. .. *Set of* 6 3·75 3·75
MS276 110×70 mm. £1.50, Queen Elizabeth and Prince Philip in landau *(horiz)*. W w **14** (sideways). P 14×14½ .. .. .. 3·50 3·75
Nos. 270/1, 272/3 and 274/5 were each printed together, *se-tenant*, in horizontal pairs throughout the sheets with the backgrounds forming composite designs.

South West Africa *see* Namibia

Sri Lanka

(*formerly* Ceylon)

CEYLON

PRICES FOR STAMPS ON COVER TO 1945

No. 1	*from* × 5
Nos. 2/12	*from* × 4
Nos. 16/17	*from* × 5
Nos. 18/59	*from* × 8
Nos. 60/2	*from* × 15
Nos. 63/72	*from* × 8
Nos. 121/38	*from* × 6
Nos. 139/41	†
Nos. 142/3	*from* × 10
Nos. 146/51	*from* × 6
Nos. 151*a*/2	†
Nos. 153/93	*from* × 8
Nos. 195/201	*from* × 12
Nos. 202/43	*from* × 6
Nos. 245/9	*from* × 4
Nos. 250/5	*from* × 5
Nos. 256/64	*from* × 4
Nos. 265/76	*from* × 3
Nos. 277/88	*from* × 4
Nos. 289/300	*from* × 8
Nos. 301/25	*from* × 2
Nos. 326/9*a*	—
Nos. 330/7*a*	*from* × 4
Nos. 338/52	*from* × 2
Nos. 353/4	—
Nos. 355/9	*from* × 2
No. 360	—
Nos. 360*a*/*g*	*from* × 2
Nos. 361/2	*from* × 5
Nos. 363/71	*from* × 3
Nos. 372/82	*from* × 2
Nos. 383/5	*from* × 3
Nos. 386/97	*from* × 2
Nos. 398/9	*from* × 8
Nos. O1/17	*from* × 30

CROWN COLONY

PRICES. The prices of the imperf stamps of Ceylon vary greatly according to condition. The following prices are for fine copies with four margins.

Poor to medium specimens can be supplied at much lower prices.

1

2

3

NOTE. Beware of stamps of Type **2** which are often offered with corners added.

(Recess P.B.)

1857 (1 April). *Blued paper. Wmk Star W* w **1**. *Imperf.*

1	**1**	6d. purple-brown	£7500	£450

Collectors should beware of proofs with faked watermark, often offered as originals.

1857 (2 July)–**59.** *Wmk Star, W* w **1**. *White paper.* (*a*) *Imperf*

2	**1**	1d. deep turquoise-blue (24.8.57)	£650	22·00
		a. Blue	£750	38·00
		b. Blued paper	—	£160
3		2d. green (*shades*) (24.8.57)	£150	55·00
		a. Yellowish green	£500	90·00
4	**2**	4d. dull rose (23.4.59)	£50000	£4500
5	**1**	5d. chestnut	£1500	£150
6		6d. purple-brown (1859)	£1800	£130
		a. Brown	£6000	£400
		b. Deep brown	£7000	£1000
		c. Light brown	—	£750
7	**2**	8d. brown (23.4.59)	£22000	£1500
8		9d. purple-brown (23.4.59)	£32000	£900
9	**3**	10d. dull vermilion	£800	£275
10		1s. slate-violet	£4500	£200
11	**2**	1s. 9d. green (23.4.59)	£700	£800
		a. Yellow-green	£3500	£2750
12		2s. dull blue (23.4.59)	£5000	£1200
		(*b*) *Unofficial perf* 7½ (*1s. 9d.*) *or roul* (*others*)		
13	**1**	1d. blue	£5000	
14		2d. green	£2250	£1200
15	**2**	1s. 9d. green	£4750	

Nos. 13/15 were privately produced, probably by commercial firms for their own convenience.

4

(Typo D.L.R.)

1857 (Oct)–**64.** *No wmk. Glazed paper.* (*a*) *Imperf*

16	**4**	½d. reddish lilac (*blued paper*)	£3250	£450
17		½d. dull mauve (1858)	£160	£160
		a. Private roul	£5500	
		(*b*) *P* 12½		
18	**4**	½d. dull mauve (1864)	£190	£150

(Recess P.B.)

1861–64. *Wmk Star, W* w **1**.

		(*a*) *Clean-cut and intermediate perf* 14 *to* 15½		
19	**1**	1d. light blue	£600	£100
		a. Dull blue	£100	12·00
20		2d. green (*shades*)	£100	26·00
		a. Imperf between (vert pair)	†	—
		b. Yellowish green	£110	24·00
21	**2**	4d. dull rose	£1800	£250
22	**1**	5d. chestnut	75·00	8·00
23		6d. brown	£1500	85·00
		a. Bistre-brown	—	£140
24	**2**	8d. brown	£1500	£425
25		9d. purple-brown	£4750	£225
26	**3**	1s. slate-violet	75·00	13·00
27	**2**	2s. dull blue	£2000	£475
		(*b*) *Rough perf* 14 *to* 15½		
28	**1**	1d. dull blue	80·00	6·00
		a. Blued paper	£375	20·00
29		2d. green	—	65·00
30	**2**	4d. rose-red	£275	50·00
		a. Deep rose-red	£300	60·00
31	**1**	6d. deep brown	£700	80·00
		a. Light brown	£1200	£100
		b. Olive-sepia	£650	70·00
32	**2**	8d. brown	£1200	£500
		a. Yellow-brown	£1200	£300
33		9d. deep brown	55·00	45·00
		a. Light brown	£650	65·00
		b. Olive-sepia	£450	40·00
34	**3**	10d. dull vermilion	£200	20·00
		a. Imperf vert (horiz pair)	†	—
35		1s. slate-violet	£225	15·00
36	**2**	1s. 9d. light green (*prepared for use, but not issued*)	£550	
37		2s. dull blue	£500	95·00
		a. Deep dull blue	£700	£120
		(*c*) *P* 12½ *by D.L.R.*		
38	**3**	10d. dull vermilion (9.64)	£225	15·00

The line machine used for Nos. 19/37 produced perforations of variable quality due to wear, poor cleaning and faulty servicing, but it is generally accepted that the clean-cut and intermediate versions occurred on stamps perforated up to March 1861 and the rough variety when the machine was used after that date.

(Recess D.L.R.)

1862. *No wmk. Smooth paper.* (*a*) *P* 13

39	**1**	1d. dull blue	85·00	6·00
40		5d. lake-brown	£1100	£150
41		6d. brown	£100	24·00
		a. Deep brown	£100	22·00
42	**2**	9d. brown	£1000	85·00
43	**3**	1s. slate-purple	£1500	75·00
		(*b*) *P* 11½, 12		
44	**1**	1d. dull blue	£950	£110
		a. Imperf between (horiz pair)	†	£7000

Nos. 39/44 were printed on paper showing a papermaker's watermark of "T H SAUNDERS 1862", parts of which can be found on individual stamps. Examples are rare and command a premium.

The 1s. is known imperforate, but was not issued in this condition.

5
(23 mm high. "CC" oval)

6
(21½ mm high. "CC" round and smaller)

(Typo (½d.) or recess (others). D.L.R.)

1863–66. *W* **5**. *Paper medium thin and slightly soft.*

		(*a*) *P* 11½, 12		
45	**1**	1d. deep blue	£2250	£275
		(*b*) *P* 13		
46	**1**	6d. sepia	£1200	£110
47	**2**	9d. sepia	£2750	£550
		(*c*) *P* 12½		
48	**4**	½d. dull mauve (1864)	28·00	19·00
		a. Reddish lilac	42·00	30·00
		b. Mauve	20·00	22·00
49	**1**	1d. deep blue	70·00	3·00
		a. Imperf		
50		2d. grey-green (1864)	45·00	7·00
		a. Imperf		
		b. Bottle-green	†	£3500
		c. Yellowish green	£7000	£400
		d. Emerald	£100	85·00
51		2d. ochre (1866)	£225	£225
52	**2**	4d. rose-carmine (1865)	£425	£100
		a. Rose	£250	50·00
53	**1**	5d. red-brown (*shades*) (1865)	£130	45·00
54		5d. grey-olive (1866)	£1300	£250
		a. Yellow-olive	£700	£180
55		6d. sepia	90·00	4·00
		a. Reddish brown	£130	11·00
		b. Blackish brown	90·00	8·00
		ba. Double print	†	£2000
56	**2**	8d. reddish brown (*shades*) (1864)	60·00	30·00
57		9d. sepia	£250	30·00
58	**3**	10d. vermilion (1866)	£1300	48·00
		a. Orange-red	£2750	£250
59	**2**	2s. steel-blue (*shades*) (1864)	£170	27·00

Watermarks as Type **5** were arranged in four panes, each of 60, with the words "CROWN COLONIES" between the panes. Parts of this marginal watermark often appear on the stamps.

The ½d. dull mauve, 2d. ochre and 5d. grey-olive with this watermark also exist imperforate, but are not known used. The 6d. sepia and 2s. steel-blue also exist imperforate on wove paper without watermark.

One used example of the 2d. grey-green is known showing private roulettes added to an imperforate stamp (*Price* £2500).

7

8

(Typo D.L.R.)

1866–68. *Wmk Crown CC.* (*a*) *P* 12½

60	**7**	3d. rose	£160	70·00
		(*b*) *P* 14		
61	**8**	1d. blue (*shades*) (1868)	15·00	6·00
62	**7**	3d. carmine-rose (1867)	55·00	27·00
		a. Bright rose	60·00	32·00

Nos. 60/1 exist imperforate.

(Recess D.L.R.)

1867–70. *W* **6**. *Specially produced hand-made paper. P* 12½.

63	**1**	1d. dull blue	90·00	6·50
		a. Deep blue	90·00	6·00
64		2d. ochre	75·00	7·50
		a. Bistre	38·00	7·00
		b. Olive-bistre	£130	20·00
		c. Yellow	38·00	5·00
65	**2**	4d. rose	£140	42·00
		a. Rose-carmine	38·00	12·00
66	**1**	5d. yellow-olive	48·00	8·50
		a. Olive-green	80·00	8·50
		b. Bronze-green	22·00	35·00
67		6d. deep brown (1869)	50·00	9·50
		a. Blackish brown	65·00	8·50
		b. Red-brown	24·00	32·00
68	**2**	8d. chocolate	40·00	45·00
		a. Lake-brown	95·00	55·00
69		9d. bistre-brown (1869)	£250	25·00
		a. Blackish brown	28·00	6·00
70	**3**	10d. dull vermilion	£1800	£140
		a. Red-orange	32·00	5·50
		b. Orange	60·00	8·00
71		1s. reddish lilac (1870)	£275	27·00
		a. Reddish violet	65·00	5·50
72	**2**	2s. steel-blue	£120	16·00
		a. Deep blue	80·00	12·00

Watermarks as Type **6** were arranged in one pane of 240 (12×20) with the words "CROWN COLONIES" twice in each side margin.

Unused examples of the 1d. dull blue, 1d. deep blue, 5d. yellow-olive, 6d. deep brown, 9d. blackish brown and 10d. red-orange with this watermark exist imperforate.

PRINTERS. All stamps from No. 121 to 367 were typographed by De La Rue & Co. Ltd, London.

(New Currency. 100 cents = 1 rupee)

9

10

11

12

13

14

15

16

17

18

19

1872–80. *Wmk Crown CC. (a) P 14.*

121 **9** 2 c. pale brown (*shades*) .. .. .. 8·00 1·75
122 **10** 4 c. grey .. .. 28·00 1·50
123 4 c. rosy-mauve (1880) .. .. .. 45·00 1·50
124 **11** 8 c. orange-yellow .. .. .. 40·00 5·50
a. Yellow .. .. 28·00 6·00
126 **12** 16 c. pale violet .. .. 60·00 2·75
127 **13** 24 c. green .. .. 38·00 2·00
128 **14** 32 c. slate (1877) .. .. £110 15·00
129 **15** 36 c. blue .. .. £100 16·00
130 **16** 48 c. rose .. .. 60·00 5·00
131 **17** 64 c. red-brown (1877) .. .. .. £200 60·00
132 **18** 96 c. drab .. .. £150 26·00
121/132 .. .. *Set of* 11 £700 £110

(b) P 14 × 12½

133 **9** 2 c. brown .. .. £350 60·00
134 **10** 4 c. grey .. .. £900 25·00
135 **11** 8 c. orange-yellow .. .. £375 42·00

(c) P 12½

136 **9** 2 c. brown £1800 £140
137 **10** 4 c. grey £950 £190

(d) P 12½ × 14

138 **19** 2 r. 50 c. dull-rose (1879) £450 £300

(e) Prepared for use and sent out to Ceylon, but not issued unsurcharged

139 **14** 32 c. slate (*p* 14 × 12½) £800
140 **17** 64 c. red-brown (*p* 14 × 12½) £950
141 **19** 2 r. 50, dull rose (*p* 12½) £1200

FORGERIES.—Beware of forged overprint and surcharge varieties on Victorian issues.

SIXTEEN

16

CENTS
(20)

1882 (Oct). *Nos.* 127 *and* 131 *surch as T* **20** *by Govt Printer.*

142 **13** 16 c. on 24 c. green .. .. .. 21·00 6·50
a. Surch inverted .. .. ..
143 **17** 20 c. on 64 c. red-brown .. .. .. 9·00 4·00
a. Surch double .. .. .. † £1100

1883–98. *Wmk Crown CA. (a) P 14.*

146 **9** 2 c. pale brown .. .. .. 48·00 1·50
147 2 c. dull green (1884) (Optd S. £180) 1·60 15
148 **10** 4 c. rosy mauve .. .. .. 2·00 30
149 4 c. rose (1884) (Optd S. £180) .. 3·25 11·00
150 **11** 8 c. orange .. .. 4·00 8·00
a. Yellow (1898) .. .. .. 3·00 7·00
151 **12** 16 c. pale violet £1100 £140

(b) Trial perforation. P 12

151*a* **9** 2 c. dull green £1800
151*b* **10** 4 c. rose £1800
151*c* **13** 24 c. brown-purple £1900

(c) Prepared for use and sent out to Ceylon, but not issued unsurcharged. P 14.

152 **13** 24 c. brown-purple (Optd S. £400) .. £900

Although delivered in 1884 it is believed that the 4 c. rose, No. 149, was not used until the early 1890s.

Postage &

FIVE
CENTS

Revenue
(21)

TEN
CENTS
(22)

Twenty
Cents
(23)

One Rupee
Twelve
Cents
(24)

1885. *T* **10/19** *surch locally as T* **21/24**.

I. *Wmk Crown CC. (a) P 14*

153 **21** 5 c. on 16 c. pale violet .. .. .. † £2250
154 5 c. on 24 c. green £1600 £100
155 5 c. on 32 c. slate .. .. .. 55·00 15·00
a. Surch inverted .. .. .. † £850
b. Dark grey .. .. 85·00 28·00
156 5 c. on 36 c. blue .. .. .. £160 8·00
a. Surch inverted .. .. .. † £1300
157 5 c. on 48 c. rose .. .. .. £700 45·00
158 5 c. on 64 c. red-brown .. .. .. 70·00 4·50
a. Surch double .. .. .. † £650
159 5 c. on 96 c. drab .. .. .. £325 60·00
161 **22** 10 c. on 16 c. pale violet £3250 £1300
162 10 c. on 24 c. green .. .. .. £325 95·00
163 10 c. on 36 c. blue £325 £150
164 10 c. on 64 c. red-brown £325 £100
165 20 c. on 24 c. green .. .. .. 45·00 17·00
166 **23** 20 c. on 32 c. slate .. .. .. 42·00 42·00
a. Dark grey .. .. 42·00 35·00
167 25 c. on 32 c. slate .. .. .. 12·00 4·50
a. Dark grey .. .. 20·00 8·00
168 28 c. on 48 c. rose .. .. .. 30·00 6·00
a. Surch double .. .. .. † £800
169 **22** 30 c. on 36 c. blue .. .. .. 8·50 7·50
a. Surch inverted £200 £100
170 56 c. on 96 c. drab .. .. .. 18·00 14·00

(b) P 14 × 12½

172 **21** 5 c. on 32 c. slate .. .. .. £400 42·00
173 5 c. on 64 c. red-brown .. .. .. £400 32·00
174 **22** 10 c. on 64 c. red-brown .. .. .. 45·00 85·00
a. Imperf between (vert pair) £2500
175 **24** 1 r. 12 c. on 2 r. 50 c. dull rose (*p* 12½) £325 80·00
176 1 r. 12 c. on 2 r. 50 c. dull rose (*p* 12½ × 14) .. .. .. 70·00 42·00

II. *Wmk Crown CA. P 14*

178 **21** 5 c. on 4 c. rose .. .. .. 17·00 3·50
a. Surch inverted .. .. .. † £275
179 5 c. on 8 c. orange-yellow .. .. .. 48·00 6·50
a. Surch double .. .. .. † £850
b. Surch inverted .. .. .. † £1100
180 5 c. on 16 c. pale violet .. .. .. 65·00 9·00
a. Surch inverted .. .. .. † £150
182 5 c. on 24 c. brown-purple .. .. .. — £500
184 **22** 10 c. on 16 c. pale violet £3250 £750
185 10 c. on 24 c. brown-purple .. .. .. 10·00 5·50
186 15 c. on 16 c. pale violet .. .. .. 8·00 6·50

Only seven examples, all used, are recorded of No. 153.

The 5 c. on 4 c. rosy mauve and 5 c. on 24 c. green, both watermarked Crown CA, previously catalogued are now considered to be forgeries.

REVENUE AND POSTAGE

5 CENTS
(25)

10 CENTS
(26)

1 R. 12 C.
(27)

1885. *T* **11/15**, **18** *and* **19** *surch with T* **25/7** *by D.L.R. P* 14.

(a) Wmk Crown CA

187 **25** 5 c. on 8 c. lilac .. .. .. 10·00 1·40
188 **26** 10 c. on 24 c. brown-purple .. .. 8·50 6·00
189 15 c. on 16 c. orange-yellow .. .. 45·00 6·00
190 28 c. on 32 c. slate .. .. .. 16·00 2·50
191 30 c. on 36 c. olive-green .. .. 28·00 14·00
192 56 c. on 96 c. drab .. .. .. 40·00 10·00

(b) Wmk Crown CC (sideways)

193 **27** 1 r. 12 c. on 2 r. 50, dull rose .. .. 35·00 80·00
187/93 .. .. *Set of* 7 £160 £110
187/93 Optd "Specimen" .. .. *Set of* 7 £650

28

29

1886. *Wmk Crown CA. P* 14.

195 **28** 5 c. dull purple .. .. .. 1·75 10
196 **29** 15 c. sage-green .. .. .. 3·50 1·25
197 15 c. olive-green .. .. .. 3·75 1·25
198 25 c. yellow-brown .. .. .. 2·75 1·00
a. Value in yellow .. .. .. 90·00 70·00
199 28 c. slate .. .. 13·00 1·40
195, 197/9 Optd "Specimen" .. *Set of* 4 £170

Six plates were used for the 5 c., No. 195, between 1885 and 1901, each being replaced by its successor as it became worn. Examples from the worn plates show thicker lines in the background and masses of solid colour under the chin, in front of the throat, at the back of the neck and at the base.

30

1887. *Wmk Crown CC (sideways). White or blued paper. P* 14.

201 **30** 1 r. 12, dull rose (Optd S. £95) .. .. 22·00 19·00
a. Wmk upright .. .. .. 40·00 55·00

Two CENTS
(31)

Two
(32)

2 Cents
(33)

Two Cents
(34)

2 Cents
(35)

1888–90. *Nos.* 148/9 *surch with T* **31/5**.

202 **31** 2 c. on 4 c. rosy mauve .. .. .. 1·00 70
a. Surch inverted .. .. .. 17·00 16·00
b. Surch double, one inverted .. .. — £140
203 2 c. on 4 c. rose .. .. .. 1·25 30
a. Surch inverted .. .. .. 13·00 14·00
b. Surch double .. .. .. — £150
204 **32** 2 (c.) on 4 c. rosy mauve 60 30
a. Surch inverted .. .. .. 28·00 30·00
b. Surch double .. .. .. 42·00 42·00
c. Surch double, one inverted .. .. 40·00 35·00
205 2 (c.) on 4 c. rose .. .. .. 3·75 20
a. Surch inverted £150
b. Surch double .. .. .. 42·00 50·00
c. Surch double, one inverted .. .. 48·00 55·00
206 **33** 2 c. on 4 c. rosy mauve .. .. 42·00 27·00
a. Surch inverted .. .. .. 70·00 35·00
b. Surch double, one inverted .. .. 90·00
207 2 c. on 4 c. rose .. .. .. 2·25 75
a. Surch inverted .. .. .. 8·50 8·00
b. Surch double .. .. .. 85·00 85·00
c. Surch double, one inverted .. .. 8·00 10·00
208 **34** 2 c. on 4 c. rosy mauve .. .. 42·00 16·00
a. Surch inverted .. .. .. 85·00 30·00
209 2 c. on 4 c. rose .. .. .. 2·00 1·10
a. Surch inverted .. .. .. 11·00 5·50
b. Surch double .. .. .. 65·00 65·00
c. Surch double, one inverted .. .. 11·00 5·50
210 **35** 2 c. on 4 c. rosy mauve .. .. 40·00 24·00
a. Surch inverted .. .. .. 50·00 40·00
b. Surch double, one inverted .. .. 60·00 60·00
c. Surch double .. .. .. — £150
d. "s" of "Cents" inverted .. .. — £275
e. As d. Whole surch inverted ..
211 2 c. on 4 c. rose .. .. .. 8·00 70
a. Surch inverted .. .. .. 12·00 5·50
b. Surch double .. .. .. 55·00 55·00
c. Surch double, one inverted .. .. 14·00 8·50
d. "s" of "Cents" inverted .. .. — £120
209, 211 Optd "Specimen" .. *Set of* 2 60·00

The 4 c. rose and the 4 c. rosy mauve are found surcharged "Postal Commission 3 (or "Three") Cents". They denote the extra commission charged by the Post Office on postal orders which had not been cashed within three months of the date of issue. For a short time the Post Office did not object to the use of these stamps on letters.

POSTAGE

Five Cents

REVENUE
(36)

FIFTEEN
CENTS
(37)

1890. *No.* 197 *surch with T* **36**.

233 5 c. on 15 c. olive-green (Optd S. £30) .. 1·50 1·75
a. Surch inverted .. .. .. 28·00 30·00
b. Surch double .. .. .. 90·00 90·00
c. "Flve" for "Five" (R. 1/1) .. .. 90·00 80·00
d. Variety as c, inverted .. .. — £750
e. "REVENUE" omitted .. .. £100 90·00
f. Inverted "s" in "Cents" .. .. 40·00 45·00
g. Variety as f, and whole surch inverted £800
h. "REVENUE" omitted and inverted "s" in "Cents" £600
i. "POSTAGE" spaced between "T" and "A" .. .. 50·00 55·00
j. Variety as i, and whole surcharge inverted .. .. — £600

1891. *Nos.* 198/9 *surch with T* **37**.

239 **29** 15 c. on 25 c. yellow-brown .. .. 7·50 10·00
240 15 c. on 28 c. slate .. .. .. 10·00 8·50

3 Cents
(38)

39

1892. *Nos.* 148/9 *and* 199 *surch with T* **38**.

241 **10** 3 c. on 4 c. rosy mauve .. .. .. 85 2·50
242 3 c. on 4 c. rose (Optd S. £30) .. .. 2·50 6·00
243 **29** 3 c. on 28 c. slate .. .. .. 2·50 3·00
a. Surch double .. .. .. 85·00
241/3 .. .. *Set of* 3 5·25 10·50

1893–99. *Wmk Crown CA. P* 14.

245 **39** 3 c. terracotta and blue-green .. .. 2·25 45
246 **10** 4 c. carmine-rose (1898) .. .. 7·50 8·00
247 **29** 30 c. bright mauve and chestnut .. 4·00 1·75
a. Bright violet and chestnut .. .. 4·75 2·25
249 **19** 2 r. 50, purple/*red* (1899) .. .. 25·00 48·00
245/9 .. .. *Set of* 4 35·00 55·00
245, 247/9 Optd "Specimen" .. .. *Set of* 3 60·00

Six Cents
(40)

2 R. 25 C.
(41)

1898 (Dec)–**99.** *(a) No.* 196 *surch with T* **40**.
250 **29** 6 c. on 15 c. sage-green 70 75

(b) As No. 138, *but colour changed and perf* 14, *surch as T* **41** (1899).
254 **19** 1 r. 50 on 2 r. 50, slate 20·00 40·00
255 2 r. 25 on 2 r. 50, yellow 32·00 70·00
250/5 Optd "Specimen" *Set of* 3 70·00

43

1899–1900. *Wmk Crown CA* (1 *r.* 50, 2 *r.* 25 *wmk Crown CC*). *P* 14.
256 **9** 2 c. pale orange-brown 1·40 30
257 **39** 3 c. deep green 1·40 55
258 **10** 4 c. yellow 1·75 2·75
259 **29** 6 c. rose and black 85 45
260 **39** 12 c. sage-green and rose 3·00 6·50
261 **29** 15 c. blue 4·75 1·25
262 **39** 75 c. black and red-brown 4·25 5·00
263 **43** 1 r. 50, rose 15·00 35·00
264 2 r. 25, dull blue 28·00 35·00
256/64 *Set of* 9 50·00 75·00
256/64 Optd "Specimen" *Set of* 9 £130

44

45

46

47

48

1903 (29 May)–**05.** *Wmk Crown CA. P* 14.
265 **44** 2 c. red-brown (21.7.03) 1·00 20
266 **45** 3 c. green (11.6.03) 1·50 1·00
267 4 c. orange-yellow and blue 1·25 3·00
268 **46** 5 c. dull purple (2.7.03) 1·50 45
269 **47** 6 c. carmine (5.11.03) 6·50 1·50
w. Wmk inverted 40·00
270 **45** 12 c. sage-green and rosine (13.8.03) 3·75 7·50
271 **48** 15 c. blue (2.7.03) 6·50 2·00
272 25 c. bistre (11.8.03) 4·00 7·50
273 30 c. dull violet and green 3·25 4·00
274 **45** 75 c. dull blue and orange (31.3.05) 2·75 17·00
275 **48** 1 r. 50, greyish slate (7.4.04) 65·00 55·00
276 2 r. 25, brown and green (12.4.04) 60·00 45·00
265/76 *Set of* 12 £140 £130
265/76 Optd "Specimen" *Set of* 12 £150

1904 (13 Sept)–**05.** *Wmk Mult Crown CA. Ordinary paper. P* 14.
277 **44** 2 c. red-brown (17.11.04) 75 10
278 **45** 3 c. green (17.11.04) 75 15
279 4 c. orange and ultramarine 75 90
280 **46** 5 c. dull purple (29.11.04) 1·75 1·25
a. Chalk-surfaced paper (5.10.05) 2·50 70
281 **47** 6 c. carmine (11.10.04) 1·10 15
282 **45** 12 c. sage-green and rosine (29.9.04) 1·50 1·75
283 **48** 15 c. blue (1.12.04) 1·00 60
284 25 c. bistre (5.1.05) 6·00 3·75
285 30 c. violet and green (7.9.05) 2·50 2·00
286 **45** 75 c. dull blue and orange (25.5.05) 5·25 8·00
287 **48** 1 r. 50, grey (5.1.05) 18·00 10·00
288 2 r. 25, brown and green (22.12.04) 18·00 29·00
277/88 *Set of* 12 50·00 50·00

50

51

1908. *Wmk Mult Crown CA. P* 14.
289 **50** 5 c. deep purple (26 May) 2·00 10
290 5 c. dull purple 2·75 30
291 **51** 6 c. carmine (6 June) 80 10
289, 291 Optd "Specimen" *Set of* 2 48·00

1910 (1 Aug)–**11.** *Wmk Mult Crown CA. P* 14.
292 **44** 2 c. brown-orange (20.5.11) 1·50 75
293 **48** 3 c. green (5.7.11) 1·00 75
294 10 c. sage-green and maroon 2·25 1·40
295 25 c. grey 2·50 90
296 50 c. chocolate 4·00 7·50
297 1 r. purple/*yellow* 7·50 10·00
298 2 r. red/*yellow* 15·00 27·00
299 5 r. black/*green* 35·00 65·00
300 10 r. black/*red* 70·00 £170
292/300 *Set of* 9 £120 £250
292/300 Optd "Specimen" *Set of* 9 £190

52

53

(A)

(B)

Most values in Type **52** were produced by two printing operations, using "Key" and "Duty" plates. Differences in the two Dies of the Key plate are described in the introduction to this catalogue.

In the Ceylon series, however, the 1 c. and 5 c. values, together with later printings of the 3 c. and 6 c., were printed from special plates at one operation. These plates can be identified by the large "C" in the value tablet (see illustration A). Examples of these values from Key and Duty plates printing have value tablet as illustration B. The 3 c. and 5 c. stamps from the single plates *resemble* Die I, and the 1 c. and 6 c. Die II, although in the latter case the inner top corners of the side panels are square and not curved.

1912–25. *Wmk Mult Crown CA. Chalk-surfaced paper* (30 *c. to* 1000 *r.*). *P* 14.

(a) Printed from single plates. Value tablet as A
301 **52** 1 c. brown (1919) 90 10
w. Wmk inverted 15·00
302 3 c. blue-green (1919) 2·50 45
w. Wmk inverted 15·00
y. Wmk inverted and reversed 20·00
303 5 c. purple 5·50 2·75
a. Wmk sideways (Crown to right of CA) £180
y. Wmk inverted and reversed 50·00
304 5 c. bright magenta 1·00 60
305 6 c. pale scarlet (1919) 8·50 85
a. Wmk sideways (Crown to left of CA) 27·00 55·00
w. Wmk inverted 20·00
306 6 c. carmine 12·00 1·25
a. Wmk sideways (Crown to right of CA) 35·00
y. Wmk inverted and reversed 20·00

(b) Printed from Key and Duty plates. Die I. 3 c. and 6 c. have value tablet as B
307 **52** 2 c. brown-orange 40 30
a. Deep orange-brown 30 20
308 3 c. yellow-green 6·50 2·25
a. Deep green (1917) 4·00 1·10
309 6 c. bright scarlet 2·25 1·00
a. Scarlet (1917) 1·10 50
310 10 c. sage-green 3·00 1·75
a. Deep sage-green (1917) 5·00 2·50
w. Wmk inverted 50·00
311 15 c. deep bright blue 3·25 2·00
a. Ultramarine (1918) 1·50 1·25
aw. Wmk inverted 20·00
312 25 c. orange and blue 6·50 4·50
a. Yellow and blue (1917) 1·75 1·75
w. Wmk inverted 50·00
313 30 c. blue-green and violet 4·00 2·25
a. Yellow-green and violet (1915) 7·00 3·25
ab. Wmk sideways (Crown to right of CA) 15·00
abw. Wmk Crown to left of CA
aw. Wmk inverted 30·00
314 50 c. black and scarlet 1·25 1·75
w. Wmk inverted 15·00
315 1 r. purple/*yellow* 2·00 3·25
a. White back (1913) (Optd S. £32) 1·75 3·75
b. On lemon (1915) (Optd S. £32) 4·00 8·00
c. On orange-buff (1918) 26·00 35·00
cw. Wmk inverted 40·00
d. On pale yellow (1922) (Optd S. £32) 4·50 10·00
316 2 r. black and red/*yellow* 3·25 8·50
a. White back (1913) (Optd S. £32) 2·50 9·00
b. On lemon (1915) (Optd S. £32) 20·00 27·00
c. On orange-buff (1919) 35·00 42·00
cw. Wmk inverted 40·00
d. On pale yellow (1921) 35·00 38·00
317 5 r. black/*green* 14·00 24·00
a. White back (1914) (Optd S. £35) 14·00 27·00
b. On blue-green (olive back) (1917) (Optd S. £40) 14·00 25·00
bw. Wmk inverted 40·00
c. Die II. *On emerald back* (1923) (Optd S. £50) 45·00 85·00
318 10 r. purple and black/*red* 55·00 65·00
aw. Wmk inverted 85·00
b. Die II (1923) 65·00 95·00
bw. Wmk inverted £150
319 20 r. black and red/*blue* 80·00 95·00
320 **53** 50 r. dull purple (Optd S. £110) £300
a. Break in scroll £600
b. Broken crown and scroll £600
321 100 r. grey-black (Optd S. £250) £1300
a. Break in scroll £2000
b. Broken crown and scroll £2000
w. Wmk inverted £2500
322 500 r. dull green (Optd S. £400) £3750
a. Break in scroll £6000
b. Broken crown and scroll £6000
323 1000 r. pur/*red* (1925) (Optd S. £800) £14000
cb. Broken crown and scroll £18000
301/18 *Set of* 14 80·00 £100
301/19 Optd "Specimen" *Set of* 15 £225

For illustrations of the varieties on Nos. 320/3 see above No. 58 of Leeward Islands.

The 2 c. exists in coils, constructed from normal sheets between 1914 and 1918.

Sideways watermark varieties are described as seen *from the back of the stamp.*

WAR STAMP
(54)

WAR STAMP ONE CENT
(55)

1918 (18 Nov)–**19.** *(a) Optd with T* **54** *by Govt Printer, Colombo.*
330 **52** 2 c. brown-orange 20 40
a. Opt inverted 30·00 35·00
b. Opt double 24·00 28·00
c. Opt omitted in pair with opt inverted £300
331 3 c. blue-green (No. 302) (1919) 90 40
332 3 c. deep green (No. 308*a*) 20 50
a. Opt double 50·00 55·00
333 5 c. purple 30 30
a. Opt double 30·00 35·00
w. Wmk inverted 50·00
334 5 c. bright magenta 1·25 1·75
a. Opt inverted 30·00 35·00
b. Opt double 24·00 32·00

(b) Surch with T **55**
335 **52** 1 c. on 5 c. purple 50 30
y. Wmk inverted and reversed 50·00
336 1 c. on 5 c. bright magenta 75 20
330/1, 333, 335 Optd "Specimen" *Set of* 4 85·00

Collectors are warned against forgeries of the errors in the "WAR STAMP" overprints.

1918. *Surch as T* **55**, *but without* "WAR STAMP".
337 **52** 1 c. on 5 c. purple (Optd S. £30) 15 25
a. Surch double £110
337*b* 1 c. on 5 c. bright magenta 1·25 2·00

1921–32. *Wmk Mult Script CA. Chalk-surfaced paper* (30 *c. to* 100 *r.*). *P* 14.

(a) Printed from single plates. Value tablet as A
338 **52** 1 c. brown (1927) 40 35
339 3 c. green (5.5.22) 2·00 75
w. Wmk inverted 15·00
340 3 c. slate-grey (1923) 40 20
a. Wmk sideways £500
w. Wmk inverted 15·00
341 5 c. purple (1927) 40 15
342 6 c. carmine-red (3.8.21) 1·25 75
w. Wmk inverted 15·00 25·00
343 6 c. bright violet (1922) 40 15
w. Wmk inverted 15·00

(b) Printed from Key and Duty plates
344 **52** 2 c. brown-orange (Die II) (1927) 30 25
345 9 c. red/*pale yellow* (Die II) (1926) 40 30
346 10 c. sage-green (Die I) (16.9.21) 80 40
aw. Wmk inverted 20·00
ay. Wmk inverted and reversed 15·00 25·00
b. Die II (1924) 90 60
c. Vert gutter pair. Die I and Die II. Nos. 346 and 346b £120
347 12 c. rose-scarlet (Die I) (1925) 3·25 5·00
a. Die II (Optd S. £50) 80 1·75
b. Vert gutter pair. Die I and Die II. Nos. 347/a 70·00
348 15 c. ultramarine (Die I) (30.5.22) 2·50 6·50
349 15 c. green/*pale yellow* (Die I) (1923) 1·25 1·25
a. Die II (1924) 1·25 1·00
aw. Wmk inverted 15·00
b. Vert gutter pair. Die I and Die II. Nos. 349/a £120
350 20 c. bright blue (Die I) (1922) 2·50 5·50
aw. Wmk inverted 20·00
b. Die II (1924) 2·00 45
c. Vert gutter pair. Die I and Die II. Nos. 350 and 350b £120
351 25 c. yellow and blue (Die I) (17.10.21) 90 1·90
a. Die II (1924) 2·25 1·25
b. Vert gutter pair. Die I and Die II. Nos. 351/a 85·00
352 30 c. yellow-green & vio (Die I) (15.3.22) 1·40 2·50
a. Die II (1924) 1·75 1·25
b. Vert gutter pair. Die I and Die II. Nos. 352/a £200
353 50 c. black and scarlet (Die II) (1922) 1·25 80
a. Die I (1932) 48·00 75·00
354 1 r. purple/*pale yellow* (Die I) (1923) 13·00 22·00
a. Die II (1925) 9·50 19·00
b. Vert gutter pair. Die I and Die II. Nos. 354/a £180
355 2 r. black & red/*pale yell* (Die II) (1923) 4·00 6·50
356 5 r. black/*emerald* (Die II) (1924) 22·00 40·00
357 20 r. black and red/*blue* (Die II) (1924) 95·00 £120
358 **53** 50 r. dull purple (1924) (Optd S. £110) £350
a. Break in scroll £550
b. Broken crown and scroll £550
359 100 r. grey-black (1924) (Optd S. £275) £1400
a. Break in scroll £1900
b. Broken crown and scroll £1900
360 100 r. dull purple and blue (24.10.27) (Optd S. £275) £1300
a. Break in scroll £1800
b. Broken crown and scroll £1800
338/56 *Set of* 19 45·00 70·00
338/57 Optd "Specimen" *Set of* 20 £350

The 2 c. to 30 c. and 1 r. values produced from Key and Duty plates were printed in sheets of 240 using two plates one above the other. Nos. 346c, 347b, 349b, 350c, 351b, 353b and 354b come from printings in 1924 and 1925 which combined Key Plate 7 (Die I) with Key Plate 12 (Die II).

No. 353a, from Key Plate 23, was a mistake; the "retired" Die I being issued in error when it became necessary to replace Key Plate 21.

For illustrations of the varieties on Nos. 358/60 see above No. 58 of Leeward Islands.

NEW INFORMATION

The editor is always interested to correspond with people who have new information that will improve or correct the Catalogue.

2 Cents.

(56)

57

(Surch at Ceylon Govt Printing Works)

1926 (27 Nov). *Surch as T* **56**.
361 **52** 2 c. on 3 c. slate-grey .. .. .. 70 1·00
a. Surch double .. .. .. 70·00
b. Bar omitted .. .. .. 65·00 75·00
362 5 c. on 6 c. bright violet 50 40
361/2 Optd "Specimen" .. .. *Set of* 2 50·00

No. 361b comes from the bottom horizontal row of the sheet which was often partially obscured by the selvedge during surcharging.

1927 (27 Nov)–**29**. *Wmk Mult Script CA. Chalk-surfaced paper. P* 14.
363 **57** 1 r. dull and bright purple (1928) .. 1·75 1·25
364 2 r. green and carmine (1929) .. .. 3·75 2·75
365 5 r. green and dull purple (1928) .. 12·00 18·00
366 10 r. green and brown-orange .. .. 28·00 80·00
367 20 r. dull purple and blue .. .. 85·00 £180
363/7 .. .. .. *Set of* 5 £120 £250
363/7 Optd "Specimen" .. .. *Set of* 5 £140

No. 364. Collectors are warned against faked 2 r. stamps, showing what purports to be a double centre.

58 Tapping Rubber

60 Adam's Peak

(Recess D.L.R. (2, 3, 20, 50 c.), B.W. (others))

1935 (1 May)–**36**. *T* **58**, **60** *and similar designs. Wmk Mult Script CA (sideways on* 10, 15, 25, 30 *c. and* 1 *r.). Various perfs.*
368 2 c. black and carmine (*p* 12 × 13) 30 40
a. Perf 14 .. .. .. 9·00 40
369 3 c. blk & ol-green (*p* 13 × 12) (1.10.35) .. 35 40
a. Perf 14 .. .. .. 24·00 35
370 6 c. black & blue (*p* 11 × 11½) (1.1.36) .. 30 30
371 9 c. green & orange (*p* 11 × 11½) (1.1.36) .. 1·00 50
372 10 c. black & purple (*p* 11½ × 11) (1.6.35) .. 1·25 2·00
373 15 c. red-brown and green (*p* 11½ × 11) .. 1·00 50
374 20 c. black & grey-blue (*p* 12 × 13) (1.1.36) .. 1·75 1·75
375 25 c. deep blue & chocolate (*p* 11½ × 11) .. 1·40 1·25
376 30 c. carm & green (*p* 11½ × 11) (1.8.35) .. 3·00 1·75
377 50 c. black and mauve (*p* 14) (1.1.36) .. .. 7·50 1·25
378 1 r. vio-bl & chocolate (*p* 11½ × 11) (1.7.35) .. 13·00 12·00
368/78 .. .. .. *Set of* 11 28·00 20·00
368/78 Perf "Specimen" .. .. *Set of* 11 £150

Designs: *Vert*—6 c. Colombo Harbour; 9 c. Plucking tea; 20 c. Coconut Palms. *Horiz*—10 c. Hill paddy (rice); 15 c. River scene; 25 c. Temple of the Tooth, Kandy; 30 c. Ancient irrigation tank; 50 c. Wild elephants; 1 r. Trincomalee.

1935 (6 May). *Silver Jubilee. As Nos.* 114/17 *of Jamaica, but ptd by D.L.R. P* 13½×14.
379 6 c. ultramarine and grey 45 30
f. Diagonal line by turret .. .. 32·00
g. Dot to left of chapel .. .. 40·00
h. Dot by flagstaff .. .. 40·00
i. Dash by turret .. .. 48·00
380 9 c. green and indigo 70 60
f. Diagonal line by turret .. .. 55·00
g. Dot to left of chapel .. .. 70·00
h. Dot by flagstaff .. .. 70·00
381 20 c. brown and deep blue .. .. 4·25 2·75
f. Diagonal line by turret £130
g. Dot to left of chapel £150
382 50 c. slate and purple .. .. 5·25 6·50
h. Dot by flagstaff £190
379/82 .. .. .. *Set of* 4 9·50 9·00
379/82 Perf "Specimen" .. .. *Set of* 4 85·00

For illustrations of plate varieties, see Omnibus section following Zimbabwe.

1937 (12 May). *Coronation. As Nos.* 118/20 *of Jamaica, but ptd by B.W. & Co. P* 11×11½.
383 6 c. carmine 65 15
384 9 c. green .. .. .. 2·50 2·50
385 20 c. blue .. .. .. 3·50 3·75
383/5 .. .. .. *Set of* 3 6·00 5·75
383/5 Perf "Specimen" .. .. *Set of* 3 60·00

69 Tapping Rubber

70 Sigiriya (Lion Rock)

71 Ancient Guard-stone, Anuradhapura

72 King George VI

Apostrophe flaw (Frame Pl 1A R.6/6) (ptg of 1 Jan 1943 only)

(Recess B.W. (stamps perf 11 × 11½ or 11½ × 11), D.L.R. (all others) T **72** typo D.L.R.)

1938–49. *T* **69/72** *and designs as* 1935–36, *but with portrait of King George VI instead of King George V, "POSTAGE & REVENUE" omitted and some redrawn. Wmk Mult Script CA (sideways on* 10, 15, 25, 30 *c. and* 1 *r.). Chalk-surfaced paper (*5 *r.). Various perfs.*
386 **69** 2 c. blk & carm (*p* 11½×13) (25.4.38) 9·50 1·75
a. Perf 13½×13 (1938) .. .. £120 1·75
b. Perf 13½ (25.4.38) 90 10
c. Perf 11×11½ (17.2.44) 55 85
cw. Wmk inverted .. .. .. — £400
d. Perf 12 (22.4.49) .. .. .. 1·50 3·50
387 **60** 3 c. black & dp blue-green (*p* 13×11½) (21.3.38) .. .. .. 9·50 30
a. Perf 13×13½ (1938) .. .. £250 7·00
b. Perf 13½ (21.3.38) .. .. 3·00 10
c. Perf 14 (7.41) £120 95
d. Perf 11½×11 (14.5.42) 70 10
da. "A" of "CA" missing from wmk .. £750 £750
e. Perf 12 (14.1.46) 55 60
387*f* – 5 c. sage-grn & orge (*p* 13½) (1.1.43) 30 10
fa. Apostrophe flaw .. .. 42·00
g. Perf 12 (1947) .. .. .. 1·25 30
388 – 6 c. black and blue (*p* 11×11½) (1.1.38) 30 10
389 **70** 10 c. blk & light bl (*p* 11½×11) (1.2.38) 1·50 10
a. Wmk upright (1.6.44) .. .. 2·50 40
390 – 15 c. grn & red-brn (*p* 11½×11) (1.1.38) 1·50 10
a. Wmk upright (23.7.45) .. .. 2·75 60
391 – 20 c. blk & grey-bl (*p* 11×11½) (15.1.38) 3·25 10
392 – 25 c. dp bl & choc (*p* 11½×11) (15.1.38) 4·00 30
a. Wmk upright (1944) .. .. 3·75 10
393 – 30 c. carm & grn (*p* 11½×11) (1.2.38) 11·00 1·25
a. Wmk upright (16.4.45) .. .. 12·00 2·75
394 – 50 c. blk & mve (*p* 13×11½) (25.4.38) .. £160 42·00
a. Perf 13×13½ (1938) .. .. £350 2·75
b. Perf 13½ (25.4.38) .. .. 13·00 30
c. Perf 14 (4.42) .. .. .. £100 27·00
d. Perf 11½×11 (14.5.42) .. .. 4·25 3·00
e. Perf 12 (14.1.46) .. .. 3·50 20
395 – 1 r. blue-violet & chocolate (*p* 11½×11) (1.2.38) .. .. .. 15·00 75
a. Wmk upright (1944) .. .. 14·00 2·25
396 **71** 2 r. blk and carm (*p* 11×11½) (1.2.38) 13·00 1·75
396*a* 2 r. blk & vio (*p* 11×11½) (15.3.47) .. 1·75 1·10
397 **72** 5 r. green and purple (*p* 14) (1.7.38) 38·00 4·00
a. Ordinary paper. *Green and pale purple* (19.2.43) .. .. 13·00 2·00
386/97a (*cheapest*) .. .. *Set of* 14 60·00 6·50
386/97 Perf "Specimen" .. .. *Set of* 14 £300

Designs: *Vert*—5 c. Coconut Palms; 6 c. Colombo Harbour; 20 c. Plucking tea. *Horiz*—15 c. River scene; 25 c. Temple of the Tooth, Kandy; 30 c. Ancient irrigation tank; 50 c. Wild elephants; 1 r. Trincomalee.

3 CENTS

(73)

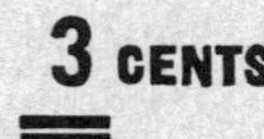

(74)

1940–41. *Nos.* 388 *and* 391 *surch.*
398 **73** 3 c. on 6 c. (10.5.41) 10 10
399 **74** 3 c. on 20 c. (5.11.40) .. .. .. 2·00 1·25

1946 (10 Dec). *Victory. As Nos.* 141/2 *of Jamaica.*
400 6 c. blue 10 10
401 15 c. brown 10 40
400/1 Perf "Specimen" .. .. *Set of* 2 55·00

75 Parliament Building

76 Adam's Peak

(Des R. Tenison and M. S. V. Rodrigo. Recess B.W.)

1947 (25 Nov). *Inauguration of New Constitution. T* **75/6** *and similar designs. Wmk Mult Script CA. P* 11 × 12 (*horiz*) *or* 12 × 11 (*vert*).
402 6 c. black and blue 10 15
403 10 c. black, orange and carmine 10 20
404 15 c. green and purple 10 40
405 25 c. ochre and emerald-green 10 20
402/5 .. .. .. *Set of* 4 35 85
402/5 Perf "Specimen" .. .. *Set of* 4 85·00

Designs: *Horiz*—15 c. Temple of the Tooth. *Vert*—25 c. Anuradhapura.

DOMINION

79 Lion Flag of Dominion

80 D. S. Senanayake

81 Lotus Flowers and Sinhalese Letters "Sri"

(Recess (flag typo) B.W.)

1949 (4 Feb–5 Apr). *First Anniv of Independence.* (*a*) *Wmk Mult Script CA (sideways on* 4 *c.). P* 12½×12 (4 *c.*) *or* 12×12½ (5 *c.*).
406 **79** 4 c. yellow, carmine and brown .. 10 20
407 **80** 5 c. brown and green 10 10

(*b*) *W* **81** (*sideways on* 15 *c.*). *P* 13 × 12½ (15 *c.*) *or* 12 × 12½ (25 *c.*) (5 April)
408 **79** 15 c. yellow, carmine and vermilion .. 25 15
409 **80** 25 c. brown and blue 15 40
406/9 .. .. .. *Set of* 4 40 75

The 15 c. is larger, measuring 28 × 12 mm.

82 Globe and Forms of Transport

83

84

(Recess D.L.R.)

1949 (10 Oct). *75th Anniv of Universal Postal Union. W* **81**. *P* 13 (25 *c.*) *or* 12 (*others*).
410 **82** 5 c. brown and bluish green 75 10
411 **83** 15 c. black and carmine .. .. .. 1·40 1·40
412 **84** 25 c. black and ultramarine .. .. 1·40 1·10
410/12 .. .. .. *Set of* 3 3·25 2·25

85 Kandyan Dancer

88 Sigiriya (Lion Rock)

89 Octagon Library, Temple of the Tooth

90 Ruins at Madirigiriya

(Recess B.W.)

1950 (4 Feb). *T* **85, 88/90** *and similar designs. W* **81.** *P* 11 × 11½ (75 c.), 11½ × 11 (1 *r.*), 12 × 12½ (*others*).

413 4 c. purple and scarlet 10 10
414 5 c. green 10 10
415 15 c. blue-green and violet .. .. .. 1·50 30
416 30 c. carmine and yellow 30 40
417 75 c. ultramarine and orange .. .. 2·50 10
418 1 r. deep blue and brown .. .. 1·75 30
413/18 .. .. *Set of* 6 5·50 95

Designs: *Vert* (*as T* **88**)—5 c. Kiri Vehera, Polonnaruwa; 15 c. Vesak Orchid.

For these values with redrawn inscriptions see Nos. 450/1, 454, 456, 460 and 462.

91 Sambars, Ruhuna National Park

92 Ancient Guard-stone, Anuradhapura

96 Star Orchid

97 Rubber Plantation

99 Tea Plantation

I. No. 424 II. No. 424a (Dot added)

(Photo Courvoisier)

1951 (1 Aug)–**54.** *T* **91/2, 96/7, 99** *and similar designs. No wmk. P* 11½.

419 2 c. brown and blue-green (15.5.54) 10 40
420 3 c. black and slate-violet (15.5.54) 10 50
421 6 c. brown-black & yellow-green (15.5.54) .. 10 20
422 10 c. green and blue-grey 75 65
423 25 c. orange-brown & bright blue (15.3.54) .. 10 20
424 35 c. red and deep green (I) (1.2.52) .. .. 1·50 1·50
 a. Type II (1954) .. .. .. 5·00 60
425 40 c. deep brown (15.5.54) .. .. .. 4·50 80
426 50 c. indigo and slate-grey (15.3.54) 30 10
427 85 c. black and deep blue-green (15.5.54) .. 50 10
428 2 r. blue and deep brown (15.5.54) .. .. 6·50 80
429 5 r. brown and orange (15.3.54) .. .. 4·75 80
430 10 r. red-brown and buff (15.3.54) .. .. 25·00 7·00
419/30 .. .. *Set of* 12 40·00 11·00

Designs: *Vert* (*as T* **91**)—6 c. Harvesting rice; 10 c. Coconut trees; 25 c. Sigiriya fresco. (*As T* **99**)—5 r. Bas-relief, Anuradhapura; 10 r. Harvesting rice. *Horiz* (*as T* **97**)—50 c. Outrigger canoe; (*as T* **99**)—2 r. River Gal Dam.

For these values with redrawn inscriptions see Nos. 448, etc.

103 Ceylon Mace and Symbols of Progress

(Photo Harrison)

1952 (23 Feb). *Colombo Plan Exhibition. Chalk-surfaced paper. W* **81** (*sideways*). *P* 14½ × 14.

431 **103** 5 c. green 10 10
432 15 c. ultramarine 20 40

104 Queen Elizabeth II

105 Ceremonial Procession

(Recess B.W.)

1953 (2 June). *Coronation. W* **81.** *P* 12 × 13.

433 **104** 5 c. green 90 10

(Recess D.L.R.)

1954 (10 Apr). *Royal Visit. W* **81** (*sideways*). *P* 13 × 12½.

434 **105** 10 c. deep blue 30 10

106 King Coconuts

107 Farm Produce

(Photo Courvoisier)

1954 (1 Dec). *No wmk. P* 11½.

435 **106** 10 c. orange, bistre-brown and buff .. 10 10

For this design with redrawn inscription see No. 453.

(Photo Harrison)

1955 (10 Dec). *Royal Agricultural and Food Exhibition. W* **81** (*sideways*). *P* 14 × 14½.

436 **107** 10 c. brown and orange 10 10

108 Sir John Kotelawala and House of Representatives

(Photo Courvoisier)

1956 (26 Mar). *Prime Minister's 25 Years of Public Service. P* 11½.

437 **108** 10 c. deep bluish green 10 10

109 Arrival of Vijaya in Ceylon

110 Lampstand and Dharmachakra

111 Hand of Peace and Dharmachakra

112 Dharmachakra encircling the Globe

(Photo Courvoisier)

1956. *Buddha Jayanti. P* 11½.

438 **109** 3 c. blue and brownish grey (23 May) .. 15 15
439 **110** 4 c. + 2 c. grnish yell & dp bl (10 May) 20 60
440 **111** 10 c. + 5 c. carm, yellow & grey (10 May) 20 60
441 **112** 15 c. bright blue (23 May) 25 10
438/41 .. .. *Set of* 4 70 1·25

113 Mail Transport

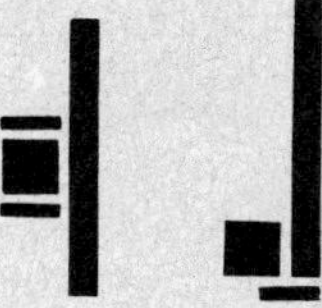

114 Stamp of 1857

(Photo Enschedé (4 c., 10 c.), Courvoisier (others))

1957 (1 Apr). *Centenary of First Ceylon Postage Stamp. P* 12½ × 13 (4 *c.*, 10 *c.*) *or* 11½ (*others*).

442 **113** 4 c. orange-red and deep bluish green 75 40
443 10 c. vermilion and blue 75 10
444 **114** 35 c. brown, yellow and blue 30 50
445 85 c. brown, yellow and grey-green .. 80 1·60
442/5 .. .. *Set of* 4 2·40 2·25

(**115**) (**116**) **117** Kandyan Dancer

1958 (15 Jan). *Nos.* 439/40 *with premium obliterated as T* **115** (4 *c.*) *or T* **116** (10 *c.*).

446 **110** 4 c. greenish yellow and deep blue .. 10 10
 a. Opt inverted .. .. .. 11·00
 b. Opt double .. .. .. 14·00
447 **111** 10 c. carmine, yellow and grey .. 10 10
 a. Opt inverted .. .. .. 13·00 15·00

The 4 c. exists with opt misplaced to right so that some stamps show the vertical bar on the left (*Price* £18 *un.*).

(Recess B.W. (4 c., 5 c., 15 c., 30 c., 75 c., 1 r.). Photo Courvoisier (others))

1958 (14 May)–**62.** *As earlier types, but inscriptions redrawn as in T* **117.** *W* **81** (4, 5, 15, 30, 75 *c.*, 1 *r.*) *or no wmk* (*others*). *P* 11×11½ (75 *c.*), 11½×11 (1 *r.*), 12×12½ (4, 5, 15 , 30 *c.*), *or* 11½ (*others*).

448 **91** 2 c. brown and blue-green 10 50
449 **92** 3 c. black and slate-violet 10 70
450 **117** 4 c. purple and scarlet 10 10
451 – 5 c. green (1.10.58) 10 50
 a. Yellow-green (13.6.61) 40 70
 b. Deep green (19.6.62) .. .. 1·75 1·25
452 – 6 c. brown-black and yellow-green .. 10 65
453 **106** 10 c. orge, bistre-brown & buff (1.10.58) 10 10
454 – 15 c. blue-green and violet (1.10.58) .. 3·50 70
455 – 25 c. orange-brown and bright blue .. 10 10
456 **88** 30 c. carmine and yellow (1.5.59) .. 15 70
457 **96** 35 c. red and deep green (II) (15.7.58) 6·50 30
459 – 50 c. indigo and slate-grey (15.7.58) .. 30 10
460 **89** 75 c. ultramarine and orange (1.5.59) 8·00 1·50
 a. Ultramarine & brown-orge (3.4.62) 8·00 1·00
461 **99** 85 c. black and deep blue-green (1.5.59) 3·75 3·75
462 **90** 1 r. deep blue and brown (1.10.58) .. 60 10
463 – 2 r. blue and deep brown .. .. 1·00 30
464 – 5 r. brown and orange .. .. 2·75 30
465 – 10 r. red-brown and buff .. .. 7·00 1·00
448/65 .. .. .. *Set of* 17 30·00 9·50

Designs: *Vert* (*as T* **117**)—5 c. Kiri Vehera Polonnaruwa; 6 c. Harvesting rice; 15 c. Vesak Orchid; 25 c. Sigiriya fresco. (*as T* **99**)—5 r. Bas-relief, Anuradhapura; 10 r. Harvesting rice. *Horiz* (*as T* **97**)—50 c. Outrigger canoe. (*as T* **99**)—2 r. River Gal Dam.

118 "Human Rights"

119 Portraits of Founders and University Buildings

(Photo Enschedé)

1958 (10 Dec). *Tenth Anniv of Declaration of Human Rights. P* 13 × 12½.

466 **118** 10 c. vermilion and dull purple 10 10
467 85 c. vermilion and deep blue-green .. 30 45

(Photo Enschedé)

1959 (31 Dec). *Institution of Pirivena Universities. P* 13 × 12½.

468 **119** 10 c. red-orange and ultramarine .. 10 10

120 Uprooted Tree

121 S.W.R.D. Bandaranaike

(Des G. Malaviachi. Litho Format)

1986 (2 Feb). *Inaugural Run of "Viceroy Special" Train from Colombo to Kandy. P* 12½.
924 **366** 1 r. multicoloured .. .. 1·50 1·50

367 Girl and Boy Students **368** D. R. Wijewardena

(Des S. Silva. Litho Heraclio Fournier, Spain)

1986 (14 Feb). *6th Anniv of Mahapola Scheme. P* 14.
925 **367** 75 c. multicoloured 40 60

(Des S. Silva. Litho J.W.)

1986 (23 Feb). *Birth Centenary of D. R. Wijewardena (newspaper publisher). P* 14 × 14½.
926 **368** 75 c. orange-brown and deep olive .. 30 60

369 Ven Welitara Gnanatillake Maha Nayake Thero **370** Red Cross Flag and Personnel

(Des S. Silva. Litho Cartor)

1986 (26 Feb). *Ven. Welitara Gnanatillake Maha Nayake Thero (scholar) Commemoration. W w* **17**. *P* 13½.
927 **369** 75 c. multicoloured 70 80

(Des W. Rohana. Litho Format)

1986 (31 Mar). *50th Anniv of Sri Lanka Red Cross Society. P* 12½.
928 **370** 75 c. multicoloured .. .. 2·00 1·50

371 Comet depicted as Goddess visiting Sun-god **372** Woman lighting Lamp

(Des W. Rohana. Litho Format)

1986 (5 Apr). *Appearance of Halley's Comet. T* **371** *and similar horiz designs. Multicoloured. P* 12½.
929 50 c. Type **371** 10 20
930 75 c. Comet and constellations of Scorpius and Sagittarius 10 20
931 6 r. 50, Comet's orbit .. .. 30 1·25
932 8 r. 50, Edmond Halley .. .. 55 1·75
929/32 .. .. *Set of* 4 75 3·00
MS933 180 × 115 mm. Nos. 929/32 .. .. 5·50 8·00

(Des B. Harischandra. Litho Format)

1986 (10 Apr). *Sinhalese and Tamil New Year. T* **372** *and similar vert designs. Multicoloured. P* 12½.
934 50 c. Type **372** 10 20
935 75 c. Woman and festive foods 10 20
936 6 r. 50, Women playing drum .. .. 30 1·60
937 8 r. 50, Anointing and making offerings at temple .. .. 55 2·00
934/7 .. .. *Set of* 4 75 3·50
MS938 178 × 108 mm. Nos. 934/7 .. .. 2·75 5·50

373 The King donating Elephant to the Brahmin **374** Ven. Kalukondayave Sri Prajnasekhara Maha Nayake Thero (Buddhist leader and social reformer)

(Des N. Bulathsinhala. Litho Format)

1986 (16 May). *Vesak. Wall paintings from Samudragiri Temple, Mirissa. T* **373** *and similar horiz designs. Multicoloured. P* 12½.
939 50 c. Type **373** 15 20
940 75 c. The Bodhisattva in the Vasavarthi heaven 15 20
941 5 r. The offering of milk rice by Sujatha .. 40 1·75
942 10 r. The offering of parched corn and honey by Thapassu and Bhalluka .. .. 60 2·25
939/42 .. .. *Set of* 4 1·10 4·00

(Des S. Silva. Litho Format)

1986 (22 May). *National Heroes. T* **374** *and similar vert designs. Multicoloured. P* 12½.
943 75 c. Type **374** 20 55
944 75 c. Brahmachari Walisinghe Harischandra (social reformer) (birth centenary) 20 55
945 75 c. Martin Wickramasinghe (author and scholar) 20 55
946 75 c. G. G. Ponnambalam (politician) .. 20 55
947 75 c. A. M. A. Azeez (Islamic scholar) (75th birth anniv) 20 55
943/7 .. .. *Set of* 5 80 2·50

375 Stylised Village and People **376** Co-op Flag and Emblem

(Des S. Herath. Litho German Bank Note Co, Leipzig)

1986 (23 June). *Gam Udawa '86 (Village Re-awakening Movement). P* 13½ × 13.
948 **375** 75 c. multicoloured .. .. 1·50 1·25

(Des A. Harischandra. Litho Format)

1986 (5 July). *75th Anniv of Sri Lanka Co-operative Movement. P* 12½.
949 **376** 1 r. multicoloured .. .. 1·50 1·25

377 Arthur V. Dias **378** Bull Elephant

(Des S. Silva. Litho Harrison)

1986 (31 July). *Birth Centenary of Arthur V. Dias (philanthropist). P* 14 × 15.
950 **377** 1 r. chestnut and dull violet-blue .. 1·50 1·25

(Des G. Ratnavira. Litho Harrison)

1986 (5 Aug). *Sri Lanka Wild Elephants. T* **378** *and similar horiz designs. Multicoloured. P* 15 × 14.
951 5 r. Type **378** .. .. 4·00 4·00
a. Horiz strip of 4. Nos. 951/4 .. .. 14·50
952 5 r. Cow elephant and calf .. .. .. 4·00 4·00
953 5 r. Cow elephant .. .. 4·00 4·00
954 5 r. Elephants bathing .. .. .. 4·00 4·00
951/4 .. .. *Set of* 4 14·50 14·50

Nos. 951/4 were printed, together, *se-tenant*, in horizontal strips of four throughout the sheet.

379 Congress Logo **380** Map showing Route of Cable and Telephone Receiver

(Des S. Silva. Litho Govt Printing Bureau, Tokyo)

1986 (14 Aug). *2nd Indo-Pacific Congress on Legal Medicine and Forensic Sciences. P* 13½ × 13.
955 **379** 8 r. 50, multicoloured .. .. .. 2·25 1·75

(Des R. Mawilmada. Litho Security Printers (M), Malaysia)

1986 (8 Sept). *SEA-ME-WE Submarine Cable Project. P* 13½ × 14.
956 **380** 5 r. 75, multicoloured .. .. .. 2·25 1·50

381 Anniversary Logo **382** Logo on Flag

(Des R. Mawilmada. Litho Format)

1986 (20 Sept). *25th Anniv of Dag Hammarskjöld Award. P* 12½.
957 **381** 2 r. multicoloured 65 65

(Des A. Harischandra. Litho Security Printers (M), Malaysia)

1986 (22 Sept). *2nd National School Games. P* 12.
958 **382** 1 r. multicoloured .. .. 2·50 1·60

383 Logo **384** College Building and Crest

(Des W. Rohana. Litho Govt Printing Bureau, Tokyo)

1986 (27 Sept). *60th Anniv of Surveyors' Institute of Sri Lanka. P* 13½ × 13.
959 **383** 75 c. red-brown and cinnamon 60 85

(Des W. Rohana. Litho Security Printers (M), Malaysia)

1986 (1 Nov). *Centenary of Ananda College, Colombo. T* **384** *and similar horiz designs. P* 12.
960 75 c. multicoloured 10 10
961 5 r. multicoloured 30 50
962 5 r. 75, multicoloured 30 50
963 6 r. carmine-red, gold and rose-lilac .. 35 60
960/3 .. .. *Set of* 4 90 1·50

Designs:—5 r. Sports field and college crest; 5 r. 75, Col. H. S. Olcott (founder), Ven. Migettuwatte Gunananda, Ven. Hikkaduwe Sri Sumangala (Buddhist leaders) and Buddhist flag; 6 r. College flag.

385 Mangrove Swamp **386** Family and Housing Estate

(Des G. Ratnavira. Litho Security Printers (M), Malaysia)

1986 (11 Nov). *Mangrove Conservation. T* **385** *and similar horiz designs. Multicoloured. P* 12.
964 35 c. Type **385** 30 10
965 50 c. Mangrove tree 40 20
966 75 c. Germinating mangrove flower 50 20
967 6 r. Fiddler Crab .. .. 3·50 4·50
964/7 .. .. *Set of* 4 4·25 4·50

(Des R. Mawilmada. Litho Govt Printing Bureau, Tokyo)

1987 (1 Jan). *International Year of Shelter for the Homeless. P* 13 × 13½.
968 **386** 75 c. multicoloured .. .. 1·50 30

387 Ven. Ambagahawatte Indasabhawaragnanasamy Thero **388** Proctor John de Silva

(Des S. Silva. Litho Security Printers (M), Malaysia)

1987 (29 Jan). *Ven. Ambagahawatte Indasabhawaragnanasamy Thero (Buddhist monk) Commemoration. P* 12.
969 **387** 5 r. 75, multicoloured .. .. 2·00 80

(Des S. Silva. Litho Security Printers (M), Malaysia)

1987 (31 Jan). *Proctor John de Silva (playwright) Commemoration. P* 12.
970 **388** 5 r. 75, multicoloured 70 70

(Des W. A. Ariyasena. Photo Courvoisier)

1960 (7 Apr). *World Refugee Year. P* 11½.
469 **120** 4 c. red-brown and gold 10 60
470 25 c. blackish violet and gold 10 15

(Photo Courvoisier)

1961 (8 Jan–15 June). *Prime Minister Bandaranaike Commemoration. P* 11½.
471 **121** 10 c. deep blue and greenish blue . . 10 10
a. Portrait redrawn (15.6.61)* . . 10 10
*Earliest known postmark date.
No. 471a can be identified by Mr. Bandaranaike's dark hair at temples.

122 Ceylon Scout Badge **123** Campaign Emblem

(Des W. A. Ariyasena. Photo Courvoisier)

1962 (26 Feb). *Golden Jubilee of Ceylon Boy Scouts Association. P* 11½.
472 **122** 35 c. buff and blue 15 10

(Photo Harrison)

1962 (7 Apr). *Malaria Eradication.* W **81**. *P* 14½ × 14.
473 **123** 25 c. red-orange and sepia 10 10

124 De Havilland D.H.85 Leopard Moth and Hawker Siddeley Comet 4 **125** "Produce" and Campaign Emblem

(Photo Courvoisier)

1963 (28 Feb). *25th Anniv of Airmail. P* 11½.
474 **124** 50 c. black and light blue 40 50

(Photo Courvoisier)

1963 (21 Mar). *Freedom from Hunger. P* 11½.
475 **125** 5 c. vermilion and blue . . . . . . 30 1·50
476 25 c. brown and yellow-olive . . . . 1·50 30

ශත
2
சதம்

(126) **127** "Rural Life"

1963 (1 June). *No.* 450 *surch with T* **126**.
477 **117** 2 c. on 4 c. purple and scarlet 10 10
a. Surch inverted . . . . . . 16·00
b. Surch double . . . . . . 22·00

(Photo Harrison)

1963 (5 July). *Golden Jubilee of Ceylon Co-operative Movement* (1962). W **81**. *P* 14 × 14½.
478 **127** 60 c. rose-red and black 70 60

128 S. W. R. D. Bandaranaike **129** Terrain, Elephant and Tree

(Recess Courvoisier)

1963 (26 Sept). *P* 11½.
479 **128** 10 c. light blue 10 10

(Photo Harrison)

1963 (9 Dec). *National Conservation Week.* W **81** (*sideways*). *P* 14 × 14½.
480 **129** 5 c. sepia and blue 60 40

130 S. W. R. D. Bandaranaike **131** Anagarika Dharmapala (Buddhist missionary)

(T 130/1. Photo Courvoisier)

1964 (1 July). *P* 11½.
481 **130** 10 c. deep violet-blue and greenish grey 10 10

1964 (16 Sept). *Birth Centenary of Anagarika Dharmapala (founder of Maha Bodhi Society). P* 11½.
482 **131** 25 c. sepia and olive-yellow 10 10

134 Southern Grackle **138** Ruins at Madirigiriya

135 D. S. Senanayake **136**

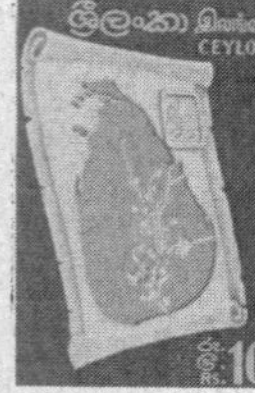

146 Tea Plantation **149** Map of Ceylon

(Des A. Dharmasiri (5 r.); P. A. Miththapala (10 r.). Photo Courvoisier (10 c. (486), 20 c.), Harrison (10 c. (487), 60 c., 1 r., 5 r., 10 r.), D.L.R. (others incl sheet))

1964 (1 Oct)–**72.** *T* **134/6**, **138**, **146**, **149** *and similar designs. No wmk* (*Nos.* 486, 489). W **81** (*others; sideways on Nos.* 487, 494, 499). *P* 11½ (*Nos.* 486, 489), 14½×14 (*No.* 494) *or* 14 (*others*).
485 **134** 5 c. multicoloured (5.2.66) . . . . 1·10 1·50
486 **135** 10 c. myrtle-green (22.3.66) 30 10
487 **136** 10 c. myrtle-green (23.9.68) 10 10
a. Imperf (pair) . . . . . . 45·00
b. Horiz pair, one stamp imperf 3 sides £100
488 – 15 c. multicoloured (5.2.66) . . . . 1·75 30
489 **138** 20 c. brown-purple and buff 10 15
494 – 60 c. multicoloured (5.2.66) . . . . 2·75 80
a. Red omitted . . . . . . 32·00
b. Blue and green omitted* . . 32·00
495 – 75 c. multicoloured (5.2.66) . . . . 1·50 50
a. No wmk (8.6.72) . . . . 8·50 8·50
497 **146** 1 r. brown and bluish green . . 1·00 30
a. Brown (tea picker, etc) omitted £150
b. Bluish green omitted . . £200
499 – 5 r. multicoloured (15.8.69) . . . . 3·50 3·00
500 **149** 10 r. multicoloured (1.10.69) . . . . 17·00 3·00
485/500 . . . . . . *Set of* 10 26·00 8·50
MS500*a* 148×174 mm. As Nos. 485, 488, 494 and 495. Imperf . . . . 7·00 11·00
Designs: *Horiz* (*as T* **134**)—15 c. Common Peafowl; 60 c. Ceylon Junglefowl; 75 c. Asian Black-headed Oriole. (*As T* **138**)—5 r. Girls transplanting rice.
*Actually only the blue printing is omitted on this sheet, but where this was printed over the yellow to form the leaves it appeared as green.
The 5 c., 75 c. and 1 r. exist with PVA gum as well as gum arabic.
No. 487b comes from a sheet which showed stamps in the third vertical row imperforate at top, bottom and at right.
In the miniature sheet the inscriptions on the 60 c. have been rearranged to conform with the style of the other values.

PRICES OF SETS

Set prices are given for many issues, generally those containing three stamps or more. Definitive sets include one of each value or major colour change, but do not cover different perforations, die types or minor shades. Where a choice is possible the set prices are based on the cheapest versions of the stamps included in the listings.

150 Exhibition Buildings and Cogwheels **151** Trains of 1864 and 1964

(Photo State Printing Works, Budapest)

1964 (1 Dec). *Industrial Exhibition. T* **150** *and similar horiz design. No wmk. P* 11.
501 – 5 c. multicoloured 10 75
a. Pair. Nos. 501/2 . . . . . . 20 2·25
502 **150** 5 c. multicoloured 10 75
No. 501 is inscribed "INDUSTRIAL EXHIBITION" in Sinhala and Tamil, No. 502 in Sinhala and English. The stamps were issued together *se-tenant* in alternate vertical rows, producing horizontal pairs.

(Photo Harrison)

1964 (21 Dec). *Centenary of Ceylon Railways. T* **151** *and similar horiz design.* W **81** (*sideways*). *P* 14 × 14½.
503 – 60 c. blue, reddish purple & yellow-grn 2·50 40
a. Pair. Nos. 503/4 . . . . . . 5·00 4·00
504 **151** 60 c. blue, reddish purple & yellow-grn 2·50 40
No. 503 is inscribed "RAILWAY CENTENARY" in Sinhala and Tamil, No. 504 in Sinhala and English. The stamps were issued together *se-tenant* in alternate horizontal rows, producing vertical pairs.

152 I.T.U. Emblem and Symbols **153** I.C.Y. Emblem

(Photo Harrison)

1965 (17 May). *I.T.U. Centenary.* W **81** (*sideways*). *P* 14½.
505 **152** 2 c. bright blue and red . . . . 50 1·10
506 30 c. brown and red . . . . . . 2·75 45
a. Value omitted £110
No. 506a was caused by the misplacement of the red.

(Photo Courvoisier)

1965 (26 June). *International Co-operation Year. T* **153** *and similar horiz design. P* 11½.
507 3 c. deep blue and rose-carmine . . . . 1·00 1·00
508 50 c. black, rose-carmine and gold . . 3·00 50
No. 508 is similar to T **153** but has the multilingual inscription "CEYLON" rearranged.

154 Town Hall, Colombo (155)

(Photo Courvoisier)

1965 (29 Oct). *Centenary of Colombo Municipal Council. P* 11 × 11½.
509 **154** 25 c. myrtle-green and sepia 10 10

1965 (18 Dec). *No.* 481 *surch with T* **155**.
510 **130** 5 c. on 10 c. dp vio-bl & greenish grey 10 30

157 Kandy and Council Crest **158** W.H.O. Building

(Photo Harrison)

1966 (15 June). *Kandy Municipal Council Centenary.* W **81**. *P* 14 × 13½.
512 **157** 25 c. multicoloured 10 10

(Litho D.L.R.)

1966 (8 Oct). *Inauguration of W.H.O. Headquarters. Geneva. P* 14.
513 **158** 4 c. multicoloured . . . . 1·75 2·25
514 1 r. multicoloured . . . . 6·75 1·50

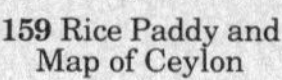

159 Rice Paddy and Map of Ceylon

160 Rice Paddy and Globe

(Photo Courvoisier)

1966 (25 Oct). *International Rice Year. P* 11½.

515	**159**	6 c. multicoloured	20	75
516	**160**	30 c. multicoloured	30	15

161 U.N.E.S.C.O. Emblem

162 Water-resources Map

(Litho State Ptg Wks, Vienna)

1966 (3 Nov). *20th Anniv of U.N.E.S.C.O. P* 12.

517	**161**	3 c. multicoloured	1·75	1·00
518		50 c. multicoloured	4·75	30

(Litho D.L.R.)

1966 (1 Dec). *International Hydrological Decade. P* 14.

519	**162**	2 c. orange-brown, greenish yellow & bl	30	85
520		2 r. orge-brn, grnish yell, bl & yell-grn	95	1·90

163 Devotees at Buddhist Temple

167 Galle Fort and Clock Tower

(Photo State Ptg Wks, Vienna)

1967 (2 Jan). *Poya Holiday System. T* **163** *and similar horiz designs. Multicoloured. P* 12.

521	5 c. Type **163**	10	40
522	20 c. Mihintale	10	10
523	35 c. Sacred Bo-tree, Anuradhapura	10	15
524	60 c. Adam's Peak	10	10
521/4	*Set of* 4	30	55

(Litho Rosenbaum Brothers, Vienna)

1967 (5 Jan). *Centenary of Galle Municipal Council. P* 13½.

525	**167**	25 c. multicoloured	50	20

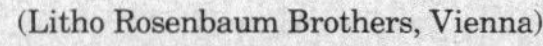

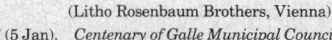

168 Field Research

(Litho Rosenbaum Bros, Vienna)

1967 (1 Aug). *Centenary of Ceylon Tea Industry. T* **168** *and similar horiz designs. Multicoloured. P* 13½.

526	4 c. Type **168**	40	80
527	40 c. Tea-tasting equipment	1·25	1·25
528	50 c. Leaves and bud	1·25	40
529	1 r. Shipping tea	1·50	10
526/9	*Set of* 4	4·00	2·25

172 Elephant Ride

173 Ranger, Jubilee Emblem and Flag

(Litho Rosenbaum Bros, Vienna)

1967 (15 Aug). *International Tourist Year. P* 13½.

530	**172**	45 c. multicoloured	1·75	60

1967 (16 Sept). *1st National Stamp Exhibition. No.* **MS**500*a optd* "FIRST NATIONAL STAMP EXHIBITION 1967".

MS531 148 × 174 mm. Nos. 485, 488, 494/5. Imperf 4·25 5·50

(Litho D.L.R.)

1967 (19 Sept). *Golden Jubilee of Ceylon Girl Guides Association. P* 12½ × 13.

532	**173**	3 c. multicoloured	30	20
533		25 c. multicoloured	40	10

174 Col. Olcott and Buddhist Flag

(Litho Rosenbaum Bros, Vienna)

1967 (8 Dec). *60th Death Anniv of Colonel H. S. Olcott (theosophist). P* 13½.

534	**174**	15 c. multicoloured	30	20

175 Independence Hall

176 Lion Flag and Sceptre

(Photo Harrison)

1968 (2 Feb). *20th Anniv of Independence. W* **81** *(sideways). P* 14.

535	**175**	5 c. multicoloured	10	55
536	**176**	1 r. multicoloured	40	10

177 Sir D. B. Jayatilleke

178 Institute of Hygiene

(Litho D.L.R.)

1968 (14 Feb). *Birth Centenary of Sir Baron Jayatilleke (scholar and statesman). P* 14.

537	**177**	25 c. yellow-brown and sepia	10	10

(Litho B.W.)

1968 (7 Apr). *20th Anniv of World Health Organization. W* **81**. *P* 12.

538	**178**	50 c. multicoloured	10	10

179 Vickers Super VC-10 Aircraft over Terminal Building

181 Open Koran and "1400"

(Des and litho B.W.)

1968 (5 Aug). *Opening of Colombo Airport. W* **81**. *P* 13½.

539	**179**	60 c. grey-blue, chestnut, red and yellow	30	10

(Des M. I. M. Mohideen. Photo Harrison)

1968 (14 Oct). *1400th Anniv of the Holy Koran. W* **81**. *P* 14.

541	**181**	25 c. multicoloured	10	10

182 Human Rights Emblem

183 All Ceylon Buddhist Congress Headquarters

(Photo Pakistan Security Printing Corp)

1968 (10 Dec). *Human Rights Year. P* 12½ × 13½.

542	**182**	2 c. multicoloured	10	15
543		20 c. multicoloured	10	10
544		40 c. multicoloured	10	10
545		2 r. multicoloured	70	3·00
542/5		*Set of* 4	75	3·00

(Des A. Dharmasiri. Litho Rosenbaum Bros, Vienna)

1968 (19 Dec). *Golden Jubilee of All Ceylon Buddhist Congress. P* 13½.

546	**183**	5 c. multicoloured	10	40

A 50 c. value showing a footprint was prepared but its release was stopped the day before it was due for issue. However, some are known to have been released in error at rural offices (*Price £28 mint*).

184 E. W. Perera (patriot)

185 Symbols of Strength in Savings

(Photo Harrison)

1969 (17 Feb). *E. W. Perera Commemoration. W* **81**. *P* 14 × 13½.

547	**184**	60 c. brown	10	10

(Des A. Dharmasiri. Photo Harrison)

1969 (20 Mar). *Silver Jubilee of National Savings Movement. W* **81**. *P* 14.

548	**185**	3 c. multicoloured	10	30

186 Seat of Enlightenment under Sacred Bodhi Tree

187 Buduresmala (Six fold Buddha-Rays)

(Des L. T. P. Manjusree. Litho D.L.R.)

1969 (10 Apr). *Vesak Day (inscr "Wesak"). W* **81** *(sideways). P* 15.

549	**186**	4 c. multicoloured	10	40
550	**187**	6 c. multicoloured	10	40
551	**186**	35 c. multicoloured	10	10
549/51		*Set of* 3	15	80

No. 549 exists with the gold apparently omitted. Normally the gold appears (without a separate plate number) over an underlay of olive-green on carmine. In one sheet we have seen, the gold only shows as tiny specks under a strong magnifying glass and as there may be intermediate stages of faint printing we do not list this.

188 A. E. Goonesinghe

189 I.L.O. Emblem

(Des and photo Harrison)

1969 (29 Apr). *Commemoration of Goonesinghe (founder of Labour Movement in Ceylon). W* **81**. *P* 14.

552	**188**	15 c. multicoloured	10	10

(Photo Harrison)

1969 (4 May). *50th Anniv of International Labour Organisation. W* **81** *(sideways). P* 14.

553	**189**	5 c. black and turquoise-blue	10	10
554		25 c. black and carmine-red	10	10

OMNIBUS ISSUES

Details, together with prices for complete sets, of the various Omnibus issues from the 1935 Silver Jubilee series to date are included in a special section following Zimbabwe at the end of Volume 2.

190 Convocation Hall, University of Ceylon

192 Uranium Atom

(Des Ahangama Edward (35 c.); L. D. P. Jayawardena (50 c.); A. Dharmasiri (60 c.); 4 c. from photograph. Litho Rosenbaum Bros, Vienna)

1969 (1 Aug). *Educational Centenary. T* **190, 192** *and similar multicoloured designs. P* 13½.

555 4 c. Type **190** 10 80
556 35 c. Lamp of Learning, Globe and flags (*horiz*) 15 10
557 50 c. Type **192** 15 10
558 60 c. Symbols of Scientific education 20 10
555/8 .. .. *Set of* 4 50 1·00

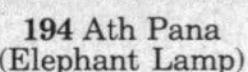

194 Ath Pana (Elephant Lamp)

195 Rock Fortress of Sigiriya

(Des from photographs. Litho Rosenbaum Bros, Vienna)

1969 (1 Aug). *Archaeological Centenary. P* 13½.

559 **194** 6 c. multicoloured 15 90
560 **195** 1 r. multicoloured 25 10

196 Leopard

197 Emblem and Symbols

(Litho Rosenbaum Bros, Vienna)

1970 (11 May). *Wildlife Conservation. T* **196** *and similar horiz designs. Multicoloured. P* 13½.

561 5 c. Water Buffalo .. .. 20 1·25
562 15 c. Slender Loris 60 30
a. Brown-black and orange-brown colours omitted .. .. 70·00
563 50 c. Spotted Deer .. .. 80 1·25
a. Imperf (in vert pair with stamp perf 3 sides) £200
564 1 r. Type **196** .. .. 90 1·75
561/4 .. .. *Set of* 4 2·25 4·00

In No. 562a the sky is blue instead of violet and the animal is in green and yellow only.

(Des A. Dharmasiri. Litho Rosenbaum Bros, Vienna)

1970 (17 June). *Asian Productivity Year. P* 13½.

565 **197** 60 c. multicoloured 10 10

198 New U.P.U. H.Q. Building

199 Oil Lamp and Caduceus

(Litho Rosenbaum Bros, Vienna)

1970 (14 Aug). *New U.P.U. Headquarters Building. P* 13½.

566 **198** 50 c. yellow-orange, black and new blue 20 10
a. New blue (Building) omitted .. 75·00
567 1 r. 10, vermilion, black and new blue 1·75 30

(Des A. Dharmasiri. Litho Rosenbaum Bros, Vienna)

1970 (1 Sept). *Centenary of Colombo Medical School. P* 13½.

568 **199** 5 c. multicoloured 40 80
a. Vert pair, bottom stamp imperf .. £170
569 45 c. multicoloured 40 60

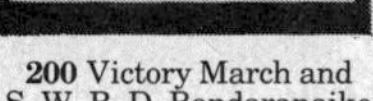

200 Victory March and S. W. R. D. Bandaranaike

201 U.N. Emblem and Dove of Peace

(Des A. Dharmasiri. Litho D.L.R.)

1970 (25 Sept). *Definitive issue marking establishment of United Front Government. P* 13½.

570 **200** 10 c. multicoloured 10 10

(Des A. Dharmasiri. Photo Pakistan Security Printing Corp)

1970 (24 Oct). *25th Anniv of United Nations. P* 12½ × 13½.

571 **201** 2 r. multicoloured .. .. .. 2·00 2·50

202 Keppetipola Dissawa

203 Ola Leaf Manuscript

(Des A. Dharmasiri. Litho Harrison)

1970 (26 Nov). *152nd Death Anniv of Keppetipola Dissawa (Kandyan patriot). P* 14 × 14½.

572 **202** 25 c. multicoloured 10 10

(Des A. Dharmasiri. Photo Pakistan Security Printing Corp)

1970 (21 Dec). *International Education Year. P* 13.

573 **203** 15 c. multicoloured .. .. .. 1·25 1·25

204 C. H. de Soysa

205 D. E. H. Pedris (patriot)

206 Lenin

(Des L. D. P. Jayawardena. Litho Pakistan Security Printing Corp)

1971 (3 Mar). *135th Birth Anniv of C. H. de Soysa (philanthropist). P* 13½.

574 **204** 20 c. multicoloured 15 40

(Des L. D. P. Jayawardena. Litho Harrison)

1971 (8 July). *D. E. H. Pedris Commemoration. P* 14 × 14½.

575 **205** 25 c. multicoloured 15 50

(Des L. D. P. Jayawardena. Litho Harrison)

1971 (31 Aug). *Lenin Commemoration. P* 14½.

576 **206** 40 c. multicoloured 15 40

207 Ananda Rajakaruna

(208)

(Des A. Dharmasiri (Nos. 577 and 579), P. A. Miththapala (Nos. 578 and 580), L. D. P. Jayawardena (No. 581). Litho Harrison)

1971 (29 Oct). *Poets and Philosophers. T* **207** *and similar vert designs. P* 14 × 13½.

577 5 c. royal blue 10 15
578 5 c. lake-brown 10 15
579 5 c. red-orange 10 15
580 5 c. deep slate-blue 10 15
581 5 c. brown 10 15
577/81 .. .. *Set of* 5 30 70

Portraits: No. 577, Type **207**; No. 578, Arumuga Navalar; No. 579, Rev. S. Mahinda; No. 580, Ananda Coomaraswamy; No. 581, Cumaratunga Munidasa.

1971 (26 Nov–2 Dec). *Nos.* 549/50, 555, 559 *and* 570 *surch as T* **208** *(obliterating shape differs).*

582 **186** 5 c. on 4 c. multicoloured .. .. 4·00 1·75
a. Surch inverted .. .. .. 5·50
b. Pair, one with "X" omitted .. 60·00
c. Surch double, one inverted .. 8·50
d. Ditto. Pair, one with "X" omitted 38·00
583 **190** 5 c. on 4 c. multicoloured .. .. 10 1·00
a. Surch inverted .. .. .. 2·75
b. Surch double, one inverted .. 8·50
584 **200** 15 c. on 10 c. multicoloured (2 Dec) 10 30
a. Surch inverted .. .. .. 2·75
b. Surch double .. .. .. 6·00
c. Surch and dot transposed .. ..
d. Surch at right, dot omitted .. ..
585 **187** 25 c. on 6 c. multicoloured 30 60
a. Surch double, one inverted .. 16·00
b. Surch inverted .. .. .. 16·00
586 **194** 25 c. on 6 c. multicoloured 30 80
a. Surch inverted .. .. .. 2·75
582/6 .. .. *Set of* 5 4·25 4·00

Nos. 584c/d were caused by a misplacement of the surcharge on one sheet.

209 Colombo Plan Emblem and Ceylon

210 Globe and CARE Package

(Des P. A. Miththapala. Litho Harrison)

1971 (28 Dec). *20th Anniv of Colombo Plan. P* 14 × 14½.

587 **209** 20 c. multicoloured 15 30

(Des A. Dharmasiri. Litho Harrison)

1971 (28 Dec). *20th Anniv of CARE (Co-operative for American Relief Everywhere). P* 14 × 13½.

588 **210** 50 c. new blue, lilac and violet 35 30

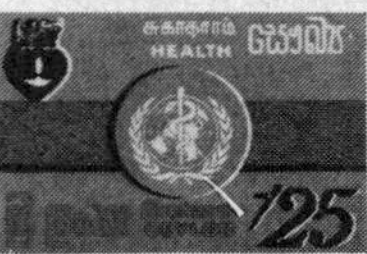

211 W.H.O. Emblem and Heart

212 Map of Asia and U.N. Emblem

(Des A. Miththapala. Litho D.L.R.)

1972 (2 May). *World Health Day. P* 13 × 13½.

589 **211** 25 c. multicoloured .. .. .. 1·75 60

(Des L. D. P. Jayawardena. Litho B.W.)

1972 (2 May). *25th Anniv of ECAFE (Economic Commission for Asia and the Far East). P* 13.

590 **212** 85 c. multicoloured .. .. .. 3·50 2·75

SRI LANKA

REPUBLIC

Ceylon became the Republic of Sri Lanka on 22 May 1972.

208 National Flower and Mountain of the Illustrious Foot

209 Map of World with Buddhist Flag

(Des L. D. P. Jayawardena. Litho D.L.R.)

1972 (22 May). *Inauguration of the Republic of Sri Lanka. P* 13.

591 **208** 15 c. multicoloured 30 30

(Des L. D. P. Jayawardena. Litho Harrison)

1972 (26 May). *Tenth Conference of the World Fellowship of Buddhists. P* 14 × 13.

592 **209** 5 c. multicoloured 30 60
a. "1972" ptd double .. ..
b. "1972" ptd double, one inverted .. 20·00

This stamp was scheduled for release in May 1971, and when finally released had the year "1972" additionally overprinted in red. Sheets are known without this overprint but their status has not been established.

210 Book Year Emblem

211 Emperor Angelfish

(Des L. D. P. Jayawardena. Photo Pakistan Security Printing Corp)

1972 (8 Sept). *International Book Year. P* 13.

593 **210** 20 c. light yellow-orange and lake-brown 20 30

(Des G. D. Kariyawasam. Litho Rosenbaum Bros, Vienna)

1972 (12 Oct). *T* **211** *and similar horiz designs showing fish. Multicoloured. P* 13 × 13½.

594 2 c. Type **211** 10 80
a. Plum colour omitted .. .. .. 3·00
595 3 c. Green Chromide 10 80
596 30 c. Skipjack Tuna .. .. .. 1·25 30
597 2 r. Black Ruby Barb .. .. .. 3·50 5·25
594/7 .. .. .. *Set of* 4 4·50 6·50

On No. 594a the stripes of the fish are in green instead of plum.

NEW INFORMATION

The editor is always interested to correspond with people who have new information that will improve or correct the Catalogue.

212 Memorial Hall

(Des R. B. Mawilmada. Litho D.L.R.)

1973 (17 May). *Opening of Bandaranaike Memorial Hall. P* 14.
598 **212** 15 c. light cobalt and deep grey-blue 30 30

213 King Vessantara giving away his Children — 214 Bandaranaike Memorial Conference Hall

(Des P. Wanigatunga. Litho D.L.R.)

1973 (3 Sept). *Rock and Temple Paintings. T* **213** *and similar vert designs. Multicoloured. P* 13½ × 14.
599 35 c. Type **213** 30 10
600 50 c. The Prince and the Grave-digger .. 35 10
601 90 c. Bearded old man 50 75
602 1 r. 55, Two female figures .. .. .. 65 1·50
599/602 .. .. *Set of* 4 1·60 2·25
MS603 115 × 141 mm. Nos. 599/602 .. .. 1·60 2·25

(Des and litho Harrison)

1974 (6 Sept). *20th Commonwealth Parliamentary Conference, Colombo. P* 14½.
604 **214** 85 c. multicoloured 30 30

215 Prime Minister Bandaranaike — 216 "UPU" and "100"

(Des and photo Harrison)

1974 (25 Sept). *P* 14½.
605 **215** 15 c. multicoloured 15 10
a. Red (face value) omitted .. .. 3·00
b. Pale blue (background) omitted .. 4·00
c. Ultramarine (country inscr) omitted .. ..
d. Imperf (pair) £100

(Des P. Jayatillake. Litho German Bank Note Ptg Co, Leipzig)

1974 (9 Oct). *Centenary of Universal Postal Union. P* 13½ × 13.
606 **216** 50 c. multicoloured 75 75

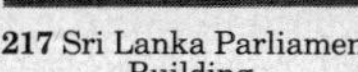

217 Sri Lanka Parliament Building — 218 Sir Ponnambalam Ramanathan (politician)

(Litho Toppan Printing Co, Japan)

1975 (1 Apr). *Inter-Parliamentary Meeting. P* 13.
607 **217** 1 r. multicoloured 30 50

(Des A. Rasiah. Litho Toppan Ptg Co, Japan)

1975 (4 Sep). *Ramanathan Commemoration. P* 13.
608 **218** 75 c. multicoloured 30 70

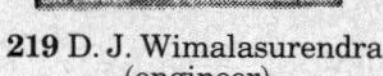

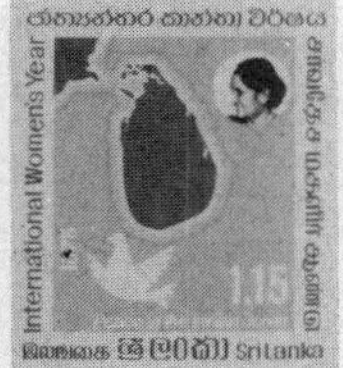

219 D. J. Wimalasurendra (engineer) — 220 Mrs. Bandaranaike, Map and Dove

(Des A. Dharmasiri. Litho Toppan Ptg Co, Japan)

1975 (17 Sept). *Wimalasurendra Commemoration. P* 13.
609 **219** 75 c. blue-black and new blue 30 70

(Des B. U. Ananda Somatilaka. Litho Toppan Ptg Co, Japan)

1975 (22 Dec). *International Women's Year. P* 13.
610 **220** 1 r. 15, multicoloured .. .. .. 2·25 1·25

221 Ma-ratmal — 222 Mahaweli Dam

(Des and litho Toppan Ptg Co, Japan)

1976 (1 Jan). *Indigenous Flora. T* **221** *and similar vert designs. Multicoloured. P* 13.
611 25 c. Type **221** 10 10
a. Imperf (pair) .. .. 60·00
612 50 c. Binara 10 10
613 75 c. Daffodil orchid 15 15
614 10 r. Diyapara .. .. 3·00 4·25
611/14 .. .. *Set of* 4 3·00 4·25
MS615 153 × 153 mm. Nos. 611/14 .. .. 8·50 11·00

A used example of No. 613 has been seen with the yellow printing apparently omitted. This results in the leaves appearing blue instead of green.

(Des R. B. Mawilmada. Litho German Bank Note Ptg Co, Leipzig)

1976 (8 Jan). *Diversion of the Mahaweli River. P* 13×12½.
616 **222** 85 c. turquoise, violet-blue and azure .. 30 80

Stamps in this design with a face value of 60 c. were not issued to post offices.

223 Dish Aerial — 224 Conception of the Buddha

(Des P. A. Miththapala. Litho German Bank Note Ptg Co, Leipzig)

1976 (6 May). *Opening of Satellite Earth Station, Padukka. P* 14 × 13½.
617 **223** 1 r. multicoloured 65 75

(Des P. Wanigatunga. Litho Toppan Ptg Co, Japan)

1976 (7 May). *Vesak. T* **224** *and similar horiz designs showing paintings from the Dambava Temple. Multicoloured. P* 13.
618 5 c. Type **224** 10 50
619 10 c. King Suddhodana and the astrologers .. 10 50
620 1 r. 50, The astrologers being entertained .. 70 60
621 2 r. The Queen in a palanquin 75 65
622 2 r. 25, Royal procession .. .. .. 85 1·40
623 5 r. Birth of the Buddha .. .. .. 1·25 2·50
618/23 .. .. *Set of* 6 3·25 5·50
MS624 161 × 95 mm. Nos. 618/23 .. .. 8·50 11·00

225 Blue Sapphire — 226 Prime Minister Mrs. S. Bandaranaike

(Des State Gem Corporation. Litho Toppan Ptg Co, Japan)

1976 (16 June). *Gems of Sri Lanka. T* **225** *and similar horiz designs. Multicoloured. P* 12 × 12½.
625 60 c. Type **225** .. .. 3·50 30
626 1 r. 15, Cat's Eye .. .. 5·00 1·50
627 2 r. Star sapphire .. .. 5·50 3·25
628 5 r. Ruby .. .. 8·00 8·50
625/8 .. .. *Set of* 4 20·00 12·00
MS629 152 × 152 mm. Nos. 625/8 .. .. 25·00 22·00

(Photo Harrison)

1976 (3 Aug). *Non-aligned Summit Conference, Colombo. P* 14×14½.
630 **226** 1 r. 15, multicoloured 25 25
631 2 r. multicoloured 40 45

NEW INFORMATION

The editor is always interested to correspond with people who have new information that will improve or correct the Catalogue.

227 Statue of Liberty — 228 Bell, Early Telephone and Telephone Lines

(Des A. Harischandra. Litho German Bank Note Ptg Co, Leipzig)

1976 (29 Nov). *Bicentenary of American Revolution. P* 13½.
632 **227** 2 r. 25, cobalt and indigo .. .. 65 1·25

(Des A. Harischandra. Litho German Bank Note Ptg Co, Leipzig)

1976 (21 Dec). *Telephone Centenary. P* 13.
633 **228** 1 r. multicoloured 50 20

229 Maitreya (pre-carnate Buddha) — 230 Kandyan Crown

(Des P. Wanigatunga. Litho German Bank Note Ptg Co, Leipzig)

1977 (1 Jan). *Centenary of Colombo Museum. T* **229** *and similar vert designs showing statues. Multicoloured. P* 12½.
634 50 c. Type **229** 25 15
635 1 r. Sundara Murti Swami (Tamil psalmist) 30 30
636 5 r. Tara (goddess) .. .. 2·25 3·75
634/6 .. .. *Set of* 3 2·50 3·75

(Des R. B. Mawilmada. Litho Toppan Ptg Co, Japan)

1977 (18 Jan). *Regalia of the Kings of Kandy. T* **230** *and similar vert design. Multicoloured. P* 13.
637 1 r. Type **230** 35 40
638 2 r. Throne and footstool .. .. .. 75 2·40

231 Sri Rahula Thero (poet) — 232 Sir Ponnambalam Arunachalam (social reformer)

(Des S. Dissanayaka. Litho Toppan Ptg Co, Japan)

1977 (23 Feb). *Sri Rahula Commemoration. P* 13.
639 **231** 1 r. multicoloured 75 75

(Litho Toppan Ptg Co, Japan)

1977 (10 Mar). *Ponnambalam Arunachalam Commemoration. P* 13.
640 **232** 1 r. multicoloured 40 55

233 Brass Lamps — 234 Siddi Lebbe (author and educationalist)

(Des A. Harischandra. Litho Toppan Ptg Co, Japan)

1977 (7 Apr). *Handicrafts. T* **233** *and similar vert designs. Multicoloured. P* 13.
641 20 c. Type **233** 15 15
642 25 c. Jewellery box 15 15
643 50 c. Caparisoned elephant 30 20
644 5 r. Mask .. .. 1·60 3·00
641/4 .. .. *Set of* 4 2·00 3·25
MS645 205 × 89 mm. Nos. 641/4 .. .. .. 3·25 3·75

(Des Sarasvati Rockwood. Litho Toppan Ptg Co, Japan)

1977 (11 June). *Siddi Lebbe Commemoration. P* 13½.
646 **234** 1 r. multicoloured 30 60

235 Girl Guide **236** Parliament Building and "Wheel of Life"

(Des and litho Asher & Co, Melbourne)

1977 (13 Dec). *60th Anniv of Sri Lanka Girl Guides Association. P* 14½ × 15.
647 **235** 75 c. multicoloured 85 30

(Des R. B. Mawilmada. Photo Enschedé)

1978 (4 Feb). *Election of New President. P* 12 × 12½.
648 **236** 15 c. gold, brt yellow-green & emerald .. 20 10
No. 648 was re-issued on 7 September 1978, additionally dated "1978.09.07" to mark the Promulgation of the Constitution for the Democratic Socialist Republic of Sri Lanka. This re-issue was only available on First Day Covers (*Price on F.D.C.* £2).
See also Nos. 680/*c*.

237 Youths Running **238** Prince Siddhartha's Renunciation

(Des M. Dissanayake. Litho Asher & Co, Melbourne)

1978 (27 Apr). *National Youth Service Council. P* 15 × 14½.
649 **237** 15 c. multicoloured 30 50

(Des P. Wanigatunga. Litho Metal Box Singapore Ltd)

1978 (16 May). *Vesak. Rock Carvings from Borobudur Temple. T* **238** *and similar horiz design in buff, brown and ultramarine. P* 13.
650 15 c. Type **238** 75 30
651 50 c. Prince Siddhartha shaving his hair .. 1·00 1·25

•05

(**239**) **240** Veera Puran Appu

1978 (18 May–20 Nov). *Nos.* 559, 601/2, 605 *and* 648/9 *surch as T* **239**.
652 5 c. on 90 c. Bearded old man (26.6) .. 75 2·00
a. Surch inverted .. .. 12·00
b. Surch double .. ..
653 10 c. on 35 c. Type **213** 50 50
a. Surch inverted .. .. 12·00
654 25 c. on 15 c. Type **215** (20.11) .. .. 3·50 3·25
a. Dot after "25" (R.3/4) .. .. .. 18·00
655 25 c. on 15 c. Type **236** (20.11) .. .. 3·50 3·25
a. Surch inverted .. .. 10·00
b. Surch quadruple .. ..
656 25 c. on 15 c. Type **237** (Blk & Pink) (20.11) 3·50 3·25
a. Surch and obliterating square inverted 9·00
ab. Surch only inverted .. .. 8·50
657 1 r. on 1 r. 55, Two female figures (17.11) 1·25 45
a. Surch inverted .. ..
652/7 .. .. *Set of* 6 11·50 11·50
No. 656 has the surcharge applied in black on a pink square, previously printed over the original face value.

(Des A. Dharmasiri. Litho Metal Box Singapore Ltd)

1978 (8 Aug). *130th Death Anniv of Veera Puran Appu (revolutionary). P* 13.
658 **240** 15 c. multicoloured 15 20

SRI LANKA

15

241 *Troides helena* (**242**)

(Des G. Ratnavira. Litho J.W. or Questa (ptgs of 25 c. from 5 Jan 1990))

1978 (28 Nov). *Butterflies. T* **241** *and similar vert designs. Multicoloured. P* 14.
659 25 c. Type **241** 40 10
660 50 c. *Cethosia nietneri* 80 10
661 5 r. *Kallima horsfieldi* (s sp *philarchus*) .. 1·50 1·25
662 10 r. *Papilio polymnestor* .. .. .. 1·75 1·75
659/62 .. .. *Set of* 4 4·00 2·75
MS663 203×147 mm. Nos. 659/62 .. .. 9·00 7·00

1979 (22 Mar). *No.* 486 *surch with T* **242** *in black and turquoise-blue.*
664 15 c. on 10 c. myrtle-green .. .. .. 1·50 1·10
a. Surch double .. .. 12·00
b. Turq-blue surch omitted .. .. .. 20·00
Type **242** shows only part of the turquoise-blue section of the overprint ("SRI LANKA"), which also includes a rectangle obliterating the original face value. The new value is printed on this rectangle in black.

243 Prince Danta and Princess Hema Mala bringing the Sacred Tooth Relic from Kalinga **244** Piyadasa Sirisena

(Des A. Dharmasiri. Litho J.W.)

1979 (3 May). *Vesak. Kelaniya Temple Paintings. T* **243** *and similar vert designs. Multicoloured. P* 13 × 13½.
665 25 c. Type **243** 10 10
666 1 r. Theri Sanghamitta bringing the Bodhi Tree branch to Sri Lanka 15 15
667 10 r. King Kirti Sri Rajasinghe offering fan of authority to the Sangha Raja .. 1·25 2·00
665/7 .. .. *Set of* 3 1·25 2·00
MS668 120 × 80 mm. Nos. 665/7 .. .. 1·40 2·00

(Des P. Jayatillake. Litho Toppan Ptg Co, Japan)

1979 (22 May). *Piyadasa Sirisena (writer) Commemoration. P* 13.
669 **244** 1 r. 25, multicoloured 40 40

245 Wrestlers **246** Dudley Senanayake

(Des R. B. Mawilmada. Litho Metal Box Singapore Ltd)

1979 (28 May). *Wood Carvings from Embekke Temple. T* **245** *and similar vert design. P* 14.
670 20 r. chocolate, ochre and deep green .. 1·25 1·50
671 50 r. agate, bistre-yellow and deep green .. 2·00 3·25
Design:—50 r. Dancer.

(Photo Heraclio Fournier)

1979 (19 June). *Dudley Senanayake (former Prime Minister) Commemoration. P* 14.
672 **246** 1 r. 25, bottle green 15 20

247 Mother with Child **248** Ceylon 1857 6d. Stamp and Sir Rowland Hill

(Des A. Dharmasiri and R. Mawilmada. Litho Metal Box Singapore Ltd)

1979 (31 July). *International Year of the Child. T* **247** *and similar horiz designs. Multicoloured. P* 12½.
673 5 c. Type **247** 10 10
674 3 r. Superimposed heads of children of different races 30 80
675 5 r. Children playing 40 90
673/5 .. .. *Set of* 3 65 1·60

(Des A. Dharmasiri. Litho Toppan Ptg Co, Japan)

1979 (27 Aug). *Death Centenary of Sir Rowland Hill. P* 13.
676 **248** 3 r. multicoloured 30 45

249 Conference Emblem and Parliament Building **250** Airline Emblem on Aircraft Tail-fin

(Des A. Harischandra. Litho Toppan Ptg Co, Japan)

1979 (28 Aug). *International Conference of Parliamentarians on Population and Development, Colombo. P* 13.
677 **249** 2 r. multicoloured 60 80

(Des S. Saparamadu. Litho Metal Box Singapore Ltd)

1979 (1 Sept). *Inauguration of "Airlanka" Airline. P* 12½.
678 **250** 3 r. black, deep blue-green & vermilion 60 85

251 Coconut Tree **252** Swami Vipulananda

(Des G. Wathuwalagedara. Litho Metal Box Singapore Ltd)

1979 (10 Sept). *10th Anniv of Asian and Pacific Coconut Community. P* 14.
679 **251** 2 r. multicoloured 60 85

1979 (10 Oct)–**87**. *Design as No.* 648 *but smaller,* 20×24 *mm. P* 12½×13.
680 **236** 25 c. gold, brt yellow-green & emerald 20 20
680*a* 50 c. gold, brt yell-grn & emer (6.6.81) 2·00 10
680*b* 60 c. gold, bright yellow-green and emerald (30.12.83) .. .. 4·75 1·25
680*c* 75 c. gold, bright yellow-green and emerald (1.7.87) 10 10
680/*c* .. .. *Set of* 4 6·25 1·50

(Des R. B. Mawilmada. Litho Metal Box Singapore Ltd)

1979 (18 Nov). *Swami Vipulananda (philosopher) Commemoration. P* 12½.
681 **252** 1 r. 25, multicoloured 20 30

253 Inscription and Crescent **254** "The Great Teacher" (Institute emblem)

(Des Q. V. Saldin. Litho Metal Box Singapore Ltd)

1979 (22 Nov). *1500th Anniv of the Hegira (Mohammedan religion). P* 12½.
682 **253** 3 r. 75, black, deep green and blue-green 35 1·25

(Des H. P. Rupasinghe. Litho Metal Box Singapore Ltd)

1979 (29 Nov). *50th Anniv of Institute of Ayurveda (school of medicine). P* 13 × 12½.
683 **254** 15 c. multicoloured 30 50

255 Ceylon Blue Magpie **256** Rotary International Emblem and Map of Sri Lanka

(Des G. Ratnavira. Litho German Bank Note Ptg Co, Leipzig)

1979 (13 Dec). *Birds (1st series). T* **255** *and similar vert designs. Multicoloured. P* 13½×14.
684 10 c. Type **255** 10 50
685 15 c. Ceylon Hanging Parrot ("Ceylon Lorikeet") 50 10
686 75 c. Ceylon Whistling Thrush ("Ceylon Arrenga") 15 15
687 1 r. Ceylon Spurfowl 15 15
688 5 r. Yellow-fronted Barbet .. .. .. 60 1·75
689 10 r. Yellow-tufted Bulbul .. .. .. 75 1·75
684/9 .. .. *Set of* 6 2·00 4·00
MS690 151×151 mm. Nos. 684/9 .. .. 4·25 4·00
See also Nos. 827/31, 985/9 and 1242/6.

(Des A. Harischandra. Litho Metal Box Singapore Ltd)

1979 (27 Dec). *50th Anniv of Sri Lanka Rotary Movement and 75th Anniv of Rotary International. P* 14.
691 **256** 1 r. 50, multicoloured . . . . 60 1·00

.35

257 A. Ratnayake (**258**) **259** Tank and Stupa (symbols of Buddhist culture)

(Photo Govt Ptg Works, Rome)

1980 (7 Jan). *80th Birth Anniv of A. Ratnayake (politician). P* 13½.
692 **257** 1 r. 25, deep grey-green 20 30

1980 (17 Mar). *No.* 680 *surch with T* **258**.
693 **236** 35 c. on 25 c. gold, brt yell-grn & emer . . 15 15
a. Surch ".33" (R. 6/1) . . . . . . 15·00
b. Dot omitted (R. 7/6) . . . . . . 3·00

(Des R. B. Mawilmada. Photo Govt Ptg Works, Rome)

1980 (25 Mar). *60th Anniv of All Ceylon Buddhist Congress. T* **259** *and similar horiz design showing symbols of Buddhist culture. Multicoloured. P* 13½.
694 10 c. Type **259** 15 70
695 35 c. Bo-leaf wheel and fan 15 20

260 Colonel Olcott

261 Patachara's Journey through Forest

(Des S. Senevirante. Litho J.W.)

1980 (17 May). *Centenary of Arrival of Colonel Olcott (campaigner for Buddhism). P* 14.
696 **260** 2 r. multicoloured . . . . . . 70 1·25

(Des A. Dharmasiri. Litho Metal Box Singapore Ltd)

1980 (23 May). *Vesak. Details from Temple Paintings, Purvaramaya, Kataluwa. T* **261** *and similar horiz design. Multicoloured. P* 13½.
697 35 c. Type **261** 30 15
698 1 r. 60, Patachara crossing river . . . . 95 1·75

262 George E. de Silva

263 Dalada Maligawa

(Des A. Rasiah. Litho German Bank Note Ptg Co, Leipzig)

1980 (8 June). *George E. de Silva (politician) Commemoration. P* 13.
699 **262** 1 r. 60, multicoloured 30 30

(Des A. Dharmasiri and R. B. Mawilmada. Litho Metal Box Singapore Ltd)

1980 (25 Aug). *U.N.E.S.C.O.—Sri Lanka Cultural Triangle Project. T* **263** *and similar horiz designs. P* 13.
700 35 c. claret 10 20
701 35 c. grey 10 20
702 35 c. rose-carmine 10 20
703 1 r. 60, olive-green 40 80
704 1 r. 60, slate-green 40 80
705 1 r. 60, sepia 40 80
700/5 . . . . . . *Set of* 6 1·40 2·75
MS706 215 × 115 mm. Nos. 700/5 . . . . 1·40 2·75
Designs:—No. 701, Dambulla; No. 702, Alahana Pirivena; No. 703, Jetavanarama; No. 704, Abhayagiri; No. 705, Sigiri.

264 Co-operation Symbols

265 Lanka Mahila Samiti Emblem

(Des R. B. Mawilmada. Litho Metal Box Singapore Ltd)

1980 (1 Oct). *50th Anniv of Co-operative Department. P* 13.
707 **264** 20 c. multicoloured 10 30

(Des R. B. Mawilmada. Photo Govt Ptg Works, Rome)

1980 (7 Nov). *50th Anniv of Lanka Mahila Samiti (Rural Women's Movement). P* 14 × 13.
708 **265** 35 c. violet, rosine and yellow 10 45

266 The Holy Family

267 Colombo Public Library

(Des L. Priyantha Silva. Litho Metal Box Singapore Ltd)

1980 (20 Nov). *Christmas. T* **266** *and similar vert design. Multicoloured. P* 12 × 11½.
709 35 c. Type **266** 10 10
710 3 r. 75, The Three Wise Men . . . . 50 1·00
MS711 125 × 75 mm. Nos. 709/10. P 13½ . . 40 1·00

(Des P. Jayatillake. Litho Toppan Ptg Co, Japan)

1980 (17 Dec). *Opening of Colombo Public Library. P* 12 × 12½.
712 **267** 35 c. multicoloured 10 10

268 Flag of Walapane Disawa

269 Fishing Cat

(Des Mrs. J. L. M. Fernando. Litho Toppan Ptg Co, Japan)

1980 (18 Dec). *Ancient Flags. T* **268** *and similar horiz designs. P* 13.
713 10 c. black, green and brown-purple 10 10
714 25 c. black, greenish yellow and brown-purple 10 10
715 1 r. 60, black, greenish yellow & brn-purple 15 20
716 20 r. black, greenish yellow and brown-purple 1·25 2·50
713/16 . . . . . . *Set of* 4 1·40 2·50
MS717 215 × 140 mm. Nos. 713/16 . . . . 1·90 2·75
Designs:—25 c. Flag of the Gajanayaka, Huduhumpola, Kandy; 1 r. 60, Sinhala royal flag; 20 r. Sinhala royal flag, Ratnapura.

(Des L. Ranasinghe. Litho J.W.)

1981 (10 Feb). *Animals. T* **269** *and similar horiz designs. Multicoloured. P* 13½ × 14.
718 2 r. 50 on 1 r. 60, Type **269** 15 15
719 3 r. on 1 r. 50, Golden Palm Civet 15 20
720 4 r. on 2 r. Indian Spotted Chevrotain . . 25 30
721 5 r. on 3 r. 75, Rusty-spotted Cat 35 45
718/21 . . . . . . *Set of* 4 80 1·00
MS722 165 × 89 mm. Nos. 718/21 . . . . 1·00 2·25
Nos. 718/21 are previously unissued stamps surcharged as in T **269**.
For redrawn designs with revised face values see Nos. 780/3 and No. 1081.

270 Heads and Houses on Map of Sri Lanka

271 Sri Lanka Light Infantry Regimental Badge

(Des D. Hemaratna. Litho Toppan Ptg Co, Japan)

1981 (2 Mar). *Population and Housing Census. P* 12½ × 12.
723 **270** 50 c. multicoloured 50 80

(Des D. Karunaratne. Litho Metal Box Singapore Ltd)

1981 (1 Apr). *Centenary of Sri Lanka Light Infantry. P* 12 × 11½.
724 **271** 2 r. multicoloured . . . . . . 1·00 75

ALTERED CATALOGUE NUMBERS

Any Catalogue numbers altered from the last edition are shown as a list in the introductory pages.

272 Panel from "The Great Stupa" in Honour of the Buddha, Sanci, India, 1st-century A.D.

273 St. John Baptist de la Salle

(Des P. Jayatillake. Litho German Bank Note Ptg Co, Leipzig)

1981 (5 May). *Vesak. T* **272** *and similar vert designs. P* 13 × 13½.
725 35 c. black, blackish green and sage-green . . 10 10
726 50 c. multicoloured 10 10
727 7 r. black and flesh . . . . . . 1·00 2·75
725/7 . . . . . . *Set of* 3 1·00 2·75
MS728 147 × 108 mm. Nos. 725/7. P 13 × 14. . . 3·50 3·50
Designs:—50 c. Silk banner representing a Bodhisattva from "Thousand Buddhas", Tun-Huang, Central Asia; 7 r. Bodhisattva from Fondukistan, Afghanistan.

(Des Grant Kenyon and Eckhardt Ltd. Litho State Printing Works, Moscow)

1981 (15 May). *300th Anniv of De La Salle Brothers (Religious Order of the Brothers of the Christian Schools). P* 12½ × 12.
729 **273** 2 r. brt rose, deep violet-blue & new blue 1·00 1·50

274 Rev. Polwatte Sri Buddadatta

275 Dr. Al-Haj T. B. Jayah

(Des G. Fernando. Litho Metal Box Singapore Ltd)

1981 (22 May). *National Heroes. T* **274** *and similar vert designs, each showing scholar, writer and Buddhist campaigner. P* 12.
730 50 c. bistre 50 80
731 50 c. brown-rose 50 80
732 50 c. deep mauve 50 80
730/2 . . . . . . *Set of* 3 1·40 2·25
Designs:—No. 731, Rev. Mohottiwatte Gunananda; No. 732, Dr. Gnanaprakasar.

(Des P. Jayatillake. Litho Metal Box Singapore Ltd)

1981 (31 May). *Dr. Al-Haj T. B. Jayah (statesman) Commemoration. P* 12.
733 **275** 50 c. grey-green 50 70

276 Dr. N. M. Perera

277 Stylised Disabled Person and Globe

(Des P. Jayatillake. Litho Metal Box Singapore Ltd)

1981 (6 June). *Dr. N. M. Perera (campaigner for social reform) Commemoration. P* 12.
734 **276** 50 c. rose-red 50 70

(Des A. Adhikari. Litho State Printing Works, Moscow)

1981 (19 June). *International Year for Disabled Persons. P* 12 × 12½.
735 **277** 2 r. vermilion, black and grey . . . . 85 1·50

278 Hand placing Vote into Ballot Box

(Des J. Vincent (50 c.), R. Mawilmada (7 r.). Litho State Printing Works, Moscow)

1981 (7 July). *50th Anniv of Universal Franchise. T* **278** *and similar multicoloured design. P* 12½ × 12 (50 c.) *or* 12 × 12½ (7 r.)
736 50 c. Type **278** 25 15
737 7 r. Ballot box, and people forming map of Sri Lanka (*vert*) . . . . . . 1·50 2·00

279 T. W. Rhys Davids (founder)

280 Federation Emblem and "25"

(Des P. Jayatillake. Litho State Printing Works, Moscow)

1981 (14 July). *Centenary of Pali Text Society. P* 12½ × 12.
738 **279** 35 c. stone, dp brown & orange-brown .. 50 20

(Des R. Mawilmada. Litho Secura, Singapore)

1981 (21 July). *25th Anniv of All Ceylon Buddhist Students' Federation. P* 13½.
739 **280** 2 r. black, greenish yellow & dull verm 60 40

281 "Plan for Happiness"

282 Dove Symbol with Acupuncture Needle and "Yin-Yang" (Chinese universe duality emblem)

(Des D. Wijesinghe. Litho Secura, Singapore)

1981 (25 Sept). *Population and Family Planning. P* 13½ × 13.
740 **281** 50 c. multicoloured 60 70

(Des F. Perera. Litho State Printing Works, Moscow)

1981 (20 Oct). *World Acupuncture Congress. P* 12 × 12½.
741 **282** 2 r. black, yellow and red-orange .. 2·50 2·75

283 Union and Sri Lanka Flags **284** "Conserve our Forests"

(Des and litho J.W.)

1981 (21 Oct). *Royal Visit. P* 14.
742 **283** 50 c. multicoloured 50 25
743 5 r. multicoloured .. .. .. 1·75 3·25
MS744 165 × 90 mm. Nos. 742/3 .. .. .. 2·75 3·50

(Des Ravi Advertising. Litho German Bank Note Co, Leipzig)

1981 (27 Nov). *Forest Conservation. T* **284** *and similar horiz designs. P* 13.
745 35 c. multicoloured 15 10
746 50 c. olive-brown and stone 20 20
747 5 r. multicoloured .. .. 1·90 3·50
745/7 .. .. *Set of* 3 2·00 3·50
MS748 180 × 90 mm. Nos. 745/7. P 14 × 13 .. 2·00 3·50
Designs:—50 c. "Plant a tree"; 5 r. Jak (tree).

285 Sir James Peiris **286** F. R. Senanayaka

(Des P. Jayatillake. Litho Metal Box Singapore Ltd)

1981 (20 Dec). *Birth Centenary of Sir James Peiris (politician). P* 12.
749 **285** 50 c. light brown 60 70

(Des M. Katugampola. Litho J.W.)

1982 (1 Jan). *Birth Centenary of F. R. Senanayaka (national hero). P* 14.
750 **286** 50 c. olive-brown 60 75

287 Philip Gunawardhane **288** Department of Inland Revenue Building, Colombo

(Des P. Jayatillake. Litho J.W.)

1982 (11 Jan). *10th Death Anniv of Philip Gunawardhane (politician). P* 14.
751 **287** 50 c. cerise 60 75

(Des S. Mallikerachchi. Litho J.W.)

1982 (9 Feb). *50th Anniv of Department of Inland Revenue. P* 14.
752 **288** 50 c. black, blue-black & reddish orange 60 75

289 Rupavahini Emblem **290** Cricketer and Ball

(Des G. Arthasad. Litho J.W.)

1982 (15 Feb). *Inauguration of Rupavahini (national television service). P* 14.
753 **289** 2 r. 50, lemon, purple-brown and grey 2·25 3·00

(Des R. Mawilmada. Litho J.W.)

1982 (17 Feb). *First Sri Lanka–England Cricket Test Match, Colombo. P* 14.
754 **290** 2 r. 50, multicoloured .. .. .. 4·00 4·00

291 *Obsbeckia wightiana* **292** Mother breast-feeding Child

(Des P. Jayatillake. Litho Security Printers (M), Malaysia)

1982 (1 Apr). *Flowers. T* **291** *and similar horiz designs. Multicoloured. P* 12.
755 35 c. Type **291** 10 10
756 2 r. *Mesua nagassarium* 20 20
757 7 r. *Rhodomyrtus tomentosa* .. .. 50 1·00
758 20 r. *Phaius tancarvilleae* .. .. .. 1·40 3·00
755/8 .. .. *Set of* 4 2·00 3·75
MS759 180 × 110 mm. Nos. 755/8 .. .. 7·00 7·50

(Des A. Ratnapala. Litho Pakistan Security Printing Corp)

1982 (6 Apr). *Food and Nutrition Policy Planning. P* 13.
760 **292** 50 c. multicoloured 85 85

293 Conference Emblem **294** King Vessantara giving away magical, rain-making White Elephant

(Des M. Hussain. Litho J.W.)

1982 (21 Apr). *World Hindu Conference. P* 14.
761 **293** 50 c. multicoloured 85 85

(Des A. Dharmasiri. Litho J.W.)

1982 (23 Apr). *Vesak. Legend of Vessantara Jataka. Details of Cloth Painting from Arattana Rajamaha Vihara (temple), Hanguranketa, District of Nuwara Eliya. T* **294** *and similar horiz designs. Multicoloured. P* 14.
762 35 c. Type **294** 45 10
763 50 c. King Vessantara with family in Vankagiri Forest 55 15
764 2 r. 50, Vessantara giving away his children as slaves .. .. 2·00 2·25
765 5 r. Vessantara and family returning to Jetuttara in royal chariot .. .. .. 2·75 3·50
762/5 .. .. *Set of* 4 5·25 5·50
MS766 160 × 115 mm. Nos. 762/5 .. .. 7·00 7·00

295 Parliament Buildings, Sri Jayawardanapura **296** Dr. C. W. W. Kannangara

(Des M. Katugampola. Litho J.W.)

1982 (29 Apr). *Opening of Parliament Building Complex, Sri Jayawardanapura, Kotte. P* 14.
767 **295** 50 c. multicoloured 85 85

(Des M. Katugampola. Litho State Printing Works, Moscow)

1982 (22 May). *Dr. C. W. W. Kannangara ("Father of Free Education") Commemoration. P* 12 × 12½.
768 **296** 50 c. yellow-olive 85 85

297 Lord Baden-Powell **298** Dr. G. P. Malalasekara

(Des W. Rohana. Litho State Printing Works, Moscow)

1982 (24 May). *125th Birth Anniv of Lord Baden-Powell. P* 12½ × 12.
769 **297** 50 c. multicoloured .. .. .. 1·75 85

(Des A. Rasiah. Litho State Printing Works, Moscow)

1982 (26 May). *Dr. G. P. Malalasekara (founder of World Fellowship of Buddhists) Commemoration. P* 12 × 12½.
770 **298** 50 c. deep bluish green 85 85

299 Wheel encircling Globe **300** Wildlife

(Des A. Ratnapala. Litho State Printing Works, Moscow)

1982 (1 June). *World Buddhist Leaders Conference. P* 12½ × 12.
771 **299** 50 c. multicoloured 85 85

(Des U. Karunaratna. Litho State Printing Works, Moscow)

1982 (5 June). *World Environment Day. P* 12½ × 12.
772 **300** 50 c. multicoloured .. .. .. 1·60 1·10

301 Sir Waitialingam Duraiswamy

(Des A. Rasiah. Litho State Printing Works, Moscow)

1982 (14 June). *Sir Waitialingam Duraiswamy (statesman and educationalist) Commemoration. P* 12 × 12½.
773 **301** 50 c. blackish brown and brown .. 85 85

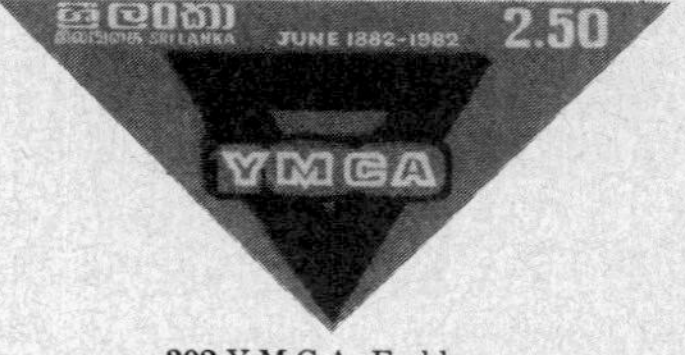

302 Y.M.C.A. Emblem

(Des R. Mawilmada. Litho State Printing Works, Moscow)

1982 (24 June). *Centenary of Colombo Y.M.C.A. P* 11½ × 11.
774 **302** 2 r. 50, multicoloured . . . . . . 3·00 3·25

303 Rev. Weliwita Sri Saranankara Sangharaja **304** Maharagama Sasana Sevaka Samithiya Emblem

(Des M. Katugampola. Litho State Printing Works, Moscow)

1982 (5 July). *Rev. Weliwita Sri Saranankara Sangharaja (Buddhist leader) Commemoration. P* 12 × 12½.
775 **303** 50 c. brown and yellow-orange 85 85

(Des A. Ratnapala. Litho Toppan Ptg Co, Japan)

1982 (4 Aug). *Silver Jubilee of Maharagama Sasana Sevaka Samithiya (Buddhist Social Reform Movement). P* 12 × 12½.
776 **304** 50 c. multicoloured 85 85

305 Dr. Robert Koch **306** Sir John Kotelawala

(Des W. Rohana. Litho Toppan Ptg Co, Japan)

1982 (21 Sept). *Centenary of Robert Koch's Discovery of Tubercle Bacillus. P* 12 × 12½.
777 **305** 50 c. multicoloured . . . . . . 1·75 1·00

(Des A. Rasiah. Litho State Printing Works, Moscow)

1982 (2 Oct). *2nd Death Anniv of Sir John Kotelawala. P* 12 × 12½.
778 **306** 50 c. deep olive 85 85

307 Eye Donation Society and Lions Club Emblems **308** 1859 4d. Dull Rose and 1948 15 c. Independence Commemorative

(Des Grant Kenyon and Eckhardt Ltd. Litho State Printing Works, Moscow)

1982 (16 Nov). *World-Wide Sight Conservation Project. P* 12 × 12½.
779 **307** 2 r. 50, multicoloured . . . . . . 3·00 3·50

(Des L. Ranasinghe. Litho Questa (5 r.) or J.W. (others))

1982 (16 Nov)–**89**. *As Nos.* 718/21, *but without surcharges and showing revised face values. P* 14.
780 2 r. 50, Type **269** (1.6.83) 20 15
781 3 r. Golden Palm Civet (21.6.83) . . . . 1·75 1·75
782 4 r. Indian Spotted Chevrotain 25 25
783 5 r. Rusty-spotted Cat (1.12.89) 25 25
780/3 . . . . . . *Set of* 4 2·25 2·25

For the 3 r. in similar design, but printed by Questa with imprint date see No. 1081.

(Des D. Karunaratne. Litho Security Printers (M), Malaysia)

1982 (2 Dec). *125th Anniv of First Postage Stamps. T* **308** *and similar horiz design. Multicoloured. P* 13 × 13½.
784 50 c. Type **308** 50 50
785 2 r. 50, 1859 1s. 9d. green and 1981 50 c. "Just Society" stamp . . . . 1·50 2·50
MS786 59 × 84 mm. Nos. 784/5 (*sold at* 5 *r.*) . . 2·00 3·00

309 Sir Oliver Goonetilleke **310** Sarvodaya Emblem

(Des A. Ratnapala. Litho State Printing Works, Moscow)

1982 (17 Dec). *4th Death Anniv of Sir Oliver Goonetilleke (statesman). P* 12 × 12½.
787 **309** 50 c. olive-grey, bistre-brown and black 60 75

(Des P. Gunasinghe. Litho Secura, Singapore)

1983 (1 Jan). *25th Anniv of Sarvodaya Movement. P* 13 × 13½.
788 **310** 50 c. multicoloured 90 90

311 Morse Key, Radio Aerial and Radio Amateur Society Emblem **312** Customs Co-operation Council Emblem and Sri Lanka Flag

(Des W. Rohana. Litho Secura, Singapore)

1983 (17 Jan). *Amateur Radio Society. P* 13 × 13½.
789 **311** 2 r. 50, multicoloured . . . . . . 2·75 3·50

(Des W. Rohana. Litho Secura, Singapore)

1983 (26 Jan). *30th Anniv of International Customs Day. P* 12 × 11½.
790 **312** 50 c. multicoloured 40 40
791 5 r. multicoloured . . . . . . 3·00 4·25

313 Bottle-nosed Dolphin **314** *Lanka Athula* (container ship)

(Des G. Ratnavira. Litho Harrison)

1983 (22 Feb). *Marine Mammals. T* **313** *and similar horiz designs. P* 14½ × 14.
792 50 c. black, new blue and grey-green . . 40 15
793 2 r. multicoloured 80 80
794 2 r. 50, black, dp grey-blue & dp bluish grey 1·75 1·75
795 10 r. multicoloured . . . . . . 4·50 5·00
792/5 . . . . . . *Set of* 4 6·75 7·00

Designs:—2 r. Dugongs; 2 r. 50, Humpback Whale; 10 r. Sperm Whale.

(Des Vision Ltd. Litho Security Printers (M), Malaysia)

1983 (1 Mar). *Ships of the Ceylon Shipping Corporation. T* **314** *and similar horiz designs. Multicoloured. P* 11½ × 12.
796 50 c. Type **314** 20 15
797 2 r. 50, Map of routes 60 60
798 5 r. *Lanka Kalyani* (freighter) . . . . 1·00 1·25
799 20 r. *Tammanna* (tanker) . . . . . . 2·00 3·75
796/9 . . . . . . *Set of* 4 3·50 5·25

315 Woman with I.W.D. Emblem and Sri Lanka Flag **316** Waterfall

(Des R. Mawilmada. Litho Secura, Singapore)

1983 (8 Mar). *International Women's Day. T* **315** *and similar vert design. Multicoloured. P* 13.
800 50 c. Type **315** 15 25
801 5 r. Woman, emblem, map and symbols of progress . . . . 70 2·00

(Des S. Lankatilake. Litho Secura, Singapore)

1983 (14 Mar). *Commonwealth Day. T* **316** *and similar horiz designs. Multicoloured. P* 13.
802 50 c. Type **316** 10 10
803 2 r. 50, Tea plucking 15 25
804 5 r. Harvesting rice 25 40
805 20 r. Decorated elephants . . . . . . 80 2·00
802/5 . . . . . . *Set of* 4 1·10 2·50

317 Lions Club International Badge **318** "The Dream of Queen Mahamaya"

(Des U. Karunaratna. Litho J.W.)

1983 (7 May). *25th Anniv of Lions Club International in Sri Lanka. P* 14.
806 **317** 2 r. 50, multicoloured . . . . . . 2·50 2·25

(Des G. Keyt and A. Dharmasiri. Litho Toppan Ptg Co, Japan)

1983 (13 May). *Vesak. Life of Prince Siddhartha from temple murals at Gotami Vihara. T* **318** *and similar vert designs. Multicoloured. P* 12½ × 12.
807 35 c. Type **318** 10 10
808 50 c. "Prince Siddhartha given to Maha Brahma" 10 10
809 5 r. "Prince Siddhartha and the Sleeping Dancers" . . . . 40 1·00
810 10 r. "The Meeting with Mara" . . . . 70 2·00
807/10 . . . . . . *Set of* 4 1·10 2·75
MS811 150 × 90 mm. Nos. 807/10 . . . . 1·25 2·75

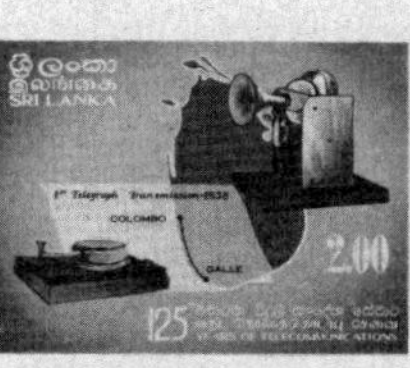

319 First Telegraph Transmission Colombo to Galle, 1858 **320** Henry Woodward Amarasuriya (philanthropist)

(Des W. Rohana. Litho Toppan Ptg Co, Japan)

1983 (17 May). *125th Anniv of Telecommunications in Sri Lanka (2 r.) and World Communications Year (10 r.). T* **319** *and similar horiz design. Multicoloured. P* 12 × 12½.
812 2 r. Type **319** 35 50
813 10 r. World Communications Year emblem . . 1·75 3·25

(Litho Security Printers (M), Malaysia (No. 810), Pakistan Security Printing Corp (others))

1983 (22 May). *National Heroes. T* **320** *and similar vert designs. P* 12 × 11½ (*No.* 814) *or* 13 (*others*).
814 50 c. bright emerald 30 80
815 50 c. new blue 30 80
816 50 c. magenta 30 80
817 50 c. turquoise-green 30 80
814/17 . . . . . . *Set of* 4 1·10 2·75

Designs:—No. 815, Father Simon Perera (historian); No. 816, Charles Lorenz (lawyer and newspaper editor); No. 817, Noordeen Abdul Cader (first President of All-Ceylon Muslim League).

A fifth design to commemorate C. W. Thamotheram Pillai was prepared for this set, but was withdrawn at the last moment when it was realised that the wrong portrait had been used. It is understood, however, that supplies were sold at some rural post offices where the instruction was not received in time. A corrected version was later issued, see No. 825.

321 Family and Village **322** Caravan of Bulls

(Des K. Gunasiri and U. Karunaratna. Litho Toppan Ptg Co, Japan)

1983 (23 June). *Gam Udawa (Village Re-awakening Movement). T* **321** *and similar horiz design. Multicoloured. P* 12 × 12½.
818 50 c. Type **321** 10 25
819 5 r. Village view . . . . 40 1·50

(Des A. Rasiah (35 c., 2 r.), D. Hemaratna (2 r. 50), U. Karunaratna (5 r.). Litho State Printing Office, Budapest)

1983 (22 Aug). *Transport. T* **322** *and similar horiz designs. Multicoloured. P* 12
820 35 c. Type **322** 10 10
821 2 r. Steam train 90 95
822 2 r. 50, Ox and cart . . . . . . 90 1·25
823 5 r. Ford motor car . . . . . . 1·50 3·00
820/3 . . . . . . *Set of* 4 3·00 4·75

323 Sir Tikiri Banda Panabokke

324 C. W. Thamotheram Pillai

(Des and litho Harrison)

1983 (2 Sept). *20th Death Anniv of Adigar Sir Tikiri Banda Panabokke. P 14 × 14½.*

824 **323** 50 c. Indian red 85 85

(Des and litho Pakistan Security Printing Corp)

1983 (1 Oct). *C. W. Thamotheram Pillai (Tamil scholar) Commemoration. P 13.*

825 **324** 50 c. orange-brown 85 85

See note below No. 817.

325 Arabi Pasha

326 Sri Lanka Wood Pigeon

(Des and litho Pakistan Security Printing Corp)

1983 (13 Nov). *Centenary of the Exile to Ceylon of Arabi Pasha (Egyptian nationalist). P 13 × 13½.*

826 **325** 50 c. green 85 85

(Des G. Ratnavira. Litho Format)

1983 (22 Nov)–**88.** *Birds (2nd series). T* **326** *and similar horiz designs. Multicoloured. P 14½.*

827 25 c. Type **326** 30 30

828 35 c. Large Sri Lanka White Eye 30 20

829 2 r. Sri Lanka Dusky Blue Flycatcher .. 30 10

829*a* 7 r. As 35 c. (28.9.88) 30 25

830 20 r. Ceylon Coucal .. .. 80 1·25

827/30 .. .. *Set of* 5 1·75 1·90

MS831 183 × 93 mm. Nos. 827/9 and 830 .. 3·75 6·50

Special packs prepared for the S.A.A.R.C. "Philex '96" stamp exhibition at Colombo contained the block of stamps from No. **MS**831 with the sheet margins removed.

327 Pelene Siri Vajiragnana

328 Mary praying over Jesus and St. Joseph welcoming Shepherds

(Des and litho Harrison)

1983 (25 Nov). *Pelene Siri Vajiragnana (scholar) Commemoration. P 14 × 14½.*

832 **327** 50 c. red-brown.. .. .. .. 80 80

(Des P. de Silva. Litho German Bank Note Co, Leipzig)

1983 (30 Nov). *Christmas. P 12½ × 13.*

833 **328** 50 c. multicoloured 10 15

834 5 r. multicoloured 25 60

MS835 85 × 141 mm. Nos. 833/4 .. .. .. 85 2·00

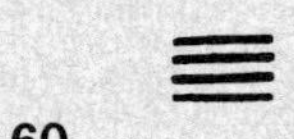

.60 .60

(**329**) (**330**)

1983 (1 Dec). *No. 680a surch with T* **329/30** *by Aitken Spence Ptg (Pte) Ltd, Sri Lanka.*

836 **236** 60 c. on 50 c. gold, bright yellow-green and emerald (surch T **329**) .. 1·50 1·00

a. Surch inverted

837 60 c. on 50 c. gold, bright yellow-green and emerald (surch T **330**) .. 3·25 3·25

331 Paddy Field, Globe and F.A.O. Emblem

(Des R. Mawilmada. Litho State Ptg Works, Moscow)

1984 (2 Jan). *World Food Day. P 12½ × 12.*

838 **331** 3 r. multicoloured .. .. .. 40 1·25

332 Modern Tea Factory

333 Students and University

(Des M. Ratnapala. Litho State Ptg Works, Moscow)

1984 (31 Jan). *Centenary of the Colombo Tea Auctions. T* **332** *and similar horiz designs. Multicoloured. P 12½ × 12.*

839 1 r. Type **332**.. .. .. 15 15

840 2 r. Logo 30 45

841 5 r. Girl picking tea.. .. .. .. 60 1·60

842 10 r. Auction in progress .. .. .. 1·25 2·50

839/42 .. .. *Set of* 4 2·10 4·25

(Des R. Mawilmada. Litho Security Printers (M), Malaysia)

1984 (10 Feb). *4th Anniv of Mahapola Scheme for Development and Education. T* **333** *and similar vert designs. Multicoloured. P 12.*

843 60 c. Type **333**.. .. .. 10 15

844 1 r. Teacher with Gnana Darsana class .. 10 15

845 5 r. 50, Student with books and microscope 35 1·25

846 6 r. Mahapola lamp symbol .. .. 40 1·25

843/6 .. .. *Set of* 4 75 2·50

334 King Daham Şonda instructing Angels

335 Development Programme Logo

(Des A. Dharmasiri. Litho D.L.R)

1984 (27 Apr). *Vesak. The Story of King Daham Sonda from ancient casket paintings. T* **334** *and similar horiz designs. Multicoloured. A. P 14. B. P 13 × 13½.*

		A		B	
847	35 c. Type **334**	15	10	35	20
848	60 c. Elephant paraded with gift of gold	30	25	35	35
849	5 r. King Daham Sonda leaps into mouth of God Sakra ..	75	2·00	85	2·50
850	10 r. God Sakra carrying King Daham Sonda	1·10	3·00	1·25	3·25
847/50	.. .. *Set of* 4	2·10	4·75	2·50	5·75
MS851	154 × 109 mm. Nos. 847/50. P 13			1·00	2·25

(Des R. Mawilmada. Litho Harrison)

1984 (5 May). *Sri Lanka Lions Clubs' Development Programme. P 14 × 14½.*

852 **335** 60 c. multicoloured .. .. .. 1·40 90

336 Dodanduwe Siri Piyaratana Tissa Mahanayake Thero (Buddhist scholar)

337 Association Emblem

(Litho State Ptg Works, Moscow)

1984 (22 May). *National Heroes. T* **336** *and similar vert designs. P 12 × 12½.*

853 60 c. yellow-bistre 30 75

854 60 c. yellow-green 30 75

855 60 c. emerald-green 30 75

856 60 c. red 30 75

857 60 c. deep yellow-brown 30 75

853/7 .. .. *Set of* 5 1·40 3·25

Designs:—No. 853, Type **336**; 854, G. P. Wickremarachchi (physician); 855, Sir Mohamed Macan Markar (politician); 856, Dr. W. Arthur de Silva (philanthropist), 857, K. Balasingham (lawyer).

(Des A. Harischandra. Litho Govt Printing Bureau, Tokyo)

1984 (16 June). *Centenary of Public Service Mutual Provident Association. P 13 × 13½.*

858 **337** 4 r. 60, multicoloured .. .. .. 45 1·75

338 Sri Lanka Village

339 World Map showing A.P.B.U. Countries

(Des S. Herath. Litho State Ptg Wks, Moscow)

1984 (23 June). *6th Anniv of "Gam Udawa" (Village Reawakening Movement). P 12 × 12½.*

859 **338** 60 c. multicoloured 30 65

(Des G. Arthasad. Litho State Ptg Wks, Moscow)

1984 (30 June). *20th Anniv of Asia-Pacific Broadcasting Union. P 12½ × 12.*

860 **339** 7 r. multicoloured .. .. .. 1·60 2·75

340 Drummers and Elephant carrying Royal Instructions

341 *Vanda memoria* Ernest Soysa (orchid)

(Des R. Mawilmada. Litho State Ptg Wks, Moscow)

1984 (11 Aug). *Esala Perahera (Procession of the Tooth), Kandy. T* **340** *and similar horiz designs. Multicoloured. P 12½ × 12.*

861 4 r. 60, Type **340** .. .. .. 85 1·50

a. Horiz strip of 4. Nos. 861/4 .. .. 3·00

862 4 r. 60, Dancers and elephants .. .. 85 1·50

863 4 r. 60, Elephant carrying Tooth Relic .. 85 1·50

864 4 r. 60, Custodian of the Sacred Tooth and attendants .. .. 85 1·50

861/4 .. .. *Set of* 4 3·00 5·50

MS865 223 × 108 mm. Nos. 861/4 .. 3·00 6·00

Nos. 861/4 were printed together, *se-tenant*, in horizontal strips of 4 throughout the sheet, forming a composite design.

(Des G. Ratnavira. Litho D.L.R.)

1984 (22 Aug). *50th Anniv of Ceylon Orchid Circle. T* **341** *and similar vert designs, showing orchids. Multicoloured. A. P 14. B. P 13½ × 13.*

		A		B	
866	60 c. Type **341**	1·50	30	50	1·00
867	4 r. 60, *Acanthephippium bicolor*	2·75	3·50	1·25	3·25
868	5 r. *Vanda tessellata var. rufescens*	3·50	3·50	90	3·25
869	10 r. *Anoectochilus setaceus* ..	3·50	4·75		†
866A/9A	.. *Set of* 4	10·00	11·00		†
866B/8B	.. *Set of* 3		†	2·40	6·75
MS870	115 × 110 mm. Nos. 866/9. P 13			7·00	10·00

342 Symbolic Athletes and Stadium

343 D. S. Senanayake, Temple and Fields

(Des M. Heenkenda. Litho Govt Printing Bureau, Tokyo)

1984 (5 Oct). *1st National School Games. P 13½ × 13.*

871 **342** 60 c. black, grey and bright new blue .. 1·50 1·25

(Des L. Jayawardena (35 c.), G. Fernando (60 c.), N. Lasantha (4 r. 60), R. Mawilmada (6 r.). Litho J.W.)

1984 (20 Oct). *Birth Centenary of D. S. Senanayake (former Prime Minister). T* **343** *and similar horiz designs. Multicoloured. P 14.*

872 35 c. Type **343**.. .. .. 10 10

873 60 c. Senanayake and statue 10 10

874 4 r. 60, Senanayake and irrigation project.. 35 50

875 6 r. Senanayake and House of Representatives 40 60

872/5 .. .. *Set of* 4 80 1·10

344 Lake House — **345** Agricultural Workers and Globe

(Des Grant Kenyon and Eckhardt Ltd. Litho State Printing Office, Budapest)

1984 (19 Nov). *150th Anniv of the "Observer" Newspaper. P* 13 × 13½.
876 **344** 4 r. 60, multicoloured .. .. .. 1·75 3·00

(Des M. Ratnapala. Litho German Bank Note Ptg Co, Leipzig)

1984 (10 Dec). *20th Anniv of World Food Programme. P* 13 × 13½.
877 **345** 7 r. multicoloured .. .. .. 1·50 1·25

346 College Emblem — **347** Dove and Stylized Figures

(Des S. Herath. Litho J.W.)

1984 (24 Dec). *Centenary of Baari Arabic College, Weligama. P* 13 × 12½.
878 **346** 4 r. 60, blackish olive, turquoise-green and turquoise-blue .. .. 1·25 2·50

(Des S. Chandrajeewa (4 r. 60), O. Weerakkody (20 r.). Litho J.W.)

1985 (1 Jan). *International Youth Year. T* **347** *and similar horiz design. Multicoloured. P* 12½ × 13.
879 4 r. 60, Type **347** 50 60
880 20 r. Dove, stylized figures and flower .. 2·00 3·00

348 Religious Symbols — **349** College Crest

(Des R. Mawilmada. Litho Security Printers (M), Malaysia)

1985 (20 Jan). *World Religion Day. P* 12.
881 **348** 4 r. 60, multicoloured .. .. .. 1·00 1·25

(Des G. Arthasad. Litho J.W.)

1985 (29 Jan). *150th Anniv of Royal College, Colombo. T* **349** *and similar vert design. P* 13 × 12½.
882 60 c. bright yellow and deep ultramarine .. 10 25
883 7 r. multicoloured .. .. 70 2·25
Design:—7 r. Royal College.

350 Banknotes, Buildings, Ship and "Wheel of Life" — **351** Wariyapola Sri Sumangala Thero

(Des R. Mawilmada. Litho J.W.)

1985 (7 Feb). *5th Anniv of Mahapola Scheme. P* 14.
884 **350** 60 c. multicoloured .. .. .. 90 1·00

(Des G. Fernando. Litho State Printing Office, Budapest)

1985 (2 Mar). *Wariyapola Sri Sumangala Thero (Buddhist priest and patriot) Commemoration. P* 13 × 13½.
885 **351** 60 c. blk, reddish brn & greenish yell 70 1·00

352 Victoria Dam — **353** Cover of 50th Edition of International Buddhist Annual, *Vesak Sirisara*

(Des G. Arthasad. Litho State Ptg Wks, Moscow)

1985 (12 Apr). *Inauguration of Victoria Hydro-electric Project. T* **352** *and similar multicoloured design. P* 12½ × 12 (60 c.) *or* 12 × 12½ (7 r.).
886 60 c. Type **352**.. .. .. 75 50
887 7 r. Map of Sri Lanka enclosing dam and power station (*vert*) .. .. .. 3·25 4·25

(Des B. Harischandra (35 c.), R. Mawilmada (others). Litho J.W.)

1985 (26 Apr). *Centenary of Vesak Poya Holiday. T* **353** *and similar vert designs. Multicoloured. P* 13 × 12½.
888 35 c. Type **353**.. .. .. 10 10
889 60 c. Buddhists worshipping at temple .. 10 10
890 6 r. Buddhist Theosophical Society Headquarters, Colombo 50 75
891 9 r. Buddhist flag .. .. 80 1·25
888/91 .. .. *Set of* 4 1·25 2·00
MS892 180 × 110 mm. Nos. 888/91 .. .. 4·00 6·00

354 Ven. Waskaduwe Sri Subhuthi (priest and scholar) — **355** Stylised Village and People

(Des S. Silva. Litho J.W.)

1985 (22 May). *Personalities. T* **354** *and similar vert designs. P* 13 × 12½.
893 60 c. black, yellow-orange and lake-brown .. 20 40
894 60 c. black, yellow-orange and deep mauve .. 20 40
895 60 c. black, yellow-orange and light brown .. 20 40
896 60 c. black, yellow-orange and emerald .. 20 40
893/6 .. .. *Set of* 4 70 1·40
Designs:— No. 893, Type **354**; 894, Revd. Fr. Peter A. Pillai (educationist and social reformer); 895, Dr. Senarath Paranavitane (scholar); 896, A. M. Wapche Marikar (architect and educationist).

(Des S. Herath. Litho German Bank Note Co, Leipzig)

1985 (23 June). *Gam Udawa '85 (Village Re-awakening Movement). P* 13½ × 13.
897 **355** 60 c. multicoloured .. .. .. 1·00 1·00

356 Emblem — **357** Kothmale Dam and Reservoir

(Des B. Harischandra. Litho German Bank Note Co, Leipzig)

1985 (25 June). *50th Anniv of Colombo Young Poets' Association. P* 14.
898 **356** 60 c. multicoloured 30 75

(Des R. Mawilmada. Litho J.W.)

1985 (24 Aug). *Inauguration of Kothmale Hydro-electric Project. T* **357** *and similar horiz design. Multicoloured. P* 14.
899 60 c. Type **357**.. .. .. 40 25
900 6 r. Kothmale Power Station .. .. 1·10 2·00

358 Federation Logo — **359** Breast Feeding

(Des R. Mawilmada. Litho J.W.)

1985 (2 Sept). *10th Asian and Oceanic Congress of Obstetrics and Gynaecology. P* 14.
901 **358** 7 r. multicoloured .. .. .. 3·25 2·50

(Des B. Harischandra. Litho Cartor)

1985 (5 Sept). *U.N.I.C.E.F. Child Survival and Development Programme. T* **359** *and similar vert designs. Multicoloured. W* w **17**. *P* 13½.
902 35 c. Type **359**.. .. .. 25 10
903 60 c. Child and oral rehydration salts .. 40 30
904 6 r. Weighing child (growth monitoring) .. 2·00 2·75
905 9 r. Immunization .. .. 2·50 3·50
902/5 .. .. *Set of* 4 4·75 6·00
MS906 99 × 180 mm. Nos. 902/5. P 12½ 4·75 6·00
w. Wmk inverted .. .. 4·75 6·00

MINIMUM PRICE

The minimum price quote is 10p which represents a handling charge rather than a basis for valuing common stamps. For further notes about prices see introductory pages.

360 Blowing Indian Chank Shell — **361** Casket containing Land Grant Deed

(Des G. Malaviachi. Litho Heraclio Fournier, Spain)

1985 (27 Sept). *10th Anniv of World Tourism Organization. T* **360** *and similar horiz designs. Multicoloured. P* 14.
907 1 r. Type **360**.. .. .. 15 10
908 6 r. Parliamentary Complex, Jayawardhanapura, Kotte 55 60
909 7 r. Tea plantation 65 75
910 10 r. Ruwanveliseya (Buddhist shrine), Anuradhapura .. .. 90 1·00
907/10 .. .. *Set of* 4 2·00 2·25
MS911 179 × 89 mm. Nos. 907/10. P 13½ .. 2·00 2·25

(Des B. Harischandra. Litho Harrison)

1985 (15 Oct). *50th Anniv of Land Development Ordinance. P* 14 × 15.
912 **361** 4 r. 60, multicoloured .. .. .. 2·00 2·50

362 Koran and Map of Sri Lanka — **363** "Our Lady of Matara" Statue

(Des R. Mawilmada. Litho Cartor)

1985 (17 Oct). *Translation of The Koran into Sinhala. W* w **17**. *P* 13½.
913 **362** 60 c. gold and bright violet 85 90

(Des S. Silva. Litho Security Printers (M), Malaysia)

1985 (5 Nov). *Christmas. T* **363** *and similar vert design. Multicoloured. P* 12.
914 60 c. Type **363**.. .. .. 25 15
915 9 r. "Our Lady of Madhu" statue .. 1·25 2·00
MS916 180 × 100 mm. Nos. 914/15 .. .. 5·00 6·50

(**364**) — **365** Linked Arms and Map of S.A.A.R.C. Countries

1985 (1 Dec)–**86**. *Nos.* 680*b*, 780, 823, 860 *and* 879 *surch as T* **364** *by Aitken Spence Ptg (Pte) Ltd, Sri Lanka.*
917 **236** 75 c. on 60 c. gold, bright yellow-green and emerald (G.) 10 10
a. Surch double .. .. .. † —
918 **347** 1 r. on 4 r. 60, mult (29.4.86) .. 1·75 1·25
919 **339** 1 r. on 7 r. multicoloured (20.1.86) .. 2·25 1·25
920 **269** 5 r. 75 on 2 r. 50, multicoloured (Br) .. 2·50 45
a. Surch double .. .. ..
921 – 7 r. on 35 c. mult (No. 828) (10.3.86) 2·50 65
a. Surch inverted .. .. ..
b. Surch double .. .. ..
c. Surch triple .. .. ..
917/21 .. .. *Set of* 5 8·00 3·25

(Des B. Harischandra. Litho J.W.)

1985 (8 Dec). *1st Summit Meeting of South Asian Association for Regional Co-operation, Dhaka, Bangladesh. T* **365** *and similar horiz design. Multicoloured. P* 14.
922 60 c. Type **365**.. .. .. 2·00 4·00
923 5 r. 50, Logo and flags of member countries .. .. 2·00 2·50
No 922 was, reportedly, withdrawn on 11 December after Pakistan objected to the boundaries shown on the map.

366 "Viceroy Special" Train

389 Mahapola Logo and Aspects of Communication

390 Dr. R. L. Brohier

(Des R. Mawilmada. Litho Security Printers (M), Malaysia)

1987 (6 Feb). *7th Anniv of Mahapola Scheme. P* 12.
971 **389** 75 c. multicoloured 75 75

(Des S. Silva. Litho Security Printers (M), Malaysia)

1987 (10 Feb). *Dr. Richard L. Brohier (historian and surveyor) Commemoration. P* 12.
972 **390** 5 r. 75, multicoloured .. .. 1·75 75

391 Tyre Corporation Building, Kelaniya, and Logo

(Des A. Harischandra. Litho Questa)

1987 (23 Mar). *25th Anniv of Sri Lanka Tyre Corporation. P* 14.
973 **391** 5 r. 75, black, lake and bright orange .. 45 45

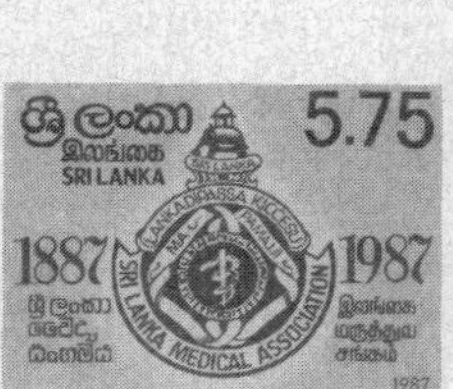

392 Logo

393 Clasped Hands, Farmer and Paddy Field

(Des A. Harischandra. Litho Govt Printing Bureau, Tokyo)

1987 (24 Mar). *Centenary of Sri Lanka Medical Association. P* 13×13½.
974 **392** 5 r. 75, lake-brown, greenish yellow & blk 1·25 1·25

(Des B. Harischandra. Litho Questa)

1987 (29 Mar). *Inauguration of Farmers' Pension and Social Security Benefit Scheme. P* 14.
975 **393** 75 c. multicoloured 45 55

394 Exhibition Logo

395 Young Children with W.H.O. and Immunization Logos

(Des W. Rohana. Litho Security Printers (M), Malaysia)

1987 (2 Apr). *Mahaweli Maha Goviya Contest and Agro Mahaweli Exhibition. P* 12.
976 **394** 75 c. multicoloured 30 30

(Des B. Harischandra. Litho Questa)

1987 (7 Apr). *World Health Day. P* 14.
977 **395** 1 r. multicoloured .. .. 2·50 40

396 Girls playing on Swing

397 Lotus Lanterns

(Des G. Fernando. Litho Security Printers (M), Malaysia)

1987 (9 Apr). *Sinhalese and Tamil New Year. T* **396** *and similar vert design. Multicoloured. P* 12.
978 75 c. Type **396** 10 10
979 5 r. Girls with oil lamp and sun symbol .. 50 50

(Des W. Rohana. Litho Security Printers (M), Malaysia)

1987 (4 May). *Vesak. T* **397** *and similar horiz designs. Multicoloured. P* 12.
980 50 c. Type **397** 10 10
981 75 c. Octagonal lanterns 10 10
982 5 r. Star lanterns 30 30
983 10 r. Gok lanterns 45 55
980/3 .. .. *Set of* 4 80 90
MS984 150×90 mm. Nos. 980/3 .. .. .. 80 1·00

398 Emerald-collared Parakeet

399 Ven. Heenatiyana Sri Dhammaloka Maha Nayake Thero (Buddhist monk)

(Des G. Ratnavira. Litho Questa)

1987 (18 May)–**91**. *Birds (3rd series). T* **398** *and similar horiz designs. Multicoloured. P* 14. *A. With imprint date at bottom right. B. Without imprint date.*

		A		B	
985	50 c. Type **398**	30	10	†	
986	1 r. Legge's Flowerpecker ..	45	10	†	
987	5 r. Ceylon White-headed Starling	1·00	1·00	1·00	1·00
988	10 r. Ceylon Jungle Babbler ..	1·50	1·75	1·50	1·75
985/8	.. .. *Set of* 4	2·75	2·75	†	
MS989	140×80 mm. Nos. 985/8	3·00	2·75	†	

Dates of issue:—9.10.90, No. 988B; 27.2.91, No. 987B.
Imprint dates: "1987", Nos. 985A/9A; "1989", No. 986A; "1990", No. 988A.

(Des S. Silva. Litho Security Printers (M), Malaysia)

1987 (22 May). *National Heroes. T* **399** *and similar vert designs. Multicoloured. P* 12.
990 75 c. Type **399** 40 35
991 75 c. P. de S. Kularatne (educationist) .. 40 35
992 75 c. M. C. Abdul Rahuman (legislator) .. 40 35
990/2 .. .. *Set of* 3 1·10 95

400 Peasant Family and Village

401 *Mesua nagassarium*

(Des J. Semage. Litho Security Printers (M), Malaysia)

1987 (23 June). *Gam Udawa '87 (Village Re-awakening Movement). P* 12.
993 **400** 75 c. multicoloured 30 30

(Des P. Hewabettage (75 c.), B. Harischandra (5 r.). Litho Security Printers (M), Malaysia)

1987 (25 June). *Forest Conservation. T* **401** *and similar horiz design. Multicoloured. P* 12.
994 75 c. Type **401** 10 10
995 5 r. Elephants in forest .. .. 1·00 70

402 Dharmaraja College, Crest and Col. H. Olcott (founder)

403 Youth Services Logo

(Des C. Kandewela. Litho Security Printers (M), Malaysia)

1987 (30 June). *Centenary of Dharmaraja College, Kandy. P* 12.
996 **402** 75 c. multicoloured .. .. 1·50 30

(Des H. Dayaratne. Litho Security Printers (M), Malaysia)

1987 (15 July). *20th Anniv of National Youth Services. P* 12.
997 **403** 75 c. multicoloured 20 20

404 Arm holding Torch and Mahaweli Logo

405 Open Bible and Logo

(Des W. Rohana. Litho Security Printers (M), Malaysia)

1987 (5 Sept). *Mahaweli Games. P* 12.
998 **404** 75 c. multicoloured .. .. .. 2·25 1·75

(Des C. Beling. Litho Security Printers (M), Malaysia)

1987 (2 Oct). *175th Anniv of Ceylon Bible Society. P* 12.
999 **405** 5 r. 75, multicoloured 30 30

406 Hurdler and Committee Symbol

407 Madonna and Child, Flowers and Oil Lamp

(Des R. Mawilmada. Litho Heraclio Fournier, Spain)

1987 (8 Oct). *50th Anniv of National Olympic Committee. P* 13.
1000 **406** 10 r. multicoloured .. .. .. 2·00 90

(Des B. Mendis. Litho Security Printers (M), Malaysia)

1987 (17 Nov). *Christmas. T* **407** *and similar vert design. Multicoloured. P* 12 *(75 c.) or* 12½×13 *(10 r.).*
1001 75 c. Type **407** 10 10
1002 10 r. Christ Child in manger, star and dove 35 40
MS1003 145×82 mm. Nos. 1001/2. P 12 .. 60 70

408 Sir Ernest de Silva

409 Society Logo

(Des P. Gunasinghe. Litho German Bank Note Co, Leipzig)

1987 (25 Nov). *Birth Centenary of Sir Ernest de Silva (philanthropist and philatelist). P* 13×13½.
1004 **408** 75 c. multicoloured 20 20

(Des W. Rohana. Litho German Bank Note Co, Leipzig)

1987 (28 Nov). *150th Anniv of Kandy Friend-in-Need Society. P* 13½×13.
1005 **409** 75 c. multicoloured 20 20

410 University Flag and Graduates

411 Father Joseph Vaz

(Des R. Samarasinghe. Litho Security Printers (M), Malaysia)

1987 (14 Dec). *First Convocation of Buddhist and Pali University. P* 12.
1006 **410** 75 c. multicoloured 20 20

(Des S. Silva. Litho Security Printers (M), Malaysia)

1987 (15 Dec). *300th Anniv of Arrival of Father Joseph Vaz in Kandy. P* 12.
1007 **411** 75 c. multicoloured 20 20

412 Wheel of Dhamma, Dagaba and Bo Leaf

413 Dharmayatra Lorry

(Des W. Rohana. Litho Security Printers (M), Malaysia)

1988 (1 Jan). *30th Anniv of Buddhist Publication Society, Kandy. P* 12.
1008 **412** 75 c. multicoloured 20 20

(Des B. Harischandra. Litho German Bank Note Co, Leipzig)

1988 (4 Jan). *5th Anniv of Mahapola Dharmayatra Service. P* 13½ × 13.
1009 **413** 75 c. multicoloured 20 20

414 Society Logo

415 National Youth Centre, Maharagama

(Des R. Samarasinghe. Litho Security Printers (M), Malaysia)

1988 (8 Jan). *Centenary of Ceylon Society of Arts. P* 12.
1010 **414** 75 c. multicoloured 30 30

(Des R. Chandrajeewa. Litho German Bank Note Co, Leipzig)

1988 (31 Jan). *Opening of National Youth Centre, Maharagama. P* 13½ × 13.
1011 **415** 1 r. multicoloured . . . . . . 2·00 30

416 Citizens with National Flag and Map of Sri Lanka

417 Graduates, Clay Lamp and Open Book

(Des R. Samarasinghe. Litho Security Printers (M), Malaysia)

1988 (4 Feb). *40th Anniv of Independence. T* **416** *and similar vert design. Multicoloured. P* 12.
1012 75 c. Type **416** 10 10
1013 8 r. 50, "40" in figures and lion emblem . . 70 70

(Des R. Samarasinghe. Litho Security Printers (M), Malaysia)

1988 (11 Feb). *8th Anniv of Mahapola Scheme. P* 12.
1014 **417** 75 c. multicoloured 20 20

418 Bus and Logo

419 Ven. Weligama Sri Sumangala Maha Nayake Thero

(Des W. Rohana. Litho Security Printers (M), Malaysia)

1988 (19 Feb). *30th Anniv of Sri Lanka Transport Board. P* 12.
1015 **418** 5 r. 75, multicoloured 45 45

(Des S. Silva. Litho Security Printers (M), Malaysia)

1988 (13 Mar). *Ven. Weligama Sri Sumangala Maha Nayake Thero (Buddhist monk) Commemoration. P* 12.
1016 **419** 75 c. multicoloured 20 20

420 Regimental Colour

421 Chevalier I. X. Pereira

(Des W. Rohana. Litho Security Printers (M), Malaysia)

1988 (20 Apr). *Centenary of Regiment of Artillery. P* 12.
1017 **420** 5 r. 75, multicoloured . . . . . . 2·00 60

(Des S. Silva. Litho Security Printers (M), Malaysia)

1988 (26 Apr). *Birth Centenary of Chevalier I. X. Pereira (politician). P* 12.
1018 **421** 5 r. 75, multicoloured 30 30

422 Invitation to the Deities and Brahmas

423 Father Ferdinand Bonnel (educationist)

(Des N. Bulathsinhala. Litho State Ptg Wks, Moscow)

1988 (13 May). *Vesak. Paintings from Narendrarama Rajamaha Temple, Suriyagoda. T* **422** *and similar horiz design. Multicoloured. P* 12½ × 12.
1019 50 c. Type **422** 15 15
1020 75 c. Bodhisathva at the Seventh Step . . 15 15
MS1021 150 × 92 mm. Nos. 1019/20 . . . . 50 50

(Des S. Silva. Litho State Ptg Wks, Moscow)

1988 (22 May). *National Heroes. T* **423** *and similar vert designs. Multicoloured. P* 12 × 12½.
1022 75 c. Type **423** 15 15
1023 75 c. Sir Razik Fareed (politician) . . 15 15
1024 75 c. W. F. Gunawardhana (scholar) . . 15 15
1025 75 c. Edward Nugawela (politician) . . 15 15
1026 75 c. Chief Justice Sir Arthur Wijeyewardene 15 15
1022/6 . . . . . . *Set of* 5 60 60

424 Stylized Figures and Reawakened Village

425 Maliyadeva College, Kurunegala, and Crest

(Des P. Gunasinghe. Litho Security Printers (M), Malaysia)

1988 (23 June). *10th Anniv of Gam Udawa (Village Re-awakening Movement). P* 12.
1027 **424** 75 c. multicoloured 20 20

(Des W. Rohana. Litho German Bank Note Co, Leipzig)

1988 (30 June). *Centenary of Maliyadeva College, Kurunegala. P* 13½ × 13.
1028 **425** 75 c. multicoloured 20 20

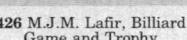

426 M.J.M. Lafir, Billiard Game and Trophy

427 Flags of Australia and Sri Lanka, Handclasp and Map of Australia

(Des S. Silva. Litho State Ptg Wks, Moscow)

1988 (5 July). *Mohamed Junaid Mohamed Lafir (World Amateur Billiards Champion, 1973) Commemoration. P* 12½ × 12.
1029 **426** 5 r. 75, multicoloured 30 30

(Des R. Samarasinghe. Litho Security Printers (M), Malaysia)

1988 (19 July). *Bicentenary of Australian Settlement. P* 12.
1030 **427** 8 r. 50, multicoloured 30 35

428 Ven. Kataluwe Sri Gunaratana Maha Nayake Thero

429 Athlete, Rice and Hydro-electric Dam

(Des S. Silva. Litho State Ptg Wks, Moscow)

1988 (11 Aug). *Ven. Kataluwe Sri Gunaratana Maha Nayake Thero (Buddhist monk) Commemoration. P* 12 × 12½.
1031 **428** 75 c. multicoloured 20 20

(Des P. Gunasinghe. Litho Security Printers (M), Malaysia)

1988 (3 Sept). *Mahaweli Games. P* 12.
1032 **429** 75 c. multicoloured 20 20

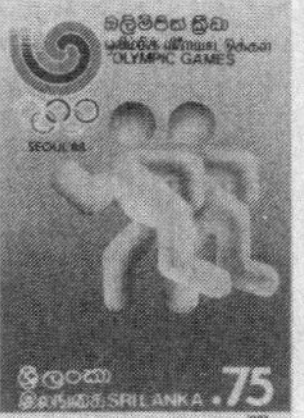

430 Athletics

431 Outline Map of Sri Lanka and Anniversary Logo

(Des P. Gunasinghe. Litho State Ptg Wks, Moscow)

1988 (6 Sept). *Olympic Games, Seoul. T* **430** *and similar vert designs. Multicoloured. P* 12 × 12½.
1033 75 c. Type **430** 10 10
1034 1 r. Swimming 10 10
1035 5 r. 75, Boxing 30 35
1036 8 r. 50, Map of Sri Lanka and logos of Olympic Committee and Seoul Games 50 55
1033/6 . . . . . . *Set of* 4 85 90
MS1037 181 × 101 mm. Nos. 1033/6 . . . . 95 1·10

(Des S. Silva. Litho Security Printers (M), Malaysia)

1988 (12 Sept). *40th Anniv of World Health Organization. P* 12.
1038 **431** 75 c. multicoloured 20 20

432 Games Logo

433 Mahatma Gandhi

(Des A. Harischandra. Litho Security Printers (M), Malaysia)

1988 (20 Sept). *3rd National School Games. P* 12.
1039 **432** 1 r. black, gold and mauve . . . . 1·40 20

(Des S. Silva. Litho Security Printers (M), Malaysia)

1988 (2 Oct). *40th Death Anniv of Mahatma Gandhi. P* 12.
1040 **433** 75 c. multicoloured 50 20

434 Globe with Forms of Transport and Communications

435 Woman with Rice Sheaf and Hydro-electric Project

(Des R. Samarasinghe. Litho State Ptg Wks, Moscow)

1988 (28 Oct). *Asia–Pacific Transport and Communications Decade. T* **434** *and similar horiz design. P* 12½ × 12.
1041 75 c. multicoloured 20 10
1042 5 r. 75, magenta, royal blue and black . . 80 50
Design:—5 r. 75, Antenna tower with dish aerials and forms of transport.

(Des B. Harischandra. Litho Security Printers (M), Malaysia)

1988 (31 Oct). *Commissioning of Randenigala Project. T* **435** *and similar horiz design. Multicoloured. P* 12.
1043 75 c. Type **435** 10 10
1044 5 r. 75, Randenigala Dam and reservoir 45 45

436 Handicrafts and Centre Logo in Cupped Hands

437 Angel, Dove, Olive Branch and Globe

(Des R. Samarasinghe. Litho Secura, Singapore)

1988 (17 Nov). *Opening of Gramodaya Folk Art Centre, Colombo. P* 13½.
1045 **436** 75 c. multicoloured 20 20

(Des B. Mendis. Litho State Ptg Wks, Moscow)

1988 (21 Nov). *Christmas. T* **437** *and similar vert design. Multicoloured. P* 12×12½.
1046 75 c. Type **437** 10 10
1047 8 r. 50, Shepherds and Star of Bethlehem 50 60
MS1048 175×100 mm. Nos. 1046/7 .. .. 60 60

438 Dr. E. W. Adikaram

439 Open Book in Tree and Children reading

(Des S. Silva. Litho Security Printers (M), Malaysia)

1988 (28 Dec). *Dr. E. W. Adikaram (educationist) Commemoration. P* 12.
1049 **438** 75 c. multicoloured 20 20

(Des Lakmini Amararatne. Litho German Bank Note Co, Leipzig)

1989 (23 Jan). *10th Anniv of Free Distribution of School Text Books. P* 13½×13.
1050 **439** 75 c. multicoloured 20 20

440 Wimalaratne Kumaragama

441 Logo and New Chamber of Commerce Building

(Des S. Silva. Litho German Bank Note Co, Leipzig)

1989 (27 Jan). *Poets of Sri Lanka. T* **440** *and similar vert designs. Multicoloured. P* 13×13½.
1051 75 c. Type **440** 15 15
1052 75 c. G. H. Perera 15 15
1053 75 c. Sagara Palansuriya 15 15
1054 75 c. P. B. Alwis Perera 15 15
1051/4 .. .. *Set of* 4 50 50

(Des Mel Ads Ltd. Litho Security Printers (M), Malaysia)

1989 (25 Mar). *150th Anniv of Ceylon Chamber of Commerce. P* 12.
1055 **441** 75 c. multicoloured 20 20

442 Bodhisatva at Lunch and Funeral Pyre

443 Parawahera Vajiragnana Thero (Buddhist monk)

(Des N. Bulathsinhala. Litho State Ptg Wks, Moscow)

1989 (15 May). *Vesak. Wall Paintings from Medawala Monastery, Harispattuwa. T* **442** *and similar horiz designs. Multicoloured. P* 12½×12.
1056 50 c. Type **442** 10 10
1057 75 c. Rescue of King Vessantara's children by god Sakra 10 10
1058 5 r. Bodhisatva ploughing and his son attacked by snake 30 35
1059 5 r. 75, King Vessantara giving away his children 30 35
1056/9 .. .. .. *Set of* 4 70 80
MS1060 150×90 mm. Nos. 1056/9 .. .. 75 75

(Des S. Silva. Litho Security Printers (M), Malaysia)

1989 (22 May). *National Heroes. T* **443** *and similar multicoloured designs. P* 12.
1061 75 c. Type **443** 15 15
1062 75 c. Father Maurice Jacques Le Goc (educationist) 15 15
1063 75 c. Hemapala Munidasa (author) .. 15 15
1064 75 c. Ananda Samarakoon (composer) .. 15 15
1065 75 c. Simon Casie Chitty (scholar) (*horiz*) 15 15
1061/5 .. .. *Set of* 5 65 65

444 College Crest

445 Dramachakra, Lamp, Buddhist Flag and Map

(Des W. Rohana. Litho Security Printers (M), Malaysia)

1989 (5 June). *150th Anniv of Hartley College, Point-Pedro* (1988). *P* 12.
1066 **444** 75 c. multicoloured 20 20

(Des P. Gunasinghe. Litho State Ptg Wks, Moscow)

1989 (18 June). *Establishment of Ministry of Buddha Sasana. P* 12½×12.
1067 **445** 75 c. multicoloured 20 20

446 Hands holding Brick and Trowel, House and Family

447 Two Families and Hand turning Cogwheel

(Des P. Gunasinghe. Litho State Ptg Wks, Moscow)

1989 (23 June). *Gam Udawa '89 (Village Re-awakening Movement). P* 12½×12.
1068 **446** 75 c. multicoloured 20 20

(Des P. Gunasinghe. Photo State Ptg Works, Moscow)

1989 (23 June)–**90**. *Janasaviya Development Programme. "1989" (75 c.) or "1990" (1 r.) imprint date at bottom right. P* 12×11½.
1069 **447** 75 c. multicoloured 20 20
1070 1 r. multicoloured (31.1.90) 20 20
a. Without imprint date at bottom right (4.12.90) 10 10

448 Dunhinda Falls

449 Rev. James Chater (missionary) and Baptist Church

(Des S. Silva. Litho State Ptg Works, Moscow)

1989 (11 Aug). *Waterfalls. T* **448** *and similar vert designs. Multicoloured. P* 12.
1071 75 c. Type **448** 10 10
1072 1 r. Rawana Falls 10 10
1073 5 r. 75, Laxapana Falls 35 40
1074 8 r. 50, Diyaluma Falls 45 50
1071/4 .. .. *Set of* 4 80 90

(Des S. Silva. Litho State Ptg Works, Moscow)

1989 (19 Aug). *177th Anniv of Baptist Church in Sri Lanka. P* 12½×12.
1075 **449** 5 r. 75, multicoloured 30 30

450 Bicentenary Logo

451 Old and New Bank Buildings and Logo

(Des R. Samarasinghe. Litho German Bank Note Co, Leipzig)

1989 (26 Aug). *Bicentenary of French Revolution. P* 13½×13.
1076 **450** 8 r. 50, black, deep blue & brt carmine 55 55

(Des W. Rohana. Litho German Bank Note Co, Leipzig)

1989 (31 Aug). *50th Anniv of Bank of Ceylon. T* **451** *and similar horiz design. Multicoloured. P* 13½×13.
1077 75 c. Type **451** 10 10
1078 5 r. "Bank of Ceylon" orchid and logo .. 45 45

452 Water Lily, Dharma Chakra and Books

453 Wilhelm Geiger

(Des P. Gunasinghe. Litho Security Printers (M), Malaysia)

1989 (22 Sept). *State Literary Festival. P* 12.
1079 **452** 75 c. multicoloured 20 20

(Des S. Silva. Litho German Bank Note Co, Leipzig)

1989 (30 Sept). *Wilhelm Geiger (linguistic scholar) Commemoration. P* 13×13½.
1080 **453** 75 c. multicoloured 20 20

(Litho Questa)

1989 (11 Oct). *As No. 781, but different printer. Face value and inscriptions in black. "1989" imprint date. P* 14.
1081 3 r. Golden Palm Civet 75 30

No. 781 has face value and inscriptions in red-brown and is without imprint date.

454 H. V. Perera, Q.C.

455 Sir Cyril de Zoysa

(Des S. Silva. Litho Security Printers (M), Malaysia)

1989 (16 Oct). *Constitutional Pioneers. T* **454** *and similar vert design. Multicoloured. P* 12.
1082 75 c. Type **454** 20 20
1083 75 c. Prof. Ivor Jennings 20 20

(Des S. Silva. Litho German Bank Note Co, Leipzig)

1989 (26 Oct). *Sir Cyril de Zoysa (Buddhist philanthropist) Commemoration. P* 13×13½.
1084 **455** 75 c. multicoloured 20 20

456 Map of South-east Asia and Telecommunications Equipment

457 Members with Offerings and Water Lily on Map of Sri Lanka

(Des W. Rohana. Litho State Ptg Works, Moscow)

1989 (1 Nov). *10th Anniv of Asia-Pacific Telecommunity. P* 12×12½.
1085 **456** 5 r. 75, multicoloured 45 45

(Des P. Gunasinghe. Litho Security Printers (M), Malaysia)

1989 (9 Nov). *50th Anniv of Sri Sucharitha Welfare Movement. P* 13.
1086 **457** 75 c. multicoloured 20 20

458 "Apollo 11" Blast-off and Astronauts

459 Shepherds

(Des W. Rohana. Litho State Ptg Works, Moscow)

1989 (10 Nov). *20th Anniv of First Manned Landing on Moon. T* **458** *and similar vert designs. Multicoloured. P* 12×12½.

1087 75 c. Type **458** 10 10
1088 1 r. Armstrong leaving lunar module Eagle 15 10
1089 2 r. Astronaut on Moon 25 25
1090 5 r. 75, Lunar surface and Earth from Moon 40 45
1087/90 .. .. *Set of* 4 75 75
MS1091 100×160 mm. Nos. 1087/90 .. .. 90 90

(Des Father P. Silva. Litho Secura, Singapore)

1989 (21 Nov). *Christmas. T* **459** *and similar vert design. Multicoloured. P* 13½.

1092 75 c. Type **459** 10 10
1093 8 r. 50, Magi with gifts .. .. .. 30 1·25
MS1094 160×100 mm. Nos. 1092/3 .. .. 75 1·50

460 Ven. Sri Devananda Nayake Thero

461 College Building, Crest and Revd. William Ault (founder)

(Des S. Silva. Litho Security Printers (M), Malaysia)

1989 (25 Nov). *Ven. Sri Devananda Nayake Thero (Buddhist monk) Commemoration. P* 12.

1095 **460** 75 c. multicoloured 20 20

(Des W. Rohana. Litho Security Printers (M), Malaysia)

1989 (29 Nov). *175th Anniv of Methodist Central College, Batticaloa. P* 12.

1096 **461** 75 c. multicoloured 20 20

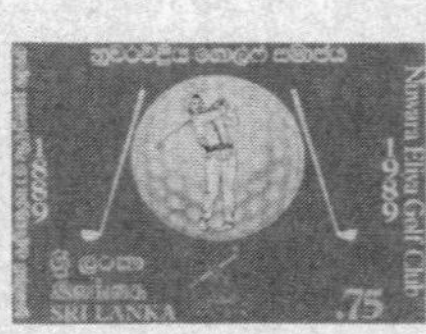

462 Golf Ball, Clubs and Logo

463 "Raja"

(Des G. Bozell. Litho Pakistan Security Ptg Corp, Karachi)

1989 (8 Dec). *Centenary of Nuwara Eliya Golf Club. T* **462** *and similar horiz design. Multicoloured. P* 13½.

1097 75 c. Type **462** 75 25
1098 8 r. 50, Course and club house .. .. 2·50 1·00

(Litho German Bank Note Co, Leipzig)

1989 (12 Dec). *"Raja" Royal Ceremonial Elephant, Kandy, Commemoration. P* 13×13½.

1099 **463** 75 c. multicoloured .. .. .. 2·00 55

464 College Building and G. Wickremarachchi (founder)

465 Ven. Udunuwara Sri Sarananda Thero

(Des S. Silva. Litho German Bank Note Co, Leipzig)

1989 (14 Dec). *60th Anniv of Gampaha Wickremarachchi Institute of Ayurveda Medicine. P* 13½×13.

1100 **464** 75 c. multicoloured 20 20

(Des S. Silva. Litho State Ptg Wks, Moscow)

1989 (20 Dec). *Ven. Udunuwara Sri Sarananda Thero (Buddhist monk) Commemoration. P* 12×12½.

1101 **465** 75 c. multicoloured 20 20

NEW INFORMATION

The editor is always interested to correspond with people who have new information that will improve or correct the Catalogue.

466 Diesel Train on Viaduct, Ella-Demodara

467 Cardinal Thomas Cooray

(Des R. Mawilmada. Litho Security Printers (M), Malaysia)

1989 (27 Dec). *125 Years of Sri Lanka Railways. T* **466** *and similar horiz designs. Multicoloured. P* 12.

1102 75 c. Type **466** 15 10
1103 2 r. Diesel train at Maradana Station .. 20 15
  a. Perf 13 .. .. 20 15
1104 3 r. Steam train 25 20
  a. Perf 13 .. .. 25 20
1105 7 r. Steam train, 1864 .. .. .. 50 40
1102/5 .. .. .. *Set of* 4 1·00 75

(Des S. Silva. Litho German Bank Note Co, Leipzig)

1989 (28 Dec). *Cardinal Thomas Cooray Commemoration. P* 13×13½.

1106 **467** 75 c. multicoloured 75 30

468 Farmer and Wife with Dagaba and Dam

469 Justin Wijayawardena

(Des P. Gunasinghe. Litho Security Printers (M), Malaysia)

1989 (29 Dec). *Agro Mahaweli Development Programme. P* 12.

1107 **468** 75 c. multicoloured 20 20

(Des S. Silva. Litho State Ptg Wks, Moscow)

1990 (14 Jan). *Justin Wijayawardena (scholar) Commemoration. P* 12×12½.

1108 **469** 1 r. multicoloured .. .. .. 1·25 20

.25

(**469***a*)

470 Ven. Induruwe Uttarananda Mahanayake Thero

1990 (16 Feb). *No.* 1059 *surch with T* **469***a*.

1108*a* 25 c. on 5 r. 75, King Vessantara giving away his children 30 20

(Des S. Silva. Litho Security Printers (M), Malaysia)

1990 (15 Mar). *4th Death Anniv of Ven. Induruwe Uttarananda Mahanayake Thero (Buddhist theologian). P* 12.

1109 **470** 1 r. multicoloured 80 80

1.00

(**470***a*)

471 Two Graduates, Lamp and Open Book

1990 (22 Mar). *No.* 1069 *surch with T* **470***a*.

1109*a* **447** 1 r. on 75 c. multicoloured 40 30

(Des P. Gunasinghe. Litho Secura, Singapore)

1990 (25 Mar). *9th Anniv of Mahapola Scheme. P* 13½.

1110 **471** 75 c. multicoloured 20 20

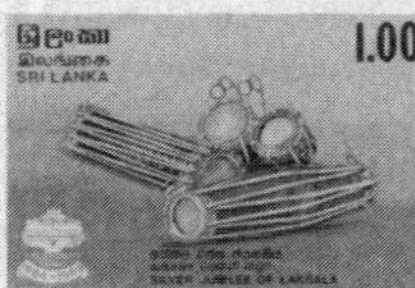

472 Traditional Drums

(Des R. Samarasinha. Litho Security Printers (M), Malaysia)

1990 (2 Apr). *25th Anniv of Laksala Traditional Handicrafts Organization. T* **472** *and similar horiz designs. Multicoloured. P* 12.

1111 1 r. Type **472** 10 10
1112 2 r. Silverware 15 15
1113 3 r. Lacquerware 20 20
1114 8 r. Dumbara mats 40 40
1111/14 .. .. *Set of* 4 75 75

473 King Maha Prathapa visiting Queen Chandra

474 Father T. Long (educationist)

(Des N. Bulathsinhala. Litho State Ptg Wks, Moscow)

1990 (2 May). *Vesak. Wall Paintings from Buduraja Maha Viharaya, Wewurukannala. T* **473** *and similar horiz designs. Multicoloured. P* 12½×12.

1115 75 c. Type **473** 10 10
1116 1 r. Execution of Prince Dharmapala .. 10 10
1117 2 r. Prince Mahinsasaka with the Water Demon 15 15
1118 8 r. King Dahamsonda with the God Sakra disguised as a demon .. 35 35
1115/18 .. .. *Set of* 4 55 55
MS1119 160×99 mm. Nos. 1115/18 .. .. 80 80

(Des S. Silva. Litho Security Printers (M), Malaysia (No. 1120), State Ptg Wks, Moscow (others))

1990 (22 May). *National Heroes. T* **474** *and similar vert designs. Multicoloured. P* 12 *(No. 1120) or* 12×12½ *(others)*.

1120 1 r. Type **474** 15 15
1121 1 r. Prof. M. Ratnasuriya (37×25 *mm*) .. 15 15
1122 1 r. D. Wijewardene (patriot) (37×25 *mm*) 15 15
1123 1 r. L. Manjusri (artist) (37×25 *mm*) .. 15 15
1120/3 .. .. *Set of* 4 50 50

475 Janasaviya Workers

476 Gold Reliquary

(Des P. Dissanayake. Litho State Ptg Wks, Moscow)

1990 (23 June). *12th Anniv of Gam Udawa and Opening of Janasaviya Centre, Pallekele. P* 12½×12.

1124 **475** 1 r. multicoloured 90 30

(Des N. Bulathsinhala. Litho Security Printers (M), Malaysia)

1990 (7 July). *Centenary of Department of Archaeology. T* **476** *and similar vert designs. P* 13 *(8 r.) or* 12 *(others)*.

1125 1 r. black and orange-yellow 10 10
1126 2 r. black and greenish grey 15 15
1127 3 r. black, apple-green and ochre .. 20 20
  a. Perf 13 .. .. 20 20
1128 8 r. black and ochre 45 35
1125/8 .. .. *Set of* 4 75 65

Designs:—2 r. Statuette of Ganesh; 3 r. Terrace of the Bodhi-tree, Isurumuniya Vihara; 8 r. Inscription of King Nissankamalla.

477 Male Tennis Player at Left

478 Spotted Loach

(Des W. Rohana. Litho Pakistan Security Ptg Corp, Karachi)

1990 (14 Aug). *75th Anniv of Sri Lanka Tennis Association. T* **477** *and similar horiz designs. Multicoloured. P* 13½.

1129 1 r. Type **477** 50 50
a. Horiz pair. Nos. 1129/30 .. .. 1·00 1·00
1130 1 r. Male tennis player at right 50 50
1131 8 r. Male tennis players .. .. .. 1·50 1·75
a. Horiz pair. Nos. 1131/2 .. .. 3·00 3·50
1132 8 r. Female tennis players .. .. 1·50 1·75
1129/32 .. .. *Set of* 4 3·50 4·00

Nos. 1129/30 and 1131/2 were each printed together, *se-tenant*, in horizontal pairs throughout the sheets, each pair forming a composite design of a singles (1 r.) or doubles (8 r.) match.

(Des R. Samarasinghe. Litho State Ptg Wks, Moscow)

1990 (14 Sept). *Endemic Fishes. T* **478** *and similar horiz designs. Multicoloured. P* 11½.

1133 25 c. Type **478** 10 10
1134 2 r. Spotted Gourami ("Ornate Paradise Fish") 20 10
1135 8 r. Mountain Labeo 50 60
1136 20 r. Cherry Barb .. .. 1·00 1·25
1133/6 .. .. *Set of* 4 1·60 1·75
MS1137 150×90 mm. Nos. 1133/6 .. .. 2·75 3·00

479 Rukmani Devi

480 Innkeeper turning away Mary and Joseph

(Litho Security Printers (M), Malaysia)

1990 (28 Oct). *12th Death Anniv of Rukmani Devi (actress and singer). P* 12.

1138 **479** 1 r. multicoloured .. .. .. 1·50 75

(Des P. Silva. Litho Security Printers (M), Malaysia)

1990 (28 Nov). *Christmas. T* **480** *and similar vert design. Multicoloured. P* 13.

1139 1 r. Type **480** 25 10
1140 10 r. Adoration of the Magi .. .. 1·50 2·00
MS1141 190×114 mm. Nos. 1139/40. P 12 .. 1·75 2·25

481 Health Worker talking to Villagers

482 Main College Building and Flag

(Des W. Rohana. Litho Security Printers (M), Malaysia)

1990 (30 Nov). *World Aids Day. T* **481** *and similar horiz design. Multicoloured. P* 12.

1142 1 r. Type **481** 45 15
1143 8 r. Emblem and Aids virus .. .. 1·50 2·00

(Des P. Gunasinghe. Litho Security Printers (M), Malaysia)

1990 (8 Dec). *50th Anniv of Dharmapala College, Pannipitiya. P* 12.

1144 **482** 1 r. multicoloured 80 70

483 Peri Sundaram

484 Letter Box, Galle, 1904

(Des W. Rohana. Litho Security Printers (M), Malaysia)

1990 (14 Dec). *Birth Centenary of Peri Sundaram (lawyer and politician). P* 12.

1145 **483** 1 r. red-brown and yellow-green .. 80 70

(Des W. Rohana. Litho Security Printers (M), Malaysia)

1990 (26 Dec). *175th Anniv of Sri Lanka Postal Service. T* **484** *and similar vert designs. Multicoloured. P* 12.

1146 1 r. Type **484** 35 10
1147 2 r. Mail runner, 1815 .. .. .. 65 25
1148 5 r. Mail coach, 1832 .. .. .. 1·00 1·25
1149 10 r. Nuwara-Eliya Post Office, 1894 .. 1·75 2·00
1146/9 .. .. *Set of* 4 3·25 3·25

485 Chemical Structure Diagram, Graduating Students and Emblem

486 Kastavahana on Royal Elephant

(Des W. Rohana. Litho Security Printers (M), Malaysia)

1991 (25 Jan). *50th Anniv of Institute of Chemistry. P* 12.

1150 **485** 1 r. multicoloured .. .. .. 1·50 75

(Des U. Karunaratne. Litho Security Printers (M), Malaysia)

1991 (17 May). *Vesak. Temple Paintings from Karagampitiya Subodarama. T* **486** *and similar horiz designs. Multicoloured. P* 12

1151 75 c. Type **486** 15 10
1152 1 r. Polo Janaka in prison 20 10
1153 2 r. Two merchants offering food to Buddha 35 35
1154 11 r. Escape of Queen .. .. .. 1·75 2·50
1151/4 .. .. *Set of* 4 2·25 2·75
MS1155 150×90 mm. Nos. 1151/4 .. .. 2·40 3·00

487 Narada Thero (Buddhist missionary)

488 Society Building

(Des S. Silva. Litho State Ptg Works, Moscow)

1991 (22 May). *National Heroes. T* **487** *and similar vert designs. Multicoloured. P* 12×12½.

1156 1 r. Type **487** 25 30
1157 1 r. Wallewatta Silva (novelist) 25 30
1158 1 r. Sir Muttu Coomaraswamy (lawyer and politician) 25 30
1159 1 r. Dr. Andreas Nell (opthalmic surgeon) 25 30
1156/9 .. .. *Set of* 4 90 1·10

(Des R. de Silva. Litho Security Printers (M), Malaysia)

1991 (31 May). *Centenary of Maha Bodhi Society. P* 12.

1160 **488** 1 r. multicoloured .. .. .. 1·00 80

489 Women working at Home

490 Globe and Plan Symbol

(Des T. Kariyawasam. Litho Security Printers (M), Malaysia)

1991 (23 June). *13th Anniv of Gam Udawa Movement. P* 12½.

1161 **489** 1 r. multicoloured .. .. .. 1·00 80

(Des R. Mawilmada. Litho Security Printers (M), Malaysia)

1991 (1 July). *40th Anniv of Colombo Plan. P* 12.

1162 **490** 1 r. bright violet and new blue .. .. 1·00 80

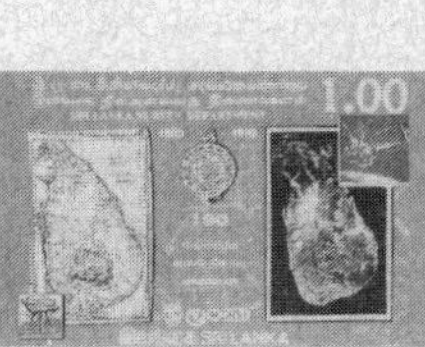

491 17th-century Map and Modern Satellite Photo of Sri Lanka

492 Ven. Henpitagedera Gnanaseeha Nayake Thero

(Des P. Miththapala. Litho Security Printers (M), Malaysia)

1991 (1 Aug). *190th Anniv of Sri Lanka Survey Department. P* 12½.

1163 **491** 1 r. multicoloured .. .. .. 1·00 80

(Des S. Silva. Litho Security Printers (M), Malaysia)

1991 (1 Aug). *10th Death Anniv of Ven. Nayak Henpitagedera Gnanaseeha Nayake Thero (Buddhist theologian). P* 12½.

1164 **492** 1 r. multicoloured .. .. .. 1·00 80

493 Police Officers of 1866 and 1991 with Badge

494 Kingswood College

(Des S. Silva. Litho Security Printers (M), Malaysia)

1991 (3 Sept). *125th Anniv of Sri Lankan Police Force. P* 12½.

1165 **493** 1 r. multicoloured 70 50

(Des W. Rohana. Litho State Ptg Wks, Moscow)

1991 (26 Oct). *Centenary of Kingswood College, Kandy. P* 12½×12.

1166 **494** 1 r. multicoloured 30 30

495 The Annunciation

496 Early Magneto Telephone

(Des P. Silva. Litho Security Printers (M), Malaysia)

1991 (19 Nov). *Christmas. T* **495** *and similar vert design. Multicoloured. P* 12½.

1167 1 r. Type **495** 20 20
1168 10 r. The Presentation of Jesus in the Temple 75 80
MS1169 90×150 mm. Nos. 1167/8 .. .. 1·00 1·75

(Des W. Rohana. Litho Security Printers (M), Malaysia)

1991 (23 Nov). *Inauguration of Sri Lankan Telecom Corporation. T* **496** *and similar vert designs. Multicoloured. P* 12½.

1170 1 r. Type **496** 15 10
1171 2 r. Manual switchboard and telephonist 20 15
1172 8 r. Satellite communications system .. 40 60
1173 10 r. Fibre optics cable and mobile phone 50 70
1170/3 .. .. *Set of* 4 1·10 1·40

497 S.A.A.R.C. Logo and Bandaranaike Memorial Hall

498 "Pancha" (Games mascot)

(Des W. Rohana (1 r.), S. Silva (8 r.). Litho Security Printers (M), Malaysia)

1991 (21 Dec). *Sixth South Asian Association for Regional Cooperation Summit, Colombo. T* **497** *and similar horiz design. P* 12½.

1174 1 r. Type **497** 15 10
1175 8 r. Logo and Hall surrounded by national flags 45 60

(Des Sri Lanka National Design Centre. Litho Secura, Singapore)

1991 (22 Dec). *5th South Asian Federation Games. T* **498** *and similar horiz designs. P* 13½×14.

1176 1 r. Type **498** 20 10
1177 2 r. Games logo 35 20
1178 4 r. Sugathadasa Stadium 70 70
1179 11 r. Asia map on globe and national flags 1·50 1·75
1176/9 .. .. *Set of* 4 2·50 2·50

COVER PRICES

Cover factors are quoted at the beginning of each country for most issues to 1945. An explanation of the system can be found on page x. The factors quoted do not, however, apply to philatelic covers.

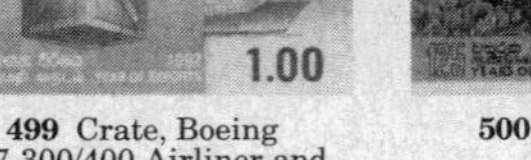

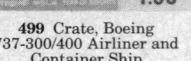

499 Crate, Boeing 737-300/400 Airliner and Container Ship   **500** Plucking Tea

(Des W. Rohana. Litho Security Printers (M), Malaysia)

1992 (13 Jan). *Exports Year. P* 12.
1180 **499** 1 r. multicoloured 85 65

(Des R. Mawilmada. Litho Secura, Singapore)

1992 (12 Feb). *125th Anniv of Tea Industry. T* **500** *and similar horiz designs. Multicoloured. P* 14.
1181 1 r. Type **500** 30 10
1182 2 r. Healthy family, tea and tea estate .. 55 20
1183 5 r. Ceylon tea symbol .. .. .. 1·25 1·50
1184 10 r. James Taylor (founder) .. .. 1·75 2·00
1181/4 .. .. *Set of* 4 3·50 3·50

501 General Ranjan Wijeratne   **502** Olcott Hall, Mahinda College

(Des W. Rohana. Litho State Ptg Wks, Moscow)

1992 (2 Mar). *1st Death Anniv of General Ranjan Wijeratne. P* 12×12½.
1185 **501** 1 r. multicoloured 20 20

(Des W. Rohana. Litho Security Printers (M), Malaysia)

1992 (2 Mar). *Centenary of Mahinda College, Galle. P* 12.
1186 **502** 1 r. multicoloured 20 20

503 Newstead College and Logo   **504** Student and Oil Lamp

(Des S. Silva. Litho Security Printers (M), Malaysia)

1992 (13 Mar). *175th Anniv of Newstead Girls' College, Negombo* (1991). *P* 12.
1187 **503** 1 r. multicoloured 20 20

(Des S. Perera. Litho Security Printers (M), Malaysia)

1992 (30 Mar). *11th Anniv of Mahapola Scholarship Fund. P* 12.
1188 **504** 1 r. multicoloured 20 20

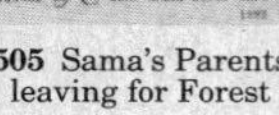

505 Sama's Parents leaving for Forest   **506** Ven. Devamottawe Amarawansa (Buddhist missionary)

(Des N. Bulathsinhala. Litho Security Printers (M), Malaysia)

1992 (5 May). *Vesak Festival. Sama Jataka Paintings from Kottimbulwala Cave Temple. T* **505** *and similar horiz designs. Multicoloured. P* 12.
1189 75 c. Type **505** 10 10
1190 1 r. Sama and parents in forest 10 10
1191 8 r. Sama leading blind parents 65 85
1192 11 r. Sama's parents grieving for wounded son .. .. 1·00 1·40
1189/92 .. .. *Set of* 4 1·60 2·25
MS1193 151×91 mm. Nos. 1189/92 .. .. 1·75 2·50

(Des S. Silva. Litho Leigh-Mardon Ltd, Melbourne)

1992 (22 May). *National Heroes. T* **506** *and similar vert designs. Multicoloured. P* 14.
1194 1 r. Type **506** 10 15
1195 1 r. Richard Mirando (Buddhist philanthropist) 10 15
1196 1 r. Gate Mudaliyar N. Canaganayagam (Buddhist social reformer) 10 15
1197 1 r. Abdul Azeez (Moorish social reformer) 10 15
1194/7 .. .. *Set of* 4 30 50

507 Map of Sri Lanka, Flag and Symbol   **508** Family in House

(Des S. Silva. Litho State Ptg Wks, Moscow)

1992 (14 June). *2300th Anniv of Arrival of Buddhism in Sri Lanka. P* 12×12½.
1198 **507** 1 r. multicoloured 20 20

(Des P. Miranda. Litho Security Printers (M), Malaysia)

1992 (23 June). *14th Anniv of Gam Udawa Movement. P* 12.
1199 **508** 1 r. multicoloured 20 20

509 Postal Activities and Award   **510** Narilata Mask

(Des W. Rohana. Litho Leigh-Mardon Ltd, Melbourne)

1992 (11 July). *Postal Service Awards. T* **509** *and similar horiz design. Multicoloured. P* 14.
1200 1 r. Type **509** 30 10
1201 10 r. Medals and commemorative cachet 1·40 1·75

(Des A. Dharmasiri. Litho Secura, Singapore)

1992 (19 Aug). *Kolam Dance Masks. T* **510** *and similar vert designs. Multicoloured. P* 12½.
1202 1 r. Type **510** 10 10
1203 2 r. Mudali mask 15 10
1204 5 r. Queen mask 25 30
1205 10 r. King mask 40 60
1202/5 .. .. *Set of* 4 80 1·00
MS1206 150×90 mm. Nos. 1202/5 .. 1·00 1·50
Special packs prepared for the S.A.A.R.C. "Philex '96" stamp exhibition at Colombo contained the strip of stamps from No. **MS**1206 with the sheet margins removed.

Barcelona'92
SHRI LANKA 1.00

511 19th and 20th-century Players and Match of 1838   **512** Running

(Des W. Rohana. Litho Secura, Singapore)

1992 (8 Sept). *160th Anniv of Cricket in Sri Lanka. P* 13.
1207 **511** 5 r. multicoloured .. .. .. 1·40 1·40

(Litho Questa)

1992 (15 Sept). *Olympic Games, Barcelona. T* **512** *and similar vert designs. Multicoloured. P* 14.
1208 1 r. Type **512** 15 10
1209 11 r. Shooting .. .. 85 1·00
1210 13 r. Swimming .. .. 1·00 1·25
1211 15 r. Weight-lifting .. .. .. 1·10 1·40
1208/11 .. .. *Set of* 4 2·75 3·25
MS1212 91×151 mm. Nos. 1208/11 .. .. 2·75 3·75

513 Vijaya Kumaratunga   **514** College Building and Crest

(Litho Secura, Singapore)

1992 (9 Oct). *Vijaya Kumaratunga (actor) Commemoration. P* 13.
1213 **513** 1 r. multicoloured 30 20

(Des W. Rohana. Litho Security Printers (M), Malaysia)

1992 (24 Oct). *Centenary of Al-Bahjathhul Ibraheemiyyah Arabic College. P* 12.
1214 **514** 1 r. multicoloured 30 20

515 Official Church Seal   **516** Nativity

(Des W. Rohana. Litho Security Printers (M), Malaysia)

1992 (25 Oct). *350th Anniv of Dutch Reformed Church in Sri Lanka. P* 12.
1215 **515** 1 r. black, yellowish grn & greenish yell 50 40

(Des S. Purnajith. Litho Security Printers (M), Malaysia)

1992 (17 Nov). *Christmas. T* **516** *and similar vert design. Multicoloured. P* 12.
1216 1 r. Type **516** 10 10
1217 9 r. Family going to church 60 80
MS1218 150×90 mm. Nos. 1216/17 .. .. 65 1·00

2.00

517 Fleet of Columbus   (**518**)

(Des and litho Questa)

1992 (1 Dec). *500th Anniv of Discovery of America by Columbus. T* **517** *and similar horiz designs. Multicoloured. P* 14.
1219 1 r. Type **517** 30 10
1220 11 r. Columbus landing in New World .. 80 90
1221 13 r. Wreck of *Santa Maria* .. .. 90 1·00
1222 15 r. Columbus reporting to Queen Isabella and King Ferdinand .. .. 1·00 1·10
1219/22 .. .. *Set of* 4 2·75 2·75
MS1223 155×95 mm. Nos. 1219/22 .. .. 2·75 3·25

1992 (1 Dec). *No.* 684 *surch with T* **518**.
1224 **255** 2 r. on 10 c. multicoloured 50 50

519 Ven. Sumedhankara Thero and Dagoba   **520** University Logo, Students and Building

(Des S. Silva. Litho Security Printers (M), Malaysia)

1992 (10 Dec). *Birth Centenary of Ven. Dambagasare Sumedhankara Nayake Thero. P* 12.
1225 **519** 1 r. multicoloured 20 20

(Des W. Rohana. Litho Security Printers (M), Malaysia)

1992 (22 Dec). *50th Anniv of University Education in Sri Lanka (1st issue). P* 12.
1226 **520** 1 r. multicoloured 20 20

521 University of Colombo Building and Logo

522 College Building and Crest

(Des W. Rohana. Litho Secura, Singapore)

1993 (23 Mar). *50th Anniv of University Education in Sri Lanka (2nd issue). P* 12½.
1227 **521** 1 r. multicoloured 20 20

(Des W. Rohana. Litho Secura, Singapore)

1993 (7 Apr). *Centenary of Zahira College, Colombo. P* 12½.
1228 **522** 1 r. multicoloured 30 30

523 Magandiya being presented to Buddha

524 Girl Guide, Badge and Camp

(Des S. Silva. Litho Security Printers (M), Malaysia)

1993 (30 Apr). *Vesak Festival. Verses from the* Dhammapada. *T* **523** *and similar vert designs. Multicoloured. P* 12.
1229 75 c. Type **523** 10 10
1230 1 r. Kisa Gotami carrying her dead baby 10 10
1231 3 r. Patachara and her dying family . . 25 30
1232 10 r. Angulimala praying 60 75
1229/32 . . . . *Set of* 4 90 1·10
MS1233 180×101 mm. Nos. 1229/32. P 12×12½ 90 1·60

(Des W. Rohana. Litho Security Printers (M), Malaysia)

1993 (10 May). *75th Anniv of Sri Lanka Girl Guides Association. T* **524** *and simlar vert design. Multicoloured. P* 12.
1234 1 r. Type **524** 25 10
1235 5 r. Girl Guide activities 75 90

525 Ven. Yagirala Pagnananda Maha Nayaka Thero (scholar)

526 Family arriving at New Home

(Des S. Silva. Litho Leigh-Mardon Ltd, Melbourne)

1993 (22 May). *National Heroes. T* **525** *and similar vert designs. Multicoloured. P* 14.
1236 1 r. Type **525** 10 10
1237 1 r. Charles de Silva (politician) . . 10 10
1238 1 r. Wilmot A. Perera (politician) . . 10 10
1239 1 r. Abdul Caffoor (philanthropist) . . 10 10
1236/9 . . . . *Set of* 4 35 40

(Des R. de Silva. Litho Secura, Singapore)

1993 (23 June). *"Gam Udawa '93". P* 12½.
1240 **526** 1 r. multicoloured 40 20

527 Consumer Movement Flag and Logo

528 Ashy-headed Laughing Thrush

(Des S. Perera. Litho Secura, Singapore)

1993 (3 July). *50th Anniv of Co-operative Consumer Movement* (1992). *P* 12½.
1241 **527** 1 r. multicoloured 40 20

(Des G. Ratnavira. Litho State Ptg Wks, Moscow)

1993 (14 July). *Birds (4th series). T* **528** *and similar horiz designs. Multicoloured. P* 12½×12.
1242 3 r. Type **528** 10 10
1243 4 r. Brown-capped Jungle Babbler . . 10 10
1244 5 r. Red-faced Malkoha 15 20
1245 10 r. Ceylon Grackle ("Ceylon Hill-Mynah") 25 30
1242/5 . . . . *Set of* 4 60 75
MS1246 151×121 mm. Nos. 1242/5 . . . . 1·75 2·50

529 Talawila Church

530 Rosette and Mail Delivery

(Des W. Rohana. Litho Secura, Singapore)

1993 (26 July). *150th Anniv of Talawila Church. P* 13.
1247 **529** 1 r. multicoloured 40 20

(Des W. Rohana. Litho Secura, Singapore)

1993 (22 Aug). *Sri Lanka Post Excellent Service Awards. P* 13.
1248 **530** 1 r. multicoloured 30 20

531 College and Flag

532 Presentation of Jesus in the Temple

(Des W. Rohana. Litho Secura, Singapore)

1993 (15 Nov). *Centenary of Musaeus College. P* 13.
1249 **531** 1 r. multicoloured 50 20

(Des S. Silva. Litho Pakistan Security Ptg Corporation, Karachi)

1993 (30 Nov). *Christmas. T* **532** *and similar horiz design. Multicoloured. P* 13½.
1250 1 r. Type **532** 10 10
1251 17 r. Boy Jesus with the Jewish teachers 70 1·00
MS1252 180×102 mm. Nos. 1250/1 . . . . 75 1·50

533 Healthy Youth and Drug Addict

(Des W. Rohana. Litho Pakistan Security Ptg Corp, Karachi)

1993 (16 Dec). *Youth and Health Campaign. P* 14.
1253 **533** 1 r. multicoloured 20 20

534 Maradana Technical College Building and Emblems

535 Trinity College Logo

(Des W. Rohana. Litho Secura, Singapore)

1993 (17 Dec). *Centenary of Technical Education. P* 13.
1254 **534** 1 r. multicoloured 30 20

(Des W. Rohana. Litho Secura, Singapore)

1994 (11 Feb). *Centenary of Trinity College, Kandy, Old Boys' Association. P* 13.
1255 **535** 1 r. multicoloured 20 20

536 College Flag

(Des W. Rohana. Litho Secura, Singapore)

1994 (10 Mar). *150th Anniv of St. Thomas' College, Matara. P* 13.
1256 **536** 1 r. lake-brown and pale new blue . . 20 20

537 Ven. Siyambalangamuwe Sri Gunaratana Thero

(Des S. Silva. Litho Secura, Singapore)

1994 (2 Apr). *Ven. Siyambalangamuwe Sri Gunaratana Thero (educationist) Commemoration. P* 12½.
1257 **537** 1 r. multicoloured 30 20

538 College Building and Arms

(Des S. Silva. Litho Secura Singapore)

1994 (4 Apr). *125th Anniv of St. Joseph's College, Trincomalee. P* 13.
1258 **538** 1 r. multicoloured 20 20

539 Man distributing Water

540 I.L.O. Monument, Geneva, Logo and Workers

(Des S. Silva. Litho Secura, Singapore)

1994 (7 May). *Vesak Festival. Dasa Paramita (Ten Virtues). T* **539** *and similar horiz designs. Multicoloured. P* 13.
1259 1 r. Type **539** 10 10
1260 2 r. Man and elephant 40 30
1261 5 r. Man surrounded by women 50 60
1262 17 r. Ruler with snake charmer . . . . 1·25 1·50
1259/62 . . . . *Set of* 4 2·00 2·25
MS1263 162×88 mm. Nos. 1259/62 . . . . 2·00 2·25

(Des W. Rohana. Litho Secura, Singapore)

1994 (12 May). *75th Anniv of International Labour Organization. P* 13.
1264 **540** 1 r. multicoloured 20 20

541 Mahakavindra Dhammaratana Thero (Buddhist theologian)

542 Conference Logo

(Des S. Silva. Litho Leigh-Mardon Ltd, Melbourne)

1994 (22 May). *National Heroes. T* **541** *and similar horiz designs. Multicoloured. P* 14.

1265	1 r. Type **541**	10	10
1266	1 r. Ranasinghe Premadasa (former President)	10	10
1267	1 r. Dr. Colvin de Silva (trade union leader)	10	10
1268	1 r. E. Periyathambipillai (Tamil poet)	10	10
1265/8	*Set of* 4	40	40

A 1 r. stamp for "Gam Udawa '94" was prepared for issue on 23 June 1994, but was not released due to the assassination of President Premadasa. Unused stamps exist from publicity examples circulated before the decision to cancel the issue was taken.

(Des R. de Silva. Litho Secura, Singapore)

1994 (9 July). *13th International Federation of Social Workers World Conference, Colombo. P* 13.

1269 **542**	8 r. multicoloured	50	70

543 Ven. Sri Somaratana Thero and Temple

544 Communication Technology and Logo

(Des S. Silva. Litho Secura, Singapore)

1994 (2 Aug). *10th Death Anniv of Ven. Sri Somaratana Thero (Buddhist religious leader). P* 13.

1270 **543**	1 r. multicoloured	30	20

(Des W. Rohana. Litho Secura, Singapore)

1994 (8 Sept). *"INFOTEL LANKA '94" International Computers and Telecommunications Exhibition. P* 13.

1271 **544**	10 r. multicoloured	40	60

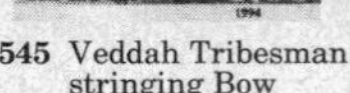

545 Veddah Tribesman stringing Bow

546 Luca Pacioli (pioneer), Logo and Equipment inside "500"

(Des R. de Silva. Litho Security Printers (M), Malaysia)

1994 (12 Sept). *Year of Indigenous People* (1993). *T* **545** *and similar vert design. Multicoloured. P* 12.

1272	1 r. Type **545**	20	10
1273	17 r. Veddah artist and rock paintings	1·25	1·25

(Des W. Rohana. Litho Secura, Singapore)

1994 (11 Oct). *500th Anniv of Accountancy. P* 13.

1274 **546**	1 r. multicoloured	30	20

547 Society Emblem

548 Airliner, I.C.A.O. Logo and Globe

(Des P. Miththapala. Litho Secura, Singapore)

1994 (24 Nov). *Centenary of Wildlife and Nature Society of Sri Lanka. T* **547** *and similar horiz designs. P* 13.

1275	1 r. bronze-green and black	10	10
1276	2 r. multicoloured	25	20
1277	10 r. multicoloured	75	80
1278	17 r. multicoloured	1·25	1·50
1275/8	*Set of* 4	2·00	2·25
MS1279	130×96 mm. Nos. 1275/8	2·00	2·25

Designs:—2 r. Horned Lizard; 10 r. Giant Squirrel; 17 r. Sloth Bear.

(Des W. Rohana. Litho Secura, Singapore)

1994 (7 Dec). *50th Anniv of International Civil Aviation Organization. P* 13.

1280 **548**	10 r. multicoloured	70	75

NEW INFORMATION

The editor is always interested to correspond with people who have new information that will improve or correct the Catalogue.

549 Christmas Crib

550 Map of Sri Lanka and Aspects of Science

(Des S. Silva. Litho Secura, Singapore)

1994 (8 Dec). *Christmas. T* **549** *and similar horiz design. Multicoloured. P* 13.

1281	1 r. Type **549**	10	10
1282	17 r. St. Joseph's carpentry workshop, Nazareth	55	75
MS1283	145×81 mm. Nos. 1281/2	80	1·25

(Des D. Gunasekera. Litho Secura, Singapore)

1994 (19 Dec). *50th Anniv of Sri Lankan Association for the Advancement of Science. P* 13.

1284 **550**	1 r. multicoloured	30	20

551 College Building and Arms

552 *Dendrobium maccarthiae*

(Des P. Nimal de Silva. Litho Secura, Singapore)

1994 (24 Dec). *Centenary of Richmond College Old Boys' Association. P* 13

1285 **551**	1 r. black, carmine-vermilion & violet-bl	20	20

(Des P. Miththapala. Litho Secura, Singapore)

1994 (27 Dec). *60th Anniv of Orchid Circle of Ceylon. T* **552** *and similar vert designs. Multicoloured. P* 13.

1286	50 c. Type **552**	10	10
1287	1 r. *Cottonia peduncularis*	10	10
1288	5 r. *Bulbophyllum wightii*	25	35
1289	17 r. *Habenaria crinifera*	65	85
1286/9	*Set of* 4	95	1·25
MS1290	127×95 mm. Nos. 1286/9	1·50	2·00

553 Father Joseph Vaz and Pope John Paul II

554 Blue Water Lily (*Nymphaea stellata*)

(Des S. Silva. Litho Japanese Govt Ptg Bureau, Tokyo)

1995 (20 Jan). *Papal Visit and Beatification of Father Joseph Vaz. P* 13.

1291 **553**	1 r. multicoloured	60	30

(Des S. Silva. Litho Leigh-Mardon Ltd, Melbourne)

1995 (22 Feb). *P* 14½×14.

1292 **554**	1 r. multicoloured	10	10

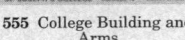

555 College Building and Arms

556 Sirimavo Bandaranaike and National Flag

(Des W. Rohana. Litho Secura, Singapore)

1995 (2 Mar). *Centenary of St. Joseph's College, Colombo. P* 13.

1293 **555**	1 r. multicoloured	10	10

(Des W. Rohana. Litho Security Printers (M), Malaysia)

1995 (17 Apr). *Election of Sirimavo Bandaranaike as Prime Minister. P* 12½×12.

1294 **556**	2 r. multicoloured	20	20

557 Man offering Water to Crew of Outrigger Canoe

558 14th-century Map of Sri Lanka and Society Arms

(Des S. Silva. Litho Security Printers (M), Malaysia)

1995 (29 Apr). *Vesak Festival. Dasa Paramita (ten virtues). T* **557** *and similar vert designs. Multicoloured. P* 12×12½.

1295	1 r. Type **557**	10	10
1296	2 r. Catching falling man	10	15
1297	10 r. Teacher with students	35	50
1298	17 r. Stopping man digging	65	80
1295/8	*Set of* 4	1·10	1·40
MS1299	170×90 mm. Nos. 1295/8. P 12½	1·40	2·00

(Litho Secura, Singapore)

1995 (17 May). *150th Anniv of Royal Asiatic Society of Sri Lanka. P* 12½.

1300 **558**	1 r. multicoloured	30	20

559 Abdul Cader

560 College Building

(Des S. Silva. Litho Bank Note Corporation of America, New York)

1995 (3 June). *120th Birth Anniv of Abdul Cader (lawyer). P* 11.

1301 **559**	2 r. multicoloured	15	15

(Des A. Hopman. Litho Security Printers (M), Malaysia)

1995 (21 June). *Centenary of St. Aloysius's College, Galle. P* 12½×12.

1302 **560**	2 r. multicoloured	15	15

561 Tikiri Ilangaratna

562 Lamps and Schools Flag

(Des S. Silva. Litho Secura, Singapore)

1995 (7 July). *Tikiri Bandara Ilangaratna (politician and author) Commemoration. P* 12½×13.

1303 **561**	2 r. multicoloured	15	15

(Des P. Gunasinghe. Litho Secura, Singapore)

1995 (3 Aug). *Centenary of Dhamma Schools Movement. P* 12½.

1304 **562**	2 r. multicoloured	15	15

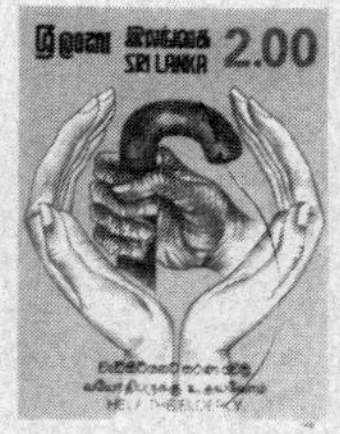

563 G.P.O. Building

564 Young Hands surrounding Old Hand

(Des S. Silva. Litho Pakistan Security Ptg Corp, Karachi)

1995 (22 Aug). *Centenary of General Post Office, Colombo. P* 13½.

1305 **563**	1 r. multicoloured	10	10

(Des S. Purnajith. Litho Enschedé)

1995 (1 Oct). *International Day for the Elderly. P* 14×13½.
1306 **564** 2 r. multicoloured 10 10

565 Sri Lankan Parliament Building and C.P.A. Logo

566 Anniversary Emblem and Map of Sri Lanka

(Des W. Rohana. Litho Pakistan Security Ptg Corp, Karachi)

1995 (8 Oct). *41st Commonwealth Parliamentary Conference, Colombo. P* 13½.
1307 **565** 2 r. multicoloured 10 10

(Des S. Purnajith. Litho Pakistan Ptg Corp, Karachi)

1995 (24 Oct). *50th Anniv of United Nations. P* 13½.
1308 **566** 2 r. multicoloured 10 10

567 Money falling into Globe Money Box

568 Diocesan Arms of Colombo and Kurunegala

(Des S. Purnajith. Litho Pakistan Ptg Corp, Karachi)

1995 (31 Oct). *71st Anniv of World Thrift Day and 110th Anniv of National Savings Bank. P* 13½.
1309 **567** 2 r. multicoloured 10 10

(Des S. Purnajith. Litho Secura, Singapore)

1995 (30 Nov). *Christmas. 150th Anniv of Anglican Diocese of Colombo. T* **568** *and similar horiz design. Multicoloured. P* 13.
1310 2 r. Type **568** 10 10
1311 20 r. Nativity scene and hands surrounding map 70 85
MS1312 150×90 mm. Nos. 1310/11 .. .. 70 85

569 Flags of Member Countries

570 School Emblem

(Des S. Purnajith. Litho Secura, Singapore)

1995 (8 Dec). *10th Anniv of South Asian Association for Regional Co-operation. P* 12½×13.
1313 **569** 2 r. multicoloured 10 10

(Des S. Purnajith. Litho Secura, Singapore)

1996 (17 Jan). *175th Anniv of Vincent Girls' High School, Batticaloa. P* 12½×13.
1314 **570** 2 r. multicoloured 10 10

571 Little Basses Lighthouse

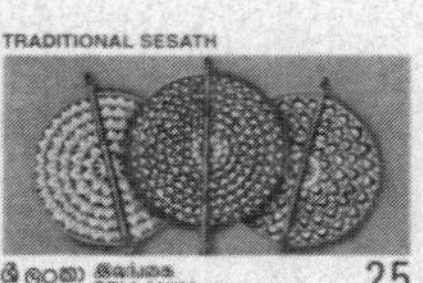

572 Traditional Sesath (umbrellas)

(Des S. Purnajith. Litho State Ptg Wks, Moscow)

1996 (22 Jan)–**97**. *Lighthouses. T* **571** *and similar vert designs. Multicoloured. P* 12.
1315 50 c. Type **571** 10 10
1316 75 c. Great Basses 10 10
1317 2 r. Devinuwara 10 10
1317*a* 2 r. 50, As 2 r. (12.2.97) 10 10
1318 20 r. Galle 50 55
1315/18 .. .. *Set of* 5 60 65
MS1319 151×91 mm. Nos. 1315/17 and 1318 .. 90 1·25

Nos. 1315/18 were printed in sheets of 50. During 1997 a printing of the 2 r. value appeared in sheets of 36.

Special packs for the S.A.A.R.C. "Philex '96" stamp exhibition at Colombo contained the strip of stamps from No. **MS**1319 with the sheet margins removed.

(Des P. Gunasinghe. Litho State Ptg Wks, Moscow)

1996 (13 Mar). *Traditional Handicrafts. T* **572** *and similar horiz designs. Multicoloured. P* 12.
1320 25 c. Type **572** 10 10
1321 8 r. 50, Pottery 20 25
1322 10 r. 50, Mats 25 30
1323 17 r. Lace 45 50
1320/3 .. .. *Set of* 4 1·00 1·10
MS1324 150×90 mm. Nos. 1320/3 .. .. 1·00 1·10

573 School Emblem and Trees

574 Upaka and Capa

(Des S. Purnajith. Litho Security Printers (M), Malaysia)

1996 (21 Mar). *Centenary of Chundikuli Girls' College, Jaffna. P* 12×12½.
1325 **573** 2 r. multicoloured 10 10

(Des S. Silva. Litho Security Printers (M), Malaysia)

1996 (3 Apr). *Vesak Festival. T* **574** *and similar vert designs. Multicoloured. P* 12.
1326 1 r. Type **574** 10 10
1327 2 r. Dantika and elephant 10 10
1328 5 r. Subha removing her eye 15 20
1329 10 r. Punna and the Brahmin 25 30
1326/9 .. .. *Set of* 4 60 70
MS1330 170×90 mm. Nos. 1326/9. P 12×12½ 60 65

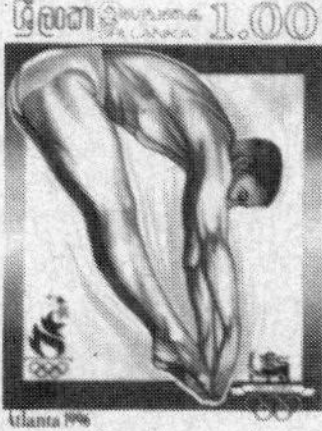

575 Diving

576 Bowler

(Des S. Purnajith. Litho Enschedé)

1996 (22 July). *Olympic Games, Atlanta. T* **575** *and similar multicoloured designs. P* 14×13½ *(vert) or* 13½×14 *(horiz).*
1331 1 r. Type **575** 10 10
1332 2 r. Volleyball 20 10
1333 5 r. Rifle shooting *(horiz)* 25 25
1334 17 r. Running *(horiz)* 55 75
1331/4 .. .. *Set of* 4 1·00 1·10

(Des S. Purnajith. Litho Enschedé)

1996 (18 Aug). *Sri Lanka's Victory in World Cup Cricket Tournament. T* **576** *and similar triangular designs. Multicoloured. P* 13½.
1335 2 r. Type **576** 25 15
1336 10 r. 50, Wicket-keeper 55 60
1337 17 r. Batsman .. .. .. 90 1·10
1338 20 r. World Cup Trophy .. .. 1·10 1·25
1335/8 .. .. *Set of* 4 2·50 2·75
MS1339 150×90 mm. Nos. 1335/8 .. .. 2·50 2·75

577 Main Building, Jaffna Central College

578 Globe in Flames and White Dove

(Des S. Purnajith. Litho Pakistan Security Printing Corp, Karachi)

1996 (7 Sept). *180th Anniv of Jaffna Central College. P* 13½×13.
1340 **577** 2 r. multicoloured 10 10
a. Black ("SRI LANKA", upper and lower panels, etc) omitted .. 60·00

(Des S. Herath. Litho Pakistan Security Ptg Corp, Karachi)

1996 (4 Nov). *50th Anniv of U.N.E.S.C.O. P* 13½.
1341 **578** 2 r. multicoloured 10 10

579 Jesus washing the Disciples' Feet

580 Cupped Hands holding Child

(Litho Oriental Press, Bahrain)

1996 (2 Dec). *Christmas. T* **597** *and similar vert design showing murals by David Paynter from Trinity College Chapel, Kandy. Multicoloured. P* 13½×13.
1342 2 r. Type **579** 10 10
1343 17 r. Parable of the Good Samaritan .. 45 50
MS1344 150×90 mm. Nos. 1342/4 .. .. 55 60

(Des P. Gunasinghe. Litho Pakistan Security Ptg Corp, Karachi)

1996 (12 Dec). *50th Anniv of U.N.I.C.E.F. P* 13×13½.
1345 **580** 5 r. multicoloured 15 20

581 Swami Vivekananda and Globe

(Des S. Silva. Litho Oriental Press, Bahrain)

1997 (15 Jan). *Centenary of Swami Vivekananda's Visit to Sri Lanka. P* 13½×13.
1346 **581** 2 r. 50, multicoloured 10 10

2.50 (582) 2.50 (583) 2.50 (584) 2.50 (585)

1997 (12 Feb). *No.* 1317 *surch with T* **582/5**.
1347 **582** 2 r. 50 on 2 r. multicoloured .. 10 10
1348 **583** 2 r. 50 on 2 r. multicoloured .. 10 10
1349 **584** 2 r. 50 on 2 r. multicoloured .. 10 10
1350 **585** 2 r. 50 on 2 r. multicoloured .. 10 10
1347/50 .. .. *Set of* 4 25 30

Nos. 1347/50 occur in separate sheets. Nos. 1347 and 1349 were surcharged by the State Ptg Corporation and Nos. 1348 and 1350 by Lakmini Printers Ltd.

586 Venerable Welivitiye Sorata Thero (scholar)

11.00 (587) 11.00 (588)

(Des S. Silva. Litho Oriental Press, Bahrain)

1997 (4 Apr). *National Heroes. T* **586** *and similar vert designs. Multicoloured. P* 13½×13.
1351 2 r. Type **586** 10 10
1352 2 r. Mahagama Sekera (writer and artist) 10 10
a. Asterisk ovpt double .. ..
b. Asterisk ovpt omitted .. ..
1353 2 r. Dr. S. A. Wickremasinghe (physician) 10 10
1354 2 r. Lt.-Gen. Denzil Kobbekaduwa .. 10 10
1351/4 .. .. *Set of* 4 20 25

No. 1352 was issued with the inscriptions at the top right and bottom left corners obliterated by rows of asterisks. A small quantity without the overprint is known to have been sold at one post office.

See also Nos. 1373/6.

1997 (6 May). *No.* 1322 *surch with T* **587/8** *by State Ptg Corporation.*

1355	**583**	11 r. on 10 r. 50, multicoloured ..	30	35
1356	**584**	11 r. on 10 r. 50, multicoloured ..	30	35

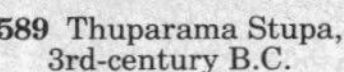

589 Thuparama Stupa, 3rd-century B.C.

590 Don Johannes Kumarage

(Des P. Gunasinghe. Litho Security Printers (M), Malaysia)

1997 (7 May). *Vesak Festival. Anauradhapura Sites. T* **589** *and similar vert designs. Multicoloured.* A. *P* 12. B. *P* 12×12½.

		A		B	
1357	1 r. Type **589**	10	10	10	10
1358	2 r. 50, Ruwanvalisaya stupa, 161–137 B.C. ..		†	10	10
1359	3 r. Abhayagiri Dagaba, 103–102 B.C	10	10	10	10
1360	17 r. Jethavana Dagaba, 276–303 A.D.	45	50		†
1357/60	(*mixed perfs*) *Set of* 4	60	70		
MS1361	170×90 mm. Nos. 1357/60		†	60	70

(Des W. Rohana. Litho Pakistan Security Ptg Corp, Karachi)

1997 (10 June). *Birth Centenary of D. J. Kumarage (Buddhist teacher). P* 13×13½.

1362 **590** 2 r. 50, multicoloured 10 10

591 *Munronia pinnata*

592 Tourist Board Logo, Airliner and Holiday Resorts

(Des D. Gunatilake. Litho Pakistan Security Ptg Corp, Karachi)

1997 (17 June). *Medicinal Herbs. T* **591** *and similar vert design. Multicoloured. P* 13½×14.

1363	2 r. 50, Type **591**	10	10
1364	14 r. *Rauwolfia serpentina*	35	40

(Des S. Kalupahana. Litho Security Printers (M), Malaysia)

1997 (11 Sept). *Visit Sri Lanka. P* 12.

1365 **592** 20 r. multicoloured 50 55

1.00

(**593**)

594 Lyre Head Lizard

1997 (22 Sept). *No.* 1321 *surch with T* **593** *by State Ptg Corporation.*

1366 1 r. on 8 r. 50, Pottery 20 25

(Des V. Perera. Litho Security Printers (M), Malaysia)

1997 (18 Oct). *Reptiles. T* **594** *and similar horiz designs. Multicoloured. P* 12½×12 (20 *r.*) *or* 12 (*others*).

1367	2 r. 50, Type **594**	10	10
1368	5 r. Boie's Roughside (snake)	15	20
1369	17 r. Common Lanka Skink	45	50
1370	20 r. Great Forest Gecko	50	55
1367/70	.. .. *Set of* 4	1·25	1·40
MS1371	170×90 mm. Nos. 1367/70. P 12 ..	1·25	1·40

595 St. Servatius' College, Matara

596 The Nativity

(Des P. Gunasinghe. Litho Security Printers (M), Malaysia)

1997 (1 Nov). *Centenary of St. Servatius' College, Matara. P* 12½×12.

1372	**595**	2 r. 50, multicoloured	10	10
		a. Perf 12×12½	10	10

(Des S. Silva. Litho Secura, Singapore)

1997 (11 Nov). *National Heroes (2nd series). Vert designs as T* **586**. *Multicoloured. P* 12½×13.

1373	2 r. 50, Sri Indasara Nayake Thero (Buddhist leader)	10	10
	a. Block of 4. Nos. 1373/6	25	
1374	2 r. 50, Abdul Aziz (trade union leader)	10	10
1375	2 r. 50, Prof. Subramaniam Vithiananthan	10	10
1376	2 r. 50, Vivienne Goonewardene (politician)	10	10
1373/6	.. .. *Set of* 4	25	30

Nos. 1373/6 were printed together, *se-tenant*, in blocks of four throughout the sheet.

(Des S. Silva. Litho Security Printers (M), Malaysia)

1997 (20 Nov). *Christmas. T* **596** *and similar vert design. Multicoloured. P* 12½.

1377	2 r. 50, Type **596**	10	70
1378	20 r. Visit of the Three Kings	50	55
MS1379	170×90 mm. Nos. 1377/8	60	65

597 Young Men's Buddhist Association Building, Colombo

(Des P. Ediriweera. Litho Security Printers (M), Malaysia)

1998 (8 Jan). *Centenary of Young Men's Buddhist Association, Colombo. P* 12½×13.

1380 **597** 2 r. 50, multicoloured 10 10

598 Sri Jayawardenapura Vidyalaya School

599 Children and Mathematical Symbols

(Des P. Gunasinghe. Litho Security Printers (M), Malaysia)

1998 (28 Jan). *175th Anniv of Sri Jayawardenapura Vidyalaya School, Kotte. P* 12½.

1381 **598** 2 r. 50, multicoloured 10 10

(Des P. Gunasinghe (No. 1383), R. Mawilmada (others). Litho Pakistan Security Ptg Corp (No. 1383), Secura, Singapore (others))

1998 (4 Feb). *50th Anniv of Independence. T* **599** *and similar horiz designs. Multicoloured. P* 13½ (*No.* 1383) *or* 12½ (*others*).

1382	2 r. Type **599**	10	10
1383	2 r. 50, Flag and 1949 4 c. Independence stamp (38×28 *mm*)	10	10
1384	2 r. 50, People with technological and industrial symbols	10	10
1385	5 r. Dancers with arts and music symbols	15	20
1386	10 r. Women with cultural and historical symbols	25	30
1382/6	.. .. *Set of* 5	60	75

600 Scouts raising Flag and Jamboree Logo

(Des W. Rohana. Litho Pakistan Security Ptg Corp, Karachi)

1998 (18 Feb). *5th National Scout Jamboree, Kandy. T* **600** *and similar vert design. Multicoloured. P* 13½.

1387	2 r. 50, Type **600**	10	10
1388	17 r. Scout saluting and Jamboree emblem	45	50

STAMP BOOKLETS

1905 (Oct). *Black on grey (No. SB1) or black on buff (No. SB1a) covers. Stapled.*

SB1 1 r. 21, booklet containing twenty-four 5 c. (No. 280) in blocks of 12 . .

SB1a 1 r. 45, booklet containing twenty-four 6 c. (No. 281) in blocks of 6 . .

1908. *Black on grey cover. Advertisement on back cover. Stapled.*

SB2 1 r. 20, booklet containing twenty-four 5 c. (No. 289) in blocks of 12 . .

1912. *Black on grey cover. Advertisement on back cover. Stapled.*

SB2a 1 r. 20, booklet containing twenty-four 5 c. (No. 304) in blocks of 12 . .

1919. *Black on orange covers. Telegraph details on back cover. Stapled.*

SB3 1 r. 44, booklet containing twenty-four 6 c. (No. 311) in blocks of 6 . .
a. Black on grey cover. Advertisement on back cover . .

SB4 1 r. 44, booklet containing twenty-four 3 c. and twelve 6 c. (Nos. 310/11) in blocks of 6 . .
a. Advertisement on back cover . .

1922. *Black on green covers. "Fiat" advertisement on back cover. Stapled.*

SB5 1 r. 44, booklet containing twenty-four 6 c. (No. 356) in blocks of 6 . .

SB6 1 r. 46, booklet containing twenty-four 3 c. and twelve 6 c. (Nos. 355/6) in blocks of 6 . .
a. Black on orange cover. "Colombo Jewelry Store" advertisement on back cover . .

1926. *Black on green covers. Kennedy & Co. (No. SB7) or Fiat (No. SB8) advertisements on back cover. Stapled.*

SB7 2 r. 06, booklet containing twelve 3 c., 5 c. on 6 c. and 9 c. (Nos. 355, 362 and 357) in blocks of 6

SB8 2 r. 16, booklet containing twenty-four 9 c. (No. 357) in blocks of 6 . .

1932. *Black on green covers. Stapled.*

SB9 1 r. 80, booklet containing thirty 6 c. (No. 356) in blocks of 6 and pane of three airmail labels £900

SB10 2 r. 70, booklet containing thirty 9 c. (No. 357) in blocks of 6 and pane of three airmail labels

1935 (May). *Silver Jubilee of King George V. Black on light blue (No. SB11) or light green (No. SB12) covers. Stapled.*

SB11 1 r. 80, booklet containing thirty 6 c. (No. 379) in blocks of 6 . . £900

SB12 2 r. 70, booklet containing thirty 9 c. (No. 380) in blocks of 6 . . £1100

1935 (Dec)–**36.** *Black on blue (No. SB13) or green (No. SB14) covers. Stapled.*

SB13 1 r. 80, booklet containing thirty 6 c. (No. 370) in blocks of 6 and pane of four airmail labels
a. Stamps in blocks of 10 . . £600

SB14 2 r. 70, booklet containing thirty 9 c. (No. 371) in blocks of 6 and pane of four airmail labels £700
a. Stamps in blocks of 10 (1936) . . £700

1937 (Apr–June). *Coronation of King George VI. Black on blue (No. SB15) or olive-green (No. SB16) covers. Stapled.*

SB15 1 r. 80, booklet containing thirty 6 c. (No. 383) in blocks of 10 and pane of four airmail labels (June) . . £750

SB16 2 r. 70, booklet containing thirty 9 c. (No. 384) in blocks of 10 and pane of four airmail labels £800

1938. *Black on blue (No. SB17) or pale green (No. SB18) covers. Stapled.*

SB17 1 r. 80, booklet containing thirty 6 c. (No. 388) in blocks of 10 and pane of four airmail labels

SB18 3 r. booklet containing fifteen 20 c. (No. 391) in blocks of 5 or 10 and pane of four airmail labels . .

1941. *Black on pink cover, with contents amended in manuscript. Stapled.*

SB19 1 r. 80, booklet containing sixty 3 c. on 6 c. (No. 398) in blocks of 10 . .
a. Black on blue cover . .

1951 (5 Dec). *Black on buff cover. Stitched.*

SB20 1 r. booklet containing twenty 5 c. (No. 414) in blocks of four and pane of airmail labels . . 12·00
a. Containing two blocks of ten 5 c. stamps and no airmail labels . .

1952 (21 Jan). *Black on green cover. Stitched.*

SB21 6 r. booklet containing eight 75 c. (No. 417) in blocks of 4 and two panes of four airmail labels . . 18·00

OFFICIAL STAMPS

1869. *Issues of 1867–68 overprinted "SERVICE" in block letters.*

Although these stamps were prepared for use and sent out to the colony, they were never issued.

Prices:

Narrow "SERVICE"		Wide "SERVICE"	
No. 64*b*, 2d.	55·00	No. 61, 1d.	50·00
67, 6d.	60·00	62, 3d.	90·00
68, 8d.	70·00		
71, 1s.	£100		
72, 2s.	95·00		
72, 2s. *imp*	£650		

Until 1 October 1895 all Official mail was carried free. After that date postage was paid on Official letters to the general public, on certain interdepartmental mail and on all packets over 1lb in weight. Nos. O1/17 were provided for ths purpose.

On

Service

(O 3)

1895. *Optd with Type* O 3 *by the Govt Printer, Colombo.*

No.	Type	Description	Unused	Used
O1	**9**	2 c. green (No. 147)	6·50	45
O2	**39**	3 c. terracotta and blue-green (No. 245)	10·00	55
O3	**28**	5 c. dull purple (No. 195)	3·00	30
O4	**29**	15 c. sage-green (No. 196)	12·00	50
O5		25 c. yellow-brown (No. 198)	10·00	1·00
O6		30 c. bright mauve and chestnut (No. 247)	13·00	50
O7	**30**	1 r. 12, dull rose (*wmk sideways*) (No. 201)	65·00	50·00
		a. Opt double, one albino	£180	
		b. Wmk upright	80·00	70·00
O1/7		*Set of* 7	£110	50·00

1899 (June)–**1900.** *Nos. 256/7 and 261/2 optd with Type* O **3.**

No.	Type	Description	Unused	Used
O 8	**9**	2 c. pale orange-brown (3.00)	6·00	60
O 9	**39**	3 c. deep green (9.00)	8·00	1·50
O10	**29**	15 c. blue (9.00)	16·00	60
O11	**39**	75 c. black and red-brown (R.)	5·50	4·75
O8/11		*Set of* 4	32·00	6·75

1903 (26 Nov)–**04.** *Nos. 265/6, 268 and 271/3 optd with Type* O **3.**

No.	Type	Description	Unused	Used
O12	**44**	2 c. red-brown (4.1.04)	9·50	85
O13	**45**	3 c. green	6·00	2·00
O14	**46**	5 c. dull purple	14·00	1·25
O15	**48**	15 c. blue	24·00	2·50
O16		25 c. bistre (15.7.04)	20·00	18·00
O17		30 c. dull violet and green (14.3.04)	8·50	1·50
O12/17		*Set of* 6	75·00	24·00

Stamps overprinted "On Service" were withdrawn on 1 October 1904.

POSTAL FISCALS

1952 (1 Dec). *As T* **72** *but inscr "REVENUE" at sides. Chalk-surfaced paper.*

F1 10 r. dull green and yellow-orange . . . . 60·00 28·00

This revenue stamp was on sale for postal use from 1 December 1952, until 14 March 1954.

F 1 Republic Crest

(Recess Harrison)

1979 (28 May)–**83.** *As Type* F **1**, *but with additional Sinhala and Tamil inscrs on either side of crest. W* **4** *of Maldive Islands. P* 13×12.

No.	Description	Unused	Used
F2	20 r. blackish green	4·75	2·75
F3	50 r. deep slate-violet	11·00	7·00
F4	100 r. deep carmine-red (14.10.83)	20·00	20·00
F2/4	*Set of* 3	32·00	27·00

The above, together with 500 and 1000 r. values, were originally released for fiscal purposes on 24 June 1974. The dates quoted are those on which they were validated for postal use. All three were withdrawn on 6 August 1984.

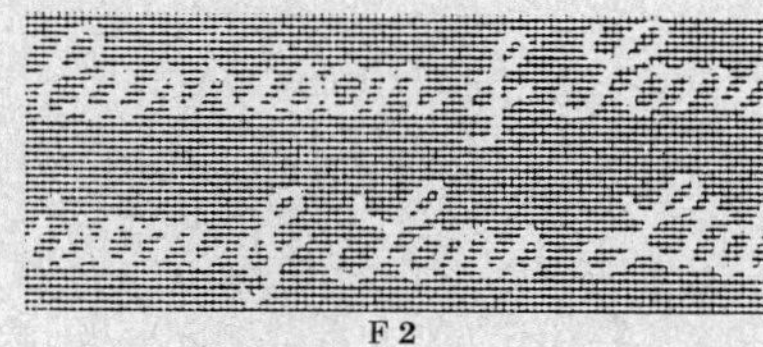

F 2

(Litho Harrison)

1984 (15 Aug). *Wmk* F **2**. *P* 14½×14.

No.	Type	Description	Unused	Used
F5	F 1	50 r. orange	24·00	11·00
F6		100 r. dull chocolate	40·00	40·00

A 500 r. value also exists, but was not valid for postal purposes.

(Recess Harrison)

1984 (21 Sept). *Wmk* F **2**. *P* 14½×14.

No.	Type	Description	Unused	Used
F7	F 1	50 r. orange-vermilion	1·25	1·40
F8		100 r. deep reddish purple	2·50	2·75

Stamps in this series with face values of 500 or 1000 r. were not valid for postal purposes.

Sudan

ANGLO-EGYPTIAN CONDOMINIUM

An Egyptian post office was opened at Suakin in 1867 and the stamps of Egypt, including postage dues and the official (No. O64), were used in the Sudan until replaced by the overprinted "SOUDAN" issue of 1897.

Cancellations have been identified from eleven post offices, using the following postmark types:

A B

C

D

E

F

G

H

I

J

K

L

BERBER (*spelt* BARBAR). *Open* 1 October 1873 *to* 20 May 1884. *Postmark type* G.
DABROUSSA. *Open* 1889? *onwards. Postmark as type* J *but with* 11 *bars in arcs.*
DONGOLA. *Open* 1 October 1873 *to* 13 June 1885 *and* 1896 *onwards. Postmark types* F, G, K, L.
GEDAREF. *Open* August 1878 *to* April 1884. *Postmark type* H.
KASSALA. *Open* 15 May 1875 *to* 30 July 1885. *Postmark type* G.
KHARTOUM. *Open* 1 October 1873 *to* 14 December 1885. *Postmark types* E (*spelt* KARTUM), G (*spelt* HARTUM), I (*with or without line of Arabic above date*).
KORTI. *Open* December 1873 *to* 14 December 1885 *and* 1897. *Postmark type* K.
SUAKIN. *Open* November 1867 *onwards. Postmark types* A, B, C (*spelt* SUAKIM), D (*spelt* SUAKIM *and also with year replaced by concentric arcs*), I (*spelt* SOUAKIN), J (*spelt* SAWAKIN, *number of bars differs*).
TANI. *Open* 1885. *Postmark type* K.
TOKAR. *Open* 1891 *onwards. Postmark type* J (7 *bars in arcs*).
WADI HALFA. *Open* 1 October 1873 *onwards. Postmark types* F (*spelt* WADI HALFE), G (*spelt* WADI HALFE), I, J (*number of bars differs*).
WADI HALFA CAMP. *Open* 1896 *onwards. Postmark type* I.

Official records also list post offices at the following locations, but no genuine postal markings from them have yet been reported: Chaka, Dara, Debeira, El Abiad, El Fasher, El Kalabat, Faras, Fashoda, Fazogl, Ishkeit, Kalkal, Karkok, Mesellemia, Sara, Sennar and Taoufikia (not to be confused with the town of the same name in Egypt.

M

The post office at Kassala was operated by Italy from 1894 until 1896, using stamps of Eritrea cancelled with postmark type M.

From the last years of the nineteenth century that part of Sudan lying south of the 5 degree North latitude line was administered by Uganda (the area to the east of the Nile) (until 1912) or by Belgium (the area to the west of the Nile, known as the Lado Enclave) (until 1910).

Stamps of Uganda or East Africa and Uganda were used at Gondokoro and Nimuli between 1901 and 1911, usually cancelled with circular date stamps or, probably in transit at Khartoum, by a lozenge-shaped grid of 18 × 17 dots.

Stamps of Belgian Congo were used from the Lado Enclave between 1897 and 1910, as were those of Uganda (1901–10) and Sudan (1902–10), although no local postmarks were supplied, examples being initially cancelled in manuscript.

Stamps of Sudan were used at Gambeila (Ethiopia) between 1910 and 10 June 1940 and from 22 March 1941 until 15 October 1956. Sudan stamps were also used at Sabderat (Eritrea) between March 1910 and 1940.

PRICES FOR STAMPS ON COVER TO 1945

Nos. 1/9	*from* × 20
Nos. 10/17	*from* × 6
Nos. 18/29	*from* × 5
Nos. 30/95	*from* × 2
Nos. D1/11	*from* × 30
Nos. O1/3	*from* × 10
Nos. O4/22	*from* × 15
Nos. A1/16	*from* × 6

(Currency. 10 milliemes = 1 piastre. 100 piastres = £1 Sudanese)

السودان
SOUDAN

(1)

1897 (1 Mar). *Nos.* 54*b*, 55*a*, 57/*a*, 58*a*, 59, 60, 62*a and* 63 *of Egypt optd as T* 1 *by Govt Ptg Wks, Bûlâq, Cairo.*

1 1 m. pale brown 1·50 2·00
a. Opt inverted £200
b. Opt omitted (in vert pair with normal) £900
c. Deep brown 1·50 2·25
3 2 m. green 1·25 1·75
a. Opt omitted (in vert pair with normal) £3000
4 3 m. orange-yellow 1·40 1·50
a. Opt omitted (in vert pair with normal) £3000
5 5 m. rose-carmine 2·00 70
a. Opt inverted £250
b. Opt omitted (in vert pair with normal) £900
6 1 p. ultramarine 7·00 2·00
7 2 p. orange-brown 50·00 13·00
8 5 p. slate 42·00 13·00
a. Opt double £2250
b. Opt omitted (in vert pair with normal) £3000
9 10 p. mauve 30·00 42·00
1/9 *Set of* 8 £120 65·00

Numerous forgeries exist including some which show the characteristics of the varieties mentioned below.

There are six varieties of the overprint on each value most of which can be supplied in vertical strips at double the catalogue price.

In some printings the large dot is omitted from the left-hand Arabic character on one stamp in the pane of 60.

Only two examples, one unused and the other used (in the Royal Collection), are known of No. 8a. In both instances one impression is partially albino.

PRINTERS. All stamps of Sudan were printed by De La Rue & Co, Ltd, London, *except where otherwise stated.*

2 Arab Postman

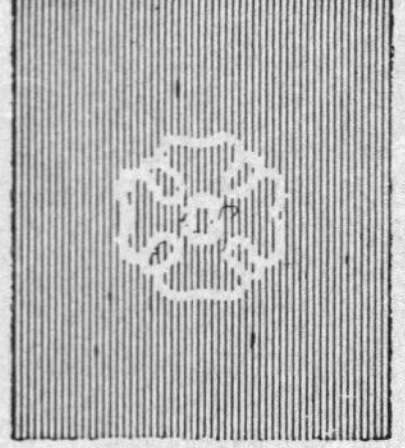

3

(Des E. A. Stanton. Typo)

1898 (1 Mar). *W* **3**. *P* 14.

10 2 1 m. brown and pink 40 1·25
11 2 m. green and brown 1·50 2·00
12 3 m. mauve and green 2·00 2·25
13 5 m. carmine and black 1·75 75
14 1 p. blue and brown 5·00 4·00
15 2 p. black and blue 22·00 7·50
16 5 p. brown and green 25·00 11·00
17 10 p. black and mauve 25·00 2·25
10/17 *Set of* 8 75·00 28·00

4

5 Milliemes

(5)

1902–21. *W* **4**. *Ordinary paper. P* 14.

18 2 1 m. brown and carmine (5.05) 1·00 10
19 2 m. green and brown (11.02) 1·75 10
20 3 m. mauve and green (7.03) 2·25 25
21 4 m. blue and bistre (20.1.07) 1·50 2·50
22 4 m. vermilion and brown (10.07) 1·50 75
23 5 m. scarlet and black (12.03) 2·00 10
24 1 p. blue and brown (12.03) 2·25 30
25 2 p. black and blue (2.08) 24·00 1·75
26 2 p. purple & orge-yellow (*chalk-surfaced paper*) (22.12.21) 3·75 9·00
27 5 p. brown and green (2.08) 22·00 30
a. Chalk-surfaced paper 28·00 3·25
28 10 p. black and mauve (2.11) 22·00 3·75
a. Chalk-surfaced paper 22·00 7·50
18/28 *Set of* 11 75·00 16·00

1903 (Sept). *No.* 16 *surch at Khartoum with T* **5**, *in blocks of* 30.

29 2 5 m. on 5 pi. brown and green 6·50 9·00
a. Surch inverted £250 £225

6

7

1921–23. *Chalk-surfaced paper. Typo. W* **4**. *P* 14.

30 6 1 m. black and orange (4.2.22) 80 3·25
31 2 m. yellow-orange and chocolate (1922) 9·00 11·00
a. Yellow and chocolate (1923) 11·00 10·00
32 3 m. mauve and green (25.1.22) 2·50 7·00
33 4 m. green and chocolate (21.3.22) 4·25 2·25
34 5 m. olive-brown and black (4.2.22) 1·75 10
35 10 m. carmine and black (1922) 1·75 10
36 15 m. bright blue and chestnut (14.12.21) 2·75 1·00
30/36 *Set of* 7 21·00 21·00

1927–41. *W* **7**. *Chalk-surfaced paper. P* 14.

37 6 1 m. black and orange 40 10
a. Ordinary paper (1941) 70 10
38 2 m. orange and chocolate 30 10
a. Ordinary paper (1941) 1·50 10
39 3 m. mauve and green 30 10
a. Ordinary paper (1941) 2·25 30
40 4 m. green and chocolate 30 10
a. Ordinary paper (1941) 2·25 30
aw. Wmk inverted 75·00
41 6 5 m. olive-brown and black 30 10
a. Ordinary paper (1941) 2·50 10
42 10 m. carmine and black 80 10
a. Ordinary paper (1941) 3·00 10
43 15 m. bright blue and chestnut 80 10
a. Ordinary paper (1941) 1·25 10
44 2 2 p. purple and orange-yellow 65 10
a. Ordinary paper (1941) 2·50 10
44*b* 3 p. red-brown and blue (1.1.40) 2·75 10
ba. Ordinary paper (1941) 12·00 10
44*c* 4 p. ultramarine and black (2.11.36) 3·50 10
45 5 p. chestnut and green 1·00 10
a. Ordinary paper (1941) 3·50 30
45*b* 6 p. greenish blue and black (2.11.36) 3·50 20
ba. Ordinary paper (1941) 20·00 1·25
45*c* 8 p. emerald and black (2.11.36) 5·50 2·25
ca. Ordinary paper (1941) 20·00 3·00
46 10 p. black and reddish purple 1·50 10
a. Ordinary paper. *Black and bright mauve* (1941) 8·00 70
46*b* 20 p. pale blue and blue (17.10.35) 2·00 10
ba. Ordinary paper (1941) 3·00 10
37/46*b* *Set of* 15 20·00 2·75

The ordinary paper of this issue is thick, smooth and opaque and was a wartime substitute for chalk-surfaced paper.

For similar stamps, but with different Arabic inscriptions, see Nos. 96/111.

AIR MAIL (8)   **AIR MAIL** (9)   **AIR** Extended foot to "R" (R.5/12)

1931 (15 Feb–Mar). *Air. Nos.* 41/2 *and* 44 *optd with T* **8** *or* **9** (2 *p.*).

47 6 5 m. olive-brown and black (Mar) 35 70
48 10 m. carmine and black 85 7·00
49 2 2 p. purple and orange-yellow 85 5·50
a. Extended foot to "R" 21·00
47/9 *Set of* 3 1·90 12·00

2½   2½

10 Statue of Gen. Gordon

AIR MAIL

٢½   ٢½

(11)

1931 (1 Sept)–**37.** *Air. Recess. W* **7** (*sideways**). *P* 14.

49*b* 10 3 m. green and sepia (1.1.33) 2·50 5·50
50 5 m. black and green 1·00 20
51 10 m. black and carmine 1·00 30
52 15 m. red-brown and sepia 40 10
aw. Wmk top of G to right
b. Perf 11½×12½ (1937) 4·50 10
53 2 p. black and orange 30 10
a. Perf 11½×12½ (1937) 4·50 15·00
53*b* 2½ p. magenta and blue (1.1.33) 3·50 10
c. Perf 11½×12½ (1936) 3·00 10
ca. Aniline magenta and blue 6·50 3·25
cx. Wmk reversed
cy. Wmk top of G to right reversed
54 3 p. black and grey 60 15
a. Perf 11½×12½ (1937) 85 35
55 3½ p. black and violet 1·50 80
a. Perf 11½×12½ (1937) 2·50 10·00
56 4½ p. red-brown and grey 10·00 15·00
57 5 p. black and ultramarine 1·00 30
a. Perf 11½×12½ (1937) 3·75 35
57*b* 7½ p. green and emerald (17.10.35) 9·00 4·50
by. Wmk top of G to right reversed
c. Perf 11½×12½ (1937) 4·00 9·00
57*d* 10 p. brown and greenish blue (17.10.35) 8·50 55
e. Perf 11½×12½ (1937) 4·00 17·00
ey. Wmk top of G to right reversed
49*b*/57*d* *Set of* 12 (*p* 14) 35·00 24·00
52b/7e *Set of* 8 (*p* 11½×12½) 24·00 45·00

*The normal sideways watermark shows the top of the G pointing left *as seen from the back of the stamp.*

1932 (18 July). *Air. No.* 44 *surch with T* **11**.

58 2 2½ p. on 2 p. purple and orange-yellow 1·40 3·50

12 Gen. Gordon (after C. Ouless)

13 Gordon Memorial College, Khartoum

14 Gordon Memorial Service, Khartoum (after R. C. Woodville)

1935 (1 Jan). *50th Death Anniv of General Gordon, Recess. W* **7**. *P* 14.

59 12 5 m. green 35 10
60 10 m. yellow-brown 85 25
61 13 m. ultramarine 85 8·00
62 15 m. scarlet 1·75 25

63 **13** 2 p. blue . . . . 1·25 20
64 5 p. orange-vermilion . . . . 1·25 40
65 10 p. purple . . . . 7·50 8·50
66 **14** 20 p. black . . . . 22·00 48·00
67 50 p. red-brown . . . . 75·00 90·00
59/67 . . *Set of* 9 £100 £140

7½ PIASTRES (15)

5 MILLIEMES (16)

1935. *Air. Nos.* 49*b*/51 *and* 56 *surch as T* **15**.
68 **10** 15 m. on 10 m. black and carmine (Apr) . . 40 10
a. Surch double . . £600 £700
69 2½ p. on 3 m. green and sepia (Apr) . . 85 5·50
a. Second arabic letter from left missing 65·00 £100
b. Small "½" . . 2·75 20·00
70 2½ p. on 5 m. black and green (Apr) . . 40 1·50
a. Second Arabic letter from left missing 35·00 55·00
b. Small "½" . . 1·75 8·00
c. Surch inverted . . £600 £700
d. Ditto with variety a. . . £2750
e. Ditto with variety b. . . £1100
71 3 p. on 4½ p. red-brown and grey (Apr) 1·75 12·00
72 7½ p. on 4½ p. red-brown and grey (Mar) 6·00 42·00
73 10 p. on 4½ p. red-brown and grey (Mar) 5·00 42·00
68/73 . . *Set of* 6 13·00 90·00

Nos. 69a and 70a occur in position 49 of the sheet of 50; the small "½" variety occurs in positions 17, 27, 32, 36, 41, 42 and 46.

The 15 m. on 10 m. surcharged in red and the 2½ p. on 3 m and 2½ p. on 5 m. in green are from proof sheets; the latter two items being known cancelled.

There were four proof sheets of the 7½ p. on 4½ p., two in red and two in black. The setting on these proof sheets showed three errors subsequently corrected before No. 72 was surcharged. Twelve positions showed an Arabic "⅓" instead of "½", one an English "¼" for "½" and another one of the Arabic letters inverted.

1938 (1 July). *Air. Nos.* 53c, 55, 57*b and* 57*d surch as T* **16**.
74 **10** 5 m. on 2½ p. mag & bl (*p* 11½×12½) 3·50 10
w. Wmk top of G to right
x. Wmk reversed
75 3 p. on 3½ p. black and violet (*p* 14) 35·00 48·00
a. Perf 11½×12½ . . £425 £550
76 3 p. on 7½ p, green and emerald (*p* 14) 7·00 6·50
ax. Wmk reversed
ay. Wmk top of G to right reversed 50·00
b. Perf 11½×12½ . . £425 £550
77 5 p. on 10 p. brown & greenish bl (*p* 14) 1·75 4·75
a. Perf 11½×12½ . . £425 £550
74/7 . . *Set of* 4 42·00 55·00

A 5 p. on 2½ p., perf 11½×12½, exists either mint or cancelled from a trial printing (*Price £350 unused*).

5 Mills. (17)

Normal ("Malime")

"Malmime" (Left-hand pane R. 5/1)

Short "mim" (Right-hand pane R. 3/1)

Broken "lam" (Right-hand pane R. 6/2)

5 M

Inserted "5" (Bottom right-hand pane R. 4/5)

1940 (25 Feb). *No.* 42 *surch with T* **17** *by McCorquodale (Sudan) Ltd, Khartoum.*
78 **6** 5 m. on 10 m. carmine and black . . 50 30
a. "Malmime" . . 45·00 50·00
b. Two dots omitted (Right-hand pane R. 8/6) . . 45·00 50·00
c. Short "mim" . . 45·00 50·00
d. Broken "lam" . . 45·00 50·00
e. Inserted "5" . . £130

4½ PIASTRES (18)

4½ Piastres (19)

1940–1. *Nos.* 41 *and* 45c *surch as T* **18** *or* **19** *at Khartoum.*
79 **6** 4½ p. on 5 m. olive-brown & blk (9.2.41) . . 48·00 3·00
80 **2** 4½ p. on 8 p. emerald and black (12.12.40) 35·00 8·00

20 Tuti Island, R. Nile, near Khartoum

21 Tuti Island, R. Nile near Khartoum

(Des Miss H. M. Hebbert. Litho Security Printing Press, Nasik, India)

1941 (25 Mar–10 Aug). *P* 14 × 13½ (*T* **20**) *or P* 13½ × 14 (*T* **21**).
81 **20** 1 m. slate and orange (10.8) . . 70 2·50
82 2 m. orange and chocolate (10.8) . . 70 2·50
83 3 m. mauve and green (10.8) . . 70 10
84 4 m. green and chocolate (10.8) . . 80 30
85 5 m. olive-brown and black (10.8) . . 30 10
86 10 m. carmine and black (10.8) . . 7·00 1·75
87 15 m. bright blue and chestnut . . 70 10
88 **21** 2 p. purple and orange-yellow (10.8) . . 3·50 60
89 3 p. red-brown and blue . . 70 10
90 4 p. ultramarine and black . . 80 10
91 5 p. chestnut and green (10.8) . . 4·50 8·00
92 6 p. greenish blue and black (10.8) . . 18·00 40
93 8 p. emerald and black (10.8) . . 14·00 45
94 10 p. slate and purple (10.8) . . 50·00 75
95 20 p. pale blue and blue (10.8) . . 50·00 28·00
81/95 . . *Set of* 15 £140 40·00

22

23

1948 (1 Jan–June). *Arabic inscriptions below camel altered. Typo. W* **7**. *Ordinary paper* (8, 10, 20 p.) *or chalk-surfaced paper (others). P* 14.
96 **22** 1 m. black and orange . . 35 2·00
97 2 m. orange and chocolate . . 80 2·75
98 3 m. mauve and green . . 30 2·75
99 4 m. deep green and chocolate . . 30 10
100 5 m. olive-brown and black . . 3·50 90
101 10 m. rose-red and black . . 4·50 10
a. Centre inverted . . † —
102 15 m. ultramarine and chestnut . . 3·50 10
103 **23** 2 p. purple and orange-yellow . . 6·00 90
104 3 p. red-brown and deep blue . . 5·50 20
105 4 p. ultramarine and black . . 3·50 1·25
106 5 p. brown-orange and deep green . . 3·50 1·00
107 6 p. greenish blue and black . . 4·50 2·75
108 8 p. bluish green and black . . 4·00 2·75
109 10 p. black and mauve . . 11·00 2·75
a. Chalk-surfaced paper (June) . . 19·00 3·50
110 20 p. pale blue and deep blue . . 4·50 20
a. Perf 13. Chalk-surfaced paper (June) . . 48·00 £120
111 50 p. carmine and ultramarine . . 6·50 1·50
96/111 . . *Set of* 16 55·00 20·00

A single used example is known of No. 101a.

For similar stamps, but with different Arabic inscriptions, see Nos. 37/46*b*.

24

25

1948 (1 Oct). *Golden Jubilee of "Camel Postman" design. Chalk-surfaced paper. Typo. W* **7**. *P* 13.
112 **24** 2 p. black and light blue . . 10 10

1948 (23 Dec). *Opening of Legislative Assembly. Chalk-surfaced paper. Typo. W* **7**. *P* 13.
113 **25** 10 m. rose-red and black . . 15 10
114 5 p. brown-orange and deep green . . 15 50

26 Blue Nile Bridge, Khartoum

(Des Col. W. L. Atkinson (2½ p., 6 p.), G. R. Wilson (3 p.), others from photographs. Recess)

1950 (1 July). *Air. T* **26** *and similar horiz designs. W* **7**. *P* 12.
115 2 p. black and blue-green . . 4·00 80
116 2½ p. light blue and red-orange . . 50 1·00
117 3 p. reddish purple and blue . . 3·00 40
118 3½ p. purple-brown and yellow-brown . . 1·00 2·50
119 4 p. brown and light blue . . 1·00 1·75
120 4½ p. black and ultramarine . . 2·25 3·50
a. Black and steel-blue . . 4·00 5·00
121 6 p. black and carmine . . 75 2·00
122 20 p. black and purple . . 1·75 3·75
115/122 . . *Set of* 8 13·00 14·00

Designs:—2½ p. Kassala Jebel; 3 p. Sagia (water wheel); 3½ p. Port Sudan; 4 p. Gordon Memorial College; 4½ p. *Gordon Pasha* (Nile mail boat); 6 p. Suakin; 20 p. G.P.O., Khartoum.

34 Ibex

35 Cotton Picking

(Des Col. W. L. Atkinson (1 m., 2 m., 4 m., 5 m., 10 m., 3 p., 3½ p., 20 p.), Col. E. A. Stanton (50 p.) others from photographs. Typo)

1951 (1 Sept)–**62**? *Designs as T* **34**/**5**. *Chalk-surfaced paper. W* **7**. *P* 14 (*millieme values*) *or* 13 (*piastre values*).
123 1 m. black and orange . . 45 1·00
124 2 m. black and bright blue . . 1·50 45
125 3 m. black and green . . 4·00 2·00
126 4 m. black and yellow-green . . 75 2·25
127 5 m. black and purple . . 1·00 10
a. Black and reddish purple (1962?) . . 3·00 40
128 10 m. black and pale blue . . 20 10
129 15 m. black and chestnut . . 2·25 10
a. Black and brown-orange (1962?) . . 2·50 10
130 2 p. deep blue and pale blue . . 20 10
a. Deep blue and very pale blue (1962?) 2·50 10
131 3 p. brown and dull ultramarine . . 3·75 10
a. Brown and deep blue (1962?) . . 6·00 90
132 3½ p. bright green and red-brown . . 90 10
133 4 p. ultramarine and black . . 50 10
a. Deep blue and black (1962?) . . 4·50 10
134 5 p. orange-brown and yellow-green . . 30 10
135 6 p. blue and black . . 5·50 2·50
a. Deep blue and black (1962?) . . 12·00 4·50
136 8 p. blue and brown . . 9·00 1·75
a. Deep blue and brown (1962?) . . 12·00 1·25
137 10 p. black and green . . 1·25 10
138 20 p. blue-green and black . . 4·50 1·10
139 50 p. carmine and black . . 12·00 75
123/139 . . *Set of* 17 42·00 10·50

Designs: *Vert as T* **34**—2 m. Whale-headed Stork; 3 m. Giraffe; 4 m. Baggara girl; 5 m. Shilluk warrior; 10 m. Hadendowa; 15 m. Policeman. *Horiz as T* **35**—3 p. Ambatch reed canoe; 3½ p. Nuba wrestlers; 4 p. Weaving; 5 p. Saluka farming; 6 p. Gum tapping; 8 p. Darfur chief; 10 p. Stack Laboratory; 20 p. Nile Lechwe. *Vert as T* **35**—50 p. Camel postman.

SELF-GOVERNMENT

51 Camel Postman

1954 (9 Jan). *Self-Government. Chalk-surfaced paper. Typo. W* **7**. *P* 13.
140 **51** 15 m. orange-brown and bright green . . 50 90
141 3 p. blue and indigo . . 50 1·40
142 5 p. black and reddish purple . . 50 90
140/2 . . *Set of* 3 1·40 2·75

Stamps as Type **51**, but dated "1953" were released in error at the Sudan Agency in London. They had no postal validity (*Price per set £16 un*).

Later issues of Sudan as an independent republic will be found in Part 14 (*Africa since Independence N–Z*) of this catalogue.

STAMP BOOKLETS

Nos. SB1/4 have one cover inscribed in English and one in Arabic.

1912. *Black on pink cover, size* 74×29 *mm. Stapled.*
SB1 100 m. booklet containing twenty 5 m. (No. 23) in pairs . . £650

1924. *Black on pink cover, size* 45×50 *mm. Stapled.*
SB2 105 m. booklet containing twenty 5 m. (No. 34) in blocks of 4

1926. *Black on pink cover, size* 45×50 *mm. Stapled.*
SB3 105 m. booklet containing twenty 5 m. (No. 41) in blocks of 4

No examples of No. SB3 are known to have survived.

1930. *Black on pink cover, size* 45×50 *mm. Stapled.*
SB4 100 m. booklet containing twenty 5 m. (No. 41) in blocks of 4 . . £950

POSTAGE DUE STAMPS

1897 (1 Mar). *Type D* **3** *of Egypt, optd with T* **1** *at Bûlâq.*
D1 2 m. green . . 1·75 8·00
a. Opt omitted (in horiz pair with normal) . . £2250
D2 4 m. maroon . . 1·75 8·00
a. Bisected (2 m.) (on cover) . . †
D3 1 p. ultramarine . . 10·00 5·00
D4 2 p. orange . . 10·00 11·00
a. Bisected (1 p.) (on cover) . . † £1200
D1/4 . . *Set of* 4 21·00 29·00

In some printings the large dot is omitted from the left-hand Arabic character on one stamp in the pane.

No. D1 has been recorded used as a bisect.

D 1 Gunboat *Zafir* D 2

1901 (1 Jan)–**26.** *Typo.* **W 4** *(sideways). Ordinary paper. P* 14.
D5 **D 1** 2 m. black and brown 55 60
a. Wmk upright (1912) .. .. £150 60·00
b. Chalk-surfaced paper (6.24*) .. 75 3·50
D6 4 m. brown and green .. .. 2·00 90
a. Chalk-surfaced paper (9.26*) .. 4·25 1·40
D7 10 m. green and mauve .. .. 3·75 3·75
a. Wmk upright (1912) .. .. £100 50·00
b. Chalk-surfaced paper (6.24*) .. 9·50 7·50
D8 20 m. ultramarine and carmine .. 3·25 3·25
D5/8 .. .. *Set of* 4 8·00 7·50

*Dates quoted for the chalk-surfaced paper printings are those of the earliest recorded postal use. These printings were despatched to the Sudan in March 1922 (10 m.) or September 1922 (others)).

The 4 m is known bisected at Khartoum or Omdurman in November/December 1901 and the 20 m. at El Obeid in 1904–05.

1927–30. **W 7.** *Chalk-surfaced paper. P* 14.
D 9 **D 1** 2 m. black and brown (1930) .. 2·50 2·50
D10 4 m. brown and green 90 80
D11 10 m. green and mauve .. .. 1·25 1·60
a. Ordinary paper .. .. 17·00
D9/11 .. .. *Set of* 3 4·25 4·50

1948 (1 Jan). *Arabic inscriptions at foot altered. Chalk-surfaced paper. Typo.* **W 7.** *P* 14.
D12 **D 2** 2 m. black and brown-orange .. .. 80 25·00
D13 4 m. brown and green .. .. 2·00 25·00
D14 10 m. green and mauve .. .. 15·00 15·00
D15 20 m. ultramarine and carmine .. 15·00 27·00
D12/15 .. .. *Set of* 4 30·00 80·00

The 10 and 20 m. were reissued in 1980 on Sudan arms watermarked paper.

OFFICIAL STAMPS

1900 (8 Feb). *5 mils of* 1897 *punctured* "S G" *by hand. The* "S" *has 14 and the* "G" *12 holes.*
O1 5 m. rose-carmine .. .. 45·00 20·00

1901 (Jan). *1 m. wmk Quatrefoil, punctured as No.* O1.
O2 1 m. brown and pink .. .. .. 42·00 30·00

Nos. O1/2 are found with the punctured "SG" inverted, reversed or inverted and reversed.

O.S.G.S. **O.S.G.S.**

(O 1) ("On Sudan Government Service") (O 2)

1902. *No.* 10 *optd at Khartoum as Type* **O 1** *in groups of* 30 *stamps.*
O3 **2** 1 m. brown and pink .. .. .. 2·00 8·50
a. Oval "O" (No. 19) .. .. .. 40·00 £100
b. Round stops. (Nos. 25 to 30) .. 7·50 35·00
c. Opt inverted £250 £325
d. Ditto and oval "O" £2500
e. Ditto and round stops £600 £750
f. Opt double £350
g. Ditto and round stops £800
h. Ditto and oval "O" .. ..

1903–12. *T* **2** *optd as Type* **O 2**, *by D.L.R. in sheets of* 120 *stamps.*

(i) *Wmk Quatrefoil* (3.06)
O 4 10 p. black and mauve .. .. 13·00 20·00
a. Malformed "O" £120

(ii) *Wmk Mult Star and Crescent*
O 5 1 m. brown and carmine (9.04) .. 50 10
a. Opt double .. ..
b. Malformed "O" .. .. 19·00
O 6 3 m. mauve and green (2.04) .. 2·50 15
a. Opt double £850 £850
b. Malformed "O" .. .. 42·00
O 7 5 m. scarlet and black (1.1.03) .. 2·50 10
a. Malformed "O" .. .. 42·00
O 8 1 p. blue and brown (1.1.03) .. 2·50 10
a. Malformed "O" .. .. 42·00
O 9 2 p. black and blue (1.1.03) .. 22·00 20
a. Malformed "O" £150
O10 5 p. brown and green (1.1.03) .. 2·00 30
a. Malformed "O" .. .. 45·00
O11 10 p. black and mauve (9.12) .. 4·00 48·00
a. Malformed "O" .. .. 65·00
O4/11 .. .. .. *Set of* 8 45·00 60·00

The malformed "O" is slightly flattened on the left-hand side and occurs on position 7 of the lower pane.

1913 (Jan)–**22.** *Nos.* 18/20 *and* 23/8 *punctured* "SG" *by machine. The* "S" *has* 12 *holes and the* "G" 13.
O12 **2** 1 m. brown and carmine .. .. 4·50 25
O13 2 m. green and brown (1915) .. .. 8·00 5·00
O14 3 m. mauve and green .. .. 7·50 70
O15 5 m. scarlet and black .. .. 4·00 15
O16 1 p. blue and brown .. .. 6·00 35
O17 2 p. black and blue .. .. 12·00 65
O18 2 p. purple and orange-yellow (*chalk-surfaced paper*) (1922) .. .. 5·50 8·00
O19 5 p. brown and green .. .. 17·00 1·50
a. Chalk-surfaced paper .. .. 17·00 2·75
O20 10 p. black and mauve (1914) .. 23·00 23·00
a. Chalk-surfaced paper .. .. 23·00 23·00
O12/20 .. .. .. *Set of* 9 80·00 35·00

1922. *Nos.* 32/5 *punctured* "SG" *by machine. The* "S" *has* 9 *holes and the* "G" 10.
O21 **6** 3 m. mauve and green .. .. 16·00 10·00
O22 4 m. green and chocolate .. .. 16·00 6·00
O23 5 m. olive-brown and black .. .. 1·00 80
O24 10 m. carmine and black .. .. 2·00 80
O21/4 .. .. *Set of* 4 32·00 16·00

1927–30. *Nos.* 39/42, 44, 45 *and* 46 *punctured* "SG" *by machine. Nos.* O25/8 *have* 9 *holes in the* "S" *and* 10 *in the* "G"; *Nos.* O29/31 12 *holes in the* "S" *and* 13 *in the* "G".
O25 **6** 3 m. mauve and green (1928) .. 8·50 3·00
O26 4 m. green and chocolate (1930) .. 70·00 48·00
O27 5 m. olive-green and black .. .. 4·00 10
O28 10 m. carmine and black .. .. 6·50 35
O29 **2** 2 p. purple and orange-yellow .. 10·00 95
O30 5 p. chestnut and green .. .. 18·00 3·50
O31 10 p. black and reddish purple .. 35·00 10·00
O25/31 .. .. .. *Set of* 7 £140 60·00

The use of Nos. O25/31 on internal official mail ceased in 1932, but they continued to be required for official mail to foreign destinations until replaced by Nos. O32/46 in 1936.

S.G. **S.G.** **S.G.**

(O 3) (O 4) (O 4*a*)

1936 (19 Sept)–**46.** *Nos.* 37a, 38a, 39/43 *optd with Type* **O 3**, *and* 44, 44ba, 44c, 45, 45ba, 45ca, 46 *and* 46ba *with Type* **O 4.** **W 7.** *P* 14.
O32 **6** 1 m. black and orange (22.11.46) .. 1·25 8·50
a. Opt double .. .. † £150
O33 2 m. orange and chocolate (*ordinary paper*) (4.45) .. .. 40 3·25
a. Chalk-surfaced paper .. ..
O34 3 m. mauve and green (*chalk-surfaced paper*) (1.37) .. .. 2·00 10
O35 4 m. grn & choc (*chalk-surfaced paper*) 2·50 2·50
O36 5 m. olive-brown and black (*chalk-surfaced paper*) (3.40) .. 60 10
a. Ordinary paper .. .. 15·00 40
O37 10 m. carmine and black (*chalk-surfaced paper*) (6.46) .. 60 10
O38 15 m. bright blue and chestnut (*chalk-surfaced paper*) (21.6.37) .. 5·00 20
a. Ordinary paper .. .. 27·00 1·75
O39 **2** 2 p. purple & orange-yellow (*chalk-surfaced paper*) (4.37) .. 8·00 10
a. Ordinary paper .. .. 26·00 2·50
O39*b* 3 p. red-brown and blue (4.46) .. 4·50 1·25
O39*c* 4 p. ultramarine and black (*chalk-surfaced paper*) (4.46) .. 20·00 2·50
ca. Ordinary paper .. .. 42·00 4·00
O40 5 p. chestnut and green (*chalk-surfaced paper*) .. .. 11·00 10
a. Ordinary paper .. .. 42·00 4·25
O40*b* 6 p. greenish blue and black (4.46) 6·50 6·00
O40*c* 8 p. emerald and black (4.46) .. 4·50 23·00
O41 10 p. black and reddish purple (*chalk-surfaced paper*) (10.37) .. 24·00 7·00
a. Ordinary paper. *Black and bright mauve* (1941) .. .. 38·00 2·50
O42 20 p. pale blue and blue (6.46) .. 21·00 19·00
O32/42 .. .. .. *Set of* 15 £100 60·00

1948 (1 Jan). *Nos.* 96/102 *optd with Type* **O 3**, *and* 103/111 *with Type* **O 4.**
O43 **22** 1 m. black and orange .. .. 30 2·75
O44 2 m. orange and chocolate .. .. 1·00 10
O45 3 m. mauve and green .. .. 1·75 4·50
O46 4 m. deep green and chocolate .. 1·75 2·50
O47 5 m. olive-brown and black .. .. 1·75 10
O48 10 m. rose-red and black .. .. 1·50 90
O49 15 m. ultramarine and chestnut .. 1·75 10
O50 **23** 2 p. purple and orange-yellow .. 1·75 10
O51 3 p. red-brown and deep blue .. 1·75 10
O52 4 p. ultramarine and black .. .. 1·75 10
a. Perf 13 (optd Type O 4*a*) .. 13·00 15·00
O53 5 p. brown-orange and deep green 2·00 10
O54 6 p. greenish blue and black .. 1·75 10
O55 8 p. bluish green and black .. .. 1·75 2·25
O56 10 p. black and mauve .. .. 2·50 20
O57 20 p. pale blue and deep blue .. 3·75 25
O58 50 p. carmine and ultramarine .. 55·00 45·00
O43/58 .. .. .. *Set of* 16 75·00 55·00

1950 (1 July). *Air. Optd with Type* **O 4***a*.
O59 2 p. black and blue-green (R.) .. .. 14·00 2·75
O60 2½ p. light blue and red-orange .. .. 1·50 1·75
O61 3 p. reddish purple and blue .. .. 80 1·00
O62 3½ p. purple-brown and yellow-brown .. 80 6·00
O63 4 p. brown and light blue .. .. 80 5·00
O64 4½ p. black and ultramarine (R.) .. 3·75 15·00
a. Black and steel-blue .. .. 5·50 15·00
O65 6 p. black and carmine (R.) .. .. 1·00 4·25
O66 20 p. black and purple (R.) .. .. 5·00 12·00
O59/66 .. .. .. *Set of* 8 25·00 42·00

1951 (1 Sept)–**62?** *Nos.* 123/9 *optd with Type* **O 3**, *and* 130/9 *with Type* **O 4***a*.
O67 1 m. black and orange (R.) .. .. 40 3·50
O68 2 m. black and bright blue (R.) .. 40 60
O69 3 m. black and green (R.) .. .. 3·00 13·00
O70 4 m. black and yellow-green (R.) .. 10 5·00
O71 5 m. black and purple (R.) 10 10
O72 10 m. black and pale blue (R.) .. 10 10
O73 15 m. black and chestnut (R.) .. 10 10
O74 2 p. deep blue and pale blue 10 10
a. Opt inverted £425
b. Deep blue and very pale blue (1962?) 50 10
O75 3 p. brown and dull ultramarine .. 3·00 10
a. Brown and deep blue (1962?) .. 3·75 85
O76 3½ p. bright green and red-brown .. 25 10
a. Light emerald & red-brown (1962?) 2·75 85
O77 4 p. ultramarine and black 30 10
a. Deep blue and black (1962?) .. 1·00 10
O78 5 p. orange-brown and yellow-green .. 25 10
O79 6 p. blue and black .. .. .. 30 2·75
a. Deep blue and black (1962?) .. 5·00 5·00
O80 8 p. blue and brown 45 10
a. Deep blue and brown (1962?) .. 3·25 1·50
O81 10 p. black and green (R.) 50 10
O81*a* 10 p. black and green (Blk.) (1958) .. 13·00 1·50
O82 20 p. blue-green and black .. .. 1·25 30
a. Opt inverted .. .. .. — £550
O83 50 p. carmine and black .. .. 3·50 1·25
O67/83 .. .. .. *Set of* 18 24·00 25·00

The 5, 10 and 15 m. values were later reissued with a thinner overprint.

ARMY SERVICE STAMPS

ARMY OFFICIAL ARMY OFFICIAL Army Service

(A 1) (A 2) (A 3)

1905 (Jan). *T* **2** *optd at Khartoum as Types* A **1** *or* A **2**. *Wmk Mult Star and Crescent.* (i) "ARMY" *reading up.*
A1 1 m. brown and carmine (A 1) .. .. 2·50 2·00
a. "!" for "1" .. .. .. 48·00 28·00
b. Opt Type A 2 .. .. .. 38·00 22·00
c. Pair. Types A 1 and A 2 *se-tenant* .. 75·00

(ii) *Overprint horizontal*
A2 1 m. brown and carmine (A 1) £325
a. "!" for "1" £3500
b. Opt Type A 2 .. .. .. £2000

The horizontal overprint exists with either "ARMY" or "OFFICIAL" reading the right way up. It did not fit the stamps, resulting in misplacements where more than one whole overprint appears, or when the two words are transposed.

(iii) *"ARMY" reading down*
A3 1 m. brown and carmine (A 1) .. .. 70·00 60·00
a. "!" for "I" £700 £700
b. Opt Type A 2 .. .. .. £600 £425

1905 (Nov). *As No.* A1, *but wmk Quatrefoil*, **W 3.**
A4 1 m. brown and pink (A 1) £120 £130
a. "!" for "1" £2750 £1600
b. Opt Type A 2 .. .. .. £1200 £1200
c. Pair. Types A 1 and A 2 *se-tenant* .. £2000

The setting used for overprinting Nos. A1/4 was 30 (6×5). The "!" for "1" variety occurs on R. 5/4 and overprint Type A **2** on R. 1/6 and 2/6 of the setting.

Two varieties of the 1 millieme
A. 1st Ptg. 14 mm between lines of opt.
B. Later Ptgs. 12 mm between lines.
All other values are Type B.

1906 (Jan)–**11.** *T* **2** *optd as Type* A **3.**

(i) *Wmk Mult Star and Crescent*, **W 4**
A 5 1 m. brown and carmine (Type A) £275 £225
A 6 1 m. brown and carmine (Type B) .. .. 1·50 20
a. Opt double, one diagonal .. .. † £650
b. Opt inverted £350 £350
c. Pair, one without opt .. ..
d. "Service" omitted .. .. † £3250
e. "A" for "A" in "Army" £150 £150
A 7 2 m. green and brown .. .. 7·50 1·00
a. Pair, one without opt .. £1600
b. "Army" omitted £2500
A 8 3 m. mauve and green .. .. 17·00 40
a. Opt inverted £1700
A 9 5 m. scarlet and black .. .. 1·50 10
a. Opt. double £190 £190
ab. Opt double, one diagonal .. £200
b. Opt inverted .. .. † £200
c. "Amry" .. .. .. † £2250
d. "A" for "A" in "Army" .. .. — £250
e. Opt double, one inverted .. £700 £350
A10 1 p. blue and brown .. .. 13·00 15
a. "Army" omitted .. .. † £2000
A11 2 p. black and blue (1.09) .. .. 45·00 13·00
a. Opt double .. .. .. † £2250
A12 5 p. brown and green (5.08) .. .. 95·00 60·00
A13 10 p. black and mauve (5.11) £450 £550
A6/10 Optd "Specimen" .. *Set of* 5 £110

There were a number of printings of these Army Service stamps; the earlier are as Type A 3; the 1908 printing has a narrower "A" in "Army" and the 1910–11 printings have the tail of the "y" in "Army" much shorter.

(ii) *Wmk Quatrefoil*, **W 3**
A14 2 p. black and blue .. .. 55·00 10·00
A15 5 p. brown and green .. .. 90·00 £130
A16 10 p. black and mauve £120 £225
A14/16 .. .. .. *Set of* 3 £225 £325
A14/16 Optd "Specimen" .. *Set of* 3 £100

1912 (1 Jan)–**22.** *Nos.* 18/20 *and* 23/8 *punctured* "AS" *by machine. The* "A" *has* 12 *holes and the* "S" 11.
A17 **2** 1 m. brown and carmine .. .. 23·00 2·50
A18 2 m. green and brown .. .. 5·50 70
A19 3 m. mauve and green .. .. 35·00 3·00
A20 5 m. scarlet and black .. .. 5·00 40
a. On No. 13 .. .. ..
A21 1 p. blue and brown .. .. 14·00 75
A22 2 p. black and blue .. .. 32·00 3·25
A23 2 p. purple and orange-yellow (*chalk-surfaced paper*) (1922) .. .. 42·00 35·00
A24 5 p. brown and green .. .. 38·00 17·00
a. Chalk-surfaced paper .. .. 38·00 17·00
A25 10 p. black and mauve (1914) £400 £225
A17/25 .. .. .. *Set of* 9 £500 £250

1922–24. *Nos.* 31a *and* 34/5 *punctured* "AS" *by machine. The* "A" *has* 8 *holes and the* "S" 9.
A26 **6** 2 m. yellow and chocolate (1924) .. 48·00 30·00
A27 5 m. olive-brown and black (4.2.22) .. 7·50 2·50
A28 10 m. carmine and black .. .. 11·00 3·00
A26/8 .. .. .. *Set of* 3 60·00 32·00

The use of Nos. A17/28 on internal Army mail ceased when the Egyptian units were withdrawn at the end of 1924, but existing stocks continued to be used on Army mail to foreign destinations until supplies were exhausted.

Swaziland

PRICES FOR STAMPS ON COVER TO 1945

Nos. 1/10	*from* × 40
Nos. 11/20	*from* × 4
Nos. 21/4	*from* × 5
Nos. 25/7	*from* × 10
Nos. 28/38	*from* × 4
Nos. 39/41	*from* × 5
Nos. D1/2	*from* × 30

TRIPARTITE GOVERNMENT

Following internal unrest and problems caused by the multitude of commercial concessions granted by the Swazi king the British and Transvaal governments intervened during 1889 to establish a tripartite administration under which the country was controlled by their representatives, acting with the agent of the Swazi king.

The Pretoria government had previously purchased the concession to run the postal service and, on the establishment of the tripartite administration, provided overprinted Transvaal stamps for use from the post offices opened at Bremersdorp, Darkton and Embekelweni.

Swazieland
(1)

1889 (18–20 Oct). *Stamps of Transvaal (South African Republic) optd with T* **1**, *in black.* (*a*) *P* 12½ × 12.

No.	Type		Un	Us
1	18	1d. carmine	17·00	16·00
		a. Opt inverted	£600	£650
2		2d. olive-bistre	80·00	16·00
		a. Opt inverted	—	£950
		b. "Swazielan"	£900	£650
3		1s. green	10·00	13·00
		a. Opt inverted	£550	£450
		(*b*) *P* 12½		
4	18	½d. grey	9·00	18·00
		a. Opt inverted	£700	£600
		b. "Swazielan"	£900	£650
		c. "Swazielan" inverted	—	£2750
5		2d. olive-bistre	14·00	15·00
		a. Opt inverted	£650	£450
		b. "Swazielan"	£425	£450
		c. "Swazielan" inverted	£2500	£2500
		d. Opt double	£2000	
6		6d. blue	17·00	30·00
7		2s. 6d. buff (20 Oct)	£200	£225
8		5s. slate-blue (20 Oct)	£140	£170
		a. Opt inverted	£1600	£1800
		b. "Swazielan"	£4000	
		c. "Swazielan" inverted		
9		10s. fawn (20 Oct)	£4500	£3000

The variety without "d" occurs on the left-hand bottom corner stamp in each sheet of certain printings.

A printing of the ½d, 1d., 2d. and 10s. with stop after "Swazieland" was made in July 1894, but such stamps were not issued.

1892 (Aug). *Optd in carmine. P* 12½.

No.	Type		Un	Us
10	18	½d. grey	7·00	15·00
		a. Opt inverted	£475	
		b. Opt double	£400	£400
		c. Pair, one without opt	—	£1300

After further negotiations in 1894 the British and Transvaal governments agreed that Swaziland would become a protectorate of the Transvaal in February 1895. The overprinted stamps were withdrawn on 7 November 1894 and replaced by ordinary issues of the Transvaal.

Shortly after the outbreak of the Boer War in 1899 the Transvaal administration withdrew from Swaziland and there was no postal service from the area until the country became a British Protectorate in March 1902. From that date, until the introduction of the 1933 definitives, the post offices listed below used Transvaal or South Africa stamps.

The following post offices or postal agencies existed in Swaziland before 1933. Dates given are those on which it is generally accepted that the offices were first opened. Some were subsequently closed before the end of the period.

Bremersdorp (1889)	Mankaiana (1913)
Darkton (1889)	Mbabane (*previously* Embabaan) (1905)
Dwaleni (1918)	M'dimba (1898)
Embabaan (1895)	Mhlotsheni (1910)
Embekelweni (1889)	Mooihoek (1918)
Ezulweni (1910)	Motshane (1929)
Forbes Reef (1906)	Nomahasha (1904)
Goedgegun (1925)	Nsoko (1927)
Hlatikulu (1903)	Piggs Peak (1899)
Hluti (1912)	Sandhlan (1903)
Ivy (1912)	Sicunusa (1913)
Kubuta (1926)	Stegi (1910)
Mahamba (1899)	Umkwakweni (1898)
Malkerns (1914)	White Umbuluzi (1925)
Malomba (1928)	

BRITISH PROTECTORATE

2 King George V

3 King George VI

(Des Rev. C. C. Tugman. Recess D.L.R.)

1933 (2 Jan). *Wmk Mult Script CA. P* 14.

No.	Type		Un	Us
11	2	½d. green	30	30
12		1d. carmine	30	20
13		2d. brown	30	45
14		3d. blue	45	1·25
15		4d. orange	1·75	2·00
16		6d. bright purple	1·00	80
17		1s. olive	1·50	2·75
18		2s. 6d. bright violet	15·00	22·00
19		5s. grey	30·00	45·00
20		10s. sepia	80·00	£100
11/20		*Set of* 10	£120	£150
11/20 Perf "Specimen"		*Set of* 10	£225	

The ½d., 1d., 2d. and 6d. values exist overprinted "OFFICIAL", but authority for their use was withdrawn before any were actually used. However, some stamps had already been issued to the Secretariat staff before instructions were received to invalidate their use (*Price* £11000 *per set un*).

1935 (4 May). *Silver Jubilee. As Nos.* 114/17 *of Jamaica. P* 11×12.

No.		Un	Us
21	1d. deep blue and scarlet	40	50
	a. Extra flagstaff	£180	
	b. Short extra flagstaff	£180	
	c. Lightning conductor	£180	
	d. Flagstaff on right-hand turret	70·00	
	e. Double flagstaff	70·00	
22	2d. ultramarine and grey-black	40	50
	a. Extra flagstaff	90·00	
	b. Short extra flagstaff	70·00	
	c. Lightning conductor	60·00	
23	3d. brown and deep blue	55	3·25
	a. Extra flagstaff	70·00	
	b. Short extra flagstaff	60·00	
	c. Lightning conductor	60·00	
24	6d. slate and purple	65	1·00
	a. Extra flagstaff	80·00	
	b. Short extra flagstaff	65·00	
	c. Lightning conductor	65·00	
21/4	*Set of* 4	1·75	4·75
21/4 Perf "Specimen"	*Set of* 4	80·00	

For illustrations of plate varieties see Omnibus section following Zimbabwe.

1937 (12 May). *Coronation. As Nos.* 118/20 *of Jamaica, but ptd by B.W. P* 11×11½.

No.		Un	Us
25	1d. carmine	50	1·00
26	2d. yellow-brown	50	15
27	3d. blue	50	50
25/7	*Set of* 3	1·40	1·50
25/7 Perf "Specimen"	*Set of* 3	65·00	

(Recess D.L.R.)

1938 (1 Apr)–**54.** *Wmk Mult Script CA. P* 13½×13.

No.	Type		Un	Us
28	3	½d. green	1·00	60
		a. Perf 13½×14 (1.43)	20	2·00
		b. Perf 13½×14. *Bronze-green* (2.50)	85	3·50
29		1d. rose-red	1·00	60
		a. Perf 13½×14 (1.43)	80	1·25
30		1½d. light blue	3·75	65
		a. Perf 14 (1941)	1·75	95
		b. Perf 13½×14 (1.43)	30	75
		ba. Printed on the gummed side	£2000	
31		2d. yellow-brown	2·50	75
		a. Perf 13½×14 (1.43)	30	50
32		3d. ultramarine	7·00	1·75
		a. Deep blue (10.38)	9·00	1·75
		b. Perf 13½×14. *Ultramarine* (1.43)	1·75	3·50
		c. Perf 13½×14. *Light ultram* (10.46)	12·00	8·00
		d. Perf 13½×14. *Deep blue* (10.47)	7·50	7·50
33		4d. orange	3·00	95
		a. Perf 13½×14 (1.43)	45	1·40
34		6d. deep magenta	7·00	1·50
		a. Perf 13½×14 (1.43)	3·50	3·50
		b. Perf 13½×14. *Reddish purple (shades)* (7.44)	3·50	1·25
		c. Perf 13½×14. *Claret* (13.10.54)	5·00	3·00
35		1s. brown-olive	7·00	1·50
		a. Perf 13½×14 (1.43)	1·25	65
36		2s. 6d. bright violet	22·00	4·00
		a. Perf 13½×14. *Violet* (1.43)	7·00	2·50
		b. Perf 13½×14. *Reddish violet* (10.47)	7·00	6·00
37		5s. grey	50·00	8·00
		a. Perf 13½×14. *Slate* (1.43)	55·00	50·00
		b. Perf 13½×14. *Grey* (5.44)	24·00	12·00
38		10s. sepia	50·00	5·50
		a. Perf 13½×14 (1.43)	6·50	6·00
28/38a		*Set of* 11	40·00	21·00
28/38 Perf "Specimen"		*Set of* 11	£225	

The above perforations vary slightly from stamp to stamp, but the average measurements are respectively: 13.3 × 13.2 comb (13½ × 13), 14.2 line (14) and 13.3 × 13.8 comb (13½ × 14).

Swaziland
(4)

1945 (3 Dec). *Victory. Nos.* 108/10 *of South Africa optd with T* 4.

No.		Un pair	Us pair	Us single
39	1d. brown and carmine	55	50	10
40	2d. slate-blue and violet	55	50	10
41	3d. deep blue and blue	55	1·75	20
39/41	*Set of* 3	1·50	2·50	30

1947 (17 Feb). *Royal Visit. As Nos.* 32/5 *of Lesotho.*

No.		Un	Us
42	1d. scarlet	10	10
43	2d. green	10	10
44	3d. ultramarine	10	10
45	1s. mauve	10	10
42/5	*Set of* 4	30	30
42/5 Perf "Specimen"	*Set of* 4	80·00	

1948 (1 Dec). *Royal Silver Wedding. As Nos.* 143/4 *of Jamaica.*

No.		Un	Us
46	1½d. ultramarine	50	10
47	10s. purple-brown	22·00	23·00

1949 (10 Oct). *75th Anniv of U.P.U. As Nos.* 145/8 *of Jamaica.*

No.		Un	Us
48	1½d. blue	20	10
49	3d. deep blue	1·00	60
50	6d. magenta	60	60
51	1s. olive	60	60
48/51	*Set of* 4	2·25	1·75

1953 (3 June). *Coronation. As No.* 153 *of Jamaica.*

No.		Un	Us
52	2d. black and yellow-brown	20	20

5 Havelock Asbestos Mine

7 Swazi Married Woman

(Recess B.W.)

1956 (2 July). *T* **5**, **7** *and similar designs. Wmk Mult Script CA. P* 13 × 13½ (*horiz*) *or* 13½ × 13 (*vert*).

No.	Type		Un	Us
53	5	½d. black and orange	10	10
54	–	1d. black and emerald	10	10
55	7	2d. black and brown	30	10
56	–	3d. black and rose-red	20	10
57	–	4½d. black and deep bright blue	60	10
58	–	6d. black and magenta	45	10
59	5	1s. black and deep olive	20	10
60	–	1s. 3d. black and sepia	1·00	1·50
61	–	2s. 6d. emerald and carmine-red	1·00	1·50
62	–	5s. deep lilac and slate-black	7·50	1·75
63	7	10s. black and deep lilac	15·00	6·50
64	–	£1 black and turquoise-blue	38·00	25·00
53/64		*Set of* 12	55·00	32·00

Designs: *Horiz*—1d., 2s. 6d. A Highveld view; *Vert*—3d., 1s. 3d. Swazi courting couple; 4½d., 5s. Swazi warrior; 6d., £1. Greater Kudu.

(New Currency. 100 cents = 1 rand)

½c	1c	2c	3½c
(11)	(12)	(13)	(14)

2½c (I) 2½c (II) 4c (I) 4c (II)

5c (I) 5c (II) 25c (I) 25c (II)

50c (I) 50c (II) 50c (III)

R1 (I) R1 (II) R1 (III) R2 (I) R2 (II)

1961 (14 Feb-May). *Nos.* 53/64 *surch as T* **11** *to* **14**.

No.		Un	Us
65	½ c. on ½d.	3·25	3·25
	a. Surch inverted	£550	
66	1 c. on 1d.	10	40
	a. Surch double*	£550	
67	2 c. on 2d.	10	50
68	2½ c. on 2d.	10	10
69	2½ c. on 3d. (Type I)	10	10
	a. Type II	10	15
70	3½ c. on 2d. (May)	10	20
71	4 c. on 4½d. (Type I)	10	10
	a. Type II	20	10
72	5 c. on 6d. (Type I)	10	10
	a. Type II	10	10
73	10 c. on 1s.	25·00	3·00
	a. Surch double*	£600	
74	25 c. on 2s. 6d. (Type I)	30	65
	a. Type II (central)	85	60
	b. Type II (bottom left)	£160	£180
75	50 c. on 5s. (Type I)	30	60
	a. Type II	4·50	2·25
	b. Type III	£300	£375
76	1 r. on 10s. (Type I)	1·50	60
	a. Type II	2·75	2·75
	b. Type III	42·00	50·00
77	2 r. on £1 (Type I)	9·00	9·00
	a. Type II (middle left)	4·50	5·50
	b. Type II (bottom)	50·00	90·00
65/77a	*Set of* 13	32·00	13·00

*On both Nos. 66a and 73a the second surcharge falls across the horizontal perforations.

No. 74b has the thin Type II surcharge at bottom left, in similar position to the thicker Type I, No. 74, with which it should not be confused.

No. 77b has the surcharge centrally placed at bottom. No. 77a has it at middle left, above "KUDU".

No. 66 with surcharge central (instead of bottom left) and No. 75a bottom left (instead of middle left) are believed to be from trial sheets released with the normal stocks. They do not represent separate printings. (No. 66 *price* £35 *un*, No. 75a *price* £120 *un*.).

(Recess B.W.)

1961. *As 1956 issue, but with values in cents and rands. Wmk Mult Script CA. P 13 × 13½ (horiz) or 13½ × 13 (vert).*
78 ½ c. black and orange (as ½d.) (14.2) .. 10 30
79 1 c. black and emerald (as 1d.) (14.2) .. 10 10
80 2 c. black and brown (as 2d.) (10.9) .. 10 1·25
81 2½ c. black and rose-red (as 3d.) (14.2) .. 15 10
82 4 c. black & dp bright bl (as 4½d) (10.9) .. 15 60
83 5 c. black and magenta (as 6d.) (10.9) .. 30 15
84 10 c. black and deep olive (as 1s.) (14.2) .. 15 10
85 12½ c. black and sepia (as 1s 3d.) (14.2) .. 1·25 40
86 25 c. emerald and carmine-red (as 2s 6d.) (1.8) 1·75 2·50
87 50 c. deep lilac & slate-blk (as 5s.) (10.9) .. 2·00 1·40
88 1 r. black and deep lilac (as 10s.) (10.9) .. 4·00 6·50
89 2 r. black and turquoise-blue (as £1) (1.8) 9·00 11·00
78/89 .. .. *Set of* 12 17·00 22·00

15 Swazi Shields

16 Battle Axe

(Des Mrs. C. Hughes. Photo Enschedé)

1962 (24 Apr)–**66.** *Various designs as T* **15/16.** *W w* **12.** *P 14×13 (horiz) or 13×14 (vert).*
90 ½ c. black, brown and yellow-brown .. 10 10
w. Wmk inverted
91 1 c. yellow-orange and black .. 10 10
w. Wmk inverted .. 1·75
92 2 c. dp bluish green, black & yellow-olive 10 50
w. Wmk inverted .. 14·00
93 2½ c. black and vermilion .. 10 10
a. Black and dull red (5.66) .. 30 10
w. Wmk inverted .. 2·25
94 3½ c. yellow-green and deep grey .. 10 40
w. Wmk inverted .. 4·00
95 4 c. black and turquoise-green .. 10 10
a. Black & deep turquoise-green (5.66) 60 10
w. Wmk inverted .. 4·00
96 5 c. black, red and orange-red .. 40 10
w. Wmk inverted .. 6·00
97 7½ c. deep brown and buff .. 60 30
a. Blackish brn & yellowish buff (5.66) 2·00 1·50
w. Wmk inverted .. 6·00
98 10 c. black and light blue .. 1·50 10
w. Wmk inverted .. 18·00
99 12½ c. carmine and grey-olive .. 1·25 2·00
100 15 c. black and bright purple .. 1·50 70
101 20 c. black and green .. 40 90
102 25 c. black and bright blue .. 50 70
w. Wmk inverted .. 18·00
103 50 c. black and rose-red .. 8·50 3·25
104 1 r. emerald and ochre .. 3·00 2·25
105 2 r. carmine-red and ultramarine .. 14·00 7·50
90/105 .. .. .. *Set of* 16 28·00 16·00

Designs: *Vert*—2 c. Forestry; 2½ c. Ceremonial headdress; 3½ c. Musical instrument; 4 c. Irrigation; 5 c. Long-tailed Whydah; 7½ c. Rock paintings; 10 c. Secretary Bird; 12½ c. Pink Arum; 15 c. Swazi married woman; 20 c. Malaria control; 25 c. Swazi warrior; 1 r. Aloes. *Horiz*—50 c. Southern Ground Hornbill; 2 r. Msinsi in flower.

1963 (4 June). *Freedom from Hunger. As No. 80 of Lesotho.*
106 15 c. reddish violet 40 15

1963 (2 Sept). *Red Cross Centenary. As Nos. 203/4 of Jamaica.*
107 2½ c. red and black 25 10
108 15 c. red and blue 65 50

31 Train and Map

(Des R. A. H. Street. Recess B.W.)

1964 (5 Nov). *Opening of Swaziland Railway. W w* **12.** *P 11½.*
109 **31** 2½ c. emerald-green and purple 55 10
110 3½ c. turquoise-blue & deep yellow-ol .. 55 60
111 15 c. red-orange and deep chocolate .. 70 60
112 25 c. olive-yellow and deep ultram .. 85 75
109/12 .. .. .. *Set of* 4 2·40 1·75

1965 (17 May). *I.T.U. Centenary. As Nos. 98/9 of Lesotho.*
113 2½ c. light blue and bistre 10 10
114 15 c. bright purple and rose 25 20

1965 (25 Oct). *International Co-operation Year. As Nos. 100/1 of Lesotho.*
115 ½ c. reddish purple and turquoise-green .. 10 10
116 15 c. deep bluish green and lavender .. 40 20

1966 (24 Jan). *Churchill Commemoration. As Nos. 102/5 of Lesotho.*
117 ½ c. new blue 10 70
118 2½ c. deep green 20 10
119 15 c. brown 35 20
w. Wmk inverted
120 25 c. bluish violet 50 65
117/20 .. .. .. *Set of* 4 1·00 1·50

1966 (1 Dec). *20th Anniv of U.N.E.S.C.O. As Nos. 342/4 of Mauritius.*
121 2½ c. slate-violet, red, yellow and orange .. 10 10
122 7½ c. orange-yellow, violet and deep olive .. 25 40
123 15 c. black, bright purple and orange .. 45 95
121/3 .. .. .. *Set of* 3 70 1·25

PROTECTED STATE

32 King Sobhuza II and Map

33 King Sobhuza II

(Des and photo Harrison)

1967 (25 Apr). *Protected State. W w* **12** *(sideways on horiz designs). P 14½.*
124 **32** 2½ c. multicoloured 10 10
125 **33** 7½ c. multicoloured 15 15
126 **32** 15 c. multicoloured 20 20
127 **33** 25 c. multicoloured 25 30
124/7 .. .. .. *Set of* 4 65 60

34 Students and University

(Des V. Whiteley. Photo Harrison)

1967 (7 Sept). *First Conferment of University Degrees. P 14 × 14½.*
128 **34** 2½ c. sepia, ultramarine & lt yellow-orge 10 10
129 7½ c. sepia, ultramarine & lt greenish bl 10 10
130 15 c. sepia, ultramarine and rose 20 25
131 25 c. sepia, ultramarine and light violet 25 30
128/31 .. .. .. *Set of* 4 55 65

35 Incwala Ceremony

36 Reed Dance

(Des Mrs. G. Ellison. Photo Harrison)

1968 (5 Jan). *Traditional Customs. P 14.*
132 **35** 3 c. silver, vermilion and black .. 10 10
133 **36** 10 c. silver, light brown, orange and black 10 10
134 **35** 15 c. gold, vermilion and black .. 15 20
135 **36** 25 c. gold, light brown, orange and black 15 20
132/5 .. .. .. *Set of* 4 40 50

(37)

38 Cattle Ploughing

1968 (1 May). *No. 96 surch with T* **37.**
136 3 c. on 5 c. black, red and orange-red .. 20 10
w. Wmk inverted .. 3·50

INDEPENDENT

(Des Mrs. G. Ellison. Photo Enschedé)

1968 (6 Sept). *Independence. T* **38** *and similar horiz designs. W w* **12** *(sideways). P 14 × 12½.*
137 3 c. multicoloured 10 10
a. Imperf (pair) .. £140
138 4½ c. multicoloured 10 10
a. Imperf (pair) .. £140
139 17½ c. yellow, green, black and gold .. 15 10
140 25 c. slate, black and gold .. 45 80
137/40 .. .. *Set of* 4 65 95
MS141 180 × 162 mm. Nos. 137/40 each × 5 .. 14·00 22·00
a. Error. Imperf .. £1300

Designs:—4½ c. Overhead cable carrying asbestos; 17½ c. Cutting sugar cane; 25 c. Iron ore mining and railway map.

Nos. 137/40 were printed in sheets of 50, but also in miniature sheets of 20 (4 × 5) containing *se-tenant* strips of each value.

INDEPENDENCE
1968
(42)

43 Cape Porcupine

1968 (6 Sept). *Nos. 90/105 optd as T* **42**, *and No.* **93** *additionally surch 3 c., by Enschedé. (a) Wmk upright.*
142 ½ c. black, brown and yellow-brown .. 10 10
a. Brown omitted .. £225
b. Albino opt .. 40·00
143 1 c. yellow-orange and black .. 10 10
w. Wmk inverted
144 2 c. dp bluish green, black & yellow-olive 10 10
w. Wmk inverted
145 2½ c. black and vermilion .. 60 75
a. Black and dull red .. 80 10
w. Wmk inverted
146 3 c. on 2½ c. black and vermilion .. 10 10
a. Black and dull red .. 10 10
w. Wmk inverted
147 3½ c. yellow-green and deep grey .. 15 10
w. Wmk inverted
148 4 c. black and turquoise-green .. 10 10
a. Black and deep turquoise-green .. 25 15
b. Black and pale turquoise-green .. 20 1·00
149 5 c. black, red and orange-red .. 1·75 10
w. Wmk inverted .. 23·00
150 7½ c. deep brown and buff .. 40 10
151 10 c. black and light blue .. 2·00 10
152 12½ c. carmine and grey-olive .. 25 45
w. Wmk inverted .. 2·75 3·50
153 15 c. black and bright purple .. 25 45
154 20 c. black and green .. 75 1·50
155 25 c. black and bright blue .. 35 40
156 50 c. black and rose-red .. 7·00 3·00
157 1 r. emerald and ochre .. 2·50 3·25
158 2 r. carmine-red and ultramarine .. 5·50 8·00

(b) Wmk sideways
159 50 c. black and rose-red .. 4·50 3·00
160 2 r. carmine-red and ultramarine .. 6·00 5·00
142/60 .. *Set of* 19 28·00 23·00

The 2½ c., 3½ c., 5 c., 12½ c., 50 c. (No. 156) and 2 r. (No. 158) exist with gum arabic only, the 1 c., 2 c., 3 c., 4 c., and 15 c. with both gum arabic and PVA gum and the remainder with PVA gum only.

(Des and litho D.L.R.)

1969 (1 Aug)–**75.** *T* **43** *and similar designs showing animals. Multicoloured. W w* **12** *(sideways on 3 c., 3½ c., 1 r., 2 r.). P 13×13½ (3, 3½ c.), 12½×13 (1, 2 r.) or 13×12½ (others).*
161 ½ c. Caracal 10 10
162 1 c. Type **43** 10 10
163 2 c. Crocodile 20 10
aw. Wmk inverted .. 4·00
b. Perf 12½×12 (29.9.75) .. 4·50 4·50
164 3 c. Lion 60 10
165 3½ c. African Elephant 60 10
166 5 c. Bush Pig 30 10
167 7½ c. Impala 35 10
168 10 c. Chacma Baboon 45 10
169 12½ c. Ratel .. .. 70 2·25
170 15 c. Leopard .. .. 1·25 70
171 20 c. Blue Wildebeest 95 60
172 25 c. White Rhinoceros .. .. 1·40 1·75
w. Wmk inverted .. 3·25
173 50 c. Common Zebra .. .. 1·50 3·25
174 1 r. Waterbuck (*vert*) .. .. 3·00 6·50
175 2 r. Giraffe (*vert*) .. .. 8·00 11·00
161/75 .. *Set of* 15 17·00 24·00

Nos. 161/73 are horizontal as Type **43** but the 3 c. and 3½ c. are larger, 35×24½ mm.

No. 163b was printed by the D.L.R. works in Bogotá, Colombia.

See also Nos. 219/20 and 229.

44 King Sobhuza II and Flags

45 King Sobhuza II, U.N. Building and Emblem

(Des D.L.R. Litho P.B.)

1969 (24 Sept). *Admission of Swaziland to the United Nations. W w* **12** *(sideways). P 13½.*
176 **44** 3 c. multicoloured 10 10
177 **45** 7½ c. multicoloured 15 10
178 **44** 12½ c. multicoloured 25 10
179 **45** 25 c. multicoloured 40 40
176/9 .. .. *Set of* 4 75 55

46 Athlete, Shield and Spears

47 *Bauhinia galpinii*

(Des L. Curtis. Litho Format)

1970 (16 July). *Ninth Commonwealth Games, Edinburgh. T* **46** *and similar vert designs. Multicoloured. W w* **12.** *P 14.*
180 3 c. Type **46** 10 10
181 7½ c. Runner 20 10
182 12½ c. Hurdler 25 10
183 25 c. Procession of Swaziland competitors .. 35 40
180/3 .. .. *Set of* 4 75 55

(Des L. Curtis from "Wild Flowers of Natal" by Dr. W. G. Wright. Litho Questa)

1971 (1 Feb). *Flowers. T* **47** *and similar vert designs. Multicoloured.* W w **12**. *P* 14½.

184 3 c. Type **47** 20 10
185 10 c. *Crocosmia aurea* 25 10
186 15 c. *Gloriosa superba* 40 15
187 25 c. *Watsonia densiflora* 55 35
184/7 . . . . *Set of* 4 1·25 60

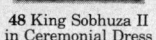

48 King Sobhuza II in Ceremonial Dress

49 UNICEF emblem

(Des L. Curtis. Litho Format)

1971 (22 Dec). *Golden Jubilee of Accession of King Sobhuza II. T* **48** *and similar vert designs. Multicoloured.* W w **12**. *P* 14.

188 3 c. Type **48** 10 10
w. Wmk inverted 50
189 3½ c. Sobhuza II in medallion 10 10
190 7½ c. Sobhuza II attending Incwala ceremony 15 10
191 25 c. Sobhuza II and aides at opening of Parliament 30 35
w. Wmk inverted 70
188/91 . . . . *Set of* 4 45 40

(Des Sylvia Goaman. Litho J.W.)

1972 (17 Apr). *25th Anniv of UNICEF.* W w **12** (*sideways*). *P* 13½.

192 **49** 15 c. black and bright lilac 15 15
193 – 25 c. black and yellow-olive 20 35

The 25 c. value is as T **49**, but the inscription is rearranged.

50 Local Dancers

(Des G. Drummond. Litho Questa)

1972 (11 Sept). *Tourism. T* **50** *and similar horiz designs. Multicoloured.* W w **12**. *P* 13½ × 14.

194 3½ c. Type **50** 10 10
195 7½ c. Swazi beehive hut 15 15
196 15 c. Ezulwini Valley 30 50
197 25 c. Fishing, Usutu River . . . . 80 1·25
194/7 . . . . *Set of* 4 1·25 1·75

51 Spraying Mosquitoes

(Des PAD Studio. Litho Questa)

1973 (21 May). *25th Anniv of W.H.O. T* **51** *and similar horiz design. Multicoloured.* W w **12**. *P* 14.

198 3½ c. Type **51** 35 10
199 7½ c. Anti-malaria vaccination 55 70

52 Mining

(Des G. Drummond. Litho Questa)

1973 (21 June). *Natural Resources. T* **52** *and similar horiz designs. Multicoloured.* W w **12**. *P* 13½.

200 3½ c. Type **52** 55 10
201 7½ c. Cattle 25 15
202 15 c. Water 30 20
203 25 c. Rice 35 50
200/3 . . . . *Set of* 4 1·25 80

53 Coat of Arms

54 Flags and Mortar-board

(Des J.W. Litho Walsall)

1973 (7 Sept). *Fifth Anniv of Independence. T* **53** *and similar horiz designs. Multicoloured (except 3 c.).* W w **12**. *P* 14.

204 3 c. Type **53** (salmon and black) 10 10
205 10 c. King Sobhuza II saluting 20 10
206 15 c. Parliament Buildings 45 65
207 25 c. National Somhlolo Stadium . . . . 55 1·25
204/7 . . . . *Set of* 4 1·10 1·75

(Des P. Powell. Litho Format)

1974 (29 Mar). *Tenth Anniv of University of Botswana, Lesotho and Swaziland. T* **54** *and similar vert designs. Multicoloured.* W w **12** (*sideways*). *P* 14.

208 7½ c. Type **54** 20 10
209 12½ c. University campus 25 10
210 15 c. Map of Southern Africa 30 20
211 25 c. University badge 40 35
208/11 . . . . *Set of* 4 1·00 60

55 King Sobhuza as College Student

56 New Post Office, Lobamba

(Des Mary Nelson; adapted PAD Studio. Litho Enschedé)

1974 (22 July). *75th Birthday of King Sobhuza II. T* **55** *and similar vert designs. Multicoloured.* W w **12**. *P* 13 × 10½.

212 3 c. Type **55** 10 10
213 9 c. King Sobhuza in middle-age 10 10
214 50 c. King Sobhuza at 75 years of age 70 60
212/14 . . . . *Set of* 3 80 60

(Des R. Granger Barrett. Litho Questa)

1974 (9 Oct). *Centenary of Universal Postal Union. T* **56** *and similar horiz designs. Multicoloured.* W w **12** (*sideways*). *P* 14.

215 4 c. Type **56** 10 10
216 10 c. Mbabane Temporary Post Office, 1902 . . 15 15
217 15 c. Carrying mail by cableway 30 50
218 25 c. Mule-drawn mail-coach 40 70
215/18 . . . . *Set of* 4 80 1·25

(New Currency. 100 cents = 1 lilangeni (*plural* emalangeni))

1975 (2 Jan). *New currency. As Nos. 174/5 but inscr in emalangeni.* W w **12** (*upright*). *P* 12½ × 13.

219 1 e. Waterbuck . . . . 1·25 2·50
220 2 e. Giraffe . . . . 2·50 4·50
w. Wmk inverted . . . . 65·00

57 Umcwasho Ceremony

58 Control Tower, Matsapa Airport

(Des PAD Studio. Litho Kynoch Press)

1975 (20 Mar). *Swazi Youth. T* **57** *and similar multicoloured designs.* W w **12** (*sideways on* 3, 10 *and* 25 *c.*). *P* 14.

221 3 c. Type **57** 10 10
222 10 c. Butimba (hunting party) 15 10
223 15 c. Lusekwane (sacred shrub) (*horiz*) 40 40
224 25 c. Goina Regiment 60 70
221/4 . . . . *Set of* 4 1·10 1·10

(Des V. Whiteley Studio. Litho Questa)

1975 (18 Aug). *Tenth Anniv of Internal Air Service. T* **58** *and similar horiz designs. Multicoloured.* W w **14** (*sideways*). *P* 14.

225 4 c. Type **58** 30 10
226 5 c. Fire engine 70 20
227 15 c. Douglas DC-3 . . . . 1·75 1·40
228 25 c. Hawker Siddeley H.S.748 . . . . 2·50 2·00
225/8 . . . . *Set of* 4 4·75 3·25

(Litho De La Rue, Bogotá, Colombia)

1975 (29 Sept). *As No. 164 but* W w **12** *upright.*

229 3 c. Lion . . . . 4·50 5·00

3c

(59)

1975 (15 Nov). *Nos. 167 and 169 surch as T* **59**.

230 3 c. on 7½ c. Impala . . . . 1·75 1·25
231 6 c. on 12½ c. Ratel . . . . 2·00 1·50

60 Elephant Symbol

(Des Mary-Jane Rostami. Litho Questa)

1975 (22 Dec). *International Women's Year. T* **60** *and similar designs.* W w **14** (*sideways on* 4 *and* 5 *c.*). *P* 14.

232 4 c. light bluish grey, black & light brt blue 10 10
233 5 c. multicoloured 10 10
234 15 c. multicoloured 30 50
235 25 c. multicoloured 50 80
232/5 . . . . *Set of* 4 80 1·40

Designs: *Horiz*—5 c. Queen Labotsibeni. *Vert*—15 c. Craftswoman; 25 c. "Women in Service".

61 African Black-headed Oriole

(Des C. Abbott. Litho Questa)

1976 (2 Jan)–**78**. *Birds. T* **61** *and similar multicoloured designs.* W w **14** (*sideways on* 1 *c.*, 3 *c.*, 2 *e.*). *Chalk-surfaced paper. P* 14.

236 1 c. Type **61** . . . . 75 1·00
237 2 c. African Green Pigeon (*vert*) . . . . 80 1·00
238 3 c. Green-winged Pytilia . . . . 1·00 80
239 4 c. Violet Starling (*vert*) 80 15
aw. Wmk inverted . . . . † 2·00
b. Ordinary paper (31.7.78) . . . . 1·50 40
240 5 c. Black-headed Heron (*vert*) 90 60
241 6 c. Stonechat (*vert*) . . . . 1·50 1·00
242 7 c. Chorister Robin Chat (*vert*) . . . . 1·40 1·25
243 10 c. Four-coloured Bush-shrike (*vert*) . . 1·50 50
244 15 c. Black-collared Barbet (*vert*) . . . . 2·25 55
245 20 c. Grey Heron (*vert*) . . . . 3·25 2·00
246 25 c. Giant Kingfisher (*vert*) . . . . 3·50 2·00
247 30 c. Verreaux's Eagle (*vert*) . . . . 3·50 2·50
248 50 c. Red Bishop (*vert*) . . . . 2·25 1·50
a. Ordinary paper (31.7.78) . . . . 90 1·00
249 1 e. Pin-tailed Whydah (*vert*) . . . . 2·50 2·75
a. Ordinary paper (31.7.78) . . . . 1·75 2·50
250 2 e. Lilac-breasted Roller . . . . 4·50 5·00
a. Ordinary paper (31.7.78) . . . . 2·50 5·00
236/50a . . . . *Set of* 15 24·00 20·00

62 Blindness from Malnutrition

63 Marathon

(Des Jennifer Toombs. Litho Questa)

1976 (15 June). *Prevention of Blindness. T* **62** *and similar horiz designs. Multicoloured.* W w **14** (*sideways*). *P* 14.

251 5 c. Type **62** 25 10
252 10 c. Infected retina 30 10
253 20 c. Blindness from trachoma 60 35
254 25 c. Medicines 65 40
251/4 . . . . *Set of* 4 1·60 80

(Des PAD Studio. Litho Walsall)

1976 (17 July). *Olympic Games, Montreal. T* **63** *and similar vert designs. Multicoloured.* W w **14** (*inverted*). *P* 14.

255 5 c. Type **63** 15 10
256 6 c. Boxing 20 10
257 20 c. Football 45 25
258 25 c. Olympic torch and flame 55 35
255/8 . . . . *Set of* 4 1·25 65

64 Footballer Shooting

65 Alexander Graham Bell and Telephone

(Des J.W. Litho Questa)

1976 (13 Sept). *F.I.F.A. Membership. T* **64** *and similar vert designs. Multicoloured. W* w **14**. *P* 14.

259	4 c. Type **64** ..	15	10
260	6 c. Heading ..	15	10
261	20 c. Goalkeeping ..	40	25
262	25 c. Player about to shoot ..	40	30
259/62	.. *Set of* 4	1·00	60

(Des J.W. Litho Walsall)

1976 (22 Nov). *Telephone Centenary. T* **65** *and similar horiz designs. W* w **14** (*sideways*). *P* 14.

263	4 c. multicoloured ..	10	10
264	5 c. multicoloured ..	10	10
265	10 c. multicoloured ..	15	10
266	15 c. multicoloured ..	30	20
267	20 c. multicoloured ..	40	30
263/7	.. *Set of* 5	95	55

Nos. 264/7 are as T **65**, but show different telephones.

66 Queen Elizabeth II and King Sobhuza II

(Des Walsall. Litho Questa)

1977 (7 Feb). *Silver Jubilee. T* **66** *and similar horiz designs. Multicoloured. W* w **14** (*sideways*). *P* 13½.

268	20 c. Type **66** ..	15	15
269	25 c. Coronation Coach at Admiralty Arch ..	15	15
270	50 c. Queen in coach ..	20	40
268/70	.. *Set of* 3	45	65

67 Matsapa College

(Des J. Cooter. Litho Questa)

1977 (2 May). *50th Anniv of Police Training. T* **67** *and similar multicoloured designs. W* w **14** (*upright on* 20 c., *sideways on others*). *P* 14.

271	5 c. Type **67** ..	10	10
272	10 c. Uniformed police and land rover ..	50	20
273	20 c. Police badge (*vert*) ..	70	85
274	25 c. Dog handling ..	80	95
271/4	.. *Set of* 4	1·90	1·90

68 Animals and Hunters

(Des BG Studio. Litho Questa)

1977 (8 Aug). *Rock Paintings. T* **68** *and similar horiz designs. Multicoloured. W* w **14** (*sideways**). *P* 14.

275	5 c. Type **68** ..	25	10
276	10 c. Four dancers in a procession ..	30	10
277	15 c. Man with cattle ..	40	20
278	20 c. Four dancers ..	45	30
275/8	.. *Set of* 4	1·25	55
MS279	103×124 mm. Nos. 275/8 ..	2·00	2·75
	w. Wmk Crown to right of CA ..	5·00	

*The normal sideways watermark shows Crown to left of CA, *as seen from the back of the stamp.*

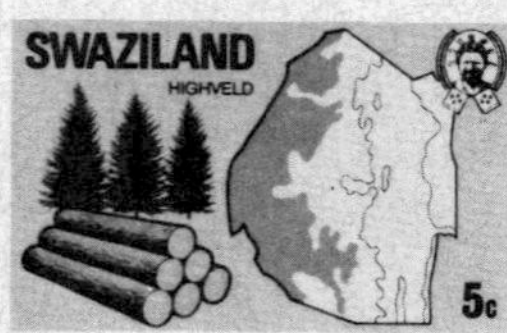

69 Timber, Highveld Region

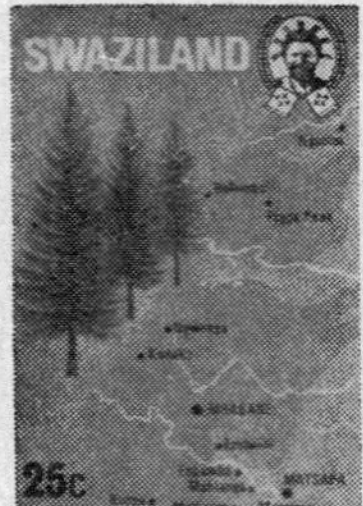

70 Timber, Highveld Region

(Des L. Curtis. Litho D.L.R.)

1977 (17 Oct). *Maps of the Regions. T* **69** *and similar horiz designs. Multicoloured. W* w **14** (*sideways*). *P* 13½.

280	5 c. Type **69** ..	25	10
281	10 c. Pineapple, Middleveld ..	30	10
282	15 c. Orange and Lemon, Lowveld ..	45	55
283	20 c. Cattle, Lubombo region ..	60	85
280/3	.. *Set of* 4	1·40	1·40
MS284	87 × 103 mm. Four 25 c. designs as T **70**, together forming a composite map of Swaziland ..	1·40	1·60

71 Cabbage Tree

(Des Jennifer Toombs. Litho Walsall)

1978 (12 Jan). *Trees of Swaziland. T* **71** *and similar horiz designs. Multicoloured* (*except* 5 c.). *W* w **14** (*sideways*). *P* 13½.

285	5 c. Type **71** (apple-green, ochre and black) ..	15	10
286	10 c. Marula ..	20	10
287	20 c. Kiaat ..	45	95
288	25 c. Lucky bean-tree ..	55	1·10
285/8	.. *Set of* 4	1·25	2·00

72 Rural Electrification at Lobamba

73 Elephant

(Des G. Drummond. Litho Questa)

1978 (6 Mar). *Hydro-electric Power. T* **72** *and similar horiz designs. W* w **14** (*sideways*). *P* 13½.

289	5 c. black and buff ..	10	10
290	10 c. black and light green ..	15	10
291	20 c. black and pale blue ..	25	30
292	25 c. black and magenta ..	30	35
289/92	.. *Set of* 4	70	65

Designs:—10 c. Edwaleni Power Station; 20 c. Switchgear, Magudza Power Station; 25 c. Turbine Hall, Edwaleni.

(Des C. Abbott. Litho Questa)

1978 (2 June). *25th Anniv of Coronation. T* **73** *and similar vert designs. P* 15.

293	25 c. chalky blue, black and sage-green ..	15	25
	a. Sheetlet. Nos. 293/5 × 2 ..	75	
294	25 c. multicoloured ..	15	25
295	25 c. chalky blue, black and sage-green ..	15	25
293/5	.. *Set of* 3	40	65

Designs:—No. 293, Queen's Lion; No. 294, Queen Elizabeth II; No. 295, Type **73**.

Nos. 293/5 were printed together in small sheets of 6, containing two *se-tenant* strips of 3, with horizontal gutter margin between.

74 Clay Pots

(Des C. Abbott. Litho Questa)

1978 (24 July). *Handicrafts* (1*st series*). *T* **74** *and similar horiz designs. Multicoloured. W* w **14** (*sideways*). *P* 13½ × 14.

296	5 c. Type **74** ..	10	10
297	10 c. Basketwork ..	10	10
298	20 c. Wooden utensils ..	15	15
299	30 c. Wooden pot ..	25	30
296/9	.. *Set of* 4	50	50

See also Nos. 310/13.

75 Defence Force

(Des BG Studio. Litho Questa)

1978 (6 Sept). *10th Anniv of Independence. T* **75** *and similar horiz designs. Multicoloured. W* w **14** (*sideways*). *P* 14.

300	4 c. Type **75** ..	15	10
301	6 c. The King's Regiment ..	15	10
302	10 c. Tinkabi tractor (agricultural development) ..	15	10
303	15 c. Water-pipe laying (self-help scheme) ..	25	10
304	25 c. Sebenta adult literacy scheme ..	30	25
305	50 c. Fire emergency service ..	1·25	50
300/5	.. *Set of* 6	2·00	85

76 Archangel Gabriel appearing before Shepherds

77 Prospecting at Phophonyane

(Des V. Whiteley Studio. Litho Harrison)

1978 (12 Dec). *Christmas. T* **76** *and similar horiz designs. Multicoloured. W* w **14**. *P* 14½ × 14.

306	5 c. Type **76** ..	10	10
307	10 c. Three Wise Men paying homage to infant Jesus ..	10	10
308	15 c. Archangel Gabriel warning Joseph ..	10	10
309	25 c. Flight into Egypt ..	20	20
306/9	.. *Set of* 4	30	35

(Des C. Abbott. Litho Walsall)

1979 (10 Jan). *Handicrafts* (2*nd series*). *Horiz designs as T* **74**. *Multicoloured. W* w **14** (*sideways*). *P* 13½.

310	5 c. Sisal bowls ..	10	10
311	15 c. Pottery ..	15	10
312	20 c. Basket work ..	20	15
313	30 c. Hide shield ..	30	20
310/13	.. *Set of* 4	60	45

(Des L. Curtis. Litho Questa)

1979 (27 Mar). *Centenary of Discovery of Gold in Swaziland. T* **77** *and similar vert designs. W* w **14**. *P* 14.

314	5 c. gold and deep ultramarine ..	25	10
315	15 c. gold and deep brown ..	45	20
316	25 c. gold and deep green ..	65	30
317	50 c. gold and carmine-red ..	90	90
314/17	.. *Set of* 4	2·00	1·25

Designs:—15 c. Early 3-stamp battery mill; 25 c. Cyanide tanks at Piggs Peak; 50 c. Pouring off molten gold.

78 "Girls at the Piano"

(Des BG Studio. Litho Questa)

1979 (8 May). *International Year of the Child. Paintings by Renoir. T* **78** *and similar horiz designs. Multicoloured. W* w **14** (*sideways*). *P* 13½.

318	5 c. Type **78** ..	10	10
319	15 c. "Madame Charpentier and her Children"	25	10
320	25 c. "Girls picking Flowers" ..	35	15
321	50 c. "Girl with Watering Can" ..	70	55
318/21	.. *Set of* 4	1·25	70
MS322	123 × 135 mm. Nos. 318/21 ..	1·25	1·75

79 1933 1d. Carmine Stamp and Sir Rowland Hill

(Des J.W. Litho Walsall)

1979 (17 July). *Death Centenary of Sir Rowland Hill. T* **79** *and similar horiz designs showing stamps and portrait of Sir Rowland Hill. Multicoloured. W* w **14** (*sideways**). *P* 14½×14.

323	10 c. 1945 3d. Victory commemorative ..	15	10
324	20 c. Type **79** ..	25	25
325	25 c. 1968 25 c. Independence commemorative	25	30
323/5	.. *Set of* 3	60	60
MS326	115×90 mm. 50 c. 1956 6d. Great Kudu Antelope definitive ..	75	85
	w. Wmk Crown to right of CA ..	7·50	

*The normal sideways watermark shows Crown to left of CA, *as seen from the back of of the stamp.*

80 Obverse and Reverse of 5 Cents

(Des G. Hutchins. Litho Walsall)

1979 (6 Sept). *Coins. T* **80** *and similar horiz designs. W* w **14** *(sideways). P* 13½.

327	5 c. black and light brown	15	10
328	10 c. black and new blue	20	10
329	20 c. black and yellowish green	35	20
330	50 c. black and yellow-orange	50	45
331	1 e. black and cerise	75	80
327/31	*Set of* 5	1·75	1·50

Designs:—10 c. Obverse and reverse of 10 cents; 20 c. Obverse and reverse of 20 cents; 50 c. Reverse of 50 cents; 1 e. Reverse of 1 lilangeni.

81 Big Bend Post Office

(Des J. Cooter. Litho Questa)

1979 (22 Nov). *Post Office Anniversaries. T* **81** *and similar designs. W* w **14** *(sideways on* 5, 20 *and* 50 c.). *P* 13½.

332	5 c. multicoloured	10	10
333	15 c. multicoloured	15	10
334	20 c. black, sage-green and magenta	20	15
335	50 c. multicoloured	40	60
332/5	*Set of* 4	70	80

Designs and commemorations: *Horiz*—5 c. Type **81** (25th anniversary of Posts and Telecommunications Services); 20 c. 1949 75th anniversary of U.P.U. 1s. commemorative stamp (10th anniversary of U.P.U. membership); 50 c. 1974 centenary of U.P.U. 25 c. commemorative stamp (10th anniversary of U.P.U. membership). *Vert*—15 c. Microwave antenna. Mount Ntondozi (25th anniversary of Posts and Telecommunications Services).

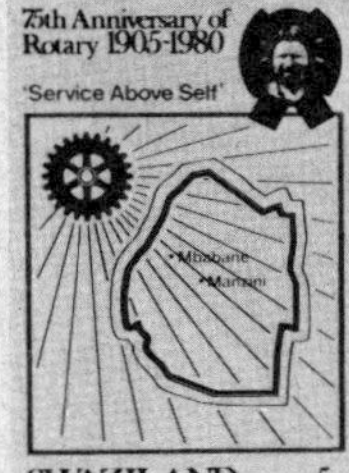

82 Map of Swaziland　**83** *Brunsvigia radulosa*

(Des BG Studio. Litho Walsall)

1980 (23 Feb). *75th Anniv of Rotary International. T* **82** *and similar vert designs in gold and bright blue. W* w **14**. *P* 13½.

336	5 c. Type **82**	25	10
337	15 c. Vitreous cutter and optical illuminator	45	10
338	50 c. Scroll	50	55
339	1 e. Rotary Headquarters, Evanston, U.S.A.	85	1·25
336/9	*Set of* 4	1·90	1·75

(Des BG Studio. Litho Secura, Singapore)

1980 (28 Apr)–**83**. *Flowers. Multicoloured designs as T* **83**.

A. *Without imprint date below design. P* 13½.

340A	1 c. Type **83**	15	10
341A	2 c. *Aloe suprafoliata*	15	10
342A	3 c. *Haemanthus magnificus*	15	10
	c. Perf 12	2·50	2·25
343A	4 c. *Aloe marlothii*	20	10
	c. Perf 12	4·25	2·75
344A	5 c. *Dicoma zeyheri*	15	10
	c. Perf 12	3·50	2·75
345A	6 c. *Aloe kniphofioides*	20	30
346A	7 c. *Cyrtanthus bicolor*	15	10
347A	10 c. *Eucomis autumnalis*	25	10
348A	15 c. *Leucospermum gerrardii*	15	10
	c. Perf 12		
349A	20 c. *Haemanthus multiflorus*	40	25
350A	30 c. *Acridocarpus natalitius*	20	20
351A	50 c. *Adenium swazicum*	30	30
352A	1 e. *Protea simplex*	55	60
353A	2 e. *Calodendrum capense*	1·10	1·25
354A	5 e. *Gladiolus ecklonii*	2·75	3·00
340A/54A	*Set of* 15	6·00	5·50

B. *With "1983" imprint date. P* 12 (12.83)

340B	1 c. Type **83**	1·00	1·00
341B	2 c. *Aloe suprafoliata*	1·00	1·00
343B	4 c. *Aloe marlothii*	1·50	75
345B	6 c. *Aloe kniphofioides*	1·75	1·75
347B	10 c. *Eucomis autumnalis*	2·00	85
349B	20 c. *Haemanthus multiflorus*	2·25	2·00
340B/9B	*Set of* 6	8·50	6·50

Nos. 347/51 are horizontal, 42 × 25 mm, and Nos. 352/4 vertical, 28 × 38 mm.

84 Mail Runner

(Des A. Theobald. Litho Walsall)

1980 (6 May). *"London 1980" International Stamp Exhibition. T* **84** *and similar horiz designs. Multicoloured. W* w **14** *(sideways*). P* 14.

355	10 c. Type **84**	15	10
356	20 c. Post Office mail truck	25	15
	w. Wmk Crown to right of CA	6·50	
357	25 c. Mail sorting office	30	20
358	50 c. Ropeway conveying mail at Bulembu	70	70
355/8	*Set of* 4	1·25	1·00

*The normal sideways watermark shows Crown to left of CA, *as seen from the back of the stamp.*

85 Scaly

(Des and litho Walsall)

1980 (25 Aug). *River Fishes. T* **85** *and similar horiz designs. Multicoloured. W* w **14** *(sideways). P* 13½.

359	5 c. Type **85**	25	10
360	10 c. Silver Catfish ("Silver Barbel")	25	10
361	15 c. Tiger Fish	45	15
362	30 c. Brown Squeaker	75	30
363	1 e. Red-breasted Tilapia ("Bream")	1·10	1·40
359/63	*Set of* 5	2·50	1·75

86 Oribi

(Des G. Drummond. Litho Harrison)

1980 (1 Oct). *Wildlife Conservation. T* **86** *and similar multicoloured designs. W* w **14** *(sideways on* 5 *and* 50 c.). *P* 14.

364	5 c. Type **86**	15	10
365	10 c. Nile Crocodile (*vert*)	30	10
366	50 c. Temminck's Ground Pangolin	75	70
367	1 e. Leopard (*vert*)	1·60	1·50
364/7	*Set of* 4	2·50	2·00

87 Public Bus Service

(Des G. Hutchins. Litho Format)

1981 (5 Jan). *Transport. T* **87** *and similar horiz designs. Multicoloured. W* w **14** *(sideways). P* 14½.

368	5 c. Type **87**	10	10
369	25 c. Royal Swazi National Airways	25	15
370	30 c. Swaziland United Transport	30	20
371	1 e. Swaziland Railway	1·25	1·75
368/71	*Set of* 4	1·60	2·00

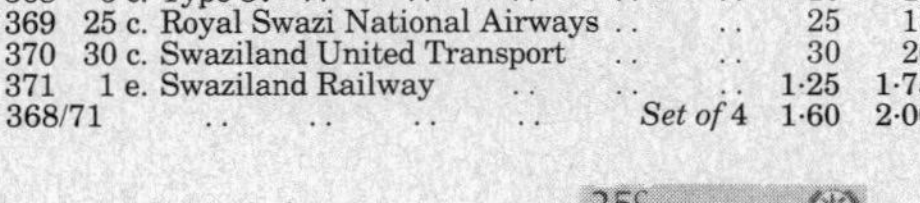

88 Mantenga Falls　**89** Prince Charles on Hike

(Des L. Curtis. Litho Format)

1981 (16 Mar). *Tourism. T* **88** *and similar horiz designs. Multicoloured. W* w **14** *(sideways). P* 14.

372	5 c. Type **88**	10	10
373	15 c. Mananga Yacht Club	15	10
374	30 c. White Rhinoceros in Mlilwane Game Sanctuary	40	30
375	1 e. Roulette wheel, playing cards and dice ("casinos")	1·10	1·60
372/5	*Set of* 4	1·50	1·90

(Des J.W. Litho Walsall)

1981 (21 July). *Royal Wedding. T* **89** *and similar vert designs. Multicoloured. W* w **14**. *P* 14.

376	10 c. Wedding bouquet from Swaziland	10	10
377	25 c. Type **89**	15	10
378	1 e. Prince Charles and Lady Diana Spencer	40	70
376/8	*Set of* 3	60	75

90 Installation of King Sobhuza II, 22 December 1921　**91** "Physical Recreation"

(Des J.W. Litho Harrison)

1981 (24 Aug). *Diamond Jubilee of King Sobhuza II. T* **90** *and similar horiz designs. Multicoloured. W* w **14** *(sideways). P* 14½.

379	5 c. Type **90**	10	10
380	10 c. Royal visit, 1947	15	10
381	15 c. King Sobhuza II and Coronation of Queen Elizabeth II, 1953	15	15
382	25 c. King Sobhuza taking Royal Salute, Independence, 1968	15	15
383	30 c. King Sobhuza in youth	20	20
384	1 e. King Sobhuza and Parliament Buildings	70	90
379/84	*Set of* 6	1·25	1·40

(Des BG Studio. Litho Questa)

1981 (5 Nov). *25th Anniv of Duke of Edinburgh Award Scheme. T* **91** *and similar vert designs. Multicoloured. W* w **14**. *P* 14.

385	5 c. Type **91**	10	10
386	20 c. "Expeditions"	10	10
387	50 c. "Skills"	25	25
388	1 e. Duke of Edinburgh in ceremonial dress	50	80
385/8	*Set of* 4	80	1·00

92 Disabled Person in Wheelchair

(Des and litho Walsall)

1981 (16 Dec). *International Year of Disabled Persons. T* **92** *and similar multicoloured designs. W* w **14** *(sideways on* 5 c. *and* 1 e.). *P* 14×14½ (5 c., 1 e.) *or* 14½×14 (*others*).

389	5 c. Type **92**	30	10
390	15 c. Teacher with disabled child (*vert*)	50	15
391	25 c. Disabled craftsman (*vert*)	75	20
392	1 e. Disabled driver in invalid carriage	2·25	1·75
389/92	*Set of* 4	3·50	2·00

93 *Papilio demodocus*　**94** Man holding a Flower, after discarding Cigarettes

(Des I. Loe. Litho Rosenbaum Bros, Vienna)

1982 (6 Jan). *Butterflies. T* **93** *and similar horiz designs. Multicoloured. W* w **14** *(sideways*). P* 14.

393	5 c. Type **93**	50	10
	w. Wmk Crown to left of CA	75	
394	10 c. *Charaxes candiope*	60	10
	w. Wmk Crown to right of CA	2·50	
395	50 c. *Papilio nireus*	2·00	85
	w. Wmk Crown to right of CA		
396	1 e. *Terias desjardinsii*	2·50	2·00
	w. Wmk Crown to left of CA		
393/6	*Set of* 4	5·00	2·75

*The normal sideways watermark shows Crown to left of CA on 10 c., 50 c. and to right on the other values, *all as seen from the back of the stamp.*

(Des PAD Studio. Litho Format)

1982 (27 Apr). *Pan-African Conference on Smoking and Health. T* **94** *and similar vert design. Multicoloured. W* w **14**. *P* 14.

397	5 c. Type **94**	50	85
398	10 c. Smoker and non-smoker climbing stairs	60	90

95 Male Fishing Owl 96 Swaziland Coat of Arms

(Des G. Drummond. Litho J.W.)

1982 (16 June). *Wildlife Conservation (1st series). Pel's Fishing Owl. T* **95** *and similar vert designs. Multicoloured.* **W** w **14**. *P* 13½ × 13.

399 35 c. Type **95** . . 5·00 3·25
a. Horiz strip of 5. Nos. 399/403 . . 22·00
400 35 c. Female Fishing Owl at nest . . 5·00 3·25
401 35 c. Pair of Fishing Owls . . 5·00 3·25
402 35 c. Fishing Owl, nest and egg . . 5·00 3·25
403 35 c. Adult Fishing Owl with youngster . . 5·00 3·25
399/403 . . *Set of* 5 22·00 14·50

Nos. 399/403 were printed together, *se-tenant*, in horizontal and vertical strips of 5 throughout the sheet.

See also Nos. 425/9 and Nos. 448/52.

(Des C. Abbott. Litho W. S. Cowells Ltd)

1982 (1 July). *21st Birthday of Princess of Wales. T* **96** *and similar vert designs. Multicoloured.* **W** w **14**. *P* 14½.

404 5 c. Type **96** . . 10 10
w. Wmk inverted . . 40·00
405 20 c. Princess leaving Eastleigh Airport, Southampton, August 1981 . . 50 10
406 50 c. Bride at Buckingham Palace . . 70 25
407 1 e. Formal portrait . . 1·25 65
w. Wmk inverted . . 75·00
404/7 . . *Set of* 4 2·25 1·00

97 Irrigation

(Des G. Hutchins. Litho Walsall)

1982 (1 Sept). *Sugar Industry. T* **97** *and similar horiz designs. Multicoloured.* **W** w **14** (*sideways*). *P* 14 × 14½.

408 5 c. Type **97** . . 10 10
409 20 c. Harvesting . . 25 15
410 30 c. Mhlume mills . . 35 25
411 1 e. Sugar transportation by train . . 1·00 1·40
408/11 . . *Set of* 4 1·50 1·75

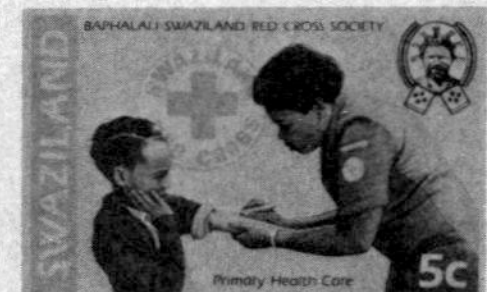

98 Nurse with Child

(Des L. Curtis. Litho Questa)

1982 (9 Nov). *Swaziland Red Cross Society (Baphaladi). T* **98** *and similar horiz designs. Multicoloured.* **W** w **14** (*sideways*). *P* 14.

412 5 c. Type **98** . . 10 10
413 20 c. Juniors carrying stretcher . . 25 15
414 50 c. Disaster relief . . 55 60
415 1 e. Henri Dunant (founder of Red Cross) . . 1·25 1·40
412/15 . . *Set of* 4 1·90 2·00

99 Taking the Oath 100 Satellite View of Earth

(Des B. Melton. Litho Format)

1982 (6 Dec). *75th Anniv of Boy Scout Movement. T* **99** *and similar horiz designs. Multicoloured.* **W** w **14** (*sideways**). *P* 14×13½.

416 5 c. Type **99** . . 10 10
417 10 c. Hiking and exploration . . 15 10
418 25 c. Community development . . 30 30
w. Wmk Crown to right of CA . . 8·00
419 75 c. Lord Baden-Powell . . 1·00 1·25
w. Wmk Crown to right of CA . . 8·00
416/19 . . *Set of* 4 1·40 1·60
MS420 107×109 mm. 1 e. World Scout badge 1·25 1·40

*The normal sideways watermark shows Crown to left of CA, *as seen from the back of the stamp.*

(Des A. Theobald. Litho Harrison)

1983 (14 Mar). *Commonwealth Day. T* **100** *and similar multicoloured designs.* **W** w **14** (*sideways on* 50 c., 1 e.). *P* 14.

421 6 c. Type **100** . . 10 10
422 10 c. King Sobhuza II . . 10 10
423 50 c. Swazi woman and beehive huts (*horiz*) . . 35 55
424 1 e. Spraying sugar crops (*horiz*) . . 70 1·00
421/4 . . *Set of* 4 1·10 1·50

(Des G. Drummond. Litho J.W.)

1983 (16 May). *Wildlife Conservation (2nd series). Lammergeier. Vert designs as T* **95**. *Multicoloured.* **W** w **14**. *P* 13½ × 13.

425 35 c. Adult male . . 2·00 2·00
a. Horiz strip of 5. Nos. 425/9 . . 9·00
426 35 c. Pair . . 2·00 2·00
427 35 c. Nest and egg . . 2·00 2·00
428 35 c. Female at nest . . 2·00 2·00
429 35 c. Adult bird with fledgling . . 2·00 2·00
425/9 . . *Set of* 5 9·00 9·00

Nos. 425/9 were printed together, *se-tenant*, in horizontal strips of 5 throughout the sheet.

101 Swaziland National Football Team 102 Montgolfier Balloon

(Des G. Vasarhelyi. Litho Format)

1983 (20 Aug). *Tour of Swaziland by English Football Clubs. Three sheets,* 101 × 72 *mm, each containing one* 75 c. *stamp as T* **101**. *Multicoloured.* **W** w **14** (*sideways*). *P* 13½.

MS430 75 c. Type **101**; 75 c. Tottenham Hotspur; 75 c. Manchester United . . *Set of* 3 *sheets* 1·75 3·00

(Des. D. Hartley-Marjoram. Litho Format)

1983 (22 Aug). *Bicentenary of Manned Flight. T* **102** *and similar multicoloured designs.* **W** w **14** (*sideways on* 10 c. *to* 50 c.). *P* 14.

431 5 c. Type **102** . . 10 10
432 10 c. Wright brothers' Flyer I (*horiz*) . . 15 10
433 25 c. Fokker F.28 Fellowship (*horiz*) . . 30 35
434 50 c. Bell XS-1 (*horiz*) . . 60 65
431/4 . . *Set of* 4 95 1·00
MS435 73×73 mm. 1 e. Space shuttle *Columbia* 1·00 1·40

103 Dr. Albert Schweitzer (Peace Prize, 1952)

(Des G. Vasarhelyi. Litho Harrison)

1983 (21 Oct). *150th Birth Anniv of Alfred Nobel. T* **103** *and similar horiz designs. Multicoloured.* **W** w **14** (*sideways*). *P* 14.

436 6 c. Type **103** . . 75 15
437 10 c. Dag Hammarskjöld (Peace Prize, 1961) 60 15
438 50 c. Albert Einstein (Physics Prize, 1921) 2·75 1·50
439 1 e. Alfred Nobel . . 3·00 3·00
436/9 . . *Set of* 4 6·25 4·25

104 Maize

(Des Jennifer Toombs. Litho Harrison)

1983 (29 Nov). *World Food Day. T* **104** *and similar horiz designs. Multicoloured.* **W** w **14** (*sideways*). *P* 14.

440 6 c. Type **104** . . 10 10
441 10 c. Rice . . 10 10
442 50 c. Cattle herding . . 70 80
443 1 e. Ploughing . . 1·25 1·60
440/3 . . *Set of* 4 1·90 2·40

105 Women's College 106 Male on Ledge

(Des C. Abbott. Litho Format)

1984 (12 Mar). *Education. T* **105** *and similar horiz designs. Multicoloured.* **W** w **14** (*sideways*). *P* 14.

444 5 c. Type **105** . . 10 10
445 15 c. Technical Training School . . 15 15
446 50 c. University . . 35 60
447 1 e. Primary school . . 65 1·10
444/7 . . *Set of* 4 1·10 1·75

(Des G. Drummond. Litho J.W.)

1984 (18 May). *Wildlife Conservation. (3rd series) Bald Ibis. T* **106** *and similar vert designs. Multicoloured.* **W** w **14**. *P* 13½ × 13.

448 35 c. Type **106** . . 3·00 3·00
a. Horiz strip of 5. Nos. 448/52 . . 13·50
449 35 c. Male and female . . 3·00 3·00
450 35 c. Bird and egg . . 3·00 3·00
451 35 c. Female on nest of eggs . . 3·00 3·00
452 35 c. Adult and fledgling . . 3·00 3·00
448/52 . . *Set of* 5 13·50 13·50

Nos. 448/52 were printed together, *se-tenant*, in horizontal strips of 5 throughout the sheet.

107 Mule-drawn Passenger Coach

(Des A. Theobald. Litho Walsall)

1984 (15 June). *Universal Postal Union Congress, Hamburg. T* **107** *and similar horiz designs. Multicoloured.* **W** w **14** (*sideways*). *P* 14½.

453 7 c. Type **107** . . 30 10
454 15 c. Ox-drawn post wagon . . 45 15
455 50 c. Mule-drawn mail coach . . 90 60
456 1 e. Bristol to London mail coach . . 1·40 1·10
453/6 . . *Set of* 4 2·75 1·75

108 Running

(Des Harrison. Litho Walsall)

1984 (27 July). *Olympic Games, Los Angeles. T* **108** *and similar horiz designs. Multicoloured.* **W** w **14** (*sideways*). *P* 14.

457 7 c. Type **108** . . 10 10
458 10 c. Swimming . . 10 10
459 50 c. Shooting . . 45 75
460 1 e. Boxing . . 90 1·60
457/60 . . *Set of* 4 1·40 2·25
MS461 100 × 70 mm. Nos. 457/60 . . 2·25 3·75

109 *Suillus bovinus*

(Des J. Spencer. Litho Format)

1984 (19 Sept). *Fungi. T* **109** *and similar multicoloured designs.* **W** w **14** (*sideways on* 10 c., 1 e.). *P* 14.

462 10 c. Type **109** . . 1·25 30
463 15 c. *Langermannia gigantea* (*vert*) . . 2·00 55
w. Wmk inverted . . 10·00
464 50 c. *Trametes versicolor* ("*Coriolus versicolor*") (*vert*) . . 2·50 2·25
465 1 e. *Boletus edulis* . . 3·25 4·25
462/5 . . *Set of* 4 8·00 6·50

110 King Sobhuza opening Railway, 1964 (111)

(Des W. Fenton. Litho Walsall)

1984 (5 Nov). *20th Anniv of Swaziland Railways. T* **110** *and similar horiz designs. Multicoloured.* **W** w **14** (*sideways*). *P* 14.

466 10 c. Type **110** . . 30 15
467 25 c. Type "15A" locomotive at Siweni Yard . . 65 40
468 30 c. Container loading, Matsapha Station . . 65 40
469 1 e. Locomotive No. 268 leaving Alto Tunnel 1·50 2·00
466/9 . . *Set of* 4 2·75 2·75
MS470 144 × 74 mm. Nos. 466/9 . . 4·25 5·50

1984 (15 Dec). *Nos.* 340B, 341A, 342A, 343A, 345B *and* 346A *surch as T* **111**.

471 10 c. on 4 c. *Aloe marlothii*
a. Surch on No. 343Ac 50 10
b. Surch on No. 343B 4·25 4·25
472 15 c. on 7 c. *Cyrtanthus bicolor* 60 20
473 20 c. on 3 c. *Haemanthus magnificus* 50 15
a. Surch on No. 342Ac 4·25 4·25
474 25 c. on 6 c. *Aloe kniphofioides* 60 20
a. Surch triple † —
b. Surch double
475 30 c. on 1 c. Type **83** 70 20
a. Surch omitted (horiz pair with normal) £375
476 30 c. on 2 c. *Aloe suprafoliata* 2·50 3·00
a. Surch on No. 341B 4·25 4·25
471a/6 *Set of* 6 4·75 3·50

112 Rotary International Logo and Map of World **113** Male Ground Hornbill

(Des G. Vasarhelyi. Litho Questa)

1985 (23 Feb). *80th Anniv of Rotary International. T* **112** *and similar horiz designs. Multicoloured. W* w **14** (*sideways*). *P* 14.

477 10 c. Type **112** 30 10
478 15 c. Teacher and handicapped children 70 20
479 50 c. Youth exchange 1·00 55
480 1 e. Nurse and children 2·00 1·10
477/80 *Set of* 4 3·50 1·75

(Des G. Drummond. Litho Harrison)

1985 (15 May). *Birth Bicentenary of John J. Audubon (ornithologist). Southern Ground Hornbills. T* **113** *and similar vert designs. Multicoloured. W* w **14**. *P* 14.

481 25 c. Type **113** 1·75 2·50
a. Horiz strip of 5. Nos. 481/5 8·00
482 25 c. Male and female Ground Hornbills 1·75 2·50
483 25 c. Female at nest 1·75 2·50
484 25 c. Ground Hornbill in nest, and egg 1·75 2·50
485 25 c. Adult and fledgeling 1·75 2·50
481/5 *Set of* 5 8·00 11·00

Nos. 481/5 were printed together, *se-tenant*, in horizontal strips of 5 throughout the sheet.

114 The Queen Mother in 1975 **115** Buick "Tourer"

(Des A. Theobald (2 e.), C. Abbott (others). Litho Questa)

1985 (7 June). *Life and Times of Queen Elizabeth the Queen Mother. T* **114** *and similar vert designs. Multicoloured. W* w **16**. *P* 14½×14.

486 10 c. The Queen Mother in South Africa, 1947 10 10
487 15 c. With the Queen and Princess Margaret, 1985 (from photo by Norman Parkinson) 10 10
488 50 c. Type **114** 25 40
489 1 e. With Prince Henry at his christening (from photo by Lord Snowdon) 50 90
486/9 *Set of* 4 80 1·40
MS490 91×73 mm. 2 e. Greeting Prince Andrew. Wmk sideways 1·25 1·40

(Des D. Hartley. Litho Walsall)

1985 (16 Sept). *Century of Motoring. T* **115** *and similar horiz designs. Multicoloured. W* w **14** (*sideways*). *P* 14.

491 10 c. Type **115** 50 10
492 15 c. Four cylinder Rover 70 20
493 50 c. De Dion Bouton 1·75 2·00
494 1 e. "Model T" Ford 2·25 3·75
491/4 *Set of* 4 4·75 5·50

116 Youths building Bridge over Ravine

(Des Vrein Barlocher. Litho Format)

1985 (2 Dec). *International Youth Year* (10, 50 c.), *and 75th Anniv of Girl Guide Movement* (*others*). *T* **116** *and similar horiz designs. Multicoloured. W* w **16** (*sideways**). *P* 14.

495 10 c. Type **116** 15 10
496 20 c. Girl Guides in camp 20 15
w. Wmk Crown to right of CA
497 50 c. Youth making model from sticks 45 75
498 1 e. Guides collecting brushwood 80 1·50
495/8 *Set of* 4 1·40 2·25

*The normal sideways watermark shows Crown to left of CA, *as seen from the back of the stamp.*

117 Halley's Comet over Swaziland **118** King Mswati III

(Des Jennifer Toombs. Litho B.D.T.)

1986 (27 Feb). *Appearance of Halley's Comet. W* w **14** (*sideways*). *P* 14.

499 **117** 1 e. 50, multicoloured 2·75 3·50

(Des A. Theobald. Litho Format)

1986 (21 Apr). *60th Birthday of Queen Elizabeth II. Vert designs as T* **230a** *of Jamaica. Multicoloured. W* w **16**. *P* 14×14½.

500 10 c. Christening of Princess Anne, 1950 10 10
501 30 c. On Palace balcony after wedding of Prince and Princess of Wales, 1981 15 25
502 45 c. Royal visit to Swaziland, 1947 15 30
503 1 e. At Windsor Polo Ground, 1984 30 60
504 2 e. At Crown Agents Head Office, London, 1983 60 1·25
500/4 *Set of* 5 1·10 2·25

(Des L. Curtis. Litho Walsall)

1986 (25 Apr). *Coronation of King Mswati III. T* **118** *and similar designs. W* w **16** (*sideways on* 20 *c. to* 2 *e.*). *P* 14½×14 (10 *c.*) *or* 14×14½ (*others*).

505 10 c. black and gold 35 10
506 20 c. multicoloured 70 30
507 25 c. multicoloured 80 35
508 30 c. multicoloured 90 50
509 40 c. multicoloured 2·00 1·75
510 2 e. multicoloured 3·50 6·00
505/10 *Set of* 6 7·50 8·00

Designs: *Horiz*—20 c. Prince with King Sobhuza II at Incwala ceremony; 25 c. At primary school; 30 c. At school in England; 40 c. Inspecting guard of honour at Matsapha Airport; 2 e. Dancing the Simemo.

119 Emblems of Round Table and Project Orbis (eye disease campaign) **120** *Precis hierta*

(Des M. Kesson, adapted G. Vasarhelyi. Litho Walsall)

1986 (6 Oct). *50th Anniv of Round Table Organization. T* **119** *and similar vert designs showing branch emblems. Multicoloured. W* w **16**. *P* 14.

511 15 c. Type **119** 20 10
512 25 c. Ehlanzeni 51 30 20
513 55 c. Mbabane 30 65 60
514 70 c. Bulembu 54 75 85
515 2 e. Manzini 44 1·75 2·50
511/15 *Set of* 5 3·25 3·75

(Des I. Loe. Litho Questa)

1987 (17 Mar). *Butterflies (1st series). T* **120** *and similar horiz designs. Multicoloured. P* 14.

516 10 c. Type **120** 40 40
517 15 c. *Hamanumida daedalus* 55 30
518 20 c. *Charaxes boueti* 55 70
519 25 c. *Abantis paradisea* 55 50
520 30 c. *Acraea anemosa* 55 70
521 35 c. *Graphium leonidas* 55 75
522 45 c. *Graphium antheus* 60 85
523 50 c. *Precis orithya* 70 85
524 55 c. *Pinacopteryx eriphia* 70 85
525 70 c. *Precis octavia* 80 1·40
526 1 e. *Mylothris chloris* 1·00 2·00
527 5 e. *Colotis regina* 1·25 1·40
528 10 e. *Spindasis natalensis* 2·50 2·75
516/28 *Set of* 13 7·50 12·00

For these designs, and similar 5 c., with different portrait of King Mswati III see Nos. 606/17.

121 Two White Rhinoceroses **122** Hybrid Tea Rose "Blue Moon"

(Des Doreen McGuinness. Litho Questa)

1987 (1 July). *White Rhinoceros. T* **121** *and similar horiz designs. Multicoloured. W* w **16** (*sideways*). *P* 14½.

529 15 c. Type **121** 2·00 45
530 25 c. Female and calf 2·75 1·00
531 45 c. Rhinoceros charging 4·25 3·25
532 70 c. Rhinoceros wallowing 6·50 7·00
529/32 *Set of* 4 14·00 10·50

(Des Josephine Martin. Litho Questa)

1987 (19 Oct). *Garden Flowers. T* **122** *and similar vert designs. Multicoloured. W* w **16**. *P* 14½.

533 15 c. Type **122** 90 20
534 35 c. Rambler Rose "Danse du feu" 1·75 80
535 55 c. Pompon Dahlia "Odin" 2·25 1·50
536 2 e. *Lilium davidii var. willmottiae* 5·75 9·00
533/6 *Set of* 4 9·50 10·50

1987 (9 Dec). *Royal Ruby Wedding. Nos.* 501/4 *optd with T* **45a** *of Kiribati in silver.*

537 30 c. On Palace balcony after wedding of Prince and Princess of Wales, 1981 20 20
538 45 c. Royal visit to Swaziland, 1947 30 30
539 1 e. At Windsor Polo Ground, 1984 50 1·25
540 2 e. At Crown Agents Head Office, London, 1983 75 2·25
537/40 *Set of* 4 1·60 3·50

123 *Zabalius aridus* (grasshopper)

(Des I. Loe. Litho Questa)

1988 (14 Mar). *Insects. T* **123** *and similar horiz designs. Multicoloured. W* w **16** (*sideways*). *P* 14.

541 15 c. Type **123** 80 15
542 55 c. *Callidea bohemani* (shieldbug) 2·00 85
543 1 e. *Phymateus viridipes* (grasshopper) 3·25 3·75
544 2 e. *Nomadacris septemfasciata* (locust) 5·00 7·00
541/4 *Set of* 4 10·00 10·50

124 Athlete with Swazi Flag and Olympic Stadium

(Des C. Abbott. Litho Format)

1988 (22 Aug). *Olympic Games, Seoul. T* **124** *and similar horiz designs. Multicoloured. W* w **16** (*sideways*). *P* 14.

545 15 c. Type **124** 25 10
546 35 c. Taekwondo 70 45
547 1 e. Boxing 1·25 1·75
548 2 e. Tennis 2·50 3·75
545/8 *Set of* 4 4·25 5·50

125 Savanna Monkey ("Green Monkey") **126** Dr. David Hynd (founder of Swazi Red Cross)

(Des I. Loe. Litho Questa)

1989 (16 Jan). *Small Mammals. T* **125** *and similar horiz designs. Multicoloured. W* w **16** (*sideways*). *P* 14.

549 35 c. Type **125** 1·25 30
550 55 c. Large-toothed Rock Hyrax ("Rock Dassie") 1·60 75
551 1 e. Zorilla 2·75 3·50
552 2 e. African Wild Cat 4·50 6·00
549/52 *Set of* 4 9·00 9·50

(Des T. Chance. Litho Security Printers (M), Malaysia)

1989 (21 Sept). *125th Anniv of International Red Cross. T* **126** *and similar horiz designs. Multicoloured. W w* **14** *(sideways). P* 12.
553 15 c. Type **126** 20 15
554 60 c. First aid training 55 40
555 1 e. Sigombeni Clinic 90 80
556 2 e. Refugee camp .. .. .. 1·40 1·40
553/6 .. .. *Set of* 4 2·75 2·50

127 King Mswati III with Prince of Wales, 1987

128 Manzini to Mahamba Road

(Des L. Curtis. Litho Harrison)

1989 (15 Nov). *21st Birthday of King Mswati III. T* **127** *and similar horiz designs. Multicoloured. P* 14×14½.
557 15 c. Type **127** 10 10
558 60 c. King with Pope John Paul II, 1988 .. 30 35
559 1 e. Introduction of Crown Prince to people, 1983 .. .. 50 55
560 2 e. King Mswati III and Queen Mother .. 95 1·00
557/60 .. .. *Set of* 4 1·60 1·75

(Des A. Theobald. Litho Questa)

1989 (18 Dec). *25th Anniv of African Development Bank. T* **128** *and similar horiz designs. Multicoloured. W w* **16** *(sideways). P* 14×14½.
561 15 c. Type **128** 10 10
562 60 c. Microwave Radio Receiver, Mbabane 30 40
563 1 e. Mbabane Government Hospital .. 50 85
564 2 e. Ezulwini Power Station switchyard .. 95 1·75
561/4 .. .. *Set of* 4 1·60 2·75

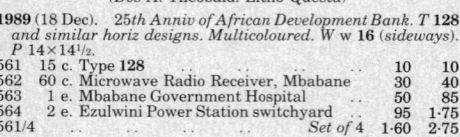

129 International Priority Mail Van

(Des G. Vasarhelyi. Litho Security Printers (M), Malaysia)

1990 (3 May). *"Stamp World London 90" International Stamp Exhibition. T* **129** *and similar horiz designs. Multicoloured. W w* **14** *(sideways). P* 12½.
565 15 c. Type **129** 15 10
566 60 c. Facsimile Service operators 40 40
567 1 e. Rural post office .. .. .. 75 1·00
568 2 e. Ezulwini Earth Station .. .. 1·40 1·90
565/8 .. .. *Set of* 4 2·40 3·00
MS569 105×85 mm. 2 e. Mail runner. Wmk upright .. .. 2·25 3·00
No. **MS**569 also commemorates the 150th anniversary of the Penny Black.

(Des D. Miller. Litho Questa)

1990 (4 Aug). *90th Birthday of Queen Elizabeth the Queen Mother. Vert designs as T* **107** *(75 c.) or* **108** *(4 e.) of Kenya. W w* **16**. *P* 14×15 *(75 c.) or* 14½ *(4 e.).*
570 75 c. multicoloured 50 50
571 4 e. brownish black & dp turquoise-green 2·25 3·00
Designs:—75 c. Queen Mother; 4 e. King George VI and Queen Elizabeth visiting Civil Resettlement Unit, Hatfield House.

130 Pictorial Teaching

131 Rural Water Supply

(Des D. Aryeequaye. Litho Questa)

1990 (21 Sept). *International Literacy Year. T* **130** *and similar horiz designs. Multicoloured. W w* **14** *(sideways). P* 14.
572 15 c. Type **130** 10 10
573 75 c. Rural class 45 45
574 1 e. Modern teaching methods 60 85
575 2 e. Presentation of certificates .. .. 1·10 1·40
572/5 .. .. *Set of* 4 2·00 2·50

(Des D. Aryeequaye. Litho Cartor)

1990 (10 Dec). *40th Anniv of United Nations Development Programme. "Helping People to Help Themselves". T* **131** *and similar vert designs. Multicoloured. W w* **14**. *P* 13½×14.
576 60 c. Type **131** 35 35
577 1 e. Seed multiplication project 60 85
578 2 e. Low-cost housing project .. .. 1·25 1·60
576/8 .. .. *Set of* 3 2·00 2·50

10c ■
(**132**)

133 Lobamba Hot Spring

1990 (17 Dec). *Nos.* 519/20, 522 *and* 524 *surch as T* **132**.
579 10 c. on 25 c. *Abantis paradisea* 30 30
580 15 c. on 30 c. *Acraea anemosa* 40 40
580*a* 15 c. on 45 c. *Graphium antheus* .. .. 10·00 10·00
581 20 c. on 45 c. *Graphium antheus* 40 40
582 40 c. on 55 c. *Pinacopteryx eriphia* .. 55 55

(Des D. Aryeequaye. Litho Harrison)

1991 (11 Feb). *National Heritage. T* **133** *and similar horiz designs. Multicoloured. W* **77** *of Brunei (sideways). P* 14½.
583 15 c. Type **133** 15 10
584 60 c. Sibebe Rock 40 45
585 1 e. Jolobela Falls 70 80
586 2 e. Mantjolo Sacred Pool .. .. .. 1·25 1·60
583/6 .. .. *Set of* 4 2·25 2·75
MS587 80×60 mm. 2 e. Usushwana River. P 14 1·75 2·50

134 King Mswati III making Speech

135 *Xerophyta retinervis*

(Des D. Aryeequaye. Litho Cartor)

1991 (24 Apr). *5th Anniv of King Mswati III's Coronation. T* **134** *and similar horiz designs. Multicoloured. W w* **14** *(sideways). P* 14×13½.
588 15 c. Type **134** 15 10
589 75 c. Butimba Royal Hunt 50 60
590 1 e. King and visiting school friends from Sherborne, 1986 .. .. .. 70 1·00
591 2 e. King opening Parliament .. .. 1·25 2·00
588/91 .. .. *Set of* 4 2·40 3·25

(Des D. Miller. Litho Questa)

1991 (17 June). *65th Birthday of Queen Elizabeth II and 70th Birthday of Prince Philip. Vert designs as T* **58** *of Kiribati. Multicoloured. W w* **16** *(sideways). P* 14½×14.
592 1 e. Prince Philip .. .. 70 1·00
a. Horiz pair. Nos. 592/3 separated by label .. .. 1·90 2·40
593 2 e. Queen Elizabeth II .. .. .. 1·25 1·40
Nos. 592/3 were printed in a similar sheet format to Nos. 366/7 of Kiribati.

(Des D. Aryeequaye. Litho Questa)

1991 (30 Sept). *Indigenous Flowers. T* **135** *and similar vert designs. Multicoloured. W w* **14** *(sideways). P* 14.
594 15 c. Type **135** 15 10
595 75 c. *Bauhinia galpinii* 60 70
596 1 e. *Dombeya rotundifolia* .. .. 80 1·25
597 2 e. *Kigelia africana* .. .. .. 1·75 2·25
594/7 .. .. *Set of* 4 3·00 3·75

136 Father Christmas arriving with Gifts

137 Lubombo Flat Lizard

(Des D. Aryeequaye. Litho Cartor)

1991 (18 Dec). *Christmas. T* **136** *and similar vert designs. Multicoloured. W w* **14**. *P* 13½.
598 20 c. Type **136** 15 10
599 70 c. Singing carols 65 50
600 1 e. Priest reading from Bible .. .. 80 1·25
601 2 e. The Nativity .. .. 1·50 2·50
598/601 .. .. *Set of* 4 2·75 3·75

(Des D. Aryeequaye. Litho Cartor)

1992 (25 Feb). *Reptiles (1st series). T* **137** *and similar horiz designs. Multicoloured. W w* **14** *(sideways). P* 13½.
602 20 c. Type **137** 65 20
603 70 c. Natal Hinged Tortoise .. .. 1·60 1·00
604 1 e. Swazi Thick-toed Gecko .. .. 2·00 2·00
605 2 e. Nile Monitor .. .. 2·75 3·50
602/5 .. .. *Set of* 4 6·25 6·00
See also Nos. 658/61.

138 *Precis hierta*

139 Missionaries visiting King Sobhuza II and Queen Lomawa

(Des I. Loe. Litho Questa)

1992 (26 Aug). *Butterflies (2nd series). Designs as Nos. 516/26 and new value (5 c.) showing different portrait of King Mswati III as in T* **138**. *Multicoloured. Without imprint date (5 c.) or with "1991" imprint date below design (others). P* 14.
606 5 c. *Colotis antevippe* 10 10
607 10 c. Type **138** 10 10
608 15 c. *Hamanumida daedalus* 10 10
609 20 c. *Charaxes boueti* 10 10
610 25 c. *Abantis paradisea* 10 10
611 30 c. *Acraea anemosa* 10 10
612 35 c. *Graphium leonidas* 10 10
613 45 c. *Graphium antheus* 10 10
614 50 c. *Precis orithya* 15 20
615 55 c. *Pinacopteryx eriphia* 15 20
616 70 c. *Precis octavia* 20 25
617 1 e. *Mylothris chloris* 25 30
606/17 .. .. *Set of* 12 1·25 1·50

(Des D. Aryeequaye. Litho Cartor)

1992 (16 Dec). *Centenary of Evangelical Alliance Missions. T* **139** *and similar vert design. Multicoloured. P* 13½×14.
620 20 c. Type **139** 25 10
621 1 e. Pioneer missionaries .. .. .. 1·25 1·75

140 Calabashes

141 King Mswati III as Baby

(Des D. Aryeequaye. Litho Cartor)

1993 (18 Mar). *Archaeological and Contemporary Artifacts. T* **140** *and similar vert designs. Multicoloured. P* 13½×14.
622 20 c. Type **140** 30 10
623 70 c. Contemporary cooking pot 75 75
624 1 e. Wooden bowl and containers .. 1·10 1·25
625 2 e. Quern for grinding seeds .. .. 1·75 2·50
622/5 .. .. *Set of* 4 3·50 4·00

(Des D. Aryeequaye. Litho Cartor)

1993 (6 Sept). *25th Birthday of King Mswati III and 25th Anniv of Independence. T* **141** *and similar vert designs. Multicoloured. P* 13½×14.
626 25 c. Type **141** 15 10
627 40 c. King Mswati III addressing meeting 20 20
628 1 e. King Sobhuza II receiving Instrument of Independence 65 90
629 2 e. King Mswati III delivering Coronation speech .. .. 1·25 1·90
626/9 .. .. *Set of* 4 2·00 2·75

142 Male and Female Common Waxbills

143 Classroom and Practical Training

(Des D. Aryeequaye. Litho Cartor)

1993 (25 Nov). *Common Waxbill. T* **142** *and similar vert designs. Multicoloured. P* 13½.
630 25 c. Type **142** 30 10
631 40 c. Waxbill and eggs in nest 45 25
632 1 e. Waxbill on nest .. .. .. 1·00 1·25
633 2 e. Waxbill feeding chicks .. .. 1·75 2·25
630/3 .. .. *Set of* 4 3·25 3·50

(Des D. Aryeequaye. Litho Cartor)

1994 (22 Feb). *25th Anniv of U.S. Peace Corps in Swaziland. T* **143** *and similar vert designs. Multicoloured. P* 13½.

634	25 c. Type **143**	15	10
635	40 c. Rural water supply	25	20
636	1 e. Americans and Swazis in traditional costumes	70	90
637	2 e. Swazi-American co-operation	1·10	1·75
634/7	*Set of* 4	2·00	2·50

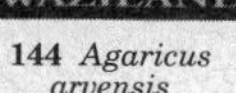

144 *Agaricus arvensis*

145 Emblem and Airliner on Runway

(Des D. Aryeequaye. Litho Cartor)

1994 (15 Sept). *Fungi. T* **144** *and similar vert designs. Multicoloured. P* 13½×14.

638	30 c. Type **144**	35	20
639	40 c. *Boletus edulis*	45	20
640	1 e. *Russula virescens*	1·00	1·25
641	2 e. *Armillaria mellea*	1·60	2·00
638/41	*Set of* 4	3·00	3·25

(Des D. Aryeequaye. Litho Walsall)

1994 (30 Nov). *50th Anniv of International Civil Aviation Organization. T* **145** *and similar horiz designs. Multicoloured. P* 14.

642	30 c. Type **145**	30	10
643	40 c. Control tower and dish aerial	35	20
644	1 e. Crash tenders	75	1·00
645	2 e. Air traffic controllers	1·25	1·75
642/5	*Set of* 4	2·40	2·75

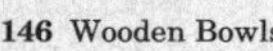

146 Wooden Bowls

147 Harvesting Maize

(Des D. Aryeequaye. Litho Cartor)

1995 (7 Apr). *Handicrafts. T* **146** *and similar vert designs. Multicoloured. P* 13½×14.

646	35 c. Type **146**	20	20
647	50 c. Chicken nests	30	35
648	1 e. Leather crafts	50	65
649	2 e. Wood carvings	90	1·25
646/9	*Set of* 4	1·75	2·25

(Des D. Aryeequaye. Litho Cartor)

1995 (5 June). *50th Anniv of Food and Agriculture Organization. T* **147** *and similar vert designs. Multicoloured. P* 13½.

650	35 c. Type **147**	20	20
651	50 c. Planting vegetables	30	35
652	1 e. Herd of cattle	50	65
653	2 e. Harvesting sorghum	90	1·25
650/3	*Set of* 4	1·75	2·25

148 Knysna Turaco

149 Waterberry

(Des D. Aryeequaye. Litho Cartor)

1995 (27 Sept). *Turacos ("Louries"). T* **148** *and simlar horiz designs. Multicoloured. P* 13½×13.

654	35 c. Type **148**	30	20
655	50 c. Knysna Turaco in flight	45	40
656	1 e. Violet-crested Turaco	70	80
657	2 e. Livingstone's Turaco	1·10	1·50
654/7	*Set of* 4	2·25	2·50

(Des D. Aryeequaye. Litho Cartor)

1996 (17 Jan). *Reptiles (2nd series). Horiz designs as T* **137** *with King's portrait at right. Multicoloured. P* 13½×13.

658	35 c. Chameleon	25	20
659	50 c. Rock Monitor	35	35
660	1 e. African Python	60	75
661	2 e. Tree Agama	90	1·50
658/61	*Set of* 4	1·90	2·50

(Des D. Aryeequaye. Litho Cartor)

1996 (23 Apr). *Trees. T* **149** *and similar vert designs. Multicoloured. P* 13×13½.

662	40 c. Type **149**	15	15
663	60 c. Sycamore Fig	20	20
664	1 e. Stem Fruit	40	50
665	2 e. Wild Medlar	80	1·10
662/5	*Set of* 4	1·40	1·75

150 Mahamba Methodist Church

(Des D. Aryeequaye. Litho Cartor)

1996 (26 Aug). *Historic Monuments. T* **150** *and similar horiz designs. Multicoloured. P* 13½×13.

666	40 c. Type **150**	15	15
667	60 c. Colonial Secretariat, Mbabane	20	20
668	1 e. King Sobhuza II Monument, Lobamba	40	50
669	2 e. First High Court Building, Hlatikulu	80	1·10
666/9	*Set of* 4	1·40	1·75

151 Children in Class

152 Klipspringer

(Litho Enschedé)

1996 (31 Dec). *50th Anniv of U.N.I.C.E.F. T* **151** *and similar multicoloured designs. P* 13½×14 (40 c.) *or* 14×13½ (*others*).

670	40 c. Type **151**	15	10
671	60 c. Child being inoculated (*vert*)	20	20
672	1 e. Child on crutches (*vert*)	40	55
673	2 e. Mother and children (*vert*)	80	1·10
670/3	*Set of* 4	1·40	1·75

(Litho Enschedé)

1997 (22 Sept). *Mammals. T* **152** *and similar multicoloured designs. P* 14×13½ (*vert*) *or* 13½×14 (*horiz*).

674	50 c. Type **152**	25	20
675	70 c. Grey Duiker	30	30
676	1 e. Antbear (*horiz*)	40	45
677	2 e. Cape Clawless Otter (*horiz*)	70	80
674/7	*Set of* 4	1·50	1·60

POSTAGE DUE STAMPS

D 1

Postage Due
2d

(D 2)

D 3

(Typo D.L.R.)

1933 (2 Jan)–**57**. *Wmk Mult Script CA. P* 14.

D1	D 1	1d. carmine	30	7·00
		a. Chalk-surfaced paper. *Dp carmine* (24.10.51)	20	11·00
		ac. Error. St Edward's Crown, W **9***b*	£150	
D2		2d. pale violet	1·75	19·00
		a. Chalk-surfaced paper (22.2.57)	4·75	26·00
		ab. Large "d"	38·00	
D1/2 Perf "Specimen"		*Set of* 2	40·00	

For illustration of No. D2ab see above No. D1 of Lesotho.

1961 (8 Feb). *No. 55 surch with Type* D **2**.

D3	7	2d. on 2d.	2·25	4·00

Another 2d. on 2d. Postage Due, with small surcharge as Type D **5**, was produced *after the currency change*, to meet the philatelic demand (*Price* 15*p unused*).

(Typo D.L.R.)

1961 (14 Feb). *Chalk-surfaced paper. Wmk Mult Script CA. P* 14.

D4	D 3	1 c. carmine	15	75
D5		2 c. violet	15	1·10
D6		5 c. green	20	1·10
D4/6		*Set of* 3	45	2·75

Postage Due
1c

(D 4)

Postage Due
1c

(D 5)

1961. *No. 55 surcharged*. A. *As Type* D **4**. (14 Feb).

D 7	7	1 c. on 2d.	1·25	2·50
D 8		2 c. on 2d.	1·25	2·50
D 9		5 c. on 2d.	2·25	2·50
D7/9		*Set of* 3	4·25	6·75

B. *As Type* D **5**. (Date?)

D10	7	1 c. on 2d.	90	2·75
D11		2 c. on 2d.	65	2·75
D12		5 c. on 2d.	1·25	2·75
D10/12		*Set of* 3	2·50	7·50

D 6

(Des and litho B.W.)

1971 (1 Feb). *Size* 18×23 *mm. W w* **12**. *P* 11½.

D13	D 6	1 c. bright rose-red	65	3·00
D14		2 c. purple	75	3·00
D15		5 c. dull green	1·00	3·50
D13/15		*Set of* 3	2·25	8·50

1977 (17 Jan). *Size* 18×23 *mm. W w* **14** (*sideways*). *P* 11½.

D16	D 6	1 c. rose-red	65	2·75
D17		2 c. purple	90	3·25
D18		5 c. dull green	1·40	4·00
D16/18		*Set of* 3	2·75	9·00

(Litho Harrison)

1978 (20 Apr)–**85**. *Size* 17½×21 *mm. W w* **14**. *P* 15×14.

D19	D 6	1 c. carmine	30	75
D19*a*		1 c. brown-red (13.3.85)	2·25	3·50
D20		2 c. purple	30	75
D21		5 c. blue-green	30	75
D19/21		*Set of* 4	2·75	5·25

(Litho Harrison)

1991 (17 July). *Size* 17½×21 *mm. With imprint date. W w* **14** (*sideways*). *P* 15×14.

D23	D 6	2 c. purple	10	10
D24		5 c. bright blue-green	10	10
D25		10 c. pale greenish blue	10	10
D26		25 c. red-brown	10	10
D23/6		*Set of* 4	25	25

Tanzania

(*formerly* Tanganyika)

TANGANYIKA

The stamps of GERMANY were used in the colony between October 1890 and July 1893 when issues for GERMAN EAST AFRICA were provided.

PRICES FOR STAMPS ON COVER TO 1945

The Mafia Island provisionals (No. M1/52) are very rare used on cover.

Nos. N1/5	*from* × 8
Nos. 45/59	*from* × 6
Nos. 60/2	—
Nos. 63/73	*from* × 6
Nos. 74/86	*from* × 8
Nos. 87/8	—
Nos. 89/92	*from* × 6
Nos. 93/106	*from* × 3
No. 107	—

MAFIA ISLAND

BRITISH OCCUPATION

Mafia Island was captured by the British from the Germans in January 1915. Letters were first sent out unstamped, then with stamps handstamped with Type M 1. Later the military were supplied with handstamps by the post office in Zanzibar. These were used to produce Nos. M11/52.

(Currency. 100 heller = 1 rupee)

(M 1)

(M 3)

1915 (Jan). *German East Africa Yacht types, handstamped with Type* M 1. *Wmk Lozenges, or no wmk* (1 *r.*, 2 *r.*). A. *In black* (2½ *h. in blackish lilac*). B. *In deep purple*. C. *In reddish violet.*

		A	B	C
M 1	2½ h. brown	£375	†	£200
	a. Pair, one without handstamp	†		† £1700
M 2	4 h. green	£500	£500	£225
	a. Pair, one without handstamp	†		† £1600
M 3	7½ h. carmine	£375	£375	£100
	a. Pair, one without handstamp	£2750		† £1300
M 4	15 h. ultramarine	£500	£475	£150
	a. Pair, one without handstamp	†		† £1400
M 5	20 h. black and red/*yellow*	£500	£500	£275
	a. Pair, one without handstamp		† £2750	£1700
M 6	30 h. black and carmine	£600	£750	£325
	a. Pair, one without handstamp	£3000		† £1700
M 7	45 h. black and mauve	£700	£700	£375
	a. Pair, one without handstamp	£3000		† £1900
M 8	1 r. carmine	£4500		† £3000
M 9	2 r. green	£5000		† £3500
M10	3 r. blue-black and red	£6000		† £3750

Prices are for unused examples.

A few contemporary Zanzibar stamps (1, 3, 6 and 15 c.) are known with the above handstamp.

(Currency. 100 cents = 1 rupee)

1915 (May). *German East Africa Yacht types with handstamped four-line surcharge* "G.R.—POST—6 CENTS—MAFIA" *in black, green or violet. Wmk Lozenges or no wmk* (1 *r.*, 2 *r.*).

M11	6 c. on 2½ h. brown	£750	£950
	a. Pair, one without handstamp		† £2750
M12	6 c. on 4 h. green	£750	£950
	a. Pair, one without handstamp	£2750	
M13	6 c. on 7½ h. carmine	£800	£950
	a. Pair, one without handstamp		
M14	6 c. on 15 h. ultramarine	£800	£1000
M15	6 c. on 20 h. black and red/*yellow*	£850	£1100
M16	6 c. on 30 h. black and carmine	£1200	£1300
M17	6 c. on 45 h. black and mauve	£1200	£1300
	a. Pair, one without handstamp		
M18	6 c. on 1 r. carmine	£7000	
M19	6 c. on 2 r. green	£8000	
M20	6 c. on 3 r. blue-black and red	£9000	

The 5, 20 and 40 pesa values of the 1901 Yacht issue are also known with the above surcharge as are the contemporary 1 c. and 6 c. Zanzibar stamps.

1915 (Sept). (*a*) *German East African fiscal stamps.* "Statistik des Waaren-Verkehrs" (*Trade Statistical Charge*) *handstamped in bluish green or violet,* "O.H.B.M.S. Mafia" *in a circle, as Type* M **3**.

M21	24 pesa, vermilion/*buff*	£600	£750
M22	12½ heller, drab	£550	£750
	a. Pair, one without handstamp	£2500	
M23	25 heller, dull green	£550	£750
M24	50 heller, slate	£550	£750
	a. Pair, one without handstamp	£2500	
M25	1 rupee, lilac	£550	£750

(*b*) *German East African* "Ubersetzungs- Gebühren" *Fee*) *stamp, overprinted as before*

M26	25 heller, grey	£550	£750

G. R. POST MAFIA (M 4)

G. R. Post MAFIA. (M 5)

(*c*) *Stamps as above, but with further opt as Type* M **4**, *in bluish green or violet*

M27	24 pesa, vermilion/*buff*	£750
M28	12½ heller, drab	£750
M29	25 heller, dull green	£750
M30	50 heller, slate	£750
M31	1 rupee, lilac	£750
M32	25 heller, grey (No. M26)	£750
	a. Pair, one without handstamp Type M 4	£2750

Type M **3** is also known handstamped on the 7½ h., 20 h. and 30 h. values of German East Africa 1905 Yacht issue and also on contemporary 1, 3, 6 and 25 c. Zanzibar stamps.

(Currency. 12 pies = 1 anna. 16 annas = 1 rupee)

1915 (Sept). *Nos.* E1/2, E4/9, E11 *and* E13 *of Indian Expeditionary Forces* (*India King George V optd* "I.E.F.") *with a further opt Type* M **4** *handstruck in green, greenish black or dull blue.*

M33	3 p. slate-grey	23·00	50·00
	a. Pair, one stamp without opt	—	£600
M34	½ a. yellow-green	40·00	55·00
	a. Pair, one stamp without opt	—	£650
M35	1 a. carmine	42·00	55·00
M36	2 a. mauve	60·00	90·00
M37	2½ a. ultramarine	80·00	£110
M38	3 a. orange-brown	85·00	£120
	a. Pair, one stamp without opt	—	£800
M39	4 a. olive-green	£100	£140
M40	8 a. purple	£170	£250
	a. Pair, one stamp without opt	—	£950
M41	12 a. dull claret	£250	£350
M42	1 r. red-brown and blue-green	£300	£375
M33/42	*Set of* 10	£1000	£1400

All values exist with the overprint inverted, and several are known with overprint double or sideways.

1916 (Oct). *Nos.* E1/2, E4/9, E11 *and* E13 *of Indian Expeditionary Forces* (*India King George V optd* "I.E.F.") *with further opt Type* M **5** *handstruck in green, greenish black, dull blue or violet.*

M43	3 p. slate-grey	95·00	£120
M44	½ a. yellow-green	95·00	£110
M45	1 a. carmine	85·00	95·00
M46	2 a. mauve	£130	£140
M47	2½ a. ultramarine	£140	£160
M48	3 a. orange-brown	£140	£160
M49	4 a. olive-green	£190	£200
M50	8 a. purple	£250	£325
M51	12 a. dull claret	£275	£400
M52	1 r. red-brown and blue-green	£325	£375
M43/52	*Set of* 10	£1500	£1900

Stamps with handstamp inverted are known.

NYASALAND-RHODESIAN FORCE

This issue was sanctioned for use by the Nyasaland-Rhodesian Force during operations in German East Africa, Mozambique and Nyasaland. Unoverprinted Nyasaland stamps were used by the Force prior to the introduction of Nos. N1/5 and, again, in 1918.

N. F.

(N 1)

1916 (7 Aug–18 Sept*). *Nos.* 83, 86, 90/1 *and* 93 *of Malawi* (*Nyasaland*) *optd with Type* N **1** *by Govt Printer, Zomba.*

N1	½d. green	1·50	7·00
N2	1d. scarlet	1·50	3·00
N3	3d. purple/*yellow* (15 Sept*)	6·00	14·00
	a. Opt double		† £7000
N4	4d. black and red/*yellow* (13 Sept*)	28·00	32·00
N5	1s. black/*green* (18 Sept*)	28·00	35·00
N1/5	*Set of* 5	60·00	80·00
N1/5 Optd "Specimen"	*Set of* 5	£200	

* Earliest known dates of use.

Of No. N3a only six copies were printed, these being the bottom row on one pane issued at M'bamba Bay F.P.O., German East Africa in March 1918.

This overprint was applied in a setting of 60 (10 rows of 6) and the following minor varieties occur on all values: small stop after "N" (R. 1/1); broken "F" (R. 4/3); very small stop after "F" (R. 6/5); no serifs at top left and bottom of "N" (R. 10/1).

TANGANYIKA

BRITISH OCCUPATION OF GERMAN EAST AFRICA

Following the invasion of German East Africa by Allied forces civilian mail was accepted by the Indian Army postal service, using Indian stamps overprinted "I.E.F.". Some offices reverted to civilian control on 1 June 1917 and these used stamps of East Africa and Uganda until the "G.E.A." overprints were ready. The last field post offices, in the southern part of the country, did not come under civilian control until 15 March 1919.

(Currency. 100 cents = 1 rupee)

G.E.A. (1) G. E. A. (2) G.E.A. (3)

1917 (Oct)–**21**. *Nos.* 44/5, 46*a*/51, 52*b*, 53/9 *and* 61 *of Kenya, Uganda and Tanganyika optd with T* **1** *and* **2**. *Wmk Mult Crown CA. Ordinary paper* (1 *c. to* 15 *c.*) *or chalk-surfaced paper* (*others*).

45	1 c. black (R.)	15	80
	ay. Wmk inverted and reversed	75·00	
	b. Vermilion opt	20·00	16·00
47	3 c. green	15	15
48	6 c. scarlet	15	10
	a. Wmk sideways	£1800	£1800
49	10 c. yellow-orange	30	40
50	12 c. slate-grey	30	1·50
	y. Wmk inverted and reversed	75·00	
51	15 c. bright blue	50	1·75
	w. Wmk inverted	90·00	
52	25 c. black and red/*yellow*	65	2·50
	a. On pale yellow (1921) (Optd S. £40)	1·40	12·00
53	50 c. black and lilac	70	3·00
54	75 c. black/*blue-green, olive back* (R.)	1·00	4·50
	a. On emerald back (1921) (Optd S. £50)	3·25	38·00
55	1 r. black/*green* (R.)	2·25	7·00
	a. On emerald back (1919)	4·25	38·00
56	2 r. red and black/*blue*	6·50	32·00
57	3 r. violet and green	12·00	60·00
58	4 r. red and green/*yellow*	17·00	75·00
59	5 r. blue and dull purple	30·00	75·00
60	10 r. red and green/*green*	50·00	£190
	a. On emerald back	55·00	£200
61	20 r. black and purple/*red*	£180	£300
62	50 r. carmine and green (Optd S. £150)	£475	£750
45/61	*Set of* 16	£275	£650
45/61 Optd "Specimen"	*Set of* 16	£375	

Early printings of the rupee values exist with very large stop after the "E" in "G.E.A." (R. 5/3). There are round stops after "E" varieties, which in one position of later printings became a small stop.

The only known used example of No. 48a is cancelled at Tanga in August 1918.

1921. *Nos.* 69/74 *of Kenya, Uganda and Tanganyika optd with T* **1** *or* **2**. *Wmk Mult Script CA. Chalk-surfaced paper* (50 *c. to* 5 *r.*).

63	12 c. slate-grey	6·00	70·00
64	15 c. bright blue	1·00	3·50
65	50 c. black and dull purple	8·50	70·00
66	2 r. red and black/*blue*	32·00	95·00
67	3 r. violet and green	50·00	£110
68	5 r. blue and dull purple	65·00	£130
63/8	*Set of* 6	£150	£425
63/8 Optd "Specimen"	*Set of* 6	£200	

1922. *Nos.* 65 *and* 68 *of Kenya, Uganda and Tanganyika optd by the Government Printer at Dar-es-Salaam with T* **3**. *Wmk Mult Script CA.*

72	1 c. black (R.)	40	12·00
73	10 c. orange	55	14·00

BRITISH MANDATED TERRITORY

(New Currency. 100 cents = 1 shilling)

4 Giraffe 5

(Recess B.W.)

1922. *Head in black. Wmk Mult Script CA.* (*a*) *P* 15 × 14.

74	4	5 c. slate-purple	1·75	20
75		10 c. green	1·40	55
76		15 c. carmine-red	1·75	10
77		20 c. orange	1·40	10
78		25 c. black	4·50	5·50
79		30 c. blue	4·50	4·00
80		40 c. yellow-brown	2·00	4·25
81		50 c. slate-grey	1·75	1·50
82		75 c. yellow-bistre	3·00	16·00

(*b*) *P* 14. A. *Wmk sideways.* B. *Wmk upright*

			A		B	
83	5	1 s. green	2·50	11·00	1·75	10·00
84		2 s. purple	4·25	12·00	3·50	18·00
85		3 s. black	8·50	26·00	†	
86		5 s. scarlet	17·00	70·00	10·00	60·00
87		10 s. deep blue	80·00	£150	40·00	80·00
88		£1 yellow-orange	£120	£225	£120	£200
74/88		*Set of* 15 (*incl* 85A)			£180	£375
74/88 Optd "Specimen"		*Set of* 15			£425	

In the £1 stamp the words of value are on a curved scroll running across the stamp above the words "POSTAGE AND REVENUE".

1925. *As* 1922. *Frame colours changed.*

89	4	5 c. green	65	1·25
90		10 c. orange-yellow	2·50	1·25
91		25 c. blue	3·25	15·00
92		30 c. purple	3·00	8·50
89/92		*Set of* 4	8·50	24·00
89/92 Optd "Specimen"		*Set of* 4	70·00	

6

7

(Typo D.L.R.)

1927–31. *Head in black. Wmk Mult Script CA. Chalk-surfaced paper* (5 *s.*, 10 *s.*, £1). *P* 14.

93	6	5 c. green	65	10
94		10 c. yellow	1·50	10
95		15 c. carmine-red	65	10
96		20 c. orange-buff	1·75	10
97		25 c. bright blue	2·00	1·75
98		30 c. dull purple	2·25	2·50
98*a*		30 c. bright blue (1931)	21·00	30
99		40 c. yellow-brown	1·75	3·50
100		50 c. grey	1·75	85
101		75 c. olive-green	2·00	8·50
102	7	1 s. green	3·00	2·00
103		2 s. deep purple	9·50	3·25
104		3 s. black	9·50	42·00
105		5 s. carmine-red	10·00	14·00

106 **7** 10 s. deep blue .. .. 48·00 80·00
107 £1 brown-orange £100 £170
93/107 .. .. *Set of* 16 £190 £300
93/107 Optd/Perf "Specimen" .. *Set of* 16 £250

Tanganyika became part of the joint East African postal administration on 1 January 1933 and subsequently used the stamps of KENYA, UGANDA AND TANGANYIKA.

INDEPENDENT REPUBLIC

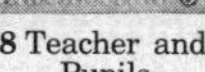

8 Teacher and Pupils

9 District Nurse and Child

14 "Maternity"

15 Freedom Torch over Mt Kilimanjaro

(Des V. Whiteley. Photo Harrison)

1961 (9 Dec)–**64**. *Independence. T* **8/9**, **14/15** *and similar designs. P* 14×15 (5 *c*., 30 *c*.), 15×14 (10 *c*., 15 *c*., 20 *c*., 50 *c*.) *or* 14½ (*others*).
108 5 c. sepia and light apple-green 10 10
109 10 c. deep bluish green 10 10
110 15 c. sepia and blue 10 10
a. Blue omitted £350
111 20 c. orange-brown 10 10
112 30 c. black, emerald and yellow 10 10
a. Inscr "UHURU 196" £425 £160
b. "1" inserted after "196" .. .. 10·00
113 50 c. black and yellow 10 10
114 1 s. brown, blue and olive-yellow .. 15 10
115 1 s. 30, red, yellow, black, brown and blue 1·75 10
a. Red, yellow, blk, brn & dp bl (10.3.64) 3·50 50
116 2 s. blue, yellow, green and brown .. 50 10
117 5 s. deep bluish green and orange-red .. 50 40
118 10 s. black, reddish purple and light blue .. 12·00 4·50
a. Reddish purple (diamond) omitted .. £150
119 20 s. red, yellow, black, brown and green .. 3·25 7·50
108/19 .. .. *Set of* 12 16·00 11·00

Designs: *Vert* (*as T* **9**)—15 c. Coffee-picking; 20 c. Harvesting maize; 50 c. Serengeti lions. *Horiz* (*as T* **8**)—30 c. Tanganyikan flag. (*As T* **14**)—2 s. Dar-es-Salaam waterfront; 5 s. Land tillage; 10 s. Diamond and mine. *Vert*—20 s. Type **15**.

No. 112a. The missing "1" in "1961" occurs on emerald Plate 1C, R. 10/10. The "1" was later inserted but it is, however, very slightly shorter and the figure is more solid than normal.

19 Pres. Nyerere inaugurating Self-help Project

20 Hoisting Flag on Mt Kilimanjaro

(Photo Harrison)

1962 (9 Dec). *Inauguration of Republic. Vert designs as T* **19/20**. *P* 14½.
120 30 c. emerald 10 10
121 50 c. yellow, black, green, red and blue .. 10 10
122 1 s. 30, multicoloured 10 10
123 2 s. 50, black, red and blue 30 30
120/3 .. .. *Set of* 4 45 35

Designs:—1 s. 30, Presidential emblem; 2 s. 50, Independence Monument.

23 Map of Republic

24 Torch and Spear Emblem

(Des M. Goaman. Photo Harrison)

1964 (7 July). *United Republic of Tanganyika and Zanzibar Commemoration. P* 14 × 14½.
124 **23** 20 c. yellow-green and light blue .. 10 10
125 **24** 30 c. blue and sepia 10 10
126 1 s. 30, orange-brown and ultramarine 10 10
127 **23** 2 s. 50, purple and ultramarine .. 80 40
124/7 .. .. *Set of* 4 1·00 50

Despite the inscription on the stamps the above issue was only on sale in Tanganyika and had no validity in Zanzibar.

STAMP BOOKLETS

1922–25. *Black on red cover.*
SB1 3 s. booklet containing 5 c., 10 c., 15 c. and 20 c. (Nos. 74/7), each in block of 6 .. ..
a. As No. SB1, but contents changed (Nos. 89/90, 76/7) (1925) .. ..

1922–26. *Black on red cover. Stapled.*
SB2 3 s. booklet containing six 10 c., and twelve 5 c. and 15 c. (Nos. 74/6) in blocks of 6 .. ..
a. As No. SB2, but contents changed (Nos. 74, 90, 76) (1925) .. ..
b. As No. SB2, but contents changed (Nos. 89/90, 76) (1926) .. ..

1927. *Black on red covers. Stapled.*
SB3 3 s. booklet containing six 10 c., and twelve 5 c. and 15 c. (Nos. 93/5) in blocks of 6 .. .. £500
SB4 3 s. booklet containing 5 c., 10 c. and 15 c. (Nos. 93/5), each in block of 10 .. ..

1961 (9 Dec). *Black on blue-green cover, size* 48×46 *mm. Stitched.*
SB5 5 s. booklet containing 10 c., 15 c., 20 c., 30 c. and 50 c. (Nos. 109/13), each in block of 4 .. 4·25

OFFICIAL STAMPS

OFFICIAL (O 1)   OFFICIAL (O 2) (3½ mm tall)

1961 (9 Dec). *Nos.* 108/14 *and* 117 *optd with Type* O **1** (10, 15, 20, 50 *c. or larger* (17 *mm*) 5, 30 *c.*) *or with Type* O **2** (1 *s. or larger* (22 *mm*) 5 *s.*).
O1 5 c. sepia and light apple-green 10 10
O2 10 c. deep bluish green 10 10
O3 15 c. sepia and blue 10 10
O4 20 c. orange-brown 10 10
O5 30 c. black, emerald and yellow 10 10
O6 50 c. black and yellow 10 10
O7 1 s. brown, blue and olive-yellow 10 10
O8 5 s. deep bluish green and orange-red .. 65 75
O1/8 .. .. *Set of* 8 90 90

ZANZIBAR

An Indian post office opened in Zanzibar in November 1868, but was closed for political reasons on 1 April of the following year. Little has survived from this period. Subsequently mail was forwarded via Seychelles or, later, Aden.

Stamps of INDIA were used in Zanzibar from 1 October 1875 until 10 November 1895, when the administration of the postal service was transferred from India to British East Africa. Separate cancellations for Zanzibar are known from 1 June 1878.

A French post office was opened on the island in January 1889 and this service used the stamps of FRANCE until 1894 when specific stamps for this office were provided. The French postal service on the island closed on 31 July 1904 and it is known that French stamps were again utilised during the final month.

A German postal agency operated in Zanzibar between 27 August 1890 and 31 July 1891, using the stamps of GERMANY.

PRICES FOR STAMPS ON COVER TO 1945

Nos. 1/2	—
Nos. 3/18	*from* × 30
Nos. 19/21	—
Nos. 22/174	*from* × 12
Nos. 175/7	—
Nos. 178/87	*from* × 20
Nos. 188/204	*from* × 15
Nos. 205/9	*from* × 20
Nos. 210/38	*from* × 15
Nos. 239/45	—
Nos. 246/59	*from* × 8
Nos. 260/f	—
Nos. 261/330	*from* × 4
Nos. D1/17	*from* × 12
Nos. D18/24	*from* × 15
Nos. D25/30	*from* × 30

PROTECTORATE

(Currency. 12 pies = 1 anna. 16 annas = 1 rupee)

Zanzibar
(1)

1895 (10 Nov)–**96**. *Nos.* 81, 85, 90/6, 98/101, 103 *and* 106/9 *of India* (*Queen Victoria*) *optd with T* 1 *by Zanzibar Gazette.*

(*a*) *In blue*
1 ½ a. blue-green £11000 £3250
2 1 a. plum £2000 £500
j. "Zanzidar" (R. 4/6, 8/5) .. .. — £11000

(*b*) *In black*
3 ½ a. blue-green .. .. 3·00 3·00
j. "Zanzidar" (R. 4/6, 8/5) £900 £600
k. "Zanibar" (R. 7/2) £950 £1300
l. Diaeresis over last "a" (R. 10/5) .. £800 £800
m. Opt double, one albino .. ..
4 1 a. plum .. .. 3·25 3·00
j. "Zanzidar" (R. 4/6, 8/5) .. .. — £2250
k. "Zanibar" (R. 7/2) £1200 £1400
l. Diaeresis over last "a" (R. 10/5) .. £1000
5 1 a. 6 p. sepia .. .. 4·00 3·00
j. "Zanzidar" (R. 4/6, 8/5) £2750 £850
k. "Zanibar" (R. 7/2) £1100 £1200
l. "Zanizbar" (R. 1/9) .. ..
m. Diaeresis over last "a" (R. 10/5) .. £800
6 2 a. pale blue .. .. 4·25 3·75
7 2 a. blue .. .. 4·50 4·00
j. "Zanzidar" (R. 4/6, 8/5) £2750 £1500
k. "Zanibar" (R. 7/2) £3000 £1600
l. Diaeresis over last "a" (R. 10/5) .. £850
m. Opt double £225
8 2½ a. yellow-green .. .. .. 6·00 4·25
j. "Zanzidar" (R. 4/6, 8/5) £2750 £1400
k. "Zanibar" (R. 7/2) £500 £950
l. "Zapzibar" .. ..
m. "Zanzipar" .. ..
n. Diaeresis over last "a" (R. 10/5) .. £850 £850
o. Second "z" italic (R. 10/1) £225 £350
p. Opt double, one albino .. ..
9 3 a. orange .. ..
10 3 a. brown-orange .. .. .. 9·00 8·50
j. "Zanzidar" (R. 4/6, 8/5) £700 £1300
k. "Zanizbar" (R. 1/9) £3250 £3500
11 4 a. olive-green .. .. .. 16·00 13·00
j. "Zanzidar" ((R. 4/6, 8/5) £4500 £3000
12 4 a. slate-green .. .. .. 8·50 11·00
l. Diaeresis over last "a" (R. 10/5) .. £1100
13 6 a. pale brown .. .. .. 15·00 10·00
j. "Zanzidar" (R. 4/6, 8/5) £4750 £3250
k. "Zanibar" (R. 7/2) £650 £1200
l. "Zanzibarr" £3250 £3250
m. Opt double .. ..
n. Opt double, one albino .. ..
o. Opt triple, two albino .. ..
14 8 a. dull mauve .. .. .. 20·00 17·00
j. "Zanzidar" (R. 4/6, 8/5) £4750 £4750
15 8 a. magenta (7.96) .. .. .. 10·00 18·00
16 12 a. purple/*red* .. .. .. 14·00 10·00
j. "Zanzidar" (R. 4/6, 8/5) £4500 £3250
17 1 r. slate .. .. 70·00 70·00
j. "Zanzidar" (R. 4/6, 8/5) £4500 £3750
18 1 r. green and aniline carmine (7.96) .. 10·00 23·00
j. Opt vert downwards £400
19 2 r. carmine and yellow-brown .. .. 35·00 60·00
j. "r" omitted £6000
k. "r" inverted £3500 £3500
20 3 r. brown and green .. .. .. 42·00 60·00
j. "r" omitted £6000
k. "r" inverted £3250 £3750
21 5 r. ultramarine and violet .. .. 42·00 60·00
j. "r" omitted £6000
k. "r" inverted £2750 £3750
l. Opt double, one inverted £750
3/21 .. .. *Set of* 15 £250 £300

There were a number of different settings for this overprint.

Values to 1 r. were initially overprinted from settings of 120 (12×10) including one which showed "Zanzidar" on R.4/6 and R.8/5 (soon corrected) and "Zanizbar" on R.1/9 (also soon corrected). Later supplies of these values were overprinted from settings of 80 (8×10) for the 6 a. only or 60 (6×10) for the others. One of these settings included "Zanibar" on R.7/2. Another late setting, size unknown, showed a diaeresis over last "a" on R.10/5.

Many forgeries of this overprint exist and also bogus errors.

MINOR VARIETIES. The following minor varieties of type exist on Nos. 1/21:

A. First "Z" antique (all values)
B. Broken "p" for "n" (all values to 1 r.)
C. Tall second "z" (all values)
D. Small second "z" (all values)
E. Small second "z" and inverted "q" for "b" (all values)
F. Second "z" Gothic (½ a. to 12 a. and 1 r.) (No. 18) (black opts only)
G. No dot over "i" (all values to 1 r.)
H. Inverted "q" for "b" (all values to 1 r.)
I. Arabic "2" for "r" (all values to 1 r.) (black opts only)

Varieties D and E are worth the same as normal examples, A (2, 3, 5 r.) and C normal plus 50%, G and I from 3 times normal, A (values to 1 r.), F and H from 4 times normal and B from 5 times normal.

2½ (2)   2½ (3)   2½ (4)   2½ (5)

1895–98. *Provisionals.* I. *Stamps used for postal purposes.*

(*a*) *No.* 5 *surch in red* (30.11.95)
22 **2** 2½ on 1½ a. sepia .. .. .. 40·00 32·00
j. "Zanzidar" £1200 £1100
k. "Zanizbar" £3500 £1800
l. Inverted "1" in "½" £1100 £900

(*b*) *No.* 4 *surch in black* (11.5.96)
23 **3** 2½ on 1 a. plum £130 £100
24 **4** 2½ on 1 a. plum £375 £250
j. Inverted "1" in "½" £1900
25 **5** 2½ on 1 a. plum £140 £100

2½ (6)   2½ (7)   2½ (8)

(*c*) *No.* 6 *surch in red* (15.8.96)
26 **6** 2½ on 2 a. pale blue .. .. .. 45·00 24·00
j. Inverted "1" in "½" £350 £275
k. Roman "I" in "½" £200 £150
l. "Zanzibar" double, one albino .. ..

27 7 2½ on 2 a. pale blue .. .. .. £130 80·00
j. "2" of "½" omitted £3750
k. "2" for "2½" £4750
l. "1" of "½" omitted £3750 £3250
m. Inverted "1" in "½" £1500
n. "Zanzibar" double, one albino ..
28 8 2½ on 2 a. pale blue £3750 £1500
No. 28 only exists with small "z"

(d) No. 5 surch in red (15.11.96)

29 6 2½ on 1½ a. sepia .. .. .. £130 95·00
j. Inverted "1" in "½" £1100 £950
k. Roman "I" in "½" £800 £750
l. Surch double, one albino ..
30 7 2½ on 1½ a. sepia £375 £325
l. Surch double, one albino ..
31 8 2½ on 1½ a. sepia £8500 £5500
No. 31 only exists with small "z".

II. *Stamps prepared for official purposes. Nos.* 4, 5 *and* 7 *surch as before in red* (1.98)

32 3 2½ on 1 a. plum £225 £500
33 4 2½ on 1 a. plum £425 £800
34 5 2½ on 1 a. plum £250 £500
35 3 2½ on 1½ a. sepia .. .. .. 75·00 £160
j. Diaeresis over last "a" £3000
36 4 2½ on 1½ a. sepia £160 £375
37 5 2½ on 1½ a. sepia £100 £200
38 3 2½ on 2 a. dull blue .. .. .. 85·00 £180
39 4 2½ on 2 a. dull blue £160 £375
40 5 2½ on 2 a. dull blue .. .. .. 95·00 £225
It is doubtful whether Nos. 32/40 were issued to the public.

1896. *Nos.* 65/6, 68 *and* 71/3 *of British East Africa* (*Queen Victoria*), *optd with T* **1**.

41 ½ a. yellow-green (23 May) .. .. .. 27·00 16·00
42 1 a. carmine-rose (1 June) .. .. .. 23·00 15·00
j. Opt double £650 £650
43 2½ a. deep blue (R.) (24 May) .. .. .. 75·00 42·00
44 4½ a. orange-yellow (12 Aug) .. .. .. 42·00 48·00
45 5 a. yellow-bistre (12 Aug) .. .. .. 48·00 27·00
j. "r" omitted .. .. .. — £2000
46 7½ a. mauve (12 Aug) .. .. .. 32·00 45·00
41/6 .. .. .. *Set of* 6 £225 £170

MINOR VARIETIES. The various minor varieties of type detailed in the note below No. 21 also occur on Nos. 22 to 46 as indicated below:

A. Nos. 23, 25, 27, 30, 35, 38, 41/6
B. Nos. 22/3, 26, 29/30, 32/3, 36, 39, 44/6
C. Nos. 22, 25/6, 32, 36, 38, 40/6
D. Nos. 22/46
E. Nos. 22/46
F. Nos. 22, 25/6, 29, 41/6
G. Nos. 25/6, 29, 35, 37/8, 40/6
H. Nos. 22, 41/6 (on the British East Africa stamps this variety occurs in the same position as variety C)
I. Nos. 26, 29, 35, 38, 41/6

The scarcity of these varieties on the surcharges (Nos. 22/40) is similar to those on the basic stamps, but examples on the British East Africa values (Nos. 41/6) are more common.

PRINTERS. All Zanzibar stamps up to Type **37** were printed by De La Rue & Co.

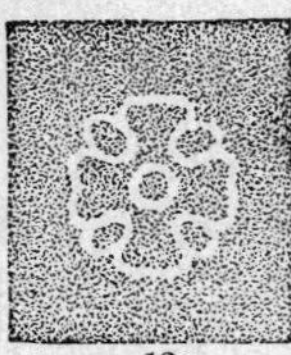

12

13

14 Sultan Seyyid Hamed-bin-Thwain

No right serif to left-hand "4" (R. 1/1)

1896 (Dec). *Recess. Flags in red on all values. W* **12**. *P* 14.

156 13 ½ a. yellow-green .. .. .. 3·25 1·50
157 1 a. indigo .. .. .. 1·25 1·50
158 1 a. violet-blue .. .. .. 3·75 3·75
159 2 a. red-brown .. .. .. 1·75 65
160 2½ a. bright blue .. .. .. 8·50 1·10
161 2½ a. pale blue .. .. .. 9·50 1·10
162 3 a. grey .. .. .. 6·50 4·25
163 3 a. bluish grey .. .. .. 7·50 6·00
164 4 a. myrtle-green .. .. .. 4·75 2·75
165 4½ a. orange .. .. .. 2·75 4·00
a. No right serif to left-hand "4" .. 65·00 75·00
b. No fraction bar at right (R. 2/1) .. 65·00 75·00
166 5 a. bistre .. .. .. 2·75 2·25
a. Bisected (2½ a.) (on cover) .. † £2750
167 7½ a. mauve .. .. .. 2·50 2·25
168 8 a. grey-olive .. .. .. 8·00 7·00
169 14 1 r. blue .. .. .. 9·00 9·00
170 1 r. deep blue .. .. .. 17·00 13·00
171 2 r. green .. .. .. 22·00 9·50
172 3 r. dull purple .. .. .. 20·00 9·50
173 4 r. lake .. .. .. 15·00 13·00
174 5 r. sepia .. .. .. 20·00 13·00
156/74 .. .. *Set of* 15 £110 75·00
156/74 Optd "Specimen" .. *Set of* 15 £180
The ½, 1, 2, 2½, 3 and 8 a. are known without wmk, these being from edges of the sheets.

1897 (5 Jan). *No.* 164 *surch as before, in red.*

175 3 2½ on 4 a. myrtle-green .. .. 55·00 35·00
176 4 2½ on 4 a. myrtle-green £180 £160
177 5 2½ on 4 a. myrtle-green .. .. 75·00 48·00
175/7 .. .. .. *Set of* 3 £275 £200

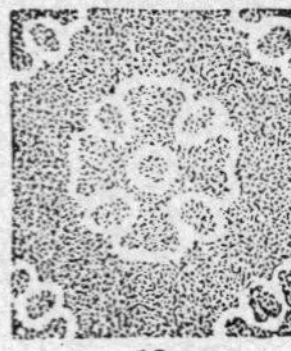

18

1898 (May). *Recess. W* **18**. *P* 14.

178 13 ½ a. yellow-green .. .. .. 1·25 35
179 1 a. indigo .. .. .. 1·00 55
a. Greenish black .. .. .. 4·25 1·50
180 2 a. red-brown .. .. .. 2·75 75
a. Deep brown .. .. .. 4·00 1·75
181 2½ a. bright blue .. .. .. 1·40 30
182 3 a. grey .. .. .. 4·00 60
183 4 a. myrtle-green .. .. .. 2·25 1·00
184 4½ a. orange .. .. .. 4·75 70
a. No right serif to left-hand "4" .. 85·00 28·00
b. No fraction bar at right (R. 2/1) .. 85·00 28·00
185 5 a. bistre .. .. .. 10·50 1·75
a. Pale bistre .. .. .. 10·50 2·00
186 7½ a. mauve .. .. .. 4·25 2·75
187 8 a. grey-olive .. .. .. 7·50 2·25
178/87 .. .. .. *Set of* 10 35·00 10·00

19

20 Sultan Seyyid Hamoud-bin-Mohammed bin Said

1899 (June)–**1901**. *Recess. Flags in red. W* **18** (*Nos.* 188/99) *or W* **12** (*others*). *P* 14.

188 19 ½ a. yellow-green .. .. .. 1·40 40
a. Wmk sideways .. .. .. 9·00 4·00
189 1 a. indigo .. .. .. 3·00 20
a. Wmk sideways .. .. .. 18·00 1·25
190 1 a. carmine (1901) .. .. .. 1·25 10
191 2 a. red-brown .. .. .. 1·75 45
192 2½ a. bright blue .. .. .. 1·40 55
193 3 a. grey .. .. .. 1·40 1·75
194 4 a. myrtle-green .. .. .. 2·25 1·00
195 4½ a. orange .. .. .. 6·50 2·25
196 4½ a. blue-black (1901) .. .. .. 10·00 10·00
197 5 a. bistre .. .. .. 2·00 1·25
198 7½ a. mauve .. .. .. 2·50 3·50
199 8 a. grey-olive .. .. .. 2·50 4·50
200 20 1 r. blue .. .. .. 15·00 12·00
201 2 r. green .. .. .. 15·00 16·00
202 3 r. dull purple .. .. .. 26·00 30·00
203 4 r. lake .. .. .. 38·00 45·00
204 5 r. sepia .. .. .. 45·00 50·00
188/204 .. .. *Set of* 17 £150 £160
188/204 Optd "Specimen" .. *Set of* 17 £180

One	Two & Half	Two & Half	Two & Half
(21)	(22)	(22*a*) Thin open "w" (R. 2/2, 3/4)	(22*b*) Serif to foot of "f" (R. 3/1)

1904. *Nos.* 194/6 *and* 198/9 *surch as T* **21** *and* **22**, *in black or lake* (L.) *by Zanzibar Gazette in setting of* 30 (6×5).

205 19 1 on 4½ a. orange .. .. .. 2·75 3·25
206 1 on 4½ a. blue-black (L.) .. .. 4·25 15·00
207 2 on 4 a. myrtle-green (L.) .. .. 13·00 16·00
208 2½ on 7½ a. mauve .. .. .. 12·00 18·00
a. Opt Type **22*a*** .. .. .. 75·00 95·00
b. Opt Type **22*b*** £110 £150
c. "Hlaf" for "Half" £9500
209 2½ on 8 a. grey-olive .. .. .. 14·00 28·00
a. Opt Type **22*a*** .. .. .. 95·00 £150
b. Opt Type **22*b*** £140 £200
c. "Hlaf" for "Half" £9000 £5000
205/9 .. .. .. *Set of* 5 40·00 70·00

23

24

Monogram of Sultan Seyyid Ali bin Hamoud bin Naherud

1904 (8 June). *Typo. Background of centre in second colour. W* **18**. *P* 14.

210 23 ½ a. green .. .. .. 1·00 80
211 1 a. rose-red .. .. .. 1·00 10
212 2 a. brown .. .. .. 1·25 45
213 2½ a. blue .. .. .. 2·25 35
214 3 a. grey .. .. .. 2·25 1·50
215 4 a. deep green .. .. .. 2·25 1·25
216 4½ a. black .. .. .. 3·00 2·50
217 5 a. yellow-brown .. .. .. 3·25 1·25
218 23 7½ a. purple .. .. .. 3·75 6·00
219 8 a. olive-green .. .. .. 3·75 2·50
220 24 1 r. blue and red .. .. .. 20·00 9·50
a. Wmk sideways .. .. .. 65·00 35·00
221 2 r. green and red .. .. .. 18·00 32·00
a. Wmk sideways £110 £140
222 3 r. violet and red .. .. .. 40·00 75·00
223 4 r. claret and red .. .. .. 45·00 90·00
224 5 r. olive-brown and red .. .. .. 48·00 95·00
210/24 .. .. .. *Set of* 15 £170 £275
210/24 Optd "Specimen" .. .. *Set of* 15 £130

25

26

27 Sultan Ali bin Hamoud

28 View of Port

1908 (May)–**09**. *Recess. W* **18** (*sideways on* 10 *r. to* 30 *r.*). *P* 14.

225 25 1 c. pearl-grey (10.09) .. .. .. 1·25 30
226 3 c. yellow-green .. .. .. 2·75 10
a. Wmk sideways .. .. .. 3·00 80
227 6 c. rose-carmine .. .. .. 5·50 10
a. Wmk sideways .. .. .. 7·50 1·50
228 10 c. brown (10.09) .. .. .. 1·60 1·75
229 12 c. violet .. .. .. 7·50 1·75
a. Wmk sideways .. .. .. 7·00 90
230 26 15 c. ultramarine .. .. .. 7·00 40
a. Wmk sideways .. .. .. 8·00 4·75
231 25 c. sepia .. .. .. 2·75 80
232 50 c. blue-green .. .. .. 4·75 3·50
233 75 c. grey-black (10.09) .. .. .. 8·00 11·00
234 27 1 r. yellow-green .. .. .. 21·00 10·00
a. Wmk sideways .. .. .. 40·00 8·00
235 2 r. violet .. .. .. 16·00 14·00
a. Wmk sideways .. .. .. 95·00 55·00
236 3 r. orange-bistre .. .. .. 21·00 45·00
237 4 r. vermilion .. .. .. 40·00 75·00
238 5 r. steel-blue .. .. .. 40·00 55·00
239 28 10 r. blue-green and brown (S. £26) .. 85·00 £180
240 20 r. black and yellow-green (S. £32) .. £180 £350
241 30 r. black and sepia (S. £42) £275 £475
242 40 r. black and orange-brown (S. £50) .. £400
243 50 r. black and mauve (S. £60) £350
244 100 r. black and steel-blue (S. £100) .. £650
245 200 r. brown and greenish black (S. £150) £950
225/38 .. .. *Set of* 14 £160 £190
225/38 Optd "Specimen" .. *Set of* 14 £150
Specimen copies of Nos. 239/45 are all overprinted.

29 Sultan Kalif bin Harub

30 Sailing Canoe

31 Dhow

1913. *Recess. W* **18** (*sideways on* 75 *c. and* 10 *r. to* 200 *r.*). *P* 14.

246 29 1 c. grey 30 20
247 3 c. yellow-green 50 20
248 6 c. rose-carmine .. .. .. 1·40 10
249 10 c. brown .. .. .. 1·10 1·25
250 12 c. violet .. .. .. 1·00 20
251 15 c. blue .. .. .. 1·25 30
252 25 c. sepia 90 45
253 50 c. blue-green .. .. .. 2·00 3·25
254 75 c. grey-black .. .. .. 2·00 2·25
a. Wmk upright £150
255 30 1 r. yellow-green .. .. .. 4·75 6·50
256 2 r. violet .. .. .. 9·00 20·00
257 3 r. orange-bistre .. .. .. 11·00 30·00
258 4 r. scarlet .. .. .. 22·00 50·00
259 5 r. steel-blue .. .. .. 30·00 32·00
260 31 10 r. green and brown .. .. .. 75·00 £130
260*a* 20 r. black and green (S. £25) £100 £225
260*b* 30 r. black and brown (S. £35) £120 £325
260*c* 40 r. black and vermilion (S. £50) .. £250 £425
260*d* 50 r. black and purple (S. £55) £225 £425
260*e* 100 r. black and blue (S. £80) £325
260*f* 200 r. brown and black (S. £110) .. £600
246/60 .. .. *Set of* 15 £140 £250
246/60 Optd "Specimen" .. *Set of* 15 £160
Specimen copies of Nos. 260*a/f* are all overprinted.

1914–22. *Wmk Mult Crown CA (sideways on 10 r.). P 14.*
261 **29** 1 c. grey 50 25
262 3 c. yellow-green 85 10
a. Dull green .. .. 2·50 15
263 6 c. deep carmine 85 10
a. Bright rose-carmine 85 10
aw. Wmk inverted .. .. .. † 75·00
264 8 c. purple/*pale yellow* (1922) .. .. 75 3·00
265 10 c. myrtle/*pale yellow* (1922) 75 30
266 15 c. deep ultramarine .. .. .. 1·10 3·50
268 50 c. blue-green .. .. 4·50 4·00
269 75 c. grey-black .. .. 3·00 18·00
270 **30** 1 r. yellow-green .. .. 4·00 3·00
271 2 r. violet .. .. 4·50 8·00
272 3 r. orange-bistre .. .. 16·00 25·00
273 4 r. scarlet .. .. 16·00 65·00
y. Wmk inverted and reversed .. 75·00
274 5 r. steel-blue .. .. 16·00 50·00
w. Wmk inverted .. .. .. 75·00
275 **31** 10 r. green and brown .. .. .. 80·00 £250
261/75 .. .. .. *Set of* 14 £130 £375
261/75 Optd "Specimen" .. .. *Set of* 14 £170

1921–29. *Wmk Mult Script CA (sideways on 10 r. to 30 r.). P 14.*
276 **29** 1 c. slate-grey .. .. 20 7·00
277 3 c. yellow-green .. .. 40 2·25
278 3 c. yellow (1922) 30 10
279 4 c. green (1922) 50 60
280 6 c. carmine-red 30 50
281 6 c. purple/*blue* (1922) 35 10
282 10 c. brown .. .. 70 6·50
283 12 c. violet 40 30
284 12 c. carmine-red (1922) 40 35
285 15 c. blue .. .. 55 6·50
286 20 c. indigo (1922) .. .. .. 1·00 30
287 25 c. sepia .. .. 75 8·00
288 50 c. myrtle-green .. .. 1·25 2·75
y. Wmk inverted and reversed .. 75·00
289 75 c. slate .. .. 2·50 38·00
290 **30** 1 r. yellow-green .. .. 3·50 2·50
291 2 r. deep violet .. .. 3·00 6·00
292 3 r. orange-bistre .. .. 4·25 7·00
293 4 r. scarlet .. .. 11·00 30·00
294 5 r. Prussian blue .. .. 17·00 60·00
w. Wmk inverted £100
295 **31** 10 r. green and brown .. .. .. 60·00 £180
296 20 r. black and green (Optd S. £65) .. £130 £300
297 30 r. black & brown (1929) (Perf S. £75) £160 £400
276/95 .. .. .. *Set of* 20 95·00 £325
276/95 Optd "Specimen" .. .. *Set of* 20 £200

32 Sultan Kalif bin Harub **33**

1926–27. *T* **32** *("CENTS" in serifed capitals). Recess. Wmk Mult Script CA. P 14.*
299 **32** 1 c. brown 20 10
300 3 c. yellow-orange 20 15
301 4 c. deep dull green 20 30
302 6 c. violet 20 10
303 8 c. slate .. .. 90 4·50
304 10 c. olive-green 85 40
305 12 c. carmine-red .. .. 1·50 10
306 20 c. bright blue 40 30
307 25 c. purple/*yellow* (1927) .. .. .. 4·00 2·50
308 50 c. claret .. .. 1·25 35
309 75 c. sepia (1927) .. .. .. 11·00 14·00
299/309 .. .. .. *Set of* 11 18·00 20·00
299/309 Optd "Specimen" .. .. *Set of* 11 £100

(New Currency. 100 cents = 1 shilling)

1936 (1 Jan). *T* **33** *("CENTS" in sans-serif capitals), and T* **30/1**, *but values in shillings. Recess. Wmk Mult Script CA. P 14×13½–14.*
310 **33** 5 c. green 10 10
311 10 c. black 10 10
312 15 c. carmine-red 10 40
313 20 c. orange 10 10
314 25 c. purple/*yellow* 10 10
315 30 c. ultramarine 10 10
316 40 c. sepia 15 10
317 50 c. claret 30 10
318 **30** 1 s. yellow-green 45 10
319 2 s. slate-violet 55 80
320 5 s. scarlet .. .. 7·00 4·75
321 7 s. 50, light blue .. .. 17·00 16·00
322 **31** 10 s. green and brown .. .. .. 16·00 16·00
310/22 .. .. .. *Set of* 13 38·00 35·00
310/22 Perf "Specimen" .. .. *Set of* 13 £120

36 Sultan Kalif bin Harub

1936 (9 Dec). *Silver Jubilee of Sultan. Recess. Wmk Mult Script CA. P 14.*
323 **36** 10 c. black and olive-green 70 30
324 20 c. black and bright purple .. .. 2·00 30
325 30 c. black and deep ultramarine .. 4·75 35
326 50 c. black and orange-vermilion .. 5·50 1·90
323/6 .. .. .. *Set of* 4 11·50 2·50
323/6 Perf "Specimen" .. .. *Set of* 4 65·00

37 *Sham Alam* (Sultan's dhow)

VICTORY ISSUE
8TH JUNE 1946
(38)

1944 (20 Nov). *Bicentenary of Al Busaid Dynasty. Recess. Wmk Mult Script CA. P 14.*
327 **37** 10 c. ultramarine .. .. 60 1·25
328 20 c. red .. .. 60 1·75
329 50 c. blue-green 60 30
330 1 s. dull purple 60 45
327/30 .. .. .. *Set of* 4 2·25 3·25
327/30 Perf "Specimen" .. .. *Set of* 4 70·00

1946 (11 Nov). *Victory. Nos. 311 and 315 optd with T* **38**.
331 **33** 10 c. black (R.) 20 20
332 30 c. ultramarine (R.) 20 40
331/2 Perf "Specimen" .. .. *Set of* 2 45·00

1949 (10 Jan). *Royal Silver Wedding. As Nos. 143/4 of Jamaica.*
333 20 c. orange 30 90
334 10 s. brown .. .. 17·00 26·00

1949 (10 Oct). *75th Anniv of U.P.U. As Nos. 145/8 of Jamaica.*
335 20 c. red-orange .. .. 40 1·50
336 30 c. deep blue .. .. 1·40 80
337 50 c. magenta .. .. 1·50 1·50
338 1 s. blue-green .. .. 1·50 2·75
335/8 .. .. .. *Set of* 4 4·25 6·00

39 Sultan Kalif bin Harub

40 Seyyid Khalifa Schools, Beit-el-Ras

1952 (26 Aug)–**55**. *Wmk Mult Script CA. P 12½ (cent values) or 13 (shilling values).*
339 **39** 5 c. black 10 10
340 10 c. red-orange 10 10
341 15 c. green .. .. 40 1·50
a. Yellow-green (12.11.53) .. .. 1·75 1·75
342 20 c. carmine-red 40 50
343 25 c. reddish purple 60 10
344 30 c. deep bluish green 30 10
a. Deep green (29.3.55) .. .. 4·25 3·75
345 35 c. bright blue .. .. 30 2·00
346 40 c. deep brown .. .. 30 1·00
a. Sepia (12.11.53) .. .. .. 1·50 1·25
347 50 c. violet .. .. 1·00 10
a. Deep violet (29.3.55) .. .. 2·00 80
348 **40** 1 s. deep green and deep brown 30 10
349 2 s. bright blue and deep purple .. 1·40 1·50
350 5 s. black and carmine-red .. .. 1·50 2·25
351 7 s. 50, grey-black and emerald .. 18·00 23·00
352 10 s. carmine-red and black .. .. 9·50 6·00
339/52 .. .. .. *Set of* 14 30·00 35·00

41 Sultan Kalif bin Harub

(Photo Harrison)

1954 (26 Aug). *Sultan's 75th Birthday. Wmk Mult Script CA. Chalk-surfaced paper. P 13 × 12.*
353 **41** 15 c. deep green 10 10
354 20 c. rose-red 10 10
355 30 c. bright blue 10 10
356 50 c. purple 15 10
357 1 s. 25, orange-red 15 60
353/7 .. .. .. *Set of* 5 40 80

42 Cloves

43 *Ummoja Wema* (dhow)

44 Sultan's Barge

45 Map of East African Coast

46 Minaret Mosque

47 Dimbani Mosque

48 Kibweni Palace

(Des W. J. Jennings (T **42**), A. Farhan (T **43**), Mrs. M. Broadbent (T **44, 46**), R. A. Sweet (T **45**), A. S. B. New (T **47**), B. J. Woolley (T **48**). Recess B.W.)

1957 (26 Aug). *W* w **12**. *P* 11½ (5 c., 10 c.), 11×11½ (15 c., 30 c., 1 s. 25), 14×13½ (20 c., 25 c., 35 c., 50 c.,), 13½×14 (40 c., 1 s., 2 s.) *or* 13×13½ (5 s., 7 s. 50, 10 s.).
358 **42** 5 c. orange and deep green 10 20
359 10 c. emerald and carmine-red 10 10
360 **43** 15 c. green and sepia .. .. .. 10 1·50
361 **44** 20 c. ultramarine 10 10
362 **45** 25 c. orange-brown and black 10 20
363 **43** 30 c. carmine-red and black 15 20
364 **45** 35 c. slate and emerald 15 20
365 **46** 40 c. brown and black 15 10
366 **45** 50 c. blue and grey-green 15 10
367 **47** 1 s. carmine and black 20 10
368 **43** 1 s. 25, slate and carmine .. .. 2·25 10
369 **47** 2 s. orange and deep green .. .. 2·25 1·25
370 **48** 5 s. deep bright blue .. .. .. 4·75 2·00
371 7 s. 50, green .. .. 4·75 4·00
372 10 s. carmine .. .. 4·75 4·25
358/72 .. .. .. *Set of* 15 18·00 12·50

49 Sultan Seyyid Sir Abdulla bin Khalifa

50 "Protein Foods"

(Recess B.W.)

1961 (17 Oct). *As T* **42/8**, *but with portrait of Sultan Sir Abdulla as in T* **49**, *W* w **12**. *P* 13×13½ (20 s.), *others as before.*
373 **49** 5 c. orange and deep green 10 30
374 10 c. emerald and carmine-red 10 10
375 **43** 15 c. green and sepia .. .. .. 40 1·50
376 **44** 20 c. ultramarine 15 10
377 **45** 25 c. orange-brown and black 15 10
378 **43** 30 c. carmine-red and black .. .. 1·25 30
379 **45** 35 c. slate and emerald .. .. .. 1·25 90
380 **46** 40 c. brown and black 30 10
381 **45** 50 c. blue and grey-green 40 10
382 **47** 1 s. carmine and black 40 40
383 **43** 1 s. 25, slate and carmine .. .. 1·50 1·00
384 **47** 2 s. orange and deep green .. .. 40 1·00
385 **48** 5 s. deep bright blue .. .. .. 2·25 5·00
386 7 s. 50, green .. .. 2·25 13·00
387 10 s. carmine .. .. 2·25 7·50
388 20 s. sepia .. .. 17·00 28·00
373/88 .. .. .. *Set of* 16 27·00 50·00

(Des M. Goaman. Photo Harrison)

1963 (4 June). *Freedom from Hunger. W* w **12**. *P* 14 × 14½.
389 **50** 1 s. 30, sepia 80 30

INDEPENDENT

51 Zanzibar Clove

53 "Religious Tolerance" (mosques and churches)

(Photo Harrison)

1963 (10 Dec). *Independence. Portrait of Sultan Seyyid Jamshid bin Abdulla. T* **51, 53** *and similar vert designs. P* 12½.
390 30 c. multicoloured 10 20
391 50 c. multicoloured 10 30
392 1 s. 30, multicoloured .. .. 10 3·25
393 2 s. 50, multicoloured .. .. 15 4·00
390/3 .. .. .. *Set of* 4 40 7·00

Designs:—50 c. "To Prosperity" (Zanzibar doorway); 2 s. 50, "Towards the Light" (Mangapwani Cave).

REPUBLIC

When the Post Office opened on 14 January 1964, after the revolution deposing the Sultan, the stamps on sale had the portrait cancelled by a manuscript cross. Stamps thus cancelled on cover or piece used between January 14 and 17 are therefore of interest.

JAMHURI 1964

(**55**= "Republic")

1964 (17 Jan). *Locally handstamped as T* **55** *in black.*

(i) *Nos.* 373/88.

No.	Type	Description	Unused	Used
394	**49**	5 c. orange and deep green	60	30
395		10 c. emerald and carmine-red	60	10
396	**43**	15 c. green and sepia	60	2·25
397	**44**	20 c. ultramarine	60	30
398	**45**	25 c. orange-brown and black	60	20
399	**43**	30 c. carmine-red and black	60	40
400	**45**	35 c. slate and emerald	60	75
401	**46**	40 c. brown and black	60	80
402	**45**	50 c. blue and grey-green	60	10
403	**47**	1 s. carmine and black	60	80
404	**43**	1 s. 25, slate and carmine	60	1·25
405	**47**	2 s. orange and deep green	1·50	1·25
406	**48**	5 s. deep bright blue	1·50	1·25
407		7 s. 50, green	2·00	1·50
408		10 s. carmine	2·00	1·25
409		20 s. sepia	2·50	4·50

(ii) *Nos.* 390/3 (*Independence*)

No.	Type	Description	Unused	Used
410		30 c. multicoloured	10	20
411		50 c. multicoloured	15	10
412		1 s. 30, multicoloured	25	40
413		2 s. 50, multicoloured	75	75
		a. Green omitted	£150	
394/413		*Set of* 20	15·00	16·00

T **55** occurs in various positions—diagonally, horizontally or vertically.

NOTE. Nos. 394 to 413 are the only stamps officially authorised to receive the handstamp but it has also been seen on Nos. 353/7, 389 and the Postage Dues. There are numerous errors but it is impossible to distinguish between cases of genuine oversight and those made deliberately at the request of purchasers.

JAMHURI 1964
(56)

JAMHURI
1964
(57)

1964 (28 Feb). *Optd by Bradbury, Wilkinson.*

(i) *As T* **56** *on Nos.* 373/88

No.	Type	Description	Unused	Used
414	**49**	5 c. orange and deep green	10	10
415		10 c. emerald and carmine-red	10	10
416	**43**	15 c. green and sepia	10	10
417	**44**	20 c. ultramarine	10	10
418	**45**	25 c. orange-brown and black	10	10
419	**43**	30 c. carmine-red and black	10	10
420	**45**	35 c. slate and emerald	10	10
421	**46**	40 c. brown and black	10	10
422	**45**	50 c. blue and grey-green	10	10
423	**47**	1 s. carmine and black	10	10
424	**43**	1 s. 25, slate and carmine	1·25	20
425	**47**	2 s. orange and deep green	50	20
426	**48**	5 s. deep bright blue	50	35
427		7 s. 50, green	65	3·50
428		10 s. carmine	1·00	3·50
429		20 s. sepia	2·00	4·00

The opt T **56** is set in two lines on Types **46/8**.

(ii) *As T* **57** *on Nos.* 390/3 (*Independence*)

No.	Type	Description	Unused	Used
430		30 c. multicoloured	10	10
431		50 c. multicoloured	10	10
432		1 s. 30, multicoloured	10	10
433		2 s. 50, multicoloured	15	30
		a. Green omitted	65·00	
414/33		*Set of* 20	6·00	11·50

The opt T **57** is set in one line on No. 432.

For the set inscribed "UNITED REPUBLIC OF TANGANYIKA AND ZANZIBAR" see Nos. 124/7 of Tanganyika.

58 Axe, Spear and Dagger

59 Zanzibari with Rifle

(Litho German Bank Note Ptg Co, Leipzig)

1964 (21 June). *T* **58/9** *and similar designs inscr.* "JAMHURI ZANZIBAR 1964". *Multicoloured. P* 13 × 13½ (*vert*) *or* 13½ × 13 (*horiz*).

No.	Type	Description	Unused	Used
434		5 c. Type **58**	10	10
435		10 c. Bow and arrow breaking chains	10	10
436		15 c. Type **58**	10	10
437		20 c. As 10 c.	30	10
438		25 c. Type **59**	30	10
439		30 c. Zanzibari breaking manacles	20	10
440		40 c. Type **59**	30	10
441		50 c. As 30 c.	20	10
442		1 s. Zanzibari, flag and Sun	20	10
443		1 s. 30, Hands breaking chains (*horiz*)	30	20
444		2 s. Hand waving flag (*horiz*)	30	20
445		5 s. Map of Zanzibar and Pemba on flag (*horiz*)	55	70
446		10 s. Flag on Map	2·50	1·75
447		20 s. National flag (*horiz*)	2·50	15·00
434/47		*Set of* 14	7·00	16·00

COVER PRICES

Cover factors are quoted at the beginning of each country for most issues to 1945. An explanation of the system can be found on page x. The factors quoted do not, however, apply to philatelic covers.

68 Soldier and Maps

69 Building Construction

(Litho German Bank Note Ptg Co, Leipzig)

1965 (12 Jan). *First Anniv of Revolution. P* 13 × 13½ (*vert*) *or* 13½ × 13 (*horiz*).

No.	Type	Description	Unused	Used
448	**68**	20 c. apple-green and deep green	10	10
449	**69**	30 c. chocolate and yellow-orange	10	10
450	**68**	1 s. 30, light blue and ultramarine	10	10
451	**69**	2 s. 50, reddish violet and rose	10	15
448/51		*Set of* 4	30	30

70 Planting Rice

(Litho German Bank Note Ptg Co, Leipzig)

1965 (17 Oct). *Agricultural Development. T* **70** *and similar horiz design. P* 13 × 12½.

No.	Type	Description	Unused	Used
452	**70**	20 c. sepia and blue	10	80
453	–	30 c. sepia and magenta	10	80
454	–	1 s. 30, sepia and yellow-orange	30	1·60
455	**70**	2 s. 50, sepia and emerald	50	3·50
452/5		*Set of* 4	85	6·00

Design:—30 c., 1 s. 30, Hands holding rice.

72 Freighter, Tractor, Factory, and Open Book and Torch

73 Soldier

(Litho German Bank Note Ptg Co, Leipzig)

1966 (12 Jan). *2nd Anniv of Revolution. P* 12½ × 13.

No.	Type	Description	Unused	Used
456	**72**	20 c. multicoloured	20	10
457	**73**	50 c. multicoloured	15	10
458	**72**	1 s. 30, multicoloured	15	10
459	**73**	2 s. 50, multicoloured	25	40
456/9		*Set of* 4	65	60

For stamps with similar inscription or inscribed "TANZANIA" only, and with commemorative date 26th April 1966, see Nos. Z142/5 of TANZANIA.

74 Tree-felling

75 Zanzibar Street

(Litho German Bank Note Ptg Co, Leipzig)

1966 (5 June). *Horiz designs as T* **74**, *and T* **75**. *P* 12½ × 13 (50 *c.,* 10 *s.*) *or* 13 × 12½ (*others*).

No.	Type	Description	Unused	Used
460		5 c. maroon and yellow-olive	30	60
461		10 c. brown-purple and bright emerald	30	60
462		15 c. brown-purple and light blue	30	60
463		20 c. ultramarine and light orange	20	20
464		25 c. maroon and orange-yellow	20	30
465		30 c. maroon and ochre-yellow	20	30
466		40 c. purple-brown and rose-pink	50	20
467		50 c. green and pale greenish yellow	50	20
468		1 s. maroon and bright blue	50	20
469		1 s. 30, maroon and turquoise	50	1·40
470		2 s. brown-purple and light blue-green	50	30
471		5 s. rose-red and pale blue	80	4·25
472		10 s. crimson and pale yellow	2·25	16·00
473		20 s. deep purple-brown and magenta	4·25	24·00
460/473		*Set of* 14	10·00	45·00

Designs:—5 c., 20 s. Type **74**; 10 c., 1 s. Clove cultivation; 15, 40 c. Chair-making; 20 c., 5 s. Lumumba College; 25 c., 1 s. 30, Agriculture; 30 c., 2 s. Agricultural workers; 50 c., 10 s. Type **75**.

81 "Education"

(Litho D.L.R.)

1966 (25 Sept). *Introduction of Free Education. P* 13½ × 13.

No.	Type	Description	Unused	Used
474	**81**	50 c. black, light blue and orange	10	75
475		1 s. 30, black, lt blue and yellow-green	15	1·25
476		2 s. 50, black, light blue and pink	40	4·00
474/6		*Set of* 3	60	5·50

82 A.S.P. Flag

(Litho D.L.R.)

1967 (5 Feb). *Tenth Anniv of Afro-Shirazi Party* (*A.S.P.*). *T* **82** *and similar multicoloured design. P* 14.

No.	Type	Description	Unused	Used
477		30 c. Type **82**	10	85
478		50 c. Vice-President M. A. Karume of Tanzania, flag and crowd (*vert*)	10	85
479		1 s. 30, As 50 c.	10	1·75
480		2 s. 50, Type **82**	30	3·25
477/80		*Set of* 4	45	6·00

84 Voluntary Workers

(Photo Delrieu)

1967 (20 Aug). *Voluntary Workers Brigade. P* 12½ × 12.

No.	Type	Description	Unused	Used
481	**84**	1 s. 30, multicoloured	15	2·00
482		2 s. 50, multicoloured	40	5·00

POSTAGE DUE STAMPS

Insufficiently prepaid.
Postage due.
1 cent.

D 1

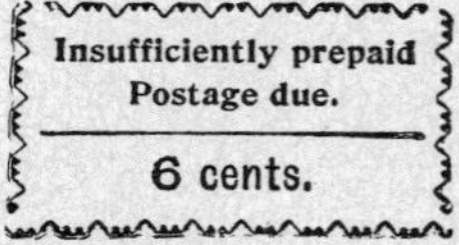
Insufficiently prepaid
Postage due.
6 cents.

D 2

(Types D **1** and D **2** typo by the Government Printer)

1927–30. *Rouletted* 10, *with imperf sheet edges. No gum.*

No.	Type	Description	Unused	Used
D 1	D **1**	1 c. black/*orange*	11·00	85·00
D 2		2 c. black/*orange*	4·50	35·00
D 3		3 c. black/*orange*	5·00	32·00
		a. "cent.s" for "cents."	95·00	
D 4		6 c. black/*orange*	—	£7000
		a. "cent.s" for "cents."	—	£15000
D 5		9 c. black/*orange*	2·75	16·00
		a. "cent.s" for "cents."	14·00	55·00
D 6		12 c. black/*orange*	£7500	£7500
		a. "cent.s" for "cents."		
D 7		12 c. black/*green*	£1300	£600
		a. "cent.s" for "cents."	£3500	£1700
D 8		15 c. black/*orange*	2·75	17·00
		a. "cent.s" for "cents."	16·00	60·00
D 9		18 c. black/*salmon*	4·00	28·00
		a. "cent.s" for "cents."	28·00	85·00
D10		18 c. black/*orange*	11·00	45·00
		a. "cent.s" for "cents."	50·00	£130
D11		20 c. black/*orange*	4·00	40·00
		a. "cent.s" for "cents."	30·00	£110
D12		21 c. black/*orange*	3·50	22·00
		a. "cent.s" for "cents."	24·00	80·00
D13		25 c. black/*magenta*	£2500	£1300
		a. "cent.s" for "cents."	£6500	£3750
D14		25 c. black/*orange*	£9000	£9000
D15		31 c. black/*orange*	9·50	55·00
		a. "cent.s" for "cents."	48·00	
D16		50 c. black/*orange*	21·00	£110
		a. "cent.s" for "cents."	90·00	
D17		75 c. black/*orange*	65·00	£225
		a. "cent.s" for "cents."	£250	

Initial printings, except the 1 c. and 2 c., contained the error "cent.s" for "cents" on R. 4/1 in the sheets of 10 (2×5). The error was corrected on subsequent supplies of the 3 c., 9 c. and 15 c.

It is known that examples of these stamps used before early 1929 were left uncancelled on the covers. Unused examples of Nos. D4, D6/7 and D13/14 which are not in very fine condition, must be assumed to have been used.

1930–33. *Rouletted 5. No gum.*
D18 D 2 2 c. black/*salmon* 9·00 20·00
D19 3 c. black/*rose* 3·00 40·00
D21 6 c. black/*yellow* 3·00 25·00
D22 12 c. black/*blue* 4·00 18·00
D23 25 c. black/*rose* 9·00 50·00
D24 25 c. black/*lilac* 10·00 38·00
D18/24 *Set of* 6 35·00 £170

D 3

(Typo D.L.R.)

1936 (1 Jan)–**62**. *Wmk Mult Script CA. P* 14.
D25 D 3 5 c. violet 1·50 5·00
a. Chalk-surfaced paper (18.7.56) 30 11·00
D26 10 c. scarlet 1·40 2·00
a. Chalk-surfaced paper (6.3.62) 30 4·50
D27 20 c. green 1·00 3·50
a. Chalk-surfaced paper (6.3.62) 30 11·00
D28 30 c. brown 4·50 13·00
a. Chalk-surfaced paper (18.7.56) 30 8·50
D29 40 c. ultramarine 4·50 18·00
a. Chalk-surfaced paper (18.7.56) 40 18·00
D30 1 s. grey 4·50 23·00
a. Chalk-surfaced paper (18.7.56) 1·00 15·00
D25/30 *Set of* 6 16·00 60·00
D25a/30a *Set of* 6 2·40 60·00
D25/30 Perf "Specimen" *Set of* 6 60·00
See footnote after No. 413.

All Zanzibar issues were withdrawn on 1 January 1968 and replaced by Tanzania issues. Zanzibar stamps remained valid for postage in Zanzibar for a limited period.

TANZANIA

The United Republic of Tanganyika and Zanzibar, formed 26 April 1964, was renamed the United Republic of Tanzania on 29 October 1964.

Issues to No. 176, except Nos. Z142/5, were also valid in Kenya and Uganda.

(Currency. 100 cents = 1 shilling)

25 Hale Hydro-Electric Scheme

26 Tanzanian Flag

27 National Servicemen

33 Dar-es-Salaam Harbour

38 Arms of Tanzania

(Des V. Whiteley. Photo Harrison)

1965 (9 Dec). *T* **25/7**, **33**, **38** *and similar designs. P* 14 × 14½ (5 *c.*, 10 *c.*, 20 *c.*, 50 *c.*, 65 *c.*), 14½ × 14 (15 *c.*, 30 *c.*, 40 *c.*), *or* 14 (*others*).
128 5 c. ultramarine and yellow-orange 10 10
129 10 c. black, greenish yellow, green & blue 10 10
130 15 c. multicoloured 10 10
131 20 c. sepia, grey-green and greenish blue 10 10
132 30 c. black and red-brown 10 10
133 40 c. multicoloured 65 20
134 50 c. multicoloured 30 10
135 65 c. green, red-brown and blue 2·50 1·50
136 1 s. multicoloured 80 10
137 1 s. 30, multicoloured 5·50 75
138 2 s. 50, blue and orange-brown 5·00 90
139 5 s. lake-brown, yellow-green and blue 80 20
140 10 s. olive-yellow, olive-green and blue 1·00 2·00
141 20 s. multicoloured 5·00 14·00
128/41 *Set of* 14 19·00 18·00

Designs: *Horiz* (*as T* **25**)—20 c. Road-building; 50 c. Common Zebras, Manyara National Park; 65 c. Mt Kilimanjaro. *Vert* (*as T* **27**)—30 c. Drum, spear, shield and stool; 40 c. Giraffes, Mikumi National Park. *Horiz* (*As T* **33**)—1 s. 30, Skull of *Zinjanthropus* and excavations, Olduvai Gorge, 2 s. 50, Fishing; 5 s. Sisal industry; 10 s. State House, Dar-es-Salaam.

MINIMUM PRICE

The minimum price quote is 10p which represents a handling charge rather than a basis for valuing common stamps. For further notes about prices see introductory pages.

Z 39 Pres. Nyerere and First Vice-Pres. Karume within Bowl of Flame

Z 40 Hands supporting Bowl of Flame

(Des J. Ahmed (Type Z **39**), G. Vasarhelyi (Type Z **40**). Photo Enschedé)

1966 (26 April). *2nd Anniv of United Republic. P* 14 × 13.
Z142 Z **39** 30 c. multicoloured 30 45
Z143 Z **40** 50 c. multicoloured 30 45
Z144 1 s. 30, multicoloured 30 45
Z145 Z **39** 2 s. 50, multicoloured 45 1·25
Z142/5 *Set of* 4 1·25 2·40

Nos. Z142/5 were on sale in Zanzibar only.

39 Black-footed Cardinalfish

40 Sobrinus Mudskipper

41 Lionfish

(Des Rena Fennessy. Photo Harrison)

1967 (9 Dec)–**73**. *Designs as T* **39/41**. *Chalk-surfaced paper. P* 14 × 15 (5 *c. to* 70 *c.*) *or* 14½ (*others*).
142 5 c. magenta, yellow-olive and black 10 85
a. Glazed, ordinary paper (22.1.71) 30 1·50
143 10 c. brown and bistre 10 10
a. Glazed, ordinary paper (27.9.72) 30 1·25
144 15 c. grey, turquoise-blue and black 10 50
a. Glazed, ordinary paper (22.1.71) 30 2·50
145 20 c. brown and turquoise-green 10 10
a. Glazed, ordinary paper (16.7.73) 30 3·50
146 30 c. sage-green and black 20 10
a. Glazed, ordinary paper (3.5.71) 6·50 1·90
147 40 c. yellow, chocolate and bright green 70 10
a. Glazed, ordinary paper (10.2.71) 70 30
148 50 c. multicoloured 20 10
a. Glazed, ordinary paper (10.2.71) 30 95
149 65 c. orange-yellow, bronze-green and black 3·50 4·25
150 70 c. multicoloured (15.9.69) 1·00 2·50
a. Glazed, ordinary paper (22.1.71) 4·25 6·50
151 1 s. orange-brown, slate-blue and maroon 30 10
a. Glazed, ordinary paper (3.2.71) 1·00 10
152 1 s. 30, multicoloured 5·00 10
153 1 s. 50, multicoloured (15.9.69) 4·75 50
a. Glazed, ordinary paper (27.9.72) 2·25 10
154 2 s. 50, multicoloured 3·25 2·00
a. Glazed, ordinary paper (27.9.72) 10·00 10
155 5 s. greenish yellow, black & turquoise-grn 6·00 2·25
a. Glazed, ordinary paper (12.12.70*) 3·25 10
156 10 s. multicoloured 2·00 2·50
a. Glazed, ordinary paper (*dull blue-green background*) (12.12.70*) 2·50 10
ab. Deep dull green background (12.9.73) 3·00 50
157 20 s. multicoloured 4·00 5·50
a. Glazed, ordinary paper (12.12.70*) 8·00 15
142/57 *Set of* 16 27·00 19·00
142a/57a *Set of* 14 35·00 17·00

*Earliest known postmark date.

Designs: *Horiz as T* **39/40**—15 c. White-spotted Puffer; 20 c. Thorny Seahorse; 30 c. Dusky Batfish; 40 c. Black-spotted Sweetlips; 50 c. Blue Birdwrasse; 65 c. Bennett's Butterflyfish; 70 c. Black-tipped Grouper. *Horiz as T* **41**:—1 s. 30, Powder-blue Surgeonfish; 1 s. 50, Yellow-finned Fusilier; 2 s. 50, Emperor Snapper; 5 s. Moorish Idol; 10 s. Painted Triggerfish; 20 s. Horned Squirrelfish.

On chalk-surfaced paper all values except the 30 c. exist with PVA gum as well as gum arabic, but the 70 c. and 1 s. 50 exist with PVA gum only. Stamps on glazed, ordinary paper come only with PVA gum.

53 *Papilio hornimani*

54 *Euphaedra neophron*

=
80c
(55)

(Des Rena Fennessy. Photo Harrison)

1973 (10 Dec)–**78**. *Various vert designs as T* **53/4**.

(*a*) *Size as T* **53**. *P* 14½×14
158 5 c. light yellow-olive, lt violet-blue & black 60 30
159 10 c. multicoloured 60 15
160 15 c. light violet-blue and black 60 30
161 20 c. reddish cinnamon, orange-yellow & blk 70 15
162 30 c. yellow, orange and black 70 10
a. Bistre-yellow, orange & black (20.4.78) 1·75 50
163 40 c. multicoloured 70 15
164 50 c. multicoloured 1·00 15
165 60 c. lt grey-brown, lemon & reddish brown 1·50 20
166 70 c. turquoise-green, pale orange and black 1·50 20

(*b*) *Size as T* **54**. *P* 14
167 1 s. multicoloured 1·50 15
168 1 s. 50, multicoloured 3·00 45
169 2 s. 50, multicoloured 3·25 80
170 5 s. multicoloured (*brt green background*) 3·00 95
a. Apple-green background (20.4.78) 4·00 60
171 10 s. multicoloured 3·75 6·00
172 20 s. multicoloured 5·50 13·00
158/72 *Set of* 15 25·00 20·00

Butterflies:—10 c. *Colotis ione*; 15 c. *Amauris hyalites* (s sp *makuyuensis*); 20 c. *Libythea labdaca* (s sp *laius*); 30 c. *Danaus chrysippus*; 40 c. *Asterope rosa*; 50 c. *Axiocerses styx*; 60 c. *Terias hecabe*; 70 c. *Acraea insignis*; 1 s. 50, *Precis octavia*; 2 s. 50, *Charaxes eupale*; 5 s. *Charaxes pollux*; 10 s. *Salamis parhassus*; 20 s. *Papilio ophidicephalus*.

Nos. 159 and 164 exist in coils, constructed from normal sheets.

A used example of No. 167 has been seen apparently showing the yellow colour omitted.

1975 (17 Nov). *Nos.* 165, 168/9 *and* 172 *surch as T* **55**.
173 80 c. on 60 c. *Terias hecabe* 2·00 2·00
174 2 s. on 1 s. 50, *Precis octavia* 3·75 6·00
175 3 s. on 2 s. 50, *Charaxes eupale* 14·00 27·00
176 40 s. on 20 s. *Papilio ophidicephalus* 6·50 12·00
173/6 *Set of* 4 24·00 42·00

1976 (15 Apr). *Telecommunications Development. As Nos.* 56/60 *of Kenya but inscr* "TANZANIA".
177 50 c. Microwave Tower 10 10
178 1 s. Cordless switchboard 15 10
179 2 s. Telephones 25 30
180 3 s. Message Switching Centre 30 40
177/80 *Set of* 4 70 70
MS181 120 × 120 mm. Nos. 177/80 1·50 1·50

Nos. 177/8 and 180 exist imperforate from stock dispersed by the liquidator of Format International Security Printers Ltd.

1976 (5 July). *Olympic Games, Montreal. As Nos* 61/5 *of Kenya but inscr* "TANZANIA".
182 50 c. Akii Bua, Ugandan hurdler 10 10
183 1 s. Filbert Bayi, Tanzanian runner 15 10
184 2 s. Steve Muchoki, Kenyan boxer 25 40
185 3 s. Olympic flame and East Africa flags 30 40
182/5 *Set of* 4 70 70
MS186 129 × 154 mm. Nos. 182/5 1·10 1·50

Nos. 182/4 exist imperforate from stock dispersed by the liquidator of Format International Security Printers Ltd.

1976 (4 Oct). *Railway Transport. As Nos.* 66/70 *of Kenya but inscr* "TANZANIA".
187 50 c. Tanzania-Zambia Railway 20 10
188 1 s. Nile Bridge, Uganda 30 10
189 2 s. Nakuru Station, Kenya 60 40
190 3 s. Class "A" locomotive, 1896 70 65
187/90 *Set of* 4 1·60 1·00
MS191 154 × 103 mm. Nos. 187/90 5·00 3·50

Nos. 187/91 exist imperforate from stock dispersed by the liquidator of Format International Security Printers Ltd.

1977 (10 Jan). *Game Fish of East Africa. As Nos.* 71/5 *of Kenya but inscr* "TANZANIA".
192 50 c. Nile Perch 35 10
193 1 s. Nile Mouthbrooder 40 10
194 3 s. Sailfish 1·75 60
195 5 s. Black Marlin 1·90 80
192/5 *Set of* 4 4·00 1·40
MS196 153×129 mm. Nos. 192/5 5·00 2·50

1977 (15 Jan). *Second World Black and African Festival of Arts and Culture, Nigeria. As Nos* 76/80 *of Kenya but inscr* "TANZANIA".
197 50 c. Maasai Manyatta (village), Kenya 15 10
198 1 s. "Heartbeat of Africa" (Ugandan dancers) 20 10
199 2 s. Makonde sculpture 45 70
200 3 s. "Early Man and Technology" (skinning hippopotamus) 55 1·00
197/200 *Set of* 4 1·25 1·75
MS201 132 × 190 mm. Nos. 197/200 1·50 3·50

1977 (5 Apr). *25th Anniv of Safari Rally. As Nos* 81/5 *of Kenya but inscr* "TANZANIA".
202 50 c. Rally-car and villagers 15 10
203 1 s. Pres. Kenyatta starting rally 15 10
204 2 s. Car fording river 30 40
205 5 s. Car and elephants 1·00 1·10
202/5 *Set of* 4 1·40 1·50
MS206 126 × 93 mm. Nos. 202/5 2·50 2·25

1977 (30 June). *Centenary of Ugandan Church. As Nos.* 86/90 *of Kenya but inscr* "TANZANIA".
207 50 c. Canon Kivebulaya 10 10
208 1 s. Modern Namirembe Cathedral 15 10
209 2 s. The first Cathedral 30 40
210 5 s. Early congregation, Kigezi 60 1·10
207/10 *Set of* 4 1·00 1·50
MS211 126 × 89 mm. Nos. 207/10 1·25 2·00

1977 (26 Sept). *Endangered Species. As Nos. 96/101 of Kenya but inscr* "TANZANIA".
212 50 c. Pancake Tortoise 20 10
213 1 s. Nile Crocodile 30 10
214 2 s. Hunter's Hartebeest .. .. .. 1·25 55
215 3 s. Red Colobus monkey .. .. .. 2·00 75
216 5 s. Dugong .. .. 2·25 1·50
212/16 .. .. *Set of* 5 5·50 2·50
MS217 127 × 101 mm. Nos. 213/16 .. .. 5·50 5·50

56 Prince Philip and President Nyerere

(Des G. Vasarhelyi. Litho Questa)

1977 (23 Nov). *Silver Jubilee. T* **56** *and similar horiz designs. Multicoloured. P* 14 × 13½.
218 50 c. Type **56** 10 10
219 5 s. Pres. Nyerere with Queen and Prince Philip 15 25
220 10 s. Jubilee emblem and Commonwealth flags 25 40
221 20 s. The Crowning 40 60
218/21 .. .. *Set of* 4 75 1·25
MS222 128 × 102 mm. Nos. 218/21 .. .. 75 1·50

57 Improvements in Rural Living Standards

(Des P. Ndembo. Litho J.W.)

1978 (5 Feb). *First Anniv of Chama Cha Mapinduzi (New Revolutionary Party). T* **57** *and similar horiz designs. P* 13½ × 14.
223 50 c. multicoloured 10 10
224 1 s. multicoloured 10 10
225 3 s. multicoloured 35 60
226 5 s. black, light green and greenish yellow 55 85
223/6 .. .. *Set of* 4 1·00 1·40
MS227 142 × 106 mm. Nos. 223/6 .. .. 1·00 1·40
Designs:—1 s. Flag raising ceremony, Zanzibar; 3 s. Handing over of TANU headquarters, Dodoma; 5 s. Chairman Julius Nyerere.

1978 (17 Apr). *World Cup Football Championship, Argentina. As Nos. 122/6 of Kenya but inscr* "TANZANIA".
228 50 c. Joe Kadenge and forwards 10 10
229 1 s. Mohamed Chuma and cup presentation 10 10
230 2 s. Omari Kidevu and goalmouth scene .. 30 60
231 3 s. Polly Ouma and forwards 40 75
228/31 .. .. *Set of* 4 75 1·25
MS232 136 × 81 mm. Nos. 228/31 .. .. 2·00 1·75

25th ANNIVERSARY CORONATION	25th ANNIVERSARY CORONATION
2nd JUNE 1953	2nd JUNE 1953
(58)	(59)

1978 (2 June). *25th Anniv of Coronation. Nos.* 218/22. A. *Optd as T* **58**. *P* 14 × 13½. B. *Optd as T* **59**. *P* 12 × 11½.

		A		B	
233	50 c. Type **56**	10	10	10	10
234	5 s. Pres. Nyerere with Queen and Prince Philip ..	20	30	20	30
235	10 s. Jubilee emblem and Commonwealth flags ..	25	40	25	40
236	20 s. The Crowning ..	40	70	40	70
233/6	.. .. *Set of* 4	75	1·25	75	1·25
MS237	128 × 102 mm. Nos. 233/6 ..	75	1·25	75	1·25

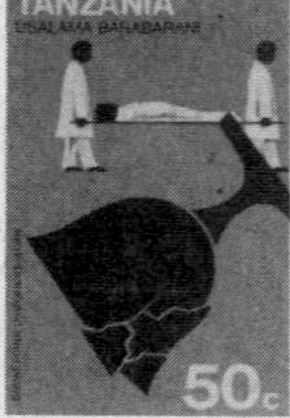

60 "Do not Drink and Drive"

61 Lake Manyara Hotel

(Des and litho J.W.)

1978 (1 July). *Road Safety. T* **60** *and similar vert designs. P* 13½ × 13.
238 50 c. multicoloured 15 10
239 1 s. multicoloured 20 10
240 3 s. orange-red, black and light brown .. 70 60
241 5 s. multicoloured .. .. 1·00 90
238/41 .. .. *Set of* 4 1·90 1·40
MS242 92 × 129 mm. Nos. 238/41. P 14 .. .. 2·00 2·00
Designs:—1 s. "Show courtesy to young, old and crippled"; 3 s. "Observe the Highway Code"; 5 s. "Do not drive a faulty vehicle".

(Des M. Raza. Litho J.W.)

1978 (11 Sept). *Game Lodges. T* **61** *and similar horiz designs. Multicoloured. P* 13½ × 13.
243 50 c. Type **61** 10 10
244 1 s. Lobo Wildlife Lodge 15 10
245 3 s. Ngorongoro Crater Lodge 25 35
246 5 s. Ngorongoro Wildlife Lodge 35 55
247 10 s. Mafia Island Lodge 50 90
248 20 s. Mikumi Wildlife Lodge .. .. .. 1·00 2·50
243/8 .. .. *Set of* 6 2·00 4·00
MS249 118 × 112 mm. Nos. 243/8 .. .. 6·00 7·50

62 "Racial Suppression"

63 Fokker F.27 Friendship

(Des local artist; adapted G. Hutchins. Litho Harrison)

1978 (24 Oct). *International Anti-Apartheid Year. T* **62** *and similar vert designs. P* 14½ × 14.
250 50 c. multicoloured 10 10
251 1 s. black, yellowish green and yellow .. 10 10
252 2 s. 50, multicoloured 30 50
253 5 s. multicoloured .. .. 60 1·00
250/3 .. .. *Set of* 4 1·00 1·50
MS254 127 × 132 mm. Nos. 250/3 .. .. 1·50 2·75
Designs:—1 s. "Racial division"; 2 s. 50, "Racial harmony"; 5 s. "Fall of suppression and rise of freedom".

(Des J. Mzinga; adapted J.W. Litho Walsall)

1978 (28 Dec). *75th Anniv of Powered Flight. T* **63** *and similar horiz designs. Multicoloured. P* 13½.
255 50 c. Type **63** 20 10
256 1 s. De Havilland D.H.84 Dragon Mk I on Zanzibar Island, 1930's 25 10
257 2 s. Concorde .. .. 1·00 45
258 5 s. Wright brothers' Flyer I, 1903 .. 1·25 85
255/8 .. .. *Set of* 4 2·40 1·25
MS259 133×97 mm. Nos. 255/8 .. .. 2·75 3·50

64 Corporation Emblem

(Des local artists; adapted BG Studio. Litho Harrison)

1979 (3 Feb). *1st Anniv of Tanzania Posts and Telecommunications Corporation. T* **64** *and similar horiz design. Multicoloured. P* 14½ × 14.
260 50 c. Type **64** 10 10
261 5 s. Headquarters buildings 50 70
MS262 82 × 97 mm. Nos. 260/1 .. .. 1·00 1·50

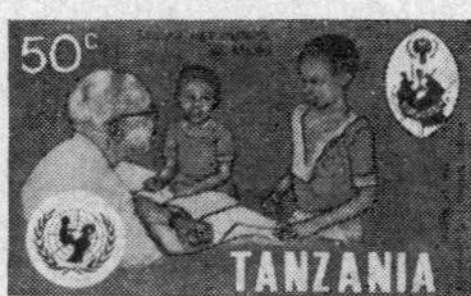

65 Pres. Nyerere (patron of National I.Y.C. Committee) with Children

30c
(66)

(Des J. Mzinga. Litho B.W.)

1979 (25 June). *International Year of the Child. T* **65** *and similar horiz designs. Multicoloured. P* 14½.
263 50 c. Type **65** 10 10
264 1 s. Day care centre 15 10
265 2 s. "Immunisation" (child being vaccinated) 25 45
266 5 s. National I.Y.C. Committee emblem .. 40 80
263/6 .. .. *Set of* 4 80 1·25
MS267 127 × 91 mm. Nos. 263/6 .. .. 1·25 1·25

1979 (Aug–Sept*). *Nos.* 159 *and* 166 *surch as T* **66** *(No. 269 has horiz bar through original value).*
268 10 c. + 30 c. multicoloured .. .. 1·25 75
a. Surch inverted .. .. .. † —
269 50 c. on 70 c. turquoise-green, pale orge & bl. 2·25 2·00
* The earliest known postmark date for No. 268 is 15 September and for No. 269 30 August.
The face value of No. 268 was 40 c.; the 30 c. surcharge being added to the original 10 c., which was not obliterated. This method was adopted because of difficulties during the actual surcharging. On No. 269 the 70 c. face value is obliterated by a bar.
Examples of No. 268a were used at Singida in December 1979.

67 Planting Young Trees

68 Mwenge Satellite Earth Station

(Des J. Mzinga. Litho J.W.)

1979 (24 Sept). *Forest Preservation. T* **67** *and similar vert designs. Multicoloured. P* 14 × 14½.
270 50 c. Type **67** 15 10
271 1 s. Replacing dead trees with saplings .. 15 10
272 2 s. Rainfall cycle 55 65
273 5 s. Forest fire warning .. .. .. 90 1·75
270/3 .. .. *Set of* 4 1·60 2·25

(Des and litho J.W.)

1979 (14 Dec). *Opening of Mwenge Satellite Earth Station. P* 13½.
274 **68** 10 c. multicoloured 10 10
275 40 c. multicoloured 15 10
276 50 c. multicoloured 15 10
277 1 s. multicoloured 25 20
274/7 .. .. *Set of* 4 55 40

69 Tabata Dispensary, Dar-es-Salaam

(Litho J.W.)

1980 (10 Apr). *75th Anniv of Rotary International. T* **69** *and similar horiz designs. Multicoloured. P* 13.
278 50 c. Type **69** 10 10
279 1 s. Ngomvu Village water project 15 10
280 5 s. Flying Doctor service (plane donation) 55 70
281 20 s. Torch and 75th Anniversary emblem .. 1·25 2·50
278/81 .. .. *Set of* 4 1·75 3·00
MS282 120 × 101 mm. Nos. 278/81. P 14 .. .. 1·75 3·00

70 Zanzibar 1896 2 r. Stamp and 1964 25 c. Definitive

'LONDON 1980'
PHILATELIC EXHIBITION
(71)

(Des J.W. Litho Questa)

1980 (21 Apr). *Death Centenary of Sir Rowland Hill* (1979). *T* **70** *and similar multicoloured designs. P* 14.
283 40 c. Type **70** 10 10
284 50 c. Tanganyika 1962 Independence 50 c. commemorative and man attaching stamp to letter (*vert*) 10 10
285 10 s. Tanganyika 1922 25 c. stamp and 1961 1 s. 30, definitive .. .. .. 70 1·25
286 20 s. Penny Black and Sir Rowland Hill (*vert*) 1·00 2·00
283/6 .. .. *Set of* 4 1·60 3·00
MS287 158 × 120 mm. Nos. 283/6 .. .. 1·60 3·00

1980 (5 May). *"London 1980" International Stamp Exhibition. Nos.* 283/7 *optd with T* **71**.
288 40 c. Type **71** 10 10
289 50 c. Tanganyika 1962 Independence 50 c. commemorative and man attaching stamp to letter 10 10
290 10 s. Tanganyika 1922 25 c. stamp and 1961 1 s. 30, definitive .. .. .. 65 1·25
291 20 s. Penny Black and Sir Rowland Hill .. 80 1·75
288/91 .. .. *Set of* 4 1·50 2·75
MS292 158 × 120 mm. Nos. 288/91 .. .. 1·50 2·75

District 920 - 55th Annual Conference, Arusha, Tanzania
(72)

1980 (23 June). *Annual Conference of District 920, Rotary International, Arusha. Nos.* 278/82 *optd as T* **72**.
293 50 c. Type **69** 20 10
294 1 s. Ngomvu Village water project 20 10
295 5 s. Flying Doctor service (plane donation) 45 70
296 20 s. Torch and 75th Anniversary of Rotary International Emblem .. .. 1·00 2·50
293/6 .. .. *Set of* 4 1·75 3·00
MS297 120 × 101 mm. Nos. 293/6 .. .. 1·75 3·00

73 Conference, Tanzanian Posts and Telecommunications Corporation and U.P.U. Emblems

(Des and litho J.W.)

1980 (1 July). *P.A.P.U. (Pan-African Postal Union) Plenipotentiary Conference, Arusha. P* 13.

298	73	50 c. black and bright violet	10	10
299		1 s. black and ultramarine	15	10
300		5 s. black and orange-red	65	70
301		10 s. black and blue-green	1·25	1·60
298/301		*Set of* 4	2·00	2·25

74 Gidamis Shahanga (marathon)

(Litho J.W.)

1980 (18 Aug). *Olympic Games, Moscow. T* **74** *and similar horiz designs. Multicoloured. P* 13.

302	50 c. Type **74**	10	15
	a. Horiz strip of 4. Nos. 302/5	1·60	
303	1 s. Nzael Kyomo (sprints)	15	15
304	10 s. Zakayo Malekwa (javelin)	60	1·00
305	20 s. William Lyimo (boxing)	1·00	1·75
302/5	*Set of* 4	1·60	2·75
MS306	172 × 117 mm. Nos. 302/305. P 14	1·60	2·75

Nos. 302/305 were printed either in separate sheets or together, *se-tenant*, in horizontal strips of 4 throughout the sheet.

75 Spring Hare 76 Impala

(Des Rena Fennessy)

1980 (1 Oct)–**85**. *Wildlife. Horiz designs as T* **75** *(10 c. to 80 c.) or T* **76** *(1 s. to 40 s.). Multicoloured.*

(a) Litho B.W. P 14 *(10 c. to 80 c.) or* 14½ *(1 s. to 40 s.)*

307	10 c. Type **75**	10	15
308	20 c. Large-spotted Genet	15	15
309	40 c. Banded Mongoose	20	10
310	50 c. Ratel (light blue panel at foot)	20	10
311	75 c. Large-toothed Rock Hyrax	20	15
312	80 c. Leopard (buff sky)	30	15
313	1 s. Type **76**	20	10
314	1 s. 50, Giraffe	30	20
315	2 s. Common Zebra	30	20
316	3 s. Buffalo	30	20
317	5 s. Lion	40	30
318	10 s. Black Rhinoceros	75	1·25
319	20 s. African Elephant	1·25	1·75
320	40 s. Cheetah	1·50	4·00
307/20	*Set of* 14	5·50	8·00

(b) Litho J.W. P 14 *(50 c., 80 c.) or* 14×14½ *(others)* (1984–85)

320*a*	50 c. Ratel (turquoise-blue panel at foot)	1·50	40
320*b*	80 c. Leopard (yellow sky)		
320*c*	1 s. Type **76**	1·50	40
320*d*	1 s. 50, Giraffe	6·00	3·00
320*e*	2 s. Common Zebra	4·00	2·75
320*f*	3 s. Buffalo	4·50	5·00
	fa. Perf 13½		
320*g*	5 s. Lion	7·50	8·00

Both formats of the Waddington printings are slightly smaller than the Bradbury Wilkinson stamps so that Nos. 320*a*/*b* measures 19½×16 mm, instead of 20×16½ mm, and the larger designs 40×23½ mm, instead of 40½×24 mm. The Swahili inscriptions on the 1 s. and 2 s. appear as one word on the Bradbury Wilkinson printings and as two words on those produced by Waddington.

1980 (22 Nov). *Nos.* O41 *and* O43 *with* "OFFICIAL" *opt Type* O **1** *obliterated by horizontal line.*

320*h*	10 c. multicoloured		
320*i*	40 c. multicoloured		

Nos. 320*h*/*i* exist on commercial mail from Morogoro. The date is that of the earliest postmark reported.

77 Ngorongoro Conservation Area Authority Emblem

ROYAL WEDDING
H.R.H. PRINCE CHARLES
29th JULY 1981
(78)

(Des D. Kyungu. Litho J.W.)

1981 (2 Feb). *60th Anniv of Ngorongoro and Serengeti National Parks. T* **77** *and similar horiz designs. P* 13.

321	50 c. multicoloured	10	10
322	1 s. black, gold and deep blue-green	10	10
323	5 s. multicoloured	35	60
324	20 s. multicoloured	1·10	2·25
321/4	*Set of* 4	1·40	2·75

Designs:—1 s. Tanzania National Parks emblem; 5 s. Friends of the Serengeti emblem; 20 s. Friends of Ngorongoro emblem.

Nos. 321/4 exist overprinted "75th ANNIVERSARY GIRL GUIDES 1910 1985" or "CONGRATULATIONS TO THE DUKE & DUCHESS OF YORK ON THE OCCASION OF THEIR MARRIAGE", but there is no evidence that these overprints were available from post offices in Tanzania.

1981 (29 July). *Royal Wedding. Nos.* 220/1 *optd with T* **78**.

325	10 s. Jubilee emblem and Commonwealth flags	35	60
326	20 s. Crowning	55	80
MS327	88×97 mm. Nos. 325/6	3·00	3·50

79 Mail Runner

(Des D. Kyungu. Litho State Printing Works, Moscow)

1981 (21 Oct). *Commonwealth Postal Administrations Conference, Arusha. T* **79** *and similar horiz designs. Multicoloured. P* 12½ × 12.

328	50 c. Type **79**	10	10
329	1 s. Letter sorting	15	15
330	5 s. Letter Post symbols	40	1·00
331	10 s. Flags of Commonwealth nations	75	2·00
328/31	*Set of* 4	1·25	3·00
MS332	130×100 mm. Nos. 328/31	1·40	3·00

80 Morris Nyunyusa (blind drummer)

(Des and litho Harrison)

1981 (30 Nov). *International Year for Disabled Persons. T* **80** *and similar horiz designs. Multicoloured. P* 14.

333	50 c. Type **80**	25	10
334	1 s. Mgulani Rehabilitation Centre, Dar-es-Salaam	30	10
335	5 s. Aids for disabled persons	2·00	2·25
336	10 s. Disabled children cleaning school compound	2·75	3·25
333/6	*Set of* 4	4·75	5·00

81 President Mwalimu Julius K. Nyerere

82 Ostrich

(Litho J.W.)

1982 (13 Jan). *20th Anniv of Independence. T* **81** *and similar horiz designs. Multicoloured. P* 13 × 13½.

337	50 c. Type **81**	10	10
338	1 s. Electricity plant, Mtoni	10	10
339	3 s. Sisal industry	35	90
340	10 s. "Universal primary education"	80	2·25
337/40	*Set of* 4	1·25	3·00
MS341	120×85 mm. Nos. 337/40	1·25	3·00

(Des and litho J.W.)

1982 (25 Jan). *Birds. T* **82** *and similar vert designs. Multicoloured. P* 13½ × 13.

342	50 c. Type **82**	70	10
343	1 s. Secretary Bird	80	10
344	5 s. Kori Bustard	2·75	2·75
345	10 s. Saddle-bill Stork	3·50	5·50
342/5	*Set of* 4	7·00	7·50

83 Jella Mtaga

(Des P. Ndembo. Litho J.W.)

1982 (2 June). *World Cup Football Championship, Spain. T* **83** *and similar horiz designs. Multicoloured. P* 14.

346	50 c. Type **83**	30	10
347	1 s. Football stadium	35	10
348	10 s. Diego Maradona	3·00	3·00
349	20 s. FIFA emblem	4·75	5·00
346/9	*Set of* 4	7·50	7·50
MS350	130×100 mm. Nos. 346/9	8·00	8·00

Nos. 346/9 exist overprinted "CONGRATULATIONS TO THE DUKE & DUCHESS OF YORK ON THE OCCASION OF THEIR MARRIAGE", but there is no evidence that these overprints were available from post offices in Tanzania.

84 "Jade" of Seronera (cheetah) with Cubs

(Des and litho Harrison)

1982 (15 July). *Animal Personalities. T* **84** *and similar horiz designs. Multicoloured. P* 14.

351	50 c. Type **84**	20	10
352	1 s. Female Golden Jackal and cubs (incorrectly inscr "Wild dog")	30	10
353	5 s. "Fifi" and two sons of "Gombe" (chimpanzees)	1·00	2·00
354	10 s. "Bahati" of Lake Manyara with twins, "Rashidi" and "Ramadhani" (elephants)	1·90	3·00
351/4	*Set of* 4	3·00	4·75
MS355	120×89 mm. Nos. 351/4. P 14½	3·50	5·00

85 Brick-laying 86 Ploughing Field

(Des P. Ndembo. Litho J.W.)

1982 (25 Aug). *75th Anniv of Boy Scout Movement. T* **85** *and similar horiz designs. Multicoloured. P* 14.

356	50 c. Type **85**	15	10
357	1 s. Camping	20	10
358	10 s. Tracing signs	1·50	2·25
359	20 s. Lord Baden-Powell	2·50	3·75
356/9	*Set of* 4	4·00	5·50
MS360	130×100 mm. Nos. 356/9	4·50	5·50

No. MS360 exists overprinted "75th ANNIVERSARY GIRL GUIDES 1910–1985", but there is no evidence that this overprint was available from post offices in Tanzania.

(Des P. Ndembo. Litho J.W.)

1982 (16 Oct). *World Food Day. T* **86** *and similar horiz designs. Multicoloured. P* 14.

361	50 c. Type **86**	10	10
362	1 s. Dairy farming	10	10
363	5 s. Maize farming	45	60
364	10 s. Grain storage	75	1·25
361/4	*Set of* 4	1·10	1·75
MS365	129×99 mm. Nos. 361/4	1·60	2·25

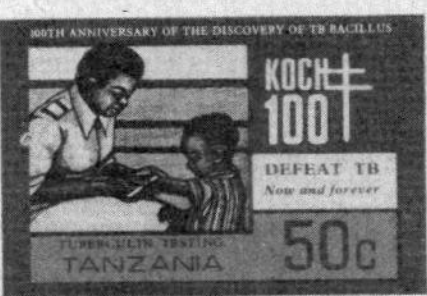

87 Immunization

(Des P. Ndembo. Litho State Printing Works, Moscow)

1982 (1 Dec). *Centenary of Robert Koch's Discovery of Tubercle Bacillus. T* **87** *and similar horiz designs. Multicoloured. P* 12½ × 12.

366	50 c. Type **87**	15	10
367	1 s. Dr. Robert Koch	20	10
368	5 s. International Union Against TB emblem	65	1·25
369	10 s. World Health Organization emblem	1·25	2·50
366/9	*Set of* 4	2·00	3·50

88 Letter Post

(Litho State Printing Works, Moscow)

1983 (3 Feb). *5th Anniv of Posts and Telecommunications Corporation. T* **88** *and similar horiz designs. Multicoloured. P* 12.

370	50 c. Type **88**	10	10
371	1 s. Training institute	10	10
372	5 s. Satellite communications	55	90
373	10 s. U.P.U., I.T.U. and T.P.T.C.C. (Tanzania Posts and Telecommunications Corporation) emblems	90	2·00
370/3	.. .. *Set of* 4	1·50	2·75
MS374	126×96 mm. Nos. 370/3	1·50	3·00

89 Pres. Mwalimu Julius Nyerere

(Litho J.W.)

1983 (14 Mar). *Commonwealth Day. T* **89** *and similar horiz designs. Multicoloured. P* 14.

375	50 c. Type **89**	10	10
376	1 s. Athletics and boxing	15	10
377	5 s. Flags of Commonwealth countries ..	40	90
378	10 s. Pres. Nyerere and members of British Royal Family	70	1·90
375/8	.. .. *Set of* 4	1·10	2·75
MS379	121×100 mm. Nos. 375/8	1·40	3·50

Nos. 375/8 exist overprinted "CONGRATULATIONS TO THE DUKE & DUCHESS OF YORK ON THE OCCASION OF THEIR MARRIAGE", but there is no evidence that these overprints were available from post offices in Tanzania.

90 Eastern and Southern African Management Institute, Arusha, Tanzania

(Des P. Ndembo. Litho State Ptg Wks, Moscow)

1983 (12 Sept). *25th Anniv of the Economic Commission for Africa. T* **90** *and similar horiz designs. Multicoloured. P* 12½ × 12.

380	50 c. Type **90**	15	10
381	1 s. 25th Anniversary inscription and U.N. logo	20	10
382	5 s. Mineral collections	2·75	2·75
383	10 s. E.C.A. Silver Jubilee logo and O.A.U. flag	2·75	3·50
380/3	.. .. *Set of* 4	5·25	5·75
MS384	132×102 mm. Nos. 380/3	5·75	5·75

91 Telephone Cables

(Des P. Ndembo. Litho J.W.)

1983 (17 Oct). *World Communications Year. T* **91** *and similar horiz designs. Multicoloured. P* 14.

385	50 c. Type **91**	15	10
386	1 s. W.C.Y. logo	15	10
387	5 s. Postal service	80	1·50
388	10 s. Microwave tower	1·10	2·50
385/8	.. .. *Set of* 4	2·00	3·75
MS389	102×92 mm. Nos. 385/88	2·00	3·75

92 Bagamoyo Boma

(Des J. de Silva and P. Ndembo. Litho State Ptg Wks, Moscow)

1983 (12 Dec). *Historical Buildings. T* **92** *and similar horiz designs. Multicoloured. P* 12½ × 12.

390	1 s. Type **92**	10	10
391	1 s. 50, Beit el Ajaib, Zanzibar	15	25
392	5 s. Anglican Cathedral, Zanzibar	40	1·00
393	10 s. Original German Government House and present State House, Dar-es-Salaam	75	2·00
390/3	.. .. *Set of* 4	1·25	3·00
MS394	130×100 mm. Nos. 390/3	1·50	3·00

93 Sheikh Abeid Amani Karume (founder of Afro-Shirazi Party)

(Des P. Ndembo. Litho J.W.)

1984 (18 June). *20th Anniv of Zanzibar Revolution. T* **93** *and similar horiz designs. Multicoloured. P* 14.

395	1 s. Type **93**	10	10
396	1 s. 50, Clove farming	15	25
397	5 s. Symbol of Industrial Development ..	40	1·00
398	10 s. New housing schemes	75	2·00
395/8	.. .. *Set of* 4	1·25	3·00
MS399	130×100 mm. 15 s. *Mapinduzi* (ferry) and map	1·50	3·00

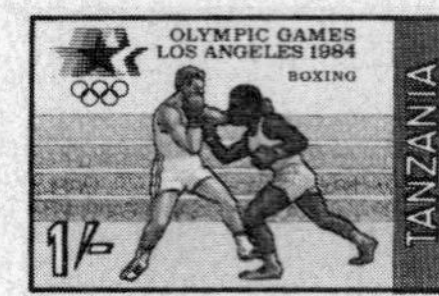

94 Boxing

(Des P. Ndembo. Litho State Ptg Wks, Moscow)

1984 (6 Aug). *Olympic Games, Los Angeles. T* **94** *and similar horiz designs. Multicoloured. P* 12½ × 12.

400	1 s. Type **94**	10	10
401	1 s. 50, Running	15	10
402	5 s. Basketball	45	60
403	20 s. Football	1·50	2·25
400/3	.. .. *Set of* 4	2·00	2·75
MS404	130×100 mm. Nos. 400/3	2·00	2·75

95 Icarus in Flight

(Des P. Ndembo. Litho J.W.)

1984 (15 Nov). *40th Anniv of International Civil Aviation Organization. T* **95** *and similar horiz designs. Multicoloured. P* 13 × 12½.

405	1 s. Type **95**	10	10
406	1 s. 50, Douglas DC-10, Boeing 737 aircraft and air traffic controller	15	20
407	5 s. Boeing 737 undergoing maintenance	55	1·25
408	10 s. I.C.A.O. badge	1·10	2·00
405/8	.. .. *Set of* 4	1·75	3·25
MS409	130×100 mm. Nos. 405/8	1·90	3·00

96 Sochi – Conical House

(Des P. Ndembo. Litho State Ptg Wks, Moscow)

1984 (20 Dec). *Traditional Houses. T* **96** *and similar horiz designs. Multicoloured. P* 12½ × 12.

410	1 s. Type **96**	10	10
411	1 s. 50, Isyenga – circular type	15	20
412	5 s. Tembe – flatroofed type	40	1·25
413	10 s. Banda – coastal type	70	2·00
410/13	.. .. *Set of* 4	1·10	3·25
MS414	129×99 mm. Nos. 410/13	1·50	3·00

97 Production of Cotton Textiles

(Des P. Ndembo. Litho J.W.)

1985 (1 Apr). *5th Anniv of Southern African Development Co-ordination Conference. T* **97** *and similar horiz designs. Multicoloured. P* 14.

415	1 s. 50, Type **97**	30	15
416	4 s. Diamond mining	2·00	1·50
417	5 s. Map of member countries and means of communication	2·00	1·50
418	20 s. Flags and signatures of member countries	2·75	3·50
415/18	.. .. *Set of* 4	6·25	6·00
MS419	110×104 mm. Nos. 415/18	8·00	8·00

98 Tortoise

(Des P. Ndembo (15s., 20s.), J. de Silva (others). Litho J.W.)

1985 (8 May). *Rare Animals of Zanzibar. T* **98** *and similar multicoloured designs. P* 12½×13 (17 *s.* 50) *or* 13×12½ (*others*).

420	1 s. Type **98**	50	10
421	4 s. Leopard	2·00	1·25
422	10 s. Civet Cat	2·50	3·50
423	17 s. 50, Red Colobus Monkey (*vert*) ..	3·25	5·00
420/3	.. .. *Set of* 4	7·50	8·75
MS424	110×93 mm. 15 s. Black Rhinoceros; 20 s. Giant Ground Pangolin	2·00	3·50

IMPERFORATE STAMPS. Nos. 425/9, 430/4, 456/68, 474/8, 508/11 and 517/21 exist imperforate from restricted printings reported as being unavailable in Tanzania.

99 The Queen Mother

(Litho Holders Press)

1985 (30 Sept). *Life and Times of Queen Elizabeth the Queen Mother. T* **99** *and similar horiz designs. Multicoloured. P* 14.

425	20 s. Type **99**	10	15
426	20 s. Queen Mother waving to crowd ..	10	15
427	100 s. Oval portrait with flowers	30	75
428	100 s. Head and shoulders portrait	30	75
425/8	.. .. *Set of* 4	70	1·60
MS429	Two sheets, each 125×63 mm. (a) Nos. 425 and 427; (b) Nos. 426 and 428. *Set of* 2 *sheets*	80	2·75

Designs as Nos. 425/9, but inscr "H.R.H. The Queen Mother" were not issued in Tanzania.

100 Locomotive No. 3022

GOLD MEDAL
HENRY TILLMAN
USA

(**101**)

(Litho Holders Press)

1985 (7 Oct). *Tanzanian Railway Locomotives* (1*st series*). *T* **100** *and similar horiz designs. Multicoloured. P* 14.

430	5 s. Type **100**	10	15
431	10 s. Locomotive No. 3107	15	30
432	20 s. Locomotive No. 6004	25	60
433	30 s. Locomotive No. 3129	40	90
430/3	.. .. *Set of* 4	80	1·75
MS434	125×93 mm. Nos. 430/3	80	2·75

See also Nos. 445/50.

1985 (22 Oct). *Olympic Games Gold Medal Winners, Los Angeles. Nos.* 400/4 *optd as T* **101**.

435	1 s. Type **94** (optd with T **101**)	10	10
436	1 s. 50, Running (optd "GOLD MEDAL USA")	15	20
437	5 s. Basketball (optd "GOLD MEDAL USA")	45	1·00
438	20 s. Football (optd "GOLD MEDAL FRANCE")	1·75	2·75
435/8	.. .. *Set of* 4	2·25	3·50
MS439	130×100 mm. Nos. 435/8	7·50	10·00

102 Cooking and Water Pots

103 Class "64" Locomotive

(Des J. Mzinga. Litho State Ptg Wks, Moscow)

1985 (4 Nov). *Pottery. T* **102** *and similar horiz designs. Multicoloured. P* 12½×12.

440 1 s. 50, Type **102** .. 20 10
441 2 s. Large pot and frying pot with cover .. 25 15
442 5 s. Trader selling pots .. 60 35
443 40 s. Beer pot .. 2·25 4·00
440/3 .. *Set of* 4 3·00 4·00
MS444 129×98 mm. 30 s. Water pots .. 3·75 3·75

(Des P. Ndembo. Litho State Ptg Wks, Moscow)

1985 (25 Nov). *Tanzanian Railway Locomotives* (2*nd series*). *T* **103** *and similar horiz designs. P* 12½×12.

445 1 s. 50, multicoloured .. 40 20
446 2 s. multicoloured .. 40 30
447 5 s. multicoloured .. 55 75
448 10 s. multicoloured .. 80 1·60
449 30 s. black, brownish black and red .. 2·00 3·25
445/9 .. *Set of* 5 3·75 5·50
MS450 130×100 mm. 15 s. black, blackish brown and rose-pink; 20 s. black, blackish brown and rose-pink .. 6·50 6·50

Designs:—2 s. Class "36" locomotive; 5 s. "DFH1013" shunting locomotive; 10 s. "DE 1001" diesel-electric locomotive; 15 s. Class "30" steam locomotive; 20 s. Class "11" steam locomotive; 30 s. Steam locomotive, Zanzibar, 1906.

Nos. 445/6 and 448/9 exist overprinted "CONGRATULATIONS TO THE DUKE & DUCHESS OF YORK ON THE OCCASION OF THEIR MARRIAGE", but there is no evidence that these overprints were available from post offices in Tanzania.

104 Young Pioneers

(Des P. Ndembo. Litho J.W.)

1986 (20 Jan). *International Youth Year. T* **104** *and similar horiz designs. P* 14.

451 1 s. 50, multicoloured .. 15 15
452 4 s. reddish brown, pale brown and black .. 30 50
453 10 s. multicoloured .. 70 1·25
454 20 s. reddish brown, pale brown and black .. 1·40 2·50
451/4 .. *Set of* 4 2·25 4·00
MS455 130×100 mm. 30 s. reddish brown, pale brown and black .. 2·25 3·50

Designs:—4 s. Child health care; 10 s. Uhuru Torch Race; 20 s. Young workers and globe; 30 s. Young people farming.

105 Rolls-Royce "20/25" (1936)

(Litho Holders Press)

1986 (10 Mar). *Centenary of Motoring. T* **105** *and similar horiz designs. Multicoloured. P* 14.

456 1 s. 50, Type **105** .. 10 10
457 5 s. Rolls-Royce "Phantom II" (1933) .. 15 25
458 10 s. Rolls-Royce "Phantom I" (1926) .. 25 60
459 30 s. Rolls-Royce "Silver Ghost" (1907) .. 40 1·50
456/9 .. *Set of* 4 80 2·25
MS460 125×93 mm. Nos. 456/9 .. 80 2·50

106 Rotary Logo and Staunton Queen Chess Piece

(Litho Holders Press)

1986 (17 Mar). *World Chess Championships, London and Leningrad. T* **106** *and similar horiz design. P* 14.

461 20 s. new blue and magenta .. 40 50
462 100 s. multicoloured .. 70 2·50
MS463 124×64 mm. Nos. 461/2 .. 1·10 3·25

Design:—100 s. Hand moving Rook.

No. 461 also commemorates Rotary International.

Slightly different versions of Nos. 461/2, incorporating the Chess Championship emblem and with "TANZANIA" and face value at top on the 100 s., were not issued.

107 Mallard

(Litho Holders Press)

1986 (22 May). *Birth Bicentenary of John J. Audubon (ornithologist)* (1985). *T* **107** *and similar horiz designs. Multicoloured. P* 14.

464 5 s. Type **107** .. 15 35
465 10 s. Eider .. 25 50
466 20 s. Scarlet Ibis .. 30 1·10
467 30 s. Roseate Spoonbill .. 40 1·25
464/7 .. *Set of* 4 1·00 2·75
MS468 122×91 mm. Nos. 464/7 .. 1·00 3·50

108 Pearls

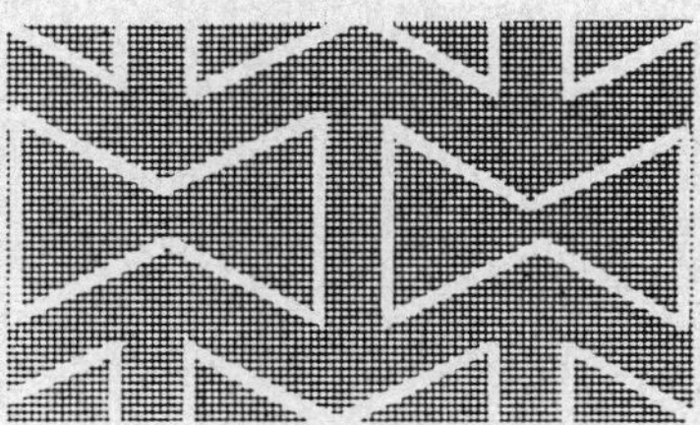

109

(Litho J.W.)

1986 (27 May). *Tanzanian Minerals. T* **108** *and similar horiz designs. Multicoloured. Phosphorised paper* (*Nos.* 469/72). *P* 14.

469 1 s. 50, Type **108** .. 80 15
470 2 s. Sapphire .. 1·10 65
471 5 s. Tanzanite .. 2·00 1·25
472 40 s. Diamonds .. 7·25 10·00
469/72 .. *Set of* 4 10·00 11·00
MS473 130×100 mm. 30 s. Rubies. W **109** .. 9·50 10·00

110 *Hibiscus calyphyllus* 111 Oryx

(Litho Holders Press)

1986 (25 June). *Flowers of Tanzania. T* **110** *and similar vert designs. Multicoloured. P* 14.

474 1 s. 50, Type **110** .. 10 10
475 5 s. *Aloe graminicola* .. 15 25
476 10 s. *Nersium oleander* .. 20 35
477 30 s. *Nymphaea caerulea* .. 40 1·25
474/7 .. *Set of* 4 75 1·75
MS478 90×119 mm. Nos. 474/7 .. 75 2·50

(Litho Holders Press)

1986 (30 June). *Endangered Animals of Tanzania. T* **111** *and similar vert designs. Multicoloured. P* 14.

479 5 s. Type **111** .. 15 15
480 10 s. Giraffe .. 20 35
481 20 s. Rhinoceros .. 25 75
482 30 s. Cheetah .. 25 1·25
479/82 .. *Set of* 4 75 2·25
MS483 91×121 mm. Nos. 479/82 .. 75 3·25

Four stamps, 10, 20, 60 and 80 s., with accompanying miniature sheets, were prepared in 1986 for the Wedding of the Duke of York, but these were not placed on sale in Tanzania.

112 Immunization 113 Angelfish

(Des P. Ndembo. Litho State Ptg Wks, Moscow)

1986 (29 July). *U.N.I.C.E.F. Child Survival Campaign. T* **112** *and similar vert designs. Multicoloured. P* 12½×12.

484 1 s. 50, Type **112** .. 15 10
485 2 s. Growth monitoring .. 25 15
486 5 s. Oral rehydration therapy .. 40 35
487 40 s. Breast feeding .. 2·00 3·25
484/7 .. *Set of* 4 2·50 3·50
MS488 110×101 mm. 30 s. Healthy baby .. 1·00 1·75

(Des P. Ndembo. Litho State Ptg Wks, Moscow)

1986 (28 Aug). *Marine Life. T* **113** *and similar horiz designs. Multicoloured. P* 12½×12

489 1 s. 50, Type **113** .. 60 10
490 4 s. Parrotfish .. 1·25 75
491 10 s. Turtle .. 2·00 2·25
492 20 s. Octopus .. 3·50 3·75
489/92 .. *Set of* 4 6·50 6·00
MS493 131×101 mm. 30 s. Corals .. 2·25 2·50

114 Team Captains shaking Hands 115 Pres. Nyerere receiving Beyond War Award

(Litho Questa)

1986 (30 Oct). *World Cup Football Championship, Mexico. T* **114** *and similar horiz designs. Multicoloured. P* 14.

494 1 s. 50, Type **114** .. 15 10
495 2 s. Referee sending player off .. 15 10
496 10 s. Goalkeeper and ball in net .. 60 80
497 20 s. Goalkeeper saving ball .. 1·00 1·75
494/7 .. *Set of* 4 1·75 2·50
MS498 95×72 mm. 30 s. Winning Argentine team .. 1·10 1·25

(Des P. Ndembo. Litho Mardon Printers Ltd, Zimbabwe)

1986 (20 Dec). *International Peace Year. T* **115** *and similar horiz designs. Multicoloured. P* 14½.

499 1 s. 50, Type **115** .. 30 10
500 2 s. Children of many races .. 50 20
501 10 s. African cosmonaut and rocket launch 1·25 1·75
502 20 s. United Nations Headquarters, New York .. 1·75 2·75
499/502 .. *Set of* 4 3·50 4·25
MS503 109×86 mm. 30 s. International Peace Year symbols .. 2·25 3·25

116 Mobile Bank Service

(Des P. Ndembo. Litho Questa)

1987 (7 Feb). *20th Anniv of National Bank of Commerce. T* **116** *and similar horiz designs. Multicoloured. P* 14.

504 1 s. 50, Type **116** .. 30 10
505 2 s. National Bank of Commerce Head Office .. 50 20
506 5 s. Pres. Mwinyi laying foundation stone 80 90
507 20 s. Cotton harvesting .. 2·00 3·25
504/7 .. *Set of* 4 3·25 4·00

117 Parade of Young Party Members

(Litho Holders Press)

1987 (10 Mar). *10th Anniv of Chama Cha Mapinduzi Party and 20th Anniv of Arusha Declaration. T* **117** *and similar horiz designs. Multicoloured. P* 14.

508 2 s. Type **117** .. 15 10
509 3 s. Harvesting coffee .. 20 10
510 10 s. Pres. Nyerere addressing Second Peace Initiative Reunion .. 30 30
511 30 s. Presidents Julius Nyerere and Ali Hassan Mwinyi .. 50 90
508/11 .. *Set of* 4 1·10 1·25

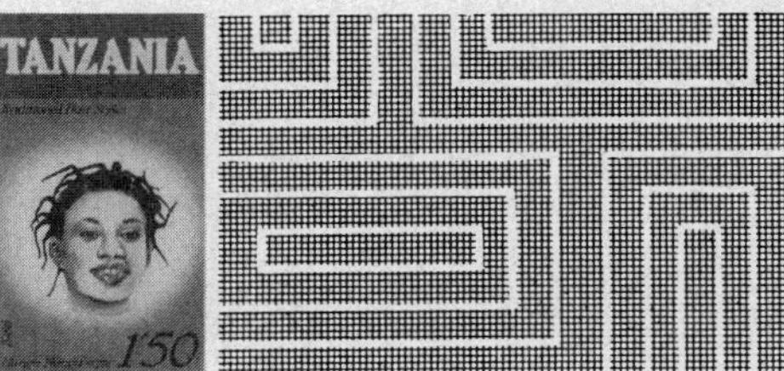

118 Nungu Nungu Hair Style 119

(Litho Leigh-Mardon Ltd, Melbourne)

1987 (16 Mar). *Traditional Hair Styles. T* **118** *and similar vert designs. Multicoloured. W* **119**. *P* 14½.

512 1 s. 50, Type **118** .. 30 10
513 2 s. Upanga wa jogoo style .. 45 20
514 10 s. Morani style .. 80 1·25
515 20 s. Twende kilioni style .. 1·50 2·50
512/15 .. *Set of* 4 2·75 3·50
MS516 110×99 mm. 30 s. Hair plaiting .. 2·75 3·50

120 Royal Family on Buckingham Palace Balcony after Trooping the Colour

(Litho Holders Press)

1987 (24 Mar). *60th Birthday of Queen Elizabeth II* (1986). *T* **120** *and similar horiz designs. Multicoloured. P* 14.

517 5 s. Type **120** 10 10
518 10 s. Queen and Prince Philip at Royal Ascot 15 20
519 40 s. Queen Elizabeth II 50 80
520 60 s. Queen Elizabeth with crowd .. .. 70 1·25
517/20 .. .. *Set of* 4 1·25 2·00
MS521 125×90 mm. Nos. 517/20 .. .. 1·25 3·00

121 *Apis mellifera* (bee) **122** Crocodile

(Litho State Ptg Wks, Moscow)

1987 (22 Apr). *Insects. T* **121** *and similar horiz designs. Multicoloured. P* $12^1/_2$×12.

522 1 s. 50, Type **121** 60 15
523 2 s. *Prostephanus truncatus* (grain borer) 80 25
524 10 s. *Glossina palpalis* (tsetse fly) .. .. 1·50 1·75
525 20 s. *Polistes* sp (wasp) .. .. .. 2·25 3·50
522/5 .. .. *Set of* 4 4·50 5·00
MS526 110×101 mm. 30 s. *Anopheles* sp (mosquito) .. .. 3·00 4·00

(Des J. Mzinga (3 s., 30 s.), P. Ndembo (others). Litho State Ptg Wks, Moscow)

1987 (2 July). *Reptiles. T* **122** *and similar horiz designs. Multicoloured. P* $12^1/_2$×12.

527 2 s. Type **122** 45 25
528 3 s. Black-striped Grass-snake 50 30
529 10 s. Adder .. .. 90 1·25
530 20 s. Green Mamba .. .. 1·60 2·00
527/30 .. .. *Set of* 4 3·00 3·50
MS531 101×101 mm. 30 s. Tortoise .. .. 1·00 1·00

123 Emblems of Posts/ Telecommunications and Railways **124** Basketry

(Des and litho Questa)

1987 (27 July). *10th Anniv of Tanzania Communications and Transport Corporations. T* **123** *and similar horiz designs. Multicoloured. P* 14.

532 2 s. Type **123** 10 10
533 8 s. Emblems of Air Tanzania and Harbours Authority 20 20
MS534 100×66 mm. 20 s. Methods of transport and communication .. .. 1·50 1·50

(Des P. Ndembo. Litho State Ptg Wks, Moscow)

1987 (15 Dec). *Traditional Handicrafts. T* **124** *and similar horiz designs. Multicoloured. P* $12^1/_2$×12.

535 2 s. Type **124** 15 10
536 3 s. Decorated gourds 15 15
537 10 s. Stools 25 20
538 20 s. Makonde carvings 40 45
535/8 .. .. *Set of* 4 85 80
MS539 89×89 mm. 40 s. Makonde carver at work 65 75

10th Anniversary of TANZANIA ZAMBIA RAILWAY AUTHORITY 1976-1986

(125)

1987 (30 Dec). *10th Anniv of Tanzania–Zambia Railway* (1986). *Nos.* 445/9 *optd with T* **125**.

540 **103** 1 s. 50, multicoloured 30 15
541 – 2 s. multicoloured 35 25
542 – 5 s. multicoloured 55 60
543 – 10 s. multicoloured .. .. 85 1·00
544 – 30 s. black, brownish black and red .. 1·50 2·75
540/4 .. .. *Set of* 5 3·25 4·25

126 Mdako (pebble game)

(Des P. Ndembo. Litho State Ptg Wks, Moscow)

1988 (15 Feb). *Traditional Pastimes. T* **126** *and similar horiz designs. Multicoloured. P* $12^1/_2$×12.

545 2 s. Type **126** 10 10
546 3 s. Wrestling 10 10
547 8 s. Bullfighting, Zanzibar 15 15
548 20 s. Bao (board game) 35 35
545/8 .. .. *Set of* 4 65 65
MS549 100×90 mm. 30 s. Archery 70 80

127 Plateosaurus

(Des G. Vasarhelyi. Litho Format)

1988 (22 Apr). *Prehistoric and Modern Animals. T* **127** *and similar trapezium-shaped designs. Multicoloured. P* $12^1/_2$.

550 2 s. Type **127** 20 25
a. *Tête-bêche* (horiz pair) 40 50
551 3 s. Pteranodon 20 25
a. *Tête-bêche* (horiz pair) 40 50
552 5 s. Apatosaurus ("Brontosaurus") .. 20 25
a. *Tête-bêche* (horiz pair) 40 50
553 7 s. Lion 30 40
a. *Tête-bêche* (horiz pair) 60 80
554 8 s. Tiger 30 40
a. *Tête-bêche* (horiz pair) 60 80
555 12 s. Orang-utan 35 55
a. *Tête-bêche* (horiz pair) .. .. .. 70 1·10
556 20 s. Elephant .. .. 70 1·00
a. *Tête-bêche* (horiz pair) .. .. .. 1·40 2·00
557 100 s. Stegosaurus .. .. 1·75 2·25
a. *Tête-bêche* (horiz pair) .. .. .. 3·50 4·50
550/7 .. .. *Set of* 8 3·50 4·75

Nos. 550/7 were issued in sheets which had the second and fourth stamps *tête-bêche* in each horizontal row of five.

128 Marchers with Party Flag **129** Population Symbols on Map

(Des P. Ndembo. Litho Questa)

1988 (1 July). *National Solidarity Walk. T* **128** *and similar horiz designs. Multicoloured. P* 14×$14^1/_2$.

558 2 s. + 1 s. Type **128** 15 15
559 3 s. + 1 s. Pres. Mwinyi leading Walk .. 15 15
MS560 121×121 mm. 50 s. + 1 s. Pres. Ali Hassan Mwinyi (35×25 *mm*). P $14^1/_2$ 75 85

(Des P. Ndembo. Litho Questa)

1988 (8 Aug). *Third National Population Census. T* **129** *and similar horiz designs. Multicoloured. P* 14.

561 2 s. Type **129** 10 10
562 3 s. Census official at work 10 10
563 10 s. Community health care 15 15
564 20 s. Population growth 1967–1988 .. .. 30 30
561/4 .. .. *Set of* 4 55 55
MS565 96×91 mm. 40 s. Development of modern Tanzania 65 65

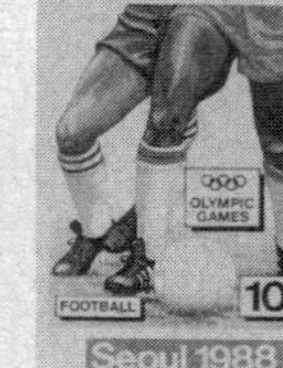

130 Javelin **131** Football

(Litho State Ptg Wks, Moscow)

1988 (5 Sept). *Olympic Games, Seoul* (1*st issue*). *T* **130** *and similar horiz designs. Multicoloured. P* $12^1/_2$×12.

566 2 s. Type **130** 30 10
567 3 s. Hurdling 30 10
568 7 s. Long distance running 65 20
569 12 s. Relay racing 90 35
566/9 .. .. *Set of* 4 1·90 65
MS570 100×70 mm. 40 s. Badminton .. .. 2·00 1·00

(Des D. Miller. Litho Questa)

1988 (5 Sept). *Olympic Games, Seoul* (2*nd issue*). *T* **131** *and similar vert designs. Multicoloured. P* 14.

571 10 s. Type **131** 10 10
572 20 s. Cycling 20 25
573 50 s. Fencing 45 50
574 70 s. Volleyball 60 65
571/4 .. .. *Set of* 4 1·25 1·40
MS575 77×92 mm. 100 s. Gymnastics .. 90 1·50

(Des D. Miller. Litho Questa)

1988 (5 Sept). *Winter Olympic Games, Calgary. Vert designs as T* **131**. *Multicoloured. P* 14.

576 5 s. Cross-country skiing 35 10
577 25 s. Figure skating 75 25
578 50 s. Downhill skiing .. .. 1·25 50
579 75 s. Bobsleighing .. .. 1·40 70
576/9 .. .. *Set of* 4 3·25 1·40
MS580 77×92 mm. 100 s. Ice hockey sticks wrapped in Olympic and Canadian colours .. 1·25 95

132 Goat **133** "Love You, Dad" (Pinocchio)

(Litho Questa)

1988 (9 Sept). *Domestic Animals. T* **132** *and similar multicoloured designs. P* 14.

581 4 s. Type **132** 15 15
582 5 s. Rabbit (*horiz*) 15 15
583 8 s. Cows (*horiz*) 20 20
584 10 s. Kitten (*horiz*) 25 25
585 12 s. Pony 30 30
586 20 s. Puppy 55 55
581/6 .. .. *Set of* 6 1·40 1·40
MS587 102×73 mm. 100 s. Chicken (*horiz*) .. 1·50 1·50

(Des Walt Disney Company. Litho Questa)

1988 (9 Sept). *Greetings Stamps. T* **133** *and similar horiz designs showing Walt Disney cartoon characters. Multicoloured. P* 14×$13^1/_2$.

588 4 s. Type **133** 10 10
589 5 s. "Happy Birthday" (Brer Rabbit and Chip n'Dale) 10 10
590 10 s. "Trick or Treat" (Daisy and Donald Duck) 15 15
591 12 s. "Be kind to Animals" (Ferdie and Mordie with Pluto) 15 15
592 15 s. "Love" (Daisy and Donald Duck) .. 20 20
593 20 s. "Let's Celebrate" (Mickey Mouse and Goofy) 30 30
594 30 s. "Keep in Touch" (Daisy and Donald Duck) 65 65
595 50 s. "Love you, Mom" (Minnie Mouse with Ferdie and Mordie) .. .. .. 1·25 1·25
588/95 .. .. *Set of* 8 2·50 2·50
MS596 Two sheets, each 127×101 mm. (a) 150 s. "Let's work together" (Goofy dressed as a fireman). (b) 150 s. "Have a super Sunday" (Goofy dressed as American footballer) *Set of* 2 *sheets* 4·75 4·50

134 *Charaxes varanes* **135** Independence Torch and Mt Kilimanjaro

(Des Jennifer Toombs. Litho Questa)

1988 (17 Oct). *Butterflies. T* **134** *and similar horiz designs. Multicoloured. P* $14^1/_2$.

597 8 s. Type **134** 30 10
598 30 s. *Neptis melicerta* 65 30
599 40 s. *Mylothris chloris* 75 40
600 50 s. *Charaxes bohemani* 90 50
601 60 s. *Myrina silenus* (s sp *ficedula*) .. 1·00 70
602 75 s. *Papilio phorcas* .. .. 1·50 90
603 90 s. *Cyrestis camillus* .. .. 1·75 1·10
604 100 s. *Salamis temora* .. .. 2·00 1·25
597/604 .. .. *Set of* 8 8·00 4·75
MS605 Two sheets, each 80×50 mm. (a) 200 s. *Asterope rosa*. (b) 250 s. *Kallima rumia* *Set of* 2 *sheets* 8·00 6·00

(Des R. Vigurs. Litho Questa)

1988 (1 Nov). *National Monuments. T* **135** *and similar vert designs. Multicoloured. P* 14.

606 5 s. Type **135** 10 10
607 12 s. Arusha Declaration Monument .. 10 10
608 30 s. Askari Monument 25 30
609 60 s. Independence Monument 55 60
606/9 .. .. *Set of* 4 80 90
MS610 100×89 mm. 100 s. Askari Monument statue .. .. 1·25 1·40

136 Eye Clinic **137** Loading Patient into Ambulance

(Des P. Ndembo. Litho National Printing & Packaging, Zimbabwe)

1988 (19 Dec). *25th Anniv of Dar-es-Salaam Lions Club. T* **136** *and similar horiz designs. Multicoloured. P* $14^{1}/_{2}$.

611 2 s. Type **136** 15 15
612 3 s. Family at shallow water well 15 15
613 7 s. Rhinoceros and map of Tanzania 20 20
614 12 s. Club presenting school desks 25 25
611/14 .. .. *Set of* 4 65 65
MS615 100×65 mm. 40 s. Lions International logo 60 65

(Des P. Ndembo. Litho State Ptg Wks, Moscow)

1988 (30 Dec). *125th Anniv of International Red Cross and Red Crescent. T* **137** *and similar horiz designs. Multicoloured. P* $12^{1}/_{2}$×12.

616 2 s. Type **137** 15 15
617 3 s. Mother and baby health clinic 15 15
618 7 s. Red Cross flag 20 20
619 12 s. Henri Dunant (founder) 30 30
616/19 .. .. *Set of* 4 70 70
MS620 90×90 mm. 40 s. Members of Red Cross International Committee, 1863 .. .. .. 75 75

138 Paradise Whydah **139** Bushbaby

(Des S. Barlowe. Litho B.D.T.)

1989 (15 Mar). *Birds. T* **138** *and similar vert designs. Multicoloured. P* $13^{1}/_{2}$.

621 20 s. Type **138** 65 65
a. Sheetlet. Nos. 621/40 .. .. .. 11·50
622 20 s. Black-collared Barbet 65 65
623 20 s. Bateleur 65 65
624 20 s. Lilac-breasted Roller and African Open-bill Storks in flight 65 65
625 20 s. Red-tufted Malachite Sunbird and African Open-bill Stork in flight 65 65
626 20 s. Dark Chanting Goshawk 65 65
627 20 s. White-fronted Bee Eater, Carmine Bee Eater and Little Bee Eaters 65 65
628 20 s. Narina Trogon and Marabou Stork in flight 65 65
629 20 s. Grey Parrot 65 65
630 20 s. Hoopoe 65 65
631 20 s. Masked Lovebird ("Yellow-collared Lovebird") 65 65
632 20 s. Yellow-billed Hornbill 65 65
633 20 s. Hammerkop 65 65
634 20 s. Violet-crested Turaco and flamingos in flight 65 65
635 20 s. Malachite Kingfisher 65 65
636 20 s. Greater Flamingos 65 65
637 20 s. Yellow-billed Storks 65 65
638 20 s. Whale-headed Stork ("Shoebill Stork") .. 65 65
639 20 s. Saddle-bill Stork and Blacksmith Plover 65 65
640 20 s. South African Crowned Crane 65 65
621/40 .. .. *Set of* 20 11·50 11·50
MS641 Two sheets, each 105×75 mm. (a) 350 s. Helmet Guineafowl (28×42 *mm*). (b) 350 s. Ostrich (28×42 *mm*). P 14 .. *Set of* 2 *sheets* 8·00 5·50

Nos. 622/41 were printed together, *se-tenant*, in a sheetlet of 20 forming a composite design of birds at a waterhole.

(Des J. Barbaris (Nos. 642/4, 648, **MS**650a), S. Barlowe (others). Litho Questa)

1989 (20 Mar). *Fauna and Flora. T* **139** *and similar multicoloured designs. P* 14.

642 5 s. Type **139** 10 10
643 10 s. Bushbaby holding insect (*horiz*) 15 15
644 20 s. Bushbaby on forked branch 25 25
645 30 s. Black Cobra on Umbrella Acacia 50 50
646 45 s. Bushbaby at night (*horiz*) 50 50
647 70 s. Red-billed Tropic Bird and Tree Ferns 2·00 2·00
648 100 s. African Tree Frog on Cocoa Tree .. 2·00 2·00
649 150 s. Black-headed Heron and Egyptian Papyrus .. .. 3·50 3·50
642/9 .. .. *Set of* 8 8·00 8·00
MS650 Two sheets. (a) 115×85 mm. 350 s. African Palm Civet (*horiz*). (b) 65×65 mm. 350 s. Pink-backed Pelican and Baobab Tree (*horiz*) *Set of* 2 *sheets* 6·50 5·50

Nos. 645, 647/9 and **MS**650 are without the World Wildlife Fund logo.

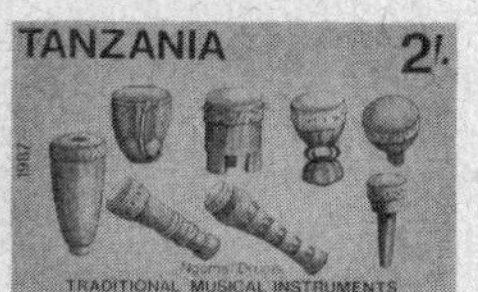

140 Juma Ikangaa (marathon runner) **141** Drums

(Des W. Storozuk. Litho Questa)

1989 (10 Apr). *International Sporting Personalities. T* **140** *and similar vert designs. Multicoloured. P* 14.

651 4 s. Type **140** 15 15
652 8 s. 50, Steffi Graf (tennis player) 65 30
653 12 s. Yannick Noah (tennis player) 70 40
654 40 s. Pelé (footballer) 80 65
655 100 s. Erhard Keller (speed skater) 90 80
656 125 s. Sadanoyama (sumo wrestler) .. .. 1·00 1·00
657 200 s. Taino (sumo wrestler) .. .. .. 1·75 1·75
658 250 s. T. Nakajima (golfer) .. .. .. 3·25 2·75
651/8 .. .. *Set of* 8 8·25 7·00
MS659 Two sheets. (a) 100×71 mm. 350 s. Joe Louis (boxer). (b) 100×76 mm. 350 s. I. Aoki (golfer) .. .. *Set of* 2 *sheets* 7·00 5·50

The captions on Nos. 658 and **MS**659b are transposed.

(Des P. Ndembo. Litho Harrison)

1989 (29 June). *Musical Instruments. T* **141** *and similar horiz designs. Multicoloured. P* 14.

660 2 s. Type **141** 30 20
661 3 s. Xylophones 30 20
662 10 s. Thumbpiano 65 60
663 20 s. Fiddles .. .. 1·00 1·25
660/3 .. .. *Set of* 4 2·00 2·00
MS664 91×80 mm. 40 s. Violins with calabash resonators 70 70

142 Chama Cha Mapinduzi Party Flag **143** Class "P36" Locomotive, U.S.S.R.

(Des P. Ndembo. Litho Questa)

1989 (1 July). *National Solidarity Walk. T* **142** *and similar multicoloured designs. P* $14^{1}/_{2}$.

665 5 s. + 1 s. Type **142** 15 20
666 10 s. + 1 s. Marchers with party flag and President Mwinyi 15 20
MS667 122×122 mm. 50 s. + 1 s. President Mwinyi (*vert*) 40 40

(Des W. Wright. Litho B.D.T.)

1989 (22 Aug). *Steam Locomotives. T* **143** *and similar multicoloured designs. P* 14.

668 10 s. Type **143** 20 20
669 25 s. Class "12", Belgium 30 30
670 60 s. Class "C62", Japan 55 55
671 75 s. Pennsylvania Railroad Class "T1", U.S.A. 65 65
672 80 s. Class "WP", India 70 70
673 90 s. East African Railways Class "59" .. 80 80
674 150 s. Class "People", China .. .. .. 1·40 1·40
675 200 s. Southern Pacific "Daylight Express" U.S.A. .. .. 1·60 1·60
668/75 .. .. *Set of* 8 5·50 5·50
MS676 Two sheets, each 114×85 mm. (a) 350 s. Stephenson's *Planet*, Great Britain (*vert*). (b) 350 s. "Coronation Scot", Great Britain (*vert*) *Set of* 2 *sheets* 5·50 6·50

(Des Design Element. Litho Questa)

1989 (17 Nov). *"World Stamp Expo '89" International Stamp Exhibition, Washington. Landmarks of Washington. Sheet 78×62 mm containing horiz design as T* **193a** *of Lesotho. Multicoloured. P* 14.

MS677 500 s. Union Station .. .. .. 4·00 5·00

Gold-USSR
Silver-Brazil
Bronze-W.Germany

144 "Luna 3" Satellite orbiting Moon, 1959 (**145**)

(Des G. Vasarhelyi. Litho Questa)

1989 (22 Nov). *History of Space Exploration and 20th Anniv of First Manned Landing on Moon. T* **144** *and similar horiz designs. Multicoloured. P* 14.

678 20 s. Type **144** 25 25
679 30 s. "Gemini 6" and "7", 1965 .. .. .. 35 35
680 40 s. Astronaut Edward White in space, 1965 .. .. 40 40
681 60 s. Astronaut Aldrin on Moon, 1969 .. .. 60 60
682 70 s. Aldrin performing experiment, 1969 .. 70 70
683 100 s. "Apollo 15" astronaut and lunar rover, 1971 .. .. 90 90
684 150 s. "Apollo 18" and "Soyuz 19" docking in space, 1975 .. .. 1·25 1·25
685 200 s. Spacelab, 1983 .. .. 1·50 1·50
678/85 .. .. *Set of* 8 5·50 5·50
MS686 Two sheets, each 110×90 mm. (a) 250 s. Lunar module *Eagle* and "Apollo 11" emblem. (b) 250 s. Projected U.S. space station *Set of* 2 *sheets* 3·50 4·50

1989 (11 Dec). *Olympic Medal Winners, Calgary and Seoul. Optd as T* **145**. *(a) On Nos.* 571/5

687 10 s. Type **131** (optd with T **145**) 40 40
688 20 s. Cycling (optd "Men's Match Sprint, Lutz Hesslich, DDR") 70 70
689 50 s. Fencing (optd "Epee, Schmitt, W. Germany") .. .. 1·00 1·00
690 70 s. Volleyball (optd "Men's Team, USA") 1·60 1·60
687/90 .. .. *Set of* 4 3·25 3·25
MS691 77×92 mm. 100 s. Gymnastics ("Women's Team, Gold – USSR") .. .. 1·50 2·25

(b) On Nos. 576/80

692 5 s. Cross-country skiing (optd "Biathlon, Peter-Roetsch, DDR") 30 30
693 25 s. Figure skating (optd "Pairs, Gordeeva & Grinkov, USSR") 55 55
694 50 s. Downhill skiing (optd "Zurbriggen, Switzerland") 95 95
695 75 s. Bobsleighing (optd "Gold – USSR Silver – DDR Bronze – DDR") .. .. .. 1·25 1·25
692/5 .. .. *Set of* 4 2·75 2·75
MS696 77×92 mm. 100 s. Ice hockey sticks wrapped in Olympic and Canadian colours (optd "Ice Hockey: Gold – USSR") .. .. .. 4·00 4·25

146 Spotted Tilapia

(Des W. Hanson Studio. Litho Questa)

1989 (14 Dec). *Reef and Freshwater Fishes of Tanzania. T* **146** *and similar multicoloured designs. P* 14.

697 9 s. Type **146** 40 40
698 13 s. Painted Triggerfish 40 40
699 20 s. Powder-blue Surgeonfish 50 50
700 40 s. Red-tailed Butterflyfish 75 75
701 70 s. Red-tailed Notho .. .. .. 1·25 1·25
702 100 s. Ansorge's Neolebias .. .. .. 1·50 1·50
703 150 s. Blue Panchax .. .. 2·00 2·00
704 200 s. Regal Angelfish .. .. .. 2·00 2·00
697/704 .. .. *Set of* 8 8·00 8·00
MS705 Two sheets, each 112×83 mm. (a) 350 s. Jewel Cichlid (50×38 *mm*). P 14×$13^{1}/_{2}$. (b) 350 s. Dusky Batfish (38×50 *mm*). P $13^{1}/_{2}$×14 *Set of* 2 *sheets* 8·00 8·00

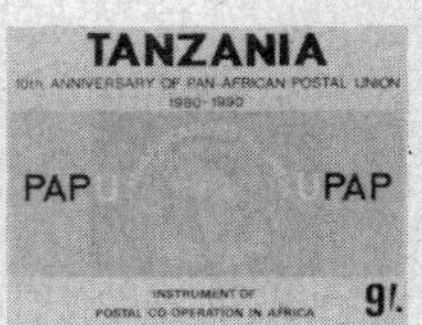

147 Rural Polling Station **148** Logo

(Des P. Ndembo. Litho State Ptg Wks, Moscow)

1989 (22 Dec). *Centenary of Inter-Parliamentary Union. T* **147** *and similar horiz designs. P* $12^{1}/_{2}$×12.

706 9 s. multicoloured 10 10
707 13 s. multicoloured 10 10
708 80 s. multicoloured 40 55
709 100 s. black, dull ultramarine and pale blue 50 75
706/9 .. .. *Set of* 4 90 1·40
MS710 90×90 mm. 40 s. multicoloured .. .. 50 1·00

Designs:—13 s. Parliament Building, Dar-es-Salaam; 40 s. Sir William Randal Cremer and Frederic Passy (founders); 80 s. Tanzania Parliament in session; 100 s. Logo.

(Des P. Ndembo. Litho Cartor)

1990 (10 Jan). *10th Anniv of Pan-African Postal Union. T* **148** *and similar horiz designs. P* $13^{1}/_{2}$.

711 9 s. greenish yellow, dull green and black 15 15
712 13 s. multicoloured 15 15
713 70 s. multicoloured 60 70
714 100 s. multicoloured .. .. 1·00 1·10
711/14 .. .. *Set of* 4 1·75 1·90
MS715 90×90 mm. 40 s. multicoloured. P $12^{1}/_{2}$ 50 1·00

Designs:—13 s. Collecting mail from post office box; 40 s. Logos of Tanzania Posts and Telecommunications Corporation, P.A.P.U. and U.P.U.; 70 s. Taking mail to post office; 100 s. Mail transport.

149 Admiral's Flag and *Nina*

(Des T. Agans. Litho Questa)

1990 (12 Feb). *500th Anniv of Discovery of America by Columbus* (1992) (50, 60, 75, 200 s.) *and Modern Scientific Discoveries* (others). *T* **149** *and similar horiz designs. Multicoloured. P* 14.

716 9 s. Bell XS-1 aircraft (first supersonic flight, 1947) 30 30
717 13 s. *Trieste* (bathyscaph) (first dive to depth of 35,000 ft, 1960) 30 30
718 50 s. Type **149** 60 60
719 60 s. Fleet flag and *Pinta* 70 70
720 75 s. Standard of Castile and León and *Santa Maria* 80 80
721 150 s. Transistor technology .. .. 1·00 1·00
722 200 s. Arms of Columbus and map of First Voyage .. .. 1·75 1·75
723 250 s. DNA molecule .. .. .. 1·75 1·75
716/23 .. .. *Set of* 8 6·50 6·50
MS724 Two sheets, each 106 x 78 mm. (a) 350 s. Caravels in the Caribbean. (b) 350 s. *Voyager II* and Neptune .. .. .. *Set of 2 sheets* 5·00 5·50

150 Tecopa Pupfish

(Des J. Genzo. Litho Questa)

1990 (20 Feb). *Extinct Species. T* **150** *and similar multicoloured designs. P* 14.

725 25 s. Type **150** 50 50
726 40 s. Thylacine 75 75
727 50 s. Quagga 90 90
728 60 s. Passenger Pigeon .. .. .. 1·50 1·50
729 75 s. Rodriguez Saddleback Tortoise .. 1·50 1·50
730 100 s. Toolache Wallaby .. .. .. 1·60 1·60
731 150 s. Texas Red Wolf .. .. .. 1·75 1·75
732 200 s. Utah Lake Sculpin .. .. .. 1·75 1·75
725/32 .. .. *Set of* 8 9·00 9·00
MS733 Two sheets. (a) 102×74 mm. 350 s. South Island Whekau. (b) 71×99 mm. 350 s. Hawaii O-o (*vert*) .. .. .. *Set of 2 sheets* 7·00 7·50

151 Camping

(Des P. Ndembo. Litho State Ptg Wks, Moscow)

1990 (22 Feb). *60th Anniv of Girl Guides Movement in Tanzania. T* **151** *and similar multicoloured designs. P* 12½×12.

734 9 s. Type **151** 15 15
735 13 s. Guides planting sapling 15 15
736 50 s. Guide teaching woman to write .. 40 60
737 100 s. Guide helping at child-care clinic .. 65 95
734/7 .. .. *Set of* 4 1·25 1·75
MS738 89×89 mm. 40 s. Guide teaching child to read (*vert*). P 12×12½ .. .. .. 60 1·00

152 Fishing **153** Footballer

(Des P. Ndembo. Litho State Ptg Wks, Moscow)

1990 (25 Apr). *25th Anniv of Union of Tanganyika and Zanzibar. T* **152** *and similar multicoloured designs. P* 12½×12 (*horiz*) *or* 12×12½ (*vert*).

739 9 s. Type **152** 15 15
740 13 s. Vineyard 15 15
741 50 s. Cloves 75 85
742 100 s. Presidents Nyerere and Karume exchanging Union instruments (*vert*) 1·50 2·00
739/42 .. .. *Set of* 4 2·25 2·75
MS743 90×90 mm. 40 s. Arms (*vert*) .. .. 1·00 1·50

(Litho B.D.T.)

1990 (1 June). *World Cup Football Championship, Italy* (1*st issue*). *T* **153** *and similar vert designs. Multicoloured. P* 14.

744 25 s. Type **153** 50 30
745 60 s. Player passing ball .. .. .. 1·00 80
746 75 s. Player turning .. .. .. 1·25 90
747 200 s. Player kicking ball .. .. .. 2·25 2·75
744/7 .. .. *Set of* 4 4·50 4·25
MS748 Two sheets, each 105×76 mm. (a) 350 s. Two players fighting for possession. (b) 350 s. Player kicking ball .. .. *Set of 2 sheets* 8·00 8·00

See also Nos. 789/93 and 794/8.

154 Miriam Makeba **155** Ring of People round Party Flag

(Des A. Fagbohun. Litho Questa)

1990 (29 June). *Famous Black Entertainers. T* **154** *and similar vert designs. Multicoloured. P* 14.

749 9 s. Type **154** 15 10
750 13 s. Manu Dibango 15 10
751 25 s. Fela 20 15
752 70 s. Smokey Robinson 50 40
753 100 s. Gladys Knight 65 55
754 150 s. Eddie Murphy .. .. .. 1·25 1·25
755 200 s. Sammy Davis Jnr. .. .. .. 1·50 1·75
756 250 f. Stevie Wonder .. .. .. 1·75 2·00
749/56 .. .. *Set of* 8 5·50 5·50
MS757 Two sheets, each 69×88 mm.(a) 350 s. Bill Cosby (30×39 *mm*). (b) 350 s. Michael Jackson (30×39 *mm*). P 14½ .. *Set of 2 sheets* 3·50 4·00

(Litho Cartor)

1990 (6 July). *Solidarity Walk,* 1990. *T* **155** *and similar multicoloured designs. P* 13½.

758 9 s. + 1 s. Type **155** 40 55
759 13 s. + 1 s. President Mwinyi 40 55
MS760 90×90 mm. 50 s. + 1 s. Handclasp on map (*vert*). P 12½ .. .. .. 90 1·25

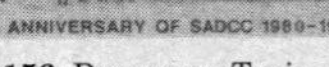

156 Passenger Train **157** Pope John Paul II

(Des P. Ndembo. Litho Cartor)

1990 (8 Aug). *10th Anniv of Southern African Development Co-ordination Conference. T* **156** *and similar horiz designs. Multicoloured. P* 13½.

761 8 s. Type **156** 50 15
762 11 s. 50, Paper-making plant 25 15
763 25 s. Tractor factory and ploughing .. 30 15
764 100 s. Map and national flags .. .. 1·50 2·00
761/4 .. .. *Set of* 4 2·25 2·25
MS765 89×89 mm. 50 s. Map of Southern Africa. P 12½ .. .. 1·25 1·50

(Des P. Ndembo. Litho Questa)

1990 (1 Sept). *Papal Visit to Tanzania. T* **157** *and similar multicoloured designs. P* 14.

766 10 s. Type **157** 15 10
767 15 s. Pope in ceremonial robes 20 10
768 20 s. Pope giving blessing 25 15
769 100 s. Papal coat of arms 70 90
766/9 .. .. *Set of* 4 1·10 1·10
MS770 172×143 mm. 50 s. Pope John Paul II (*horiz*); 50 s. St. Joseph's Cathedral, Dar-es-Salaam (*horiz*); 50 s. Christ the King Cathedral, Moshi (*horiz*); 50 s. Saint Theresa's Cathedral, Tabora (*horiz*); 50 s. Cathedral of the Epiphany, Bugando Mwanza (*horiz*); 50 s. St. Mathias Mulumba Kalemba Cathedral, Songea (*horiz*) 2·75 3·00
a. Error. Imperf .. .. † —

158 Mickey and Minnie Mouse in Herby the Love Bug

(Des Walt Disney Co. Litho Questa)

1990 (7 Nov). *Motor Cars from Disney Films. T* **158** *and similar horiz designs. Multicoloured. P* 14×13½.

771 20 s. Type **158** 20 20
772 30 s. The Absent-minded Professor's car .. 25 25
773 45 s. Chitty-Chitty Bang-Bang 35 35
774 60 s. Mr. Toad's car 55 55
775 75 s. Scrooge's limousine 65 65
776 100 s. The Shaggy Dog's car 90 90
777 150 s. Donald Duck's nephews cleaning car 1·40 1·40
778 200 s. Fire engine from *Dumbo* .. .. 1·60 1·60
771/8 .. .. *Set of* 8 5·50 5·50
MS779 Two sheets, each 127×112, (a) 350 s. The Mickeymobile. (b) 350 s. Cruella De Vil and dog wagon from *101 Dalmations* .. *Set of 2 sheets* 6·00 7·00

159 "St. Mary Magdalen in Penitence" (detail) **160** Klinsmann of West Germany

(Litho Questa)

1990 (7 Nov). *Paintings by Titian. T* **159** *and similar vert designs. Multicoloured. P* 13½×14.

780 5 s. Type **159** 10 10
781 10 s. "Averoldi Polyptych" (detail) .. 10 10
782 15 s. "Saint Margaret" (detail) 15 15
783 50 s. "Venus and Adonis" (detail) 40 40
784 75 s. "Venus and the Lutenist" (detail) .. 55 55
785 100 s. "Tarquin and Lucretia" (detail) .. 70 70
786 125 s. "Saint Jerome" (detail) 90 90
787 150 s. "Madonna and Child in Glory with Saints" (detail) .. .. .. 1·00 1·00
780/7 .. .. *Set of* 8 3·50 3·50
MS788 Three sheets. (a) 95×110 mm. 300 s. "Adoration of the Holy Trinity" (detail). (b) 95×110 mm. 300 s. "St. Catherine of Alexandria at Prayer" (detail). (c) 110×95 mm. 300 s. "The Supper at Emmaus" (detail) .. *Set of 3 sheets* 6·50 7·00

(Des Young Phillips Studio. Litho Questa)

1990 (17 Nov). *World Cup Football Championship, Italy* (2*nd issue*). *T* **160** *and similar vert designs. Multicoloured. P* 14.

789 10 s. Type **160** 30 20
790 60 s. Serena of Italy 75 60
791 100 s. Nicol of Scotland .. .. .. 1·25 1·25
792 300 s. Susic of Yugoslavia .. .. .. 2·75 3·25
789/92 .. .. *Set of* 4 4·50 4·75
MS793 Two sheets, each 85×95 mm. (a) 400 s. Montero of Costa Rica. (b) 400 s. Seifo of Belgium *Set of 2 sheets* 7·00 7·50

161 Throw-in

(Litho Questa)

1990 (17 Nov). *World Cup Football Championship, Italy* (3*rd issue*). *T* **161** *and similar horiz designs. Multicoloured. P* 14.

794 9 s. Type **161** 20 15
795 13 s. Penalty kick 20 15
796 25 s. Dribbling 30 25
797 100 s. Corner kick .. .. 1·10 1·75
794/7 .. .. *Set of* 4 1·60 2·10
MS798 82×82 mm. 50 s. World Cup and world map .. .. 1·25 1·75

162 Canoe

(Des M. Raza. Litho State Ptg Works, Moscow)

1990 (24 Nov). *Marine Transport. T* **162** *and similar horiz designs. Multicoloured. P* 12½×12.

799 9 s. Type **162** 10 10
800 13 s. Sailing canoe 15 10
801 25 s. Dhow 25 15
802 100 s. Freighter .. .. 1·10 1·75
799/802 .. .. *Set of* 4 1·40 1·90
MS803 90×90 mm. 40 s. Mashua dhow .. .. 1·25 1·50

ALTERED CATALOGUE NUMBERS

Any Catalogue numbers altered from the last edition are shown as a list in the introductory pages.

163 Lesser Masked Weaver

164 Lesser Flamingo

(Litho Questa)

1990 (15 Dec)–**91**. *Birds. Horiz designs as T* **163** (5 *s. to* 30 *s.*) *or* **164** (40 *s. to* 500 *s.*). *Multicoloured. P* 14.

804 5 s. Type **163** 10 10
a. Booklet pane. Nos. 804/9 each × 2 with margins all round 90
805 9 s. African Emerald Cuckoo 15 10
806 13 s. Little Bee Eater 15 10
807 15 s. Red Bishop 15 10
808 20 s. Bateleur 20 10
809 25 s. Scarlet-chested Sunbird 20 10
809*a* 30 s. African Wood Pigeon (1.7.91) .. 20 10
810 40 s. Type **164** 20 10
811 70 s. Helmet Guineafowl 30 20
812 100 s. Eastern White Pelican 40 25
813 170 s. Saddle-bill Stork 55 50
814 200 s. South African Crowned Crane .. 65 55
814*a* 300 s. Pied Crow (1.7.91) 85 85
814*b* 400 s. White-headed Vulture (1.7.91) .. 1·00 1·10
815 500 s. Ostrich .. .. 1·10 1·25
804/15 .. .. *Set of* 15 5·50 4·75
MS816 100×102 mm. 40 s. Superb Starling; 60 s. Lilac-breasted Roller .. .. 1·75 2·00

165 Athletics

(Des P. Ndembo. Litho Questa)

1990 (29 Dec). *14th Commonwealth Games, Auckland, New Zealand. T* **165** *and similar multicoloured designs. P* 14.

817 9 s. Type **165** 25 15
818 13 s. Netball (*vert*) 45 15
819 25 s. Pole vaulting 60 20
820 100 s. Long jumping (*vert*) .. .. 1·50 2·25
817/20 .. .. *Set of* 4 2·50 2·50
MS821 100×100 mm. 40 s. Boxing (*vert*) .. 50 1·00

166 Former German Post Office, Dar-es-Salaam

(Litho Questa)

1991 (10 Jan). *150th Anniv of the Penny Black and "Stamp World London 90" International Stamp Exhibition. T* **166** *and similar horiz designs. Multicoloured. P* 14.

822 50 s. Type **166** 55 55
a. Horiz pair. Nos. 822/3 .. .. 1·10 1·10
823 50 s. *Reichstag* (German mail steamer), 1890 .. .. 55 55
824 75 s. Dhows, Zanzibar 75 75
a. Horiz pair. Nos. 824/5 .. .. 1·50 1·50
825 75 s. Cobham's Short S. 5 Singapore I flying boat, Mwanza, Lake Victoria, 1928 75 75
826 100 s. Air Tanzania Fokker F. 27 Friendship over Livingstone's House, Zanzibar 1·00 1·00
a. Horiz pair. Nos. 826/7 .. .. 2·00 2·00
827 100 s. Mail train at Moshi station .. .. 1·00 1·00
828 100 s. English mail coach, 1840 .. .. 1·00 1·00
829 150 s. Stephenson's *Rocket* and mail coach, 1838 .. .. 1·75 1·75
830 200 s. Imperial Airways Handley Page H.P.42 at Croydon .. .. .. 1·90 1·90
822/30 .. .. *Set of* 9 8·00 8·00
MS831 Two sheets, each 85×65 mm. (a) 350 s. Sir Rowland Hill and Penny Black. (b) 350 s. Thurn and Taxis letter of 1860 .. *Set of* 2 *sheets* 5·00 6·00

Nos. 822/3, 824/5 and 826/7 were each printed together, *se-tenant*, in horizontal pairs throughout the sheets.

Nos. 822/7 and **MS**831a overprinted "40th Anniversary of the Accession H. M. Queen Elizabeth II 1952–1992" are reported as not being issued in Tanzania.

167 Petersberg Railway, West Germany

(Litho Questa)

1991 (10 Jan). *Cog Railways. T* **167** *and similar horiz designs. Multicoloured. P* 14.

832 8 s. Type **167** 40 30
833 25 s. *Waumbek* (locomotive), Mount Washington Railway, U.S.A. .. 60 60
834 50 s. Dubrovnik–Sarajevo line, Yugoslavia 75 75
835 100 s. Cog railway, Budapest, Hungary .. 1·00 1·00
836 150 s. Steam locomotive, Vordenberg–Eisenerz line, Austria .. .. 1·50 1·50
837 200 s. Last train on Rimutaka Incline, New Zealand, 1955 .. .. .. 1·60 1·60
838 250 s. John Stevens' cog locomotive, U.S.A., 1825 .. .. 1·60 1·75
839 300 s. Pilatusbahn cog railcar, Switzerland 1·75 1·75
832/9 .. .. *Set of* 8 8·25 8·25
MS840 Two sheets, each 117×87 mm. (a) 400 s. Sylvester Marsh and Presidential excursion train, U.S.A., 1869 (51×38 *mm*). (b) 400 s. Steam locomotive Schneebergbahn, Austria (51×38 *mm*). P 13½ .. .. *Set of* 2 *sheets* 6·00 7·00

(Des Walt Disney Co. Litho Questa)

1991 (10 Jan). *International Literacy Year* (1*st issue*). *Designs as T* **246** *of Maldive Islands showing Walt Disney cartoon characters illustrating the Alphabet. Multicoloured. P* 13½×14.

841/67 1, 2, 3, 5, 10, 15, 18, 20, 25, 30, 35, 40, 45, 50, 55, 60, 75, 80, 90, 100, 120, 125, 145, 150, 160, 175, 200 s. .. .. *Set of* 27 11·00 13·00
MS868 Two sheets, each 128×112 mm. (a) 600 s. Tiger Lily and Lost Boys. P 14×13½. (b) 600 s. Mickey Mouse driving miniature railway locomotive (*vert*). P 13½×14 .. *Set of* 2 *sheets* 8·00 9·00

Nos. 841/67 were issued in three sheetlets, each of nine, the first containing Nos. 841/3, 846, 855, 858, 861, 863, 867, the second Nos. 845, 848, 850, 852, 854, 856, 860, 862, 864 and the third Nos. 844, 847, 849, 851, 853, 857, 859, 865/6.

See also Nos. 905/9.

(Litho Questa)

1991 (10 Jan). *Olympic Games, Barcelona* (1*st issue*). *Vert designs as T* **202** *of Lesotho. Multicoloured. P* 14.

869 5 s. Archery 30 20
870 10 s. Women's gymnastics 30 20
871 25 s. Boxing 40 30
872 50 s. Canoeing 60 50
873 100 s. Volleyball .. .. .. 1·25 1·25
874 150 s. Men's gymnastics .. .. 1·40 1·50
875 200 s. 4 × 100 metres relay .. .. 1·75 2·00
876 300 s. Judo .. .. 2·00 2·25
869/76 .. .. *Set of* 8 7·25 7·25
MS877 Two sheets, each 102×71 mm. (a) 400 s. Cycling. (b) 400 s. 400 metres men's hurdles *Set of* 2 *sheets* 6·00 7·00

See also Nos. 1309/13 and 1404/12.

(Litho Questa)

1991 (18 Jan). *"EXPO '90" International Garden and Greenery Exhibition, Osaka. Orchids. Multicoloured designs as T* **198** *of Lesotho, but vert. P* 14.

878 10 s. *Phalaenopsis* "Lipperose" 20 15
879 25 s. *Lycoste* "Aquila" 30 20
880 30 s. *Vuylstekeara* "Cambria Plush" .. 30 20
881 50 s. *Vuylstekeara* "Monica Burnham" .. 45 35
882 90 s. *Odontocidium* "Crowborough Plush" 85 85
883 100 s. *Oncidioda* "Crowborough Chelsea" .. 85 85
884 250 s. *Sophrolaeliocattleya* "Phena Saturn" 1·40 1·60
885 300 s. *Laeliocattleya* "Lykas" .. .. 1·50 1·75
878/85 .. .. *Set of* 8 5·25 5·50
MS886 Two sheets, each 100×69 mm. (a) 400 s. *Cymbidium* "Baldoyle Melbury". (b) 400 s. *Cymbidium* "Tapestry Long Beach" *Set of* 2 *sheets* 4·50 5·50

168 Olympic "Soling" Class Yacht Racing

(Litho Questa)

1991 (18 Jan). *Record-breaking Sports Events. T* **168** *and similar multicoloured designs. P* 14.

887 5 s. Type **168** 20 20
888 20 s. Olympic downhill skiing 50 35
889 30 s. "Tour de France" cycle race 75 50
890 40 s. Le Mans 24-hour endurance motor race 80 60
891 75 s. Olympic two-man bobsleighing .. 90 90
892 100 s. Belgian Grand Prix motor cycle race 1·40 1·25
893 250 s. Indianapolis 500 motor race .. 2·00 2·25
894 300 s. Gold Cup power boat championship 2·00 2·50
887/94 .. .. *Set of* 8 7·75 7·75
MS895 Two sheets, each 85×64 mm. (a) 400 s. Colorado 500 motor cycle race (*vert*). (b) 400 s. Schneider Trophy air race (*vert*) *Set of* 2 *sheets* 7·00 8·00

169 Mickey Mouse as Cowboy

(Des Walt Disney Co. Litho Questa)

1991 (20 Feb). *Mickey Mouse in Hollywood. T* **169** *and similar horiz designs showing Walt Disney cartoon characters as actors. Multicoloured. P* 14×13½.

896 5 s. Type **169** 30 30
897 10 s. Mickey as boxer 30 30
898 15 s. Mickey as astronaut 30 30
899 20 s. Mickey and Minnie as lovers .. 30 30
900 100 s. Mickey as pirate rescuing Minnie .. 1·25 1·25
901 200 s. Mickey and Donald Duck as policemen arresting Big Pete .. 2·50 2·50
902 350 s. Mickey and Donald with Goofy in historical drama .. .. 2·75 2·75
903 450 s. Mickey, Donald and Goofy as sailors 2·75 2·75
896/903 .. .. *Set of* 8 9·50 9·50
MS904 Two sheets, each 127×96 mm. (a) 600 s. Mickey, Minnie and Donald in the mummy's tomb. (b) 600 s. Mickey as Canadian Mountie rescuing Minnie from Big Pete .. *Set of* 2 *sheets* 7·50 8·50

170 Women learning to Read

(Litho Questa)

1991 (15 Mar). *International Literacy Year* (2*nd issue*). *T* **170** *and similar horiz designs. Multicoloured. P* 14.

905 9 s. Type **170** 20 15
906 13 s. Teacher with blackboard 25 15
907 25 s. Literacy aids 35 20
908 100 s. Reading newspaper .. .. .. 1·40 2·00
905/8 .. .. *Set of* 4 2·00 2·25
MS909 104×73 mm. 50 s. Adult education class 75 1·00

171 Ngorongoro Crater

172 Stegosaurus

(Litho National Printing and Packaging, Zimbabwe)

1991 (28 Mar). *Historical Craters and Caves. T* **171** *and similar horiz designs. Multicoloured. P* 14×14½.

910 3 s. Type **171** 60 60
911 5 s. Prehistoric rock painting, Kondoa Caves 60 60
912 9 s. Inner crater, Mt Kilimanjaro 75 75
913 12 s. Olduvai Gorge .. .. .. 1·00 1·00
910/13 .. .. *Set of* 4 2·75 2·75
MS914 91×92 mm. 10 s. Discarded bottles, Amboni Caves; 10 s. Rock paintings, Amboni Caves; 10 s. Entrance to Amboni Caves; 10 s. Rock formation, Amboni Caves .. .. 5·50 5·50

(Litho Questa)

1991 (28 Apr). *350th Death Anniv of Rubens. Cartoons for Decius Mus Tapestries. Multicoloured designs as T* **250** *of Maldive Islands. P* 14×13½.

915 85 s. "Proclamation of the Vision" .. .. 1·00 1·00
a. Sheetlet. Nos. 915/20 .. .. 6·00
916 85 s. "Divining of the Entrails" .. .. 1·00 1·00
917 85 s. "Dispatch of the Lictors" .. .. 1·00 1·00
918 85 s. "Dedication to Death" .. .. 1·00 1·00
919 85 s. "Victory and Death of Decius Mus" .. 1·00 1·00
920 85 s. "Funeral Rites" .. .. .. 1·00 1·00
915/20 .. .. *Set of* 6 6·00 6·00
MS921 70×100 mm. 500 s. "Trophy of War" (detail) (*vert*). P 13½×14 .. .. .. 5·50 7·00

(Litho State Ptg Wks, Moscow)

1991 (3 June). *Prehistoric Creatures. T* **172** *and similar vert designs. Multicoloured. P* 12×12½.

922 10 s. Type **172** 25 25
923 15 s. Triceratops 25 25
924 25 s. Edmontosaurus 40 40
925 30 s. Plateosaurus 40 40
926 35 s. Diplodocus 45 45
927 100 s. Iguanodon .. .. 1·40 1·40
928 200 s. Silviasaurus .. .. .. 2·00 2·00
922/8 .. .. *Set of* 7 4·75 4·75
MS929 90×90 mm. 150 s. Rhamphorhynchus 2·25 2·75

173 Dairy Farming

174 Pres. Mwinyi leading Walk

(Litho Questa)

1991 (7 June). *20th Anniv of Tanzania Investment Bank. T* **173** *and similar horiz designs. Multicoloured. P* 14.

930 10 s. Type **173** 20 15
931 13 s. Industrial development 25 15
932 25 s. Engineering 30 15
933 100 s. Tea picking 1·25 1·75
930/3 *Set of* 4 1·75 2·00
MS934 93×91 mm. Nos. 930/3 1·75 2·00

(Litho Cartor)

1991 (5 July). *National Solidarity Walk. T* **174** *and similar horiz designs. Multicoloured. P* 13½.

935 4 s. + 1 s. Type **174** 40 55
936 30 s. + 1 s. Pres. Mwinyi planting sapling 40 55
MS937 91×91 mm. 50 s. + 1 s. Pres. Mwinyi sorting cloves. P 12½ 1·10 1·50

(Des K. Gromell. Litho Questa)

1991 (15 Aug). *"Phila Nippon '91" International Stamp Exhibition, Tokyo. Japanese Railway Locomotives. Multicoloured designs as T* **257** *of Maldive Islands, but horiz. P* 14.

938 10 s. First steam locomotive in Japan 50 50
939 25 s. Class "4500" steam locomotive 75 75
940 35 s. Class "C 62" steam locomotive 85 85
941 50 s. Class "Mikado" steam locomotive 1·00 1·00
942 75 s. Class "6250" steam locomotive 1·25 1·25
943 100 s. Class "C 11" steam locomotive 1·50 1·50
944 200 s. Class "E 10" steam locomotive 1·75 1·75
945 300 s. Class "8550" steam locomotive 2·00 2·00
938/45 *Set of* 8 8·50 8·50
MS946 Four sheets, each 102×71 mm. (a) 400 s. Class "400" electric train. (b) 400 s. Class "EH 10" electric locomotive. (c) 400 s. Class "DD 51" diesel locomotive. (d) 400 s. Class "EF 58" electric locomotive *Set of* 4 *sheets* 8·00 9·00

175 Zebra and Golden-winged Sunbird, Ngorongoro Crater

176 *Eronia cleodora*

(Des Mary Walters. Litho Questa)

1991 (22 Aug). *National Game Parks. T* **175** *and similar horiz designs. Multicoloured. P* 14.

947 10 s. Type **175** 50 50
948 25 s. Greater Kudu and Elephant, Ruaha Park 80 80
949 30 s. Sable Antelope and Red and Yellow Barbet, Mikumi Park 80 80
950 50 s. Leopard and Wildebeest, Serengeti Park 90 90
951 90 s. Giraffe and Starred Robin, Ngurdoto Park 1·75 1·75
952 100 s. Eland and Abbott's Duiker, Kilimanjaro Park 1·75 1·75
953 250 s. Lion and Impala, Lake Manyara Park 2·75 2·75
954 300 s. Black Rhinoceros and Ostrich, Tarangire Park 3·50 3·50
947/54 *Set of* 8 11·50 11·50
MS955 Two sheets, each 99×68 mm. (a) 400 s. Blue-breasted Kingfisher and Defassa Waterbuck, Selous Game Reserve. (b) 400 s. Paradise Whydah and Oryx, Mkomazi Game Reserve *Set of* 2 *sheets* 9·25 9·25

(Des I. Maclaury. Litho Questa)

1991 (28 Aug). *Butterflies. T* **176** *and similar vert designs. Multicoloured. P* 14.

956 10 s. Type **176** 45 45
957 15 s. *Precis westermanni* 60 60
958 35 s. *Antanartia delius* 90 90
959 75 s. *Bematistes aganice* 1·60 1·60
960 100 s. *Kallima jacksoni* 1·75 1·75
961 150 s. *Apaturopsis cleochyaris* 2·50 2·50
962 200 s. *Colotis aurigineus* 2·75 2·75
963 300 s. *Iolaus crawshayi* 3·00 3·00
956/63 *Set of* 8 12·00 12·00
MS964 Four sheets, each 117×76 mm. (a) 400 s. *Charaxes zoolina*. (b) 400 s. *Papilio phorcas*. (c) 400 s. *Charaxes ethalion*. (d) 400 s. *Papilio nobilis* *Set of* 4 *sheets* 14·00 15·00

177 Microwave Tower and Dish Aerial

178 Rice Cultivation

(Litho Questa)

1991 (5 Sept). *25th Anniv of Intelsat Satellite System. T* **177** *and similar horiz designs. Multicoloured. P* 14.

965 10 s. Type **177** 30 20
966 25 s. Satellite picture of Earth 45 30
967 100 s. Mwenge "B" Earth station 1·25 1·25
968 500 s. Mwenge "A" Earth station 3·75 4·50
965/8 *Set of* 4 5·25 5·50
MS969 90×86 mm. 50 s. Satellite links on world map 1·40 1·75

(Litho Cartor)

1991 (16 Sept). *40th Anniv of United Nations Development Programme. T* **178** *and similar designs. P* 13½.

970 10 s. multicoloured 10 10
971 15 s. multicoloured 15 10
972 100 s. multicoloured 1·00 1·10
973 500 s. multicoloured 3·50 4·50
970/3 *Set of* 4 4·25 5·00
MS974 90×90 mm. 40 s. pale new blue and black. P 12½ 80 1·25

Designs: *Horiz*—15 s. Vocational and Civil Service training; 100 s. Terrace farming. *Vert*—40 s. U.N.D.P. anniversary emblem; 500 s. Renovated Arab door.

179 Netball

180 "TELECOM '91" Logo

(Litho State Ptg Wks, Moscow)

1991 (20 Sept). *All-Africa Games, Cairo. T* **179** *and similar multicoloured designs. P* 12½×12 *(Nos. 976, 979) or* 12×12½ *(others).*

975 10 s. Type **179** 20 15
976 15 s. Football *(horiz)* 20 15
977 100 s. Tennis 1·25 1·25
978 200 s. Athletics 1·60 1·60
979 500 s. Baseball *(horiz)* 4·50 5·00
975/9 *Set of* 5 7·00 7·25
MS980 80×60 mm. 500 s. Basketball 4·75 5·50

(Litho Cartor)

1991 (1 Oct). *"TELECOM '91" International Telecommunication Exhibition, Geneva (10, 15 s.) and World Telecommunications Day (others). T* **180** *and similar multicoloured designs. P* 13½×14 *(vert) or* 14×13½ *(horiz).*

981 10 s. Type **180** 10 10
982 15 s. "TELECOM '91" logo and address on envelope *(horiz)* 15 10
983 35 s. Symbolic telecommunication signals 25 20
984 100 s. Symbolic telecommunication signals *(horiz)* 70 1·00
981/4 *Set of* 4 1·00 1·25

181 Japanese Bobtail Cat

(Des Mary Walters. Litho Questa)

1991 (28 Oct). *Cats. T* **181** *and similar horiz designs. Multicoloured. P* 14.

985 50 s. Type **181** 55 55
a. Sheetlet. Nos. 985/1000 8·00
986 50 s. Cornish Rex 55 55
987 50 s. Malayan 55 55
988 50 s. Tonkinese 55 55
989 50 s. Abyssinian 55 55
990 50 s. Russian Blue 55 55
991 50 s. Cymric 55 55
992 50 s. Somali 55 55
993 50 s. Siamese 55 55
994 50 s. Himalayan 55 55
995 50 s. Singapura 55 55
996 50 s. Manx 55 55
997 50 s. Oriental Shorthair 55 55
998 50 s. Maine Coon 55 55
999 50 s. Persian 55 55
1000 50 s. Birman 55 55
985/1000 *Set of* 16 8·00 8·00

Nos. 985/1000 were printed together, *se-tenant*, as a sheetlet of 16.

182 Shire Horse

(Des Mary Walters. Litho Questa)

1991 (28 Oct). *Horses and Ponies. T* **182** *and similar horiz designs. Multicoloured. P* 14.

1001 50 s. Type **182** 60 60
a. Sheetlet. Nos. 1001/16 8·50
1002 50 s. Thoroughbred 60 60
1003 50 s. Kladruber 60 60
1004 50 s. Appaloosa 60 60
1005 50 s. Hanoverian 60 60
1006 50 s. Arab 60 60
1007 50 s. Breton 60 60
1008 50 s. Exmoor 60 60
1009 50 s. Connemara 60 60
1010 50 s. Lipizzaner 60 60
1011 50 s. Shetland 60 60
1012 50 s. Percheron 60 60
1013 50 s. Pinto 60 60
1014 50 s. Orlov 60 60
1015 50 s. Palomino 60 60
1016 50 s. Welsh Cob 60 60
1001/16 *Set of* 16 8·50 8·50

Nos. 1001/16 were printed together, *se-tenant*, as a sheetlet of 16, with the backgrounds of each horizontal strip of 4 forming a composite design.

183 Yellow Tetra

184 African Elephant

(Des Mary Walters. Litho Questa)

1991 (28 Oct). *Aquarium Fishes. T* **183** *and similar horiz designs. Multicoloured. P* 14.

1017 75 s. Type **183** 65 65
a. Sheetlet. Nos. 1017/32 9·00
1018 75 s. Five-banded Barb 65 65
1019 75 s. Simpson Platy 65 65
1020 75 s. Guppy 65 65
1021 75 s. Zebra Danio 65 65
1022 75 s. Neon Tetra 65 65
1023 75 s. Siamese Fighting Fish 65 65
1024 75 s. Tiger Barb 65 65
1025 75 s. Two-striped Lyretail 65 65
1026 75 s. Fan-tailed Goldfish 65 65
1027 75 s. Pearl Gourami 65 65
1028 75 s. Freshwater Angelfish 65 65
1029 75 s. Clown Loach 65 65
1030 75 s. Red Swordtail 65 65
1031 75 s. Blue Discus 65 65
1032 75 s. Rosy Barb 65 65
1017/32 *Set of* 16 9·00 9·00

Nos. 1017/32 were printed together, *se-tenant*, as a sheetlet of 16, with the backgrounds of each stamp forming a composite design.

(Des Mary Walters. Litho Questa)

1991 (28 Oct). *African Elephants. T* **184** *and similar vert designs. Multicoloured. P* 14.

1033 75 s. Type **184** 75 75
a. Sheetlet. Nos. 1033/48 11·00
1034 75 s. Two elephants fighting 75 75
1035 75 s. Elephant facing forward and tree 75 75
1036 75 s. Elephant facing left and tree 75 75
1037 75 s. Cow elephant and calf facing right standing in water 75 75
1038 75 s. Cow watching over calf in water 75 75
1039 75 s. Two adults and calf in water 75 75
1040 75 s. Cow and calf facing left standing in water 75 75
1041 75 s. Elephant facing right 75 75
1042 75 s. Elephants feeding 75 75
1043 75 s. Elephant feeding 75 75
1044 75 s. Elephant and Zebra 75 75
1045 75 s. Cow and calf drinking 75 75
1046 75 s. Calf suckling 75 75
1047 75 s. Bull elephant 75 75
1048 75 s. Cow with small calf 75 75
1033/48 *Set of* 16 11·00 11·00

Nos. 1033/48 were printed together, *se-tenant*, as a sheetlet of 16, with each horizontal strip of 4 forming a composite design.

185 Budgerigar

186 Indian Elephant

(Des Mary Walters. Litho Questa)

1991 (28 Oct). *Pet Birds. T* **185** *and similar horiz designs. Multicoloured. P* 14.

1049 75 s. Type **185** 60 60
a. Sheetlet. Nos. 1049/64 8·50
1050 75 s. Orange-breasted Bunting ("Rainbow Bunting") 60 60
1051 75 s. Golden-fronted Leafbird 60 60

1052 75 s. Black-headed Caique 60 60
1053 75 s. Java Sparrow 60 60
1054 75 s. Diamond Firetail Finch 60 60
1055 75 s. Peach-faced Lovebird 60 60
1056 75 s. Golden Conure 60 60
1057 75 s. Military Macaw 60 60
1058 75 s. Yellow-faced Parrotlet 60 60
1059 75 s. Sulphur-crested Cockatoo 60 60
1060 75 s. White-fronted Amazon ("Spectacled Amazon Parrot") 60 60
1061 75 s. Paradise Tanager 60 60
1062 75 s. Gouldian Finch 60 60
1063 75 s. Masked Lovebird 60 60
1064 75 s. Hill Mynah 60 60
1049/64 .. .. *Set of* 16 8·50 8·50

Nos. 1049/64 were printed together, *se-tenant*, as a sheetlet of 16, forming a composite design.

(Litho Questa)

1991 (20 Nov). *Death Centenary of Vincent van Gogh (artist) (1990). Multicoloured designs as T* **255** *of Maldive Islands. P* 13½×14.
1065 10 s. "Peasant Woman Sewing" 25 25
1066 15 s. "Head of Peasant Woman with Greenish Lace Cap" 35 35
1067 35 s. "Flowering Orchard" 60 60
1068 75 s. "Portrait of a Girl" .. .. .. 1·00 1·00
1069 100 s. "Portrait of a Woman with Red Ribbon" .. .. 1·25 1·25
1070 150 s. "Vase with Flowers" .. .. 1·75 1·75
1071 200 s. "Houses in Antwerp" .. .. 2·00 2·00
1072 400 s. "Seated Peasant Woman with White Cap" .. .. 4·00 4·00
1065/72 .. .. *Set of* 8 10·00 10·00
MS1073 Two sheets, each 127×112 mm. (a) 400 s. "Bulb Fields" (*horiz*). (b) 400 s. "The Parsonage Garden at Nuenen in the Snow" (*horiz*). Imperf .. .. *Set of* 2 *sheets* 8·50 10·00

(Des J. Puvilland. Litho State Ptg Wks, Moscow)

1991 (28 Nov). *Elephants. T* **186** *and similar multicoloured designs. P* 12×12½ (*vert*) *or* 12½×12 (*horiz*).
1074 10 s. Type **186** 40 40
1075 15 s. Indian Elephant uprooting tree .. 55 55
1076 25 s. Indian Elephant with calf 70 70
1077 30 s. African Elephant 70 70
1078 35 s. Head of African Elephant (*horiz*) .. 75 75
1079 100 s. African Elephant and calf bathing (*horiz*) .. .. 1·60 1·60
1080 200 s. Two African Elephants (*horiz*) .. 2·75 2·75
1074/80 .. .. *Set of* 7 6·75 6·75
MS1081 90×90 mm. 400 s. Mammoth (*horiz*) 4·00 4·50

187 Russian Steam Locomotive, 1930

(Litho State Ptg Wks, Moscow)

1991 (10 Dec). *Locomotives of the World. T* **187** *and similar multicoloured designs. P* 12½×12 (*horiz*) *or* 12×12½ (*vert*).
1082 10 s. Type **187** 25 25
1083 15 s. Japanese electric locomotive, 1964 35 35
1084 25 s. Russian steam locomotive, 1834 (*vert*) 45 45
1085 35 s. French electric locomotive, 1979 .. 55 55
1086 60 s. French diesel railcar, 1972 .. 80 80
1087 100 s. U.K. diesel locomotive, 1972 .. 1·40 1·40
1088 300 s. Russian steam locomotive, 1837 (*vert*) .. .. 3·00 3·00
1082/8 .. .. *Set of* 7 6·00 6·00
MS1089 91×91 mm. 100 s. French electric locomotive, 1952 (*vert*) .. .. .. 1·40 1·60

(Des Walt Disney Co. Litho Questa)

1991 (24 Dec). *Christmas. Walt Disney Christmas Cards. Multicoloured designs as T* **228** *of St. Vincent. P* 14×13½ (*horiz*) *or* 13½×14 (*vert*).
1090 10 s. Disney characters in "JOY", 1968 (*horiz*) 20 20
1091 25 s. Mickey, Donald, Pluto and Goofy hanging up stockings, 1981 (*horiz*) 40 40
1092 35 s. Characters from Disney film *Robin Hood*, 1973 (*horiz*) 45 45
1093 75 s. Mickey looking at Christmas tree, 1967 (*horiz*) 90 90
1094 100 s. Goofy, Mickey, Donald and Chip n' Dale on film set, 1969 .. .. 1·25 1·25
1095 150 s. Mickey on giant bauble, 1976 .. 1·60 1·60
1096 200 s. Clarabelle Cow with electric cow bell, 1935 .. .. 2·00 2·00
1097 300 s. Mickey's nephews with book, 1935 2·75 2·75
1090/7 .. .. *Set of* 8 8·50 8·50
MS1098 Two sheets, each 127×102 mm. (a) 500 s. Mickey handing out presents, 1935. (b) 500 s. Disney cartoon characters, 1968 *Set of* 2 *sheets* 10·00 11·00

188 Bruce Lee

189 Sand Tilefish

(Des J. Iskowitz. Litho Questa)

1992 (14 Feb). *Entertainers. T* **188** *and similar vert designs. P* 13½.
1099/134 75 s. × 36 multicoloured *Set of* 36 20·00 22·00
MS1135 Four sheets, each 78×108 mm. 500 s. × 4 multicoloured (Bruce Lee, Marilyn Monroe, Elvis Presley, Kouyate & Kouyate, each 28×42 *mm*). P 14 .. .. .. *Set of* 4 *sheets* 20·00 22·00

Nos. 1099/134 were issued as four sheetlets, each of nine different designs, depicting Bruce Lee, Marilyn Monroe, Elvis Presley and black entertainers (Scott Joplin, Sammy Davis Jnr, Joan Armatrading, Louis Armstrong, Miriam Makeba, Lionel Ritchie, Whitney Houston, Bob Marley, Tina Turner).

(Des P. Ndembo. Litho State Ptg Wks, Moscow)

1992 (9 Mar). *Fishes. T* **189** *and similar horiz designs. Multicoloured. P* 12½×12.
1136 10 s. Type **189** 30 30
1137 15 s. Five-banded Cichlid 35 35
1138 25 s. Pearly Lamprologus 50 50
1139 35 s. Jewel Cichlid 60 60
1140 60 s. Two-striped Lyretail 80 80
1141 100 s. Reef Stonefish .. .. .. 1·25 1·25
1142 300 s. Ahl's Lyretail .. .. .. 3·50 3·50
1136/42 .. .. .. *Set of* 7 6·50 6·50
MS1143 90×90 mm. 100 s. Oarfish .. .. 1·40 1·60

190 Chimpanzee in Tree

191 Pope John Paul II in Dominican Republic, 1979

(Des Mary Walters. Litho Questa)

1992 (30 Mar). *Common Chimpanzee. T* **190** *and similar vert designs. Multicoloured. P* 14.
1144 10 s. Type **190** 40 40
1145 15 s. Feeding 45 45
1146 35 s. Two chimpanzees 70 70
1147 75 s. Adult male with arms folded .. 1·10 1·10
1148 100 s. Breaking branch .. .. .. 1·25 1·25
1149 150 s. Young chimpanzee in tree .. 1·75 1·75
1150 200 s. Female holding young .. .. 2·50 2·50
1151 300 s. Chimpanzee sitting in tree .. 3·00 3·00
1144/51 .. .. .. *Set of* 8 10·00 10·00
MS1152 Two sheets, each 99×68 mm. (a) 400 s. Eating termites. (b) 400 s. Swinging through trees .. .. *Set of* 2 *sheets* 6·25 6·25

(Litho Questa)

1992 (13 Apr). *Papal Visits. T* **191** *and similar vert designs. P* 14.
1153/272 100 s. × 120 multicoloured *Set of* 120 70·00 70·00

Nos. 1153/272 were issued in ten sheetlets, each of 12 different designs arranged round a common block of four stamp-sized labels.

192 Balcony

193 Gogo Costume

(Des J. da Silva. Litho State Ptg Wks, Moscow)

1992 (15 Apr). *Zanzibar Stone Town. T* **192** *and similar multicoloured designs. P* 12½×12 (200 s.) *or* 12×12½ (*others*).
1273 10 s. Type **192** 25 20
1274 20 s. Bahlnara Mosque 45 35
1275 30 s. High Court Building 55 40
1276 200 s. National Museum (*horiz*) .. 2·75 3·50
1273/6 .. .. .. *Set of* 4 3·50 4·00
MS1277 91×91 mm. 150 s. Old Fort (*horiz*); 300 s. Maruhubi ruins (*horiz*). P 12½×12 .. 4·25 5·00

(Des P. Ndembo. Litho National Printing and Packaging, Zimbabwe)

1992 (30 Apr). *Traditional Costumes. T* **193** *and similar vert designs. Multicoloured. P* 14½.
1278 3 s. Type **193** 30 30
1279 5 s. Swahili 30 30
1280 9 s. Hehe and Makonde 35 35
1281 12 s. Maasai 40 40
1278/81 .. .. .. *Set of* 4 1·25 1·25
MS1282 91×91 mm. 40 s. Mwarusha .. .. 1·50 1·75

194 Melisa and Mike (chimpanzees)

(Des P. Ndembo. Litho B.D.T.)

1992 (29 May). *Chimpanzees of the Gombe. Multicoloured. P* 14.

(*a*) *Horiz designs as T* **194**
1283 10 s. Type **194** 20 20
1284 15 s. Leakey and David Greybeard .. 25 25
1285 30 s. Fifi termiting 30 30
1286 35 s. Galahad 35 35
1283/6 .. .. .. *Set of* 4 1·00 1·00
MS1287 90×90 mm. 100 s. Fifi, Flo and Faben 1·25 1·75

(*b*) *Vert designs showing individual chimpanzees*
1288 10 s. Leakey 50 50
a. Sheetlet. Nos. 1288/95 .. .. 4·25
1289 15 s. Fifi 50 50
1290 20 s. Faben 50 50
1291 30 s. David Greybeard 50 50
1292 35 s. Mike 50 50
1293 50 s. Galahad 50 50
1294 100 s. Melisa 70 70
1295 200 s. Flo 90 90
1288/95 .. .. .. *Set of* 8 4·25 4·25

Nos. 1288/95 were printed together, *se-tenant*, in sheetlets of 8.

195 Sorghum Farming, Serena

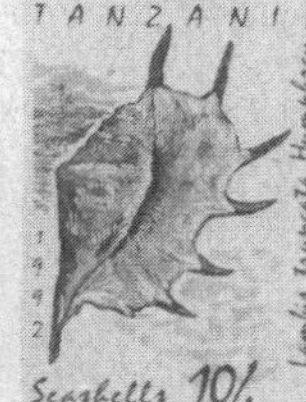

196 Giant Spider Conch (*Lambis truncata*)

(Des P. Ndembo. Litho Questa)

1992 (22 June). *25th Anniv of National Bank of Commerce. T* **195** *and similar multicoloured designs. P* 14.
1296 10 s. Type **195** 20 15
1297 15 s. Samora Avenue Branch and computer operator (*vert*) 25 25
1298 35 s. Training centre 35 35
1299 40 s. Women dyeing textiles 40 45
1296/9 .. .. .. *Set of* 4 1·10 1·10
MS1300 111×117 mm. 30 s. Bank Head Office 50 75

(Litho State Ptg Wks, Moscow)

1992 (30 June). *Shells. T* **196** *and similar vert designs. Multicoloured. P* 12×12½.
1301 10 s. Type **196** 30 30
1302 15 s. Bull-mouth Helmet (*Cypraecassis rufa*) 35 35
1303 25 s. Rugose Mitre (*Vexillum rugosum*) 50 50
1304 30 s. Lettered Cone (*Conus litteratus*) .. 50 50
1305 35 s. True Heart Cockle (*Corculum cardissa*) 50 50
1306 50 s. Ramose Murex (*Murex ramosus*) .. 70 70
1307 250 s. Indian Volute (*Melo melo*) .. 2·75 3·25
1301/7 .. .. .. *Set of* 7 5·00 5·50
MS1308 91×91 mm. 300 s. Giant Clam (*Tridacna gigas*) .. .. .. 3·50 4·00

197 Basketball

198 British-designed Radar, Pearl Harbor

(Des A. Nabola. Litho State Ptg Wks, Moscow)

1992 (23 July). *Olympic Games, Barcelona (2nd issue). T* **197** *and similar vert designs. Multicoloured. P* 12×12½.

1309	40 s. Type **197**	45	30
1310	100 s. Billiards	75	60
1311	200 s. Table Tennis	1·25	1·40
1312	400 s. Darts	2·75	3·25
1309/12	*Set of* 4	4·75	5·00
MS1313	91×8 mm. 500 s. Weightlifting	2·75	3·50

(Des J. Batchelor. Litho Questa)

1992 (1 Aug). *50th Anniv of Japanese Attack on Pearl Harbor. T* **198** *and similar horiz designs. Multicoloured. P* 14½.

1314	75 s. Type **198**	1·00	1·00
	a. Sheetlet. Nos. 1314/23	9·00	
1315	75 s. Winston Churchill	1·00	1·00
1316	75 s. Sinking of H.M.S. *Repulse* (battle cruiser)	1·00	1·00
1317	75 s. Sinking of H.M.S. *Prince of Wales* (battleship)	1·00	1·00
1318	75 s. Surrender of Singapore	1·00	1·00
1319	75 s. Sinking of H.M.S. *Hermes* (aircraft carrier)	1·00	1·00
1320	75 s. Japanese attack on Malayan airfield	1·00	1·00
1321	75 s. Japanese gun crew, Hong Kong	1·00	1·00
1322	75 s. Japanese landing craft	1·00	1·00
1323	75 s. *Haguro* (Japanese cruiser)	1·00	1·00
1314/23	*Set of* 10	9·00	9·00

Nos. 1314/23 were printed together, *se-tenant*, in sheetlets of 10 with the stamps arranged in two horizontal strips of 5 separated by a gutter showing H.M.S. *Exeter* at Battle of Java Sea.

199 French Resistance Monument and Medal

(Litho Questa)

1992 (1 Aug). *Birth Centenary of Charles de Gaulle (French statesman)* (1990). *T* **199** *and similar multicoloured designs. P* 14.

1324	25 s. Type **199**	50	40
1325	30 s. Free French tank on Omaha Beach, D-Day	50	40
1326	150 s. Concorde at Charles de Gaulle Airport	3·50	4·00
1324/6	*Set of* 3	4·00	4·25
MS1327	115×92 mm. 500 s. Free French local Cross of Lorraine opt on Petain 1 f. 50 and De Gaulle label postmarked 25 August 1944 (39×51 *mm*)	4·50	5·00

200 Scout Badge, Giraffe and Elephant

(Litho Questa)

1992 (1 Aug). *50th Death Anniv of Lord Baden-Powell (founder of Boy Scout movement)* (1991). *T* **200** *and similar multicoloured designs. P* 14.

1328	10 s. Type **200**	40	30
1329	15 s. Scouts in boat	40	30
1330	400 s. John Glenn's space capsule	4·00	4·50
1328/30	*Set of* 3	4·25	4·50
MS1331	90×117 mm. 500 s. Tanzanian Scout (39×51 *mm*). P 13½	4·00	4·50

201 Marcella Sembrich as Zerlina in *Don Giovanni*

202 Lucky Omens

(Litho Questa)

1992 (1 Aug). *Death Bicentenary of Mozart. T* **201** *and similar designs. P* 14.

1332	10 s. black and deep mauve	50	40
1333	50 s. multicoloured	1·25	1·10
1334	300 s. black and deep mauve	3·75	4·25
1332/4	*Set of* 3	5·00	5·25
MS1335	115×87 mm. 500 s. grey-brown, stone and black	5·00	6·00

Designs: *Horiz*—50 s. Planet Jupiter (Symphony No. 41); 300 s. Luciano Pavarotti as Idamente in *Idomeneo. Vert* (35×47 *mm*)—500 s. Wolfgang Amadeus Mozart.

(Litho B.D.T.)

1992 (1 Aug). *"Granada '92" International Stamp Exhibition, Spain. Paintings. Designs as T* **68** *of St. Kitts-Nevis (Nevis). P* 13.

1336	25 s. Indian red and black	25	25
1337	35 s. multicoloured	30	30
1338	50 s. multicoloured	40	40
1339	75 s. multicoloured	60	60
1340	100 s. black, brown and flesh	90	90
1341	150 s. Indian red and black	1·40	1·40
1342	200 s. Indian red and black	1·75	1·75
1343	300 s. multicoloured	2·40	2·40
1336/43	*Set of* 8	7·25	7·25
MS1344	Two sheets, each 121×95 mm. (a) 400 s. multicoloured. (b) 400 s. multicoloured. Imperf *Set of* 2 *sheets*	6·25	6·75

Designs: *Horiz* (49½×36 *mm*)—25 s. "A Picador, mounted on a Chulo's Shoulders, spears a Bull" (Goya); 150 s. "Another Madness (of Martincho) in the Plaza de Zaragoza" (Goya); 200 s. "Recklessness of Martincho in the Plaza de Zaragoza" (Goya). (111×86 *mm*)—400 s. (No. **MS**1344a) "Two Men at Table" (Velasquez); 400 s. (No. **MS**1344b) "Seascape" (Mariana Salvador Maella). *Vert*—35 s. "Philip IV at Fraga" (Velasquez); 50 s. "Head of a Stag" (Velasquez); 75 s. "The Cardinal-Infante Ferdinand as a Hunter" (Velasquez); 100 s. "The Dream of Reason brings forth Monsters" (Goya); 300 s. "Pablo de Valladolid" (Velasquez).

(Des P. Ndembo. Litho State Ptg Wks, Moscow)

1992 (30 Sept). *500th Anniv of Discovery of America by Columbus. T* **202** *and similar multicoloured designs. P* 12×12½ (*vert*) *or* 12½×12 (*horiz*).

1345	10 s. Type **202**	20	20
1346	15 s. Map and compass	25	25
1347	25 s. Look-out in crow's nest	35	35
1348	30 s. Amerindians sighting ships (*horiz*)	40	40
1349	35 s. *Pinta* and *Nina* (*horiz*)	45	45
1350	75 s. *Santa Maria* (*horiz*)	70	70
1351	250 s. Wreck of *Santa Maria*	1·50	2·00
1345/51	*Set of* 7	3·50	4·00
MS1352	93×93 mm. 200 s. Columbus	1·50	2·00

203 Superb Starling

15th Anniversary

(**204**)

(Des P. Ndembo. Litho State Ptg Wks, Moscow)

1992 (15 Oct). *Birds. T* **203** *and similar multicoloured designs. P* 12×12½.

1353	5 s. Type **203**	15	15
1354	10 s. Golden Bishop ("Canary")	20	20
1355	15 s. Four-coloured Bush Shrike	30	30
1356	25 s. Grey-headed Kingfisher	35	35
1357	30 s. Common Kingfisher	35	35
1358	35 s. Yellow-billed Oxpecker	40	40
1359	150 s. Black-throated Honeyguide	1·40	1·40
1353/9	*Set of* 7	2·75	2·75
MS1360	93×92 mm. 300 s. European Cuckoo (*horiz*). P 12½×12	2·50	2·75

1992 (15 Oct). *15th Death Anniv of Elvis Presley. Nos.* 1117/25 *optd with T* **204**.

1361	75 s. Looking pensive	65	65
	a. Sheetlet. Nos. 1361/9	5·50	
1362	75 s. Wearing black and yellow striped shirt	65	65
1363	75 s. Singing into microphone	65	65
1364	75 s. Wearing wide-brimmed hat	65	65
1365	75 s. With microphone in right hand	65	65
1366	75 s. In Army uniform	65	65
1367	75 s. Wearing pink shirt	65	65
1368	75 s. In yellow shirt	65	65
1369	75 s. In jacket and bow tie	65	65
1361/9	*Set of* 9	5·50	5·50

205 Iguanodon

(Des S. Barlowe. Litho Questa)

1992 (5 Nov). *African Dinosaurs. T* **205** *and similar horiz designs. Multicoloured. P* 14.

1370	100 s. Type **205**	65	65
	a. Sheetlet. Nos. 1370/85	9·00	
1371	100 s. Saltasaurus	65	65
1372	100 s. Cetiosaurus	65	65
1373	100 s. Camarasaurus	65	65
1374	100 s. Spinosaurus	65	65
1375	100 s. Stegosaurus	65	65
1376	100 s. Allosaurus	65	65
1377	100 s. Ceratosaurus	65	65
1378	100 s. Lesothosaurus	65	65
1379	100 s. Anchisaurus	65	65
1380	100 s. Ornithomimus	65	65
1381	100 s. Baronyx	65	65
1382	100 s. Pachycephalosaurus	65	65
1383	100 s. Heterodontosaurus	65	65
1384	100 s. Dryosaurus	65	65
1385	100 s. Coelophysis	65	65
1370/85	*Set of* 16	9·00	9·00

Nos. 1370/85 were printed together, *se-tenant*, in sheetlets of 16, forming a composite design.

206 Spotted Tilapia

(Litho B.D.T.)

1992 (5 Nov). *Fishes. T* **206** *and similar horiz designs. Multicoloured. P* 13½.

1386	100 s. Type **206**	65	65
	a. Sheetlet. Nos. 1386/97	7·00	
1387	100 s. Butterfly Barb	65	65
1388	100 s. Blunthead Moliro Cichlid	65	65
1389	100 s. Angel Squeaker	65	65
1390	100 s. Dickfeld's Julie	65	65
1391	100 s. Nile Mouthbrooder	65	65
1392	100 s. Blue-finned Notho	65	65
1393	100 s. Crabro Mbuna	65	65
1394	100 s. Pearl-scaled Lamprologus	65	65
1395	100 s. Zebra Mbuna	65	65
1396	100 s. Marlier's Julie	65	65
1397	100 s. Brichard's Chalinochromis	65	65
1386/97	*Set of* 12	7·00	7·00
MS1398	Three sheets, each 71×55 mm. (a) 500 s. Palmqvist's Notho. (b) 500 s. Electric Blue Haplochromis. (c) 500 s. Short Lamprologus *Set of* 3 *sheets*	9·00	9·50

Nos. 1386/97 were printed together, *se-tenant*, in sheetlets of 12, forming a composite design.

207 Hunting Birds with Catapults

208 *Couroupita guianensis*

(Litho Cartor)

1992 (25 Nov). *Traditional Hunting. T* **207** *and similar horiz designs. Multicoloured. P* 13½.

1399	20 s. Type **207**	30	30
1400	70 s. Hunting antelope with bow and arrow	55	55
1401	100 s. Hunting antelopes with dogs	75	75
1402	150 s. Hunting lion with spears and shields	1·40	1·40
1399/1402	*Set of* 4	2·75	2·75
MS1403	100×100 mm. 40 s. Traditional hunting weapons. P 12½×12	1·00	1·50

(Litho Questa)

1992 (30 Nov). *Olympic Games, Albertville and Barcelona (3rd issue). Multicoloured designs as T* **216** *of Lesotho. P* 14.

1404	20 s. Men's 4000 metre pursuit cycling	15	15
1405	40 s. Men's double sculls rowing (*horiz*)	20	20
1406	50 s. Waterpolo (*horiz*)	20	20
1407	70 s. Women's single luge (*horiz*)	30	30
1408	100 s. Marathon (*horiz*)	50	50
1409	150 s. Women's asymmetrical bars gymnastics (*horiz*)	90	90
1410	200 s. Ice hockey	1·25	1·25
1411	400 s. Men's rings gymnastics	2·50	2·50
1404/11	*Set of* 8	5·50	5·50
MS1412	Two sheets, each 100×71 mm. (a) 500 s. Tennis. (b) 500 s. Football *Set of* 2 *sheets*	8·00	8·50

(Des Walt Disney & Co. Litho Questa)

1992 (30 Nov). *Mickey's Portrait Gallery. Multicoloured designs as T* **70** *of St. Kitts-Nevis (Nevis) showing Walt Disney cartoon characters. P* 13½×14.

1413	25 s. Donald Duck in *Sea Scouts*, 1939	15	15
1414	25 s. Minnie Mouse in *Hawaiian Holiday*, 1937	15	15
1415	25 s. Pluto in *Society Dog Show*, 1939	15	15
1416	35 s. Donald in *Fire Chief*, 1940	20	20
1417	50 s. Donald in *Truant Officer Donald*, 1941	25	25
1418	75 s. Goofy in *Clock Cleaners*, 1937	35	35
1419	100 s. Goofy in *Goofy and Wilbur*, 1939	40	40
1420	100 s. Mickey Mouse in *Magician Mickey*, 1937	40	40
1421	200 s. Minnie in *The Nifty Nineties*, 1941	75	75
1422	300 s. Mickey and Pluto in *Society Dog Show*, 1939	95	95
1423	400 s. Pluto and pups in *Pluto's Quin-Puplets*, 1937	1·25	1·25
1424	500 s. Daisy and Donald in *Mr. Duck Steps Out*, 1940	1·40	1·40
1413/24	*Set of* 12	5·75	5·75

MS1425 Three sheets. (a) 127×102 mm. 600 s. Goofy in *Forever Goofy*. P 13½×14. (b) 127×102 mm. 600 s. Daisy in *Don Donald*, 1937. P 13½×14. (c) 112×104 mm. 600 s. Mickey and Minnie in *Brave Little Tailor*, 1938 (*horiz*). P 14×13½ .. .. .. *Set of 3 sheets* 8·00 9·00

(Des Jennifer Toombs. Litho Questa)

1992 (1 Dec). *Botanical Gardens of the World. Rio de Janeiro. T* **208** *and similar vert designs showing African plants. Multicoloured. P* 14½×14.
1426/45 70 s.×20 .. .. .. *Set of* 20 9·50 11·00
MS1446 110×74 mm. 500 s. Avenue of Royal Palms .. .. 3·00 3·75
Nos. 1426/45 were issued as a *se-tenant* sheetlet of 20 (5×4).

209 Abyssinian Cat

210 Count Ferdinand von Zeppelin

(Litho State Ptg Wks, Moscow)

1992 (3 Dec). *Cats. T* **209** *and similar vert designs. Multicoloured. P* 12×12½.

1447	20 s. Type **209**	30	30
1448	30 s. Havana cat	30	30
1449	50 s. Persian black cat	35	35
1450	70 s. Persian blue cat	50	50
1451	100 s. European silver tabby cat	70	70
1452	150 s. Persian silver tabby cat	1·00	1·00
1453	200 s. Maine Coon cat	1·25	1·25
1447/53	*Set of* 7	4·00	4·00
MS1454	90×90 mm. 300 s. European cat	2·50	2·75

(Des W. Hanson. Litho B.D.T.)

1992 (10 Dec). *"Genova '92" International Stamp Exhibition. Toy Trains manufactured by Lionel. Horiz designs as T* **253** *of Sierra Leone. Multicoloured. P* 14.

1455	10 s. B. & O. tunnel locomotive No. 5, 1904	25	25
1456	20 s. "Liberty Bell" locomotive, 1930	35	35
1457	30 s. Armoured rail car, 1917	40	40
1458	50 s. Open trolley No. 202, 1910–14	60	60
1459	70 s. "Macy Special" electric locomotive	70	70
1460	100 s. "Milwaukee Road" bi-polar electric locomotive, 1929	80	80
1461	200 s. New York Central "S" type locomotive, 1912	1·25	1·25
1462	300 s. Locomotive No. 7, 1914	1·50	1·50
1455/62	*Set of* 8	5·25	5·25

MS1463 Two sheets. (a) 91×75 mm. 500 s. Display model locomotive in clear plastic, 1947. (b) 71×89 mm. 500 s. Mickey and Minnie Mouse on clockwork handcar, 1936 .. *Set of 2 sheets* 5·50 6·50

(Des W. Wright and W. Hanson (Nos. 1464, 1471, **MS**1475a), W. Wright and L. Fried (Nos. 1466, 1473, **MS**1475c), J. Genzo (Nos. 1474, **MS**1475e), W. Wright (others). Litho B.D.T.)

1992 (15 Dec). *Anniversaries and Events. T* **210** *and similar multicoloured designs. P* 14.

1464	30 s. Type **210**	30	30
1465	70 s. *Santa Maria*	55	55
1466	70 s. "Apollo-Soyuz" link-up, 1975	55	55
1467	150 s. African Elephant	1·00	1·00
1468	150 s. Child being offered apple	1·00	1·00
1469	200 s. Zebra	1·10	1·10
1470	200 s. Trying on glasses	1·10	1·10
1471	300 s. Airship LZ-127 *Graf Zeppelin*, 1929	1·60	1·60
1472	300 s. Christopher Columbus	1·60	1·60
1473	400 s. Space shuttle	2·25	2·25
1474	400 s. Wolfgang Amadeus Mozart (*vert*)	2·25	2·25
1464/74	*Set of* 11	12·00	12·00

MS1475 Five sheets. (a) 110×82 mm. 500 s. LZ-5 Zeppelin airship. (b) 114×81 mm. 500 s. Head of Columbus. (c) 110×82 mm. 500 s. "Voyager 2" space probe. (d) 114×81 mm. 500 s. African Elephant (*different*). (e) 110×68 mm. 500 s. Queen of the Night from *The Magic Flute* (*vert*) *Set of 5 sheets* 13·00 14·00

Anniversaries and Events:—Nos. 1464, 1471, **MS**1475a, 75th death anniv of Count Ferdinand von Zeppelin; Nos. 1465, 1472, **MS**1475b, 500th anniv of Discovery of America by Columbus; Nos. 1466, 1473, **MS**1475c, International Space Year; Nos. 1467, 1469, **MS**1475d, Earth Summit '92, Rio; No. 1468, International Conference on Nutrition, Rome; No. 1470, 75th anniv of International Association of Lions Clubs; Nos. 1474, **MS**1475e, Death bicent of Mozart.

(Litho Walsall)

1992 (15 Dec). *Bicentenary of the Louvre, Paris. Paintings by Jean Chardin. Multicoloured designs as T* **221** *of Lesotho. P* 12.

1476	100 s. "Young Draughtsman sharpening Pencil"	50	50
	a. Sheetlet. Nos. 1476/83	3·50	
1477	100 s. "The Buffet"	50	50
1478	100 s. "Return from the Market"	50	50
1479	100 s. "The Hard-working Mother"	50	50
1480	100 s. "Grace"	50	50
1481	100 s. "The Copper Water Urn"	50	50
1482	100 s. "The House of Cards"	50	50
1483	100 s. "Boy with a Top"	50	50
1476/83	*Set of* 8	3·50	3·50

MS1484 100×70 mm. 500 s. "The Ray" (85×52 *mm*). P 14½ .. .. 2·50 2·75
Nos. 1476/83 were printed together, *se-tenant*, in sheetlets of 8 stamps and one centre label.

TANZANIA

211 Carved Head

212 Russian Cycle, 1813

(Litho State Ptg Wks, Moscow)

1992 (24 Dec). *Makonde Art. T* **211** *and similar vert designs showing various carvings. P* 12×12½.

1485	20 s. multicoloured	15	15
1486	30 s. multicoloured	15	15
1487	50 s. multicoloured	20	20
1488	70 s. multicoloured	30	30
1489	100 s. multicoloured	40	40
1490	150 s. multicoloured	70	70
1491	200 s. multicoloured	80	80
1485/91	*Set of* 7	2·40	2·40
MS1492	91×91 mm. 350 s. multicoloured	1·75	2·00

(Litho State Ptg Wks, Moscow)

1992 (30 Dec). *Bicycles of the World. T* **212** *and similar horiz designs. Multicoloured. P* 12½×12.

1493	20 s. Type **212**	20	20
1494	30 s. German, 1840	20	20
1495	50 s. German, 1818	30	30
1496	70 s. German, 1850	40	40
1497	100 s. Italian, 1988	50	50
1498	150 s. Swedish, 1982	80	80
1499	300 s. Italian, 1989	1·25	1·25
1493/9	*Set of* 7	3·25	3·25
MS1500	90×90 mm. 350 s. British penny-farthing, 1887	1·75	2·00

213 Seal

214 Boxing

(Litho Questa)

1993 (1 Mar). *Large Sea Creatures. T* **213** *and similar horiz designs. Multicoloured. P* 14.

1501	20 s. Type **213**	40	40
1502	30 s. Whale	65	65
1503	70 s. Shark	75	75
1504	100 s. Walrus	90	90
1501/4	*Set of* 4	2·40	2·40
MS1505	99×91 mm. 500 s. Sea Turtle	3·50	4·00

(Litho State Ptg Wks, Moscow)

1993 (28 May). *Sports. T* **214** *and similar multicoloured designs. P* 12×12½.

1506	20 s. Type **214**	15	15
1507	50 s. Hockey	30	20
1508	70 s. Show jumping	40	40
1509	100 s. Marathon running	45	45
1510	150 s. Football	60	60
1511	200 s. Diving	70	70
1512	400 s. Basketball	1·25	1·50
1506/12	*Set of* 7	3·50	3·50
MS1513	91×91 mm. 300 s. High jumping (*horiz*). P 12½×12	1·75	2·00

(Des Kerri Schiff. Litho Questa)

1993 (10 June). *40th Anniv of Coronation. Vert designs as T* **224** *of Lesotho. P* 13½×14.

1514	100 s. multicoloured	50	50
	a. Sheetlet. Nos. 1514/17×2	6·50	
1515	150 s. multicoloured	75	75
1516	200 s. blackish lilac and black	1·00	1·00
1517	300 s. multicoloured	1·25	1·25
1514/17	*Set of* 4	3·25	3·25
MS1518	102×70 mm. 500 s. multicoloured. P 14	2·50	2·75

Designs:—100 s. Queen Elizabeth II at Coronation (photograph by Cecil Beaton); 150 s. Gold salt-cellar; 200 s. Prince Philip at Coronation; 300 s. Queen Elizabeth II and Prince Andrew. (28½×42½ *mm*)—500 s. "Princess Elizabeth opening the New Broadgate, Coventry" (detail) (Dame Laura Knight).
Nos. 1514/17 were printed together in sheetlets of 8, containing two *se-tenant* blocks of 4.

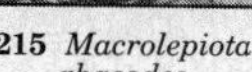

215 *Macrolepiota rhacodes*

216 *Geochelone elephantopus* (tortoise)

(Des Mary Walters. Litho Questa)

1993 (18 June). *Fungi. T* **215** *and similar vert designs. Multicoloured. P* 14.

1519	20 s. Type **215**	20	20
1520	40 s. *Mycena pura*	30	30
1521	50 s. *Chlorophyllum molybdites*	30	30
1522	70 s. *Agaricus campestris*	40	40
1523	100 s. *Volvariella volvacea*	45	45
1524	150 s. *Leucoagaricus naucinus*	70	70
1525	200 s. *Oudemansiella radicata*	80	80
1526	300 s. *Clitocybe nebularis*	1·00	1·00
1519/26	*Set of* 8	3·75	3·75

MS1527 Two sheets, each 100×70 mm. (a) 500 s. *Omphalotus olearius*. (b) 500 s. *Lepista nuda* *Set of 2 sheets* 4·00 4·25

(Litho State Ptg Wks, Moscow)

1993 (28 June). *Reptiles. T* **216** *and similar multicoloured designs. P* 12×12½ (*vert*) *or* 12½×12 (*horiz*).

1528	20 s. Type **216**	20	20
1529	50 s. *Iguana iguana*	30	30
1530	70 s. *Varanus salvator* (lizard) (*horiz*)	40	40
1531	100 s. *Naja oxiana* (cobra)	45	45
1532	150 s. *Chamaeleo jacksoni* (*horiz*)	70	70
1533	200 s. *Eunectes murinus* (snake) (*horiz*)	80	80
1534	250 s. *Alligator mississippensis* (*horiz*)	90	90
1528/34	*Set of* 7	3·25	3·25
MS1535	90×90 mm. 500 s. *Vipera berus* (snake)	3·00	3·50

217 Pancake Tortoise on Rock

218 Elephant

(Des L. Birmingham. Litho Questa)

1993 (30 June). *Endangered Species. Pancake Tortoise. T* **217** *and similar horiz designs. Multicoloured. P* 14.

1536	20 s. Type **217**	20	20
1537	30 s. Drinking	25	25
1538	50 s. Under rock	35	35
1539	70 s. Tortoise hatching	45	45
1536/9	*Set of* 4	1·10	1·10

(Des L. Birmingham. Litho Questa)

1993 (30 June). *Wildlife. T* **218** *and similar multicoloured designs. P* 14.
1540/87 100 s.×48 .. .. .. *Set of* 48 15·00 16·00
MS1588 Two sheets, each 100×71 mm. (a) 500 s. Lion cub (*horiz*). (b) 500 s. Elephant calf (*horiz*) *Set of 2 sheets* 4·00 4·50

Nos. 1540/87 were issued together, *se-tenant*, as four sheetlets each of twelve different vertical designs. The species depicted are, in addition to Type **218**, Gazelle, Hartebeest, Duiker, Genet, Civet, Eastern White Pelican, Waterbuck, Blacksmith Plover, Lesser Pied Kingfisher, Black-winged Stilt, Bush Pig, Brown-hooded Kingfisher, Sable Antelope, Impala, Buffalo, Leopard, Aardvark, Hippopotamus, Spotted Hyena, South African Crowned Crane, Crocodile, Greater Flamingo, Baboon, Potto, Lesser Flamingo, Grey-headed Kingfisher, Red Colobus Monkey, Dik-Dik, Aardwolf (incorrectly inscribed "ARDWOLF"), Black-backed Jackal, Tree Pangolin, Serval, Yellow-billed Hornbill, Pygmy Mongoose, Bat-eared Fox, Bushbaby, Egyptian Vulture, Ostrich, Greater Kudu, Diana Monkey, Giraffe, Cheetah, Wildebeest, Chimpanzee, Warthog, Zebra and Rhinoceros.

219 Grant's Zebra galloping

220 Valentina Tereshkova (first woman in space)

(Des P. Ndembo. Litho B.D.T.)

1993 (30 June). *Wild Animals. T* **219** *and similar horiz designs. Multicoloured. P* 14.

1589 100 s. Type **219** 50 50
a. Sheetlet. Nos. 1589/94 .. .. 2·75
1590 100 s. Grant's Zebra standing 50 50
1591 100 s. Grant's Gazelle doe 50 50
1592 100 s. Grant's Gazelle buck 50 50
1593 100 s. Thomson's Gazelle 50 50
1594 100 s. White-bearded Gnu with calf .. 50 50
1595 100 s. Female Cheetah with cubs .. 50 50
a. Sheetlet. Nos. 1595/1600 .. .. 2·75
1596 100 s. Young Cheetah drinking 50 50
1597 100 s. Lioness carrying cub in mouth .. 50 50
1598 100 s. Pair of Hunting Dogs 50 50
1599 100 s. Three Hunting Dogs 50 50
1600 100 s. Four Hunting Dogs 50 50
1589/1600 .. .. *Set of* 12 5·50 5·50
MS1601 Two sheets, each 106×76 mm. (a) 500 s. African Elephant. (b) 500 s. Rhinoceros *Set of* 2 *sheets* 6·25 6·25

Nos. 1589/94 and 1595/1600 were printed together, *se-tenant*, in sheetlets of 6.

(Des J. Iskowitz. Litho Questa)

1993 (15 July). *Famous 20th-century Women. T* **220** *and similar vert designs. Multicoloured. P* 14.

1602 20 s. Type **220** 30 30
a. Sheetlet. Nos. 1602/9 .. .. 4·00
1603 40 s. Marie Curie (physicist) 30 30
1604 50 s. Indira Gandhi (Prime Minister of India) 30 30
1605 70 s. Wilma Rudolph (Olympic athlete) .. 30 30
1606 100 s. Margaret Mead (anthropologist) .. 40 40
1607 150 s. Golda Meir (Prime Minister of Israel) 60 60
1608 200 s. Dr. Elizabeth Blackwell (first female medical doctor) 70 70
1609 400 s. Margaret Thatcher (Prime Minister of Great Britain) .. .. .. 1·50 1·50
1602/9 .. .. *Set of* 8 4·00 4·00
MS1610 116×80 mm. 500 s. Mother Teresa (humanitarian) .. .. 2·50 2·75

Nos. 1602/9 were printed together, *se-tenant*, in sheetlets of 8.

221 *Iolaus aphnaeoides*

222 Arthur Ashe (tennis)

(Des Jennifer Toombs. Litho Cartor)

1993 (15 July). *Butterflies. T* **221** *and similar horiz designs. Multicoloured. P* 13.

1611/54 100 s. × 44 .. .. .. *Set of* 44 15·00 16·00
MS1655 Four sheets, each 69×58 mm. (a) 500 s. *Cymothoe sangaris*. (b) 500 s. *Precis octavia*. (c) 500 s. *Charaxes violetta*. (d) 500 s. *Papilio nobilis* *Set of* 4 *sheets* 8·00 8·50

Nos. 1611/54 were printed *se-tenant* in two sheetlets of 12 (Nos. 1611/34) and one of 20 (Nos. 1635/54). The species depicted are *Iolaus aphnaeoides, Charaxes eupale, Danaus formosa, Antanartia hippomene, Mylothris sagala, Charaxes anticlea, Salamis temora, Nepheronia argia, Acraea pseudolycia, Hypolimnas antevorta, Colotis hildebrandti, Acraea bonasia, Eurema desjardinsi, Myrina silenus, Iolaus ismenias, Charaxes candiope, Precis artaxia, Danaus chrysippus, Axiocerses bambana, Precis orithya, Pinacopteryx eriphia, Iolaus coecolus, Precis hierta, Colotis regina, Euphaedra neophron, Mylothris poppea, Aphaneus flavescens, Eronia leda, Charaxes zoolina, Papilio bromius, Cyrestis camillus, Hypolycaena buxtoni, Charaxes achaemenes, Asterope rosa, Graphium antheus, Charaxes acuminatus, Kallima rumia, Leptosia alcesta, Pseudacraea boisduvali, Iolaus sidus, Salamis parhassus, Charaxes protoclea azota, Charaxes bohemani* and *Papilio ophidicephalus.*

(Des J. Iskowitz. Litho Questa)

1993 (15 July). *Black Sporting Personalities. T* **222** *and similar multicoloured designs. P* 14.

1656 20 s. Type **222** 30 30
a. Sheetlet. Nos. 1656/63 .. .. 4·00
1657 40 s. Michael Jordan (basketball) .. 30 30
1658 50 s. Daley Thompson (decathlon) .. 30 30
1659 70 s. Jackie Robinson (baseball) .. 30 30
1660 100 s. Kareem Abdul-Jabbar (basketball) 40 40
1661 150 s. Florence Joyner (athletics) .. 60 60
1662 200 s. Jesse Owens (athletics) 70 70
1663 400 s. Jack Johnson (boxing) .. .. 1·50 1·50
1656/63 .. .. *Set of* 8 4·00 4·00
MS1664 72×101 mm. 500 s. Muhammad Ali (boxing) (*horiz*) .. .. 2·50 2·75

Nos. 1656/63 were printed together, *se-tenant*, in sheetlets of 8.

223 Short-finned Mako

(Litho State Ptg Wks, Moscow)

1993 (27 July). *Sharks. T* **223** *and similar multicoloured designs. P* 12½×12.

1665 20 s. Type **223** 15 15
1666 30 s. Lantern Shark 20 20
1667 50 s. Tiger Shark 25 25
1668 70 s. African Angelshark 35 35
1669 100 s. "*Pristiophorus cirratus*" 45 45
1670 150 s. White-tipped Reef Shark 65 65
1671 200 s. Scalloped Hammerhead 75 75
1665/71 .. .. *Set of* 7 2·50 2·50
MS1672 91×91 mm. 350 s. Six-gilled Shark (*vert*). P 12×12½ .. .. 1·40 1·75

224 Alpha Jet

225 Gordon Setter

(Litho State Ptg Wks, Moscow)

1993 (30 Aug). *Military Aircraft. T* **224** *and similar multicoloured designs. P* 12½×12.

1673 20 s. Type **224** 20 20
1674 30 s. Northrop F-5E 25 25
1675 50 s. Dassault Mirage 3NG 30 30
1676 70 s. MB 339C 45 45
1677 100 s. MiG-31 .. .. 50 50
1678 150 s. C-101 Aviojet 70 70
1679 200 s. General Dynamics F-16 Fighting Falcon 80 80
1673/9 .. .. *Set of* 7 3·00 3·00
MS1680 91×91 mm. 500 s. EAP fighter (*vert*). P 12×12½ .. .. 1·50 1·75

(Litho State Ptg Wks, Moscow)

1993 (27 Sept). *Dogs. T* **225** *and similar vert designs. Multicoloured. P* 12×12½.

1681 20 s. Type **225** 20 20
1682 30 s. Zwergschnauzer 25 25
1683 50 s. Labrador Retriever 30 30
1684 70 s. Wire Fox Terrier 45 45
1685 100 s. English Springer Spaniel 50 50
1686 150 s. Newfoundlander 70 70
1687 200 s. Moscow Toy Terrier 80 80
1681/7 .. .. *Set of* 7 3·00 3·00
MS1688 91×91 mm. 350 s. Dobermann Pinscher 1·40 1·60

226 Rhinoceros, Ngorongoro Crater

227 *Ansellia africana*

(Litho State Ptg Wks, Moscow)

1993 (29 Oct). *National Parks. T* **226** *and similar multicoloured designs. P* 12½×12.

1689 20 s. Type **226** 20 20
1690 50 s. Buffalo, Ngurdoto Crater 20 20
1691 70 s. Leopard, Kilimanjaro 30 30
1692 100 s. Baboon, Gombe 35 35
1693 150 s. Lion, Selous 45 45
1694 200 s. Giraffe, Mikumi 65 65
1695 250 s. Zebra, Serengeti 70 70
1689/95 .. .. *Set of* 7 2·50 2·50
MS1696 91×91 mm. 500 s. Elephant, Lake Manyara (*vert*). P 12×12½ .. .. 1·50 1·75

(Litho Cartor)

1993 (8 Nov). *Flowers. T* **227** *and similar vert designs. Multicoloured. P* 13½.

1697 20 s. Type **227** 10 10
1698 30 s. *Saintpaulia ionantha* 15 15
1699 40 s. *Stapelia semota lutea* 20 20
1700 50 s. *Impatiens walleriana* 20 20
1701 60 s. *Senecio petraeus* 20 20
1702 70 s. *Kalanchoe velutina* 25 25
1703 100 s. *Kaempferia brachystemon* 30 30
1704 150 s. *Nymphaea colorata* 45 45
1705 200 s. *Thunbergia battiscombei* 55 55
1706 250 s. *Crossandra nilotica* 65 65
1707 300 s. *Spathodea campanulata* 75 75
1708 350 s. *Ruttya fruticosa* 85 85
1697/1708 .. .. .. *Set of* 12 4·25 4·25
MS1709 Two sheets, each 100×70 mm. (a) 500 s. *Streptocarpus saxorum*. (b) 500 s. *Glorioso verschurii*. P 13 .. .. .. *Set of* 2 *sheets* 5·25 5·50

228 Norman-Arab

229 Berts Warrior

(Litho State Ptg Wks, Moscow)

1993 (30 Nov). *Horses. T* **228** *and similar multicoloured designs. P* 12½×12.

1710 20 s. Type **228** 20 20
1711 40 s. Nonius 30 30
1712 50 s. Boulonnais 30 30
1713 70 s. Arab 40 40
1714 100 s. Anglo-Arab 45 45
1715 150 s. Tarpon 70 70
1716 200 s. Thoroughbred 80 80
1710/16 .. .. *Set of* 7 2·75 2·75
MS1717 91×91 mm. 400 s. Anglo-Norman (*vert*). P 12×12½ .. .. 1·50 1·75

No. 1716 is inscribed "THOROUGBLED" in error.

(Litho State Ptg Wks, Moscow)

1993 (30 Dec). *Traditional African Costumes. T* **229** *and similar vert designs. Multicoloured. P* 12×12½.

1718 20 s. Type **229** 10 10
1719 40 s. Galla 15 15
1720 50 s. Guinean 15 15
1721 70 s. Goloff 20 25
1722 100 s. Peul 30 30
1723 150 s. Abyssinian 45 45
1724 200 s. Pahuin 55 55
1718/24 .. .. *Set of* 7 1·75 1·75
MS1725 91×91 mm. 350 s. Zulu .. .. 1·10 1·25

(Litho Questa)

1994 (10 Feb). *Hummel Figurines. Vert designs as T* **256** *of Maldive Islands. Multicoloured. P* 14.

1726 20 s. Boy playing accordion 15 15
1727 40 s. Girl with guitar and boy with lute 20 20
1728 50 s. Boy playing euphonium 20 20
1729 70 s. Boy playing mouth organ 25 25
1730 100 s. Boy with trumpet on fence .. 30 30
1731 150 s. Boy playing recorder 45 45
1732 200 s. Boy with trumpet and bird on feet 60 65
1733 300 s. Girl playing banjo 80 85
1734 350 s. Boy carrying double bass on back .. 1·00 1·10
1735 400 s. Girls with banjo and song sheet .. 1·10 1·25
1726/35 .. .. *Set of* 10 4·50 4·75
MS1736 Two sheets, each 70×101 mm. (a) 500 s. Carol singers. (b) 500 s. Angels with trumpets in bell tower .. .. .. *Set of* 2 *sheets* 5·00 5·50

230 Downhill Skiing

231 Ruud Gullit (Netherlands)

(Litho State Ptg Wks, Moscow)

1994 (12 Feb). *Winter Olympic Games, Lillehammer, Norway. T* **230** *and similar vert designs. Multicoloured. P* 12×12½.

1737 40 s. Type **230** 20 20
1738 50 s. Ice hockey 20 20
1739 70 s. Speed skating 30 30
1740 100 s. Bobsleighing 35 35
1741 120 s. Figure skating 40 40
1742 170 s. Free style skiing 55 55
1743 250 s. Biathlon 75 75
1737/43 .. .. *Set of* 7 2·50 2·50
MS1744 93×91 mm. 500 s. Cross-country skiing 1·50 1·75

(Litho Questa)

1994 (14 Feb). *World Cup Football Championship, U.S.A.* (1*st issue*). *T* **231** *and similar vert designs. Multicoloured. P* 14.

1745 20 s. Type **231** 20 20
1746 30 s. Kevin Sheedy (Ireland) 20 20
1747 50 s. Giuseppe Giannini (Italy) 30 30
1748 70 s. Julio Cesar (Brazil) 35 35
1749 250 s. John Barnes (England) and Grun (Belgium) 90 90
1750 300 s. Chendo (Spain) .. .. .. 1·00 1·00
1751 350 s. Frank Rijkaard (Netherlands) .. 1·10 1·10
1752 400 s. Lothar Matthaeus (Germany) .. 1·25 1·25
1745/52 .. .. *Set of* 8 4·75 4·75
MS1753 Two sheets. (a) 76×106 mm. 500 s. Nicola Berti (Italy). (b) 106×76 mm. 500 s. Des Walker (England) .. .. *Set of* 2 *sheets* 5·25 5·75

See also Nos. 1838/46 and 1892/9

(Des W. Hanson. Litho Questa)

1994 (18 Feb). *"Hong Kong '94" International Stamp Exhibition. Horiz designs as T* **293** *of Maldive Islands. Multicoloured. P* 14.

1754 350 s. Blue-barred Orange Parrotfish and Red Cap White Pearl-scale Goldfish at right .. .. 1·25 1·25
a. Horiz pair. Nos. 1754/5 .. .. .. 2·50 2·50
1755 350 s. Regal Angelfish and Red Cap White Pearl-scale Goldfish at left .. 1·25 1·25

Nos. 1754/5 were printed together, *se-tenant*, in horizontal pairs throughout the sheet with the centre part of each pair forming a composite design.

232 Mickey Mouse, Goofy, Pluto and Donald Duck boarding Airliner

(Des Rosemary DeFiglio. Litho Questa)

1994 (13 Mar). *65th Anniv of Mickey Mouse. T* **232** *and similar multicoloured designs showing Walt Disney cartoon characters on World Tour. P* 14×13½ *(horiz) or* 13½×14 *(vert).*

1756 10 s. Type **232** 15 15
1757 20 s. Daisy Duck and Minnie Mouse dancing, Tonga 20 20
1758 30 s. Mickey and Goofy playing bowls, Australia 20 20
1759 40 s. Mickey, Donald and Goofy building igloo, Arctic Circle 25 25
1760 50 s. Pluto, Goofy, Mickey and Donald on guard at Buckingham Palace, London 25 25
1761 60 s. Pluto at Esna Bazaar, Egypt .. 30 30
1762 70 s. Donald being chased by Zsambox herders, Hungary *(vert)* 30 30
1763 100 s. Donald and Daisy on Grand Canal, Venice *(vert)* 35 35
1764 150 s. Goofy dancing, Bali *(vert)* 60 60
1765 200 s. Donald with monks, Thailand *(vert)* 75 75
1766 300 s. Goofy water skiing at Taj Mahal, India *(vert)* .. .. 1·00 1·00
1767 400 s. Mickey, Minnie, Goofy and Donald being carried by Sherpas, Nepal .. 1·25 1·25
1756/67 .. .. *Set of* 12 5·00 5·00
MS1768 Three sheets. (a) 127×102 mm. 500 s. Mickey at Livingstone's memorial, Ujiji *(vert)*. (b) 127×102 mm. 500 s. Mickey at Kigoma railway station, Tanzania *(vert)*. (c) 102×127 mm. 500 s. Mickey climbing Mt Kilimanjaro *(vert)* *Set of* 3 *sheets* 6·00 6·50

233 Bonelli's Eagle ("African Hawk Eagle")

234 Henry Ford and Model "T"

(Des P. Ndembo. Litho Questa)

1994 (17 Apr). *Birds. T* **233** *and similar multicoloured designs. P* 14.

1769 20 s. Type **233** 30 30
a. Sheetlet. Nos. 1769/74 .. .. 2·25
1770 30 s. Whale-headed Stork ("Shoe-bill Stork") 30 30
1771 50 s. Brown Harrier Eagle 35 35
1772 70 s. Black-casqued Hornbill 40 40
1773 100 s. Crowned Cranes 45 45
1774 150 s. Greater Flamingos 60 60
1775 200 s. Pair of Eastern White Pelicans *(horiz)* 65 65
a. Sheetlet. Nos. 1775/80 .. .. 4·50
1776 250 s. African Jacana and Black Crake *(horiz)* 70 70
1777 300 s. Pair of Ostriches *(horiz)* 80 80
1778 350 s. Pair of Helmet Guineafowl *(horiz)* 90 90
1779 400 s. Malachite Kingfisher *(horiz)* .. 1·00 1·00
1780 500 s. Pair of Saddle-bill Storks *(horiz)* .. 1·10 1·10
1769/80 .. .. *Set of* 12 6·75 6·75

Nos. 1769/74 and 1775/80 were printed together, *se-tenant*, in sheetlets of 6.

(Litho Questa)

1994 (25 Apr). *Centenaries of Henry Ford's First Petrol Engine (Nos. 1781, 1783,* **MS**1785a*) and Karl Benz's First Four-wheeled Car (others). T* **234** *and similar horiz designs. Multicoloured. P* 14.

1781 200 s. Type **234** 65 65
1782 200 s. Benz, 1893, and "500 SEL", 1993 .. 65 65
1783 400 s. Ford, 1893, Mustang Cobra and emblem .. .. 1·00 1·00
1784 400 s. Karl Benz and emblem .. .. .. 1·00 1·00
1781/4 .. .. *Set of* 4 3·00 3·00
MS1785 Two sheets, each 106×71 mm. (a) 500 s. Henry Ford outside first factory. (b) 500 s. Benz emblem and bonnet of 1937 "540k" *Set of* 2 *sheets* 4·00 4·50

235 Sopwith Pup Biplane

236 Jahazi (sailing canoe)

(Litho Questa)

1994 (25 Apr). *Aviation Anniversaries. T* **235** *and similar multicoloured designs. P* 14.

1786 200 s. Type **235** 65 65
1787 200 s. Inflating hot-air balloons 65 65
1788 400 s. Hawker Siddeley Harrier and design drawing .. .. 1·00 1·00
1789 400 s. Jean-Pierre Blanchard and his balloon .. .. 1·00 1·00
1786/9 .. .. *Set of* 4 3·00 3·00
MS1790 Two sheets, each 105×71 mm. (a) 500 s. Supermarine Spitfire. (b) 500 s. Hot-air balloons in flight *(vert)* .. .. *Set of* 2 *sheets* 3·25 3·50

Anniversaries:—Nos. 1786, 1788, **MS**1790a, 75th anniv of Royal Air Force; Nos. 1787, 1789, **MS**1790b, Bicentenary of first balloon flight in the U.S.A.

(Litho State Ptg Wks, Moscow)

1994 (20 May). *Sailing Ships. T* **236** *and similar vert designs. Multicoloured. P* 12×12½.

1791 40 s. Type **236** 15 15
1792 50 s. Caravel 15 15
1793 70 s. Pirate carrack 25 25
1794 100 s. Baltic galeass 30 30
1795 170 s. Frigate (inscr "Battle-ship") 55 55
1796 200 s. British ship of the line (inscr "Frigate") 65 65
1797 250 s. Brig 75 75
1791/7 .. .. *Set of* 7 2·50 2·50
MS1798 91×91 mm. 500 s. Clipper .. .. 1·60 1·75

237 Diatryma

238 Koala Bear with Cub

(Litho State Ptg Wks, Moscow)

1994 (30 June). *Prehistoric Animals. T* **237** *and similar vert designs. Multicoloured. P* 12×12½.

1799 40 s. Type **237** 20 20
1800 50 s. Tyrannosaurus rex 20 20
1801 100 s. Uintaterius 35 35
1802 120 s. Stiracosaurus 45 45
1803 170 s. Diplodocus 60 60
1804 250 s. Archaeopteryx 80 80
1805 300 s. Sordes 90 90
1799/1805 .. .. *Set of* 7 3·25 3·25
MS1806 91×91 mm. 500 s. Dimetrodon .. 1·60 1·75

No. 1799 is inscribed "DIATRUMA" in error.

(Litho State Ptg Wks, Moscow)

1994 (29 July). *Endangered Species. T* **238** *and similar multicolourd designs. P* 12½×12.

1807 40 s. Type **238** 15 15
1808 70 s. Giant Panda with cub 25 25
1809 100 s. Eagles 35 35
1810 120 s. African Elephant with calf 45 45
1811 250 s. Caribbean Monk Seals 75 75
1812 400 s. Dolphins .. .. 1·00 1·00
1813 500 s. Whales .. .. 1·25 1·25
1807/13 .. .. *Set of* 7 3·75 3·75
MS1814 90×90 mm. 500 s. Tiger *(vert)*. P 12×12½ .. .. 1·60 1·75

No. 1808 shows the incorrect scientific species name.

239 Pres. Salmin Amour of Zanzibar

240 Lorry at Customs Post

(Litho State Ptg Wks, Moscow)

1994 (1 Aug). *30th Anniv of Zanzibar Revolution. T* **239** *and similar multicoloured designs. P* 12½×12 *(120 s.) or* 12×12½ *(others).*

1815 40 s. Type **239** 15 10
1816 70 s. Amani Karume (first President of Zanzibar) 25 20
1817 120 s. Harvesting cloves *(horiz)* 45 45
1818 250 s. Carved door .. .. 75 1·00
1815/18 .. .. *Set of* 4 1·40 1·50
MS1819 91×91 mm. 500 s. Hands clasped over map .. .. 1·50 1·75

(Litho Cartor)

1994 (23 Aug). *81st/82nd Customs Co-Operation Council Meeting, Arusha. T* **240** *and similar multicoloured designs. P* 14×13½.

1820 20 s. Type **240** 15 10
1821 50 s. Container ship 20 10
1822 100 s. Passengers and airliner 35 30
1823 150 s. Customs and U.P.U. logos 50 65
1820/3 .. .. *Set of* 4 1·10 1·00
MS1824 99×99 mm. 500 s. Customs arms (30×40 *mm*). P 12½ .. .. 2·00 2·25

241 Tanzanian Family

242 *Trombidium* sp

(Litho State Ptg Wks, Moscow)

1994 (30 Aug). *International Year of the Family. T* **241** *and similar multicoloured designs. P* 12½×12 *(170 s.) or* 12×12½ *(others).*

1825 40 s. Type **241** 15 10
1826 120 s. Father playing with children 35 35
1827 170 s. Family clinic *(horiz)* 50 55
1828 250 s. Woman harvesting tobacco 70 80
1825/8 .. .. *Set of* 4 1·50 1·60
MS1829 91×91 mm. 300 s. Emblem .. .. 1·25 1·40

(Litho State Ptg Wks, Moscow)

1994 (31 Aug). *Arachnids. T* **242** *and similar multicoloured designs. P* 12½×12 *(horiz) or* 12×12½ *(vert).*

1830 40 s. Type **242** 20 20
1831 50 s. *Eurypelma* sp 20 20
1832 100 s. *Salticus* sp 30 30
1833 120 s. *Micrommata rosea* *(vert)* 35 35
1834 170 s. *Araneus* sp *(vert)* 50 50
1835 250 s. *Micrathena* sp *(vert)* 70 70
1836 300 s. *Araneus diadematus* *(vert)* 80 80
1830/6 .. .. *Set of* 7 2·75 2·75
MS1837 92×92 mm. 500 s. Claw of *Hadogenes* sp *(vert)* .. .. 1·50 1·75

243 Giuseppe Signori (Italy)

244 Bateleur

1994 (26 Sept). *World Cup Football Championship, U.S.A. (2nd issue). T* **243** *and similar vert designs. Multicoloured. Litho. P* 14.

1838 300 s. Type **243** 80 80
a. Sheetlet. Nos. 1838/45 .. .. 5·75
1839 300 s. Ruud Gullit (Netherlands) 80 80
1840 300 s. Roberto Mancini (Italy) 80 80
1841 300 s. Marco van Basten (Netherlands) .. 80 80
1842 300 s. Dennis Bergkamp (Netherlands) .. 80 80
1843 300 s. Oscar Ruggeri (Argentina) 80 80
1844 300 s. Frank Rijkaard (Netherlands) .. 80 80
1845 300 s. Peter Schmeichel (Denmark) .. 80 80
1838/45 .. .. *Set of* 8 5·75 5·75
MS1846 100×70 mm. 1000 s. World Cup trophy 3·25 3·50

Nos. 1838/45 were printed together, *se-tenant*, in sheetlets of 8.

(Litho State Ptg Wks, Moscow)

1994 (30 Sept). *Birds of Prey. T* **244** *and similar multicoloured designs. P* 12½×12 *(170, 400 s.) or* 12×12½ *(others).*

1847 40 s. Type **244** 20 20
1848 50 s. Ornate Hawk Eagle 20 20
1849 100 s. Osprey 35 35
1850 120 s. Andean Condor 40 40
1851 170 s. African Fish Eagle *(horiz)* 60 60
1852 250 s. King Vulture 80 80
1853 400 s. Peregrine Falcon *(horiz)* .. .. 1·25 1·25
1847/53 .. .. *Set of* 7 3·50 3·50
MS1854 90×90 mm. 500 s. African White-backed Vulture .. .. 1·75 1·90

245 Afghan Hound **246** Players and Flags from Group B

(Des G. Bibby. Litho B.D.T.)

1994 (30 Sept). *Dogs of the World. T* **245** *and similar vert designs. Multicoloured. P* 14.

1855/63 120 s. × 9 (Type **245**; Basenji; Siberian Husky; Irish Setter; Norwegian Elkhound; Bracco Italiano; Australian Cattle Dog; German Short-haired Pointer; Rhodesian Ridgeback)
 a. Sheetlet. Nos. 1855/63 .. .. 3·00 3·25
1864/72 120 s. × 9 (Alsatian; Japanese Chin; Shetland Sheepdog; Italian Spinone; Great Dane; English Setter; Welsh Corgi; St. Bernard; Irish Wolfhound)
 a. Sheetlet. Nos. 1864/72 .. .. 3·00 3·25
1873/81 120 s. × 9 (Doberman Pinscher; Chihuahua; Bloodhound; Keeshond; Tibetan Spaniel; Japanese Akita; Tervueren; Chow; Pharaoh Hound)
 a. Sheetlet. Nos. 1873/81 .. .. 3·00 3·25
1882/90 120 s. × 9 (Alaskan Malamute; Scottish Cairn Terrier; American Foxhound; British Bulldog; Boston Terrier; Borzoi; Shar Pei; Saluki; Bernese Mountain Dog)
 a. Sheetlet. Nos. 1882/90 .. .. 3·00 3·25
1855/90 .. .. *Set of* 36 11·00 12·00
MS1891 Two sheets, each 76×106 mm. 1000 s. As No. 1856. (b) 1000 s. As No. 1868 *Set of* 2 *sheets* 8·00 8·50

Nos. 1855/63, 1864/72, 1873/81 and 1882/90 were printed together, *se-tenant*, in sheetlets of 9.

(Litho State Ptg Wks, Moscow)

1994 (30 Sept). *World Cup Football Championship, U.S.A. (3rd issue). T* **246** *and similar horiz designs. Multicoloured. P* 12½×12.

1892 40 s. Type **246** 30 30
1893 50 s. Players and flags from Group C .. 30 30
1894 70 s. Players and flags from Group D .. 45 45
1895 100 s. Players and flags from Group E .. 55 55
1896 170 s. Players and flags from Group A .. 90 90
1897 200 s. Players and World Cup .. .. 1·10 1·10
1898 250 s. Players and flags from Group F .. 1·40 1·40
1892/8 .. .. .. *Set of* 7 4·50 4·50
MS1899 92×92 mm. 500 s. Player heading ball 3·00 3·50

Nos. 1892/9 have been seen with cancelled-to-order postmarks of 17 June 1994.

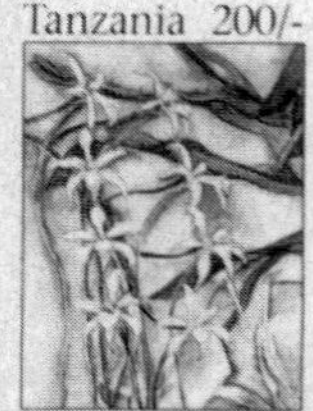

247 *Rangaeris amaniensis* **248** *Dicentra spectabilis*

(Des Marilyn Abromowitz. Litho Questa)

1994 (7 Oct). *Orchids. T* **247** *and similar multicoloured designs. P* 14.

1900 200 s. Type **247** 60 60
 a. Sheetlet. Nos. 1900/7 .. .. 4·25
1901 200 s. *Eulophia macowanii* 60 60
1902 200 s. *Cytorchis arcuata* 60 60
1903 200 s. *Centrostigma occultans* 60 60
1904 200 s. *Cirrhopetalum umbellatum* .. 60 60
1905 200 s. *Ansellia gigantea* 60 60
1906 200 s. *Angraecum ramosum* 60 60
1907 200 s. *Disa englerana* 60 60
1908 200 s. *Nervilia stolziana* 60 60
 a. Sheetlet. Nos. 1908/15 .. .. 4·25
1909 200 s. *Satyrium orbiculare* 60 60
1910 200 s. *Schizochilus sulphureus* 60 60
1911 200 s. *Disa stolzii* 60 60
1912 200 s. *Platycornye mediocris* 60 60
1913 200 s. *Satyrium breve* 60 60
1914 200 s. *Eulophia nuttii* 60 60
1915 200 s. *Disa ornithantha* 60 60
1900/15 .. .. .. *Set of* 16 8·50 8·50
MS1916 Two sheets, each 106×76 mm. (a) 1000 s. *Phaius tankervilliae* (*horiz*). (b) 1000 s. *Eulophia thomsonii* (*horiz*) .. *Set of* 2 *sheets* 7·50 8·00

Nos. 1900/7 and 1908/15 were printed together, *se-tenant*, in sheetlets of 8.

(Litho State Ptg Wks. Moscow)

1994 (31 Oct). *Flowers. T* **248** *and similar vert designs. Multicoloured. P* 12×12½.

1917 40 s. Type **248** 20 20
1918 100 s. *Thunbergia alata* 30 30
1919 120 s. *Cyrtanthus minimiflorus* 35 35
1920 170 s. *Nepenthes hybrida* 50 50
1921 250 s. *Allamanda cathartica* 65 65
1922 300 s. *Encyclia pentotis* 75 75
1923 400 s. *Protea lacticolor* 90 90
1917/23 .. .. .. *Set of* 7 3·25 3·25
MS1924 91×92 mm. 500 s. Tradescantia .. 1·60 1·75

249 *Limenitis sydyi*

(Des Mary Walters. Litho Questa)

1994 (19 Nov). *Butterflies. T* **249** *and similar horiz designs. Multicoloured. P* 14.

1925 120 s. Type **249** 40 40
 a. Sheetlet. Nos. 1925/33 .. .. 3·25
1926 120 s. *Agraulis vanillae* 40 40
1927 120 s. *Danaus chrysippus* 40 40
1928 120 s. *Eurytides marcellus* 40 40
1929 120 s. *Artopoetes pryeri* 40 40
1930 120 s. *Heliconius charitonius* 40 40
1931 120 s. *Limenitis weidemeyerii* 40 40
1932 120 s. *Phoebis sennae* 40 40
1933 120 s. *Timelaea albescens* 40 40
1934 120 s. *Papilio glaucus* 40 40
 a. Sheetlet. Nos. 1934/42 .. .. 3·25
1935 120 s. *Danaus plexippus* 40 40
1936 120 s. *Papilio troilus* 40 40
1937 120 s. *Hypolimnas antevorta* 40 40
1938 120 s. *Cirrochroa imperatrix* 40 40
1939 120 s. *Vanessa atalanta* 40 40
1940 120 s. *Limenitis archippus* 40 40
1941 120 s. *Hypolimnas pandarus* 40 40
1942 120 s. *Anthocharis belia* 40 40
1925/42 .. .. .. *Set of* 18 6·50 6·50
MS1943 Two sheets, each 101×70 mm. (a) 1000 s. *Papilio polyxenes*. (b) 1000 s. *Vanessa cardui* .. .. .. *Set of* 2 *sheets* 6·50 7·00

Nos. 1925/33 and 1934/42 were printed together, *se-tenant*, in sheetlets 9.

250 Donald Duck and Goofy with Safari Equipment

(Litho Questa)

1994 (26 Nov). *Mickey Mouse Safari Club. T* **250** *and similar multicoloured designs showing Walt Disney cartoon characters on safari. P* 14×13½.

1944 70 s. Type **250** 25 25
1945 70 s. Donald and Mickey Mouse with leopard cubs 25 25
1946 100 s. Donald photographing antelope .. 30 30
1947 100 s. Donald between elephant's legs .. 30 30
1948 120 s. Mickey with monkeys 40 40
1949 120 s. Donald with hippopotamuses .. 40 40
1950 150 s. Goofy carrying equipment 50 50
1951 150 s. Mickey, Donald and Goofy sheltering under elephant's ears 50 50
1952 200 s. Goofy with zebras 60 60
1953 200 s. Donald, Goofy and Mickey with lion 60 60
1954 250 s. Donald filming monkeys 70 70
1955 250 s. Giraffe licking Mickey 70 70
1944/55 .. .. .. *Set of* 12 5·00 5·00
MS1956 Three sheets, each 101×121 mm. (a) 1000 s. Goofy in tree with camera (*vert*). (b) 1000 s. Donald and Goofy with camera (*vert*). (c) 1000 s. Donald and Mickey with camera (*vert*). P 13½×14 .. .. .. *Set of* 3 *sheets* 8·50 9·50

251 Plan indicating Moon Landing Point

(Des G. Vasarhelyi. Litho Questa)

1994 (30 Nov). *25th Anniv of First Moon Landing. T* **251** *and similar horiz designs. Multicoloured. P* 14.

1957 150 s. Type **251** 50 50
 a. Sheetlet. Nos. 1957/65 .. .. 4·00
1958 150 s. Photograph showing Sea of Tranquility 50 50
1959 150 s. Lunar surface 50 50
1960 150 s. Lift-off 50 50
1961 150 s. Jettisoning first stage rocket .. 50 50
1962 150 s. Jettisoning second stage rocket .. 50 50
1963 150 s. Lunar module *Eagle* leaving command module 50 50
1964 150 s. *Eagle* descending towards lunar surface 50 50
1965 150 s. Armstrong and Aldrin (astronauts) inside *Eagle* 50 50
1966 150 s. "Apollo 11" crew in space suits .. 50 50
 a. Sheetlet. Nos. 1966/74 .. .. 4·00
1967 150 s. *Eagle* on lunar surface 50 50
1968 150 s. Armstrong descending to lunar surface 50 50
1969 150 s. Astronaut, *Eagle* and experiment .. 50 50
1970 150 s. Astronaut setting-up equipment .. 50 50
1971 150 s. Reflection in astronaut's visor .. 50 50
1972 150 s. Astronaut and U.S.A. flag .. 50 50
1973 150 s. Astronaut carrying equipment .. 50 50
1974 150 s. *Eagle* blasting off from Moon .. 50 50
1975 150 s. Command module 50 50
 a. Sheetlet. Nos. 1975/83 .. .. 4·00
1976 150 s. *Eagle* leaving Moon 50 50
1977 150 s. Capsule leaving Moon orbit .. 50 50
1978 150 s. Capsule heading for Earth .. 50 50
1979 150 s. Capsule re-entering Earth's atmosphere 50 50
1980 150 s. Capsule in sea 50 50
1981 150 s. Recovery crew opening hatch .. 50 50
1982 150 s. Transferring astronauts by helicopter 50 50
1983 150 s. Armstrong, Collins and Aldrin (astronauts) after recovery .. 50 50
1957/83 .. .. .. *Set of* 27 12·00 12·00

Nos. 1957/65, 1966/74 and 1975/83 were printed together, *se-tenant*, in sheetlets of 9.

252 *Astacus leptodactytus*

(Litho State Ptg Wks, Moscow)

1994 (30 Nov). *Crabs. T* **252** *and similar multicoloured designs. P* 12½×12 (*horiz*) *or* 12×12½ (*vert*).

1984 40 s. Type **252** 15 15
1985 100 s. *Eriocheir sinensis* (*vert*) 35 35
1986 120 s. *Caneer opillo* (*vert*) 40 40
1987 170 s. *Cardisoma quanhumi* 55 55
1988 250 s. *Birgus latro* (*vert*) 70 70
1989 300 s. *Menippe mercenaria* 80 80
1990 400 s. *Dromia vulgaris* (*vert*) 95 95
1984/90 .. .. .. *Set of* 7 3·50 3·50
MS1991 92×92 mm. 500 s. Coral and crab's claw 1·60 1·75

(Des Kerri Schiff. Litho Questa)

1994 (12 Dec). *Centenary of International Olympic Committee. Gold Medal Winners. Vert designs as T* **303** *of Maldive Islands. Multicoloured. P* 14.

1992 350 s. Kristin Otto (Germany) (50 metres freestyle swimming), 1988 .. 1·00 1·00
1993 500 s. Carl Lewis (U.S.A.) (various track and field events), 1984 and 1988 .. 1·40 1·40
MS1994 74×104 mm. 1000 s. Oksana Baiul (Ukraine) (figure skating), 1994 .. .. 2·75 3·00

(Des J. Batchelor. Litho Questa)

1994 (12 Dec). *50th Anniv of D-Day* (*1st issue*). *Horiz designs as T* **304** *of Maldive Islands. Multicoloured. P* 14.

1995 350 s. Troops leaving landing craft .. 1·00 1·00
1996 600 s. Amphibious tank and troops, Omaha Beach .. .. .. 1·60 1·60
MS1997 104×74 mm. 1000 s. Loading landing ship in England .. .. .. 2·75 3·00

253 Supermarine Spitfire over Beaches **254** Deinonychus

(Des R. Vigurs. Litho Questa)

1994 (12 Dec). *50th Anniv of D-Day (2nd issue). T* **253** *and similar horiz designs. Multicoloured. P* 14.

1998	200 s.	Type **253**	60	60
		a. Sheetlet. Nos. 1998/2003	3·25	
1999	200 s.	D.U.K.W.s landing on Gold Beach	60	60
2000	200 s.	Canadian troops landing on Juno Beach	60	60
2001	200 s.	Canadian cyclists disembarking, Juno Beach	60	60
2002	200 s.	Amphibious Sherman tank on beach	60	60
2003	200 s.	German gun implacement	60	60
2004	200 s.	General Montgomery and British troops on beach	60	60
		a. Sheetlet. Nos. 2004/9	3·25	
2005	200 s.	British engineers with AVRE Churchill tank, Gold Beach ..	60	60
2006	200 s.	U.S.S. *Thompson* (destroyer) being refuelled	60	60
2007	200 s.	H.M.S. *Warspite* (battleship) ..	60	60
2008	200 s.	Royal Marines on Juno Beach ..	60	60
2009	200 s.	Sherman Mark 1 flail tank leaving landing craft	60	60
2010	200 s.	General Eisenhower and U.S. troops on Omaha Beach	60	60
		a. Sheetlet. Nos. 2010/15	3·25	
2011	200 s.	North American P-51 Mustang escorting ships	60	60
2012	200 s.	U.S. coastguard cutter alongside landing craft	60	60
2013	200 s.	U.S. troops in landing craft ..	60	60
2014	200 s.	U.S. troops landing on Omaha Beach	60	60
2015	200 s.	U.S. troops on Omaha Beach ..	60	60
1998/2015		.. .. .. *Set of* 18	9·50	9·50

MS2016 Two sheets, each 99×70 mm. (a) 1000 s. U.S. marines amongst beach obstacles. (b) 1000 s. U.S. troops landing on Utah Beach *Set of* 2 *sheets* 6·00 6·50

Nos. 1998/2003, 2004/9 and 2010/15 were each printed together, *se-tenant*, in sheetlets of 6.

No. 2004 is inscribed "COMMANDER-IN-CHEIF" and No. 2010 "OPERATION OVERLOAD", both in error.

(Des G. Bibby. Litho Questa)

1994 (26 Dec). *Prehistoric Animals. T* **254** *and similar designs. P* 14.

2017/48	120 s. × 32 multicoloured		11·00	12·00
MS2049	80×110 mm. 1000 s. multicoloured ..		3·00	3·25

Designs: *Vert*—No. 2018, Styracosaurus; No. 2019, Anatosaurus; No. 2020, Plateosaurus; No. 2021, Iguanodon; No. 2022, Oviraptor; No. 2023, Dimorphodons; No. 2024, Ornithomimus; No. 2025, Lambeosaurus; No. 2026, Megalosaurus; No. 2027, Cetiosaurus; No. 2028, Hypsilophodon; No. 2029, Rhamphorynchus; No. 2030, Scelidosaurus; No. 2031, Antrodemus; No. 2032, Dimetrodon; No. **MS**2049, Brachiosaurus. *Horiz*—No. 2033, Brontosaurus; No. 2034, Albertosaurus; No. 2035, Parasaurolophus; No. 2036, Pteranodons; No. 2037, Stegosaurus; No. 2038, Tyrannosaurus rex; No. 2039, Triceratops; No. 2040, Ornitholestes; No. 2041, Camarasaurus; No. 2042, Ankylosaurus; No. 2043, Trachodon; No. 2044, Allosaurus; No. 2045, Corythosaurus; No. 2046, Struthiomimus; No. 2047, Camptosaurus; No. 2048, Heterodontosaurus.

Nos. 2017/32 and 2033/48 were printed together, *se-tenant*, in sheetlets of 16, Nos. 2033/48 forming a composite design.

255 "Hubble" Space Telescope

(Litho State Ptg Wks, Moscow)

1994 (30 Dec). *Space Research. T* **255** *and similar horiz designs. Multicoloured. P* 12½×12.

2050	40 s.	Type **255**	15	15
2051	100 s.	"Mariner"	35	35
2052	120 s.	"Voyager 2"	40	40
2053	170 s.	"Work Package-03"	55	55
2054	250 s.	Orbiting solar observer	70	70
2055	300 s.	"Magellan"	80	80
2056	400 s.	"Galilei"	95	95
2050/6		.. .. *Set of* 7	3·50	3·50
MS2057		91×91 mm. 500 s. "Fobos"	1·60	1·75

STAMP BOOKLETS

1965 (9 Dec). *Black on blue (No. SB6) or buff (No. SB7) covers, size 48×46 mm. Stitched.*

SB6 3 s. booklet containing four 15 c. and eight 30 c. (Nos. 130, 132) in blocks of 4 .. .. 3·75
SB7 5 s. booklet containing four 15 c. and 50 c., and eight 30 c. (Nos. 130, 132, 134) in blocks of 4 3·75

1967 (9 Dec). *Black on blue (No. SB8) or buff (No. SB9) covers, size 48×45 mm. Stitched.*

SB8 3 s. booklet containing four 15 c. and eight 30 c. (Nos. 144, 146) in blocks of 4 .. .. 3·00
SB9 5 s. booklet containing 10 c., 15 c., 20 c., 30 c. and 50 c. (Nos. 143/6, 148), each in block of 4 .. 3·50

1971 (15 Dec). *Black printed (No. SB10) or black on claret (No. SB11) covers, size 48×46 mm. Stitched.*

SB10 5 s. booklet containing four 10 c., 15 c. and 40 c., and eight 30 c. (Nos. 143, 144a, 146, 147a) in blocks of 4 .. .. .. 20·00
SB11 10 s. booklet containing four 10 c., 20 c., 30 c. and 50 c., and eight 70 c. (Nos. 143, 145/6, 148a, 150a) in blocks of 4 .. .. .. 26·00

1973 (13 June). *Black printed cover, size 48×46 mm. Stitched.*

SB12 5 s. booklet containing four 10 c., 15 c. and 40 c., and eight 30 c. (Nos. 143a, 144a, 146a, 147a) in blocks of 4 .. .. .. 16·00

1973 (10 Dec). *Black on yellow (No. SB13) or blue (No. SB14) covers, size 54×41 mm. Stitched.*

SB13 5 s. booklet containing 5 c., 10 c., 20 c., 40 c. and 50 c. (Nos. 158/9, 161, 163/4), each in block of 4 .. .. .. 10·00
SB14 10 s. booklet containing four 10 c., 20 c., 30 c. and 50 c., and eight 70 c. (Nos. 159, 161/2, 164, 166) in blocks of 4 .. .. .. 16·00

1980 (Nov). *Black printed (No. SB15) or black on red (No. SB16) covers, size 66×47 mm. Stitched.*

SB15 6 s. booklet containing eight 10 c. and 20 c., and four 40 c. and 50 c. (Nos. 307/10) in blocks of 4 .. .. .. 3·00
SB16 14 s. booklet containing four 1 s. and two 2 s. and 3 s. (Nos. 313, 315/16) in pairs .. .. 3·50

1990 (15 Dec). *Black on yellow cover, size 99×58 mm. Pane attached by selvedge.*

SB17 174 s. booklet containing *se-tenant* pane of twelve (No. 804a) 90

OFFICIAL STAMPS

(Opt photo Harrison)

1965 (9 Dec). *Nos. 128/32, 134, 136, 139 optd as Types* O **1** *(15 c., 30 c. or larger (17 mm) 5 c., 10 c., 20 c., 50 c.), or with* O **2** *of Tanganyika (1 s., 5 s.).*

O 9 5 c. ultramarine and yellow-orange .. 10 30
O10 10 c. black, greenish yellow, green & blue .. 10 30
O11 15 c. multicoloured 10 30
O12 20 c. sepia, grey-green and greenish blue .. 10 30
O13 30 c. black and red-brown 10 30
O14 50 c. multicoloured 15 30
O15 1 s. multicoloured 30 30
O16 5 s. lake-brown, yellow-green and blue .. 1·75 5·00
O9/16 .. .. .. *Set of* 8 2·25 6·50

OFFICIAL

(O 3) (3 mm tall)

(Opt litho Govt Printer, Dar-es-Salaam)

1967 (10–18 Nov). *Nos. 134, 136 and 139 optd as No.* O14 *(50 c.) or with Type* O **3** *(others).*

O17 50 c. multicoloured (18.11) .. .. ..
O18 1 s. multicoloured (18.11) .. .. 16·00 4·50
O19 5 s. lake-brown, yellow-green and blue .. 9·00 8·00

The issue dates given are for the earliest known postmarked copies.

Nos. O9/16 were overprinted by Harrison in photogravure and Nos. O17/19 have litho overprints by the Government Printer, Dar-es-Salaam. On No. O17 the overprint is the same size (17 mm long) as on No. O14.

1967 (9 Dec)–**71**. *Nos. 142/6, 148, 151 and 155 optd as Type* O **1**, *but larger (measuring 17 mm) (5 c. to 50 c.) or as Type* O **2** *of Tanganyika (1 s. and 5 s.). Chalk-surfaced paper.*

O20 5 c. magenta, yellow-olive and black .. 10 1·50
a. Glazed, ordinary paper (22.1.71) .. 1·50 3·50
O21 10 c. brown and bistre 10 50
O22 15 c. grey, turquoise-blue and black .. 10 1·25
a. Glazed, ordinary paper (22.1.71) .. 1·50 4·00
O23 20 c. brown and turquoise-green .. 10 30
O24 30 c. sage-green and black 10 30
O25 50 c. multicoloured 15 80
a. Glazed, ordinary paper (22.1.71) .. 1·50 3·50
O26 1 s. orange-brown, slate-blue and maroon .. 30 1·50
a. Glazed, ordinary paper (3.2.71) .. 5·00 4·00
O27 5 s. greenish yellow, black & turquoise-grn. 2·50 8·00
a. Glazed, ordinary paper (3.2.71) .. 12·00 14·00
O20/7 .. .. .. *Set of* 8 3·00 12·50
O20a/7a .. .. .. *Set of* 5 †19·00 26·00

The chalk-surfaced paper exists with both PVA gum and gum arabic, but the glazed, ordinary paper exists PVA gum only.

OFFICIAL (O 4) **OFFICIAL** (O 5)

1970 (10 Dec)–**73**. *Nos. 142/8, 151 and 155 optd locally by letterpress as Type* O **4** *(5 to 50 c.) or as Type* O **2** *of Tanganyika, but measuring 28 mm (1 s. and 5 s.).*

(a) *Chalk-surfaced paper*

O28 5 c. magenta, yellow-olive and black .. 10 2·00
a. "OFFCIAL" (R.7/6) .. .. ..
O29 10 c. brown and bistre 10 90
a. "OFFCIAL" (R.7/6) .. .. ..
O30 20 c. brown and turquoise-green .. 20 1·00
O31 30 c. sage-green and black .. .. 25 1·00
O28/31 .. .. .. *Set of* 4 55 4·50

(b) *Glazed, ordinary paper* (1973)

O32 5 c. magenta, yellow-olive and black .. — 2·00
a. "OFFCIAL" (R.7/6) .. .. — 30·00
b. "OFFICIA" (R.10/9) .. .. — 35·00
O33 10 c. brown and bistre .. .. ..
a. "OFFCIAL" (R.7/6) .. .. ..
O34 15 c. grey, turquoise-blue and black .. ..
a. "OFFCIAL" (R.7/6) .. .. ..
O35 20 c. brown and turquoise-green .. ..
O36 40 c. yellow, chocolate and bright green .. — 2·50
a. Opt double .. .. ..
b. "OFFICIA" (R.10/9) .. .. — 50·00
O37 50 c. multicoloured .. .. — 2·00
a. "OFFCIAL" (R.7/6) .. .. — 40·00
O38 1 s. orange-brown, slate-blue and maroon .. — 10·00
a. Opt double .. .. ..
O39 5 s. greenish yellow, black & turquoise-grn — 25·00

The letterpress overprint can be distinguished from the photogravure by its absence of screening dots and the overprint showing through to the reverse, apart from the difference in length.

1973 (10 Dec). *Nos. 158/9, 161, 163/4 and 166/70 optd with Type* O **1** *of Tanganyika (5 to 70 c.) or Type* O **5** *(others).*

O40 5 c. light yellow-olive, lt violet-blue & black 50 1·25
O41 10 c. multicoloured 65 30
O42 20 c. reddish cinnamon, orange-yellow & blk 80 30
O43 40 c. multicoloured .. .. .. 1·25 30
O44 50 c. multicoloured .. .. .. 1·25 30
O45 70 c. turquoise-green, pale orange and black .. 1·50 65
O46 1 s. multicoloured .. .. .. 1·50 30
O47 1 s. 50, multicoloured .. .. 3·50 2·50
a. Pair, one without opt .. .. † —
O48 2 s. 50, multicoloured .. .. 4·00 5·50
O49 5 s. multicoloured .. .. .. 4·50 6·50
O40/9 .. .. .. *Set of* 10 17·00 16·00

No. O47a is due to a paper fold and comes from a sheet used at Kigoma in 1974.

1977 (Feb). *Nos. 159, 161 and 163/4 optd locally by letterpress as Type* O **4**.

O50 10 c. multicoloured .. .. — 2·00
a. "OFFCIAL" (R. 7/6) .. .. — 38·00
O51 20 c. multicoloured .. .. — 2·00
a. "OFFCIAL" (R. 7/6) .. .. — 40·00
b. Opt inverted .. .. ..
c. Opt double .. .. ..
O52 40 c. multicoloured .. .. ..
a. "OFFCIAL" (R. 7/6) .. .. — 2·50
O53 50 c. multicoloured .. .. — 50·00
a. "OFFCIAL" (R. 7/6) .. .. — 2·50
b. Opt inverted .. .. — 48·00

OFFICIAL (O 6) OFFICIAL (O 6a) OFFICIAL (O 7) OFFICIAL (O 7a)

1980 (Nov)–**85**. (a) *Bradbury Wilkinson printings. Nos. 307/12 optd with Type* O **6** *(10 mm long) and Nos. 313 and 315/17 optd with Type* O **7** *(13½ mm long).*

O54 10 c. Type **75** 20 30
O55 20 c. Large-spotted Genet 25 30
O56 40 c. Banded Mongoose 30 30
O57 50 c. Ratel (light blue panel at foot) .. 30 30
O58 75 c. Large-toothed Rock Hyrax .. 40 50
O59 80 c. Leopard 55 60
O60 1 s. Type **76** 55 30
O61 2 s. Common Zebra .. .. .. 85 1·50
O62 3 s. African Buffalo .. .. 1·00 1·75
O63 5 s. Lion .. .. .. 1·50 2·50
O54/63 .. .. .. *Set of* 10 5·50 7·50

(b) *John Waddington printings. No. 320a optd with Type* O **6a** *(8½ mm long) and Nos. 320c/g optd with Type* O **7a** *(13 mm long) (1984–85)*

O64 50 c. Ratel (turquoise-blue panel at foot) 1·50 1·50
O65 1 s. Type **76** .. .. .. 1·75 1·75
O66 1 s. 50, Giraffe .. .. .. 3·50 3·75
O67 2 s. Common Zebra .. .. 4·50 5·00
O68 3 s. African Buffalo .. .. 6·00 7·00
O69 5 s. Lion .. .. .. 9·00 10·00
O64/9 .. .. .. *Set of* 6 24·00 26·00

On the Bradbury Wilkinson printings the overprint reads downwards on the 10 c., 50 c., 2 s., 5 s. and upwards on the others. All values of the John Waddington printing show the overprint reading upwards.

OFFICIAL (O 8) **OFFICIAL** (O 9)

1990 (15 Dec)–**91**. *Nos. 804/12 optd with Type* O **8** *(5 s. to 30 s.) or Type* O **9** *(40 s. to 100 s.).*

O70 5 s. Type **163** 10 10
O71 9 s. African Emerald Cuckoo 10 10
O72 13 s. Little Bee Eater 10 10
O73 15 s. Red Bishop 10 10
O74 20 s. Bateleur 10 10
O75 25 s. Scarlet-chested Sunbird 10 10
O76 30 s. African Wood Pigeon (1.7.91) .. 10 10
O77 40 s. Type **164** 10 10
O78 70 s. Helmet Guineafowl 15 20
O79 100 s. Eastern White Pelican 20 25
O70/9 .. .. .. *Set of* 10 65 80

Official overprints were reported as being used for normal postal purposes during 1992.

POSTAGE DUE STAMPS

Postage Due stamps of Kenya and Uganda were issued for provisional use as such in Tanganyika on 1 July 1933. The postmark is the only means of identification.

The Postage Due stamps of Kenya, Uganda and Tanganyika were used in Tanganyika until 2 January 1967.

D 1

D 2

(Litho D.L.R.)

1967 (3 Jan). *P* 14 × 13½.

D1 D 1 5 c. scarlet .. .. .. 35 5·50
D2 10 c. green .. .. .. 45 6·00
D3 20 c. deep blue .. .. .. 70 7·00
D4 30 c. red-brown .. .. .. 70 8·00
D5 40 c. bright purple .. .. .. 70 12·00
D6 1 s. orange .. .. .. 1·25 12·00
D1/6 .. .. .. *Set of* 6 3·75 45·00

1969–71. *As Nos.* D1/6, *but perf* 14 × 15.
A. *Chalk-surfaced paper* (19.12.69).
B. *Glazed, ordinary paper* (13.7.71).

			A		B	
D 7 D 1	5 c. scarlet	..	30	8·00	3·50	8·00
D 8	10 c. green	..	65	5·50	75	3·75
D 9	20 c. deep blue	..	40	8·00	2·50	9·00
D10	30 c. red-brown	..	50	13·00	85	6·50
D11	40 c. bright purple	..	2·00	13·00	5·50	25·00
D12	1 s. orange	..	†		4·75	25·00
D7A/11A	.. *Set of* 5		3·50	42·00		
D7B/12B	.. *Set of* 6				16·00	70·00

The stamps on chalk-surfaced paper exist only with gum arabic, but the stamps on glazed paper exist only with PVA gum.

1973 (12 Dec). *As Nos.* D1/6, *but glazed ordinary paper. P* 15.

D13 D 1 5 c. scarlet .. .. .. 50 8·00
D14 10 c. emerald .. .. .. 50 6·00
D15 20 c. deep blue .. .. .. 70 9·00
D16 30 c. red-brown .. .. .. 85 9·50
D17 40 c. bright mauve .. .. .. 90 14·00
D18 1 s. bright orange .. .. .. 1·25 15·00
D13/18 .. .. .. *Set of* 6 4·25 55·00

(Litho Questa)

1978 (31 July). *Chalk-surfaced paper. P* 13½×14.

D19 D 1 5 c. brown-red .. .. .. 15 1·75
D20 10 c. emerald .. .. .. 20 1·75
D21 20 c. steel-blue .. .. .. 30 1·90
D22 30 c. red-brown .. .. .. 45 2·75
D23 40 c. bright purple .. .. .. 50 3·75
D24 1 s. bright orange .. .. .. 70 4·50
D19/24 .. .. .. *Set of* 6 2·10 15·00

1984 (?). *Chalk-surfaced paper. P* 15×14.

D25 D 1 10 c. emerald .. .. ..
D26 20 c. deep dull blue .. .. ..
D27 30 c. reddish brown .. .. ..
D28 40 c. bright purple .. .. ..
D29 1 s. bright orange .. .. ..

(Litho Questa)

1990 (15 Dec). *P* 14½×14.

D30 D 2 50 c. myrtle-green 10 10
D31 80 c. ultramarine 10 10
D32 1 s. orange-brown 10 10
D33 2 s. yellow-olive 10 10
D34 3 s. purple 10 10
D35 5 s. grey-brown 10 10
D36 10 s. reddish brown 10 10
D37 20 s. brown-ochre 10 10
D30/7 .. .. .. *Set of* 8 40 40

Appendix

The following stamps have either been issued in excess of postal needs, or have not been made available to the public in reasonable quantities at face value. Miniature sheets, imperforate stamps, etc., are excluded from this section.

1985

Life and Times of Queen Elizabeth the Queen Mother. As Nos. 425/8 *but embossed on gold foil.* 20 s. × 2, 100 s. × 2.
Tanzanian Railway Locomotives (1st series). As Nos. 430/3, *but embossed on gold foil.* 5, 10, 20, 30 s.

1986

Caribbean Royal Visit. Optd in silver and gold on previous issues. (a) Nos. 425/8 20 s. × 2, 100 s. × 2. *(b) On Nos.* 430/3, 5, 10, 20, 30 s.
"Ameripex" International Stamp Exhibition, Chicago. Optd on Nos. 425/8. 20 s. × 2, 100 s. × 2.

1988

Centenary of Statue of Liberty (1986). 1, 2, 3, 4, 5, 6, 7, 8, 10, 12, 15, 18, 20, 25, 30, 35, 40, 45, 50, 60 s.
Royal Ruby Wedding. Optd on No. 378. 10 s.
125th Anniv of Red Cross. Optd on Nos. 486/7. 5, 40 s.
63rd Anniv of Rotary International in Africa. Optd on Nos. 422/3. 10 s., 17 s. 50.

Tasmania *see* Australia

Togo

The stamps of GERMANY were used in the colony from March 1888 until June 1897 when issues for TOGO were provided.

PRICES FOR STAMPS ON COVER

Nos. H1/22	*from* × 6
Nos. H23/33	—
Nos. H34/58	*from* × 6

ANGLO-FRENCH OCCUPATION

French forces invaded southern Togo on 8 August 1914 and the British landed at Lomé on 12 August. The German administration surrendered on 26 August 1914.

The territory was jointly administered under martial law, but was formally divided between Great Britain and France, effective 1 October 1920. League of Nations mandates were issued for both areas from 20 July 1922.

(Currency. 100 pfennig = 1 mark)

Stamps of German Colonial issue Yacht Types 1900 and 1909–14 (5 pf. and 10 pf.)

TOGO
Anglo-French
Occupation
(1)

Half penny
(2)

SETTINGS. Nos. H1/33 were all overprinted or surcharged by the Catholic Mission, Lome.

The initial setting for the 3 pf. to 80 pf. was of 50 (10×5), repeated twice on each sheet of 100. Overprints from this setting, used for Nos. H1/9, had the lines of type 3 mm apart.

Nos. H1/2 were subsequently surcharged, also from a setting of 50, to form Nos. H12/13. The surcharge setting showed a thin dropped "y" with small serifs on R. 1/1–2, 2/1, 3/1, 4/1 and 5/1–2.

The type from the overprint and surcharge was then amalgamated in a new setting of 50 on which the lines of the overprint were only 2 mm apart. On this amalgamated setting, used for Nos. H27/8, the thin "y" varieties were still present and R. 4/7 showed the second "O" of "TOGO" omitted.

The surcharge was subsequently removed from this "2 mm" setting which was then used to produce Nos. H17/19. The missing "O" was spotted and corrected before any of the 30 pf. stamps were overprinted.

The remaining low values of the second issue, Nos. H14/16 and H20/2, were overprinted from settings of 25 (5×5), either taken from the last setting of 50 or from an amended version on which there was no space either side of the hyphen. This slightly narrower overprint was subsequently used for Nos. H29/33. It shows the top of the second "O" broken so that it resembles a "U" on R. 1/5.

The mark values were overprinted from settings of 20 (5×4), showing the same differences in the spacing of the lines as on the low values.

It is believed that odd examples of some German colonial values were overprinted from individual settings in either spacing.

1914 (24 Sept). *Optd with T* **1** *by Catholic Mission, Lome. Wide setting. Lines 3 mm apart.*

H 1	3 pf. brown	£110	95·00
H 2	5 pf. green	£100	90·00
H 3	10 pf. carmine (Wmk Lozenges)	£120	£100
	a. Opt inverted	£7500	£3000
	b. Opt *tête-bêche* in vert pair	†	£6500
	c. No wmk	†	£5500
H 4	20 pf. ultramarine	28·00	35·00
H 5	25 pf. black and red/*yellow*	28·00	27·00
H 6	30 pf. black and orange/*buff*	30·00	45·00
H 7	40 pf. black and carmine	£225	£250
H 8	50 pf. black and purple/*buff*	£9000	£7000
H 9	80 pf. black and carmine/*rose*	£225	£275
H10	1 m. carmine	£5000	£2500
H11	2 m. blue	£8000	£8500
	a. "Occupation" double	£13000	£11000
	b. Opt inverted	£9500	

The *tête-bêche* overprint on the 10 pf. is due to the sheet being turned round after the upper 50 stamps had been overprinted so that vertical pairs from the two middle rows have the overprint *tête-bêche.*

1914 (1 Oct). *Nos.* H1 *and* H2 *surch as T* **2**.

H12	½d. on 3 pf. brown	£160	£140
	a. Thin "y" in "penny"	£400	£350
H13	1d. on 5 pf. green	£160	£140
	a. Thin "y" in "penny"	£400	£350

TOGO
Anglo-French
Occupation
(3)

TOGO
Anglo-French
Occupation
Half penny
(4)

1914 (Oct). (*a*) *Optd with T* **3**. *Narrow Setting. Lines* 2 *mm apart.* "Anglo-French" *measures* 16 *mm.*

H14	3 pf. brown	£4500	£900
H15	5 pf. green	£1100	£700
H16	10 pf. carmine	†	£2500
H17	20 pf. ultramarine	15·00	12·00
	a. "TOG"	£4000	£4000
	b. Nos. H4 and H17 *se-tenant* (vert pair)	£6500	
H18	25 pf. black and red/*yellow*	19·00	29·00
	a. "TOG"	£12000	
H19	30 pf. black and orange/*buff*	19·00	29·00
H20	40 pf. black and carmine	£4500	£1500
H21	50 pf. black and purple/*buff*	†	£6000
H22	80 pf. black and carmine/*rose*	£1800	£1800
H23	1 m. carmine	£7000	£4000
H24	2 m. blue	†	£8500
H25	3 m. violet-black	†	£38000
H26	5 m. lake and black	†	£38000

(*b*) *Narrow setting, but including value, as T* **4**

H27	½d. on 3 pf. brown	28·00	26·00
	a. "TOG"	£425	£300
	b. Thin "y" in "penny"	60·00	60·00
H28	1d. on 5 pf. green	4·00	4·25
	a. "TOG"	£130	£110
	b. Thin "y" in "penny"	12·00	15·00

In the 20 pf. one half of a sheet was overprinted with the wide setting (3 mm), and the other half with the narrow setting (2 mm), so that vertical pairs from the middle of the sheet show the two varieties of the overprint.

TOGO
Anglo-French
Occupation
(6)

TOGO
ANGLO-FRENCH
OCCUPATION
(7)

TOGO
ANGLO-FRENCH
OCCUPATION
(8)

1915 (7 Jan). *Optd as T* **6**. *The words* "Anglo-French" *measure* 15 *mm instead of* 16 *mm as in T* **3**.

H29	3 pf. brown	£7500	£2500
H30	5 pf. green	£200	£130
	a. "Occupation" omitted	£6500	
H31	10 pf. carmine	£200	£130
	a. No wmk	†	£7000
H32	20 pf. ultramarine	£1400	£475
H32*a*	40 pf. black and carmine	†	£7500
H33	50 pf. black and purple/*buff*	£12000	£9500

This printing was made on another batch of German Togo stamps, found at Sansane-Mangu.

Stamps of Ghana (Gold Coast) overprinted

1915 (May). *Nos.* 70/81, 82*a and* 83/4 *of Gold Coast* (*King George V*) *optd at Govt Press, Accra, with T* **7** ("OCCUPATION" 14½ *mm long*).

H34	½d. green	30	60
	g. Opt double	£700	£800
H35	1d. red	30	30
	g. Opt double	£325	£450
	h. Opt inverted	£160	£250
	ha. Ditto. "TOGO" omitted		
H36	2d. grey	30	40
H37	2½d. bright blue	40	2·00
H38	3d. purple/*yellow*	65	80
	a. White back	3·50	11·00
H40	6d. dull and bright purple	65	1·75
H41	1s. black/*green*	1·25	4·00
	g. Opt double	£900	
H42	2s. purple and blue/*blue*	7·50	9·00
H43	2s. 6d. black and red/*blue*	4·50	15·00
H44	5s. green and red/*yellow* (*white back*)	8·00	15·00
H45	10s. green and red/*green*	32·00	55·00
H46	20s. purple and black/*red*	£120	£120
H34/46	*Set of* 12	£150	£190

Varieties (*Nos. indicate positions in pane*).
A. *Small* "F" *in* "FRENCH" (25, 58 *and* 59).
B. *Thin* "G" *in* "TOGO" (24).
C. *No hyphen after* "ANGLO" (5).
D. *Two hyphens after* "ANGLO" (5).
E. "CUPATION" *for* "OCCUPATION" (33).
F. "CCUPATION" *for* "OCCUPATION" (57).

Varieties C and E also occur together on position 28 of the ½d. value only.

Prices are for unused. Used are worth more

		A	B	C	D	E	F
H34	½d.	1·50	3·00	3·00	†	80·00	48·00
H35	1d.	1·75	4·25	4·25	†	†	£120
	h. Inverted	£1200	£3000	£3000	†	†	†
H36	2d.	1·75	5·50	60·00	38·00	†	£120
H37	2½d.	2·50	8·00	28·00	40·00	†	£100
H38	3d.	2·50	8·00	30·00	†	†	£120
	a. White back	14·00	48·00	†	†	†	†
H40	6d.	4·25	9·50	†	†	†	£170
H41	1s.	4·25	9·50	†	†	†	95·00
H42	2s.	24·00	48·00	£120	†	†	£275
H43	2s. 6d.	18·00	38·00	£110	†	†	£425
H44	5s.	30·00	55·00	£150	†	†	£275
H45	10s.	75·00	£160	†	†	†	£400
H46	20s.	£250	£450	†	†	†	£600

1916 (Apr)–**20.** *Nos.* 70/84 *of Gold Coast* (*King George V*) *optd in London with T* **8** ("OCCUPATION" 15 *mm long*). *Heavy type and thicker letters showing through on back.*

H47	½d. green	15	1·75
H48	1d. red	15	85
H49	2d. grey	35	45
H50	2½d. bright blue	45	1·50
H51	3d. purple/*yellow*	80	70
H52	6d. dull and bright purple	55	1·00
	w. Wmk inverted	75·00	
H53	1s. black/*green*	1·75	3·00
	a. On blue-green (*olive back*) (1918)	3·25	8·00
	b. On emerald-green (*olive back*) (1920)	£300	
	c. On emer-grn (*emer-grn back*) (1920)	£200	£425
H54	2s. purple and blue/*blue*	4·50	8·00
H55	2s. 6d. black and red/*blue*	4·50	7·00
H56	5s. green and red/*yellow*	8·00	25·00
	a. On orange-buff (1919)	8·00	27·00
	b. On buff (1920)		
H57	10s. green and red/*green*	24·00	60·00
	a. On blue-green (*olive back*) (1920)	16·00	50·00
H58	20s. purple and black/*red*	£120	£130
H47/58	*Set of* 12	£140	£200
H47/58 Optd "Specimen"	*Set of* 12	£300	

Nos. H47/58 were withdrawn in October 1920 when Gold Coast stamps were introduced.

The mandates were transferred to the United Nations in January 1946. The inhabitants of the British mandate voted to join Ghana in 1957.

Tokelau *see after* New Zealand

Tonga

The Tongan Post Office was established in 18‿5 and FIJI 2d. and 6d. stamps are recorded in use until the arrival of Nos. 1/4.

PRICES FOR STAMPS ON COVER TO 1945

Nos. 1/4	*from* × 60
Nos. 5/9	*from* × 20
Nos. 10/28	*from* × 8
Nos. 29/31	*from* × 7
Nos. 32/7	*from* × 6
Nos. 38/54	*from* × 5
Nos. 55/63	*from* × 6
Nos. 64/70	*from* × 3
Nos. 71/87	*from* × 2
Nos. O1/10	*from* × 25

PROTECTORATE KINGDOM

King George I, 1845–93

1 King George I

2

(Eng Bock and Cousins. Plates made and typo Govt Ptg Office, Wellington)

1886–88. *W* **2**. *P* 12½ (*line*) *or* 12 × 11½ (*comb*)*.

1	1	1d. carmine (*p* 12½) (27.8.86)	£300	6·00
		a. Perf 12½ × 10		
		b. Perf 12 × 11½ (15.7.87)	10·00	3·25
		ba. Pale carmine (*p* 12 × 11½)	16·00	8·50
2		2d. pale violet (*p* 12½) (27.8.86)	50·00	10·00
		a. Bright violet	70·00	3·50
		b. Perf 12 × 11½ (15.7.87)	28·00	2·75
		ba. Bright violet (*p* 12 × 11½)	40·00	3·00
3		6d. blue (*p* 12½) (9.10.86)	60·00	2·25
		a. Perf 12 × 11½ (15.10.88)	50·00	2·25
		ab. Dull blue (*p* 12 × 11½)	25·00	2·25
4		1s. pale green (*p* 12½) (9.10.86)	85·00	4·50
		a. Deep green (*p* 12½)	95·00	2·25
		b. Perf 12 × 11½ (15.10.88)	55·00	6·00
		ba. Deep green (*p* 12 × 11½)	55·00	3·25

*See note after New Zealand, No. 186.

FOUR
PENCE.
(3)

EIGHT
PENCE.
(4)

(Surch Messrs Wilson & Horton, Auckland, N.Z.)

1891 (10 Nov). *Nos.* 1b *and* 2b *surch.*

5	3	4d. on 1d. carmine	2·50	11·00
		a. No stop after "PENCE"	45·00	£100
6	4	8d. on 2d. violet	35·00	90·00
		a. Short "T" in "EIGHT"	£150	£250

No. 5a occurred on R. 6/8 and 9, R. 10/11, all from the righthand pane.

1891 (23 Nov). *Optd with stars in upper right and lower left corners. P* 12½.

7	1	1d. carmine	38·00	48·00
		a. Three stars	£275	
		b. Four stars	£375	
		c. Five stars	£550	
		d. Perf 12 × 11½	£250	
		da. Three stars	£425	
		db. Four stars	£500	
		dc. Five stars	£750	
8		2d. violet	60·00	38·00
		a. Perf 12 × 11½	£300	

1892 (15 Aug). *W* **2**. *P* 12 × 11½.

9	1	6d. yellow-orange	14·00	26·00

5 Arms of Tonga   6 King George I

Damaged "O" in "TONGA" (R. 1/1, later corrected)

(Dies eng A. E. Cousins. Typo at Govt Printing Office, Wellington, N.Z.)

1892 (10 Nov). *W* **2**. *P* 12 × 11½.

No.	Type	Description	Unused	Used
10	**5**	1d. pale rose	12·00	17·00
		a. Bright rose	12·00	17·00
		b. Bisected diag (½d.) (1893) (on cover)	†	£850
		c. Damaged "O"	£100	
11	**6**	2d. olive	13·00	15·00
12	**5**	4d. chestnut	45·00	70·00
13	**6**	8d. bright mauve	55·00	£130
14		1s. brown	75·00	£110
10/14		*Set of* 5	£180	£300

No. 10b was used from 31 May 1893 to provide a 2½d. rate before the arrival of No. 15, and on subsequent occasions up to 1895.

½ d. (7)   2½d. (8)   FIVE PENCE. (9)   7½d. (10)

1893. *Printed in new colours and surch with T* **7/10** *by Govt Printing Office, Wellington. (a) In carmine. P* 12½ (21 Aug).

No.	Type	Description	Unused	Used
15	**5**	½d. on 1d. bright ultramarine	23·00	25·00
		a. Surch omitted		
16	**6**	2½d. on 2d. green	14·00	12·00
17	**5**	5d. on 4d. orange	4·00	6·50
18	**6**	7½d. on 8d. carmine	24·00	75·00
		(*b*) *In black. P* 12×11½ (Nov)		
19	**5**	½d. on 1d. dull blue	45·00	48·00
20	**6**	2½d. on 2d. green	17·00	17·00
		a. Surch double	—	£1500
		b. Fraction bar completely omitted (R. 3/3)		

King George II, 1893–1918

SURCHARGE. HALF-PENNY (11)   SURCHARGE, 2½d. (12)   HALF-PEI Small "F" in "HALF"

(Surch at the *Star* Office, Auckland, N.Z.)

1894 (June–Nov). *Surch with T* **11** *or* **12**.

No.	Type	Description	Unused	Used
21	**5**	½d. on 4d. chestnut (B.) (Nov)	1·75	7·00
		a. "SURCHARCE"	9·00	20·00
		b. Small "F"	9·00	20·00
22	**6**	½d. on 1s. brown	1·75	11·00
		a. "SURCHARCE"	10·00	38·00
		b. Small "F"	10·00	38·00
		c. Surch double	£275	
		d. Surch double with "SURCHARCE"	£900	
23		2½d. on 8d. bright mauve	5·00	8·00
		a. No stop after "SURCHARGE"	32·00	55·00
24		2½d. on 1s. deep green (No. 4*a*) (Nov)	50·00	22·00
		a. No stop after "SURCHARGE"	£160	
		b. Perf 12×11½	15·00	32·00
		ba. No stop after "SURCHARGE"	55·00	

Nos. 21/4 were surcharged in panes of 60 (6×10) with No. 21a occurring on R. 2/6, 4/6, 5/6, 8/6 and 10/6, No. 21b on R. 1/4, 3/4, 6/4, 7/4 and 9/4, No. 22a on R. 1/6, 3/6, 5/6, 8/6 and 10/6, No. 22b on R. 2/4, 4/4, 6/4, 7/4 and 9/4 (both after the setting had been rearranged), No. 23a on R. 3/1–3 and Nos. 24a and 24ba on R. 6/3 and R. 7/3 or R. 7/1–2.

Sheets used for these provisionals were surcharged with the remains of the tissue interleaving still in place. This sometimes subsequently fell away taking parts of the surcharge with it.

Deformed "E" in "PENI" (R. 2/2)

(Design resembling No. 11 litho and surch at *Star* Office Auckland, N.Z.)

1895 (22 May*). *As T* **6** *surch as T* **11** *and* **12**. *No wmk. P* 12.

No.	Type	Description	Unused	Used
25	**11**	1d. on 2d. pale blue (C.)	42·00	22·00
		a. Deformed "E"		
26	**12**	1½d. on 2d. pale blue (C.)	60·00	27·00
		a. Deformed "E"		
		b. Perf 12×11	42·00	27·00
		ba. Deformed "E"		
27		2½d. on 2d. pale blue (C.)†	40·00	45·00
		a. No stop after "SURCHARGE"	£225	£225
		b. Deformed "E"		
28		7½d. on 2d. pale blue (C.)	£375	
		a. Deformed "E"		
		b. Perf 12×11	60·00	45·00
		ba. Deformed "E"		

* Earliest known date of use.

†The 2½d. on 2d. is the only value which normally has a stop after the word "SURCHARGE".

No. 27a occurs on R.1/3 of the right-hand pane.

12*a* King George II

13 King George II

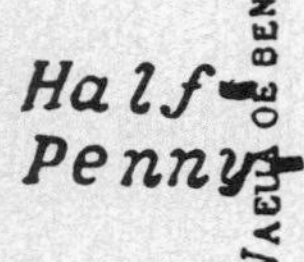

(14)

"BU" joined (R. 1/1)

Missing eyebrow (R.2/4)

"7" for "1" in "½d." (R. 2/1)

1895 (20 June*). *Unissued stamp surch as in T* **12a**. *No wmk. P* 12.

No.	Type	Description	Unused	Used
29	**11**	½d. on 2½d. vermilion	30·00	32·00
		a. "BU" joined	75·00	
		b. "SURCHARCE"	70·00	
		c. Missing eyebrow	75·00	
		d. Stop after "POSTAGE" (R. 2/5)	75·00	
		e. "7" for "1" in "½d."		
30		1d. on 2½d. vermilion	50·00	32·00
		a. "BU" joined	95·00	
		c. Missing eyebrow	95·00	
		d. Stop after "POSTAGE" (R. 2/5)	95·00	
		e. "7" for "1" in "½d."		
31	**12**	7½d. on 2½d. vermilion	50·00	50·00
		a. "BU" joined	95·00	
		c. Missing eyebrow	95·00	
		d. Stop after "POSTAGE" (R. 2/5)	95·00	
		e. "7" for "1" in "½d."		

*Earliest known date of use.

No. 29b occurs on R. 1/6 and 3/6 of both the right and the left pane.

In the ½d. surcharge there is a stop after "SURCHARGE" and not after "PENNY". In the 1d. and 7½d. the stop is after the value only.

"Black Eye" flaw (Rt pane R. 2/4)

(Litho *Star* Office, Auckland, N.Z.)

1895 (9 July–Sept). *No wmk. P* 12.

No.	Type	Description	Unused	Used
32	**13**	1d. olive-green	15·00	26·00
		a. Bisected diagonally (½d.) (on cover) (9.95)	†	£750
		b. Imperf between (horiz pair)	—	£6000
33		2½d. rose	20·00	20·00
		a. Stop (flaw) after "POSTAGE" (R. 4/5)	60·00	60·00
34		5d. blue	18·00	48·00
		a. "Black eye" flaw		
		b. Perf 12×11	20·00	48·00
		ba. "Black eye" flaw		
		c. Perf 11	£325	
		ca. "Black eye" flaw		
35		7½d. orange-yellow	26·00	42·00
		a. Yellow	26·00	42·00

1896 (May). *Nos.* 26a *and* 28a *with typewritten surcharge* "Half-Penny-", *in violet, and Tongan surcharge, in black, as T* **14**.

A. *Tongan surch reading downwards* (*right panes*)
B. *Tongan surch reading upwards* (*left panes*)

No.	Type	Description	A		B	
36	**6**	½d. on 1½d. on 2d.	£400	—	£375	£375
		a. Perf 12	£375	£375	£400	£400
		ab. "Haalf"	†		£1700	—
		c. "H" double	†		—	—
		d. Tongan surch omitted	†		£3750	—
		e. "Halef"	£4250	—	†	
37		½d. on 7½d. on 2d.	75·00	£100	75·00	£100
		a. "Hafl" for "Half"	£1300	£1400	†	
		b. "Hafl" ("Penny" omitted)	£2750	—	†	
		c. "PPenny"	£600	—	†	
		d. Stops instead of hyphens	£800	—	£850	—
		e. "Halyf"	—	—	†	
		f. "Half-penny-" inverted	£1700	—	£2250	—
		g. No hyphen after "Penny"	—	—	†	
		h. "Hwlf"	†		—	—
		i. No hyphen after "Half"	†		£800	—
		j. "Penny" double	†		—	—
		k. "Penny" twice, with "Half" on top of upper "Penny"	†		£3000	—
		l. Capital "P" over small "p"	—	—	†	
		m. "Half-H"	†		£700	—
		n. Tongan surch double	†		£1100	—
		o. Two hyphens between "Half" and "Penny"	†		—	—
		p. Perf 12	£650	—	£650	—
		pa. No hyphen after "Half"	—	—	†	

Nos. 26a and 28a were in sheets of 48 (2 panes 6×4). The panes were separated before the surcharges were applied.

There are variations in the relative positions of the words "Half" and "Penny", both vertically and horizontally.

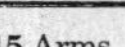

15 Arms

16 Ovava Tree, Kana-Kubolu

17 King George II

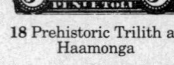

18 Prehistoric Trilith at Haamonga

19 Bread Fruit

20 Coral

21 View of Haapai

22 Red Shining Parrot

23 View of Vavau Harbour

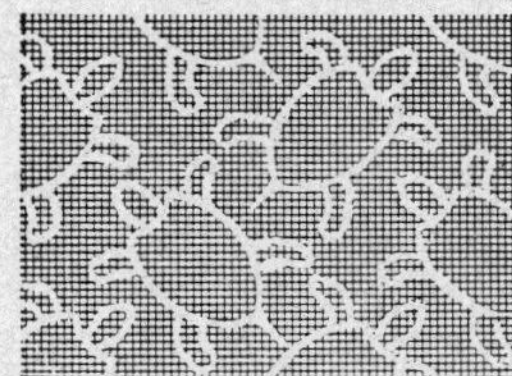

24 Tortoises (*upright*)

Types of 2d.:

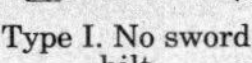

Type I. No sword hilt

Type II. Top of hilt showing

Normal

Lopped branch (R. 8/5) (ptgs from 1934 onwards)

Normal

Small "2" (R. 1/2, 1/4–5, 2/8, 4/4, 5/4 and 6/1)

Normal

Both "O"'s small in "HOGOFULU" (R. 1/7)

Small second "O" in "HOGOFULU" (R. 2/7)

WATERMARKS. Stamps with W 24 upright show all the tortoise heads pointing upwards, or downwards if inverted. On stamps with sideways watermark the heads point upwards or downwards alternately.

(Recess D.L.R.)

1897 (1 June). *W* **24**. *P* 14.

38 **15** ½d. indigo .. .. 3·25 2·75
a. Wmk sideways .. .. 70 2·25
39 **16** 1d. black and scarlet 80 80
a. Wmk sideways .. .. 4·50 3·00
b. Lopped branch .. .. 32·00
40 **17** 2d. sepia and bistre (I) .. .. .. 12·00 5·50
a. Wmk sideways .. .. 12·00 3·50
b. Small "2" .. .. 35·00 15·00
41 2d. sepia and bistre (II) .. .. .. 75·00 9·00
a. Wmk sideways .. .. 50·00 9·00
b. Small "2" .. .. £120 25·00
42 2d. grey and bistre (II) .. .. .. 24·00 3·25
a. Wmk sideways .. .. 13·00 3·00
b. Small "2" .. .. 32·00 5·50
43 2½d. black and blue .. .. .. 6·00 1·25
a. No fraction bar in "½" (R. 2/10) .. 95·00 85·00
b. Wmk sideways .. .. 3·50 1·40
ba. No fraction bar in "½" (R. 2/10) 60·00 60·00
44 **18** 3d. black and yellow-green .. .. 3·50 5·50
a. Wmk sideways .. .. 2·50 5·00
45 **19** 4d. green and purple .. .. .. 3·75 4·00
a. Wmk sideways .. .. 4·00 4·50
46 **17** 5d. black and orange .. .. .. 30·00 12·00
a. Wmk sideways .. .. ..
47 **20** 6d. red .. .. 13·00 4·50
a. Wmk sideways .. .. 8·50 3·75
48 **17** 7½d. black and green .. .. .. 14·00 23·00
a. Centre inverted £3750
49 10d. black and lake .. .. .. 40·00 40·00
a. Wmk sideways .. .. ..
b. Both "O"'s small .. .. ..
c. Small second "O" £225 £225
50 1s. black and red-brown .. .. .. 14·00 7·50
a. No hyphen before "TAHA" (R. 3/5) £140 £140
b. Wmk sideways .. .. ..
51 **21** 2s. black and ultramarine .. .. 60·00 65·00
a. Wmk sideways .. .. .. 19·00 26·00
52 **22** 2s. 6d. deep purple .. .. .. 48·00 30·00
a. Wmk sideways .. .. .. 65·00 48·00
53 **23** 5s. black and brown-red .. .. .. 45·00 42·00
a. Wmk sideways .. .. .. 26·00 32·00
38a/53a .. .. *Set of* 14 £200 £170

The 1d., 3d. and 4d. are known bisected and used for half their value.

T - L

1 June, 1899.

(25)

26 Queen Salote

1899 (1 June). *Royal Wedding. No. 39a optd with T* **25** *at "Star" Office, Auckland, N.Z.*

54 **16** 1d. black and scarlet (hyphen 2 mm long) 27·00 55·00
a. "1889" for "1899" (R. 8/1, 8/4) .. £200 £350
b. Hyphen 3 mm long .. .. .. 38·00 75·00
c. Wmk upright .. .. .. 50·00 85·00
ca. "1889" for "1899" (R. 8/1, 8/4) .. £375 £500
cb. Hyphen 3 mm long .. .. .. 75·00 £130

The letters "T L" stand for Taufa'ahau, the King's family name, and Lavinia, the bride.

No. 54 was overprinted from a setting of 30 (3×10) applied twice to the sheets of 60. The setting contains twenty-one examples of the 2 mm hyphen and nine of the 3 mm.

Queen Salote, 1918–65

Dies of the 2d.:

Die I (As used for 1897 issue)

Die II

Normal

"2½" recut (note lines on "2" and different "½") (R. 1/1)

Retouched (small) hyphen (R. 3/5)

(Recess D.L.R.)

1920 (Apr)–**37**. *W* **24** (*sideways*). *P* 14.

55 **15** ½d. yellow-green (1934) .. .. 80 1·25
a. Wmk upright .. .. .. 13·00 17·00
56 **26** 1½d. grey-black (1935) .. .. 30 2·50
57 2d. agate and aniline violet (Die I) .. 7·00 13·00
a. Wmk upright .. .. .. 15·00 32·00
b. Small "2" .. .. .. 60·00
c. Black and slate-violet (1924) .. 6·50 2·00
ca. Wmk upright .. .. ..
cb. Small "2" .. .. .. 55·00
d. Black and deep purple (1925) ..
db. Small "2" .. .. ..
57*e* 2d. black & blackish lilac (Die II) (1937) 4·00 4·75
58 2½d. black and blue (3.21) .. .. 4·50 30·00
59 2½d. bright ultramarine (1934) .. 1·75 60
a. Recut "2½" .. .. .. 18·00 8·50
60 5d. black and orange-vermilion (1922) 3·25 4·50
61 7½d. black and yellow-green (1922) .. 1·75 1·75
62 10d. black and lake (1922) .. .. 2·50 4·75
a. Both "O"'s small .. .. ..
b. Small second "O" .. .. 28·00 45·00
c. Black and aniline carmine (9.25) ..
ca. Both "O"'s small .. .. ..
cb. Small second "O" .. .. ..
63 1s. black and red-brown (1922) .. 1·25 2·25
a. Retouched (small) hyphen .. ..
b. Wmk upright .. .. .. 18·00 18·00
ba. Retouched (small) hyphen .. ..
55/63 .. .. .. *Set of* 10 24·00 50·00
55/63 Optd/Perf "Specimen" *Set of* 9 £180

In Die II the ball of the "2" is larger and the word "PENI-E-UA" is re-engraved and slightly shorter; the "U" has a spur on the left side.

For illustration of No. 62a see above No. 38.

TWO PENCE

PENI-E-UA

(27)

TWO PENCE

PENI-E-UA

(28)

1923 (20 Oct)–**24**. *Nos. 46, 48/9, 50, 51/2 and 53a surch as T* **27** (*vert stamps*) *or* **28** (*horiz stamps*).

64 **17** 2d. on 5d. black and orange (B.) .. 85 85
a. Wmk sideways .. .. .. 4·50 4·50
65 2d. on 7½d. black and green (B.) .. 13·00 20·00
a. Wmk sideways .. .. .. 38·00 48·00
66 2d. on 10d. black and lake (B.) .. 5·50 42·00
a. Wmk sideways .. .. .. 26·00 70·00
b. Both "O"'s small .. .. ..
c. Small second "O" .. .. 60·00
67 2d. on 1s. black and red-brown (B.) .. 38·00 22·00
a. No hyphen before "TAHA" (R. 3/5) £275
b. Wmk sideways .. .. .. 60·00 55·00
68 **21** 2d. on 2s. black and ultramarine (R.) .. 13·00 14·00
a. Wmk sideways .. .. .. 7·50 4·50
69 **22** 2d. on 2s. 6d. deep purple (R.) .. 25·00 6·50
a. Wmk sideways .. .. .. 90·00 50·00
70 **23** 2d. on 5s. black and brown-red (R.) .. 9·00 9·50
a. Wmk sideways .. .. .. 2·75 2·50
64/70a .. .. *Set of* 7 80·00 90·00

29 Queen Salote

(Recess D.L.R.)

1938 (12 Oct). *20th Anniv of Queen Salote's Accession. Tablet at foot dated "1918–1938". W* **24** (*sideways*). *P* 13½.

71 **29** 1d. black and scarlet .. .. .. 55 3·00
72 2d. black and purple .. .. .. 5·50 2·25
73 2½d. black and ultramarine .. .. 5·50 3·00
71/3 .. .. *Set of* 3 10·50 7·50
71/3 Perf "Specimen" .. .. *Set of* 3 65·00

For Silver Jubilee issue in a similar design, see Nos. 83/87.

Further die of 2d.:

Die III

(Recess D.L.R.)

1942–49. *Wmk Mult Crown CA* (*sideways on* 5s.). *P* 14.

74 **15** ½d. yellow-green .. .. .. 15 1·75
75 **16** 1d. black and scarlet .. .. .. 90 1·75
a. Lopped branch .. .. .. 22·00
76 **26** 2d. black and purple (Die II) .. .. 2·50 1·50
a. Die III (4.49) .. .. .. 3·75 7·00
77 2½d. bright ultramarine .. .. .. 80 1·00
a. Recut "2½" .. .. .. 20·00
78 **18** 3d. black and yellow-green .. .. 30 1·75
79 **20** 6d. red .. .. 1·75 1·75
80 **26** 1s. black and red-brown .. .. 1·50 2·50
a. Retouched (small) hyphen .. ..
81 **22** 2s. 6d. deep purple (1943) .. .. 23·00 20·00
82 **23** 5s. black and brown-red (1943) .. 16·00 40·00
74/82 .. .. *Set of* 9 42·00 65·00
74/82 Perf "Specimen" .. .. *Set of* 9 £170

In Die III the foot of the "2" is longer than in Die II and extends towards the right beyond the curve of the loop; the letters of "PENI-E-UA" are taller and differently shaped.

Damage to the "2" on R. 4/9 of No. 77 was frequently corrected by hand-painting.

For illustration of No. 75a see above No. 38 and of No. 77a see above No. 55.

PRICES OF SETS

Set prices are given for many issues, generally those containing three stamps or more. Definitive sets include one of each value or major colour change, but do not cover different perforations, die types or minor shades. Where a choice is possible the set prices are based on the cheapest versions of the stamps included in the listings.

UANIMA TA'U 'OE PULE 'A 'ENE 'AFIO 1918-1943

30

(Recess D.L.R.)

1944 (25 Jan). *Silver Jubilee of Queen Salote's Accession. As T* **29**, *but inscr* "1918–1943" *at foot, as T* **30**. *Wmk Mult Script CA. P* 14.

83	1d. black and carmine	15	60
84	2d. black and purple	15	60
85	3d. black and green	15	60
86	6d. black and orange	45	1·10
87	1s. black and brown	45	1·10
83/7	*Set of* 5	1·25	3·50
83/7 Perf "Specimen"	*Set of* 5	70·00	

1949 (10 Oct). *75th Anniv of U.P.U. As Nos. 145/8 of Jamaica.*

88	2½d. ultramarine	40	40
89	3d. olive	1·25	2·25
90	6d. carmine-red	50	30
91	1s. red-brown	50	35
88/91	*Set of* 4	2·40	3·00

31 Queen Salote 33

32 Queen Salote

(Photo Waterlow)

1950 (1 Nov). *Queen Salote's Fiftieth Birthday. Wmk Mult Script CA. P* 12½.

92	**31**	1d. carmine	40	1·25
93	**32**	5d. green	40	1·25
94	**33**	1s. violet	40	1·75
92/4		*Set of* 3	1·10	3·75

34 Map 35 Palace, Nuku'alofa

(Recess Waterlow)

1951 (2 July). *50th Anniv of Treaty of Friendship between Great Britain and Tonga. T* **34/5** *and similar designs. Wmk Mult Script CA. P* 12½ (3d.), 13 × 13½ (½d.), 13½ × 13 (*others*).

95	½d. green	20	1·75
96	1d. black and carmine	15	1·25
97	2½d. green and brown	30	1·75
98	3d. yellow and bright blue	1·25	1·75
99	5d. carmine and green	75	70
100	1s. yellow-orange and violet	75	70
95/100	*Set of* 6	3·00	7·00

Designs: *Horiz*—2½d. Beach scene; 5d. Flag; 1s. Arms of Tonga and G.B. *Vert*—3d. H.M.N.Z.S. *Bellona*.

40 Royal Palace, Nuku'alofa 43 Swallows' Cave, Vava'u

52 Queen Salote 53 Arms of Tonga

(Des J. Berry. Centre litho, frame recess (£1), recess (others) B.W.)

1953 (1 July). *T* **40**, **43**, **52/3** *and similar designs. W* **24** (*sideways*). *P* 11×11½ (*vert*) *or* 11½×11 (*horiz*).

101	1d. black and red-brown	10	10
102	1½d. blue and emerald	10	10
103	2d. deep turquoise-green and black	75	20
104	3d. blue and deep bluish green	40	20
105	3½d. yellow and carmine-red	40	70
106	4d. yellow and deep rose-carmine	65	10
107	5d. blue and red-brown	40	10
108	6d. black and deep blue	40	30
109	8d. emerald and deep reddish violet	90	40
110	1s. blue and black	60	10
111	2s. sage-green and brown	3·00	60
112	5s. orange-yellow and slate-lilac	24·00	6·50
113	10s. yellow and black	5·50	6·50
114	£1 yellow, scarlet, ultramarine & dp brt bl	8·00	6·50
101/14	*Set of* 14	40·00	20·00

Designs: *Horiz* (*as T* **40**)—1½d. Shore fishing with throw-net; 2d. *Hifofua* and *Aoniu* (ketches); 3½d. Map of Tongatapu; 4d. Vava'u Harbour; 5d. Post Office, Nuku'alofa; 6d. Aerodrome, Fua'amotu; 8d. *Matua* (inter-island freighter) at Nuku'alofa wharf; 2s. Lifuka, Ha'apai; 5s. Mutiny on the *Bounty*. *Vert* (*as T* **43**)—1s. Map of Tonga Islands.

54 Stamp of 1886 55 Whaling Ship and Whaleboat

(Des D. Bakeley. Photo Harrison)

1961 (1 Dec). *75th Anniv of Tongan Postal Service. T* **54/5** *and similar horiz designs. W* **24** (*sideways*). *P* 14½×13½.

115	1d. carmine and brown-orange	10	10
116	2d. ultramarine	60	25
117	4d. blue-green	15	25
118	5d. violet	60	25
119	1s. red-brown	60	25
115/19	*Set of* 5	1·75	1·00

Designs:—4d. Queen Salote and Post Office, Nuku'alofa; 5d. *Aoniu II* (inter-island freighter); 1s. Douglas DC-4 mailplane over Tongatapu.

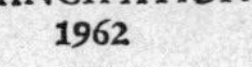

(59)

60 "Protein Foods"

1962 (7 Feb). *Centenary of Emancipation. Nos.* 101, 104, 107/10, 112, 117 *optd with T* **59** (*No.* 126 *surch also*), *in red, by R. S. Wallbank, Govt Printer.*

120	1d. black and red-brown	10	30
121	4d. blue-green	10	40
122	5d. blue and red-brown	15	40
123	6d. black and deep blue	20	50
124	8d. emerald and deep reddish violet	40	80
125	1s. blue and black	20	50
	a. Opt inverted	£375	£190
126	2s. on 3d. blue and deep bluish green	40	2·50
	a. Missing fraction-bar in surch	10·00	
127	5s. orange-yellow and slate-lilac	5·50	2·75
	a. Opt inverted	£180	£275
120/127	*Set of* 8	6·00	7·25

(Des M. Goaman. Photo Harrison)

1963 (4 June). *Freedom from Hunger. W* **24**. *P* 14 × 14½.

128	**60**	11d. ultramarine	50	15

61 Coat of Arms

62 Queen Salote

63 Queen Salote

(Des Ida West. Die-cut Walsall)

1963 (17 June). *First Polynesian Gold Coinage Commemoration. Circular designs. Embossed on gold foil, backed with paper, inscr overall* "TONGA THE FRIENDLY ISLANDS". *Imperf.*

(*a*) *Postage*. ¼ *koula coin. Diameter* 1⅝ *in.*

129	**61**	1d. carmine	10	10
130	**62**	2d. deep blue	10	10
131	**61**	6d. blue-green	15	15
132	**62**	9d. bright purple	15	15
133	**61**	1s. 6d. violet	25	25
134	**62**	2s. light emerald	30	30

(*b*) *Air*. (i) ½ *koula coin. Diam* 2⅛ *in.*

135	**63**	10d. carmine	20	20
136	**61**	11d. blue-green	20	20
137	**63**	1s. 1d. deep blue	20	20

(ii) 1 *koula coin. Diam* 3⅛ *in.*

138	**63**	2s. 1d. bright purple	35	30
139	**61**	2s. 4d. light emerald	40	35
140	**63**	2s. 9d. violet	40	40
129/140 *and* O17		*Set of* 13	6·50	8·00

Examples of a 9d. Postage value in the design of the 1s. 6d. exists, but these have been identified as proofs.

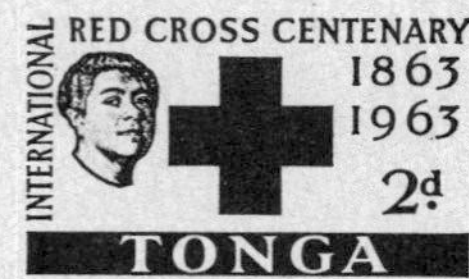

64 Red Cross Emblem

(Des V. Whiteley. Litho B.W.)

1963 (7 Oct). *Red Cross Centenary. W* **24** (*sideways*). *P* 13½.

141	**64**	2d. red and black	25	10
142		11d. red and blue	50	90

65 Queen Salote

66 Map of Tongatapu

(Des M. Meers. Die-cut Walsall)

1964 (19 Oct). *Pan-Pacific South-East Asia Women's Association Meeting, Nuku'alofa. Embossed on gold foil, backed with paper inscr overall* "TONGA THE FRIENDLY ISLANDS". *Imperf.*

(*a*) *Postage*

143	**65**	3d. pink	15	15
144		9d. light blue	20	20
145		2s. yellow-green	35	35
146		5s. lilac	65	65

(*b*) *Air*

147	**66**	10d. blue-green	20	15
148		1s. 2d. black	30	25
149		3s. 6d. cerise	50	50
150		6s. 6d. violet	85	95
143/150		*Set of* 8	2·75	2·75

(67)

1965 (18 Mar). *"Gold Coin" stamps of* 1963 *surch as T* **67** *by Walsall Lithographic Co. New figures of value in gold; obliterating colours shown in brackets.* (*a*) *Postage.*

151	**61**	1s. 3d. on 1s. 6d. violet (R.)	15	15
152	**62**	1s. 9d. on 9d. bright purple (W.)	15	20
153	**61**	2s. 6d. on 6d. blue-green (R.)	20	35
154		5s. on 1d. carmine	14·00	17·00
155	**62**	5s. on 2d. deep blue	2·50	3·25
156		5s. on 2s. light emerald	60	75
		(*b*) *Air*		
157	**63**	2s. 3d. on 10d. carmine	15	25
158	**61**	2s. 9d. on 11d. blue-green (W.)	20	35
159	**63**	4s. 6d. on 2s. 1d. bright purple (R.)	10·00	13·00
160	**61**	4s. 6d. on 2s. 4d. light emerald (R.)	10·00	13·00
161	**63**	4s. 6d. on 2s. 9d. violet (R.)	7·00	8·00
151/161 *and* O18		*Set of* 12	42·00	55·00

King Taufa'ahau IV, 16 December 1965

1866-1966
TUPOU COLLEGE
& SECONDARY
EDUCATION

(68)

AIRMAIL
1866 CENTENARY 1966
TUPOU COLLEGE
&
SECONDARY EDUCATION
10d **XX**

(69)

OU COLLE
&
ARY EDUC

Misplaced "&" (R. 5/5)

1966 (18 June). *Centenary of Tupou College and Secondary Education. Nos.* 115/16 *and* 118/19 *optd or surch.* (*a*) *Postage. As T* **68**.

162	1d. carmine and brown-orange (P.)	10	10
163	3d. on 1d. carmine and brown-orange (P.)	10	10
	a. Misplaced "3d" (R.2/5)	2·25	
	b. Surch inverted	†	—
164	6d. on 2d. ultramarine (R.)	10	10
165	1s. 2d. on 2d. ultramarine (R.)	20	10
166	2s. on 2d. ultramarine (R.)	40	10
167	3s. on 2d. ultramarine (R.)	40	15
	(*b*) *Air. As T* **69**		
168	5d. violet	10	10
	b. Misplaced "&"	2·25	
169	10d. on 1d. carmine and brown-orange	10	10
	b. Misplaced "&"	2·50	
170	1s. red-brown	10	10
	b. Misplaced "&"	2·50	
171	2s. 9d. on 2d. ultramarine	40	15
	a. Sideways second "X" (R.3/4)	7·50	
	b. Misplaced "&"	5·50	
172	3s. 6d. on 5d. violet	45	15
	a. Sideways second "X" (R.3/4)	7·50	
	b. Misplaced "&"	5·50	
173	4s. 6d. on 1s. red-brown	50	15
	a. Sideways second "X" (R.3/4)	7·50	
	b. Misplaced "&"	5·50	
162/173 and O19/20	*Set of* 14	4·00	1·75

On No. 163a the "d" is 20 mm from the "X" instead of the normal 22 mm.

(70)

(71)

1966 (16 Dec). *Queen Salote Commemoration. Nos.* 143/4 *and* 147/8 *optd as T* **70/1**, *or surch also, by Walsall Lithographic Co. Inscriptions and new figures of value in first colour and obliterating shapes in second colour given.*

		(*a*) *Postage. Optd as T* **70**		
174	**65**	3d. (silver and ultramarine)	10	10
175		5d. on 9d. (silver and black)	15	10
176		9d. (silver and black)	20	10
177		1s. 7d. on 3d. (silver and ultramarine)	40	40
178		3s. 6d. on 9d. (silver and black)	60	60
179		6s. 6d. on 3d. (silver and ultramarine)	1·00	1·10
		(*b*) *Air. Optd as T* **71**		
180	**66**	10d. (silver and black)	20	10
181		1s. 2d. (black and gold)	25	20
182		4s. on 10d. (silver and black)	70	60
183		5s. 6d. on 1s. 2d. (black and gold)	90	90
184		10s. 6d. on 1s. 2d. (gold and black)	1·25	1·50
174/184		*Set of* 11	5·00	5·00

(New Currency. 100 seniti = 1 pa'anga)

10
Seniti
10

1 SENITI 1

(72) **(73)**

1967 (25 Mar). *Decimal currency. Various stamps surch as T* **72/3**.

185	1 s. on 1d. (No. 101)	10	10
186	2 s. on 4d. (No. 106)	20	10
187	3 s. on 5d. (No. 107)	10	10
188	4 s. on 5d. (No. 107)	30	30
189	5 s. on 3½d. (No. 105)	10	10
190	6 s. on 8d. (No. 109)	30	10
191	7 s. on 1½d. (No. 102)	10	10
192	8 s. on 6d. (No. 108)	30	10
193	9 s. on 3d. (No. 104)	15	15
194	10 s. on 1s. (No. 110)	15	15
195	11 s. on 3d. on 1d. (No. 163)	30	20
	a. Misplaced "3d" (R. 2/5)	5·00	
196	21 s. on 3s. on 2d. (No. 167)	25	35
197	23 s. on 1d. (No. 101)	25	35
198	30 s. on 2s. (No. 111)* (R.)	2·25	2·50
199	30 s. on 2s. (No. 111)* (R.)	2·50	3·00
200	50 s. on 6d. (No. 108) (R.)	1·25	1·75
201	60 s. on 2d. (No. 103) (R.)	1·50	2·00
185/201 and O21	*Set of* 18	12·00	12·00

The above surcharges come in a variety of types and sizes.
*No. 198 has the surcharged value expressed horizontally; No. 199 has the figures "30" above and below "SENITI".

74 Coat of Arms (reverse)

75 King Taufa'ahau IV (obverse)

(Die-cut Walsall)

1967 (4 July). *Coronation of King Taufa'ahau IV. Circular designs. Embossed on palladium foil, backed with paper inscr overall* "The Friendly Islands Tonga", *etc. Imperf.*

Sizes

(*a*) *Diameter* 1½ *in.*	(*d*) *Diameter* $2\frac{3}{10}$ *in.*
(*b*) *Diameter* $1\frac{7}{10}$ *in.*	(*e*) *Diameter* $2\frac{7}{10}$ *in.*
(*c*) *Diameter* 2 *in.*	(*f*) *Diameter* $2\frac{9}{10}$ *in.*

		(*a*) *Postage*		
202	**74**	1 s. orange and greenish blue (*b*)	10	10
203	**75**	2 s. greenish blue and deep magenta (*c*)	10	10
204	**74**	4 s. emerald and bright purple (*d*)	10	10
205	**75**	15 s. turquoise and violet (*e*)	30	25
206	**74**	28 s. black and bright purple (*a*)	70	60
207	**75**	50 s. carmine-red and ultramarine (*c*)	1·00	1·00
208	**74**	1 p. blue and carmine (*f*)	1·75	2·00
		(*b*) *Air*		
209	**75**	7 s. carmine-red and black (*b*)	15	10
210	**74**	9 s. brown-purple and emerald (*c*)	15	10
211	**75**	11 s. greenish blue and orange (*d*)	20	15
212	**74**	21 s. black and emerald (*e*)	40	30
213	**75**	23 s. bright purple and light emerald (*a*)	55	45
214	**74**	29 s. ultramarine and emerald (*c*)	70	60
215	**75**	2 p. bright purple and orange (*f*)	2·50	2·75
202/15		*Set of* 14	7·75	7·50

The commemorative coins depicted in reverse (Type **74**) are inscribed in various denominations as follows: 1 s.—"20 SENITI"; 4 s.—"PA'ANGA"; 9 s.—"50 SENITI"; 21 s.—"TWO PA'ANGA"; 28 s.—"QUARTER HAU"; 29 s.—"HALF HAU"; 1 p. "HAU".

The
Friendly Islands
welcome the
United States
Peace Corps

S

(76)

1967 (15 Dec). *Arrival of U.S. Peace Corps in Tonga. As Nos.* 101/14, *but imperf in different colours and surch as T* **76**.

	(*a*) *Postage.*		
216	1 s. on 1d. black and orange-yellow	10	10
217	2 s. on 2d. ultramarine and carmine-red	10	10
218	3 s. on 3d. chestnut and yellow	10	10
219	4 s. on 4d. reddish violet and yellow	10	10
220	5 s. on 5d. green and yellow	10	10
221	10 s. on 1s. carmine-red and yellow	10	10
222	20 s. on 2s. claret and new blue	20	15
223	50 s. on 5s. sepia and orange-yellow	75	35
224	1 p. on 10s. orange-yellow	70	55
	(*b*) *Air*		
225	11 s. on 3½d. ultramarine (R.)	15	10
226	21 s. on 1½d. emerald	30	20
227	23 s. on 3½d. ultramarine	30	20
216/27 *and* O26/8	*Set of* 15	4·25	3·00

On Nos. 219 and 224 the opt is smaller, and in four lines instead of five. On Nos. 216/20 the surcharge takes the form of an alteration to the currency name as in T **76**.

10
SENITI
10

2 SENITI 2

(77) **(78)**

1968 (6 Apr). *Various stamps surch as T* **77/8**.

	(*a*) *Postage*		
228	1 s. on 1d. (No. 101) (R.)	10	10
229	2 s. on 4d. (No. 106)	10	10
230	3 s. on 3d. (No. 104) (B.)	10	10
231	4 s. on 5d. (No. 107) (R.)	10	10
232	5 s. on 2d. (No. 103) (R.)	10	10
233	6 s. on 6d. (No. 108) (R.)	10	10
234	7 s. on 1½d. (No. 102) (R.)	10	15
235	8 s. on 8d. (No. 109) (R.)	10	15
236	9 s. on 3½d. (No. 105)	20	20
237	10 s. on 1s. (No. 110) (R.)	20	20
238	20 s. on 5s. (No. 112) (R.)	90	40
239	2 p. on 2s. (No. 111) (R.)	1·50	2·00
	(*b*) *Air. Surch as T* **78** *with* "AIRMAIL" *added*		
240	11 s. on 10s. (No. 113) (R.)	25	25
241	21 s. on 10s. (No. 113) (R.)	40	40
242	23 s. on 10s. (No. 113) (R.)	40	40
228/42 *and* O22/5	*Set of* 19	7·00	7·50

H M'S BIRTHDAY
4 JULY 1968

(79)

Friendly Islands
Field & Track Trials
South Pacific Games
Port Moresby
1969

S

(80)

1968 (4 July). 50*th Birthday of King Taufa'ahua IV. Nos.* 202/15 *optd as T* **79**. (*a*) *Postage.*

243	**74**	1 s. orange and greenish blue (*b*) (R.)	10	10
244	**75**	2 s. greenish blue & dp magenta (*b*) (B.)	10	10
245	**74**	4 s. emerald and bright purple (*d*) (R.)	15	10
246	**75**	15 s. turquoise and violet (*e*) (B.)	40	15
247	**74**	28 s. black and bright purple (*a*) (R.)	80	30
248	**75**	50 s. carmine-red and ultramarine (*c*) (B.)	1·40	80
249	**74**	1 p. blue and carmine (*f*) (R.)	2·75	2·25
		(*b*) *Air*		
250	**75**	7 s. carmine-red and black (*b*) (B.)	20	10
251	**74**	9 s. brown-purple and emerald (*c*) (R.)	25	10
252	**75**	11 s. greenish blue and orange (*d*) (B.)	30	10
253	**74**	21 s. black and emerald (*e*) (R.)	65	25
		a. Opt (gold only) double	£275	
254	**75**	23 s. bright purple & lt emerald (*a*) (B.)	65	25
255	**74**	29 s. ultramarine and emerald (*c*) (R.)	85	35
256	**75**	2 p. bright purple and orange (*f*) (B.)	4·75	4·00
243/56 *and* O29/32		*Set of* 18	21·00	16·00

The overprints vary in size, but are all crescent-shaped as Type **79** and inscribed "H.M'S BIRTHDAY 4 JULY 1968" (Type **79**) or "HIS MAJESTY'S 50th BIRTHDAY" (others).

1968 (19 Dec). *South Pacific Games Field and Track Trials, Port Moresby, Papua New Guinea. Nos.* 101/13, *but imperf, in different colours and surch as T* **80**. (*a*) *Postage.*

257	5 s. on 5d. green and yellow (R.)	10	10
258	10 s. on 1s. carmine-red and yellow	10	10
259	15 s. on 2s. claret and new blue	15	15
260	25 s. on 2d. ultramarine and carmine-red	20	15
261	50 s. on 1d. black and orange-yellow	35	35
262	75 s. on 10s. orange-yellow (G.)	60	50
	(*b*) *Air*		
263	6 s. on 6d. black and yellow*	10	10
264	7 s. on 4d. reddish violet and yellow	10	10
265	8 s. on 8d. black and greenish yellow	10	10
	a. Surch 11½ mm as on 6d.	£160	£100
266	9 s. on 1½d. emerald	10	10
267	11 s. on 3d. chestnut and yellow	15	10
268	21 s. on 3½d. ultramarine	20	15
269	38 s. on 5s. sepia and orange-yellow	50	30
270	1 p. on 10s. orange-yellow	70	50
257/70 *and* O33/4	*Set of* 16	3·50	3·00

*On No. 263 the surcharge is smaller (11½ mm wide).

1s (81) 1s (82)

1969. *Emergency Provisionals. Various stamps (Nos. 273/6 are imperf and in different colours) surch as T* **81** *or* **82**. *(a) Postage.*

No.		Description		
271		1 s. on 1s. 2d. on 2d. ultramarine (No. 165)	1·50	1·75
272		1 s. on 2s. on 2d. ultramarine (No. 166) ..	1·50	1·75
273		1 s. on 6d. black and yellow (as No. 108)	50	50
274		2 s. on 3½d. ultramarine (as No. 105) ..	55	50
275		3 s. on 1½d. emerald (as No. 102) ..	55	50
276		4 s. on 8d. blk & greenish yell (as No. 109)	80	80
		(b) Air. Nos. 171/3 surch with T **82**		
277		1 s. on 2s. 9d. on 2d. ultramarine ..	1·50	1·75
		a. Sideways second "X" (R.3/4) ..	12·00	
		b. Misplaced "&" ..	8·00	
278		1 s. on 3s. 6d. on 5d. violet ..	1·50	1·75
		a. Sideways second "X" (R.3/4) ..	12·00	
		b. Misplaced "&" ..	8·00	
279		1 s. on 4s. 6d. on 1s. red-brown ..	1·50	1·75
		a. Sideways second "X" (R.3/4) ..	12·00	
		b. Misplaced "&" ..	8·00	
271/9		*Set of* 9	9·00	10·00

SELF-ADHESIVE ISSUES. From No. 280 until No. 922 all stamps were manufactured by Walsall Security Printers Ltd and are self-adhesive. The backing paper is separated by roulette or perforations (from No. 780 onwards), and shows on its reverse the words *"TONGA where time begins"*, or, from No. 568 onwards, various texts or illustrations. This also applies to the Official stamps.

83 Banana

1969 (21 Apr). *Coil stamps.*

No.	Type	Description		
280	**83**	1 s. scarlet, black and greenish yellow ..	50	60
281		2 s. brt green, black & greenish yellow ..	60	70
282		3 s. violet, black and greenish yellow ..	70	80
283		4 s. ultramarine, black & greenish yell	80	90
284		5 s. bronze-green, black & greenish yell	90	1·00
280/4		*Set of* 5	3·25	3·50

Nos. 280/4 were produced in rolls of 200, each even stamp having a number applied to the front of the backing paper, with the usual inscription on the reverse.

See also Nos. 325/9, 413/17 and 675/89.

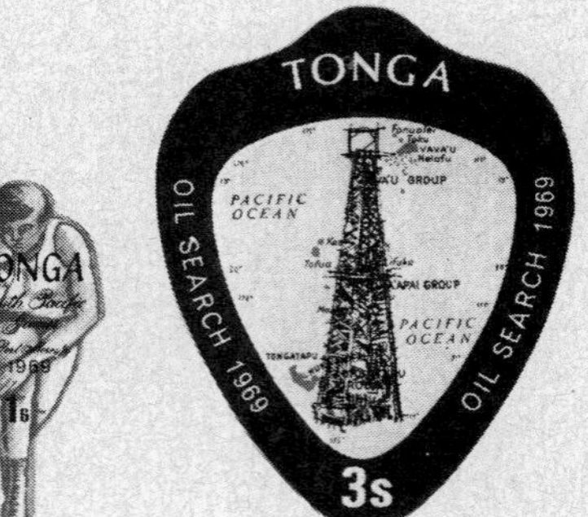

84 Putting the Shot **86** Oil Derrick and Map

1969 (13 Aug). *Third South Pacific Games, Port Moresby. T* **84** *and similar design. (a) Postage.*

No.	Type	Description		
285	**84**	1 s. black, red and buff ..	10	10
286		3 s. bright green, red and buff ..	10	10
287		6 s. blue, red and buff ..	10	10
288		10 s. bluish violet, red and buff ..	10	10
289		30 s. blue, red and buff ..	15	20
		(b) Air		
290	–	9 s. black, violet and orange ..	10	10
291	–	11 s. black, ultramarine and orange ..	10	10
292	–	20 s. black, bright green and orange ..	15	15
293	–	60 s. black, cerise and orange ..	45	65
294	–	1 p. black, blue-green and orange ..	70	1·00
285/94 *and* O35/6		*Set of* 12	2·75	3·50

Design:—9, 11, 20, 60 s., 1 p. Boxing.

1969 (23 Dec). *First Oil Search in Tonga. T* **86** *and similar vert design.*

No.	Type	Description		
		(a) Postage		
295	**86**	3 s. multicoloured ..	15	10
296		7 s. multicoloured ..	20	15
297		20 s. multicoloured ..	50	40
298		25 s. multicoloured ..	55	45
299		35 s. multicoloured ..	80	80
		(b) Air		
300	–	9 s. multicoloured ..	30	20
301	–	10 s. multicoloured ..	30	20
302	–	24 s. multicoloured ..	60	45
303	–	29 s. multicoloured ..	70	70
304	–	38 s. multicoloured ..	80	80
295/304 *and* O37/8		*Set of* 12	10·00	10·00

Design:—Nos. 300/4, Oil derrick and island of Tongatapu.

87 Members of the British and Tongan Royal Families

1970 (7 Mar). *Royal Visit. T* **87** *and similar design. Multicoloured.*

No.	Type	Description		
		(a) Postage		
305	**87**	3 s. multicoloured ..	20	15
306		5 s. multicoloured ..	25	15
307		10 s. multicoloured ..	40	30
308		25 s. multicoloured ..	1·00	65
309		50 s. multicoloured ..	2·00	1·75
		(b) Air		
310	–	7 s. multicoloured ..	35	20
311	–	9 s. multicoloured ..	40	30
312	–	24 s. multicoloured ..	1·00	65
313	–	29 s. multicoloured ..	1·25	70
314	–	38 s. multicoloured ..	1·50	90
305/14 *and* O39/41		*Set of* 13	18·00	16·00

Design:—Nos. 310/14, Queen Elizabeth II and King Taufa'ahau Tupou IV.

TONGA The Friendly Islands POSTAGE 3s Commonwealth Member JUNE 1970

89 Book, Tongan Rulers and Flag

1970 (4 June). *Entry into British Commonwealth. T* **89** *and similar design. (a) Postage.*

No.	Type	Description		
315	**89**	3 s. multicoloured ..	10	15
316		7 s. multicoloured ..	15	20
317		15 s. multicoloured ..	35	20
318		25 s. multicoloured ..	45	25
319		50 s. multicoloured ..	75	75
		(b) Air		
320	–	9 s. turquoise-blue, gold and scarlet ..	15	20
321	–	10 s. bright purple, gold and greenish blue	15	20
322	–	24 s. olive-yellow, gold and green ..	45	30
323	–	29 s. new blue, gold and orange-red ..	50	30
324	–	38 s. deep orange-yellow, gold & brt emer	60	40
315/24 *and* O42/4		*Set of* 13	7·50	7·00

Design: *"Star" shaped* (44 × 51 *mm*)—Nos. 320/4, King Taufa'ahau Tupou IV.

90 Coconut

1970 (9 June). *Coil stamps. (a) As T* **83** *but colours changed.*

No.	Type	Description		
325	**83**	1 s. greenish yellow, bright purple & blk	45	50
326		2 s. greenish yellow, ultramarine & black	55	60
327		3 s. greenish yellow, chocolate and black	55	60
328		4 s. greenish yellow, emerald and black	55	60
329		5 s. greenish yellow, orge-red & bl ..	60	65
		(b) T **90**. *Multicoloured; colour of face value given*		
330	**90**	6 s. rose-carmine ..	70	80
331		7 s. bright purple ..	75	85
332		8 s. bluish violet ..	85	95
333		9 s. turquoise ..	95	1·10
334		10 s. pale orange ..	95	1·10
325/34		*Set of* 10	6·25	7·00

Nos. 325/34 and O45/54 were produced in rolls of 200, each even stamp having a number applied to the front of the backing paper, with the usual inscription on the reverse.

MINIMUM PRICE

The minimum price quote is 10p which represents a handling charge rather than a basis for valuing common stamps. For further notes about prices see introductory pages.

91 "Red Cross"

(Litho (postage) or litho and die-stamped (air))

1970 (17 Oct). *Centenary of British Red Cross. T* **91** *and similar "cross" shaped design. (a) Postage.*

No.	Type	Description		
335	**91**	3 s. vermilion, black and light green ..	10	10
336		7 s. vermilion, black and ultramarine ..	15	15
337		15 s. vermilion and bright purple ..	40	40
338		25 s. vermilion, black and turquoise-blue	70	70
339		75 s. vermilion and deep red-brown ..	4·50	4·50
		(b) Air		
340	–	9 s. vermilion and silver ..	20	20
341	–	10 s. vermilion and bright purple ..	20	20
342	–	18 s. vermilion and green ..	50	50
343	–	38 s. vermilion and ultramarine ..	2·25	2·25
344	–	1 p. vermilion and turquoise-blue ..	5·50	5·50
335/44 *and* O55/7		*Set of* 13	22·00	22·00

Design: *As T* **91**—Nos. 340/4 as Nos. 335/9 but with inscription rearranged and coat of arms omitted.

On Nos. 335/6 and 338 the black colour is produced as a composite of the other two colours used.

(92)

(93)

1971 (30 Jan). *Fifth Death Anniv of Queen Salote. Nos. 174/84 surch as T* **92/3**. *Obliterating shapes in black; inscriptions and figures of value in colour given. (a) Postage. Surch as T* **92**.

No.	Type	Description		
345	**65**	2 s. on 5d. on 9d. (silver) ..	20	20
346		3 s. on 9d. (orange-red) ..	20	20
347		5 s. on 3d. (bright green) ..	30	20
348		15 s. on 3s. 6d. on 9d. (orange-brown)	90	35
		a. Surch double ..	—	30·00
349		25 s. on 6s. 6d. on 3d. (purple) ..	1·50	80
350		50 s. on 1s. 7d. on 3d. (gold) ..	2·50	1·75
		(b) Air. Surch as T **93**		
351	**66**	9 s. on 10d. (silver) ..	60	20
352		24 s. on 4s. on 10d. (orange-brown) ..	1·50	75
353		29 s. on 5s. 6d. on 1s. 2d. (orange-red)	1·75	1·00
354		38 s. on 10s. 6d. on 1s. 2d. (bright green)	2·50	1·50
345/54 *and* O58/61		*Set of* 14	23·00	16·00

(94)

HONOURING JAPANESE POSTAL CENTENARY 1871-1971 15s

(95)

1971 (17 Apr). *"Philatokyo 1971" Stamp Exhibition. As Nos. 101/2, 106 and 109/11, but imperf, colours changed and surch as T* **94** *(Nos. 355/6, 358/61 and 363), as T* **95** *(Nos. 357, 362) or with similar surcharge in four lines (No. 364). (a) Postage.*

No.	Type	Description		
355		3 s. on 8d. blk & greenish yellow (Blk. & R.)	10	10
356		7 s. on 4d. reddish violet & yellow (Blk. & R.)	10	10
357		15 s. on 1s. carmine, red and yellow	20	20
358		25 s. on 1d. black & orange-yellow (Blk. & R.)	30	30
359		75 s. on 2s. claret & new blue (Blk. & R.) ..	1·25	1·25
		(b) Air. Additionally surch "AIRMAIL"		
360		9 s. on 1½d. emerald (Blk. and R.)	10	10
361		10 s. on 4d. reddish violet & yellow (Blk. & R.)	10	10
362		18 s. on 1s. carmine-red and yellow (V.)	25	25
363		38 s. on 1d. black & orange-yellow (Blk. & R.)	50	50
364		1 p. on 2s. claret and new blue ..	1·50	1·50
355/64 *and* O62/4		*Set of* 13	7·50	7·25

96 Wristwatch

97 Pole-vaulter

1971 (20 July)–**72**. *Air. Backed with paper bearing advertisements.*

365	**96**	14 s. multicoloured	1·50	1·50
365*a*		17 s. multicoloured (20.7.72)	1·75	1·75
366		21 s. multicoloured	1·75	1·75
366*a*		38 s. multicoloured (20.7.72)	2·75	2·75
365/6*a and* O65/6*a*		*Set of* 8	14·00	14·00

1971 (20 July). *Fourth South Pacific Games, Tahiti. T* **97** *and similar design. (a) Postage.*

367	**97**	3 s. multicoloured	10	10
368		7 s. multicoloured	10	10
369		15 s. multicoloured	20	20
370		25 s. multicoloured	30	35
371		50 s. multicoloured	60	90
		(b) Air		
372	–	9 s. multicoloured	10	10
373	–	10 s. multicoloured	10	10
374	–	24 s. multicoloured	30	35
375	–	29 s. multicoloured	40	50
376	–	38 s. multicoloured	55	70
367/76 *and* O67/9		*Set of* 13	4·75	6·50

Design: *Horiz*—Nos. 372/6, High-jumper.

98 Medal of Merit (reverse)

99 Child

1971 (30 Oct). *Investiture of Royal Tongan Medal of Merit. T* **98** *and similar "medal" shaped design. Multicoloured; colour of medal given.*

		(a) Postage		
377	**98**	3 s. gold	10	10
378		24 s. silver	25	25
379	–	38 s. brown	50	50
		(b) Air		
380	–	10 s. gold	15	15
381	–	75 s. silver	90	1·00
382	**98**	1 p. brown	1·10	1·25
377/82 *and* O70/2		*Set of* 9	5·00	5·50

Design: *As T* **98**—Nos. 379/81, Obverse of the Medal of Merit.

1971 (31 Dec). *25th Anniv of UNICEF. T* **99** *and similar design.*

		(a) Postage		
383	**99**	2 s. multicoloured	10	10
384		4 s. multicoloured	10	10
385		8 s. multicoloured	10	10
386		16 s. multicoloured	25	25
387		30 s. multicoloured	45	45
		(b) Air		
388	–	10 s. multicoloured	15	15
389	–	15 s. multicoloured	25	25
390	–	25 s. multicoloured	40	40
391	–	50 s. multicoloured	85	1·00
392	–	1 p. multicoloured	1·75	2·00
383/92 *and* O73/5		*Set of* 13	8·00	9·00

Design: *Vert* (21 x 42 *mm*)—Nos. 388/92, Woman.

100 Map of South Pacific, and *Olovaha*

1972 (14 Apr). *Merchant Marine Routes. T* **100** *and similar design.*

		(a) Postage		
393	**100**	2 s. multicoloured	30	30
394		10 s. multicoloured	60	20
395		17 s. multicoloured	90	30
396		21 s. multicoloured	1·00	40
397		60 s. multicoloured	4·25	3·25
		(b) Air		
398	–	9 s. multicoloured	60	25
399	–	12 s. multicoloured	75	25
400	–	14 s. multicoloured	85	25
401	–	75 s. multicoloured	4·50	3·50
402	–	90 s. multicoloured	4·75	4·75
393/402 *and* O76/8		*Set of* 13	25·00	21·00

Design:—Nos. 398/402, Map of South Pacific and *Niuvakai*.

101 ¼ Hau Coronation Coin

1972 (15 July). *Fifth Anniv of Coronation. T* **101** *and similar design.*

		(a) Postage		
403	**101**	5 s. multicoloured	10	10
404		7 s. multicoloured	10	10
405		10 s. multicoloured	15	15
406		17 s. multicoloured	30	20
407		60 s. multicoloured	1·00	75
		(b) Air		
408	–	9 s. multicoloured	15	15
409	–	12 s. multicoloured	20	15
410	–	14 s. multicoloured	25	20
411	–	21 s. multicoloured	35	20
412	–	75 s. multicoloured	1·25	75
403/12 *and* O79/81		*Set of* 13	8·00	5·50

Design (47 × 41 *mm*):—Nos. 408/12, as T **101**, but with coins above inscription instead of beneath it.

102 Water Melon

1972 (30 Sept). *Coil stamps. (a) As T* **83**, *but inscription altered, omitting "Best in the Pacific", and colours changed.*

413	**83**	1 s. light yellow, scarlet and black	25	10
414		2 s. light yellow, ultramarine and black	30	15
415		3 s. light yellow, yellow-green and black	35	20
416		4 s. light yellow, royal blue and black	35	20
417		5 s. light yellow, reddish brn & bl	35	20
		(b) As T **90** *but colours changed. Colour of face value given*		
418	**90**	6 s. dull orange	40	20
419		7 s. ultramarine	45	25
420		8 s. bright magenta	45	25
421		9 s. brown-orange	45	25
422		10 s. bright new blue	55	30
		(c) T **102**. *Colour of face value given*		
423	**102**	15 s. new blue	1·00	45
424		20 s. reddish orange	1·25	60
425		25 s. chocolate	1·40	70
426		40 s. yellow-orange	2·50	1·50
427		50 s. lemon	2·50	1·75
413/27		*Set of* 15	11·50	6·50

Nos. 413/27 and O82/96 were produced in rolls, each even stamp having a number applied to the front of the backing paper, with the usual inscription on the reverse.

■ 7s

NOVEMBER 1972
INAUGURAL
Internal Airmail
Nuku'alofa — Vava'u

(103)

1972 (2 Nov). *Inaugural Internal Airmail. No. 398 surch with T* **103**.

428	7 s. on 9 s. multicoloured	1·25	2·25

104 Hoisting Tongan Flag

1972 (9 Dec). *Proclamation of Sovereignty over Minerva Reefs. T* **104** *and similar design. (a) Postage.*

429	**104**	5 s. multicoloured	10	10
430		7 s. multicoloured	10	10
431		10 s. multicoloured	15	15
432		15 s. multicoloured	25	20
433		40 s. multicoloured	80	55
		(b) Air		
434	–	9 s. multicoloured	15	15
435	–	12 s. multicoloured	20	15
436	–	14 s. multicoloured	25	15
437	–	38 s. multicoloured	75	55
438	–	1 p. multicoloured	2·00	2·00
429/38 *and* O97/9		*Set of* 13	8·00	7·50

Design: *Spherical* (52 *mm diameter*)—Nos. 434/8, Proclamation in Govt Gazette.

105 Coins around Bank

1973 (30 Mar). *Foundation of Bank of Tonga. T* **105** *and similar design. (a) Postage.*

439	**105**	5 s. multicoloured	10	10
440		7 s. multicoloured	10	10
441		10 s. multicoloured	15	10
442		20 s. multicoloured	40	20
443		30 s. multicoloured	60	30
		(b) Air		
444	–	9 s. multicoloured	20	10
445	–	12 s. multicoloured	20	10
446	–	17 s. multicoloured	35	15
447	–	50 s. multicoloured	1·25	80
448	–	90 s. multicoloured	2·50	2·00
439/48 *and* O100/2		*Set of* 13	12·00	9·00

Design: *Horiz* (64 × 52 *mm*)—Nos. 444/8, Bank and banknotes.

106 Handshake and Scout in Outrigger Canoe

1973 (29 June). *Silver Jubilee of Scouting in Tonga. T* **106** *and similar design. (a) Postage.*

449	**106**	5 s. multicoloured	20	10
450		7 s. multicoloured	30	15
451		15 s. multicoloured	95	40
452		21 s. multicoloured	1·25	50
453		50 s. multicoloured	4·50	2·25
		(b) Air		
454	–	9 s. multicoloured	50	25
455	–	12 s. multicoloured	60	30
456	–	14 s. multicoloured	85	50
457	–	17 s. multicoloured	95	60
458	–	1 p. multicoloured	12·00	6·50
449/58 *and* O103/5		*Set of* 13	95·00	42·00

Design: *Square* (53 × 53 *mm*)—Nos. 454/8, Scout badge.

ALTERED CATALOGUE NUMBERS

Any Catalogue numbers altered from the last edition are shown as a list in the introductory pages.

107 Excerpt from Cook's Log-book

1973 (2 Oct). *Bicentenary of Capt. Cook's Visit to Tonga. T* **107** *and similar design. (a) Postage.*

No.	Type	Description		
459	**107**	6 s. multicoloured	40	30
460		8 s. multicoloured	40	35
461		11 s. multicoloured	60	40
462		35 s. multicoloured	4·00	2·25
463		40 s. multicoloured	4·00	2·50
		(b) Air		
464	–	9 s. multicoloured	70	30
465	–	14 s. multicoloured	1·25	50
466	–	29 s. multicoloured	4·00	2·00
467	–	38 s. multicoloured	4·50	2·50
468	–	75 s. multicoloured	8·50	4·50
459/68 *and* O106/8		*Set of* 13	45·00	26·00

Design: *Vert*—Nos. 464/8, H.M.S. *Resolution*.

(108) 109 Red Shining Parrot

1973 (19 Dec). *Commonwealth Games, Christchurch, New Zealand. Various stamps surch as T* **108** *(No. 474 optd "AIRMAIL" in addition). (a) Postage.*

No.	Description		
469	5 s. on 50 s. (No. 371) (Blk. and Gold)	15	10
470	12 s. on 38 s. (No. 379) (R. and Silver)	30	15
471	14 s. on 75 s. (No. 381) (R. and Gold)	30	15
472	20 s. on 1 p. (No. 382) (Blk. and Gold)	50	30
473	50 s. on 24 s. (No. 378) (Blk. and Silver)	1·25	1·00
	(b) Air		
474	7 s. on 25 s. (No. 370) (Blk. and Silver)	15	10
475	9 s. on 38 s. (No. 376) (V.)	20	10
476	24 s. (No. 374)	60	30
477	29 s. on 9 s. (No. 454) (B.)	70	40
478	40 s. on 14 s. (No. 456)	1·00	90
469/78 *and* O109/11	*Set of* 13	9·00	8·00

1974 (20 Mar). *Air.*

No.	Type	Description		
479	**109**	7 s. multicoloured	70	35
480		9 s. multicoloured	75	40
481		12 s. multicoloured	80	50
482		14 s. multicoloured	85	50
483		17 s. multicoloured	95	75
484		29 s. multicoloured	1·75	1·00
485		38 s. multicoloured	2·25	1·25
486		50 s. multicoloured	2·75	3·25
487		75 s. multicoloured	4·00	4·75
479/87		*Set of* 9	13·50	11·50

Nos. 479/87 and O112/20 were produced in rolls, each stamp having a number applied to the front of the backing paper, with the usual inscription on the reverse.

110 "Stamped Letter"

1974 (20 June). *Centenary of Universal Postal Union. T* **110** *and similar design. (a) Postage.*

No.	Type	Description		
488	**110**	5 s. multicoloured	10	15
489		10 s. multicoloured	15	15
490		15 s. multicoloured	25	25
491		20 s. multicoloured	30	30
492		50 s. multicoloured	1·00	1·50
		(b) Air		
493	–	14 s. multicoloured	25	25
494	–	21 s. multicoloured	35	35
495	–	60 s. multicoloured	1·10	1·60
496	–	75 s. multicoloured	1·25	1·75
497	–	1 p. multicoloured	1·50	2·00
488/97 *and* O121/3		*Set of* 13	7·50	10·50

Design: *Horiz*—Nos. 493/7, Carrier pigeon scattering letters over Tonga.

111 Girl Guide Badges

1974 (11 Sept). *Tongan Girl Guides. T* **111** *and similar design.*

No.	Type	Description		
		(a) Postage		
498	**111**	5 s. multicoloured	40	30
499		10 s. multicoloured	60	30
500		20 s. multicoloured	1·50	65
501		40 s. multicoloured	3·25	1·75
502		60 s. multicoloured	4·00	2·75
		(b) Air		
503	–	14 s. multicoloured	1·00	45
504	–	16 s. multicoloured	1·00	45
505	–	29 s. multicoloured	2·00	1·00
506	–	31 s. multicoloured	2·25	1·25
507	–	75 s. multicoloured	5·50	3·50
498/507 *and* O124/6		*Set of* 13	32·00	20·00

Design: *Vert*—Nos. 503/7, Girl Guide leaders.

112 H.M.S. *Resolution*

1974 (11 Dec). *Establishment of Royal Marine Institute. T* **112** *and similar design. (a) Postage.*

No.	Type	Description		
508	**112**	5 s. multicoloured	1·25	50
509		10 s. multicoloured	1·40	50
		a. Vert roul omitted (horiz pair)		
510		25 s. multicoloured	2·75	80
511		50 s. multicoloured	4·00	3·00
512		75 s. multicoloured	5·50	4·50
		(b) Air		
513	–	9 s. multicoloured	1·25	30
514	–	14 s. multicoloured	1·75	55
515	–	17 s. multicoloured	2·00	60
516	–	60 s. multicoloured	4·25	3·75
517	–	90 s. multicoloured	6·00	5·50
508/17 *and* O127/9		*Set of* 13	35·00	25·00

Design: *Horiz* (51×46 *mm*)—Nos. 513/17, *James Cook* (bulk carrier).

113 Dateline Hotel, Nuku'alofa

1975 (11 Mar). *South Pacific Forum and Tourism. T* **113** *and similar vert designs. (a) Postage.*

No.	Type	Description		
518	**113**	5 s. multicoloured	10	10
519		10 s. multicoloured	10	10
520		15 s. multicoloured	20	20
521		30 s. multicoloured	45	45
522		1 p. multicoloured	1·60	2·00
		(b) Air		
523	–	9 s. multicoloured	10	10
524	–	12 s. multicoloured	15	15
525	–	14 s. multicoloured	20	20
526	–	17 s. multicoloured	20	20
527	–	38 s. multicoloured	55	65
518/27 *and* O130/2		*Set of* 13	8·00	8·00

Designs (46 × 60 *mm*):—9, 12, 14 s. Beach; 17, 38 s. Surf and sea.

114 Boxing

1975 (11 June). *Fifth South Pacific Games, Guam. T* **114** *and similar "star"-shaped design. (a) Postage.*

No.	Type	Description		
528	**114**	5 s. multicoloured	15	10
529		10 s. multicoloured	20	10
530		20 s. multicoloured	30	25
531		25 s. multicoloured	35	35
532		65 s. multicoloured	80	90
		(b) Air		
533	–	9 s. multicoloured	20	10
534	–	12 s. multicoloured	25	15
535	–	14 s. multicoloured	25	15
536	–	17 s. multicoloured	30	20
537	–	90 s. multicoloured	1·10	1·40
528/37 *and* O133/5		*Set of* 13	6·25	6·50

Design (37 × 43 *mm*):—Nos. 533/7, Throwing the Discus.

115 Commemorative Coin

1975 (3 Sept). *F.A.O. Commemoration. T* **115** *and similar designs.*

No.	Description		
	(a) Postage		
538	5 s. multicoloured	15	10
539	20 s. multicoloured	35	15
540	50 s. new blue, black and silver	75	35
541	1 p. ultramarine, black and silver	1·50	1·25
542	2 p. black and silver	2·50	2·25
	(b) Air		
543	12 s. multicoloured	30	15
544	14 s. multicoloured	30	15
545	25 s. vermilion, black and silver	45	20
546	50 s. bright magenta, black and silver	70	50
547	1 p. black and silver	1·50	1·25
538/47	*Set of* 10	7·50	5·75

Nos. 539/47 are as T **115** but show different coins. Nos. 542 and 544 are horiz, size 75 × 42 mm.

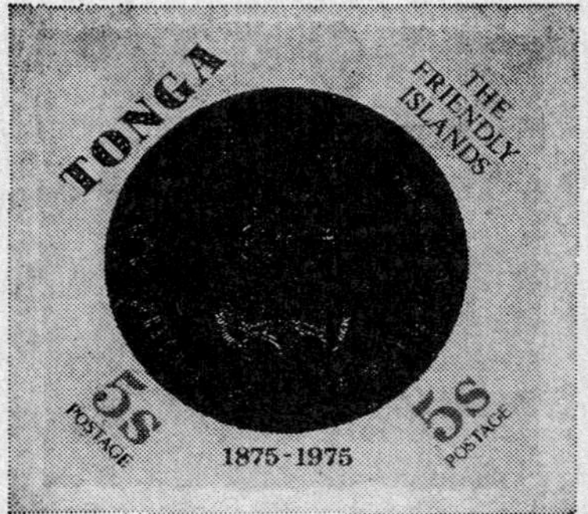

116 Commemorative Coin

1975 (4 Nov). *Centenary of Tongan Constitution. T* **116** *and similar designs showing coinage. Multicoloured. (a) Postage.*

No.	Description		
548	5 s. Type **116**	15	10
549	10 s. King George I	25	10
550	20 s. King Taufa'ahau IV	40	25
551	50 s. King George II	90	60
552	75 s. Tongan arms	1·50	1·40

(b) Air

No.	Type	Description	Unused	Used
553		9 s. King Taufa'ahau IV	25	10
554		12 s. Queen Salote	30	15
555		14 s. Tongan arms	30	15
556		38 s. King Taufa'ahau IV	70	35
557		1 p. Four monarchs	1·75	1·75
548/57 *and* O136/8		*Set of* 13	9·00	7·50

Sizes:—60 × 40 mm, Nos. 549 and 551; 76 × 76 mm, Nos. 552 and 557; 57 × 56 mm, others.

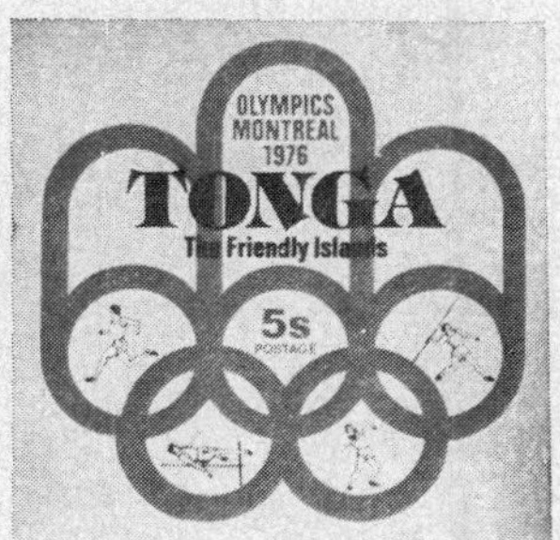

117 Montreal Logo

1976 (24 Feb). *First Participation in Olympic Games. (a) Postage.*

No.	Type	Description	Unused	Used
558	**117**	5 s. vermilion, black and blue	30	15
559		10 s. vermilion, black and emerald	35	15
560		25 s. vermilion, black and bistre	1·00	35
561		35 s. vermilion, black and mauve	1·25	40
562		70 s. vermilion, black and olive-yellow	2·75	1·25

(b) Air. Montreal logo optd on Girl Guide stamps (Nos. 500 etc)

No.	Type	Description	Unused	Used
563	**111**	12 s. on 20 s. multicoloured	50	15
564	–	14 s. on 16 s. multicoloured	50	15
565	–	16 s. multicoloured	55	15
566	**111**	38 s. on 40 s. multicoloured	1·75	45
567	–	75 s. multicoloured	3·00	1·25
558/67 *and* O139/41		*Set of* 13	20·00	8·00

118 Signatories of Declaration of Independence

1976 (26 May). *Bicentenary of American Revolution. T* **118** *and similar horiz designs showing signatories to the Declaration of Independence. (a) Postage.*

No.	Type	Description	Unused	Used
568	**118**	9 s. multicoloured	40	15
569	–	10 s. multicoloured	40	15
570	–	15 s. multicoloured	60	45
571	–	25 s. multicoloured	1·00	70
572	–	75 s. multicoloured	2·75	2·50

(b) Air

No.	Type	Description	Unused	Used
573	–	12 s. multicoloured	50	15
574	–	14 s. multicoloured	60	20
575	–	17 s. multicoloured	70	35
576	–	38 s. multicoloured	1·40	75
577	–	1 p. multicoloured	3·50	3·50
568/77 *and* O142/4		*Set of* 13	16·00	13·00

119 Nathaniel Turner and John Thomas (Methodist missionaries)

1976 (25 Aug). *150th Anniv of Christianity in Tonga. T* **119** *and similar design. (a) Postage.*

No.	Type	Description	Unused	Used
578	**119**	5 s. multicoloured	20	25
579		10 s. multicoloured	30	25
580		20 s. multicoloured	50	40
581		25 s. multicoloured	55	45
582		85 s. multicoloured	2·25	2·25

(b) Air. Design showing Missionary Ship "Triton" (45 × 59 mm)

No.	Type	Description	Unused	Used
583	–	9 s. multicoloured	30	25
584	–	12 s. multicoloured	35	30
585	–	14 s. multicoloured	40	35
586	–	17 s. multicoloured	50	40
587	–	38 s. multicoloured	1·25	1·00
578/87 *and* O145/7		*Set of* 13	12·00	11·00

120 Emperor Wilhelm I and King George Tupou I

1976 (1 Nov). *Centenary of Treaty of Friendship with Germany.*

(a) Postage

No.	Type	Description	Unused	Used
588	**120**	9 s. multicoloured	20	20
589		15 s. multicoloured	30	30
590		22 s. multicoloured	40	45
591		50 s. multicoloured	90	1·25
592		73 s. multicoloured	1·40	1·90

(b) Air. Circular design (52 mm diameter) showing Treaty Signing

No.	Type	Description	Unused	Used
593	–	11 s. multicoloured	25	25
594	–	17 s. multicoloured	40	45
595	–	18 s. multicoloured	40	45
596	–	31 s. multicoloured	60	80
597	–	39 s. multicoloured	70	90
588/97 *and* O148/50		*Set of* 13	9·50	11·50

121 Queen Salote and Coronation Procession

1977 (7 Feb). *Silver Jubilee. (a) Postage.*

No.	Type	Description	Unused	Used
598	**121**	11 s. multicoloured	60	30
599		20 s. multicoloured	40	30
600		30 s. multicoloured	50	30
601		50 s. multicoloured	70	65
602		75 s. multicoloured	90	85

(b) Air. Square design (59 × 59 mm) showing Queen Elizabeth and King Taufa'ahau

No.	Type	Description	Unused	Used
603	–	15 s. multicoloured	40	25
604	–	17 s. multicoloured	40	30
605	–	22 s. multicoloured	4·50	1·25
		a. Horiz roul omitted (vert pair)		
606	–	31 s. multicoloured	40	40
607	–	39 s. multicoloured	40	40
598/607 *and* O151/3		*Set of* 13	10·50	5·50

122 Tongan Coins

1977 (4 July). *Tenth Anniv of King's Coronation. (a) Postage.*

No.	Type	Description	Unused	Used
608	**122**	10 s. multicoloured	20	20
609		15 s. multicoloured	25	25
610		25 s. multicoloured	35	45
611		50 s. multicoloured	75	90
612		75 s. multicoloured	1·00	1·50

(b) Air. Oval design (64 × 46 mm) showing 1967 Coronation Coin

No.	Type	Description	Unused	Used
613	–	11 s. multicoloured	25	20
614	–	17 s. multicoloured	30	30
615	–	18 s. multicoloured	30	30
616	–	39 s. multicoloured	45	60
617	–	1 p. multicoloured	1·50	2·25
608/17 *and* O154/6		*Set of* 13	7·50	9·50

COVER PRICES

Cover factors are quoted at the beginning of each country for most issues to 1945. An explanation of the system can be found on page x. The factors quoted do not, however, apply to philatelic covers.

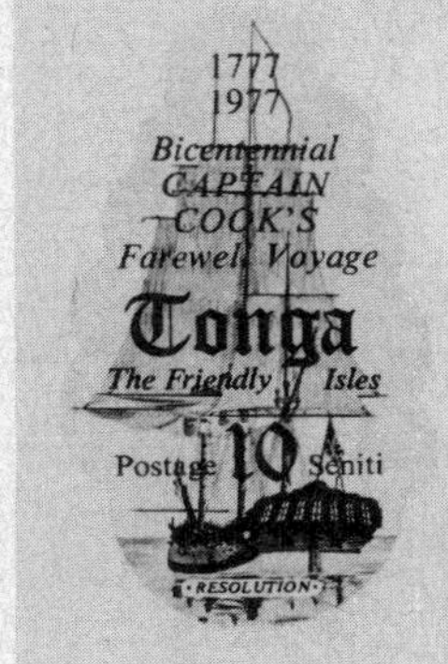

123 H.M.S. *Resolution*

1977 (28 Sept). *Bicentenary of Capt. Cook's Last Voyage.*

(a) Postage.

No.	Type	Description	Unused	Used
618	**123**	10 s. multicoloured	1·75	75
619		17 s. multicoloured	2·25	1·10
620		25 s. multicoloured	3·75	2·00
621		30 s. multicoloured	3·75	2·75
622		40 s. multicoloured	4·50	4·50

(b) Air. Horiz design (52×46 mm) showing medal and extract from Cook's journal

No.	Type	Description	Unused	Used
623	–	15 s. multicoloured	1·75	2·25
624	–	22 s. multicoloured	2·75	2·25
625	–	31 s. multicoloured	3·25	2·75
626	–	50 s. multicoloured	4·50	4·50
627	–	1 p. multicoloured	8·00	8·50
618/27 *and* O157/9		*Set of* 13	48·00	45·00

124 Humpback Whale **(125)**

1977 (16 Dec). *Whale Conservation. (a) Postage.*

No.	Type	Description	Unused	Used
628	**124**	15 s. black, grey and bright blue	2·50	70
629		22 s. black, grey and dull green	2·75	1·00
630		31 s. black, grey and orange	3·25	1·50
631		38 s. black, grey and bright lilac	3·50	2·00
632		64 s. black, grey and red-brown	5·50	4·50

(b) Air. Hexagonal design (66 × 51 mm) showing Sei and Fin Whales

No.	Type	Description	Unused	Used
633	–	11 s. multicoloured	2·50	60
634	–	17 s. multicoloured	2·75	80
635	–	18 s. multicoloured	2·75	90
636	–	39 s. multicoloured	3·75	2·00
637	–	50 s. multicoloured	4·75	2·75
628/37 *and* O160/2		*Set of* 13	45·00	27·00

1978 (17 Feb). *Various stamps surch as T* **125**. *(a) Postage.*

No.	Type	Description	Unused	Used
638	**115**	15 s. on 5 s. multicoloured	1·50	1·75
639	**119**	15 s. on 5 s. multicoloured (Br.)	1·50	1·75
640	**117**	15 s. on 10 s. verm, blk & emerald (G.)	1·50	1·75
641	**119**	15 s. on 10 s. multicoloured	1·50	1·75
642	**121**	15 s. on 11 s. multicoloured (Blk. & Sil.)	1·50	2·75
643	**114**	15 s. on 20 s. multicoloured	1·50	1·75
644	–	15 s. on 38 s. mult (No. O133) (V.)	1·50	1·75

(b) Air

No.	Type	Description	Unused	Used
645	–	17 s. on 9 s. multicoloured (No. 533)	1·75	2·00
646	–	17 s. on 9 s. multicoloured (583) (V.)	1·75	2·00
		a. Surch double	£150	
647	–	17 s. on 12 s. multicoloured (534) (V.)	1·75	2·00
648	–	17 s. on 12 s. mult (573) (R. & Gold)	1·75	2·00
649	–	17 s. on 18 s. mult (595) (Olive & Br)	1·75	2·00
650	–	17 s. on 38 s. multicoloured (527) (G.)	1·75	2·00
651	–	17 s. on 38 s. multicoloured (556)	1·75	2·00
652	–	1 p. on 35 s. mult (O151) (Silver & B.)	20·00	27·00
653	–	1 p. on 38 s. mult (576) (V & Gold)	8·50	9·00
654	–	1 p. on 75 s. mult (572) (G. & Sil.)	8·50	9·00
638/54		*Set of* 17	55·00	65·00

The surcharges on Nos. 638/9 are formed by adding a figure "1" to the existing face value.

The surcharge on No. 644 includes the word "POSTAGE".

126 Flags of Canada and Tonga

1978 (5 May). *Commonwealth Games, Edmonton. (a) Postage.*

655	**126**	10 s. blue, red and black	15	15
656		15 s. multicoloured	25	25
657		20 s. turquoise-green, black and red	35	35
658		25 s. red, blue and black	40	40
659		45 s. black and red	90	1·00
		(b) Air. Leaf-shaped design (39 × 40 mm) showing Maple Leaf		
660	–	17 s. black and red	30	30
661	–	35 s. black, red and blue	60	65
662	–	38 s. black, red and turquoise-green	75	85
663	–	40 s. black, red and green	80	90
664	–	65 s. black, red and chestnut	1·40	1·60
655/64 *and* O163/5		*Set of* 13	8·00	9·00

127 King Taufa'ahau Tupou IV

1978 (4 July). *60th Birthday of King Taufa'ahau Tupou IV.*

(a) Postage

665	**127**	2 s. black, deep blue and cobalt	10	20
666		5 s. black, deep blue and rose-pink	10	20
667		10 s. black, deep blue and mauve	20	20
668		25 s. black, deep blue and brownish grey	45	35
669		75 s. black, deep blue and yellow-ochre	1·10	1·25
		(b) Air. Star-shaped design (44 × 51 mm) showing portrait of King		
670	–	11 s. black, dp blue & greenish yellow	20	20
671	–	15 s. black, deep blue and cinnamon	30	25
672	–	17 s. black, deep blue and bright lilac	35	25
673	–	39 s. black, dp blue & turquoise-green	60	55
674	–	1 p. black, deep blue and pink	1·75	1·75
665/74 *and* O166/8		*Set of* 13	7·00	7·00

128 Banana

1978 (29 Sept)–**82**. *(a) Coil stamps. Designs as T* **128** *showing bananas (the number coinciding with the face value).*

675	1 s. black and greenish yellow	20	30
676	2 s. deep blue and greenish yellow	20	30
677	3 s. purple-brown, yellow and greenish yellow	30	30
678	4 s. deep blue, yellow and greenish yellow	30	30
679	5 s. vermilion, yellow and greenish yellow	30	30
	(b) Coil stamps. Coconut-shaped design (18 × 26 mm)		
680	6 s. purple, emerald and bistre-brown	40	40
681	7 s. greenish blue, emerald and light brown	40	40
682	8 s. vermilion, emerald and light brown	40	40
683	9 s. deep mauve, emerald and light brown	40	40
684	10 s. emerald and light brown	40	40
	(c) Coil stamps. Pineapple-shaped design (17 × 30 mm)		
684*a*	13 s. deep mauve, emerald and cinnamon (17.12.82)	6·00	5·00
685	15 s. blue-green, orange-brown and emerald	1·25	1·25
686	20 s. brown, orange-brown and emerald	1·40	1·40
687	30 s. magenta, orange-brown and emerald	1·60	1·60
688	50 s. black, orange-brown and emerald	2·00	2·00
689	1 p. purple, orange-brown and emerald	2·50	3·00
	(d) Mixed fruit oval design (55 × 29 mm)		
689*a*	2 p. multicoloured (17.12.82)	8·50	9·00
689*b*	3 p. multicoloured (17.12.82)	10·00	11·00
675/89*b*	*Set of* 18	32·00	35·00

Nos. 675/89 and O169/83 were produced in rolls, each even stamp having a number applied to the backing paper, with the usual inscription on the reverse.

129 Humpback Whale

1978 (15 Dec). *Endangered Wildlife Conservation. T* **129** *and similarly shaped designs. Multicoloured. (a) Postage.*

690	15 s. Type **129**	2·25	1·00
691	18 s. Insular Flying Fox	2·25	1·00
692	25 s. Turtle	2·25	1·25
693	28 s. Red Shining Parrot	3·50	1·75
694	60 s. Type **129**	6·00	4·50
	(b) Air		
695	17 s. Type **129**	2·25	1·00
696	22 s. As 18 s.	2·25	1·00
697	31 s. As 25 s.	2·25	1·75
698	39 s. As 28 s.	4·50	2·75
699	45 s. Type **129**	5·00	3·25
690/9 *and* O184/6	*Set of* 13	42·00	28·00

130 Metrication Symbol

1979 (16 Feb). *Decade of Progress. T* **130** *and other multi-angular designs in ultramarine and gold (31 s.) or multicoloured (others).*

(a) Postage

700	5 s. Type **130**	10	10
701	11 s. Map of South Pacific Islands	15	15
702	18 s. "Building wall of progress" with the assistance of the United States Peace Corps	25	20
703	22 s. New churches	35	25
704	50 s. Map showing air routes	80	50
	(b) Air		
705	15 s. As 50 s.	20	20
706	17 s. As 11 s.	25	20
707	31 s. Rotary International emblem	45	35
708	39 s. Government offices	60	40
709	1 p. "Communications"	1·60	1·25
700/9 *and* O187/9	*Set of* 13	7·50	5·00

131 Various Envelopes bearing Self-adhesive Stamps

1979 (1 June). *Death Centenary of Sir Rowland Hill and 10th Anniv of Tongan Self-adhesive Stamps. (a) Postage.*

710	**131**	5 s. multicoloured	20	10
711		10 s. multicoloured	30	15
712		25 s. multicoloured	65	35
713		50 s. multicoloured	1·25	60
714		1 p. multicoloured	2·00	1·25
		a. Horiz roul omitted (vert pair)		
		(b) Air. Multi-angular design (53 × 53 mm) showing various self-adhesive stamps		
715	–	15 s. multicoloured	40	20
716	–	17 s. multicoloured	45	25
717	–	18 s. multicoloured	45	25
718	–	31 s. multicoloured	75	40
719	–	39 s. multicoloured	90	45
710/19 *and* O190/2		*Set of* 13	10·50	6·00

132

(Des R. Edge and K. Jones)

1979 (17 Aug)–**82**. *Air. Coil stamps.*

720	**132**	5 s. black and cobalt	40	50
721		11 s. black and bright blue	50	50
722		14 s. black and violet	50	50
723		15 s. black and mauve	55	50
724		17 s. black and bright magenta	55	50
725		18 s. black and bright rose-red	55	50
726		22 s. black and orange-vermilion	65	50
726*a*		29 s. black and rose (17.12.82)	8·00	5·00
727		31 s. black and orange-yellow	85	1·00
727*a*		32 s. black and yellow-ochre (17.12.82)	9·00	5·50
728		39 s. black and bright yellow-green	1·00	1·00
728*a*		47 s. black and light brown (17.12.82)	9·00	6·50
729		75 s. black and bright blue-green	1·50	2·50
730		1 p. black and emerald	2·00	3·25
720/30		*Set of* 14	30·00	25·00

Nos. 720/30 and O193/203 were produced in rolls, each even stamp having a number applied to the backing paper, with the usual inscription on the reverse.

133 Rain Forest, Island of 'Eua

1979 (23 Nov). *Views as seen through the Lens of a Camera.*

(a) Postage

731	**133**	10 s. multicoloured	25	25
732		18 s. multicoloured	30	30
733		31 s. multicoloured	40	40
734		50 s. multicoloured	70	85
735		60 s. multicoloured	80	1·25
		(b) Air. Design as T **133** *but showing Isle of Kao*		
736	–	5 s. multicoloured	15	20
737	–	15 s. multicoloured	30	30
738	–	17 s. multicoloured	30	30
739	–	39 s. multicoloured	60	60
740	–	75 s. multicoloured	90	1·25
731/40 *and* O204/6		*Set of* 13	6·50	8·00

134 King George Tupou I, Admiral Du Bouzet and Map of Tonga

(**135**)

1980 (9 Jan). *125th Anniv of France–Tonga Treaty of Friendship.*

(a) Postage

741	**134**	7 s. multicoloured	15	15
742		10 s. multicoloured	20	20
743		14 s. multicoloured	30	30
744		50 s. multicoloured	1·25	1·25
745		75 s. multicoloured	1·75	2·00
		(b) Air. Design as T **134** *but showing King George Tupou I, Napoleon III and "L'Aventure" (French warship)*		
746	–	15 s. multicoloured	30	30
747	–	17 s. multicoloured	35	35
748	–	22 s. multicoloured	55	55
749	–	31 s. multicoloured	90	90
750	–	39 s. multicoloured	1·00	1·00
741/50 *and* O207/9		*Set of* 13	10·50	11·00

1980 (30 Apr). *Olympic Games, Moscow. Nos. 710/19 surch or optd only (No. 755) as T* **135** *in black on silver background.*

(a) Postage

751	**131**	13 s. on 5 s. multicoloured	35	35
752		20 s. on 10 s. multicoloured	55	55
753		25 s. multicoloured	70	70
754		33 s. on 50 s. multicoloured	85	85
755		1 p. multicoloured	3·25	3·50
		(b) Air		
756	–	9 s. on 15 s. multicoloured	30	30
757	–	16 s. on 17 s. multicoloured	50	50
758	–	29 s. on 18 s. multicoloured	80	80
759	–	32 s. on 31 s. multicoloured	90	90
760	–	47 s. on 39 s. multicoloured	1·50	1·75
751/60 *and* O210/12		*Set of* 13	14·00	14·50

136 Scout at Campfire

1980 (30 Sept). *South Pacific Scout Jamboree, Tonga and 75th Anniv of Rotary International. (a) Postage.*
761 **136** 9 s. multicoloured 30 15
762 13 s. multicoloured 40 20
763 15 s. multicoloured 40 20
764 30 s. multicoloured 75 40

(b) Air. Design as T **136** *showing Scout activities and Rotary emblem*
765 – 29 s. multicoloured 75 45
766 – 32 s. multicoloured 80 45
767 – 47 s. multicoloured 1·10 70
768 – 1 p. multicoloured 2·00 1·25
761/8 *and* O214/15 *Set of* 10 9·50 6·50

(137) **138** Red Cross and Tongan Flags, with Map of Tonga

1980 (3 Dec)–**82.** *Various stamps surch as T* **137**. *(a) Postage.*
769 **117** 9 s. on 35 s. vermilion, black and mauve 40 40
770 **119** 13 s. on 20 s. multicoloured 55 55
771 13 s. on 25 s. multicoloured 55 55
772 – 19 s. on 25 s. multicoloured (No. 571) 75 75
773 **114** 1 p. on 65 s. multicoloured 3·00 3·75
773*a* – 5 p. on 25 s. multicoloured (No. O214) (B.) (4.1.82) 12·00 14·00
773*b* – 5 p. on 2 p. multicoloured (No. O215) (B.) (4.1.82) 12·00 14·00
ba. Stamp omitted (centre stamp of strip of 3)

(b) Air
774 – 29 s. on 14 s. multicoloured (No. 585) 90 90
775 – 29 s. on 39 s. multicoloured (No. 597) 90 90
776 – 32 s. on 12 s. multicoloured (No. 554) 1·10 1·10
777 – 32 s. on 14 s. multicoloured (No. 574) 1·10 1·10
778 – 47 s. on 12 s. multicoloured (No. 524) 1·60 1·60
779 – 47 s. on 12 s. multicoloured (No. 584) 1·60 1·60
769/79 *and* O216 *Set of* 14 35·00 42·00

On No. 773ba the centre stamp in a vertical strip of 3 became detached so that the surcharge was applied to the white backing paper.

No. 773*b* exists with map on reverse or with plain back. No. 773*a* comes with map on back only.

1981 (9 Sept). *International Year of Disabled Persons.*

(a) Postage. P 14½ × 14.
780 **138** 2 p. multicoloured 2·00 1·25
781 3 p. multicoloured 2·25 1·50

(b) Air. Vert design (25 × 33 mm) showing Red Cross flag and map depicting Tongatapu and Eua. P 13½
782 – 29 s. multicoloured 50 20
783 – 32 s. multicoloured 60 25
784 – 47 s. multicoloured 70 30
780/4 *Set of* 5 5·50 3·25

139 Prince Charles and King Taufa'ahau Tupou IV

1981 (21 Oct). *Royal Wedding and Centenary of Treaty of Friendship between Tonga and Great Britain. T* **139** *and similar vert designs. Multicoloured. P* 13½.
785 13 s. Type **139** 30 20
786 47 s. Prince Charles and Lady Diana Spencer 60 30
787 1 p. 50, Prince Charles and Lady Diana (*different*) 1·00 90
a. Imperf backing paper (pair) 75·00
788 3 p. Prince and Princess of Wales after wedding ceremony 1·40 1·40
785/8 *Set of* 4 3·00 2·50

140 Report of Printing in *Missionary Notices*

1981 (25 Nov). *Christmas. 150th Anniv of first Books Printed in Tonga. T* **140** *and similar horiz designs. Multicoloured. P* 13½.
789 9 s. Type **140** 25 25
790 13 s. *Missionary Notices* report (*different*) 30 30
791 32 s. Type in chase 85 85
792 47 s. Bible class 1·40 1·40
789/92 *Set of* 4 2·50 2·50

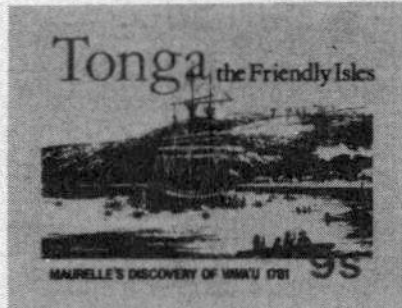

141 Landing Scene

1981 (25 Nov). *Bicentenary of Maurelle's Discovery of Vava'u. T* **141** *and similar horiz designs. Multicoloured. P* 14 × 14½.
793 9 s. Type **141** 40 40
794 13 s. Map of Vava'u 60 50
795 47 s. *La Princesa* 2·75 1·50
796 1 p. *La Princesa* (*different*) 5·00 6·50
793/6 *Set of* 4 8·00 8·00
MS797 100 × 78 mm. As No. 796. Imperf 8·50 10·00

The stamp from No. **MS**797 is as No. 796 but without inscription at foot of design.

142 Battle Scene

1981 (16 Dec). *175th Anniv of Capture of "Port au Prince" (ship). T* **142** *and similar horiz designs in black and new blue. P* 13½.
798 29 s. Type **142** 90 45
799 32 s. Battle scene (*different*) 1·00 55
800 47 s. Map of Ha'apai Group 1·25 1·25
801 47 s. Native canoes preparing to attack 1·25 1·25
802 1 p. *Port au Prince* 1·75 2·00
798/802 *Set of* 5 5·50 5·00

The 47 s. values were printed together, *se-tenant*, in horizontal and vertical pairs throughout the sheet.

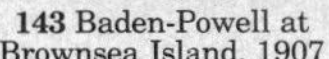

CYCLONE RELIEF
T$1+50s
POSTAGE & RELIEF

143 Baden-Powell at Brownsea Island, 1907 (144)

1982 (22 Feb). *75th Anniv of Boy Scout Movement and 125th Birth Anniv of Lord Baden-Powell. T* **143** *and similar vert designs. P* 13½.
803 29 s. Type **143** 80 30
804 32 s. Baden-Powell on his charger "Black Prince" 90 35
805 47 s. Baden-Powell at Imperial Jamboree, 1924 1·25 45
806 1 p. 50, Cover of first *Scouting for Boys* journal 3·00 1·75
807 2 p. 50, Newsboy, 1900 and Mafeking Siege 3d. stamp 5·25 4·00
803/7 *Set of* 5 10·00 6·00

1982 (14 Apr). *Cyclone Relief. No. 788 optd with T* **144** *in silver.*
808 1 p. + 50 s. on 3 p. Prince and Princess of Wales after wedding ceremony 1·60 2·50
a. Imperf backing paper (pair) £200

145 Ball Control

146 *Olovaha II* (inter-island freighter)

1982 (7 July). *World Cup Football Championship, Spain. T* **145** *and similar vert designs. Multicoloured. P* 13½.
809 32 s. Type **145** 55 45
810 47 s. Goalkeeping 75 60
811 75 s. Heading 1·10 95
812 1 p. 50, Shooting 1·90 1·75
809/12 *Set of* 4 3·75 3·25

1982 (11 Aug). *Inter-Island Transport. T* **146** *and similar horiz design. Multicoloured. P* 14 × 14½.
813 9 s. Type **146** 45 15
814 13 s. Type **146** 50 25
815 47 s. SPIA De Havilland D.H.C.6 Twin Otter 300 1·25 1·00
816 1 p. As 47 s. 2·25 3·00
813/16 *Set of* 4 4·00 4·00

147 Mail Canoe

148 Decathlon

1982 (29 Sept). *Tin Can Mail Centenary. T* **147** *and similar vert designs. P* 13½ × 14.
817 13 s. multicoloured 15 15
818 32 s. multicoloured 25 25
819 47 s. multicoloured 35 35
820 2 p. black and pale turquoise-green 1·40 1·40
817/20 *Set of* 4 2·00 2·00
MS821 135 × 90 mm. Nos. 817/19. Imperf 1·25 2·00
MS822 135 × 89 mm. As No. 820 but with gold inscriptions. Imperf 3·00 4·25

Designs:—32 s. Mail canoe and ship; 47 s. Collecting Tin Can mail; 2 p. Map of Niuafo'ou.

1982 (25 Oct). *Commonwealth Games, Brisbane. T* **148** *and similar multicoloured design. P* 13½.
823 32 s. Type **148** 50 30
824 1 p. 50, Tongan Police band at opening ceremony (*horiz*) 4·50 4·50

Christmas
Greetings
1982

149 Pupils (150)

1982 (25 Oct). *Tonga College Centenary. T* **149** *and similar multicoloured designs. P* 13½ (*Nos.* 825/6) *or* 14 × 14½ (*others*).
825 5 s. Type **149** (Tongan inscription) 50 65
a. Pair. Nos. 825/6 1·00 1·25
826 5 s. Type **149** (English inscription) 50 65
827 29 s. School crest and monument (Tongan inscr) (29×22 *mm*) 2·00 2·25
a. Block of 4. Nos. 827/9 7·00
828 29 s. As No. 827, but inscr in English 2·00 2·25
829 29 s. King George Tupou I (founder) and school (Tongan inscr) (29×22 *mm*) 2·00 2·25
830 29 s. As No. 829, but inscr in English 2·00 2·25
825/30 *Set of* 6 8·00 9·25

Nos. 825/6 were printed together, *se-tenant*, in horizontal and vertical pairs and Nos. 827/30 in different combinations throughout the sheet, giving four blocks of 4 and four single stamps.

1982 (17 Nov). *Christmas. Nos.* 817/19 *optd as T* **150** *in bright carmine (13 s.) or silver (others).*
831 13 s. Type **147** 15 20
a. Bright purple opt
832 32 s. Mail boat and ship 45 55
833 47 s. Collecting Tin Can mail 55 65
831/3 *Set of* 3 1·00 1·25

151 H.M.S. *Resolution*, and S. S. *Canberra*

1983 (22 Feb). *Sea and Air Transport. T* **151** *and similar horiz designs. Multicoloured. P* 14.
834 29 s. Type **151** (sage-green background) 2·75 1·75
835 32 s. Type **151** (buff background) 2·75 1·75
836 47 s. Montgolfier's balloon and Concorde (pale blue background) 4·00 2·75
837 1 p. 50, As No. 836 (lilac background) 6·00 8·00
834/7 *Set of* 4 14·00 13·00
MS838 120×165 mm. 2 p. 50, *Canberra* (liner) and Concorde 4·00 6·00

152 Globe and Inset of Tonga

153 SPIA De Havilland D.H.C.6 Twin Otter 300

1983 (14 Mar). *Commonwealth Day. T* **152** *and similar horiz designs. Multicoloured. P* 14.

No.	Description	Mint	Used
839	29 s. Type **152**	35	45
840	32 s. Tongan dancers	6·00	4·00
841	47 s. Trawler	50	80
842	1 p. 50, King Taufa'ahau Tupou IV and flag	1·75	4·00
839/42	*Set of* 4	7·75	8·25

1983 (11 May). *Inauguration of Niuafo'ou Airport. T* **153** *and similar horiz design. Multicoloured. P* 14 × 14½.

No.	Description	Mint	Used
843	32 s. Type **153**	75	30
844	47 s. Type **153**	85	35
845	1 p. SPIA Boeing 707	1·50	1·25
846	1 p. 50, As 1 p.	2·25	1·75
843/6	*Set of* 4	4·75	3·25

154 "Intelsat IV" Satellite

155 Obverse and Reverse of Pa'anga Banknote

1983 (22 June). *World Communications Year. T* **154** *and similar multicoloured designs. P* 11 (2 *p.*) *or* 14 × 14½ (*others*).

No.	Description	Mint	Used
847	29 s. Type **154**	40	20
848	32 s. "Intelsat IVA" satellite	50	25
849	75 s. "Intelsat V" satellite	1·00	70
850	2 p. Moon post cover (45 × 32 *mm*)	2·00	2·00
847/50	*Set of* 4	3·50	2·75

1983 (3 Aug). *10th Anniv of Bank of Tonga. P* 14.

No.	Description	Mint	Used
851	**155** 1 p. multicoloured	1·25	1·50
852	2 p. multicoloured	2·25	2·50

STAMP DUTY. Stamps of Tonga and Niuafo'ou overprinted or surcharged "STAMP DUTY", "STAMP DUTY ONLY" or similar wording were for fiscal use and were not valid for postal purposes.

156 Early Printing Press

157 Yacht off Coast

(Des A. Benjamin and R. Edge)

1983 (22 Sept). *Printing in Tonga. T* **156** *and similar vert designs. Multicoloured. P* 14.

No.	Description	Mint	Used
853	13 s. Type **156**	20	15
854	32 s. Arrival of W. Woon	40	30
855	1 p. Early Tongan print	95	95
856	2 p. *The Tonga Chronicle*	1·50	2·00
853/6	*Set of* 4	2·75	3·00

1983 (17 Nov). *Christmas. Yachting off Vava'u. T* **157** *and similar vert designs. Multicoloured. P* 11.

No.	Description	Mint	Used
857	29 s. Type **157**	60	35
858	32 s. View of yacht from cave	60	35
859	1 p. 50, Anchored yacht	2·00	2·25
860	2 p. 50, Yacht off coast (*different*)	2·75	3·50
857/60	*Set of* 4	5·50	5·75

158 Abel Tasman and *Zeehan*

159 Chaste Mitre (*Scabrida casta*)

(Des R. Edge)

1984 (12 Mar). *Navigators and Explorers of the Pacific* (1*st series*). *T* **158** *and similar horiz designs. P* 14.

No.	Description	Mint	Used
861	32 s. deep dull green and black	1·50	1·50
862	47 s. reddish violet and black	2·00	2·00
863	90 s. light brown and black	3·75	3·75
864	1 p. 50, royal blue and black	5·00	5·00
861/4	*Set of* 4	11·00	11·00

Designs:—47 s. Samuel Wallis and H.M.S. *Dolphin*; 90 s. William Bligh and H.M.S. *Bounty*; 1 p. 50, James Cook and H.M.S. *Resolution*.

See also Nos. 896/9.

STAMPS DIE-CUT OR PERFORATED. During 1985 developments took place in the production of Tonga and Niuafo'ou self-adhesive stamps. Since 1981 these had been produced in traditional formats on backing paper perforated in the usual way. The individual stamps were, however, separated by the removal of the margins between them by the die-cutting process.

As an experiment some supplies of Tonga Nos. 870, 896, **MS**904, 905/9, 915/18, O225 and Niuafo'ou Nos. 56/60, together with the entire printing of Tonga Nos. 910/14, were produced with the margins intact so that both stamps and backing paper were perforated through.

Such issues are usually inscribed "Bend forward and peel off backing paper" on the reverse.

1984 (10 Apr)–**85.** *Marine Life. T* **159** *and similar multicoloured designs. Stamps die-cut and backing paper perf* 14 (1, 2, 3, 5 *p.*) *or* 14½ (*others*).

No.	Description	Mint	Used
865	1 s. Type **159**	30	50
866	2 s. *Porites* sp (26.6.84)	40	50
867	3 s. Red Squirrelfish (18.5.84)	40	60
868	5 s. Green Map Cowrie (*Cypraea mappa viridis*)	40	60
869	6 s. *Dardanus megistos* (crab) (17.9.84)	55	70
870	9 s. Variegated Shark (18.5.84)	55	45
	b. Stamp perforated (28.5.85)	75	45
871	10 s. Bubble Cone (*Conus bullatus*)	70	65
872	13 s. Lionfish (18.5.84)	80	55
873	15 s. Textile or Cloth of Gold Cone (*Conus textile*)	90	75
874	20 s. White-tailed Dascyllus (18.5.84)	1·25	85
875	29 s. Princely Cone (*Conus aulicus*)	1·75	70
876	32 s. Powder-blue Surgeonfish (18.5.84)	2·00	80
877	47 s. Giant Spider Conch (*Lambis truncata*)	2·50	1·60
878	1 p. *Millepora dichotoma* (26.6.84)	5·50	5·50
879	2 p. *Birgus latro* (crab) (17.9.84)	9·00	9·50
880	3 p. Rose-branch Murex (*Chicoreus palma rosae*)	9·00	11·00
881	5 p. Yellow-finned Tuna (18.5.84)	11·00	13·00
865/81	*Set of* 17	42·00	42·00

Nos. 878/81 are horizontal, 38×23 mm.

For 1, 2, 5, 6, 10, 15, 20, 32 s., 2 p., 3 p. and 5 p. with normal gum and perforations see Nos. 976*a*/*b*, 999/1017*a* and 1087/95.

For some of these designs redrawn with face value at foot see Nos. 1218/34 and 1346/7.

160 Printer checking Newspaper

161 U.S.A. Flag and Running

1984 (26 June). *20th Anniv of* Tonga Chronicle (*newspaper*). *Die-cut.*

No.	Description	Mint	Used
882	**160** 3 s. grey-brown and bright blue	10	10
	a. Sheetlet of 12	50	
883	32 s. grey-brown and vermilion	40	45
	a. Sheetlet of 12	4·75	

Nos. 882/3 were each printed in sheetlets of 12, the designs being superimposed on a reproduction of the front page from the first edition. This was printed in grey and is in Tongan for the 3 s. and English for the 32 s.

(Des R. Edge)

1984 (23 July). *Olympic Games, Los Angeles. T* **161** *and similar horiz designs, each showing U.S. flag. Each printed in black, scarlet-vermilion and bright new blue. P* 14 × 14½.

No.	Description	Mint	Used
884	29 s. Type **161**	25	25
885	47 s. Javelin-throwing	30	30
886	1 p. 50, Shot-putting	1·00	1·00
887	3 p. Olympic torch	1·90	1·90
884/7	*Set of* 4	3·00	3·00

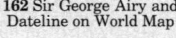

162 Sir George Airy and Dateline on World Map

163 Australia 1914 Laughing Kookaburra 6d. Stamp

(Des R. Edge)

1984 (20 Aug). *Centenary of International Dateline. T* **162** *and similar horiz design. Multicoloured. P* 14.

No.	Description	Mint	Used
888	47 s. Type **162**	1·25	1·00
889	2 p. Sir Sandford Fleming and Map of Pacific time zones	4·25	4·50

1984 (17 Sept). *"Ausipex" International Stamp Exhibition, Melbourne. T* **163** *and similar vert design. Multicoloured. P* 14.

No.	Description	Mint	Used
890	32 s. Type **163**	1·00	75
891	1 p. 50, Tonga 1897 Red Shining Parrot 2s. 6d. stamp	3·00	3·00
MS892	90×100 mm. As Nos. 890/1, but without exhibition logo and with "TONGA" and face values in gold. Die-cut	2·75	2·75

Examples of No. **MS**892 without face values are Exhibition Banquet souvenirs without postal validity.

164 Beach at Sunset ("Silent Night")

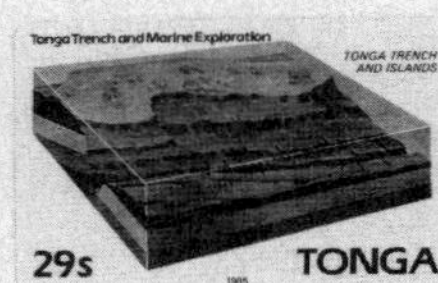

165 Section of Tonga Trench

(Des R. Edge)

1984 (12 Nov). *Christmas. Carols. T* **164** *and similar vert designs. Multicoloured. P* 14.

No.	Description	Mint	Used
893	32 s. Type **164**	60	45
894	47 s. Hut and palm trees ("Away in a Manger")	85	65
895	1 p. Sailing boats ("I Saw Three Ships")	1·75	2·75
893/5	*Set of* 3	2·75	3·50

Nos. 893/5 were each issued in sheets of 20 stamps with 5 labels, in the central vertical row, showing progressive stages of the design.

(Des R. Edge)

1985 (27 Feb). *Navigators and Explorers of the Pacific* (2*nd series*). *Horiz designs as T* **158**. *Stamps die-cut and backing paper perf* 14.

No.	Description	Mint	Used
896	32 s. black and turquoise-blue	2·75	1·25
	b. Stamp perforated	25·00	32·00
897	47 s. black and blue-green	3·00	1·50
898	90 s. black and scarlet	5·50	4·00
899	1 p. 50, black and buff	7·00	6·50
896/9	*Set of* 4	16·00	12·00

Designs:—32 s. Willem Schouten and *Eendracht*; 47 s. Jacob Le Maire and *Hoorn*; 90 s. Fletcher Christian and *Bounty*; 1 p. 50, Francisco Maurelle and *La Princessa*.

No. 896b has no inscription on the reverse.

1985 (10 Apr). *Geological Survey of the Tonga Trench. T* **165** *and similar multicoloured designs. Stamps die-cut and backing paper perf* 14.

No.	Description	Mint	Used
900	29 s. Type **165**	1·25	1·00
901	32 s. Diagram of marine seismic survey	1·25	1·00
902	47 s. Diagram of aerial oil survey (*vert*)	1·50	1·50
903	1 p. 50, Diagram of sea bed survey (*vert*)	4·75	6·00
900/3	*Set of* 4	8·00	8·50
MS904	100×100 mm. 1 p. 50, Bearded Angler (fish). Die-cut	6·00	4·50
	b. Stamp perforated	6·00	5·50

166 *Port au Prince* at Gravesend, 1805

167 Quintal (Byron Russell) and Capt. Bligh (Charles Laughton)

1985 (18 June). *175th Anniv of Will Mariner's Departure for England. T* **166** *and similar horiz designs. Multicoloured. A. Stamp die-cut and backing paper perf* 14. *B. Both stamp and backing paper perf* 14.

No.	Description	A		B	
905	29 s. Type **166**	70	70	60	50
906	32 s. Capture of *Port au Prince*, Tonga, 1806	70	70	60	50
907	47 s. Will Mariner on Tongan canoe, 1807	80	80	80	70
908	1 p. 50, Mariner boarding brig *Favourite*, 1810	2·25	2·75	2·25	2·75
909	2 p. 50, *Cuffnells* in English Channel, 1811	3·75	4·25	3·50	4·25
905/9	*Set of* 5	7·50	8·25	7·00	8·00

1985 (16 July). *50th Anniv of Film "Mutiny on the Bounty". T* **167** *and similar horiz designs showing film stills. Multicoloured. Both stamp and backing paper perf* 14.

No.	Description	Mint	Used
910	47 s. Type **167**	6·00	6·00
	a. Horiz strip of 5. Nos. 910/14	27·00	
911	47 s. Captain Bligh and prisoners	6·00	6·00
912	47 s. Fletcher Christian (Clark Gable)	6·00	6·00
913	47 s. Mutineers threatening Bligh	6·00	6·00
914	47 s. Bligh and Roger Byam (Franchot Tone) in boat	6·00	6·00
910/14	*Set of* 5	27·00	27·00

Nos. 910/14 were printed together, *se-tenant*, in horizontal strips of 5 throughout the sheet.

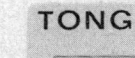

168 Lady Elizabeth Bowes-Lyon, 1910

169 Mary and Joseph arriving at Inn

1985 (20 Aug). *Life and Times of Queen Elizabeth the Queen Mother and 75th Anniv of Girl Guide Movement. T* **168** *and similar horiz designs. A. Stamp die-cut and backing paper perf* 14. B. *Both stamp and backing paper perf* 14.

		A		B	
915	32 s. black, salmon-pink and reddish brown	75	75	1·25	1·00
916	47 s. black, pale rose-lilac and reddish brown	1·00	1·25	1·75	1·50
917	1 p. 50, black, olive-yellow and reddish brown	3·00	3·50	5·00	4·00
918	2 p. 50, multicoloured	4·75	5·50	7·50	7·00
915/18	.. .. .. *Set of* 4	8·50	10·00	14·00	12·00

Designs:—47 s. Duchess of York at Hadfield Girl Guides' Rally, 1931; 1 p. 50, Duchess of York in Girl Guide uniform; 2 p. 50, Queen Mother in 1985 (from photo by Norman Parkinson).

1985 (12 Nov). *Christmas. T* **169** *and similar vert designs. Multicoloured. P* 14.

919	32 s. Type **169**..	55	30
920	42 s. The shepherds	60	40
921	1 p. 50, The Three Wise Men	2·25	3·00
922	2 p. 50, The Holy Family	3·25	4·00
919/22	.. .. *Set of* 4	6·00	7·00

PRINTER AND PROCESS. All issues from No. 923 were printed in lithography by Walsall Security Printers Ltd, *unless otherwise stated*, and have the normal form of gum, except for Nos. 972/6 which are self-adhesive.

170 Comet and Slogan "Maybe Twice in a Lifetime"

4s ▬ 4s
(**171**)

1986 (26 Mar). *Appearance of Halley's Comet. T* **170** *and similar horiz designs. Multicoloured. P* 14.

923	42 s. Type **170**..	2·50	2·50
	a. Horiz strip of 5. Nos. 923/7	11·00	
924	42 s. Edmond Halley	2·50	2·50
925	42 s. Solar System	2·50	2·50
926	42 s. Telescope	2·50	2·50
927	42 s. *Giotto* spacecraft	2·50	2·50
928	57 s. Type **170**..	2·75	2·75
	a. Horiz strip of 5. Nos. 928/32 ..	12·00	
929	57 s. As No. 924	2·75	2·75
930	57 s. As No. 925	2·75	2·75
931	57 s. As No. 926	2·75	2·75
932	57 s. As No. 927	2·75	2·75
923/32	.. .. *Set of* 10	23·00	23·00

Nos. 923/7 and 928/32 were each printed together, *se-tenant*, in horizontal strips of five, forming composite designs, throughout the sheets.

1986 (16 Apr). *Nos.* 866/7, 869/70, 872, 874, 879 *and* 881 *surch as T* **171**.

933	4 s. on 2 s. *Porites* sp.	70	80
934	4 s. on 13 s. Lionfish	70	80
935	42 s. on 3 s. Red Squirrelfish	1·25	80
936	42 s. on 9 s. Variegated Shark	1·25	80
937	57 s. on 6 s. *Dardanus megistos*	1·75	1·25
938	57 s. on 20 s. White-tailed Dascyllus ..	1·75	1·25
939	2 p. 50 on 2 p. *Birgus latro*	4·75	6·00
940	2 p. 50 on 5 p. Yellow-finned Tuna ..	4·75	6·00
933/40	.. .. *Set of* 8	15·00	16·00

172 King Taufa'ahau Tupou IV of Tonga

1986 (22 May). *Royal Links with Great Britain and 60th Birthday of Queen Elizabeth II. T* **172** *and similar designs. P* 14.

941	**172**	57 s. multicoloured	75	1·00
		a. Horiz pair. Nos. 941/2	1·50	2·00
942	–	57 s. multicoloured	75	1·00
943	–	2 p. 50, reddish brown, blk & pale new bl	3·25	3·75
941/3		.. .. .. *Set of* 3	4·25	5·25

Designs: *Horiz* (*as T* **172**)—No. 942, Queen Elizabeth II. *Square* (40×40 *mm*)—No. 943, Queen Elizabeth II and King Taufa'ahau Tupou IV, Tonga, 1970.

Nos. 941/2 were printed together, *se-tenant*, in horizontal pairs throughout the sheet, and No. 943 in sheetlets of five stamps and one stamp-size label.

173 Peace Corps Nurse giving Injection

174 Hockey (World Hockey Cup for Men, London)

1986 (22 May). *"Ameripex '86" International Stamp Exhibition, Chicago. 25th Anniv of United States Peace Corps. T* **173** *and similar horiz design. Multicoloured. P* 14.

944	57 s. Type **173**..	1·25	1·00
945	1 p. 50, Peace Corps teacher and pupil ..	2·25	2·75
MS946	90×90 mm. Nos. 944/5, magnifying glass and tweezers. Imperf	3·00	4·00

1986 (23 July). *Sporting Events. T* **174** *and similar vert designs. Multicoloured. P* 14.

947	42 s. Type **174**..	1·00	75
948	57 s. Handball (13th Commonwealth Games, Edinburgh)	1·10	85
949	1 p. Boxing (13th Commonwealth Games, Edinburgh)	1·75	2·25
950	2 p. 50, Football (World Cup Football Championship, Mexico)	4·00	5·00
947/50	.. .. *Set of* 4	7·00	8·00

175 1886 1d. King George I Definitive

(Des A. Benjamin)

1986 (27 Aug). *Centenary of First Tonga Stamps. T* **175** *and similar multicoloured designs. P* 14.

951	32 s. Type **175**..	1·25	95
952	42 s. 1897 7½d. King George II inverted centre error	1·50	1·00
953	57 s. 1950 Queen Salote's 50th Birthday 1d.	2·00	1·25
954	2 p. 50, 1986 Royal Links with Great Britain 2 p. 50	4·00	5·50
951/4	.. .. *Set of* 4	8·00	8·00
MS955	132×104 mm. 50 s.×8 Vert designs forming montage of Tonga stamps	8·00	9·00

Nos. 951/5 were printed with an overall pattern similar to watermark W **24**.

176 Girls wearing Shell Jewellery

BOY SCOUT JAMBOREE 5th–10th DEC '86
(**177**)

1986 (12 Nov). *Christmas. T* **176** *and similar multicoloured designs. P* 14.

956	32 s. Type **176**..	90	55
957	42 s. Boy with wood carvings (*vert*)	1·25	75
958	57 s. Children performing traditional dance (*vert*)	1·50	1·10
959	2 p. Children in dugout canoe	4·00	6·00
956/9	.. .. *Set of* 4	7·00	7·50

1986 (2 Dec). *Scout Jamboree, Tongatapu. Nos.* 957/8 *optd with T* **177** *in silver.*

960	42 s. Boy with wood carvings (*vert*)	1·75	1·75
961	57 s. Children performing traditional dance (*vert*)	2·25	2·25

178 Dumont D'Urville and *L'Astrolabe*

179 Noah's Ark

1987 (24 Feb). *150th Anniv of Dumont D'Urville's Second Voyage. T* **178** *and similar horiz designs. Multicoloured. P* 14.

962	32 s. Type **178**..	2·75	1·50
963	42 s. Tongan girls (from *Voyage au Pole et dans l'Oceanie*)	2·75	1·75
964	1 p. Contemporary chart	6·00	5·50
965	2 p. 50, Wreck of *L'Astrolabe*	11·00	12·00
962/5	.. .. *Set of* 4	20·00	19·00

1987 (6 May). *World Wildlife Fund. Sheet* 115×110 *mm containing T* **179** *and similar vert designs. Multicoloured. P* 13½.

MS966 42 s. Type **179**; 42 s. American Bald Eagles; 42 s. Giraffes and birds; 42 s. Gulls; 42 s. Ostriches and elephants; 42 s. Elephant; 42 s. Lions, zebras, antelopes and giraffes; 42 s. Chimpanzees; 42 s. Frogs and antelopes; 42 s. Lizard and tigers; 42 s. Snake and tiger; 42 s. *Papilio machaon* (butterfly) .. .. .. 26·00 26·00

The stamps within No. **MS**966 show a composite design of animals entering Noah's Ark.

180 Two Paddlers in Canoe

181 King Taufa'ahau Tupou IV

(Des C. Abbott. Litho Questa)

1987 (1 July). *"Siv'a'alo" (Tonga-Fiji-Samoa) Canoe Race. T* **180** *and similar square designs. Multicoloured. P* 14.

967	32 s. Type **180**..	55	40
968	42 s. Five paddlers	65	50
969	57 s. Paddlers and canoe bow	80	65
	a. Value omitted (R. 3/2)	£350	
970	1 p. 50, Two paddlers (different)	2·10	2·75
967/70	.. .. *Set of* 4	3·50	3·75
MS971	153×59 mm. Nos. 967/70	3·50	4·25

The stamps within No. **MS**971 show a composite design of two canoes racing.

No. 969a occurred on a batch of fifty sheets distributed to local post offices in Tonga. The remainder of the first printing was withdrawn and replaced, later in the month, by sheets showing the error corrected.

1987 (1 July)–**88**. *20th Anniv of Coronation of King Taufa'ahau Tupou IV. Self-adhesive. Stamps die-cut.*

972	**181**	1 s. black and olive-green	15	30
		a. Booklet pane. Nos. 972×2, 974×4, 975 × 2 and 976 × 4	3·00	
		b. Booklet pane. Nos. 972, 972*d*×2, 973×2, 974×4 and 975×3 (4.7.88)	5·00	
		c. Booklet pane. Nos. 972×4, 972*d*×2 and 976×6 (4.7.88)	6·00	
972*d*		2 s. black and pale orange (4.7.88) ..	1·50	1·75
973		5 s. black and pale magenta ..	15	30
		a. Booklet pane. Nos. 973×7, 974×2 and 975×3..	2·00	
974		10 s. black and reddish lilac	20	30
975		15 s. black and rose-red..	25	40
976		32 s. black and turquoise-blue	45	60
972/6		.. .. *Set of* 6	2·40	3·25

Nos. 972/6 were only available from stamp booklets. These are self-adhesive stamps and the backing card forms the booklet cover.

1987 (Sept). *As Nos.* 871 *and* 876 *(previously self-adhesive), but printed with normal gum and perforations. Multicoloured. P* 14½.

976*a*	10 s. *Conus bullatus*	5·00	5·00
976*b*	32 s. Powder-blue Surgeonfish	12·00	12·00

Nos. 976*a*/*b* were printed from the same plates as the self-adhesive issue. They are without imprint date at foot and show a space of 23 mm between the two horizontal lines across each design.

For redrawn versions of these stamps with imprint date see Nos. 1005 and 1008.

182 Arms and Tongan Citizens

183 Father Christmas Octopus and Rat with Sack of Presents

1987 (23 Sept). *125th Anniv of First Parliament. P* 14½ × 14.

977	**182**	32 s. multicoloured	40	30
978		42 s. multicoloured	50	40
979		75 s. multicoloured	90	1·00
980		2 p. multicoloured	2·25	2·75
977/80		.. .. .. *Set of* 4	3·50	4·00

1987 (25 Nov). *Christmas. T* **183** *and similar horiz designs showing cartoons. Multicoloured. P* 13½ × 14.

981	42 s. Type **183**	70	45
982	57 s. Delivering presents by outrigger canoe	90	65
983	1 p. Delivering presents by motorised tricycle	1·75	2·00
984	3 p. Drinking cocktails	4·50	5·50
981/4	.. .. *Set of* 4	7·00	7·75

PRICES OF SETS

Set prices are given for many issues, generally those containing three stamps or more. Definitive sets include one of each value or major colour change, but do not cover different perforations, die types or minor shades. Where a choice is possible the set prices are based on the cheapest versions of the stamps included in the listings.

184 King Taufa'ahau Tupou IV, *Olovaha II* (inter-island freighter), Oil Rig and Pole Vaulting

1988 (4 July). *70th Birthday of King Taufa'ahau Tupou IV. T* **184** *and similar horiz designs, each showing portrait. Multicoloured. P* 11½.

985 32 s. Type **184** .. .. 1·00 70
986 42 s. Banknote, coins, Ha'amonga Trilithon and woodcarver .. .. .. 1·00 75
987 57 s. Rowing, communications satellite and Red Cross worker .. .. .. 1·25 90
988 2 p. 50, Scout emblem, 1982 47 s. Scout stamp and Friendly Islands Airways De Havilland D.H.C.6 Twin Otter 200/300 aircraft .. .. .. 5·00 6·00
985/8 .. .. *Set of* 4 7·50 7·50

Nos. 985/8 exist overprinted "XX U.P.U. CONGRESS WASHINGTON DC 1989" on the reverse in blue and come from albums distributed at this event.

For similar designs issued in 1990 for the King's Silver Jubilee see Nos. 1082/5.

185 Capt. Cook and Journal

186 Athletics

1988 (11 July). *Bicentenary of Australian Settlement. Sheet* 115 × 110 *mm containing T* **185** *and similar vert designs. Multicoloured. P* 13½.

MS989 42 s. Type **185**; 42 s. Ships in Sydney Harbour and Governor Philip; 42 s. Australia 1952 2s. 6d. aborigine definitive and early settlement; 42 s. Burke and Wills (explorers); 42 s. Emu, opals and gold prospector's licence; 42 s. ANZAC cap badge and soldier; 42 s. Cover from first overland mail by Trans Continental; 42 s. Ross Smith, England–Australia flown cover and G.B. 1969 1s. 9d. commemorative stamp; 42 s. Don Bradman and Harold Larwood (cricketers); 42 s. World War II campaign medals; 42 s. Australia 1978 18 c. Flying Doctor Service stamp and sheep station; 42 s. Sydney Opera House .. .. 16·00 17·00

No. **MS**989 exists overprinted on the reverse as described below Nos. 985/8.

1988 (11 Aug). *Olympic Games, Seoul. T* **186** *and similar vert designs. Multicoloured. P* 14.

990 57 s. Type **186** 60 65
991 75 s. Yachting 90 95
992 2 p. Cycling .. .. 2·75 3·00
993 3 p. Tennis .. .. 4·00 4·25
990/3 .. .. *Set of* 4 7·50 8·00

187 Traditional Tongan Fale

1988 (9 Sept). *Music in Tonga. T* **187** *and similar horiz designs. Multicoloured. P* 14.

994 32 s. Type **187** 30 35
995 42 s. Church choir 40 45
996 57 s. Tonga Police Band outside Royal Palace 75 80
997 2 p. 50, "The Jets" pop group .. .. 2·40 3·25
994/7 .. .. *Set of* 4 3·50 4·25

188 Olympic Flame

1988 (9 Sept). *"Sport Aid '88". Sheet* 105 × 75 *mm, containing T* **188** *and design as No.* 997. *Multicoloured. P* 14.

MS998 57 s. Type **188**; 57 s. As No. 997 .. 1·10 1·40

Two types of 42 s.:

Type I. Background shading in bright blue extending to the perforation margin. Plumage is light brown.

Type II. Background shading in oval of new blue bleeding off at edges. Plumage is sepia.

1988 (4 Oct)–**92.** *Redrawn designs as Nos.* 865/6, 868/9, 871/6, 879/81 *(previously self-adhesive) and new values* (7, 35, 42, 57 *s.,* 1 *p.,* 1 *p.* 50, 10 *p.*), *all with normal gum, perforations and imprint date at foot. Multicoloured. Chalk-surfaced paper* (4, 7, 35, 42, 50, 57 *s.,* 1 *p.,* 1 *p.* 50., 2 *p.,* 5 *p.,* 10 *p.*). *P* 14 (1 *p. to* 10 *p.*) *or* 14½×14 (*others*).

999 1 s. Type **159** 30 40
1000 2 s. *Porites* sp (18.10.88) 40 50
a. Chalk-surfaced paper (4.90) 50 70
1001 4 s. Lionfish (2.3.89) 70 80
1002 5 s. Green Map Cowrie (*Cypraea mappa viridis*) 50 60
a. Chalk-surfaced paper (4.90) .. .. 90 1·00
1003 6 s. *Dardanus megistos* (crab) (18.10.88) 70 1·00
1004 7 s. Wandering Albatross (2.3.89) .. 1·50 1·25
1005 10 s. Bubble Cone (*Conus bullatus*) .. 60 50
a. Chalk-surfaced paper (4.90) 90 90
1006 15 s. Textile or Cloth of Gold Cone (*Conus textile*) (18.10.88) 60 60
1007 20 s. White-tailed Dascyllus 90 90
1008 32 s. Powder-blue Surgeonfish .. .. 1·00 60
a. Chalk-surfaced paper (4.90) .. .. 1·00 1·00
1009 35 s. Seahorse (2.3.89) .. .. .. 1·75 1·50
1010 42 s. Lesser Frigate Bird (I) (18.10.88) .. 1·50 60
a. Type II .. .. 23·00
1011 50 s. Princely Cone (*Conus aulicus*) (2.3.89) .. .. 1·00 80
1012 57 s. Brown Booby (18.10.88) .. .. 2·00 90
1013 1 p. *Chelonia mydas* (turtle) (2.3.89) .. 2·50 2·50
1014 1 p. 50, Humpback Whale (2.3.89) .. 6·00 4·50
1015 2 p. *Birgus latro* (crab) (19.1.89) .. 3·50 4·50
1016 3 p. Rose-branch Murex (*Chicoreus palma rosae*) (18.10.88) .. .. .. 2·75 4·50
1017 5 p. Yellow-finned Tuna (19.1.89) .. 8·50 11·00
1017*a* 10 p. Variegated Shark (12.5.92) .. 13·00 16·00
999/1017*a* .. .. .. *Set of* 20 45·00 48·00

Nos. 1013/17 are horizontal, 41×26 mm and No. 1017*a* vertical, 26×41 mm.

Imprint dates: "1988", Nos. 999/1000, 1002/3, 1005/8, 1010, 1012, 1016; "1989", Nos. 1001, 1004, 1009, 1013/15, 1017; "1990", Nos. 1000a, 1002a, 1005a, 1008a; "1992", No. 1017*a*.

On the redrawn designs there is a larger gap between the two horizontal lines on each design. On Nos. 1005 and 1008 this measures 25 mm. For these two values with a gap of 23 mm and no imprint date see Nos. 976*a*/*b*.

For 2, 5, 10, 15 and 32 s. values in a smaller format see Nos. 1087/95.

For some of these designs redrawn with face value at foot see Nos. 1218/34 and 1345/9.

189 Capt. Cook's H.M.S. *Resolution*

190 Girl in Hospital Bed

1988 (20 Oct). *Centenary of Tonga–U.S.A. Treaty of Friendship. T* **189** *and similar horiz designs. Multicoloured. P* 14.

1018 42 s. Type **189** 80 70
1019 57 s. *Santa Maria* .. .. 1·00 80
1020 2 p. Cook and Christopher Columbus .. 3·25 4·00
1018/20 .. .. *Set of* 3 4·50 5·00
MS1021 140 × 115 mm. Nos. 1018/20 .. .. 4·50 5·50

Nos. 1018/21 exist overprinted on the reverse as described below Nos. 985/8.

1988 (17 Nov). *Christmas. 125th Anniv of International Red Cross and 25th Anniv of Tongan Red Cross. T* **123** *and similar horiz designs. Multicoloured. P* 14½.

1022 15 s. Type **190** (A) 15 20
a. Horiz pair. Nos. 1022/3 .. .. 30 40
1023 15 s. Type **190** (B) 15 20
1024 32 s. Red Cross nurse reading to boy (A) .. 30 35
a. Horiz pair. Nos. 1024/5 .. .. 60 70
1025 32 s. Red Cross nurse reading to boy (B) .. 30 35
1026 42 s. Red Cross nurse taking pulse (A) .. 40 45
a. Horiz pair. Nos. 1026/7 .. .. 80 85
1027 42 s. Red Cross nurse taking pulse (B) .. 40 45
1028 57 s. Red Cross nurse with sleeping child (A) 55 60
a. Horiz pair. Nos. 1028/9 .. .. 1·10 1·25
1029 57 s. Red Cross nurse with sleeping child (B) 55 60
1030 1 p. 50, Boy in wheelchair (A) .. .. 1·40 2·00
a. Horiz pair. Nos. 1030/1 .. .. 2·75 4·00
1031 1 p. 50, Boy in wheelchair (B) .. .. 1·40 2·00
1022/31 .. .. *Set of* 10 5·00 6·50

Nos. 1022/3, 1024/5, 1026/7, 1028/9 and 1030/1 were printed together, *se-tenant,* in horizontal pairs throughout the sheets with the first stamp in each pair inscribed "INTERNATIONAL RED CROSS 125th ANNIVERSARY" (A) and the second "SILVER JUBILEE OF TONGAN RED CROSS" (B).

Nos. 1022, 1024, 1026, 1028 and 1030 exist overprinted on the reverse as described below Nos. 985/8.

191 Map of Tofua Island and Breadfruit

192 *Hypolimnas bolina*

1989 (28 Apr). *Bicentenary of Mutiny on the* Bounty. *T* **191** *and similar multicoloured designs. P* 13½×14.

1032 32 s. Type **191** .. .. 2·00 1·25
1033 42 s. H.M.S. *Bounty* and chronometer .. 3·00 1·50
1034 57 s. Captain Bligh and *Bounty*'s launch cast adrift .. .. 4·00 2·75
1032/4 .. .. *Set of* 3 8·00 5·00
MS1035 106×80 mm. 2 p. Fletcher Christian on H.M.S. *Bounty* (*vert*); 3 p. Bligh cast adrift. P 14×13½ (2 p.) or 13½×14×13½×13½ (3 p.) 6·00 7·50

Nos. 1032/5 exists overprinted on the reverse as described below Nos. 985/8.

1989 (18 May). *Butterflies. T* **192** *and similar vert designs. Multicoloured. P* 14½×14.

1036 42 s. Type **192** .. .. 1·00 70
1037 57 s. *Jamides bochus* .. .. .. 1·25 90
1038 1 p. 20, *Melanitis leda* .. .. .. 2·25 2·50
1039 2 p. 50, *Danaus plexippus* .. .. 3·75 5·00
1036/9 .. .. *Set of* 4 7·50 8·00

Nos. 1036/9 exist overprinted on the reverse as described below Nos. 985/8.

193 Football at Rugby School, 1870

194 Short S.30 Modified "G" Class Flying Boat *Aotearoa*, 1939 (50th anniv of first flight)

1989 (22 Aug). *Inauguration of National Sports Stadium and South Pacific Mini Games, Tonga. T* **193** *and similar horiz designs showing development of rugby, tennis and cricket. Multicoloured. P* 14.

1040 32 s. Type **193** 55 55
a. Sheetlet. Nos. 1040/4×2 .. .. 5·00
1041 32 s. D. Gallaher (All Black's captain, 1905) and Springboks rugby match, 1906 55 55
1042 32 s. King George V with Cambridge team, 1922 and W. Wakefield (England captain, 1926) 55 55
1043 32 s. E. Crawford (Ireland captain, 1926) and players on cigarette cards .. 55 55
1044 32 s. S. Mafi (Tonga captain, 1970s) and modern rugby match 55 55
1045 42 s. Royal tennis, 1659 .. .. .. 85 85
a. Sheetlet. Nos. 1045/9×2 .. .. 7·50
1046 42 s. Major Wingfield and lawn tennis, 1873 .. .. 85 85
1047 42 s. Oxford and Cambridge tennis teams, 1884 .. .. 85 85
1048 42 s. Bunny Ryan, 1910, and players on cigarette cards 85 85
1049 42 s. Boris Becker and modern tennis match 85 85
1050 57 s. Cricket match, 1743, and F. Pilch memorial .. .. 1·25 1·25
a. Sheetlet. Nos. 1050/4×2 .. .. 11·00
1051 57 s. W. G. Grace (19th-century cricketer) 1·25 1·25
1052 57 s. *Boys Own Paper* cricket article, 1909 1·25 1·25
1053 57 s. Australian cricket team, 1909, and players on cigarette cards .. .. 1·25 1·25
1054 57 s. The Ashes urn, and modern cricket match .. .. 1·25 1·25
1040/54 .. .. *Set of* 15 12·00 12·00

Nos. 1040/4, 1045/9 and 1050/4 were each issued in sheetlets of ten containing two horizontal strips of five separated by a central inscribed gutter.

1989 (23 Oct). *Aviation in Tonga. T* **194** *and similar horiz designs. Multicoloured. P* 14½×14.

1055 42 s. Type **194** .. .. 1·75 1·10
1056 57 s. Chance Vought F4U Corsair, 1943 .. 2·25 1·50
1057 90 s. Boeing 737 at Fua'amotu Airport .. 3·50 3·50
1058 3 p. Montgolfier balloon, Wright Flyer I biplane, Concorde and space shuttle (97×26 *mm*) .. .. 8·50 10·00
1055/8 .. .. *Set of* 4 14·50 14·50

PRICES OF SETS

Set prices are given for many issues, generally those containing three stamps or more. Definitive sets include one of each value or major colour change, but do not cover different perforations, die types or minor shades. Where a choice is possible the set prices are based on the cheapest versions of the stamps included in the listings.

195 CASA C-212 Aviocar landing

196 Rowland Hill, Mulready Cover and Penny Blacks

(Des G. Bennett)

1989 (9 Nov). *Christmas. "Flying Home". T* **195** *and similar vert designs. P* 14×13½.

1059 32 s. blue-green, deep brown & dull orange .. 1·00 70
1060 42 s. blue-green, deep brown and emerald .. 1·10 70
1061 57 s. blue-green, deep brown and vermilion .. 1·40 90
1062 3 p. blue-green, deep brown & deep mauve .. 5·50 6·50
1059/62 .. .. *Set of* 4 8·00 8·00

Designs:—42 s. Villagers waving to CASA C-212 Aviocar aircraft; 57 s. Outrigger canoe and CASA C-212 Aviocar aircraft; 3 p. CASA C-212 Aviocar aircraft over headland.

1989 (17 Nov). *20th Universal Postal Union Congress, Washington. Sheet* 115×110 *mm containing T* **196** *and similar vert designs. Multicoloured. P* 13½.

MS1063 57 s. Type **196**; 57 s. Early train and steam ship; 57 s. Stage coach, Pony Express poster and rider; 57 s. French hot-air balloon and flown cover; 57 s. Samuel Morse and telegraph key; 57 s. Early British mail van and pillar box; 57 s. Unloading De Havilland D.H.4.M mail biplane; 57 s. *Queen Mary* (liner) and Airship LZ-127 *Graf Zeppelin* flown cover; 57 s. Westland Dragonfly helicopter and mail van; 57 s. Computer and fax machine; 57 s. "Apollo 11" emblem and space cover; 57 s. U.P.U. Monument and space shuttle .. .. 19·00 21·00

No. **MS**1063 exists overprinted on the reverse as described below Nos. 985/8.

197 1989 U.P.U. Congress Stamps

198 Boxing

1989 (17 Nov). *"World Stamp Expo '89" International Stamp Exhibition, Washington. P* 14.

1064 **197** 57 s. multicoloured .. .. 1·40 1·25

No. 1064 exists overprinted on the reverse as described below Nos. 985/8.

1990 (14 Feb). *14th Commonwealth Games, Auckland. T* **198** *and similar vert designs. Multicoloured. P* 14.

1065 42 s. Type **198** 90 70
1066 57 s. Archery .. .. 1·50 1·10
1067 1 p. Bowls .. .. 2·00 2·50
1068 2 p. Swimming .. .. 3·50 4·50
1065/8 .. .. *Set of* 4 7·00 8·00

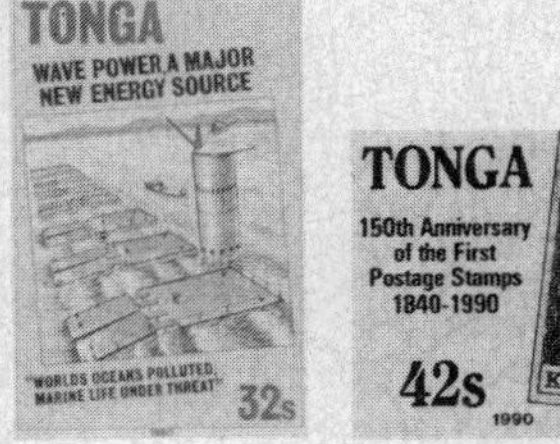

199 Wave Power Installation

200 Penny Black

1990 (11 Apr). *Alternative Sources of Electricity. T* **199** *and similar vert designs. Multicoloured. P* 14.

1069 32 s. Type **199** .. .. 1·00 65
1070 57 s. Wind farm .. .. 1·50 1·10
1071 1 p. 20, Experimental solar cell vehicle .. 3·00 4·25
1069/71 .. .. *Set of* 3 5·00 5·50
MS1072 110×90 mm. 2 p. 50, Planet Earth .. 7·00 8·00

1990 (1 May). *150th Anniv of the Penny Black. T* **200** *and similar horiz designs showing stamps. P* 14.

1073 42 s. multicoloured .. .. .. 1·25 1·25
a. Horiz pair. Nos. 1073/4 .. .. 2·50 2·50
1074 42 s. multicoloured .. .. .. 1·25 1·25
1075 57 s. scarlet and black .. .. .. 1·50 1·25
1076 1 p. 50, multicoloured .. .. .. 3·50 4·00
1077 2 p. 50, multicoloured .. .. .. 5·00 5·50
1073/7 .. .. *Set of* 5 11·00 12·00

Designs:—42 s. (No. 1074) Great Britain 1840 Twopence Blue; 57 s. Tonga 1886 1d.; 1 p. 50, 1980 South Pacific Scout Jamboree and Rotary 75th anniv 2 p. official stamp; 2 p. 50, 1990 Alternative Sources of Electricity 57 s.

Nos. 1073/4 were printed together, *se-tenant*, in horizontal pairs throughout the sheet.

Nos. 1073/7 show a faint grey pattern similar to W **24** in the background.

201 Departure of Canoe

202 Iguana searching for Food

(Des G. Bennett)

1990 (6 June). *Polynesian Voyages of Discovery. T* **201** *and similar vert designs. P* 14½.

1078 32 s. deep blue-green 75 65
1079 42 s. deep dull blue .. .. .. 1·00 80
1080 1 p. 20, reddish brown .. .. .. 2·75 3·00
1081 3 p. deep reddish violet .. .. .. 5·50 8·00
1078/81 .. .. *Set of* 4 9·00 11·00

Designs:—42 s. Navigating by night; 1 p. 20, Canoe and sea birds; 3 p. Landfall.

1990 (4 July). *Silver Jubilee of King Taufa'ahau Tupou IV. Designs as Nos.* 985/8, *but inscribed* "Silver Jubilee of His Majesty King Taufa'ahau Tupou IV. 1965–1990" *and with* "TONGA" *and values in silver. P* 11½.

1082 32 s. As Type **184** .. .. .. 1·00 70
1083 42 s. Banknote, coins, Ha'amonga Trilithon and woodcarver .. .. .. 1·10 75
1084 57 s. Rowing, communications satellite and Red Cross worker .. .. .. 1·40 85
1085 2 p. 50, Scout emblem, 1982 47 s. Scout stamp and Friendly Island Airways De Havilland D.H.C.6 Twin Otter aircraft .. .. 5·00 6·50
1082/5 .. .. *Set of* 4 7·75 8·00

1990 (6 July)–**92**. *Designs as Nos.* 1000, 1002, 1003 (*value changed*), 1005 *and* 1008 *redrawn smaller,* 19×22 *mm. Multicoloured. Chalk-surfaced paper. P* 14.

1087 2 s. *Porites* sp 40 50
a. Booklet pane. No. 1087×10 (4.9.90) .. 3·00
1089 5 s. Green Map Cowrie (*Cypraea mappa viridis*) 40 50
a. Booklet pane. No. 1089×10 (4.9.90) 3·00
1092 10 s. Bubble Cone (*Conus bullatus*) .. 40 50
a. Booklet pane. No. 1092×10 (4.9.90) 3·00
1093 15 s. *Dardanus megistos* (crab) (as No. 1003) (12.5.92) 80 80
1095 32 s. Powder-blue Surgeonfish 40 50
a. Booklet pane. No. 1095×10 (4.9.90) 3·00
1087/95 .. .. *Set of* 5 2·25 2·50

The outer edges of booklet panes Nos. 1087a, 1089a, 1092a, 1095a are imperforate so that stamps from them have one or two adjacent sides imperforate.

Imprint dates: "1990", Nos. 1087, 1089, 1092, 1095; "1992", Nos. 1087, 1089, 1092/3.

(Des G. Drummond)

1990 (12 Sept). *Endangered Species. Banded Iguana. T* **202** *and similar horiz designs. Multicoloured. P* 14.

1105 32 s. Type **202** .. .. 1·50 75
1106 42 s. Head of male .. .. 1·75 85
1107 57 s. Pair of iguanas during courtship .. 2·25 1·25
1108 1 p. 20, Iguana basking .. .. .. 5·00 6·00
1105/8 .. .. *Set of* 4 9·50 8·00

203 Tourism

204 Boy

(Des A. Benjamin and R. Edge)

1990 (25 Oct). *40th Anniv of United Nations Development Programme. T* **203** *and similar horiz designs. Multicoloured. P* 13½×14.

1109 57 s. Type **203** .. .. 1·25 1·25
a. Pair. Nos. 1109/10 .. .. .. 2·50 2·50
1110 57 s. Agriculture and Fisheries .. .. 1·25 1·25
1111 3 p. Education .. .. 6·00 7·00
a. Pair. Nos. 1111/12 .. .. .. 12·00 14·00
1112 3 p. Healthcare .. .. 6·00 7·00
1109/12 .. .. *Set of* 4 13·00 15·00

The two designs for each value were printed together, *se-tenant*, in horizontal and vertical pairs throughout the sheets.

1990 (28 Nov). *Christmas. Rotary International Interact Project. T* **204** *and similar vert designs. Multicoloured. P* 14.

1113 32 s. Type **204** 70 40
1114 42 s. Young boys 90 55
1115 2 p. Girls in western clothes .. .. 3·50 4·00
1116 3 p. Girls in traditional costumes .. .. 4·50 5·00
1113/16 .. .. *Set of* 4 8·75 9·00

205 Safety at Work

206 Yacht at Dawn

(Des C. Abbott)

1991 (10 Apr–11 Aug). *Accident Prevention. T* **205** *and similar vert designs. Multicoloured. P* 14½×14.

1117 32 s. Type **205** (English inscription) .. 80 80
a. Horiz pair. Nos. 1117/18 .. .. 1·60 1·60
1118 32 s. Safety at home (English inscription) 80 80
1119 32 s. As No. 1118 (Tongan inscription) .. 80 80
a. Horiz pair. Nos. 1119/20 .. .. 1·60 1·60
b. Horiz pair. Nos. 1119/20a (11 Aug) 18·00 18·00
1120 32 s. As Type **205** (Tongan inscription) .. 80 80
a. Tongan inscription corrected to "Ngaue tokanga" (11 Aug) .. 18·00 18·00
1121 42 s. Safety in cars (English inscription) .. 1·25 1·25
a. Horiz pair. Nos. 1121/2 .. .. 2·50 2·50
1122 42 s. Safety on bikes (English inscription) 1·25 1·25
1123 42 s. As No. 1122 (Tongan inscription) .. 1·25 1·25
a. Horiz pair. Nos. 1123/4 .. .. 2·50 2·50
1124 42 s. As No. 1121 (Tongan inscription) .. 1·25 1·25
1125 57 s. Safety at sea (English inscription) .. 1·50 1·50
a. Horiz pair. Nos. 1125/6 .. .. 3·00 3·00
1126 57 s. Safety on the beach (English inscription) .. .. .. 1·50 1·50
1127 57 s. As No. 1126 (Tongan inscription) .. 1·50 1·50
a. Horiz pair. Nos. 1127/8 .. .. 3·00 3·00
1128 57 s. As No. 1125 (Tongan inscription) .. 1·50 1·50
1117/28 .. .. *Set of* 12 13·00 13·00

Nos. 1117/28 were printed in sheets of 20, two panes (2×5) separated by a vertical gutter, for each value with the left-hand panes containing *se-tenant* horizontal pairs of the designs with English inscriptions and the right-hand panes similar pairs inscribed in Tongan.

No. 1120 is incorrectly inscribed in Tongan "Ngauo tokanga".

(Des D. Miller)

1991 (2 July). *Around the World Yacht Race. Sheet* 120×103 *mm containing T* **206** *and similar vert designs. Multicoloured. P* 14½×14.

MS1129 1 p. Type **206**; 1 p. Yacht in the morning; 1 p. Yacht at midday; 1 p. Yacht in the evening; 1 p. Yacht at night .. .. .. 6·75 7·50

207 Fishes in the Sea

208 Tonga Temple

(Des D. Miller)

1991 (2 July). *Heilala Week. T* **207** *and similar vert designs. Multicoloured. P* 14½×14.

1130 42 s. Type **207** 70 55
1131 57 s. Island and yacht 90 65
1132 2 p. Pile of fruit .. .. 2·75 3·50
1133 3 p. Turtle on beach .. .. .. 3·50 4·00
1130/3 .. .. *Set of* 4 7·00 8·00

(Des R. Edge)

1991 (19 Aug). *Centenary of Church of Latter Day Saints in Tonga. T* **208** *and similar vert design. Multicoloured. P* 14½.

1134 42 s. Type **208** .. .. 1·10 1·10
1135 57 s. Temple at night .. .. .. 1·40 1·40

209 Making T.V. Childcare Programme

(Des R. Edge)

1991 (15 Oct). *Telecommunications in Tonga. T* **209** *and similar horiz designs. Multicoloured. P* 14½.

1136 15 s. Type **209** 35 35
a. Horiz strip of 3. Nos. 1136/8 . . 95
1137 15 s. T.V. satellite 35 35
1138 15 s. Mothers watching programme . . 35 35
1139 32 s. Man on telephone and woman with computer 65 65
a. Horiz strip of 3. Nos. 1139/41 . . 1·75
1140 32 s. Telecommunications satellite . . 65 65
1141 32 s. Overseas customer on telephone . . 65 65
1142 42 s. Sinking coaster 90 90
a. Horiz strip of 3. Nos. 1142/4 . . 2·40
1143 42 s. Coastguard controller 90 90
1144 42 s. Maritime rescue 90 90
1145 57 s. Weather satellite above Southern Hemisphere . . . . 1·10 1·10
a. Horiz strip of 3. Nos. 1145/7 . . 3·00
1146 57 s. Meteorologist collecting data . . 1·10 1·10
1147 57 s. T.V. weather map and storm . . 1·10 1·10
1136/47 . . . . *Set of* 12 8·00 8·00

The three designs for each value were printed together, *se-tenant*, in horizontal strips of three throughout the sheets.

210 Women's Rowing Eight

(Des D. Miller)

1991 (29 Oct). *"Siu'a'alo" Rowing Festival. T* **210** *and similar horiz designs. Multicoloured. P* 14.

1148 42 s. Type **210** 85 45
1149 57 s. Longboat . . . . 1·00 55
1150 1 p. Outrigger canoe . . . . . . 2·00 2·00
1151 2 p. Stern of fautasi (large canoe) . . 3·25 4·00
a. Horiz pair. Nos. 1151/2 . . 6·50 8·00
1152 2 p. Bow of fautasi . . . . . . 3·25 4·00
1148/52 . . . . *Set of* 5 9·25 10·00

Nos. 1151/2 were printed together, *se-tenant*, in horizontal pairs throughout the sheet, forming a composite design

211 Turtles pulling Santa's Sledge

212 *Pangai* (patrol boat)

1991 (11 Nov). *Christmas. T* **211** *and similar horiz designs. Multicoloured. P* 14.

1153 32 s. Type **211** 85 35
1154 42 s. Santa Claus on roof of fala (Tongan house) 95 45
1155 57 s. Family opening presents . . . . 1·10 60
1156 3 p. 50, Family waving goodbye to Santa 6·50 8·00
1153/6 . . . . *Set of* 4 8·50 8·50

(Des R. Edge)

1991 (15 Dec). *Royal Tongan Defence Force. T* **212** *and similar multicoloured designs. P* 14.

1157 42 s. Type **212** . . . . 1·00 1·00
a. Horiz pair. Nos. 1157/8 . . 2·00 2·00
1158 42 s. Marine in battle dress . . . . 1·00 1·00
1159 57 s. Tonga Royal Guards . . . . 1·25 1·25
a. Horiz pair. Nos. 1159/60 . . 2·50 2·50
1160 57 s. Raising the ensign on *Neiafu* (patrol boat) . . . . 1·25 1·25
1161 2 p. *Savea* (patrol boat) (*horiz*) . . 3·00 3·50
a. Horiz pair. Nos. 1161/2 . . 6·00 7·00
1162 2 p. King Taufa'ahau Tupou IV inspecting parade (*horiz*) . . . . . . 3·00 3·50
1157/62 . . . . *Set of* 6 9·50 10·50

The two designs for each value were printed together, *se-tenant*, in horizontal pairs throughout the sheets.

XXX

1s

(213)

214 Columbus and Signature

1992 (19 Mar). *No.* 1007 *surch with T* **213**.

1163 1 s. on 20 s. White-tailed Dascyllus . . 55 55

(Des R. Edge)

1992 (28 Apr). 500*th Anniv of Discovery of America by Columbus. Sheet* 119×109 *mm containing T* **214** *and similar vert designs. Multicoloured. P* 13½.

MS1164 57 s. Type **214**; 57 s. Monastery of Santa Maria de la Chevas; 57 s. Obverse and reverse of coin of Ferdinand and Isabella; 57 s. Spain commemorative stamps of 1930; 57 s. Compass and astrolabe; 57 s. Model of *Santa Maria*; 57 s. Sketch map and signature; 57 s. 15th-century woodcut of Columbus arriving in New World; 57 s. Lucayan artefacts and parrot; 57 s. Pineapple, bird pendant and Indian nose ring; 57 s. Columbus reporting to Spanish Court; 57 s. Medal showing Columbus and signature . . 15·00 17·00

215 U.S.S. *Arizona* under attack, Pearl Harbor, 1941

216 Boxing

(Des R. Edge)

1992 (26 May). 50*th Anniv of Outbreak of Pacific War. T* **215** *and similar horiz designs. Multicoloured. P* 14.

1165 42 s. Type **215** 80 80
a. Sheetlet. Nos. 1165/76 . . 8·50
1166 42 s. Japanese invasion of the Philippines 80 80
1167 42 s. U.S. landings in the Gilbert Islands 80 80
1168 42 s. Landing on Iwo Jima 80 80
1169 42 s. Admiral Nimitz and Battle of Midway map 80 80
1170 42 s. General MacArthur and liberation of Philippines map 80 80
1171 42 s. Lt-Gen. Holland Smith and map of landings on Saipan and Tinian . . 80 80
1172 42 s. Major-Gen. Curtis Lemay and bombing of Japan map 80 80
1173 42 s. Japanese Mitsubishi A6M Zero-Sen 80 80
1174 42 s. Douglas SBD Dauntless 80 80
1175 42 s. Grumman FM-2 Wildcat 80 80
1176 42 s. Supermarine Seafire Mk III . . 80 80
1165/76 . . . . *Set of* 12 8·50 8·50

Nos. 1165/76 were printed together, *se-tenant*, in sheetlets of 12 (4×3) on which the top row formed a composite design.

(Des J. Smith)

1992 (16 June). *Olympic Games, Barcelona. T* **216** *and similar vert designs. Multicoloured. P* 14.

1177 42 s. Type **216** 75 50
1178 57 s. Diving 95 55
1179 1 p. 50, Tennis . . . . 4·00 4·25
1180 3 p. Cycling . . . . 6·00 6·50
1177/80 . . . . *Set of* 4 10·50 10·50

217 King Taufa'ahau Tupou IV and Queen Halaevalu

45s ▬ 45s

(218)

(Des R. Edge)

1992 (4 July). 25*th Anniv of the Coronation of King Tupou IV. T* **217** *and similar horiz designs. P* 13½×13 (45 *s.*) *or* 12 (*others*).

1181 45 s. multicoloured 75 45
1182 80 s. multicoloured . . . . . . 1·50 1·75
a. Horiz strip of 3. Nos. 1182/4 . . 4·00
1183 80 s. black and cinnamon . . . . 1·50 1·75
1184 80 s. multicoloured . . . . . . 1·50 1·75
1185 2 p. multicoloured . . . . . . 3·50 4·00
1181/5 . . . . *Set of* 5 8·00 8·75

Designs: (48×35 *mm*)—No. 1182, King Tupou IV and Crown; No. 1183, Extract from Investiture ceremony; No. 1184, King Tupou IV and 1967 Coronation 2 p. commemorative; No. 1185, As Type **217**, but larger.

Nos. 1181/5 show the King's first name incorrectly spelt as "Tauf'ahau".

Nos. 1182/4 were printed together, *se-tenant*, in horizontal strips of 3 throughout the sheet.

1992 (11 Aug). *No.* 1095 *surch with T* **218**.

1186 45 s. on 32 s. Powder-blue Surgeonfish . . 2·25 1·50

MINIMUM PRICE

The minimum price quote is 10p which represents a handling charge rather than a basis for valuing common stamps. For further notes about prices see introductory pages.

60

(219)

220 Bats flying Home

1992 (11 Aug). *Nos.* 1121/4 *surch with T* **219** *in black on red.*

1187 60 s. on 42 s. Safety in cars (English inscription) . . . . 2·25 2·25
a. Horiz pair. Nos. 1187/8 . . 4·50 4·50
1188 60 s. on 42 s. Safety on bikes (English inscription) . . . . 2·25 2·25
1189 60 s. on 42 s. As No. 1187 (Tongan inscr) 2·25 2·25
a. Horiz pair. Nos. 1189/90 . . 4·50 4·50
1190 60 s. on 42 s. As No. 1188 (Tongan inscr) 2·25 2·25
1187/90 . . . . *Set of* 4 8·00 8·00

Nos. 1187/90 differ from the unsurcharged printing by showing the order of the stamps in each horizontal pair reversed.

(Des G. Bennett (Nos. 1191/5), D. Miller (No. **MS**1196))

1992 (20 Oct). *Sacred Bats of Kolovai. T* **220** *and similar multicoloured designs. P* 14.

1191 60 s. Type **220** . . . . 1·60 1·60
a. Horiz strip of 5. Nos. 1191/5 . . 7·25
1192 60 s. Tongan Fruit Bat . . . . . . 1·60 1·60
1193 60 s. Bats alighting on branches . . . . 1·60 1·60
1194 60 s. Bats hanging from tree . . . . 1·60 1·60
1195 60 s. Tongan Fruit Bat in tree . . . . 1·60 1·60
1191/5 . . . . *Set of* 5 7·25 7·25

MS1196 96×112 mm. 45 s. Kula leaving Tonga; 45 s. Kula watching Chief's daughter dancing; 2 p. Kula between fires and Hina; 2 p. Kula leaving Samoa with bats (*each* 38×30 *mm*). P 14×14½ . . . . 8·50 9·50

Nos. 1191/5 were printed together, *se-tenant*, in horizontal strips of five throughout the sheet each strip forming a composite design.

221 Tongan Pearls

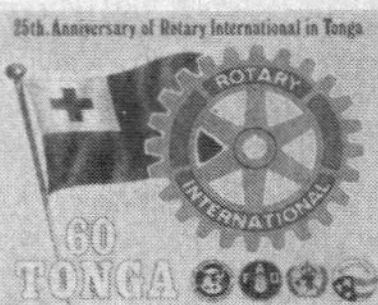

222 Tonga Flag and Rotary Emblem (25th anniv of Rotary International in Tonga)

1992 (10 Nov). *Christmas. T* **221** *and similar horiz designs. Multicoloured. P* 14.

1197 60 s. Type **221** 70 65
1198 80 s. Reef fish 90 80
1199 2 p. Pacific orchids . . . . . . 4·25 4·75
1200 3 p. Red Shining Parrots from Eua . . 5·50 6·50
1197/1200 . . . . *Set of* 4 10·00 11·50

1992 (15 Dec). *Anniversaries and Events. T* **222** *and similar horiz designs. P* 14×14½.

1201 60 s. multicoloured . . . . . . 1·00 65
1202 80 s. multicoloured . . . . . . 1·25 90
1203 1 p. 50, deep violet, pale lilac and black 2·75 3·50
1204 3 p. 50, multicoloured . . . . 5·50 6·50
1201/4 . . . . *Set of* 4 9·50 10·50

Designs:—80 s. Pres. Kennedy and Peace Corps emblem (25th anniv of Peace Corps in Tonga); 1 p. 50, F.A.O. and W.H.O. emblems (International Conference); 3 p. 50, Globe and Rotary Foundation emblem (75th anniv of Rotary Foundation).

223 Mother and Child

(Des G. Bennett)

1993 (26 Jan). *Family Planning. T* **223** *and similar vert designs. P* 14×13½.

1205 15 s. black, new blue & mag (English inscr) 40 40
a. Horiz pair. Nos. 1205/6 . . 80 80
1206 15 s. black, new blue & mag (Tongan inscr) 40 40
1207 45 s. black, greenish yellow and bright yellow-green (English inscr) . . 90 90
a. Horiz pair. Nos. 1207/8 . . 1·75 1·75

1208 45 s. black, greenish yellow and bright yellow-green (Tongan inscr) .. 90 90
1209 60 s. black, dull vermilion and chrome-yellow (English inscr) .. .. 1·90 1·90
a. Horiz pair. Nos. 1209/10 .. .. 3·75 3·75
1210 60 s. black, dull vermilion and chrome-yellow (Tongan inscr) .. .. 1·90 1·90
1211 2 p. black, greenish yellow and red-orange (English inscr) .. .. .. 4·00 4·00
a. Horiz pair. Nos. 1211/12 .. .. 8·00 8·00
1212 2 p. black, greenish yellow and red-orange (Tongan inscr) .. .. .. 4·00 4·00
1205/12 .. .. *Set of* 8 13·00 13·00

Designs:—45 s. Child on bike; 60 s. Girl with cats; 2 p. Old man and boy playing chess.

The two designs for each value were printed in horizontal *se-tenant* pairs throughout the sheets with those on the right inscribed in Tongan and those on the left, which have the designs reversed, in English.

224 Anti-smoking and Anti-drugs Symbols with Healthy Food

(Des D. Miller)

1993 (16 Mar). *Health and Fitness Campaign. T* **224** *and similar horiz designs. Multicoloured. P* 14.

1213 60 s. Type **224** .. .. 1·25 90
1214 80 s. Anti-smoking symbol and weight training .. .. 1·60 1·10
1215 1 p. 50, Anti-drugs symbol and water sports .. .. 2·75 3·50
1216 2 p. 50, Healthy food with cyclist and jogger .. .. 5·00 6·00
1213/16 .. .. *Set of* 4 9·50 10·50

xx

10s

(225)

226 Chaste Mitre (*Scabricola casta*)

1993 (29 Mar). *Nos.* 1001 *and* 1087 *surch as T* **225** *in blue.*

1217 10 s. on 2 s. *Porites* sp .. .. .. 50·00 15·00
1217*a* 20 s. on 4 s. Lionfish £400

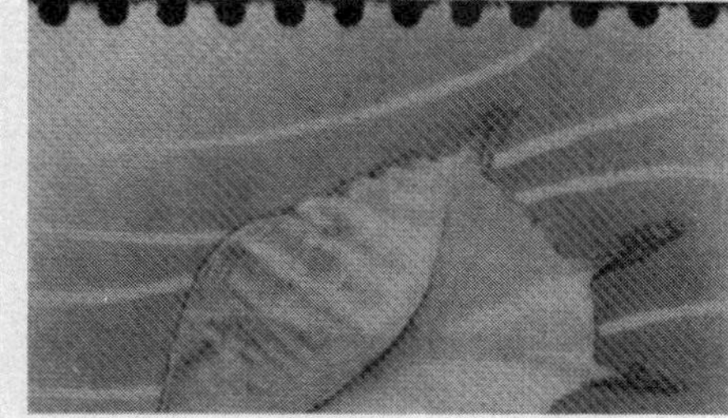

I

II

Two types of 10, 20, 45, 60 and 80 s.:

Type I. Diffuse central oval extends to top perforations. Dated "1993".

Type II. Central design and oval with sharper outlines well clear of the perforations. Some in different shades. Dated "1995".

1993 (12 May)–**95.** *Multicoloured designs as Nos.* 867, 872, 875, 877, 999, 1002, 1005, 1007, 1013, 1015/16 *and* 1017*a*, *some with new face values, redrawn as in T* **226** *with species inscr at foot. Chalk-surfaced paper. P* 13 (1, 5, 45, 60 *s.*) *or* 14 (*others*).

1218 1 s. Type **226** 10 10
1219 3 s. Red Squirrelfish 10 10
1220 5 s. Green Map Cowrie (*Cypraea mappa viridis*) 10 10
1221 10 s. Bubble Cone (*Conus bullatus*) (I) (grey background) 30 30
a. Type II (sage-green background) (25.9.95) 10 10
1223 20 s. White-tailed Dascyllus (I) (sage-green background) 40 40
a. Type II (yell-ol background) (25.9.95) 20 25
1225 45 s. Giant Spider Conch (*Lambis truncata*) (as No. 877) (I) 70 60
a. Perf 14. Type II (25.9.95) 40 45
1227 60 s. Princely Cone (*Conus aulicus*) (as No. 875) (I) 90 80
a. Perf 14. Type II (25.9.95) 50 55
1229 80 s. Lionfish (as No. 872) (I) .. .. 1·10 1·10
a. Type II (25.9.95) 70 75
1230 1 p. *Chelonia mydas* (turtle) (21.6.94) .. 1·25 1·25
1231 2 p. *Birgus latro* (crab) (21.6.94) .. 2·25 2·50
1232 3 p. Rose-branch Murex (*Chicoreus palma rosae*) (21.6.94) .. .. .. 3·25 3·75
1233 5 p. Humpback Whale (as No. 1014) (21.9.94) .. .. 6·50 7·00
1234 10 p. Variegated Shark (18.1.95) .. .. 14·00 15·00
1218/34 .. .. *Set of* 13 26·00 28·00

Nos. 1218/29 are 19×22 mm, Nos. 1230/3 40×28 mm and No. 1234 28×40 mm.

Imprint dates: "1993", Nos. 1218/29; "1994", Nos. 1230/3; "1995", Nos. 1221a, 1223a, 1225a, 1227a, 1229a, 1234.

Nos. 1233/4 were each issued in sheets of 10 stamps and two stamp-sized labels in the centre of the sheets.

For 1 p. to 10 p. redrawn with species inscriptions at top left see Nos. 1345/9.

227 Fire Brigade Badge

228 Old Map of Islands

(Des D. Miller)

1993 (18 May). *25th Annivs of Police Training College and Fire Service. T* **227** *and similar horiz designs. Multicoloured. P* 14.

1235 45 s. Type **227** .. .. 1·50 1·50
a. Horiz pair. Nos. 1235/6 .. .. 3·00 3·00
1236 45 s. Police badge and van .. .. 1·50 1·50
1237 60 s. Police band .. .. 1·75 1·75
a. Horiz pair. Nos. 1237/8 .. .. 3·50 3·50
1238 60 s. Fire engine at fire .. .. .. 1·75 1·75
1239 2 p. Fire engine at station .. .. 4·00 4·50
a. Horiz pair. Nos. 1239/40 .. .. 8·00 9·00
1240 2 p. Policeman and dog handler .. .. 4·00 4·50
1235/40 .. .. *Set of* 6 13·00 14·00

The two designs for each value were printed together, *se-tenant*, in horizontal pairs throughout the sheets.

(Des G. Bennett)

1993 (21 June). *350th Anniv of Abel Tasman's Discovery of Eua. T* **228** *and similar vert designs. Multicoloured. P* 14×13½.

1241 30 s. Type **228** 80 55
1242 60 s. *Heemskirk* and *Zeehaan* at sea .. 1·25 85
1243 80 s. Tongan canoes welcoming ships .. 1·60 1·25
1244 3 p. 50, Tasman landing on Eua .. 6·00 8·00
1241/4 .. .. *Set of* 4 8·75 9·50

229 King Taufa'ahau Tupou IV and Musical Instruments

230 Christmas Feast

(Des D. Miller)

1993 (1 July). *75th Birthday of King Taufa'ahau Tupou IV. T* **229** *and similar vert designs. Multicoloured. P* 13×13½ (45 *s.*) *or* 12 (*others*).

1245 45 s. Type **229** 60 45
1246 80 s. King Tupou IV and sporting events (38½ × 51 *mm*) .. .. .. 1·00 1·40
a. Strip of 3. Nos. 1246/8 .. .. 2·75
1247 80 s. King Tupou IV and ancient landmarks (38½ × 51 *mm*) .. .. 1·00 1·40
1248 80 s. King Tupou IV and Royal Palace (38½ × 51 *mm*) .. .. .. 1·00 1·40
1249 2 p. As Type **229**, but larger (38½ × 51 *mm*) .. .. 2·50 3·25
1245/9 .. .. *Set of* 5 5·50 7·00

Nos. 1246/8 were printed together, *se-tenant*, in horizontal and vertical strips of 3 throughout the sheet of 9.

(Des G. Bennett)

1993 (10 Nov). *Christmas. T* **230** *and similar vert designs. Multicoloured. P* 14.

1250 60 s. Type **230** 90 60
1251 80 s. Firing home-made cannon .. .. 1·25 80
1252 1 p. 50, Band playing carols .. .. 2·50 3·25
1253 3 p. Going to church .. .. .. 5·00 6·00
1250/3 .. .. *Set of* 4 8·75 9·50

231 "Land of Sun, Sea and Sand" (Kiley and Peter Moala)

232 Boy holding Cockerel

1993 (1 Dec). *Winners of Children's Painting Competition. T* **231** *and similar vert designs. P* 14.

1254 **231** 10 s. multicoloured 30 50
a. Horiz strip of 6. Nos. 1254/9 .. 1·60
1255 – 10 s. multicoloured 30 50
1256 – 10 s. multicoloured 30 50
1257 – 10 s. multicoloured 30 50
1258 – 10 s. black and grey-black 30 50
1259 – 10 s. black and grey-black 30 50
1260 **231** 80 s. multicoloured .. .. .. 1·40 1·60
a. Horiz strip of 6. Nos. 1260/5 .. 7·50
1261 – 80 s. multicoloured .. .. .. 1·40 1·60
1262 – 80 s. multicoloured .. .. .. 1·40 1·60
1263 – 80 s. multicoloured .. .. .. 1·40 1·60
1264 – 80 s. multicoloured .. .. .. 1·40 1·60
1265 – 80 s. multicoloured .. .. .. 1·40 1·60
1254/65 .. .. *Set of* 12 9·00 11·00

Designs:—Nos. 1255 and 1261, "Maui, Fisher God of Tonga" (Kiley and Peter Moala); Nos. 1256 and 1262, "Traditional Island Transport" (Kiley and Peter Moala); Nos. 1257 and 1263, "Young Girl making Kava" (Pulotu Pole'o); Nos. 1258 and 1264, "Maui and his Hook" (Salome Tapou); Nos. 1259 and 1265, "Communications in the South Pacific" (Fe'ofa'aki Taufa).

Nos. 1254/9 and 1260/5 were each printed in sheetlets of 12, of one value, each sheetlet containing two *se-tenant* strips of six.

(Des G. Bennett

1994 (14 Jan). *Animal Welfare. Sheet,* 122×100 *mm, containing T* **232** *and similar vert designs. Multicoloured. P* 14½.

MS1266 60 s. Type **232**; 60 s. Girl with butterfly; 60 s. Dog and puppies; 60 s. Boy with puppy; 80 s. Boy holding puppy; 80 s. Girl holding cat 6·00 7·00

233 Tiger Shark

(Des G. Bennett)

1994 (28 Feb). *Game Fishing. T* **233** *and similar horiz designs. Multicoloured. P* 12½×12.

1267 60 s. Type **233** .. .. 1·10 85
1268 80 s. Dolphin (fish) .. .. 1·50 1·10
1269 1 p. 50, Yellow-finned Tuna .. .. .. 2·75 3·25
1270 2 p. 50, Blue Marlin .. .. 3·50 4·00
1267/70 .. .. *Set of* 4 8·00 8·25

234 Hands holding World Cup

235 Policewoman

(Des D. Miller)

1994 (1 June). *World Cup Football Championship, U.S.A. T* **234** *and similar horiz designs. Multicoloured. P* 14×14½.

1271 80 s. Type **234** .. .. 1·50 1·50
a. Pair. Nos. 1271/2 .. .. .. 3·00 3·00
1272 80 s. Player's legs .. .. 1·50 1·50
1273 2 p. German player (black shorts) .. 3·25 4·00
a. Pair. Nos. 1273/4 .. .. .. 6·50 8·00
1274 2 p. American player .. .. .. 3·25 4·00
1271/4 .. .. *Set of* 4 8·50 10·00

Nos. 1271/2 and 1273/4 were printed together, *se-tenant*, in horizontal and vertical pairs throughout the sheets.

(Des D. Miller)

1994 (18 Aug). *Pan Pacific and South East Asia Women's Association Conference, Tonga. T* **235** *and similar vert designs. Multicoloured. P* 14½.

1275 45 s. Type **235** . . . . . . 1·50 1·50
a. Pair. Nos. 1275/6 . . . . . . 3·00 3·00
1276 45 s. Woman barrister . . . . . . 1·50 1·50
1277 2 p. 50, Nurse . . . . . . 4·25 4·75
a. Pair. Nos. 1277/8 . . . . . . 8·50 9·50
1278 2 p. 50, Woman doctor . . . . 4·25 4·75
1275/8 . . . . . . *Set of* 4 10·50 11·50

Nos. 1275/6 and 1277/8 were each printed together, *se-tenant*, in horizontal and vertical pairs throughout the sheets.

60

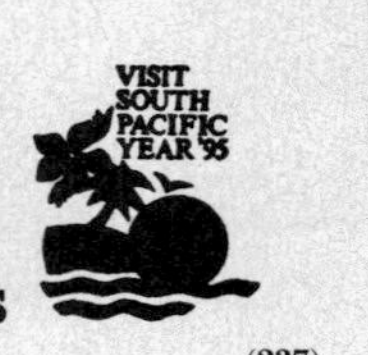

MERRY
CHRISTMAS

(236) (237)

1994 (10 Nov). *Christmas. No.* **MS**1266 *optd with T* **236** *or equivalent in Tongan.*

MS1279 60 s. Type **232**; 60 s. Girl with butterfly; 60 s. Dog and puppies; 60 s. Boy with puppy; 80 s. Boy holding puppy; 80 s. Girl holding cat 5·00 5·50

T **236** appears on five of the stamps from the miniature sheet. The 60 s. in the centre of the bottom row (dog and puppies) is overprinted "KILISIMASI FIEFIA".

1994 (17 Nov). *Visit South Pacific Year '95 (1st issue). No.* 1204 *surch with T* **237** *in blue.*

1280 60 s. on 3 p. 50, multicoloured . . . . 1·25 1·25

See also Nos. 1297/1308.

1994 (14 Dec). *25th Anniv of Tongan Self-adhesive Stamps.*

(*a*) *Various previous self-adhesive designs, some in smaller size, with new values.* (i) *Postage*

1281 **128** 10 s. black & greenish yell (21×9 *mm*) 20 30
a. Booklet pane. Nos. 1281×12 and 1284×3 . . . . . . 5·00
1282 **124** 60 s. black, grey and red-brown . . 1·40 1·75
a. Booklet pane. Nos. 1282/3 and O243 . . . . . . 5·00
1283 – 60 s. multicoloured (as Nos. O214/15) 1·40 1·75

(ii) *Air*

1284 **109** 25 s. multicoloured (27×36 *mm*) . . 1·00 1·25

(*b*) *As Nos.* 915A/18A, *but new face value and inscr* "SELF-ADHESIVE ANNIVERSARY 1969–1994"

1285 **168** 45 s. black, salmon-pink & reddish brn 75 85
a. Booklet pane. Nos. 1285/6 each × 3, 1287×2 and 1288 . . 5·00
1286 – 45 s. black, pale-rose lilac and reddish brown (as No. 916A) 75 85
1287 – 45 s. black, olive-yellow and reddish brown (as No. 917A) . . 1·25 1·50
1288 – 45 s. multicoloured (as No. 918A) . . 2·75 3·25

(*c*) *Hologram design, 39×29 mm, showing Tongastar 1 satellite*

1289 – 2 p. multicoloured . . . . . . 5·00 6·00
a. Booklet pane of 1 . . . . 5·00
1281/9 . . . . . . *Set of* 9 13·00 16·00

Nos. 1281/9 and O243 were only available from 10 p. self-adhesive booklets.

238 Farmer, Produce and Emblem

(Des K. McGee)

1995 (16 May). *50th Anniv of Food and Agriculture Organization. P* 14.

1290 **238** 5 p. multicoloured . . . . . . 7·00 8·00

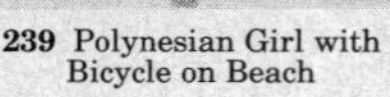

239 Polynesian Girl with Bicycle on Beach

240 Three Players running with Ball

(Des K. McGee)

1995 (6 June). *25th Anniv of Tonga's Entry into Commonwealth. Children with Bicycles. T* **239** *and similar horiz designs. Multicoloured. P* 14.

1291 45 s. Type **239** 65 45
1292 60 s. Children and skyscrapers, Hong Kong 80 60
1293 80 s. Boy in African village . . . . 1·00 80
1294 2 p. Indian boy and palace . . . . 2·50 3·00
1295 2 p. 50, English children and village church . . . . . . 3·00 3·50
1291/5 . . . . . . *Set of* 5 7·00 7·50

(Des G. Bennett)

1995 (20 June). *World Cup Rugby Championship, South Africa. Two sheets, each 84×117 mm, containing T* **240** *and similar vert designs. P* 14½.

MS1296 (a) 80 s. × 2 Type **240**; 80 s. × 2 Two players running with ball. (b) 2 p. × 2 Player making pass; 2 p. × 2 Player receiving pass *Set of* 2 *sheets* 15·00 16·00

The miniature sheets contain two of each design.

60

WHERE TIME BEGINS

(241)

1995 (30 June). *Visit South Pacific Year '95 (2nd issue).*

(*a*) *Nos.* 1149/52 *optd or surch as T* **241**, *but inscr* "VISIT SOUTH PACIFIC YEAR '95"

1297 60 s. on 57 s. Longboat 75 60
1298 80 s. on 2 p. Stern of fautasi (large canoe) 1·00 1·25
a. Horiz pair. Nos. 1298/9 . . . . 2·00 2·50
1299 80 s. on 2 p. Bow of fautasi . . . . 1·00 1·25
1300 1 p. Outrigger canoe . . . . . . 1·40 1·60
1297/1300 . . . . . . *Set of* 4 3·75 4·25

(*b*) *Nos.* 1197/1200 *surch as T* **241** *inscr either* (A) "WHERE TIME BEGINS" or (B) "THE 21st CENTURY STARTS HERE"

1301 60 s. on 60 s. Type **221** (A) 75 75
a. Horiz pair. Nos. 1301/2 . . . . 1·50 1·50
1302 60 s. on 60 s. Type **221** (B) 75 75
1303 60 s. on 80 s. Reef Fish (A) 75 75
a. Horiz pair. Nos. 1303/4 . . . . 1·50 1·50
1304 60 s. on 80 s. Reef Fish (B) 75 75
1305 60 s. on 2 p. Pacific orchids (A) 75 75
a. Horiz pair. Nos. 1305/6 . . . . 1·50 1·50
1306 60 s. on 2 p. Pacific orchids (B) 75 75
1307 60 s. on 3 p. Red Shining Parrots from Eua (A) 75 75
a. Horiz pair. Nos. 1307/8 . . . . 1·50 1·50
1308 60 s. on 3 p. Red Shining Parrots from Eua (B) 75 75
1301/8 . . . . . . *Set of* 8 5·50 5·50

Nos. 1298/9, 1301/2, 1303/4, 1305/6 and 1307/8 were each printed together, *se-tenant*, in horizontal pairs throughout the sheets.

242 Soldier on Scrambling Net

243 1995 Commonwealth 45 s. Stamp and Exhibition Emblem

(Des D. Miller)

1995 (1 Aug). *50th Anniv of End of Second World War in the Pacific. T* **242** *and similar vert designs. P* 14½.

1309 **242** 60 s. greenish yellow, black & new blue 1·10 1·10
a. Sheetlet. Nos. 1309/18 . . . . 10·00
1310 – 60 s. greenish yellow, black & new blue 1·10 1·10
1311 – 60 s. greenish yellow, black & new blue 1·10 1·10
1312 – 60 s. multicoloured . . . . . . 1·10 1·10
1313 – 60 s. multicoloured . . . . . . 1·10 1·10
1314 **242** 80 s. greenish yellow, black and rosine 1·10 1·10
1315 – 80 s. greenish yellow, black and rosine 1·10 1·10
1316 – 80 s. greenish yellow, black and rosine 1·10 1·10
1317 – 80 s. multicoloured . . . . . . 1·10 1·10
1318 – 80 s. multicoloured . . . . . . 1·10 1·10
1309/18 . . . . . . *Set of* 10 10·00 10·00

Designs:—Nos. 1310 and 1315, U.S.S. *Nevada* (battleship) with troops in foreground; Nos. 1311 and 1316 U.S.S. *West Virginia* (battleship) and rear of landing craft; Nos. 1312 and 1317, U.S.S. *Idaho* (battleship) and front of landing craft; Nos. 1313 and 1318, Map of South-east Asia and Pacific.

Nos. 1309/18 were printed together, *se-tenant*, in sheetlets of 10 with the horizontal strips of 5 forming the same composite design.

(Des K. McGee)

1995 (1 Sept). *"Singapore '95" International Stamp Exhibition. T* **243** *and similar horiz designs. Multicoloured. P* 12.

1319 45 s. Type **243** . . . . . . 1·00 1·25
a. Horiz pair. Nos. 1319/20 . . . . 2·00 2·50
1320 60 s. 1995 Commonwealth 60 s. stamp and emblem . . . . . . 1·00 1·25

MS1321 110×70 mm. 2 p. Boy on bicycle and Singapore skyscrapers . . . . . . 2·75 3·00

Nos. 1319/20 were printed together, *se-tenant* horizontally, in sheets of 10.

244 Mt Song
(*Illustration reduced. Actual size* 84½×51½ *mm*)

(Des Li Defu)

1995 (14 Sept). *Beijing International Coin and Stamp Show '95. Sheet* 143×87 *mm. P* 14½.

MS1322 **244** 1 p. 40, multicoloured . . . . 2·00 2·50

245 Holocaust Victims

(Des K. McGee)

1995 (20 Oct). *50th Anniv of United Nations and End of Second World War. T* **245** *and similar designs. P* 13×13½.

1323 60 s. multicoloured 75 85
a. Horiz strip of 3. Nos. 1323/5 . . 2·00
1324 60 s. black and bright blue 75 85
1325 60 s. multicoloured 75 85
1326 80 s. multicoloured . . . . . . 1·00 1·25
a. Horiz strip of 3. Nos. 1326/8 . . 2·75
1327 80 s. bright blue and black . . . . 1·00 1·25
1328 80 s. multicoloured . . . . . . 1·00 1·25
1323/8 . . . . . . *Set of* 6 4·75 5·50

Designs: *Horiz* (*as Type* **245**)—No. 1323, Type **245**; No. 1325, Children of Holocaust survivors with balloons; No. 1326, Atomic explosion, Hiroshima; No. 1328, U.S. Space Shuttle. *Vert* (23×35 *mm*)—Nos. 1324 and 1327, U.N. anniversary emblem.

Nos. 1323/5 and 1326/8 were printed together, *se-tenant*, in horizontal strips of 3 throughout the sheets.

246 *Calanthe triplicata*

247 Humpback Whale

(Des G. Bennett)

1995 (15 Nov). *Greetings Stamps. Orchids. T* **246** *and similar square designs inscribed either* "MERRY CHRISTMAS" (A) *or* "A HAPPY 1996" (B). *Multicoloured. P* 14×14½.

1329 20 s. Type **246** (A) 50 50
1330 45 s. *Spathoglottis plicata* (A) 75 75
1331 45 s. As No. 1330 (B) 75 75
1332 60 s. *Dendrobium platygastrium* (A) . . 90 90
1333 60 s. As No. 1332 (B) 90 90
1334 80 s. *Goodyera rubicunda* (B) . . . . 1·25 1·25
1335 2 p. *Dendrobium toki* (B) . . . . 2·75 3·00
1336 2 p. 50, *Phaius tankervillae* (A) . . . . 3·50 3·75
1329/36 . . . . . . *Set of* 8 10·00 10·50

(Des G. Bennett)

1996 (7 Feb). *Endangered Species. Humpback Whale. T* **247** *and similar horiz designs. Multicoloured. P* 14.

1337 45 s. Type **247** 85 60
1338 60 s. Whale and calf . . . . . . 1·25 75
1339 1 p. 50, Whale's tail and Herald Petrels 2·75 3·00
1340 2 p. 50, Whale breaking surface . . 4·25 4·75
1337/40 . . . . . . *Set of* 4 8·00 8·00

248 Rats and Top Left Quarter of Clock Face

249 Running

Two types of 60 s.:

60 I   60 II

(Des A. Benjamin)

1996 (7 Feb–27 June). *Chinese New Year ("Year of the Rat"). Sheets, 127×85 mm, containing T* **248** *and similar horiz designs showing rats and quarter segments of clock face. Multicoloured. P* 14.
MS1341 10 s. Type **248**; 10 s. Top right quarter; 10 s. Bottom left quarter; 10 s. Bottom right quarter (27 June) .. .. 75 1·00
MS1342 20 s. Type **248**; 20 s. Top right quarter; 20 s. Bottom left quarter; 20 s. Bottom right quarter (27 June) .. .. 1·50 1·75
MS1343 45 s. Type **248**; 45 s. Top right quarter; 45 s. Bottom left quarter; 45 s. Bottom right quarter (27 June) .. .. 3·00 3·50
MS1344 60 s. Type **248** (I); 60 s. Top right quarter (I); 60 s. Bottom left quarter (I); 60 s. Bottom right quarter (I) .. .. 4·00 4·50
a. Face values as Type II (27 June) .. 5·00 6·00

On Nos. **MS**1341/3 and **MS**1344a the face values were applied by typography. They also include "Sheet Value" inscriptions at bottom right.

For similar designs for "Year of the Ox" see No. **MS**1370

1996 (31 May). *Multicoloured designs as Nos. 1230/4, but redrawn with species inscriptions at top left. Chalk-surfaced paper. P* 14.
1345 1 p. *Chelonia mydas* (turtle) 90 95
1346 2 p. *Birgus latro* (crab) .. .. 1·75 1·90
1347 3 p. Rose Branch Murex (*Chicoreus palma-rosae*) .. .. 2·50 2·75
1348 5 p. Humpback Whale .. .. 4·25 4·50
1349 10 p. Variegated Shark (*vert*) .. .. .. 8·75 9·00
1345/9 .. .. *Set of* 5 18·00 19·00

Imprint date: "1996", Nos. 1345/9.

Nos. 1348/9 were each issued in sheets of 10 stamps and 2 stamp-size labels in the centre of the sheets.

(Des D. Miller)

1996 (2 July). *Centennial Olympic Games, Atlanta. T* **249** *and similar vert designs showing ancient Greek and modern athletes. Multicoloured. P* 14.
1350 45 s. Type **249** 90 65
1351 80 s. Throwing the discus .. .. .. 1·50 1·10
1352 2 p. Throwing the javelin .. .. .. 4·00 4·25
1353 3 p. Equestrian dressage .. .. .. 5·50 6·00
1350/3 .. .. *Set of* 4 10·50 11·00

250 Aspects of Prehistoric Life

(Des D. Miller)

1996 (5 Sept). *13th Congress of International Union of Prehistoric and Protohistoric Sciences, Forli, Italy. T* **250** *and similar horiz design. Multicoloured. P* 12.
1354 1 p. Type **250** .. .. 1·75 1·75
a. Horiz pair. Nos. 1354/5 .. .. .. 3·50 3·50
1355 1 p. Aspects of Egyptian, Greek and Roman civilisations .. .. 1·75 1·75

Nos. 1354/5 were printed together, *se-tenant*, in sheetlets of 6 (2×3).

PRICES OF SETS

Set prices are given for many issues, generally those containing three stamps or more. Definitive sets include one of each value or major colour change, but do not cover different perforations, die types or minor shades. Where a choice is possible the set prices are based on the cheapest versions of the stamps included in the listings.

251 "Virgin and Child" (Sassoferrato)

252 Athletics and Rugby

(Des D. Miller)

1996 (21 Oct). *Christmas. Religious Paintings. T* **251** *and similar horiz designs. Multicoloured. P* 14.
1356 20 s. Type **251** 45 40
1357 60 s. "Adoration of the Shepherds" (Murillo) .. .. 1·10 75
1358 80 s. "Virgin and Child" (Delaroche) .. 1·40 1·00
1359 3 p. "Adoration of the Shepherds" (Champaigne) .. .. 4·50 5·50
1356/9 .. .. *Set of* 4 6·75 7·00

(Des D. Miller)

1996 (29 Oct). *50th Anniv of U.N.I.C.E.F. Children's Sports. T* **252** *and similar vert designs. Multicoloured. P* 14.
1360 80 s. Type **252** .. .. 1·40 1·60
a. Horiz strip of 3. Nos. 1360/2 .. .. 3·75
1361 80 s. Tennis .. .. 1·40 1·60
1362 80 s. Cycling .. .. 1·40 1·60
1360/2 .. .. *Set of* 3 3·75 4·25

Nos. 1360/2 were printed together, *se-tenant*, in horizontal strips of three throughout the sheet, each strip forming a composite design.

253 Queen Halaevalu Mata'aho and Flag

(Des D. Miller and K. Jones)

1996 (27 Nov). *70th Birthday of Queen Halaevalu Mata'aho. T* **253** *and similar horiz designs. Multicoloured. P* 12.
1363 60 s. Type **253** .. .. 1·00 65
1364 2 p. Queen and obverse (portrait) of commemorative coin .. .. .. 3·25 3·75
a. Horiz pair. Nos. 1364/5 .. .. .. 6·50 7·50
1365 2 p. Queen and reverse (arms) of commemorative coin .. .. .. 3·25 3·75
1363/5 .. .. *Set of* 3 6·75 7·25

Nos. 1364/5 were printed together, *se-tenant*, as horizontal pairs in sheets of 6.

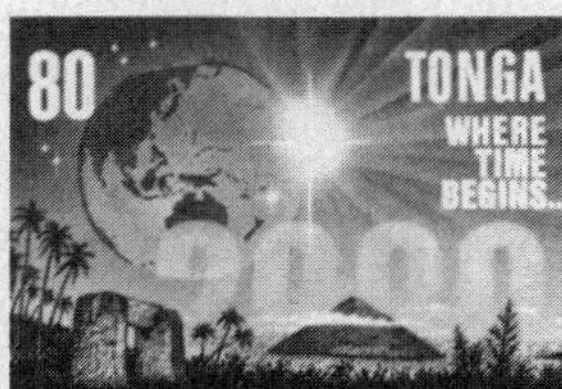

254 Globe, the Ha'amonga and Kao Island

(Des D. Miller)

1996 (9 Dec). *"Towards the Millennium". T* **254** *and similar horiz design. Multicoloured. P* 12.
1366 80 s. Type **254** .. .. 1·50 1·50
a. Horiz pair. Nos. 1366/7 .. .. .. 3·00 3·00
1367 80 s. Mount Talau, Royal Palace and satellite .. .. 1·50 1·50
1368 2 p. Type **254** .. .. 3·25 3·75
a. Horiz pair. Nos. 1368/9 .. .. .. 6·50 7·50
1369 2 p. As No. 1367 .. .. 3·25 3·75
1366/9 .. .. *Set of* 4 8·50 9·50

Nos. 1366/7 and 1368/9 were printed together, *se-tenant*, as horizontal pairs in sheets of 6.

(Des A. Benjamin)

1997 (24 Jan). *Chinese New Year ("Year of the Ox"). Sheet 126×85 mm, containing horiz designs as T* **248**, *showing ox and quarter segments of clock face. Multicoloured. P* 14.
MS1370 60 s. Top left quarter; 60 s. Top right quarter; 80 s. Bottom left quarter; 2 p. Bottom right quarter .. .. 5·50 6·50

10

(255)

1997 (3 Mar). *Nos. 1235/40 surch as T* **255** *in black.*
1371 10 s. on 45 s. Type **227** .. .. .. 1·50 1·50
a. Horiz pair. Nos. 1371/2 .. .. .. 3·00 3·00
1372 10 s. on 45 s. Police badge and van .. 1·50 1·50
1373 10 s. on 60 s. Police band .. .. .. 1·50 1·50
a. Horiz pair. Nos. 1373/4 .. .. .. 3·00 3·00
1374 10 s. on 60 s. Fire engine at fire .. .. 1·50 1·50
1375 20 s. on 2 p. Fire engine at station .. 1·75 1·75
a. Horiz pair. Nos. 1375/6 .. .. .. 3·50 3·50
1376 20 s. on 2 p. Policeman and dog handler .. 1·75 1·75
1371/6 .. .. *Set of* 6 8·50 8·50

10
FAKAMANATU
TA'U 75 'OE
'AKAPULU 'IUNIONI
'I TONGA

(256)

10
A
SILVER
FOR
TONGA

(257)

1997 (24 Mar). *75th Anniv of Tongan Rugby Union. No.* **MS**1296 *surch* (A) *as T* **256** *or* (B) "75th ANNIVERSARY TONGA RUGBY FOOTBALL UNION".
MS1377 Two sheets, each 84×117 mm. (a) 10 s. on 80 s. Type **240** (A); 10 s. on 80 s. Type **240** (B); 10 s. on 80 s. Two players running with ball (A); 10 s. on 80 s. Two players running with ball (B). (b) 1 p. on 2 p. Player making pass (A); 1 p. on 2 p. Player making pass (B); 1 p. on 2 p. Player receiving pass (A); 1 p. on 2 p. Player receiving pass (B) .. .. *Set of 2 sheets* 5·00 5·50

1997 (24 Mar). *Tongan Medal Winner at Atlanta Olympic Games. Nos. 1350/3 surch as T* **257** *or optd only* (3 *p.*).
1378 10 s. on 45 s. Type **249** 30 30
1379 10 s. on 80 s. Throwing the discus 30 30
1380 10 s. on 2 p. Throwing the javelin 30 30
1381 3 p. Equestrian dressage .. .. .. 3·00 3·50
1378/81 .. .. *Set of* 4 3·50 4·00

258 Captain James Wilson and *Duff*

(Des D. Miller)

1997 (28 Apr). *Birth Bicentenary of King George I and Bicentenary of Christianity in Tonga* (1*st issue*). *T* **258** *and similar horiz designs. Multicoloured. P* 14.
1382 10 s. Type **258** 50 50
a. Sheetlet. Nos. 1382, 1383×3 and 1384/5 .. .. 2·75
1383 10 s. King George Tupou I 50 50
1384 10 s. Missionaries landing at Tongatapu 50 50
1385 10 s. Missionaries and Tongans 50 50
1386 60 s. Type **258** 70 70
a. Horiz strip of 3. Nos. 1386/8 .. .. 1·90
1387 60 s. As No. 1384 .. .. 70 70
1388 60 s. As No. 1385 .. .. 70 70
1389 80 s. Type **258** 80 80
a. Horiz strip of 3. Nos. 1389/91 .. .. 2·25
1390 80 s. As No. 1384 .. .. 80 80
1391 80 s. As No. 1385 .. .. 80 80
1382/91 .. .. *Set of* 10 6·00 6·00

Nos. 1382, 1383 x 3, and 1384/5 were printed together, *se-tenant*, in sheetlets of 6. Nos. 1386/8 and 1389/91 were each printed together, *se-tenant*, as horizontal strips of 3 in sheetlets of 9.

For 10 p. values as Nos. 1382/5, but smaller, 28×18 mm, see Nos. 1415/18.

259 Pacific Swallow

(Des D. Miller)

1997 (30 May). *"Pacific '97" International Stamp Exhibition, San Francisco. Sheet 84×110 mm. P* 14.
MS1392 **259** 2 p. multicoloured .. .. .. 2·75 3·00

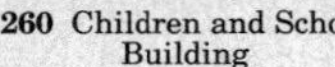

260 Children and School Building

261 King and Queen of Tonga during Coronation

(Des D. Miller)

1997 (4 June). *50th Anniv of Tonga High School. T* **260** *and similar horiz designs. Multicoloured. P* 14.

1393	20 s. Type **260**	45	40
1394	60 s. Athletic team	1·00	75
1395	80 s. School band	1·25	90
1396	3 p. 50, Athletics meeting	4·00	4·50
1393/6	*Set of* 4	6·00	6·00

(Des D. Miller)

1997 (30 June). *King and Queen of Tonga's Golden Wedding and 30th Anniv of the Coronation. T* **261** *and similar vert designs. Multicoloured. (a) Size* 23×34 *mm. P* 13×13½.

1397	10 s. Type **261**	30	30
	a. Horiz strip of 3. Nos. 1397/9	80	
1398	10 s. Moment of Crowning and procession	30	30
1399	10 s. King and Queen of Tonga	30	30
1400	45 s. Royal Crown	65	65
	(b) Size 50×37 *mm. P* 12		
1401	60 s. As Type **261**	75	75
	a. Horiz strip of 3. Nos. 1401/3	2·00	
1402	60 s. As No. 1398	75	75
1403	60 s. As No. 1399	75	75
1404	2 p. As No. 1400	2·25	2·50
1397/1404	*Set of* 8	5·50	5·75

Nos. 1397/9 and 1400 were each printed in sheets of 9, the 10 s. as horiz *se-tenant* strips of three. Nos. 1401/3 and 1404 were in sheets of six, the 60 s. as horiz strips of three.

1997 (27 Aug). *Birth Bicentenary of King George I and Bicentenary of Christianity in Tonga (2nd issue). As Nos.* 1382/5, *but smaller,* 28×18 *mm. P* 14.

1405	10 s. Type **258**	20	20
	a. Sheetlet. Nos. 1405/7, each × 2, and 1408×6	2·25	
1406	10 s. As No. 1384	20	20
1407	10 s. As No. 1385	20	20
1408	10 s. As No. 1383	20	20
1405/8	*Set of* 4	70	70

Nos. 1405/8 were printed together, *se-tenant*, in sheetlets of 12.

262 *Lenzites elegans*

(Des D. Miller)

1997 (8 Sept). *Fungi. T* **262** *and similar vert designs. Multicoloured. P* 14. *(a) Size* 18×28 *mm.*

1409	10 s. Type **262**	25	25
	a. Horiz strip of 6. Nos. 1409/14	1·25	
1410	10 s. *Marasmiellus semiustus*	25	25
1411	10 s. *Aseroe rubra*	25	25
1412	10 s. *Podoscypha involuta*	25	25
1413	10 s. *Microporus xanthopus*	25	25
1414	10 s. *Lentinus tuber-regium*	25	25
	(b) Size 28×42 *mm*		
1415	20 s. Type **262**	40	40
	a. Horiz pair. Nos. 1415/16	80	80
	b. Sheetlet. Nos. 1415/20	5·50	
1416	20 s. As No. 1410	40	40
1417	60 s. As No. 1411	75	75
	a. Horiz pair. Nos. 1417/18	1·50	1·50
1418	60 s. As No. 1412	75	75
1419	2 p. As No. 1413	2·00	2·00
	a. Horiz pair. Nos. 1419/20	4·00	4·00
1420	2 p. As No. 1414	2·00	2·00
1409/20	*Set of* 12	6·75	6·75

Nos. 1409/14 were printed together, *se-tenant*, in horizontal strips of 6 throughout the sheet with the backgrounds forming a composite design. Nos. 1415/20 were printed in sheetlets of 6 (2×3) containing either *se-tenant* horizontal pairs of the two designs for each value or all six stamps.

STAMP BOOKLETS

1987 (1 July)–**88.** *20th Anniv of Coronation of King Taufa'ahau Tupou IV. Black, rosine and deep turquoise-green covers showing Royal Palace, 68×49 mm. Self-adhesive.*

SB1 1 p. booklet containing *se-tenant* pane of 12 (No. 973a) .. .. 2·00
a. As No. SB1 but containing *se-tenant* pane No. 972b (4.7.88) .. .. 5·00

SB2 2 p. booklet containing *se-tenant* pane of 12 (No. 972a) .. .. 3·00
a. As No. SB2 but containing *se-tenant* pane No. 972c (4.7.88) .. .. 6·00

1990 (4 Sept). *Turquoise printed covers, 131×41 mm, in four different designs showing marine life. Stitched.*
(a) *Dascyllus aruanus*
(b) *Cypraea mappa viridis*
(c) *Dardanus megistos*
(d) *Holocentrus ruber*

SB3 4 p. 90, booklet containing 2 s., 5 s., 10 s. and 32 s., each in pane of 10 (Nos. 1087a, 1089a, 1092a, 1095a) *(any cover)* .. .. 10·00
Set of 4 *different covers* 35·00

1994 (14 Dec). *25th Anniv of Tongan Self-adhesive Stamps. Multicoloured cover showing photograph of Pacific from Space with cut out to show stamp on pane No. 1289a. Stitched.*

SB4 10 p. booklet containing panes Nos. 1281a/2a, 1285a and 1289a .. .. 17·00

EXPRESS STAMP

E 1 Short-eared Owl in Flight

1990 (21 Feb). *Air. P* 11½.

E1 E 1 10 p. black, vermilion and ultramarine .. 8·75 9·00

OFFICIAL STAMPS

G.F.B. (O 1) 1D ½ (O 2)

(G.F.B. = Gaue Faka Buleaga = On Government Service)

1893 (13 Feb). *Optd with Type* O **1** *by Govt Printing Office, Wellington, N.Z. W* **2.** *P* 12 × 11½.

O1 **5** 1d. ultramarine (C.) .. .. .. 10·00 42·00
a. Bisected diagonally (½d.) (on cover)
O2 **6** 2d. ultramarine (C.) .. .. .. 27·00 48·00
O3 **5** 4d. ultramarine (C.) .. .. .. 45·00 90·00
O4 **6** 8d. ultramarine (C.) .. .. .. 85·00 £160
O5 1s. ultramarine (C.) .. .. .. 95·00 £180
O1/5 .. .. .. *Set of* 5 £225 £475

Above prices are for stamps in good condition and colour. Faded and stained stamps from the remainders are worth much less.

1893 (Dec). *Nos* O1 *to* O5 *variously surch with new value, sideways as Type* O **2.**

O 6 **5** ½d. on 1d. ultramarine .. .. 15·00 48·00
O 7 **6** 2½d. on 2d. ultramarine .. .. 21·00 40·00
O 8 **5** 5d. on 4d. ultramarine .. .. 21·00 40·00
O 9 **6** 7½d. on 8d. ultramarine .. .. 21·00 70·00
a. "D" of "7½D." omitted £1100
b. Surch double £1800
O10 10d. on 1s. ultramarine .. .. 25·00 75·00
O6/10 .. .. *Set of* 5 95·00 £250

OFFICIAL AIR MAIL 1862 TAU'ATAINA EMANCIPATION 1962 (O 3)

OFFICIAL AIRMAIL 40 SENITI (O 4)

1962 (7 Feb). *Air. Centenary of Emancipation. Nos.* 112/14, 116 *and* 118/19 *optd with Type* O **3** *in red by R. S. Wallbank, Govt Printer.*

O11 – 2d. ultramarine .. .. .. 11·00 6·00
a. "OFFICIAI" .. .. .. 20·00 11·00
b. "MAII" .. .. .. 20·00 11·00
O12 – 5d. violet .. .. .. 12·00 6·50
a. "OFFICIAI" .. .. .. 22·00 12·00
b. "MAII" .. .. .. 22·00 12·00
O13 – 1s. red-brown .. .. .. 7·50 3·75
a. "OFFICIAI" .. .. .. 25·00 11·00
b. "MAII" .. .. .. 25·00 11·00
c. Opt double £350
ca. "OFFICIAI" £600
cb. "MAII" £600
O14 – 5s. orange-yellow and slate-lilac .. 90·00 55·00
a. "MAII" .. .. .. £200 75·00
b. "OFFICIAI" .. .. ..
O15 **52** 10s. yellow and black .. .. 42·00 22·00
a. "MAII" £100
O16 **53** £1 yellow, scarlet, ultram & dp brt blue 70·00 35·00
a. "MAII" £150
b. "OFFICIAI" .. .. ..
O11/16 .. .. *Set of* 6 £200 £120

SET PRICES. Official stamps from here onwards are included in the complete commemorative set prices given for any corresponding Postage issues.

1963 (15 July). *Air. First Polynesian Gold Coinage Commemoration. As T* **63** *but inscr* "OFFICIAL AIRMAIL". 1 *koula coin (diam* 3⅛ *in.). Imperf.*

O17 **63** 15s. black .. .. 4·50 6·00

1965 (18 Mar). *No.* O17 *surch as T* **67**.

O18 **63** 30s. on 15s. black .. .. .. 3·00 3·75

1966 (18 June). *Air. Centenary of Tupou College and Secondary Education. No.* 117 *surch with* "OFFICIAL AIRMAIL" *and new value, with commemorative inscription as in T* **69** *but in italic capital letters.*

O19 10s. on 4d. blue-green 80 35
a. Surch inverted £300 £150
O20 20s. on 4d. blue-green .. .. .. 1·00 50

1967 (25 Mar). *Air. Decimal currency. No.* 112 *surch* "OFFICIAL AIRMAIL ONE PA'ANGA" *in three lines, in red.*

O21 1 p. on 5s. .. .. 3·50 2·25
a. "AIRMAIL" above "OFFICIAL" .. £150

No. O21a occurred once in a number of sheets until it was corrected.

1967 (4 July). *Air. No.* 114 *surch in various denominations as Type* O 4.

O22 **53** 40 s. on £1 .. .. 50 60
O23 60 s. on £1 .. .. 70 80
O24 1 p. on £1 .. .. 90 1·25
O25 2 p. on £1 .. .. 1·50 1·75

Nos. O22/5 were first used on 4 July 1967, but supplies of unused stamps were not made available until April 1968.

The Friendly Islands welcome the United States Peace Corps Official Airmail 30s (O 5)

Friendly Islands Trials Field & Track South Pacific Games Port Moresby 1969 T$ 1·00 OFFICIAL AIRMAIL (O 6)

1967 (15 Dec). *Air. Arrival of U.S. Peace Corps in Tonga. As No.* 114, *but imperf, and background colour changed, and surch as Type* O **5**.

O26 **53** 30 s. on £1 yellow, scarlet, ultramarine and emerald-green 50 25
O27 70 s. on £1 yellow, scarlet, ultramarine and emerald-green 70 45
O28 1 p. 50, on £1 yellow, scarlet, ultramarine and emerald-green .. .. 1·00 85

1968 (4 July). *Air. 50th Birthday of King Taufa'ahua IV. No.* 207 *surch* "HIS MAJESTY'S 50th BIRTHDAY" *(as T* **79**), "OFFICIAL AIRMAIL" *and new value.*

O29 **75** 40 s. on 50 s. (Turq.) .. .. .. 1·25 70
O30 60 s. on 50 s. (G.) .. .. .. 1·75 1·25
O31 1 p. on 50 s. (V.) .. .. .. 2·50 2·50
O32 2 p. on 50 s. (P.) .. .. .. 4·50 4·50

1968 (19 Dec). *Air. South Pacific Games Field and Track Trials, Port Moresby, New Guinea. As No.* 114, *but imperf, background colour changed and surch as Type* O **6**.

O33 **53** 20 s. on £1 yellow, scarlet, ultramarine and emerald-green 20 15
O34 1 p. on £1 yellow, scarlet, ultramarine and emerald-green 70 50

1969 (13 Aug). *Air. Third South Pacific Games, Port Moresby. Design as Nos.* 290/4.

O35 70 s. carmine-red, bright green and turquoise 45 70
O36 80 s. carmine-red, orange and turquoise .. 55 80

OFFICIAL AIRMAIL 1969 OIL SEARCH 90s (O 7)

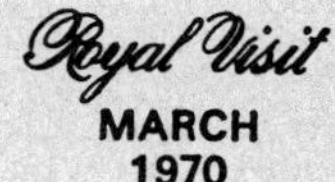

OFFICIAL AIRMAIL T$1·25 (O 8)

1969 (23 Dec). *Air. First Oil Search in Tonga. As No.* 114 *but imperf, background colour changed to emerald-green, and surch as Type* O **7**.

O37 **53** 90 s. on £1 multicoloured .. .. 3·50 3·50
a. "1966" for "1969" (R.3/5) £140
O38 1 p. 10 on £1 multicoloured (R.) .. 3·50 3·50
a. "1966" for "1969" (R.3/5) £140

The "1966" error does not occur on every sheet. It is possible that Nos. O37/8 were surcharged in sheets of 120 containing two panes of 60 (6×10).

No. O38 is surch as Type O 7, but without "OFFICIAL AIRMAIL".

1970 (7 Mar). *Royal Visit. As No.* 110 *but imperf, colours changed, and surch as Type* O **8**.

O39 75 s. on 1s. carmine-red and yellow .. 3·50 3·25
O40 1 p. on 1s. carmine-red and yellow (B.) .. 4·00 3·75
O41 1 p. 25 on 1s. carmine-red & yellow (G.) .. 4·75 5·00

(O 9)

1970 (4 June). *Air. Entry into British Commonwealth. As No.* 112 *but imperf, background colour changed, and surch as Type* O **9**.

O42 50 s. on 5s. orange-yellow and sepia .. 1·00 90
O43 90 s. on 5s. orange-yellow and sepia (R.) .. 1·40 1·40
O44 1 p. 50 on 5s. orange-yellow & sepia (G.) .. 2·25 2·50

1970 (4 June). *As Nos.* 325/34, *but inscr.* "OFFICIAL POST". *Colour of* "TONGA" *given for* 6 *to* 10 *s.*

O45 **83** 1 s. greenish yellow, brt purple & blk .. 45 50
O46 2 s. greenish yellow, ultram & black .. 55 60
O47 3 s. greenish yellow, chocolate & blk .. 55 60
O48 4 s. greenish yellow, emerald and black 55 60
O49 5 s. greenish yellow, orange-red & blk .. 60 65
O50 **90** 6 s. ultramarine 70 80
O51 7 s. deep mauve 75 85
O52 8 s. gold 85 95
O53 9 s. bright carmine .. .. .. 95 1·10
O54 10 s. silver .. .. 95 1·10
O45/54 .. .. .. *Set of* 10 6·25 7·00

The note after No. 334 also applies here.
See also Nos. O82/91.

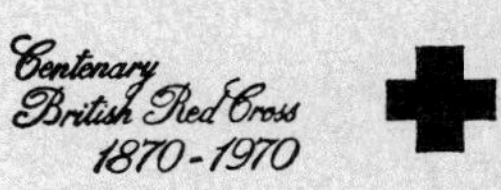

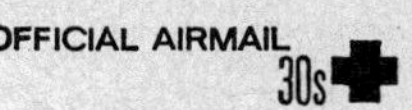

(O 10)

1970 (17 Oct). *Centenary of British Red Cross. As Nos.* 102 *and* 112 *but imperf, colours changed and surch as Type* O **10**.
O55 30 s. on 1½d. emerald (Blk. and R.) .. 1·75 1·75
O56 80 s. on 5s. orange-yellow & sepia (B. & R.).. 4·25 4·25
O57 90 s. on 5s. orange-yellow & sepia (B. & R.).. 4·25 4·25

(O 11) (O 12)

1971 (30 Jan). *Air. Fifth Death Anniv of Queen Salote. As No.* 113, *but imperf, colours changed and surch as Type* O **11**.
O58 **52** 20 s. on 10s. orange-yellow .. .. 1·25 80
O59 30 s. on 10s. orange-yellow (V.) .. 1·50 1·00
O60 50 s. on 10s. orange-yellow (B.) .. 2·50 1·75
O61 2 p. on 10s. orange-yellow (G.) .. 8·50 7·00

1971 (17 Apr). *Air. "Philatokyo 1971" Stamp Exhibition. Unissued Red Cross surcharges on No.* 107, *but imperf, colours changed and additionally surch as Type* O **12**.
O62 30 s. on 5d. green and yellow (B. & R.) .. 70 55
O63 80 s. on 5d. green and yellow (Blk. & R.) .. 1·50 1·50
O64 90 s. on 5d. green and yellow (P. & R.) .. 1·75 1·75

1971 (20 July)–**72**. *Air. As Nos.* 365/6*a*, *but inscr* "OFFICIAL AIRMAIL".
O65 **96** 14 s. multicoloured .. .. .. 1·50 1·50
O65*a* 17 s. multicoloured (20.7.72) .. .. 1·75 1·75
O66 21 s. multicoloured .. .. .. 1·75 1·75
O66*a* 38 s. multicoloured (20.7.72) .. .. 2·75 2·75

O **13** Football

1971 (20 July). *Air. Fourth South Pacific Games, Tahiti.*
O67 O **13** 50 s. multicoloured 60 90
O68 90 s. multicoloured .. .. .. 85 1·50
O69 1 p. 50, multicoloured .. .. 1·25 1·75

INVESTITURE 1971
OFFICIAL 60s AIRMAIL

(O 14)

(*Illustration reduced. Actual size* 61 × 13 *mm*)

1971 (30 Oct). *Air. Investiture of Royal Tongan Medal of Merit. Nos.* 315, 318 *and* 316 *surch as Type* O **14**.
O70 **89** 60 s. on 3 s. multicoloured 70 80
O71 80 s. on 25 s. multicoloured .. .. 90 1·00
O72 1 p. 10 on 7 s. multicoloured .. .. 1·00 1·25

O **15** "UNICEF" and Emblem

1971 (31 Dec). *Air. 25th Anniv of UNICEF.*
O73 O **15** 70 s. multicoloured .. .. .. 1·40 1·60
O74 80 s. multicoloured .. .. .. 1·50 1·75
O75 90 s. multicoloured .. .. .. 1·60 1·90

1972 (14 Apr). *Air. Merchant Marine Routes. Design similar to T* **100**, *but inscr* "OFFICIAL AIRMAIL".
O76 20 s. multicoloured .. .. 1·25 80
O77 50 s. multicoloured .. .. 2·75 2·50
O78 1 p. 20, multicoloured .. .. .. 5·50 6·50
Design:—Nos. O76/8, Map of South Pacific, and *Aonia*.

1972 (15 July). *Air. Fifth Anniv of Coronation. Design similar to T* **101**, *but inscr* "OFFICIAL AIRMAIL".
O79 50 s. multicoloured .. .. 1·00 75
O80 70 s. multicoloured .. .. 1·40 1·00
O81 1 p. 50, multicoloured .. .. .. 2·75 1·75
Design (47 × 57 *mm*):—Nos. O79/81, As T **101**, but with different background.

1972 (30 Sept). *As Nos.* 413/27, *but inscr* "OFFICIAL POST".

(*a*) *As Nos.* 413/17
O82 **83** 1 s. light yellow, scarlet and black .. 20 10
O83 2 s. light yellow, dp blue-green & black 25 15
O84 3 s. light yellow, yellow-green and black 30 20
O85 4 s. light yellow and black 30 20
O86 5 s. light yellow and black 30 20

(*b*) *As Nos.* O50/4, *but colours changed. Colour of* "TONGA" *given*
O87 **90** 6 s. light green 35 20
O88 7 s. light green 40 25
O89 8 s. light green 40 25
O90 9 s. light green 40 25
O91 10 s. light green 50 30

(*c*) *As Nos.* 423/7. *Colour of face value given*
O92 **102** 15 s. new blue 85 45
O93 20 s. reddish orange .. .. .. 1·00 60
O94 25 s. chocolate .. .. 1·10 70
O95 40 s. yellow-orange .. .. .. 2·25 1·50
O96 50 s. royal blue .. .. 2·50 1·75
O82/96 .. .. *Set of* 15 10·00 6·50
The note after No. 427 also applies here.

1972 (9 Dec). *Air. Proclamation of Sovereignty over Minerva Reefs. Design similar to T* **104**, *but inscr* "OFFICIAL AIRMAIL".
O97 25 s. multicoloured 40 35
O98 75 s. multicoloured .. .. 1·25 1·25
O99 1 p. 50, multicoloured .. .. .. 2·50 2·75
Design: *Horiz* (64 × 39 *mm*)—Nos. O97/9, Flags and map.

TONGA
1973
ESTABLISHMENT
BANK OF TONGA
40s
OFFICIAL AIRMAIL

(O 16)

1973 (30 Mar). *Air. Foundation of Bank of Tonga. No.* 396 *surch as Type* O **16**.
O100 **100** 40 s. on 21 s. mult (Blk. & G.) .. 1·50 1·25
O101 85 s. on 21 s. multicoloured (B. & G.) 2·75 2·00
O102 1 p. 25 on 21 s. multicoloured (Br.).. 3·50 3·00

SILVER JUBILEE
TONGAN SCOUTING
1948 · 1973

(O 17)

1973 (29 June). *Silver Jubilee of Scouting in Tonga. Nos.* O76, O74 *and* 319 *variously optd or surch as Type* O **17** *in silver* (*Nos.* O103/4) *or silver and blue* (*No.* O105).
O103 – 30 s. on 20 s. multicoloured .. .. 12·00 2·75
O104 O **15** 80 s. multicoloured .. .. .. 28·00 10·00
O105 **89** 1 p. 40 on 50 s. multicoloured .. 42·00 25·00

1973 (2 Oct). *Air. Bicentenary of Capt. Cook's Visit. Design similar to T* **107**, *but inscr* "OFFICIAL AIRMAIL".
O106 25 s. multicoloured .. .. 3·25 1·50
O107 80 s. multicoloured .. .. 8·50 4·50
O108 1 p. 30, multicoloured .. .. .. 10·00 7·50
Design: *Horiz* (52 × 45 *mm*)—Nos. O106/8, *James Cook* (bulk carrier).

1974
Commonwealth
Games
Christchurch
OFFICIAL AIRMAIL
50s

(O 18)

1973 (19 Dec). *Air. Commonwealth Games. Nos.* O67/9 *optd with Type* O **18**.
O109 O **13** 50 s. multicoloured (B.) .. .. 1·00 1·10
O110 90 s. multicoloured (Blk.) .. .. 1·75 1·75
O111 1 p. 50, multicoloured (G.) .. .. 2·50 2·50
a. Opt double £150

O **19** Dove of Peace

1974 (20 Mar). *Air.*
O112 O **19** 7 s. turq-grn, reddish vio & orge-red 60 20
O113 9 s. turq-grn, reddish vio & red-brn 65 25
O114 12 s. turq-grn, reddish vio & yell-orge 70 35
O115 14 s. turquoise-green, reddish violet and bistre-yellow 75 40
O116 17 s. multicoloured 85 60
O117 29 s. multicoloured .. .. .. 1·50 1·00
O118 38 s. multicoloured .. .. .. 2·00 1·25
O119 50 s. multicoloured .. .. .. 2·50 2·75
O120 75 s. multicoloured .. .. .. 3·75 4·25
O112/120 .. .. *Set of* 9 12·00 10·00

1974 (20 June). *Air. Centenary of Universal Postal Union. Design similar to T* **110**, *but inscr* "OFFICIAL AIRMAIL".
O121 25 s. dp red-orange, lt yellow-green & black 50 60
O122 35 s. lemon, magenta and black 60 75
O123 70 s. deep orange, bright blue and black .. 1·25 2·00
Design: *Square* (40 × 40 *mm*)—Letters "UPU".

1974 (11 Sept). *Air. Tongan Girl Guides. Design similar to T* **111**, *but inscr* "OFFICIAL AIRMAIL".
O124 45 s. multicoloured .. .. 4·00 2·00
O125 55 s. multicoloured .. .. 4·25 2·25
O126 1 p. multicoloured .. .. 7·50 5·50
Design: *Oval* (35 × 52 *mm*)—Lady Baden-Powell.

(O 20)

1974 (11 Dec). *Air. Establishment of Royal Marine Institute. Nos.* 446 *and* 451 *surch as Type* O **20**, *each obliterating the centre part of the original design.*
O127 30 s. on 15 s. multicoloured (Gold, B. & P.) 2·50 1·75
O128 35 s. on 15 s. multicoloured (Sil., B. & Blk.) 2·75 2·00
a. Black ("TONGA TONGA") omitted .. £150
O129 80 s. on 17 s. multicoloured (Blk. & R.) .. 4·25 4·50

1975 (11 Mar). *Air. South Pacific Forum and Tourism. Designs similar to T* **113** *but inscr* "OFFICIAL AIRMAIL".
O130 50 s. multicoloured .. .. 1·10 1·00
O131 75 s. multicoloured .. .. 1·75 1·50
O132 1 p. 25, multicoloured .. .. .. 2·50 2·25
Designs: (49 × 43 *mm*)—50 s. Jungle arch; others, Sunset scene.

1975 (11 June). *Air. Fifth South Pacific Games. Design similar to T* **114** *but inscr* "OFFICIAL AIRMAIL".
O133 38 s. multicoloured 55 50
O134 75 s. multicoloured .. .. 90 1·00
O135 1 p. 20, multicoloured .. .. .. 1·60 2·00
Design: *Oval* (51 × 27 *mm*):—Runners on track.

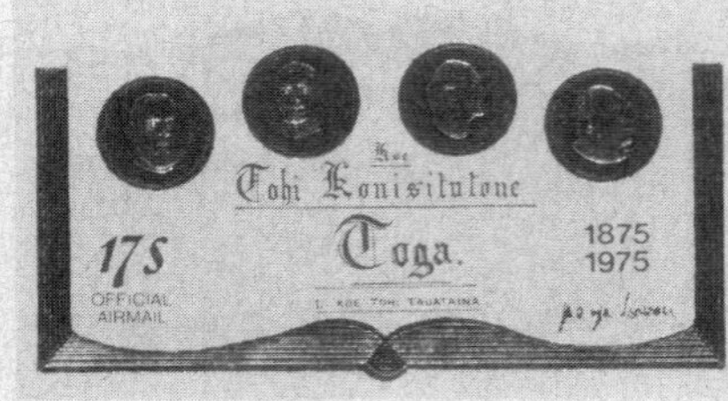

O **21** Tongan Monarchs

1975 (4 Nov). *Air. Centenary of Tongan Constitution.*
O136 O **21** 17 s. multicoloured 55 30
O137 60 s. multicoloured .. .. .. 1·25 1·25
O138 90 s. multicoloured .. .. .. 1·75 1·75

1976 (24 Feb). *Air. First Participation in Olympic Games. Design similar to T* **117** *but inscr* "OFFICIAL AIRMAIL".
O139 45 s. multicoloured .. .. 2·75 85
O140 55 s. multicoloured .. .. 3·00 1·00
O141 1 p. multicoloured .. .. 5·00 2·50
Design: *Oval* (36 × 53 *mm*)—Montreal logo.

1976 (26 May). *Air. Bicentenary of American Revolution. Designs as T* **118** *showing signatories to the Declaration of Independence. Inscr* "OFFICIAL AIRMAIL".
O142 20 s. multicoloured 90 50
O143 50 s. multicoloured .. .. 1·75 1·50
O144 1 p. 15, multicoloured .. .. .. 3·75 3·50

1976 (25 Aug). *Air. 150th Anniv of Christianity in Tonga. Hexagonal design* (65 × 52 *mm*) *showing Lifuka Chapel.*
O145 65 s. multicoloured .. .. 1·75 1·60
O146 85 s. multicoloured .. .. 2·00 2·00
O147 1 p. 15, multicoloured .. .. .. 2·75 2·75

1976 (1 Nov). *Air. Centenary of Treaty of Friendship with Germany. Rectangular design* (51 × 47 *mm*) *showing text.*
O148 30 s. multicoloured 60 70
O149 60 s. multicoloured .. .. 1·40 1·75
O150 1 p. 25, multicoloured .. .. .. 2·75 3·50

1977 (7 Feb). *Air. Silver Jubilee. Vert design* (57 × 66 *mm*) *showing flags of Tonga and the U.K.*
O151 35 s. multicoloured .. .. 1·25 40
O152 45 s. multicoloured 50 30
O153 1 p. 10, multicoloured 65 50

1977 (4 July). *Air. Tenth Anniv of King's Coronation. Square design* (50 × 50 *mm*) *showing* 1967 *Coronation Coin.*

O154	20 s. multicoloured	40	45
O155	40 s. multicoloured	80	1·00
O156	80 s. multicoloured	1·75	2·25

1977 (28 Sept). *Air. Bicentenary of Capt. Cook's Last Voyage. Rectangular design* (52 × 46 *mm*) *showing text.*

O157	20 s. multicoloured	2·75	2·50
O158	55 s. on 20 s. multicoloured	6·00	6·50
O159	85 s. on 20 s. multicoloured (V. and Blk.)	8·50	9·00

The face values of Nos. O158/9 are surcharged on the stamps, the original face value being incorrect.

1977 (16 Dec). *Air. Whale Conservation. Hexagonal design* (66 × 51 *mm*) *showing Blue Whale.*

O160	45 s. multicoloured	4·50	2·75
O161	65 s. multicoloured	6·00	4·50
O162	85 s. multicoloured	7·50	5·50

1978 (5 May). *Air. Commonwealth Games, Edmonton. "Tear-drop" design* (35 × 52 *mm*) *showing Games Emblem.*

O163	30 s. black, blue and red	45	50
O164	60 s. black, red and blue	1·00	1·25
O165	1 p. black, red and blue	1·60	1·75

1978 (4 July). *Air. 60th Birthday of King Taufa'ahau Tupou IV. Medal-shaped design* (21 × 45 *mm*) *showing portrait of King.*

O166	26 s. black, vermilion and yellow	35	30
O167	85 s. black, light brown and yellow	1·10	1·25
O168	90 s. black, bright violet and yellow	1·25	1·25

1978 (29 Sept). *Coil stamps.* (a) *Designs similar to Nos.* 675/9 *but inscr* "OFFICIAL POST".

O169	1 s. purple and greenish yellow	20	20
O170	2 s. brown and greenish yellow	20	20
O171	3 s. carmine, yellow and greenish yellow	30	30
O172	4 s. brown, yellow and greenish yellow	30	30
O173	5 s. blue-green, yellow and greenish yellow	30	30

(b) *Designs similar to Nos.* 680/4 *but inscr* "OFFICIAL POST"

O174	6 s. yellow-brown, emerald and light brown	40	40
O175	7 s. blue-black, emerald and light brown	40	40
O176	8 s. magenta, emerald and light brown	40	40
O177	9 s. red-brown, emerald and light brown	40	40
O178	10 s. deep green, emerald and light brown	40	40

(c) *Designs similar to Nos.* 685/9 *but inscr* "OFFICIAL POST"

O179	15 s. grey-black, orange-brown and emerald	1·00	1·00
O180	20 s. vermilion, orange-brown and emerald	1·10	1·10
O181	30 s. emerald and orange-brown	1·25	1·50
O182	50 s. new blue, orange-brown and emerald	1·50	1·75
O183	1 p. reddish violet, orange-brown & emer	2·25	2·75
O169/83	*Set of* 15	9·25	10·00

1978 (15 Dec). *Air. Endangered Wildlife Conservation. Designs as Nos.* 690/2 *but inscr* "OFFICIAL AIRMAIL".

O184	40 s. Type **129**	4·00	3·00
O185	50 s. Insular Flying Fox	4·00	3·00
O186	1 p. 10, Turtle	6·00	6·00

1979 (16 Feb). *Air. Decade of Progress. Designs similar to Nos.* 700/9 *but inscr* "OFFICIAL AIRMAIL".

O187	38 s. Tonga Red Cross emblem	65	40
O188	74 s. As No. 702	1·25	75
O189	80 s. As No. 701	1·40	80

1979 (1 June). *Air. Death Centenary of Sir Rowland Hill and 10th Anniv of Tongan Self-adhesive Stamps. Hand-shaped design* (45 × 53 *mm*) *showing self-adhesive stamps being removed from backing paper.*

O190	45 s. multicoloured	1·00	60
O191	65 s. multicoloured	1·40	85
O192	80 s. multicoloured	1·75	1·10

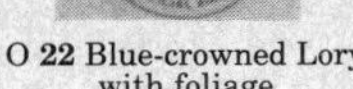

O **22** Blue-crowned Lory with foliage

O **23** Blue-crowned Lory without foliage

1979 (17 Aug). *Air. Coil stamps.*

O193	O **22**	5 s. mult (face value in black)	50	40
O194		11 s. multicoloured	55	40
O195		14 s. multicoloured	55	40
O196		15 s. multicoloured	60	40
O197		17 s. multicoloured	60	40
O198		18 s. multicoloured	60	40
O199		22 s. multicoloured	70	45
O200		31 s. multicoloured	75	65
O201		39 s. multicoloured	90	80
O202		75 s. multicoloured	1·75	2·50
O203		1 p. multicoloured	2·25	3·25
O193/203		*Set of* 11	8·75	9·00

See also No. O213.

1979 (23 Nov). *Air. Views as seen through the Lens of a Camera. Design as T* **133** *but showing Niuatoputapu and Tafahi.*

O204	35 s. multicoloured	55	55
O205	45 s. multicoloured	65	65
O206	1 p. multicoloured	1·40	2·00

1980 (9 Jan). *Air. 125th Anniv of France-Tonga Treaty of Friendship. Design as T* **134** *but showing the Establishment of the Principle of Religious Freedom in the Pacific Islands.*

O207	40 s. multicoloured	1·00	1·00
O208	55 s. multicoloured	1·25	1·25
O209	1 p. 25, multicoloured	2·50	2·75

1980 (30 Apr). *Air. Olympic Games, Moscow. Nos.* O190/2 *surch as T* **135** *in black on silver background.*

O210	26 s. on 45 s. multicoloured	85	85
O211	40 s. on 65 s. multicoloured	1·40	1·40
O212	1 p. 10, on 1 p. multicoloured	3·50	3·75

1980 (May). *No.* O193 *redrawn without foliage as Type* O **23**.

O213	O **23** 5 s. mult (face value in magenta)	£100	

1980 (30 Sept). *Air. South Pacific Scout Jamboree, Tonga and 75th Anniv of Rotary International. Design showing Scout camp and Rotary emblem.*

O214	25 s. multicoloured	70	40
O215	2 p. multicoloured	3·50	3·00

Nos. O214/15 show maps of Tonga on the reverse.

T$2 OFFICIAL (O 24) — **OFFICIAL** (O 25) — OFFICIAL (O 26)

1980 (3 Dec). *Air. No.* O145 *surch with Type* O **24**.

O216	2 p. on 65 s. multicoloured	4·50	5·50

1983 (22 Feb–Mar). *Nos.* 834/6 *handstamped with Type* O **25** (29 *s.*, 32 *s.*) *or optd with Type* O **26** (47 *s.*).

O217	29 s. Type **151**	3·25	3·50
O218	32 s. Type **151**	3·75	4·00
O219	47 s. Montgolfier's balloon and Concorde (Mar)	6·50	7·00
O217/19	*Set of* 3	12·00	13·00

OFFICIAL (O 27) — ***OFFICIAL*** (O 28) — *OFFICIAL* (O 29)

1984 (10 Apr)–**85**. *Nos.* 865/79 *and* 881 *optd with Type* O **27** (1, 5, 10, 15, 29, 47 *s.*) *or with Type* O **28** (*others*).

O220	1 s. Type **159**	10	10
O221	2 s. *Porites* sp (26.6.84)	10	10
O222	3 s. Red Squirrelfish (18.5.84)	15	15
O223	5 s. Green Map Cowrie (*Cypraea mappa viridis*)	15	15
O224	6 s. *Dardanus megistos* (17.9.84)	15	15
O225	9 s. Variegated Shark (18.5.84)	20	20
	b. Optd on No. 870b (28.5.85)	60	60
O226	10 s. Bubble Cone (*Conus bullatus*)	30	30
O227	13 s. Lionfish (18.5.84)	40	40
O228	15 s. Textile or Cloth of Gold Cone (*Conus textile*)	50	50
O229	20 s. White-tailed Dascyllus (18.5.84)	50	50
O230	29 s. Princely Cone (*Conus aulicus*)	60	60
O231	32 s. Powder-blue Surgeonfish (18.5.84)	60	60
O232	47 s. Giant Spider Conch (*Lambis truncata*)	70	70
O233	1 p. *Millepora dichotoma* (26.6.84)	1·50	1·50
O234	2 p. *Birgus latro* (17.9.84)	3·00	3·00
O235	5 p. Yellow-finned Tuna (28.5.85)	7·00	7·00
O220/35	*Set of* 16	14·00	14·00

Examples of the 3 p., No. 880, were also prepared with this overprint, but were not used for Official mail. It is believed that most examples were further overprinted "STAMP DUTY" for fiscal use.

1986 (16 Apr). *Nos.* 933/9 *optd with Type* O **29**.

O236	4 s. on 2 s. *Porites* sp.	60	60
O237	4 s. on 13 s. Lionfish	60	60
O238	42 s. on 3 s. Red Squirrelfish	1·50	1·50
O239	42 s. on 9 s. Variegated Shark	1·50	1·50
O240	57 s. on 6 s. *Dardanus megistos*	1·75	1·75
O241	57 s. on 20 s. White-tailed Dascyllus	1·75	1·75
O242	2 p. 50 on 2 p. *Birgus latro*	6·00	7·00
O236/42	*Set of* 7	12·50	13·50

1994 (14 Dec). *Air. 25th Anniv of Tongan Self-adhesive Stamps. Design as No.* O192, *but inscr* "25th ANNIVERSARY OF THE INTRODUCTION OF SELFADHESIVE STAMPS 1969–1994 BERNARD MECHANICK: 1915–80 INVENTOR FREEFORM SELFADHESIVE STAMPS" *at centre foot.*

O243	80 s. multicoloured	2·75	3·25

POSTAGE & REVENUE

TONGA 10s OFFICIAL

O **30** Bubble Cone (*Conus bullatus*)

1995 (25 Sept)–**96**. *Designs as Nos.* 1221a, 1223a, 1225a, 1227a, 1229a *and* 1345/9, *but inscr as Type* O **30**. *Chalk-surfaced paper. P* 14.

O247	10 s. Type O **30**	10	10
O249	20 s. White-tailed Dascyllus	15	20
O251	45 s. Giant Spider Conch (*Lambis truncata*)	40	45
O253	60 s. Princely Cone (*Conus aulicus*)	50	55
O255	80 s. Lionfish	70	75
O256	1 p. *Chelonia mydas* (turtle) (31.5.96)	90	95
O257	2 p. *Birgus latro* (crab) (31.5.96)	1·75	1·90
O258	3 p. Rose Branch Murex (*Chicoreus palma-rosae*) (31.5.96)	2·50	2·75
O259	5 p. Humpback Whale (31.5.96)	4·25	4·50
O260	10 p. Variegated Shark (*vert*) (31.5.96)	8·75	9·00
O247/60	*Set of* 10	20·00	21·00

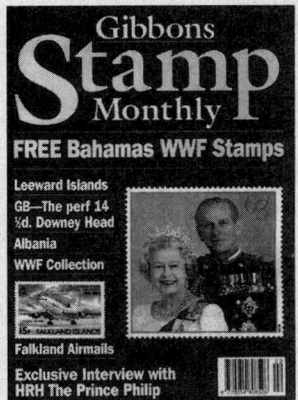

NIUAFO'OU

The following stamps were provided for the remote island of Niuafo'ou and were not valid for postage in the remainder of Tonga.

SELF-ADHESIVE ISSUES. Nos. 1/63 were manufactured by Walsall Security Printers using the self-adhesive system as described above Tonga No. 280.

T$1

1 Map of Niuafo'ou

NIUAFO'OU
KINGDOM OF TONGA

(2)

1983 (11 May). (*a*) *P* 14.
1 1 1 s. pale stone, black and rosine 20 40
2 2 s. pale stone, black and light emerald 20 40
3 3 s. pale stone, black & dull ultram 20 50
4 3 s. pale stone, black and chestnut 20 50
5 5 s. pale stone, black and deep magenta 30 50
6 6 s. pale stone, black and greenish blue 30 50
7 9 s. pale stone, black & dull yell-grn 30 50
8 10 s. pale stone, black & dull ultram 30 50
9 13 s. pale stone, black and light emerald 55 55
10 15 s. pale stone, black and chestnut 60 80
11 20 s. pale stone, black and greenish blue 65 80
12 29 s. pale stone, black and deep magenta 90 70
13 32 s. pale stone, black & dull yellow-green 1·00 80
14 47 s. pale stone, black and rosine 1·40 1·25

(*b*) *No.* 820 *of Tonga surch* (*No.* 15) *with T* 2 *by lithography or optd only* (*No.* 16) *by typography. P* 13½
15 1 p. on 2 p. pale turquoise-green & black (V.) 2·50 2·75
a. Deep mauve surch in typography 12·00 13·00
16 2 p. pale turquoise-green (Gold) 3·50 4·25
1/16 *Set of* 16 12·00 14·00

Most examples of No. 15 have the surcharge printed by lithography. A small quantity did, however, receive a typography surcharge in a different shade to form No. 15a. In addition to the colour the typography printing can be identified by the white rims to the letters and figures. All examples of No. 16 were printed by typography.

1983 (11 May). *Inauguration of Niuafo'ou Airport. As T* **153** *of Tonga. P* 14 × 14½.
17 29 s. multicoloured 80 1·00
18 1 p. multicoloured 2·50 3·25

3s

(3)

4 Eruption of Niuafo'ou

1983 (30 May). *As T* 1, *but without value, surch with T* 3 *by Tonga Government Printer.*
19 3 s. pale stone, black and royal blue 20 20
20 5 s. pale stone, black and royal blue 20 20
21 32 s. pale stone, black and royal blue 1·50 1·25
a. Surch inverted £600
b. Surch double
22 2 p. pale stone, black and royal blue 8·00 9·00
a. Surch inverted 90·00
b. Surch double £100
c. Albino surch
19/22 *Set of* 4 9·00 9·50

At least one example of No. 21a was caused by the self-adhesive stamp in the last position of the bottom row being inverted when the sheet was surcharged.

STAMP DUTY. Stamps of Tonga and Niuafo'ou overprinted or surcharged "STAMP DUTY", "STAMP DUTY ONLY" or similar wording were for fiscal use and were not valid for postal purposes.

(Des R. Edge)

1983 (29 Sept). *25th Anniv of Re-settlement. T* 4 *and similar horiz designs. Multicoloured. P* 14.
23 5 s. Type 4 40 30
24 29 s. Lava flow 1·00 1·00
25 32 s. Islanders fleeing to safety 1·10 1·00
26 1 p. 50, Evacuation by canoe 3·50 5·00
23/6 *Set of* 4 5·50 6·50

5 Purple Swamphen

6 Green Turtle

(Des N. Arlott)

1983 (15 Nov). *Birds of Niuafo'ou. T* **5** *and similar designs. P* 11 (1 *p.*, 2 *p.*), 14 (20 *s. to* 47 *s.*) *or* 14½ (*others*).
27 1 s. black and deep mauve 60 70
28 2 s. black and bright blue 60 70
29 3 s. black and blue-green 60 70
30 5 s. black and yellow 80 75
31 6 s. black and red-orange 90 85
32 9 s. multicoloured 1·10 85
33 10 s. multicoloured 1·25 1·25
34 13 s. multicoloured 1·50 1·25
35 15 s. multicoloured 1·50 1·50
36 20 s. multicoloured 1·75 1·75
37 29 s. multicoloured 2·00 1·50
38 32 s. multicoloured 2·00 1·60
39 47 s. multicoloured 2·75 2·25
40 1 p. multicoloured 4·50 6·00
41 2 p. multicoloured 6·50 8·50
27/41 *Set of* 15 25·00 28·00

Designs: *Vert* (22 × 29 *mm*)—2 s. White-collared Kingfisher; 3 s. Red-headed Parrot Finch; 5 s. Banded Rail; 6 s. Polynesian Scrub Hen ("Niuafo'ou Megapode"); 9 s. Green Honeyeater; 10 s. Purple Swamphen (*different*); (22 × 36 *mm*)—29 s. Red-headed Parrot Finch (*different*); 32 s. White-collared Kingfisher (*different*); (29 × 42 *mm*)—1 p. As 10 s. *Horiz* (29 × 22 *mm*)—13 s. Banded Rail (*different*); 15 s. Polynesian Scrub Hen ("Niuafo'ou Megapode") (*different*); (36 × 22 *mm*)—20 s. As 13 s.; 47 s. As 15 s.; (42 × 29 *mm*)—2 p. As 15 s.

(Des R. Edge)

1984 (7 Mar). *Wildlife and Nature Reserve. T* **6** *and similar multicoloured designs. P* 14.
42 29 s. Type **6** 70 70
43 32 s. Insular Flying Fox (*vert*) 70 70
44 47 s. Humpback Whale 2·00 1·60
45 1 p. 50, Polynesian Scrub Hen ("Niuafo-ou Megapode") (*vert*) 4·00 5·00
42/5 *Set of* 4 6·75 7·25

7 Diagram of Time Zones

8 Australia 1913 £2 Kangaroo Definitive

(Des R. Edge)

1984 (20 Aug). *Centenary of International Dateline. T* **7** *and similar horiz design. Multicoloured. P* 14.
46 47 s. Type **7** 60 50
47 2 p. Location map showing Niuafo'ou 1·90 2·75

1984 (17 Sept). *"Ausipex" International Stamp Exhibition, Melbourne. T* **8** *and similar vert design. Multicoloured. P* 14.
48 32 s. Type **8** 75 60
49 1 p. 50, Niuafo'ou 1983 10 s. map definitive 2·25 3·00
MS50 90 × 100 mm. As Nos. 48/9, but without exhibition logo and with face value at foot. Die cut. 1·75 2·50

Examples of No. **MS**50 without face values are Exhibition Banquet souvenirs without postal validity.

9 Dutch Brass Band entertaining Tongans

10 *Ysabel*, 1902

(Des R. Edge)

1985 (20 Feb). *400th Birth Anniv of Jacob Le Maire* (*discoverer of Niuafo'ou*). *T* **9** *and similar vert designs. P* 14.
51 13 s. purple-brown, pale cinnamon & brt orge 25 40
52 32 s. purple-brn, pale cinnamon & brt new bl 55 60
53 47 s. purple-brn, pale cinnamon & brt green 75 80
54 1 p. 50, purple-brn, pale cinnamon & lemon 2·25 3·00
51/4 *Set of* 4 3·50 4·25
MS55 90 × 90 mm. 1 p. 50, purple-brown, pale cinnamon and new blue. Imperf 1·50 2·00

Designs:—No. 52, Tongans preparing kava; No. 53, Tongan canoes and outriggers; Nos. 54/5, *Eendracht* at anchor off Tafahi Island.

1985 (22 May). *Mail Ships. T* **10** *and similar horiz designs. Multicoloured. A. Stamp die-cut and backing paper perf* 14. *B. Both stamp and backing paper perf* 14.

		A		B	
56	9 s. Type **10**	50	50	35	55
57	13 s. *Tofua I*, 1908	60	55	50	80
58	47 s. *Mariposa*, 1934	1·50	1·25	1·10	1·60
59	1 p. *Matua*, 1936	3·00	3·50	2·50	4·00
56/9	*Set of* 4	5·00	5·25	4·00	6·25

For description of the two forms of perforation see after Tonga No. 864.

11 Preparing to fire Rocket

12 Halley's Comet, 684 A.D.

1985 (5 Nov). *Niuafo'ou Rocket Mails. T* **11** *and similar horiz designs. Multicoloured. P* 14.
60 32 s. Type **11** 80 80
61 42 s. Rocket in flight 1·00 1·00
62 57 s. Ship's crew watching rocket's descent 1·40 1·40
63 1 p. 50, Islanders reading mail 3·25 4·00
60/3 *Set of* 4 5·75 6·50

(Des and litho Walsall)

1986 (26 Mar). *Appearance of Halley's Comet. T* **12** *and similar vert designs. Multicoloured. P* 14.
64 42 s. Type **12** 4·00 3·00
a. Horiz strip of 5. Nos. 64/8 18·00
65 42 s. Halley's Comet, 1066, from Bayeux Tapestry 4·00 3·00
66 42 s. Edmond Halley 4·00 3·00
67 42 s. Halley's Comet, 1910 4·00 3·00
68 42 s. Halley's Comet, 1986 4·00 3·00
69 57 s. Type **12** 4·50 3·50
a. Horiz strip of 5. Nos. 69/73 20·00
70 57 s. As No. 65 4·50 3·50
71 57 s. As No. 66 4·50 3·50
72 57 s. As No. 67 4·50 3·50
73 57 s. As No. 68 4·50 3·50
64/73 *Set of* 10 38·00 29·00

Nos. 64/8 and 69/73 were each printed together, *se-tenant*, in horizontal strips of five, forming composite designs, throughout the sheets.

X X

(13)

14 Swimmers with Mail

1986 (16 Apr). *Nos.* 32/9 *surch as T* **13** *in blue.*
74 4 s. on 9 s. Green Honeyeater 65 80
75 4 s. on 10 s. Purple Swamphen 65 80
76 42 s. on 13 s. Banded Rail 1·50 1·25
77 42 s. on 15 s. Polynesian Scrub Hen 1·50 1·25
78 57 s. on 29 s. Red-headed Parrot Finch 2·00 1·75
79 57 s. on 32 s. White-collared Kingfisher 2·00 1·75
80 2 p. 50 on 20 s. Banded Rail 5·50 6·00
81 2 p. 50 on 47 s. Polynesian Scrub Hen 5·50 6·00
74/81 *Set of* 8 17·00 18·00

(Des and litho Walsall)

1986 (22 May). *"Ameripex '86" International Stamp Exhibition, Chicago. 25th Anniv of United States Peace Corps. Horiz designs as T* **173** *of Tonga. Multicoloured. P* 14.
82 57 s. Peace Corps surveyor and pipeline 1·25 1·25
83 1 p. 50, Inspecting crops 2·25 2·75
MS84 90 × 90 mm. Nos. 82/3, magnifying glass and tweezers. Imperf 3·75 5·00

(Des Walsall. Litho Questa)

1986 (27 Aug). *Centenary of First Tonga Stamps. T* **14** *and similar horiz designs showing Niuafo'ou mail transport. Multicoloured. P* 14.
85 42 s. Type **13** 90 90
86 57 s. Collecting tin can mail 1·10 1·10
87 1 p. Ship firing mail rocket 2·00 2·50
88 2 p. 50, "Collecting the Mails" (detail) (C. Mayger) 3·50 4·50
85/8 *Set of* 4 6·75 8·00
MS89 135 × 80 mm. No. 88 5·00 7·00

Nos. 85/8 were issued in sheets of twenty stamps and five *se-tenant* labels, in the central vertical column, showing the colour separations of the designs.

PRINTER AND PROCESS. The following issues were lithographed by Walsall Security Printers Ltd, *unless otherwise stated.*

15 Woman with Nourishing Foods ("Eat a balanced diet")

16 Hammerhead

(Des C. Abbott)

1987 (11 Mar). *Red Cross. Preventive Medicine. T* **15** *and similar horiz designs. Multicoloured. P* 14×14½.

90 15 s. Type **15** 60 60
91 42 s. Nurse with baby ("Give them post-natal care") .. .. 1·60 1·60
92 1 p. Man with insecticide ("Insects spread disease") .. .. 2·50 3·00
93 2 p. 50, Boxer ("Say no to alcohol, drugs, tobacco") .. .. 4·00 4·75
90/3 .. .. *Set of* 4 8·00 9·00

1987 (29 Apr). *Sharks. T* **16** *and similar horiz designs. Multicoloured. P* 14.

94 29 s. Type **16** .. .. 1·75 1·75
95 32 s. Tiger Shark .. .. 1·75 1·75
96 47 s. Grey Nurse Shark .. .. 2·25 2·25
97 1 p. Great White Shark .. .. 3·75 4·50
94/7 .. .. *Set of* 4 8·50 9·25
MS98 90×90 mm. 2 p. Shark and fishes .. .. 9·00 10·00

17 Capt. E. C. Musick and Sikorsky S.42A Flying Boat *Samoan Clipper*

1987 (2 Sept). *Air Pioneers of the South Pacific. T* **17** *and similar horiz designs. Multicoloured. P* 14.

99 42 s. Type **17** .. .. 1·40 1·40
100 57 s. Capt. J. W. Burgess and Short S.30 modified "G" Class flying boat *Aotearoa* 1·75 1·75
101 1 p. 50, Sir Charles Kingsford Smith and Fokker F.VIIa/3m *Southern Cross* .. 2·50 3·00
102 2 p. Amelia Earhart and Lockheed 10E Electra .. .. 3·00 3·50
99/102 .. .. *Set of* 4 7·75 8·75

18 Polynesian Scrub Hen and 1983 1 s. Map Definitive

19 Sailing Ship and Ship's Boat

1988 (18 May). *5th Anniversaries of First Niuafo'ou Postage Stamp (42, 57 s.) or Niuafo'ou Airport Inauguration (1, 2 p.). T* **18** *and similar horiz designs. Multicoloured. P* 14.

103 42 s. Type **18** 80 75
104 57 s. As Type **18** but with stamp at left .. 1·00 95
105 1 p. Concorde and 1983 Airport Inauguration 29 s. stamp .. .. .. 3·00 3·00
106 2 p. As 1 p., but with stamp at left .. 3·50 3·75
103/6 .. .. *Set of* 4 7·50 7·50

1988 (11 July). *Bicentenary of Australian Settlement. Sheet 115 × 110 mm containing T* **19** *and similar vert designs. Multicoloured. P* 13½.

MS107 42 s. Type **19**; 42 s. Aborigines; 42 s. Early settlement; 42 s. Marine and convicts; 42 s. Sheep station; 42 s. Mounted stockman; 42 s. Kangaroos and early Trans Continental locomotive; 42 s. Kangaroos and train carriages; 42 s. Flying Doctor aircraft; 42 s. Cricket match; 42 s. Wicket and Sydney skyline; 42 s. Fielders and Sydney Harbour Bridge .. .. .. 24·00 24·00

Each horizontal strip of 4 within No. **MS**107 shows a composite design.

No. **MS**107 exists overprinted on the reverse as described below Nos. 985/8 of Tonga.

20 Audubon's Shearwaters and Blowholes, Houma, Tonga

21 Sextant

1988 (18 Aug). *Islands of Polynesia. T* **20** *and similar vert designs. Multicoloured. P* 14.

108 42 s. Type **20** 95 95
109 57 s. Brown Kiwi at Akaroa Harbour, New Zealand .. .. 1·40 1·40
110 90 s. Red-tailed Tropic Birds at Rainmaker Mountain, Samoa .. .. .. 2·00 2·25
111 2 p. 50, Laysan Albatross at Kapoho Volcano, Hawaii .. .. 4·50 5·50
108/11 .. .. *Set of* 4 8·00 9·00

1989 (28 Apr). *Bicentenary of Mutiny on the* Bounty. *Sheet 115×110 mm containing T* **21** *and similar vert designs. Multicoloured. P* 13½.

MS112 42 s. Type **21**; 42 s. Capt. Bligh; 42 s. Lieutenant, 1787; 42 s. Midshipman, 1787; 42 s. Tahitian woman and contemporary newspaper; 42 s. Breadfruit plant; 42 s. Pistol and extract from *Mutiny on the Bounty*; 42 s. Book illustration of Bligh cast adrift; 42 s. Profile of Tahitian woman and extract from contemporary newspaper; 42 s. Signatures of *Bounty* officers; 42 s. Fletcher Christian; 42 s. Tombstone of John Adams, Pitcairn Island .. .. .. 11·50 12·50

22 Spiny Hatchetfish

23 Formation of Earth's Surface

1989 (2 June). *Fishes of the Deep. T* **22** *and similar horiz designs. Multicoloured. P* 14.

113 32 s. Type **22** .. .. 85 1·00
114 42 s. Snipe Eel .. .. 1·00 1·00
115 57 s. Viperfish .. .. 1·25 1·50
116 1 p. 50, Football Anglerfish .. .. .. 3·00 3·75
113/16 .. .. *Set of* 4 5·50 6·50

Nos. 113/16 exist overprinted on the reverse as described below Nos. 985/8 of Tonga.

(Des R. Edge)

1989 (6 June)–**93**. *The Evolution of the Earth. T* **23** *and similar vert designs. Multicoloured.*

(*a*) *Size* 27×35½ *mm. P* 14½

117 1 s. Type **23** 10 10
118 2 s. Cross-section of Earth's crust 10 10
119 5 s. Volcano 10 10
120 10 s. Cross-section of Earth during cooling .. 10 10
120*a* 13 s. Gem stones (3.5.93) 15 20
121 15 s. Sea 15 20
122 20 s. Mountains 15 20
123 32 s. River gorge 25 30
124 42 s. Early plant life, Silurian era 35 40
124*a* 45 s. Early marine life (3.5.93) 40 45
125 50 s. Fossils and Cambrian lifeforms 45 50
126 57 s. Carboniferous forest and coal seams .. 50 55
126*a* 60 s. Dinosaurs feeding (3.5.93) 50 55
126*b* 80 s. Tyrannosaurus fighting Triceratops (3.5.93) 70 75

(*b*) *Size* 25½×40 *mm. P* 14

127 1 p. Dragonfly and amphibians, Carboniferous era (1.8.89) 90 95
128 1 p. 50, Dinosaurs, Jurassic era (1.8.89) 1·25 1·40
129 2 p. Archaeopteryx and mammals, Jurassic era (1.8.89) .. .. .. 1·75 1·90
130 5 p. Human family and domesticated dog, Pleistocene era (1.8.89) .. .. .. 4·25 4·50
130*a* 10 p. Mammoth and Sabre-tooth Tiger (14.9.93) .. .. 8·75 9·00
117/30*a* .. .. *Set of* 19 20·00 22·00

Nos. 130/*a* were each printed in sheetlets of 12 (3×4) containing 10 stamps and 2 stamp-size labels in the centre of rows 2 and 3.

24 Astronaut on Moon and Newspaper Headline

25 Lake Vai Lahi

1989 (17 Nov). *"World Stamp Expo '89" International Stamp Exhibition, Washington. P* 14.

131 **24** 57 s. multicoloured .. .. 1·00 1·00

1989 (17 Nov). *20th Universal Postal Union Congress, Washington. Miniature sheet, 185 × 150 mm, containing designs as Nos. 117/31, but with U.P.U. emblem at top right and some new values. P* 14½×14 (*top two rows*) *or* 14 (*bottom row*).

MS132 32 s. × 5 (as Nos. 117/21); 42 s. × 5 (as Nos. 122/6); 57 s. × 5 (as Nos. 127/31) .. 15·00 16·00

On No. **MS**132 the row of five 57 s. values are at the foot of the sheet and are perforated in a different gauge from the top two rows.

No. **MS**132 exists overprinted on the reverse as described below Nos. 985/8 of Tonga.

1990 (4 Apr). *Niuafo'ou Crater Lake. T* **25** *and similar horiz designs. Multicoloured. P* 14.

133 42 s. Type **25** 70 90
  a. Sheetlet. Nos. 133/8 .. .. .. 5·50
134 42 s. Islands in centre of lake 70 90
135 42 s. South-west end of lake and islet .. 70 90
136 1 p. Type **25** .. .. 1·40 1·50
137 1 p. As No. 134 .. .. 1·40 1·50
138 1 p. As No. 135 .. .. 1·40 1·50
133/8 .. .. *Set of* 6 5·50 6·50

Nos. 133/8 were printed together, *se-tenant*, as a sheetlet of six containing horizontal strips of three of each value forming composite designs and separated by an inscribed horizontal gutter.

26 Penny Black and Tin Can Mail Service

1990 (1 May). *150th Anniv of the Penny Black. T* **26** *and similar horiz designs, each showing stamp and Tin Can Mail. Multicoloured. P* 14.

139 42 s. Type **26** 80 80
140 57 s. U.S.A. 1847 10 c. .. .. .. 1·10 1·25
141 75 s. Western Australia 1854 1d. .. .. 1·25 1·50
142 2 p. 50, Mafeking Siege 1900 1d. .. .. 4·00 4·75
139/42 .. .. *Set of* 4 6·50 7·50

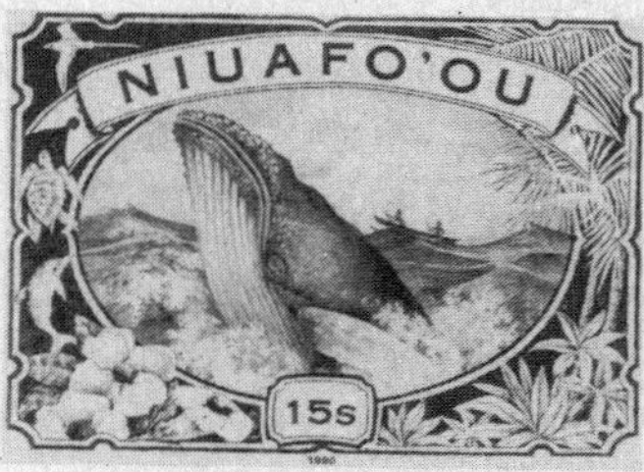

27 Humpback Whale surfacing

(Des G. Bennett)

1990 (6 June–4 Sept). *Polynesian Whaling. T* **27** *and similar horiz designs. Multicoloured. P* 11½.

143 15 s. Type **27** .. .. 1·10 1·10
144 42 s. Whale diving under canoe .. .. 1·75 1·75
145 57 s. Tail of Blue Whale .. .. .. 1·90 1·90
146 2 p. Old man and pair of whales .. .. 4·75 4·75
143/6 .. .. *Set of* 4 8·50 8·50
MS147 120×93 mm. 1 p. Pair of whales (38×30 *mm*). P 14×14½ (4 Sept) .. .. .. 9·00 10·00

No. **MS**147 shows "1990A" as an imprint on the 1p. stamp. Examples of this miniature sheet with "1990" as the imprint were mainly used for the surcharge, No. **MS**156, although a few unsurcharged examples with this imprint were used on Niuafo'ou in 1991.

(Des A. Benjamin and R. Edge)

1990 (25 Oct). *40th Anniv of United Nations Development Programme. Horiz designs as T* **203** *of Tonga. Multicoloured. P* 13½×14.

148 57 s. Agriculture and Fisheries .. .. 90 1·25
  a. Pair. Nos. 148/9 .. .. 1·75 2·50
149 57 s. Education .. .. 90 1·25
150 2 p. 50, Healthcare .. .. 3·25 3·75
  a. Pair. Nos. 150/1 .. .. 6·50 7·50
151 2 p. 50, Communications .. .. .. 3·25 3·75
148/51 .. .. *Set of* 4 7·50 9·00

The two designs for each value were printed together, *se-tenant*, in horizontal and vertical pairs throughout the sheets.

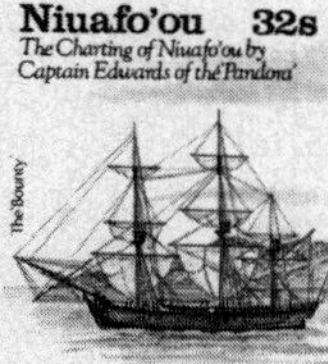

28 H.M.S. *Bounty*

X X

1991 ORNITHOLOGICAL AND SCIENTIFIC EXPEDITION.

T$1

(29)

(Des D. Miller)

1991 (25 July). *Bicentenary of Charting of Niuafo'ou. T* **28** *and similar vert designs. Multicoloured. P* 14½×14.

152 32 s. Type **28** .. .. 1·00 1·25
  a. Horiz strip of 3. Nos. 152/4 .. .. 3·00
153 42 s. Chart of *Pandora*'s course .. .. 1·10 1·40
154 57 s. H.M.S. *Pandora* (frigate) .. .. 1·25 1·50
152/4 .. .. *Set of* 3 3·00 3·75
MS155 120×93 mm. 2 p. Capt. Edwards of the *Pandora*; 3 p. Capt. Bligh of the *Bounty* .. 9·00 10·00

Nos. 152/4 were printed together, *se-tenant*, in horizontal strips of three throughout the sheet.

1991 (31 July). *Ornithological and Scientific Expedition to Niuafo'ou. No.* **MS**147 *surch with T* **29** *in blue by Govt. Printer, Tonga.*

MS156 120×93 mm. 1 p. on 1 p. multicoloured .. 2·25 3·00

No. **MS**156 shows "1990" as the imprint date.

30 Longhorned Beetle Grub

31 Heina meeting the Eel

(Des G. Bennett)

1991 (11 Sept). *Longhorned Beetle. T* **30** *and similar vert designs. Multicoloured. P* 14½×14.

157 42 s. Type **30** 80 80
158 57 s. Adult beetle 90 90
159 1 p. 50, Grub burrowing .. .. .. 2·75 3·00
160 2 p. 50, Adult on treetrunk .. .. 4·00 4·25
157/60 .. .. *Set of* 4 7·50 8·00

(Des D. Miller)

1991 (12 Nov). *Christmas. The Legend of the Coconut Tree. T* **31** *and similar horiz designs. Multicoloured. P* 14×14½.

161 15 s. Type **31** 35 40
162 42 s. Heina crying over the eel's grave .. 90 1·00
MS163 96×113 mm. 15 s. Type **31**; 42 s. No. 162; 1 p. 50, Heina's son collecting coconuts; 3 p. Milk flowing from coconut .. .. 9·00 10·00

(Des R. Edge)

1992 (28 Apr). *500th Anniv of Discovery of America by Columbus. Sheet* 119×109 *mm. containing vert designs as T* **214** *of Tonga. Multicoloured. P* 13½.

MS164 57 s. Columbus; 57 s. Queen Isabella and King Ferdinand; 57 s. Columbus being blessed by Abbot of Palos; 57 s. 15th-century compass; 57 s. Wooden traverse, windrose and the *Nina*; 57 s. Bow of *Santa Maria*; 57 s. Stern of *Santa Maria*; 57 s. The *Pinta*; 57 s. Crew erecting cross; 57 s. Sailors and Indians; 57 s. Columbus reporting to King and Queen; 57 s. Coat of Arms 13·00 14·00

(Des R. Edge)

1992 (12 May). *50th Anniv of Outbreak of Pacific War. Horiz designs as T* **215** *of Tonga, each showing contemporary newspaper headline. Multicoloured. P* 14.

165 42 s. American battleship ablaze, Pearl Harbor .. .. 1·10 1·25
a. Sheetlet. Nos. 165/76 .. .. 12·00
166 42 s. Destroyed American Douglas B-18 Bolo aircraft, Hawaii .. .. .. 1·10 1·25
167 42 s. Japanese Mitsubishi A6M Zero-Sen fighter .. .. 1·10 1·25
168 42 s. Pres. Roosevelt signing Declaration of War .. .. 1·10 1·25
169 42 s. Japanese T 95 light tank and Gen. MacArthur .. .. 1·10 1·25
170 42 s. Douglas SBD Dauntless dive bomber and Admiral Nimitz .. .. .. 1·10 1·25
171 42 s. Bren gun and Gen. Sir Thomas Blamey 1·10 1·25
172 42 s. Australian mortar crew, Kokoda .. 1·10 1·25
173 42 s. U.S.S. *Mississippi* (battleship) in action and Maj-Gen. Julian C. Smith .. 1·10 1·25
174 42 s. U.S.S. *Enterprise* (aircraft carrier) .. 1·10 1·25
175 42 s. American marine and Maj-Gen. Curtis Lemay .. .. 1·10 1·25
176 42 s. Boeing B-29 Superfortress bomber and Japanese surrender, Tokyo Bay .. 1·10 1·25
165/76 .. .. *Set of* 12 12·00 13·50

Nos. 165/76 were printed together, *se-tenant*, in sheetlets of 12 (4×3) with each horizontal row forming a composite design.

(Des R. Edge)

1992 (4 July). *25th Anniv of the Coronation of King Tupou IV. Horiz designs as T* **217** *of Tonga. P* 13½×13 (45 *s.*) *or* 12 (*others*).

177 45 s. multicoloured 75 75
178 80 s. multicoloured .. .. 1·50 1·75
a. Horiz strip of 3. Nos. 178/80 .. .. 4·00
179 80 s. black and cinnamon .. .. .. 1·50 1·75
180 80 s. multicoloured .. .. 1·50 1·75
181 2 p. multicoloured .. .. 2·50 3·00
177/81 .. .. *Set of* 5 7·00 8·00

Designs: (34×23 *mm*)—No. 177, King Taufa'ahau Tupou IV and Queen Halaevalu during Coronation; (48×35 *mm*)—No. 178. King Tupou IV and Tongan national anthem; No. 179, Extract from Investiture ceremony; No. 180 Tongan choir; No. 181, As 45 s.

Nos. 177/81 show the King's first name incorrectly spelt as "Tauf'ahau".

Nos. 178/80 were printed together, *se-tenant*, in horizontal strips of 3 throughout the sheet.

32 Male and Female Scrub Hens searching for Food

33 1983 2s. Map and 1993 60s. Dinosaur Definitives

(Des G. Bennett)

1992 (15 Sept). *Endangered Species. Polynesian Scrub Hen. T* **32** *and similar horiz designs. P* 14.

182 45 s. Type **32** .. .. 1·00 1·25
183 60 s. Female guarding egg .. .. .. 1·25 1·40
184 80 s. Chick .. .. 1·60 1·75
185 1 p. 50, Head of male .. .. .. 2·75 3·50
182/5 .. .. *Set of* 4 6·00 7·00

(Des D. Miller)

1993 (3 May). *10th Anniv of First Niuafo'ou Stamp. T* **33** *and similar horiz design. Multicoloured. P* 14×14½.

186 60 s. Type **33** .. .. 1·00 1·10
187 80 s. 1983 5 s. map and 1993 80 s. dinosaur definitives .. .. 1·25 1·40

34 De Havilland D.H.C.6 Twin Otter 200/300 of South Pacific Island Airways

35 Blue-crowned Lory

(Des D. Miller)

1993 (3 May). *10th Anniv of First Flight to Niuafo'ou. T* **34** *and similar horiz design. Multicoloured. P* 14×14½.

188 1 p. Type **34** .. .. 1·50 2·00
189 2 p. 50, De Havilland D.H.C.6 Twin Otter 200/300 of Friendly Islands Airways 3·50 4·25

(Des D. Miller)

1993 (1 July). *75th Birthday of King Taufa'ahau Tupou IV. Vert designs as T* **229** *of Tonga. Multicoloured. P* 13×13½ (45 *s.*) *or* 12 (*others*).

190 45 s. King Tupou IV and *Pangai* (patrol boat) 55 55
191 80 s. King Tupou IV and musical instruments (38½×51 *mm*) .. .. 1·25 1·75
a. Strip of 3. Nos. 191/3 .. .. 3·25
192 80 s. King Tupou IV and sporting events (38½×51 *mm*) .. .. .. 1·25 1·75
193 80 s. King Tupou IV with De Havilland D.H.C.6 Twin Otter 200/300 aircraft and telecommunications (38½×51 *mm*) .. .. 1·25 1·75
194 2 p. As 45 s., but larger (38½×51 *mm*) .. 2·75 3·00
190/4 .. .. *Set of* 5 6·50 8·00

Nos. 191/3 were printed together, *se-tenant*, in horizontal and vertical strips of 3 throughout the sheet of 9.

(Des G. Bennett)

1993 (10 Aug). *Natural History of Lake Vai Lahi. T* **35** *and similar vert designs. Multicoloured. P* 14.

195 60 s. Type **35** .. .. 1·00 1·25
a. Horiz strip of 5. Nos. 195/9 .. .. 4·50
196 60 s. White-tailed Tropic Bird and Eastern Reef Heron .. .. 1·00 1·25
197 60 s. Black Admiral (butterfly) and Niuafo'ou Coconut Beetle .. .. 1·00 1·25
198 60 s. Niuafo'ou Dragonfly, Spotbill Ducks and Niuafo'ou Moths .. .. 1·00 1·25
199 60 s. Niuafo'ou Megapode .. .. .. 1·00 1·25
195/9 .. .. *Set of* 5 4·50 5·50

Nos. 195/9 were printed together, *se-tenant*, in horizontal strips of five throughout the sheet, each strip forming a composite design.

1993 (1 Dec). *Children's Painting Competition Winners. Vert designs as T* **231** *of Tonga. P* 14.

200 10 s. multicoloured 40 55
a. Pair. Nos. 200/1 .. .. .. 80 1·10
201 10 s. black and grey-black 40 55
202 1 p. multicoloured .. .. 2·75 3·00
a. Pair. Nos. 202/3 .. .. .. 5·50 6·00
203 1 p. multicoloured .. .. 2·75 3·00
200/3 .. .. *Set of* 4 5·75 6·50

Designs:—Nos. 200 and 202, "Crater Lake Megapode and Volcano" (Paea Puletau); Nos. 201 and 203, "Ofato Beetle Grubs of Niuafo'ou" (Peni Finau).

Nos. 200/1 and 202/3 were each printed together, *se-tenant*, in horizontal and vertical pairs throughout separate sheetlets of 12.

36 *Scarabaeidea*

37 Stern of H.M.S. *Bounty*

(Des G. Bennett)

1994 (15 Mar). *Beetles. T* **36** *and similar horiz designs. Multicoloured. P* 14.

204 60 s. Type **36** .. .. 85 1·00
205 80 s. *Coccinellidea* .. .. 1·10 1·40
206 1 p. 50, *Cerambycidea* .. .. .. 2·00 2·50
207 2 p. 50, *Pentatomidae* .. .. .. 3·75 4·25
204/7 .. .. *Set of* 4 7·00 8·25

(Des G. Bennett)

1994 (21 June). *Sailing Ships. T* **37** *and similar vert designs. Multicoloured. P* 14.

208 80 s. Type **37** .. .. 1·75 2·00
a. Horiz strip of 5. Nos. 208/12 .. .. 8·00
209 80 s. Bow of H.M.S. *Bounty* .. .. 1·75 2·00
210 80 s. H.M.S. *Pandora* (frigate) .. .. 1·75 2·00
211 80 s. Whaling ship .. .. 1·75 2·00
212 80 s. Trading schooner .. .. .. 1·75 2·00
208/12 .. .. *Set of* 5 8·00 9·00

Nos. 208/12 were printed together, *se-tenant*, in horizontal strips of 5 throughout the sheet.

SAVE THE WHALES

38 Blue-crowned Lory and Lava Flows

(39)

(Des D. Miller)

1994 (21 Sept). *Volcanic Eruptions on Niuafo'ou. T* **38** *and similar vert designs. Multicoloured. P* 14½.

213 80 s. Type **38** .. .. 1·25 1·50
a. Horiz strip. Nos. 213/17 .. .. 5·75
214 80 s. Spotbill Ducks over lava flows .. 1·25 1·50
215 80 s. Megapodes and palm trees .. .. 1·25 1·50
216 80 s. White-tailed Tropic Birds and inhabitants .. .. 1·25 1·50
217 80 s. Eastern Reef Heron and evacuation, 1946 .. .. 1·25 1·50
213/17 .. .. *Set of* 5 5·75 6·75

Nos. 213/17 were printed together, *se-tenant*, in horizontal strips of 5 throughout the sheet with the backgrounds forming a composite design.

1995 (30 June). *Visit South Pacific Year '95. Save the Whales. Nos. 143/7 surch as T* **39** *in blue.*

218 60 s. on 42 s. Whale diving under canoe .. 80 80
219 80 s. on 15 s. Type **27** .. .. .. 1·10 1·10
220 80 s. on 57 s. Tail of Blue Whale .. .. 1·10 1·10
221 2 p. on 2 p. Old man and pair of whales .. 2·50 3·00
218/21 .. .. *Set of* 4 5·00 5·50
MS222 120×93 mm. 1 p. 50 on 1 p. Pair of whales (38×30 *mm*) .. .. 2·25 2·75

(Des D. Miller)

1995 (1 Aug). *50th Anniv of End of Second World War in the Pacific. Vert designs as T* **242** *of Tonga. P* 14½.

223 60 s. greenish yellow, black and new blue 1·00 1·00
a. Sheetlet. Nos. 223/32 .. .. 8·75
224 60 s. greenish yellow, black and new blue 1·00 1·00
225 60 s. greenish yellow, black and new blue 1·00 1·00
226 60 s. greenish yellow, black and new blue 1·00 1·00
227 60 s. greenish yellow, black and new blue 1·00 1·00
228 80 s. greenish yellow, black and rosine .. 1·00 1·00
229 80 s. greenish yellow, black and rosine .. 1·00 1·00
230 80 s. greenish yellow, black and rosine .. 1·00 1·00
231 80 s. greenish yellow, black and rosine .. 1·00 1·00
232 80 s. greenish yellow, black and rosine .. 1·00 1·00
223/32 .. .. *Set of* 10 8·75 8·75

Designs:—Nos. 223 and 228, American marine; Nos. 224 and 229, Marine firing and side of tank; Nos. 225 and 230, Tank; Nos. 226 and 231, Marines leaving landing craft; Nos. 227 and 232, Beach assault and palm trees.

Nos. 223/32 were printed together, *se-tenant*, in sheetlets of 10 with the horizontal strips of 5 forming the same composite design.

(Des. D. Miller)

1995 (1 Sept). *"Singapore '95" International Stamp Exhibition. Multicoloured designs as T* **243** *of Tonga each with exhibition emblem. P* 12.

233 45 s. Dinosaurs feeding (as No. 126a) (*vert*) 1·00 1·25
a. Vert pair. Nos. 233/4 .. .. 2·00 2·50
234 60 s. Tyrannosaurus fighting Triceratops (as No. 126b) (*vert*) .. .. .. 1·00 1·25
MS235 110×70 mm. 2 p. Plesiosaurus .. 2·50 3·00

Nos. 233/4 were printed together, *se-tenant* vertically, in sheets of 10.

(Des Li Defu)

1995 (14 Sept). *Beijing International Coin and Stamp Show '95. Sheet* 143×87 *mm, containing horiz design as T* **244** *of Tonga. Multicoloured. P* 14½.

MS236 1 p. 40, The Great Wall of China .. 2·00 2·50

(Des K. McGee)

1995 (20 Oct). *50th Anniv of United Nations and End of Second World War. Designs as T* **245** *of Tonga. P* 13×13½.

237	60 s. multicoloured		1·00	1·00
	a. Horiz strip of 3. Nos. 237/9		2·75	
238	60 s. black and bright blue		1·00	1·00
239	60 s. multicoloured		1·00	1·00
240	80 s. multicoloured		1·25	1·25
	a. Horiz strip of 3. Nos. 240/2		3·25	
241	80 s. bright blue and black		1·25	1·25
242	80 s. multicoloured		1·25	1·25
237/42		*Set of* 6	6·00	6·00

Designs: *Horiz (as Type* **245** *of Tonga)*—No. 237, St. Paul's Cathedral and searchlights; No. 239, Concorde; No. 240, Allied prisoners of war and Burma Railway; No. 242, Mt Fuji and express train. *Vert* (25×35 *mm*)—Nos. 238 and 241, U.N. anniversary emblem.

Nos. 237/9 and 240/2 were printed together, *se-tenant*, in horizontal strips of 3 throughout the sheets.

40 Charles Ramsay and Swimmers with Poles — **41** Island and Two Canoes

(Des A. Benjamin (3 p.), G. Bennett (others))

1996 (21 Aug). *Tin Can Mail Pioneers. T* **40** *and similar horiz designs. Multicoloured. P* 14.

243	45 s. Type **40**		90	90
244	60 s. Charles Ramsay and encounter with shark		1·25	1·25
245	1 p. Walter Quensell and transferring mail from canoes to ship		2·00	2·00
246	3 p. Walter Quensell and Tin Can Mail cancellations		6·00	6·00
243/6		*Set of* 4	9·00	9·00

(Des D. Miller)

1996 (5 Sept). *13th Congress of International Union of Prehistoric and Protohistoric Sciences, Forli, Italy. Horiz design as T* **250** *of Tonga. Multicoloured. P* 12.

247	1 p. Cave painting, lake village and hunter	2·00	2·00
	a. Horiz pair. Nos. 247/8	4·00	4·00
248	1 p. Egyptians with Pyramid, Greek temple, and Romans with Colosseum	2·00	2·00

Nos. 247/8 were printed together, *se-tenant*, in sheetlets of 6 (2×3).

(Des D. Miller)

1996 (29 Oct). *50th Anniv of U.N.I.C.E.F. Children's Toys. Vert designs as T* **252** *of Tonga. Multicoloured. P* 14.

249	80 s. Dolls, model truck and counting balls		1·25	1·25
	a. Horiz strip of 3. Nos. 249/51		3·50	
250	80 s. Teddy bear, tricycle and model car		1·25	1·25
251	80 s. Book, model helicopter, pedal car and roller skates		1·25	1·25
249/51		*Set of* 3	3·50	3·50

Nos. 249/51 were printed together, *se-tenant*, in horizontal strips of three throughout the sheet, each strip forming a composite design.

(Des G. Bennett)

1996 (2 Dec). *50th Anniv of Evacuation of Niuafo'ou. T* **41** *and similar vert designs. Multicoloured. P* 14.

252	45 s. Type **41**		70	75
	a. Horiz strip of 5. Nos. 252/6		3·25	
253	45 s. Erupting volcano and canoes		70	75
254	45 s. End of island, volcanic cloud and canoe		70	75
255	45 s. Family and livestock in outrigger canoe		70	75
256	45 s. Islanders reaching Matua		70	75
257	60 s. Type **41**		95	1·00
	a. Horiz strip of 5. Nos. 257/61		4·25	
258	60 s. As No. 253		95	1·00
259	60 s. As No. 254		95	1·00
260	60 s. As No. 255		95	1·00
261	60 s. As No. 256		95	1·00
252/61		*Set of* 10	7·50	8·00

Nos. 252/6 and 257/61 were each printed together, *se-tenant*, in sheetlets of 10 with the horizontal strips of 5 forming the same composite design.

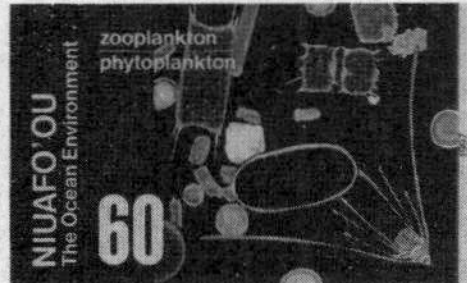

42 Plankton

(Des D. Miller)

1997 (19 May). *The Ocean Environment. T* **42** *and similar horiz designs showing different plankton. P* 14.

262	60 s. multicoloured		85	85
263	80 s. multicoloured		1·10	1·10
264	1 p. 50, multicoloured		2·00	2·25
265	2 p. 50, multicoloured		2·75	3·00
262/5		*Set of* 4	6·00	6·50

(Des D. Miller)

1997 (30 May). *"Pacific '97" International Stamp Exhibition, San Francisco. Sheet* 85×110 *mm, containing design as T* **259** *of Tonga. Multicoloured. P* 14.

MS266	2 p. Black-naped Tern	2·75	3·00

(Des D. Miller)

1997 (30 June). *King and Queen of Tonga's Golden Wedding and 30th Anniv of Coronation. Multicoloured designs as T* **261** *of Tonga, but* 50×37 *mm. P* 12.

267	80 s. King and Queen on wedding day	1·25	1·25
	a. Vert pair. Nos. 267/8	2·50	2·50
268	80 s. King Tupou in Coronation robes	1·25	1·25
MS269	82×70 mm. 5 p. King Tupou with pages (*horiz*)	7·00	7·00

Nos. 267/8 were printed together, *se-tenant*, as vertical pairs in sheets of 6.

Transjordan

PRICES FOR STAMPS ON COVER

Nos. 1/88*a*	*from* × 10
Nos. 89/142	*from* × 5
Nos. 143/243	*from* × 3
Nos. D112/24	*from* × 5
Nos. D159/248	*from* × 3
No. O117	*from* × 5

Transjordan was part of the Turkish Empire from 1516 to 1918.

Turkish post offices are known to have existed at Ajlun ("Adjiloun"), Amman ("Omman"), Amman Station, Kerak ("Kerek"), Ma'an ("Mohan" or "Maan"), Qatrana, Salt and Tafila ("Tafile"). Stamps cancelled "Ibin" may have been used at Ibbin.

The area was overrun by British and Arab forces, organised by Colonel T. E. Lawrence, in September 1918, and as Occupied Enemy Territory (East), became part of the Syrian state under the Emir Faisal, who was king of Syria from 11 March to 24 July 1920. During 1920 the stamps of the Arab Kingdom of Syria were in use. On 25 April 1920 the Supreme Council of the Allies assigned to the United Kingdom a mandate to administer both Palestine and Transjordan, as the area to the east of the Jordan was called. The mandate came into operation on 29 September 1923.

E.E.F. post offices, using the stamps of Palestine, operated in the area from September 1918.

BRITISH MANDATED TERRITORY

(Currency. 1000 milliemes = 100 piastres = £1 Egyptian)

"EAST". Where the word "East" appears in the Arabic overprints it is not used in its widest sense but as implying the land or government "East of Jordan".

("East of Jordan")
(1)

(1*a*)

(Optd at Greek Orthodox Convent, Jerusalem)

1920 (Nov). *T* 3 *of Palestine optd with T* 1. (*a*) *P* 15 × 14.

No.	Type	Description	Unused	Used
1	1	1 m. sepia	50	1·25
		a. Opt inverted	£120	
2		2 m. blue-green	7·00	8·50
		a. Silver opt	£250	£300
3		3 m. yellow-brown	90	1·25
		a. Opt Type 1*a*	£1100	
4		4 m. scarlet	95	1·25
5		5 m. yellow-orange	1·00	1·25
5*a*		1 p. deep indigo (Silver)	£2000	
6		2 p. olive	2·75	5·50
		a. Opt Type 1*a*	£850	
7		5 p. deep purple	23·00	28·00
		a. Opt Type 1*a*	£1200	
8		9 p. ochre	£800	£1400
1/7 (*ex* 5*a*)		*Set of* 7	32·00	42·00
		(*b*) *P* 14		
9	1	1 m. sepia	1·25	1·40
		a. Opt inverted	£150	
10		2 m. blue-green	50	70
		a. Silver opt	£550	
11		3 m. yellow-brown	16·00	16·00
12		4 m. scarlet	15·00	18·00
13		5 m. orange	2·00	80
14		1 p. deep indigo (Silver)	1·50	1·75
15		2 p. deep olive	3·25	3·00
16		5 p. purple	2·50	6·00
17		9 p. ochre	3·50	20·00
18		10 p. ultramarine	4·00	20·00
19		20 p. pale grey	8·00	35·00
9/19		*Set of* 11	50·00	£110

Nos. 1/9 were surcharged from five different settings of 120 (12×10) which produced eight sub-types of Type 1. Type 1*a* occurred on R. 8/12 from one setting.

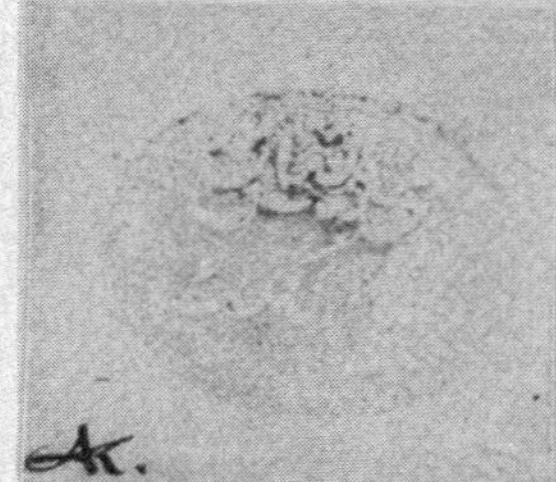

1*b* Moab District Seal (*full size*)

1920. *Issued at Kerak. Handstamped. Manuscript initials "AK" in violet. Imperf.*

No.	Type	Description	Unused	Used
19*a*	1*b*	(1 p.) pale blue	£3500	£4000

No. 19*a* was issued in late 1920 by the political officer for Moab District, Captain (later Sir) Alex Kirkbride, and was used until supplies of Nos. 1/19 reached the area in March 1921. The local Turkish canceller was used as a postmark.

Emir Abdullah, 1 April 1921–22 May 1946

Abdullah, a son of the King of the Hejaz, was made Emir of Transjordan in 1921. On 26 May 1923 Transjordan was recognised as an autonomous state and on 20 February 1928 it was accorded a degree of independence.

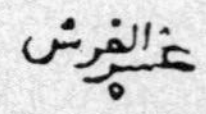

("Tenth of a piastre")
(2)

("Piastre")
(3)

1922 (Nov). *Nos.* 1/19 *additionally handstamped with steel dies at Amman as T* 2 *or* 3. (*a*) *P* 15 × 14.

No.	Type	Description	Unused	Used
20	2	1/10 p. on 1 m. sepia	25·00	45·00
		a. Red surch	70·00	70·00
		b. Violet surch	70·00	70·00
21		2/10 p. on 2 m. blue-green	28·00	28·00
		a. Error. Surch "3/10" for "2/10"	£110	£110
		b. Red surch	80·00	80·00
		c. Violet surch	£100	£100
22		3/10 p. on 3 m. yellow-brown	10·00	10·00
		a. Pair, one without surch	£750	
		b. Opt Type 1*a*	£1500	
		c. Violet surch	£150	£150
		ca. Opt Type 1*a*	£2750	
23		4/10 p. on 4 m. scarlet	50·00	50·00
24		5/10 p. on 5 m. yellow-orange	£180	£100
		a. Violet surch	£250	£225
25	3	2 p. on 2 p. olive	£250	75·00
		aa. Opt Type 1*a*	£1300	
		a. Red surch	£325	80·00
		b. Violet surch	£300	90·00
26		5 p. on 5 p. deep purple	50·00	70·00
		a. Opt Type 1*a*	£1500	
27		9 p. on 9 p. ochre	£300	£350
		a. Red surch	£130	£140
		(*b*) *P* 14		
28	2	1/10 p. on 1 m. sepia	20·00	25·00
		a. Red surch	60·00	60·00
		b. Violet surch	£250	£300
29		2/10 p. on 2 m. blue-green	25·00	25·00
		a. Error. Surch "3/10" for "2/10"	£100	£100
		b. Red surch	80·00	80·00
		c. Violet surch	80·00	80·00
30		5/10 p. on 5 m. orange	£225	£100
		a. Violet surch	£275	
31	3	1 p. on 1 p. deep indigo (R.)	£200	60·00
		a. Pair, one without surch	£1800	
		b. Violet surch	£400	
32		9 p. on 9 p. ochre (R.)	£500	£500
33		10 p. on 10 p. ultramarine	£850	£1000
34		20 p. on 20 p. pale grey	£650	£850
		a. Violet surch	£900	£950

T 3 *of Palestine* (*perf* 15×14) *similarly surch*

No.	Type	Description	Unused	Used
35	3	10 p. on 10 p. ultramarine	£1800	£2500
36		20 p. on 20 p. pale grey	£2500	£3000

T 2 reads "tenths of a piastre" and T 3 "the piastre", both with Arabic figures below. These surcharges were supplied in order to translate the Egyptian face values of the stamps into terms intelligible to the local population, *i.e.* tenths of a piastre (= milliemes) and piastres of the Turkish gold pound, but the actual face value of the stamps remained unchanged.

Being handstamped the surcharge may be found either at the top or bottom of the stamp, and exists double on most values.

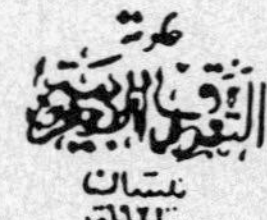

("Arab Government of the East, April 1921")
(4)

1922 (Dec). *Stamps of* 1920, *handstamped with a steel die as T* 4 *in red-purple, violet or black.** (*a*) *P* 15 × 14.

No.	Type	Description	Unused	Used
37	4	1 m. sepia (R.P.)	25·00	25·00
		a. Violet opt	28·00	28·00
		b. Black opt	22·00	22·00
38		2 m. blue-green (R.P.)	22·00	22·00
		a. Violet opt	20·00	20·00
		b. Black opt	18·00	18·00
39		3 m. yellow-brown (R.P.)	40·00	40·00
		a. Opt Type 1*a*	£1600	
		b. Violet opt	7·00	7·00
		ba. Pair, one without opt	£1000	
		bb. Opt Type 1*a*	£1500	£2000
		c. Black opt	8·00	8·00
40		4 m. scarlet (R.P.)	45·00	50·00
		a. Opt Type 1 omitted	£750	
		b. Violet opt	45·00	50·00
		c. Black opt	45·00	50·00
41		5 m. yellow-orange (R.P.)	35·00	10·00
		a. Violet opt	15·00	10·00
42		2 p. olive (No. 6) (R.P.)	55·00	40·00
		a. Violet opt	20·00	15·00
		b. Black opt	12·00	10·00
		c. On No. 6*a* (R.P.)	£1500	
		d. On No. 6*a* (V.)	£1500	£1300
43		5 p. deep purple (R.P.)	£100	£120
		aa. Pair, one without opt	£1500	
		a. Violet opt	60·00	80·00
44		9 p. ochre (R.P.)	£400	£450
		a. Violet opt	£200	£250
		ab. Opt Type 1*a*	£2250	
		b. Black opt	65·00	80·00
		(*b*) *P* 14		
45	4	1 m. sepia (R.P.)	12·00	15·00
		a. Pair, one without opt	£1000	
		b. Violet opt	22·00	20·00
		c. Black opt	18·00	18·00
46		2 m. blue-green (R.P.)	25·00	25·00
		a. Violet opt	8·00	8·00
		b. Black opt	10·00	10·00
46*c*		3 m. yellow-brown (V.)	£800	£350
47	4	5 m. orange (R.P.)	£300	75·00
		a. Violet opt	25·00	20·00
48		1 p. deep indigo (R.P.)	25·00	15·00
		a. Violet opt	15·00	9·00
49		2 p. deep olive (V.)	75·00	80·00
50		5 p. purple (R.P.)	90·00	£100
		a. Violet opt	£100	£110
51		9 p. ochre (V.)	£900	£1000
52		10 p. ultramarine (R.P.)	£1800	£1900
		a. Violet opt	£1100	£1600
53		20 p. pale grey (R.P.)	£1600	£2000
		a. Violet opt	£1100	£1800

*The ink of the "black" overprint is not a true black, but is caused by a mixture of inks from different ink-pads. The colour is, however, very distinct from either of the others. Other values may exist with "black" overprint.

Most values are known with inverted and/or double overprints.

حكومة الشرق
العربية

("Arab Government of the East, April 1921")
(5)

1923 (1 Mar). *Stamps of* 1920, *with typographed overprint, T* 5.

(*a*) *P* 15×14

No.	Type	Description	Unused	Used
54	5	1 m. sepia (Gold)	£1400	£1800
55		2 m. blue-green (Gold)	20·00	22·00
56		3 m. yellow-brown (Gold)	12·00	15·00
		a. Opt double	£500	
		b. Opt inverted	£550	
		c. Black opt	75·00	85·00
57		4 m. scarlet	10·00	12·00
58		5 m. yellow-orange	50·00	45·00
		a. Opt Type 1 albino	£1200	£1400
59		2 p. olive (No. 6) (Gold)	15·00	15·00
		a. Black opt	£250	£250
		b. On No. 6*a* (Gold)	£1200	£1000
60		5 p. deep purple (No. 7) (Gold)	60·00	80·00
		a. Opt inverted	£225	
		b. On No. 7*a*	£1500	
		ba. Ditto. Gold opt inverted	£2500	
		c. Black opt inverted	£1500	
		(*b*) *P* 14		
62	5	1 m. sepia (Gold)	16·00	24·00
		a. Opt inverted	£600	
63		2 m. blue-green (Gold)	14·00	18·00
		a. Opt inverted	£350	£350
		b. Opt double	£275	
		c. Black opt	£300	
64		5 m. orange	10·00	12·00
65		1 p. deep indigo (Gold)	10·00	14·00
		a. Opt double	£450	£475
		b. Black opt	£800	£850
66		9 p. ochre	75·00	£100
67		10 p. ultramarine (Gold)	70·00	£100
68		20 p. pale grey (Gold)	70·00	£100
		a. Opt inverted	£350	
		b. Opt double	£425	
		c. Opt double, one inverted	£425	
		e. Opt double, one gold, one black, latter inverted	£700	
		f. Opt treble, one inverted	£1000	
		g. Black opt	£800	
		ga. Black opt inverted	£1000	
		gb. Black opt inverted, one inverted	£1200	

The gold overprints were created by sprinkling gold dust on wet black ink.

There are numerous constant minor varieties in this overprint in all values.

The 20 p. exists with top line of overprint only or with the lines transposed, both due to misplacement.

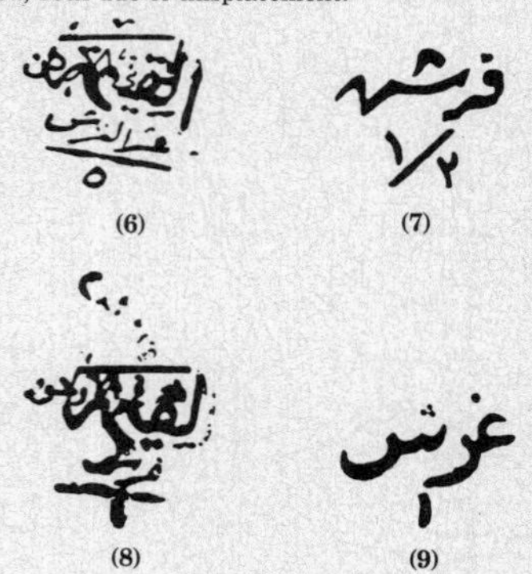

(6) (7) (8) (9)

1923 (Apr–Oct). *Stamps of the preceding issues further surch by means of handstamps.* (*a*) *Issue of Nov* 1920.

No.	Type	Description	Unused	Used
70	–	2½/10ths p. on 5 m. (13) (B.–Blk.)	£160	£160
		a. Black surch	£160	£160
		b. Violet surch	£160	£160
70*c*	6	5/10 p. on 5 m. (13)		
		(*b*) *Stamp of Palestine*		
71	6	5/10 p. on 3 m. (7)	£7500	
		(*c*) *Issue of Nov* 1922		
72	6	5/10 p. on 3 m. (22)	£7000	
73		5/10 p. on 5 p. (26) (V.)	70·00	80·00
		a. Opt Type 3 omitted	£1200	
73*b*		5/10 p. on 9 p. (27*a*)	£800	£850
74	7	½ p. on 5 p. (26)	70·00	80·00
		a. Pair, one without surch	£750	
75		½ p. on 9 p. (27)	£7500	
		a. On No. 27*a*	£350	£400
		ab. Opt Type 1*a*	£3500	
76		½ p. on 9 p. (32)	—	£8000
77	8	1 p. on 5 p. (26)	80·00	£100

(d) Issue of Dec 1922

No.	Type	Description	Unused	Used
78	6	5/10 p. on 3 m. (39)	85·00	£100
		a. On No. 39a	£750	
		b. On No. 39b	40·00	50·00
		ba. Pair, one without surch	£1400	
		c. On No. 39c	40·00	50·00
		ca. Without numeral of value	£150	
79		5/10 p. on 5 p. (43a)	8·00	14·00
		c. Pair, one without surch	£500	
79*d*		5/10 p. on 9 p. (44b)	—	£1200
		e. Surch on No. 44a	—	£1300
80	7	½ p. on 2 p. (42)	£100	£120
		b. On No. 42a	80·00	£110
		c. On No. 42b	60·00	£110
		ca. Pair, one without surch	£1000	
		f. On No. 42c	£2000	
81		½ p. on 5 p. (43a)	£3000	
82		½ p. on 5 p. (50)	£1800	
		a. On No. 50a	£2500	
83	8	1 p. on 5 p. (43)	£3750	
		b. On No. 43a	£2000	£2250
83*c*		1 p. on 5 p. (50)	£2500	

(e) Issue of 1 March 1923

No.	Type	Description	Unused	Used
84	6	5/10 p. on 3 m. (56)	25·00	30·00
		a. On No. 56c	£700	
85	7	½ p. on 9 p. (*p* 15×14)	90·00	£150
		a. Pair, one without surch		
86		½ p. on 9 p. (66)	£150	
87	9	1 p. on 10 p. (67)	£2250	£2500
		a. Violet surch	£2750	
88		2 p. on 20 p. (68)	60·00	80·00
88*a*		2 p. on 20 p. (68g)	£2000	

The handstamp on No. 88 has an Arabic "2" in place of the "1" shown in the illustration of Type **9**.

Being handstamped many of the above exist inverted or double.

TYPES OF SAUDI ARABIA. The following illustrations are repeated here for convenience from Saudi Arabia.

11

20

21

22

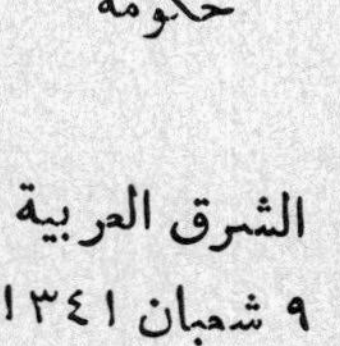

("Arab Government of the East, 9 Sha'ban 1341")
(10)

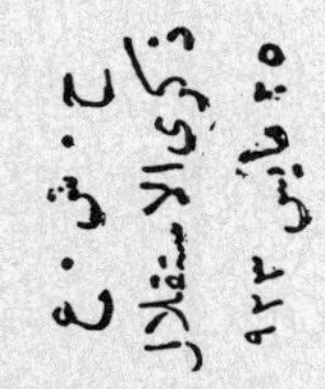

("Arab Government of the East. Commemoration of Independence, 25 May 1923")
(11)

It should be noted that as Arabic is read from right to left, the overprint described as reading downwards appears to the English reader as though reading upwards. Our illustration of Type **11** shows the overprint reading downwards.

1923 (April). *Stamps of Saudi Arabia.* T **11**, *with typographed opt,* T **10**.

No.	Type	Description	Unused	Used
89	10	⅛ p. chestnut	2·00	1·75
		a. Opt double	£200	
		b. Opt inverted	£110	
90		½ p. scarlet	2·00	1·75
91		1 p. blue	1·25	80
		a. Opt inverted	£120	£140
92		1½ p. lilac	1·50	1·75
		a. Opt double	£150	
		b. Top line omitted	—	£225
		c. Pair, one without opt	£250	
93		2 p. orange	2·00	5·50
94		3 p. brown	3·00	8·00
		a. Opt inverted	£225	
		b. Opt double	£225	£250
		c. Pair, one without opt	£375	
95		5 p. olive	5·00	9·00
89/95		*Set of* 7	15·00	26·00

On same stamps, surcharged with new values (Saudi Arabia, Nos. 47 and 49)

No.	Type	Description	Unused	Used
96	10	¼ p. on ⅛ p. chestnut	4·00	5·50
		a. Opt and surch inverted	£150	
		b. Ditto. but 2nd and 3rd lines of opt omitted	£200	
97		10 p. on 5 p. olive	15·00	22·00
		a. Top line omitted	£350	

In this setting the third line of the overprint measures 19–21 mm. On 35 stamps out of the setting of 36 the Arabic "9" (right-hand character in bottom line) is widely spaced from the rest of the inscription. Minor varieties of this setting exist on all values.

For later setting, varying from the above, see Nos. 121/4.

٩٢٣ ٩٣٣

Normal. "923" Error. "933"

An error reading "933" instead of "923" occurs as No. 2 in the setting of 24 on all values. As only 24 stamps were overprinted for each of Nos. 103A, 105B and 107B only one example of the error can exist for each. No such examples have so far been recorded.

1923 (25 May). T **3** *of Palestine optd with* T **11**, *reading up or down, in black or gold.* A. *Reading downwards.* B. *Reading upwards.*

No.	Description	A Unused	A Used	B Unused	B Used
98	1 m. (Blk.)	17·00	17·00	90·00	£100
	a. Opt double, one inverted (Blk.)	£650	£650	†	
	b. Arabic "933"	85·00	—	£250	—
	c. Gold opt	£150	£160	£150	£160
	ca. Opt double, one inverted (Gold)	£900	—	†	
	cb. Opt double (Blk. + Gold)	£900	£900	†	
	cc. Arabic "933"	£300	—	£350	—
99	2 m. (Blk.)	28·00	35·00	45·00	50·00
	a. Arabic "933"	£140	—	£200	—
100	3 m. (Blk.)	10·00	12·00	90·00	£100
	a. Arabic "933"	70·00	—	£250	—
101	4 m. (Blk.)	10·00	12·00	25·00	32·00
	a. Arabic "933"	70·00	—	£130	—
102	5 m. (Blk.)	50·00	60·00	†	
	a. Arabic "933"	£250	—	—	—
103	1 p. (Gold)	£650	£750	50·00	60·00
	a. Opt double	£750	£850	£600	—
	b. Black opt	†		—	—
	c. Arabic "933"	—	—	£250	—
104	2 p. (Blk.)	50·00	70·00	£750	—
	a. Arabic "933"	£250	—	—	—
105	5 p. (Gold)	60·00	70·00	£750	£550
	a. Opt double (Gold)	£650	—	†	
	b. Arabic "933"	£275	—	—	—
	c. Opt double (Blk.)	£1500	—	†	
106	5 p. (Blk.)	70·00	90·00	50·00	60·00
	a. Arabic "933"	£300	—	£250	—
107	10 p. (Blk.)	60·00	80·00	£500	—
	a. Arabic "933"	£275	—	—	—
108	20 p. (Blk.)	£700	—	70·00	90·00
	a. Arabic "933"	£2500	—	£300	—

The 9 and 10 p. are perf 14, all the other values being perf 15×14.

No. 107A surch with T **9**

No.	Description	Unused	Used
109	1 p. on 10 p. ultramarine	£6000	

(12)

1923 (Sept). *No.* 92 *surch with T* **12**. *(a) Handstamped.*

No.	Type	Description	Unused	Used
110	12	½ p. on 1½ p. lilac	6·00	6·00
		a. Surch and opt inverted	55·00	
		b. Opt double	75·00	
		c. Opt double, one inverted	90·00	£100
		d. Pair, one without opt	£150	

This handstamp is known inverted, double and double, one inverted.

(b) Typographed

No.	Type	Description	Unused	Used
111	12	½ p. on 1½ p. lilac	50·00	50·00
		a. Surch inverted	£150	
		b. Surch double	£180	
		c. Pair, one without surch	£500	

(13*a*) **(13*b*)**
("Arab Government of the East, 9 Sha'ban, 1341")

These two types differ in the spacing of the characters and in the position of the bottom line which is to the left of the middle line in T **13*a*** and centrally placed in T **13*b***.

1923 (Oct). *T* **11** *of Saudi Arabia handstamped as T* **13*a*** *or* **13*b***.

No.	Type	Description	Unused	Used
112	13*a*	½ p. scarlet	6·00	7·00
113	13*b*	½ p. scarlet	6·00	7·00

No. 112 exists with handstamp inverted.

ملك العرب

(15 "Arab Government of the East")

("Commemorating the coming of His Majesty the King of the Arabs" and date)
(16)

1924 (Jan). *T* **11** *of Saudi Arabia with typographed opt T* **15**.

No.	Type	Description	Unused	Used
114	15	½ p. scarlet	6·00	8·00
		a. Opt inverted	£180	
115		1 p. blue	£300	£200
116		1½ p. lilac	£350	

The ½ p. exists with thick, brown gum, which tints the paper, and with white gum and paper.

1924 (18 Jan). *Visit of King Hussein of Hejaz. T* **11** *of Saudi Arabia optd with T* **15** *and with further typographed opt T* **16**.

A. *In Black.* B. *In Gold*

No.	Type	Description	A Unused	A Used	B Unused	B Used
117	16	½ p. scarlet	1·00	1·00	2·00	2·00
		a. Type **15** omitted	£150	—	†	
		b. Type **16** inverted	£150	—	†	
		c. Imperf between (pr)	£110	—	£250	—
118		1 p. blue	1·25	1·25	2·00	2·00
		a. Type **15** omitted	£150	—	†	
		b. Both opts inverted	£200	—	£300	—
		d. Imperf between (pr)	†		£225	—
119		1½ p. lilac	2·00	2·00	3·00	3·00
		a. Type **15** inverted	£130	—	£150	—
120		2 p. orange	4·00	4·00	6·00	6·00

The spacing of the lines of the overprint varies considerably, and a variety dated "432" for "342" occurs on the twelfth stamp in each sheet (*Price* £75 *un*).

حكومة

الشرق العربية

٩ شعبان ١٣٤١

(16*a*)

شعبان شعبال شعبن

"Shaban" (normal) — "Shabal" (R.4/6) — "Shabn" (R.5/3)

1924 (Mar–May). *T* **11** *of Saudi Arabia optd with T* **16*a*** *(new setting of Type* **10**).

No.	Description	Unused	Used
121	⅛ p. chestnut	10·00	8·00
	a. Opt inverted	£100	
122	½ p. scarlet	3·00	3·00
	a. "Shabal"	50·00	
	b. "Shabn"	50·00	
	c. Opt inverted	£120	
123	1 p. blue	5·00	2·00
	a. "Shabal"	75·00	
	b. "Shabn"	75·00	
	c. Opt double	£120	
124	1½ p. lilac	7·50	8·50
	a. "Shabal"	90·00	
	b. "Shabn"	90·00	

This setting is from fresh type with the third line measuring 18¼ mm.

On all stamps in this setting (except Nos. 1, 9, 32 and 33) the Arabic "9" is close to the rest of the inscription.

The dots on the character "Y" (the second character from the left in the second line) are on many stamps vertical (:) instead of horizontal (..).

On some sheets of the ⅛ p. and ½ p. the right-hand character, "H", in the first line, was omitted from the second stamp in the first row of the sheet.

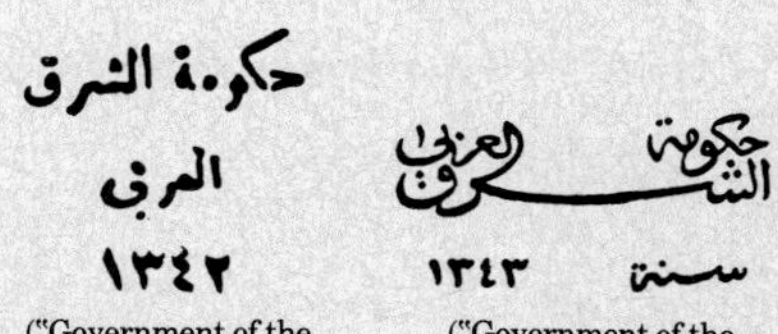

("Government of the Arab East, 1342")
(17)

("Government of the Arab East, 1343")
(18)

1924 (Sept–Nov). *T* **11** *of Saudi Arabia with type-set opt as T* **17**.

No.	Type	Description	Unused	Used
125	17	⅛ p. chestnut	35	25
		a. Opt inverted	£130	
126		¼ p. green	30	30
		a. *Tête-bêche* (pair, both opts normal)	7·50	10·00
		b. Opt inverted	85·00	
		c. *Tete-bêche* (pair, one with opt inverted)	£300	
127		½ p. bright scarlet	30	30
		a. Deep rose-red		
129		1 p. blue	2·50	1·50
		a. Imperf between (horiz pair)	£130	
		b. Opt inverted		
130		1½ p. lilac	2·50	2·50
131		2 p. orange	2·00	2·00
132		3 p. brown-red	1·50	1·50
		a. Opt inverted	£100	
		b. Opt double	£100	
133		5 p. olive	2·00	2·50
134		10 p. brown-purple and mauve (R.)	4·00	5·00
		a. Centre inverted		
		b. Black opt	£200	
125/34		*Set of* 9	14·00	14·00

Varieties may be found with dates "1242" or "1343", with "1" or "2" inverted, and other errors exist.

Type **11** of Saudi Arabia was printed in sheets of 36 (6×6). The ¼ p. value had the bottom three rows inverted, giving six vertical *tête-bêche* pairs. A few sheets were overprinted with the normal setting of Type **17**, with the result that the overprints on the bottom rows were inverted in relation to the stamp, including on one of the stamps in the *tête-bêche* pair (No. 126c). A corrected setting with the overprint inverted on the lower rows was used for the majority of the printing giving *tête-bêche* pairs with the overprints both normal in relation to the stamps (No. 126a).

1925 (Aug). *T* **20/22** *of Saudi Arabia with lithographed opt T* **18**.

135 **18** 1/8 p. chocolate 30 70
a. Imperf between (horiz pair) .. £110 £130
b. Opt inverted .. .. .. 60·00
136 1/4 p. ultramarine 30 70
a. Opt inverted .. .. .. 60·00
137 1/2 p. carmine 50 40
a. Opt inverted .. .. .. 60·00
138 1 p. green 40 40
139 1 1/2 p. orange .. .. .. 90 1·75
a. Opt inverted .. .. .. 60·00
140 2 p. blue .. .. .. 1·25 2·00
a. Opt treble £150 £200
141 3 p. sage-green (R.) .. .. 1·75 3·00
a. Imperf between (horiz pair) .. £110 £160
b. Opt inverted .. .. .. 80·00
c. Black opt £120 £150
142 5 p. chestnut .. .. .. 2·00 7·00
a. Opt inverted .. .. .. 80·00
135/42 .. .. .. *Set of* 8 6·75 14·00

All values exist imperforate.

No. 141 with gold overprint comes from a presentation sheet for the Emir.

("East of the Jordan")
(19)

22 Emir Abdullah

23 Emir Abdullah

(Opt typo by Waterlow)

1925 (1 Nov). *Stamps of Palestine,* 1922 (*without the three-line Palestine opt*), *optd with T* **19**. *Wmk Mult Script CA*. (*a*) *P* 14.

143 **19** 1 m. deep brown 10 40
144 2 m. yellow 10 30
145 3 m. greenish blue 10 30
146 4 m. carmine-pink 10 40
147 5 m. orange 10 20
a. *Yellow-orange* .. .. .. 35·00 20·00
148 6 m. blue-green 15 30
149 7 m. yellow-brown 15 30
150 8 m. scarlet 20 30
151 13 m. ultramarine 50 60
152 1 p. grey 50 50
153 2 p. olive .. .. .. 75 1·00
a. *Olive-green* .. .. .. £100 25·00
154 5 p. deep purple .. .. .. 3·00 3·75
155 9 p. ochre .. .. .. 6·00 7·50
156 10 p. light blue .. .. .. 11·00 13·00
a. Error. "E.F.F." in bottom panel .. £750 £800
157 20 p. bright violet .. .. .. 20·00 24·00
143/57 .. .. .. *Set of* 15 38·00 48·00
143/57 Optd "Specimen" .. *Set of* 15 £150

(*b*) *P* 15 × 14

157*a* **19** 9 p. ochre £850 £1000
158 10 p. blue .. .. .. 75·00 85·00
158*a* 20 p. bright violet £850 £850

(New Currency. 1000 milliemes = £1 Palestinian)

(Recess Perkins, Bacon & Co)

1927 (1 Nov)–**29**. *New Currency. Wmk Mult Script CA. P* 14.

159 **22** 2 m. greenish blue 15 30
160 3 m. carmine-pink 20 40
161 4 m. green .. .. .. 50 1·00
162 5 m. orange 25 30
163 10 m. scarlet 50 75
164 15 m. ultramarine 60 30
165 20 m. olive-green 80 90
166 **23** 50 m. purple .. .. .. 2·50 3·50
167 90 m. bistre .. .. .. 5·50 10·00
168 100 m. blue .. .. .. 8·00 7·50
169 200 m. violet .. .. .. 17·00 23·00
170 500 m. brown (1929) .. .. 60·00 85·00
171 1000 m. slate-grey (1929) £100 £140
159/71 .. .. .. *Set of* 13 £180 £250
159/71 Optd/perf "Specimen" .. *Set of* 13 £180

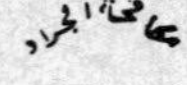

("Constitution")
(24)

(27)

(Optd at Cairo)

1928 (1 Sept). *New Constitution of* 20 *February* 1928. *Optd with T* **24**.

172 **22** 2 m. greenish blue .. .. .. 80 1·75
173 3 m. carmine-pink .. .. .. 90 2·75
174 4 m. green .. .. .. 1·00 3·00
175 5 m. orange .. .. .. 1·00 1·75
176 10 m. scarlet .. .. .. 1·50 3·50
177 15 m. ultramarine .. .. .. 1·50 1·75
178 20 m. olive-green .. .. .. 3·00 7·50
179 **23** 50 m. purple .. .. .. 5·00 8·50
180 90 m. bistre .. .. .. 14·00 38·00
181 100 m. blue .. .. .. 22·00 42·00
182 200 m. violet .. .. .. 65·00 £100
172/82 .. .. .. *Set of* 11 £100 £180

(Optd at Alexandria by Whitehead, Morris & Co)

1930 (1 Apr). *Locust Campaign. Optd as T* **27**.

183 **22** 2 m. greenish blue .. .. .. 1·10 3·50
a. Opt inverted £200 £500
184 3 m. carmine-pink .. .. .. 1·50 4·00
185 4 m. green .. .. .. 1·50 4·50
186 5 m. orange .. .. .. 14·00 14·00
a. Opt double £300 £500
b. Pair, one without bottom line .. £500
187 10 m. scarlet .. .. .. 1·50 4·00
188 15 m. ultramarine .. .. .. 1·50 2·25
a. Opt inverted £180 £275
189 20 m. olive-green .. .. .. 1·50 4·00
190 **23** 50 m. purple .. .. .. 5·00 9·00
191 90 m. bistre .. .. .. 10·00 38·00
192 100 m. blue .. .. .. 12·00 38·00
193 200 m. violet .. .. .. 30·00 85·00
194 500 m. brown .. .. .. 75·00 £150
a. "C" of "LOCUST" omitted (R. 5/3) £700 £800
183/94 .. .. .. *Set of* 12 £140 £325

28

29

(Re-engraved with figures of value at left only. Recess Perkins, Bacon)

1930 (1 June)–**39**. *Wmk Mult Script CA. P* 14.

194*b* **28** 1 m. red-brown (6.2.34) .. .. 30 1·00
c. Perf 13½ × 13 (1939) .. .. 2·75 3·25
195 2 m. greenish blue 30 50
a. Perf 13½ × 13. *Bluish green* (1939) .. .. .. 7·50 2·00
196 3 m. carmine-pink 40 70
196*a* 3 m. green (6.2.34) 85 85
b. Perf 13½ × 13 (1939) .. .. 13·00 4·25
197 4 m. green .. .. .. 60 1·75
197*a* 4 m. carmine-pink (6.2.34) .. .. 1·50 90
b. Perf 13½ × 13 (1939) .. .. 50·00 15·00
198 5 m. orange 40 40
a. Coil stamp. P 13½ × 14 (1936) .. 18·00 13·00
b. Perf 13½ × 13 (1939) .. .. 50·00 3·00
199 10 m. scarlet 70 15
a. Perf 13½ × 13 (1939) .. .. 80·00 4·25
200 15 m. ultramarine 65 20
a. Coil stamp. P 13½ × 14 (1936) .. 18·00 13·00
b. Perf 13½ × 13 (1939) .. .. 32·00 3·75
201 20 m. olive-green .. .. .. 1·25 35
a. Perf 13½ × 13 (1939) .. .. 55·00 12·00
202 **29** 50 m. purple .. .. .. 1·50 1·25
203 90 m. bistre .. .. .. 2·50 4·25
204 100 m. blue .. .. .. 3·75 4·25
205 200 m. violet .. .. .. 8·50 14·00
206 500 m. brown .. .. .. 20·00 38·00
207 £P1 slate-grey .. .. .. 45·00 80·00
194*b*/207 .. .. .. *Set of* 16 80·00 £130
194*b*/207 Perf "Specimen" .. *Set of* 16 £160

For stamps perf 12 see Nos. 230/43, and for T **28** lithographed, perf 13½, see Nos. 222/9.

30 Mushetta

31 Threshing Scene

32 The Khazneh at Petra

33 Emir Abdullah

(Vignettes from photographs; frames des Yacoub Sukker. Recess Bradbury, Wilkinson)

1933 (1 Feb). *As T* **30** (*various designs*) *and T* **31/3**. *Wmk Mult Script CA. P* 12.

208 1 m. black and maroon .. .. 50 1·40
209 2 m. black and claret .. .. 50 1·00
210 3 m. blue-green .. .. .. 60 1·40
211 4 m. black and brown .. .. 1·00 2·25
212 5 m. black and orange .. .. 1·00 1·25
213 10 m. carmine .. .. .. 1·50 3·00
214 15 m. blue .. .. .. 2·50 1·25
215 20 m. black and sage-green .. .. 3·50 5·00
216 50 m. black and purple .. .. 9·00 10·00
217 90 m. black and yellow .. .. 13·00 24·00
218 100 m. black and blue .. .. 13·00 24·00
219 200 m. black and violet .. .. 45·00 60·00
220 500 m. scarlet and red-brown £130 £170
221 £P1 black and yellow-green £350 £550
208/21 .. .. .. *Set of* 14 £500 £750
208/21 Perf "Specimen" .. *Set of* 14 £500

Designs: *As T* **30**—2 m. Nymphaeum, Jerash; 3 m. Kasr Kharana; 4 m. Kerak Castle; 5 m. Temple of Artemis, Jerash; 10 m. Ajlun Castle; 20 m. Allenby Bridge over the Jordan.

The 90 m., 100 m. and 200 m. are similar to the 3 m., 5 m. and 10m. respectively, but are larger (33½ × 23½ mm). The 500 m. is similar to T **32**, but larger (23½ × 33½ mm).

34

(Litho Survey Dept, Cairo)

1942 (18 May). *T* **28**, *but with Arabic characters above portrait and in top left circle modified as in T* **34**. *No wmk. P* 13½.

222 **34** 1 m. red-brown .. .. .. 80 3·00
223 2 m. green .. .. .. 1·50 1·50
224 3 m. yellow-green .. .. .. 2·00 2·25
225 4 m. carmine-pink .. .. .. 2·00 3·00
226 5 m. yellow-orange .. .. .. 3·25 1·00
227 10 m. scarlet .. .. .. 3·00 2·75
228 15 m. blue .. .. .. 5·00 1·75
229 20 m. olive-green .. .. .. 8·50 11·00
222/9 .. .. .. *Set of* 8 23·00 23·00

(Recess Bradbury, Wilkinson)

1943 (1 Jan)–**44**. *Wmk Mult Script CA. P* 12.

230 **28** 1 m. red-brown 20 75
231 2 m. bluish green 70 75
232 3 m. green .. .. .. 1·75 1·25
233 4 m. carmine-pink .. .. .. 1·75 1·25
234 5 m. orange .. .. .. 1·25 20
235 10 m. red .. .. .. 3·00 1·25
236 15 m. blue .. .. .. 3·00 30
237 20 m. olive-green (5.44) .. .. 2·75 1·00
238 **29** 50 m. purple (5.44) .. .. 3·00 1·00
239 90 m. bistre (5.44) .. .. 4·75 4·00
240 100 m. blue (5.44) .. .. 5·00 1·75
241 200 m. violet (5.44) .. .. 9·00 6·00
242 500 m. brown (5.44) .. .. 13·00 12·00
243 £P1 slate-grey (5.44) .. .. 24·00 20·00
230/43 .. .. .. *Set of* 14 65·00 45·00

Nos. 237/43 were released in London by the Crown Agents about May 1944 but were not put on sale in Transjordan until 26 August 1946.

Printings of the 3, 4, 10, 12, 15 and 20 m. in changed colours were released on 12 May 1947.

POSTAGE DUE STAMPS

حكومة
مستحق
الشرق العربية
٩ شعبان ١٣٤١

مستحق

(D 12 "Due")

(D 13)

1923 (Sept). *Issue of April, 1923, with opt T* **10**, *with further typographed opt Type* D **12** (*the 3 p. with handstamped surch as T* **12** *at top*).

D112 ½ p. on 3 p. brown .. .. .. 12·00 15·00
a. "Due" inverted .. .. .. 50·00 55·00
b. "Due" double .. .. .. 50·00 60·00
ba. "Due" double, one inverted .. £150
c. Arabic "t" & "h" transposed .. £100
ca. As c, inverted £250
d. Surch at foot of stamp .. .. 25·00
da. Ditto, but with var. c £120
e. Surch omitted £200
D113 1 p. blue .. .. .. 8·00 9·00
a. Type **10** inverted .. .. .. 80·00
b. "Due" inverted .. .. .. 45·00 40·00
c. "Due" double .. .. .. 50·00
d. "Due" double, one inverted .. £150
e. Arabic "t" & "h" transposed .. 70·00
f. "Due" omitted (in vertical pair) .. £200
D114 1½ p. lilac .. .. .. 8·00 9·00
a. "Due" inverted .. .. .. 45·00 45·00
b. "Due" double .. .. .. 50·00
ba. "Due" double, one diagonal .. 75·00
c. Arabic "t" & "h" transposed .. 70·00
ca. As c, inverted £200
d. "Due" omitted (in pair) £200
D115 2 p. orange .. .. .. 9·00 10·00
a. "Due" inverted .. .. .. 60·00 60·00
b. "Due" double .. .. .. 65·00
ba. "Due" double, one diagonal .. £100
c. "Due" treble £150
d. Arabic "t" & "h" transposed .. 70·00
e. Arabic "h" omitted .. .. 90·00

The variety, Arabic "t" and "h" transposed, occurred on No. 2 in the first row of all values in the first batch of sheets printed. The variety, Arabic "h" omitted, occurred on every stamp in the first three rows of at least three sheets of the 2 p.

Handstamped in four lines as Type D **13** *and surch as on No.* D112

D116 ½ p. on 3 p. brown .. .. .. 40·00 50·00
a. Opt and surch inverted £200
b. Opt double £200
c. Surch omitted £225
d. Opt inverted. Surch normal, but at foot of stamp £150
e. Opt omitted and opt inverted (pair) £300
f. "Due" double, one inverted .. £160
g. "Due" double, one larger .. £180
h. Surch double £250

حكومة

الشرق العربية
مستحق
٩ شعبان ١٣٤١

(D 14)

مستحق
شرق الاردن

("Due. East of the Jordan")
(D 20)

1923 (Oct). *T* **11** *of Saudi Arabia handstamped with Type* D **20**.

D117	½ p. scarlet	1·00	2·00
D118	1 p. blue	1·50	2·25
D119	1½ p. lilac	1·75	3·00
D120	2 p. orange	2·25	3·50
D121	3 p. brown	3·75	7·00
	a. Pair, one without handstamp	£200	
D122	5 p. olive	6·50	10·00
D117/22	*Set of* 6	15·00	25·00

There are three types of this handstamp, differing in some of the Arabic characters. They occur inverted, double etc.

1923 (Nov). *T* **11** *of Saudi Arabia with opt similar to Type* D **14** *but first three lines typo and fourth handstruck.*

D123	1 p. blue	50·00	
D124	5 p. olive	6·00	

(Opt typo by Waterlow)

1925 (Nov). *Stamps of Palestine* 1922 (*without the three-line Palestine opt*), *optd with Type* D **20**. *P* 14.

D159	1 m. deep brown	1·40	4·00
D160	2 m. yellow	1·75	2·75
D161	4 m. carmine-pink	2·75	4·50
D162	8 m. scarlet	3·75	7·00
D163	13 m. ultramarine	4·50	7·00
D164	5 p. deep purple	5·00	9·00
	a. Perf 15 × 14	40·00	55·00
D159/64	*Set of* 6	17·00	30·00
D159/64 Optd "Specimen"	*Set of* 6	60·00	

Stamps as No. D164, but with a different top line to overprint Type D **20**, were for revenue purposes.

مستحق

١ مليم (1 m.) (D 21) ٢ مليم (2 m.) ٤ مليم (4 m.)

٨ مليم (8 m.) ١٣ مليم (13 m.) ٥ قروش (5 p.)

(Surch typo at Jerusalem)

1926. *Postage stamps of* 1 *November* 1925, *surch "Due" and new value as Type* D **21**. *Bottom line of surcharge differs for each value as illustrated.*

D165	1 m. on 1 m. deep brown	2·00	4·00
D166	2 m. on 1 m. deep brown	2·25	4·00
D167	4 m. on 3 m. greenish blue	2·50	5·00
D168	8 m. on 3 m. greenish blue	2·50	5·50
D169	13 m. on 13 m. ultramarine	2·50	6·00
D170	5 p. on 13 m. ultramarine	3·50	8·00
D165/70	*Set of* 6	14·00	29·00

١ مستحق ١

(D 25 "Due")

D 26

D 35

(Surch at Cairo)

1929 (1 Jan). *Nos.* 159 *etc. optd only or surch in addition as Type* D **25**.

D183	**22**	1 m. on 3 m. carmine-pink	70	2·50
D184		2 m. greenish blue	80	2·50
		a. Pair, one without surch	£300	
D185		4 m. on 15 m. ultramarine	1·25	3·00
		a. Surch inverted	£120	£180
D186		10 m. scarlet	1·25	3·00
D187	**23**	20 m. on 100 m. blue	3·75	8·50
		a. Vert pair, one without surch	£300	
D188		50 m. purple	4·75	11·00
		a. Pair, one without surch	£325	
D183/8		*Set of* 6	11·00	27·00

(Recess Perkins, Bacon)

1929 (1 Apr)–**39**. *Wmk Mult Script CA. P* 14.

D189	D **26**	1 m. red-brown	60	2·50
		a. Perf 13½×13 (1939)	80·00	50·00
D190		2 m. orange-yellow	60	3·00
D191		4 m. green	60	3·25
D192		10 m. scarlet	1·50	3·75
D193		20 m. olive-green	5·50	9·50
D194		50 m. blue	7·00	13·00
D189/94		*Set of* 6	14·00	30·00
D189/94 Perf "Specimen"		*Set of* 6	60·00	

(Litho Survey Dept, Cairo)

1942 (22 Dec). *Redrawn. Top line of Arabic in taller lettering. No wmk. P* 13½.

D230	D **35**	1 m. red-brown	1·10	7·50
D231		2 m. orange-yellow	5·50	7·50
D232		10 m. scarlet	6·00	5·50
D230/2		*Set of* 3	11·50	18·00

(Recess Bradbury, Wilkinson)

1944. *Wmk Mult Script CA. P* 12.

D244	D **26**	1 m. red-brown	15	2·00
D245		2 m. orange-yellow	30	2·50
D246		4 m. green	55	3·75
D247		10 m. carmine	85	4·25
D248		20 m. olive-green	20·00	30·00
D244/8		*Set of* 5	20·00	38·00

OFFICIAL STAMP

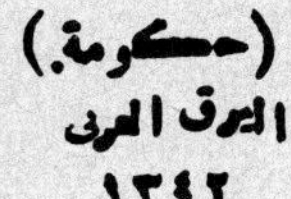

("Arab Government of the East, 1342" = 1924)
(O 16)

1924. *T* **11** *of Saudi Arabia with typographed opt, Type* O **16**.

O117	½ p. scarlet	20·00	£100
	a. Arabic "1242" (R. 2/2, 3/6, 4/5, 4/6)	£150	

By treaty of 22 March 1946 with the United Kingdom, Transjordan was proclaimed an independent kingdom on 25 May 1946.

Later issues are listed under JORDAN in Part 19 (*Middle East*) of this catalogue.

Transvaal
see South Africa

Trinidad and Tobago

TRINIDAD

CROWN COLONY

The first post office was established at Port of Spain in 1800 to deal with overseas mail. Before 1851 there was no post office inland service, although a privately-operated one along the coast did exist, for which rates were officially fixed (see No. 1). During 1851 the colonial authorities established an inland postal system which commenced operation on 14 August. Responsibility for the overseas mails passed to the local post authorities in 1858.

No. CC1 is recorded in the G.P.O. Record Book on 21 March 1852, but no examples have been recorded used on cover before February 1858. From March 1859 it was used with the early Britannia 1d. stamps to indicate prepayment of the additional overseas rate in cash or, later, to show that letters were fully franked with adhesive stamps. This is the normal usage of the handstamp and commands little, if any premium over the cover price quoted below for the stamps involved. The use of the handstamp without an adhesive is rare.

PORT OF SPAIN

CROWNED-CIRCLE HANDSTAMPS

CC 1

CC1 CC 1 TRINIDAD (R.) (*without additional adhesive stamp*) (21.3.52) *Price on cover* £500

PRICES FOR STAMPS ON COVER

No. 1	*from* × 2
Nos. 2/12	*from* × 5
No. 8	—
Nos. 13/20	*from* × 2
Nos. 25/9	*from* × 10
No. 30	—
Nos. 31/44	*from* × 3
No. 45	—
Nos. 46/59	*from* × 3
Nos. 60/3	*from* × 4
Nos. 64/8	*from* × 3
Nos. 69/79	*from* × 10
No. 87	—
Nos. 98/102	*from* × 5
No. 103	—
Nos. 104/5	*from* × 15
Nos. 106/12	*from* × 8
No. 113	—
Nos. 114/21	*from* × 4
Nos. 122/4	—
No. 125	*from* × 10
Nos. 126/30	*from* × 5
No. 131	—
Nos. 132/43	*from* × 3
Nos. 144/5	—
Nos. 146/8	*from* × 3
Nos. D1/17	*from* × 12

1

2 Britannia

1847 (16 Apr). *Litho. Imperf.*

1	**1**	(5 c.) blue	£13000	£7000

The "LADY McLEOD" stamps were issued in April 1847, by David Bryce, owner of the S.S. *Lady McLeod*, and sold at five cents each for the prepayment of the carriage of letters by his vessel between Port of Spain and San Fernando.

The price quoted for used examples of No. 1 is for pen-cancelled. Stamps cancelled by having a corner skimmed-off are worth less.

(Recess P.B.)

1851 (14 Aug)–**56**. *No value expressed. Imperf. Blued paper.*

2	**2**	(1d.) purple-brown (1851)	7·00	55·00
3		(1d.) blue *to* deep blue (12.51)	7·00	38·00
4		(1d.) deep blue (1852)*	£150	70·00
5		(1d.) grey (11.52)	40·00	50·00
6		(1d.) brownish grey (1853)	28·00	60·00
7		(1d.) brownish red (1853)	£300	45·00
8		(1d.) brick-red (1856)	£120	50·00

*No. 4 shows the paper deeply and evenly blued, especially on the back. It has more the appearance of having been printed on blue paper rather than on white paper that has become blued.

1854–57. *Imperf. White paper.*

9	**2**	(1d.) deep purple (1854)	16·00	55·00
10		(1d.) dark grey (1854)	25·00	65·00
11		(1d.) blue (? date)		
12		(1d.) rose-red (1857)	£1500	50·00

PRICES. Prices quoted for the unused of most of the above issues and Nos. 25 and 29 are for "remainders" with original gum, found in London. Old colours that have been out to Trinidad are of much greater value.

3 Britannia 4

The following provisional issues were lithographed in the Colony (from die engraved by Charles Petit), and brought into use to meet shortages of the Perkins Bacon stamps during the following periods:

(1) Sept 1852–May 1853; (2) March 1855–June 1855; (3) Dec 1856–Jan 1857; (4) Oct 1858–Jan 1859; (5) March 1860–June 1860.

1852–60. *No value expressed. Imperf.*

A. *First Issue* (Sept 1852). *Fine impression; lines of background clear and distinct.* (i) *Yellowish paper*

13	**3**	(1d.) blue	£8500	£1600

(ii) *Bluish cartridge paper* (Feb 1853)

14	**3**	(1d.) blue	—	£1800

B. *Second issue* (March 1855). *Thinner paper. Impression less distinct than before*

15	**3**	(1d.) pale blue *to* greenish blue	—	£900

C. *Third issue* (August 1856). *Background often of solid colour, but with clear lines in places*

16	**3**	(1d.) bright blue *to* deep blue	£4500	£1000

D. *Fourth issue* (October 1858). *Impression less distinct, and rarely showing more than traces of background lines*

17	**3**	(1d.) very deep greenish blue	—	£650
18		(1d.) slate-blue	£4000	£650

E. *Fifth issue* (March 1860). *Impression shows no* (*or hardly any*) *background lines*

19	**3**	(1d.) grey *to* bluish grey	£4000	£400
20		(1d.) red (*shades*)	12·00	£450

In the worn impression of the fourth and fifth issues, the impression varies according to the position on the stone. Generally speaking, stamps of the fifth issue have a flatter appearance and cancellations are often less well defined. The paper of both these issues is thin or very thin. In all issues except 1853 (Feb) the gum tends to give the paper a toned appearance.

Stamps in the slate-blue shade (No. 18) also occur in the fifth issue, but are not readily distinguishable.

(Recess P.B.)

1859 (9 May). *Imperf.*

25	4	4d. grey-lilac	60·00	£275
28		6d. deep-green	—	£425
29		1s. indigo	60·00	£275
30		1s. purple-slate		

No. 30 may be of unissued status.

1859 (Sept). (*a*) *Pin-perf* 12½.

31	2	(1d.) rose-red	£500	45·00
32		(1d.) carmine-lake	£500	42·00
33	4	4d. dull lilac	—	£700
34		4d. dull purple	£2750	£700
35		6d. yellow-green	£1800	£150
36		6d. deep green	£1800	£130
37		1s. purple-slate	£2750	£850
		(*b*) *Pin-perf* 13½–14		
38	2	(1d.) rose-red	80·00	19·00
39		(1d.) carmine-lake	£120	17·00
40	4	4d. dull lilac	£650	65·00
40*a*		4d. brownish purple	65·00	85·00
41		4d. dull purple	£200	85·00
42		6d. yellow-green	£300	60·00
43		6d. deep green	£250	55·00
43*a*		6d. bright yellow-green	65·00	70·00
		b. Imperf between (vert pair)	£3500	
44		1s. purple-slate	£3000	£550
		(*c*) *Compound pin-perf* 13½–14 × 12½		
45	2	(1d.) carmine-lake	†	£3000
45*a*	4	4d. dull purple	†	—

PRICES. The Pin-perf stamps are very scarce with perforations on all sides and the prices quoted above are for good average specimens.

The note after No. 12 also applies to Nos. 38, 40*a*, 43*a*, 46, 47 and 50.

1860 (Aug). *Clean-cut perf* 14–16½.

46	2	(1d.) rose-red	85·00	48·00
		a. Imperf vert (horiz pair)	£1100	
47	4	4d. brownish lilac	90·00	70·00
48		4d. lilac	—	£225
49		6d. bright yellow-green	£275	75·00
50		6d. deep green	£180	£120

1861 (June). *Rough perf* 14–16½.

52	2	(1d.) rose-red	70·00	22·00
53		(1d.) rose	70·00	18·00
54	4	4d. brownish lilac	£160	60·00
55		4d. lilac	£350	60·00
		a. Imperf		
56		6d. yellow-green	£150	60·00
57		6d. deep green	£350	55·00
58		1s. indigo	£600	£160
59		1s. deep bluish purple	£750	£250

(Recess D.L.R.)

1862–63. *Thick paper.* (*a*) *P* 11½, 12.

60	2	(1d.) crimson-lake	75·00	12·00
61	4	4d. deep purple	£110	45·00
62		6d. deep green	£600	60·00
63		1s. bluish slate	£700	65·00
		(*b*) *P* 11½, 12, *compound with* 11		
63*a*	2	(1d.) crimson-lake	£1500	£350
63*b*	4	6d. deep green	—	£5000
		(*c*) *P* 13 (1863)		
64	2	(1d.) lake	29·00	15·00
65	4	6d. emerald-green	£275	48·00
67		1s. bright mauve	£2750	£225
		(*d*) *P* 12½ (1863)		
68	2	(1d.) lake	28·00	16·00

1863–76. *Wmk Crown CC.* (*a*) *P* 12½.

69	2	(1d.) lake	32·00	4·00
		a. Wmk sideways	£110	10·00
		b. Rose	32·00	1·40
		ba. Imperf (pair)		
		c. Scarlet	32·00	1·25
		d. Carmine	32·00	1·50
70	4	4d. bright violet	85·00	8·00
		a. Pale mauve	£140	9·50
		b. Dull lilac	£100	11·00
71		4d. grey (1872)	85·00	3·50
		a. Bluish grey	85·00	4·00
72		6d. emerald-green	60·00	11·00
		a. Deep green	£200	7·50
		b. Yellow-green	45·00	3·00
		c. Apple-green	45·00	4·50
		d. Blue-green	80·00	5·50
73		1s. bright deep mauve	£100	6·50
		a. Lilac-rose	85·00	6·00
		b. Mauve (aniline)	75·00	4·25
74		1s. chrome-yellow (1872)	£110	1·00
		(*b*) *P* 14 (1876)		
75	2	(1d.) lake	16·00	60
		a. Bisected (½d.) (on cover)	†	£550
		b. Rose-carmine	16·00	1·00
		c. Scarlet	32·00	75
76	4	4d. bluish grey	80·00	70
77		6d. bright yellow-green	70·00	1·25
		a. Deep yellow-green	75·00	1·00
78		1s. chrome-yellow	85·00	2·50
		(*c*) *P* 14×12½ (1876)		
79	4	6d. yellow-green	—	£4750

The 1s. perforated 12½ in purple-slate is a colour changeling.

5

(Typo D.L.R.)

1869. *Wmk Crown CC. P* 12½.

87	5	5s. rose-lake	£140	70·00

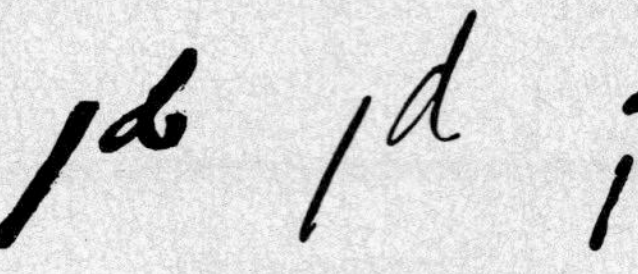

(6) (7)

1879–82. *Surch with T* **6** *or* **7**. *P* 14.

		(*a*) *Wmk Crown CC* (June 1879)		
98	2	½d. lilac	9·00	5·50
99		½d. mauve	9·00	5·50
		a. Wmk sideways	48·00	48·00
		(*b*) *Wmk Crown CA* (1882)		
100	2	½d. lilac	£180	60·00
101		1d. rosy carmine	17·00	50
		a. Bisected (½d.) (on cover)	†	£425

1882. *Wmk Crown CA. P* 14.

102	4	4d. bluish grey	£140	5·50

(8) Various styles

1882 (9 May). *Surch by hand in various styles as T* **8** *in red or black ink and the original value obliterated by a thick or thin bar or bars, of the same colour.*

103	1d. on 6d. (No. 77) (Bk.)	—	£1500
104	1d. on 6d. (No. 77) (R.)	4·50	3·50
105	1d. on 6d. (No. 77*a*) (R.)	4·75	3·50
	a. Bisected (½d.) (on cover)	†	£300

10 · 11 Britannia · 12 Britannia

(Typo D.L.R.)

1883–94. *P* 14. (*a*) *Wmk Crown CA.*

106	10	½d. dull green	1·75	80
107		1d. carmine	6·00	30
		a. Bisected (½d.) (on cover)	†	£475
108		2½d. bright blue	8·50	30
110		4d. grey	2·25	40
111		6d. olive-black (1884)	3·00	3·00
112		1s. orange-brown (1884)	3·00	1·75
		(*b*) *Wmk Crown CC*		
113	5	5s. maroon (1894)	42·00	70·00
106/13		*Set of* 7	60·00	70·00
106/12 Optd "Specimen"		*Set of* 6	£400	

Two types of 1d. value:

ONE PENNY (I) (round "o") **ONE PENNY** (II) (oval "o")

(Typo D.L.R.)

1896 (17 Aug)–**1900.** *P* 14. (*a*) *Wmk Crown CA.*

114	11	½d. dull purple and green	2·50	30
115		1d. dull purple and rose (I)	3·25	10
116		1d. dull purple and rose (II) (1900)	£180	3·75
117		2½d. dull purple and blue	4·00	15
118		4d. dull purple and orange	5·00	12·00
119		5d. dull purple and mauve	5·50	11·00
120		6d. dull purple and black	6·00	4·50
121		1s. green and brown	7·00	5·00
		(*b*) *Wmk CA over Crown. Ordinary paper*		
122	12	5s. green and brown	35·00	65·00
123		10s. green and ultramarine	£120	£160
124		£1 green and carmine	95·00	£140
		a. Chalk-surfaced paper		
114/24		*Set of* 10	£250	£350
114/24 Optd "Specimen"		*Set of* 10	£150	

No. 119, surcharged "3d." was prepared for use but not issued (*Price £2750 unused*). It also exists overprinted "Specimen" (*Price £75*).

Collectors are warned against apparently postally used copies of this issue which bear "REGISTRAR-GENERAL" obliterations and are of very little value.

13 Landing of Columbus

(Recess D.L.R.)

1898. *400th Anniv of Discovery of Trinidad. Wmk Crown CC. P* 14.

125	13	2d. brown and dull violet	2·00	90
125 Optd "Specimen"			50·00	

1901–06. *Colours changed. Wmk Crown CA or CA over Crown (5s.). Ordinary paper. P* 14.

126	11	½d. grey-green (1902)	55	1·50
127		1d. black/*red* (II)	1·00	10
		a. Value omitted	£10000	
		w. Wmk inverted		
128		2½d. purple and blue/*blue* (1902)	11·00	25
129		4d. green and blue/*buff* (1902)	1·75	9·50
		a. Chalk-surfaced paper	3·25	9·50
130		1s. black and blue/*yellow* (1903)	18·00	4·00
131	12	5s. lilac and mauve	38·00	60·00
		a. Deep purple and mauve (1906)	48·00	75·00
		ab. Chalk-surfaced paper	60·00	80·00
126/31		*Set of* 6	65·00	65·00
126/31 Optd "Specimen"		*Set of* 6	£100	

A pane of sixty of No. 127a was found in a post office in Trinidad but not more than nine copies are believed to have been sold, and the rest withdrawn.

1904–09. *Wmk Mult Crown CA. Ordinary paper* (½d., 1d., 2½d. (*No.* 137)) *or chalk-surfaced paper* (*others*). *P* 14.

132	11	½d. grey-green	2·00	80
		a. Chalk-surfaced paper	3·50	1·50
133		½d. blue-green (1906)	7·50	2·00
134		1d. black/*red* (II)	2·75	10
		a. Chalk-surfaced paper	3·75	10
135		1d. rose-red (1907)	1·00	10
136		2½d. purple and blue/*blue*	17·00	90
137		2½d. blue (1906)	1·50	15
138		4d. grey and red/*yellow* (1906)	1·00	6·00
		a. Black and red/yellow	9·00	20·00
139		6d. dull purple and black (1905)	13·00	14·00
140		6d. dull and bright purple (1906)	5·50	6·00
141		1s. black and blue/*yellow*	17·00	7·50
142		1s. purple and blue/*golden yellow*	9·00	10·00
143		1s. black/*green* (1906)	1·50	1·25
144	12	5s. deep purple and mauve (1907)	42·00	75·00
145		£1 green and carmine (1907)	95·00	£160
132/45		*Set of* 14	£180	£250
135, 137/8, 140, 142/3 Optd "Specimen"		*Set of* 6	£100	

No. 135 is from a new die, the letters of "ONE PENNY" being short and thick, while the point of Britannia's spear breaks the uppermost horizontal line of shading in the background.

14 · 15 · 16

(Typo D.L.R.)

1909. *Wmk Mult Crown CA. P* 14.

146	14	½d. green	1·75	10
147	15	1d. rose-red	1·00	10
148	16	2½d. blue	7·50	2·75
146/8		*Set of* 3	9·25	2·75
146/8 Optd "Specimen"		*Set of* 3	50·00	

TOBAGO

Although a Colonial Postmaster was appointed in January 1765 it was not until 1841 that the British G.P.O. established a branch office at Scarborough, the island capital, to handle the overseas mail.

The stamps of Great Britain were in use from May 1858 to the end of April 1860 when the control of the postal service passed to the local authorities.

From April 1860 Nos. CC1/2 were again used on overseas mail, pending the introduction of Tobago stamps in 1879.

SCARBOROUGH

CROWNED-CIRCLE HANDSTAMPS

CC 1

CC 2

CC1	CC 1	TOBAGO (R.) (31.10.1851)	*Price on cover*	£700
CC2	CC 2	TOBAGO (R.) (1875)	*Price on cover*	£2250

Stamps of GREAT BRITAIN *cancelled* "A 14" *as Type* Z 1 *of Jamaica.*

1858 *to* **1860**.
Z 1 1d. rose-red (1857), *perf* 14 .. .. £650
Z 2 4d. rose (1857) £225
Z 3 6d. lilac (1856) £200
Z 4 1s. green (1856) £700

PRICES FOR STAMPS ON COVER	
Nos. 1/4	*from* × 25
Nos. 5/7	—
Nos. 8/12	*from* × 10
Nos. 13/19	*from* × 6
Nos. 20/4	*from* × 40
Nos. 26/33	*from* × 25

CANCELLATIONS. Beware of early stamps of Tobago with fiscal endorsements removed and forged wide "A 14" postmarks added.

1

2

2½ PENCE
(3)

(T 1 and 2. Typo D.L.R.)

1879 (1 Aug). *Fiscal stamps issued provisionally pending the arrival of stamps inscr* "POSTAGE". *Wmk Crown CC. P* 14.
1 1 1d. rose .. .. 75·00 60·00
2 3d. blue .. .. 70·00 40·00
3 6d. orange .. .. 30·00 42·00
4 1s. green .. .. £350 60·00
a. Bisected (6d.) (on cover) ..
5 5s. slate £550 £500
6 £1 mauve £4000

The stamps were introduced for fiscal purposes on 1 July 1879.
Stamps of T 1, watermark Crown CA, are fiscals which were never admitted to postal use.

1880 (Nov). *No. 3 bisected vertically and surch with pen and ink.*
7 1 1d. on half of 6d. orange £4500 £750

1880 (20 Dec). *Wmk Crown CC. P* 14.
8 2 ½d. purple-brown .. .. .. 26·00 42·00
9 1d. Venetian red .. .. .. 80·00 45·00
a. Bisected (½d.) (on cover) .. .. † £1500
10 4d. yellow-green .. .. .. £180 25·00
a. Bisected (2d.) (on cover) .. .. † £1500
b. Malformed "CE" in "PENCE" .. £1200 £400
11 6d. stone .. .. .. £250 90·00
12 1s. yellow-ochre .. .. .. 50·00 60·00

For illustration of Nos. 10b, 18a, 22b, 30a, 31a and 33b see above No. 4 of Dominica.

1883 (Apr). *No. 11 surch with T* 3.
13 2 2½d. on 6d. stone .. .. .. 32·00 32·00
a. Surch double £2500 £1200
b. Large "2" with long tail £100 £110

"SLASH" FLAW. Stamps as Type 2 were produced from Key and Duty plates. On the Key plate used for consignments between 2 October 1892 and 16 December 1896, damage in the form of a large cut or "slash" shows after the "E" of "POSTAGE" on R.1/4.

After 1896 an attempt was made to repair the "slash". This resulted in its disappearance, but left an incomplete edge to the circular frame at right.

1882–84. *Wmk Crown CA. P* 14.
14 2 ½d. purple-brown (1882) .. .. 1·00 12·00
15 1d. Venetian red (1882) .. .. 2·00 1·25
a. Bisected diag (½d.) (on cover) ..
16 2½d. dull blue (1883) .. .. 18·00 95
a. Bright blue .. .. 3·25 75
b. Ultramarine .. .. 3·25 75
c. "Slash" flaw .. .. 25·00 28·00
ca. "Slash" flaw repaired .. 70·00
18 4d. yellow-green (1882) .. .. £170 90·00
a. Malformed "CE" in "PENCE" .. £1100 £450
19 6d. stone (1884) £500 £475

1885–96. *Colours changed and new value. Wmk Crown CA. P* 14.
20 2 ½d. dull green (1886) 80 30
a. "Slash" flaw .. .. 15·00 22·00
ab. "Slash" flaw repaired .. 30·00
21 1d. carmine (1889) .. .. 1·25 20
a. "Slash" flaw .. .. 20·00 20·00
ab. "Slash" flaw repaired .. 40·00
22 2 4d. grey (1885) 80 55
a. Imperf (pair) .. £1700
b. Malformed "CE" in "PENCE" .. 50·00 80·00
c. "Slash" flaw .. .. 55·00 90·00
ca. "Slash" flaw repaired .. 80·00
23 6d. orange-brown (1886) .. .. 75 2·50
a. "Slash" flaw .. .. 55·00 90·00
ab. "Slash" flaw repaired .. 80·00
24 1s. olive-yellow (1894) .. .. 90 11·00
a. Pale olive-yellow .. .. 6·50
b. "Slash" flaw .. .. 65·00 £140
ba. "Slash" flaw repaired .. 90·00
24c 1s. orange-brown (1896) .. .. 4·75 42·00
ca. "Slash" flaw .. .. 85·00
20, 21 and 23 Optd "Specimen" .. *Set of* 3 £170

No. 24*c* was printed in the colour of the 6d. by mistake.

½ PENNY (4)   2½ PENCE (5)   ½d POSTAGE (6)

1886–89. *Nos.* 16, 19 *and* 23 *surch as T* 4.
26 ½d. on 2½d. dull blue (4.86) .. .. 3·50 8·00
a. Figure further from word .. .. 16·00 42·00
b. Surch double £1500 £1200
c. Surch omitted. Vert pair with No. 26 .. £8000
d. Ditto with No. 26a £15000
27 ½d. on 6d. stone (1.86) .. .. 2·25 16·00
a. Figure further from word .. .. 25·00 £110
b. Surch inverted £1300
c. Surch double £1500
28 ½d. on 6d. orange-brown (8.87) .. .. 80·00 £100
a. Figure further from word £250 £275
b. Surch double .. .. — £1000
29 1d. on 2½d. dull blue (7.89) .. .. 38·00 14·00
a. Figure further from word .. .. £110 75·00

The surcharge is in a setting of 12 (two rows of 6) repeated five times in the pane. Nos. 7, 9 and 10 in the setting have a raised "P" in "PENNY", and No. 10 also shows the wider spacing between figure and word.

1891–92. *No. 22 surch with T* 4 *or* 5.
30 ½d. on 4d. grey (3.92) .. .. 10·00 35·00
a. Malformed "CE" in "PENCE" .. £200 £350
b. Surch double £1800
31 2½d. on 4d. grey (8.91) .. .. 3·50 6·50
a. Malformed "CE" in "PENCE" .. £120 £200
b. Surch double £1800 £1800

1896. *Fiscal stamp (T* 1, *value in second colour, wmk Crown CA, P* 14), *surch with T* 6.
33 ½d. on 4d. lilac and carmine .. .. 42·00 26·00
a. Space between "½" and "d" .. 85·00 55·00
b. Malformed "CE" in "PENCE" .. £400 £400

Tobago became a ward of Trinidad on 1 January 1899. Stamps of Trinidad were used until issues inscribed "TRINIDAD AND TOBAGO" appeared in 1913.

TRINIDAD AND TOBAGO

PRICES FOR STAMPS ON COVER	
Nos. 149/55	*from* × 3
Nos. 156/7	—
Nos. 174/89	*from* × 10
Nos. 206/56	*from* × 2
Nos. D18/25	*from* × 12

17

18

(Typo D.L.R.)

1913–23. *Wmk Mult Crown CA. Ordinary paper* (½d. *to* 4d. *and* 1s.) *or chalk-surfaced paper (others). P* 14.
149 17 ½d. green .. .. .. 2·50 10
a. Yellow-green (1915) .. .. 2·75 15
b. Blue-green (thick paper) (1917) .. 5·50 90
ba. Wmk sideways .. .. † £1300
c. Blue-green/bluish (3.18) .. 13·00 12·00
w. Wmk inverted
150 1d. bright red .. .. 1·25 10
a. Red (thick paper) (1916) .. 2·50 10
b. Pink (1918) .. .. 13·00 1·75
c. Carmine-red (5.18) .. .. 1·75 10
151 2½d. ultramarine .. .. 4·00 40
a. Bright blue (thick paper) (1916) .. 4·50 40
b. Bright blue (thin paper) (1918) .. 6·50 40
152 4d. black and red/*yellow* ..
a. Chalk-surfaced paper .. .. 70 4·50
b. White back (12.13) (Optd S. £18) 1·75 8·50
c. On lemon (1917) .. .. 10·00
d. On pale yellow (1923) (Optd S. £22) 4·75 8·00
153 6d. dull and reddish purple .. 5·50 5·00
a. Dull and deep purple (1918) .. 5·50 3·75
b. Dull purple and mauve (2.18) .. 8·00 8·00
154 1s. black/*green* .. .. 1·60 3·75
a. White back (Optd S. £18) .. 1·00 4·00
b. On blue-green, olive back .. 5·50 7·00
c. On emerald back (Optd S. £22) .. 1·50 2·50
155 18 5s. dull purple and mauve (1914) .. 48·00 90·00
a. Deep purple and mauve (1918) .. 50·00 90·00
b. Lilac and violet .. .. 85·00 £120
c. Dull purple and violet .. .. 90·00 £130
d. Brown-purple and violet .. 38·00 90·00
156 £1 grey-green and carmine (1914) .. £100 £140
a. Deep yellow-green and carmine (1918) £100 £140
149/56 .. .. .. *Set of* 8 £140 £225
149/56 Optd "Specimen" .. *Set of* 8 £140

No. 156*a* is from a plate showing background lines very worn.

18*a*

1914 (18 Sept). *Red Cross Label authorised for use as* ½*d. stamp. Typo. P* 11–12.
157 18*a* (½d.) Red .. .. .. 9·00 £190

The above was authorised for internal use on one day only, to raise funds for the Red Cross. The used price is for stamp on cover.

21. 10. 15.
(19)

19. 10. 16.
(19*a*)

1915 (21 Oct). *Optd with T* 19. *Cross in red with outline and date in black.*
174 17 1d. red .. .. .. 1·00 1·00
a. Cross 2 mm to right .. .. 16·00 16·00
b. "1" of "15" forked foot .. .. 8·00 11·00
c. Broken "0" in "10" .. .. 12·00 14·00

The varieties occur in the following positions on the *pane* of 60: a. No. 11. b. No. 42. c. No. 45. Variety a. is only found on the right-hand pane.

1916 (19 Oct). *Optd with T* 19*a*. *Cross in red with outline and date in black.*
175 17 1d. scarlet 30 85
a. No stop after "16" .. .. 6·50 22·00
b. "19.10.16" omitted ..
c. Red shading on cross omitted ..

No. 175a appears on stamp No. 36 on the right-hand pane only.

FORGERIES. Beware of forgeries of the "War Tax" errors listed below. There are also other unlisted errors which are purely fakes.

WAR TAX (19*b*)   WAR TAX (20)   WAR TAX (21)   WAR TAX (22)

1917 (2 Apr). *Optd with T* 19*b*.
176 17 1d. red .. .. .. 1·00 2·00
a. Opt inverted £140
b. Scarlet .. .. .. 1·00 2·00
w. Wmk inverted ..

1917 (May). *Optd with T* 20.
177 17 ½d. green 10 10
a. Pair, one without opt £250
178 1d. red 20 95
a. Pair, one without opt £250
b. Scarlet .. .. .. 1·75 70
ba. Opt double .. .. 80·00

The varieties without overprint were caused by the type being shifted over towards the left so that one stamp in the lowest row of each pane escaped.

1917 (21 June). *Optd with T* 21.
179 17 ½d. yellow-green .. .. .. 1·00 4·25
a. Pale green .. .. .. 10 3·75
b. Deep green .. .. .. 85 4·25
180 1d. red 10 50
a. Pair, one without opt .. ..

No. 180a was caused by a shifting of the type to the left-hand side, but only a few stamps on the right-hand vertical row escaped the overprint and such pairs are very rare.

1917 (21 July–Sept). *Optd with T* 22.
181 17 ½d. yellow-green .. .. .. 3·25 4·50
a. Deep green .. .. .. 10 2·00
182 1d. red (Sept) .. .. .. 1·50 75

WAR TAX (23)   WAR TAX (24)   WAR TAX (25)

1917 (1 Sept). *Optd with T* 23 *(closer spacing between lines of opt).*
183 17 ½d. deep green .. .. .. 10 2·00
a. Pale yellow-green .. ..
184 1d. red .. .. .. 26·00 20·00

1917 (31 Oct). *Optd with T* 24.
185 17 1d. scarlet 30 75
a. Opt inverted .. .. 70·00

1918 (7 Jan). *Optd with T* **25**.
186 **17** 1d. scarlet 55 10
a. Opt double £130 £130
b. Opt inverted .. .. 80·00 80·00

War Tax (26) War Tax (26a) 27

1918 (13 Feb–May). *Optd with T* **26**.
187 **17** ½d. bluish green .. .. 10 1·25
a. Pair, one without opt £425
188 1d. scarlet 40 80
a. Opt double .. .. 80·00
b. Rose-red (1.5.18) 10 50
The ½d. exists with "TAX" omitted caused by a paper fold.

1918 (14 Sept). *New printing as T* **26**, *but 19 stamps on each sheet have the letters of the word "Tax" wider spaced, the "x" being to the right of "r" of "War" as T* **26a**. *Thick bluish paper.*
189 **17** 1d. scarlet ("Tax" spaced) .. .. .. 35 3·50
a. Opt double £140

1921–22. *Wmk Mult Script CA. Chalk-surfaced paper* (6d. *to* £1). *P* 14.
206 **17** ½d. green .. .. 1·10 1·50
207 1d. scarlet 30 30
208 1d. brown (17.2.22) 30 85
209 2d. grey (17.2.22) .. .. 1·00 1·25
210 2½d. bright blue .. .. 70 9·00
211 3d. bright blue (17.2.22) .. .. .. 2·00 2·25
212 6d. dull and bright purple .. .. .. 1·50 14·00
213 **18** 5s. dull purple and purple (1921) .. .. 45·00 £110
214 5s. deep purple and purple (1922) .. .. 45·00 £110
215 £1 green and carmine .. .. 75·00 £180
206/15 .. .. *Set of* 9 £110 £275
206/15 Optd "Specimen" .. .. *Set of* 9 £200

(Typo D.L.R.)

1922–28. *P* 14. *Chalk-surfaced paper* (4d. *to* £1).

(*a*) *Wmk Mult Crown CA*
216 **27** 4d. black and red/*pale yellow* .. .. 12·00 3·50
217 1s. black/*emerald* .. .. 2·00 7·50

(*b*) *Wmk Mult Script CA*
218 **27** ½d. green 30 10
219 1d. brown 30 10
w. Wmk inverted .. .. 25·00
220 1½d. bright rose .. .. 1·50 10
aw. Wmk inverted .. ..
b. Scarlet 90 30
bw. Wmk inverted .. ..
222 2d. grey 40 80
223 3d. blue 40 80
224 4d. black and red/*pale yellow* (1928) .. 3·00 2·75
225 6d. dull purple and bright magenta .. 2·00 21·00
226 6d. green and red/*emerald* (1924) .. 1·00 30
227 1s. black/*emerald* .. .. 4·50 1·25
228 5s. dull purple and mauve .. .. .. 18·00 28·00
229 £1 green and bright rose .. .. .. 85·00 £180
216/29 .. .. *Set of* 13 £110 £225
216/29 Optd "Specimen" .. .. *Set of* 13 £225

(New Currency. 100 cents = 1 West Indian, later Trinidad and Tobago dollar)

28 First Boca

29 Imperial College of Tropical Agriculture

(Recess B.W.)

1935 (1 Feb)–**37**. *T* **28/9** *and similar horiz designs. Wmk Mult Script CA* (*sideways*). *P* 12.
230 1 c. blue and green 30 30
a. Perf 13×12½ (1936) 15 10
231 2 c. ultramarine and yellow-brown 30 30
a. Perf 13×12½ (1936) 40 10
232 3 c. black and scarlet 45 10
a. Perf 13×12½ (1936) .. .. .. 1·00 10
233 6 c. sepia and blue .. .. 2·75 1·25
a. Perf 13×12½ (1937) .. .. .. 3·25 2·00
234 8 c. sage-green and vermilion .. .. 2·00 2·00
235 12 c. black and violet .. .. 2·00 1·00
a. Perf 13×12½ (1937) .. .. .. 2·75 3·25
236 24 c. black and olive-green .. .. .. 1·25 85
a. Perf 13×12½ (1937) .. .. .. 8·50 4·75
237 48 c. deep green .. .. 5·50 12·00
238 72 c. myrtle-green and carmine .. .. 27·00 25·00
230/8 .. .. *Set of* 9 38·00 38·00
230/8 Perf "Specimen" .. .. *Set of* 9 £100
Designs:—3 c. Mt Irvine Bay, Tobago; 6 c. Discovery of Lake Asphalt; 8 c. Queen's Park, Savannah; 12 c. Town Hall, San Fernando; 24 c. Government House; 48 c. Memorial Park; 72 c. Blue Basin.

1935 (6 May). *Silver Jubilee. As Nos.* 114/17 *of Jamaica. P* 11×12.
239 2 c. ultramarine and grey-black 30 40
a. Extra flagstaff .. .. 32·00
b. Short extra flagstaff .. .. .. 32·00
c. Lightning conductor .. .. .. 24·00
d. Flagstaff on right-hand turret .. .. 45·00
240 3 c. deep blue and scarlet 30 75
a. Extra flagstaff .. .. 50·00
c. Lightning conductor .. .. .. 35·00
241 6 c. brown and deep blue .. .. .. 1·50 1·75
a. Extra flagstaff .. .. 85·00
b. Short extra flagstaff .. .. .. 80·00
c. Lightning conductor .. .. .. 65·00
242 24 c. slate and purple .. .. 4·00 11·00
a. Extra flagstaff £110
c. Lightning conductor .. .. .. 80·00
d. Flagstaff on right-hand turret £130
e. Double flagstaff £140
239/42 .. .. *Set of* 4 5·50 12·50
239/42 Perf "Specimen" .. .. *Set of* 4 75·00
For illustrations of plate varieties see Omnibus section following Zimbabwe.

1937 (12 May). *Coronation. As Nos.* 118/20 *of Jamaica.*
243 1 c. green 15 10
244 2 c. yellow-brown 35 10
245 8 c. orange .. .. 1·25 85
243/5 .. .. *Set of* 3 1·60 90
243/5 Perf "Specimen" .. .. *Set of* 3 55·00

37 First Boca

47 King George VI

(Recess B.W.)

1938 (2 May)–**44**. *T* **37** *and similar horiz designs, and T* **47**. *Wmk Mult Script CA* (*sideways on* 1 c. *to* 60 c.).

(*a*) *P* 11½×11
246 1 c. blue and green 45 20
247 2 c. blue and yellow-brown 45 20
248 3 c. black and scarlet .. .. 11·00 90
248*a* 3 c. green and purple-brown (1941) 30 20
ab. "A" of "CA" missing from wmk .. ..
249 4 c. chocolate .. .. 29·00 1·00
249*a* 4 c. scarlet (1941) 40 60
249*b* 5 c. magenta (1.5.41) 30 15
250 6 c. sepia and blue .. .. 1·50 60
251 8 c. sage-green and vermilion .. .. 1·40 75
252 12 c. black and purple .. .. 14·00 1·10
a. Black and slate-purple (1944) .. .. 2·50 10
253 24 c. black and olive-green 75 10
254 60 c. myrtle-green and carmine .. .. 8·50 1·25

(*b*) *T* **47**. *P* 12
255 $1.20, blue-green (1.40) .. .. .. 10·00 85
256 $4.80, rose-carmine (1.40) .. .. .. 20·00 21·00
246/56 .. .. *Set of* 14 75·00 25·00
246/56 *exc* 249*b* Perf "Specimen" .. *Set of* 13 £190
Designs:—2 c. Imperial College of Tropical Agriculture; 3 c. Mt Irvine Bay, Tobago; 4 c. Memorial Park; 5 c. G.P.O. and Treasury; 6 c. Discovery of Lake Asphalt; 8 c. Queen's Park, Savannah; 12 c. Town Hall, San Fernando; 24 c. Government House; 60 c. Blue Basin.

1946 (1 Oct). *Victory. As Nos.* 141/2 *of Jamaica.*
257 3 c. chocolate 10 10
258 6 c. blue 10 90
257/8 Perf "Specimen" .. .. *Set of* 2 45·00

1948 (22 Nov). *Royal Silver Wedding. As Nos.* 143/4 *of Jamaica, but* $4.80 *in recess.*
259 3 c. red-brown 10 10
260 $4.80, carmine .. .. 17·00 20·00

1949 (10 Oct). *75th Anniv of U.P.U. As Nos.* 145/8 *of Jamaica.*
261 5 c. bright reddish purple 40 40
262 6 c. deep blue .. .. 1·00 55
263 12 c. violet 40 65
264 24 c. olive 40 40
261/4 .. .. *Set of* 4 2·00 1·75

1951 (16 Feb). *University College of B.W.I. As Nos.* 149/50 *of Jamaica.*
265 3 c. green and red-brown 20 40
266 12 c. black and reddish violet 20 40

48 First Boca

49 Mt Irvine Bay, Tobago

(Recess B.W.)

1953 (20 Apr)–**59**. *Designs previously used for King George VI issue, but with portrait of Queen Elizabeth II as in T* **48** (1 c., 2 c., 12 c.) *or* **49** (*other values*). *Wmk Mult Script CA. P* 12 (*dollar values*) *or* 11½×11 (*others*).
267 1 c. blue and green 20 30
a. Blue and bluish green (10.6.59) .. .. 3·50 3·50
268 2 c. indigo and orange-brown 20 30
269 3 c. deep emerald and purple-brown 20 10
270 4 c. scarlet 20 30
271 5 c. magenta 30 30
272 6 c. brown and greenish blue 30 30
273 8 c. deep yellow-green and orange-red .. 90 30
274 12 c. black and purple 30 10
275 24 c. black and yellow-olive .. .. .. 1·00 30
a. Black and olive (16.11.55) .. .. 2·50 55
b. Black and greenish olive (12.12.56) .. 4·00 1·00
276 60 c. blackish green and carmine .. .. 18·00 90
277 $1.20, bluish green .. .. 1·00 1·00
a. Perf 11½ (19.1.55) .. .. .. 1·25 30
278 $4.80, cerise .. .. 6·50 17·00
a. Perf 11½ (16.12.55) .. .. .. 8·50 11·00
267/78a .. .. *Set of* 12 26·00 12·50
Designs: *Horiz*—2 c. Imperial College of Tropical Agriculture; 4 c. Memorial Park; 5 c. G.P.O. and Treasury; 6 c. Discovery of Lake Asphalt; 8 c. Queen's Park, Savannah; 12 c. Town Hall, San Fernando; 24 c. Government House; 60 c. Blue Basin. *Vert* (18 × 21 *mm*)—$1.20, $4.80, Queen Elizabeth II.

1953 (3 June). *Coronation. As No.* 153 *of Jamaica.*
279 3 c. black and green 20 10

ONE CENT
(**50**)

1956 (20 Dec). *No.* 268 *surch with T* **50**.
280 1 c. on 2 c. indigo and orange-brown .. 70 95

1958 (22 Apr). *Inauguration of British Caribbean Federation. As Nos.* 175/7 *of Jamaica.*
281 5 c. deep green 20 10
282 6 c. blue 25 80
283 12 c. scarlet 25 10
281/3 .. .. *Set of* 3 65 90

PRINTERS. Nos. 284 to 354 were printed in photogravure by Harrison & Sons, *unless otherwise stated.*

51 Cipriani Memorial

52 Queen's Hall

53 Copper-rumped Hummingbird

54 Map of Trinidad and Tobago

(Des V. Whiteley (1, 2, 12, 35, 60 c., $4.80), J. Matthews (5 c.), H. Baxter (6, 8, 10, 15 c.), M. Goaman (25 c., 50 c., $1.20))

1960 (24 Sept)–**67**. *Designs as T* **51/4**. *W w* **12** (*upright*). *P* 13½×14½ (1 c., 60 c., $1.20, $4.80) *or* 14½×13½ (*others*).
284 1 c. stone and black 10 10
285 2 c. bright blue 10 10
a. Blue (23.6.64) .. .. 2·25 10
b. New blue (18.4.67) .. .. 2·25 10
w. Wmk inverted .. .. 4·00
286 5 c. chalky blue 10 10
w. Wmk inverted .. .. 4·50 1·25
287 6 c. red-brown 10 10
a. Pale chestnut (13.4.67) .. .. .. 2·25 30
w. Wmk inverted .. .. 18·00
288 8 c. yellow-green 10 10
289 10 c. deep lilac 10 10
290 12 c. vermilion 10 10
291 15 c. orange 90 45
291*a* 15 c. orange (15.9.64) .. .. 2·50 10
292 25 c. rose-carmine and deep blue 70 10
w. Wmk inverted .. .. 3·25 90
293 35 c. emerald and black .. .. 2·50 10
294 50 c. yellow, grey and blue 35 40
295 60 c. vermilion, yellow-green and indigo .. 55 30
a. Perf 14½ (1.10.65)* .. .. .. £100 35·00
296 $1.20, multicoloured .. .. 13·00 2·00
297 $4.80, apple-green and pale blue .. .. 7·00 7·50
284/97 .. .. *Set of* 15 24·00 10·00
Designs: *Vert as T* **51**—60 c. Anthurium Lilies. *Horiz as T* **52**—5 c. Whitehall; 6 c. Treasury Building; 8 c. Governor-General's House; 10 c. General Hospital, San Fernando; 12 c. Oil refinery; 15 c. (No. 291), Crest; 15 c. (No. 291*a*), Coat of arms; 25 c. Scarlet Ibis; 35 c. Pitch Lake; 50 c. Mohammed Jinnah Mosque.
*This is the earliest date reported to us. It comes from an unannounced printing which was despatched to Trinidad on 3 December 1964.
The 2, 5, 6, 12 and 25 c. exist with PVA gum as well as gum arabic.
See also No. 317.

65 Scouts and Gold Wolf Badge

1961 (4 Apr). *Second Caribbean Scout Jamboree. Design multicoloured; background colours below. W w* **12**. *P* 13½ × 14½.
298 **65** 8 c. light green 15 10
299 25 c. light blue 15 10
w. Wmk inverted .. ..

INDEPENDENT

66 "Buccoo Reef" (painting by Carlisle Chang)

71 "Protein Foods"

1962 (31 Aug). *Independence. T* **66** *and similar horiz designs. W* w **12**. *P* 14½.

300	5 c. bluish green	..	10	10
301	8 c. grey	..	15	10
302	25 c. reddish violet	..	15	10
303	35 c. brown, yellow, green and black	..	2·25	15
304	60 c. red, black and blue	..	2·50	2·75
300/4	..	*Set of* 5	4·75	2·75

Designs:—8 c. Piarco Air Terminal; 25 c. Hilton Hotel, Port-of-Spain; 35 c. Greater Bird of Paradise and map; 60 c. Scarlet Ibis and map.

(Des M. Goaman)

1963 (4 June). *Freedom from Hunger. W* w **12**. *P* 14 × 13½.

305	**71**	5 c. brown-red	..	10	10
306		8 c. yellow-bistre	..	10	20
307		25 c. violet-blue	..	20	20
305/7		..	*Set of* 3	35	40

72 Jubilee Emblem

1964 (15 Sept). *Golden Jubilee of Trinidad and Tobago Girl Guides' Association. W* w **12**. *P* 14½ × 14.

308	**72**	6 c. yellow, ultramarine and rose-red	..	10	20
309		25 c. yellow, ultramarine and bright blue		15	20
310		35 c. yellow, ultramarine & emerald-grn		15	20
308/10		..	*Set of* 3	30	55

73 I.C.Y. Emblem

(Litho State Ptg Wks, Vienna)

1965 (15 Nov). *International Co-operation Year. P* 12.

311	**73**	35 c. red-brown, dp green & ochre-yell	..	50	20

74 Eleanor Roosevelt, Flag and U.N. Emblem

1965 (10 Dec). *Eleanor Roosevelt Memorial Foundation. W* w **12**. *P* 13½ × 14.

312	**74**	25 c. black, red and ultramarine	..	15	10

75 Parliament Building

FIFTH YEAR OF INDEPENDENCE 31st AUGUST 1967

(79)

1966 (8 Feb). *Royal Visit. T* **75** *and similar horiz designs. Multicoloured. W* w **12** (*sideways*). *P* 13½ × 14½.

313	5 c. Type **75**	..	15	10
314	8 c. Map, Royal Yacht *Britannia* and Arms		2·25	70
315	25 c. Map and flag	..	2·25	55
316	35 c. Flag and panorama	..	2·25	70
313/16	..	*Set of* 4	6·00	1·75

1966 (15 Nov). *As No.* 284 *but W* w **12** (*sideways**).

317	1 c. stone and black	..	10	50
	w. Wmk Crown to right of CA	..		

*The normal sideways watermark shows Crown to left of CA, *as seen from the back of the stamp.*

No. 317 exists with PVA gum as well as gum arabic.

1967 (31 Aug). *Fifth Year of Independence. Nos.* 288/9, 291*a and* 295 *optd as T* **79**.

318	8 c. yellow-green	..	10	10
319	10 c. deep lilac	..	10	10
320	15 c. orange	..	10	10
321	60 c. vermilion, yellow-green and indigo	..	25	10
318/21	..	*Set of* 4	30	20

On No. 321 the overprint is in five lines.

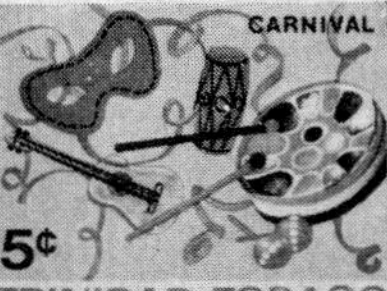

80 Musical Instruments

81 Calypso King

1968 (17 Feb). *Trinidad Carnival. Horiz designs as T* **80** (15 *and* 25 *c.*), *or vert designs as T* **81** (35 *and* 60 *c.*). *Multicoloured. P* 12.

322	5 c. Type **80**	..	10	10
323	10 c. Type **81**	..	10	10
324	15 c. Steel band	..	10	10
325	25 c. Carnival procession	..	20	10
326	35 c. Carnival King	..	20	10
327	60 c. Carnival Queen	..	35	1·00
322/7	..	*Set of* 6	75	1·25

86 Doctor giving Eye-Test

87 Peoples of the World and Emblem

1968 (7 May). *20th Anniv of World Health Organization. W* w **12** (*sideways*). *P* 14.

328	**86**	5 c. red, blackish brown and gold	..	15	10
329		25 c. orange, blackish brown and gold	..	25	10
330		35 c. bright blue, black and gold	..	40	15
328/30		..	*Set of* 3	80	30

1968 (5 Aug). *Human Rights Year. W* w **12** (*sideways*). *P* 13½ × 14.

331	**87**	5 c. cerise, black and greenish yellow	..	10	10
332		10 c. new blue, black and greenish yellow		15	10
333		25 c. apple-green, black & greenish yell	..	30	15
331/3		..	*Set of* 3	45	30

88 Cycling

(Des G. Vasarhelyi. Islands additionally die-stamped in gold (5 c. to 35 c.))

1968 (14 Oct). *Olympic Games, Mexico. T* **88** *and similar horiz designs. Multicoloured. W* w **12**. *P* 14.

334	5 c. Type **88**	..	20	10
	w. Wmk inverted	..	†	£180
335	15 c. Weightlifting	..	20	10
	w. Wmk inverted	..	6·00	
336	25 c. Relay-racing	..	20	10
337	35 c. Sprinting	..	20	10
338	$1.20 Maps of Mexico and Trinidad	..	70	30
334/8	..	*Set of* 5	1·40	50

93 Cocoa Beans

94 Green Hermit

(Des G. Vasarhelyi. Queen's profile die-stamped in gold (G.) or silver (S.), also the Islands on 20, 25 c.)

1969–72. *Designs as T* **93/4**. *W* w **12** (*sideways* on* 1 *to* 8 *c.*, 40 *c.*, 50 *c.*). *P* 14×14½ ($2.50, $5) *or* 14 (*others*).

A. *Chalk-surfaced paper* (1.4.69)
B. *Glazed, ordinary paper* (24.3.72†)

			A		B	
339	1 c. multicoloured (S.)	..	10	65	10	10
	a. Queen's head omitted	..	80·00	—	†	
	w. Wmk Crown to right of CA	..	—	—	—	—
340	3 c. multicoloured (G.)	..	10	10	10	10
	w. Wmk Crown to right of CA	..	—	—	—	—
341	5 c. multicoloured (G.)	..	2·00	10	1·50	10
	a. Queen's head omitted	..	†		—	—
	b. Imperf (pair)	..	†		£200	—
	ba. Ditto and Queen's head omitted	..	†		£325	—
	w. Wmk Crown to right of CA	..	†		4·50	—

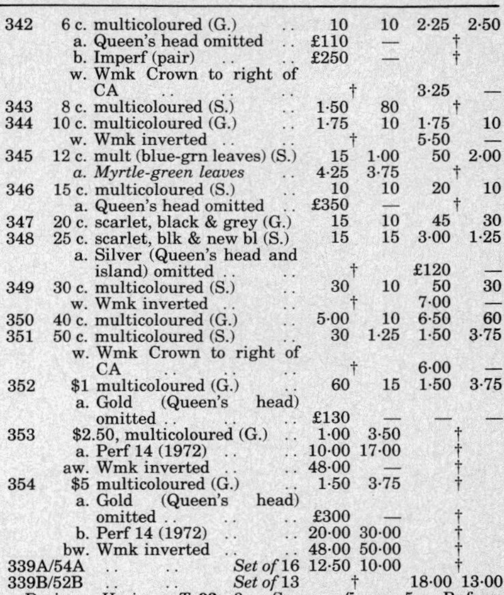

342	6 c. multicoloured (G.)	..	10	10	2·25	2·50
	a. Queen's head omitted	..	£110	—	†	
	b. Imperf (pair)	..	£250	—	†	
	w. Wmk Crown to right of CA	..	†		3·25	—
343	8 c. multicoloured (S.)	..	1·50	80	†	
344	10 c. multicoloured (G.)	..	1·75	10	1·75	10
	w. Wmk inverted	..	†		5·50	—
345	12 c. mult (blue-grn leaves) (S.)		15	1·00	50	2·00
	a. Myrtle-green leaves	..	4·25	3·75	†	
346	15 c. multicoloured (S.)	..	10	10	20	10
	a. Queen's head omitted	..	£350	—	†	
347	20 c. scarlet, black & grey (G.)		15	10	45	30
348	25 c. scarlet, blk & new bl (S.)		15	15	3·00	1·25
	a. Silver (Queen's head and island) omitted	..	†		£120	—
349	30 c. multicoloured (S.)	..	30	10	50	30
	w. Wmk inverted	..	†		7·00	—
350	40 c. multicoloured (G.)	..	5·00	10	6·50	60
351	50 c. multicoloured (S.)	..	30	1·25	1·50	3·75
	w. Wmk Crown to right of CA	..	†		6·00	—
352	$1 multicoloured (G.)	..	60	15	1·50	3·75
	a. Gold (Queen's head) omitted	..	£130	—	—	—
353	$2.50, multicoloured (G.)	..	1·00	3·50	†	
	a. Perf 14 (1972)	..	10·00	17·00	†	
	aw. Wmk inverted	..	48·00	—	†	
354	$5 multicoloured (G.)	..	1·50	3·75	†	
	a. Gold (Queen's head) omitted	..	£300	—	†	
	b. Perf 14 (1972)	..	20·00	30·00	†	
	bw. Wmk inverted	..	48·00	50·00	†	
339A/54A	..	*Set of* 16	12·50	10·00	†	
339B/52B	..	*Set of* 13	†		18·00	13·00

Designs: *Horiz as T* **93**—3 c. Sugar refinery; 5 c. Rufous-vented Chachalaca; 6 c. Oil refinery; 8 c. Fertilizer plant; 40 c. Scarlet Ibis; 50 c. Maracas Bay; $2.50, Fishing; $5 Red House. *Vert as T* **94**—12 c. Citrus fruit; 15 c. Arms of Trinidad and Tobago; 20, 25 c. Flag and outline of Trinidad and Tobago; 30 c. Chaconia plant; $1, Poui tree.

*The normal sideways watermark shows the Crown to the left of CA, *as seen from the back of the stamp.*

†This was the date of receipt at the G.P.O.; the dates of issue are not known.

The listed missing die-stamped heads have the heads completely omitted and, except for No. 352a which results from a shift, show a blind impression of the die. They should not be confused with stamps from sheets containing a row of partially missing heads progressing down to mere specks of foil. The 20 c. value also exists with the gold omitted from the map only. We have also seen stamps with an additional "blind" profile cutting into the rear of the head but without a second die-stamped impression. Varieties of this nature are outside the scope of this catalogue.

See also Nos. 428/30 and 473.

108 Captain A. A. Cipriani (labour leader) and Entrance to Woodford Square

(Photo State Ptg Works, Vienna)

1969 (1 May). *50th Anniv of International Labour Organization. T* **108** *and similar horiz design. P* 12.

355	6 c. black, gold and carmine-red	..	15	15
356	15 c. black, gold and new blue	..	15	15

Design:—15 c. Arms of Industrial Court and entrance to Woodford Square.

110 Cornucopia and Fruit

111 Map showing "CARIFTA" Countries

(Des and photo State Ptg Works, Vienna)

1969 (1 Aug). *First Anniv of CARIFTA (Caribbean Free Trade Area). T* **110/11** *and similar multicoloured designs. P* 13½.

357	6 c. Type **110**	..	10	10
358	10 c. British and member nations' flags (*horiz*)	..	10	10
359	30 c. Type **111**	..	30	20
360	40 c. Boeing 727-100 "Sunjet" in flight (*horiz*)	..	55	70
357/60	..	*Set of* 4	90	90

114 Space Module landing on Moon

(Des G. Vasarhelyi. Litho D.L.R.)

1969 (2 Sept). *First Man on the Moon. T* **114** *and similar multi-coloured designs. P* 14.

361	6 c. Type **114** . .	10	10
362	40 c. Space module and astronauts on Moon (*vert*)	15	10
363	$1 Astronauts seen from inside space module	45	20
361/3	*Set of* 3	65	30

The above were released by the Philatelic Agency in the U.S.A. on 1 September, but not sold locally until 2 September.

117 Parliamentary Chamber, Flags and Emblems

(Photo Harrison)

1969 (23 Oct*). *15th Commonwealth Parliamentary Association Conference, Port-of-Spain. T* **117** *and similar horiz designs. Multicoloured. W w* **12**. *P* 14½ × 13½.

364	10 c. Type **117** . .	10	10
365	15 c. J.F. Kennedy College	10	10
366	30 c. Parliamentary maces	25	40
367	40 c. Cannon and emblem	25	40
364/7	*Set of* 4	60	75

*This was the local release date; the Philatelic Agency in New York released the stamps ten days earlier.

121 Congress Emblem **122** Emblem and Islands at Daybreak

(Photo Rosenbaum Bros, Vienna)

1969 (3 Nov). *International Congress of the Junior Chamber of Commerce. T* **121/2** *and similar vert design. P* 13½.

368	6 c. black, red and gold	10	10
369	30 c. gold, lake and light blue . .	25	40
370	40 c. black, gold and ultramarine	25	40
368/70	*Set of* 3	50	75

Design:—40 c. Emblem, palm-trees and ruin.

The above were released by the Philatelic Agency in the U.S.A. on 2 November, but not sold locally until 3 November.

124 "Man in the Moon" **129** Statue of Gandhi

(Des V. Whiteley. Litho Questa)

1970 (6 Feb). *Carnival Winners. T* **124** *and similar multicoloured designs. W w* **12** *(sideways on 40 c.). P* 14.

371	5 c. Type **124**	10	10
372	6 c. "City beneath the Sea"	10	10
373	15 c. "Antelope" God Bamibara	15	10
	w. Wmk inverted	—	12·00
374	30 c. "Chanticleer" Pheasant Queen of Malaya	25	10
375	40 c. Steel Band of the Year (*horiz*)	25	20
371/5	*Set of* 5	70	40

The above were released by the Philatelic Agency in the U.S.A. on 2 February, but not sold locally until 6 February.

(Photo State Printing Works, Vienna)

1970 (2 Mar). *Gandhi Centenary Year* (1969). *T* **129** *and similar multicoloured design. P* 12.

376	10 c. Type **129** . .	25	10
377	30 c. Head of Gandhi and Indian flag (*horiz*) . .	45	20

131 Symbols of Culture, Science, Arts and Technology

132 New U.P.U. H.Q. Building

(Des G. Lee. Photo State Printing Works, Vienna)

1970 (26 June). *25th Anniv of United Nations. T* **131/2** *and similar designs. Multicoloured. P* 12 *(30 c.),* 13½ × 14 *(10 c.) or* 13½ *(others).*

378	5 c. Type **131** . .	10	10
379	10 c. Children of different races, map and flag (34 × 25 *mm*)	25	10
380	20 c. Noah's Ark, rainbow and dove (35 × 24 *mm*)	35	30
381	30 c. Type **132** . .	35	30
378/81	*Set of* 4	95	60

NATIONAL
COMMERCIAL
BANK
ESTABLISHED
1.7.70

(**133**)

134 "East Indian Immigrants" (J. Cazabon)

1970 (1 July). *Inauguration of National Commercial Bank. No.* 341A *optd with T* **133**.

382	5 c. multicoloured	30	10

(Des from paintings by Cazabon. Litho Questa)

1970 (Oct). *125th Anniv of San Fernando. T* **134** *and similar designs. W w* **12** *(sideways on 5 c. and 40 c.). P* 13½.

383	3 c. multicoloured	10	65
	w. Wmk inverted	—	32·00
384	5 c. black, blue and yellow-ochre	10	10
385	40 c. black, blue and yellow-ochre	60	20
383/5	*Set of* 3	70	85

Designs: *Horiz*—5 c. "San Fernando Town Hall"; 40 c. "San Fernando Harbour, 1860".

135 "The Adoration of the Shepherds" (detail, School of Seville)

(Des G. Drummond. Litho Format)

1970 (8 Dec). *Christmas. Paintings. T* **135** *and similar vert designs. Multicoloured. P* 13½.

386	3 c. Type **135** . .	10	10
387	5 c. "Madonna and Child with Saints" (detail, Titian)	10	10
388	30 c. "The Adoration of the Shepherds" (detail, Le Nain) . .	20	20
389	40 c. "The Virgin and Child, St. John and an Angel" (Morando)	20	10
390	$1 "The Adoration of the Kings" (detail, Veronese)	70	1·50
386/90	*Set of* 5	1·10	1·75
MS391	114 × 153 mm. Nos. 386/9	1·75	2·75

136 Red Brocket

(Des State Printing Works, Vienna. Litho Questa)

1971 (9 Aug). *Trinidad Wildlife. T* **136** *and similar horiz designs. Multicoloured. W w* **12** *(sideways*). P* 13½.

392	3 c. Type **136**	20	30
393	5 c. Collared Peccary ("Quenk") . .	25	15
394	6 c. Paca ("Lappe")	30	50
	w. Wmk Crown to left of CA		
395	30 c. Brazilian Agouti	1·25	3·50
396	40 c. Ocelot	1·25	2·75
392/6	*Set of* 5	3·00	6·50

*The normal sideways watermark shows Crown to right of CA, *as seen from the back of the stamp.*

137 A. A. Cipriani **138** "Virgin and Child with St. John" (detail, Bartolommeo)

(Litho D.L.R.)

1971 (30 Aug*). *Ninth Anniv of Independence. T* **137** *and similar vert design. Multicoloured. W w* **12**. *P* 14.

397	5 c. Type **137** . .	10	10
398	30 c. Chaconia medal . .	30	60

*This was the local release date, but the New York agency issued the stamps on 25 August.

(Litho Harrison)

1971 (25 Oct). *Christmas. T* **138** *and similar vert designs. Multicoloured. W w* **12** *(sideways* on* 10 *and* 15 *c.). P* 14×14½.

399	3 c. Type **138**	15	15
400	5 c. Local crèche	20	10
401	10 c. "Virgin and Child with Saints Jerome and Dominic" (detail, Lippi) . .	25	10
402	15 c. "Virgin and Child with St. Anne" (detail, Gerolamo dai Libri) . .	30	20
	w. Wmk Crown to right of CA	15·00	
399/402	*Set of* 4	80	40

*The normal sideways watermark shows Crown to left of CA, *as seen from the back of the stamp.*

139 Satellite Earth Station, Matura

(Litho Harrison)

1971 (18 Nov). *Satellite Earth Station. T* **139** *and similar vert designs. Multicoloured. W w* **12** *(sideways on 10 c.). P* 14 *(10 c.) or* 14 × 13½ *(others).*

403	10 c. Type **139** . .	10	10
404	30 c. Dish antennae	25	40
405	40 c. Satellite and the earth . .	35	50
403/5	*Set of* 3	65	85
MS406	140 × 76 mm. Nos. 403/5 (wmk sideways). Imperf	1·25	2·00
	a. Yellow and pale blue omitted		

140 *Morpho peleides* × *achilleana*

(Des G. Drummond. Photo Harrison)

1972 (18 Feb). *Butterflies. T* **140** *and similar horiz designs. Multicoloured. W w* **12** *(sideways on* 5 *c.). P* 14.

407	3 c. Type **140**	75	30
	w. Wmk inverted	19·00	
408	5 c. *Eryphanis polyxena*	80	10
409	6 c. *Phoebis philea*	85	30
	w. Wmk inverted	11·00	
410	10 c. *Prepona laertes*	1·00	15
411	20 c. *Eurytides telesilaus*	1·75	1·60
	w. Wmk inverted	2·00	
412	30 c. *Eurema proterpia*	2·00	2·50
407/12	*Set of* 6	6·50	4·50

NEW INFORMATION

The editor is always interested to correspond with people who have new information that will improve or correct the Catalogue.

141 *Lady McLeod* (paddle-steamer) and McLeod Stamp **142** Trinity Cross

(Des J. Cooter. Litho Harrison)

1972 (24 Apr*). *125th Anniv. of First Trinidad Postage Stamp. T* **141** *and similar horiz designs.* W w **12**. *P* 14.
413 5 c. multicoloured 15 10
414 10 c. multicoloured 25 10
415 30 c. greenish blue, reddish chestnut & blk 70 45
  w. Wmk inverted .. .. .. 20·00
413/15 .. .. *Set of* 3 1·00 55
MS416 83×140 mm. Nos. 413/15 .. .. 1·00 1·25
  a. Wmk sideways .. .. 20·00 25·00
  w. Wmk inverted .. .. .. 22·00

Designs:—10 c. Map and Lady McLeod stamp; 30 c. Lady McLeod stamp and inscription.

*This was the local release date, but the New York Agency issued the stamps on 12 April.

(Des G. Drummond. Photo Enschedé)

1972 (28 Aug). *Tenth Anniv of Independence. T* **142** *and similar vert designs. Multicoloured.* W w **12**. *P* 13½ × 13.
417 5 c. Type **142** 10 10
418 10 c. Chaconia Medal 10 10
419 20 c. Hummingbird Medal 15 15
420 30 c. Medal of Merit 15 20
417/20 .. .. *Set of* 4 40 40
MS421 93 × 121 mm. Nos. 417/20 .. .. 60 1·00

One example of MS421 has been seen with the blue (background and frame) omitted from the 10 c. Another example has been seen with carmine (background and frame) omitted from the 30 c.

See also Nos. 440/4.

143 Bronze Medal, 1964 Relay

(Des G. Drummond. Litho Questa)

1972 (7 Sept). *Olympic Games, Munich. T* **143** *and similar horiz designs. Multicoloured.* W w **12**. *P* 14.
422 10 c. Type **143** 15 10
423 20 c. Bronze, 1964 200 metres 35 25
424 30 c. Silver, 1952 weightlifting 45 25
425 40 c. Silver, 1964 400 metres 45 25
426 50 c. Silver, 1948 weightlifting .. .. 50 1·75
422/6 .. .. *Set of* 5 1·75 2·25
MS427 153×82 mm. Nos. 422/6 .. .. 1·75 2·25
  w. Wmk inverted .. .. .. 18·00

1972–74. *Nos. 340/2, but* W w **12** *(upright). Glazed, ordinary paper.*
428 3 c. multicoloured (7.11.72*) .. .. 4·50 10·00
429 5 c. multicoloured (1973) .. .. .. 7·50 1·75
  a Yellow (background) omitted .. £130
430 6 c. multicoloured (1974) .. .. .. 3·50 2·75
  w. Wmk inverted .. .. ..
428/30 .. .. *Set of* 3 14·00 13·00

*Earliest known postmark date.

144 "Adoration of the Kings" (detail, Dosso)

(Des G. Drummond. Photo J.W.)

1972 (9 Nov). *Christmas. T* **144** *and similar horiz design. Multicoloured.* W w **12**. *P* 14.
431 3 c. Type **144** 10 10
432 5 c. "The Holy Family and a Shepherd" (Titian) 10 10
433 30 c. As 5 c. 70 55
431/3 .. .. *Set of* 3 80 60
MS434 73×99 mm. Nos. 431/3 .. .. 1·25 1·50
  w. Wmk inverted .. .. ..

145 E.C.L.A. Building, Chile

(Des G. Drummond. Litho Questa)

1973 (15 Aug). *Anniversaries. Events described on stamps. T* **145** *and similar horiz designs. Multicoloured.* W w **12**. *P* 14.
435 10 c. Type **145** 10 10
  w. Wmk inverted .. .. .. 10·00
436 20 c. Interpol emblem 45 30
437 30 c. W.M.O. emblem 45 30
438 40 c. University of the West Indies .. 45 80
435/8 .. .. *Set of* 4 1·25 80
MS439 155×92 mm. Nos. 435/8 .. .. 1·25 1·25
  w. Wmk inverted .. .. .. 20·00

(Des J. Cooter. Litho Harrison)

1973 (30 Aug). *Eleventh Anniv of Independence. Vert designs as T* **142**. *Multicoloured.* W w **12**. *P* 14½ × 14.
440 10 c. Trinity Cross 10 10
441 20 c. Medal of Merit 20 35
442 30 c. Chaconia Medal 20 40
443 40 c. Hummingbird Medal 30 40
440/3 .. .. *Set of* 4 70 1·10
MS444 75×122 mm. Nos. 440/3. P 14 .. .. 70 1·25
  w. Wmk inverted .. .. .. 27·00

146 G.P.O., Port-of-Spain **147** "Madonna with Child" (Murillo)

(Des J. Cooter. Photo J.W.)

1973 (8 Oct). *Second Commonwealth Conference of Postal Administrations, Trinidad. T* **146** *and similar horiz design. Multicoloured.* W w **12** *(sideways*)*. *P* 14.
445 30 c. Type **146** 20 50
446 40 c. Conference Hall, Chaguaramas .. 30 50
MS447 115×115 mm. Nos. 445/6 .. .. 90 1·00
  w. Wmk Crown to right of CA .. .. 18·00

No. 446 is wrongly inscribed "CHAGARAMAS".

*The normal sideways watermark shows Crown to left of CA, *as seen from the back of the stamp.*

(Des PAD Studio. Photo Harrison)

1973 (22 Oct). *Christmas.* W w **12**. *P* 14½×14.
448 **147** 5 c. multicoloured 10 10
  w. Wmk inverted .. .. .. 26·00
449 $1 multicoloured .. .. .. 75 1·25
MS450 94×88 mm. Nos. 448/9. Wmk sideways*. P 14 .. .. 85 1·40
  w. Wmk Crown to right of CA .. 15·00

*The normal sideways watermark shows Crown to left of CA, *as seen from the back of the stamp.*

148 Berne H.Q. within U.P.U. Emblem

(Des PAD Studio. Photo Harrison)

1974 (18 Nov). *Centenary of Universal Postal Union. T* **148** *and similar horiz design. Multicoloured.* W w **12** *(sideways)*. *P* 13 × 14.
451 40 c. Type **148** 45 15
452 50 c. Map within emblem 45 85
MS453 117 × 104 mm. Nos. 451/2. P 13 × 14½ 15·00 20·00

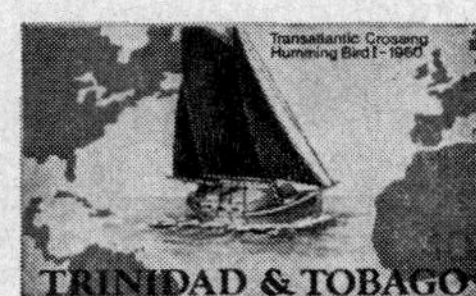

149 *Humming Bird I* (ketch) crossing Atlantic Ocean (1960)

(Des and photo Harrison)

1974 (2 Dec). *First Anniv of World Voyage by H. and K. La Borde. T* **149** *and similar horiz design. Multicoloured.* W w **12** *(sideways)*. *P* 14.
454 40 c. Type **149** 50 15
455 50 c. *Humming Bird II* (ketch) crossing globe 60 75
MS456 109×84 mm. Nos. 454/5. Wmk upright. 1·50 4·00
  w. Wmk inverted .. .. .. 3·25 4·50

150 "Sex Equality"

(Des Hetty J. Mejias de Grannes; adapted V. Whiteley. Litho Harrison)

1975 (23 June). *International Women's Year.* W w **14** *(sideways)*. *P* 14.
457 **150** 15 c. multicoloured 15 20
458 30 c. multicoloured 35 70

151 Common Vampire Bat, Microscope and Syringe

(Des PAD Studio. Photo Harrison)

1975 (23 Sept). *Isolation of Rabies Virus. T* **151** *and similar horiz design. Multicoloured.* W w **14**. *P* 14 × 14½.
459 25 c. Type **151** 40 40
460 30 c. Dr. Pawan, instruments and book .. 50 50
  w. Wmk inverted .. .. .. 5·00

152 Route-map and Tail of Boeing 707

(Des C. Abbott. Litho Walsall)

1975 (27 Nov). *35th Anniv of British West Indian Airways. T* **152** *and similar horiz designs.* W w **14** *(sideways*)*. *P* 14.
461 20 c. Type **152** 40 20
462 30 c. 707 on ground 60 85
463 40 c. 707 in flight .. .. 70 1·00
  w. Wmk Crown to right of CA .. ..
461/3 .. .. *Set of* 3 1·50 1·90
MS464 119×110 mm. Nos. 461/3 .. .. 1·50 2·00

*The normal sideways watermark shows Crown to left of CA, *as seen from the back of the stamp.*

153 "From the Land of the Humming Bird"

1976 (12 Jan). *Carnival. 1974 Prizewinning Costumes. T* **153** *and similar horiz design. Multicoloured.* W w **14** *(sideways*)*. *P* 14.
465 30 c. Type **153** 10 10
466 $1 "The Little Carib" 40 50
MS467 83×108 mm. Nos. 465/6 .. .. 1·10 1·10
  w. Wmk Crown to right of CA .. .. 5·00

*The normal sideways watermark shows Crown to left of CA, *as seen from the back of the stamp.*

154 Angostura Building, Port-of-Spain

(Des Jennifer Toombs. Litho J.W.)

1976 (14 July). *150th Anniv. of Angostura Bitters. T* **154** *and similar horiz designs. Multicoloured.* W w **14** *(sideways)*. *P* 13.
468 5 c. Type **154** 10 10
469 35 c. Medal, New Orleans 1885/6 .. .. 20 35
470 45 c. Medal, Sydney 1879 .. .. .. 25 40
471 50 c. Medal, Brussels 1897 .. .. .. 25 80
468/71 .. .. *Set of* 4 65 1·50
MS472 119×112 mm. Nos. 468/71. P 14 .. 90 1·50

REPUBLIC

1976 (2 Aug). *As Nos. 344B but* W w **14**.
473 10 c. multicoloured .. .. .. 75 1·00
  w. Wmk inverted .. .. .. 7·50

1976 (4 Oct). *West Indian Victory in World Cricket Cup. As Nos. 419/20 of Jamaica.*

No.	Description	Unused	Used
474	35 c. Caribbean map	45	30
475	45 c. Prudential Cup	55	40
MS476	80 × 80 mm. Nos. 474/5	1·75	2·75

155 "Columbus sailing through the Bocas" (Campins)

(Des J.W. Litho Questa)

1976 (1 Nov)–**78**. *Paintings, Hotels and Orchids. Horiz designs as T* **155**. *Multicoloured. W w* **14**. *P* 14.

No.	Description	Unused	Used
479	5 c. Type **155**	1·25	10
	w. Wmk inverted	3·25	
480	6 c. Robinson Crusoe Hotel, Tobago (17.1.78)	20	1·25
482	10 c. "San Fernando Hill" (J. Cazabon)	20	10
483	12 c. *Paphinia cristata* (7.6.78)	2·00	2·25
484	15 c. Turtle Beach Hotel (17.1.78)	50	1·25
485	20 c. "East Indians in a Landscape" (J. Cazabon)	70	10
486	25 c. Mt Irvine Hotel (17.1.78)	60	10
487	30 c. *Caularthon bicornutum* (7.6.78)	2·00	1·10
488	35 c. "Los Gallos Point" (J. Cazabon)	1·00	10
	w. Wmk inverted	6·50	
489	40 c. *Miltassia* (7.6.78)	2·00	10
490	45 c. "Corbeaux Town" (J. Cazabon)	1·00	10
491	50 c. *Oncidium ampliatum* (7.6.78)	2·00	20
	w. Wmk inverted	†	—
492	70 c. Beach facilities, Mt Irvine Hotel (17.1.78)	70	1·00
494	$2.50, *Oncidium papilio* (7.6.78)	2·25	1·00
495	$5 Trinidad Holiday Inn (17.1.78)	1·50	6·00
479/95	*Set of* 15	15·00	12·50
MS497	171 × 100 mm. Nos. 479, 482, 485, 488 and 490. Wmk sideways	2·00	1·50
MS498	171 × 88 mm. Nos. 480, 484, 486, 492 and 495. Wmk sideways (17.1.78)	3·00	6·50
MS499	170 × 90 mm. Nos. 483, 487, 489, 491 and 494. Wmk sideways (7.6.78)	3·75	4·00

156 Hasely Crawford and Olympic Gold Medal

(Des J.W. Litho D. L. R.)

1977 (4 Jan). *Hasely Crawford Commemoration. W w* **14** *(sideways). P* 12 × 12½.

No.	Description	Unused	Used
501 **156**	25 c. multicoloured	20	50
MS502	93 × 70 mm. No. 501	50	1·25

157 Lindbergh's Sikorsky "S–38", 1929 — **158** National Flag

(Des and litho J.W.)

1977 (4 Apr). *50th Anniv of Airmail Service. T* **157** *and similar horiz designs. Multicoloured. W w* **14** *(sideways). P* 13.

No.	Description	Unused	Used
503	20 c. Type **157**	45	20
504	35 c. Arrival of Charles and Anne Lindbergh	55	35
505	45 c. Boeing "707", c. 1960	70	60
506	50 c. Boeing "747", 1969	1·40	3·25
503/6	*Set of* 4	2·75	4·00
MS507	130 × 100 mm. Nos. 503/6. P 14	3·75	4·00

(Des and litho J.W.)

1977 (26 July). *Inauguration of the Republic. T* **158** *and similar vert designs. Multicoloured. W w* **14**. *P* 13.

No.	Description	Unused	Used
508	20 c. Type **158**	40	15
509	35 c. Coat of Arms	60	65
510	45 c. Government House	70	85
508/10	*Set of* 3	1·50	1·50
MS511	125×84 mm. Nos. 508/10. P 14	1·00	2·25

OMNIBUS ISSUES

Details, together with prices for complete sets, of the various Omnibus issues from the 1935 Silver Jubilee series to date are included in a special section following Zimbabwe at the end of Volume 2.

159 White Poinsettia — **160** Miss Janelle (Penny) Commissiong with Trophy

(Des J.W. Litho Walsall)

1977 (11 Oct). *Christmas. T* **159** *and similar vert design. Multicoloured. W w* **14**. *P* 14 × 14½.

No.	Description	Unused	Used
512	10 c. Type **159**	20	10
513	35 c. Type **159**	35	10
514	45 c. Red Poinsettia	45	30
515	50 c. As 45 c.	55	1·50
512/15	*Set of* 4	1·40	1·75
MS516	112 × 142 mm. Nos. 512/15	1·40	2·50

(Des BG Studio. Litho Questa)

1978 (2 Aug). *Miss Janelle (Penny) Commissiong ("Miss Universe 1977") Commemoration. T* **160** *and similar vert designs showing Miss Commissiong. Multicoloured. W w* **14**. *P* 14½.

No.	Description	Unused	Used
517	10 c. Type **160**	25	10
	w. Wmk inverted	†	9·50
518	35 c. Portrait	50	60
519	45 c. In evening dress	60	75
517/19	*Set of* 3	1·25	1·25
MS520	186×120 mm. Nos. 517/19	1·25	1·75
	a. 45 c. value imperf on three sides	£500	

161 Tayra — **162** "Burst of Beauty"

(Des G. Drummond. Litho Walsall)

1978 (7 Nov). *Wildlife. T* **161** *and similar horiz designs. Multicoloured. W w* **14** *(sideways). P* 13½.

No.	Description	Unused	Used
521	15 c. Type **161**	20	20
522	25 c. Ocelot	30	30
523	40 c. Brazilian Tree Porcupine	50	30
524	70 c. Tamandua	65	2·00
521/4	*Set of* 4	1·50	2·50
MS525	128×101 mm. Nos. 521/4	1·50	3·25

(Des C. Abbott. Litho Format)

1979 (1 Feb). *Carnival* 1978. *T* **162** *and similar vert designs. P* 13½.

No.	Description	Unused	Used
526	5 c. multicoloured	10	10
527	10 c. multicoloured	10	10
528	35 c. multicoloured	10	10
529	45 c. multicoloured	10	10
530	50 c. yellow-brown, rosine and deep lilac	10	15
531	$1 multicoloured	20	65
526/31	*Set of* 6	50	85

Designs:—10 c. Rain worshipper; 35 c. "Zodiac"; 45 c. Praying mantis; 50 c. "Eye of the Hurricane"; $1 Steel orchestra.

163 Day Care — **164** Geothermal Exploration

(Des BG Studio. Litho J.W.)

1979 (5 June). *International Year of the Child. T* **163** *and similar vert designs. Multicoloured. P* 13.

No.	Description	Unused	Used
532	5 c. Type **163**	10	10
533	10 c. School feeding programme	10	10
534	35 c. Dental care	30	15
535	45 c. Nursery school	30	20
536	50 c. Free bus transport	30	40
537	$1 Medical care	65	1·50
532/7	*Set of* 6	1·60	2·25
MS538	114 × 132 mm. Nos. 532/7. P 14 × 13½	1·60	2·25

(Des local artist; adapted L. Curtis. Litho Format)

1979 (3 July). *4th Latin American Geological Congress. T* **164** *and similar horiz designs. Multicoloured. W w* **14** *(sideways). P* 13½.

No.	Description	Unused	Used
539	10 c. Type **164**	20	10
540	35 c. Hydrogeology	35	35
541	45 c. Petroleum exploration	40	40
542	70 c. Environmental preservation	55	1·60
539/42	*Set of* 4	1·40	2·25
MS543	185 × 89 mm. Nos. 539/42	1·50	2·00

165 1879 1d. rose and Map of Tobago

(Des J. Cooter. Litho Format)

1979 (1 Aug). *Tobago Stamp Centenary. T* **165** *and similar horiz designs in black, rose-lilac and dull orange* ($1) *or multicoloured (others). W w* **14** *(sideways*). P* 13½×14.

No.	Description	Unused	Used
544	10 c. Type **165**	10	10
545	15 c. 1879 3d. and 1880 ½d. surcharged on half of 6d.	15	10
546	35 c. 1879 6d. and 1886 ½d. surcharged on 6d.	25	20
547	45 c. 1879 1s. and 1886 ½d. surcharged on 2½d.	30	20
548	70 c. 1879 5s. and Great Britain 1856 1s. with "A14" (Scarborough, Tobago) postmark	40	1·50
549	$1 1879 £1 and General Post Office, Scarborough, Tobago	50	1·75
544/9	*Set of* 6	1·50	3·25
MS550	165×155 mm. Nos. 544/9	2·00	4·00
	w. Wmk Crown to left of CA	40·00	

*The normal sideways watermark on Nos. 544/9 shows Crown to left of CA and on No. **MS**550 Crown to right of CA, *as seen from the back of the stamp.*

166 1962 60 c. Independence Commemorative and Sir Rowland Hill

(Des and litho J.W.)

1979 (4 Oct). *Death Centenary of Sir Rowland Hill. T* **166** *and similar horiz designs showing stamps and Sir Rowland Hill. Multicoloured. W w* **14** *(sideways*). P* 13.

No.	Description	Unused	Used
551	25 c. Type **166**	30	15
552	45 c. 1977 35 c. Inauguration of Republic commemorative	40	20
553	$1 1879 Trinidad ½d. surcharge and Tobago 1880 4d.	65	1·25
551/3	*Set of* 3	1·25	1·40
MS554	115×125 mm. Nos. 551/3. P 13½×14	1·25	1·50
	w. Wmk Crown to right of CA	35·00	

*The normal sideways watermark on Nos. 551/3 shows Crown to right of CA, and on No. **MS**554 Crown to left of CA, *as seen from the back of the stamp.*

167 Poui Tree in Churchyard

1844–
1980
POPULATION
CENSUS
12th MAY 1980

(168)

(Des G. Hutchins. Litho Format)

1980 (21 Jan). *Centenary of Princes Town. T* **167** *and similar horiz designs. Multicoloured. W w* **14** *(sideways). P* 14½ × 14.

No.	Description	Unused	Used
555	5 c. Type **167**	10	10
556	10 c. Princes Town Court House	10	10
557	50 c. Locomotive of the Royal Train, 1880	60	90
558	$1.50, H.M.S. *Bacchante* (screw corvette)	1·00	2·00
555/8	*Set of* 4	1·60	2·75
MS559	177×102 mm. Nos. 555/8	1·90	2·75

1980 (8 Apr). *Population Census. Nos. 479/80 and 482 optd with T* **168**.

No.	Description	Unused	Used
560	5 c. Type **155**	20	20
561	6 c. Robinson Crusoe Hotel, Tobago	20	80
562	10 c. "San Fernando Hill" (Cazabon)	20	20
560/2	*Set of* 3	55	1·10

169 Scarlet Ibis (male) **170** Silver and Bronze Medals for Weightlifting, 1948 and 1952

(Des G. Drummond. Litho Questa)

1980 (6 May). *Scarlet Ibis. T* **169** *and similar vert designs. Multicoloured.* W w **14**. *P* 14.

563 50 c. Type **169** .. .. 1·00 1·25
a. Strip of 5. Nos. 563/7 .. .. .. 4·50
564 50 c. Male and female .. .. 1·00 1·25
565 50 c. Hen and nest .. .. 1·00 1·25
566 50 c. Nest and eggs .. .. 1·00 1·25
567 50 c. Chick in nest .. .. 1·00 1·25
563/7 .. .. *Set of* 5 4·50 5·50

Nos. 563/7 were printed together, *se-tenant*, in horizontal and vertical strips of 5 throughout.

(Des G. Hutchins. Litho Walsall)

1980 (22 July). *Olympic Games, Moscow. T* **170** *and similar designs.* W w **14** (*sideways*). *P* 14.

568 10 c. multicoloured 10 10
569 15 c. multicoloured 10 10
570 70 c. multicoloured 45 65
568/70 .. .. *Set of* 3 50 70
MS571 110 × 149 mm. $2.50, black, silver and orange-vermilion (wmk upright) .. .. .. 1·50 2·25

Designs: *Horiz*—15 c. Hasely Crawford (100 metres sprint winner, 1976) and gold medal; 70 c. Silver medal for 400 metres and bronze medals for 4 × 400 metres relay, 1964. *Vert*—$2.50, Olympic Games emblems for Moscow, 1980, Olympia, 776 B.C. and Athens, 1896.

171 Charcoal Production

(Des J. Cooter. Litho Walsall)

1980 (8 Sept). *11th Commonwealth Forestry Conference. T* **171** *and similar horiz designs. Multicoloured.* W w **14** (*sideways*). *P* 14.

572 10 c. Type **171** 10 10
573 55 c. Logging 25 25
574 70 c. Teak plantation 35 60
575 $2.50, Watershed management .. .. .. 85 2·25
572/5 .. .. *Set of* 4 1·40 2·75
MS576 135 × 87 mm. Nos. 572/5 .. .. .. 1·50 2·75

172 Beryl McBurnie (dance and culture) and Audrey Jeffers (social worker)

(Des BG Studio. Litho Questa)

1980 (29 Sept). *Decade for Women (1st issue). T* **172** *and similar horiz designs. Multicoloured.* W w **14** (*sideways*). *P* 14.

577 $1 Type **172** 45 55
578 $1 Elizabeth Bourne (judiciary) and Isabella Teshier (government) 45 55
579 $1 Dr. Stella Abidh (public health) and Louise Horne (nutrition).. .. .. .. 45 55
577/9 .. .. *Set of* 3 1·25 1·50

See also Nos. 680/2.

173 Netball Stadium

(Des BG Studio. Litho Format)

1980 (21 Oct). *World Netball Tournament.* W w **14** (*sideways*). *P* 13½ × 14.

580 **173** 70 c. multicoloured 30 45

174 I.Y.D.P. Emblem, Athlete and Disabled Person **175** "Our Land Must Live"

(Des BG Studio. Litho Format)

1981 (23 Mar). *International Year for Disabled Persons. T* **174** *and similar horiz designs.* W w **14**. *P* 14½.

581 10 c. black, vermilion and dull yellowish green 15 10
582 70 c. black, vermilion and buff 40 70
583 $1.50, black, vermilion and cobalt .. .. 60 1·40
584 $2 black, vermilion and flesh .. .. .. 60 1·75
581/4 .. .. *Set of* 4 1·60 3·50

Designs:—70 c. I.Y.D.P. emblem and doctor with disabled person; $1.50, Emblem, and blind man and woman; $2 Emblem and inscription.

(Des Debbie Galt; adapted G. Vasarhelyi. Litho J.W.)

1981 (7 July). *Environmental Preservation. T* **175** *and similar horiz designs. Multicoloured.* W w **14** (*sideways*). *P* 13 × 13½.

585 10 c. Type **175** 15 10
586 55 c. "Our seas must live" 45 30
587 $3 "Our skies must live" .. .. 1·60 1·60
585/7 .. .. *Set of* 3 2·00 1·75
MS588 142 × 89 mm. Nos. 585/7 .. .. .. 3·00 5·00

176 "Food or Famine" **177** "First Aid Skills"

(Des and litho Harrison)

1981 (16 Oct). *World Food Day. T* **176** *and similar horiz designs. Multicoloured.* W w **14** (*sideways**). *P* 14½×14.

589 10 c. Type **176** 10 10
w. Wmk Crown to right of CA .. ..
590 15 c. "Produce more" (threshing and milling rice) 10 10
w. Wmk Crown to right of CA .. ..
591 45 c. "Fish for food" (Bigeye) 30 20
592 55 c. "Prevent hunger" 35 25
593 $1.50, "Fight malnutrition" 85 90
w. Wmk Crown to right of CA .. .. 19·00
594 $2 "Fish for food" (Small-mouthed Grunt) 1·10 1·25
589/94 .. .. *Set of* 6 2·40 2·40
MS595 164×98 mm. Nos. 589/94 .. .. .. 2·75 4·00

*The normal sideways watermark shows Crown to left of CA, *as seen from the back of the stamp.*

(Des L. Curtis. Litho Format)

1981 (17 Nov). *President's Award Scheme. T* **177** *and similar vert designs. Multicoloured.* W w **14**. *P* 14.

596 10 c. Type **177** 20 10
597 70 c. "Motor mechanics" 40 45
598 $1 "Expedition" 50 55
599 $2 Presenting an award .. .. 90 1·40
596/9 .. .. *Set of* 4 1·75 2·25

178 Pharmacist at Work **179** "Production"

(Des C. Abbott. Litho Questa)

1982 (12 Feb). *Commonwealth Pharmaceutical Conference. T* **178** *and similar vert designs.* W w **14**. *P* 14½ × 14.

600 10 c. Type **178** 15 10
601 $1 Gerritoute (plant) .. .. 1·75 2·25
602 $2 Rachette (plant) .. .. 2·75 4·25
600/2 .. .. *Set of* 3 4·25 6·00

(Des Debbie Galt; adapted G. Vasarhelyi. Litho Questa)

1982 (28 June). *75th Anniv of Boy Scout Movement. T* **179** *and similar vert designs. Multicoloured.* W w **14**. *P* 14.

603 15 c. Type **179** 60 10
604 55 c. "Tolerance" .. .. 1·50 30
605 $5 "Discipline" .. .. 5·50 6·50
603/5 .. .. *Set of* 3 7·00 6·50

180 Charlotteville **181** "Pa Pa Bois"

(Des Harrison. Litho Format)

1982 (18 Oct). *25th Anniv of Tourist Board. T* **180** *and similar vert designs. Multicoloured.* W w **14**. *P* 13½ × 14.

606 55 c. Type **180** 30 25
607 $1 Boating 40 55
608 $3 Fort George .. .. 1·25 1·90
606/8 .. .. *Set of* 3 1·75 2·40

(Des D. Louison. Litho Harrison)

1982 (8 Nov). *Folklore. Local Spirits and Demons. T* **181** *and similar horiz designs. Multicoloured.* W w **14** (*sideways*). *P* 14.

609 10 c. Type **181** 10 10
610 15 c. "La Diablesse" 10 10
611 65 c. "Lugarhoo", "Phantom" and "Soucouyant" 35 30
612 $5 "Bois de Soleil", "Davens" and "Mamma de l'Eau" .. .. 2·50 3·25
609/12 .. .. *Set of* 4 2·75 3·25
MS613 133 × 100 mm. Nos. 609/12 .. .. 4·25 6·00

182 Cane Harvesting

((Des W. Fenton. Litho Harrison)

1982 (13 Dec). *Canefarmers' Association Centenary. T* **182** *and similar horiz designs. Multicoloured.* W w **14** (*sideways*). *P* 14.

614 30 c. Type **182** 30 15
615 70 c. Farmers loading bullock cart 60 85
616 $1.50, Cane field in bloom .. .. .. 1·10 1·75
614/16 .. .. *Set of* 3 1·75 2·50
MS617 72 × 117 mm. Nos. 614/16. P 14½. .. 1·40 1·50

183 National Stadium

(Des McCombie Skinner. Litho Harrison)

1982 (28 Dec). *20th Anniv of Independence. T* **183** *and similar horiz designs. Multicoloured.* W w **14** (*sideways**). *P* 13×14.

618 10 c. Type **183** 15 10
w. Wmk Crown to right of CA .. .. 7·00
619 35 c. Caroni water treatment plant 20 15
620 50 c. Mount Hope Maternity Hospital 45 25
621 $2 National Insurance Board Mall, Tobago .. .. 90 1·75
618/21 .. .. *Set of* 4 1·50 2·00

*The normal sideways watermark shows Crown to left of CA, *as seen from the back of the stamp.*

184 Commonwealth Flags

(Des C. Abbott. Litho Harrison)

1983 (14 Mar). *Commonwealth Day. T* **184** *and similar multicoloured designs.* W w **14** (*sideways on* 10, 55 *c.*). *P* 14.

622 10 c. Type **184** 10 10
623 55 c. Satellite view of Trinidad and Tobago .. 25 20
624 $1 "Nodding donkey" oil pump (*vert*) .. 40 60
625 $2 Map of Trinidad and Tobago (*vert*) .. 85 1·25
622/5 .. .. *Set of* 4 1·40 1·90

185 Lockheed L-1011 TriStar 500 *Flamingo*

(Des D. Miller. Litho Format)

1983 (11 July). *10th Anniv of CARICOM.* W w **14** (*sideways*). *P* 14.

626 **185** 35 c. multicoloured .. .. 70 1·25

186 V.D.U. Operator

(Des G. Vasarhelyi. Litho Harrison)

1983 (5 Aug). *World Communications Year. T* **186** *and similar horiz designs. Multicoloured.* W w **14** (*sideways*). *P* 14.

627	15 c. Type **186** ..	20	10
628	55 c. Scarborough Post Office, Tobago ..	50	20
629	$1 Textel building ..	85	70
630	$3 Morne Blue E.C.M.S. station ..	2·00	2·50
627/30	.. .. *Set of* 4	3·25	3·25

187 Financial Complex

(Des D. Miller. Litho Format)

1983 (19 Sept). *Conference of Commonwealth Finance Ministers.* W w **14** (*sideways*). *P* 14.

631 **187** $2 multicoloured .. .. .. 80 1·25

188 King Mackerel **189** Bois Pois

(Des N. Weaver. Litho Format)

1983 (17 Oct). *World Food Day. T* **188** *and similar horiz designs. Multicoloured.* W w **14** (*sideways*). *P* 14 × 13½ (10 *c.*, 55 *c.*) *or* 13½ (*others*).

632	10 c. Type **188** ..	20	10
633	55 c. Four-winged Flyingfish ..	1·00	40
634	70 c. Queen or Pink Conch ..	1·25	1·40
635	$4 Red Shrimp ..	4·50	7·00
632/5	.. .. *Set of* 4	6·25	8·00

(Des I. Loe. Litho Questa)

1983 (14 Dec)–**84**. *Flowers. T* **189** *and similar multicoloured designs.* W w **14** (*sideways on* 5 *c. to* $1.50). *P* 14. *A. Without imprint date. B. With imprint date* (10.84).

		A		B	
636	5 c. Type **189** ..	60	70	1·25	1·75
637	10 c. Maraval Lily ..	60	40	75	80
638	15 c. Star Grass ..	60	30	1·00	1·25
639	20 c. Bois Caco ..	30	15	†	
640	25 c. Strangling Fig ..	70	90	1·50	2·00
641	30 c. *Cassia moschata* ..	40	15	†	
642	50 c. Chalice Flower ..	30	30	†	
643	65 c. Black Stick ..	55	30	†	
644	80 c. *Columnea scandens* ..	65	75	†	
645	95 c. Cat's Claw ..	80	80	†	
646	$1 Bois L'agli ..	1·00	50	†	
647	$1.50, *Eustoma exaltatum* ..	1·25	1·00	†	
648	$2 Chaconia ..	1·50	1·50	†	
649	$2.50, *Chrysothemis pulchella*	1·25	2·25	†	
650	$5 *Centratherum punctatum* ..	3·00	6·50	†	
651	$10 Savanna Flower ..	4·25	8·50	†	
636A/51A	.. *Set of* 16	16·00	22·00	†	
636B/40B	.. *Set of* 4			4·00	5·25

Nos. 648/51 are horizontal, 39×29 mm.

The 10 c. value shows an incorrect botanical name. This should read "*Spathiphyllum cannaefolium*".

Imprint dates: "1984", Nos. 636B/8B, 640B; "1985", No. 637B; "1987", No. 637B; "1989", No. 637B.

For these designs watermarked w **16** see Nos. 686/701.

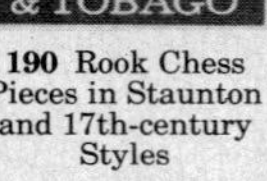

190 Rook Chess Pieces in Staunton and 17th-century Styles **191** Swimming

(Des L. Curtis. Litho Questa)

1984 (14 Sept). *60th Anniv of International Chess Federation. T* **190** *and similar vert designs. Multicoloured.* W w **14**. *P* 14.

652	50 c. Type **190** ..	2·75	50
653	70 c. Staunton and 12th-century Lewis Bishops ..	3·00	2·00
654	$1.50, Staunton and 13th-century Swedish Queens ..	4·00	5·00
655	$2 Staunton and 19th-century Chinese Kings ..	5·00	6·50
652/5	.. .. *Set of* 4	13·50	12·50

(Des Garden Studio. Litho Harrison)

1984 (21 Sept). *Olympic Games, Los Angeles. T* **191** *and similar vert designs. Multicoloured.* W w **14**. *P* 14 × 14½.

656	15 c. Type **191** ..	10	10
	w. Wmk inverted ..	75	1·00
657	55 c. Track and field events ..	30	20
658	$1.50, Sailing ..	1·00	1·50
659	$4 Cycling ..	3·25	3·75
656/9	.. *Set of* 4	4·25	5·00
MS660	132×85 mm. Nos. 656/9 ..	4·50	6·50

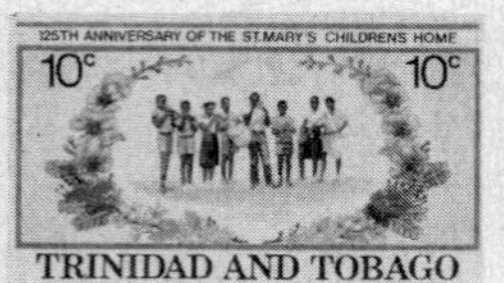

192 Slave Schooner and Shackles **193** Children's Band

(Des O. Bell. Litho Walsall)

1984 (22 Oct). *150th Anniv of Abolition of Slavery. T* **192** *and similar vert designs. Multicoloured.* W w **14**. *P* 13½ × 13.

661	35 c. Type **192** ..	85	30
662	55 c. Slave and "Slave Triangle" map ..	1·25	50
663	$1 *Capitalism and Slavery* (book by Dr. Eric Williams) ..	2·00	1·75
664	$2 Toussaint l'Ouverture (Haitian revolutionary) ..	2·50	4·00
661/4	.. *Set of* 4	6·00	6·00
MS665	95 × 100 mm. Nos. 661/4 ..	6·00	7·50

(Des G. Vasarhelyi. Litho J.W.)

1984 (13 Nov). *125th Anniv of St. Mary's Children's Home. T* **193** *and similar horiz designs. Multicoloured.* W w **14** (*sideways*). *P* 13½.

666	10 c. Type **193** ..	15	10
667	70 c. St. Mary's Children's Home ..	50	50
668	$3 Group of children ..	2·25	2·75
666/8	.. *Set of* 3	2·50	3·00

194 Parang Band **195** Capt. A. A. Cipriani and T. U. B. Butler

(Des D. Miller. Litho Questa)

1984 (26 Nov). *Parang Festival. T* **194** *and similar horiz designs. Multicoloured.* W w **14** (*sideways*). *P* 14 × 14½.

669	10 c. Type **194** ..	20	10
670	30 c. Music and poinsettia ..	50	15
671	$1 Bandola, bandolin and cuatro (musical instruments) ..	1·25	90
672	$3 Double bass, fiddle and guitar (musical instruments) ..	2·50	3·50
669/72	.. *Set of* 4	4·00	4·25

(Des G. Vasarhelyi. Litho Questa)

1985 (17 June). *Labour Day. Labour Leaders. T* **195** *and similar vert designs.* W w **14**. *P* 14.

673	55 c. black and bright rose ..	80	80
674	55 c. black and orange-yellow ..	80	80
675	55 c. black and emerald ..	80	80
673/5	.. *Set of* 3	2·25	2·25

Designs:—No. 674, C. P. Alexander and Q. O'Connor; 675, A. Cola Rienzi and C. T. W. E. Worrell.

196 *Lady Nelson* (1928)

(Des E. Nisbet. Litho Format)

1985 (20 Aug). *Ships. T* **196** *and similar horiz designs. Multicoloured.* W w **14**. *P* 14½ × 14.

676	30 c. Type **196** ..	70	25
677	95 c. *Lady Drake* (1928) ..	1·50	1·75
678	$1.50, *Federal Palm* (1961) ..	2·00	3·00
679	$2 *Federal Maple* (1961) ..	2·50	3·50
676/9	.. *Set of* 4	6·00	7·75

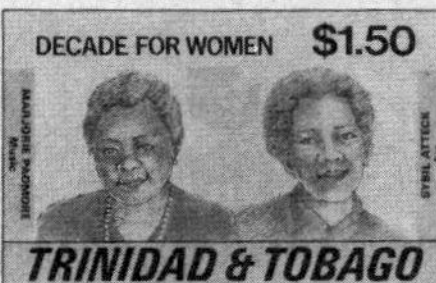

197 Marjorie Padmore (music) and Sybil Atteck (art)

(Des Julijana Zappin. Litho Walsall)

1985 (11 Nov). *Decade for Women (2nd issue). T* **197** *and similar horiz designs. Multicoloured.* W w **16** (*sideways*). *P* 14.

680	$1.50, Type **197** ..	1·40	1·75
681	$1.50, May Cherrie (medical social worker) and Evelyn Tracey (social worker) ..	1·40	1·75
682	$1.50, Umilta McShine (education) and Jessica Smith-Phillips (public service) ..	1·40	1·75
680/2	.. *Set of* 3	3·75	4·75

198 Badge of Trinidad and Tobago Cadet Force (75th Anniv) **199** Anne-Marie Javouhey (foundress)

(Des D. Slater. Litho Harrison)

1985 (9 Dec). *International Youth Year. T* **198** *and similar horiz designs. Multicoloured.* W w **16** (*sideways*). *P* 14 × 14½.

683	10 c. Type **198** ..	45	10
684	65 c. Guide badges (75th anniv of Girl Guide movement) ..	2·00	2·25
685	95 c. Young people of Trinidad ..	2·50	2·75
683/5	.. *Set of* 3	4·50	4·50

1985 (Dec)–**89**. *As Nos.* 636/7, 639/41 *and* 643/51, *but* W w **16** (*sideways on* 5, 10, 20, 25, 30, 65, 80, 95 *c.*, $1, $1.50). *With imprint date. P* 14.

686	5 c. Type **189** ..	2·00	80
687	10 c. Maraval Lily (4.8.86) ..	30	30
689	20 c. Bois Caco (8.88) ..	60	1·25
690	25 c. Strangling Fig (8.88) ..	60	1·25
691	30 c. *Cassia moschata* (5.87) ..	1·25	1·25
693	65 c. Black Stick (5.87) ..	1·25	1·75
694	80 c. *Columnea scandens* (5.87) ..	2·00	2·50
695	95 c. Cat's Claw ..	50	60
696	$1 Bois L'agli ..	65	30
697	$1.50, *Eustoma exaltatum* (5.87) ..	3·00	3·25
698	$2 Chaconia (39×29 *mm*) (5.87) ..	1·50	3·00
699	$2.50, *Chrysothemis pulchella* (39×29 *mm*) (5.89) ..	8·50	8·50
700	$5 *Centratherum punctatum* (39×29 *mm*)	1·75	1·75
	w. Wmk inverted ..	4·00	
701	$10 Savanna Flower (39×29 *mm*) ..	3·50	4·25
	w. Wmk inverted ..	8·50	
686/701	.. *Set of* 14	25·00	28·00

Imprint dates: "1985", Nos. 686. 695/6, 700/1; "1986", No. 687; "1987", Nos. 687, 691, 693/8, 700/1; "1988", Nos. 687, 689/91, 693/6, 700/1; "1989", Nos. 687, 689/91, 693, 696/701.

(Des Joan Thompson. Litho Format)

1986 (19 Mar). *150th Anniv of Arrival of Sisters of St. Joseph de Cluny. T* **199** *and similar vert designs. Multicoloured.* W w **16** (*sideways*). *P* 14 × 14½.

702	10 c. Type **199** ..	10	10
703	65 c. St. Joseph's Convent, Port-of-Spain ..	45	90
704	95 c. Children and statue of Anne-Marie Javouhey ..	65	1·25
702/4	.. *Set of* 3	1·10	2·00

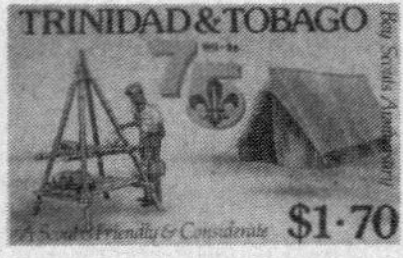

200 Tank Locomotive *Arima* **201** Scout Camp

(Des J.W. Litho Format)

1986 (26 May). *"Ameripex '86" International Stamp Exhibition, Chicago. Trinidad Railway Locomotives. T* **200** *and similar horiz designs.* W w **16**. *P* 14½ × 14.

705	65 c. Type **200** ..	25	35
706	95 c. Canadian-built locomotive No. 22 ..	35	60
707	$1.10, Tender engine ..	40	95
708	$1.50, Saddle tank ..	60	1·25
705/8	.. *Set of* 4	1·40	2·75
MS709	105×80 mm. Nos. 705/8 ..	1·40	2·75

(Des N. Shewring. Litho Questa)

1986 (21 July). *75th Anniv of Trinidad and Tobago Boy Scouts. T* **201** *and similar horiz design. Multicoloured.* W w **16** (*sideways*). *P* 14.

710	$1.70, Type **201** ..	1·00	1·60
711	$2 Scouts of 1911 and 1986 ..	1·25	1·90

NEW INFORMATION

The editor is always interested to correspond with people who have new information that will improve or correct the Catalogue.

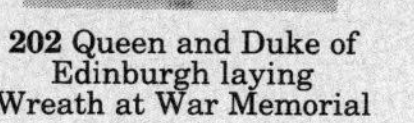

202 Queen and Duke of Edinburgh laying Wreath at War Memorial

203 Eric Williams at Graduation, 1935

(Des C. Abbott. Litho Walsall)

1986 (16 Sept). *60th Birthday of Queen Elizabeth II. T* **202** *and similar vert designs. Multicoloured.* W w **16**. *P* 14½×14.

712 10 c. Type **202** .. 30 10
713 15 c. Queen with Trinidadian dignitaries aboard *Britannia* .. 55 20
714 30 c. With President Ellis Clarke .. 65 25
715 $5 Receiving bouquet .. 3·00 5·50
712/15 .. *Set of 4* 4·00 5·50

(Des D. Miller. Litho Format)

1986 (25 Sept). *75th Birth Anniv of Dr. Eric Williams. T* **203** *and similar multicoloured designs.* W w **14** (*sideways* on 95 c., $5*). *P* 14.

716 10 c. Type **203** .. 30 10
717 30 c. Premier Eric Williams (wearing red tie) 55 20
w. Wmk inverted
718 30 c. As No. 717, but wearing black and orange tie .. 55 20
719 95 c. Arms of University of West Indies and Dr. Williams as Pro-Chancellor (*horiz*) 1·00 1·25
720 $5 Prime Minister Williams and Whitehall (*horiz*) .. 2·25 4·25
w. Wmk Crown to right of CA .. 22·00
716/20 .. *Set of 5* 4·25 5·50
MS721 105×100 mm. Nos. 716/17 and 719/20. Wmk sideways .. 6·00 8·50

*The normal sideways watermark shows Crown to left of CA, *as seen from the back of the stamp.*

204 "PEACE" Slogan and Outline Map of Trinidad and Tobago

205 Miss Giselle La Ronde and BWIA Airliner

(Adapted L. Curtis. Litho Questa)

1986 (3 Nov). *International Peace Year. T* **204** *and similar horiz design. Multicoloured.* W w **16** (*sideways*). *P* 14.

722 95 c. Type **204** .. 40 50
723 $3 Peace dove with olive branch .. 1·25 2·25

(Des D. Miller. Litho Walsall)

1987 (27 July). *Miss World 1986. T* **205** *and similar vert designs. Multicoloured.* W w **16**. *P* 14.

724 10 c. Type **205** .. 40 10
725 30 c. In swimsuit on beach .. 85 25
726 95 c. Miss Giselle La Ronde .. 2·00 2·25
727 $1.65, Wearing Miss World sash .. 2·75 3·50
w. Wmk inverted .. 17·00
724/7 .. *Set of 4* 5·50 5·50

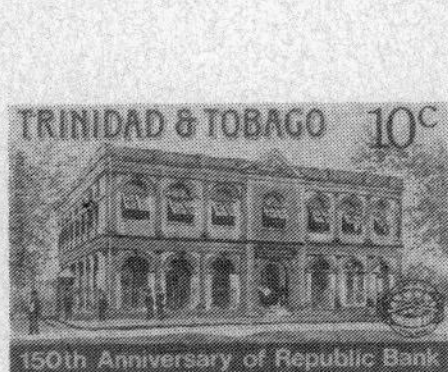

206 Colonial Bank, Port-of-Spain

207 Sergeant in Parade Order and Soldiers in Work Dress and Battle Dress

(Des J.W. Litho Walsall)

1987 (21 Dec). *150th Anniv of Republic Bank. T* **206** *and similar horiz designs. Multicoloured.* W w **14** (*sideways*). *P* 14.

728 10 c. Type **206** .. 10 10
729 65 c. Cocoa plantation .. 50 70
730 95 c. Oil field .. 1·00 1·50
731 $1.10, Belmont Tramway Company tramcar .. 1·25 2·00
728/31 .. *Set of 4* 2·50 3·75

(Des C. Abbott. Litho Questa)

1988 (29 Feb). *25th Anniv of Defence Force. T* **207** *and similar vert designs. Multicoloured.* W w **16** (*sideways*). *P* 14.

732 10 c. Type **207** .. 55 15
733 30 c. Women soldiers .. 1·25 30
734 $1.10, Defence Force officers .. 2·50 2·75
735 $1.50, Naval ratings and patrol boat .. 3·25 3·50
732/5 .. *Set of 4* 6·75 6·00

(Des D. Hartley and L. Curtis. Litho Walsall)

1988 (6 June). *West Indian Cricket. Horiz designs as T* **243***a of Jamaica, each showing portrait, cricket equipment and early belt buckle. Multicoloured.* W w **14** (*sideways**). *P* 14.

736 30 c. George John .. 1·00 30
737 65 c. Learie Constantine .. 2·00 1·00
w. Wmk Crown to right of CA .. 24·00
738 95 c. Sonny Ramadhin .. 2·25 1·75
739 $1.50, Gerry Gomez .. 2·75 3·00
740 $2.50, Jeffrey Stollmeyer .. 4·00 5·00
736/40 .. *Set of 5* 11·00 10·00

*The normal sideways watermark shows Crown to left of CA, *as seen from the back of the stamp.*

208 Uriah Butler (labour leader)

209 Mary Werges and Santa Rosa Church

(Des G. Vasarhelyi. Litho Walsall)

1988 (11 July). *50th Anniv of Oilfield Workers Trade Union* (1987). *T* **208** *and similar vert designs. Multicoloured.* W w **16**. *P* 14½ × 14.

741 10 c. Type **208** .. 10 10
742 30 c. Adrian Rienzi (O.W.T.U. president, 1937-42) .. 10 10
743 65 c. John Rojas (O.W.T.U. president, 1943-62) .. 15 25
744 $5 George Weekes (O.W.T.U. president, 1962-87) .. 1·25 2·25
741/4 .. *Set of 4* 1·40 2·40

(Des O. Bell. Litho Walsall)

1988 (22 Aug). *Centenary of Borough of Arima. T* **209** *and similar horiz designs. Multicoloured.* W w **16** (*sideways*). *P* 14 × 14½.

745 20 c. Type **209** .. 15 10
746 30 c. Governor W. Robinson and Royal Charter .. 15 10
747 $1.10, Arrival of Governor Robinson .. 60 95
748 $1.50, Mayor J. F. Wallen and Centenary logo .. 90 1·50
745/8 .. *Set of 4* 1·60 2·40

(Des D. Miller (30 c.), S. Noon and D. Miller (others). Litho Questa)

1988 (21 Nov). *300th Anniv of Lloyd's of London. Multicoloured designs as T* **167***a of Malawi.* W w **16** (*sideways on* $1.10, $1.55). *P* 14.

749 30 c. Queen Mother at Topping-out of new building, 1984 .. 50 20
750 $1.10, BWIA Lockheed L-1011 TriStar 500 *Flamingo* airliner (*horiz*) .. 1·75 1·40
751 $1.55, Steel works, Trinidad (*horiz*) .. 1·75 1·75
752 $2 *Atlantic Empress* (tanker) on fire off Tobago, 1979 .. 3·25 2·75
749/52 .. *Set of 4* 6·50 5·50

210 Colonial Arms of Trinidad & Tobago and 1913 1d. Stamp

(Des W. Carr, adapted D. Miller. Litho Questa)

1989 (20 Mar). *Centenary of Union of Trinidad and Tobago. T* **210** *and similar horiz designs. Multicoloured.* W w **16** (*sideways*). *P* 14½.

753 40 c. Type **210** .. 50 10
754 $1 Pre-1889 Tobago emblem and Tobago 1896 ½d. on 4d. stamp .. 1·25 1·00
755 $1.50, Pre-1889 Trinidad emblem and Trinidad 1883 4d. stamp .. 1·75 2·25
756 $2.25, Current Arms of Trinidad and Tobago and 1977 45 c. Republic stamp 2·25 3·00
753/6 .. *Set of 4* 5·25 5·75

211 Common Piping Guan

212 Blind Welfare (75th Anniversary)

(Des Doreen McGuinness. Litho Walsall)

1989 (31 July). *Rare Fauna of Trinidad and Tobago. T* **211** *and similar horiz designs. Multicoloured.* W w **14** (*sideways*). *P* 14×14½.

757 $1 Type **211** .. 2·75 3·00
a. Vert strip of 5. Nos. 757/61 .. 12·00
758 $1 *Phyllodytes auratus* (frog) .. 2·75 3·00
759 $1 *Cebus albifrons trinitatis* (monkey) .. 2·75 3·00
760 $1 Tamandua .. 2·75 3·00
761 $1 *Lutra longicaudis* (otter) .. 2·75 3·00
757/61 .. *Set of 5* 12·00 13·00

Nos. 757/61 were printed together, *se-tenant*, in vertical strips of 5 throughout the sheet, forming a composite background design.

(Des S. Noon. Litho Walsall)

1989 (2 Oct). *Anniversaries. T* **212** *and similar vert designs. Multicoloured.* W w **14**. *P* 14½×14.

762 10 c. Type **212** .. 30 15
w. Wmk inverted .. 5·50
763 40 c. Port-of-Spain City Hall (75th anniv) 35 20
764 $1 Guides and Brownies (75th anniv) .. 1·50 60
765 $2.25, Red Cross members (50th anniv) 2·25 2·50
762/5 .. *Set of 4* 4·00 3·00

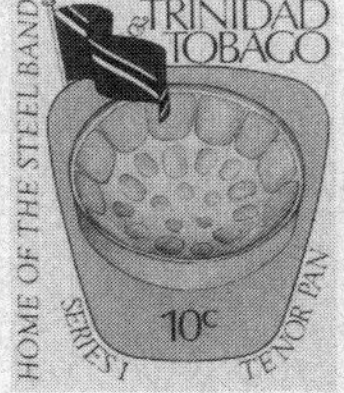

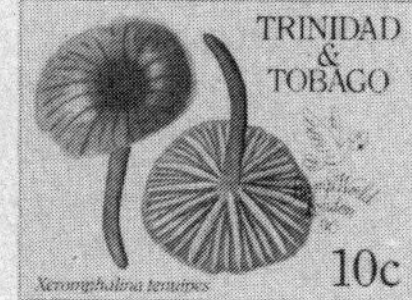

213 Tenor Pan

214 *Xeromphalina tenuipes*

(Des T. Mussio, adapted D. Miller. Litho Questa)

1989 (30 Nov). *Steel Pans (1st series). T* **213** *and similar vert designs. Multicoloured.* W w **16**. *P* 14½×14.

766 10 c. Type **213** .. 10 10
767 40 c. Guitar pans .. 15 15
768 $1 Cello pans .. 45 60
769 $2.25, Bass pans .. 85 1·75
766/9 .. *Set of 4* 1·40 2·40

See also Nos. 828/31.

(Des McCombie Skinner. Litho Questa)

1990 (3 May). *"Stamp World London 90" International Stamp Exhibition, London. Fungi. T* **214** *and similar horiz designs. Multicoloured.* W w **16** (*sideways*). *P* 14×13½.

770 10 c. Type **214** .. 25 20
771 40 c. *Phallus indusiatus* ("*Dictyophora indusiata*") .. 50 25
772 $1 *Leucocoprinus birnbaumii* .. 1·10 90
773 $2.25, *Crinipellis perniciosa* .. 2·00 3·50
770/3 .. *Set of 4* 3·50 4·25

215 Scarlet Ibis in Immature Plumage

216 Princess Alice and Administration Building

(Litho Questa)

1990 (7 Sept). *Scarlet Ibis. T* **215** *and similar horiz designs. Multicoloured.* W w **16** (*sideways*). *P* 14.

774 40 c. Type **215** .. 1·00 25
775 80 c. Pair in pre-nuptial display .. 1·25 1·00
776 $1 Male in breeding plumage .. 1·50 1·00
777 $2.25, Adult on nest with chick .. 2·25 3·50
774/7 .. *Set of 4* 5·50 5·25

(Des L. Curtis. Litho B.D.T.)

1990 (15 Oct). *40th Anniv of University of West Indies. T* **216** *and similar horiz designs. Multicoloured.* W w **14** (*sideways*). *P* 13½×14.

778 40 c. Type **216** .. 40 15
779 80 c. Sir Hugh Wooding and Library .. 70 60
780 $1 Sir Allen Lewis and Faculty of Engineering .. 90 80
781 $2.25, Sir Shridath Ramphal and Faculty of Medical Sciences .. 2·25 3·00
778/81 .. *Set of 4* 3·75 4·00

217 Lockheed L.18 Lodestar

218 Yellow Oriole

(Des E. Nisbet. Litho B.D.T)

1990 (27 Nov). *50th Anniv of British West Indies Airways. T* **217** *and similar horiz designs. Multicoloured. W* w **14** *(sideways). P* 14.

782 40 c. Type **217** 80 20
783 80 c. Vickers Viking 1A .. .. 1·25 1·00
784 $1 Vickers Viscount 702 .. .. .. 1·40 1·00
785 $2.25, Boeing 707 .. .. 2·75 3·75
782/5 .. .. *Set of* 4 5·50 5·50
MS786 77×52 mm. $5 Lockheed L-1011 TriStar 500 .. .. 3·25 4·00

(Des D. Miller. Litho Questa)

1990 (17 Dec). *Birds. T* **218** *and similar vert designs. Multicoloured. W* w **16** *(sideways). P* 14.

787 20 c. Type **218** 10 10
788 25 c. Green-rumped Parrotlet 20 20
789 40 c. Fork-tailed Flycatcher 10 10
790 50 c. Copper-rumped Hummingbird 30 20
791 $1 Bananaquit 20 25
792 $2 Violaceous Euphonia 45 50
793 $2.25, Channel-billed Toucan 45 50
794 $2.50, Bay-headed Tanager 50 55
795 $5 Green Honeycreeper .. .. 1·75 2·00
796 $10 Cattle Egret .. .. 2·00 2·25
797 $20 Golden-olive Woodpecker .. .. .. 4·00 4·25
798 $50 Peregrine Falcon .. .. 10·00 10·50
787/98 .. .. *Set of* 12 19·00 20·00

For some of these values watermarked w **14** (sideways) see Nos. 837/844.

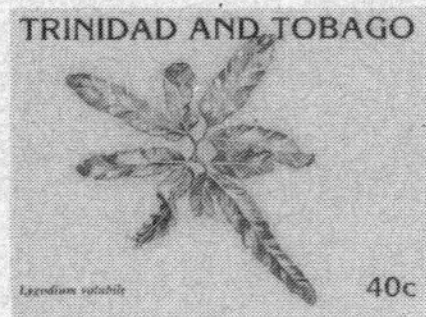

219 *Lygodium volubile*

(Des T. Musio. Litho B.D.T)

1991 (1 July). *Ferns. T* **219** *and similar horiz designs. Multicoloured. W* w **14** *(sideways). P* 13½×14.

799 40 c. Type **219** 35 15
800 80 c. *Blechnum occidentale* 65 60
801 $1 *Gleichenia bifida* 75 75
802 $2.25, *Polypodium lycopodioides* .. .. 1·75 3·00
799/802 .. .. *Set of* 4 3·25 4·00

220 Trinidad and Tobago Regiment Anti-aircraft Battery

221 H. E. Rapsey (founder)

(Des A. Theobald. Litho Questa)

1991 (7 Dec). *50th Anniv of Second World War. T* **220** *and similar horiz designs. Multicoloured. W* w **16** *(sideways). P* 13½×14.

803 40 c. Type **220** 75 20
804 80 c. Fairey Barracuda Mk III attacking U-boat .. .. 1·00 80
805 $1 Avro Type 683 Lancaster .. .. .. 1·25 90
806 $2.25, H.M.S. *Wye* (frigate) escorting convoy .. .. 2·25 3·25
803/6 .. .. *Set of* 4 4·75 4·75
MS807 117×85 mm. $2.50, Presentation Supermarine Spitfire; $2.50, Presentation Vickers-Armstrong Wellington bomber .. 5·50 6·00

(Des G. Vasarhelyi. Litho B.D.T.)

1992 (30 Mar). *Anniversaries. T* **221** *and similar vert designs. Multicoloured. W* w **14.** *P* 14.

808 40 c. Type **221** (centenary of Trinidad Building and Loan Assoc) 25 10
809 80 c. *Inca clathrata quesneli* (beetle) (Trinidad & Tobago Field Naturalists' Club) 70 75
810 $1 Holy Name Convent (centenary) .. 80 85
808/10 .. .. *Set of* 3 1·60 1·50

222 Baptism (Baptist)

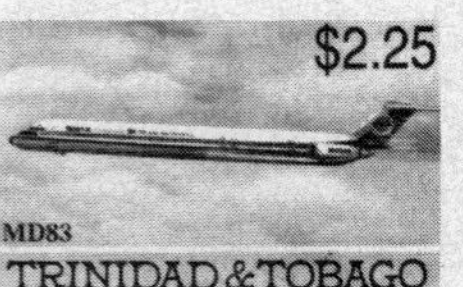

223 McDonnell Douglas MD-83

(Des Jennifer Toombs. Litho Questa)

1992 (21 Apr). *Religions of Trinidad and Tobago. T* **222** *and similar vert designs. Multicoloured. W* w **14.** *P* 14.

811 40 c. Type **222** 50 50
812 40 c. Minaret with star and crescent (Islam) 50 50
813 40 c. Logo (Hinduism) 50 50
814 40 c. Cross (Christian) 50 50
815 40 c. Logo (Baha'i) 50 50
811/15 .. .. *Set of* 5 2·25 2·25

(Des G. Vasarhelyi. Litho B.D.T.)

1992 (6 Aug). *Aircraft. T* **223** *and similar horiz design. Multicoloured. W* w **14** *(sideways). P* 14.

816 $2.25, Type **223** .. .. 1·50 1·75
817 $2.25, Lockheed L-1011 TriStar aircraft .. 1·50 1·75

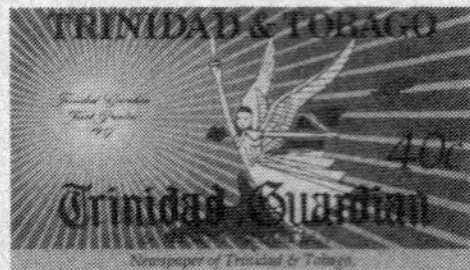

224 *Trinidad Guardian* Title (75th anniv of newspaper)

(Des Jennifer Toombs (No. 819), N. Shewring (others). Litho Questa)

1992 (7–30 Dec). *Anniversaries. T* **224** *and similar multicoloured designs. W* w **16** *(sideways on horiz designs). P* 14½.

818 40 c. Type **224** 10 10
819 40 c. Nativity scene (Christmas) (*vert*) (21 Dec) 10 10
820 $1 National Museum and Art Gallery (centenary) (23 Dec) 35 40
821 $2.25, Cover to St. James Internment Camp, 1942 (50th anniv of Trinidad and Tobago Philatelic Society) (30 Dec) 80 1·25
818/21 .. .. *Set of* 4 1·25 1·60

225 Derek Walcott, Sir Shridath Ramphal and William Demas with Caribbean Maps (*illustration reduced. Actual size* 100×22 *mm*)

(Des O. Ball and D. Miller. Litho B.D.T.)

1994 (31 Jan). *20th Anniv of CARICOM (Caribbean Economic Community). Recipients of Order of the Caribbean Community. T* **225** *and similar design. W* w **14** *(sideways). P* 13×13½.

822 **225** 50 c. multicoloured 20 20
823 $1.50, multicoloured 45 60
824 $2.75, multicoloured .. .. .. 85 1·10
825 $3 multicoloured .. .. 1·00 1·40
822/5 .. .. *Set of* 4 2·25 3·00
MS826 90×90 mm. $6 multicoloured (Insignia of the Order (34½×51½ *mm*)). Wmk upright. P 13½×13 .. .. 2·00 3·00

226 Aldwyn Roberts Kitchener (bass player)

227 Quadrophonic Pans

(Des G. Vasarhelyi. Litho Walsall)

1994 (11 Feb). *"Land of Calypso". W* w **14.** *P* 14.

827 **226** 50 c. multicoloured 55 55

(Des D. Miller. Litho B.D.T.)

1994 (11 Feb). *Steel Pans (2nd series). T* **227** *and similar horiz designs. W* w **16** *(sideways). P* 14×15.

828 50 c. Type **227** 20 20
829 $1 Tenor base pans 35 30
830 $2.25, Six pans .. .. 80 1·25
831 $2.50, Rocket pans .. .. 90 1·25
828/31 .. .. *Set of* 4 2·00 2·75

1994 (18 Feb). *"Hong Kong '94" International Stamp Exhibition. Nos.* 789, 792, 837 *and as* 796 *but W* w **14** *(sideways), optd as T* **272** *of Jamaica.*

832 25 c. Green-rumped Parrotlet 30 20
833 40 c. Fork-tailed Flycatcher 35 20
834 $2 Violaceous Euphonia .. .. .. 95 1·25
835 $10 Cattle Egret .. .. 3·25 4·00
832/5 .. .. *Set of* 4 4·25 5·00

1994 (Aug)–**96.** *As Nos.* 788, 790/2 *and* 795, *but W* w **14** *(sideways). P* 14.

837 25 c. Green-rumped Parrotlet 10 10
839 50 c. Copper-rumped Hummingbird (4.95) 10 10
840 $1 Bananaquit (3.3.97) 20 25
841 $2 Violaceous Euphonia (3.3.97) 40 45
844 $5 Green Honeycreeper (6.96) .. .. 1·00 1·10
837/44 .. .. *Set of* 5 1·75 2·00

On some sheets from the April 1995 printing of Nos. 837 and 839 the watermark is indistinct.

For miniature sheet containing the $5 see No. **MS**872.

228 Trinidad Hilton

229 Boa Constrictor

(Des D. Miller. Litho Walsall)

1994 (10 Aug). *Hotels and Lodgings. T* **228** *and similar horiz designs. Multicoloured. W* w **14** *(sideways). P* 14×14½.

848 $3 Type **228** .. .. 90 1·25
849 $3 Sandy Point Village, Tobago .. .. 90 1·25
850 $3 Asa Wright Nature Centre and Lodge 90 1·25
851 $3 M.L.'s Bed and Breakfast .. .. .. 90 1·25
848/51 .. .. *Set of* 4 3·25 4·50

(Des R. Watton. Litho Walsall)

1994 (19 Sept). *Snakes. T* **229** *and similar horiz designs. Multicoloured. W* w **14** *(sideways). P* 14.

852 50 c. Type **229** 20 20
853 $1.25, Vine Snake 45 55
854 $2.50, Bushmaster .. .. 80 1·10
855 $3 Large Coral Snake .. .. 95 1·25
852/5 .. .. *Set of* 4 2·25 2·75

230 "Snowballman" (painting, Mahmoud Alladin)

231 Loggerhead Turtle

(Des D. Miller. Litho Walsall)

1995 (6 Mar). *50th Anniv of the Trinidad Art Society. T* **230** *and similar vert designs. Multicoloured. W* w **16.** *P* 14½.

856 50 c. Type **530** 35 45
857 50 c. "Fishermen" (painting, Sybil Atteck) 35 45
858 50 c. Copper sculpture (Ken Morris) .. 35 45
856/8 .. .. *Set of* 3 95 1·25

(Des D. Miller. Litho Walsall)

1995 (7 Aug). *Conservation. T* **231** *and similar multicoloured designs. W* w **16** *(sideways on horiz designs). P* 14½.

859 $1.25, Type **231** 40 50
860 $2.50, Port-of-Spain Lighthouse (*vert*) .. 80 1·00
861 $3 "Knowsley" (location of Ministry of Foreign Affairs) .. .. 1·00 1·25
859/61 .. .. *Set of* 3 2·00 2·50

232 Brian Lara

233 Red Cross Economy Label on Envelope

(Des S. Noon. Litho Cartor)

1996 (15 May). *Brian Lara (cricketer) Commemoration. T* **232** *and similar vert designs showing cricket scenes. W* w **14.** *P* 13×13½.

862 50 c. multicoloured 20 10
863 $1.25, multicoloured 45 35
864 $2.50, multicoloured .. .. 75 1·00
865 $3 multicoloured .. .. 90 1·25
862/5 .. .. *Set of* 4 2·10 2·40
MS866 62×75 mm. $3.75, multicoloured; $5.01, multicoloured .. .. 2·40 3·00

(Des R. Watton. Litho Cot Printery Ltd, Barbados)

1996 (7 June). *50th Anniv of End of Second World War* (1995). *T* **233** *and similar horiz designs. Multicoloured. W* w **14** *(sideways). P* 14.

867 50 c. Type **233** 20 10
868 $1.25, U.S.S. *Missouri* (battleship), 1944 45 35
869 $2.50, U.S. servicemen playing baseball, 1942 .. .. 75 1·00
870 $3 Fleet Air Arm Fulmar 1 (fighter) .. 90 1·25
867/70 .. .. *Set of* 4 2·10 2·40
MS871 116×85 mm. $3 Fleet Air Arm Grumman Mackinnon G-21C Goose flying boat; $3 U.S. Navy airship .. .. 1·60 1·90

1997 (3 Feb). *"HONG KONG '97" International Stamp Exhibition. Sheet* 130×90 *mm, containing design as No.* 795. *Multicoloured. W* w **14** *(sideways). P* 14.

MS872 $5 Green Honeycreeper .. .. 1·25 1·50

STAMP BOOKLETS

1925.

SB1 2s. booklet containing eight ½d., 1d. and 1½d. (Nos. 218/20) in blocks of 4 .. .. ..

1931–32. *Black on pink covers.*

SB2 1s. 8d. booklet containing eight ½d. and sixteen 1d. (Nos. 218/19) in blocks of 8 .. .. ..
SB3 2s. booklet containing eight ½d., 1d. and 1½d. (Nos. 218/20) in blocks of 8 .. .. ..

1935.

SB4 48 c. booklet containing eight 1, 2 and 3 c. (Nos. 230/2) in blocks of 4 .. .. ..

1970 (8 Dec). *Christmas. Olive-green printed cover inscr* "CHRISTMAS GREETINGS".

SB5 $1.78, booklet containing six 3 c., four 5 c. and two 30 c. and 40 c. (Nos. 386/9) in pairs .. .. 4·00

POSTAGE DUE STAMPS

D 1

D 2

(Typo D.L.R.)

1885 (1 Jan). *Wmk Crown CA. P* 14.

D1 D 1 ½d. slate-black .. .. 15·00 40·00
D2 1d. slate-black .. .. 3·25 15
D3 2d. slate-black .. .. 17·00 15
D4 3d. slate-black .. .. 42·00 40
D5 4d. slate-black .. .. 24·00 3·00
D6 5d. slate-black .. .. 22·00 60
D7 6d. slate-black .. .. 35·00 4·00
D8 8d. slate-black .. .. 48·00 3·00
D9 1s. slate-black .. .. 48·00 5·00
D1/9 .. .. *Set of* 9 £225 50·00

1905–06. *Wmk Mult Crown CA. P* 14.

D10 D 1 1d. slate-black .. .. .. 2·75 15
D11 2d. slate-black .. .. .. 13·00 15
D12 3d. slate-black .. .. .. 6·00 2·25
w. Wmk inverted .. .. ..
D13 4d. slate-black .. .. .. 10·00 9·50
D14 5d. slate-black .. .. .. 10·00 9·00
D15 6d. slate-black .. .. .. 6·00 9·50
D16 8d. slate-black .. .. .. 12·00 14·00
D17 1s. slate-black .. .. .. 12·00 26·00
D10/17 .. .. *Set of* 8 65·00 65·00

1923–45. *Wmk Mult Script CA. P* 14.

D18 D 1 1d. black (1923) .. .. .. 60 1·00
D19 2d. black (1923) .. .. .. 60 1·00
D20 3d. black (1925) .. .. .. 60 1·75
D21 4d. black (1929) .. .. .. 2·00 15·00
D22 5d. black (1944) .. .. .. 29·00 70·00
D23 6d. black (1945) .. .. .. 38·00 24·00
D24 8d. black (1945) .. .. .. 38·00 £110
D25 1s. black (1945) .. .. .. 55·00 85·00
D18/25 .. .. *Set of* 8 £150 £275
D18/25 Optd/Perf "Specimen" .. *Set of* 8 £140

1947 (1 Sept)–**61.** *Values in cents. Wmk Mult Script CA. Ordinary paper. P* 14.

D26 D 1 2 c. black .. .. 95 2·25
a. Chalk-surfaced paper (20.1.53) .. 20 3·25
ab. Error. Crown missing. W **9***a* .. 60·00
ac. Error. St. Edward's Crown. W **9***b* 24·00
D27 4 c. black .. .. 85 3·00
a. Chalk-surfaced paper (10.8.55) .. 1·75 4·00
D28 6 c. black .. .. 95 6·00
a. Chalk-surfaced paper (20.1.53) .. 30 6·50
ab. Error. Crown missing. W **9***a* .. £160
ac. Error. St. Edward's Crown. W **9***b* 55·00
D29 8 c. black .. .. 90 17·00
a. Chalk-surfaced paper (10.9.58) .. 35 14·00
D30 10 c. black .. .. 85 2·75
a. Chalk-surfaced paper (10.8.55) .. 2·75 8·00
D31 12 c. black .. .. 90 15·00
a. Chalk-surfaced paper (20.1.53) .. 40 14·00
ab. Error. Crown missing. W **9***a* .. £190
ac. Error. St. Edward's Crown. W **9***b* 85·00
D32 16 c. black .. .. 2·00 35·00
a. Chalk-surfaced paper (22.8.61) .. 7·00 35·00
D33 24 c. black .. .. 6·00 7·50
a. Chalk-surfaced paper (10.8.55) .. 2·75 26·00
D26/33 .. .. *Set of* 8 12·00 80·00
D26/33a .. .. *Set of* 8 14·00 £100
D26/33 Perf "Specimen" .. .. *Set of* 8 £140

(Litho B.W.)

1969 (25 Nov)–**70.** *Size* 19 × 24 *mm. P* 14 × 13½.

D34 D 2 2 c. pale blue-green .. .. .. 15 2·50
D35 4 c. magenta (1970) .. .. .. 25 3·25
D36 6 c. brown (1970) .. .. .. 50 4·50
D37 8 c. slate-lilac (1970) .. .. .. 65 4·75
D38 10 c. dull red (1970) .. .. .. 65 4·75
D39 12 c. pale orange (1970) .. .. .. 80 4·75
D40 16 c. bright apple-green (1970) .. .. 80 3·25
D41 24 c. grey (1970) .. .. 80 3·50
D42 50 c. grey-blue (1970) .. .. .. 85 4·00
D43 60 c. sage-green (1970) .. .. .. 85 4·00
D34/43 .. .. *Set of* 10 5·50 35·00

(Litho Questa)

1976 (3 May)*–**77.** *Redrawn in smaller size* (17 × 21 *mm*). *P* 13½ × 14.

D44 D 2 2 c. pale blue-green (31.3.77) .. .. 20 1·00
D45 4 c. light claret .. .. 25 1·00
D46 6 c. brown (31.3.77) .. .. .. 25 1·25
D47 8 c. bright lilac (31.3.77) .. .. 30 1·25
D48 10 c. dull red (31.3.77) .. .. .. 30 1·25
D49 12 c. pale orange .. .. 50 1·75
D44/9 .. .. *Set of* 6 1·60 6·75

*The date for the 4 and 12 c. is the local date; the Crown Agents released the stamps on 19 March.

"TOO LATE" STAMPS

A handstamp with the words "TOO LATE" was used upon letters on which a too-late fee had been paid, and was sometimes used for cancelling the stamps on such letters.

OFFICIAL STAMPS

O S (O 1) OFFICIAL (O 2) OFFICIAL (O 3)

1894. *Optd with Type* O **1.** *(a) On Nos.* 106/12. *Wmk Crown CA. P* 14.

O1 **10** ½d. dull green .. .. 30·00 50·00
O2 1d. carmine .. .. 32·00 55·00
O3 2½d. bright blue .. .. 42·00 80·00
O4 4d. grey .. .. 42·00 85·00
O5 6d. olive-black .. .. 42·00 85·00
O6 1s. orange-brown .. .. 60·00 £110

(b) On No. 87. *Wmk Crown CC. P* 12½.

O7 **5** 5s. rose-lake £140 £300

1909. *Nos.* 133 *and* 135 *optd with Type* O **2.** *Wmk Mult Crown CA. P* 14.

O8 **11** ½d. blue-green .. .. 40 4·00
O9 1d. rose-red .. .. 40 4·00
a. Opt double .. .. — £225
b. Opt vertical .. .. 55·00
c. Opt inverted .. .. — £160

1910. *No.* 146 *optd with Type* O **2.** *Wmk Mult Crown CA. P* 14.

O10 **14** ½d. green .. .. 2·50 4·00

1913. *No.* 149 *optd with Type* O **3.**

O11 **17** ½d. green .. .. 60 3·75
a. Opt vertical .. ..

OFFICIAL (O 4) OFFICIAL (O 5) OFFICIAL (O 6)

1914. *No.* 149 *optd with Type* O **4.**

O12 **17** ½d. green .. .. 1·10 8·00

1914–17. *No.* 149 *optd with Type* O **5** *(without stop).*

O13 **17** ½d. green .. .. 2·00 9·00
a. Blue-green (thick paper) (1917) .. 40 6·00

1916. *No.* 149*a optd with Type* O **5** *(with stop).*

O14 **17** ½d. yellow-green .. .. .. 60 1·25
a. Opt double .. .. .. 24·00

1917 (22 Aug). *No.* 149 *optd with Type* O **6.**

O15 **17** ½d. green .. .. 1·60 10·00
a. Yellow-green .. .. .. 2·25 13·00
b. Blue-green (thick paper) .. .. 75 11·00

Tristan Da Cunha

Although first settled in 1817 no surviving mail is known from Tristan da Cunha until two whaler's letters written in 1836 and 1843, these being carried home in other whaling ships. Then there is a long gap until the late 1800's when other letters are known—surprisingly only some seven in number, up to 1908 when the first of the island cachet handstamps came into use.

The collecting of postal history material from 1908 to 1952, when Tristan's first stamps were issued, revolves around the numerous cachets of origin which were struck on mail from the island during these 44 years. The handstamps producing these cachets were supplied over the years by various people particularly interested in the island and the islanders, and were mostly used by the clergymen who volunteered to go and serve as the community's ministers.

The postal cachets are illustrated below. The use of the different cachets on mail frequently overlapped, at one period in 1930 there were five different types of handstamp in use. As there was no official source for providing them they appeared on the island from various donors; then disappeared without trace once they became worn out. Only one of these early rubber handstamps has apparently survived, Cachet Va.

Covers bearing the cachets are recognised collector's items, but are difficult to value in general terms. As elsewhere the value is discounted by poor condition of the cover, and may be increased by use on a scarce date or with additional postal markings.

Cachet Types V and VII on cover are the commonest, Type Va, used only for three months, and Type IVa are the scarcest, equalling the scarcest use of Type I examples. All cacheted covers, particularly if non-philatelic, are desirable forerunner items. Even a philatelic cover of Type V is, at present, worth in the region of £35.

Dates given are of the first recorded use.

Cachet I   Cachet II

Cat. No.			*Value on cover*
C1	**1908** (May).	Cachet I	*from* £4000
C2	**1919** (31 July).	Cachet II	*from* £425

Cachet III

C3	**1921** (8 Feb).	Cachet III	*from* £275

Cachet IVa

C4	**1927** (1 Oct).	Cachet IV (*as* IVa, *but without centre label*)	*from* £800
C5	**1928** (28 Oct).	Cachet IVa	*from* £5500

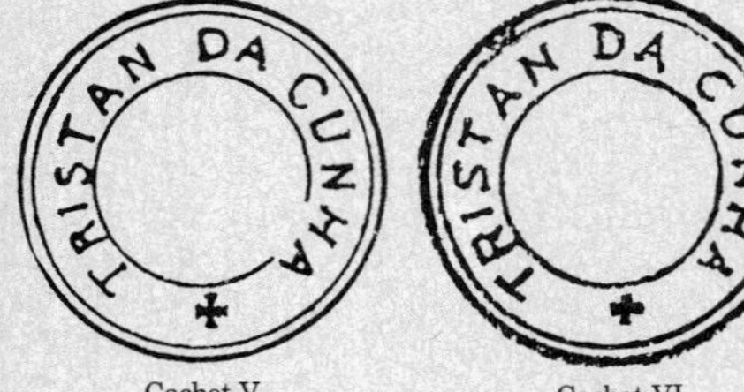

Cachet V   Cachet VI

C6	**1929** (24 Feb).	Cachet V	*from* 35·00
C7	**1929** (15 May).	Cachet Va (*as* V, *but without break in inner ring. Shows* "T" "C" *and* "N" *damaged*)	*from* £6500
C8	**1936** (Aug).	Cachet VI	*from* 60·00

Cachet VII

C9	**1936** (1 Feb).	Cachet VII	*from* 22·00

During World War II there was little mail from the island as its function as a meteorological station was cloaked by security. Such covers as are known are generally struck with the "tombstone" naval censor mark and postmarked "maritime mail" or have South African postal markings. A few philatelic items from early in the war bearing cachets exist, but this usage was soon stopped by the military commander and the handstamps were put away until peace returned. Covers from the period would be worth from £75 to, at least, £350.

Cachet VIII

C10	**1946** (8 May).	Cachet VIII	*from* 85·00

Cachet IX

C11	**1948** (2 Feb).	Cachet IX	*from* 45·00

Cachet X

C12	**1948** (29 Feb).	Cachet X	*from* 55·00

Cachet XI

Cachet XII

RESETTLEMENT
SURVEY - 1962

Cachet XIII

Cachets XI to XIII from the 1961/63 "volcano eruption" and "return to the island" period vary in value from £30 to £120, due to philatelic usage on the one hand and scarce mailings from the small survey parties on shore during this period on the other.

**TRISTAN
DA CUNHA**

(1)

1952 (1 Jan). *Nos.* 131, 135a/40 *and* 149/51 *of St. Helena optd with T* 1.

1	½d. violet	15	85
2	1d. black and green	50	1·25
3	1½d. black and carmine	50	1·25
4	2d. black and scarlet	50	1·50
5	3d. grey	70	1·25
6	4d. ultramarine	3·00	2·00
7	6d. light blue	4·00	2·50
8	8d. sage-green	3·00	3·00
9	1s. sepia	4·00	2·00
10	2s. 6d. maroon	19·00	14·00
11	5s. chocolate	23·00	23·00
12	10s. purple	40·00	45·00
1/12	*Set of* 12	85·00	85·00

1953 (2 June). *Coronation. As No.* 153 *of Jamaica.*

13	3d. black and grey-green	50	1·25

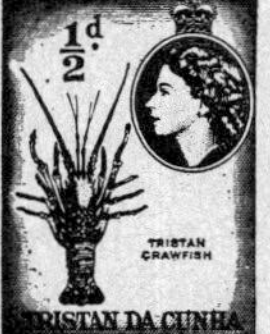

2 Tristan Crawfish

3 Carting Flax for Thatching

(Recess D.L.R.)

1954 (2 Jan). *T* **2/3** *and similar designs. Wmk Mult Script CA. P* 12½ × 13 (*horiz*) *or* 13 × 12½ (*vert*).

14	½d. red and deep brown	10	10
15	1d. sepia and bluish green	10	40
16	1½d. black and reddish purple	1·75	90
17	2d. grey-violet and brown-orange	30	20
18	2½d. black and carmine-red	1·50	60
19	3d. ultramarine and olive-green	80	75
20	4d. turquoise-blue and deep blue	90	90
21	5d. emerald and black	90	70
22	6d. deep green and violet	90	75
23	9d. reddish violet and Venetian red	90	45
24	1s. deep yellow-green and sepia	90	45
25	2s. 6d. deep brown and light blue	24·00	10·00
26	5s. black and red-orange	48·00	16·00
27	10s. brown-orange and purple	30·00	20·00
14/27	*Set of* 14	£100	45·00

Designs: *Vert*—1½d. Rockhopper Penguin; 3d. Island longboat. *Horiz*—2d. Big Beach factory; 2½d. Yellow-nosed Albatross; 4d. Tristan from the south-west; 5d. Girls on donkeys; 6d. Inaccessible Island from Tristan; 9d. Nightingale Island; 1s. St. Mary's Church; 2s. 6d. Southern Elephant-Seal at Gough Island; 5s. Inaccessible Island Rail; 10s. Island spinning wheel.

16 Starfish

17 Concha Wrasse

(Des Mr. and Mrs. G. F. Harris. Recess Waterlow)

1960 (1 Feb). *Marine Life. Vert designs as T* **16/17**. *W* w **12**. *P* 13.

28	½d. black and orange	15	40
29	1d. black and bright purple	15	20
30	1½d. black and light turquoise-blue	15	50
31	2d. black and bluish green	20	50
32	2½d. black and sepia	25	40
33	3d. black and brown-red	40	20
34	4d. black and yellow-olive	40	40
35	5d. black and orange-yellow	55	40
36	6d. black and blue	70	40
37	9d. black and rose-carmine	75	40
38	1s. black and light brown	90	30
39	2s. 6d. black and ultramarine	10·00	15·00
40	5s. black and light emerald	13·00	20·00
41	10s. black and violet	38·00	40·00
28/41	*Set of* 14	55·00	70·00

Designs:—1½d. Two-spined Thornfish; 2d. Atlantic Saury; 2½d. Bristle Snipefish; 3d. Tristan Crawfish; 4d. False Jacopever; 5d. Five-fingered Morwong; 6d. Long-finned Scad; 9d. Christophersen's Medusafish; 1s. Blue Medusafish; 2s. 6d. Snoek; 5s. Blue Shark; 10s. Black Right Whale.

NEW INFORMATION

The editor is always interested to correspond with people who have new information that will improve or correct the Catalogue.

1961 (15 Apr). *As Nos.* 28/30 *and* 32/41 *but values in South African decimal currency.*

42 ½ c. black and orange (as ½d.) 10 70
43 1 c. black and bright purple (as 1d.) . . 15 70
44 1½ c. black and light turquoise-blue (as 1½d.) 35 70
45 2 c. black and sepia (as 2½d.) 40 70
46 2½ c. black and brown-red (as 3d.) 50 70
47 3 c. black and yellow-olive (as 4d.) . . 65 70
48 4 c. black and orange-yellow (as 5d.) . . 80 70
49 5 c. black and blue (as 6d) 85 70
50 7½ c. black and rose-carmine (as 9d.) . . 90 70
51 10 c. black and light brown (as 1s.) . . 1·75 70
52 25 c. black and ultramarine (as 2s. 6d.) . . 6·00 11·00
53 50 c. black and light emerald (as 5s.) . . 14·00 24·00
54 1 r. black and violet (as 10s.) . . . . 38·00 42·00
42/54 . . . . *Set of* 13 55·00 70·00

Following a volcanic eruption the island was evacuated on 10 October 1961, but resettled in 1963.

TRISTAN DA CUNHA RESETTLEMENT 1963

(30)

1963 (12 Apr). *Tristan Resettlement. As Nos.* 176/88 *of St. Helena, but Wmk Mult Script CA (sideways on* 1d., 2d., 7d., 10d., 2s. 6d., 10s), *optd with T* **30**.

55 1d. bright blue, dull violet, yellow & carmine 15 50
56 1½d. yellow, green, black and light drab . . 20 30
57 2d. scarlet and grey 25 50
58 3d. light blue, black, pink and deep blue . . 30 50
a. Black printed double* £275
w. Wmk inverted . . . .
59 4½d. yellow-green, green, brown and grey . . 50 50
60 6d. red, sepia and light yellow-olive . . 85 30
61 7d. red-brown, black and violet 50 30
62 10d. brown-purple and light blue 50 30
63 1s. greenish yellow, bluish green & brown 50 30
64 1s. 6d. grey, black and slate-blue . . 3·00 60
65 2s. 6d. red, pale yellow and turquoise . . 1·00 45
66 5s. yellow, brown and green . . . . 6·00 1·25
w. Wmk inverted . . . . 65·00
67 10s. orange-red, black and blue . . . . 6·50 1·25
55/67 . . . . . . *Set of* 13 18·00 6·00

*No. 58a shows the outline round the Queen's head printed double.

1963 (2 Oct). *Freedom from Hunger. As No.* 80 *of Lesotho.*

68 1s. 6d. carmine 50 30

1964 (1 Feb). *Red Cross Centenary. As Nos.* 203/4 *of Jamaica.*

69 3d. red and black 25 15
70 1s. 6d. red and blue 50 20

31 South Atlantic Map

32 Queen Elizabeth II

(Queen's portrait by Anthony Buckley. Des, eng and recess B.W.)

1965 (17 Feb)–**67**. *Designs as T* **31/2**. *W w* **12** *(sideways on* £1). *P* 11½ × 11 *(vert) or* 11 × 11½ *(horiz).*

71 ½d. black and ultramarine 15 15
72 1d. black and emerald-green 30 15
73 1½d. black and blue 30 15
74 2d. black and purple 30 15
75 3d. black and turquoise-blue . . 30 15
75*a* 4d. black and orange (1.9.67) . . 5·50 4·00
76 4½d. black and brown 30 15
77 6d. black and green 30 15
78 7d. black and rose-red 30 30
79 10d. black and chocolate 30 55
80 1s. black and carmine 30 30
81 1s. 6d. black and yellow-olive . . 3·50 2·50
82 2s. 6d. black and orange-brown . . 2·75 2·75
83 5s. black and violet . . . . 5·00 3·50
84 10s. deep blue and carmine . . . . 1·75 1·25
84*a* 10s. black and deep turquoise-blue (1.9.67) 17·00 15·00
84*b* £1 deep blue and orange-brown (1.9.67) . . 17·00 18·00
71/84*b* . . . . . . *Set of* 17 48·00 45·00

Designs: *Horiz as T* **31**—1d. Flagship of Tristão da Cunha, 1506; 1½d. *Heemstede* (Dutch East Indiaman), 1643; 2d. *Edward* (American whaling ship), 1864; 3d. *Shenandoah* (Confederate warship), 1862; 4d. H.M.S. *Challenger* (survey ship), 1873; 4½d. H.M.S. *Galatea* (screw frigate), 1867; 6d. H.M.S. *Cilicia* (transport), 1942; 7d. Royal Yacht *Britannia*; 10d. H.M.S. *Leopard* (frigate); 1s. *Tjisadane* (liner); 1s. 6d. *Tristania* (crayfish trawler); 2s. 6d. *Boissevain* (cargo liner); 5s. *Bornholm* (liner); 10s. (No. 84*a*), *R.S.A.* (research vessel). *Vert*—10s. (No. 84), £1, Type **32**.

1965 (11 May*). *I.T.U. Centenary. As Nos.* 98/9 *of Lesotho.*

85 3d. orange-red and grey 30 15
86 6d. reddish violet and yellow-orange . . 40 15

*This is the local date of issue; the stamps were not released in London until 17 May.

1965 (25 Oct). *International Co-operation Year. As Nos.* 100/1 *of Lesotho.*

87 1d. reddish purple and turquoise-green . . 20 15
88 6d. deep bluish green and lavender 75 25

1966 (24 Jan). *Churchill Commemoration. As Nos.* 102/5 *of Lesotho.*

89 1d. new blue 35 30
a. Value omitted £425
90 3d. deep green . . . . . . 1·50 45
91 6d. brown . . . . . . 2·00 55
92 1s. 6d. bluish violet . . . . 2·25 65
89/92 . . . . . . *Set of* 4 5·50 1·75

No. 89a was caused by misplacement of the gold and also shows the country inscription moved to the right.

45 H.M.S. *Falmouth* (frigate) at Tristan and Soldier of 1816

(Des V. Whiteley. Litho Harrison)

1966 (15 Aug). *150th Anniv of Tristan Garrison. W w* **12** *(sideways*). P* 14½.

93 **45** 3d. multicoloured 20 10
w. Wmk Crown to right of CA . . 4·00
94 6d. multicoloured 20 15
95 1s. 6d. multicoloured 30 25
96 2s. 6d. multicoloured 30 25
93/6 . . . . . . *Set of* 4 90 65

*The normal sideways watermark shows Crown to left of CA, *as seen from the back of the stamp.*

1966 (1 Oct*). *World Cup Football Championships. As Nos.* 57/8 *of Pitcairn Islands.*

97 3d. violet, yellow-grn, lake & yell-brn 20 10
98 2s. 6d. chocolate, blue-grn, lake & yellow-brn 50 20

*Released in St. Helena on 1 July in error.

1966 (1 Oct). *Inauguration of W.H.O. Headquarters, Geneva. As Nos.* 185/6 *of Montserrat.*

99 6d. black, yellow-green and light blue . . 50 30
100 5s. black, light purple and yellow-brown . . 75 70

1966 (1 Dec). *20th Anniv of U.N.E.S.C.O. As Nos.* 342/4 *of Mauritius.*

101 10d. slate-violet, red, yellow and orange . . 50 15
w. Wmk Crown to right of CA . . . . 32·00
102 1s. 6d. orange-yellow, violet and deep olive 60 20
103 2s. 6d. black, bright purple and orange . . 70 25
101/3 . . . . . . *Set of* 3 1·60 55

*The normal sideways watermark shows Crown to left of CA, *as seen from the back of the stamp.*

46 Calshot Harbour

(Des V. Whiteley. Litho D.L.R.)

1967 (2 Jan). *Opening of Calshot Harbour. P* 14 × 14½.

104 **46** 6d. multicoloured 10 10
105 10d. multicoloured 10 10
106 1s. 6d. multicoloured 10 10
107 2s. 6d. multicoloured 15 15
104/7 . . . . . . *Set of* 4 30 30

(47)

48 Prince Alfred, First Duke of Edinburgh

1967 (10 May). *No.* 76 *surch with T* **47**.

108 4d. on 4½d. black and brown 10 10

(Des M. Goaman. Litho Harrison)

1967 (10 July). *Centenary of First Duke of Edinburgh's Visit to Tristan. W w* **12**. *P* 14½.

109 **48** 3d. multicoloured 10 10
110 6d. multicoloured 10 10
111 1s. 6d. multicoloured 10 10
112 2s. 6d. multicoloured 15 10
109/12 . . . . . . *Set of* 4 30 20

49 Wandering Albatross

(Des V. Whiteley. Photo Harrison)

1968 (15 May). *Birds. T* **49** *and similar horiz designs. Multicoloured. W w* **12**. *P* 14 × 14½.

113 4d. Type **49** 40 20
114 1s. Wilkins's Finch 45 20
115 1s. 6d. Tristan Thrush 50 35
116 2s. 6d. Greater Shearwater 90 45
113/16 . . . . . . *Set of* 4 2·00 1·10

53 Union Jack and Dependency Flag

(Des Jennifer Toombs. Litho D.L.R.)

1968 (1 Nov). *30th Anniv of Tristan da Cunha as a Dependency of St. Helena. T* **53** *and similar horiz design. W w* **12** *(sideways). P* 14.

117 **53** 6d. multicoloured 10 15
118 – 9d. sepia, blue and turquoise-blue . . 10 20
119 **53** 1s. 6d. multicoloured 15 25
120 – 2s. 6d. carmine, blue and turquoise-blue 20 25
117/20 . . . . . . *Set of* 4 50 75

Design:—9d., 2s. 6d. St. Helena and Tristan on chart.

55 Frigate

(Des and recess B.W.)

1969 (1 June). *Clipper Ships. T* **55** *and similar horiz designs. W w* **12**. *P* 11 × 11½.

121 4d. new blue 40 20
122 1s. carmine (full-rigged ship) . . 40 25
123 1s. 6d. blue-green (barque) 45 50
124 2s. 6d. chocolate (full-rigged clipper) . . 50 55
121/4 . . . . . . *Set of* 4 1·60 1·40

59 Sailing Ship off Tristan da Cunha

(Des Jennifer Toombs. Litho Format)

1969 (1 Nov). *United Society for the Propagation of the Gospel. T* **59** *and similar horiz designs. Multicoloured. W w* **12** *(sideways). P* 14½ × 14.

125 4d. Type **59** 30 20
126 9d. Islanders going to first Gospel service . . 15 20
127 1s. 6d. Landing of the first minister . . 15 25
128 2s. 6d. Procession outside St. Mary's Church 20 30
125/8 . . . . . . *Set of* 4 70 85

63 Globe and Red Cross Emblem

(Des and litho B.W.)

1970 (1 June). *Centenary of British Red Cross. T* **63** *and similar designs. W w* **12** *(sideways on vert designs). P* 13.

129 **63** 4d. lt emerald, scarlet & dp bluish green 10 15
130 9d. bistre, scarlet and deep bluish green 15 20
131 – 1s. 9d. light drab, scarlet & ultramarine 25 30
132 – 2s. 6d. reddish purple, scarlet & ultram 30 40
129/32 . . . . . . *Set of* 4 70 95

Design: *Vert*—1s. 9d., 2s. 6d., Union Jack and Red Cross Flag.

MINIMUM PRICE

The minimum price quote is 10p which represents a handling charge rather than a basis for valuing common stamps. For further notes about prices see introductory pages.

64 Crawfish and Longboat

(65)

(Des Harrison. Litho Enschedé)

1970 (1 Nov). *Crawfish Industry. T* **64** *and similar horiz design. Multicoloured.* W w **12**. *P* 12½ × 13.

133 4d. Type **64** 20 20
134 10d. Packing and storing Crawfish 25 25
135 1s. 6d. Type **64** 35 45
136 2s. 6d. As 10d. 40 50
133/6 .. .. *Set of* 4 1·10 1·25

1971 (14 Feb).* *Decimal Currency. As Nos.* 72/4, 75*a*, 77/83 *and* 84*a surch as T* **65**, *by B.W. in typo. Glazed paper.*

137 ½p. on 1d. black and emerald-green .. 15 15
138 1p. on 2d. black and purple 15 15
139 1½p. on 4d. black and orange 30 15
140 2½p. on 6d. black and green 30 15
141 3p. on 7d. black and rose-red 30 15
142 4p. on 10d. black and chocolate 30 20
143 5p. on 1s. black and carmine 30 20
144 7½p. on 1s. 6d. black and yellow-olive .. 1·75 1·75
145 12½p. on 2s. 6d. black and orange-brown .. 2·75 2·50
146 15p. on 1½d. black and blue .. .. 2·75 3·00
147 25p. on 5s. black and violet .. .. 2·75 5·50
148 50p. on 10s. black and deep turquoise-blue 5·00 11·00
137/48 .. .. *Set of* 12 15·00 22·00

*This was the local release date, but the Crown Agents issued the stamps one day later.

66 *Quest*

(Des V. Whiteley. Litho J.W.)

1971 (1 June). *50th Anniv of Shackleton–Rowett Expedition. T* **66** *and similar horiz designs.* W w **12** (*sideways*). *P* 13½ × 14.

149 1½p. multicoloured 80 30
150 4p. sepia, pale green and apple-green .. 80 40
151 7½p. black, bright purple and pale green .. 80 40
152 12½p. multicoloured 90 45
149/52 .. .. *Set of* 4 3·00 1·40

Designs:—4p. Presentation of Scout Troop flag; 7½p. Cachet on pair of 6d. G.B. stamps; 12½p. Shackleton, postmarks and longboat taking mail to the *Quest*.

67 H.M.S. *Victory* at Trafalgar and Thomas Swain catching Nelson

68 Cow Pudding

(Des R. Granger Barrett. Litho Questa)

1971 (1 Nov). *Island Families. T* **67** *and similar horiz designs showing ships and the names of families associated with them. Multicoloured.* W w **12** (*sideways*). *P* 13½.

153 1½p. Type **67** 20 40
154 2½p. *Emily of Stonington* (American schooner) (P. W. Green) 30 50
155 4p. *Italia* (barque) (Lavarello and Repetto) 35 60
156 7½p. H.M.S. *Falmouth* (frigate) (William Glass) 45 70
157 12½p. American whaling ship (Rogers and Hagan) 50 85
153/7 .. .. *Set of* 5 1·60 2·75

(Des M. and Sylvia Goaman. Recess and litho B.W. (50p., £1); Litho A. & M. (others))

1972 (29 Feb). *T* **68** *and similar multicoloured designs showing flowering plants.* W w **12** (*sideways** *on horiz designs*). *P* 13.

158 ½p. Type **68** 20 15
w. Wmk inverted 30 30
159 1p. Peak Berry 40 15
w. Wmk inverted 40 40
160 1½p. Sand Flower (*horiz*) 40 20
161 2½p. N.Z. Flax (*horiz*) 40 20
w. Wmk Crown to right of CA 60 60
162 3p. Island Tree 40 20
w. Wmk inverted 60 60
163 4p. Bog Fern 40 25
w. Wmk inverted 75 75
164 5p. Dog Catcher 85 25
w. Wmk inverted .. .. .. 1·25 1·00
165 7½p. Celery .. .. 3·00 50
w. Wmk inverted .. .. .. 3·25 1·25
166 12½p. Pepper Tree .. .. .. 1·75 60
w. Wmk inverted .. .. .. 27·00 27·00
167 25p. Foul Berry (*horiz*) .. .. .. 1·75 1·50
w. Wmk Crown to right of CA .. .. 4·00 4·00
168 50p. Tussock .. .. 6·50 1·75
169 £1 Tussac (*horiz*) .. .. .. 4·00 2·50
158/69 .. .. *Set of* 12 18·00 7·50

*The normal sideways watermark shows Crown to left of CA, *as seen from the back of the stamp.*

69 Launching

(Des R. Svensson. Litho Walsall)

1972 (1 June). *Tristan Longboats. T* **69** *and similar multicoloured designs.* W w **12** (*sideways on* 2½*p. and* 4*p.*). *P* 14.

170 2½p. Type **69** 15 10
171 4p. Under oars 20 10
172 7½p. Coxswain Arthur Repetto (*vert*) .. 25 15
173 12½p. Under sail for Nightingale Island (*vert*) 30 20
170/73 .. .. *Set of* 4 80 50

70 Tristan Thrushes and Wandering Albatrosses

(Des (from photographs by D. Groves) and photo Harrison)

1972 (20 Nov). *Royal Silver Wedding. Multicoloured; background colours given.* W w **12**. *P* 14 × 14½.

174 **70** 2½p. red-brown 25 30
w. Wmk inverted .. .. .. 9·00
175 7½p. dull ultramarine 10 30
w. Wmk inverted .. .. .. 80·00

71 Church Altar

(Des J. Cooter. Litho Questa)

1973 (8 July). *Golden Jubilee of St. Mary's Church.* W w **12**. *P* 13½.

176 **71** 25p. multicoloured 40 40

72 H.M.S. *Challenger's* Laboratory

(Des V. Whiteley Studio. Litho Questa)

1973 (15 Oct). *Centenary of H.M.S. Challenger's Visit. T* **72** *and similar horiz designs. Multicoloured.* W w **12**. *P* 13½.

177 4p. Type **72** 20 25
178 5p. H.M.S. *Challenger* off Tristan .. 20 25
179 7½p. *Challenger's* pinnace off Nightingale Is 20 30
180 12½p. Survey route 30 40
177/80 .. .. *Set of* 4 80 1·10
MS181 145 × 96 mm. Nos. 177/80 .. .. 1·10 3·50

73 Approaching English Port

(Des Jennifer Toombs. Litho Questa)

1973 (10 Nov). *Tenth Anniv of Return to Tristan da Cunha. T* **73** *and similar horiz designs. Multicoloured (except 4p.).* W w **12**. *P* 14.

182 4p. Type **73** (reddish brn, lemon & gold) 20 25
183 5p. Survey party 20 25
184 7½p. Embarking on *Bornholm* 20 35
w. Wmk inverted £140
185 12½p. Approaching Tristan 30 45
w. Wmk inverted .. .. .. 1·50
182/5 .. .. *Set of* 4 80 1·10

1973 (14 Nov). *Royal Wedding. As Nos.* 322/3 *of Montserrat.*

186 7½p. bright blue 15 10
187 12½p. light turquoise-green 15 10

74 Rockhopper Penguin and Egg

(Des R. Granger Barrett. Litho Questa)

1974 (1 May). *Rockhopper Penguins. T* **74** *and similar horiz designs.* W w **12**. *P* 14.

188 2½p. Type **74** .. .. 3·00 90
189 5p. Rockhopper Colony, Inaccessible Island 3·50 1·25
190 7½p. Penguin fishing .. .. .. 4·00 1·40
w. Wmk inverted .. .. ..
191 25p. Adult and fledgling .. .. .. 4·50 1·75
188/91 .. .. *Set of* 4 13·50 4·75

75 Map with Rockhopper Penguin and Wandering Albatross

(Des J.W. Litho Questa)

1974 (1 Oct). *"The Lonely Island". Sheet* 154×104 *mm.* W w **12** (*sideways**). *P* 13½.

MS192 **75** 35p. multicoloured .. .. 2·75 3·25
w. Wmk Crown to right of CA .. £200

*The normal sideways watermark shows Crown to left of CA, *as seen from the back of the stamp.*

76 Blenheim Palace

(Des Sylvia Goaman. Litho Questa)

1974 (30 Nov). *Birth Centenary of Sir Winston Churchill. T* **76** *and similar horiz design.* W w **14** (*sideways*). *P* 14.

193 7½p. pale yellow and black 10 10
194 25p. black, sepia and grey 30 25
MS195 93 × 93 mm. Nos. 193/4. W w **12** (sideways) 55 1·60

Design:—25p. Churchill with Queen Elizabeth II.

77 *Plocamium fuscorubrum*

(Des Sylvia Goaman. Litho Harrison)

1975 (16 Apr). *Sea Plants. T* **77** *and similar horiz designs.* W w **12** (*sideways**). *P* 13×13½.

196 4p. rose-carmine, light lilac and black .. 15 10
197 5p. apple-green, light violet-blue and deep bluish green 15 15
198 10p. red-orange, stone and brown-purple .. 20 15
w. Wmk Crown to right of CA .. .. 75·00
199 20p. multicoloured 30 25
196/9 .. .. *Set of* 4 70 60

Designs:—5p. *Ulva lactua*; 10p. *Epymenia flabellata*; 20p. *Macrocystis pyrifera*.

*The normal sideways watermark shows Crown to left of CA, *as seen from the back of the stamp.*

78 Killer Whale

(Des G. Drummond. Litho Walsall)

1975 (1 Nov). *Whales. T* **78** *and similar horiz designs. Multicoloured.* W w **12** (*sideways*). *P* 13½.

200	2p. Type **78**	65	35
201	3p. Rough-toothed Dolphin	65	35
202	5p. Black Right Whale	80	40
203	20p. Fin Whale	1·60	85
200/3	*Set of* 4	3·25	1·75

79 ½d. Stamp of 1952 — 80 Island Cottage

(Des C. Abbott. Litho J.W.)

1976 (27* May). *Festival of Stamps, London. T* **79** *and similar designs.* W w **14** (*sideways on* 5 *and* 25*p*). *P* 13½.

204	5p. black, violet and light lilac	20	15
205	9p. black, deep green and turquoise	25	15
206	25p. multicoloured	40	40
204/6	*Set of* 3	75	65

Designs: *Vert*—9p. 1953 Coronation stamp. *Horiz*—25p. Mail carrier *Tristania II*.

*This is the local date of issue. The stamps were released by the Crown Agents on 4 May.

For miniature sheet containing No. 206 see No. **MS**218 of Ascension.

(Des C. Abbott. Litho Questa)

1976 (4 Oct). *Paintings by Roland Svensson* (*1st series*). *T* **80** *and similar multicoloured designs.* W w **14** (*sideways on* 5*p.*, 10*p. and* **MS**211). *P* 14.

207	3p. Type **80**	15	15
208	5p. The potato patches (*horiz*)	15	15
209	10p. Edinburgh from the sea (*horiz*)	20	20
210	20p. Huts, Nightingale Island	30	35
207/10	*Set of* 4	70	70
MS211	125 × 112 mm. Nos. 207/10	90	1·75

See also Nos. 234/8 and 272/6.

81 The Royal Standard

(Des and litho J.W.)

1977 (7 Feb). *Silver Jubilee. T* **81** *and similar horiz designs. Multicoloured.* W w **14** (*sideways*). *P* 13.

212	10p. Royal Yacht *Britannia*	15	20
213	15p. Type **81**	15	20
214	25p. Royal family	20	20
212/14	*Set of* 3	45	55

For Nos. 213/14 surcharged, see Nos. 232/3.

82 H.M.S. *Eskimo* (frigate)

(Des L. Curtis. Litho Walsall)

1977 (1 Oct). *Ships' Crests. T* **82** *and similar horiz designs. Multicoloured.* W w **14** (*sideways*). *P* 14.

215	5p. Type **82**	15	15
216	10p. H.M.S. *Naiad* (frigate)	20	15
217	15p. H.M.S. *Jaguar* (frigate)	25	25
218	20p. H.M.S. *London* (destroyer)	30	30
215/18	*Set of* 4	80	75
MS219	142×140 mm. Nos. 215/18	1·00	1·50

83 Great-winged Petrel

(Des BG Studio. Litho Walsall)

1977 (1 Dec). *Multicoloured designs as T* **83** *showing birds.* W w **14** (*sideways on* 1 *and* 2*p.*). *P* 13½.

220	1p. Type **83**	15	40
221	2p. White-faced Storm Petrel	20	65
222	3p. Hall's Giant Petrel	20	65
223	4p. Soft-plumaged Petrel	60	80
224	5p. Wandering Albatross	60	80
225	10p. Kerguelen Petrel	60	80
226	15p. Swallow-tailed Tern	60	1·00
227	20p. Greater Shearwater	1·00	1·00
228	25p. Broad-billed Prion	1·25	1·00
229	50p. Great Skua	1·50	1·00
230	£1 Common Diving Petrel	2·00	2·00
231	£2 Yellow-nosed Albatross	4·50	3·25
220/31	*Set of* 12	12·00	12·00

The 3p. to £2 are vertical designs.

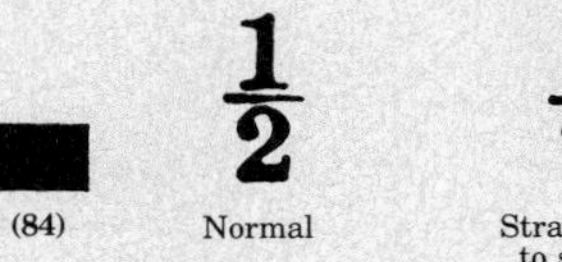

4p — (84) — Normal — Straight top to serif in "½" (Pl 1C R. 5/1–5)

1978 (19 Jan*). *Provisional definitives. Nos.* 213/14 *surch as T* **84**.

232	4p. on 15p. Type **81**	1·50	4·00
233	7½p. on 25p. Royal family	1·50	4·00
	a. Straight top to serif	13·00	

*This is the local date of issue. Covers dated 26 November 1977 are philatelic mail forwarded to the island for cancellation, the stamps having been released in London on 31 October 1977. Supplies for the island population did not arrive until 19 January.

(Des C. Abbott. Litho Questa)

1978 (1 Mar). *Paintings by Roland Svensson* (*2nd series*). *Horiz designs as T* **80**. *Multicoloured.* W w **14** (*sideways**). *P* 14.

234	5p. St. Mary's Church	15	15
235	10p. Longboats	15	15
236	15p. A Tristan home	20	25
237	20p. The harbour, 1970	20	25
	w. Wmk Crown to right of CA	70·00	
234/7	*Set of* 4	65	70
MS238	115×128 mm. Nos. 234/7	1·10	2·00

*The normal sideways watermark shows Crown to left of CA, *as seen from the back of the stamp.*

85 King's Bull — 86 Sodalite

(Des Jennifer Toombs. Litho Questa)

1978 (21 Apr). *25th Anniv of Coronation. T* **85** *and similar vert designs.* W w **14**. *P* 15.

239	25p. bistre, bright violet and silver	25	30
	aw. Wmk inverted	17·00	
	b. Sheetlet. Nos. 239/41×2	1·10	
	bw. Wmk inverted	90·00	
240	25p. multicoloured	25	30
	aw. Wmk inverted	17·00	
241	25p. bistre, bright violet and silver	25	30
	aw. Wmk inverted	17·00	
239/41	*Set of* 3	65	30

Designs:—No. 239, Type **85**; No. 240, Queen Elizabeth II; No. 241, Tristan crawfish.

Nos. 239/41 were printed together in small sheets of 6, containing two *se-tenant* strips of 3, with horizontal gutter margin between.

(Des J.W. Litho Questa)

1978 (9 June). *Local Minerals. T* **86** *and similar horiz designs. Multicoloured.* W w **14** (*sideways*). *P* 13½.

242	3p. Type **86**	25	20
243	5p. Aragonite	30	25
244	10p. Sulphur	45	30
245	20p. Lava containing pyroxene crystal	65	35
242/5	*Set of* 4	1·50	1·00

87 Two-spined Thornfish

(Des R. Granger Barrett. Litho Harrison)

1978 (29 Sept). *Fish. T* **87** *and similar horiz designs.* W w **14** (*sideways*). *P* 14.

246	5p. black, yellow-brown and yellow-green	10	10
247	10p. black, yellow-brown and emerald	15	15
248	15p. multicoloured	20	20
249	20p. multicoloured	30	25
246/9	*Set of* 4	65	60

Designs:–10p. Five-fingered Morwong; 15p. Concha Wrasse; 20p. Tristan Jacopever.

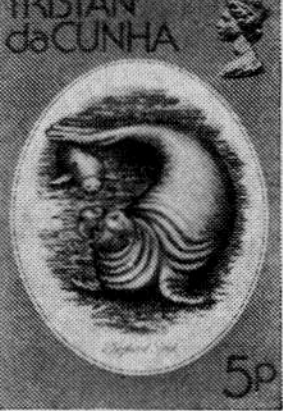

88 R.F.A. *Orangeleaf* (tanker) — 89 Southern Elephant Seal

(Des R. Granger Barrett. Litho Cartor)

1978 (24 Nov). *Royal Fleet Auxiliary Vessels. T* **88** *and similar horiz designs. Multicoloured.* W w **14** (*sideways*). *P* 12½ × 12.

250	5p. Type **88**	15	10
251	10p. R.F.A. *Tarbatness* (store carrier)	20	10
252	20p. R.F.A. *Tidereach* (tanker)	30	25
253	25p. R.F.A. *Reliant* (store carrier)	35	30
250/3	*Set of* 4	90	65
MS254	136×140 mm. Nos. 250/3 (Wmk inverted)	90	2·75

(Des J.W. Litho Questa)

1979 (3 Jan). *Wildlife Conservation. T* **89** *and similar vert designs. Multicoloured.* W w **14**. *P* 14.

255	5p. Type **89**	10	10
256	10p. Afro-Australian Fur Seal	15	15
257	15p. Tristan Thrush	25	20
258	20p. Nightingale Finch	35	25
255/8	*Set of* 4	75	60

90 Tristan Longboat

(Des R. Granger Barrett. Litho Questa)

1979 (8 Feb). *Visit of* Queen Elizabeth 2. *T* **90** *and similar horiz designs. Multicoloured.* W w **14** (*sideways**). *P* 14½.

259	5p. Type **90**	15	20
	w. Wmk Crown to right of CA	6·00	
260	10p. *Queen Mary* (liner)	15	20
261	15p. *Queen Elizabeth* (liner)	20	30
262	20p. *Queen Elizabeth 2* (liner)	20	30
259/62	*Set of* 4	65	90
MS263	148×96 mm. 25p. *Queen Elizabeth 2* (liner) (131×27 *mm*)	75	1·50
	w. Wmk Crown to right of CA	12·00	

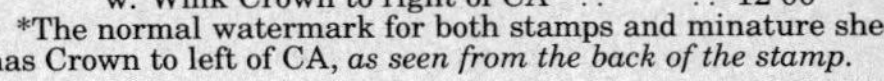

*The normal watermark for both stamps and miniature sheet has Crown to left of CA, *as seen from the back of the stamp.*

91 1952 "TRISTAN DA CUNHA" overprinted St. Helena 10s. Definitive

(Des J.W. Litho Questa)

1979 (27 Aug). *Death Centenary of Sir Rowland Hill. T* **91** *and similar designs showing stamps.* W w **14** (*sideways** *on* 5 *and* 10*p.*). *P* 14.

264	5p. black, lilac and bistre-yellow	10	15
	w. Wmk Crown to right of CA	13·00	
265	10p. black, red and apple-green	15	20
266	25p. multicoloured	30	30
	w. Wmk inverted	7·00	
264/6	*Set of* 3	50	60
MS267	83×103 mm. 50p. black and vermilion	60	70

Designs: *Horiz*—10p. 1954 5s. definitive. *Vert*—25p. 1963 3d. Tristan da Cunha Resettlement commemorative; 50p. 1946 1d. 4 Potatoes local label.

*The normal sideways watermark shows Crown to left of CA, *as seen from the back of the stamp.*

92 "The Padre's House"

93 *Tristania II* (crayfish trawler)

(Des G. Hutchins. Litho Questa)

1979 (26 Nov). *International Year of the Child. Children's Drawings. T* **92** *and similar horiz designs. Multicoloured. W* w **14** *(sideways). P* 14.

268	5p. Type **92**	10	10
269	10p. "Houses in the Village"	15	15
270	15p. "St. Mary's Church"	15	15
271	20p. "Rockhopper Penguins"	20	25
268/71	*Set of* 4	50	60

(Des C. Abbott. Litho Questa)

1980 (29 Feb). *Paintings by Roland Svensson (3rd series). Landscapes. Multicoloured designs as T* **80**. *W* w **14** *(sideways on 5 and 10p.). P* 14.

272	5p. "Stoltenhoff Island" *(horiz)*	10	10
273	10p. "Nightingale from the East" *(horiz)*	15	20
274	15p. "The Administrator's Abode"	15	25
275	20p. "Ridge where the Goat jump off"	20	30
272/5	*Set of* 4	50	75
MS276	126 × 109 mm. Nos. 272/5 (wmk sideways)	70	1·25

(Des C. Abbott. Litho Walsall)

1980 (6 May). *"London 1980" International Stamp Exhibition. T* **93** *and similar vert designs. Multicoloured. W* w **14**. *P* 14.

277	5p. Type **93**	10	10
278	10p. Unloading mail at Calshot Harbour	15	15
279	15p. Tractor transporting mail to Post Office	15	20
280	20p. Ringing the "dong" to summons people to Post Office	20	20
281	25p. Distributing mail	25	25
277/81	*Set of* 5	70	80

94 Queen Elizabeth the Queen Mother at Royal Opera House, 1976

95 *Golden Hind*

(Des Harrison. Litho Questa)

1980 (11 Aug*). *80th Birthday of Queen Elizabeth the Queen Mother. W* w **14** *(sideways). P* 14.

282 **94**	14p. multicoloured	25	25

*This is the local date of issue. The Crown Agents released this stamp in London on 4 August.

(Des G. Vasarhelyi. Litho Walsall)

1980 (6 Sept). *400th Anniv of Sir Francis Drake's Circumnavigation of the World. T* **95** *and similar vert designs. Multicoloured. W* w **14**. *P* 14½ × 14.

283	5p. Type **95**	10	10
284	10p. Drake's route	15	15
285	20p. Sir Francis Drake	20	20
286	25p. Queen Elizabeth I	25	25
283/6	*Set of* 4	65	65

96 "Humpty Dumpty"

97 South Atlantic Ocean showing Islands on Mid-Atlantic Ridge

(Des G. Vasarhelyi. Litho J.W.)

1980 (31 Oct). *Christmas. Scenes from Nursery Rhymes. T* **96** *and similar horiz designs. Multicoloured. W* w **14** *(sideways). P* 13.

287	15p. Type **96**	15	25
	a. Sheetlet Nos. 287/95	1·25	
288	15p. "Mary had a little Lamb"	15	25
289	15p. "Little Jack Horner"	15	25
290	15p. "Hey Diddle Diddle"	15	25
291	15p. "London Bridge"	15	25
292	15p. "Old King Cole"	15	25
293	15p. "Sing a Song of Sixpence"	15	25
294	15p. "Tom, Tom the Piper's Son"	15	25
295	15p. "The Owl and the Pussy Cat"	15	25
287/95	*Set of* 9	1·25	1·75

Nos. 287/95 were printed together, *se-tenant*, within a small sheet of 9 stamps.

(Des A. Crawford, adapted BG Studio. Litho Rosenbaum Bros, Vienna)

1980 (15 Dec). *150th Anniv of Royal Geographical Society. Maps. T* **97** *and similar vert designs. Multicoloured. W* w **14**. *P* 13½.

296	5p. Type **97**	15	20
297	10p. Tristan da Cunha group (Beauforts Survey, 1806)	15	25
298	15p. Tristan Island (Crawford, 1937–38)	20	30
299	20p. Gough Island (1955–56)	25	40
296/9	*Set of* 4	65	1·00

98 Revd. Edwin Dodgson as Young Man

99 Detail from Captain Denham's Plan, 1853

(Des Jennifer Toombs. Litho Questa)

1981 (23 Mar). *Centenary of Revd. Edwin Dodgson's Arrival on Tristan da Cunha. T* **98** *and similar multicoloured designs. W* w **14** *(sideways on 20p.). P* 14.

300	10p. Type **98**	15	15
301	20p. Dodgson and view of Tristan da Cunha *(horiz)*	25	30
302	30p. Dodgson with people of Tristan da Cunha	35	45
300/2	*Set of* 3	65	80
MS303	140×134 mm. Nos. 300/2. Wmk sideways*	75	1·40
	w. Wmk Crown to right of CA	22·00	

*The normal sideways watermark on No. **MS**303 shows Crown to left of CA, *as seen from the back of the stamp.*

(Des L. McCombie. Litho Questa)

1981 (22 May). *Early Maps. T* **99** *and similar horiz designs. Multicoloured. W* w **14** *(sideways*). P* 13½×14.

304	5p. Type **99**	15	10
	w. Wmk Crown to right of CA	40·00	
305	14p. Detail from map by A. Dalrymple, 17 March 1781	30	20
306	21p. Detail from Captain Denham's plan, 1853 *(different)*	40	30
304/6	*Set of* 3	75	55
MS307	110×70 mm. 35p. Detail from map by J. van Keulen, *circa* 1700	50	60
	w. Wmk Crown to right of CA	60·00	

*The normal sideways watermark shows Crown to left of CA, *as seen from the back of the stamp or minature sheet.*

100 Wedding Bouquet from Tristan da Cunha

101 Explorer with Rucksack

(Des J.W. Litho Walsall)

1981 (22 July). *Royal Wedding. T* **100** *and similar vert designs. Multicoloured. W* w **14**. *P* 14.

308	5p. Type **100**	10	10
309	20p. Prince of Wales at Investiture	15	15
310	50p. Prince Charles and Lady Diana Spencer	45	45
308/10	*Set of* 3	60	60

(Des BG Studio. Litho Questa)

1981 (14 Sept). *25th Anniv of Duke of Edinburgh Award Scheme. T* **101** *and similar vert designs. Multicoloured. W* w **14**. *P* 14.

311	5p. Type **101**	10	10
312	10p. Explorer at campsite	10	10
313	20p. Explorer map reading	20	20
314	25p. Duke of Edinburgh	25	25
311/14	*Set of* 4	55	55

102 Inaccessible Island Rail on Nest

(Des R. Granger Barrett. Litho Walsall)

1981 (1 Nov). *Inaccessible Island Rail. T* **102** *and similar horiz designs. Multicoloured. W* w **14** *(sideways*). P* 13½×14.

315	10p. Type **102**	25	30
	a. Strip of 4. Nos. 315/18	90	
	aw. Wmk Crown to right of CA (strip of 4)	£130	
316	10p. Inaccessible Island Rail eggs	25	30
317	10p. Rail chicks	25	30
318	10p. Adult Rail	25	30
315/18	*Set of* 4	90	1·10

*The normal sideways watermark shows Crown to left of CA, *as seen from the back of the stamp.*

Nos. 315/18 were printed together, *se-tenant*, in horizontal and vertical strips of 4 throughout the sheet.

103 Six-gilled Shark

(Des I. Loe. Litho Enschedé)

1982 (8 Feb). *Sharks. T* **103** *and similar horiz designs. Multicoloured. W* w **14** *(sideways*). P* 13½.

319	5p. Type **103**	20	10
	w. Wmk Crown to right of CA	60·00	
320	14p. Porbeagle	30	20
	w. Wmk Crown to right of CA	60·00	
321	21p. Blue Shark	40	35
322	35p. Golden Hammerhead	50	50
319/22	*Set of* 4	1·25	1·00

*The normal sideways watermark shows Crown to left of CA, *as seen from the back of the stamp.*

104 *Marcella* (barque)

105 Lady Diana Spencer at Windsor, July 1981

(Des J. Cooter. Litho Questa)

1982 (5 Apr). *Sailing Ships (1st series). T* **104** *and similar horiz designs. Multicoloured. W* w **14** *(sideways). P* 13½.

323	5p. Type **104**	25	35
324	15p. *Eliza Adams* (full-rigged ship)	30	50
325	30p. *Corinthian* (American whaling ship)	45	80
326	50p. *Samuel and Thomas* (American whaling ship)	70	1·10
323/6	*Set of* 4	1·50	2·50

See also Nos. 341/4.

(Des Jennifer Toombs. Litho Walsall)

1982 (1 July). *21st Birthday of Princess of Wales. T* **105** *and similar vert designs. Multicoloured. W* w **14**. *P* 14½ × 14.

327	5p. Tristan da Cunha coat of arms	10	10
328	15p. Type **105**	40	20
329	30p. Prince and Princess of Wales in wedding portrait	45	40
330	50p. Formal portrait	1·25	60
327/30	*Set of* 4	2·00	1·10

106 Lord Baden-Powell

1ST PARTICIPATION COMMONWEALTH GAMES 1982

(107)

(Des C. Abbott. Litho J.W.)

1982 (20 Sept). *75th Anniv of Boy Scout Movement. T* **106** *and similar multicoloured designs. W* w **14** *(sideways on No. 333). P 13 × 13½ (50p.) or 13½ × 13 (others).*

331 5p. Type **106** 15 15
332 20p. First Scout camp, Brownsea, 1907 .. 30 35
333 50p. Local Scouts on parade (*horiz*) .. 65 75
331/3 .. .. *Set of* 3 1·00 1·10
MS334 88 × 104 mm. 50p. Moral of the Acorn and the Oak. P 14 .. .. 1·10 1·40

1982 (28 Sept). *Commonwealth Games, Brisbane. Nos. 224 and 228 optd with T* **107**.

335 5p. Wandering Albatross 15 10
336 25p. Broad-billed Prion 40 30
w. Wmk inverted .. .. 27·00

108 Formation of Island

109 Tractor pulling Trailer

(Des J.W. Litho Questa)

1982 (1 Nov). *Volcanoes. T* **108** *and similar horiz designs. Multicoloured. W* w **14** *(sideways). P 14 × 14½.*

337 5p. Type **108** 15 15
338 15p. Plan of surface cinder cones and cross-section of volcano showing feeders .. 30 35
339 25p. Eruption 45 50
340 35p. 1961 Tristan eruption 65 70
337/40 .. .. *Set of* 4 1·40 1·50

(Des J. Cooter. Litho Questa)

1983 (1 Feb). *Sailing Ships (2nd series). Multicoloured designs as T* **104**. *W* w **14** *(sideways on 20p., 35p.). P 13½.*

341 5p. *Islander* (barque) (*vert*) 25 15
342 20p. *Roscoe* (full-rigged ship) 45 35
343 35p. *Columbia* (whaling ship) 60 55
344 50p. *Emeline* (schooner) (*vert*) 80 80
341/4 .. .. *Set of* 4 1·90 1·75

(Des C. Abbott. Litho Format)

1983 (2 May). *Land Transport. T* **109** *and similar horiz designs. Multicoloured. W* w **14** *(sideways). P 14.*

345 5p. Type **109** 10 15
346 15p. Pack donkeys 15 25
347 30p. Bullock cart 30 40
348 50p. Landrover 50 60
345/8 .. .. *Set of* 4 90 1·25

110 Early Chart of South Atlantic

111 "Christ's Charge to St. Peter" (detail) (Raphael)

(Des L. Curtis. Litho Questa)

1983 (1 Aug). *Island History. T* **110** *and similar horiz designs. Multicoloured (except 50p. black, bright scarlet and buff). W* w **14** *(sideways*). P 14.*

349 1p. Type **110** 30 30
350 3p. Tristao da Cunha's caravel 40 30
351 4p. Notice left by Dutch on first landing, 1643 40 30
352 5p. 17th-century views of the island .. 40 30
353 10p. British army landing party, 1815 .. 45 40
354 15p. 19th-century view of the settlement .. 55 50
355 18p. Governor Glass's house 55 50
356 20p. The Revd. W. F. Taylor and Peter Green 65 65
357 25p. *John and Elizabeth* (American whaling ship) 85 75
358 50p. Letters Patent declaring Tristan da Cunha a dependency of St. Helena .. 1·40 1·25
359 £1 Commissioning H.M.S. *Atlantic Isle*, 1944 .. .. 2·50 2·50
w. Wmk Crown to right of CA .. .. 2·50
360 £2 Evacuation, 1961 .. .. .. 3·75 4·00
w. Wmk Crown to right of CA .. .. 4·00
349/60 .. .. .. *Set of* 12 11·00 10·50

*The normal sideways watermark shows Crown to left of CA, *as seen from the back of the stamp.*

(Des and litho Walsall)

1983 (27 Oct). *500th Birth Anniv of Raphael. T* **111** *and similar designs, showing different details of "Christ's Charge to St. Peter". W* w **14**. *P 14½.*

361 10p. multicoloured 15 20
362 25p. multicoloured 25 35
363 40p. multicoloured 45 60
361/3 .. .. *Set of* 3 75 1·00
MS364 115 × 90 mm. 50p. multicoloured (*horiz*). Wmk sideways 70 80

On No. **MS**364 the Queen's head has been replaced by the Royal Cypher.

112 1952 6d. Stamp

113 *Agrocybe praecox var. cutefracta*

(Des C. Abbott. Litho Questa)

1984 (3 Jan). *150th Anniv of St. Helena as a British Colony. T* **112** *and similar horiz designs showing 1952 overprints on St. Helena stamps. Multicoloured. W* w **14** *(sideways). P 14.*

365 10p. Type **112** 15 30
366 15p. 1952 1s. stamp 25 40
367 25p. 1952 2s. 6d. stamp 35 60
368 60p. 1952 10s. stamp .. .. 85 1·25
365/8 .. .. *Set of* 4 1·40 2·25

(Des McCombie Skinner Studio. Litho Questa)

1984 (25 Mar). *Fungi. T* **113** *and similar multicoloured designs. W* w **14** *(sideways on 30 p., 50 p.). P 14.*

369 10p. Type **113** 65 85
370 20p. *Laccaria tetraspora* .. .. .. 95 1·25
371 30p. *Agrocybe cylindracea* (*horiz*) .. .. 1·10 1·40
372 50p. *Sacoscypha coccinea* (*horiz*) .. .. 1·40 1·75
369/72 .. .. *Set of* 4 3·75 4·75

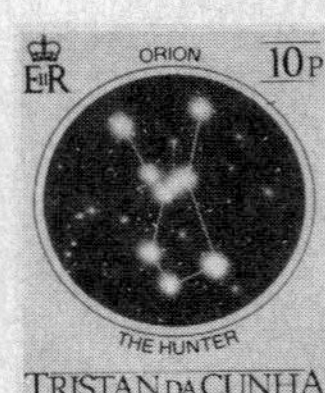

114 Constellation of "Orion"

115 Sheep-shearing

(Des Harrison. Litho Questa)

1984 (30 July). *The Night Sky. T* **114** *and similar vert designs. Multicoloured. W* w **14**. *P 14½ × 14.*

373 10p. Type **114** 45 80
374 20p. "Scorpius" .. .. 65 1·00
375 25p. "Canis Major" .. .. 75 1·10
376 50p. "Crux" .. .. 1·10 1·40
373/6 .. .. *Set of* 4 2·75 3·75

(Des G. Wilby. Litho Walsall)

1984 (1 Oct). *Tristan Woollens Industry. T* **115** *and similar vert designs. Multicoloured. W* w **14**. *P 14½.*

377 9p. Type **115** 20 45
378 17p. Carding wool 30 60
379 29p. Spinning 50 90
380 45p. Knitting .. .. 75 1·10
377/80 .. .. *Set of* 4 1·60 2·75
MS381 120 × 85 mm. As Nos. 377/80, but without white borders around the designs.. .. .. 1·25 3·00

116 "Christmas Dinner-table"

117 "H.M.S. *Julia* (sloop) Ashore, 1817" (Midshipman C. W. Browne)

(Des G. Vasarhelyi. Litho Questa)

1984 (3 Dec). *Christmas. Children's Drawings. T* **116** *and similar horiz designs. Multicoloured. W* w **14** *(sideways). P 14.*

382 10p. Type **116** 20 35
383 20p. "Santa Claus in ox cart" 30 50
384 30p. "Santa Claus in longboat" 40 80
385 50p. "The Nativity" .. .. 75 1·10
382/5 .. .. *Set of* 4 1·50 2·50

(Des A. Crawford, adapted G. Vasarhelyi. Litho Questa)

1985 (4 Feb). *Shipwrecks (1st series). T* **117** *and similar designs. W* w **14** *(sideways on 35p.). P 14 × 13½ (10, 25p.) or 13½ × 14 (35, 60p.).*

386 10p. royal blue and light grey-blue 70 80
387 25p. red-brown and emerald .. .. .. 1·25 1·40
388 35p. yellow-brown and orange-yellow .. 1·40 1·60
386/8 .. .. *Set of* 3 3·00 3·50
MS389 142 × 101 mm. 60p. multicoloured. Wmk sideways .. .. 1·00 2·25

Designs: *Vert*—25p. *Mabel Clark's* bell, St. Mary's Church. *Horiz*—35p. "Barque *Glenhuntley* foundering, 1898" (John Hagan); 60p. Map of Tristan da Cunha showing sites of shipwrecks.

See also Nos. 411/14 and 426/9.

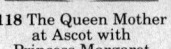

118 The Queen Mother at Ascot with Princess Margaret

119 Jonathan Lambert and "Isles of Refreshment" Flag, 1811

(Des A. Theobald (80p.), C. Abbott (others). Litho Questa)

1985 (7 June). *Life and Times of Queen Elizabeth the Queen Mother. T* **118** *and similar vert designs. Multicoloured. W* w **16**. *P 14½ × 14.*

390 10p. The Queen Mother and Prince Charles, 1954 .. .. 20 30
w. Wmk inverted .. .. 8·00 10·00
391 20p. Type **118** 30 60
w. Wmk inverted .. .. 8·00 10·00
392 30p. Queen Elizabeth the Queen Mother .. 40 85
393 50p. With Prince Henry at his christening 70 1·25
390/3 .. .. *Set of* 4 1·40 2·75
MS394 91×73 mm. 80p. The Queen Mother and the young Princess Anne at Trooping the Colour. Wmk sideways .. .. 1·75 2·75

(Des D. Slater. Litho J.W.)

1985 (30 Sept). *Flags. T* **119** *and similar multicoloured designs. W* w **16** *(sideways on 10p., inverted on others). P 14.*

395 10p. Type **119** 80 80
396 15p. 21st Light Dragoons guidon and cannon from Fort Malcolm (1816–17) (*vert*) .. .. 1·00 1·00
397 25p. White Ensign and H.M.S. *Falmouth* (frigate) offshore, 1816 (*vert*) .. .. 1·40 1·60
398 60p. Union Jack and Tristan da Cunha (*vert*) .. .. 2·75 3·00
395/8 .. .. *Set of* 4 5·50 5·75

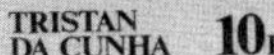

120 Lifeboat heading for Barque *West Riding*

121 Halley's Comet, 1066, from Bayeux Tapestry

(Des D. Miller. Litho Format)

1985 (28 Nov). *Centenary of Loss of Island Lifeboat. T* **120** *and similar vert designs. Multicoloured. W* w **14**. *P 14 × 13½.*

399 10p. Type **120** 25 60
w. Wmk inverted 75
400 30p. Map of Tristan da Cunha .. .. 55 1·25
w. Wmk inverted .. .. 1·25
401 50p. Memorial plaque to lifeboat crew .. 85 1·75
399/401 .. .. *Set of* 3 1·50 3·25

(Des D. Miller. Litho Walsall)

1986 (3 Mar). *Appearance of Halley's Comet. T* **121** *and similar horiz designs. Multicoloured. W* w **16** *(sideways). P 14.*

402 10p. Type **121** 40 65
403 20p. Path of Comet .. .. 65 1·00
404 30p. Comet over Inaccessible Island .. 85 1·40
405 50p. H.M.S. *Paramour* (pink) and map of South Atlantic .. .. 1·40 1·75
402/5 .. .. *Set of* 4 3·00 4·25

(Des A. Theobald. Litho Questa)

1986 (21 Apr). *60th Birthday of Queen Elizabeth II. Vert designs as T* **230a** *of Jamaica. Multicoloured. W* w **16**. *P 14½×14.*

406 10p. With Prince Charles, 1950 .. .. 15 30
w. Wmk inverted 60
407 15p. Queen at Trooping the Colour 20 40
408 25p. In robes of Order of the Bath, Westminster Abbey, 1972 .. .. 35 60
a. Silver (cypher and logo) omitted .. £275
409 45p. In Canada, 1977 .. .. .. 55 1·00
w. Wmk inverted .. .. 1·40
410 65p. At Crown Agents Head Office, London, 1983 .. .. 75 1·50
406/10 .. .. *Set of* 5 1·75 3·50

122 "*Allanshaw* wrecked on East Beach, 1893" (drawing by John Hagan)

123 Wandering Albatross

(Des A. Crawford, adapted G. Vasarhelyi. Litho J.W.)

1986 (2 June). *Shipwrecks* (*2nd series*). *T* **122** *and similar designs. W* w **16** (*sideways on 9p.*). *P* 13½×13 (*9p.*) *or* 13×13½ (*others*).

411	9p. dp turquoise-blue, dp grey-blue & black	30	80
412	20p. grey-olive, olive-yellow and black ..	60	1·40
413	40p. bright blue, bright violet and black ..	1·10	1·90
411/13	.. .. *Set of* 3	1·75	3·50
MS414	142×80 mm. 65p. orange-brown and black. Wmk sideways*. P 13½×13 ..	1·75	3·25
	w. Wmk Crown to left of CA	20·00	

Designs: *Vert*—20p. Church font from wreck of *Edward Vittery*, 1881; 40p. Ship's figurehead. *Horiz*—65p. Gaetano Lavarello and Andrea Repetto, survivors from *Italia*, 1892.

*The normal sideways watermark on the minature sheet shows Crown to right of CA, *as seen from the back of the sheet.*

(Des D. Miller. Litho Questa)

1986 (23 July). *Royal Wedding. Square designs as T* **231***a of Jamaica. Multicoloured. W* w **16**. *P* 14.

415	10p. Prince Andrew and Miss Sarah Ferguson	20	50
	w. Wmk inverted	30·00	
416	40p. Prince Andrew piloting helicopter, Digby, Canada, 1985	80	1·50
	w. Wmk inverted	35·00	

(Des A. Theobald. Litho Questa)

1986 (30 Sept). *Flora and Fauna of Inaccessible Island. T* **123** *and similar vert designs. Multicoloured. W* w **16**. *P* 14.

417	5p. Type **123**	40	60
418	10p. *Lagenophora nudicaulis* (daisy) ..	40	70
	w. Wmk inverted	—	25·00
419	20p. *Cynthia virginiensis* (butterfly) ..	90	1·40
420	25p. Wilkin's Finch	95	1·50
	w. Wmk inverted	—	23·00
421	50p. White-chinned Petrel	1·40	1·75
417/21	.. .. *Set of* 5	3·50	5·50

124 *Dimorphinoctua cunhaensis* (flightless moth) and Edinburgh.

125 Castaways from *Blenden Hall* attacking Sea Elephant, 1821

(Des C. Abbott. Litho Walsall)

1987 (23 Jan). *Island Flightless Insects and Birds. T* **124** *and similar vert designs. Multicoloured. W* w **14**. *P* 14½.

422	10p. Type **124**	25	60
423	25p. *Tristanomyia frustilifera* (fly) and Crater Lake	55	1·25
424	35p. Inaccessible Island Rail and Inaccessible Island	1·25	2·00
425	50p. Gough Island Moorhen and Gough Island	1·75	2·25
422/5	.. .. *Set of* 4	3·50	5·50

(Des A. Crawford, adapted G. Vasarhelyi. Litho Walsall)

1987 (2 Apr*). *Shipwrecks* (*3rd series*). *T* **125** *and similar designs. W* w **16** (*sideways on 17p.*). *P* 13½×14 (*17p.*) *or* 14×13½ (*others*).

426	11p. black and olive-brown	60	90
427	17p. black and bright lilac	80	1·40
428	45p. black and deep blue-green	1·25	1·75
426/8	.. .. *Set of* 3	2·40	3·50
MS429	131×70 mm. 70p. royal blue, bright green and pale blue. Wmk sideways†. P 13½×14	2·50	3·00
	w. Wmk Crown to right of CA	32·00	

Designs: *Horiz*—17p. Barquentine *Henry A. Paull* stranded at Sandy Point, 1879; 70p. Map of Inaccessible Island showing sites of shipwrecks. *Vert*—45p. Gustav Stoltenhoff, 1871, and Stoltenhoff Island.

*This is the local date of issue. The Crown Agents placed the stamps on the sale from 2 February 1987.

†The normal sideways watermark on the miniature sheet shows Crown to left of CA, *as seen from the back of the sheet.*

126 Rockhopper Penguin swimming

127 Microscope and Published Report

(Des I. Strange. Litho Questa)

1987 (22 June). *Rockhopper Penguins. T* **126** *and similar horiz designs. Multicoloured. W* w **16** (*sideways*). *P* 14½.

430	10p. Type **126**	65	75
431	20p. Adult with egg	1·00	1·25
432	30p. Adult with juvenile	1·25	1·60
433	50p. Head of Rockhopper Penguin ..	1·75	2·00
430/3	.. .. *Set of* 4	4·25	5·00

(Des N. Shewring. Litho Questa)

1987 (7 Dec). *50th Anniv of Norwegian Scientific Expedition. T* **127** *and similar square designs. Multicoloured. W* w **16** (*10p., 20p.*) *or* w **14** (*30p., 50p.*) (*all sideways*). *P* 14.

434	10p. Type **127**	90	1·00
435	20p. Scientists ringing Yellow-nosed Albatross	1·90	2·00
436	30p. Expedition hut, Little Beach Point ..	2·25	2·50
437	50p. S.S. *Thorshammer* (whale factory ship)	3·25	3·50
434/7	.. .. *Set of* 4	7·50	8·00

1988 (9 Mar). *Royal Ruby Wedding. Nos.* 406/10 *optd with T* **45***a of Kiribati in silver.*

438	10p. Princess Elizabeth with Prince Charles, 1950	20	25
439	15p. Queen Elizabeth II at Trooping the Colour	30	35
440	25p. In robes of Order of the Bath, Westminster Abbey, 1972	50	55
441	45p. In Canada, 1977	95	95
442	65p. At Crown Agents Head Office, London, 1983	1·00	1·40
438/42	.. .. *Set of* 5	2·75	3·25

128 Nightingale Finch ("Tristan Bunting")

129 Painted Penguin Eggs

(Des A. Theobald. Litho Questa)

1988 (21 Mar). *Fauna of Nightingale Island. T* **128** *and similar vert designs. Multicoloured. W* w **16**. *P* 14.

443	5p. Type **128**	40	40
444	10p. Tristan Thrush (immature) ..	55	55
445	20p. Yellow-nosed Albatross (chick) ..	75	80
446	25p. Greater Shearwater	75	85
447	50p. Elephant Seal	1·25	1·75
443/7	.. .. *Set of* 5	3·25	3·75

(Des O. Bell. Litho Questa)

1988 (30 May). *Tristan da Cunha Handicrafts. T* **129** *and similar horiz designs. Multicoloured. W* w **16** (*sideways**). *P* 14×14½.

448	10p. Type **129**	25	35
	w. Wmk Crown to right of CA ..	35·00	
449	15p. Moccasins	35	50
	w. Wmk Crown to right of CA ..	25·00	
450	35p. Knitwear	75	1·00
	w. Wmk Crown to right of CA ..	35·00	
451	50p. Model longboat	1·10	1·40
	w. Wmk Crown to right of CA ..	25·00	
448/51	.. .. *Set of* 4	2·25	3·00

*The normal sideways watermark show Crown to left of CA, *as seen from the back of the stamp.*

130 Processing Blubber

(Des N. Shewring. Litho Questa)

1988 (6 Oct). *19th-century Whaling. T* **130** *and similar horiz designs. Multicoloured. W* w **16** (*sideways**). *P* 14×14½.

452	10p. Type **130**	65	65
	w. Wmk Crown to right of CA ..		
453	20p. Harpoon guns	85	85
454	30p. Scrimshaw (carved whale bone) ..	1·00	1·00
455	50p. Whaling ships	1·75	2·00
	w. Wmk Crown to right of CA ..	50·00	
452/5	.. .. *Set of* 4	3·75	4·00
MS456	76×56 mm. £1 Right Whale	2·50	2·50

*The normal sideways watermark shows Crown to left of CA, *as seen from the back of the stamp.*

(Des E. Nisbet and D. Miller (25, 35p.), D. Miller (others). Litho Harrison)

1988 (7 Nov). *300th Anniv of Lloyd's of London. Designs as T* **167***a of Malawi. W* w **16** (*sideways on 25, 35p.*). *P* 14.

457	10p. multicoloured	30	40
458	25p. multicoloured	1·00	1·10
459	35p. brownish black and emerald ..	1·40	1·50
460	50p. brownish black and carmine-red ..	1·75	1·90
457/60	.. .. *Set of* 4	4·00	4·50

Designs: *Vert*—10p. New Lloyd's Building, 1988; 50p. *Kobenhavn* (cadet barque), 1928. *Horiz*—25p. *Tristania II* (crayfish trawler); 35p. *St. Helena* (mail ship).

131 "Government House"

132 Hall's Giant Petrel

(Des N. Harvey. Litho Walsall)

1988 (10 Dec). *Augustus Earle's Paintings, 1824. T* **131** *and similar horiz designs. Multicoloured. W* w **16** (*sideways**). *P* 14.

461	1p. Type **131**	20	30
462	3p. "Squall off Tristan"	30	40
463	4p. "Rafting Blubber"	35	40
464	5p. "View near Little Beach"	35	40
465	10p. "Man killing Albatross"	45	50
466	15p. "View on The Summit"	70	70
467	20p. "Nightingale Island"	85	85
468	25p. "Earle on Tristan"	1·00	1·00
469	35p. "Solitude–Watching the Horizon" ..	1·25	1·25
470	50p. "Northeaster"	1·50	1·50
	w. Wmk Crown to right of CA ..	35·00	
471	£1 "Tristan Village"	2·75	2·75
472	£2 "Governor Glass at Dinner" ..	4·25	4·25
461/72	.. .. *Set of* 12	12·50	13·00

*The normal sideways watermark shows Crown to left of CA, *as seen from the back of the stamp.*

Examples of Nos. 461/72 showing Earle's dates as "1793–1835" were sold by the U.S.A. agents, and by the authorities on Ascension, in error. Supplies sent to Tristan da Cunha show the correct dates "1793–1838".

(Des A. Theobald. Litho Walsall)

1989 (6 Feb). *Fauna of Gough Island. T* **132** *and similar vert designs. Multicoloured. W* w **16**. *P* 14.

473	5p. Type **132**	50	50
474	10p. Gough Island Moorhen	60	60
475	20p. Gough Island Finch ("Gough Bunting")	80	80
476	25p. Sooty Albatross	90	90
477	50p. Amsterdam Fur Seal	1·40	1·60
473/7	.. .. *Set of* 5	3·75	4·00

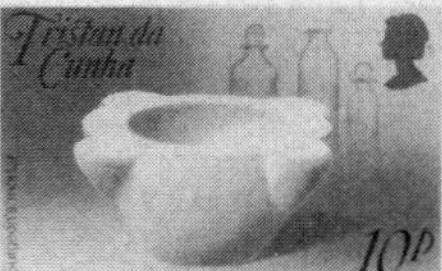

133 *Eriosorus cheilanthoides*

134 Surgeon's Mortar

(Des Jane Fern. Litho Walsall)

1989 (22 May). *Ferns. T* **133** *and similar vert designs. Multicoloured. W* w **14**. *P* 14×13½.

478	10p. Type **133**	35	35
479	25p. *Asplenium alvarezense*	75	75
480	35p. *Elaphoglossum hybridum*	85	85
481	50p. *Ophioglossum opacum*	1·40	1·40
478/81	.. .. *Set of* 4	3·00	3·00

(Des Jennifer Toombs. Litho Questa)

1989 (25 Sept). *Nautical Museum Exhibits. T* **134** *and similar horiz designs. Multicoloured. W* w **16** (*sideways*). *P* 14.

482	10p. Type **134**	35	35
483	20p. Parts of darting-gun harpoon ..	60	60
484	30p. Ship's compass with binnacle-hood ..	80	80
485	60p. Rope-twisting device	1·60	1·60
482/5	.. .. *Set of* 4	3·00	3·00

135 Cattle Egret　　136 *Peridroma saucia*

(Des Josephine Martin and Sally Hynard. Litho Questa)

1989 (20 Nov). *Vagrant Birds. T* **135** *and similar vert designs. Multicoloured.* W w **16**. *P* 14.

486　10p. Type **135** 1·00 85
487　25p. Spotted Sandpiper 1·75 1·75
488　35p. Purple Gallinule 2·00 2·00
489　50p. Barn Swallow 2·25 2·50
486/9　*Set of* 4 6·25 6·25

(Des I. Loe. Litho Questa)

1990 (1 Feb). *Moths. T* **136** *and similar horiz designs. Multicoloured.* W w **14** (*sideways*). *P* 14.

490　10p. Type **136** 70 60
491　15p. *Ascalapha odorata* 90 90
492　35p. *Agrius cingulata* 1·50 1·50
493　60p. *Eumorpha labruscae* 2·00 2·25
490/3　*Set of* 4 4·50 4·75

137 Sea Urchin　　138 H.M.S. *Pyramus* (frigate), 1829

(Des Anna Hecht. Litho Questa)

1990 (12 June). *Echinoderms. T* **137** *and similar vert designs showing starfishes.* W w **14**. *P* 13½×14.

494　10p. multicoloured 60 55
495　20p. multicoloured 85 85
496　30p. multicoloured 1·00 1·00
497　60p. multicoloured 1·75 2·00
494/7　*Set of* 4 3·75 4·00

(Des D. Miller. Litho Questa)

1990 (4 Aug). *90th Birthday of Queen Elizabeth the Queen Mother. Vert designs as T* **107** (25p.) *or* **108** (£1) *of Kenya.* W w **16**. *P* 14×15 (25p.) *or* 14½ (£1).

498　25p. multicoloured 75 75
499　£1 agate and Prussian blue 2·50 3·00

Designs:—25p. Queen Mother at the London Coliseum; £1 Queen Elizabeth broadcasting to women of the Empire, 1939.

(Des L. Curtis. Litho Walsall)

1990 (13 Sept). *Maiden Voyage of* St. Helena II. *Horiz designs as T* **162** *of St. Helena. Multicoloured.* W w **14** (*sideways*). *P* 14×14½.

500　10p. *Dunnottar Castle* (liner), 1942 70 70
501　15p. *St. Helena* (mail ship) at Tristan 1·00 1·00
502　35p. Launch of *St. Helena II* (mail ship) 1·60 1·75
503　60p. Duke of York launching *St. Helena II* 2·50 2·75
500/3　*Set of* 4 5·25 5·50
MS504　100×100 mm. £1 *St. Helena II* and outline map of Tristan da Cunha 3·00 4·50

No. **MS**504 also contains two imperforate designs of similar stamps from Ascension and St. Helena without face values.

(Des E. Nisbet. Litho Questa)

1990 (30 Nov). *Ships of the Royal Navy* (1*st series*). *T* **138** *and similar horiz designs. Multicoloured.* W w **14** (*sideways*). *P* 14.

505　10p. Type **138** 1·00 90
506　25p. H.M.S. *Penguin* (sloop), 1815 2·00 2·00
507　35p. H.M.S. *Thalia* (screw corvette), 1886 2·25 2·25
508　50p. H.M.S. *Sidon* (paddle frigate), 1858 2·75 3·25
505/8　*Set of* 4 7·25 7·75

See also Nos. 509/12 and 565/8.

(Des E. Nisbet. Litho Questa)

1991 (4 Feb). *Ships of the Royal Navy* (2*nd series*). *Horiz designs as T* **138**. *Multicoloured.* W w **14** (*sideways*). *P* 14.

509　10p. H.M.S. *Milford* (sloop), 1938 1·00 90
510　25p. H.M.S. *Dublin* (cruiser), 1923 2·00 2·00
511　35p. H.M.S. *Yarmouth* (cruiser), 1919 2·25 2·25
512　50p. H.M.S. *Carlisle* (cruiser), 1937 2·75 3·25
509/12　*Set of* 4 7·25 7·75

No. 512 is inscribed "1938" in error.

139 *Royal Viking Sun* (cruise liner)

(Des L. Curtis. Litho B.D.T.)

1991 (1 Apr). *Visit of* Royal Viking Sun. *Sheet* 62×47 *mm.* W w **16** (*sideways*). *P* 14.

MS513　**139** £1 multicoloured 4·50 5·50

140 Prince Alfred and H.M.S. *Galatea* (screw frigate), 1867

(Des D. Miller. Litho Questa)

1991 (10 June). *70th Birthday of Prince Philip, Duke of Edinburgh. T* **140** *and similar horiz designs.* W w **16** (*sideways*). *P* 14.

514　10p. brownish black, pale blue & dp dull bl 1·25 1·25
515　25p. brownish black, pale blue-green and myrtle-green 1·75 2·00
516　30p. black, deep brown & pale bistre-yellow 2·25 2·50
517　50p. multicoloured 2·50 2·75
514/17　*Set of* 4 7·00 7·75

Designs:—25p. Prince Philip meeting local inhabitants, 1957; 30p. Prince Philip and Royal Yacht *Britannia*, 1957; 50p. Prince Philip and Edinburgh settlement.

141 Pair of Gough Island Moorhens　　142 Coats' Perch

(Des G. Vasarhelyi. Litho Questa)

1991 (1 Oct). *Endangered Species. Birds. T* **141** *and similar horiz designs. Multicoloured.* W w **14** (*sideways*). *P* 14.

518　8p. Type **141** 1·25 1·25
519　10p. Gough Island Finch 1·40 1·40
520　12p. Gough Island Moorhen on nest 1·50 1·50
521　15p. Gough Island Finch feeding chicks 1·60 1·60
518/21　*Set of* 4 5·25 5·25

(Des R. Watton. Litho Walsall)

1992 (23 Jan). *500th Anniv of Discovery of America by Columbus and Re-enactment Voyages. Horiz designs as T* **168** *of St. Helena. Multicoloured.* W w **14** (*sideways*). *P* 13½×14.

522　10p. Map of re-enactment voyages and *Eye of the Wind* (cadet brig) 75 75
523　15p. Compass rose and *Soren Larsen* (cadet brigantine) 1·00 1·00
524　35p. Ships of Columbus 2·00 2·25
525　60p. Columbus and *Santa Maria* 2·25 2·50
522/5　*Set of* 4 5·50 6·00

(Des. D. Miller. Litho Questa (65p.), Walsall (others))

1992 (6 Feb). *40th Anniv of Queen Elizabeth II's Accession. Horiz designs as T* **113** *of Kenya. Multicoloured.* W w **14** (*sideways*). *P* 14.

526　10p. Tristan from the sea 35 40
527　20p. Longboat under sail 60 70
528　25p. Aerial view of Edinburgh 70 80
529　35p. Three portraits of Queen Elizabeth 90 1·00
530　65p. Queen Elizabeth II 1·75 2·00
526/30　*Set of* 5 4·00 4·50

(Des Ann Hecht. Litho Questa)

1992 (1 June). *Fishes. T* **142** *and similar horiz designs. Multicoloured.* W w **14** (*sideways*). *P* 14×13½.

531　10p. Type **142** 65 65
532　15p. Lined Trumpeter 90 90
533　35p. Karrer's Morid Cod 2·00 2·25
534　60p. Long-finned Scad 2·25 2·50
531/4　*Set of* 4 5·25 5·75

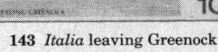

143 *Italia* leaving Greenock　　144 *Stenoscelis hylastoides*

(Des E. Nisbet. Litho Questa)

1992 (16 Sept). *Centenary of the Wreck of Barque* Italia. *T* **143** *and similar horiz designs.* W w **14** (*sideways*). *P* 13½×14.

535　10p. Type **143** 75 75
536　45p. In mid-Atlantic 2·00 2·25
537　65p. Driving ashore on Stony Beach 2·50 2·75
535/7　*Set of* 3 4·75 5·25
MS538　101×75 mm. £1 *Italia* becalmed 5·50 6·00

Nos. **MS**538 also commemorates "Genova '92" International Thematic Stamp Exhibition.

(Des G. Marx. Litho Questa)

1993 (2 Feb). *Insects. T* **144** *and similar vert designs. Multicoloured.* W w **16**. *P* 14×13½.

539　15p. Type **144** 85 90
540　45p. *Trogloscaptomyza brevilamellata* 2·00 2·25
541　60p. *Senilites tristanicola* 2·50 2·75
539/41　*Set of* 3 4·75 5·50

145 Ampulla and Anointing Spoon

(Des D. Miller. Litho Walsall)

1993 (14 June). *40th Anniv of Coronation. T* **145** *and similar vert designs.* W w **16**. *P* 14½×14.

542　10p. emerald and black 65 70
543　15p. magenta and black 90 1·00
544　35p. violet and black 1·40 1·75
545　60p. new blue and black 2·00 2·50
542/5　*Set of* 4 4·50 5·50

Designs:—15p. Orb; 35p. Imperial State Crown; 60p. St. Edward's Crown.

146 *Tristania* and *Frances Repetto* (crayfish trawlers)

(Des E. Nisbet. Litho Questa)

1993 (10 Nov). *30th Anniv of Resettlement of Tristan. T* **146** *and similar horiz designs. Multicoloured.* W w **16** (*sideways*). *P* 13½×14.

546　35p. Type **146** 1·75 2·00
　a. Horiz pair. Nos. 546/7 3·50 4·00
547　35p. *Boissevain* (cargo liner) 1·75 2·00
548　50p. *Bornholm* (liner) and longboat 2·25 2·75
546/8　*Set of* 3 5·25 6·00

Nos. 546/7 were printed together, *se-tenant*, in horizontal pairs throughout the sheet.

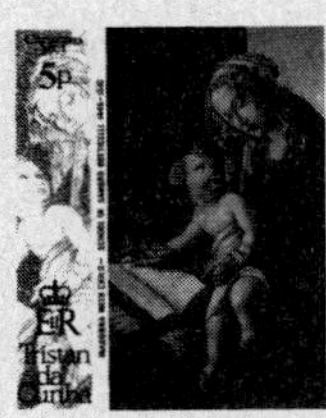

147 "Madonna with Child" (School of Botticelli)　　148 *Duchess of Atholl* (liner)

(Des D. Miller. Litho Cartor)

1993 (30 Nov). *Christmas. Religious Paintings. T* **147** *and similar vert designs. Multicoloured.* W w **14**. *P* 13.

549　5p. Type **147** 60 60
550　15p. "The Holy Family" (Daniel Gran) 1·25 1·25
551　35p. "The Holy Virgin and Child" (Rubens) 2·25 2·50
552　65p. "The Mystical Marriage of St. Catherine with the Holy Child" (Jan van Balen) 2·75 3·25
549/52　*Set of* 4 6·25 7·00

(Des R. Watton. Litho Questa)

1994 (3 Feb). *Ships. T* **148** *and similar horiz designs. Multicoloured.* W w **16** (*sideways*). *P* 14.

553　1p. Type **148** 10 10
554　3p. *Empress of Australia* (liner) 10 10
555　5p. *Anatolia* (freighter) 10 10
556　8p. *Viceroy of India* (liner) 15 20
557　10p. *Rangitata* (transport) 20 25
558　15p. *Caronia* (liner) 30 35
559　20p. *Rotterdam* (liner) 40 45
560　25p. *Leonardo da Vinci* (liner) 50 55

561	35p. *Vistafjord* (liner)	70	75
562	£1 *World Discoverer* (liner)	2·00	2·10
563	£2 *Astor* (liner)	4·00	4·25
564	£5 *St. Helena II* (mail ship)	10·00	10·50
553/64	.. .. *Set of* 12	18·00	19·00

(Des E. Nisbet. Litho Questa)

1994 (2 May). *Ships of the Royal Navy (3rd series). Horiz designs as T* **138**. *Multicoloured. W* w **14** *(sideways). P* 14×14½.

565	10p. H.M.S. *Nigeria* (cruiser), 1948 ..	75	75
566	25p. H.M.S. *Phoebe* (cruiser), 1949 ..	1·50	1·50
567	35p. H.M.S. *Liverpool* (cruiser), 1949 ..	1·75	1·75
568	50p. H.M.S. *Magpie* (frigate), 1955 ..	2·00	2·00
565/8	.. .. *Set of* 4	5·50	5·50

149 Blue Shark

(Des Anne Hecht. Litho Questa)

1994 (8 Aug). *Sharks. T* **149** *and similar horiz designs. Multicoloured. W* w **16** *(sideways). P* 14½.

569	10p. Type **149**	70	70
570	45p. Seven-gilled Shark	2·00	2·25
571	65p. Short-finned Mako	2·50	3·00
569/71	.. .. *Set of* 3	4·75	5·50

150 Pair of Donkeys

(Des Josephine Martin. Litho Questa)

1994 (21 Nov). *Island Livestock (1st series). T* **150** *and similar horiz designs. Multicoloured. W* w **14** *(sideways). P* 13½×14.

572	10p. Type **150**	60	60
573	20p. Cattle	1·00	1·00
574	35p. Ducks and geese	1·75	2·00
575	60p. Girl bottle-feeding lamb	2·25	2·50
572/5	.. .. *Set of* 4	5·00	5·50

See also Nos. 620/3.

151 Pick-up Truck

152 Queen Elizabeth the Queen Mother

(Des A. Theobald. Litho Walsall)

1995 (27 Feb). *Local Transport. T* **151** *and similar horiz designs. Multicoloured. W* w **16** *(sideways). P* 14.

576	15p. Type **151**	80	80
577	20p. Sherpa van	1·00	1·00
578	45p. Scooter and Yamaha motorcycle ..	1·75	2·00
579	60p. Administrator's Landrover	2·25	2·50
576/9	.. .. *Set of* 4	5·25	5·50

(Des R. Watton. Litho Cartor (Nos. 580/3) or Questa (No. **MS**584))

1995 (10 July). *50th Anniv of End of Second World War. Multicoloured designs as T* **75** *of Kiribati. W* w **14** *(sideways). P* 13½.

580	15p. Sailors training on Lewis guns ..	80	80
581	20p. Tristan Defence Volunteers	1·00	1·00
582	45p. Wireless and meteorological station ..	1·75	2·00
583	60p. H.M.S. *Birmingham* (cruiser) ..	2·25	2·50
580/3	.. .. *Set of* 4	5·25	5·50
MS584	75×85 mm. £1 Reverse of 1939–45 War Medal (*vert*). Wmk upright. P 14	2·00	2·50

(Des Jennifer Toombs. Litho Questa)

1995 (4 Aug). *95th Birthday of Queen Elizabeth the Queen Mother. Sheet* 75×103 *mm. W* w **14** *(sideways). P* 14½×14.

MS585	**152** £1.50, multicoloured	3·75	4·50

COVER PRICES

Cover factors are quoted at the beginning of each country for most issues to 1945. An explanation of the system can be found on page x. The factors quoted do not, however, apply to philatelic covers.

153 Sub-Antarctic Fur Seal on Rock

(Des R. Watton. Litho Cartor)

1995 (3 Nov). *Seals. T* **153** *and similar horiz designs. Multicoloured. W* w **14** *(sideways). P* 14×13½.

586	10p. Type **153**	60	60
587	35p. Sub-Antarctic Fur Seals with pups ..	1·50	1·50
588	45p. Southern Elephant Seal asleep with pups	1·75	1·75
589	50p. Southern Elephant Seals in water ..	1·75	1·75
586/9	.. .. *Set of* 4	5·00	5·00

(Des A. Theobald. Litho Cartor)

1996 (23 Jan). *50th Anniv of United Nations. Horiz designs as T* **284** *of Jamaica. Multicoloured. W* w **14** *(sideways). P* 13½×13.

590	20p. Bedford 4-ton lorry	90	90
591	30p. Saxon armoured personnel carrier ..	1·25	1·25
592	45p. Mi26 heavy lift helicopter	2·00	2·00
593	50p. R.F.A. *Sir Tristram* (landing ship) ..	2·00	2·00
590/3	.. .. *Set of* 4	5·50	5·50

(Des D. Miller. Litho Cartor)

1996 (22 Apr). *70th Birthday of Queen Elizabeth II. Vert designs as T* **55** *of New Zealand (Tokelau), each incorporating a different photograph of the Queen. W* w **14**. *P* 13½×14.

594	15p. Tristan from the sea	50	60
595	20p. Traditional cottage	65	75
596	45p. The Residency	1·25	1·50
597	60p. The Queen and Prince Philip ..	1·75	2·00
594/7	.. .. *Set of* 4	3·75	4·25

154 Old Harbour and *St. Helena I* (mail ship)

(Des C. Abbott. Litho Cartor)

1996 (5 July). *Construction of New Harbour. T* **154** *and similar horiz designs. Multicoloured. W* w **14** *(sideways). P* 13 *(15, 60p.) or* 14×13½ *(20, 45p.).*

598	15p. Type **154**	70	70
599	20p. Excavator and dump truck (44×27 *mm*)	80	80
600	45p. Construction of new mole (44×27 *mm*)	1·40	1·60
601	60p. New harbour and *St. Helena II* (mail ship)	2·00	2·25
598/601	.. .. *Set of* 4	4·50	4·75

155 Gough Island Moorhen

156 19th-century Map

(Des I. Loe. Litho Walsall)

1996 (1 Oct). *Declaration of Gough Island as World Heritage Site. Birds. T* **155** *and similar vert designs. Multicoloured. W* w **14**. *P* 14.

602	15p. Type **155**	65	70
603	20p. Wandering Albatross	75	80
604	45p. Sooty Albatross	1·40	1·60
605	60p. Gough Island Finch ("Gough Bunting")	1·75	2·00
602/5	.. .. *Set of* 4	4·00	4·50

For 60p. design in miniature sheet see No. **MS**619.

(Des G. Vasarhelyi. Litho Cartor)

1996 (18 Dec). *Centenary of the Presentation of the Queen Victoria Portrait to Tristan. T* **156** *and similar vert designs. Multicoloured. W* w **14**. *P* 13½.

606	20p. Type **156**	75	80
607	30p. H.M.S. *Magpie* (gunboat)	1·10	1·25
608	45p. Governor Peter Green	1·25	1·50
609	50p. "Queen Victoria" (H. von Angeli) (detail)	1·40	1·60
606/9	.. .. *Set of* 4	4·00	4·75

157 Archelon (turtle)

(Des N. Shewring. Litho B.D.T.)

1997 (10 Feb). *Atlantic Marine Life of the Cretaceous Period. Sheet* 92×100 *mm containing T* **157** *and similar horiz designs. Multicoloured. W* w **16** *(sideways). P* 14.

MS610	35p. Type **157**; 35p. Trinacromerum; 35p. Platecarpus; 35p. Clidastes	3·25	3·75

158 Smoke Signals

159 *Hilary* and *Melodie*

(Des D. Miller. Litho Walsall)

1997 (1 May). *Visual Communications. T* **158** *and similar horiz designs. Multicoloured. W* w **16** *(sideways). P* 14×14½.

611	10p. Type **158**	30	30
	a. Horiz pair. Nos. 611/12	60	60
612	10p. H.M.S. *Eurydice* (frigate)	30	30
613	15p. H.M.S. *Challenger* (survey ship) ..	50	50
	a. Horiz pair. Nos. 613/14	1·00	1·00
614	15p. Flag hoists	50	50
615	20p. Semaphore	65	65
	a. Horiz pair. Nos. 615/16	1·25	1·25
616	20p. H.M.S. *Carlisle* (cruiser)	65	65
617	35p. Aldis lamp	80	80
	a. Horiz pair. Nos. 617/18	1·60	1·60
618	35p. H.M.S. *Cilicia* (transport)	80	80
611/18	.. .. *Set of* 8	4·00	4·00

Nos. 611/12, 613/14, 615/16 and 617/18 were each printed together, *se-tenant*, in horizontal pairs forming composite designs.

(Litho Walsall)

1997 (20 June). *Return of Hong Kong to China. Sheet,* 130×90 *mm, containing designs as No.* 605, *but with "1997" imprint date. W* w **14**. *P* 14.

MS619	60p. Gough Island Finch ("Gough Bunting")	1·50	1·75

(Des Josephine Martin. Litho Walsall)

1997 (26 Aug). *Island Livestock (2nd series). Horiz designs as T* **150**. *Multicoloured. W* w **16** *(sideways). P* 13½×14.

620	20p. Chickens	60	60
621	30p. Bull	80	80
622	45p. Sheep	1·25	1·25
623	50p. Collie dogs	1·25	1·25
620/3	.. .. *Set of* 4	3·50	3·50

(Des N. Shewring (No. **MS**630), D. Miller (others). Litho Questa (No. **MS**630), B.D.T. (others))

1997 (20 Nov). *Golden Wedding of Queen Elizabeth and Prince Philip. Multicoloured designs as T* **87** *of Kiribati. W* w **14**. *P* 13½.

624	15p. Queen Elizabeth	45	45
	a. Horiz pair. Nos. 624/5	90	90
625	15p. Prince Philip playing polo	45	45
626	20p. Queen Elizabeth with horse	55	55
	a. Horiz pair. Nos. 626/7	1·10	1·10
627	20p. Prince Philip	55	55
628	45p. Queen Elizabeth with Prince Philip in R.A.F. uniform	1·25	1·25
	a. Horiz pair. Nos. 628/9	2·25	2·25
629	45p. Princess Anne on horseback	1·25	1·25
624/9	.. .. *Set of* 6	3·75	3·75
MS630	110×70 mm. £1.50, Queen Elizabeth and Prince Philip in landau (*horiz*). Wmk sideways. P 14×14½	3·50	3·75

Nos. 624/5, 626/7 and 628/9 were each printed together, *se-tenant*, in horizontal pairs throughout the sheetlets with the backgrounds forming composite designs.

(Des N. Shewring. Litho Questa)

1998 (6 Feb). *50th Anniv of First Lobster Survey. Lobster Trawlers. T* **159** *and similar vert designs. Multicoloured. W* w **14**. *P* 14½×14.

631	15p. Type **159**	45	45
632	20p. *Tristania II* and *Hekla*	55	55
633	30p. *Pequena* and *Frances Repetto* ..	75	75
634	45p. *Tristania* and *Gillian Gaggins* ..	1·25	1·25
635	50p. *Kelso* and *Edinburgh*	1·25	1·25
631/5	.. .. *Set of* 5	3·75	3·75
MS636	100×80 mm. £1.20, Revd. C. P. Lawrence and lobster	3·25	3·50

STAMP BOOKLETS

1957 (30 May)–**58.** *Black on blue cover. Postmarked "MY 30 57" on back cover. Stapled.*

SB1	3s. 6d. booklet containing eight ½d. and four 1d., 1½d., 3d. and 4d. (Nos. 14/16, 19/20) in blocks of 4	£350
	a. Postmarked "JA 24 58" on back cover (24.1.58)	£325
	b. Without postmark	£300

1958 (Jan). *Black on red cover. Without postmark. Stapled.*

SB2	3s. 6d. Contents as No. SB1	75·00

1960 (Feb). *Black on green cover. Stitched.*

SB3	3s. 6d. booklet containing eight ½d. and four 1d., 1½d., 3d. and 4d. (Nos. 28/30, 33/4) in blocks of 4	40·00

1965 (17 Feb). *Black on green cover. Stapled.*

SB4	4s. 2d. booklet containing eight ½d. and four 1d., 1½d., 3d. and 6d. (Nos. 71/3, 75, 77) in blocks of 4	7·00

The booklet covers were reprinted with amended postage rates and released by the Crown Agents on 21 September 1970.

POSTAGE DUE STAMPS

D 1

3d — Normal

3d — Lower serif at left of "3" missing (R. 9/1)

(Typo D.L.R.)

1957 (1 Feb). *Chalk-surfaced paper. Wmk Mult Script CA. P* 14.

D1	D 1	1d. scarlet	1·75	10·00
D2		2d. orange-yellow	2·25	4·75
		a. Large "d"	16·00	
D3		3d. green	3·50	5·50
		a. Missing serif	35·00	
D4		4d. ultramarine	7·00	7·00
D5		5d. lake	5·00	23·00
D1/5		*Set of* 5	18·00	45·00

For illustration of No. D2a see above No. D1 of Lesotho.

D 2

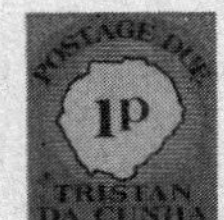

D 3 Outline Map of Tristan da Cunha

(Des J.W. Litho Questa)

1976 (27 May*). *W w* **12** *(sideways). P* 13½ × 14.

D 6	D 2	1p. magenta	10	75
D 7		2p. dull emerald	15	85
D 8		4p. bluish violet	20	85
D 9		5p. new blue	20	85
D10		10p. chestnut	20	1·25
D6/10		*Set of* 5	75	4·00

*This is the local date of issue; the Crown Agents released the stamps four days later.

1976 (3 Sept). *W w* **14** *(sideways*). P* 13½×14.

D11	D 2	1p. magenta	10	40
D12		2p. dull emerald	15	40
D13		4p. bluish violet	20	45
D14		5p. new blue	20	50
D15		10p. chestnut	20	65
		w. Wmk Crown to right of CA	90·00	
D11/15		*Set of* 5	75	2·25

*The normal sideways watermark shows Crown to left of CA, *as seen from the back of the stamp.*

(Des L. Curtis. Litho Questa)

1986 (20 Nov). *W w* **16**. *P* 14½×14.

D16	D 3	1p. deep brown and cinnamon	10	10
D17		2p. deep brown and bright orange	10	10
D18		5p. deep brown and orange-vermilion	10	15
D19		7p. black and bright reddish violet	15	20
D20		10p. black and violet-blue	20	25
D21		25p. black and pale emerald	50	55
D16/21		*Set of* 6	95	1·10

POSTAL FISCAL STAMPS

NATIONAL
SAVINGS

(F 1)

(F 2)

1970 (15 May). *No. 77 optd with Type* F **1** *in red.*

F1	6d. black and green	20	30

No. F1 was originally intended as a National Savings Stamp, but also retained postal validity.

(Handstamped locally by rubber handstamp)

1971 (14 Feb). *Decimal currency. No.* F 1 *handstamped with Type* F **2**, *in violet.*

F2	2½p. on 6d. black and green	3·50	5·00
	a. Pair, one without handstamp	£375	£375

Beware of forgeries of this handstamp.

Trucial States

The Trucial States consisted of Abu Dhabi, Ajman (with Manama), Dubai, Fujeira, Ras al Khaima, Sharjah and Umm al Qiwain. However the following issue of stamps was only put into use in Dubai, despite the inscription "TRUCIAL STATES".

The first organised postal service in Dubai commenced on 19 August 1909 when an Indian Branch Office, administered from Karachi, was opened, using the unoverprinted stamps of India, principally the ½ a. and 1 a. values.

The initial cancellation was a single-ring type inscribed "DUBAI B.O. PERSIAN GULF", which remained in use until 1933.

1909 Cancellation

Its replacement was of the Indian double-circle type showing a similar inscription.

Dubai was upgraded to Sub-Post Office status on 1 April 1942 and this change was reflected in a new double-ring mark inscribed "DUBAI" only. At the same time the office was provided with a single-ring handstamp which also incorporated a cancelling device of seven wavy lines.

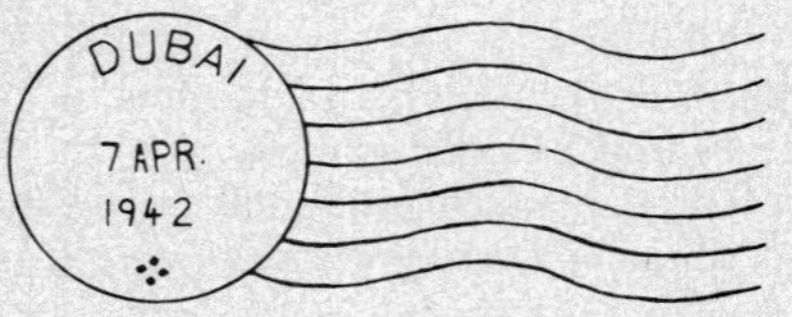

1942 Handstamp

(*illustration reduced: actual size* 65 × 27 *mm*)

A further version of the double-ring type appeared in 1946, showing the "PERSIAN GULF" inscription restored to the lower segment of the postmark.

In October 1947 control of the Dubai Post Office passed to Pakistan whose stamps were used there until the end of March 1948.

On 1 April 1948 the post office was transferred, yet again, to British control and Great Britain stamps surcharged for use in the British Postal Agencies in Eastern Arabia were then sold in Dubai until 6 January 1961, being cancelled with British style single and double-ring postmarks.

(Currency. 100 naye paise = 1 rupee)

1 Palms

2 Dhow

(Des M. Goaman. Photo Harrison (T 1). Des M. Farrar-Bell. Recess D.L.R. (T 2))

1961 (7 Jan). *P* 15 × 14 (*T* 1) *or* 13 × 12½ (*T* **2**).

1	**1**	5 n.p. green	30	10
2		15 n.p. red-brown	30	10
3		20 n.p. bright blue	40	10
4		30 n.p. orange-red	40	10
5		40 n.p. reddish violet	40	10
6		50 n.p. bistre	40	10
7		75 n.p. grey	60	10
8	**2**	1 r. green	3·00	1·25
9		2 r. black	3·00	11·00
10		5 r. carmine-red	4·50	14·00
11		10 r. deep ultramarine	12·00	21·00
1/11		*Set of* 11	22·00	42·00

The Dubai Post Department took over the postal services on 14 June 1963. Later issues for Dubai will be found in Part 19 (*Middle East*) of this catalogue.

Turks and Caicos Islands

TURKS ISLANDS

DEPENDENCY OF JAMAICA

A branch of the British Post Office opened at Grand Turk on 11 December 1854 replacing an earlier arrangement under which mail for the islands was sorted by local R.M.S.P. agents.

No. CC1 is known used between 22 October 1857 and 20 April 1862.

GRAND TURK

CROWNED-CIRCLE HANDSTAMPS

CC 1

CC1 **CC 1** TURKS-ISLANDS (1857) *Price on cover* £4250

PRICES FOR STAMPS ON COVER TO 1945	
Nos. 1/5	*from* × 25
No. 6	—
Nos. 7/20	*from* × 30
Nos. 20a/48	—
Nos. 49/52	*from* × 5
Nos. 53/7	*from* × 6
Nos. 58/65	*from* × 15
Nos. 66/9	*from* × 5
Nos. 70/2	*from* × 10
Nos. 101/9	*from* × 8
Nos. 110/26	*from* × 6
Nos. 129/39	*from* × 4
Nos. 140/53	*from* × 12
Nos. 154/90	*from* × 3
Nos. 191/3	*from* × 10
Nos. 194/205	*from* × 2

1

Throat flaw (R.3/4)

(Recess P.B.)

1867 (4 Apr). *No wmk. P* 11–12.

1	**1**	1d. dull rose	42·00	42·00
		a. Throat flaw	£130	£140
2		6d. black	80·00	95·00
3		1s. dull blue	70·00	60·00

1873–79. *Wmk Small Star. W* w **2** (*sideways on Nos.* 5 *and* 6). *P* 11–12 × 14½–15½.

4	**1**	1d. dull rose-lake (7.73)	45·00	45·00
		a. Throat flaw	£140	£150
		b. Wmk sideways	75·00	75·00
		ba. Throat flaw	£225	£225
5		1d. dull red (1.79)	50·00	60·00
		a. Imperf between (horiz pair)	£11000	
		b. Throat flaw	£160	£180
		c. Wmk upright		
6		1s. lilac (1.79)	£5000	£2000

1881 (1 Jan). *Stamps of the preceding issues surcharged locally, in black.*

There are twelve different settings of the ½d., nine settings of the 2½d., and six settings of the 4d.

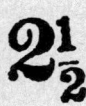

(2) (3)

Setting 1. *T* **2**. *Long fraction bar. Two varieties repeated fifteen times in the sheet.*

7	½ on 6d. black	65·00	90·00

Setting 2. *T* **3**. *Short fraction bar. Three varieties in a vertical strip repeated ten times in sheet.*

Setting 3. *Similar to setting* 2, *but the middle stamp of the three varieties has a longer bar.*

8	½ on 6d. black (*setting* 2 *only*)	55·00	85·00
9	½ on 1s. dull blue	80·00	£130
	a. Surch double	£4500	

(4) (5) (6)

Three varieties in a vertical strip repeated ten times in sheet.

Section 4. *Types* **4, 5, 6.**

Setting 5. *Types* **4** (*without bar*), **5, 6**.

Setting 6. *Types* **4, 5, 6** (*without bar*).

Setting 7. *Types* **4** (*shorter thick bar*), **6, 6**.

10	½ on 1d. dull red (*setting* 7 *only*) (T **6**)		
	a. Type **4** (shorter thick bar)	£5500	
11	½ on 1s. dull blue (*setting* 6 *and* 7) (T **4**)	£900	
	a. Type **4** (shorter thick bar)	£1100	
	b. Type **5**	£900	
	c. Type **6**	£800	
	d. Type **6** (without bar)	£900	
	e. Surch double (T **6** without bar)		
12	½ on 1s. lilac (T **4**)	£225	£325
	a. Without bar	£475	
	b. With short thick bar	£450	
	c. Surch double	£2500	
	cb. Surch double and short thick bar	£4500	
13	½ on 1s. lilac (T **5**)	£110	£160
	a. Surch double	£2250	
14	½ on 1s. lilac (T **6**)	£110	
	a. Without bar	£475	
	b. Surch double	£3250	
	ba. Surch double and without bar	£4500	

Care should be taken in the identification of Types **6** and **7** which are very similar. For the 1s. value some varieties of No. 9 are often confused with Nos. 11b/c.

(7) (8) (9) (10)

Setting 8. *T* **7**. *Three varieties in a vertical strip. All have a very short bar.*

15	½ on 1d. dull red	55·00	85·00
	a. Throat flaw	£180	

Setting 9. *T* **8**. *Three varieties in a vertical strip. Bars long and thick and "1" leaning a little to left.*

16	½ on 1d. dull red	£180	£200
	a. Surch double		
	b. Throat flaw	£450	

Setting 10. *T* **9** *and* **10**. *Fifteen varieties repeated twice in a sheet. Ten are of T* **9** (*Rows* 1 *and* 2), *five of T* **10** (*Row* 3).

17	½ on 1d. dull red (T **9**)	50·00	85·00
	a. Surch double	£2500	
18	½ on 1d. dull red (T **10**)	80·00	£120
	a. Surch double		
	b. Throat flaw	£200	
19	½ on 1s. lilac (T **9**)	80·00	£130
20	½ on 1s. lilac (T **10**)	£140	£225
20*a*	½ on 1s. dull blue (T **9**)	£7000	
20*b*	½ on 1s. dull blue (T **10**)	£10000	

Types **9** and **11**. The difference is in the position of the "2" in relation to the "1". In setting 10 the "2" is to the left of the "1" except on No. 10 (where it is directly below the "1") and in setting 11 it is to the right except on No. 2 (where it is to the left, as in setting 10).

(11) (12) (13) (14)

Setting 11. *T* **9** *and* **11** *to* **14**. *Fifteen varieties repeated twice in a sheet. Nine of T* **11**, *three of T* **12**, *and one each of T* **9**, **13** *and* **14**.

Setting 12. *Similar to last, but T* **13** *replaced by another T* **12**.

21	½ on 1d. dull red (T **11**)	90·00	
22	½ on 1d. dull red (T **12**)	£190	
	a. Throat flaw	£850	
23	½ on 1d. dull red (T **13**)	£1000	
	a. Throat flaw	£1000	
24	½ on 1d. dull red (T **14**)	£425	
24*a*	½ on 1s. dull blue (T **11**)	£10000	

Type **9** from these settings, where it occurs on position 2, can only be distinguished from similar stamps from setting 10 when *se-tenant* with Type **11**.

(15) (16)

Setting 1. *T* **15**. *Fraction in very small type.*

25	2½ on 6d. black	£7000	

Setting 2. *T* **16**. *Two varieties repeated fifteen times in a sheet. Large "2" on level with top of the "1", long thin bar.*

26	2½ on 6d. black	£275	£325
	a. Imperf between (horiz pair)	£10000	
	b. Surch double	£5500	

2½ (17) 2½ (18) 2½ (19)

Setting 3. *T* **17**. *As T* **16**, *but large "2" not so high up.*

No.	Type	Description	Unused	Used
27		2½ on 1s. lilac	£1700	

Setting 4. *T* **18**. *Three varieties in a vertical strip repeated ten times in sheet. Large "2" placed lower and small bar.*

No.	Type	Description	Unused	Used
28		2½ on 6d. black	£140	£200
		a. Surch double		

Setting 5. *T* **19**. *Three varieties in a vertical strip repeated ten times in sheet "2" further from "½", small fraction bar.*

No.	Type	Description	Unused	Used
29		2½ on 1s. lilac	£550	£800

2½ (20) 2½ (21)

Setting 6. *T* **20** *and* **21**. *Fifteen varieties. Ten of T* **20** *and five of T* **21**, *repeated twice in a sheet.*

No.	Type	Description	Unused	Used
30		2½ on 1s. lilac (T **20**)	£6500	
31		2½ on 1s. lilac (T **21**)	£9500	

2½ (22) 2½ (23) 2½ (24)

Setting 7. *T* **22**. *Three varieties in a vertical strip, repeated ten times in a sheet.*

No.	Type	Description	Unused	Used
32		2½ on 6d. black	£7500	
33		2½ on 1s. dull blue	£11000	

Setting 8. *T* **23** *and* **24**. *Fifteen varieties. Ten of T* **23** *and five of T* **24**, *repeated twice in a sheet.*

No.	Type	Description	Unused	Used
34		2½ on 1d. dull red (T **23**)	£600	
35		2½ on 1d. dull red (T **24**)	£1200	
		a. Throat flaw		
36		2½ on 1s. lilac (T **23**)	£500	£650
		a. Surch "½" double	£2750	
37		2½ on 1s. lilac (T **24**)	£1200	
		a. Surch "½" double	£4250	

2½ (25) 2½ (26)

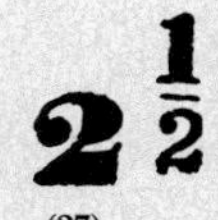

(27)

Setting 9. *T* **25**, **26**, *and* **27**. *Fifteen varieties. Ten of T* **25**, *three of T* **26**, *one of T* **26** *without bar, and one of T* **27**, *repeated twice in a sheet.*

No.	Type	Description	Unused	Used
38		2½ on 1s. dull blue (T **25**)	£700	
39		2½ on 1s. dull blue (T **26**)	£1700	
40		2½ on 1s. dull blue (T **26**) (without bar)	£6000	
41		2½ on 1s. dull blue (T **27**)	£6000	

4 (28) 4 (29) 4 (30)

Setting 1. *T* **28**. *"4" 8 mm high, pointed top.*

No.	Type	Description	Unused	Used
42		4 on 6d. black	£250	£300

Settings 2–6. *T* **29** *and* **30**.

No.	Type	Description	Unused	Used
43		4 on 6d. black (T **29**)	65·00	85·00
44		4 on 6d. black (T **30**)	£325	£375
45		4 on 1s. lilac (T **29**)	£375	
		a. Surch double		
46		4 on 1s. lilac (T **30**)	£2000	
		a. Surch double		
47		4 on 1d. dull red (T **29**)	£700	£475
48		4 on 1d. dull red (T **28**)	£800	£550

The components of these settings can only be distinguished when in blocks. Details are given in the handbook by John J. Challis.

31

One Penny

(32)

(Type D.L.R.)

1881. *Wmk Crown CC (sideways on T* **1**). *P* 14.

No.	Type	Description	Unused	Used
49	**1**	1d. brown-red (Oct)	55·00	75·00
		a. Throat flaw	£150	£160
50	**31**	4d. ultramarine (Die I) (Aug)	85·00	60·00
51	**1**	6d. olive-black (Oct)	80·00	£110
52		1s. slate-green (Oct)	£110	£100

1882–85. *Wmk Crown CA. P* 14.

No.	Type	Description	Unused	Used
53	**31**	½d. blue-green (Die I) (2.82)	8·00	19·00
		a. Pale green (12.85)	2·00	3·50
		b. Top left triangle detached	70·00	
55	**1**	1d. orange-brown (10.83)	48·00	30·00
		a. Bisected (½d.) (on cover)	†	£1800
		b. Throat flaw	£120	80·00
56	**31**	2½d. red-brown (Die I) (2.82)	13·00	10·00
57		4d. grey (Die I) (10.84)	10·00	2·00
		a. Bisected (2d.) (on cover)	†	£1800

For illustration of "top left triangle detached" variety see above No. 6 of Montserrat.

1887 (July)–**89.** *Wmk Crown CA.* (*a*) *P* 12.

No.	Type	Description	Unused	Used
58	**1**	1d. crimson-lake	9·50	2·50
		a. Imperf between (horiz pair)	£9500	
		b. Throat flaw	28·00	10·00

(*b*) *P* 14

No.	Type	Description	Unused	Used
59	**1**	6d. yellow-brown (2.89) (Optd S. £60)	2·50	2·75
60		1s. sepia	4·00	2·75

During a shortage of 1d. stamps a supply of JAMAICA No. 27 was sent to the Turks and Caicos Islands in April 1889 and used until replaced by No. 61.

1889 (May). *Surch at Grand Turk with T* **32**.

No.	Type	Description	Unused	Used
61	**31**	1d. on 2½d. red-brown	6·50	9·50
		a. "ONE" omitted		
		b. Bisected (½d.) (on cover)	†	—

No. 61a was caused by misplacement of the surcharge. Stamps from the same sheet can be found with the surcharge reading "Penny One".

Neck flaw (R.3/2)

1889–93. *Wmk Crown CA. P* 14.

No.	Type	Description	Unused	Used
62	**1**	1d. crimson-lake (7.89)	3·00	3·50
		a. Bisected (½d.) (on cover)	†	—
		b. Throat flaw	13·00	14·00
		c. Neck flaw	16·00	18·00
63		1d. lake	2·00	2·25
		a. Bisected (½d.) (on cover)	†	—
		b. Throat flaw	8·00	8·50
		c. Neck flaw	10·00	12·00
64		1d. pale rosy lake	1·40	3·75
		b. Throat flaw	4·75	13·00
		c. Neck flaw	7·00	17·00
65	**31**	2½d. ultram (Die II) (4.93) (Optd S. £55)	2·00	1·25

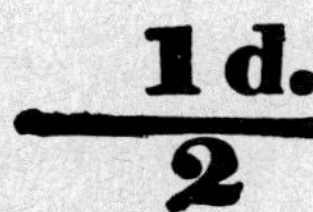

(33)

34

1893 (July). *No. 57 surch at Grand Turk with T* **33**.

Setting 1. *Bars between "1d." and "2" separate, instead of continuous across the rows of stamps.*

No.	Type	Description	Unused	Used
66		½d. on 4d. grey	£600	£300

Setting 2. *Continuous bars. Thin and thick bar* 10¾ *mm apart. "2" under the "1".*

No.	Type	Description	Unused	Used
67		½d. on 4d. grey	£130	£130

Setting 3. *As last, but bars* 11¾ *mm apart.*

No.	Type	Description	Unused	Used
68		½d. on 4d. grey	£120	£120

Setting 4. *Bars* 11 *mm apart. Five out of the six varieties in the strip have the "2" below the space between the "1" and "d".*

No.	Type	Description	Unused	Used
69		½d. on 4d. grey	£120	£130

There is a fifth setting, but the variation is slight.

(Typo D.L.R.)

1894–95. *Wmk Crown CA. P* 14.

No.	Type	Description	Unused	Used
70	**31**	½d. dull green (Die II) (1894)	1·50	1·50
71		4d. dull purple & ultram (Die II) (5.95)	8·00	11·00
72	**34**	5d. olive-green and carmine (6.94)	3·25	10·00
		a. Bisected (2½d.) (on cover)	†	£2750
70/2		*Set of* 3	11·50	20·00
71/2 Optd "Specimen"		*Set of* 2	£100	

TURKS AND CAICOS ISLANDS

35 Badge of the Islands **36**

The dates on the stamps have reference to the political separation from Bahamas.

(Recess D.L.R.)

1900 (10 Nov)–**04.** *Wmk Crown CA* (½*d. to* 1*s.*) *or Wmk Crown CC* (2*s.,* 3*s.*). *P* 14.

No.	Type	Description	Unused	Used
101	**35**	½d. green	2·75	4·00
		x. Wmk reversed		
102		1d. red	3·50	75
		w. Wmk inverted		
103		2d. sepia	75	1·25
		w. Wmk inverted		
		x. Wmk reversed		
104		2½d. blue	6·50	15·00
		a. Greyish blue (1904)	1·75	1·00
		aw. Wmk inverted	60·00	
		ay. Wmk inverted and reversed		
105		4d. orange	3·50	7·00
106		6d. dull mauve	1·75	6·50
107		1s. purple-brown	2·25	14·00
108	**36**	2s. purple	40·00	55·00
109		3s. lake	50·00	70·00
101/9		*Set of* 9	95·00	£140
101/9 Optd "Specimen"		*Set of* 9	£225	

1905–08. *Wmk Mult Crown CA. P* 14.

No.	Type	Description	Unused	Used
110	**35**	½d. green	2·75	15
111		1d. red	11·00	50
		w. Wmk inverted		
112		3d. purple/*yellow* (1908) (Optd S. £50)	1·50	6·00
		w. Wmk inverted		
110/12		*Set of* 3	14·00	6·00

37 Turk's-head Cactus **38**

(Recess D.L.R.)

1909 (2 Sept)–**11.** *Wmk Mult Crown CA. P* 14.

No.	Type	Description	Unused	Used
115	**37**	¼d. rosy mauve (1910)	1·25	1·00
		w. Wmk inverted		
116		¼d. red (1911)	30	30
		w. Wmk inverted		
117	**38**	½d. yellow-green	45	30
		w. Wmk inverted		
		x. Wmk reversed	40·00	
		y. Wmk inverted and reversed		
118		1d. red	55	30
119		2d. greyish slate	90	1·40
120		2½d. blue	1·25	3·75
		w. Wmk inverted		
		x. Wmk reversed	50·00	
121		3d. purple/*yellow*	1·75	2·00
122		4d. red/*yellow*	3·25	7·00
123		6d. purple	6·00	7·00
124		1s. black/*green*	6·00	8·50
		w. Wmk inverted		
125		2s. red/*green*	26·00	48·00
126		3s. black/*red*	26·00	35·00
115/26		*Set of* 12	65·00	£100
115/26 Optd "Specimen"		*Set of* 12	£200	

See also Nos. 154 and 162.

39

WAR TAX

(40)

1913 (1 Apr)–**21.** *Wmk Mult Crown CA. P* 14.

No.	Type	Description	Unused	Used
129	**39**	½d. green	40	1·75
		w. Wmk inverted		
130		1d. red	1·00	2·25
		a. Bright rose-scarlet	1·10	2·00
		ax. Wmk reversed	40·00	
		b. Rose-carmine (1918)	3·25	4·50
131		2d. greyish slate	1·40	3·00
132		2½d. ultramarine	2·25	2·50
		aw. Wmk inverted		
		b. Bright blue (1918)	3·75	2·50
133		3d. purple/*yellow*	2·25	8·00
		a. On lemon	15·00	
		b. On yellow-buff	3·75	7·50
		c. On orange-buff	1·75	
		cx. Wmk reversed	60·00	
		d. On pale yellow	2·00	7·00
134		4d. red/*yellow*	1·00	8·50
		a. On orange-buff (Optd S. £48)	1·60	7·00
		b. Carmine on pale yellow	6·50	15·00
135		5d. pale olive-green (18.5.16)	6·50	18·00
136		6d. dull purple	2·25	3·25
		w. Wmk inverted		
		x. Wmk reversed		

137 **39** 1s. brown-orange 1·50 4·00
w. Wmk inverted
138 2s. red/*blue-green* 7·50 25·00
a. On greenish white (1919) 24·00 70·00
b. On emerald (3.21) (Optd S. £48) 48·00 70·00
bx. Wmk reversed £100
139 3s. black/*red* 15·00 25·00
129/39 *Set of* 11 35·00 85·00
129/39 Optd "Specimen" *Set of* 11 £180

1917 (3 Jan). *Optd with T* **40** *at bottom of stamp.*
140 **39** 1d. red 10 1·00
a. Opt double £160
b. "TAX" omitted
c. "WAR TAX" omitted in vert pair with normal £325
d. Opt inverted at top 65·00
e. Opt double, one inverted* £100
f. Opt inverted only, in pair with No. 140e* £450
141 3d. purple/*yellow-buff* 85 3·00
a. Opt double 55·00
b. Purple/lemon 1·75 4·25
ba. Opt double 55·00
bb. Opt double, one inverted £250

*In Nos. 140e/f the inverted overprint is at foot and reads "TAX WAR" owing to displacement. No. 140e also exists with "WAR" omitted from the inverted overprint.

In both values of the first printings the stamp in the bottom left-hand corner of the sheet has a long "T" in "TAX", and on the first stamp of the sixth row the "X" is damaged and looks like a reversed "K".

1917 (Oct). *Second printing with overprint at top or in middle of stamp.*
143 **39** 1d. red 10 75
a. Inverted opt at bottom or centre 42·00
c. Opt omitted (in pair with normal) £300
d. Opt double, one at top, one at bottom 45·00
e. As d., but additional opt in top margin £100
f. Vertical pair, one as d., the other normal £200
g. Pair, one opt inverted, one normal £325
h. Double opt at top (in pair with normal) £200
i. Opt double 40·00 40·00
144 3d. purple/*yellow* 60 1·50
a. Opt double 28·00
b. Opt double, one inverted £225
c. Purple/lemon 2·50

1918. *Overprinted with T* **40**.
145 **39** 3d. purple/*yellow* (R.) 8·00 20·00
a. Opt double £275

WAR TAX (41) · WAR TAX (42) · WAR TAX (43)

1918. *Optd with T* **41** *in London by D.L.R.*
146 **39** 1d. rose-carmine 20 1·25
a. Bright rose-scarlet 15 1·25
aw. Wmk inverted
147 3d. purple/*yellow* 1·00 2·50
146/7 Optd "Specimen" *Set of* 2 80·00

1919. *Optd with T* **41** *in London by D.L.R.*
148 **39** 3d. purple/*orange-buff* (R.) 10 1·50
148 Optd "Specimen" 40·00

1919. *Local overprint. T* **40**, *in violet.*
149 **39** 1d. bright rose-scarlet 15 2·50
a. "WAR" omitted £110
b. Opt double 20·00
c. Opt double in pair with normal £110
d. Opt double, one inverted
e. Rose-carmine 6·50 14·00
ea. Opt double
w. Wmk inverted 25·00

1919. *Optd with T* **42**.
150 **39** 1d. scarlet 10 80
a. Opt double £130 £150
b. Opt double, one albino and reversed
151 3d. purple/*orange-buff* 30 2·25
w. Wmk inverted 25·00
x. Wmk reversed 25·00

1919 (17 Dec). *Optd with T* **43**.
152 **39** 1d. scarlet 10 1·75
a. Opt inverted
153 3d. purple/*orange-buff* 20 2·00
w. Wmk inverted 25·00
x. Wmk reversed 25·00
y. Wmk inverted and reversed 12·00

The two bottom rows of this setting have the words "WAR" and "TAX" about 1 mm further apart.

1921 (23 Apr). *Wmk Mult Script CA. P* 14.
154 **37** ¼d. rose-red 2·50 9·00
155 **39** ½d. green 2·75 5·00
156 1d. carmine-red 1·00 4·50
157 2d. slate-grey 1·00 15·00
y. Wmk inverted and reversed 45·00
158 2½d. bright blue 1·75 6·50
159 5d. sage-green 7·00 35·00
160 **39** 6d. purple 6·50 38·00
w. Wmk inverted
x. Wmk reversed 45·00
161 1s. brown-orange 6·50 21·00
154/61 *Set of* 8 26·00 £120
154/61 Optd "Specimen" *Set of* 8 £140

44 · **45**

(Recess D.L.R.)

1922 (20 Nov)–**26.** *P* 14. (*a*) *Wmk Mult Script CA*
162 **37** ¼d. black (11.10.26) 60 80
163 **44** ½d. yellow-green 1·00 1·75
a. Bright green 1·00 1·50
b. Apple-green 4·25 9·00
164 1d. brown 40 3·00
165 1½d. scarlet (24.11.25) 5·50 11·00
166 2d. slate 40 3·75
167 2½d. purple/*pale yellow* 40 1·50
168 3d. bright blue 40 3·75
169 4d. red/*pale yellow* 85 10·00
ax. Wmk reversed
b. Carmine/pale yellow 4·50 13·00
170 5d. sage-green 75 16·00
y. Wmk inverted and reversed 45·00
171 6d. purple 60 3·50
x. Wmk reversed
172 1s. brown-orange 70 11·00
173 2s. red/*emerald* 2·00 7·00

(*b*) *Wmk Mult Crown CA*
174 **44** 2s. red/*emerald* (24.11.25) 25·00 65·00
175 3s. black/*red* (24.11.25) 5·00 18·00
162/75 *Set of* 14 38·00 £140
162/75 Optd "Specimen" *Set of* 14 £200

1928 (1 Mar). *Inscr* "POSTAGE & REVENUE". *Wmk Mult Script CA. P* 14.
176 **45** ½d. green 60 40
177 1d. brown 60 70
178 1½d. scarlet 50 2·50
179 2d. grey 45 30
180 2½d. purple/*yellow* 45 3·25
181 3d. bright blue 45 4·00
182 6d. purple 45 5·50
183 1s. brown-orange 3·75 5·50
184 2s. red/*emerald* 5·50 32·00
185 5s. green/*yellow* 11·00 32·00
186 10s. purple/*blue* 42·00 90·00
176/86 *Set of* 11 60·00 £160
176/86 Optd "Specimen" *Set of* 11 £140

1935 (6 May). *Silver Jubilee. As Nos.* 114/17 *of Jamaica, but ptd by Waterlow. P* 11×12.
187 ½d. black and green 20 60
k. Kite and vertical log 24·00
l. Kite and horizontal log 24·00
188 3d. brown and deep blue 1·75 3·50
k. Kite and vertical log 60·00
189 6d. light blue and olive-green 1·75 3·75
k. Kite and vertical log 60·00
190 1s. slate and purple 1·75 3·25
k. Kite and vertical log 60·00
187/90 *Set of* 4 5·00 10·00
187/90 Perf "Specimen" *Set of* 4 75·00

For illustrations of plate varieties see Omnibus section following Zimbabwe.

1937 (12 May). *Coronation. As Nos.* 118/20 *of Jamaica.*
191 ½d. myrtle-green 10 10
a. Deep green 40·00
192 2d. grey-black 50 40
193 3d. bright blue 60 40
191/3 *Set of* 3 1·00 75
191/3 Perf "Specimen" *Set of* 3 55·00

46 Raking Salt · **47** Salt Industry

(Recess Waterlow)

1938 (18 June)–**45.** *Wmk Mult Script CA. P* 12½.
194 **46** ¼d. black 10 10
195 ½d. yellowish green 3·25 15
a. Deep green (6.11.44) 70 70
196 1d. red-brown 60 10
197 1½d. scarlet 60 15
198 2d. grey 60 30
199 2½d. yellow-orange 4·00 80
a. Orange (6.11.44) 2·00 1·50
200 3d. bright blue 50 30
201 6d. mauve 7·50 1·25
201*a* 6d. sepia (9.2.45) 20 20
202 1s. yellow-bistre 3·25 7·50
202*a* 1s. grey-olive (9.2.45) 20 20
203 **47** 2s. deep rose-carmine 42·00 11·00
a. Bright rose-carmine (6.11.44) 17·00 14·00
204 5s. yellowish green 48·00 13·00
a. Deep green (6.11.44) 35·00 17·00
205 10s. bright violet 12·00 5·50
194/205 *Set of* 14 70·00 35·00
194/205 Perf "Specimen" *Set of* 14 £200

1946 (4 Nov). *Victory. As Nos.* 141/2 *of Jamaica.*
206 2d. black 10 10
207 3d. blue 15 10
206/7 Perf "Specimen" *Set of* 2 55·00

1948 (13 Sept). *Royal Silver Wedding. As Nos.* 143/4 *of Jamaica.*
208 1d. red-brown 15 10
209 10s. mauve 6·50 9·00

50 Badge of the Islands · **53** Queen Victoria and King George VI

(Recess Waterlow)

1948 (14 Dec). *Centenary of Separation from Bahamas. T* **50**, **53** *and similar designs. Wmk Mult Script CA. P* 12½.
210 **50** ½d. blue-green 40 15
211 2d. carmine 75 15
212 – 3d. blue 1·00 15
213 – 6d. violet 50 20
214 **53** 2s. black and bright blue 55 55
215 5s. black and green 90 1·50
216 10s. black and brown 90 3·25
210/16 *Set of* 7 4·50 5·50

Designs: *Horiz*—3d. Flag of Turks and Caicos Islands; 6d. Map of islands.

1949 (10 Oct). *75th Anniv of U.P.U. As Nos.* 145/8 *of Jamaica.*
217 2½d. red-orange 40 55
218 3d. deep blue 1·10 50
219 6d. brown 50 50
220 1s. olive 50 35
217/20 *Set of* 4 2·25 1·75

65 Bulk Salt Loading

66 Dependency's Badge

(Recess Waterlow)

1950 (1 Aug). *T* **65** *and similar horiz designs, and T* **66**. *Wmk Mult Script CA. P* 12½.
221 ½d. green 30 40
222 1d. red-brown 30 75
223 1½d. deep carmine 60 55
224 2d. red-orange 30 40
225 2½d. grey-olive 50 50
226 3d. bright blue 30 40
227 4d. black and rose 2·50 70
228 6d. black and blue 2·00 50
229 1s. black and blue-green 80 40
230 1s. 6d. black and scarlet 5·00 3·25
231 2s. emerald and ultramarine 2·25 3·50
232 5s. blue and black 12·00 6·00
233 10s. black and violet 15·00 15·00
221/33 *Set of* 13 38·00 28·00

Designs:—1d. Salt Cay; 1½d. Caicos mail; 2d. Grand Turk; 2½d. Sponge diving; 3d. South Creek; 4d. Map; 6d. Grand Turk Light; 1s. Government House; 1s. 6d. Cockburn Harbour; 2s. Government Offices; 5s. Loading salt.

1953 (2 June). *Coronation. As No.* 153 *of Jamaica, but ptd by B.W. & Co.*
234 2d. black and orange-red 20 80

67 M.V. *Kirksons*

(Recess Waterlow)

1955 (1 Feb). *T* **67** *and similar horiz design. Wmk Mult Script CA. P* 12½.
235 5d. black and bright green 30 30
236 8d. black and brown 2·25 30

Design:—8d. Greater Flamingoes in flight.

69 Queen Elizabeth II (after Annigoni)

70 Bonefish

82 Dependency's Badge

(Recess B.W.)

1957 (25 Nov). *T* **69/70**, **82** *and similar horiz designs as T* **70**. *W w* **12**. *P* 13½×14 (1d.), 14 (10s.) *or* 13½ (*others*).

No.	Description	Unused	Used
237	1d. deep blue and carmine	15	20
238	1½d. grey-green and orange	15	30
239	2d. red-brown and olive	15	15
240	2½d. carmine and green	15	15
241	3d. turquoise-blue and purple	15	15
242	4d. lake and black	20	15
243	5d. slate-green and brown	40	40
244	6d. carmine-rose and blue	2·00	55
245	8d. vermilion and black	3·00	20
246	1s. deep blue and black	40	10
247	1s. 6d. sepia and deep ultramarine	6·50	70
248	2s. deep ultramarine and brown	7·50	2·50
249	5s. black and carmine	1·25	2·00
250	10s. black and purple	12·00	8·00
237/250 *and* 253	*Set of* 15	65·00	28·00

Designs:—2d. Red Grouper; 2½d. Spiny Lobster; 3d. Albacore; 4d. Mutton Snapper; 5d. Permit; 6d. Queen or Pink Conch; 8d. Greater Flamingoes; 1s. Spanish Mackerel; 1s. 6d. Salt Cay; 2s. *Uakon* (Caicos sloop); 5s. Cable Office.

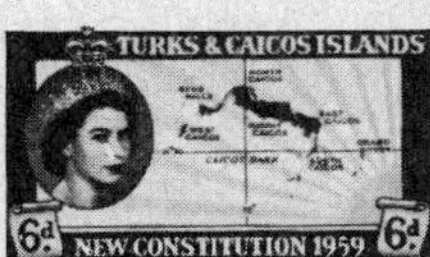
83 Map of the Turks and Caicos Islands

(Photo D.L.R.)

1959 (4 July). *New Constitution. Wmk Mult Script CA.* *P* 13½ × 14.

No.	Type	Description	Unused	Used
251	**83**	6d. deep olive and light orange	45	40
252		8d. violet and light orange	45	40

84 Brown Pelican

(Des Mrs. S. Hurd. Photo Harrison)

1960 (1 Nov). *W w* 12. *P* 14 × 14½.

No.	Type	Description	Unused	Used
253	**84**	£1 sepia and deep red	40·00	16·00

CROWN COLONY

1963 (4 June). *Freedom from Hunger. As No.* 80 *of Lesotho.*

No.	Description	Unused	Used
254	8d. carmine	30	15

1963 (2 Sept). *Red Cross Centenary. As Nos.* 203/4 *of Jamaica.*

No.	Description	Unused	Used
255	2d. red and black	15	30
256	8d. red and blue	30	30

1964 (23 Apr). 400*th Birth Anniv of William Shakespeare. As No.* 156 *of Montserrat.*

No.	Description	Unused	Used
257	8d. green	15	10

1965 (17 May). *I.T.U. Centenary. As Nos.* 98/9 *of Lesotho.*

No.	Description	Unused	Used
258	1d. vermilion and brown	10	10
259	2s. light emerald and turquoise-blue	20	20

1965 (25 Oct). *International Co-operation Year. As Nos.* 100/1 *of Lesotho.*

No.	Description	Unused	Used
260	1d. reddish purple and turquoise-green	10	15
261	8d. deep bluish green and lavender	20	15

1966 (24 Jan). *Churchill Commemoration. As Nos.* 102/5 *of Lesotho.*

No.	Description	Unused	Used
262	1d. new blue	10	10
263	2d. deep green	20	10
264	8d. brown	25	10
	a. Gold ptg double	£130	
265	1s. 6d. bluish violet	30	45
262/5	*Set of* 4	70	55

1966 (4 Feb). *Royal Visit. As Nos.* 183/4 *of Montserrat.*

No.	Description	Unused	Used
266	8d. black and ultramarine	25	10
267	1s. 6d. black and magenta	45	20

85 Andrew Symmer going ashore

(Des V. Whiteley. Photo D.L.R.)

1966 (1 Oct). *Bicentenary of "Ties with Britain" T* **85** *and similar horiz designs. P* 13½.

No.	Description	Unused	Used
268	1d. deep blue and orange	10	10
269	8d. red, blue and orange-yellow	20	15
270	1s. 6d. multicoloured	25	20
268/70	*Set of* 3	50	40

Designs:—8d. Andrew Symmer and Royal Warrant; 1s. 6d. Arms and Royal Cypher.

1966 (1 Dec). 20*th Anniv of U.N.E.S.C.O. As Nos.* 342/4 *of Mauritius.*

No.	Description	Unused	Used
271	1d. slate-violet, red, yellow and orange	10	10
272	8d. orange-yellow, violet and deep olive	15	10
273	1s. 6d. black, bright purple and orange	20	40
271/3	*Set of* 3	35	50

88 Turk's-head Cactus

89 Boat-building

90 Arms of Turks and Caicos Islands

91 Queen Elizabeth II

(Des V. Whiteley. Photo Harrison)

1967 (1 Feb). *Designs as T* **88/91**. *W w* **12**. *P* 14½ × 14 (*vert*) *or* 14 × 14½ (*horiz*).

No.	Description	Unused	Used
274	1d. olive-yellow, vermilion & brt bluish vio	10	10
275	1½d. brown and orange-yellow	20	10
276	2d. deep slate and deep orange-yellow	20	10
277	3d. agate and dull green	20	10
278	4d. bright mauve, black and turquoise	85	10
279	6d. sepia and new blue	40	10
280	8d. yellow, turquoise-blue and deep blue	20	10
281	1s. maroon and turquoise	20	10
282	1s. 6d. orange-yellow, lake-brn & dp turq-bl	50	20
283	2s. multicoloured	60	1·50
284	3s. maroon and turquoise-blue	55	40
285	5s. ochre, blue and new blue	1·25	2·50
286	10s. multicoloured	1·75	3·00
287	£1 Prussian blue, silver and crimson	3·50	6·00
274/287	*Set of* 14	8·50	12·50

Designs: *Vert as T* **88**—2d. Donkey; 3d. Sisal industry; 6d. Salt industry; 8d. Skin-diving; 1s. 6d. Water-skiing. *Horiz as T* **89**—4d. Conch industry; 1s. Fishing; 2s. Crawfish industry; 3s. Maps of Turks and Caicos Islands and West Indies; 5s. Fishing industry.

102 Turks Islands 1d. Stamp of 1867

(Des R. Granger Barrett. Photo Harrison)

1967 (1 May). *Stamp Centenary. T* **102** *and similar horiz designs. W w* **12**. *P* 14½.

No.	Description	Unused	Used
288	1d. black and light magenta	15	10
	w. Wmk inverted	28·00	
289	6d. black and bluish grey	25	15
290	1s. black and turquoise-blue	25	15
288/90	*Set of* 3	60	30

Designs:—6d. Queen Elizabeth "stamp" and Turks Islands 6d. stamp of 1867; 1s. Turks Islands 1s. stamp of 1867.

104 Human Rights Emblem and Charter

(Des R. Granger Barrett. Photo Harrison)

1968 (1 Apr). *Human Rights Year. W w* **12**. *P* 14 × 14½.

No.	Type	Description	Unused	Used
291	**104**	1d. multicoloured	10	10
292		8d. multicoloured	15	15
293		1s. 6d. multicoloured	15	15
291/3		*Set of* 3	30	30

105 Dr Martin Luther King and "Freedom March"

(Des V. Whiteley. Photo Harrison)

1968 (1 Oct). *Martin Luther King Commemoration. W w* **12**. *P* 14 × 14½.

No.	Type	Description	Unused	Used
294	**105**	2d. yellow-brown, blackish brn & dp bl	10	10
295		8d. yellow-brown, blackish brn & lake	15	15
296		1s. 6d. yellow-brn, blackish brn & vio	15	15
294/6		*Set of* 3	30	30

(New Currency. 100 cents=1 dollar)

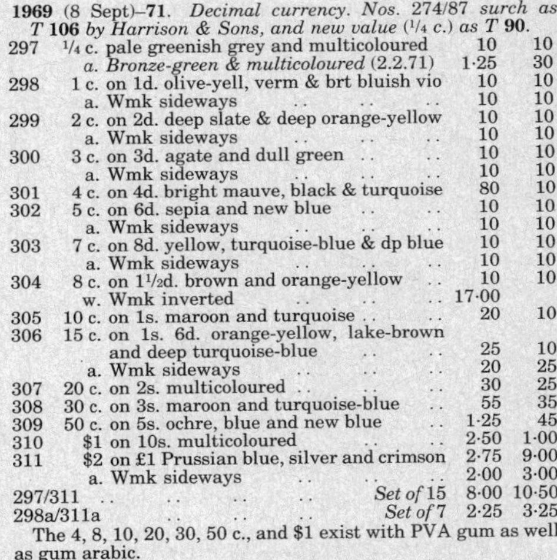

1c

(106)

107 "The Nativity with John the Baptist"

1969 (8 Sept)–**71**. *Decimal currency. Nos.* 274/87 *surch as T* **106** *by Harrison & Sons, and new value* (¼ *c.*) *as T* **90**.

No.	Description	Unused	Used
297	¼ c. pale greenish grey and multicoloured	10	10
	a. Bronze-green & multicoloured (2.2.71)	1·25	30
298	1 c. on 1d. olive-yell, verm & brt bluish vio	10	10
	a. Wmk sideways	10	10
299	2 c. on 2d. deep slate & deep orange-yellow	10	10
	a. Wmk sideways	10	10
300	3 c. on 3d. agate and dull green	10	10
	a. Wmk sideways	10	10
301	4 c. on 4d. bright mauve, black & turquoise	80	10
302	5 c. on 6d. sepia and new blue	10	10
	a. Wmk sideways	10	10
303	7 c. on 8d. yellow, turquoise-blue & dp blue	10	10
	a. Wmk sideways	10	10
304	8 c. on 1½d. brown and orange-yellow	10	10
	w. Wmk inverted	17·00	
305	10 c. on 1s. maroon and turquoise	20	10
306	15 c. on 1s. 6d. orange-yellow, lake-brown and deep turquoise-blue	25	10
	a. Wmk sideways	20	25
307	20 c. on 2s. multicoloured	30	25
308	30 c. on 3s. maroon and turquoise-blue	55	35
309	50 c. on 5s. ochre, blue and new blue	1·25	45
310	$1 on 10s. multicoloured	2·50	1·00
311	$2 on £1 Prussian blue, silver and crimson	2·75	9·00
	a. Wmk sideways	2·00	3·00
297/311	*Set of* 15	8·00	10·50
298a/311a	*Set of* 7	2·25	3·25

The 4, 8, 10, 20, 30, 50 c., and $1 exist with PVA gum as well as gum arabic.

No. 311 was only on sale through the Crown Agents.

(Des adapted by V. Whiteley. Litho D.L.R.)

1969 (20 Oct). *Christmas. Scenes from 16th-cent Book of Hours. T* **107** *and similar vert design. Multicoloured. W w* **12**. *P* 13 × 12½.

No.	Description	Unused	Used
312	1 c. Type **107**	10	10
313	3 c. "The Flight into Egypt"	10	10
314	15 c. Type **107**	15	10
315	30 c. As 3 c.	25	20
312/15	*Set of* 4	40	40

109 Coat of Arms

110 "Christ bearing the Cross"

(Des L. Curtis. Litho B.W.)

1970 (2 Feb). *New Constitution. Multicoloured; background colours given. W w* **12** (*sideways*). *P* 13 × 12½.

No.	Type	Description	Unused	Used
316	**109**	7 c. brown	20	15
317		35 c. deep violet-blue	35	25

For similar $10 design, but without commemorative inscription, see No. 946.

(Des, recess and litho Enschedé)

1970 (17 Mar). *Easter. Details from the "Small Engraved Passion" by Dürer. T* **110** *and similar vert designs. W w* **12** *(sideways). P* 13 × 13½.

318 5 c. olive-grey and blue 10 10
319 7 c. olive-grey and vermilion 10 10
320 50 c. olive-grey and red-brown 50 60
318/20 .. .. *Set of* 3 60 70

Designs:—7 c. "Christ on the Cross"; 50 c. "The Lamentation of Christ".

113 Dickens and Scene from *Oliver Twist*

(Des Sylvia Goaman. Recess and litho D.L.R.)

1970 (17 June). *Death Centenary of Charles Dickens. T* **113** *and similar horiz designs. W w* **12** *(sideways). P* 13.

321 1 c. black and yellow-brown/*yellow* 10 15
322 3 c. black and Prussian blue/*flesh* 10 15
323 15 c. black and grey-blue/*flesh* 20 20
324 30 c. black and drab/*blue* 40 40
321/4 .. .. *Set of* 4 60 80

Designs (each incorporating portrait of Dickens as in T **113**, and a scene from one of his novels):—3 c. *A Christmas Carol*; 15 c. *Pickwick Papers*; 30 c. *The Old Curiosity Shop*.

114 Ambulance—1870

(Des Harrison. Litho B.W.)

1970 (4 Aug). *Centenary of British Red Cross. T* **114** *and similar horiz design. Multicoloured. W w* **12**. *P* 13½ × 14.

325 1 c. Type **114** 10 10
326 5 c. Ambulance—1970 .. .. 20 10
a. Wmk sideways 20 10
ab. Grey omitted £250
327 15 c. Type **114** 40 15
a. Wmk sideways 40 10
328 30 c. As 5 c. 50 20
a. Wmk sideways 55 40
325/8 .. .. *Set of* 4 1·00 45

115 Duke of Albemarle and Coat of Arms

(Des V. Whiteley. Litho Enschedé)

1970 (1 Dec). *Tercentenary of Issue of Letters Patent. T* **115** *and similar horiz design. Multicoloured. W w* **12**. *P* 12½ × 13½.

329 1 c. Type **115** 10 15
330 8 c. Arms of Charles II and Elizabeth II .. 20 30
331 10 c. Type **115** 20 15
332 35 c. As 8 c. 40 75
329/32 .. .. *Set of* 4 75 1·25

116 Boat-building

117 Lined Seahorse

1971 (2 Feb). *Designs as T* **88/91** *etc., but inscr in decimal currency as in T* **116**. *W w* **12** *(sideways on* 1 c., 2 c., 3 c., 5 c., 7 c., 15 c. *and* $2).

333 1 c. olive-yell, verm & brt bluish vio (as 1d.) 10 10
334 2 c. deep slate & deep orange-yell (as 2d.) 10 10
335 3 c. agate and dull green (as 3d.) 15 10
336 4 c. brt mauve, black & turquoise (as 4d.) 1·25 10
337 5 c. sepia and new blue (as 6d.) 40 10
338 7 c. yellow, turquoise-blue & dp bl (as 8d.) 30 10
339 8 c. brown and orange-yellow .. .. 1·00 10
340 10 c. maroon and turquoise (as 1s.) 75 10
341 15 c. orange-yellow, lake-brown and deep turquoise-blue (as 1s. 6d.) .. .. 1·00 65
342 20 c. multicoloured (as 2s.) .. .. .. 1·50 2·25
343 30 c. maroon and turquoise-blue (as 3s.) .. 2·00 1·00
344 50 c. ochre, blue and new blue (as 5s.) .. 2·75 2·00
345 $1 multicoloured (as 10s.) .. .. .. 3·00 3·00
a. Green omitted .. ..
w. Wmk inverted .. .. 4·00 5·00
346 $2 Prussian blue, silver & crimson (as £1) 4·00 7·50
333/46 .. .. *Set of* 14 16·00 15·00

The ¼ c. value was also re-issued and is listed as No. 297*a*.

(Des G. Vasarhelyi. Litho J.W.)

1971 (4 May). *Tourist Development. T* **117** *and similar multicoloured designs. W w* **12** *(sideways on Nos.* 348/50). *P* 14 × 14½ (1 c.) *or* 14½ × 14 *(others)*.

347 1 c. Type **117** 10 10
348 3 c. Queen or Pink Conch Shell (*horiz*) .. 15 10
349 15 c. Oystercatcher (*horiz*) 60 20
350 30 c. Sailfish ("Blue Marlin") (*horiz*) .. 60 25
347/50 .. .. *Set of* 4 1·25 55

118 Pirate Sloop

119 The Wilton Diptych (Left Wing)

(Des and litho J.W.)

1971 (27 July). *Pirates. T* **118** *and similar horiz designs. Multicoloured. W w* **12** *(sideways). P* 14.

351 2 c. Type **118** 10 10
352 3 c. Pirate treasure 10 10
353 15 c. Marooned sailor 45 15
354 30 c. Buccaneers 70 45
351/4 .. .. *Set of* 4 1·25 70

(Des J.W. Litho Questa)

1971 (12 Oct). *Christmas. T* **119** *and similar vert design. Multicoloured. W w* **12**. *P* 13½.

355 2 c. Type **119** 10 10
a. Horiz pair. Nos. 355/6 .. .. .. 10 10
356 2 c. The Wilton Diptych (Right Wing) .. 10 10
357 8 c. Type **119** 10 10
a. Horiz pair. Nos. 357/8 .. .. .. 20 20
358 8 c. As No. 356 .. .. 10 10
359 15 c. Type **119** 20 10
a. Horiz pair. Nos. 359/60 .. .. .. 40 20
360 15 c. As No. 356 .. .. 20 10
355/60 .. .. *Set of* 6 65 45

The two stamps of each denomination were printed in horizontal *se-tenant* pairs throughout the sheet.

120 Cape Kennedy Launching Area

121 "Christ before Pilate" (Rembrandt)

(Des V. Whiteley. Litho A. & M.)

1972 (21 Feb). *Tenth Anniv of Colonel Glenn's Splashdown. T* **120** *and similar multicoloured designs. W w* **12** *(sideways* on* 5, 10 *and* 15 *c.). P* 13½.

361 5 c. Type **120** 10 10
w. Wmk Crown to right of CA 20 20
362 10 c. "Friendship 7" space capsule 10 10
w. Wmk Crown to right of CA 30 30
363 15 c. Map of Islands and splashdown .. 15 10
w. Wmk Crown to right of CA 30 30
364 20 c. N.A.S.A. Space Medal (*vert*) 15 10
w. Wmk inverted 30 30
361/4 .. .. *Set of* 4 40 30

*The normal sideways watermark shows Crown to left of CA, *as seen from the back of the stamp.*

(Des and litho J.W.)

1972 (21 Mar). *Easter. T* **121** *and similar designs. W w* **12** *(sideways on* 15 *c.). P* 13½.

365 2 c. black and lilac 10 10
366 15 c. black and rose-pink 20 10
367 30 c. black and greenish yellow 30 15
365/7 .. .. *Set of* 3 50 30

Designs: *Horiz*—15 c. "The Three Crosses" (Rembrandt). *Vert*—30 c. "The Descent from the Cross" (Rembrandt).

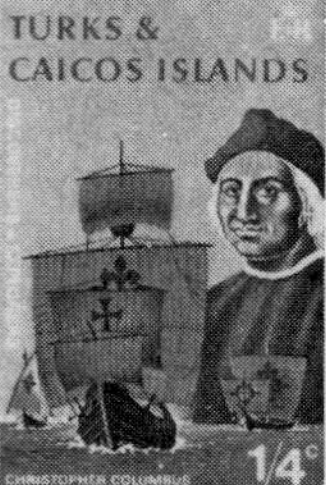

122 Christopher Columbus

123 Turk's-head Cactus and Spiny Lobster

(Des P. Powell. Litho J.W.)

1972 (28 July*). *Discoverers and Explorers. T* **122** *and similar multicoloured designs. W w* **12** *(sideways on* 8 *and* 30 *c.). P* 13½.

368 ¼ c. Type **122** 15 10
369 8 c. Sir Richard Grenville (*horiz*) 70 10
370 10 c. Capt. John Smith 80 10
371 30 c. Juan Ponce de Leon (*horiz*) .. .. 1·50 90
368/71 .. .. *Set of* 4 2·75 1·00

*This was the local date of issue; the Crown Agents released the stamps on 4 July.

(Des (from photograph by D. Groves) and photo Harrison)

1972 (20 Nov). *Royal Silver Wedding. Multicoloured; background colour given. W w* **12**. *P* 14 × 14½.

372 **123** 10 c. dull ultramarine 15 10
373 20 c. myrtle-green 15 10

124 Treasure Hunting, *circa* 1700

125 Arms of Jamaica and Turks & Caicos Islands

(Des C. Abbott. Litho Questa)

1973 (18 Jan). *Treasure. T* **124** *and similar vert designs. W w* **12** *(sideways*). P* 14×14½.

374 3 c. multicoloured 10 10
375 5 c. reddish purple, silver and black .. 10 10
376 10 c. magenta, silver and black 20 10
w. Wmk Crown to right of CA .. ..
377 30 c. multicoloured 60 30
374/7 .. .. *Set of* 4 85 35
MS378 127×108 mm. Nos. 374/7 .. .. 1·50 2·00

Designs:—5 c. Silver Bank medallion (obverse); 10 c. Silver Bank medallion (reverse); 30 c. Treasure hunting, 1973.

*The normal sideways watermark shows Crown to left of CA, *as seen from the back of the stamp.*

(Des PAD Studio. Litho Walsall)

1973 (16 Apr). *Centenary of Annexation to Jamaica. W w* **12** *(sideways). P* 13½ × 14.

379 **125** 15 c. multicoloured 25 10
380 35 c. multicoloured 45 20

126 Sooty Tern

127 Bermuda Sloop

(Des R. Granger Barrett. Litho Questa)

1973 (1 Aug). *Birds. T* **126** *and similar vert designs. W w* **12** *(sideways*). P* 14.

381 ¼ c. Type **126** 10 40
382 1 c. Magnificent Frigate Bird 30 60
383 2 c. Common Noddy 30 60
w. Wmk Crown to right of CA .. .. 40·00
384 3 c. Blue-grey Gnatcatcher 85 50
385 4 c. Little Blue Heron .. .. 35 1·25
w. Wmk Crown to right of CA .. .. 65·00
386 5 c. Catbird 30 30
w. Wmk Crown to right of CA .. .. 1·00
387 7 c. Black-whiskered Vireo .. .. .. 4·50 30
w. Wmk Crown to right of CA .. .. 70·00
388 8 c. Osprey .. .. 5·00 2·50
389 10 c. Greater Flamingo 70 90
390 15 c. Brown Pelican .. .. 1·25 50
w. Wmk Crown to right of CA .. .. 75·00
391 20 c. Parula Warbler .. .. 3·50 1·25
392 30 c. Northern Mockingbird .. .. .. 1·75 90
393 50 c. Ruby-throated Hummingbird .. .. 3·25 3·75
394 $1 Bananaquit .. .. 3·50 4·00
w. Wmk Crown to right of CA .. .. 7·00
395 $2 Cedar Waxwing .. .. 4·50 5·50
381/95 .. .. *Set of* 15 27·00 21·00

*The normal sideways watermark shows Crown to left of CA, *as seen from the back of the stamp.*

See also Nos. 411/14 and 451/64.

(Des R. Granger Barrett. Litho Questa)

1973 (14 Aug). *Vessels. T* **127** *and similar horiz designs. Multicoloured.* W w **12**. P 13½.

396	2 c. Type **127**	20	40
397	5 c. H.M.S. *Blanche* (screw sloop)	35	10
398	8 c. *Grand Turk* (American privateer) and *Hinchinbrook II* (British packet), 1813	40	50
399	10 c. H.M.S. *Endymion* (frigate), 1790	40	15
400	15 c. *Medina* (paddle-steamer)	45	70
401	20 c. H.M.S. *Daring* (brig), 1804	50	1·25
396/401	*Set of* 6	2·10	2·75
MS402	198×101 mm. Nos. 396/401	2·10	3·00

1973 (14 Nov). *Royal Wedding. As Nos.* 322/3 *of Montserrat.*

403	12 c. light turquoise-blue	10	10
	w. Wmk Crown to right of CA	42·00	
404	18 c. dull indigo	10	10

*The normal sideways watermark shows Crown to left of CA, *as seen from the back of the stamp.*

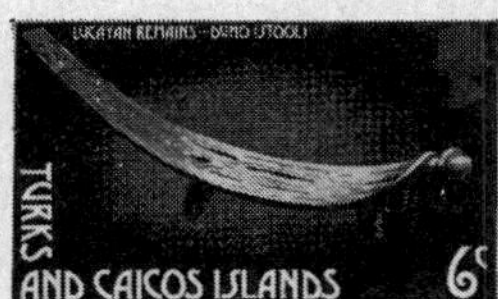

128 Duho (stool)

(Des Jennifer Toombs. Litho Questa)

1974 (17 July). *Lucayan Remains. T* **128** *and similar horiz designs. Multicoloured.* W w **12** (*sideways**). P 14½×14.

405	6 c. Type **128**	10	10
406	10 c. Broken wood bowl	15	10
	w. Wmk Crown to right of CA	1·75	
407	12 c. Greenstone axe	15	10
408	18 c. Wood bowl	15	10
409	35 c. Fragment of duho	20	20
405/9	*Set of* 5	65	40
MS410	240×90 mm. Nos. 405/9	1·10	1·75

*The normal sideways watermark shows Crown to left of CA, *as seen from the back of the stamp.*

1974–75. *As Nos.* 381 *etc, but* W w **12** (*upright*).

411	1 c. Magnificent Frigate Bird (11.6.75)	1·00	1·50
412	2 c. Common Noddy (27.9.74)	2·00	1·00
413	3 c. Blue-grey Gnatcatcher (19.3.75)	3·00	1·00
	w. Wmk inverted	11·00	
414	20 c. Parula Warbler (11.6.75)	2·25	3·75
411/14	*Set of* 4	7·50	6·50

Nos. 415/25 vacant.

129 G.P.O., Grand Turk

(Des G. Drummond. Litho Questa)

1974 (9 Oct). *Centenary of Universal Postal Union. T* **129** *and similar horiz designs. Multicoloured.* W w **12**. P 14.

426	4 c. Type **129**	10	10
427	12 c. Sloop and island map	20	10
428	18 c. "U.P.U." and globe	20	10
429	55 c. Posthorn and emblem	35	35
426/9	*Set of* 4	75	55

130 Churchill and Roosevelt

131 Spanish Captain, *circa* 1492

(Des V. Whiteley. Litho Questa)

1974 (30 Nov). *Birth Centenary of Sir Winston Churchill. T* **130** *and similar horiz design. Multicoloured.* W w **14** (*sideways*). P 14.

430	12 c. Type **130**	15	15
431	18 c. Churchill and vapour-trails	15	15
MS432	85 × 85 mm. Nos. 430/1	40	55

(Des J.W. Litho Questa)

1975 (26 Mar). *Military Uniforms. T* **131** *and similar vert designs. Multicoloured.* W w **14**. P 14.

433	5 c. Type **131**	10	10
434	20 c. Officer, Royal Artillery, 1783	30	15
435	25 c. Officer, 67th Foot, 1798	35	15
436	35 c. Private, 1st West India Regt, 1833	45	25
433/6	*Set of* 4	1·10	50
MS437	145 × 88 mm. Nos. 433/6	1·25	2·00

132 Ancient Windmill, Salt Cay

133 Star Coral

(Des P. Powell. Litho Questa)

1975 (16 Oct). *Salt-raking Industry. T* **132** *and similar multi-coloured designs.* W w **12** (*sideways on* 10 *and* 20 *c.*). P 14.

438	6 c. Type **132**	15	10
439	10 c. Salt pans drying in sun (*horiz*)	15	10
440	20 c. Salt-raking (*horiz*)	25	25
441	25 c. Unprocessed salt heaps	30	30
	w. Wmk inverted	28·00	
438/41	*Set of* 4	75	60

(Des C. Abbott. Litho Questa)

1975 (4 Dec). *Island Coral. T* **133** *and similar horiz designs. Multicoloured.* W w **14** (*sideways**). P 14.

442	6 c. Type **133**	15	10
443	10 c. Elkhorn Coral	20	10
444	20 c. Brain Coral	35	15
	w. Wmk Crown to right of CA	42·00	
445	25 c. Staghorn Coral	40	20
442/5	*Set of* 4	1·00	40

*The normal sideways watermark shows Crown to left of CA, *as seen from the back of the stamp.*

134 American Schooner

135 1s. 6d. Royal Visit Stamp of 1966

(Des J.W. Litho Questa)

1976 (28 May). *Bicentenary of American Revolution. T* **134** *and similar vert designs. Multicoloured.* W w **14**. P 13½.

446	6 c. Type **134**	25	15
447	20 c. British ship of the line	40	20
448	25 c. American privateer *Grand Turk*	40	25
	w. Wmk inverted	60·00	
449	55 c. British ketch	50	65
	w. Wmk inverted	5·00	
446/9	*Set of* 4	1·40	1·10
MS450	95×151 mm. Nos. 446/9	1·50	4·50

Each value depicts, at the top, the engagement between the *Grand Turk* and the P.O. Packet *Hinchinbrooke*, as in T **134**.

1976–77. *As Nos.* 381/95, *and new value* ($5), *but* W w **14** (*upright*).

451	¼ c. Type **126** (12.77)	75	2·75
452	1 c. Magnificent Frigate Bird (12.77)	75	2·00
453	2 c. Common Noddy (12.77)	75	2·75
454	3 c. Blue-grey Gnatcatcher (14.6.76)	90	70
455	4 c. Little Blue Heron (12.77)	1·50	2·25
456	5 c. Catbird (12.77)	1·25	2·75
457	10 c. Greater Flamingo (12.77)	1·25	2·75
458	15 c. Brown Pelican (12.77)	1·50	2·50
459	20 c. Parula Warbler (30.11.76)	1·50	75
460	30 c. Northern Mockingbird (12.77)	1·25	2·25
461	50 c. Ruby-throated Hummingbird (12.77)	1·50	2·25
462	$1 Bananaquit (12.77)	2·25	2·75
463	$2 Cedar Waxwing (12.77)	5·00	4·50
464	$5 Painted Bunting (24.11.76)	2·25	2·75
451/64	*Set of* 14	19·00	30·00

No. 465 vacant.

(Des V. Whiteley Studio. Litho Walsall)

1976 (14 July). *Tenth Anniv of Royal Visit. T* **135** *and similar horiz design. Multicoloured.* W w **14** (*sideways*). P 14½ × 14.

466	20 c. Type **135**	30	30
467	25 c. 8d. Royal Visit stamp	40	30

136 "The Virgin and Child with Flowers" (C. Dolci)

137 Balcony Scene, Buckingham Palace

(Des G. Drummond. Litho Questa)

1976 (10 Nov). *Christmas. T* **136** *and similar vert designs. Multicoloured.* W w **14**. P 13½.

468	6 c. Type **136**	10	10
469	10 c. "Virgin and Child with St. John and an Angel" (Studio of Botticelli)	10	10
470	20 c. "Adoration of the Magi" (Master of Paraiso)	30	15
471	25 c. "Adoration of the Magi" (French miniature)	30	20
468/71	*Set of* 4	65	35

(Des J.W. (**MS**475), C. Abbott (others) Litho Questa)

1977 (7 Feb–6 Dec). *Silver Jubilee. T* **137** *and similar vert designs. Multicoloured.* W w **14**. P 14 × 13½ (**MS**475) *or* 13½ (*others*).

472	6 c. Queen presenting O.B.E. to E.T. Wood	10	10
	w. Wmk inverted	25·00	
473	25 c. The Queen with regalia	15	20
474	55 c. Type **137**	30	45
472/4	*Set of* 3	40	60
MS475	120×97 mm. $5 Queen Elizabeth II (6.12.77)	80	80

138 Col. Glenn's "Mercury" Capsule

139 "Flight of the Holy Family" (Rubens)

(Des and litho J.W.)

1977 (20 June). *25th Anniv of U.S. Tracking Station. T* **138** *and similar multicoloured designs.* W w **14** (*sideways on horiz designs*). P 13½.

476	1 c. Type **138**	10	10
477	3 c. Moon buggy "Rover" (*vert*)	10	10
478	6 c. Tracking Station, Grand Turk	10	10
479	20 c. Moon landing craft (*vert*)	15	15
480	25 c. Col. Glenn's rocket launch (*vert*)	20	20
481	50 c. "Telstar 1" satellite	30	40
476/81	*Set of* 6	70	80

(Des J.W. Litho Questa)

1977 (23 Dec). *Christmas and 400th Birth Anniv of Rubens. T* **139** *and similar vert designs. Multicoloured.* P 14.

482	¼ c. Type **139**	10	10
483	½ c. "Adoration of the Magi" (1634)	10	10
484	1 c. "Adoration of the Magi" (1624)	10	10
485	6 c. "Virgin within Garland"	15	10
486	20 c. "Madonna and Child Adored by Angels"	15	10
487	$2 "Adoration of the Magi" (1618)	1·25	1·25
482/7	*Set of* 6	1·40	1·25
MS488	100 × 81 mm. $1 detail of 20 c.	1·40	1·40

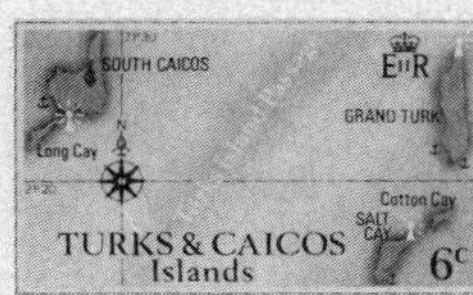

140 Map of Passage

(Des R. Granger Barrett. Litho J.W.)

1978 (2 Feb). *Turks Islands Passage. T* **140** *and similar horiz designs. Multicoloured.* P 13½. A. *No wmk.* B. W w **14** (*sideways*).

		A		B	
489	6 c. Type **140**	15	15	15	15
490	20 c. Caicos sloop passing Grand Turk Lighthouse	45	65	45	65
491	25 c. Motor cruiser	45	75	45	75
492	55 c. *Jamaica Planter* (freighter)	95	2·00	95	2·00
489/92	*Set of* 4	1·75	3·25	1·75	3·25
MS493	136×88 mm. Nos. 489/92. P 14½	1·50	2·50	30·00	—

141 "Queen Victoria" (Sir George Hayter)

142 Ampulla and Anointing Spoon

(Manufactured by Walsall (Nos. 499/501). Des PAD Studio. Litho Questa (others))

1978 (2 June-July). *25th Anniv of Coronation. Multicoloured.*

(*a*) *Sheet stamps. Vert designs as T* **141** *showing British monarchs in coronation robes. P* 14

494 6 c. Type **141** 10 10
495 10 c. "King Edward VII" (Sir Samuel Fildes) .. 10 10
496 25 c. King George V 20 10
497 $2 King George VI 50 70
494/7 .. .. *Set of* 4 75 75
MS498 161 × 113 mm. $2.50, Queen Elizabeth II 75 75

(*b*) *Booklet stamps. Vert designs as T* **142**. *Imperf × roul* 5*. *Self-adhesive* (July)

499 15 c. Type **142** 15 30
a. Booklet pane. Nos. 499/501 .. .. 1·10
b. Booklet pane. Nos. 499/500, each × 3 .. 80
500 25 c. St. Edward's Crown 15 30
501 $2 Queen Elizabeth II in coronation robes .. 1·00 2·25
499/501 .. .. *Set of* 3 1·10 2·50

Nos. 494/7 also exist perf 12 (*Price for set of* 4 75p *mint or used*) from additional sheetlets of 3 stamps and 1 label. Stamps perforated 14 are from normal sheets of 50.

Nos. 499/501 are separated by various combinations of rotary-knife (giving a straight edge) and roulette.

143 Wilbur Wright and Wright Type A

(Des Curtis Design. Litho Format)

1978 (29 June). *75th Anniv of Powered Flight. T* **143** *and similar horiz designs. Multicoloured. P* 14½.

502 1 c. Type **143** 10 10
503 6 c. Wright brothers and Cessna 337 Super Skymaster 10 10
504 10 c. Orville Wright and Lockheed L.188 Electra 10 10
505 15 c. Wilbur Wright and Douglas C-47 Skytrain 15 15
506 35 c. Wilbur Wright and Britten Norman Islander 35 35
507 $2 Wilbur Wright and Wright Type A .. 1·00 1·75
502/7 .. .. *Set of* 6 1·50 2·25
MS508 111×84 mm. $1 Orville Wright and Wright glider No. III .. .. 60 1·40

No. 502 is inscribed "FLYER III" in error.

144 Hurdling

(Des J.W. Litho Format)

1978 (3 Aug). *Commonwealth Games, Edmonton. T* **144** *and similar horiz designs. Multicoloured. P* 14½.

509 6 c. Type **144** 10 10
510 20 c. Weightlifting 15 15
511 55 c. Boxing 20 30
512 $2 Cycling .. .. 50 1·25
509/12 .. .. *Set of* 4 75 1·50
MS513 105 × 79 mm. $1 Sprinting .. .. 55 1·25

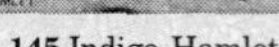

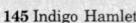

145 Indigo Hamlet

146 "Madonna of the Siskin"

(Des G. Drummond. Litho Questa)

1978 (17 Nov)–**83**. *Fishes. Horiz designs as T* **145**. *Multicoloured.*

A. *No imprint date. P* 14

514A 1 c. Type **145** 15 50
515A 2 c. Tobacco Fish (19.1.79) 75 50
516A 3 c. Bar Jack 30 30
517A 4 c. Porkfish (19.1.79) 75 50
518A 5 c. Spanish Grunt 30 40
519A 7 c. Yellow-tailed Snapper (19.1.79) .. 1·00 60
520A 8 c. Four-eyed Butterflyfish (19.1.79) .. 1·00 15
521A 10 c. Yellow-finned Grouper 30 15
522A 15 c. Beau Gregory 75 30
523A 20 c. Queen Angelfish 30 30
524A 30 c. Hogfish (19.1.79) .. .. .. 1·50 40
525A 50 c. Royal Gramma ("Fairy Basslet") (19.1.79) .. .. 1·00 65
526A $1 Fin-spot Wrasse (19.1.79) .. .. 1·75 1·60
527A $2 Stoplight Parrotfish (19.1.79) .. .. 3·25 2·50
528A $5 Queen Triggerfish (19.1.79) .. .. 3·25 6·50
514A/28A .. .. *Set of* 15 14·00 13·50

B. *With imprint date at foot of design. P* 14 (15 *c.*) *or* 12 (*others*)

514B 1 c. Type **145** (15.12.81) .. .. .. 2·25 2·25
518B 5 c. Spanish Grunt (15.12.81) .. .. 2·75 2·75
521B 10 c. Yellow-finned Grouper (15.12.81) .. 2·75 2·75
522B 15 c. Beau Gregory (25.1.83) .. .. 2·50 2·25
523B 20 c. Queen Angelfish (15.12.81) .. .. 1·25 1·00
a. Perf 14 (25.1.83) .. .. .. 85 1·25
525B 50 c. Royal Gramma ("Fairy Basslet") (15.12.81) .. .. 7·00 6·00
526B $1 Fin-spot Wrasse (15.12.81) .. .. 3·25 3·00
a. Perf 14 (25.1.83) .. .. .. 2·00 3·00
527B $2 Stoplight Parrotfish (15.12.81) .. 5·50 5·00
a. Perf 14 (25.1.83) .. .. .. 2·50 4·50
528B $5 Queen Triggerfish (15.12.81) .. .. 9·50 11·00
a. Perf 14 (25.1.83) .. .. .. 5·50 9·00
514B/28B .. .. *Set of* 9 25·00 30·00

Imprint dates: "1981", Nos. 514B, 518B, 521B, 523B, 525B/8B; "1983", Nos. 522B, 523Ba, 526Ba, 527Ba, 528Ba.

(Des BG Studio. Litho Questa)

1978 (11 Dec). *Christmas. Paintings by Dürer. T* **146** *and similar multicoloured designs. P* 14.

529 6 c. Type **146** 15 10
530 20 c. "The Virgin and Child with St. Anne" .. 20 15
531 35 c. "Paumgärtner Nativity" (*horiz*) 35 15
532 $2 "Praying Hands" .. .. 85 1·25
529/32 .. .. *Set of* 4 1·40 1·40
MS533 137 × 124 mm. $1 "Adoration of the Magi" (*horiz*) .. .. 2·25 3·25

147 Osprey

(Des G. Drummond. Litho Questa)

1979 (29 May). *Endangered Wildlife. T* **147** *and similar horiz designs. Multicoloured. P* 14.

534 6 c. Type **147** 75 20
535 20 c. Green Turtle 65 20
536 25 c. Queen or Pink Conch 75 25
537 55 c. Rough-toothed Dolphin 90 50
538 $1 Humpback Whale .. .. 2·00 2·00
534/8 .. .. *Set of* 5 4·50 2·75
MS539 117×85 mm. $2 Iguana .. .. .. 2·50 3·75

148 "The Beloved" (painting by D. G. Rossetti)

(Des G. Vasarhelyi. Litho Questa)

1979 (2 July). *International Year of the Child. T* **148** *and similar horiz designs showing paintings and I.Y.C. emblem. Multicoloured. P* 14.

540 6 c. Type **148** 10 10
541 25 c. "Tahitian Girl" (P. Gauguin) 15 10
542 55 c. "Calmady Children" (Sir Thomas Lawrence) 25 20
543 $1 "Mother and Daughter" (detail, P. Gauguin) 45 45
540/3 .. .. *Set of* 4 80 70
MS544 112 × 85 mm. $2 "Marchesa Elena Grimaldi" (A. van Dyck) .. .. 55 1·25

149 *Medina* (paddle-steamer) and Handstamped Cover

150 Cuneiform Script

(Des J.W. Litho Questa (Nos. 545/51). Des and litho Walsall (Nos. 552/64))

1979 (27 Aug)–**80**. *Death Centenary of Sir Rowland Hill.*

(*a*) *Sheet stamps. Horiz designs as T* **149**. *Multicoloured. P* 12 ($2) *or* 14 (*others*)

545 6 c. Type **149** 10 10
546 20 c. Sir Rowland Hill and map of Caribbean 15 15
547 45 c. *Orinoco I* (mail paddle-steamer) and cover bearing Penny Black stamp .. 20 20
548 75 c. *Shannon* (screw steamer) and letter to Grand Turk 30 30
549 $1 *Trent I* (paddle-steamer) and map of Caribbean 35 35
550 $2 Turks Islands 1867 and Turks and Caicos Islands 1900 1d. stamps (6.5.80) 2·00 2·00
545/50 .. .. *Set of* 6 2·75 2·75
MS551 170×113 mm. As No. 550. P 14 .. 75 1·50

Nos. 545/9 also exist perf 12 (*Price for set of* 5 £1·10 *mint or used*) from additional sheetlets of 5 stamps and 1 label. No. 550 only exists in this format and has the inscription "International Stamp Exhibition Earls Court—London 6–14 May 1980. LONDON 1980" overprinted on the sheet margin. The individual stamps are not overprinted. Stamps perforated 14 are from normal sheets of 40.

(*b*) *Booklet stamps. Designs as T* **150**. *Imperf × roul* 5*. *Self-adhesive* (27.9.79)

552 5 c. black and bright emerald 10 10
a. Booklet pane. Nos. 552/7 80
553 5 c. black and bright emerald 10 10
554 5 c. black and bright emerald 10 10
555 15 c. black and light blue 20 20
556 15 c. black and light blue 20 20
557 15 c. black and light blue 20 20
558 25 c. black and light blue 30 30
a. Booklet pane. Nos. 558/63 .. .. 2·25
559 25 c. black and light blue 60 45
560 25 c. black and light blue 30 30
561 40 c. black and bright rosine 45 45
562 40 c. black and bright rosine 45 45
563 40 c. black and bright rosine 45 45
564 $1 black and lemon .. .. .. 70 1·25
a. Booklet pane of 1 70

Designs: *Horiz*—No. 552, Type **150**; No. 553, Egyptian papyrus; No. 554, Chinese paper; No. 555, Greek runner; No. 556, Roman post horse; No. 557, Roman post ship; No. 558, Pigeon post; No. 559, Railway post; No. 560, Packet paddle-steamer; No. 561, Balloon post; No. 562, First airmail; No. 563, Supersonic airmail. *Vert*—No. 564, Original stamp press.

*Nos. 552/63 are separated by various combinations of rotary knife (giving a straight edge) and roulette. No. 564 exists only with straight edges.

BRASILIANA 79

(**151**)

152 "St. Nicholas", Prikra, Ukraine

1979 (10 Sept). *"Brasiliana 79" International Stamp Exhibition, Rio de Janeiro. No.* **MS**551 *optd with T* **151**.

MS565 170 × 113 mm. $2 Turks Islands 1867 and Turks and Caicos Islands 1900 1d. stamps .. 65 1·50

Stamps from Nos. **MS**551 and **MS**565 are identical as the overprint on **MS**565 appears on the margin of the sheet.

(Des M. Diamond. Litho Questa)

1979 (19 Oct). *Christmas. Art. T* **152** *and similar vert designs. Multicoloured. P* 13½ × 14.

566 1 c. Type **152** 10 10
567 3 c. "Emperor Otto II with Symbols of Empire" (Master of the Registrum Gregorii) .. 10 10
568 6 c. "Portrait of St. John" (Book of Lindisfarne) 10 10
569 15 c. "Adoration of the Majestas Domini" (Prayer Book of Otto II) 10 10
570 20 c. "Christ attended by Angels" (Book of Kells) 15 15
571 25 c. "St. John the Evangelist" (Gospels of St. Medard of Soissons), Charlemagne .. 20 15
572 65 c. "Christ Pantocrator", Trocany, Ukraine 30 25
573 $1 "Portrait of St. John" (Canterbury Codex Aureus) 45 45
566/73 .. .. *Set of* 8 1·10 1·10
MS574 106 × 133 mm. $2 "Portrait of St. Matthew" (Book of Lindisfarne) .. .. 70 1·50

153 Pluto and Starfish

(Litho Format)

1979 (2 Nov). *International Year of the Child. Walt Disney Cartoon Characters. T* **153** *and similar vert designs showing characters at the seaside. Multicoloured. P* 11.

575 ¼ c. Type **153** 10 10
576 ½ c. Minnie Mouse in summer outfit 10 10
577 1 c. Mickey Mouse underwater 10 10
578 2 c. Goofy and turtle 10 10
579 3 c. Donald Duck and dolphin 10 10

580 4 c. Mickey Mouse fishing 10 10
581 5 c. Goofy surfing 10 10
582 25 c. Pluto and crab 45 20
583 $1 Daisy water-skiing .. .. 1·50 2·25
575/83 .. .. *Set of* 9 2·00 2·50
MS584 126 × 96 mm. $1.50, Goofy after water-skiing accident. P 13½. .. .. 1·25 1·60
a. Error. Imperf £180

154 "Christina's World" (painting by Andrew Wyeth)

(Des J.W. Litho Format)

1979 (19 Dec). *Works of Art. T* **154** *and similar multicoloured designs. P* 13½.
585 6 c. Type **154** 10 10
586 10 c. Ivory Leopards, Benin (19th-cent) .. 10 10
587 20 c. "The Kiss" (painting by Gustav Klimt) (*vert*) 15 15
588 25 c. "Portrait of a Lady" (painting by R. van der Weyden) (*vert*) 15 15
589 80 c. Bull's head harp, Sumer, *c.* 2600 B.C. (*vert*) 30 30
590 $1 "The Wave" (painting by Hokusai) .. 45 45
585/90 .. .. *Set of* 6 95 95
MS591 110 × 140 mm. $2 "Holy Family" (painting by Rembrandt) (*vert*) .. .. 70 1·25

155 Pied-billed Grebe

156 Stamp, Magnifying Glass and Perforation Gauge

(Des G. Drummond. Litho Questa)

1980 (20 Feb). *Birds. T* **155** *and similar horiz designs. Multicoloured. P* 14.
592 20 c. Type **155** 70 30
593 25 c. Ovenbirds at nest 75 30
594 35 c. Hen Harrier .. .. 1·00 45
595 55 c. Yellow-bellied Sapsucker .. .. 1·25 50
596 $1 Blue-winged Teal .. .. .. 1·50 1·75
592/6 .. .. *Set of* 5 4·75 3·00
MS597 107 × 81 mm. $2 Glossy Ibis .. .. 2·75 2·25

(Des BG Studio. Litho Questa)

1980 (6 May). *"London 1980" International Stamp Exhibition. T* **156** *and similar horiz designs. P* 14.
598 25 c. black and chrome-yellow 15 15
599 40 c. black and bright green 15 25
MS600 76 × 97 mm. $2 vermilion, black and blue 70 1·10
Designs:—40 c. Stamp, tweezers and perforation gauge; $2, Earls Court Exhibition Centre.

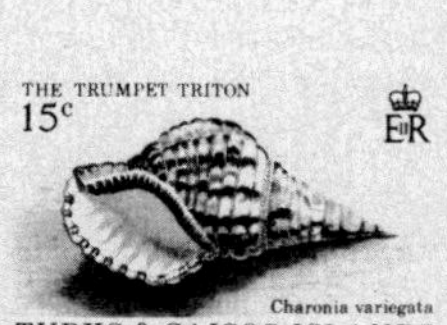

157 Atlantic Trumpet Triton (*Charonia variegata*)

158 Queen Elizabeth the Queen Mother

(Des G. Drummond. Litho Questa)

1980 (26 June). *Shells. T* **157** *and similar horiz designs. Multicoloured. P* 14.
601 15 c. Type **157** 20 20
602 20 c. Measled Cowrie (*Cypraea zebra*) .. 25 25
603 30 c. True Tulip (*Fasciolaria tulipa*) .. 35 35
604 45 c. Lion's-paw Scallop (*Lyropecten nodosa*) 45 45
605 55 c. Sunrise Tellin (*Tellina radiata*) .. 55 55
606 70 c. Crown Cone (*Conus regius*) 70 70
601/6 .. .. *Set of* 6 2·25 2·25

(Des G. Vasarhelyi. Litho Questa)

1980 (4 Aug). *80th Birthday of Queen Elizabeth the Queen Mother. P* 14.
607 **158** 80 c. multicoloured .. .. .. 50 1·25
MS608 57 × 80 mm. **158** $1.50, multicoloured. P 12. 80 2·00

COVER PRICES

Cover factors are quoted at the beginning of each country for most issues to 1945. An explanation of the system can be found on page x. The factors quoted do not, however, apply to philatelic covers.

159 Doctor examining Child and Lions International Emblem

(Des Design Images. Litho Questa)

1980 (29 Aug). *"Serving the Community". T* **159** *and similar horiz designs. Multicoloured. P* 14.
609 10 c. Type **159** 15 10
610 15 c. Students receiving scholarships and Kiwanis International emblem 20 10
611 45 c. Teacher with students and Soroptimist emblem 40 35
612 $1 Lobster trawler and Rotary International emblem 75 80
609/12 .. .. *Set of* 4 1·40 1·25
MS613 101 × 74 mm. $2 School receiving funds and Rotary International emblem .. .. 1·25 2·00
No. **MS**613 also commemorates the 75th anniversary of Rotary International.

(Litho Walsall)

1980 (30 Sept). *Christmas. Scenes from Walt Disney's Cartoon Film "Pinocchio". Horiz designs as T* **153**. *Multicoloured. P* 11.
614 ¼ c. Scene from *Pinocchio* 10 10
615 ½ c. As puppet 10 10
616 1 c. Pinocchio changed into a boy 10 10
617 2 c. Captured by fox 10 10
618 3 c. Pinocchio and puppeteer 10 10
619 4 c. Pinocchio and bird's nest nose 10 10
620 5 c. Pinocchio eating 10 10
621 75 c. Pinocchio with ass ears .. .. .. 1·00 90
622 $1 Pinocchio underwater .. .. .. 1·25 1·00
614/22 .. .. *Set of* 9 2·25 2·00
MS623 127 × 102 mm. $2 Pinocchio dancing (*vert*) 2·50 2·50

160 Martin Luther King Jr

(Des Design Images. Litho Questa)

1980 (22 Dec). *Human Rights. Personalities. T* **160** *and similar horiz designs. Multicoloured. P* 14 × 13½.
624 20 c. Type **160** 15 10
625 30 c. John F. Kennedy 30 25
626 45 c. Roberto Clemente (baseball player) .. 45 35
627 70 c. Sir Frank Worrel (cricketer) 90 90
628 $1 Harriet Tubman .. .. 1·10 1·25
624/8 .. .. *Set of* 5 2·50 2·50
MS629 103 × 80 mm. $2 Marcus Garvey .. 1·10 1·25

161 Yachts

162 Night Queen Cactus

(Litho Questa)

1981 (29 Jan). *South Caicos Regatta. T* **161** *and similar horiz designs. Multicoloured. P* 14.
630 6 c. Type **161** 10 10
631 15 c. Trophy and yachts 15 15
632 35 c. Spectators watching speedboat race .. 25 20
633 $1 Caicos sloops 60 60
630/3 .. .. *Set of* 4 90 90
MS634 113 × 85 mm. $2 Queen Elizabeth II and map of South Caicos (*vert*) .. .. .. 80 1·75

(Des J. Cooter. Litho Questa)

1981 (10 Feb). *Flowering Cacti. T* **162** *and similar vert designs. Multicoloured. P* 13½ × 14.
635 25 c. Type **162** 25 25
636 35 c. Ripsaw Cactus 35 35
637 55 c. Royal Strawberry Cactus 40 60
638 80 c. Caicos Cactus .. .. 60 1·00
635/8 .. .. *Set of* 4 1·40 2·00
MS639 72 × 86 mm. $2 Turks Head Cactus. P 14½ 1·00 2·00

(Litho Format)

1981 (16 Feb). *50th Anniv of Walt Disney's Cartoon Character, Pluto. Vert designs as T* **153**. *Multicoloured. P* 13½.
640 10 c. Pluto playing on beach with Queen or Pink Conch shell 10 10
641 75 c. Pluto on raft, and porpoise 75 90
MS642 127×101 mm. $1.50 Pluto in scene from film *Simple Things* .. .. .. 1·60 2·25

(Litho Format)

1981 (20 Mar). *Easter. Walt Disney Cartoon Characters. Vert designs as T* **153**. *Multicoloured. P* 11.
643 10 c. Donald Duck and Louie 20 20
644 25 c. Goofy and Donald Duck 40 40
645 60 c. Chip and Dale .. .. 70 1·00
646 80 c. Scrooge McDuck and Huey .. .. 90 1·40
643/6 .. .. *Set of* 4 2·00 2·75
MS647 126 × 101 mm. $4 Chip (or Dale). P 13½ 4·00 3·50

163 "Woman with Fan"

164 Kensington Palace

(Des J.W. Litho Questa)

1981 (28 May). *Birth Centenary of Picasso. T* **163** *and similar vert designs. Multicoloured. P* 13½ × 14.
648 20 c. Type **163** 20 15
649 45 c. "Woman with Pears" 25 30
650 80 c. "The Accordionist" 45 50
651 $1 "The Aficionado" 60 80
648/51 .. .. *Set of* 4 1·40 1·60
MS652 102 × 127 mm. $2 "Girl with a Mandolin" 1·40 1·25

(Des J.W. Litho Questa)

1981 (23 June). *Royal Wedding. T* **164** *and similar vert designs. Multicoloured. P* 14.
653 35 c. Prince Charles and Lady Diana Spencer 15 10
654 65 c. Type **164** 20 20
655 90 c. Prince Charles as Colonel of the Welsh Guards 25 30
653/5 .. .. *Set of* 3 50 50
MS656 96 × 82 mm. $2 Glass Coach 50 55
Nos. 653/5 also exist perforated 12 (*price for set of* 3 50*p. mint or used*) from additional sheetlets of five stamps and one label. The 65 c. and 90 c. values from these sheetlets have changed background colours.

165 Lady Diana Spencer

166 Marine Biology Observation

(Manufactured by Walsall)

1981 (7 July). *Royal Wedding. Booklet stamps. T* **165** *and similar vert designs. Multicoloured. Roul* 5 × *imperf**. *Self-adhesive.*
657 20 c. Type **165** 25 30
a. Booklet pane. Nos. 657/8, each × 3 .. 1·60
658 $1 Prince Charles 35 70
659 $2 Prince Charles and Lady Diana Spencer 1·10 2·25
a. Booklet pane of 1 .. .. 1·10
657/9 .. .. *Set of* 3 1·50 3·00
*The 20 c. and $1 values were each separated by various combinations of rotary knife (giving a straight edge) and roulette. The $2 value exists only with straight edges.

(Des G. Drummond. Litho Questa)

1981 (21 Aug). *Diving. T* **166** *and similar horiz designs. Multicoloured. P* 14.
660 15 c. Type **166** 20 15
661 40 c. Underwater photography 50 35
662 75 c. Wreck diving 90 70
663 $1 Diving with dolphins .. .. .. 1·25 1·00
660/3 .. .. *Set of* 4 2·50 2·00
MS664 91 × 75 mm. $2 Diving flag .. .. 1·75 2·25

(Litho Questa)

1981 (2 Nov). *Christmas. Horiz designs as T* **153** *showing scenes from Walt Disney's cartoon film "Uncle Remus". P* 13½.
665 ¼ c. multicoloured 10 10
666 ½ c. multicoloured 10 10
667 1 c. multicoloured 10 10
668 2 c. multicoloured 10 10
669 3 c. multicoloured 10 10
670 4 c. multicoloured 10 10
671 5 c. multicoloured 10 10
672 75 c. multicoloured .. .. 1·00 80
673 $1 multicoloured .. .. 1·25 1·00
665/73 .. .. *Set of* 9 2·25 1·90
MS674 128 × 103 mm. $2 multicoloured .. .. 1·75 2·25

167 Map of Grand Turk, and Lighthouse

168 *Junonia evarete*

(Des J.W. Litho Questa)

1981 (1 Dec). *Tourism. T* **167** *and similar horiz designs. Multicoloured. P* 14.

675 20 c. Type **167** 40 45
a. Vert strip of 10. Nos. 675/84 .. .. 3·50
676 20 c. Map of Salt Cay, and "industrial archaeology" 40 45
677 20 c. Map of South Caicos, and "island flying" 40 45
678 20 c. Map of East Caicos, and "beach combing" 40 45
679 20 c. Map of Grand Caicos (middle), and cave exploring 40 45
680 20 c. Map of North Caicos, and camping and hiking 40 45
681 20 c. Map of North Caicos, Parrot Cay, Dellis Cay, Fort George Cay, Pine Cay and Water Cay, and "environmental studies" 40 45
682 20 c. Map of Providenciales, and scuba diving 40 45
683 20 c. Map of West Caicos, and "cruising and bird sanctuary" 40 45
684 20 c. Turks and Caicos Islands flag 40 45
675/84 .. .. *Set of* 10 3·50 4·00

Nos. 675/84 were printed together, *se-tenant*, in vertical strips of 10 throughout the sheet of 40, the two panes (2 × 10), separated by a gutter margin, being *tête-bêche*.

(Des J. Cooter. Litho Questa)

1982 (21 Jan). *Butterflies. T* **168** *and similar vert designs. Multicoloured. P* 14.

685 20 c. Type **168** 30 30
686 35 c. *Strymon maesites* 50 55
687 65 c. *Agraulis vanillae* .. .. 90 1·25
688 $1 *Eurema dina* .. .. 1·40 2·00
685/8 .. .. *Set of* 4 2·75 3·75
MS689 72×56 mm. $2 *Anaea intermedia* .. 2·75 3·75

169 Flag Salute on Queen's Birthday

170 Footballer

(Litho Questa)

1982 (17 Feb). *75th Anniv of Boy Scout Movement. T* **169** *and similar vert designs. Multicoloured. P* 14.

690 40 c. Type **169** 50 50
691 50 c. Raft building 60 60
692 75 c. Sea scout cricket match .. .. .. 1·10 1·60
693 $1 Nature study .. .. 1·50 1·75
690/3 .. .. *Set of* 4 3·25 4·00
MS694 100 × 70 mm. $2 Lord Baden-Powell and scout salute .. .. 2·50 3·00

(Des G. Vasarhelyi. Litho Questa)

1982 (30 Apr). *World Cup Football Championship, Spain. T* **170** *and similar designs showing footballers. P* 14.

695 10 c. multicoloured 15 15
696 25 c. multicoloured 20 20
697 45 c. multicoloured 25 25
698 $1 multicoloured 80 80
695/8 .. .. *Set of* 4 1·25 1·25
MS699 117 × 83 mm. $2 multicoloured (*horiz*) .. 1·25 2·00

171 Washington crossing the Delaware and Phillis Wheatley (poetess)

172 "Second Thoughts"

(Des Design Images. Litho Questa)

1982 (3 May). *250th Birth Anniv of George Washington* (20, 35 *c.*) *and Birth Centenary of Franklin D. Roosevelt* (65, 80 *c.*). *T* **171** *and similar horiz designs. Multicoloured. P* 14.

700 20 c. Type **171** 30 30
701 35 c. George Washington and Benjamin Banneker (surveyor) 45 45
702 65 c. Franklin D. Roosevelt meeting George Washington Carver (agricultural researcher) 65 80
703 80 c. Roosevelt as stamp collector .. .. 80 1·00
700/3 .. .. *Set of* 4 2·00 2·25
MS704 100 × 70 mm. $2 Roosevelt with stamp showing profile of Washington .. .. .. 2·00 2·50

(Litho Questa)

1982 (23 June). *Norman Rockwell (painter) Commemoration. T* **172** *and similar vert designs. Multicoloured. P* 14 × 13½.

705 8 c. Type **172** 15 10
706 15 c. "The Proper Gratuity" 20 20
707 20 c. "Doctor's Office" (inscr "Before the Shot") 25 30
708 25 c. "Bottom of the Sixth" (inscr "The Three Umpires") 25 30
705/8 .. .. *Set of* 4 75 80

173 Princess of Wales

174 Cessna 337 Super Skymaster over Caicos Cays

(Des PAD Studio. Litho Questa)

1982 (1 July–18 Nov). *21st Birthday of Princess of Wales. T* **173** *and similar vert designs. Multicoloured. P* 14½ × 14.

(*a*) *Sheet stamps. Pale green frames*

709 55 c. Sandringham 35 45
710 70 c. Prince and Princess of Wales 60 55
711 $1 Type **173** 90 80
709/11 .. .. *Set of* 3 1·75 1·75
MS712 102 × 76 mm. $2 Princess Diana (*different*) 1·50 1·75

(*b*) *Booklet stamps. As Nos.* 709/11 *but printed with new values and blue frame* (18.11.82)

713 8 c. Sandringham 15 35
714 35 c. Prince and Princess of Wales .. .. 55 1·00
715 $1.10, Type **173** .. .. 80 2·00
713/15 .. .. *Set of* 3 1·40 3·00

Nos. 713/15 also exist from sheets printed in horizontal *tête-bêche* pairs throughout.

(Des MBI Studios. Litho Questa)

1982 (23 Aug). *Aircraft. T* **174** *and similar horiz designs. Multicoloured. P* 14.

716 8 c. Type **174** 15 15
717 15 c. Lockheed JetStar II over Grand Turk .. 20 25
718 65 c. Sikorsky S.58 helicopter over South Caicos 65 80
719 $1.10, Cessna 182 Skylane seaplane over Providenciales .. .. 1·10 1·25
716/19 .. .. *Set of* 4 1·90 2·25
MS720 99×69 mm. $2 Boeing 727-200 over Turks and Caicos Islands .. .. .. 2·00 2·50

(Litho Questa)

1982 (1 Dec). *Christmas. Scenes from Walt Disney's Cartoon Film "Mickey's Christmas Carol". Horiz designs as T* **153**. *Multicoloured. P* 13½.

721 1 c. Donald Duck, Mickey Mouse and Scrooge 10 10
722 1 c. Goofy (Marley's ghost) and Scrooge .. 10 10
723 2 c. Jiminy Cricket and Scrooge 10 10
724 2 c. Huey, Dewey and Louie 10 10
725 3 c. Daisy Duck and youthful Scrooge .. 10 10
726 3 c. Giant and Scrooge 10 10
727 4 c. Two bad wolves, a wise pig and a reformed Scrooge 10 10
728 65 c. Donald Duck and Scrooge .. .. 1·00 75
729 $1.10, Mortie and Scrooge .. .. .. 1·60 1·25
721/9 .. .. *Set of* 9 2·50 2·00
MS730 126 × 101 mm. $2 Mickey and Minnie Mouse with Mortie .. .. 2·75 2·50

175 West Caicos Trolley Tram

(Des N. Waldman. Litho Questa)

1983 (18 Jan). *Trams and Locomotives. T* **175** *and similar horiz designs. Multicoloured. P* 14

731 15 c. Type **175** 20 25
732 55 c. West Caicos steam locomotive 65 70
733 90 c. East Caicos sisal locomotive .. .. 90 1·00
734 $1.60, East Caicos steam locomotive .. 1·75 1·90
731/4 .. .. *Set of* 4 3·25 3·50
MS735 99 × 69 mm. $2.50, Steam engine pulling cars of sisal .. .. 2·25 2·25

176 Policewoman on Traffic Duty

177 "St. John and the Virgin Mary" (detail)

(Des N. Waldman. Litho Questa)

1983 (14 Mar). *Commonwealth Day. T* **176** *and similar horiz designs. Multicoloured. P* 14

736 1 c. Type **176** 15 20
a. Vert strip of 4. Nos. 736/9 .. .. 2·40
737 8 c. Stylised sun and weather vane 15 20
738 65 c. Yacht 85 90
739 $1 Cricket .. .. 1·50 1·60
736/9 .. .. *Set of* 4 2·40 2·50

Nos. 736/9 were printed together, *se-tenant*, in vertical strips of four throughout the sheet.

(Des Design Images. Litho Questa)

1983 (7 Apr). *Easter. T* **177** *and similar vert designs showing details from the "Mond Crucifixion" by Raphael. Multicoloured. P* 13½ × 14.

740 35 c. Type **177** 25 25
741 50 c. "Two Women" 35 35
742 95 c. "Angel with two jars" 55 60
743 $1.10, "Angel with one jar" 75 80
740/3 .. .. *Set of* 4 1·75 2·00
MS744 100 × 130 mm. $2.50, "Christ on the Cross" 1·60 2·00

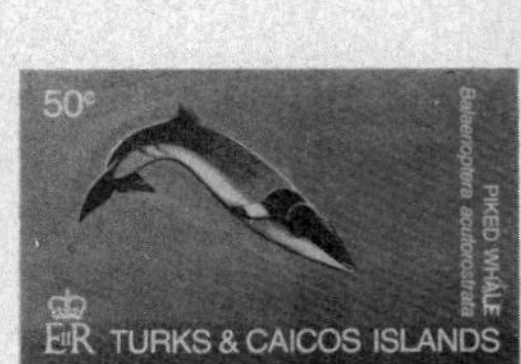

178 Minke Whale

179 First Hydrogen Balloon *The Globe*, 1783

(Des D. Hamilton. Litho Questa)

1983 (16 May–11 July). *Whales. T* **178** *and similar horiz designs. Multicoloured. P* 13½.

745 50 c. Type **178** .. .. 2·00 2·00
746 65 c. Black Right Whale (11.7.83) .. .. 2·25 2·25
747 70 c. Killer Whale (13.6.83) .. .. .. 2·50 2·50
748 95 c. Sperm Whale (13.6.83) .. .. .. 2·75 2·75
749 $1.10, Cuvier's Beaked Whale (11.7.83) .. 3·00 3·00
750 $2 Blue Whale (13.6.83) .. .. .. 5·00 5·00
751 $2.20, Humpback Whale .. .. .. 5·50 5·50
752 $3 Long-finned Pilot Whale .. .. 6·25 6·25
745/52 .. .. *Set of* 8 26·00 26·00
MS753 112×82 mm. $3 Fin Whale (11.7.83) .. 5·50 5·00

Nos. 745/52 were each issued in sheetlets of four.

(Des BG Studio. Litho Questa)

1983 (30 Aug). *Bicentenary of Manned Flight. T* **179** *and similar vert designs. Multicoloured. P* 14.

754 25 c. Type **179** 25 25
755 35 c. *Friendship 7* 35 35
756 70 c. First hot air balloon *Le Martial*, 1783 70 70
757 95 c. Space shuttle *Columbia* 90 90
754/7 .. .. *Set of* 4 2·00 2·00
MS758 112×76 mm. $2 Montgolfier balloon and Space shuttle .. .. 1·50 2·00

180 Fiddler Pig

181 Bermuda Sloop

(Litho Format)

1983 (4 Oct). *Christmas. Walt Disney Cartoon Characters. T* **180** *and similar vert designs. Multicoloured. P* 11.

759 1 c. Type **180** 10 10
760 1 c. Fifer Pig 10 10
761 2 c. Practical Pig 10 10
762 2 c. Pluto 10 10
763 3 c. Goofy 10 10

764 3 c. Mickey Mouse 10 10
765 35 c. Gyro Gearloose 35 35
766 50 c. Ludwig von Drake 50 60
767 $1.10, Huey, Dewey and Louie .. .. 1·00 1·25
759/67 .. .. *Set of* 9 1·75 2·00
MS768 127 × 102 mm. $2.50, Mickey and Minnie Mouse with Huey, Dewey and Louie. P 13½ .. 3·25 4·00

(Des G. Drummond. Litho Questa)

1983 (5 Oct)–**85**. *Ships. T* **181** *and similar horiz designs. Multicoloured. A. P* 14. B. *P* 12½ × 12.

		A		B	
769	4 c. Arawak dug-out canoe ..	40	1·25	1·75	2·00
770	5 c. *Santa Maria*	65	1·25	70	1·00
771	8 c. British and Spanish ships in battle	2·00	1·25	2·50	1·00
772	10 c. Type **181**	2·00	90	2·50	90
773	20 c. U.S. privateer *Grand Turk*	70	1·25	50	70
774	25 c. H.M.S. *Boreas* (frigate)	3·00	1·25	50	70
775	30 c. H.M.S. *Endymion* (frigate) attacking French ship, 1790s	3·00	90	3·00	80
776	35 c. *Caesar* (barque) ..	1·25	1·75	60	70
777	50 c. *Grapeshot* (American schooner)	3·50	1·25	60	80
778	65 c. H.M.S. *Invincible* (battle cruiser)	4·50	2·50	2·50	2·50
779	95 c. H.M.S. *Magicienne* (cruiser)	4·50	2·50	2·50	2·50
780	$1.10, H.M.S. *Durban* (cruiser)	5·50	3·75	7·00	3·50
781	$2 *Sentinel* (cable ship)	7·00	4·00	2·50	3·50
782	$3 H.M.S. *Minerva* (frigate)	7·50	7·50	8·00	15·00
783	$5 Caicos sloop	7·50	11·00	14·00	16·00
769/83	.. .. *Set of* 15	48·00	38·00	45·00	45·00

Dates of issue:—5.10.83, Nos. 772A, 775A, 778A, 780A/2A; 16.12.83, Nos. 771A, 774A, 777A, 779A; 9.1.84, Nos. 769A/70A, 773A, 776A, 783A; 3.85, Nos. 769B, 771B/2B, 775B, 778B, 780B, 783B; 12.8.85, Nos. 770B, 773B/4B, 776B/7B, 779B, 781B; 12.85, No. 782B.

182 President Kennedy and Signing of Civil Rights Legislation

(Des Design Images. Litho Questa)

1983 (22 Dec). *20th Death Anniv of President J. F. Kennedy. P* 14.
784 **182** 20 c. multicoloured 20 15
785 $1 multicoloured .. .. 1·10 1·25

183 Clarabelle Cow Diving

(Litho Questa)

1984 (21 Feb–Apr). *Olympic Games, Los Angeles. T* **183** *and similar horiz designs showing Disney cartoon characters in Olympic events. Multicoloured. A. Inscr* "1984 LOS ANGELES". *P* 14 × 13½. B. *Inscr* "1984 OLYMPICS LOS ANGELES" *and Olympic emblem. P* 14 × 13½ (**MS** 795B) *or* 12 (*others*) (4.84).

		A		B	
786	1 c. Type **183**	10	10	10	10
787	1 c. Donald Duck in 500m kayak race	10	10	10	10
788	2 c. Huey, Dewey and Louie in 1000m kayak race..	10	10	10	10
789	2 c. Mickey Mouse in single kayak	10	10	10	10
790	3 c. Donald Duck highboard diving	10	10	10	10
791	3 c. Minnie Mouse in kayak slalom	10	10	10	10
792	25 c. Mickey Mouse freestyle swimming	45	45	45	45
793	75 c. Donald Duck playing water-polo	1·40	1·40	1·60	1·40
794	$1 Uncle Scrooge and Donald Duck yachting ..	1·75	1·75	2·00	1·75
786/94	.. .. *Set of* 9	3·50	3·50	3·75	3·50
MS795	117 × 90 mm. $2 Pluto platform diving	3·75	4·25	3·75	4·75

ALTERED CATALOGUE NUMBERS

Any Catalogue numbers altered from the last edition are shown as a list in the introductory pages.

184 "Cadillac V–16", 1933 **185** "Rest during the Flight to Egypt, with St. Francis"

(Des N. Waldman. Litho Questa)

1984 (15 Mar). *Classic Cars and 125th Anniv of first Commercial Oil Well. T* **184** *and similar horiz designs. Multicoloured. P* 14.
796 4 c. Type **184** 20 10
797 8 c. Rolls-Royce "Phantom III", 1937 .. 25 15
798 10 c. Saab "99", 1969 .. .. .. 25 15
799 25 c. Maserati "Bora", 1973 .. .. 60 40
800 40 c. Datsun "260Z", 1970 .. .. 85 65
801 55 c. Porsche "917", 1971 .. .. 1·00 80
802 80 c. Lincoln "Continental", 1939 .. 1·25 90
803 $1 Triumph "TR3A", 1957 .. .. 1·40 1·25
796/803 .. .. *Set of* 8 5·25 4·00
MS804 70 × 100 mm. $2 Daimler, 1886 .. .. 2·00 2·50

(Des S. Karp. Litho Walsall)

1984 (9 Apr). *Easter. 450th Death Anniv of Correggio (painter). T* **185** *and similar vert designs. Multicoloured. P* 14.
805 15 c. Type **185** 20 15
806 40 c. "St. Luke and St. Ambrose" .. 45 40
807 60 c. "Diana and her Chariot".. .. 65 65
808 95 c. "The Deposition of Christ" .. 80 80
805/8 .. .. .. *Set of* 4 1·90 1·75
MS809 100 × 79 mm. $2 "The Nativity with Saints Elizabeth and John the younger" (*horiz*).. .. 2·00 2·50

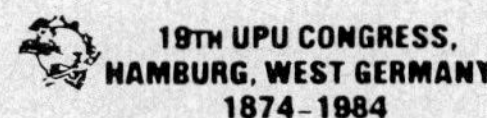

(**186**)

1984 (19 June). *Universal Postal Union Congress, Hamburg. Nos.* 748/9 *and* **MS**753 *optd with T* **186**.
810 95 c. Sperm Whale .. .. .. 2·50 2·00
811 $1.10, Cuvier's Beaked Whale .. .. 2·50 2·00
MS812 112 × 82 mm. $3 Fin Whale .. .. 4·25 4·25

187 "The Adventure of the Second Stain" **188** Orange Clownfish

(Des S. Karp. Litho Walsall)

1984 (16 July). *125th Birth Anniv of Sir Arthur Conan Doyle (author). T* **187** *and similar horiz designs showing scenes from Sherlock Holmes stories. Multicoloured. P* 14.
813 25 c. Type **187** .. .. 2·25 1·50
814 45 c. "The Adventure of the Final Problem" .. 3·00 2·25
815 70 c. "The Adventure of the Empty House" .. 4·50 3·50
816 85 c. "The Adventure of the Greek Interpreter" 5·50 4·00
813/16 .. .. .. *Set of* 4 13·50 10·00
MS817 100 × 70 mm. $2 Sir Arthur Conan Doyle 8·50 9·00

(Des Susan David. Litho Walsall)

1984 (22 Aug). *"Ausipex" International Stamp Exhibition, Melbourne. 175th Birth Anniv of Charles Darwin. T* **188** *and similar vert designs. Multicoloured. P* 14 × 13½.
818 5 c. Type **188**.. .. .. .. 55 40
819 35 c. Monitor Lizard .. .. .. 2·00 1·75
820 50 c. Rainbow Lory .. .. .. 2·75 2·75
821 $1.10, Koalas .. .. 3·50 3·75
818/21 .. .. .. *Set of* 4 8·00 8·00
MS822 100 × 70 mm. $2 Eastern Grey Kangaroo .. .. 3·50 4·50

189 Donald Duck cutting down Christmas Tree

(Litho Questa)

1984 (8 Oct–26 Nov). *Christmas. Walt Disney Cartoon Characters. T* **189** *and similar horiz designs showing scenes from "Toy Tinkers". Multicoloured. P* 12 (75 c.) *or* 14 × 13½ (*others*).
823 20 c. Type **189**.. .. .. .. 85 45
824 35 c. Donald Duck and Chip n'Dale playing with train set .. .. .. 1·10 75
825 50 c. Donald Duck and Chip n'Dale playing with catapult .. .. .. 1·60 1·10
826 75 c. Donald Duck, Chip n'Dale and Christmas tree (26.11).. .. .. 2·25 1·75
827 $1.10, Donald Duck, toy soldier and Chip n'Dale .. .. 2·50 2·50
823/7 .. .. .. *Set of* 5 7·50 6·00
MS828 126 × 102 mm. $2 Donald Duck as Father Christmas .. .. 3·25 4·00
No. 826 was printed in sheetlets of 8 stamps.

190 Magnolia Warbler **191** Leonardo da Vinci and Illustration of Glider Wing (15th century)

(Des Susan David. Litho Walsall)

1985 (28 Jan). *Birth Bicentenary of John J. Audubon (ornithologist). T* **190** *and similar vert designs. Multicoloured. P* 14.
829 25 c. Type **190**.. .. .. .. 2·00 75
830 45 c. Short-eared Owl.. .. .. 3·00 1·50
831 70 c. Mourning Dove and eggs .. .. 3·50 2·75
832 85 c. Caribbean Martin .. .. .. 3·50 3·00
829/32 .. .. *Set of* 4 11·00 7·25
MS833 100×70 mm. $2 Oystercatcher and chicks .. .. 4·25 4·50

(Des K. Gromol. Litho Walsall)

1985 (22 Feb). *40th Anniv of International Civil Aviation Organization. Aviation Pioneers. T* **191** *and similar horiz designs. Multicoloured. P* 14.
834 8 c. Type **191** 50 20
835 25 c. Sir Alliott Verdon Roe and Avro (Canada) CF-102 jetliner (1949) .. 1·50 40
836 65 c. Robert H. Goddard and first liquid fuel rocket (1926).. .. .. .. 2·50 1·50
837 $1 Igor Sikorsky and Vought-Sikorsky VS-300 helicopter prototype (1939) 3·50 2·75
834/7 .. .. *Set of* 4 7·25 4·25
MS838 100×70 mm. $2 Amelia Earhart's Lockheed 10E Electra (1937) .. .. 2·75 3·25

192 Benjamin Franklin and Marquis de Lafayette

(Des Susan David. Litho Walsall)

1985 (28 Mar). *Centenary of the Statue of Liberty's Arrival in New York. T* **192** *and similar horiz designs. Multicoloured. P* 14.
839 20 c. Type **192** 80 80
840 30 c. Frederic Bartholdi (designer) and Gustave Eiffel (engineer) 90 80
841 65 c. *Isere* (French screw warship) arriving in New York with statue, 1885 .. 2·25 1·75
842 $1.10, United States fund raisers Louis Agassiz, Charles Sumner, H. W. Longfellow and Joseph Pulitzer .. .. 2·50 2·00
839/42 .. .. *Set of* 4 5·75 4·75
MS843 99×69 mm. $2 Dedication ceremony, 1886 .. .. 3·00 3·50

193 Sir Edward Hawke and H.M.S. *Royal George* (ship of the line), 1782

(Des Susan David. Litho Walsall)

1985 (17 Apr). *Salute to the Royal Navy. T* **193** *and similar multicoloured designs. P* 14.

844 20 c. Type **193** .. .. 2·25 1·75
845 30 c. Lord Nelson and H.M.S. *Victory* (ship of the line), 1805 .. .. .. 2·75 2·25
846 65 c. Admiral Sir George Cockburn and H.M.S. *Albion* (ship of the line), 1802 3·75 3·00
847 95 c. Admiral Sir David Beatty and H.M.S. *Indefatigable* (battle cruiser), 1916 4·75 4·25
844/7 .. .. *Set of* 4 12·00 10·00
MS848 99×69 mm. $2 18th-century sailor and cannon (*vert*) .. .. 3·25 4·00

194 Mark Twain riding on Halley's Comet

195 The Queen Mother outside Clarence House

(Des J. Iskowitz. Litho Walsall)

1985 (17 May). *International Youth Year. Birth Annivs of Mark Twain* (150*th*) *and Jakob Grimm* (*Bicentenary*). *T* **194** *and similar multicoloured designs. P* 13½×14 (25, 35 c., $2) *or* 14×13½ (50, 95 c.).

849 25 c. Type **194** .. .. 1·00 40
850 35 c. *Grand Turk* (Mississippi river steamer) .. .. 1·50 55
851 50 c. Hansel and Gretel and gingerbread house (*vert*) .. .. 1·75 85
852 95 c. Rumpelstiltskin (*vert*) .. .. .. 2·50 2·00
849/52 .. .. *Set of* 4 6·00 3·50
MS853 99×68 mm. $2 Mark Twain and the Brothers Grimm .. .. 3·50 4·50

(Des J.W. Litho Questa)

1985 (15 July). *Life and Times of Queen Elizabeth the Queen Mother. T* **195** *and similar multicoloured designs. P* 14.

854 30 c. Type **195** 45 45
855 50 c. Visiting Biggin Hill airfield (*horiz*) .. 75 75
856 $1.10, 80th birthday portrait .. .. 1·75 1·90
854/6 .. .. *Set of* 3 2·75 2·75
MS857 56×85 mm. $2 With Prince Charles at Garter ceremony, Windsor Castle, 1968 .. 2·00 3·00

196 King George II and Score of "Zadok the Priest" (1727)

197 Harley-Davidson Dual Cylinder (1915) on Middle Caicos

(Des Susan David. Litho Format)

1985 (17 July). 300*th Birth Anniv of George Frederick Handel* (*composer*). *T* **196** *and similar vert designs. P* 15.

858 4 c. multicoloured 65 50
859 10 c. multicoloured .. .. 1·00 50
860 50 c. multicoloured .. .. 2·75 2·50
861 $1.10, multicoloured .. .. 4·75 5·50
858/61 .. .. *Set of* 4 8·25 8·00
MS862 101×76 mm. $2 black, deep dull purple and dull violet-blue .. .. 6·00 7·50

Designs:—10 c. Queen Caroline and score of "Funeral Anthem" (1737); 50 c. King George I and score of "Water Music" (1714); $1.10, Queen Anne and score of "Or la Tromba" from *Rinaldo* (1711); $2 George Frederick Handel.

(Des Susan David. Litho Format)

1985 (17 July). 300*th Birth Anniv of Johann Sebastian Bach* (*composer*). *Vert designs as T* **204***a of Maldive Islands. Multicoloured. P* 15.

863 15 c. Bassoon .. .. 1·00 40
864 40 c. Natural Horn .. .. 2·00 85
865 60 c. Viola D'Amore .. .. 2·50 1·25
866 95 c. Clavichord .. .. 3·00 2·25
863/6 .. .. *Set of* 4 7·75 4·25
MS867 102×76 mm. $2 Johann Sebastian Bach .. .. 5·00 4·00

(Des Mary Walters. Litho Questa)

1985 (4 Sept). *Centenary of the Motor Cycle. T* **197** *and similar multicoloured designs. P* 14.

868 8 c. Type **197** 60 30
869 25 c. Triumph "Thunderbird" (1950) on Grand Turk .. .. 1·25 70
870 55 c. BMW "K100RS" (1985) on North Caicos .. .. 2·25 1·75
871 $1.20, Honda "1100 Shadow" (1985) on South Caicos .. .. 3·25 5·00
868/71 .. .. *Set of* 4 6·75 7·00
MS872 106×77 mm. $2 Daimler single track (1885) (*vert*) .. .. 3·75 4·00

198 Pirates in Prison

(Des Walt Disney Productions. Litho Questa)

1985 (4 Oct). 30*th Anniv of Disneyland, U.S.A. T* **198** *and similar horiz designs showing scenes from "Pirates of the Caribbean" exhibition. Multicoloured. P* 14×13½.

873 1 c. Type **198** 10 10
874 1 c. The fate of Captain William Kidd .. 10 10
875 2 c. Bartholomew Roberts 10 10
876 2 c. Two buccaneers 10 10
877 3 c. Privateers looting 10 10
878 3 c. Auction of captives 10 10
879 35 c. Singing pirates .. .. 1·50 80
880 75 c. Edward Teach—"Blackbeard" .. .. 3·00 3·25
881 $1.10, Sir Henry Morgan .. .. .. 3·50 4·00
873/81 .. .. *Set of* 9 7·50 7·50
MS882 123×86 mm. $2.50, Mary Read and Anne Bonney .. .. 4·50 4·50

199 Brownies from China, Turks and Caicos and Papua New Guinea

(Des Mary Walters. Litho Questa)

1985 (4 Nov). 75*th Anniv of Girl Guide Movement and* 35*th Anniv of Grand Turk Company. T* **199** *and similar horiz designs. Multicoloured. P* 14.

883 10 c. Type **199** 75 40
884 40 c. Brownies from Surinam, Turks and Caicos and Korea .. .. .. 1·75 1·25
885 70 c. Guides from Australia, Turks and Caicos and Canada .. .. .. 2·50 3·00
886 80 c. Guides from West Germany, Turks and Caicos and Israel .. .. .. 2·75 3·00
883/6 .. .. *Set of* 4 7·00 7·00
MS887 107×76 mm. $2 75th anniversary emblem .. .. 3·00 3·50

200 Iguana and Log

201 Duke and Duchess of York after Wedding

(Des I. MacLaury. Litho Questa)

1986 (20 Nov). *Turks and Caicos Ground Iguana. T* **200** *and similar horiz designs. Multicoloured. P* 14.

888 8 c. Type **200** .. .. 2·25 1·25
889 10 c. Iguana on beach .. .. 2·25 1·25
890 20 c. Iguana at nest .. .. 3·50 2·50
891 35 c. Iguana eating flowers .. .. .. 6·50 4·50
888/91 .. .. *Set of* 4 13·00 8·50
MS892 105×76 mm. $2 Map showing habitat .. 10·00 14·00

(Litho Questa)

1986 (19 Dec). *Royal Wedding. T* **201** *and similar vert designs. Multicoloured. P* 14.

893 35 c. Type **201** 75 55
894 65 c. Miss Sarah Ferguson in wedding carriage .. .. 1·25 1·40
895 $1.10, Duke and Duchess of York on Palace balcony after wedding .. .. 2·00 2·75
893/5 .. .. *Set of* 3 3·50 4·25
MS896 85×85 mm. $2 Duke and Duchess of York leaving Westminster Abbey .. .. 2·50 3·50

202 "The Prophecy of the Birth of Christ to King Achaz"

203 H.M.S. *Victoria* (ship of the line), 1859, and Victoria Cross

(Litho Questa)

1987 (9 Dec). *Christmas. T* **202** *and similar vert designs, each showing illuminated illustration by Giorgio Clovio from "Farnese Book of Hours". Multicoloured. P* 14.

897 35 c. Type **202** .. .. 1·25 85
898 50 c. "The Annunciation" .. .. .. 1·75 1·75
899 65 c. "The Circumcision" .. .. .. 2·25 2·25
900 95 c. "Adoration of the Kings" .. .. 3·25 4·00
897/900 .. .. *Set of* 4 7·75 8·00
MS901 76×106 mm. $2 "The Nativity" .. .. 4·25 5·50

(Litho Questa)

1987 (24 Dec). 150*th Anniv of Accession of Queen Victoria. T* **203** *and similar horiz designs. Multicoloured. P* 14.

902 8 c. Type **203** .. .. 1·50 1·00
903 35 c. *Victoria* (paddle-steamer) and gold sovereign .. .. 2·50 2·25
904 55 c. Royal Yacht *Victoria and Albert I* and 1840 Penny Black stamp .. .. 2·75 2·75
905 95 c. Royal Yacht *Victoria and Albert II* and Victoria Public Library .. .. 3·75 4·50
902/5 .. .. *Set of* 4 9·50 9·50
MS906 129×76 mm. $2 *Victoria* (barque) .. 6·00 7·50

(Des and litho Questa)

1987 (31 Dec). *Bicentenary of U.S. Constitution. Multicoloured designs as T* **210***a of Sierra Leone. P* 14.

907 10 c. State Seal, New Jersey 25 35
908 35 c. 18th-century family going to church ("Freedom of Worship") (*vert*) 75 75
909 65 c. U.S. Supreme Court, Judicial Branch, Washington (*vert*) .. .. .. 1·40 1·75
910 80 c. John Adams (statesman) (*vert*) .. 1·60 2·25
907/10 .. .. *Set of* 4 3·50 4·50
MS911 105×75 mm. $2 George Mason (Virginia delegate) (*vert*) .. .. 2·40 3·75

Nos. 907/10 were each printed in sheetlets of five stamps and one stamp-size label, which appears in the centre of the bottom row.

204 *Santa Maria*

205 Arawak Artifact and Scouts in Cave, Middle Caicos

(Litho Questa)

1988 (20 Jan). 500*th Anniv of Discovery of America by Columbus* (1992) (1*st issue*). *T* **204** *and similar horiz designs. Multicoloured. P* 14.

912 4 c. Type **204** 35 15
913 25 c. Columbus meeting Tainos Indians .. 85 60
914 70 c. *Santa Maria* anchored off Indian village .. .. 2·50 3·00
915 $1 Columbus in field of grain .. .. 2·75 3·25
912/15 .. .. *Set of* 4 5·75 6·25
MS916 105 × 76 mm. $2 *Santa Maria, Pinta* and *Nina* .. .. 3·50 4·50

See also Nos. 947/51, 1028/36, 1072/80 and 1166/76.

(Litho Questa)

1988 (12 Feb). *World Scout Jamboree, Australia. T* **205** *and similar multicoloured designs. P* 14.

917 8 c. Type **205** 20 15
918 35 c. *Santa Maria*, scouts and Hawks Nest Island (*horiz*) 55 55
919 65 c. Scouts diving to wreck of galleon .. 95 1·25
920 95 c. Visiting ruins of 19th-century sisal plantation (*horiz*) .. .. .. 1·40 1·75
917/20 .. .. *Set of* 4 2·75 3·25
MS921 118 × 82 mm. $2 Splashdown of John Glenn's "Mercury" capsule, 1962 .. .. 3·75 5·00

No. **MS**921 is inscribed "Sight" in error.

40TH WEDDING ANNIVERSARY

H.M. QUEEN ELIZABETH II

H.R.H. THE DUKE OF EDINBURGH

(206)

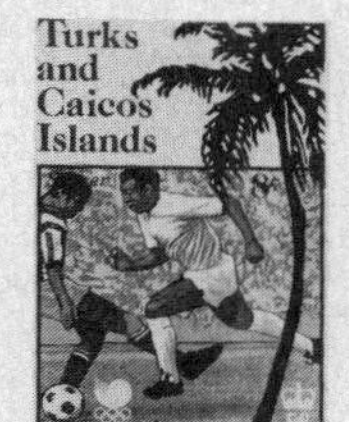

207 Football

1988 (14 Mar). *Royal Ruby Wedding. Nos.* 772A, 774A *and* 781A *optd with T* **206**.

922	10 c. Type **181**	40	40
923	25 c. H.M.S. *Boreas* (frigate)	70	55
924	$2 *Sentinel* (cable ship)	3·25	4·25
922/4	.. .. *Set of* 3	4·00	4·75

(Des L. Fried. Litho B.D.T.)

1988 (29 Aug). *Olympic Games, Seoul. T* **207** *and similar vert designs. Multicoloured. P* 14.

925	8 c. Type **207**	30	15
926	30 c. Yachting	60	50
927	70 c. Cycling	1·75	2·00
928	$1 Athletics	1·75	2·25
925/8	.. .. *Set of* 4	4·00	4·50
MS929	102 × 71 mm. $2 Swimming	2·75	3·50

208 Game-fishing Launch and Swordfish

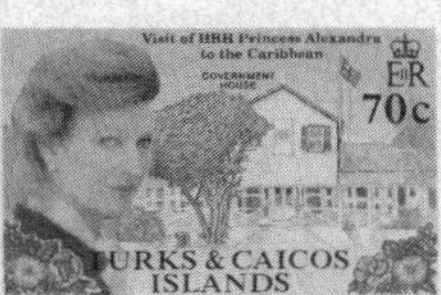

209 Princess Alexandra and Government House

(Des L. Birmingham. Litho Questa)

1988 (5 Sept). *Billfish Tournament. T* **208** *and similar multicoloured designs. P* 14.

930	8 c. Type **208**	40	20
931	10 c. Competitors with swordfish catch ..	45	20
932	70 c. Game-fishing launch	2·00	2·50
933	$1 Atlantic Blue Marlin	2·50	3·25
930/3	.. .. *Set of* 4	4·75	5·50
MS934	119×85 mm. $2 Stylized Sailfish (*horiz*)	4·00	5·50

(Litho Questa)

1988 (24 Oct). *Christmas. 500th Birth Anniv of Titian (artist). Vert designs as T* **186***a of Lesotho inscr* "CHRISTMAS 1988" *and with royal cypher at top right. Multicoloured. P* 13½×14.

935	15 c. "Madonna and Child with Saint Catherine"	40	30
936	25 c. "Madonna with a Rabbit"	50	40
937	35 c. "Virgin and Child with Saints" ..	60	50
938	40 c. "The Gypsy Madonna"	70	60
939	50 c. "The Holy Family and a Shepherd" ..	80	70
940	65 c. "Madonna and Child"	95	85
941	$3 "Madonna and Child with Saints" ..	4·25	6·00
935/41	.. .. *Set of* 7	7·50	8·50
MS942	Two sheets, each 110 × 95 mm. (a) $2 "Adoration of the Magi" (detail). (b) $2 "The Annunciation" (detail) .. .. *Set of 2 sheets*	6·00	7·50

(Des and litho Questa)

1988 (14 Nov). *Visit of Princess Alexandra. T* **209** *and similar multicoloured designs. P* 14.

943	70 c. Type **209**	1·50	1·50
944	$1.40, Princess Alexandra and map of islands	3·00	3·25
MS945	92 × 72 mm. $2 Princess Alexandra (*vert*)	5·50	6·50

210 Coat of Arms

210*a* Andrew Jackson and *De Witt Clinton* Railway Locomotive

(Des and litho Questa)

1988 (15 Dec). *P* 14½×15.

946	**210** $10 multicoloured	11·00	13·00

(Des D. Miller. Litho Questa)

1989 (15 May). *500th Anniv of Discovery of America by Columbus (1992) (2nd issue). Pre-Columbian Carib Society. Multicoloured designs as T* **69** *of St. Vincent Grenadines. P* 14.

947	10 c. Cutting tree bark for canoe	15	15
948	50 c. Body painting (*horiz*)	80	80
949	65 c. Religious ceremony (*horiz*)	95	1·10
950	$1 Canoeing	1·50	1·75
947/50	.. .. *Set of* 4	3·00	3·50
MS951	84×70 mm. $2 Cave pictograph (*horiz*)	3·50	4·50

(Des Design Element. Litho Questa)

1989 (17 Nov). *"World Stamp Expo '89" International Stamp Exhibition, Washington (1st issue). Sheet 77×62 mm containing horiz design as T* **193***a of Lesotho. Multicoloured. P* 14.

MS952	$1.50, Lincoln Memorial	2·50	3·25

(Des W. Hanson Studio. Litho Questa)

1989 (19 Nov). *"World Stamp Expo '89" International Stamp Exhibition, Washington (2nd issue). Bicentenary of the U.S. Presidency. T* **210***a and similar horiz designs. Multicoloured. P* 14.

953	50 c. Type **210***a*	80	80
	a. Sheetlet. Nos. 953/8	4·25	
954	50 c. Martin van Buren, Moses Walker and early baseball game	80	80
955	50 c. William H. Harrison and campaign parade	80	80
956	50 c. John Tyler, Davy Crockett and the Alamo, Texas	80	80
957	50 c. James K. Polk, California gold miner and first U.S. postage stamp ..	80	80
958	50 c. Zachary Taylor and Battle of Buena Vista, 1846	80	80
959	50 c. Rutherford B. Hayes and end of Confederate Reconstruction	80	80
	a. Sheetlet. Nos. 959/64	4·25	
960	50 c. James A. Garfield and Battle of Shiloh	80	80
961	50 c. Chester A. Arthur and opening of Brooklyn Bridge, 1883	80	80
962	50 c. Grover Cleveland, Columbian Exposition, Chicago, 1893, and commemorative stamp	80	80
963	50 c. Benjamin Harrison, Pan-American Union Building and map of Americas	80	80
964	50 c. William McKinley and Rough Rider Monument	80	80
965	50 c. Herbert Hoover, Sonya Heine (skater) and Ralph Metcalf (athlete) ..	80	80
	a. Sheetlet. Nos. 965/70	4·25	
966	50 c. Franklin D. Roosevelt with dog and in wheelchair	80	80
967	50 c. Statue of Washington by Frazer and New York World's Fair, 1939 ..	80	80
968	50 c. Harry S. Truman, Veterans Memorial Building, San Francisco, and U.N. emblem	80	80
969	50 c. Dwight D. Eisenhower and U.S. troops landing in Normandy, 1944 ..	80	80
970	50 c. John F. Kennedy and "Apollo 11" astronauts on Moon, 1969	80	80
953/70	.. .. *Set of* 18	13·00	13·00

Nos. 953/8, 959/64 and 965/70 were each printed together, *se-tenant*, in sheetlets of six stamps.

(Litho Questa)

1989 (18 Dec). *Christmas. Paintings by Bellini. Vert designs as T* **193***b of Lesotho. Multicoloured. P* 14.

971	15 c. "Madonna and Child"	40	40
972	25 c. "The Madonna of the Shrubs" ..	50	50
973	35 c. "The Virgin and Child"	60	60
974	40 c. "The Virgin and Child with a Greek Inscription"	70	70
975	50 c. "The Madonna of the Meadow" ..	80	80
976	65 c. "The Madonna of the Pear"	1·50	1·50
977	70 c. "The Virgin and Child" (*different*) ..	1·75	1·75
978	$1 "Madonna and Child" (*different*) ..	2·50	2·50
971/8	.. .. *Set of* 8	8·00	8·00
MS979	Two sheets, each 96 × 72 mm. (a) $2 "The Virgin and Child enthroned". (b) $2 "The Madonna with John the Baptist and another Saint" .. .. .. *Set of 2 sheets*	9·00	11·00

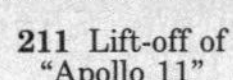
211 Lift-off of "Apollo 11"

212 *Zephyranthes rosea*

(Des W. Hanson Studio. Litho Questa)

1990 (8 Jan). *20th Anniv of First Manned Landing on Moon. T* **211** *and similar vert designs. Multicoloured. P* 14.

980	50 c. Type **211**	60	80
	a. Sheetlet. Nos. 980/4 and 5 labels	2·75	
981	50 c. Lunar module *Eagle* on Moon ..	60	80
982	50 c. Aldrin gathering dust sample ..	60	80
983	50 c. Neil Armstrong with camera ..	60	80
984	50 c. *Eagle* re-united with command module *Columbia*	60	80
980/4	.. .. *Set of* 5	2·75	3·50

Nos. 980/4 were printed together, *se-tenant*, in sheetlets of five stamps, and five stamp-size labels, with Nos. 981/3 forming a composite design.

(Des C. Abbott. Litho Questa)

1990 (11 Jan)–**94**. *Island Flowers. T* **212** *and similar vert designs. Multicoloured.* A. *P* 14. B. *P* 12 (1994).

		A		B	
985	8 c. Type **212**	30	20	30	20
986	10 c. *Sophora tomentosa* ..	30	20	30	20
987	15 c. *Coccoloba uvifera* ..	40	25	40	25
988	20 c. *Encyclia gracilis* ..	40	30	40	30
989	25 c. *Tillandsia streptophylla*	50	35	50	35
990	30 c. *Maurandella antirrhiniflora*	70	70	70	60
991	35 c. *Tillandsia balbisiana* ..	60	50	60	50
992	50 c. *Encyclia rufa*	1·25	1·25	1·00	1·00
993	65 c. *Aechmea lingulata* ..	1·40	1·50	1·25	1·25
994	80 c. *Asclepias curassavica* ..	1·40	1·50	1·40	1·50
995	$1 *Caesalpinia bahamensis*	1·50	1·60	1·50	1·60
996	$1.10, *Capparis cynophallophora*	2·00	2·75	2·00	2·75
997	$1.25, *Stachytarpheta jamaicensis*	2·50	3·00	2·50	3·00
998	$2 *Cassia biflora*	3·00	4·00	3·00	4·00
999	$5 *Clusia rosea*	7·00	9·00	7·00	9·00
1000	$10 *Opuntia bahamana* (21.5.90)	14·00	17·00	14·00	17·00
985/1000	.. .. *Set of* 16	35·00	40·00	35·00	40·00

213 Queen Parrotfish

(Des J. Barbaris. Litho B.D.T.)

1990 (12 Feb). *Fishes. T* **213** *and similar horiz designs. Multicoloured. P* 14.

1001	8 c. Type **213**	25	20
1002	10 c. Queen Triggerfish	25	20
1003	25 c. Sergeant Major	60	45
1004	40 c. Spotted Goatfish	85	75
1005	50 c. Neon Goby	1·00	85
1006	75 c. Nassau Grouper	1·50	1·50
1007	80 c. Yellow-headed Jawfish	1·75	2·00
1008	$1 Blue Tang	1·75	2·00
1001/8	.. .. *Set of* 8	7·00	7·00
MS1009	Two sheets, each 115×80 mm. (a) $2 Butter Hamlet. (b) $2 Queen Angelfish *Set of 2 sheets*	12·00	13·00

214 Yellow-billed Cuckoo

215 *Anartia jatrophae*

(Des W. Wright. Litho B.D.T.)

1990 (19 Feb). *Birds (1st series). T* **214** *and similar horiz designs. Multicoloured. P* 14.

1010	10 c. Type **214**	50	30
1011	15 c. White-tailed Tropic Bird	65	40
1012	20 c. Kirtland's Warbler	80	65
1013	30 c. Yellow-crowned Night Heron ..	90	70
1014	50 c. Black-billed Whistling Duck ("West Indian Tree Duck")	1·50	1·00
1015	80 c. Yellow-bellied Sapsucker	2·00	2·00
1016	$1 American Kestrel	2·25	2·25
1017	$1.40, Northern Mockingbird	3·00	3·50
1010/17	.. .. *Set of* 8	10·50	9·75
MS1018	Two sheets, each 104×78 mm. (a) $2 Yellow Warbler. (b) $2 Osprey .. *Set of 2 sheets*	14·00	14·00

See also Nos. 1050/8.

(Des Linda Vorovik. Litho Questa)

1990 (19 Mar). *Butterflies (1st series). T* **215** *and similar multicoloured designs. P* 14.

1019	15 c. Type **215**	60	30
1020	25 c. *Phoebis sennae* (*horiz*)	80	50
1021	35 c. *Euptoieta hegesia* (*horiz*)	95	65
1022	40 c. *Hylephila phylaeus* (*horiz*)	1·00	70
1023	50 c. *Eurema chamberlaini* (*horiz*) ..	1·10	90
1024	60 c. *Brephidium exilis*	1·40	1·25
1025	90 c. *Papilio aristodemus* (*horiz*)	2·25	2·75
1026	$1 *Marpesia eleuchea*	2·40	3·00
1019/26	.. .. *Set of* 8	9·50	9·00
MS1027	Two sheets, each 106×76 mm. (a) $2 *Hemiargus thomasi* (*horiz*). (b) $2 *Danaus gilippus* (*horiz*) .. .. .. *Set of 2 sheets*	9·50	11·00

See also Nos. 1081/9.

(Des Mary Walters. Litho Questa)

1990 (2 Apr). *500th Anniv of Discovery of America by Columbus (1992) (3rd issue). New World Natural History – Fishes. Horiz designs as T* **60** *of Nevis (St. Kitts-Nevis). Multicoloured. P* 14.

1028	10 c. Rock Beauty	50	30
1029	15 c. Coney	60	40
1030	25 c. Red Hind	85	60
1031	50 c. Banded Butterflyfish	1·40	1·25

1032 60 c. French Angelfish .. .. .. 1·75 1·50
1033 75 c. Black-barred Soldierfish .. .. 1·90 1·90
1034 90 c. Stoplight Parrotfish .. .. 2·00 2·25
1035 $1 French Grunt .. .. .. 2·25 2·40
1028/35 .. .. *Set of 8* 10·00 9·50
MS1036 Two sheets, each 109×75 mm. (a) $2 Blue Chromis. (b) $2 Grey Angelfish *Set of 2 sheets* 8·50 10·00

216 Penny "Rainbow Trial" in Blue

217 Pillar Box No. 1, 1855

(Des M. Pollard. Litho B.D.T.)

1990 (3 May). *150th Anniv of the Penny Black. T* **216** *and similar vert designs. P* 14.
1037 25 c. deep violet-blue 85 60
1038 75 c. lake-brown .. .. .. 2·00 2·00
1039 $1 blue .. .. 2·50 2·75
1037/9 .. .. .. *Set of 3* 4·75 4·75
MS1040 144×111 mm. $2 brownish black .. 4·25 4·75
Designs:—75 c. 1d. red-brown colour trial of December, 1840; $1 2d. blue of 1840; $2 Penny Black.

(Des M. Pollard. Litho B.D.T.)

1990 (3 May). *"Stamp World London 90" International Stamp Exhibition. British Pillar Boxes. T* **217** *and similar vert designs. P* 14.
1041 35 c. purple-brown and brownish grey .. 65 65
1042 50 c. deep violet-blue and brownish grey .. 90 1·00
1043 $1.25, dull ultramarine & brownish grey 2·25 3·00
1041/3 .. .. .. *Set of 3* 3·50 4·25
MS1044 143×111 mm. $2 brown-lake and black 4·00 4·50
Designs:—50 c. Penfold box, 1866; $1.25, Air mail box, 1935; $2 "K" type box, 1979.

218 Queen Elizabeth the Queen Mother

219 Stripe-headed Tanager

(Des D. Miller. Litho Questa)

1990 (20 Aug). *90th Birthday of Queen Elizabeth the Queen Mother. T* **218** *and similar vert designs showing recent photographs of the Queen Mother. P* 14.
1045 10 c. multicoloured 25 15
1046 25 c. multicoloured 60 50
1047 75 c. multicoloured .. .. .. 1·40 1·60
1048 $1.25, multicoloured .. .. .. 2·00 2·50
1045/8 .. .. .. *Set of 4* 3·75 4·25
MS1049 70×73 mm. $2 multicoloured .. .. 3·75 4·50

(Des Tracy Pedersen. Litho Questa)

1990 (24 Sept). *Birds (2nd series). T* **219** *and similar multicoloured designs. P* 14.
1050 8 c. Type **219** 45 40
1051 10 c. Black-whiskered Vireo (*horiz*) .. 45 40
1052 25 c. Blue-grey Gnatcatcher (*horiz*) .. 80 60
1053 40 c. Lesser Scaup (*horiz*) .. .. 1·25 90
1054 50 c. Bahama Pintail (*horiz*) .. .. 1·25 1·00
1055 75 c. Black-necked Stilt (*horiz*) .. .. 1·75 1·75
1056 80 c. Oystercatcher .. .. .. 1·75 2·00
1057 $1 Louisiana Heron (*horiz*) .. .. 2·25 2·50
1050/7 .. .. .. *Set of 8* 9·00 8·50
MS1058 Two sheets, each 98×69 mm. (a) $2 American Coot (*horiz*). (b) $2 Bahama Woodstar (*horiz*) .. .. .. *Set of 2 sheets* 7·50 8·50

220 "Triumph of Christ over Sin and Death" (detail, Rubens)

221 Canoeing

(Litho Questa)

1990 (17 Dec). *Christmas. 350th Death Anniv of Rubens. T* **220** *and similar vert designs. Multicoloured. P* 13½×14.
1059 10 c. Type **220** 10 10
1060 35 c. "St. Theresa Praying" (detail) .. 40 45
1061 45 c. "St. Theresa Praying" (different detail) 55 60
1062 50 c. "Triumph of Christ over Sin and Death" (different detail) .. 60 65
1063 65 c. "St. Theresa Praying" (different detail) 80 85
1064 75 c. "Triumph of Christ over Sin and Death" (different detail) .. 90 95
1065 $1.25, "St. Theresa Praying" (different detail) .. .. .. 1·50 1·60
1059/65 .. .. .. *Set of 7* 4·75 5·25
MS1066 Two sheets, each 70×100 mm. (a) $2 "Triumph of Christ over Sin and Death" (different detail). (b) $2 "St. Theresa Praying" (different detail) .. .. *Set of 2 sheets* 5·00 5·25

(Des D. Miller. Litho Questa)

1991 (7 Jan). *Olympic Games, Barcelona* (1992). *T* **221** *and similar vert designs. Multicoloured. P* 14.
1067 10 c. Type **221** 20 20
1068 25 c. 100 metre sprint 50 50
1069 75 c. Pole vaulting .. .. .. 1·25 1·50
1070 $1.25, Javelin .. .. .. 1·90 2·25
1067/70 .. .. .. *Set of 4* 3·50 4·00
MS1071 109×70 mm. $2 Baseball .. .. 3·75 4·25

(Des T. Agans. Litho Questa)

1991 (15 Apr). *500th Anniv of Discovery of America by Columbus* (1992) (*4th issue*). *History of Exploration. Multicoloured designs as T* **64** *of Nevis (St. Kitts-Nevis). P* 14.
1072 5 c. Henry Hudson in Hudson's Bay, 1611 10 10
1073 10 c. Roald Amundsen's airship N.1 *Norge*, 1926 .. .. .. 10 10
1074 15 c. Amundsen's *Gjoa* in the Northwest Passage, 1906 .. .. 20 25
1075 50 c. U.S.S. *Nautilus* (submarine) under North Pole, 1958 .. .. 60 65
1076 75 c. Robert Scott's *Terra Nova*, 1911 .. 90 95
1077 $1 Byrd and Bennett's Fokker F.VIIa/3m *Josephine Ford* aircraft over North Pole, 1926 .. .. 1·25 1·40
1078 $1.25, Lincoln Ellsworth's Northrop Gamma *Polar Star* on trans-Antarctic flight, 1935 .. .. .. 1·50 1·60
1079 $1.50, Capt. James Cook in the Antarctic, 1772–1775 .. .. 1·75 1·90
1072/9 .. .. .. *Set of 8* 6·50 7·00
MS1080 Two sheets, each 116×76 mm. (a) $2 *Santa Maria* (*vert*). (b) $2 Bow of *Nina* (*vert*) *Set of 2 sheets* 5·00 5·25

222 *Anartia jatrophae*

(Des D. Miller. Litho Questa)

1991 (13 May). *Butterflies (2nd series). T* **222** *and similar horiz designs. Multicoloured. P* 14.
1081 5 c. Type **222** 30 30
1082 25 c. *Historis osius* 70 50
1083 35 c. *Agraulis vanillae* 80 65
1084 45 c. *Junonia evarete* 95 80
1085 55 c. *Dryas julia* .. .. .. 1·10 1·00
1086 65 c. *Siproeta stelenes* .. .. .. 1·40 1·40
1087 70 c. *Appias drusilla* .. .. .. 1·50 1·60
1088 $1 *Ascia monuste* .. .. .. 1·75 1·90
1081/8 .. .. .. *Set of 8* 7·75 7·25
MS1089 Two sheets, each 114×72 mm. (a) $2 *Phoebis philea*. (b) $2 *Pseudolycaena marsyas* *Set of 2 sheets* 9·00 10·00

223 Protohydrochoerus

(Des R. Frank. Litho Questa)

1991 (3 June). *Extinct Species of Fauna. T* **223** *and similar horiz designs. Multicoloured. P* 14.
1090 5 c. Type **223** 10 10
1091 10 c. Phororhacos 10 10
1092 15 c. Prothylacynus 20 25
1093 50 c. Borhyaena 60 65
1094 75 c. Smilodon 90 95
1095 $1 Thoatherium .. .. .. 1·25 1·40
1096 $1.25, Cuvieronius .. .. .. 1·50 1·60
1097 $1.50, Toxodon .. .. .. 1·75 1·90
1090/7 .. .. .. *Set of 8* 6·50 7·00
MS1098 Two sheets, each 79×59 mm. (a) $2 Astrapotherium. (b) $2 Mesosaurus *Set of 2 sheets* 5·00 5·25

(Des D. Miller. Litho Walsall)

1991 (8 June). *65th Birthday of Queen Elizabeth II. Horiz designs as T* **210** *of Lesotho. Multicoloured. P* 14.
1099 25 c. Queen and Prince Philip at St. Paul's Cathedral, 1988 .. .. .. 65 45
1100 35 c. Queen and Prince Philip 80 60
1101 65 c. Queen and Prince Philip at Garter Ceremony, 1988 .. .. .. 1·40 1·40
1102 80 c. Queen at Windsor, May 1988 .. 1·75 2·00
1099/1102 .. .. .. *Set of 4* 4·25 4·00
MS1103 68×90 mm. $2 Separate photographs of Queen and Prince Philip .. .. .. 4·00 4·50

224 *Pluteus chrysophlebius*

(Des Wendy Smith-Griswold. Litho Questa)

1991 (24 June). *Fungi. T* **224** *and similar multicoloured designs. P* 14.
1104 10 c. Type **224** 10 10
1105 15 c. *Leucopaxillus gracillimus* 20 25
1106 20 c. *Marasmius haematocephalus* .. 25 30
1107 35 c. *Collybia subpruinosa* 40 45
1108 50 c. *Marasmius atrorubens* (*vert*) .. 60 65
1109 65 c. *Leucocoprinus birnbaumii* (*vert*) .. 80 85
1110 $1.10, *Trogia cantharelloides* (*vert*) .. 1·40 1·50
1111 $1.25, *Boletellus cubensis* (*vert*) .. 1·50 1·60
1104/11 .. .. .. *Set of 8* 5·25 5·75
MS1112 Two sheets, each 85×59 mm. (a) $2 *Pyrrhoglossum pyrrhum* (*vert*). (b) $2 *Gerronema citrinum* .. .. .. *Set of 2 sheets* 5·00 5·25

(Des D. Miller. Litho Walsall)

1991 (29 July). *10th Wedding Anniv of Prince and Princess of Wales. Horiz designs as T* **210** *of Lesotho. Multicoloured. P* 14.
1113 10 c. Prince and Princess of Wales, 1987 .. 30 25
1114 45 c. Separate photographs of Prince, Princess and sons .. .. .. 1·25 90
1115 50 c. Prince Henry in fire engine and Prince William applauding .. .. .. 1·50 1·25
1116 $1 Princess Diana in Derbyshire, 1990, and Prince Charles .. .. .. 2·00 2·50
1113/16 .. .. .. *Set of 4* 4·50 4·50
MS1117 68×90 mm. $2 Prince, Princess and family, Majorca, 1990 .. .. .. 4·50 5·00

(Litho B.D.T.)

1991 (26 Aug). *Death Centenary of Vincent van Gogh (artist)* (1990). *Multicoloured designs as T* **255** *of Maldive Islands. P* 13.
1118 15 c. "Weaver with Spinning Wheel" (*horiz*) 20 25
1119 25 c. "Head of a Young Peasant with Pipe" 30 35
1120 35 c. "Old Cemetery Tower at Nuenen" .. 40 45
1121 45 c. "Cottage at Nightfall" (*horiz*) .. 55 60
1122 50 c. "Still Life with Open Bible" (*horiz*) .. 60 65
1123 65 c. "Lane, Jardin du Luxembourg" (*horiz*) 80 85
1124 80 c. "Pont du Carrousel and Louvre, Paris" (*horiz*) .. .. .. 1·00 1·10
1125 $1 "Vase with Poppies, Cornflowers, Peonies and Chrysanthemums" .. 1·25 1·40
1118/25 .. .. .. *Set of 8* 5·00 5·50
MS1126 Two sheets, each 117×80 mm. (a) $2 "Ploughed Field" (*horiz*). (b) $2 "Entrance to the Public Park" (*horiz*). Imperf .. *Set of 2 sheets* 5·00 5·25

225 Series "8550" Steam Locomotive

(Litho Questa)

1991 (4 Nov). *"Phila Nippon '91" International Stamp Exhibition, Tokyo. Japanese Steam Locomotives. T* **225** *and similar horiz designs. Multicoloured. P* 14.
1127 8 c. Type **225** 10 10
1128 10 c. Class "C 57" 10 10
1129 45 c. Series "4110" 55 60
1130 50 c. Class "C 55" 60 65
1131 65 c. Series "6250" 80 85
1132 80 c. Class "E 10" .. .. .. 1·00 1·10
1133 $1 Series "4500" .. .. .. 1·25 1·40
1134 $1.25, Class "C 11" .. .. .. 1·50 1·60
1127/34 .. .. .. *Set of 8* 6·00 6·50
MS1135 Two sheets, each 112×80 mm. (a) $2 Class "C 58". (b) $2 Class "C 62" .. *Set of 2 sheets* 5·00 5·25

(Litho Walsall)

1991 (23 Dec). *Christmas. Religious Paintings by Gerard David. Vert designs as T* **211** *of Lesotho. Multicoloured. P* 12.
1136 8 c. "Adoration of the Shepherds" (detail) 20 15
1137 15 c. "Virgin and Child Enthroned with Two Angels" 35 25
1138 35 c. "The Annunciation" (outer wings) .. 65 50
1139 45 c. "The Rest on the Flight to Egypt" .. 80 70
1140 50 c. "The Rest on the Flight to Egypt" (*different*) 90 90
1141 65 c. "Virgin and Child with Angels" .. 1·25 1·25

1142 80 c. "Adoration of the Shepherds" .. 1·50 1·75
1143 $1.25, "Perussis Altarpiece" (detail) .. 2·25 2·50
1136/43 .. .. *Set of* 8 7·00 7·25
MS1144 Two sheets, each 102×127 mm. (a) $2 "The Nativity". (b) $2 "Adoration of the Kings". P 14 .. .. .. *Set of* 2 *sheets* 8·00 9·00

(Des D. Miller. Litho Questa)

1992 (6 Feb). *40th Anniv of Queen Elizabeth II's Accession. Horiz designs as T* **214** *of Lesotho. Multicoloured. P* 14.
1145 10 c. Garden overlooking sea 30 30
1146 20 c. Jetty 55 55
1147 25 c. Small bay 60 60
1148 35 c. Island road 75 75
1149 50 c. Grand Turk .. .. 1·00 1·00
1150 65 c. Beach .. .. 1·40 1·40
1151 80 c. Marina .. .. 1·50 1·50
1152 $1.10, Grand Turk (*different*) .. .. 1·60 1·60
1145/52 .. .. *Set of* 8 7·00 7·00
MS1153 Two sheets, each 75×97 mm. (a) $2 Beach (*different*). (b) $2 Foreshore, Grand Turk *Set of* 2 *sheets* 7·00 8·00

(Litho B.D.T.)

1992 (26 May). *"Granada '92" International Stamp Exhibition, Spain. Religious Paintings. Vert designs as T* **68** *of St. Kitts-Nevis (Nevis). Multicoloured. P* 13.
1154 8 c. "St. Monica" (Luis Tristán) 10 10
1155 20 c. "The Vision of Ezekiel: The Resurrection of the Flesh" (detail) (Francisco Collantes) 25 30
1156 45 c. "The Vision of Ezekiel: The Resurrection of the Flesh" (different detail) (Collantes) 55 60
1157 50 c. "The Martyrdom of St. Phillip" (José de Ribera) 60 65
1158 65 c. "St. John the Evangelist" (Juan Ribalta) 80 85
1159 80 c. "Archimedes" (De Ribera) .. .. 1·00 1·10
1160 $1 "St. John the Baptist in the Desert" (De Ribera) .. .. .. 1·25 1·40
1161 $1.25, "The Martyrdom of St. Phillip" (detail) (De Ribera) .. .. 1·50 1·60
1154/61 .. .. *Set of* 8 6·00 6·50
MS1162 Two sheets, each 95×120 mm. (a) $2 "The Baptism of Christ" (Juan Fernández Navarrete). (b) $2 "Battle at El Sotillo" (Francisco Zurbarán). Imperf .. *Set of* 2 *sheets* 5·00 5·25

226 Boy Scout on Duty at New York World's Fair, 1964

(Des W. Hanson Studio. Litho Questa)

1992 (6 July). *17th World Scout Jamboree, Korea. T* **226** *and similar multicoloured designs. P* 14.
1163 $1 Type **226** .. .. 2·00 2·25
1164 $1 Lord Baden-Powell (*vert*) .. .. 2·00 2·25
MS1165 117×89 mm. $2 Silver Buffalo award 4·00 5·00

227 *Nina* and Commemorative Coin

(Litho Questa)

1992 (12 Oct). *500th Anniv of Discovery of America by Columbus (5th issue). T* **227** *and similar horiz designs, each showing a commemorative coin. Multicoloured. P* 14.
1166 10 c. Type **227** 10 10
1167 15 c. Departure from Palos 20 25
1168 20 c. Coat of Arms of Columbus 25 30
1169 25 c. Ships of Columbus 30 35
1170 30 c. *Pinta* 35 40
1171 35 c. Landfall in the New World 40 45
1172 50 c. Christopher Columbus 60 65
1173 65 c. *Santa Maria* 80 85
1174 80 c. Erecting commemorative cross .. 1·00 1·25
1175 $1.10, Columbus meeting Amerindian .. 1·40 1·50
1166/75 .. .. *Set of* 10 5·50 6·00
MS1176 Two sheets, each 70×100 mm. (a) $2 Coins showing ships of Columbus. (b) $2 Coins showing landing in the New World *Set of* 2 *sheets* 5·00 5·25

(Litho Questa)

1992 (7 Dec). *Christmas. Religious Paintings. Vert designs as T* **218** *of Lesotho. Multicoloured. P* 13½×14.
1177 8 c. "Nativity" (detail) (Simon Bening) .. 20 15
1178 15 c. "Circumcision" (detail) (Bening) .. 40 30
1179 35 c. "Flight to Egypt" (detail) (Bening) .. 75 60
1180 50 c. "Massacre of the Innocents" (detail) (Bening) 90 80
1181 65 c. "The Annunciation" (Dieric Bouts) .. 1·25 1·25
1182 80 c. "The Visitation" (Bouts) .. .. 1·50 1·50
1183 $1.10, "Adoration of the Angels" (Bouts) 1·60 1·75
1184 $1.25, "Adoration of the Wise Men" (Bouts) .. .. 1·75 2·00
1177/84 .. .. *Set of* 8 7·50 7·50
MS1185 Two sheets, each 77×102 mm. (a) $2 "The Virgin seated with the Child" (detail) (Bouts). (b) $2 "The Virgin and Child" (detail) (Bouts) .. .. *Set of* 2 *sheets* 8·00 9·00

228 American Astronaut repairing Satellite

Royal Visit
HRH Duke of Edinburgh
20th March 1993

(**229**)

(Des W. Wright and L. Fried (Nos. 1186, 1191, **MS**1192a), W. Wright (others). Litho Questa)

1993 (8 Mar). *Anniversaries and Events. T* **228** *and similar horiz designs. Multicoloured. P* 14.
1186 25 c. Type **228** 60 50
1187 50 c. Dead and flourishing trees 90 80
1188 65 c. Food and World map .. .. 1·25 1·25
1189 80 c. Polluted and clean seas .. .. 1·75 1·75
1190 $1 Lions Club emblem .. .. .. 1·90 1·90
1191 $1.25, Projected orbiting quarantine modules .. .. 2·25 2·25
1186/91 .. .. *Set of* 6 7·75 7·75
MS1192 Two sheets, each 107×80 mm. (a) $2 Projected orbital Martian vehicle. (b) $2 Industrialised town and clean beach *Set of* 2 *sheets* 8·00 9·00

Anniversaries and Events:—Nos. 1186, 1191, **MS**1192a, International Space Year; Nos. 1187, 1189, **MS**1192b, Earth Summit '92, Rio; No. 1188, International Conference on Nutrition, Rome; No. 1190, 75th anniv of International Association of Lions Clubs.

1993 (20 Mar). *Visit of the Duke of Edinburgh. Nos.* 1100/1 *and* **MS**1103 *optd with T* **229**.
1193 35 c. Queen and Prince Philip (R.) .. 60 60
1194 65 c. Queen and Prince Philip at Garter Ceremony, 1988 (R.) .. .. 1·00 1·00
MS1195 68×90 mm. $2 Separate photographs of Queen and Prince Philip .. .. .. 2·75 3·00

(Des Kerri Schiff. Litho Questa)

1993 (2 June). *40th Anniv of Coronation. Vert designs as T* **224** *of Lesotho. P* 13½×14.
1196 15 c. multicoloured 20 25
a. Sheetlet. Nos. 1196/9×2 .. .. 7·00
1197 50 c. multicoloured 60 65
1198 $1 deep emerald and black .. .. 1·25 1·40
1199 $1.25, multicoloured .. .. .. 1·50 1·60
1196/9 .. .. *Set of* 4 3·50 4·00
MS1200 70×100 mm. $2 multicoloured. P 14 2·50 2·75

Designs:—15 c. Communion Chalice and Plate; 50 c. Queen Elizabeth II at Coronation (photograph by Cecil Beaton); $1 Queen Elizabeth during Coronation ceremony; $1.25, Queen Elizabeth and Prince Philip. (28½×42½ *mm*)—$2 "Queen Elizabeth II" (detail).

Nos. 1196/9 were printed together in sheetlets of 8, containing two *se-tenant* blocks of 4.

230 Omphalosaurus

(Litho Questa)

1993 (15 Nov). *Prehistoric Animals. T* **230** *and similar horiz designs. Multicoloured. P* 14.
1201 8 c. Type **230** 10 10
1202 15 c. Coelophysis 20 25
1203 20 c. Triceratops 25 30
1204 35 c. Dilophosaurus 45 50
1205 50 c. Pterodactylus 60 65
1206 65 c. Elasmosaurus 80 85
1207 80 c. Stegosaurus .. .. 1·00 1·10
1208 $1.25, Euoplocephalus .. .. .. 1·50 1·60
1201/8 .. .. *Set of* 8 5·00 5·25
MS1209 Two sheets, each 100×70 mm. (a) $2 As 20 c. (b) $2 As 35 c. .. .. *Set of* 2 *sheets* 5·00 5·25

(Litho Questa)

1993 (29 Nov). *Christmas. Religious Paintings. Designs as T* **76** *of Nevis (St. Kitts–Nevis). Black, pale lemon and red (Nos.* 1210/12, 1217 *and* **MS**1218) *or multicoloured (others). P* 13½×14.
1210 8 c. "Mary, Queen of the Angels" (detail) (Dürer) 20 10
1211 20 c. "Mary, Queen of the Angels" (different detail) (Dürer) 40 30
1212 35 c. "Mary, Queen of the Angels" (different detail) (Dürer) 60 50
1213 50 c. "Virgin and Child with St. John the Baptist" (Raphael) 80 70
1214 65 c. "The Canagiani Holy Family" (detail) (Raphael) .. .. 1·10 1·10
1215 80 c. "The Holy Family with the Lamb" (detail) (Raphael) .. .. .. 1·25 1·25
1216 $1 "Virgin and Child with St. John the Baptist" (different detail) (Raphael) 1·50 1·50
1217 $1.25, "Mary, Queen of the Angels" (different detail) (Dürer) .. .. 1·75 2·00
1210/17 .. .. *Set of* 8 7·00 6·75
MS1218 Two sheets, each 102×127 mm. (a) $2 "Mary, Queen of the Angels" (different detail) (Dürer). P 13½×14. (b) $2 "The Canagiani Holy Family" (different detail) (Raphael) (*horiz*). P 14×13½ .. .. .. *Set of* 2 *sheets* 6·00 6·50

231 Blue-headed Wrasse

(Des J. Genzo. Litho Questa)

1993 (15 Dec). *Fishes. T* **231** *and similar horiz designs. Multicoloured. P* 14.
1219 10 c. Type **231** 20 10
1220 20 c. Honeycomb Cowfish 40 30
1221 25 c. Glass-eyed Snapper 40 35
1222 35 c. Spotted Drum 55 50
1223 50 c. Jolt-headed Porgy 80 70
1224 65 c. Small-mouthed Grunt .. .. 1·00 1·00
1225 80 c. Candy Basslet ("Peppermint Bass") 1·25 1·40
1226 $1.10, Indigo Hamlet .. .. .. 1·75 2·00
1219/26 .. .. *Set of* 8 5·75 5·75
MS1227 Two sheets, each 106×75 mm. (a) $2 Bonnethead. (b) $2 Atlantic Sharp-nosed Shark *Set of* 2 *sheets* 6·50 7·00

The captions on No. **MS**1227 have been transposed in error.

232 Killdeer

(Des I. MacLaury. Litho Questa)

1993 (30 Dec). *Birds. T* **232** *and similar multicoloured designs. P* 14.
1228 10 c. Type **232** 30 30
1229 15 c. Yellow-crowned Night Heron (*vert*) 50 25
1230 35 c. Northern Mockingbird 75 55
1231 50 c. Eastern Kingbird (*vert*) 90 75
1232 65 c. Magnolia Warbler .. .. .. 1·25 1·25
1233 80 c. Cedar Waxwing (*vert*) .. .. 1·50 1·50
1234 $1.10, Ruby-throated Hummingbird .. 1·75 1·75
1235 $1.25, Painted Bunting (*vert*) .. .. 1·90 2·00
1228/35 .. .. *Set of* 8 8·00 7·50
MS1236 Two sheets, each 100×70 mm. (a) $2 Ruddy Duck. (b) $2 American Kestrel (*vert*) *Set of* 2 *sheets* 6·50 7·00

233 Sergio Goycoechea (Argentina)

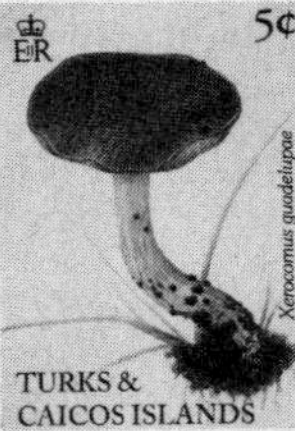

234 *Xerocomus guadelupae*

(Litho Questa)

1994 (26 Sept). *World Cup Football Championship, U.S.A. T* **233** *and similar multicoloured designs. P* 14.
1237 8 c. Type **233** 20 10
1238 10 c. Bodo Illgner (Germany) 20 10
1239 50 c. Nico Claesen (Belgium), Bossis and Amoros (France) 85 70
1240 65 c. German players celebrating .. .. 1·10 1·10
1241 80 c. Cameroun players celebrating .. 1·40 1·40
1242 $1 Cuciuffo (Argentina), Santin and Francescoli (Uruguay) .. .. .. 1·50 1·60
1243 $1.10, Hugo Sanchez (Mexico) .. .. 1·60 1·75
1237/43 .. .. *Set of* 8 6·00 6·00
MS1244 Two sheets, each 100×70 mm. (a) $2 The Silverdome, Michigan. (b) $2 Michel Platini (France) (*vert*) .. .. *Set of* 2 *sheets* 5·25 5·75

No. 1237 is inscribed "Segio Goycoechea" and No. 1238 "Bado Illgner", both in error.

(Litho Questa)

1994 (10 Oct). *Fungi. T* **234** *and similar multicoloured designs. P* 14.
1245 5 c. Type **234** 10 10
1246 10 c. *Volvariella volvacea* 10 10
1247 35 c. *Hygrocybe atrosquamosa* (*horiz*) .. 40 45
1248 50 c. *Pleurotus ostreatus* (*horiz*) 60 65
1249 65 c. *Marasmius pallescens* (*horiz*) .. 80 85
1250 80 c. *Coprinus plicatilis* .. .. .. 1·00 1·10
1251 $1.10, *Bolbitius vitellinus* (*horiz*) .. 1·40 1·50
1252 $1.50, *Pyrrhoglossum lilaceipes* .. 1·75 1·90
1245/52 .. .. *Set of* 8 6·25 6·75
MS1253 Two sheets, each 102×72 mm. (a) $2 *Russula cremeolilacina*. (b) $2 *Lentinus edodes* (*horiz*) .. .. .. *Set of* 2 *sheets* 5·00 5·25

NEW INFORMATION

The editor is always interested to correspond with people who have new information that will improve or correct the Catalogue.

235 "The Annunciation"

(Litho Questa)

1994 (5 Dec). *Christmas. Illustrations from 15th-century French Book of Hours. T* **235** *and similar vert designs. P* 14.
1254 25 c. Type **235** 45 35
1255 50 c. "The Visitation" 80 75
1256 65 c. "Annunciation to the Shepherds" .. 1·10 1·10
1257 80 c. "The Nativity" .. .. 1·25 1·40
1258 $1 "Flight into Egypt" .. .. 1·50 1·60
1254/8 .. .. *Set of* 5 4·50 4·75
MS1259 63×86 mm. $2 "The Adoration of the Magi" .. .. 3·25 3·75

236 *Dryas julia*

(Litho Questa)

1994 (12 Dec). *Butterflies. T* **236** *and similar horiz designs. Multicoloured. P* 14.
1260 15 c. Type **236** 20 25
1261 20 c. *Urbanus proteus* 25 30
1262 25 c. *Colobura dirce* 30 35
1263 50 c. *Papilio homerus* 60 65
1264 65 c. *Chiodes catillus* 80 85
1265 80 c. *Eurytides zonaria* .. .. .. 1·00 1·10
1266 $1 *Hypolymnas misippus* .. .. .. 1·25 1·40
1267 $1.25, *Phoebis avellaneda* .. .. .. 1·50 1·60
1260/7 .. .. *Set of* 8 6·00 6·50
MS1268 Two sheets, each 100×70 mm. (a) $2 *Eurema adamsi.* (b) $2 *Morpho peleides* *Set of 2 sheets* 5·00 5·25

237 General Montgomery and British Troops landing on Juno Beach

(Des J. Iskowitz. Litho Questa)

1994 (19 Dec). *50th Anniv of D-Day. T* **237** *and similar horiz designs. Multicoloured. P* 14.
1269 10 c. Type **237** 10 10
1270 15 c. Admiral Ramsay and British commandos at Sword Beach .. 20 25
1271 35 c. Gun crew on H.M.S. *Belfast* (cruiser) 40 45
1272 50 c. Montgomery and Eisenhower with Air Chief Marshal Tedder 60 65
1273 65 c. General Eisenhower and men of U.S. 101st Airborne Division 80 85
1274 80 c. Lt-Gen. Bradley and U.S. troops landing on Omaha Beach .. .. 1·00 1·10
1275 $1.10, Arrival of U.S. reinforcements 1·40 1·50
1276 $1.25, Eisenhower at briefing .. .. 1·50 1·60
1269/76 .. .. *Set of* 8 6·00 6·50
MS1277 Two sheets, each 100×70 mm. (a) $2 Landing craft and barrage balloon. (b) $2 Eisenhower and Montgomery .. *Set of 2 sheets* 5·00 5·25

238 *Cattleya deckeri*

(Des Dorothy Novak. Litho Questa)

1995 (5 Jan). *Orchids. T* **238** *and similar horiz designs. Multicoloured. P* 14.
1278 8 c. Type **238** 30 20
1279 20 c. *Epidendrum carpophorum* 50 30
1280 25 c. *Epidendrum ciliare* 50 35
1281 50 c. *Encyclia phoenicea* 85 70
1282 65 c. *Bletia patula* .. .. 1·10 1·10
1283 80 c. *Brassia caudata* .. .. 1·25 1·25
1284 $1 *Brassavola nodosa* .. .. .. 1·50 1·50
1285 $1.25, *Bletia purpurea* .. .. .. 1·75 2·00
1278/85 .. .. *Set of* 8 7·00 6·75
MS1286 Two sheets, each 100×70 mm. (a) $2 *Vanilla planifolia.* (b) $2 *Ionopsis utricularioides* *Set of 2 sheets* 6·00 6·50

(Des W. Hanson. Litho Questa)

1995 (9 Jan). *25th Anniv of First Moon Landing. Multicoloured designs as T* **302** *of Maldive Islands. P* 14.
1287 10 c. "Apollo 11" 10 10
1288 20 c. Moon landing simulation 25 30
1289 25 c. "Astronauts on the Moon" (detail) (Kovales) 30 35
1290 35 c. First human foot on Moon 45 50
1291 50 c. Astronaut Aldrin conducting solar wind experiment 60 65
1292 65 c. Astronauts planting U.S.A. flag .. 80 85
1293 80 c. Space module *Columbia* over lunar surface .. .. 1·00 1·10
1294 $1.10, "Apollo 11" after splashdown .. 1·40 1·50
1287/94 .. .. *Set of* 8 5·00 5·25
MS1295 Two sheets, each 104×84 mm. (a) $2 Sample of Moon rock. (b) $2 "Apollo 11" lift-off, Cape Canaveral (*vert*) .. .. *Set of 2 sheets* 5·00 5·25

239 Elasmosaurus **240** Fencing

(Des Mary Walters. Litho Questa)

1995 (23 Jan). *Jurassic Marine Reptiles. T* **239** *and similar horiz designs. Multicoloured. P* 14.
1296 35 c. Type **239** 40 45
a. Sheetlet. Nos. 1296/307 .. .. 4·75
1297 35 c. Plesiosaurus 40 45
1298 35 c. Ichthyosaurus 40 45
1299 35 c. Archelon 40 45
1300 35 c. Askeptosaurus 40 45
1301 35 c. Macroplata 40 45
1302 35 c. Ceresiosaurus 40 45
1303 35 c. Lipoleurodon 40 45
1304 35 c. Henodus 40 45
1305 35 c. Muraenosaurus 40 45
1306 35 c. Placodus 40 45
1307 35 c. Kronosaurus 40 45
1296/1307 .. .. *Set of* 12 4·75 5·50
Nos. 1296/307 were printed together, *se-tenant*, in sheetlets of 12 forming a composite design.

(Des D. Miller. Litho Questa)

1995 (6 Feb). *Centenary of International Olympic Committee. T* **240** *and similar vert designs. Multicoloured. P* 14.
1308 8 c. Type **240** 20 15
1309 10 c. Speed skating 20 15
1310 15 c. Diving 30 25
1311 20 c. Cycling 50 30
1312 25 c. Ice hockey 60 35
1313 35 c. Figure skating 65 50
1314 50 c. Football 80 70
1315 65 c. Bob-sleighing .. .. 1·10 1·10
1316 80 c. Supergiant slalom .. .. .. 1·25 1·40
1317 $1.25, Show jumping .. .. .. 1·75 2·00
1308/17 .. .. *Set of* 10 6·50 6·25
MS1318 Two sheets, 89×110 mm. (a) $2 Downhill skiing. (b) $2 Gymnastics *Set of 2 sheets* 6·50 7·00
Both miniature sheets are incorrectly dated "1984–1994" on the margin.

241 Cat and Kitten **242** Belted Kingfisher

(Des Mary Walters. Litho Questa)

1995 (3 July). *Cats. T* **241** *and similar horiz designs. Multicoloured. P* 14.
1319 15 c. Type **241** 20 25
1320 20 c. Tabby on branch 25 30
1321 35 c. Cat and ladybird 40 45
1322 50 c. Black and white cat 60 65
1323 65 c. Red cat with flower in paw 80 85
1324 80 c. White cat on pink pillow .. .. 1·00 1·10
1325 $1 Siamese with flower in paws .. 1·25 1·40
1326 $1.25, Cats preening .. .. .. 1·50 1·60
1319/26 .. .. *Set of* 8 6·00 6·50
MS1327 Two sheets, each 106×76 mm. (a) $2 Kitten and ladybirds. (b) $2 Kittens asleep *Set of 2 sheets* 5·00 5·25

(Des Helen Bultfield. Litho B.D.T.)

1995 (2 Aug). *Birds. T* **242** *and similar multicoloured designs. P* 13½×13.
1328 10 c. Type **242** 10 10
1329 15 c. Clapper Rail 20 25
1330 20 c. American Redstart 25 30
1331 25 c. Roseate Tern 30 35
1332 35 c. Purple Gallinule 40 45
1333 45 c. Turnstone 55 60
1334 50 c. Barn Owl 60 65
1335 60 c. Brown Booby 75 80
1336 80 c. Great Blue Heron .. .. .. 1·00 1·10
1337 $1 Antillean Nighthawk .. .. .. 1·25 1·40
1338 $1.25, Thick-billed Vireo .. .. 1·50 1·60
1339 $1.40, American Flamingo .. .. 1·75 1·90
1340 $2 Wilson's Plover .. .. 2·50 2·75
1341 $5 Blue-winged Teal .. .. .. 6·25 6·50
1342 $10 Pair of Reddish Egrets (50×28 *mm*) 12·50 13·00
1328/42 .. .. *Set of* 15 30·00 32·00

(Des and litho Questa)

1995 (4 Aug). *95th Birthday of Queen Elizabeth the Queen Mother. Vert designs as T* **321** *of Maldive Islands. P* 13½×14.
1344 50 c. orange-brown, pale brown and black 60 65
a. Sheetlet. Nos. 1344/7×2 .. .. 4·75
1345 50 c. multicoloured 60 65
1346 50 c. multicoloured 60 65
1347 50 c. multicoloured 60 65
1344/7 .. .. *Set of* 4 2·40 2·60
MS1348 102×127 mm. $2 multicoloured .. 2·50 2·75
Designs:—No. 1344, Queen Elizabeth the Queen Mother (pastel drawing); No. 1345, Wearing tiara; No. 1346, At desk (oil painting); No. 1347, Wearing blue dress; No. **MS**1348, Wearing pale blue dress and hat
Nos. 1344/7 were printed together in sheetlets of 8, containing two *se-tenant* horizontal strips of 4.

(Des R. Sauber. Litho Questa)

1995 (14 Aug). *50th Anniv of End of Second World War in Europe. Horiz designs as T* **317** *of Maldive Islands. Multicoloured. P* 14.
1349 10 c. Churchill, Roosevelt and Stalin at Yalta Conference 10 10
1350 15 c. Liberated Allied prisoners of war .. 20 25
1351 20 c. Meeting of American and Soviet soldiers at River Elbe 25 30
1352 25 c. Pres. Roosevelt's funeral cortege .. 30 35
1353 60 c. U.S. bugler sounding cease-fire .. 75 80
1354 80 c. U.S. sailor kissing nurse, New York 1·00 1·10
1355 $1 Nuremburg Trials .. .. .. 1·25 1·40
1349/55 .. .. *Set of* 7 3·75 4·25
MS1356 104×74 mm. $2 Fireworks over Allied capitals .. .. 2·50 2·75

243 William James Scuba, 1825

(Des L. Birmingham. Litho Questa)

1995 (1 Sept). *"Singapore '95" International Stamp Exhibition. Deep Sea Diving. T* **243** *and similar horiz designs. Multicoloured. P* 14×14½.
1357 60 c. Type **243** 75 80
a. Sheetlet. Nos. 1357/65 .. .. 6·75
1358 60 c. Rouquayrol apparatus, 1864 .. 75 80
1359 60 c. Fluess oxygen-rebreathing apparatus, 1878 .. .. 75 80
1360 60 c. Armoured diving suit, 1900 .. .. 75 80
1361 60 c. Diving on the *Lusitania* in Peress armoured diving suit, 1935 .. .. 75 80
1362 60 c. Cousteau Gagnan aqualung, 1943 .. 75 80
1363 60 c. Underwater camera, 1955 .. .. 75 80
1364 60 c. Sylvia Earle's record dive, 1979 .. 75 80
1365 60 c. Spider propeller-driven rigid suit, 1984 .. .. 75 80
1357/65 .. .. *Set of* 9 6·75 7·00
MS1366 Two sheets, each 107×77 mm. (a) $2 Helmet diver, 1935. (b) $2 Jacques-Yves Cousteau (aqualung pioneer) .. *Set of 2 sheets* 5·00 5·25
Nos. 1357/65 were printed together, *se-tenant*, in sheetlets of 9.

(Litho Questa)

1995 (29 Dec). *Christmas. Religious Paintings by Piero di Cosimo. Vert designs as T* **98** *of St. Kitts-Nevis (Nevis). Multicoloured. P* 13½×14.
1367 20 c. "Madonna and Child with St. Giovannino" 25 30
1368 25 c. "Adoration of the Child" 30 35
1369 60 c. "Madonna and Child with St. Giovannino, St. Margherita and Angel" 75 80
1370 $1 "Madonna and Child with Angel" .. 1·25 1·40
1367/70 .. .. *Set of* 4 2·50 2·75
MS1371 76×106 mm. $2 "Madonna and Child with Angels and Saints" (detail) .. .. 2·50 2·75

244 Daisies and Female Symbol ("Rights of Women and Children")

(Litho Questa)

1996 (26 Feb). *50th Anniv of the United Nations. T* **244** *and similar horiz designs. Multicoloured. P* 14×13½.

1372 15 c. Type **244** 20 25
1373 60 c. Peace dove escaping from prison .. 75 80
1374 80 c. Symbolic candles ("Human Rights") 1·00 1·10
1375 $1 People on open book .. .. 1·25 1·40
1372/5 .. .. *Set of* 4 3·25 3·50
MS1376 107×78 mm. $2 National flags forming "50" .. .. 2·50 2·75

245 Farmer on Tractor

(Litho Questa)

1996 (26 Feb). *50th Anniv of Food and Agriculture Organization. Sheet* 111×80 *mm. P* 14×13½.

MS1377 **245** $2 multicoloured .. .. .. 2·50 2·75

(Litho Questa)

1996 (21 Apr). *70th Birthday of Queen Elizabeth II. Vert designs as T* **334** *of Maldive Islands. Multicoloured. P* 13½×14.

1378 80 c. As Type **334** of Maldive Islands .. 1·00 1·10
a. Strip of 3. Nos. 1378/80 .. .. 3·00
1379 80 c. In blue coat and hat .. .. 1·00 1·10
1380 80 c. At Trooping the Colour .. .. 1·00 1·10
1378/80 .. .. *Set of* 3 3·00 3·25
MS1381 125×104 mm. $2 In yellow dress and hat .. .. 2·50 2·75

Nos. 1378/80 were printed together, *se-tenant*, in horizontal or vertical strips of 3 throughout the sheet.

246 Glaucus, God of Divers, 2500 B.C. **247** Show Jumping

(Des L. Birmingham. Litho Questa)

1996 (13 May). *"China '96" Asian International Philatelic Exhibition, Beijing. Underwater Exploration (1st series). T* **246** *and similar horiz designs. Multicoloured. P* 14×14½.

1382 55 c. Type **246** 65 70
a. Sheetlet. Nos. 1382/90 .. .. 5·75
1383 55 c. Alexander the Great, 332 B.C. .. 65 70
1384 55 c. Salvage diver, 1430 .. .. .. 65 70
1385 55 c. Borelli's rebreathing device, 1680 .. 65 70
1386 55 c. Edmund Halley's diving bell, 1690 .. 65 70
1387 55 c. John Lethbridge's diving machine, 1715 .. .. 65 70
1388 55 c. Klingert's diving apparatus, 1789 .. 65 70
1389 55 c. Drieberg's triton, 1808 .. .. 65 70
1390 55 c. Seibe's diving helmet, 1819 .. 65 70
1382/90 .. .. *Set of* 9 5·75 6·25
MS1391 Two sheets, each 102×77 mm. (a) $2 12th-century Arab diver. (b) $2 Caribbean pearl diver, 1498 .. .. .. *Set of* 2 *sheets* 5·00 5·25

Nos. 1382/90 were printed together, *se-tenant*, in sheetlets of 9.

(Des L. Birmingham. Litho Questa)

1996 (13 May). *"Capex '96" World Stamp Exhibition, Toronto. Underwater Exploration (2nd series). Multicoloured designs as T* **246**. *P* 14×14½.

1392 60 c. Jim Jarrat exploring *Lusitania*, 1935 75 80
a. Sheetlet. Nos. 1392/1400 .. .. 6·75
1393 60 c. Cousteau's first use of scuba gear for exploration, 1952 .. .. .. 75 80
1394 60 c. Discovery of oldest shipwreck, 1959 75 80
1395 60 c. Raising of the *Vasa*, 1961 .. .. 75 80
1396 60 c. Mel Fisher discovering *Atocha*, 1971 75 80
1397 60 c. Barry Clifford discovering *Whydah*, 1984 .. .. 75 80
1398 60 c. Argo robot over the *Bismarck*, 1989 75 80
1399 60 c. Discovery of *Land Tortoise* in Lake George, New York, 1991 .. .. 75 80
1400 60 c. Nuclear submarine recovering artefacts from Roman shipwreck, 1994 .. .. 75 80
1392/1400 .. .. *Set of* 9 6·75 7·25
MS1401 Two sheets, each 102×77 mm. (a) $2 Diver investigates the *Edmund Fitzgerald*. (b) $2 *Alvin* exploring the *Titanic* .. *Set of* 2 *sheets* 5·00 5·25

Nos. 1392/1400 were printed together, *se-tenant*, in sheetlets of 9.

(Litho Questa)

1996 (27 May). *Olympic Games, Atlanta. T* **247** *and similar vert designs showing sports on medals. Multicoloured. P* 13½×14.

1402 55 c. Type **247** 65 70
1403 55 c. Cycling 65 70
1404 55 c. Fencing 65 70
1405 55 c. Gymnastics 65 70
1406 55 c. Pole vaulting 65 70
1407 55 c. Sprinting 65 70
1408 55 c. Swimming 65 70
1409 55 c. Diving 65 70
1410 55 c. Hurdling 65 70
1411 55 c. Long-distance running 65 70
1402/11 .. .. *Set of* 10 6·50 7·00

248 James McCartney (First Chief Minister) **249** Space Dog

1996 (8 July). *20th Anniv of Ministerial Government. Litho. P* 14.

1412 **248** 60 c. multicoloured 75 80

No. 1412 was printed in sheetlets of 9 with a large illustrated margin at right.

(Des Mary Walters. Litho Questa)

1996 (8 Sept). *Working Dogs. T* **249** *and similar vert designs. Multicoloured. P* 14.

1413 25 c. Type **249** 30 35
a. Sheetlet. Nos. 1413/24 .. .. 3·50
1414 25 c. Greyhound 30 35
1415 25 c. St. Bernard 30 35
1416 25 c. Dog with medals 30 35
1417 25 c. Retriever 30 35
1418 25 c. Dog with bone 30 35
1419 25 c. "Hearing ear" dog 30 35
1420 25 c. Husky 30 35
1421 25 c. Police Alsatian 30 35
1422 25 c. Guard dog 30 35
1423 25 c. Boxer 30 35
1424 25 c. Sniffer dog 30 35
1413/24 .. .. *Set of* 12 3·50 4·25
MS1425 Two sheets, each 106×76 mm. (a) $2 Labrador guide dog. (b) $2 Border sheep dog *Set of* 2 *sheets* 5·00 5·25

Nos. 1413/24 were printed together, *se-tenant*, in sheetlets of 12.

250 Winnie the Pooh asleep in Chair **251** Giant Milkweed

1996 (25 Nov). *Christmas. Winnie the Pooh. T* **250** *and similar vert designs. Multicoloured. Litho. P* 13½×14.

1426 15 c. Type **250** 20 25
1427 20 c. Piglet holding star decoration .. 25 30
1428 35 c. Tigger carrying presents 40 45
1429 50 c. Pooh, Tigger and Piglet singing carols 60 65
1430 60 c. Winnie and Rabbit 75 80
1431 80 c. Tigger and Roo .. .. .. 1·00 1·10
1432 $1 Santa Pooh filling stockings .. 1·25 1·40
1433 $1.25, Christopher Robin and Winnie the Pooh .. .. 1·50 1·60
1426/33 .. .. *Set of* 8 6·00 6·50
MS1434 Two sheets. (a) 124×98 mm. $2 Piglet decorating biscuits. (b) 98×124 mm. $2.60, Piglet placing star on tree .. *Set of* 2 *sheets* 5·75 6·00

1997 (10 Feb). *Flowers. T* **251** *and similar vert designs. Multicoloured. Litho. P* 14.

1435 20 c. Type **251** 25 30
a. Sheetlet. Nos. 1435/8, each × 2 .. 2·00
1436 20 c. Geiger Tree 25 30
1437 20 c. Passion Flower 25 30
1438 20 c. Hibiscus 25 30
1439 60 c. Yellow Elder 75 80
a. Sheetlet. Nos. 1439/42, each × 2 .. 6·00
1440 60 c. Prickly Poppy 75 80
1441 60 c. Frangipani 75 80
1442 60 c. Seaside Mahoe 75 80
1435/42 .. .. *Set of* 8 4·00 4·25
MS1443 Two sheets, each 105×76 mm. (a) $2 Firecracker. (b) $2 Chain of Love *Set of* 2 *sheets* 5·00 5·25

Nos. 1435/8 and 1439/42 were each printed together, *se-tenant*, in sheetlets of 8 containing two of each design.

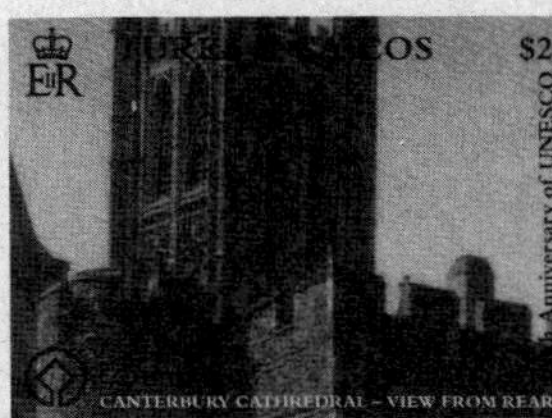

252 Canterbury Cathedral Tower

(Litho Questa)

1997 (24 Mar). *50th Anniv of U.N.E.S.C.O. Two sheets, each* 127×102 *mm, containing T* **252** *and similar horiz design. Multicoloured. P* 14×13½.

MS1444 (a) $2 Type **252**; (b) $2 High Altar, Canterbury Cathedral .. .. *Set of* 2 *sheets* 5·00 5·25

The miniature sheets of No. **MS**1444 are inscribed "CATHREDRAL" in error.

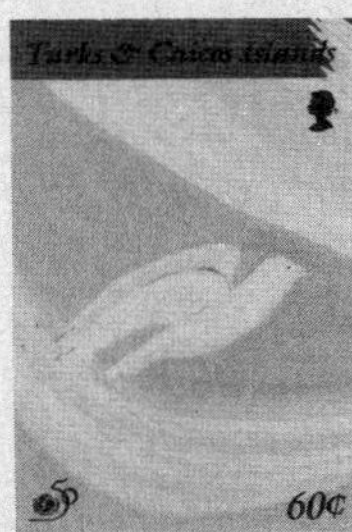

253 White Dove (face value at right)

(Des Claire Fejes. Litho)

1997 (24 Mar). *50th Anniv of U.N.I.C.E.F. T* **253** *and similar vert designs. Multicoloured. P* 14.

1445 60 c. Type **253** 75 80
a. Sheetlet. Nos. 1445/8 .. .. 3·00
1446 60 c. White dove (with face value at left) 75 80
1447 60 c. Three children 75 80
1448 60 c. Two children with pets 75 80
1445/8 .. .. *Set of* 4 3·00 3·25

Nos. 1445/8 were printed together, *se-tenant*, in sheetlets of 4

(Litho Questa)

1997 (21 Apr). *Golden Wedding of Queen Elizabeth and Prince Philip. Horiz designs as T* **350** *of Maldive Islands. Multicoloured. P* 14.

1449 60 c. Queen Elizabeth II 75 80
a. Sheetlet. Nos. 1449/54 .. .. 4·50
1450 60 c. Royal coat of arms 75 80
1451 60 c. Queen Elizabeth and Prince Philip in carriage 75 80
1452 60 c. Queen Elizabeth and Prince Philip on royal visit 75 80
1453 60 c. Windsor Castle 75 80
1454 60 c. Prince Philip 75 80
1449/54 .. .. *Set of* 6 4·50 4·75
MS1455 100×70 mm. $2 Princess Elizabeth and Duke of Edinburgh on wedding day .. .. 2·50 2·75

Nos. 1449/54 were printed together, *se-tenant*, in sheetlets of 6.

(Des J. Iskowitz. Litho Questa)

1997 (1 July). *"Pacific '97" International Stamp Exhibition, San Francisco. Death Centenary of Heinrich von Stephan (founder of the U.P.U. Horiz designs as T* **351** *of Maldive Islands. P* 14.

1456 50 c. mauve 60 65
a. Sheetlet. Nos. 1456/8 .. .. 1·75
1457 50 c. chestnut 60 65
1458 50 c. deep blue 60 65
1456/8 .. .. *Set of* 3 1·75 1·90
MS1459 80×117 mm. $2 bright mauve and black 2·50 2·75

Designs:—No. 1456, British mail coach, 1700's; No. 1457, Von Stephan and Mercury; No. 1458, Space Shuttle; No. **MS**1459, Von Stephan and Ancient Greek messenger.

Nos. 1456/8 were printed together, *se-tenant*, in sheets of 3 with enlarged right-hand margin.

STAMP BOOKLETS

1977 (7 Feb). *Silver Jubilee. Multicoloured cover, 80×55 mm. Stapled.*
SB1 $1.60, booklet containing 25 c. and 55 c. (Nos. 473/4), each in pair .. .. 1·10

1978 (July). *25th Anniv of Coronation. Cover, 165×92 mm, black and purple on front showing Westminster Abbey and multicoloured on back. Stitched.*
SB2 $3.60, booklet containing *se-tenant* panes of 3 and 6 (Nos. 499a/b) .. .. 1·90

1979 (27 Sept). *Death Centenary of Sir Rowland Hill. Multicoloured cover, 165×92 mm, showing Penny Black stamp and Sir Rowland Hill. Stitched.*
SB3 $3.55, booklet containing two different *se-tenant* panes of 6 and pane of 1 $1 (Nos. 552a, 558a, 564a) .. .. 3·25

1981 (7 July). *Royal Wedding. Cover, 165×90 mm; blue, gold and black on front showing Prince of Wales emblem and multicoloured on back. Stitched.*
SB4 $5.60, booklet containing *se-tenant* pane of 6 and pane of 1 $2 (Nos. 657a, 659a) .. .. 2·40

1981 (1 Dec). *Tourism. Multicoloured cover, 114×58 mm, showing tourist attractions. Stapled.*
SB5 $4 booklet containing twenty 20 c. (Nos. 675/84), in *se-tenant* blocks of 4 .. .. .. 6·00

1982 (18 Nov). *21st Birthday of Princess of Wales. Multicoloured cover, 101×49 mm, showing rainbow over South Caicos Harbour. Stapled.*
SB6 $4.60, booklet containing 8 c., 35 c. and $1.10 (Nos. 713/15), each in strip of 3 .. .. 4·25

CAICOS ISLANDS

CAICOS ISLANDS

(1)

1981 (24 July). *Nos.* 514A, 518A, 520A, 523A *and* 525A/7A *of Turks and Caicos Islands optd with T* **1**.

1	1 c. Indigo Hamlet	15	15
2	5 c. Spanish Grunt	20	20
3	8 c. Four-eyed Butterflyfish	20	20
4	20 c. Queen Angelfish	45	30
5	50 c. Royal Gramma ("Fairy Basslet")	85	1·00
6	$1 Fin-spot Wrasse	1·50	1·75
7	$2 Stoplight Parrotfish	2·50	3·25
1/7	*Set of* 7	5·25	6·00

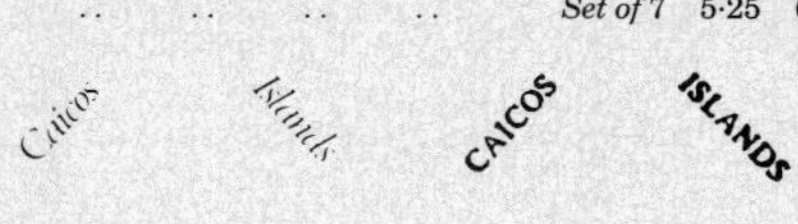

(2) (3)

1981 (24 July). *Royal Wedding. Nos.* 653/6 *of Turks and Caicos Islands optd. A. With T* **2** *in London. B. With T* **3** *in New York.*

		A		B	
8	35 c. Prince Charles and Lady Diana Spencer	20	25	50	70
	a. Opt inverted	†		£110	—
9	65 c. Kensington Palace	30	40	70	1·00
	a. Opt inverted	†		80·00	—
10	90 c. Prince Charles as Colonel of the Welsh Guards	40	50	90	1·50
	a. Opt inverted	†		90·00	—
	b. Opt double	†		90·00	—
8/10	*Set of* 3	80	1·00	1·90	3·00
MS11	96 × 82 mm. $2 Glass Coach	1·00	2·00	1·00	2·50
	a. Opt inverted	†		—	—

Nos. 8B/10 come either in sheets of 40 (2 panes 4×5) or in sheetlets of 5 stamps and one label. Examples of Nos. 8Ba, 9Ba and 10Ba are known from both formats, but No. 10Bb only exists from sheetlets.

Nos. 8/10 also exist perforated 12 (*Price for set of 3 with London opt £2 or with New York opt £5, mint or used*) from additional sheetlets of five stamps and one label.

1981 (29 Oct). *Royal Wedding. Booklet stamps. As Nos.* 657/9 *of Turks and Caicos Islands, but each inscr* "Caicos Islands". *Multicoloured. Roul* 5 × *imperf*. Self-adhesive.*

12	20 c. Lady Diana Spencer	30	40
	a. Booklet pane. Nos. 12/13, each × 3	3·00	
13	$1 Prince Charles	80	1·25
14	$2 Prince Charles and Lady Diana Spencer	5·50	5·50
	a. Booklet pane of 1	5·50	
12/14	*Set of* 3	6·00	6·50

*The 20 c. and $1 values were each separated by various combinations of rotary knife (giving a straight edge) and roulette. The $2 value exists only with straight edges.

4 Queen or Pink Conch and Lobster Fishing, South Caicos

(Des J. Cooter (8 c. to 20 c.). Litho)

1983 (6 June)–**84**. *T* 4 *and similar horiz designs. Multicoloured. P* 14.

15	8 c. Type **4**	70	50
16	10 c. Hawksbill Turtle, East Caicos	70	50
17	20 c. Arawak Indians and idol, Middle Caicos	70	50
18	35 c. Boat-building, North Caicos	1·25	85
19	50 c. Marine biologist at work, Pine Cay	1·75	90
20	95 c. Boeing 707 airliner at new airport, Providenciales	3·75	2·25
21	$1.10, Columbus' *Pinta*, West Caicos	3·75	2·50
22	$2 Fort George Cay (18.5.84)	3·50	3·75
23	$3 Pirates Anne Bonny and Calico Jack at Parrot Cay (18.5.84)	6·00	4·75
15/23	*Set of* 9	20·00	15·00

5 Goofy and Patch

6 "Leda and the Swan"

(Litho Walsall)

1983 (7 Nov). *Christmas. T* **5** *and similar vert designs showing Disney cartoon characters. Multicoloured. P* 11.

30	1 c. Type **5**	10	10
31	1 c. Chip and Dale	10	10
32	2 c. Morty	10	10
33	2 c. Morty and Ferdie	10	10
34	3 c. Goofy and Louie	10	10
35	3 c. Donald Duck, Huey, Dewey and Louie	10	10
36	50 c. Uncle Scrooge	2·50	2·00
37	70 c. Mickey Mouse and Ferdie	2·75	2·50
38	$1.10, Pinocchio, Jiminy Cricket and Figaro	3·50	3·50
30/8	*Set of* 9	8·00	7·50
MS39	126 × 101 mm. $2 Morty and Ferdie. P 13½ × 14	3·50	3·50

(Des and litho Questa)

1983 (15 Dec). *500th Birth Anniv of Raphael. T* **6** *and similar vert designs. Multicoloured. P* 14.

40	35 c. Type **6**	75	50
41	50 c. "Study of Apollo for Parnassus"	1·00	70
42	95 c. "Study of two figures for the battle of Ostia"	2·00	1·25
43	$1.10, "Study for the Madonna of the Goldfinch"	2·00	1·50
40/3	*Set of* 4	5·25	3·50
MS44	71 × 100 mm. $2.50, "The Garvagh Madonna"	3·50	3·25

7 High Jumping

8 Horace Horsecollar and Clarabelle Cow

(Litho Questa)

1984 (1 Mar). *Olympic Games, Los Angeles. T* **7** *and similar designs. P* 14.

45	4 c. multicoloured	10	10
46	25 c. multicoloured	20	20
47	65 c. black, deep grey-blue and new blue	50	50
48	$1.10, multicoloured	85	85
45/8	*Set of* 4	1·50	1·50
MS49	105 × 75 mm. $2 multicoloured	2·25	3·00

Designs: *Vert*—25 c. Archery; 65 c. Cycling; $1.10, Football. *Horiz*—$2 Show jumping.

(Des Walt Disney Productions. Litho Questa)

1984 (23 Apr). *Easter. Walt Disney Cartoon Characters. T* **8** *and similar horiz designs. Multicoloured. P* 14 × 13½.

50	35 c. Type **8**	70	60
51	45 c. Mickey and Minnie Mouse, and Chip	85	75
52	75 c. Gyro Gearloose, Chip 'n Dale	1·40	1·25
53	85 c. Mickey Mouse, Chip 'n Dale	1·50	1·40
50/3	*Set of* 4	4·00	3·50
MS54	127 × 101 mm. $2.20, Donald Duck	4·25	3·75

UNIVERSAL POSTAL UNION 1874-1984 

(9)

AUSIPEX 1984

(10)

1984 (19 June). *Universal Postal Union Congress, Hamburg. Nos.* 20/1 *optd with T* **9**.

55	95 c. Boeing 707 airliner at new airport, Providenciales	1·00	1·25
56	$1.10, Columbus' *Pinta*, West Caicos	1·25	1·50

1984 (22 Aug). *"Ausipex" International Stamp Exhibition, Melbourne. No.* 22 *optd with T* **10**.

57	$2 Fort George Cay	2·40	2·50

11 Seamen sighting American Manatees

(Des L. Lightbourne. Litho Walsall)

1984 (12 Sept). *492nd Anniv of Columbus' First Landfall. T* **11** *and similar horiz designs. Multicoloured. P* 14.

58	10 c. Type **11**	75	50
59	70 c. Fleet of Columbus	2·75	2·50
60	$1 First landing in West Indies	3·25	3·00
58/60	*Set of* 3	6·00	5·50
MS61	99 × 69 mm. $2 Fleet of Columbus (*different*)	2·75	3·00

NEW INFORMATION

The editor is always interested to correspond with people who have new information that will improve or correct the Catalogue.

12 Donald Duck and Mickey Mouse with Father Christmas

(Litho Questa)

1984 (26 Nov). *Christmas. Walt Disney Cartoon Characters. T* **12** *and similar vert designs. Multicoloured. P* 12 ($2) *or* 13½ × 14 (*others*).

62	20 c. Type **12**	1·00	75
63	35 c. Donald Duck opening refrigerator	1·40	1·00
64	50 c. Mickey Mouse, Donald Duck and toy train	1·90	1·50
65	75 c. Donald Duck and parcels	2·50	2·25
66	$1.10, Donald Duck and carol singers	2·75	2·75
62/6	*Set of* 5	8·50	7·50
MS67	127 × 102 mm. $2 Donald Duck as Christmas tree	3·75	4·00

No. 65 was printed in sheetlets of 8 stamps.

13 Thick-billed Vireo

14 Two Children learning to Read and Write (Education)

(Des Susan David. Litho Walsall)

1985 (12 Feb). *Birth Bicentenary of John J. Audubon (ornithologist). T* **13** *and similar horiz designs. Multicoloured. P* 14.

68	20 c. Type **13**	1·60	50
69	35 c. Black-faced Grassquit	1·90	75
70	50 c. Pearly-eyed Thrasher	2·25	1·10
71	$1 Greater Antillean Bullfinch	2·50	1·90
68/71	*Set of* 4	7·50	3·75
MS72	100 × 70 mm. $2 Stripe-headed Tanager	3·25	3·50

(Des C. Walters. Litho Walsall)

1985 (8 May). *International Youth Year and 40th Anniv of United Nations. T* **14** *and similar vert designs. Multicoloured. P* 14.

73	16 c. Type **14**	20	25
74	35 c. Two children on playground swings (Health)	50	55
75	70 c. Boy and girl (Love)	1·00	1·10
76	90 c. Three children (Peace)	1·25	1·40
73/6	*Set of* 4	2·75	3·00
MS77	101 × 71 mm. $2 Child, dove carrying ears of wheat and map of the Americas	2·75	3·00

15 Air Caicos Douglas DC-3 on Ground

16 The Queen Mother visiting Foundation for the Disabled, Leatherhead

(Des K. Gromol. Litho Walsall)

1985 (23 May). *40th Anniv of International Civil Aviation Organization. T* **15** *and similar horiz designs. Multicoloured. P* 14.

78	35 c. Type **15**	1·50	55
79	75 c. Air Caicos Convair CV 440 Metropolitan	2·75	1·25
80	90 c. TCNA Britten Norman Islander	3·00	1·40
78/80	*Set of* 3	6·50	3·00
MS81	100×70 mm. $2.20, Hang-gliding over the Caicos Islands	3·00	3·25

(Des J.W. Litho Questa)

1985 (8 July). *Life and Times of Queen Elizabeth the Queen Mother. T* **16** *and similar multicoloured designs. P* 14.

82	35 c. Type **16**	50	55
83	65 c. With Princess Anne (*horiz*)	90	95
84	95 c. At Epsom, 1961	1·40	1·60
82/4	*Set of* 3	2·50	2·75
MS85	56×85 mm. $2 Visiting Royal Hospital, Chelsea	2·75	3·00

(Des Walt Disney Productions. Litho Questa)

1985 (5 Dec). *150th Birth Anniv of Mark Twain (author). Multicoloured designs as T* **160a** *of Lesotho, but horiz, showing Walt Disney cartoon characters in scenes from "Tom Sawyer, Detective". P* 14×13½.

86 8 c. Huckleberry Finn (Goofy) and Tom Sawyer (Mickey Mouse) reading reward notice 60 20
87 35 c. Huck and Tom meeting Jake Dunlap .. 1·75 65
88 95 c. Huck and Tom spying on Jubiter Dunlap .. .. 3·25 2·00
89 $1.10, Huck and Tom with hound (Pluto) .. 3·25 2·25
86/9 .. .. *Set of* 4 8·00 4·75
MS90 127×101 mm. $2 Tom unmasking Jubiter Dunlap .. .. 3·50 4·00

(Des Walt Disney Productions. Litho Questa)

1985 (5 Dec). *Birth Bicentenaries of Grimm Brothers (folklorists). Multicoloured designs as T* **160b** *of Lesotho, but horiz, showing Walt Disney cartoon characters in scenes from "Six Soldiers of Fortune". P* 14×13½.

91 16 c. The Soldier (Donald Duck) with his meagre pay 75 30
92 25 c. The Soldier meeting the Strong Man (Horace Horsecollar) .. .. 1·00 45
93 65 c. The Soldier meeting the Marksman (Mickey Mouse) .. .. 2·00 1·25
94 $1.35, The Fast Runner (Goofy) winning the race against the Princess (Daisy Duck) .. 2·75 2·25
91/4 .. .. *Set of* 4 6·00 3·75
MS95 126×101 mm. $2 The Soldier and the Strong Man with sack of gold .. .. 3·25 3·50

STAMP BOOKLET

1981 (29 Oct). *Royal Wedding. As No. SB4 of Turks and Caicos Islands.*

SB1 $5.60, booklet containing *se-tenant* pane of 6 and pane of 1 $2 (Nos. 12a, 14a) .. .. 8·00

Tuvalu

Formerly known as the Ellice Islands when they shared a joint administration with the Gilbert group. On 1 January 1976 the two island-groups separated and the Ellice Islands were renamed Tuvalu.

CROWN COLONY

(Currency. 100 cents = 1 Australian dollar)

1 Gilbertese and Tuvaluan

(Des Iakopo Nivatui; adapted J. Cooter. Litho Questa)

1976 (1 Jan). *Separation of the Islands. T* **1** *and similar multicoloured designs. W w* 14 (*sideways* on 4 and 35 c.*). *P* 13½.

1 4 c. Type **1** 35 80
2 10 c. Map of the islands (*vert*) .. 50 1·00
3 35 c. Canoes .. .. 70 1·50
w. Wmk Crown to right of CA .. 5·50
1/3 .. *Set of* 3 1·40 3·00

*The normal sideways watermark shows Crown to left of CA, *as seen from the back of the stamp.*

TUVALU

(2)

3 50 c. Coin and Octopus

1976 (1 Jan). *Nos. 173 etc. of Gilbert & Ellice Is optd as T* **2** *in silver (35 c.) or blue (others). (a) W w* 12 (*upright*).

4 2 c. Lagoon fishing .. £900 £140
5 5 c. Gilbertese canoe .. 80 60
6 8 c. Weaving pandanus fronds .. 80 60
7 10 c. Weaving a basket .. 80 80
w. Wmk inverted .. 6·00
8 50 c. Local handicrafts .. 22·00 13·00
9 $1 Weaving coconut screen .. 50·00 65·00

(*b*) W w **12** (*sideways*)

10 2 c. Lagoon fishing .. £140 30·00
11 3 c. Cleaning pandanus leaves .. 75 60
12 5 c. Gilbertese canoe .. 2·25 1·00
w. Wmk Crown to right of CA .. 6·50
13 25 c. Loading copra .. 4·00 1·75

(*c*) W w **14** (*inverted*)

14 1 c. Cutting toddy .. 30 30
15 6 c. De-husking coconuts .. 80 40
16 15 c. Tiger Shark .. 80 50
17 50 c. Local handicrafts .. 80 65
18 $1 Weaving coconut screen .. 80 85
19 $2 Coat of arms .. 1·00 85

(*d*) W w **14** (*sideways**)

20 2 c. Lagoon fishing .. 80 40
w. Wmk Crown to right of CA .. 70·00
21 3 c. Cleaning pandanus leaves .. 80 40
22 4 c. Casting nets .. 80 45
23 20 c. Beating a rolled pandanus leaf .. 80 60
24 25 c. Loading copra .. 80 60
25 35 c. Fishing at night .. 85 70
5/7 and 14/25 .. *Set of* 15 10·00 7·50

*The normal sideways watermark shows Crown to left of CA, *as seen from the back of the stamp.*

(Des G. Drummond. Litho Walsall)

1976 (21 Apr). *New Coinage. Vert designs, each showing coin as in T* **3**. *Multicoloured. W w* **14** (*inverted*). *P* 13½.

26 5 c. Type **3** .. 30 15
27 10 c. Red-eyed Crab .. 40 20
28 15 c. Flying Fish .. 55 25
29 35 c. Green Turtle .. 70 45
26/9 .. *Set of* 4 1·75 95

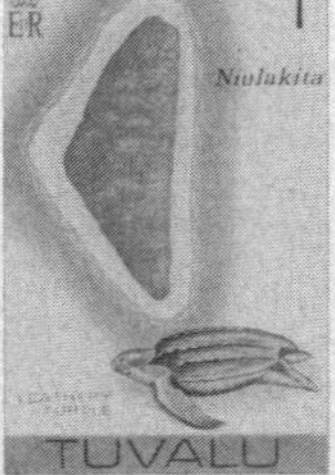

4 Niulakita and Seven-ridged Leathery Turtle

5 Title page of New Testament

(Des J. Cooter. Litho Questa)

1976 (1 July–1 Sept). *Vert designs showing maps (1 to 25 c.) or horiz designs showing scenes (others). Multicoloured. W w* **14** (*sideways on 35 c. to $5*). *P* 13½.

30 1 c. Type **4** .. 85 70
31 2 c. Nukulaelae and sleeping mat .. 40 55
32 4 c. Nui and talo (vegetable) .. 40 50
33 5 c. Nanumanga and grass skirt .. 80 50
34 6 c. Nukufetau and Coconut Crab .. 70 55
35 8 c. Funafuti and Banana tree .. 75 70
36 10 c. Map of Tuvalu .. 75 40
37 15 c. Niutao and Flying fish .. 1·00 20
38 20 c. Vaitupu and Maneapa (meeting hall) 70 50
39 25 c. Nanumea and fish-hook .. 1·40 90
w. Wmk inverted .. 60·00
40 35 c. Te Ano (game) .. 60 20
41 50 c. Canoe pole fishing .. 75 30
42 $1 Reef fishing by flare .. 80 40
43 $2 Living house .. 80 40
44 $5 M.V. *Nivanga* (1.9.76) .. 9·50 9·00
30/44 .. *Set of* 15 18·00 14·00

See also Nos. 58/69.

(Des G. Drummond. Litho Harrison)

1976 (6 Oct). *Christmas. T* **5** *and similar horiz designs. Multicoloured. W w* **14**. *P* 14 × 14½.

45 5 c. Type **5** .. 25 30
46 20 c. Lotolelei Church .. 25 30
47 25 c. Kelupi Church .. 25 30
48 30 c. Mataloa o Tuvalu Church .. 30 30
49 35 c. Palatasio o Keliso Church .. 30 30
45/9 .. *Set of* 5 1·25 1·40

Nos. 45/9 were each printed in sheets of ten stamps and two *se-tenant* stamp-size labels.

6 Queen Elizabeth and Prince Philip

(Des G. Vasarhelyi. Litho Format)

1977 (9 Feb). *Silver Jubilee. T* **6** *and similar horiz designs. Multicoloured. P* 13½.

50 15 c. Type **6** .. 15 10
51 35 c. Prince Philip carried ashore at Vaitupu 20 15
52 50 c. Queen and attendants .. 30 20
50/2 .. *Set of* 3 60 40
MS53 98 × 144 mm. Nos. 50/2. P 15 .. 1·00 1·00

7 "Health"

(Des I. Oliver. Litho Format)

1977 (4 May). *30th Anniv of South Pacific Commission. T* **7** *and similar horiz designs. Multicoloured. P* 13½.

54 5 c. Type **7** .. 15 20
55 20 c. "Education" .. 15 20
56 30 c. "Fruit-growing" .. 15 20
57 35 c. Map of S.P.C. area .. 20 25
54/7 .. *Set of* 4 60 75

1977 (13 June)–**78**. *As Nos. 30/6, 38/9 and 44, but no wmk, or new values and designs (30, 40 c.).*

58 1 c. Type **4** (4.78) .. 50 15
59 2 c. Nukulaelae and sleeping mat (4.78) .. 20 25
60 4 c. Nui and talo (vegetable) (4.78) .. 20 15
61 5 c. Nanumanga and grass skirt (9.77) .. 25 15
62 6 c. Nukufetau and Coconut Crab (3.78) .. 20 35
63 8 c. Funafuti and Banana tree (4.78) .. 20 25
64 10 c. Map of Tuvalu (4.78) .. 20 20
65 20 c. Vaitupu and Maneapa (meeting house) (9.77) .. 50 1·25
66 25 c. Nanumea and fish hook (9.77) .. 1·40 20
67 30 c. Fatele (local dancing) (19.4.78) .. 30 20
68 40 c. Screw Pine (19.4.78) .. 30 15
69 $5 M.V. *Nivanga* .. 2·00 3·00
58/69 .. *Set of* 12 5·50 5·50

Examples of the 15 c. and 35 c. values are known on unwatermarked paper, but there is no evidence that such printings were issued without the Independence overprint of 1 October 1978 (Nos. 94/100).

8 Scout Promise

(Des I. Oliver. Litho Format)

1977 (10 Aug). *50th Anniv of Scouting in the Central Pacific. T* **8** *and similar horiz designs. Multicoloured. P* 13½.

73 5 c. Type **8** .. 15 20
74 20 c. Canoeing .. 15 20
75 30 c. Scout shelter .. 20 25
76 35 c. Lord Baden-Powell .. 20 25
73/6 .. *Set of* 4 65 80

9 Hurricane Beach (Expedition photo)

(Des I. Oliver. Litho Format)

1977 (2 Nov). *Royal Society Expeditions, 1896/7. T* **9** *and similar designs. P* 13½ × 14 (5 *and* 35 *c.*) *or* 14 × 13½ (*others*).

77 5 c. multicoloured .. 15 15
78 20 c. black and light blue .. 15 20
79 30 c. black and light blue .. 20 20
80 35 c. multicoloured .. 20 20
77/80 .. *Set of* 4 65 65

Designs: *Vert*—20 c. Boring apparatus on H.M.S. *Porpoise*; 30 c. Dredging chart. *Horiz*—35 c. Charles Darwin and H.M.S. *Beagle*.

10 Pacific Pigeon

11 *Lawedua* (inter-island coaster)

(Des G. Drummond. Litho Format)

1978 (25 Jan). *Wild Birds. T* **10** *and similar vert designs. Multicoloured. P* 14 × 13½.

81 8 c. Type **10** .. 40 25
82 20 c. Eastern Reef Heron .. 55 40
83 30 c. White Tern .. 65 50
84 40 c. Lesser Frigate Bird .. 65 55
a. Magenta offset from 20 c. value on back
81/4 .. *Set of* 4 2·00 1·50

No. 84a shows an inverted impression of the magenta plate used for the 20 c. on the reverse.

(Des I. Oliver. Litho Format)

1978 (5 Apr). *Ships. T* **11** *and similar horiz designs. Multicoloured. P* 13½ × 14.

85 8 c. Type **11** .. 25 15
86 10 c. *Wallacia* (tug) .. 25 15
87 30 c. *Cenpac Rounder* (freighter) .. 25 20
88 40 c. *Pacific Explorer* (freighter) .. 30 20
85/8 .. *Set of* 4 95 65

(Des G. Drummond. Litho Format)

1978 (2 June). *25th Anniv of Coronation. Horiz designs as Nos. 422/5 of Montserrat. Multicoloured. P* 13½ × 14.

89	8 c. Canterbury Cathedral	10	10
90	30 c. Salisbury Cathedral	10	10
91	40 c. Wells Cathedral	10	10
92	$1 Hereford Cathedral	30	30
89/92	.. .. *Set of* 4	40	40
MS93	137 × 108 mm. Nos. 89/92. P 15	60	90

Nos. 89/92 were each printed in sheets containing 2 *se-tenant* stamp-size labels.

INDEPENDENT

INDEPENDENCE
1ST OCTOBER
1978

(12)

13 White Frangipani

1978 (1 Oct). *Independence. Nos.* 63/4, 65, 67/8 *and as Nos.* 37 *and* 40, *but without wmk, optd as T* **12**.

94	8 c. Funafuti and Banana tree	10	10
95	10 c. Map of Tuvalu	10	10
96	15 c. Niutao and Four-winged Flyingfish ..	10	10
97	20 c. Vaitupu and Maneapa (house) ..	15	15
98	30 c. Fatele (local dancing)	15	15
99	35 c. Te Ano (game)	20	20
100	40 c. Screw Pine	20	20
94/100	.. .. *Set of* 7	75	75

(Des J. Cooter. Litho Format)

1978 (4 Oct). *Wild Flowers. T* **13** *and similar vert designs. Multicoloured. P* 14.

101	8 c. Type **13**	10	10
102	20 c. Susana	10	10
103	30 c. Tiale	15	15
104	40 c. Inato	20	25
101/4	.. .. *Set of* 4	50	55

14 Squirrelfish

(Des G. Drummond. Litho Format)

1979 (24 Jan)–**81**. *Fishes (1st series). Multicoloured designs as T* **14**. *P* 14.

105	1 c. Type **14**	10	10
106	2 c. Band-tailed Goatfish	10	10
107	4 c. Regal Angelfish	10	10
108	5 c. Melon Butterflyfish	15	10
109	6 c. Semi-circle Angelfish	15	10
110	8 c. Blue-striped Snapper	15	10
111	10 c. Clown Anemonefish	25	10
112	15 c. Chevron Butterflyfish	25	10
113	20 c. Yellow-edged Lyretail ("Fairy Cod") ..	35	15
114	25 c. Clown Triggerfish	35	20
115	30 c. Long-nosed Butterflyfish	35	10
116	35 c. Yellow-finned Tuna	40	20
117	40 c. Spotted Eagle Ray	40	10
117*b*	45 c. Black-tipped Grouper (16.6.81) ..	1·50	2·00
118	50 c. Hammerhead	40	20
119	70 c. Lionfish (*vert*)	40	30
120	$1 Painted Triggerfish (*vert*) ..	40	40
121	$2 Copper-banded Butterflyfish ("Beaked Coralfish") (*vert*)	70	40
122	$5 Tiger Shark (*vert*)	90	55
105/22	.. .. .. *Set of* 19	6·50	4·25

Nos. 105/22 were each printed in sheets containing 2 *se-tenant* stamp-size printed labels.

Both fine (300 lines of dots per linear inch) and coarse (175 lines of dots per linear inch) screens were used to produce plates for this issue. Examples of the 1, 5, 8, 10, 30 and 40 c. values exist with either screen, the 2, 4, 6, 20, 70 c., $1, $2, $5 only with the fine screen, and the 15, 25, 35, 45 and 50 c. only with the coarse.

See also Nos. 770/81.

15 "Explorer of the Pacific"

(Des J. Cooter. Litho Format)

1979 (14 Feb). *Death Bicentenary of Captain Cook. T* **15** *and similar horiz designs. Multicoloured. P* 14 × 14½.

123	8 c. Type **15**	15	20
	a. Horiz strip of 4. Nos. 123/6 ..	75	
	ab. Imperf. Horiz strip of 4		
124	30 c. "A new island is discovered" ..	20	20
125	40 c. "Transit of Venus, Tahiti, 3 June, 1769"	20	20
126	$1 Death of Captain Cook, Hawaii, 14 February, 1779	30	30
123/6	.. .. *Set of* 4	75	80

Nos. 123/6 were printed together, *se-tenant*, in horizontal strips of 4 throughout the sheet.

16 Grumman Mackinnon G-21C Goose Flying Boat and Nukulaelae Island

(Des J. Cooter. Litho Format)

1979 (16 May). *Internal Air Service. T* **16** *and similar horiz designs. Multicoloured. P* 13½.

127	8 c. Type **16**	15	15
128	20 c. Goose and Vaitupu	15	20
129	30 c. Goose and Nui	20	30
130	40 c. Goose and Funafuti	25	35
127/30	.. .. *Set of* 4	65	90

17 Sir Rowland Hill, 1976 4 c. Separation Commemorative and London's First Pillar Box, 1855

18 Child's Face

(Des J. Cooter. Litho Format)

1979 (27 Aug). *Death Centenary of Sir Rowland Hill. T* **17** *and similar horiz designs. Multicoloured. P* 13½ × 14.

131	30 c. Type **17**	15	15
132	40 c. Sir Rowland Hill, 1976 10 c. Separation commemorative and Penny Black ..	15	15
133	$1 Sir Rowland Hill, 1976 35 c. Separation commemorative and mail coach ..	35	30
131/3	.. .. *Set of* 3	60	55
MS134	148 × 140 mm. Nos. 131/3. P 15	70	1·25

(Des G. Vasarhelyi. Litho Format)

1979 (20 Oct). *International Year of the Child. T* **18** *and similar vert designs showing children's faces. P* 14 × 13½.

135	8 c. multicoloured	10	10
136	20 c. multicoloured	10	10
137	30 c. multicoloured	10	15
138	40 c. multicoloured	15	25
135/8	.. .. *Set of* 4	40	55

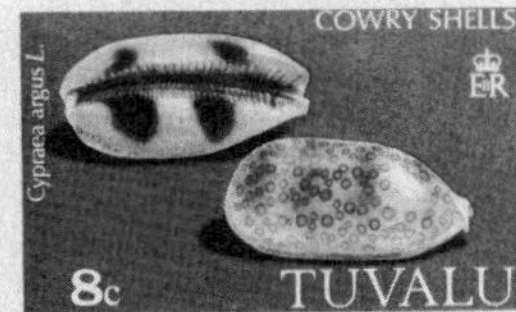

19 Eyed Cowrie (*Cypraea argus*)

(Des J. Cooter. Litho Format)

1980 (20 Feb). *Cowrie Shells. T* **19** *and similar horiz designs. Multicoloured. P* 13½ × 14.

139	8 c. Type **19**	10	10
140	20 c. Jester Cowrie (*Cypraea scurra*) ..	10	10
141	30 c. Closely-related Carnelian Cowrie (*Cypraea carneola propinqua*) ..	15	15
142	40 c. Golden Cowrie (*Cypraea aurantium*) ..	25	20
139/42	.. .. *Set of* 4	55	45

20 Philatelic Bureau, Funafuti, and 1976 8 c. Definitive

21 Queen Elizabeth the Queen Mother at Royal Variety Performance, 1978

(Des J. Cooter. Litho Questa)

1980 (30 Apr). *"London 1980" International Stamp Exhibition. T* **20** *and similar horiz designs. Multicoloured. P* 13½ × 14.

143	10 c. Type **20**	10	10
144	20 c. Gilbert and Ellice Islands stamp with Nukulaelae postmark of 1946 and 1976 2 c. definitive	15	15
145	30 c. Fleet Post Office, U.S. Navy, airmail letter of 1943	15	20
146	$1 Tuvalu coat of arms and map ..	35	40
143/6	.. .. *Set of* 4	65	75
MS147	160 × 136 mm. Nos. 143/6	65	1·10

(Des G. Drummond. Litho Format)

1980 (14 Aug). *80th Birthday of Queen Elizabeth the Queen Mother. P* 13½.

148 **21**	50 c. multicoloured	25	20

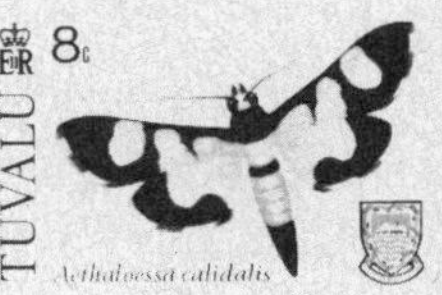

22 *Aethaloessa calidalis*

(Des J. Cooter. Litho Format)

1980 (20 Aug). *Moths. T* **22** *and similar horiz designs. Multicoloured. P* 14.

149	8 c. Type **22**	10	10
150	20 c. *Parotis suralis*	15	10
151	30 c. *Dudua aprobola*	20	15
152	40 c. *Decadarchis simulans*	20	15
149/52	.. .. *Set of* 4	60	45

23 Air Pacific De Havilland D.H.114 Heron 2

45
CENTS

(24)

(Des G. Drummond. Litho Format)

1980 (5 Nov). *Aviation Commemorations. T* **23** *and similar horiz designs. Multicoloured. P* 13½ × 14.

153	8 c. Type **23**	10	10
154	20 c. Hawker Siddeley H.S.748	15	10
155	30 c. Short S.25 Sunderland flying boat ..	15	15
156	40 c. Orville Wright and Wright Flyer III	20	15
153/6	.. .. *Set of* 4	55	45

Commemorations:—8 c. 1st regular air service to Tuvalu, 1964; 20 c. Air service to Tuvalu; 30 c. War time R.N.Z.A.F. flying boat service to Funafuti, 1945; 40 c. Wright Brothers' 1st flight, 17 December 1903.

TWO TYPES OF SURCHARGE FOR NO. 157

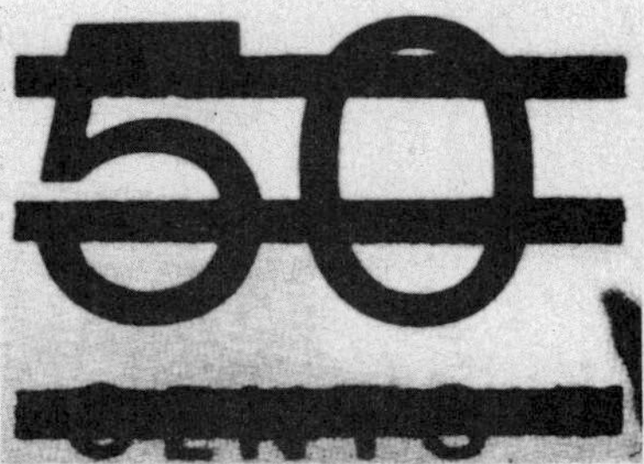

Type I

Type II

Type I. Applied by lithography. Clean lines with an even distribution of the ink.

Type II. Applied by typography. Ragged lines with an uneven distribution of the ink, especially at the edges of the figures and bars. On some stamps the impression of the surcharge is visible on the back.

1981 (19 Jan). *No.* 118 *surch with T* **24**.

157	45 c. on 50 c. Hammerhead (I)	25	40
	a. Type II (typo) surch	2·75	2·75

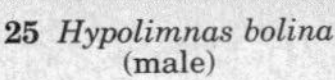

25 *Hypolimnas bolina* (male)

26 *Elizabeth* (brig), 1809

(Des J. Cooter. Litho Questa)

1981 (3 Feb). *Butterflies. T* **25** *and similar horiz designs. Multicoloured. P* 14 × 14½.

158 8 c. Type **25** 15 10
159 20 c. *Hypolimnas bolina* (female) 20 15
160 30 c. *Hypolimnas bolina* (female) (*different*) 20 20
161 40 c. *Precis villida* 25 20
158/61 .. .. *Set of* 4 70 60

(Des R. Granger Barrett. Litho Format)

1981 (13 May). *Ships* (*1st series*). *T* **26** *and similar horiz designs. Multicoloured. W* w **15** (*sideways*). *P* 14.

162 10 c. Type **26** 20 20
163 25 c. *Rebecca* (brigantine), 1819 .. .. 20 25
164 35 c. *Independence II* (whaling ship), 1821 25 30
165 40 c. H.M.S. *Basilisk* (paddle-sloop), 1872 30 35
166 45 c. H.M.S. *Royalist* (screw-corvette), 1890 35 40
167 50 c. *Olivebank* (barque), 1920 .. .. 35 40
162/7 .. .. *Set of* 6 1·50 1·75

Nos. 162/7 were each produced in sheets of six stamps and two labels, these occurring in the second horizontal row.

See also Nos. 235/40, 377/80 and 442/5.

(Des D. Shults. Litho Questa)

1981 (10 July–26 Nov). *Royal Wedding. Horiz designs as T* **26/27** *of Kiribati. Multicoloured.* (a) *W* w **15**. *P* 14.

168 10 c. *Carolina* 10 15
a. Sheetlet. No. 168 × 6 and No. 169 .. 90
169 10 c. Prince Charles and Lady Diana Spencer 35 50
170 45 c. *Victoria and Albert III* 10 15
a. Sheetlet. No. 170 × 6 and No. 171 .. 90
171 45 c. As No. 169 .. .. 40 65
172 $2 *Britannia* 35 50
a. Sheetlet No. 172 × 6 and No. 173 .. 2·75
173 $2 As No. 169 .. .. 1·00 1·50
168/73 .. .. *Set of* 6 2·00 3·00
MS174 120 × 109 mm. $1.50, As No. 169. Wmk sideways. P 12 (26 Nov) 50 75

(b) *Booklet stamps. No wmk. P* 12 (26 No

175 10 c. As No. 168 .. .. 10 15
a. Booklet pane. No. 175×4 with margins all round 35
176 45 c. As No. 171 .. .. 30 80
a. Booklet pane. No. 176×2 with margins all round 60

Nos. 168/73 were printed in sheetlets of seven stamps of the same face value, each containing six of the "Royal Yacht" design and one of the larger design showing Prince Charles and Lady Diana.

Nos. 175/6 come from $1.70 stamp booklets.

27 U.P.U. Emblem

28 Map of Funafuti and Anchor

(Des, eng and recess Harrison)

1981 (19 Nov). *U.P.U. Membership. W* **4** *of Maldive Islands. P* 14½ × 14.

177 **27** 70 c. deep ultramarine 20 30
178 $1 red-brown 30 45
w. Wmk inverted .. .. .. 22·00
MS179 86×71 mm. Nos. 177/8. No wmk .. 90 2·25

(Des J. Cooter. Litho Questa)

1982 (17 Feb). *Amatuku Maritime School. T* **28** *and similar horiz designs. Multicoloured. W* w **15** (*sideways*). *P* 13½ × 14.

180 10 c. Type **28** 10 10
181 25 c. Motor launch 20 20
182 35 c. School buildings and jetty 25 30
183 45 c. School flag and freighters 30 35
180/3 .. .. *Set of* 4 75 85

29 Caroline of Brandenburg–Ansbach, Princess of Wales, 1714

TONGA CYCLONE
RELIEF
1982 +20c
(30)

(Des D. Shults and J. Cooter. Litho Format)

1982 (19 May). *21st Birthday of Princess of Wales. T* **29** *and similar vert designs. Multicoloured. W* w **15**. *P* 13½ × 14.

184 10 c. Type **29** 10 10
185 45 c. Coat of arms of Caroline of Brandenburg-Ansbach 10 10
w. Wmk inverted .. .. .. 18·00
186 $1.50, Diana, Princess of Wales 50 30
w. Wmk inverted .. .. .. 26·00
184/6 .. .. *Set of* 3 60 40

1982 (20 May). *Tonga Cyclone Relief. Nos.* 170/1 *surch as T* **30** (*words in one line on No.* 188).

187 45 c. + 20 c. *Victoria and Albert III* 15 30
a. Sheetlet. No. 187 × 6 and No. 188 .. 1·25
b. Surch inverted .. .. .. 4·00
c. Surch inverted (horiz pair) .. .. 7·50
d. Surch double .. .. .. 3·50
188 45 c. + 20 c. Prince Charles and Lady Diana Spencer 45 95
a. Surch inverted .. .. .. 11·00
b. Surch double .. .. .. 11·00

No. 187c shows the long surcharge, intended for No. 188, inverted and struck across a horizontal pair of No. 187. No. 188a shows two examples of Type **30** inverted on the same stamp.

1982 (14 July). *Birth of Prince William of Wales. Nos.* 184/6 *optd with T* **19** *of St. Kitts.*

189 10 c. Type **29** 10 10
190 45 c. Coat of arms of Caroline of Brandenburg-Ansbach 10 10
a. Opt inverted .. .. .. 20·00
w. Wmk inverted .. .. .. 18·00
191 $1.50, Diana, Princess of Wales 30 30
189/91 .. .. *Set of* 3 40 40

31 Tuvalu and World Scout Badges

32 Tuvalu Crest and Duke of Edinburgh's Standard

(Des J. Cooter. Litho Walsall)

1982 (18 Aug). *75th Anniv of Boy Scout Movement. T* **31** *and similar horiz designs. Multicoloured. W* w **15** (*sideways*). *P* 13½ × 14.

192 10 c. Type **31** 15 15
193 25 c. Camp-fire 40 40
194 35 c. Parade 45 45
195 45 c. Boy Scout 55 55
192/5 .. .. *Set of* 4 1·40 1·40

(Des J. Cooter. Litho Format)

1982 (26 Oct). *Royal Visit. T* **32** *and similar vert designs. Multicoloured. W* w **15**. *P* 14.

196 25 c. Type **32** 15 20
197 45 c. Tuvalu flag and Royal Standard .. 25 30
198 50 c. Portrait of Queen Elizabeth II 25 30
196/8 .. .. *Set of* 3 60 70
MS199 104×85 mm. Nos. 196/8. Wmk inverted .. .. 60 1·50

33 Fisherman's Hat and Equipment

(Des G. Drummond. Litho Walsall)

1983 (14 Mar)–**84**. *Handicrafts. T* **33** *and similar multicoloured designs. W* w **15** (*sideways on* 1 c. *to* 45 c.). *P* 14.

200 1 c. Type **33** 30 10
201 2 c. Cowrie shell handbags 30 10
202 5 c. Wedding and babyfood baskets .. 30 10
203 10 c. Model canoe 30 10
203*a* 15 c. Ladies' sun hats (30.4.84) .. .. 2·00 1·40
204 20 c. Palm climbing rope and platform with toddy pot 30 20
205 25 c. Pandanus baskets 30 20
205*a* 30 c. Basket tray and coconut stands (18.4.84) 2·00 1·40
206 35 c. Pandanus pillows and shell necklaces .. 40 30
207 40 c. Round baskets and fans 30 35
208 45 c. Reef sandals and fish trap 35 40
209 50 c. Rat trap (*vert*) 40 45
209*a* 60 c. Fisherman's waterproof boxes (*vert*) (18.4.84) .. .. 2·75 1·40
210 $1 Pump drill and adze (*vert*) 60 55
211 $2 Fisherman's hat and canoe bailers (*vert*) 60 70
212 $5 Fishing rod, lures and scoop nets (*vert*) .. 1·25 90
200/12 .. .. *Set of* 16 11·00 7·50

34 *Te Tautai* (trawler)

(Des G. Drummond. Litho Format)

1983 (14 Mar). *Commonwealth Day. T* **34** *and similar horiz designs. Multicoloured. W* w **15** (*sideways*). *P* 14.

213 20 c. Type **34** 15 15
214 35 c. Traditional dancing, Motufoua School .. 15 25
215 45 c. Satellite view of Pacific 20 30
216 50 c. *Morning Star* (container ship) 25 40
213/16 .. .. *Set of* 4 65 1·00

No. 214 is incorrectly inscribed "MOTOFOUA SCHOOL".

35 *Pantala flavescens*

(Des J. Cooter. Litho Format)

1983 (25 May). *Dragonflies. T* **35** *and similar horiz designs. Multicoloured. W* w **15** (*sideways*). *P* 14.

217 10 c. Type **35** 15 10
218 35 c. *Anax guttatus* 35 35
219 40 c. *Tholymis tillarga* 35 40
220 50 c. *Diplacodes bipunctata* 40 50
217/20 .. .. *Set of* 4 1·10 1·25

36 Brigade Members Racing

60c
(37)

(Des J. Cooter. Litho Format)

1983 (10 Aug). *Centenary of Boys' Brigade. T* **36** *and similar multicoloured designs. W* w **15** (*sideways on* 10 c., 35 c.). *P* 13½.

221 10 c. Type **36** 10 10
222 35 c. B. B. members in outrigger canoe .. 25 30
223 $1 On parade (*vert*) .. .. .. 65 1·00
221/3 .. .. *Set of* 3 90 1·25

1983 (26 Aug). *No.* 210 *surch with T* **37**.

224 60 c. on $1 Pump drill and adze 70 70

38 Montgolfier Balloon, 1783

39 Early Communications

(Des A. Theobald. Litho Format)

1983 (21 Sept). *Bicentenary of Manned Flight. T* **38** *and similar multicoloured designs. W* w **15** (*sideways on* 35 c., 45 c.). *P* 14.

225 25 c. Type **38** 15 20
w. Wmk inverted .. .. .. 25·00
226 35 c. Grumman Mackinnon G-21E Turbo Goose (*horiz*) 20 25
a. No wmk .. .. ..
227 45 c. Beech 200 Super King Air (*horiz*) .. 20 30
228 50 c. *Double Eagle II* balloon 25 35
w. Wmk inverted .. .. .. 32·00
225/8 .. .. *Set of* 4 70 1·00
MS229 114×145 mm. Nos. 225/8. Wmk sideways 70 1·00

(Des J.W. Litho Questa)

1983 (18 Nov). *World Communications Year. T* **39** *and similar horiz designs. Multicoloured. W* w **15**. *P* 14.

230 25 c. Type **39** 20 20
231 35 c. Radio operator 25 25
232 45 c. Modern telephone 25 25
233 50 c. Funafuti transmitting station 30 30
230/3 .. .. *Set of* 4 90 90

30c

(40)

1984 (1 Feb). *No.* 208 *surch with T* **40**.

234 30 c. on 45 c. Reef sandals and fish trap .. 35 40

(Des R. Granger Barrett. Litho Format)

1984 (16 Feb). *Ships* (*2nd series*). *Horiz designs as T* **26**. *Multicoloured. W* w **15** (*sideways**). *P* 14.

235 10 c. *Titus* (freighter), 1897 .. .. 15 15
w. Wmk POST OFFICE reading upwards 50·00
236 20 c. *Malaita* (freighter), 1905 .. .. 20 15
w. Wmk POST OFFICE reading upwards 90·00
237 25 c. *Aymeric* (freighter), 1906 .. .. 20 15
w. Wmk POST OFFICE reading upwards 50·00
238 35 c. *Anshun* (freighter), 1965 .. .. 25 25
239 45 c. *Beaverbank* (freighter), 1970 .. .. 30 30
240 50 c. *Benjamin Bowring* (freighter), 1981 .. 30 30
235/40 .. .. *Set of* 6 1·25 1·10

*The normal sideways watermark shows "POST OFFICE" reading downwards.

Nos. 235/40 were each produced in sheets of six stamps and two labels, these occurring in the second horizontal row.

41 Class "GS-4"

(Des J.W. Litho Format)

1984 (29 Feb). *Leaders of the World. Railway Locomotives* (1st *series*). *T* **41** *and similar horiz designs, the first in each pair showing technical drawings and the second the locomotive at work. P* 12½.

241 1 c. multicoloured 10 10
a. Vert pair. Nos. 241/2 .. .. .. 10 10
242 1 c. multicoloured 10 10
243 15 c. multicoloured 20 25
a. Vert pair. Nos. 243/4 .. .. .. 40 50
244 15 c. multicoloured 20 25
245 40 c. multicoloured 25 35
a. Vert pair. Nos. 245/6 .. .. .. 50 70
246 40 c. multicoloured 25 35
247 60 c. multicoloured 35 45
a. Vert pair. Nos. 247/8 .. .. .. 70 90
248 60 c. multicoloured 35 45
241/8 .. .. *Set of* 8 1·40 2·00

Designs:—Nos. 241/2, Class "GS-4", U.S.A. (1941); 243/4, Class "AD 60", Australia (1952); 245/6, Class "C 38", Australia (1943); 247/8, *Lord of the Isles*, Great Britain (1892).

See also Nos. 253/68, 273/80, 313/20 and 348/55.

42 *Ipomoea pes-caprae*

(Des Michael and Sylvia Goaman. Litho Questa)

1984 (30 May). *Beach Flowers. T* **42** *and similar horiz designs. Multicoloured. W w* **15**. *P* 14.

249 25 c. Type **42** 25 25
250 45 c. *Ipomoea macrantha* 40 40
251 50 c. *Triumfetta procumbens* 45 45
252 60 c. *Portulaca quadrifida* 50 50
249/52 .. .. *Set of* 4 1·40 1·40

(Des J.W. Litho Format)

1984 (27 June). *Leaders of the World, Railway Locomotives* (2nd *series*). *Designs as T* **41**, *the first in each pair showing technical drawings and the second the locomotive at work. P* 12½.

253 10 c. multicoloured 10 10
a. Vert pair. Nos. 253/4 .. .. .. 15 15
254 10 c. multicoloured 10 10
255 15 c. multicoloured 10 15
a. Vert pair. Nos. 255/6 .. .. .. 20 30
256 15 c. multicoloured 10 15
257 20 c. multicoloured 10 15
a. Vert pair. Nos. 257/8 .. .. .. 20 30
258 20 c. multicoloured 10 15
259 25 c. multicoloured 10 15
a. Vert pair. Nos. 259/60 .. .. .. 20 30
260 25 c. multicoloured 10 15
261 40 c. multicoloured 15 20
a. Vert pair. Nos. 261/2 .. .. .. 30 40
262 40 c. multicoloured 15 20
263 50 c. multicoloured 15 20
a. Vert pair. Nos. 263/4 .. .. .. 30 40
264 50 c. multicoloured 15 20
265 60 c. multicoloured 15 25
a. Vert pair. Nos. 265/6 .. .. .. 30 50
266 60 c. multicoloured 15 25
267 $1 multicoloured 20 30
a. Vert pair. Nos. 267/8 .. .. .. 40 60
268 $1 multicoloured 20 30
253/68 .. .. *Set of* 16 1·75 2·75

Designs:—Nos. 253/4, "Casey Jones" type engine, U.S.A. (1896); 255/6, Triplex type, U.S.A. (1914); 257/8, Class "370" Advanced Passenger Train, Great Britain (1981); 259/60, Class "4F", Great Britain (1924); 261/2, Class "Tornado Rover", Great Britain (1888); 263/4, *Broadlands*, Great Britain (1967); 265/6, *Locomotion No.* 1, Great Britain (1825); 267/8, Class "C57", Japan, (1937).

Nos. 253/68 were issued in a similar sheet format to Nos. 241/8.

43 Exhibition Emblem

44 A. Shrewsbury

(Des G. Drummond. Litho Format)

1984 (21 Aug). *"Ausipex" International Stamp Exhibition, Melbourne* (*Nos.* 269/70) *and 15th South Pacific Forum* (*others*). *T* **43** *and similar horiz designs. Multicoloured, W w* **15** (*sideways*). *P* 14.

269 60 c. Type **43** 20 30
270 60 c. Royal Exhibition Building, Melbourne .. 20 30
271 60 c. Arms of Tuvalu 20 30
272 60 c. Tuvalu flag 20 30
269/72 .. .. *Set of* 4 70 1·10

IMPERFORATES AND MISSING COLOURS. Various issues between Nos. 273 and 529 exist either imperforate or with colours omitted. Such items are not listed as there is no evidence that they fulfil the criteria outlined on page xi of this catalogue.

(Des J.W. Litho Format)

1984 (4 Oct). *Leaders of the World. Railway Locomotives* (3rd *series*). *Horiz designs as T* **41**, *the first in each pair showing technical drawings and the second the locomotive at work. P* 12½.

273 1 c. multicoloured 10 10
a. Vert pair. Nos. 273/4 .. .. .. 10 10
b. Error. Wmk w **15** .. .. .. 4·50
ba. Vert pair. Nos. 273b/4b .. .. .. 9·00
274 1 c. multicoloured 10 10
b. Error. Wmk w **15** .. .. .. 4·50
275 15 c. multicoloured 15 20
a. Vert pair. Nos. 275/6 .. .. .. 30 40
276 15 c. multicoloured 15 20
277 30 c. multicoloured 20 30
a. Vert pair. Nos. 277/8 .. .. .. 40 60
b. Error. Wmk w **15** .. .. .. 4·50
ba. Vert pair. Nos. 277b/8b .. .. .. 9·00
278 30 c. multicoloured 20 30
b. Error. Wmk w **15** .. .. .. 4·50
279 $1 multicoloured 40 80
a. Vert pair. Nos. 279/80 .. .. .. 80 1·60
b. Error. Wmk w **15** .. .. .. 8·00
ba. Vert pair. Nos. 279b/80b .. .. 16·00
280 $1 multicoloured 40 80
b. Error. Wmk w **15** .. .. .. 8·00
273/80 .. .. *Set of* 8 1·40 2·40

Designs:—Nos. 273/4, Class "9700", Japan (1897); 275/6, Class "231" C/K, France (1909); 277/8, Class "640", Italy (1907); 279/80, Class "4500", France (1906).

Nos. 273/80 were issued in a similar sheet format to Nos. 241/8.

(Des Court House Studio. Litho Format)

1984 (5 Nov). *Leaders of the World. Cricketers. T* **44** *and similar vert designs, the first listed in each pair showing the cricketer in action and the second a head portrait. P* 12½.

281 5 c. multicoloured 10 10
a. Horiz pair. Nos. 281/2 .. .. .. 10 20
282 5 c. multicoloured 10 10
283 30 c. multicoloured 25 35
a. Horiz pair. Nos. 283/4 .. .. .. 50 70
284 30 c. multicoloured 25 35
285 50 c. multicoloured 30 40
a. Horiz pair. Nos. 285/6 .. .. .. 60 80
286 50 c. multicoloured 30 40
287 60 c. multicoloured 40 45
a. Horiz pair. Nos. 287/8 .. .. .. 80 90
288 60 c. multicoloured 40 45
281/8 .. .. *Set of* 8 1·75 2·40

Designs:—Nos. 281/2, A. Shrewsbury; 283/4, H. Verity; 285/6, E. H. Hendren; 287/8, J. Briggs.

Nos. 281/2, 283/4, 285/6 and 287/8 were printed together, *se-tenant*, in horizontal pairs throughout the sheets.

Similar stamps showing Close (5 c.), (Boycott (15 c.), Bairstow (30 c.), and Evans ($1) were prepared, but not issued. They exist imperforate from stock dispersed by the liquidator of Format International Security Printers Ltd.

45 Trees and Stars

(Des Jennifer Toombs. Litho Format)

1984 (14 Nov). *Christmas. Children's Drawings. T* **45** *and similar horiz designs. Multicoloured. W w* **15** (*sideways*). *P* 14½ × 14.

289 15 c. Type **45** 10 10
290 40 c. Fishing from outrigger canoes 20 20
291 50 c. Three Wise Men bearing gifts 25 25
292 60 c. The Holy Family 35 35
289/92 .. .. *Set of* 4 75 75

46 Morris Minor

47 Common Flicker

(Des J.W. ($1), Artists International (others). Litho Format)

1984 (7 Dec). *Leaders of the World. Automobiles* (1st *series*). *T* **46** *and similar horiz designs, the first in each pair showing technical drawings and the second paintings. P* 12½.

293 1 c. black, pale cinnamon and yellow-ochre .. 10 10
a. Vert pair. Nos. 293/4 .. .. .. 10 10
294 1 c. multicoloured 10 10
295 15 c. black, pale flesh and brown-lilac .. 10 15
a. Vert pair. Nos. 295/6 .. .. .. 20 30
296 15 c. multicoloured 10 15
297 50 c. black, pale cinnamon and dull mauve .. 20 20
a. Vert pair. Nos. 297/8 .. .. .. 40 60
298 50 c. multicoloured 20 30
299 $1 black, pale green and cobalt 30 40
a. Vert pair. Nos. 299/300 .. .. .. 60 80
300 $1 multicoloured 30 40
293/300 .. .. *Set of* 8 1·10 1·60

Designs:—Nos. 293/4, Morris "Minor"; 295/6, Studebaker "Avanti"; 297/8, Chevrolet "International Six"; 299/300, Allard "J2".

Nos. 293/4, 295/6, 297/8 and 299/300 were printed together, *se-tenant*, in vertical pairs throughout the sheets.

See also Nos. 321/8, 356/71, 421/32 and 446/70.

(Des R. Vigurs. Litho Format)

1985 (12 Feb). *Leaders of the World. Birth Bicentenary of John J. Audubon (ornithologist). T* **47** *and similar vert designs. Multicoloured. P* 12½.

301 1 c. Type **47** 10 10
a. Horiz pair. Nos. 301/2 .. .. .. 10 10
302 1 c. Say's Phoebe 10 10
303 25 c. Townsend's Warbler 30 30
a. Horiz pair. Nos. 303/4 .. .. .. 60 60
304 25 c. Bohemian Waxwing 30 30
305 50 c. Prothonotary Warbler 40 50
a. Horiz pair. Nos. 305/6 .. .. .. 80 1·00
306 50 c. Worm-eating Warbler 40 50
307 70 c. Broad-winged Hawk 50 75
a. Horiz pair. Nos. 307/8 .. .. .. 1·00 1·50
308 70 c. Hen Harrier 50 75
301/8 .. .. *Set of* 8 2·25 2·75

Nos. 301/2, 303/4, 305/6 and 307/8 were printed together, *se-tenant*, in horizontal pairs throughout the sheets.

48 Black-naped Tern

(Des G. Drummond. Litho Format)

1985 (27 Feb). *Birds and their Eggs. T* **48** *and similar horiz designs. Multicoloured. W w* **15** (*sideways*). *P* 14.

309 15 c. Type **48** 50 20
310 40 c. White-capped Noddy 85 50
311 50 c. White-tailed Tropicbird 95 60
312 60 c. Sooty Tern .. .. 1·00 70
309/12 .. .. *Set of* 4 3·00 1·75

(Des J.W. (5 c., $1), T. Hadler (others). Litho Format)

1985 (19 Mar). *Leaders of the World. Railway Locomotives* (4th *series*). *Horiz designs as T* **41** *the first in each pair showing technical drawings and the second the locomotive at work. P* 12½.

313 5 c. multicoloured 10 10
a. Vert pair. Nos. 313/14 .. .. .. 10 10
314 5 c. multicoloured 10 10
315 10 c. multicoloured 10 10
a. Vert pair. Nos. 315/16 .. .. .. 20 20
316 10 c. multicoloured 10 10
317 30 c. multicoloured 30 35
a. Vert pair. Nos. 317/18 .. .. .. 60 70
318 30 c. multicoloured 30 35
319 $1 multicoloured .. .. 75 1·00
a. Vert pair. Nos. 319/20 .. .. .. 1·50 2·00
320 $1 multicoloured .. .. 75 1·00
313/20 .. .. *Set of* 8 2·25 2·75

Designs:—Nos. 313/14, "Churchward 28XX", Great Britain (1905); 315/16, Class "KF", China (1935); 317/18, Class "99.77", East Germany (1952); 319/20, Pearson type, Great Britain (1853).

Nos. 313/20 were issued in a similar sheet format to Nos. 241/8.

(Des Artists International. Litho Format)

1985 (3 Apr). *Leaders of the World. Automobiles* (2nd *series*). *Horiz designs as T* **46**, *the first in each pair showing technical drawings and the second paintings. P* 12½.

321 1 c. black, apple green and deep dull green 10 10
a. Vert pair. Nos. 321/2 .. .. .. 10 10
322 1 c. multicoloured 10 10
323 20 c. black, pink and rose-red 15 20
a. Vert pair. Nos. 323/4 .. .. .. 30 40
324 20 c. multicoloured 15 20
325 50 c. black, dull violet-blue & brt reddish vio 20 30
a. Vert pair. Nos. 325/6 .. .. .. 40 60
326 50 c. multicoloured 20 30
327 70 c. black, dull pink and grey-brown .. 20 35
a. Vert pair. Nos. 327/8 .. .. .. 40 70
328 70 c. multicoloured 20 35
321/8 .. .. *Set of* 8 1·00 1·50

Designs:—Nos. 321/2, Rickenbacker (1923); 323/4, Detroit-Electric Two Door Brougham (1914); 325/6, Packard "Clipper" (1941): 327/8, Audi "Quattro" (1982).

Nos. 321/8 were issued in a similar sheet format to Nos. 293/300.

49 Curtiss P-40N Warhawk

50 Queen Elizabeth the Queen Mother

(Des A. Theobald. Litho Questa)

1985 (29 May). *World War II Aircraft. T* **49** *and similar horiz designs. Multicoloured. W* w **15**. *P* 14.
329 15 c. Type **49** .. .. 1·25 45
330 40 c. Consolidated B-24 Liberator .. .. 1·60 1·00
331 50 c. Lockheed PV-1 Ventura .. .. 1·75 1·25
332 60 c. Douglas C-54 .. .. .. 1·75 1·50
329/32 .. .. *Set of* 4 5·50 3·75
MS333 110×108 mm. Nos. 329/32. Wmk sideways .. .. 4·00 2·75

(Des D. Ewart ($1.20), Maxine Marsh (others). Litho Format)

1985 (4 July). *Leaders of the World. Life and Times of Queen Elizabeth the Queen Mother. Various vertical portraits as T* **50**. *P* 12½.
334 5 c. multicoloured 10 10
a. Horiz pair. Nos. 334/5 .. .. .. 10 10
335 5 c. multicoloured 10 10
336 30 c. multicoloured 10 15
a. Horiz pair. Nos. 336/7 .. .. .. 15 30
337 30 c. multicoloured 10 15
338 60 c. multicoloured 15 20
a. Horiz pair. Nos. 338/9 .. .. .. 30 40
339 60 c. multicoloured 15 20
340 $1 multicoloured 15 35
a. Horiz pair. Nos. 340/1 .. .. .. 30 70
341 $1 multicoloured 15 35
334/41 .. .. *Set of* 8 70 1·40
MS342 85×114 mm. $1.20, multicoloured; $1.20, multicoloured .. .. 60 1·50

The two designs of each value were issued, *se-tenant*, in horizontal pairs within the sheets.

Each *se-tenant* pair shows a floral pattern across the bottom of the portraits which stops short of the left-hand edge on the left-hand stamp and of the right-hand edge on the right-hand stamp.

Designs as Nos. 336/7 and 338/9, but with face values of $3×2 and $2×2, also exist in additional miniature sheets from a restricted printing issued 10 January 1986.

51 Guide playing Guitar 52 Stalk-eyed Ghost Crab

(Des Jennifer Toombs. Litho Format)

1985 (28 Aug). *75th Anniv of Girl Guide Movement. T* **51** *and similar vert designs. Multicoloured. W* w **15** (*sideways*). *P* 15.
343 15 c. Type **51** 15 20
344 40 c. Building camp-fire 40 45
345 50 c. Patrol Leader with Guide flag 50 55
346 60 c. Guide saluting 60 65
343/6 .. .. *Set of* 4 1·50 1·60
MS347 141×77 mm. Nos. 343/6. Wmk upright 1·50 2·00

(Des J.W. (10 c.), T. Hadler (others). Litho Format)

1985 (18 Sept). *Leaders of the World. Railway Locomotives* (5*th series*). *Horiz designs as T* **41**, *the first in each pair showing technical drawings and the second the locomotive at work. P* 12½.
348 10 c. multicoloured 10 15
a. Vert pair. Nos. 348/9 .. .. .. 15 30
349 10 c. multicoloured 10 15
350 40 c. multicoloured 20 30
a. Vert pair. Nos. 350/1 .. .. .. 40 60
351 40 c. multicoloured 20 30
352 65 c. multicoloured 30 45
a. Vert pair. Nos. 352/3 .. .. .. 60 90
353 65 c. multicoloured 30 45
354 $1 multicoloured 40 70
a. Vert pair. Nos. 354/5 .. .. .. 80 1·40
355 $1 multicoloured 40 70
348/55 .. .. *Set of* 8 1·75 2·75

Designs:—Nos. 348/9, *Green Arrow*, Great Britain (1936); 350/1, Class "SD-50" diesel, U.S.A. (1982); 352/3, D.R.G. *Flying Hamburger*, Germany (1932); 354/5, Class "1070", Japan (1908).

Nos. 348/55 were issued in a similar sheet format to Nos. 241/8.

(Des Artists International. Litho Format)

1985 (8 Oct). *Leaders of the World. Automobiles* (3*rd series*). *Horiz designs as T* **46**, *the first in each pair showing technical drawings and the second paintings. P* 12½.
356 5 c. black, grey and bright mauve 10 10
a. Vert pair. Nos. 356/7 .. .. .. 10 15
357 5 c. multicoloured 10 10
358 10 c. black, pale salmon-pink and Indian red 10 15
a. Vert pair. Nos. 358/9 .. .. .. 15 30
359 10 c. multicoloured 10 15
360 15 c. black, light brown and Indian red .. 10 15
a. Vert pair. Nos. 360/1 .. .. .. 20 30
361 15 c. multicoloured 10 15
362 35 c. black, brown-red & light turq-blue .. 20 30
a. Vert pair. Nos. 362/3 .. .. .. 40 60
363 35 c. multicoloured 20 30
364 40 c. black, dull yellow-grn & yellowish grn 20 30
a. Vert pair. Nos. 364/5 .. .. .. 40 60
365 40 c. multicoloured 20 30
366 55 c. black, pale stone and brown-olive .. 20 30
a. Vert pair. Nos. 366/7 .. .. .. 40 60
367 55 c. multicoloured 20 30
368 $1 black, brown and lake-brown 30 45
a. Vert pair. Nos. 368/9 .. .. .. 60 90
369 $1 multicoloured 30 45
370 $1.50, black, flesh and dull scarlet 40 60
a. Vert pair. Nos. 370/1 .. .. .. 80 1·10
371 $1.50, multicoloured 40 60
356/71 .. .. *Set of* 16 2·75 4·00

Designs:—Nos. 356/7, Cord "L-29" (1929); 358/9, Horch "670 V-12" (1932); 360/1, Lanchester (1901); 362/3, Citroen "2 CV" (1950); 364/5, MGA (1957); 366/7, Ferrari "250 GTO" (1962); 368/9, Ford "V-8" (1932); 370/1, Aston Martin "Lagonda" (1977).

Nos. 356/71 were issued in a similar sheet format to Nos. 293/300.

(Des G. Drummond. Litho Format)

1986 (7 Jan). *Crabs. T* **52** *and similar horiz designs. Multicoloured. P* 15.
372 15 c. Type **52** 50 50
373 40 c. Red and White Painted Crab 70 75
374 50 c. Red-spotted Crab .. .. .. 75 1·00
375 60 c. Red Hermit Crab .. .. .. 85 1·40
372/5 .. .. *Set of* 4 2·50 3·25

53 Chess Knight on Board and Flags of U.S. and U.S.S.R. (World Chess Championships) 54 Peace Dove carrying Wreath and Rainbow

(Des Court House Studio. Litho Format)

1986 (19 Mar). *International Events. Sheet* 148×127 *mm, containing T* **53** *and similar vert design. Multicoloured. P* 12½.
MS376 $3 Type **53**: $3 Emblem (80th anniv of Rotary .. .. 5·00 7·00

The margins of No. **MS**376 are inscribed "TUVALU" and "Anniversary of Scouting" with two emblems either on a plain apple-green background or with illustrations of types of fungi added.

Overprints on this miniature sheet commemorating "Capex 87" International Stamp Exhibition, Toronto, were not authorised by the Tuvalu administration.

(Des R. Granger Barrett. Litho Format)

1986 (14 Apr). *Ships* (3*rd series*). *Missionary Vessels. Horiz designs as T* **26**. *Multicoloured. W* w **15**. *P* 15.
377 15 c. *Messenger of Peace* (schooner) .. 40 40
378 40 c. *John Wesley* (brig) 65 70
379 50 c. *Duff* (full-rigged ship) 70 80
380 60 c. *Triton* (brigantine) .. .. .. 80 1·10
377/80 .. .. *Set of* 4 2·25 2·75

(Des Court House Studio. Litho Format)

1986 (21 Apr–14 June). *60th Birthday of Queen Elizabeth II. Multicoloured designs as T* **117a** *of Montserrat. P* 12½.
381 10 c. Queen wearing ceremonial cloak, New Zealand, 1977 .. .. 10 10
382 90 c. Before visit to France, 1957 .. .. 25 35
383 $1.50, Queen in 1982 .. .. .. 45 65
384 $3 In Canberra, 1982 (*vert*) .. .. 80 1·25
381/4 .. .. *Set of* 4 1·40 2·10
MS385 85×115 mm. $4 Queen carrying bouquet (14.6) .. .. 3·25 4·50

The 10 c., 90 c. and $1.50 values exist with PVA gum as well as gum arabic.

(Des Gloria McConnaghy. Litho Questa)

1986 (22 May). *25th Anniv of United States Peace Corps.* W w **15**. *P* 14.
386 **54** 50 c. multicoloured 80 90

55 Island and Flags of Tuvalu and U.S.A. 56 South Korean Player

(Des Court House Studio. Litho Questa)

1986 (22 May). *"Ameripex" International Stamp Exhibition, Chicago.* W w **15**. *P* 14×13½.
387 **55** 60 c. multicoloured 85 95

(Des Court House Studio. Litho Format)

1986 (30 June). *World Cup Football Championship, Mexico. T* **56** *and similar multicoloured designs. P* 15 (1 c. *to* 40 c.) *or* 12½ (*others*).
388 1 c. Type **56** 10 10
389 5 c. French player 10 10
390 10 c. West German captain with World Cup trophy, 1974 .. .. 10 10
391 40 c. Italian player 50 50
392 60 c. World Cup final, 1974 (59×39 *mm*) .. 65 65
393 $1 Canadian team (59×39 *mm*) .. .. 80 1·00
394 $2 Northern Irish team (59×39 *mm*) .. 1·50 2·00
395 $3 English team (59×39 *mm*) .. .. 2·50 3·00
388/95 .. .. *Set of* 8 5·50 6·50
MS396 Two sheets, each 85×114 mm. (a) $1.50, As No. 393; (b) $2·50, As No. 394 *Set of* 2 *sheets* 3·50 5·00

(Litho Format)

1986 (18 July–15 Oct). *Royal Wedding* (1*st issue*). *Multicoloured designs as T* **118a** *of Montserrat. P* 12½.
397 60 c. Prince Andrew and Miss Sarah Ferguson 25 35
a. Pair. Nos. 397/8 .. .. .. 50 70
398 60 c. Prince Andrew with prizewinning bull 25 35
399 $1 Prince Andrew at horse trials (*horiz*) .. 30 65
a. Pair. Nos. 399/400 .. .. .. 60 1·25
400 $1 Miss Sarah Ferguson and Princess Diana (*horiz*) 30 65
397/400 .. .. *Set of* 4 1·00 1·75
MS401 85×115 mm. $6 Duke and Duchess of York after wedding (*horiz*) (15.10) .. .. 2·25 5·50

Nos. 397/8 and 399/400 were printed together, *se-tenant*, in horizontal and vertical pairs throughout the sheets.

Nos. 397/400 imperforate come from souvenir stamp booklets.

See also Nos. 433/6

57 Mourning Gecko (58)

(Des Jennifer Toombs. Litho Questa)

1986 (30 July). *Lizards. T* **57** *and similar horiz designs. Multicoloured. W* w **15**. *P* 14.
402 15 c. Type **57** 55 55
403 40 c. Oceanic Stump-toed Gecko .. .. 1·00 1·00
404 50 c. Azure-tailed Skink .. .. .. 1·25 1·50
405 60 c. Moth Skink .. .. 1·50 2·00
402/5 .. .. *Set of* 4 4·00 4·50

1986 (4 Aug). *"Stampex '86" Stamp Exhibition, Adelaide. No.* 386 *optd with T* **58**.
406 **54** 50 c. multicoloured 55 65

59 Map and Flag of Australia

(Des G. Drummond. Litho Format)

1986 (4 Aug). *15th Anniv of South Pacific Forum. T* **59** *and similar horiz designs showing maps and national flags. Multicoloured. W* w **15**. *P* 15.
407 40 c. Type **59** 55 60
a. Sheetlet. Nos. 407/20 .. .. 6·50
408 40 c. Cook Islands 55 60
409 40 c. Micronesia 55 60
410 40 c. Fiji 55 60
411 40 c. Kiribati 55 60
412 40 c. Western Samoa 55 60
413 40 c. Nauru 55 60
414 40 c. Vanuatu 55 60
415 40 c. New Zealand 55 60
416 40 c. Tuvalu 55 60
417 40 c. Tonga 55 60
418 40 c. Solomon Islands 55 60
419 40 c. Papua New Guinea 55 60
420 40 c. Niue 55 60
407/20 .. .. *Set of* 14 6·50 7·50

Nos. 407/20 were printed together, *se-tenant*, as a sheetlet of fourteen stamps arranged round a central label.

(Des Court House Studio. Litho Format)

1986 (13 Oct). *Automobiles* (4*th series*). *Horiz designs as T* **46**, *the first in each pair showing technical drawings and the second paintings. P* 12½.
421 15 c. multicoloured 15 15
a. Vert pair. Nos. 421/2 .. .. .. 30 30
422 15 c. multicoloured 15 15
423 40 c. multicoloured 20 25
a. Vert pair. Nos. 423/4 .. .. .. 40 50
424 40 c. multicoloured 20 25
425 50 c. multicoloured 25 30
a. Vert pair. Nos. 425/6 .. .. .. 50 60
426 50 c. multicoloured 25 30
427 60 c. multicoloured 30 35
a. Vert pair. Nos. 427/8 .. .. .. 60 70
428 60 c. multicoloured 30 35
429 90 c. multicoloured 30 40
a. Vert pair. Nos. 429/30 .. .. .. 60 80
430 90 c. multicoloured 30 40
431 $1.50, multicoloured 45 65
a. Vert pair. Nos. 431/2 .. .. .. 90 1·25
432 $1.50, multicoloured 45 65
421/32 .. .. *Set of* 12 3·00 3·75

Designs:—Nos. 421/2, Cooper "500" (1953); 423/4, Rover "2000" (1964); 425/6, Ruxton (1930); 427/8, Jowett "Jupiter" (1950); 429/30, Cobra "Daytona Coupe" (1964); 431/2, Packard Model F "Old Pacific" (1903).

Nos. 421/32 were issued in a similar sheet format to Nos. 293/300.

1986 (28 Oct). *Royal Wedding (2nd issue). Nos. 397/400 optd as T* **121** *of Montserrat in silver.*
433 60 c. Prince Andrew and Miss Sarah Ferguson .. .. 70 1·00
a. Pair. Nos. 433/4.. .. .. 1·40 2·00
434 60 c. Prince Andrew with prizewinning bull 70 1·00
435 $1 Prince Andrew at horse trials (*horiz*) .. 1·25 1·40
a. Pair. Nos. 435/6.. .. .. 2·50 2·75
436 $1 Miss Sarah Ferguson and Princess Diana (*horiz*) .. .. 1·25 1·40
433/6 .. .. *Set of* 4 3·50 4·25

60 Sea Star

61 *Nephrolepis saligna*

(Des G. Drummond. Litho Questa)

1986 (5 Nov). *Coral Reef Life (1st series). T* **60** *and similar horiz designs. Multicoloured. P* 14.
437 15 c. Type **60** 70 70
438 40 c. Pencil Urchin .. .. 1·40 1·75
439 50 c. Fragile Coral .. .. 1·60 1·90
440 60 c. Pink Coral .. .. 1·75 2·00
437/40 .. .. *Set of* 4 5·00 5·75
See also Nos. 498/501 and 558/62.

(Des Court House Studio. Litho Format)

1986 (24 Nov). *Centenary of Statue of Liberty. Vert views of Statue as T* **121***a of Montserrat in separate miniature sheets. Multicoloured. P* 14×13½.
MS441 Nine sheets, each 85×115 mm. $1.25; $1.50; $1.80; $2; $2.25; $2.50; $3; $3.25; $3.50 .. .. *Set of* 9 *sheets* 5·00 9·00

(Des R. Granger Barrett. Litho Questa)

1987 (4 Feb). *Ships (4th series). Missionary Steamers. Horiz designs as T* **26**. *Multicoloured. P* 14.
442 15 c. *Southern Cross IV* 75 75
443 40 c. *John Williams VI* .. .. 1·50 1·75
444 50 c. *John Williams IV* .. .. 1·75 2·00
445 60 c. *M.S. Southern Cross* .. .. .. 1·90 2·00
442/5 .. .. *Set of* 4 5·50 6·00

(Litho Format)

1987 (7 May–6 June). *Automobiles (5th series). Horiz designs as T* **46**, *the first in each pair showing technical drawings and the second paintings. P* 12½.
446 1 c. multicoloured 10 10
a. Vert pair. Nos. 446/7 .. .. 10 10
447 1 c. multicoloured 10 10
448 2 c. multicoloured 10 10
a. Vert pair. Nos. 448/9 .. .. 10 10
449 2 c. multicoloured 10 10
450 5 c. multicoloured 10 10
a. Vert pair. Nos. 450/1 .. .. 10 15
451 5 c. multicoloured 10 10
452 10 c. multicoloured 15 20
a. Vert pair. Nos. 452/3 .. .. 30 40
453 10 c. multicoloured 15 20
454 20 c. multicoloured 20 25
a. Vert pair. Nos. 454/5 .. .. 40 50
455 20 c. multicoloured 20 25
456 30 c. multicoloured 25 30
a. Vert pair. Nos. 456/7 .. .. 50 60
457 30 c. multicoloured 25 30
458 40 c. multicoloured 30 35
a. Vert pair. Nos. 458/9 .. .. 60 70
459 40 c. multicoloured 30 35
460 50 c. multicoloured 35 40
a. Vert pair. Nos. 460/1 .. .. 70 80
461 50 c. multicoloured 35 40
462 60 c. multicoloured 35 40
a. Vert pair. Nos. 462/3 .. .. 70 80
463 60 c. multicoloured 35 40
464 70 c. multicoloured 40 45
a. Vert pair. Nos. 464/5 .. .. 80 90
465 70 c. multicoloured 40 45
466 75 c. multicoloured 40 45
a. Vert pair. Nos. 466/7 .. .. 80 90
467 75 c. multicoloured 40 45
468 $1 multicoloured 55 70
a. Vert pair. Nos. 468/9 .. .. 1·10 1·40
469 $1 multicoloured 55 70
446/9 .. .. *Set of* 24 5·50 6·50
MS470 100×85 mm. Nos. 468/9 (6.6) .. .. 2·00 3·25
Designs:—Nos. 446/7, Talbot-Lago (1938); 448/9, Du Pont "Model G" (1930); 450/1, Riley "RM" (1950); 452/3, Chevrolet "Baby Grand" (1915); 454/5, Shelby "Mustang GT 500 KR" (1968); 456/7, Ferrari "212 Export Barchetta" (1952); 458/9, Peerless "Model 48-Six" (1912); 460/1, Sunbeam "Alpine" (1954); 462/3, Matra-Ford "MS 80" (1969); 464/5, Squire 1½ Litre (1934); 466/7, Talbot "105" (1931); 468/9, Plymouth "Model Q" (1928).
Nos. 446/69 were issued in a similar sheet format to Nos. 293/300.

(Des J. Cooter. Litho Questa)

1987 (7 July). *Ferns. T* **61** *and similar vert designs. Multicoloured. W w* **15** *(sideways). P* 14.
471 15 c. Type **61** 40 45
472 40 c. *Asplenium nidus* 70 80
473 50 c. *Microsorum scolopendria* .. .. .. 85 1·10
474 60 c. *Pteris tripartita* .. .. 95 1·25
471/4 .. .. *Set of* 4 2·50 3·25
MS475 62×62 mm. $1.50, *Psilotum nudum*. Wmk upright .. .. 2·25 3·50

62 Floral Arrangement

63 Queen Victoria, 1897 (photo by Downey)

(Des Jennifer Toombs. Litho Questa)

1987 (12 Aug). *Flowers and "Fous". T* **62** *and similar vert designs showing either floral arrangements or "fous" (women's headdresses). Multicoloured. W w* **15** *(sideways). P* 14.
476 15 c. Type **62** 25 25
a. Horiz pair. Nos. 476/7 .. .. 50 50
477 15 c. "Fou" 25 25
478 40 c. "Fou" 55 65
a. Horiz pair. Nos. 478/9 .. .. 1·10 1·25
479 40 c. Floral arrangement 55 65
480 50 c. Floral arrangement 65 80
a. Horiz pair. Nos. 480/1 .. .. 1·25 1·60
481 50 c. "Fou" 65 80
482 60 c. "Fou" 75 90
a. Horiz pair. Nos. 482/3 .. .. 1·50 1·75
483 60 c. Floral arrangement 75 90
476/83 .. .. *Set of* 8 4·00 4·75
The two designs of each value were printed together, *se-tenant*, in horizontal pairs throughout the sheets.

(Litho Format)

1987 (15 Oct). *Royal Ruby Wedding and 150th Anniv of Queen Victoria's Accession. T* **63** *and similar square designs. P* 15.
484 40 c. brownish black, black and deep olive .. 45 50
485 60 c. purple-black, black and deep blue-green 65 75
486 80 c. brownish black, black and deep dull blue 85 1·00
487 $1 brownish black, black and deep claret .. 1·10 1·25
488 $2 multicoloured .. .. 1·90 2·50
484/8 .. .. *Set of* 5 4·50 5·50
MS489 86×101 mm. $3 brownish black .. .. 2·25 3·50
Designs:—60 c. Wedding of Princess Elizabeth and Duke of Edinburgh, 1947; 80 c. Queen, Duke of Edinburgh and Prince Charles, *c.* 1950; $1 Queen with Princess Anne, 1950; $2 Queen Elizabeth II, 1970; $3 Queen and Prince Charles at Princess Anne's christening, 1950.

64 Coconut Crab

(Des M. Pollard. Litho Questa)

1987 (11 Nov). *Crustaceans. T* **64** *and similar diamond-shaped designs. Multicoloured. W w* **15**. *P* 14.
490 40 c. Type **64** .. .. 1·00 1·00
491 50 c. Painted Crayfish .. .. 1·25 1·25
492 60 c. Ocean Crayfish .. .. 1·40 1·75
490/2 .. .. *Set of* 3 3·25 3·50

65 Aborigine and Ayers Rock

(Des Young Philips. Litho Format)

1987 (2 Dec). *World Scout Jamboree, Australia, and Bicent of Australian Settlement. T* **65** *and similar horiz designs. Multicoloured. P* 12½.
493 40 c. Type **65** 30 45
494 60 c. Capt. Cook and H.M.S. *Endeavour* .. 90 1·00
495 $1 Scout saluting and Scout Park entrance 95 1·25
496 $1.50, Koala and kangaroo .. .. .. 1·00 1·50
493/6 .. .. *Set of* 4 2·75 3·75
MS497 115×85 mm. $2.50, Lord and Lady Baden-Powell .. .. 2·00 3·25

(Des G. Drummond. Litho Format)

1988 (29 Feb). *Coral Reef Life (2nd series). Horiz designs as T* **60**. *Multicoloured. P* 15.
498 15 c. Spanish Dancer (*Hexabranchus sanguineus*) 60 60
499 40 c. Hard corals .. .. 1·00 1·25
500 50 c. Feather Stars .. .. 1·00 1·50
501 60 c. Staghorn corals .. .. 1·00 1·50
498/501 .. .. *Set of* 4 3·25 4·25

66 Red Junglefowl

67 Henri Dunant (founder)

(Des Jennifer Toombs. Litho Format)

1988 (2 Mar). *Birds. T* **66** *and similar horiz designs. Multicoloured. P* 15.
502 5 c. Type **66** 15 15
503 10 c. White Tern 20 20
504 15 c. Common Noddy.. .. .. 30 20
505 20 c. Phoenix Petrel 40 40
506 25 c. American Golden Plover 45 45
507 30 c. Crested Tern 50 45
508 35 c. Sooty Tern 50 50
509 40 c. Bristle-thighed Curlew.. .. .. .. 60 40
510 45 c. Bar-tailed Godwit 65 45
511 50 c. Eastern Reef Heron 70 50
512 55 c. Great Frigate Bird 80 70
513 60 c. Red-footed Booby 85 75
514 70 c. Rufous-necked Sandpiper ("Red-necked Stint") .. .. 85 1·00
515 $1 Long-tailed Koel ("Long-tailed Cuckoo").. .. .. 85 1·50
516 $2 Red-tailed Tropic Bird .. .. 1·00 3·00
517 $5 Banded Rail .. .. 1·75 6·00
502/17 .. .. *Set of* 16 9·50 15·00

(Des M. Pollard. Litho Format)

1988 (9 May). *125th Anniv of International Red Cross. T* **67** *and similar horiz designs. P* 12½.
518 15 c. vermilion and pale reddish brown .. 10 15
519 40 c. vermilion and ultramarine 20 35
520 50 c. vermilion and turquoise-green 25 40
521 60 c. vermilion and purple 35 60
518/21 .. .. *Set of* 4 80 1·40
MS522 96 × 66 mm. $1.50, vermilion & emerald 1·25 2·25
Designs:—40 c. Junior Red Cross members on parade; 50 c. Red Cross worker with boy in wheelchair; 60 c. First aid training; $1.50, Lecture.

68 H.M.S. *Endeavour*

(Litho Format)

1988 (15 June). *Voyages of Captain Cook. T* **68** *and similar horiz designs. Multicoloured. P* 12½.
523 20 c. Type **68** 75 80
524 40 c. Stern of H.M.S. *Endeavour* .. .. 90 1·10
525 50 c. Cook preparing to land at Tahiti (*vert*) 1·00 1·25
526 60 c. Maori chief (*vert*) .. .. .. 1·00 1·40
527 80 c. H.M.S. *Resolution* and Hawaiian canoe 1·25 1·75
528 $1 "Captain Cook" (after Nathaniel Dance) (*vert*) .. .. 1·40 1·90
523/8 .. .. *Set of* 6 5·50 7·50
MS529 115 × 85 mm. $2.50, H.M.S. *Resolution* in Antarctica .. .. 6·00 8·00

69 *Ganoderma applanatum*

(Des J. Cooter. Litho Format)

1988 (25 July). *Fungi (1st series). T* **69** *and similar vert designs. Multicoloured. P* 15.
530 40 c. Type **69** .. .. 1·25 1·40
531 50 c. *Pseudoepicoccum cocos* (brown leaf spot) .. .. 1·40 1·50
532 60 c. *Rigidoporus lineatus* ("*Rigidoporus zonalis*") .. .. 1·60 1·75
533 90 c. *Rigidoporus microporus* .. .. .. 1·75 2·00
530/3 .. .. *Set of* 4 5·50 6·00
See also 554/7.

COVER PRICES

Cover factors are quoted at the beginning of each country for most issues to 1945. An explanation of the system can be found on page x. The factors quoted do not, however, apply to philatelic covers.

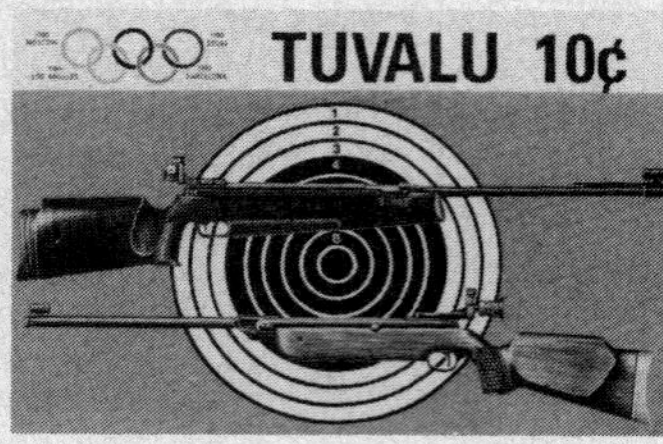

70 Rifle-shooting

(Litho Format)

1988 (19 Aug). *Olympic Games, Seoul. T* **70** *and similar horiz designs. Multicoloured. P* 12½.

534 10 c. Type **70** 25 35
535 20 c. Judo 35 45
536 40 c. Canoeing 60 65
537 60 c. Swimming 80 95
538 80 c. Yachting .. .. 1·00 1·40
539 $1 Gymnastics .. .. 1·25 1·60
534/9 .. .. *Set of* 6 3·75 4·75

71 Queen Elizabeth II in Ceremonial Canoe

72 Virgin Mary

(Des and litho Questa)

1988 (28 Sept). *10th Anniv of Independence. T* **71** *and similar designs showing scenes from Royal Visit of* 1982. *W w* **15** *(sideways on* 60, 90 *c.,* $1.20). *P* 14.

540 60 c. multicoloured 60 70
541 90 c. multicoloured .. .. 90 1·10
542 $1 multicoloured (*horiz*) .. .. 1·00 1·40
543 $1.20, multicoloured .. .. 1·25 1·75
540/3 .. .. *Set of* 4 3·50 4·50
MS544 Designs as Nos. 540/3 in separate miniature sheets, each 85 × 85 mm *Set of* 4 *sheets* 3·50 4·50

(Des M. Pollard. Litho Questa)

1988 (5 Dec). *Christmas. T* **72** *and similar diamond-shaped designs. Multicoloured. P* 14.

545 15 c. Type **72** 35 30
546 40 c. Christ Child 70 65
547 60 c. Joseph .. .. 90 1·40
545/7 .. .. *Set of* 3 1·75 2·10
MS548 73 × 99 mm. $1.50, Angel .. .. 1·40 2·25

73 Dancing Skirt and Dancer

(Des Jennifer Toombs. Litho Questa)

1989 (31 Mar). *Traditional Dancing Skirts. T* **73** *and similar designs showing skirts and dancer silhouettes. P* 14½.

549 40 c. multicoloured 70 90
550 50 c. multicoloured .. .. 80 1·00
551 60 c. multicoloured .. .. 90 1·25
552 90 c. multicoloured .. .. 1·40 1·75
549/52 .. .. *Set of* 4 3·50 4·50
MS553 110×75 mm. $1.50, multicoloured (dancer) (*vert*) .. .. 3·50 5·00

(Litho Questa)

1989 (24 May). *Fungi (2nd series). Vert designs as T* **69**. *Multicoloured. P* 14.

554 40 c. *Trametes marianna* ("*Trametes muelleri*") .. .. 1·75 1·75
555 50 c. *Pestalotiopsis palmarum* (grey leaf spot) .. .. 1·90 1·90
556 60 c. *Trametes cingulata* .. .. .. 2·00 2·00
557 90 c. *Schizophyllum commune* .. .. 2·75 2·75
554/7 .. .. *Set of* 4 7·50 7·50

(Des G. Drummond. Litho Questa)

1989 (31 July). *Coral Reef Life (3rd series). Horiz designs as T* **60**. *Multicoloured. P* 14.

558 40 c. Pennant Coralfish .. .. .. 1·50 1·50
559 50 c. Orange-finned Anemonefish .. .. 1·75 1·75
560 60 c. Narrow-banded Batfish .. .. .. 2·00 2·00
561 90 c. Thread-finned Butterflyfish .. .. 2·50 2·50
558/61 .. .. *Set of* 4 7·00 7·00
MS562 110×85 mm. Nos. 558/61 .. .. 8·00 9·00

74 *Nivaga II*

75 Trumpet Triton Shell

(Des M. Pollard. Litho Questa)

1989 (9 Oct). *Delivery of* Nivaga II *(new inter-island ship). Sheet* 116×85 *mm. P* 14.

MS563 **74** $1.50, multicoloured .. .. 3·75 4·50

(Des Jennifer Toombs. Litho Questa)

1989 (29 Nov). *Christmas. T* **75** *and similar vert designs. Multicoloured. P* 14.

564 40 c. Type **75** 75 75
565 50 c. Posy of flowers 90 90
566 60 c. Germinating coconut .. .. .. 1·10 1·10
567 90 c. Jewellery .. .. 2·00 2·40
564/7 .. .. *Set of* 4 4·25 4·75

76 *Cocus nucifera*

77 Penny Black with "Stamp World London 90" Emblem

(Des M. Pollard. Litho Questa)

1990 (28 Feb). *Tropical Trees. T* **76** *and similar vert designs. Multicoloured. P* 14½.

568 15 c. Type **76** 60 60
569 30 c. *Rhizophora samoensis* 90 90
570 40 c. *Messerschmidia argentea* .. .. 1·10 1·10
571 50 c. *Pandanus tectorius* .. .. .. 1·25 1·40
572 60 c. *Hernandia nymphaeifolia* .. .. 1·40 1·60
573 90 c. *Pisonia grandis* .. .. .. 1·90 2·25
568/73 .. .. *Set of* 6 6·50 7·00

(Des M. Pollard. Litho Questa)

1990 (3 May). *150th Anniv of the Penny Black, and "Stamp World London 90" International Stamp Exhibition. P* 14.

574 **77** 15 c. multicoloured .. .. 1·00 1·00
575 40 c. multicoloured .. .. 2·25 2·25
576 90 c. multicoloured .. .. 3·50 3·75
574/6 .. .. *Set of* 3 6·00 6·25
MS577 115×85 mm. **77** $2 multicoloured .. 5·00 6·00

78 Japanese Camouflaged Freighter

79 *Erythrina fusca*

(Litho Questa)

1990 (25 July). *Second World War Ships* (1*st series*). *T* **78** *and similar horiz designs. Multicoloured. P* 14.

578 15 c. Type **78** 75 75
579 30 c. U.S.S *Unimack* (seaplane tender) .. 1·25 1·25
580 40 c. *Amagiri* (Japanese destroyer) .. 1·40 1·40
581 50 c. U.S.S *Platte* (attack transport) .. 1·50 1·50
582 60 c. Japanese "Shumushu" Class escort .. 1·60 1·60
583 90 c. U.S.S *Independence* (aircraft carrier) 2·25 2·25
578/83 .. .. *Set of* 6 8·00 8·00

See also Nos. 613/16.

(Des Jennifer Toombs. Litho Questa)

1990 (21 Sept). *Flowers. T* **79** *and similar vert designs. Multicoloured. P* 14½×14.

584 15 c. Type **79** 30 30
585 30 c. *Capparis cordifolia* 50 50
586 40 c. *Portulaca pilosa* 60 60
587 50 c. *Cordia subcordata* 75 85
588 60 c. *Scaevola taccada* .. .. .. 80 1·00
589 90 c. *Suriana maritima* .. .. .. 1·25 1·75
584/9 .. .. *Set of* 6 3·75 4·50

80 Land Resources Survey

81 Mary and Joseph travelling to Bethlehem

(Litho Questa)

1990 (20 Nov). *40th Anniv of United Nations Development Programme. T* **80** *and similar horiz designs. P* 14.

590 40 c. Type **80** 80 80
591 60 c. Satellite earth station .. .. .. 1·50 1·50
592 $1.20, *Te Tautai* (trawler) .. .. 3·25 3·50
590/2 .. .. *Set of* 3 5·00 5·25

(Des M. Pollard. Litho Questa)

1990 (20 Nov). *Christmas. T* **81** *and similar square designs. Multicoloured. P* 14.

593 15 c. Type **81** 55 55
594 40 c. The Nativity .. .. 1·00 1·00
595 60 c. Shepherds with flock .. .. .. 1·50 1·50
596 90 c. Wise Men bearing gifts .. .. .. 2·00 2·00
593/6 .. .. *Set of* 4 4·50 4·50

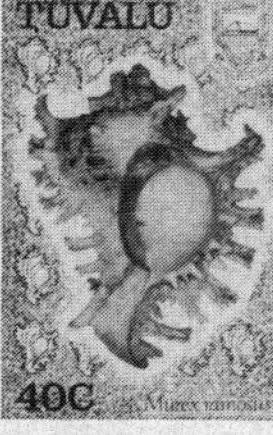

82 Ramose Murex (*Murex ramosus*)

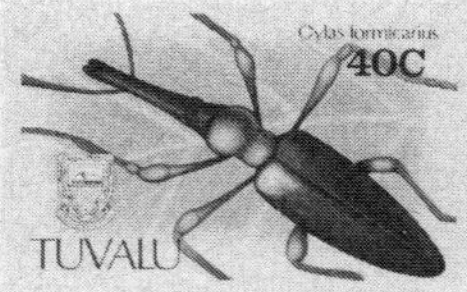

83 *Cylas formicarius* (beetle)

(Des D. Miller. Litho Questa)

1991 (18 Jan). *Sea Shells. T* **82** *and similar vert designs. Multicoloured. P* 14.

597 40 c. Type **82** .. .. 1·25 1·25
598 50 c. Marble Cone (*Conus marmoreus marmoreus*) .. .. 1·40 1·40
599 60 c. Commercial Trochus (*Trochus niloticus*) .. .. 1·60 1·60
600 $1.50, Green Map Cowrie (*Cypraea mappa viridis*) .. .. 3·25 3·75
597/600 .. .. *Set of* 4 6·75 7·25

(Des D. Miller. Litho Questa)

1991 (22 Mar). *Insects. T* **83** *and similar horiz designs. Multicoloured. P* 14.

601 40 c. Type **83** .. .. 1·60 1·40
602 50 c. *Heliothis armiger* (moth) .. .. 1·75 1·50
603 60 c. *Spodoptera litura* (moth) .. .. 2·00 2·00
604 $1.50, *Agrius convolvuli* (moth) .. .. 4·75 6·00
601/4 .. .. *Set of* 4 9·00 9·75

84 Green Turtle

85 Football

(Des D. Miller. Litho Questa)

1991 (31 May). *Endangered Marine Life. T* **84** *and similar vert designs. Multicoloured. P* 14.

605 40 c. Type **84** 90 80
606 50 c. Humpback Whale .. .. 1·25 1·00
607 60 c. Hawksbill Turtle .. .. 1·25 1·40
608 $1.50, Sperm Whale .. .. 3·00 4·00
605/8 .. .. *Set of* 4 5·75 6·50

(Des D. Miller. Litho Questa)

1991 (31 July). *9th South Pacific Games. T* **85** *and similar vert designs. Multicoloured. P* 14.

609 40 c. Type **85** .. .. 1·00 1·00
610 50 c. Volleyball .. .. 1·60 1·60
611 60 c. Lawn tennis .. .. 2·25 2·25
612 $1.50, Cricket .. .. 4·50 4·50
609/12 .. .. *Set of* 4 8·50 8·50

NEW INFORMATION

The editor is always interested to correspond with people who have new information that will improve or correct the Catalogue.

86 U.S.S. *Tennessee* (battleship)

87 Traditional Dancers

(Des D. Miller. Litho Questa)

1991 (15 Oct). *Second World War Ships (2nd series). T* **86** *and similar horiz designs. Multicoloured. P* 14.

613 40 c. Type **86** . . . . 1·75 1·50
614 50 c. *Haguro* (Japanese cruiser) . . . . 2·00 1·75
615 60 c. H.M.N.Z.S. *Achilles* (cruiser) . . . . 2·25 2·25
616 $1.50, U.S.S. *North Carolina* (battleship) 4·50 5·00
613/16 . . . . *Set of* 4 9·50 9·50

(Des. D. Miller. Litho Questa)

1991 (13 Dec). *Christmas. T* **87** *and similar vert designs. Multicoloured. P* 14.

617 40 c. Type **87** . . . . 1·40 1·25
618 50 c. Solo dancer . . . . 1·60 1·50
619 60 c. Dancers in green costumes . . . . 2·00 1·75
620 $1.50, Dancers in multicoloured costumes 4·00 5·00
617/20 . . . . *Set of* 4 8·00 8·50

88 Southern Fish Constellation

89 King George VI and Cargo Liner

(Des D. Miller. Litho Questa)

1992 (29 Jan). *Pacific Star Constellations. T* **88** *and similar vert designs. Multicoloured. P* 14.

621 40 c. Type **88** . . . . 1·60 1·50
622 50 c. Scorpion . . . . 1·90 1·75
623 60 c. Archer . . . . 2·25 2·25
624 $1.50, Southern Cross . . . . . . 4·75 5·50
621/4 . . . . *Set of* 4 9·50 10·00

(Des D. Miller. Litho Questa)

1992 (23 Mar). *Centenary of British Occupation of Tuvalu. T* **89** *and similar horiz designs. P* 14.

625 40 c. Type **89** . . . . 1·50 1·25
626 50 c. King George V and freighter with barges at wharf . . . . . . 1·75 1·40
627 60 c. King Edward VII and freighter . . 2·00 1·75
628 $1.50, Queen Victoria and warship . . 3·75 4·50
625/8 . . . . *Set of* 4 8·00 8·00

It is probable that the ship shown on No. 628 is intended to be H.M.S. *Royalist* (corvette) launched 1883, but the vessel depicted appears to be H.M.S. *Royalist* (cruiser) launched 1915.

90 Columbus with King Ferdinand and Queen Isabella of Spain

(Des D. Miller. Litho Questa)

1992 (22 May). 500*th Anniv of Discovery of America by Columbus. T* **90** *and similar horiz designs. P* 14.

629 40 c. deep new blue and black 70 70
630 50 c. brown-purple and black 80 80
631 60 c. myrtle-green and black . . . . 90 1·00
632 $1.50, deep purple and black . . . . 2·25 3·00
629/32 . . . . *Set of* 4 4·25 5·00

Designs:—50 c. Columbus and Polynesians; 60 c. Columbus and South American Indians; $1.50, Columbus and North American Indians.

OMNIBUS ISSUES

Details, together with prices for complete sets, of the various Omnibus issues from the 1935 Silver Jubilee series to date are included in a special section following Zimbabwe at the end of Volume 2.

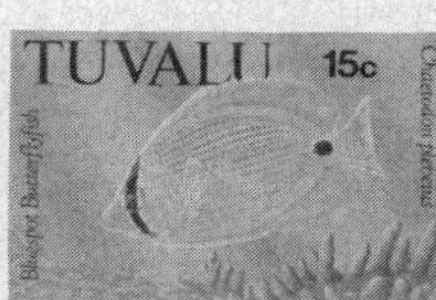

91 Blue-spotted Butterflyfish

92 Discus Throwing

(Des D. Miller. Litho Questa)

1992 (15 July). *Fishes. T* **91** *and similar multicoloured designs. P* 14.

633 15 c. Type **91** 30 20
634 20 c. Bridled Parrotfish 35 25
635 25 c. Clown Surgeonfish 35 30
636 30 c. Moon Wrasse 40 35
637 35 c. Harlequin Filefish 45 40
638 40 c. Bird Wrasse 50 45
639 45 c. Black-finned Pigfish 55 50
640 50 c. Blue Damselfish 60 55
641 60 c. Hump-headed Wrasse 70 70
642 70 c. Ornate Butterflyfish (*vert*) 80 85
643 90 c. Saddle Butterflyfish (*vert*) . . . . 1·00 1·10
644 $1 Vagabond Butterflyfish (*vert*) . . . . 1·10 1·25
645 $2 Pennant Coralfish (*vert*) . . . . 2·00 2·40
646 $3 Moorish Idol (*vert*) . . . . . . 3·00 3·50
633/46 . . . . *Set of* 14 11·00 11·50

(Des D. Miller. Litho Questa)

1992 (27 July). *Olympic Games, Barcelona. T* **92** *and similar vert designs. Multicoloured. P* 14.

647 40 c. Type **92** 90 80
648 50 c. Javelin throwing . . . . . . 1·00 90
649 60 c. Shotput . . . . 1·25 1·25
650 $1.50, Competitor's foot . . . . . . 2·75 3·50
647/50 . . . . *Set of* 4 5·50 5·75
MS651 100×71 mm. $2 Olympic stadium, Barcelona . . . . 3·00 4·00

93 Blue Coral

(94)

(Des G. Drummond. Litho Questa)

1992 (1 Sept). *Endangered Species. Blue Coral. T* **93** *and similar horiz designs showing different coral formations. P* 14.

652 10 c. multicoloured 75 75
653 25 c. multicoloured . . . . 1·60 1·60
654 30 c. multicoloured . . . . 1·75 1·75
655 35 c. multicoloured . . . . 1·90 1·90
652/5 . . . . *Set of* 4 5·50 5·50

1992 (1 Sept). *"Kuala Lumpur '92" International Philatelic Exhibition. Nos.* 636, 638 *and* 640/1 *optd with T* **94**.

656 30 c. Moon Wrasse . . . . 1·25 1·25
657 40 c. Bird Wrasse . . . . 1·40 1·40
658 50 c. Blue Damselfish . . . . . . 1·50 1·50
659 60 c. Hump-headed Wrasse . . . . . . 1·60 1·60
656/9 . . . . *Set of* 4 5·25 5·25

95 Fishermen and Angel

96 *Calophyllum inophyllum*

(Des D. Miller. Litho Questa)

1992 (25 Dec). *Christmas. T* **95** *and similar vert designs. Multicoloured. P* 14.

660 40 c. Type **95** 70 60
661 50 c. Fishing canoes following star 80 70
662 60 c. Nativity scene 90 90
663 $1.50, Christmas gifts . . . . . . 1·75 2·50
660/3 . . . . *Set of* 4 3·75 4·25

(Des D. Miller. Litho Questa)

1993 (2 Feb). *Flowers. T* **96** *and similar vert designs. Multicoloured. P* 14.

664 40 c. Type **96** 80 70
665 50 c. *Hibiscus tiliaceus* 95 90
666 60 c. *Lantana camara* . . . . . . 1·10 1·10
667 $1.50, *Plumeria rubra* . . . . . . 2·50 3·25
664/7 . . . . *Set of* 4 4·75 5·50

97 Japanese Nakajima B5N "Kate" Bombers attacking Island

98 *Cepora perimale*

(Des D. Miller. Litho Questa)

1993 (23 Apr). 50*th Anniv of War in the Pacific. T* **97** *and similar multicoloured designs. P* 14.

668 40 c. Type **97** . . . . 1·25 1·00
669 50 c. Japanese anti-aircraft gun (*vert*) . . 1·40 1·25
670 60 c. American troops storming beach . . 1·50 1·50
671 $1.50, Map of Funafuti Atoll (*vert*) . . 3·25 4·00
668/71 . . . . *Set of* 4 6·75 7·00

(Des Patricia Altman. Litho and die-stamped Southern Colour Print, Dunedin)

1993 (29 May). *"Indopex '93" International Stamp Exhibition", Surabaya, Indonesia. Sheet* 81×111 *mm. P* 14.

MS672 **98** $1.50 multicoloured . . . . . . 3·25 3·75

See also Nos. **MS**682, **MS**683 and **MS**693.

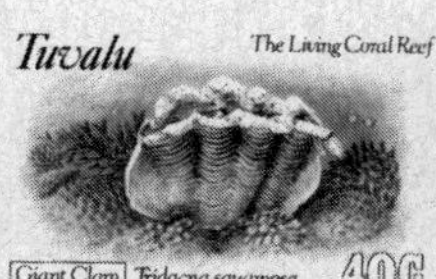

99 Fluted Giant Clam (*Tridacna squamosa*)

100 Queen Elizabeth II and Prince Philip in Land Rover

(Des D. Miller. Litho Questa)

1993 (29 June). *Marine Life. T* **99** *and similar horiz designs. Multicoloured. P* 14.

673 40 c. Type **99** 75 75
674 50 c. Anemone Crab 85 85
675 60 c. Octopus 95 95
676 $1.50, Green Turtle . . . . . . 2·25 2·75
673/6 . . . . *Set of* 4 4·25 4·75

(Litho Questa)

1993 (5 July). 40*th Anniv of Coronation. T* **100** *and similar horiz designs. P* 14.

677 40 c. multicoloured 85 75
678 50 c. multicoloured 95 90
679 60 c. multicoloured . . . . 1·10 1·10
680 $1.50, multicoloured . . . . . . 2·50 3·00
677/80 . . . . *Set of* 4 4·75 5·25
MS681 88×88 mm. $2 blackish olive, pale lemon and black . . . . 4·50 5·00

Designs:—50 c. Queen Elizabeth drinking kava; 60 c. Queen Elizabeth with parasol; $1.50, Ceremonial welcome; $2 Crowning of Queen Elizabth II, 1953.

(Des Patricia Altman. Litho and die-stamped Southern Colour Print, Dunedin)

1993 (14 Aug). *"Taipei '93" International Stamp Exhibition, Taiwan. Sheet* 85×85 *mm containing multicoloured design as T* **98**. *P* 14½×14.

MS682 $1.50, *Geoffroyi godart* (*vert*) . . . . 3·00 4·00

(Des Patricia Altman. Litho and die-stamped Southern Colour Print, Dunedin)

1993 (1 Oct). *"Bangkok 1993" International Stamp Exhibition, Thailand. Sheet* 86×86 *mm containing horiz design as T* **98**. *P* 14.

MS683 $1.50, *Paradisea staudinger* . . . . 2·00 3·00

101 Hermit Crab and Shells on Beach

102 Virgin and Child with Christmas Tree

(Des Patricia Altman. Litho Southern Colour Print, Dunedin)

1993 (2 Nov). *Environmental Protection. T* **101** *and similar vert designs. Multicoloured. P* 13½.

684 40 c. Type **101** 75 65
685 50 c. Conch shell and starfish 85 80
686 60 c. Crab, seaweed and shells 95 95
687 $1.50, Herring Gull and human footprint on beach . . . . 2·25 3·00
684/7 . . . . *Set of* 4 4·25 4·75
MS688 126×80 mm. Nos. 684/7. P 14½×14 . . 5·00 6·00

(Des Patricia Altman. Litho Southern Colour Print, Dunedin)

1993 (3 Dec). *Christmas. T* **102** *and similar vert designs. Multicoloured. P* 13½.

689	40 c. Type **102**	80	70
690	50 c. Candle	90	80
691	60 c. Angel	1·00	1·00
692	$1.50, Decorated palm tree	2·25	3·00
689/92	*Set of* 4	4·50	5·00

(Des Patricia Altman. Litho Southern Colour Print, Dunedin)

1994 (18 Feb). *"Hong Kong '94" International Stamp Exhibition. Sheet* 85×85 *mm containing multicoloured design as T* **98**. *P* 14½×14.

MS693	$2 *Danaus plexippus* (*vert*)	4·00	4·50

103 Beach **104** Irish Red Setter

(Des D. Miller. Litho Questa)

1994 (18 Feb). *Island Scenery. T* **103** *and similar horiz designs. Multicoloured. P* 14.

694	40 c. Type **103**	80	70
695	50 c. Lagoon	90	80
696	60 c. Distant island	1·00	1·00
697	$1.50, Launch and outrigger canoes on beach	2·25	3·00
694/7	*Set of* 4	4·50	5·00

(Des D. Miller. Litho Questa)

1994 (23 Apr). *Chinese New Year ("Year of the Dog"). T* **104** *and similar vert designs. Multicoloured. P* 14.

698	40 c. Type **104**	80	80
699	50 c. Golden Retriever	90	90
700	60 c. West Highland Terrier	1·00	1·00
701	$1.50, German Shepherd	2·50	3·25
698/701	*Set of* 4	4·75	5·50

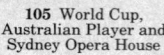

105 World Cup, Australian Player and Sydney Opera House

106 Giant Button Top (*Umbonium giganteum*)

(Des D. Miller. Litho Questa)

1994 (7 June). *World Cup Football Championship, U.S.A. T* **105** *and similar vert designs. Multicoloured. P* 14.

702	40 c. Type **105**	50	50
703	50 c. English player and Big Ben, London	60	60
704	60 c. Argentinian player and House of Assembly, Buenos Aires	70	75
705	$1.50, German player and Brandenburg Gate, Berlin	2·00	2·50
702/5	*Set of* 4	3·50	4·00
MS706	105×99 mm. $2 American player and Statue of Liberty, New York	4·00	4·50

(Des D. Miller. Litho Questa

1994 (16 Aug). *Sea Snails. T* **106** *and similar vert designs. Multicoloured. P* 14.

707	40 c. Type **106**	80	65
708	50 c. Tapestry Turban (*Turbo petholatus*)	90	75
709	60 c. *Planaxis savignyi*	1·00	1·00
710	$1.50, Green-lined Paper Bubble (*Hydatina physis*)	2·50	3·25
707/10	*Set of* 4	4·75	5·00

107 Pekingese and Logo **(108)**

(Des D. Miller. Litho Questa)

1994 (16 Aug). *"Philakorea '94" International Stamp Exhibition, Seoul. Sheet* 106×72 *mm. P* 14.

MS711	**107** $1.50, multicoloured	2·75	3·50

1994 (31 Aug). *"Singpex '94" Stamp Exhibition, Singapore. Nos.* 502/3 *and* 509/10 *optd with T* **108**.

712	5 c. Type **66**	20	25
713	10 c. White Tern	20	25
714	40 c. Bristle-thighed Curlew	50	55
715	45 c. Bar-tailed Godwit	60	65
712/15	*Set of* 4	1·40	1·50

109 "Saturn V" Launch **110** Boys swimming with Log

(Des D. Miller. Litho Questa)

1994 (21 Oct). *25th Anniv of First Moon Landing. T* **109** *and similar vert designs. Multicoloured. P* 14.

716	40 c. Type **109**	75	75
	a. Horiz strip of 4. Nos. 716/19	4·25	
717	50 c. "Apollo 11" capsule	85	85
718	60 c. Neil Armstrong and American flag	1·00	1·00
719	$1.50, Capsule re-entry	2·00	2·00
716/19	*Set of* 4	4·25	4·25

Nos. 716/19 were printed together, *se-tenant*, in horizontal strips of 4 throughout the sheet of 16.

(Des D. Miller. Litho Questa)

1994 (15 Dec). *Christmas. Local Customs. T* **110** *and similar horiz designs. Multicoloured. P* 14.

720	40 c. Type **110**	75	60
721	50 c. Fishermen landing catch	85	75
722	60 c. Christmas dinner	95	95
723	$1.50, Traditional dancers	2·00	2·50
720/3	*Set of* 4	4·00	4·25

111 Pig asleep

(Des D. Miller. Litho Questa)

1995 (30 Jan). *Chinese New Year ("Year of the Pig"). T* **111** *and similar horiz designs. Multicoloured. P* 14.

724	40 c. Type **111**	65	60
725	50 c. Two pigs and vegetation	75	70
726	60 c. Three pigs	85	85
727	$1.50, Sow suckling piglets	1·75	2·25
724/7	*Set of* 4	3·50	4·00

112 Emblem and Man with Produce in Wheelbarrow

(Litho Questa)

1995 (31 Mar). *50th Anniv of Food and Agriculture Organization. T* **112** *and similar horiz designs. Multicoloured. P* 14.

728	40 c. Type **112**	70	60
729	50 c. Man holding basket of food	80	70
730	60 c. Woman slicing produce	90	90
731	$1.50, Woman mixing food	2·00	2·50
728/31	*Set of* 4	4·00	4·25

113 Beach and Lagoon

(Litho Questa)

1995 (26 May). *Visit South Pacific Year. T* **113** *and similar horiz designs. Multicoloured. P* 14.

732	40 c. Type **113**	70	60
733	50 c. Catamaran	80	70
734	60 c. Traditional hut	90	90
735	$1.50, Village on beach	2·00	2·50
732/5	*Set of* 4	4·00	4·25

114 *Dendrobium comptonii*

(Des Sue Wickison. Litho Questa)

1995 (28 July). *Pacific Coastal Orchids. T* **114** *and similar horiz designs. Multicoloured. P* 14.

736	40 c. Type **114**	80	70
737	50 c. *Dendrobium involutum*	90	80
738	60 c. *Dendrobium rarum*	1·00	1·00
739	$1.50, *Grammatophyllum scriptum*	2·25	2·75
736/9	*Set of* 4	4·50	4·75

115 Japanese Soldier and Maps of Tuvalu and Japan **116** Tuvalu Dancer

(Des D. Miller. Litho Questa)

1995 (19 Aug). *50th Anniv of End of Second World War. T* **115** *and similar horiz designs. Multicoloured. P* 14.

740	40 c. Type **115**	90	80
741	50 c. American soldier and beach landing	1·00	90
742	60 c. American marine and tree	1·25	1·25
743	$1.50, American soldier and atomic explosion	2·50	2·75
740/3	*Set of* 4	5·00	5·25

(Litho and die-stamped Southern Colour Print, Dunedin)

1995 (19 Aug). *"JAKARTA '95" Stamp Exhibition, Indonesia. Sheet* 85×85 *mm. P* 12.

MS744	**116** $1 multicoloured	1·75	2·00

117 *Phalaenopsis amabillis* **118** Tuvaluans in Outrigger Canoes

(Litho and die-stamped Southern Colour Print, Dunedin)

1995 (1 Sept). *"Singapore '95" International Stamp Exhibition. Sheet* 85×85 *mm. P* 12.

MS745	**117** $1 multicoloured	1·75	2·00

(Des D. Miller. Litho Questa)

1995 (24 Oct). *50th Anniv of United Nations. Sheet* 83×70 *mm, containing T* **118** *and similar vert design. Multicoloured. P* 15×14½.

MS746	$1 Type **118**; $1 U.N. headquarters, New York	2·50	3·25

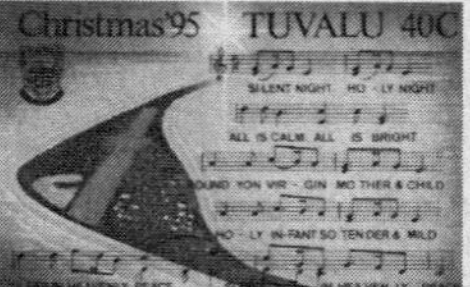

119 "Silent Night" and Aerial View of Airfield

(Des D. Miller. Litho Questa)

1995 (15 Dec). *Christmas. T* **119** *and similar horiz designs showing Christmas carols. Multicoloured. P* 14.

747 40 c. Type **119** 70 60
748 50 c. "O Come all ye Faithful" and choir boys 85 75
749 60 c. "The First Nowell" and choir girls .. 1·00 1·00
750 $1.50, "Hark the Herald Angels sing" and angel .. .. 2·50 3·00
747/50 .. .. *Set of* 4 4·50 4·75

120 1976 Separation 4 c. Stamp

121 Rat with Jar

(Des D. Miller. Litho Questa)

1996 (1 Jan). *20th Anniv of Separation from Gilbert Islands and of First Tuvalu Postage Stamps. Sheet* 108×82 *mm, containing T* **120** *and similar horiz designs showing values from* 1976 *Separation issue. P* 14.

MS751 40 c. Type **120**; 60 c. 1976 10 c. stamp; $1 1976 35 c. stamp .. .. 3·25 3·75

(Des Sophie Zhang. Litho Questa)

1996 (23 Feb). *Chinese New Year ("Year of the Rat"). Sheet* 130×87 *mm containing T* **121** *and similar vert design. Multicoloured. P* 14×14½.

MS752 50 c. Type **121**; 50 c. Rat drinking from jar .. .. 1·40 1·60

1996 (23 Feb). *"HONGPEX '96" International Stamp Exhibition. Sheet as No.* **MS**752, *but additionally inscr with* "HONGPEX '96" *emblem on sheet margin. P* 14×14½.

MS753 50 c. Type **121**; 50 c. Rat drinking from jar .. .. 1·40 1·60

(**122**) **123** Volleyball

1996 (21 Mar). *"indonesia 96" International Youth Stamp Exhibition, Bandung. No.* **MS**744 *optd with T* **122** *in gold.*

MS754 85×85 mm. **116** $1 multicoloured .. 1·25 1·50

A further overprint as Type **122** appears on the sheet margin.

1996 (18 May). *"CHINA '96" 9th Asian International Stamp Exhibition, Peking. Sheet as No.* **MS**752, *but additionally inscr with* "CHINA '96" *emblem and puppet holding envelope on sheet margin. P* 14×14½.

MS755 50 c. Type **121**; 50 c. Rat drinking from jar .. .. 1·40 1·60

(Des D. Miller. Litho Questa)

1996 (11 Sept). *Olympic Games, Atlanta. T* **123** *and similar horiz designs. Multicoloured. P* 14.

756 40 c. Type **123** 50 45
757 50 c. Swimming 60 55
758 60 c. Weightlifting 70 70
759 $1.50, Boxing .. .. 1·75 2·00
756/9 .. .. *Set of* 4 3·25 3·25

(**124**)

1996 (21 Oct). *"TAIPEI 96" 10th Asian International Stamp Exhibition, Taiwan. No.* 639 *surch with T* **124**.

760 $1 on 45 c. Black-finned Pigfish .. .. 1·25 1·40

MINIMUM PRICE

The minimum price quote is 10p which represents a handling charge rather than a basis for valuing common stamps. For further notes about prices see introductory pages.

125 Children being Immunised

126 Wise Men following Star

(Des D. Miller. Litho Questa)

1996 (28 Oct). *50th Anniv of U.N.I.C.E.F. T* **125** *and similar horiz designs. Multicoloured. P* 14.

761 40 c. Type **125** 55 45
762 50 c. Teacher and children 65 55
763 60 c. Domestic water tanks and child .. 75 75
764 $1.50, Children in hydroponic greenhouse 1·90 2·25
761/4 .. .. *Set of* 4 3·50 3·50

(Litho Walsall)

1996 (25 Nov). *Christmas. T* **126** *and similar vert designs. Multicoloured. P* 14½.

765 40 c. Type **126** 55 45
766 50 c. Shepherds and star 65 55
767 60 c. Wise men presenting gifts 75 75
768 $1.50, The Nativity .. .. .. 1·90 2·25
765/8 .. .. *Set of* 4 3·50 3·50

127 Ox ploughing

128 White Pekin Ducks

(Des Colleen Corlett. Litho Walsall)

1997 (12 Feb). *"HONG KONG '97" International Stamp Exhibition. Chinese New Year ("Year of the Ox"). Sheet* 97×83 *mm. P* 14.

MS769 **127** $2 multicoloured .. .. .. 2·40 2·50

(Des G. Drummond. Litho Questa)

1997 (15 Mar). *Fishes (2nd series). Horiz designs as T* **14**. *Multicoloured. P* 14.

770 25 c. Sehel's Grey Mullet 25 30
771 30 c. Leatherback 25 30
772 40 c. Hump-backed Snapper ("Paddletail") 35 40
773 45 c. Long-nosed Emperor 40 45
774 50 c. Blue-spined Unicornfish 45 50
775 55 c. Oblique-banded Snapper 50 55
776 60 c. Twin-spotted Snapper ("Red Bass") .. 50 55
777 70 c. Rusty Jobfish 60 65
778 90 c. Leopard Flounder 80 85
779 $1 Ruby Snapper 90 95
780 $2 Yellow-striped Snapper .. .. 1·75 1·90
781 $3 Black Jack .. .. 2·50 2·75
770/81 .. .. *Set of* 12 9·25 10·00

(Des Colleen Corlett. Litho Walsall)

1997 (29 May). *"Pacific '97" International Stamp Exhibition, San Francisco. Ducks. T* **128** *and similar horiz designs. Multicoloured. P* 14½.

782 40 c. Type **128** 55 45
783 50 c. Muscovy Ducks 65 55
784 60 c. Pacific Black Ducks 75 75
785 $1.50, Mandarin Ducks .. .. .. 1·75 2·00
782/5 .. .. *Set of* 4 3·25 3·25

129 Korat King Cat

(Des Colleen Corlett. Litho Walsall)

1997 (20 June). *Cats. T* **129** *and similar horiz designs. Multicoloured. P* 14½.

786 40 c. Type **129** 55 45
787 50 c. Long-haired ginger kitten 65 55
788 60 c. Shaded Cameo 75 75
789 $1.50, Maine Coon .. .. 1·75 2·00
786/9 .. .. *Set of* 4 3·25 3·25

(Litho Walsall)

1997 (20 June). *Return of Hong Kong to China. Sheet,* 130×90 *mm, containing design as No.* 780, *but with imprint date. W w* **14** *(sideways). P* 14.

MS790 $2 Yellow-striped Snapper .. .. 2·40 2·50

(Des N. Shewring (No. **MS**797), D. Miller (others). Litho Questa (No. **MS**797) or Walsall (others))

1997 (1 Oct). *Golden Wedding of Queen Elizabeth and Prince Philip. Multicoloured designs as T* **87** *of Kiribati. W w* **14**. *P* 14½.

791 40 c. Queen Elizabeth and Prince Philip in Land Rover 35 40
a. Horiz pair. Nos. 791/2 .. .. 70 80
792 40 c. Queen Elizabeth 35 40
793 50 c. Queen Elizabeth accepting ceremonial gift 45 50
a. Horiz pair. Nos. 793/4 .. .. 90 1·00
794 50 c. Prince Philip 45 50
795 60 c. Three portraits of Queen Elizabeth .. 50 55
a. Horiz pair. Nos. 795/6 .. .. 1·00 1·10
796 60 c. Queen Elizabeth and Prince Philip leaving Philatelic Bureau 50 55
791/6 .. .. *Set of* 6 2·50 2·75

MS797 110×70 mm. $2 Queen Elizabeth and Prince Philip in landau (*horiz*). Wmk sideways. P 14×14½ .. .. 1·75 1·90

Nos. 791/2, 793/4 and 795/6 were each printed together, *se-tenant*, in horizontal pairs throughout the sheets with the backgrounds forming composite designs.

130 Turtle Hunting

(Des O. Bell. Litho Cartor)

1997 (25 Nov). *Christmas. T* **130** *and similar horiz designs. Multicoloured. W w* **14** *(sideways). P* 13½×13.

798 40 c. Type **130** 35 40
799 50 c. Pole fishing 45 50
800 60 c. Canoe racing 50 55
801 $1.50, Traditional dancing .. .. .. 1·25 1·40
798/801 .. .. *Set of* 4 2·50 2·75

131 Tiger

(Des V. Ambrus. Litho Cartor)

1998 (2 Feb). *Chinese New Year ("Year of the Tiger"). Sheet* 110×69 *mm. W w* **14** *(sideways). P* 13.

MS802 **131** $1.40, multicoloured .. .. 1·25 1·40

(Des D. Miller. Litho Questa)

1998 (31 Mar). *Diana, Princess of Wales Commemoration. Sheet,* 145×70 *mm, containing vert designs as T* **91** *of Kiribati. Multicoloured. W w* **14** *(sideways). P* 14½×14.

MS803 80 c. Wearing pearl drop earrings, 1990; 80 c. Wearing black evening dress, 1995; 80 c. Wearing tiara, 1992; 80 c. Wearing beige coat (*sold at* $3.20 + 20 c. *charity premium*) .. 3·00 3·25

(Des A. Theobald. Litho Cartor)

1998 (1 Apr). *80th Anniv of the Royal Air Force. Horiz designs as T* **270** *of Samoa. Multicoloured. W w* **14** *(sideways). P* 13½.

804 40 c. Hawker Woodcock 35 40
805 50 c. Vickers Victoria 45 50
806 60 c. Bristol Brigand 50 55
807 $1.50, De Havilland D.H.C.1 Chipmunk 1·25 1·40
804/7 .. .. *Set of* 4 2·50 2·75

MS808 110×77 mm. $1 Sopwith Pup; $1 Armstrong Whitworth F.K.8; $1 North American Harvard; $1 Vultee Vengeance .. 3·50 3·75

STAMP BOOKLETS

1978 (20 July). *25th Anniv of Coronation. Multicoloured cover, 85×52 mm, showing Coronation ceremony on front and Westminster Abbey on reverse. Stapled.*

SB1	$3.56, booklet containing 8 c., 30 c., 40 c. and $1 (Nos. 89/92), each in pair	1·00

1980 (20 Feb). *Brown and blue-green cover, 100×60 mm, showing Lionfish. Stapled.*

SB2	$3.92, booklet containing 8 c., 20 c., 30 c. and 40 c. (Nos. 110, 113, 115, 117), each in block of 4	2·00

1981 (16 June). *Violet on blue cover, 100×63 mm, showing stylized shark. Stapled.*

SB3	$4.60, booklet containing 10 c., 25 c., 35 c. and 45 c. (Nos. 111, 114, 116, 117*b*), each in block of 4	6·50

1981 (26 Nov). *Royal Wedding. Multicoloured cover, 105×65 mm, showing* The Carolina. *Stitched.*

SB4	$1.70, booklet containing two panes of four 10 c. (No. 175a) and pane of two 45 c. (No. 176a)	1·00

1984 (18 Apr). *Vermilion printed cover, 98×50 mm, showing Tuvalu crest. Stamps attached by selvedge.*

SB5	$1.20, booklet containing two 30 c. and one 60 c. (Nos. 205*a*, 209*a*)	4·75

1986 (18 July). *Royal Wedding. Silver* (No. SB6) *or gold* (No. SB7) *on rosine covers, 152×80 mm. Stapled.*

SB6	$6.40, booklet (State Coach) containing 60 c. and $1 (Nos. 397/400, but imperf) each value in block of 4	2·40
SB7	$7.20, booklet (Westminster Abbey) containing twelve 60 c. (Nos. 397/8) in blocks of 4	2·75

POSTAGE DUE STAMPS

D 1 Tuvalu Crest

(Des G. Drummond. Litho Questa)

1981 (3 May). *P* 13½×14.

No.	Type	Description	Unused	Used
D1	D 1	1 c. black and bright purple	10	10
D2		2 c. black and greenish blue	10	10
D3		5 c. black and ochre	10	10
D4		10 c. black and blue-green	10	15
D5		20 c. black and purple-brown	15	25
D6		30 c. black and bright orange	20	30
D7		40 c. black and blue	25	40
D8		50 c. black and yellow-green	30	45
D9		$1 black and deep mauve	50	80
D1/9		*Set of* 9	1·50	2·25

1982 (25 Nov)–**83**. *As Nos.* D1/9 *but P* 14½ × 15 *and with imprint date at foot.*

No.	Type	Description	Unused	Used
D10	D 1	1 c. black and bright purple	10	20
D11		2 c. black and greenish blue	10	20
D12		5 c. black and ochre	10	20
D13		10 c. black and blue-green	10	20
D14		20 c. black and purple-brown	15	30
D15		30 c. black and bright orange (25.5.83)	25	30
D16		40 c. black and blue (25.5.83)	35	40
D17		50 c. black and yellow-green (25.5.83)	45	50
D18		$1 black and deep mauve (25.5.83)	85	90
D10/18		*Set of* 9	2·00	2·75

The imprint date on Nos. D10/14 is "1982" and on Nos. D15/18 "1983".

OFFICIAL STAMPS

For the use of the Philatelic Bureau.

OFFICIAL (O 1) OFFICIAL (O 2)

TWO TYPES OF OVERPRINT FOR NOS. O1/19

This issue was overprinted using two different processes.

All values, except for the 35, 45 and 50 c., come with the overprint applied by typography. This process results in ragged lines, uneven distribution of the ink, especially at the edges of the letters, and often has the impression of the letters visible from the reverse.

In addition nine of these values have been found with overprints applied by lithography. These show clean lines and an even distribution of the ink.

The 35, 45 and 50 c. values have only been seen with overprints applied by lithography.

1981 (2 July). *Nos.* 105/22 *optd with Type* O **1**.

No.	Description	Unused	Used
O 1	1 c. Type **14**	10	10
	a. Litho opt	1·25	
O 2	2 c. Band-tailed Goatfish	10	10
O 3	4 c. Regal Angelfish	10	10
O 4	5 c. Melon Butterflyfish	10	10
O 5	6 c. Semi-circle Angelfish	10	10
	a. Litho opt	1·25	1·25
O 6	8 c. Blue-striped Snapper	10	10
O 7	10 c. Clown Anemonefish	15	15
	a. Litho opt	1·25	1·25
O 8	15 c. Chevron Butterflyfish	20	20
O 9	20 c. Yellow-edged Lyretail ("Fairy Cod")	25	25
O10	25 c. Clown Triggerfish	25·00	
	a. Litho opt	30	30
O11	30 c. Long-nosed Butterflyfish	30	30
	a. Litho opt		
O12	35 c. Yellow-finned Tuna (*litho opt*)	35	35
O13	40 c. Spotted Eagle Ray	40	40
O14	45 c. Black-tipped Grouper (*litho opt*)	45	45
O15	50 c. Hammerhead (*litho opt*)	50	50
O16	70 c. Lionfish	60	60
	a. Litho opt	3·25	3·00
O17	$1 Painted Triggerfish	65	60
	a. Litho opt	2·50	2·50
O18	$2 Copper-banded Butterflyfish	1·75	1·50
	a. Litho opt	1·50	1·50
O19	$5 Tiger Shark	1·75	1·50
	a. Litho opt	15·00	12·00
O1/19	*Set of* 19	6·50	6·50

The 1 c. (typo opt), 8 c. and 30 c. exist with either screen, the 2 c., 4 c., 6 c. (both opts), 10 c. (typo opt), 20 c., 70 c. (both opts), $1 (both opts), $2 (both opts) and $5 (both opts) with the fine screen and the 1 c. (litho opt), 5 c., 10 c. (litho opt), 15 c., 25 c. (both opts), 35 c., 40 c., 45 c. and 50 c. with the coarse.

1983 (26 Aug)–**85**. *Nos.* 202/3a, 205/12, 224 *and* 234 *optd as Type* O **1**, *but* 20½×4 *mm.* (5 c.) *or as Type* O **2** (*others*), *both applied by lithography.*

No.	Description	Unused	Used
O20	5 c. Wedding and baby food baskets (1.2.84)	10	30
	a. Optd as Type O **2** (5.85)	30	30
O21	10 c. Hand-carved model of canoe (1.2.84)	10	30
O22	15 c. Ladies' sun hats (30.4.84)	15	50
O23	25 c. Pandanus baskets (1.2.84)	25	50
O24	30 c. on 45 c. Reef sandals and fish trap (1.2.84)	50	60
O25	30 c. Basket tray and coconut stand (30.4.84)	30	50
O26	35 c. Pandanus pillows and shell necklaces (1.2.84)	40	65
O27	40 c. Round baskets and fans (1.2.84)	45	65
O28	45 c. Reef sandals and fish trap (1.2.84)	45	65
O29	50 c. Rat trap (1.2.84)	50	65
O30	60 c. on $1 Pump drill and adze	75	70
O31	60 c. Fisherman's waterproof boxes (30.4.84)	60	80
	a. Typo opt (19.2.85*)		
O32	$1 Pump drill and adze (1.2.84)	75	1·00
O33	$2 Fisherman's hat and canoe bailers (1.2.84)	1·25	1·00
O34	$5 Fishing rod, lures and scoop nets (1.2.84)	3·00	2·50
O20/34	*Set of* 15	8·50	10·00

*No. O31a comes from an emergency overprinting by typography undertaken in Fiji to meet Tuvalu government requirements for this value. Examples are known used between 19 February 1985 and August 1988. Further supplies of the lithography overprint were subsequently obtained from Great Britain.

For the different characteristics of litho and typo overprints see above No. O1.

OFFICIAL

(O 3)

1989 (22 Feb). *Nos.* 502/17 *optd with Type* O 3.

No.	Description	Unused	Used
O35	5 c. Type **66**	15	30
O36	10 c. White Tern	15	30
O37	15 c. Common Noddy	30	30
O38	20 c. Phoenix Petrel	30	30
O39	25 c. American Golden Plover	40	50
O40	30 c. Crested Tern	40	50
O41	35 c. Sooty Tern	45	55
O42	40 c. Bristle-thighed Curlew	45	55
O43	45 c. Bar-tailed Godwit	55	65
O44	50 c. Eastern Reef Heron	60	70
O45	55 c. Great Frigate Bird	60	70
O46	60 c. Red-footed Booby	70	80
O47	70 c. Rufous-necked Sandpiper ("Red-necked Stint")	80	90
O48	$1 Long-tailed Koel ("Long-tailed Cuckoo")	1·10	1·10
O49	$2 Red-tailed Tropic Bird	2·00	1·90
O50	$5 Banded Rail	4·25	4·50
O35/50	*Set of* 16	12·00	13·00

Appendix

The following issues for individual islands of Tuvalu fall outside the criteria for full listing as detailed on page xi of this edition.

FUNAFUTI

1984

Leaders of the World. Railway Locomotives (1st series). *Two designs for each value, the first showing technical drawings and the second the locomotive at work.* 15, 20, 30, 40, 50, 60 c., *each* × 2

Leaders of the World. Automobiles (1st series). *Two designs for each value, the first showing technical drawings and the second the car in action.* 1, 10, 40 c., $1, *each* × 2

Leaders of the World. Railway Locomotives (2nd series). *Two designs for each value, the first showing technical drawings and the second the locomotive at work.* 5, 15, 25, 35, 40, 55, 60 c., $1, *each* × 2

1985

Leaders of the World. Automobiles (2nd series). *Two designs for each value, the first showing technical drawings and the second the car in action.* 1, 30, 55, 60 c., *each* × 2

Leaders of the World. Railway Locomotives (3rd series). *Two designs for each value, the first showing technical drawings and the second the locomotive at work.* 5, 15, 35, 40, 50 c., $1, *each* × 2

Leaders of the World. Life and Times of Queen Elizabeth the Queen Mother. Two designs for each value, showing different portraits. 5, 25, 80 c., $1.05, *each* × 2

1986

60th Birthday of Queen Elizabeth II. 10, 50 c., $1.50, $3.50

Royal Wedding (1st issue). 60 c., $1, *each* × 2

Royal Wedding (2nd issue). *Previous Royal Wedding stamps optd* "Congratulations T.R.H. The Duke & Duchess of York". 60 c., $1, *each* × 2

Railway Locomotives (4th series). *Two designs for each value, the first showing technical drawings and the second the locomotive at work.* 20, 40, 60 c., $1.50, *each* × 2

1987

Automobiles (3rd series). *Two designs for each value, the first showing technical drawings and the second the car in action.* 10, 20, 40, 60, 75, 80 c., $1, $1.50, *each* × 2

Royal Ruby Wedding. 20, 50, 75 c., $1.20, $1.75

1988

Olympic Games, Seoul. 10, 20, 40, 50, 80, 90 c.

NANUMAGA

1984

Leaders of the World. Automobiles (1st series). *Two designs for each value, the first showing technical drawings and the second the car in action.* 5, 10, 25, 30, 40 c., $1, *each* × 2

Leaders of the World. British Monarchs. Two designs for each value, forming a composite picture. 10, 20, 30, 40, 50 c., $1, *each* × 2

Leaders of the World. Automobiles (2nd series). *Two designs for each value, the first showing technical drawings and the second the car in action.* 5, 10, 50 c., $1, *each* × 2

1985

Leaders of the World. Railway Locomotives. Two designs for each value, the first showing technical drawings and the second the locomotive at work. 10, 25, 50, 60 c., *each* × 2

Leaders of the World. Flowers. 25, 30, 40, 50 c., *each* × 2

Leaders of the World. Automobiles (3rd series). *Two designs for each value, the first showing technical drawings and the second the car in action.* 10, 25, 75 c., $1, *each* × 2

Leaders of the World. Life and Times of Queen Elizabeth the Queen Mother. Two designs for each value, showing different portraits. 15, 55, 65, 90 c., *each* × 2

1986

60th Birthday of Queen Elizabeth II. 5 c., $1, $1.75, $2.50

World Cup Football Championship, Mexico. 1, 5, 5, 10, 20, 35, 50, 60, 75 c., $1, $2, $4

Royal Wedding (1st issue). 60 c., $1, *each* × 2

Royal Wedding (2nd issue). *Previous Royal Wedding stamps optd as for Funafuti.* 60 c., $1, *each* × 2

1987

Automobiles (4th series). *Two designs for each value, the first showing technical drawings and the second the car in action.* 5, 10, 15, 20, 25, 40, 60 c., $1, *each* × 2

Royal Ruby Wedding. 15, 35, 60 c., $1.50, $1.75

NANUMEA

1984

Leaders of the World. Railway Locomotives (1st series). *Two designs for each value, the first showing technical drawings and the second the locomotive at work.* 15, 20, 30, 40, 50, 60 c., *each* × 2

Leaders of the World. Famous Cricketers. Two designs for each value, the first showing a portrait and the second the cricketer in action. 1, 10, 40 c., $1, *each* × 2

1985

Leaders of the World. Automobiles (1st series). *Two designs for each value, the first showing technical drawings and the second the car in action.* 5, 40, 50, 60 c., *each* × 2

Leaders of the World. Railway Locomotives (2nd series). *Two designs for each value, the first showing technical drawings and the second the locomotive at work.* 1, 35, 50, 60 c., *each* × 2

Leaders of the World. Automobiles (2nd series). *Two designs for each value, the first showing technical drawings and the second the car in action.* 15, 20, 50, 60 c., *each* × 2

Leaders of the World. Cats. 5, 30, 50 c., $1, *each* × 2

Leaders of the World. Life and Times of Queen Elizabeth the Queen Mother. Two designs for each value, showing different portraits. 5, 30, 75 c., $1.05, *each* × 2

1986

60th Birthday of Queen Elizabeth II. 10, 80 c., $1.75, $3

World Cup Football Championship, Mexico. 1, 2, 5, 10, 25, 40, 50, 75, 90 c., $1, $2.50, $4

Royal Wedding (1st issue). 60 c., $1, *each* × 2

Royal Wedding (2nd issue). *Previous Royal Wedding stamps optd as for Funafuti.* 60 c., $1, *each* × 2

Automobiles (3rd series). *Two designs for each value, the first showing technical drawings and the second the car in action.* 10, 20, 35, 50, 75 c., $2, *each* × 2

1987

Royal Ruby Wedding. 40, 60, 80 c., $1, $2

NIUTAO

1984

Leaders of the World. Automobiles (1st series). *Two designs for each value, the first showing technical drawings and the second the car in action.* 15, 30, 40, 50 c., *each* × 2

Leaders of the World. Railway Locomotives (1st series). *Two designs for each value, the first showing technical drawings and the second the locomotive at work.* 5, 10, 20, 40, 50 c., $1, *each* × 2

1985

Leaders of the World. Famous Cricketers. Two designs for each value, the first showing a portrait and the second the cricketer in action. 1, 15, 50 c., $1, *each* × 2

Leaders of the World. Birth Bicent of John J. Audubon (ornithologist). Birds. 5, 15, 25 c., $1, *each* × 2

Leaders of the World. Automobiles (2nd series). *Two designs for each value, the first showing technical drawings and the second the car in action.* 20, 25, 40, 60 c., *each* × 2

Leaders of the World. Railway Locomotives (2nd series). *Two designs for each value, the first showing technical drawings and the second the locomotive at work.* 10, 30, 45, 60, 75 c., $1.20, *each* × 2

Leaders of the World. Life and Times of Queen Elizabeth the Queen Mother. Two designs for each value, showing different portraits. 15, 35, 70, 95 c., *each* × 2

1986

60th Birthday of Queen Elizabeth II. 5, 60 c., $1.50, $3.50

Royal Wedding (1st issue). 60 c., $1, *each* × 2

Royal Wedding (2nd issue). *Previous Royal Wedding stamps optd as for Funafuti.* 60 c., $1, *each* × 2

1987

Royal Ruby Wedding. 60th Birthday of Queen Elizabeth II issue of 1986 optd "40th WEDDING ANNIVERSARY OF H.M. QUEEN ELIZABETH II". 5, 60 c., $1.50, $3.50

NUI

1984

Leaders of the World. Railway Locomotives (1st series). *Two designs for each value, the first showing technical drawings and the second the locomotive at work.* 15, 25, 30, 50 c., *each* × 2

Leaders of the World. British Monarchs. Two designs for each value, forming a composite picture. 1, 5, 15, 40, 50 c., $1, *each* × 2

1985

Leaders of the World. Railway Locomotives (2nd series). *Two designs for each value, the first showing technical drawings and the second the locomotive at work.* 5, 15, 25 c., $1, *each* × 2

Leaders of the World. Automobiles (1st series). *Two designs for each value, the first showing technical drawings and the second the car in action.* 25, 30, 40, 50 c., *each* × 2

Leaders of the World. Famous Cricketers. Two designs for each value, the first showing a portrait and the second the cricketer in action. 1, 40, 60, 70 c., *each* × 2

Leaders of the World. Life and Times of Queen Elizabeth the Queen Mother. Two designs for each value, showing different portraits. 5, 50, 75, 85 c., *each* × 2

Leaders of the World. Automobiles (2nd series). *Two designs for each value, the first showing technical drawings and the second the car in action.* 5, 15, 40, 60, 90 c., $1.10, *each* × 2

1986

60th Birthday of Queen Elizabeth II. 10, 80 c., $1.75, $3

Royal Wedding (1st issue). 60 c., $1, *each* × 2

Royal Wedding (2nd issue). *Previous Royal Wedding stamps optd as for Funafuti.* 60 c., $1, *each* × 2

1987

Railway Locomotives (3rd series). *Two designs for each value, the first showing technical drawings and the second the locomotive at work.* 10, 25, 35, 40, 60, 75 c., $1, $1.25, *each* × 2

Royal Ruby Wedding. 20, 50, 75 c., $1.20, $1.75

1988

Railway Locomotives (4th series). *Two designs for each value, the first showing technical drawings and the second the locomotive at work.* 5, 10, 20, 25, 40, 50, 60, 75 c., *each* × 2

NUKUFETAU

1984

Leaders of the World. Automobiles (1st series). *Two designs for each value, the first showing technical drawings and the second the car in action.* 10, 25, 30, 50, 60 c., *each* × 2

Leaders of the World. British Monarchs. Two designs for each value, forming a composite picture. 1, 10, 30, 50, 60 c., $1, *each* × 2

1985

Leaders of the World. Famous Cricketers. Two designs for each value, the first showing a portrait and the second the cricketer in action. 1, 10, 55 c., $1, *each* × 2

Leaders of the World. Railway Locomotives (1st series). *Two designs for each value, the first showing technical drawings and the second the locomotive at work.* 1, 10, 60, 70 c., *each* × 2

Leaders of the World. Automobiles (2nd series). *Two designs for each value, the first showing technical drawings and the second the car in action.* 5, 10, 15, 20, 50, 60, 75 c., $1.50, *each* × 2

Leaders of the World. Life and Times of Queen Elizabeth the Queen Mother. Two designs for each value, showing different portraits. 10, 45, 65 c., $1, *each* × 2

1986

Leaders of the World. Railway Locomotives (2nd series). *Two designs for each value, the first showing technical drawings and the second the locomotive at work.* 20, 40, 60 c., $1.50, *each* × 2

60th Birthday of Queen Elizabeth II. 5, 40 c., $2, $4

Royal Wedding (1st issue). 60 c., $1, *each* × 2

Royal Wedding (2nd issue). *Previous Royal Wedding stamps optd as for Funafuti.* 60 c., $1, *each* × 2

1987

Railway Locomotives (3rd series). *Two designs for each value, the first showing technical drawings and the second the locomotive at work.* 5, 10, 15, 25, 30, 50, 60 c., $1, *each* × 2

Royal Ruby Wedding. 60th Birthday of Queen Elizabeth II issue of 1986 optd as for Niutao. 5, 40 c., $2, $4

NUKULAELAE

1984

Leaders of the World. Railway Locomotives (1st series). *Two designs for each value, the first showing technical drawings and the second the locomotive at work.* 5, 15, 40 c., $1, *each* × 2

Leaders of the World. Famous Cricketers. Two designs for each value, the first showing a portrait and the second the cricketer in action. 5, 15, 30 c., $1, *each* × 2

Leaders of the World. Railway Locomotives (2nd series). *Two designs for each value, the first showing technical drawings and the second the locomotive at work.* 5, 20, 40 c., $1, *each* × 2

1985

Leaders of the World. Automobiles. Two designs for each value, the first showing technical drawings and the second the car in action. 5, 35, 50, 70 c., *each* × 2

Leaders of the World. Dogs. 5, 20, 50, 70 c., *each* × 2

Leaders of the World. Railway Locomotives (3rd series). *Two designs for each value, the first showing technical drawings and the second the locomotive at work.* 10, 25, 50 c., $1, *each* × 2

Leaders of the World. Automobiles (2nd series). *Two designs for each value, the first showing technical drawings and the second the car in action.* 10, 25, 35, 50, 75 c., $1, *each* × 2

Leaders of the World. Life and Times of Queen Elizabeth the Queen Mother. Two designs for each value, showing different portraits. 5, 25, 85 c., $1, *each* × 2

1986

60th Birthday of Queen Elizabeth II. 10 c., $1, $1.50, $3

Railway Locomotives (4th series). *Two designs for each value, the first showing technical drawings and the second the locomotive at work.* 10, 15, 25, 40, 50, 80 c., $1, $1.50, *each* × 2

Royal Wedding (1st issue). 60 c., $1, *each* × 2

Royal Wedding (2nd issue). *Previous Royal Wedding stamps optd as for Funafuti.* 60 c., $1, *each* × 2

1987

Royal Ruby Wedding. 15, 35, 60 c., $1.50, $1.75

VAITUPU

1984

Leaders of the World. Automobiles (1st series). *Two designs for each value, the first showing technical drawings and the second the car in action.* 15, 25, 30, 50 c., *each* × 2

Leaders of the World. British Monarchs. Two designs for each value, forming a composite picture. 1, 5, 15, 40, 50 c., $1, *each* × 2

Leaders of the World. Automobiles (2nd series). *Two designs for each value, the first showing technical drawings and the second the car in action.* 5, 15, 25, 30, 40, 50, 60 c., $1, *each* × 2

1985

Leaders of the World. Railway Locomotives (1st series). *Two designs for each value, the first showing technical drawings and the second the locomotive at work.* 10, 25, 50, 60 c., *each* × 2

Leaders of the World, Butterflies. 5, 15, 50, 75 c., *each* × 2

Leaders of the World. Automobiles (3rd series). *Two designs for each value, the first showing technical drawings and the second the car in action.* 15, 30, 40, 60 c., *each* × 2

Leaders of the World. Life and Times of Queen Elizabeth the Queen Mother. Two designs for each value, showing different portraits. 15, 40, 65, 95 c., *each* × 2

1986

Leaders of the World. Railway Locomotives (2nd series). *Two designs for each value, the first showing technical drawings and the second the locomotive at work.* 5, 25, 80 c., $1, *each* × 2

60th Birthday of Queen Elizabeth II. 5, 60 c., $2, $3.50

Royal Wedding (1st issue). 60 c., $1, *each* × 2

Royal Wedding (2nd issue). *Previous Royal Wedding stamps optd as for Funafuti.* 60 c., $1, *each* × 2

1987

Railway Locomotives (3rd series). *Two designs for each value, the first showing technical drawings and the second the locomotive at work.* 10, 15, 25, 35, 45, 65, 85 c., $1, *each* × 2

Royal Ruby Wedding. 60th Birthday of Queen Elizabeth II issue of 1986 optd as for Niutao. 5, 60 c., $2, $3.50

Uganda

PRICES FOR STAMPS ON COVER TO 1945

The type-written stamps of Uganda, Nos. 1/53, are very rare used on cover.

Nos. 54/60	*from* × 20
No. 61	—
Nos. 70/5	*from* × 12
No. 76	—
Nos. 84/90	*from* × 20
No. 91	—
Nos. 92/3	*from* × 40

PROTECTORATE

Following a period of conflict between Islamic, Protestant and Roman Catholic factions, Uganda was declared to be in the British sphere of influence by the Anglo-German Agreement of July 1890. The British East Africa Company exercised a variable degree of control until 27 August 1894 when the country was declared a British Protectorate.

Before the introduction of Nos. 84/91 the stamps of Uganda were only valid for internal postage. Letters for overseas were franked with British East Africa issues on arrival at Mombasa.

(Currency. 200 cowries = 1 rupee)

'U G' 50

1

'U G' 20

2

TYPE-WRITTEN STAMPS. Nos. 2/53 were type-written by the Revd. E. Millar at Mengo for the Uganda administration. For all "printings" a thin laid paper was used, and all issues were imperforate.

The original typewriter used had wide letters, but in late April, 1895 Millar obtained a new machine on which the type face was in a narrower fount.

Each sheet was made up of whatever values were required at the time, so that different values can be found *se-tenant* or *tête-bêche*. These last were caused by the paper being inverted in the machine so that space at the foot could be utilised.

For the first issue the sheets were of 117 (9 × 13), but with the introduction of the narrower width (Nos. 17 onwards) a larger number of stamps per sheet, 143 (11 × 13), was adopted.

The manuscript provisionals, Nos. 9*a*/16, come from the Mission at Ngogwe, most of the manuscript surcharges including the initials of the Revd. G. R. Blackledge stationed there.

1895 (20 Mar). *Wide letters. Wide stamps,* 20 *to* 26 *mm wide.*

No.	Type	Description	Unused	Used
2	1	10 (c.) black	£2000	£1100
4		20 (c.) black	£3000	£1100
		a. "U A" for "U G"	†	£2500
6		30 (c.) black	£1300	£1200
7		40 (c.) black	£2000	£1200
8		50 (c.) black	£1100	£1000
9		60 (c.) black	£1500	£1500

It is now believed that the 5, 15 and 25 cowries values in this width, previously Nos. 1, 3 and 5, do not exist.

A strip of three of No. 2 is known on cover of which one stamp has the value "10" altered to "5" in manuscript and initialled "E.M.".

1895 (May). *Wide stamps with pen-written surcharges, in black.*

No.	Type	Description	Unused	Used
9*a*	1	10 on 30 (c.) black	†	£28000
10		10 on 50 (c.) black	†	£22000
11		15 on 10 (c.) black	†	£22000
12		15 on 20 (c.) black	†	£26000
13		15 on 40 (c.) black	†	£22000
14		15 on 50 (c.) black	†	£28000
15		25 on 50 (c.) black	†	£28000
16		50 on 60 (c.) black	†	£28000

1895 (April). *Wide letters. Narrow stamps,* 16 *to* 18 *mm wide.*

No.	Type	Description	Unused	Used
17	1	5 (c.) black	£1200	£950
18		10 (c.) black	£1300	£1000
19		15 (c.) black	£900	£1000
20		20 (c.) black	£1000	£650
21		25 (c.) black	£850	£900
22		30 (c.) black	£6500	£6500
23		40 (c.) black	£6000	£6000
24		50 (c.) black	£2750	
25		60 (c.) black	£3500	£3500

1895 (May). *Narrow letters. Narrow stamps* 16 *to* 18 *mm wide.*

No.	Type	Description	Unused	Used
26	2	5 (c.) black	£600	
27		10 (c.) black	£550	
28		15 (c.) black	£600	
29		20 (c.) black	£450	
30		25 (c.) black	£600	
31		30 (c.) black	£600	
32		40 (c.) black	£700	
33		50 (c.) black	£550	
34		60 (c.) black	£1200	

1895 (Nov). *Narrow letters. Narrow stamps,* 16–18 *mm wide. Change of colour.*

No.	Type	Description	Unused	Used
35	2	5 (c.) violet	£425	£450
36		10 (c.) violet	£400	£400
37		15 (c.) violet	£450	£375
38		20 (c.) violet	£325	£275
		a. "G U" for "U G"		
39		25 (c.) violet	£550	£550
40		30 (c.) violet	£800	£600
41		40 (c.) violet	£650	£650
42		50 (c.) violet	£650	£700
43		100 (c.) violet	£2500	£2500

Stamps of 35 (c.) and 45 (c.) have been recorded in violet. They were never prepared for postal use, and did not represent a postal rate, but were type-written to oblige a local official. (*Price* £2500 *each, unused*)

'V.96.R' 25 'Uganda'

3

1896 (June).

No.	Type	Description	Unused	Used
44	3	5 (c.) violet	£400	£425
45		10 (c.) violet	£350	£350
46		15 (c.) violet	£400	£425
47		20 (c.) violet	£275	£200
48		25 (c.) violet	£400	
49		30 (c.) violet	£450	£550
50		40 (c.) violet	£450	£550
51		50 (c.) violet	£550	£600
52		60 (c.) violet	£1300	
53		100 (c.) violet	£1200	£1200

(New Currency. 16 annas = 1 rupee)

UGANDA POSTAGE V✝R 1 ANNA PROTECTORATE

4 (Thin "1")

UGANDA POSTAGE V✝R 1 ANNA PROTECTORATE

5 (Thick "1")

UGANDA POSTAGE V✝R 4 ANNAS PROTECTORATE

6

UGANDA POSTAGE V✝R L 4 ANNAS PROTECTORATE

7

In the 2 a. and 3 a. the dagger points upwards; the stars in the 2 a. are level with the top of "VR". The 8 a. is as T 6 but with left star at top and right star at foot. The 1 r. has three stars at foot. The 5 r. has central star raised and the others at foot.

(Type-set by the Revd. F. Rowling at Lubwa's, in Usoga)

1896 (7 Nov). (*a*) *Types* **4/6**.

A. *Normal.* B. *Small* "o" *in* "POSTAGE"

No.	Type	Description	A Unused	A Used	B Unused	B Used
54	4	1 a. black	80·00	70·00	£350	£325
55	5	1 a. black	13·00	16·00	48·00	55·00
56	6	2 a. black	17·00	19·00	60·00	65·00
57		3 a. black	17·00	20·00	60·00	75·00
58		4 a. black	17·00	19·00	60·00	70·00
59		8 a. black	20·00	22·00	75·00	80·00
60		1 r. black	60·00	70·00	£200	£275
61		5 r. black	£160	£200	£450	£550

(*b*) *Optd* "L", *in black as in T* **7** *for local use, by a postal official, R. R. Racey, at Kampala*

No.	Type	Description	A Unused	A Used	B Unused	B Used
70	4	1 a. black	£130	£100	£700	£600
71	6	2 a. black	60·00	80·00	£200	£275
72		3 a. black	£150	£170	£750	£850
73		4 a. black	70·00	£110	£300	—
74		8 a. black	£120	£160	£650	£800
75		1 r. black	£225	£275	£850	—
76		5 r. black	£7000	£7000	—	—

Tête-bêche pairs of all values may be found owing to the settings of 16 (4 × 4) being printed side by side or above one another. They are worth a premium. The variety with small "O" occurs on R. 3/1.

8

9

UGANDA

(10)

(Recess D.L.R.)

1898 (Nov)–**1902.** *P* 14. (*a*) *Wmk Crown CA.*

No.	Type	Description	Unused	Used
84	8	1 a. scarlet	1·75	1·50
		a. Carmine-rose (1902)	1·50	75
86		2 a. red-brown	1·50	4·00
87		3 a. pale grey	6·00	15·00
		a. Bluish grey	6·00	10·00
88		4 a. deep green	2·00	6·00
89		8 a. pale olive	6·00	22·00
		a. Grey-green	6·50	25·00

(*b*) *Wmk Crown CC*

No.	Type	Description	Unused	Used
90	9	1 r. dull blue	25·00	32·00
		a. Bright blue	35·00	35·00
91		5 r. brown	60·00	85·00
84/91		*Set of* 7	90·00	£140
84/91 Optd "Specimen"		*Set of* 7	£150	

On 1 April 1901 the postal administrations of British East Africa and Uganda were merged. Subsequent issues to 1962 are listed under KENYA, UGANDA and TANGANYIKA.

1902 (Feb). *T* **11** *of British East Africa* (*Kenya, Uganda, and Tanganyika*) *optd with T* **10**.

No.	Description	Unused	Used
92	½ a. yellow-green	1·75	1·10
	a. Opt omitted (in pair with normal)	£2750	
	b. Opt inverted (at foot)	£1100	
	c. Opt double	£1200	
93	2½ a. deep blue (R.)	1·75	2·50
	a. Opt double	£600	
	b. Inverted "S" (R. 1/1)	42·00	70·00

The Eastern Province of Uganda was transferred to British East Africa on 1 April 1902.

SELF-GOVERNMENT

(New Currency. 100 cents = 1 East African, later Uganda shilling)

11 Ripon Falls and Speke Memorial

(Des S. Scott. Recess B.W.)

1962 (28 July). *Centenary of Speke's Discovery of Source of the Nile. W w* **12**. *P* 14.

No.	Type	Description	Unused	Used
95	11	30 c. black and red	15	10
96		50 c. black and slate-violet	15	10
97		1 s. 30, black and green	30	10
98		2 s. 50, black and blue	1·40	1·10
95/8		*Set of* 4	1·75	1·25

INDEPENDENT

12 Murchison Falls

13 Tobacco-growing

14 Mulago Hospital

(Des V. Whiteley. Photo Harrison)

1962 (9 Oct)–**64**. *Independence. Various designs as T* **12/14**. *P* 15×14 (5 *c. to* 50 *c.*) *or* 14½ (*others*).

99	5 c. deep bluish green	10	10
100	10 c. reddish brown	10	10
	a. Brown (coil)	10	10
	b. Deep yellow-brown (17.10.64)	10	10
101	15 c. black, red and green	10	10
102	20 c. plum and buff	10	10
103	30 c. blue	10	10
104	50 c. black and turquoise-green	10	10
105	1 s. sepia, red and turquoise-green	15	10
106	1 s. 30, yellow-orange and violet	20	10
107	2 s. black, carmine and light blue	40	40
108	5 s. vermilion and deep green	4·00	1·00
109	10 s. slate and chestnut	1·75	1·75
110	20 s. brown and blue	4·50	11·00
99/110	*Set of* 12	10·50	13·00

Designs: *As T* **12/13**—10 c. Tobacco growing; 15 c. Coffee growing; 20 c. Ankole cattle; 30 c. Cotton; 50 c. Mountains of the Moon. *As T* **14**—1 s. 30, Cathedrals and Mosque; 2 s. Makerere College; 5 s. Copper mining; 10 s. Cement industry; 20 s. Parliament Buildings.

15 South African Crowned Crane

(Photo Harrison)

1965 (20 Feb). *International Trade Fair, Kampala. P* 14½ × 14.

111	**15**	30 c. multicoloured	10	10
112		1 s. 30, multicoloured	20	10

16 Black Bee Eater

17 African Jacana

18 Ruwenzori Turaco

(Des Mrs. R. Fennessy. Photo Harrison)

1965 (9 Oct). *Birds. Various designs as T* **16/18**. *P* 15 × 14 (5 *c.*, 15 *c.*, 20 *c.*, 40 *c.*, 50 *c.*), 14 × 15 (10 *c.*, 30 *c.*, 65 *c.*) *or* 14½ (*others*).

113	5 c. multicoloured	10	10
114	10 c. chestnut, black and light blue	10	10
115	15 c. yellow and sepia	20	10
116	20 c. multicoloured	20	10
117	30 c. black and brown-red	1·50	10
118	40 c. multicoloured	90	50
119	50 c. grey-blue and reddish violet	25	10
	a. White bird (grey-blue omitted)	£225	
120	65 c. orange-red, black and light grey	2·50	2·00
121	1 s. multicoloured	50	10
122	1 s. 30, chestnut, black and yellow	5·50	30
123	2 s. 50, multicoloured	4·25	65
124	5 s. multicoloured	7·00	3·50
125	10 s. multicoloured	11·00	9·00
126	20 s. multicoloured	21·00	32·00
113/26	*Set of* 14	48·00	42·00

Designs: *Vert as T* **16**—15 c. Orange Weaver; 20 c. Narina Trogon; 40 c. Blue-breasted Kingfisher; 50 c. Whale-headed Stork. *Horiz as T* **17**—30 c. Sacred Ibis; 65 c. Red-crowned Bishop. *As T* **18**. *Vert*—1 s. 30, African Fish Eagle; 5 s. Lilac-breasted Roller. *Horiz*—2 s. 50, Great Blue Turaco; 10 s. Black-collared Lovebird; 20 s. South African Crowned Crane.

The 15 c., 40 c., 65 c., and 1s. exist with PVA gum as well as gum arabic.

19 Carved Screen

(Des Mrs. R. Fennessy. Photo Harrison)

1967 (26 Oct). *13th Commonwealth Parliamentary Association Conference. T* **19** *and similar horiz designs. Multicoloured. P* 14.

127	30 c. Type **19**	10	10
128	50 c. Arms of Uganda	10	10
129	1 s. 30, Parliamentary Building	10	10
130	2 s. 50, Conference Chamber	15	1·00
127/30	*Set of* 4	30	1·00

20 *Cordia abyssinica*

21 *Acacia drepanolobium*

(Des Mrs. R. Fennessy. Photo Harrison)

1969 (9 Oct)–**74**. *Flowers. Various designs as T* **20/1**. *Chalk-surfaced paper. P* 14½×14 (5 *c. to* 70 *c.*) *or* 14 (*others*).

131	5 c. brown, green and light olive-yellow	10	85
	a. Glazed, ordinary paper (11.4.73)	40	10
132	10 c. multicoloured	10	10
	a. Glazed, ordinary paper (27.9.72)	40	10
133	15 c. multicoloured	40	10
134	20 c. bluish violet, yellow-ol & pale sage-grn	15	10
	a. Glazed, ordinary paper (27.9.72)	40	10
135	30 c. multicoloured	20	10
136	40 c. reddish violet, yell-grn & pale ol-grey	20	10
137	50 c. multicoloured	20	10
138	60 c. multicoloured	45	90
	a. Glazed, ordinary paper (9.5.73)	7·50	40
139	70 c. multicoloured	35	30
	a. Glazed, ordinary paper (27.9.72)	1·00	45
140	1 s. multicoloured	20	10
	a. Glazed, ordinary paper (22.1.71)	80	10
141	1 s. 50, multicoloured (cobalt background)	35	10
	a. Glazed, ordinary paper (3.2.71)	50	10
	b. Azure background (chalk-surfaced paper) (21.1.74)	55	20
142	2 s. 50, multicoloured	70	1·25
	a. Glazed, ordinary paper (3.2.71)	1·25	10
143	5 s. multicoloured	80	1·60
	a. Glazed, ordinary paper (3.2.71)	1·75	10
144	10 s. multicoloured	1·25	4·00
	a. Glazed, ordinary paper (3.2.71)	3·75	10
145	20 s. multicoloured	2·00	5·00
	a. Glazed, ordinary paper (22.1.71)	11·00	15
131/45	*Set of* 15	6·50	13·00
131a/45a	*Set of* 11	26·00	1·40

Designs: *As T* **20**—10 c. *Grewia similis*; 15 c. *Cassia didymobotrya*; 20 c. *Coleus barbatus*; 30 c. *Ockna ovata*; 40 c. *Ipomoea spathulata*; 50 c. *Spathodea nilotica*; 60 c. *Oncoba spinosa*; 70 c. *Carissa edulis*. *As T* **21**—1 s. 50, *Clerodendrum myricoides*; 2 s. 50, *Acanthus arboreus*; 5 s. *Kigelia aethiopium*; 10 s. *Erythrina abyssinica*; 20 s. *Monodora myristica*.

Some of the glazed ordinary paper printings were available in Uganda some time before the London release dates which are quoted in the listings.

2/

(**22**)

1975 (29 Sept). *Nos.* 141/2 *and* 145a *surch as T* **22**.

146	2 s. on 1 s. 50, multicoloured	2·00	1·50
147	3 s. on 2 s. 50, multicoloured	20·00	40·00
148	40 s. on 20 s. multicoloured	5·50	3·50
	a. Surch on No. 145	6·50	3·50
146/8	*Set of* 3	25·00	40·00

23 Millet

24 Maize

(Des Mrs. R. Fennessy. Photo Harrison)

1975 (9 Oct). *Ugandan Crops. T* **23/4** *and similar horiz designs. P* 14 × 14½ (10 *to* 80 *c.*) *or* 14 (*others*).

149	10 c. black, apple-green and yellow-brown	10	10
150	20 c. multicoloured	10	10
151	30 c. multicoloured	10	10
152	40 c. multicoloured	10	10
153	50 c. multicoloured	10	10
154	70 c. black, apple-green and light blue-green	15	15
155	80 c. multicoloured	15	15
156	1 s. multicoloured	15	15
157	2 s. multicoloured	30	30
158	3 s. multicoloured	50	45
159	5 s. multicoloured	50	75
160	10 s. multicoloured	65	1·25
161	20 s. apple-green, black and bright purple	90	2·50
162	40 s. apple-green, black and yellow-orange	1·50	5·50
149/62	*Set of* 14	4·50	10·00

Designs: *As T* **23**—20 c. Sugar; 30 c. Tobacco; 40 c. Onions; 50 c. Tomatoes; 70 c. Tea; 80 c. Bananas. *As T* **24**—2 s. Pineapples; 3 s. Coffee; 5 s. Oranges; 10 s. Groundnuts; 20 s. Cotton; 40 s. Runner Beans.

Face value colours: 5 s. green; 10 s. brown; 20 s. bright purple; 40 s. yellow-orange. For 5 s. to 40 s. with colours changed see Nos. 220/3.

Nos. 149 and 153 exist in coils constructed from normal sheets.

1976 (15 Apr). *Telecommunications Development. As Nos.* 56/60 *of Kenya, but inscr* "UGANDA".

163	50 c. Microwave tower	10	10
164	1 s. Cordless switchboard	10	10
165	2 s. Telephone	20	25
166	3 s. Message Switching Centre	30	45
163/6	*Set of* 4	60	70
MS167	120 × 120 mm. Nos. 163/6	90	1·25

Nos. 164 and 166 exist imperforate from stock dispersed by the liquidator of Format International Security Printers Ltd.

1976 (5 July). *Olympic Games, Montreal. As Nos.* 61/5 *of Kenya, but inscr* "UGANDA".

168	50 c. Akii Bua, hurdler	10	10
169	1 s. Filbert Bayi, runner	10	10
170	2 s. Steve Muchoki, boxer	30	30
171	3 s. East African flags	40	45
168/71	*Set of* 4	75	75
MS172	129 × 154 mm. Nos. 168/71	4·50	5·00

Nos. 168/70 exist imperforate from stock dispersed by the liquidator of Format International Security Printers Ltd.

1976 (4 Oct). *Railway Transport. As Nos.* 66/70 *of Kenya, but inscr* "UGANDA".

173	50 c. Tanzania–Zambia railway	15	10
174	1 s. Nile Bridge, Uganda	15	10
175	2 s. Nakuru Station, Kenya	50	45
176	3 s. Class A loco, 1896	55	55
173/6	*Set of* 4	1·25	1·00
MS177	154 × 103 mm. Nos. 173/6	2·75	2·50

Nos. 173/7 exist imperforate from stock dispersed by the liquidator of Format International Security Printers Ltd.

1977 (10 Jan). *Game Fish of East Africa. As Nos.* 71/5 *of Kenya, but inscr* "UGANDA".

178	50 c. Nile Perch	15	10
179	1 s. Nile Mouthbrooder	20	10
180	3 s. Sailfish	70	40
181	5 s. Black Marlin	1·00	60
178/81	*Set of* 4	1·90	1·00
MS182	153×129 mm. Nos. 178/81	4·75	2·00

1977 (15 Jan). *Second World Black and African Festival of Arts and Culture, Nigeria. As Nos.* 76/80 *of Kenya, but inscr* "UGANDA".

183	50 c. Maasai Manyatta (village)	10	10
184	1 s. "Heartbeat of Africa" (Ugandan dancers)	10	10
185	2 s. Makonde sculpture	25	55
186	3 s. "Early Man and Technology" (skinning hippopotamus)	35	85
183/6	*Set of* 4	75	1·40
MS187	132 × 109 mm. Nos. 183/6	1·50	2·25

1977 (5 Apr). *25th Anniv of Safari Rally. As Nos.* 81/5 *of Kenya, but inscr* "UGANDA".

188	50 c. Rally-car and villagers	10	10
189	1 s. Starting-line	10	10
190	2 s. Car fording river	25	35
191	5 s. Car and elephants	80	1·00
188/91	*Set of* 4	1·10	1·40
MS192	126 × 93 mm. Nos. 188/91	1·75	2·50

1977 (30 June). *Centenary of Ugandan Church. As Nos.* 86/90 *of Kenya, but inscr* "UGANDA".

193	50 c. Canon Kivebulaya	10	10
194	1 s. Modern Namirembe Cathedral	10	10
195	2 s. Old Namirembe Cathedral	20	40
196	5 s. Early congregation, Kigezi	45	90
193/6	*Set of* 4	75	1·25
MS197	126 × 89 mm. Nos. 193/6	1·00	1·75

80c

(**25**)

26 Shot Putting

1977 (22 Aug). *Design as No.* 155 *surch with T* **25** *in mauve by Harrison.*

198	80 c. on 60 c. multicoloured	30	20
	a. Surch omitted	£180	

A 60 c. stamp was to have been added to Nos. 149/62 using the design of the 80 c. (bananas), but it was cancelled and those already printed were surcharged to make No. 198.

1977 (26 Sept). *Endangered Species. As Nos.* 96/101 *of Kenya, but inscr* "UGANDA".

199	50 c. Pancake Tortoise	30	10
200	1 s. Nile Crocodile	45	10
201	2 s. Hunter's Hartebeest	2·00	40
202	3 s. Red Colobus monkey	2·50	75
203	5 s. Dugong	2·50	1·00
199/203	*Set of* 5	7·00	2·00
MS204	127 × 101 mm. Nos. 200/3	7·00	4·00

1978 (10 Apr). *World Cup Football Championship, Argentina (1st issue). As Nos.* 122/6 *of Kenya but inscr* "UGANDA".

205	50 c. Joe Kadenge and forwards	15	10
206	1 s. Mohamed Chuma and cup presentation	15	10
207	2 s. Omari Kidevu and goalmouth scene	30	35
208	5 s. Polly Ouma and forwards	50	85
205/8	*Set of* 4	1·00	1·10
MS209	136 × 81 mm. Nos. 205/8	2·00	2·75

(Litho Questa)

1978 (28 Aug). *Commonwealth Games, Edmonton. T* **26** *and similar horiz designs. Multicoloured. P* 14.

210	50 c. Type **26**	10	10
211	1 s. Long jumping	15	10
212	2 s. Running	20	30
213	5 s. Boxing	40	70
210/13	*Set of* 4	75	1·00
MS214	114×85 mm. Nos. 210/13. P 12½×12	1·50	3·00

1978 (11 Sept). *World Cup Football Championship, Argentina (2nd issue). Designs as Nos. 205/8 but additionally inscr* "WORLD CUP 1978".

215 50 c. Polly Ouma and forwards 15 10
216 2 s. Omari Kidevu and goalmouth scene .. 30 40
217 5 s. Joe Kadenge and forwards 60 90
218 10 s. Mohamed Chuma and cup presentation 90 1·60
215/18 .. .. *Set of* 4 1·75 2·75
MS219 140×87 mm. Nos. 215/18. P 12×11½ .. 2·00 2·75

(Litho Questa)

1978. *As Nos.* 159/62 *but printing process and colours changed.*

220 5 s. multicoloured (face value in blue) .. 55 70
221 10 s. multicoloured (face value in magenta) .. 60 1·00
222 20 s. multicoloured (face value in brown) .. 70 1·00
223 40 s. multicoloured (face value in red) .. 1·00 1·40
220/3 .. .. *Set of* 4 2·50 3·75

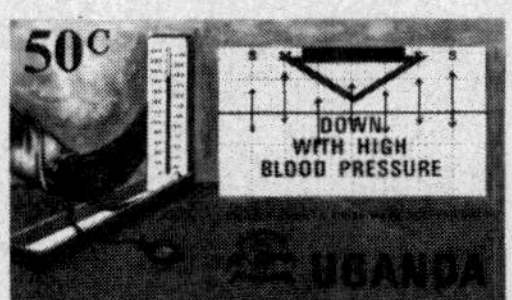

27 Measurements of High Blood Pressure

(Litho Questa)

1978 (25 Sept). *"Down with High Blood Pressure". T* **27** *and similar horiz designs. Multicoloured. P* 14 × 13½.

224 50 c. Type **27** 15 10
225 1 s. Hypertension and the heart 15 10
226 2 s. Fundus of the eye in hypertension .. 40 35
227 5 s. Kidney and high blood pressure.. .. 75 1·00
224/7 .. .. *Set of* 4 1·25 1·40
MS228 180 × 115 mm. Nos. 224/7 .. .. 2·00 2·75

28 Off Loading Cattle

(Litho Questa)

1978 (16 Dec). *75th Anniv of Powered Flight. T* **28** *and similar horiz designs. Multicoloured. P* 14.

229 1 s. Type **28** 20 10
230 1 s. 50, "Domestic services" (passengers boarding Britten Norman Islander light aircraft) 30 15
231 2 s. 70, Export of Uganda coffee 30 35
232 10 s. "Time machines in the air" (Wright Flyer III and Concorde) .. .. 1·00 1·25
229/32 .. .. *Set of* 4 1·60 1·60
MS233 166×110 mm. Nos. 229/32 .. .. 2·25 2·75

29 Queen Elizabeth II leaving Owen Falls Dam

(Des BG Studio. Litho Ashton-Potter)

1979 (15 Feb). *25th Anniv of Coronation* (1978). *T* **29** *and similar horiz designs. Multicoloured. P* 12½ × 12.

234 1 s. Type **29** 15 10
235 1 s. 50, Regalia 20 10
236 2 s. 70, Coronation ceremony 45 20
237 10 s. Royal family on balcony of Buckingham Palace 80 80
234/7 .. .. *Set of* 4 1·40 1·00
MS238 150 × 102 mm. Nos. 234/7 .. .. 1·40 1·25

30 Dr. Joseph Kiwanuka (first Ugandan bishop)

(Des G. Vasarhelyi. Litho Questa)

1979 (15 Feb). *Centenary of Catholic Church in Uganda. T* **30** *and similar horiz designs. Multicoloured. P* 14.

239 1 s. Type **30** 10 10
240 1 s. 50, Lubaga Cathedral 10 10
241 2 s. 70, Ugandan pilgrimage to Rome, Holy Year, 1975 .. .. 15 25
242 10 s. Friar Lourdel-Mapeera (early missionary) 50 80
239/42 .. .. *Set of* 4 75 1·10
MS243 128 × 91 mm. Nos. 239/42 .. .. 1·00 2·00

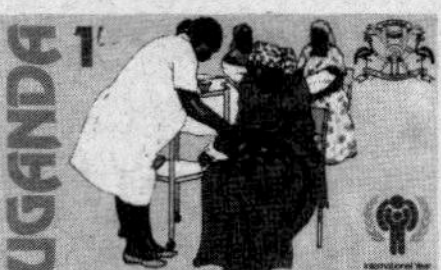

31 Immunisation of Children

(Des J.W. Litho Questa)

1979 (28 June). *International Year of the Child. T* **31** *and similar horiz designs. Multicoloured. P* 14.

244 1 s. Type **31** 10 10
245 1 s. 50, Handicapped children at play .. 15 20
246 2 s. 70, Ugandan I.Y.C. emblem 20 35
247 10 s. Children in class.. .. .. .. 60 90
244/7 .. .. *Set of* 4 85 1·40
MS248 136 × 113 mm. Nos. 244/7 .. .. 1·10 2·00

UGANDA LIBERATED 1979 (32)

UGANDA LIBERATED 1979 (33)

UGANDA LIBERATED 1979 (34)

1979 (12 July–16 Aug?). *Liberation.*

(*a*) *Nos.* 149/55 *optd with T* **32** *and* 156/62 *with T* **33** (12 July)

249 10 c. black, apple-green and yellow-brown .. 10 10
250 20 c. multicoloured 10 10
251 30 c. multicoloured 10 10
252 40 c. multicoloured 10 10
253 50 c. multicoloured 10 10
254 70 c. black, apple-green and light blue-green 10 10
255 80 c. multicoloured 10 10
a. Opt double £110
256 1 s. multicoloured 15 15
257 2 s. multicoloured 20 25
258 3 s. multicoloured 35 40
259 5 s. multicoloured 55 60
260 10 s. multicoloured .. .. 80 1·25
261 20 s. apple-green, black and bright purple .. 1·50 2·40
262 40 s. apple-green, black and yellow-orange .. 3·00 4·75
a. Opt double £130

(*b*) *Nos.* 210/13 (*Commonwealth Games*) *optd with T* **34** (1 Aug)

263 50 c. Type **26** 10 10
264 1 s. Long jumping 15 20
265 2 s. Running 25 30
266 5 s. Boxing 60 65

(*c*) *Nos.* 207, 215 *and* 217/18 (*World Cup Football Championships*) *optd with T* **34** (1 Aug)

267 50 c. Polly Ouma and forwards 10 10
268 2 s. Omari Kidevu and goal-mouth scene .. 20 30
a. Optd on No. 216 .. .. 9·00 17·00
269 5 s. Joe Kadenge and forwards 55 65
270 10 s. Mohamed Chuma and cup presentation 1·00 1·40

(*d*) *Nos.* 220/3 *optd with T* **33** (1979)

271 5 s. multicoloured 55 60
272 10 s. multicoloured .. .. 80 1·25
273 20 s. multicoloured .. .. 1·25 2·40
274 40 s. multicoloured .. .. 2·00 4·75

(*e*) *Nos.* 229/32 (*75th Anniv of Powered Flight*) *optd with T* **34** (1 Aug)

275 1 s. Type **28** 30 20
276 1 s. 50, "Domestic services" (passengers boarding Britten Norman Islander light aircraft) 40 25
277 2 s. 70, Export of Uganda coffee 50 55
278 10 s. "Time machines in the air" (Wright Flyer III and Concorde) .. .. 2·25 2·00

(*f*) *Nos.* 234/7 (*25th Anniv of Coronation*) *optd as T* **33** *or surch also and No.* **MS**238 *additionally inscr* "Diplomatic Relations Normalised" *with Ugandan and British flags replacing portrait of Amin* (12 July)

279 1 s. Type **29** 10 20
280 1 s. 50, Regalia 15 20
281 2 s. 70, Coronation ceremony 20 30
282 15 s. on 10 s. Royal family on balcony of Buckingham Palace .. .. .. 85 1·50
MS283 150×102 mm. Nos. 234/6 and 15 s. as No. 237* .. .. 2·00 3·25

* The sheet contains unoverprinted stamps; the additional inscriptions and changes in design appear only on the sheet margin.

(*g*) *Nos.* 239/42 (*Centenary of Catholic Church in Uganda*) *optd with T* **34** *and No.* **MS**243 *with additional inscr* "FREEDOM OF WORSHIP DECLARED" *replacing part of the margin decoration* (1 Aug)

284 1 s. Type **30** 10 20
285 1 s. 50, Lubaga Cathedral 15 25
286 2 s. 70, Ugandan pilgrimage to Rome, Holy Year, 1975 .. .. 30 45
287 10 s. Friar Lourdel-Mapeera (early missionary) .. .. 90 1·60
MS288 128×91 mm. Nos. 239/42*. P 12½×12 (1979) .. .. 2·25 2·75

* The sheet contains the original unoverprinted stamps; the additional inscription appears on the sheet margin.

(*h*) *Nos.* 244/8 (*International Year of the Child*) *optd with T* **34** (16 Aug)

289 1 s. Type **31** 15 20
290 1 s. 50, Handicapped children at play .. 20 25
291 2 s. 70, Ugandan I.Y.C. emblem 40 45
292 10 s. Children in class.. .. .. .. 1·25 1·40
MS293 136 × 113 mm. Nos. 289/92 .. .. 2·50 3·25
249/82, 284/7 *and* 289/92 .. .. *Set of* 42 20·00 29·00

MINIMUM PRICE

The minimum price quote is 10p which represents a handling charge rather than a basis for valuing common stamps. For further notes about prices see introductory pages.

35 Radio Wave Symbol

(Des G. Vasarhelyi. Litho Questa)

1979 (11 Sept). *50th Anniv of International Consultative Radio Committee and International Telecommunications Union. P* 14.

294 **35** 1 s. multicoloured 10 10
295 1 s. 50, multicoloured 15 10
296 2 s. 70, multicoloured 20 35
297 10 s. multicoloured .. .. 60 1·10
294/7 .. .. *Set of* 4 90 1·50

36 20s. Definitive Stamp of 1965 and Sir Rowland Hill

(Des BG Studio. Litho Questa)

1979 (Oct). *Death Centenary of Sir Rowland Hill. T* **36** *and similar horiz designs showing stamps and Sir Rowland Hill. Multicoloured. P* 14.

298 1 s. Type **36** 10 10
299 1 s. 50, 1967 13th Commonwealth Parliamentary Association Conference 50 c. commemorative 15 10
300 2 s. 70, 1962 Independence 20 s. commemorative 20 30
301 10 s. Uganda Protectorate 1898 1 a. .. 60 1·25
298/301.. .. .. *Set of* 4 85 1·40
MS302 154×98 mm. Nos. 298/301 .. .. 90 1·50

37 Impala **38** Lions with Cub

(Des G. Drummond. Litho Questa)

1979 (3 Dec)–**82.** *Wildlife. Horiz designs as T* **37** (10 *to* 80 *c.*) *or T* **38** (1 *to* 40 *s.*). *Multicoloured. P* 14×13½ (10 *to* 80 *c.*) *or* 14 (1 *to* 40 *s.*) A. *No imprint date.* B. *With* "1982" *imprint date at foot of design* (1982).

			A		B	
303	10 c. Type **37**	10	20	†	
304	20 c. Large-spotted Genet ..	10	20	†	
305	30 c. Thomson's Gazelle ..	15	20	†	
306	50 c. Lesser Bushbaby.. ..	15	10	†	
307	80 c. Hunting Dog	20	10	†	
308	1 s. Type **38**	30	10	20	10
309	1 s. 50, Gorilla	45	10	†	
310	2 s. Common Zebra	45	20	30	20
311	2 s. 70, Leopard with cub ..	60	20	†	
312	3 s. 50, Black Rhinoceros ..	70	55	†	
313	5 s. Waterbuck	70	55	40	85
314	10 s. African Buffalo	70	1·00	†	
315	20 s. Hippopotamus	1·00	2·00	†	
316	40 s. African Elephant ..	1·75	3·50	†	
303A/16A	.. *Set of* 14	6·50	8·00	†	
308B/13B	.. *Set of* 3	†		80	1·00

For designs as Nos. 308/12 and 315/16, but with face values in revalued currency, see Nos. 433/9.

LONDON 1980

(39)

40 Rotary Emblem

1980 (6 May). *"London 1980" International Stamp Exhibition. Nos.* 298/302 *optd as T* **39**.

317 1 s. Type **36** 15 10
318 1 s. 50, 1967 13th Commonwealth Parliamentary Association Conference 50 c. commemorative 20 10
319 2 s. 70, 1962 Independence 20s. commemorative 35 25
320 10 s. Uganda Protectorate 1898 1a. 80 80
317/20 .. .. *Set of* 4 1·40 1·10
MS321 154 × 99 mm. Nos. 317/20 .. .. 1·40 1·75

(Des BG Studio. Litho Questa)

1980 (25 Aug). *75th Anniv of Rotary International. T* **40** *and similar multicoloured design. P* 14.

322 1 s. Type **40** 10 10
323 20 s. Paul Harris (founder) with wheel-barrow containing "Rotary projects" (*horiz*) .. 1·50 1·75
MS324 100 × 76 mm. Nos. 322/3. Imperf. .. .. 2·10 2·50

FOOTBALL
GOLD MEDALISTS, C.S.S.R.

41 Football (42)

(Des G. Vasarhelyi. Litho Questa)

1980 (29 Dec). *Olympic Games, Moscow. T* **41** *and similar horiz designs. Multicoloured. P* 14.

325 1 s. Type **41** 10 10
326 2 s. Relay 10 10
327 10 s. Hurdles 35 65
328 20 s. Boxing .. .. 60 1·75
325/8 .. .. *Set of* 4 1·00 2·25
MS329 118×90 mm. 2 s. 70, 3 s., 5 s., 25 s. As Nos. 325/8 .. .. 1·25 2·25

1980 (29 Dec). *Olympic Games, Moscow. Medal Winners. Nos.* 325/9 *optd as T* **42**.

330 1 s. Type **41** 10 10
331 2 s. Relay 10 15
332 10 s. Hurdles 35 60
333 20 s. Boxing .. .. 60 1·25
330/3 .. .. *Set of* 4 1·00 1·75
MS334 118×90 mm. 2 s. 70, 3 s., 5 s., 25 s. As Nos. 330/3 .. .. 1·00 2·50

Overprints:—2s. "RELAY GOLD MEDALIST U.S.S.R."; 10s. "HURDLES 110 m. GOLD MEDALIST THOMAS MUNKLET, D.D.R."; 20s. "BOXING WELTERWEIGHT SILVER MEDALIST JOHN MUGABI, UGANDA".

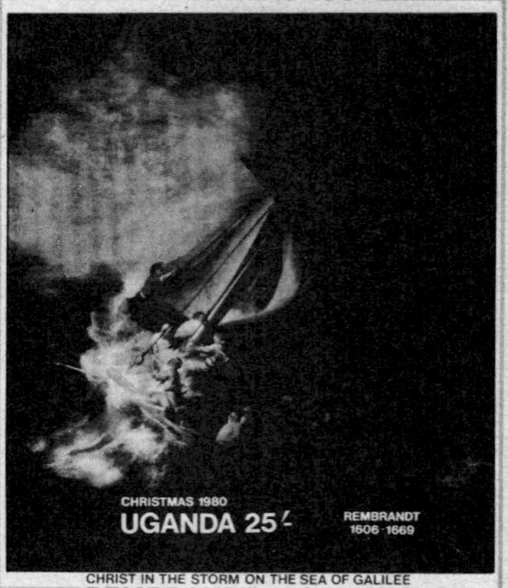

43 "Christ in the Storm on the Sea of Galilee" (painting, Rembrandt)

1980 (31 Dec). *Christmas. Sheet* 79 × 101 *mm. Litho. Imperf.*

MS335 **43** 25 s. multicoloured .. .. .. 4·25 4·75

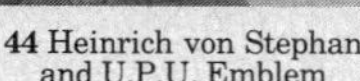

44 Heinrich von Stephan and U.P.U. Emblem 45 Tower of London

(Des BG Studio. Litho Questa)

1981 (2 June). *150th Birth Anniv of Heinrich von Stephan (founder of U.P.U.). T* **44** *and similar horiz designs. Multicoloured. P* 14.

336 1 s. Type **44** 10 10
337 2 s. U.P.U. Headquarters 15 15
338 2 s. 70, Air mail, 1935 .. .. 40 20
339 10 s. Mail transport by train, 1927 .. .. 1·10 80
336/9 .. .. *Set of* 4 1·60 1·10
MS340 112 × 95 mm. Nos. 336/9 .. .. .. 2·75 1·90

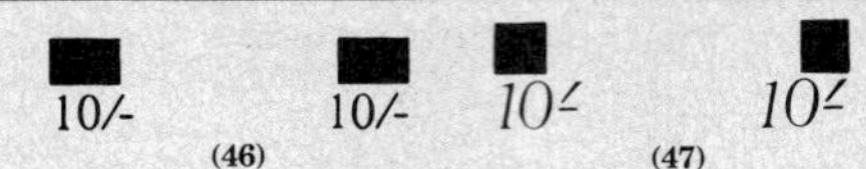

(46) (47)

(Des J.W. Litho Questa)

1981 (July). *Royal Wedding. T* **45** *and similar vert designs. Multicoloured. P* 14. (*a*) *Unissued stamps surcharged* (13 July). A. *As T* **46.** B. *As T* **47**.

		A		B	
341	10 s. on 1 s. Prince Charles and Lady Diana Spencer	20	50	15	20
	a. Surch on 5 s. value ..	23·00	—	†	
	b. Surch on 20 s. value ..	21·00	—	†	
	c. Surch omitted	50·00	—	†	
342	50 s. on 5 s. Type **45**	30	70	20	30
	a. Surch omitted	40·00	—	†	
343	200 s. on 20 s. Prince Charles at Balmoral	60	2·00	45	80
	a. Surch omitted	75·00	—	†	
	b. Surch inverted	25·00	—	†	
	c. Surch inverted on 1 s. value	25·00	—	†	
	d. Surch inverted on 5 s. value	25·00	—	†	
341/3	.. .. .. *Set of* 3	1·00	2·75	70	1·10
MS344	95×80 mm. 250 s. on 25 s. Royal Mews	3·50	6·00	1·00	1·00
	a. Surch omitted	—	—	†	

(*b*) *Redrawn with new face values. Background colours changed* (29 July)

345 10 s. As No. 341 .. .. 10 15
346 50 s. Type **45** 15 20
347 200 s. As No. 343 .. .. 30 40
345/7 .. .. *Set of* 3 40 65
MS348 95 × 80 mm. 250 s. As No. **MS**344 .. 50 65

Nos. 345/7 also exist perforated 12 (*price for set of* 3 40*p mint or used*) from additional sheetlets of 5 stamps and one label. These stamps have changed background colours.

The issue was originally printed with face values of 1, 5 and 20 s. and 25 s. for the miniature sheet. Before it could be placed on sale the Uganda currency was devalued and the stamps were surcharged, and later reprinted with corrected face values.

48 "Sleeping Woman before Green Shutters"

(Des J.W. Litho Questa)

1981 (21 Sept). *Birth Centenary of Picasso. T* **48** *and similar multicoloured designs. P* 14 × 13½.

349 10 s. Type **48** 10 10
350 20 s. "Bullfight" 20 20
351 30 s. "Detail of a Nude asleep in a Landscape" 25 30
352 200 s. "Interior with a Girl Drawing" .. .. 2·25 3·25
349/52 .. .. *Set of* 4 2·50 3·50
MS353 120 × 146 mm. 250 s. "Minotaure" (112 × 139 *mm*). Imperf .. .. 3·50 4·00

49 Deaf People using Sign Language

(Des Design Images. Litho Format)

1981 (28 Dec). *International Year of Disabled Persons. T* **49** *and similar horiz designs. Multicoloured. P* 15.

354 1 s. Type **49** 10 10
355 10 s. Disabled teacher in classroom 15 10
356 50 s. Teacher and disabled children 70 50
357 200 s. Blind person with guide dog .. .. 2·00 2·00
354/7 .. .. *Set of* 4 2·50 2·25
MS358 122×93 mm. Nos. 354/7 .. .. 5·00 4·00

50 Footballers

(Des G. Vasarhelyi. Litho Questa)

1982 (11 Jan). *World Cup Football Championship, Spain. T* **50** *and similar horiz designs showing World Cup* (250 *s.*) *or footballers* (*others*). *P* 14.

359 1 s. multicoloured 10 10
360 10 s. multicoloured 15 10
361 50 s. multicoloured 70 50
362 200 s. multicoloured .. .. 2·00 2·00
359/62 .. .. *Set of* 4 2·50 2·25
MS363 116×77 mm. 250 s. multicoloured .. 3·00 3·00

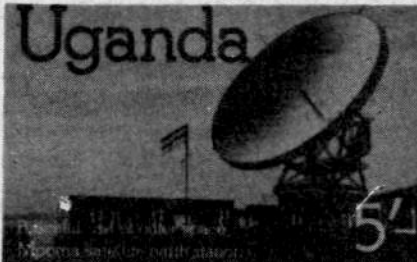

51 Mpoma Satellite Earth Station

(Des Artists International. Litho Format)

1982 (10 May). *"Peaceful Use of Outer Space". T* **51** *and similar horiz designs. Multicoloured. P* 15.

364 5 s. Type **51** 25 15
365 10 s. *Pioneer II* (satellite) 35 35
366 50 s. Space Shuttle .. .. 1·75 2·00
367 100 s. *Voyager* 2 (satellite) .. .. .. 2·75 4·00
364/7 .. .. *Set of* 4 4·75 6·00
MS368 118×89 mm. 150 s. Space Shuttle (*different*) .. .. 3·75 2·00

No. 364 exists imperforate from stock dispersed by the liquidator of Format International Security Printers Ltd.

21st BIRTHDAY
HRH Princess of Wales
JULY 1 1982

52 Dr. Robert Koch (53)

(Des R. Vigurs. Litho Questa)

1982 (14 June). *Centenary of Robert Koch's Discovery of Tubercle Bacillus. T* **52** *and similar multicoloured designs. P* 14.

369 1 s. Type **52** 30 10
370 10 s. Microscope .. .. 1·25 40
371 50 s. Ugandans receiving vaccinations .. 3·00 2·50
372 100 s. Tubercle virus .. .. 4·50 4·25
369/72 .. .. *Set of* 4 8·00 6·50
MS373 85 × 64 mm. 150 s. Medical College classroom scene (*horiz*) .. .. 7·00 3·25

1982 (7 July). *21st Birthday of Princess of Wales. Nos.* 345/8 *optd with T* **53.** *P* 14.

374 10 s. Prince Charles and Lady Diana Spencer 20 10
375 50 s. Type **45** 50 40
376 200 s. Prince Charles at Balmoral .. .. 1·50 1·25
374/6 .. .. *Set of* 3 2·00 1·50
MS377 95 × 82 mm. 250 s. Royal Mews .. .. 2·50 2·00

Nos. 374/6 also exist perforated 12 (*price for set of* 3 £1·25 *mint or used*) from additional sheetlets of 5 stamps and one label. These stamps have changed background colours.

Nos. 374/7, and the sheetlets, also exist with the top line of the overprint shown as "21st Birthday" instead of "21st BIRTHDAY" as in Type **53** (*Price for set of* 3 *and miniature sheet* £6 *mint*).

Examples of an unissued 150 s. miniature sheet for the 20th Anniversary of Independence exist from stock dispersed by the liquidator of Format International Security Printers Ltd.

54 Yellow-billed Hornbill 55 Scout Band

(Des Artists International. Litho Questa)

1982 (12 July). *Birds. T* **54** *and similar vert designs. Multicoloured. P* 14.

378 1 s. Type **54** 15 10
379 20 s. Superb Starling 60 35
380 50 s. Bateleur .. .. 1·25 1·75
381 100 s. Saddle-bill Stork .. .. 2·00 2·50
378/81 .. .. *Set of* 4 3·50 4·25
MS382 115×85 mm. 200 s. Laughing Dove .. 9·00 9·00

(Des G. Vasarhelyi. Litho Questa)

1982 (23 Aug). *75th Anniv of Boy Scout Movement. T* **55** *and similar horiz designs. Multicoloured. P* 14.

383 5 s. Type **55** 40 10
384 20 s. Scout receiving Bata Shoe trophy .. 1·10 45
385 50 s. Scouts with wheelchair patient .. .. 2·25 2·25
386 100 s. First aid instruction .. .. .. 3·00 3·50
383/6 .. .. *Set of* 4 6·00 5·75
MS387 112×85 mm. 150 s. Lord Baden-Powell .. .. 4·00 3·00

NEW INFORMATION

The editor is always interested to correspond with people who have new information that will improve or correct the Catalogue.

56 Swearing-in of Roosevelt

(Des Design Images. Litho Format)

1982 (8 Nov). *250th Birth Anniv of George Washington (Nos. 389/90) and Birth Centenary of Franklin D. Roosevelt (others). T* **56** *and similar horiz designs. Multicoloured. P* 15.

388 50 s. Type **56** 30 30
389 200 s. Swearing-in of Washington .. .. 75 1·25
MS390 100×69 mm. 150 s. Washington at Mt Vernon .. .. 1·00 1·25
MS391 100×70 mm. 150 s. Roosevelt at Hyde Park Mansion .. .. 1·00 1·25

Nos. 388/91 exist imperforate from stock dispersed by the liquidator of Format International Security Printers Ltd.

57 Italy v West Germany

(Des D. Miller. Litho Format)

1982 (30 Dec). *World Cup Football Championship Winners. T* **57** *and similar horiz designs. Multicoloured. P* 14½.

392 10 s. Type **57** 30 25
393 200 s. Victorious Italian team .. .. .. 1·50 3·50
MS394 97×117 mm. 250 s. Espana '82 emblem with Spanish and Italian flags .. .. .. 1·50 2·00

Nos. 392/4 exist imperforate from stock dispersed by the liquidator of Format International Security Printers Ltd.

58 Dancers

500th ANNIVERSARY BIRTH OF RAPHAEL

Saint George and the Dragon

UGANDA 5/-

59 "St. George and the Dragon" (Raphael)

(Des and litho Questa)

1983 (14 Mar). *Commonwealth Day. Cultural Art. T* **58** *and similar horiz designs. Multicoloured. P* 14.

395 5 s. Type **58** 10 10
396 20 s. Traditional currency 15 20
397 50 s. Homestead 35 55
398 100 s. Drums .. .. 70 1·10
395/8 .. .. *Set of* 4 1·10 1·75

(Des Design Images. Litho Questa)

1983 (16 Apr). *500th Birth Anniv of Raphael (painter). T* **59** *and similar vert designs. Multicoloured. P* 13½.

399 5 s. Type **59** 10 10
400 20 s. "St. George and the Dragon" (*different*) 40 30
401 50 s. "Crossing the Red Sea" (*detail*) 80 80
402 200 s. "The Expulsion of Heliodorus" (*detail*) .. 1·50 3·25
399/402 .. .. *Set of* 4 2·50 4·00
MS403 126×101 mm. 250 s. "The Meeting of Pope Leo the Great and Attila the Hun" (*detail*) .. .. 1·40 1·40

60 Map showing Namibia and U.N. Flag

(Des R. Vigurs. Litho Format)

1983 (15 Aug). *Commemorations. T* **60** *and similar horiz design. Multicoloured. P* 15.

404 5 s. Type **60** 10 10
405 200 s. 7th Non-aligned Summit Conference logo 80 2·25

No. 404 exists imperforate from stock dispersed by the liquidator of Format International Security Printers Ltd.

BOYS BRIGADE CENTENARY 1883-1983

61 Elephants in Grassland (**62**)

(Des J. Iskowitz. Litho Format)

1983 (22 Aug). *Endangered Species (1st series). T* **61** *and similar multicoloured designs. P* 15.

406 5 s. Elephants in "Elephants' Graveyard" 1·25 40
407 10 s. Type **61** .. .. 1·60 40
408 30 s. Elephants at waterhole .. .. 3·50 2·50
409 70 s. Elephants having dust bath .. .. 5·50 6·00
406/9 .. .. *Set of* 4 10·50 8·50
MS410 87×64 mm. 300 s. Grevy's Zebra drinking (*vert*) .. .. 5·00 3·25

See also Nos. 642 and 988/92.

1983 (19 Sept). *Centenary of Boys' Brigade. Nos. 383/7 optd with T* **62** *or surch also.*

411 5 s. Type **55** 10 10
412 20 s. Scout receiving Bata Shoe trophy .. 15 15
413 50 s. Scouts with wheelchair patient .. 25 30
414 400 s. on 100 s. First aid instruction .. 2·40 2·75
411/14 .. .. *Set of* 4 2·50 3·00
MS415 112×85 mm. 150 s. Lord Baden-Powell .. 90 1·25

100/-

63 Mpoma Satellite Earth Station (**64**)

(Des D. Dorfman. Litho Format)

1983 (3 Oct). *World Communications Year. T* **63** *and similar horiz designs. Multicoloured. P* 15.

416 20 s. Type **63** 25 15
417 50 s. Railroad computer and operator .. 65 85
418 70 s. Cameraman filming lions .. .. 75 1·50
419 100 s. Aircraft cockpit .. .. .. 95 2·00
416/19 .. .. *Set of* 4 2·40 4·00
MS420 128×103 mm. 300 s. Communications satellite .. .. 1·25 1·75

No. 416 has the "o" omitted from "Station".

1983 (7 Oct). *Nos.* 303, 305/7, 308A, 309 *and* 313A *surch as T* **64**.

421 100 s. on 10 c. Type **37** 65 55
422 135 s. on 1 s. Type **38** 80 70
423 175 s. on 30 c. Thomson's Gazelle 95 85
424 200 s. on 50 c. Lesser Bushbaby .. .. 1·10 1·00
425 400 s. on 80 c. Hunting Dog .. .. 2·00 2·00
426 700 s. on 5 s. Waterbuck .. .. .. 3·25 4·00
427 1000 s. on 1 s. 50, Gorilla .. .. 5·50 7·00
421/7 .. .. *Set of* 7 13·00 14·50

65 The Nativity

(Des PAD Studio. Litho Questa)

1983 (12 Dec). *Christmas. T* **65** *and similar horiz designs. Multicoloured. P* 14.

428 10 s. Type **65** 10 10
429 50 s. Shepherds and Angels 25 30
430 175 s. Flight into Egypt .. .. .. 80 1·25
431 400 s. Angels blowing trumpets .. .. 1·90 2·75
428/31 .. .. *Set of* 4 2·75 4·00
MS432 85×57 mm. 300 s. The Three Kings .. 1·40 1·75

1983 (19 Dec). *Designs as Nos.* 308/12 *and* 315/16 *but with face values in revalued currency. Without imprint date.*

433 100 s. Type **38** 90 35
434 135 s. Gorilla .. .. 1·25 50
435 175 s. Common Zebra .. .. .. 1·40 80
436 200 s. Leopard with cub .. .. .. 1·75 90
437 400 s. Black Rhinoceros .. .. .. 3·00 3·25
438 700 s. African Elephant .. .. .. 6·00 6·50
439 1000 s. Hippopotamus .. .. .. 5·50 7·50
433/9 .. .. *Set of* 7 17·00 18·00

66 Ploughing with Oxen

(Des J.W. Litho Questa)

1984 (16 Jan). *World Food Day. T* **66** *and similar horiz design. Multicoloured. P* 14.

440 10 s. Type **66** 15 10
441 300 s. Harvesting bananas .. .. .. 4·25 5·50

67 Ruth Kyalisiima, Sportsman of the Year 1983

(Des J. Iskowitz. Litho Format)

1984 (1 Oct). *Olympic Games, Los Angeles. T* **67** *and similar multicoloured designs. P* 15.

442 5 s. Type **67** 10 10
443 115 s. Javelin-throwing 50 80
444 155 s. Wrestling 60 90
445 175 s. Rowing .. .. 70 1·00
442/5 .. .. *Set of* 4 1·60 2·50
MS446 108×79 mm. 500 s. Fund-raising walk (*vert*) .. .. 90 1·25

68 Entebbe Airport

(Des BG Studio. Litho Format)

1984 (29 Oct). *40th Anniv of International Civil Aviation Organization. T* **68** *and similar horiz designs. Multicoloured. P* 15.

447 5 s. Type **68** 15 10
448 115 s. Loading cargo plane .. .. .. 1·50 1·75
449 155 s. Uganda police helicopter .. .. 2·50 2·75
450 175 s. East African Civil Flying School, Soroti 2·75 3·25
447/50 .. .. *Set of* 4 6·25 7·00
MS451 100×70 mm. 250 s. Balloon race .. 2·00 1·75

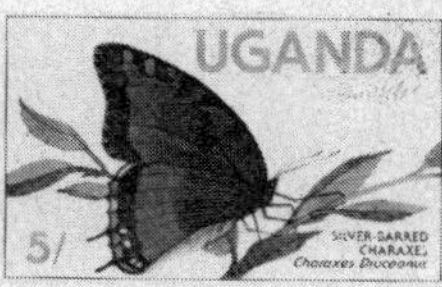

69 *Charaxes druceanus*

(Des J. Johnson. Litho Questa)

1984 (19 Nov). *Butterflies. T* **69** *and similar horiz designs. Multicoloured. P* 14.

452 5 s. Type **69** 30 10
453 115 s. *Papilio lormieri* .. .. .. 2·50 2·00
454 155 s. *Druryia antimachus* .. .. .. 3·00 2·50
455 175 s. *Salamis temora* .. .. .. 4·25 3·25
452/5 .. .. *Set of* 4 9·00 7·00
MS456 127×90 mm. 250 s. *Colotis protomedia* 2·25 2·25

70 Blue-finned Notho

(Des Associated Creative Designers. Litho Format)

1985 (1 Apr–10 June). *Lake Fishes. T* **70** *and similar horiz designs. Multicoloured. P* 15.

457 5 s. Type **70** 30 40
458 10 s. Semutundu 40 40
459 50 s. Grey Bichir 75 30
460 100 s. Walking Catfish 85 30
461 135 s. Elephant-snout Fish (10 June) .. 1·25 1·00
462 175 s. Lake Victoria Squeaker .. .. 1·40 1·60
463 205 s. Brown's Haplochromis .. .. 1·40 2·00
464 400 s. Nile Perch .. .. 1·50 2·25
465 700 s. African Lungfish .. .. .. 1·75 2·75
466 1000 s. Radcliffe's Barb .. .. .. 1·75 3·00
467 2500 s. Electric Catfish (10 June) .. .. 1·75 3·75
457/67 .. .. *Set of* 11 12·00 16·00

71 The Last Supper

(Des Associated Creative Designers. Litho Questa)

1985 (13 May). *Easter. T* **71** *and similar horiz designs. Multicoloured. P* 14.

468 5 s. Type **71** 10 10
469 115 s. Christ showing the nail marks to Thomas .. .. 1·25 1·25
470 155 s. The raising of the Cross .. .. 1·40 2·00
471 175 s. Pentecost .. .. 1·75 2·50
468/71 .. .. *Set of* 4 4·00 5·25
MS472 99×70 mm. 250 s. The last prayer in the Garden .. .. 80 1·25

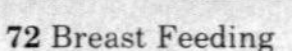

72 Breast Feeding

73 Queen Elizabeth the Queen Mother

(Des Associated Creative Designers. Litho Questa)

1985 (29 July). *U.N.I.C.E.F. Child Survival Campaign. T* **72** *and similar horiz designs. Multicoloured. P* 14.

473	5 s. Type **72**	10	10
474	115 s. Growth monitoring	1·75	1·75
475	155 s. Immunisation	2·25	2·25
476	175 s. Oral re-hydration therapy	2·50	2·50
473/6	*Set of* 4	6·00	6·00
MS477	75×55 mm. 500 s. Pregnant woman preparing nourishing food	4·25	5·00

(Des J.W. Litho Questa)

1985 (21 Aug). *Life and Times of Queen Elizabeth the Queen Mother and Decade for Women. T* **73** *and similar vert design. Multicoloured. P* 14.

478	1000 s. Type **73**	1·40	2·10
MS479	57×81 mm. 1500 s. The Queen Mother inspecting Kings African Rifles, Kampala	2·25	3·50

74 Sedge Warbler

GOLD MEDALIST
BENITA BROWN-FITZGERALD
USA

(75)

(Des S. Heinmann. Litho Questa)

1985 (21 Aug). *Birth Bicentenary of John J. Audubon (ornithologist) (1st issue). T* **74** *and similar vert designs. Multicoloured. P* 14.

480	115 s. Type **74**	2·00	1·50
481	155 s. Cattle Egret	2·25	1·75
482	175 s. Crested Lark	2·50	2·25
483	500 s. Tufted Duck	3·25	4·50
480/3	*Set of* 4	9·00	9·00
MS484	99×69 mm. 1000 s. Tawny Owl	11·00	10·00

See also Nos. 494/8.

1985 (21 Aug). *Olympic Gold Medal Winners, Los Angeles. Nos. 442/6 optd or surch as T* **75** *in gold.*

485	5 s. Type **67** (optd T **75**)	10	10
486	115 s. Javelin-throwing (optd "GOLD MEDALIST ARTO HAERKOENEN FINLAND")	30	30
487	155 s. Wrestling (optd "GOLD MEDALIST ATSUJI MIYAHARA JAPAN")	40	40
488	1000 s. on 175 s. Rowing (surch "GOLD MEDALIST WEST GERMANY")	2·00	2·00
485/8	*Set of* 4	2·50	2·50
MS489	108×79 mm. 1200 s. on 500 s. Fund-raising walk (surch "MEN'S HURDLES EDWIN MOSES USA")	2·25	2·50

On No. **MS**489 only the new value appears on the stamp, the remainder of the surcharge is on the sheet margin.

76 Women carrying National Women's Day Banner

77 Man beneath Tree laden with Produce (F.A.O.)

(Des and litho Questa)

1985 (1 Nov). *Decade for Women. T* **76** *and similar multicoloured designs. P* 14.

490	5 s. Type **76**	10	10
491	115 s. Girl Guides (*horiz*)	1·75	2·00
492	155 s. Mother Teresa (Nobel Peace Prize winner, 1979)	3·00	3·25
490/2	*Set of* 3	4·25	4·75
MS493	85×59 mm. 1500 s. As 115 s.	4·00	4·00

Nos. 491 and **MS**493 also commemorate the 75th anniversary of the Girl Guide movement.

(Litho Questa)

1985 (23 Dec). *Birth Bicentenary of John J. Audubon (ornithologist) (2nd issue). Multicoloured designs as T* **201** *of Maldive Islands, but horiz, showing original paintings. P* 12.

494	5 s. Rock Ptarmigan	55	10
495	155 s. Sage Grouse	2·00	1·75
496	175 s. Lesser Yellowlegs	2·00	2·50
497	500 s. Brown-headed Cowbird	3·25	4·50
494/7	*Set of* 4	7·00	8·00
MS498	72×102 mm. 1000 s. Whooping Crane. P 14	9·50	9·50

Nos. 494/7 were each printed in sheetlets of 5 stamps and one stamp-size label which appears in the centre of the bottom row.

(Des BG Studio. Litho Format)

1986 (1 Apr). *40th Anniv of United Nations Organization. T* **77** *and similar designs. P* 15.

499	10 s. multicoloured	10	10
500	180 s. multicoloured	50	30
501	200 s. new blue, agate and bright green	55	35
502	250 s. new blue, brownish blk & scar-verm	55	40
503	2000 s. multicoloured	1·75	5·00
499/503	*Set of* 5	3·00	5·50
MS504	69×69 mm. 2500 s. multicoloured	2·00	2·75

Designs: *Horiz*—180 s. Soldier of U.N. Peace-Keeping Force; 250 s. Hands releasing peace dove. *Vert*—200 s. U.N. emblem; 2000 s. Flags of U.N. and Uganda; 2500 s. U.N. Building, New York, and flags of member nations.

78 Goalkeeper catching Ball

NRA LIBERATION
1986

(79)

(Des Shelley Haas. Litho Questa)

1986 (17 Apr). *World Cup Football Championship, Mexico. T* **78** *and similar multicoloured designs. P* 14.

505	10 s. Type **78**	10	10
506	180 s. Player with ball	85	55
507	250 s. Two players competing for ball	1·00	65
508	2500 s. Player running with ball	5·50	6·00
505/8	*Set of* 4	6·75	6·50
MS509	87×66 mm. 3000 s. Player kicking ball (*vert*)	4·75	3·50

1986 (30 Apr). *Liberation by National Resistance Army. Nos. 462, 464/7 and* **MS**493 *optd with T* **79** *or larger (22×8 mm) (No.* **MS**493).

510	175 s. Lake Victoria Squeaker (Sil.)	70	70
511	400 s. Nile Perch	1·25	1·25
512	700 s. African Lungfish (Sil.)	2·00	2·50
513	1000 s. Radcliffe's Barb	2·25	3·00
514	2500 s. Electric Catfish	4·25	6·00
510/14	*Set of* 5	9·50	12·00
MS514*a*	85×59 mm. 1500 s. Girl Guides	4·00	2·50

Nos. 510/14 also exist with the overprint colours transposed.

(Des W. Hanson. Litho Questa)

1986 (30 Apr). *Appearance of Halley's Comet (1st issue). Horiz designs as T* **162***a of Lesotho. Multicoloured. P* 14.

515	50 s. Tycho Brahe and Arecibo Radio Telescope, Puerto Rico	20	10
516	100 s. Recovery of astronaut John Glenn from sea, 1962	35	15
517	140 s. "The Star in the East" (painting by Giotto)	50	30
518	2500 s. Death of Davy Crockett at the Alamo, 1835	3·75	6·00
515/18	*Set of* 4	4·25	6·00
MS519	102×70 mm. 3000 s. Halley's Comet over Uganda	5·50	4·00

See also Nos. 544/8.

80 Niagara Falls

81 *Gloria* (Colombia)

(Des Mary Walters. Litho Format)

1986 (22 May). *"Ameripex '86" International Stamp Exhibition, Chicago. American Landmarks. T* **80** *and similar horiz designs. Multicoloured. P* 15.

520	50 s. Type **80**	15	10
521	100 s. Jefferson Memorial, Washington D.C.	25	15
522	250 s. Liberty Bell, Philadelphia	50	35
523	1000 s. The Alamo, San Antonio, Texas	1·50	2·25
524	2500 s. George Washington Bridge, New York–New Jersey	2·25	5·00
520/4	*Set of* 5	4·25	7·00
MS525	87×64 mm. 3000 s. Grand Canyon	2·50	3·25

Nos. 522/3 exist imperforate from stock dispersed by the liquidator of Format International Security Printers Ltd.

(Litho Questa)

1986 (24 May). *60th Birthday of Queen Elizabeth II. Vert designs as T* **163***a of Lesotho. P* 14.

526	100 s. black and yellow	50	15
527	140 s. multicoloured	50	20
528	2500 s. multicoloured	3·25	4·00
526/8	*Set of* 3	3·75	4·00
MS529	120×85 mm. 3000 s. black & grey-brown	3·25	4·00

Designs:—100 s. Princess Elizabeth at London Zoo; 140 s. Queen Elizabeth at race meeting, 1970; 2500 s. With Prince Philip at Sandringham, 1982; 3000 s. Engagement photograph, 1947.

(Des J. Iskowitz. Litho Questa)

1986 (2 July). *Centenary of Statue of Liberty. T* **81** *and similar multicoloured designs showing cadet sailing ships. P* 14.

530	50 s. Type **81**	55	20
531	100 s. *Mircea* (Rumania)	85	30
532	140 s. *Sagres II* (Portugal) (*horiz*)	1·50	1·00
533	2500 s. *Gazela Primiero* (U.S.A.) (*horiz*)	6·50	9·50
530/3	*Set of* 4	8·50	10·00
MS534	113×82 mm. 3000 s. Statue of Liberty	3·25	3·50

No. 533 is inscribed "Primero" in error.

(Des and litho Questa)

1986 (23 July). *Royal Wedding. Multicoloured designs as T* **170***a of Lesotho. P* 14.

535	50 s. Prince Andrew and Miss Sarah Ferguson (*horiz*)	10	10
536	140 s. Prince Andrew with Princess Anne at shooting match (*horiz*)	20	20
537	2500 s. Prince Andrew and Miss Sarah Ferguson at Ascot (*horiz*)	2·75	3·75
535/7	*Set of* 3	2·75	3·75
MS538	88×88 mm. 3000 s. Prince Andrew and Miss Sarah Ferguson (*different*)	3·00	3·25

WINNERS

Argentina 3 W.Germany 2

(82)

1986 (15 Sept). *World Cup Football Championship Winners, Mexico. Nos. 505/9 optd as T* **82**, *or surch also, in gold.*

539	50 s. on 10 s. Type **78**	10	10
540	180 s. Player with ball	25	25
541	250 s. Two players competing for ball	35	35
542	2500 s. Player running with ball	2·75	4·00
539/42	*Set of* 4	3·00	4·25
MS543	87×66 mm. 3000 s. Player kicking ball (*vert*)	4·50	3·25

1986 (15 Oct). *Appearance of Halley's Comet (2nd issue). Nos. 515/19 optd with T* **213***b of Maldive Islands (in silver on 3000 s.).*

544	50 s. Tycho Brahe and Arecibo Radio Telescope, Puerto Rico	20	15
545	100 s. Recovery of astronaut John Glenn from sea, 1962	35	20
546	140 s. "The Star in the East" (painting by Giotto)	55	40
547	2500 s. Death of Davy Crockett at the Alamo, 1835	5·50	7·50
544/7	*Set of* 4	6·00	7·50
MS548	102×70 mm. 3000 s. Halley's Comet over Uganda	3·50	4·00

83 St. Kizito

(Des Associated Creative Designers. Litho Questa)

1986 (15 Oct). *Christian Martyrs of Uganda. T* **83** *and similar horiz designs. Multicoloured. P* 14.

549	50 s. Type **83**	10	10
550	150 s. St. Kizito instructing converts	25	25
551	200 s. Martyrdom of Bishop James Hannington, 1885	30	30
552	1000 s. Burning of Bugandan Christians, 1886	1·50	2·75
549/52	*Set of* 4	1·90	3·00
MS553	89×59 mm. 1500 s. King Mwanga of Buganda passing sentence on Christians	1·50	2·25

84 "Madonna of the Cherries" (Titian)

(Litho Questa)

1986 (26 Nov). *Christmas. Religious Paintings. T* **84** *and similar multicoloured designs. P* 14.

554	50 s. Type **84**	25	15
555	150 s. "Madonna and Child" (Dürer) (*vert*)	60	30
556	200 s. "Assumption of the Virgin" (Titian) (*vert*)	70	40
557	2500 s. "Praying Hands" (Dürer) (*vert*)	5·50	8·00
554/7	*Set of* 4	6·25	8·00
MS558	Two sheets, each 102×76 mm. (a) 3000 s. "Presentation of the Virgin in the Temple" (Titian). (b) 3000 s. "Adoration of the Magi" (Dürer) *Set of* 2 *sheets*	6·50	7·50

85 Red-billed Fire Finch and Glory Lily

(Litho Format)

1987 (22 July). *Flora and Fauna. T* **85** *and similar horiz designs. Multicoloured. P* 15.
559 2 s. Type **85** 35 30
560 5 s. African Pygmy Kingfisher and Nandi Flame 45 30
561 10 s. Scarlet-chested Sunbird and Crown of Thorns 55 30
562 25 s. White Rhinoceros and Yellow-billed Oxpecker .. .. 1·00 80
563 35 s. Lion and Elephant Grass .. .. 1·00 1·10
564 45 s. Cheetahs and Doum Palm .. .. 1·25 1·50
565 50 s. Red-cheeked Cordon Bleu and Desert Rose .. .. 1·40 2·00
566 100 s. Giant Eland and Acacia .. .. 2·25 3·50
559/66 .. .. *Set of* 8 7·50 8·75
MS567 Two sheets, each 98×67 mm. (a) 150 s. Carmine Bee Eaters and Sausage Tree. (b) 150 s. Cattle Egret and Zebras .. *Set of 2 sheets* 6·50 7·50
No. 563 exists imperforate from stock dispersed by the liquidator of Format International Security Printers Ltd.

86 Tremml's *Eagle* (longest man-powered flight), 1987

(Des W. Hanson. Litho Format)

1987 (14 Aug). *Milestones of Transportation. T* **86** *and similar horiz designs. Multicoloured. P* 15.
568 2 s. Type **86** 20 20
569 3 s. Junkers W.33 *Bremen* (first east-west transatlantic flight), 1928 .. .. 20 20
570 5 s. Lockheed Vega 5 *Winnie Mae* (Post's first solo round-the-world flight), 1933 30 30
571 10 s. *Voyager* (first non-stop round-the-world flight), 1986 .. .. .. 40 40
572 15 s. Chanute biplane glider, 1896 .. 60 60
573 25 s. Airship N.1 *Norge* and Polar Bear (first transpolar flight), 1926 .. 90 90
574 35 s. Curtiss Golden Flyer biplane and U.S.S. *Pennsylvania* (battleship) (first take-off and landing from ship), 1911 1·25 1·25
575 45 s. Shepard and "Freedom 7" spacecraft (first American in space), 1961 .. 1·40 1·50
576 100 s. Concorde (first supersonic passenger flight) .. .. 4·25 5·50
568/76 .. .. *Set of* 9 8·50 9·75

87 Olympic Torch-bearer

(Litho Questa)

1987 (5 Oct). *Olympic Games, Seoul* (1988) (*1st issue*). *T* **87** *and similar horiz designs. Multicoloured. P* 14.
577 5 s. Type **87** 10 10
578 10 s. Swimming 20 25
579 50 s. Cycling .. .. 1·00 1·25
580 100 s. Gymnastics .. .. 2·00 2·50
577/80 .. .. *Set of* 4 3·00 3·75
MS581 100×75 mm. 150 s. Boxing .. .. 3·00 4·00
See also Nos. 628/32.

88 Child Immunization **89** Golden-backed Weaver

(Des Associated Creative Designers. Litho Questa)

1987 (8 Oct) *25th Anniv of Independence. T* **88** *and similar horiz designs. P* 14.
582 5 s. multicoloured 15 10
583 10 s. multicoloured 30 25
584 25 s. multicoloured 70 70
585 50 s. multicoloured .. .. 1·25 1·50
582/5 .. .. *Set of* 4 2·25 3·25
MS586 90×70 mm. 100 s. black, bright scarlet and greenish yellow .. .. 2·00 2·75
Designs:—10 s. Mulago Hospital, Kampala; 25 s. Independence Monument, Kampala City Park; 50 s. High Court, Kampala; 100 s. Stylized head of Crested Crane, "25" and Ugandan flag.

(Des Jennifer Toombs. Litho Questa)

1987 (19 Oct). *Birds of Uganda. T* **89** *and similar multicoloured designs. P* 14.
587 5 s. Type **89** 65 60
588 10 s. Hoopoe .. .. 1·25 90
589 15 s. Red-throated Bee Eater .. .. 1·40 1·00
590 25 s. Lilac-breasted Roller .. .. 1·75 1·60
591 35 s. African Pygmy Goose .. .. 2·00 1·75
592 45 s. Scarlet-chested Sunbird .. .. 2·25 2·25
593 50 s. South African Crowned Crane .. 2·25 2·50
594 100 s. Long-tailed Fiscal .. .. .. 3·50 4·00
587/94 .. .. *Set of* 8 13·50 13·00
MS595 Two sheets, each 80×60 mm. (a) 150 s. African Fish Eagle. (b) 150 s. Barn Owl *Set of 2 sheets* 6·50 8·00

90 Hippocrates (physician) and Surgeons performing Operation

(Des L. Nelson. Litho Questa)

1987 (2 Nov). *Great Scientific Discoveries. T* **90** *and similar multicoloured designs. P* 14.
596 5 s. Type **90** 50 30
597 25 s. Einstein and Deep Space (Theory of Relativity) .. .. 1·75 1·75
598 35 s. Isaac Newton and diagram from *Opticks* (Theory of Colour and Light) .. 2·00 2·50
599 45 s. Karl Benz, early Benz and modern Mercedes cars .. .. 2·50 3·00
596/9 .. .. *Set of* 4 6·00 6·75
MS600 97×70 mm. 150 s. *Challenger* (space shuttle) (*vert*) .. .. 3·25 4·00

91 Scout with Album and Uganda Stamps

(Des Mary Walters. Litho Questa)

1987 (20 Nov). *World Scout Jamboree, Australia. T* **91** *and similar horiz designs. Multicoloured. P* 14.
601 5 s. Type **91** 20 10
602 25 s. Scouts planting tree 70 70
603 35 s. Canoeing on Lake Victoria 90 85
604 45 s. Hiking .. .. 1·25 1·10
601/4 .. .. *Set of* 4 2·75 2·50
MS605 95×65 mm. 150 s. Jamboree and Uganda scout emblems .. .. 3·00 4·00

92 "The Annunciation"

(Litho Questa)

1987 (18 Dec). *Christmas. T* **92** *and similar multicoloured designs showing scenes from French diptych, c.* 1250. *P* 14.
606 5 s. Type **92** 10 10
607 10 s. "The Nativity" 20 25
608 50 s. "Flight into Egypt" .. .. .. 1·00 1·25
609 100 s. "The Adoration of the Magi" .. .. 2·00 2·50
606/9 .. .. *Set of* 4 3·00 3·50
MS610 76×105 mm. 150 s. "Mystic Wine" (tapestry detail) (*vert*) .. .. 3·00 4·00

93 Class "12" Light Shunter Locomotive **94** Columbite-Tantalite

(Des BG Studio. Litho Questa)

1988 (18 Jan). *Locomotives of East Africa Railways. T* **93** *and similar horiz designs. Multicoloured. P* 14.
611 5 s. Type **93** 35 35
612 10 s. Class "92" diesel-electric 45 45
613 15 s. Locomotive No. 2506 .. .. .. 60 60
614 25 s. Tank locomotive No. 126 .. .. 85 85
615 35 s. Class "31" locomotive .. .. .. 1·10 1·10
616 45 s. Class "31" locomotive (*different*) .. 1·40 1·40
617 50 s. Class "59" Double Garratt locomotive 1·60 1·60
618 100 s. Class "87" diesel-electric shunter .. 2·40 2·40
611/18 .. .. *Set of* 8 8·00 8·00
MS619 Two sheets, each 100 × 74 mm. (a) 150 s. Class "31". (b) 150 s. Class "59" Double Garratt *Set of 2 sheets* 4·25 5·50

(Des Mary Walters. Litho Questa)

1988 (18 Jan). *Minerals. T* **94** *and similar vert designs. Multicoloured. P* 14.
620 1 s. Type **94** 15 15
621 2 s. Galena 20 20
622 5 s. Malachite 35 35
623 10 s. Cassiterite 55 55
624 35 s. Ferberite .. .. 1·50 1·50
625 50 s. Emerald .. .. 2·00 2·00
626 100 s. Monazite .. .. 3·00 3·00
627 150 s. Microcline .. .. 4·00 4·00
620/7 .. .. *Set of* 8 10·50 10·50

95 Hurdling

(Des BG Studio. Litho Questa)

1988 (16 May). *Olympic Games, Seoul* (*2nd issue*). *T* **95** *and similar horiz designs. Multicoloured. P* 14.
628 5 s. Type **95** 10 10
629 25 s. High jumping 40 50
630 35 s. Javelin throwing 45 55
631 45 s. Long jumping 55 70
628/31 .. .. *Set of* 4 1·25 1·60
MS632 85 × 114 mm. 150 s. Olympic medals .. 1·00 1·50

96 *Spathodea campanulata*

(Des L. Nelson. Litho Format)

1988 (29 July). *Flowers. T* **96** *and similar multicoloured designs. P* 15.
633 5 s. Type **96** 15 15
634 10 s. *Gloriosa simplex* 15 15
635 20 s. *Thevetica peruviana* (*vert*) 20 20
636 25 s. *Hibiscus schizopetalus* 20 25
637 35 s. *Aframomum sceptrum* 20 30
638 45 s. *Adenium obesum* 20 35
639 50 s. *Kigelia africana* (*vert*) 25 40
640 100 s. *Clappertonia ficifolia* 35 75
633/40 .. .. *Set of* 8 1·50 2·25
MS641 Two sheets, each 109 × 79 mm. (a) 150 s. *Costus spectabilis.* (b) 150 s. *Canarina abyssinica* (*vert*) .. .. *Set of 2 sheets* 2·00 2·75

97 Elephants in Grassland (Type **61** redrawn)

(Litho Questa)

1988 (29 July). *Endangered Species* (*2nd series*). *P* 14.
642 **97** 10 s. multicoloured .. ..

98 Red Cross Worker vaccinating Baby **99** Giraffes, Kidepo Valley National Park

(Des Associated Creative Art Designers. Litho Questa)

1988 (28 Oct). *125th Anniv of International Red Cross. T* **98** *and similar designs. P* 14.
643 10 s. bright scarlet, pale yellow and black 25 15
644 40 s. multicoloured 70 70
645 70 s. multicoloured .. .. 1·50 2·00
646 90 s. multicoloured .. .. 2·00 2·25
643/6 .. .. *Set of* 4 4·00 4·50
MS647 110 × 78 mm. 150 s. multicoloured .. 1·00 1·60
Designs: *Horiz*—10 s. "AIDS" with test tube as "I"; 70 s. Distributing food to refugees; 90 s. Red Cross volunteers with accident victim. *Vert*—150 s. Henri Dunant (founder).

(Litho Questa)

1988 (31 Oct). *500th Birth Anniv of Titian (artist). Vert designs as T* **186a** *of Lesotho. Multicoloured. P* 13½×14.

648	10 s. "Portrait of a Lady"	15	15
649	20 s. "Portrait of a Man"	20	20
650	40 s. "Isabella d'Este"	35	35
651	50 s. "Vincenzo Mosti"	45	45
652	70 s. "Pope Paul III Farnese"	60	60
653	90 s. "Violante"	75	75
654	100 s. "Titian's Daughter Lavinia"	85	85
655	250 s. "Dr. Parma"	1·90	1·90
648/55	*Set of* 8	4·75	4·75
MS656	Two sheets, each 110 × 95 mm. (a) 350 s. "The Speech of Alfonso D'Avalos" (detail). (b) 350 s. "Cain and Abel" (detail) *Set of* 2 *sheets*	6·50	7·50

(Des Mary Walters. Litho Questa)

1988 (18 Nov). *National Parks of Uganda. T* **99** *and similar vert designs. Multicoloured. P* 14.

657	10 s. Type **99**	50	20
658	25 s. Zebras, Lake Mburo National Park	1·00	30
659	100 s. African Buffalo, Murchison Falls National Park	2·00	2·50
660	250 s. Eastern White Pelicans, Queen Elizabeth National Park	5·00	6·50
657/60	*Set of* 4	7·75	8·50
MS661	97×68 mm. 350 s. Roan Antelopes, Lake Mburo National Park	2·50	3·75

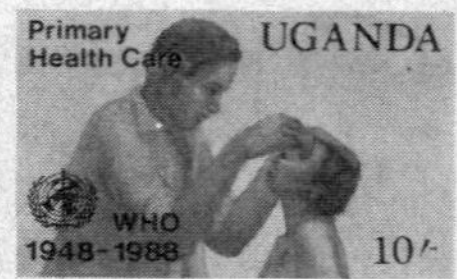

100 Doctor examining Child's Eyes

(Des L. Watkins. Litho Questa)

1988 (1 Dec). *40th Anniv of World Health Organization. T* **100** *and similar horiz designs. Multicoloured. P* 14.

662	10 s. Type **100**	20	15
663	25 s. Mental health therapist with patient	40	30
664	45 s. Surgeon performing operation	60	60
665	100 s. Dentist treating girl	1·25	1·50
666	200 s. Doctor examining child	2·00	2·50
662/6	*Set of* 5	4·00	4·50
MS667	107 × 88 mm. 350 s. Delegates approving Declaration of Alma-Ata, 1978	2·50	3·50

100a Father Christmas with List

110 M HURDLES
R. KINGDOM
USA

(**101**)

(Des Walt Disney Co. Litho Questa)

1988 (2 Dec). *Christmas. "Santa's Helpers". T* **100a** *and similar vert designs showing Walt Disney cartoon characters. Multicoloured. P* 13½×14.

668	50 s. Type **100a**	85	1·00
	a. Sheetlet. Nos. 668/75	6·00	
669	50 s. Goofy carrying presents	85	1·00
670	50 s. Mickey Mouse on toy train	85	1·00
671	50 s. Reindeer at window	85	1·00
672	50 s. Donald Duck's nephew with building blocks	85	1·00
673	50 s. Donald Duck holding sack	85	1·00
674	50 s. Chip n'Dale on conveyor belt	85	1·00
675	50 s. Donald Duck's nephew operating conveyor belt	85	1·00
668/75	*Set of* 8	6·00	7·00
MS676	Two sheets, each 127×102 mm. (a) 350 s. Mickey Mouse loading sack of toys on sleigh (*horiz*). P 14×13½. (b) 350 s. Mickey Mouse and Chip n'Dale grooming reindeer. P 13½×14 *Set of* 2 *sheets*	7·50	8·50

Nos. 668/75 were printed together, *se-tenant* as a composite design, in sheetlets of eight.

1989 (30 Jan). *Olympic Gold Medal Winners, Seoul. Nos.* 628/32 *optd as T* **101** *or surch also.*

677	5 s. Type **95** (optd with T **101**)	10	10
678	25 s. High jumping (optd "HIGH JUMP G. AVDEENKO USSR")	20	25
679	35 s. Javelin throwing (optd "JAVELIN T. KORJUS FINLAND")	25	30
680	300 s. on 45 s. Long jumping (optd "LONG JUMP C. LEWIS USA")	2·25	2·75
677/80	*Set of* 4	2·50	3·00
MS681	85×114 mm. 350 s. on 150 s. Olympic medals with medal table optd on sheet margin	3·00	4·00

102 Goalkeeper with Ball

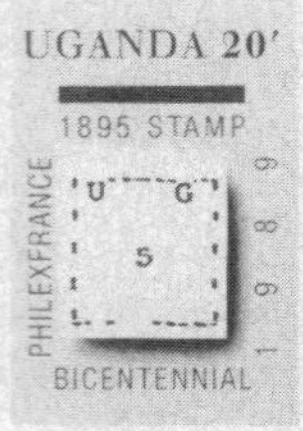

103 1895 5 Cowries Stamp

(Des J. Genzo. Litho Questa)

1989 (24 Apr). *World Cup Football Championship, Italy* (1990) (*1st issue*). *T* **102** *and similar multicoloured designs. P* 14.

682	10 s. Type **102**	25	15
683	25 s. Player kicking ball (*horiz*)	55	40
684	75 s. Heading ball towards net (*horiz*)	1·25	1·10
685	200 s. Tackling	2·25	2·75
682/5	*Set of* 4	3·75	4·00
MS686	118×87 mm. 300 s. Football and World Cup trophy (*horiz*)	2·25	3·00

See also Nos. 849/53.

(Litho Questa)

1989 (15 May). *Japanese Art. Paintings by Hokusai. Horiz designs as T* **187a** *of Lesotho. Multicoloured. P* 14×13½.

687	10 s. "Fuji and the Great Wave off Kanagawa"	20	20
688	15 s. "Fuji from Lake Suwa"	30	30
689	20 s. "Fuji from Kajikazawa"	30	30
690	60 s. "Fuji from Shichirigahama"	70	70
691	90 s. "Fuji from Ejiri in Sunshu"	90	90
692	120 s. "Fuji above Lightning"	1·10	1·10
693	200 s. "Fuji from Lower Meguro in Edo"	1·90	1·90
694	250 s. "Fuji from Edo"	2·10	2·10
687/94	*Set of* 8	6·75	6·75
MS695	Two sheets, each 102×76 mm. (a) 500 s. "The Red Fuji from the Foot". (b) 500 s. "Fuji from Umezawa" *Set of* 2 *sheets*	7·00	8·00

Nos. 687/94 were each printed in sheetlets of 10 containing two horizontal strips of 5 stamps separated by printed labels commemorating Emperor Hirohito.

(Des U. Purins. Litho B.D.T.)

1989 (7 July). *"Philexfrance 89" International Stamp Exhibition, Paris. T* **103** *and similar vert designs. P* 14.

696	20 s. black, brt scarlet & pale grey-brown	40	35
697	70 s. black, yellowish green and azure	1·00	1·00
698	100 s. black, dull violet and pale brown-rose	1·25	1·50
699	250 s. black, orange-yell & pale greenish yell	2·25	2·75
696/9	*Set of* 4	4·50	5·00
MS700	176×131 mm. Nos. 696/9 (*sold at* 500 s.)	6·00	7·00

Designs:—70 s. 1895 10 on 50 cowries stamp; 100 s. 1896 25 cowries stamp; 250 s. 1896 1 rupee stamp.

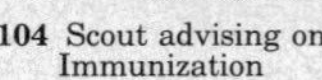

104 Scout advising on Immunization

UGANDA
10/-

105 *Suillus granulatus*

(Des Associated Creative Designers. Litho Questa)

1989 (3 Aug). *2nd All African Scout Jamboree, Uganda, and 75th Anniv of Ugandan Scout Movement. T* **104** *and similar multicoloured designs. P* 14.

701	10 s. Type **104**	30	15
702	70 s. Poultry keeping	90	80
703	90 s. Scout on crutches leading family to immunization centre	1·40	1·25
704	100 s. Scouts making bricks	1·40	1·75
701/4	*Set of* 4	3·50	3·50
MS705	99×67 mm. 500 s. Ugandan Scout logo (*vert*)	3·25	4·25

(Des Mary Walters. Litho B.D.T.)

1989 (14 Aug). *Fungi. T* **105** *and similar vert designs. Multicoloured. P* 14.

706	10 s. Type **105**	30	30
707	15 s. *Omphalotus olearius*	40	40
708	45 s. *Oudemansiella radicata*	1·00	1·00
709	50 s. *Clitocybe nebularis*	1·10	1·10
710	60 s. *Macrolepiota rhacodes*	1·25	1·25
711	75 s. *Lepista nuda*	1·40	1·40
712	150 s. *Suillus luteus*	2·50	2·50
713	200 s. *Agaricus campestris*	2·75	2·75
706/13	*Set of* 8	9·50	9·50
MS714	Two sheets, each 100×68 mm. (a) 350 s. *Bolbitius vitellinus*. (b) 350 s. *Schizophyllum commune* *Set of* 2 *sheets*	9·00	9·00

COVER PRICES

Cover factors are quoted at the beginning of each country for most issues to 1945. An explanation of the system can be found on page x. The factors quoted do not, however, apply to philatelic covers.

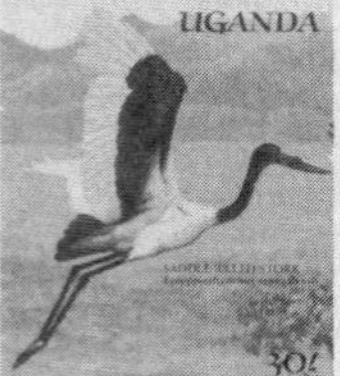

106 Saddle-bill Stork

UGANDA
10/-

107 Rocket on Launch Pad

(Des S. Barlowe. Litho Questa)

1989 (12 Sept). *Wildlife at Waterhole. T* **106** *and similar vert designs. Multicoloured. P* 14½×14.

715	30 s. Type **106**	55	55
	a. Sheetlet. Nos. 715/34	10·00	
716	30 s. Eastern White Pelican	55	55
717	30 s. Marabou Stork	55	55
718	30 s. Egyptian Vulture	55	55
719	30 s. Bateleur	55	55
720	30 s. African Elephant	55	55
721	30 s. Giraffe	55	55
722	30 s. Goliath Heron	55	55
723	30 s. Black Rhinoceros	55	55
724	30 s. Common Zebra and Oribi	55	55
725	30 s. African Fish Eagle	55	55
726	30 s. Hippopotamus	55	55
727	30 s. Black-backed Jackal and Eastern White Pelican	55	55
728	30 s. African Buffalo	55	55
729	30 s. Olive Baboon	55	55
730	30 s. Bohar Reedbuck	55	55
731	30 s. Lesser Flamingo and Serval	55	55
732	30 s. Whale-headed Stork ("Shoebill Stork")	55	55
733	30 s. South African Crowned Crane	55	55
734	30 s. Impala	55	55
715/34	*Set of* 20	10·00	10·00
MS735	Two sheets, each 99×68 mm. (a) 500 s. Lion. (b) 500 s. Long-crested Eagle *Set of* 2 *sheets*	6·50	7·50

Nos. 715/34 were printed together, *se-tenant*, in a sheetlet of 20 stamps, forming a composite design showing wildlife at a waterhole.

(Des T. Agans. Litho Questa)

1989 (20 Oct). *20th Anniv of First Manned Landing on Moon. T* **107** *and similar multicoloured designs. P* 14.

736	10 s. Type **107**	20	20
737	20 s. Lunar module *Eagle* on Moon	30	30
738	30 s. "Apollo 11" command module	40	40
739	50 s. *Eagle* landing on Moon	60	60
740	70 s. Astronaut Aldrin on Moon	85	85
741	250 s. Neil Armstrong alighting from *Eagle* (*vert*)	2·50	2·50
742	300 s. *Eagle* over Moon	2·50	2·50
743	350 s. Astronaut Aldrin on Moon (*vert*)	2·75	2·75
736/43	*Set of* 8	9·00	9·00
MS744	Two sheets, each 77×104 mm. (a) 500 s. "Saturn" rocket (*vert*). (b) 500 s. "Apollo 11" capsule on parachutes (*vert*) *Set of* 2 *sheets*	7·00	8·00

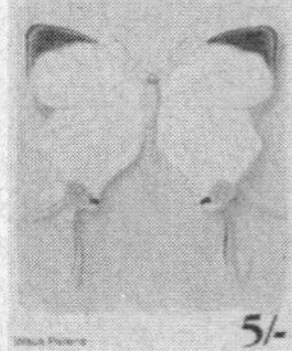

108 *Aphniolaus pallene*

109 John Hanning Speke and Map of Lake Victoria

(Des S. Heimann. Litho Questa)

1989 (13 Nov). *Butterflies. T* **108** *and similar vert designs showing "UGANDA" in black. Multicoloured. Without imprint date. P* 14.

745	5 s. Type **108**	25	20
746	10 s. *Hewitsonia boisduvali*	35	25
747	20 s. *Euxanthe wakefieldi*	45	30
748	30 s. *Papilio echerioides*	50	30
749	40 s. *Acraea semivitrea*	60	40
750	50 s. *Colotis antevippe*	60	40
751	70 s. *Acraea perenna*	70	70
752	90 s. *Charaxes cynthia*	70	70
753	100 s. *Euphaedra neophron*	70	70
754	150 s. *Cymothoe beckeri*	1·00	1·00
755	200 s. *Vanessula milca*	1·10	1·25
756	400 s. *Mimacraea marshalli*	1·75	2·25
757	500 s. *Axiocerses amanga*	2·00	2·50
758	1000 s. *Precis hierta*	2·50	3·50
745/58	*Set of* 14	12·00	13·00

For these, and similar, designs showing "UGANDA" in blue, see Nos. 864/80.

(Des A. Granberg. Litho Questa)

1989 (15 Nov). *Exploration of Africa. T* **109** *and similar horiz designs. Multicoloured. P* 14.

760	10 s. Type **109**	45	35
761	25 s. Sir Richard Burton and map of Lake Tanganyika	60	50
762	40 s. Richard Lander and Bakota bronze	70	65
763	90 s. René Caillié and mosque, Timbuktu	1·00	1·00
764	125 s. Sir Samuel Baker and Dorcas Gazelle	1·25	1·25
765	150 s. Pharaoh Necho and ancient Phoenician merchant ship	1·50	1·50

766	250 s. Vasco da Gama and 15th-century caravel	2·25	2·50
767	300 s. Sir Henry Morton Stanley and *Lady Alice* (sectional boat)	2·50	2·75
760/7	.. .. *Set of* 8	9·25	9·50

MS768 Two sheets, each 73×103 mm. (a) 500 s. Dr. David Livingstone and steam launch *Ma Robert;* (b) 500 s. Mary Kingsley and map of Ogooué River .. .. .. *Set of 2 sheets* 8·50 9·50

110 Logo (25th anniv of African Development Bank)

111 *Aerangis kotschyana*

(Des D. Miller. Litho Questa)

1989 (12 Dec). *Anniversaries. T* **110** *and similar horiz designs. Multicoloured. P* 14.

769	10 s. Type **110**	15	15
770	20 s. Arrows and dish aerials (World Telecommunications Day)	20	20
771	75 s. Two portraits of Nehru (birth centenary)	1·50	1·50
772	90 s. Pan Am Boeing 314A flying boat *Dixie Clipper* (50th anniv of first scheduled trans-Atlantic airmail flight) ..	1·50	1·50
773	100 s. George Stephenson and *Locomotion,* 1825 (175th anniv of first practical steam locomotive)	1·60	1·60
774	150 s. Concorde cockpit (20th anniv of first test flight)	2·75	2·75
775	250 s. *Wapen von Hamburg* and *Leopoldus Primus* (galleons) (800th anniv of Port of Hamburg)	2·75	2·75
776	300 s. Concorde and cockpit interior (20th anniv of first test flight) ..	3·00	3·00
769/76	.. .. *Set of* 8	12·00	12·00

MS777 Two sheets (a) 91×87 mm. 500 s. Revolutionary with musket and Bastille, Paris (bicentenary of French Revolution). (b) 110×82 mm. 500 s. Emperor Frederick I Barbarossa and Hamburg charter (800th anniv of Port of Hamburg) .. .. .. *Set of 2 sheets* 5·50 6·50

(Des W. Wright. Litho Questa)

1989 (18 Dec). *Orchids. T* **111** *and similar vert designs. Multicoloured. P* 14.

778	10 s. Type **111**	25	25
779	15 s. *Angraecum infundibulare*	30	30
780	45 s. *Cyrtorchis chailluana*	70	70
781	50 s. *Aerangis rhodosticta*	75	75
782	100 s. *Eulophia speciosa*	1·50	1·50
783	200 s. *Calanthe sylvatica*	2·25	2·25
784	250 s. *Vanilla imperialis*	2·40	2·40
785	350 s. *Polystachya vulcanica*	2·75	2·75
778/85	.. .. .. *Set of* 8	9·75	9·75

MS786 Two sheets, each 110×82 mm. (a) 500 s. *Ansellia africana.* (b) 500 s. *Ancistrochilus rothschildianus* .. .. .. *Set of 2 sheets* 6·00 7·00

(Litho Questa)

1989 (21 Dec). *Christmas. Paintings by Fra Angelico Vert designs as T* **193***b of Lesotho. Multicoloured. P* 14.

787	10 s. "Madonna and Child"	15	10
788	20 s. "Adoration of the Magi"	20	15
789	40 s. "Virgin and Child enthroned with Saints"	40	30
790	75 s. "The Annunciation"	70	60
791	100 s. "Virgin and Child" (detail, "St. Peter Martyr" triptych)	85	75
792	150 s. "Virgin and Child enthroned with Saints" (*different*)	1·25	1·25
793	250 s. "Virgin and Child enthroned" ..	1·75	2·00
794	350 s. "Virgin and Child" (from Annalena altarpiece)	2·00	2·75
787/94	.. .. *Set of* 8	6·50	7·00

MS795 Two sheets, each 72×96 mm. (a) 500 s. "Virgin and Child" (from Bosco ai Frati altarpiece). (b) 500 s. "Madonna and Child with Twelve Angels" .. .. *Set of 2 sheets* 5·00 6·00

112 *Thevetia peruviana*

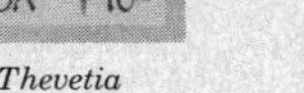

(**113**)

(Des Jennifer Toombs. Litho B.D.T.)

1990 (17 Apr). *"EXPO '90" International Garden and Greenery Exhibition, Osaka (1st issue). Flowering Trees. T* **112** *and similar vert designs. Multicoloured. P* 14.

796	10 s. Type **112**	15	15
797	20 s. *Acanthus eminens*	20	20
798	90 s. *Gnidia glauca*	50	50
799	150 s. *Oncoba spinosa*	70	70
800	175 s. *Hibiscus rosa-sinensis*	75	75
801	400 s. *Jacaranda mimosifolia*	1·25	1·50
802	500 s. *Erythrina abyssinica*	1·40	1·75
803	700 s. *Bauhinia purpurea*	1·60	2·00
796/803	.. .. .. *Set of* 8	6·00	6·75

MS804 Two sheets, each 93×85 mm. (a) 1000 s. *Delonix regia.* (b) 1000 s. *Cassia didymobotrya* *Set of 2 sheets* 7·50 8·00

See also Nos. 820/8.

(Des W. Wright. Litho Questa)

1990 (8 June). *50th Anniv of Second World War. Multicoloured designs as T* **242** *of Maldive Islands. P* 14.

805	5 s. Allied penetration of German West Wall, 1944	25	25
806	10 s. Flags of the Allies, VE Day, 1945 ..	35	35
807	20 s. Capture of Okinawa, 1945	45	45
808	75 s. Appointment of Gen. De Gaulle to command all Free French forces, 1944	60	60
809	100 s. Invasion of Saipan, 1944	75	75
810	150 s. Airborne landing, Operation Market Garden, 1944	1·25	1·25
811	200 s. MacArthur's return to Philippines, 1944	1·40	1·40
812	300 s. Japanese attack on U.S. carrier, Coral Sea, 1942	1·50	1·50
813	350 s. First Battle of El Alamein, 1942 ..	1·60	1·60
814	500 s. Naval Battle of Guadalcanal, 1942 ..	2·00	2·00
805/14	.. .. .. *Set of* 10	9·00	9·00
MS815	112×83 mm. 1000 s. Battle of Britain, 1940 (*vert*)	3·50	4·00

(Des Young Phillips Studio. Litho Questa)

1990 (5 July). *90th Birthday of Queen Elizabeth the Queen Mother. Vert designs as T* **198***a of Lesotho, showing portraits, 1940–49. P* 14.

816	250 s. black, deep magenta and new blue ..	80	1·00
	a. Strip of 3. Nos. 816/18	2·25	
817	250 s. black, deep magenta and new blue ..	80	1·00
818	250 s. black, deep magenta and new blue ..	80	1·00
816/18	.. .. .. *Set of* 3	2·25	2·75
MS819	90×75 mm. 1000 s. multicoloured ..	2·75	3·25

Designs:—No. 816, Queen Elizabeth with corgi; Nos. 817, **MS**819, Queen Elizabeth wearing feathered hat; No. 818, Queen Elizabeth at wartime inspection.

Nos. 816/18 were printed together, horizontally and vertically *se-tenant*, in sheetlets of 9 (3×3).

1990 (30 July). *"EXPO 90" International Garden and Greenery Exhibition, Osaka (2nd issue). Nos. 778/86 optd as T* **113** *in silver.*

820	10 s. Type **111**	30	20
821	15 s. *Angraecum infundibulare*	30	20
822	45 s. *Cyrtorchis chailluana*	55	45
823	50 s. *Aerangis rhodosticta*	55	45
824	100 s. *Eulophia speciosa*	70	60
825	200 s. *Calanthe sylvatica*	1·10	1·25
826	250 s. *Vanilla imperialis*	1·25	1·50
827	350 s. *Polystachya vulcanica*	1·25	1·75
820/7	.. .. .. *Set of* 8	5·50	5·75

MS828 Two sheets, each 110×82 mm. (a) 500 s. *Ansellia africana.* (b) 500 s. *Ancistrochilus rothschildianus* .. .. .. *Set of 2 sheets* 5·50 6·00

The overprint on No. **MS**828 occurs on the sheet margin and includes an additional inscription.

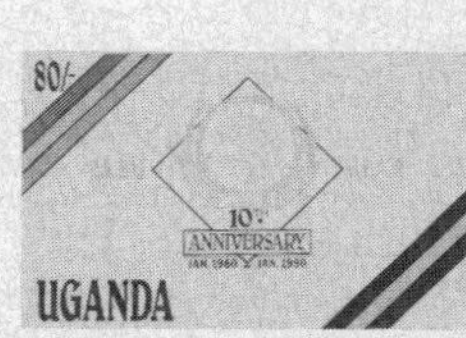

114 P.A.P.U. Emblem

115 Unissued G. B. "V R" Penny Black

(Des L. Fried. Litho B.D.T.)

1990 (3 Aug). *Tenth Anniv of Pan-African Postal Union* (80 s.) *and Second United Nations Conference on Least Developed Countries, Paris* (750 s.). *T* **114** *and similar horiz design. P* 14.

829	80 s. multicoloured	50	50
MS830	97×67 mm. 750 s. black and new blue	2·50	3·25

Design:—750 s. Clasped hands.

(Des and litho B.D.T.)

1990 (6 Aug). *150th Anniv of the Penny Black. T* **115** *and similar vert designs. P* 14.

831	25 s. multicoloured	15	15
832	50 s. brown-lake, blk & pale turquoise-grn	25	25
833	100 s. multicoloured	45	45
834	150 s. multicoloured	65	75
835	200 s. multicoloured	75	85
836	300 s. multicoloured	1·00	1·10
837	500 s. multicoloured	1·25	1·50
838	600 s. multicoloured	1·25	1·50
831/8	.. .. .. *Set of* 8	5·25	6·00

MS839 Two sheets (a) 107×77 mm. 1000 s. multicoloured. (b) 119×85 mm. 1000 s. black and rosine .. .. .. *Set of 2 sheets* 6·00 7·00

Designs:—50 s. Canada 1858-59 3d. Beaver; 100 s. Baden 1851 9 k. on green error; 150 s. Basel 1845 2½ r. Dove; 200 s. U.S.A. 1918 24 c. Inverted "Jenny" error; 300 s. Western Australia 1854 1d. Black Swan; 500 s. Uganda 1895 20 c. "narrow" typewritten stamp; 600 s. Great Britain Twopenny blue; 1000 s. (No. **MS**839a), Uganda 1895 20 c. "wide" typewritten stamp; 1000 s. (No. **MS**839b), Sir Rowland Hill.

No. **MS**839 also commemorates "Stamp World London 90" International Stamp Exhibition.

116 African Jacana

(Des P. Gonzalez. Litho Questa)

1990 (3 Sept). *Wild Birds of Uganda. T* **116** *and similar multicoloured designs. P* 14.

840	10 s. Type **116**	40	30
841	15 s. Southern Ground Hornbill	45	35
842	45 s. Kori Bustard (*vert*)	60	50
843	50 s. Secretary Bird	60	50
844	100 s. Egyptian Geese	85	75
845	300 s. Goliath Heron (*vert*)	1·75	2·00
846	500 s. Ostrich with chicks (*vert*)	2·25	2·50
847	650 s. Saddle-bill Stork (*vert*)	2·50	2·75
840/7	.. .. *Set of* 8	8·50	8·75

MS848 Two sheets, each 98×69 mm. (a) 1000 s. Lesser Flamingo (*vert*). (b) 1000 s. Vulturine Guineafowl (*vert*) .. .. *Set of 2 sheets* 7·00 8·50

117 Roger Milla of Cameroun

(Des Young Phillips Studio. Litho Questa)

1990 (21 Sept). *World Cup Football Championship, Italy* (2nd *issue*). *T* **117** *and similar horiz designs. Multicoloured. P* 14.

849	50 s. Type **117**	35	25
850	100 s. Ramzy of Egypt	55	45
851	250 s. David O'Leary of Ireland ..	1·25	1·25
852	600 s. Littbarsky of West Germany ..	1·75	2·00
849/52	.. .. .. *Set of* 4	3·50	3·50

MS853 Two sheets, each 75×90 mm. (a) 1000 s. Ali McCoist of Scotland. (b) 1000 s. Ekstrom of Sweden .. .. *Set of 2 sheets* 6·50 7·50

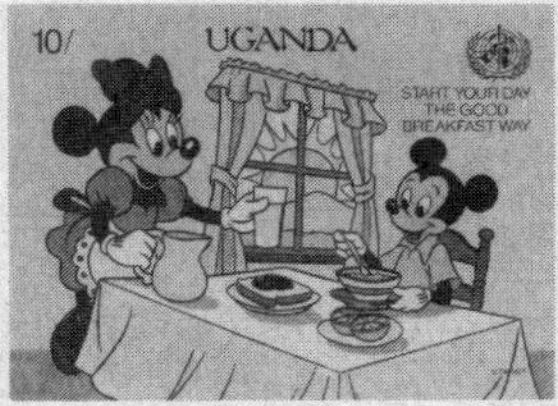

118 Mickey and Minnie Mouse at Breakfast

(Des Walt Disney Co. Litho B.D.T.)

1990 (19 Oct). *Health and Safety Campaign. T* **118** *and similar multicoloured designs showing Walt Disney cartoon characters. P* 13.

854	10 s. Type **118**	15	10
855	20 s. Donald Duck's nephews doing kerb drill	20	15
856	50 s. Donald and Mickey stopping Big Pete smoking	45	35
857	90 s. Mickey stopping Donald choking ..	60	40
858	100 s. Mickey and Goofy using seat belts ..	65	45
859	250 s. Mickey and Minnie dancing ..	1·25	1·25
860	500 s. Donald Duck's fitness class	2·25	2·75
861	600 s. Mickey's nephews showing lights at night	2·50	3·00
854/61	.. .. .. *Set of* 8	7·25	7·50

MS862 Two sheets, each 135×115 mm. (a) 1000 s. Mickey weighing nephew (*vert*). (b) 1000 s. Mickey and Pluto walking (*vert*) *Set of 2 sheets* 6·50 7·50

(Litho Questa)

1990 (1 Nov)–**92.** *As Nos. 746/55 and new values, showing butterflies, as T* **108** *with* "UGANDA" *in blue. Multcoloured. P* 14. A. *Without imprint date.* B. *With* "1991" *imprint date.*

		A		B	
864	10 s. *Hewitsonia boisduvali*	15	15	†	
865	20 s. *Euxanthe wakefieldi* ..	20	20	30	30
866	30 s. *Papilio echerioides* ..	20	20	†	
867	40 s. *Acraea semivitrea* ..	20	20	†	
868	50 s. *Colotis antevippe* ..	†		30	30
869	70 s. *Acraea perenna* ..	30	30	†	
870	90 s. *Charaxes cynthia* ..	30	30	†	
871	100 s. *Euphaedra neophron*	40	40	40	40
872	150 s. *Cymothoe beckeri* ..	40	40	†	
873	200 s. *Vanessula milca* ..	60	60	60	60
874	400 s. *Mimacraea marshalli*	†		1·00	1·00
875	500 s. *Axiocerses amanga* ..	†		1·00	1·00
876	1000 s. *Precis hierta*	†		2·00	2·00
877	2000 s. *Precis hierta*	4·50	6·00	3·25	4·25
878	3000 s. *Euphaedra eusemoides*	6·50	7·00	†	
879	4000 s. *Acraea natalica* ..	8·00	8·50	†	
880	5000 s. *Euphaedra themis* ..	8·00	9·50	†	
864A/80A	.. .. *Set of* 13	27·00	30·00	†	
865B/77B	.. .. *Set of* 8	†		8·00	9·25

Dates of issue:—1.11.90, Nos. 864A/77A; 4.11.91, Nos. 865B, 868B, 871B, 873B/7B; 9.10.92, 878A/80A.

(Litho Questa)

1990 (17 Dec). *Christmas. 350th Death Anniv of Rubens. Multicoloured designs as T* **250** *of Maldive Islands, but inscr* "CHRISTMAS 1990". *P* 13½×14.
881 10 s. "Baptism of Christ" (detail) (*vert*) 10 10
882 20 s. "St. Gregory the Great and other Saints" (detail) (*vert*) 10 10
883 100 s. "Saints Nereus, Domitilla and Achilleus" (detail) (*vert*) 35 35
884 150 s. "St. Gregory the Great and other Saints" (different detail) (*vert*) 50 60
885 300 s. "Saint Augustine" (detail) (*vert*) 90 1·25
886 400 s. "St. Gregory the Great and other Saints" (different detail) (*vert*) 1·10 1·40
887 500 s. "Baptism of Christ" (different detail) (*vert*) 1·25 1·60
888 600 s. "St. Gregory the Great and other Saints (different detail) (*vert*) 1·25 1·75
881/8 *Set of* 8 5·00 6·50
MS889 Two sheets, each 110×71 mm. (a) 1000 s. "The Triumph of Faith" (detail). (b) 1000 s. "The Victory of Eucharistic Truth over Heresy" (detail). P 14×13½ *Set of* 2 *sheets* 7·00 8·00

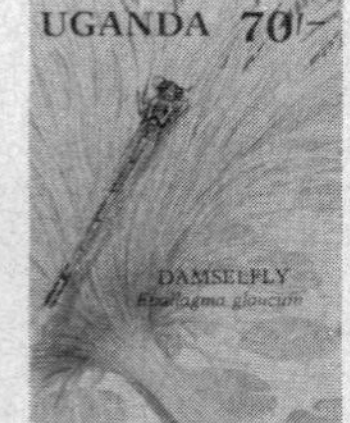

119 Census Emblem **120** Damselfly

(Litho Questa)

1990 (28 Dec). *National Population and Housing Census. T* **119** *and similar horiz design. Multicoloured. P* 14.
890 20 s. Type **119** 30 30
MS891 105×73 mm. 1000 s. Symbolic people and dwellings 4·00 4·50

(Des I. Maclaury. Litho B.D.T.)

1991 (8 Jan). *Fauna of Uganda's Wetlands. T* **120** *and similar multicoloured designs. P* 14.
892 70 s. Type **120** 50 50
a. Sheetlet of 16. Nos. 892/907 7·00
893 70 s. Purple Swamphen ("Gallinule") 50 50
894 70 s. Sitatunga 50 50
895 70 s. Western Reef Heron ("Purple Heron") 50 50
896 70 s. Bushpig 50 50
897 70 s. Vervet Monkey 50 50
898 70 s. Long Reed Frog 50 50
899 70 s. Malachite Kingfisher 50 50
900 70 s. Marsh Mongoose 50 50
901 70 s. Painted Reed Frog 50 50
902 70 s. African Jacana 50 50
903 70 s. Charaxes butterfly 50 50
904 70 s. Nile Crocodile 50 50
905 70 s. Herald Snake 50 50
906 70 s. Dragonfly 50 50
907 70 s. Lungfish 50 50
892/907 *Set of* 16 7·00 7·00
MS908 118×78 mm. 1000 s. Nile Monitor (*horiz*) 5·25 5·75
Nos. 892/907 were printed together, *se-tenant*, in sheetlets of 16 forming a composite design.

121 Slug Haplochromis

(Des Susan Fuller. Litho B.D.T.)

1991 (18 Jan). *Fishes of Uganda. T* **121** *and similar horiz designs. Multicoloured. P* 14.
909 10 s. Type **121** 10 10
910 20 s. Palmquist's Notho 15 15
911 40 s. Silver Distichodus 20 20
912 90 s. Sauvage's Haplochromis 40 40
913 100 s. Blue Calliurum 45 45
914 350 s. Johnston's Haplochromis 1·10 1·10
915 600 s. Colour-tailed Haplochromis 2·25 2·25
916 800 s. Jewel Cichlid 2·50 2·50
909/16 *Set of* 8 6·50 6·50
MS917 Two sheets, each 100×74 mm. (a) 1000 s. Haplochromis. (b) 1000 s. Striped Panchax *Set of* 2 *sheets* 9·00 10·00

(Des B. Grout. Litho Questa)

1991 (25 Feb). *Olympic Games, Barcelona* (1992). *Multicoloured designs as T* **202** *of Lesotho. P* 14.
918 20 s. Women's 100 metres hurdles 25 15
919 40 s. Long jump 30 20
920 125 s. Table tennis 70 60
921 250 s. Football 1·00 1·25
922 500 s. Men's 800 metres 1·60 2·25
918/22 *Set of* 5 3·50 4·00
MS923 Two sheets, each 110×71 mm. (a) 1200 s. Opening Ceremony at Seoul Games (*horiz*). (b) 1200 s. Women's 4 × 100 metres relay (*horiz*) *Set of* 2 *sheets* 8·50 9·50

122 Class "10" Steam Locomotive, Zimbabwe

(Des O. Fernandez. Litho Walsall)

1991 (2 Apr). *African Railway Locomotives. T* **122** *and similar horiz designs. Multicoloured. P* 14.
924 10 s. Type **122** 30 30
925 20 s. Class "12" steam locomotive, Zimbabwe 45 45
926 80 s. Class "Tribal" steam locomotive, Tazara Railway 80 80
927 200 s. 4-6-0 type steam locomotive, Egypt 1·50 1·50
928 300 s. Mikado type steam locomotive, Sudan 1·60 1·60
929 400 s. Class "Mountain" Garrat steam locomotive, Uganda 1·60 1·60
930 500 s. Mallet type steam locomotive, Uganda 1·75 1·75
931 1000 s. 5 F 1 electric locomotive, South Africa 2·25 2·25
924/31 *Set of* 8 9·00 9·00
MS932 Four sheets, each 100×70 mm. (a) 1200 s. Atlantic type steam locomotive, Egypt. (b) 1200 s. 4-8-2 type steam locomotive, Zimbabwe. (c) 1200 s. 4-8-2 type steam locomotive, Angola. (d) 1200 s. Mallet compound type steam locomotive, Natal *Set of* 4 *sheets* 13·00 14·00

123 Lord Baden-Powell and Scout Emblem **124** General Charles de Gaulle

(Des W. Hanson Studio. Litho Questa)

1991 (27 May). *World Scout Jamboree Mount Sorak, Korea. T* **123** *and similar horiz designs. P* 14.
933 20 s. multicoloured 30 30
934 80 s. multicoloured 65 65
935 100 s. multicoloured 75 75
936 150 s. black and pale yellow-olive 1·00 1·00
937 300 s. multicoloured 1·50 1·50
938 400 s. multicoloured 1·60 1·60
939 500 s. multicoloured 1·75 1·75
940 1000 s. multicoloured 2·50 2·50
933/40 *Set of* 8 9·00 9·00
MS941 Two sheets. (a) 76×115 mm. 1200 s. black and stone. (b) 115×76mm. 1200 s. black and dull violet-blue *Set of* 2 *sheets* 9·00 9·50
Designs:—80 s. Scouts and Uganda 1982 100 s. anniversary stamp; 100 s. Scout encampment, New York World's Fair, 1939; 150 s. Cover and illustration from *Scouting for Boys*; 300 s. Cooking on campfire; 400 s. Aldrin and Armstrong on Moon; 500 s. Scout salutes; 1000 s. Statue to the Unknown Scout, Gillwell Park; 1200 s. (**MS**941a) Jamboree emblem; 1200 s. (**MS**941b) Lord Baden-Powell, W. Boyce and Revd. L. Hadley.

(Des Walt Disney Co. Litho Questa)

1991 (29 May). *"Phila Nippon '91" International Stamp Exhibition, Tokyo. Multicoloured designs as T* **204** *of Lesotho showing Walt Disney cartoon characters and Japanese traditions. P* 14×13½.
942 10 s. Uncle Scrooge celebrating Ga-No-Iwai 15 15
943 20 s. Mickey Mouse removing shoes 20 20
944 70 s. Goofy leading cart-horse 50 50
945 80 s. Daisy Duck and Minnie Mouse exchanging gifts 60 60
946 300 s. Minnie kneeling at doorway 1·50 1·50
947 400 s. Donald Duck and Mickey taking a hot volcanic sand bath 1·60 1·60
948 500 s. Clarabelle Cow burning incense 1·75 1·75
949 1000 s. Mickey and Minnie writing New Year cards 2·50 2·50
942/9 *Set of* 8 8·00 8·00
MS950 Two sheets, each 127×112 mm. (a) 1200 s. Mickey conducting (*vert*). (b) 1200 s. Mickey in public bath (*vert*). P 13½×14 *Set of* 2 *sheets* 9·00 9·00

(Litho Walsall)

1991 (26 June). *Death Centenary of Vincent van Gogh* (*artist*) (1990). *Multicoloured designs as T* **255** *of Maldive Islands. P* 13½.
951 10 s. "Snowy Landscape with Arles" (*horiz*) 15 15
952 20 s. "Peasant Woman binding Sheaves" 20 20
953 60 s. "The Drinkers" (*horiz*) 40 40
954 80 s. "View of Auvers" (*horiz*) 50 50
955 200 s. "Mourning Man" 1·00 1·00
956 400 s. "Still Life: Vase with Roses" (*horiz*) 1·50 1·50
957 800 s. "The Raising of Lazarus" (*horiz*) 2·25 2·25
958 1000 s. "The Good Samaritan" 2·40 2·40
951/8 *Set of* 8 7·50 7·50
MS959 Two sheets each 102×76 mm. (a) 1200 s. "First Steps" (95×71 *mm*). (b) 1200 s. "Village Street and Steps in Auvers" (95×71 *mm*). Imperf *Set of* 2 *sheets* 8·50 9·50

(Des D. Miller. Litho Walsall)

1991 (5 July). *65th Birthday of Queen Elizabeth II. Horiz designs as T* **210** *of Lesotho. Multicoloured. P* 14.
960 70 s. Queen and Prince Charles after polo match 45 45
961 90 s. Queen at Balmoral, 1976 55 55
962 500 s. Queen with Princess Margaret, August 1980 2·00 2·00
963 600 s. Queen and Queen Mother leaving St. George's Chapel, Windsor 2·00 2·00
960/3 *Set of* 4 4·50 4·50
MS964 68×90 mm. 1200 s. Separate photographs of Queen and Prince Philip 3·25 3·75

(Des D. Miller. Litho Walsall)

1991 (5 July). *10th Wedding Anniv of Prince and Princess of Wales. Horiz designs as T* **210** *of Lesotho. Multicoloured. P* 14.
965 20 s. Prince and Princess of Wales in July 1986 20 15
966 100 s. Separate photographs of Prince, Princess and sons 55 45
967 200 s. Prince Henry and Prince William 1·00 1·00
968 1000 s. Separate photographs of Prince and Princess in 1988 3·25 3·25
965/8 *Set of* 4 4·50 4·50
MS969 68×90 mm. 1200 s. Princes William and Henry on Majorca and Prince and Princess of Wales in Cameroun 3·25 3·75

(Litho Questa)

1991 (15 July). *Birth Centenary of Charles de Gaulle* (*French statesman*) (1990). *T* **124** *and similar multicoloured designs. P* 14.
970 20 s. Type **124** 15 15
971 70 s. Liberation of Paris, 1944 35 35
972 90 s. De Gaulle with King George VI, 1940 45 45
973 100 s. Reviewing Free French troops, 1940 (*horiz*) 50 50
974 200 s. Broadcasting to France, 1940 (*horiz*) 85 85
975 500 s. De Gaulle in Normandy, 1944 (*horiz*) 1·50 1·50
976 600 s. De Gaulle at Albert Hall, 1940 (*horiz*) 1·60 1·60
977 1000 s. Inauguration as President, 1959 2·25 2·25
970/7 *Set of* 8 7·00 7·00
MS978 Two sheets. (a) 104×76 mm. 1200 s. De Gaulle entering Paris, 1944. (b) 107×76 mm. 1200 s. De Gaulle with Eisenhower, 1942 (*horiz*) *Set of* 2 *sheets* 7·50 8·50

125 *Volvariella bingensis* **126** *Anigozanthos manglesii*

(Des K. Botis. Litho Questa)

1991 (19 July). *Fungi. T* **125** *and similar multicoloured designs. P* 14.
979 20 s. Type **125** 20 20
980 70 s. *Agrocybe broadwayi* 45 45
981 90 s. *Camarophyllus olidus* 55 55
982 140 s. *Marasmius arborescens* 80 80
983 180 s. *Marasmiellus subcinereus* 90 90
984 200 s. *Agaricus campestris* 1·00 1·00
985 500 s. *Chlorophyllum molybdites* 2·00 2·00
986 1000 s. *Agaricus bingensis* 3·25 3·25
979/86 *Set of* 8 8·25 8·25
MS987 Two sheets, each 96×65 mm. (a) 1200 s. *Leucocoprinus cepaestipes* (*horiz*). (b) 1200 s. *Laccaria ohiensis* ("*Laccaria lateritia*") (*horiz*) *Set of* 2 *sheets* 8·00 8·50

(Des J. Iskowitz (Nos. 988/91), O. Fernandez (No. **MS**992). Litho Questa (Nos. 988/91) or Cartor (No. **MS**992))

1991 (1 Aug). *Endangered Species* (3*rd series*). *As Nos.* 406/9, *but with changed face values, and additional horiz designs as T* **61**. *Multicoloured. P* 14.
988 100 s. Elephants in "Elephants' Graveyard" 55 45
989 140 s. Type **61** 75 75
990 200 s. Elephants at waterhole 90 90
991 600 s. Elephants having dust bath 2·25 3·00
988/91 *Set of* 4 4·00 4·50
MS992 Two sheets, each 102×74 mm. (a) 1200 s. Giraffe. (b) 1200 s. Rhinoceros and Red-billed Oxpecker. P 13×12 *Set of* 2 *sheets* 11·00 12·00

(Des Jennifer Toombs. Litho Questa)

1991 (25 Nov). *Botanical Gardens of the World. T* **126** *and similar vert designs. Multicoloured. P* 14½.
993/1032 90 s. × 20, 100 s. × 20 *Set of* 40 13·00 15·00
MS1033 Two sheets, each 110×75 mm. (a) 1400 s. The Pagoda, Kew. (b) 1400 s. Temple of the Winds, Melbourne *Set of* 2 *sheets* 9·00 10·00
Nos. 993/1032 were issued together, *se-tenant*, as two sheetlets of 20. The 90 s. values show *Anigozanthos manglesii, Banksia grandis, Clianthus formosus, Gossypium sturtianum, Callistemon lanceolatus, Saintpaulia ionantha, Calodendrum capense, Aloe ferox* × *arborescens, Bolusanthus speciousus, Lithops schwantesii, Protea repens, Plumbago capensis, Clerodendrum thomsoniae, Thunbergia alata, Schotia latifolia, Epacris impressa, Acacia pycnantha, Telopea speciosissima, Wahlenbergia gloriosa, Eucalyptus globulus* from Melbourne, and the 100 s. *Cypripedium calceolus, Rhododendron thomsonii, Ginkgo biloba, Magnolia campbellii, Wisteria sinensis, Clerodendrum ugandense, Eulophia horsfallii, Aerangis*

rhodosticta, Abelmoschus moschatus, Gloriosa superba, Carissa edulis, Ochna kirkii, Canarina abyssinica, Nymphaea caerulea, Ceropegia succulenta, Strelitzia reginae, Strongylodon macrobotrys, Victoria amazonica, Orchis militaris and *Sophora microphylla* from Kew.

20/-

(127)

1991 (4 Dec). *Nos.* 573, 597 *and* 614 *surch as T* **127**.
1034 20 s. on 25 s. Airship N.1 *Norge* and Polar Bear (first transpolar flight), 1926
1035 20 s. on 25 s. Einstein and Deep Space (Theory of Relativity) .. ..
1035*a* 20 s. on 25 s. Tank locomotive No. 126 ..

(Litho Walsall)

1991 (18 Dec). *Christmas. Paintings by Piero della Francesca. Vert designs as T* **211** *of Lesotho. Multicoloured. P* 12.
1036 20 s. "Madonna with Child and Angels" 20 15
1037 50 s. "The Baptism of Christ" 30 15
1038 80 s. "Polyptych of Mercy" 40 30
1039 100 s. "Polyptych of Mercy" (detail) .. 45 30
1040 200 s. "The Annunciation" from "The Legend of the True Cross" .. 80 80
1041 500 s. "Pregnant Madonna" .. .. 1·60 1·75
1042 1000 s. "The Annunciation" from "Polyptych of St. Anthony" .. .. 2·50 2·75
1043 1500 s. "The Nativity" .. .. .. 3·25 4·00
1036/43 .. .. *Set of* 8 8·50 9·25
MS1044 Two sheets, each 102×127 mm. (a) 1800 s. "The Brera Altarpiece". (b) 1800 s. "Madonna and Child" from "Polyptych of St. Anthony". P 14 .. .. *Set of* 2 *sheets* 8·50 9·00

128 Boy Scout Monument, New York, and Ernest Thompson (first Chief Scout of U.S.A.)

(Des W. Hanson (Nos. 1045/6, **MS**1050b). W. Wright (Nos. 1047, **MS**1050a). Litho Questa)

1992 (6 Jan). *Anniversaries and Events. T* **128** *and similar multicoloured designs. P* 14.
1045 20 s. Type **128** 40 30
1046 50 s. Treehouse design and Daniel Beard (*vert*) 55 40
1047 400 s. Lilienthal's signature and *Flugzeug Nr. 8* .. .. 1·25 1·40
1048 500 s. Demonstrator demolishing Berlin Wall .. .. 1·40 2·00
1049 700 s. *The Magic Flute* .. .. .. 2·00 2·25
1045/9 .. .. *Set of* 5 5·00 5·75
MS1050 Two sheets. (a) 114×85 mm. 1200 s. Electric train leaving tunnel. (b) 117×89 mm. 1500 s. Ugandan Boy Scout badge *Set of* 2 *sheets* 6·50 7·00

Anniversaries and Events:—Nos. 1045/6, **MS**1050b, 50th death anniv of Lord Baden-Powell and World Scout Jamboree, Korea; No. 1047, Centenary of Otto Lilienthal's first gliding experiments; No. 1048, Bicentenary of Brandenburg Gate, Berlin; No. 1049, Death bicentenary of Mozart; No. **MS**1050a, Centenary of Trans-Siberian Railway.

129 U.S.S. *Vestal* (repair ship) under Attack

(Des W. Hanson Studio. Litho Questa)

1992 (6 Jan). *50th Anniv of Japanese Attack on Pearl Harbor. T* **129** *and similar horiz designs. Multicoloured. P* 14½.
1051 200 s. Type **129** 60 60
a. Sheetlet. Nos. 1051/60 .. .. 5·50
1052 200 s. Japanese Mitsubishi A6M Zero-Sen 60 60
1053 200 s. U.S.S. *Arizona* (battleship) on fire 60 60
1054 200 s. U.S.S. *Nevada* (battleship) passing burning ships 60 60
1055 200 s. Japanese Aichi D3A "Val" bomber attacking 60 60
1056 200 s. Douglas SBD Dauntless bombers attacking *Hiryu* (carrier) at Midway 60 60
1057 200 s. Japanese Mitsubishi A6M Zero-Sen aircraft attacking Midway Island .. 60 60
1058 200 s. U.S. Marine Brewster F2A Buffalo (fighter) defending Midway .. 60 60
1059 200 s. American Grumman F6F Hellcat aircraft and carrier 60 60
1060 200 s. U.S.S. *Yorktown* (carrier) torpedoed 60 60
1051/60 .. .. *Set of* 10 5·50 5·50

Nos. 1051/60 were printed together, *se-tenant*, in sheetlets of 10 with the stamps arranged in two horizontal strips of 5 forming composite designs separated by a gutter showing photograph of Pearl Harbor model and text.

130 Three Modern Hot Air Balloons

(Litho Questa)

1992 (6 Jan). *120th Anniv of Paris Balloon Post* (1990). *T* **130** *and similar horiz designs. Multicoloured. P* 14.
1061 200 s. Type **130** 60 60
a. Sheetlet. Nos. 1061/9 .. .. 4·75
1062 200 s. Sport balloons and top of *Double Eagle II* 60 60
1063 200 s. Pro Juventute balloon and top of Branson's *Virgin Otsuka Pacific Flyer* 60 60
1064 200 s. Blanchard and Jeffries' balloon .. 60 60
1065 200 s. Nadar's *Le Geant* and centre of *Double Eagle II* 60 60
1066 200 s. Branson's *Virgin Otsuka Pacific Flyer* 60 60
1067 200 s. Montgolfier balloon 60 60
1068 200 s. *Double Eagle II* basket and Paris balloons of 1870 .. .. .. 60 60
1069 200 s. Henri Giffard's balloon *Le Grand Ballon Captif* 60 60
1061/9 .. .. *Set of* 9 4·75 4·75

Nos. 1061/9 were printed together, *se-tenant*, as a sheetlet of 9 forming a composite design.

(Des Walt Disney Co. Litho B.D.T.)

1992 (20 Feb). *Mickey's World Tour. Multicoloured designs as T* **264** *of Maldive Islands showing Walt Disney cartoon characters in different countries. P* 13.
1070 20 s. Mickey Mouse and Goofy on African safari (*horiz*) 20 10
1071 50 s. Mickey charming Pluto's tail, India (*horiz*) 30 10
1072 80 s. Minnie Mouse, Donald and Daisy Duck as Caribbean calypso band (*horiz*) 40 20
1073 200 s. Goofy pulling Donald and Daisy in rickshaw, China (*horiz*) 70 40
1074 500 s. Mickey and Minnie on camel, Egypt (*horiz*) .. .. 1·00 1·00
1075 800 s. Donald and Pete sumo wrestling, Japan (*horiz*) .. .. .. 1·40 1·60
1076 1000 s. Goofy bullfighting, Spain (*horiz*) .. 1·60 1·90
1077 1500 s. Mickey playing football, Italy (*horiz*) .. .. 2·25 3·00
1070/7 .. .. *Set of* 8 7·00 7·50
MS1078 Two sheets, each 83×104 mm. (a) 2000 s. Mickey as Cossack dancer, Russia. (b) 2000 s. Daisy as Wagnerian diva, Germany *Set of* 2 *sheets* 7·50 8·00

(Des D. Miller. Litho Questa)

1992 (26 Feb). *40th Anniv of Queen Elizabeth II's Accession. Horiz designs as T* **214** *of Lesotho. Multicoloured. P* 14.
1079 100 s. Lake Victoria 45 25
1080 200 s. Lake and mountains 75 60
1081 500 s. Lakeside fields .. .. .. 1·50 1·60
1082 1000 s. River Nile .. .. .. 2·50 2·75
1079/82 .. .. *Set of* 4 4·75 4·75
MS1083 Two sheets, each 74×97 mm. (a) 1800 s. Waterfalls. (b) 1800 s. Owen Falls Dam *Set of* 2 *sheets* 8·00 9·00

(Des D. Burkhart, Litho Walsall)

1992 (8 Apr). *Prehistoric Animals. Horiz designs as T* **217** *of Lesotho. Multicoloured. P* 14.
1084 50 s. Kentrosaurus 35 30
1085 200 s. Iguanodon 70 70
1086 250 s. Hypsilophodon 80 80
1087 300 s. Brachiosaurus .. .. .. 1·00 1·00
1088 400 s. Peloneustes .. .. .. 1·10 1·10
1089 500 s. Pteranodon .. .. .. 1·25 1·25
1090 800 s. Tetralophodon .. .. .. 1·75 1·75
1091 1000 s. Megalosaurus .. .. .. 1·90 1·90
1084/91 .. .. *Set of* 8 8·00 8·00
MS1092 Two sheets, each 100×70 mm. (a) 2000 s. As 250 s. (b) 2000 s. As 1000 s. *Set of* 2 *sheets* 9·00 9·50

131 "The Entry into Jerusalem" (detail) (Giotto)

132 Adungu

(Litho Questa)

1992 (7 May). *Easter. Religious Paintings. T* **131** *and similar vert designs. Multicoloured. P* 13½×14.
1093 50 s. Type **131** 30 15
1094 100 s. "Pilate and the Watch" (Psalter of Robert de Lisle) 40 25
1095 200 s. "The Kiss of Judas" (detail) (Giotto) 65 55
1096 250 s. "Christ washing the Feet of the Disciples" (Vita Christi manuscript) 75 75
1097 300 s. "Christ seized in the Garden" (Melissende Psalter) 85 85
1098 500 s. "Doubting Thomas" (Vita Christi manuscript) .. .. .. 1·25 1·50
1099 1000 s. "The Marys at the Tomb" (detail) (anon) .. .. 2·00 2·75
1100 2000 s. "The Ascension" (Florentine manuscript) .. .. 3·50 4·50
1093/100 .. .. *Set of* 8 8·75 10·00
MS1101 Two sheets, each 72×102 mm. (a) 2500 s. "The Piercing of Christ's Side" (detail) (Limoges enamel). (b) 2500 s. "Agony at Gethsemane" (detail) (Limoges enamel) *Set of* 2 *sheets* 9·50 10·00

(Des R. Sauber. Litho Questa)

1992 (20 July). *Traditional Musical Instruments. T* **132** *and similar vert designs. Multicoloured. P* 14.
1102 50 s. Type **132** 20 20
1103 100 s. Endingidi 35 35
1104 200 s. Akogo 60 60
1105 250 s. Nanga 65 65
1106 300 s. Engoma 75 75
1107 400 s. Amakondere 80 80
1108 500 s. Akakyenkye .. .. .. 1·10 1·25
1109 1000 s. Ennanga .. .. 2·25 2·75
1102/9 .. .. *Set of* 8 6·00 6·50

133 Map of Known World, 1486

(Des A. Granberg. Litho Questa)

1992 (27 July). *500th Anniv of Discovery of America by Columbus and "World Columbian Stamp Expo '92" Exhibition, Chicago. T* **133** *and similar multicoloured designs. P* 14.
1110 50 s. Type **133** 20 20
1111 100 s. Map of Africa, 1508 .. .. 30 30
1112 150 s. Map of West Indies, 1500 .. 50 50
1113 200 s. *Nina* and astrolabe 60 60
1114 600 s. *Pinta* and quadrant .. .. 1·50 1·50
1115 800 s. Sand glass .. .. .. 1·60 1·60
1116 900 s. 15th-century compass .. .. 1·75 1·75
1117 2000 s. Map of World, 1492 .. .. 3·50 3·50
1110/17 .. .. *Set of* 8 9·00 9·00
MS1118 Two sheets, each 95×75 mm. (a) 2500 s. Sections of globe, 1492. (b) 2500 s. Europe and Africa from map by Henricus Martellus, 1490 (*vert*) .. .. *Set of* 2 *sheets* 7·50 9·00

(Litho Questa)

1992 (28 Aug). *Hummel Figurines. Vert designs as T* **256** *of Maldive Islands. Multicoloured. P* 14.
1119 50 s. Girl with washing 20 20
1120 200 s. Girl scrubbing floor 50 50
1121 250 s. Girl sweeping floor 60 60
1122 300 s. Girl with baby 70 70
1123 600 s. Boy mountaineer .. .. .. 1·50 1·50
1124 900 s. Girl knitting .. .. .. 2·00 2·00
1125 1000 s. Boy on stool .. .. .. 2·25 2·25
1126 1500 s. Boy with telescope .. .. 2·50 2·50
1119/26 .. .. *Set of* 8 9·25 9·25
MS1127 Two sheets, each 97×122 mm. (a) 500 s. As No. 1119; 500 s. As No. 1120; 500 s. As No. 1121; 500 s. As No. 1122. (b) 500 s. As No. 1124; 500 s. As No. 1123; 500 s. As No. 1125; 500 s. As No. 1126 .. .. .. *Set of* 2 *sheets* 8·00 9·00

134 Spotted Hyena

135 Red-headed Falcon

(Litho Questa)

1992 (25 Sept). *Wildlife. T* **134** *and similar horiz designs. Multicoloured. P* 14.
1128 50 s. Type **134** 15 15
1129 100 s. Impala 25 25
1130 200 s. Giant Forest Hog 35 35
1131 250 s. Pangolin 45 45
1132 300 s. Golden Monkey 50 50
1133 800 s. Serval .. .. 1·40 1·40
1134 1000 s. Small-spotted Genet ("Bush Genet") 1·60 1·60
1135 3000 s. Waterbuck .. .. .. 4·25 4·50
1128/35 .. .. *Set of* 8 8·00 8·25
MS1136 Two sheets, each 100×70 mm. (a) 2500 s. Gorilla. (b) 2500 s. Hippopotamus *Set of* 2 *sheets* 9·00 9·50

(Litho Questa)

1992 (2 Oct). *Olympic Games, Barcelona. Multicoloured designs as T* **216** *of Lesotho. P* 14.

1137 50 s. Men's javelin 20 20
1138 100 s. Men's highjump (*horiz*) 30 30
1139 200 s. Fencing (Pentathlon) 45 45
1140 250 s. Men's volleyball 50 50
1141 300 s. Women's platform diving .. 55 55
1142 500 s. Men's team cycling .. .. 1·25 1·25
1143 1000 s. Women's tennis .. .. .. 2·00 2·00
1144 2000 s. Boxing (*horiz*) .. .. .. 3·00 3·00
1137/44 .. .. *Set of* 8 7·50 7·50
MS1145 Two sheets, each 100×70 mm. (a) 2500 s. Men's basketball. (b) 2500 s. Baseball *Set of* 2 *sheets* 8·50 9·00

(Litho Questa)

1992 (9 Oct). *Birds. T* **135** *and similar vert designs. Multicoloured. P* 15×14.

1146 20 s. Type **135** 10 10
1147 30 s. Yellow-billed Hornbill 15 10
1148 50 s. Purple Heron 15 10
1149 100 s. Regal Sunbird 20 20
1150 150 s. White-browed Robin Chat .. 25 25
1151 200 s. Shining-blue Kingfisher 30 30
1152 250 s. Great Blue Turaco 45 40
1153 300 s. African Emerald Cuckoo 55 45
1154 500 s. Abyssinian Roller 90 90
1155 800 s. South African Crowned Crane .. 1·40 1·50
1156 1000 s. Doherty's Bush Shrike .. .. 1·75 1·90
1157 2000 s. Splendid Glossy Starling .. .. 3·00 3·50
1158 3000 s. Little Bee Eater .. .. .. 4·50 5·50
1159 4000 s. Red-faced Lovebird ("Red-headed Lovebird") .. .. .. 6·00 7·00
1146/59 .. .. *Set of* 14 18·00 20·00

(Des Kerri Schiff. Litho Questa)

1992 (28 Oct). *Postage Stamp Mega Event, New York. Sheet* 100×70 *mm. containing vert design as T* **219** *of Lesotho. Multicoloured. P* 14.

MS1160 2500 s. United Nations Headquarters 3·25 3·75

136 Goofy in *Hawaiian Holiday*, 1937

137 "The Annunciation" (Zurbaran)

(Des Walt Disney Co. Litho Questa)

1992 (2 Nov). *60th Anniv of Goofy. T* **136** *and similar multicoloured designs. P* 13½.

1162 50 s. Type **136** 20 20
1163 100 s. Riding pennyfarthing cycle, 1941 20 20
1164 200 s. Goofy and Mickey Mouse as firemen, 1935 .. .. .. 35 35
1165 250 s. Skiing, 1941 (*horiz*) 40 40
1166 300 s. One man band, 1937 (*horiz*) .. 50 50
1167 1000 s. Asleep against boat, 1938 (*horiz*) 1·75 2·00
1168 1500 s. Ancient Olympic champion, 1942 2·50 2·75
1169 2000 s. Pole vaulting, 1942 .. .. 3·00 3·50
1162/9 .. .. *Set of* 8 8·00 9·00
MS1170 Two sheets. (a) 105×115 mm. 3000 s. Goofy and Wilbur the grasshopper, 1939 (*horiz*). (b) 92×116 mm. 3000 s. Wyatt Goofy and Goofy today .. .. *Set of* 2 *sheets* 8·50 9·00

(Litho Questa)

1992 (16 Nov). *Christmas. Religious Paintings by Francisco Zurbaran. T* **137** *and similar vert designs. Multicoloured. P* 13½×14.

1171 50 s. Type **137** 20 15
1172 200 s. "The Annunciation" (*different*) .. 50 35
1173 250 s. "The Virgin of the Immaculate Conception" 60 45
1174 300 s. "The Virgin of the Immaculate Conception" (detail) 65 50
1175 800 s. "Holy Family with Saints Anne, Joachim and John the Baptist" .. 1·75 2·00
1176 900 s. "Holy Family with Saints Anne, Joachim and John the Baptist" (detail) .... 1·90 2·25
1177 1000 s. "Adoration of the Magi" .. .. 2·00 2·25
1178 2000 s. "Adoration of the Magi" (detail) 3·50 4·25
1171/8 .. .. *Set of* 8 10·00 11·00
MS1179 Two sheets, each 76×102 mm. (a) 2500 s. "The Virgin of the Immaculate Conception (*different*). (b) 2500 s. "The Virgin of the Immaculate Conception" (*different*) *Set of* 2 *sheets* 9·50 10·00

138 Man cleaning Granary

(Des W. Wright and L. Fried (Nos. 1184, 1189, **MS**1191a). Litho Questa)

1992 (7 Dec). *Anniversaries and Events. T* **138** *and similar horiz designs. Multicoloured. P* 14.

1180 50 s. Type **138** 15 15
1181 200 s. Mother breast feeding 40 40
1182 250 s. Mother feeding baby 50 50
1183 300 s. Boy collecting water from pump .. 60 60
1184 300 s. "Voyager 2" passing Jupiter .. 75 75
1185 800 s. Mother and baby .. .. .. 1·40 1·40
1186 800 s. Impala .. .. 1·40 1·40
1187 1000 s. Mountain Zebra .. .. .. 1·90 1·90
1188 1000 s. Count Ferdinand von Zeppelin and airship .. .. .. 1·90 1·90
1189 2000 s. "Voyager 2" passing Neptune .. 4·00 4·00
1190 3000 s. Count Ferdinand von Zeppelin and Clement-Bayard airship *Fleurus* 5·00 5·00
1180/90 .. .. *Set of* 11 16·00 16·00
MS1191 Four sheets, each 115×85 mm. (a) 2500 s. "Voyager 2" and Jupiter. (b) 2500 s. Warthog. (c) 2500 s. Count Ferdinand von Zeppelin with Robert Brothers and Colin Hullin balloon. (d) 2500 s. Doctor inoculating boy *Set of* 4 *sheets* 17·00 18·00

Anniversaries and Events—Nos. 1180/3, 1185, United Nations World Health Organization Projects; Nos. 1184, 1189, **MS**1191a, International Space Year; Nos. 1186/7, **MS**1191b, Earth Summit '92, Rio; Nos. 1188, 1190, **MS**1191c, 75th death anniv of Count Ferdinand von Zeppelin (airship pioneer); **MS**1191d, 75th anniv of International Association of Lions Clubs.

139 Hands releasing Dove with Lubaga and Kampala Catholic Cathedrals

(Des Susan Rini. Litho Questa)

1993 (1 Feb). *Visit of Pope John Paul II. T* **139** *and similar multicoloured designs. P* 14.

1192 50 s. Type **139** 20 10
1193 200 s. Pope and Kampala Cathedral .. 35 30
1194 250 s. Pope and Catholic worshipper .. 40 35
1195 300 s. Ugandan bishops and Pope .. 45 40
1196 800 s. Pope John Paul II waving .. 1·25 1·40
1197 900 s. Pope and Kampala Cathedral (*different*) .. .. .. 1·25 1·50
1198 1000 s. Pope, national flag and Kampala Cathedral .. .. .. 1·40 1·60
1199 2000 s. Pope and national flag .. .. 2·75 3·00
1192/9 .. .. *Set of* 8 7·25 7·75
MS1200 Two sheets, each 100×70 mm. (a) 3000 s. Pope on aircraft steps (*vert*). (b) 3000 s. Pope delivering blessing (*vert*) .. *Set of* 2 *sheets* 8·00 8·50

A 5000 s. value embossed on gold foil exists from a limited printing.

(Litho Walsall)

1993 (5 Apr). *Bicentenary of the Louvre, Paris. Paintings by Rembrandt. Multicoloured designs as T* **221** *of Lesotho. P* 12.

1201 500 s. "Self-portrait at Easel" 60 65
a. Sheetlet. Nos. 1201/8 .. .. 4·75
1202 500 s. "Birds of Paradise" 60 65
1203 500 s. "The Carcass of Beef" 60 65
1204 500 s. "The Supper at Emmaus" 60 65
1205 500 s. "Hendrickje Stoffels" 60 65
1206 500 s. "The Artist's Son, Titus" 60 65
1207 500 s. "The Holy Family" (left detail) .. 60 65
1208 500 s. "The Holy Family" (right detail" .. 60 65
1201/8 .. .. *Set of* 8 4·75 5·25
MS1209 100×70 mm. 2000 s. "The Philosopher in Meditation" (89×57 *mm*). P 14½ .. 3·00 3·25

Nos. 1201/8 were printed together, *se-tenant*, in sheetlets of 8 stamps and one centre label.

140 Afghan Hound

141 Gutierrez (Uruguay) and Voeller (Germany)

(Des J. Barbaris. Litho Questa)

1993 (28 May). *Dogs of the World. T* **140** *and similar multicoloured designs. P* 14.

1210 50 s. Type **140** 10 10
1211 100 s. Newfoundland 10 10
1212 200 s. Siberian Huskies 25 30
1213 250 s. Briard 30 35
1214 300 s. Saluki 35 40
1215 800 s. Labrador guide-dog (*vert*) .. 95 1·00
1216 1000 s. Greyhound .. .. .. 1·25 1·40
1217 1500 s. Pointer .. .. 1·75 1·90
1210/17 .. .. *Set of* 8 5·00 5·50
MS1218 Two sheets, each 103×80 mm. (a) 2500 s. Cape Hunting Dog. (b) 2500 s. Norwegian Elkhound pup .. *Set of* 2 *sheets* 6·00 6·25

(Des Kerri Schiff. Litho Questa)

1993 (2 June). *40th Anniv of Coronation. Vert designs as T* **224** *of Lesotho. Multicoloured. P* 13½.

1219 50 s. Queen Elizabeth II at Coronation (photograph by Cecil Beaton) .. 10 10
a. Sheetlet. Nos. 1219/22×2 .. 5·50
1220 200 s. Orb and Sceptre 25 30
1221 500 s. Queen Elizabeth during Coronation 60 65
1222 1500 s. Queen Elizabeth II and Princess Margaret .. .. 1·75 1·90
1219/22 .. .. *Set of* 4 2·75 3·00
MS1223 69×100 mm. 2500 s. "The Crown" (detail) (Grace Wheatley) (28½×42½ *mm*). P 14 3·00 3·25

Nos. 1219/22 were printed in sheetlets of 8, containing two *se-tenant* blocks of 4.

(Des Kerri Schiff. Litho Questa)

1993 (22 Sept). *Asian International Stamp Exhibitions. Multicoloured designs as T* **263** *of St. Vincent, but vert. P* 13½×14.

(*a*) *"Indopex '93", Surabaya, Indonesia. Javanese Wayang Puppets*

1224 600 s. Bupati karma, Prince of Wangga .. 70 75
a. Sheetlet. Nos. 1224/9 .. .. 4·25
1225 600 s. Rahwana 70 75
1226 600 s. Sondjeng Sandjata 70 75
1227 600 s. Raden Damar Wulan 70 75
1228 600 s. Unidentified puppet 70 75
1229 600 s. Hanaman 70 75
1224/9 .. .. *Set of* 6 4·25 4·50
MS1230 135×105 mm. 2500 s. Candi Mendut Temple, Java .. .. 3·00 3·25

(*b*) *"Taipei '93", Taiwan. Funerary Pottery Figures*

1231 600 s. Tomb guardian god in green armour 70 75
a. Sheetlet. Nos. 1231/6 .. .. 4·25
1232 600 s. Civil official and shrine 70 75
1233 600 s. Tomb guardian god in green and gold armour 70 75
1234 600 s. Civil official in red robe 70 75
1235 600 s. Chimera (tomb guardian) 70 75
1236 600 s. Civil official in red and green robe 70 75
1231/6 .. .. *Set of* 6 4·25 4·50
MS1237 135×105 mm. 2500 s. Statue of the Sacred Mother, Taiyuan .. .. .. 3·00 3·25

(*c*) *"Bangkok '93", Thailand. Sculptured Figures*

1238 600 s. Standing Buddha in gilded red sandstone, 13th–15th century .. 70 75
a. Sheetlet. Nos. 1238/43 .. .. 4·25
1239 600 s. Crowned Buddha in bronze, 13th century 70 75
1240 600 s. Thepanom in stone, 15th century .. 70 75
1241 600 s. Crowned Buddha in bronze, 12th century 70 75
1242 600 s. Avalokitesvara in bronze, 9th century 70 75
1243 600 s. Lop Buri standing Buddha in bronze, 13th–century 70 75
1238/43 .. .. *Set of* 6 4·25 4·50
MS1244 135×105 mm. 2500 s. Buddha, Wat Mahathat .. .. 3·00 3·25

Nos. 1224/9, 1231/6 and 1238/43 were each printed together, *se-tenant*, in sheetlets of 6.

(Des Rosemary DeFiglio. Litho Questa)

1993 (1 Oct). *World Cup Football Championship, U.S.A. (1994) (1st issue). T* **141** *and similar multicoloured designs. P* 14.

1245 50 s. Type **141** 15 10
1246 200 s. Tomas Brolin (Sweden) 35 30
1247 250 s. Gary Lineker (England) 40 35
1248 300 s. Munoz and Butragueno (Spain) .. 45 40
1249 800 s. Carlos Valderrama (Colombia) .. 1·25 1·25
1250 900 s. Diego Maradona (Argentina) .. 1·40 1·40
1251 1000 s. Pedro Troglio (Argentina) .. 1·50 1·50
1252 2000 s. Enzo Scifo (Belgium) .. .. 2·75 3·25
1245/52 .. .. *Set of* 8 7·50 7·75
MS1253 Two sheets, each 103×72 mm. (a) 2500 s. Brazilians celebrating. (b) 2500 s. De Napoli (Italy) and Skuhravy (Czechoslovkia) (*horiz*) .. .. *Set of* 2 *sheets* 7·50 8·00

See also Nos. 1322/8.

142 York Minster, England

143 Mickey Mouse asleep on Stegosaurus

(Des G. Bibby. Litho Questa)

1993 (3 Nov). *Cathedrals of the World. T* **142** *and similar vert designs. Multicoloured. P* 14.

1254 50 s. Type **142** 15 10
1255 100 s. Notre Dame, Paris 20 10
1256 200 s. Little Metropolis, Athens 35 30
1257 250 s. St. Patrick's, New York 40 35
1258 300 s. Ulm, Germany 45 40
1259 800 s. St. Basil's, Moscow .. .. 1·25 1·25
1260 1000 s. Roskilde, Denmark .. .. 1·50 1·50
1261 2000 s. Seville, Spain .. .. .. 2·75 3·25
1254/61 .. .. *Set of* 8 6·25 6·50
MS1262 Two sheets, each 70×100 mm. (a) 2500 s. Namirembe, Uganda. (b) 2500 s. St. Peter's, Vatican City .. .. *Set of* 2 *sheets* 6·50 7·50

(Litho Questa)

1993 (19 Nov). *Christmas. Religious Paintings. Vert designs as T* **76** *of Nevis (St. Kitts–Nevis). Black, pale lemon and red (Nos.* 1263, 1265, 1267, 1270 *and* **MS**1271a) *or multicoloured (others).*

1263 50 s. "Virgin with Carthusian Monks" (detail) (Dürer) 15 10
1264 100 s. "Sacred Family" (detail) (Raphael) 20 10
1265 200 s. "Virgin with Carthusian Monks" (different detail) (Dürer) 35 30
1266 250 s. "The Virgin of the Rose" (Raphael) 40 35
1267 300 s. "Virgin with Carthusian Monks" (different detail) (Dürer) 45 40
1268 800 s. "Sacred Family" (different detail) (Raphael) .. .. 1·25 1·25
1269 1000 s. "Virgin with Beardless Joseph" (Raphael) .. .. 1·50 1·50
1270 2000 s. "Virgin with Carthusian Monks" (different detail) (Dürer) .. .. 2·75 3·25
1263/70 .. .. *Set of* 8 6·25 6·50
MS1271 Two sheets, each 102×127 mm. (a) 2500 s. "Virgin with Carthusian Monks" (different detail) (Dürer). (b) 2500 s. "Sacred Family" (different detail) (Raphael) *Set of* 2 *sheets* 7·00 8·00

Nos. **MS**1271 is inscribed "Canthusian Monks" in error.

(Des Walt Disney Co. Litho Questa)

1993 (22 Dec). *Prehistoric Animals. T* **143** *and similar horiz designs showing Walt Disney cartoon characters. Multicoloured. P* 14×13½.

1272 50 s. Type **143** 15 10
1273 100 s. Minnie Mouse on pterandon 20 10
1274 200 s. Mickey being licked by mamenchisaurus 35 30
1275 250 s. Mickey doing cave painting .. 40 35
1276 300 s. Mickey wind-surfing on dinosaur 45 45
1277 500 s. Mickey and Donald Duck sliding on diplodocus 75 75
1278 800 s. Mamenchisaurus carrying Mickey 1·25 1·40
1279 1000 s. Pluto on triceratops .. .. 1·50 1·60
1272/9 .. .. *Set of* 8 4·50 4·50
MS1280 Two sheets, each 128×102 mm. (a) 2500 s. Mickey and Minnie. (b) 2500 s. Mickey feeding tyrannosaurus rex .. *Set of* 2 *sheets* 7·00 7·50

No. 1273 is inscribed "PTERANDOM" and No. 1278 "MAMENSHISAURUS", both in error.

144 "Woman in Yellow" (Picasso)

145 Passion Fruit

(Litho Questa)

1993 (29 Dec). *Anniversaries and Events. T* **144** *and similar multicoloured designs. P* 14.

1281 100 s. Type **144** 10 10
1282 200 s. Head of cow and syringe 35 30
1283 250 s. "Gertrude Stein" (Picasso) .. 30 35
1284 500 s. Early telescope 75 75
1285 800 s. "Creation" (S. Witkiewicz after J. Glogowski) .. .. 1·25 1·25
1286 1000 s. Modern telescope .. .. .. 1·50 1·50
1287 1000 s. "For the Right to Work" (A. Strumillo) .. .. 1·50 1·50
1281/7 .. .. *Set of* 7 5·25 5·25
MS1288 Three sheets. (a) 75×105 mm. 2500 s. "Woman by a Window" (detail) (Picasso). (b) 105×75 mm. 2500 s. Copernicus. (c) 105×75 mm. 2500 s. "Temptation of Saint Antony I" (detail) (S. Witkiewicz) (*horiz*) .. *Set of* 3 *sheets* 9·50 10·00

Anniversaries and Events:—Nos. 1281, 1283, **MS**1288a, 20th death anniv of Picasso (artist); No. 1282, Pan African Rinderpest Campaign; Nos. 1284, 1286, **MS**1288b, 450th death anniv of Copernicus (astronomer); Nos. 1285, 1287, **MS**1288c, "Polska '93" International Stamp Exhibition, Poznań.

(Litho Questa)

1994 (13 Jan). *Fruits and Crops. T* **145** *and similar multicoloured designs. P* 14.

1289 50 s. Type **145** 15 10
1290 100 s. Sunflower 15 10
1291 150 s. Bananas 25 25
1292 200 s. Runner beans 35 30
1293 250 s. Pineapple 40 35
1294 300 s. Jackfruit 45 45
1295 500 s. Sorghum 75 85
1296 800 s. Maize .. .. 1·25 1·50
1289/96 .. .. *Set of* 8 3·25 3·50
MS1297 Two sheets, each 101×71 mm. (a) 2000 s. Sesame. (b) 2000 s. Coffee (*horiz*) *Set of* 2 *sheets* 5·50 6·00

146 Ford Model "A", 1903

(Litho Questa)

1994 (18 Jan). *Centenaries of Henry Ford's First Petrol Engine (Nos.* 1298/1301, **MS**1306a) *and Karl Benz's First Four-wheeled Car (others). T* **146** *and similar multicoloured designs. P* 14.

1298 700 s. Type **146** 85 90
a. Horiz strip of 4. Nos. 1298/1301 .. 3·50
1299 700 s. Ford Model "T" snowmobile, 1932 85 90
1300 700 s. Ford "Mustang" 85 90
1301 700 s. Lotus-Ford racing car, 1965 .. 85 90
1302 800 s. Mercedes-Benz "S600" coupe, 1994 95 1·00
a. Horiz strip of 4. Nos. 1302/5 .. 3·75
1303 800 s. Mercedes-Benz "W196" racing car, 1955 .. .. 95 1·00
1304 800 s. Mercedes-Benz "W125" road speed record car, 1938 .. .. .. 95 1·00
1305 800 s. Benz "Viktoria", 1893 .. .. 95 1·00
1298/1305 .. .. *Set of* 8 7·25 7·50
MS1306 Two sheets, each 85×85 mm. (a) 2500 s. Henry Ford (*vert*). (b) 2500 s. Karl Benz (*vert*) *Set of* 2 *sheets* 6·00 6·25

Nos. 1298/1301 and 1302/5 were printed together, *se-tenant*, in horizontal strips of 4 throughout the sheet.

(Des W. Hanson. Litho Questa)

1994 (18 Feb). *"Hong Kong '94" International Stamp Exhibition (1st issue). Horiz designs as T* **293** *of Maldive Islands. Multicoloured. P* 14.

1307 500 s. Hong Kong 1988 60 c. Catholic Cathedral stamp and Religious shrines, Repulse Bay 60 65
a. Horiz pair. Nos. 1307/8 .. .. 1·10 1·25
1308 500 s. Uganda 1993 2500 s. Namirembe Cathedral stamp and Religious shrines, Repulse Bay (*different*) .. 60 65

Nos. 1307/8 were printed together, *se-tenant*, in horizontal pairs throughout the sheet with the centre part of each pair forming a composite design.

(Des Kerri Schiff. Litho Questa)

1994 (18 Feb). *"Hong Kong '94" International Stamp Exhibition (2nd issue). Ching Dynasty Snuff Boxes. Vert designs as T* **294** *of Maldive Islands. Multicoloured. P* 14.

1309 200 s. Glass box with pavilion design .. 25 30
a. Sheetlet. Nos. 1309/14 .. .. 1·50
1310 200 s. Porcelain box with quail design .. 25 30
1311 200 s. Porcelain box with floral design .. 25 30
1312 200 s. Porcelain box with openwork design 25 30
1313 200 s. Agate box with carved Lion-dogs .. 25 30
1314 200 s. Agate box with man on donkey design 25 30
1309/14 .. .. *Set of* 6 1·50 1·75

Nos. 1309/14 were printed together, *se-tenant*, in sheetlets of 6.

Captions for Nos. 1310/11 are transposed.

147 Meteorological Weather Station

(Des Associated Creative Designs. Litho Questa)

1994 (15 Mar). *World Meteorological Day. T* **147** *and similar multicoloured designs. P* 14.

1315 50 s. Type **147** 15 10
1316 200 s. Weather observatory at training school, Entebbe (*vert*) 35 30
1317 250 s. Satellite link 40 35
1318 300 s. Recording temperatures 45 45
1319 400 s. Automatic weather station (*vert*) .. 60 70
1320 800 s. Crops damaged by hailstones .. 1·25 1·50
1315/20 .. .. *Set of* 6 2·75 3·00
MS1321 105×75 mm. 2500 s. Barograph .. 3·50 3·75

(Des J. Iskowitz. Litho Questa)

1994 (27 June). *World Cup Football Championship, U.S.A. (2nd issue). Horiz designs as T* **268** *of Sierra Leone. Multicoloured. P* 14.

1322 500 s. Georges Grun (Belgium) 95 95
a. Sheetlet. Nos. 1322/7 .. .. 5·00
1323 500 s. Oscar Ruggeri (Argentina) 95 95
1324 500 s. Frank Rijkaard (Netherlands) .. 95 95
1325 500 s. Magid "Tyson" Musisi (Uganda) .. 95 95
1326 500 s. Ronald Koeman (Netherlands) .. 95 95
1327 500 s. Igor Shalimov (Russia) 95 95
1322/7 .. .. *Set of* 6 5·00 5·00
MS1328 Two sheets, each 70×100 mm. (a) 2500 s. Ruud Gullit (Netherlands). (b) 2500 s. Player and R.F.K. Stadium, Washington D.C. *Set of* 2 *sheets* 8·00 8·50

Nos. 1322/7 were printed together, *se-tenant*, in sheetlets of 6. No. 1326 is inscribed "DONALD KOEMAN" in error.

148 Milking Cow

(Des Associated Creative Designs. Litho Questa)

1994 (29 June). *50th Anniv of Heifer Project International. P* 14.

1329 **148** 100 s. multicoloured 30 20

149 *Lobobunaea goodii* (wings spread)

150 Wooden Stool

(Des D. Burkhart. Litho Questa)

1994 (13 July). *Moths. T* **149** *and similar vert designs. Multicoloured. P* 14.

1330 100 s. Type **149** 20 10
1331 200 s. *Bunaeopsis hersilia* 35 30
1332 300 s. *Rufoglanis rosea* 45 40
1333 350 s. *Acherontia atropos* 50 50
1334 400 s. *Rohaniella pygmaea* 60 60
1335 450 s. *Euchloron megaera* 65 65
1336 500 s. *Epiphora rectifascia* 75 75
1337 1000 s. *Polyphychus coryndoni* .. .. 1·50 2·00
1330/7 .. .. *Set of* 8 4·50 4·75
MS1338 Two sheets, each 117×88 mm. (a) 2500 s. As Type **149**. (b) 2500 s. *Lobobunaea goodii* (wings folded) .. .. *Set of* 2 *sheets* 7·50 8·00

(Litho Questa)

1994 (18 July). *Crafts. T* **150** *and similar vert designs. Multicoloured. P* 14.

1339 100 s. Type **150** 15 10
1340 200 s. Wood and banana fibre chair .. 35 30
1341 250 s. Raffia and palm leaves basket .. 40 35
1342 300 s. Wool tapestry showing tree planting 45 40
1343 450 s. Wool tapestry showing hair grooming 65 65
1344 500 s. Wood sculpture of a drummer .. 75 75
1345 800 s. Gourds .. .. 1·25 1·50
1346 1000 s. Bark cloth handbag .. .. 1·40 1·60
1339/46 .. .. *Set of* 8 4·75 5·00
MS1347 Two sheets, each 100×70 mm. (a) 2500 s. Raffia baskets. (b) 2500 s. Papyrus hats *Set of* 2 *sheets* 6·50 7·50

151 Turkish Angora Cat and Blue Mosque

152 Child carrying Building Block

(Des J. Genzo. Litho Questa)

1994 (22 July). *Cats. T* **151** *and similar multicoloured designs. P* 14.

1348 50 s. Type **151** 10 10
1349 100 s. Japanese Bobtail and Mt Fuji .. 10 10
1350 200 s. Norwegian Forest Cat and windmill, Holland 25 30
1351 300 s. Egyptian Mau and Pyramids (*vert*) 35 40
1352 450 s. Rex and Stonehenge, England (*vert*) 55 60
1353 500 s. Chartreux and Eiffel Tower, France 60 65
1354 1000 s. Burmese and Shwe Dagon Pagoda (*vert*) .. .. 1·25 1·40
1355 1500 s. Maine Coon and Pemaquid Point Lighthouse (*vert*) .. .. .. 1·75 1·90
1348/55 .. .. *Set of* 8 5·00 5·50
MS1356 Two sheets, each 100×76 mm. (a) 2500 s. Russian Blue. (b) 2500 s. Manx *Set of* 2 *sheets* 6·00 6·25

(Des Associated Creative Designs. Litho Questa)

1994 (29 July). *75th Anniv of International Labour Organization. P* 14.

1357 **152** 350 s. multicoloured 60 60

(Des W Hanson. Litho B.D.T.)

1994 (11 Aug). *25th Anniv of First Moon Landing. Astronauts. Horiz designs as T* **302** *of Maldive Islands. Multicoloured. P* 14.

1358 50 s. Alan Shepard Jnr 10 10
a. Sheetlet. Nos. 1358/64 .. .. 2·50
1359 100 s. M. Scott Carpenter 10 10
1360 200 s. Virgil Grissom 25 30
1361 300 s. L. Gordon Cooper Jnr 35 40
1362 400 s. Walter Schirra Jnr 50 55
1363 500 s. Donald Slayton 60 65
1364 600 s. John Glenn Jnr 70 75
1358/64 .. .. *Set of* 7 2·50 2·75
MS1365 88×91 mm. 3000 s. "Apollo 11" anniversary emblem .. .. 3·50 3·75

Nos. 1358/64 were printed together, *se-tenant*, in sheetlets of 7 with 2 stamp-size labels depicting rocket launches.

(Des Kerri Schiff. Litho Questa)

1994 (11 Aug). *Centenary of International Olympic Committee. Gold Medal Winners. Multicoloured designs as T* **303** *of Maldive Islands. P* 14.

1366 350 s. John Akii-Bua (Uganda) (400 metres hurdles), 1972 (*horiz*) 40 45
1367 900 s. Heike Herkel (Germany) (high jump), 1992 (*horiz*) .. .. .. 1·10 1·25
MS1368 107×76 mm. 2500 s. Aleski Urmanov (Russia) (figure skating), 1994 .. .. 3·00 3·25

(Des J. Batchelor. Litho Questa)

1994 (11 Aug). *50th Anniv of D-Day. Horiz designs as T* **304** *of Maldive Islands. Multicoloured. P* 14.

1369 300 s. Mulberry Harbour pier 35 40
1370 1000 s. Mulberry Harbour floating bridge 1·25 1·40
MS1371 105×76 mm. 2500 s. Aerial view of Mulberry Harbour .. .. 3·00 3·25

(Litho Questa)

1994 (11 Aug). *"Philakorea '94" International Stamp Exhibition, Seoul. Horiz designs as T* **305** *of Maldive Islands. Multicoloured. P* 14.

1372 100 s. Sari Pagoda, Paekyangsa .. 10 10
1373 350 s. Ch'omsongdae 40 45
1374 1000 s. Pulguksa Temple .. .. 1·25 1·40
1372/4 .. .. *Set of* 3 1·75 2·00
MS1375 76×106 mm. 2500 s. Bronze mural, Pagoda Park, Seoul .. .. 3·00 3·25

153 Ugandan Family

(Litho Questa)

1994 (11 Aug). *International Year of the Family. P* 14.

1376 **153** 100 s. multicoloured 20 10

154 Baby Simba

(Des Alvin White Studios. Litho Questa)

1994 (30 Sept). *The Lion King. T* **154** *and similar multi-coloured designs showing characters from Walt Disney's cartoon film. P* 14.

1377 100 s. Type **154** 15 15
a. Sheetlet. Nos. 1377/85 .. .. 1·25
1378 100 s. Mufasa, Simba and Sarabi .. 15 15
1379 100 s. Young Simba and Nala 15 15
1380 100 s. Timon 15 15
1381 100 s. Rafiki 15 15
1382 100 s. Pumbaa 15 15
1383 100 s. The Hyenas 15 15
1384 100 s. Scar 15 15
1385 100 s. Zazu 15 15
1386 200 s. Rafiki and Mufasa 35 35
a. Sheetlet. Nos. 1386/94 .. .. 2·75
1387 200 s. Rafiki holding Simba with Mufasa and Sarabi 35 35
1388 200 s. Rafiki holding Simba aloft .. 35 35
1389 200 s. Scar and Zazu 35 35
1390 200 s. Rafiki having vision 35 35
1391 200 s. Simba and Scar 35 35
1392 200 s. Simba and Nala 35 35
1393 200 s. Simba with mane of leaves .. 35 35
1394 200 s. Simba, Nala and Zazu 35 35
1395 250 s. Scar and Simba 40 40
a. Sheetlet. Nos. 1395/1403 .. .. 3·25
1396 250 s. Mufasa rescues Simba 40 40
1397 250 s. Scar killing Mufasa 40 40
1398 250 s. Simba falling off cliff 40 40
1399 250 s. Timon, Pumbaa and Simba at pool 40 40
1400 250 s. Simba, Timon and Pumbaa .. 40 40
1401 250 s. Rafiki with staff 40 40
1402 250 s. Simba and Nala 40 40
1403 250 s. Simba looking into pool 40 40
1377/1403 .. .. *Set of* 27 7·25 7·25
MS1404 Three sheets. (a) 127×94 mm. 2500 s. Jungle animals. P 14×13½. (b) 127×102 mm. 2500 s. Simba and Timon on branch. P 14×13½. (c) 127×94 mm. 2500 s. Simba with parents and Rafiki (*vert*). P 13½×14 .. .. *Set of* 3 *sheets* 10·00 11·00

Nos. 1377/85, 1386/94 and 1395/1403 were each printed together, *se-tenant*, in sheetlets of 9.

A 5000 s. in a similar design, embosed on gold foil, also exists from a limited printing.

(Des Kerri Schiff. Litho B.D.T.)

1994 (9 Nov). *Centenary of Sierra Club (environmental protection society) (1992). Endangered Species. Multicoloured designs as T* **296** *of Maldive Islands. P* 14.

(*a*) *Vert designs*

1405 100 s. Chimpanzee with arms folded .. 10 10
a. Sheetlet. Nos. 1405/12 .. .. 4·50
1406 200 s. Head of Chimpanzee 25 30
1407 250 s. Head of African Wild Dog .. 30 35
1408 300 s. Head of Cheetah 35 40
1409 500 s. Geleda Baboon 60 65
1410 600 s. Geleda Baboon from back .. 70 75
1411 800 s. Head of Grevy's Zebra .. .. 95 1·00
1412 1000 s. Geleda Baboon siting on rock .. 1·25 1·40

(*b*) *Horiz designs*

1413 200 s. Pair of Cheetahs 25 30
a. Sheetlet. Nos. 1413/19 plus label 4·25
1414 250 s. Cheetah cubs 30 35
1415 300 s. African Wild Dog at rest 35 40
1416 500 s. Head of African Wild Dog .. 60 65
1417 600 s. Grevy's Zebra 70 75
1418 800 s. Chimpanzee lying down .. .. 95 1·00
1419 1000 s. Grevy's Zebra feeding .. .. 1·25 1·40
1405/19 .. .. *Set of* 15 8·75 9·75

Nos. 1405/12 and 1413/19 were each printed together, *se-tenant*, in sheetlets of 8 stamps (Nos. 1405/12) or 7 stamps and one label (at top left) (Nos. 1413/19).

155 Terminal Building, Entebbe International Airport

156 Game Poachers

(Des Creative Graphics. Litho B.D.T.)

1994 (14 Nov). *50th Anniv of International Civil Aviation Organization. T* **155** *and similar horiz design. Multicoloured. P* 14.

1420 100 s. Type **155** 20 10
1421 250 s. Control tower, Entebbe International Airport 50 60

(Des Creative Graphics. Litho B.D.T.)

1994 (15 Nov). *Ecology. T* **156** *and similar vert designs. Multicoloured. P* 14.

1422 100 s. Type **156** 15 10
1423 250 s. Villagers at rubbish dump .. 45 40
1424 350 s. Fishermen 60 60
1425 500 s. Deforestation .. .. .. 90 1·10
1422/5 .. .. *Set of* 4 1·90 2·00

157 "Adoration of the Christ Child" (Filippino Lippi)

158 "Self-portrait" (Tintoretto)

(Litho Questa)

1994 (5 Dec). *Christmas. Religious Paintings. T* **157** *and similar vert designs. Multicoloured. P* 13½×14.

1426 100 s. Type **157** 20 10
1427 200 s. "The Holy Family rests on the Flight into Egypt" (Annibale Carracci) 35 30
1428 300 s. "Madonna with Christ Child and St. John" (Piero di Cosimo) 45 40
1429 350 s. "The Conestabile Madonna" (Raphael) 55 45
1430 450 s. "Madonna and Child with Angels" (after Antonio Rossellino) .. 65 65
1431 500 s. "Madonna and Child with St. John" (Raphael) 75 75
1432 900 s. "Madonna and Child" (Luca Signorelli) .. .. 1·40 1·50
1433 1000 s. "Madonna with the Child Jesus, St. John and an Angel" (pseudo Pier Francesco Fiorentino) .. .. 1·50 1·60
1426/33 .. .. *Set of* 8 5·25 5·25
MS1434 Two sheets, each 115×95 mm. (a) 2500 s. "The Madonna of the Magnificat" (detail) (Sandro Botticelli). (b) 2500 s. "Adoration of the Magi" (detail) (Fra Angelico and Filippo Lippi) *Set of* 2 *sheets* 7·00 7·50

No. 1426 is inscribed "Fillipino" in error.

(Des Pauline Cianciolo. Litho B.D.T.)

1995 (7 Feb). *400th Death Anniv of Jacopo Tintoretto (painter)* (1994). *T* **158** *and similar multicoloured designs. P* 13.

1435 100 s. Type **158** 15 10
1436 300 s. "A Philosopher" 45 40
1437 400 s. "The Creation of the Animals" (detail) (*horiz*) 60 55
1438 450 s. "The Feast of Belshazzar" (detail) (*horiz*) 65 60
1439 500 s. "The Raising of the Brazen Serpent" 75 75
1440 1000 s. "Elijah fed by the Angel" .. 1·50 1·75
1435/40 .. .. *Set of* 6 3·50 3·75
MS1441 Two sheets. (a) 114×124 mm. 2000 s. "Moses striking Water from a Rock" (detail). (b) 124×114 mm. 200 s. "Finding of Moses" (detail) *Set of* 2 *sheets* 5·50 6·00

159 White-faced Whistling Duck ("White-faced Tree-duck")

1995 (24 Apr). *Waterfowl and Wetland Birds of Uganda. T* **159** *and similar horiz designs. Multicoloured. Litho. P* 14.

1442 200 s. Type **159** 25 30
a. Sheetlet. Nos. 1442/57 .. .. 4·00
1443 200 s. Common Shoveler ("European Shoveler") 25 30
1444 200 s. Hartlaub's Duck 25 30
1445 200 s. Verreaux's Eagle Owl ("Milky Eagle-owl") 25 30
1446 200 s. Avocet 25 30
1447 200 s. African Fish Eagle 25 30
1448 200 s. Spectacled Weaver 25 30
1449 200 s. Black-headed Gonolek 25 30
1450 200 s. Great Crested Grebe 25 30
1451 200 s. Red-knobbed Coot 25 30
1452 200 s. Woodland Kingfisher 25 30
1453 200 s. Pintail 25 30
1454 200 s. Squacco Heron 25 30
1455 200 s. Purple Swamphen ("Purple Gallinule") 25 30
1456 200 s. African Darter 25 30
1457 200 s. African Jacana 25 30
1442/57 .. .. *Set of* 16 4·00 4·75
MS1458 Two sheets, each 106×76 mm. (a) 2500 s. African Pygmy Goose. (b) 2500 s. Fulvous Whistling Duck ("Fulvous Tree-duck") *Set of* 2 *sheets* 6·00 6·25

Nos. 1442/57 were printed together, *se-tenant*, in sheetlets of 16 forming a composite design.

18th World Scout Jamboree
Mondial, Holland, August 1995

(**160**)

1995 (1 June). *18th World Scout Jamboree, Netherlands. Nos.* 701/4 *and* **MS**941b *optd or surch as T* **160**.

1459 100 s. Scouts making bricks 10 10
1460 450 s. on 70 s. Poultry keeping 55 60
1461 800 s. on 90 s. Scout on crutches leading family to immunization centre .. 95 1·00
1462 1500 s. on 10 s. Type **104** .. .. 1·75 1·90
1459/62 .. .. *Set of* 4 3·25 3·50
MS1463 115×76 mm. 2500 s. on 1200 s. Lord Baden-Powell, W. Boyce and Revd. L. Hadley 3·00 3·25

No. **MS**1463 is overprinted "18th World Scout Jamboree, August 1995, The Netherlands" on the sheet margin with the surcharge appearing on the stamp.

(Des W. Wright. Litho Questa)

1995 (6 July). *50th Anniv of End of Second World War in Europe. Horiz designs as T* **317** *of Maldive Islands. Multicoloured. P* 14.

1464 500 s. Soviet artillery in action 60 65
a. Sheetlet. Nos. 1464/71 .. .. 4·75
1465 500 s. Soviet tanks on the Moltke Bridge 60 65
1466 500 s. Kaiser Wilhelm Memorial Church, Berlin 60 65
1467 500 s. Soviet tanks and Brandenburg Gate 60 65
1468 500 s. U.S. Boeing B-17 Flying Fortress .. 60 65
1469 500 s. Soviet tanks enter Berlin 60 65
1470 500 s. Ruins of the Chancellery 60 65
1471 500 s. The Reichstag on fire 60 65
1464/71 .. .. *Set of* 8 4·75 5·25
MS1472 104×74 mm. 2500 s. Hoisting the Soviet flag on the Reichstag (57×42½ *mm*) .. .. 3·00 3·25

Nos. 1464/71 were printed together, *se-tenant*, in sheetlets of 8 with the stamps arranged in two horizontal strips of 4 separated by a gutter showing map of the Soviet advance.

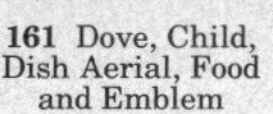

161 Dove, Child, Dish Aerial, Food and Emblem

162 Australian Flag in Form of "VJ"

(Litho Questa)

1995 (6 July). *50th Anniv of United Nations. T* **161** *and similar multicoloured designs. P* 14.

1473 450 s. Type **161** 55 60
1474 1000 s. Hands releasing bird and insects 1·25 1·40
MS1475 100×70 mm. 2000 s. Child's hand holding adult's finger (*horiz*) .. .. .. 2·40 2·50

(Litho Questa)

1995 (6 July). *50th Anniv of Food and Agriculture Organization. Vert designs as T* **320** *of Maldive Islands. Multicoloured. P* 14.

1476 350 s. Woman peeling maize 40 45
a. Horiz strip of 3. Nos. 1476/8 .. 1·25
1477 350 s. Woman and child with maize .. 40 45
1478 350 s. Woman and baby with maize .. 40 45
1476/8 .. .. *Set of* 3 1·25 1·40
MS1479 100×70 mm. 2000 s. Child and head of cow .. .. 2·40 2·50

Nos. 1476/8 were printed together, *se-tenant*, as horizontal strips of 3 in sheets of 9, each strip forming a composite design.

(Litho Questa)

1995 (6 July). *90th Anniv of Rotary International. Designs as T* **299** *of St. Vincent, but vert. Multicoloured. P* 14.

1480 2000 s. Paul Harris (founder) and logo .. 2·40 2·50
MS1481 70×100 mm. 2000 s.. National flag and logo .. .. 2·40 2·50

(Litho Questa)

1995 (6 July). *95th Birthday of Queen Elizabeth the Queen Mother. Vert designs as T* **321** *of Maldive Islands. P* 13½×14.

1482 500 s. orange-brown, pale brown and black 60 65
a. Sheetlet. Nos. 1482/5×2 .. .. 4·75
1483 500 s. multicoloured 60 65
1484 500 s. multicoloured 60 65
1485 500 s. multicoloured 60 65
1482/5 .. .. *Set of* 4 2·40 2·50
MS1486 102×127 mm. 2500 s. multicoloured 3·00 3·25

Designs:—No. 1482, Queen Elizabeth the Queen Mother (pastel drawing); No. 1483, With bouquet of flowers; No. 1484, At desk (oil painting); No. 1845, Wearing turquoise-blue dress; No. **MS**1486, Wearing pale blue dress.

Nos. 1482/5 were printed together in sheetlets of 8, containing two *se-tenant* horizontal strips of 4.

(Des J. Batchelor. Litho Questa)

1995 (6 July). *50th Anniv of End of Second World War in the Pacific. T* **162** *and similar horiz designs showing national flags as* "VJ". *P* 14.

1487 600 s. scarlet-vermilion, bluish violet & blk 70 75
a. Sheetlet. Nos. 1487/92 .. .. 4·25
1488 600 s. scarlet-vermilion, bluish violet & blk 70 75
1489 600 s. scarlet vermilion, bluish violet & blk 70 75
1490 600 s. multicoloured 70 75
1491 600 s. scarlet-vermilion, pale orange & blk 70 75
1492 600 s. scarlet-vermilion and black .. 70 75
1487/92 .. .. *Set of* 6 4·25 4·50
MS1493 108×76 mm. 2500 s. multicoloured .. 3·00 3·25

Designs:—No. 1487, Type **162**; No. 1488, Great Britain; No. 1489, New Zealand; No. 1490, United States of America; No. 1491, People's Republic of China; No. 1492, Canada; No. **MS**1493 American soldier and flag.

Nos. 1487/92 were printed together, *se-tenant*, in sheetlets of 6 with the stamps arranged in two horizontal strips of 3 separated by a gutter showing the raising of the U.S.A. flag on Iwo Jima.

163 Velociraptor

(Des B. Regal. Litho B.D.T.)

1995 (15 July). *Prehistoric Animals. T* **163** *and similar multicoloured designs. P* 14.

1494 150 s. Type **163** 20 25
1495 200 s. Head of Psittacosaurus 25 30
1496 300 s. Archaeopteryx (*vert*) 35 40
a. Sheetlet. Nos. 1496/1507 .. .. 4·00
1497 300 s. Quetzalcoatlus and volcano (*vert*) 35 40
1498 300 s. Pteranodon and volcano (*vert*) .. 35 40
1499 300 s. Brachiosaurus (*vert*) 35 40
1500 300 s. Tsintaosaur (*vert*) 35 40
1501 300 s. Allosaur (*vert*) 35 40
1502 300 s. Tyrannosaurus (*vert*) 35 40
1503 300 s. Apatosaur (*vert*) 35 40
1504 300 s. Giant Dragonfly (*vert*) 35 40
1505 300 s. Dimorphodon (*vert*) 35 40
1506 300 s. Triceratops (*vert*) 35 40
1507 300 s. Compsognathus (*vert*) 35 40
1508 350 s. Head of Dilophosaurus 40 45
1509 400 s. Kentrosaurus 50 55
1510 500 s. Stegosaurus 60 65
1511 1500 s. Pterodaustro .. .. .. 1·75 1·90
1494/1511 .. .. *Set of* 18 7·75 8·75
MS1512 Two sheets, each 106×75 mm. (a) 2000 s. Head of Parasaurolophus. (b) 2000 s. Head of Shunosaurus .. .. *Set of 2 sheets* 4·75 5·00

Nos. 1496/1507 were printed together, *se-tenant*, in sheetlets of 12 with the backgrounds forming a composite design.

No. 1502 is inscribed "Tyranosaur" and No. 1506 "Tricreatops", both in error.

164 Rough-scaled Bush Viper

165 Bell's Hinged Tortoise

(Des R. Rundo. Litho Questa)

1995 (21 Aug–20 Nov). *Reptiles. Multicoloured.*

(*a*) *Square designs as T* **164**. *P* 14×15.

1513 50 s. Type **164** 10 10
1514 100 s. Pygmy Python 10 10
1515 150 s. Three-horned Chameleon 20 25
1516 200 s. African Rock Python 25 30
1517 350 s. Nile Monitor 40 45
1518 400 s. Savannah Monitor 50 55
1519 450 s. Bush Viper 55 60
1520 500 s. Nile Crocodile 60 65

(*b*) *Horiz designs as T* **165**. *P* 14.

1521 700 s. Type **165** 85 90
1522 900 s. Rhinoceros Viper .. .. .. 1·10 1·25
1523 1000 s. Gaboon Viper .. .. .. 1·25 1·40
1524 2000 s. Spitting Cobra .. .. .. 2·40 2·50
1525 3000 s. Leopard Tortoise (20 Nov) .. 3·50 3·75
1526 4000 s. Puff Adder (20 Nov) .. .. 4·75 5·00
1527 5000 s. Common House Gecko (20 Nov) .. 6·00 6·25
1528 6000 s. Dwarf Chameleon (20 Nov) .. 7·25 7·50
1529 10000 s. Boomslang (snake) (20 Nov) .. 12·00 12·50
1513/29 .. .. *Set of* 17 40·00 42·00

166 Nsambya Church

(Litho Questa)

1995 (7 Sept). *Local Anniversaries. T* **166** *and similar horiz designs. Multicoloured. P* 14.

1530 150 s. Type **166** 20 25
1531 450 s. Namilyango College 55 60
1532 500 s. Figures with symbolic wheel .. 60 65
1533 1000 s. Volunteers with food sacks .. 1·25 1·40
1530/3 .. .. *Set of* 4 2·50 2·75

Anniversaries:—Nos. 1530/1, Centenary of Mill Hill Missionaries in Uganda; No. 1532, Centenary of International Co-operative Alliance; No. 1533, 25th anniversary of U.N. volunteers.

167 Bwindi Forest

(Litho Questa)

1995 (14 Sept). *Landscapes. T* **167** *and similar horiz designs. Multicoloured. P* 14.

1534 50 s. Type **167** 10 10
1535 100 s. Karamoja 10 10
1536 450 s. Sunset, Lake Mburo National Park 55 60
1537 500 s. Sunset, Gulu District 60 65
1538 900 s. Mist, Kabale District .. .. 1·10 1·25
1539 1000 s. Ruwenzori Mountains .. .. 1·25 1·40
1534/9 .. .. *Set of* 6 3·75 4·00

(Litho Questa)

1995 (14 Sept). *Waterfalls. Multicoloured designs as T* **167**. *P* 14.

1540 50 s. Sipi Falls (*vert*) 10 10
1541 100 s. Murchison Falls 10 10
1542 450 s. Bujagali Falls 55 60
1543 500 s. The Two Falls at Murchison .. 60 65
1544 900 s. Falls, Ruwenzori Mountains (*vert*) 1·10 1·25
1545 1000 s. Falls, Ruwenzori Mountains (*different*) (*vert*) .. .. .. 1·25 1·40
1540/5 .. .. *Set of* 6 3·75 4·00

168 Peter Rono (1500 metres), 1988

(Des R. Sauber. Litho Questa)

1995 (21 Sept). *Olympic Games, Atlanta* (1996). *T* **168** *and similar multicoloured designs. P* 14.

1546 50 s. Type **168** 10 10
1547 350 s. Reiner Klimke (dressage), 1984 .. 40 45
1548 450 s. German team (cycling time trials), 1988 .. .. 55 60
1549 500 s. Grace Birungi (athlete) 60 65
1550 900 s. Francis Ogola (athlete) .. .. 1·10 1·25
1551 1000 s. Nyakana Godfrey (boxer) .. 1·25 1·40
1546/51 .. .. *Set of* 6 4·00 4·25
MS1552 Two sheets, each 106×76 mm. (a) 2500 s. Sebastian Coe (1500 metres), 1980 and 1984. (b) 2500 s. Rolf Dannenberg (discus), 1984 (*vert*) .. .. *Set of 2 sheets* 6·00 6·25

169 Peacock

170 Scouts putting Child on Scales

(Litho Questa)

1995 (2 Oct). *Domestic Animals. T* **169** *and similar horiz designs. Multicoloured. P* 14.

1553 200 s. Type **169** 25 30
a. Sheetlet. Nos. 1553/68 .. .. 4·00
1554 200 s. Pouter Pigeon 25 30
1555 200 s. Rock Doves 25 30
1556 200 s. Rouen Duck 25 30
1557 200 s. Guineafowl 25 30
1558 200 s. Donkey 25 30
1559 200 s. Shetland ponies 25 30
1560 200 s. Palomino horse 25 30
1561 200 s. Pigs 25 30
1562 200 s. Border Collie 25 30
1563 200 s. Merino sheep 25 30
1564 200 s. Milch goat 25 30
1565 200 s. Black Dutch rabbit 25 30
1566 200 s. Lop rabbit 25 30
1567 200 s. Somali cat 25 30
1568 200 s. Asian cat 25 30
1553/68 .. .. *Set of* 16 4·00 4·75
MS1569 Two sheets, each 106×76 mm. (a) 2500 s. Saddle-bred horses. (b) 2500 s. Oxen *Set of 2 sheets* 6·00 6·25

Nos. 1553/68 were printed together, *se-tenant*, in sheetlets of 16 forming a composite design.

(Litho Questa)

1995 (18 Oct). *Uganda Boy Scouts in the Community. T* **170** *and similar multicoloured designs. P* 14.

1570 150 s. Type **170** 20 25
1571 350 s. Scouts carrying children 40 45
1572 450 s. Checking health cards (*horiz*) .. 55 60
1573 800 s. Holding child for immunization (*horiz*) .. .. 95 1·00
1574 1000 s. Weighing child before immunization .. .. 1·25 1·40
1570/4 .. .. *Set of* 5 3·25 3·75

171 Hermann Staudinger (1953 Chemistry)

172 *Ansellia africana*

(Des R. Cassila. Litho Questa)

1995 (31 Oct). *Centenary of Nobel Prize Trust Fund. T* **171** *and similar vert designs. Multicoloured. P* 14.

1575 300 s. Type **171** 35 40
a. Sheetlet. Nos. 1575/86 .. .. 4·25
1576 300 s. Fritz Haber (1918 Chemistry) .. 35 40
1577 300 s. Bert Sakmann (1991 Medicine) .. 35 40
1578 300 s. Adolf Windaus (1926 Chemistry) .. 35 40
1579 300 s. Wilhelm Wien (1911 Physics) .. 35 40
1580 300 s. Ernest Hemingway (1954 Literature) 35 40

1581 300 s. Richard Willstätter (1915 Chemistry) 35 40
1582 300 s. Stanley Cohen (1986 Medicine) 35 40
1583 300 s. Hans Jensen (1963 Physics) 35 40
1584 300 s. Otto Warburg (1931 Medicine) 35 40
1585 300 s. Heinrich Wieland (1927 Chemistry) 35 40
1586 300 s. Albrecht Kossel (1910 Medicine) 35 40
1587 300 s. Hideki Yukawa (1949 Physics) 35 40
a. Sheetlet. Nos. 1587/98 4·25
1588 300 s. F. W. de Klerk (1993 Peace) 35 40
1589 300 s. Nelson Mandela (1993 Peace) 35 40
1590 300 s. Odysseus Elytis (1979 Literature) 35 40
1591 300 s. Ferdinand Buisson (1927 Peace) 35 40
1592 300 s. Lev Landau (1962 Physics) 35 40
1593 300 s. Halldor Laxness (1955 Literature) 35 40
1594 300 s. Wole Soyinka (1986 Literature) 35 40
1595 300 s. Desmond Tutu (1984 Peace) 35 40
1596 300 s. Susumu Tonegawa (1987 Medicine) 35 40
1597 300 s. Louis de Broglie (1929 Physics) 35 40
1598 300 s. George Seferis (1963 Literature) 35 40
1575/98 *Set of* 24 8·25 9·50
MS1599 Two sheets, each 105×76 mm. (a) 2000 s. Nelly Sachs (1966 Literature). (b) 2000 s. Werner Forssmann (1956 Medicine) *Set of 2 sheets* 4·75 5·00

Nos. 1575/86 and 1587/98 were each printed together, *se-tenant*, in sheetlets of 12 forming composite designs.

(Litho Questa)

1995 (30 Nov). *Christmas. Religious Paintings. Vert designs as T* **98** *of St. Kitts-Nevis (Nevis). Multicoloured. P* 13½×14.

1600 150 s. "The Virgin and Child" (Holbein the Younger) 20 25
1601 350 s. "Madonna" (Procaccini) 40 45
1602 500 s. "The Virgin and Child" (Pisanello) 60 65
1603 1000 s. "Madonna and Child" (Crivelli) 1·25 1·40
1604 1500 s. "The Nativity of the Virgin" (Le Nain) 1·75 1·90
1600/4 *Set of* 5 4·25 4·75
MS1605 Two sheets, each 102×127 mm. (a) 2500 s. "Madonna and Child" (detail) (Bellini). (b) 2500 s. "The Holy Family" (detail) (Andrea del Sarto) *Set of 2 sheets* 6·00 6·25

(Litho Questa)

1995 (8 Dec). *Orchids. T* **172** *and similar vert designs. Multicoloured. P* 14½×14.

1606 150 s. Type **172** 20 25
1607 350 s. *Aerangis iuteoalba* 40 45
a. Sheetlet. Nos. 1607/15 3·50
1608 350 s. *Satyrium sacculatum* 40 45
1609 350 s. *Bolusiella maudiae* 40 45
1610 350 s. *Habenaria attenuata* 40 45
1611 350 s. *Cyrtorchis arcuata* 40 45
1612 350 s. *Eulophia angolensis* 40 45
1613 350 s. *Tridactyle bicaudata* 40 45
1614 350 s. *Eulophia horsfallii* 40 45
1615 350 s. *Diaphananthe fragrantissima* 40 45
1616 450 s. *Satyricum crassicaule* 55 60
1617 500 s. *Polystachya cultriformis* 60 65
1618 800 s. *Disa erubescens* 95 1·00
1606/18 *Set of* 13 6·00 6·50
MS1619 Two sheets, each 66×76 mm. (a) 2500 s. *Rangaeris amaniensis*. (b) 2500 s. *Diaphananthe pulchella*. P 13½×14 *Set of 2 sheets* 6·00 6·25

Nos. 1607/15 were printed together, *se-tenant*, in sheetlets of 9.

173 Rat and Purple Grapes

(Des Y. Lee. Litho B.D.T.)

1996 (29 Jan). *Chinese New Year ("Year of the Rat"). T* **173** *and similar horiz designs. Multicoloured. P* 14.

1620 350 s. Type **173** 40 45
a. Block of 4. Nos. 1620/3 1·60
1621 350 s. Rat and radishes 40 45
1622 350 s. Rat eating corn 40 45
1623 350 s. Rat eating cucumber 40 45
1620/3 *Set of* 4 1·60 1·75
MS1624 100×74 mm. Nos. 1620/3 1·60 1·75
MS1625 106×76 mm. 2000 s. Rat and green grapes 2·40 2·50

Nos. 1620/3 were printed together, *se-tenant*, as blocks of 4 in sheets of 16.

174 Wild Dog and Pup

(Des R. Rundo. Litho Questa)

1996 (27 Mar). *Wildlife of Uganda. Multicoloured designs as T* **174**. *P* 14.

(*a*) *Horiz designs*

1626 150 s. Type **174** 20 25
a. Sheetlet. Nos. 1626/33 3·50
1627 200 s. African Fish Eagle 25 30
1628 250 s. Hippopotamus 30 35
1629 350 s. Leopard 40 45
1630 400 s. Lion 50 55
1631 450 s. Lioness 55 60
1632 500 s. Meerkats 60 65
1633 550 s. Pair of Black Rhinoceroses 65 70

(*b*) *Vert designs*

1634 150 s. Gorilla 20 25
a. Sheetlet. Nos. 1634/41 3·50
1635 200 s. Cheetah 25 30
1636 250 s. African Elephant 30 35
1637 350 s. Thomson's Gazelle 40 45
1638 400 s. Crowned Crane 50 55
1639 450 s. Saddlebill 55 60
1640 500 s. Vulture 60 65
1641 550 s. Zebra 65 70
1626/41 *Set of* 16 6·75 7·50
MS1642 Two sheets. (a) 72×102 mm. 2000 s. Grey Heron (*horiz*). (b) 102×72 mm. 2000 s. Giraffe *Set of 2 sheets* 4·75 5·00

Nos. 1626/33 and 1634/41 were each printed together, *se-tenant*, in sheetlets of 8 with enlarged left or top margin.

175 Mickey Mouse and Goofy on Platform at Calais

176 "Autumn Pond"

(Des Walt Disney Co. Litho Questa)

1996 (15 Apr). *Mickey's Orient Express. T* **175** *and similar horiz designs showing Walt Disney cartoon characters. Multicoloured. P* 14×13½.

1643 50 s. Type **175** 10 10
1644 100 s. Mickey and Goofy at Athens 10 10
1645 150 s. Mickey showing Donald Duck his Pullman ticket 20 25
1646 200 s. Daisy and Donald Duck in Pullman car 25 30
1647 250 s. Mickey and Minnie Mouse in dining car 30 35
1648 300 s. Goofy as guard assisting Mickey and Minnie 35 40
1649 600 s. Mickey and Donald preparing for bed 70 75
1650 700 s. Mickey and Minnie at Orient Express accident, Frankfurt, 1901 85 90
1651 800 s. Mickey and Goofy building snowman and Orient Express in snowdrift, 1929 95 1·00
1652 900 s. Disney characters filming *Murder on the Orient Express* 1·10 1·25
1643/52 *Set of* 10 5·00 5·50
MS1653 Two sheets, each 132×106 mm. (a) 2500 s. Donald driving Orient Express. (b) 2500 s. Mickey, Minnie and Goofy on observation platform *Set of 2 sheets* 6·00 6·25

(Litho Questa)

1996 (8 May). *"CHINA '96" 9th Asian International Stamp Exhibition, Peking* (1*st issue*). *Paintings by Qi Baishi. T* **176** *and similar vert designs. Multicoloured. P* 15×14.

1654 50 s. Type **176** 10 10
a. Sheetlet. Nos. 1654/63 3·25
1655 100 s. "Partridge and Smartweed" 10 10
1656 150 s. "Begonias and Mynah" 20 25
1657 200 s. "Chrysanthemums, Cocks and Hens" 25 30
1658 250 s. "Crabs" 30 35
1659 300 s. "Wisterias and Bee" 35 40
1660 350 s. "Smartweed and Ink-drawn Butterflies" 40 45
1661 400 s. "Lotus and Mandarin Ducks" 50 55
1662 450 s. "Lichees and Locust" 55 60
1663 500 s. "Millet and Praying Mantis" 60 65
1654/63 *Set of* 10 3·25 3·75
MS1664 135×114 mm. 800 s. "Morning Glories and Locust" (50×38 *mm*); 800 s. "Shrimps" (50×38 *mm*). P 14×13½ 1·90 2·00

The painting titles on 150 s. and 200 s. are transposed in error with "CHRYSANTHEMUMS" shown as "RYSANTHEMUMS".

Nos. 1654/63 were printed together, *se-tenant*, in sheetlets of 10.

MINIMUM PRICE

The minimum price quote is 10p which represents a handling charge rather than a basis for valuing common stamps. For further notes about prices see introductory pages.

177 Tomb Mural, Xi'an

1996 (13 May). *"CHINA '96" 9th Asian International Stamp Exhibition, Peking* (2*nd issue*). *Sheet* 140×90 *mm. Litho. P* 13½×14.

MS1664*a* **177** 500 s. multicoloured 60 65

178 *Coprinus disseminatus*

179 *Catopsilia philea*

1996 (24 June). *African Fungi. T* **178** *and similar vert designs. Multicoloured. Litho. P* 14.

1665 150 s. Type **178** 20 25
a. Sheetlet. Nos. 1665/72 4·50
1666 300 s. *Coprinus radians* 35 40
1667 350 s. *Hygrophorus coccineus* 40 45
1668 400 s. *Marasmius siccus* 50 55
1669 450 s. *Cortinarius collinitus* 55 60
1670 500 s. *Cortinarius cinnabarinus* 60 65
1671 550 s. *Coltricia cinnamomea* 65 70
1672 1000 s. *Mutinus elegans* 1·25 1·40
1665/72 *Set of* 8 4·50 5·00
MS1673 Two sheets, each 110×80 mm. (a) 2500 s. *Inocybe sororia*. (b) 2500 s. *Flammulina velutipes* *Set of 2 sheets* 6·00 6·25

Nos. 1665/72 were printed together, *se-tenant*, in sheetlets of 8.

(Des D. Burkhardt. Litho Questa)

1996 (26 June). *Butterflies. T* **179** *and similar horiz designs. Multicoloured. P* 14.

1674 50 s. Type **179** 10 10
a. Sheetlet. Nos. 1674/85 4·75
1675 100 s. *Dione vanillae* 10 10
1676 150 s. *Metamorpha dido* 20 25
1677 200 s. *Papilio sesostris* 25 30
1678 250 s. *Papilio neophilus* 30 35
1679 300 s. *Papilio thoas* 35 40
1680 350 s. *Diorina periander* 40 45
1681 400 s. *Morpho cipris* 50 55
1682 450 s. *Catonephele numilia* 55 60
1683 500 s. *Heliconius doris* 60 65
1684 550 s. *Prepona antimache* 65 70
1685 600 s. *Eunica alcmena* 70 75
1674/85 *Set of* 12 4·75 5·25
MS1686 Two sheets, each 100×70 mm. (a) 2500 s. *Caligo martia*. (b) 2500 s. *Heliconius doris* (*different*) *Set of 2 sheets* 6·00 6·25

Nos. 1674/85 were printed together, *se-tenant*, in sheetlets of 12.

(Litho Questa)

1996 (10 July). *70th Birthday of Queen Elizabeth II. Vert designs as T* **334** *of Maldive Islands showing different photographs. Multicoloured. P* 13½×14.

1687 500 s. As Type **334** of Maldive Islands 60 65
a. Strip of 3. Nos. 1687/9 1·75
1688 500 s. In evening dress 60 65
1689 500 s. Wearing red coat and hat 60 65
1687/9 *Set of* 3 1·75 1·90
MS1690 125×103 mm. 2000 s. Queen Elizabeth II 2·40 2·50

Nos. 1687/9 were printed together, *se-tenant*, in horizontal and vertical strips of 3 throughout sheets of 9.

(Litho Questa)

1996 (10 July). *50th Anniv of U.N.I.C.E.F. Multicoloured designs as T* **335** *of Maldive Islands. P* 14.

1691 450 s. Asian children (*horiz*) 55 60
1692 500 s. South American children (*horiz*) 60 65
1693 550 s. Boy holding pencil (*horiz*) 65 70
1691/3 *Set of* 3 1·75 1·90
MS1694 74×104 mm. 2000 s. African mother and child 2·40 2·50

(Des M. Freedman and Dena Rubin. Litho Questa)

1996 (10 July). *50th Anniv of U.N.E.S.C.O. Horiz designs as T* **348** *of Maldive Islands. Multicoloured. P* 14×13½.

1695 450 s. Darien National Park, Panama 55 60
1696 500 s. Los Glaciares National Park, Argentina 60 65
1697 550 s. Tubbatha Reef Marine Park, Philippines 65 70
1695/7 *Set of* 3 1·75 1·90
MS1698 104×74 mm. 2500 s. Ruwenzori Mountains National Park, Uganda 3·00 3·25

No. **MS**1698 is inscribed "RWENZORI" in error.

180 Statue of Menorah, Knesset

(Des R. Sauber. Litho Questa)

1996 (10 July). *3000th Anniv of Jerusalem. T* **180** *and similar vert designs. Multicoloured. P* 14.
MS1699 114×95 mm. 300 s. Type **180**, 500 s. Jerusalem Theatre. 1000 s. Israel Museum .. 2·10 2·25
MS1700 104×74 mm. 2000 s. Grotto of the Nativity .. .. 2·40 2·50

(Des R. Sauber. Litho Questa)

1996 (10 July). *Centenary of Radio. Entertainers. Vert designs as T* **326** *of St. Vincent. Multicoloured. P* 13½×14.
1701 200 s. Ella Fitzgerald 25 30
1702 300 s. Bob Hope 35 40
1703 500 s. Nat "King" Cole 60 65
1704 800 s. George Burns and Gracie Allen .. 95 1·00
1701/4 .. .. *Set of* 4 2·10 2·40
MS1705 74×104 mm. 2000 s. Jimmy Durante 2·40 2·50

181 Electric Locomotive Type BBB, 1968 (Japan)

1996 (25 July). *Railway Locomotives. T* **181** *and similar horiz designs. Multicoloured. Litho. P* 14.
1706 450 s. Type **181** 55 60
a. Sheetlet. Nos. 1706/11 .. .. 3·25
1707 450 s. Stephenson's *Rocket*, 1829 .. 55 60
1708 450 s. *Austria*, 1843 .. .. .. 55 60
1709 450 s. Early American steam locomotive 55 60
1710 450 s. Steam locomotive, 1947 (India) .. 55 60
1711 450 s. Electric locomotive Type CO.CO.DB (Germany) 55 60
1712 550 s. *Lady of Lynn* (England) 65 70
a. Sheetlet. Nos. 1712/17 .. .. 4·00
1713 550 s. Steam locomotive, 1930 (China) .. 65 70
1714 550 s. Meyer-Kitson steam locomotive (Chile) 65 70
1715 550 s. Union Pacific "Centennial" Type diesel locomotive (U.S.A.) 65 70
1716 550 s. Type "581" diesel locomotive, 1968 (Japan) 65 70
1717 550 s. Electric locomotive Type CO.CO. series 120 (Germany) 65 70
1706/17 .. .. *Set of* 12 7·25 7·75
MS1718 Two sheets, each 106×76 mm. (a) 2500 s. Type 99 steam locomotive (Germany); (b) 2500 s. *Mallard*, Great Britain .. *Set of* 2 *sheets* 6·00 6·25
Nos. 1706/11 and 1712/17 were each printed, *se-tenant*, in sheetlets of 6.

182 Postal and Telecommunications Corporation Emblem

(Litho Questa)

1996 (30 Aug). *Centenary of Postal Services. T* **182** *and similar horiz designs. Multicoloured. P* 14.
1719 150 s. Type **182** 20 25
1720 450 s. Loading postbus 55 60
1721 500 s. Modern postal transportation .. 60 65
1722 550 s. 1896 25 c. violet and 1 r. black stamps 65 70
1719/22 .. .. *Set of* 4 2·00 2·25

ALTERED CATALOGUE NUMBERS

Any Catalogue numbers altered from the last edition are shown as a list in the introductory pages.

183 Two American River Steamers and 1904 Games, St. Louis

184 Mango

(Litho B.D.T.)

1996 (23 Sept). *Olympic Games, Atlanta* (1st issue). *T* **183** *and similar multicoloured designs. P* 14.
1723 350 s. Type **183** 40 45
1724 450 s. George Finnegan (U.S.A.) (boxing), 1904 .. .. 55 60
1725 500 s. Chariot racing 60 65
1726 800 s. John Flanagan (U.S.A.) (hammer), 1904 (*vert*) .. .. 95 1·00
1723/6 .. .. *Set of* 4 2·50 2·75
See also Nos. 1764/81

(Litho B.D.T.)

1996 (8 Oct). *Fruit. T* **184** *and similar multicoloured designs. P* 14.
1727 150 s. Type **184** 20 25
1728 350 s. Orange 40 45
1729 450 s. Pawpaw 55 60
1730 500 s. Avocado 60 65
1731 550 s. Watermelon (*horiz*) 65 70
1727/31 .. .. *Set of* 5 2·40 2·75

(Litho Questa)

1996 (18 Nov). *Christmas. Religious Paintings. Multicoloured designs as T* **337** *of St. Vincent. P* 13½×14.
1732 150 s. "Annunciation" (Lorenzo di Credi) 20 25
1733 350 s. "Madonna of the Loggia" (detail) (Botticelli) 40 45
1734 400 s. "Virgin in Glory with Child and Angels" (Lorenzetti) 50 55
1735 450 s. "Adoration of the Child" (Lippi) .. 55 60
1736 500 s. "Madonna of the Loggia" (Botticelli) 60 65
1737 550 s. "The Strength" (Botticelli) 65 70
1732/7 .. .. *Set of* 6 3·00 3·25
MS1738 Two sheets, each 106×76 mm. (a) 2500 s. "Holy Allegory" (Bellini) (*horiz*); (b) 2500 s. "The Virgin on the Throne with Child and the Saints" (Ghirlandaio) (*horiz*). P 14×13½ *Set of* 2 *sheets* 6·00 6·25

(Des Shannon. Litho Questa)

1996 (21 Nov). *20th Anniv of* Rocky (*film*). *Sheet* 143×182 *mm, containing vert design as T* **338** *of St. Vincent. Multicoloured. P* 14×13½.
MS1739 800 s. × 3 Sylvester Stallone in *Rocky III* 2·75 3·00

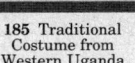

185 Traditional Costume from Western Uganda

186 Ox

(Litho B.D.T.)

1997 (2 Jan). *Traditional Costumes. T* **185** *and similar multicoloured designs. P* 14.
1740 150 s. Type **185** 20 25
1741 300 s. Acholi headdress 35 40
a. Sheetlet. Nos. 1741/6 .. .. 2·10
1742 300 s. Alur headdress 35 40
1743 300 s. Bwola dance headdress 35 40
1744 300 s. Madi headdress 35 40
1745 300 s. Karimojong headdress with plume 35 40
1746 300 s. Karimojong headdress with two feathers 35 40
1747 350 s. Karimojong women 40 45
1748 450 s. Ganda traditional dress (*horiz*) .. 55 60
1749 500 s. Acholi traditional dress (*horiz*) .. 60 65
1740/9 .. .. *Set of* 10 3·75 4·25
Nos. 1741/6 were printed together, *se-tenant*, in sheetlets of 6.

(Des Y. Lee. Litho Questa)

1997 (24 Jan). *Chinese New Year* ("*Year of the Ox*"). *T* **186** *and similar multicoloured designs. P* 14.
1750 350 s. Type **186** 40 45
a. Vert strip of 4. Nos. 1750/3 .. 1·60
1751 350 s. Cow suckling calf 40 45
1752 350 s. Cow and calf lying down 40 45
1753 350 s. Ox lying down 40 45
1750/3 .. .. *Set of* 4 1·60 1·75
MS1754 111×83 mm. Nos. 1750/3 .. .. 1·60 1·75
MS1755 76×106 mm. 1500 s. Young calf (*vert*) 1·75 1·90
Nos. 1750/3 were printed together, *se-tenant*, as vertical strips of 4 in sheets of 16.

187 Giraffe running

188 "The Constitution" on Open Book

(Des D. Burkhart. Litho Questa)

1997 (12 Feb). *Endangered Species. Rothschild's Giraffe. T* **187** *and similar multicoloured designs. P* 14.
1756 300 s. Type **187** 35 40
a. Horiz strip of 4. Nos. 1756/9 .. 1·40
1757 300 s. Two adult giraffes 35 40
1758 300 s. Head of giraffe 35 40
1759 300 s. Giraffe with calf 35 40
1756/9 .. .. *Set of* 4 1·40 1·60
MS1760 75×109 mm. 2500 s. Head of giraffe (*different*) (*horiz*) .. .. 3·00 3·25
Nos. 1756/9 were printed together, *se-tenant*, both horizontally and vertically in sheets of 12 containing three of each design.

(Litho Questa)

1997 (25 Feb). *Promulgation of New Constitution* (8 *Oct* 1995). *T* **188** *and similar multicoloured designs. P* 13½×14 (550 s.) *or* 14×13½ (*others*).
1761 150 s. Type **188** 20 25
1762 350 s. "The Constitution" on scroll .. 40 45
1763 550 s. "THE CONSTITUTION" on closed book (*vert*) 65 70
1761/3 .. .. *Set of* 3 1·25 1·40

189 Kitel Son (Japan) (marathon), 1936

190 "Red Plum Blossom and Daffodil"

(Des J. Puvilland. Litho Questa)

1997 (3 Mar). *Olympic Games, Atlanta* (2nd issue). *Previous Gold Medal Winners. T* **189** *and similar vert designs. Multicoloured. P* 14.
1764 150 s. Type **189** 20 25
a. Sheetlet. Nos. 1764, 1766, 1768, 1770, 1772, 1774, 1776, 1778, 1780 3·75
1765 150 s. Bob Hayes (U.S.A.) (100m), 1964 .. 20 25
a. Sheetlet. Nos. 1765, 1767, 1769, 1771, 1773, 1775, 1777, 1779, 1781 3·75
1766 200 s. Walter Davis (U.S.A.) (high jump), 1952 .. .. 25 30
1767 200 s. Rod Milburn (110m hurdles), 1972 25 30
1768 250 s. Matthes (swimming), 1968 .. 30 35
1769 250 s. Filbert Bayi (Tanzania) (athletics), 1976 .. .. 30 35
1770 300 s. Akii Bua (Uganda) (400m hurdles), 1972 .. .. 35 40
1771 300 s. H. Kipchoge Keino (Kenya) (steeple chase), 1972 .. .. 35 40
1772 350 s. Nordwig (Germany) (pole vault), 1972 .. .. 40 45
1773 350 s. Ron Ray (U.S.A.) (athletics), 1976 40 45
1774 400 s. Wilma Rudolph (U.S.A.) (100m relay), 1960 .. .. 50 55
1775 400 s. Joe Frazer (U.S.A.) (boxing), 1976 50 55
1776 450 s. Abebe Bikila (Ethiopia) (marathon), 1964 .. .. 55 60
1777 450 s. Carl Lewis (U.S.A.) (100m), 1984 .. 55 60
1778 500 s. Edwin Moses (U.S.A.) (400m hurdles), 1984 .. .. 60 65
1779 500 s. Gisela Mauermayer (Germany) (discus), 1936 .. .. 60 65
1780 550 s. Rady Williams (U.S.A.) (long jump), 1972 .. .. 65 70
1781 550 s. Dietmar Mogenburg (Germany) (high jump), 1984 .. .. 65 70
1764/81 .. .. *Set of* 18 7·50 8·50
Nos. 1764, 1766, 1768, 1770, 1772, 1774, 1776, 1778 and 1780 and 1765, 1767, 1769, 1771, 1773, 1775, 1777, 1779 and 1781 were each printed together, *se-tenant*, in sheetlets of 9 with the backgrounds forming composite designs.
No. 1769 is incorrectly inscribed "Eiilbert" and is dated "1976". Filbert Bayi did not participate in the 1976 Games. No. 1779 is incorrectly inscribed "Mauemayer" and wrongly identifies the event as the shotput.

(Des Y. Lee. Litho B.D.T.)

1997 (5 Mar). *"HONG KONG '97" International Stamp Exhibition. Paintings by Wu Changshuo. T* **190** *and similar multicoloured designs. P* 14×15.
1782 50 s. Type **190** 10 10
a. Sheetlet. Nos. 1782/91 .. .. 3·25
1783 100 s. "Peony" 10 15
1784 150 s. "Rosaceae" 20 25
1785 200 s. "Pomegranate" 25 30
1786 250 s. "Peach, Peony and Plum Blossom" 30 35
1787 300 s. "Calyx Canthus" 35 40
1788 350 s. "Chrysanthemum" 40 45
1789 400 s. "Calabash" 50 55
1790 450 s. "Chrysanthemum" (*different*) .. 55 60
1791 500 s. "Cypress Tree" 60 65
1782/91 .. .. *Set of* 10 3·25 3·75
MS1792 137×105 mm. 550 s. "Litchi" (50×37 *mm*); 1000 s. "Water Lily" (50×37 *mm*). P 14 65 70
Nos. 1782/91 were printed together, *se-tenant*, in sheetlets of 10.

191 Woody

192 "Pioneer 10"

(Des Rosemary DeFiglio. Litho Questa)

1997 (2 Apr). *Disney's* Toy Story *(cartoon film). T* **191** *and similar multicoloured designs. P* 13½×14 (*vert*) *or* 14×13½ (*others*).
1793 100 s. Type **191** 10 15
a. Sheetlet. Nos. 1793/8 60
1794 100 s. Buzz Lightyear 10 15
1795 100 s. Bo Peep 10 15
1796 100 s. Hamm 10 15
1797 100 s. Slinky 10 15
1798 100 s. Rex 10 15
1799 150 s. Woody on bed (*horiz*) 20 25
a. Sheetlet. Nos. 1799/1807 .. .. 1·75
1800 150 s. Woody at microphone (*horiz*) .. 20 25
1801 150 s. Bo Peep (*horiz*) 20 25
1802 150 s. Buzz Lightyear (*horiz*) 20 25
1803 150 s. Slinky and Rex (*horiz*) 20 25
1804 150 s. Woody hiding (*horiz*) 20 25
1805 150 s. "Halt ! Who goes there" (*horiz*) .. 20 25
1806 150 s. Rex, Slinky and Buzz Lightyear (*horiz*) 20 25
1807 150 s. "You're just an action figure !" (*horiz*) 20 25
1808 200 s. "I'm the only sherrif in these parts" (*horiz*) 25 30
a. Sheetlet. Nos. 1808/16 .. .. 2·25
1809 200 s. Green toy soldiers (*horiz*) 25 30
1810 200 s. Woody and Buzz (*horiz*) 25 30
1811 200 s. Woody pointing (*horiz*) 25 30
1812 200 s. Buzz Lightyear (*horiz*) 25 30
1813 200 s. Green aliens (*horiz*) 25 30
1814 200 s. "This is an intergalactic emergency" (*horiz*) 25 30
1815 200 s. Buzz and Woody argue (*horiz*) .. 25 30
1816 200 s. Buzz and Woody in buggy (*horiz*) .. 25 30
1793/1816 .. .. *Set of* 24 4·50 5·75
MS1817 Three sheets, each 133×108 mm. (a) 133×108 mm. 2000 s. Woody; (b) 108×133 mm. 2000 s. Buzz Lightyear, Rex and other toys; (c) 2000 s. Buzz Lightyear .. .. *Set of* 3 *sheets* 7·25 7·50
Nos. 1793/8, 1799/1807 and 1808/16 were each printed, *se-tenant*, in sheetlets of 6 (Nos. 1793/8) or 9.

(Des W. Wright. Litho Questa)

1997 (16 Apr). *Space Exploration. T* **192** *and similar multicoloured designs. P* 14.
1818 250 s. Type **192** 30 35
a. Sheetlet. Nos. 1818/25 .. .. 2·40
1819 250 s. "Voyager 1" 30 35
1820 250 s. "Viking Orbiter" 30 35
1821 250 s. "Pioneer – Venus 1" 30 35
1822 250 s. "Mariner 9" 30 35
1823 250 s. "Galileo" Entry Probe 30 35
1824 250 s. "Mariner 10" 30 35
1825 250 s. "Voyager 2" 30 35
1826 300 s. "Sputnik 1" 35 40
a. Sheetlet. Nos. 1826/33 .. .. 2·75
1827 300 s. "Apollo" space craft 35 40
1828 300 s. "Soyuz" space craft 35 40
1829 300 s. "Intelsat 1" 35 40
1830 300 s. Manned manoeuvring Unit 35 40
1831 300 s. "Skylab" 35 40
1832 300 s. "Telstar 1" 35 40
1833 300 s. Hubble Telescope 35 40
1818/33 .. .. *Set of* 16 5·25 6·00
MS1834 Two sheets, each 103×73 mm. (a) 2000 s. Space Shuttle *Challenger* (35×61 *mm*). (b) 2000 s. "Viking Lander" on Mars (61×35 *mm*) *Set of* 2 *sheets* 4·75 5·00
Nos. 1818/25 and 1826/33 were each printed together, *se-tenant*, in sheetlets of 8 with the backgrounds forming composite designs.

193 Deng Xiaoping and Port

194 Water Hyacinth and Pebbles

(Des Y. Lee. Litho Questa)

1997 (9 May). *Deng Xiaoping (Chinese statesman) Commemoration. T* **193** *and similar horiz design. P* 14.
1835 **193** 500 s. multicoloured 60 65
a. Sheetlet. Nos. 1835/7 .. 2·50
1836 550 s. multicoloured 65 70
1837 1000 s. multicoloured .. .. 1·25 1·40
1835/7 .. .. *Set of* 3 2·50 2·75
MS1838 100×70 mm. 2000 s. multicoloured (Deng Xiaoping and Shenzhen) .. .. 2·40 2·50
Nos. 1835/7 were printed together, *se-tenant*, in sheetlets of 3 with an enlarged illustrated margin at right.

(Des R. Martin. Litho Questa)

1997 (14 May). *Environmental Protection. T* **194** *and similar vert designs. Multicoloured. P* 14.
1839 500 s. Water hyacinth and Lake Victoria (inscr at top left) 60 65
a. Sheetlet. Nos. 1839/42 .. 2·40
1840 500 s. Water hyacinth and Lake Victoria (inscr at top right) 60 65
1841 500 s. Type **194** 60 65
1842 500 s. Larger clump of Water hyacinth and pebbles 60 65
1843 550 s. Buffalo 65 70
a. Sheetlet. Nos. 1843/6 .. 2·50
1844 550 s. Uganda Kob 65 70
1845 550 s. Guinea Fowl 65 70
1846 550 s. Marabou Stork 65 70
1839/46 .. .. *Set of* 8 5·00 5·50
MS1847 106×76 mm. 2500 s. Gorilla .. .. 3·00 3·25
Nos. 1839/42 and 1843/6 were each printed together, *se-tenant*, in sheetlets of 4 with the backgrounds forming composite designs, and an enlarged illustrated margin at right.
No. 1845 is inscribed "GUINEA FOWEL" and No. 1846 "MALIBU STORK", both in error.

(Litho Questa)

1997 (21 May). 10*th Anniv of Chernobyl Nuclear Disaster. Vert designs as T* **347** *of St. Vincent. P* 13½×14.
1848 500 s. As Type **347** of St. Vincent .. 60 65
1849 700 s. As No. 1848 but inscribed "CHABAD'S CHILDREN OF CHERNOBYL" at foot 85 90

(Des J. Iskowitz. Litho Questa)

1997 (2 June). 50*th Death Anniv of Paul Harris (founder of Rotary International). Horiz designs as T* **113** *of St. Kitts-Nevis (Nevis). Multicoloured. P* 14.
1850 1000 s. Paul Harris and child drinking .. 1·25 1·40
MS1851 78×107 mm. 2500 s. The first Rotarians 3·00 3·25

(Litho Questa)

1997 (2 June). *Golden Wedding of Queen Elizabeth and Prince Philip. Horiz designs as T* **350** *of Maldive Islands. Multicoloured. P* 14.
1852 200 s. Queen Elizabeth II 25 30
a. Sheetlet. Nos. 1852/7 .. 1·50
1853 200 s. Royal coat of arms 25 30
1854 200 s. Queen Elizabeth and Prince Philip at reception 25 30
1855 200 s. Queen Elizabeth and Prince Philip on royal visit 25 30
1856 200 s. Buckingham Palace 25 30
1857 200 s. Prince Philip in military uniform .. 25 30
1852/7 .. .. *Set of* 6 1·50 1·75
MS1858 100×70 mm. 2000 s. Princess Elizabeth in wedding dress .. .. 2·40 2·50
Nos. 1852/7 were printed together, *se-tenant*, in sheetlets of 6.

(Des J. Iskowitz. Litho Questa)

1997 (2 June). *"Pacific '97" International Stamp Exhibition, San Francisco. Death Centenary of Heinrich von Stephan (founder of the U.P.U.). Horiz designs as T* **351** *of Maldive Islands. P* 14.
1859 800 s. deep blue .. .. 95 1·00
a. Sheetlet. Nos. 1859/61 .. 2·75
1860 800 s. chestnut .. .. 95 1·00
1861 800 s. blue-green .. .. 95 1·00
1859/61 .. .. *Set of* 3 2·75 3·00
MS1862 82×119 mm. 2500 s. dull blue and grey-blue .. .. 3·00 3·25
Designs:—No. 1859, Chinese post boat; No. 1860, Von Stephan and Mercury; No. 1861, Russian post cart; No. **MS**1862, Von Stephan and French postman on stilts.
Nos. 1859/61 were printed together, *se-tenant*, in sheets of 3 with enlarged right-hand margin.

COVER PRICES

Cover factors are quoted at the beginning of each country for most issues to 1945. An explanation of the system can be found on page x. The factors quoted do not, however, apply to philatelic covers.

195 Men's Slalom

196 Main Building, Makerere University

(Litho Questa)

1997 (23 June). *Winter Olympic Games, Nagano, Japan* (1998). *T* **195** *and similar multicoloured designs. P* 14.
1863 350 s. Type **195** 40 45
1864 450 s. Two-man bobsled 55 60
1865 500 s. Ski-jumping (*horiz*) 60 65
a. Sheetlet. Nos. 1865/70 .. .. 3·50
1866 500 s. Giant slalom (*horiz*) 60 65
1867 500 s. Cross-country skiing (*horiz*) .. 60 65
1868 500 s. Ice hockey (*horiz*) 60 65
1869 500 s. Pairs figure skating (man) (*horiz*) 60 65
1870 500 s. Pairs figure skating (woman) (*horiz*) 60 65
1871 800 s. Women's slalom (*horiz*) .. .. 95 1·00
1872 2000 s. Men's speed skating (*horiz*) .. 2·40 2·50
1863/72 .. .. *Set of* 10 7·75 8·50
MS1873 Two sheets, each 103×72 mm. (a) 2500 s. Downhill skiing (*horiz*). (b) 2500 s. Women's figure skating (*horiz*) .. *Set of* 2 *sheets* 6·00 6·25
Nos. 1865/70 were printed together, *se-tenant*, in sheetlets of 6 with the backgrounds forming a composite design.

(Litho Questa)

1997 (31 July). 75*th Anniv of Makerere University. T* **196** *and similar multicoloured designs. P* 14×13½ (*horiz*) *or* 13½×14 (*vert*).
1874 150 s. Type **196** 20 25
1875 450 s. East African School of Librarianship building (*vert*) 55 60
1876 500 s. Buyana Stock Farm, Makerere University 60 65
1877 550 s. Ceramic dish from School of Architecture and Fine Arts .. 65 70
1874/7 .. .. *Set of* 4 2·00 2·25

1997 (3 Oct). *World Cup Football Championship, France* (1998). *Multicoloured* (*except Nos.* 1878, 1880, 1883 *and* 1886) *designs as T* **246** *of Lesotho. P* 13½×14 (*vert*) *or* 14×13½ (*horiz*).
1878 200 s. Fritz Walter, Germany (agate) .. 25 30
a. Sheetlet. Nos. 1878 and 1896/1900 3·00
1879 250 s. Paulo Rossi (*horiz*) 25 30
a. Sheetlet. Nos. 1879/87 .. .. 2·25
1880 250 s. Mario Kempes (black) (*horiz*) .. 25 30
1881 250 s. Gerd Muller (*horiz*) 25 30
1882 250 s. Grzegorz Lato (*horiz*) 25 30
1883 250 s. Ademir (black) (*horiz*) 25 30
1884 250 s. Eusebio Ferreica da Silva (*horiz*) .. 25 30
1885 250 s. Salvatore Schillaci (*horiz*) 25 30
1886 250 s. Leonidas da Silva (black) (*horiz*) .. 25 30
1887 250 s. Gary Lineker (*horiz*) 25 30
1888 250 s. Argentine and West German player chasing ball (*horiz*) 25 30
a. Sheetlet. Nos. 1888/95 and central label .. .. 2·00
1889 250 s. Azteca Stadium (*horiz*) 25 30
1890 250 s. Maradona holding World Cup (*horiz*) 25 30
1891 250 s. Argentine and West German players with goal keeper (*horiz*) 25 30
1892 250 s. West German player tackling Argentine player (*horiz*) 25 30
1893 250 s. Ball in back of net (*horiz*) 25 30
1894 250 s. Argentine team (*horiz*) 25 30
1895 250 s. Players competing to head ball (*horiz*) 25 30
1896 300 s. Daniel Pasarella, Argentina 35 40
1897 450 s. Dino Zoff, Italy 55 60
1898 500 s. Bobby Moore, England 60 65
1899 550 s. Franz Beckenbauer, West Germany 65 70
1900 600 s. Diego Maradona, Argentina .. 70 75
1878/1900 .. .. *Set of* 23 7·25 8·50
MS1901 Two sheets. (a) 102×127 mm. 2000 s. Celebrating West German players, 1990 (*horiz*). (b) 127×102 mm. 2000 s. Bobby Moore, 1966 (*horiz*) .. .. .. *Set of* 2 *sheets* 4·75 5·00
Nos. 1878 with 1896/900, 1879/87 and 1888/95 were each printed together in sheets of 6 (Nos. 1878 with 1896/900), 9 (Nos. 1879/87) or 8 stamps and 1 central label (Nos. 1888/95) (depicts 1986 World Cup final between Argentina and West Germany).

197 Mahatma Gandhi

198 "Cupid and Dolphin" (Andrea del Verrocchio)

(Des J. Iskowitz. Litho Questa)

1997 (5 Oct). *50th Death Anniv of Mahatma Gandhi* (1998). *T* **197** *and similar vert designs showing different portraits. P* 14.

1902 600 s. reddish brown and black 70 75
1903 700 s. reddish brown and black 85 90
MS1904 73×103 mm. 1000 s. multicoloured . . 1·25 1·40

(Litho B.D.T.)

1997 (1 Dec). *Christmas. Paintings and Sculptures. T* **198** *and similar multicoloured designs. P* 14.

1905 200 s. Type **198** 25 30
1906 300 s. "The Fall of the Rebel Angels" (Pieter Brueghel the Elder) 35 40
1907 400 s. "The Immaculate Conception" (Bartolome Murillo) 50 55
1908 500 s. "Music-making Angel" (Rosso Fiorentino) 60 65
1909 600 s. "Cupid and Psyche" (Adolphe-William Bougereau) 70 75
1910 700 s. "Cupid and Psyche" (Antonio Canova) 85 90
1905/10 . . . . *Set of* 6 3·25 3·50
MS1911 Two sheets, each 105×96 mm. (a) 2500 s. Mary and Angels (detail, "The Assumption of the Virgin") (El Greco) (*horiz*). (b) 2500 s. Angel holding baby (detail, "The Assumption of the Virgin") (El Greco) (*horiz*) *Set of* 2 *sheets* 6·00 6·25

199 Diana, Princess of Wales

200 Tiger

(Des Deb Hoeffner. Litho Questa)

1997 (8 Dec). *Diana, Princess of Wales Commemoration. P* 14.

1912 **199** 600 s. multicoloured 70 75
a. Sheetlet. No. 1912×6 . . . . 4·25

No. 1912 were printed in sheetlets of 6 stamps with an enlarged illustrated right-hand margin.

(Litho Cartor)

1998 (16 Jan). *Chinese New Year ("Year of the Tiger"). T* **200** *and similar horiz designs. Multicoloured. P* 13½.

1913 350 s. Type **200** 40 45
a. Sheetlet. Nos. 1913/16 . . . . 1·60
1914 350 s. Tiger leaping 40 45
1915 350 s. Tiger resting 40 45
1916 350 s. Tiger yawning 40 45
1913/16 . . . . . . *Set of* 4 1·60 1·75
MS1917 106×76 mm. 1500 s. Tiger . . . . 1·75 1·90

Nos. 1913/16 were printed together, *se-tenant*, in sheetlets of 4.

201 Mountain Gorilla

(Litho Questa)

1998 (18 Jan). *18th Anniv of Pan African Postal Union. P* 14.

1918 **201** 300 s. + 150 s. multicoloured . . 55 60

STAMP BOOKLETS

1962 (9 Oct). *Black on buff cover. Stitched.*

SB1 5 s. booklet containing 10 c., 15 c., 20 c., 30 c. and 50 c. (Nos. 100/4), each in block of 4 . . 6·50

1965. *Black on blue* (*No.* SB2) *or buff* (*No.* SB3) *covers. Stitched.*

SB2 3 s. booklet containing four 15 c. and eight 30 c. (Nos. 115, 117) in blocks of 4 . . . . 9·50
SB3 5 s. booklet containing four 15 c. and 50 c., and eight 30 c. (Nos. 115, 117, 119) in blocks of 4 11·00

1970. *Black on blue* (*No.* SB4) *or buff* (*No.* SB5) *covers. Stitched.*

SB4 3 s. booklet containing four 5 c. and 10 c., and eight 30 c. (Nos. 131/2, 135) in blocks of 4 . . 6·00
SB5 5 s. booklet containing four 5 c., 10 c. and 50 c., and eight 30 c. (Nos. 131/2, 135, 137) in blocks of 4 . . . . 6·00

1971 (15 Dec). *Black on salmon* (*No.* SB6) *or lilac* (*No.* SB7) *covers. Stitched.*

SB6 5 s. booklet containing four 10 c., 15 c. and 40 c., and eight 30 c. (Nos. 132/3, 135/6) in blocks of 4 . . . . 6·50
SB7 10 s. booklet containing four 10 c., 20 c., 30 c. and 50 c., and eight 70 c. (Nos. 132, 134/5, 137, 139) in blocks of 4 . . . . . . 9·00

1975 (9 Oct). *Black on blue* (*No.* SB8) *or yellow* (*No.* SB9) *covers. Stitched.*

SB8 5 s. booklet containing ten 50 c. (No. 153) in two blocks of 4 and one pair . . . . . . 2·75
SB9 10 s. booklet containing four 10 c., 20 c., 40 c. and 80 c., and eight 50 c. (Nos. 149/50, 152/3, 155) in blocks of 4 . . . . 3·25

POSTAGE DUE STAMPS

The Postage Due stamps of Kenya, Uganda and Tanganyika were used in Uganda until 2 January 1967.

D 1

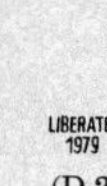

(D 2)

D 3 Lion

(Litho D.L.R.)

1967 (3 Jan). *Chalk-surfaced paper. P* 14 × 13½.

D1 D 1 5 c. scarlet . . . . 20 4·00
D2 10 c. green . . . . 20 4·00
D3 20 c. deep blue . . . . 35 4·00
D4 30 c. red-brown . . . . 40 5·50
D5 40 c. bright purple . . . . 60 8·50
D6 1 s. orange . . . . 1·50 12·00
D1/6 . . . . *Set of* 6 3·00 35·00

1970 (31 Mar). *As Nos.* D1/6, *but on glazed ordinary paper. P* 14 × 15.

D 7 D 1 5 c. scarlet . . . . . . 15 2·25
D 8 10 c. green . . . . . . 15 2·25
D 9 20 c. deep blue . . . . . . 25 2·75
D10 30 c. red-brown . . . . . . 35 3·75
D11 40 c. bright purple . . . . . . 55 4·25
D7/11 . . . . . . *Set of* 5 1·25 13·50

1973 (12 Dec). *Glazed, ordinary paper. P* 15.

D12 D 1 5 c. scarlet . . . . . . 80 4·50
D13 10 c. emerald . . . . . . 80 4·50
D14 20 c. deep blue . . . . . . 1·25 5·00
D15 30 c. red-brown . . . . . . 1·50 7·00
D16 40 c. bright mauve . . . . . . 2·00 9·50
D17 1 s. bright orange . . . . . . 2·75 10·00
D12/17 . . . . . . *Set of* 6 8·00 35·00

"UGANDA LIBERATED" OVERPRINTS. Nos. D1/17 were overprinted "UGANDA LIBERATED 1979", in very limited quantities, using a style of overprint similar to Type **32** (*Prices: Nos.* D1/6 *set of* 6 £225; D7/11 *set of* 5 £75; D12, 14/17 *set of* 5 £60; D13 £80, *all mint*).

(Litho Questa)

1979 (Dec). *Liberation. As Nos.* D1/6 *optd with Type* D **2**. *Chalk-surfaced paper. P* 13½ × 14.

D18 D 1 5 c. scarlet 20 40
D19 10 c. green 20 40
D20 20 c. dull ultramarine 25 40
D21 30 c. red-brown 25 60
D22 40 c. bright purple 30 60
D23 1 s. orange 30 60
D18/23 . . . . . . *Set of* 6 1·40 2·75

(Litho Questa)

1985 (11 Mar). *Animals. Type* D **3** *and similar vert designs. P* 14½ × 14.

D24 5 s. black and bright turquoise-green . . 15 20
D25 10 s. black and dull rose-lilac 15 20
D26 20 s. black and dull orange 30 40
D27 40 s. black and bright lilac 60 75
D28 50 s. black and pale greenish blue . . 60 75
D29 100 s. black and mauve . . . . 1·00 1·25
D24/9 . . . . *Set of* 6 2·50 3·25

Designs:—10 s. African Buffalo; 20 s. Kob; 40 s. African Elephant; 50 s. Common Zebra; 100 s. Black Rhinoceros.

Vanuatu

(*formerly* New Hebrides)

NEW HEBRIDES

Stamps of NEW SOUTH WALES were used by various Postal Agencies in the New Hebrides from August 1891 onwards. From late 1892 the N.S.W. agency at Port Vila was run by the Australian New Hebrides Company who, from 1897, issued local 1d and 2d. stamps for the carriage of mail on the Company's ships. These can be found used in combination with N.S.W. issues. Similar Postal Agencies supplying the stamps of NEW CALEDONIA were opened from 1903 onwards.

PRICES FOR STAMPS ON COVER TO 1945

Nos. 1/8 (F1/5)	*from* × 10
No. 9	*from* × 2
Nos. 10/16 (F6/10)	*from* × 8
Nos. 18/28 (F11/32)	*from* × 6
Nos. 30/4 (F33/7)	*from* × 4
No. 35 (F32*a*)	—
Nos. 36/9	*from* × 3
Nos. 40/2 (F38/41)	*from* × 4
Nos. 43/51 (F42/52)	*from* × 5
Nos. 52/63 (F53/64)	*from* × 3
Nos. D1/10 (FD53/69)	*from* × 8

ANGLO-FRENCH CONDOMINIUM

The New Hebrides, an island group in the south-west Pacific, were recognised as an area of joint Anglo-French influence in 1878. The position was regularised by the Convention of 20 October 1906 which created a Condominium, the two nations having equal rights and shares in the administration of the islands.

Stamps inscribed in English or French were issued concurrently and had equal validity throughout the islands. A common currency was reflected in the face values from 1938.

Where common designs were used the main differences between stamps inscribed in English and those in French are as follows:

(a) Inscriptions in English or French.
(b) Position of cyphers. French issues normally have "RF" to the right or above the British royal cypher.
(c) French issues are without watermark, *unless otherwise stated.*

Inscriptions in English

Inscriptions in French

I. STAMPS INSCRIBED IN ENGLISH

NEW HEBRIDES.
CONDOMINIUM.
(1)

NEW HEBRIDES
CONDOMINIUM
(2)

1908 (29 Oct). *T* **23** *and* **24** *of Fiji optd with T* **1** *by Govt Printing Establishment, Suva. On the bicoloured stamps the word "FIJI" obliterated by a bar in the colour of the word. P* 14.

(a) Wmk Multiple Crown CA. Ordinary paper (½d., 1d.) or chalk-surfaced paper (1s.)

No.	Description	Unused	Used
1	½d. green and pale green (No. 115)	2·75	14·00
1a	½d. green (No. 118)	40	7·00
2	1d. red	45	40
	a. Opt omitted (in vert pair with normal)	£5000	
3	1s. green and carmine	16·00	5·50

(b) Wmk Crown CA

No.	Description	Unused	Used
4	½d. green and grey-green	50·00	80·00
5	2d. dull purple and orange	60	70
6	2½d. dull purple and blue/*blue*	60	70
7	5d. dull purple and green	80	2·00
8	6d. dull purple and carmine	70	1·25
9	1s. green and carmine	£150	£200
1/9	*Set of* 9	£180	£250

1910 (15 Dec). *Types as last optd with T* **2** *by D.L.R. Wmk Multiple Crown CA. Ordinary paper (½d. to 2½d.) or chalk-surfaced paper (5d., 6d., 1s.). P* 14.

No.	Description	Unused	Used
10	½d. green	3·50	24·00
11	1d. red	10·00	8·50
12	2d. grey	60	3·00
13	2½d. bright blue	65	3·75
14	5d. dull purple and olive-green	80	5·50
15	6d. dull and deep purple	1·00	5·00
16	1s. black/*green* (R.)	1·00	7·50
10/16	*Set of* 7	16·00	50·00
10/16 Optd "Specimen"	*Set of* 7	£250	

3 Weapons and Idols

1d.

(4)

(Des J. Giraud. Recess D.L.R.)

1911 (25 July). *Wmk Mult Crown CA. P* 14.

No.	Type	Description	Unused	Used
18	3	½d. green	85	1·60
19		1d. red	3·25	2·00
20		2d. grey	6·00	4·00
21		2½d. ultramarine	2·00	5·00
24		5d. sage-green	3·75	5·50
25		6d. purple	3·00	5·00
26		1s. black/*green*	2·00	12·00
27		2s. purple/*blue*	17·00	22·00
28		5s. green/*yellow*	32·00	48·00
18/28		*Set of* 9	65·00	95·00
18/28 Optd "Specimen"		*Set of* 9	£160	

1920 (June)–**21**. *Surch with T* **4** *at Govt Printing Establishment, Suva.*

(a) On Nos. 24 and 26/8

No.	Type	Description	Unused	Used
30	3	1d. on 5d. sage-green (10.3.21)	7·00	60·00
		a. Surch inverted	£1400	
31		1d. on 1s. black/*green*	1·25	11·00
32		1d. on 2s. purple/*blue*	1·00	10·00
33		1d. on 5s. green/*yellow*	1·00	10·00

(b) On No. F16

No.	Type	Description	Unused	Used
34	3	2d. on 40 c. red/*yellow*	1·00	15·00

(c) On No. F27

No.	Type	Description	Unused	Used
35	3	2d. on 40 c. red/*yellow*	£120	£425

1921 (Sept–Oct). *Wmk Mult Script CA. P* 14.

No.	Type	Description	Unused	Used
36	3	1d. scarlet	2·00	14·00
37		2d. slate-grey	3·25	29·00
39		6d. purple	13·50	70·00
36/9		*Set of* 3	17·00	£100
36/9 Optd "Specimen"		*Set of* 3	65·00	

1924 (1 May). *Surch as T* **4**, *at Suva.*

No.	Type	Description	Unused	Used
40	3	1d. on ½d. green (No. 18)	3·75	20·00
41		3d. on 1d. scarlet (No. 36)	3·75	11·00
42		5d. on 2½d. ultramarine (No. 21)	7·00	20·00
		a. Surch inverted	£1200	
40/2		*Set of* 3	13·00	45·00

5

(Recess D.L.R.)

1925 (June). *Wmk Mult Script CA. P* 14.

No.	Type	Description	Unused	Used
43	5	½d. (5 c.) black	1·25	7·50
44		1d. (10 c.) green	1·00	7·00
45		2d. (20 c.) slate-grey	1·75	2·50
46		2½d. (25 c.) brown	1·00	10·00
47		5d. (50 c.) ultramarine	2·75	2·50
48		6d. (60 c.) purple	3·50	9·00
49		1s. (1.25 fr.) black/*emerald*	3·25	18·00
50		2s. (2.50 fr.) purple/*blue*	6·00	20·00
51		5s. (6.25 fr.) green/*yellow*	6·00	23·00
43/51		*Set of* 9	23·00	90·00
43/51 Optd "Specimen"		*Set of* 9	£180	

(New Currency. 100 gold centimes = 1 gold franc)

The currency used for the face values of issues to 1977 was an artificial, rather than an actual, monetary unit. The actual currencies in use were Australian dollars and the local franc.

6 Lopevi Is and Outrigger Canoe

(Des J. Kerhor. Eng J. G. Hall. Recess B.W.)

1938 (1 June). *Gold Currency. Wmk Mult Script CA. P* 12.

No.	Type	Description	Unused	Used
52	6	5 c. blue-green	2·50	2·75
53		10 c. orange	1·25	80
54		15 c. bright violet	3·00	2·75
55		20 c. scarlet	1·60	1·60
56		25 c. reddish brown	1·60	1·60
57		30 c. blue	1·90	1·25
58		40 c. grey-olive	4·50	3·25
59		50 c. purple	1·60	80
60		1 f. red/*green*	4·00	7·50
61		2 f. blue/*green*	30·00	16·00
62		5 f. red/*yellow*	70·00	48·00
63		10 f. violet/*blue*	£200	75·00
52/63		*Set of* 12	£300	£140
52/63 Perf "Specimen"		*Set of* 12	£225	

(Recess Waterlow)

1949 (10 Oct). *75th Anniv of U.P.U. As Nos. 145/8 of Jamaica. Wmk Mult Script CA. P* 13½×14.

No.	Description	Unused	Used
64	10 c. red-orange	30	15
65	15 c. violet	30	15
66	30 c. ultramarine	30	15
67	50 c. purple	40	20
64/7	*Set of* 4	1·10	60

NEW INFORMATION

The editor is always interested to correspond with people who have new information that will improve or correct the Catalogue.

7 Outrigger Sailing Canoes

(Des C. Hertenberger (1 f. to 5 f.), R. Serres (others). Recess Waterlow)

1953 (30 Apr). *T* **7** *and similar horiz designs. Wmk Mult Script CA. P* 12½.

No.	Description	Unused	Used
68	5 c. green	60	10
69	10 c. scarlet	60	10
70	15 c. yellow-ochre	60	10
71	20 c. ultramarine	60	10
72	25 c. olive	60	10
73	30 c. brown	60	10
74	40 c. blackish brown	60	10
75	50 c. violet	1·00	10
76	1 f. orange	7·50	70
77	2 f. reddish purple	7·50	9·00
78	5 f. scarlet	12·00	32·00
68/78	*Set of* 11	29·00	38·00

Designs:—5 to 20 c. Type **7**; 25 to 50 c. Native carving; 1 to 5 f. Two natives outside hut.

1953 (2 June). *Coronation. As No. 153 of Jamaica.*

No.	Description	Unused	Used
79	10 c. black and carmine	60	50

10 Quirós Galleon and Map

(Photo Harrison)

1956 (20 Oct). *50th Anniv of Condominium. T* **10** *and similar horiz design. Wmk Mult Script CA. P* 14½ × 14.

No.	Description	Unused	Used
80	5 c. emerald	15	10
81	10 c. scarlet	15	10
82	20 c. deep bright blue	10	10
83	50 c. deep lilac	15	15
80/3	*Set of* 4	45	30

Designs:—5, 10 c. Type **10**; 20, 50 c. "Marianne", "Talking Drum" and "Britannia".

12 Port Vila: Iririki Islet

13 River Scene and Spear Fisherman

(Des H. Cheffer (T **12**), P Gandon (others). Recess Waterlow)

1957 (3 Sept). *Wmk Mult Script CA. T* **12/13** *and similar horiz design. P* 13½.

No.	Type	Description	Unused	Used
84	12	5 c. green	40	50
85		10 c. scarlet	30	10
86		15 c. yellow-ochre	50	50
87		20 c. ultramarine	40	10
88	13	25 c. olive	45	10
89		30 c. brown	45	10
90		40 c. sepia	45	10
91		50 c. violet	45	10
92	–	1 f. orange	1·00	80
93	–	2 f. mauve	6·00	4·00
94	–	5 f. black	15·00	6·00
84/94		*Set of* 11	23·00	11·00

Design:—1 to 5 f. Woman drinking from coconut.

1963 (2 Sept). *Freedom from Hunger. As No. 80 of Lesotho.*

No.	Description	Unused	Used
95	60 c. green	50	15

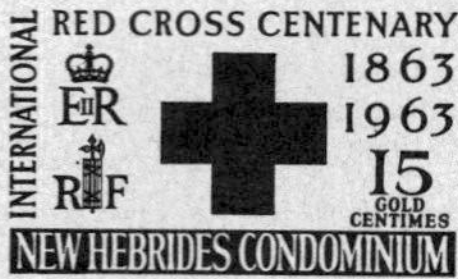

15 Red Cross Emblem

(Des V. Whiteley. Litho B.W.)

1963 (2 Sept). *Red Cross Centenary. W w* **12**. *P* 13½.

No.	Type	Description	Unused	Used
96	15	15 c. red and black	35	10
97		45 c. red and blue	45	20

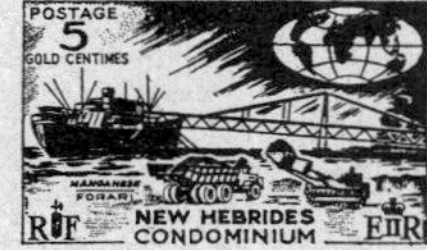

16 Exporting Manganese, Forari

17 Cocoa Beans

(Des V. Whiteley, from drawings by J. White (10 c., 20 c.), K. Penny (40 c.), C. Robin (3 f.). Photo Harrison. Des C. Robin (5 c., 1 f.), J. White (15 c.), G. Vasarhelyi (25 c., 5 f.), A. Larkins, Turrell and Thomas (30 c., 50 c., 2 f.). Recess Govt Printing Works, Paris)

1963 (25 Nov)–**72**. *T* **16/17** *and similar horiz designs. W* w **12** (10 c., 20 c., 40 c., 3 f.) *or no wmk (others). P* 14 (3 f.), 12½ (10 c., 20 c., 40 c.) *or* 13 (*others*).

98 5 c. lake, purple-brn & greenish bl (15.8.66) 90 40
a. Lake and greenish blue (29.2.72)* .. 35·00 35·00
99 10 c. light brown, buff and emerald (16.8.65) 15 10
100 15 c. yellow-bistre, red-brown & deep violet 15 10
101 20 c. black, olive-grn & greenish bl (16.8.65) 45 10
102 25 c. reddish violet, orange-brown & crimson (15.8.66) 50 70
103 30 c. chestnut, bistre and violet 75 10
104 40 c. vermilion and deep blue (16.8.65) .. 80 1·40
105 50 c. green, yellow and greenish blue .. 60 10
106 1 f. red, black & deep bluish green (15.8.66) 2·50 3·25
107 2 f. black, brown-purple and yellow-olive 2·50 1·75
108 3 f. deep violet, orange-brown, emerald and black (16.8.65) .. .. .. 13·00 8·00
w. Wmk inverted .. .. .. 15·00
109 5 f. blue, deep blue and black (24.1.67) 18·00 20·00
98/109 .. .. *Set of* 12 35·00 32·00

Designs:—15 c. Copra; 20 c. Fishing from Palikulo Point; 25 c. Painted Triggerfish; 30 c. New Caledonian Nautilus shell; 40 c. Lionfish; 50 c. Clown Surgeonfish; 1 f. Cardinal Honeyeater; 2 f. Buff-bellied Flycatcher; 3 f. Thicket Warbler; 5 f. White-collared Kingfisher.

*In No. 98*a* the globe is printed in the same colour as the centre, instead of in purple-brown.

See also No. 129.

28 I.T.U. Emblem

(Des M. Goaman. Litho Enschedé)

1965 (17 May). *I.T.U. Centenary. W* w **12**. *P* 11 × 11½.

110 **28** 15 c. scarlet and drab 20 10
111 60 c. blue and light red 35 20

29 I.C.Y. Emblem

(Des V. Whiteley. Litho Harrison)

1965 (24 Oct). *International Co-operation Year. W* w **12**. *P* 14½.

112 **29** 5 c. reddish purple and turquoise-green 15 10
113 55 c. deep bluish green and lavender .. 20 20

30 Sir Winston Churchill and St. Paul's Cathedral in Wartime

(Des Jennifer Toombs. Photo Harrison)

1966 (24 Jan). *Churchill Commemoration. W* w **12**. *P* 14.

114 **30** 5 c. black, cerise, gold and new blue .. 20 10
115 15 c. black, cerise, gold and deep green .. 40 10
116 25 c. black, cerise, gold and brown .. 50 10
117 30 c. black, cerise, gold and bluish violet 50 10
114/17 .. .. *Set of* 4 1·40 35

31 Footballer's Legs, Ball and Jules Rimet Cup

(Des V. Whiteley. Litho Harrison)

1966 (1 July). *World Cup Football Championships. W* w **12** (*sideways*). *P* 14.

118 **31** 20 c. violet, yellow-green, lake & yell-brn 20 15
119 40 c. chocolate, blue-grn, lake & yell-brn 30 15

32 W.H.O. Building

(Des M. Goaman. Litho Harrison)

1966 (20 Sept). *Inauguration of W.H.O. Headquarters, Geneva. W* w **12** (*sideways*). *P* 14.

120 **32** 25 c. black, yellow-green and light blue .. 20 10
121 60 c. black, light purple and yellow-brown 55 20

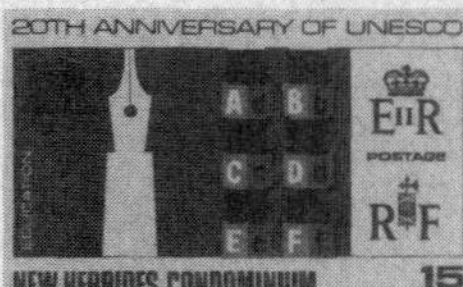

33 "Education"

(Des Jennifer Toombs. Litho Harrison)

1966 (1 Dec). *20th Anniv of U.N.E.S.C.O. W* w **12** (*sideways*). *T* **33** *and similar horiz designs. P* 14.

122 15 c. slate-violet, red, yellow and orange .. 20 10
123 30 c. orange-yellow, violet and deep olive .. 65 10
124 45 c. black, bright purple and orange 70 15
122/4 .. .. *Set of* 3 1·40 30

Designs:—30 c. "Science"; 45 c. "Culture".

36 The Coast Watchers

(Des R. Granger Barrett. Photo Enschedé)

1967 (26 Sept). *25th Anniv of the Pacific War. T* **36** *and similar horiz designs. Multicoloured. W* w **12**. *P* 14 × 13.

125 15 c. Type **36** 15 10
126 25 c. Map of war zone, U.S. marine and Australian soldier 40 15
127 60 c. H.M.A.S. *Canberra* (cruiser) 50 20
128 1 f. Boeing B-17 Flying Fortress 55 30
125/8 .. .. *Set of* 4 1·40 65

1967 (5 Dec). *New value with W* w **12** *sideways*.

129 60 c. vermilion and deep blue (as No. 104) .. 40 15

40 Globe and Hemispheres

(Des and eng J. Combet. Recess Govt Printing Works, Paris)

1968 (23 May). *Bicentenary of Bougainville's World Voyage. T* **40** *and similar horiz designs. P* 13.

130 15 c. emerald, slate-violet and red 15 10
131 25 c. deep olive, maroon and ultramarine .. 30 10
132 60 c. bistre-brown, brown-pur & myrtle-grn .. 35 10
130/2 .. .. *Set of* 3 70 30

Designs:—25 c. Ships *La Boudeuse* and *L'Etoile*, and map; 60 c. Bougainville, ship's figure-head and bougainvillea flowers.

43 Concorde and Vapour Trails

45 Kauri Pine

(Des S. W. Moss (25 c.), R. Granger Barrett (60 c.). Litho D.L.R.)

1968 (9 Oct). *Anglo-French Concorde Project. T* **43** *and similar horiz design. W* w **12** (*sideways*). *P* 14.

133 25 c. lt blue, orange-red & deep violet-blue 50 20
134 60 c. red, black and bright blue 60 25

Design:—60 c. Concorde in flight.

(Des V. Whiteley. Litho Format)

1969 (30 June). *Timber Industry. W* w **12**. *P* 14½.

135 **45** 20 c. multicoloured (*shades*) 10 10

No. 135 was issued in small sheets of 9 (3 × 3) printed on a simulated wood-grain background and with a decorative border showing various stages of the local timber industry. There is a wide range of shades on the printing.

ALTERED CATALOGUE NUMBERS

Any Catalogue numbers altered from the last edition are shown as a list in the introductory pages.

46 Cyphers, Flags and Relay Runner receiving Baton

48 Diver on Platform

(Des C. Haley. Photo Delrieu)

1969 (13 Aug). *Third South Pacific Games, Port Moresby. T* **46** *and similar horiz design. Multicoloured. P* 12½.

136 25 c. Type **46** 10 10
137 1 f. Cyphers, flags and relay runner passing baton 20 20

(Des V. Whiteley. Litho P.B.)

1969 (15 Oct). *Pentecost Island Land Divers. T* **48** *and similar vert designs. Multicoloured. W* w **12** (*sideways*). *P* 12½.

138 15 c. Type **48** 10 10
139 25 c. Diver jumping 10 10
140 1 f. Diver at end of fall 20 20
138/40 .. .. *Set of* 3 30 30

51 U.P.U. Emblem and New Headquarters Building

52 General Charles de Gaulle

(Des and eng J. Gauthier. Recess Govt Ptg Wks, Paris)

1970 (20 May). *Inauguration of New U.P.U. Headquarters Building. P* 13.

141 **51** 1 f. 05, slate, red-orange & bright purple 15 15

(Des V. Whiteley. Photo Govt Ptg Wks, Paris)

1970 (20 July). *30th Anniv of New Hebrides' Declaration for the Free French Government. P* 13.

142 **52** 65 c. multicoloured 35 40
143 1 f. 10, multicoloured 45 40

35

(**53**)

54 "The Virgin and Child" (Bellini)

1970 (15 Oct). *As No. 101, but W* w **12** (*sideways*) *and surch with T* **53**.

144 35 c. on 20 c. black, ol-grn & greenish black .. 30 30

(Des V. Whiteley. Litho Harrison)

1970 (30 Nov). *Christmas. T* **54** *and similar vert design. Multicoloured. W* w **12** (*sideways*). *P* 14½ × 14.

145 15 c. Type **54** 10 10
146 50 c. "The Virgin and Child" (Cima) 20 20

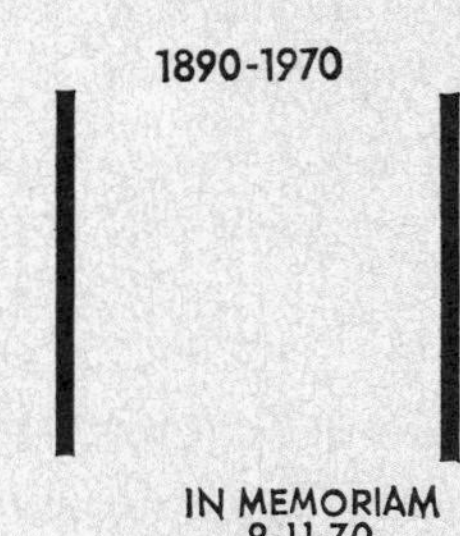

(**55**)

1971 (19 Jan). *Death of General Charles de Gaulle. Nos.* 142/3 *optd with T* **55**, *vertical bars in black, inscriptions in gold.*

147	**52**	65 c. multicoloured	15	10
148		1 f. 10, multicoloured	15	20

56 Football

(Des G. Bétemps. Photo Delrieu)

1971 (13 July). *Fourth South Pacific Games, Papeete, French Polynesia. T* **56** *and similar multicoloured design. P* 12½.

149	20 c. Type **56**	10	10
150	65 c. Basketball (*vert*)	30	20

57 Kauri Pine, Cone and Arms of Royal Society

58 "The Adoration of the Shepherds" (detail, Louis le Nain)

(Des P. Powell. Litho Harrison)

1971 (7 Sept). *Royal Society Expedition to New Hebrides,* 1971. *W w* **12** (*sideways*). *P* 14½ × 14.

151	**57**	65 c. multicoloured	20	15

(Des G. Drummond. Litho Questa)

1971 (23 Nov). *Christmas. T* **58** *and similar vert design. Multicoloured. W w* **12**. *P* 14 × 13½.

152	25 c. Type **58**	10	10
153	50 c. "The Adoration of the Shepherds" (detail, Tintoretto)	30	40

59 De Havilland D.H.A.3 Drover 3

60 Ceremonial Headdress, South Malekula

(Des M. Goaman. Photo Delrieu)

1972 (29 Feb). *Aircraft. T* **59** *and similar horiz designs. Multicoloured. P* 13.

154	20 c. Type **59**	40	15
155	25 c. Short S.25 Sandringham 4 flying boat	40	15
156	30 c. De Havilland D.H.89 Dragon Rapide	40	15
157	65 c. Sud Aviation SE210 Caravelle	1·00	1·25
154/7	*Set of* 4	2·00	1·50

(Des Odette Baillais (bird designs), Pierrette Lambert (others). Photo Govt Printing Works, Paris)

1972 (24 July). *T* **60** *and similar vert designs. Multicoloured. P* 12½ × 13.

158	5 c. Type **60**	10	10
159	10 c. Baker's Pigeon	25	10
160	15 c. Gong and carving, North Ambrym	15	15
161	20 c. Red-headed Parrot Finch	40	25
162	25 c. Gaskoin's Cowrie (*Cypraea gaskoini*) (shell)	40	25
163	30 c. Red-lip Olive (*Oliva rubrolabiata*) (shell)	50	30
164	35 c. Chestnut-bellied Kingfisher	65	40
165	65 c. Pretty Conch (*Strombus plicatus pulchellus*) (shell)	75	60
166	1 f. Gong (North Malekula) and carving (North Ambrym)	90	1·00
167	2 f. Palm Lorikeet	4·00	4·50
168	3 f. Ceremonial headdress, South Malekula (*different*)	3·00	6·00
169	5 f. Great Green Turban (*Turbo marmoratus*) (shell)	6·50	14·00
158/69 *and* 199	*Set of* 13	24·00	42·00

NEW INFORMATION

The editor is always interested to correspond with people who have new information that will improve or correct the Catalogue.

61 "Adoration of the Kings" (Spranger)

62 Royal and French Cyphers

(Des G. Drummond. Litho J.W.)

1972 (25 Sept). *Christmas. T* **61** *and similar vert design. Multicoloured. W w* **12**. *P* 14.

170	25 c. Type **61**	10	10
171	70 c. "The Virgin and Child in a Landscape" (Provoost)	20	20

(Des (from photographs by D. Groves) and photo Harrison)

1972 (20 Nov). *Royal Silver Wedding. Multicoloured; background colour given. W w* **12**. *P* 14 × 14½.

172	**62**	35 c. violet-black	15	10
		w. Wmk inverted	23·00	
173		65 c. yellow-olive	20	10

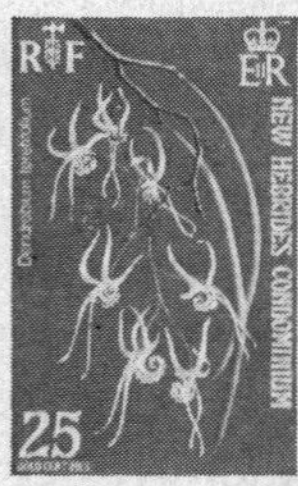

63 *Dendrobium teretifolium*

64 New Wharf at Vila

(Des Jennifer Toombs. Litho Questa)

1973 (26 Feb). *Orchids. T* **63** *and similar vert designs. Multicoloured. W w* **12** (*sideways**). *P* 14×14½.

174	25 c. Type **63**	30	10
	w. Wmk Crown to right of CA	1·25	
175	30 c. *Ephemerantha comata*	35	10
	w. Wmk Crown to right of CA	7·00	
176	35 c. *Spathoglottis petri*	40	10
177	65 c. *Dendrobium mohlianun*	75	55
174/7	*Set of* 4	1·60	70

*The normal sideways watermark shows Crown to left of CA, *as seen from the back of the stamp.*

(Des PAD Studio. Litho Questa)

1973 (14 May). *Opening of New Wharf at Vila. P* 14 × 14½ (25 c.) *or* 14½ × 14 (70 c.).

178	**64**	25 c. multicoloured	20	10
179	–	70 c. multicoloured	40	30

The 70 c. is as T **64**, but in a horizontal format.

65 Wild Horses

66 Mother and Child

(Des Pierrette Lambert. Photo Govt Printing Works, Paris)

1973 (13 Aug). *Tanna Island. T* **65** *and similar horiz design. Multicoloured. P* 13 × 12½.

180	35 c. Type **65**	30	15
181	70 c. Yasur Volcano	55	20

(Des Moutouh (35 c.), Tatin d'Avesnières (70 c.); adapted PAD Studio. Litho Questa)

1973 (19 Nov). *Christmas. T* **66** *and similar vert design. Multicoloured. W w* **12** (*sideways*). *P* 13½.

182	35 c. Type **66**	10	10
183	70 c. Lagoon scene	20	20

67 Pacific Pigeon

ROYAL VISIT 1974

(**68**)

(Des J. and H. Bregulla. Photo Govt Printing Works, Paris)

1974 (11 Feb). *Wild Life. T* **67** *and similar horiz designs. Multicoloured. P* 13 × 12½.

184	25 c. Type **67**	80	35
185	35 c. *Lyssa curvata* (moth)	80	60
186	70 c. Green Sea Turtle	80	70
187	1 f. 15, Grey-headed Flying Fox	1·00	1·50
184/7	*Set of* 4	3·00	2·75

1974 (11 Feb). *Royal Visit of Queen Elizabeth II. Nos.* 164 *and* 167 *optd with T* **68**.

188	35 c. Chestnut-bellied Kingfisher (R.)	25	10
189	2 f. Palm Lorikeet	40	40

69 Old Post Office

(Des Odette Baillais. Photo Govt Printing Works, Paris)

1974 (6 May). *Inauguration of New Post Office, Vila. T* **69** *and similar triangular design. Multicoloured. P* 12.

190	35 c. Type **69**	15	50
	a. *Tête-bêche* (pair). Nos. 190/1	30	1·10
191	70 c. New Post Office	15	60

Nos. 190/1 were printed together, in *tête-bêche* pairs throughout the sheet.

70 Capt. Cook and Map

(Des J. Cooter. Litho J.W.)

1974 (1 Aug). *Bicentenary of Discovery. T* **70** *and similar horiz designs. Multicoloured. W w* **12** (*sideways on* 1 *f.* 15). *P* 11 (1 *f.* 15) *or* 13 (*others*).

192	35 c. Type **70**	1·75	2·00
	a. Horiz strip of 3. Nos. 192/4	4·75	
193	35 c. William Wales and beach landing	1·75	2·00
194	35 c. William Hodges and island scene	1·75	2·00
195	1 f. 15, Capt Cook, map and H.M.S. *Resolution* (59 × 34 *mm*)	3·50	4·50
192/5	*Set of* 4	8·00	9·50

Nos. 192/4 were printed together, *se-tenant*, in horizontal strips of 3 throughout the sheet forming a composite design.

71 U.P.U. Emblem and Letters

72 "Adoration of the Magi" (Velazquez)

(Des Pierrette Lambert. Photo Govt Printing Works, Paris)

1974 (9 Oct). *Centenary of Universal Postal Union. P* 13 × 12½.

196	**71**	70 c. multicoloured	30	70

(Des J. Cooter. Litho Questa)

1974 (14 Nov). *Christmas. T* **72** *and similar multicoloured design. W w* **12** (*sideways* on* 70 *c.*). *P* 14×13½ (35 *c.*) *or* 13½×14 (70 *c.*).

197	35 c. Type **72**	10	10
198	70 c. "The Nativity" (Gerard van Honthorst) (*horiz*)	20	20
	w. Wmk Crown to right of CA	2·25	

*The normal sideways watermark shows Crown to left of CA, *as seen from the back of the stamp.*

73 Charolais Bull

74 Canoeing

(Des and eng J. Pheulpin. Recess Govt Printing Works, Paris)

1975 (29 Apr). *P* 13 × 12½.

199	**73**	10 f. bistre-brown, green & dull ultram	9·50	20·00

(Des J. Cooter. Litho Questa)

1975 (5 Aug). *World Scout Jamboree, Norway. T* **74** *and similar vert designs. Multicoloured. P* 13½.

200	25 c. Type **74**	20	10
201	35 c. Preparing meal	20	10
202	1 f. Map-reading	50	15
203	5 f. Fishing	1·75	2·50
200/3	*Set of* 4	2·40	2·50

75 "Pitti Madonna" (Michelangelo)

(Des PAD Studio. Litho Harrison)

1975 (11 Nov). *Christmas. Michelangelo's Sculptures. T* **75** *and similar vert designs. Multicoloured. W w* **12** *(sideways*). P* 14½×14.

204	35 c. Type **75**	10	10
205	70 c. "Bruges Madonna"	15	10
206	2 f. 50, "Taddei Madonna"	70	50
	w. Wmk Crown to right of CA	30·00	
204/6	*Set of* 3	85	55

*The normal sideways watermark shows Crown to left of CA, *as seen from the back of the stamp.*

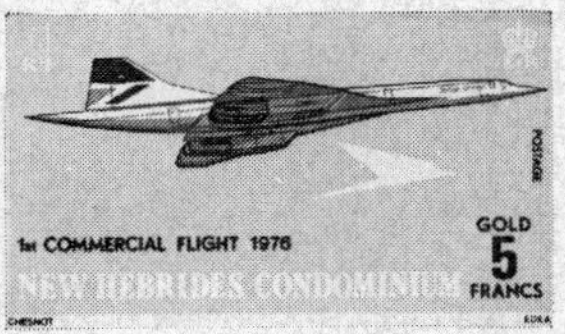

76 Concorde

(Des J. B. F. Chesnot. Typo Edila)

1976 (30 Jan). *First Commercial Flight of Concorde. P* 13.

207 **76**	5 f. multicoloured	6·00	5·00

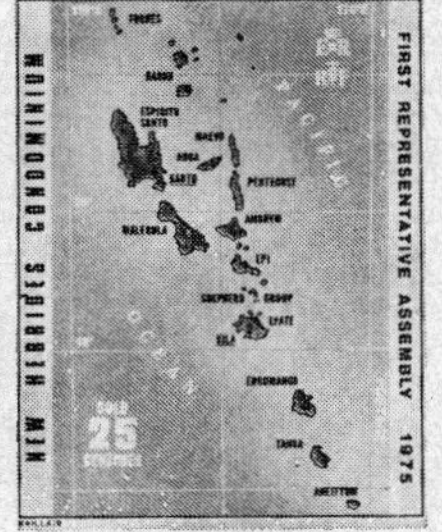

77 Telephones of 1876 and 1976 — **78** Map of the Islands

(Des J. Gauthier. Photo Delrieu)

1976 (31 Mar). *Telephone Centenary. T* **77** *and similar vert designs. Multicoloured. P* 13½.

208	25 c. Type **77**	15	10
209	70 c. Alexander Graham Bell	30	10
210	1 f. 15, Satellite and Nouméa Earth Station	50	50
208/10	*Set of* 3	85	60

(Des Odette Baillais. Photo Govt Printing Works, Paris)

1976 (29 June). *Constitutional Changes. T* **78** *and similar multicoloured designs. P* 13 *(25 c.) or* 13 × 12½ *(others).*

211	25 c. Type **78**	30	15
212	1 f. View of Santo (36×27 *mm*)	55	60
213	2 f. View of Vila (36×27 *mm*)	75	1·25
211/13	*Set of* 3	1·40	1·75

No. 211 shows the incorrect longitude, 116°E instead of 166°E.

Nos. 212/13 are inscribed "MUNICIPAL COUNCIL". Similar designs exist inscribed "FIRST REPRESENTATIVE ASSEMBLY 1975" and the name of the town. These stamps were not available in the New Hebrides.

79 "The Flight into Egypt" (Lusitano) — **80** Royal Visit, 1974

(Des J. Cooter. Litho Walsall)

1976 (8 Nov). *Christmas. T* **79** *and similar vert designs. Multicoloured. W w* **14**. *P* 13½.

214	35 c. Type **79**	10	10
215	70 c. "Adoration of the Shepherds"	15	10
216	2 f. 50, "Adoration of the Magi"	45	50
214/16	*Set of* 3	60	55

Nos. 215/16 show retables by the Master of Santos-o-Novo.

(Des BG Studio. Litho Walsall)

1977 (7 Feb). *Silver Jubilee. T* **80** *and similar vert designs. Multicoloured. W w* **14**. *P* 13½.

217	35 c. Type **80**	10	10
218	70 c. Imperial State Crown	15	10
	w. Wmk inverted	55·00	
219	2 f. The Blessing	30	65
217/19	*Set of* 3	45	70

(New Currency: 100 centimes=1 New Hebrides franc)

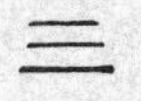

FNH — FNH — FNH — 25 FNH

(**81**) (5 f.) — (**82**) (10 f., 20 f.) — (**83**) (15 f.) — (**84**)

1977 (1 July). *Currency change. Surch by Govt. Ptg Works, Paris. Nos. 220/3 as T* **81/3**, *others as T* **84**.

220	5 f. on 5 c. Type **60**	40	45
221	10 f. on 10 c. Baker's Pigeon	80	35
222	15 f. on 15 c. Gong and carving	60	70
223	20 f. on 20 c. Red-headed Parrot Finch	1·25	55
224	25 f. on 25 c. Gaskoin's Cowrie (*Cypraea gaskoini*) (shell)	1·00	1·00
225	30 f. on 30 c. Red-lip Olive (*Oliva rubrolabiata*) (shell)	1·25	50
226	35 f. on 35 c. Chestnut-bellied Kingfisher	1·75	1·25
227	40 f. on 65 c. Pretty Conch (*Strombus plicatus pulchellus*) (shell)	1·25	1·50
228	50 f. on 1 f. Gong and carving	1·50	1·50
229	70 f. on 2 f. Palm Lorikeet	3·00	1·00
230	100 f. on 3 f. Ceremonial headdress	1·75	4·25
231	200 f. on 5 f. Great Green Turban (*Turbo marmoratus*) (shell)	7·00	14·00
232	500 f. on 10 f. Type **73**	10·00	24·00
220/32	*Set of* 13	27·00	45·00

FNH — FNH — FNH

(**85**) (5 f.) — (**86**) (10 f.) — (**87**) (15 f.)

Two settings of 35 f. and 200 f. surcharges:
Setting I. Space of 1.4 mm between figures and "FNH".
Setting II. Space of 2.1 mm between figures and "FNH".

1977 (18 July)–**78**. *Nos. 158/60, 162/5 and 169 surch by I.P.V., Port Vila, in typography with T* **85/7** *or similar surcharges.*

233	5 f. on 5 c. Type **60** (10.8.77)	50	15
	a. Surch double	£350	
234	10 f. on 10 c. Baker's Pigeon (10.7.77)	50	15
235	15 f. on 15 c. Gong and carving (18.7.77)	3·00	1·25
	b. Short bar in surcharge (5.8.77)	1·50	90
	ba. Surch inverted		
236	25 f. on 25 c. Gaskoin's Cowrie (*Cypraea gaskoini*) (shell) (10.9.77)	50·00	20·00
	a. "FHN" for "FNH" (R. 5/1)	£400	
237	30 f. on 30 c. Red-lip Olive (*Oliva rubrolabiata*) (shell) (10.9.77)	£250	75·00
	a. "FHN" for "FNH" (R. 5/1)	£1300	£600
238	35 f. on 35 c. Chestnut-bellied Kingfisher (Setting I) (10.9.77)	2·00	55
	a. Setting II (6.1.78)		
239	40 f. on 65 c. Pretty Conch (*Strombus plicatus pulchellus*) (shell) (12.9.77)	1·50	55
240	200 f. on 5 f. Great Green Turban (*Turbo marmoratus*) (shell) (Setting I) (22.8.77)	17·00	13·00
	a. Setting II (13.1.78)		
241	500 f. on 10 f. Type **73** (14.9.77)	19·00	13·00
233/41	*Set of* 9	£300	£110

50 f. and 100 f. local surcharges were also prepared but these were not put on general sale, being available from the Philatelic Bureau only (*Price for set of* 2 *£50 mint, £35 used*).

Dates are those on which the various values were surcharged.

Surcharges on Nos. 236/41 are similar to Type **84**, but with new currency inscription as Type **86**.

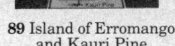

89 Island of Erromango and Kauri Pine — **90** "Tempi Madonna" (Raphael)

(Des L. Curtis. Litho J.W. (15, 30, 40 f.), Walsall (10, 35, 70, 500 f.), Questa (others))

1977 (6 Sept)–**78**. *Maps of the Islands. T* **89** *and similar vert designs. Multicoloured. W w* **14**. *P* 13½ × 13 *(15, 30, 40 f.) or* 14 *(others).*

242	5 f. Type **89**	30	10
243	10 f. Territory map and copra-making (9.5.78)	40	30
244	15 f. Espiritu Santo and cattle (23.11.77)	30	30
245	20 f. Efate and Vila P.O.	30	25
246	25 f. Malekula and headdresses (23.11.77)	40	40
247	30 f. Aoba, Maewo and pigs' tusks (23.11.77)	45	50
248	35 f. Pentecost and land diver (9.5.78)	50	65
249	40 f. Tanna and John Frum cross (23.11.77)	70	60
250	50 f. Shepherd Island and canoe	90	40
251	70 f. Banks Island and dancers (9.5.78)	1·75	2·75
252	100 f. Ambrym and idols	1·75	90
253	200 f. Aneityum and baskets	1·75	2·50
254	500 f. Torres Islands and archer fisherman (9.5.78)	4·00	7·50
242/54	*Set of* 13	12·00	15·00

(Des J.W. Litho Cartor)

1977 (8 Dec). *Christmas. T* **90** *and similar vert designs. Multicoloured. W w* **14**. *P* 12.

255	10 f. Type **90**	15	15
	w. Wmk inverted	65	
256	15 f. "The Flight into Egypt" (Gerard David)	25	20
	w. Wmk inverted	85	
257	30 f. "Virgin and Child" (Batoni)	35	60
	w. Wmk inverted	1·25	
255/7	*Set of* 3	65	85

91 Concorde over New York — **92** White Horse of Hanover

(Des BG Studio. Litho Rosenbaum Bros, Vienna)

1978 (9 May). *Concorde Commemoration. T* **91** *and similar horiz designs. Multicoloured. W w* **14** *(sideways*). P* 13½.

258	10 f. Type **91**	1·00	75
	w. Wmk Crown to right of CA	10·00	
259	20 f. Concorde over London	1·25	1·00
	w. Wmk Crown to right of CA	10·00	
260	30 f. Concorde over Washington	1·60	1·40
	w. Wmk Crown to right of CA	10·00	
261	40 f. Concorde over Paris	1·90	1·60
	w. Wmk Crown to right of CA	12·00	
258/61	*Set of* 4	5·25	4·25

*The normal sideways watermark shows Crown to left of CA, *as seen from the back of the stamp.*

(Des Jennifer Toombs. Litho Questa)

1978 (2 June). *25th Anniv of Coronation. T* **92** *and similar vert designs. P* 15.

262	40 f. sepia, turquoise-blue and silver	15	30
	a. Sheetlet. Nos. 262/4, each × 2	75	
263	40 f. multicoloured	15	30
264	40 f. sepia, turquoise-blue and silver	15	30
262/4	*Set of* 3	40	80

Designs:—No. 262, Type **92**. No. 263, Queen Elizabeth II; No. 264, Gallic Cock.

Nos. 262/4 were printed together in small sheets of 6, containing two *se-tenant* strips of 3 with horizontal gutter margin between.

93 "Madonna and Child" — (**94**)

(Des C. Abbott. Litho Questa)

1978 (1 Dec). *Christmas. Paintings by Dürer. T* **93** *and similar vert designs. Multicoloured. W w* **14**. *P* 14 × 13½.

265	10 f. Type **93**	10	10
266	15 f. "The Virgin and Child with St. Anne"	10	10
267	30 f. "Madonna of the Siskin"	15	10
268	40 f. "The Madonna of the Pear"	20	15
265/8	*Set of* 4	50	30

1979 (11 Jan). *1st Anniv of Internal Self-Government. As No.* 211 *surch as T* **94**.

269 **78**	10 f. on 25 c. multicoloured (blue background)	10	10
270	40 f. on 25 c. multicoloured (pale blue-green background)	20	20

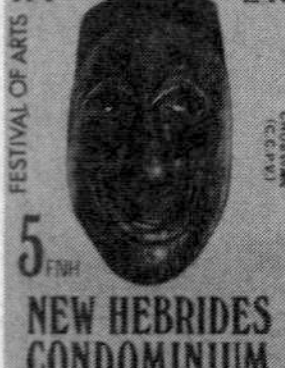

95 1938 5 c. Stamp and Sir Rowland Hill — **96** Chubwan Mask

(Des J.W. Litho Questa)

1979 (10 Sept). *Death Centenary of Sir Rowland Hill. T* **95** *and similar horiz designs showing stamps and Sir Rowland Hill. Multicoloured. W w* **14** *(sideways). P* 14.

No.	Description	Unused	Used
271	10 f. Type **95**	15	10
272	20 f. 1969 25 c. Pentecost Island Land Divers commemorative	20	10
273	40 f. 1925 2d. (20 c.)	25	20
271/3	*Set of* 3	55	30
MS274	143 × 94 mm. No. 272 and as No. F286, but W w **14** (sideways)	75	90

(Des BG Studio. Litho Format)

1979 (16 Nov). *Festival of Arts. T* **96** *and similar vert designs. Multicoloured. W w* **14**. *P* 14.

No.	Description	Unused	Used
275	5 f. Type **96**	10	10
276	10 f. Nal-Nal clubs and spears	10	10
277	20 f. Ritual puppet	15	10
278	40 f. Neqatmalow headdress	25	15
275/8	*Set of* 4	55	30

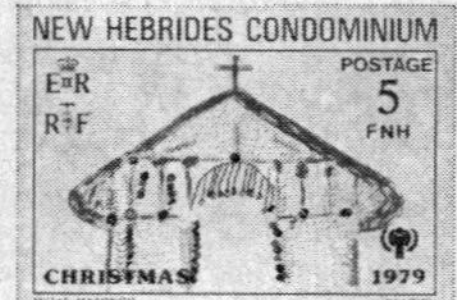

97 "Native Church" (Metas Masongo)

(Litho Delrieu)

1979 (4 Dec). *Christmas and International Year of the Child. Children's Drawings. T* **97** *and similar multicoloured designs. No wmk. P* 13 × 13½ *(horiz) or* 13½ × 13 *(vert)*.

No.	Description	Unused	Used
279	5 f. Type **97**	10	10
280	10 f. "Priest and Candles" (Herve Rutu)	10	10
281	20 f. "Cross and Bible" (Mark Deards) (*vert*)	10	10
282	40 f. "Green Candle and Santa Claus" (Dev Raj) (*vert*)	15	15
279/82	*Set of* 4	30	30

98 White-bellied Honeyeater

(Des G. Drummond. Litho Walsall)

1980 (27 Feb). *Birds. T* **98** *and similar horiz designs. Multicoloured. W w* **14** *(sideways). P* 14.

No.	Description	Unused	Used
283	10 f. Type **98**	50	10
284	20 f. Scarlet Robin	70	10
285	30 f. Yellow-fronted White Eye	90	45
286	40 f. Fan-tailed Cuckoo	1·00	70
283/6	*Set of* 4	2·75	1·25

STAMP BOOKLETS

1980. *Multicoloured cover, 109×74 mm. Stamps attached by selvedge.*

No.	Description	Price
SB1	200 f. booklet containing 5 f., 10 f., 15 f. and 20 f. (Nos. 242/5), each in block of 4	10·00

POSTAGE DUE STAMPS

POSTAGE DUE (D 1) — **POSTAGE DUE** (D 2) — **POSTAGE DUE** (D 3)

1925 (June). *Optd with Type* D **1**, *by D.L.R.*

No.	Type	Description	Unused	Used
D1	**5**	1d. (10 c.) green	40·00	1·00
D2		2d. (20 c.) slate-grey	48·00	1·00
D3		3d. (30 c.) red	50·00	2·50
D4		5d. (50 c.) ultramarine	55·00	4·50
D5		10d. (1 f.) carmine/*blue*	60·00	5·50
D1/5		*Set of* 5	£225	13·00
D1/5 Optd "Specimen"		*Set of* 5	£225	

1938 (1 June). *Optd with Type* D **2**, *by B.W.*

No.	Type	Description	Unused	Used
D 6	**6**	5 c. blue-green	20·00	28·00
D 7		10 c. orange	20·00	28·00
D 8		20 c. scarlet	26·00	42·00
D 9		40 c. grey-olive	35·00	55·00
D10		1 f. red/*green*	45·00	65·00
D6/10		*Set of* 5	£130	£200
D6/10 Perf "Specimen"		*Set of* 5	£120	

1953 (30 Apr). *Nos. 68/9, 71, 74 and 76 optd with Type* D **3**, *by Waterlow.*

No.	Description	Unused	Used
D11	5 c. green	5·00	9·00
D12	10 c. scarlet	1·75	6·50
D13	20 c. ultramarine	6·00	15·00
D14	40 c. blackish brown	8·50	25·00
D15	1 f. orange	6·00	25·00
D11/15	*Set of* 5	24·00	70·00

1957 (3 Sept). *Nos. 84/5, 87, 90 and 92 optd with Type* D **3**, *by Waterlow.*

No.	Type	Description	Unused	Used
D16	**12**	5 c. green	30	1·50
D17		10 c. scarlet	30	1·50
D18		20 c. ultramarine	1·25	2·00
D19	**13**	40 c. sepia	2·50	3·75
D20	–	1 f. orange	4·00	7·00
D16/20		*Set of* 5	7·50	14·00

II. STAMPS INSCRIBED IN FRENCH

(Currency. 100 centimes = 1 French franc)

NOUVELLES HEBRIDES (F 1) — NOUVELLES-HEBRIDES (F 2)

1908 (21 Nov). *T* **15/17** *of New Caledonia optd with Types* F **1** *or* F **2** *(1 f.), by Govt Ptg Wks, Paris.*

No.	Description	Unused	Used
F1	5 c. green	2·75	2·75
F2	10 c. carmine	3·25	3·50
F3	25 c. blue/*greenish* (R.)	4·00	3·75
F4	50 c. red/*orange*	5·50	5·25
F5	1 f. blue/*green* (R.)	11·50	11·50
F1/5	*Set of* 5	24·00	24·00

CONDOMINIUM (F 3) — 10c. (F 4)

1910 (Aug)–**11**. *Nos. F1/5 further optd with Type* F **3**, *or larger (1 f.), by Govt Ptg Wks, Paris.*

No.	Description	Unused	Used
F 6	5 c. green	2·00	1·75
F 7	10 c. carmine	2·00	70
F 8	25 c. blue/*greenish* (R.) (1911)	2·25	3·50
F 9	50 c. red/*orange* (1911)	6·50	6·50
F10	1 f. blue/*green* (R.)	13·00	16·00
F6/10	*Set of* 5	23·00	25·00

All the above were released in Paris on 16 March 1910. The 5 c., 10 c. and 1 f. were issued in New Hebrides in August but the 25 c. and 50 c. were not received until 1911 after the issue of the definitive stamps and they were placed in reserve, although some may have been issued on request.

1911 (12 July). *Wmk Mult Crown CA. P* 14.

No.	Type	Description	Unused	Used
F11	**3**	5 c. green	1·00	2·25
F12		10 c. carmine	45	75
F13		20 c. greyish slate	1·10	1·75
F14		25 c. ultramarine	3·50	6·50
F15		30 c. brown/*yellow*	6·50	3·75
F16		40 c. red/*yellow*	1·40	3·25
F17		50 c. sage-green	2·00	3·00
F18		75 c. orange	6·75	15·00
F19		1 f. red/*blue*	2·25	2·50
F20		2 f. violet	8·50	18·00
F21		5 f. red/*green*	12·00	24·00
F11/21		*Set of* 11	40·00	70·00

1913. *As last but wmk "R F" in sheet or without wmk.*

No.	Type	Description	Unused	Used
F22	**3**	5 c. green	80	3·75
F23		10 c. carmine	80	3·25
F24		20 c. greyish slate	90	3·00
F25		25 c. ultramarine	85	3·75
F26		30 c. brown/*yellow*	2·25	7·50
F27		40 c. red/*yellow*	32·00	48·00
F28		50 c. sage-green	14·00	18·00
F29		75 c. orange	14·00	28·00
F30		1 f. red/*blue*	6·50	7·50
F31		2 f. violet	12·00	23·00
F32		5 f. red/*green*	16·00	38·00
F22/32		*Set of* 11	90·00	£160

The above were placed on sale in Paris on 29 April 1912.

1920–21. *Surch as Type* F **4**, *at Govt Printing Establishment, Suva, Fiji.* (*a*) *On stamps of* 1908–11 (June 1920).

No.	Type	Description	Unused	Used
F32*a*		5 c. on 50 c. red/*orange* (F4)	£400	£400
F33		5 c. on 50 c. red/*orange* (F9)	2·50	6·50
F33*a*		10 c. on 25 c. blue/*greenish* (F8)	50	1·25
		(*b*) *On stamps of* 1911–13 (10.3.21)		
F34	**3**	5 c. on 40 c. red/*yellow* (F27)	26·00	75·00
F35		20 c. on 30 c. brown/*yellow* (F15)	9·50	45·00
F36		20 c. on 30 c. brown/*yellow* (F26)	14·00	55·00
		(*c*) *On Inscr in English* (10.3.21)		
F37	**3**	10 c. on 5d. sage-green (24)	15·00	38·00

1924 (1 May). *Stamps of* 1911–13 *surch as Type* F **4**, *at Suva.*

No.	Type	Description	Unused	Used
F38	**3**	10 c. on 5 c. green (F22)	1·60	3·00
F39		30 c. on 10 c. carmine (F23)	1·75	1·75
F40		50 c. on 25 c. ultramarine (F14)	32·00	70·00
F41		50 c. on 25 c. ultramarine (F25)	3·25	20·00
F38/41		*Set of* 4	35·00	85·00

F 5

France Libre (F 6)

(Recess D.L.R.)

1925 (June). *Wmk "R F" in sheet or without wmk. P* 14.

No.	Type	Description	Unused	Used
F42	F **5**	5 c. (½d.) black	1·50	8·00
F43		10 c. (1d.) green	1·50	7·50
F44		20 c. (2d.) greyish slate	1·50	2·50
F45		25 c. (2½d.) brown	2·00	9·00
F46		30 c. (3d.) red	1·50	4·50
F47		40 c. (4d.) red/*yellow*	1·50	4·50
F48		50 c. (5d.) ultramarine	1·50	3·25
F49		75 c. (7½d.) yellow-brown	2·00	9·50
F50		1 f. (10d.) carmine/*blue*	2·00	3·00
F51		2 f. (1/8) violet	4·25	20·00
F52		5 f. (4s.) carmine/*green*	5·50	21·00
F42/52		*Set of* 11	22·00	80·00
F42/52 Optd "Specimen"		*Set of* 11	£250	

In July 1929 a batch of mail was carried by aircraft from Port Vila to the French cruiser *Tourville* for sorting and forwarding at Nouméa, New Caledonia. Stamps of the above issue (including those with English inscriptions) were affixed to covers and handstamped "PAR AVION" before cancellation.

(New Currency. 100 gold centimes = 1 gold franc)

1938 (1 June). *Gold Currency. Wmk "R F" in sheet or without wmk. P* 12.

No.	Type	Description	Unused	Used
F53	**6**	5 c. blue-green	1·60	2·50
F54		10 c. orange	1·60	1·60
F55		15 c. bright violet	1·25	2·50
F56		20 c. scarlet	1·60	2·25
F57		25 c. reddish brown	4·00	2·50
F58		30 c. blue	4·00	2·00
F59		40 c. grey-olive	1·25	5·00
F60		50 c. purple	1·25	1·60
F61		1 f. lake/*pale green* (*shades*)	1·60	3·25
F62		2 f. blue/*pale green* (*shades*)	25·00	25·00
F63		5 f. red/*yellow*	50·00	38·00
F64		10 f. violet/*blue*	£120	80·00
F53/64		*Set of* 12	£190	£150
F53/64 Perf "Specimen"		*Set of* 12	£300	

1941 (15 Apr). *Adherence to General de Gaulle. Optd with Type* F **6**, *at Nouméa, New Caledonia.*

No.	Type	Description	Unused	Used
F65	**6**	5 c. blue-green	2·50	20·00
F66		10 c. orange	4·00	19·00
F67		15 c. bright violet	6·00	26·00
F68		20 c. scarlet	14·00	24·00
F69		25 c. reddish brown	14·00	27·00
F70		30 c. blue	14·00	25·00
F71		40 c. grey-olive	14·00	27·00
F72		50 c. purple	14·00	24·00
F73		1 f. lake/*pale green*	14·00	24·00
F74		2 f. blue/*pale green*	14·00	27·00
F75		5 f. red/*yellow*	14·00	27·00
F76		10 f. violet/*blue*	14·00	27·00
F65/76		*Set of* 12	£120	£275

1949 (10 Oct). *75th Anniv of U.P.U. As Nos. 64/7. Wmk "R F" in sheet or without wmk. P* 13½.

No.	Description	Unused	Used
F77	10 c. red-orange	2·25	4·00
F78	15 c. violet	3·50	6·50
F79	30 c. ultramarine	5·00	9·50
F80	50 c. purple	6·00	10·00
F77/80	*Set of* 4	15·00	27·00

1953 (30 Apr). *As Nos. 68/78. Wmk "R F" in sheet or without wmk. P* 12½.

No.	Type	Description	Unused	Used
F81	**7**	5 c. green	40	1·00
F82		10 c. scarlet	70	75
F83		15 c. yellow-ochre	70	1·00
F84		20 c. ultramarine	70	75
F85	–	25 c. olive	70	75
F86	–	30 c. brown	70	75
F87	–	40 c. blackish brown	70	90
F88	–	50 c. violet	70	75
F89	–	1 f. orange	19·00	5·50
F90	–	2 f. reddish purple	21·00	42·00
F91	–	5 f. scarlet	28·00	70·00
F81/91		*Set of* 11	65·00	£110

1956 (20 Oct). *Fiftieth Anniv of Condominium. As Nos. 80/3. Wmk "R F" in sheet or without wmk. P* 14½ × 14.

No.	Type	Description	Unused	Used
F92	**10**	5 c. emerald	1·50	1·25
F93		10 c. scarlet	1·50	1·25
F94	–	20 c. deep bright blue	1·50	1·50
F95	–	50 c. deep lilac	1·50	2·00
F92/5		*Set of* 4	5·50	5·50

1957 (3 Sept). *As Nos. 84/94. Wmk "R F" in sheet or without wmk. P* 13½.

No.	Type	Description	Unused	Used
F 96	**12**	5 c. green	80	60
F 97		10 c. scarlet	80	40
F 98		15 c. orange-yellow	1·25	60
F 99		20 c. ultramarine	1·25	50
F100	**13**	25 c. yellow-olive	1·25	50
F101		30 c. brown	1·25	60
F102		40 c. sepia	1·25	60
F103		50 c. reddish violet	1·25	50
F104	–	1 f. red-orange	8·00	2·75
F105	–	2 f. mauve	22·00	27·00
F106	–	5 f. black	32·00	35·00
F96/106		*Set of* 11	65·00	65·00

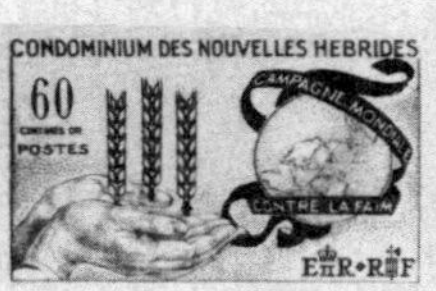

F 7 Emblem and Globe

F 8 Centenary Emblem

(Des and eng J. Derrey. Recess Govt Ptg Wks, Paris)

1963 (2 Sept). *Freedom from Hunger. P* 13.
F107 **F 7** 60 c. deep bluish green and chestnut .. 17·00 11·00

(Des and eng J. Combet. Recess Govt Ptg Wks, Paris)

1963 (2 Sept). *Red Cross Centenary. P* 13.
F108 **F 8** 15 c. red, grey and orange .. .. 10·00 6·00
F109 45 c. red, grey and yellow-bistre .. 18·00 18·00

1963 (25 Nov)–**72.** *As Nos.* 98/109 *and* 129. *No wmk. P* 12½ (10, 20, 40, 60 *c.*), 14 (3 *f.*) *or* 13 (*others*).
F110 5 c. lake, purple-brown and greenish blue (15.8.66) 60 30
a. Lake and greenish blue (29.2.72) .. 50·00 50·00
F111 10 c. lt brown, buff & emerald* (16.8.65) .. 80 80
F112 10 c. lt brown, buff and emerald (5.8.68) .. 65 15
F113 15 c. yellow-bistre, red-brown & dp violet .. 10·00 40
F114 20 c. black, ol-green & grnsh bl* (16.8.65) .. 2·25 3·00
F115 20 c. black, ol-green & grnsh bl (5.8.68) .. 1·75 25
F116 25 c. reddish violet, orange-brown and crimson (15.8.66) 60 60
F117 30 c. chestnut, bistre and violet .. .. 11·00 60
F118 40 c. vermilion and deep blue* (16.8.65) .. 3·50 6·00
F119 50 c. green, yellow and greenish blue .. 11·00 60
F120 60 c. vermilion and deep blue (5.12.67) .. 1·50 80
F121 1 f. red, black & dp bluish grn (15.8.66) .. 2·00 3·25
F122 2 f. black, brown-purple & yellow-olive .. 24·00 9·00
F123 3 f. multicoloured* (16.8.65) .. .. 11·00 20·00
F124 3 f. multicoloured (5.8.68) .. .. 9·00 11·00
F125 5 f. blue, deep blue and black (24.1.67) .. 20·00 28·00
F110/25 .. .. *Set of* 16 £100 75·00

*Normally all French New Hebrides issues have the "RF" inscription on the right to distinguish them from the British New Hebrides stamps which have it on the left. The stamps indicated by an asterisk have "RF" wrongly placed on the left.

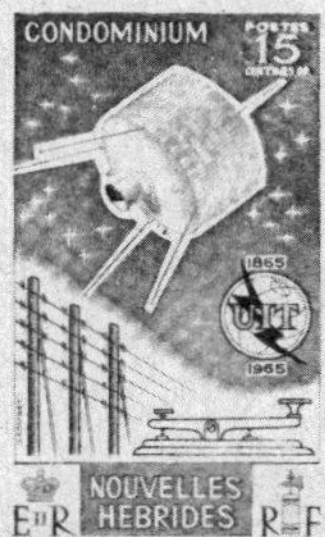

F **9** "Syncom" Communications Satellite, Telegraph Poles and Morse Key

(Des and eng J. Combet. Recess Govt Ptg Wks, Paris)

1965 (17 May). *Air. I.T.U. Centenary. P* 13.
F126 **F 9** 15 c. blue, chocolate and emerald .. 10·00 6·00
F127 60 c. carmine, dp bluish green & slate 22·00 22·00

1965 (24 Oct). *International Co-operation Year. As Nos.* 112/13. *P* 14½.
F128 **29** 5 c. dp reddish purple & turquoise-grn 4·00 3·00
F129 55 c. deep bluish green and lavender .. 10·00 9·00

1966 (24 Jan). *Churchill Commemoration. As Nos.* 114/17. *P* 14.
F130 **30** 5 c. black, cerise, gold and new blue .. 1·00 75
F131 15 c. black, cerise, gold and deep green .. 2·75 1·00
F132 25 c. black, cerise, gold and brown .. 3·00 3·50
F133 30 c. black, cerise, gold and bluish violet 3·75 4·50
F130/3 .. .. *Set of* 4 9·50 8·75

1966 (1 July). *World Cup Football Championships. As Nos.* 118/19. *P* 14.
F134 **31** 20 c. violet, yellow-grn, lake & yell-brn 3·50 2·75
F135 40 c. chocolate, bl-grn, lake & yell-brn 5·00 4·25

1966 (20 Sept). *Inauguration of W.H.O. Headquarters, Geneva. As Nos.* 120/1. *P* 14.
F136 **32** 25 c. black, yellow-green and light blue 3·00 2·00
F137 60 c. black, mauve and yellow-ochre .. 5·00 5·00

1966 (1 Dec). *20th Anniv of U.N.E.S.C.O. As Nos.* 122/4. *P* 14.
F138 **33** 15 c. slate-violet, red, yellow and orange 1·75 1·25
F139 – 30 c. orange-yellow, violet & dp olive .. 2·75 2·50
F140 – 45 c. black, bright purple and orange .. 3·00 3·00
F138/40 .. .. *Set of* 3 6·75 6·00

1967 (26 Sept). *25th Anniv of the Pacific War. As Nos.* 125/8. *P* 14 × 13.
F141 15 c. Type **36** 75 40
F142 25 c. Map of war zone, U.S. marine and Australian soldier .. .. .. 1·25 50
F143 60 c. H.M.A.S. *Canberra* (cruiser) .. .. 1·75 1·25
F144 1 f. Boeing B-17 Flying Fortress .. 2·25 2·00
F141/4 .. .. *Set of* 4 5·50 3·75

1968 (23 May). *Bicentenary of Bougainville's World Voyage. As Nos.* 130/2. *P* 13.
F145 **40** 15 c. emerald, slate-violet and red .. 20 20
F146 – 25 c. dp olive, maroon & ultramarine .. 40 40
F147 – 60 c. bistre-brn, brn-pur & myrtle-grn .. 90 90
F145/7 .. .. *Set of* 3 1·40 1·40

1968 (9 Oct). *Anglo-French Concorde Project. As Nos.* 133/4. *P* 14.
F148 **43** 25 c. lt blue, orange-red & dp violet-bl .. 2·25 1·50
F149 – 60 c. red, black and bright blue .. .. 3·75 3·00

1969 (30 June). *Timber Industry. As No.* 135. *P* 14½.
F150 **45** 20 c. multicoloured (*shades*) 20 30

1969 (13 Aug). *3rd South Pacific Games, Port Moresby, Papua New Guinea. As Nos.* 136/7. *Multicoloured. P* 12½.
F151 25 c. Type **46** 40 30
F152 1 f. Runner passing baton, and flags .. 1·60 1·75

1969 (15 Oct). *Pentecost Island Land Divers. As Nos.* 138/40. *Multicoloured. P* 12½.
F153 15 c. Type **48** 30 30
F154 25 c. Diver jumping 40 40
F155 1 f. Diver at end of fall .. .. .. 1·40 1·40
F153/5 .. .. *Set of* 3 1·90 1·90

1970 (20 May). *Inauguration of New U.P.U. Headquarters Building, Berne. As No.* 141. *P* 13.
F156 **51** 1 f. 05, slate, red-orange & brt purple .. 50 70

1970 (20 July). *30th Anniv of New Hebrides' Declaration for the Free French Government. As Nos.* 142/3. *P* 13.
F157 **52** 65 c. multicoloured 65 65
F158 1 f. 10, multicoloured .. .. .. 1·25 1·25

1970 (15 Oct). *No.* F115 *surch with T* **53**.
F159 35 c. on 20 c. black, ol-green & greenish blue 60 50

1970 (30 Nov). *Christmas. As Nos.* 145/6. *Multicoloured. P* 14½ × 14.
F160 15 c. Type **54** 15 15
F161 50 c. "The Virgin and Child" (G. Cima) .. 25 40

1971 (19 Jan). *Death of General Charles de Gaulle. Nos.* F157/8 *optd with T* **55**, *the vertical bars in black and inscriptions in gold.*
F162 **52** 65 c. multicoloured 75 55
a. Gold opt omitted .. .. ..
F163 1 f. 10, multicoloured .. .. 1·50 1·50

On No. F162a the vertical black bars are still present.

1971 (13 July). *4th South Pacific Games, Papeete, French Polynesia. As Nos.* 149/50. *Multicoloured. P* 12½.
F164 20 c. Type **56** 35 20
F165 65 c. Basketball (*vert*) 95 80

1971 (7 Sept). *Royal Society's Expedition to New Hebrides. As No.* 151. *P* 14½ × 14.
F166 **57** 65 c. multicoloured 50 50

1971 (23 Nov). *Christmas. As Nos.* 152/3. *Multicoloured. P* 14 × 13½.
F167 25 c. Type **58** 15 20
F168 50 c. "Adoration of the Shepherds" (J. Tintoretto) 30 35

1972 (29 Feb). *Aircraft. As Nos.* 154/7. *Multicoloured. P* 13.
F169 20 c. Type **59** .. .. 1·00 60
F170 25 c. Short S.25 Sandringham 4 flying boat 1·00 70
F171 30 c. De Havilland D.H.89 Dragon Rapide 1·10 80
F172 65 c. Sud Aviation SE 210 Caravelle .. 3·00 4·50
F169/72 .. .. *Set of* 4 5·50 6·00

1972 (24 July). *As Nos.* 158/69. *Multicoloured. P* 12½ × 13.
F173 5 c. Type **60** 40 10
F174 10 c. Baker's Pigeon .. .. .. 1·75 50
F175 15 c. Gong and carving, North Ambrym 50 15
F176 20 c. Red-headed Parrot Finch .. .. 2·25 30
F177 25 c. Gaskoin's Cowrie (*Cypraea gaskoini*) (shell) .. .. .. 1·75 30
F178 30 c. Red-lip Olive (*Oliva rubrolabiata*) (shell) .. .. .. 1·75 30
F179 35 c. Chestnut-bellied Kingfisher .. 3·00 40
F180 65 c. Pretty Conch (*Strombus plicatus pulchellus*) (shell) .. .. 2·50 60
F181 1 f. Gong, North Malekula and carving, North Ambrym .. .. 2·50 1·75
F182 2 f. Palm Lorikeet .. .. .. 15·00 10·00
F183 3 f. Ceremonial headdress, South Malekula (*different*) .. .. 9·50 13·00
F184 5 f. Great Green Turban (*Turbo marmoratus*) (shell) .. .. .. 17·00 22·00
F173/84 *and* F213 .. .. *Set of* 13 75·00 75·00

1972 (25 Sept). *Christmas. As Nos.* 170/1. *Multicoloured. P* 14.
F185 25 c. Type **61** 25 20
F186 70 c. "Virgin and Child" (Provoost) .. 50 45

1972 (20 Nov). *Royal Silver Wedding. As Nos.* 172/3. *W* **w 12.** *P* 14 × 14½.
F187 **62** 35 c. multicoloured 40 40
F188 65 c. multicoloured .. .. .. 50 1·00

1973 (26 Feb). *Orchids. As Nos.* 174/7. *Multicoloured. P* 14 × 14½.
F189 25 c. Type **63** .. .. 2·00 60
F190 30 c. *Ephemerantha comata* .. .. .. 2·00 80
F191 35 c. *Spathoglottis petri* .. .. .. 2·00 95
F192 65 c. *Dendrobium mohlianum* .. .. 3·50 4·75
F189/92 .. .. *Set of* 4 8·50 6·50

1973 (14 May). *Opening of New Wharf, Vila. As Nos.* 178/9. *Multicoloured. P* 14 × 14½ (25 *c.*) *or* 14½ × 14 (70 *c.*).
F193 25 c. Type **64** 60 50
F194 70 c. View of wharf (*horiz*) .. .. 90 1·50

1973 (13 Aug). *Tanna Island. As Nos.* 180/1. *Multicoloured. P* 13 × 12½.
F195 35 c. Type **65** .. .. 2·25 1·25
F196 70 c. Yasur Volcano .. .. .. 3·25 3·25

1973 (19 Nov). *Christmas. As Nos.* 182/3. *Multicoloured. P* 14 × 13½.
F197 35 c. Type **66** 40 35
F198 70 c. Lagoon scene 70 75

1974 (11 Feb). *Wild Life. As Nos.* 184/7. *Multicoloured. P* 13 × 12½.
F199 25 c. Type **67** .. .. 3·75 1·50
F200 35 c. *Lyssa curvata* .. .. .. 5·50 1·75
F201 70 c. Green Sea Turtle .. .. .. 5·50 4·00
F202 1 f. 15, Grey-headed Flying Fox .. 6·00 10·00
F199/202 .. .. *Set of* 4 19·00 15·00

VISITE ROYALE
1974
(F 10)

1974 (11 Feb). *Royal Visit of Queen Elizabeth II. Nos.* F179 *and* F182 *optd with Type* F **10**.
F203 35 c. Chestnut-bellied Kingfisher (R.) .. 2·00 50
F204 2 f. Palm Lorikeet .. .. 5·00 6·00

1974 (6 May). *Inauguration of New Post Office, Vila. As Nos.* 190/1. *Multicoloured. P* 12.
F205 35 c. Type **69** 50 65
a. *Tête-bêche* (pair). Nos. F205/6 .. 1·10 1·50
F206 70 c. New Post Office 60 85

1974 (1 Aug). *Bicentenary of Discovery. As Nos.* 192/5. *Multicoloured. P* 11 (1 *f.* 15) *or* 13 × 13½ (*others*).
F207 35 c. Type **70** .. .. 4·50 4·00
a. Horiz strip of 3. Nos. F207/9 .. .. 12·00
F208 35 c. William Wales and beach landing .. 4·50 4·00
F209 35 c. William Hodges and island scene .. 4·50 4·00
F210 1 f. 15, Capt. Cook, *Resolution* and map of islands (64 × 39 *mm*) .. .. 10·00 8·50
F207/10 .. .. *Set of* 4 21·00 18·00

1974 (9 Oct). *Centenary of Universal Postal Union. As No.* 196. *P* 13 × 12½.
F210*a* **71** 70 c. dp turquoise-blue, rosine & black 1·50 1·75

1974 (4 Nov). *Christmas. As Nos.* 197/8. *Multicoloured. P* 14 × 13½ (35 *c.*) *or* 13½ × 14 (70 *c.*).
F211 35 c. Type **72** 25 20
F212 70 c. "The Nativity" (G. van Honthorst) (*horiz*) 55 45

1975 (29 Apr). *As No.* 199. *P* 13 × 12½.
F213 **73** 10 f. bistre-brown, yellow-green & blue 28·00 35·00

1975 (5 Aug). *World Scout Jamboree, Norway. As Nos.* 200/3. *Multicoloured. P* 14 × 13½.
F214 25 c. Type **74** 55 20
F215 35 c. Preparing meal 65 30
F216 1 f. Map-reading .. .. 1·25 1·10
F217 5 f. Fishing .. .. 5·50 9·00
F214/17 .. .. *Set of* 4 7·00 9·50

1975 (11 Nov). *Christmas. As Nos.* 204/6. *Multicoloured. P* 14½ × 14.
F218 35 c. Type **75** 25 15
F219 70 c. "Bruges Madonna" 40 25
F220 2 f. 50, "Taddei Madonna" .. .. 1·75 2·75
F218/20 .. .. *Set of* 3 2·25 2·75

1976 (30 Jan). *First Commercial Flight of Concorde. As No.* 207. *P* 13.
F221 **76** 5 f. multicoloured .. .. .. 15·00 14·00

1976 (31 Mar). *Telephone Centenary. As Nos.* 208/10. *Multicoloured. P* 13½.
F222 25 c. Type **77** 55 40
F223 70 c. Alexander Graham Bell .. .. 1·40 1·50
F224 1 f. 15, Satellite and Earth Station, Nouméa 1·75 2·50
F222/4 .. .. *Set of* 3 3·50 4·00

1976 (29 June). *Constitutional Changes. As Nos.* 211/13. *Multicoloured. P* 13 (25 *c.*) *or* 13 × 12½ (*others*).
F225 25 c. Type **78** 50 30
F226 1 f. Luganville (36×27 *mm*) .. .. 1·50 1·25
F227 2 f. Vila (36×27 *mm*) .. .. .. 2·50 2·25
F225/7 .. .. *Set of* 3 4·00 3·50

No. F225 shows the incorrect longitude, 116°E, instead of 166°E.

Nos. F226/7 are inscribed "PREMIERE MUNICIPALITE". Similar designs exist with the inscription "PREMIERE ASSEMBLEE REPRESENTATIVE 1975" and the name of the town. These stamps were not available in the New Hebrides.

1976 (8 Nov). *Christmas. As Nos.* 214/16. *Multicoloured. P* 13½.
F228 35 c. Type **79** 25 15
F229 70 c. "Adoration of the Shepherds" 40 25
F230 2 f. 50, "Adoration of the Magi" .. .. 1·75 2·75
F228/30 .. .. *Set of* 3 2·25 2·75

1977 (7 Feb). *Silver Jubilee. As Nos.* 217/19. *Multicoloured. P* 13½.
F231 35 c. Type **80** 30 15
F232 70 c. Imperial State Crown 50 25
F233 2 f. The Blessing 60 60
F231/3 .. .. *Set of* 3 1·25 90

(New Currency. 100 centimes = 1 New Hebrides franc)

1977 (1 July). *Currency Change. Nos.* F173/84 *and* F214 *surch as T* **81**/**3** (Nos. F234/7) *or as T* **84** (*others*) *by Govt Ptg Wks, Paris.*
F234 5 f. on 5 c. Type **60** 40 40
F235 10 f. on 10 c. Baker's Pigeon 85 40
F236 15 f. on 15 c. Gong and carving, North Ambrym 70 60
F237 20 f. on 20 c. Red-headed Parrot Finch 1·50 85
F238 25 f. on 25 c. Gaskoin's Cowrie (*Cypraea gaskoini*) (shell) .. .. 1·50 1·00
F239 30 f. on 30 c. Red-lip Olive (*Oliva rubrolabiata*) (shell) .. .. 1·75 1·50
F240 35 f. on 35 c. Chestnut-bellied Kingfisher 2·50 1·50
F241 40 f. on 65 c. Pretty Conch (*Strombus plicatus pulchellus*) (shell) .. 2·50 2·00
F242 50 f. on 1 f. Gong, North Malekula, and carving, North Ambrym .. 2·50 2·00
F243 70 f. on 2 f. Palm Lorikeet .. .. 4·25 2·75
a. Surch double .. .. ..
F244 100 f. on 3 f. Ceremonial headdress, South Malekula .. .. .. 4·50 4·50
F245 200 f. on 5 f. Great Green Turban (*Turbo marmoratus*) (shell) .. .. 14·00 19·00
F246 500 f. on 10 f. Type **73** .. .. 26·00 35·00
F234/46 .. .. .. *Set of* 13 55·00 65·00

1977 (18 July)–**78**. *Nos.* F173/5, F177/180, F184 *and* F213 *surch by I.P.V., Port Vila, in typography with T* **85/7** *or similar surcharges.*

F247	5 f. on 5 c. Type **60** (10.8.77)	1·25	1·00
F248	10 f. on 10 c. Baker's Pigeon (20.7.77)	2·50	55
F249	15 f. on 15 c. Gong and carving (18.7.77)	3·25	1·50
	a. Short bar in surcharge (5.8.77)	2·75	2·25
F250	25 f. on 25 c. Gaskoin's Cowrie (*Cypraea gaskoini*) (shell) (10.9.77)	£130	65·00
	a. "FHN" for "FNH" (R. 5/1)	£750	
F251	30 f. on 30 c. Red-lip Olive (*Oliva rubrolabiata*) (shell) (10.9.77)	£375	75·00
	a. "FHN" for "FNH" (R. 5/1)	£1500	£600
F252	35 f. on 35 c. Chestnut-bellied Kingfisher (Setting I) (10.9.77)	5·00	4·25
	a. "NH" for "FNH" (R. 4/2)	£500	
	b. Setting II (6.1.78)	24·00	14·00
F253	40 f. on 65 c. Pretty Conch (*Strombus plicatus pulchellus*) (shell) (12.9.77)	4·50	4·50
F254	200 f. on 5 f. Great Green Turban (*Turbo marmoratus*) (shell) (Setting I) (22.8.77)	40·00	48·00
	a. Setting II (13.1.78)	45·00	48·00
F255	500 f. on 10 f. Type **73** (14.9.77)	42·00	48·00
F247/55	*Set of* 9	£550	£225

Dates are those on which the various values were surcharged.
50 f., 70 f. and 100 f. local surcharges were also prepared, but were not put on general sale, being available from the Philatelic Bureau only (*Price £70 each mint*).

1977 (7 Sept)–**78**. *Maps of the Islands. As Nos.* 242/54. *Multicoloured. P* 13½ × 13 (15, 30, 40 *f.*) *or* 14 (*others*).

F256	5 f. Type **89**	65	20
F257	10 f. Territory map and copra-making (9.5.78)	75	20
F258	15 f. Espiritu Santo and cattle (23.11.77)	75	20
F259	20 f. Efate and Vila Post Office	1·00	30
F260	25 f. Malekula and headdresses (23.11.77)	80	40
F261	30 f. Aoba, Maewo and pigs' tusks (23.11.77)	80	45
F262	35 f. Pentecost and land diver (9.5.78)	2·25	60
F263	40 f. Tanna and John Frum cross (23.11.77)	1·25	75
F264	50 f. Shepherd Island and canoe	2·00	75
F265	70 f. Banks Island and dancers (9.5.78)	4·50	3·25
F266	100 f. Ambrym and idols	3·00	2·50
F267	200 f. Aneityum and baskets	4·75	9·00
F268	500 f. Torres Islands and archer fisherman (9.5.78)	11·00	15·00
F256/68	*Set of* 13	30·00	30·00

1977 (8 Dec). *Christmas. As Nos.* 255/7. *Multicoloured. P* 12.

F269	10 f. Type **90**	20	20
F270	15 f. "The Flight into Egypt" (G. David)	35	35
F271	30 f. "Virgin and Child" (Pompeo Batoni)	85	85
F269/71	*Set of* 3	1·25	1·25

1978 (9 May). *Concorde Commemoration. As Nos.* 258/61. *Multicoloured. P* 13½.

F272	10 f. Type **91**	2·50	1·00
F273	20 f. Concorde over London	2·75	1·50
F274	30 f. Concorde over Washington	3·25	2·00
F275	40 f. Concorde over Paris	3·75	3·25
F272/5	*Set of* 4	11·00	7·00

1978 (2 June). *25th Anniv of Coronation. As Nos.* 262/4. *P* 15.

F276 **92**	40 f. sepia, turquoise-blue and silver	25	60
	a. Sheetlet. Nos. F276/8 × 2	1·25	
F277 –	40 f. multicoloured	25	60
F278 –	40 f. sepia, turquoise-blue and silver	25	60
F276/8	*Set of* 3	65	1·60

Nos. F276/278 were printed together in small sheets of 6, containing two *se-tenant* strips of 3, with horizontal gutter margin between.

1978 (1 Dec). *Christmas. As Nos.* 265/8. *Multicoloured. P* 14 × 13½.

F279	10 f. Type **93**	20	20
F280	15 f. "The Virgin and Child with St. Anne"	25	30
F281	30 f. "The Madonna with the Goldfinch"	40	60
F282	40 f. "The Madonna with the Child"	50	70
F279/82	*Set of* 4	1·25	1·60

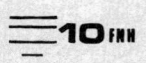

(F 11)

1979 (11 Jan). *1st Anniv of Internal Self-Government. As No.* F225 *surch as Type* **F 11**.

F283 **78**	10 f. on 25 c. multicoloured (blue background)	55	30
F284	40 f. on 25 c. multicoloured (pale blue-green background)	1·25	1·50

1979 (10 Sept). *Death Centenary of Sir Rowland Hill. As Nos.* 271/3. *Multicoloured. P* 14.

F285	10 f. Type **95**	30	35
F286	20 f. 1969 Land Divers 25 c. commemorative	45	55
F287	40 f. 1925 20 c. (2d.)	65	75
F285/7	*Set of* 3	1·25	1·50

For miniature sheet containing No. F286, see No. **MS**274.

1979 (16 Nov). *Festival of Arts. As Nos.* 275/8. *Multicoloured. P* 14.

F288	5 f. Type **96**	20	10
F289	10 f. Nal-Nal clubs and spears	25	15
F290	20 f. Ritual puppet	35	40
F291	40 f. Neqatmalow headdress	60	1·00
F288/91	*Set of* 4	1·25	1·50

1979 (4 Dec). *Christmas and International Year of the Child. As Nos.* 279/82. *Multicoloured. P* 13 × 13½ (*horiz*) *or* 13½ × 13 (*vert*).

F292	5 f. Type **97**	65	35
F293	10 f. "Priest and Candles" (Herve Rutu)	85	35
F294	20 f. "Cross and Bible" (Mark Deards) (*vert*)	1·25	1·00
F295	40 f. "Green Candle and Santa Claus" (Dev Raj) (*vert*)	2·00	2·00
F292/5	*Set of* 4	4·25	3·25

1980 (27 Feb). *Birds. As Nos.* 283/6. *Multicoloured. P* 14.

F296	10 f. Type **98**	1·50	45
F297	20 f. Scarlet Robin	1·75	1·00
F298	30 f. Yellow-fronted White Eye	2·00	1·75
F299	40 f. Fan-tailed Cuckoo	2·00	2·25
F296/9	*Set of* 4	6·50	5·00

STAMP BOOKLETS

1980. *Cover as No.* SB1.

FSB1	200 f. As No. SB1, but containing Nos. F256/9	35·00

POSTAGE DUE STAMPS

CHIFFRE TAXE (FD 1) — CHIFFRE TAXE (FD 2) — TIMBRE-TAXE (FD 3)

1925 (June). *Optd with Type* FD 1, *by D.L.R.*

FD53 **F 5**	10 c. (1d.) green	48·00	3·00
FD54	20 c. (2d.) greyish slate	48·00	3·00
FD55	30 c. (3d.) red	48·00	3·00
FD56	50 c. (5d.) ultramarine	48·00	3·00
FD57	1 f. (10d.) carmine/*blue*	48·00	3·00
FD53/7	*Set of* 5	£225	13·50
FD53/7 Optd "Specimen"	*Set of* 5	£225	

Although on sale in Paris, the Postmaster would not issue any in unused condition for about a year and most copies are cancelled-to-order.

1938 (1 June). *Optd with Type* FD 2, *by Bradbury, Wilkinson.*

FD65 **6**	5 c. blue-green	14·00	32·00
FD66	10 c. orange	17·00	32·00
FD67	20 c. scarlet	23·00	42·00
FD68	40 c. grey-olive	45·00	80·00
FD69	1 f. lake/*pale green*	48·00	90·00
FD65/9	*Set of* 5	£130	£250
FD65/9 Perf "Specimen"	*Set of* 5	£200	

1941 (15 Apr). *Nos.* FD65/9 *optd with Type* F 6 *at Nouméa, New Caledonia.*

FD77 **6**	5 c. blue-green	8·75	32·00
FD78	10 c. orange	8·75	32·00
FD79	20 c. scarlet	8·75	32·00
FD80	40 c. grey-olive	8·75	32·00
FD81	1 f. lake/*pale green*	17·00	32·00
FD77/81	*Set of* 5	48·00	£140

1953 (30 Apr). *Optd with Type* FD 3, *by Waterlow.*

FD92 **7**	5 c. green	4·00	15·00
FD93	10 c. scarlet	4·00	13·00
FD94	20 c. ultramarine	12·00	20·00
FD95 –	40 c. blackish brown	15·00	42·00
FD96 –	1 f. orange	25·00	45·00
FD92/6	*Set of* 5	55·00	£120

1957 (3 Sept). *Optd with Type* FD 3, *by Waterlow.*

FD107 **12**	5 c. green	2·25	7·00
FD108	10 c. scarlet	2·25	7·00
FD109	20 c. ultramarine	5·50	9·50
FD110 **13**	40 c. sepia	11·00	17·00
FD111 –	1 f. red-orange	13·00	20·00
FD107/11	*Set of* 5	30·00	55·00

VANUATU

The former Condominium of the New Hebrides became the Republic of Vanuatu on 30 July 1980 and was admitted as a member of the Commonwealth.

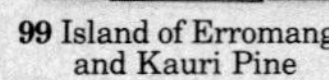

99 Island of Erromango and Kauri Pine

100 Rotary International

(Des L. Curtis. Litho J.W. (15, 30, 40 f.), Walsall (10, 35, 70, 500 f.), Questa (others))

1980 (30 July). *As Nos.* 242/54 *of New Hebrides but inscr* "VANUATU" *and without cyphers as in T* **99**. *P* 13 (15, 30, 40 *f.*) *or* 14 (*others*).
E. *Inscr in English. W* w **14**. F. *Inscr in French. No wmk.*

		E		F	
287	5 f. Type **99**	15	15	35	15
288	10 f. Territory map and copra making	15	15	40	15
289	15 f. Espiritu Santo and cattle	25	25	45	25
290	20 f. Efate and Vila P.O.	30	30	50	30
291	25 f. Malakula and headdresses	35	35	55	35
292	30 f. Aoba, Maewo and pigs' tusks	45	45	55	45
293	35 f. Pentecost and land diver	50	50	60	50
294	40 f. Tanna and John Frum cross	60	60	90	60
295	50 f. Shepherd Island and outrigger canoe	65	70	1·00	70
296	70 f. Banks Island and custom dancers	1·00	1·00	1·40	1·00
297	100 f. Ambrym and idols	1·25	80	1·50	1·10
298	200 f. Aneityum and baskets	1·40	1·40	1·75	1·75
299	500 f. Torres Island and archer fisherman	2·50	3·00	4·00	3·50
287/99	*Set of* 13	8·50	8·50	12·50	9·50

(Des L. Curtis. Litho Walsall)

1980 (16 Sept). *75th Anniv of Rotary International. T* **100** *and similar multicoloured design. P* 14. E. *Inscr in English. W* w **14** (*sideways on* 10 *f.*). F. *Inscr in French. No wmk.*

		E		F	
300	10 f. Type **100**	10	10	10	10
301	40 f. Rotary emblem (*vert*)	30	30	30	30

101 Kiwanis Emblem and Globe

102 "The Virgin and Child enthroned with Saints and Angels" (Umkreis Michael Pacher)

(Des L. Curtis. Litho Walsall)

1980 (16 Sept). *Kiwanis International (service club), New Zealand District Convention, Port Vila. T* **101** *and similar design. P* 14. E. *Inscr in English. W* w **14** (*sideways on* 40 *f.*). F. *Inscr in French. No wmk.*

		E		F	
302	10 f. gold, ultram & chestnut	10	10	30	10
303	40 f. gold, blue-grn & brt bl	30	40	70	50

Design: *Horiz*—40 f. Kiwanis and Convention emblems.

(Des BG Studio. Litho Questa)

1980 (12 Nov). *Christmas. Details from Paintings. T* **102** *and similar vert designs. Multicoloured. W* w **14**. *P* 14 × 13½.

304	10 f. Type **102**	10	10
305	15 f. "The Virgin and Child with Saints, Angels and Donors" (Hans Memling)	10	10
306	30 f. "The Rest on the Flight to Egypt" (Adriaen van der Werff)	20	20
304/6	*Set of* 3	35	35

103 Blue-faced Parrot Finch

104 Tribesman with Portrait of Prince Philip

(Des G. Drummond. Litho Questa)

1981 (18 Feb). *Birds* (*1st series*). *T* **103** *and similar vert designs. Multicoloured. W* w **14**. *P* 14.

307	10 f. Type **103**	50	20
308	20 f. Emerald Dove	70	40
309	30 f. Golden Whistler	1·00	70
310	40 f. Silver-shouldered Fruit Dove	1·10	90
307/10	*Set of* 4	3·00	2·00

See also Nos. 327/30.

(New Currency. Vatus)

(Des A. Theobald. Litho Format)

1981 (10 June). *60th Birthday of Prince Philip, Duke of Edinburgh. T* **104** *and similar vert designs. Multicoloured.* W w **14.** *P* 14 × 14½.
311 15 v. Type **104** 10 15
312 25 v. Prince Philip in casual dress .. 15 20
313 35 v. Queen and Prince Philip with Princess Anne and Master Peter Phillips .. 15 25
314 45 v. Prince Philip in ceremonial dress .. 20 35
311/14 .. .. *Set of* 4 55 85

105 Prince Charles with his Dog, Harvey

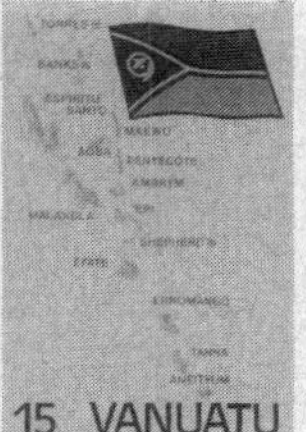

106 National Flag and Map of Vanuatu

(Des J.W. Litho Walsall)

1981 (22 July). *Royal Wedding. T* **105** *and similar vert designs. Multicoloured.* W w **14.** *P* 14.
315 15 v. Wedding bouquet from Vanuatu .. 10 10
316 45 v. Type **105** 20 15
317 75 v. Prince Charles and Lady Diana Spencer 35 45
315/17 .. .. *Set of* 3 55 60

(Des C. Abbott. Litho Format)

1981 (30 July). *First Anniv of Independence. T* **106** *and similar designs.* W w **14** (*sideways on* 25 *and* 45 *v.*). *P* 14.
318 15 v. multicoloured 15 15
w. Wmk inverted .. .. .. 30·00
319 25 v. multicoloured 15 15
320 45 v. greenish yellow and brown-lake .. 20 20
321 75 v. multicoloured 35 70
w. Wmk inverted .. .. ..
318/21 .. .. *Set of* 4 75 1·10
Designs: *Horiz*—25 v. Vanuatu emblem; 45 v. Vanuatu national anthem. *Vert*—75 v. Vanuatu coat of arms.

107 Three Shepherds

108 New Caledonian Myiagra Flycatcher

(Adapted G. Vasarhelyi. Litho Questa)

1981 (11 Nov). *Christmas. Children's Paintings. T* **107** *and similar multicoloured designs.* W w **14** (*sideways on* 25 *and* 45 *v.*). *P* 14.
322 15 v. Type **107** 10 10
323 25 v. Vanuatu girl with lamb (*vert*) .. 15 15
324 35 v. Angel as butterfly 15 20
325 45 v. Boy carrying torch and gifts (*vert*) .. 25 30
322/5 .. .. *Set of* 4 60 65
MS326 133 × 94 mm. Nos. 322/5 (wmk sideways) 80 1·25

(Des G. Drummond. Litho Questa)

1982 (8 Feb). *Birds (2nd series). T* **108** *and similar vert designs. Multicoloured.* W w **14.** *P* 14½ × 14.
327 15 v. Type **108** 45 20
w. Wmk inverted .. .. ..
328 20 v. Rainbow Lorys 50 30
w. Wmk inverted .. .. ..
329 25 v. Buff-bellied Flycatchers 55 35
330 45 v. Collared Grey Fantails 80 65
327/30 .. .. *Set of* 4 2·10 1·40

109 *Flickingeria comata*

110 Scouts round Campfire

(Des Jennifer Toombs. Litho Enschedé)

1982 (15 June). *Orchids. Multicoloured designs as T* **109.** W w **14** (*sideways* on* 35, 45, 50 *and* 75 *v.*). *P* 13½.
331 1 v. Type **109** 10 40
332 2 v. *Calanthe triplicata* 10 40
333 10 v. *Dendrobium sladei* 15 20
334 15 v. *Dendrobium mohlianum* 20 20
335 20 v. *Dendrobium macrophyllum* 25 30
336 25 v. *Dendrobium purpureum* 30 35
337 30 v. *Robiquetia mimus* 35 40
338 35 v. *Dendrobium mooreanum* (*horiz*) .. 50 50
339 45 v. *Spathoglottis plicata* (*horiz*) .. 55 70
340 50 v. *Dendrobium seemannii* (*horiz*) .. 60 80
341 75 v. *Dendrobium conanthum* (*horiz*) .. 95 1·50
w. Wmk Crown to right of CA .. — 10·00
342 100 v. *Dendrobium macranthum* .. .. 1·25 1·50
343 200 v. *Coelogyne lamellata* .. .. 2·25 2·50
344 500 v. *Bulbophyllum longioscapum* .. 5·00 6·00
331/44 .. .. *Set of* 14 11·00 14·00
*The normal sideways watermark shows Crown to left of CA, *as seen from the back of the stamp.*

(Des L. Curtis. Litho Questa)

1982 (1 Sept). *75th Anniv of Boy Scout Movement. T* **110** *and similar horiz designs. Multicoloured.* W w **14** (*sideways*). *P* 14.
345 15 v. Type **110** 50 20
346 20 v. First aid 55 25
347 25 v. Constructing tower 60 40
348 45 v. Constructing raft 90 70
349 75 v. Scout saluting .. .. .. 1·25 1·25
345/9 .. .. *Set of* 5 3·50 2·50

111 Baby Jesus

112 *Euploea sylvester*

(Des G. Vasarhelyi. Litho Questa)

1982 (1 Nov). *Christmas. Nativity Scenes. T* **111** *and similar multicoloured designs.* W w **14** (*sideways on* 15, 25 *v.*). *P* 14.
350 15 v. Type **111** 40 15
351 25 v. Mary and Joseph 60 45
352 35 v. Shepherds (*vert*) .. .. .. 75 1·00
353 45 v. Kings bearing gifts (*vert*) .. .. 80 1·40
350/3 .. .. *Set of* 4 2·25 2·75
MS354 132 × 92 mm. As Nos. 350/3 but without yellow borders .. .. 2·25 3·25

(Des J. Cooter. Litho Questa)

1983 (17 Jan). *Butterflies. T* **112** *and similar horiz designs. Multicoloured.* W w **14** (*sideways*). *P* 14 × 14½.
355 15 v. Type **112** 65 35
a. Pair. Nos. 355/6 .. .. .. 1·25 70
356 15 v. *Hypolimnas octocula* 65 35
357 20 v. *Papilio canopus* 80 50
a. Pair. Nos. 357/8 .. .. .. 1·60 1·00
358 20 v. *Polyura sacco* 80 50
359 25 v. *Luthrodes cleotas* 80 55
a. Pair. Nos. 359/60 .. .. .. 1·60 1·10
360 25 v. *Danaus pumila* 80 55
355/60 .. .. *Set of* 6 4·00 2·50
Nos. 355/6, 357/8 and 359/60 were each printed in *se-tenant* pairs, horizontally and vertically throughout the sheets.

113 President Afi George Sokomanu

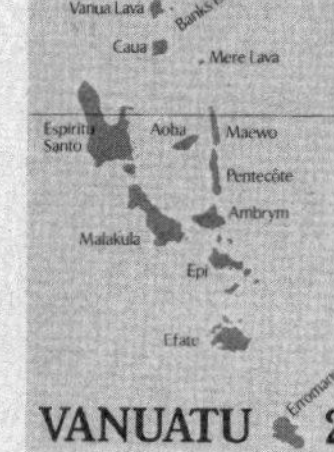

114 Map of Northern Vanuatu

(Des L. Curtis. Litho Enschedé)

1983 (14 Mar). *Commonwealth Day. T* **113** *and similar horiz designs. Multicoloured.* W w **14** (*sideways**). *P* 13½×14.
361 15 v. Type **113** 15 10
362 20 v. Fisherman and liner *Oriana* 20 15
w. Wmk Crown to right of CA .. 1·00
363 25 v. Herdsman and cattle 25 15
364 75 v. World map showing position of Vanuatu with Commonwealth and Vanuatu flags 50 70
w. Wmk Crown to right of CA .. .. 11·00
361/4 .. .. *Set of* 4 1·00 1·00
*The normal sideways watermark shows Crown to left of CA, *as seen from the back of the stamp.*

(Des A. Theobald. Litho Harrison)

1983 (23 May). *Economic Zone. Sheet* 120 × 120 *mm containing T* **114** *and similar vert designs. Multicoloured.* W w **14.** *P* 13½ × 13.
MS365 25 v. × 6 Yellow-finned Tuna; Type **114**; Map of Matthew Island; Map of Hunter Island; Cornet Grouper; Skipjack Tuna .. .. 2·50 2·50

NEW INFORMATION

The editor is always interested to correspond with people who have new information that will improve or correct the Catalogue.

115 Montgolfier Balloon of De Rozier and D'Arlandes, 1783

116 Mail at Bauerfield Airport

(Des A. Theobald. Litho Questa)

1983 (4 Aug). *Bicentenary of Manned Flight. T* **115** *and similar multicoloured designs, each with manned flight logo.* W w **14** (*sideways on* 35, 40 *and* 45 *v.*). *P* 13½.
366 15 v. Type **115** 15 15
367 20 v. J. A. C. Charles hydrogen balloon (first use of hydrogen), 1783 .. .. 25 25
368 25 v. Blanchard and Jeffries crossing English Channel, 1785 .. .. 30 30
369 35 v. Giffard's steam-powered dirigible airship, 1852 (*horiz*) 40 40
370 40 v. *La France* (airship of Renard and Krebs), 1884 (*horiz*) 45 45
371 45 v. LZ-127 *Graf Zeppelin* (first aerial circumnavigation), 1929 (*horiz*) .. 55 55
366/71 .. .. *Set of* 6 1·90 1·90

(Des L. McCombie. Litho Questa)

1983 (10 Oct). *World Communications Year. T* **116** *and similar horiz designs. Multicoloured.* W w **14** (*sideways*). *P* 14.
372 15 v. Type **116** 20 25
373 20 v. Switchboard operator 30 35
374 25 v. Telex operator 35 40
375 45 v. Satellite Earth station 65 70
372/5 .. .. *Set of* 4 1·40 1·50
MS376 138 × 95 mm. Nos. 372/5 .. .. 2·00 2·50

117 *Cymatoderma elegans var lamellatum*

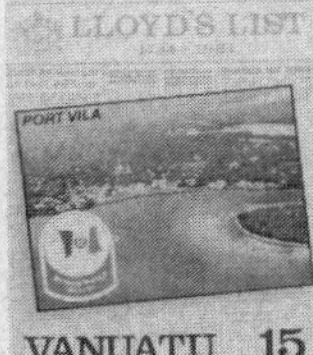

118 Port Vila

(Des P. Cox. Litho Questa)

1984 (9 Jan). *Fungi. T* **117** *and similar multicoloured designs.* W w **14** (*sideways on* 35 *v., inverted on* 45 *v.*). *P* 14.
377 15 v. Type **117** 70 45
378 25 v. *Lignosus rhinocerus* 90 85
379 35 v. *Stereum ostrea* (*horiz*) .. .. 1·25 1·25
380 45 v. *Ganoderma boninense* .. .. 1·60 1·90
377/80 .. .. *Set of* 4 4·00 4·00

(Des D. Miller. Litho Questa)

1984 (30 Apr). *250th Anniv of "Lloyd's List" (newspaper). T* **118** *and similar vert designs. Multicoloured.* W w **14.** *P* 14½ × 14.
381 15 v. Type **118** 20 25
382 20 v. *Induna* (container ship) 30 35
383 25 v. Air Vanuatu Boeing 737 aircraft .. 35 40
384 45 v. *Brahman Express* (container ship) .. 65 70
381/4 .. .. *Set of* 4 1·40 1·50

(Des A. Theobald. Litho Questa)

1984 (11 June). *Universal Postal Union Congress, Hamburg. As No.* 371 *but inscribed* "UPU CONGRESS HAMBURG" *and with U.P.U. logo.* W w **14** (*sideways*). *P* 13½ × 14.
385 45 v. multicoloured 80 80

119 Charolais

(Des Doreen McGuinness. Litho J.W.)

1984 (24 July). *Cattle. T* **119** *and similar horiz designs. Multicoloured.* W w **14** (*sideways*). *P* 14.
386 15 v. Type **119** 20 25
387 25 v. Charolais-afrikander 35 40
388 45 v. Friesian 65 70
389 75 v. Charolais-brahman .. .. .. 1·10 1·25
386/9 .. .. *Set of* 4 2·10 2·40

120 *Makambo*

(Des L. Dunn. Litho Walsall)

1984 (7 Sept). *"Ausipex" International Stamp Exhibition, Melbourne. T* **120** *and similar horiz designs showing inter-island freighters. Multicoloured. W* w **14** *(sideways). P* 14.

390 25 v. Type **120** 70 50
391 45 v. *Rockton* .. .. 1·10 90
392 100 v. *Waroonga* .. .. 2·00 3·50
390/2 .. .. *Set of* 3 3·50 4·50
MS393 140 × 70 mm. Nos. 390/2 .. .. .. 4·00 5·00

121 Father Christmas in Children's Ward

═ (**122**)

(Des D. Slater. Litho Questa)

1984 (19 Nov). *Christmas. T* **121** *and similar horiz designs. Multicoloured. W* w **14** *(sideways). P* 14.

394 25 v. Type **121** 45 40
395 45 v. Nativity play 80 70
396 75 v. Father Christmas distributing presents 1·40 1·25
394/6 .. .. *Set of* 3 2·40 2·10

1985 (16 Jan). *No. 331 surch with T* **122**.

397 5 v. on 1 v. Type **109** 65 50

123 Ambrym Island Ceremonial Dance

124 Peregrine Falcon diving

(Des D. Slater. Litho Questa)

1985 (22 Jan). *Traditional Costumes. T* **123** *and similar vert designs. Multicoloured. W* w **14**. *P* 14.

398 20 v. Type **123** 30 35
399 25 v. Pentecost Island marriage ceremony .. 35 40
400 45 v. Women's grade ceremony, South West Malakula 65 70
401 75 v. Ceremonial dance, South West Malakula .. .. 1·10 1·25
398/401 .. .. *Set of* 4 2·10 2·40

(Des N. Arlott. Litho Questa)

1985 (26 Mar). *Birth Bicentenary of John J. Audubon (ornithologist). Peregrine Falcon. T* **124** *and similar vert designs. Multicoloured. W* w **14**. *P* 14.

402 20 v. Type **124** 60 35
403 35 v. Peregrine Falcon in flight 75 50
404 45 v. Peregrine Falcon perched on branch 90 80
405 100 v. "Peregrine Falcon" (John J. Audubon) .. .. 1·60 1·75
402/5 .. .. *Set of* 4 3·50 3·00

125 The Queen Mother on her 80th Birthday

126 *Mala* (patrol boat)

(Des A. Theobald (100 v.), C. Abbott (others). Litho Questa)

1985 (7 June). *Life and Times of Queen Elizabeth the Queen Mother. T* **125** *and similar vert designs. Multicoloured. W* w **16**. *P* 14½ × 14.

406 5 v. Duke and Duchess of York on wedding day, 1923 .. .. 10 15
w. Wmk inverted .. .. † —
407 20 v. Type **125** 35 35
408 35 v. At Ancona, Italy 55 55
409 55 v. With Prince Henry at his christening (from photo by Lord Snowdon) .. 85 90
406/9 .. .. *Set of* 4 1·60 1·75
MS410 91×73 mm. 100 v. At Royal Opera House, Covent Garden. Wmk sideways .. 1·40 1·50

(Des A. Theobald. Litho Format)

1985 (26 July). *5th Anniv of Independence and "Expo '85" World Fair, Japan. T* **126** *and similar horiz designs. Multicoloured. W* w **16** *(sideways). P* 14.

411 35 v. Type **126** 45 50
412 45 v. Japanese fishing fleet 65 70
413 55 v. Vanuatu Mobile Force Band 75 85
414 100 v. Prime Minister Fr. Walter H. Lini .. 1·00 1·75
411/14 .. .. *Set of* 4 2·50 3·50
MS415 116×102 mm. Nos. 411/14 .. .. 3·25 4·25

127 "Youth Activities" (Alain Lagaliu)

(Des D. Miller. Litho Questa)

1985 (16 Sept). *International Youth Year. Children's Paintings. T* **127** *and similar horiz designs. Multicoloured. W* w **14** *(sideways*). P* 14.

416 20 v. Type **127** 55 35
w. Wmk Crown to right of CA .. .. 15·00
417 30 v. "Village" (Peter Obed) 65 45
w. Wmk Crown to right of CA .. .. 15·00
418 50 v. "Beach and "PEACE" Slogan" (Mary Estelle) .. .. 1·10 75
w. Wmk Crown to right of CA .. .. 5·00
419 100 v. "Youth Activities" (*different*) (Abel Merani) .. .. 1·75 1·50
w. Wmk Crown to right of CA .. .. 9·00
416/19 .. .. *Set of* 4 3·50 2·75

*The normal sideways watermark shows Crown to left of CA, *as seen from the back of the stamp.*

128 Map of Vanuatu with National and U.N. Flags

129 Elizabeth's Nudibranch (*Chromodoris elisabethina*)

(Des D. Hartley. Litho Questa)

1985 (24 Oct). *4th Anniv of United Nations Membership. W* w **14** *(sideways). P* 14.

420 **128** 45 v. multicoloured 70 70

(Des A. Riley. Litho Questa)

1985 (11 Nov). *Marine Life (1st series). Sea Slugs. T* **129** *and similar multicoloured designs. W* w **14** *(sideways on 35, 55 v.). P* 14½ × 14 *(20, 100 v.) or* 14 × 14½ *(others).*

421 20 v. Type **129** 30 35
422 35 v. Tessellated Nudibranch (*Halgerda aurantiomaculata*) (*horiz*) 45 50
423 55 v. *Chromodoris kuniei* (*horiz*) 75 80
424 100 v. *Notodoris minor* .. .. .. 1·40 1·50
421/4 .. .. *Set of* 4 2·50 2·75

See also Nos. 442/5 and 519/22.

130 Scuba Diving

131 Liner S.S. *President Coolidge* leaving San Francisco

(Des O. Bell. Litho Walsall)

1986 (22 Jan). *Tourism. T* **130** *and similar vert designs. Multicoloured. W* w **16**. *P* 14.

425 30 v. Type **130** 85 40
w. Wmk inverted .. .. 1·00
426 35 v. Yasur volcano, Tanna .. .. .. 1·40 45
w. Wmk inverted .. .. 1·75
427 55 v. Land diving, Pentecost Island .. .. 1·40 70
428 100 v. Windsurfing .. .. 1·50 1·50
425/8 .. .. *Set of* 4 4·50 2·75

For miniature sheet containing Nos. 427/8 with additional Australian Bicentenary symbol see No. **MS**501.

(Des A. Theobald. Litho Format)

1986 (21 Apr). *60th Birthday of Queen Elizabeth II. Vert designs as T* **230a** *of Jamaica. Multicoloured. W* w **16**. *P* 14×14½.

429 20 v. With Prince Charles and Princess Anne, 1951 .. .. 15 30
430 35 v. Prince William's Christening, 1982 .. 20 45
w. Wmk inverted .. .. 8·00
431 45 v. In New Hebrides, 1974 .. .. .. 25 60
432 55 v. On board Royal Yacht *Britannia*, Mexico, 1974 .. .. 30 70
433 100 v. At Crown Agents Head Office, London, 1983 .. .. 40 1·25
429/33 .. .. *Set of* 5 1·10 3·00

(Des L. Curtis. Litho Walsall)

1986 (19 May). *"Ameripex '86" International Stamp Exhibition, Chicago. Sinking of S.S.* President Coolidge. *T* **131** *and similar horiz designs. Multicoloured. W* w **16** *(sideways). P* 14.

434 45 v. Type **131** 85 60
435 55 v. S.S. *President Coolidge* as troopship, 1942 .. .. 95 70
436 135 v. Map of Espiritu Santo showing site of sinking, 1942 .. .. 1·90 1·75
434/6 .. .. *Set of* 3 3·25 2·75
MS437 80×105mm. Nos. 434/6 .. .. .. 4·25 3·00

132 Halley's Comet and Vanuatu Statue

(Des Jennifer Toombs. Litho Questa)

1986 (23 June). *Appearance of Halley's Comet. T* **132** *and similar horiz designs. Multicoloured. W* w **16** *(sideways). P* 14½.

438 30 v. Type **132** 90 50
439 45 v. Family watching Comet .. .. .. 1·25 1·00
440 55 v. Comet passing Earth .. .. .. 1·40 1·25
441 100 v. Edmond Halley .. .. 2·00 3·25
438/41 .. .. *Set of* 4 5·00 5·50

133 Daisy Coral

(Des I. Loe. Litho Walsall)

1986 (27 Oct). *Marine Life (2nd series). Corals. T* **133** *and similar horiz designs. Multicoloured. W* w **16** *(sideways). P* 14.

442 20 v. Type **133** 60 40
443 45 v. Organ Pipe Coral 90 75
444 55 v. Sea Fan .. .. 1·00 1·10
445 135 v. Soft Coral .. .. 2·25 3·50
442/5 .. .. *Set of* 4 4·25 5·25

134 Children of Different Races

135 Datsun "240Z" (1969)

(Des C. Austin. Litho Harrison)

1986 (3 Nov). *Christmas. International Peace Year. T* **134** *and similar horiz designs. Multicoloured. W* w **14** *(sideways). P* 14.

446 30 v. Type **134** 90 50
447 45 v. Church and boy praying .. .. .. 1·25 85
448 55 v. U.N. discussion and Headquarters Building, New York .. .. .. 1·40 1·40
449 135 v. People of different races at work .. 2·75 5·00
446/9 .. .. *Set of* 4 5·75 7·00

(Des J.W. Litho Questa)

1987 (22 Jan). *Motor Vehicles. T* **135** *and similar horiz designs. Multicoloured. W* w **14** *(sideways). P* 14.

450 20 v. Type **135** 30 30
451 45 v. Ford "Model A" (1927) 60 60
452 55 v. Unic lorry (1924–5) 70 70
453 135 v. Citroen "DS19" (1975) .. .. .. 1·60 2·25
450/3 .. .. *Set of* 4 3·00 3·50

(136) **137** Young Coconut Plants

1987 (12 May). *Hurricane Relief Fund. No.* 332, *already surch as T* **122**, *and Nos.* 429/33, *all surch as T* **136**.
454 20 v. + 10 v. on 2 v. *Calanthe triplicata* .. 45 60
455 20 v. + 10 v. Princess Elizabeth with Prince Charles and Princess Anne, 1951 .. 45 60
456 35 v. + 15 v. Prince William's Christening, 1982 .. .. 75 90
457 45 v. + 20 v. Queen in New Hebrides, 1974 90 1·10
458 55 v. + 25 v. Queen on board Royal Yacht *Britannia*, Mexico, 1974 .. .. 1·10 1·50
459 100 v. + 50 v. Queen at Crown Agents Head Office, London, 1983 .. .. .. 1·75 2·75
454/9 .. .. *Set of* 6 4·75 6·75
The surcharge as T **136** on No. 454 includes the word "Surcharge" in addition to the inscription illustrated.

(Des R. Corringe. Litho Format)

1987 (13 May). *25th Anniv of I.R.H.O. Coconut Research Station. T* **137** *and similar horiz designs. Multicoloured. W* w **16** (*sideways*). *P* 14.
460 35 v. Type **137** 40 45
461 45 v. Coconut flower and fronds 55 60
462 100 v. Coconuts .. .. 1·10 1·40
463 135 v. Research Station .. .. .. 1·60 2·00
460/3 .. .. *Set of* 4 3·25 4·00
The inscriptions on Nos. 462/3 are in French.

138 Spotted Hawkfish **139** *Xylotrupes gideon* (beetle)

(Des N.Harvey. Litho Questa)

1987 (15 July). *Fishes. T* **138** *and similar horiz designs. Multicoloured. W* w **16** (*sideways**). *P* 14×14½.
464 1 v. Type **138** 10 10
465 5 v. Moorish Idol 15 10
466 10 v. Black-saddled Pufferfish 15 10
467 15 v. Dusky Anemonefish 20 20
468 20 v. Striped Surgeonfish 30 25
469 30 v. Six-barred Wrasse 40 35
470 35 v. Yellow-striped Anthias ("Purple Queenfish") 45 40
471 40 v. Squirrelfish 50 45
472 45 v. Clown Triggerfish 60 55
473 50 v. Dragon Wrasse 65 65
474 55 v. Regal Angelfish 70 70
475 65 v. Lionfish 80 80
476 100 v. Freckled Hawkfish .. .. .. 1·40 1·40
477 300 v. Undulate Triggerfish .. .. 3·50 4·00
w. Wmk Crown to right of CA .. 50·00
478 500 v. Saddle Butterflyfish .. .. 5·50 6·00
464/78 .. .. *Set of* 15 14·00 14·50
*The normal sideways watermark shows Crown to left of CA, *as seen from the back of the stamp.*

(Des I. Loe. Litho Questa)

1987 (22 Sept). *Insects. T* **139** *and similar horiz designs. Multicoloured. W* w **16** (*sideways*). *P* 14.
479 45 v. Type **139** 55 60
480 55 v. *Phyllodes imperialis* (moth) 65 70
481 65 v. *Cyphogastra* sp (beetle) 75 85
482 100 v. *Othreis fullonia* (moth) .. .. 1·10 1·75
479/82 .. .. *Set of* 4 2·75 3·50

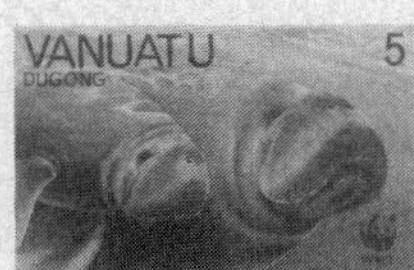

140 Away in a Manger" **141** Dugong Cow and Calf

(Des Josephine Martin. Litho Security Printers (M), Malaysia)

1987 (10 Nov). *Christmas. Christmas Carols. T* **140** *and similar vert designs. Multicoloured. W* w **14**. *P* 13½ × 14.
483 20 v. Type **140** 45 30
484 45 v. "Once in Royal David's City" .. 80 65
485 55 v. "While Shepherds watched their Flocks" 90 90
486 65 v. "We Three Kings of Orient Are" .. 1·00 1·00
483/6 .. .. *Set of* 4 2·75 2·50

1987 (9 Dec). *Royal Ruby Wedding. Nos.* 429/33 *optd with T* **45a** *of Kiribati in silver.*
487 20 v. Princess Elizabeth with Prince Charles and Princess Anne, 1951 .. 30 30
488 35 v. Prince William's Christening, 1982 45 45
w. Wmk inverted .. .. .. 11·00
489 45 v. Queen in New Hebrides, 1974 60 60
490 55 v. Queen on board Royal Yacht *Britannia*, Mexico, 1974 .. .. 70 70
491 100 v. Queen at Crown Agents Head Office, London, 1983 .. .. .. 1·25 1·25
487/91 .. .. *Set of* 5 3·00 3·00

(Des Doreen McGuinness. Litho Walsall)

1988 (29 Feb). *Endangered Species. Dugong. T* **141** *and similar horiz designs. Multicoloured. W* w **16** (*sideways*). *P* 13×13½.
492 5 v. Type **141** 90 35
493 10 v. Dugong underwater .. .. 1·40 35
494 20 v. Two dugongs surfacing to breathe .. 1·90 1·00
495 45 v. Four dugongs swimming .. .. 2·75 2·50
492/5 .. .. *Set of* 4 6·25 3·75

142 *Tambo* **143** Captain James Cook

(Des E. Nisbet. Litho Security Printers (M), Malaysia)

1988 (18 May). *Bicentenary of Australian Settlement. Freighters. T* **142** *and similar horiz designs. Multicoloured. W* w **14** (*sideways**). *P* 12.
496 20 v. Type **142** 20 25
w. Wmk Crown to right of CA .. .. 6·50
497 45 v. *Induna* 50 55
w. Wmk Crown to left of CA .. .. 7·50
498 55 v. *Morinda* 60 65
499 65 v. *Marsina* 70 75
w. Wmk Crown to right of CA .. .. 13·00
496/9 .. .. *Set of* 4 1·75 2·00
*The normal sideways watermark shows Crown to left of CA on the 20 v. and 65 v. and to right of CA on 45 v. and 55 v., *all as seen from the back of the stamp.*

(Des A. Theobald. Litho Format)

1988 (29 July). *"Sydpex '88" National Stamp Exhibition, Sydney. W* w **16**. *P* 14.
500 **143** 45 v. black and rosine 75 75
No. 500 was printed in small sheets of 10 (5 × 2), the two strips separated by a horizontal gutter of five illustrated stamp-size labels. The outer edges of the sheet are imperforate so that the stamps have one or two adjacent sides imperforate.

(Des O. Bell, adapted D. Miller. Litho Walsall)

1988 (24 Aug). *"Expo '88" World Fair, Brisbane. Sheet* 100 × 80 *mm. containing designs as Nos.* 427/8, *but with addition of Australian Bicentenary symbol and imprint date. Multicoloured. W* w **14**. *P* 14.
MS501 55 v. Land diving, Pentecost Island; 100 v. Windsurfing .. .. 2·25 1·90

144 Boxer in training **145** Agricultural Crops

(Des S. Noon. Litho Security Printers (M), Malaysia)

1988 (19 Sept). *Olympic Games, Seoul. T* **144** *and similar vert designs. Multicoloured. W* w **14**. *P* 13½ × 14.
502 20 v. Type **144** 20 25
w. Wmk inverted .. .. .. 3·00
503 45 v. Athletics 50 55
504 55 v. Signing Olympic agreement 60 65
505 65 v. Soccer 70 75
w. Wmk inverted .. .. .. 3·50
502/5 .. .. *Set of* 4 1·75 2·00
MS506 54×66 mm. 150 v. Tennis. P 13½ .. 2·00 2·00

(Des O. Bell and D Miller (55, 65 v.), D. Miller (20, 145 v.). Litho Questa)

1988 (25 Oct). *300th Anniv of Lloyd's of London. Multicoloured designs as T* **167a** *of Malawi. W* w **16** (*sideways on* 55, 65 *v.*). *P* 14.
507 20 v. Interior of new Lloyd's Building, 1988 30 25
508 55 v. *Shirrabank* (freighter) (*horiz*) .. 1·10 65
509 65 v. *Adela* (ferry) (*horiz*) .. .. 1·25 75
510 145 v. *General Slocum* (excursion paddle-steamer) on fire, New York, 1904 .. 2·25 1·75
507/10 .. .. *Set of* 4 4·50 3·00

(Des A. Edmonston. Litho Format)

1988 (14 Nov). *Food and Agriculture Organization. T* **145** *and similar multicoloured designs. W* w **16** (*sideways on* 45, 120 *v.*). *P* 14½ × 14 (*horiz*) *or* 14 × 14½ (*vert*).
511 45 v. Type **145** 45 55
512 55 v. Fisherman with catch (*vert*) 50 65
513 65 v. Livestock on smallholding (*vert*) .. 55 75
514 120 v. Market women with produce .. 80 1·40
511/14 .. .. *Set of* 4 2·10 3·00

146 Virgin and Child ("Silent Night") **147** *Periclimenes brevicarpalis*

(Des Josephine Martin. Litho Format)

1988 (1 Dec). *Christmas. Carols. T* **146** *and similar horiz designs. Multicoloured. W* w **16** (*sideways**). *P* 14½×14.
515 20 v. Type **146** 25 25
516 45 v. Angels ("Angels from the Realms of Glory") 45 55
517 65 v. Shepherd boy with lamb ("O Come all ye Faithful") 55 75
w. Wmk Crown to right of CA .. 2·25
518 155 v. Baby ("In that Poor Stable how Charming Jesus Lies") .. .. 1·50 1·90
w. Wmk Crown to right of CA .. 2·25
515/18 .. .. *Set of* 4 2·50 3·00
*The normal sideways watermark shows Crown to left of CA, *as seen from the back of the stamp.*

(Des A. Riley. Litho Questa)

1989 (1 Feb). *Marine Life (3rd series). Shrimps. T* **147** *and similar horiz designs. Multicoloured. W* w **16** (*sideways*). *P* 14.
519 20 v. Type **147** 40 25
520 45 v. *Lysmata grabhami* 70 55
521 65 v. *Rhynchocinetes* sp 95 75
522 150 v. *Stenopus hispidus* .. .. .. 2·25 2·50
519/22 .. .. *Set of* 4 3·75 3·50

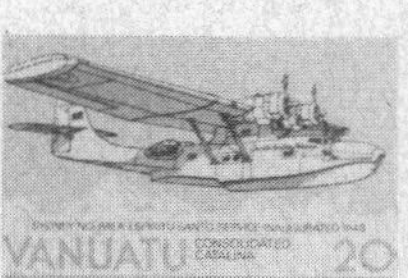

148 Consolidated PBY-5 Catalina Flying Boat **149** Porte de Versailles Hall No. 1

(Des A. Theobald. Litho Security Printers (M), Malaysia)

1989 (5 Apr). *Economic and Social Commission for Asia and the Pacific. Aircraft. T* **148** *and similar horiz designs. W* w **14** (*sideways*). *P* 12.
523 20 v. black and cobalt 75 30
524 45 v. black and turquoise-green .. .. 1·10 65
525 55 v. black and orange-yellow .. .. 1·50 80
526 200 v. black and orange-red .. .. 4·00 3·00
523/6 .. .. *Set of* 4 6·50 4·25
Designs:—45 v. Douglas DC-3; 55 v. Embraer EMB-110 Bandeirante; 200 v. Boeing 737-300.

(Des O. Bell (Nos. 527/8), D. Miller (No. **MS**529). Litho Security Printers, Malaysia (Nos. 527/8), B.D.T. (No. **MS**529))

1989 (5 July). *"Philexfrance '89" International Stamp Exhibition, Paris. T* **149** *and similar horiz designs. W* w **14**. *P* 12.
527 **149** 100 v. multicoloured .. .. 1·90 1·40
a. Horiz pair. Nos. 527/8 .. 3·75 2·75
528 – 100 v. multicoloured (Eiffel Tower) 1·90 1·40
MS529 115×101 mm. 100 v. black, grey and scarlet (Revolt of French troops, Nancy, 1790 (42×28 *mm*)). W w **16** (sideways). P 14 .. 1·40 1·50
Nos. 527/8 were printed together, *se-tenant*, in horizontal pairs throughout the sheet, each pair forming a composite design.

(Des A. Theobald (100 v.), D. Miller (others). Litho Questa)

1989 (20 July). *20th Anniv of First Manned Landing on Moon. Multicoloured designs as T* **51a** *of Kiribati. W* w **16** (*sideways on* 55, 65 *v.*). *P* 14×13½ (45, 120 *v.*) *or* 14 (*others*).
530 45 v. Command module seen from lunar module .. .. 1·00 80
531 55 v. Crew of "Apollo 17" (30×30 *mm*) .. 1·10 90
532 65 v. "Apollo 17" emblem (30×30 *mm*) .. 1·25 1·00
533 120 v. Launch of "Apollo 17" .. .. 2·00 2·00
530/3 .. .. *Set of* 4 4·75 4·25
MS534 99×82 mm. 100 v. Recovery of "Apollo 11". Wmk inverted. P 14×13½ .. .. 1·75 1·75

100 /

(150) **151** New Hebrides 1978 Concorde 30 f. (French inscr) Stamp

1989 (18 Oct). *"Melbourne Stampshow '89". No. 332 surch with T* **150**.
535 100 v. on 2 v. *Calanthe triplicata* . . . . 3·50 4·00

(Des A. Theobald. Litho Leigh-Mardon Ltd, Melbourne)

1989 (6 Nov). *"World Stamp Expo '89", International Stamp Exhibition, Washington. T* **151** *and similar horiz designs. Multicoloured. W w* **16** (*inverted*). *P* 13½.
536 65 v. Type **151** . . . . 2·25 2·25
MS537 105×100 mm. 65 v. New Hebrides 1978 Concorder 10 f. (English inscr) stamp; 100 v. White House, Washington . . . . . . 6·50 7·50

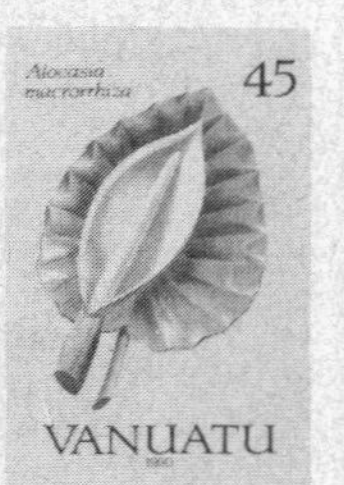

152 *Alocasia macrorrhiza*

153 Kava (National plant)

(Des Jennifer Toombs. Litho Security Printers (M), Malaysia)

1990 (5 Jan). *Flora. T* **152** *and similar vert designs. Multicoloured. W w* **14**. *P* 12.
538 45 v. Type **152** 60 55
539 55 v. *Acacia spirorbis* 70 70
540 65 v. *Metrosideros collina* 80 80
541 145 v. *Hoya australis* . . . . . . 1·75 2·50
538/41 . . . . *Set of* 4 3·50 4·00

(Des O. Bell. Litho Security Printers (M), Malaysia)

1990 (30 Apr). *"Stamp World London 90" International Stamp Exhibition. T* **153** *and similar vert designs. Multicoloured. W w* **14** (*sideways*). *P* 13½.
542 45 v. Type **153** 80 55
543 65 v. Luganville Post Office . . . . 1·00 95
544 100 v. Embraer EMB-110 Bandeirante mail plane and sailing packet . . . . 1·90 2·00
545 200 v. Penny Black and Vanuatu 1980 10 f. definitive . . . . . . 3·00 3·75
542/5 . . . . *Set of* 4 6·00 6·50
MS546 110×70 mm. 150 v. New Hebrides 1974 New Post Office *tête-bêche* pair with first day postmark. Wmk upright . . . . . . 4·00 4·00

154 National Council of Women Logo

(Des D. Ashby. Litho Security Printers (M), Malaysia)

1990 (30 July). *10th Anniv of Independence. T* **154** *and similar horiz designs. W w* **14** (*sideways*). *P* 14×13½.
547 25 v. black and pale blue 35 30
548 50 v. multicoloured 60 70
549 55 v. bright purple, black and buff . . 65 70
550 65 v. multicoloured 70 90
551 80 v. multicoloured . . . . . . 85 1·25
547/51 . . . . *Set of* 5 2·75 3·50
MS552 109×82 mm. 150 v. multicoloured. Wmk upright . . . . 4·00 4·50
Designs:—50 v. President Frederick Kalomuana Timakata; 55 v. Preamble to the Constitution; 65 v. Vanuaaku Pati party flag; 80 v. Reserve Bank of Vanuatu; 150 v. Prime Minister Fr. Walter Lini taking oath.
No. **MS**552 also commemorates the South Pacific Forum, Port Vila, 1990.

155 General De Gaulle at Bayeux, 1944

156 Angel facing Right

(Des G. Vasarhelyi. Litho B.D.T)

1990 (22 Nov). *Birth Centenary of General Charles de Gaulle (French statesman). T* **155** *and similar horiz designs. Multicoloured. W w* **14** (*sideways*). *P* 14.
553 20 v. Type **155** . . . . 1·25 1·50
a. Sheetlet. Nos. 553/4, and 555/8 each × 2 . . . . 8·00
554 25 v. Generals De Lattre de Tassigny, De Gaulle, Devers and Patch in Alsace, 1945 . . . . 1·25 1·50
555 30 v. De Gaulle as President of the French Republic 70 80
556 45 v. De Gaulle at Biggin Hill, 1942 . . 75 85
557 55 v. Roosevelt, De Gaulle and Churchill, Casablanca, 1943 . . . . . . 80 90
558 65 v. General De Gaulle and Liberation of Paris, 1944 . . . . . . 85 95
553/8 . . . . *Set of* 6 5·00 5·50
Nos. 553/8 were printed together, *se-tenant*, in sheetlets of 12 (4×3) containing one each of the 20 c. and 25 c. values and two each of the others plus two labels, showing the Cross of Lorraine, at each end of the centre row.

(Des Jennifer Toombs. Litho Cartor)

1990 (2 Dec). *Christmas. T* **156** *and similar vert designs. Multicoloured. W w* **14** (*sideways*). *P* 13.
559 25 v. Type **156** 45 55
a. Horiz strip of 5. Nos. 559/63 . . . . 3·25
560 50 v. Shepherds 70 90
561 65 v. Nativity . . . . . . 80 1·00
562 70 v. Three Kings . . . . . . 85 1·10
563 80 v. Angel facing left . . . . . . 85 1·25
559/63 . . . . *Set of* 5 3·25 4·25
Nos. 559/63 were printed together, *se-tenant*, in horizontal strips of 5 throughout the sheet, forming a composite design.

157 *Parthenos sylvia*

158 Dance Troupe from South-west Malakula

(Des I. Loe. Litho Questa)

1991 (9 Jan). *Butterflies. T* **157** *and similar horiz designs. Multicoloured. W w* **16**. *P* 14×14½.
564 25 v. Type **157** 45 30
565 55 v. *Euploea leucostictus* 80 60
566 80 v. *Lampides boeticus* . . . . . . 1·25 1·25
567 150 v. *Danaus plexippus* . . . . . . 2·00 2·75
564/7 . . . . *Set of* 4 4·00 4·50
Nos. 564/7 were each printed in sheets of 10 with the two horizontal rows of five being separated by a row of labels illustrating the butterfly's life cycle.

(Des Sue Wickison. Litho Cartor)

1991 (2 May). *Second National Art Festival, Luganville. T* **158** *and similar vert designs. Multicoloured. W w* **14**. *P* 13½×14.
568 25 v. Type **158** 35 30
569 65 v. Women weavers and baskets . . 85 85
570 80 v. Woodcarver and carved animals, masks, dish and ceremonial figures 1·10 1·25
571 150 v. Musicians playing bamboo flute, youtatau and pan pipes . . . . 1·90 2·25
568/71 . . . . *Set of* 4 3·75 4·25

20
═
(**159**)

20
═
(**159a**)

160 White-collared Kingfisher

Type **159**. Surch by Mercury-Walch Pty, Hobart. 2½ mm between "20" and bars. Bars 5½ mm long.
Type **159a**. Surch by Southern Colour Print, Dunedin. 2 mm between "20" and bars. Bars 6½ mm long.

1991 (12 June–3 Dec). *Nos. 332/4 and 337 surch as T* **159** *by Mercury-Walch Pty, Hobart.*
572 20 v. on 2 v. *Calanthe triplicata* 50 50
a. Surch with Type **159a** (3 Dec) . . 85 85
573 60 v. on 10 v. *Dendrobium sladei* . . 1·25 1·60
574 70 v. on 15 v. *Dendrobium mohlianum* . . 1·40 1·75
575 80 v. on 30 v. *Robiquetia mimus* . . 1·40 1·75
572/5 . . . . *Set of* 4 4·00 5·00
See also No. 622.

(Des D. Miller. Litho Questa)

1991 (17 June). *65th Birthday of Queen Elizabeth II and 70th Birthday of Prince Philip. Vert designs as T* **58** *of Kiribati. Multicoloured. W w* **16** (*sideways*). *P* 14½×14.
576 65 v. Queen Elizabeth II . . . . . . 80 1·00
a. Horiz pair. Nos. 576/7 separated by label . . . . 1·60 2·00
577 70 v. Prince Philip . . . . 80 1·00
Nos. 576/7 were printed in a similar sheet format as Nos. 366/7 of Kiribati.

(Des N. Arlott. Litho Questa)

1991 (15 Nov). *"Phila Nippon '91" International Stamp Exhibition, Tokyo. Birds. T* **160** *and similar vert designs. Multicoloured. W w* **14**. *P* 14½×14.
578 50 v. Type **160** 65 70
579 55 v. Palm Lorikeet 70 75
580 80 v. Scarlet Robin . . . . . . 95 1·10
581 100 v. Pacific Swallow . . . . . . 1·10 1·75
578/81 . . . . *Set of* 4 3·25 3·75
MS582 75×56 mm. 150 v. Eastern Reef Heron 2·25 3·00

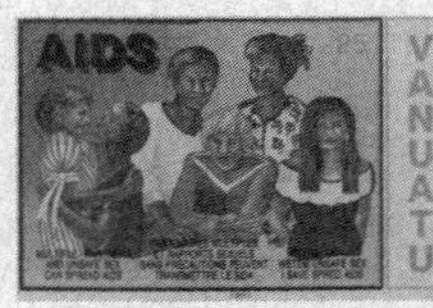

161 Group of Islanders

(Des C. Bulewal and Sue Wickison (80 v.), Sue Wickison (others). Litho Questa)

1991 (29 Nov). *World AIDS Day. T* **161** *and similar horiz designs. Multicoloured. W w* **16** (*sideways*). *P* 14.
583 25 v. Type **161** 45 30
584 65 v. Caring for AIDS victim 90 85
585 80 v. AIDS Shark . . . . 1·10 1·25
586 150 v. Children's playground . . . . 1·75 2·25
583/6 . . . . *Set of* 4 3·75 4·25

(Des D. Miller. Litho Questa (70 v.), Leigh-Mardon Ltd, Melbourne (others))

1992 (6 Feb). *40th Anniv of Queen Elizabeth II's Accession. Horiz designs as T* **113** *of Kenya. Multicoloured. W w* **14** (*sideways*) (70 v.) *or w* **16** (*sideways*) (*others*). *P* 14.

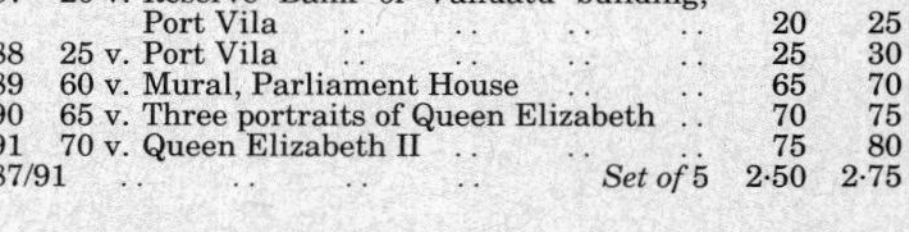

587 20 v. Reserve Bank of Vanuatu building, Port Vila 20 25
588 25 v. Port Vila 25 30
589 60 v. Mural, Parliament House 65 70
590 65 v. Three portraits of Queen Elizabeth . . 70 75
591 70 v. Queen Elizabeth II 75 80
587/91 . . . . *Set of* 5 2·50 2·75

162 Grumman F4F Wildcat

163 Meteorological Station, Port Vila

(Des E. Nisbet, Litho Enschedé)

1992 (22 May). *50th Anniv of Outbreak of the Pacific War (1st issue). T* **162** *and similar horiz designs, Multicoloured. W w* **14** (*sideways*). *P* 13½×14.
592 50 v. Type **162** . . . . 1·25 1·00
593 55 v. Douglas SBD-3 Dauntless . . . . 1·25 1·10
594 65 v. Consolidated PBY-5A Catalina . . 1·50 1·50
595 80 v. U.S.S. *Hornet* (aircraft carrier) . . 2·00 2·00
592/5 . . . . *Set of* 4 5·50 5·00
MS596 94×62 mm. 200 v. Vought-Sikorsky OS-2-3 Kingfisher over Port Vila . . . . 5·50 5·50
See also Nos. 623/7.

(Des Sue Wickison. Litho Leigh-Mardon Ltd, Melbourne)

1992 (24 June). *10th Anniv of Vanuatu's Membership of World Meteorological Organization. T* **163** *and similar horiz designs. Multicoloured. W w* **14**. *P* 14.
597 25 v. Type **163** 40 30
598 60 v. Satellite picture of tropical cyclone . . 80 80
599 80 v. Weather chart of Pacific showing cyclone . . . . 1·00 1·25
600 105 v. Radio Vanuatu broadcasting cyclone warning . . . . 1·25 1·75
597/600 . . . . *Set of* 4 3·00 3·50

164 Vanuatu National Football Team

165 Breast-feeding

(Des S. Noon. Litho Questa)

1992 (20 July). *Vanuatu's Participation in Melanesian Football Cup and Olympic Games, Barcelona. T* **164** *and similar horiz designs. Multicoloured. W w* **14** (*sideways*). *P* 13½×14.
601 20 v. Type **164** 35 35
602 65 v. Melanesian Cup Final, 1990 . . . . 1·00 1·00
603 70 v. Baptiste Firiam (800 metres) . . 1·10 1·10
604 80 v. Mary Estelle Kapalu (400, 400 hurdles and 800 metres) . . . . . . 1·25 1·25
601/4 . . . . *Set of* 4 3·25 3·25

(Des Sue Wickison. Litho B.D.T.)

1992 (16 Oct). *World Food Day. T* **165** *and similar vert designs. Each reddish brown and bronze-green. W w* **16**. *P* 14×13½.

605 20 v. Type **165** 25 25
606 70 v. Central Hospital, Port Vila 85 90
607 80 v. Children eating .. .. .. 95 1·00
608 150 v. Nutritious food .. .. .. 1·60 2·25
605/8 .. .. *Set of* 4 3·25 4·00

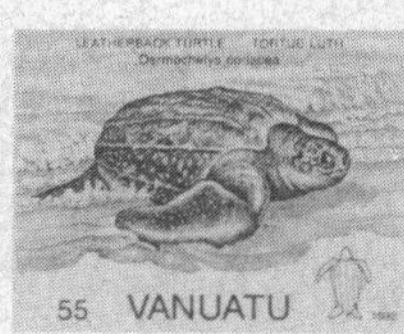

166 Leatherback Turtle

167 *Hibiscus rosa-sinensis* "Agnes Goult"

(Des Sue Wickison. Litho Questa)

1992 (15 Dec). *Turtles. T* **166** *and similar horiz designs. Multicoloured. W w* **16** *(sideways). P* 14×14½.

609 55 v. Type **166** .. .. 1·25 1·10
610 65 v. Loggerhead Turtle laying eggs .. 1·40 1·25
611 70 v. Hawksbill Turtle swimming .. .. 1·60 1·40
612 80 v. Green Turtle under water .. .. 2·25 2·00
609/12 .. .. *Set of* 4 6·00 5·25
MS613 81×96 mm. 200 v. Green Turtle hatchlings on beach. Wmk upright .. .. 3·75 4·25

(Des Jennifer Toombs. Litho Questa)

1993 (3 Mar). *Hibiscus Flowers (1st series). T* **167** *and similar vert designs. Multicoloured. W w* **16**. *P* 14.

614 25 v. Type **167** 30 30
615 55 v. *Hibiscus tiliaceus* 70 70
616 80 v. *Hibiscus rosa-sinensis linnaeus* .. 95 1·00
617 150 v. *Hibiscus rosa-sinensis* "Rose of China" 1·60 2·25
614/17 .. .. *Set of* 4 3·25 3·75

See also Nos. 682/5 and 736/9.

WORLD ORCHID
CONFERENCE 1993

40
══
(168)

20
══
(169)

1993 (2 Apr). *14th World Orchid Conference, Glasgow. Nos.* 339 *and* 341/3 *surch as T* **168**.

618 40 v. on 45 v. *Spathoglottis plicata (horiz)* 50 50
619 55 v. on 75 v. *Dendrobium conanthum (horiz)* 70 75
620 65 v. on 100 v. *Dendrobium macranthum* 75 80
621 150 v. on 200 v. *Coelogyne lamellata* .. 1·60 2·25
618/21 .. .. *Set of* 4 3·25 3·75

1993 (30 Apr*). *No.* 338 *surch with T* **169**.

622 20 v. on 35 v. *Dendrobium mooreanum* .. 3·00 50

*Earliest known date of use.

(Des E. Nisbet. Litho B.D.T.)

1993 (30 June). *50th Anniv of Outbreak of the Pacific War (2nd issue). Horiz designs as T* **162**. *Multicoloured. W w* **14** *(sideways). P* 13½.

623 20 v. Grumman F6F Hellcat 65 45
624 55 v. Lockheed P-38F Lightning .. .. 1·25 90
625 65 v. Grumman TBF Avenger .. .. 1·40 1·25
626 80 v. U.S.S. *Essex* (aircraft carrier) .. 1·75 2·00
623/6 .. .. *Set of* 4 4·50 4·25
MS627 82×58 mm. 200 v. Douglas C-47 Skytrain .. .. 4·50 4·50

170 Port Vila and Iririki Island

171 Commercial Trochus (*Trochus niloticus*)

(Des D. Miller. Litho Leigh-Mardon Ltd, Melbourne)

1993 (7 July). *Local Scenery. T* **170** *and similar multicoloured designs. W w* **14** *(sideways on vert designs). P* 14×14½ *(horiz) or* 14½×14 *(vert)*.

628 5 v. Type **170** 10 10
629 10 v. Yachts and Iririki Island 10 10
630 15 v. Court House, Port Vila 15 20
631 20 v. Two girls, Pentecost Island 20 25
632 25 v. Women dancers, Tanna Island .. 25 30
633 30 v. Market, Port Vila 30 35
634 45 v. Man in canoe, Erakor Island (*vert*) .. 50 55
635 50 v. Coconut trees, Champagne Beach .. 55 60
636 55 v. Coconut trees, North Efate Islands 60 65
637 60 v. Underwater shoal of fishes, Banks Group 65 70
638 70 v. Sea Fan, Tongoa Island (*vert*) .. 75 80
639 75 v. Santo Island 80 85
640 80 v. Sunset, Port Vila harbour (*vert*) .. 85 90
641 100 v. Mele Waterfall (*vert*) .. .. 1·10 1·25
642 300 v. Yasur Volcano, Tanna Island (*vert*) 3·25 3·50
643 500 v. Aerial view of Erakor Island .. 5·50 5·75
628/43 .. .. *Set of* 16 15·00 16·00

For miniature sheet containing Nos. 629, 636/7 and 639 see No. **MS**673.

(Des Sue Wickison. Litho Walsall)

1993 (15 Sept). *Shells (1st series). T* **171** *and similar vert designs. Multicoloured. W w* **14**. *P* 14½.

644 55 v. Type **171** .. .. 1·00 85
645 65 v. Camp Pitar Venus (*Lioconcha castrensis*) .. .. 1·10 95
646 80 v. Tapestry Turban (*Turbo petholatus*) 1·40 1·40
647 150 v. Trapezium Horse Conch (*Fasciolaria trapezium*) .. .. 2·25 2·75
644/7 .. .. *Set of* 4 5·25 5·50

See also Nos. 665/8 and 692/5.

172 "St. Joseph the Carpenter" (detail) (De La Tour)

(Des D. Miller. Litho B.D.T.)

1993 (10 Nov). *Christmas. Bicentenary of the Louvre, Paris. Religious Paintings by Georges de la Tour. T* **172** *and similar horiz designs. Multicoloured. W w* **14** *(sideways). P* 14.

648 25 v. Type **172** 35 30
649 55 v. "Holy Child" (detail) 70 65
650 80 v. "Adoration of the Shepherds" (detail) 90 1·00
651 150 v. "Adoration of the Shepherds" (different detail) .. .. .. 1·60 2·25
648/51 .. .. *Set of* 4 3·25 3·75

SOUTH PACIFIC MINI GAMES
PORT VILA DECEMBER 1993
15/

(173)

174 Charity Horse Race and Kiwanis Emblem

1993 (6 Dec). *South Pacific Mini Games, Port Vila. Nos.* 602, 604, 631 *and* 633 *surch as T* **173**.

652 15 v. on 20 v. Two girls, Pentecost Island .. 25 25
653 25 v. on 30 v. Market, Port Vila 35 35
654 55 v. on 65 v. Melanesian Cup Final, 1990 75 75
655 70 v. on 80 v. Mary Estelle Kapalu (400, 400 hurdles and 800 metres) .. .. 80 1·10
652/5 .. .. *Set of* 4 1·90 2·25

(Des E. Nisbet. Litho B.D.T.)

1994 (18 Feb). *"Hong Kong '94" International Stamp Exhibition. Charitable Organizations. T* **174** *and similar multicoloured designs. W w* **14** *(sideways on horiz designs). P* 14×15 *(vert) or* 15×14 *(horiz)*.

656 25 v. Type **174** 35 30
657 60 v. Twin Otter airplane and Lions Club emblem (*horiz*) 70 75
658 75 v. Mosquito and Rotary International emblem .. .. 90 1·00
659 150 v. Blood donor service ambulance and Red Cross emblem (*horiz*) .. .. 1·60 2·25
656/9 .. .. *Set of* 4 3·25 3·75
MS660 126×96 mm. 200 v. Charity emblems (*horiz*) .. .. 2·40 3·00

175 Silhouetted Family

176 Traditional Sculpture and Hut

(Des Sue Wickison. Litho Questa)

1994 (2 Mar). *International Year of the Family. W w* **14**. *P* 14.

661 **175** 25 v. purple-brown and bluish violet .. 35 30
662 60 v. myrtle-green and vermilion .. 70 75
663 90 v. deep brown and emerald .. 1·00 1·10
664 150 v. bluish violet and yellow-brown .. 1·60 2·00
661/4 .. .. *Set of* 4 3·25 3·75

(Des Sue Wickison. Litho Southern Colour Print, Dunedin)

1994 (31 May). *Shells (2nd series). Vert designs as T* **171**. *Multicoloured. P* 12.

665 60 v. Eyed Cowrie (*Cypraea argus*) .. 1·25 1·00
666 70 v. Marble Cone (*Conus marmoreus*) .. 1·25 1·10
667 85 v. Chiragra Spider Conch (*Lambis chiragra*) .. .. 1·40 1·40
668 155 v. Adusta Murex (*Murex brunneus*) .. 2·25 2·75
665/8 .. .. *Set of* 4 5·50 5·50

(Des C. Abbott. Litho Southern Colour Print, Dunedin)

1994 (27 July). *Tourism. T* **176** *and similar vert designs. Multicoloured. P* 13½.

669 25 v. Type **176** 70 80
a. Horiz strip of 4. Nos. 669/72 .. 6·00
670 75 v. Outrigger canoe and inflatable dinghy 1·40 1·50
671 90 v. Yachts, airliner and parrot .. .. 1·75 1·90
672 200 v. Helicopter and local woman with fruit 2·75 3·00
669/72 .. .. *Set of* 4 6·00 6·50

Nos. 669/72 were printed together, *se-tenant*, in horizontal strips of 4 forming a composite design.

(Des D. Miller. Litho Leigh-Mardon Ltd, Melbourne)

1994 (10 Aug). *"Philakorea '94" International Stamp Exhibition. Sheet* 130×68 *mm, containing Nos.* 629, 636/7 *and* 639. *Multicoloured. P* 14×14½.

MS673 10 v. Yachts and Iririki Island; 55 v. Coconut trees, North Efate Islands; 60 v. Underwater shoal of fishes, Banks Group; 75 v. Santo Island .. .. 2·75 3·50

177 Pink Anemonefish

178 Consolidated PBY-5 Catalina Flying Boat

(Des Sue Wickison. Litho Southern Colour Print, Dunedin)

1994 (16 Aug). *Anemonefish. T* **177** *and similar horiz designs. Multicoloured. P* 12.

674 55 v. Type **177** 90 80
675 70 v. Yellow-tailed Anemonefish .. .. 1·25 1·00
676 80 v. Fire Anemonefish .. .. .. 1·40 1·40
677 140 v. Orange-finned Anemonefish .. 2·50 3·00
674/7 .. .. *Set of* 4 5·50 5·50
MS678 80×60 mm. No. 677 .. .. .. 2·50 3·00

No. **MS**678 shows the "Philakorea '94" International Stamp Exhibition logo on the sheet margin.

(Des C. Abbott. Litho Southern Colour Print, Dunedin)

1994 (7 Dec). *50th Anniv of International Civil Aviation Organization. T* **178** *and similar horiz designs. Multicoloured. P* 12.

679 25 v. Type **178** 65 45
680 60 v. Douglas DC-3 .. .. .. 1·10 90
681 75 v. De Havilland D.H.A.3 Drover .. 1·25 1·40
682 90 v. Boeing 737 on runway .. .. 1·50 2·00
679/82 .. .. *Set of* 4 4·00 4·25

179 *Hibiscus rosa-sinensis* "The Path"

180 *Emoia nigromarginata*

(Des Patricia Altman. Litho Southern Colour Print, Dunedin)

1995 (1 Feb). *Hibiscus Flowers (2nd issue). T* **179** *and similar horiz designs. Multicoloured. P* 12.

683 25 v. Type **179** 60 45
684 60 v. *Hibiscus rosa-sinensis* "Old Frankie" 1·10 1·00
685 90 v. *Hibiscus sinensis* "Fijian White" .. 1·60 1·75
686 200 v. *Hibiscus rosa-sinensis* "Surfrider" .. 3·25 3·75
683/6 .. .. *Set of* 4 6·00 6·25

(Des Sue Wickison. Litho Southern Colour Print, Dunedin)

1995 (12 Apr). *Lizards. T* **180** *and similar horiz designs. Multicoloured. P* 12.

687 25 v. Type **180** 50 45
688 55 v. *Nactus multicarinatus* .. .. 1·00 1·00
689 70 v. *Lepidodactylus* .. .. .. 1·25 1·25
690 80 v. *Emoia caeruleocauda* .. .. 1·40 1·40
691 140 v. *Emoia sanfordi* .. .. .. 2·25 2·75
687/91 .. .. *Set of* 5 5·75 6·25

(Des Sue Wickison. Litho Southern Colour Print, Dunedin)

1995 (1 June). *Shells (3rd series). Vert designs as T* **171**. *Multicoloured. P* 12.

692 25 v. *Epitonium scalare* 60 50
693 55 v. *Strombus latissimus* .. .. 1·25 1·25
694 90 v. *Conus bullatus* .. .. .. 1·75 1·75
695 200 v. *Pteryonotus pinnatus* .. .. 3·50 4·00
692/5 .. .. *Set of* 4 6·25 6·75

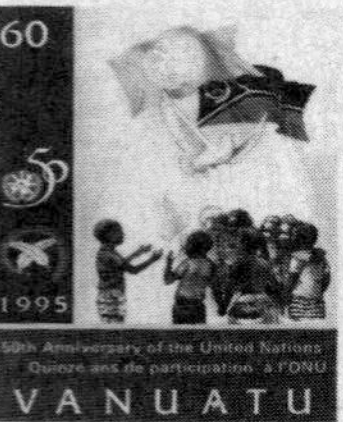

181 "Tanna Girls" (A. Toni) **182** Children with Doves and Flags

(Des Red Cactus Design Ltd. Litho Enschedé)

1995 (28 July). *15th Anniv of Independence. T* **181** *and similar multicoloured designs. P* 14×13½ *(horiz) or* 13½×14 *(vert).*
696 25 v. Type **181** 45 40
697 55 v. "Black Coral Dancers" (sculpture, E. Watt) *(vert)* 90 90
698 75 v. Erromango tapestry by Juliet Peta *(vert)* .. .. 1·25 1·25
699 90 v. "Parade Day" (H. Di-Donna) .. 1·40 1·60
700 140 v. "Banks Dancers" (J. John) .. .. 2·00 2·75
696/700 .. .. *Set of* 5 5·50 6·25
MS701 100×75 mm. No. 699 .. .. .. 2·25 2·50
No. **MS**701 also includes the "Singapore '95" International Stamp Exhibition logo on the sheet margin.

(Des G. Vasarhelyi, adapted Red Cactus Design Ltd. Litho Enschedé)

1995 (28 July). *50th Anniv of United Nations. P* 13½×14.
702 **182** 60 v. multicoloured .. .. .. 1·25 1·00

(Des E. Nisbet (Nos. 703/6), G. Vasarhelyi (No. **MS**707). Litho Enschedé)

1995 (1 Sept). *50th Anniv of End of Second World War in the Pacific. Horiz designs as T* **162** *showing aircraft. Multicoloured. P* 12½.
703 60 v. Curtiss SB2C Helldiver .. .. 1·25 1·00
704 70 v. Supermarine Spitfire Mk VIII .. 1·40 1·10
705 75 v. Chance Vought F4U-1A Corsair .. 1·50 1·40
706 80 v. Lockheed PV-1 Ventura .. .. 1·50 1·40
703/6 .. .. *Set of* 4 5·00 4·50
MS707 94×68 mm. 140 v. Japanese delegation at signing of Unconditional Surrender, Tokyo Bay. P 13½×14 .. .. 2·50 3·00
No. **MS**707 also includes the "Singapore '95" International Stamp Exhibition logo on the sheet margin.

183 Rambaramp (effigy), Malakula **184** Boy throwing Cast Net

(Des C. Abbott. Litho Enschedé)

1995 (22 Nov). *Opening of New National Museum. Artefacts. T* **183** *and similar vert designs. Multicoloured. P* 13½×13.
708 25 v. Type **183** 35 30
a. Horiz strip of 4. Nos. 708/11 .. .. 3·00
709 60 v. Pot from Wusi, Espiritu Santo .. 75 70
710 75 v. Slit gong from Mele, Efate 90 90
711 90 v. Tapa cloth, Erromango .. .. 1·25 1·40
708/11 .. .. *Set of* 4 3·00 3·00
In addition to separate sheets of 50, Nos. 708/11 were also available in sheets of 48 with the stamps *se-tenant* horizontally.

(Des R. Youmans. Litho Questa)

1996 (1 Feb). *Fishing. T* **184** *and similar multicoloured designs. P* 14.
712 55 v. Type **184** 70 65
713 75 v. Fishing canoes 90 85
714 80 v. *Etelis* (fishing boat) and deep water fish *(vert)* 95 95
715 140 v. Game fisherman catching sailfish *(vert)* .. .. 2·00 2·25
712/15 .. .. *Set of* 4 4·00 4·25

185 *Pteropus anetianus* **186** Immunization Programme

(Des Sue Wickison. Litho Southern Colour Print, Dunedin)

1996 (3 Apr). *Endangered Species. Flying Foxes. T* **185** *and similar multicoloured designs. P* 14.
716 25 v. Type **185** 40 40
717 25 v. *Notopteris macdonaldi* upside down eating fruit *(horiz)* 40 40
718 25 v. *Pteropus anetianus* hanging on branch 40 40
719 25 v. *Notopteris macdonaldi* on branch *(horiz)* 40 40
716/19 .. .. *Set of* 4 1·40 1·40

(Des C. Abbott (No. **MS**720), Sue Wickison (No. **MS**721). Litho Southern Colour Print, Dunedin)

1996 (18 May). *"CHINA '96" 9th Asian International Stamp Exhibition, Peking. P* 14.
MS720 75×85 mm. No. 711 .. .. .. 1·25 1·40
MS721 75×85 mm. 90 v. *Pteropus tonganus* (flying fox); 140 v. *Pteropus tonganus (different)* 3·25 3·50

(Des Karen Odiam. Litho Questa)

1996 (5 June). *50th Anniv of U.N.I.C.E.F. T* **186** *and similar horiz design. Multicoloured. P* 14.
722 55 v. Type **186** 90 90
723 60 v. Breast-feeding programme 90 90

187 Airliner and Radio Waves

(Des C. Abbott. Litho Questa)

1996 (5 June). *Centenary of Radio. T* **187** *and similar horiz designs. Multicoloured. P* 14½.
724 60 v. Type **187** 75 80
a. Block of 4. Nos. 724/7 .. .. 3·25
725 75 v. Radio Vanuatu broadcaster 90 95
726 80 v. Guglielmo Marconi .. .. .. 95 1·00
727 90 v. Cruise liner and radio waves .. 1·00 1·10
724/7 .. .. *Set of* 4 3·25 3·50
In addition to separate sheets of 50, Nos. 724/7 were also available in sheets of 48 with the stamps in *se-tenant* blocks of 4, forming a composite aerial view of Port Vila.

188 Marie Kapalu, Tawai Keiruan, Baptiste Firiam and Tava Kalo

(Des S. Coburn. Litho Southern Colour Print, Dunedin)

1996 (17 July). *Centenary of Modern Olympics Games. T* **188** *and similar horiz designs. Multicoloured. P* 14.
728 25 v. Type **188** 35 30
a. Horiz strip of 4. Nos. 728/31 .. .. 4·50
729 70 v. Athletes training 95 95
730 75 v. Athletes from 1950s .. .. 1·00 1·00
731 200 v. Athletes in 1896 .. .. .. 2·75 3·00
728/31 .. .. *Set of* 4 4·50 4·75
In addition to separate sheets of 50, Nos. 728/31 were also available in sheets of 48 with the stamps *se-tenant* horizontally.

189 Children in Front of Presbyterian Church and Roman Catholic Cathedral **190** *Hibiscus rosa-sinensis* "Lady Cilento"

(Des Josephine Martin. Litho Southern Colour Print, Dunedin)

1996 (11 Sept). *Christmas. Religious Buildings. T* **189** *and similar vert designs. Multicoloured. P* 14.
732 25 v. Type **189** 35 30
a. Horiz strip of 4. Nos. 732/5 .. .. 3·00
733 60 v. Children and Church of Christ .. 80 80
734 75 v. Children and Seventh Day Adventist and Apostolic churches 95 95
735 90 v. Children and Anglican church .. 1·25 1·40
732/5 .. .. *Set of* 4 3·00 3·00
In addition to separate sheets of 50, Nos. 732/5 were also available in sheets of 48 with the stamps *se-tenant* horizontally.

(Des Sue Wickison. Litho Walsall)

1996 (13 Nov). *Hibiscus Flowers (3rd issue). T* **190** *and similar horiz designs. Multicoloured. P* 13½.
736 25 v. Type **190** 40 30
737 60 v. *Hibiscus rosa-sinensis* "Kinchen's Yellow" 90 70
738 90 v. *Hibiscus rosa-sinensis* "D. J. O'Brien" 1·25 1·25
739 200 v. *Hibiscus rosa-sinensis* "Cuban Variety" .. .. 3·00 3·25
736/9 .. .. *Set of* 4 5·00 5·00
For miniature sheet containing Nos. 736 and 739 see No. **MS**745.

191 Coral Garden

(Des G. Ryan. Litho Questa)

1997 (15 Jan). *Diving. T* **191** *and similar horiz designs. Multicoloured. P* 14½×14.
740 70 v. Type **191** 90 80
741 75 v. Carving on the *President Coolidge* .. 95 85
742 90 v. "Boris" (Giant Grouper) .. .. 1·25 1·25
743 140 v. Wreck of the *President Coolidge* .. 2·25 2·50
740/3 .. .. *Set of* 4 4·75 4·75
MS744 124×75 mm. Nos. 740/3 .. .. 4·75 5·00
For further miniature sheet containing Nos. 741 and 743 see No. **MS**750.

(Des Sue Wickison. Litho Walsall)

1997 (12 Feb). *"HONG KONG '97" International Stamp Exhibition. Sheet, 100×85 mm, containing Nos. 736 and 739. Multicoloured. P* 13½.
MS745 25 v. Type **190**; 200 v. *Hibiscus rosa-sinensis* "Cuban Variety" .. .. .. 2·40 2·50

192 View from Cockpit

(Des C. Abbott. Litho Enschedé)

1997 (2 Apr). *10th Anniv of Air Vanuatu. T* **192** *and similar horiz designs. Multicoloured. P* 15×14.
746 25 v. Type **192** 25 30
747 60 v. 737-400 airliner being serviced, Bauerfield International Airport, Port Vila *(81×31 mm)* 65 70
748 90 v. Air stewardess serving drinks .. 95 1·00
749 200 v. Passengers disembarking .. .. 2·10 2·40
746/9 .. .. *Set of* 4 4·00 4·50

(Des G. Ryan. Litho Questa)

1997 (29 May). *"Pacific '97" International Philatelic Exhibition, San Francisco. Sheet, 100×86 mm, containing Nos. 741 and 743. Multicoloured. P* 14½×14.
MS750 75 v. Carving on the *President Coolidge*; 140 v. Wreck of the *President Coolidge* .. 2·40 2·50

193 Sharp-tailed Sandpiper

(Des P. Martinson. Litho Enschedé)

1997 (4 June). *Birds (1st issue). Coastal Birds. T* **193** *and similar multicoloured designs. P* 13½×14 *(horiz) or* 14×13½ *(vert).*
751 25 v. Type **193** 25 30
752 55 v. Crested Tern 60 65
753 60 v. Little Pied Cormorant 65 70
754 75 v. Brown Booby 80 85
755 80 v. Reef Heron *(vert)* 85 90
756 90 v. Red-tailed Tropic Bird *(vert)* .. 1·00 1·10
751/6 .. .. *Set of* 6 4·25 4·50

NEW INFORMATION

194 Thomas Edison and Light Bulb

195 Yellow-faced Angelfish

(Des C. Abbott. Litho Southern Colour Print, Dunedin)

1997 (27 Aug). *150th Birth Anniv of Thomas Edison (inventor). T* **194** *and similar horiz designs. Multicoloured. P* 12.

757 60 v. Type **194** 65 70
a. Horiz pair. Nos. 757/8 .. .. 1·40
758 70 v. Hydro-electric dam, Espiritu Santo 75 80
759 200 v. Port Vila at dusk (80×29 *mm*) .. 2·10 2·25
757/9 .. .. *Set of* 3 3·50 3·75

Nos. 757/9 were printed together, *se-tenant*, in blocks of 3 showing the two smaller designs separated from the 200 v. by an inscribed gutter. Each sheet contained six such blocks.

(Des Sue Wickison. Litho Questa)

1997 (12 Nov). *Angelfish. T* **195** *and similar vert designs. Multicoloured. P* 14×13½.

760 25 v. Type **195** 25 30
761 55 v. Flame Angelfish 60 65
762 60 v. Lemonpeel Angelfish 65 70
763 70 v. Emperor Angelfish 75 80
764 140 v. Multi-barred Angelfish .. .. 1·50 1·60
760/4 .. .. *Set of* 5 3·75 4·00

197 Fale, Espiritu Santo

(Des C. Abbott. Litho Southern Colour Print, Dunedin)

1998 (12 Feb). *Local Architecture. T* **197** *and similar square designs. Multicoloured. P* 14½.

766 30 v. Type **197** 30 35
767 65 v. National Cultural Centre 70 75
768 80 v. University of South Pacific 85 90
769 150 v. Chiefs' Nakamal .. .. .. 1·60 1·75
766/9 .. .. *Set of* 4 3·50 3·75

(Des D. Miller. Litho Questa)

1998 (31 Mar). *Diana, Princess of Wales Commemoration. Vert designs as T* **91** *of Kiribati. Multicoloured. P* 14½×14.

770 95 v. Wearing black jacket, 1997 .. .. 1·00 1·10
MS771 145×70 mm. 75 v. Wearing green jacket, 1987; 85 v. Wearing cream jacket and hat, 1991; 95 v. No. 769; 145 v. Wearing red dress, 1992 (*sold at* 400 v. + 50 v. *charity premium*) .. 4·75 5·00

STAMP BOOKLETS

1980 (July). *Multicoloured cover,* 110×75 *mm, showing Vanuatu flag. Stamps attached by selvedge. E. Stamps inscr in English. F. Stamps inscr in French.*

E F
SB2 200 f. As No. SB1, but containing Nos. 287/90, each in block of 4 .. .. 3·75 3·75

1982 (15 June). *Multicoloured cover,* 92×74 *mm, showing orchid. Stamps attached by selvedge.*

SB3 230 v. booklet containing 20 v. (No. 335) in block of 4, and 10 v. and 15 v. (Nos. 333/4) in blocks of 6 .. .. 3·75

1987 (15 July). *Multicoloured cover,* 90×85 *mm, showing diver and coral reef. Stamps attached by selvedge.*

SB4 360 v. booklet containing 5 v., 10 v., 35 v. and 40 v. (Nos. 465/6, 470/1), each in block of 4 .. 4·00

1993 (7 July). *Local Scenery. Multicoloured cover,* 90×85 *mm, showing view of Champagne Beach. Stamps attached by selvedge.*

SB5 440 v. booklet containing 5 v., 10 v., 45 v. and 50 v. (Nos. 628/9, 634/5), each in block of 4 .. 4·75

Victoria
see Australia

Victoria *see* Australia

Virgin Islands
see British Virgin Islands

Western Australia
see Australia

Western Samoa
see Samoa

Zambia
(*formerly* Northern Rhodesia)

NORTHERN RHODESIA

The north-eastern and north-western provinces of Rhodesia, previously administered by the British South Africa Company, became a Crown Colony on 1 April 1924.

The current stamps of Rhodesia (the "Admiral design" first issued in 1913) remained in use until 31 March 1925 and continued to be valid for postal purposes until 30 September of that year.

PRICES FOR STAMPS ON COVER TO 1945

Nos. 1/21	*from* × 2
Nos. 22/4	*from* × 5
Nos. 25/45	*from* × 2
Nos. D1/4	*from* × 15

1

2

(Eng W. G. Fairweather. Recess Waterlow)

1925 (1 April)–**29.** *Wmk Mult Script CA. P* 12½.

No.	Type	Description	Unused	Used
1	1	½d. green	90	60
2		1d. brown	1·00	10
3		1½d. carmine-red	60	30
4		2d. yellow-brown	1·75	10
5		3d. ultramarine	1·75	90
6		4d. violet	2·50	50
7		6d. slate-grey	2·50	40
8		8d. rose-purple	3·75	32·00
9		10d. olive-green	3·75	32·00
10	2	1s. yellow-brown and black	2·50	1·25
11		2s. brown and ultramarine	12·00	18·00
12		2s. 6d. black and green	13·00	5·00
13		3s. violet and blue (1929)	22·00	12·00
14		5s. slate-grey and violet	25·00	15·00
15		7s. 6d. rose-purple and black	85·00	£130
16		10s. green and black	55·00	60·00
17		20s. carmine-red and rose-purple	£140	£160
1/17		*Set of* 17	£325	£425
1/17 Optd/Perf "Specimen"		*Set of* 17	£750	

A used example of the 4d. exists imperforate between the stamp and a fragment of another below it.

1935 (6 May). *Silver Jubilee. As Nos.* 114/17 *of Jamaica, but ptd by D.L.R. P* 13½×14.

No.	Description	Unused	Used
18	1d. light blue and olive-green	50	90
	f. Diagonal line by turret	35·00	
	h. Dot by flagstaff	55·00	
	i. Dash by turret	55·00	
19	2d. green and indigo	50	80
	f. Diagonal line by turret	45·00	
	g. Dot to left of chapel	70·00	
20	3d. brown and deep blue	2·50	4·25
	f. Diagonal line by turret	80·00	
	g. Dot to left of chapel	£120	
21	6d. slate and purple	2·00	1·25
	a. Frame printed double, one albino	£1600	
	h. Dot by flagstaff	£120	
18/21	*Set of* 4	5·00	6·50
18/21 Perf "Specimen"	*Set of* 4	85·00	

For illustrations of plate varieties see Omnibus section following Zimbabwe.

THERN_RHODE

Hyphen between "NORTHERN" AND "RHODESIA" (R. 9/6)

1937 (12 May). *Coronation. As Nos.* 118/20 *of Jamaica, but ptd by B.W. P* 11×11½.

No.	Description	Unused	Used
22	1½d. carmine	40	35
23	2d. buff	55	35
24	3d. blue	80	1·75
	a. Hyphen flaw	£130	
22/4	*Set of* 3	1·60	2·25
22/4 Perf "Specimen"	*Set of* 3	65·00	

3

4

"Tick bird" flaw (R. 7/1 of ptgs from Sept 1938 onwards)

(Recess Waterlow)

1938 (1 Mar)–**52.** *Wmk Mult Script CA. P* 12½.

No.	Type	Description	Unused	Used
25	3	½d. green	10	10
		a. "C" of "CA" missing from wmk		
26		½d. chocolate (15.11.51)	10	70
		a. Perf 12½×14 (22.10.52)	1·40	4·50
27		1d. brown	10	10
		a. *Chocolate* (1948)	1·60	60
28		1d. green (15.11.51)	60	90
29		1½d. carmine-red	45·00	30
		a. Imperf between (horiz pair)	£11000	
		b. "Tick bird" flaw	£1700	£150
30		1½d. yellow-brown (10.1.41)	30	10
		b. "Tick bird" flaw	48·00	22·00
31		2d. yellow-brown	60·00	95
32		2d. carmine-red (10.1.41)	30	20
33		2d. purple (1.12.51)	45	75
34		3d. ultramarine	30	10
35		3d. scarlet (1.12.51)	50	1·50
36		4d. dull violet	30	40
37		4½d. blue (5.5.52)	40	4·00
38		6d. grey	30	10
39		9d. violet (5.5.52)	40	2·00
40	4	1s. yellow-brown and black	2·00	40
41		2s. 6d. black and green	7·00	1·75
42		3s. violet and blue	13·00	4·00
43		5s. grey and dull violet	9·00	5·00
44		10s. green and black	12·00	12·00
45		20s. carmine-red and rose-purple	38·00	45·00
25/45		*Set of* 21	£170	70·00
25/45 Perf "Specimen"		*Set of* 15	£275	

Nos. 26a and 28 exist in coils, constructed from normal sheets.

1946 (26 Nov). *Victory. As Nos.* 141/2 *of Jamaica. P* 13½×14.

No.	Description	Unused	Used
46	1½d. red-orange	10	10
	a. Perf 14×13½	9·50	10·00
47	2d. carmine	10	30
46/7 Perf "Specimen"	*Set of* 2	50·00	

1948 (1 Dec). *Royal Silver Wedding. As Nos.* 143/4 *of Jamaica, but 20s. ptd in recess.*

No.	Description	Unused	Used
48	1½d. orange	30	10
49	20s. brown-lake	40·00	45·00

1949 (10 Oct). *75th Anniv of U.P.U. As Nos.* 145/8 *of Jamaica.*

No.	Description	Unused	Used
50	2d. carmine	30	30
51	3d. deep blue	1·90	1·25
52	6d. grey	1·00	1·25
53	1s. red-orange	1·00	1·00
50/3	*Set of* 4	3·75	3·50

5 Cecil Rhodes and Victoria Falls

(Recess D.L.R.)

1953 (30 May). *Birth Centenary of Cecil Rhodes. Wmk Mult Script CA. P* 12 × 11½.

No.	Type	Description	Unused	Used
54	5	½d. brown	50	50
55		1d. green	40	40
56		2d. mauve	40	15
57		4½d. blue	40	3·25
58		1s. orange and black	75	4·00
54/8		*Set of* 5	2·25	7·50

6 Arms of the Rhodesias and Nyasaland

(Recess Waterlow)

1953 (30 May). *Rhodes Centenary Exhibition. Wmk Mult Script CA. P* 14 × 13½.

No.	Type	Description	Unused	Used
59	6	6d. violet	40	60

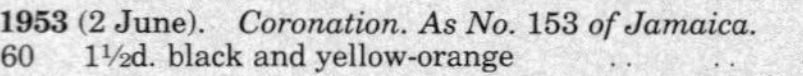

1953 (2 June). *Coronation. As No.* 153 *of Jamaica.*

No.	Description	Unused	Used
60	1½d. black and yellow-orange	30	10

7

8

(Recess Waterlow)

1953 (15 Sept). *Wmk Mult Script CA. P* 12½ × 14 (*pence values*) *or* 12½ × 13½ (*shilling values*).

No.	Type	Description	Unused	Used
61	7	½d. deep brown	65	10
62		1d. bluish green	65	10
63		1½d. orange-brown	80	10
64		2d. reddish purple	75	10
65		3d. scarlet	60	10
66		4d. slate-lilac	1·25	1·25
67		4½d. deep blue	90	3·25
68		6d. grey-black	1·25	10
		w. Wmk inverted	£900	£500
69		9d. violet	60	3·25
70	8	1s. orange-brown and black	60	10
71		2s. 6d. black and green	6·50	2·75
72		5s. grey and dull purple	6·50	12·00
73		10s. green and black	6·00	22·00
74		20s. rose-red and rose-purple	20·00	25·00
61/74		*Set of* 14	40·00	60·00

For issues from 1954 to 1963, see RHODESIA AND NYASALAND.

9 Arms 10

(Photo Harrison)

1963 (10 Dec). *Arms black, orange and blue; portrait and inscriptions black; background colours below. P* 14½ (*T* **9**) *or* 13½ × 13 (*T* **10**).

No.	Type	Description	Unused	Used
75	9	½d. bright violet	40	60
		a. Value omitted	£650	
76		1d. light blue	60	10
		a. Value omitted	11·00	
77		2d. brown	30	10
78		3d. yellow	20	10
		a. Value omitted	75·00	
		b. Value and orange (eagle) omitted	£140	
		c. Eagle printed double	£2000	
		d. Orange (eagle) omitted	£1000	
79		4d. green	30	20
		a. Value omitted	90·00	
80		6d. light olive-green	30	10
		a. Value omitted	£450	
81		9d. yellow-brown	30	80
		a. Value omitted	£375	
		b. Value and orange (eagle) omitted	£275	
82		1s. slate-purple	30	10
83		1s. 3d. bright purple	1·25	10
84	10	2s. orange	1·00	2·00
85		2s. 6d. lake-brown	1·00	90
86		5s. magenta	4·50	4·50
		a. Value omitted	£1400	
87		10s. mauve	4·00	10·00
88		20s. blue	5·00	14·00
		a. Value omitted	£850	
75/88		*Set of* 14	17·00	30·00

Nos. 75/6 exist in coils, constructed from normal sheets.

The stamps of Northern Rhodesia were withdrawn on 23 October 1964 when the territory attained independence as the Republic of Zambia.

ZAMBIA

INDEPENDENT

11 Pres. Kaunda and Victoria Falls

12 College of Further Education, Lusaka

(Des M. Goaman (3d., 6d.), Gabriel Ellison (1s. 3d.). Photo Harrison)

1964 (24 Oct). *Independence. T* **11/12** *and similar vert design. P* 13½ × 14½ (6d.) *or* 14½ × 13½ (*others*).

91	3d. sepia, yellow-green and blue	10	10
92	6d. deep violet and yellow	15	10
93	1s. 3d. red, black, sepia and orange	20	15
91/3	*Set of* 3	40	30

Design:—1s. 3d. Barotse dancer.

14 Maize-Farmer and Silo

15 Health—Radiographer

21 Fishing at Mpulungu

22 Tobacco Worker

(Des Gabriel Ellison. Photo Harrison)

1964 (24 Oct). *T* **14/15, 21/2** *and similar designs. P* 14½ (½d. *to* 4d.), 14½ × 13½ (1s. 3d., 2s. *and* £1) *or* 13½ × 14½ (*others*).

94	½d. red, black and yellow-green	10	20
95	1d. brown, black and bright blue	10	10
96	2d. red, deep brown and orange	10	10
97	3d. black and red	10	10
98	4d. black, brown and orange	15	10
99	6d. orange, deep brown & deep bluish green	15	10
100	9d. carmine, black and bright blue	15	10
101	1s. black, yellow-bistre and blue	15	10
102	1s. 3d. light red, yellow, black and blue	20	10
103	2s. bright blue, black, deep brown & orange	25	10
104	2s. 6d. black and orange-yellow	60	35
105	5s. black, yellow and green	1·00	45
106	10s. black and orange	3·50	3·50
107	£1 black, brown, yellow and red	2·50	4·25
94/107	*Set of* 14	8·00	8·00

Designs: *Vert* (*as T* **15**)—2d. Chinyau dancer; 3d. Cotton-picking. (*As T* **22**)—2s. Tonga basket-making; £1 Makishi dancer. *Horiz* (*as T* **14**)—4d. Angoni bull. (*As T* **21**)—6d. Communications, old and new; 9d. Zambezi sawmills and Redwood flower; 2s. 6d. Luangwa Game Reserve; 5s. Education—student; 10s. Copper mining.

Nos. 94/5 and 97 exist in coils, constructed from normal sheets.

28 I.T.U. Emblem and Symbols

29 I.C.Y. Emblem

(Photo Harrison)

1965 (26 July). *I.T.U. Centenary. P* 14 × 14½.

108	**28**	6d. light reddish violet and gold	15	10
109		2s. 6d. brownish grey and gold	85	1·50

(Photo Harrison)

1965 (26 July). *International Co-operation Year. P* 14½.

110	**29**	3d. turquoise and gold	10	10
111		1s. 3d. ultramarine and gold	35	45

30 State House, Lusaka

34 W.H.O. Building and U.N. Flag

(Des Gabriel Ellison. Photo Harrison)

1965 (18 Oct). *First Anniv of Independence. T* **30** *and similar multicoloured designs. No wmk. P* 13½ × 14½ (3d.), 14 × 13½ (6d.) *or* 13½ × 14 (*others*).

112	3d. Type **30**	10	10
113	6d. Fireworks, Independence Stadium	10	10
	a. Bright purple (fireworks) omitted	75·00	
114	1s. 3d. Clematopsis (*vert*)	15	10
115	2s. 6d. *Tithonia diversifolia* (*vert*)	30	80
112/15	*Set of* 4	50	90

(Des M. Goaman. Photo Harrison)

1966 (18 May). *Inauguration of W.H.O. Headquarters, Geneva. P* 14½.

116	**34**	3d. lake-brown, gold and new blue	20	10
		a. Gold omitted	90·00	
117		1s. 3d. gold, new blue & deep bluish vio	60	60

35 University Building

36 National Assembly Building

(Des Gabriel Ellison. Photo Harrison)

1966 (12 July). *Opening of Zambia University. P* 14½.

118	**35**	3d. blue-green and copper-bronze	10	10
119		1s. 3d. reddish violet and copper-bronze	20	10

(Des Gabriel Ellison. Photo Harrison)

1967 (2 May). *Inauguration of National Assembly Building. P* 14½.

120	**36**	3d. black and copper-bronze	10	10
121		6d. olive-green and copper-bronze	10	10

37 Airport Scene

(Des Gabriel Ellison. Photo Harrison)

1967 (2 Oct). *Opening of Lusaka International Airport. P* 13½ × 14½.

122	**37**	6d. violet-blue and copper-bronze	15	10
123		2s. 6d. brown and copper-bronze	60	80

38 Youth Service Badge

39 "Co-operative Farming"

(Des Gabriel Ellison. Photo Harrison)

1967 (23 Oct). *National Development. T* **38/9** *and similar designs. P* 13½ × 14½ (6d., 1s. 6d.) *or* 14½ × 13½ (*others*).

124	4d. black, red and gold	10	10
125	6d. black, gold and violet-blue	10	10
126	9d. black, grey-blue and silver	15	30
127	1s. multicoloured	50	10
128	1s. 6d. multicoloured	70	1·75
124/8	*Set of* 5	1·40	2·00

Designs: *Vert*—9d "Communications"; 1s. Coalfields. *Horiz*—1s. 6d. Road link with Tanzania.

(New Currency. 100 ngwee=1 kwacha)

43 Lusaka Cathedral

44 Baobab Tree

52 Chokwe Dancer

53 Kafue Railway Bridge

(Des Gabriel Ellison. Photo Harrison)

1968 (16 Jan). *Decimal Currency. T* **43/4, 52/3** *and similar designs. P* 13½ × 14½ (1, 3, 15, 50 *n.*) *or* 14½ × 13½ (*others*).

129	1 n. multicoloured	10	10
	a. Copper-bronze (including value) omitted	90·00	
	b. Ultramarine (windows) omitted	90·00	
130	2 n. multicoloured	10	10
131	3 n. multicoloured	10	10
132	5 n. bistre-brown and copper-bronze	10	10
133	8 n. multicoloured	15	10
	a. Copper-bronze (background) omitted		
	b. Blue (of costumes) omitted	70·00	
134	10 n. multicoloured	25	10
135	15 n. multicoloured	2·75	10
136	20 n. multicoloured	4·00	10
137	25 n. multicoloured	25	10
138	50 n. chocolate, red-orange & copper-bronze	30	15
139	1 k. royal blue and copper-bronze	4·00	20
140	2 k. black and copper-bronze	2·25	1·25
129/40	*Set of* 12	12·50	1·75

Designs: *Horiz* (*as T* **43**)—3 n. Zambia Airways Vickers VC-10 jetliner. (*As T* **53**)—15 n. *Imbrasia zambesina* (moth); 2 k. Eland. *Vert* (*as T* **44**)—5 n. National Museum, Livingstone; 8 n. Vimbuza dancer; 10 n. Tobacco picking. (*As T* **52**)—20 n. South African Crowned Cranes; 25 n. Angoni warrior.

All values exist with PVA gum as well as gum arabic.

Nos. 129/30 and 132 exist in coils, constructed from normal sheets.

55 Ndola on Outline of Zambia

56 Human Rights Emblem and Heads

(Des Gabriel Ellison. Photo Harrison)

1968 (29 June). *Trade Fair, Ndola. P* 14.

141	**55**	15 n. green and gold	10	10

(Des Gabriel Ellison. Photo and die-stamped (gold emblem) Harrison)

1968 (23 Oct). *Human Rights Year. P* 14.

142	**56**	3 n. deep blue, pale violet and gold	10	10

57 W.H.O. Emblem

58 Group of Children

(Des Gabriel Ellison. Photo and die-stamped (gold staff and "20") Harrison)

1968 (23 Oct). *20th Anniv of World Health Organization. P* 14.

143	**57**	10 n. gold and bluish violet	10	10

(Des Gabriel Ellison. Photo and die-stamped (gold children) Harrison)

1968 (23 Oct). *22nd Anniv. of U.N.I.C.E.F. P* 14.

144	**58**	25 n. black, gold and ultramarine	15	70

59 Copper Miner

61 Zambia outlined on Map of Africa

(Des Gabriel Ellison. Photo Harrison)

1969 (18 June). *50th Anniv of International Labour Organization. T* **59** *and similar design. P* 14½ × 13½ (3 *n.*) *or* 13½ × 14½ (25 *n.*).

145	3 n. copper-bronze and deep violet	25	10
146	25 n. pale yell, copper-bronze & blackish brn	1·00	1·00

Design: *Horiz*—25 n. Poling a furnace.

A used example of No. 145 exists with the copper-bronze omitted.

(Des Gabriel Ellison. Photo Harrison)

1969 (23 Oct). *International African Tourist Year. T* **61** *and similar multicoloured designs. P* 14 × 14½ (5 *n.*, 25 *n.*) *or* 14½ × 14 (*others*).

147	5 n. Type **61**	10	10
148	10 n. Waterbuck (*horiz*)	15	10
149	15 n. Kasaba Bay Golden Perch (*horiz*)	35	40
150	25 n. Carmine Bee Eater	1·00	1·50
147/50	*Set of* 4	1·40	1·75

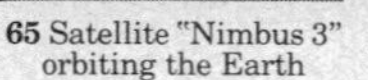

65 Satellite "Nimbus 3" orbiting the Earth   **66** Woman collecting Water from Well

(Des Gabriel Ellison. Litho Enschedé)

1970 (23 Mar). *World Meteorological Day. P* 13 × 10½.
151 **65** 15 n. multicoloured 20 50

(Des V. Whiteley (from local designs). Litho B.W.)

1970 (4 July). *Preventive Medicine. T* **66** *and similar vert designs. P* 13½ × 12.
152 3 n. multicoloured 15 10
153 15 n. multicoloured 40 20
154 25 n. greenish blue, rosine and sepia .. 80 35
152/4 .. .. *Set of* 3 1·25 55
Designs:—15 n. Child on scales; 25 n. Child being immunized.

67 "Masks" (mural by Gabriel Ellison   **68** Ceremonial Axe

(Des Gabriel Ellison. Litho Harrison)

1970 (8 Sept). *Conference of Non-Aligned Nations. P* 14 × 14½.
155 **67** 15 n. multicoloured 30 30

(Des Gabriel Ellison. Litho D.L.R.)

1970 (30 Nov). *Traditional Crafts. T* **68** *and similar multicoloured designs. P* 13½ (15 *n.*), 12½ (25 *n.*) *or* 14 (*others*).
156 3 n. Type **68** 10 10
157 5 n. Clay Smoking-Pipe Bowl 15 10
158 15 n. Makishi Mask (30 × 47 *mm*) 45 45
159 25 n. Kuomboka Ceremony (72 × 19 *mm*) .. 85 1·25
156/9 .. .. *Set of* 4 1·40 1·75
MS160 133 × 83 mm. Nos. 156/9. Imperf. .. .. 10·00 13·00

69 Dag Hammarskjöld and U.N. General Assembly

(Des J.W. Litho Questa)

1971 (18 Sept). *Tenth Death Anniv of Dag Hammarskjöld. T* **69** *and similar horiz designs, each with portrait of Hammarskjöld. Multicoloured. P* 13½.
161 4 n. Type **69** 10 10
162 10 n. Tail of aircraft 20 10
163 15 n. Dove of Peace 25 25
164 25 n. Memorial tablet .. .. 45 1·50
161/4 .. .. *Set of* 4 85 1·75

70 Red-breasted Tilapia   **71** North African Crested Porcupine

(Des G. Drummond. Litho J.W.)

1971 (10 Dec). *Fish. T* **70** *and similar horiz designs. Multicoloured. P* 13½.
165 4 n. Type **70** 50 10
166 10 n. Long-finned Tilapia ("Green-headed Bream") 85 40
167 15 n. Tigerfish .. .. 1·10 2·25
165/7 .. .. *Set of* 3 2·25 2·50

(Des and litho J.W.)

1972 (15 Mar). *Conservation Year* (1*st issue*). *T* **71** *and similar multicoloured designs. P* 13½.
168 4 n. Cheetah (58 × 21 *mm*) 20 25
169 10 n. Lechwe (58 × 21 *mm*) 50 60
170 15 n. Type **71** 80 85
171 25 n. African Elephant .. .. 2·00 3·00
168/71 .. .. *Set of* 4 3·25 4·25

(Des and litho J.W.)

1972 (30 June). *Conservation Year* (2*nd issue*). *Designs similar to T* **71**. *Multicoloured. P* 13½.
172 4 n. Soil conservation 20 20
173 10 n. Forestry 30 45
174 15 n. Water (58 × 21 *mm*) 50 80
175 25 n. Maize (58 × 21 *mm*) .. .. .. 90 1·60
172/5 .. .. *Set of* 4 1·75 2·75

72 Giraffe and Common Zebra

(Des and litho J.W.)

1972 (30 June). *National Parks. Sheet* 114 × 140 *mm containing T* **72** *and similar vert designs. Multicoloured. P* 13½.
MS176 10 n. (× 4). Type **72**; Black Rhinoceros; Hippopotamus and Common Panther; Lion .. 8·00 14·00
Each design includes part of a map showing Zambian National Parks, the four forming a composite design.

73 Zambian Flowers

(Des and litho J.W.)

1972 (22 Sept). *Conservation Year* (3*rd issue*). *T* **73** *and similar horiz designs. Multicoloured. P* 13½.
177 4 n. Type **73** 30 30
178 10 n. *Papilio demodocus* (butterfly) 90 80
179 15 n. *Apis mellifera* (bees) .. .. .. 1·40 1·40
180 25 n. *Nomadacris septemfasciata* (locusts) 2·25 2·25
177/80 .. .. *Set of* 4 4·25 4·25

74 Mary and Joseph   **75** Oudenodon and Rubidgea

(Des V. Whiteley. Litho Questa)

1972 (1 Dec). *Christmas. T* **74** *and similar horiz designs. Multicoloured. P* 14.
181 4 n. Type **74** 10 10
182 9 n. Mary, Joseph and Jesus 10 10
183 15 n. Mary, Jesus and the shepherds 10 10
184 25 n. The Three Wise Men 20 40
181/4 .. .. *Set of* 4 35 50

(Des Gabriel Ellison; adapted J.W. Litho Questa)

1973 (1 Feb). *Zambian Prehistoric Animals. T* **75** *and similar horiz designs. Multicoloured. P* 14 × 13½ (4 *n.*) *or* 13½ × 14 (*others*).
185 4 n. Type **75** 85 85
186 9 n. Broken Hill Man 90 90
187 10 n. Zambiasaurus .. .. 1·00 1·50
188 15 n. *Luangwa drysdalli* .. .. .. 1·10 2·00
189 25 n. Glossopteris .. .. 1·25 3·00
185/9 .. .. *Set of* 5 4·50 7·50
Nos. 186/9 are smaller, 38×21 mm.

76 "Dr. Livingstone, I Presume"

(Des J.W. Litho Format)

1973 (1 May). *Death Centenary of Dr. Livingstone. T* **76** *and similar horiz designs. Multicoloured. P* 13½.
190 3 n. Type **76** 30 15
191 4 n. Scripture Lesson 30 15
192 9 n. Victoria Falls 60 40
193 10 n. Scattering slavers 60 45
194 15 n. Healing the sick .. .. 60 1·60
195 25 n. Burial place of Livingstone's heart .. 70 2·75
190/5 .. .. *Set of* 6 2·75 5·00

77 Parliamentary Mace

(Des Gabriel Ellison. Litho Questa)

1973 (24 Sept). *Third Commonwealth Conference of Speakers and Presiding Officers, Lusaka. P* 13½.
196 **77** 9 n. multicoloured 60 65
197 15 n. multicoloured .. .. 75 1·50
198 25 n. multicoloured .. .. 85 2·00
196/8 .. .. *Set of* 3 2·00 3·75

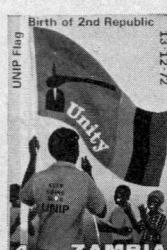

78 Inoculation   **79** U.N.I.P. Flag

(Des Gabriel Ellison. Litho Questa)

1973 (16 Oct). *25th Anniv of W.H.O. T* **78** *and similar multicoloured designs. P* 14.
199 4 n. Mother washing baby (*vert*) .. .. 48·00 23·00
200 9 n. Nurse weighing baby (*vert*) .. .. 45 2·25
201 10 n. Type **78** .. .. 50 3·00
202 15 n. Child eating meal .. .. .. 90 5·00
199/202 .. .. *Set of* 4 48·00 30·00
Only a small quantity of No. 199 was produced, and most examples were issued to post offices for local use.

(Des Gabriel Ellison. Litho Questa)

1973 (13 Dec). *1st Anniv of Second Republic. T* **79** *and similar vert designs. Multicoloured. P* 14 × 13½.
203 4 n. Type **79** .. .. 7·00 7·00
204 9 n. Freedom House .. .. 30 1·50
205 10 n. Army band .. .. 30 2·00
206 15 n. "Celebrations" (dancers) .. .. 50 3·25
207 25 n. Presidential chair .. .. .. 75 5·00
203/7 .. .. *Set of* 5 8·00 17·00

80 President Kaunda at Mulungushi   **81** Nakambala Sugar Estate

(Des Gabriel Ellison. Litho Harrison)

1974 (28 Apr). *President Kaunda's 50th Birthday. T* **80** *and similar horiz designs. Multicoloured. P* 14½ × 14 (4 *n.*) *or* 14 × 14½ (*others*).
208 4 n. Type **80** 55 55
209 9 n. President's former residence 30 30
210 15 n. President holding Independence flame .. 70 1·75
208/10 .. .. *Set of* 3 1·40 2·40

(Des G. Vasarhelyi. Litho Questa)

1974 (23 Oct). *Tenth Anniv of Independence. T* **81** *and similar horiz designs. Multicoloured. P* 13½.
211 3 n. Type **81** 15 10
212 4 n. Local market 15 10
213 9 n. Kapiri glass factory 20 10
214 10 n. Kafue hydro-electric scheme 25 10
215 15 n. Kafue Railway Bridge 50 95
216 25 n. Non-aligned Conference, Lusaka, 1970 60 1·75
211/16 .. .. *Set of* 6 1·60 2·25
MS217 141 × 105 mm. 15 n. (× 4) Academic Education; Teacher Training College; Technical Education; Zambia University .. .. 6·00 8·50

82 Mobile Post-van

(Des Gabriel Ellison. Litho Format)

1974 (15 Nov). *Centenary of Universal Postal Union. T* **82** *and similar horiz designs. Multicoloured. P* 13½.

No.	Description	Unused	Used
218	4 n. Type **82**	20	15
219	9 n. Hawker Siddeley H.S.748 airplane on tarmac	30	30
220	10 n. Chipata Post Office	30	40
221	15 n. Modern training centre	45	1·75
218/21	*Set of* 4	1·10	2·40

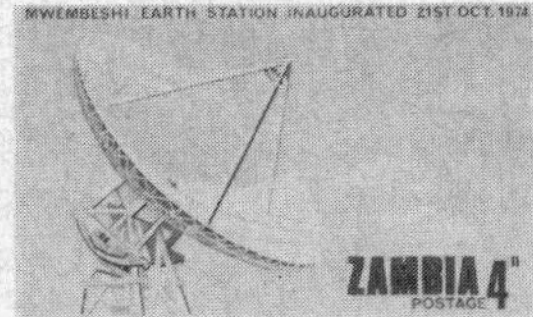

83 Dish Aerial

(Des Gabriel Ellison. Litho Questa)

1974 (16 Dec). *Opening of Mwembeshi Earth Station (21 October). T* **83** *and similar horiz designs. Multicoloured. P* 13½.

No.	Description	Unused	Used
222	4 n. Type **83**	30	20
223	9 n. View at dawn	40	30
224	15 n. View at dusk	55	70
225	25 n. Aerial view	70	1·50
222/5	*Set of* 4	1·75	2·40

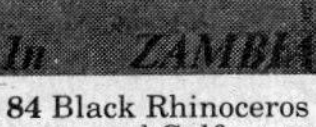

84 Black Rhinoceros and Calf 85 Independence Monument

(Des Gabriel Ellison. Litho J.W.)

1975 (3 Jan). *T* **84/5** *and similar horiz designs. Multicoloured.*

(*a*) *Size as T* **84**. *P* 13½ × 14

No.	Description	Unused	Used
226	1 n. Type **84**	50	30
227	2 n. Helmet Guineafowl	30	30
228	3 n. National Dancing Troupe	15	30
229	4 n. African Fish Eagle	40	10
230	5 n. Knife-edge Bridge	85	50
231	8 n. Sitatunga (antelope)	75	50
232	9 n. African Elephant, Kasaba Bay	85	20
233	10 n. Temminck's Ground Pangolin	20	10

(*b*) *Size as T* **85**. *P* 13

No.	Description	Unused	Used
234	15 n. Type **85**	30	10
	a. Magenta omitted	£700	
235	20 n. Harvesting groundnuts	85	95
236	25 n. Tobacco-growing	1·25	30
237	50 n. Flying-Doctor service	1·75	1·75
238	1 k. Lady Ross's Turaco	3·00	1·75
239	2 k. Village scene	3·00	5·50
226/39	*Set of* 14	12·50	11·00

No. 234a shows much of the design in yellow-green due to the omission of the magenta which was used as an overlay on other colours.

Nos. 226/7 exist in coils, constructed from normal sheets.

86 Map of Namibia 87 Erection of Sprinkler Irrigation

(Des PAD Studio. Litho Questa)

1975 (26 Aug). *Namibia Day. P* 13½.

No.	Type	Description	Unused	Used
240	**86**	4 n. green and light yellow-green	20	20
241		9 n. steel-blue and light turquoise-green	25	30
242		15 n. orange-yellow and greenish yellow	40	75
243		25 n. orange and light orange	50	1·25
240/3		*Set of* 4	1·25	2·25

(Des and litho J.W.)

1975 (16 Dec). *Silver Jubilee of the International Commission on Irrigation and Drainage. T* **87** *and similar horiz designs. Multicoloured. P* 13.

No.	Description	Unused	Used
244	4 n. Type **87**	15	15
245	9 n. Sprinkler irrigation (*different*)	30	40
246	15 n. Furrow irrigation	65	1·25
244/6	*Set of* 3	1·00	1·60

88 Mutondo

(Des A. Chimfwembe. Litho J.W.)

1976 (22 Mar). *World Forestry Day. T* **88** *and similar horiz designs showing trees. Multicoloured. P* 13.

No.	Description	Unused	Used
247	3 n. Type **88**	25	10
248	4 n. Mukunyu	25	10
249	9 n. Mukusi	45	25
250	10 n. Mopane	45	25
251	15 n. Musuku	70	1·40
252	25 n. Mukwa	85	1·75
247/52	*Set of* 6	2·75	3·50

89 Passenger Train

(Des A. Chimfwembe. Litho J.W.)

1976 (10 Dec). *Opening of Tanzania-Zambia Railway. T* **89** *and similar horiz designs. Multicoloured. P* 13½ (**MS**257) *or* 13 (*others*).

No.	Description	Unused	Used
253	4 n. Type **89**	30	30
254	9 n. Copper exports	55	55
255	15 n. Machinery imports	90	95
256	25 n. Goods train	1·40	1·75
253/6	*Set of* 4	2·75	3·25
MS257	140 × 106 mm. 10 n. Clearing bush; 15 n. Laying track; 20 n. Railway workers; 25 n. Completed track	3·50	4·00

90 Kayowe Dance 91 Grimwood's Longclaw

(Des BG Studio. Litho Questa)

1977 (18 Jan). *Second World Black and African Festival of Arts and Culture, Nigeria. T* **90** *and similar horiz designs. Multicoloured. P* 13½.

No.	Description	Unused	Used
258	4 n. Type **90**	15	10
259	9 n. Lilombola dance	15	15
260	15 n. Initiation ceremony	30	40
261	25 n. Munkhwele dance	55	1·00
258/61	*Set of* 4	1·00	1·50

(Des Gabriel Ellison. Litho Questa)

1977 (1 July). *Birds of Zambia. T* **91** *and similar vert designs. Multicoloured. P* 14½.

No.	Description	Unused	Used
262	4 n. Type **91**	40	10
263	9 n. Shelley's Sunbird	55	60
264	10 n. Black-cheeked Lovebird	55	60
265	15 n. Locust Finch	1·25	2·00
266	20 n. Black-chinned Tinkerbird	1·40	2·25
267	25 n. Chaplin's Barbet	1·50	2·75
262/7	*Set of* 6	5·00	7·50

92 Girls with Building Blocks

(Des Gabriel Ellison. Litho Questa)

1977 (20 Oct). *Decade for Action to Combat Racism and Racial Discrimination. T* **92** *and similar horiz designs. Multicoloured. P* 14 × 14½.

No.	Description	Unused	Used
268	4 n. Type **92**	10	10
269	9 n. Women dancing	15	20
270	15 n. Girls with dove	25	70
268/70	*Set of* 3	45	90

93 Angels and Shepherds

(Des Gabriel Ellison. Litho J.W.)

1977 (20 Dec). *Christmas. T* **93** *and similar horiz designs. Multicoloured. P* 14.

No.	Description	Unused	Used
271	4 n. Type **93**	10	10
272	9 n. The Holy Family	10	10
273	10 n. The Magi	10	15
274	15 n. Jesus presented to Simeon	20	60
271/4	*Set of* 4	40	85

=8n

94 African Elephant and Road Check (95)

(Des Gabriel Ellison. Litho Questa)

1978 (1 Aug). *Anti-Poaching Campaign. T* **94** *and similar horiz designs. Multicoloured. P* 14 × 14½.

No.	Description	Unused	Used
275	8 n. Type **94**	35	10
276	18 n. Lechwe and canoe patrol	40	65
277	28 n. Warthog and Bell 206 JetRanger helicopter	75	95
278	32 n. Cheetah and game guard patrol	80	1·25
275/8	*Set of* 4	2·10	2·75

1979 (15 Mar). *Nos.* 228, 232, 234 *and* 236 *surch as T* **95**.

No.	Description	Unused	Used
279	8 n. on 9 n. African Elephant, Kasaba Bay	60	10
	a. Surch inverted	50·00	
280	10 n. on 3 n. National Dancing Troupe	10	10
	a. Surch inverted	50·00	
	b. Surch omitted (in pair with normal)		
281	18 n. on 25 n. Tobacco-growing	15	15
	a. Surch inverted		
282	28 n. on 15 n. Type **85**	20	25
	a. Surch inverted	8·00	
	b. Albino surch		
279/82	*Set of* 4	90	55

No. 280b was caused by a corner paper fold.

96 Kayowe Dance 97 "Kalulu and the Tug of War"

(Des Gabriel Ellison. Litho Questa)

1979 (1 Aug). *Commonwealth Summit Conference, Lusaka. T* **96** *and similar horiz designs. Multicoloured. P* 14.

No.	Description	Unused	Used
283	18 n. Type **96**	15	25
284	32 n. Kutambala dance	20	40
285	42 n. Chitwansombo drummers	20	60
286	58 n. Lilombola dance	25	80
283/6	*Set of* 4	70	1·90

(Des Gabriel Ellison. Litho Questa)

1979 (21 Sept). *International Year of the Child. Illustrations from Children's Books. T* **97** *and similar vert designs. Multicoloured. P* 14.

No.	Description	Unused	Used
287	18 n. Type **97**	20	30
288	32 n. "Why the Zebra has no Horns"	30	55
289	42 n. "How the Tortoise got his Shell"	40	85
290	58 n. "Kalulu and the Lion"	50	1·10
287/90	*Set of* 4	1·25	2·50
MS291	90 × 120 mm. Nos. 287/90	2·25	2·75

98 Children of Different Races holding Anti-Apartheid Emblem

(Des Gabriel Ellison. Litho Questa)

1979 (13 Nov). *International Anti-Apartheid Year. T* **98** *and similar horiz designs showing children of different races together. Multicoloured. P* 14½.

No.	Description	Unused	Used
292	18 n. Type **98**	15	25
293	32 n. Children with toy car	25	40
294	42 n. Young children with butterfly	35	60
295	58 n. Children with microscope	50	80
292/5	*Set of* 4	1·10	1·90

99 Sir Rowland Hill and 2s. Definitive Stamp of 1964

LONDON 1980

(100)

(Des Gabriel Ellison. Litho Format)

1979 (20 Dec). *Death Centenary of Sir Rowland Hill.* T **99** *and similar horiz designs. Multicoloured. P* 14½.

296	18 n. Type **99**	20	25
297	32 n. Sir Rowland Hill and mailman	30	55
298	42 n. Sir Rowland Hill and Northern Rhodesia 1963 ½d. definitive stamp	40	70
299	58 n. Sir Rowland Hill and mail-carrying oxwaggon	50	1·10
296/9	*Set of* 4	1·25	2·40
MS300	112 × 89 mm. Nos. 296/9	1·25	2·50

1980 (16 May). *"London 1980" International Stamp Exhibition. Nos.* 296/300 *optd with* T **100**.

301	18 n. Type **99**	25	40
302	32 n. Sir Rowland Hill and mailman	30	60
303	42 n. Sir Rowland Hill and Northern Rhodesia 1963 ½d. definitive stamp	40	75
304	58 n. Sir Rowland Hill and mail-carrying oxwaggon	60	90
301/4	*Set of* 4	1·40	2·40
MS305	112 × 89 mm. Nos. 301/4	3·00	3·75

101 Rotary Anniversary Emblem

(Des J.W. Litho Questa)

1980 (18 June). *75th Anniv of Rotary International. P* 14.

306 **101**	8 n. multicoloured	10	10
307	32 n. multicoloured	40	55
308	42 n. multicoloured	45	80
309	58 n. multicoloured	70	1·00
306/9	*Set of* 4	1·50	2·25
MS310	115 × 89 mm. Nos. 306/9	2·00	2·50

102 Running

(Des Gabriel Ellison. Litho J.W.)

1980 (19 July). *Olympic Games, Moscow.* T **102** *and similar horiz designs. Multicoloured. P* 13.

311	18 n. Type **102**	25	25
312	32 n. Boxing	40	45
313	42 n. Football	50	80
314	58 n. Swimming	80	1·25
311/14	*Set of* 4	1·75	2·50
MS315	142 × 144 mm. Nos. 311/14. P 14	1·75	2·75

103 *Euphaedra zaddachi*

104 Zambia Coat of Arms

(Des Gabriel Ellison. Litho Questa)

1980 (27 Aug). *Butterflies.* T **103** *and similar horiz designs. Multicoloured. P* 14.

316	18 n. Type **103**	15	15
317	32 n. *Aphnaeus questiauxi*	25	40
318	42 n. *Abantis zambesiaca*	40	80
319	58 n. *Spindasis modesta*	60	1·60
316/19	*Set of* 4	1·25	2·75
MS320	114×86 mm. Nos. 316/19	3·75	3·00

(Des Gabriel Ellison. Litho Format)

1980 (27 Sept). *26th Commonwealth Parliamentary Association Conference, Lusaka. P* 14.

321 **104**	18 n. multicoloured	15	25
322	32 n. multicoloured	25	45
323	42 n. multicoloured	30	65
324	58 n. multicoloured	40	1·25
321/4	*Set of* 4	1·00	2·40

105 Nativity and St. Francis of Assisi (stained glass window, Ndola Church)

106 Musikili

(Des Gabriel Ellison. Litho Questa)

1980 (3 Nov). *50th Anniv of Catholic Church on the Copperbelt. P* 13½.

325 **105**	8 n. multicoloured	10	10
326	28 n. multicoloured	40	70
327	32 n. multicoloured	40	70
328	42 n. multicoloured	60	95
325/8	*Set of* 4	1·40	2·25

(Des Gabriel Ellison. Litho Questa)

1981 (21 Mar). *World Forestry Day. Seedpods.* T **106** *and similar horiz designs. Multicoloured. P* 14.

329	8 n. Type **106**	10	10
330	18 n. Mupapa	20	45
331	28 n. Mulunguti	25	80
332	32 n. Mulama	25	1·25
329/32	*Set of* 4	70	2·25

107 I.T.U. Emblem

108 Mask Maker

(Des J.W. Litho Format)

1981 (15 May). *World Telecommunications and Health Day.* T **107** *and similar vert design. Multicoloured. P* 14½.

333	8 n. Type **107**	20	10
334	18 n. W.H.O. emblems	35	35
335	28 n. Type **107**	50	60
336	32 n. As 18 n.	60	75
333/6	*Set of* 4	1·50	1·60

(Des Gabriel Ellison. Litho Harrison)

1981 (2 June)–**83**. *Multicoloured designs as* T **108**. *P* 14 × 13½ (50 *n.*, 75 *n.*, 1 *k.*, 2 *k.*) *or* 14½ (*others*).

337	1 n. Type **108**	10	10
338	2 n. Blacksmith	10	10
339	5 n. Pottery making	10	10
340	8 n. Straw-basket fishing	10	10
341	10 n. Thatching	10	10
342	12 n. Mushroom picking (17.2.83)	3·00	1·75
343	18 n. Millet grinding on stone	30	10
344	28 n. Royal Barge paddler (11.11.81)	50	10
345	30 n. Makishi tightrope dancer (11.11.81)	50	10
346	35 n. Tonga Ila granary and house (11.11.81)	55	10
347	42 n. Cattle herding (11.11.81)	55	80
348	50 n. Traditional healer (38 × 26 *mm*) (11.11.81)	55	10
349	75 n. Women carrying water (38 × 26 *mm*) (17.2.83)	55	60
350	1 k. Pounding maize (38 × 26 *mm*) (17.2.83)	55	60
351	2 k. Pipe-smoking, Gwembe Valley Belle (38 × 26 *mm*)	55	60
337/51	*Set of* 15	7·00	4·50

Nos. 338/9 and 341 exist in coils, constructed from normal sheets.

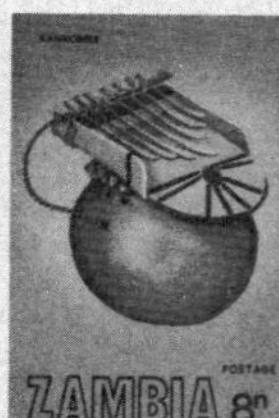

109 Kankobele

110 Banded Ironstone

(Des Gabriel Ellison. Litho Format)

1981 (30 Sept*). *Traditional Musical Instruments.* T **109** *and similar vert designs. Multicoloured. P* 15.

356	8 n. Type **109**	30	10
357	18 n. Inshingili	40	55
358	28 n. Ilimba	50	1·50
359	32 n. Bango	60	1·75
356/9	*Set of* 4	1·60	3·50

*It has been reported that the Ndola Philatelic Bureau inadvertently sold some of these stamps some days earlier, and that cancelled-to-order examples exist postmarked 14 or 15 September.

Nos. 356 and 358/9 exist imperforate from stock dispersed by the liquidator of Format International Security Printers Ltd.

(Des Gabriel Ellison. Litho Questa)

1982 (5 Jan). *Minerals* (*1st series*). T **110** *and similar vert designs. Multicoloured. P* 14.

360	8 n. Type **110**	80	10
361	18 n. Cobaltocalcite	1·75	80
362	28 n. Amazonite	2·25	1·90
363	32 n. Tourmaline	2·50	2·25
364	42 n. Uranium ore	2·75	3·25
360/4	*Set of* 5	9·00	7·50

See also Nos. 370/4.

111 Zambian Scouts

(Des Gabriel Ellison. Litho Questa)

1982 (30 Mar). *75th Anniv of Boy Scout Movement.* T **111** *and similar horiz designs. Multicoloured. P* 14.

365	8 n. Type **111**	30	10
366	18 n. Lord Baden-Powell and Victoria Falls	70	40
367	28 n. African Buffalo and Zambian Scout patrol pennant	70	50
368	1 k. African Fish Eagle and Zambian Conservation badge	2·25	4·50
365/8	*Set of* 4	3·50	5·00
MS369	105×78 mm. Nos. 365/8	3·50	5·00

(Des Gabriel Ellison. Litho Questa)

1982 (1 July). *Minerals* (*2nd series*). *Vert designs as* T **110**. *Multicoloured. P* 14.

370	8 n. Bornite	95	10
371	18 n. Chalcopyrite	2·25	90
372	28 n. Malachite	2·75	3·00
373	32 n. Azurite	2·75	3·00
374	42 n. Vanadinite	3·25	4·25
370/4	*Set of* 5	11·00	10·00

112 Drilling Rig, 1926

(Des Gabriel Ellison. Litho Harrison)

1983 (26 Jan). *Early Steam Engines.* T **112** *and similar horiz designs. Multicoloured. P* 14 × 14½.

375	8 n. Type **112**	60	10
376	18 n. Fowler road locomotive, 1900	80	70
377	28 n. Borsig ploughing engine, 1925	1·25	2·25
378	32 n. Class "7" railway locomotive, 1900	1·60	2·50
375/8	*Set of* 4	3·75	5·00

113 Cotton Picking

114 *Eulophia cucullata*

(Des Gabriel Ellison. Litho Harrison)

1983 (10 Mar). *Commonwealth Day.* T **113** *and similar horiz designs. Multicoloured. P* 14 × 13½.

379	12 n. Type **113**	20	10
380	18 n. Mining	40	30
381	28 n. Ritual pot and traditional dances	30	50
382	1 k. Violet-crested Turaco and Victoria Falls	2·75	5·00
379/82	*Set of* 4	3·25	5·50

(Des Gabriel Ellison. Litho Questa)

1983 (26 May). *Wild Flowers.* T **114** *and similar vert designs. Multicoloured. P* 14.

383	12 n. Type **114**	25	10
384	28 n. *Kigelia africana*	35	40
385	35 n. *Protea gaguedi*	40	80
386	50 n. *Leonotis nepetifolia*	60	2·00
383/6	*Set of* 4	1·40	3·00
MS387	141 × 71 mm. Nos. 383/6. P 12	1·50	3·25

115 Giraffe

(Des Gabriel Ellison. Litho Harrison)

1983 (21 July). *Zambia Wildlife. T* **115** *and similar horiz designs. Multicoloured. P* 14 × 13½.
388 12 n. Type **115** 70 10
a. Orange-brown and brown (inscr and face value) omitted £300
389 28 n. Blue Wildebeest 90 70
390 35 n. Lechwe .. .. 1·25 90
391 1 k. Yellow-backed Duiker .. .. .. 2·50 4·25
388/91 .. .. *Set of* 4 4·75 5·50

116 Tigerfish

117 The Annunciation

(Des Gabriel Ellison. Litho J.W.)

1983 (29 Sept). *Zambia Fishes. T* **116** *and similar horiz designs. Multicoloured. P* 14.
392 12 n. Type **116** 40 15
393 28 n. Silver Catfish 70 65
394 35 n. Large-spotted Squeaker .. .. .. 80 1·50
395 38 n. Red-breasted Tilapia .. .. .. 90 1·50
392/5 .. .. *Set of* 4 2·50 3·50

(Des Gabriel Ellison. Litho J.W.)

1983 (12 Dec). *Christmas. T* **117** *and similar vert designs. Multicoloured. P* 14.
396 12 n. Type **117** 15 10
397 28 n. The Shepherds 30 40
398 35 n. Three Kings .. .. 40 1·00
399 38 n. Flight into Egypt .. .. 45 1·50
396/9 .. .. *Set of* 4 1·10 2·75

118 Boeing 737

(Des Gabriel Ellison. Litho Harrison)

1984 (26 Jan). *Air Transport. T* **118** *and similar horiz designs. Multicoloured. P* 14 × 13½.
400 12 n. Type **118** 25 10
401 28 n. De Havilland D.H.C.2 Beaver 45 40
402 35 n. Short S.45A Solent 3 flying boat .. 55 70
403 1 k. De Havilland D.H.66 Hercules *City of Basra* .. .. 1·00 2·50
400/3 .. .. *Set of* 4 2·00 3·25

119 Receiving Flowers

120 Football

(Des and litho J.W.)

1984 (28 Apr). *60th Birthday of President Kaunda. T* **119** *and similar multicoloured designs. P* 14½ × 14 (12 *n*., 60 *n*.) *or* 14 × 14½ (*others*).
404 12 n. Type **119** 30 10
405 28 n. Swearing-in ceremony (*vert*) 45 40
406 60 n. Planting cherry tree .. .. .. 90 2·00
407 1 k. Opening of 5th National Assembly (*vert*) 1·25 3·00
404/7 .. .. *Set of* 4 2·50 5·00

(Des Gabriel Ellison. Litho Format)

1984 (18 July). *Olympic Games, Los Angeles. T* **120** *and similar vert designs. Multicoloured. P* 14½ × 14.
408 12 n. Type **120** 25 10
409 28 n. Running 30 50
410 35 n. Hurdling 40 80
411 50 n. Boxing .. .. 45 1·40
408/11 .. .. *Set of* 4 1·25 2·50

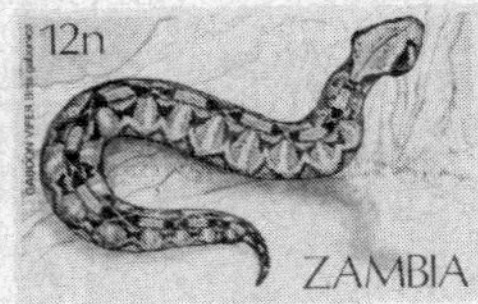

121 Gaboon Viper

(Des Gabriel Ellison. Litho Harrison)

1984 (5 Sept). *Reptiles. T* **121** *and similar horiz designs. Multicoloured. P* 14.
412 12 n. Type **121** 20 10
413 28 n. Chameleon 40 50
414 35 n. Nile Crocodile 50 70
415 1 k. Blue-headed Agama .. .. .. 1·00 2·75
412/15 .. .. *Set of* 4 1·90 3·50
MS416 120 × 101 mm. Nos. 412/15 .. .. 2·00 4·00

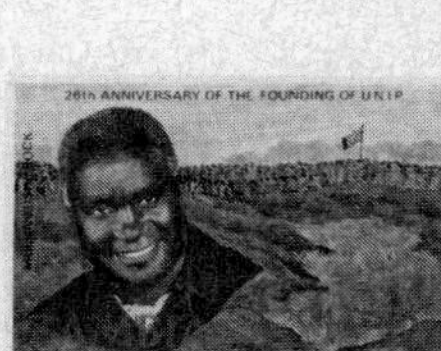
122 Pres. Kaunda and Mulungushi Rock

123 *Amanita flammeola*

(Des Gabriel Ellison. Litho Harrison)

1984 (22 Oct). *26th Anniv of United National Independence Party* (12 *n*.) *and 20th Anniv of Independence* (*others*) (1*st issue*). *T* **122** *and similar horiz designs. Multicoloured. P* 14.
417 12 n. Type **122** 30 10
418 28 n. Freedom Statue 50 50
419 1 k. Pres. Kaunda and agricultural produce ("Lima Programme") .. .. .. 1·25 3·00
417/19 .. .. *Set of* 3 1·75 3·25
See also Nos. 438/40.

(Des Gabriel Ellison. Litho J.W.)

1984 (12 Dec). *Fungi. T* **123** *and similar vert designs. Multicoloured. P* 14 × 14½.
420 12 n. Type **123** .. .. 1·10 30
421 28 n. *Amanita zambiana* .. .. 1·50 1·25
422 32 n. *Termitomyces letestui* .. .. .. 2·00 2·25
423 75 n. *Cantharellus miniatescens* .. .. 3·25 4·50
420/3 .. .. *Set of* 4 7·00 7·50

(**124**)

125 Chacma Baboon

1985 (5 Mar). *No.* 237 *surch with T* **124**.
424 5 k. on 50 n. Flying-doctor service .. .. 1·75 2·00

(Des Gabriel Ellison. Litho Harrison)

1985 (25 Apr). *Zambian Primates. T* **125** *and similar horiz designs. Multicoloured. P* 14.
425 12 n. Type **125** 55 10
426 20 n. Diademed Monkey 75 40
427 45 n. Diademed Monkey (*different*) .. .. 1·50 1·25
428 1 k. Savanna Monkey .. .. 2·50 4·25
425/8 .. .. *Set of* 4 4·75 5·50

126 Map showing S.A.D.C.C. Member States

127 The Queen Mother in 1980

(Des Gabriel Ellison. Litho Harrison)

1985 (9 July). *5th Anniv of Southern African Development Co-ordination Conference. T* **126** *and similar horiz designs. P* 14.
429 20 n. multicoloured 75 15
430 45 n. black, new blue and pale blue .. .. 1·75 1·10
431 1 k. multicoloured .. .. 2·00 3·25
429/31 .. .. *Set of* 3 4·00 4·00
Designs:—45 n. Mining; 1 k. Flags of member states and Mulungushi Hall.

(Des and litho Harrison)

1985 (2 Aug). *Life and Times of Queen Elizabeth the Queen Mother. T* **127** *and similar designs. P* 14.
432 25 n. multicoloured 10 10
433 45 n. deep violet-blue and gold 10 15
434 55 n. deep violet-blue and gold 15 25
435 5 k. multicoloured .. .. 1·25 2·25
432/5 .. .. *Set of* 4 1·40 2·50
Designs: *Vert*—45 n. The Queen Mother at Clarence House, 1963. *Horiz*—55 n. With the Queen and Princess Margaret, 1980; 5 k. At Prince Henry's christening, 1984.

20n
(**128**)

129 Postman and Lusaka Post Office, 1958

1985 (12 Sept–25 Nov). *Nos.* 340 *and* 342 *surch as T* **128** *in chestnut* (20 *n*.) *or greenish blue* (25 *n*.).
436 20 n. on 12 n. Mushroom picking .. .. 2·75 30
a. Horiz pair, one without surch .. £500
437 25 n. on 8 n. Straw-basket fishing (25.11) 1·00 65

1985 (23 Oct). *26th Anniv of United National Independence Party* (*No.* 438) *and 20th Anniv of Independence* (*others*) (2*nd issue*). *Designs as Nos.* 417/19 *but larger,* 55 × 34 *mm, embossed on gold foil. P* 10.
438 5 k. Type **122** .. .. 1·00 2·00
439 5 k. Freedom Statue .. .. 1·00 2·00
440 5 k. Pres. Kaunda and agricultural produce ("Lima Programme") .. .. .. 1·00 2·00
438/40 .. .. *Set of* 3 2·75 5·50

(Des Gabriel Ellison. Litho J.W.)

1985 (12 Dec). *10th Anniv of Posts and Telecommunication Corporation. T* **129** *and similar horiz designs. Multicoloured. P* 13 × 12½.
441 20 n. Type **129** 55 10
442 45 n. Postman and Livingstone Post Office, 1950 .. .. 85 25
443 55 n. Postman and Kalomo Post Office, 1902 .. .. 1·00 70
444 5 k. Africa Trans-Continental Telegraph Line under construction, 1900 .. .. 3·25 5·50
441/4 .. .. *Set of* 4 5·00 6·00

130 Boy in Maize Field

131 *Mylabris tricolor*

(Des Gabriel Ellison. Litho Harrison)

1985 (19 Dec). *40th Anniv of United Nations Organization. T* **130** *and similar vert designs. P* 14.
445 20 n. multicoloured 40 10
446 45 n. black, new blue and brownish black .. 65 20
447 1 k. multicoloured .. .. 1·25 2·00
448 2 k. multicoloured .. .. 1·75 3·00
445/8 .. .. *Set of* 4 3·50 4·75
Designs:—45 n. Logo and "40"; 1 k. President Kaunda addressing U.N. General Assembly, 1970; 2 k. Signing of U.N. Charter, San Francisco, 1945.

(Des Gabriel Ellison. Litho Harrison)

1986 (20 Mar). *Beetles. T* **131** *and similar horiz designs. Multicoloured. P* 14.
449 35 n. Type **131** 15 10
450 1 k. *Phasgonocnema melanianthe* 20 20
451 1 k. 70, *Amaurodes passerinii* 30 50
452 5 k. *Ranzania petersiana* .. .. .. 85 2·00
449/52 .. .. *Set of* 4 1·40 2·50

(Des A. Theobald. Litho Format)

1986 (21 Apr). *60th Birthday of Queen Elizabeth II. Vert designs as T* **230a** *of Jamaica. Multicoloured. W w* **16**. *P* 14 × 14½ (1 *k*. 95) *or* 14 × 13½ (*others*).
453 35 n. Princess Elizabeth at Flower Ball, Savoy Hotel, 1951 .. .. .. 10 10
a. Perf 14 × 14½ .. .. 1·00
454 1 k. 25, With Prince Andrew, Lusaka Airport, 1979 .. .. 15 20
a. Perf 14 × 14½ .. .. 6·00
455 1 k. 70, With President Kaunda 15 25
a. Perf 14 × 14½ .. .. 10·00
456 1 k. 95, In Luxembourg, 1976 .. .. 15 30
457 5 k. At Crown Agents Head Office, London, 1983 .. .. 40 85
453/7 .. .. *Set of* 5 85 1·50

(Des D. Miller. Litho Questa)

1986 (23 July). *Royal Wedding. Square designs as T* **231a** *of Jamaica. Multicoloured. W w* **16**. *P* 14.
458 1 k. 70, Prince Andrew and Miss Sarah Ferguson 30 35
459 5 k. Prince Andrew in Zambia, 1979 .. 80 1·40

ALTERED CATALOGUE NUMBERS

Any Catalogue numbers altered from the last edition are shown as a list in the introductory pages.

132 Goalkeeper saving Goal

133 Sculpture of Edmond Halley by Henry Pegram

(Des Gabriel Ellison. Litho Mardon Printers Ltd, Zimbabwe)

1986 (30 July). *World Cup Football Championship, Mexico. T* **132** *and similar vert designs. Multicoloured. P* 14½.

460	35 n. Type **132**	85	15
461	1 k. 25, Player kicking ball	2·00	1·40
462	1 k. 70, Two players competing for ball	2·25	1·90
463	5 k. Player scoring goal	3·25	6·00
460/3	*Set of* 4	7·50	8·50

(Des Jennifer Toombs. Litho Mardon Printers Ltd, Zimbabwe)

1986 (6 Aug). *Appearance of Halley's Comet. T* **133** *and similar horiz designs. P* 14½.

464	1 k. 25, multicoloured	1·00	55
465	1 k. 70, multicoloured	1·25	85
466	2 k. multicoloured	1·75	1·75
467	5 k. light blue and blue-black	3·50	6·00
464/7	*Set of* 4	6·75	8·00

Designs:—1 k. 70, *Giotto* spacecraft approaching nucleus of Comet; 2 k. Studying Halley's Comet in 1682 and 1986; 5 k. Part of Halley's chart of southern sky.

134 The Nativity

(Des and litho Harrison)

1986 (15 Dec). *Christmas. Children's Paintings. T* **134** *and similar horiz designs. Multicoloured. P* 14.

468	35 n. Type **134**	40	10
469	1 k. 25, The Visit of the Three Kings	1·50	75
470	1 k. 60, The Holy Family with Shepherd and King	1·75	1·60
471	5 k. Angel and Christmas Tree	3·75	6·00
468/71	*Set of* 4	6·75	7·50

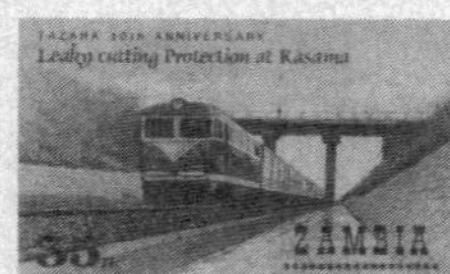

135 Train in Kasama Cutting

(Des G. Vasarhelyi. Litho Questa)

1986 (22 Dec). *10th Anniv of Tanzania-Zambia Railway. T* **135** *and similar horiz designs. Multicoloured. P* 14.

472	35 n. Type **135**	25	10
473	1 k. 25, Train leaving Tunnel No. 21	45	50
474	1 k. 70, Train between Tunnels No. 6 and 7	50	70
475	5 k. Trains at Mpika Station	1·00	2·50
472/5	*Set of* 4	2·00	3·50

136 President Kaunda and Graduate

137 Arms of Kitwe

(Litho Harrison)

1987 (27 Jan). *20th Anniv of University of Zambia. T* **136** *and similar multicoloured designs. P* 14.

476	35 n. Type **136**	30	10
477	1 k. 25, University Badge (*vert*)	75	60
478	1 k. 60, University Statue	85	1·00
479	5 k. President Kaunda laying foundation stone (*vert*)	3·00	5·50
476/9	*Set of* 4	4·50	6·50

(Litho Harrison)

1987 (26 Mar). *Arms of Zambian Towns. T* **137** *and similar vert designs. Multicoloured. P* 14.

480	35 n. Type **137**	10	10
481	1 k. 25, Ndola	15	20
482	1 k. 70, Lusaka	20	25
483	20 k. Livingstone	2·75	5·00
480/3	*Set of* 4	2·75	5·00

138 Chestnut-headed Crake

139 Look-out Tree, Livingstone

Two types of surcharge for 20 n., 75 n.:

20n 20n 75n 75n
I II I II

I Surch by Format in Great Britain
II Surch in Zambia

(Des Gabriel Ellison. Litho Questa)

1987 (16 Apr)–**88**. *Birds* (1*st series*). *T* **138** *and similar vert designs, some additionally surch as T* **128**. *Multicoloured. P* 11×13. (5 *n. to* 40 *n.*, 75 *n.*, 1 *k.* 65) *or* 14 (*others*).

484	5 n. Cloud-scraping Cisticola (8.10.87)	10	10
485	10 n. White-winged Starling (8.10.87)	10	10
486	20 n. on 1 n. Yellow Swamp Warbler (I) (10.3.88)	30	20
	a. Surch Type II	20	20
487	25 n. Type **138**	1·50	1·00
488	30 n. Red-fronted Barbet ("Miombo Pied Barbet") (8.10.87)	10	10
489	35 n. Black and Rufous Swallow	1·75	1·25
490	40 n. Wattled Crane (8.10.87)	10	10
491	50 n. Red-throated Heron ("Slaty Egret") (8.10.87)	10	10
492	75 n. on 2 n. Olive-flanked Robin Chat (I) (10.3.88)	30	50
	a. Surch Type II	30	50
	b. Surch omitted		
493	1 k. Bradfield's Hornbill	1·75	40
494	1 k. 25, Boulton's Puff-back Flycatcher ("Margaret's Batis")	1·75	1·50
495	1 k. 60, Anchieta's Sunbird	1·75	1·50
496	1 k. 65 on 30 n. Red-fronted Barbet (10.3.88)	30	35
497	1 k. 70, Boehm's Bee Eater	2·00	1·75
498	1 k. 95, Perrin's Bush Shrike	2·00	1·75
499	2 k. Whale-headed Stork ("Shoebill") (8.10.87)	35	35
500	5 k. Taita Falcon	2·50	80
501	10 k. on 50 n. Red-throated Heron (10.3.88)	1·10	2·00
502	20 k. on 2 k. Whale-headed Stork (10.3.88)	2·10	3·25
484/502	*Set of* 19	17·00	15·00

Nos. 491, 493/5 and 497/502 are larger, size 24×39 mm.

The 1 n. and 2 n. values were not officialy issued without surcharge, but examples with c-t-o cancellations of 10 March 1988 are known.

No. 502 is surcharged "K 20" only. For "K 20·00" surcharge see No. 594.

For further surcharges see Nos. 587/95, and for different designs see Nos. 625/38.

(Litho Questa)

1987 (30 June). *Tourism. T* **139** *and similar horiz designs. Multicoloured. P* 14.

503	35 n. Type **139**	30	15
504	1 k. 25, Rafting on Zambezi	30	25
505	1 k. 70, Tourists photographing lions, Luangwa Valley	1·75	90
506	10 k. Eastern White Pelicans	6·50	6·50
503/6	*Set of* 4	8·00	7·00

= K3

(140)

141 De Havilland D.H.C.2 Beaver

1987 (14 Sept). *Various stamps surch as T* **140**.

(*a*) *On Nos.* 432/5 *in gold*

507	**127**	3 k. on 25 n. multicoloured	55	55
508	–	6 k. on 45 n. deep violet-blue and gold	1·00	1·00
509	–	10 k. on 55 n. deep violet-blue and gold	1·60	1·60
510	–	20 k. on 5 k. multicoloured	3·25	3·75

(*b*) *On Nos.* 453/7

511		3 k. on 35 n. Princess Elizabeth at Flower Ball, Savoy Hotel, 1951	55	55
512		4 k. on 1 k. 25, With Prince Andrew, Lusaka Airport, 1979	65	65
513		6 k. on 1 k. 70, With President Kaunda	1·00	1·00
514		10 k. on 1 k. 95, In Luxembourg, 1976	1·60	1·60
515		20 k. on 5 k. At Crown Agents Head Office, London, 1983	3·25	3·75

(*c*) *On Nos.* 460/3

516		3 k. on 35 n. Type **132**	55	55
517		6 k. on 1 k. 25, Player kicking ball	1·00	1·00
518		10 k. on 1 k. 70, Two players competing for ball	1·60	1·60
519		20 k. on 5 k. Player scoring goal	3·25	3·75

(*d*) *On Nos.* 464/7 *in gold*

520	**133**	3 k. on 1 k. 25, multicoloured	90	70
		a. Surch omitted (in horiz pair with normal)	80·00	
521	–	6 k. on 1 k. 70, multicoloured	1·50	1·25
522	–	10 k. on 2 k. multicoloured	2·50	2·50
523	–	20 k. on 15 k. light blue and blue-black	4·50	5·00
507/23		*Set of* 17	26·00	28·00

(Des and litho Questa)

1987 (21 Sept). *20th Anniv of Zambia Airways. T* **141** *and similar horiz designs showing aircraft. Multicoloured. P* 14.

524	35 c. Type **141**	65	10
525	1 k. 70, Douglas DC-10	1·50	70
526	5 k. Douglas DC-3	3·50	3·50
527	10 k. Boeing 707	5·50	6·50
524/7	*Set of* 4	10·00	9·75

142 Friesian/Holstein Cow

143 Mpoloto Ne Mikobango

(Des Gabriel Ellison. Litho Format)

1987 (1 Oct). *40th Anniv of Food and Agriculture Organization. T* **142** *and similar horiz designs. Multicoloured. P* 14½×15.

528	35 n. Type **142**	10	10
529	1 k. 25, Simmental bull	20	25
530	1 k. 70, Sussex bull	25	30
531	20 k. Brahman bull	1·50	3·00
528/31	*Set of* 4	1·75	3·25

(Litho Format)

1987 (3 Nov). *People of Zambia. T* **143** *and similar vert designs. Multicoloured. P* 12½.

532	35 n. Type **143**	10	10
533	1 k. 25, Zintaka	20	25
534	1 k. 70, Mufuluhi	25	30
535	10 k. Ntebwe	1·25	1·50
536	20 k. Kubangwa Aa Mbulunga	2·25	3·00
532/6	*Set of* 5	3·50	4·50

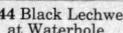

144 Black Lechwe at Waterhole

145 Cassava Roots

(Des Gabriel Ellison. Litho Questa)

1987 (21 Dec). *Black Lechwe. T* **144** *and similar multicoloured designs. P* 14.

537	50 n. Type **144**	65	10
538	2 k. Black Lechwe resting by pool (*horiz*)	1·75	40
539	2 k. 50, Running through water (*horiz*)	1·75	80
540	10 k. Watching for danger	4·50	5·50
537/40	*Set of* 4	7·75	6·00

MS541 Two sheets, each 105×74 mm. (a) 20 k. Caracal (predator). (b) 20 k. Cheetah (predator) *Set of 2 sheets* 8·00 7·50

(Des Gabriel Ellison. Litho Questa)

1988 (20 May). *International Fund for Agricultural Development. T* **145** *and similar horiz designs. Multicoloured. P* 14.

542	50 n. Type **145**	10	10
543	2 k. 50, Fishing	60	50
544	2 k. 85, Farmer and cattle	65	55
545	10 k. Picking coffee beans	1·25	1·40
542/5	*Set of* 4	2·40	2·25

146 Breast feeding

147 Asbestos Cement

(Des Gabriel Ellison. Litho Format)

1988 (12 Sept). *U.N.I.C.E.F. Child Survival Campaign. T* **146** *and similar vert designs. Multicoloured. P* 12½.

546	50 n. Type **146**	20	10
547	2 k. Growth monitoring	50	30
548	2 k. 85, Immunization	60	60
549	10 k. Oral rehydration	1·25	3·00
546/9	*Set of* 4	2·25	3·50

(Des Gabriel Ellison. Litho Format)

1988 (10 Oct). *Preferential Trade Area Fair. T* **147** *and similar vert designs. Multicoloured. P* 12½.

550	50 n. Type **147**	10	10
551	2 k. 35, Textiles	20	30
552	2 k. 50, Tea	20	40
553	10 k. Poultry	75	2·50
550/3	*Set of* 4	1·10	3·00

148 Emergency Food Distribution

(Des Gabriel Ellison. Litho Questa)

1988 (20 Oct). *125th Anniv of International Red Cross. T* **148** *and similar horiz designs. Multicoloured. P* 14.

554	50 n. Type **148**	20	10
555	2 k. 50, Giving first aid	50	60
556	2 k. 85, Practising bandaging	55	70
557	10 k. Henri Dunant (founder)	1·75	3·00
554/7	*Set of* 4	2·75	4·00

149 Aardvark

(Des Gabriel Ellison. Litho Questa)

1988 (5 Dec). *Endangered Species of Zambia. T* **149** *and similar horiz designs. Multicoloured. P* 14.

558	50 n. Type **149**	25	10
559	2 k. Temminck's Ground Pangolin	50	40
560	2 k. 85, Hunting Dog	60	75
561	20 k. Black Rhinoceros and calf	6·00	7·00
558/61	*Set of* 4	6·50	7·50

150 Boxing — 151 Red Toad

(Des Gabriel Ellison. Litho Questa)

1988 (30 Dec). *Olympic Games, Seoul. T* **150** *and similar horiz designs. Multicoloured. P* 14.

562	50 n. Type **150**	15	10
563	2 k. Athletics	35	40
564	2 k. 50, Hurdling	40	65
565	20 k. Football	3·50	6·00
562/5	*Set of* 4	4·00	6·50
MS566	Two sheets, each 97×72 mm. (a) 30 k. Tennis. (b) 30 k. Karate .. *Set of* 2 *sheets*	8·00	11·00

(Des Gabriel Ellison. Litho Format)

1989 (25 Jan). *Frogs and Toads. T* **151** *and similar horiz designs. Multicoloured. P* $12^{1/2}$.

567	50 n. Type **151**	15	10
568	2 k. 50, Puddle Frog	50	50
569	2 k. 85, Marbled Reed Frog	55	65
570	10 k. Young Reed Frogs	1·60	3·00
567/70	*Set of* 4	2·50	3·75

152 Common Slit-faced Bat — 153 Pope John Paul II and Map of Zambia

(Des Gabriel Ellison. Litho Format)

1989 (22 Mar). *Bats. T* **152** *and similar horiz designs. Multicoloured. P* $12^{1/2}$.

571	50 n. Type **152**	15	10
572	2 k. 50, Little Free-tailed Bat	45	55
573	2 k. 85, Hildebrandt's Horseshoe Bat	55	75
574	10 k. Peters' Epauletted Fruit Bat	1·50	3·00
571/4	*Set of* 4	2·40	4·00

Nos. 572/3 exist imperforate from stock dispersed by the liquidator of Format International Security Printers Ltd.

(Des and litho Harrison)

1989 (2 May). *Visit of Pope John Paul II. T* **153** *and similar vert designs each with inset portrait. Multicoloured. P* $12^{1/2}$.

575	50 n. Type **153**	75	20
576	6 k. 85, Peace dove with olive branch	2·75	2·75
577	7 k. 85, Papal arms	3·00	3·25
578	10 k. Victoria Falls	4·50	4·50
575/8	*Set of* 4	10·00	9·75

K19.50 = (154)

K20.00 = (155)

1989 (1 July–1 Nov). *Various stamps surch.*

(*a*) *Nos.* 339, 341/3, 345/6, 349 *and* 351 *surch as T* **154** (1 *k.* 20, 19 *k.* 50, 20 *k.* 50) *or as T* **155** (*others*)

579	1 k. 20 on 35 n. Tonga Ila granary and house (Br.) (1 Nov)	15	15
580	3 k. 75 on 5 n. Pottery making	20	20
581	8 k. 11 on 10 n. Thatching	40	50
582	9 k. on 30 n. Makishi tightrope dancer	40	50
583	10 k. on 75 n. Women carrying water (38×26 *mm*)	40	50
584	18 k. 50 on 2 k. Pipe-smoking Gwembe Valley belle (38×26 *mm*)	1·00	1·25
585	19 k. 50 on 12 n. Mushroom picking (Br.) (1 Nov)	2·00	2·00
	a. Two stops between "K19" and "50" (R.8/1)		
586	20 k. 50 on 18 n. Millet grinding on stone (V.) (1 Nov)	1·00	1·25

(*b*) *Nos.* 484, 489, 493/5 *and* 497/500 *surch as T* **155**

587	70 n. on 35 n. Black and Rufous Swallow	40	15
	a. Bars printed twice	†	—
588	3 k. on 5 n. Cloud-scraping Cisticola	50	30
589	8 k. on 1 k. 25, Boulton's Puff-back Flycatcher	70	60
590	9 k. 90 on 1 k. 70, Boehm's Bee Eater	80	80
591	10 k. 40 on 1 k. 60, Anchieta's Sunbird	80	80
592	12 k. 50 on 1 k. Bradfield's Hornbill	90	1·00
593	15 k. on 1 k. 95, Perrin's Bush Shrike	95	1·10
594	20 k. on 2 k. Whale-headed Stork	1·50	1·75
595	20 k. 35 on 5 k. Taita Falcon	1·50	1·75
579/95	*Set of* 17	12·00	13·00

No. 587a shows a second pair of bars applied by typography, the original surcharge in lithography being misplaced. One example of this error includes an extraneous "7".

No. 594 shows the surcharge as "K20·00". The previously listed 20 k. on 2 k., No. 502, is surcharged "K20" only.

156 *Parinari curatellifolia* — 157 *Lamarckiana* sp

(Des Gabriel Ellison. Litho Questa)

1989 (26 July). *Edible Fruits. T* **156** *and similar vert designs. Multicoloured. P* $14^{1/2}$.

596	50 n. Type **156**	15	10
597	6 k. 50, *Uapaca kirkiana*	1·25	1·50
598	6 k. 85, Wild Fig	1·25	1·75
599	10 k. Bottle Palm	2·25	2·75
596/9	*Set of* 4	4·50	5·50

(Des Gabriel Ellison. Litho Cartor)

1989 (8 Nov). *Grasshoppers. T* **157** *and similar horiz designs. Multicoloured. P* 14×$13^{1/2}$.

600	70 n. Type **157**	15	10
601	10 k. 40, *Dictyophorus* sp	1·25	1·50
602	12 k. 50, *Cymatomera* sp	1·50	2·25
603	15 k. *Phymateus iris*	2·00	2·75
600/3	*Set of* 4	4·50	6·00

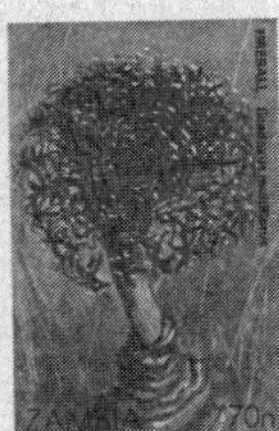

158 Fireball — 159 Postvan, Postman on Bicycle and Main Post Office, Lusaka

(Des Gabriel Ellison. Litho National Printing & Packaging, Zimbabwe)

1989 (6 Dec). *Christmas. Flowers. T* **158** *and similar vert designs. Multicoloured. P* $14^{1/2}$.

604	70 n. Type **158**	15	10
605	10 k. 40, Flame Lily	1·00	1·25
606	12 k. 50, Foxglove Lily	1·40	1·75
607	20 k. Vlei Lily	2·40	3·50
604/7	*Set of* 4	4·50	6·00

(Des D. Miller. Litho Questa)

1990 (2 May). *"Stamp World London 90" International Stamp Exhibition. T* **159** *and similar horiz designs. Multicoloured. P* 14.

608	1 k. 20, Type **159**	10	10
609	19 k. 50, Zambia 1980 18 n. butterflies stamp	2·00	2·50
610	20 k. 50, Rhodesia and Nyasaland 1962 9d. and Northern Rhodesia 1925 ½d. stamps	2·00	2·50
611	50 k. 1840 Penny Black and Maltese Cross cancellation	4·25	5·00
608/11	*Set of* 4	7·50	9·00

160 Footballer and Ball — 161 Road Tanker

(Des R. Vigurs. Litho Questa)

1990 (7 July). *World Cup Football Championship, Italy. T* **160** *and similar vert designs showing football scenes. P* 14.

612	1 k. 20, multicoloured	10	10
613	18 k. 50, multicoloured	2·00	2·50
614	19 k. 50, multicoloured	2·00	2·50
615	20 k. 50, multicoloured	2·00	2·50
612/15	*Set of* 4	5·50	6·50
MS616	100×73 mm. 50 k. multicoloured	6·00	7·00

No. **MS**616 also exists imperforate from a limited printing.

(Litho Harrison)

1990 (23 July). *10th Anniv of Southern African Development Co-ordination Conference. T* **161** *and similar horiz designs, each showing map of Southern Africa. Multicoloured. P* $12^{1/2}$.

617	1 k. 20, Type **161**	15	10
618	19 k. 50, Telecommunications	1·50	2·00
619	20 k. 50, "Regional Co-operation"	1·50	2·00
620	50 k. Transporting coal by cable	5·50	6·50
617/20	*Set of* 4	7·75	9·50

162 Irrigation — 163 The Bird and the Snake

(Des Gabriel Ellison. Litho Questa)

1990 (23 Oct). *26th Anniv of Independence. T* **162** *and similar horiz designs. Multicoloured. P* 14.

621	1 k. 20, Type **162**	10	10
622	19 k. 50, Shoe factory	1·10	1·40
623	20 k. 50, Mwembeshi II satellite earth station	1·25	1·60
624	50 k. "Mother and Child" (statue)	2·50	3·75
621/4	*Set of* 4	4·50	6·00

(Des Gabriel Ellison. Litho Questa)

1990 (30 Oct)–**91**. *Birds (2nd series). Vert designs as T* **138**. *Multicoloured. P* 11×13 (10, 15, 30, 50 *n.*, 1 *k.*, 1 *k.* 20, 2 *k.*, 3 *k.*, 5 *k.*) *or* 14 (*others*).

625	10 n. Livingstone's Flycatcher	10	10
626	15 n. Bar-winged Weaver	10	10
627	30 n. Purple-throated Cuckoo Shrike	10	10
628	50 n. Retz's Red-billed Helmet Shrike	10	10
629	50 n. As 10 n. (7.5.91)	75	30
630	1 k. As 15 n. (7.5.91)	75	40
631	1 k. 20, Bronze-naped Pigeon	20	10
632	2 k. As 30 n. (7.5.91)	75	50
633	3 k. As 50 n. (No. 628) (7.5.91)	75	50
634	5 k. As 1 k. 20 (7.5.91)	80	60
635	15 k. Corncrake	30	20
636	20 k. Dickinson's Kestrel (7.5.91)	90	80
637	20 k. 50, As 20 k.	30	25
638	50 k. Barrow's Bustard ("Denham's Bustard")	45	45
625/38	*Set of* 14	5·50	4·00

Nos. 635/8 are larger, size 23×39 mm.

(Des Gabriel Ellison. Litho Questa)

1991 (11 Jan). *International Literacy Year. Folklore. T* **163** *and similar vert designs. Multicoloured. P* 14.

639	1 k. 20, Type **163**	15	10
640	18 k. 50, Kalulu and the Leopard	1·75	2·00
641	19 k. 50, The Mouse and the Lion	1·75	2·00
642	20 k. 50, Kalulu and the Hippopotamus	1·75	2·00
639/42	*Set of* 4	4·75	5·50

164 Genet

K2 = (165)

(Des Gabriel Ellison. Litho Questa)

1991 (25 Jan). *Small Carnivores. T* **164** *and similar horiz designs. Multicoloured. P* 14.

643	1 k. 20, Type **164**	20	10
644	18 k. 50, Civet	2·25	2·50
645	19 k. 50, Serval	2·25	2·50
646	20 k. 50, African Wild Cat	2·00	2·50
643/6	*Set of* 4	6·00	6·50

1991 (4 Mar). *Nos. 441/4 surch with T* **165**.

647	2 k. on 20 n. Type **129**	2·00	2·50
648	2 k. on 45 n. Postman and Livingstone Post Office, 1950	2·00	2·50
649	2 k. on 55 n. Postman and Kalomo Post Office, 1902	2·00	2·50
650	2 k. on 5 k. African Trans-Continental Telegraph Line under construction, 1900	2·00	2·50
647/50	*Set of* 4	7·00	9·00

166 Woman Cooking

167 Chilubula Church near Kasama

(Des A. Mwansa and Daniela Schepp. Litho Cartor)

1991 (28 June). *Soya Promotion Campaign. T* **166** *and similar vert designs. Multicoloured. P* 13½.

651	1 k. Type **166**	10	10
652	2 k. Soya bean and field	10	10
653	5 k. Mother feeding child	20	15
654	20 k. Healthy and malnourished children	1·25	1·75
655	50 k. President Kaunda holding child	2·25	3·00
651/5	*Set of* 5	3·50	4·50

1991 (5 July). *Various stamps surch as T* **165**.

656	**130**	2 k. on 20 n. multicoloured
657	**127**	2 k. on 25 n. multicoloured (Gold)
658	–	2 k. on 28 n. multicoloured (No. 344)
659	–	2 k. on 28 n. multicoloured (No. 393)
660	–	2 k. on 28 n. multicoloured (No. 401)
661	–	2 k. on 28 n. multicoloured (No. 418)
662	–	2 k. on 32 n. multicoloured (No. 422)
663	–	2 k. on 35 n. multicoloured (No. 453)
664	**134**	2 k. on 35 n. multicoloured
665	**137**	2 k. on 35 n. multicoloured
666	–	2 k. on 45 n. multicoloured (No. 427)
667	–	2 k. on 45 n. black, new blue and pale blue (No. 430)
668	–	2 k. on 45 n. deep violet-blue and gold (No. 433)
669	–	2 k. on 45 n. black, new blue & brownish black (No. 446) (Gold + Blk.)
670	–	2 k. on 1 k. 60, multicoloured (No. 470)
671	–	2 k. on 1 k. 70, multicoloured (No. 451)
672	–	2 k. on 1 k. 70, multicoloured (No. 482)
673	–	2 k. on 5 k. multicoloured (No. 435)
674	–	2 k. on 5 k. multicoloured (No. 452)
675	–	2 k. on 6 k. 50, multicoloured (No. 597)
676	–	2 k. on 6 k. 85, multicoloured (No. 576)
677	–	2 k. on 6 k. 85, multicoloured (No. 598)
678	–	2 k. on 7 k. 85, multicoloured (No. 577)

The surcharge for No. 669 shows "K2" in gold and the bars in black over gold.

(Des Gabriel Ellison. Litho Cartor)

1991 (18 July). *500th Birth Anniv of St. Ignatius Loyola. T* **167** *and similar vert designs. Multicoloured. P* 13½.

679	1 k. Type **167**	10	10
680	2 k. Chikuni Church near Monze	15	15
681	20 k. Bishop Joseph du Pont	1·75	2·00
682	50 k. Saint Ignatius Loyola	3·00	3·75
679/82	*Set of* 4	4·50	5·50

168 *Adansonia digitata*

169 *Disa hamatopetala*

(Des Gabriel Ellison. Litho Cartor)

1991 (28 Nov). *Flowering Trees. T* **168** *and similar horiz designs. Multicoloured. P* 13½.

683	1 k. Type **168**	10	10
684	2 k. *Dichrostachys cinerea*	15	15
685	10 k. *Stereospermum kunthianum*	90	1·00
686	30 k. *Azana garckeana*	2·25	3·00
683/6	*Set of* 4	3·00	3·75

No. 685 is inscribed "Sterospermum" in error.

(Des D. Miller. Litho Cartor)

1992 (6 Feb). *40th Anniv of Queen Elizabeth II's Accession. Horiz designs as T* **113** *of Kenya. Multicoloured. W w* **14** *(sideways). P* 13½.

687	4 k. Queen's House	10	10
688	32 k. Traditional village	80	60
689	35 k. Fishermen hauling nets	80	80
690	38 k. Three portraits of Queen Elizabeth	95	95
691	50 k. Queen Elizabeth II	1·25	2·25
687/91	*Set of* 5	3·50	4·25

(Des Gabriel Ellison. Litho Cartor)

1992 (28 Feb). *Orchids. T* **169** *and similar vert designs. Multicoloured. P* 13½.

692	1 k. Type **169**	30	15
693	2 k. *Eulophia paivaeana*	30	20
694	5 k. *Eulophia quartiniana*	60	40
695	20 k. *Aerangis verdickii*	2·75	3·50
692/5	*Set of* 4	3·50	3·75

170 Kasinja Mask

171 Bushbuck

(Des Gabriel Ellison. Litho Cartor)

1992 (10 Mar). *Tribal Masks. T* **170** *and similar vert designs. Multicoloured. P* 13½.

696	1 k. Type **170**	10	10
697	2 k. Chizaluke	10	10
698	10 k. Mwanapweu	35	35
699	30 k. Maliya	1·25	1·75
696/9	*Set of* 4	1·50	2·00

(Des Gabriel Ellison. Litho Questa)

1992 (14 Sept). *Antelopes. T* **171** *and similar horiz designs. Multicoloured. P* 14.

700	4 k. Type **171**	10	10
701	40 k. Eland	40	40
702	45 k. Roan Antelope	45	45
703	100 k. Sable Antelope	1·10	1·75
700/3	*Set of* 4	1·75	2·40

172 De Havilland D.H.66 Hercules *City of Basra*

(Des Gabriel Ellison. Litho Questa)

1992 (24 Nov). *60th Anniv of Airmail Service. T* **172** *and similar horiz designs. Multicoloured. P* 14.

704	4 k. Type **172**	30	20
705	40 k. Vickers Super VC-10	1·25	75
706	45 k. Short S.45A Solent 3 flying boat *Severn*	1·25	75
707	100 k. Douglas DC-10	2·25	3·25
704/7	*Set of* 4	4·50	4·50

173 Wise Men with Gifts

174 Hurdling

(Litho Questa)

1992 (23 Dec). *Christmas. T* **173** *and similar horiz designs. Multicoloured. P* 14.

708	10 k. Type **173**	10	10
709	80 k. Nativity	1·10	1·25
710	90 k. Angelic choir	1·25	1·40
711	100 k. Angel and shepherds	1·40	1·60
708/11	*Set of* 4	3·25	3·75
MS712	209×57 mm. Nos. 708/11	5·50	6·50

(Des R. Vigurs. Litho Questa)

1992 (28 Dec). *Olympic Games, Barcelona. T* **174** *and similar vert designs. Multicoloured. P* 14.

713	10 k. Type **174**	10	10
714	40 k. Boxing	40	40
715	80 k. Judo	80	1·25
716	100 k. Cycling	1·50	1·75
713/16	*Set of* 4	2·50	3·00

175 Nkundalila Falls

176 Athlete and Cardiograph

(Des Gabriel Ellison. Litho Cartor)

1993 (30 Sept). *Waterfalls. T* **175** *and similar horiz designs. Multicoloured. P* 13½.

717	50 k. Type **175**	10	10
718	200 k. Chishimba Falls	20	25
719	250 k. Chipoma Falls	25	30
720	300 k. Lumangwe Falls	30	35
717/20	*Set of* 4	80	95

(Litho National Printing & Packaging, Zimbabwe)

1993 (20 Oct). *Heartbeat Campaign. T* **176** *and similar vert design. Multicoloured. P* 14½.

721	(O) Type **176**	50	55
722	(P) Heart and cardiograph	50	55

These stamps were initially sold at 50 k. (No. 721) for ordinary post and 80 k. (No. 722) for priority mail. These face values were increased to reflect postage rates increases. See note below Nos. 723/38.

177 Bronze Sunbird

178 Tiger Snake

(Des Gabriel Ellison. Litho Cartor)

1994 (30 May). *Sunbirds. T* **177** *and similar horiz designs. Multicoloured. P* 13. *(a) Face values as T* **177**.

723	20 k. Type **177**	10	10
724	50 k. Violet-backed Sunbird	10	10
725	100 k. Scarlet-chested Sunbird	10	10
726	150 k. Bannerman's Sunbird	15	20
727	200 k. Oustalet's White-bellied Sunbird	20	25
728	250 k. Anchieta's Sunbird ("Red and Blue Sunbird")	25	30
729	300 k. Olive Sunbird	30	35
730	350 k. Green-headed Sunbird	35	40
731	400 k. Red-tufted Malachite Sunbird	40	45
732	500 k. Variable Sunbird	50	55
733	800 k. Coppery Sunbird	75	80
734	1000 k. Orange-tufted Sunbird	95	1·00
735	1500 k. Amethyst Sunbird ("Black Sunbird")	1·40	1·50
736	2000 k. Green-throated Sunbird	1·90	2·00
	(b) Face values shown as capital letters		
737	(O) Mariqua Sunbird ("Marico Sunbird")	50	55
738	(P) Eastern Double-collared Sunbird	50	55
723/38	*Set of* 16	8·25	9·00

Nos. 737/8 were initially sold at 50 k. for ordinary post (No. 737) and 80 k. for priority mail (No. 738). These rates were increased to 100 k. for ordinary post and 150 k. for priority mail on 20 June 1994. On 1 March 1995 the difference between the two rates was abolished and both "O" and "P" stamps were sold at 500 k. This was reduced to 400 k. each on 1 April 1995, but the rate reverted to 500 k. on 8 February 1996.

(Litho Questa)

1994 (28 Sept). *Snakes. T* **178** *and similar vert designs. Multicoloured. P* 14.

739	50 k. Type **178**	10	10
740	200 k. Egyptian Cobra	20	25
741	300 k. African Python	30	35
742	500 k. Green Mamba	50	55
739/42	*Set of* 4	1·00	1·25

179 Women working on Road

(Des Gabriel Ellison. Litho Questa)

1995 (3 Apr). *75th Anniv of International Labour Organization. T* **179** *and similar horiz design. Multicoloured. P* 14.

743	100 k. Type **179**	10	10
744	450 k. Women making cement blocks	45	50

180 Angel playing Kalimba and Flowers

181 Anniversary Emblem, Rainbow and Map

(Des Gabriel Ellison. Litho Walsall)

1995 (29 Aug). *Christmas* (1994). *T* **180** *and similar diamond-shaped designs. Multicoloured. P* 14×14½.

745	100 k. Type **180**	10	10
746	300 k. Angel at prayer and animals	30	35
747	450 k. Angel with flute and birds	45	50
748	500 k. Angel with drum and Baobab trees	50	55
745/8	*Set of* 4	1·40	1·50

(Photo Courvoisier)

1995 (30 Dec). *50th Anniv of United Nations. Granite paper. P* 11½.

749 **181**	700 k. multicoloured	70	75

182 David Livingstone (missionary) and Memorial

183 Saddle-bill Stork

(Des Gabriel Ellison. Litho Questa)

1996 (21 Feb). *Monuments. T* **182** *and similar vert designs. Multicoloured. P* 14.

750	100 k. Type **182**	10	10
751	300 k. Mbereshi Mission	30	35
752	450 k. Von Lettow-Vorbeck Monument	45	50
753	500 k. Niamkolo Church	50	55
750/3	*Set of* 4	1·40	1·50

(Des Gabriel Ellison. Litho Walsall)

1996 (27 Nov). *Endangered Species. Birds. T* **183** *and similar horiz designs. Multicoloured. P* 14×14½.

754	200 k. Type **183**	20	25
755	300 k. Black-cheeked Lovebird	30	35
756	500 k. Pair of Black-cheeked Lovebirds	50	55
757	900 k. Saddle-bill Stork and chicks	90	95
754/7	*Set of* 4	1·90	2·10
MS758	120×90 mm. Nos. 754/7	50·00	50·00

O

═

(184)

1996 (18 Dec). *Christmas. Nos.* 709/10 *surch as T* **184**.

759	(O) on 90 k. Angelic Choir	50	55
760	900 k. on 80 k. Nativity	85	90

No. 759 was sold at 500 k., which was the minimum local postage rate for ordinary post.

STAMP BOOKLETS

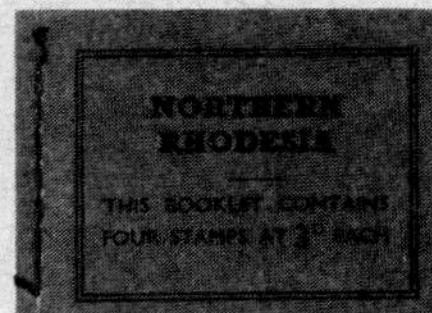

B 1

1964. *Black on blue cover as Type* B **1**. *Stitched.*

SB1	1s. booklet containing 3d. (No.78) in block of 4	8·00

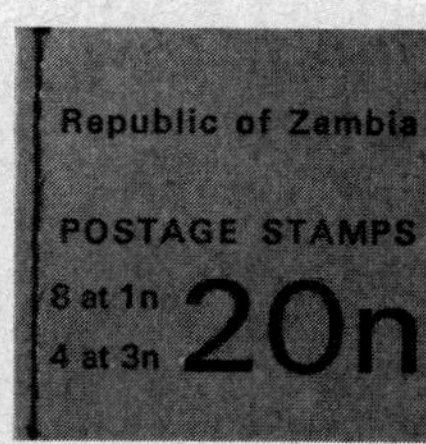

B 2

1968. *Black on buff covers as Type* B **2** (*No.* SB2), *or size* 82×58 *mm* (*No.* SB3). *Stitched.*

SB2	20 n. booklet containing eight 1 n. and four 3 n. (Nos. 129, 131) in blocks of 4	4·00
SB3	30 n. booklet containing twelve 1 n. and six 3 n. (Nos. 129, 131) in blocks of 6	4·00

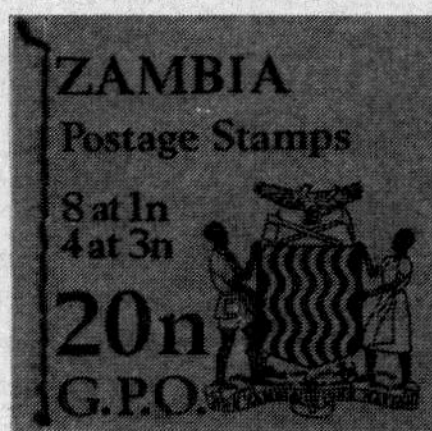

B 3

1970 (26 Aug). *Black on green cover as Type* B **3** (*No.* SB4) *or black on rose cover, size* 82×58 *mm* (*No.* SB5). *Stitched.*

SB4	20 n. booklet containing eight 1 n. and four 3 n. (Nos. 129, 131) in blocks of 4	3·75
SB5	30 n. booklet containing twelve 1 n. and six 3 n. (Nos. 129, 131) in blocks of 6	4·00

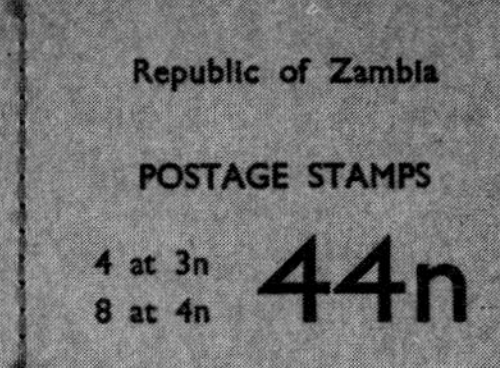

B 4

1976. *Black on green cover as Type* B **4**, (*No.* SB6), *or black on blue cover, size* 101×54 *mm* (*No.* SB7). *Stitched.*

SB6	44 n. booklet containing four 3 n. and eight 4 n. (Nos. 228/9) in blocks of 4	6·50
SB7	78 n. booklet containing 4 n. and 9 n. (Nos. 229, 232), each in block of 6	7·50

B 5

1981 (2 June). *Black on emerald* (*No.* SB8) *or orange* (*No.* SB9) *covers as Type* B **5**. *Stitched.*

SB8	66 n. booklet containing 1 n., 2 n. and 8 n. (Nos. 337/8, 340), each in block of 6	2·50
SB9	1 k. 08, booklet containing 8 n. and 10 n. (Nos. 340/1), each in block of 6	2·75

POSTAGE DUE STAMPS

D 1

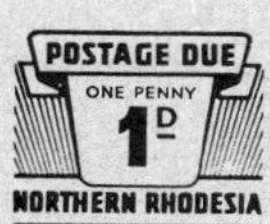

D 2

(Typo D.L.R.)

1929–52. *Wmk Mult Script CA. Ordinary paper. P* 14.

D1 D **1**	1d. grey-black	2·50	2·50
	a. Chalk-surfaced paper. *Blk* (22.1.52)	20·00	75·00
	ab. Error. St. Edward's Crown, W9*b*	£1200	
D2	2d. grey-black	3·00	3·00
D3	3d. grey-black	3·00	22·00
	a. Chalk-surfaced paper. *Blk* (22.1.52)	7·00	65·00
	ab. Error. Crown missing, W9*a*	£200	
	ac. Error. St. Edward's Crown, W9*b*	£150	
D4	4d. grey-black	9·00	27·00
D1/4	*Set of* 4	16·00	48·00
D1/4 Perf "Specimen"	*Set of* 4	85·00	

The 2d. is known bisected and used as a 1d. at Luanshya or Nkana on various dates between 1937 and 1951 and on understamped letters from South Africa at Chingola in May 1950 (*Price on cover* £350).

Following the increase in the internal letter rate from 1½d. to 2d. on 1 July 1953 stocks of postage due stamps at Mkushi became exhausted. As an emergency measure the sub-postmaster was authorised to surcharge examples of Nos. 28 and 55 "POSTAGE DUE (or "postage due") 1d." in red by typewriter. Examples properly used on cover between 6 July and 15 September 1953 are of considerable scarcity (*Price on cover* £2000). No unused examples exist.

(Des D. Smith. Litho Govt Ptr, Lusaka)

1963 (10 Dec). *P* 12½.

D 5 D **2**	1d. orange	80	3·00
D 6	2d. deep blue	80	3·25
D 7	3d. lake	90	3·75
D 8	4d. ultramarine	90	5·50
D 9	6d. purple	4·50	7·50
D10	1s. light emerald	5·50	17·00
	a. Imperf (vert pair)	£170	
	b. Block of four imperf horiz and imp between vert	£650	
D5/10	*Set of* 6	12·00	32·00

In all values the stamps in the right-hand vertical row of the sheet are imperforate on the right.

D 3

(Des D. Smith. Litho Govt Printer, Lusaka)

1964 (24 Oct). *P* 12½.

D11 D **3**	1d. orange	30	1·00
D12	2d. deep blue	35	1·40
D13	3d. lake	45	1·60
D14	4d. ultramarine	45	2·00
D15	6d. purple	45	2·25
D16	1s. light emerald	55	4·25
D11/16	*Set of* 6	2·25	11·50

In all values the left-hand vertical row of the sheet is imperf at left and the bottom horizontal row is imperf at bottom. The above were crudely perforated, resulting in variations in the sizes of the stamps.

The above were withdrawn on 15 January 1968 and thereafter decimal currency postage stamps were used for postage due purposes with appropriate cancellations.

Appendix

The following stamps have either been issued in excess of postal needs, or have not been made available to the public in reasonable quantities at face value. Miniature sheets, imperforate stamps etc., are excluded from this section.

1984

Olympic Games, Los Angeles. 90 *n.* × 5, *each embossed on gold foil.*

1987

Classic Cars. 1 *k.* 50×25, *each embossed on gold foil.*

Zanzibar *see* Tanzania

Zimbabwe
(formerly Rhodesia)

SOUTHERN RHODESIA

PRICES FOR STAMPS ON COVER TO 1945
Nos. 1/61 *from* × 2

SELF-GOVERNMENT

The southern part of Rhodesia, previously administered by the British South Africa Company, was annexed by the British Government and granted the status of a self-governing colony from 1 October 1923.

The existing stamps of Rhodesia (the "Admiral" design first issued in 1913) remained in use until 31 March 1924 and continued to be valid for postal purposes until 30 April of that year.

1

2 King George V

3 Victoria Falls

(Recess Waterlow)

1924 (1 Apr)–**29**. *P* 14.

No.	Type	Description	Unused	Used
1	1	½d. blue-green	1·00	10
		a. Imperf between (horiz pair)	£650	£700
		b. Imperf between (vert pair)	£650	£700
		c. Imperf vert (horiz pair)	£700	
2		1d. bright rose	1·60	10
		a. Imperf between (horiz pair)	£600	£650
		b. Imperf between (vert pair)	£1000	
		c. Perf 12½ (coil) (1929)	2·75	80·00
3		1½d. bistre-brown	1·00	45
		a. Imperf between (horiz pair)	£7500	
		b. Imperf between (vert pair)	£4250	
		c. Printed double, once albino	£250	
4		2d. black and purple-grey	2·00	40
		a. Imperf between (horiz pair)	£8500	
5		3d. blue	2·25	2·00
6		4d. black and orange-red	2·00	2·75
7		6d. black and mauve	2·00	2·75
		a. Imperf between (horiz pair)	£15000	
8		8d. purple and pale green	11·00	42·00
9		10d. blue and rose	11·00	42·00
10		1s. black and light blue	5·00	3·75
11		1s. 6d. black and yellow	19·00	28·00
12		2s. black and brown	17·00	17·00
13		2s. 6d. blue and sepia	35·00	60·00
14		5s. blue and blue-green	60·00	£100
1/14		*Set of* 14	£150	£275

Prices for "imperf between" varieties are for adjacent stamps from the same pane and not for those separated by wide gutter margins between vertical or horizontal pairs, which come from the junction of two panes.

(T 2 recess by B.W.; T 3 typo by Waterlow)

1931 (1 April)–**37**. *T* **2** (*line perf* 12 *unless otherwise stated) and* **3** (*comb perf* 15 × 14). (*The* 11½ *perf is comb.*).

No.	Type	Description	Unused	Used
15	2	½d. green	85	75
		a. Perf 11½ (1933)	65	20
		b. Perf 14 (1935)	1·60	30
16		1d. scarlet	1·00	40
		a. Perf 11½ (1933)	1·50	20
		b. Perf 14 (1935)	50	20
16c		1½d. chocolate (3.3.33)	60·00	42·00
		d. Perf 11½ (1.4.32)	2·50	55
17	3	2d. black and sepia	3·75	1·00
18		3d. deep ultramarine	10·00	11·00
19	2	4d. black and vermilion	1·25	90
		a. Perf 11½ (1935)	17·00	5·00
		b. Perf 14 (10.37)	32·00	48·00
20		6d. black and magenta	2·25	1·75
		a. Perf 11½ (1933)	15·00	1·25
		b. Perf 14 (1936)	10·00	60
21		8d. violet and olive-green	1·75	3·25
		a. Perf 11½ (1934)	17·00	30·00
21b		9d. vermilion and olive-green (1.9.34)	6·00	9·00
22		10d. blue and scarlet	7·00	3·00
		a. Perf 11½ (1933)	6·00	13·00
23		1s. black and greenish blue	2·00	2·25
		a. Perf 11½ (1935)	90·00	60·00
		b. Perf 14 (10.37)	£200	£140
24		1s. 6d. black and orange-yellow	10·00	16·00
		a. Perf 11½ (1936)	50·00	95·00
25		2s. black and brown	20·00	5·50
		a. Perf 11½ (1933)	35·00	30·00
26		2s. 6d. blue and drab	32·00	35·00
		a. Perf 11½ (1933)	28·00	30·00
27		5s. blue and blue-green	48·00	48·00
		a. Printed on gummed side	£3750	
15/27		*Set of* 15	£120	£110

No. 16c was only issued in booklets.

PRINTERS. All stamps from Types **4** to **29** were recess-printed by Waterlow and Sons, Ltd, London, except where otherwise stated.

4

1932 (1 May). *P* 12½.

No.	Type	Description	Unused	Used
29	4	2d. green and chocolate	3·00	50
30		3d. deep ultramarine	3·50	1·75
		a. Imperf horiz (vert pair)	£6000	£7000
		b. Imperf between (vert pair)	£12000	

5 Victoria Falls

1935 (6 May). *Silver Jubilee. P* 11×12.

No.	Type	Description	Unused	Used
31	5	1d. olive and rose-carmine	3·25	1·75
32		2d. emerald and sepia	5·50	5·00
33		3d. violet and deep blue	5·50	10·00
34		6d. black and purple	8·00	13·00
31/4		*Set of* 4	20·00	27·00

1935–41. *Inscr* "POSTAGE AND REVENUE".

No.	Type	Description	Unused	Used
35	4	2d. green and chocolate (*p* 12½)	2·00	7·50
		a. Perf 14 (1941)	1·00	10
35b		3d. deep blue (*p* 14) (1938)	2·75	10

6 Victoria Falls and Railway Bridge

7 King George VI

1937 (12 May). *Coronation. P* 12½.

No.	Type	Description	Unused	Used
36	6	1d. olive and rose-carmine	80	50
37		2d. emerald and sepia	80	1·25
38		3d. violet and blue	3·75	7·00
39		6d. black and purple	2·25	3·25
36/9		*Set of* 4	7·00	11·00

1937 (25 Nov). *P* 14.

No.	Type	Description	Unused	Used
40	7	½d. green	50	10
41		1d. scarlet	30	10
42		1½d. red-brown	1·00	10
43		4d. red-orange	1·50	10
44		6d. grey-black	1·50	20
45		8d. emerald-green	2·00	1·00
46		9d. pale blue	1·50	30
47		10d. purple	2·25	1·75
48		1s. black and blue-green	1·75	10
		a. Double print of frame	£900	
49		1s. 6d. black and orange-yellow	9·00	1·50
50		2s. black and brown	12·00	55
51		2s. 6d. ultramarine and purple	8·00	4·25
52		5s. blue and blue-green	26·00	2·00
40/52		*Set of* 13	60·00	10·50

Nos. 40/1 exist in coils, constructed from normal sheets.

8 British South Africa Co's Arms

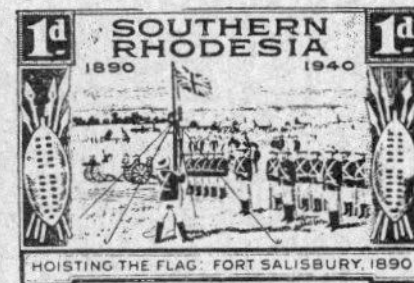

9 Fort Salisbury, 1890

10 Cecil John Rhodes (after S. P. Kendrick)

15 Lobengula's Kraal and Govt House, Salisbury

MINIMUM PRICE

The minimum price quote is 10p which represents a handling charge rather than a basis for valuing common stamps. For further notes about prices see introductory pages.

Recut shirt collar (R. 6/1)

"Cave" flaw (R. 6/6)

(Des Mrs. L. E. Curtis (½d., 1d., 1½d., 3d.), Mrs I. Mount (others))

1940 (3 June). *British South Africa Company's Golden Jubilee. T* **8/10**, **15** *and similar designs. P* 14.

No.	Type	Description	Unused	Used
53		½d. slate-violet and green	10	45
54		1d. violet-blue and scarlet	10	10
55		1½d. black and red-brown	15	70
		a. Recut shirt collar	19·00	
56		2d. green and bright violet	30	50
57		3d. black and blue	30	1·00
		a. Cave flaw	26·00	
58		4d. green and brown	1·75	2·00
59		6d. chocolate and green	30	1·75
60		1s. blue and green	45	1·75
53/60		*Set of* 8	3·00	7·50

Designs: *Horiz* (*as T* 8)—2d. Fort Victoria; 3d. Rhodes makes peace. *Vert* (*as T* 10)—4d. Victoria Falls Bridge; 6d. Statue of Sir Charles Coghlan.

16 Mounted Pioneer

Hat brim retouch (P1 1B R. 1/8)

(Roto South African Govt Printer, Pretoria)

1943 (1 Nov). *50th Anniv of Occupation of Matabeleland. W* **9** *of South Africa* (*Mult Springbok*) *sideways. P* 14.

No.	Type	Description	Unused	Used
61	16	2d. brown and green	20	40
		a. Hat brim retouch	17·00	

17 Queen Elizabeth II when Princess and Princess Margaret

1947 (1 Apr). *Royal Visit. T* **17** *and similar horiz design. P* 14.

No.	Type	Description	Unused	Used
62		½d. black and green	15	50
63		1d. black and scarlet	15	50

Design:—1d. King George VI and Queen Elizabeth.

19 Queen Elizabeth

20 King George VI

21 Queen Elizabeth II when Princess

22 Princess Margaret

Damage to right-hand frame (R.1/10)

1947 (8 May). *Victory. P* 14.
64 **19** 1d. carmine — 10 10
65 **20** 2d. slate — 10 10
a. Double print — £1000
b. Damaged frame — 8·50
66 **21** 3d. blue — 55 30
67 **22** 6d. orange — 30 55
64/7 — *Set of* 4 — 90 90

(Recess B.W.)

1949 (10 Oct). *75th Anniv of U.P.U. As Nos.* 146/7 *of Jamaica.*
68 2d. slate-green — 80 20
69 3d. blue — 1·10 2·75

23 Queen Victoria, Arms and King George VI

1950 (12 Sept). *Diamond Jubilee of Southern Rhodesia. P* 14.
70 **23** 2d. green and brown — 30 60

24 "Medical Services"

(Des A. R. Winter (2d.), Mrs. J. M. Enalim (others))

1953 (15 Apr). *Birth Centenary of Cecil Rhodes. T* **24** *and similar horiz designs. P* 14.
71 ½d. pale blue and sepia — 15 1·40
72 1d. chestnut and blue-green — 15 10
73 2d. grey-green and violet — 15 10
74 4½d. deep blue-green & deep ultramarine — 75 2·50
75 1s. black and red-brown — 3·00 80
71/5 — *Set of* 5 — 3·75 4·25

Designs:—1d. "Agriculture"; 2d. "Building"; 4½d. "Water Supplies"; 1s. "Transport".

No. 74 also commemorates the Diamond Jubilee of Matabeleland.

1953 (30 May). *Rhodes Centenary Exhibition, Bulawayo. As No.* 59 *of Zambia, but without watermark.*
76 6d. violet — 30 50

30 Queen Elizabeth II

(Recess D.L.R.)

1953 (1 June). *Coronation. P* 12 × 12½.
77 **30** 2s. 6d. carmine — 5·50 6·00

31 Sable Antelope

33 Rhodes's Grave

34 Farm Worker

42 Basket Maker

43 Balancing Rocks

44 Coat of Arms

(Recess, centre typo (4d.), B.W.)

1953 (31 Aug). *T* **31, 33/4, 42/4** *and similar designs. P* 13½ × 14 (*2d., 6d., 5s.*), 14 (*10s., £1*) *or* 14 × 13½ (*others*).
78 ½d. grey-green and claret — 30 40
79 1d. green and brown — 30 10
80 2d. deep chestnut and reddish violet — 30 10
81 3d. chocolate and rose-red — 55 70
82 4d. red, green and indigo — 3·25 10
83 4½d. black and deep bright blue — 2·00 2·75
84 6d. brown-olive & deep turquoise-green — 3·00 60
85 9d. deep blue and reddish brown — 3·50 2·75
86 1s. reddish violet and light blue — 1·25 10
87 2s. purple and scarlet — 11·00 3·50
88 2s. 6d. yellow-olive and orange-brown — 6·50 3·75
89 5s. yellow-brown and deep green — 14·00 8·50
90 10s. red-brown and olive — 17·00 35·00
91 £1 rose-red and black — 27·00 35·00
78/91 — *Set of* 14 — 80·00 80·00

Designs: *Vert* (*as T* **31**)—1d. Tobacco planter. (*As T* **33**)—6d. Baobab tree. *Horiz* (*as T* **34**)—4d. Flame Lily; 4½d. Victoria Falls; 9d. Lion; 1s. Zimbabwe Ruins; 2s. Birchenough Bridge; 2s. 6d. Kariba Gorge.

For issues from 1954 to 1963 see under RHODESIA AND NYASALAND.

45 Maize

50 Flame Lily

56 Cattle

58 Coat of Arms

(Des V. Whiteley. Photo Harrison)

1964 (19 Feb). *T* **45, 50, 56, 58** *and similar horiz designs. P* 14½ (*½d. to 4d.*), 13½ × 13 (*6d. to 2s. 6d.*) *or* 14½ × 14 (*others*).
92 ½d. yellow, yellow-green and light blue — 20 1·25
93 1d. reddish violet and yellow-ochre — 15 10
a. Reddish violet omitted — £1400
94 2d. yellow and deep violet — 60 10
95 3d. chocolate and pale blue — 20 10
96 4d. yellow-orange and deep green — 30 10
97 6d. carmine-red, yellow & deep dull green — 40 10
98 9d. red-brown, yellow and olive-green — 2·50 80
99 1s. blue-green and ochre — 4·00 10
a. Blue-green (Queen and emeralds) omitted — £1600
100 1s. 3d. red, violet and yellow-green — 3·75 10
101 2s. blue and ochre — 3·00 1·25
102 2s. 6d. ultramarine and vermilion — 5·00 70
a. Vermilion omitted — £1800
b. Ultramarine omitted — £4250
103 5s. light brown, bistre-yellow & light blue — 5·00 2·25
104 10s. black, yell-ochre, lt blue & carmine-red — 13·00 6·50
105 £1 brown, yellow-grn, buff & salmon-pink — 7·00 16·00
92/105 — *Set of* 14 — 40·00 26·00

Designs: (*As T* **45**)—1d. African Buffalo; 2d. Tobacco; 3d. Greater Kudu; 4d. Citrus. (*As T* **50**)—9d. Ansellia Orchid; 1s. Emeralds; 1s. 3d. Aloe; 2s. Lake Kyle; 2s. 6d. Tigerfish. (*As T* **56**)—10s. Helmet Guineafowl.

Nos. 92 and 93 exist in coils constructed from normal sheets.

Nos. 102a and 102b occur on different sheets and involve one vertical row of stamps in each instance. They were caused by the printing press being stopped and then restarted. Three such sheets showing No. 102a have been reported.

See also Nos. 359/72 of Rhodesia.

In October 1964 Southern Rhodesia was renamed Rhodesia.

RHODESIA

59 "Telecommunications"

60 Bangala Dam

(Des V. Whiteley. Photo Harrison)

1965 (17 May). *I.T.U. Centenary. P* 14½.
351 **59** 6d. violet and light yellow-olive — 1·50 40
352 1s. 3d. violet and lilac — 1·50 40
353 2s. 6d. violet and light brown — 2·50 4·50
351/3 — *Set of* 3 — 5·00 4·75

(Des V. Whiteley. Photo Harrison)

1965 (19 July). *Water Conservation. T* **60** *and similar vert designs. Multicoloured. P* 14.
354 3d. Type **60** — 30 10
355 4d. Irrigation canal — 1·00 1·25
356 2s. 6d. Cutting sugar cane — 2·25 3·50
354/6 — *Set of* 3 — 3·25 4·25

63 Sir Winston Churchill, Quill, Sword and Houses of Parliament

(Des H. Baxter. Photo Harrison)

1965 (16 Aug). *Churchill Commemoration. P* 14½.
357 **63** 1s. 3d. black and bright blue — 60 35

UNILATERAL DECLARATION OF INDEPENDENCE

Independence was declared by Rhodesia on 11 November 1965 but this was not recognised by the British Government. Following a conference in London during 1979 it was agreed that the British Government should resume control, pending elections to be held in February 1980.

After the elections Rhodesia became an independent republic within the Commonwealth on 18 April 1980, as ZIMBABWE.

64 Coat of Arms

(Des Col. C. R. Dickenson. Litho Mardon Printers, Salisbury)

1965 (8 Dec). *"Independence". P* 11.
358 **64** 2s. 6d. multicoloured — 15 15
a. Imperf (pair) — £600

INDEPENDENCE
11th November
1965

INDEPENDENCE
11th November 1965
(65)

= 5/-
(66)

1966 (17 Jan). (*a*) *Nos.* 92/105 *optd with T* **65** *or larger* (*5s. to £1*) *by Mardon Printers, Salisbury.*
359 ½d. yellow, yellow-green and light blue — 10 10
a. Pair, one stamp without opt. — £2750
360 1d. reddish violet and yellow-ochre — 10 10
361 2d. yellow and deep violet — 10 10
362 3d. chocolate and pale blue — 10 10
363 4d. yellow-orange and deep green — 15 10
364 6d. carmine-red, yellow & dp dull green — 15 10
365 9d. red-brown, yellow and olive-green — 30 10
a. Opt double — £325
366 1s. blue-green and ochre — 40 10
a. Opt double — £325
367 1s. 3d. red, violet and yellow-green — 80 20
368 2s. blue and ochre — 90 3·25
369 2s. 6d. ultramarine and vermilion — 60 1·00
370 5s. light brown, bistre-yellow & lt blue — 2·50 5·50
a. Opt double — £425
371 10s. black, yellow-ochre, lt bl & carm-red — 3·00 2·25
372 £1 brown, yell-green, buff & salmon-pink — 1·25 2·25

(*b*) *No.* 357 *surch with T* **66**
373 5s. on 1s. 3d. black and bright blue (R.) — 8·00 25·00
a. "5/-" omitted
359/73 — *Set of* 15 — 16·00 35·00

Owing to the existence of forgeries, No. 370a should only be purchased when accompanied by a certificate of genuineness. Other overprint errors exist from the clandestine use of the original settings.

67 Emeralds

68 Zeederberg Coach, *circa* 1895

(Des V. Whiteley. Photo Harrison)

1966 (9 Feb). *As Nos.* 92/105, *but inscr* "RHODESIA" *as T* **67**. *Some designs and colours changed. P* 14½ (1*d. to* 4*d.*), 13½×13 (6*d. to* 2*s.* 6*d*) *or* 14½×14 (5*s. to* £1).

374 – 1d. reddish violet and yellow-ochre .. 10 10
375 – 2d. yellow-orange and dp grn (as No. 96) 10 10
a. Yellow-orange omitted £1000
376 – 3d. chocolate and pale blue 10 10
a. Chocolate omitted £1700
b. Pale blue omitted £1300
377 **67** 4d. emerald and sepia 70 10
378 **50** 6d. carmine-red, yellow & dp dull green 15 10
379 – 9d. yellow and deep violet (as No. 94) .. 15 20
380 **45** 1s. yellow, yellow-green and light blue 15 10
381 – 1s. 3d. blue and ochre (as No. 101) .. 25 15
a. Ochre omitted £1900
382 – 1s. 6d. red-brn, yell & ol-grn (as No. 98) 1·75 25
383 – 2s. red, violet and yell-grn (as No. 100) 40 80
384 – 2s. 6d. blue, vermilion & turquoise-blue 40 20
385 **56** 5s. light brown, bistre-yellow & lt blue 40 90
386 – 10s. black, yell-ochre, lt blue & carm-red 2·25 4·00
387 **58** £1 brown, yell-grn, buff & salmon-pink 10·00 8·00
374/87 .. .. *Set of* 14 14·00 13·00

Nos. 379/80 are in larger format, as T **50**.

No. 374 exists in coils constructed from normal sheets. Coil-vending machines were withdrawn from service in 1967.

No. 375a occured on single rows from two separate sheets, No. 376a in the bottom row of a sheet, No. 376b in the top two rows of a sheet and No. 381a in the third vertical row on two sheets.

For stamps printed by lithography, see Nos. 397/407.

PRINTERS. All the following stamps were printed by lithography by Mardon Printers, Salisbury.

(Des V. Whiteley (Nos. 388/90))

1966 (2 May). *28th Congress of Southern Africa Philatelic Federation* ("*Rhopex*"). *T* **68** *and similar horiz designs. P* 14½.

388 3d. multicoloured 25 10
389 9d. grey-buff, sepia and grey-green 30 40
390 1s. 6d. pale blue and black 50 50
391 2s. 6d. salmon-pink, pale dull grn & blk 55 80
388/91 .. .. *Set of* 4 1·40 1·50
MS392 126×84 mm. Nos. 388/91 (*toned paper*) 11·00 20·00
a. White paper .. .. 17·00 25·00

Designs:—9d. Sir Rowland Hill; 1s. 6d. The Penny Black; 2s. 6d. Rhodesian stamp of 1892 (No. 12).

The 3d., 2s. 6d. and minature sheet exist imperforate from sheets prepared for presentation purposes.

69 De Havilland D.H.89 Dragon Rapide (1946)

70 Kudu

1966 (1 June). *20th Anniv of Central African Airways. T* **69** *and similar horiz designs. P* 14½ × 14.

393 6d. black, blue, yellow and green .. .. 1·00 50
394 1s. 3d. blue, yellow-orange, black and green 1·25 55
395 2s. 6d. black, blue, yellow and green .. 3·50 2·50
396 5s. black and blue .. .. 6·00 5·50
393/6 .. .. *Set of* 4 10·50 8·00

Aircraft:—1s. 3d. Douglas DC-3 (1953); 2s. 6d. Vickers Viscount 748 *Matopos* (1956); 5s. B.A.C. One Eleven 200.

The 6d., 2s. 6d. and 5s. values exist imperforate from sheets prepared for presentation purposes.

1966–69. *As Nos.* 374/87 *but litho. P* 14½ (1*d. to* 2*s.*) *or* 14½ × 14 (*others*).

397 1d. reddish violet and yellow-ochre (*shades*) (2.6.66) 15 10
398 2d. orange and green (1.11.67) 85 65
399 3d. chocolate-brn & pale grnsh bl (29.1.68).. 1·00 10
400 4d. emerald, bistre-brown & drab (21.9.66) 65 10
401 6d. carmine-red, yell & ol-grey (1.11.66) .. 60 50
402 9d. yellow and light violet (20.11.67) .. 30 10
403 1s. 3d. blue and ochre (1.11.66) .. .. 2·75 30
404 2s. dull red, violet & sage-green (18.7.66) .. 2·75 4·50
405 5s. yellow-brown, deep bistre-yellow and light blue (25.6.66) .. .. .. 3·25 4·50
406 10s. black, buff, lt bl & carm-red (10.8.66) .. 15·00 22·00
407 £1 pale brown, yellow-green, brown-ochre and salmon (10.8.66) .. .. 20·00 28·00
397/407 .. .. *Set of* 11 42·00 55·00

In addition to the change in printing process from photogravure to lithography and the difference in perforation in the 6d. to 2s. values (14½ instead of 13½ × 13) and shade variations, the oval portrait frame is larger (and in some values thicker) in the 1d. to 2s., and in the 1s. 3d. the Queen's head is also larger.

Trial printings, made in June 1966, exist of the 5s., 10s. and £1 values on a slightly thinner paper. These are rare.

The 1d., 3d. and 5s. values exist imperforate from sheets prepared for presentation purposes.

1967–68. *Dual Currency Issue. As Nos.* 376, 380 *and* 382/4 *but value in decimal currency in addition as in T* **70**. *P* 14½. *White gum* (*No.* 408) *or cream gum* (*others*).

408 3d./2½ c. chocolate-brown and pale greenish blue (15.3.67) 60 20
409 1s./10 c. yell, grn & greenish bl (1.11.67) .. 70 45
410 1s. 6d./15 c. red-brown, yellow and yellow-green (11.3.68) .. .. 4·75 50
411 2s./20 c. dull red, viol and sage-grn (11.3.68) 5·50 7·50
412 2s. 6d./25 c. ultramarine-blue, vermilion and bright turquoise-blue (9.12.68) .. 35·00 48·00
408/12 .. .. *Set of* 5 42·00 50·00

71 Dr. Jameson (administrator)

(Des from painting by F. M. Bennett)

1967 (17 May). *Famous Rhodesians* (*1st issue*) *and 50th Death Anniv of Dr. Jameson. P* 14½.

413 **71** 1s. 6d. multicoloured 30 35

See also Nos. 426, 430, 457, 458, 469, 480, 488 and 513.

72 Soapstone Sculpture (Joram Mariga)

1967 (12 July). *Tenth Anniv of Opening of Rhodes National Gallery. T* **72** *and similar vert designs. P* 14½ × 14 (3*d.*, 9*d.*) *or* 14 (*others*).

414 3d. reddish chestnut, yellow-olive and black 10 10
415 9d. lt greenish blue, dp olive-brown & black 20 20
a. Perf 13½ .. .. 7·50 18·00
416 1s. 3d. multicoloured 20 25
417 2s. 6d. multicoloured 25 35
414/17 .. .. *Set of* 4 65 75

Designs:—9d. "The Burgher of Calais" (detail, Rodin); 1s. 3d. "The Knight" (stamp design wrongly inscr) (Roberto Crippa); 2s. 6d. "John the Baptist" (M. Tossini).

73 Baobab Tree

1967 (6 Sept). *Nature Conservation. T* **73** *and similar designs. P* 14½.

418 4d. light brown and black 25 25
419 4d. yellow-olive and black 25 25
420 4d. deep grey and black 25 25
421 4d. yellow-orange and black.. .. .. 25 25
418/21 .. .. *Set of* 4 90 90

Designs: *Horiz*—No. 418, Type **73**; No. 419, White Rhinoceros; No. 420, African Elephants. *Vert*—No. 421, Wild Gladiolus.

74 Wooden Hand Plough

(Des Rose Martin)

1968 (26 Apr). *15th World Ploughing Contest, Norton, Rhodesia. T* **74** *and similar horiz designs. P* 14½.

422 3d. pale orange, orange-verm & lake-brown 10 10
423 9d. multicoloured 25 25
424 1s. 6d. multicoloured 35 65
425 2s. 6d. multicoloured 45 95
422/5 .. .. *Set of* 4 1·00 1·75

Designs:—9d. Early wheel plough; 1s. 6d. Steam powered tractor, and ploughs; 2s. 6d. Modern tractor, and plough.

75 Alfred Beit (national benefactor)

76 Raising the Flag, Bulawayo, 1893

(Des from painting by A. Haywood)

1968 (15 July). *Famous Rhodesians* (*2nd issue*). *P* 14½.

426 **75** 1s. 6d. pale orange, black and brown .. 30 30

(Des Rose Martin)

1968 (4 Nov). *75th Anniv of Matabeleland. T* **76** *and similar vert designs. P* 14½.

427 3d. pale orange, red-orange and black .. 15 10
428 9d. multicoloured 25 20
429 1s. 6d. pale turquoise-green, deep emerald and blackish green 25 60
427/9 .. .. *Set of* 3 60 80

Designs:—9d. View and coat of arms of Bulawayo; 1s. 6d. Allan Wilson (combatant in the Matabele War).

77 Sir William Henry Milton (administrator)

(Des from painting by S. Kendrick)

1969 (15 Jan). *Famous Rhodesians* (*3rd issue*). *P* 14½.

430 **77** 1s. 6d. multicoloured 20 55

78 2 ft Gauge Steam Locomotive, Beira-Salisbury Line, 1899

(Des Rose Martin)

1969 (22 May). *70th Anniv of Opening of Beira-Salisbury Railway. T* **78** *and similar horiz designs showing locomotives. Multicoloured. P* 14½.

431 3d. Type **78** .. .. 1·00 20
432 9d. Steam locomotive, 1904 .. .. .. 1·50 75
433 1s. 6d. Articulated steam locomotive, 1950 .. 4·50 3·25
434 2s. 6d. Diesel locomotive, 1955 .. .. 6·50 7·00
431/4 .. .. *Set of* 4 12·00 10·00

79 Low Level Bridge

(Des Rose Martin)

1969 (18 Sept). *Bridges of Rhodesia. T* **79** *and similar horiz designs. Multicoloured. P* 14½.

435 3d. Type **79** 75 20
436 9d. Mpudzi bridge .. .. 1·00 30
437 1s. 6d. Umniati bridge .. .. .. 2·50 2·00
438 2s. 6d. Birchenough bridge .. .. .. 3·50 3·00
435/8 .. .. *Set of* 4 7·00 5·00

(New Currency. 100 cents = 1 dollar)

80 Harvesting Wheat

81 Devil's Cataract, Victoria Falls

(Des from colour-transparencies (3, 6 c.), Rose Martin (others))

1970 (17 Feb)–**73.** *Decimal Currency. T* **80/1** *and similar horiz designs. P* 14½.

439 1 c. multicoloured 10 10
a. Booklet pane of 4 30
440 2 c. multicoloured 10 10
441 2½ c. multicoloured 10 10
a. Booklet pane of 4 35

441*c* 3 c. multicoloured (1.1.73) .. .. 1·25 10
ca. Booklet pane of 4 .. .. .. 4·50
442 3½ c. multicoloured 10 10
a. Booklet pane of 4 65
442*b* 4 c. multicoloured (1.1.73) .. .. 1·75 40
ba. Booklet pane of 4 .. .. .. 6·00
443 5 c. multicoloured 15 10
443*b* 6 c. multicoloured (1.1.73) .. .. 4·00 3·75
443*c* 7½ c. multicoloured (1.1.73) .. .. 7·50 80
444 8 c. multicoloured .. .. .. 1·25 20
445 10 c. multicoloured 60 10
446 12½ c. multicoloured .. .. .. 1·00 10
446*a* 14 c. multicoloured (1.1.73) .. .. 15·00 90
447 15 c. multicoloured .. .. .. 2·50 15
448 20 c. multicoloured .. .. .. 1·75 15
449 25 c. multicoloured .. .. .. 4·00 90
450 50 c. turquoise and ultramarine .. .. 2·25 55
451 $1 multicoloured .. .. .. 4·00 1·75
452 $2 multicoloured .. .. .. 10·00 23·00
439/52 .. .. *Set of* 19 48·00 28·00

Designs: *Size as T* **80**—2 c. Pouring molten metal; 2½ c. Zimbabwe Ruins; 3 c. Articulated lorry; 3½ c. and 4 c. Statute of Cecil Rhodes; 5 c. Mine headgear. *Size as T* **81**—6 c. Hydrofoil *Seaflight;* 7½ c. As 8 c.; 10 c. Yachting on Lake McIlwaine; 12½ c. Hippopotamus in river; 14 c. and 15 c. Kariba Dam; 20 c. Irrigation canal. *As T* **80/1** *but larger* (31×26 *mm*)—25 c. Bateleurs; 50 c. Radar antenna and Vickers Viscount 810; $1 "Air Rescue"; $2 Rhodesian flag.

Booklet panes Nos. 439a, 441a, 441ca, 442a and 442ba have margins all round.

82 Despatch Rider, *circa* 1890

(Des Rose Martin)

1970 (1 July). *Inauguration of Posts and Telecommunications Corporation. T* **82** *and similar horiz designs. Multicoloured. P* 14½.
453 2½ c. Type **82** 35 10
454 3½ c. Loading mail at Salisbury airport .. 75 50
455 15 c. Constructing telegraph line, *circa* 1890 1·50 2·25
456 25 c. Telephone and modern telecommunications equipment .. .. .. 2·25 4·00
453/6 .. .. *Set of* 4 4·25 6·00

83 Mother Patrick (Dominican nurse and teacher)

(Des Rose Martin from photograph)

1970 (16 Nov). *Famous Rhodesians* (4*th issue*). *P* 14½.
457 **83** 15 c. multicoloured 60 50

84 Frederick Courteney Selous (big-game hunter, explorer and pioneer)

(Des from painting by L. C. Dickinson)

1971 (1 Mar). *Famous Rhodesians* (5*th issue*). *P* 14½.
458 **84** 15 c. multicoloured 40 60

85 Hoopoe

86 Porphyritic Granite

(Des from photographs by Peter Ginn)

1971 (1 June). *Birds of Rhodesia* (1*st series*). *T* **85** *and similar multicoloured designs. P* 14½.
459 2 c. Type **85** .. .. 1·25 20
460 2½ c. Half-collared Kingfisher (*horiz*) .. 1·25 20
461 5 c. Golden-breasted Bunting .. .. 3·50 70
462 7½ c. Carmine Bee Eater .. .. 4·00 1·25
463 8 c. Red-eyed Bulbul .. .. .. 4·00 1·50
464 25 c. Senegal Wattled Plover (*horiz*) .. 8·50 3·25
459/64 .. .. *Set of* 6 20·00 6·50

See also Nos. 537/42.

(Des from photographs by University of Rhodesia and Dept of Geological Survey)

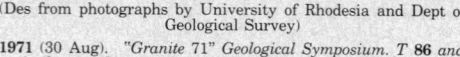

1971 (30 Aug). *"Granite 71" Geological Symposium. T* **86** *and similar vert designs. Multicoloured. P* 14.
465 2½ c. Type **86** 85 10
466 7½ c. Muscovite mica seen through microscope .. .. 2·25 1·25
467 15 c. Granite seen through microscope .. 3·00 3·75
468 25 c. Geological map of Rhodesia .. .. 3·50 5·50
465/8 .. .. *Set of* 4 8·75 9·50

87 Dr. Robert Moffat (missionary)

1972 (14 Feb). *Famous Rhodesians* (6*th issue*). *P* 14½.
469 **87** 13 c. multicoloured .. .. .. 65 1·40

88 Bird ("Be Airwise")

89 "The Three Kings"

(Des C. Lawton)

1972 (17 July). *"Prevent Pollution". T* **88** *and similar horiz designs. Multicoloured. P* 14½.
470 2½ c. Type **88** 20 10
471 3½ c. Antelope ("Be Countrywise") 20 20
472 7 c. Fish ("Be Waterwise") 30 45
473 13 c. City ("Be Citywise") 45 70
470/3 .. .. *Set of* 4 1·00 1·25

1972 (28 Aug). *"Rhophil '72". As Nos.* 439a, 441a *and* 442a *with commemorative inscr in margins. Each* 66 × 78 *mm.*
MS474 1 c. multicoloured .. .. .. 1·75 3·00
MS475 2½ c. multicoloured .. .. .. 1·75 3·00
MS476 3½ c. multicoloured .. .. .. 1·75 3·00
MS474/6 .. .. .. *Set of* 3 *sheets* 4·75 8·00

(Des Rose Martin)

1972 (18 Oct). *Christmas. P* 14.
477 **89** 2 c. multicoloured 10 10
478 5 c. multicoloured 20 25
479 13 c. multicoloured 50 75
477/9 .. .. *Set of* 3 70 1·00

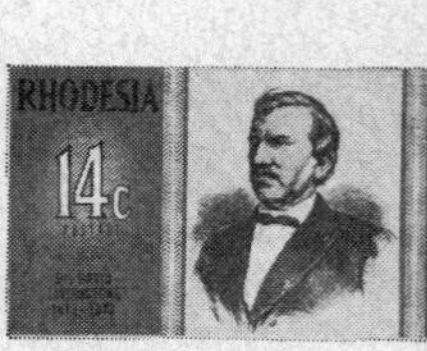

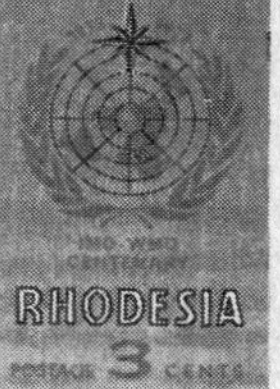

90 Dr. David Livingstone

91 W.M.O. Emblem

1973 (2 Apr). *Famous Rhodesians* (7*th issue*). *P* 14.
480 **90** 14 c. multicoloured 70 85

(Des S. J. Ivey)

1973 (2 July). *I.M.O./W.M.O. Centenary. P* 14.
481 **91** 3 c. multicoloured 15 10
482 14 c. multicoloured 80 80
483 25 c. multicoloured .. .. .. 1·25 2·50
481/3 .. .. *Set of* 3 2·00 3·00

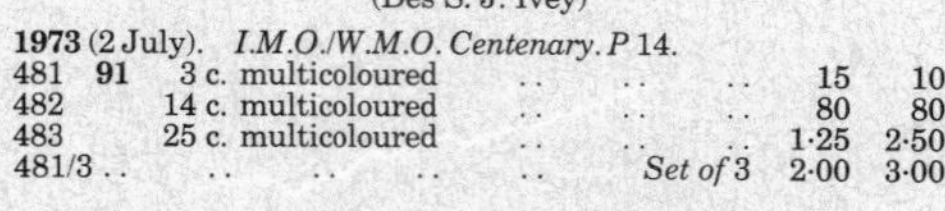

92 Arms of Rhodesia

1973 (10 Oct). 50*th Anniv of Responsible Government. P* 14.
484 **92** 2½ c. multicoloured 15 10
485 4 c. multicoloured 25 20
486 7½ c. multicoloured 40 80
487 14 c. multicoloured .. .. .. 70 2·50
484/7 .. .. *Set of* 4 1·40 3·25

93 George Pauling (construction engineer)

(Des P. Birch)

1974 (15 May). *Famous Rhodesians* (8*th issue*). *P* 14.
488 **93** 14 c. multicoloured .. .. .. 80 1·75

94 Greater Kudu

95 Thunbergia

96 *Charaxes varanes*

(Des J. Huntly)

1974 (14 Aug)–**76**. *Various vert designs as T* **94/6**. *Multicoloured. P* 14½ (1 *to* 14 *c.*) *or* 14 (*others*). (*a*) *Antelopes. Size as T* **94**.
489 1 c. Type **94** 10 10
490 2½ c. Eland 75 10
a. Booklet pane of 4 .. .. .. 2·75
491 3 c. Roan Antelope 10 10
a. Booklet pane of 4 70
492 4 c. Reedbuck 30 10
a. Booklet pane of 4 .. .. .. 1·00
493 5 c. Bushbuck 40 10

(*b*) *Wild Flowers. Size as T* **95**
494 6 c. Type **95** 40 10
495 7½ c. Flame Lily .. .. 3·00 35
496 8 c. As 7½ c. (1.7.76) 40 10
497 10 c. Devil Thorn 40 10
498 12 c. Hibiscus (1.7.76) .. .. .. 70 2·00
499 12½ c. Pink Sabi Star .. .. .. 4·00 50
500 14 c. Wild Pimpernel .. .. .. 4·00 50
501 15 c. As 12½ c. (1.7.76) 70 75
502 16 c. As 14 c. (1.7.76) 70 45

(*c*) *Butterflies. Size as T* **96**
503 20 c. Type **96** .. .. 2·50 35
504 24 c. *Precis hierta* (s sp *cebrene*) (1.7.76) .. 1·25 40
505 25 c. As 24 c. .. .. 6·00 3·50
506 50 c. *Colotis regina* 70 90
507 $1 *Graphium antheus* .. .. .. 70 1·50
508 $2 *Hamanumida daedalus* .. .. 80 2·25
489/508 .. .. .. *Set of* 20 24·00 12·50

97 Collecting Mail

98 Thomas Baines (artist)

(Des M. Chase)

1974 (20 Nov). *Centenary of Universal Postal Union. T* **97** *and similar horiz designs. Multicoloured. P* 14.
509 3 c. Type **97** 15 10
510 4 c. Sorting mail 25 10
511 7½ c. Mail delivery 70 75
512 14 c. Weighing parcel .. .. .. 1·40 2·25
509/12 .. .. *Set of* 4 2·25 2·75

(Des from self-portrait)

1975 (12 Feb). *Famous Rhodesians* (9*th issue*). *P* 14.
513 **98** 14 c. multicoloured .. .. .. 90 1·25

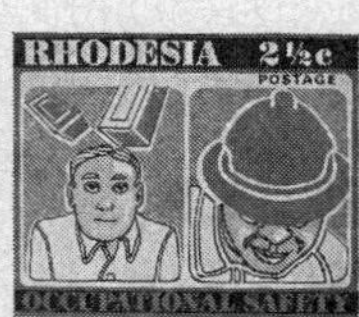

99 *Euphorbia confinalis*

100 Prevention of Head Injuries

(Des Nancy Abrey)

1975 (16 July). *International Succulent Congress, Salisbury ("Aloe '75"). T* **99** *and similar vert designs. Multicoloured. P* 14½.
514 2½ c. Type **99** 20 10
515 3 c. *Aloe excelsa* 20 10
516 4 c. *Hoodia lugardii* 30 10
517 7½ c. *Aloe orthlopha* 45 10
518 14 c. *Aloe musapana* .. .. .. 1·00 20
519 25 c. *Aloe saponaria* .. .. .. 1·50 3·00
514/19 .. .. *Set of* 6 3·25 3·00

(Des Val Bond)

1975 (15 Oct). *Occupational Safety. T* **100** *and similar horiz designs. Multicoloured. P* 14.

520	2½ c. Type **100**	15	10
521	4 c. Bandaged hand and gloved hand	20	10
522	7½ c. Broken glass and eye	35	25
523	14 c. Blind man and welder with protective mask	50	75
520/3	*Set of* 4	1·10	1·00

8c

101 Telephones, 1876 and 1976 (**102**)

(Des M. Chase)

1976 (10 Mar). *Telephone Centenary. T* **101** *and similar vert design. P* 14.

524	3 c. grey-black and pale blue	10	10
525	14 c. brownish black and light stone	20	55

Design:—14 c. Alexander Graham Bell.

1976 (1 July). *Nos.* 495, 500 *and* 505 *surch as T* **102**.

526	8 c. on 7½ c. Flame Lily	15	15
	a. Surch double, one albino		
527	16 c. on 14 c. Wild Pimpernel	20	15
528	24 c. on 25 c. *Precis hierta* (s sp *cebrene*)	30	80
526/8	*Set of* 3	60	1·00

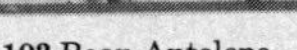

103 Roan Antelope **104** Msasa

(Des N. Pedersen)

1976 (21 July). *Vulnerable Wildlife. T* **103** *and similar horiz designs. Multicoloured. P* 14.

529	4 c. Type **103**	15	10
530	6 c. Brown Hyena	15	30
531	8 c. Hunting Dog	25	20
532	16 c. Cheetah	35	35
529/32	*Set of* 4	80	75

(Des Nancy Abrey)

1976 (17 Nov). *Trees of Rhodesia. T* **104** *and similar vert designs. Multicoloured. P* 14.

533	4 c. Type **104**	15	10
534	6 c. Red Mahogany	15	10
535	8 c. Mukwa	20	15
536	16 c. Rhodesian Teak	25	65
533/6	*Set of* 4	65	75

105 Common Bulbul **106** "Lake Kyle" (Joan Evans)

(Des B. Finch)

1977 (16 Mar). *Birds of Rhodesia (2nd series). T* **105** *and similar vert designs. Multicoloured. P* 14.

537	3 c. Type **105**	20	10
538	4 c. Yellow-mantled Whydah	20	10
539	6 c. Cape Longclaw	25	35
540	8 c. Eastern Long-tailed Shrike	35	50
541	16 c. Lesser Blue-eared Glossy Starling	55	1·10
542	24 c. Green Wood Hoopoe	70	1·50
537/42	*Set of* 6	2·00	3·25

1977 (20 July). *Landscape Paintings. T* **106** *and similar horiz designs. Multicoloured. P* 14.

543	3 c. Type **106**	10	10
544	4 c. "Chimanimani Mountains" (Joan Evans)	10	10
545	6 c. "Rocks near Bonsor Reef", (Alice Balfour)	15	40
546	8 c. "A Dwala near Devil's Pass" (Alice Balfour)	20	10
547	16 c. "Zimbabwe" (Alice Balfour)	25	40
548	24 c. "Victoria Falls" (Thomas Baines)	30	75
543/8	*Set of* 6	1·00	1·50

107 Virgin and Child **108** Fair Spire

(Des Dianne Deudney)

1977 (16 Nov). *Christmas. P* 14.

549	**107**	3 c. multicoloured	10	10
550		6 c. multicoloured	10	20
551		8 c. multicoloured	15	10
552		16 c. multicoloured	30	75
549/52		*Set of* 4	60	95

1978 (15 Mar). *Trade Fair Rhodesia, Bulawayo. T* **108** *and similar vert design. Multicoloured. P* 14.

553	4 c. Type **108**	15	10
554	8 c. Fair Spire (*different*)	20	25

109 Morganite **110** White Rhinoceros

111 Odzani Falls

(Des N. Pedersen (1 to 17 c.), D. Myles (21 c. to $2))

1978 (16 Aug). *Multicoloured.*

(*a*) *Horiz designs as T* **109** *showing gemstones. P* 14½

555	1 c. Type **109**	20	10
556	3 c. Amethyst	30	10
557	4 c. Garnet	30	10
558	5 c. Citrine	30	10
559	7 c. Blue Topaz	30	10

(*b*) *Horiz designs as T* **110** *showing wild animals. P* 14½

560	9 c. Type **110**	20	10
561	11 c. Lion	20	30
562	13 c. Warthog	20	45
563	15 c. Giraffe	20	30
564	17 c. Common Zebra	20	10

(*c*) *Horiz designs as T* **111** *showing waterfalls. P* 14

565	21 c. Type **111**	20	40
566	25 c. Goba Falls	20	40
567	30 c. Inyangombi Falls	25	30
568	$1 Bridal Veil Falls	35	80
569	$2 Victoria Falls	50	1·00
555/69	*Set of* 15	3·00	3·75

112 Wright Flyer I

(Des C. Herbert)

1978 (18 Oct). *75th Anniv of Powered Flight. T* **112** *and similar horiz designs. Multicoloured. P* 14.

570	4 c. Type **112**	10	10
571	5 c. Bleriot XI	10	10
572	7 c. Vickers Vimy *Silver Queen II*	10	10
573	9 c. Armstrong Whitworth A.W.15 Atlanta	10	10
574	17 c. Vickers Viking 1B *Zambezi*	15	15
575	25 c. Boeing 720B	20	30
570/5	*Set of* 6	65	65

ZIMBABWE

REPUBLIC

Rhodesia became independent under majority rule on 18 April 1980 and was renamed Zimbabwe.

PRINTERS. All stamps of Zimbabwe were printed in lithography by Mardon Printers (Pvt) Ltd, subsequently (from Nos. 724/7) National Printing and Packaging, Harare, *unless otherwise stated.*

113 Morganite **114** Rotary Anniversary Emblem

1980 (18 Apr)–**83.** *As Nos.* 555/69 *and new value* (40 c.), *all inscr* "ZIMBABWE" *as in T* **113**.

576	1 c. Type **113**	20	30
577	3 c. Amethyst	30	30
578	4 c. Garnet	30	10
	a. Imperf (pair)	£140	
579	5 c. Citrine	35	10
580	7 c. Blue Topaz	35	10
581	9 c. White Rhinoceros	15	10
582	11 c. Lion	15	15
583	13 c. Warthog	15	15
584	15 c. Giraffe	15	20
585	17 c. Common Zebra	15	20
586	21 c. Odzani Falls	20	25
587	25 c. Goba Falls	25	30
588	30 c. Inyangombi Falls	30	50
588*a*	40 c. Bundi Falls (14.3.83)	6·00	4·50
589	$1 Bridal Veil Falls	50	2·00
590	$2 Victoria Falls	75	3·75
576/90	*Set of* 16	9·25	11·50

1980 (18 June). *75th Anniv of Rotary International. P* 14½.

591	**114**	4 c. multicoloured	10	10
592		13 c. multicoloured	15	30
593		21 c. multicoloured	20	55
594		25 c. multicoloured	20	80
591/4		*Set of* 4	50	1·60
MS595		140 × 84 mm. Nos. 591/4	75	1·60

115 Olympic Rings

(Des Nancy Abrey)

1980 (19 July). *Olympic Games, Moscow. P* 14½.

596	**115**	17 c. multicoloured	30	40

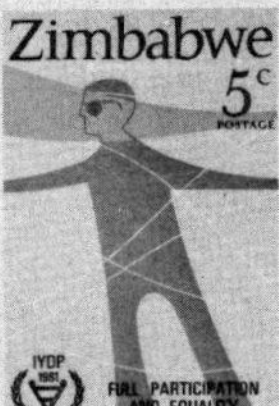

116 Gatooma Post Office, 1912 **117** Stylised Blind Person

(Des Mortimer Tiley and Partners Ltd)

1980 (17 Oct). *75th Anniv of Post Office Savings Bank. T* **116** *and similar horiz designs. P* 14.

597	5 c. black and yellow-brown	10	10
598	7 c. black and red-orange	10	10
599	9 c. black and olive-yellow	10	10
600	17 c. black and light blue	25	25
597/600	*Set of* 4	40	40
MS601	125 × 84 mm. Nos. 597/600	55	1·25

Designs:—7 c. Salisbury Post Office, 1912; 9 c. Umtali Post Office, 1901; 17 c. Bulawayo Post Office, 1895.

(Des Rose Martin)

1981 (23 Sept). *International Year of Disabled Persons. T* **117** *and similar vert designs showing stylised figures. Multicoloured. P* 14.

602	5 c. Type **117**	15	10
603	7 c. Deaf person	15	10
604	11 c. Person with one leg	20	15
605	17 c. Person with one arm	25	35
602/5	*Set of* 4	65	60

118 Msasa

119 Painting from Gwamgwadza Cave, Mtoko Area

(Des Nancy Abrey)

1981 (4 Dec). *National Tree Day. T* **118** *and similar vert designs. Multicoloured. P* 14½.

606	5 c. Type **118**	10	10
607	7 c. Mopane	15	15
608	21 c. Flat-crowned Acacia	45	85
609	30 c. Pod Mahogany	60	1·40
606/9	*Set of* 4	1·10	2·25

1982 (17 Mar). *Rock Paintings. T* **119** *and similar horiz designs showing paintings from various locations. Multicoloured. P* 14½.

610	9 c. Type **119**	75	20
611	11 c. Epworth Mission, near Harare	1·00	20
612	17 c. Diana's Vow, near Harare	1·00	65
613	21 c. Gwamgwadza Cave, Mtoko Area (*different*)	1·40	1·25
614	25 c. Mucheka Cave, Msana Communal Land	1·75	2·00
615	30 c. Chinzwini Shelter, Chiredzi Area	2·00	2·25
610/15	*Set of* 6	7·00	6·00

120 Scout Emblem

121 Dr. Robert Koch

(Des Rose Martin)

1982 (21 July). *75th Anniv of Boy Scout Movement. T* **120** *and similar vert designs. Multicoloured. P* 14½ × 14.

616	9 c. Type **120**	35	15
617	11 c. Scouts around campfire	35	15
618	21 c. Scouts map-reading	55	1·25
619	30 c. Lord Baden-Powell	65	2·00
616/19	*Set of* 4	1·75	3·25

(Des Rose Martin)

1982 (17 Nov). *Centenary of Dr. Robert Koch's Discovery of Tubercle Bacillus. T* **121** *and similar horiz design. P* 14.

620	11 c. salmon, black and greenish grey	85	25
621	30 c. multicoloured	1·40	3·25

Design:—30 c. Man looking through microscope.

122 "Wing Woman" (Henry Mudzengerere)

123 Traditional Ploughing Team (moving right)

1983 (14 Mar). *Commonwealth Day. Sculptures. T* **122** *and similar multicoloured designs. P* 14.

622	9 c. Type **122**	10	10
623	11 c. "Telling Secrets" (Joseph Ndandarika) (*horiz*)	10	10
624	30 c. "Hornbill Man" (John Takawira) (*horiz*)	20	45
625	$1 "The Chief" (Nicholas Mukomberanwa)	55	1·75
622/5	*Set of* 4	80	2·00

(Des Rose Martin)

1983 (13 May). *30th World Ploughing Contest, Zimbabwe. T* **123** *and similar horiz designs. Multicoloured. P* 14.

626	21 c. Type **123**	25	35
	a. Horiz pair. Nos. 626/7	50	70
627	21 c. Traditional ploughing team (moving left)	25	35
628	30 c. Tractor ploughing	40	65
	a. Horiz pair. Nos. 628/9	80	1·25
629	30 c. Modern plough	40	65
626/9	*Set of* 4	1·25	1·75

The two designs of each value were issued in horizontal *se-tenant* pairs, forming composite designs, throughout the sheets.

124 Postman on Cycle

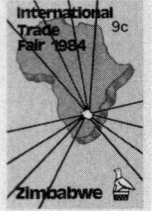

125 Map of Africa showing Zimbabwe

(Des R. Phillips)

1983 (12 Oct). *World Communications Year. T* **124** *and similar multicoloured designs. P* 14.

630	9 c. Type **124**	20	10
631	11 c. Aircraft controller directing airliner	25	10
632	15 c. Switchboard operator	30	30
633	17 c. Printing works	35	30
634	21 c. Road transport (*horiz*)	50	60
635	30 c. Rail transport (*horiz*)	75	1·25
630/5	*Set of* 6	2·10	2·40

(Des Bunty Woods and Nancy Abrey)

1984 (11 Apr). *Zimbabwe International Trade Fair. T* **125** *and similar vert designs. Multicoloured. P* 14½.

636	9 c. Type **125**	10	10
637	11 c. Globe	15	10
638	30 c. Zimbabwe flag and Trade Fair logo	45	50
636/8	*Set of* 3	65	60

126 Cycling

(Des Vivienne Fick (11 c.), Joanna Hogg (21 c.), Blessing Chikoore (30 c.), Wayne Gubb (40 c.))

1984 (18 July). *Olympic Games, Los Angeles. Children's Pictures. T* **126** *and similar horiz designs. Multicoloured. P* 14½.

639	11 c. Type **126**	35	15
640	21 c. Swimming	45	50
641	30 c. Running	65	85
642	40 c. Hurdling	80	1·75
639/42	*Set of* 4	2·00	3·00

127 Liberation Heroes

128 African Fish Eagle

(Des N. Pearce (11 c.), J. Akester (others))

1984 (8 Aug). *Heroes' Days. T* **127** *and similar multicoloured designs showing various aspects of Heroes' Acre. P* 14½.

643	9 c. Type **127**	25	10
644	11 c. Symbolic tower and flame (*vert*)	25	10
645	17 c. Bronze sculpture (*vert*)	40	60
646	30 c. Section of bronze mural	55	95
643/6	*Set of* 4	1·25	1·50

(Des B. Finch)

1984 (10 Oct). *Birds of Prey. T* **128** *and similar vert designs. Multicoloured. P* 14½.

647	9 c. Type **128**	50	20
648	11 c. Long-crested Eagle	50	20
649	13 c. Bateleur	65	55
650	17 c. Verreaux's Eagle	80	55
651	21 c. Martial Eagle	90	1·40
652	30 c. Bonelli's Eagle	1·25	2·25
647/52	*Set of* 6	4·25	4·75

129 Class "9" Locomotive No. 86

130 "Intelsat V" Telecommunications Satellite

(Des G. Cameron)

1985 (15 May). *"Zimbabwe Steam Safaris". Railway Locomotives. T* **129** *and similar horiz designs. Multicoloured. P* 14½.

653	9 c. Type **129**	85	20
654	11 c. Class "12" No. 190	85	20
655	17 c. Class "Garratt 15A" *Isilwane*	1·50	1·00
656	30 c. Class "Garratt 20A" *Gwaai*	2·50	3·00
653/6	*Set of* 4	5·25	4·00

1985 (8 July). *Earth Satellite Station, Mazowe. T* **130** *and similar multicoloured design. P* 14½ × 14 (26 c.) *or* 14½ (57 c.).

657	26 c. Type **130**	1·50	60
658	57 c. Earth Satellite Station, Mazowe (65 × 25 *mm*)	3·00	6·00

131 Tobacco

132 Chief Mutapa Gatsi Rusere and 17th-century Seal

(Des Rose Rigden)

1985 (21 Aug)–**88**. *National Infrastructure. T* **131** *and similar horiz designs. Multicoloured. P* 14½.

659	1 c. Type **131**	10	10
	a. Perf 14	—	40
660	3 c. Maize	10	10
	a. Perf 14	—	40
661	4 c. Cotton	15	10
	a. Perf 14	—	40
662	5 c. Tea	30	10
	a. Perf 14	—	40
663	10 c. Cattle	20	10
	a. Perf 14	—	40
664	11 c. Birchenough Bridge	75	10
665	12 c. Ore stamp mill	1·00	10
666	13 c. Gold pouring	1·75	15
	a. Perf 14	—	75
667	15 c. Dragline coal mining	1·25	15
	a. Perf 14	—	75
668	17 c. Uncut amethyst	2·00	40
669	18 c. Electric locomotive	2·00	30
670	20 c. Kariba Dam	1·25	15
	a. Perf 14	—	75
671	23 c. Elephants at water hole	1·75	45
672	25 c. Sunset over Zambezi	65	30
	a. Perf 14	—	1·00
673	26 c. Baobab tree	65	20
674	30 c. Ruins of Great Zimbabwe	75	50
675	35 c. Traditional dancing	60	30
676	45 c. Village women crushing maize	75	40
677	57 c. Woodcarving	75	70
678	$1 Playing Mbira (musical instrument)	1·25	90
	a. Perf 14		
679	$2 Mule-drawn Scotch cart	2·00	3·00
680	$5 Zimbabwe coat-of-arms	3·75	5·50
659/80	*Set of* 22	21·00	12·00

The stamps perforated 14 date from the introduction of a new perforating head in 1988.

(Des C. Herbert)

1985 (18 Sept). *50th Anniv of National Archives. T* **132** *and similar horiz designs. Multicoloured. P* 14½.

681	12 c. Type **132**	20	15
682	18 c. Chief Lobengula, seal and 1888 Treaty	25	40
683	26 c. Exhibition gallery	35	45
684	35 c. National Archives building	45	75
681/4	*Set of* 4	1·10	1·60

MACHINE LABELS. From 24 October 1985 gummed labels in the above design varying in value from 1 c. to $99.99, were available from four automatic machines located at the Philatelic Bureau and at post offices in Bulawayo, Gwelo and Harare. Two further machines were installed at Harare offices in 1985–86, but by this time the Bureau example had ceased to function. Paper showing an overall pattern of rhinoceroses appeared briefly in 1991, but it is reported that all machines were withdrawn during 1993.

133 Computer Operator

(Des C. Herbert)

1985 (13 Nov). *United Nations Decade for Women. T* **133** *and similar horiz designs. Multicoloured. P* 14½.

685	10 c. Type **133**	40	10
686	17 c. Nurse giving injection	75	70
687	26 c. Woman student	1·25	2·50
685/7	*Set of* 3	2·25	3·00

134 Harare Conference Centre

(Des C. Herbert)

1986 (29 Jan). *Harare International Conference Centre. T* **134** *and similar horiz design. Multicoloured. P* 14½.
688 26 c. Type **134**.. .. .. 60 30
689 35 c. Interior of conference hall .. .. 1·00 1·40

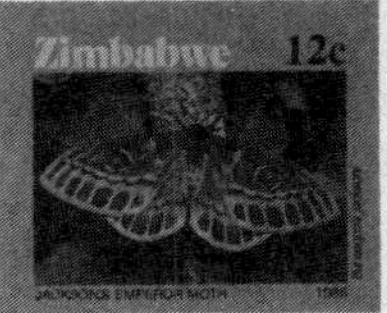

135 Grain Storage Silo **136** *Bunaeopsis jacksoni*

(Des C. Herbert)

1986 (1 Apr). *6th Anniv of Southern African Development Co-ordination Conference. T* **135** *and similar horiz designs. Multicoloured. P* 14½.
690 12 c. Type **135**.. .. .. 55 20
691 18 c. Rhinoceros and hawk at sunset .. 2·50 1·50
692 26 c. Map showing S.A.D.C.C. member states, and Boeing "737" .. .. 2·50 2·00
693 35 c. Map and national flags of S.A.D.C.C. members.. .. .. 2·75 2·25
690/3 .. .. *Set of* 4 7·50 5·50

1986 (18 June). *Moths of Zimbabwe. T* **136** *and similar horiz designs. Multicoloured. P* 14½×14.
694 12 c. Type **136** .. .. 1·10 20
695 18 c. *Deilephila nerii* .. .. 1·60 1·10
696 26 c. *Bunaeopsis zaddachi* .. .. .. 2·00 1·50
697 35 c. *Heniocha apollonia* .. .. .. 2·40 4·25
694/7 .. .. *Set of* 4 6·50 6·25

137 Victoria Falls **138** Sopwith Motorcycle (1921)

(Des C. Herbert)

1986 (26 Aug). *8th Non-Aligned Summit Conference. T* **137** *and similar horiz design. Multicoloured. P* 14½×14 (26 c.) *or* 14½ ($1).
698 26 c. Type **137**.. .. .. 1·75 30
699 $1 Ruins of Great Zimbabwe (62×24 *mm*) .. .. 4·25 5·50

(Des G. Cameron)

1986 (8 Oct). *Centenary of Motoring. T* **138** *and similar horiz designs. Multicoloured. P* 14½.
700 10 c. Type **138**.. .. .. 65 10
701 12 c. Gladiator motor car (1902) 65 30
702 17 c. Douglas motorcycle (1920) .. .. 1·00 40
703 26 c. Ford "Model A" (1930) .. .. .. 1·40 70
704 35 c. Schacht motor car (1909) .. .. 1·75 2·25
705 40 c. Benz three-wheeled car (1886) .. 1·75 2·25
700/5 .. .. *Set of* 6 6·50 5·50

139 Growth Monitoring **140** Barred Owlet

(Des Barbara Chalk)

1987 (11 Feb). *Child Survival Campaign. T* **139** *and similar vert designs. Multicoloured. P* 14×14½.
706 12 c. Type **139**.. .. .. 1·50 1·75
a. Block of 4. Nos. 706/9 .. .. .. 5·50
707 12 c. Breast-feeding .. .. 1·50 1·75
708 12 c. Oral rehydration therapy .. .. 1·50 1·75
709 12 c. Immunization .. .. 1·50 1·75
706/9 .. .. *Set of* 4 5·50 6·25
Nos. 706/9 were printed together, *se-tenant*, in blocks of four throughout the sheet.

(Des B. Finch)

1987 (15 Apr). *Owls (1st series). T* **140** *similar vert designs. Multicoloured. P* 14½.
710 12 c. Type **140**.. .. .. 2·00 30
711 18 c. Pearl-spotted Owlet .. .. .. 2·50 1·25
712 26 c. White-faced Scops Owl .. .. .. 3·00 1·75
713 35 c. African Scops Owl .. .. .. 4·00 4·50
710/13 .. .. *Set of* 4 10·50 7·00
See also Nos. 850/3.

141 Brownie, Guide and Ranger saluting ("Commitment") **142** Common Grey Duiker

(Des Barbara Connelly)

1987 (24 June). *75th Anniv of Girl Guides' Association of Zimbabwe. T* **141** *and similar horiz designs. Multicoloured. P* 14½.
714 15 c. Type **141**.. .. .. 55 15
715 23 c. Guides preparing meal over campfire ("Adventure") 75 30
716 35 c. Guide teaching villagers to read ("Service") 85 45
717 $1 Handshake and globe ("International Friendship") .. .. 2·00 3·00
714/17 .. .. *Set of* 4 3·75 3·50

(Des Patricia Wilson)

1987 (7 Oct). *Duikers of Africa Survey. T* **142** *and similar horiz designs, each showing duiker and distribution map. Multicoloured. P* 14½×14.
718 15 c. Type **142**.. .. .. 70 15
719 23 c. Zebra Duiker 80 25
720 25 c. Yellow-backed Duiker 80 90
721 30 c. Blue Duiker .. .. 95 1·10
722 35 c. Jentink's Duiker .. .. 95 1·25
723 38 c. Red Duiker .. .. 1·00 1·75
718/23 .. .. *Set of* 6 4·75 4·75

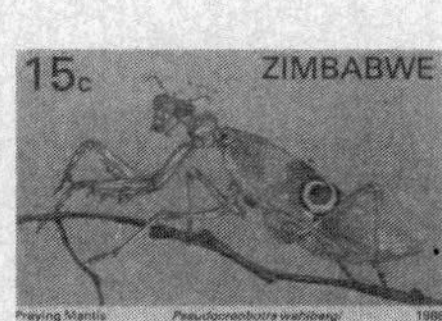

143 *Pseudocreobotra wahlberghi* (mantid) **144** "Cockerel" (Arthur Azevedo)

(Des Janet Duff)

1988 (12 Jan). *Insects. T* **143** *and similar horiz designs. Multicoloured. P* 14½.
724 15 c. Type **143** 70 15
725 23 c. *Dicranorrhina derbyana* (beetle) .. 85 30
726 35 c. *Dictyophorus spumans* (grasshopper) 1·10 85
727 45 c. *Chalcocoris rutilus* (bug) .. .. 1·40 2·00
724/7 .. .. *Set of* 4 3·50 3·00

1988 (14 Apr). *30th Anniv of National Gallery of Zimbabwe. T* **144** *and similar multicoloured designs showing painting (38 c.) or sculptures (others). P* 14 × 14½ *(vert) or* 14½ × 14 *(horiz).*
728 15 c. Type **144** 20 10
729 23 c. "Man into Hippo" (Bernard Matemera) 30 20
730 30 c. "Spirit Python" (Henry Munyaradzi) .. 35 30
731 35 c. "Spirit Bird carrying People" (Thomas Mukarobgwa) *(horiz)* 35 30
732 38 c. "The Song of the Herd Boy" (George Nene) *(horiz)* 35 40
733 45 c. "War Victim" (Joseph Muzondo) *(horiz)* 40 50
728/33 .. .. *Set of* 6 1·75 1·60

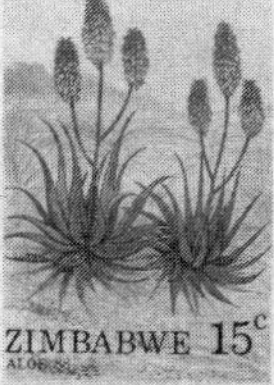
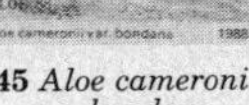

145 *Aloe cameronii var. bondana* **146** White-faced Whistling Duck

(Des Nancy Abrey)

1988 (14 July). *Aloes. T* **145** *and similar vert designs. Multicoloured. P* 14½.
734 15 c. Type **145** 20 10
735 23 c. *Orbeopsis caudata* 35 20
736 25 c. *Euphorbia wildii* 35 35
737 30 c. *Euphorbia fortissima* 40 45
738 35 c. *Aloe aculeata* 40 55
739 38 c. *Huernia zebrina* 45 70
734/9 .. .. *Set of* 6 2·00 2·00

(Des B. Finch and C. Herbert)

1988 (6 Oct). *Wild Ducks and Geese of Zimbabwe. T* **146** *and similar horiz designs. Multicoloured. P* 14½ × 14.
740 15 c. Type **146** 50 15
741 23 c. African Pygmy Goose 60 20
742 30 c. Hottentot Teal 75 65
743 35 c. Comb Duck ("Knob-billed Duck") .. 80 80
744 38 c. White-backed Duck 80 90
745 45 c. Maccoa Duck .. .. 1·10 1·75
740/5 .. .. *Set of* 6 4·00 4·00

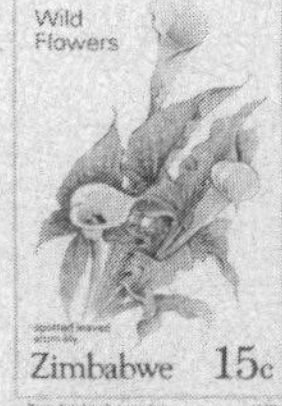

147 O'Shaughnessy's Banded Gecko **148** Spotted Leaved Arum-Lily

1989 (10 Jan). *Geckos. T* **147** *and similar horiz designs. Multicoloured. P* 14½.
746 15 c. Type **147** 70 15
747 23 c. Tiger Rock Gecko 85 40
748 35 c. Tasman's Gecko .. .. 1·25 1·25
749 45 c. Bibron's Gecko .. .. 1·50 2·00
746/9 .. .. *Set of* 4 3·75 3·50

1989 (12 Apr). *Wild Flowers. T* **148** *and similar vert designs. Multicoloured. P* 14½.
750 15 c. Type **148** 35 10
751 23 c. Grassland Vlei-lily 45 25
752 30 c. Manica Protea 45 40
753 35 c. Flame Lily 50 40
754 38 c. Poppy Hibiscus 55 55
755 45 c. Blue Sesbania 65 65
750/5 .. .. *Set of* 6 2·75 2·00

149 Red-breasted Tilapia **150** Black Rhinoceros

(Des C. Herbert)

1989 (12 July). *Fishes (1st series). T* **149** *and similar horiz designs. Multicoloured. P* 14½.
756 15 c. Type **149** 60 15
757 23 c. Chessa 80 25
758 30 c. Eastern Bottlenose 90 70
759 35 c. Vundu 90 70
760 38 c. Large-mouthed Black Bass .. .. 1·00 1·00
761 45 c. Lesser Tigerfish .. .. 1·40 1·75
756/61 .. .. *Set of* 6 5·00 4·00
See also Nos. 864/9.

1989 (10 Oct). *Endangered Species. T* **150** *and similar horiz designs. Multicoloured. P* 14½×14.
762 15 c. Type **150** .. .. 1·25 40
763 23 c. Cheetah .. .. 1·25 45
764 30 c. Wild Dog .. .. 1·40 90
765 35 c. Pangolin .. .. 1·40 1·25
766 38 c. Brown Hyena .. .. 1·50 2·00
767 45 c. Roan Antelope .. .. 1·60 2·25
762/7 .. .. *Set of* 6 7·50 6·50

151 Giant Tigerfish **152** Headrest

153 Bicycles

(Des Janet Duff (1 to 9 c.), Rose Rigden (15 to 30 c.), Nancy Abrey (33 c. to $2))

1990 (2 Jan). *Multicoloured.*

(a) Horiz designs as T **151** *showing wildlife. P* 14
768 1 c. Type **151** 15 10
a. Perf 14½ 30 10
769 2 c. Helmet Guineafowl 20 10
a. Perf 14½ 30 10
770 3 c. Scrub Hare 20 10
a. Perf 14½ 30 10
771 4 c. Temminck's Ground Pangolin .. 20 10
a. Perf 14½ 30 10

772 5 c. Greater Kudu 30 10
a. Perf 14½ 30 10
b. Imperf (pair) £160
773 9 c. Black Rhinoceros 50 30
a. Perf 14½ 50 30

(b) Horiz designs as T **152** *showing cultural artifacts. P* 14½×14
774 15 c. Type **152** 20 20
775 20 c. Hand axe and adze 20 20
776 23 c. Gourd and water pot 20 20
777 25 c. Snuff container 20 20
778 26 c. Winnowing tray and basket 30 30
779 30 c. Grinding stone 30 30

(c) Horiz designs as T **153** *showing transport. P* 14½
780 33 c. Type **153** 40 30
781 35 c. Buses 70 40
782 38 c. Passenger train 70 40
783 45 c. Mail motorcycle and trailer 70 40
784 $1 Air Zimbabwe Boeing 737 airliner 1·50 90
785 $2 Lorry 1·50 1·60
768/85 *Set of* 18 7·50 5·50

154 Pres. Mugabe and Joshua Nkomo at Signing of Unity Accord, 1987

155 Runhare House, 1986

(Adapted Nancy Abrey)

1990 (17 Apr). *10th Anniv of Independence. T* **154** *and similar horiz designs. Multicoloured. P* 14½×14.
786 15 c. Type **154** 40 10
787 23 c. Conference Centre, Harare 45 20
788 30 c. Children in class 50 40
789 35 c. Intelsat aerial, Mazowe Earth Satellite Station 60 70
790 38 c. National Sports Stadium 60 80
791 45 c. Maize field 90 1·40
786/91 *Set of* 6 3·00 3·25

1990 (11 July). *Centenary of the City of Harare. T* **155** *and similar horiz designs. Multicoloured. P* 14½.
792 15 c. Type **155** 30 10
793 23 c. Market Hall, 1894 50 20
794 30 c. Charter House, 1959 55 35
795 35 c. Supreme Court, 1927 60 80
796 38 c. Standard Chartered Bank, 1911 60 90
797 45 c. The Town House, 1933 80 1·40
792/7 *Set of* 6 3·00 3·25

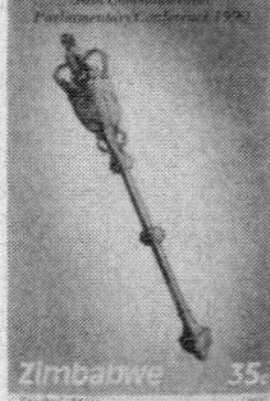

156 Speaker's Mace

157 Small-spotted Genet

1990 (17 Sept). *36th Commonwealth Parliamentary Conference, Harare. T* **156** *and similar vert design. Multicoloured. P* 14½.
798 35 c. Type **156** 50 25
799 $1 Speaker's chair 1·25 2·00

(Des Barbara Chalk)

1991 (15 Jan). *Small Mammals. T* **157** *and similar horiz designs. Multicoloured. P* 14½×14.
800 15 c. Type **157** 80 20
801 23 c. Red Squirrel 85 30
802 35 c. Night-ape 1·25 1·25
803 45 c. Bat-eared Fox 1·75 2·25
800/3 *Set of* 4 4·25 3·50

158 Hosho (rattles)

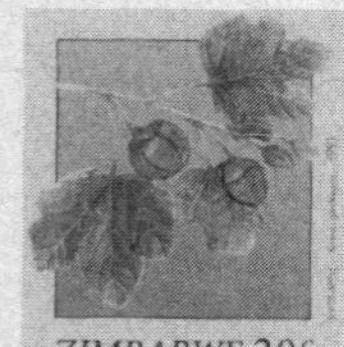

159 Snot-apple

(Des R. Pletts)

1991 (16 Apr). *Traditional Musical Instruments. T* **158** *and similar vert designs. Multicoloured. P* 14½.
804 15 c. Type **158** 45 10
805 23 c. Mbira (thumb piano) 50 15
806 30 c. Ngororombe (pan pipes) 55 40
807 35 c. Chipendani (mouth bow) 65 70
808 38 c. Marimba (xylophone) 65 80
809 45 c. Ngoma (drum) 75 1·10
804/9 *Set of* 6 3·25 2·75

(Des Barbara Chalk)

1991 (17 July). *Wild Fruits. T* **159** *and similar vert designs. Multicoloured. P* 14×14½.
810 20 c. Type **159** 50 10
811 39 c. Marula 55 30
812 51 c. Mobola Plum 60 80
813 60 c. Water Berry 70 85
814 65 c. Northern Dwaba Berry 75 85
815 77 c. Mahobohobo 85 1·10
810/15 *Set of* 6 3·50 3·50

160 Bridal Veil Falls

161 Lion

(Des R. Jeffrey)

1991 (16 Oct). *Commonwealth Heads of Government Meeting, Harare. T* **160** *and similar vert designs. Multicoloured. P* 14½.
816 20 c. Type **160** 55 15
817 39 c. Meeting logo 55 35
818 51 c. Chinhoyi Caves 70 75
819 60 c. Kariba Dam 80 1·00
820 65 c. Victoria Falls 90 1·25
821 77 c. Balancing rocks 95 1·50
816/21 *Set of* 6 4·00 4·50

(Des R. Pletts)

1992 (8 Jan). *Wildlife Conservation. Big Cats. T* **161** *and similar horiz designs. Multicoloured. P* 14½×14.
822 20 c. Type **161** 65 15
823 39 c. Leopard 95 40
824 60 c. Cheetah 1·40 1·75
825 77 c. Serval 1·75 2·00
822/5 *Set of* 4 4·25 3·75

162 *Amanita zambiana*

163 Common Bulbul

(Des R. Pletts)

1992 (8 Apr). *Edible Mushrooms. T* **162** *and similar vert designs. Multicoloured. P* 14×14½.
826 20 c. Type **162** 50 20
827 39 c. *Boletus edulis* 70 40
828 51 c. *Termitomyces* sp 75 75
829 60 c. *Cantharellus densifolius* 90 1·00
830 65 c. *Cantharellus longisporus* 1·00 1·25
831 77 c. *Cantharellus cibarius* 1·25 1·50
826/31 *Set of* 6 4·50 4·50

(Des R. Pletts)

1992 (7 July). *Birds. T* **163** *and similar vert designs. Multicoloured. P* 14½.
832 25 c. Type **163** 45 15
833 59 c. Fiscal Shrike 65 45
834 77 c. Forktailed Drongo 75 80
835 90 c. Cardinal Woodpecker 80 95
836 98 c. Yellow-billed Hornbill 80 95
837 $1.16, Crested Francolin 95 1·40
832/7 *Set of* 6 4·00 4·25

164 *Charaxes jasius*

165 Uranium

(Des R. Pletts)

1992 (15 Oct). *Butterflies. T* **164** *and similar horiz designs. Multicoloured. P* 14½×14.
838 25 c. Type **164** 75 20
839 59 c. *Eronia leda* 1·25 75
840 77 c. *Princeps ophidicephalus* 1·50 1·25
841 90 c. *Junonia oenone* 1·75 1·75
842 98 c. *Danaus chrysippus* 1·90 1·90
843 $1.16, *Junonia octavia* 2·00 2·25
838/43 *Set of* 6 8·25 7·25

(Des R. Jeffrey)

1993 (12 Jan). *Minerals. T* **165** *and similar horiz designs. Multicoloured. P* 14½×14.
844 25 c. Type **165** 60 20
845 59 c. Chrome 90 55
846 77 c. Copper 1·25 1·00
847 90 c. Coal 1·50 1·50
848 98 c. Gold 1·75 1·75
849 $1.16, Emerald 1·90 2·25
844/9 *Set of* 6 7·00 6·50

(Des B. Finch)

1993 (6 Apr). *Owls (2nd series). Vert designs as T* **140**. *Multicoloured. P* 14½.
850 25 c. African Wood Owl 80 30
851 59 c. Pel's Fishing Owl 1·40 65
852 90 c. Spotted Eagle Owl 2·00 2·00
853 $1.16, Verreaux's Eagle Owl ("Giant Eagle Owl") 2·25 2·50
850/3 *Set of* 4 5·75 5·00

166 Hadyana (relish pot)

167 *Polystachya dendrobiflora*

(Des Dianne Deudney)

1993 (13 July). *Household Pottery. T* **166** *and similar horiz designs. Multicoloured. P* 14½×14.
854 25 c. Type **166** 40 10
855 59 c. Chirongo (water jar) 55 30
856 77 c. Mbiya (relish bowl) 65 60
857 90 c. Pfuko (water jar) 75 85
858 98 c. Tsaya (cooking pot) 75 85
859 $1.16, Gate (beer pot) 85 1·00
854/9 *Set of* 6 3·50 3·25

(Des Paula Ware)

1993 (12 Oct). *Orchids. T* **167** *and similar vert designs. Multicoloured. P* 14×14½.
860 35 c. Type **167** 65 20
861 $1 *Diaphananthe subsimplex* 1·25 75
862 $1.50, *Ansellia gigantea* 1·75 1·90
863 $1.95, *Vanilla polyepis* 2·00 2·50
860/3 *Set of* 4 5·00 4·75

(Des C. Herbert)

1994 (20 Jan). *Fishes (2nd series). Horiz designs as T* **149**. *Multicoloured. P* 14½.
864 35 c. Manyame Labeo ("Hunyani Salmon") 30 10
865 $1 Sharp-toothed Catfish ("Barbel") 55 30
866 $1.30, Rainbow Trout 65 65
867 $1.50, African Mottled Eel 70 70
868 $1.65, Common Carp 75 85
869 $1.95, Nembwe ("Robustus Bream") 85 1·00
864/9 *Set of* 6 3·50 3·25

168 City Hall, 1940

169 Strelitzia

(Des Janet Duff)

1994 (5 Apr). *Centenary of Bulawayo. T* **168** *and similar horiz designs. Multicoloured. P* 14½.
870 35 c. Type **168** 15 10
871 80 c. Cresta Churchill Hotel, 1974 30 20
872 $1.15, High Court, 1938 40 40
873 $1.75, Douslin House, 1902 50 70
874 $1.95, Goldfields Building, 1895 60 90
875 $2.30, Parkade Centre, 1975 85 1·25
870/5 *Set of* 6 2·50 3·00

(Des Dianne Deudney)

1994 (12 July). *Export Flowers. T* **169** *and similar vert designs. Multicoloured. P* 14½.
876 35 c. Type **169** 25 10
877 80 c. Protea 45 25
878 $1.15, Phlox 60 50
879 $1.75, Chrysanthemum 70 80
880 $1.95, Ullum 90 1·00
881 $2.30, Rose 1·10 1·40
876/81 *Set of* 6 3·50 3·50

170 The Annunciation

171 Harvesting Maize

(Des Paula Ware)

1994 (11 Oct). *Christmas. T* **170** *and similar vert designs. Multicoloured. P* 14½.

882	35 c. Type **170**	20	10
883	80 c. Journey to Bethlehem	30	15
884	$1.15, The Nativity	45	40
885	$1.75, Shepherds	60	80
886	$1.95, Wise Men	70	90
887	$2.30, Mary and Jesus	80	1·25
882/7	*Set of* 6	2·75	3·25

(Des R. Pletts (1 c. to 4 c.), C. Herbert (5 c. on 50 c.), D. Hobert (70 c. to $10))

1995 (17 Jan)–**96.** *Zimbabwe Culture. T* **171** *and similar horiz designs. Multicoloured. P* 14.

888	1 c. Type **171**	10	10
889	2 c. Loading sugar cane	10	10
890	3 c. Sunflowers	10	10
891	4 c. Sorghum	10	10
892	5 c. Miners	10	10
893	10 c. Drilling for gold	10	10
894	20 c. Opencast coal mining, Wankie	10	10
895	30 c. Chrome smelting, Kwekwe	10	10
896	40 c. Opencast iron extraction, Redcliff	10	10
896*a*	45 c. Underground mining team (3.6.96)	10	10
897	50 c. Gold smelting	10	10
898	70 c. Bogie Clock Tower, Gweru	10	10
899	80 c. Masvingo Watchtower	10	10
900	$1 Hanging Tree, Harare	10	10
901	$2 Cecil House, Harare	15	20
902	$5 The Toposcope, Harare	35	40
903	$10 Paper House, Kwekwe	65	70
888/903	*Set of* 17	1·40	1·60

172 Spider-hunting Wasp

173 Football

(Des Janet Duff)

1995 (4 Apr). *Insects. T* **172** *and similar horiz designs. Multicoloured. P* 14½.

904	35 c. Type **172**	25	10
905	$1.15, Emperor Dragonfly	55	40
906	$1.75, Foxy Charaxes (butterfly)	70	80
907	$2.30, Antlion	1·00	1·40
904/7	*Set of* 4	2·25	2·40

(Des Paula Ware)

1995 (11 July). *6th All-Africa Games, Harare. T* **173** *and similar vert designs, each showing sport within map of Africa. Multicoloured. P* 14×14½.

908	35 c. Type **173**	15	10
909	80 c. Running	25	20
910	$1.15, Boxing	30	25
911	$1.75, Swimming	40	45
912	$1.95, Hockey	60	70
913	$2.30, Volleyball	70	80
908/13	*Set of* 6	2·25	2·25

174 Weighing Baby (Health)

175 Fernandoa Tree

(Des Jane Debney)

1995 (17 Oct). *50th Anniv of United Nations. T* **174** *and similar horiz designs. Multicoloured. P* 14½×14.

914	35 c. Type **174**	15	10
915	$1.15, Women at pump (Environment)	30	30
916	$1.75, Workers on lorry (Food Distribution)	50	55
917	$2.30, Teacher and children (Education)	60	75
914/17	*Set of* 4	1·40	1·50

(Des Janet Duff)

1996 (24 Jan). *Indigenous Flowering Trees. T* **175** *and similar vert designs. Multicoloured. P* 14½.

918	45 c. Type **175**	15	10
919	$1 Round Leaf Mukwa	30	20
920	$1.50, Luckybean Tree	45	45
921	$2.20, Winter Cassia	60	65
922	$2.50, Sausage Tree	65	70
923	$3 Sweet Thorn	75	85
918/23	*Set of* 6	2·50	2·50

176 Mazvikadei Dam

(Des R. Pletts)

1996 (9 Apr). *Dams of Zimbabwe. T* **176** *and similar horiz designs. Multicoloured. P* 14½.

924	45 c. Type **176**	15	10
925	$1.50, Mutirikwi Dam	45	35
926	$2.20, Ncema Dam	65	70
927	$3 Odzani Dam	75	90
924/7	*Set of* 4	1·75	1·75

177 Matusadonha National Park at Sunset

178 Carved Frog

(Des Paula Ware)

1996 (18 July). *Scenic Views. T* **177** *and similar horiz designs. Multicoloured* . *P* 14½.

928	45 c. Type **177**	15	10
929	$1.50, Juliasdale rocky outcrop	45	35
930	$2.20, Honde Valley	75	75
931	$3 Finger Rocks at Morgenster Mission	85	95
928/31	*Set of* 4	2·00	1·90

(Des M. Nyoni)

1996 (15 Oct). *Animal Wood Carvings. T* **178** *and similar horiz designs. Multicoloured. P* 14½×14.

932	45 c. Type **178**	15	10
933	$1.50, Tortoise	30	20
934	$1.70, Kudu	35	35
935	$2.20, Chimpanzee	50	55
936	$2.50, Porcupine	55	60
937	$3 Rhinoceros	60	70
932/7	*Set of* 6	2·25	2·25

179 Mashona Cow

(Des R. Pletts)

1997 (7 Jan). *Cattle Breeds. T* **179** *and similar horiz designs. Multicoloured. P* 14½.

938	45 c. Type **179**	10	10
939	$1.50, Tuli cow	20	15
940	$2.20, Nkoni bull	30	30
941	$3 Brahman bull	35	40
938/41	*Set of* 4	80	80

180 Cycad

(Des Paula Ware)

1997 (15 Apr). *10th Meeting of Convention on International Trade in Endangered Species Members, Harare. T* **180** *and similar horiz designs. Multicoloured. P* 14½.

942	45 c. Type **180**	10	10
943	$1.50, Peregrine Falcon	20	20
944	$1.70, Temminck's Ground Pangolin	25	25
945	$2.20, Black Rhinoceros	30	30
946	$2.50, African Elephant	35	40
947	$3 Python	35	45
942/7	*Set of* 6	1·40	1·50

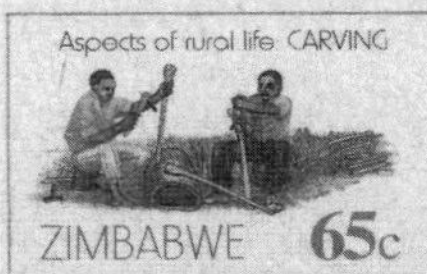

181 Wood Carving

(Des Dianne Deudney)

1997 (22 July). *Rural Life. T* **181** *and similar horiz designs. Multicoloured. P* 14½.

948	65 c. Type **181**	15	10
949	$1 Winnowing	15	10
950	$2.40, Dancing	25	25
951	$2.50, Ploughing	25	25
952	$3.10, Stamping cereals	30	35
953	$4.20, Fetching water	40	45
948/53	*Set of* 6	1·40	1·40

STAMP BOOKLETS

1928 (1 Jan). *Black on blue cover. Stitched.*
SB1 2s. 6d. booklet containing twelve ½d. and twenty-four 1d. (Nos. 1/2) in blocks of 6 .. .. £2500

1931. *Black on blue cover. Stitched.*
SB2 2s. 6d. booklet containing twelve ½d. and twenty-four 1d. (Nos. 15/16) in blocks of 6 .. .. £3000

1933 (3 Mar). *Black on red cover, size 69×53 mm. Stitched.*
SB3 3s. booklet containing twelve ½d., 1d. and 1½d. (Nos. 15, 16, 16*c*) in blocks of 6 .. .. £1800

1938 (31 Mar). *Black on yellow cover. Stitched.*
SB4 2s. 6d. booklet containing twenty-four ½d. and eighteen 1d. (Nos. 40/1) in blocks of 6 .. £225

1954 (Jan). *Black on yellow cover, size 71×54 mm. Stitched.*
SB5 2s. 6d. booklet containing twelve ½d. and twenty-four 1d. (Nos. 78/9) in blocks of 6 .. .. 80·00

1964 (19 Feb). *Black on orange cover, size 57×45 mm. Stitched.*
SB6 1s. booklet containing 3d. (No. 95) in block of 4 4·00

1967 (Feb). *Black on orange cover, size 57×45 mm. Stitched.*
SB7 1s. booklet containing 3d. (No. 376) in block of 4 5·50

Although not issued in Rhodesia until February 1967, No. SB7 was released in London in June 1966.

1968 (21 Dec). *Black on yellow cover, size 51×94 mm. Stapled.*
SB8 5s. booklet containing twelve 1d. and 3d., and six 2d. (Nos. 397/9) in blocks of 6 .. .. 22·00

1970 (17 Feb). *Red on yellow cover. Stapled.*
SB9 46 c. booklet containing twelve 1 c., eight 2½ c. and four 3½ c. in panes of 4 (Nos. 439a, 441a, 442a) .. .. 5·00

1972 (10 Apr). *Green on yellow cover. Stapled.*
SB10 48 c. booklet containing eight 1 c. and sixteen 2½ c. in panes of 4 (Nos. 439a, 441a) .. 13·00

1973 (7 May). *Blue on yellow cover. Stapled.*
SB11 50 c. booklet containing four 2½ c. and 4 c., and eight 3 c. in panes of 4 (Nos. 441a, 441ca, 442ba) .. .. 18·00

1974 (14 Aug). *White on blue cover. Stapled.*
SB12 50 c. booklet containing four 2½ c. and 4 c., and eight 3 c. in panes of 4 (Nos. 490a, 491a, 492a) .. .. 6·00

POSTAGE DUE STAMPS

SOUTHERN

RHODESIA

(D 1)

POSTAGE DUE 1D ONE PENNY RHODESIA

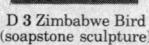

D 2

1951 (1 Oct). *Postage Due stamps of Great Britain optd with Type* D 1.

D1 D 1	½d. emerald (No. D27)		3·25	13·00
D2	1d. violet-blue (No. D36)		3·00	2·50
D3	2d. agate (No. D29)		4·00	1·75
D4	3d. violet (No. D30)		2·75	1·75
D5	4d. blue (No. D38)		1·75	3·00
D6	4d. dull grey-green (No. D31)		£160	£500
D7	1s. deep blue (No. D33)		3·00	2·25
D1/5, 7	.. ..	*Set of* 6	16·00	22·00

No. D6 is reported to have been issued to Fort Victoria and Gwelo main post offices only.

(Typo Printing and Stationery Dept, Salisbury)

1965 (17 June). *Roul* 9.

D 8 D 2	1d. orange-red (*roul* 5)		70	12·00
	a. Roul 9		3·25	12·00
D 9	2d. deep blue		50	8·00
D10	4d. green		60	8·00
D11	6d. plum		60	6·00
D8a/11	.. ..	*Set of* 4	2·25	30·00

The 2d. has a stop below the "D".

D 3 Zimbabwe Bird (soapstone sculpture)

D 4 Zimbabwe Bird (soapstone sculpture)

(Litho Mardon Printers, Salisbury)

1966 (15 Dec). *P* 14½.

D12 D 3	1d. red		1·00	3·25
D13	2d. bluish violet		1·25	2·50
D14	4d. pale green		1·25	4·25
D15	6d. reddish violet		1·25	2·25
D16	1s. red-brown		1·25	2·25
D17	2s. black		1·50	5·00
D12/17	.. ..	*Set of* 6	6·50	18·00

1970 (17 Feb)–**73.** *Decimal Currency. As Type* D **3**, *but larger* (26 × 22½ *mm*). *P* 14½.

D18 D 3	1 c. bright green		1·00	1·75
D19	2 c. ultramarine		1·00	80
	a. Printed on the gummed side ..		65·00	
D20	5 c. bright reddish violet		2·50	2·75
D21	6 c. pale lemon (7.5.73)		4·25	3·75
D22	10 c. cerise		2·50	4·25
D18/22	.. ..	*Set of* 5	10·00	12·00

1980. *P* 14½.

D23 D 4	1 c. bright green		25	80
D24	2 c. ultramarine		30	90
D25	5 c. bright reddish violet		40	90
	a. Imperf (pair)		90·00	
D26	6 c. pale lemon		50	1·60
D27	10 c. cerise		65	2·00
D23/7	.. ..	*Set of* 5	1·90	5·75

Zimbabwe 1C TO PAY

D 5

25

(D 6)

1985 (21 Aug). *P* 14½.

D28 D 5	1 c. yellow-orange		10	30
D29	2 c. magenta		15	30
D30	6 c. blue-green		25	40
D31	10 c. orange-brown		30	40
D32	13 c. new blue		30	40
D28/32	.. ..	*Set of* 5	1·00	1·60

1990 (2 Jan). *No. D27 surch with Type* D **6**.

D33 D 4 25 c. on 10 c. cerise .. .. .. 6·00 6·00

No. D33 is reported to have been issued to the main post offices at Bulawayo, Gweru, Harare and Mutare.

D 7

1995 (17 Jan). *P* 14½.

D34 D 7	1 c. lemon		10	10
D35	2 c. yellow-orange		10	10
D36	5 c. mauve		10	10
D37	10 c. pale blue		10	10
D38	25 c. bright reddish violet		10	10
D39	40 c. bright blue-green		10	10
D40	60 c. red-orange		10	10
D41	$1 brown		10	10
D34/41	.. ..	*Set of* 8	45	45

Zululand
see South Africa

Addenda

PAKISTAN

510 Faiz Ahmed Faiz

511 Golden Jubilee and O.I.C. Emblems

1997 (12 Feb). 86*th Birth Anniv of Faiz Ahmed Faiz* (*poet*). *P* 13.

1011 **510** 3 r. multicoloured 10 15

1997 (23 Mar). *Special Summit Conference of Organization of Islamic Countries commemorating* 50*th anniv of Pakistan*. *P* 13.

1012 **511** 2 r. multicoloured 10 10

512 Amir Timur

513 Jalal-al-din Moulana Rumi

1997 (8 Apr). 660*th Birth Anniv of Timur* (*founder of Timurid Empire*). *P* 13.

1013 **512** 3 r. multicoloured 10 15

1997 (21 Apr). *Pakistan–Iran Joint Issue. T* **513** *and similar vert design. P* 13½.

1014 3 r. Type **513** 10 15
1015 3 r. Allama Mohammad Iqbal (poet) .. 10 15

514 Apple

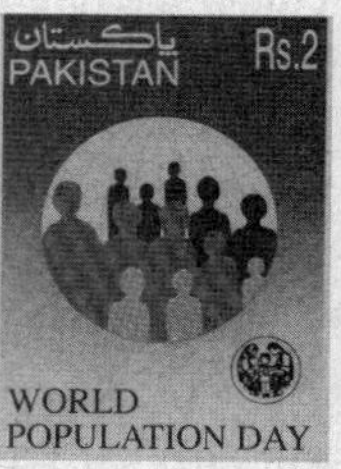

515 People on Globe

1997 (8 May). *Fruit. P* 13.

1016 **514** 2 r. multicoloured 10 10

1997 (11 July). *World Population Day. P* 13.

1017 **515** 2 r. multicoloured 10 10

Note: The first Supplement recording new stamps not in this catalogue or the Addenda appeared in the September 1998 number of *Gibbons Stamp Monthly*.

Set Prices for British Commonwealth Omnibus Issues

The composition of these sets is in accordance with the tables on the following pages. Only such items considered basic stamps are included; varieties such as shades, perforation changes and watermark changes are excluded. Great Britain issues which come on both ordinary paper and on paper with phosphor bands are however covered.

Stamps issued in connection with any of the events by countries which are no longer in the British Commonwealth and which are not listed in the Part 1 Catalogue are omitted.

		Price Un	Used
1935. Silver Jubilee.	*Complete set of* 250 *stamps*	£900	£1100

The concept initiated by the 1935 Silver Jubilee omnibus issue has provided a pattern for a series of Royal commemoratives over the past 50 years which have introduced countless collectors to the hobby.

The Crown Colony Windsor Castle design by Harold Fleury is, surely, one of the most impressive produced in the 20th-century and its reproduction in the recess process by three of the leading stamp-printing firms of the era has provided a subject for philatelic research which has yet to be exhausted.

Each of the three, Bradbury, Wilkinson & Co. and Waterlow and Sons, who both produced fifteen issues, together with De La Rue & Co. who printed fourteen, used a series of vignette (centre) plates coupled with individual frame plates for each value. All were taken from dies made by Waterlow. Several worthwhile varieties exist on the frame plates, but most interest has been concentrated on the centre plates, each of which was used to print a considerable number of different stamps.

Sheets printed by Bradbury, Wilkinson were without printed plate numbers, but research has now identified eleven centre plates which were probably used in permanent pairings. A twelfth plate awaits confirmation. Stamps from some of these centre plates have revealed a number of prominent plate flaws, the most famous of which, the extra flagstaff, has been eagerly sought by collectors for many years.

Extra flagstaff (Plate "1" R.9/1)

Short extra flagstaff (Plate "2" R.2/1)

Lightning conductor (Plate "3" R.2/5)

Flagstaff on right-hand turret (Plate "5" R.7/1)

Double flagstaff (Plate "6" R.5/2)

De La Rue sheets were initially printed with plate numbers, but in many instances these were subsequently trimmed off. Surviving examples do, however, enable a positive identification of six centre plates, 2A, 2B, (2A), (2B), 4 and 4/ to be made. The evidence of sheet markings and plate flaws clearly demonstrates that there were two different pairs of plates numbered 2A 2B. The second pair is designated (2A) (2B) by specialist collectors to avoid further confusion. The number of major plate flaws is not so great as on the Bradbury, Wilkinson sheets, but four examples are included in the catalogue.

Diagonal line by turret (Plate 2A R.10/1 and 10/2)

Dot to left of chapel (Plate 2B R.8/3)

Dot by flagstaff (Plate 4 R.8/4)

Dash by turret (Plate 4/ R.3/6)

Much less is known concerning the Waterlow centre plate system as the sheets did not show plate numbers. Ten individual plates have, so far, been identified and it is believed that these were used in pairs. The two versions of the kite and log flaw from plate "2" show that this plate exists in two states.

Damaged turret (Plate "1" R.5/6)

Kite and vertical log (Plate "2A" R.10/6)

Kite and horizontal log (Plate "2B" R.10/6)

Bird by turret (Plate "7" R.1/5)

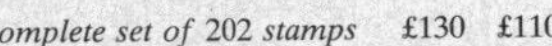

1937. Coronation.	*Complete set of* 202 *stamps*	£130	£110

1945–46. Victory.	*Complete set of* 164 *stamps*	30·00	27·00

1948–49. Royal Silver Wedding.	*Complete set of* 138 *stamps*	£1700	£1600

1949. U.P.U. 75th Anniversary	*Complete set of* 310 *stamps*	£325	£325

1951. B.W.I. University College	*Complete set of* 28 *stamps*	10·00	10·50

1953. Coronation.	*Complete set of* 106 *stamps*	£100	70·00

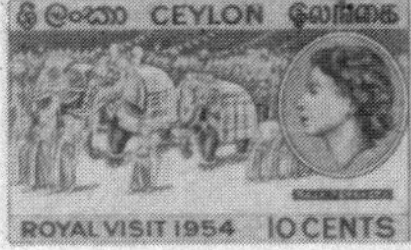

1953–54. Royal Visit.	*Complete set of* 13 *stamps*	3·00	3·25

1958. Caribbean Federation.	*Complete set of* 30 *stamps*	17·00	14·50

1963. Freedom from Hunger.
Complete set of 77 *stamps* £190 90·00

1963. Red Cross Centenary.
Complete set of 108 *stamps and* 2 *miniature sheets* £275 £190

1964. Shakespeare. 400th Birth Anniversary.
Complete set of 25 *stamps* 21·00 19·00

1965. I.T.U. Centenary.
Complete set of 112 *stamps and* 1 *miniature sheet* £160 90·00

1965. I.C.Y.
Complete set of 107 *stamps and* 2 *miniature sheets* £120 70·00

1965–67. Churchill. *Complete set of* 182 *stamps* £250 £130

1966. Royal Visit to the Caribbean.
Complete set of 34 *stamps* 30·00 12·00

1966. World Cup Football Championship.
Complete set of 68 *stamps and* 1 *miniature sheet* 75·00 42·00

1966. W.H.O. New Headquarters.
Complete set of 58 *stamps and* 1 *miniature sheet* 75·00 35·00

1966–67. U.N.E.S.C.O. 20th Anniversary.
Complete set of 110 *stamps and* 1 *miniature sheet* £150 85·00

1972. Royal Silver Wedding.
Complete set of 78 *stamps* 27·00 25·00

1973. Royal Wedding.
Complete set of 72 *stamps and* 6 *miniature sheets* 26·00 17·00

1977. Silver Jubilee. *Set of* 220 *stamps* 55·00 60·00
Set of 24 *miniature sheets* 20·00 26·00

1977. Royal Visit. *Set of* 46 *stamps* 7·50 9·00
Set of 8 *miniature sheets* 5·50 9·00

1978. Coronation. 25th Anniversary.
Set of 195 *stamps* 42·00 50·00
Set of 21 *sheetlets* 22·00
Set of 27 *miniature sheets* 32·00 22·00

1980. Queen Mother's Birthday.
Set of 41 *stamps* 20·00 22·00
Set of 12 *miniature sheets* 20·00 22·00

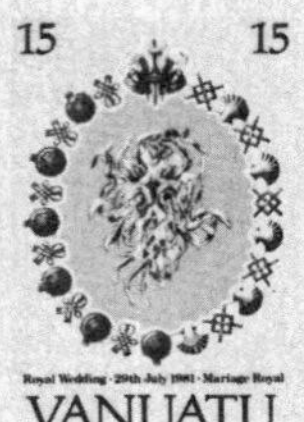

1981. Royal Wedding. *Set of* 244 *stamps* 90·00 95·00
Set of 35 *miniature sheets* 45·00 50·00

1982. Princess Diana's 21st Birthday.
Set of 162 *stamps* 85·00 90·00
Set of 19 *miniature sheets* 42·00 42·00

1982. Birth of Prince William.

Set of 124 stamps 95·00 85·00
Set of 22 miniature sheets 42·00 45·00

The Life and Times of Her Majesty Queen Elizabeth The Queen Mother

(*Illustration reduced*)

1985. Life and Times of Queen Elizabeth the Queen Mother.

Set of 226 stamps 95·00 £130
Set of 47 miniature sheets 85·00 £110

1986. 60th Birthday of Queen Elizabeth II.

Set of 233 stamps £120 £170
Set of 28 miniature sheets 85·00 £110

1986. Royal Wedding.

Set of 142 stamps £100 £130
Set of 24 miniature sheets 85·00 £110

1987. Royal Ruby Wedding.

Set of 117 stamps £100 £130
Set of 14 miniature sheets 42·00 55·00

1990. 90th Birthday of Queen Elizabeth the Queen Mother.

Set of 127 stamps £140 £160
Set of 22 miniature sheets £100 £110

1991. 65th Birthday of Queen Elizabeth II and 70th Birthday of Prince Philip.

Set of 99 stamps £110 £120
Set of 14 miniature sheets 35·00 40·00

1992. 40th Anniversary of Queen Elizabeth II's Accession.

Set of 195 stamps £160 £180
Set of 30 miniature sheets 95·00 £110

1993. 40th Anniv of Coronation.

Set of 135 stamps £120 £140
Set of 18 miniature sheets 48·00 55·00

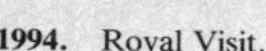

1994. Royal Visit.

Set of 27 stamps	23·00	26·00
Set of 2 miniature sheets	6·00	6·50

1995. 95th Birthday of Queen Elizabeth the Queen Mother.

Set of 64 stamps	55·00	60·00
Set of 14 sheetlets	55·00	
Set of 18 miniature sheets	55·00	55·00

1996. Queen Elizabeth II's 70th Birthday.

Set of 86 stamps	90·00	£100
Set of 13 sheetlets	29·00	
Set of 19 miniature sheets	55·00	60·00

1997. Royal Golden Wedding

Set of 216 stamps	£120	£130
Set of 13 sheetlets	35·00	
Set of 37 miniature sheets	90·00	£100

1935 SILVER JUBILEE TO 1973 ROYAL WEDDING

Issuing Countries	1935 *Silver Jubilee*	1937 *Coronation*	1945–46 *Victory*	1948 *Silver Wedding*	1949 *U.P.U.*	1951 *B.W.I. Univ*	1953 *Coronation*	1953–54 *Royal Visit*	1958 *Caribbean Fed.*	1963 *F.F.H.*	1963 *Red Cross*	1964 *Shakespeare*	1965 *I.T.U.*	1965 *I.C.Y.*	1965–66 *Churchill*	1966 *Royal Visit*	1966 *Football Cup*	1966 *W.H.O.*	1966–67 *UNESCO*	1972 *Silver Wedding*	1973 *Royal Wedding*
Great Britain	4	1	2	2	4	—	4	—	—	2+2	3+3	5+4	2+2	2+2	2+2	—	3+3	—	—	2	2
Guernsey	—	—	—	—	—	—	—	—	—	—	—	—	—	—	—	—	—	—	—	4	1
Isle of Man	—	—	—	—	—	—	—	—	—	—	—	—	—	—	—	—	—	—	—	—	1
Jersey	—	—	—	—	—	—	—	—	—	—	—	—	—	—	—	—	—	—	—	4	2
Anguilla	—	—	—	—	—	—	—	—	—	—	—	—	—	—	—	—	—	—	—	2	2
Antigua	4	3	2	2	4	2	1	—	3	1	2	1	2	2	4	2	2	2	3	2	2+**MS**
Barbuda	—	—	—	—	—	—	—	—	—	—	—	—	—	—	—	—	—	—	—	—	2
Ascension	4	3	2	2	4	—	1	—	—	1	2	—	2	2	4	—	2	2	3	2	2
Australia	3	—	3	—	1	—	3	3	—	—	1	—	1	1	1	—	—	—	—	—	—
Bahamas	4	3	2	2	4	—	1	—	—	1	2	1	2	2	4	2	2	2	3	2	—
Bahrain	—	—	—	2	4	—	4	—	—	—	—	—	—	—	—	—	—	—	—	—	—
Barbados	4	3	2	2	4	2	1	—	3	—	—	—	2	—	4	2	—	—	3	—	—
Belize/British Honduras	4	3	2	2	4	2	1	—	—	1	2	—	2	2	4	—	—	—	—	2	2
Bermuda	4	3	2	2	4	—	1	1	—	1	2	—	2	2	4	—	2	—	3	2	2
Botswana/Bechuanaland	4	3	3×2	2	4	—	1	—	—	1	2	1	2	2	4	—	—	—	—	—	—
British Antarctic Territory	—	—	—	—	—	—	—	—	—	—	—	—	—	—	4	—	—	—	—	2	2
British Indian Ocean Terr.	—	—	—	—	—	—	—	—	—	—	—	—	—	—	—	—	—	—	—	2	—
British P.A.'s in Eastern Arabia	—	—	—	2	4	—	4	—	—	—	—	—	—	—	—	—	—	—	—	—	—
British Virgin Islands	4	3	2	2	4	2	1	—	—	1	2	1	2	2	4	2	—	—	3	2	2
Brunei	—	—	—	—	4	—	—	—	—	1	—	—	2	2	4	—	2	2	3	2	2
Burma	—	—	4	—	—	—	—	—	—	—	—	—	—	—	—	—	—	—	—	—	—
Canada	6	1	—	—	—	—	1	—	—	—	—	—	—	1	1	—	—	—	—	—	—
Newfoundland	4	14	—	—	—	—	—	—	—	—	—	—	—	—	—	—	—	—	—	—	—
Cayman Islands	4	3	2	2	4	—	1	—	—	1	2	1	2	2	4	2	2	2	3	2	2
Cook Islands	3	3	4	—	—	—	2	—	—	—	—	—	—	—	6	—	—	—	—	4	3+**MS**
Aitutaki	—	—	—	—	—	—	—	—	—	—	—	—	—	—	—	—	—	—	—	2	2+**MS**
Penrhyn	—	—	—	—	—	—	—	—	—	—	—	—	—	—	—	—	—	—	—	—	3
Cyprus	4	3	2	2	4	—	1	—	—	2	2	4	3	2	—	—	—	—	1	—	—
Dominica	4	3	2	2	4	2	1	—	3	1	2	1	2	2	4	2	2	2	3	2	2+**MS**
Egypt/British Forces in Egypt	1	—	—	—	—	—	—	—	—	—	—	—	—	—	—	—	—	—	—	—	—
Falkland Islands	4	3	2	2	4	—	1	—	—	1	2	1	2	2	4	—	—	—	—	2	2
Falkland Islands Dependencies	—	—	2	2	4	—	1	—	—	—	—	—	—	—	—	—	—	—	—	—	—
South Georgia	—	—	—	—	—	—	—	—	—	—	—	—	—	—	—	—	—	—	—	2	2
Fiji	4	3	2	2	4	—	1	1	—	1	2	—	2	2	4	—	2	2	—	2	—
Gambia	4	3	2	2	4	—	1	—	—	1	2	1	2	—	3	—	—	—	—	—	—
Ghana/Gold Coast	4	3	2	2	4	—	1	—	—	3	4+**MS**	—	4+**MS**	4+**MS**	—	—	5+**MS**	4+**MS**	5+**MS**	—	—
Gibraltar	4	3	2	2	4	—	1	1	—	1	2	1	2	2	4	—	2	2	3	2	2
Gilbert and Ellice Islands	4	3	2	2	4	—	1	—	—	1	2	—	2	2	4	—	2	2	3	2	2
Grenada	4	3	2	2	4	2	1	—	3	1	2	—	2	2	4	2	2	2	3	2	2+**MS**
Grenadines	—	—	—	—	—	—	—	—	—	—	—	—	—	—	—	—	—	—	—	—	2+**MS**
Guyana/British Guiana	4	3	2	2	4	2	1	—	—	1	2	—	2	2	2	2	—	—	—	—	—
Hong Kong	4	3	2	2	4	—	1	—	—	1	2	—	2	2	4	—	—	2	3	2	2
India	7	—	4	—	4	—	—	—	—	1	1	—	1	1	—	—	—	—	—	—	—
Hyderabad	—	—	1	—	—	—	—	—	—	—	—	—	—	—	—	—	—	—	—	—	—
Ireland	—	—	—	—	—	—	—	—	—	2	2	—	2	2	—	—	—	—	—	—	—
Jamaica	4	3	2	2	4	2	1	1	3	2	2	—	1	—	2	4	—	—	—	—	—
K.U.T./East Africa	4	3	2	2	4	—	1	1	—	4	2	—	4	4	—	—	—	—	4	—	—
Kuwait	—	—	—	2	4	—	4	—	—	—	—	—	—	—	—	—	—	—	—	—	—
Leeward Islands	4	3	2	2	4	2	1	—	—	—	—	—	—	—	—	—	—	—	—	—	—
Lesotho/Basutoland	4	3	3×2	2	4	—	1	—	—	1	2	—	2	2	4	—	—	—	4	—	—
Malawi/Nyasaland	4	3	2	2	4	—	1	—	—	—	—	—	—	—	—	—	—	—	—	—	—
Malayan States, etc.	4	3	—	22	44	—	11	—	—	3	—	—	3	—	—	—	—	—	—	—	—
North Borneo	—	—	—	2	4	—	1	—	—	1	—	—	—	—	—	—	—	—	—	—	—
Sarawak	—	—	—	2	4	—	1	—	—	1	—	—	—	—	—	—	—	—	—	—	—
Maldive Islands	—	—	—	—	—	—	—	—	—	7	5	—	—	5+**MS**	6	—	—	—	6	—	—
Malta	4	3	2	2	4	—	1	1	—	1	2	—	—	—	4	—	—	—	—	—	—
Mauritius	4	3	2	2	4	—	1	—	—	1	2	—	2	2	4	—	—	—	3	—	—
Montserrat	4	3	2	2	4	2	1	—	3	1	2	1	2	2	4	2	—	2	3	2	2
Morocco Agencies/Tangier	15	3	2	4	4	—	4	—	—	—	—	—	—	—	—	—	—	—	—	—	—
Namibia/South West Africa	4	8×2	3×2	1×2	3×2	—	5	—	—	—	2	—	—	—	—	—	—	—	—	—	—
Nauru	4	4	—	—	—	—	—	—	—	—	—	—	—	—	—	—	—	—	—	—	—
New Zealand	3	3	11	—	—	—	5	2	—	—	—	—	1	1	1	—	—	—	—	—	—
Tokelau Islands	—	—	—	—	—	—	1	—	—	—	—	—	—	—	—	—	—	—	—	—	—
Nigeria	4	3	2	2	4	—	1	—	—	2	3+**MS**	—	3	3	—	—	—	—	3	—	—
Niue	3	3	4	—	—	—	2	—	—	—	—	—	—	—	—	—	—	—	—	—	—
Pakistan	—	—	—	—	—	—	—	—	—	2	1	—	1	2	—	—	—	—	1	—	—
Bahawalpur Postage and Officials	—	—	1	—	4+4	—	—	—	—	—	—	—	—	—	—	—	—	—	—	—	—
P.N.G./Papua	4	4	—	—	—	—	—	—	—	—	1	—	—	—	—	—	—	—	—	—	—
New Guinea	2	4	—	—	—	—	—	—	—	—	—	—	—	—	—	—	—	—	—	—	—
Pitcairn Islands	—	—	2	2	4	—	1	—	—	1	2	—	2	2	4	—	2	2	3	2	2
Rhodesia and Nyasaland	—	—	—	—	—	—	—	—	—	—	1	—	—	—	—	—	—	—	—	—	—
St. Helena	4	3	2	2	4	—	1	—	—	1	2	—	2	2	4	—	2	2	3	2	2
St. Kitts-Nevis	4	3	2	2	4	2	1	—	3	—	2	—	2	2	4	2	2	2	3	2	2
St. Lucia	4	3	2	2	4	2	1	—	3	1	2	1	2	2	4	2	2	2	3	2	2
St. Vincent	4	3	2	2	4	2	1	—	3	1	2	—	2	—	4	2	—	2	3	2	2
Grenadines	—	—	—	—	—	—	—	—	—	—	—	—	—	—	—	—	—	—	—	—	2
Samoa	3	—	4	—	—	—	2	—	—	—	—	—	—	—	—	—	—	4	—	—	—
Seychelles	4	3	2	2	4	—	1	—	—	1	2	—	2	2	4	—	2	2	3	2	2
Sierra Leone	4	3	2	2	4	—	1	—	—	2	3	—	—	—	11	—	—	—	—	—	—
Singapore	—	—	—	2	4	—	1	—	—	—	—	—	—	—	—	—	—	—	—	—	—
Solomon Islands	4	3	2	2	4	—	1	—	—	1	2	—	2	2	4	—	2	2	3	2	2
Somaliland Protectorate	4	3	2	2	4	—	1	—	—	—	—	—	—	—	—	—	—	—	—	—	—
South Africa	4×2	5×2	3×2	1×2	3×2	—	1	—	—	—	2	—	2	—	—	—	—	—	—	—	—
South Arabian Fed./Aden	—	3	2	2	4	—	1	1	—	1	2	—	—	2	4	—	2	2	3	—	—
Seiyun	—	—	2	2	4	—	1	—	—	—	—	—	7	—	1	—	7	—	—	—	—
Shihr and Mukalla	—	—	2	2	4	—	1	—	—	—	—	—	—	8	3	—	8	—	—	—	—
Sri Lanka/Ceylon	4	3	2	—	3	—	1	1	—	2	—	—	2	2	—	—	—	2	2	—	—
Swaziland	4	3	3×2	2	4	—	1	—	—	1	2	—	2	2	4	—	—	—	3	—	—
Tanzania/Zanzibar	—	—	2	2	4	—	—	—	—	1	—	—	—	—	—	—	—	—	—	—	—
Tonga	—	—	—	—	4	—	—	—	—	1	2	—	—	—	—	—	—	—	—	—	—
Trinidad and Tobago	4	3	2	2	4	2	1	—	3	3	—	—	—	1	—	4	—	—	—	—	—
Tristan da Cunha	—	—	—	—	—	—	1	—	—	1	2	—	2	2	4	—	2	2	3	2	2
Turks and Caicos Islands	4	3	2	2	4	—	1	—	—	1	2	1	2	2	4	2	—	—	3	2	2
Vanuatu/New Hebrides (English & French inscr)	—	—	—	—	4+4	—	1	—	—	1+1	2+2	—	2+2	2+2	4+4	—	2+2	2+2	3+3	2+2	—
Zambia/Northern Rhodesia	4	3	2	2	4	—	1	—	—	—	—	—	2	2	—	—	—	2	—	—	—
Zimbabwe/Southern Rhodesia	4	4	4	—	2	—	1	—	—	—	—	—	3	—	1	—	—	—	—	—	—
Total number of stamps	250	202	164	138	310	28	106	13	30	77	108 +2 **MS**	25	112 +**MS**	107 +2 **MS**	182	34	68 + **MS**	58 + **MS**	110 + **MS**	78	72 +6 **MS**

BRITISH COMMONWEALTH OMNIBUS ISSUES

NOTE Countries marked with an asterisk are those which comprise the Crown Agents Omnibus issue.

1977 SILVER JUBILEE

Country	*Catalogue Nos.*	*Stamps*	*MS*
Great Britain	1033/7	5	—
Guernsey	149/50	2	—
Isle of Man	94/6	3	—
Jersey	168/70	3	—
Anguilla	269/73	4	1
Antigua	526/31	5	1
Barbuda	298/304, 323/28	11	2
Ascension*	222/4	3	—
Australia	645/6	2	—
Christmas Island	83	1	—
Norfolk Island	196	1	—
Bahamas	488/92	4	1
Bangladesh	93/6	3	1
Barbados*	574/6	3	—
Belize*	449/51	3	—
Bermuda*	371/3	3	—
Botswana*	391/3	3	—
British Antarctic Territory*	83/5	3	—
British Virgin Islands*	364/6	3	—
Brunei	264/6	3	—
Canada	855	1	—
Cayman Islands*	427/9	3	—
Cook Islands	564/70	6	1
Aitutaki	225/9	4	1
Penrhyn	100/3	3	1
Cyprus	485	1	—
Dominica	562/7	5	1
Falkland Islands*	325/7	3	—
South Georgia*	50/2	3	—
Fiji*	536/8	3	—
Gambia*	365/7	3	—
Gibraltar	371/3	2	1
Grenada	857/62	5	1
Grenadines of Grenada	215/18	3	1
Hong Kong*	361/3	3	—
Kenya	91/5	4	2
Kiribati / Gilbert Islands*	48/50	3	—
Maldive Islands	673/9	6	1
Mauritius*	516/18	3	—
Montserrat	396/8	3	—
New Zealand	**MS**1137	—	1
Niue	213/15	2	1
Papua New Guinea	330/2	3	—
Pitcairn Islands*	171/3	3	—
St. Helena*	332/4	3	—
St. Kitts-Nevis*	367/9	3	—
St. Lucia	443/7	4	1
St. Vincent	502/14	12	1
Grenadines of St. Vincent	93/5	3	—
Samoa	479/82	4	—
Seychelles	393/401	8	1
Sierra Leone	597/8	2	—
Solomon Islands*	334/6	3	—
Swaziland*	268/70	3	—
Tanzania	218/22	4	1
Tonga	598/607, O151/3	13	—
Tristan da Cunha*	212/14	3	—
Turks and Caicos Islands*	472/5	3	1
Tuvalu	50/3	3	1
Vanuatu/New Hebrides* (English & French inscr)	217/19 F231/3	3+3	—
Total number of items		220	24

The Turks and Caicos Islands miniature sheet, **MS**475, did not form part of the Crown Agents Omnibus issue.

1977 ROYAL VISIT

Country	*Catalogue Nos.*	*Stamps*	*MS*
Anguilla	298/302	4	1
Antigua	548/53	5	1
Barbuda	345/54	8	2
Bahamas	500/4	4	1
Barbados	590/2	3	—
British Virgin Islands	371/3	3	—
Dominica	591/6	5	1
Grenada	894/9	5	1
Grenadines of Grenada	239/42	3	1
Montserrat	409/11	3	—
St. Vincent	540	1	—
Grenadines of St. Vincent	104/5	2	—
Total number of items		46	8

1978 CORONATION ANNIVERSARY

Country	*Catalogue Nos.*	*Stamps*	*Sheetlets*	*MS*
Great Britain	1059/62	4	—	—
Guernsey	167	1	—	—
Isle of Man	132	1	—	—
Jersey	195/6	2	—	—
Anguilla	320/4	4	—	1
Antigua	581/6	5	—	1
Barbuda	408/20, 445/6	12	—	3
Ascension*	233/5	3	1	—
Australia				
Christmas Island*	96/8	3	1	—
Norfolk Island	207/8	2	—	—
Bahamas	515/17	2	—	1
Bangladesh	116/20	4	—	1
Barbados*	597/9	3	1	—
Belize*	464/6, 495/503	11	1	2
Bermuda	384/6	3	—	—
British Antarctic Territory*	86/8	3	1	—
British Virgin Islands*	384/6	3	1	—
Brunei	267/9	3	—	—
Cayman Islands*	468/70	3	1	—
Cook Islands	593/601	8	—	1
Aitutaki	257/60	3	—	1
Penrhyn	121/4	3	—	1
Dominica	612/15	3	—	1
Falkland Islands*	348/50	3	1	—
South Georgia*	67/9	3	1	—
Fiji*	549/51	3	1	—
Gambia*	397/9	3	1	—
Gibraltar	400/3	4	—	—
Grenada	946/9	3	—	1
Grenadines of Grenada	272/5	3	—	1
Hong Kong	373/4	2	—	—
Kiribati/Gilbert Islands*	68/70	3	1	—
Maldive Islands	755/61	6	—	1
Mauritius*	549/51	3	1	—
Montserrat	422/6	4	—	1
New Zealand				
Tokelau	61/4	4	—	—
Niue	245/8	3	—	1
Pitcairn Islands	**MS**189	—	—	1
St. Helena*	338/40	3	1	—
St. Kitts-Nevis*	389/91	3	1	—
St. Lucia	468/72	4	—	1
St. Vincent	556/60	4	—	1
Grenadines of St. Vincent	130/4	4	—	1
Samoa*	508/10	3	1	—
Seychelles	428/32	4	—	1
Sierra Leone	601/3	3	—	—
Solomon Islands*	357/9	3	1	—
Swaziland	293/5	3	1	—
Tanzania	233/7	4	—	1
Tristan da Cunha*	239/41	3	1	—
Turks and Caicos Islands	494/8	4	—	1
Tuvalu	89/93	4	—	1
Uganda	234/8	4	—	1
Vanuatu/New Hebrides* (English & French inscr)	262/4, F276/8	3+3	1+1	—
Total number of items		195	21	27

The Crown Agents Omnibus issue was printed in matching sheetlets, each containing two *se-tenant* strips of the three designs.

Barbuda Nos. 445/6 form part of a general anniversaries issue.

Belize Nos. 495/503 were not part of the Crown Agents Omnibus issue.

1980 QUEEN MOTHER's 80th BIRTHDAY

Country	*Catalogue Nos.*	*Stamps*	MS
Great Britain	1129	1	—
Anguilla	411/15	4	1
Antigua	663/5	2	1
Barbuda	533/5	2	1
Ascension*	269	1	—
Australia			
Norfolk Island	252/3	2	—
Bangladesh	172/4	2	1
Belize	592/3	1	1
Bermuda*	425	1	—
Cayman Islands*	506	1	—
Cook Islands	701/2	1	1
Penrhyn	150/1	1	1
Dominica	732/4	2	1
Falkland Islands*	383	1	—
Gambia*	440	1	—
Gibraltar*	436	1	—
Hong Kong*	390	1	—
Lesotho	423/5	3	—
Maldive Islands	886/7	1	1
Niue	364/5	1	1
Pitcairn Islands*	206	1	—
St. Helena*	366	1	—
St. Kitts-Nevis			
St. Kitts	48	1	—
Nevis	50	1	—
St. Lucia	534/6	2	1
Samoa*	572	1	—
Solomon Islands*	421	1	—
Tristan da Cunha*	282	1	—
Turks and Caicos Islands	607/8	1	1
Tuvalu	148	1	—
Total number of items		41	12

1981 ROYAL WEDDING

Country	*Catalogue Nos.*	*Stamps*	MS
Great Britain	1160/1	2	—
Guernsey	232/9	7	1
Isle of Man	202/4	2	1
Jersey	284/5	2	—
Anguilla	464/7	3	1
Antigua	702/5	3	1
Barbuda	565/75	9	2
Ascension*	302/4	3	—
Australia	821/2	2	—
Cocos (Keeling) Islands	70/1	2	—
Norfolk Island*	262/4	3	—
Bahamas	586/8	2	1
Barbados*	674/6	3	—
Belize	614/20	6	1
Bermuda*	436/8	3	—
British Virgin Islands*	463/5	3	—
Brunei*	304/6	3	—
Cayman Islands*	534/6	3	—
Cook Islands	812/14	2	1
Aitutaki	391/3	3	—
Penrhyn	223/8	5	1
Cyprus	580	1	—
Turkish Cypriot Posts	121	1	—
Dominica	747/50	3	1
Falkland Islands*	402/4	3	—
Dependencies*	95/7	3	—
Fiji*	612/14	3	—
Gambia*	454/6	3	—
Ghana	948/54	6	1
Gibraltar	450	1	—
Grenada	1130/5	5	1
Grenadines of Grenada	444/9	5	1
Guyana	769/70, 841/3, 930/6	12	—
Hong Kong*	399/401	3	—
Jamaica	516/20	4	1
Kenya	207/11	4	1
Kiribati	149/55	6	1
Lesotho*	451/4	3	1
Maldive Islands	918/21	3	1
Mauritius*	615/17	3	—
Montserrat	510/15	6	1
New Zealand	1247/8	2	—
Niue	430/3	3	1
Pitcairn Islands*	219/21	3	—
St. Helena*	378/80	3	—
St. Kitts-Nevis			
St. Kitts	75/81	6	1
Nevis	72/8	6	1
St. Lucia	576/9	3	1
St. Vincent	668/74	6	1
Grenadines of St. Vincent	195/201	6	1
Samoa*	599/601	3	—
Seychelles	505/11	6	1
Zil Elwagne Sesel	23/9	6	1
Sierra Leone*	668/74	6	1
Solomon Islands*	445/7	3	—
Swaziland*	376/8	3	—
Tanzania	325/7	2	1
Tonga	785/8	4	—
Tristan da Cunha*	308/10	3	—
Turks and Caicos Islands	653/6	3	1
Caicos Islands	8/11	3	1
Tuvalu	168/74	6	1
Uganda	341/8	6	2
Vanuatu*	315/17	3	—
Total number of items		244	35

The Lesotho miniature sheet, No. **MS**454, and Sierra Leone Nos. 671/3 do not form part of the Crown Agents Omnibus issue.

1982 PRINCESS DIANA'S 21st BIRTHDAY

Country	*Catalogue Nos.*	*Stamps*	*MS*
Anguilla	507/14	6	2
Antigua	748/51	3	1
Barbuda	624/30	6	2
Ascension*	322/5	4	—
Bahamas*	622/5	4	—
Barbados*	705/8	4	—
Belize	680/6	6	1
British Antarctic Territory*	109/12	4	—
British Virgin Islands*	488/91	4	—
Cayman Islands*	549/52	4	—
Cook Islands	833/7	4	1
Aitutaki	411/14	3	1
Penrhyn	250/5	5	1
Dominica	821/4	3	1
Falkland Islands*	426/9	4	—
Dependencies*	108/11	4	—
Fiji*	640/3	4	—
Gambia*	476/9	4	—
Grenada	1188/94	6	1
Grenadines of Grenada	493/9	6	1
Guyana	979/81	3	—
Jamaica	551/7	6	1
Kiribati	183/5	3	—
Lesotho*	514/17	4	—
Maldive Islands	964/7	3	1
Mauritius*	643/6	4	—
Montserrat	542/4	3	—
Niue	454/7	3	1
Pitcairn Islands*	226/9	4	—
St. Helena*	397/400	4	—
St. Kitts-Nevis			
St. Kitts	95/7	3	—
Nevis	85/7	3	—
St. Lucia	625/8	3	1
St. Vincent	694/6	3	—
Grenadines of St. Vincent	229/31	3	—
Sierra Leone	707/10	3	1
Solomon Islands*	467/70	4	—
Swaziland*	404/7	4	—
Tristan da Cunha*	327/30	4	—
Turks and Caicos Islands	709/12	3	1
Tuvalu	184/6	3	—
Uganda	374/7	1	1
Total number of items		162	19

1982 BIRTH OF PRINCE WILLIAM

Country	*Catalogue Nos.*	*Stamps*	*MS*
Great Britain			
Isle of Man	**MS**227	—	1
Antigua	757/60	3	1
Barbuda	613/16, 632/5	6	2
Belize	707/20	12	2
Cook Islands	838/47, 856/61	13	3
Aitutaki	415/24	9	1
Penrhyn	256/72	15	2
Dominica	830/3	3	1
Grenada	1200/6	6	1
Grenadines of Grenada	505/11	6	1
Guyana	982/7	6	—
Jamaica	558/64	6	1
Kiribati	186/8	3	—
Lesotho	521/2	2	—
Maldive Islands	968/72	4	1
Mauritius	647	1	—
Niue	458/74	13	4
St. Kitts-Nevis			
St. Kitts	98/100	3	—
Nevis	88/90	3	—
St. Vincent	699/701	3	—
Grenadines of St. Vincent	234/6	3	—
Sierra Leone	711/14	3	1
Tuvalu	189/91	3	—
Total number of items		124	22

1985 LIFE AND TIMES OF QUEEN ELIZABETH THE QUEEN MOTHER

Country	Catalogue Nos.	Stamps	MS
Anguilla	655/8	3	1
Antigua	946/9	3	1
Barbuda	776/82, 809/15 826/9	17	1
Ascension*	376/80	4	1
Australia			
Norfolk Island*	364/8	4	1
Bahamas*	712/16	4	1
Barbados*	779/83	4	1
Belize	827/31	4	1
Bermuda*	494/8	4	1
British Virgin Islands	579/87	8	1
Cook Islands	1035/9	4	1
Aitutaki	523/7	4	1
Penrhyn	378/82	4	1
Dominica	949/52	3	1
Falkland Islands*	505/9	4	1
Dependencies*	129/33	4	1
Fiji*	701/5	4	1
Gambia	586/9	3	1
Ghana	1140/3	3	1
Grenada	1426/9	3	1
Grenadines of Grenada	689/92	3	1
Guyana	1536/9	3	1
Hong Kong*	493/6	4	—
Jamaica*	625/9	4	1
Lesotho	635/9	4	1
Maldive Islands	1099/102	4	1
Mauritius*	699/703	4	1
Montserrat	636/44	8	1
Niue	587/90	3	1
Pitcairn Islands*	268/72	4	1
St. Helena*	454/8	4	1
St. Kitts-Nevis			
Nevis	309/17	8	1
St. Lucia	832/40	8	1
St. Vincent	910/18	8	1
Grenadines of St. Vincent	403/11	8	1
Samoa*	700/4	4	1
Seychelles*	614/18	4	1
Zil Elwannyen Sesel*	115/19	4	1
Sierra Leone	872/5	3	1
Solomon Islands*	538/42	4	1
Swaziland*	486/90	4	1
Tanzania	425/9	4	1
Tonga	915/18	4	—
Tristan da Cunha*	390/4	4	1
Turks and Caicos Islands	854/7	3	1
Caicos Islands	82/5	3	1
Tuvalu	334/42	8	1
Uganda	478/9	1	1
Vanuatu*	406/10	4	1
Zambia	432/5	4	—
Total number of items		226	47

1986 QUEEN ELIZABETH II's 60th BIRTHDAY

Country	Catalogue Nos.	Stamps	MS
Great Britain	1316/19	4	—
Guernsey	365	1	—
Isle of Man	328/30	3	—
Jersey	389	1	—
Anguilla	711/14	3	1
Antigua	1005/8	3	1
Barbuda	861/4, 872/5	6	2
Ascension*	397/401	5	—
Australia	1009	1	—
Norfolk Island	389/92	4	—
Bahamas*	741/5	5	—
Barbados*	810/14	5	—
Belize	905/9	4	1
Bermuda*	524/8	5	—
British Virgin Islands	600/4	4	1
Cayman Islands*	621/5	5	—
Cook Islands	1065/8	3	1
Aitutaki	542/3	1	1
Penrhyn	394/6	3	—
Cyprus—Turkish Cypriot Posts	201	1	—
Dominica	998/1001	3	1
Falkland Islands*	522/6	5	—
Fiji*	714/18	5	—
Gambia	641/4	3	1
Gibraltar	540	1	—
Grenada	1499/502	3	1
Grenadines of Grenada	753/6	3	1
Guyana	1684/5	1	1
Hong Kong*	512/16	5	—
Jamaica*	646/50	5	—
Kiribati*	251/5	5	—
Lesotho	701/4	3	1
Maldive Islands	1170/3	3	1
Mauritius*	724/8	5	—
Montserrat	677/81	4	1
Niue	615/19	3	2
Papua New Guinea*	520/4	5	—
Pitcairn Islands*	285/9	5	—
St. Helena*	477/81	5	—
St. Kitts-Nevis			
St. Kitts	185/8	4	—
Nevis	384/8	4	1
St. Lucia	876/85	8	2
St. Vincent	978/82, 996/1000	8	2
Grenadines of St. Vincent	459/63	4	1
Samoa*	726/30	5	—
Seychelles*	639/43	5	—
Zil Elwannyen Sesel*	128/32	5	—
Sierra Leone	937/40	3	1
Solomon Islands*	562/6	5	—
South Georgia and South Sandwich Islands*	153/7	5	—
Swaziland*	500/4	5	—
Tanzania	517/21	4	1
Tonga	941/3	3	—
Trinidad and Tobago	712/15	4	—
Tristan da Cunha*	406/10	5	—
Tuvalu	381/5	4	1
Uganda	526/9	3	1
Vanuatu*	429/33	5	—
Zambia*	453/7	5	—
Total number of items		233	28

1986 ROYAL WEDDING

Country	Catalogue Nos.	Stamps	MS
Great Britain	1333/4	2	—
Guernsey	369/70	2	—
Isle of Man	326/7	2	—
Jersey	395/6	2	—
Anguilla	720/4	4	1
Antigua	1019/22	3	1
Barbuda	891/4	3	1
Ascension*	407/8	2	—
Australia			
Christmas Island*	220/1	2	—
Bahamas*	756/7	2	—
Barbados*	822/3	2	—
Belize	941/4	3	1
British Virgin Islands	605/9	4	1
Cayman Islands*	633/4	2	—
Cook Islands	1075/7	3	—
Aitutaki	547/8	1	1
Penrhyn	400/1	2	—
Cyprus—Turkish Cypriot Posts	200	1	—
Dominica	1018/21	3	1
Falkland Islands	536/8	3	1
Gambia	664/7	3	1
Gibraltar	**MS**545	—	1
Grenada	1512/15	3	1
Grenadines of Grenada	762/5	3	1
Jamaica*	656/7	2	—
Lesotho	736/9	3	1
Maldive Islands	1179/82	3	1
Montserrat	691/5, 705/8	8	1
Niue	625/6	1	1
Pitcairn Islands*	290/1	2	—
St. Helena*	486/7	2	—
St. Kitts-Nevis			
St. Kitts*	189/90	2	—
Nevis	406/10, 454/7	8	1
St. Lucia	890/3, 897/901	8	1
St. Vincent	1009/13, 1022/5	8	1
Grenadines of St. Vincent	481/5, 486/9	8	1
Seychelles*	651/2	2	—
Zil Elwannyen Sesel*	133/4	2	—
Sierra Leone	946/9	3	1
Solomon Islands*	568/9	2	—
South Georgia and South Sandwich Islands	158/60	3	—
Tristan da Cunha*	415/16	2	—
Turks and Caicos Islands	893/6	3	1
Tuvalu	397/401, 433/6	8	1
Uganda	535/8	3	1
Zambia*	458/9	2	—
Total number of items		142	24

1987 ROYAL RUBY WEDDING

Country	Catalogue Nos.	Stamps	MS
Anguilla	788/91	4	—
Antigua	1149/53	4	1
Barbuda	1029/33	4	1
Ascension*	447/51	5	—
Belize	980/4	4	1
Cook Islands	1193/4	2	—
Aitutaki	572/4	3	—
Penrhyn	413/14	2	—
Dominica	1109/13	4	1
Gambia	765/9	4	1
Grenada	1737/41	4	1
Grenadines of Grenada	928/32	4	1
Guyana	2233/4	1	1
Kiribati*	279/83	5	—
Lesotho	806/9	3	1
Maldive Islands	1282/5	3	1
Montserrat	739/42	8	—
Niue	657/8	2	—
St. Helena*	514/18	5	—
St. Vincent	1079/84	5	1
Grenadines of St. Vincent	536/41	5	1
Seychelles*	674/8	5	—
Zil Elwannyen Sesel*	157/61	5	—
Sierra Leone	1116/20	4	1
Swaziland*	537/40	4	—
Tristan da Cunha*	438/42	5	—
Turks and Caicos Islands	922/4	3	—
Tuvalu	484/9	5	1
Vanuatu*	487/91	5	—
Total number of items		117	14

1990 QUEEN MOTHER'S 90th BIRTHDAY

Country	Catalogue Nos.	Stamps	MS
Great Britain	1507/10	4	–
Isle of Man	448	1	–
Anguilla	859	1	–
Antigua	1415/19	4	1
Barbuda	1206/10	4	1
Ascension*	525/6	2	–
Bahamas*	880/1	2	–
Barbados*	919/20	2	–
British Antarctic Territory*	186/7	2	—
British Indian Ocean Territory*	106/7	2	—
British Virgin Islands	746/50	4	1
Cayman Islands*	711/12	2	—
Cook Islands	1246/7	1	1
Aitutaki	**MS**614	—	1
Penrhyn	445/6	1	1
Dominica	1373/7	4	1
Falkland Islands*	606/7	2	—
Gambia	1060/3	3	1
Grenada	2131/4	3	1
Grenadines of Grenada	1262/5	3	1
Guyana	2754/61, E**MS**31/3	8	3
Kenya*	545/6	2	—
Kiribati*	341/2	2	—
Lesotho	967/70	3	1
Maldive Islands	1396/9	3	1
Niue	689/90	1	1
Pitcairn Islands*	378/9	2	—
St. Helena*	570/1	2	—
St. Kitts-Nevis			
Nevis	555/8	3	1
St. Lucia*	1053/4	2	—
St. Vincent	1536/9	3	1
Grenadines of St. Vincent	705/32	27	1
Seychelles*	782/3	2	—
Zil Elwannyen Sesel*	212/13	2	—
Sierra Leone	1493/6	3	1
Solomon Islands*	675/6	2	—
South Georgia and South Sandwich Islands*	195/6	2	—
Swaziland*	570/1	2	—
Tristan da Cunha*	498/9	2	—
Turks and Caicos Islands	1045/9	4	1
Uganda	816/19	3	1
Total number of items		127	22

1991 65th BIRTHDAY OF QUEEN ELIZABETH II AND 70th BIRTHDAY OF PRINCE PHILIP

Country	Catalogue Nos.	Stamps	MS
Antigua	1534/8	4	1
Barbuda	1303/12	4	1
Ascension*	539/40	2	—
Australia	1286	1	—
Bahamas*	913/14	2	—
Belize*	1104/5	2	—
Bermuda*	634/5	2	—
Cook Islands	1255	1	—
Aitutaki	622	1	—
Penrhyn	456	1	—
Dominica	1433/7	4	1
Gambia	1165/9	4	1
Grenada	2299/303	4	1
Grenada Grenadines	1393/7	4	1
Guyana	3146/52	6	1
Kiribati*	366/7	2	—
Maldive Islands	1506/10	4	1
Mauritius*	849/50	2	—
Niue	706	1	—
Pitcairn Islands*	399/400	2	—
St. Helena*	591/2	2	—
St. Kitts-Nevis			
St. Kitts*	336/7	2	—
Nevis	622/6	4	1
St. Vincent	1686/90	4	1
Grenadines of St. Vincent	750/4	4	1
Samoa*	861/2	2	—
Seychelles*	799/800	2	—
Zil Elwannyen Sesel*	234/5	2	—
Sierra Leone	1639/43	4	1
Solomon Islands*	692/5	2	—
South Georgia and South Sandwich Islands*	201/2	2	—
Swaziland*	592/3	2	—
Tristan da Cunha	514/17	4	—
Turks and Caicos Islands	1099/1103	4	1
Uganda	960/4	4	1
Vanuatu*	576/7	2	—
Total number of items		99	14

1992 40th ANNIVERSARY OF QUEEN ELIZABETH II'S ACCESSION

Country	Catalogue Nos.	Stamps	MS
Great Britain	1602/6	5	—
Guernsey	552/5	4	—
Isle of Man	508/12	5	—
Antigua	1604/8	4	2
Barbuda	1384/8	4	2
Ascension*	569/73	5	—
Bahamas*	928/32	5	—
Bermuda*	640/4	5	—
British Indian Ocean Territory*	119/23	5	—
British Virgin Islands	813/17	4	1
Cayman Islands*	737/41	5	—
Cook Islands	1324/7	4	—
Dominica	1515/19	4	2
Falkland Islands*	647/51	5	—
Gambia	1284/8	4	2
Gibraltar*	673/7	5	—
Grenada	2375/9	4	2
Grenada Grenadines	1469/73	4	2
Guyana	3294/8	4	2
Hong Kong*	691/5	5	—
Kenya*	565/9	5	—
Kiribati*	377/81	5	—
Lesotho	1084/8	4	1
Maldive Islands	1626/30	4	2
Niue	759/62	4	—

Country	*Catalogue Nos.*	*Stamps*	*MS*
Pitcairn Islands*	409/13	5	—
St. Helena*	607/11	5	—
St. Kitts-Nevis			
St. Kitts*	350/4	5	—
Nevis	655/9	4	2
St. Vincent	1861/5	4	2
St. Vincent Grenadines	809/13	4	2
Samoa*	876/80	5	—
Seychelles*	810/14	5	—
Zil Elwannyen Sesel*	240/4	5	—
Sierra Leone	1774/8	4	2
Solomon Islands*	713/17	5	—
South Georgia and South Sandwich Islands*	209/13	5	—
Tristan da Cunha*	526/30	5	—
Turks and Caicos Islands	1145/53	8	2
Uganda	1079/83	4	2
Vanuatu*	587/91	5	—
Zambia*	687/91	5	—
Total number of items		195	30

1993 40th ANNIVERSARY OF CORONATION

Country	*Catalogue Nos.*	*Stamps*	*MS*
Great Britain			
Jersey	634	1	—
Anguilla	917/21	4	1
Antigua	1772/6	4	1
	1777/1808	32	—
Bahamas	962/5	4	—
British Virgin Islands	841/5	4	1
Cook Islands	1328/30	3	—
Aitutaki	650/2	3	—
Penrhyn	480	1	—
Dominica	1700/4	4	1
Gambia	1521/5	4	1
Ghana	1844/8	4	2
Grenada	2518/22	4	1
Grenada Grenadines	1623/7	4	1
Guyana	3551/5	4	1
Hong Kong	741/4	4	—
Lesotho	1159/63	4	1
Maldive Islands	1805/8	4	—
Montserrat	913/14	2	—
New Zealand			
Tokelau	197/200	4	—
Niue	773	1	—
Pitcairn Islands	430	1	—
St. Kitts-Nevis			
St. Kitts	378/81	4	—
Nevis	753/7	4	1
St. Vincent	2264/8	4	1
Sierra Leone	2059, 2061, 2064, **MS**2067b	3	1
Tanzania	1514/18	4	1
Tristan da Cunha	542/5	4	—
Turks and Caicos Islands	1196/1200	4	1
Tuvalu	677/81	4	1
Uganda	1218/22	4	1
Total number of items		135	18

1994 ROYAL VISIT

Country	*Catalogue Nos.*	*Stamps*	*MS*
Bahamas	999/1002	4	—
Belize	1157/60	4	—
Bermuda	699/701	3	—
Cayman Islands	774/7	4	—
Dominica	1844/8	4	1
Guyana	3873/7	4	1
Jamaica	843/6	4	—
Total number of items		27	2

1995 QUEEN MOTHER'S 95th BIRTHDAY

Country	*Catalogue Nos.*	*Stamps*	*MS*
Antigua	2127/31	4	1
Barbuda	1662, 1814/18	5	1
Cayman Islands	**MS**810	—	1
Cook Islands	1378	1	—
Aitutaki	688	1	—
Penrhyn	515	1	—
Dominica	1993/7	4	1
Gambia	2025/9	4	1
Ghana	2191/5	4	1
Grenada	2902/6	4	1
Grenada Grenadines	1980/4	4	1
Guyana	4414/18	4	1
Jamaica	**MS**883	—	1
Maldive Islands	2274/8	4	1
Pitcairn Islands	**MS**478	—	1
St. Kitts-Nevis			
Nevis	923/7	4	1
St. Vincent	2927/31	4	1
Seychelles	852/5	4	—
Sierra Leone	2335/9	4	1
Tristan da Cunha	**MS**585	—	1
Turks and Caicos Islands	1344/8	4	1
Uganda	1482/6	4	1
Total number of items		64	18

1996 QUEEN ELIZABETH II's 70th BIRTHDAY

Country	*Catalogue Nos.*	*Stamps*	*MS*
Great Britain			
Jersey	738	1	—
Antigua	2355/8	3	1
Barbuda	1782/5	3	1
Ascension*	671/4	4	—
Australia	1589	1	—
British Antarctic Territory*	270/3	4	—
British Indian Ocean Territory*	180/4	4	1
British Virgin Islands*	920/4	4	1
Cook Islands	1392/5	3	1
Aitutaki	694	1	—
Penrhyn	521	1	—
Dominica	2118/21	3	1
Falkland Islands*	761/4	4	—
Gambia	2247/50	3	1
Ghana	2325/8	3	1
Grenada	3078/81	3	1
Grenadines of Grenada	2126/9	3	1
Maldive Islands	2489/92	3	1
New Zealand			
Tokelau*	240/4	4	1
Pitcairn Islands*	493/6	4	—
St. Helena*	716/20	4	1
St. Kitts-Nevis			
Nevis	1018/21	3	1
St. Vincent	3326/9	3	1
Samoa*	983/7	4	1
Sierra Leone	2559/62	3	1
Tristan da Cunha*	594/7	4	—
Turks and Caicos Islands	1378/81	3	1
Uganda	1687/90	3	1
Total number of items		86	19

1997 ROYAL GOLDEN WEDDING

Country	*Catalogue Nos.*	*Stamps*	*MS*
Great Britain	1978/9, 2011/14	6	—
Guernsey	754/9	6	—
Isle of Man	768/71	4	—
Jersey	834/6	2	1
Antigua	2464/9	6	1
Barbuda	1894/9	6	1
Ascension*	719/24	6	1
Australia			
Norfolk Island*	647/51	4	1
Bahamas*	1114/20	6	1
Bermuda*	778/80	2	1
British Indian Ocean Territory*	195/200	6	1
British Virgin Islands*	959/64	6	1
Cayman Islands*	841/7	6	1
Cook Islands	1419/20	1	1
Aitutaki	697/8	1	1
Penrhyn	523/4	1	1
Dominica	2296/302	6	1
Falkland Islands*	788/94	6	1
Gambia	2595/601	6	1
Ghana	2441/7	6	1
Gibraltar*	810/11	2	—
Grenada	3352/8	6	1
Grenadines of Grenada	2310/17	6	1
Kiribati*	535/41	6	1
Maldive Islands	2753/9	6	1
Nauru	469/71	2	1
New Zealand	2117	1	—
Papua New Guinea*	813/19	6	1
Pitcairn Islands*	516/21	6	—
St. Helena*	746/52	6	1
St. Kitts-Nevis			
St. Kitts*	485/91	6	1
Nevis	1083/9	6	1
St. Lucia*	1160/6	6	1
St. Vincent	3694/700	6	1
Samoa*	1007/13	6	1
Seychelles*	876/82	6	1
Sierra Leone	2697/703	6	1
Solomon Islands*	889/93	4	1
South Georgia and South Sandwich Islands*	270/6	6	1
Tristan da Cunha*	624/30	6	1
Turks and Caicos Islands	1449/55	6	1
Tuvalu*	791/7	6	1
Uganda	1852/8	6	1
Total number of items		216	37

Index

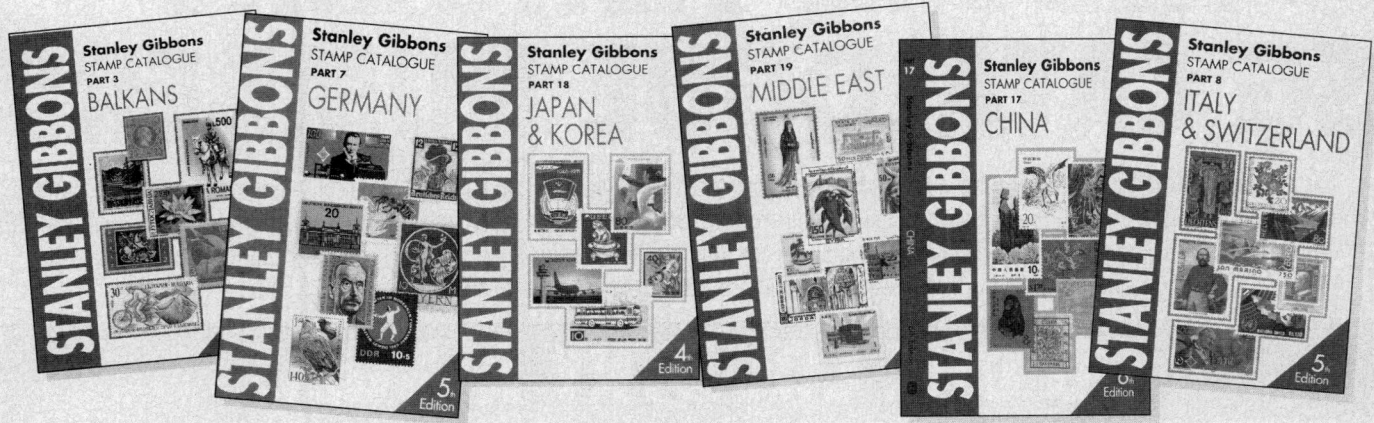